A TENNYSON CONCORDANCE

A CONCORDANCE

TO THE

POETICAL AND DRAMATIC WORKS

OF

ALFRED, LORD TENNYSON

INCLUDING THE POEMS CONTAINED IN THE "LIFE OF ALFRED, LORD TENNYSON," AND THE "SUPPRESSED POEMS," 1830-1868.

BY

ARTHUR E. (rnest) BAKER, F.R.HIST.S., F.L.A.

SECRETARY AND LIBRARIAN, TAUNTON.

AUTHOR OF

"A BRIEF ACCOUNT OF THE PUBLIC LIBRARY MOVEMENT IN TAUNTON," ETC.

B&N 1873

Barnes & Noble, Inc.

NEW YORK

First published 1914
reissued
in the United States of America
1966
Reprinted 1967

Printed in Great Britain

TO THE MEMORY

OF

MY MOTHER,

MY FIRST AND BEST TEACHER,

THIS BOOK IS

AFFECTIONATELY DEDICATED.

"*Until the day break, and the shadows flee away.*"

PREFATORY NOTE

Origin of the Work.

It may, perhaps, not be out of place to say a word or two as to how I came to undertake the compilation of this work. Some years ago, when occupying the position of Deputy-Librarian in a public library in the North of England, I received numerous enquiries from readers at that institution for a Concordance to the Works of Tennyson. Realising that here was a distinct *desideratum* in the library of the student of English Literature, I there and then decided to undertake the compilation of such a Work. Taking from one of the Book-presses a copy of the poet's Works, and opening it, my eyes fell on the following quotation :—

> "Make knowledge circle with the winds ;
> But let her herald, Reverence, fly
> Before her to whatever sky
> Bear seed of men and growth of minds."
> —*Love thou thy land.*

I jotted down the lines under their respective key-words, and thus the work was commenced.

Shortly afterwards it happened that I removed to my present position in the South of England; consequently the matter was for some time "shelved"; but at the end of 1907 I returned to the subject, and after about eight years of what has been to me a labour of love, I present my humble labour to the public, with a sincere hope that students, and lovers of Tennyson, and others, will find it of interest and utility.

Contents.

The volume consists of Verbal Indexes to the Poetical and Dramatic Works of the author comprised in the *Complete Edition*, published by Messrs Macmillan & Co., to the *Poems* contained in the *Life of Lord Tennyson* by his son, and published by the same publishers; also to the *Suppressed Poems*, edited by J. C. Thomson, and published by Messrs Sands & Co.

Arrangement.

The Concordance has been arranged in strict alphabetical sequence; the different senses or grammatical functions of a word are frequently distinguished under separate headings; the dialect words are paraphrased; all proper names are included, and occasionally some indication has been added of their identity.

Line-references.

Line-references are given, thereby greatly facilitating the finding of a quotation or reference, particularly in the larger poems.

Method of numbering Lines.

As each one has to number the lines for himself in all but school editions of Tennyson's Works, I must explain the method, or rather methods, of numbering for the purpose of this Concordance. In the *Poems* the lines have been numbered without regard to the typographical peculiarities of the standard edition, which has two columns to a page. The following lines, here reprinted as they stand in that edition, were numbered 1-6, thus :—

1 THESE to His Memory—since he held
them dear,
2 Perchance as finding there unconsciously
3 Some image of himself—I dedicate,
4 I dedicate, I consecrate with tears—
5 These Idylls.
6 And indeed He seems to me
—*Idylls of the King. Dedication.*

That is to say, a line broken into two by the printer was counted as one; a line broken by the poet was counted as two.

In the *Dramatic Works*, another and merely mechanical system was adopted. There every line of print as it occurs in Macmillan's one-volume edition of the *Complete Works* was numbered separately, even if only containing a single word. Thus :—

1 *Cranmer.* To Strasburg, Antwerp,
2 Frankfort, Zurich, Worms,
3 Geneva, Basle—our Bishops from their
4 sees
5 Or fled, they say, or flying—Poinet,
6 Barlow,
—*Queen Mary, Act i., Scene ii.*

Metrically, of course, there are only three lines here, not six. A method of numbering that is not to be avoided in the prose portions of the plays has intentionally been extended also to the blank verse in order to facilitate rapid reference to copies of the text in which the lines are not already numbered. On receiving a reference, say to line 560 of *The Falcon,* a reader using Macmillan's standard edition in one volume can quickly reckon out the page and even the column in which the quotation appears, by remembering that the column contains approximately fifty lines of print. Had the lines been numbered metrically he would have had to count from the beginning of the piece. Only the lines of the text proper, not the stage-directions, have been numbered.

Cross-references.

Cross-references are supplied in the case of compounds and dialect forms—*e.g.*, **Life** (*See also* **After-life, Loife**).

Duplicate Titles and Headings of Poems.

In the *Collected Works*, two poems appear bearing the same title—viz., *To the Queen.* The one which appears on page 474, immediately preceding the *Lover's Tale,* has been described as *To the Queen ii,* in contradistinction to the one which appears on page 1. Then there are a few poems with no distinct titles, but simply headed thus : *To ——*, *Song, Sonnet,* etc. To avoid confusion, these are referred to in the Concordance by the first two or three words of each poem.

Omitted Words.

No quotations are furnished for the following words. A few quotations, however, may be found under those marked with an asterisk (*Poetical Works*) or dagger (*Dramatic Works*) but they are there to illustrate some especial use, and by no means represent every occurrence of the word:—

A	But	†If	Ourself	Too
About	By	In	Out	'Twas
Above	Can	*Indeed	Over	'Twere
Adown	Cannot	Into	Perchance	'Twill
†After	Canst	Is	*Round	*Under
Again	†Could	It	*Scarce	Until
Against	Couldst	Its	Scarcely	Unto
Ago	Did	Itself	Seldom	Up
Ah	Didst	Lest	Shall	Upon
Albeit	*Do	Let	Shalt	Us
†All	Does	May	She	*†Very
Almost	Done	May'st	Should	*†Was
*Along	Dost	Me	Shouldst	Wast
Aloof	Doth	*Mid	Since	We
Already	Down	Might	So	*†Well
Also	†Downward	Might'st	*†Some	Were
Although	Each	†Mine	*†Something	Wert
Alway	E'er	More	Soon	What
Always	*Either	Most	Still (adv.)	Whate'er
Am	Else	Must	*†Such	Whatsoever
Among	Ere	My	Than	*†When
An	Even	Myself	That	Whence
And	†Ever	Near	The	Whene'er
†Any	*Every	Nearly	Thee	Where
Are	For	*Need	Their	Whereat
Around	Forth	Ne'er	Theirs	Whether
Art	From	†Neither	Them	Which
As	'Gainst	*Never	*Then	Whicheve
At	Had	*No	Thence	While
Athwart	Hadst	*None	There	Who
Atwain	Has	Nor	Therefore	Whom
Atween	Hast	Not	These	†Whose
Away	Have	Nothing	They	Why
*Ay	Having	†Now	Thine	*Will
Back	He	O	†This	Wilt
Be	Hence	O'er	Tho'	With
Because	Henceforth	Of	Those	Within
Been	Her	Off	Thou	Without
*Before	Here	Oft	Though	Would
Behind	Herself	Often	Thro'	Wouldst
Being	Him	Oh	Through	Ye
Below	Himself	On	Thus	Yea
Beneath	His	Once	Thy	Yes
Beside	*How	*†Only	Thyself	Yet
Between	Howe'er	*Onward	Till	You
Betwixt	However	Or	'Tis	Your
Beyond	Howsoe'er	Our	To	Yours
Both	*I	Ours	Together	Yourself

It was originally intended, in order to curtail the heavy expenditure entailed in publication, to omit various adjectives and other words; but as enquiries were made regarding their omission, it was decided later to insert these words as far as it was possible. As, however, the letters A-D (*Poetical Works* only) had already been printed, it was impossible to make these entries, consequently many ordinary adjectives under the above letters are omitted.

Poems in Duplicate.

The following poems in the *Life* occur also in the *Collected Works*, or in the *Suppressed Poems*, and are, of course, treated only once:—

As when a man that sails in a balloon. (See *Suppressed Poems* under *Dream of Fair Women.*)
Check every outflash, every ruder sally. (See *Suppressed Poems.*)
Farewell, Macready, since to-night we part. (See *Collected Works* under *To W. C. Macready.*)
First drink a health, this solemn night. (See *Suppressed Poems* under *Hands all Round.*) A few readings peculiar to the *Life* are, however, recorded in their place.
God bless our Prince and Bride! (See *Suppressed Poems.*)
Grave mother of majestic works. (See *Collected Works* under *Of old sat Freedom.*)
Helen's Tower, here I stand. (See *Collected Works*, under *Helen's Tower.*) The sole variant is duly recorded, however.
Here often when a child I lay reclined. (See *Suppressed Poems* under *Mablethorpe.*) Important variants in the *Life* are recorded.
Me my own Fate to lasting sorrow doometh. (See *Suppressed Poems.*)
Rise, Britons, rise, if manhood be not dead. (See *Suppressed Poems* under *Britons, guard your own.*) Important variants in the *Life* are recorded.
Row us out from Desenzano, to your Sirmione row! (See *Collected Works* under *Frater Ave Atque Vale.*)
The North wind fall'n in the new-starréd night. (See *Suppressed Poems* under *The Hesperides.*)
Therefore your Halls, your ancient Colleges. (See *Suppressed Poems* under *Cambridge.*) The significant variants are all recorded.
Thy prayer was "Light — more Light — while time shall last!" (See *Collected Works* under *Epitaph on Caxton.*)

The poem *Lover's Tale* appears in the *Collected Works* and also in the *Suppressed Poems.* The portion common to both versions have not been indexed twice; they have been neglected in making the Concordance to the *Suppressed Poems.*

Alphabetizing and Checking.

The volume contains approximately 150,000 quotations and references; and as each quotation or reference was written on a separate slip, which was then placed in its alphabetical order, and afterwards classified according to the sense or grammatical function of the key-word, it can better be imagined than described what an immense amount of labour and time was thus bestowed upon the work.

Appreciation.

In this respect my acknowledgments are due, and are hereby tendered, to Miss Beatrice Hewlett (the hon. librarian of the Crewe Green Parish Library, Cheshire), and to my two sisters, Miss Mary E. Baker and Miss Miriam Maud Mary Baker, for their valuable assistance in this portion of the work. At the same time, I beg to tender my hearty thanks to those who have from time to time written me encouraging letters, which have greatly assisted me in

my arduous task, and in this respect I would specially mention Mr Lionel R. M. Strachan, English Lecturer in Heidelberg University, for the great interest he has invariably evinced in the compilation of the work—particularly for his valuable help in the checking of the proofs—and for his readiness at all times to render assistance.

A. E. B.

TAUNTON,
1914.

CORRIGENDA

Page 132 Dawn (verb) *Tiresias* 206 *read* Dawn (s).
„ 252 Gave (*See also* Gied, Giv) *read* Gave (*See also* Gev, Gied, Giv).
„ 256 Gev (give) *read* Gev (gave).
„ 258 Give (*See also* Gev, Gie) *read* Give (*See also* Gie).
„ 334 Hope (verb) *Supp. Confessions* 31 *read* Hope (s).
„ 832 Alight (lighted) *read* Alight.
„ 832 Alighted. *See* Lighted—*delete.*

CONTENTS

LIST OF SHORT TITLES AND ABBREVIATIONS

Achilles over the T.	Achilles over the Trench.
(*adj.*)	adjective.
(*adv.*)	adverb.
A gate and a field	A gate and a field half ploughed.
Akbar's D., Hymn	Akbar's Dream. Hymn.
Akbar's D., Inscrip.	Akbar's Dream. Inscription.
Along this glimmering	Along this glimmering gallery.
Arabian Nights	Recollections of the Arabian Nights.
Are those the far-famed	Are those the far-famed Victor Hours ?
A spirit haunts	A spirit haunts the year's last hours.
A surface man	A surface man of many theories.
Batt. of Brunanburh	Battle of Brunanburh.
Beauty, Good, etc.	Beauty, Good, and Knowledge are three sisters.
Because she bore	Because she bore the iron name.
Blow ye the trumpet	Blow ye the trumpet, gather from afar.
Bold Havelock	Bold Havelock march'd.
Bright is the moon	Bright is the moon on the deep.
Britons, guard	Britons, guard your own.
By an Evolution.	By an Evolutionist.
Check every outflash	Check every outflash, every ruder sally.
Church-warden, etc.	Church-warden and the Curate.
Com. of Arthur	Coming of Arthur.
Come not, when, etc.	Come not, when I am dead.
(*compar.*)	comparative.
Could I outwear	Could I outwear my present state of woe.
D. of F. Women	Dream of Fair Women.
D. of the Duke of C.	Death of the Duke of Clarence and Avondale.
D. of the O. Year	Death of the Old Year.
Day-Dm., Pro.	Day-Dream, Prologue.
" *Sleep. P.*	" Sleeping Palace.
" *Sleep. B.*	" Sleeping Beauty.
" *Depart.*	" Departure.
" *Ep.*	" Epilogue.
Ded. of Idylls	Idylls of the King. Dedication.
Ded. Poem Prin. Alice	Dedicatory Poem to the Princess Alice.
Deep glens I found	Deep glens I found, and sunless gulfs.
Def. of Lucknow	Defence of Lucknow.
Demeter and P.	Demeter and Persephone.
De Prof., Two G.	De Profundis: The Two Greetings.
" *Human C.*	" The Human Cry.
Early-wise	Early-wise, and pure, and true.
England and Amer.	England and America.
Epit. on Caxton	Epitaph on Caxton.
Epit. on Gordon	Epitaph on General Gordon.
Epit. on Stratford	Epitaph on Lord Stratford de Redcliffe.
Every day, etc.	Every day hath its night.
Faded ev'ry violet	Faded ev'ry violet, all the roses.
Far off in the dun	Far off in the dun, dark occident.
First drink a health	First drink a health, this solemn night.
Flow. in cran. wall	Flower in the crannied wall.
Frater Ave, etc.	Frater Ave atque Vale.
Frenchman, etc.	Frenchman, a hand is thine !
From shape to shape	From shape to shape at first within the womb
Full light aloft	Full light aloft doth the laverock spring.
G. of Swainston	In the Garden at Swainston.
Gardener's D.	Gardener's Daughter.
Gareth and L.	Gareth and Lynette.
Geraint and E.	Geraint and Enid.
God and the Univ.	God and the Universe.
God bless our Prince	God bless our Prince and Bride.
Gone into Darkness	Gone into darkness that full light.
He was too good	He was too good and kind and sweet.
Hear you the sound	Hear you the sound of wheels ?
Heavy Brigade	Charge of the Heavy Brigade at Balaclava.
Here, I that stood	Here, I that stood in On beside the flow.
Here often when a child	Here often when a child I lay reclined.
High. Pantheism	Higher Pantheism.
Hither, when all	Hither, when all the deep, unsounded skies
Hold thou, my friend	Hold thou, my friend, no lesser life in scorn.
Home they brought him	Home they brought him slain with spears.
How glad am I	How glad am I to walk.
How is it that men	How is it that men have so little grace ?
How strange it is	How strange it is, O God, to wake.
I keep no more	I keep no more a lone distress.
I, loving Freedom	I, loving Freedom for herself.
In Mem., Pro.	In Memoriam, Prologue.
" *Con.*	" Conclusion.
" *W. G. Ward*	" William George Ward.
I met in all	I met in all the close green ways.
(*interj.*)	interjection.
In the Child. Hosp.	In the Children's Hospital.
(*intrans.*)	intransitive.
June Bracken, etc.	June Bracken and Heather.
L. C. V. de Vere	Lady Clara Vere de Vere.
L. of Burleigh	Lord of Burleigh.
L. of Shalott	Lady of Shalott.
Lancelot and E.	Lancelot and Elaine.
Leonine Eleg.	Leonine Elegiacs.
Life of the Life	Life of the Life within my blood.
Light Brigade	Charge of the Light Brigade.
Lit. Squabbles	Literary Squabbles.
Little Aubrey	Little Aubrey in the West !
Locksley H., Sixty	Locksley Hall, Sixty Years after.
Long as the heart	Long as the heart beats life within the breast.
Lotos-Eaters, C. S.	Lotos-Eaters. Choric Song.
Love, Pride, etc.	Love, Pride, and Forgetfulness.
Mariana in the S.	Mariana in the South.
Marr. of Geraint	Marriage of Geraint.
May Queen, N. Y.'s E.	May Queen, New Year's Eve.
" *Con.*	" Conclusion.
M. d'Arthur	Morte d'Arthur.

M. d'Arthur, Ep.	Morte d'Arthur, Epilogue.
Me my own fate	Me my own fate to lasting sorrow doometh.
Merlin and the G.	Merlin and the Gleam.
Merlin and V.	Merlin and Vivien.
Methought I saw	Methought I saw a face whose every line.
Miller's D.	Miller's Daughter.
Move eastward	Move eastward, happy earth, and leave.
My life is full	My life is full of weary days.
N. Farmer, N. S.	Northern Farmer, New Style.
" O. S.	" Old Style.
New Timon	The New Timon and the Poets.
North. Cobbler	Northern Cobbler.
Not a whisper	Not a whisper stirs the gloom.
Not such were those	Not such were those whom Freedom claims.
Not to Silence	Not to Silence would I build.
Ode on Well.	Ode on the Death of the Duke of Wellington.
Ode Inter. Exhib.	Ode sung at the Opening of the International Exhibition.
O God, make this age	O God, make this age great that we may be.
Oh, Beauty	Oh, beauty, passing beauty.
O leave not thou	O leave not thou thy son forlorn.
Of old sat Freedom	Of old sat Freedom on the heights.
Old ghosts	Old ghosts whose day was done ere mine began
On Jub. Q. Victoria	On the Jubilee of Queen Victoria.
On One who effec. E. M.	On One who affected an Effeminate Manner.
One was the Tishbite	One was the Tishbite, whom the raven fed.
Open. I. and C. Exhib.	Opening of the Indian and Colonial Exhibition by the Queen.
Oriana	Ballad of Oriana.
O sad No more!	O sad *No more!* O sweet *No more!*
Pallid thunderstricken	The pallid thunderstricken sigh for gain.
(part.)	participle.
Pass. of Arthur	Passing of Arthur.
Pelleas and E.	Pelleas and Ettarre.
Poets and their B.	Poets and their Bibliographies.
Popular, Popular	Popular, Popular, Unpopular!
Pref. Poem. Broth. S.	Prefatory Poem to my Brother's Sonnets.
(prep.)	preposition.
Prin. Beatrice	To H.R.H. Princess Beatrice.
Princess, Pro.	Princess, Prologue.
" Con.	" Conclusion.
Pro. to Gen. Hamley	Prologue to General Hamley.
Prog. of Spring	Progress of Spring.
Prom. of May	Promise of May.
(pron.)	pronoun.
Remember you	Remember you the clear moonlight?
Remembering him	Remembering him who waits thee far away.
Rise, Britons, rise	Rise, Britons, rise, if manhood be not dead.
Romney's R.	Romney's Remorse.
Roses on the T.	Roses on the Terrace.
(s).	substantive.
St. S. Stylites	St. Simeon Stylites.
Shall the hag	Shall the hag Evil die.
Sir J. Franklin	Sir John Franklin.
Sir J. Oldcastle	Sir John Oldcastle, Lord Cobham.
Sir L. and Q. G.	Sir Launcelot and Queen Guinevere.
Sisters (E. and E.)	Sisters (Evelyn and Edith).
Speak to me	Speak to me from the stormy sky!
Spec. of Iliad	Specimen of a Translation of the Iliad in Blank Verse.
Spinster's S's	Spinster's Sweet-Arts.
Spurge with fairy	Spurge with fairy crescent set.
Steersman	Steersman, be not precipitate in thine act.
Sugg. by Reading	Suggested by reading an article in a newspaper.
Supp. Confessions	Supposed Confessions of a Second-rate Sensitive Mind.
Take, Lady	Take, Lady, what your loyal nurses give.
That is his portrait	That is his portrait, painted by himself.
That the voice	That the voice of a satisfied people may keep.
The child was sitting	The child was sitting on the bank.
The form, the form	The form, the form alone is eloquent.
The lamps were bright	The lamps were bright and gay.
The lintwhite	The lintwhite and the throstlecock.
The night, etc.	The night with sudden odour reel'd.
The noblest men	The noblest men methinks are bred.
The winds, etc.	The winds, as at their hour of birth.
There are three things	There are three things that fill my heart with sighs.
Therefore your Halls	Therefore your Halls, your ancient Colleges.
They say, etc.	They say some foreign powers have laid their heads together.
They wrought, etc.	They wrought a work which time reveres.
Third of Feb.	Third of February, 1852.
Thou may'st remember	Thou may'st remember that I said.
Though night	Though Night hath climbed.
Thy soul is like	Thy soul is like a landskip, friend.
'Tis not alone	'Tis not alone the warbling woods.
To a Lady Sleep.	To a Lady Sleeping.
To A. Tennyson	To Alfred Tennyson, My Grandson.
To C. North	To Christopher North.
To F. D. Maurice	To the Rev. F. D. Maurice.
To J. M. K.	Sonnet To J. M. K.
To One who ran down Eng.	To One who ran down the English.
To Prof. Jebb	To Professor Jebb.
To Marq. of Dufferin	To the Marquis of Dufferin and Ava.
To Master of B.	To the Master of Balliol.
To Prin. F. of H.	To the Princess Frederica of Hanover on her Marriage.
To thee with whom	To thee with whom my true affections dwell.
To W. H. Brookfield	To the Rev. W. H. Brookfield.
Townsmen, etc.	Townsmen, or of the hamlet, young or old.
(trans.)	transitive.
Trans. of Homer	On Translations of Homer.
V. of Cauteretz	In the Valley of Cauteretz.
V. of Maeldune	Voyage of Maeldune.
Vicar of this	Vicar of this pleasant spot.
Voice and the P.	Voice and the Peak.
Voice spake, etc.	A Voice spake out of the Skies.
W. to Alexandra	A Welcome to Alexandra.
W. to Marie Alex.	A Welcome to Her Royal Highness Marie Alexandrovna, Duchess of Edinburgh.
Walk. to the Mail	Walking to the Mail.
Wan Sculptor	Wan sculptor, weepest thou.
We lost you	We lost you for how long a time.
Well, as to Fame	Well, as to Fame, who strides the earth.
What rustles	What rustles hither in the dark?
What time I wasted	What time I wasted youthful hours.
Wherever evil	Wherever evil customs thicken.
While I live	While I live, the owls!
Why suffers	Why suffers human life so soon eclipse?
Will Water	Will Waterproof's Lyrical Monologue.
Window. At the W.	Window. At the Window.
" Marr. Morn	" Marriage Morning.
Woman of noble	Woman of noble form and noble mind!
Yon huddled cloud	Yon huddled cloud his motion shifts.
You ask me, why,	You ask me, why, tho' ill at ease.
You might have won	You might have won the Poet's name.
Young is the grief	Young is the grief I entertain.
Youth, lapsing	Youth, lapsing thro' fair solitudes.

A CONCORDANCE TO THE POETICAL WORKS

OF

ALFRED, LORD TENNYSON.

A mouthing out his hollow oes and *aes*, — *The Epic* 50
Äage (age) owd *a* as 'appy as iver I can, — *Owd Roä* 3
'Äair (hair) an' cryin' and teärin' 'er '*a* — *North. Cobbler* 34
Äale (ale) Says that I moänt 'a naw moor *a*: — *N. Farmer, O. S.*, 3
Git ma my *a*, (repeat) — ,, 4, 36, 68
I've 'ed my point o' *a* ivry noight — ,, 7
an' doesn bring ma the *a*? — ,, 65
an' droonk wi' the farmer's *a*, — *Village Wife* 77
An' the taäble staäin'd wi' 'is *a*, — *Spinster's S's.* 99
tha mun nobbut hev' one glass of *a*. — *Owd Roä* 20
'Äapoth (half-pennyworth) Joänes, as 'ant not a '*a* o' sense, — *N. Farmer, O. S.*, 49
Äaste (haste) thaw summun said it in '*a*: — ,, 27
Abaddon *A* and Asmodeus caught at me. — *St. S. Stylites* 172
Abase *A* those eyes that ever loved — *Princess ii* 427
Abash'd so forlorn As I am!' half *a* him; — *Enoch Arden* 288
Enid, all *a* she knew not why, — *Marr. of Geraint* 765
man of thine to-day *A* us both, — *Balin and Balan* 71
A Lavaine, whose instant reverence, — *Lancelot and E.* 418
beauty of her flesh *a* the boy, — *Pelleas and E.* 78
Abate *A* the stride, which speaks of man — *Princess ii* 429
Abbess Our simple-seeming *A* and her nuns, — *Guinevere* 309
till in time their *A* died. — ,, 692
Was chosen *A*, there, an *A*, lived For three brief years, and there, an *A*, past — ,, 696
Abbey 'Come out,' he said, 'To the *A*: — *Princess, Pro.*, 51
But we went back to the *A*, — ,, *Con.*, 106
fellow hath broken from some *A*, — *Gareth and L.* 456
The helmet in an *a* far away — *Holy Grail* 6
Abbey-ruin Carved stones of the *A-r* — *Princess, Pro.*, 14
Abbey-wall I see the moulder'd *A-w's*, — *Talking Oak* 3
Abbot An *a* on an ambling pad, — *L. of Shalott ii* 20
Abdiel Titan angels, Gabriel, *A*, — *Milton* 5
A-beälin' (bellowing) An' thou was *a-b* likewise, — *Owd Roä* 89
Abeär (bear) for I couldn *a* to see it. — *N. Farmer, O. S.*, 64
An' I can't *a* 'em, I can't, — *Church-warden, etc.*, 13
Abeat Eats scarce enow to keep his pulse *a*; — *Balin and Balan* 105
A-begging I never came *a-b* for myself, — *Dora* 141
Abeyance Those winters of *a* all worn out, — *Princess iv* 440
Abhor I hate, *a*, spit, sicken at him; — *Lucretius* 199
Abhorr'd they fell and made the glen *a*: — *Lancelot and E.* 42
Abhorrent *A* of a calculation crost, — *Enoch Arden* 473
Abide 'Trust me, in bliss I shall *a* — *Palace of Art* 18
Tho' much is taken, much *a's*; — *Ulysses* 65
In whose least act *a's* the nameless charm — *Princess v* 70
you failing, I *a* What end soever: — ,, 405
hate me not, but *a* your lot, — *Spiteful Letter* 11
A: thy wealth is gather'd in, — *In Mem. lii* 15
A a little longer here, — ,, *lviii* 11
Dare I bid her *a* by her word? — *Maud I xvi* 25
but *a* Without, among the cattle — *Gareth and L.* 273
A: take counsel; for this lad — ,, 730
shalt *a* her judgment on it; — *Marr. of Geraint* 584
'I will *a* the coming of my lord, — *Geraint and E.* 131
thou art man, and canst *a* a truth, — *Balin and Balan* 501
Yet better if the King *a*, — *Last Tournament* 109

Abide (*continued*) the wife Whom he knows false, *a* — *Guinevere* 515
which thou wilt *a*, if thou be wise, — *Ancient Sage* 35
Wretch you must *a* it . . . — *Forlorn* 52
Abidest *a* lame and poor, Calling thyself — *Two Voices* 197
Abiding *A* with me till I sail To seek thee — *In Mem. cxxv* 13
Able-bodied Grew plump and *a-b*; — *The Goose* 18
Abler A quarter-sessions chairman, *a* none; — *Princess, Con.*, 90
Abode at the farm *a* William and Dora. — *Dora* 1
those four *a* Within one house — ,, 169
Wherein the younger Charles *a* — *Talking Oak* 297
she *a* his coming, and said to him — *Geraint and E.* 139
stately Queen *a* For many a week, — *Guinevere* 146
mightiest of my knights, *a* with me, — ,, 430
Clave to him, and *a* in his own land. — ,, 440
Time and Grief *a* too long with Life, — *Lover's Tale i* 107
Abodest While thou *a* in the bud. — *Two Voices* 158
Abolish Caught at the hilt, as to *a* him: — *Marr. of Geraint* 210
Abominable The *A*, that uninvited came — *Œnone* 224
shapes of lust, unspeakable, *A*, — *Lucretius* 158
and shatter it, hold it *a*, — *Boädicea* 65
Abreast One walk'd *a* with me, — *Lover's Tale ii* 86
Abruptly broke the sentence in his heart *A*, — *Geraint and E.* 42
Absence she mourn'd his *a* as his grave, — *Enoch Arden* 247
in his *a* full of light and joy, — *Lover's Tale i* 425
Absolution find A sort of *a* in the sound — *Sea Dreams* 61
Absolution-seller *a-s's*, monkeries — *Sir John Oldcastle* 93
Absorb in its onward current it *a's* — *Isabel* 31
Absorbing *A* all the incense of sweet thoughts — *Lover's Tale i* 469
Abstraction They do so that affect *a* — *Princess ii* 359
A-buried I'll hev 'im *a-b* wi'mma — *North. Cobbler* 106
Abû Saïd (Sufee Poet) him *A S*—a sun but dimly seen — *Akbar's Dream* 94
Abuse (s) 'lest from the *a* of war, — *Princess v* 126
bore without *a* The grand old name — *In Mem. cxi* 21
Perchance from some *a* of Will — *Epilogue* 24
Abuse (verb) wayward grief *a* The genial hour — *In Mem. cv* 9
my Leonard, use and not *a* your day, — *Locksley H., Sixty*, 265
Abused God's great gift of speech *a* — *A Dirge* 44
Abysm fell into the *a* Of forms outworn, — *Lover's Tale i* 796
weigh'd him down into the *a*— — *Columbus* 137
into the *a*, The *A* of all *A's*, — *Ancient Sage* 39
downward too into the *a*. — *Locksley H., Sixty*, 146
Abyss and the waste wide Of that *a*, — *Two Voices* 120
to sound the *a* Of science, — *Princess ii* 176
lighten thro' The secular *a* to come, — *In Mem. lxxvi* 6
O, from the distance of the *a* — ,, *xciii* 11
upheaven from the *a* By fire, to sink into the *a* again; — *Pass. of Arthur* 82
bubble bursts above the *a* Of Darkness, — *Romney's R.* 52
Acacia Was lispt about the *a's*, — *Princess vii* 251
The slender *a* would not shake — *Maud I xxii* 45
Academe The softer Adams of your *A*, — *Princess ii* 197
this your *A*, Whichever side be Victor, — ,, 230
A-callin' *a-c* ma 'hugly' mayhap to my faäce — *Spinster's S's.* 91
kep *a-c'* o' Roä till 'e waggled 'is taäil — *Owd Roä* 105
Acanthus-wreath many a wov'n *a-w* divine! — *Lotos-Eaters, C. S.*, 97

Accent an *a* very low In blandishment, *Isabel* 19
She replies, in *a's* fainter, *L. of Burleigh* 5
With nearing chair and lower'd *a*) *Aylmer's Field* 267
Accept God *a* him, Christ receive him. *Ode on Well.* 281
do *a* my madness, and would die *Maud I xviii* 44
to *a* this cloth of gold, *Gareth and L.* 398
that I *a* thee aught the more ,, 766
a thee aught the more, Scullion, ,, 839
a this old imperfect tale, *To the Queen ii* 36
dark lord *a* and love the Sun, *Demeter and P.* 137
Acceptance Blithe would her brother's *a* be. *Maud I x* 27
Access closed her *a* to the wealthier farms, *Aylmer's Field* 503
down the lane of *a* to the King, *Gareth and L.* 661
Acclaim tumult of their *a* is roll'd *Dying Swan* 33
And follow'd with *a's*, *Will Water.* 138
let a people's voice In full *a*, *Ode on Well.* 143
Is wrought with tumult of *a*. *In Mem. lxxv* 20
Accompanied and oft *a* By Averill: *Aylmer's Field* 137
Accompanying brethren slowly with bent brows *A*, *Lancelot and E.* 1139
Accomplice The *a* of your madness unforgiven, *Princess vi* 276
Accomplish 'Which did *a* their desire, *Two Voices* 217
A thou my manhood and thyself; *Princess vii* 365
A that blind model in the seed, *Prog. of Spring* 114
Accomplish'd (*See also* **All-accomplish'd**, **Full-accomplished**)
Who, thro' their own desire *a*, *Aylmer's Field* 776
I have *a* what I came to do. *Columbus* 65
My mission be *a*!' *Akbar's Dream* 199
Accomplishment win all eyes with all *a*: *The form, the form* 4
Miss the full flower of this *a*.' *Gareth and L.* 1297
Accord (s) when both were brought to full *a*, *Last Tournament* 722
Faith and Work were bells of full *a*, *In Mem. W. G. Ward* 2
Accord (verb) I *a* it easily as a grace.' *Gareth and L.* 975
Accorded Prince *A* with his wonted courtesy, *Lancelot and E.* 638
According That mind and soul, *a* well, *In Mem., Pro.*, 27
would work *a* as he will'd. *Holy Grail* 784
lady's love, *A* to her promise, *Pelleas and E.* 162
A to the Highest in the Highest. *Ancient Sage* 90
for my sake, *A* to my word?' *Romney's R.* 130
To pray, to do *a* to the prayer, *Akbar's Dream* 8
Account (s) dodged me with a long and loose *a*. *Sea Dreams* 149
a hard friend in his loose *a's*, ,, 162
of the crowd you took no more *a* *Lancelot and E.* 105
Account (verb) Eat and be glad, for I
a you mine' *Geraint and E.* 647
whatsoever he *a's* Of all his treasures *Lover's Tale iv* 233
Accounted Is thy white blamelessness *a* blame!' *Merlin and V.* 799
Accoutrement Among piled arms and rough *a's*, *Princess v* 55
Accrue Delight a hundredfold *a*, *In Mem. cxvii* 8
Accurate your fine epithet Is *a* too, *Merlin and V.* 533
Accurst-Accursed Thro' you, my life will be *accurst*.' *The Letters* 36
Accursed, who from the wrongs *Gareth and L.* 347
Accursed, who strikes nor lets the hand ,, 435
Accursèd were she!' (repeat) *Kapiolani* 21, 24
Accusation Like bitter *a* ev'n to death, *Love and Duty* 81
people's talk And *a* of uxoriousness *Marr. of Geraint* 83
breathe but *a* vast and vague, *Merlin and V.* 701
Accuse sent for Blanche to *a* her *Princess iv* 239
A her of the least immodesty: *Geraint and E.* 111
Accused You never once *a* me, *Happy* 69
Achæan nor join'd The *A's*— *Achilles over the T.* 16
Ache (s) (*See also* **Finger-ache**, **Haäche**)
In coughs, *a's*, stitches, *St. S. Stylites* 13
And ills and *a's*, and teethings, *Holy Grail* 554
Ache (verb) would not let your little finger *a* *Godiva* 22
The sight that throbs and *a's* *Lover's Tale i* 33
a's in the grasp of an idiot power, *Despair* 43
Achievable if our end were less *a* *Princess iii* 283
Achieve Gone! He will *a* his greatness *Tiresias* 168
spoken true Of all we shall *a*, *Mechanophilus* 26
Achieved sword and golden circlet were *a*. *Pelleas and E.* 170
a, The loneliest ways are safe *Last Tournament* 101
Achieving some have striven, *A* calm, *Two Voices* 209
Achilles see the great *A*, whom we knew. *Ulysses* 64
Then rose *A* dear to Zeus; *Achilles over the T.* 2
Acknowledge in my heart of hearts I did *a* nobler. *Lancelot and E.* 1211

A-cleänin' as we was *a-c* the floor, *Spinster's S's.* 49
Aconite Their rich ambrosia tasted *a*. *Demeter and P.* 105
Acorn An *a* in her breast. *Talking Oak* 228
nor yet Thine *a* in the land. ,, 260
Acorn-ball wear Alternate leaf and *a-b* ,, 287
Acquiescing the Queen But coldly *a*, *Last Tournament* 23
A-crawin' (crowing) cocks kep *a-c* an' crawin' *Owd Roä* 106
Acre (*See also* **Five-acre**, **Haäcre**) dinner To
the men of many *a's*, *Maud I xx* 32
Acreage No coarse and blockish God of *a* *Aylmer's Field* 651
A-creeäpin (creeping) wur *a-c* about my waäist; *Spinster's S's.* 26
Acrimony flow'd in shallower *acrimonies*: *Aylmer's Field* 563
A-cryin' then I seed 'er *a-c*, I did. *Owd Roä* 80
Act (s) A saying, hard to shape in *a*; *Love thou thy land* 49
swift mind, In *a* to throw: *M. d'Arthur* 61
king demand An *a* unprofitable, ,, 96
In *a* to render thanks. *Gardener's D.* 162
which I clothed in *a*, *Princess i* 195
a tiger-cat In *a* to spring ,, *ii* 451
by single *a* Of immolation ,, *iii* 284
And all creation in one *a* at once, ,, 325
One *a* a phantom of succession: ,, 329
makes Such head from *a* to *a*, ,, *iv* 452
least *a* abides the nameless charm ,, *v* 70
creatures native unto gracious *a*, ,, *vii* 27
How much of *a* at human hands *In Mem. lxxxv* 38
bold in heart and *a* and word was he, *Com. of Arthur* 176
graced the lowliest *a* in doing it. *Gareth and L.* 490
dream she could be guilty of foul *a*, *Marr. of Geraint* 120
hearts who see but *a's* of wrong: ,, 438
So splendid in his *a's* and his attire, ,, 620
Balin graspt, but while in *a* to hurl, *Balin and Balan* 368
FROM noiseful arms, and *a's* of prowess *Holy Grail* 1
one last *a* of knighthood shalt thou see. *Pass. of Arthur* 163
the swift mind, In *a* to throw: ,, 229
king demand An *a* unprofitable, ,, 264
beautiful in Past of *a* or place, *Lover's Tale i* 135
with her highest *a* the placid face ,, 216
power on thine own *a* and on the world. *De Prof. Two G.* 56
A first, this Earth, a stage *The Play* 1
may show In some fifth *A* ,, 4
Act (verb) up and *a*, nor shrink For fear *Princess iii* 265
For who can always *a*? *In Mem. cxi* 9
be born and think, And *a* and love, ,, *Con.*, 127
Not he, not yet! and time to *a*— *The Flight* 73
Acted weaker grows thro' *a* crime, *Will* 12
If more and *a* on, what follows? *Princess ii* 229
after madness *a* question ask'd: *Geraint and E.* 813
thro' the journey home, *A* her hest, *Pelleas and E.* 203
Acting (*See also* **Over-acting**) *A* the law we
live by without fear; *Œnone* 148
Action 'Which in all *a* is the end of all; ,, 122
until endurance grow Sinew'd with *a*, ,, 165
enough of *a*, and of motion we, *Lotos-Eaters, C. S.*, 105
I myself must mix with *a*, *Locksley Hall* 98
A life in civic *a* warm, *In Mem. cxiii* 9
shape His *a* like the greater ape, ,, *cxx* 11
unfathom'd woe Reflex of *a*. *Lover's Tale i* 747
mould it into *a* pure as theirs. *Tiresias* 129
Acton (Sir Roger) *See* **Roger Acton**
Actor let the dying *a* mouth his last *Locksley H., Sixty*, 152
Adair (Ellen) *See* **Ellen Adair**
A-dallackt (overdrest) An' hallus *a-d* an' dizen'd out, *Village Wife* 37
Adam The gardener *A* and his wife *L. C. V. de Vere* 51
when *A* first embraced his Eve *Day-Dm., L'Envoi* 41
The softer *A's* of your Academe, *Princess ii* 197
there be Two *A's*, two mankinds, *Columbus* 54
Adam's wine I a' nowt but *A w*: *North. Cobbler* 5
an' a beslings-puddin' an' *A w*; ,, 112
Add *a* A crimson to the quaint Macaw, *Day-Dm., Pro.*, 15
Nor *a* and alter, many times, *Will Water.* 15
a my diamonds to her pearls; *Lancelot and E.* 1224
months will *a* themselves and make *Guinevere* 625
Added set the words, and *a* names I knew. *Audley Court* 61
'Swear' *a* Enoch sternly 'on the book.' *Enoch Arden* 842

Added (*continued*) Put on more calm and *a* supplantly: *Princess vi* 215
Had surely *a* praise to praise. *In Mem. xxxi* 8
faith, I fain had *a*—Knight, *Gareth and L.* 1162
weight is *a* only grain by grain, *Marr. of Geraint* 526
Then Balan *a* to their Order *Balin and Balan* 91
a, of her wit, A border fantasy *Lancelot and E.* 10
a plain Sir Torre, 'Yea, since I cannot ,, 198
'A fair large diamond, *a* plain Sir Torre, ,, 230
a wound to wound, And ridd'n away ,, 567
Were *a* mouths that gaped, ,, 1249
a to the griefs the great must bear, *Guinevere* 205
each other They should have *a*), *Lover's Tale i* 263
Your viceregal days Have *a* fulness *To Marq. of Dufferin* 11
Adder I thought it was an *a's* fold, *Lover's Tale i* 691
harm an *a* thro' the lust for harm, *Ancient Sage* 271
Addition Balin, 'the Savage'—that *a* *Balin and Balan* 53
Addle (earn) Mun be a guvness, lad, or summut, and *a* her breäd: *N. Farmer, N. S.*, 26
Address Began to *a* us, and was moving on *Princess ii* 184
Address'd-Addrest faces toward us and *address'd* Their motion: ,, *iv* 551
now *address'd* to speech—Who spoke few words ,, *Con.*, 93
suddenly *addrest* the hoary Earl: *Marr. of Geraint* 402
address'd More to the inward than the outward *Lover's Tale i* 720
Adeline Faintly smiling *A*, *Adeline* 2
Shadowy, dreaming *A*? (repeat) *Adeline* 10, 39
Spiritual *A*? (repeat) ,, 22, 64
Who talketh with thee, *A*? ,, 24
Thou faint smiler, *A*? ,, 48
Than your twin-sister, *A* *Margaret* 48
Adieu uttered it, And bade *a* for ever *Love and Duty* 83
What more? we took our last *a*, *The Daisy* 85
'*A*, *a*,' for evermore. *In Mem. lvii* 16
For tho' my lips may breathe *a*, ,, *cxxiii* 11
Adit yourself and yours shall have Free *a*; *Princess vi* 302
Adjust *a* My vapid vegetable loves *Talking Oak* 182
Admiral Chains for the *A* of the Ocean! *Columbus* 19
Chains! we are *A's* of the Ocean, ,, 28
Ocean—of the Indies—*A's* we— ,, 31
Admire *a* Joints of cunning workmanship *Vision of Sin* 185
not to desire or *a*, if a man *Maud I iv* 41
Admired which when now *a* By Edith *Aylmer's Field* 231
Admiring sat beside the couch, *A* him, *Marr. of Geraint* 80
the two Were turning and *a* it, ,, 637
Admission beat *a* in a thousand years, *Princess iii* 155
Admit Nor other thought her mind *a's* *In Mem. xxxii* 2
The time *a's* not flowers or leaves ,, *cvii* 5
Ado why make we such *a*? *May Queen, Con.*, 56
Adoration Meet *a* to my household gods, *Ulysses* 42
shaken voice, And flutter'd *a*, *Merlin and V.* 158
Adore How many measured words *a* *Eleänore* 45
To stand apart, and to *a*, ,, 79
on the meadow grass, and *a*, *Maud I v* 26
Strong in the power that all men *a*, ,, *x* 14
Adored was *a*; He, loved for her *Aylmer's Field* 178
A her, as the stateliest and the best *Marr. of Geraint* 20
Call'd on the Power *a* by the Christian, *Kapiolani* 32
Adoring *A* That who made, and makes, *Akbar's Dream* 123
Kneel *a* Him the Timeless ,, *D. Hymn* 8
Adorn brought to *a* her with, The jewels, *Last Tournament* 715
Adorn'd her I loved, *a* with fading flowers. *Lover's Tale iii* 40
A-dressin' an' jessmine *a-d* it greeän, *Spinster's S's.* 105
A-drooping locks *a-d* twined Round thy neck *Adeline* 57
Adulation golden eloquence And amorous *a*, *Lancelot and E.* 650
Adulterer My knights are all *a's* like his own, *Last Tournament* 84
'*A*, Go back to thine adulteress and die!' *Death of Œnone* 47
Adulteress Go back to thine *a* and die!' ,, 48
Adultery mother of the foul *adulteries* *Aylmer's Field* 376
adulteries, Wife-murders,— *Romney's R.* 133
Advance (s) But these are the days of *a*, *Maud I i* 25
Advance (verb) 'The years with change *a*: *Two Voices* 52
How gain in life, as life *a's* *To F. D. Maurice* 39
Let all my genial spirits *a* *In Mem., Con.*, 77
'*A* and take, as fairest of the fair, *Marr. of Geraint* 553

Advance (verb) (*continued*) '*A* and take thy prize The diamond'; *Lancelot and E.* 503
wreaths of all that would *a*, *To Victor Hugo* 5
Advanced Something far *a* in State, *Ode on Well.* 275
a The monster, and then paused, *Gareth and L.* 1384
who *a*, Each growling like a dog, *Geraint and E.* 558
the King himself *A* to greet them, ,, 879
Advancing up and down *A* nor retreating. *Sisters (E. and E.)* 179
Advantage He took *a* of his strength to be *Princess ii* 152
Forebore his own *a*, (repeat) *Guinevere* 331, 333
Advent Wink at our *a*: help my prince *Princess iii* 160
dividing clove An *a* to the throne: ,, *iv* 284
Expecting still his *a* home; *In Mem. vi* 21
Adventure battle, bold *a*, dungeon, wreck, *Aylmer's Field* 98
mad for strange *a*, dash'd away *Balin and Balan* 289
then, with small *a* met, Sir Bors *Holy Grail* 660
Bound upon solitary *a*, saw *Pelleas and E.* 275
Adversary robbers mock at a barbarous *a*. *Boädicea* 18
hearing her tumultuous *adversaries* ,, 78
Advice he wouldn't take my *a*. *Grandmother* 4
Adviser Horace, you the wise *A* *Poets and their B.* 6
A-dying For the old year lies *a-d*. *D. of the O. Year* 5
Æakidês So rang the clear voice of *Æ*; *Achilles over the T.* 21
cry of *Æ* Was heard among the Trojans, ,, 22
Ægis Pallas flung Her fringed *æ*, ,, 4
Æolian *Æ* harp that wakes No certain air, *Two Voices* 436
Scarce living in the *Æ* harmony, *Lover's Tale i* 477
Æon the great *Æ* sinks in blood, *In Mem. cxxvii* 16
Whirl'd for a million *æ's* *De Prof. Two G.* 3
Many an *Æ* moulded earth before her highest, *Locksley H., Sixty*, 205
Many an *Æ* too may pass ,, 206
Shall not *æ* after *æ* pass and touch *Making of Man* 4
Æonian Draw down *Æ* hills, and sow *In Mem. xxxv* 11
Æ music measuring out The steps ,, *xcv* 41
Æ Evolution, swift or slow, *The Ring* 44
Aërially And less *a* blue, *Margaret* 51
a murmur heard *a*, *Boädicea* 24
Ætna as *Æ* does The Giant of Mythology *Lover's Tale iv* 17
and *Æ* kept her winter snow *Demeter and P.* 115
Afear'd (afraid) But Squire wur *a* o' 'is son, *Village Wife* 63
allus *a* of a man's gittin' ower fond, *Spinster's S's.* 27
I wasn't *a*, or I thinks leästwaäys as I wasn't *a*; *Owd Roä* 86
Affair For I never whisper'd a private *a* *Maud II v* 47
kinsman travelling on his own *a* *Merlin and V.* 717
Affect They do so that *a* abstraction *Princess ii* 359
Affection The still *a* of the heart *Miller's D.* 225
he spoke, Part banter, part *a* *Princess, Pro.*, 167
old and strange *a* of the house. ,, *i* 13
cared not for the *a* of the house; ,, 26
like a flash the weird *a* came: ,, *v* 477
wing'd *a's* clipt with crime: ,, *vii* 316
My old *a* of the tomb, (repeat) *In Mem. lxxxv* 75, 77
With what divine *a's* bold ,, *xciv* 2
A, and the light of victory, *Gareth and L.* 331
a mood Of over-strain'd *a*, *Merlin and V.* 522
'Stabb'd through the heart's *a's* ,, 868
with full *a* said, 'Lancelot, *Lancelot and E.* 1355
if *A* Living slew Love, *Lover's Tale ii* 30
Affiance when I dwelt upon your old *a*, *Princess iii* 139
in whom I have Most joy and most *a*, *Lancelot and E.* 1357
Affianced *a* years ago To the Lady Ida: *Princess ii* 215
A, Sir? love-whispers may not ,, 221
with Melissa Florian, I With mine *a*. ,, *iii* 356
Affirm *A's* your Psyche thieved her theories, ,, 92
Affirm'd she *a* not, or denied: ,, *iv* 234
Affirming *A* each his own philosophy— *Lucretius* 216
A that his father left him gold, *Marr. of Geraint* 451
A that as long as either lived, *Lover's Tale iv* 277
Affluence (*See also* **Heart-Affluence**) You, that wanton in *a*, *On Jub. Q. Victoria* 28
Affright nothing there her maiden grace *a*! *Maud I xviii* 71
like a man in a mortal *a*; *V. of Maeldune* 74
Affrighted Round *a* Lisbon drew *Ode on Well.* 103
Affronted *A* with his fulsome innocence? *Pelleas and E.* 266
Afire (on fire) the house is *a*,' she said. *Owd Roä* 68

Afire (*continued*) 'But the stairs is *a*,' she said ; *Owd Roä* 80
A-flyin' wool of a thistle *a-f* an' seeädin' *Spinster's S's.* 79
Afraid *See* **Afear'd, Half-afraid.**
Afric On capes of *A* as on cliffs of Kent, *W. to Marie Alex.* 17
African Indian, Australasian, *A*, *On Jub. Q. Victoria* 61
After-age Thro' *a-a's* in the love of Truth, *Akbar's Dream* 101
After-beauty that *a-b* makes Such head *Princess iv* 451
After-days It grows to guerdon *a-d*: *Love thou thy land* 27
After-dinner It seems in *a-d* talk *Miller's D.* 31
'Twas but an *a-d's* nap. *Day-Dm., Revival* 24
After-fulness from the *a-f* of my heart, *Lover's Tale i* 146
After-hands whence *a-h* May move the world, *Princess iii* 263
After-heat It might have drawn from *a-h.*' *In Mem. lxxxi* 12
After-life my dead face would vex her *a-l.* *Enoch Arden* 891
she will pass me by in *a-l* *Princess v* 91
After-love *A-l's* of maids and men *Window, No Answer* 25
Aftermath a sweep Of meadow smooth from *a* *Audley Court* 14
After-morn Which left my *a-m* content. *In Mem. ciii* 4
That man can have no *a-m*, *Epilogue* 73
Afternoon In the *a* they came unto a land *Lotos-Eaters* 3
In which it seemed always *a*. ,, 4
Bright was that *a*, Sunny but chill ; *Enoch Arden* 669
Half-sickening of his pension'd *a*, *Aylmer's Field* 461
'That *a* the Princess rode *Princess iii* 169
all That *a* a sound arose ,, *vi* 379
in the all-golden *a* A guest, *In Mem. lxxxix* 25
But in the falling *a* return'd *Geraint and E.* 591
It made the laughter of an *a* *Merlin and V.* 163
Here in the never-ended *a*, *Last Tournament* 584
For brief repast or *a* repose *Guinevere* 395
and yester *a* I dream'd,— *Akbar's Dream* 169
Aftertime I am sung or told In *a*, *M. d'Arthur* 35
relic of my lord Should be to *a*, ,, 99
some old man speak in the *a* ,, 107
a, And that full voice which circles *Princess ii* 44
sole men we shall prize in the *a*, ,, *v* 412
I am sung or told In *a*, *Pass. of Arthur* 203
relic of my lord Should be to *a*, ,, 267
some old man speak in the *a* ,, 275
After-years *a-y* Will learn the secret of our Arthur's birth.' *Com. of Arthur* 158
Agape A rabbit mouth that is ever *a*— *Maud I x* 31
ye seem *a* to roar ! *Gareth and L.* 1306
Agaric learned names of *a*, moss and fern, *Edwin Morris* 17
as one That smells a foul-flesh'd *a* *Gareth and L.* 747
Agate Turkis and *a* and almondine *The Merman* 32
bottom *a's* seen to wave and float *Princess ii* 327
Agavè One tall *A* above the lake. *The Daisy* 84
A-gawin' (going) I beänt *a-g* to breäk my rule. *N. Farmer, O. S.*, 4
A-gawinin' (staring) an' foälk stood *a-g'* in, *North. Cobbler* 81
Age (*See also* **Aäge, After-age, Mother-age**) There hath he lain for *a's* and will lie. *The Kraken* 11
'I know that *a* to *a* succeeds, *Two Voices* 205
makes me talk too much in *a*. *Miller's D.* 194
And the great *a's* onward roll. *To J. S.* 72
Now the most blessed memory of mine *a*. *Gardener's D.* 279
thrifty too beyond her *a*. *Dora* 16
until he grows Of *a* to help us.' ,, 127
old sore breaks out from *a* to *a* *Walk. to the Mail* 79
Of different *a's*, like twin-sisters *Edwin Morris* 32
suffer'd long For *a's* and for *a's* !' *St. S. Stylites* 100
float about the threshold of an *a*, *Golden Year* 16
an *a*, when every hour Must sweat ,, 68
Old *a* hath yet his honour *Ulysses* 50
Immortal *a* beside immortal youth, *Tithonus* 22
thro' the *a's* one increasing purpose *Locksley Hall* 137
I the heir of all the *a's*, ,, 178
As all were order'd, *a's* since. *Day-Dm., Sleep. P.*, 54
'Tis vain ! in such a brassy *a* *Amphion* 65
found My spirits in the golden *a*. *To E. L.* 12
tonsured head in middle *a* forlorn, *The Brook* 200
when *this* Aylmer came of *a*— *Aylmer's Field* 407
huge cathedral fronts of every *a*, *Sea Dreams* 218
palsy, death-in-life, And wretched *a*— *Lucretius* 155
every clime and *a* Jumbled together ; *Princess, Pro.*, 16

Age (*continued*) 'The climax of his *a* ! *Princess, Pro.*, *ii* 50
Amazon As emblematic of a nobler *a* ; *Princess ii* 127
some *a's* had been lost ; ,, 153
second-sight of some Astræan *a*, ,, 443
reasons drawn from *a* and state, ,, *v* 357
you got a friend of your own *a*, ,, *vi* 251
To such a name for *a's* long, *Ode on Well.* 76
For many and many an *a* proclaim ,, 226
tho' the Giant *A's* heave the hill ,, 259
at your *a*, Annie, I could have wept (repeat) *Grandmother* 20, 100
And *a* is a time of peace, ,, 97
I hear the roll of the *a's*. *Spiteful Letter* 8
Milton, a name to resound for *a's* ; *Milton* 4
to-morrow, And that's an *a* away.' *Window, When* 14
left for human deeds In endless *a* ? *In Mem. lxxiii* 12
take the print Of the golden *a*— *Maud I i* 30
many a million of *a's* have gone ,, *iv* 35
Wretchedest *a*, since Time began, ,, *II v* 21
His *a* hath slowly droopt, *Gareth and L.* 79
sadder *a* begins To war against ill uses ,, 1129
suffering thus he made Minutes an *a*: *Geraint and E.* 115
flatter his own wish in *a* for love, *Merlin and V.* 185
Who paced it, *a's* back : ,, 553
more fitly yours, not thrice your *a* : *Lancelot and E.* 953
Built by old kings, *a* after *a*, *Holy Grail* 340
I found Only one man of an exceeding *a*. ,, 431
In the white winter of his *a*, *Pass. of Arthur* 4
weight as if of *a* upon my limbs, *Lover's Tale i* 125
she, my love, is of an *a* with me ,, 196
poisons of his heart In his old *a*.' ,, 357
the fool this *A* that doubts of all— *Sisters (E. and E.)* 141
in that flight of *a's* which are God's *Columbus* 202
but thine *a*, by *a* as winter-white *Tiresias* 19
And oldest *a* in shadow from the night, ,, 104
and the human heart, and the *A*. *Despair* 40
For these are the new dark *a's*, ,, 88
And cap our *a* with snow ?' *Ancient Sage* 98
The poet whom his *A* would quote ,, 146
well might fool a dotard's *a*. *Locksley H., Sixty*, 10
Some thro' *a* and slow diseases, ,, 46
A's after, while in Asia, ,, 81
an *a* of noblest English names, ,, 83
When was *a* so cramm'd with menace ? ,, 108
Bring the old dark *a's* back without the faith, ,, 137
well, it scarce becomes mine *a*— ,, 151
Gone at eighty, mine own *a*, ,, 281
tho', in this lean *a* forlorn, *Epilogue* 71
Light among the vanish'd *a's* ; *To Virgil* 25
May we find, as *a's* run, *Open. I. and C. Exhib.* 11
darkness Dawns into the Jubilee of the *A's*. *On Jub. Q. Victoria* 71
the morning when you came of *a* *The Ring* 77
girls of equal *a*, but one was fair, ,, 160
My ring too when she comes of *a*, ,, 289
For *A* will chink the face, *Happy* 46
gloom of *A* And suffering cloud *Romney's R.* 64
And over the flight of the *A's* ! *Parnassus* 3
What hast thou done for me, grim Old *A*, *By an Evolution.* 9
I have climb'd to the snows of *A*, ,, 17
all but deaf thro' *a* and weariness, *St. Telemachus* 41
and ere the crowning *A* of *a's*, *Making of Man* 3
When I make for an *A* of gold, *The Dreamer* 7
Helter-skelter runs the *a* ; *Poets and Critics* 2
Agent (*See also* **Agint**) Thro' many *a's* making strong, *Love thou thy land* 39
Aghast (*See also* **Half-Aghast**) all that mark'd him were *a*. *Gareth and L.* 1399
not a word !' and Enid was *a* ; *Geraint and E.* 18
men and women staring and *a*, ,, 804
a the maiden rose, White as her veil, *Guinevere* 362
Agincourt 'this,' he said, 'was Hugh's at *A* ; *Princess, Pro.*, 25
Agint (Agent) Yer Honour's own *a*, he says to me *Tomorrow* 63
Agitated people around the royal chariot *a*, *Boädicea* 73
Aglaïa a double April old, *A* slept. *Princess ii* 111
my sweet *A*, my one child : ,, *v* 101
Came Psyche, sorrowing for *A*. ,, *vi* 29
A-glare all the Hells *a-g* in either eye, *Akbar's Dream* 115

Aglow '*My* Rose' set all your face *a*, *Roses on the T.* 3
Agned-Cathregonion And up in *A-C* too, *Lancelot and E.* 300
Agoän (gone) whoy, Doctor's abeän an' *a*: *N. Fårmer, O. S.*, 2
Agony ancient melody Of an inward *a*, *Claribel* 7
one voice an *a* Of lamentation, *M. d'Arthur* 200
kill'd with some luxurious *a*, *Vision of Sin* 43
modest bosom prest In *a*, *Aylmer's Field* 417
as cried Christ ere His *a* ,, 793
wail of women and children, multitudinous *agonies*. *Boädicea* 26
Roman slaughter, multitudinous *agonies*. ,, 84
With *agonies*, with energies, *In Mem.* cxiii 18
Travail, and throes and *agonies* of the life, *Com. of Arthur* 76
into wastes and solitudes For *a*, *Lancelot and E.* 253
up the side, sweating with *a*, ,, 494
Brain-feverous in his heat and *a*, ,, 854
one voice, an *a* Of lamentation, *Pass. of Arthur* 368
All joy, to whom my *a* was a joy. *Lover's Tale i* 656
and in his *a* conceives A shameful sense ,, 793
these in my *a* Did I make bare ,, *ii* 47
my dull *a*, Ideally to her transferr'd, ,, 136
Dead of some inward *a*—is it so? *To W. H. Brookfield* 10
Twisted hard in mortal *a* *Locksley H., Sixty*, 98
A-grawin' (growing) hes now be *a-g* sa howd, *Village Wife* 107
Agreed *a* That much allowance must be made *Aylmer's Field* 409
so it was *a* when first they came; *Princess iii* 36
A to, this, the day fled on ,, 176
his wish, whereto the Queen *a* *Lancelot and E.* 1169
then they were *a* upon a night *Guinevere* 96
he sent, an' the father *a*; *First Quarrel* 18
An' Molly an' me was *a*, *Spinster's S's.* 49
Agrin His visage all *a* as at a wake, *Princess v* 521
Agrippina and the Roman brows Of *A* ,, *ii* 85
Agypt (Egypt) Thim ould blind nagers in *A*, *Tomorrow* 69
A-hawking We ride *a-h* with Sir Lancelot *Merlin and V.* 95
Ahead he rode on *a*, as he waved his blade *Heavy Brigade* 9
Aid (s) knew not whither he should turn for *a*. *Com. of Arthur* 40
for lack of gentle maiden's *a*. *Lancelot and E.* 765
He needs no *a* who doth his lady's will.' *Pelleas and E.* 281
following thy true counsel, by thine *a*, *Akbar's Dream* 154
Aid (verb) Us, who stand now, when we should *a* the right— *Poland* 13
O Lord, *A* all this foolish people; *St. S. Stylites* 223
a me, give me strength Not to tell her, *Enoch Arden* 785
a me Heaven when at mine uttermost, *Marr. of Geraint* 502
Aiding serve them both in *a* her— *Princess vii* 268
Aidless to leave thee thus, *A*, alone, *M. d'Arthur* 41
to leave thee thus, *A*, alone, *Pass. of Arthur* 209
Aïdoneus car Of dark *A* rising rapt thee *Demeter and P.* 39
Ail mother thought, What *a's* the boy? *Miller's D.* 93
What *a's* us, who are sound, *Walk. to the Mail* 105
Ail'd What *a* her then, that ere she enter'd, *Enoch Arden* 518
told his gentle wife What *a* him, *Geraint and E.* 504
Aileth What *a* thee? whom waitest thou *Adeline* 45
Ailing 'Anything *a*,' I ask'd her, 'with baby?' *The Wreck* 61
only—you Were always *a*. *The Ring* 311
Ailment Yours has been a slighter *a*, *Locksley H., Sixty*, 17
Aim (s) Embrace our *a's*: work out your freedom. *Princess ii* 89
For fear our solid *a* be dissipated ,, *iii* 266
works Without a conscience or an *a*. *In Mem.* xxxiv 8
so I wake to the higher *a's* *Maud III vi* 38
he kept his mind on one sole *a*, *Merlin and V.* 626
a's Were sharpen'd by strong hate *Guinevere* 19
Because all other Hope had lower *a*; *Lover's Tale i* 455
Ready! take *a* at their leaders— *Def. of Lucknow* 42
Look to your butts, and take good *a's*! *Riflemen form!* 16
Aim (verb) one would *a* an arrow fair, *In Mem.* lxxxvii 25
Aim'd fairy arrows *a* All at one mark, *Aylmer's Field* 94
Nay, but she *a* not at glory, *Wages* 4
A at the helm, his lance err'd; *Geraint and E.* 157
better *a* are your flank fusillades— *Def. of Lucknow* 57
Aiming near storm, and *a* at his head, *Aylmer's Field* 727
In *a* at an all but hopeless mark *The Ring* 346
Aimless three days, *a* about the land, *Pelleas and E.* 391
Air (atmosphere) Till the *a* And the ground *Nothing will Die* 27
Or breathe into the hollow *a*, *Supp. Confessions* 58
Air (atmosphere) (*continued*) fires and fluid range Of lawless *a's*, *Supp. Confessions* 148
The living *a's* of middle night *Arabian Nights* 69
a is damp, and hush'd, and close, *A spirit haunts* 13
Life in dead stones, or spirit in *a*; *A Character* 9
Wide, wild, and open to the *a*, *Dying Swan* 2
Or when little *a's* arise, *Adeline* 33
With melodious *a's* lovelorn, ,, 55
reveal'd themselves to English *a*, *Eleänore* 2
a Sleepeth over all the heaven, ,, 38
Like softened *a's* that blowing steal, *Two Voices* 406
The very *a* about the door *Miller's D.* 103
earth and *a* seem only burning fire.' *Œnone* 268
the summer *a's* blow cool *May Queen, N. Y's. E.* 27
the languid *a* did swoon, *Lotos-Eaters* 5
Falls, and floats adown the *a*. ,, *C. S.*, 31
warm *a's* lull us, blowing lowly) ,, 89
was no motion in the dumb dead *a*, *D. of F. Women* 65
round them sea and *a* are dark *Love thou thy land* 63
made the *a* Of Life delicious, *Gardener's D.* 69
murmur broke the stillness of that *a* ,, 147
Felt earth as *a* beneath me, ,, 212
A soft *a* fans the cloud apart; *Tithonus* 32
deep *a* listen'd round her as she rode, *Godiva* 54
I yearn to breathe the *a's* of heaven *Sir Galahad* 63
Are touch'd, are turn'd to finest *a*. ,, 72
And clouds are highest up in *a*, *Lady Clare* 2
All the *a* was torn in sunder, *The Captain* 43
Like Fancy made of golden *a*, *The Voyage* 66
green From draughts of balmy *a*. *Sir L. and Q. G.* 9
black yew gloom'd the stagnant *a*, *The Letters* 2
sweet half-English Neilgherry *a* *The Brook* 17
breath Of tender *a* made tremble ,, 202
at a touch of light, an *a* of heaven, *Aylmer's Field* 5
rush of the *a* in the prone swing, ,, 86
to flush his blood with *a*, ,, 459
Drank the large *a*, and saw, *Sea Dreams* 34
towering o'er him in serenest *a*, *Lucretius* 178
flushing the guiltless *a*, Spout ,, 239
soul flies out and dies in the *a*.' ,, 274
sweet as English *a* could make her, *Princess, Pro.*, 155
each light *a* On our mail'd heads: ,, *v* 244
'for this wild wreath of *a*, ,, 318
went The enamour'd *a* sighing ,, *vi* 79
with a tender foot, light as on *a*, ,, 88
shake To the same sweet *a*, ,, *vii* 69
Naked, a double light in *a* and wave, ,, 167
like a broken purpose waste in *a*: ,, 214
In that fine *a* I tremble, ,, 354
Thro' the long-tormented *a* Heaven *Ode on Well.* 128
Flash'd as they turn'd in *a* *Light Brigade* 28
Clash, ye bells, in the merry March *a*! *W. to Alexandra* 18
diviner *a* Breathe thro' the world *W. to Marie Alex.* 43
And snowy dells in a golden *a*. *The Daisy* 68
bird in *a*, and fishes turn'd *The Victim* 19
cloud in my heart, and a storm in the *a*! *Window, Gone* 6
no ruder *a* perplex Thy sliding keel, *In Mem.* ix 9
Calm and deep peace in this wide *a*, ,, xi 13
And circle moaning in the *a*: ,, xii 15
Was as the whisper of an *a* ,, xvii 3
As light as carrier-birds in *a*; ,, xxv 6
seem to have reach'd a purer *a*, ,, xxxiii 2
Sweet after showers, ambrosial *a*, ,, lxxxvi 1
And shook to all the liberal *a* ,, lxxxix 7
drink the cooler *a*, and mark ,, 15
The memory like a cloudless *a*, ,, xciv 11
With summer spice the humming *a*; ,, ci 8
the stirring *a* The life re-orient ,, cxvi 5
Thy voice is on the rolling *a*; ,, cxxx 1
ruin'd woodlands drove thro' the *a*. *Maud I i* 12
essences turn'd the live *a* sick ,, xiii 11
fed With honey'd rain and delicate *a*, ,, xviii 21
Melody on branch, and melody in mid *a*. *Gareth and L.* 183
solid turrets topsy-turvy in *a*: ,, 255
under one long lane of cloudless *a* *Bâlin and Balan* 461

Air (atmosphere) (*continued*) their foreheads felt the cooling *a*, — *Balin and Balan* 589
for God's love, a little *a*! — *Lancelot and E.* 505
a that smites his forehead is not *a* — *Holy Grail* 914
choice from *a*, land, stream, and sea, — *Pelleas and E.* 149
my rose, that sweeten'd all mine *a*— — ,, 403
started thro' mid *a* Bearing an eagle's nest: — *Last Tournament* 14
stump Pitch-blacken'd sawing the *a*, — ,, 67
heather-scented *a*, Pulsing full man; — ,, 691
spouting from a cliff Fails in mid *a*, — *Guinevere* 609
could not breathe in that fine *a* — ,, 645
outward circling *a* wherewith I breathe, — *Lover's Tale i* 167
seem'd a gossamer filament up in *a*, — ,, 413
moon, Half-melted into thin blue *a*, — ,, 421
flowing odour of the spacious *a*, — ,, 478
to all that draw the wholesome *a*, — ,, 500
the gentlest *a's* of Heaven Should kiss — ,, 738
A morning *a*, sweet after rain, — ,, *iii* 3
Bore her free-faced to the free *a's* — ,, *iv* 38
veil, that seemed no more than gilded *a*, — ,, 290
and horrible fowls of the *a*, — *Rizpah* 39
'O diviner *A*.' (repeat) — *Sisters* (*E. and E.*) 4
Breathe, diviner *A*! — ,, 13
but as welcome as free *a's* of heaven — ,, 197
God's free *a*, and hope of better things. — *Sir J. Oldcastle* 10
jewell'd throne thro' the fragrant *a*, — *V. of Maeldune* 59
where the water is clearer than *a*: — ,, 77
all that suffers on land or in *a* or the deep, — *Despair* 45
Yon summit half-a-league in *a*— — *Ancient Sage* 11
And now one breath of cooler *a* — ,, 117
side by side in God's free light and *a*, — *The Flight* 81
The woods with living *a's* — *Early Spring* 19
Light *a's* from where the deep, — ,, 21
there In haunts of jungle-poison'd *a* — *To Marq. of Dufferin* 31
pierce the glad and songful *a*, — *Demeter and P.* 45
we will feed her with our mountain *a*, — *The Ring* 319
up the tower—an icy *a* Fled by me.— — ,, 445
marvel how in English *a* My yucca, — *To Ulysses* 20
her bare To breaths of balmier *a*; — *Prog. of Spring* 13
Air (strain of music) Æolian harp that wakes No certain *a*, — *Two Voices* 437
With the *a* of the trumpet round him, — *Princess v* 162
slightest *a* of song shall breathe — *In Mem. xlix* 7
She is singing an *a* that is known to me, — *Maud I v* 3
while I past he was humming an *a*, — ,, *xiii* 17
playest that *a* with Queen Isolt, — *Last Tournament* 263
hum An *a* the nuns had taught her; — *Guinevere* 163
play That *a* which pleased her first. — *Lover's Tale i* 21
amid eddies of melodious *a's*, — ,, 450
'*A* and Words,' Said Hubert, — *The Ring* 24
Air (manner) I KNOW her by her angry *a*, — *Kate* 1
A cold *a* pass'd between us, — *The Ring* 380
'Air (hair) was stroäkin ma down wi' the '*a*, — *Spinster's S's.* 19
An' 'is '*a* coom'd off i' my 'ands — *Owd Roä* 100
Air'd into the world, And *a* him there: — *Aylmer's Field* 468
Airing *A* a snowy hand and signet gem, — *Princess i* 121
Airm (arm) blacksmith 'e strips me the thick ov 'is *a*, — *North. Cobbler* 85
Airth But *a* was at pace nixt mornin', — *Tomorrow* 25
Aisle 'Dark porch,' I said, 'and silent *a*, — *The Letters* 47
but in the middle *a* Reel'd, — *Aylmer's Field* 818
ambrosial *a's* of lofty lime — *Princess, Pro.*, 87
giant *a's*, Rich in model and design; — *Ode Inter. Exhib.* 12
sombre, old, colonnaded *a's*. — *The Daisy* 56
often I and Amy in the mouldering *a* have stood, — *Locksley H., Sixty*, 31
Ajalon like Joshua's moon in *A*! — *Locksley Hall* 180
Ajar THEY have left the doors *a*; — *Sisters* (*E. and E.*) 1
A-joompin' (jumping) An' hallus *a-j'* about ma — *Spinster's S's.* 89
Akbar (Mogul Emperor) ask'd his Chronicler Of *A* — *Akbar's Dream* 2
turning slowly toward him, *A* said — ,, 4
Akin (*See also* **Half-akin**) Maud to him is nothing *a*: — *Maud I xiii* 38
lawful and lawless war Are scarcely even *a*. — ,, *II v* 95
swallow and the swift are near *a*, — *Com. of Arthur* 313
Akrokeraunian The vast *A* walls, — *To E. L.* 4
A-laäid (lying) fun 'um theer *a-l* on 'is faäce — *N. Farmer, O. S.*, 33
Alarm when fresh from war's *a's*, — *D. of F. Women* 149
Alarm (*continued*) I shook her breast with vague *a's*— — *The Letters* 38
our sallies, their lying *a's*, — *Def. of Lucknow* 75
a's Sounding 'To arms! to arms!' — *Prog. of Spring* 103
Alas with many a vain '*A*!' — *Doubt and Prayer* 2
Albert 'And with him *A* came on his. — *Talking Oak* 105
Albert (Prince Consort) Hereafter, thro' all times, *A* the Good. — *Ded. of Idylls* 43
Albion laborious, Patient children of *A* — *On Jub. Q. Victoria* 59
Alcestis The true *A* of the time. — *Romney's R.* 91
Alchemise *a* old hates into the gold Of Love, — *Akbar's Dream* 163
Alcor Red-pulsing up thro' Alioth and *A*, — *Last Tournament* 480
Alder blowing over meadowy holms And *a's*, — *Edwin Morris* 96
Came wet-shod *a* from the wave, — *Amphion* 41
But here will sigh thine *a* tree, — *A Farewell* 9
Balin's horse Was fast beside an *a*, — *Balin and Balan* 29
Ale (*See also* **Aäle**) mellow'd all his heart with *a*, — *The Brook* 155
A mockery to the yeomen over *a*, — *Aylmer's Field* 497
A-leaning Weak Truth *a-l* on her crutch, — *Clear-headed friend* 18
Ale-house Jack on his *a-h* bench — *Maud I iv* 9
Alexandra SEA-KING's daughter from over the sea, *A*! — *W. to Alexandra* 2
Danes in our welcome of thee, *A*! — ,, 5
all Dane in our welcome of thee, *A*! — ,, 34
Alexandrovna (*See also* **Marie, Marie Alexandrovna**)
Prince his own imperial Flower, *A*. — *W. to Marie Alex.* 5
sultry palms of India known, *A*. — ,, 15
gives its throne a wife, *A*! — ,, 25
thy young lover hand in hand *A*! — ,, 35
and change the hearts of men, *A*? — ,, 45
Alfred—*A*! — ,, 50
Alfred (King of England) Truth-teller was our England's *A* named; — *Ode on Well.* 188
Alfred (Duke of Edinburgh, 1844-1900) *A*—Alexandrovna! — *W. to Marie Alex.* 50
Alice My own sweet *A*, we must die. — *Miller's D.* 18
Pray, *A*, pray, my darling wife, — ,, 23
But, *A*, what an hour was that, — ,, 57
Sweet *A*, if I told her all?' — ,, 120
Go fetch your *A* here,' she said: — ,, 143
But, *A*, you were ill at ease; — ,, 146
foolish song I gave you, *A*, on the day — ,, 162
none so fair as little *A* — *May Queen* 7
In there came old *A* the nurse, — *Lady Clare* 13
said *A* the nurse, (repeat) — *Lady Clare* 17, 23, 33, 41, 45
Alien I am but an *a* and a Genovese. — *Columbus* 243
Alif The *A* of Thine alphabet of Love.' — *Akbar's Dream* 31
A-liggin' (lying) wheere thou was *a-l*, my lad, — *Owd Roä* 87
Alighted (*See also* **Lighted**) To Francis just *a* from the boat, — *Audley Court* 7
Alioth Red-pulsing up thro' *A* and Alcor, — *Last Tournament* 480
Alive That thou, if thou wert yet *a*, — *Supp. Confessions* 100
Joying to feel herself *a*, — *Palace of Art* 178
pass away before, and yet *a* I am; — *May Queen, Con.*, 1
palace-front *A* with fluttering scarfs — *Princess v* 509
not always certain if they be *a* — *Grandmother* 84
there's none of them left *a*; — ,, 85
strive To keep so sweet a thing *a*:' — *In Mem. xxxv* 7
Dark bulks that tumble half *a*, — ,, *lxx* 11
at fifty Should Nature keep me *a*, — *Maud I vi* 32
with beatings in it, as if *a*, — *Holy Grail* 118
marvel among us that one should be left *a*, — *Def. of Lucknow* 78
And doom'd to burn *a*. — *Sir J. Oldcastle* 183
But we old friends are still *a*, — *To E. Fitzgerald* 42
The love that keeps this heart *a* — *The Flight* 35
the dead are not dead but *a*. — *Vastness* 36
'All (hall) sin fust a coom'd to the '*A*; — *N. Farmer, O. S.*, 55
walks down fro' the '*A* to see, — *North. Cobbler* 91
Alla both, to worship *A*, but the prayers, — *Akbar's Dream* 9
are faint And pale in *A's* eyes — ,, 11
A be my guide! — ,, 16
'Mine is the one fruit *A* made for man.' — ,, 40
pulse of *A* beats Thro' all His world. — ,, 41
Yet '*A*,' says their sacred book, 'is Love,' — ,, 73
Yea, *A* here on earth, who caught — ,, 84
was not *A* call'd In old Irân — ,, 86

Alla (*continued*) Who all but lost himself in *A*, *Akbar's Dream* 93
One *A* ! one Kalifa ! ,, 167
'All praise to *A* by whatever hands ,, 198
All-accomplish'd modest, kindly, *a-a*, wise *Ded. of Idylls* 18
All-amorous Brushing his instep, bow'd the *a-a* Earl *Geraint and E.* 360
Allan WITH Farmer *A* at the farm *Dora* 1
a day When *A* call'd his son, ,, 10
bells were ringing, *A* call'd His niece ,, 41
said *A*, 'did I not Forbid you, Dora?' ,, 91
A said, 'I see it is a trick ,, 95
seal, that hung From *A's* watch, ,, 136
A set him down, and Mary said : ,, 139
All-arm'd *A-a* I ride, whate'er betide, *Sir Galahad* 83
All-assuming The *a-a* months and years *In Mem. lxxxv* 67
All-comprehensive express *A-c* tenderness, ,, 47
Allegiance from all neighbour crowns Alliance and *a*, *Œnone* 125
my rose, there my *a* due. *Sir J. Oldcastle* 59
One full voice of *a*, *On Jub. Q. Victoria* 22
Allegory I SEND you here a sort of *a*, *To—— With Pal. of Art* 1
the third fool of their *a*.' *Gareth and L.* 1085
four fools have suck'd their *a* ,, 1199
Allen (Francis) *See* **Francis, Francis Allen**
All-enduring like the *a-e* camel, *Lover's Tale i* 136
Alley From the long *a's* latticed shade *Arabian Nights* 112
plaited *a's* of the trailing rose, *Ode to Memory* 106
a's falling down to twilight grots, ,, 107
every hollow cave and *a* lone *Lotos-Eaters, C. S.*, 103
And *a's*, faded places, *Amphion* 86
firefly-like in copse And linden *a*: *Princess i* 209
as she rode The woodland *a's*, *Balin and Balan* 439
There among the glooming *a's* *Locksley H., Sixty*, 219
All-fragrant slip at once *a-f* into one. *Princess vii* 70
All-generating *a-g* powers and genial heat Of Nature, *Lucretius* 97
All-golden in the *a-g* afternoon A guest, *In Mem. lxxxix* 25
All-graceful *A-g* head, so richly curl'd, *Day-Dm., L'Envoi* 38
All-heal with a bunch of *a-h* in her hand, *Vastness* 12
Alliance from all neighbour crowns *A* *Œnone* 125
longs For this *a*: *Sisters (E. and E.)* 29
Allied However she came to be so *a*. *Maud I xiii* 36
Allies backward reel'd the Trojans and *a* ; *Achilles over the T.* 31
All-in-all Is like another, *a i a*.' *Two Voices* 36
with that mood or this, Is *a-i-a* to all : *Will Water.* 108
Philip was her children's *a-i-a* ; *Enoch Arden* 348
her good Philip was her *a-i-a*, ,, 525
take them *a-i-a*, Were we ourselves *Princess v* 200
'trust me not at all or *a i a*' (repeat) *Merlin and V.* 384, 398, 449
Love Were not his own imperial *a-i-a*. *Sisters (E. and E.)* 227
Out of His whole World-self and *a-i-a*— *De Prof. Two G.* 49
What England is, and what her *a-i-a*, *The Fleet* 2
fleet of England is her *a-i-a* ; ,, 13
been till now each other's *a-i-a*. *The Ring* 53
Within us, as without, that *A-i-a*, *Akbar's Dream* 146
All-kindled *A-k* by a still and sacred fire, *Enoch Arden* 71
Allot The sphere thy fate *a's* : *Will Water.* 218
Allotted (part.) quit the post *A* by the Gods : *Lucretius* 149
show'd an empty tent *a* her, *Geraint and E.* 885
Allow *one of less desert* a's *This laurel* *To the Queen* 6
fly no more : I *a* thee for an hour. *Gareth and L.* 892
A me for mine hour, and thou wilt find ,, 902
our true King Will then *a* your pretext, *Lancelot and E.* 153
answer for a noble knight? *A* him ! ,, 202
Will well *a* my pretext, ,, 586
Allowance much *a* must be made for men. *Aylmer's Field* 410
Made more and more *a* for his talk ; *Sea Dreams* 75
To make *a* for us all. *In Mem. li* 16
Allow'd leave To see the hunt, *a* it easily. *Marr. of Geraint* 155
loyal worship is *a* Of all men : *Lancelot and E.* 110
Lightly, her suit *a*, she slipt away, ,, 778
Scorn was *a* as part of his defect, *Guinevere* 43
thro' his cowardice *a* Her station, ,, 516
Allowing (*See also* **Half-allowing**) *A* it, the Prince and Enid rode, *Marr. of Geraint* 43
Alloy Bright metal all without *a* *Rosalind* 21
All-perfect *A-p*, finish'd to the finger nail. *Edwin Morris* 22
All-puissant noble breast and *a-p* arms, *Marr. of Geraint* 86
All-seeing or of older use *A-s* Hyperion— *Lucretius* 126
All-shamed I rode *a-s*, hating the life *Geraint and E.* 852
All-silent Sigh fully, or *a-s* gaze upon him *Merlin and V.* 182
All-subtilising *A-s* intellect : *In Mem. lxxxv* 48
All-too-full *a-t-f* in bud For puritanic stays : *Talking Oak* 59
Allure beacon-blaze *a's* The bird of passage, *Enoch Arden* 728
Allured *A* him, as the beacon-blaze allures ,, 728
a The glance of Gareth *Gareth and L.* 1315
the sweet name *A* him first, *Last Tournament* 399
Allusion phrases of the hearth, And far *a*, *Princess ii* 316
Ally (Alfred) GOLDEN-HAIR'D *A* whose name is one *To A. Tennyson* 1
Ally (s) True we have got—*such* a faithful *a* *Riflemen form!* 24
Ally (verb) *a* Your fortunes, justlier balanced, *Princess ii* 65
Almesbury sat There in the holy house at *A* *Guinevere* 2
she to *A* Fled all night long ,, 127
when she came to *A* she spake ,, 138
As even here they talk at *A* ,, 208
saw One lying in the dust at *A*, *Pass. of Arthur* 77
Almighty (*See also* **Amoighty**) O God *A*, blessed Saviour, Thou *Enoch Arden* 782
SIR AYLMER-AYLMER, that *a* man, *Aylmer's Field* 13
Almond-blossom *The sunlit* a-b *shakes*— *To the Queen* 16
Almondine Turkis and agate and *a*: *The Merman* 32
Alms set himself, Scorning an *a*, to work *Enoch Arden* 812
free of *a* her hand—The hand that *Aylmer's Field* 697
life of prayer, Praise, fast and *a* ; *Holy Grail* 5
She gave herself, to fast and *a*. ,, 77
cripple, one that held a hand for *a*— *Pelleas and E.* 542
fling free *a* into the beggar's bowl, *Ancient Sage* 260
From the golden *a* of Blessing *Locksley H., Sixty*, 87
Almsdeed wear out in *a* and in prayer *Guinevere* 687
Aloän (alone) an' if Sally be left *a*, *North. Cobbler* 105
Hallus *a* wi' 'is booöks, *Village Wife* 27
one night I wur sittin' *a*, *Owd Roä* 29
Aloe Of olive, *a*, maize and vine. *The Daisy* 4
Alone (*See also* **Aloän**) moon cometh, And looketh down *a*. *Claribel* 14
While I do pray to Thee *a*, *Supp. Confessions* 12
A and warming his five wits, (repeat) *The Owl, I.* 6, 13
My friend, with you to live *a*, *Ode to Memory* 119
Death, walking all *a* beneath a yew, *Love and Death* 5
A I wander to and fro, *Oriana* 8
A merman bold, Sitting *a*, Singing *a* *The Merman* 3
mermaid fair, Singing *a*, *The Mermaid* 3
Springing *a* With a shrill inner sound, ,, 19
For sure thou art not all *a*. *Adeline* 25
broad river rushing down *a*, *Mine be the strength* 2
'Ah,' she sang, 'to be all *a*, (repeat) *Mariana in the S.* 11, 23
'but I wake *a*, I sleep forgotten, ,, 35
She thought, 'My spirit is here *a*, ,, 47
'Sweet Mother, let me not here *a* ,, 59
So be *a* for evermore.' ,, 68
Is this the end to be left *a*, ,, 71
'But thou shalt be *a* no more.' ,, 76
And day and night I am left *a* ,, 83
When I shall cease to be all *a*, ,, 95
And you and I were all *a*. *Miller's D.* 136
Came up from reedy Simois all *a*. *Œnone* 52
from that time to this I am *a*, ,, 193
And I shall be *a* until I die. ,, 194
I will not die *a*, (repeat) *Œnone* 246, 257
some one pacing there *a*, *Palace of Art* 66
Nor these *a*, but every landscape fair, ,, 89
Nor these *a*: but every legend ,, 125
prolong Her low preamble all *a*, ,, 174
Flash'd thro' her as she sat *a*, ,, 214
And all *a* in crime : ,, 272
But I shall lie *a*, mother, *May Queen, N. Y's. E.* 20
why should we toil *a*, *Lotos-Eaters, C. S.*, 15
Let us *a*. Time driveth onward ,, 43
Let us *a*. What is it that will last? ,, 45
Let us *a*. What pleasure can we have ,, 48
'Not so, nor once *a* ; *D. of F. Women* 203
That standeth there *a*, *D. of the O. Year* 50
Falls off, and love is left *a*. *To J. S.* 16
leave thee thus, Aidless, *a*, *M. d'Arthur* 41

Alone (*continued*) For not *a* this pillar-punishment, Not this *a* — *St. S. Stylites* 60
I might be more *a* with thee, — ,, 85
In which we sat together and *a*, — *Love and Duty* 60
both with those That loved me, and *a*; — *Ulysses* 9
About the hall, among his dogs, *a*, — *Godiva* 17
She lying on her couch *a*, — *Day-Dm., Sleep. B.*, 2
Ah, let the rusty theme *a*! — *Will Water.* 177
fell Sun-stricken, and that other lived *a* — *Enoch Arden* 570
who speaks with Him, seem all *a*, — ,, 620
'*A*,' I said, 'from earlier than I know, — *Princess vii* 311
When ill and weary, *a* and cold, — *The Daisy* 96
A, *a*, to where he sits, — *In Mem. xxiii* 3
When I contemplate all *a* — ,, *lxxxiv* 1
light Went out, and I was all *a*, — ,, *xcv* 20
Which not *a* had guided me, — ,, *cxiii* 3
she will let me *a*. — *Maud I i* 74
For am I not, am I not, here *a* — ,, *vi* 65
I am here at the gate *a*; — ,, *xxii* 4
When will the dancers leave her *a*? — ,, 21
That thou art left for ever *a*: — ,, *II iii* 4
a And all the world asleep, — *Com. of Arthur* 118
sought The King *a*, and found, and told — *Gareth and L.* 541
and they were left *a*. — *Geraint and E.* 244
endured Strange chances here *a*;' — ,, 810
I was all *a* upon the flood, — *Lancelot and E.* 1046
shaped, it seems, By God for thee *a*, — ,, 1367
leave me all *a* with Mark and hell. — *Last Tournament* 536
leave thee thus, Aidless, *a*, — *Pass. of Arthur* 209
didst sit *a* in the inner house, — *Lover's Tale i* 112
To me *a*, Push'd from his chair — ,, 117
Our general mother meant for me *a*, — ,, 245
They tell me we would not be *a*,— — ,, 252
many weary moons I lived *a*—*A*, — ,, *ii* 2
day waned; *A* I sat with her: — ,, 140
I will be all *a* with all I love, — ,, *iv* 47
Found, as it seem'd, a skeleton *a*, — ,, 139
dark eyes! and not her eyes *a*, — ,, 166
I am all *a* in the world, — *First Quarrel* 8
go, go, you may leave me *a*— — *Rizpah* 79
I was there *a*: The phantom — *Sisters (E. and E.)* 113
I lying here bedridden and *a*, — *Columbus* 164
when I left my darling *a*.' — *The Wreck* 97
a on that lonely shore— — *Despair* 33
I am left *a* on the land, she is all *a* — ,, 63
Nor canst not prove that thou art body *a*, — *Ancient Sage* 59
Nor canst thou prove that thou art spirit *a*, — ,, 60
when I Sat all *a*, revolving — ,, 230
but we were left *a*: — *The Flight* 77
sitting on the wreck *a*. — *Locksley H., Sixty*, 16
Thou *a*, my boy, of Amy's kin — ,, 56
wearying to be left *a*, — ,, 57
first dark hour of his last sleep *a*. — ,, 238
gazing from this height *a*, — *Pro. to Gen. Hamley* 9
he dash'd up *a* Thro' the great gray slope — *Heavy Brigade* 16
Or Might must rule *a*; — *Epilogue* 29
And he sung not *a* of an old sun set, — *Dead Prophet* 41
To forage for herself *a*; — *Open. I. and C. Exhib.* 29
I parted from her, and I went *a*. — *The Ring* 437
would he live and die *a*? — *Happy* 5
but I wept *a*, and sigh'd — ,, 69
Listen! we three were *a* in the dell — *Bandit's Death* 19
of that Power which *a* is great, — *God and the Univ.* 5
Along six tall men haling a seventh *a*, — *Gareth and L.* 811
Alongside if t'one stick *a* t'uther — *Church-warden, etc.*, 10
A-loving When I was *a-l* you all along — *First Quarrel* 65
Alphabet The Alif of Thine *a* of Love.' — *Akbar's Dream* 31
Alphabet-of-heaven-in-man *A-o-h-i-m* Made vocal— — ,, 136
Alpine In gazing up an *A* height, — *Two Voices* 362
an *A* harebell hung with tears — *Princess vii* 115
Alps Sun-smitten *A* before me lay. — *The Daisy* 62
Alraschid *See* **Haroun Alraschid**
Altar (*See also* **Isle-altar, Mountain-altars**) Leads her to the village *a*, — *L. of Burleigh* 11
And saw the *a* cold and bare. — *The Letters* 4

Altar (*continued*) 'Cold *a*, Heaven and earth shall meet — *The Letters* 7
fire, That burn'd as on an *a*. — *Enoch Arden* 72
at the *a* the poor bride Gives her harsh groom — *Princess v* 377
The Priest in horror about his *a* — *The Victim* 7
Burnt and broke the grove and *a* — *Boädicea* 2
sacred *a* blossom'd white with May, — *Com. of Arthur* 461
Beheld before a golden *a* lie — *Balin and Balan* 410
from the *a* glancing back upon her, — *Sisters (E. and E.)* 210
to pray Before *that a*—so I think; — ,, 239
There, brooding by the central *a*, — *Ancient Sage* 33
Tower and *a* trembling . . . — *Forlorn* 34
fire from off a pure Pierian *a*, — *Parnassus* 17
Altar-cloth Fair gleams the snowy *a-c*, — *Sir Galahad* 33
as thine *a-c* From that best blood — *Gareth and L.* 599
Altar-fashion'd smooth rock Before it, *a-f*, — *Tiresias* 147
Altar-fire As mounts the heavenward *a-f*, — *In Mem. xli* 3
Altar-flame made my life a perfumed *a-f*; — *Maud I xviii* 24
Altar-shrine before The stateliest of her *a-s's*, — *Com. of Arthur* 455
Altar-stairs Upon the great world's *a-s* — *In Mem. lv* 15
Altar-stone To the *a-s* she sprang alone, — *The Victim* 67
Alter Sequel of guerdon could not *a* me — *Œnone* 153
Nor add and *a*, many times, — *Will Water.* 15
Persuasion, no, nor death could *a* her: — *Aylmer's Field* 418
as the fiery Sirius *a's* hue, — *Princess v* 262
Alter'd For I was *a*, and began — *Miller's D.* 94
tho' you have grown You scarce have *a*: — *Princess ii* 306
Alum chalk and *a* and plaster are sold — *Maud I i* 39
Amaracus Violet, *a*, and asphodel, — *Œnone* 97
Amaranth propt on beds of *a* and moly, — *Lotos-Eaters, C. S.*, 88
in heaven With Milton's *a*. — *Romney's R.* 111
Amaryllis A milky-bell'd *a* blew. — *The Daisy* 16
A-maying Had been, their wont, *a-m* — *Guinevere* 23
Amaze (*See also* **Half-amaze**) In much *a* he stared On eyes — *The Brook* 205
Up went the hush'd *a* of hand and eye. — *Princess iii* 138
Suddenly honest, answer'd in *a*, — *Geraint and E.* 410
sister's vision, fill'd me with *a*; — *Holy Grail* 140
And some of us, all in *a*, — *Heavy Brigade* 35
a Our brief humanities; — *Epilogue* 56
set the mother waking in *a* — *Demeter and P.* 57
Amazed (*See also* **Half-amazed, Part-amazed**) *A* and melted all who listen'd — *Enoch Arden* 649
Averill solaced as he might, *a*: — *Aylmer's Field* 343
half *a* half frighted all his flock: — ,, 631
A he fled away Thro' the dark land, — *Princess v* 48
'*A* am I to hear Your Highness: — ,, *vi* 324
a They glared upon the women, — ,, 360
brake on him, till, *a*, He knew not — *Com. of Arthur* 39
those who went with Gareth were *a*, — *Gareth and L.* 197
and all hearers were *a*. — ,, 655
Enid ask'd, *a*, 'If Enid errs, — *Marr. of Geraint* 131
the armourer turning all *a* — ,, 283
plover's human whistle *a* Her heart, — *Geraint and E.* 49
when he found all empty, was *a*; — ,, 216
A am I, Beholding how ye butt — ,, 676
He much *a* us; after, when we sought — *Balin and Balan* 115
A were these; 'Lo there' she cried— — ,, 465
more *a* Than if seven men had set — *Lancelot and E.* 350
the Queen *a*, 'Was he not with you? — ,, 572
He *a*, 'Torre and Elaine! why here? — ,, 795
So that the angels were *a*, — *Holy Grail* 451
ye look *a*, Not knowing they were lost — *Last Tournament* 41
babble about his end *A* me; — ,, 671
I sware, Being *a*: but this went by— — ,, 674
dead world's winter dawn *A* him, — *Pass. of Arthur* 443
nor lights nor feast Dazed or *a*, — *Lover's Tale iv* 311
mask that I saw so *a* me, — *The Wreck* 117
I stood there, naked, *a* — *Despair* 77
still in her cave, *A*, — *Death of Œnone* 70
Amazement stood Stock-still for sheer *a*. — *Will Water.* 136
all the guests in mute *a* rose— — *Lover's Tale iv* 305
which made the *a* more, — ,, 334
Amazing *See* **Maäzin'**
Amazon Glanced at the legendary *A* — *Princess ii* 126
Ambassador My father sent *a's* with furs — ,, *i* 42

Ambassador (*continued*) Sir Lancelot went *a*, at first, *Merlin and V.* 774
A, to lead her to his lord *Guinevere* 383
Ambassadress 'are you *a'es* From him to me? *Princess iii* 203
Amber (adj.) lights, rose, *a*, emerald, blue, *Palace of Art* 169
Purple or *a*, dangled a hundred fathoms *V. of Maeldune* 56
Like the tender *a* round, *Margaret* 19
and the *a* eves When thou and I, Camilla, *Lover's Tale i* 52
Ran *a* towards the west, and nigh the sea ,, 432
Amber (s) fans Of sandal, *a*, ancient rosaries, *Princess, Pro.*, 19
Ambition No madness of *a*, avarice, none: *Lucretius* 212
lawless perch Of wing'd *a's*, *Ded. of Idylls* 23
Down with *a*, avarice, pride, *Maud I x* 47
Ambrosia Hebes are they to hand *a*, *Princess iii* 113
Their rich *a* tasted aconite. *Demeter and P.* 105
Ambrosial oak-tree sigheth, Thick-leaved, *a*, *Claribel* 5
her deep hair *A*, golden *Œnone* 178
Sweet after showers, *a* air, *In Mem. lxxxvi* 1
Ambrosially fruit of pure Hesperian gold, That smelt *a*, *Œnone* 67
Ambrosius fellow-monk among the rest, *A*, *Holy Grail* 9
monk *A* question'd Percivale: ,, 17
Then spake the monk *A*, asking him, ,, 203
I told him all thyself hast heard, *A*, ,, 737
Ambuscade In every wavering brake an *a*. *Geraint and E.* 51
Ambush (*See also* **Lilac-ambush**) Lances in *a* set; *D. of F. Women* 28
Ambush'd meanings *a* under all they saw, *Tiresias* 5
Ambushing poisonous counsels, wayside *a's*— *Gareth and L.* 432
Amen yet I take it with *A*. *Lancelot and E.* 1223
A! Nay, I can burn, *Sir J. Oldcastle* 172
Amend might *a* it by the grace of Heaven, *Geraint and E.* 53
Amends Can thy love, Thy beauty, make *a*, *Tithonus* 24
She made me divine *a* *Maud I vi* 13
Well, we will make *a*.' *Gareth and L.* 300
A hereafter by some gaudy-day, *Marr. of Geraint* 818
Courteous—*a* for gauntness— *Merlin and V.* 104
our *a* for all we might have done— *Columbus* 34
Amethyst chrysoprase, Jacynth, and a— ,, 86
Amid gap they had made—Four *a* thousands! *Heavy Brigade* 24
Golden branch *a* the shadows, *To Virgil* 27
Why not bask *a* the senses *By an Evolution.* 6
bracken *a* the gloom of the heather. *June Bracken, etc.*, 9
Amiss There's somewhat in this world *a* *Miller's D.* 19
Kind to Maud? that were not *a*. *Maud I xix* 82
pray you check me if I ask *a*— *Guinevere* 324
Amity idioted By the rough *a* of the other, *Aylmer's Field* 591
Ammon my race Hew'd *A*, hip and thigh, *D. of F. Women* 238
Ammonian *A* Oasis in the waste. *Alexander* 8
Ammonite Huge *A's*, and the first bones of Time; *Princess, Pro.*, 15
Amo 'Io t'*a*'—and these diamonds— *The Ring* 70
This very ring Io t'*a*? ,, 134
This ring 'Io t'*a*' to his best beloved, ,, 210
cried 'I see him, Io t'*a*, Io t'*a*.' ,, 223
call thro' this 'Io t'*a*' to the heart Of Miriam; ,, 234
'Io t'*a*, all is well then.' Muriel fled. ,, 271
You love me still 'Io t'*a*.'— ,, 291
'Io t'*a*, Io t'*a*'!' flung herself ,, 397
even that 'Io t'*a*,' those three sweet Italian words, ,, 406
Amoighty (Almighty) 'The *a's* a taäkin o' you to 'issén, (repeat) *N. Farmer, O. S.*, 10, 26
Amorous (*See also* **All-amorous, Human-amorous**)
with argent-lidded eyes *A*, *Arabian Nights* 136
Of temper *a*, as the first of May, *Princess i* 2
High nature *a* of the good, *In Mem. cix* 9
Amorously kiss Thy taper fingers *a*, *Madeline* 44
shall we dandle it *a*? *Boädicea* 33
A-mountin' we 'eärd 'im *a-m* oop 'igher an' 'igher, *North. Cobbler* 47
Amourist your modern *a* is of easier, earthlier make. *Locksley H., Sixty*, 18
Amphion In days of old *A*, *Amphion* 10
Amuck Ran a Malayan *a* against the times, *Aylmer's Field* 463
Amulet What *a* drew her down ,, 507
kept it as a sacred *a* About me,— *The Ring* 442
Amurath (Turkish Emperor) Or *A* of the East? *Sir J. Oldcastle* 97
Amy I said, 'My cousin *A*, speak, *Locksley Hall* 23
O my *A*, mine no more! ,, 39
A's arms about my neck— *Locksley H., Sixty*, 13

Amy (*continued*) *A* loved me, *A* fail'd me, *A* was a timid child; *Locksley H., Sixty*, 19
often I and *A* in the mouldering aisle have stood, ,, 31
Lies my *A* dead in child-birth, ,, 36
Here to-day was *A* with me, ,, 53
of *A's* kin and mine art left to me. ,, 56
our latest meeting—*A*—sixty years ago— ,, 177
Amygdaloid trap and tuff, *A* and trachyte, *Princess iii* 363
Ana Ere days, that deal in *a*, *Will Water.* 199
Anadem Lit light in wreaths and *a's*, *Palace of Art* 186
A-naggin' Moother 'ed beän *a-n* about the gell *Owd Roä* 69
Anakim I felt the thews of *A*, *In Mem. ciii* 31
Analyse and *a* Our double nature, *Supp. Confessions* 174
Anarch wearied of Autocrats, *A's*, and Slaves, *The Dreamer* 10
Anathema Thunder '*A*,' friend, at you; *To F. D. Maurice* 8
Anatolian Ghost Crag-cloister; *A G*; *To Ulysses* 43
Anatomic not found among them all One *a*.' *Princess iii* 307
Ancestor those fixt eyes of painted *a's* *Aylmer's Field* 832
Anchor (s) with silver *a* left afloat, *Arabian Nights* 93
there was no *a*, none, To hold by.' *The Epic* 20
Nor *a* dropt at eve or morn; *The Voyage* 82
A's of rusty fluke, and boats *Enoch Arden* 18
Cast all your cares on God; that *a* holds. ,, 222
lay At *a* in the flood below; *In Mem. ciii* 20
my love Waver'd at *a* with me, *Lover's Tale i* 65
Anchor (verb) Why not yet *A* thy frailty there, *Supp. Confessions* 124
To *a* by one gloomy thought; *Two Voices* 459
Anchor'd Tho' *a* to the bottom, such is he.' *Princess iv* 257
A tawny pirate *a* in his port, *Merlin and V.* 558
Half-swallow'd in it, *a* with a chain; *Holy Grail* 803
Anchorite *a* Would haunt the desolated fane, *St. Telemachus* 12
Ancients (s) For we are *A's* of the earth, *Day-Dm., L'Envoi* 19
Ancle *See* **Ankle**
'And (hand) an' thy muther coom to '*a*, *N. Farmer, N. S.*, 21
But I puts it inter 'er '*a's* *North. Cobbler* 72
an' poonch'd my '*a* wi' the hawl, ,, 78
Fur I couldn't 'owd '*a's* off gin, ,, 84
An' 'e spanks 'is '*a* into mine, ,, 92
new Squire's coom'd wi' 'is taäil in 'is '*a*, (repeat) *Village Wife* 14, 121
'e 'ed hallus a booök i' 'is '*a*, ,, 26
an' our Nelly she gied me 'er '*a*, ,, 111
An' that squeedg'd m t'*a* i' the shed, *Spinster's S's.* 39
Or sits wi' their '*a's* afoor 'em, ,, 86
An' 'is 'air coom'd off i' my '*a's* *Owd Roä* 100
Anemone (*See also* **'Enemies)** burn'd The red *a*. *D. of F. Women* 72
Crocus, *a*, violet, *To F. D. Maurice* 44
among the gardens, auriculas, *a's*, *City Child* 4
'Ang'd (hanged) Noäks wur '*a* for it oop at 'soize— *N. Farmer, O. S.*, 36
Angel (adj.) So sweet a face, such *a* grace, *Beggar Maid* 13
With books, with flowers, with *A* offices, *Princess vii* 26
a dearer being, all dipt In *A* instincts, ,, 321
Rings to the roar of an *a* onset— *Milton* 8
And be found of *a* eyes *Helen's Tower* 11
The toll of funeral in an *A* ear *D. of the Duke of C.* 10
Angel (s) (*See also* **Earth-Angel, Hangel)**
When *a's* spake to men aloud, *Supp. Confessions* 25
once by man and *a's* to be seen, *The Kraken* 14
Like that strange *a* which of old, *Clear-headed friend* 24
thyself a little lower 'Than *a's*. *Two Voices* 199
temper'd with the tears Of *a's* *To—— With Pal. of Art* 19
slept St. Cecily; An *a* look'd at her. *Palace of Art* 100
a's rising and descending met ,, 143
March-morning I heard the *a's* call; *May Queen, Con.*, 25
saw An *a* stand and watch me, *St. S. Stylites* 35
Is that the *a* there That holds ,, 203
Three *a's* bear the holy Grail: *Sir Galahad* 42
And, stricken by an *a's* hand, ,, 69
been as God's good *a* in our house. *Enoch Arden* 423
Fair as the *A* that said 'Hail!' *Aylmer's Field* 681
himself Were that great *A*; *Sea Dreams* 27
devil in man, there is an *a* too, ,, 278
His *a* broke his heart. ,, 280
'lest some classic *A* speak In scorn *Princess iii* 70
the woman's *A* guards you, ,, *v* 410
No *A*, but a dearer being, ,, *vii* 320

Angel (s) (*continued*) Whose Titan *a's*, Gabriel, Abdiel, *Milton* 5
My guardian *a* will speak out *In Mem. xliv* 15
I found an *a* of the night; ,, *lxix* 14
An *a* watching an urn Wept *Maud I viii* 3
ship and sail and *a's* blowing on it: *Balin and Balan* 365
a's of our Lord's report. *Merlin and V.* 16
I pray him, send a sudden *A* down *Lancelot and E.* 1424
So that the *a's* were amazed, *Holy Grail* 451
a's, awful shapes, and wings and eyes. ,, 848
I, and Arthur and the *a's* hear, *Last Tournament* 350
we are not *a's* here Nor shall be: ,, 698
face, Which then was as an *a's*, *Guinevere* 596
I to her became Her guardian and her *a*, *Lover's Tale i* 393
Come like an *a* to a damned soul, ,, 673
like the waft of an *A's* wing; *In the Child. Hosp.* 38
Till you find the deathless *A* *Locksley H., Sixty*, 278
mountain-walls Young *a's* pass. *Early Spring* 12
hear a death-bed *A* whisper 'Hope.' *Romney's R.* 148

Angelo The bar of Michael *A*. *In Mem. lxxxvii* 40

Anger (s) Delicious spites and darling *a's*, *Madeline* 6
Then wax'd her *a* stronger. *The Goose* 30
as with a kind of *a* in him, *Enoch Arden* 392
his *a* reddens in the heavens; *Princess iv* 386
their ravening eagle rose In *a*, *Ode on Well.* 120
troubled, as if with *a* or pain: *Grandmother* 65
all their *a* in miraculous utterances, *Boädicea* 23
an *a*, not by blood to be satiated. ,, 52
The bitter springs of *a* and fear; *Maud I x* 49
Till I with as fierce an *a* spoke, ,, *II i* 17
vassals of wine and *a* and lust, ,, 43
strength of *a* thro' mine arms, *Gareth and L.* 948
And when his *a* tare him, ,, 1340
ruth began to work Against his *a* *Geraint and E.* 102
or hot, God's curse, with *a*— ,, 661
beast, whose *a* was his lord. *Balin and Balan* 488
As some wild turn of *a*, *Merlin and V.* 521
turn of *a* born Of your misfaith; ,, 531
Vivien, frowning in true *a*, ,, 691
breaths of *a* puff'd Her fairy nostril ,, 848
his *a* slowly died Within him, ,, 891
too faint and sick am I For *a*: *Lancelot and E.* 1087
first her *a*, leaving Pelleas, *Pelleas and E.* 289
storm of *a* brake From Guinevere, *Guinevere* 361
as *a* falls aside And withers *Lover's Tale i* 9
so fluster'd with *a* were they *V. of Maeldune* 25
and in *a* we sail'd away. ,, 54
great God, Arês, burns in *a* still *Tiresias* 11
climbing from the bath In *a*; ,, 41
And *a's* of the Gods for evil done ,, 62
and quench The red God's *a*, ,, 158
And who, when his *a* was kindled, *The Wreck* 17
moment's *a* of bees in their hive?— *Vastness* 35
sound of *a* like a distant storm. *The Ring* 119
wild horse, *a*, plunged To fling me, *Akbar's Dream* 118
Rolling her *a* Thro' blasted valley *Kapiolani* 11

Anger (verb) *A's* thee most, or *a's* thee at all? *Lucretius* 75

Anger-charm'd Sat *a-c* from sorrow, *Aylmer's Field* 728

Anger'd (adj.) (*See also* **Half-anger'd**) The flush of *a* shame O'erflows *Madeline* 32
Those dragon eyes of *a* Eleanor *D. of F. Women* 255
Gareth spake *A*, 'Old Master, *Gareth and L.* 280
Sick? or for any matter *a* at me?' *Balin and Balan* 276
most of these were mute, some *a*, *Last Tournament* 210
I was jealous, *a*, vain, *Happy* 66

Anger'd (verb) jealousies Which *a* her. Who *a* James? *The Brook* 100
'So Merlin riddling *a* me; *Com. of Arthur* 412
a saying that *a* her. *Last Tournament* 628
But he *a* me all the more, *First Quarrel* 64
an' he *a* me more and more. ,, 66
Eh! how I *a* Arundel asking me *Sir J. Oldcastle* 135

Angerly Again thou blushest *a*; *Madeline* 45

Angle (corner) We rub each other's *a's* down, *In Mem. lxxxix* 40

Angle (race of people) Saxon and *A* from Over the broad billow *Batt. of Brunanburh* 118

Angled But *a* in the higher pool. *Miller's D.* 64
a with them for her pupil's love: *Princess iii* 93

Angling left That *a* to the mother. *The Ring* 356

Angrier I never ate with *a* appetite *Geraint and E.* 233

Angry Hungry for honour, *a* for his king. *Princess v* 314
Hortensia pleading: *a* was her face. ,, *vii* 132
—it makes me *a* now. *Grandmother* 44
makes me *a* yet to speak of it— *Lover's Tale iv* 135

Anguisant (King of Erin) With *A* of Erin, Morganore, *Com. of Arthur* 115

Anguish Life, *a*, death, immortal love, *Arabian Nights* 73
'Thine *a* will not let thee sleep, *Two Voices* 49
'Or that this *a* fleeting hence, ,, 235
down in hell Suffer endless *a*, *Lotos-Eaters, C. S.*, 124
Beauty and *a* walking hand in hand *D. of F. Women* 15
She loveth her own *a* deep *To J. S.* 42
Shall I heed them in their *a*? *Boädicea* 9
My deeper *a* also falls, *In Mem. xix* 15
My *a* hangs like shame. *Maud II iv* 74
in her *a* found The casement: *Guinevere* 586
Sweat, writhings, *a*, labouring *Pass. of Arthur* 115
in the sudden *a* of her heart *Lover's Tale i* 702
became *A* intolerable. ,, *ii* 138
Life with its *a*, and horrors, and errors— *Despair* 48

Animal (adj.) With *a* heat and dire insanity? *Lucretius* 163

Animal (s) The single pure and perfect *a*, *Princess vii* 306

Animalism Hetairai, curious in their art, Hired *a's*, *Lucretius* 53

Ankle-Ancle From head to *ancle* fine, *Talking Oak* 224
One praised her *ancles*, one her eyes, *Beggar Maid* 11
At last I hook'd my *ankle* in a vine, *Princess iv* 268
Behind his *ankle* twined her hollow feet *Merlin and V.* 240

Ankle-bells To make her smile, her golden *a-b*. ,, 579

Ankle-bones feet unmortised from their *a-b* ,, 552

Ankle-deep And brushing *a-d* in flowers, *In Mem. lxxxix* 49

Ankle-wing as it were with Mercury's *a-w*, *Lucretius* 201

Anlaf (Danish King) Sparing not any of Those that with *A*, *Batt. of Brunanburh* 46
Earls of the army of *A* Fell ,, 53
nor had *A* With armies so broken ,, 81

Annal-book Merlin did In one great *a-b*, *Com. of Arthur* 158

Annals Holding the folded *a* of my youth; *Gardener's D.* 244
Told him, with other *a* of the port, *Enoch Arden* 702
with a day Blanch'd in our *a*, *Princess vi* 63
Read the wide world's *a*, you, *Locksley H., Sixty*, 104
glorious *a* of army and fleet, *Vastness* 7

Anne is gone, you say, little *A*? *Grandmother* 1
I had not wept, little *A*, not since ,, 63

Annie (*See also* **Annie Lee, Hannie**) While *A* still was mistress; *Enoch Arden* 26
and make a home For *A*: ,, 48
a home For *A*, neat and nestlike, ,, 59
Enoch and *A*, sitting hand-in-hand, ,, 69
set *A* forth in trade With all that seamen ,, 138
moving homeward came on *A* pale, ,, 149
to break his purposes To *A*, ,, 156
A fought against his will: ,, 158
Bought *A* goods and stores, ,, 169
A seem'd to hear Her own death-scaffold ,, 174
would work for *A* to the last, ,, 180
A's fears, Save, as his *A's*, ,, 183
'*A*, this voyage by the grace of God ,, 190
A, come, cheer up before I go.' ,, 200
A, the ship I sail in passes here ,, 214
'*A*, my girl, cheer up, be comforted, ,, 218
When *A* would have raised him ,, 232
A from her baby's forehead clipt ,, 235
same week when *A* buried it, ,, 271
but *A*, seated with her grief, ,, 280
'*A*, I came to ask a favour of you.' ,, 285
A, now—Have we not known each other ,, 305
A—for I am rich and well-to-do. ,, 311
A with her brows against the wall ,, 314
ask'd 'Then you will let me, *A*?' ,, 323
for *A's* sake, Fearing the lazy gossip ,, 334

Annie (*continued*) Philip did not fathom *A's* mind: *Enoch Arden* 344
one evening *A's* children long'd To go „ 362
And *A* would go with them; „ 364
For was not *A* with them? „ 371
'Listen, *A*, How merry they are „ 388
Tired, *A*?' for she did not speak „ 390
And *A* said 'I thought not of it: „ 395
'*A*, there is a thing upon my mind, „ 399
O *A*, It is beyond all hope, „ 402
answer'd *A*; tenderly she spoke: „ 422
'*A*, as I have waited all my life „ 435
fearing night and chill for *A*, „ 443
At *A's* door he paused and gave „ 447
'*A*, when I spoke to you, „ 448
A weeping answer'd 'I am bound.' „ 451
'Take your own time, *A*, take „ 466
A could have wept for pity of him; „ 467
chanced That *A* could not sleep, „ 490
never merrily beat *A's* heart. „ 513
The babes, their babble, *A*, „ 606
home Where *A* lived and loved him, „ 685
His gazing in on *A*, his resolve, „ 863
tell my daughter *A*, whom I saw „ 882
For, *A*, you see, her father was not the man *Grandmother* 5
I cannot cry for him, *A*: „ 15
Why do you look at me, *A*? „ 17
at your age, *A*, I could have wept (repeat) „ 20, 100
I mean your grandfather, *A*: „ 23
But soiling another, *A*, „ 36
Shadow and shine is life, little *A*, „ 60
children, *A*, they're all about me yet. „ 76
my *A* who left me at two, „ 77
my own little *A*, an *A* like you: „ 78
in this Book, little *A*, the message „ 96
Get me my glasses, *A*: „ 106
Hall but Miss *A*, the heldest, *Village Wife* 8
but Miss *A* she said it wur draäins, „ 11
Hoänly Miss *A* were saw stuck oop, „ 59
An' es for Miss *A* es call'd me afoor „ 105
taäke it kindly ov owd Miss *A* „ 109
O *A*, what shall I do?' *In the Child. Hosp.* 47
A consider'd. 'If I,' said the wise little *A*, „ 48
That was a puzzle for *A*. „ 55
Annie Lee (*See also* **Annie**) *A L*, The prettiest little damsel *Enoch Arden* 11
A later but a loftier *A L*, „ 748
Annihilate eagle's beak and talon *a* us? *Boädicea* 11
Announced *A* the coming doom, and fulminated *Sea Dreams* 22
Annulet And into many a listless *a*, *Geraint and E.* 258
Answer (s) Our thought gave *a* each to each, *Sonnet To——* 10
The sullen *a* slid betwixt: *Two Voices* 226
There must be *a* to his doubt, „ 309
I spoke, but *a* came there none: „ 425
To which my soul made *a* readily: *Palace of Art* 17
Not rendering true *a*, *M. d'Arthur* 74
some sweet *a*, tho' no *a* came, *Gardener's D.* 159
let me have an *a* to my wish; *Dora* 30
before thine *a* given Departest, *Tithonus* 44
an *a* peal'd from that high land, *Vision of Sin* 221
Rejoicing at that *a* to his prayer. *Enoch Arden* 127
such a voluble *a* promising all, „ 903
And Leolin's horror-stricken *a*, *Aylmer's Field* 318
hush'd itself at last Hopeless of *a*: „ 543
therewithal an *a* vague as wind: *Princess i* 45
In this report, this *a* of a king, „ 70
Her *a* was 'Leave me to deal with that.' „ *iii* 149
a which, half-muffled in his beard, „ *v* 234
oozed All o'er with honey'd *a* „ 242
I lagg'd in *a* loth to render up „ 299
shall have her *a* by the word.' „ 327
Last, Ida's *a*, in a royal hand, „ 371
what *a* should I give? „ *vii* 6
The noblest *a* unto such Is perfect *Lit. Squabbles* 19
it seem'd that an *a* came. *The Victim* 24

Answer (s) (*continued*) Bark an *a*, Britain's raven! *Boädicea* 13
doubts and *a's* here proposed, *In Mem. xlviii* 3
What hope of *a*, or redress? „ *lvi* 27
But Death returns an *a* sweet: „ *lxxxi* 9
A faithful *a* from the breast, „ *lxxxv* 14
win An *a* from my lips, „ *ciii* 50
Make *a*, Maud my bliss, *Maud I xviii* 57
old Seer made *a* playing on him *Gareth and L.* 252
said your say; Mine *a* was my deed. „ 1175
being still rebuked, would *a* still „ 1249
Made *a* sharply that she should not *Marr. of Geraint* 196
So moving without *a* to her rest „ 530
He made a wrathful *a*: 'Did I wish *Geraint and E.* 76
he flung a wrathful *a* back: „ 146
Made *a*, either eyelid wet *Merlin and V.* 379
Is that an *a* for a noble knight? *Lancelot and E.* 201
Full simple was her *a*, 'What know I? „ 671
all their *a's* were as one: *Holy Grail* 284
And when his *a* chafed them, „ 673
Percivale made *a* not a word. *Pelleas and E.* 534
Well then, what *a*?' *Last Tournament* 713
voice about his feet Sent up an *a* „ 761
when she drew No *a*, by and by *Guinevere* 162
a mournful *a* made the Queen: „ 341
Not rendering true *a*, *Pass. of Arthur* 242
Had made a silent *a*: *Lover's Tale iv* 96
to that passionate *a* of full heart *Sisters (E. and E.)* 259
an *a* came Not from the nurse— *The Wreck* 143
all the night an *a* shrill'd, *Demeter and P.* 61
Answer (verb) And *a's* to his mother's calls *Supp. Confessions* 159
I shall know Thy voice, and *a* *My life is full* 10
Or *a* should one press his hands? *Two Voices* 245
He *a's* not, nor understands. „ 246
'But thou canst *a* not again. „ 310
Or thou wilt *a* but in vain. „ 312
O will she *a* if I call? *Miller's D.* 118
you dare to *a* thus! *Dora* 26
To that man My work shall *a*, *Love and Duty* 29
He will *a* to the purpose, *Locksley Hall* 55
Scarce *a* to my whistle; *Amphion* 68
in gentle murmur, When they *a* *L. of Burleigh* 50
could *a* him, If question'd, *Enoch Arden* 653
to *a*, Madam, all those hard things *Princess ii* 345
Madam, *you* should *a*, *we* would ask) „ 353
told me she would *a* us to-day, „ *iii* 166
a, echoes, dying, dying, dying. (repeat) „ *iv* 6, 12
a, echoes, *a*, dying, dying, dying. „ *iv* 18
(*A*, O *a*) We give you his life.' *The Victim* 15
'O wife, what use to *a* now? „ 55
A each other in the mist. *In Mem. xxviii* 4
Love would *a* with a sigh, „ *xxxv* 13
whatever is ask'd her, *a's* 'Death.' *Maud I i* 4
wilt thou not *a* this? „ *xviii* 59
musing 'Shall I *a* yea or nay?' *Com. of Arthur* 426
but *a* scorn with scorn. *Gareth and L.* 953
it shall *a* for me. Listen to it. *Merlin and V.* 386
But shall it? *a*, darling, *a*, no. „ 397
To *a* that which came: *Holy Grail* 12
he had Scarce any voice to *a*, „ 434
Doth question'd memory *a* not, *Lover's Tale i* 277
if my neighbour whistle *a's* him— „ *iv* 161
Highlanders *a* with conquering cheers, *Def. of Lucknow* 99
Who then will have to *a*, *Columbus* 213
'give it to me,' but he would not *a* me— *Bandit's Death* 27
Answer'd To which he *a* scoffingly; *Two Voices* 37
in that time and place she *a* me, *Gardener's D.* 231
But William *a* short; *Dora* 22
William *a* madly; bit his lips, „ 33
he *a* me; And well his words *Edwin Morris* 24
plagiarised a heart, And *a* *Talking Oak* 20
in mimic cadence *a* James— *Golden Year* 53
She *a* to my call, *Will Water.* 106
A all queries touching those at home *Aylmer's Field* 465
Echo *a* in her sleep From hollow fields: *Princess, Pro.*, 66
a sharply that I talk'd astray. „ *iii* 140

Answer'd (*continued*) I *a* nothing, doubtful in myself *Princess iii* 272
when have I *a* thee? ,, *vii* 4
Gods have *a*; We give them the wife!' *The Victim* 78
Doubt not ye the Gods have *a*, *Boädicea* 22
The 'wilt thou' *a*, and again *In Mem. Con.*, 54
and *a* me In riddling triplets *Com. of Arthur* 401
Gareth *a* them With laughter, *Gareth and L.* 208
Sir Gareth *a*, laughingly, ,, 1007
thou hast ever *a* courteously, ,, 1167
reviled, hast *a* graciously, ,, 1269
A Sir Gareth graciously to one ,, 1414
ask'd it of him, Who *a* as before; *Marr. of Geraint* 205
a with such craft as women use, *Geraint and E.* 352
not dead!' she *a* in all haste. ,, 542
Enid *a*, harder to be moved ,, 694
truest eyes that ever *a* Heaven, ,, 842
I am *a*, and henceforth *Merlin and V.* 879
ever well and readily *a* he: *Lancelot and E.* 269
Lancelot spoke And *a* him at full, ,, 286
in her heart she *a* it and said, ,, 786
he *a* not, Or short and coldly, ,, 886
whom she *a* with all calm. ,, 997
He *a* with his eyes upon the ground, ,, 1352
Lancelot *a* nothing, but he went, ,, 1387
a not, but, sharply turning, *Holy Grail* 739
she *a*, and she laugh'd, *Pelleas and E.* 132
Gawain *a* kindly tho' in scorn, ,, 333
a them Even before high God. ,, 462
he *a* not, 'Or hast thou other griefs? ,, 598
was *a* softly by the King *Guinevere* 44
I should have *a* his farewell. ,, 615
To all their queries *a* not a word, *Lover's Tale iv* 333
Julian, sitting by her, *a* all: ,, 340
he *a* her wail with a song— *The Dreamer* 16
Answering *a* under crescent brows; *Princess ii* 428
a now my random stroke *In Mem. xxxix* 2
a not one word, she led the way. *Geraint and E.* 495
to the court of Arthur *a* yea. *Com. of Arthur* 446
Ant one whose foot is bitten by an *a*, *Pelleas and E.* 184
What is it all but a trouble of *a's* *Vastness* 4
Antagonism in the teeth of clench'd *a's* *Princess iv* 465
And toppling over all *a* *Marr. of Geraint* 491
And, toppling over all *a*, *Geraint and E.* 834
Anthem *a* sung, is charm'd and tied *D. of F. Women* 193
sound of the sorrowing *a* roll'd *Ode on Well.* 60
Anther With *a's* and with dust: *Talking Oak* 184
Antibabylonianism And loud-lung'd *A's* *Sea Dreams* 252
Antichrist He leans on *A*; or that his mind, *Sir J. Oldcastle* 74
That mock-meek mouth of utter *A*, ,, 170
Antiquity A front of timber-crost *a*, *Enoch Arden* 692
Anton (a knight) This is the son of A, not the King.' *Com. of Arthur* 74
Arthur born of Gorloïs, Others of *A*? ,, 171
And gave him to Sir *A*, ,, 222
else the child of *A*, and no king, ,, 233
Antony (Mark) *See* **Mark Antony**
Anvil silver hammers falling On silver *a's*, *Princess i* 217
iron-clanging *a* bang'd With hammers; ,, *v* 504
Anything He never meant us *a t* but good. *Enoch Arden* 887
Behold, we know not *a*; *In Mem. liv* 13
can see elsewhere, *a* so fair. *Marr. of Geraint* 499
Henceforth in all the world at *a*, *Geraint and E.* 649
Apartment died Of fright in far *a's*. *Princess vi* 371
Ape (s) In bed like monstrous *a's* *St. S. Stylites* 174
And let the *a* and tiger die. *In Mem. cxviii* 28
His action like the greater *a*, ,, *cxx* 11
moods of tiger, or of *a*? *Making of Man* 2
Ape (verb) should *a* Those monstrous males *Princess iii* 309
as far As I could *a* their treble, ,, *iv* 92
Aphroditè Herè comes to-day, Pallas and *A*, *Œnone* 86
Idalian *A* beautiful, ,, 174
Apocalyptic as if he held The *A* millstone, *Sea Dreams* 26
Apollo strange song I heard *A* sing, *Tithonus* 62
another of our Gods, the Sun, *A*, *Lucretius* 125
Apology But ended with *a* so sweet, *Geraint and E.* 394
No less than one divine *a*. *Lover's Tale iv* 169

Apostle shrive myself No, not to an *A*.' *Sir J. Oldcastle* 147
Apothegm My curse upon the Master's *a*, *Romney's R.* 37
Appal *A* me from the quest.' *Gareth and L.* 1331
Appall'd cliff-side, *a* them, and they said, *Lancelot and E.* 1253
In our most need, *a* them, *Columbus* 71
Apparel in her hand A suit of bright *a*, *Marr. of Geraint* 678
store of rich *a*, sumptuous fare, ,, 709
a as might well beseem His princess, ,, 758
clothed her in *a* like the day. *Geraint and E.* 948
Appeal (s) She the *a* Brook'd not, *Princess vi* 139
'Thou makest thine *a* to me: *In Mem. lvi* 5
tho' it spake and made *a* ,, *xcii* 4
she lifted up A face of sad *a*, *Merlin and V.* 234
Appeal (verb) *a* Once more to France or England; *Columbus* 57
Appeal'd *a* To one that stood beside. *D. of F. Women* 99
And with a larger faith *a* *Talking Oak* 15
Appealing *A* to the bolts of Heaven; *Princess iv* 372
Appear Shadows of the world *a*. *L. of Shalott ii* 12
made *a* Still-lighted in a secret shrine, *Mariana in the S.* 17
Falling had let *a* the brand of John— *Aylmer's Field* 509
things *a* the work of mighty Gods. *Lucretius* 102
Thy marble bright in dark *a's*, *In Mem. lxvii* 5
Which makes *a* the songs I made ,, *Con.*, 21
Shall I *a*, O Queen, at Camelot, *Lancelot and E.* 142
beauties of the work *a* The darkest faults: *Sisters (E. and E.)* 105
and now the morn *a's*, *The Flight* 18
Miriam your Mother might *a* to me. *The Ring* 137
Appear'd The very graves *a* to smile, *The Letters* 45
now that shadow of mischance *a* *Enoch Arden* 128
blew and blew, but none *a*: *Princess v* 336
the work To both *a* so costly, *Marr. of Geraint* 638
a, low-built but strong; *Balin and Balan* 333
never yet Had heaven *a* so blue, *Holy Grail* 365
Appearing *A* ere the times were ripe, *In Mem. Con.*, 139
dark in the golden grove *A*, *Last Tournament* 380
Appeased holy Gods, they must be *a*, *The Victim* 47
Appertain all That *a's* to noble maintenance. *Marr. of Geraint* 712
Appetite I never ate with angrier *a* *Geraint and E.* 233
Applauded mildly, that all hearts *A*, ,, 958
Applause (*See also* **Self-applause**) might reap the *a* of Great, *Princess iii* 262
the Trojans roar'd *a*; *Spec. of Iliad* 1
Shall he for whose *a* I strove, *In Mem. li* 5
To laughter and his comrades to *a*. *Geraint and E.* 296
Apple full-juiced *a*, waxing over-mellow, *Lotos-Eaters, C. S.*, 33
swung an *a* of the purest gold, *Marr. of Geraint* 170
a's by the brook Fallen, and on the lawns. *Holy Grail* 384
and ate The goodly *a's*, ,, 388
The warm white *a* of her throat, *Last Tournament* 717
peak of the mountain was *a's*, *V. of Maeldune* 63
Apple-arbiter beardless *a-a* Decided fairest. *Lucretius* 91
Apple-blossom Fresh *a-b*, blushing for a boon. *The Brook* 90
cheek of *a-b*, Hawk-eyes; *Gareth and L.* 589
Apple-cheek'd a bevy of Eroses *a-c*, *The Islet* 11
Apple-tree and o'er the brook Were *a-t's*, *Holy Grail* 384
Appliances With half a night's *a*, *Lover's Tale iv* 93
Application And liberal *a's* lie In Art *Day-Dm., Moral* 13
Appraised *A* his weight, and fondled *Enoch Arden* 154
A the Lycian custom, *Princess ii* 128
Apprehend And thro' thick veils to *a* *Two Voices* 296
Approach (s) less achievable By slow *a'es*, *Princess iii* 284
Preserve a broad *a* of fame, *Ode on Well.* 78
Approach (verb) and let him presently *A*, *St. S. Stylites* 216
a To save the life despair'd of, *Enoch Arden* 830
A and fear not; *Princess vii* 353
Morning-Star, *a*, Arm me,' *Gareth and L.* 924
'*A* and arm me!' ,, 1112
Approach'd *a* Melissa, tinged with wan *Princess iii* 24
A between them toward the King, *Gareth and L.* 441
as the great knight *A* them: *Lancelot and E.* 180
A him, and with full affection said, ,, 1355
Approaching *A*, press'd you heart to heart. *Miller's D.* 160
A thro' the darkness, call'd; *Lancelot and E.* 1000
Approve And wishes me to *a* him, *Maud I xix* 71
Approved She wore the colours I *a*. *The Letters* 16

Approved (*continued*) *A* him, bowing at their own deserts *The Brook* 128
and all the knights *A* him, *Balin and Balan* 210
Approven he by miracle was *a* King: *Guinevere* 296
Approvingly often talk'd of him *A*, *Aylmer's Field* 474
'Appy (happy) as *'a* as 'art could think, *North. Cobbler* 15
I loovs tha to maäke thysen *'a*, *Spinster's S's.* 57
maäke 'is owd aäge as *'a* as iver I can, *Owd Roä* 3
A-preächin' Fur *they*'ve bin *a-p mea* down, *Church-warden, etc.*, 53
Apricot blanching *a* like snow in snow. *Prog. of Spring* 30
April (adj.) When *A* nights began to blow, *Miller's D.* 106
A hopes, the fools of chance; *Vision of Sin* 164
And breathes in *A* autumns. *The Brook* 196
clad her like an *A* daffodilly *Princess ii* 324
Can trouble live with *A* days, *In Mem. lxxxiii* 7
Thro' all the years of *A* blood; ,, *cix* 12
and my regret Becomes an *A* violet, ,, *cxv* 19
For all an *A* morning, till the ear *Lancelot and E.* 897
gustful *A* morn That puff'd *Holy Grail* 14
Green prelude, *A* promise, glad new-year *Lover's Tale i* 281
April (s) ('Twas *A* then), I came and sat *Miller's D.* 59
And *A's* crescent glimmer'd cold, ,, 107
balmier than half-opening buds Of *A*, *Tithonus* 60
May or *A*, he forgot, The last of *A* *The Brook* 151
Her maiden babe, a double *A* old, *Princess ii* 110
To rain an *A* of ovation round Their statues, ,, *vi* 66
From *A* on to *A* went, *In Mem. xxii* 7
Make *A* of her tender eyes; ,, *xl* 8
That keenlier in sweet *A* wakes, ,, *cxvi* 2
(For then was latter *A*) *Com. of Arthur* 451
in *A* suddenly Breaks from a coppice *Marr. of Geraint* 338
With *A* and the swallow. *The Ring* 60
Apt supple, sinew-corded, *a* at arms; *Princess v* 535
a at arms and big of bone *Marr. of Geraint* 489
A-raägin' (raging) fire was *a-r* an' raävin' *Owd Roä* 110
Arab delicate *A* arch of her feet *Maud I xvi* 15
Arâbi (Leader of Egyptian Revolt, 1882) And Wolseley overthrew *A*, *Pro. to Gen. Hamley* 31
Arabian nodding together In some *A* night? *Maud I vii* 12
I know not, your *A* sands; *To Ulysses* 35
plunge old Merlin in the *A* sea: *Gareth and L.* 211
Arac (Prince) Not ev'n her brother *A*, *Princess i* 153
rumour of Prince *A* hard at hand. ,, *v* 112
speak with *A*: *A's* word is thrice ,, 226
midmost and the highest Was *A*: ,, 257
The genial giant, *A*, roll'd himself ,, 274
but we will send to her,' Said *A*, ,, 325
whereas I know Your prowess, *A*, ,, 404
Down From those two bulks at *A's* side, ,, 499
From *A's* arm, as from a giant's flail, ,, 500
but *A* rode him down: ,, 532
A, satiate with his victory. ,, *vii* 90
Arbaces *A*, and Phenomenon, and the rest, *The Brook* 162
Arbiter *See* **Apple-arbiter**
Arbitrate to-morrow, *a* the field; *Last Tournament* 104
Arbitration Before his throne of *a* ,, 162
Arbour They read in *a's* clipt and cut, *Amphion* 85
Arbutus there? yon *a* Totters; *Lucretius* 184
Arc thro' a little *a* Of heaven, *To J. S.* 26
Bear had wheel'd Thro' a great *a* *Princess iv* 213
sine and *a*, spheroïd and azimuth, ,, *vi* 256
Run out your measured *a's*, *In Mem. cv* 27
bridge of single *a* Took at a leap; *Gareth and L.* 908
Arcady To many a flute of *A*. *In Mem. xxiii* 24
Arch (s) (*See also* **Innocent-arch, Portal-arch**) Thro' little crystal *a'es* low *Arabian Nights* 49
shadow'd grots of *a'es* interlaced, *Palace of Art* 51
Many an *a* high up did lift, ,, 142
round and round, and whirl'd in an *a*, *M. d'Arthur* 138
to three *a'es* of a bridge Crown'd *Gardener's D.* 43
Yet all experience is an *a* wherethro' Gleams *Ulysses* 19
we past an *a*, Whereon a woman-statue *Princess i* 209
Or under *a'es* of the marble bridge ,, *ii* 458
bloom profuse and cedar *a'es* Charm, *Milton* 11
the delicate Arab *a* of her feet *Maud I xvi* 15

Arch (s) (*continued*) round and round, and whirl'd in an *a*, *Pass. of Arthur* 306
Straining his eyes beneath an *a* of hand, ,, 464
thro' the *a* Down those loud waters, *Lover's Tale i* 58
Arch (verb) fires that *a* this dusky dot— *Epilogue* 52
Archbishop *A*, Bishop, Priors, Canons, *Sir J. Oldcastle* 159
Arched *See* **High-arched**
Arching (*See also* **Slow-arching**) now *a* leaves her bare To breaths *Prog. of Spring* 12
Architect You, the Patriot *A*, *On Jub. Q. Victoria* 42
Archives of crimeful record all My mortal *a*. *St. S. Stylites* 159
Archway Gleam thro' the Gothic *a* in the wall. *Godiva* 64
so thou pass Beneath this *a*, *Gareth and L.* 268
a shatter'd *a* plumed with fern; *Marr. of Geraint* 316
While I shelter'd in this *a* *Locksley H., Sixty*, 259
Arctic would dare Hell-heat or *A* cold, *Ancient Sage* 116
Arden (surname) (*See also* **Enoch, Enoch Arden**) 'You *A*, you! nay,—sure he was a foot Higher *Enoch Arden* 854
Eh, let me fetch 'em, *A*,' ,, 871
Arden (forest) face again, My Rosalind in this *A*— *Sisters (E. and E.)* 119
'Are (hare) An' 'e niver not shot one *'a*, *Village Wife* 42
Arês great God, *A*, burns in anger still *Tiresias* 11
hail of *A* crash Along the sounding walls. ,, 96
yesternight, To me, the great God *A*, ,, 111
Argent The polish'd *a* of her breast *D. of F. Women* 158
To yonder *a* round; *St. Agnes' Eve* 16
Argent-lidded Serene with *a-l* eyes Amorous, *Arabian Nights* 135
Argive On *A* heights divinely sang, *In Mem. xxiii* 22
Argosy *argosies* of magic sails, *Locksley Hall* 121
Arguing *A* boundless forbearance: *Aylmer's Field* 317
seem As *a* love of knowledge and of power; *Princess ii* 57
Argument Half-buried in some weightier *a*, *Lucretius* 9
A-rilin' thowt she was nobbut *a-r* ma then. *Owd Roä* 74
Arimathæan Joseph *See* **Joseph**
A-ringing we heard them *a-r* the bell, *First Quarrel* 21
Arise Scarce outward signs of joy *a*, *Supp. Confessions* 49
Come forth, I charge thee, *a*, *Ode to Memory* 46
I feel the tears of blood *a* *Oriana* 77
Or when little airs *a*, *Adeline* 33
Many suns *a* and set. *Miller's D.* 205
A, and let us wander forth, ,, 239
I will *a* and slay thee with my hands.' *M. d'Arthur* 132
yearning for thy yoke, *a*, *Tithonus* 40
mighty wind *a's*, roaring seaward, *Locksley Hall* 194
Expecting when a fountain should *a*: *Vision of Sin* 8
The thoughts that *a* in me. *Break, break, etc.* 4
pillars of the hearth *A* to thee; *Princess vii* 217
'*A*, and get thee forth and seek *In Mem. lxxxv* 79
A and fly The reeling Faun, ,, *cxviii* 25
Morning *a's* stormy and pale, *Maud I vi* 1
And ah for a man to *a* in me, ,, *x* 67
A, my God, and strike, for we hold ,, *II i* 45
war would *a* in defence of the right, *Maud III vi* 19
saw the dreary phantom *a* and fly ,, 36
saying, '*A*, and help us thou! *Com. of Arthur* 44
A And quickly pass to Arthur's hall, *Gareth and L.* 983
these from all his life *a*, and cry, ,, 1131
Until my lord *a* and look upon me?' *Geraint and E.* 650
Till yonder man upon the bier *a*, ,, 657
my dear lord *a* and bid me do it, ,, 665
Until himself *a* a living man, ,, 706
And by the great Queen's name, *a* *Balin and Balan* 482
A, go forth and conquer as of old.' *Pass. of Arthur* 64
I will *a* and slay thee with my hands.' ,, 300
A in open prospect—heath and hill, *Lover's Tale i* 397
A, my own true sister, come forth! *The Flight* 96
Arisen (*See also* **Half-arisen**) mountains have *a* since With cities *Merlin and V.* 675
Arising at Bible meetings, o'er the rest *A*, *Sea Dreams* 195
from the floor, Tusklike, *a*, *Balin and Balan* 316
horse, *A* wearily at a fallen oak, ,, 425
goblet with a priceless wine *A*, *Lover's Tale iv* 228
Ilion falling, Rome *a*, *To Virgil* 3
Aristocrat what care I, *A*, democrat, autocrat— *Maud I x* 65

Ark sought'st to wreck my mortal *a*,	*Two Voices* 389
I leave this mortal *a* behind,	*In Mem. xii* 6
Rich *a's* with priceless bones	*Balin and Balan* 110
Arm (s) (*See also* **Airm, Hairm**) enormous polypi Winnow with giant *a's*	*The Kraken* 10
And with a sweeping of the *a*,	*A Character* 16
Of wrath her right *a* whirl'd,	*The Poet* 54
Sweet faces, rounded *a's*,	*Sea Fairies* 3
Fold thine *a's*, turn to thy rest.	*A Dirge* 3
right *a* debased The throne of Persia,	*Alexander* 1
A glowing *a*, a gleaming neck,	*Miller's D.* 78
When, *a* in *a*, we went along,	,, 163
Round my true heart thine *a's* entwine	,, 216
The kiss, The woven *a's*, seem	,, 232
Puts forth an *a*, and creeps	*Œnone* 4
when I look'd, Paris had raised his *a*,	,, 189
that my *a's* Were wound about thee,	,, 202
Sat smiling, babe in *a*.	*Palace of Art* 96
my *a* was lifted to hew down	*D. of F. Women* 45
humid *a's* festooning tree to tree,	,, 70
mailed Bacchus leapt into my *a's*,	,, 151
kneeling, with one *a* about her king,	,, 270
He held a goose upon his *a*,	*The Goose* 5
He took the goose upon his *a*,	,, 41
an *a* Rose up from out the bosom	*M. d'Arthur* 29
rose an *a* Clothed in white samite,	,, 143
behold an *a*, Clothed in white samite,	,, 158
with pain, reclining on his *a*,	,, 168
One *a* aloft—Gown'd in pure white,	*Gardener's D.* 125
in the circle of his *a's* Enwound us both ;	,, 216
thrust him in the hollows of his *a*,	*Dora* 132
To Francis, with a basket on his *a*,	*Audley Court* 6
Sleep, Ellen, folded in thy sister's *a*,	,, 63
sleeping, haply dream her *a* is mine.	,, 64
'Sleep, Ellen, folded in Emilia's *a* ;	,, 65
in my weak, lean *a's* I lift the cross,	*St. S. Stylites* 118
leg and *a* with love-knots gay,	*Talking Oak* 65
She sank her head upon her *a*	,, 207
close and dark my *a's* I spread,	,, 225
I wither slowly in thine *a's*,	*Tithonus* 6
Roll'd in one another's *a's*,	*Locksley Hall* 58
Glows forth each softly-shadow'd *a*	*Day-Dm. Sleep. B.* 13
AND on her lover's *a* she leant,	,, *Depart.* 1
Mute with folded *a's* they waited—	*The Captain* 39
HER *a's* across her breast she laid	*Beggar Maid* 1
We rush'd into each other's *a's*.	*The Letters* 40
laid the feeble infant in his *a's* ;	*Enoch Arden* 152
strong *a's* about his drooping wife,	,, 228
babe, who rear'd his creasy *a's*,	,, 751
he rose, he spread his *a's* abroad	,, 912
grovelike, each huge *a* a tree,	*Aylmer's Field* 510
a's stretch'd as to grasp a flyer :	,, 588
sideways up he swung his *a's*,	*Sea Dreams* 24
waved my *a* to warn them off ;	,, 132
raised your *a*, you tumbled down	,, 141
soft *a*, which, like the pliant bough	,, 290
roll thy tender *a's* Round him,	*Lucretius* 82
her *a* lifted, eyes on fire—	*Princess, Pro.*, 41
long *a's* and hands Reach'd out,	,, *i* 28
lapt In the *a's* of leisure,	,, *ii* 168
holding out her lily *a's* Took both his hands,	,, 303
Herself and Lady Psyche the two *a's* ;	,, *iii* 35
then Oaring one *a*, and bearing in my left	,, *iv* 183
drew My burthen from mine *a's* ;	,, 192
A Niobëan daughter, one *a* out,	,, 371
She stretch'd her *a's* and call'd	,, 496
From Arac's *a*, as from a giant's flail,	,, *v* 500
Ida stood With Psyche's babe in *a* :	,, *vi* 31
on every side A thousand *a's*	,, 37
glittering axe was broken in their *a's*,	,, 51
a's were shatter'd to the shoulder blade.	,, 52
and with the babe yet in her *a's*,	,, 74
reach its fatling innocent *a's*	,, 138
in your own *a's* To hold your own,	,, 177
breast that fed or *a* that dandled you,	,, 181
Arm (s) (*continued*) from mine *a's* she rose Glowing	*Princess vii* 159
and Jenny hung on his *a*.	*Grandmother* 42
he turn'd and claspt me in his *a's*,	,, 55
So dear a life your *a's* enfold	*The Daisy* 93
She cast her *a's* about the child.	*The Victim* 32
He stay'd his *a's* upon his knee :	,, 54
And moves his doubtful *a's*, and feels	*In Mem. xiii* 3
When Science reaches forth her *a's*	,, *xxi* 18
Laid their dark *a's* about the field. (repeat)	*In Mem. xcv* 16, 52
They mix in one another's *a's*	*In Mem. cii* 23
That watch'd her on her nurse's *a*,	,, *Con.* 46
To find the *a's* of my true love	*Maud II iv* 3
So well thine *a* hath wrought for me to-day.'	*Com. of Arthur* 127
a's Stretch'd under all the cornice	*Gareth and L.* 218
with a kindly hand on Gareth's *a*	,, 578
bears a skeleton figured on his *a's*,	,, 640
lifted either *a*, 'Fie on thee, King !	,, 657
His *a's*, the rosy raiment, and the star.	,, 938
Sun Heaved up a ponderous *a*	,, 1045
writhed his wiry *a's* Around him,	,, 1150
Lifted an *a*, and softly whisper'd,	,, 1361
a's on which the standing muscle sloped,	*Marr. of Geraint* 76
'O noble breast and all-puissant *a's*,	,, 86
Not to be folded more in these dear *a's*,	,, 99
Claspt the gray walls with hairy-fibred *a's*,	,, 323
Down by the length of lance and *a*	*Geraint and E.* 463
and she cast her *a's* About him,	,, 761
His *a* half rose to strike again, but fell :	*Balin and Balan* 223
If *a* of flesh could lay him.'	,, 299
either lock'd in either's *a*.	,, 632
woven paces and with waving *a's*,	*Merlin and V.* 207
curved an *a* about his neck,	,, 241
made her lithe *a* round his neck Tighten,	,, 614
gentle wizard cast a shielding *a*.	,, 908
rose, Her *a's* upon her breast across,	,, 910
sloping down to make *A's* for his chair,	*Lancelot and E.* 438
battle-writhen *a's* and mighty hands	,, 812
innocently extending her white *a's*,	,, 932
armlet for the roundest *a* on earth,	,, 1183
an *a* to which the Queen's Is haggard,	,, 1226
Caught from his mother's *a's*—	,, 1405
often in her *a's* She bare me,	,, 1410
milky *a* Red-rent with hooks of bramble,	*Holy Grail* 210
she rose Opening her *a's* to meet me,	,, 395
Open'd his *a's* to embrace me as he came,	,, 417
every moment glanced His silver *a's*	,, 493
Hold her a wealthy bride within thine *a's*,	,, 621
in her white *a's* Received,	*Last Tournament* 23
Why ye not wear on *a*, or neck, or zone	,, 36
Right *a* of Arthur in the battlefield,	,, 202
wert lying in thy new leman's *a's*.'	,, 625
For feel this *a* of mine—	,, 690
milkwhite *a's* and shadowy hair	*Guinevere* 416
while yet Sir Lancelot, my right *a*	,, 429
Then she stretch'd out her *a's* and cried	,, 606
an *a* Rose up from out the bosom	*Pass. of Arthur* 197
rose an *a* Clothed in white samite,	,, 311
behold an *a*, Clothed in white samite,	,, 326
with pain, reclining on his *a*,	,, 336
on one *a* The flaxen ringlets of our infancies	*Lover's Tale i* 233
Bent o'er me, and my neck his *a* upstay'd.	,, 690
Love's *a's* were wreath'd about the neck of Hope,	,, 815
I wound my *a's* About her :	,, *ii* 200
softly put his *a* about her neck	,, *iv* 71
Holding his golden burthen in his *a's*,	,, 89
To greet us, her young hero in her *a's* !	,, 171
bearing high in *a's* the mightly babe,	,, 295
bearing on one *a* the noble babe,	,, 370
sisters closed in another's *a's*,	*Sisters (E. and E.)* 155
'Emmie, you put out your *a's*,	*In the Child. Hosp.* 56
It's the little girl with her *a's* lying out	,, 58
little *a's* lying out on the counterpane ;	,, 70
I spread mine *a's*, God's work, I said,	*Sir J. Oldcastle* 136
As I lean'd away from his *a's*—	*The Wreck* 102

Arm (s) (*continued*) 'Woman'—he graspt at my *a*— *The Wreck* 120
Ah, clasp me in your *a's*, sister, *The Flight* 5
O would I were in Edwin's *a's*— ,, 45
I feel'd thy *a* es I stood *Spinster's S's.* 26
Amy's *a's* about my neck— *Locksley H., Sixty*, 13
'Mother!' and I was folded in thine *a's*. *Demeter and P.* 22
here, my child, tho' folded in thine *a's*, ,, 40
And dying rose, and rear'd her *a's*, *The Ring* 222
happy had I died within thine *a's*, *Death of Œnone* 31
and Rome was a babe in *a's*, *The Dawn* 9
'O what an *a*,' said the king. *The Tourney* 12
Arm (verb) to *a* in proof, and guard about *Supp. Confessions* 65
Morning-star, approach, *A* me,' *Gareth and L.* 925
'Approach and *a* me!' ,, 1112
Arm-chair Her father left his good *a-c*, *Talking Oak* 103
small goodman Shrinks in his *a-c* *Princess v* 454
When asleep in this *a-c*? *Maud I vii* 4
So I sits i' my oän *a-c* *Spinster's S's.* 9
Arm'd (*See also* **All-arm'd, Full-arm'd, Plump-armed**)
one that *a* Her own fair head, *Princess, Pro.*, 32
Sleep must lie down *a*, for the villainous *Maud I i* 41
fair, strong, *a*—But to be won by force— *Gareth and L.* 104
who alway rideth *a* in black, ,, 636
These *a* him in blue arms, and gave ,, 931
damsel came, And *a* him in old arms, ,, 1115
wholly *a*, behind a rock In shadow, *Geraint and E.* 57
horsemen waiting, wholly *a*, ,, 121
And each of them is wholly *a*, ,, 143
issuing *a* he found the host and cried, ,, 407
he *a* himself and went, *Balin and Balan* 22
There two stood *a*, and kept the door; *Lancelot and E.* 1247
and we ride, *A* as ye see, *Pelleas and E.* 65
knights *A* for a day of glory before the King. *Last Tournament* 55
a by day and night Against the Turk; *Montenegro* 3
Armlet *a* for the roundest arm on earth, *Lancelot and E.* 1183
a for an arm to which the Queen's ,, 1226
Armour And as he rode his *a* rung, *L. of Shalott iii* 17
This mortal *a* that I wear, *Sir Galahad* 70
His own forefathers' arms and *a* hung. *Princess, Pro.*, 24
Your very *a* hallow'd, and your statues ,, *v* 413
When *a* clash'd or jingled, ,, *vi* 363
he had ask'd For horse and *a*: *Gareth and L.* 474
so ye cleave His *a* off him, ,, 1095
hew'd great pieces of his *a* off him, ,, 1142
youth who scour'd His master's *a*; *Marr. of Geraint* 258
slay him and will have his horse And *a*, *Geraint and E.* 63
and possess your horse And *a*, ,, 75
three gay suits of *a* which they wore, ,, 95
bound the suits Of *a* on their horses, ,, 97
Their three gay suits of *a*, each from each, ,, 181
heap'd The pieces of his *a* in one place, ,, 374
glimmer'd on his *a* in the room. ,, 386
'Take Five horses and their *a's*;' ,, 409
palfrey heart enough To bear his *a*? ,, 490
Bled underneath his *a* secretly, ,, 502
A light of *a* by him flash, *Balin and Balan* 326
moved Among us in white *a*, Galahad. *Holy Grail* 135
one that on me moved In golden *a* ,, 410
horse In golden *a* jewell'd everywhere: ,, 412
In silver *a* suddenly Galahad shone ,, 458
In silver-shining *a* starry-clear; ,, 511
Wherefore now thy horse And *a*: *Pelleas and E.* 355
Behold his horse and *a*. ,, 373
he that hath His horse and *a*: ,, 378
In blood-red *a* sallying, *Last Tournament* 443
And all her golden *a* on the grass, *Tiresias* 45
Armour'd And *a* all in forest green, *Last Tournament* 170
Armourer riding further past an *a's*, Who, *Marr. of Geraint* 266
Whereat the *a* turning all amazed ,, 283
Armoury from Jehovah's gorgeous *armouries*, *Milton* 6
Arms (weapons) *a, or power of brain, or birth* *To the Queen* 3
Those men thine *a* withstood, *England and Amer.* 7
one might show it at a joust of *a*, *M. d'Arthur* 102
broke a close with force and *a*: *Edwin Morris* 131
His own forefathers' *a* and armour hung. *Princess, Pro.*, 24

Arms (weapons) (*continued*) clash'd in *a*, By glimmering lanes *Princess, Pro.*, *v* 5
piled *a* and rough accoutrements, ,, 55
horses yell'd; they clash'd their *a*; ,, 250
two armies and the noise Of *a*; ,, 346
none to trust Since our *a* fail'd— ,, 427
supple, sinew-corded, apt at *a*; ,, 535
whose *a* Champion'd our cause and won it ,, *vi* 61
Roll of cannon and clash of *a*, *Ode on Well.* 116
Arthur yet had done no deed of *a*, *Com. of Arthur* 46
many of these in richer *a* than he, ,, 52
Closed in her castle from the sound of *a*. *Gareth and L.* 163
his *a* Clash'd; and the sound was good ,, 311
A for her son, and loosed him from his vow. ,, 530
Gareth ere he parted flash'd in *a*. ,, 689
Mounted in *a*, threw up their caps ,, 697
'Bound upon a quest With horse and *a*— ,, 709
few goodlier than he) Shining in *a*, ,, 745
These arm'd him in blue *a*, ,, 931
strength of anger thro' mine *a*, ,, 948
and take his horse And *a*, ,, 956
Hath overthrown thy brother, and hath his *a*.' ,, 1037
damsel came, And arm'd him in old *a*, ,, 1115
His *a* are old, he trusts the harden'd skin— ,, 1139
on a nightblack horse, in nightblack *a*, ,, 1381
a On loan, or else for pledge; *Marr. of Geraint* 219
a, *a*, *a* to fight my enemy? ,, 282
A? truth! I know not: ,, 289
thought to find *A* in your town, ,, 418
if ye know Where I can light on *a*, ,, 422
heard me praise Your feats of *a*, ,, 435
true heart,' replied Geraint, 'but *a*, ,, 474
'*A*, indeed, but old And rusty, ,, 477
Who being apt at *a* and big of bone ,, 489
Yniol's rusted *a* Were on his princely person, ,, 543
will not fight my way with gilded *a*, *Geraint and E.* 21
Three horses and three goodly suits of *a*, ,, 124
Two sets of three laden with jingling *a*, ,, 188
take A horse and *a* for guerdon; ,, 218
one with *a* to guard his head and yours, ,, 427
paid with horses and with *a*; ,, 486
loosed the fastenings of his *a*, ,, 511
grow In use of *a* and manhood, *Lancelot and E.* 64
while she watch'd their *a* far-off Sparkle, ,, 395
earth shake, and a low thunder of *a*. ,, 460
glittering in enamell'd *a* the maid ,, 619
FROM noiseful *a*, and acts of prowess *Holy Grail* 1
a Hack'd, and their foreheads grimed ,, 264
Lend me thine horse and *a*, *Pelleas and E.* 345
Pelleas lent his horse and all his *a*, ,, 358
one might show it at a joust of *a*, *Pass. of Arthur* 270
Gold, jewels, *a*, whatever it may be. *Lover's Tale iv* 235
and shoutings and soundings to *a*, *Def. of Lucknow* 76
The warrior hath forgot his *a*, *Ancient Sage* 138
alarms Sounding 'To *a*! to *a*!' *Prog. of Spring* 104
clatter of *a*, and voices, and men passing *Bandit's Death* 24
Arms (ensigns armorial) His *a* were carven only; but if twain His *a* were blazon'd also; *Gareth and L.* 412
then was painting on it fancied *a*, *Merlin and V.* 474
guess'd a hidden meaning in his *a*, *Lancelot and E.* 17
quartering your own royal *a* of Spain, *Columbus* 115
Arm's-length Paris held the costly fruit Out at *a-l*, *Œnone* 136
Army crying there was an *a* in the land, *Princess iv* 484
compassed by two *armies* and the noise ,, *v* 345
Charging an *a*, while All the world *Light Brigade* 30
To preach our poor little *a* down, *Maud I x* 38
councils thinn'd, And *armies* waned, *Merlin and V.* 573
Earls of the *a* of Anlaf Fell *Batt. of Brunanburh* 53
nor had Anlaf With *armies* so broken ,, 82
Her dauntless *a* scatter'd, and so small, *The Fleet* 11
glorious annals of *a* and fleet, *Vastness* 7
Arno unfamiliar *A*, and the dome *The Brook* 189
Arnon from Aroer On *A* unto Minneth.' *D. of F. Women* 239
Aroer from *A* On Arnon unto Minneth.' ,, 238
Aromat from the blessed land of *A*— *Holy Grail* 48

Arose *a*, and I releas'd The casement, *Two Voices* 403
a wind *a*, And overhead the wandering ivy *Œnone* 98
THE rain had fallen, the Poet *a*, *Poet's Song* 1
and *a* Eager to bring them down, *Enoch Arden* 871
not to die a listener, I *a*, *The Brook* 163
a the labourers' homes, *Aylmer's Field* 147
footstool from before him, and *a*; ,, 327
wind *a* and rush'd upon the South, *Princess i* 97
a Once more thro' all her height, ,, *vi* 159
That afternoon a sound *a* of hoof And chariot, ,, 379
Star after star, *a* and fell; ,, *vii* 50
on one side *a* The women up in wild revolt, ,, 122
Then thorpe and byre *a* in fire, *The Victim* 3
Thro' four sweet years *a* and fell, *In Mem., xxii* 3
Since our first Sun *a* and set. ,, *xxiv* 8
Till at the last *a* the man; ,, *cxviii* 12
till I could bear it no more, But *a*, *Maud I iii* 10
Nor ever *a* from below, ,, *II ii* 36
on the further side *A* a silk pavilion, *Gareth and L.* 910
a, and raised Her mother too, *Marr. of Geraint* 535
in their halls *a* The cry of children, *Geraint and E.* 964
damsel bidden *a* And stood with folded hands *Merlin and V.* 68
with smiling face *a*, *Lancelot and E.* 552
and all the knights *a*, And staring *Holy Grail* 192
King *a* and went To smoke the ,, 213
words of Arthur flying shriek'd, *a*, *Last Tournament* 139
She clear'd her sight, she *a*, *Dead Prophet* 31
call'd *a*, and, slowly plunging down *St. Telemachus* 28
from the ruin *a* The shriek and curse *Akbar's Dream* 189
Aroused So sleeping, so *a* from sleep *Day-Dm., L'Envoi* 21
A the black republic on his elms, *Aylmer's Field* 529
a Lancelot, who rushing outward *Guinevere* 106
Arrange Dispute the claims, *a* the chances; *To F. D. Maurice* 31
A the board and brim the glass; *In Mem., cvii* 16
Arranged *a* Her garden, sow'd her name *Aylmer's Field* 87
men and maids *A* a country dance, *Princess, Pro.*, 84
A the favour, and assumed the Prince. ,, *iv* 602
Arras (adj.) In Arthur's *a* hall at Camelot: *Merlin and V.* 250
Arras (s) hung with *a* green and blue, *Palace of Art* 61
Array (s) Singing of men that in battle *a*, *Maud I v* 8
Array'd with her own white hands *A* *Marr. of Geraint* 17
took them, and *a* herself therein, ,, 139
took it, and *a* herself therein. ,, 849
there the Queen *a* me like the sun: *Geraint and E.* 701
Arraying morn by morn, *a* her sweet self *Lancelot and E.* 906
Arrival will harangue The fresh *a's* of the week *Princess ii* 96
Arrive *A* at last the blessed goal, *In Mem. lxxxiv* 41
Arrived *A* and found the sun of sweet content *The Brook* 168
a, by Dubric the high saint, *Com. of Arthur* 453
Arriving *A* all confused among the rest *Princess iv* 224
A at a time of golden rest, *Merlin and V.* 142
Arrogance They said with such heretical *a* *Sir J. Oldcastle* 15
Arrow viewless *a's* of his thoughts were headed *The Poet* 11
The bitter *a* went aside, *Oriana* 37
The false, false *a* went aside, ,, 39
The damned *a* glanced aside, ,, 41
Within thy heart my *a* lies, ,, 80
shoot into the dark *A's* of lightnings. *To J. M. K.* 14
A random *a* from the brain. *Two Voices* 345
look'd a flight of fairy *a's* aim'd *Aylmer's Field* 94
Fly twanging headless *a's* at the hearts, *Princess ii* 402
When one would aim an *a* fair, *In Mem. lxxxvii* 25
Or into silver *a's* break The sailing ,, *ci* 15
Before an ever-fancied *a*, made *Geraint and E.* 531
a whizz'd to the right, one to the left, *Balin and Balan* 419
lest an *a* from the bush Should leave me *Last Tournament* 535
jingle of bits, Shouts, *a's*, *Tiresias* 94
Struck by a poison'd *a* in the fight, *Death of Œnone* 26
Arrowing *a* light from clime to clime, *Akbar's D. Hymn* 5
Arrowlet blows a globe of after *a's*, *Gareth and L.* 1029
Arrow-seed like the *a-s's* of the field flower, *The Poet* 19
Arrow-slain With loss of half his people *a-s*; *Merlin and V.* 565
Arrow-wounded your *a-w* fawn Came flying *Princess ii* 270
Arsenic *A*, *a*, sure, would do it, *Maud II v* 62
Art discovery And newness of thine *a* so pleased *Ode to Memory* 88

Art (*continued*) knowledge of his *a* Held me *D. of F. Women* 9
words, tho' cull'd with choicest *a*, ,, 285
I and he, Brothers in *A*; *Gardener's D.* 4
'will you climb the top of *A*. ,, 169
liberal applications lie In *A* like Nature, *Day-Dm. Moral* 14
Her *a*, her hand, her counsel *Aylmer's Field* 151
Hetairai, curious in their *a*, *Lucretius* 52
At wine, in clubs, of *a*, of politics; *Princess, Pro.*, 161
in *a's* of government Elizabeth and others; *a's* of war The peasant Joan and others; *a's* of grace Sappho and others ,, *ii* 161
with inmost terms Of *a* and science: ,, 447
Two great statues, *A* And Science, ,, *iv* 200
Science, *A*, and Labour have outpour'd *Ode Inter. Exhib.* 5
shapes and hues of *A* divine! ,, 22
piece of inmost Horticultural *a*, *Hendecasyllabics* 20
And owning but a little *a* *In Mem. xxxvii* 14
From *a*, from nature, from the schools, ,, *xlix* 1
on mind and *a*, And labour, ,, *lxxxvii* 22
The graceful tact, the Christian *a*; ,, *cx* 16
That all, as in some piece of *a*, ,, *cxxviii* 23
letters, dear to Science, dear to *A*, *Ded. of Idylls* 40
served King Uther thro' his magic *a*; *Com. of Arthur* 152
Knowing all *a's*, had touch'd, *Gareth and L.* 307
knew the range of all their *a's*, *Merlin and V.* 167
since ye seem the Master of all *A*, ,, 468
Or *A* with poisonous honey stol'n from France, *To the Queen ii* 56
Heirlooms, and ancient miracles of *A*, *Lover's Tale iv* 192
Repell'd by the magnet of *A* *The Wreck* 22
with the living hues of *A*. *Locksley H., Sixty*, 140
A and Grace are less and less: ,, 245
And here the Singer for his *A* *Epilogue* 79
You see your *A* still shrined in *Poets and their B.* 11
a nation purer through their *a*. *To W. C. Macready* 8
the fault is less In me than *A*. *Romney's R.* 9
A! Why should I so disrelish ,, 10
seem'd my lodestar in the Heaven of *A*, ,, 39
Of ancient *A* in Paris, or in Rome. ,, 87
This *A*, that harlot-like ,, 115
I replied 'Nay, Lord, for *A*,' ,, 131
'Art (heart) as 'appy as '*a* could think, *North. Cobbler* 15
Artemisia (Carian) *See* **Carian Artemisia**
Arthur (Epic poem) 'he burnt His epic, his King *A*, *The Epic* 28
Arthur (King) Until King *A's* table, man by man, *M. d'Arthur* 3
fallen in Lyonnesse about their Lord, King *A*: ,, 5
spake King *A* to Sir Bedivere: (repeat) ,, 13, 66
replied King *A*, faint and pale: ,, 72
'King *A's* sword, Excalibur, ,, 103
spoke King *A*, breathing heavily: ,, 113
replied King *A*, much in wrath: ,, 118
Then spoke King *A*, drawing thicker breath: ,, 148
answer made King *A*, breathing hard: ,, 162
as he walk'd, King *A* panted hard, ,, 176
murmur'd *A*, 'Place me in the barge,' ,, 204
like that *A* who, with lance in rest, ,, 222
my Lord *A*, whither shall I go? ,, 227
slowly answer'd *A* from the barge: ,, 239
sail with *A* under looming shores, ,, *Ep.* 17
King *A*, like a modern gentleman ,, 22
cried '*A* is come again: he cannot die.' ,, 24
For many a petty king ere *A* came *Com. of Arthur* 5
man was less and less, till *A* came. ,, 12
after these King *A* for a space, ,, 16
for he heard of *A* newly crown'd, ,, 41
A yet had done no deed of arms, ,, 46
A, looking downward as he past, ,, 55
A, passing thence to battle, ,, 75
When *A* reach'd a field-of-battle ,, 96
till *A* by main might, And mightier ,, 109
A call'd to stay the brands ,, 120
in the heart of *A* joy was lord. ,, 124
A said, 'Man's word is God in man: ,, 133
'Knowest thou aught of *A's* birth?' ,, 147
learn the secret of our *A's* birth?' ,, 159
By this King *A* as by thee to-day, ,, 162

Arthur (King) (*continued*) *A* born of Gorloïs, Others of Anton? *Com. of Arthur* 170
Hold ye this *A* for King Uther's son?' ,, 172
Knighted by *A* at his crowning, ,, 175
like a loyal sister cleaved To *A*,— ,, 192
before his time Was *A* born, ,, 212
Brought *A* forth, and set him in the hall, ,, 229
clamour'd for a king, Had *A* crown'd; ,, 236
A were the child of shamefulness, ,, 239
Ye come from *A's* court. ,, 249
and *A* sat Crown'd on the daïs, ,, 257
from the casement over *A*, smote Flame-colour, ,, 274
friends Of *A*, gazing on him, ,, 278
A row'd across and took it— ,, 298
sad was *A's* face Taking it, ,, 305
therefore *A's* sister?' ask'd the King. ,, 317
when did *A* chance upon thee first?' ,, 338
Back to the court of *A* answering yea. ,, 446
A charged his warrior whom he loved ,, 447
A said, 'Behold, thy doom is mine. ,, 467
A's knighthood sang before the King:— ,, 481
Rome or Heathen rule in *A's* realm? ,, 485
A spake, 'Behold, for these have sworn ,, 507
and *A* strove with Rome. ,, 514
A and his knighthood for a space ,, 515
knight of *A*, working out his will, *Gareth and L.* 24
A gave him back his territory, ,, 78
both thy brethren are in *A's* hall, ,, 82
thou shalt go disguised to *A's* hall, ,, 152
A's wars in weird devices done, ,, 225
three Queens, the friends Of *A*, ,, 230
Merlin's hand, the Mage at *A's* court, ,, 306
everywhere At *A's* ordinance, ,, 308
heard A voice, the voice of *A*, ,, 318
Said *A*, 'Whether would ye? ,, 340
A, 'Have thy pleasant field again, ,, 343
A, 'We sit King, to help the wrong'd ,, 371
heard that *A* of his grace Had made ,, 393
A cried To rend the cloth, (repeat) ,, 400, 417
this was *A's* custom in his hall; ,, 410
A mightiest on the battle-field— ,, 496
'Comfort thyself,' said *A*, ,, 601
A mindful of Sir Gareth ask'd, ,, 624
and *A* glancing at him, Brought ,, 652
without the door King *A's* gift, ,, 677
most ungentle knight in *A's* hall.' ,, 757
A's men are set along the wood; ,, 788
a stalwart Baron, *A's* friend. ,, 818
'I well believe You be of *A's* Table,' ,, 836
being *A's* kitchen-knave!— ,, 838
this morn I stood in *A's* hall, ,, 855
A all at once gone mad replies, ,, 863
champion thou hast brought from *A's* hall? ,, 916
And quickly pass to *A's* hall, ,, 984
'Here is a kitchen-knave from *A's* hall ,, 1036
'No star of thine, but shot from *A's* heaven ,, 1100
meek withal As any of *A's* best, ,, 1169
knight of *A*, here lie thrown by whom I know not, ,, 1233
on the day when *A* knighted him.' ,, 1240
truth if not in *A's* hall, In *A's* presence? ,, 1254
A's harp tho' summer-wan, ,, 1314
challenge the chief knight Of *A's* hall?' ,, 1417
Geraint, a knight of *A's* court, *Marr. of Geraint* 1
Weeping for some gay knight in *A's* hall.' ,, 118
For *A* on the Whitsuntide before ,, 145
Cavall, King *A's* hound of deepest mouth, ,, 186
That eat in *A's* hall at Camelot. ,, 432
Shalt ride to *A's* court, ,, 582
rising up, he rode to *A's* court, ,, 591
A knight of *A's* court, who laid *Geraint and E.* 775
made a knight of *A's* Table Round, ,, 793
will not go To *A*, then will *A* come to you,' ,, 815
past With *A* to Caerleon upon Usk. ,, 946
wherefore *A* call'd His treasurer, *Balin and Balan* 4
A laugh'd upon him. 'Old friend, ,, 16

Arthur (King) (*continued*) spirit of his youth return'd On *A's* heart; *Balin and Balan* 22
'Fair Sirs,' said *A*, 'wherefore sit ,, 31
we be mightier men than all In *A's* court; ,, 34
'I too,' said *A*, 'am of *A's* hall, ,, 37
A lightly smote the brethren down, ,, 41
A seeing ask'd 'Tell me your names; ,, 49
Said *A* 'Thou hast ever spoken truth; ,, 73
A's host Proclaim'd him Victor, ,, 89
Then *A*, 'Let who goes before me, ,, 134
learn what *A* meant by courtesy, ,, 158
A, when Sir Balin sought him, ,, 198
all the kindly warmth of *A's* hall ,, 236
(for *A's* knights Were hated strangers ,, 351
thou from *A's* hall, and yet So simple! ,, 357
ye men of *A* be but babes.' ,, 361
to thy guest, Me, me of *A's* Table. ,, 380
some high lord-prince of *A's* hall, ,, 466
if from *A's* hall, To help the weak. ,, 472
A the blameless, pure as any maid, ,, 479
The slights of *A* and his Table, *Merlin and V.* 7
follow'd, Sir, In *A's* household?'— ,, 20
A bound them not to singleness ,, 28
'This *A* pure! ,, 49
If I were *A*, I would have thy blood. ,, 53
Perchance, one curl of *A's* golden beard. ,, 58
A, him Ye scarce can overpraise, ,, 91
A in the highest Leaven'd the world, ,, 140
While all the heathen lay at *A's* feet, ,, 144
wily Vivien stole from *A's* court. ,, 149
A walking all alone, Vext ,, 152
leaving *A's* court he gain'd the beach; ,, 197
In *A's* arras hall at Camelot: ,, 250
I rose and fled from *A's* court ,, 297
many-corridor'd complexities Of *A's* palace: ,, 733
the royal rose In *A's* casement ,, 740
A, blameless King and stainless man?' ,, 779
jousts, Which *A* had ordain'd, *Lancelot and E.* 32
A, long before they crown'd him King, ,, 34
A came, and labouring up the pass, ,, 47
A, holding then his court Hard ,, 74
Has *A* spoken aught? ,, 117
'*A*, my lord, *A*, the faultless King, ,, 121
I am yours, Not *A's*, as ye know, ,, 135
After the King, who eat in *A's* halls. ,, 184
'Known am I, and of *A's* hall, and known, ,, 188
till our good *A* broke The Pagan ,, 279
you know Of *A's* glorious wars.' ,, 285
having been With *A* in the fight ,, 287
where he sat At *A's* right, with smiling face arose, ,, 552
A to the banquet, dark in mood, ,, 564
'Our true *A*, when he learns, ,, 585
A's wars were render'd mystically, ,, 801
of *A's* palace toward the stream, ,, 1178
In which as *A's* Queen I move and rule: ,, 1221
For some do hold our *A* cannot die, ,, 1258
So *A* bad the meek Sir Percivale ,, 1264
But *A* spied the letter in her hand, ,, 1270
'My lord liege *A*, and all ye that hear, ,, 1290
A answer'd, 'O my knight, ,, 1326
A leading, slowly went The marshall'd ,, 1331
Then *A* spake among them, 'Let her tomb ,, 1339
A, who beheld his cloudy brows, ,, 1354
Alas for *A's* greatest knight, a man Not after *A's* heart! ,, 1419
A and his knighthood call'd The Pure, *Holy Grail* 3
one of those who eat in *A's* hall; ,, 24
Sin against *A* and the Table Round, ,, 79
when King *A* made His Table Round, ,, 89
not *A's* use To hunt by moonlight;' ,, 110
Said *A*, when he dubb'd him knight; ,, 137
Did *A* take the vow?' ,, 204
For dear to *A* was that hall of ours, ,, 222
Which Merlin built for *A* long ago! ,, 226
statue in the mould Of *A*, made by Merlin, ,, 239
twelve great windows blazon *A's* wars, ,, 248

Arthur (King) (*continued*) A finds the brand Excalibur. *Holy Grail* 253
'Lo now,' said A, 'have ye seen a cloud? ,, 286
voice Shrilling along the hall to A, call'd, 'But I, Sir A, saw ,, 289
the great table of our A closed ,, 329
Had Camelot seen the like, since A came; ,, 332
A's wars are render'd mystically, ,, 359
the gate of A's wars.' ,, 539
I remember'd A's warning word, ,, 598
thou shalt be as A in our land.' ,, 606
follow'd—almost A's words— ,, 669
seven clear stars of A's Table Round— ,, 684
Or was there sooth in A's prophecy, ,, 709
there sat A on the daïs-throne, ,, 721
and A turn'd to whom at first He saw not, ,, 751
A kept his best until the last; ,, 763
King A made new knights to fill *Pelleas and E.* 1
and A made him knight. ,, 16
I will be thine A when we meet.' ,, 47
A made vast banquets, and strange knights ,, 147
For A, loving his young knight, ,, 159
A had the jousts Down in the flat field ,, 163
our A made Knight of his table; ,, 319
'Gawain am I, Gawain of A's court, ,, 371
he, Gasping, 'Of A's hall am I, ,, 514
Had made mock-knight of A's Table Round, *Last Tournament* 2
For A and Sir Lancelot riding once ,, 10
brought A maiden babe; which A pitying took, ,, 21
So she, delivering it to A, said, ,, 30
A turn'd to Kay the seneschal, ,, 89
A rose and Lancelot follow'd him, ,, 112
words of A flying shriek'd, arose, ,, 139
Right arm of A in the battlefield, ,, 202
Dagonet, skipping, 'A, the King's; ,, 262
so thou breakest A's music too.' ,, 266
thank the Lord I am King A's fool. ,, 320
call the harp of A up in heaven?' ,, 333
With A's vows on the great lake of fire. ,, 345
I, and A and the angels hear, ,, 350
A with a hundred spears Rode far, ,, 420
'Lo there,' said one of A's youth, ,, 429
But A waved them back. ,, 437
He ended: A knew the voice; ,, 455
A deign'd not use of word or sword, ,, 458
in the heart of A pain was lord. ,, 486
other was the Tristram, A's knight! ,, 634
Had A right to bind them to himself? ,, 684
A make me pure As any maiden child? ,, 692
That night came A home, and while ,, 755
disruption in the Table Round Of A, *Guinevere* 18
knight of A's noblest dealt in scorn; ,, 40
Which good King A founded, years ago, ,, 221
the bard Sang A's glorious wars, ,, 286
And that was A; and they foster'd him ,, 295
to lead her to his lord A, ,, 384
silk pavilions of King A raised ,, 394
think How sad it were for A, should he live, ,, 496
'Oh A!' there her voice brake suddenly, ,, 607
There came on A sleeping, *Pass. of Arthur* 30
A woke and call'd, 'Who spake? ,, 45
Then spake King A to Sir Bedivere: (repeat) *Pass. of Arthur* 65, 136, 181, 234
ever yet had A fought a fight Like this *Pass. of Arthur* 93
and ev'n on A fell Confusion, ,, 98
while A at one blow, Striking ,, 167
Until King A's Table, man by man, ,, 172
fall'n in Lyonnesse about their lord, King A. ,, 174
replied King A, faint and pale: ,, 240
'King A's sword, Excalibur, ,, 271
spoke King A, breathing heavily: ,, 281
replied King A, much in wrath: ,, 286
Then spoke King A, drawing thicker breath: ,, 316
answer made King A, breathing hard: ,, 330
as he walk'd, King A panted hard, ,, 344
murmur'd A, 'Place me in the barge.' ,, 372

Arthur (King) (*continued*) like that A who, with lance in rest, *Pass. of Arthur* 390
my Lord A, whither shall I go? ,, 395
slowly answer'd A from the barge: ,, 407
friends Of A, who should help him ,, 456
city and palace Of A the king; *Merlin and the G.* 66
on the forehead Of A the blameless ,, 73
A had vanish'd I knew not whither, ,, 77
Arthur (Sir, a local magnate) To show Sir A's deer. *The Brook* 133
Arthur (A. H. Hallam, 1811-1833) With my lost A's loved remains, *In Mem. ix* 3
My A, whom I shall not see ,, 17
That holy Death ere A died ,, *lxxx* 2
My A, found your shadows fair, ,, *lxxxix* 6
Artificer A and subject, lord and slave, *Lover's Tale, ii* 103
Artist Well hast thou done, great a Memory, *Ode to Memory* 80
A more ideal A he than all, (repeat) *Gardener's D.* 25, 173
wife, an unknown a's orphan child— *Sea Dreams* 2
golden moods Of sovereign a's; *Princess, v.* 195
portrait of his friend Drawn by an a, *Sisters (E. and E.)* 135
What A ever yet Could make pure light *Romney's R.* 9
wife and children drag an A down! ,, 38
'This model husband, this fine A'! ,, 124
Artist-like A-l, Ever retiring thou dost gaze *Ode to Memory* 92
'Arty (hearty) glad to seeä tha sa 'a an' well. *North. Cobbler* 2
Arundel (Archbishop of Canterbury) (*See also* **Caiaphas-Arundel**) Against the proud archbishop A— *Sir J. Oldcastle* 16
this mitred A Dooms our unlicensed preacher ,, 104
how I anger'd A asking me To worship ,, 135
Arviragus there the heathen Prince, A, *Holy Grail* 61
A-sailing a-s with wind an' tide. *First Quarrel* 42
Ascalon that was old Sir Ralph's at A: *Princess, Pro.* 26
Ascend Take wings of fancy, and a, *In Mem. lxxvi* 1
thy deeds in light, A's to thee; *Ded. Poem Prin. Alice* 10
Ascended shouts A, and there brake *Gareth and L.* 801
as Kapiolani a her mountain, *Kapiolani* 28
Ascending A tired, heavily slept till morn. *Enoch Arden* 181
with the dawn a lets the day Strike *Geraint and E.* 692
with slow sad steps A, fill'd *Last Tournament* 144
Ascension spheroïd and azimuth, And right a, *Princess vi* 257
Ascent in steepness overcome, And victories of a, *Lover's Tale i* 387
Ash (tree) (*See also* **Esh**) Young a'es pirouetted down *Amphion* 27
Delaying as the tender a delays *Princess, iv* 106
Nor hoary knoll of a and haw *In Mem. c* 9
Ashaämed (ashamed) an' I wur dreädful a; *North. Cobbler* 40
Ashamed (*See also* **Ashaämed, Half-ashamed, Shaämed**)
Shall I believe him a to be seen? *Maud I. xiii* 25
'A boon, Sir King (his voice was all a), *Gareth and L.* 442
A am I that I should tell it thee. *Marr. of Geraint* 577
Your hand shakes. I am a. *Romney's R.* 25
A-shawin' (showing) mun be fools to be hallus a-s your claws, *Spinster's S's.* 61
Ashbud hair More black than a's in the front of March.' *Gardener's D.* 28
Ashen-gray seems But an a-g delight. *Maud I. vi* 22
Ashes And heap their a on the head; *Love thou thy land* 70
And all I was, in a. *Tithonus* 23
Who will not let his a rest! *You might have won* 28
Slipt into a, and was found no more. *Aylmer's Field* 6
A to a, dust to dust; *Ode on Well.* 270
And from his a may be made *In Mem. xviii* 3
And dust and a all that is; ,, *xxxiv* 4
who knows? we are a and dust. *Maud I i* 32
I spring Like flame from a.' *Gareth and L.* 546
champion from the a of his hearth.' ,, 899
who lay Among the a and wedded ,, 904
youth gone out Had left in a: *Merlin and V.* 246
dead a and all fire again Thrice in a second, *Lover's Tale iv* 323
but now to silent a fall'n away. *Locksley H., Sixty,* 41
Had the fierce a of some fiery peak *St. Telemachus* 1
Ashore I've ninety men and more that are lying sick a. *The Revenge* 10
And a day less or more At sea or a, ,, 87
But the blind wave cast me a, *Despair* 61
Ashy quivering brine With a rains, *The Voyage* 43
Asia Ages after, while in A, *Locksley H., Sixty,* 81
A-singein' Fur 'e smell'd like a herse a-s, *Owd Roä* 110

A-singin' Theer wur a lark a-s 'is best — North. Cobbler 46
Ask A the sea At midnight, — Supp. Confessions 125
When I a her if she love me, — Lilian 3
A's what thou lackest, — Two Voices 98
a thou not my name: — D. of F. Women 93
You a me, why, tho' ill at ease, — You ask me, why, 1
he has a mint of reasons: a. — The Epic 33
'Annie, I came to a a favour of you.' — Enoch Arden 285
This is the favour that I came to a.' — ,, 313
what is it that you a?' — ,, 427
O then to a her of my shares, — Sea Dreams 115
That Sheba came to a of Solomon.' — Princess ii 346
you should answer, we would a) — ,, 353
'O a me nothing,' I said: — ,, iii 59
a for him Of your great head— — ,, vi 313
A me no more: (repeat) — Princess vii 1, 5, 6, 9, 10, 11, 15
would but a you to fulfil yourself: — Princess vii 146
I a you nothing: only, if a dream, — ,, 148
A her to marry me by and by? — Window, Letter 6
And a a thousand things of home; — In Mem. xiv 12
Let no one a me how it came to pass; — Maud I xviii 49
If one should a me whether The habit, — ,, xx 17
I will not a thee why — ,, II iii 2
Or if I a thee why, — ,, 6
Or to a her, 'Take me, sweet, — ,, iv 87
Before thou a the King to make thee knight, — Gareth and L. 145
and loathe to a thee aught. — ,, 356
I scarce can a it thee for hate, — ,, 361
or thyself be mad, I a not: — ,, 877
'So this damsel a it of me Good— — ,, 974
'I charge thee, a not, but obey.' — Marr. of Geraint 133
'Then will I a it of himself,' — ,, 197
I swear I will not a your meaning in it: — Geraint and E. 743
I am silent then, And a no kiss;' — Merlin and V. 254
a your boon, for boon I owe you — ,, 306
wherefore a; And take this boon — ,, 309
will ye never a some other boon? — ,, 375
Who feels no heart to a another boon. — ,, 382
has tript a little: a thyself. — ,, 602
never could undo it: a no more: — ,, 686
I a you, is it clamour'd by the child, — ,, 771
a me not Hereafter ye shall know me— — Lancelot and E. 191
a you not to see the shield he left, — ,, 653
should a some goodly gift of him — ,, 912
'A me not, for I may not speak of it: — Holy Grail 758
yield me sanctuary, nor a Her name — Guinevere 141
and they spared To a it. — ,, 145
pray you check me if I a amiss— — ,, 324
Ye a me, friends, When I began to love. — Lover's Tale i 144
Ye know not what ye a. — ,, 150
I a you now, should this first master — ,, iv 265
let me a you then, Which voice — Sisters (E. and E.) 29
Edith wrote: 'My mother bids me a' — ,, 181
Did he believe it? did you a him? — The Ring 225
a 'Why left you wife and children? — Romney's R. 128
Ask'd (See also **Hax'd**) for I a him, and he said, — Dora 145
once I a him of his early life, — Edwin Morris 23
I a him half-sardonically. — ,, 59
she knew it not, And would if a deny it. — Enoch Arden 44
till I a If James were coming. — The Brook 105
To learn the price and what the price he a, — ,, 142
a her 'Are you from the farm?' — ,, 209
wonder'd at her strength, and a her of it: — Sea Dreams 113
And a; but not a word; — ,, 116
and a That which I a the woman — ,, 146
her we a of that and this, — Princess i 231
and when I a her 'how,' — ,, iii 29
'Tell us,' Florian a, 'How grew this feud — ,, 76
mutual pardon a and given — ,, v 46
a but space and fairplay for her scheme; — ,, 282
Ay or no, if a to her face? — Window, Letter 9
again The 'wilt thou' a, — In Mem. Con. 55
whatever is a her, answers 'Death.' — Maud I i 4
therefore Arthur's sister?' a the King. — Com. of Arthur 317
a him if these things were truth— — ,, 398
Ask'd (continued) A me to tilt with him, — Gareth and L. 27
he had a For horse and armour: — ,, 473
I a for thy chief knight, — ,, 658
bound to thee for any favour a!' — ,, 977
a it of him, Who answer'd as before; — Marr. of Geraint 204
after madness acted question a: — Geraint and E. 813
a her not a word, But went apart — ,, 880
Arthur seeing a 'Tell me your names; — Balin and Balan 49
Balin was bold, and a To bear — ,, 199
at feast Sir Galon likewise a — ,, 347
a this very boon, Now a again: — Merlin and V. 323
died Thrice than have a it once— — ,, 919
proof of trust—so often a in vain! — ,, 920
they a of court and Table Round, — Lancelot and E. 268
when he a 'Is it for Lancelot, — ,, 1104
and eyes that a 'What is it?' — ,, 1249
a us, knight by knight, if any Had seen it, — Holy Grail 283
'O brother,' a Ambrosius,—'for in sooth — ,, 540
then he a, 'Where is he? — ,, 638
scarce had pray'd or a it for myself— — ,, 691
sharply turning, a Of Gawain, — ,, 739
Lancelot,' a the King, 'my friend, — ,, 764
'Dead, is it so?' she a. 'Ay, ay,' said he, — Pelleas and E. 384
'Have ye fought?' She a of Lancelot. — ,, 593
a, 'Why skipt ye not, Sir Fool?' — Last Tournament 256
she a, I know not what, and a, — Lover's Tale i 706
and a If I would see her burial: — ,, ii 70
in his fantasy, I never a: — ,, iv 13
she rais'd an eye that a 'Where?' — ,, 94
then he suddenly a her if she were. — ,, 328
once my prattling Edith a him 'why?' — Sisters (E. and E.) 58
'Anything ailing,' I a her, 'with baby?' — The Wreck 61
a the waves that moan about the world — Demeter and P. 64
and I a About my Mother, — The Ring 102
'Why weird?' I a him; — ,, 197
Had a us to their marriage, — ,, 430
paused—and then a Falteringly, — Death of Œnone 94
a 'Is earth On fire to the West? — St. Telemachus 18
of the nations' a his Chronicler Of Akbar — Akbar's Dream 1
her name? what was it? I a her. — Charity 35
Askew all his conscience and one eye a'—(repeat) — Sea Dreams 180, 184
Asking (See also **Haxin'**) grant mine a with a smile, — Tithonus 16
Nor a overmuch and taking less, — Enoch Arden 252
a, one Not fit to cope your quest. — Gareth and L. 1173
therefore at thine a, thine. — Marr. of Geraint 479
not so strange as my long a it, — Merlin and V. 312
braved a riotous heart in a for it. — Lancelot and E. 359
a him, 'What said the King? — Holy Grail 203
a whence Had Arthur right to bind — Last Tournament 683
Arundel a me To worship Holy Cross! — Sir J. Oldcastle 135
A-sleeäpin' (sleeping) cat wur a-s alongside Roäver, — Owd Roä 33
Asleep (See also **Deep-asleep, Half-asleep, Warm-asleep**)
smiling a, Slowly awaken'd, — Eleänore 84
but I fall a at morn; — May Queen, N. Y's. E. 50
Falling a in a half-dream! — Lotos-Eaters, C.S. 56
Since that dear soul hath fall'n a. — To J. S. 34
To fall a with all one's friends; — Day-Dm., L'Envoi 4
If e'er when faith had fall'n a, — In Mem. cxxiv 9
When a in this arm-chair? — Maud I vii 4
But come to her waking, find her a, — ,, II ii 81
himself alone And all the world a, — Com. of Arthur 119
vext his day, but blesses him a— — Gareth and L. 1286
half a she made comparison — Marr. of Geraint 651
fell a again; And dreamt herself — ,, 653
He fell a, and Enid had no heart — Geraint and E. 369
not seem as dead, But fast a, — Lancelot and E. 1161
when they fall a Into delicious dreams, — Lover's Tale i 161
First falls a in swoon, wherefrom awaked, — ,, 791
I have done it, while you were a— — Rizpah 19
we believed her a again— — In the Child. Hosp. 69
ere the dotard fall a? — Locksley H., Sixty, 153
fall of water lull'd the noon a. — Romney's R. 83
But such a tide as moving seems a, — Crossing the Bar 5
A-smilin' An' Squire wur hallus a-s, — Village Wife 33
Asmodeus Abaddon and A caught at me. — St. S. Stylites 172

Aspasia not for all *A's* cleverness, *Princess ii* 344
Aspect Of pensive thought and *a* pale, *Margaret* 6
More bounteous *a's* on me beam, *Sir Galahad* 21
Under the selfsame *a* of the stars, *Lover's Tale i* 199
Aspen (*See also* **Aspen-tree**) Willows whiten, *a's* quiver, *L. of Shalott i* 10
And here thine *a* shiver ; *A Farewell* 10
Aspen-tree in the meadows tremulous *a-t's* *Lancelot and E.* 410
showers, And ever-tremulous *a-t's*, ,, 524
Asphodel Violet, amaracus, and *a*, *Œnone* 97
weary limbs at last on beds of *a*. *Lotos-Eaters, C. S.* 125
Along the silent field of *A*. *Demeter and P.* 153
Aspick Showing the *a's* bite.) *D. of F. Women* 160
A-squeälin' an' *a-s*, as if tha was bit, *Owd Roä* 89
and thou was *a-s'* thysen, ,, 107
Ass (an animal) whisper'd '*A'es'* ears,' among the sedge, *Princess ii* 113
one of thy long *a'es'* ears, *Last Tournament* 273
swine, goats, *a'es*, rams and geese ,, 321
'Then were swine, goats, *a'es*, geese ,, 325
Ass (a stupid fellow) Sam, thou's an *a* for thy paaïns: *N. Farmer, N.S.* 3
we boäth on us thinks tha an *a*. (repeat) ,, 12, 38
an *a* as near as mays nowt— ,, 39
Assail To *a* this gray preëminence of man! *Princess iii* 234
Assail'd brother king, Urien, *a* him: *Com. of Arthur* 36
They that *a*, and they that held *Lancelot and E.* 455
Assassin earls, and caitiff knights, *A's*, *Marr. of Geraint* 36
Sanctuary granted To bandit, thief, *a*— *Sir J. Oldcastle* 113
Assault Sharp is the fire of *a*, *Def. of Lucknow* 57
Ever the mine and *a*, our sallies, ,, 75
Assay 'I shall *a*,' said Gareth *Gareth and L.* 783
A it on some one of the Table Round, *Merlin and V.* 689
Assaye Against the myriads of *A* *Ode on Well.* 99
Assemble plans, And phantom hopes *a*; *Will Water.* 30
Assembled Narrowing in to where they sat *a* *Vision of Sin* 16
Assent I gave *a*: Yet how to bind *Princess, Con.* 7
Assented Enoch all at once *a* to it, *Enoch Arden* 126
Assert *a* None lordlier than themselves *Princess ii* 143
a's his claim In that dread sound *Ode on Well.* 70
Assign'd purpose of God, and the doom *a*. *Maud III vi* 59
quest *A* to her not worthy of it, *Lancelot and E.* 825
kiss the child That does the task *a*, ,, 829
Assize *See* **'Soize**
Association A fresh *a* blow, *In Mem. ci* 18
Assoil'd And the Holy man he *a* us, *V. of Maeldune* 126
Assume law The growing world *a*, *England and Amer.* 17
lose the child, *a* The woman: *Princess i* 137
Assumed Arranged the favour, and *a* the Prince. ,, *iv* 602
A from thence a half-consent ,, *vii* 82
A that she had thank'd him, *Geraint and E.* 646
Assuming *See* **All-assuming**
Assumption heart In its *a's* up to heaven; *In Mem. lxiii* 4
quench'd herself In that *a* of the bridesmaid— *Sisters (E. and E).* 234
Assurance *A* only breeds resolve.' *Two Voices* 315
Assure may now *a* you mine; *Merlin and V.* 549
Assured *See* **Half-assured**
Assyrian oil'd and curl'd *A* Bull Smelling of musk *Maud I vi* 44
A kings would flay Captives *Locksley H., Sixty,* 79
A-stanning (standing) 'What's i' tha bottle *a's* theer?' *North. Cobbler* 7
A-steppin' yon laädy *a-s* along the streeät, ,, 107
Astolat (*See also* **Lord of Astolat, Maid of Astolat**)
Elaine, the lily maid of *A*, *Lancelot and E.* 2
Ran to the Castle of *A*, ,, 167
And issuing found the Lord of *A* ,, 173
then the Lord of *A*: 'Whence comest thou, ,, 180
said the Lord of *A*, 'Here is Torre's: ,, 195
And came at last, tho' late, to *A*: ,, 618
came The Lord of *A* out, to whom the Prince ,, 627
the Lord of *A*, 'Bide with us, ,, 632
About the maid of *A*, and her love. ,, 723
'The maid of *A* loves Sir Lancelot, ,, 725
Sir Lancelot loves the maid of *A*.' ,, 726
But far away the maid in *A*, ,, 745
To *A* returning rode the three. ,, 905
Then spake the lily maid of *A*: ,, 1085
So that day there was dole in *A*. ,, 1136
the lily maid of *A* Lay smiling, ,, 1242
Astolat (*continued*) I, sometime call'd the maid of *A*, *Lancelot and E.* 1273
Astride men and boys *a* On wyvern, *Holy Grail* 349
A-stroäkin' (stroking) as I be *a-s* o' you, *Spinster's S's.* 19
Astræan second-sight of some *A* age, *Princess ii* 443
Astrology brought to understand A sad *a*, *Maud I xviii* 36
Astronomy their cosmogonies, their *astronomies*: *Columbus* 42
Dead the new *a* calls her . . . *Locksley H., Sixty,* 175
A and Geology, terrible Muses! *Parnassus* 16
Asunder each as each, Not to be pluck'd *a*; *Holy Grail* 777
They might be pluck'd *a*. ,, 780
save they could be pluck'd *a*, ,, 782
To tear the twain *a* in my heart, ,, 786
As if 'twere drawn *a* by the rack. *Lover's Tale ii* 57
shook us *a*, as if she had struck *The Wreck* 108
'At (hat) doesn not touch thy *'a* to the Squire;' *North. Cobbler* 25
says Parson, and laäys down 'is *'a*, ,, 89
A-taäkin' (taking) what a's doing *a-t* o' meä? *N. Farmer, O.S.* 45
A-talkin' Me an' thy muther, Sammy, 'as beän *a-t* o' thee; ,, *N.S.* 9
Atar infuse Rich *a* in the bosom of the rose, *Lover's Tale i* 270
Ate *A* with young lads his portion *Gareth and L.* 480
Sat down beside him, *a* and then began. ,, 872
Sir Gareth drank and *a*, and all his life ,, 1280
let the horses graze, and *a* themselves. *Geraint and E.* 211
Geraint *A* all the mowers' victual ,, 215
I never *a* with angrier appetite ,, 233
a with tumult in the naked hall, ,, 605
That ever among ladies *a* in hall, *Lancelot and E.* 255
drank the brook, and *a* The goodly apples, *Holy Grail* 387
our solemn feast—we *a* and drank, *Lover's Tale iv* 221
Atheist Authors—essayist, *a*, *Locksley H., Sixty,* 139
On whom the women shrieking '*A*' *Akbar's Dream* 91
Atheling (*See also* **Edmund Atheling**) Also the brethren, King and *A*, *Batt. of Brunanburh* 100
Athelstan (King of England) *A* King, Lord among Earls, ,, 1
Athene (Pallas) *See* **Pallas, Pallas Athene**
Athens when *A* reign'd and Rome, *Freedom* 9
Athlete Until she be an *a* bold, *Clear-headed friend* 21
an *a*, strong to break or bind *Palace of Art* 153
Athos Tomohrit, *A*, all things fair, *To E. L.* 5
Atlantic waste *A* roll'd On her and us *Third of Feb.* 21
I wish they were a whole *A* broad.' *Princess, Con.* 71
same bones back thro' the *A* sea, *Columbus* 214
Atmosphere Floating thro' an evening *a*, *Eleänore* 100
For love possess'd the *a*, *Miller's D.* 91
Cold in that *a* of Death, *In Mem. xx* 14
Atom If all be *a's*, how then should the Gods *Lucretius* 114
Vanishing, *a* and void, *a* and void, ,, 258
Boundless inward, in the *a*, *Locksley H., Sixty,* 212
Atomic Being *a* not be dissoluble, *Lucretius* 115
Atom-stream I saw the flaring *a-s's* And torrents ,, 38
Atomy Crowded with driving *atomies*, *Lover's Tale ii* 174
Atonement morning shine So rich in *a* as this *Maud I xix* 6
Attach phantasm of the form It should *a* to? *Lover's Tale i* 647
Attain *A* the wise indifference of the wise; *A Dedication* 8
Attain'd (*See also* **Half-attained**) have *a* Rest in a happy place *Œnone* 130
Attempt Vivien should *a* the blameless King. *Merlin and V.* 164
Attend each ear was prick'd to *a* A tempest, *Princess vi* 280
And in his presence I *a* To hear *In Mem. cxxvi* 2
Attendance And make her dance *a*; *Amphion* 62
You come with no *a*, page or maid, *Geraint and E.* 322
Attended So she goes by him *a*, *L. of Burleigh* 25
Attest *A* their great commander's claim *Ode on Well.* 148
Attic And round the *a's* rumbled, *The Goose* 46
single sordid *a* holds the living and the dead. *Locksley H., Sixty,* 222
Attire She in her poor *a* was seen: *Beggar Maid* 10
So splendid in his acts and his *a*, *Marr. of Geraint* 620
Attired women who *a* her head, ,, 62
than Geraint to greet her thus *a*; ,, 772
Attorney *See* **'Turney**
Attracted *a*, won, Married, made one with, *Lover's Tale i* 133
Attribute all the gentle *a's* Of his lost child, *Aylmer's Field* 730
Or, crown'd with *a's* of woe *In Mem. cxviii* 18
A-tuggin' Roäver *a-t* an' teärin' my slieäve. *Owd Roä* 60

A-tuggin' (*continued*) *a-t* an' teärin' me wuss nor afoor, *Owd Roä* 66
A-turnin 'be *a-t* ma hout upo' Christmas Eäve'? ,, 59
A-twizzen'd (twisted) Wi' haäfe o' the chimleys *a-t* ,, 22
Aubrey (Ellen) *See* **Ellen, Ellen Aubrey**
Audacious *See* **Outdacious**
Audible Shaped by the *a* and visible, Moulded the *a* and visible; *Lover's Tale ii* 104
Audibly Half inwardly, half *a* she spoke, *Marr. of Geraint* 109
Audience at the palace craved *A* of Guinevere, *Lancelot and E.* 1163
Audley *A* feast Humm'd like a hive *Audley Court* 4
Audley Court Let us picnic there At *A C.*' ,, 3
Auger hammer and axe, *A* and saw, *Enoch Arden* 174
Auger-hole Boring a little *a-h* in fear, *Godiva* 68
Aught—what, I would not *a* of false— *Princess v* 402
Unfaith in *a* is want of faith in all. *Merlin and V.* 389
less than swine, A naked *a*— *Last Tournament* 309
Augury how shall Britain light upon *auguries* happier? *Boädicea* 45
Now with prosperous *auguries* *On Jub. Q. Victoria* 9
Augustine (of Hippo) and besides, The great *A* wrote *Columbus* 52
Aunt came Trustees and *A's* and Uncles. *Edwin Morris* 121
maiden *A* Took this fair day for text, *Princess, Pro.,* 107
'Why not now?' the maiden *A*. ,, 208
the maiden *A* (A little sense of wrong ,, 218
She fixt a showery glance upon her *a*, ,, *Con.* 33
Aurelian (Roman Emperor) the Palmyrene That fought *A*, ,, *ii* 84
Aurelius (King of Britain) *A* lived and fought and died, *Com. of Arthur* 13
A Emrys would have scourged thee dead, *Gareth and L.* 375
Auricula among the gardens, *a's*, anemones, *City Child* 4
Ausonian stay'd the *A* king to hear *Palace of Art* 111
Austerely master took Small notice, or *a*, *Lucretius* 8
Australasian the long wash of *A* seas Far off, *The Brook* 194
Indian, *A*, African, *On Jub. Q. Victoria* 61
Australian black *A* dying hopes he shall return, *Locksley H., Sixty,* 70
Author *A's*—essayist, atheist, ,, 139
Authority *A* forgets a dying king, *M. d'Arthur* 121
see that some one with *a* Be near her *Princess vi* 236
All people said she had *a*— ,, 238
And simple words of great *a*, *Com. of Arthur* 261
A forgets a dying king, *Pass. of Arthur* 289
Autocrat Aristocrat, democrat, *a*— *Maud I x* 65
wearied of *A's*, Anarchs, and Slaves, *The Dreamer* 10
Autumn (adj.) then one low roll Of *A* thunder, *Last Tournament* 153
Autumn (s) (*See also* **Fall**) *A* and summer Are gone long ago; *Nothing will Die* 18
A, in a bower Grape-thicken'd *Eleänore* 35
Till *A* brought an hour For Eustace, *Gardener's D.* 207
That *a* into *a* flash'd again, *Enoch Arden* 456
And breathes in April *a's*. *The Brook* 196
parcel-bearded with the traveller's-joy In *A*, *Aylmer's Field* 154
A's mock sunshine of the faded woods ,, 610
breadth Of *A*, dropping fruits of power: *Princess vi* 55
after *A* past—if left to pass His *a* *A Dedication* 9
And *A*, with a noise of rooks, *In Mem. lxxxv* 71
A laying here and there A fiery finger ,, *xcix* 11
storms Of *A* swept across the city, *Demeter and P.* 71
and bless Their garner'd *A* also, ,, 147
Spring and Summer and *A* and Winter, *Vastness* 29
like May-blossoms in mid *a*— *The Ring* 255
mist of *a* gather from your lake, ,, 329
Autumn-changed Then; and then *A-c*, *The Oak* 8
Autumn-dripping in a death-dumb *a-d* gloom, *Last Tournament* 756
Autumn-fields In looking on the happy *A-f*, *Princess iv* 42
Autumn-sheaf Than of the garner'd *A-s*. *Two Voices* 114
Autumn-tide High over all the yellowing *A-t*, *Last Tournament* 241
Avail (s) 'I count it of no more *a*, Dame, *Geraint and E.* 715
Avail (verb) Let this *a*, just, dreadful, *St. S. Stylites* 9
Nor branding summer suns *a* *In Mem. ii* 11
Avail'd hath this Quest *a* for thee?' *Holy Grail* 765
Avalon Lay, dozing in the vale of *A*, *Palace of Art* 107
Avanturine Like sparkles in the stone *A*. *Gareth and L.* 930
Avarice No madness of ambition, *a*, *Lucretius* 212
evil tyrannies, all her pitiless *a*, *Boädicea* 80
Down with ambition, *a*, pride, *Maud I x* 47

Avarice (*continued*) the lust, Villainy, violence, *a*, *Columbus* 172
Opulent *A*, lean as Poverty; *Vastness* 20
Avaunt '*A*,' they cried, 'our lady loves *Pelleas and E.* 369
Ave '*A*, *A*, *A*,' said, 'Adieu, adieu' *In Mem. lvii* 15
singin' yer '*A's*' an' 'Pathers' *Tomorrow* 96
Ave atque Vale Came that '*A a V*' of the Poet's *Frater Ave, etc.* 5
Ave Mary But '*A M*,' made she moan, And '*A M*,' night and morn, *Mariana in the S.* 9
And '*A M*,' was her moan, ,, 21
Avenge Peace! there are those to *a* us *Princess iv* 501
felon knight, I *a* me for my friend.' *Gareth and L.* 1220
'I will *a* this insult, noble Queen, *Marr. of Geraint* 215
God's *A* on stony hearts *Death of Œnone* 41
I cried to the Saints to *a* me. *Bandit's Death* 14
crying 'I dare her, let Peelè *a* herself'! *Kapiolani* 32
Avenged it was a crime Of sense *a* by sense *Vision of Sin* 214
Avenging learn his name, *A* this great insult *Marr. of Geraint* 425
Avenue (*See also* **Lily-avenue**) Down at the far end of an *a*, *Enoch Arden* 358
And ever-echoing *a's* of song. *Ode on Well.* 79
city glitter'd, Thro' cypress *a's*, *The Daisy* 48
flash'd again Down the long *a's* *Gareth and L.* 785
thro' the slowly-mellowing *a's* *Last Tournament* 360
Entering all the *a's* of sense *Lover's Tale i* 630
in yon arching *a* of old elms, *The Ring* 172
Aver *a* That all thy motions gently pass *In Mem. xv* 9
I, clasping brother-hands, *a* I could not, *In Mem. lxxxv* 102
Averill *A A* at the Rectory Thrice over; *Aylmer's Field* 37
might not *A*, had he will'd it so, ,, 46
Not proven' *A* said, or laughingly 'Some other race of *A's*'— ,, 53
his brother, living oft With *A*, ,, 58
A was a decade and a half His elder, ,, 82
He wasted hours with *A*; ,, 109
and oft accompanied By *A*: ,, 138
To let that handsome fellow *A* walk ,, 269
foam'd away his heart at *A's* ear: whom *A* solaced ,, 342
A seeing How low his brother's mood ,, 403
Forbad her first the house of *A*, ,, 502
A wrote And bad him with good heart ,, 543
A went and gazed upon his death. ,, 599
Long o'er his bent brows linger'd *A*, ,, 625
Averring *A* it was clear against all rules *Princess i* 178
Averse with sick and scornful looks *a*, *D. of F. Women* 101
Avilion To the island-valley of *A*; *M. d'Arthur* 259
'He passes to the Isle *A*, *Gareth and L.* 502
To the island-valley of *A*; *Pass. of Arthur* 427
A-waäitin' (waiting) An' she wur *a-w* fo'mma, *North. Cobbler* 34
Awaäke (awake) but I wur *a*, *Owd Roä* 33
Await Some draught of Lethe might *a* *Two Voices* 350
slow-develop'd strength *a's* Completion *Love thou thy land* 57
come; for all the vales *A* thee; *Princess vii* 216
Yea, let all good things *a* Him who cares *Ode on Well.* 198
and happier hours *A* them. *In Mem. Con.* 66
A the last and largest sense *Ancient Sage* 180
Awaiting Beheld her first in field *a* him, *Marr. of Geraint* 540
Awake (adj.) (*See also* **Awaäke, Half-awake**) All night I lie *a*, *May Queen, N. Y's. E.* 50
lying broad *a* I thought of you and Effie ,, *Con.* 29
deep-asleep he seem'd, yet all *a*, *Lotos-Eaters* 35
That I might kiss those eyes *a*! *Day-Dm. L'Envoi* 28
but watch'd *a* A cypress in the moonlight *The Daisy* 81
I have walk'd *a* with Truth. *Maud I xix* 4
the rose was *a* all night for your sake, ,, *xxii* 49
The lilies and roses were all *a*, ,, 51
shook his drowsy squire *a* and cried, *Marr. of Geraint* 125
her mother grasping her To get her well *a*; ,, 677
Held her *a*: or if she slept, *Guinevere* 75
Wherein we nested sleeping or *a*, *Lover's Tale i* 231
our palace is *a*, and morn Has lifted *Akbar's Dream* 200
Awake (verb) bee Is lily-cradled: I alone *a*. *Œnone* 30
strike it, and *a* her with the gleam; *Lancelot and E.* 6
may death *A* them with heaven's music *Lover's Tale i* 761
and *a* to a livid light, *The Wreck* 7
A! the creeping glimmer steals, *The Flight* 4

Awaked (*See also* **Half-awaked**) myself have *a*, as it seems, *Maud III vi* 56
falls asleep in swoon, wherefrom *a*, *Lover's Tale i* 791
Awaken if the King *a* from his craze, *Gareth and L.* 724
Awaken'd (*See also* **Half-awaken'd**) Slowly *a*, grow so full and deep *Eleänore* 85
Awaking *A* knew the sword, and turn'd *Pelleas and E.* 489
A-walkin' murnin' when we was *a-w* togither, *Spinster's S's.* 23
Award would seem to *a* it thine, *Œnone* 73
Aware After a lingering,—ere she was *a*,— *Enoch Arden* 268
Enid was *a* of three tall knights *Geraint and E.* 56
she by tact of love was well *a* *Lancelot and E.* 984
Awe springs of life, the depths of *a*, *Two Voices* 140
shall hold a fretful realm in *a*, *Locksley Hall* 129
heart beat thick with passion and with *a*; *Princess iii* 190
To feel once more, in placid *a*, *In Mem. cxxii* 5
but all in *a*, For twenty strokes *Lancelot and E.* 719
he wellnigh kiss'd her feet For loyal *a*, ,, 1173
tenderness of manner, and chaste *a*, *Pelleas and E.* 110
with the excess of sweetness and of *a*, *Lover's Tale ii* 155
Awearied For I was much *a* of the Quest: *Holy Grail* 744
Aweary She said, 'I am *a*, *a*, (repeat) *Mariana* 11, 23, 35, 47, 59, 71
She wept, 'I am *a*, *a*, *Mariana* 83
And I am all *a* of my life. *Œnone* 33
Awed *a* and promise-bounden she forbore, *Enoch Arden* 869
Still It *a* me.' *Sea Dreams* 205
And my dream *a* me:—well— ,, 247
eyes *A* even me at first, thy mother— *Demeter and P.* 24
Awe-stricken hold *A-s* breaths at a work divine, *Maud I x* 17
Awful But all she is and does is *a*; *Princess i* 140
Awl *See* **Hawl**
Awning ample *a's* gay Betwixt the pillars, *Princess ii* 25
A blood-red *a* waver overhead, *St. Telemachus* 52
Awoke And last with these the king *a*, *Day-Dm. Revival* 17
night-light flickering in my eyes *A* me.' *Sea Dreams* 104
desire that *a* in the heart of the child, *Maud I xix* 48
Leodogran *a*, and sent Ulfius, *Com. of Arthur* 444
these *a* him, and by great mischance *Marr. of Geraint* 112
Refused her to him, then his pride *a*; ,, 448
strongly striking out her limbs *a*; *Geraint and E.* 380
every evil deed I ever did, *A* *Holy Grail* 374
mantle clung, And pettish cries *a*, *Last Tournament* 214
owl-whoop and dorhawk-whirr *A* me not, *Lover's Tale ii* 117
Awry wherefore do we grow *a* From roots *Supp. Confessions* 77
To woman, superstition all *a*: *Princess ii* 137
Stampt into dust—tremulous, all *a*, *Romney's R.* 113
Axe (*See also* **Battle-axe**) ere the falling *a* did part *Margaret* 38
see the woodman lift His *a* to slay my kin. *Talking Oak* 236
Nor wielded *a* disjoint, ,, 262
hammer and *a*, Auger and saw, *Enoch Arden* 173
The woodmen with their *a's*: *Princess vi* 44
glittering *a* was broken in their arms, ,, 51
train of dames: by *a* and eagle sat, ,, *vii* 128
'Churl, thine *a*!' he cried, *Balin and Balan* 295
Axelike That *a* edge unturnable, *Princess ii* 203
Axle war Rides on those ringing *a's*! *Tiresias* 93
Ay Why? For its *a a*, *a a*. *Window. Ay.* 18
A-year my two 'oonderd *a-y* to mysen; *Spinster's S's.* 12
but my two 'oonderd *a-y*. ,, 22
fro' my oän two 'oonderd *a-y*. ,, 58
Aylmer (*See also* **Lawrence Aylmer**)
Sɪʀ *A A* that almighty man, *Aylmer's Field* 13
A followed *A* at the Hall ,, 36
like an *A* in his Aylmerism, ,, 123
Sir *A* half forgot his lazy smile ,, 197
Sir *A* past, And neither loved ,, 249
did Sir *A* know That great pock-pitten ,, 255
had Sir *A* heard—Nay, but he must— ,, 261
did Sir *A* (deferentially With nearing chair ,, 266
Sir *A A* slowly stiffening spoke: ,, 273
They parted, and Sir *A A* watch'd. ,, 277
Things in an *A* deem'd impossible, ,, 305
Sir *A* reddening from the storm within, ,, 322
To shame these mouldy *A's* in their graves: ,, 396
when *this A* came of age— ,, 407
Aylmer (*continued*) and Sir *A* watch'd them all, *Aylmer's Field* 552
and with her the race of *A*, past. ,, 577
Aylmer-Averill There was an *A-A* marriage once. ,, 49
Aymerism like an Aylmer in his *A*, ,, 123
A-yowlin' *a-y* an' yaupin' like mad; *Owd Roä* 88
An' the dogs was *a-y* all round, ,, 107
Azimuth sine and arc, spheroïd and *a*, *Princess vi* 256
Azores Aᴛ Fʟᴏʀᴇs in the *A* Sir Richard Greville lay, *The Revenge* 1
Azrael the black-wing'd *A* overcame, *Akbar's Dream* 186
Azure Her eyes a bashful *a*, and her hair *The Brook* 71
he stared On eyes a bashful *a*, ,, 206
Inmingled with Heaven's *a* waveringly, *Gareth and L.* 936
A, an Eagle rising or, the Sun *Merlin and V.* 475
Shallow skin of green and *a*— *Locksley H., Sixty*, 208
and, men, below the dome of *a* *Akbar's D. Hymn* 7
Azure-circled High over all the *a-c* earth, *Lover's Tale i* 390

B

Baäcon (bacon) *B* an' taätes, an' a beslings puddin' *North. Cobbler* 112
Baäked (baked) fever 'ed *b* Jinny's 'eäd as bald *Village Wife* 102
Baäl and honour thy brute *B*, *Aylmer's Field* 644
came a Lord in no wise like to *B*. ,, 647
Babble (s) the *b* of the stream Fell, *Mariana in the S.* 51
The babes, their *b*, Annie, *Enoch Arden* 606
night goes In *b* and revel and wine. *Maud I xxii* 28
But *b*, merely for *b*. ,, *II v* 46
Merlin's mystic *b* about his end *Last Tournament* 670
laughter and *b* and earth's new wine, *To A. Tennyson* 2
And you liken—boyish *b*— *Locksley H., Sixty*, 6
B, *b*; our old England may go down in *b* ,, 8
—words, Wild *b*. *Romney's R.* 32
Babble (verb) by the poplar tall rivulets *b* and fall. *Leonine Eleg.* 4
I *b* on the pebbles. *The Brook* 42
Howe'er you *b*, great deeds cannot die; *Princess iii* 254
brook shall *b* down the plain, *In Mem. ci* 10
Began to scoff and jeer and *b* of him *Marr. of Geraint* 58
because ye dream they *b* of you.' *Merlin and V.* 690
ye set yourself To *b* about him, *Last Tournament* 340
Babbled *b* for the golden seal, that hung *Dora* 135
b for you, as babies for the moon, *Princess iv* 428
Had *b* 'Uncle' on my knee; *In Mem. lxxxiv* 13
He moving homeward *b* to his men, *Geraint and E.* 362
While thus they *b* of the King, *Lancelot and E.* 1260
their tongues may have *b* of me— *The Wreck* 41
I myself have often *b* doubtless *Locksley H., Sixty*, 7
she said, I *b*, Mother, Mother— *The Ring* 115
Babbler garrulously given, A *b* in the land. *Talking Oak* 24
she, like many another *b*, hurt *Guinevere* 354
mothers with their *b's* of the dawn, *Tiresias* 103
Babbling runlets *b* down the glen. *Mariana in the S.* 44
his wheat-suburb, *b* as he went. *The Brook* 123
My words are like the *b's* in a dream Of nightmare, when the *b's* break the dream. *Ancient Sage* 106
Babby (*See also* **Babe, Baby**) An' then the *b* wur burn, *North. Cobbler* 16
an' she an' the *b* beäl'd, ,, 37
An' the *b's* faäce wurn't wesh'd ,, 42
Thou's rode of 'is back when a *b*, *Owd Roä* 5
Babe (*See also* **Babby, Baby**) Sat smiling, *b* in arm. *Palace of Art* 96
With his first *b's* first cry, *Enoch Arden* 85
Nursing the sickly *b*, her latest-born. ,, 150
Pray'd for a blessing on his wife and *b's* ,, 188
be comforted, Look to the *b's*, ,, 219
To give his *b's* a better bringing-up ,, 299
know his *b's* were running wild Lik e colts ,, 304
A gilded dragon, also, for the *b's*. ,, 540
The *b's*, their babble, Annie, ,, 606
lived and loved him, and his *b's* ,, 685
rosy, with his *b* across his knees; ,, 746
and a ring To tempt the *b*, ,, 751
mother glancing often toward her *b*, ,, 754
saw the *b* Hers, yet not his, ,, 759

Babe (*continued*) I shall see him, My *b* in bliss: *Enoch Arden* 898
The *b* shall lead the lion. *Aylmer's Field* 648
the *b* Too ragged to be fondled ,, 685
One *b* was theirs, a Margaret, *Sea Dreams* 3
the *b*, Their Margaret cradled near ,, 56
Her maiden *b*, a double April old, *Princess ii* 110
Father will come to his *b* in the nest, ,, *iii* 13
vassals to be beat, nor pretty *b's* ,, *iv* 146
my *b*, my blossom, ah, my child, ,, *v* 82
My *b*, my sweet Aglaïa, my one child: ,, 101
With Psyche's *b*, was Ida watching us, ,, 512
Ida stood With Psyche's *b* in arm: ,, *vi* 31
with the *b* yet in her arms, ,, 74
b that by us, Half-lapt in glowing gauze ,, 133
burst The laces toward her *b*; ,, 149
Laid the soft *b* in his hard-mailed hands. ,, 208
Not tho' he built upon the *b* restored; ,, *vii* 75
'Here's a leg for a *b* of a week!' *Grandmother* 11
for the *b* had fought for his life. ,, 64
bring her *b*, and make her boast, *In Mem. xl* 26
From youth and *b* and hoary hairs: ,, *lxix* 10
Mammonite mother kills her *b* for a burial fee, *Maud I i* 45
red man's *b* Leap, beyond the sea. ,, *xvii* 19
now we poison our *b's*, poor souls! ,, *II v* 63
in the flame was borne A naked *b*, and rode to Merlin's feet, Who stoopt and caught the *b*, *Com. of Arthur* 384
naked *b*, of whom the Prophet spake, *Gareth and L.* 501
lad and girl—yea, the soft *b*! ,, 1341
ye men of Arthur be but *b's*.' *Balin and Balan* 361
As clean as blood of *b's*, *Merlin and V.* 344
his wife And two fair *b's*, ,, 707
seven-months' *b* had been a truer gift. ,, 711
broken shed, And in it a dead *b*; *Holy Grail* 399
brought A maiden *b*; which Arthur pitying took, *Last Tournament* 21
But the sweet body of a maiden *b*. ,, 48
cursed The dead *b* and the follies ,, 163
In honour of poor Innocence the *b*, ,, 292
bearing high in arms the mighty *b*, *Lover's Tale iv* 295
And over all her *b* and her the jewels ,, 298
bearing on one arm the noble *b*, ,, 370
Whereat the very *b* began to wail; ,, 375
a truth the *b* Will suck in with his milk *Columbus* 37
b in lineament and limb Perfect, *De Prof. Two G.* 11
and the wail Of a beaten *b*, *The Wreck* 123
Saving women and their *b's*, *Locksley H., Sixty,* 64
a cotter's *b* is royal-born by right divine; ,, 125
many a time ranged over when a *b*. *The Ring* 151
senseless, worthless, wordless *b*, ,, 304
all her talk was of the *b* she loved; ,, 353
She used to shun the wailing *b*, ,, 358
In your sweet *b* she finds but you— ,, 365
bending by the cradle of her *b*. ,, 415
linger, till her own, the *b* She lean'd to ,, 483
found Paris, a naked *b*, among the woods *Death of Œnone* 54
I was lilting a song to the *b*, *Bandit's Death* 20
Screams of a *b* in the red-hot palms *The Dawn* 2
and Rome was a *b* in arms, ,, 9
Babe-faced He came with the *b-f* lord; *Maud II i* 13
Babel let be Their cancell'd *B's*: *Princess iv* 77
clamour grew As of a new-world *B*, ,, 487
Baby (adj.) Moulded thy *b* thought. *Eleänore* 5
Baby (s) in her bosom bore the *b*, Sleep. *Gardener's D.* 268
As ruthless as a *b* with a worm, *Walk. to the Mail* 108
Then lightly rocking *b's* cradle *Enoch Arden* 194
from her *b's* forehead clipt A tiny curl, ,, 235
His *b's* death, her growing poverty, ,, 705
What does little *b* say, *Sea Dreams* 301
B says, like little birdie, ,, 303
B, sleep a little longer, ,, 305
B too shall fly away. ,, 308
babies roll'd about Like tumbled fruit *Princess, Pro.,* 82
babbled for you, as *babies* for the moon, ,, *iv* 428
I knew them all as *babies*, *Grandmother* 88

Baby (s) (*continued*) The *b* new to earth and sky, *In Mem. xlv* 1
I cannot bide Sir *B*. *Pelleas and E.* 190
I have gather'd my *b* together— *Rizpah* 20
My *b*, the bones that had suck'd me, ,, 53
kill Their *babies* at the breast *Columbus* 180
'Anything ailing,' I asked her, 'with *b*?' *The Wreck* 61
Baby-germ gamboll'd on the greens A *b-g*, *Talking Oak* 78
Baby-girl a *b-g*, that had never look'd on the light: *Despair* 71
Babyism In *b's*, and dear diminutives *Aylmer's Field* 539
Babylon Shall *B* be cast into the sea; *Sea Dreams* 28
and life Pass in the fire of *B*! *Sir J. Oldcastle* 124
For *B* was a child new-born, *The Dawn* 9
Babylonian The foundress of the *B* wall, *Princess ii* 80
Baby-oak magnetise The *b-o* within. *Talking Oak* 256
Baby-rose The *b-r's* in her cheeks; *Lilian* 17
Baby-sole tender pink five-beaded *b-s's*, *Aylmer's Field* 186
Baby-wife nor wail of *b-w*, Or Indian widow; *Akbar's Dream* 196
Bacchanal like wild *B's* Fled onward *Lover's Tale iii* 25
Bacchante *B*, what you will; *Romney's R.* 6
Bacchus mailed *B* leapt into my arms, *D. of F. Women* 151
Back wear an undress'd goatskin on my *b*; *St. S. Stylites* 116
How she mouths behind my *b*. *Vision of Sin* 110
Read rascal in the motions of his *b* *Sea Dreams* 167
hear my father's clamour at our *b's* *Princess i* 105
Her *b* against a pillar, her foot ,, *iii* 180
Them as 'as coäts to their *b's* an' taäkes *N. Farmer, N.S.* 46
The daily burden for the *b*. *In Mem. xxv* 4
b turn'd, and bow'd above his work, *Marr. of Geraint* 267
brutes of mountain *b* That carry kings *Merlin and V.* 576
long *b's* of the bushless downs, (repeat) *Lancelot and E.* 400, 789
Look at the cloäths on 'er *b*, *North. Cobbler* 109
Backbiter Face-flatterer and *b* are the same. *Merlin and V.* 824
Back'd *See* **Bow-back'd**
Bacon (Francis) *See* **Verulam**
Bacon *See* **Baäcon**
Bad (adj.) O base and *b*! what comfort? *Princess v* 78
for she wur a *b* un, sheä. *N. Farmer, O.S.* 22
the poor in a loomp is *b*. ,, *N.S.* 48
What is she now? My dreams are *b*. *Maud I i* 73
And here beneath it is all as *b*, ,, *II v* 14
good ye are and *b*, and like to coins, *Holy Grail* 25
Ya was niver sa *b* as that. *Church-warden, etc.* 26
Bad (s) I fear to slide from *b* to worse. *Two Voices* 231
sa o' coorse she be gone to the *b*! *Village Wife* 98
I wur gawin' that waäy to the *b*, *Owd Roä* 71
Bad-bade (verb) I made a feast: I *bad* him come; *The Sisters* 13
and do the thing I *bad* thee, *M. d'Arthur* 81
utter'd it, And *bade* adieu for ever. *Love and Duty* 83
bade him cry, with sound of trumpet, *Godiva* 36
bad him with good heart sustain himself— *Aylmer's Field* 544
He *bad* you guard the sacred coasts. *Ode on Well.* 172
my three brethren *bad* me do it, *Gareth and L.* 1410
'Fair Sir, they *bad* me do it. ,, 1417
Thro' which he *bad* her lead him on, *Geraint and E.* 29
bad the host Call in what men ,, 285
Prince *bad* him a loud good-night. ,, 361
In this poor gown he *bad* me clothe myself, ,, 702
Nor waved his hand, Nor *bad* farewell, *Lancelot and E.* 987
who *bad* a thousand farewells to me, ,, 1056
Lancelot, who coldly went, nor *bad* me one: ,, 1057
So Arthur *bad* the meek Sir Percivale ,, 1264
I left her and I *bad* her no farewell; ,, 1304
when he saw me, rose, and *bad* me hail, *Holy Grail* 725
and do the thing I *bade* thee, *Pass. of Arthur* 249
bad them to a banquet of farewells. *Lover's Tale iv* 186
bad his menials bear him from the door, ,, 260
We *bad* them no farewell, ,, 386
bad them remember my father's death, *V. of Maeldune* 70
bad his trumpeter sound To the charge, *Heavy Brigade* 8
I *bad* her keep, Like a seal'd book, *The Ring* 122
bad the man engrave 'From Walter' on the ring, ,, 235
Badger live like an old *b* in his earth, *Holy Grail* 629
Badon broke the Pagan yet once more on *B* hill.' *Lancelot and E.* 280
on the mount Of *B* I myself beheld ,, 303
Baffle 'Thy glory *b's* wisdom. *Akbar's Dream* 28

Baffled Havelock *b*, or beaten, *Def. of Lucknow* 91
B her priesthood, Broke the Taboo, *Kapiolani* 29
Baffling winds variable, Then *b*, a long course of them; *Enoch Arden* 546
blown by *b* winds, Like the Good Fortune, ,, 628
Bag not plunge His hand into the *b*: *Golden Year* 72
with *b* and sack and basket, *Enoch Arden* 63
Bagdat By *B's* shrines of fretted gold, *Arabian Nights* 7
mooned domes aloof In inmost *B*, ,, 128
Bagpipe *b's*, revelling, devil's-dances, *Sir J. Oldcastle* 149
Bailey-gate storm at the *B-g*! storm, *Def. of Lucknow* 37
Bailiff his *b* brought A Chartist pike. *Walk. to the Mail* 70
how he sent the *b* to the farm *The Brook* 141
how the *b* swore that he was mad, ,, 143
He met the *b* at the Golden Fleece, ,, 146
He found the *b* riding by the farm, ,, 153
Bairn (*See also* **Barne**) 'See your *b's* before you go! *Enoch Arden* 870
But fur thy *b's*, poor Steevie, *Spinster's S's*. 82
thou was es fond o' thy *b's* ,, 83
wi' my b *i' 'is mouth to the winder* *Owd Roä* 92
Bait the *b's* Of gold and beauty, *Aylmer's Field* 486
Christ the *b* to trap his dupe and fool; *Sea Dreams* 191
hinted love was only wasted *b*, *The Ring* 360
Baited so spurn'd, so *b* two whole days— *Sir J. Oldcastle* 163
Bake whose brain the sunshine *b's*; *St. S. Stylites* 164
Baked (*See also* **Baäked**) Over all the meadow *b* and bare, *Sisters (E. and E.)* 8
Baking not earn'd my cake in *b* of it? *Gareth and L.* 575
Bala south-west that blowing *B* lake *Geraint and E.* 929
Balan Balin and *B* sitting statuelike, *Balin and Balan* 24
on the left Of *B B's* near a poplartree. ,, 30
Balin and *B* answer'd 'For the sake ,, 32
Then Balin rose, and *B*, ,, 43
and my better, this man here, *B*. ,, 55
fury on myself, Saving for *B*: ,, 63
Than twenty Balins, *B* knight. ,, 69
Then *B* added to their Order ,, 91
Said *B* 'I'! So claim'd the quest ,, 137
B warn'd, and went; Balin remain'd: ,, 153
He took the selfsame track as *B*, ,, 290
and *B* lurking there (His quest was unaccomplish'd) ,, 546
shield of *B* prick'd The hauberk ,, 559
had chanced, and *B* moan'd again. ,, 604
Balance (equipoise) As the wind-hover hangs in *b*, *Aylmer's Field* 321
Balance (verb) who would cast and *b* at a desk, *Audley Court* 44
LIKE souls that *b* joy and pain, *Sir L. and Q. G.* 1
Balanced (*See also* **Self-balanced**) Your fortunes, justlier *b*, *Princess ii* 66
Well, she *b* this a little, ,, *iii* 165
And *b* either way by each, *Lover's Tale iv* 269
Balcony Under tower and *b*, *L. of Shalott iv* 37
And lean'd upon the *b*. *Mariana in the S.* 88
Bald Jinny's 'eäd as *b* as one o' them heggs, *Village Wife* 102
Baldness (*See also* **Earth-baldness**) Began to wag their *b* up and down, *Princess v* 19
Baldric from his blazon'd *b* slung *L. of Shalott iii* 15
Bale dropping down with costly *b's*; *Locksley Hall* 122
tho' they brought but merchants' *b's*, *In Mem. xiii* 19
Balin *B* and Balan sitting statuelike, *Balin and Balan* 24
on the right of *B B's* horse Was fast ,, 28
B and Balan answer'd 'For the sake ,, 32
Then *B* rose, and Balan, ,, 43
B the stillness of a minute broke ,, 51
B, 'the Savage'—that addition thine— ,, 53
Than twenty *B's*, Balan knight. ,, 69
Thereafter, when Sir *B* enter'd hall, ,, 80
heretofore with these And *B*, ,, 93
Embracing *B*, 'Good my brother, ,, 139
Balan warn'd, and went; *B* remain'd: ,, 153
B marvelling oft How far beyond ,, 171
Arthur, when Sir *B* sought him, said ,, 198
B was bold, and ask'd To bear ,, 199
'No shadow' said Sir *B* 'O my Queen, ,, 206
B bare the crown, and all the knights ,, 209
chanced, one morning, that Sir *B* sat ,, 240

Balin (*continued*) Follow'd the Queen; Sir *B* heard her *Balin and Balan* 250
and *B* started from his bower. ,, 280
B cried 'Him, or the viler devil ,, 299
B answer'd him 'Old fabler, ,, 306
Said *B* 'For the fairest and the best ,, 339
B said 'The Queen we worship, ,, 348
A goblet on the board by *B*, ,, 362
This *B* graspt, but while in act to hurl, ,, 368
Sir *B* with a fiery 'Ha! ,, 393
B by the banneret of his helm ,, 398
B drew the shield from off his neck, ,, 429
And *B* rose, 'Thither no more! ,, 483
Said *B* to her 'Is this thy courtesy— ,, 494
Sir *B* spake not word, But snatch'd ,, 553
B's horse Was wearied to the death, ,, 560
they clash'd, Rolling back upon *B*, ,, 562
B first woke, and seeing that true face, ,, 590
'O *B*, *B*, I that fain had died To save ,, 599
B told him brokenly, and in gasps, ,, 603
'O brother' answer'd *B* 'woe is me! ,, 618
B answer'd low 'Goodnight, ,, 627
and slept the sleep With *B*, ,, 632
Balk'd with a worm I *b* his fame. *D. of F. Women* 155
Ball (globe) 'No compound of this earthly *b* *Two Voices* 35
Ball (game) Had tost his *b* and flown his kite, *Aylmer's Field* 84
Flung *b*, flew kite, and raced the purple fly, *Princess ii* 248
others tost a *b* Above the fountain-jets, ,, 461
Quoit, tennis, *b*—no games? ,, *iii* 215
And we took to playing at *b*, *V. of Maeldune* 94
Ball (round object) whereon the gilded *b* Danced *Princess, Pro.*, 63
like a *b* The russet-bearded head roll'd *Geraint and E.* 728
he made me the cowslip *b*, *First Quarrel* 13
Ball (orb) To him who grasps a golden *b*, *In Mem. cxi* 3
Ball (the sun) The day comes, a dull red *b* *Maud II iv* 65
Ball (the heel) Dagonet, turning on the *b* of his foot, *Last Tournament* 329
Ball (entertainment of dancing) But I came on him once at a *b*, *The Wreck* 47
Ball (plaything) Is to be the *b* of Time, *Vision of Sin* 105
Ball (*See also* **Acorn-ball, Blossom-ball, Cannon-ball, Cowslip Ball, Football**)
Ballad time to time, some *b* or a song *Princess, Pro.*, 241
something in the *b's* which they sang, ,, *Con.* 14
flung A *b* to the brightening moon: *In Mem. lxxxix* 28
A passionate *b* gallant and gay, *Maud I v* 4
To the *b* that she sings. *Maud II iv* 43
carolling as he went A true-love *b*, *Lancelot and E.* 705
lay At thy pale feet this *b* *Ded. Poem Prin. Alice* 20
Ballad-burthen Like *b-b* music, kept, *The Daisy* 77
Ballast we laid them on the *b* down below; *The Revenge* 18
Balliol loved by all the younger gown There at *B*, *To Master of B.* 3
Balloon *See* **Fire-balloon**
Balm steep our brows in slumber's holy *b*; *Lotos-Eaters, C. S.* 21
desires, like fitful blasts of *b* *Gardener's D.* 68
spikenard, and *b*, and frankincense. *St. S. Stylites* 211
caress The ringlet's waving *b*— *Talking Oak* 178
Beat *b* upon our eyelids. *Princess iii* 123
Be thine the *b* of pity, *Merlin and V.* 80
Strowing *b*, or shedding poison *Locksley H., Sixty*, 274
who breathe the *b* Of summer-winters *To Ulysses* 10
'From the South I bring you *b*, *Prog. of Spring* 66
whatever herb or *b* May clear the blood *Death of Œnone* 35
Balm-cricket The *b-c* carols clear In the green *A Dirge* 47
Balm-dew drop *B-d's* to bathe thy feet! *Talking Oak* 268
Balm'd swathed and *b* it for herself, *Lover's Tale i* 682
Balmier kisses *b* than half-opening buds *Tithonus* 59
B and nobler from her bath of storm, *Lucretius* 175
Baltic shaker of the *B* and the Nile, *Ode on Well.* 137
side of the Black and the *B* deep, *Maud III vi* 51
Baluster And leaning there on those *b's*, *Princess iii* 119
Balustrade stairs Ran up with golden *b*, *Arabian Nights* 118
Bamboo Your cane, your palm, tree-fern, *b*, *To Ulysses* 36
Band (bond, strip) bind with *b's* That island queen *Buonaparte* 2
Sleep had bound her in his rosy *b*, *Caress'd or chidden* 6
A *b* of pain across my brow; *The Letters* 6

Band (bond, strip) (*continued*) single *b* of gold about her hair, *Princess v* 513
No spirit ever brake the *b* *In Mem. xciii* 2
bars Of black and *b's* of silver, *Lover's Tale iv* 59
an' twined like a *b* o' haäy. *Owd Roä* 22
Band (a company) held debate, a *b* Of youthful friends, *In Mem. lxxxvii* 21
in a dream from a *b* of the blest, *Maud III vi* 10
if he live, we will have him of our *b* ; *Geraint and E.* 553
thanks to the Blessed Saints that I came on none of his *b* ; *Bandit's Death* 40
b will be scatter'd now their gallant captain is dead, ,, 41
Bandage raised the blinding *b* from his eyes: *Princess i* 244
Banded (*See also* **Snowy-banded, Yellow-banded**)
but after, the great lords *B*, *Com. of Arthur* 237
Bandied *B* by the hands of fools. *Vision of Sin* 106
Bandit redden'd with no *b's* blood: *Aylmer's Field* 597
bridge, ford, beset By *b's*, *Gareth and L.* 595
I saw three *b's* by the rock *Geraint and E.* 72
Struck thro' the bulky *b's* corselet home, ,, 159
now so long By *b's* groom'd, ,, 193
Was half a *b* in my lawless hour, ,, 795
One from the *b* scatter'd in the field, ,, 818
Scaped thro' a cavern from a *b* hold, *Holy Grail* 207
Thieves, *b's*, leavings of confusion, *Last Tournament* 95
Sanctuary granted To *b*, thief, *Sir J. Oldcastle* 113
tho' I *am* the *B's* bride. *Bandit's Death* 6
But the *B* had woo'd me in vain, ,, 10
Bandit-haunted past The marches, and by *b-h* holds, *Geraint and E.* 30
Bane courtesies of household life, Became her *b* ; *Guinevere* 87
mockery of my people, and their *b*.' ,, 526
Bang Let us *b's* these dogs of Seville, *The Revenge* 30
good manners *b* thruf to the tip o' the taäil. *Spinster's S's.* 66
Bang'd palace *b*, and buzz'd and clackt, *Day-Dm., Revival,* 14
iron-clanging anvil *b* With hammers ; *Princess v* 504
Banished born And *b* into mystery, *De Prof. Two G.* 42
Banishment causer of his *b* and shame, *Balin and Balan* 221
Bank (*See also* **River-bank, Sea-bank**) In cool soft turf upon the *b*, *Arabian Nights* 96
wave-worn horns of the echoing *b*, *Dying Swan* 39
Shadow forth the *b's* at will: *Eleänore* 110
From the *b* and from the river *L. of Shalott, iii* 33
broad stream in his *b's* complaining, ,, *iv* 3
The little life of *b* and brier, *You might have won* 30
With many a curve my *b's* I fret *The Brook* 43
maidens glimmeringly group'd In the hollow *b*. *Princess iv* 191
shadowing bluff that made the *b's*, *In Mem. ciii* 22
Behind a purple-frosty *b* Of vapour, ,, *cvii* 3
Full to the *b's*, close on the promised good *Maud I xviii* 6
Rough-thicketed were the *b's* and steep ; *Gareth and L.* 907
star of morn Parts from a *b* of snow, *Marr. of Geraint* 735
Tho' happily down on a *b* of grass, *Geraint and E.* 507
like a *b* Of maiden snow mingled *Last Tournament* 148
leaves Low *b's* of yellow sand ; *Lover's Tale i* 535
thaw the *b's* o' the beck be sa high, *Village Wife* 83
Plunges and heaves at a *b* *Def. of Lucknow* 39
slushin' down fro' the *b* to the beck, *Owd Roä* 41
Here on this *b* in *some* way live the life *Akbar's Dream* 144
Bankrupt *b* of all claim On your obedience, *Romney's R.* 70
Banner (*See also* **Flame-banner**) Here droops the *b* on the tower, *Day-Dm., Sleep. P.,* 13
hedge broke in, the *b* blew, *Day-Dm. Revival* 9
unfurl the maiden *b* of our rights, *Princess iv* 503
undulated The *b* : anon to meet us ,, *v* 254
With *b* and with music, *Ode on Well.* 81
March with *b* and bugle and fife *Maud I v* 10
hail once more to the *b* of battle unroll'd ! *Maud III vi* 42
So when the King had set his *b* broad, *Com. of Arthur* 101
with black *b*, and a long black horn *Gareth and L.* 1366
b's of twelve battles overhead Stir, *Balin and Balan* 88
deeds Of England, and her *b* in the East ? *Ded. Poem Prin. Alice* 21
B of England, not for a season, O *b* *Def. of Lucknow* 1
topmost roof our *b* of England blew. (repeat) *Def. of Lucknow* 6, 30, 45, 60, 94
topmost roof our *b* in India blew. *Def. of Lucknow* 72

Banner (*continued*) on the palace roof the old *b* of England blew. *Def. of Lucknow* 106
Thraldom who walks with the *b* of Freedom, *Vastness* 10
b's blazoning a Power That is not seen *Akbar's Dream* 137
Banneret a slender *b* fluttering. *Gareth and L.* 913
Balin by the *b* of his helm Dragg'd *Balin and Balan* 398
Banquet (*See also* **Marriage-banquet, Mid-banquet**)
Each baron at the *b* sleeps, *Day-Dm., Sleep. P.,* 37
beeswing from a binn reserved For *b's*, *Aylmer's Field* 406
distant blaze of those dull *b's*, ,, 489
with this our *b's* rang ; *Princess i* 132
With *b* in the distant woods ; *In Mem. lxxxix* 32
flowers or leaves To deck the *b*. ,, *cvii* 6
Spice his fair *b* with the dust of death ? *Maud I xviii* 56
at the *b* those great Lords from Rome, *Com. of Arthur* 504
Faint in the low dark hall of *b* : *Balin and Balan* 343
(She sat beside the *b* nearest Mark), *Merlin and V.* 18
made him leave The *b*, and concourse *Lancelot and E.* 562
Arthur to the *b*, dark in mood, ,, 564
ev'n the knights at *b* twice or thrice ,, 736
against the floor Beneath the *b*, ,, 743
While the great *b* lay along the hall, *Holy Grail* 180
Then Arthur made vast *b's*, *Pelleas and E.* 147
bad them to a *b* of farewells. *Lover's Tale iv* 186
cries about the *b*—' Beautiful ! ,, 239
To make their *b* relish ? *Ancient Sage* 18
Banqueted Let the needy be *b*, *On Jub. Q. Victoria* 35
Banquet-hall Into the fair Peleïan *b-h*, *Œnone* 225
Banter (s) he spoke, Part *b*, part affection. *Princess, Pro.,* 167
They hated *b*, wish'd for something real, ,, *Con.,* 18
Banter (verb) With solemn gibe did Eustace *b* me. *Gardener's D.* 168
Banter'd I *b* him, and swore They said *Golden Year* 8
With which we *b* little Lilia first: *Princess, Con.,* 12
Bantling Then let the *b* scald at home, *Princess, v* 458
Lo their precious Roman *b*, *Boädicea* 31
Baptis (Baptist) Fur I wur a *B* wonst, *Church-warden, etc.* 11
tha *mun* speäk hout to the *B'es* here i' the town, ,, 51
Bar (barrier) (*See also* **Harbour-bar, Window-bars**)
Sang looking thro' his prison *b's* ? *Margaret* 35
salt pool, lock'd in with *b's* of sand, *Palace of Art* 249
My spirit beats her mortal *b's*, *Sir Galahad* 46
Low breezes fann'd the belfry *b's*, *The Letters* 43
Save for the *b* between us, loving *Enoch Arden* 880
I linger by my shingly *b's* ; *The Brook* 180
Baronet yet had laid No *b* between them : *Aylmer's Field* 118
nor conscious of a *b* Between them, ,, 134
squeezed himself betwixt the *b's*, *Princess, Pro.,* 112
Who breaks his birth's invidious *b*, *In Mem. lxiv* 5
Unloved, by many a sandy *b*, ,, *ci* 9
Rave over the rocky *b*, *Voice and the P.* 6
those that hand the dish across the *b*. *Gareth and L.* 155
may there be no moaning of the *b*, *Crossing the Bar* 3
When I have crost the *b*. ,, 16
Bar (band) long night in silver streaks and *b's*, *Lover's Tale, ii* 112
b's Of black and bands of silver, ,, *iv* 58
Bar (iron rod) casting *b* or stone Was counted best ; *Gareth and L.* 518
Bar (bony ridge) The *b* of Michael Angelo *In Mem. lxxxvii* 40
Bar (ray) stream'd thro' many a golden *b*, *Day-Dm., Depart.* 15
Bar (tribunal) himself The prisoner at the *b*, *Sea Dreams* 176
Bar (body of barristers) year or two before Call'd to the *b*, *Aylmer's Field* 59
Bar (division of music) Whistling a random *b* of Bonny Doon, *The Brook* 82
Bar (verb) doors that *b* The secret bridal chambers *Gardener's D.* 248
block and *b* Your heart with system *Princess iv* 462
Thro' the gates that *b* the distance *Faith* 6
Barbarian Till that o'ergrown *B* in the East *Poland* 7
gray *b* lower than the Christian child. *Locksley Hall* 174
' Who ever saw such wild *b's*. ? Girls ?— *Princess iii* 42
B's, grosser than your native bears— ,, *iv* 537
Barbarous These women were too *b*, ,, *ii* 298
Barcelona At *B*—tho' you were not *Columbus* 8
Bard *b* has honour'd beech or lime, *Talking Oak* 291
O little *b*, is your lot so hard, *Spiteful Letter* 5
b's of him will sing Hereafter ; *Com. of Arthur* 414

Bard (*continued*) not then the Riddling of the *B's*? *Gareth and L.* 286
Was also *B*, and knew the starry heavens; *Merlin and V.* 169
her *b*, her silver star of eve, Her God, ,, 954
many a *b*, without offence, *Lancelot and E.* 111
all the sacred madness of the *b*, *Holy Grail* 877
thy Paynim *b* Had such a mastery *Last Tournament* 326
'Yea, one, a *b*; of whom my father said, *Guinevere* 277
the *b* Sang Arthur's glorious wars, ,, 285
we chanted the songs of the *B's* *V. of Maeldune* 90
B whose fame-lit laurels glance *To Victor Hugo* 4
B's, that the mighty Muses have raised *Parnassus* 2
Bare (adj.) plain was grassy, wild and *b*, *Dying Swan* 1
God, before whom ever lie *b* *Palace of Art* 222
argent of her breast to sight Laid *b*. *D. of F. Women* 159
And saw the altar cold and *b*. *The Letters* 4
our love and reverence left them *b*? *Aylmer's Field* 785
walks were stript as *b* as brooms, *Princess, Pro.*, 184
strip a hundred hollows *b* of Spring, ,, *vi* 65
Flash'd all their sabres *b*, *Light Brigade* 27
B of the body, might it last, *In Mem. xliii* 6
breathing *b* The round of space, ,, *lxxxvi* 4
shield was blank and *b* without a sign *Gareth and L.* 414
Worn by the feet that now were silent, wound *B* to the sun, *Marr. of Geraint* 322
in my agony Did I make *b* *Lover's Tale ii* 48
Over all the meadow baked and *b*, *Sisters (E. and E.)* 8
strip your own foul passions *b*; *Locksley H., Sixty*, 141
His friends had stript him *b*, *Dead Prophet* 14
An' haäfe on 'im *b* as a bublin'. *Owd Roä* 102
honest Poverty, *b* to the bone; *Vastness* 19
now arching leaves her *b* To breaths *Prog. of Spring* 12
Bare (to bear) hoofs *b* on the ridge of spears *Princess v* 489
and *b* Straight to the doors: ,, *vi* 348
first that ever I *b* was dead *Grandmother* 59
b The use of virtue out of earth: *In Mem. lxxxii* 9
This *b* a maiden shield, a casque; *Gareth and L.* 680
down upon him *b* the bandit three. *Geraint and E.* 84
he, she dreaded most, *b* down upon him. ,, 156
B victual for the mowers: ,, 202
b her by main violence to the board. ,, 654
Balin *b* the crown, and all the knights *Balin and Balan* 209
Trampled ye thus on that which *b* the Crown?' ,, 602
he that always *b* in bitter grudge *Merlin and V.* 6
great and guilty love he *b* the Queen, *Lancelot and E.* 245
In battle with the love he *b* his lord, ,, 246
all together down upon him *B*, ,, 482
came the hermit out and *b* him in, ,, 519
often in her arms She *b* me, ,, 1411
none might see who *b* it, and it past. *Holy Grail* 190
his creatures took and *b* him off, *Guinevere* 109
Bare (to lay open) Falsehood shall *b* her plaited brow: *Clear-headed friend* 11
To *b* the eternal Heavens again, *In Mem. cxxii* 4
Bared The rites prepared, the victim *b*, *The Victim* 65
tho' it spake and *b* to view *In Mem. xcii* 9
b the knotted column of his throat, *Marr. of Geraint* 74
b her forehead to the blistering sun, *Geraint and E.* 515
Barefoot For *b* on the keystone, *Gareth and L.* 214
Bare-footed *B-f* came the beggar maid *Beggar Maid* 3
B-f and bare-headed three fair girls *Gareth and L.* 926
Bare-grinning Flash'd the *b-g* skeleton of death! *Merlin and V.* 847
Bare-headed Some cowled, and some *b-h*, *Princess vi* 77
Bare-footed and *b-h* three fair girls *Gareth and L.* 926
Bareness To make old *b* picturesque *In Mem. cxxviii* 19
Bargain they closed a *b*, hand in hand. *The Brook* 156
May rue the *b* made.' *Princess i* 74
Barge Slide the heavy *b's* trail'd *L. of Shalott i* 20
Then saw they how there hove a dusky *b*, *M. d'Arthur* 193
'Place me in the *b*,' And to the *b* they came. ,, 204
slowly answered Arthur from the *b*: ,, 239
b with oar and sail Moved from the brink, ,, 265
and a *b* Be ready on the river, *Lancelot and E.* 1122
to that stream whereon the *b*, ,, 1141
slowly past the *b* Whereon the lily maid ,, 1241
the *b*, On to the palace-doorway sliding, ,, 1245
Barge (*continued*) *b* that brought her moving down, *Lancelot and E.* 139
that unhappy child Past in her *b*: *Last Tournament* 45
Then saw they how there hove a dusky *b*, *Pass. of Arthur* 361
'Place me in the *b*.' So to the *b* they came. ,, 372
slowly answer'd Arthur from the *b*: ,, 407
b with oar and sail Moved from the brink, ,, 433
Barge-laden creeps on, *B-l*, to three arches *Gardener's D.* 43
Bark (vessel) (*See also* **Crescent-bark**) a *b* that, blowing forward, bore *M. d'Arthur Ep.* 21
I find a magic *b*; *Sir Galahad* 38
swiftly stream'd ye by the *b*! *The Voyage* 50
lading and unlading the tall *b's*, *Enoch Arden* 816
this frail *b* of ours, when sorely tried, *Aylmer's Field* 715
I sit within a helmless *b*, *In Mem. iv* 3
unhappy *b* That strikes by night ,, *xvi* 12
spare thee, sacred *b*; ,, *xvii* 14
b had plunder'd twenty nameless isles; *Merlin and V.* 559
Down on a *b*, and overbears the *b*, *Lancelot and E.* 485
Bark (of a tree) silver-green with gnarled *b*: *Mariana* 42
And rugged *b's* begin to bud, *My life is full* 18
Could slip its *b* and walk. *Talking Oak* 188
Bark (verb) *B* an answer, Britain's raven! *b* and blacken innumerable, *Boädicea* 13
Let the fox *b*, let the wolf yell. *Pelleas and E.* 472
and the dog couldn't *b*. *V. of Maeldune* 18
Barketh *B* the shepherd-dog cheerly; *Leonine Eleg.* 5
Barking *b* for the thrones of kings; *Ode on Well.* 121
Bark's-bosom Borne in the *b-b*, *Batt. of Brunanburh* 49
Barley Long fields of *b* and of rye, *L. of Shalott i* 2
In among the bearded *b*, ,, 29
And raked in golden *b*. *Will Water.* 128
Barley-sheaves He rode between the *b-s*, *L. of Shalott iii* 2
Barley-spear *b-s's* Were hollow-husk'd, *Demeter and P.* 112
Barmaid 'Bitter *b*, waning fast! *Vision of Sin* 67
Barn got to the *b*, fur the *b* wouldn't burn *Owd Roä* 103
but the *b* was as cowd as owt, ,, 111
Barne (bairn) Bessy Marris's *b*. (repeat) *N. Farmer, O.S.* 14, 21
Baron (title) Each *b* at the banquet sleeps, *Day-Dm., Sleep. P.*, 37
The *b's* swore, with many words, ,, *Revival* 23
gaunt old *B* with his beetle brow *Princess ii* 240
bush-bearded *B's* heaved and blew, ,, *v* 21
In doubt if you be of our *B's*' breed— *Third of Feb.* 32
Lords and *B's* of his realm *Com. of Arthur* 65
B's and the kings prevail'd, ,, 105
fought against him in the *B's*' war, *Gareth and L.* 77
A knight of Uther in the *B's*' war, ,, 353
a stalwart *B*, Arthur's friend. ,, 818
B saying, 'I well believe ,, 835
the *B* set Gareth beside her, ,, 851
Setting this knave, Lord *B*, at my side. ,, 854
His *B* said 'We go but harken: *Balin and Balan* 9
Heard from the *B* that, ten years *Lancelot and E.* 272
Count, *b*—whom he smote, he overthrew. ,, 465
Bracelet-bestower and *B* of *B's*, *Batt. of Brunanburh* 4
Baronet hoar hair of the *B* bristle up *Aylmer's Field* 42
B yet had laid No bar between them: ,, 117
No little lily-handed *B* he, *Princess, Con.* 84
Barr'd All *b* with long white cloud *Palace of Art* 83
Every door is *b* with gold, *Locksley Hall* 100
door shut, and window *b*. *Godiva* 41
home-circle of the poor They *b* her: *Aylmer's Field* 505
But now fast *b*: *Princess v* 367
and entering *b* her door, *Lancelot and E.* 15
ribb'd And *b* with bloom on bloom. *Lover's Tale i* 416
Barren But it is wild and *b*, *Amphion* 2
The soil, left *b*, scarce had grown *In Mem. liii* 7
Barren-beaten He left the *b-b* thoroughfare, *Lancelot and E.* 161
Barricade Should pile her *b's* with dead. *In Mem. cxxvii* 8
death at our slight *b*, *Def. of Lucknow* 15
Barrier trumpet blared At the *b* *Princess v* 486
burst All *b's* in her onward race *In Mem. cxiv* 14
Back to the *b*; then the trumpets *Lancelot and E.* 500
almost burst the *b's* in their heat, *Holy Grail* 336
voice that billow'd round the *b's* *Last Tournament* 167

Barrier (*continued*) Russia bursts our Indian *b*, *Locksley H., Sixty*, 115
b that divided beast from man Slipt, *St. Telemachus* 60
Barring out graver than a schoolboy's *b o*; *Princess Con.* 66
Barrow grassy *b's* of the happier dead. *Tithonus* 71
behind it a gray down With Danish *b's*; *Enoch Arden* 7
Pass from the Danish *b* overhead; ,, 442
Barter not being bred To *b*, ,, 250
Base (adj.) *him that utter'd nothing* b; *To the Queen* 8
Counts nothing that she meets with *b*, *On a Mourner* 4
'Ungenerous, dishonourable, *b*, *Aylmer's Field* 292
O *b* and bad! what comfort? *Princess v* 78
is he not too *b*? *Maud I iv* 36
And myself so languid and *b*. ,, *v* 18
And therefore splenetic, personal, *b*, ,, *x* 33
Nor know I whether I be very *b* *Marr. of Geraint* 468
Not only to keep down the *b* in man, *Guinevere* 480
spared the flesh of thousands, the coward and the *b*, *Happy* 17
Base (s) (*See also* **Meadow-bases**) Wrapt in dense cloud from *b* to cope. *Two Voices* 186
The seas that shock thy *b*! *England and Amer.* 15
Upon the hidden *b's* of the hills.' *M. d'Arthur* 106
people hum About the column's *b*, *St. S. Stylites* 39
The broken *b* of a black tower, *Aylmer's Field* 511
a pillar'd porch, the *b's* lost In laurel: *Princess i* 230
He has a solid *b* of temperament: ,, *iv* 254
roots of earth and *b* of all; ,, *v* 446
fangs Shall move the stony *b's* of the world. ,, *vi* 58
roar that breaks the Pharos from his *b* ,, 339
great the crush was, and each *b*, ,, 353
It sees itself from thatch to *b* *Requiescat* 3
drown The *b's* of my life in tears. *In Mem. xlix* 16
a hundred feet Up from the *b*: *Balin and Balan* 171
lash'd it at the *b* with slanting storm; *Merlin and V.* 635
at the *b* we found On either hand, *Holy Grail* 497
earthquake shivering to your *b* Split you, *Pelleas and E.* 465
gathering at the *b* Re-makes itself, ,, 609
Upon the hidden *b's* of the hills.' *Pass. of Arthur* 274
iceberg splits From cope to *b*— *Lover's Tale i* 604
wander round the *b's* of the hills, ,, *ii* 121
plunge to the *b* of the mountain walls, *V. of Maeldune* 14
Baseborn Call him *b*, and since his ways *Com. of Arthur* 180
and no king, Or else *b*.' ,, 234
Based (*See also* **Broad-based, Firm-based**) *b* His feet on juts of slippery crag *M. d'Arthur* 188
b His feet on juts of slippery crag *Pass. of Arthur* 356
Basement Modred brought His creatures to the *b* *Guinevere* 104
Baseness 'He knows a *b* in his blood *Two Voices* 301
equal *b* lived in sleeker times *Princess v* 385
Is there no *b* we would hide? *In Mem. li* 3
She finds the *b* of her lot, ,, *lx* 6
there is no *b* in her.' *Merlin and V.* 127
To leave an equal *b*; ,, 830
Puts his own *b* in him by default *Pelleas and E.* 81
Basest ALTHO' I be the *b* of mankind, *St. S. Stylites* 1
The *b*, far into that council-hall *Lucretius* 171
All that is noblest, all that is *b*, *Vastness* 32
Bashful reddens, cannot speak, So *b*, *Balin and Balan* 520
Bashfulness His *b* and tenderness at war, *Enoch Arden* 289
His broken utterances and *b*, *Pelleas and E.* 111
Basilisk hornless unicorns, Crack'd *b's*, *Holy Grail* 718
Basis All but the *b* of the soul. *Love thou thy land* 44
Bask or to *b* in a summer sky: *Wages* 9
To you that *b* below the Line, *To Ulysses* 5
Why not *b* amid the senses *By an Evolution.* 6
Bask'd *b* and batten'd in the woods. *In Mem. xxxv* 24
wealthy enough to have *b* *The Wreck* 45
Basket To Francis, with a *b* on his arm, *Audley Court* 6
holiday, With bag and sack and *b*, *Enoch Arden* 63
set down His *b*, and dismounting *Geraint and E.* 210
skin Clung but to crate and *b*, *Merlin and V.* 625
Basking city Of little Monaco, *b*, glow'd. *The Daisy* 8
summer *b* in the sultry plains *Prog. of Spring* 77
Bassa by the shore Of Duglas; that on *B*; *Lancelot and E.* 290
Bassoon (*continued*) liquid treble of that *b*, my throat; *Princess ii* 426
Bassoon heard The flute, violin, *b*; *Maud I xxii* 14
Basting be for the spit, Larding and *b*. *Gareth and L.* 1083
Bastion A looming *b* fringed with fire. *In Mem. xv* 20
Bastion'd from the *b* walls Like threaded spiders, *Princess i* 107
Bat After the flitting of the *b's*, *Mariana* 17
this Mock-Hymen were laid up like winter *b's* *Princess iv* 144
b's wheel'd, and owls whoop'd, *Princess, Con.*, 110
b's went round in fragrant skies, *In Mem. xcv* 9
For the black *b*, night, has flown, *Maud I xxii* 2
A home of *b's*, in every tower an owl. *Balin and Balan* 336
When the *b* comes out of his cave, *Despair* 89
Batchelor Molly Magee wid her *b*, Danny O'Roon— *Tomorrow* 10
Bath the *b's* Of all the western stars, *Ulysses* 60
His wife a faded beauty of the *B's*, *Aylmer's Field* 27
Balmier and nobler from her *b* of storm, *Lucretius* 175
dipt in *b's* of hissing tears, *In Mem. cxviii* 23
Pallas Athene climbing from the *b* In anger; *Tiresias* 40
fuse themselves to little spicy *b's*, *Prog. of Spring* 33
The *B's*, the Forum gabbled of his death, *St. Telemachus* 74
Bathe Balm-dews to *b* thy feet! *Talking Oak* 268
Coldly thy rosy shadows *b* me, *Tithonus* 66
Soft lustre *b's* the range of urns *Day-Dm., Sleep. P.*, 9
she *b's* the Saviour's feet *In Mem. xxxii* 11
Bathed (*See also* **New-bathed**) lying *b* In the green gleam *Princess i* 93
Vivien *b* your feet before her own? *Merlin and V.* 284
So *b* we were in brilliance. *Lover's Tale i* 313
So fair in southern sunshine *b*, *Freedom* 5
B in that lurid crimson— *St. Telemachus* 18
Batin' (beating) set me heart *b* to music wid ivery word! *Tomorrow* 34
Batten And *b* on her poisons? *Lover's Tale i* 777
Batten'd bask'd and *b* in the woods. *In Mem. xxxv* 24
Battenest Thou *b* by the greasy gleam *Will Water.* 221
Battening lie *B* upon huge seaworms *The Kraken* 12
Batter some one *b's* at the dovecote-doors, *Princess iv* 169
Batter'd (*See also* **Bone-batter'd**) flints *b* with clanging hoofs; *D. of F. Women* 21
He *b* at the doors; none came: *Princess v* 337
Cyril, *b* as he was, Trail'd himself ,, *vi* 154
And *b* with the shocks of doom *In Mem. cxviii* 24
and so left him bruised And *b*, *Pelleas and E.* 547
Battering *B* the gates of heaven *St. S. Stylites* 7
Battery-smoke Plunged in the *b's* *Light Brigade* 32
Battle (s) (*See also* **Field-of-battle, Mahratta-battle**) We heard the steeds to *b* going, *Oriana* 15
The *b* deepen'd in its place, ,, 51
The distant *b* flash'd and rung. *Two Voices* 126
Peal after peal, the British *b* broke, *Buonaparte* 7
all day long the noise of *b* roll'd *M. d'Arthur* 1
drunk delight of *b* with my peers, *Ulysses* 16
boyish histories Of *b*, bold adventure, *Aylmer's Field* 98
That beat to *b* where he stands *Princess iv* 578
And gives the *b* to his hands: ,, 580
prove Your knight, and fight your *b*, ,, 595
Breathing and sounding beauteous *b*, ,, *v* 161
doing *b* with forgotten ghosts, ,, 480
I and mine have fought Your *b*: ,, *vi* 225
From talk of *b's* loud and vain, *Ode on Well.* 247
Some ship of *b* slowly creep, *To F. D. Maurice* 26
War with a thousand *b's*, *Maud I i* 48
months ran on and rumour of *b* grew, ,, *III vi* 29
Far into the North, and *b*, ,, 37
hail once more to the banner of *b* unroll'd! ,, 42
Arthur, passing thence to *b*, felt *Com. of Arthur* 75
long-lanced *b* let their horses run. ,, 104
like a painted *b* the war stood Silenced, ,, 122
in twelve great *b's* overcame The heathen hordes, ,, 518
Grant me some knight to do the *b* for me, *Gareth and L.* 362
King had saved his life In *b* twice, ,, 494
thou send To do the *b* with him, ,, 619
To bring thee back to do the *b* ,, 1294
loving the *b* as well As he that rides him.' ,, 1301
ride with him to *b* and stand by, *Marr. of Geraint* 94

Battle (s) (*continued*) 'Do *b* for it then,' no more ; *Marr. of Geraint* 561
In the great *b* fighting for the King. " 596
soldiers wont to hear His voice in *b*, *Geraint and E.* 175
In *b*, fighting for the blameless King. " 970
banners of twelve *b's* overhead stir, *Balin and Balan* 88
My father died in *b* for thy King, *Merlin and V.* 72
ever-moaning *b* in the mist, " 192
after furious *b* turfs the slain " 657
In *b* with the love he bare his lord, *Lancelot and E.* 246
in the four loud *b's* by the shore Of Duglas ; " 289
hast been in *b* by my side, " 1358
twelve great *b's* of our King. *Holy Grail* 250
Knights that in twelve great *b's* " 311
with one Who gets a wound in *b*, *Pelleas and E.* 529
Fought in her father's *b's* ? wounded *Last Tournament* 592
Isolt ?—I fought his *b's*, for Isolt ! " 604
In open *b* or the tilting-field (repeat) *Guinevere* 330, 332
In twelve great *b's* ruining " 432
Far down to that great *b* in the west, " 571
ere he goes to the great *B* ? " 652
ere that last weird *b* in the west, *Pass. of Arthur* 29
is this *b* in the west Whereto we move, " 66
last, dim, weird *b* of the west. " 94
old ghosts Look in upon the *b* ; " 104
King glanced across the field Of *b* : " 127
held the field of *b* was the King : " 138
all day long the noise of *b* roll'd " 170
The darkness of that *b* in the West, *To the Queen ii* 65
In *b* with the glooms of my dark will, *Lover's Tale i* 744
God of *b's*, was ever a *b* like this *The Revenge* 62
Floated in conquering *b* or flapt *Def. of Lucknow* 2
kings Of Spain than all their *b's* ! *Columbus* 23
And we took to playing at *b*, *V. of Maeldune* 95
For the passion of *b* was in us, " 96
Till the passion of *b* was on us, " 111
Gaining a lifelong Glory in *b*, *Batt. of Brunanburh* 8
That they had the better In perils of *b* " 85
himself Blood-red from *b*, *Tiresias* 113
flay Captives whom they caught in *b*— *Locksley H., Sixty*, 80
mad for the charge and the *b* were we, *Heavy Brigade* 41
Stately purposes, valour in *b*, *Vastness* 7
crimson with *b's*, and hollow with graves, *The Dreamer* 12
Storm of *b* and thunder of war ! *Riflemen form !* 3
Battle (verb) For them I *b* till the end, *Sir Galahad* 15
Battle-axe Bloodily, bloodily fall the *b-a*, *Boädicea* 56
fall *b* upon helm, Fall *b*, *Com. of Arthur* 486
Clang *b* and clash brand ! (repeat) *Com. of Arthur* 493, 496, 499
crash Of *b's* on shatter'd helms, *Pass. of Arthur* 110
Battle-bolt *b-b* sang from the three-decker *Maud I i* 50
Battle-club *b-c's* From the isles of palm : *Princess, Pro.*, 21
Battle-cry battle or flapt to the *b-c* ! *Def. of Lucknow* 2
and could raise such a *b-c* *V. of Maeldune* 23
Battled (adj.) glow Beneath the *b* tower. *D. of F. Women* 220
Battled (verb) Who *b* for the True, the Just, *In Mem. lvi* 18
Battle-field Be shot for sixpence in a *b-f*, *Audley Court* 41
Descends upon thee in the *b-f* : *Com. of Arthur* 129
Arthur mightiest on the *b-f*— *Gareth and L.* 496
Right arm of Arthur in the *b*, *Last Tournament* 202
A galleried palace, or a *b*, *The Ring* 246
Battle-flag and the *b-f's* were furl'd *Locksley Hall* 127
Battlement The *b* overtopt with ivytods, *Balin and Balan* 335
Battle-plain springs Of Dircê laving yonder *b-p*, *Tiresias* 139
Battleshield Hack'd the *b*, *Batt. of Brunanburh* 13
Battle-song hear again The chivalrous *b-s* *Maud I x* 54
Battle-thunder thine the *b-t* of God,' *Boädicea* 44
the *b-t* broke from them all. *The Revenge* 49
with her *b-t* and flame ; " 59
Battle-twig (earwig) 'Twur es bad es a *b-t* 'ere *Spinster's S's.* 80
Battle-writhen *b-w* arms and mighty hands *Lancelot and E.* 812
Baulk (beam) 'eärd the bricks an' the *b's* *Owd Roä* 109
Bawl throats of Manchester may *b*, *Third of Feb.* 43
Millions of throats would *b* for civil rights, *Princess v* 387
shamed to *b* himself a kitchen-knave. *Gareth and L.* 717
b's this frontless kitchen-knave, " 860
Bawl'd you *b* the dark side of your faith *Despair* 39

Bay (arm of the sea) (*See also* **Lover's Bay**) spangle dances in bight and *b*, *Sea-Fairies* 24
glassy *b's* among her tallest towers.' *Œnone* 119
where the *b* runs up its latest horn. *Audley Court* 11
farmer's son, who lived across the *b*, " 75
lower down The *b* was oily calm ; " 86
That he sings in his boat on the *b* ! *Break, break, etc.* 8
I bubble into eddying *b's*, *The Brook* 41
By *b's*, the peacock's neck in hue ; *The Daisy* 14
In caves about the dreary *b*, *Sailor Boy* 10
long waves that roll in yonder *b* ? *Maud I xviii* 63
pleasant breast of waters, quiet *b*, *Lover's Tale i* 6
borne about the *b* or safely moor'd " 54
growing holier as you near'd the *b*, " 338
into the sympathy Of that small *b*, " *i* 435
curving round The silver-sheeted *b* : " *ii* 76
Moved with one spirit round about the *b*, " *iii* 17
their gloom, the mountains and the *B*, " *iv* 16
After their marriage lit the lover's *B*, " 28
I with our lover to his native *B*. " 155
and flung them in bight and *b*, *V. of Maeldune* 53
that dropt to the brink of his *b*, *The Wreck* 73
that *b* with the colour'd sand— " 135
Bay (a tree) the boar hath rosemaries and *b*. *Gareth and L.* 1074
that wear a wreath of sweeter *b*, *Poets and their B.* 7
Bay (at bay) Where he greatly stood at *b*, *Ode on Well.* 106
heard The noble hart at *b*, *Marr. of Geraint* 233
Bay (verb) Not less, tho' dogs of Faction *b*, *Love thou thy land* 85
Baying chiefly for the *b* of Cavall, *Marr. of Geraint* 185
Bay-window from some *b-w* shake the night ; *Princess i* 106
lands in your view From this *b-w* *Sisters (E. and E.)* 52
Beach rib and fret The broad-imbased *b*, *Supp. Confessions* 128
To watch the crisping ripples on the *b*, *Lotos-Eaters, C.S.* 61
rounded by the stillness of the *b* *Audley Court* 10
Here about the *b* I wander'd, *Locksley Hall* 11
on this *b* a hundred years ago, *Enoch Arden* 10
here and there, on sandy *b'es* *The Daisy* 15
The breaker breaking on the *b*. *In Mem. lxxi* 16
the scream of a madden'd *b* *Maud I iii* 12
shore-cliff's windy walls to the *b*, *Geraint and E.* 164
leaving Arthur's court he gain'd the *b* ; *Merlin and V.* 197
tremulously as foam upon the *b* *Guinevere* 364
the narrow fringe Of curving *b*— *Lover's Tale i* 39
the fig ran up from the *b* *V. of Maeldune* 58
Beacon (s) like a *b* guards thee home. *In Mem. xvii* 12
prophet's *b* burn'd in vain, *Ancient Sage* 142
Beacon (verb) Not in vain the distance *b's*. *Locksley Hall* 181
Beacon-blaze *b-b* allures The bird of passage, *Enoch Arden* 728
Beacon-star Each with a *b-s* upon his head, *Guinevere* 241
Beacon-tower Fixt like a *b-t* above the waves *Princess iv* 493
Bead (*See also* **Frost-bead**) And number'd *b*, and shrift, *Talking Oak* 46
Beaded (*See also* **Black-beaded, Five-beaded**) And woolly breasts and *b* eyes ; *In Mem. xcv* 12
Beak hawk stood with the down on his *b*, *Poet's Song* 11
swoops The vulture, *b* and talon, *Princess v* 383
ever-ravening eagle's *b* and talon *Boädicea* 11
And all unscarr'd from *b* or talon, *Last Tournament* 20
Beaker *b* brimm'd with noble wine. *Day-Dm., Sleep. P.*, 36
Beäl'd (bellowed) she *b* 'Ya mun saäve little Dick, *Owd Roä* 81
an' she an' the babby *b*, *North. Cobbler* 37
an' 'e *b* to ya 'Lad coom hout' *Church-warden, etc.* 28
Beam (ray) So many minds did gird their orbs with *b's* *The Poet* 29
'Or will one *b* be less intense, *Two Voices* 40
into two burning rings All *b's* of Love, *D. of F. Women* 175
deep-blue gloom with *b's* divine : " 186
the white dawn's creeping *b's*, " 261
fresh *b* of the springing east ; *M. d'Arthur* 214
like a lane of *b's* athwart the sea, *Golden Year* 50
b's, that thro' the Oriel shine, *Day-Dm., Sleep. P.*, 34
Pure spaces clothed in living *b's*, *Sir Galahad* 66
b of Heaven Dawn'd sometime *Aylmer's Field* 684
Was it the first *b* of my latest day ? *Lucretius* 59

Beam (ray) (*continued*) a *b* Had slanted forward, *Princess ii* 138
' Fresh as the first *b* glittering on a sail, ,, *iv* 44
b Of the East, that play'd upon them, ,, *v* 258
A *b* in darkness: let it grow. *In Mem. Pro.*, 24
A chequer-work of *b* and shade ,, *lxxii* 15
Pale with the golden *b* of an eyelash *Maud I iii* 3
Like a *b* of the seventh Heaven, ,, *xiv* 21
smitten by the dusty sloping *b*, *Marr. of Geraint* 262
Stream'd thro' my cell a cold and silver *b*, *Holy Grail* 116
down the long *b* stole the Holy Grail, (repeat) ,, 117, 188
Grail Past, and the *b* decay'd, ,, 122
A crimson grail within a silver *b*; ,, 155
b of light seven times more clear than day: ,, 187
Smote by the fresh *b* of springing east; *Pass. of Arthur* 382
crown of *b's* about his brows— *Lover's Tale i* 672
And solid *b* of isolated light, ,, *ii* 173
Beam (timber) (*See also* **Baulk, Rigtree**) shape it plank and *b* for roof *Princess vi* 46
Beam (verb) More bounteous aspects on me *b*, *Sir Galahad* 21
Beam'd Love's white star *B* thro' *Gardener's D.* 166
b, Beneath a manelike mass *Aylmer's Field* 67
ghostly grace *B* on his fancy, *Lancelot and E.* 886
Beän 'ere a *b* an' yonder a peä; *N. Farmer, O.S.* 46
Bear (an animal) grosser than your native *b's*— *Princess iv* 537
dog, and wolf and boar and *b* *Com. of Arthur* 23
Albeit grizzlier than a *b*, to ride *Pelleas and E.* 193
Bear (constellation) *B* had wheel'd Thro' a great arc *Princess iv* 212
Bear (verb) (*See also* **Abeär, Bore**) That *b's* relation to the mind. *Two Voices* 177
' His sons grow up that *b* his name, ,, 256
how canst thou *b* my weight? *Œnone* 237
I know you proud to *b* your name, *L.C.V. de Vere* 10
whatever sky *B* seed of men *Love thou thy land* 20
As we *b* blossom of the dead; ,, 94
I will not *b* it longer.' *The Goose* 32
And *b* me to the margin; *M. d'Arthur* 165
Less burthen, by ten-hundred-fold, to *b*, *St. S. Stylites* 24
B witness, if I could have found ,, 55
in truth (thou wilt *b* witness here) ,, 129
that which *b's* but bitter fruit? *Locksley Hall* 65
and he *b's* a laden breast, ,, 143
Three angels *b* the holy Grail: *Sir Galahad* 42
Which *b's* a season'd brain about, *Will Water.* 85
b me with thee, smoothly borne, *Move eastward* 9
beseech you by the love you *b* Him *Enoch Arden* 307
' Too hard to *b*! why did they take me ,, 781
boat that *b's* the hope of life ,, 830
thought to *b* it with me to my grave; ,, 896
b's about A silent court of justice *Sea Dreams* 173
jam the doors, and *b* The keepers down, *Lucretius* 169
not he, who *b's* one name with her ,, 235
The king would *b* him out;' *Princess i* 182
Earth Should *b* a double growth ,, *ii* 180
think I *b* that heart within my breast, ,, 334
much I *b* with her: ,, *iii* 81
hear me, for I *b*, Tho' man, yet human, ,, *iv* 424
if thou needs must *b* the yoke, ,, *vi* 205
skater on ice that hardly *b's* him, *Hendecasyllabics* 6
But help thy foolish ones to *b*; *In Mem. Pro.*, 31
Help thy vain worlds to *b* thy light. ,, 32
To *b* thro' Heaven a tale of woe, ,, *xii* 2
Come then, pure hands, and *b* the head ,, *xviii* 9
I loved the weight I had to *b*, ,, *xxv* 7
A life that *b's* immortal fruit ,, *xl* 18
To that ideal which he *b's*? ,, *lii* 10
She often brings but one to *b*, ,, *lv* 12
He *b's* the burthen of the weeks ,, *lxxx* 11
growing, till I could *b* it no more, *Maud I iii* 9
b's a skeleton figured on his arms, *Gareth and L.* 640
heart enough To *b* his armour? *Geraint and E.* 490
b him hence out of this cruel sun? ,, 544
take him up, and *b* him to our hall: ,, 552
pray the King To let me *b* some token *Balin and Balan* 188
said ' What wilt thou *b*?' ,, 199
and ask'd To *b* her own crown-royal ,, 200

Bear (verb) (*continued*) ladies living gave me this to *b*.' *Balin and Balan* 340
best and purest, granted me To *b* it!' ,, 351
Thee will I *b* no more,' ,, 432
b's, with all Its stormy crests *Lancelot and E.* 483
Then will I *b* it gladly;' ,, 1106
But I myself must *b* it.' ,, 1108
seize me by the hair and *b* me far, ,, 1425
see thou, that it may *b* its flower. *Holy Grail* 887
cannot *b* to dream you so forsworn: *Pelleas and E.* 300
added to the griefs the great must *b*, *Guinevere* 205
B with me for the last time ,, 454
And *b* me to the margin; *Pass. of Arthur* 333
B witness, that rememberable day, *To the Queen ii* 3
that perfectness Which I do *b* within me: *Lover's Tale i* 89
bade his menials *b* him from the door, ,, *iv* 260
How could I *b* with the sights and the loathsome smells *In the Child. Hosp.* 25
Him, who should *b* the sword Of Justice— *Sir J. Oldcastle* 87
Why should we *b* with an hour of torture, *Despair* 81
sorrow that I *b* is sorrow for *his* sake. *The Flight* 64
and I and you will *b* the pall; *Locksley H., Sixty*, 281
B witness you, that yesterday *To Prof. Jebb* 2
younger kindlier Gods to *b* us down, *Demeter and P.* 131
creed and race Shall *b* false witness, *Akbar's Dream* 98
The flood may *b* me far, *Crossing the Bar* 14
Beard *b* Was tagg'd with icy fringes *St. S. Stylites* 31
His *b* a foot before him, and his hair *Godiva* 18
' By holy rood, a royal *b*! *Day-Dm., Revival* 20
My *b* has grown into my lap.' ,, 22
paw'd his *b*, and muttered 'catalepsy.' *Princess i* 20
answer which, half-muffled in his *b*, ,, *v* 234
father's face and reverend *b* ,, *vi* 103
b That looks as white as utter truth, *Gareth and L.* 280
Broad-faced with under-fringe of russet *b*, *Geraint and E.* 537
took his russet *b* between his teeth; ,, 713
one curl of Arthur's golden *b*. *Merlin and V.* 58
to part The lists of such a *b* ,, 245
shaggy mantle of his *b* Across her neck ,, 256
no more sign of reverence than a *b*. ,, 279
b that clothed his lips with light— *Last Tournament* 668
and his white *b* fell to his feet, *V. of Maeldune* 118
we kiss'd the fringe of his *b* ,, 125
Beard-blown *b-b* goat Hang on the shaft, *Princess iv* 78
Bearded (*See also* **Black-bearded, Bush-bearded, Lichen-Bearded, Long-bearded, Parcel-bearded, Russet-bearded**) In among the *b* barley, *L. of Shalott i* 29
Some *b* meteor, trailing light, ,, *iii* 26
the *b* grass Is dry and dewless. *Miller's D.* 245
tho' you were not then So *b*. *Columbus* 9
Beardless *b* apple-arbiter Decided fairest. *Lucretius* 91
Bearer Save under pall with *b's*. *Aylmer's Field* 827
Bearest love thou *b* The first-born *Ode to Memory* 91
Bearing (part.) *b* on My shallop thro' *Arabian Nights* 35
B a lifelong hunger in his heart. *Enoch Arden* 79
b hardly more Than his own shadow *Aylmer's Field* 29
and, as *b* in myself the shame ,, 355
Oaring one arm, and *b* in my left *Princess iv* 183
as underhand, not openly *b* the sword. *Maud I i* 28
B all down in thy precipitancy— *Gareth and L.* 8
b in their common bond of love, *Balin and Balan* 150
sent him to the Queen *B* his wish, *Lancelot and E.* 1169
started thro' mid air *B* an eagle's nest: *Last Tournament* 15
b round about him his own day, *Lover's Tale i* 510
b high in arms the mighty babe, ,, *iv* 295
b on one arm the noble babe, ,, 370
from our fiery beech Were *b* off the mast, *Pro. to Gen. Hamley* 4
Bearing (mien) face nor *b*, limbs nor voice, *Com. of Arthur* 71
thro' these Princelike his *b* shone; *Marr. of Geraint* 545
And all her *b* gracious; *Holy Grail* 394
gazed upon the man Of princely *b*, *Pelleas and E.* 306
I dream'd the *b* of our knights *Last Tournament* 120
Bearing (bringing forth) *b* and the training of a child *Princess v* 465
Bearing (armorial) gateway she discerns With armorial *b's* *L. of Burleigh* 43
Bearing (force) To change the *b* of a word, *In Mem. cxxviii* 16

Beast (*See also* **Beäst, Man-Beast**) but a little more Than b's, Two Voices 197
people here, a b of burden slow, Palace of Art 149
one deep cry Of great wild b's; ,, 283
I a b To take them as I did? Edwin Morris 71
and even b's have stalls, St. S. Stylites 109
Like a b with lower pleasures, like a b Locksley Hall 176
The many-headed b should know.' You might have won 20
like a b hard-ridden, breathing hard. Aylmer's Field 291
there surely lives in man and b Sea Dreams 68
What b has heart to do it? Lucretius 233
b or bird or fish, or opulent flower: ,, 249
biting laws to scare the b's of prey Princess v 393
envy not the b that takes His license In Mem. xxvii 5
Move upward, working out the b, ,, cxviii 27
Like Paul with b's, I fought with Death; ,, cxx 4
Wherein the b was ever more and more, Com. of Arthur 11
wet woods, and many a b therein, ,, 21
none or few to scare or chase the b; ,, 22
between the man and b we die.' ,, 45
slew the b, and fell'd The forest, ,, 59
between the man and b they die. ,, 79
lift her from this land of b's Up to my throne, ,, 80
b and man had had their share of me: ,, 163
b's, and surely would have torn the child ,, 217
Have foughten like wild b's ,, 226
noise of ravage wrought by b and man, Gareth and L. 437
Care not, good b's, so well I care ,, 1308
skins the wild b after slaying him, Geraint and E. 93
first as sullen as a b new-caged, ,, 856
In lieu of this rough b upon my shield, Balin and Balan 196
maws ensepulchre Their brother b, ,, 488
yell, Unearthier than all shriek of bird or b, ,, 545
beauteous b Scared by the noise Merlin and V. 421
weak b seeking to help herself ,, 498
b's themselves would worship; ,, 575
in the lowest b's are slaying men, And in the second men are slaying b's, Holy Grail 234
great b's rose upright like a man, ,, 821
the b's Will tear thee piecemeal.' ,, 824
b—he, she, or I? myself most fool; Pelleas and E. 475
B too, as lacking human wit— ,, 476
made his b that better knew it, swerve ,, 551
what evil b Hath drawn his claws Last Tournament 62
Reel back into the b, and be no more?' ,, 125
And men from b's—Long live the king ,, 358
thro' ever harrying thy wild b's— ,, 635
art grown wild b thyself. ,, 637
like a subtle b Lay couchant Guinevere 10
subtle b, Would track her guilt ,, 59
my realm Reels back into the b, Pass. of Arthur 26
As ignorant and impolitic as a b— Columbus 128
That gray b, the wolf of the weald. Batt. of Brunanburh 110
the multitudinous b, The dragon, Tiresias 15
fierce b found A wiser than herself, ,, 151
curb the b would cast thee in the mire, Ancient Sage 276
Sisters, brothers,—and the b's— Locksley H., Sixty, 102
Have we risen from out the b, then back into the b again? ,, 148
house with all its hateful needs no cleaner than the b, Happy 32
starved the wild b that was linkt By an Evolution. 11
But I hear no yelp of the b, ,, 19
caged b Yell'd, as he yell'd of yore St. Telemachus 45
barrier that divided b from man Slipt, ,, 60
that stare of a b of prey. Charity 10
is prized for it smells of the b, The Dawn 14
Beäst nor a mortal b o' the feäld. North. Cobbler 38
An' I says 'Git awaäy, ya b,' Owd Roä 62
Beastlier B than any phantom of his kind Lucretius 196
Beastlike b as I find myself, Not manlike ,, 231
Beat (s) (*See also* **Heart-beat**) nigh to burst with violence of the b, Gareth and L. 763
Beat (verb) (*See also* **Beät**) The cloud fleets, The heart b's, Nothing will Die 12
The heart will cease to b; All Things will Die 12
And the blue wave b the shore; ,, 43

Beat (verb) (*continued*) From winter rains that b his grave. Two Voices 261
My frozen heart began to b, ,, 422
B time to nothing in my head Miller's D. 67
And her heart would b against me, ,, 177
I should know if it b right, ,, 179
dog howl, mother, or the death-watch b, May Queen, Con. 21
wind, that b's the mountain, blows To J. S. 1
'B quicker, for the time Is pleasant, On a Mourner 12
b me down and marr'd and wasted me, Tithonus 19
b the twilight into flakes of fire. ,, 42
heart of existence b for ever like a boy's? Locksley Hall 140
where my life began to b; ,, 154
Music in his heart B's quick Day-Dm. Arrival 27
My spirit b's her mortal bars, Sir Galahad 46
But never merrily b Annie's heart. Enoch Arden 513
b's out his weary life. ,, 730
May b a pathway out to wealth Aylmer's Field 439
Long since her heart had b remorselessly, ,, 799
B breast, tore hair, cried out Lucretius 277
Had b her foes with slaughter Princess, Pro., 34
but convention b's them down: ,, 128
B balm upon our eyelids. ,, iii 123
wave May b admission in a thousand years, ,, 155
My heart b thick with passion ,, 190
vassals to be b, nor pretty babes ,, iv 146
That b to battle where he stands; ,, 578
and they will b my girl ,, v 88
clash'd their arms; the drum B; ,, 251
One pulse that b's true woman, ,, vi 180
greater than all knowledge, b her down. ,, vii 238
faith in womankind B's with his blood, ,, 329
b with rapid unanimous hand, Boädicea 79
dance with death, to b the ground In Mem. i 12
clock B's out the little lives of men. ,, ii 8
'What is it makes me b so low?' ,, iv 8
Hath still'd the life that b from thee. ,, vi 12
my heart was used to b So quickly, ,, vii 3
A flower b with rain and wind, ,, viii 15
darken'd heart that b no more; ,, xix 2
hearts that b from day to day, ,, lviii 6
plays with threads, he b's his chair ,, lxvi 13
My pulses therefore b again In Mem. lxxxv 57
That b's within a lonely place, ,, 110
But seeks to b in time with one ,, 115
crash'd the glass and b the floor; ,, lxxxvii 20
At last he b his music out. ,, xcvi 10
hearts of old have b in tune, ,, xcvii 10
But let no footstep b the floor, ,, cv 17
my heart was used to b So quickly, ,, cxix 1
heart b stronger And thicker, Maud I viii 8
B to the noiseless music of the night! ,, xviii 77
B, happy stars, timing with things below, ,, 81
B with my heart more blest than heart ,, 82
My heart would hear her and b, ,, xxii 69
My dust would hear her and b, ,, 71
Is it gone? my pulses b— ,, II i 36
But the broad light glares and b's, ,, iv 89
the hoofs of the horses b, b, The hoofs of the horses b, B into my scalp and my brain, ,, v 8
heart of a people b with one desire; ,, III vi 49
fierce light which b's upon a throne, Ded. of Idylls 27
and by this will b his foemen down.' Com. of Arthur 309
B thro' the blindless casement Marr. of Geraint 71
Invaded Britain, 'But we b him back, ,, 746
Not b him back, but welcomed him ,, 748
B, till she woke the sleepers, Geraint and E. 404
while the sun yet b a dewy blade, ,, 446
And b the cross to earth, and break Balin and Balan 458
Vivien, tho' ye b me like your dog, ,, 582
Across the iron grating of her cell B, Holy Grail 82
blood b's, and the blossom blows, ,, 671
felt the sun B like a strong knight Pelleas and E. 23
let my lady b me if she will: ,, 335
And b's upon the faces of the dead, Pass. of Arthur 141

Beat (verb) (*continued*) tho' there *b* a heart in either eye ; *Lover's Tale i* 34
Death drew nigh and *b* the doors of Life ; ,, 111
noons *B* from the concave sand ; ,, 140
felt the blast *B* on my heated eyelids : ,, *iii* 28
Hearts that had *b* with such a love ,, *iv* 69
It *b*—the heart—it *b* : Faint—but it *b* : ,, 80
They *b* me for that, they *b* me— *Rizpah* 48
and *b* Thro' all the homely town *Columbus* 82
heart alive *b's* on it night and day— *The Flight* 35
heart that once had *b* beside her own. *Locksley H., Sixty,* 58
when life has ceased to *b*. *Happy* 52
'*B*, little heart—I give you this and this' *Romney's R.* 1
'*B* upon mine, little heart ! *b*, *b* ! ,, 94
'*B* upon mine ! you are mine, my sweet ! ,, 95
'*B* little heart' on this fool brain ,, 155
pulse of Alla *b's* Thro' all His world. *Akbar's Dream* 41
b back The menacing poison ,, 164
Harmony Whereto the worlds *b* time, *D. of the Duke of C.* 16

Beät (verb) An' it *b's* ma to knaw wot she died on, *Church-warden, etc.* 6

Beaten (*See also* **Barren-beaten, Breaker-beaten, Hollow-beaten, Thrice-beaten, Weather-beaten**)
B with some great passion at her heart, *Princess iv* 388
B I had been for a little fault *Com. of Arthur* 341
seems no bolder than a *b* hound ; *Geraint and E.* 61
forward by a way which, *b* broad, ,, 436
b back, and *b* back Settles, *Merlin and V.* 371
took To bitter weeping like a *b* child, ,, 855
Of every dint a sword had *b* in it, *Lancelot and E.* 19
lance had *b* down the knights, *Holy Grail* 363
There was I *b* down by little men ,, 789
a traitor proven, or hound *B*, *Pelleas and E.* 440
save for dread of thee had *b* me, *Last Tournament* 525
many a heathen sword Had *b* thin ; *Pass. of Arthur* 167
Drooping and *b* by the breeze, *Lover's Tale i* 700
better ha' *b* me black an' blue *First Quarrel* 72
Havelock baffled, or *b*, *Def. of Lucknow* 91
thus was I *b* back, *Columbus* 55

Beating (*See also* **Batin**) When will the heart be aweary of *b* ? *Nothing will Die* 6
in joyance is *b* Full merrily ; *All Things will Die* 6
Do *b* hearts of salient springs *Adeline* 26
music in his ears his *b* heart did make. *Lotos-Eaters* 36
heard with *b* heart The Sweet-Gale *Edwin Morris* 109
bosom *b* with a heart renew'd. *Tithonus* 36
B it in upon his weary brain, *Enoch Arden* 796
b up thro' all the bitter world, ,, 802
two-cell'd heart *b*, with one full stroke, *Princess vii* 307
B from the wasted vines *Ode on Well.* 109
Rose-red with *b's* in it, as if alive, *Holy Grail* 118
own steps, and his own heart *B*, *Pelleas and E.* 417
Heart *b* time to heart, *Lover's Tale i* 260
found her *b* the hard Protestant doors. *Sisters (E. and E.)* 240
warriors *b* back the swarm Of Turkish *Montenegro* 10
O the deathwatch *b* ! *Forlorn* 24

Beatitude Fulfils him with *b*. *Supp. Confessions* 62

Beauteous The reflex of a *b* form, *Miller's D.* 77
To find my heart so near the *b* breast, *The form, the form* 7
when the *b* hateful isle Return'd *Enoch Arden* 617
Breathing and sounding *b* battle, *Princess v* 161
In whispers of the *b* world. *In Mem. lxxix* 12
Come, *b* in thine after form, ,, *xci* 15
the *b* beast Scared by the noise *Merlin and V.* 421
Paris, himself as *b* as a God. *Death of Œnone* 18
Paris, no longer *b* as a God, ,, 25

Beautiful spirit-thrilling eyes so keen and *b* : *Ode to Memory* 39
And said the earth was *b*. *A Character* 12
Her *b* bold brow, *The Poet* 38
B Paris, evil-hearted Paris, *Œnone* 50
Idalian Aphroditè *b*, ,, 174
How *b* a thing it was to die For God *D. of F. Women* 231
Twin-sisters differently *b*. *Edwin Morris* 33
ever thus thou growest *b* In silence, *Tithonus* 43
'She is more *b* than day.' *Beggar Maid* 8
his own children tall and *b*, *Enoch Arden* 762

Beautiful (*continued*) the stars about the moon Look *b*, *Spec. of Iliad* 12
made His darkness *b* with thee. *In Mem. lxxiv* 12
Perfectly *b* ; let it be granted her : *Maud I ii* 4
pride flash'd over her *b* face. ,, *iv* 16
Silence, *b* voice ! ,, *v* 19
O *b* creature, what am I ,, *xvi* 10
Not *b* now, not even kind ; ,, *II v* 66
He had not dream'd she was so *b*. *Lancelot and E.* 353
Beyond my knowing of them, *b*, *Holy Grail* 103
B in the light of holiness. ,, 105
'God make thee good as thou art *b*,' ,, 136
'Is Guinevere herself so *b* ?' *Pelleas and E.* 70
And enter it, and make it *b* ? *Pass. of Arthur* 17
Forgetting how to render *b* Her countenance *Lover's Tale i* 96
The *b* in Past of act or place, ,, 135
Of all his treasures the most *b*, ,, *iv* 234
cries about the banquet—'*B* ! ,, 239
That which is thrice as *b* as these, ,, 248
Of all my treasures the most *b*, ,, 318
pity, if one so *b* Prove, ,, 338
both are *b* : Evelyn is gayer, *Sisters (E and E)* 35
Both *b* alike, nor can I tell ,, 276
So *b*, vast, various, *Ancient Sage* 84
one was dark, and both were *b*. *The Ring* 161
Bountiful, *b*, apparell'd gay, *Prog. of Spring* 62

Beautiful-brow'd *B-b* Œnone, my own soul, *Œnone* 71

Beautifully So lightly, *b* built : *Palace of Art* 294
dress her *b* and keep her true'— *Geraint and E.* 40
that beauty should go *b* : (repeat) ,, 681, 684

Beauty (*See also* **After-beauty**) solid form Of constant *b*. *Supp. Confessions* 150
He spake of *b* : that the dull *A Character* 7
I see thy *b* gradually unfold, *Eleänore* 70
Light Hope at *B's* call would perch *Caress'd or chidden* 3
they live with *B* less and less, ,, 9
'But now thy *b* flows away, *Mariana in the S.* 67
I loved his *b* passing well. *The Sisters* 23
love *B* only (*B* seen In all varieties *To—— With Pal. of Art* 6
And Knowledge for its *b* ; ,, 8
Good only for its *b*, seeing not That *B*, Good, and Knowledge, are three sisters ,, 9
B and anguish walking hand in hand *D. of F. Women* 15
'I had great *b* : ask thou not my name : ,, 93
B such a mistress of the world. *Gardener's D.* 58
Her *b* grew ; till Autumn brought ,, 207
many a group Of *beauties*, *Talking Oak* 62
glorious in his *b* and thy choice, *Tithonus* 12
Can thy love, Thy *b*, make amends, ,, 24
Thou wilt renew thy *b* morn by morn ; ,, 74
Her constant *b* doth inform Stillness *Day-Dm. Sleep. B.* 15
His wife a faded *b* of the Baths, *Aylmer's Field* 27
Edith, whose pensive *b*, perfect else, ,, 70
made pleasant the baits Of gold and *b*, ,, 487
sank down shamed At all that *b* ; *Lucretius* 64
murmurs of her *b* from the South, *Princess i* 36
All *b* compass'd in a female form, ,, *ii* 34
beauties every shade of brown and fair ,, 437
underneath the crag, Full of all *b*. ,, *iii* 337
brief the moon of *b* in the South. ,, *iv.* 113
Another kind of *b* in detail ,, 448
We hunt them for the *b* of their skins ; ,, *v* 156
became Her former *b* treble ; ,, *vii* 25
All of *b*, all of use, *Ode. Inter. Exhib.* 23
Willy, my *b*, my eldest-born, *Grandmother* 9
So Willy has gone, my *b*, my eldest-born, ,, 101
She's a *b* thou thinks— *N. Farmer, N. S.* 14
—wot's a *b* ?—the flower as blaws. ,, 15
Maäybe she warn't a *b* :— ,, 23
His *b* still with his years increased, *The Victim* 34
this orb of flame, Fantastic *b* ; *In Mem. xxxiv* 6
Who shall rail Against her *b* ? ,, *cxiv* 2
of the singular *b* of Maud ; *Maud I i* 67
Done but in thought to your *b*, ,, *iii* 6
O child, you wrong your *b*, ,, *iv* 17
and *B* fair in her flower ; ,, 25

Beggar (s) (*continued*) I am a *b* born,' she said, — *Lady Clare* 71
her, he loved, a *b*: then he pray'd — *Enoch Arden* 117
tho' she were a *b* from the hedge, — *Marr. of Geraint* 230
fling free alms into the *b's* bowl, — *Ancient Sage* 260
And a *b* began to cry, 'Food, food — *Voice spake, etc.* 5
Beggar'd and I fell *B* for ever— — *Lover's Tale i* 670
Beggar Maid Bare-footed came the *b m* — *Beggar Maid* 3
'This *b m* shall be my queen!' — ,, 16
Beggar-Woman silken rag, the *b-w's* weed: — *Geraint and E.* 680
Begged then they *b* For Father Philip — *Enoch Arden* 364
At last she *b* a boon, — *Princess i* 146
Begin fret Of that sharp-headed worm *b's* — *Supp. Confessions* 186
And rugged barks *b* to bud, — *My life is full* 18
That to *b* implies to end; — *Two Voices* 339
When meres *b* to uncongeal, — ,, 407
call me loud when the day *b's* to break: — *May Queen* 10
O look! the sun *b's* to rise, — *May Queen, Con.*, 49
lights *b* to twinkle from the rocks: — *Ulysses* 54
B's to move and tremble. — *Will Water.* 32
Till the graves *b* to move, And the dead *b* to dance. — *Vision of Sin* 165
B's the scandal and the cry: — *You might have won* 16
Which made a selfish war *b*; — *To F. D. Maurice* 30
The noise of life *b's* again, — *In Mem. vii* 10
From whence clear memory may *b*, — ,, *xlv* 10
overhead *B's* the clash and clang — ,, *Con.* 61
sadder age *b's* To war against — *Gareth and L.* 1129
b's to play That air which pleased her — *Lover's Tale i* 20
an' saw she *b's* to cry, — *North. Cobbler* 71
Evelyn *b's* it 'O diviner Air.' — *Sisters (E. and E.)* 4
listen how the birds *B* to warble — *The Flight* 61
Beginner fair *b's* of a nobler time, — *Com. of Arthur* 457
Beginning (part.) world's great work is heard *B*, — *In Mem. cxxi* 11
B to faint in the light that she loves — *Maud I xxii* 9
B at the sequel know no more. — *Lover's Tale iv* 158
And he *b* languidly— — ,, 274
The boat was *b* to move, — *First Quarrel* 21
Beginning (s) end and the *b* vex His reason: — *Two Voices* 298
blind *b's* that have made me man, — *Lucretius* 246
break The low *b's* of content. — *In Mem. lxxxiv* 48
And be the fair *b* of a time. — *Guinevere* 466
Begone 'You must *b*,' said Death, — *Love and Death* 7
B: we will not look upon you more. — *Princess iv* 547
B! my knave!—belike and like — *Gareth and L.* 713
thou *b*, take counsel, and away, — ,, 1002
Begotten (*See also* **Want-begotten**) My father hath *b* me in his wrath. — *Balin and Balan* 283
Beguile To *b* her melancholy; — *Maud I xx* 3
Beguil'd well, well, well, I *may* be *b* — ,, *vi* 89
Begun help me as when life *b*: — *Locksley Hall* 185
into my heart, and *b* to darken my eyes. — *Rizpah* 16
My brain had *b* to reel— — *In the Child. Hosp.* 60
A juster epoch has *b*. — *Epilogue* 6
The light of days when life *b*, — *Pref. Poem Broth. S.* 23
Altho' the months have scarce *b*, — *To Ulysses* 22
this bare dome had not *b* to gleam — *To Mary Boyle* 41
O weary one, has it *b*? — *The Dreamer* 26
Beheld *b* Thy mild deep eyes upraised, — *Supp. Confessions* 73
I *b* great Herè's angry eyes, — *Œnone* 190
Since I *b* young Laurence dead. — *L. C. V. de Vere* 28
ere a star can wink, *b* her there. — *Gardener's D.* 122
I *b* her ere she knew my heart, — ,, 276
when the boy *b* His mother, — *Dora* 137
B the dead flame of the fallen day — *Enoch Arden* 441
b His wife his wife no more, — ,, 758
Turning *b* the Powers of the House — *Aylmer's Field* 287
I *b* her, when she rose The yesternight, — *Princess v* 175
The Priest *b* him, And cried — *The Victim* 37
And what I am *b* again — *In Mem. cxxiv* 21
b The death-white curtain drawn; — *Maud I xiv* 33
I *b* From eye to eye thro' all their Order — *Com. of Arthur* 269
likewise I *b* Excalibur — ,, 295
when her son *B* his only way to glory — *Gareth and L.* 159
b Far over heads in that long-vaulted — ,, 318
B the long street of a little town — *Marr. of Geraint* 242

Beheld (*continued*) Geraint *B* her first in field, — *Marr. of Geraint* 540
Turn'd, and *b* the four, and all — ,, 558
b A little town with towers, — *Geraint and E.* 196
I never yet *b* a thing so pale. — ,, 615
Have I *b* a lily like yourself. — ,, 620
true eyes *B* the man you loved — ,, 847
b Balin and Balan sitting Statuelike, — *Balin and Balan* 23
B before a golden altar lie — ,, 410
B the Queen and Lancelot get to horse. — *Merlin and V.* 102
b the King Charge at the head — *Lancelot and E.* 303
Arthur, who *b* his cloudy brows, — ,, 1354
every knight *b* his fellow's face — *Holy Grail* 191
Another hath *b* it afar off, — ,, 897
b That victor of the Pagan — *Last Tournament* 664
b three spirits mad with joy — *Guinevere* 252
B at noon in some delicious dale — ,, 393
glancing up *b* the holy nuns All round her, — ,, 666
some *b* the faces of old ghosts — *Pass. of Arthur* 103
When I *b* her weep so ruefully; — *Lover's Tale i* 773
b All round about him that which — ,, *iv* 53
never yet *b* a thing so strange, — ,, 303
when before have Gods or men *b* The Life — *Demeter and P.* 29
b A blood-red awning waver — *St. Telemachus* 51
Behest Then not to disobey her lord's *b*, — *Geraint and E.* 450
Behold Where'er they fell, *b*, Like to — *The Poet* 22
'*B*, it is the Sabbath morn.' — *Two Voices* 402
B this fruit, whose gleaming rind — *Œnone* 72
Mayst well *b* them unbeheld, — ,, 89
when I look'd again, *b* an arm, — *M. d'Arthur* 158
B her there, As I beheld her — *Gardener's D.* 275
'Who is this? *b* thy bride,' — *Love and Duty* 49
some one spake: '*B*! it was a crime — *Vision of Sin* 213
In such a shape dost thou *b* thy God. — *Aylmer's Field* 657
in me *b* the Prince Your countryman, — *Princess ii* 214
B your father's letter.' — ,, *iv* 468
reverent people *b* The towering car, — *Ode on Well.* 54
'*B* the man that loved and lost, — *In Mem. i* 15
B me, for I cannot sleep, — ,, *vii* 6
B a man raised up by Christ! — ,, *xxxi* 13
An inner trouble I *b*, — ,, *xli* 18
B, we know not anything; — ,, *liv* 13
B their brides in other hands; — ,, *xc* 14
B, I dream a dream of good, — ,, *cxxix* 11
O happy hour, *b* the bride — ,, *Con.* 69
Arthur said, '*B* thy doom is mine. — *Com. of Arthur* 467
'*B*, for these have sworn To wage my wars, — ,, 507
did Enid, keeping watch, *b* — *Geraint and E.* 118
B me overturn and trample on him. — ,, 843
b me come To cleanse this common — ,, 894
father, I *b* him in my dreams — *Lancelot and E.* 763
B it, crying, 'We have still a King.' — *Holy Grail* 245
b a woman at a door Spinning; — ,, 391
when they led me into hall, *b*, — ,, 577
looking up, *B*, the enchanted towers — ,, 813
'In happy time *b* our pilot-star! — *Pelleas and E.* 63
'*B* me, Lady, A prisoner, — ,, 240
B his horse and armour. — ,, 373
b This day my Queen of Beauty — *Last Tournament* 208
Till the High God *b* it from beyond, — *Pass. of Arthur* 16
B, I seem but King among the dead.' — ,, 146
when I look'd again, *b* an arm, — ,, 326
in her *b* Of all my treasures — *Lover's Tale iv* 317
Behind this darkness, I *b* her still, — *Tiresias* 52
when these *b* their Lord, — *Akbar's Dream* 142
Beholden But being so *b* to the Prince, — *Marr. of Geraint* 623
shame the Prince To whom we are *b*; — ,, 727
Beholding *B* how the years which are not Time's — *Aylmer's Field* 601
B one so bright in dark estate, — *Marr. of Geraint* 786
B how ye butt against my wish, — *Geraint and E.* 677
B it was Edyrn son of Nudd, — ,, 781
b her Tho' pale, yet happy, — ,, 879
b him so strong, she thought — *Pelleas and E.* 117
Behoof break them more in their *b*, — *Princess vi* 61
To mask, tho' but in his own *b*, — *Maud I vi* 48
Being changes should control Our *b*, — *Love thou thy land* 42

Being (*continued*) all the current of my b sets to thee.' *Locksley Hall* 24
and spoils My bliss in b ; *Lucretius* 222
No Angel, but a dearer b, *Princess vii* 320
Her peaceful b slowly passes by *Requiescat* 7
And all the wheels of B slow. *In Mem. l* 4
His b working in mine own, *In Mem. lxxxv* 43
And strike his b into bounds, ,, *Con.* 124
b he loved best in all the world, *Geraint and E.* 103
and he felt his b move In music *Balin and Balan* 211
glad new-year Of B, which with earliest *Lover's Tale i* 282
Beknaved Gareth following was again b. *Gareth and L.* 786
Bel Till the face of B be brighten'd, *Boädicea* 16
Belabour'd so b him on rib and cheek *Princess v* 341
Belaud blush to b myself a moment— *Hendecasyllabics* 18
Beldam Then glided a vulturous B forth, *Dead Prophet* 25
Beleaguerer Blown by the fierce b's of a town, *Achilles over the T.* 20
Belfry white owl in the b sits. (repeat) *The Owl I.* 7, 14
Low breezes fann'd the b bars, *The Letters* 43
Belied liars b in the hubbub of lies ; *Maud I iv* 51
Belief Think my b would stronger grow ! *Supp. Confessions* 13
but my b In all this matter— *Com. of Arthur* 183
Beyond mine old b in womanhood, *Lancelot and E.* 955
I am quicker of b Than you believe me, ,, 1204
and he believed in her b. *Holy Grail* 165
or that which most Enchains b, *Lover's Tale ii* 134
Believable that he sinn'd is not b ; *Merlin and V.* 760
Believe (*See also* **Make-believes**) Why not b then ? *Supp. Confessions* 123
But I b she wept. *Talking Oak* 164
I b, if you were fast my wife, *Enoch Arden* 414
Save Christ as we b him— *Aylmer's Field* 573
Gods there are, for all men so b. *Lucretius* 117
there is iron in the blood, And I b it. *Princess vi* 231
we b him Something far advanced *Ode on Well.* 274
nor b me Too presumptuous, *Hendecasyllabics* 15
I heard a voice, 'b no more' *In Mem. cxxiv* 10
you wrong your beauty, b it, *Maud I iv* 17
Shall I b him ashamed to be seen ? ,, *xiii* 25
I well b You be of Arthur's Table,' *Gareth and L.* 835
I do b yourself against yourself, *Geraint and E.* 744
world will not b a man repents : ,, 900
I well b this damsel, and the one *Balin and Balan* 612
we b all evil of thy Mark— *Merlin and V.* 93
and half b her true : ,, 186
I well b that all about this world ,, 541
I well b she tempted them and fail'd, ,, 819
I might b you then, Who knows ? ,, 922
noble it is, I well b, the noblest— *Lancelot and E,* 361
if I could b the things you say ,, 1097
I may not well b that you b.' ,, 1196
I am quicker of belief Than you b me, ,, 1205
with him, to b as he believed. *Holy Grail* 487
Our Lady says it, and we well b : ,, 604
greatest hardly will b he saw ; ,, 896
lie to me : I b. Will ye not lie ? *Last Tournament* 645
I should all as soon b that his, *Guinevere* 350
to b it—'tis so sweet a thought, *Lover's Tale i* 275
can well b, for he look'd so coarse *In the Child. Hosp.* 7
'O soul of little faith, slow to b ! *Columbus* 147
who b These hard memorials ,, 195
speak the truth that no man may b.' *Tiresias* 50
were used to b everlasting would die : *Despair* 54
Did *he* b it ? did you ask him ? *The Ring* 225
That no man would b. *Mechanophilus* 28
Believed The woman cannot be b. *The Letters* 32
b This filthy marriage-hindering *Aylmer's Field* 373
when he came again, his flock b— ,, 600
and saw, but scarce b *Sea Dreams* 34
often she b that I should die : *Princess vii* 100
I b that in the living world My spirit ,, 157
Queen b that when her son *Gareth and L.* 158
Not less Geraint b it ; *Marr. of Geraint* 28
I b myself Unconquerable, *Geraint and E.* 835
He spoke, and Enid easily b, ,, 874
and half b her true, (repeat) *Merlin and V.* 400, 893

Believed (*continued*) and he b in her belief. *Holy Grail* 165
One with him, to believe as he b. ,, 487
in vows when men b the King ! *Last Tournament* 649
every knight B himself a greater ,, 677
we b her asleep again— *In the Child. Hosp.* 69
And if I b in a God, I would *Despair* 70
Believing B where we cannot prove ; *In Mem., Pro.,* 4
own soul to hers, B her ; *Pelleas and E.* 84
B, 'lo mine helpmate, one to feel *Guinevere* 485
Only, b I loved Edith, *Sisters (E. and E.)* 138
b that the girl's Lean fancy, *The Ring* 335
people b that Peelè the Goddess *Kapiolani* 8
Bell (*See also* **Ankle-bells, Bindweed-bell, Chapel Bell, Church-bell, Flower-bells, Marriage-bell**) Nine times goes the passing b : *All Things will Die* 35
dropping low their crimson b's Half-closed, *Arabian Nights* 62
with white b's the clover-hill swells *Sea-Fairies* 14
The bridle b's rang merrily *L. of Shalott iii* 13
The foxglove cluster dappled b's.' *Two Voices* 72
The sweet church b's began to peal. ,, 408
in the towers I placed great b's that swung, *Palace of Art* 129
those great b's Began to chime. ,, 157
midnight b's cease ringing suddenly, *D. of F. Women* 247
At this a hundred b's began to peal, *M. d'Arthur, Ep.,* 29
sound of funeral or of marriage b's ; *Gardener's D.* 36
from them clash'd The b's ; we listen'd ; ,, 221
when the b's were ringing, Allan call'd *Dora* 41
I do not hear the b's upon my cap, *Edwin Morris* 56
blow The sound of minster b's. *Talking Oak* 272
shrill b rings, the censer swings, *Sir Galahad* 35
There comes a sound of marriage b's. *The Letters* 48
were wed, and merrily rang the b's, (repeat) *Enoch Arden* 80, 511
Merrily rang the b's and they were wed ,, 512
heard the pealing of his parish b's ; ,, 615
hark the b For dinner, let us go !' *Princess ii* 432
the chapel b's Call'd us : we left ,, 470
half open'd b of the woods ! ,, *vi* 193
like a b Toll'd by an earthquake ,, 331
Let the b be toll'd : (repeat) *Ode on Well.* 53, 58
Clash, ye b's, in the merry March air ! *W. to Alexandra* 18
Saäint's daäy—they was ringing the b's. *N. Farmer, N. S.* 13
'lights and rings the gateway b, *In Mem. viii* 3
I hear the b struck in the night : ,, *x* 2
The Christmas b's from hill to hill ,, *xxviii* 3
Before I heard those b's again : ,, 16
The merry merry b's of Yule. ,, 20
One set slow b will seem to toll ,, *lvii* 10
A single peal of b's below, ,, *civ* 5
That these are not the b's I know. ,, 8
Ring out, wild b's, to the wild sky, ,, *cvi* 1
Ring, happy b's, across the snow : ,, 6
The dead leaf trembles to the b's. ,, *Con.* 64
Is cap and b's for a fool. *Maud I vi* 62
Not a b was rung, not a prayer was read ; ,, *II v* 24
she tower'd ; her b's, Tone under tone, *Merlin and V.* 131
ye, that follow but the leader's b' *Holy Grail* 298
thence at intervals A low b tolling. *Lover's Tale ii* 83
came on me The hollow tolling of the b, ,, *iii* 10
by slow degrees the sullen b Toll'd quicker, ,, 13
Four b's instead of one began to ring, ,, 20
Four merry b's, four merry marriage-bells, ,, 21
b's Lapsed into frightful stillness ; ,, 29
again the b's Jangled and clang'd : ,, 52
the b's, Those marriage-bells, ,, *iv* 2
Heard yet once more the tolling b, ,, 29
we heard them a-ringing the b, *First Quarrel* 21
butted each other with clashing of b's, *V. of Maeldune* 108
the clash and boom of the b's rang ,, 110
The tolling of his funeral b *Tiresias* 192
Ring little b's of change *Early Spring* 41
b's that rang without a hand, *The Ring* 411
where the loyal b's Clash welcome— ,, 482
Bridal b's with tolling ! . . . *Forlorn* 70
A spike of half-accomplish'd b's— *To Ulysses* 24
lin-lan-lone of evening b's Far-far-away. *Far-far-away* 5

Bell (*continued*) Faith and Work were *b's* of full accord, *In Mem., W. G. Ward* 2
many a pendent *b* and fragrant star, *Death of Œnone* 13
people ring the *b* from love to Thee. *Akbar's Dream, Inscrip.* 4
in praise of Whom The Christian *b*, *Akbar's Dream* 149
Twilight and evening *b*, *Crossing the Bar* 9
Bell'd *See* **Milky-Bell'd**
Bellerophon White Rose, *B*, the Jilt, *The Brook* 161
Bellicent (Queen) the Queen of Orkney, *B*, (repeat) *Com. of Arthur* 190, 245
last tall son of Lot and *B*, *Gareth and L.* 1
Then *B* bemoan'd herself and said, ,, 72
son Of old King Lot and good Queen *B*, ,, 1231
Belling Last in a roky hollow, *b*, heard *Last Tournament* 502
Bell-like many a deep-hued *b-l* flower *Eleänore* 37
Bell-mouth'd whom the *b-m* glass had wrought, *Princess iv* 155
Bellow'd (*See also* **Beäl'd**) ever overhead *B* the tempest, *Merlin and V.* 957
Bellowing (*See also* **A-bealin', Hollower-bellowing**) *B* victory, *b* doom : *Ode on Well.* 66
b thro' the darkness on to dawn, *Gareth and L.* 177
Hell burst up your harlot roofs *B*, *Pelleas and E.* 467
Bellringer Friars, *b's*, Parish-clerks— *Sir J. Oldcastle* 160
Belong'd booöks, I ha' see'd 'em, *b* to the Squire, *Village Wife* 71
an' 'is gells es *b* to the land ; ,, 112
my Fathers *b* to the church of old, *The Wreck* 1
Belonging things *b* to thy peace and ours ! *Aylmer's Field* 740
I knew it—Of and *b* to me, *Lucretius* 44
Beloved (*See also* **Much-beloved, Well-beloved**) *Revered, b—O you that hold* *To the Queen* 1
O this world's curse,—*b* but hated— *Love and Duty* 47
For love reflects the thing *b* ; *In Mem. lii* 2
Maud the *b* of my mother, *Maud I i* 72
the liquid note *b* of men Comes *Marr. of Geraint* 336
friend, the neighbour, Lionel, the *b*, *Lover's Tale i* 653
b for a kindliness Rare in Fable *On Jub. Q. Victoria* 4
This ring 'Io t'amo' to his best *b*, *The Ring* 210
Belt (s) (*See also* **Blossom-belt, Sword-belt**) A gleaming crag with *b's* of pines. *Two Voices* 189
Unclasp'd the wedded eagles of her *b*, *Godiva* 43
glories of the broad *b* of the world, *Enoch Arden* 579
A *b*, it seem'd, of luminous vapour, *Sea Dreams* 209
ridge Of breaker issued from the *b*, ,, 212
same as that Living within the *b*) ,, 216
past into the *b* and swell'd again ,, 222
Half-lost in *b's* of hop and breadths of wheat ; *Princess, Con.*, 45
From *b* to *b* of crimson seas *In Mem. lxxxvi* 13
By summer *b's* of wheat and vine ,, *xcviii* 4
a mighty purse, Hung at his *b*, *Geraint and E.* 23
seem a sword beneath a *b* of three, *Merlin and V.* 510
faltering sideways downward to her *b*, ,, 850
crimson in the *b* a strange device, *Holy Grail* 154
round thee, maiden, bind my *b*. ,, 159
Belt (verb) woods that *b* the gray hill-side, *Ode to Memory* 55
and from the woods That *b* it rise *Lover's Tale i* 536
deeps that *b* the changeful West, *Prog. of Spring* 98
Belt (built) an' *b* long afoor my daäy *Owd Roä* 21
Belted with puff'd cheek the *b* hunter blew *Palace of Art* 63
B his body with her white embrace, *Last Tournament* 513
Bemoan'd Then Bellicent *b* herself and said, *Gareth and L.* 72
Bench Jack on his ale-house *b* has as many *Maud I iv* 9
I saw, No *b* nor table, painting *Holy Grail* 829
Down on a *b*, hard-breathing. *Pelleas and E.* 592
Bench'd stately theatres *B* crescent-wise. *Princess ii* 370
Bencher wrinkled *b's* often talk'd of him *Aylmer's Field* 473
Bend chafes me that I could not *b* One will ; *D. of F. Women* 137
How sweet are looks that ladies *b* *Sir Galahad* 13
fathers *b* Above more graves, *In Mem. xcviii* 15
On me she *b's* her blissful eyes ,, *Con.* 29
tyranny now should *b* or cease, *Maud III vi* 20
O ay—the winds that *b* the brier ! *Last Tournament* 731
Bending erect, but *b* from his height *Aylmer's Field* 119
b by the cradle of her babe. *The Ring* 415
Bengal For which, in branding summers of *B*, *The Brook* 16
Bent lowly *b* With melodious airs *Adeline* 54

Bent (*continued*) From yon blue heavens above us *b* *L. C. V. de Vere* 50
b or broke The lithe reluctant boughs *Enoch Arden* 380
b as he was To make disproof of scorn, *Aylmer's Field* 445
Nor *b*, nor broke, nor shunn'd *Princess, Pro.*, 38
seal was Cupid *b* above a scroll, ,, *i* 242
B their broad faces toward us ,, *iv* 551
Her head a little *b* ; and on her mouth ,, *vi* 269
The King *b* low, with hand on brow, *The Victim* 53
a straight staff *b* in a pool ; *High. Pantheism* 16
thrice as large as man he *b* To greet *In Mem. ciii* 42
either spear *B* but not brake, *Gareth and L.* 964
b he seem'd on going the third day, *Marr. of Geraint* 604
B as he seem'd on going this third day, ,, 625
since her mind was *b* On hearing, *Pelleas and E.* 114
round him *b* the spirits of the hills *Guinevere* 283
but he *B* o'er me, and my neck *Lover's Tale i* 690
so feeble : she *b* above me, too ; ,, 693
the mast *b* and the ravin wind ,, *ii* 170
And the pikes were all broken or *b*, *The Revenge* 80
Bow'd the spoiler, *B* the Scotsman, *Batt. of Brunanburh* 21
The plowman passes, *b* with pain, *Ancient Sage* 144
Bequeath'd This ring *b* you by your mother, *The Ring* 75
Bereave nothing can *b* him Of the force *Ode on Well.* 272
Berg goes, like glittering *b's* of ice, *Princess iv* 71
Berkshire weed the white horse on the *B* hills *Geraint and E.* 936
Berried about my feet The *b* briony fold.' *Talking Oak* 148
Berry With bunch and *b* and flower *Œnone* 102
red *berries* charm the bird, *Gareth and L.* 85
With ever-scattering *berries*, and on *Last Tournament* 173
Married among the red *berries*, *First Quarrel* 40
and the branch with *berries* on it, *Columbus* 73
And the crimson and scarlet of *berries* *V. of Maeldune* 61
But in every *b* and fruit was the ,, 62
Clomb the mountain, and flung the *berries*, *Kapiolani* 6
handle or gather the *berries* of Peelè ! ,, 20
Into the flame-billow dash'd the *berries*, ,, 33
Beryl sardius, Chrysolite, *b*, topaz, *Columbus* 85
Beseech I do *b* you by the love you bear *Enoch Arden* 307
Beseem might well *b* His princess, *Marr. of Geraint* 758
Beseem'd true answer, as *b* Thy fëalty, *M. d'Arthur* 74
true answer, as *b* Thy fëalty, *Pass. of Arthur* 242
Besiege so *b's* her To break her will, *Gareth and L.* 616
Besieged (*See also* **Strait-Besieged**) *b* Ygerne within Tintagil, *Com. of Arthur* 198
Besotted A drowning life, *b* in sweet self, *Princess vii* 314
So far *b* that they fail to see *Balin and Balan* 359
Besought *B* him, supplicating, if he cared *Enoch Arden* 163
the knight *b* him, 'Follow me, *Geraint and E.* 807
B Lavaine to write as she devised *Lancelot and E.* 1103
B me to be plain and blunt, ,, 1301
Bess (horse) Black *B*, Tantivy, Tallyho, *The Brook* 160
Bess (Christian name) MILK for my sweet-'arts, *B* ! *Spinster's S's.* 1
Mew ! mew !—*B* wi' the milk ! ,, 113
I says 'I'd be good to tha, *B*, *Owd Roä* 75
Bessy Marris 'bout *B M's* barne. *N. Farmer, O. S.* 14
B M's barne ! tha knaws she laäid ,, 21
Best (*See also* **Earthly-best, Heavenly-best**) at *b* A vague suspicion of the breast : *Two Voices* 335
they say : Kind nature is the *b* : *Walk to the Mail* 64
b That ever came from pipe. *Will Water.* 75
He gave the people of his *b* : *You might have won* 25
His worst he kept, his *b* he gave. ,, 26
You chose the *b* among us—a strong man : *Enoch Arden* 293
Their *b* and brightest, when they dwelt *Aylmer's Field* 69
so true that second thoughts are *b* ? *Sea Dreams* 65
Arising, did his holy oily *b*, ,, 195
sit the *b* and stateliest of the land ? *Lucretius* 172
who love *b* have *b* the grace to know *W. to Marie Alex.* 28
I could have wept with the *b*. (repeat) *Grandmother* 20, 100
fur them as 'as it's the *b*. *N. Farmer, N. S.* 44
And do their little *b* to bite *Lit. Squabbles* 6
And cancell'd nature's *b* : *In Mem. lxxii* 20
Fair words were *b* for him who fights *Gareth and L.* 946
as the stateliest and the *b* *Marr. of Geraint* 20
my dear child is set forth at her *b*, ,, 728

Best (*continued*) arms for guerdon; choose the *b*.' — *Geraint and E.* 218
desired the humbling of their *b*, — ,, 637
fairest and the *b* Of ladies living — *Balin and Balan* 339
I, and all, As fairest, *b* and purest, — ,, 350
I have seen; but *b*, *B*, purest? — ,, 356
From homage to the *b* and purest, — ,, 376
women, worst and *b*, as Heaven and Hell. — *Merlin and V.* 815
Win shall I not, but do my *b* to win: — *Lancelot and E.* 221
Young as I am, yet would I do my *b*.' — ,, 222
with meats and vintage of their *b* — ,, 266
Lives for his children, ever at its *b* — ,, 336
when they love their *b*, Closest — ,, 869
she deem'd she look'd her *b*, — ,, 907
having loved God's *b* And greatest, — ,, 1093
'Let love be free; free love is for the *b*: — ,, 1381
What should be *b*, if not so pure a love — ,, 1383
Arthur kept his *b* until the last; — *Holy Grail* 763
'Then,' I said, 'I'm none o' the *b*.' — *First Quarrel* 61
he would have been one of his *b*. — *Rizpah* 28
our Lawrence the *b* of the brave: — *Def. of Lucknow* 11
their marksmen were told of our *b*, — ,, 19
sees the *B* that glimmers thro' the Worst, — *Ancient Sage* 72
an' I knaws it be all fur the *b*. — *Spinster's S's.* 52
Is girlish talk at *b*; — *Epilogue* 43
rank with the *b*, Garrick — *To W. C. Macreday* 6
so fickle are men—the *b*! — *The Ring* 392
and body is foul at *b*. — *Happy* 28
Phra-Chai, the Shadow of the *B*, — *To Ulysses* 41
The *b* in me that sees the worst in me, — *Romney's R.* 44
the Highest is the wisest and the *b*, — *Faith* 1

Bestial Courteous or *b* from the moment, — *Gareth and L.* 631
Best-natured 'Which was prettiest, *B-n*?' — *Princess i* 234
Bestrode he *b* my Grandsire, when he fell, — ,, *ii* 242
Bethink *B* thee, Lord, while thou and all — *St. S. Stylites* 105
Bethlehem Not least art thou, thou little *B* In Judah, — *Sir J. Oldcastle* 24
Bethought Then she *b* her of a faded silk, — *Marr. of Geraint* 134
and *b* her of her promise given — ,, 602
b her how she used to watch, — ,, 647
Betide All-arm'd I ride, whate'er *b*, — *Sir Galahad* 83
I meet my fate, whatever ills *b*! — *The Flight* 95
Betray wouldst *b* me for the precious hilt; — *M. d'Arthur* 126
Break lock and seal: *b* the trust: — *You might have won* 18
They know me not. I should *b* myself. — *Enoch Arden* 789
and said, '*B* me not, but help— — *Pelleas and E.* 360
Simpler than any child, *b's* itself. — *Guinevere* 371
wouldst *b* me for the precious hilt; — *Pass. of Arthur* 294
you knew that he meant to *b* me— — *Charity* 12
Betray'd 'Thou hast *b* thy nature and thy name, — *M. d'Arthur* 73
B my secret penance, so that all — *St. S. Stylites* 68
let them know themselves *b*; — *Aylmer's Field* 524
b her cause and mine— — *Princess v* 76
'Thou hast *b* thy nature and thy name, — *Pass. of Arthur* 241
Betraying statesman there, *b* His party-secret, — *Maud II v* 34
Betrothed (*See also* **Long-betroth'd**) her far-off cousin and *b*, — *The Brook* 75
b To one, a neighbouring Princess: — *Princess i* 32
I spake of why we came, And my *b*. — ,, 120
B us over their wine, — *Maud I xix* 39
Betrothment how the strange *b* was to end: — *Princess v* 474
Betted they *b*; made a hundred friends, — *Princess, Pro.* 163
Better how much *b* than to own A crown, — *Ode to Memory* 120
Were it not *b* not to be?' — *Two Voices* 3
Is boundless *b*, boundless worse. — ,, 27
Surely 'twere *b* not to be. — ,, 48
'Twere *b* not to breathe or speak, — ,, 94
A murmur, 'Be of *b* cheer.' — ,, 429
'Twere *b* I should cease Although — *To J. S.* 66
are men *b* than sheep or goats — *M. d'Arthur* 250
Something *b* than his dog, — *Locksley Hall* 50
B thou wert dead before me, — ,, 56
B thou and I were lying, — ,, 57
held it *b* men should perish one by one, — ,, 179
B to me the meanest weed — *Amphion* 93

Better (*continued*) griefs Like his have worse or *b*, — *Enoch Arden* 741
B not be at all Than not be noble. — *Princess ii* 93
B to clear prime forests, — ,, *iii* 127
Methinks he seems no *b* than a girl; — ,, 218
You hold the woman is the *b* man; — ,, *iv* 410
Almost our maids were *b* at their homes, — ,, *v* 428
b or worse Than the heart of the citizen — *Maud I i* 23
peace or war? *b*, war! loud war — ,, 47
far *b* to be born To labour — *Maud I xviii* 33
myself have awaked, as it seems, to the *b* mind; — ,, *III vi* 56
It is *b* to fight for the good — ,, 57
A worse were *b*; yet no worse would I. — *Gareth and L.* 17
But truly foul are *b*, for they send — ,, 947
b were I laid in the dark earth, — *Marr. of Geraint* 97
sigh'd 'Was I not *b* there with him?' — *Balin and Balan* 292
b have died Thrice than have ask'd — *Merlin and V.* 918
B the King's waste hearth and — *Guinevere* 524
are men *b* than sheep or goats — *Pass. of Arthur* 418
b that than his, than he The friend, — *Lover's Tale i* 652
B have sent Our Edith thro' — *Sisters (E. and E.)* 224
B a rotten borough or so — *Riflemen form!* 17
Go, therefore, thou! thy *b's* went — *Will Water.* 185
Thine elders and thy *b's*. — ,, 192
Thy *b* born unhappily from thee, — *Aylmer's Field* 675
in the distance pealing news Of *b*, — *Princess iv* 82
My brother and my *b*, this man here, — *Balin and Balan* 54
By striking at her *b*, miss'd, — *Merlin and V.* 499
That they had the *b* In perils of battle — *Batt. of Brunanburh* 84
And then I will let you a *b*.' — *By an Evolution.* 4
ever cared to *b* his own kind, — *Sea Dreams* 201
his work, That practice *b's*?' — *Princess iii* 299
voice that—you scarce could *b* that. — *Sisters (E. and E.)* 14
B fifty years of Europe than a cycle — *Locksley Hall* 184
for I love him all the *b* for it— — *Enoch Arden* 196
B the waste Atlantic roll'd On her — *Third of Feb.* 21
For himself has done much *b*. — *Spiteful Letter* 4
I loved him *b* than play; — *First Quarrel* 12
an' I loved him *b* than all. — ,, 14
I had *b* ha' put my naked hand in a hornets' nest. — ,, 50
you had *b* ha' beaten me black an' blue — ,, 72

Bettering ill for him who, *b* not with time, — *Will* 10
Beugh (bough) togither like birds on a *b*; — *North. Cobbler* 54
Beverley Burnt too, my faithful preacher, *B*! — *Sir J. Oldcastle* 80
Bevy a *b* of Eroses apple-cheek'd, — *The Islet* 11
Bewail Let golden youth *b* the friend, — *To Mary Boyle* 53
Bewail'd maidens with one mind *B* their lot; — *In Mem. ciii* 46
Beware *b* Lest, where you seek — *Princess, vi* 171
Bewitch'd thaw it wur summat *b* — *North. Cobbler* 82
Bib their bottles o' pap, an' their mucky *b's*, — *Spinster's S's.* 87
Bible oft at *B* meetings, o'er the rest — *Sea Dreams* 194
read me a *B* verse of the Lord's good will — *Rizpah* 61
But as a Latin *B* to the crowd; — *Sir J. Oldcastle* 18
Bicker To *b* down a valley. — *The Brook* 26
And *b's* into red and emerald, — *Princess v* 263
men may *b* with the things they love, — *Geraint and E.* 325
and the points of lances *b* in it. — ,, 449
Bicker'd Flicker'd and *b* From helmet — *Merlin and the G.* 70
Bid Friends, I was *b* to speak of such a one — *Aylmer's Field* 677
of him I was not *b* to speak— — ,, 710
lest I should *b* thee live; — *Princess vii* 9
Dare I *b* her abide by her word? — *Maud I xvi* 25
b him bring Charger and palfrey.' — *Geraint and E.* 400
my dear lord arise and *b* me do it, — ,, 665
And *b* me cast it. — ,, 707
we shall never *b* again Goodmorrow— — *Balin and Balan* 622
I *b* the stranger welcome. — *Merlin and V.* 270
She needs must *b* farewell to sweet Lavaine. — *Lancelot and E.* 341
and *b* call the ghostly man Hither, — ,, 1099
Send! *b* him come;' but Lionel was away— — *Lover's Tale iv* 101
when he came to *b* me goodbye. — *First Quarrel* 78
I had *b* him my last goodbye; — *Rizpah* 41
Edith wrote: 'My mother *b's* me ask' — *Sisters (E. and E.)* 181
Not there to *b* my boy farewell, — *To Marq. of Dufferin* 42
as 'ull hallus do as 'e's *b*.' — *Owd Roä* 79
B him farewell for me, and tell him— — *Romney's R.* 147

Bidden I knock'd and, *b*, enter'd; *Princess iii* 130
Rise!' and the damsel *b* rise arose *Merlin and V.* 68
The foot that loiters, *b* go,— *Last Tournament* 117
Bidding *b* him Disband himself, and scatter *Geraint and E.* 797
And in my vision *b* me dream on, *Lover's Tale ii* 119
Bide 'Were this not well, to *b* mine hour, *Two Voices* 76
Will you not *b* your year as I *b* mine?' *Enoch Arden* 438
Philip answer'd 'I will *b* my year.' ,, 439
why she should *B* by this issue: *Princess v* 326
bound am I to *b* with thee.' *Gareth and L.* 805
B ye here the while. *Merlin and V.* 97
'Go! I *b* the while.' ,, 99
To whom the Lord of Astolat, '*B* with us, *Lancelot and E.* 632
if I *b*, lo! this wild flower for me!' ,, 644
B,' answer'd he: 'we needs must hear ,, 756
I cannot *b* Sir Baby. *Pelleas and E.* 190
yourselves: how can ye *b* at peace, ,, 265
But never let me *b* one hour at peace.' ,, 387
thou canst not *b*, unfrowardly, ,, 597
will draw me into sanctuary, And *b* my doom.' *Guinevere* 122
I *b* no more, I meet my fate, *The Flight* 95
Bided ever *b* tryst at village stile, *Merlin and V.* 378
They heard, they *b* their time. *Bandit's Death* 14
Bideford Men of *B* in Devon, *The Revenge* 17
Biding leave Thine easeful *b* here, *Gareth and L.* 128
Bier (*See also* **Chariot-bier**, **Litter-bier**) This truth came borne with *b* and pall, *In Mem. lxxxv* 1
cast him and the *b* in which he lay *Geraint and E.* 572
Till yonder man upon the *b* arise, ,, 657
Wreathed round the *b* with garlands: *Lover's Tale ii* 79
those six virgins which upheld the *b*, ,, 84
and all The vision of the *b*. ,, *iii* 11
those that held the *b* before my face, ,, 16
on the sand Threw down the *b*; ,, 33
She from her *b*, as into fresher life, ,, 42
I stood stole beside the vacant *b*. ,, 58
I hate the black negation of the *b*, *Ancient Sage* 204
Who saw you kneel beside your *b*, *Happy* 54
The bridal garland falls upon the *b*, *D. of the Duke of C.* 1
Big being apt at arms and *b* of bone *Marr. of Geraint* 489
Cried out with a *b* voice, 'What, is he dead?' *Geraint and E.* 541
as *b* i' the mouth as a cow, *Village Wife* 103
Bigger With me, Sir, enter'd in the *b* boy, *Princess ii* 404
No *b* than a glow-worm shone the tent ,, *iv* 25
Bight the spangle dances in *b* and bay, *Sea-Fairies* 24
and flung them in *b* and bay, *V. of Maeldune* 53
Bill (beak) With that gold dagger of thy *b* *The Blackbird* 11
A golden *b*! the silver tongue, ,, 13
Bill (parliamentary measure) I had heard it was this *b* that past, *Walk. to the Mail* 67
My lord, and shall we pass the *b* *Day-Dm., Revival* 27
Bill (an account) But 'e niver looökt ower a *b*, *Village Wife* 51
Bill of Sale (A *b o s* gleam'd thro' the drizzle) *Enoch Arden* 688
Billow (*See also* **Flame-billow**) to the *b* the fountain calls: *Sea-Fairies* 9
a *b*, blown against, Falls back, *Two Voices* 316
the wanton *b* wash'd Them over, *Lover's Tale ii* 9
the upblown *b* ran Shoreward ,, 178
flow'd away To those unreal *b's*: ,, 196
jarring breaker, the deep-sea *b*, *Batt. of Brunanburh* 97
Saxon and Angle from Over the broad *b* ,, 119
Billow'd heard The voice that *b* round *Last Tournament* 167
Billowing Blanching and *b* in a hollow of it, *Lucretius* 31
Enring'd a *b* fountain in the midst; *Princess ii* 28
and his river *b* ran, *Maud I iv* 32
Billy (horse) '*B*,' says 'e, 'hev a joomp!'— *Village Wife* 83
But *B* fell bakkuds o' Charlie, ,, 85
Billy-rough-un (horse) Fur he ca'd 'is 'erse *B-r-u*, ,, 84
Bin (*See also* **Corn-bin**) In musty *b's* and chambers, *Will Water.* 102
Bind cords that *b* and strain The heart *Clear-headed friend* 4
We must *b* And keep you fast, *Rosalind* 42
We'll *b* you fast in silken cords, ,, 49
b with bands That island Queen *Buonaparte* 2
an athlete, strong to break or *b* *Palace of Art* 153
Life, that, working strongly, *b's*— *Love thou thy land* 34

Bind (*continued*) rent The woodbine wreaths that *b* her, *Amphion* 34
Faster *b's* a tyrant's power; *Vision of Sin* 128
dream That Love could *b* them closer *Aylmer's Field* 41
my vow *B's* me to speak, *Princess ii* 202
Psyche, wont to *b* my throbbing brow, ,, 250
b the scatter'd scheme of seven ,, *Con.* 8
he may read that *b's* the sheaf, *In Mem. xxxvi* 13
the frame that *b's* him in His isolation ,, *xlv* 11
I took the thorns to *b* my brows, ,, *lxix* 7
May *b* a book, may line a box, ,, *lxxvii* 6
King Will *b* thee by such vows, *Gareth and L.* 270
would *b* The two together; *Marr. of Geraint* 790
what is worthy love Could *b* him, *Lancelot and E.* 1379
yet thee She fail'd to *b*, ,, 1385
round thee, maiden, *b* my belt. *Holy Grail* 159
'*B* him, and bring him in.' *Pelleas and E.* 232
B him as heretofore, and bring him in: ,, 271
Far less to *b*, your victor, and thrust him ,, 293
let my lady *b* me if she will, ,, 334
vow that *b's* too strictly snaps itself— *Last Tournament* 657
Had Arthur right to *b* them to himself? ,, 684
To *b* them by inviolable vows, ,, 688
B me to one? The wide world laughs ,, 695
What! shall I *b* him more? *Lover's Tale iv* 346
b the maid to love you by the ring; *The Ring* 202
Binding *b* his good horse To a tree, *Pelleas and E.* 30
Bindweed-bell fragile *b-b's* and briony rings; *The Brook* 203
Bine When burr and *b* were gather'd; *Aylmer's Field* 113
berries that flamed upon *b* and vine, *V. of Maeldune* 61
Binn beeswing from a *b* reserved For banquets, *Aylmer's Field* 405
Birch (*See also* **Birk**) Our *b'es* yellowing and from each *Pro. to Gen. Hamley* 1
Bird (*See also* **Birdie**, **Wild-bird**, **Carrier-bird**, **Sea-bird**) voice of the *b* Shall no more be heard, *All Things will Die* 24
heart of the garden the merry *b* chants. *Poet's Mind* 22
b would sing, nor lamb would bleat, *Mariana in the S.* 37
Not any song of *b* or sound of rill; *D. of F. Women* 66
singing clearer than the crested *b* ,, 179
lusty *b* takes every hour for dawn: *M. d'Arthur, Ep.* 11
Sang loud, as tho' he were the *b* of day. *Gardener's D.* 96
These *b's* have joyful thoughts. ,, 99
Slides the *b* o'er lustrous woodland, *Locksley Hall* 162
every *b* of Eden burst In carol, *Day-Dm., L'Envoi* 43
Like long-tail'd *b's* of Paradise ,, *Ep.* 7
fly, like a *b*, from tree to tree; *Edward Gray* 30
b that pipes his lone desire *You might have won* 31
Like the caged *b* escaping suddenly, *Enoch Arden* 269
lightning flash of insect and of *b*, ,, 575
beacon-blaze allures The *b* of passage, ,, 729
Philip chatter'd more than brook or *b*; *The Brook* 51
'The *b's* were warm, (repeat) *Aylmer's Field* 260
Returning, as the *b* returns, at night, *Sea Dreams* 43
and every *b* that sings: ,, 102
b Makes his heart voice amid *Lucretius* 100
b or fish, or opulent flower: ,, 249
the *b*, the fish, the shell, the flower, *Princess ii* 383
As flies the shadow of a *b*, she fled. ,, *iii* 96
not see The *b* of passage flying south ,, 210
earliest pipe of half-awaken'd *b's* ,, *iv* 50
wild *b's* on the light Dash themselves dead. ,, 495
b's that piped their Valentines, ,, *v* 239
a *b*, That early woke to feed ,, *vii* 251
Make music, O *b*, in the new-budded *W. to Alexandra* 11
There is but one *b* with a musical throat, *The Islet* 27
And *b* in air, and fishes turn'd *The Victim* 19
B's' love, and *b's'* song *Window, Spring* 1
B's' song and *b's'* love, (repeat) ,, 3, 5
We'll be *b's* of a feather, ,, 14
Be merry, all *b's*, to-day, ,, *Ay.* 1
Like *b's* the charming serpent draws, *In Mem. xxxiv* 14
Wild *b*, whose warble, liquid sweet, ,, *lxxxviii* 1
Flits by the sea-blue *b* of March; ,, *xci* 4
So loud with voices of the *b's*, ,, *xcix* 2
low love-language of the *b* ,, *cii* 11
happy *b's*, that change their sky ,, *cxv* 15

Bird (*continued*) I hear a chirp of *b's*; *In Mem. cxix* 5
Beginning, and the wakeful *b*; ,, *cxxi* 11
B's in the high Hall-garden (repeat) *Maud I xii* 1, 25
B's in our wood sang ,, 9
And the *b* of prey will hover, ,, *xx* 28
Till a silence fell with the waking *b*, ,, *xxii* 17
My *b* with the shining head, ,, *II iv* 45
red berries charm the *b*, *Gareth and L* 85
b's made Melody on branch, ,, 182
'O *b's*, that warble to the morning sky, O *b's* that warble as the day goes by, ,, 1075
'What knowest thou of *b's*, ,, 1078
and as the sweet voice of a *b*, *Marr. of Geraint* 329
Moves him to think what kind of *b* it is ,, 331
by the *b's* song ye may learn the nest,' ,, 359
Among the dancing shadows of the *b's*, ,, 601
all about were *b's* Of sunny plume ,, 658
we will live like two *b's* in one nest. *Geraint and E.* 627
than all shriek of *b* or beast, *Balin and Balan* 545
the *b* Who pounced her quarry *Merlin and V.* 134
took his brush and blotted out the *b*, ,, 478
foul *b* of rapine whose whole prey ,, 728
Then as a little helpless innocent *b*, *Lancelot and E.* 894
b's of passage piping up and down, *Holy Grail* 146
once the shadow of a *b* Flying, *Pelleas and E.* 38
Beneath the shadow of some *b* of prey; ,, 608
head all night, like *b's* of prey, *Last Tournament* 138
like wild *b's* that change Their season *Pass. of Arthur* 38
sent his soul Into the songs of *b's*, *Lover's Tale i* 321
the *b* That will not hear my call, ,, *iv* 159
togither like *b's* on a beugh; *North. Cobbler* 54
And a pinnace, like a flutter'd *b*, *The Revenge* 2
b's make ready for their bridal-time *Sisters (E. and E.)* 71
Some *b's* are sick and sullen when they moult. ,, 73
not arter the *b's* wi' 'is gun, *Village Wife* 41
a score of wild *b's* Cried *V. of Maeldune* 27
And the shouting of these wild *b's* ,, 33
And we left the dead to the *b's* ,, 36
flight of *b's*, the flame of sacrifice, *Tiresias* 6
b with a warble plaintively sweet *The Wreck* 81
b's could make This music in the *b*? *Ancient Sage* 21
shell must break before the *b* can fly. ,, 154
listen how the *b's* Begin to warble *The Flight* 60
whishper was sweet as the lilt of a *b*! *Tomorrow* 33
av the *b* 'ud come to me call, ,, 45
thy chuckled note, Thou twinkling *b*, *Early Spring* 38
The summer *b* is still, *Pref. Poem Broth. S.* 18
FAINT as a climate-changing *b* that flies *Demeter and P.* 1
I envied human wives, and nested *b's*, ,, 53
my ravings hush'd The *b*, ,, 109
b's that circle round the tower *The Ring* 85
B's and brides must leave the nest. ,, 89
bright *b* that still is veering there ,, 332
My *b's* would sing, You heard not. *To Mary Boyle* 18
scaled the buoyant highway of the *b's*, *Prog. of Spring* 80
Sing like a *b* and be happy, *Parnassus* 14
waked a *b* of prey that scream'd and past; *Death of Œnone* 87
Warble *b*, and open flower, *Akbar's D., Hymn* 7
Birdie Sleep, little *b*, sleep! *Sea Dreams* 282
Without her 'little *b*'? well then. ,, 283
sleep, And I will sing you '*b*.' ,, 284
What does little *b* say ,, 293
Let me fly, says little *b*, ,, 295
B, rest a little longer, ,, 297
Baby says, like little *b*, ,, 303
Bird's-eye-view *b-e-v* of all the ungracious past *Princess ii* 125
Birk Shadows of the silver *b* *A Dirge* 5
ere thy maiden *b* be wholly clad, *Prog. of Spring* 50
Birth *arms, or power of brain, or* b *To the Queen* 3
The old earth Had a *b*, *All Things will Die* 38
Her temple and her place of *b*, *Supp. Confessions* 53
winds, as at their hour of *b*, *The Winds, etc.* 1
At the moment of thy *b*, *Eleänore* 15
range of evil between death and *b*, *If I were loved* 3
hadst not between death and *b* *Two Voices* 169
Birth (*continued*) From that first nothing ere his *b* *Two Voices* 332
Would God renew me from my *b* *Miller's D.* 27
slew him with your noble *b*. *L. C. V. de Vere* 48
Titanic forces taking *b* In divers *Day-Dm., L'Envoi* 17
'He does not love me for my *b*, *Lady Clare* 9
marriage, and the *b* Of Philip's child: *Enoch Arden* 708
one act at once, The *b* of light: *Princess iii* 326
The time draws near the *b* of Christ: *In Mem. xxviii* 1
Beyond the second *b* of Death. ,, *xlv* 16
Who breaks his *b's* individous bar, ,, *lxiv* 5
Evil haunts The *b*, the bridal; ,, *xcviii* 14
Memories of bridal, or of *b*, ,, *xcix* 15
The time draws near the *b* of Christ; ,, *civ* 1
Becoming, when the time has *b*, ,, *cxiii* 14
shaping an infant ripe for his *b*, *Maud I iv* 34
mine by a right, from *b* till death. ,, *xix* 42
By the home that gave me *b*, ,, *II iv* 7
'Knowest thou aught of Arthur's *b*?' *Com. of Arthur* 147
learn the secret of our Arthur's *b*.' ,, 159
the cloud that settles round his *b* *Gareth and L.* 130
had tended on him from his *b*, ,, 179
creatures voiceless thro' the fault of *b*, *Geraint and E.* 266
that weird legend of his *b*, *Last Tournament* 669
mystery From all men, like his *b*; *Guinevere* 298
govern a whole life from *b* to death, *Lover's Tale i* 76
like each other was the *b* of each! (repeat) ,, 197, 201
Gives *b* to a brawling brook, ,, 526
Rose of Lancaster, Red in thy *b*, *Sir J. Oldcastle* 53
Have I not been about thee from thy *b*? *Columbus* 148
and was noble in *b* as in worth, *V. of Maeldune* 3
sweet mother land which gave them *b* *Tiresias* 122
Youth and Health, and *b* and wealth, *By an Evolution.* 8
how far? from o'er the gates of *B*, *Far-far-away* 13
the *b* of a baseborn child. *Charity* 28
Birthday Each month, a *b-d* coming on, *Will Water.* 93
the night Before my Enid's *b*, *Marr. of Geraint* 458
given her on the night Before her *b*, ,, 633
I send a *b* line Of greeting; *To E. Fitzgerald* 45
on your third September *b* *The Ring* 130
And sent it on her *b*. ,, 211
She in wrath Return'd it on her *b*, ,, 212
And on your Mother's *b*—all but yours— ,, 248
This *b*, death-day, and betrothal ring, ,, 276
Your *b* was her death-day. ,, 301
forgotten it was your *b*, child— ,, 378
Your fifth September *b*. ,, 423
Every morning is thy *b* *Akbar's D., Hymn* 2
b came of a boy born happily dead. *Charity* 34
Biscay The *B*, roughly ridging eastward, *Enoch Arden* 529
Bishop Archbishop, *B*, Priors, Canons, *Sir J. Oldcastle* 159
Ay, an' ya seed the *B*. *Church-warden, etc.* 17
an' sits o' the *B's* throän. ,, 20
an' thou'll be a *B* yit. ,, 50
Bit (s) or *b's* of roasting ox Moan *Lucretius* 131
Nobbut a *b* on it's left, *N. Farmer, O.S.* 41
an' a nicetish *b* o' land. ,, *N.S.* 22
Vext me a *b*, till he told me *First Quarrel* 36
I am going to leave you a *b*— ,, 80
'tha mun breäk 'im off *b* by *b*.' *North. Cobbler* 88
jingle of *b's*, Shouts, arrows, *Tiresias* 93
like a *b* of yisther-day in a dhrame— *Tomorrow* 8
Now I'll gie tha a *b* o' my mind *Church-warden, etc.* 21
if tha wants to git forrads a *b*, ,, 49
Bit (verb) *b* his lips, And broke away. *Dora* 33
crack'd the helmet thro', and *b* the bone, *Marr. of Geraint* 573
clench'd her fingers till they *b* the palm, *Lancelot and E.* 611
an' a-squeälin, as if tha was *b*, *Owd Roä* 89
Bite (s) Showing the aspick's *b*.) *D. of F. Women* 160
An' it wasn't a *b* but a burn, *Owd Roä* 90
Bite (verb) *b's* it for true heart and not for harm, *Princess, Pro.*, 174
And do their little best to *b* *Lit. Squabbles* 6
B, frost, *b*! (repeat) *Window, Winter* 7, 13
b far into the heart of the house, ,, 11
Biting *b* laws to scare the beasts of prey *Princess v* 393
Modred *b* his thin lips was mute, *Gareth and L.* 31

Bitten (*See also* **Root-bitten**) *b* the heel of the going year. *Window, Winter* 6
b into the heart of the earth, ,, 18
one whose foot is *b* by an ant, *Pelleas and E.* 184
Scratch'd, *b*, blinded, marr'd me *Last Tournament* 526
Bitter (*See also* **Seeming-bitter, Wormwood-bitter**) Failing to give the *b* of the sweet, *D. of F. Women* 286
O sweet and *b* in a breath, *In Mem. iii* 3
My own less *b*, rather more: ,, *vi* 6
If I find the world so *b* *Maud I vi* 33
Then the world were not so *b* (repeat) ,, 38, 94
canst abide a truth, Tho' *b*. *Balin and Balan* 502
she tempted them and fail'd, Being so *b*: *Merlin and V.* 820
b death must be: Love, thou art *b*; *Lancelot and E.* 1010
Bitterer Yet *b* from his readings: *Aylmer's Field* 553
Bitterly *B* weeping I turn'd away: (repeat) *Edward Gray* 6, 34
'*B* wept I over the stone: ,, 33
long and *b* meditating, *Boädicea* 35
spake the Queen and somewhat *b*, *Guinevere* 271
Bittern *See* **Butter-bump**
Bitterness Sweet in their utmost *b*, *Supp. Confessions* 117
Have fretted all to dust and *b*.' *Princess vi* 264
wake The old *b* again, *In Mem. lxxxiv* 47
By reason of the *b* and grief *Com. of Arthur* 210
they were, A *b* to me!— *Last Tournament* 41
his spirit From *b* of death. *Lover's Tale i* 143
Bivouac Gone the comrades of my *b*, *Locksley H., Sixty,* 45
Blabbing physician, *b* The case of his patient— *Maud II v* 36
Prophet, curse me the *b* lip, ,, 57
Black (*See also* **Coal-black, Jet-black**) *B* the garden-bowers and grots *Arabian Nights* 78
In the yew-wood *b* as night, *Oriana* 19
foreground *b* with stones and slags, *Palace of Art* 81
that hair More *b* than ashbuds *Gardener's D.* 28
in its coarse *b*'s or whites, *W. to the Mail* 107
The streets were *b* with smoke *In Mem. lxix* 3
To *b* and brown on kindred brows. ,, *lxxix* 16
who alway rideth arm'd in *b*, *Gareth and L.* 636
B, with *b* banner, and a long *b* horn ,, 1366
ready on the river, clothed in *b*. *Lancelot and E.* 1123
Part *b*, part whiten'd with the bones *Holy Grail* 500
B as the harlot's heart— *Pelleas and E.* 468
Wear *b* and white, and be a nun *Guinevere* 677
stoled from head to foot in flowing *b*; *Lover's Tale ii* 85
bars Of *b* and bands of silver, ,, *iv* 59
better ha' beaten me *b* an' blue *First Quarrel* 72
An' yer hair as *b* as the night, *Tomorrow* 32
b in white above his bones. *Locksley H., Sixty,* 44
B with bridal favours mixt! *Forlorn* 69
B was the night when we crept away *Bandit's Death* 25
the dumb Hour, clothed in *b*, *Silent Voices* 1
Black (Sea) side of the *B* and the Baltic deep, *Maud III vi* 51
Black-beaded Glancing with *b-b* eyes, *Lilian* 15
Black-bearded stern *b-b* kings with wolfish eyes, *D. of F. Women* 111
Black Bess (Horse) *B B*, Tantivy, Tallyho, *The Brook* 160
Blackbird (*See also* **Merle**) O *B*! sing me something well: *The Blackbird* 1
while the *b* on the pippin hung *Audley Court* 38
The *b*'s have their wills, (repeat) *Early Spring* 5, 47
Black-blue *b-b* Irish hair and Irish eyes *Last Tournament* 404
Blackcap The *b* warbles, and the turtle purrs, *Prog. of Spring* 55
Black'd *B* with thy branding thunder, *St. S. Stylites* 76
Blacken pierces the liver and *b*'s the blood; *The Islet* 35
bark and *b* innumerable, *Boädicea* 13
B round the Roman carrion, ,, 14
upon a throne, And *b*'s every blot: *Ded. of Idylls* 28
City children soak and *b* *Locksley H., Sixty,* 218
b round The corpse of every man *Romney's R.* 122
Blacken'd (*See also* **Pitch-blacken'd**) So *b* all her world in secret, *Princess vii* 42
the walls *B* about us, ,, *Con* 110
His countenance *b*, and his forehead *Balin and Balan* 391
Blackening *b* over heath and holt, *Locksley Hall* 191
And *b* in the sea-foam sway'd *Holy Grail* 802
B against the dead-green stripes *Pelleas and E.* 554
Blackening (*continued*) *b*, swallow'd all the land, *Guinevere* 82
Was *b* on the slopes of Portugal, *Sisters (E. and E.)* 62
Blackest lie which is half a truth is ever the *b* of lies, *Grandmother* 30
To lie, to lie—in God's own house—the *b* of all lies! *The Flight* 52
Black-heart unnetted *b-h*'s ripen dark, *The Blackbird* 7
Black-hooded Black-stoled, *b-h*, like a dream *M. d'Arthur* 197
Black-stoled, *b-h*, like a dream *Pass. of Arthur* 365
Blackness In the gross *b* underneath. *Supp. Confessions* 187
With *b* as a solid wall, *Palace of Art* 274
The *b* round the tombing sod, *On a Mourner* 27
dark was Uther too, Wellnigh to *b*; *Com. of Arthur* 330
she make My darkness *b*? *Balin and Balan* 193
Blackshadow'd there, *b* nigh the mere *Gareth and L.* 809
Blacksmith *b* border-marriage—one they knew— *Aylmer's Field* 263
b 'e strips me the thick ov 'is airm, *North. Cobbler* 85
Black-stoled *B-s*, black-hooded, like a dream *M. d'Arthur* 197
B-s, black-hooded, like a dream *Pass. of Arthur* 365
Blackthorn never see The blossom on the *b*, *May Queen, N. Y's. E.* 8
Blackthorn-blossom *b-b* fades and falls and leaves the bitter sloe, *The Flight* 15
Black-wing'd the *b-w* Azrael overcame, *Akbar's Dream* 186
Blade (of grass) varying year with *b* and sheaf *Day-Dm., Sleep. P.* 1
In bud or *b*, or bloom, may find, ,, *Moral* 10
While life was yet in bud and *b*, *Princess i* 32
while the sun yet beat a dewy *b*, *Geraint and E.* 446
voice clings to each *b* of grass, *Lancelot and E.* 107
From buried grain thro' springing *b*, *Demeter and P.* 146
Blade (of sword) pure and true as *b*'s of steel. *Kate* 16
My good *b* carves the casques of men, *Sir Galahad* 1
She bore the *b* of Liberty. *The Voyage* 72
struck out and shouted; the *b* glanced, *Princess v* 540
Geraint's, who heaved his *b* aloft, *Marr. of Geraint* 572
b so bright That men are blinded *Com. of Arthur* 300
but turn the *b* and ye shall see, ,, 303
these will turn the *b*.' *Gareth and L.* 1095
the *b* flew Splintering in six, *Balin and Balan* 395
waved his *b* To the gallant three hundred *Heavy Brigade* 9
drove the *b* that had slain my husband *Bandit's Death* 34
Blade (of dagger) with the *b* he prick'd his hand, *Aylmer's Field* 239
'From Edith' was engraven on the *b*. ,, 598
Blade (shoulder-bone) (*See also* **Shoulder blade**) arms were shatter'd to the shoulder *b*. *Princess vi* 52
Blain face deform'd by lurid blotch and *b*— *Death of Œnone* 72
Blame (s) But he is chill to praise or *b*. *Two Voices* 258
Joyful and free from *b*. *D. of F. Women* 80
Shall smile away my maiden *b* ,, 214
The crime of malice, and is equal *b*.' *Vision of Sin* 216
Nor yours the *b*—for who beside *Aylmer's Field* 735
Which he has worn so pure of *b*, *Ode on Well.* 72
I had such reverence for his *b*, *In Mem. li* 6
white blamelessness accounted *b*!' *Merlin and V.* 799
mine the *b* that oft I seem as he *Last Tournament* 115
Received unto himself a part of *b*, *Lover's Tale i* 786
lines I read Nor utter'd word of *b*, *Pro. to Gen. Hamley* 18
Blame (verb) in truth You must *b* Love. *Miller's D.* 192
'I have been to *b*—to *b*. *Dora* 159
I have been to *b*. Kiss me, my children.' ,, 161
Am I to *b* for this, *St. S. Stylites* 124
she had a will; was he to *b*? *Princess i* 48
yet I *b* you not so much for fear; ,, *iv* 506
'Ida—'sdeath! you *b* the man; ,, *vi* 221
'*b* not thyself too much,' I said, 'nor *b* ,, *vii* 255
They are all to *b*, they are all to *b*. *Sailor Boy* 20
knot thou the winds that make *In Mem. xlix* 10
b not thou thy plaintive song,' ,, *lii* 5
Nor *b* I Death, because he bare ,, *lxxxii* 9
Nor count me all to *b* if I ,, *Con.* 85
She did not wish to *b* him— *Maud I xx* 5
'Damsel,' he said, 'you be not all to *b*, *Gareth and L.* 1171
who should *b* me then?' *Merlin and V.* 661
'To *b*, my lord Sir Lancelot, much to *b*! *Lancelot and E.* 97
the girl was the most to *b*. *First Quarrel* 26
An' I felt I had been to *b*; ,, 90
You praise when you should *b* *Epilogue* 4

Blazon'd (*continued*) *b* lions o'er the imperial tent *Princess v* 9
Bright let it be with its *b* deeds, *Ode on Well.* 56
The giant windows' *b* fires, *The Daisy* 58
b fair In diverse raiment *Palace of Art* 167
Some *b*, some but carven, *Gareth and L.* 406
if twain His arms were *b* also ; ,, 413
all true hearts be *b* on her tomb *Lancelot and E.* 1344
purple *b* with armorial gold. *Godiva* 52
lamps *b* like Heaven and Earth *Princess i* 223
monsters *b* what they were, ,, *iv* 345
The prophet *b* on the panes ; *In Mem. lxxxvii* 8
shield of Gawain *b* rich and bright, *Gareth and L.* 416
All the devices *b* on the shield *Lancelot and E.* 9
Blazoning silken case with braided *b's*, ,, 1149
banners *b* a Power That is not seen *Akbar's Dream* 137
Bleach'd wizard brow *b* on the walls : *Merlin and V.* 597
lay till all their bones were *b*, *Lancelot and E.* 43
Bleat *b* Of the thick-fleeced sheep *Ode to Memory* 65
bird would sing, nor lamb would *b*, *Mariana in the S.* 37
motherless *b* of a lamb in the storm *In the Child. Hosp.* 64
Bleating I hear the *b* of the lamb. *May Queen, Con.* 2
Sent out a bitter *b* for its dam ; *Princess iv* 392
Bled when her Satrap *b* At Issus *Alexander* 2
B underneath his armour secretly, *Geraint and E.* 502
Bleed strain The heart until it *b's*, *Clear-headed friend* 5
For which her warriors *b*, *Epilogue* 35
Bleedeth my true breast *B* for both ; *To J. S.* 63
Blemish stain or *b* in a name of note, *Merlin and V.* 832
'Small *b* upon the skin ! *Dead Prophet* 66
Blench make thee somewhat *b* or fail, *In Mem. lxii* 2
Blend all their voices *b* in choric Hallelujah *Making of Man* 7
Blent hatred of her weakness, *b* with shame. *Princess vii* 30
Bless But that God *b* thee, dear— *Miller's D.* 235
And *b* him for the sake of him (repeat) *Dora* 70, 94
'God *b* him !' he said, 'and may he ,, 149
And *b* me, mother, ere I go.' *Lady Clare* 56
b him, he shall sit upon my knees *Enoch Arden* 197
God *b* you for it, God reward you ,, 424
softly whisper '*B*, God *b* 'em : *Aylmer's Field* 187
And forty blest ones *b* him, ,, 372
God *b* the narrow sea which keeps *Princess, Con.* 51
God *b* the narrow seas ! ,, 70
O for thy voice to soothe and *b* ! *In Mem. lvi* 26
And *b* thee, for thy lips are bland, ,, *cxix* 9
That which we dare invoke to *b* ; ,, *cxxiv* 1
And cried, 'God *b* the King, *Gareth and L.* 698
vext his day, but *b'es* him asleep— ,, 1286
God *b* you, my own little Nell.' *First Quarrel* 22
the Saviour lives but to *b*. *Rizpah* 64
that men May *b* thee as we *b* thee, *De Prof. Two G.* 17
dream of a shadow, go—God *b* you. *To W. H. Brookfield* 14
He *b'es* the wife. *To Prin. F. of H.* 4
Love your enemy, *b* your haters, *Locksley H., Sixty* 85
and *b* Their garner'd Autumn also, *Demeter and P.* 146
and '*b*' Whom ? even 'your persecutors' ! *Akbar's Dream* 76
a woman, God *b* her, kept me from Hell. *Charity* 4
Blessed *See* **Blest**
Blessedness Or is there *b* like theirs ? *In Mem. xxxii* 16
Blessin' for a *b* 'ud come wid the green !' *Tomorrow* 64
Blessing tell her that I died *B* her, *Enoch Arden* 879
spent in *b* her and praying for her. ,, 884
tell my son that I died *b* him. ,, 885
b those that look on them. *Princess iii* 256
B the wholesome white faces *Def. of Lucknow* 101
B his field, or seated in the dusk *Demeter and P.* 125
With *b's* beyond hope or thought, *Miller's D.* 237
With *b's* which no words can find. ,, 238
O *b's* on his kindly voice *May Queen, Con.* 13
And *b's* on his whole life long, ,, 14
O *b's* on his kindly heart ,, 15
be tended by My *b* ! *Love and Duty* 88
God's *b* on the day ! *Lady Clare* 8
Pray'd for a *b* on his wife and babes *Enoch Arden* 188
calling down a *b* on his head ,, 327
And *b's* on the falling out *Princess ii* 6

Blessing (*continued*) from Heaven A *b* on her labours *Princess ii* 479
Blazon your mottoes of *b* and prayer ! *W. to Alexandra* 12
My *b*, like a line of light, *In Mem. xvii* 10
We yield all *b* to the name ,, *xxxvi* 3
crown'd with *b* she doth rise ,, *xl* 5
Why do they prate of the *b's* of Peace ? *Maud I i* 21
she was deaf To *b* or to cursing *Geraint and E.* 579
Thy *b*, stainless King ! *Merlin and V.* 54
take withal Thy poet's *b*, *To the Queen ii* 46
hold the hand of *b* over them, *Lover's Tale i* 754
saved by the *b* of Heaven ! *Def. of Lucknow* 104
'Bread—Bread left after the *b* ?' *Sir J. Oldcastle* 154
From the golden alms of *B* *Locksley H., Sixty* 87
Blest-Blessed And forty *blest* ones bless him, *Aylmer's Field* 372
Sammy, I'm *blest* If it isn't the saäme oop yonder, *N. Farmer, N.S.* 43
soul laments, which hath been *blest*, *D. of F. Women* 281
fruit of thine by Love is *blest*, *Talking Oak* 249
Thy name was *blest* within the narrow door ; *W. to Marie Alex.* 38
Marie, shall thy name be *blest*, ,, 39
As if the quiet bones were *blest* *In Mem. xviii* 6
what may count itself as *blest*, ,, *xxvii* 9
Thrice *blest* whose lives are faithful prayers, ,, *xxxii* 13
my heart more *blest* than heart can tell, *Maud I. xviii* 82
Blest, but for some dark undercurrent ,, 83
'*Blessed* be thou, Sir Gareth ! *Gareth and L.* 1258
They might as well have *blest* her : *Geraint and E.* 578
blest be Heaven That brought thee *Holy Grail* 616
Blessed are Bors, Lancelot and Percivale, ,, 874
blessed be the King, who hath forgiven *Guinevere* 634
Blest be the voice of the Teacher *Kapiolani* 2
fancy made me for a moment *blest* *The form, the form* 6
She desires no isles of the *blest*, *Wages* 8
As she looks among the *blest*, *Maud II iv* 84
in a dream from a band of the *blest*, ,, *III vi* 10
fellowship Would make me wholly *blest* : *Balin and Balan* 148
follow Edwin to those isles, those islands of the *Blest* ! *The Flight* 42
I *blest* them, and they wander'd on : *Two Voices* 424
A thousand times I *blest* him, *May Queen, Con.* 16
bless'd herself, and cursed herself, *The Goose* 15
say to Philip that I *blest* him too ; *Enoch Arden* 886
Perceived the waving of his hands that *blest*. *Guinevere* 584
saw not his daughter—he *blest* her : *To Prin. F. of H.* 3
And they *blest* him in their pain, *The Revenge* 20
Blew breeze of a joyful dawn *b* free *Arabian Nights* 1
B his own praises in his eyes, *A Character* 22
hunter *b* His wreathed bugle-horn. *Palace of Art* 63
sweet Europa's mantle *b* unclasp'd, ,, 117
The glass *b* in, the fire *b* out, *The Goose* 49
Her cap *b* off, her gown *b* up, ,, 51
full-fed with perfume, *b* Beyond us, *Gardener's D.* 113
The hedge broke in, the banner *b*, *Day-Dm., Revival* 9
A light wind *b* from the gates of the sun, *Poet's Song* 3
from the tiny pitted target *b* *Aylmer's Field* 93
the wind *b* ; The rain of heaven, ,, 427
b the swoll'n cheek of a trumpeter, *Princess ii* 364
bush-bearded Barons heaved and *b*, ,, *v* 21
he *b* and *b*, but none appear'd : ,, 336
stood four-square to all the winds that *b* ! *Ode on Well.* 39
Last, the Prussian trumpet *b* ; ,, 127
A milky-bell'd amaryllis *b*. *The Daisy* 16
all the bugle breezes *b* Reveillée *In Mem. lxviii* 7
Altho' the trumpet *b* so loud. ,, *xcvi* 24
cloth of gold, the trumpets *b*, *Com. of Arthur* 480
other *b* A hard and deadly note *Gareth and L.* 1110
that ye *b* your boast in vain ?' ,, 1229
and lights, and once again he *b* ; ,, 1371
O'er the four rivers the first roses *b*, *Geraint and E.* 764
and anon The trumpets *b* ; *Lancelot and E.* 454
trumpets *b* Proclaiming his the prize, ,, 500
sun Shone, and the wind *b*, thro' her, *Holy Grail* 99
And *b* my merry maidens all about ,, 748
to the summit, and the trumpets *b*. *Pelleas and E.* 167
ever the wind *b*, and yellowing leaf *Last Tournament* 154
Far off a solitary trumpet *b*. *Guinevere* 529

Blew (*continued*) from the North, and *b* The mist aside, *Pass. of Arthur* 124
and *b* Fresh fire into the sun, *Lover's Tale i* 318
and *b* Coolness and moisture and all smells „ *iii* 4
and *b* it far Until it hung, „ 35
ever that evening ended a great gale *b*, *The Revenge* 114
topmost roof our banner of England *b*. (repeat) *Def. of Lucknow* 6, 30, 45, 60, 94
topmost roof our banner in India *b*. „ 72
the old banner of England *b*. „ 106
a sudden blast *b* us out and away *V. of Maeldune* 10
whirlwind blow these woods, as never *b* before. *The Flight* 12
All at once the trumpet *b*, *Happy* 75
Bleys (Merlin's master) (so they call him) *B*, *Com. of Arthur* 153
B Laid magic by, and sat him down, „ 155
B, our Merlin's master, as they say, „ 360
Blight (s) *B* and famine, plague and earthquake, *Lotos-E's., C. S.*, 115
The *b* of low desires— *Aylmer's Field* 673
b Of ancient influence and scorn. *Princess ii* 168
And *b* and famine on all the lea: *The Victim* 46
like a *b* On my fresh hope, *Maud I xix* 102
b Lives in the dewy touch of pity *Lover's Tale i* 694
if the blossom can doat on the *b*, *The Wreck* 19
Blight (verb) Which would *b* the plants. *Poet's Mind* 18
Shall sharpest pathos *b* us, *Love and Duty* 85
b thy hope or break thy rest, *Faith* 2
Blighted 'your pretty bud, So *b* here, *The Ring* 317
Blind (sightless) (*See also* **Half-blind, Hoodman-blind**)
All night long on darkness *b*. *Adeline* 44
this dreamer, deaf and *b*, *Two Voices* 175
men, whose reason long was *b*, „ 370
parch'd and wither'd, deaf and *b*, *Fatima* 6
those, not *b*, who wait for day, *Love thou thy land* 15
almost *b*, And scarce can recognise *St. S. Stylites* 39
mate is *b* and captain lame, *The Voyage* 91
b or lame or sick or sound, „ 93
for he groped as *b*, and seem'd *Aylmer's Field* 821
wept her true eyes *b* for such a one, *Princess iv* 134
b with rage she miss'd the plank, „ 177
I cried myself well-nigh *b*, *Grandmother* 37
And shall I take a thing so *b*, *In Mem. iii* 13
He would not make his judgment *b*, „ *xcvi* 14
not *b* To the faults of his heart *Maud I xix* 67
He mark'd not this, but *b* and deaf *Balin and Balan* 318
were I stricken *b* That minute, *Lancelot and E.* 426
one hath seen, and all the *b* will see. *Holy Grail* 313
on the splendour came, flashing me *b*; „ 413
thrice as *b* as any noonday owl, „ 866
Being too *b* to have desire to see. „ 872
Mute, *b* and motionless as then I lay; *Lover's Tale i* 607
B, for the day was as the night „ 610
Almost *b* With ever-growing cataract, *Sisters (E. and E.)* 191
'Henceforth be *b*, for thou hast seen *Tiresias* 49
Or power as of the Gods gone *b* *Ancient Sage* 80
leave him, *b* of heart and eyes, „ 113
For wert thou born or *b* or deaf, „ 175
no man halt, or deaf or *b*; *Locksley H., Sixty*, 163
Fur the dog's stoän-deäf, an' e's *b*, *Owd Roä* 2
an' seeäm'd as *b* as a poop, „ 101
A barbarous people, *B* to the magic, *Merlin and the G.* 26
Blind (screen) (*See also* **Lattice-blind**) Sometimes your shadow cross'd the *b*. *Miller's D.* 124
Blind (verb) lest the gems Should *b* my purpose, *M. d'Arthur* 153
Ere yet they *b* the stars, *Tithonus* 39
To *b* the truth and me: *Princess iii* 112
He shall not *b* his soul with clay.' „ *vii* 331
good King means to *b* himself, *Merlin and V.* 783
b's himself and all the Table Round „ 784
lest the gems Should *b* my purpose, *Pass. of Arthur* 321
b your pretty blue eyes with a kiss! *Romney's R.* 101
Blinded (*See also* **Half-blinded, Self-blinded**)
those whom passion hath not *b*, *Ode to Memory* 117
blissful tears *b* my sight *Oriana* 23
and *b* With many a deep-hued *Eleänore* 36
Droops *b* with his shining eye: *Fatima* 38

Blinded (*continued*) I, *b* with my tears, 'Still strove *D. of F. Women* 108
Not with *b* eyesight poring *Locksley Hall* 172
so bright That men are *b* by it— *Com. of Arthur* 301
Blasted and burnt, and *b* as I was, *Holy Grail* 844
Scratch'd, bitten, *b*, marr'd me *Last Tournament* 526
Too early *b* by the kiss of death— *Romney's R.* 103
May leave the windows *b*, „ 146
He stumbled in, and sat *B*; *St. Telemachus* 49
Blinder Nature made them *b* motions *Locksley Hall* 150
'Gawain, and *b* unto holy things *Holy Grail* 870
Blind Fate Rail at '*B F*' with many *Doubt and Prayer* 2
Blindfold Drug down the *b* sense of wrong *In Mem. lxxi* 7
from what side The *b* rummage *Balin and Balan* 416
Blinding Struck up against the *b* wall. *Mariana in the S.* 56
Dash'd together in *b* dew: *Vision of Sin* 42
his fire is on my face *B*, *Lucretius* 145
raised the *b* bandage from his eyes: *Princess i* 244
suck the *b* splendour from the sand, „ *vii* 39
all in mail Burnish'd to *b*, *Gareth and L.* 1027
Are *b* desert sand; we scarce can *Akbar's Dream* 30
Blindless the *b* casement of the room, *Marr. of Geraint* 71
Blindly That read his spirit *b* wise, *Two Voices* 287
And, while now she wonders *b*, *L. of Burleigh* 53
'The stars,' she whispers, '*b* run; *In Mem. iii* 5
And staggers *b* ere she sink? „ *xvi* 14
muffled motions *b* drown „ *xlix* 15
b rush'd on all the rout behind. *Geraint and E.* 466
Blindness That in this *b* of the frame *In Mem. xciii* 15
for talk Which lives with *b*, *Sisters (E. and E.)* 249
curse Of *b* and their unbelief, *Tiresias* 59
Blink those that did not *b* the terror, *Gareth and L.* 1402
Blinkt *B* the white morn, sprays grated, *Balin and Balan* 385
Bliss Then in madness and in *b*, *Madeline* 42
Weak symbols of the settled *b*, *Miller's D.* 233
Above the thunder, with undying *b* *Œnone* 132
'Trust me, in *b* I shall abide *Palace of Art* 18
move Me from my *b* of life, *D. of F. Women* 210
I rose up Full of his *b*, *Gardener's D.* 211
A man had given all other *b*, *Sir L. and Q. G.* 42
I shall see him, My babe in *b*: *Enoch Arden* 898
and spoils My *b* in being; *Lucretius* 222
A central warmth diffusing *b* *In Mem. lxxxiv* 6
I triumph in conclusive *b*, „ *lxxxv* 91
O *b*, when all in circle drawn „ *lxxxix* 21
With gods in unconjectured *b*, „ *xciii* 10
A wither'd violet is her *b*: „ *xcvii* 26
For fuller gain of after *b*: „ *cxvii* 4
Nor have I felt so much of *b* „ *Con.* 5
Make answer, Maud my *b*, *Maud I xviii* 57
My dream? do I dream of *b*? „ *xix* 3
Sun, that wakenest all to *b* or pain, *Gareth and L.* 1060
thrills of *b* That strike across the soul *Lover's Tale i* 363
b stood round me like the light of Heaven,— „ 495
tell him of the *b* he had with God— „ 674
sunder'd With smiles of tranquil *b*, „ *ii* 143
O *b*, what a Paradise there! *V. of Maeldune* 78
whose one *b* Is war, and human sacrifice— *Tiresias* 111
Twelve times in the year Bring me *b*, *The Ring* 6
'Sleep, little blossom, my honey, my *b*! *Romney's R.* 99
I had one brief summer of *b*. *Bandit's Death* 9
Blissful here are the *b* downs and dales, *Sea-Fairies* 22
While *b* tears blinded my sight *Oriana* 23
As from some *b* neighbourhood, *Two Voices* 430
sleep down from the *b* skies. *Lotos-Eaters, C.S.* 7
With *b* treble ringing clear. *Sir L. and Q. G.* 22
b palpitations in the blood, *Princess iv* 28
B bride of a *b* heir, *W. to Alexandra* 27
led him thro' the *b* climes, *In Mem. lxxxv* 25
On me she bends her *b* eyes „ *Con.* 29
Blister'd *B* every word with tears, *Forlorn* 81
Blistering bared her forehead to the *b* sun, *Geraint and E.* 515
Blithe New-year *b* and bold, my friend, *D. of the O. Year* 35
B would her brother's acceptance be. *Maud I x* 27
Bloat *b* himself, and ooze All over *Sea Dreams* 154

Bloated forehead veins *B*, and branch'd ; *Balin and Balan* 392
merry *b* things Shoulder'd the spigot, *Guinevere* 267
Block (s) (*See also* **Yule-block**) on black *b's* A breadth of thunder. *Princess iii* 291
as a *b* Left in the quarry ; ,, *vii* 230
(Huge *b's*, which some old trembling *Lover's Tale ii* 45
Block (verb) *b* and bar Your heart with system *Princess iv* 462
Block'd knew mankind, And *b* them out ; ,, *vi* 328
Blockish No coarse and *b* God of acreage *Aylmer's Field* 651
Blonde rosy *b*, and in a college gown, *Princess ii* 323
Blood *And leave us rulers of your* b *To the Queen* 21
Ice with the warm *b* mixing ; *All Things will Die* 33
Which mixing with the infant's *b*, *Supp. Confessions* 61
till his own *b* flows About his hoof. ,, 155
was no *b* upon her maiden robes *The Poet* 41
I feel the tears of *b* arise *Oriana* 77
her sacred *b* doth drown The fields, *Poland* 4
A matter to be wept with tears of *b* ! ,, 14
Till her *b* was frozen slowly, *L. of Shalott iv* 30
It was the stirring of the *b*. *Two Voices* 159
' He knows a baseness in his *b* ,, 301
The prudent partner of his *b* ,, 415
my swift *b* that went and came *Fatima* 16
my vigour, wedded to thy *b*, *Œnone* 161
She mix'd her ancient *b* with shame. *The Sisters* 8
phantasms weeping tears of *b*, *Palace of Art* 239
The guilt of *b* is at your door : *L.C.V. de Vere* 43
And simple faith than Norman *b*, ,, 56
ever-shifting currents of the *b* *D. of F. Women* 133
That Principles are rain'd in *b* ; *Love thou thy land* 80
Who sprang from English *b* ! *England and Amer.* 10
his brow Striped with dark *b* : *M. d'Arthur* 212
Vex'd with a morbid devil in his *b* *Walk. to the Mail* 19
' The slight she-slips of loyal *b*, *Talking Oak* 57
felt my *b* Glow with the glow *Tithonus* 55
stays the *b* along the veins. *Day-Dm., Sleep. P.* 4
grapes with bunches red as *b* ; ,, 44
Ah, blessed vision ! *b* of God! *Sir Galahad* 45
Let Whig and Tory stir their *b* ; *Will Water.* 53
To make my *b* run quicker, ,, 110
And I,' said he, ' the next in *b*— *Lady Clare* 84
Burnt in each man's *b*. *The Captain* 16
scatter'd *B* and brains of men. ,, 48
In their *b*, as they lay dying, ,, 55
' We are men of ruin'd *b* ; *Vision of Sin* 99
down thro' all his *b* Drew in *Enoch Arden* 659
now there is but one of all my *b* ,, 892
distant kinship to the gracious *b* *Aylmer's Field* 62
to flush his *b* with air, ,, 459
redden'd with no bandit's *b* : ,, 597
Runs in a river of *b* to the sick sea. ,, 768
swept away The men of flesh and *b*, *Sea Dreams* 237
Confused the chemic labour of the *b*, *Lucretius* 20
thought that all the *b* by Sylla shed ,, 47
keep him from the lust of *b* ,, 83
strikes thro' the thick *b* Of cattle, ,, 98
lust or lusty *b* or provender : ,, 198
made her *b* in sight of Collatine ,, 238
none of all our *b* should know *Princess i* 8
thoughts enrich the *b* of the world.' ,, *ii* 181
b Was sprinkled on your kirtle, ,, 273
That was fawn's *b*, not brother's, ,, 275
blissful palpitations in the *b*, ,, *iv* 28
what mother's *b* You draw from, *Princess v* 404
The brethren of our *b* and cause, ,, *vi* 71
dabbled with the *b* Of his own son, ,, 104
' I've heard that there is iron in the *b*, ,, 230
faith in womankind Beats with his *b*, ,, *vii* 329
Mourn for the man of long-enduring *b*, *Ode on Well.* 24
Shall lash all Europe into *b* ; *To F. D. Maurice* 34
pierces the liver and blackens the *b* ; *The Islet* 35
To spill his *b* and heal the land : *The Victim* 44
anger, not by *b* to be satiated. *Boädicea* 52
Into my heart and my *b* ! *Window, Marr. Morn.* 16
I seem to fail from out my *b* *In Mem. ii* 15

Blood (*continued*) Or crush her, like a vice of *b*, *In Mem. iii* 15
Moved in the chambers of the *b* ; ,, *xxiii* 20
Oh, sacred be the flesh and *b* ,, *xxxiii* 11
This use may lie in *b* and breath, ,, *xlv* 13
b creeps, and the nerves prick ,, *l* 2
Defects of doubt, and taints of *b* ; ,, *liv* 4
O Sorrow, wilt thou rule my *b*, ,, *lix* 5
Delayest the sorrow in my *b*, *In Mem. lxxxiii* 14
branches of thy *b* ; Thy *b*, my friend, *In Mem. lxxxiv* 8
My *b* an even tenor kept, ,, *lxxxv* 17
Ring out false pride in place and *b*, ,, *cvi* 21
Thro' all the years of April *b* ; ,, *cix* 12
By *b* a king, at heart a clown ; ,, *cxi* 4
Till all my *b*, a fuller wave, ,, *cxxii* 12
And the great Æon sinks in *b*, ,, *cxxvii* 16
Remade the *b* and changed the frame, ,, *Con.* 11
drip with a silent horror of *b*, *Maud I i* 3
sweeter *b* by the other side ; ,, *xiii* 34
never yet so warmly ran my *b* ,, *xviii* 3
household Fury sprinkled with *b* ,, *xix* 32
true *b* spilt had in it a heat ,, 44
soul of the rose went into my *b*, ,, *xxii* 33
A cry for a brother's *b* : ,, *II i* 34
Am I guilty of *b* ? ,, *ii* 73
fear they are not roses, but *b* ; ,, *v* 78
sun with smoke and earth with *b*, *Com. of Arthur* 37
and clarions shrilling unto *b*, ,, 103
And mine is living *b* : *Gareth and L.* 10
he had glamour enow In his own *b*, ,, 210
that best *b* it is a sin to spill.' ,, 600
ev'n Sir Lancelot thro' his warm *b* ,, 1398
Prince's *b* spirted upon the scarf, *Marr. of Geraint* 208
fail'd to draw The quiet night into her *b*, ,, 532
b Of their strong bodies, flowing, ,, 568
nay ; I do not mean *b* : *Geraint and E.* 338
fearing for his hurt and loss of *b*, ,, 777
nature's prideful sparkle in the *b* ,, 827
vicious quitch Of *b* and custom ,, 904
Fill'd all the genial courses of his *b* ,, 927
Born with the *b*, not learnable, *Balin and Balan* 175
starve not thou this fire within thy *b*, ,, 453
Reputed to be red with sinless *b*, ,, 557
If I were Arthur, I would have thy *b*. *Merlin and V.* 53
As clean as *b* of babes, ,, 344
for my *b* Hath earnest in it ,, 556
sin that practice burns into the *b*, ,, 762
pale *b* of the wizard at her touch ,, 949
Red as the rising sun with heathen *b*, *Lancelot and E.* 308
the *b* Sprang to her face and fill'd ,, 376
And half his *b* burst forth, ,, 517
For twenty strokes of the *b*, ,, 720
far *b*, which dwelt at Camelot ; ,, 803
when the *b* ran lustier in him again, ,, 881
Ev'n to the death, as tho' ye were my *b*, ,, 960
Was rather in the fantasy than the *b*. ,, 1132
what are they ? flesh and *b* ? ,, 1256
no further off in *b* from me Than sister ; *Holy Grail* 69
White Horse in his own heathen *b*— ,, 312
my *b* danced in me, and I knew ,, 366
Our race and *b*, a remnant ,, 663
b beats, and the blossom blows, ,, 671
slept that night for pleasure in his *b*, *Pelleas and E.* 138
have risen against me in their *b* ,, 461
No *b* of mine, I trow ; *Last Tournament* 201
be no rubies, this is frozen *b*, ,, 413
Showing a shower of *b* in a field noir, ,, 433
flesh and *b* Of our old kings : ,, 686
flesh and *b* perforce would violate : ,, 689
comforted the *b* With meats and wines, ,, 724
reverencing king's *b* in a bad man, *Guinevere* 37
To save his *b* from scandal, ,, 514
drew Down with his *b*, till all his heart *Pass. of Arthur* 97
a brow Striped with dark *b* : ,, 380
countenance with quick and healthful *b*— *Lover's Tale i* 97
And hourly visitation of the *b*, ,, 206

Blood (*continued*) stream of life, one stream, one life, one *b*, *Lover's Tale i* 239
As mountain streams Our *b's* ran free: ,, 327
I was as the brother of her *b*, ,, 559
my *b* Crept like marsh drains ,, *ii* 52
I weänt shed a drop on 'is *b*, *North. Cobbler* 114
Now reddest with the *b* of holy men, *Sir J. Oldcastle* 54
a cross of flesh and *b* And holier. ,, 137
Blue *b* of Spain, *Columbus* 114
blue *b* and black *b* of Spain, ,, 116
innocent hospitalities quench'd in *b*, ,, 176
and the boast of our ancient *b*, *V. of Maeldune* 88
red with *b* the Crescent reels *Montenegro* 6
All the field with *b* of the fighters Flow'd, *Batt. of Brunanburh* 24
wholesome heat the *b* had lost, *To E. Fitzgerald* 24
crowd would roar For *b*, for war, *Tiresias* 65
Spain in his *b* and the Jew— *The Wreck* 15
are both of them turn'd into *b*, *Despair* 91
Her *b* is in your bloom. *Ancient Sage* 166
evil thought may soil thy children's *b*; ,, 275
yer Honour's the thrue ould *b* *Tomorrow* 5
on that founder of our *b*. *Locksley H., Sixty* 32
shriek'd and slaked the light with *b*. ,, 90
Like drops of *b* in a dark-gray sea, *Heavy Brigade* 43
O follow, leaping *b*, *Early Spring* 25
Their idol smear'd with *b*, *Freedom* 28
crescent moon, and changed it into *b*. *Happy* 44
Diffuse thyself at will thro' all my *b*, *Prog. of Spring* 24
hopes, which race the restless *b*, ,, 115
herb or balm May clear the *b* from poison, *Death of Œnone* 36
as he yell'd of yore for Christian *b*. *St. Telemachus* 46
dust send up a steam of human *b*, ,, 53
hour Dark with the *b* of man ,, 80
warms the *b* of Shiah and Sunnee, *Akbar's Dream* 107
gentleman, heart, *b* and bone, *Bandit's Death* 2
For he reek'd with the *b* of Piero; ,, 13
a ray red as *b* Glanced on the strangled face— ,, 31
Rang the stroke, and sprang the *b*, *The Tourney* 9
Blood-eagle red '*B-e*' of liver and heart; *Dead Prophet* 71
Blooded *See* **Cold-blooded, Pale-blooded**
Bloodier the hands of power Were *b*, *Aylmer's Field* 453
Bloodily *B* flow'd the Tamesa rolling *Boädicea* 27
B, *b* fall the battle-axe, ,, 56
Bloodless now, the *b* point reversed, *The Voyage* 71
b east began To quicken to the sun, *Marr. of Geraint* 534
Blood-red dabbled with *b-r* heath, *Maud I i* 2
flames The *b-r* blossom of war ,, *III vi* 53
the *b-r* light of dawn Flared *Lancelot and E.* 1025
but always in the night *B-r*, and sliding down the blacken'd marsh *B-r*, and on the naked mountain top *B-r*, and in the sleeping mere below *B-r*. *Holy Grail* 473
In *b-r* armour sallying, *Last Tournament* 443
himself *B-r* from battle, *Tiresias* 113
Bloodshed hold were all as free From cursed *b*, *Gareth and L.* 599
Bloody shovell'd up into some *b* trench *Audley Court* 42
see the raw mechanic's *b* thumbs *Walk. to the Mail* 75
Where the *b* conduit runs, *Vision of Sin* 144
take such *b* vengeance on you both?— *Princess iv* 534
Bloom (s) (*See also* **Chestnut-bloom, Milk-bloom, Orange-bloom**) inlay Of braided *b's* unmown, *Arabian Nights* 29
lovely freight Of overflowing *b's*, *Ode to Memory* 17
throng with stately *b's* the breathing spring *The Poet* 27
Whence that aery *b* of thine, *Adeline* 11
violet eyes. and all her Hebe *b*, *Gardener's D.* 137
In bud or blade, or *b*, may find, *Day-Dm., Moral* 10
many a slope was rich in *b* *To E. L.* 20
fair in our sad world's best *b*, *The Brook* 218
scatter'd, each a nest in *b*. *Aylmer's Field* 150
cheek and bosom brake the wrathful *b* *Princess iv* 383
bud ever breaks into *b* on the tree, *The Islet* 32
The chestnut towers in his *b*; *Voice and the P.* 18
b profuse and cedar arches Charm, *Milton* 11
not for thee the glow, the *b*, *In Mem. ii* 9
And every spirit's folded *b* ,, *xliii* 2
Bloom (s) (*continued*) Which sicken'd every living *b*, *In Mem. lxxii* 7
over brake and *b* And meadow, ,, *lxxxvi* 3
And passion pure in snowy *b* ,, *cix* 11
azure *b* of a crescent of sea, *Maud I iv* 5
wild-wood hyacinth and the *b* of May. *Balin and Balan* 271
and her *b* A rosy dawn kindled *Pelleas and E.* 71
ribb'd And barr'd with *b* on *b*. *Lover's Tale i* 416
We was busy as beeäs i' the *b* *North. Cobbler* 15
Edith—all One *b* of youth, *Sisters (E. and E.)* 120
'How far thro' all the *b* and brake *Ancient Sage* 19
wake The *b* that fades away? ,, 94
Her blood is in your *b*. ,, 166
lifts her buried life from gloom to *b*, *Demeter and P.* 98
rounder cheek had brighten'd into *b*. *The Ring* 351
vernal *b* from every vale and plain *To Mary Boyle* 9
Bloom (verb) She saw the water-lily *b*, *L. of Shalott iii* 39
Lotos *b's* below the barren peak: *Lotos-Eaters, C.S.* 100
b's the garden that I love. *Gardener's D.* 34
That if it can it there may *b*, *In Mem. viii* 23
from marge to marge shall *b* the eternal landscape ,, *xlvi* 7
Will *b* to profit, otherwhere. ,, *lxxxii* 12
hearts are warm'd and faces *b*, ,, *Con.* 82
my white heather only *b's* in heaven *Romney's R.* 110
B's in the Past, but close to me to-day *Roses on the T.* 6
Bloomed thro' The low and *b* foliage, *Arabian Nights* 13
Blooming The maid-of-honour *b* fair; *Day-Dm., Sleep. P.* 28
By Cupid-boys of *b* hue— ,, *Ep.* 10
her *b* mantle torn, *Princess vi* 145
Blossom (s) (*See also* **Almond-blossom, Apple-blossom, Blackthorn-blossom, Lake-blossom, May-blossom, Orange-blossom**) Atween the *b's*, 'We are free.' *The Winds, etc.* 8
Bursts into *b* in his sight. *Fatima* 35
He prest the *b* of his lips to mine, *Œnone* 78
The *b* on the blackthorn, the leaf *May Queen, N. Y's. E.* 8
As we bear *b* of the dead; *Love thou thy land* 94
b fades, and they that loved *Walk. to the Mail* 57
The maiden *b's* of her teens *Talking Oak* 79
break In full and kindly *b*. *Will Water.* 24
as Nature packs Her *b* or her seedling, *Enoch Arden* 179
With here a *b* sailing, *The Brook* 56
Gather'd the *b* that rebloom'd, *Aylmer's Field* 142
Into a land all sun and *b*, *Sea Dreams* 101
caught the *b* of the flying terms, *Princess, Pro.* 164
Perch'd on the pouted *b* of her lips: ,, 199
Fruit, *b*, viand, amber wine, and gold. ,, *iv* 35
my babe, my *b*, ah, my child, ,, *v* 82
lay my little *b* at my feet, ,, 100
the *b* wavering fell, ,, *vi* 80
Scatter the *b* under her feet! *W. to Alexandra* 9
Or rosy *b* in hot ravine, *The Daisy* 32
they tumble the *b*, the mad little tits! *Window, Ay.* 9
The tender *b* flutter down, *In Mem. ci* 2
flames The blood-red *b* of war *Maud III vi* 53
sun, and rain! and the free *b* flows: *Com. of Arthur* 409
near her, like a *b* vermeil-white, *Marr. of Geraint* 364
tints the *b* of the quince *Balin and Balan* 267
wayside *b's* open to the blaze. ,, 449
that will strike my *b* dead. *Lancelot and E.* 971
blood beats, and the *b* blows, *Holy Grail* 671
groves that look'd a paradise Of *b*, *Guinevere* 390
little *b*, O mine, and mine *To A. Tennyson* 4
Had set the *b* of her health again, *Sisters (E. and E.)* 151
And starr'd with a myriad *b* *V. of Maeldune* 40
B and *b*, and promise of *b*, ,, 51
if the *b* can doat on the blight, *The Wreck* 19
tastes the fruit before the *b* falls, *Ancient Sage* 75
Jet upward thro' the mid-day *b*. *Demeter and P.* 47
hillock, Would break into *b*; *Merlin and the G.* 108
'Sleep, little *b*, my honey, my bliss! *Romney's R.* 99
From each fair plant the *b* choicest-grown *Akbar's Dream* 22
Blossom (verb) A little garden *b*. *Amphion* 104
wilderness shall *b* as the rose. *Aylmer's Field* 649
buds and *b's* like the rest. *In Mem. cxv* 20
And *b* in purple and red. *Maud I xxii* 74

Blossom (verb) (*continued*) where the winter thorn *B's* at Christmas, *Holy Grail* 52
b an' spring from the grass, *Tomorrow* 89
B again on a colder isle. *To Prof. Jebb* 12
Blossom-ball Made *b-b* or daisy-chain, *Aylmer's Field* 87
Blossom-belt Above the garden's glowing *b-b's*, *Princess v* 363
Blossom-dust like the working bee in *b-d*, *Enoch Arden* 366
Foot-gilt with all the *b-d* *Merlin and V.* 282
Blossom'd (adj.) (*See also* **Daisy-blossomed, Heavy-blossom'd**) white robe like a *b* branch *Princess iv* 179
On the *b* gable-ends *Maud I vi* 9
O *b* portal of the lonely house, *Lover's Tale i* 280
Blossom'd (verb) branch'd And *b* in the zenith, *Enoch Arden* 586
b up From out a common vein *Princess ii* 313
when the wreath of March has *b*, *To F. D. Maurice* 43
Great garlands swung and *b*; *Lover's Tale iv* 191
Blossom-flake elmtree's ruddy-hearted *b-f* *To Mary Boyle* 3
Blossom-fragrant *b-f* slipt the heavy dews *Princess v* 243
Blossoming (*See also* **Many-blossoming**) and the happy *b* shore? *Sea-Fairies* 8
Blot (s) With *b's* of it about them, *Aylmer's Field* 620
'Tis the *b* upon the brain *Maud II iv* 60
a throne, And blackens every *b*: *Ded. of Idylls* 28
Gareth's eyes had flying *b's* *Gareth and L.* 1031
square of text that looks a little *b*, *Merlin and V.* 671
Far-off, a *b* upon the stream, *Lancelot and E.* 1392
A *b* in heaven, the Raven, *Guinevere* 133
Blot (verb) *B* out the slope of sea *Princess vii* 38
Blotch face deform'd by lurid *b* and blain— *Death of Œnone* 72
Blotted (*See also* **Mist-blotted**) took his brush and *b* out the bird, *Merlin and V.* 478
Blow (s) (*See also* **Death-blow, Head-blow**) O cursed hand! O cursed *b*! *Oriana* 82
stood like one that had received a *b*: *Sea Dreams* 161
red-hot iron to be shaped with *b's*. *Princess v* 209
clench'd his purpose like a *b*! ,, 306
b's rain'd, as here and everywhere ,, 501
With their own *b's* they hurt themselves, ,, *vi* 49
Back to France with countless *b's*, *Ode on Well.* 111
knife uprising toward the *b* *The Victim* 66
Phantom sound of *b's* descending, *Boädicea* 25
breasts the *b's* of circumstance, *In Mem. lxiv* 7
But in the present broke the *b*. ,, *lxxxv* 56
shocks of Chance—The *b's* of Death. ,, *xcv* 43
That must have life for a *b*. *Maud II i* 27
red life spilt for a private *b*— ,, *v* 93
mightier of his hands with every *b*, *Com. of Arthur* 110
Three with good *b's* he quieted, *Gareth and L.* 813
mightful hand striking great *b's* *Marr. of Geraint* 95
lash'd at each So often and with such *b's*, ,, 564
Descended, and disjointed it at a *b*: *Balin and Balan* 296
Kill'd with a word worse than a life of *b's*! *Merlin and V.* 870
each had slain his brother at a *b*; *Lancelot and E.* 41
hardly won with bruise and *b*, ,, 1165
while Arthur at one *b*, Striking *Pass. of Arthur* 167
live to fight again and to strike another *b*.' *The Revenge* 95
Rode flashing *b* upon *b*, *Heavy Brigade* 32
Blow (verb) (*See also* **Blaw**) The stream flows, The wind *b's*, *Nothing will Die* 10
make the winds *b* Round and round, ,, 23
The wind will cease to *b*; *All Things will Die* 10
loud the Norland whirlwinds *b*, *Oriana* 6
Round thee *b*, self-pleached deep, *A Dirge* 29
And tell me if the woodbines *b*. *My life is full* 25
Gazing where the lilies *b* *L. of Shalott i* 7
That all about the thorn will *b* *Two Voices* 59
When April nights began to *b*, *Miller's D.* 106
gales, as from deep gardens, *b* Before him, *Fatima* 24
the wind *b's* the foam, and all my heart *Œnone* 62
by the meadow-trenches *b* the faint sweet cuckoo-flowers; *May Queen* 30
from the dry dark wold the summer airs *b* cool *May Queen, N. Y's. E.* 27
and all the flowers that *b*, ,, *Con.* 7
Lotos *b's* by every winding creek: *Lotos-Eaters, C. S.* 101
b's More softly round the open wold, *To J. S.* 1
Blow (verb) (*continued*) Nor ever wind *b's* loudly; *M. d'Arthur* 261
or then While the gold-lily *b's*, *Edwin Morris* 146
I saw Your own Olivia *b*, *Talking Oak* 76
light as any wind that *b's* So fleetly ,, 129
The full south-breeze around thee *b* ,, 271
winds from all the compass shift and *b*, *Godiva* 33
wildweed-flower that simply *b's*? *Day-Dm., Moral* 6
B, flute, and stir the stiff-set sprigs, *Amphion* 63
weed That *b's* upon its mountain, ,, 94
she makes The violet of a legend *b* *Will Water.* 147
It was the time when lilies *b*, *Lady Clare* 1
And the wind did *b*; *The Captain* 34
To *b* these sacrifices thro' the world— *Aylmer's Field* 758
Low, low, breathe and *b*, *Princess iii* 3
and *b*, *B* him again to me; ,, 6
B, bugle, *b*, set the wild echoes flying, (repeat) ,, *iv* 5 17
B, bugle; answer, echoes, dying, (repeat) ,, 6 12
B, let us hear the purple glens replying: ,, 11
A moment, while the trumpets *b*, ,, 581
let the mournful martial music *b*; *Ode on Well.* 17
To Britain, when her flowers begin to *b*! *W. to Marie Alex.* 7
Wet west wind how you *b*, you *b*! *Window, No Answer* 14
B then, *b*, and when I am gone, ,, ,, 17
And make them pipes whereon to *b*. *In Mem. xxi* 4
With blasts that *b* the poplar white, ,, *lxxii* 3
fan my brows and *b* The fever from my cheek, ,, *lxxxvi* 8
from the garden and the wild A fresh association *b*, ,, *ci* 18
There in due time the woodbine *b's*, ,, *cv* 7
By ashen roots the violets *b*. ,, *cxv* 4
And all the breeze of Fancy *b's*, ,, *cxxii* 17
woodland lilies, Myriads *b* together. *Maud I xii* 8
lily and rose That *b* by night, ,, *II v* 75
and rain! and the free blossom *b's*: *Com. of Arthur* 409
'*B* trumpet, for the world is white with May; ,, 482
B trumpet, the long night hath roll'd away! ,, 483
B thro' the living world— ,, 484
'*B* trumpet! he will lift us from the dust. ,, 491
B trumpet! live the strength and die the lust! ,, 492
'*B*, for our Sun is mighty in his May! ,, 497
B, for our Sun is mightier day by day! ,, 498
flower, That *b's* a globe of after arrowlets, *Gareth and L.* 1029
flowers that close when day is done, *B* sweetly: ,, 1068
King gave order to let *b* His horns *Marr. of Geraint* 152
we *b* with breath, or touch with hand, *Holy Grail* 114
blood beats, and the blossom *b's*, ,, 671
But such a blast, my King, began to *b*, ,, 795
clash the shield, and *b* the horn. *Last Tournament* 436
I hear the trumpet *b*: They summon me *Guinevere* 569
Nor ever wind *b's* loudly; *Pass. of Arthur* 429
trust that Heaven Will *b* the tempest *To the Queen ii* 47
whirlwind *b* these woods, as never blew before. *The Flight* 12
gather the roses whenever they *b*, *Romney's R.* 107
Let *b* the trumpet strongly while I pray, *Doubt and Prayer* 10
Blower 'O hunter, and O *b* of the horn, Harper, *Last Tournament* 542
Blowing (*See also* **Blawin', Equal-blowing, Merrily-blowing, Trumpet-blowings**) When will the wind be aweary of *b* Over the sky? *Nothing will Die* 3
south winds are *b* Over the sky. *All Things will Die* 3
myrrh-thickets *b* round The stately cedar, *Arabian Nights* 104
Winds were *b*, waters flowing, *Oriana* 14
Aloud the hollow bugle *b*, ,, 17
B a noise of tongues and deeds, *Two Voices* 206
Like soften'd airs that *b* steal, ,, 406
wind is *b* in turret and tree. (repeat) *The Sisters* 3, 33
(while warm airs lull us, *b* lowly) *Lotos-Eaters, C. S.* 89
a bark that, *b* forward, bore King Arthur, *M. d'Arthur, Ep.* 21
wind *b* over meadowy holms And alders, *Edwin Morris* 95
and *b* havenward With silks, and fruits, *Golden Year* 44
Summer woods, about them *b*, *L. of Burleigh* 19
B the ringlet from the braid: *Sir L. and Q. G.* 39
and *b* bosks of wilderness, *Princess i* 111
The horns of Elfland faintly *b*! ,, *iv* 10
'Fear not, isle of *b* woodland, *Boädicea* 38
No joy the *b* season gives, *In Mem. xxxviii* 5
Over glowing ships; Over *b* seas, *Maud I xvii* 13

Boane (bone) when an' wheere to bury his *b*. *Owd Roä* 8
Boanerges Our *B* with his threats of doom, *Sea Dreams* 251
Boar dog, and wolf and *b* and bear Came *Com. of Arthur* 23
wherewithal deck the *b's* head? Flowers? nay, the *b* hath rosemaries and bay. *Gareth and L.* 1073
Board (table) 'This was cast upon the *b*, *Œnone* 79
cast the golden fruit upon the *b*, ,, 226
I pledge her silent at the *b*; *Will Water.* 25
cups and silver on the burnish'd *b* *Enoch Arden* 742
There at a *b* by tome and paper sat, *Princess ii* 32
And on the *b* the fluttering urn: *In Mem. xcv* 8
Arrange the *b* and brim the glass; ,, *cvii* 16
seating Gareth at another *b*, Sat down *Gareth and L.* 871
boil'd the flesh, and spread the *b*, *Marr. of Geraint* 391
knife's haft hard against the *b*, *Geraint and E.* 600
bare her by main violence to the *b*, ,, 654
Along the walls and down the *b*; *Balin and Balan* 84
A goblet on the *b* by Balin, ,, 362
all the light that falls upon the *b* *Holy Grail* 249
Who spake so low and sadly at our *b*; ,, 701
left me gazing at a barren *b*, ,, 893
Are ye but creatures of the *b* and bed, *Pelleas and E.* 267
Before the *b*, there paused and stood, *Lover's Tale iv* 307
Board (ship) he served a year On *b* a merchantman, *Enoch Arden* 53
Am I so like her? so they said on *b*. *The Brook* 223
I leap on *b*: no helmsman steers: *Sir Galahad* 39
Board (for a game) That pushes us off from the *b*, *Maud I iv* 27
Board (floor) Pattering over the *b's*, (repeat) *Grandmother* 77, 79
Board (list, register) hastily subscribed, We enter'd on the *b's*: *Princess ii* 74
Boarding *B's* and rafters and doors— *Def. of Lucknow* 67
Boast (s) To shame the *b* so often made, *Love thou thy land* 71
And bring her babe, and make her *b*, *In Mem. xl* 26
that ye blew your *b* in vain?' *Gareth and L.* 1229
to mar the *b* Thy brethren of thee make— ,, 1242
Abash'd us both, and brake my *b*. *Balin and Balan* 71
and the *b* of our ancient blood, *V. of Maeldune* 88
crime, of her eldest-born, her glory, her *b*, *Despair* 73
Boast (verb) you know it—I will not *b*: *Princess iv* 353
the clipt palm of which they *b*; *The Daisy* 26
and *b*, 'Behold the man that loved and lost, *In Mem i* 14
heard them *b* That they would slay you, *Geraint and E.* 73
b's his life as purer than thine own; *Balin and Balan* 104
Boasted each of them *b* he sprang from the oldest race *V. of Maeldune* 4
Boastful ruled the hour, Tho' seeming *b*: *Aylmer's Field* 195
Boat (*See also* **Pleasure-boat**) leaping lightly from the *b*, *Arabian Nights* 92
Down she came and found a *b* *L. of Shalott iv* 6
Francis just alighted from the *b*, *Audley Court* 7
B, island, ruins of a castle, built *Edwin Morris* 6
That he sings in his *b* on the bay! *Break, break, etc.* 8
Anchors of rusty fluke, and *b's* updrawn; *Enoch Arden* 18
To purchase his own *b*, and make a home ,, 47
He purchased his own *b*, and made a home For Annie, ,, 58
sell the *b*—and yet he loved her well— ,, 134
The horse he drove, the *b* he sold, ,, 609
b that bears the hope of life approach ,, 830
till as when a *b* Tacks, *Princess ii* 185
b's and bridges for the use of men. ,, *vi* 47
The *b* is drawn upon the shore; *In Mem. cxxi* 6
The market *b* is on the stream, ,, 13
There found a little *b*, and stept into it; *Merlin and V.* 198
the *b* Drave with a sudden wind across ,, 200
He saw two cities in a thousand *b's* ,, 561
Up the great river in the boatman's *b*. *Lancelot and E.* 1038
with exceeding swiftness ran the *b*, If *b* it were— *Holy Grail* 514
or had the *b* Become a living creature ,, 518
blackening in the sea-foam sway'd a *b*, ,, 802
I burst the chain, I sprang into the *b*. ,, 807
And felt the *b* shock earth, ,, 812
Then from the *b* I leapt, ,, 819
be yon dark Queens in yon black *b*, *Pass. of Arthur* 452
The *b* was beginning to move, *First Quarrel* 21
an' go to-night by the *b*.' ,, 88
Boat (*continued*) the *b* went down that night—(repeat) *First Quarrel* 92
till I saw that a *b* was nearing us— *The Wreck* 123
and there in the *b* I lay With sad eyes ,, 125
his *b* was on the sand; *The Flight* 37
And lay on that funereal *b*, *To Marq. of Dufferin* 34
Had parted from his comrade in the *b*, *The Ring* 308
b's of Dahomey that float upon human blood! *The Dawn* 5
Boated I *b* over, ran My craft aground, *Edwin Morris* 108
They *b* and they cricketed; *Princess, Pro.* 160
Boat-head did I turn away The *b-h* *Arabian Nights* 25
as the *b-h* wound along The willowy hills *L. of Shalott iv* 24
Boatman wrought To make the *boatmen* fishing-nets, *Enoch Arden* 815
By the great river in a *b's* hut. *Lancelot and E.* 278
Up the great river in a *b's* boat. ,, 1038
Boatswain China-bound, And wanting yet a *b*. *Enoch Arden* 123
Boboli Or walks in *B's* ducal bowers. *The Daisy* 44
Bode thither wending there that night they *b*. *Lancelot and E.* 412
And Lancelot *b* a little, till he saw ,, 461
There *b* the night: but woke with dawn, ,, 846
And *b* among them yet a little space ,, 921
And there awhile it *b*; and if a man *Holy Grail* 54
spake not any word, But *b* his hour, *Last Tournament* 386
Bodied Is *b* forth the second whole. *Love thou thy land* 66
Bodily were she the prize of *b* force, *Marr. of Geraint* 541
Body I wrapt his *b* in the sheet, *The Sisters* 34
A *b* slight and round, and like a pear *Walk. to the Mail* 53
I was strong and hale of *b* then; *St. S. Stylites* 29
touch my *b* and be heal'd, and live: ,, 79
bodies and the bones of those That strove *Day-Dm., Arrival* 9
'Here lies the *b* of Ellen Adair; *Edward Gray* 27
There lies the *b* of Ellen Adair! ,, 35
Bore to earth her *b*, drest In the dress *L. of Burleigh* 98
He cast his *b*, and on we swept. *The Voyage* 80
Like that long-buried *b* of the king, *Aylmer's Field* 3
adulteries That saturate soul with *b*. ,, 377
His *b* half flung forward in pursuit, ,, 587
as not passing thro' the fire *Bodies*, but souls— ,, 672
that break *B* toward death, and palsy, *Lucretius* 154
unlaced my casque And grovell'd on my *b*, *Princess vi* 28
and to dance Its *b*, and reach ,, 138
There lay the sweet little *b* *Grandmother* 62
I look'd at the still little *b*— ,, 66
this weight of *b* and limb, *High. Pantheism* 5
phantom *bodies* of horses and men; *Boädicea* 27
and back return To where the *b* sits, *In Mem. xii* 19
cheeks drop in; the *b* bows Man dies: ,, *xxxv* 3
Bare of the *b*, might it last, ,, *xliii* 6
in the ghastly pit long since a *b* was found, *Maud I i* 5
sworn to bury All this dead *b* of hate, ,, *xix* 97
Hath *b* enow to hold his foemen down?' *Com. of Arthur* 253
blood Of their strong *bodies*, flowing, *Marr. of Geraint* 569
And let the *bodies* lie, but bound *Geraint and E.* 96
And being weak in *b* said no more; *Lancelot and E.* 839
'Faith of my *b*,' he said, 'and art thou not— *Pelleas and E.* 318
But the sweet *b* of a maiden babe. *Last Tournament* 48
Belted his *b* with her white embrace, ,, 513
A *b* journeying onward, sick with toil. *Lover's Tale i* 124
breathless *b* of her good deeds past. ,, 217
soul and heart and *b* are all at ease: ,, 556
had the ghastliest That ever lusted for a *b*, ,, 648
She took the *b* of my past delight, ,, 681
'*b* and soul And life and limbs, ,, *iv* 282
sank his *b* with honour down into the deep, *The Revenge* 109
He veils His flesh in bread, *b* and bread together.' *Sir J. Oldcastle* 157
'No bread, no bread. God's *b*!' ,, 159
Thou canst not prove that thou art *b* alone, *Ancient Sage* 59
they laid this *b* they foun' an the grass *Tomorrow* 73
nurse of ailing *b* and mind, *Locksley H., Sixty* 51
lustier *b*, larger mind? ,, 164
out of his *b* she drew The red 'Blood-eagle' *Dead Prophet* 70
You say your *b* is so foul— *Happy* 25
Your *b* is not foul to me, and *b* is foul at best. ,, 28
If my *b* come from brutes, (repeat) *By an Evolution.* 5, 13
Where I sank with the *b* at times ,, 18

Body (*continued*) that dark *b* which had lain Of old — *Death of Œnone* 93
bodies and souls go down in a common wreck, — *The Dawn* 13
Bog (*See also* **Irish Bog**) last month they wor diggin' the *b*, — *Tomorrow* 61
bad scran to the *b's* whin they swallies the man — ,, 66
sorra the *b* that's in Hiven — ,, 67
aisier work av they lived be an Irish *b*. — ,, 72
Boggle (ghost) Theer wur a *b* in it, — *N. Farmer, O. S.* 30
Bog-wather foun' Dhrownded in black *b-w* — *Tomorrow* 62
Boil hell beneath Made me *b* over. — *St. S. Stylites* 171
Boil'd burn'd in fire, or *b* in oil, — ,, 52
b the flesh, and spread the board, — *Marr. of Geraint* 391
Bold (*See also* **Half-bold, Over-bold**) so clear and *b* and free As you, — *Rosalind* 17
Kate loves well the *b* and fierce; — *Kate* 29
But none are *b* enough for Kate — ,, 30
wide in soul and *b* of tongue, — *Two Voices* 124
New-year blithe and *b*, my friend, — *D. of the O. Year* 35
A man more pure and *b* and just — *To J. S.* 31
tho' keen and *b* and soldierly Sear'd — *Aylmer's Field* 192
You are *b* indeed: — *Princess iii* 250
Among the wise and the *b*. — *Ode on Well.* 52
If you be fearful, then must we be *b*. — *Third of Feb.* 19
men are *b* and strongly say their say;— — *W. to Marie Alex.* 32
With what divine affections *b* — *In Mem. xciv* 2
b to dwell On doubts that drive the coward — ,, *xcv* 29
b in heart and act and word was he, — *Com. of Arthur* 176
And wholly *b* thou art, and meek — *Gareth and L.* 1168
Am I so *b*, and could I so stand by, — *Marr. of Geraint* 102
B will I be— — *Balin and Balan* 194
Balin was *b*, and ask'd To bear — ,, 199
B was mine answer, 'Had thyself — *Holy Grail* 277
'Art thou so *b* and hast not seen the Grail?' — ,, 279
This heard the *b* Sir Bedivere and spake: — *Pass. of Arthur* 50
death And silence made him *b*— — *Lover's Tale iv* 73
Had they been *b* enough then, — *Def. of Lucknow* 66
still be *b* Not only to slight praise — *To Duke of Argyll* 3
Bolden'd *b* by the silence of his King,— — *Holy Grail* 857
Bolder And me this knowledge *b* made, — *To J. S.* 5
seems no *b* than a beaten hound; — *Geraint and E.* 61
Not risen to, she was *b*. — *The Ring* 361
Boldest drawn of fairest Or *b* since, — *Ode to Memory* 90
their oldest and their *b* said, — *Death of Œnone* 100
Boldly for such a face had *b* died,' — *D. of F. Women* 98
Enoch faced this morning of farewell Brightly and *b*. — *Enoch Arden* 183
And *b* ventured on the liberties. — *Princess i* 205
I offer *b*: we will seat you highest: — ,, *iii* 159
B they rode and well, — *Light Brigade* 23
Boldness Should licensed *b* gather force, — *In Mem. cxiii* 13
B and royal knighthood of the bird — *Merlin and V.* 134
Bole (*See also* **Elm-tree-boles**) stanzas that you made About my 'giant *b*;' — *Talking Oak* 136
wind And double in and out the *b's*, — *Princess iv* 262
a thousand rings of Spring In every *b*, — ,, *v* 238
glancing thro' the hoary *b's*, he saw, — *Pelleas and E.* 50
Bolster'd An' the fences all on 'em *b* oop — *Owd Roä* 32
Bolt (*See also* **Battle-bolt**) and if a *b* of fire Would rive — *Supp. Confessions* 10
b's are hurl'd Far below them in the valleys, — *Lotos-Eaters, C.S.* 111
Appealing to the *b's* of Heaven; — *Princess iv* 372
Scarce had she ceased, when out of heaven a *b* — *Merlin and V.* 934
Pray Heaven, they be not smitten by the *b*.' — *Holy Grail* 221
slant His *b* from falling on your head— — *Happy* 81
b of war dashing down upon cities — *The Dawn* 8
Bolted gate Is *b*, and the master gone. — *Tiresias* 201
Bond (adj.) dwarf'd or godlike, *b* or free: — *Princess vii* 260
Bond (s) Unmanacled from *b's* of sense, — *Two Voices* 236
break or bind All force in *b's* that might endure, — *Palace of Art* 154
Seeing obedience is the *b* of rule. — *M. d'Arthur* 94
Then broke all *b's* of courtesy, — *Aylmer's Field* 323
Which breaks all *b's* of ours; — ,, 425
broke the *b* which they desired to break, — ,, 778
all her *b's* Crack'd; and I saw — *Lucretius* 37
his dearest *b* is this, — *Princess vii* 277

Bond (s) (*continued*) Has broke the *b* of dying use. — *In Mem. cv* 12
Than some strong *b* which is to be. — ,, *cxvi* 16
Gareth loosed his *b's* and on free feet — *Gareth and L.* 817
all Their bearing in their common *b* of love, — *Balin and Balan* 150
purity Beyond the limit of their *b*, — *Merlin and V.* 27
For such a supersensual sensual *b* — ,, 109
our *b* Had best be loosed for ever: — ,, 341
world howling forced them into *b's*, — ,, 744
yours, Not Arthur's, as ye know, save by the *b*. — *Lancelot and E.* 135
Not violating the *b* of like to like.' — ,, 241
daughter fled From *b's* or death, — ,, 277
Our *b*, as not the *b* of man and wife, — ,, 1191
Our *b* is not the *b* of man and wife. — ,, 1206
needs must break These *b's* that so defame me: — ,, 1421
More bondsman in his heart than in his *b's*. — *Pelleas and E.* 239
may be ye shall slay him in his *b's*.' — ,, 272
let who will release him from his *b's*. — ,, 294
gazed upon the man Of princely bearing, tho' in *b's*, — ,, 306
sprang Gawain, and loosed him from his *b's*, — ,, 315
bound, save by white *b's* and warm, — ,, 353
brakest thro' the scruple of my *b*, — *Last Tournament* 568
Seeing obedience is the *b* of rule. — *Pass. of Arthur* 262
Is but a burthen: loose the *b*, and go. — *To the Queen ii* 17
it was a *b* and seal Of friendship, — *Lover's Tale ii* 181
Were these not *b's*? nay, nay, — *Sisters (E. and E.)* 167
that mystic *b* betwixt the twins— — ,, 256
For I broke the *b*. — *The Wreck* 59
snap the *b* that link'd us life to life, — *Happy* 61
since my will Seal'd not the *b*— — *Princess v* 399
To dissolve the previous seal on a *b*, — *Maud I xix* 45
Bondslave bound by precontract Your bride, your *b*! — *Princess iv* 542
Bondsman My will is *b* to the dark; — *In Mem. iv* 2
More *b* in his heart than in his bonds. — *Pelleas and E.* 239
Bone (*See also* **Ankle-bones, Boän, Boane, Breast-bone, Collar-bone, Cross-bones**) To feed thy *b's* with lime, — *Two Voices* 326
green Christmas crams with weary *b's*. — *Wan Sculptor* 14
lay the mighty *b's* of ancient men, — *M. d'Arthur* 47
burn a fragrant lamp before my *b's*, — *St. S. Stylites* 196
bodies and the *b's* of those That strove — *Day-Dm., Arrival* 9
'You are *b's*, and what of that? — *Vision of Sin* 175
From the fashion of your *b's*. — ,, 182
his *b's* long laid within the grave, — *Lucretius* 256
Ammonites, and the first *b's* of Time; — *Princess, Pro.* 15
chanted on the blanching *b's* of men?' — ,, *ii* 199
cut this epitaph above my *b's*; — ,, 207
stuck out The *b's* of some vast bulk — ,, *iii* 294
'As these rude *b's* to us, are we to her — ,, 296
and spilt our *b's* in the flood— — ,, *iv* 532
Echo round his *b's* for evermore. — *Ode on Well.* 12
Be glad, because his *b's* are laid by thine! — ,, 141
Thy roots are wrapt about the *b's*. — *In Mem. ii* 4
As if the quiet *b's* were blest — ,, *xviii* 6
Old warder of these buried *b's*, — ,, *xxxix* 1
grins on a pile of children's *b's*, — *Maud I i* 46
And my *b's* are shaken with pain, — ,, *II v* 5
b's for his o'ergrown whelp to crack; — ,, 55
being apt at arms and big of *b* — *Marr. of Geraint* 489
crack'd the helmet thro', and bit the *b*, — ,, 573
when his good *b* Seems to be pluck'd at — *Geraint and E.* 559
and he fears To lose his *b*, and lays his foot — ,, 562
arks with priceless *b's* of martyrdom, — *Balin and Balan* 110
lay till all their *b's* were bleach'd, — *Lancelot and E.* 43
part whiten'd with the *b's* of men, — *Holy Grail* 500
Fool to the midmost marrow of his *b's*, — *Pelleas and E.* 258
Like a dry *b* cast to some hungry hound? — *Last Tournament* 196
lay the mighty *b's* of ancient men, — *Pass. of Arthur* 215
I have number'd the *b's*, — *Rizpah* 10
but *b* of my *b* was left— — ,, 51
the *b's* that had suck'd me, the *b's* that had laughed — ,, 53
Do you think I was scared by the *b's*? — ,, 55
every *b* seem'd out of its place— — *In the Child. Hosp.* 13
can prayer set a broken *b*?' — ,, 20
'Behold the *b's* of Christopher Colon'— — *Columbus* 210
'These same chains Bound these same *b's* — ,, 214

Bone (*continued*) in these spasms that grind *B* against *b*. *Columbus* 221
the white North has thy *b's*; *Sir J. Franklin* 1
There blanch the *b's* of whom she slew, *Tiresias* 150
black in white above his *b's*. *Locksley H., Sixty* 44
moulder'd nest On its barkless *b's*, *Dead Prophet* 19
honest Poverty, bare to the *b*; *Vastness* 19
save breaking my *b's* on the rack? *By an Evolution*. 9
gentleman, heart, blood and *b*, *Bandit's Death* 2
Bone-batter'd being all *b-b* on the rock, Yielded; *Gareth and L.* 1050
Bonnet Or the frock and gipsy *b* *Maud I xx* 19
Bonny Doon Whistling a random bar of *B D*, *The Brook* 82
Book (*See also* **Annal-book, Booök, Statute-book**)
Take, Madam, this poor b *of song;* *To the Queen* 17
burnt His epic, his King Arthur, some twelve *b's*'— *The Epic* 28
these twelve *b's* of mine Were faint ,, 38
old Sir Robert's pride, His *b's*— *Audley Court* 59
faces grow between me and my *b*; *St. S. Stylites* 176
eyesight poring over miserable *b's*— *Locksley Hall* 172
prose O'er *b's* of travell'd seamen, *Amphion* 82
Nor yet the fear of little *b's* *Will Water*. 195
the priest, above his *b* Leering *Vision of Sin* 117
And bought them needful *b's*, *Enoch Arden* 332
Then desperately seized the holy *B*, ,, 495
she closed the *B* and slept: ,, 499
swear upon the *b* Not to reveal it, ,, 838
'on the *b*.' And on the *b*, half-frighted, ,, 842
After his *b's*, to flush his blood with air, Then to his *b's* again. *Aylmer's Field* 459
'Show me the *b's*!' *Sea Dreams* 148
'The *b's*! the *b's*!' but he, he could not ,, 150
great *B's* (see Daniel seven and ten) ,, 152
'O miracle of women,' said the *b*, *Princess, Pro*. 35
(I kept the *b* and had my finger in it) ,, 53
which brought My *b* to mind: ,, 120
on lattice edges lay Or *b* or lute; ,, *ii* 30
'can he not read—no *b's*? ,, *iii* 214
but brooding turn The *b* of scorn, ,, *v* 142
rout of saucy boys Brake on us at our *b's*, ,, 395
to and fro With *b's*, with flowers, ,, *vii* 26
was cramm'd with theories out of *b's*, ,, *Con*. 35
in this *B*, little Annie, the message *Grandmother* 96
Still in the little *b* you lent me, *The Daisy* 99
May bind a *b*, may line a box, *In Mem. lxxvii* 6
One lesson from one *b* we learn'd, ,, *lxxix* 14
Discuss'd the *b's* to love or hate, ,, *lxxxix* 34
With festal cheer, With *b's* and music, ,, *cvii* 22
in their hand Is Nature like an open *b*; ,, *Con*. 132
She sits by her music and *b's* *Maud I xiv* 13
a palm As glitters gilded in thy *B* of Hours. *Gareth and L.* 46
Read but one *b*, and ever reading *Merlin and V.* 622
and his *b* came down to me.' ,, 650
'Ye have the *b*: the charm is written in it: ,, 652
'Thou read the *b*, my pretty Vivien! ,, 667
cities on their flanks—thou read the *b*! ,, 676
'From our old *b's* I know That Joseph *Holy Grail* 59
For so they say, these *b's* of ours, ,, 65
'for in sooth These ancient *b's*— ,, 541
Of Geoffrey's *b*, or him of Malleor's, *To the Queen ii* 42
gie fur a howry owd *b* thutty pound an' moor, *Village Wife* 45
An' 'e'd wrote an owd *b*, his awn sen, ,, 46
I am written in the Lamb's own *B* of Life *Columbus* 88
dipt In some forgotten *b* of mine *To E. Fitzgerald* 47
He would open the *b's* that I prized, *The Wreck* 21
We had read their know-nothing *b's* *Despair* 55
their knowing and know-nothing *b's* ,, 93
knows not ev'n the *b* he wrote, *Ancient Sage* 148
knew no *b's* and no philosophies, ,, 218
there were *b's* and dresses—left to me, *The Ring* 113
I bad her keep, Like a seal'd *b*, ,, 123
scarce have learnt the title of your *b*, ,, 126
'The *b's*, the miniature, the lace are hers, ,, 288
my friend, To prize your various *b*, *To Ulysses* 47
thought to myself I would offer this *b* to you, *June Bracken, etc.* 4
'Alla,' says their sacred *b*, 'is Love,' *Akbar's Dream* 73
Booklearned *See* **Boooklarn'd.**
Booklearning *See* **Boooklarnin'.**
Bookless Your flight from out your *b* wilds *Princess ii* 56
Boom (s) air was torn in sunder, Crashing went the *b* *The Captain* 44
clash and *b* of the bells rang *V. of Maeldune* 110
Boom (verb) His captain's-ear has heard them *b* *Ode on Well.* 65
b and blanch on the precipices, *Boädicea* 76
Boometh At eve the beetle *b* *Claribel* 9
Booming Listens the muffled *b* indistinct *Lover's Tale i* 637
Boon (adj.) Fled all the *b* companions of the Earl, *Geraint and E.* 477
Boon (s) *b* from me, From me, Heaven's Queen, *Œnone* 126
Fresh apple-blossom, blushing for a *b*. *The Brook* 90
At last she begg'd a *b*, *Princess i* 146
widow crying to the King, 'A *b*, Sir King! *Gareth and L.* 334
No *b* is here, But justice, ,, 345
'A *b*, Sir King! Thine enemy, King, am I. ,, 351
'A *b*, Sir King! I am her kinsman, I. ,, 365
came Sir Kay, the seneschal, and cried, 'A *b*, Sir King! ,, 368
the wholesome *b* of gyve and gag.' ,, 370
b, Sir King (his voice was all ashamed), ,, 442
youth and worth a goodlier *b*! ,, 449
'A *b*, Sir King—this quest!' then— ,, 647
'To what request for what strange *b*,' *Merlin and V.* 264
B, ay, there was a *b*, one not so strange— ,, 287
ask your *b*, for *b* I owe you thrice, ,, 306
take this *b* so strange and not so strange.' ,, 310
Whenever I have ask'd this very *b*, ,, 323
Yield my *b*, Till which I scarce can yield ,, 351
Why will ye never ask some other *b*? ,, 375
Who feels no heart to ask another *b*. ,, 382
Not ever be too curious for a *b*, ,, 486
Lo, there my *b*! What other? ,, 494
To snare her royal fancy with a *b* *Lancelot and E.* 71
tale of diamonds for his destined *b*) ,, 91
Booök (book) 'e 'ed hallus a *b* i' 'is 'and, *Village Wife* 26
Hallus aloän wi' 'is *b's*, ,, 27
An' *b's*, what's *b's*? ,, 28
niver knawd nowt but *b's*, an' *b's*, ,, 52
why shouldn't thy *b's* be sowd? ,, 69
I hears es soom o' thy *b's* mebbe worth ,, 70
Heäps an' heäps o' *b's*, I ha' see'd 'em, ,, 71
moäst on 'is owd big *b's* fetch'd ,, 73
Sa 'is taäil wur lost an' 'is *b's* wur gone ,, 87
B's, es I said afoor, thebbe neyther 'ere nor theer! ,, 113
Boooklarn'd (booklearned) An' I 'oäps es 'e beänt *b*: ,, 23
Boooklarnin' (booklearning) an' we haätes *b* 'ere. ,, 24
Booöt (boot) I could fettle and clump owd *b's* *North. Cobbler* 13
And browt me the *b's* to be cobbled ,, 94
Boor-tree (elder-tree) in wan grave be the dead *b-t*, *Tomorrow* 87
Boot (*See also* **Booöt**) Leisurely tapping a glossy *b*, *Maud I xiii* 19
an' the mud o' 'is *b's* o' the stairs, *Spinster's S's*. 99
Boot (in addition) Will pay thee all thy wages, and to *b*. *Gareth and L.* 1005
Booth sport and song, in *b* and tent, *In Mem. xcviii* 28
Bootless proxy-wedded with a *b* calf *Princess i* 34
Booty chance of *b* from the morning's raid, *Geraint and E.* 565
Border (adj.) A *b* fantasy of branch and flower, *Lancelot and E.* 11
Border (s) Morn broaden'd on the *b's* of the dark, *D. of F. Women* 265
From out the *b's* of the morn, *On a Mourner* 24
Close on the *b's* of a territory, *Marr. of Geraint* 34
on the *b* of her couch they sat *Guinevere* 101
There on the *b* Of boundless Ocean, *Merlin and the G.* 116
Border'd the yellow down *B* with palm, *Lotos-Eaters* 22
Border-marriage land was ringing of it—This blacksmith *b-m*— *Aylmer's Field* 263
Border-race such counter-terms, my son, Are *b-r's*, *Ancient Sage* 251
Bore (to burrow) hedgehog underneath the plaintain *b's*, *Aylmer's Field* 850
Bore (to bear) winds which *b* Them earthward till they lit; *The Poet* 17
The broad stream *b* her far away, *L. of Shalott iv* 17
B and forbore, and did not tire, *Two Voices* 218
That *b* a lady from a leaguer'd town; *D. of F. Women* 47
Branches they *b* of that enchanted stem, *Lotos-Eaters* 28
b him to a chapel nigh the field. *M. d'Arthur* 8
And rising *b* him thro' the place of tombs. ,, 175

Bore (to bear) (*continued*) blowing forward, *b* King Arthur, *M. d'Arthur, Ep.* 21
in her bosom *b* the baby, Sleep. *Gardener's D.* 268
But Dora *b* them meekly, *Dora* 36
knowest I *b* this better at the first, *St. S. Stylites* 28
Not this alone I *b*: ,, 61
I *b*, whereof, O God, thou knowest all. ,, 70
and love her for the love she *b*? *Locksley Hall* 73
she Not less thro' all *b* up, till, *Godiva* 62
Right down by smoky Paul's they *b*, *Will Water.* 141
Three fair children first she *b* him, *L. of Burleigh* 87
B to earth her body, drest In the dress ,, 98
She *b* the blade of Liberty. *The Voyage* 72
A light-green tuft of plumes she *b* *Sir L. and Q. G.* 26
B him another son, a sickly one: *Enoch Arden* 109
grieving held his will, and *b* it thro'. ,, 167
do the thing he will'd, and *b* it thro'. ,, 295
weight of the dead leaf *b* it down: ,, 678
And Enoch *b* his weakness cheerfully. ,, 827
To be the ghost of one who *b* your name *The Brook* 219
yet she *b* it: yet her cheek *Aylmer's Field* 505
loneliness of grief *B* down in flood, ,, 633
her own people *b* along the nave Her pendent hands, ,, 812
motion of the boundless deep *B* thro' the cave, *Sea Dreams* 92
motion of the great deep *b* me on, ,, 111
They *b* her back into the tent: *Princess iv* 193
Yet I *b* up in part from ancient love, ,, 303
Yet I *b* up in hope she would be known: ,, 320
b down a Prince, And Cyril, one. ,, *v* 518
me they *b* up the broad stairs, ,, *vi* 374
He *b* but little game in hand; *The Victim* 42
And *b* thee where I could not see *In Mem. xxii* 17
And thus he *b* without abuse ,, *cxi* 21
In either hand he *b* What dazzled all, *Gareth and L.* 386
And he that *b* The star, when mounted, ,, 950
with a costrel *b* The means of goodly welcome, *Marr. of Geraint* 386
best by her that *b* her understood. ,, 511
b Down by the length of lance and arm *Geraint and E.* 462
b him to the naked hall of Doorm, ,, 570
She *b* me there, for born from death was I *Merlin and V.* 44
He *b* a knight of old repute to the earth, *Lancelot and E.* 492
he *b* the prize and could not find The victor, ,, 629
thus they *b* her swooning to her tower. ,, 968
reverently they *b* her into hall. ,, 1266
b them down, And broke thro' all, *Holy Grail* 479
b him to a chapel nigh the field, *Pass. of Arthur* 176
And rising *b* him thro' the place of tombs. ,, 343
she that *b* Camilla close beneath *Lover's Tale i* 202
converse sweet, In which our voices *b* least part. ,, 542
A whirlwind caught and *b* us; ,, *ii* 197
so they *b* her (for in Julian's land ,, *iv* 36
B her free-faced to the free airs ,, 38
So *b* her thro' the solitary land ,, 90
Sir Richard *b* in hand all his sick men *The Revenge* 15
stately Spanish men to their flagship *b* him ,, 97
She *b* a child, whom reverently we call'd *Sisters (E. and E.)* 268
and the love I *b* them both— ,, 281
we, who *b* the Cross Thither, *Columbus* 191
And so, when I *b* him a girl, *The Wreck* 33
Nature who knew not that which she *b*! *Despair* 34
on an earth that *b* not a flower; ,, 44
wheat Of Egypt *b* a grain as sweet *To Prof. Jebb* 6
As we *b* down the Gods before us? *Demeter and P.* 132
yesterday They *b* the Cross before you *Happy* 48
In a while I *b* him a son, *Bandit's Death* 15

Borest Ah little rat that *b* in the dyke *Merlin and V.* 112

Boring *B* a little auger-hole in fear, *Godiva* 68

Born (*See also* **Burn, Devil-born, Eldest-born, Equal-born, First-born, Gentle-born, King-born, Lame-born, Latest-born, New-born, Royal-born, Sickly-born, Spleen-born**)
Nothing was *b*; Nothing will die; *Nothing will Die* 36
All things were *b*. *All Things will Die* 47
And Thou and peace to earth were *b*. *Supp. Confessions* 26
THE poet in a golden clime was *b*, *The Poet* 1

Born (*continued*) Two children in one hamlet *b* and bred; *Circumstance* 8
Thou wert *b*, on a summer morn, *Eleänore* 7
Truth is *b* Beyond the polar gleam *Two Voices* 181
features of her child Ere it is *b*: *Œnone* 253
never child be *b* of me, Unblest, ,, 254
which mood was *b* Scorn of herself; *Palace of Art* 230
call me before the day is *b*. *May Queen, N. Y's. E.* 49
thousand times I would be *b* and die. *D. of F. Women* 204
Was never *b* into the earth. *To J. S.* 32
With that fair child betwixt them *b*. *On a Mourner* 25
B out of everything I heard and saw, *Gardener's D.* 66
days went on, there was *b* a boy To William; *Dora* 48
sinful man, conceived and *b* in sin: *St. S. Stylites* 122
group Of beauties, that were *b* In teacup-times of hood *Talking Oak* 62
'But I was *b* too late: the fair new forms, *Golden Year* 15
glimpse of that dark world where I was *b*. *Tithonus* 33
And thought and time be *b* again, *Day-Dm., Sleep. P.* 50
serving-man As any *b* of woman. *Will Water.* 152
I'm a beggar *b*,' she said, *Lady Clare* 37
I am a beggar *b*,' she said, ,, 71
'If you are not the heiress *b*, (repeat) ,, 83, 85
honour Unto which she was not *b*. *L. of Burleigh* 80
Every moment dies a man, Every moment one is *b*. (repeat) *Vision of Sin* 98, 122
but when her child was *b*, *Enoch Arden* 522
In those far-off seven happy years were *b*; ,, 686
B of a village girl, carpenter's son, *Aylmer's Field* 668
Thy better *b* unhappily from thee, ,, 675
A CITY clerk, but gently *b* and bred; *Sea Dreams* 1
chiefly you were *b* for something great, *Princess iv* 307
Ere you were *b* to vex us? ,, *vi* 248
dead before he was *b*, (repeat) *Grandmother* 59, 68
naw, naw, tha was not *b* then; *N. Farmer, O. S.* 29
The linnet *b* within the cage, *In Mem. xxvii* 3
The light that shone when Hope was *b*. ,, *xxx* 32
In these brief lays, of Sorrow *b*, ,, *xlviii* 1
In that dark house where she was *b*. ,, *lx* 12
It is the day when he was *b*, ,, *cvii* 1
And, *b* of love, the vague desire ,, *cx* 19
But I was *b* to other things. ,, *cxx* 12
Result in man, be *b* and think, ,, *Con.* 126
it seem'd far better to be *b* To labour *Maud I xviii* 33
On the day when Maud was *b*; ,, *xix* 40
O Rivulet, *b* at the Hall, ,, *xxi* 8
Is a juggle *b* of the brain? ,, *II ii* 42
tickle the maggot *b* in an empty head, ,, *v* 38
Some calling Arthur *b* of Gorloïs, Others of Anton? *Com. of Arthur* 170
all before his time Was Arthur *b*, ,, 212
Or *b* the son of Gorloïs, after death, Or Uther's son, and *b* before his time, ,, 240
Else, wherefore *b*?' *Gareth and L.* 119
saying thou wert basely *b*. ,, 355
God wot, so thou wert nobly *b*, ,, 1064
Stript from the three dead wolves of woman *b* *Geraint and E.* 94
creatures gently *b* But into bad hands ,, 191
B with the blood, not learnable, *Balin and Balan* 175
We two were *b* together, and we die ,, 629
bore me there, for *b* from death was I *Merlin and V.* 44
turn of anger *b* Of your misfaith; ,, 531
but *b* of sickness, could not live: *Lancelot and E.* 880
sons *B* to the glory of thy name and fame, ,, 1372
Well is it that no child is *b* of thee. *Guinevere* 424
children *b* of thee are sword and fire, ,, 425
Like the last echo *b* of a great cry, *Pass. of Arthur* 459
Life knows not when young Life was *b*, *Lover's Tale i* 156
falsehood of all starcraft!) we were *b*. ,, 200
So were we *b*, so orphan'd. ,, 218
Because my grief as yet was newly *b* ,, 613
Back to the mother's house where she was *b*. ,, *iv* 91
b Not from believing mind, ,, 104
and that day a boy was *b*, Heir ,, 128
But the boy was *b* i' trouble, *First Quarrel* 2
The boy was *b* in wedlock, ,, 6
For the lawyer is *b* but to murder— *Rizpah* 64

Bottom (s) (*continued*) made a plunge To the *b*, and dispersed, *Enoch Arden* 380
fox—where started—kill'd In such a *b*: *Aylmer's Field* 254
Tho' anchor'd to the *b*, such is he.' *Princess iv* 257
the sand danced at the *b* of it. *Balin and Balan* 27
b of the well, Where Truth is hidden. *Merlin and V.* 47
glances from the *b* of the pool, *The Ring* 371

Bough (*See also* **Beechen-bough, Beugh**) beneath the dome Of hollow *b's*. *Arabian Nights* 42
garlanding the gnarled *b's* With bunch *Œnone* 101
Whose thick mysterious *b's* in the dark morn ,, 213
came To rest beneath thy *b's*.—(repeat) *Talking Oak* 36, 156
Olivia came To sport beneath thy *b's*. ,, 100
till thy *b's* discern The front of Sumner-place. ,, 247
bent or broke The lithe reluctant *b's* *Enoch Arden* 381
one soft arm, which, like the pliant *b* *Sea Dreams* 290
grasping down the *b's* I gain'd the shore. *Princess iv* 189
and while the holly *b's* Entwine *In Mem. xxix* 9
I found a wood with thorny *b's*: ,, *lxix* 6
And sow the sky with flying *b's*, ,, *lxxii* 24
Unwatch'd, the garden *b* shall sway, ,, *ci* 1
Came on the hoarhead woodman at a *b* Wearily hewing. *Balin and Balan* 294
He burst his lance against a forest *b*, ,, 329
canker'd *b's* without Whined in the wood; ,, 345
and old *b's* Whined in the wood. ,, 385
made him quickly dive Beneath the *b's*, ,, 423
and on the *b's* a shield Showing *Last Tournament* 432
and the wind among the *b's*. ,, 489
shot forth *B's* on each side, *Lover's Tale i* 230
beechen *b's* Of our New Forest. *Sisters (E. and E.)* 112
Look, he stands, Trunk and *b*, *The Oak* 14

Bought (*See also* **Bowt**) have *b* A mansion incorruptible. *Deserted House* 20
B Annie goods and stores, and set *Enoch Arden* 169
b them needful books, and everyway, ,, 332
b Quaint monsters for the market of those times, ,, 538
We *b* the farm we tenanted before. *The Brook* 222
B? what is it he cannot buy? *Maud I x* 32
sold and sold had *b* them bread: *Marr. of Geraint* 641
who *b* me for his slave: *The Flight* 19

Boulder found a glen, gray *b* and black tarn. *Lancelot and E.* 36

Bound (adj.) (*See also* **China-bound, Seaward-bound**)
B on a matter he of life and death: *Sea Dreams* 151
'Was he so *b*, poor soul?' ,, 169
B for the Hall, I am sure was he: *Maud I x* 25
B for the Hall, and I think for a bride. ,, 26
'*B* upon a quest With horse and arms— *Gareth and L.* 708
B on a foray, rolling eyes of prey, *Geraint and E.* 538
B upon solitary adventure, *Pelleas and E.* 275
Whither are you *b*? For Naples *The Ring* 57

Bound (limit) *make The* b's *of freedom wider yet* *To the Queen* 32
Transgress his ample *b* to some new crown:— *Poland* 8
And mete the *b's* of hate and love— *Two Voices* 135
Beyond the utmost *b* of human thought. *Ulysses* 32
You that have dared to break our *b*, *Princess iv* 539
And music in the *b's* of law, *In Mem. lxxxvii* 34
And strike his being into *b's*, ,, *Con.* 124
b's of heaven and earth were lost— *Com. of Arthur* 372
shun to break those *b's* of courtesy *Lancelot and E.* 1220
Drew from before Sir Tristram to the *b's*, *Last Tournament* 185
Back to the sunset *b* of Lyonnesse— *Pass. of Arthur* 81
charged the winds With spiced May-sweets from *b* to *b*, *Lover's Tale i* 318
Nor understandest *b* nor boundlessness, *Ancient Sage* 48
and the *b's* Determining concession; *To Duke of Argyll* 2
Narrowing the *b's* of night.' *Prog. of Spring* 91
all the *b's* of earth, Far-far-away? *Far-far-away* 14
I spy nor term nor *b*. *Mechanophilus* 20

Bound (spring) but a single *b*, and with a sweep *Geraint and E.* 727

Bound (verb) wild winds *b* within their cell, *Mariana* 54
Two lives *b* fast in one *Circumstance* 5
Sleep had *b* her in his rosy band, *Caress'd or chidden* 6
Art thou so *b* To men, *Two Voices* 109
Which only to one engine *b* ,, 347

Bound (verb) (*continued*) In front they *b* the sheaves. *Palace of Art* 78
earth is every way *B* by gold chains *M. d'Arthur* 255
'I am *b*: you have my promise— *Enoch Arden* 437
I am always *b* to you, but you are free.' ,, 450
Annie weeping answer'd 'I am *b*.' ,, 451
she knew that she was *b*— ,, 462
B in an immemorial intimacy, *Aylmer's Field* 39
nor by plight or broken ring *B*, ,, 136
you think me *b* In some sort, *Princess i* 158
given us letters, was he *b* to speak? ,, 181
I b by precontract Your bride, ,, *iv* 541
each beside his chariot *b* his own; *Spec. of Iliad* 3
lost the links that *b* Thy changes; *In Mem. xli* 6
Had *b* us one to the other, *Maud I xix* 38
B them by so strait vows to his own self, *Com. of Arthur* 262
vows, as is a shame A man should not be *b* by, *Gareth and L.* 271
b my lord to cast him in the mere.' ,, 803
'*B* am I to right the wrong'd, ,, 804
straitlier *b* am I to bide with thee.' ,, 805
I *b* to thee for any favour ask'd!' ,, 977
b the suits Of armour on their horses, *Geraint and E.* 96
b them on their horses, each on each, ,, 182
B are they To speak no evil. *Balin and Balan* 145
Arthur *b* them not to singleness *Merlin and V.* 28
They b to holy vows of chastity! ,, 695
then he *b* Her token on his helmet, *Lancelot and E.* 373
but free love will not be *b*.' ,, 1379
'Free love, so *b*, were freëst,' ,, 1380
bright boy-knight, and *b* it on him, *Holy Grail* 156
'All men, to one so *b* by such a vow, ,, 565
Seized him, and *b* and plunged him into a cell ,, 675
Give ye the slave mine order to be *b*, *Pelleas and E.* 270
rose up, and *b*, and brought him in. ,, 288
Not to be *b*, save by white bonds ,, 353
and *b* his horse Hard by the gates. ,, 413
B on her brow, were Gawain and Ettarre. ,, 435
the King hath *b* And sworn me to this brotherhood; ,, 448
earth is every way *B* by gold chains *Pass. of Arthur* 423
So *b* to me by common love and loss— *Lover's Tale iv* 345
Harry was *b* to the Dorsetshire farm *First Quarrel* 19
only done my duty as a man is *b* to do: *The Revenge* 102
I had not *b* myself by words, *Sisters (E. and E.)* 137
I was *b* to her; I could not free myself ,, 160
b Not by the sounded letter of the word, ,, 161
broken chain that *b* me to my kind. *Locksley H., Sixty* 52
the laughing shepherd *b* with flowers; *To Virgil* 16
b to follow, wherever she go Stark-naked, *Dead Prophet* 45
for twenty years *B* by the golden cord *The Ring* 429

Bound *See also* **Brow-bound, Charm-bound**

Boundary Close at the *b* of the liberties; *Princess i* 172

Bounded motions *b* in a shallower brain: *Locksley Hall* 150
a spirit *b* and poor; *Maud I iv* 38
Death's dark war-horse *b* forward *Gareth and L.* 1401
Then *b* forward to the castle walls, *Pelleas and E.* 363
b forth and vanish'd thro' the night. ,, 487
Seeing it is not *b* save by love.' *Last Tournament* 703

Bounden (*See also* **Long-bounden, Promise-bounden**)
and lying *b* there In darkness *Holy Grail* 676
those he overthrew Be *b* straight, *Pelleas and E.* 236
but thrust him *b* out of door. ,, 314
Thus to be *b*, so to see her face, ,, 326
tho' she hath me *b* but in spite, ,, 329
Let me be *b*, I shall see her face; ,, 331

Bounding *b* forward 'Leave them to the wolves.' *Balin and Balan* 588

Boundless Feels that the deep is *b*, *Ancient Sage* 192
Sent the shadow of Himself, the *b*, *Locksley H., Sixty* 211
B inward, in the atom, *b* outward, ,, 212

Boundlessness Nor understandest bound nor *b*, *Ancient Sage* 48

Bounteous Of whom were any *b*, merciful, *Gareth and L.* 423

Bounteous Isle And we came to the *B I*, *V. of Maeldune* 83
Till we hated the *B I* and the sunbright hand ,, 92

Bounteously *b* made, And yet so finely, *Aylmer's Field* 74

Bountiful Spare not now to be *b*, *On Jub. Q. Victoria* 29
B, beautiful, apparell'd gay, *Prog. of Spring* 62

Bounty God only thro' his *b* hath thought fit, *St. S. Stylites* 186
Here he lives in state and *b*, *L. of Burleigh* 57
Or Heaven in lavish *b* moulded, grew. *Aylmer's Field* 107
Bourg Ye think the rustic cackle of your *b* *Marr. of Geraint* 276
They take the rustic murmur of their *b* ,, 419
Bourn-Bourne and rang Beyond the *bourn* of sunset; *Princess, Con.* 100
from out our *bourne* of Time and Place *Crossing the Bar* 13
Bovadilla *B*, one As ignorant and impolitic *Columbus* 127
Bow (respectful inclination) O the formal mocking *b*, *The Flight* 29
Bow (an instrument) spirit ever strung Like a new *b*, *Kate* 11
Bow (rainbow) great *b* will waver in the sun, *Palace of Art* 43
And every dew-drop paints a *b*, *In Mem. cxxii* 18
For there beyond a bridge of treble *b*, *Gareth and L.* 1086
Bow (part of a ship) figure-head Stared o'er the ripple feathering from her *b's*: *Enoch Arden* 544
huge sea-castles heaving upon the weather *b*. *The Revenge* 24
Bow (s) *See* **Foam-bow, Saddle-bow, Torrent-bow**
Bow (verb) *B* myself down, where thou hast knelt, *Supp. Confessions* 80
B down one thousand and two hundred *St. S. Stylites* 111
gay domestic *B's* before him at the door. *L. of Burleigh* 48
as when a field of corn *B's* all its ears *Princess i* 237
She *b's*, she bathes the Saviour's feet *In Mem. xxxii* 11
cheeks drop in; the body *b's* Man dies: ,, *xxxv* 3
made him flush, and *b* Lowly, to kiss his hand, *Gareth and L.* 548
O ay—the winds that *b* the grass! *Last Tournament* 735
To thee, dead wood, I *b* not head nor knees. *Sir J. Oldcastle* 128
Bow-back'd supporters on a shield, *B-b* with fear: *Princess vi* 359
Bow'd Like Thine own mother's when she *b* Above Thee, *Supp. Confessions* 23
A group of Houris *b* to see The dying Islamite, *Palace of Art* 102
power in his eye That *b* the will. *M. d'Arthur* 123
She *b* upon her hands, *Dora* 103
She *b* down her head, ,, 105
She *b* down And wept in secret; ,, 107
My knees are *b* in crypt and shrine: *Sir Galahad* 18
Enoch as a brave God-fearing man *B* himself down, *Enoch Arden* 186
Enoch was so brown, so *b*, So broken— ,, 703
'My God has *b* me down to what I am; ,, 856
b her state to them, that they might grow *Princess ii* 166
She *b* as if to veil a noble tear; ,, *iii* 289
handmaid on each side *B* toward her, ,, *iv* 276
B on her palms and folded up from wrong, ,, 288
She *b*, she set the child on the earth; ,, *vi* 120
thine own land has *b* to Tartar hordes *W. to Marie Alex.* 23
save Thy sailor,—while thy head is *b*, *In Mem. vi* 14
When have I *b* to her father, *Maud I iv* 13
not to her brother I *b*; I *b* to his lady-sister ,, 14
the budded peaks of the wood are *b* ,, *vi* 4
redden'd her cheek When I *b* to her ,, *xix* 66
Gareth *b* himself With all obedience *Gareth and L.* 487
Low *b* the tributary Prince, *Marr. of Geraint* 174
with back turn'd, and *b* above his work, ,, 267
lifted adoring eyes, *B* at her side *Geraint and E.* 305
b the all-amorous Earl, ,, 360
low *b* the Prince, and felt His work ,, 920
b black knees Of homage, *Merlin and V.* 577
then *b* his homage, bluntly saying, *Last Tournament* 206
he *b* to kiss the jewell'd throat, ,, 751
and *b* down upon her hands Silent, *Guinevere* 158
and *b* her head nor spake. ,, 310
power in his eye That *b* the will. *Pass. of Arthur* 291
B the spoiler, Bent the Scotsman, *Batt. of Brunanburh* 20
b myself down as a slave to his intellectual throne, *The Wreck* 66
Edith *b* her stately head, *The Tourney* 13
Edith Montfort *b* her head, ,, 15
Bower (*See also* **Garden-bower, Tree-bower**) Creeping thro' blossomy rushes and *b's* of rose-blowing bushes, *Leonine Eleg.* 3
day Was sloping toward his western *b*. *Mariana* 80
Dwelling amid these yellowing *b's*: *A spirit haunts* 2
Youngest Autumn, in a *b* Grape-thicken'd *Eleänore* 35
Then to the *b* they came, *Œnone* 94
they came to that smooth-swarded *b*, ,, 95
And I was left alone within the *b*; ,, 192
honeysuckle round the porch has wov'n its wavy *b's*, *May Queen* 29

Bower (*continued*) Leaving the promise of my bridal *b*, *D. of F. Women* 218
bulk Of mellow brickwork on an isle of *b's*. *Edwin Morris* 12
Pursue thy loves among the *b's* *Talking Oak* 199
Droops the heavy-blossom'd *b*, *Locksley Hall* 163
Then fled she to her inmost *b*, *Godiva* 42
but even then she gain'd Her *b*; ,, 77
The peacock in his laurel *b*, *Day-Dm., Sleep. P.* 15
From havens hid in fairy *b's*, *The Voyage* 54
she moved To meet me, winding under woodbine *b's*, *The Brook* 88
from a *b* of vine and honeysuckle: *Aylmer's Field* 156
broader-grown the *b's* Drew the great night *Princess vii* 48
music, O bird, in the new-budded *b's*! *W. to Alexandra* 11
Or walks in Boboli's ducal *b's*. *The Daisy* 44
and make her a *b* All of flowers, *Window, At the W.* 5
out of her *b* All of flowers, ,, 12
light Dies off at once from *b* and hall, *In Mem. viii* 6
That sweeps with all its autumn *b's*, ,, *xi* 10
have clothed their branchy *b's* With fifty Mays, ,, *lxxvi* 13
With thy lost friend among the *b's*, ,, *cii* 15
glowing like the moon Of Eden on its bridal *b*: ,, *Con.* 28
And tends upon bed and *b*, *Maud I xiv* 4
out of *b* and casement shyly glanced *Gareth and L.* 313
walk of lilies crost it to the *b*: *Balin and Balan* 243
long white walk of lilies toward the *b*. ,, 249
and Balin started from his *b*. ,, 280
Remembering that dark *b* at Camelot, ,, 526
'Had ye not held your Lancelot in your *b*, *Pelleas and E.* 182
spied not any light in hall or *b*, ,, 419
In her high *b* the Queen, Working a tapestry, *Last Tournament* 128
then slowly to her *b* Parted, ,, 238
Thro' many a league-long *b* he rode. ,, 374
saw The great Queen's *b* was dark,— ,, 758
in thy *b's* of Camelot or of Usk *Guinevere* 503
vanish'd from my sight Beneath the *b* *Lover's Tale ii* 43
they were swallow'd in the leafy *b's*, ,, *iii* 57
All the *b's* and the flowers, *Sisters (E. and E.)* 10
Fainting flowers, faded *b's*, ,, 11
Over all the woodland's flooded *b's*, ,, 20
piping underneath his beechen *b's*; *To Virgil* 14
wealth of tropic *b* and brake; *To Ulysses* 37
Bower'd (*See also* **Close-bower'd**) garden *b* close With plaited alleys of the trailing rose, *Ode to Memory* 105
Bower-eaves Look out below your *b-e*, *Margaret* 66
A BOW-SHOT from her *b-e*, *L. of Shalott iii* 1
Boweth Earthward he *b* the heavy stalks *A spirit haunts* 7
Bowing Approved him, *b* at their own deserts: *The Brook* 128
and *b* o'er the brook A tonsured head ,, 199
She spoke, and *b* waved Dismissal: *Princess ii* 99
b over him, Low to her own heart *Marr. of Geraint* 84
b lowly down before thee, *Akbar's D., Hymn* 3
Bowl (*See also* **Wassail-bowl**) Nor robb'd the farmer of his *b* of cream: *Princess v* 223
Nor *b* of wassail mantle warm; *In Mem. cv* 18
fling free alms into the beggar's *b*, *Ancient Sage* 260
Bowl'd a herd of boys with clamour *b* *Princess, Pro.* 81
Bowl-shaped saw, *B-s*, thro' tops of many thousand pines *Gareth and L.* 796
Bowman *See* **Master-bowman**
Bow-shot A *B-s* from her bower-eaves, *L. of Shalott iii* 1
Bow-string His *b-s* slacken'd, languid Love, *Eleänore* 117
Bowt (bought) An' 'e *b* owd money, es wouldn't goä, *Village Wife* 49
An' 'e *b* little statues all-naäkt ,, 50
Box (a case) (*See also* **Deal-box**) A long green *b* of mignonette, *Miller's D.* 83
and the *b* of mignonette. *May Queen, N. Y's. E.* 48
May bind a book, may line a *b*, *In Mem. lxxvii* 6
Box (compartment) Old *b'es*, larded with the steam *Will Water.* 223
Shall call thee from the *b'es*. ,, 240
Box (boxful) 'e snifft up a *b* in a daäy, *Village Wife* 40
Box (a shrub) breath Of the fading edges of *b* beneath, *A spirit haunts* 19
Boy (*See also* **Cupid-boys, Orphan-boy**) A merry *b* in sun and shade? *Two Voices* 321
'A merry *b* they call'd him then, ,, 322

Boy (*continued*) To be the long and listless b Late-left *Miller's D.* 33
My mother thought, What ails the b? ,, 93
'No fair Hebrew b Shall smile away *D. of F. Women* 213
'You will not, b! you dare to answer thus! *Dora* 26
there was born a b To William; ,, 48
Mary sat And look'd with tears upon her b, ,, 57
let me take the b, ,, 66
he may see the b, And bless him for the sake ,, 69
Well—for I will take the b; ,, 99
So saying, he took the b that cried aloud ,, 101
the b's cry came to her from the field, ,, 104
Mary saw the b Was not with Dora. ,, 111
Dora said, 'My uncle took the b; ,, 114
now I think, he shall not have the b, ,, 119
I will have my b, and bring him home; ,, 122
b set up betwixt his grandsire's knees, ,, 131
but when the b beheld His mother, ,, 137
now, Sir, let me have my b, ,, 152
and with his b Betwixt his knees, *Walk. to the Mail* 40
was as a b Destructive, ,, 81
So seems she to the b. *Talking Oak* 108
Eager-hearted as a b when first he leaves *Locksley Hall* 112
heart of existence beat for ever like a b's? ,, 140
A something-pottle-bodied b *Will Water.* 131
O well for the fisherman's b, *Break, break, etc.* 5
two years after came a b to be The rosy idol *Enoch Arden* 89
Now let me put the b and girl to school: ,, 312
Philip put the b and girl to school, ,, 331
the youngest, hardly more than b, ,, 563
like her mother, and the b, my son.' ,, 791
Prattling the primrose fancies of the b, *The Brook* 19
So much the b foreran; *Aylmer's Field* 80
b might get a notion into him; ,, 271
girl and b, Sir, know their differences!' ,, 274
Last he said, 'B, mark me! ,, 300
'B, should I find you by my doors ,, 324
twenty b's and girls should marry on it, ,, 371
a herd of b's with clamour bowl'd *Princess, Pro.* 81
embower the nest, Some b would spy it.' ,, 148
daughter and his housemaid were the b's: ,, *i* 190
'Wretched b, How saw you not the inscription ,, *ii* 193
With me, Sir, enter'd in the bigger b, ,, 404
'Poor b,' she said, 'can he not read— ,, *iii* 214
when a b, you stoop'd to me From all high places, ,, *iv* 429
more Than growing b's their manhood; ,, 457
As b's that slink From ferule ,, *v* 37
B, when I hear you prate I almost think ,, 152
B, there's no rose that's half so dear ,, 159
idle b's are cowards to their shame, ,, 309
'B's!' shriek'd the old king, ,, 328
rout of saucy b's Brake on us at our books, ,, 394
B, The bearing and the training of a child ,, 464
The little b's begin to shoot and stab, ,, *Con.* 61
Among six b's, head under head, ,, 83
Godfather, come and see your b: *To F. D. Maurice* 2
'O b, tho' thou art young and proud, *Sailor Boy* 7
We give them the b.' *The Victim* 40
Cut the Roman b to pieces in his lust *Boădicea* 66
For they controll'd me when a b; *In Mem. xxviii* 18
A sober man, among his b's, ,, *liii* 2
When he was little more than b, ,, *lxii* 6
and b's of thine Had babbled 'Uncle' on my knee; ,, *lxxxiv* 12
and b's That crash'd the glass and beat the floor; ,, *lxxxvii* 19
And like an inconsiderate b, ,, *cxxii* 14
b Will have plenty: so let it be.' (repeat) *Maud I vii* 7, 15
Read with a b's delight, ,, 10
To take a wanton dissolute b For a man ,, *x* 58
so the b, Sweet mother, neither clomb, *Gareth and L.* 55
ye are yet more b than man.' ,, 98
the b Is noble-natured. ,, 467
the b Was half beyond himself for ecstasy. ,, 523
the might and breath of twenty b's.' ,, 1106
Issued the bright face of a blooming b ,, 1408
fears And horrors only proven a blooming b. ,, 1425
'B,' said he, 'I have eaten all, *Geraint and E.* 217

Boy (*continued*) 'I take it as free gift, then,' said the b, *Geraint and E.* 222
b return'd And told them of a chamber, ,, 260
bone Seems to be pluck'd at by the village b's ,, 560
as a b lame-born beneath a height, *Balin and Balan* 164
old sun-worship, b, will rise again, ,, 457
Hither, b—and mark me well. ,, 502
'Live on, Sir B,' she cried. ,, 584
men and b's astride On wyvern, lion, *Holy Grail* 349
beauty of her flesh abash'd the b, *Pelleas and E.* 78
as the wholesome mothers tell their b's. ,, 197
b Paused not, but overrode him, shouting, ,, 544
on whom the b, Across the silent seeded meadow-grass ,, 560
thronging fancies come To b's and girls *Lover's Tale i* 555
so love that men and b's may say, ,, 756
that day a b was born, Heir of his face and land, ,, *iv* 128
Another, if the b were hers: ,, 332
But the b was born i' trouble, *First Quarrel* 2
the b can hold up his head, ,, 5
The b was born in wedlock, ,, 6
He fought the b's that were rude, ,, 14
I was near my time wi' the b, ,, 82
But say nothing hard of my b, *Rizpah* 22
I kiss'd my b in the prison, ,, 23
hear that cry of my b that was dead, ,, 45
But I go to-night to my b, ,, 74
For I cared so much for my b that the Lord ,, 75
if my b be gone to the fire? ,, 78
and gain her then: no wavering, b! *Sisters (E. and E.)* 39
for all that, my b, Some birds are sick ,, 72
booöks wur gone an' 'is b wur deäd, *Village Wife* 87
Here was a b—I am sure that some of our children *In the Child. Hosp.* 11
Here was a b in the ward, ,, 13
what! the kingly, kindly b; *Sir J. Oldcastle* 88
thou comest, darling b; Our own; *De Prof. Two G.* 10
Down yon dark sea, thou comest, darling b. ,, 34
To younger England in the b my son. *To Victor Hugo* 14
said to me 'Pity it isn't a b.' *The Wreck* 34
for oft On me, when b, there came *Ancient Sage* 217
what had he lost, the b? ,, 227
For the b's wor about her agin *Tomorrow* 43
a bouncin' b an' a gell. *Spinster's S's.* 82
Thou alone, my b, of Amy's kin *Locksley H., Sixty* 56
a shatter'd wheel? a vicious b ,, 215
Not there to bid my b farewell, *To Marq. of Dufferin* 42
haunt him when a b, Far-far-away? *Far-far-away* 8
Turn'd him again to b, for up he sprang, *St. Telemachus* 58
that the b never cried again. *Bandit's Death* 28
birthday came of a b born happily dead. *Charity* 34
Boyhood Then, in the b of the year, *Sir L. and Q. G.* 19
Sweet love on pranks of saucy b: *Princess vii* 344
One whispers, 'Here thy b sung Long since *In Mem. cii* 9
Wander'd back to living b while I heard *Locksley H., Sixty* 3
Eyes that lured a doting b ,, 10
Feed the budding rose of b ,, 143
I was then in early b, ,, 258
Boy-knight saw the bright b-k, and bound it on him, *Holy Grail* 156
Boy-love this b-l of yours with mine. *Locksley H., Sixty* 6
Boy-phrase my b-p 'The Passion of the Past.' *Ancient Sage* 219
Bräain (brain) moor sense i' one o' 'is legs nor in all thy b's. *N. Farmer, N.S.* 4
'Sottin' thy b's Guzzlin' an' soäkin' *North. Cobbler* 23
Brace b Of twins may weed her of her folly. *Princess v* 463
and then against his b Of comrades, *Geraint and E.* 87
Braced Had b my purpose to declare myself: *Sisters (E. and E.)* 143
Bracelet With b's of the diamond bright: *Day-Dm., Sleep. B.* 14
Bracelet-bestower B-b and Baron of Barons, *Batt. of Brunanburh* 3
Bracken when the b rusted on their crags, *Edwin Morris* 100
Nowt at all but b an' fuzz, *N. Farmer, O. S.* 38
Breast-high in that bright line of b stood: *Pelleas and E.* 56
Among our heath and b. *The Ring* 318
When I look'd at the b so bright *June Bracken, etc.* 3
As the green of the b amid the gloom ,, 9
Bracken-rooft Furze-cramm'd, and b-r, *Last Tournament* 377

Bracket statuette Of my dear Mother on your *b* here— *The Ring* 110
Brag (s) Said Gareth, 'Old, and over-bold in *b*! *Gareth and L.* 1107
Brag (verb) *b* to his fellow rakes of his conquest *Charity* 18
Bragging armies so broken A reason for *b* *Batt. of Brunanburh* 83
Brahmin *B*, and Buddhist, Christian, and Parsee, *Akbar's Dream* 25
Braid wound Her looser hair in *b*, *Gardener's D.* 158
fire-flies tangled in a silver *b*. *Locksley Hall* 10
Forth streaming from a *b* of pearl: *Day-Dm., Sleep. B.* 6
Blowing the ringlet from the *b*: *Sir L. and Q. G.* 39
the *b* Slipt and uncoil'd itself, *Merlin and V.* 888
Braided (*See also* **Vapour-braided**) *b* thereupon All the devices blazon'd *Lancelot and E.* 8
precious crystal into which I *b* Edwin's hair! *The Flight* 34
Brain (*See also* **Braäin, Full-brain, Half-brain**) *arms, or power of* b, *or birth* *To the Queen* 3
Right to the heart and *b*, tho' undescried, *Isabel* 22
From the *b* of the purple mountain *Poet's Mind* 29
falling axe did part The burning *b* from the true heart, *Margaret* 39
A random arrow from the *b*. *Two Voices* 345
From some odd corner of the *b*. *Miller's D.* 68
In my dry *b* my spirit soon, *Fatima* 26
Devil, large in heart and *b*, *To—With Pal. of Art* 5
great thought strikes along the *b*, *D. of F. Women* 43
dawn's creeping beams, Stol'n to my *b*, ,, 262
Drawn from the spirit thro' the *b*, *To J. S.* 38
nourish a blind life within the *b*, *M. d'Arthur* 251
Simeon, whose *b* the sunshine bakes; *St. S. Stylites* 164
Better the narrow *b*, the stony heart, *Love and Duty* 15
mist of tears, that weigh'd Upon my *b*, ,, 44
that his *b* is overwrought: *Locksley Hall* 53
blinder motions bounded in a shallower *b*: ,, 150
On secrets of the *b*, the stars, *Day-Dm., L'Envoi* 11
Which bears a season'd *b* about, *Will Water.* 85
were scatter'd Blood and *b's* of men. *The Captain* 48
Beating it in upon his weary *b*, *Enoch Arden* 796
tickling the brute *b* within the man's *Lucretius* 21
but as his *b* Began to mellow, *Princess i* 179
Besides the *b* was like the hand, ,, *ii* 150
Then while I dragg'd my *b's* for such a song, ,, *iv* 154
Whose *b's* are in their hands and in their heels, ,, 518
upon whose hand and heart and *b* *Ode on Well.* 239
Perchance, to charm a vacant *b*, *The Daisy* 106
dash the *b's* of the little one out, *Boädicea* 68
But, for the unquiet heart and *b*, *In Mem. v* 5
And marvel what possess'd my *b*; ,, *xiv* 16
I make a picture in the *b*; ,, *lxxx* 9
As but the canker of the *b*; ,, *xcii* 3
Pallas from the *b* Of Demons? ,, *cxiv* 12
I think we are not wholly *b*, ,, *cxx* 2
And like is darken'd in the *b*. ,, *cxxi* 8
would not marvel at either, but keep a temperate *b*; *Maud I iv* 40
What was it? a lying trick of the *b*? ,, *II i* 37
Is a juggle born of the *b*? ,, *ii* 42
'Tis the blot upon the *b* That *will* show ,, *iv* 60
Beat into my scalp and my *b*, ,, *v* 10
So dark a forethought roll'd about his *b*, *Merlin and V.* 230
may make My scheming *b* a cinder, ,, 933
Skip to the broken music of my *b's* *Last Tournament* 258
'Save for that broken music in thy *b's*, ,, 267
and clove him thro' the *b*. ,, 754
nourish a blind life within the *b*, *Pass. of Arthur* 419
springing from her fountains in the *b*, *Lover's Tale i* 83
clear brow, bulwark of the precious *b*, ,, 130
Past thro' into his citadel, the *b*, ,, 631
O'erbore the limits of my *b*: ,, 689
meaning of the letters shot into My *b*; ,, *ii* 9
In my *b* The spirit seem'd to flag ,, 50
thro' my eyes into my innermost *b*, ,, 95
Flatter'd the fancy of my fading *b*; ,, 107
love is of the *b*, the mind, the soul: ,, *iv* 156
her *b* broke With over-acting, *Sisters (E. and E.)* 235
My *b* had begun to reel— *In the Child. Hosp.* 60
brute bullet broke thro' the *b* *Def. of Lucknow* 20
For I am emptier than a friar's *b's*; *Sir J. Oldcastle* 7
rang into the heart and the *b*, *V. of Maeldune* 110

Brain (*continued*) My *b* is full of the crash of wrecks, *The Wreck* 4
for my *b* was drunk with the water, *Despair* 65
statesman's *b* that sway'd the past *Ancient Sage* 134
Set the feet above the *b* and swear the *b* is in the feet. *Locksley H., Sixty* 136
oust the madness from your *b*. ,, 241
Works of subtle *b* and hand, *Open. I. and C. Exhib.* 7
'Beat little heart' on this fool *b* of mine. *Romney's R.* 155
Who was a shadow in the *b*, *Mechanophilus* 15
Brain-feverous *B-f* in his heat and agony, *Lancelot and E.* 854
Brain-labour And prodigal of all *b-l* he, *Aylmer's Field* 447
Brainless Insolent, *b*, heartless! ,, 368
Brainpan Than if my *b* were an empty hull, *Princess ii* 398
Brake (s) Close-matted, bur and *b* and briar, *Day-Dm., Sleep. P.* 46
gloom Of evening over *b* and bloom And meadow, *In Mem. lxxxvi* 3
And bristles all the *b's* and thorns ,, *cvii* 9
In every wavering *b* an ambuscade. *Geraint and E.* 51
'How far thro' all the bloom and *b* *Ancient Sage* 19
wealth of tropic bower and *b*; *To Ulysses* 37
downy drift against the *b's*, *Prog. of Spring* 27
Brake (verb) at their feet the crocus *b* like fire, *Œnone* 96
B with a blast of trumpets from the gate, *Princess, Pro.* 42
from my breast the involuntary sigh *B*, ,, *iii* 192
over brow And cheek and bosom *b* the wrathful bloom ,, *iv* 383
titter, out of which there *b* On all sides, ,, *v* 16
a rout of saucy boys *B* on us at our books, ,, 395
then *b* out my sire, Lifting his grim head ,, *vi* 271
For on them *b* the sudden foe; *The Victim* 4
Suddenly from him *b* his wife, ,, 70
No spirit ever *b* the band That stays him *In Mem. xciii* 2
fires of Hell *b* out of thy rising sun, *Maud II i* 9
b on him, till, amazed, He knew not whither *Com. of Arthur* 39
they swerved and *b* Flying, ,, 119
great lords Banded, and so *b* out in open war.' ,, 237
neither clomb, nor *b* his neck, But *b* his very heart in pining for it, *Gareth and L.* 56
That lookt half-dead, *b* bright, ,, 685
there *b* a servingman Flying from out of the black wood, ,, 801
either spear Bent but not *b*, ,, 964
Clash'd his, and *b* it utterly to the hilt. ,, 1148
and thrice they *b* their spears. *Marr. of Geraint* 562
then *b* short, and down his enemy roll'd, *Geraint and E.* 160
Abash'd us both, and *b* my boast. Thy will?' *Balin and Balan* 71
I *b* upon thy rest, And now full loth ,, 499
the storm *B* on the mountain and I cared not *Merlin and V.* 503
and the skull *B* from the nape, *Lancelot and E.* 50
b a sudden-beaming tenderness Of manners ,, 328
then out she *b*: 'Going? ,, 925
when the next sun *b* from underground, ,, 1137
B from the vast oriel-embowering vine ,, 1198
Stoopt, took, *b* seal, and read it; ,, 1271
'But when the next day *b* from under ground— *Holy Grail* 338
Then blush'd and *b* the morning of the jousts, *Pelleas and E.* 157
comes again'—there she *b* short; ,, 295
Reel'd in the smoke, *b* into flame, and fell. ,, 519
It chanced that both *B* into hall together, ,, 587
and the Red Knight *B* in upon me *Last Tournament* 72
B with a wet wind blowing, ,, 137
B up their sports, then slowly to her bower ,, 238
maid, who brook'd No silence, *b* it, *Guinevere* 160
storm of anger *b* From Guinevere, ,, 361
there her voice *b* suddenly, ,, 607
b the petty kings, and fought with Rome, *Pass. of Arthur* 68
wan wave *B* in among dead faces, ,, 130
while they *b* them, own'd me King. ,, 158
B the shield-wall, *Batt. of Brunanburh* 11
Brakest *b* thro' the scruple of my bond, *Last Tournament* 568
Bramble arm Red-rent with hooks of *b*, *Holy Grail* 211
and *b's* mixt And overgrowing them, *Pelleas and E.* 422
Bramble Rose *B r's*, faint and pale, *A Dirge* 30
Branch (s) (*See also* **Willow-branches**) Like to some *b* of stars we see *L. of Shalott iii* 11
B'es they bore of that enchanted stem, *Lotos-Eaters* 28
With winds upon the *b*, ,, *C. S.* 27
curved *b'es*, fledged with clearest green, *D. of F. Women* 59

Branch (s) (*continued*) paused, And dropt the *b* she held, *Gardener's D.* 157
Whose topmost *b'es* can discern The roofs *Talking Oak* 31
And from thy topmost *b* discern The roofs ,, 95
From spray, and *b*, and stem, ,, 190
Stagger'd and shook, holding the *b*, *Enoch Arden* 767
whirl'd her white robe like a blossom'd *b* *Princess iv* 179
the *b'es* thereupon Spread out at top, ,, 205
and shook the *b'es* of the deer ,, *Con.* 98
That makes the barren *b'es* loud; *In Mem. xv* 13
On all the *b'es* of thy blood; ,, *lxxxiv* 8
lie, while these long *b'es* sway, *Maud I xviii* 29
Melody on *b*, and melody in mid air. *Gareth and L.* 183
high on a *b* Hung it, *Balin and Balan* 432
Tore from the *b*, and cast on earth, ,, 539
and the rotten *b* Snapt in the rushing *Merlin and V.* 957
A border fantasy of *b* and flower, *Lancelot and E.* 11
puff'd the swaying *b'es* into smoke *Holy Grail* 15
were our mothers' *b'es* of one stem? *Lover's Tale ii* 25
and the *b* with berries on it, *Columbus* 73
Golden *b* amid the shadows, *To Virgil* 27
Who lops the moulder'd *b* away. *Hands all round* 8
gliding thro' the *b'es* over-bower'd *Death of Œnone* 6
Branch (verb) But *b'es* current yet in kindred veins.' *Princess ii* 245
o'er the friths that *b* and spread *In Mem., Con.* 115
a name that *b'es* o'er the rest, *Balin and Balan* 182
Branch'd cloisters, *b* like mighty woods, *Palace of Art* 26
whisper of huge trees that *b* And blossom'd in the zenith, *Enoch Arden* 585
that *b* itself Fine as ice-ferns *Aylmer's Field* 221
throve and *b* from clime to clime, *In Mem. cxviii* 13
dress All *b* and flower'd with gold, *Marr. of Geraint* 631
forehead veins Bloated, and *b*; *Balin and Balan* 392
Branching empires *b*, both, in lusty life!— *W. to Marie Alex.* 21
trace On paler heavens the *b* grace Of leafless elm, *To Ulysses* 15
Branch-work Beneath *b-w* of costly sardonyx *Palace of Art* 95
Brand (a mark) a part Falling had let appear the *b* of John— *Aylmer's Field* 509
Brand (a sword) (*See also* **Levin-brand**) The *b*, the buckler, and the spear— *Two Voices* 129
Thou therefore take my *b* Excalibur, *M. d'Arthur* 27
There drew he forth the *b* Excalibur, ,, 52
'And if indeed I cast the *b* away, ,, 88
The great *b* Made lightnings in the splendour ,, 136
So flash'd and fell the *b* Excalibur: ,, 142
The hard *b's* shiver on the steel, *Sir Galahad* 6
And, ringing, springs from *b* and mail; ,, 54
—*b*, mace, and shaft, and shield— *Princess v* 503
Arthur call'd to stay the *b's* *Com. of Arthur* 120
So this great *b* the king Took, ,, 308
Flash *b* and lance, fall battleaxe ,, 486
Fall battleaxe, and flash *b*! (repeat) ,, 487, 490, 502
Clang battleaxe and clash *b*! (repeat) ,, 493, 496, 499
Gareth lash'd so fiercely with his *b* *Gareth and L.* 968
Sir Gareth's *b* Clash'd his, ,, 1147
neither hunting-dress Nor weapon, save a golden-hilted *b*, *Marr. of Geraint* 166
Swung from his *b* a windy buffet out Once, *Geraint and E.* 90
and tearing out of sheath The *b*, *Balin and Balan* 393
Where Arthur finds the *b* Excalibur. *Holy Grail* 253
The *b* Excalibur will be cast away. ,, 257
Shield-breakings, and the clash of *b's*, *Pass. of Arthur* 109
b's that once had fought with Rome, ,, 133
There drew he forth the *b* Excalibur, ,, 220
'And if indeed I cast the *b* away, ,, 256
The great *b* Made lightnings in the splendour ,, 304
So flash'd and fell the *b* Excalibur: ,, 310
Sons of Edward with hammer'd *b's*. *Batt. of Brunanburh* 14
Brand (verb) power to burn and *b* His nothingness into man. *Maud I xviii* 39
b us, after, of whose fold we be: *Merlin and V.* 764
Earth and Hell will *b* your name, *Forlorn* 51
Brandagoras King *B* of Latangor, *Com. of Arthur* 114
Brandish'd caught him by the hilt, and *b* him (repeat) *M. d'Arthur* 145, 160
caught him by the hilt, and *b* him (repeat) *Pass. of Arthur* 313, 328

C*

Brandishing *B* in her hand a dart *Boädicea* 71
Brass crag-platform smooth as burnish'd *b* I chose. *Palace of Art* 5
Two handfuls of white dust, shut in an urn of *b*! *Lotos-Eaters C.S.* 68
A flying splendour out of *b* and steel, *Princess vi* 365
Among the knightly *b'es* of the graves, *Merlin and V.* 752
Brastias (a knight) Ulfius, and *B*, and Bedivere, (repeat) *Com. of Arthur* 136, 165, 445
Ulfius and *B* answer'd, 'Ay.' *Com. of Arthur* 173
Brat I hevn't naw likin' fur *b's*; *Spinster's S's.* 84
Brave (adj.) *B* the Captain was: *The Captain* 5
few his knights, however *b* they be— *Com. of Arthur* 252
but all *b*, all of one mind with him; ,, 255
Truth-speaking, *b*, good livers, *Gareth and L.* 424
till she left Not even Lancelot *b*, *Merlin and V.* 805
All *b*, and many generous, and some chaste. ,, 817
Each was as *b* in the fight *V. of Maeldune* 5
being true as he was *b*; *Locksley H., Sixty* 59
Brave (s) our Lawrence the best of the *b*: *Def. of Lucknow* 11
Follow'd by the *b* of other lands, *Ode on Well.* 194
whatsoe'er He wrought of good or *b* *Epilogue* 76
Brave (verb) never: here I *b* the worst:' *Edwin Morris* 118
However we *b* it out, we men are a little breed. *Maud I iv* 30
Braved She *b* a riotous heart in asking for it. *Lancelot and E.* 359
Bravery Lancelot, the flower of *b*, ,, 113
Bravest Fought with the *b* among us, *Def. of Lucknow* 71
Brawl (s) creature wholly given to *b's* and wine, *Marr. of Geraint* 441
Brawl (verb) Cease to wail and *b*! *Two Voices* 199
I care not what the sects may *b*. *Palace of Art* 210
left the drunken king To *b* at Shushan *Princess iii* 230
b Their rights or wrongs like potherbs ,, *v* 458
our free press should cease to *b*, *Third of Feb.* 3
Is perfect stillness when they *b*. *Lit. Squabbles* 20
Brawler 'What fear ye, *b's*? *Princess iv* 498
Brawling brook o'er a shingly bed *B*, *Marr. of Geraint* 249
Romans *b* of their monstrous games; *St. Telemachus* 40
Bray loud rung out the bugle's *b's*, *Oriana* 48
in the blast and *b* of the long horn *Princess v* 252
Brazen-headed O'erthwarted with the *b-h* spear *Œnone* 139
Breach One has leapt up on the *b*, *Def. of Lucknow* 64
Breach'd *b* the belting wall of Cambalu, *Columbus* 108
Bread (*See also* **Bread**) I speak the truth, as I live by *b*! *Lady Clare* 26
Taking her *b* and theirs: *Enoch Arden* 111
wine And *b* from out the houses brought, *Spec. of Iliad* 6
chalk and alum and plaster are sold to the poor for *b*, *Maud I i* 39
Where *b* and baken meats and good red wine *Gareth and L.* 1190
in her veil enfolded, manchet *b*. *Marr. of Geraint* 389
sold and sold had bought them *b*: ,, 641
smote itself into the *b*, and went; *Holy Grail* 467
But, *b*, merely for *b*. *Sir J. Oldcastle* 14
'*B*—*B* left after the blessing?' ,, 153
now He veils His flesh in *b*, body and *b* ,, 157
'No *b*, no *b*. (repeat) ,, 159, 161
Hast thou brought *b* with thee? ,, 198
I have not broken *b* for fifty hours. ,, 199
For holding there was *b* where *b* was none—No *b*. ,, 201
I am not like to die for lack of *b*. ,, 205
B enough for his need till the labourless day *V. of Maeldune* 86
dream, now and then, of a hand giving *b* and wine, *The Wreck* 114
Master scrimps his haggard sempstress of her daily *b*, *Locksley H., Sixty* 221
Breäd Mun be a guvness, lad, or summut, and addle her *b*: *N. Farmer, N. S.* 26
Breadth *B's* of tropic shade and palms in cluster, *Locksley Hall* 160
left but narrow *b* to left and right *Enoch Arden* 674
shattering on black blocks A *b* of thunder. *Princess iii* 292
whence they need More *b* of culture: ,, *v* 188
a *b* Of Autumn, dropping fruits of power: ,, *vi* 54
She mental *b*, nor fail in childward care, ,, *vii* 283
tower Half-lost in belts of hop and *b's* of wheat; ,, *Con.* 45
with all thy *b* and height Of foliage, *In Mem. lxxxix* 3
highway running by it leaves a *b* Of sward to left and right, *Sisters (E. and E.)* 80
from over the *b* of a street, *Def. of Lucknow* 23
she with all the *b* of man, *Locksley H., Sixty* 48

Break (s) Across a *b* on the mist-wreathen isle *Enoch Arden* 632
At *b* of day the College Portress came: *Princess ii* 15
I climb'd the roofs at *b* of day; *The Daisy* 61

Break (verb) (*See also* **Breäk**) passion fann'd, About thee *b's* and dances: *Madeline* 30
breaking heart that will not *b*, *Oriana* 64
athlete, strong to *b* or bind All force *Palace of Art* 153
'No voice *b's* thro' the stillness ,, 259
You thought to *b* a country heart *L. C. V. de Vere* 3
Nor would I *b* for your sweet sake ,, 13
call me loud when the day begins to *b*: *May Queen* 10
lest a cry Should *b* his sleep by night, *Walk. to the Mail* 74
same old sore *b's* out from age to age ,, 79
Faltering, would *b* its syllables, *Love and Duty* 39
He *b's* the hedge: he enters there: *Day-Dm., Arrival* 18
But *b* it. In the name of wife, ,, *L'Envoi* 53
B up the heavens, O Lord! *St. Agnes' Eve* 21
barren commonplaces *b* In full and kindly blossom. *Will Water.* 23
B lock and seal: betray the trust: *You might have won* 18
B, *b*, *b*, On thy cold gray stones, *Break, break, etc.* 1
B, *b*, *b*, At the foot of thy crags, ,, 13
But had no heart to *b* his purposes To Annie, *Enoch Arden* 155
I think your kindness *b's* me down; ,, 318
Help me not to *b* in upon her peace. ,, 787
Which *b's* all bonds but ours; *Aylmer's Field* 425
Who broke the bond which they desired to *b*, ,, 778
trifle makes a dream, a trifle *b's*.' *Sea Dreams* 144
that *b* Body toward death, *Lucretius* 153
which *b's* As I am breaking now! ,, 241
In iron gauntlets: *b* the council up.' *Princess i* 89
wherefore *b* her troth? ,, 95
To *b* my chain, to shake my mane: ,, *ii* 424
Kill up with pity, *b* us with ourselves— ,, *iii* 258
tho' the rough kex *b* The starr'd mosaic, ,, *iv* 77
did I *b* Your precinct; ,, 421
On me, me, me, the storm first *b's*: ,, 499
You that have dared to *b* our bound, ,, 539
she's yet a colt—Take, *b* her: ,, *v* 456
takes, and *b's*, and cracks, and splits, ,, 527
fear we not To *b* them more in their behoof, ,, *vi* 61
Nemesis *B* from a darken'd future, ,, 175
We *b* our laws with ease, ,, 323
your Highness *b's* with ease The law ,, 325
roar that *b's* the Pharos from his base ,, 339
sorrowing in a pause I dared not *b*; ,, *vii* 249
b the shore, and evermore Make and *b*, *Ode on Well.* 260
War, who *b's* the converse of the wise; *Third of Feb.* 8
Tho' all the storm of Europe on us *b*; ,, 14
B, happy land, into earlier flowers! *W. to Alexandra* 10
everywhere, The blue heaven *b*, *W. to Marie Alex.* 43
To *b* the blast of winter, stand; *To F. D. Maurice* 22
the bud ever *b's* into bloom on the tree, *The Islet* 32
b the works of the statuary, *Boädicea* 64
immeasurable heavens *B* open to their highest, *Spec. of Iliad* 15
Must I take you and *b* you, *Window, The Answer* 3
I must take you, and *b* you, ,, 5
take—*b*, *b*—*B*—you may *b* my heart. ,, 7
B, *b* and all's done. ,, 10
B, thou deep vase of chilling tears, *In Mem. iv* 11
To evening, but some heart did *b*. ,, *vi* 8
On the bald street *b's* the blank day. ,, *vii* 12
B's hither over Indian seas, ,, *xxvi* 14
that my hold on life would *b* Before I heard ,, *xxviii* 15
That *b's* about the dappled pools: ,, *xlix* 4
Who *b's* his birth's invidious bar, ,, *lxiv* 5
and *b* The low beginnings of content. ,, *lxxxiv* 47
And *b* the livelong summer day ,, *lxxxix* 31
b's The rocket molten into flakes Of crimson ,, *xcviii* 30
Or into silver arrows *b* The sailing moon ,, *ci* 15
the rolling brine That *b's* the coast. ,, *cvii* 15
Will let his coltish nature *b* ,, *cxi* 7
And every thought *b's* out a rose. ,, *cxxii* 20
million emeralds *b* from the ruby-budded lime *Maud I iv* 1
Can *b* her word were it even for me? ,, *xvi* 29
B not, O woman's-heart, *Ded. of Idylls* 44

Break (verb) (*continued*) *B* not, for thou art Royal, but endure, *Ded. of Idylls* 45
'Climb not lest thou *b* thy neck, *Gareth and L.* 54
To *b* him from the intent to which he grew, ,, 140
so besieges her To *b* her will, and make her wed ,, 617
Running too vehemently to *b* upon it. *Marr. of Geraint* 78
Here often they *b* covert at our feet.' ,, 183
Then will I fight him, and will *b* his pride, ,, 221
and in April suddenly *B's* from a coppice ,, 339
That lightly *b's* a faded flower-sheath, ,, 365
fight and *b* his pride and have it of him. ,, 416
I will *b* his pride, and learn his name, ,, 424
In next day's tourney I may *b* his pride.' ,, 476
b perforce Upon a head so dear in thunder, *Geraint and E.* 12
as a man upon his tongue May *b* it, ,, 43
chance That *b's* upon them perilously, ,, 354
nature's prideful sparkle in the blood *B* into furious flame; ,, 828
b Into some madness ev'n before the Queen?' *Balin and Balan* 229
and *b* the King And all his Table.' ,, 458
knight, we *b* on thy sweet rest, ,, 470
now full loth am I to *b* thy dream, ,, 500
Began to *b* her sports with graver fits, *Merlin and V.* 180
in the slippery sand before it *b's*? ,, 293
fled from Arthur's court To *b* the mood. ,, 298
that wave about to *b* upon me And sweep me ,, 302
tiny-trumpeting gnat can *b* our dream When sweetest; *Lancelot and E.* 137
crying Christ and him, And *b* them; ,, 306
Would he *b* faith with one I may not name? ,, 685
discourtesy To blunt or *b* her passion.' ,, 974
(He meant to *b* the passion in her) ,, 1079
Would shun to *b* those bounds of courtesy ,, 1220
To *b* her passion, some discourtesy ,, 1302
I needs must *b* These bonds that so defame me: ,, 1420
b thro' all, till one will crown thee king *Holy Grail* 161
'I never heard his voice But long'd to *b* away. *Pelleas and E.* 256
said Tristram, 'I would *b* thy head. *Last Tournament* 268
and after the great waters *b* Whitening ,, 464
make the smouldering scandal *b* and blaze *Guinevere* 91
Stands in a wind, ready to *b* and fly, ,, 365
b the heathen and uphold the Christ, ,, 470
—let my heart *B* rather— *Lover's Tale i* 738
Not to *b* in on what I say by word ,, *iv* 352
B, diviner light! *Sisters (E. and E.)* 23
one of those who would *b* their jests on the dead, *In the Child. Hosp.* 8
B thro' the yews and cypress of thy grave, *Ded. Poem Prin. Alice* 12
would *b* down and raze The blessed tomb *Columbus* 98
Years that make And *b* the vase of clay, *Ancient Sage* 92
B into 'Thens' and 'Whens' ,, 104
when the babblings *b* the dream. ,, 107
Scarce feels the senses *b* away ,, 152
shell must *b* before the bird can fly. ,, 154
B the State, the Church, the Throne, *Locksley H., Sixty* 138
thro' this midnight *b's* the sun *Pref. Poem Broth. S.* 21
Might *b* thro' clouded memories *Demeter and P.* 10
And *b's* into the crocus-purple hour ,, 50
b The sunless halls of Hades into Heaven? ,, 135
b's her latest earthy link With me to-day. *The Ring* 47
Your 'Miriam *b's*'—is making ,, 50
No pliable idiot I to *b* my vow; ,, 402
made one barren effort to *b* it at the last. *Happy* 72
groundflame of the crocus *b's* the mould, *Prog. of Spring* 1
The mortal hillock, Would *b* into blossom; *Merlin and the G.* 108
blight thy hope or *b* thy rest, *Faith* 2

Breäk (verb) fur I beänt a-gawin' to *b* my rule. *N. Farmer, O. S.* 4
I weänt *b* rules fur Doctor, ,, 67
B me a bit o' the esh for his 'eäd, ,, *N. S.* 41
Tis'n them as 'as munny as *b's* into 'ouses ,, 45
an' sweär'd as I'd *b* ivry stick *North. Cobbler* 35
'tha mun *b* 'im off bit by bit.' ,, 88
runs out when ya *b's* the shell. *Village Wife* 4

Breaker (one who breaks) A *b* of the bitter news from home, *Aylmer's Field* 594

Breaker (one who breaks) (*continued*) Nor those horn-handed *b's* of the glebe, *Princess ii* 159
Breaker (wave) long swells of *b* sweep The nutmeg rocks *The Voyage* 39
following up And flying the white *b*, *Enoch Arden* 21
hard upon the cry of '*b's*' came " 548
a ridge Of *b* issued from the belt, *Sea Dreams* 212
The mellow *b* murmur'd Ida. *Princess iv* 436
roaring *b's* boom and blanch on the precipices, *Boädicea* 76
The *b* breaking on the beach. *In Mem. lxxi* 16
And the fringe Of that great *b*, *Com. of Arthur* 387
And steps that met the *b*! *Holy Grail* 816
chafed *b's* of the outer sea Sank powerless, *Lover's Tale i* 8
the *b's* on the shore Sloped into louder surf: " *iii* 14
Javelins over The jarring *b*, *Batt. of Brunanburh* 97
came thro' the roar of the *b* a whisper, *Despair* 13
The *b's* lash the shores: *Pref. Poem Broth. S.* 2
Breaker-beaten For leagues along that *b-b* coast *Enoch Arden* 51
Breakest so thou *b* Arthur's music too.' *Last Tournament* 266
Breaking (part) (*See also* **Ever-breaking**) Just *b* over land and main? *Two Voices* 84
heart is *b*, and my eyes are dim, *Œnone* 32
They say his heart is *b*, mother— *May Queen* 22
The thunders *b* at her feet: *Of old sat Freedom* 2
while on all sides *b* loose Her household fled *The Goose* 53
Old elms came *b* from the vine, *Amphion* 45
LONG lines of cliff *b* have left a chasm; *Enoch Arden* 1
Nor let him be, but often *b* in, " 701
he saw An end, a hope, a light *b* upon him. *Aylmer's Field* 480
b that, you made and broke your dream: *Sea Dreams* 143
which breaks As I am *b* now! *Lucretius* 241
nation weeping, and *b* on my rest? *Ode on Well.* 82
B their mailed fleets and armed towers, *Ode Inter. Exhib.* 39
Or *b* into song by fits, *In Mem. xxiii* 2
The breaker *b* on the beach. " *lxxi* 16
And *b* let the splendour fall " *Con.* 119
why come you so cruelly meek, *B* a slumber *Maud I iii* 2
B up my dream of delight. " *xix* 2
and *b* into song Sprang out, *Com. of Arthur* 320
heard The world's loud whisper *b* into storm, *Marr. of Geraint* 27
Then *b* his command of silence given, *Geraint and E.* 390
Vivien *b* in upon him, said: *Merlin and V.* 600
Outram and Havelock *b* their way through *Def. of Lucknow* 96
O young life *B* with laughter *De. Prof. Two G.* 18
Who *b* in upon us yestermorn, *Akbar's Dream* 114
Breaking (s) (*See also* **Shield-breaking**) Until the *b* of the light, *Clear-headed friend* 25
Yours came but from the *b* of a glass, *Sea Dreams* 248
crave His pardon for thy *b* of his laws. *Gareth and L.* 986
Red ruin, and the *b* up of laws, *Guinevere* 426
making a new link *B* an old one? *The Ring* 51
save *b* my bones on the rack? *By an Evolution.* 9
Breast (s) Naiad Throbbing in mild unrest holds him beneath in her *b*. *Leonine Eleg.* 12
Showering thy gleaned wealth into my open *b* *Ode to Memory* 23
Fold thy palms across thy *b*, *A Dirge* 2
Take the heart from out my *b*. *Adeline* 8
To find my heart so near the beauteous *b* *The form, the form* 7
Dominion in the head and *b*.' *Two Voices* 21
'His palms are folded on his *b*: " 247
A vague suspicion of the *b*: " 336
fill'd the *b* with purer breath. *Miller's D.* 92
I crush'd them on my *b*, my mouth; *Fatima* 12
Over her snow-cold *b* and angry cheek *Œnone* 142
His ruddy cheek upon my *b*, *The Sisters* 20
hundred winters snow'd upon his *b*. *Palace of Art* 139
as I lie upon your *b*— *May Queen, Con.* 59
polish'd argent of her *b* to sight *D. of F. Women* 158
and my true *b* Bleedeth for both; *To J. S.* 62
So muscular he spread, so broad of *b*. *Gardener's D.* 8
wave of such a *b* As never pencil drew. " 139
breathing health and peace upon her *b*: *Audley Court* 68
An acorn in her *b*. *Talking Oak* 228
crimson comes upon the robin's *b*; *Locksley Hall* 17
press me from the mother's *b*. " 90
Breast (s) (*continued*) and he bears a laden *b*, *Locksley Hall* 143
in its *b* a thunderbolt. " 192
old Earl's daughter died at my *b*; *Lady Clare* 25
HER arms across her *b* she laid; *Beggar Maid* 1
I shook her *b* with vague alarms— *The Letters* 38
silent court of justice in his *b*, *Sea Dreams* 174
stood out the *b's*, The *b's* of Helen, *Lucretius* 60
blasting the long quiet of my *b* " 162
Beat *b*, tore hair, cried out upon herself " 277
think I bear that heart within my *b*, *Princess ii* 334
Rest, rest, on mother's *b*, " *iii* 11
My secret, seem'd to stir within my *b*; " 44
from my *b* the involuntary sigh Brake, " 191
I smote him on the *b*; " *iv* 164
now her *b*, Beaten with some great passion " 387
Her noble heart was molten in her *b*; " *vi* 119
if you loved The *b* that fed or arm " 181
Thy helpless warmth about my barren *b* " 202
something wild within her *b*, " *vii* 237
Sent from a dewy *b* a cry for light: " 253
Chop the *b's* from off the mother, *Boädicea* 68
And dead calm in that noble *b* *In Mem. xi* 19
And onward drags a labouring *b*, " *xv* 18
Be tenants of a single *b*, " *xvi* 3
Against the circle of the *b*, " *xlv* 3
A faithful answer from the *b*, " *lxxxv* 14
That warms another living *b*. " 116
They haunt the silence of the *b*, " *xciv* 9
And woolly *b's* and beaded eyes; " *xcv* 12
A single murmur in the *b*, " *civ* 7
and in my *b* Spring wakens too; " *cxv* 17
And enter in at *b* and brow, " *cxxii* 11
A warmth within the *b* would melt " *cxxiv* 13
opulence jewel-thick Sunn'd itself on his *b* *Maud I xiii* 13
Lord of the pulse that is lord of her *b*, " *xvi* 13
ruddy shield on the Lion's *b*. " *III vi* 14
o'er her *b* floated the sacred fish; *Gareth and L.* 223
The massive square of his heroic *b*, *Marr. of Geraint* 75
'O noble *b* and all-puissant arms, " 86
weep True tears upon his broad and naked *b*, " 111
thro' his manful *b* darted the pang " 121
Sank her sweet head upon her gentle *b*; " 527
fell'd him, and set foot upon his *b*, " 574
Drave the long spear a cubit thro' his *b* *Geraint and E.* 86
Her arms upon her *b* across, *Merlin and V.* 910
pleasant *b* of waters, quiet bay, *Lover's Tale i* 6
anger falls aside And withers on the *b* of peaceful love; " 10
Her *b* as in a shadow-prison, " *iv* 58
her *b* Hard-heaving, and her eyes upon her feet, " 307
her thin hands crost on her *b*— *In the Child. Hosp.* 39
kill Their babies at the *b* *Columbus* 180
And from her virgin *b*, and virgin eyes *Tiresias* 46
ah, fold me to your *b*! *The Flight* 5
pluck from this true *b* the locket that I wear, " 33
well-used to move the public *b*. *To W. C. Macready* 3
gave Thy *b* to ailing infants in the night, *Demeter and P.* 56
my loving head upon your leprous *b*. *Happy* 26
let me lean my head upon your *b*. *Romney's R.* 154
blade that had slain my husband thrice thro' his *b*. *Bandit's Death* 34
Breast (verb) *b's* the blows of circumstance, *In Mem. lxiv* 7
Breast-bone white *b-b*, and barren ribs of Death, *Gareth and L.* 1382
Breast-deep all night long *b-d* in corn, *Princess ii* 387
Breasted *See* **Full-breasted, Man-breasted, White-breasted.**
Breast-high *B-h* in that bright line *Pelleas and E.* 56
Breath (*See also* **Morning-breath**) Her subtil, warm, and golden *b*, *Supp. Confessions* 60
b Of the fading edges of box beneath, *A spirit haunts* 18
There is frost in your *b* *Poet's Mind* 17
the *b* Of the lilies at sunrise? *Adeline* 36
I lose my colour, I lose my *b*, *Eleänore* 137
No life that breathes with human *b* *Two Voices* 395
fill'd the breast with purer *b*. *Miller's D.* 92
As half-asleep his *b* he drew, *The Sisters* 28
Long labour unto aged *b*, *Lotos-Eater's, C. S.* 85

Breath (*continued*) Dan Chaucer, the first warbler, whose sweet *b* — *D. of F. Women* 5
Drew forth the poison with her balmy *b*, — ,, 271
but empty *b* And rumours of a doubt? — *M. d'Arthur* 99
spoke King Arthur, drawing thicker *b*: — ,, 148
Clothed with his *b*, and looking, — ,, 182
my ears could hear Her lightest *b*; — *Edwin Morris* 65
but ever at a *b* She linger'd, — *Godiva* 44
My *b* to heaven like vapour goes: — *St. Agnes' Eve* 3
'Greet her with applausive *b*, — *Vision of Sin* 135
While we keep a little *b*! — ,, 192
The *b* of heaven came continually — *Enoch Arden* 535
my latest *b* Was spent in blessing her — ,, 883
a low *b* Of tender air made tremble — *The Brook* 201
ice-ferns on January panes Made by a *b*. — *Aylmer's Field* 223
on a sudden rush'd Among us, out of *b*, — *Princess iv* 375
b of life; O more than poor men wealth, — ,, 459
body that never had drawn a *b*. — *Grandmother* 62
O sweet and bitter in a *b*, — *In Mem. iii* 3
And scarce endure to draw the *b*, — ,, *xx* 15
And so the Word had *b*, and wrought — ,, *xxxvi* 9
This use may lie in blood and *b*, — ,, *xlv* 13
spirit does but mean the *b* I know no more.' — ,, *lvi* 7
Death's twin-brother, times my *b*; — ,, *lxviii* 2
new life that feeds thy *b* Throughout — *In Mem. lxxxvi* 10
East and West, without a *b*, — *In Mem. xcv* 62
To where he breathed his latest *b*, — ,, *xcviii* 5
Who wakenest with thy balmy *b* — ,, *xcix* 13
I trust I have not wasted *b*: — ,, *cxx* 1
Be quicken'd with a livelier *b*, — ,, *cxxii* 13
Awe-stricken *b's* at a work divine, — *Maud I x* 17
Prickle my skin and catch my *b*, — ,, *xiv* 36
Catch not my *b*, O clamorous heart, — ,, *xvi* 31
Not die; but live a life of truest *b*, — *Maud I xviii* 53
Seal'd her mine from her first sweet *b*. — ,, *xix* 41
mix'd my *b* With a loyal people shouting — ,, *III vi* 34
with the might and *b* of twenty boys.' — *Gareth and L.* 1106
Sent all his heart and *b* thro' all the horn. — ,, 1369
Here ceased the kindly mother out of *b*; — *Marr. of Geraint* 732
fits of prayer, at every stroke a *b*. — *Geraint and E.* 155
Sweet lady, never since I first drew *b* — ,, 619
and the *b* Of her sweet tendance — ,, 925
b's of anger puff'd Her fairy nostril — *Merlin and V.* 848
At last he got his *b* and answer'd, 'One, — *Lancelot and E.* 422
whereat she caught her *b*; — ,, 623
blow with *b*, or touch with hand, — *Holy Grail* 114
She felt the King's *b* wander o'er her neck, — *Guinevere* 582
but empty *b* And rumours of a doubt? — *Pass. of Arthur* 267
spoke King Arthur, drawing thicker *b*: — ,, 316
Clothed with his *b*, and looking, — ,, 350
I feel thy *b*; I come, great Mistress — *Lover's Tale i* 21
Thy *b* is of the pinewood; — ,, 23
faints, and hath no pulse, no *b*— — ,, 268
rose as it were *b* and steam of gold, — ,, 402
my name was borne Upon her *b*. — ,, 444
by that name I moved upon her *b*; — ,, 560
Love drew in her *b* In that close kiss, — ,, 816
about my brow Her warm *b* floated — ,, *ii* 141
at once, soul, life And *b* and motion, — ,, 195
And parted lips which drank her *b*, — ,, 204
Took the *b* from our sails, and we stay'd. — *The Revenge* 42
but never a murmur, a *b*— — *V. of Maeldune* 19
their *b* met us out on the seas, — ,, 37
thro' life to my latest *b*; — *The Wreck* 79
thro' the roar of the breaker a whisper, a *b*, — *Despair* 13
And now one *b* of cooler air — *Ancient Sage* 117
A *b*, a whisper—some divine farewell— — ,, 225
to feel his *b* Upon my cheek— — *The Flight* 45
b that past With all the cold of winter. — *The Ring* 32
and felt An icy *b* play on me, — ,, 131
an icy *b*, As from the grating of a sepulchre, — ,, 399
leaves her bare To *b's* of balmier air; — *Prog. of Spring* 13
Blown into glittering by the popular *b*, — *Romney's R.* 49
a *b* From some fair dawn beyond — *Far-far-away* 10
open-door'd To every *b* from heaven, — *Akbar's Dream* 180

Breathe in her first sleep earth *b's* stilly: — *Leonine Eleg.* 7
Or *b* into the hollow air, — *Supp. Confessions* 58
odorous wind *B's* low between the sunset — *Eleänore* 124
But *b* it into earth and close it up — *Wan Sculptor* 12
'Twere better not to *b* or speak, — *Two Voices* 94
'To *b* and loathe, to live and sigh, — ,, 104
No life that *b's* with human breath — ,, 395
I least should *b* a thought of pain. — *Miller's D.* 26
wind *b's* low with mellower tone: — *Lotos-Eaters, C. S.* 102
How hard he *b's*! — *D. of the O. Year* 37
to sit, to sleep, to wake, to *b*.' — *Edwin Morris* 40
I do not *b*, Not whisper, any murmur — *St. S. Stylites* 21
When that, which *b's* within the leaf, — *Talking Oak* 187
As tho' to *b* were life. — *Ulysses* 24
I yearn to *b* the airs of heaven — *Sir Galahad* 63
A carefuller in peril, did not *b* — *Enoch Arden* 50
And *b's* in April-autumns. — *The Brook* 196
love-whispers may not *b* Within this vestal limit, — *Princess ii* 221
Low, low, *b* and blow, — ,, *iii* 3
let us *b* for one hour more in Heaven' — ,, 69
'Alas your Highness *b's* full East,' — ,, 231
Where shall I *b*? — ,, *v* 77
that each May *b* himself, and quick! — ,, 316
b upon my brows; — ,, *vii* 353
To let the people *b*? — ,, *Con.* 104
diviner air *B* thro' the world and change — *W. to Marie Alex.* 44
To *b* thee over lonely seas. — *In Mem. xvii* 4
That *b* a thousand tender vows, — ,, *xx* 2
The slightest air of song shall *b* — ,, *xlix* 7
And *b's* a novel world, the while — ,, *lxii* 9
And, while we *b* beneath the sun, — ,, *lxxv* 14
To *b* my loss is more than fame, — ,, *lxxvii* 15
summer's hourly-mellowing change May *b*, — ,, *xci* 10
I find no place that does not *b* Some gracious memory — ,, *c* 3
Nor landmark *b's* of other days, — ,, *civ* 11
Thro' which the spirit *b's* no more? — ,, *cv* 20
For tho' my lips may *b* adieu, — ,, *cxxiii* 11
Left the still King, and passing forth to *b*, — *Com. of Arthur* 369
only *b* Short fits of prayer, — *Geraint and E.* 154
'You *b* but accusation vast and vague, — *Merlin and V.* 701
No keener hunter after glory *b's*. — *Lancelot and E.* 156
there *b's* not one of you Will deem this prize — ,, 540
'Look, He haunts me—I cannot *b*— — *Pelleas and E.* 227
thought I could not *b* in that fine air — *Guinevere* 645
B but a little on me, — *Lover's Tale i* 26
outward circling air wherewith I *b*, — ,, 167
b with her as if in heaven itself; — ,, 391
Which pass with that which *b's* them? — ,, 481
B, diviner Air! — *Sisters (E. and E.)* 13
none could *b* Within the zone of heat; — *Columbus* 52
can I *b* divorced from the Past? — *Despair* 113
And all that *b* are one Slight ripple — *Ancient Sage* 188
who *b* the balm Of summer-winters — *To Ulysses* 10

Breathed *B* low around the rolling earth — *The Winds, etc.* 3
She *b* in sleep a lower moan, — *Mariana in the S.* 45
Rose slowly to a music slowly *b*, — *Œnone* 41
B, like the covenant of a God, — *Gardener's D.* 209
I *b* In some new planet: — *Edwin Morris* 114
I *b* upon her eyes Thro' all the summer — *Talking Oak* 210
the low wind hardly *b* for fear. — *Godiva* 55
on him *b* Far purelier in his rushings — *Aylmer's Field* 457
while I *b* in sight of haven, he, Poor fellow, — *The Brook* 157
he had *b* the Proctor's dogs; — *Princess, Pro.* 113
And look on Spirits *b* away, — *In Mem. xl* 2
That *b* beneath the Syrian blue: — ,, *lii* 12
Where all things round me *b* of him. — ,, *lxxxv* 32
To where he *b* his latest breath, — ,, *xcviii* 5
He *b* the spirit of the song; — ,, *cxxv* 10
living words of life *B* in her ear. — ,, *Con.* 53
Whenever slander *b* against the King— — *Com. of Arthur* 177
God hath *b* a secret thing. — ,, 501
twice they fought, and twice they *b*, — *Marr. of Geraint* 567
Queen's fair name was *b* upon, — *Geraint and E.* 951
B in a dismal whisper 'It is truth.' — *Balin and Balan* 527

Breathed (*continued*) emerald center'd in a sun Of silver rays, that lighten'd as he *b*; *Lancelot and E.* 296
Whereof the chill, to him who *b* it, *Pass. of Arthur* 96
Has *b* a race of mightier mountaineers. *Montenegro* 14
No sound is *b* so potent to coerce, *Tiresias* 120
warm winds had gently *b* us away from the land— *The Wreck* 63
Breather those we call the dead Are *b's* of an ampler day *In Mem. cxviii* 6
Breathing (*See also* **Hard-breathing**) *B* Light against thy face, *Adeline* 56
Old letters, *b* of her worth, *Mariana in the S.* 62
A hint, a whisper *b* low, *Two Voices* 434
B like one that hath a weary dream. *Lotos-Eaters* 6
spoke King Arthur, *b* heavily: *M. d'Arthur* 113
answer made King Arthur, *b* hard: „ 162
alighted from the boat, And *b* of the sea. *Audley Court* 8
'Sleep, *b* health and peace upon her breast: „ 68
Sleep, *b* love and trust against her lip: „ 69
her *b's* are not heard In palace chambers *Day-Dm., Sleep. B.* 17
warm-blue *b's* of a hidden hearth Broke *Aylmer's Field* 155
like a beast hard-ridden, *b* hard. „ 291
b down From over her arch'd brows, *Princess ii* 38
B and sounding beauteous battle, „ *v* 161
In Angel instincts, *b* Paradise, „ *vii* 321
Closer is He than *b*, and nearer than hands *High. Pantheism* 12
Would *b* thro' his lips impart *In Mem. xviii* 15
slowly *b* bare The round of space, „ *lxxxvi* 4
By meadows *b* of the past, „ *xcix* 7
Bright English lily, *b* a prayer *Maud I xix* 55
hear him *b* low and equally. *Geraint and E.* 372
she glided out Among the heavy *b's* of the house, „ 402
Beside the placid *b's* of the King, *Guinevere* 69
spoke King Arthur, *b* heavily: *Pass. of Arthur* 281
answer made King Arthur, *b* hard: „ 330
b on each other, Dreaming together *Lover's Tale i* 261
and joy In *b* nearer heaven; „ 389
b hard at the approach of Death,— „ 585
Is *b* in his sleep, *Early Spring* 23
changest, *b* it, the sullen wind, *Prog. of Spring* 110
Breathing-space ballad or a song To give us *b-s*.' *Princess, Pro.* 242
Breathing-while Except when for a *b-w* at eve, *Aylmer's Field* 449
Bred (*See also* **Home-bred, Wisdom-bred**) Two children in one hamlet born and *b*; *Circumstance* 8
upon the board, And *b* this change; *Œnone* 227
for his sake I *b* His daughter Dora: *Dora* 19
not being *b* To barter, *Enoch Arden* 249
A CITY clerk, but gently born and *b*; *Sea Dreams* 1
her will *B* will in me to overcome *Princess v* 351
From out the doors where I was *b*, *In Mem. ciii* 2
'e wur burn an' *b* i' the 'ouse, *Spinster's S.'s* 69
opiate then *B* this black mood? *Romney's R.* 62
Brede in glowing gauze and golden *b*, *Princess vi* 134
Breed (s) looks not like the common *b* That with the napkin dally; *Will Water.* 117
In doubt if you be of our Barons' *b*— *Third of Feb.* 32
we men are a little *b*. *Maud I iv* 30
Breed (verb) Assurance only *b's* resolve.' *Two Voices* 315
graze and wallow, *b* and sleep; *Palace of Art* 202
like *b's* like, they say: *Walk. to the Mail* 63
could he understand how money *b's*, *The Brook* 6
much loth to *b* Dispute betwixt myself *Princess i* 156
in thunderstorms, And *b* up warriors! „ *v* 440
earth's embrace May *b* with him, *In Mem. lxxxii* 4
Breeding Softness *b* scorn of simple life, *To the Queen ii* 53
Breeze (*See also* **River-breeze, South-breeze**) The *b's* pause and die, *Claribel* 2
LOW-FLOWING *b's* are roaming the broad valley *Leonine Eleg.* 1
WHEN the *b* of a joyful dawn blew free *Arabian Nights* 1
fann'd With *b's* from our oaken glades, *Eleänore* 10
Coming in the scented *b*, „ 24
Little *b's* dusk and shiver *L. of Shalott i* 11
And heard her native *b's* pass, *Mariana in the S.* 43
A *b* thro' all the garden swept, *Day-Dm., Revival* 6
Warm broke the *b* against the brow, *The Voyage* 9
Low *b's* fann'd the belfry bars, *The Letters* 43

Breeze (*continued*) Made noise with bees and *b* from end to end. *Princess, Pro.* 88
long *b's* rapt from inmost south „ *iv* 431
roll'd With music in the growing *b* of Time, „ *vi* 56
such a *b* Compell'd thy canvas, *In Mem. xvii* 1
all the bugle *b's* blew Reveillée „ *lxviii* 7
And round thee with the *b* of song „ *lxxv* 11
A *b* began to tremble o'er The large leaves „ *xcv* 54
And all the *b* of Fancy blows, „ *cxxii* 17
tells The joy to every wandering *b*; „ *Con.* 62
blown by the *b* of a softer clime, *Maud I iv* 4
sighing for Lebanon In the long *b* „ *xviii* 16
For a *b* of morning moves, „ *xxii* 7
Drooping and beaten by the *b*, *Lover's Tale i* 700
Thoughts of the *b's* of May blowing *Def. of Lucknow* 83
sat each on the lap of the *b*; *V. of Maeldune* 38
a balmier *b* curl'd over a peacefuller sea, *The Wreck* 133
lark has past from earth to Heaven upon the morning *b*! *The Flight* 62
Flies back in fragrant *b's* to display *Prog. of Spring* 64
Brendan (Irish Saint) who had sail'd with St. *B* of yore, *V. of Maeldune* 115
Brethren (*See also* **Brother**) so that all My *b* marvell'd greatly. *St. S. Stylites* 69
And of her *b*, youths of puissance; *Princess i* 37
Not ev'n her brother Arac, nor the twins Her *b*, „ 154
The *b* of our blood and cause, „ *vi* 71
To where her wounded *b* lay; „ 90
O let me have him with my *b* here „ 123
bite And pinch their *b* in the throng, *Lit. Squabbles* 7
grieve Thy *b* with a fruitless tear? *In Mem. lviii* 10
till Doubt and Death, Ill *b*, „ *lxxxvi* 12
both my *b* are in Arthur's hall, *Gareth and L.* 82
b, and a fourth And of that four the mightiest, „ 614
younger *b* have gone down Before this youth; „ 1102
to mar the boast Thy *b* of thee make— „ 1243
my three *b* bad me do it, „ 1410
Among his burnish'd *b* of the pool; *Marr. of Geraint* 650
B, to right and left the spring, *Balin and Balan* 25
Arthur lightly smote the *b* down, „ 41
Thy chair, a grief to all the *b*, „ 78
My *b* have been all my fellowship; *Lancelot and E.* 672
came her *b* saying, 'Peace to thee, „ 996
those two *b* slowly with bent brows Accompanying, „ 1138
So those two *b* from the chariot took „ 1146
friends in testimony, Her *b*, and her father, „ 1300
Where all the *b* are so hard, *Holy Grail* 618
Also the *b*, King and Atheling, *Batt. of Brunanburh* 100
Breton on the *B* strand! *B*, not Briton; *Maud II ii* 29
Back from the *B* coast, „ 43
touching *B* sands, they disembark'd. *Merlin and V.* 202
cried the *B*, 'Look, her hand is red! *Last Tournament* 412
Breviary read but on my *b* with ease, *Holy Grail* 545
Brew'd found a witch Who *b* the philtre *Lucretius* 16
Brewer gloomy *b's* soul Went by me, *Talking Oak* 55
Brewis The kitchen *b* that was ever supt *Gareth and L.* 781
Briar (*See also* **Brier**) bur and brake and *b*, *Day-Dm., Sleep. P.* 46
Bribe a costly *b* To guerdon silence, *Princess i* 203
which for *b* had wink'd at wrong, *Geraint and E.* 939
Bribed *B* with large promises the men *Marr. of Geraint* 453
Brick When we made *b's* in Egypt. *Princess iv* 128
mantles all the mouldering *b's*— *Locksley H., Sixty* 257
as graw'd hall ower the *b*; *Owd Roä* 26
'eärd the *b's* an' the baulks „ 109
Brickwork Tudor-chimnied bulk Of mellow *b* *Edwin Morris* 12
Bridal (adj.) Leapt lightly clad in *b* white— *Lover's Tale iii* 44
Thy Soldier-brother's *b* orange-bloom Break *Ded. Poem Prin. Alice* 11
THE *b* garland falls upon the bier, *D. of the Duke of C.* 1
Bridal (s) Then reign the world's great *b's*, *Princess vii* 294
Evil haunts The birth, the *b*; *In Mem. xcviii* 14
Memories of *b*, or of birth, „ *xcix* 15
Will clothe her for her *b's* like the sun.' *Marr. of Geraint* 231
clothed her for her *b's* like the sun; „ 836
Bridal-gift poor bride Gives her harsh groom for *b-g* a scourge; *Princess v* 378

Brief (*continued*) *B*, *b* is a summer leaf, *Spiteful Letter* 21
if Thou willest, let my day be *b*, *Doubt and Prayer* 13
Brier (*See also* **Briar**) whom Gideon school'd with *b's*. *Buonaparte* 14
The little life of bank and *b*, *You might have won* 30
drench'd with ooze, and torn with *b's*, *Princess v* 28
I have heard of thorns and *b's*. *Window, Marr. Morn.* 20
Over the thorns and *b's*, „ 21
the winds that bend the *b* ! *Last Tournament* 731
wild *b* had driven Its knotted thorns *Lover's Tale i* 619
rough *b* tore my bleeding palms ; „ *ii* 18
Brig (bridge) An' I'll run oop to the *b*, *N. Farmer, N. S.* 55
Brigade Glory to all the three hundred, and all the *B* ! *Heavy Brigade* 66
Brigade, Heavy *See* **Heavy Brigade**
Brigade, Light *See* **Light Brigade**
Bright (adj.) *See also* **Over-bright, Rosy-bright, Summer-bright)**
Clear and *b* it should be ever, *Poet's Mind* 5
B as light, and clear as wind. „ 7
met with two so full and *b*—Such eyes ! *Miller's D.* 86
I made my dagger sharp and *b*. *The Sisters* 26
but none so *b* as mine ; *May Queen* 5
Make *b* our days and light our dreams, *Of old sat Freedom* 22
B was that afternoon, Sunny but chill ; *Enoch Arden* 669
B with the sun upon the stream *Sea Dreams* 97
b and fierce and fickle is the South, *Princess iv* 97
B let it be with its blazon'd deeds, *Ode on Well.* 56
Phosphor, *b* As our pure love, *In Mem. ix* 10
Thy marble *b* in dark appears, „ *lxvii* 5
The voice was low, the look was *b* ; „ *lxix* 15
And *b* the friendship of thine eye ; „ *cxix* 10
To-day the grave is *b* for me, „ *Con.* 73
b and light as the crest Of a peacock, *Maud I xvi* 16
soft splendours that you look so *b* ? „ *xviii* 79
dawn of Eden *b* over earth and sky, „ *II i* 8
in a weary world my one thing *b* ; „ *III vi* 17
Geraint with eyes all *b* replied, *Marr. of Geraint* 494
strange *b* and dreadful thing, a court, „ 616
she knew That all was *b* ; „ 658
Beholding one so *b* in dark estate, „ 786
keep him *b* and clean as heretofore, *Geraint and E.* 937
She with a face, *b* as for sin forgiven, *Lancelot and E.* 1102
her look *B* for all others, *Pelleas and E.* 177
our eyes met : hers were *b*, and mine Were dim *Lover's Tale i* 441
an' I keeäps 'im cleän an' *b*, *North. Cobbler* 97
Far from out a sky for ever *b*, *Sisters (E. and E.)* 19
an' yer eyes as *b* as the day ! *Tomorrow* 32
How *b* you keep your marriage-ring ! *Romney's R.* 59
morning that looks so *b* from afar ! *By an Evolution.* 10
When I look'd at the bracken so *b* *June Bracken, etc.* 3
Bright (s) level lake with diamond-plots Of dark and *b*. *Arabian Nights* 86
Remaining betwixt dark and *b* : *Margaret* 28
Of this flat lawn with dusk and *b* ; *In Mem. lxxxix* 2
B and Dark have sworn that I, *Demeter and P.* 96
Beyond the darker hour to see the *b*, *Prog. of Spring* 88
Brighten cheek brighten'd as the foam-bow *b's* *Œnone* 61
stars above them seem to *b* as they pass ; *May Queen* 34
Thy sweet eyes *b* slowly close to mine, *Tithonus* 38
it *b's* and darkens down on the plain. *Window, On the Hill* 2
it *b's* and darkens and *b's* like my hope, And it darkens and *b's* and darkens like my fear, „ 18
And *b* like the star that shook *In Mem., Con.* 31
b's at the clash of 'Yes' and 'No,' *Ancient Sage* 71
b's thro' the Mother's tender eyes, *Prin. Beatrice* 4
Brighten'd cheek *b* as the foam-bow brightens *Œnone* 61
For so mine own was *b* : *Aylmer's Field* 683
Till the face of Bel be *b*, *Boädicea* 16
Your pretty sports have *b* all again. *Merlin and V.* 305
The rounder cheek had *b* into bloom. *The Ring* 351
Brightening (*See also* **Ever-brightening**) Like sheet lightning, Ever *b* *Poet's Mind* 26
B the skirts of a long cloud, *M. d'Arthur* 54
Unseen, is *b* to his bridal morn. *Gardener's D.* 73
Brightening (*continued*) Enid listen'd *b* as she lay : *Marr. of Geraint* 733
B the skirts of a long cloud, *Pass. of Arthur* 222
And slowly *b* Out of the glimmer, *Merlin and the G.* 88
Brighter broader and *b* The Gleam flying onward, „ 95
Brightest Their best and *b*, when they dwelt on hers, *Aylmer's Field* 69
Brightly Enoch faced this morning of farewell *B* *Enoch Arden* 183
Brightness as babies for the moon, Vague *b* ; *Princess iv* 429
false sense in her own self Of my contrasting *b*, overbore *Marr. of Geraint* 801
set apart Their motions and their *b* from the stars, *Lover's Tale i* 174
The *b* of a burning thought, „ 743
Brilliance star The black earth with *b* rare. *Ode to Memory* 20
So bathed we were in *b*. *Lover's Tale i* 313
Brim (s) By garden porches on the *b*, *Arabian Nights* 16
He froth'd his bumpers to the *b* ; *D. of the O. Year* 19
New stars all night above the *b* *The Voyage* 25
Brim (verb) I *b* with sorrow drowning song. *In Mem. xix* 12
Arrange the board and *b* the glass ; „ *cvii* 16
Brimful heart, *B* of those wild tales, *D. of F. Women* 12
Brimm'd (*See also* **Broad-brimm'd**) *B* with delirious draughts of warmest life. *Eleänore* 139
And beaker *b* with noble wine. *Day-Dm., Sleep. P.* 36
Brine Lulling the *b* against the Coptic sands. *Buonaparte* 8
Fresh-water springs come up through bitter *b*. *If I were loved* 8
hear and see the far-off sparkling *b*, *Lotos-Eaters, C. S.* 98
Gloom'd the low coast and quivering *b* *The Voyage* 42
Should gulf him fathom-deep in *b* ; *In Mem. x* 18
To darken on the rolling *b* That breaks „ *cvii* 14
Bring *b* me my love, Rosalind. *Leonine Eleg.* 14
'*B* this lamb back into Thy fold, *Supp. Confessions* 105
Music that *b's* sweet sleep down *Lotos-Eaters, C. S.* 7
And in its season *b* the law ; *Love thou thy land* 32
Certain, if knowledge *b* the sword, That knowledge takes „ 87
For nature *b's* not back the Mastodon, *The Epic* 36
Watch what thou seëst, and lightly *b* me word.' *M. d'Arthur* 38
Watch what I see, and lightly *b* thee word.' „ 44
I bad thee, watch, and lightly *b* me word.' „ 81
A word could *b* the colour to my cheek ; *Gardener's D.* 196
I will have my boy, and *b* him home ; *Dora* 122
b me offerings of fruit and flowers : *St. S. Stylites* 128
Love himself will *b* The drooping flower *Love and Duty* 23
sweet hours that *b* us all things good, „ 57
sad hours that *b* us all things ill, „ 58
Nay, but Nature *b's* thee solace ; *Locksley Hall* 87
my latest rival *b's* thee rest. „ 89
B truth that sways the soul of men ? *Day-Dm., Sleep. P.* 52
And *b* the fated fairy Prince. „ 56
'*B* the dress and put it on her, *L. of Burleigh* 95
B me spices, *b* me wine ; *Vision of Sin* 76
Will *b* fair weather yet to all of us. *Enoch Arden* 191
I warrant, man, that we shall *b* you round.' „ 841
and arose Eager to *b* them down, „ 872
b Their own gray hairs with sorrow to the grave— *Aylmer's Field* 776
And *b* her in a whirlwind : *Princess i* 65
b's our friends up from the underworld. „ *iv* 45
an' doesn *b* ma the aäle ? *N. Farmer, O. S.* 65
The seasons *b* the flower again, *In Mem. ii* 5
And *b* the firstling to the flock ; „ 6
So *b* him : we have idle dreams : „ *x* 9
And not the burthen that they *b*. „ *xiii* 20
If one should *b* me this report, „ *xiv* 1
And all was good that Time could *b*, „ *xxiii* 18
They *b* me sorrow touch'd with joy, „ *xxviii* 19
Which *b's* no more a welcome guest „ *xxix* 5
And *b* her babe, and make her boast, „ *xl* 26
She often *b's* but one to bear, „ *lv* 12
I *b* to life, I *b* to death : „ *lvi* 6
Then *b* an opiate trebly strong, „ *lxxi* 6
In verse that *b's* myself relief, „ *lxxv* 2
B orchis, *b* the foxglove spire, „ *lxxxiii* 9
Demanding, so to *b* relief „ *lxxxv* 6
Ah, take the imperfect gift I *b*, „ 117

Bring (*continued*) *B* in great logs and let them lie, *In Mem. cvii* 17
Which every hour his couriers *b*. ,, *cxxvi* 4
She may *b* me a curse. *Maud I i* 73
how God will *b* them about ,, *iv* 44
to ride forth And *b* the Queen ;— *Com. of Arthur* 449
b him here, that I may judge the right, *Gareth and L.* 380
And could not wholly *b* him under, ,, 1144
To *b* thee back to do the battle with him. ,, 1294
ere you wed with any, *b* your bride, *Marr. of Geraint* 228
Call the host and bid him *b* Charger and palfrey.' *Geraint and E.* 400
'Go thou with him and him and *b* it *Balin and Balan* 6
I *b* thee back, When I have ferreted *Merlin and V.* 54
charged by Valence to *b* home the child. ,, 718
one dark hour which *b's* remorse, ,, 763
Joust for it, and win, and *b* it in an hour, *Lancelot and E.* 204
let me *b* your colour back ; ,, 387
b us where he is, and how he fares, ,, 547
'Bind him, and *b* him in.' *Pelleas and E.* 232
Bind him as heretofore, and *b* him in : ,, 271
to flout me, when they *b* me in, ,, 330
third night hence will *b* thee news of gold.' ,, 357
Watch what thou seëst, and lightly *b* me word.' *Pass. of Arthur* 206
Watch what I see, and lightly *b* thee word.' ,, 212
I bade thee, watch, and lightly *b* me word.' ,, 249
b's And shows them whatsoever he accounts *Lover's Tale iv* 232
b's and sets before him in rich guise ,, 247
To *b* Camilla down before them all. ,, 285
be none left here to *b* her back : ,, 367
b on both the yoke Of stronger states, *Tiresias* 69
God curse him and *b* him to nought ! *Despair* 106
morning *b's* the day I hate and fear ; *The Flight* 2
which *b's* our Edwin home. ,, 92
B the old dark ages back without the faith, *Locksley H., Sixty* 137
Moother 'ed tell'd ma to *b* tha down, *Owd Roä* 50
Twelve times in the year *B* me bliss, *The Ring* 6
Hubert *b's* me home With April ,, 59
once more I *b* you these. *Happy* 22
'From the South I *b* you balm, *Prog. of Spring* 66
The shepherd *b's* his adder-bitten lamb, *Death of Œnone* 38
B me my horse—my horse ? *Mechanophilus* 9
And *b* or chase the storm, ,, 14
B's the Dreams about my bed, *Silent Voices* 2
Bringer something more, A *b* of new things ; *Ulysses* 28
Bringest Thou *b* the sailor to his wife, *In Mem. x* 5
Come quick, thou *b* all I love. ,, *xvii* 8
thou *b* Not peace, a sword, a fire. *Sir J. Oldcastle* 35
Bringeth poetess singeth, that Hesperus all things *b*, *Leonine Eleg.* 13
Bringing And *b* me down from the Hall *Maud I xxi* 2
the new sun rose *b* the new year. *Pass. of Arthur* 469
Bringing-up give his child a better *b-u* *Enoch Arden* 87
To give his babes a better *b-u* ,, 299
It is but *b u* : no more than that : *Princess, Pro.* 129
Brink Betwixt the green *b* and the running foam, *Sea-fairies* 2
now shake hands across the *b* Of that deep grave *My life is full* 6
barge with oar and sail Moved from the *b*, *M. d'Arthur* 266
the woman walk'd upon the *b* : *Sea Dreams* 112
Leapt fiery Passion from the *b's* of death ; *Princess vii* 156
And voices hail it from the *b* ; *In Mem. cxxi* 14
But if a man who stands upon the *b* *Geraint and E.* 472
barge with oar and sail Moved from the *b*, *Pass. of Arthur* 434
lianas that dropt to the *b* of his bay, *The Wreck* 73
Briony about my feet The berried *b* fold.' *Talking Oak* 148
fragile bindweed-bells and *b* rings ; *The Brook* 203
Briony-vine *b-v* and ivy-wreath Ran forward *Amphion* 29
Bristle (s) Figs out of thistles, silk from *b's*, *Last Tournament* 356
Bristle (verb) half stands up And *b's* ; *Walk. to the Mail* 32
The hoar hair of the Baronet *b* up *Aylmer's Field* 42
And *b's* all the brakes and thorns *In Mem. cvii* 9
Britain The name of *B* trebly great— *You ask me, why* 22
And keeps our *B*, whole within herself, *Princess, Con.* 52
Our *B* cannot salve a tyrant o'er. *Third of Feb.* 20
welcome Russian flower, a people's pride, To *B*, *W. to Marie Alex.* 7
Girt by half the tribes of *B*, *Boädicea* 5
call us *B's* barbarous populaces, ,, 7
Tear the noble heart of *B*, ,, 12

Britain (*continued*) Bark an answer, *B's* raven ! *Boädicea* 13
shall *B* light upon auguries happier ? ,, 45
Nor *B's* one sole God be the millionaire : *Maud III vi* 22
Chief of the church in *B*, *Com. of Arthur* 454
flying over many a windy wave To *B*, *Marr. of Geraint* 338
Roman Cæsar first Invaded *B*, ,, 746
Brought the great faith to *B* *Balin and Balan* 103
dread Pendragon, *B's* Kings of kings, *Lancelot and E.* 424
Isolt of *B* and his bride, *Last Tournament* 408
Isolt of *B* dash'd Before Isolt ,, 588
for crest the golden dragon clung Of *B* ; *Guinevere* 595
The voice of *B*, or a sinking land, *To the Queen ii* 24
O banner of *B*, hast thou Floated *Def. of Lucknow* 1
Nor thou in *B*, little Lutterworth, *Sir J. Oldcastle* 26
Broke into *B* with Haughty war-workers *Batt. of Brunanburh* 120
Makes the might of *B* known ; *Open. I. and C. Exhib.* 19
B fought her sons of yore— ,, 21
B fail'd ; and never more, ,, 22
B's myriad voices call, ,, 35
One with *B*, heart and soul ! ,, 38
At times our *B* cannot rest, *To Marq. of Dufferin* 1
British Peal after peal, the *B* battle broke, *Buonaparte* 7
With a stony *B* stare. *Maud I xiii* 22
And curse me the *B* vermin, the rat ; ,, *II v* 58
Howiver was *B* farmers to stan' ageän o' their feeät. *Owd Roä* 46
Briton set His *B* in blown seas and storming showers, *Ode on Well.* 155
Up my *B's*, on my chariot, *Boädicea* 69
Breton, not *B* : here Like a shipwreck'd man *Maud II ii* 30
Beyond the race of *B's* and of men. *Com. of Arthur* 331
B's, hold your own ! (repeat) *Open. I. and C. Exhib.* 10, 20, 30, 40
Britoness haled the yellow-ringleted *B*— *Boädicea* 55
Brittany (*See also* **Breton**) From overseas in *B* return'd, *Last Tournament* 175
Her daintier namesake down in *B*— ,, 265
Was it the name of one in *B*, ,, 396
He seem'd to pace the strand of *B* ,, 407
Before Isolt of *B* on the strand, ,, 589
Broach-turner Dish-washer and *b-t*, loon !— *Gareth and L.* 770
Broad Grows green and *b*, and takes no care, *Lotos-Eaters, C. S.* 28
Make *b* thy shoulders to receive my weight, *M. d'Arthur* 164
muscular he spread, so *b* of breast. *Gardener's D.* 8
Alas, I was so *b* of girth, *Talking Oak* 139
rain, That makes thee *b* and deep ! ,, 280
those that saunter in the *b* Cries *Aylmer's Field* 744
I wish they were a whole Atlantic *b*.' *Princess, Con.* 71
Make *b* thy shoulders to receive my weight, *Pass. of Arthur* 332
Broad-based *B-b upon her people's will*, *To the Queen* 35
B-b flights of marble stairs Ran up *Arabian Nights* 117
Broad-blown *b-b* comeliness, red and white, *Maud I xiii* 9
Broad-brimm'd *b-b* hawker of holy things, ,, *x* 41
Broadcast shower the fiery grain Of freedom *b* *Princess v* 422
Broaden Freedom slowly *b's* down From precedent *You ask me, why* 11
To *b* into boundless day. *In Mem. xcv* 64
B the glowing isles of vernal blue. *Prog. of Spring* 60
Broaden'd Morn *b* on the borders of the dark, *D. of F. Women* 265
Broadening (*See also* **Ever-broadening**) *b* from her feet, And blackening, *Guinevere* 81
Broader Sun Grew *b* toward his death *Princess iii* 364
B and higher than any in all the lands ! *Holy Grail* 247
b and brighter The Gleam flying onward, *Merlin and the G.* 95
Broader-grown *b-g* the bowers Drew the great night *Princess vii* 48
Broad-faced *B-f* with under-fringe of russet beard, *Geraint and E.* 537
Broad-flung tide in its *b-f* shipwrecking roar, *Maud I iii* 11
Broad-limb'd there alone The *b-l* Gods at random thrown *To E. L.* 15
Broad-shoulder'd great *b-s* genial Englishman, *Princess, Con.* 85
Brocade That stood from out a stiff *b* *Aylmer's Field* 204
He found an ancient dame in dim *b* ; *Marr. of Geraint* 363
Broceliande And in the wild woods of *B*, *Merlin and V.* 2
Ev'n to the wild woods of *B*. ,, 204
Broider'd (*See also* **Costly-broider'd, Star-broider'd**)
'A red sleeve *B* with pearls,' *Lancelot and E.* 373
sleeve of scarlet, *b* with great pearls, ,, 604
Broidering Among her damsels *b* sat, *Merlin and V.* 138
Broidery-frame take the *b-f*, and add A crimson *Day-Dm., Pro.* 15
Broidry Rare *b* of the purple clover. *A Dirge* 38

Bronzed on the cheek, And bruised and b, Lancelot and E. 259
Brooch Pull off, pull off, the b of gold, Lady Clare 39
read and earn our prize, A golden b: Princess iii 301
Brood (s) If there were many Lilias in the b, ,, Pro. 146
tell her, Swallow, that thy b is flown: ,, iv 108
He sees his b about thy knee; ,, 582
Because her b is stol'n away. In Mem. xxi 28
O sound to rout the b of cares, ,, lxxxix 17
Her own b lost or dead, Com. of Arthur 28
Heathen, the b by Hengist left; Guinevere 16
Brood (verb) with downcast eyes we muse and b, Sonnet to—— 1
About him b's the twilight dim: Two Voices 263
To muse and b and live again in memory, Lotos-Eaters, C. S. 65
That b's above the fallen sun, To J. S. 51
happy birds, that change their sky To build and b; In Mem. cxv 16
nevermore to b On a horror of shatter'd limbs Maud I i 55
sunshine seem'd to b More warmly on the heart Lover's Tale i 327
What use to b? this life of mingled pains To Mary Boyle 49
Brooded stillness of that air Which b round about her: Gardener's D. 148
while she b thus And grew half-guilty Guinevere 407
tender love Of him she b over. Lover's Tale i 617
B one master-passion evermore, ,, ii 60
Broodeth But where the sunbeam b warm, In Mem. xci 14
Brooding ragged rims of thunder b low, Palace of Art 75
Sit b in the ruins of a life, Love and Duty 12
Across my fancy, b warm, Day-Dm., Pro. 10
but b turn The book of scorn, Princess v 141
wordless b's on the wasted cheek— ,, vii 112
But b on the dear one dead, In Mem. xxxvii 17
But over all things b slept ,, lxxviii 7
felt that tempest b round his heart, Geraint and E. 11
There, b by the central altar, Ancient Sage 33
She that in her heart is b Locksley H., Sixty 23
Brook (s) (See also **Beck, Mountain-brook, Yabbok brook**) Past Yabbok b the livelong night, Clear-headed friend 27
b that loves To purl o'er matted cress Ode to Memory 58
deep b groan'd beneath the mill; Miller's D. 113
I thirsted for the b's, the showers: Fatima 10
long b falling thro' the clov'n ravine Œnone 8
O mountain b's, I am the daughter ,, 37
'The torrent b's of hallow'd Israel D. of F. Women 181
and leap the rainbows of the b's, Locksley Hall 171
Here, by this b, we parted; The Brook 1
yet the b he loved, ,, 15
'O b,' he says, 'O babbling b,' ,, 20
and the b, why not? replies. ,, 22
Philip's farm where b and river meet. ,, 38
Philip chatter'd more than b or bird; ,, 51
Beyond the b, waist-deep in meadow-sweet. ,, 118
and bowing o'er the b A tonsured head ,, 199
Little about it stirring save a b! Aylmer's Field 32
where the b Vocal, with here and there a silence, ,, 145
part were drown'd within the whirling b: Princess, Pro. 47
Cataract b's to the ocean run, The Islet 17
b's of Eden mazily murmuring, Milton 10
Oh is it the b, or a pool, Window, On the Hill 4
Spring that swells the narrow b's, In Mem. lxxxv 70
The b alone far-off was heard, ,, xcv 7
On yon swoll'n b that bubbles fast ,, xcix 6
The b shall babble down the plain, ,, ci 10
slopes a wild b o'er a little stone, Marr. of Geraint 77
a broad b o'er a shingly bed Brawling, ,, 248
And at the inrunning of a little b Lancelot and E. 1388
By grove, and garden-lawn, and rushing b, Holy Grail 230
saw deep lawns, and then a b, ,, 380
and o'er the b Were apple-trees, and apples by the b Fallen, ,, 383
But even while I drank the b, ,, 387
Stay'd in the wandering warble of a b; Last Tournament 254
Blaze by the rushing b or silent well. Guinevere 400
blue valley and the glistening b's, Lover's Tale i 331
With falling b or blossom'd bush— ,, 405
Gives birth to a brawling b, ,, 526
echoes of the hollow-banked b's ,, 566
the chillness of the sprinkled b Smote ,, 633
black b's Of the midforest heard me— ,, ii 11
Brook (s) (continued) I cast them in the noisy b beneath, Lover's Tale ii 41
moanings in the forest, the loud b, ,, 114
b's glitter'd on in the light without sound, V. of Maeldune 13
I found these cousins often by the b, The Ring 158
b that feeds this lakelet murmur'd 'debt,' ,, 171
following her old pastime of the b, ,, 354
the secret splendour of the b's. Prog. of Spring 21
thunder of the b Sounded 'Œnone'; Death of Œnone 23
Brook (verb) I must b the rod And chastisement Supp. Confessions 107
I would not b my fear Of the other: D. of F. Women 154
We b no further insult but are gone.' Princess vi 342
shall I b to be supplicated? Boädicea 9
I scarce could b the strain and stir In Mem. xv 12
Who cannot b the shadow of any lie.' Gareth and L. 293
I cannot b to gaze upon the dead.' Balin and Balan 586
I cannot b to see your beauty marr'd Pelleas and E. 298
thine eyes not b in forest-paths, Prog. of Spring 31
Brook'd B not the expectant terror of her heart, Enoch Arden 493
but she b no more: Aylmer's Field 798
She b it not; but wrathful, Lucretius 14
She the appeal B not, but clamouring out Princess vi 140
until the little maid, who b No silence, Guinevere 159
Brooking b not the Tarquin in her veins, Lucretius 237
peculiar treasure, b not Exchange or currency: Lover's Tale i 447
Brooks B, for they call'd you so that knew you best, Old B, who loved so well to mouth To W. H. Brookfield 1
Broom walks were stript as bare as b's, Princess, Pro. 184
Gilded with b, or shatter'd into spires, Lover's Tale i 400
Broth wicked b Confused the chemic labour Lucretius 19
Brother (See also **Brethren, Soldier-brother, Twin-brother**) my b's they: B's in Christ— Supp. Confessions 28
vexed eddies of its wayward b: Isabel 33
Each to each is dearest b; Madeline 21
Oh rest ye, b mariners, Lotos-Eaters, C. S. 128
I knew your b: his mute dust I honour To J. S. 29
Who miss the b of your youth? ,, 59
Thy b's and immortal souls. Love thou thy land 8
I and he, B's in Art; Gardener's D. 4
She is my b's daughter: Dora 17
Come, blessed b, come. St. S. Stylites 204
Sun flies forward to his b Sun; Golden Year 23
Men, my b's, men the workers, Locksley Hall 117
b's of the weather stood Stock-still Will Water. 135
Hob-and-nob with b Death! Vision of Sin 194
My dearest b, Edmund, sleeps, The Brook 187
My b James is in the harvest-field: ,, 227
Leolin, his b, living oft With Averill, Aylmer's Field 57
his, a b's love, that hung With wings ,, 138
thro' the bright lawns to his b's ran, ,, 341
'B, for I have loved you more as son Than b, ,, 351
b, where two fight The strongest wins, ,, 364
'O b, I am grieved to learn your grief— ,, 398
How low his b's mood had fallen, ,, 404
Sent to the harrow'd b, praying him ,, 607
shall thy b man, the Lord from Heaven, ,, 667
they see no men, Not ev'n her b Arac, Princess i 153
'My b!' 'Well, my sister.' ,, ii 188
Here lies a b by a sister slain, ,, 208
That was fawn's blood, not b's, ,, 275
be swerved from right to save A prince, a b? ,, 291
I give thee to death My b! ,, 308
Till, one of those two b's, half aside ,, v 302
'O b, you have known the pangs we felt, ,, 374
B's, the woman's Angel guards you, ,, 410
'He saved my life: my b slew him for it.' ,, vi 108
to wait upon him, Like mine own b. ,, 299
Help, father, b, help; ,, 305
'Your b, Lady,—Florian,—ask for him ,, 313
but the Prince Her b came; ,, 345
Did those twin b's, risen again ,, vii 89
My friend, the b of my love; In Mem. ix 16
More than my b's are to me. ,, 20
'Where wert thou, b, those four days?' ,, xxxi 5
Roves from the living b's face, ,, xxxii 7

Brother (*continued*) 'More than my *b's* are to me,'— *In Mem. lxxix* 1
I met her to-day with her *b*, but not to her *b* I bow'd: *Maud I iv* 14
and chuckle, and grin at a *b's* shame; ,, 29
Her *b*, from whom I keep aloof, ,, *vi* 46
Blithe would her *b's* acceptance be. ,, *x* 27
All, all upon the *b*. ,, *xiii* 43
her *b* lingers late With a roystering company) ,, *xiv* 14
Her *b* is coming back to-night, ,, *xix* 1
only Maud and the *b* Hung over her dying bed— ,, 35
This *b* had laugh'd her down, ,, 60
her *b* comes, like a blight On my fresh hope, ,, 102
her *b* ran in his rage to the gate, ,, *II i* 12
A cry for a *b's* blood: ,, 34
'O that ye had some *b*, pretty one, *Com. of Arthur* 335
my husband's *b* had my son Thrall'd in his castle, *Gareth and L.* 357
Our noblest *b*, and our truest man, ,, 565
second *b* in their fool's parable— ,, 1004
'What dost thou, *b*, in my marches here?' ,, 1034
Hath overthrown thy *b*, and hath his arms.' ,, 1037
the third *b* shouted o'er the bridge, ,, 1096
My *b* and my better, this man here, *Balin and Balan* 54
Embracing Balin, 'Good my *b*, hear! ,, 139
on his dying *b* cast himself Dying; ,, 593
'*B*, I dwelt a day in Pellam's hall: ,, 605
'O *b*' answer'd Balin 'woe is me! ,, 618
darken thine, Goodnight, true *b*.' ,, 626
'Goodnight, true *b* here! goodmorrow there! ,, 628
two *b's*, one a king, had met And fought *Lancelot and E.* 39
each had slain his *b* at a blow; ,, 41
brought the yet-unblazon'd shield, His *b's*; ,, 380
rosy-kindled with her *b's* kiss— ,, 393
Sir Modred's *b*, and the child of Lot, ,, 558
Came on her *b* with a happy face ,, 791
Full ill then should I quit your *b's* love, ,, 944
the *b's* heard, and thought With shuddering, ,, 1021
'Sweet *b's*, yesternight I seem'd ,, 1034
'Fret not yourself, dear *b*, nor be wroth, ,, 1074
'O *b*, I have seen this yew-tree smoke, *Holy Grail* 18
what drove thee from the Table Round, My *b*? ,, 29
'Sweet *b*, I have seen the Holy Grail: ,, 107
b, fast thou too and pray, And tell thy *b* knights to fast and pray, ,, 125
and himself her *b* more than I. ,, 142
'Sister or *b* none had he; ,, 143
b, In our great hall there stood ,, 166
b, had you known our mighty hall, ,, 225
b, had you known our hall within, ,, 246
b, when I told him what had chanced, ,, 271
(*B*, the King was hard upon his knights) ,, 299
O *b*, had you known our Camelot, ,, 339
'O *b*,' ask'd Ambrosius,— ,, 540
O *b*, saving this Sir Galahad, ,, 561
my *b*, Why wilt thou shame me to confess ,, 566
was the one, *B*, and that one only, ,, 579
O me, my *b*! but one night my vow ,, 607
For, *b*, so one night, because they roll ,, 685
'And that can I, *B*, and truly; ,, 712
B, I need not tell thee foolish words,— ,, 855
Art thou the purest, *b*? *Last Tournament* 192
b, thou nor I have made the world; ,, 203
is the King thy *b* fool?' ,, 352
ay, my *b* fool, the king of fools! ,, 354
A goodly *b* of the Table Round ,, 431
Slain was the *b* of my paramour ,, 448
So *b*, pluck and spare not.' *Lover's Tale i* 351
'*B*,' she said, 'let this be call'd ,, 461
I was as the *b* of her blood, ,, 559
deem'd I wore a *b's* mind: she call'd me *b*: ,, 741
Deem that I love thee but as *b's* do, ,, 767
Praise to our Indian *b's*, *Def. of Lucknow* 69
Drove me and my good *b's* home in chains, *Columbus* 134
He with his *b*, Edmund Atheling, *Batt. of Brunanburh* 5
Christ, our human *b* and friend, *Despair* 25
the tears, O *b*, mine or thine, *Ancient Sage* 186
Sisters, *b's*—and the beasts— *Locksley H., Sixty* 102

Brother (*continued*) Rip your *b's'* voices open, *Locksley H., Sixty* 141
True *b*, only to be known By those who love *Pref. Poem Broth. S.* 7
Sons and *b's* that have sent, *Open. I. and C. Exhib.* 3
B's, must we part at last? ,, 32
Is *b* of the Dark one in the lowest, *Demeter and P.* 95
He, the *b* of this Darkness, ,, 116
Will my Indian *b* come? *Romney's R.* 143
Well spake thy *b* in his hymn to heaven *Akbar's Dream* 27
Meanwhile, my *b's*, work, and wield *Mechanophilus* 29
Father, and my *B*, and my God! *Doubt and Prayer* 8
Brother-brute ever butted his rough *b-b* For lust *Lucretius* 197
Brother-hands I, clasping *b-h*, aver I could not, *In Mem. lxxxv* 102
Brotherhood And all men work in noble *b*, *Ode Inter. Exhib.* 38
To fight the *b* of Day and Night— *Gareth and L.* 857
hast thou so defamed Thy *b* *Pelleas and E.* 322
hath bound And sworn me to this *b*;' ,, 449
Unlawful and disloyal *b*— *Sisters (E. and E.)* 174
Brother-in-law that mock-sister there—*B-i-l* ,, 173
Brother-knight Lo! he hath slain some *b-k*, *Balin and Balan* 549
Brother-like kiss'd her with all pureness, *b-l*, *Geraint and E.* 884
Brother-oak honours that, Thy famous *b-o*, *Talking Oak* 296
Brother-sister are you That *b-s* Psyche, *Princess ii* 254
Brother-slayer Not from the skeleton of a *b-s*, *Last Tournament* 47
Brother-star *b-s*, why shine ye here so low? *Gareth and L.* 1097
Brother-worm and its last *b-w* will have fled *Despair* 85
Brought (*See also* **Browt, Far-brought**) Is not my human pride *b* low? *Supp. Confessions* 14
from the outward to the inward *b*, *Eleänore* 4
The oriental fairy *b*, ,, 14
I marvell'd how the mind was *b* To anchor *Two Voices* 458
slowly was my mother *b* To yield consent *Miller's D.* 137
Although the loss had *b* us pain, ,, 229
light-foot Iris *b* it yester-eve, *Œnone* 83
I won his love, I *b* him home. *The Sisters* 14
and *b* Into the gulfs of sleep. *D. of F. Women* 51
Where'er I came I *b* calamity.' ,, 96
then at my request He *b* it; *The Epic* 48
every morning *b* a noble chance, And every chance *b* out a noble knight. *M. d'Arthur* 230
till Autumn *b* an hour For Eustace, *Gardener's D.* 207
B out a dusky loaf that smelt of home, *Audley Court* 22
his bailiff *b* A Chartist pike. *Walk. to the Mail* 70
b the night In which we sat together *Love and Duty* 59
all the mothers *b* Their children, *Godiva* 14
The pint, you *b* me, was the best *Will Water.* 75
Lord Ronald *b* a lily-white doe *Lady Clare* 3
lily-white doe Lord Ronald had *b* ,, 61
then with what she *b* Buy goods and stores— *Enoch Arden* 137
b the stinted commerce of those days; ,, 817
letter which he *b*, and swore besides *Aylmer's Field* 522
She *b* strange news. *Sea Dreams* 267
which he *b*, and I Dived in a hoard of tales *Princess, Pro.* 28
which *b* My book to mind: ,, 119
these *b* back A present, a great labour ,, *i* 43
He *b* it, and himself, a sight to shake ,, 200
She *b* us Academic silks, ,, *ii* 16
'I *b* a message here from Lady Blanche.' ,, 319
from the Queen's decease she *b* her up. ,, *iii* 86
—or *b* her chain'd, a slave, ,, *v* 139
Home they *b* her warrior dead: ,, *vi* 1
B from under every star, *Ode Inter. Exhib.* 25
And bread from out the houses *b*, *Spec. of Iliad* 6
As tho' they *b* but merchants' bales, *In Mem. xiii* 19
Such precious relics *b* by thee; ,, *xvii* 18
And he that *b* him back is there. ,, *xxxii* 4
He *b* an eye for all he saw; ,, *lxxxix* 9
she *b* the harp and flung A ballad ,, 27
And *b* a summons from the sea: ,, *ciii* 16
Large elements in order *b*, ,, *cxii* 13
and *b* to understand A sad astrology, *Maud I xviii* 35
B Arthur forth, and set him in the hall, *Com. of Arthur* 229
Or *b* by Merlin, who, they say, ,, 347
B down a momentary brow. *Gareth and L.* 653
champion thou hast *b* from Arthur's hall? ,, 916
ere his horse was *b*, Glorying; ,, 934

Brought (*continued*) *b* a helm With but a drying evergreen — *Gareth and L.* 1115
Gareth *b* him grovelling on his knees, — ,, 1124
Enid *b* sweet cakes to make them cheer, — *Marr. of Geraint* 388
and he *b* me to a goodly house; — ,, 713
like a madman *b* her to the court, — ,, 725
promise, that whatever bride I *b*, — ,, 783
b a mantle down and wrapt her in it, — ,, 824
Prince had *b* his errant eyes Home — *Geraint and E.* 245
And wine and food were *b*, — ,, 289
as they *b* upon their forays out — ,, 567
men *b* in whole hogs and quarter beeves, — ,, 602
they *b* report 'we hardly found, — *Balin and Balan* 94
who first *B* the great faith to Britain — ,, 103
b By holy Joseph hither, — ,, 112
b report of azure lands and fair, — ,, 168
as he That *b* her hither. — ,, 187
To save thy life, have *b* thee to thy death. — ,, 600
miss'd, and *b* Her own claw back, — *Merlin and V.* 499
He lightly scatter'd theirs and *b* her off, — ,, 564
He *b*, not found it therefore: — ,, 719
I by mere mischance have *b*, my shield. — *Lancelot and E.* 189
red sleeve Broider'd with pearls,' and *b* it: — ,, 373
Returning *b* the yet-unblazon'd shield, — ,, 379
And *b* his horse to Lancelot where he lay. — ,, 493
the shield was *b*, and Gawain saw — ,, 662
have *b* thee, now a lonely man Wifeless — ,, 1370
saw the barge that *b* her moving down, — ,, 1391
Joseph, journeying *B* to Glastonbury, — *Holy Grail* 51
b thee here to this poor house of ours — ,, 617
they fell from, *b* us to the hall. — ,, 720
Joseph *b* of old to Glastonbury?' — ,, 735
bounden straight, and so they *b* him in. — *Pelleas and E.* 236
rose up, and bound, and *b* him in. — ,, 288
Waited, until the third night *b* a moon — ,, 393
b A maiden babe; which Arthur pitying took, — *Last Tournament* 20
b to adorn her with, The jewels, — ,, 715
when both were *b* to full accord, — ,, 722
And hither *b* by Tristram for his last — ,, 747
Modred *b* His creatures to the basement — *Guinevere* 103
and my tears have *b* me good: — ,, 202
he that *b* The heathen back among us, — *Pass. of Arthur* 151
every morning *b* a noble chance, And every chance *b* out a noble knight. — ,, 398
Looking on her that *b* him to the light: — *Lover's Tale i* 160
the shuddering moonlight *b* its face — ,, 650
rare or fair Was *b* before the guest: — ,, *iv* 204
He slowly *b* them back to Lionel. — ,, 371
caught and *b* him in To their charm'd circle, — ,, 376
For we *b* them all aboard, — *The Revenge* 19
On whom I *b* a strange unhappiness, — *Sisters (E. and E.)* 89
So took her thence, and *b* her here, — ,, 267
He had *b* his ghastly tools: — *In the Child. Hosp.* 69
Hast thou *b* bread with thee? — *Sir J. Oldcastle* 198
b out a broad sky Of dawning over— — *Columbus* 77
Whatever wealth I *b* from that new world — ,, 101
I had *b* your Princes gold enough — ,, 105
I *b* From Solomon's now-recover'd Ophir — ,, 111
This creedless people will be *b* to Christ — ,, 189
That day my nurse had *b* me the child. — *The Wreck* 59
Dead! 'Is it *he* then *b* so low?' — *Dead Prophet* 6
Until I *b* thee hither, — *Demeter and P.* 8
I *b* you to that chamber on your — *The Ring* 129
I *b* you, you remember, these roses, — *Happy* 73
b you down A length of staghorn-moss, — *Romney's R.* 78
'hast *thou b* us down a new Korân — *Akbar's Dream* 116
when I met you first—when *he b* you!— — *Charity* 9

Brow *This laurel greener from the* b's — *To the Queen* 7
Among the thorns that girt Thy *b*, — *Supp. Confessions* 6
when with *b's* Propt on thy knees, — ,, 69
An image with profulgent *b's*, — ,, 145
Upon her bed, across her *b*. — *Mariana* 56
Falsehood shall bare her plaited *b*: — *Clear-headed friend* 11
Frowns perfect-sweet along the *b* — *Madeline* 15
o'er black *b's* drops down A sudden-curved frown: (repeat) — ,, 34, 46

Brow (*continued*) a *b* of pearl Tressed with redolent ebony, — *Arabian Nights* 137
Even as a maid, whose stately *b* — *Ode to Memory* 13
Her beautiful bold *b*, — *The Poet* 38
With thy soften'd, shadow'd *b*, — *Adeline* 46
wearing on my swarthy *b's* The garland — *Kate* 23
His broad clear *b* in sunlight glow'd; — *L. of Shalott iii* 28
From *b* and bosom slowly down — *Mariana in the S.* 14
Look up, the fold is on her *b*. — *Two Voices* 192
blow Before him, striking on my *b*. — *Fatima* 25
and the charm of married *b's*.' — *Œnone* 76
drew From her warm *b's* and bosom her deep hair — ,, 177
steep our *b's* in slumber's holy balm; — *Lotos-Eaters, C. S.* 21
Whereto the other with a downward *b*: — *D. of F. Women* 117
lying dead, my crown about my *b's*, — ,, 162
dropping bitter tears against his *b* — *M. d'Arthur* 211
But the full day dwelt on her *b's*, — *Gardener's D.* 136
Love with knit *b's* went by, — ,, 245
whose bald *b's* in silent hours become — *St. S. Stylites* 165
I waited long; My *b's* are ready. — ,, 206
glimmer steals From thy pure *b's*, — *Tithonus* 35
Her sweet face from *b* to chin: — *L. of Burleigh* 62
Warm broke the breeze against the *b*, — *The Voyage* 9
A band of pain across my *b*; — *The Letters* 6
sleepy light upon their *b's* and lips— — *Vision of Sin* 9
we know the hue Of that cap upon her *b's*. — ,, 142
And gain'd a laurel for your *b* — *You might have won* 3
Annie with her *b's* against the wall — *Enoch Arden* 314
o'er his bent *b's* linger'd Averill, — *Aylmer's Field* 625
often placed upon the sick man's *b* — ,, 700
breathing down From over her arch'd *b's*, — *Princess ii* 39
and the Roman *b's* Of Agrippina. — ,, 84
gaunt old baron with his beetle *b* Sun-shaded — ,, 240
Psyche, wont to bind my throbbing *b*, — ,, 250
Star-sisters answering under crescent *b's*; — ,, 428
lilylike Melissa droop'd her *b's*; — ,, *iv* 161
manlike, but his *b's* Had sprouted, — ,, 204
With hooded *b's* I crept into the hall, — ,, 225
made the single jewel on her *b* Burn — ,, 273
till over *b* And cheek and bosom brake — ,, 382
raised the cloak from *b's* as pale and smooth — ,, *v* 73
veil'd her *b's*, and prone she sank, — ,, 107
she laid A feeling finger on my *b's*, — ,, *vi* 121
With *b* to *b* like night and evening — ,, 131
fear not; breathe upon my *b's*; — ,, *vii* 353
King bent low, with hand on *b*, — *The Victim* 53
gladness even crown'd The purple *b's* of Olivet. — *In Mem. xxxi* 12
Urania speaks with darken'd *b*: — ,, *xxxvii* 1
I took the thorns to bind my *b's*, — ,, *lxix* 7
Lift as thou may'st thy burthen'd *b's* — ,, *lxxii* 21
So, dearest, now thy *b's* are cold, — ,, *lxxiv* 5
turn'd To black and brown on kindred *b's*. — ,, *lxxix* 16
fan my *b's* and blow The fever from my cheek, — ,, *lxxxvi* 8
Be large and lucid round thy *b*. — ,, *xci* 8
And enter in at breast and *b*, — ,, *cxxii* 11
Broad *b's* and fair, a fluent hair and fine, — *Gareth and L.* 464
a *b* May-blossom, and a cheek of apple-blossom, — ,, 588
Brought down a momentary *b*. — ,, 653
Then seeing cloud upon the mother's *b*, — *Marr. of Geraint* 777
with droopt *b* down the long glades he rode; — *Balin and Balan* 311
drawing down the dim disastrous *b* — ,, 597
a wizard *b* bleach'd on the walls: — *Merlin and V.* 597
two brethren slowly with bent *b's* Accompanying, — *Lancelot and E.* 1138
kiss'd her quiet *b's*, and saying — ,, 1150
Arthur, who beheld his cloudy *b's*, — ,, 1354
the circlet of the jousts Bound on her *b*, — *Pelleas and E.* 435
circlet of the tourney round her *b's*, — ,, 454
under her black *b's* a swarthy one Laugh'd — *Last Tournament* 216
laid His *b's* upon the drifted leaf and dream'd. — ,, 406
a *b* Like hillsnow high in heaven, — ,, 666
dropping bitter tears against a *b* — *Pass. of Arthur* 379
To pass my hands across my *b's*, — *Lover's Tale i* 31
clear *b*, bulwark of the precious brain, — ,, 130
brood More warmly on the heart than on the *b*. — ,, 328

Brow (continued) for her b's And mine made garlands — Lover's Tale i 342
Beyond the nearest mountain's bosky b's, — ,, 396
knotted thorns thro' my unpaining b's, — ,, 620
sprinkled brook Smote on my b's, — ,, 634
great crown of beams about his b's— — ,, 672
walk'd abreast with me, and veil'd his b, — ,, ii 86
and from his b drew back His hand to push — ,, 92
about my b Her warm breath floated — ,, 140
Upon my fever'd b's that shook and throbb'd — ,, iii 7
walk'd behind with one who veil'd his b. — ,, 12
Cold were his b's when we kiss'd him— — Def. of Lucknow 12
in your raised b's I read Some wonder — Columbus 1
Why, what a b was there ! — The Wreck 48
The broad white b of the Isle— — ,, 135
dreamer stoopt and kiss'd her marble b. — Locksley H., Sixty 38
out of the field, And over the b and away. — Heavy Brigade 64
Unfurnish'd b's, tempestuous tongues— — Freedom 38
But seen upon the silent b when life — Happy 52
when I let him kiss my b ; — ,, 65
round her b's a woodland culver flits, — Prog. of Spring 18
till the heat Smote on her b, — Death of Œnone 98
Me they front With sullen b's. — Akbar's Dream 52

Brow-beat while the worn-out clerk B-b's his desk below. — To J. M. K. 12
Brow-bound eyes, B-b with burning gold. — D. of F. Women 128
Brow'd See **Beautiful-brow'd, Dark-brow'd, Large-brow'd**
Brow-high the hemlock, B-h, did strike my forehead — Lover's Tale ii 19
Brown in a silent shade of laurel b Apart — Alexander 9
Her streaming curls of deepest b — Mariana in the S. 16
B, looking hardly human, strangely clad, — Enoch Arden 638
Enoch was so b, so bow'd, — ,, 703
beauties every shade of b and fair — Princess ii 437
all her autumn tresses falsely b, — ,, 449
I watch the twilight falling b — To F. D. Maurice 14
To black and b on kindred brows. — In Mem. lxxix 16
park and suburb under b Of lustier leaves ; — ,, xcviii 24
Unloved, that beech will gather b, — ,, ci 3
bracken so bright and the heather so b, — June Bracken, etc. 3
Browsed b by deep-udder'd kine, — Gardener's D. 46
Browt (brought) I b what tha seeäs stannin' theer, — North. Cobbler 70
b me the booöts to be cobbled — ,, 94
So I b tha down, an' I says — Owd Roä 97
I b 'im down, an' we got to the barn, — ,, 103
An' I b Roä round, but Moother — ,, 113
Bruise Hard-won and hardly won with b and blow, — Lancelot and E. 1165
Bruised cursed and scorn'd, and b with stones : — Two Voices 222
that there Lie b and maim'd, — Princess vi 72
Had b the herb and crush'd the grape, — In Mem. xxxv 23
swordcut on the cheek, And b and bronzed, — Lancelot and E. 259
and so left him b And batter'd, — Pelleas and E. 546
Nor b the wildbird's egg. — Lover's Tale ii 21
b and butted with the shuddering War-thunder — Tiresias 99
Brunanburh Slew with the sword-edge There by B, — Batt. of Brunanburh 10
Brunelleschi Arno, and the dome Of B ; — The Brook 190
Brunette A quick b, well-moulded, — Princess ii 106
Brush (pencil) took his b and blotted out the bird, — Merlin and V. 478
Brush (tail of fox) 'Peter had the b, My Peter, first :' — Aylmer's Field 254
Brush (verb) to b the dew From thine own lily, — Supp. Confessions 84
Brush'd b Thro' the dim meadow toward his — Aylmer's Field 530
when, this gad-fly b aside, — Princess v 414
and b My fallen forehead in their to and fro, — Lover's Tale i 700
Brushing And b ankle-deep in flowers, — In Mem. lxxxix 49
with his brandish'd plume B his instep, — Geraint and E. 360
Brushwood elm-tree-boles did stoop and lean Upon the dusky b — D. of F. Women 58
Brute (See also **Brother-brute**) Take my b, and lead him in, — Vision of Sin 65
Thou madest Life in man and b; — In Mem., Pro. 6
No longer half-akin to b, — ,, Con. 133
he had not been a Sultan of b's, — Maud II v 81
b's of mountain back That carry kings — Merlin and V. 576
O great and sane and simple race of b's — Pelleas and E. 480
Come from the b, poor souls— — Despair 36

Brute (continued) no souls—and to die with the b— — Despair 36
and burn the kindlier b's alive. — Locksley H., Sixty 96
B's, the b's are not your wrongers— — ,, 97
let the house of a b to the soul of a man, — By an Evolution. 1
If my body come from b's, (repeat) — ,, 5, 13
I, the finer b rejoicing in my hounds, — ,, 7
and rule thy Province of the b. — ,, 16
these Are like wild b's new-caged— — Akbar's Dream 50
The Ghost of the B that is walking — The Dawn 23
Brutus (Lucius Junius) See **Lucius Junius Brutus**
Bubble (s) watch'd Or seem'd to watch the dancing b, — Princess iii 24
colour'd b bursts above the abyss — Romney's R. 52
Bubble (verb) I b into eddying bays, — The Brook 41
On yon swoll'n brook that b's fast — In Mem. xcix 6
And yet b's o'er like a city, with gossip, — Maud I iv 8
Bubbled at mine ear B the nightingale — Princess iv 266
The milk that b in the pail, — In Mem. lxxxix 51
oilily b up the mere. — Gareth and L. 816
Bubbling See **Life-bubbling**
Bublin' (young unfledged bird) An' haäfe on 'im bare as a b.' — Owd Roä 102
Bucket rope that haled the b's from the well, — St. S. Stylites 64
helpt to pass a b from the well — To Mary Boyle 39
Buckled B with golden clasps before ; — Sir L. and Q. G. 25
Buckler The brand, the b, and the spear— — Two Voices 129
Clash the darts and on the b beat — Boädicea 79
snatch'd a sudden b from the Squire, — Balin and Balan 554
Bud (s) (See also **Chestnut-bud, Sea-bud**) While thou abodest in the b. — Two Voices 158
chestnuts, when their b's Were glistening — Miller's D. 60
flowers, and b's and garlands gay, — May Queen 11
folded leaf is woo'd from out the b — Lotos-Eaters, C. S. 26
Sweet as new b's in Spring. — D. of F. Women 272
all-too-full in b For puritanic stays : — Talking Oak 59
kisses balmier than half-opening b's Of April, — Tithonus 59
In b or blade, or bloom, may find, — Day-Dm., Moral 10
burst In carol, every b to flower, — ,, L'Envoi 44
While life was yet in b and blade, — Princess i 32
'Pretty b ! Lily of the vale ! — ,, vi 192
b ever breaks into bloom on the tree, — The Islet 32
longs to burst a frozen b And flood — In Mem. lxxxiii 15
O when her life was yet in b, — ,, Con. 33
flower tell What sort of b it was, — Lover's Tale i 152
from within Burst thro' the heated b's, — ,, 320
No b, no leaf, no flower, no fruit — ,, 725
and all smells of b And foliage from the dark — ,, iii 5
spies the summer thro' the winter b, — Ancient Sage 74
fleets the shower, And burst the b's, — Early Spring 14
'your pretty b, So blighted here, — The Ring 316
Thy warmths from b to b Accomplish — Prog. of Spring 113
Bud (verb) And rugged barks begin to b, — My life is full 18
times, when some new thought can b, — Golden Year 27
out of tyranny tyranny b's. — Boädicea 83
And b's and blossoms like the rest. — In Mem. cxv 20
Budded See **New-budded, Ruby-budded**
Buddhist Brahmin, and B, Christian, and Parsee, — Akbar's Dream 25
Bude the thundering shores of B and Bos, — Guinevere 291
Buffet (s) with a stronger b he clove the helm — Gareth and L. 1406
Swung from his brand a windy b — Geraint and E. 90
Buffet (verb) echo flap And b round the hills, — Golden Year 77
Strove to b to land in vain. — Princess iv 185
Buffeted See **Tempest-buffeted**
Bugle (adj.) all the b breezes blew Reveillée — In Mem. lxviii 7
Bugle (s) Aloud the hollow b blowing, — Oriana 17
Loud, loud rung out the b's brays, — ,, 48
A mighty silver b hung, — L. of Shalott iii 16
Blow, b, blow, set the wild echoes (repeat) — Princess iv 5, 17
Blow, b ; answer, echoes, dying, (repeat) — ,, 6, 12
and bray of the long horn And serpent-throated b, — ,, v 253
With blare of b, clamour of men, — Ode on Well. 115
Warble, O b, and trumpet, blare ! — W. to Alexandra 14
March with banner and b and fife — Maud I v 10
raised a b hanging from his neck, — Pelleas and E. 364
waits below the wall, Blowing his b — ,, 381
and on shield A spear, a harp, a b— — Last Tournament 174

Bugle (s) (*continued*) *B's* and drums in the darkness, *Def. of Lucknow* 76
Bugle-horn belted hunter blew His wreathed *b-h.* *Palace of Art* 64
when you want me, sound upon the *b-h.* *Locksley Hall* 2
call me, sounding on the *b-h,* ,, 145
Build *b* up all My sorrow with my song, *Œnone* 39
built When men knew how to *b,* *Edwin Morris* 7
I would *b* Far off from men a college *Princess, Pro.* 134
She had founded; they must *b.* ,, *ii* 145
I, that have lent my life to *b* up yours, ,, *iv* 351
b some plan Foursquare to opposition.' ,, *v* 230
On God and Godlike men we *b* our trust. *Ode on Well.* 266
b's the house, or digs the grave, *In Mem. xxxvi* 14
change their sky To *b* and brood; ,, *cxv* 16
Gave him an isle of marsh whereon to *b*; *Holy Grail* 62
he groan'd, 'ye *b* too high.' *Pelleas and E.* 555
b a wall betwixt my life and love, *Lover's Tale i* 176
none but Gods could *b* this house *Ancient Sage* 83
Builded The house was *b* of the earth, *Deserted House* 15
Building like enow They are *b* still, *Gareth and L.* 276
Built (*See also* **Belt, Half-built, Low-built, Sand-built, Woman-built**) *b* up everywhere An under-roof *Dying Swan* 3
I *B* my soul a lordly pleasure-house, *Palace of Art* 1
Thereon I *b* it firm. ,, 9
In this great mansion, that is *b* for me, ,, 19
'My spacious mansion *b* for me, ,, 234
palace towers, that are So lightly, beautifully *b*: ,, 294
b When men knew how to build, *Edwin Morris* 6
And *b* herself an everlasting name. *Godiva* 79
B for pleasure and for state. *L. of Burleigh* 32
b their castles of dissolving sand *Enoch Arden* 19
b, and thatch'd with leaves of palm, ,, 559
Rhodope, that *b* the pyramid, *Princess ii* 82
vapour streak the crowned towers *B* to the Sun:' ,, *iii* 345
'The plan was mine. I *b* the nest' ,, *iv* 365
conscious of what temper you are *b,* ,, 400
Far off from men I *b* a fold for them: ,, *v* 390
tho' he *b* upon the babe restored; ,, *vii* 75
And towers fall'n as soon as *b*— *In Mem. xxvi* 8
Who *b* him fanes of fruitless prayer, ,, *lvi* 12
New as his title, *b* last year, *Maud I x* 19
city of Enchanters, *b* By fairy Kings.' *Gareth and L.* 199
and whether this be *b* By magic, ,, 247
Fairy Queens have *b* the city, son; ,, 259
And *b* it to the music of their harps. ,, 262
seeing the city is *b* To music, therefore never *b* at all, ,, 276
And therefore *b* for ever.' ,, 278
B that new fort to overawe my friends, *Marr. of Geraint* 460
that low church he *b* at Glastonbury. *Balin and Balan* 367
Had *b* the King his havens, ships, *Merlin and V.* 168
there he *b* with wattles from the marsh *Holy Grail* 63
Which Merlin *b* for Arthur long ago! ,, 226
Climbs to the mighty hall that Merlin *b.* ,, 231
B by old kings, age after age, ,, 340
some ancient king Had *b* a way, ,, 502
saw High up in heaven the hall that Merlin *b,* *Pelleas and E.* 553
B for a summer day with Queen Isolt *Last Tournament* 378
There be some hearts so airily *b,* that they, *Lover's Tale i* 803
Timur *b* his ghastly tower of eighty thousand *Locksley H., Sixty* 82
Served the poor, and *b* the cottage, ,, 268
Son's love *b* me, and I hold Mother's love *Helen's Tower* 3
b their shepherd-prince a funeral pile; *Death of Œnone* 63
whose pious hand had *b* the cross, *St. Telemachus* 9
Bulbul Died round the *b* as he sung; *Arabian Nights* 70
'O *B*, any rose of Gulistan Shall burst *Princess iv* 122
Bulge cheek *B* with the unswallow'd piece, *Geraint and E.* 631
Bulk Tudor-chimnied *b* Of mellow brickwork *Edwin Morris* 11
bones of some vast *b* that lived and roar'd *Princess iii* 294
Down From those two *b's* at Arac's side, ,, *v* 499
and grown a *b* Of spanless girth, ,, *vi* 35
Dark *b's* that tumble half alive, *In Mem. lxx* 11
strike him, overbalancing his *b,* *Last Tournament* 460
Bulk'd an old-world mammoth *b* in ice, *Princess v* 148
Bull grasp'd The mild *b's* golden horn. *Palace of Art* 120
Bull (*continued*) oil'd and curl'd Assyrian *B* Smelling of musk *Maud I vi* 44
Kay near him groaning like a wounded *b*— *Gareth and L.* 648
whom his shaking vassals call'd the *B,* *Geraint and E.* 439
brainless *b's*, Dead for one heifer!' *Balin and Balan* 578
like a *b* gotten loose at a faäir, *North. Cobbler* 33
and the *b* couldn't low, and the dog *V. of Maeldune* 18
Bull (Inn Sign) 'THE *B*, the Fleece are cramm'd, *Audley Court* 1
Bull (Edward) *See* **Edward Bull**
Bullet (*See also* **Cannon-bullet, Musket-bullet, Rifle-bullet**) *B's* fell like rain; *The Captain* 46
b struck him that was dressing it *The Revenge* 67
And caught the laming *b.* *Sisters (E. and E.)* 65
the brute *b* broke thro' the brain *Def. of Lucknow* 20
B's would sing by our foreheads, and *b's* would rain ,, 21
Bulrush sword-grass, and the *b* in the pool. *May Queen, N. Y's. E.* 28
mid-thigh-deep in *b'es* and reed, *Gareth and L.* 810
Bulrush-bed plunged Among the *b-b's*, and clutch'd the sword, *M. d'Arthur* 135
plunged Among the *b-b's*, and clutch'd the sword, *Pass. of Arthur* 303
Bulwark now they saw their *b* fallen, *Geraint and E.* 168
Bummin' (buzzing) *b'* awaäy loike a buzzard-clock *N. Farmer, O. S.* 18
Bump'd I *b* the ice into three several stars, *The Epic* 12
Bumper He froth'd his *b's* to the brim; *D. of the O. Year* 19
Bunch (*See also* **Fruit-bunches, Vine-bunches**) With *b* and berry and flower *Œnone* 102
grapes with *b'es* red as blood; *Day-Dm., Sleep. P.* 44
Craft with a *b* of all-heal in her hand, *Vastness* 12
Bundle now hastily caught His *b*, waved his hand, *Enoch Arden* 238
Buoy (*See also* **Harbour-buoy**) WE left behind the painted *b* *The Voyage* 1
The *b* that rides at sea, and dips *Gareth and L.* 1146
Buoy'd range Of vapour *b* the crescent-bark, *Day-Dm., Depart.* 22
B upon floating tackle and broken *Enoch Arden* 551
Bur (*See also* **Burr**) *b* and brake and briar, *Day-Dm., Sleep. P.* 46
like a wall of *b's* and thorns; *Sea Dreams* 119
Burden (*See also* **Burthen**) people here, a beast of *b* slow, *Palace of Art* 149
prepared The daily *b* for the back. *In Mem. xxv* 4
Burdock eft and snake, In grass and *b,* *Holy Grail* 571
Burgeon space to *b* out of all Within her— *Princess vii* 271
Now *b's* every maze of quick *In Mem. cxv* 2
Burgher Knight and *b*, lord and dame, *L. of Shalott iv* 43
Burial (adj.) Mammonite mother kills her babe for a *b* fee, *Maud I i* 45
Burial (s) at a *b* to hear The creaking cords *Supp. Confessions* 35
Fresh from the *b* of her little one, *Enoch Arden* 281
A summer *b* deep in hollyhocks; *Aylmer's Field* 164
That hears his *b* talk'd of by his friends, *Princess vii* 152
Now to glorious *b* slowly borne, *Ode on Well.* 193
Pray for my soul, and yield me *b.* *Lancelot and E.* 1280
place of *b* Far lovelier than its cradle; *Lover's Tale i* 529
and ask'd If I would see her *b*: ,, *ii* 71
At some precipitance in her *b.* ,, *iv* 107
Past thro' his visions to the *b*; ,, 357
borne in white To *b* or to burning, *Ancient Sage* 208
Those that in barbarian *b's* kill'd the slave, *Locksley Hall, Sixty* 67
Beyond our *b* and our buried eyes, *The Ring* 296
Buried (*See also* **A-buried, Half-buried, Long-buried**) I *b* her like my own sweet child, *Lady Clare* 27
that same week when Annie *b* it, *Enoch Arden* 271
And when they *b* him the little port ,, 916
Old scandals *b* now seven decads deep *Aylmer's Field* 442
Half *b* in some weightier argument, *Lucretius* 9
have they not *b* me deep enough? *Maud II v* 96
Dead, whom we *b*; more than one of us *Balin and Balan* 122
rummage *b* in the walls Might echo, ,, 416
see that she be *b* worshipfully.' *Lancelot and E.* 1329
maiden *b*, not as one unknown, ,, 1334
I kiss'd 'em, I *b* 'em all— *Rizpah* 55
She died and she was *b* ere we knew. *Sisters (E. and E.)* 241
So feyther an' son was *b* togither, *Village Wife* 90
as God's truer images Are daily *b.*' *Sir J. Oldcastle* 141
I will have them *b* in my grave. *Columbus* 201
his Riverence *b* thim both in wan grave *Tomorrow* 87
There, there! he *b* you, the Priest; *Happy* 105

Burleigh *See* **Lord of Burleigh**
Burleigh-house *B-h* by Stamford-town. *L. of Burleigh* 92
Burlesque Had ever seem'd to wrestle with *b*, *Princess, Con.* 16
Burn (stream) Over the pools in the *b* water-gnats *Leonine Eleg.* 8
tall firs and our fast-falling *b's*; *Gareth and L.* 91
Burn (burnt place) An' it was'nt a bite but a *b*, *Owd Roä* 90
Burn (verb) cricket chirps: the light *b's* low: *D. of the O. Year* 40
While the stars *b*, the moons increase, *To J. S.* 71
And *b* a fragrant lamp before my bones, *St. S. Stylites* 196
And *b* the threshold of the night, *The Voyage* 18
but my cheek Began to *b* and *b*, *Princess iii* 46
b's Above the unrisen morrow:' ,, *iv* 82
made the single jewel on her brow *B* ,, 274
Wherefore in me *b's* an anger, *Boädicea* 52
Burst the gates, and *b* the palaces, ,, 64
fires *b* clear, And frost is here *Window, Winter* 4
And with the thought her colour *b's*; *In Mem. vi* 34
And calm that let the tapers *b* ,, *xcv* 5
This maple *b* itself away; ,, *ci* 4
Cold fires, yet with power to *b* *Maud I xviii* 39
beneath there *b's* A jewell'd harness, *Gareth and L.* 687
Made her cheek *b* and either eyelid fall, *Marr. of Geraint* 775
Made her cheek *b* and either eyelid fall. *Geraint and E.* 434
sin that practice *b's* into the blood, *Merlin and V.* 762
Made my tears *b*—is also past— *Guinevere* 542
Amen! Nay, I can *b*, so that the Lord *Sir J. Oldcastle* 173
And doom'd to *b* alive. ,, 183
So, caught, I *b*. *B*? ,, 184
God willing, I will *b* for Him. ,, 193
for the bright-eyed goddess made it *b*. *Achilles over the T.* 29
great God, Arês, *b's* in anger still *Tiresias* 11
noonday crag made the hand *b*; ,, 35
—but how my temples *b*! *The Flight* 73
and *b* the kindlier brutes alive. *Locksley H., Sixty* 96
fur the barn wouldn't *b* *Owd Roä* 103
What star could *b* so low? not Ilion yet. *Death of Œnone* 83
'Who *b's* upon the pyre?' ,, 99
Burn (born) Cooms of a gentleman *b*: *N. Farmer, N. S.* 38
Gentleman *b*! what's gentleman *b*? ,, 42
An' then the babby wur *b*, *North. Cobbler* 16
For 'e warn't not *b* to the land, *Village Wife* 44
'e wur *b* an' bred i' the 'ouse, *Spinster's S's.* 69
Burn'd (*See also* **Burnt**) *B* like one burning flame together, *L. of Shalott iii* 22
green grasses *b* The red anemone. *D. of F. Women* 71
Or *b* in fire, or boil'd in oil, *St. S. Stylites* 52
that, which in me *b*, The love, *Talking Oak* 10
eye, That *b* upon its object thro' such tears *Love and Duty* 63
At times the whole sea *b*, *The Voyage* 51
sacred fire, That *b* as on an altar. *Enoch Arden* 72
But still the foeman spoil'd and *b*, *The Victim* 17
Last night, when the sunset *b* *Maud I vi* 8
b Full on her knights in many an evil name *Pelleas and E.* 289
one low light betwixt them *b* *Guinevere* 4
great light of heaven *B* at his lowest *Pass. of Arthur* 91
And *b* alive as heretics! *Sir J. Oldcastle* 48
o'er the great Peleion's head *B*, *Achilles over the T.* 29
The prophet's beacon *b* in vain, *Ancient Sage* 142
Burning A love still *b* upward, *Isabel* 18
All earth and air seem only *b* fire.' *Œnone* 268
Larger constellations *b*, mellow moons *Locksley Hall* 159
The tapers *b* fair. *Sir Galahad* 32
with life-long injuries *b* unavenged, *Geraint and E.* 696
On *them* the smell of *b* had not past. *Sir J. Oldcastle* 177
borne in white To burial or to *b*, *Ancient Sage* 208
Burnish to scream, to *b*, and to scour, *Princess iv* 520
Burnish'd sitting, *b* without fear The brand, *Two Voices* 128
That glitter *b* by the frosty dark; *Princess v* 261
and all in mail *B* to blinding, *Gareth and L.* 1027
Burnt (*See also* **Burn'd**) *B* like a fringe of fire. *Palace of Art* 48
he *b* His epic, his King Arthur, *The Epic* 27
Mere chaff and draff, much better *b*.' ,, 40
B in each man's blood. *The Captain* 16
and *b*, Now chafing at his own great self *Aylmer's Field* 536
the good Sir Ralph had *b* them all— *Princess, Pro.* 236
Burnt (*continued*) grandsire *b* Because he cast no shadow, *Princess i* 6
Nor *b* the grange, nor buss'd the milking-maid, ,, *v* 222
other thoughts than Peace *B* in us, ,, 246
B and broke the grove and altar *Boädicea* 2
the rest Slew on and *b*, crying, *Com. of Arthur* 439
So *b* he was with passion, *Marr. of Geraint* 560
smoulder'd wrong that *b* him all within; *Geraint and E.* 107
many of those who *b* the hold, *Holy Grail* 264
but one night my vow *B* me within, ,, 608
Blasted and *b*, and blinded as I was, ,, 844
B as a living fire of emeralds, *Pelleas and E.* 35
and in it Far cities *b*, *Guinevere* 83
took and hang'd, Took, hang'd and *b*— *Sir J. Oldcastle* 46
B—good Sir Roger Acton, my dear friend! ,, 79
B too, my faithful preacher, Beverley! ,, 80
B, *b*! and while this mitred Arundel ,, 104
Not *b* were they. On *them* the smell of burning ,, 176
b at midnight, found at morn, *Locksley H., Sixty* 97
the smoke, The pyre he *b* in.'— *The Ring* 340
Burr (*See also* **Bur**) When *b* and bine were gather'd; *Aylmer's Field* 113
Burrowing I have ferreted out their *b's*, *Merlin and V.* 55
Burst (s) Preluded those melodious *b's* *D. of F. Women* 6
Caught in a *b* of unexpected storm, *Aylmer's Field* 285
more than mortal in the *b* Of sunrise, *Princess, Pro.* 40
but given to starts and *b's* Of revel; ,, *i* 54
B's of great heart and slips in sensual mire, ,, *v* 199
after some quick *b* of sudden wrath, *Balin and Balan* 216
now the storm, its *b* of passion spent, *Merlin and V.* 961
interspaces gush'd in blinding *b's* The incorporate blaze of sun *Lover's Tale i* 408
and bosom'd the *b* of the spray, *V. of Maeldune* 103
Burst (verb) *B's* into blossom in his sight. *Fatima* 35
shrine-doors *b* thro' heated blasts *D. of F. Women* 29
all at once the old man *b* in sobs:— *Dora* 158
with hoggish whine They *b* my prayer. *St. S. Stylites* 178
Or to *b* all links of habit— *Locksley Hall* 157
every bird of Eden *b* In carol, *Day-Dm., L'Envoi* 43
All heaven *b's* her starry floors, *St. Agnes' Eve* 27
Now high on waves that idly *b* *The Voyage* 69
b away In search of stream or fount, *Enoch Arden* 634
B his own wyvern on the seal, *Aylmer's Field* 516
the great organ almost *b* his pipes, *Princess ii* 474
rose of Gulistan Shall *b* her veil: ,, *iv* 123
Ready to *b* and flood the world with foam: ,, 474
clad in iron *b* the ranks of war, ,, 504
in the saddle, then *b* out in words. ,, *v* 275
Descending, *b* the great bronze valves, ,, *vi* 75
b The laces toward her babe; ,, 148
made the serf a man, and *b* his chain— *W. to Marie Alex.* 3
B the gates, and burn the palaces, *Boädicea* 64
That longs to *b* a frozen bud *In Mem. lxxxiii* 15
fiery-hot to *b* All barriers ,, *cxiv* 13
And yearn'd to *b* the folded gloom, ,, *cxxii* 3
Ready to *b* in a colour'd flame; *Maud I vi* 19
should *b* and drown with deluging storms ,, *II i* 42
should make your Enid *b* Sunlike *Marr. of Geraint* 788
pavement echoing, *b* Their drowse; *Geraint and E.* 271
fringe of coppice round them *b* A sprangled pursuivant, *Balin and Balan* 46
b his lance against a forest bough, ,, 329
pearl-necklace of the Queen, That *b* *Merlin and V.* 452
And half his blood *b* forth, *Lancelot and E.* 517
b away To weep and wail in secret; ,, 1244
almost *b* the barriers in their heat, *Holy Grail* 336
I *b* the chain, I sprang into the boat. ,, 807
Hell *b* up your harlot roofs Bellowing *Pelleas and E.* 466
from within *B* thro' the heated buds, *Lover's Tale i* 320
Methought a light *B* from the garland ,, 366
b through the cloud of thought Keen, ,, *ii* 164
B vein, snap sinew, and crack heart, *Sir J. Oldcastle* 123
wish yon moaning sea would rise and *b* the shore, *The Flight* 11
Russia *b's* our Indian barrier, *Locksley H., Sixty* 115
B like a thunderbolt, Crash'd like a hurricane, *Heavy Brigade* 27
fleets the shower, And *b* the buds, *Early Spring* 14

C

Call (verb) (*continued*) 'Me you *c* great: mine is the firmer seat, *Lancelot and E.* 446
'Father, you *c* me wilful, and the fault Is yours ,, 750
Would *c* her friend and sister, sweet Elaine, ,, 865
I needs must follow death, who *c's* for me; *C* and I follow, I follow! let me die.' ,, 1017
I know not what you *c* the highest; ,, 1080
and bid *c* the ghostly man Hither, ,, 1099
To this I *c* my friends in testimony, ,, 1299
Art thou not he whom men *c* light-of-love?' *Pelleas and E.* 361
We *c* the harp of Arthur up in heaven?' *Last Tournament* 333
strike against the man they *c* My sister's son— *Guinevere* 572
how dare I *c* him mine? The shadow of another ,, 617
Nor shun to *c* me sister, dwell with you; ,, 676
But *c* not thou this traitor of my house *Pass. of Arthur* 155
Both for themselves and those who *c* them friend? ,, 421
we came To what our people *c* 'The Hill of Woe.' *Lover's Tale i* 374
Why should he *c* me to-night, *Rizpah* 3
and you, will you *c* it a theft?— ,, 52
he used but to *c* in the dark, ,, 83
he *c's* to me now from the church ,, 84
Good-night. I am going. He *c's*. ,, 86
An' Doctor 'e *c's* o' Sunday *North. Cobbler* 87
Their favourite—which I *c* 'The Tables Turned.' *Sisters (E. and E.)* 3
An' 'e *c's* fur 'is son, *Village Wife* 62
'but then if I *c* to the Lord, *In the Child. Hosp.* 53
if what we *c* The spirit flash not all at once *Ded. Poem Prin. Alice* 4
Without a roof that I can *c* mine own, *Columbus* 168
the waters—you hear them *c*! *Despair* 47
c on that Infinite Love that has served us ,, 95
set The lamps alight, and *c* For golden music, *Ancient Sage* 196
My Edwin loved to *c* us then *The Flight* 80
What did they *c* her, yer Honour? *Tomorrow* 4
I *c's* 'em arter the fellers *Spinster's S's.* 4
while I heard the curlews *c*, *Locksley H., Sixty* 3
curse your fellow-victim? *c* him dotard in your rage ,, 9
used to *c* the very flowers Sisters, brothers— ,, 101
Dead the new astronomy *c's* her . . . ,, 175
Britain's myriad voices *c*, *Open. I. and C. Exhib.* 35
C your poor to regale with you, *On Jub. Q. Victoria* 30
you used to *c* me once The lonely maiden-Princess *The Ring* 64
I Would *c* thro' this 'Io t'amo' ,, 234
There! I heard Our cuckoo *c*. *To Mary Boyle* 6
Down to the haven, *C* your companions, *Merlin and the G.* 125
the palm *C* to the cypress 'I alone am fair'? *Akbar's Dream* 38
Teacher who *c's* to them 'Set yourselves free!' *Kapiolani* 2
C me not so often back, *Silent Voices* 3
C me rather, silent voices, ,, 7

Call'd We are *c*—we must go. *All Things will Die* 20
Old voices *c* her from without. *Mariana* 68
'A merry boy they *c* him then, *Two Voices* 322
Far-off the torrent *c* me from the cleft: *Œnone* 54
Which men *c* Aulis in those iron years: *D. of F. Women* 106
And *c* him by his name, complaining loud, *M. d'Arthur* 210
C to me from the years to come, *Gardener's D.* 180
came a day When Allan *c* his son, and said, *Dora* 10
bells were ringing, Allan *c* His niece and said: ,, 41
c him Crichton, for he seem'd All-perfect, *Edwin Morris* 21
her business often *c* her from it, *Enoch Arden* 264
play'd with him And *c* him, Father Philip. ,, 354
For Father Philip (as they *c* him) too: ,, 365
'After the Lord has *c* me she shall know, ,, 810
He *c* aloud for Miriam Lane and said ,, 836
and *c* old Philip out To show the farm: *The Brook* 120
C to the bar, but ever *c* away *Aylmer's Field* 59
C all her vital spirits into each ear To listen: ,, 201
the great Sicilian *c* Calliope to grace his golden verse— *Lucretius* 93
enter'd an old hostel, *c* mine host To council, *Princess i* 173
Above an entry: riding in, we *c*; ,, 225
the chapel bells *C* us: we left the walks; ,, *ii* 471
Girl after girl was *c* to trial: ,, *iv* 228
she *c* For Psyche's child to cast it from the doors; ,, 237

Call'd (*continued*) stretch'd her arms and *c* Across the tumult *Princess iv* 496
pique at what she *c* The raillery, or grotesque, ,, 587
C him worthy to be loved, ,, *vi* 6
prest Their hands, and *c* them dear deliverers, ,, 92
or *c* On flying Time from all their silver tongues— ,, *vii* 104
They *c* me in the public squares *In Mem. lxix* 11
They *c* me fool, they *c* me child: ,, 13
and Arthur *c* to stay the brands *Com. of Arthur* 120
and *c* A hoary man, his chamberlain, ,, 144
And one—they *c* her Fame; and one,— *Gareth and L.* 114
they *c* To Gareth, 'Lord, the gateway is alive.' ,, 234
Sir Gareth *c* from where he rose, ,, 645
Of any save of him whom I *c*— ,, 859
Why came ye not, when *c*? and wherefore now Come ye, not *c*? ,, 1247
And *c* her like that maiden in the tale, *Marr. of Geraint* 742
c For Enid, and when Yniol made report ,, 755
Or hasty judger would have *c* her guilt, *Geraint and E.* 433
whom his shaking vassals *c* the Bull, ,, 439
And *c* for flesh and wine to feed his spears. ,, 601
They *c* him the great Prince and man of men. ,, 961
wherefore Arthur *c* His treasurer, *Balin and Balan* 4
The people *c* him Wizard; *Merlin and V.* 170
And *c* herself a gilded summer fly ,, 258
So Vivien *c* herself, But rather seem'd ,, 261
Who *c* her what he *c* her— ,, 864
C her to shelter in the hollow oak, ,, 894
Since, if I be what I am grossly *c*, ,, 915
And *c* him dear protector in her fright, ,, 946
she *c* him lord and liege, Her seer, her bard, ,, 953
Lancelot Would, tho' he *c* his wound a little hurt *Lancelot and E.* 852
Approaching thro' the darkness, *c*; ,, 1000
And *c* her song 'The Song of Love and Death,' ,, 1005
and *c* The father, and all three in hurry ,, 1023
I, sometime *c* the maid of Astolat, ,, 1273
Whom Arthur and his knighthood *c* The Pure, *Holy Grail* 3
but some *C* him a son of Lancelot, ,, 144
And Merlin *c* it 'The Siege perilous,' ,, 172
Shrilling along the hall to Arthur, *c*, ,, 289
Across the forest *c* of Dean, to find Caerleon *Pelleas and E.* 21
And this was *c* 'The Tournament of Youth:' ,, 158
She *c* them, saying, 'There he watches yet, ,, 262
he *c*, 'I strike upon thy side—The caitiffs!' ,, 279
the poor Pelleas whom she *c* her fool? ,, 474
rider, who *c* out from the dark field, ,, 575
And when I *c* upon thy name as one *Last Tournament* 73
By these in earnest those in mockery *c* ,, 135
'Isolt Of the white hands' they *c* her: ,, 398
Who *c* him the false son of Gorloïs: *Guinevere* 288
he, the King, *C* me polluted: ,, 620
His hope he *c* it; but he never mocks, ,, 632
Arthur woke and *c*, 'Who spake? A dream. *Pass. of Arthur* 45
And *c* him by his name, complaining loud, ,, 378
'let this be *c* henceforth The Hill of Hope;' *Lover's Tale i* 461
I wore a brother's mind: she *c* me brother: ,, 741
he *c* me his own little wife; *First Quarrel* 10
he *c* in the dark to me year after year— *Rizpah* 47
one of those about her knowing me *C* me to join them; *Sisters (E. and E.)* 123
She bore a child, whom reverently we *c* Edith; ,, 268
An' es for Miss Annie es *c* me afoor *Village Wife* 105
Our doctor had *c* in another, *In the Child. Hosp.* 1
Softly she *c* from her cot to the next, ,, 46
how many—thirty-nine—*C* it revellion— *Sir J. Oldcastle* 47
I changed the name; San Salvador I *c* it; *Columbus* 76
Brooks, for they *c* you so that knew you best, *To W. H. Brookfield* 1
standing, shouted, and Pallas far away *C*; *Achilles over the T.* 18
our trembling fathers *c* The God's own son. *Tiresias* 16
and he *c* to me 'Kiss me!' and there— *The Wreck* 104
On me, when boy, there came what then I *c*, *Ancient Sage* 217
They *c* her Molly Magee. *Tomorrow* 4
C from her cabin an' tould her to come ,, 20

Call'd (*continued*) Thin a slip of a gossoon *c*, *Tomorrow* 78
c me es pretty es ony lass i' the Shere ; *Spinster's S's.* 13
poet *c* the Bringer home of all good things. *Locksley H., Sixty* 185
he *c* ' Left wheel into line ! ' *Heavy Brigade* 6
They *c* her ' Reverence ' here upon earth, *Dead Prophet* 27
Then I *c* out Roä, Roä, Roä, *Owd Roä* 91
I raised her, *c* her ' Muriel, *The Ring* 449
and *c* arose, and, slowly plunging down *St. Telemachus* 28
c ' Forbear In the great name of Him who died for men, ,, 62
Alla *c* In old Irân the Sun of Love ? *Akbar's Dream* 86
An' ya *c* 'im a clown, ya did, *Church-Warden, etc.* 30
C on the Power adored by the Christian, *Kapiolani* 32
Callest *C* thou that thing a leg ? *Vision of Sin* 89
Callin' o' use to be *c* 'im Roä, Roä, Roä, *Owd Roä* 1
Calling (part) (*See also* **A-callin'**, **Callin'**) Hark ! death is *c* While I speak *All Things will Die* 28
C thyself a little lower ' Than angels. *Two Voices* 198
To hear the dewy echoes *c* From cave to cave *Lotos-Eaters, C. S.* 94
Then *c* down a blessing on his head *Enoch Arden* 327
And *c*, here and there, about the wood. ,, 383
Maud, Maud, They were crying and *c*. *Maud I xii* 4
Were crying and *c* to her, Where is Maud, ,, 26
Some *c* Arthur born of Gorloïs, Others of Anton ? *Com. of Arthur* 170
c two That still had tended on him *Gareth and L.* 178
and *c* ' Damsel, is this he, The champion ,, 915
And chafing his pale hands, and *c* to him. *Geraint and E.* 582
And chafing his faint hands, and *c* to him ; ,, 585
Moaning and *c* out of other lands, *Merlin and V.* 962
But he pursued her, *c* ' Stay a little ! *Lancelot and E.* 683
the King Look'd up, *c* aloud, ' Lo, there ! *Holy Grail* 219
named us each by name, *C* ' God speed ! ' ,, 352
And *c* me the greatest of all knights, ,, 595
Then *c* her three knights, she charged them, *Pelleas and E.* 219
C me thy white hind, and saying to me *Last Tournament* 569
rollers on the cliffs Clash'd, *c* to each other, *Lover's Tale i* 58
And voices in the distance *c* to me ,, *ii* 118
cuckoo of a joyless June Is *c* out of doors : *Pref. Poem Broth. S.* 4
cuckoo of a worse July Is *c* thro' the dark : ,, 12
Are *c* to each other thro' a dawn *The Ring* 37
all Stood round it, hush'd, or *c* on his name. *Death of Œnone* 66
very well just now to be *c* me darling and sweet, *Charity* 7
Calling (s) There came so loud a *c* of the sea, *Enoch Arden* 910
Calliope called *C* to grace his golden verse— *Lucretius* 94
Calm (adj.) reign the world's great bridals, chaste and *c* : *Princess vii* 294
C is the morn without a sound, *C* as to suit a calmer grief, *In Mem. xi* 1
if calm at all, If any calm, a *c* despair : ,, 16
His eye was *c*, and suddenly she took *Merlin and V.* 854
' May her life be as blissfully *c*, *The Wreck* 139
The night was *c*, the morn is *c*, *The Flight* 10
Calm (s) The summer *c* of golden charity, *Isabel* 8
No tranced summer *c* is thine, *Madeline* 2
My shallop through the star-strown *c*, *Arabian Nights* 36
I cannot hide that some have striven, Achieving *c*, *Two Voices* 209
' There is no joy but *c* ! ' *Lotos-Eaters, C. S.* 23
lower down The bay was oily *c* ; *Audley Court* 86
star of phosphorescence in the *c*, ,, 87
Then follow'd *c's*, and then winds variable, *Enoch Arden* 545
That mock'd him with returning *c*, *Lucretius* 25
fain Would follow, center'd in eternal *c*. ,, 79
to mar Their sacred everlasting *c* ! ,, 110
Not all so fine, nor so divine a *c*, ,, 111
Put on more *c* and added suppliantly : *Princess vi* 215
C and deep peace on this high wold, *In Mem. xi* 5
C and still light on yon great plain ,, 9
C and deep peace in this wide air, ,, 13
if *c* at all, If any *c*, a calm despair : ,, 15
C on the seas, and silver sleep, ,, 17
And dead *c* in that noble breast ,, 19
The touch of change in *c* or storm ; ,, *xvi* 6
And *c* that let the tapers burn Unwavering : ,, *xcv* 5
And tracts of *c* from tempest made, *In Mem. cxii* 14
And moulded in colossal *c*. ,, *Con.* 16
Long have I sigh'd for a *c* : *Maud I ii* 1
Calm (s) (*continued*) And presently thereafter follow'd *c*, *Com. of Arthur* 391
whom she answer'd with all *c*. *Lancelot and E.* 997
sway and whirl Of the storm dropt to windless *c*, *Lover's Tale ii* 207
Calming *C* itself to the long-wish'd-for end, *Maud I xviii* 5
Calpe From *C* unto Caucasus they sung, *The Poet* 15
Calumet celts and *c's*, Claymore and snowshoe, *Princess, Pro.* 18
Calumny Sweeter tones than *c* ? *A Dirge* 17
Calve *See* **Cauve**
Cama throne of Indian *C* slowly sail'd *Palace of Art* 115
Cambalu breach'd the belting wall of *C*, *Columbus* 108
Came (*See also* **Coom'd**, **Kem**) From the dark fen the oxen's low *C* to her : *Mariana* 29
In marvel whence that glory *c* Upon me, *Arabian Nights* 94
I *c* upon the great Pavilion of the Caliphat. ,, 113
It would fall to the ground if you *c* in. *Poet's Mind* 23
It would shrink to the earth if you *c* in. ,, 37
But if any *c* near I would call, *The Mermaid* 38
Fancy *c* and at her pillow sat, *Caress'd or chidden* 5
A moment *c* the tenderness of tears, *The form, the form* 9
C two young lovers lately wed ; *L. of Shalott ii* 34
The sun *c* dazzling thro' the leaves, ,, *iii* 3
Down she *c* and found a boat Beneath a willow ,, *iv* 6
Out upon the wharfs they *c*, ,, 42
There *c* a sound as of the sea ; *Mariana in the S.* 86
C out clear plates of sapphire mail. *Two Voices* 12
' Or if thro' lower lives I *c*— ,, 364
I spoke, but answer *c* there none : ,, 425
I *c* and sat Below the chestnuts, *Miller's D.* 59
That went and *c* a thousand times. ,, 72
From off the wold I *c*, and lay ,, 111
From my swift blood that went and *c* *Fatima* 16
Hither *c* at noon Mournful Œnone, *Œnone* 15
C up from reedy Simois all alone. ,, 52
Went forth to embrace him coming ere he *c*. ,, 63
river of speech *C* down upon my heart. ,, 69
Then to the bower they *c*, Naked they *c* ,, 94
They *c*, they cut away my tallest pines, ,, 208
in the dark morn The panther's roar *c* muffled, ,, 214
The Abominable, that uninvited *c* ,, 224
On corpses three-months-old at noon she *c*, *Palace of Art* 243
Too proud to care from whence I *c*. *L. C. V. de Vere* 12
As I *c* up the valley whom think ye should I see, *May Queen* 13
Till Charles's Wain *c* out above the tall white chimney-tops. *May Queen, N. Y's. E.* 12
To die before the snowdrop *c*, *May Queen, Con.* 4
There *c* a sweeter token when the night ,, 22
up the valley *c* a swell of music on the wind. ,, 32
And up the valley *c* again the music ,, 36
once again it *c*, and close beside the window-bars, ,, 39
In the afternoon they *c* unto a land *Lotos-Eaters* 3
mild-eyed melancholy Lotos-eaters *c*. ,, 27
Where'er I *c* I brought calamity.' *D. of F. Women* 95
Strength *c* to me that equall'd my desire. ,, 230
You *c* to us so readily, *D. of the O. Year* 7
mighty voice *C* rolling on the wind. *Of old sat Freedom* 8
(for so we held it then), What *c* of that ?' *The Epic* 27
C on the shining levels of the lake. *M. d'Arthur* 51
And to the barge they *c*. ,, 205
Then *c* a bark that, blowing forward, ,, *Ep.* 21
Artist he than all, *C*, drew your pencil from you, *Gardener's D.* 26
C voices of the well-contented doves. ,, 89
some sweet answer, tho' no answer *c*, ,, 159
little words, More musical than ever *c* ,, 233
while I mused *c* Memory with sad eyes, ,, 243
farewells—Of that which *c* between, ,, 252
Then there *c* a day When Allan call'd his son, *Dora* 9
then distresses *c* on him ; ,, 49
Dora *c* and said : ' I have obey'd my uncle ,, 58
all thro' me This evil *c* on William at the first. ,, 61
Far off the farmer *c* into the field ,, 74
when the morrow *c*, she rose and took The child ,, 80
c and said : ' Where were you yesterday ? ,, 87
the boy's cry *c* to her from the field, ,, 104
Remembering the day when first she *c*, ,, 106

Came (*continued*) they *c* in: but when the boy beheld His mother, *Dora* 137
I never *c* a-begging for myself, " 141
all his love *c* back a hundred-fold; " 166
c again together on the king With heated faces; *Audley Court* 36
C to the hammer here in March— " 60
I went and *c*; Her voice fled *Edwin Morris* 66
out they *c* Trustees and Aunts and Uncles. " 120
There *c* a mystic token from the king " 132
those that *c* To touch my body and be heal'd, *St. S. Stylites* 78
c To rest beneath thy boughs.—(repeat) *Talking Oak* 35, 155
c To sport beneath thy boughs. " 99
'And with him Albert *c* on his. " 105
here she *c*, and round me play'd, " 133
c Like Death betwixt thy dear embrace *Love and Duty* 47
cheek and forehead *c* a colour and a light, *Locksley Hall* 25
from the valleys underneath *C* little copses climbing. *Amphion* 32
C wet-shod alder from the wave, *C* yews, a dismal coterie; " 41
Old elms *c* breaking from the vine, " 45
Cruelly *c* they back to-day: *Edward Gray* 18
was the best That ever *c* from pipe. *Will Water.* 76
For since I *c* to live and learn, " 81
I think he *c* like Ganymede, " 119
C crowing over Thames. " 140
thy betters went Long since, and *c* no more; " 186
In there *c* old Alice the nurse, *Lady Clare* 13
great in story, Wheresoe'er he *c*. *The Captain* 20
Joyful *c* his speech: " 30
And he *c* to look upon her, *L. of Burleigh* 93
We *c* to warmer waves, and deep Across *The Voyage* 37
Again to colder climes we *c*, " 89
C in a sun-lit fall of rain. *Sir L. and Q. G.* 4
Bare-footed *c* the beggar maid *Beggar Maid* 3
A youth *c* riding toward a palace-gate. *Vision of Sin* 2
And from the palace *c* a child of sin, " 5
C floating on for many a month and year, " 54
there *c* a further change: " 207
two years after *c* a boy to be The rosy idol *Enoch Arden* 89
c a change, as all things human change. " 101
hearing his mischance, *C*, for he knew the man " 121
Then moving homeward *c* on Annie pale, " 149
blessing on his wife and babes Whatever *c* to him: " 189
when the last of those last moments *c*, " 217
when the day, that Enoch mention'd, *c*, " 239
Expectant of that news which never *c*, " 258
'Annie, I *c* to ask a favour of you.' " 285
'I *c* to speak to you of what he wish'd, " 291
This is the favour that I *c* to ask.' " 313
When you *c* in my sorrow broke me down; " 317
Scarce could the woman when he *c* upon her, " 345
and no news of Enoch *c*. " 361
I know not when it first *c* there, " 401
c the children laden with their spoil; " 445
Then the new mother *c* about her heart, " 524
breath of heaven *c* continually And sent her " 535
upon the cry of 'breakers' *c* The crash of ruin, " 548
sunny and rainy seasons *c* and went " 623
his lonely doom *C* suddenly to an end. " 627
None of these *C* from his country, " 653
and he *c* upon the place. " 681
and *c* out upon the waste. " 777
a langour *c* Upon him, gentle sickness, " 823
There *c* so loud a calling of the sea, " 910
For here I *c*, twenty years back— *The Brook* 77
her father *c* across With some long-winded tale, " 108
'Have you not heard?' said Katie, 'we *c* back. " 221
C from a grizzled cripple, whom I saw Sunning himself *Aylmer's Field* 8
With half a score of swarthy faces *c*. " 191
like a storm he *c*, And shook the house, " 215
The next day *c* a neighbour. " 251
c Her sicklier iteration. " 298
—when *this* Aylmer *c* of age— " 407
C at the moment Leolin's emissary, " 518

Came (*continued*) But passionately restless *c* and went, *Aylmer's Field* 546
And *c* upon him half-arisen from sleep, " 584
And when he *c* again, his flock believed— " 600
Then *c* a Lord in no wise like to Baäl. " 647
when the second Christmas *c*, escaped His keepers, " 838
C, with a month's leave given them, *Sea Dreams* 6
forth they *c* and paced the shore, " 32
when I *c* To know him more, I lost it, " 71
'It *c*,' she said, 'by working in the mines:' " 114
C men and women in dark clusters round, " 226
Yours *c* but from the breaking of a glass, " 248
blood by Sylla shed *C* driving rainlike *Lucretius* 48
but satiated at length *C* to the ruins. *Princess, Pro.* 91
C murmurs of her beauty from the South, " *i* 36
I spake of why we *c*, And my betroth'd. " 119
and a stable wench *C* running at the call, " 227
when we *c* where lies the child We lost " *ii* 10
At break of day the College Portress *c*: " 15
c to chivalry: When some respect, however slight, " 135
(what other way was left) I *c*.' " 217
arrow-wounded fawn *C* flying while you sat " 271
as you *c*, to slip away To-day, to-morrow, " 296
stood, so rapt, we gazing, *c* a voice, " 318
That Sheba *c* to ask of Solomon.' " 346
if you *c* Among us, debtors for our lives " 354
Will wonder why they *c*: " 432
often *c* Melissa hitting all we saw with shafts " 467
C furrowing all the orient into gold. " *iii* 18
so it was agreed when first they *c*; " 36
Then *c* these dreadful words out one by one, " 57
when your sister *c* she won the heart Of Ida: " 87
Hither *c* Cyril, and yawning 'O hard task,' " 123
demanded who we were, And why we *c*? " 136
He ceasing, *c* a message from the Head. " 168
On a sudden my strange seizure *c* Upon me, " 183
we *c* to where the river sloped To plunge in cataract, " 290
For many weary moons before we *c*, " 319
c On flowery levels underneath the crag, " 335
all The rosy heights *c* out above the lawns. " 365
How *c* you here?' I told him: " *iv* 221
as we *c*, the crowd dividing clove An advent " 283
Then *c* your new friend: " 298
What student *c* but that you planed her path " 315
Then *c* these wolves: *they* knew her: " 321
I *c* to tell you: found that you had gone, " 342
c a little stir About the doors, " 373
C all in haste to hinder wrong, " 401
C in long breezes rapt from inmost south " 431
A man I *c* to see you: but, indeed, " 441
Yet that I *c* not all unauthorized " 467
While I listen'd, *c* On a sudden the weird seizure and the doubt: " 559
This went by As strangely as it *c*, " 569
touch of all mischance but *c* As night to him " 573
morions, washed with morning, as they *c*. " *v* 264
He batter'd at the doors; none *c*: " 337
C sallying thro' the gates, and caught his hair, " 340
With message and defiance, went and *c*; " 370
Then *c* a postscript dash'd across the rest. " 424
And like a flash the weird affection *c*: " 477
c As comes a pillar of electric cloud, " 523
Like summer tempest *c* her tears— " *vi* 15
after him *C* Psyche, sorrowing for Aglaïa. " 29
'Our enemies have fall'n, have fall'n: they *c*; (repeat) " 38, 43
on they *c*, Their feet in flowers, her loveliest: " 77
At distance follow'd: so they *c*: " 83
When first she *c*, all flush'd you said " 250
these men *c* to woo Your Highness— " 328
but the Prince Her brother *c*, " 345
maidens *c*, they talk'd, They sang, " *vii* 22
down she *c*, And found fair peace once more " 43
with her oft, Melissa *c*; for Blanche had gone, " 56
on a day When Cyril pleaded, Ida *c* behind " 78
with me oft she sat: Then *c* a change; " 92
a touch *C* round my wrist, and tears upon my hand " 138

Came (*continued*) when she c From barren deep to conquer all with love; *Princess vii* 163
when we ceased There c a minute's pause, ,, *Con.* 4
C thro' the jaws of Death, *Light Brigade* 46
Remember how we c at last To Como; *The Daisy* 69
Up there c a flower, *The Flower* 3
at last it seem'd that an answer c. *The Victim* 24
And looking back to whence I c, *In Mem. xxiii* 7
'I murmur'd, as I c along, ,, *xxxvii* 21
The path we c by, thorn and flower, ,, *xlvi* 2
c In whispers of the beauteous world. ,, *lxxix* 11
This truth c borne with bier and pall, ,, *lxxxv* 1
But if they c who past away, ,, *xc* 13
c on that which is, and caught The deep pulsations ,, *xcv* 39
c at length To find a stronger faith his own; ,, *xcvi* 16
And out of darkness c the hands ,, *cxxiv* 23
they went and c, Remade the blood ,, *Con.* 10
if an enemy's fleet c yonder round the hill, *Maud I i* 49
when the morning c In a cloud, it faded, ,, *vi* 20
C out of her pitying womanhood, ,, 64
She c to the village church, ,, *viii* 1
Last week c one to the county town, ,, *x* 37
However she c to be so allied. ,, *xiii* 36
snow-limb'd Eve from whom she c. ,, *xviii* 28
Let no one ask me how it c to pass; ,, 49
And at last, when each c home, ,, *xix* 61
He c with the babe-faced lord; ,, *II i* 13
hard mechanic ghost That never c from on high ,, *ii* 35
C glimmering thro' the laurels At the quiet evenfall, ,, *iv* 77
Everything c to be known. ,, *v* 51
for he c not back From the wilderness, ,, 53
know not whether he c in the Hanover ship, ,, 59
man was less and less, till Arthur c. *Com. of Arthur* 12
wolf and boar and bear C night and day, ,, 24
But heard the call, and c: ,, 47
when they c before him, the King said, ,, 166
c to Cameliard, With Gawain and young Modred, ,, 243
I know not whether of himself he c, ,, 346
Why, Gawain, when he c With Modred hither *Gareth and L.* 25
c an ancient man, Long-bearded, ,, 240
They c from out a sacred mountain-cleft ,, 260
Then c a widow crying to the King, ,, 333
C yet another widow crying to him, ,, 350
Then c Sir Kay, the seneschal, and cried, ,, 367
Then c in hall the messenger of Mark, ,, 384
suppliant crying c With noise of ravage ,, 436
out of kitchen c The thralls in throng, ,, 694
Out of the smoke he c, and so my lance Hold, ,, 722
'Well that Ye c, or else these caitiff rogues ,, 819
Wherethro' the serpent river coil'd, they c. ,, 906
three fair girls in gilt and rosy raiment c: ,, 927
Then when he c upon her, spake 'Methought, ,, 991
The savour of thy kitchen c upon me ,, 993
damsel c, And arm'd him in old arms, ,, 1114
unhappiness Of one who c to help thee, ,, 1238
Why c ye not, when call'd? ,, 1247
a page Who c and went, and still reported ,, 1338
anon C lights and lights, and once again he blew; ,, 1371
Remembering when first he c on her *Marr. of Geraint* 140
Before him c a forester of Dean, ,, 148
C quickly flashing thro' the shallow ford ,, 167
And thither c Geraint, and underneath ,, 241
C forward with the helmet yet in hand ,, 285
c again with one, A youth, ,, 385
thither c the twain, and when Geraint Beheld her ,, 539
and errant knights And ladies c, ,, 546
There c a clapping as of phantom hands. ,, 566
and c to loathe His crime of traitor, ,, 593
c A stately queen whose name was Guinevere, ,, 666
therewithal one c and seized on her, ,, 673
C one with this and laid it in my hand, ,, 699
I c among you here so suddenly, ,, 794
Remembering how first he c on her, ,, 842
from the place There c a fair-hair'd youth, *Geraint and E.* 201
when the fair-hair'd youth c by him, said, ,, 205

Came (*continued*) c upon him, and he sigh'd; *Geraint and E.* 249
Crost and c near, lifted adoring eyes, ,, 304
I thought, but that your father c between, ,, 314
Suddenly c, and at his side all pale Dismounting, ,, 510
She rested, and her desolation c Upon her, ,, 518
C riding with a hundred lances up; ,, 539
ere he c, like one that hails a ship, ,, 540
out of her there c a power upon him; ,, 613
Neigh'd with all gladness as they c, ,, 755
C purer pleasure unto mortal kind ,, 765
o'er her meek eyes c a happy mist ,, 769
And you c—But once you c,— ,, 845
thither c The King's own leech to look ,, 922
For whatsoever knight against us c *Balin and Balan* 35
and c To learn black magic, and to hate his kind ,, 126
the great Queen C with slow steps, ,, 245
under open blue C on the hoarhead woodman at a bough ,, 294
scream of that Wood-devil I c to quell!' ,, 548
a wanton damsel c, And sought for Garlon ,, 609
no quest c, but all was joust and play, *Merlin and V.* 145
turn'd to tyrants when they c to power) ,, 518
They said a light c from her when she moved: ,, 567
and his book c down to me.' ,, 650
C to her old perch back, and settled there. ,, 903
Her eyes and neck glittering went and c; ,, 960
How c the lily maid by that good shield Of Lancelot, *Lancelot and E.* 28
Arthur c, and labouring up the pass, ,, 47
Then c an old, dumb, myriad-wrinkled man, ,, 170
across him c a cloud Of melancholy severe, ,, 324
Past inward, as she c from out the tower. ,, 346
Then c on him a sort of sacred fear, ,, 354
Then c the hermit out and bare him in, ,, 519
C round their great Pendragon, saying ,, 528
since the knight C not to us, ,, 544
c at last, tho' late, to Astolat: ,, 618
c The Lord of Astolat out, ,, 626
One old dame C suddenly on the Queen ,, 730
C on her brother with a happy face ,, 791
She c before Sir Lancelot, for she thought ,, 908
Then c her father, saying in low tones, ,, 994
c her brethren saying, 'Peace to thee, ,, 996
the King C girt with knights: ,, 1261
c the fine Gawain and wonder'd at her, And Lancelot later c and mused at her, ,, 1267
To answer that which c: *Holy Grail* 12
I know That Joseph c of old to Glastonbury, ,, 60
And when she c to speak, behold her eyes ,, 102
touch with hand, Was like that music as it c; ,, 115
'Then c a year of miracle: ,, 166
'Then on a summer night it c to pass, ,, 179
Had Camelot seen the like, since Arthur c; ,, 332
to the Gate of the three Queens we c, ,, 358
C like a driving gloom across my mind. ,, 370
And on the splendour c, flashing me blind; ,, 413
Open'd his arms to embrace me as he c, ,, 417
I saw not whence it c. ,, 515
return'd To whence I c, the gate of Arthur's wars.' ,, 539
C ye on none but phantoms in your quest, ,, 562
And now I c upon her once again, ,, 585
c a night Still as the day was loud; ,, 682
My madness c upon me as of old, ,, 787
I c All in my folly to the naked shore, ,, 792
But if indeed there c a sign from heaven, ,, 873
out of those to whom the vision c ,, 895
and the sunshine c along with him. *Pelleas and E.* 6
And as he c away, The men who met him ,, 141
strange knights From the four winds c in: ,, 148
out they c, But Pelleas overthrew them ,, 220
Then when he c before Ettarre, ,, 237
from a tiny cave C lightening downward, ,, 426
c the village girls And linger'd talking, ,, 508
Then a long silence c upon the hall, ,, 609
C Tristram, saying, 'Why skip ye so, *Last Tournament* 9

Came (*continued*) they *c* Not from the skeleton of a brother-slayer, *Last Tournament* 46
Fool, I *c* late, the heathen wars were o'er, ,, 269
Who knew thee swine enow before I *c*, ,, 304
That night *c* Arthur home, ,, 755
In the dead night, grim faces *c* and went Before her, *Guinevere* 70
when she *c* to Almesbury she spake ,, 138
a rumour wildly blown about *C*, ,, 154
remembering Her thought when first she *c*, ,, 182
when at last he *c* to Camelot, ,, 260
there was no man knew from whence he *c*; ,, 289
There *c* a day as still as heaven, ,, 292
Lancelot *c*, Reputed the best knight ,, 381
C to that point where first she saw the King ,, 403
then *c* silence, then a voice, ,, 419
Then *c* thy shameful sin with Lancelot; ,, 487
Then *c* the sin of Tristram and Isolt; ,, 488
Until it *c* a kingdom's curse with thee— ,, 550
There *c* on Arthur sleeping, Gawain *Pass. of Arthur* 30
c A bitter wind, clear from the North, ,, 123
C on the shining levels of the lake. ,, 219
So to the barge they *c*. ,, 373
therewithal *c* on him the weird rhyme, ,, 444
Then from the dawn it seem'd there *c*, ,, 457
There *c* a glorious morning, such a one *Lover's Tale i* 299
first we *c* from out the pines at noon, ,, 310
sounds of joy That *c* on the sea-wind. ,, 326
Last we *c* To what our people call ,, 373
yet to both there *c* The joy of life ,, 385
Hither we *c*, And sitting down upon the golden moss, ,, 539
then *c* in The white light of the weary moon ,, 639
Had I not learnt my loss before he *c*? ,, 665
Could that be more because he *c* my way? ,, 666
the wind *C* wooingly with woodbine smells. ,, *ii* 36
I *c* upon The rear of a procession, ,, 74
c a broad And solid beam of isolated light, ,, 172
I *c* one day and sat among the stones ,, *iii* 1
Then *c* on me The hollow tolling of the bell, ,, 9
hand she reach'd to those that *c* behind, ,, 48
Julian *c* again Back to his mother's house ,, *iv* 14
wrapping her all over with the cloak He *c* in, ,, 87
'Here! and how *c* I here?' ,, 97
An hour or two, Camilla's travail *c* Upon her, ,, 127
Suddenly *c* her notice and we past, ,, 154
So sweetly and so modestly she *c* To greet us, ,, 170
And crossing her own picture as she *c*, ,, 286
So she *c* in:—I am long in telling it, ,, 302
some other question'd if she *c* From foreign lands, ,, 330
he was a child, an' he *c* to harm; *First Quarrel* 23
when Harry *c* home for good. ,, 30
And Harry *c* home at last, ,, 35
Harry *c* in, an' I flung him the letter ,, 57
watch'd him, an' when he *c* in I felt ,, 75
when he *c* to bid me goodbye. ,, 78
I *c* into court to the Judge and the lawyers. *Rizpah* 33
like a flutter'd bird, *c* flying from far away: *The Revenge* 2
sailed away from Flores till the Spaniard *c* in sight, ,, 23
And the rest they *c* aboard us, ,, 52
For a dozen times they *c* with their pikes ,, 53
and the stars *c* out far over the summer sea, ,, 56
their high-built galleons *c*, Ship after ship, ,, 58
I *c* on lake Llanberris in the dark, *Sisters (E. and E.)* 95
Then *c* the day when I, Flattering myself ,, 139
And the doctor *c* at his hour, *In the Child. Hosp.* 68
Why there? they *c* to hear their preacher. *Sir J. Oldcastle* 42
And *c* upon the Mountain of the World, *Columbus* 26
I have accomplish'd what I *c* to do. ,, 65
Then *c* two voices from the Sepulchre, ,, 95
what was mine, *c* happily to the shore. ,, 141
And we *c* to the isle in the ocean, *V. of Maeldune* 9
And we *c* to the Silent Isle ,, 11
And we *c* to the Isle of Shouting, ,, 27
And we *c* to the Isle of Flowers: ,, 37
And we *c* to the Isle of Fruits: ,, 55
And we *c* to the Isle of Fire: ,, 71

Came (*continued*) And we *c* to the Bounteous Isle, *V. of Maeldune* 83
And we *c* in an evil time to the Isle ,, 105
And we *c* to the Isle of a Saint ,, 115
And we *c* to the Isle we were blown from, ,, 127
c back That wholesome heat the blood *To E. Fitzgerald* 23
dreadful light *C* from her golden hair, *Tiresias* 44
But I *c* on him once at a ball, *The Wreck* 47
wail *c* borne in the shriek of a growing wind, ,, 87
then *c* the crash of the mast. ,, 92
an answer *c* Not from the nurse— ,, 143
O Mother, she *c* to me there. ,, 148
That you *c* unwish'd for, uncall'd, *Despair* 5
there *c* thro' the roar of the breaker a whisper, ,, 13
Hoped for a dawn and it *c*, ,, 27
foam in the dusk *c* playing about our feet. ,, 50
From out his ancient city *c* a Seer *Ancient Sage* 2
The Nameless never *c* Among us, ,, 54
oft On me, when boy, there *c* what then I call'd, ,, 217
And yet no comfort *c* to me, *The Flight* 18
You *c*, and look'd and loved the view *Pro. to Gen. Hamley* 5
C that 'Ave atque Vale' of the Poet's hopeless woe, *Frater Ave, etc.* 5
from all the world the voices *c* *Demeter and P.* 66
c On three gray heads beneath a gleaming rift. ,, 82
Given on the morning when you *c* of age *The Ring* 77
then a woman *c* And caught me from my nurse. ,, 117
She *c* to you, not me. ,, 138
Vext, that you thought my Mother *c* to me? ,, 140
one silent voice *C* on the wind, ,, 154
And she that *c* to part them all too late, ,, 216
one day *c* And saw you, shook her head, ,, 312
I *c*, I went, was happier day by day; ,, 348
She always *c* to meet me carrying you, ,, 352
She *c* no more to meet me, carrying you, ,, 385
A beauty *c* upon your face, *Happy* 51
c, my friend, To prize your various book, *To Ulysses* 46
You *c* not, friend; *To Mary Boyle* 17
There no one *c*, the turf was fresh, *Prog. of Spring* 72
so to the land's Last limit I *c*— *Merlin and the G.* 110
c of your own will To wait on one so broken, *Romney's R.* 16
shouted, and the shepherds heard and *c*. *Death of Œnone* 56
shape with wings *C* sweeping by him, *St. Telemachus* 25
Love and Justice *c* and dwelt therein; (repeat) *Akbar's Dream* 181, 194
that I *c* on none of his band; *Bandit's Death* 40
would it matter so much if I *c* on the street? *Charity* 8
—a widow *c* to my door: ,, 26
birthday *c* of a boy born happily dead. ,, 34

Camel *c's* knelt Unbidden, and the brutes *Merlin and V.* 575
And like the all-enduring *c*, driven *Lover's Tale i* 136

Cameliard Leodogran, the King of *C*, *Com. of Arthur* 1
And thus the land of *C* was waste, ,, 20
came to *C*, With Gawain and young Modred, ,, 243

Camelot road runs by To many-tower'd *C*; *L. of Shalott i* 5
island in the river Flowing down to *C*. ,, 14
shallop flitteth silken-sail'd Skimming down to *C*: ,, 23
river winding clearly, Down to tower'd *C*: ,, 32
A curse is on her if she stay To look down to *C*. ,, *ii* 5
she sees the highway near Winding down to *C*: ,, 14
long-hair'd page in crimson clad, Goes by to tower'd *C*; ,, 23
with plumes and lights And music, went to *C*: ,, 32
As he rode down to *C*: (repeat) *L. of Shalott iii* 14, 23, 32
She look'd down to *C*. *L. of Shalott iii* 41
Heavily the low sky raining Over tower'd *C*; ,, *iv* 5
With a glassy countenance Did she look to *C*. ,, 14
Thro' the noises of the night She floated down to *C*: ,, 23
her eyes were darken'd wholly, Turn'd to tower'd *C*. ,, 32
Silent into *C*. ,, 41
they cross'd themselves for fear, All the knights at *C*: ,, 50
Walking about the gardens and the halls Of *C*, *M. d'Arthur* 21
Shot thro' the lists at *C*, ,, 224
plain That broaden'd toward the base of *C*, *Gareth and L.* 188
then enter'd with his twain *C*, ,, 303
king, Was ev'n upon his way to *C*; ,, 392
helping back the dislocated Kay To *C*, ,, 1214

Capitol the pillar'd Parthenon, The glittering *C*; *Freedom* 4
Caprera which here The warrior of *C* set, *To Ulysses* 26
Captain melting the mighty hearts Of *c's* and of kings. *D. of F. Women* 176
The *c* of my dreams Ruled in the eastern sky. ,, 263
Brave the *C* was: *The Captain* 5
harsh and cruel Seem'd the *C's* mood. ,, 14
Then the *C's* colour heighten'd, ,, 29
beneath the water Crew and *C* lie; ,, 68
Now mate is blind, and *c* lame, *The Voyage* 91
He got it; for their *c* after fight, *Aylmer's Field* 226
Without the *c's* knowledge: ,, 717
Communing with his *c's* of the war. *Princess i* 67
young *c's* flash'd their glittering teeth, ,, *v* 20
to meet us lightly pranced Three *c's* out; ,, 255
every *c* waits Hungry for honour, ,, 313
Foremost *c* of his time, *Ode on Well.* 31
those deep voices our dead *c* taught The tyrant, ,, 69
To a lord, a *c*, a padded shape, *Maud I x* 29
the crew were gentle, the *c* kind; *The Wreck* 129
band will be scatter'd now their gallant *c* is dead, *Bandit's Death* 41
Captain's-ear His *c-e* has heard them boom *Ode on Well.* 65
Captive 'sdeath! and he himself Your *c*, *Princess v* 277
The *c* void of noble rage, *In Mem xxvii* 2
Ye cage a buxom *c* here and there. *Merlin and V.* 542
seized upon my papers, loosed My *c's*, *Columbus* 131
void of joy, Lest she be taken *c*— *Tiresias* 102
flay *C's* whom they caught in battle— *Locksley H., Sixty* 80
Car reverent people behold The towering *c*, *Ode on Well.* 55
Fixt by their *c's*, waited the golden dawn. *Spec. of Iliad* 22
thro' which the *c* Of dark Aïdoneus rising *Demeter and P.* 38
Caracole round the gallery made his horse *C*; *Last Tournament* 206
Carádos (King) *C*, Urien, Cradlemont of Wales, *Com. of Arthur* 112
Caravel frailer *c*, With what was mine, *Columbus* 140
Carbonek the enchanted towers of *C*, *Holy Grail* 813
Carcanet Make a *c* of rays, *Adeline* 59
a *c* Of ruby swaying to and fro, *Last Tournament* 6
c Vext her with plaintive memories of the child: ,, 28
Because the twain had spoil'd her *c*. ,, 419
Tristram show'd And swung the ruby *c*. ,, 740
Carcase make the *c* a skeleton, *Boädicea* 14
Many a *c* they left to be carrion, *Batt. of Brunanburh* 105
Card Insipid as the Queen upon a *c*: *Aylmer's Field* 28
Care (s) and *the* c *That yokes with empire*, *To the Queen* 9
He hath no *c* of life or death; *Supp. Confessions* 48
sure it is a special *c* Of God, ,, 63
Thee nor carketh *c* nor slander; *A Dirge* 8
And little other *c* hath she, *L. of Shalott ii* 8
Grows green and broad, and takes no *c*, *Lotos-Eaters, C. S.* 28
a low voice, full of *c*, Murmur'd *D. of F. Women* 249
took with *c*, and kneeling on one knee, *M. d'Arthur* 173
Come, *C* and Pleasure, Hope and Pain, *Day-Dm., Sleep. P.* 55
Thy *c* is, under polish'd tins, *Will Water.* 227
Cast all your *c's* on God: *Enoch Arden* 222
mother cared for it With all a mother's *c*: ,, 263
no kin, no *c*, No burthen, save my *c* for you ,, 418
The common *c* whom no one cared for, *Aylmer's Field* 688
Seam'd with the shallow *c's* of fifty years: ,, 814
takes a lady's finger with all *c*, *Princess, Pro.* 173
each by other drest with *c* Descended ,, *iii* 19
She had the *c* of Lady Ida's youth, ,, 85
either she will die from want of *c*, ,, *v* 85
out of long frustration of her *c*, ,, *vii* 101
mental breadth, nor fail in childward *c*, ,, 283
Come, when no graver *c's* employ, *To F. D. Maurice* 1
Which once she foster'd up with *c*; *In Mem. viii* 16
Is this the end of all my *c*?' ,, *xii* 14
If any *c* for what is here Survive ,, *xxxviii* 9
Her *c* is not to part and prove; ,, *xlviii* 5
And falling with my weight of *c's* ,, *lv* 14
O sound to rout the brood of *c's*, ,, *lxxxix* 17
A song that slights the coming *c*, ,, *xcix* 10
Let *c's* that petty shadows cast, ,, *cv* 13
Ring out the want, the *c*, the sin, ,, *cvi* 17
And if the song were full of *c*, ,, *cxxv* 9

Care (s) (*continued*) Shall I not take *c* of all that I think, *Maud I xv* 7
Forgetful of his princedom and its *c's*. *Marr. of Geraint* 54
he thought, 'In spite of all my *c*, ,, 115
Told him that her fine *c* had saved his life. *Lancelot and E.* 863
so forgot herself A moment, and her *c's*: *Last Tournament* 26
took with *c*, and kneeling on one knee, *Pass. of Arthur* 341
offices Of watchful *c* and trembling tenderness. *Lover's Tale i* 226
But there from fever and my *c* of him ,, *iv* 143
the Lord has look'd into my *c*, *Rizpah* 75
lad will need little more of your *c*.' *In the Child. Hosp.* 17
days' of fever, and want of *c*! *The Wreck* 147
Muriel nursed you with a mother's *c*; *The Ring* 349
made you leper in His loving *c* for both, *Happy* 91
With politic *c*, with utter gentleness, *Akbar's Dream* 128
Care (verb) You *c* not for another's pains, *Rosalind* 19
random eyes, That *c* not whom they kill, ,, 38
Nor *c's* to lisp in love's delicious creeds; *Caress'd or chidden* 11
She still will take the praise, and *c* no more. *The form, the form* 14
Nor *c* to sit beside her where she sits— *Wan Sculptor* 10
I *c* not what the sects may brawl. *Palace of Art* 210
Too proud to *c* from whence I came. *L. C. V. de Vere* 12
but I *c* not what they say, *May Queen* 19
I *c* not if I go to-day. ,, *Con.* 43
But if you *c* indeed to listen, hear *Golden Year* 20
Like wealthy men who *c* not how they give. *Tithonus* 17
be happy! wherefore should I *c*? *Locksley Hall* 97
To choose your own you did not *c*; *Day-Dm., L'Envoi* 30
And that for which I *c* to live. ,, 56
I *c* no longer, being all unblest: *Come not, when etc.* 8
What *c* I for any name? *Vision of Sin* 85
'His head is low, and no man *c's* for him. *Enoch Arden* 850
if my children *c* to see me dead, ,, 888
Would *c* no more for Leolin's walking *Aylmer's Field* 124
Slight was his answer 'Well—I *c* not for it:' ,, 238
I *c* not for it either;' ,, 248
wherefore need he *c* Greatly for them, *Lucretius* 150
'*C* not thou! Thy duty? What is duty? ,, 280
c not while we hear A trumpet in the distance *Princess iv* 80
myself, what *c* I, war or no? ,, *v* 278
And, right or wrong, I *c* not: ,, 290
nor *c's* to walk With Death and Morning ,, *vii* 203
Him who *c's* not to be great, *Ode on Well.* 199
what do I *c* for Jane, let her speak of you *Grandmother* 51
shall we *c* to be pitiful? *Boädicea* 32
Nor *c's* to fix itself to form, *In Mem. xxxiii* 4
I *c* for nothing, all shall go. ,, *lvi* 4
I *c* not in these fading days ,, *lxxv* 9
Whatever they call him, what *c* I, *Maud I x* 64
But now shine on, and what *c* I, ,, *xviii* 41
C not thou to reply: ,, *II iii* 7
C not for shame: thou art not knight but knave.' *Gareth and L.* 1006
'And *c* not for the cost; the cost is mine.' *Geraint and E.* 288
Nor did I *c* or dare to speak with you, ,, 871
He *c's* not for me: only here to-day *Lancelot and E.* 126
nor *c's* For triumph in our mimic wars, ,, 311
she cried, 'I *c* not to be wife, ,, 937
I *c* not howsoever great he be, ,, 1069
And this am I, so that ye *c* for me *Holy Grail* 615
C's but to pass into the silent life. ,, 899
And pass and *c* no more. *Pelleas and E.* 77
wherefore shouldst thou *c* to mingle with it, *Last Tournament* 105
since I *c* not for thy pearls. ,, 314
C not for her! patient, and prayerful, ,, 607
I the King should greatly *c* to live; *Guinevere* 452
Not greatly *c* to lose; ,, 495
And *c* not thou for dreams from him, *Pass. of Arthur* 58
Do you think that I *c* for *my* soul if my boy *Rizpah* 78
I c not for a name—no fault of mine. *Sisters (E. and E.)* 77
Not es I *c's* fur to hear ony harm, *Village Wife* 22
Ah why should we *c* what they say? *In the Child. Hosp.* 71
heart of the father will *c* for his own.' *The Wreck* 98
Fly—*c* not. Birds and brides must leave *The Ring* 89
their music here be mortal need the singer greatly *c*? *Parnassus* 18
Cared Which you had hardly *c* to see. *L. C. V. de Vere* 32
nor heard of her, nor *c* to hear. Nor *c* to hear? *Edwin Morris* 138

Case (circumstance) (*continued*) it was all but a hopeless *c*: *In the Child. Hosp.* 14
And it was but a hopeless *c*, ,, 16
Casement (*See also* **Chancel-casement**) Or at the *c* seen her stand? *L. of Shalott i* 25
I arose, and I released The *c*, *Two Voices* 404
And all the *c* darken'd there. *Miller's D.* 128
And fires your narrow *c* glass, ,, 243
As one that from a *c* leans his head, *D. of F. Women* 246
gardener's lodge, With all its *c's* bedded, *Audley Court* 18
Many a night from yonder ivied *c*, *Locksley Hall* 7
Flew over roof and *c*: *Will Water.* 134
and he clamour'd from a *c*, 'Run' *The Brook* 85
The *c* slowly grows a glimmering square; *Princess iv* 52
All night has the *c* jessamine stirr'd *Maud I xxii* 15
Down from the *c* over Arthur, smote Flame-colour, *Com. of Arthur* 274
out of bower and *c* shyly glanced Eyes *Gareth and L.* 313
Beat thro' the blindless *c* of the room, *Marr. of Geraint* 71
rang Clear thro' the open *c* of the hall, ,, 328
Push'd thro' an open *c* down, *Balin and Balan* 413
royal rose In Arthur's *c* glimmer'd chastely *Merlin and V.* 740
Unclasping flung the *c* back, *Lancelot and E.* 981
Down in a *c* sat, A low sea-sunset glorying *Last Tournament* 507
and in her anguish found The *c*: *Guinevere* 587
From that *c* where the trailer mantles *Locksley H., Sixty* 257
Close beneath the *c* crimson with the shield ,, 34
Casement-curtain She drew her *c-c* by, *Mariana* 19
Casement-edge That morning, on the *c-e* *Miller's D.* 82
Cask when their *c's* were fill'd they took aboard: *Enoch Arden* 646
Casket since The key to that weird *c*, *Ancient Sage* 254
Casque And loosed the shatter'd *c*, and chafed his hands, *M. d'Arthur* 209
My good blade carves the *c's* of men, *Sir Galahad* 1
knightlike in his cap instead of *c*, *Princess iv* 600
unlaced my *c* And grovell'd on my body, ,, *vi* 27
This bare a maiden shield, a *c*; *Gareth and L.* 680
jangling, the *c* Fell, and he started up *Geraint and E.* 388
dismount and loose their *c's* *Balin and Balan* 573
there first she saw the *c* Of Lancelot on the wall: *Lancelot and E.* 805
a crown of gold About a *c* all jewels; *Holy Grail* 411
I saw The pelican on the *c* of our Sir Bors ,, 635
I remember now That pelican on the *c*: ,, 700
That ware their ladies' colours on the *c*, *Last Tournament* 184
And loosed the shatter'd *c*, and chafed his hands, *Pass. of Arthur* 377
C's were crack'd, and hauberks hack'd *The Tourney* 7
Cassandra Talk with the wild *C*, *Œnone* 263
C, Hebe, Joan, *Romney's R.* 4
Cassia turning round a *c*, full in view, *Love and Death* 4
Cassiopëia had you been Sphered up with *C*, *Princess iv* 438
Cássivëlaún (British king) hear it, Spirit of *C*! *Boädicea* 20
sweeter then the bride of *C*, Flur, *Marr. of Geraint* 744
Cast (mould) take the *c* Of those dead lineaments *Wan Sculptor* 1
Not only cunning *c's* in clay: *In Mem. cxx* 5
Cast (vomit) Lies the hawk's *c*, *Aylmer's Field* 849
Cast (throw) Jephtha vows his child . . . to one *c* of the dice. *The Flight* 26
Cast (verb) Low on her knees herself she *c*, *Mariana in the S.* 27
'Let me not *c* in endless shade *Two Voices* 5
I *c* me down, nor thought of you, *Miller's D.* 63
'This was *c* upon the board, *Œnone* 79
And *c* the golden fruit upon the board, ,, 226
those That are *c* in gentle mould. *To J. S.* 4
Memory standing near *C* down her eyes, ,, 54
'And if indeed I *c* the brand away, *M. d'Arthur* 88
Dora *c* her eyes upon the ground, *Dora* 89
who would *c* and balance at a desk, *Audley Court* 44
'Yet, since I first could *c* a shade, *Talking Oak* 85
Had *c* upon its crusty side *Will Water.* 103
overboard one stormy night He *c* his body, *The Voyage* 80
C all your cares on God; *Enoch Arden* 222
C his strong arms about his drooping wife, ,, 228
'Enoch, poor man, was *c* away and lost, ,, 713
Repeated muttering '*c* away and lost;' ,, 715
she *c* back upon him A piteous glance, *Aylmer's Field* 283
But they that *c* her spirit into flesh, ,, 481
He had *c* the curtains of their seat aside— ,, 803

Cast (verb) (*continued*) Shall Babylon be *c* into the sea; *Sea Dreams* 28
The mountain there has *c* his cloudy slough, *Lucretius* 177
grandsire burnt Because he *c* no shadow, *Princess i* 7
entering here, to *c* and fling The tricks, ,, *ii* 62
eddied into suns, that wheeling *c* The planets: ,, 118
Psyche's child to *c* it from the doors; ,, *iv* 238
turn'd her face, and *c* A liquid look on Ida, ,, 368
But a *c* oop, thot a did, *N. Farmer, O. S.* 14
in a golden hour I *c* to earth a seed. *The Flower* 2
She *c* her arms about the child. *The Victim* 32
Or *c* as rubbish to the void, *In Mem. liv* 7
And if thou *c* thine eyes below, ,, *lxi* 5
Tho' if an eye that's downward *c* ,, *lxii* 1
To chances where our lots were *c* ,, *xcii* 5
Let cares that petty shadows *c*, ,, *cv* 13
I seem to *c* a careless eye On souls, ,, *cxii* 7
Uther *c* upon her eyes of love: *Com. of Arthur* 193
written in the speech ye speak yourself, '*C* me away!" ,, 305
time to *c* away Is yet far-off.' ,, 307
rend In pieces, and so *c* it on the hearth. *Gareth and L.* 401
rend the cloth and *c* it on the hearth. ,, 418
cloth of roughest web, and *c* it down, ,, 683
bound my lord to *c* him in the mere.' ,, 803
rough dog, to whom he *c* his coat, ,, 1011
but straining ev'n his uttermost *C*, ,, 1153
saw That Death was *c* to ground, ,, 1403
Who, moving, *c* the coverlet aside, *Marr. of Geraint* 73
At this she *c* her eyes upon her dress, ,, 609
And *c* it on the mixen that it die.' ,, 672
she could *c* aside A splendour dear to women, ,, 807
she *c* about For that unnoticed failing *Geraint and E.* 46
c him and the bier in which he lay ,, 572
c his lance aside, And doff'd his helm: ,, 595
this poor gown I will not *c* aside ,, 705
arise a living man, And bid me *c* it. ,, 707
and she *c* her arms About him, ,, 761
c his eyes On each of all whom Uther left ,, 932
Stumbled headlong, and *c* his face to ground. *Balin and Balan* 426
And there in gloom *c* himself all along, ,, 434
Tore from the branch, and *c* on earth, the shield, ,, 539
on his dying brother *c* himself Dying; ,, 593
As Love, if Love be perfect, *c's* out fear, So Hate, if Hate be perfect, *c's* out fear. *Merlin and V.* 40
C herself down, knelt to the Queen, ,, 66
Where children *c* their pins and nails, ,, 430
The gentle wizard *c* a shielding arm. ,, 908
For if his own knight *c* him down, *Lancelot and E.* 313
stay'd; and *c* his eyes on fair Elaine: ,, 640
Leaf after leaf, and tore, and *c* them off, ,, 1199
The brand Excalibur will be *c* away. *Holy Grail* 257
all but hold, and then—*c* her aside, ,, 622
binding his good horse To a tree, *c* himself down; *Pelleas and E.* 31
c himself down, And gulf'd his griefs ,, 515
but *c* himself Down on a bench, hard-breathing. ,, 591
a knight *c* down Before his throne of arbitration *Last Tournament* 161
Like a dry bone *c* to some hungry hound? ,, 196
So dame and damsel *c* the simple white, ,, 232
and *c* thee back Thine own small saw, ,, 711
And *c* him as a worm upon the way; *Guinevere* 35
'And if indeed I *c* the brand away, *Pass. of Arthur* 256
Are morning shadows huger than the shapes That *c* them, *To the Queen ii* 64
we found The dead man *c* upon the shore? *Lover's Tale i* 295
I *c* them in the noisy brook beneath, ,, *ii* 41
But *c* a parting glance at me, ,, *iv* 4
'He *c's* me out,' she wept, 'and goes' ,, 103
She shook, and *c* her eyes down, ,, 329
Yet *c* her not away so suddenly, ,, 366
'*C* awaäy on a disolut land wi' a vartical soon!' *North. Cobbler* 3
And *c* it to the Moor: *Columbus* 111
I heard his voice, 'Be not *c* down. ,, 158
C off, put by, scouted by court and king— ,, 165
C at thy feet one flower that fades *To Dante* 7
A planet equal to the sun Which *c* it, *To E. Fitzgerald* 36

Cattle (*continued*) And *c* died, and deer in wood, *The Victim* 18
The *c* huddled on the lea; *In Mem. xv* 6
abide Without, among the *c* of the field. *Gareth and L.* 274
half of the *c* went lame, *V. of Maeldune* 31
drive Innocent *c* under thatch, *Locksley H., Sixty* 96
Catullus All composed in a metre of *C*, *Hendecasyllabics* 4
Thro' this metrification of *C*, ,, 10
Sweet *C's* all-but-island, *Frater Ave, etc.* 9
C, whose dead songster never dies; *Poets and their B.* 8
Caucasian Which the supreme *C* mind Carved *Palace of Art* 126
Where our *C's* let themselves be sold. *Aylmer's Field* 349
Caucasus From Calpe unto *C* they sung, *The Poet* 15
Elburz and all the *C* have heard; *W. to Marie Alex.* 13
Cauf (calf) 'Cushie wur craäzed fur 'er *c*' *Spinster's S's.* 115
'thank God that I hevn't naw *c* o' my oän.' ,, 116
Caught (*See also* **Cotch'd**) eddying of her garments *c* from thee The light *Ode to Memory* 31
And there a vision *c* my eye; *Miller's D.* 76
C in the frozen palms of Spring. *The Blackbird* 24
She *c* the white goose by the leg, *The Goose* 9
She dropt the goose, and *c* the pelf, ,, 13
c him by the hilt, and brandish'd him Three times, (repeat) *M. d'Arthur* 145, 160
the last night's gale had *c*, *Gardener's D.* 124
And there he *c* the younker tickling trout— *Walk. to the Mail* 33
C in flagrante—what's the Latin word? ,, 34
Thou wouldst have *c* me up into thy rest, *St. S. Stylites* 18
Abaddon and Asmodeus *c* at me. ,, 172
C up the whole of love and utter'd it, *Love and Duty* 82
Like truths of Science waiting to be *c*— *Golden Year* 17
The page has *c* her hand in his: *Day-Dm., Sleep P.* 29
Lady's-head upon the prow *C* the shrill salt, *The Voyage* 12
C the sparkles, and in circles, *Vision of Sin* 30
C each other with wild grimaces, ,, 35
now hastily *c* His bundle, waved his hand, *Enoch Arden* 237
C at his hand, and wrung it passionately, ,, 328
C at and ever miss'd it, and they laugh'd; ,, 752
about the fields you *c* His weary daylong chirping, *The Brook* 52
great pock-pitten fellow had been *c*? *Aylmer's Field* 256
C in a burst of unexpected storm, ,, 285
And *c* the blossom of the flying terms, *Princess, Pro.* 164
and the flood drew: yet I *c* her; ,, *iv* 182
Right on this we drove and *c*, ,, 188
And falling on my face was *c* and known. ,, 270
as if *c* at once from bed And tumbled ,, 285
On one knee Kneeling, I gave it, which she *c*, ,, 470
Like tender things that being *c* feign death, ,, *v* 108
Were *c* within the record of her wrongs, ,, 143
Came sallying thro' the gates, and *c* his hair, ,, 340
not less one glance he *c* Thro' open doors ,, 342
And reach'd the ship and *c* the rope, *Sailor Boy* 3
He *c* her away with a sudden cry; *The Victim* 69
And Fancy light from Fancy *c*, *In Mem. xxiii* 14
And *c* once more the distant shout, ,, *lxxxvii* 9
c The deep pulsations of the world, ,, *xcv* 39
C and cuff'd by the gale: *Maud I vi* 5
and *c* By that you swore to withstand? ,, 79
Last year, I *c* a glimpse of his face, ,, *xiii* 27
For how often I *c* her with eyes all wet, ,, *xix* 23
Who stoopt and *c* the babe, and cried *Com. of Arthur* 385
c And stay'd him, 'Climb not lest thou break *Gareth and L.* 53
The listening rogue hath *c* the manner of it. ,, 778
C at the hilt, as to abolish him: *Marr. of Geraint* 210
Yniol *c* His purple scarf, and held, ,, 376
Edyrn's men had *c* them in their flight, ,, 642
Her by both hands he *c*, and sweetly said, ,, 778
he sharply *c* his lance and shield, *Balin and Balan* 287
'And passing gentle' *c* his hand away ,, 371
C in a great old tyrant spider's web, *Merlin and V.* 259
one of Satan's shepherdesses *c* And meant to stamp him ,, 758
plunged, and *c* And set it on his head, *Lancelot and E.* 54
The heathen *c* and reft him of his tongue. ,, 273
and him they *c* and maim'd; ,, 275
whereat she *c* her breath; ,, 623

Caught (*continued*) Lady of the Lake *C* from his mother's arms— *Lancelot and E.* 1405
the holy cup Was *c* away to Heaven, *Holy Grail* 58
c his hand, Held it, and there, half-hidden by him, ,, 753
she *c* the circlet from his lance, *Pelleas and E.* 173
C his unbroken limbs from the dark field, ,, 585
Then Tristram laughing *c* the harp, *Last Tournament* 730
c him by the hilt, and brandish'd him Three times, (repeat) *Pass. of Arthur* 313, 328
round and round A whirlwind *c* and bore us; *Lover's Tale ii* 197
they turn'd, and *c* and brought him in ,, *iv* 376
old Sir Richard *c* at last, *The Revenge* 98
And *c* the laming bullet. *Sisters (E. and E.)* 65
Had *c* her hand, her eyelids fell— ,, 148
C in a mill and crush'd— *In the Child. Hosp.* 14
So, *c*, I burn, Burn? heathen men have borne *Sir J. Oldcastle* 184
I *c* the wreath that was flung. *The Wreck* 40
flay Captives whom they *c* in battle— *Locksley H., Sixty* 80
And his eloquence *c* like a flame *Dead Prophet* 34
And *c* her chaplet here—and there *To Marg. of Dufferin* 30
woman came And *c* me from my nurse. *The Ring* 118
C by the flower that closes on the fly, ,, 344
Who never *c* one gleam of the beauty *Happy* 60
c and held His people by the bridle-rein *Akbar's Dream* 84
And he *c* my little one from me: *Bandit's Death* 22
died of a fever *c* when a nurse *Charity* 41
Cause embattail and to wall about thy *c* *To J. M. K.* 8
more *c* to weep have I: My tears, no tears of love, *Wan Sculptor* 6
Nor in a merely selfish *c*— *Two Voices* 147
'In some good *c*, not in mine own, ,, 148
This woman was the *c*. *D. of F. Women* 104
only love were *c* enough for praise.' *Gardener's D.* 105
no *c*; James had no *c*: but when I prest the *c*, *The Brook* 97
who most have *c* to sorrow for her— *Aylmer's Field* 678
such extremes, I told her, well might harm The woman's *c*. *Princess iii* 145
Or, falling, protomartyr of our *c*, Die: ,, *iv* 505
twice I sought to plead my *c*, ,, 552
betray'd her *c* and mine— ,, *v* 76
and storming in extremes, Stood for her *c*, ,, 177
why, the *c's* weigh'd, Fatherly fears— ,, 215
in our noble sister's *c*? More, more, for honour: ,, 312
I would not aught of false—Is not our *c* pure? ,, 403
you The sole men to be mingled with our *c*, ,, 411
our side was vanquish'd and my *c* For ever lost, ,, *vi* 24
whose arms Champion'd our *c* and won it ,, 62
The brethren of our blood and *c*, ,, 71
To dream thy *c* embraced in mine, ,, 200
She pray'd me not to judge their *c* from her ,, *vii* 235
that know The woman's *c* is man's: ,, 259
With such compelling *c* to grieve *In Mem. xxix* 1
Ring out a slowly dying *c*, ,, *cvi* 13
can he tell Whether war be a *c* or a consequence? *Maud I x* 45
I cleaved to a *c* that I felt to be pure *Maud III vi* 31
We have proved we have hearts in a *c*, ,, 55
good *c* is theirs To hate me, *Gareth and L.* 820
'Sound sleep be thine! sound *c* to sleep hast thou. ,, 1282
Am I the *c*, I the poor *c* that men Reproach you, *Marr. of Geraint* 87
I *am* the *c*, because I dare not speak ,, 89
'Graver *c* than yours is mine, To curse ,, 308
you that most had *c* To fear me, fear no longer, *Geraint and E.* 824
Yourself were first the blameless *c* ,, 826
And made her good man jealous with good *c*. *Merlin and V.* 605
Some *c* had kept him sunder'd from his wife: ,, 715
Could call him the main *c* of all their crime; ,, 788
now remains But little *c* for laughter: *Lancelot and E.* 597
that I gave No *c*, not willingly, for such a love: ,, 1298
hither had she fled, her *c* of flight Sir Modred; *Guinevere* 9
come my way! to twit me with the *c*! *Lover's Tale i* 661
So much God's *c* was fluent in it— *Sir J. Oldcastle* 17
some less *c*, some *c* far less than mine; ,, 187
For every other *c* is less than mine. ,, 188
To this great *c* of Freedom drink, my friends, (repeat) *Hands all Round* 11, 35
Death for the right *c*, death for the wrong *c*, *Vastness* 8

Causer *c* of his banishment and shame, *Balin and Balan* 221
him The *c* of that scandal, fought and fell; *The Ring* 215
Causeway from the *c* heavily to the swamp Fall, *Last Tournament* 461
Cauve (calve). Wi' aäf the cows to *c* *N. Farmer, O.S.* 52
Cavalier A *c* from off his saddle-bow, *D. of F. Women* 46
Cavall (King Arthur's hound) chiefly for the baying of *C*, *Marr. of Geraint* 185
Cave (*see also* **Charnel-cave, Temple-cave**) And sweet is the colour of cove and *c*, *Sea-Fairies* 30
O *C's* That house the cold crown'd snake! *Œnone* 36
within the *c* Behind yon whispering tuft ,, 87
rock-thwarted under bellowing *c's*, *Palace of Art* 71
To hear the dewy echoes calling From *c* to *c* *Lotos-Eaters, C.S.* 95
Thro' every hollow *c* and alley lone ,, 103
Dry clash'd his harness in the icy *c's* *M. d'Arthur* 186
A narrow *c* ran in beneath the cliff: *Enoch Arden* 23
a *c* Of touchwood, met a single flourishing spray. *Aylmer's Field* 511
All sand and cliff and deep-inrunning *c*, *Sea Dreams* 17
Ran in and out the long sea-framing *c's*, ,, 33
dark *c's* that run beneath the cliffs. ,, 90
motion of the boundless deep Bore thro' the *c*, ,, 92
I found Only the landward exit of the *c*, ,, 96
along the valley, by rock and *c* and tree, *V. of Cauteretz* 9
In *c's* about the dreary bay, *Sailor Boy* 10
help and shelter to the hermit's *c*. *Gareth and L.* 1209
A *c*, Sir Lancelot, is hard by, ,, 1275
woodman show'd the *c* From which he sallies, *Balin and Balan* 131
Look to the *c*.' ,, 306
As on a dull day in an Ocean *c* The blind wave *Merlin and V.* 231
But into some low *c* to crawl, ,, 884
massive columns, like a shorecliff *c*, *Lancelot and E.* 406
shot red fire and shadows thro' the *c*, ,, 414
across the poplar grove Led to the *c's*: ,, 805
city to the fields, Thence to the *c*: ,, 848
rivulet from a tiny *c* Came lightening downward, *Pelleas and E.* 425
Dry clash'd his harness in the icy *c's* *Pass. of Arthur* 354
the *c*, Storm, sunset, glows and glories of the moon *Lover's Tale ii* 109
stately vestibules To *c's* and shows of Death: ,, 126
Strewn in the entry of the moaning *c*; ,, *iii* 2
Dragon's *c* Half hid, they tell me, *Tiresias* 143
When the bat comes out of his *c*, *Despair* 89
seem to draw From yon dark *c*, *Ancient Sage* 10
I peer'd thro' tomb and *c*, *Demeter and P.* 70
Œnone sat within the *c* from out *Death of Œnone* 1
still in her *c*, Amazed, and ever seeming stared ,, 69
in his *c* The man, whose pious hand had built *St. Telemachus* 8
Reason in the dusky *c* of Life, *Akbar's Dream* 121
dragg'd me up there to his *c* in the mountain, *Bandit's Death* 11
We return'd to his *c*—the link was broken— ,, 29
slept Ay, till dawn stole into the *c*, ,, 31
Cavern shoulder under gloom Of *c* pillars; *To E. L.* 18
a hut, Half hut, half native *c*. *Enoch Arden* 560
I long to creep Into some still *c* deep, *Maud II iv* 96
And told him of a *c* hard at hand, *Gareth and L.* 1189
Scaped thro' a *c* from a bandit hold, *Holy Grail* 207
Beneath a low-brow'd *c*, where the tide Plash'd, *Lover's Tale i* 55
Is scoop'd a *c* and a mountain hall, ,, 517
The hollow *c's* heard me— ,, *ii* 11
Chiefly I sought the *c* and the hill ,, 33
old man before A *c* whence an affluent *Ancient Sage* 7
Gnome of the *c*, Griffin and Giant, *Merlin and the G.* 39
Cavern-chasm mark'd not on his right a *c-c* *Balin and Balan* 312
Cavern-mouth *c-m*, Half overtrailed with a wanton weed, *Lover's Tale i* 524
All day I sat within the *c-m*, ,, *ii* 37
Cavern-shadowing wilderness, And *c-s* laurels. *Lucretius* 205
Caw The building rook 'll *c* *May Queen, N. Y's. E.* 17
Cease The stream will *c* to flow; The wind will *c* to blow; The clouds will *c* to fleet; The heart will *c* to beat; *All Things will Die* 9
trust and hope till things should *c*, *Supp. Confessions* 31
When I shall *c* to be all alone, *Mariana in the S.* 95
A wither'd palsy *c* to shake?' *Two Voices* 57
C to wail and brawl! ,, 199

Cease (*continued*) Not make him sure that he shall *c*? *Two Voices* 282
And the wicked *c* from troubling, *May Queen, Con.* 60
fold our wings, And *c* from wanderings, *Lotos-Eaters, C. S.* 20
In silence; ripen, fall and *c*: ,, 52
When midnight bells *c* ringing suddenly, *D. of F. Women* 247
'Twere better I should *c* *To J. S.* 66
the wise of heart would *c* To hold his hope *Love thou thy land* 81
Shall I *c* here? Is this enough to say *Gardener's D.* 236
I will not *c* to grasp the hope I hold Of saintdom, *St. S. Stylites* 5
Yet *c* I not to clamour and to cry, ,, 42
I muse on joy that will not *c*, *Sir Galahad* 65
thou shalt *c* To pace the gritted floor, *Will Water.* 241
For blasts would rise and rave and *c*, *The Voyage* 85
I cannot *c* to follow you, *Princess iv* 455
Nor did her father *c* to press my claim, ,, *vii* 87
But *c* to move so near the Heavens, and *c* ,, 195
That our free press should *c* to brawl, *Third of Feb.* 3
hearts that change not, love that cannot *c*, *W. to Marie Alex.* 46
the Judge of us all when life shall *c*; *Grandmother* 95
Her quiet dream of life this hour may *c*. *Requiescat* 6
They have their day and *c* to be: *In Mem., Pro.* 18
jaws Of vacant darkness and to *c*. ,, *xxxiv* 16
And those cold crypts where they shall *c*. ,, *lviii* 8
That the man I am may *c* to be! *Maud I x* 68
Pass and *c* to move about! ,, *II iv* 59
iron tyranny now should bend or *c*, ,, *III vi* 20
c not from your quest until ye find.' *Lancelot and E.* 548
wherefore *c*, Sweet father, and bid call ,, 1098
I would that wars should *c*, *Epilogue* 11
silver year should *c* to mourn and sigh— *To Mary Boyle* 57
Ceased heart of Poland hath not *c* To quiver, *Poland* 3
A little *c*, but recommenced. *Two Voices* 318
I *c*, and sat as one forlorn. ,, 400
She *c*, and Paris held the costly fruit *Œnone* 135
'Here she *c*, And Paris ponder'd, ,, 168
But all these things have *c* to be, *May Queen, Con.* 48
She *c* in tears, fallen from hope and trust: *D. of F. Women* 257
Before he *c* I turn'd, *Gardener's D.* 121
He *c*; and Miriam Lane Made such a voluble answer *Enoch Arden* 902
And then the motion of the current *c*, *Sea Dreams* 117
cloud That not one moment *c* to thunder, ,, 125
I *c*, and all the ladies, each at each, *Princess iv* 117
Scarce had I *c* when from a tamarisk near ,, 258
She *c*: the Princess answer'd coldly, ,, 359
I *c*; he said, 'Stubborn, but she may sit ,, *v* 438
C all on tremble: piteous was the cry: ,, *vi* 142
when we *c* There came a minute's pause, ,, *Con.* 3
We *c*: a gentler feeling crept Upon us: *In Mem. xxx* 17
him who had *c* to share her heart, *Maud I xix* 30
sod and shingle *c* to fly Behind her, *Gareth and L.* 761
Here *c* the kindly mother out of breath; *Marr. of Geraint* 732
She *c*; his evil spirit upon him leapt, *Balin and Balan* 537
He *c*, and then—for Vivien sweetly said *Merlin and V.* 17
She *c*, and made her lithe arm round his neck ,, 614
Scarce had she *c*, when out of heaven a bolt ,, 934
He spoke and *c*: the lily maid Elaine, *Lancelot and E.* 242
She *c*: her father promised; ,, 1130
Then, when he *c*, in one cold passive hand ,, 1201
'He *c*; and Arthur turn'd to whom at first *Holy Grail* 751
leave this land for ever.' Here he *c*. *Lover's Tale iv* 368
But never a moment *c* the fight *The Revenge* 57
And when I *c* to speak, the king, *Columbus* 14
now thy long day's work hath *c*, *Epit. on Stratford* 2
Nor ever *c* to clamour for the ring; *The Ring* 389
when life has *c* to beat. *Happy* 52
Ceasing *C* not, mingled, unrepress'd, *Arabian Nights* 74
He *c*, came a message from the Head. *Princess iii* 168
'So speaking, and here *c*, *Holy Grail* 853
Cecily Wound with white roses, slept St. *C*; *Palace of Art* 99
Cedar (*See also* **Cedar-wood**) The stately *c*, tamarisks, *Arabian Nights* 105
A *c* spread his dark-green layers of shade. *Gardener's D.* 116
Beam'd thro' the thicken'd *c* in the dusk. ,, 166
in halls Of Lebanonian *c*: *Princess ii* 352

Cedar *(continued)* bloom profuse and *c* arches Charm, *Milton* 11
Sighing for Lebanon, Dark *c*, *Maud I xviii* 18
Cedar-tree A voice by the *c t* In the meadow ,, *v* 1
red man dance By his red *c-t*, ,, *xvii* 18
Cedar-wood A mile beneath the *c-w*. *Eleänore* 8
Cede learn if Ida yet would *c* our claim, *Princess v* 333
Ceiling (*See also* **Hall-ceiling**) men Walk'd like the fly on *c's*? *Columbus* 51
Celandine in varnish'd glory shine Thy stars of *c*. *Prog. of Spring* 39
Celebrate To *c* the golden prime *Arabian Nights* 131
Celebrated thine the deeds to be *c*, *Boädicea* 41
Celibacy Into the suburb—their hard *c*, *Sir J. Oldcastle* 107
Celidon gloomy skirts Of *C* the forest; *Lancelot and E.* 292
Cell From many a wondrous grot and secret *c* *The Kraken* 8
And wild winds bound within their *c*, *Mariana* 54
'Not less the bee would range her *c's*, *Two Voices* 70
From *c's* of madness unconfined, ,, 371
Made havock among those tender *c's*, *Lucretius* 22
And weave their petty *c's* and die. *In Mem. l* 12
track Suggestion to her inmost *c*. ,, *xcv* 32
The tiny *c* is forlorn, *Maud II ii* 13
Thro' *c's* of madness, haunts of horror ,, *III vi* 2
in your frosty *c's* ye feel the fire! *Balin and Balan* 446
c's and chambers: all were fair and dry; *Lancelot and E.* 407
When they gain'd the *c* wherein he slept, ,, 811
Across the iron grating of her *c* Beat, *Holy Grail* 81
Stream'd thro' my *c* a cold and silver beam, ,, 116
Till all the white walls of my *c* were dyed ,, 119
I never stray'd beyond the *c*, ,, 628
bound and plunged him into a *c* Of great piled stones; ,, 675
such a craziness as needs A *c* and keeper), *Lover's Tale iv* 165
They had fasten'd the door of his *c*. *Rizpah* 42
Like worldly beauties in the *C*, *The Ring* 143
Cellar in the *c's* merry bloated things *Guinevere* 267
Celled *See* **Full-celled, Two-cell'd**
Celt (race of people) Teuton or *C*, or whatever we be, *W. to Alexandra* 32
The blind hysterics of the *C*; *In Mem. cix* 16
Celt (stone implement) *c's* and calumets, Claymore and snowshoe, *Princess, Pro.* 17
Censer incense free From one *c* in one shrine, *Eleänore* 59
The shrill bell rings, the *c* swings, *Sir Galahad* 35
A *c*, either worn with wind and storm; *Gareth and L.* 222
Censure England's honest *c* went too far; *Third of Feb.* 2
It might be safe our *c's* to withdraw; ,, 11
Cent mellow metres more than *c* for *c*; *The Brook* 5
Center'd *See* **Centred**
Centre Earth is dry to the *c*, *Nothing will Die* 20
Till toward the *c* set the starry tides, *Princess ii* 117
thoughts that wait On you, their *c*: ,, *iv* 444
in the *c* stood The common men with rolling eyes; ,, *vi* 359
Whose faith has *c* everywhere, *In Mem. xxxiii* 3
The *c* of a world's desire; ,, *lxiv* 16
In the *c* stood A statue veil'd, ,, *ciii* 11
Safe, damsel, as the *c* of this hall. *Gareth and L.* 604
To *c* in this place and time. *Lover's Tale i* 552
the *c* and crater of European confusion, *Beautiful City* 1
Centre-bit *c-b's* Grind on the wakeful ear *Maud I i* 41
Centred-Center'd music *centred* in a doleful song *Lotos-Eaters, C. S.* 117
centred in the sphere Of common duties, *Ulysses* 39
Would follow, *center'd* in eternal calm. *Lucretius* 79
one emerald *center'd* in a sun Of silver rays, *Lancelot and E.* 295
Century When the *centuries* behind me like a fruitful land *Locksley Hall* 13
A maiden of our *c*, yet most meek; *The Brook* 68
thro' the *centuries* let a people's voice *Ode on Well.* 142
Had I lain for a *c* dead; *Maud I xxii* 72
years will roll into the *centuries*, *Guinevere* 626
speak to the *centuries*, All the *centuries*, *On Jub. Q. Victoria* 48
The *c's* three strong eights have met *To Ulysses* 7
Ceremonial Hail the fair *C* Of this year of her Jubilee. *On Jub. Q. Victoria* 23
in his heart rejoice At this glad *C*, ,, 37
Of this great *C*, ,, 50
Ceremony Long summers back, a kind of *c*— *Princess i* 124
in the darkness, at the mystical *c*, *Boädicea* 36
suit of fray'd magnificence, Once fit for feasts of *c*) *Marr. of Geraint* 297
And there be wedded with all *c*. ,, 608
They twain were wedded with all *c*. ,, 839
Chaänge (change) I thowt shall I *c* my staäte? *Spinster's S's.* 44
Chaänged (changed) But arter I *c* my mind, *North. Cobbler* 105
Chaängin' (changing) all the while I wur *c* my gown, *Spinster's S's.* 43
Chace-Chase (*See also* **Sumner-chace**) That stand within the *chace*. *Talking Oak* 4
And overlook the *chace*; ,, 94
Look further through the *chace*, ,, 246
Then crost the common into Darnley *chase* *The Brook* 132
Chafe yet it *c's* me that I could not bend *D. of F. Women* 137
Began to *c* as at a personal wrong. *Enoch Arden* 474
Chafed *c* his hands, And call'd him by his name, *M. d'Arthur* 209
And when his answer *c* them, *Holy Grail* 673
c his hands, And call'd him by his name, *Pass. of Arthur* 377
I took And *c* the freezing hand. *The Ring* 452
Chaff Mere *c* and draff, much better burnt.' *The Epic* 40
will be *c* For every gust of chance, *Princess iv* 355
And vacant *c* well meant for grain. *In Mem. vi* 4
and grope, And gather dust and *c*, ,, *lv* 18
Chaffering *C's* and chatterings at the market-cross, *Holy Grail* 558
Chafing *c* at his own great self defied, *Aylmer's Field* 537
But *c* me on fire to find my bride) *Princess i* 166
and the squire *C* his shoulder: *Geraint and E.* 27
c his pale hands, and calling to him. ,, 582
c his faint hands, and calling to him; ,, 585
Chain (s) (*See also* **Daisy-chain, Ruby-chain**) to chain with *c's*, and bind with bands *Buonaparte* 2
loosed the *c*, and down she lay; *L. of Shalott iv* 16
such a *c* Of knitted purport, *Two Voices* 167
Bound by gold *c's* about the feet of God. *M. d'Arthur* 255
But dallied with his golden *c*, *Day-Dm., Revival* 31
Twofooted at the limit of his *c*, *Aylmer's Field* 127
To break my *c*, to shake my mane: *Princess ii* 424
From growing commerce loose her latest *c*, *Ode Inter. Exhib.* 33
made the serf a man, and burst his *c*— *W. to Marie Alex.* 3
boat, Half-swallow'd in it, anchor'd with a *c*; *Holy Grail* 803
I burst the *c*, I sprang into the boat. ,, 807
Bound by gold *c's* about the feet of God. *Pass. of Arthur* 423
seem'd as tho' a link Of some tight *c* *Lover's Tale i* 595
sat as if in *c's*—to whom he said: ,, *iv* 362
He workt me the daisy *c*— *First Quarrel* 13
but am led by the creak of the *c*, *Rizpah* 7
They hang'd him in *c's* for a show— ,, 35
C's, my good lord: in your raised brows *Columbus* 1
C's for the Admiral of the Ocean! *c's* For him who gave a new heaven, ,, 19
c's for him Who push'd his prows ,, 23
C's! we are Admirals of the Ocean, ,, 28
Drove me and my good brothers home in *c's*, ,, 134
the *c's*, what do *they* mean—the *c's*?' ,, 211
'These same *c's* Bound these same bones ,, 213
wept with me when I return'd in *c's*, ,, 231
She that link'd again the broken *c* *Locksley H., Sixty* 52
c's of mountain, grains of sand ,, 208
The slave, the scourge, the *c*; *Freedom* 12
all the gold from each laburnum *c* *To Mary Boyle* 11
Down hill 'Too-quick,' the *c*. *Politics* 12
Chain (verb) to *c* with chains, and bind with bands *Buonaparte* 2
And *c's* regret to his decease, *In Mem. xxix* 3
Chain'd My right leg *c* into the crag, *St. S. Stylites* 73
—or brought her *c*, a slave, *Princess v* 139
so *c* and coupled with the curse Of blindness *Tiresias* 58
dog: it was *c*, but its horrible yell *Bandit's Death* 35
Chaining But *c* fancy now at home *To Ulysses* 31
Chair (*See also* **Arm-chair, Elbow-chair**) If one but speaks or hems or stirs his *c*, *Sonnet To——* 5
In yonder *c* I see him sit, *Miller's D.* 9
And the long shadow of the *c* ,, 126
Two years his *c* is seen Empty *To J. S.* 22
farmer vext packs up his beds and *c's*, *Walk. to the Mail* 39

Chair (*continued*) Sweat on his blazon'd *c's*; *Walk. to the Mail* 76
And in his *c* himself uprear'd, *Day-Dm., Revival* 18
But kept the house, his *c*, and last his bed. *Enoch Arden* 826
With nearing *c* and lower'd accent) *Aylmer's Field* 267
I cry to vacant *c's* and widow'd walls, ,, 720
They come and sit by my *c*, *Grandmother* 83
spirits sink To see the vacant *c*, *In Mem. xx* 19
The *c's* and thrones of civil power? ,, *xxi* 16
He plays with threads, he beats his *c* ,, *lxvi* 13
Why sits he here in his father's *c*? *Maud I xiii* 23
Gareth went, and hovering round her *c* Ask'd, *Gareth and L.* 33
pushing could move The *c* of Idris. *Marr. of Geraint* 543
in their *c's* set up a stronger race *Geraint and E.* 940
Thy *c*, a grief to all the brethren, *Balin and Balan* 78
sloping down to make Arms for his *c*, *Lancelot and E.* 438
In our great hall there stood a vacant *c*, *Holy Grail* 167
Merlin sat In his own *c*, and so was lost; ,, 176
Galahad would sit down in Merlin's *c*. ,, 181
now his *c* desires him here in vain, ,, 901
fill'd his double-dragon'd *c*. *Last Tournament* 144
Push'd from his *c* of regal heritage, *Lover's Tale i* 118
Led his dear lady to a *c* of state. ,, *iv* 321
I mash'd the taäbles an' *c's*, *North. Cobbler* 37
an' the mark o' 'is 'eäd o' the *c's*! *Spinster's S's.* 100
An' I slep i' my *c* hup-on-end, *Owd Roä* 54
An' I slep' i' my *c* ageän ,, 65
Sa I kep i' my *c*, fur I thowt she was nobbut ,, 74
she skelpt ma haäfe ower i' the *c*, ,, 76
Chairman A quarter-sessions *c*, abler none; *Princess, Con.* 90
Chaise Within the low-wheel'd *c*, *Talking Oak* 110
Chalcedony *C*, emerald, sardonyx, sardius, *Columbus* 84
Chalice The *c* of the grapes of God; *In Mem. x* 16
C and salver, wines that, Heavens knows when, *Lover's Tale iv* 193
Chalk all his joints Are full of *c*? *Audley Court* 47
Tumbles a billow on *c* and sand; *To F. D. Maurice* 24
c and alum and plaster are sold to the poor *Maud I i* 39
Chalk'd *c* her face, and wing'd Her transit *Princess iv* 377
Chalk-hill On the *c-h* the bearded grass Is dry *Miller's D.* 245
Chalk-quarry white *c-q* from the hill Gleam'd ,, 115
Challenge madness made thee *c* the chief knight *Gareth and L.* 1416
a jubilant *c* to Time and to Fate; *Vastness* 21
Challenging *c* And overthrowing every knight *Balin and Balan* 12
Chamber (*See also* **Chaumber**) *faults were thick as dust In vacant* c's, *To the Queen* 19
thick-moted sunbeam lay Athwart the *c's*, *Mariana* 79
door that bar The secret bridal *c's* of the heart, *Gardener's D.* 249
breathings are not heard In palace *c's* far apart. *Day-Dm., Sleep B.* 18
till he find The quiet *c* far apart. ,, *Arrival* 28
In musty bins and *c's*, *Will Water.* 102
till the comrade of his *c's* woke, *Aylmer's Field* 583
To one deep *c* shut from sound, *Princess vi* 376
all The *c's* emptied of delight: *In Mem. viii* 8
The field, the *c* and the street, ,, 11
Moved in the *c's* of the blood; ,, *xxiii* 20
About its echoing *c's* wide, *Maud I vi* 74
In the *c* or the street, ,, *II iv* 83
But hire us some fair *c* for the night, *Geraint and E.* 238
the boy return'd And told them of a *c*, ,, 261
the two remain'd Apart by all the *c's* width, ,, 265
High in her *c* up a tower to the east *Lancelot and E.* 3
cells and *c's*: all were fair and dry; ,, 407
Past to her *c*, and there flung herself ,, 609
The lucid *c's* of the morning star, *Lover's Tale i* 28
Shut in the secret *c's* of the rock. ,, 521
Death in our innermost *c*, *Def. of Lucknow* 15
read Some wonder at our *c* ornaments. *Columbus* 2
That *c* in the tower. *The Ring* 94
What *c*, child? Your nurse is here? ,, 95
You took me to that *c* in the tower, ,, 111
I brought you to that *c* ,, 129
Chamber-door (*See also* **Chaumber-door**) As lightly as a sick man's *c-d*, *Enoch Arden* 776
Chamberlain call'd A hoary man, his *c*, *Com. of Arthur* 145
Then spake the hoary *c* and said, ,, 148
Chamian Apart the *C* Oracle divine *Alexander* 10
Champaign river-sunder'd *c* clothed with corn, *Œnone* 114
high Above the empurpled *c*, drank the gale *Princess iii* 120
shadowing down the *c* till it strikes On a wood, ,, *v* 526
Champion My *c* from the ashes of his hearth.' *Gareth and L.* 899
c thou hast brought from Arthur's hall? ,, 916
but have ye slain The damsel's *c*? ,, 1099
Lady Lyonors Had sent her coming *c*, ,, 1192
Champion'd *C* our cause and won it *Princess vi* 62
Chance (s) I shut my life from happier *c*. *Two Voices* 54
Many a *c* the years beget. *Miller's D.* 206
For that is not a common *c* *To J. S.* 47
every morning brought a noble *c*, And every *c* brought out a noble knight. *M. d'Arthur* 230
April hopes, the fools of *c*; *Vision of Sin* 164
'Drink to Fortune, drink to *C*, ,, 191
It is beyond all hope, against all *c*, *Enoch Arden* 403
He gave them line: and how by *c* *The Brook* 150
rate your *c* Almost at naked nothing.' *Princess i* 160
With open eyes, and we must take the *c*. ,, *iii* 143
dread His wildness, and the *c's* of the dark.' ,, *iv* 244
will be chaff For every gust of *c*, ,, 356
my flitting *c* Were caught within the record ,, *v* 142
she's comely; there's the fairer *c*: ,, 460
or was it *c*, She past my way. ,, *vi* 97
Dispute the claims, arrange the *c's*; *To F. D. Maurice* 31
And grasps the skirts of happy *c*, *In Mem. lxiv* 6
To *c's* where our lots were cast ,, *xcii* 5
steps of Time—the shocks of *C*— ,, *xcv* 42
And leaps into the future *c*, ,, *cxiv* 7
can a sweeter *c* ever come to me here? *Maud I i* 62
if it had not been For a *c* of travel, ,, *ii* 8
an often *c* In those brain-stunning shocks, *Gareth and L.* 88
some *c* to mar the boast Thy brethren ,, 1242
good *c* that we shall hear the hounds: *Marr. of Geraint* 182
What *c* is this? how is it I see you *Geraint and E.* 309
A common *c*—right well I know it— ,, 331
Guilty or guiltless, to stave off a *c* ,, 353
Their *c* of booty from the morning's raid, ,, 565
ye surely have endured Strange *c's* here alone;' ,, 810
Queen demanded as by *c* 'Know ye the stranger woman?' *Merlin and V.* 128
This *c* of noble deeds will come and go Unchallenged, *Holy Grail* 318
Our fear of some disastrous *c* for thee On hill, ,, 727
Ready to spring, waiting a *c*: *Guinevere* 12
Some evil *c* Will make the smouldering scandal ,, 90
c and craft and strength in single fights, *Pass. of Arthur* 106
every morning brought a noble *c*, And every *c* brought out a noble knight. ,, 398
Above the perilous seas of Change and *C*; *Lover's Tale i* 806
c's of dividend, consol, and share— *The Wreck* 30
Like a clown—by *c* he met me— *Locksley H., Sixty* 256
Chance (verb) when did Arthur *c* upon thee first?' *Com. of Arthur* 338
However that might *c*! *Gareth and L.* 458
boast Thy brethren of thee make—which could not *c*— ,, 1243
Chance-comer You set before *c-c's*, *Will Water.* 6
Chanced It *c* one evening Annie's children *Enoch Arden* 362
At last one night it *c* That Annie could not sleep, ,, 489
Now it *c* that I had been, *Princess i* 31
and if their *c* a joust, *Gareth and L.* 519
then by what thereafter *c*, ,, 1214
At last, it *c* that on a summer morn *Marr. of Geraint* 69
It *c* the song that Enid sang was one ,, 345
with her mind all full of what had *c*, *Geraint and E.* 778
King's own ear Speak what has *c*; ,, 809
Then *c*, one morning, that Sir Balin sat *Balin and Balan* 240
All that had *c*, and Balan moan'd again. ,, 604
And as it *c* they are happy, being pure.' *Merlin and V.* 745
'These jewels, whereupon I *c* Divinely, *Lancelot and E.* 58
one morn it *c* He found her in among the garden yews, ,, 922
I told him what had *c*, My sister's vision, *Holy Grail*, 271
And then I *c* upon a goodly town ,, 573
It *c* that both Brake into hall together *Pelleas and E.* 586

Chanced (*continued*) For thus it *c* one morn when all the court, — *Guinevere* 21
c that, when half of the short summer night was gone, — *The Revenge* 65
and it *c* on a day Soon as the blast — *Def. of Lucknow* 31
Chance-gift eating not, Except the spare *c-g* — *St. S. Stylites* 78
Chancel A broken *c* with a broken cross, — *M. d'Arthur* 9
I peer'd athwart the *c* pane — *The Letters* 3
A broken *c* with a broken cross, — *Pass. of Arthur* 177
and mute below the *c* stones, — *Locksley H., Sixty* 43
Chancel-casement Upon the *c-c*, and upon that grave — *May Queen, N. Y's. E.* 21
Chancellor The *c*, sedate and vain, — *Day-Dm., Revival* 29
C, or what is greatest would he be— — *Aylmer's Field* 397
Chance-met cross-lightnings of four *c-m* eyes — ,, 129
Change (s) Truth may stand forth unmoved of *c*, — *Supp. Confessions* 144
oxen's low Came to her: without hope of *c*, — *Mariana* 29
And airy forms of flitting *c*. — *Madeline* 7
run thro' every *c* of sharp and flat; — *Caress'd or Chidden* 4
I said, 'The years with *c* advance: — *Two Voices* 52
'Then comes the check, the *c*, the fall, — ,, 163
upon the board, And bred this *c*; — *Œnone* 227
fit for every mood And *c* of my still soul. — *Palace of Art* 60
Full-welling fountain-heads of *c*, — ,, 166
but all hath suffer'd *c*: — *Lotos-Eaters, C.S.* 71
'I govern'd men by *c*, and so I sway'd — *D. of F. Women* 130
thro' all *c* Of liveliest utterance. — ,, 167
Lie still, dry dust, secure of *c*. — *To J. S.* 76
Meet is it *c's* should control Our being, — *Love thou thy land* 41
So let the *c* which comes be free — ,, 45
Of many *c's*, aptly join'd, — ,, 65
And sick of home went overseas for *c*. — *Walk. to the Mail* 24
And fear of *c* at home, that drove him hence. — ,, 68
With all the varied *c's* of the dark, — *Edwin Morris* 36
shrivelling thro' me, and a cloudlike *c*, — *St. S. Stylites* 199
Changed with thy mystic *c*, — *Tithonus* 55
spin for ever down the ringing grooves of *c*. — *Locksley Hall* 182
And, rapt thro' many a rosy *c*, — *Day-Dm., Depart* 23
The flower and quintessence of *c*. — ,, *L'Envoi* 24
voice grew faint: there came a further *c*: — *Vision of Sin* 207
came a *c*, as all things human change. — *Enoch Arden* 101
So much to look to—such a *c*— — ,, 461
and the *c* and not the *c*, — *Aylmer's Field* 831
dismal lyrics, prophesying *c* Beyond all reason: — *Princess i* 142
woman wed is not as we, But suffers *c* of frame. — ,, *v* 463
Then came a *c*: for sometimes I would catch — ,, *vii* 92
Till notice of a *c* in the dark world — ,, 250
the *c*, This truthful *c* in thee has kill'd it. — ,, 349
I perceived no touch of *c*, — *In Mem. xiv* 17
The touch of *c* in calm or storm; — ,, *xvi* 6
Each voice four *c's* on the wind, — ,, *xxviii* 9
I have lost the links that bound Thy *c's*; here upon the ground No more partaker of thy *c*. — ,, *xli* 7
we talk'd Of men and minds, the dust of *c*, — ,, *lxxi* 10
There cannot come a mellower *c*, — ,, *lxxxi* 3
For *c's* wrought on form and face; — ,, *lxxxii* 2
Recalls, in *c* of light or gloom, — ,, *lxxxv* 74
Or touch'd the *c's* of the state, — ,, *lxxxix* 35
When summer's hourly-mellowing *c* May breathe, — ,, *xci* 9
abyss Of tenfold-complicated *c*, — ,, *xciii* 12
For *c* of place, like growth of time, — ,, *cv* 11
O earth, what *c's* hast thou seen! — ,, *cxxiii* 2
His very face with *c* of heart is changed. — *Geraint and E.* 899
in *c* of glare and gloom Her eyes and neck — *Merlin and V.* 959
Naked of glory for His mortal *c*, — *Holy Grail* 448
with living waters in the *c* Of seasons: — *Pelleas and E.* 511
Above the perilous seas of *C* and Chance; — *Lover's Tale i* 806
In marvel at that gradual *c*, I thought — ,, *iii* 19
their bridal-time By *c* of feather: — *Sisters (E. and E.)* 72
Glance at the wheeling Orb of *c*, — *To E. Fitzgerald* 3
Over the range and the *c* of the world — *The Wreck* 70
After all the stormy *c's* shall we find — *Locksley H., Sixty* 156
Far away beyond her myriad coming *c's* — ,, 231
Ring little bells of *c* From word to word. — *Early Spring* 41
By *c's* all too fierce and fast — *Freedom* 22
c of the tide—what is all of it worth? — *Vastness* 30

Change (s) (*continued*) glimmer of relief In *c* of place. — *To Mary Boyle* 48
That after many *c's* may succeed Life, — *Prog. of Spring* 116
Change (verb) (*See also* **Chaänge**) All things will *c* Thro' eternity. — *Nothing will Die* 15
It will *c*, but it will not fade — ,, 31
All things will *c*. — ,, 38
Not swift nor slow to *c*, but firm: — *Love thou thy land* 31
Or *c* a word with her he calls his wife, — *Dora* 44
'It cannot be: my uncle's mind will *c*!' — ,, 47
full music seem'd to move and *c* — *Edwin Morris* 35
iris *c's* on the burnish'd dove; — *Locksley Hall* 19
She *c's* with that mood or this, — *Will Water.* 107
'*C*, reverting to the years, — *Vision of Sin* 159
Then came a change, as all things human *c*. — *Enoch Arden* 101
If our old halls could *c* their sex, — *Princess, Pro.* 140
you began to *c*—I saw it and grieved— — ,, *iv* 298
one that wishes at a dance to *c* The music— — ,, 589
When your skies *c* again: — ,, *vi* 278
Some patient force to *c* them when we will, — ,, *Con.* 56
and *c* the hearts of men, — *W. to Marie Alex.* 44
But hearts that *c* not, love that cannot cease, — ,, 46
Nor *c* to us, although they *c*; — *In Mem. xxx* 24
Will *c* my sweetness more and more, — ,, *xxxv* 15
And every winter *c* to spring. — ,, *liv* 16
Thy ransom'd reason *c* replies — ,, *lxi* 2
fly The happy birds, that *c* their sky — ,, *cxv* 15
To *c* the bearing of a word, — ,, *cxxviii* 16
the wind will never *c* again.' — *Gareth and L.* 1140
Let Gareth, an he will, *C* his for mine, — ,, 1300
and the wine will *c* your will.' — *Geraint and E.* 663
The music in him seem'd to *c*, — *Balin and Balan* 217
Must our true man *c* like a leaf at last? — *Lancelot and E.* 686
The twain together well might *c* the world. — *Guinevere* 301
like wild birds that *c* Their season in the night — *Pass. of Arthur* 38
Nevertheless, we did not *c* the name. — *Lover's Tale i* 464
Yet must you *c* your name: — *Sisters (E. and E.)* 69
To *c* with her horizon, — ,, 226
A wish in you To *c* our dark Queen-city, — *To Mary Boyle* 65
Changed (*See also* **Chaänged, Autumn-changed, Counter-changed**) Till all the crimson *c*, and past — *Mariana in the S.* 25
'O cruel heart,' she *c* her tone, — ,, 69
You *c* a wholesome heart to gall. — *L. C. V. de Vere* 44
but ere my flower to fruit *C*, — *D. of F. Women* 208
thy flute-notes are *c* to coarse, — *The Blackbird* 18
We all are *c* by still degrees, — *Love thou thy land* 43
flower of knowledge *c* to fruit Of wisdom. — *Love and Duty* 24
C with thy mystic change, — *Tithonus* 55
And her spirit *c* within. — *L. of Burleigh* 64
the rim *C* every moment as we flew. — *The Voyage* 28
Moved with violence, *c* in hue, — *Vision of Sin* 34
but that name has twice been *c*— — *Enoch Arden* 859
my mind is *c*, for I shall see him, — ,, 897
tost on thoughts that *c* from hue to hue, — *Princess iv* 210
Our mind is *c*: we take it to ourself.' — ,, 362
and her hue *c*, and she said: — ,, *vi* 107
Walk'd at their will, and everything was *c*. — ,, 384
And one is sad; her note is *c*, — *In Mem. xxi* 27
crying, How *c* from where it ran — ,, *xxiii* 9
A grief, then *c* to something else, — ,, *lxxvii* 11
O grief, can grief be *c* to less? — ,, *lxxviii* 16
Thy place is *c*; thou art the same. — ,, *cxxi* 20
Remade the blood and *c* the frame, — ,, *Con.* 11
Of her whose gentle will has *c* my fate, — *Maud I xviii* 23
mood is *c*, for it fell at a time of year — ,, *III vi* 4
Till with a wink his dream was *c*, — *Com. of Arthur* 441
but the wind hath *c*: — *Gareth and L.* 994
'Hath not the good wind, damsel, *c* again?' — ,, 1054
being young, he *c* and came to loathe His crime — *Marr. of Geraint* 593
To fear me, fear no longer, I am *c*. — *Geraint and E.* 825
But kept myself aloof till I was *c*; And fear not, cousin; I am *c* indeed.' — ,, 872
have ye seen how nobly *c*? — ,, 897
His very face with change of heart is *c*. — ,, 899
her hue *C* at his gaze: — *Balin and Balan* 279

Changed (*continued*) And c itself and echo'd in her heart, Lancelot and E. 782
I doubt not that however c, ,, 1218
I was c to wan And meagre, Holy Grail 571
find thy favour c and love thee not '— Last Tournament 500
Denouncing judgment, but tho' c, Guinevere 421
I c the name ; San Salvador I call'd it ; Columbus 75
And c her into dust. Ancient Sage 162
We never c a bitter word, The Flight 86
And then had c ? so fickle are men— The Ring 392
clove the Moslem crescent moon, and c it into blood. Happy 44
I that heard, and c the prayer ,, 55
A man who never c a word with men, St. Telemachus 10
Changeless thee the c in thine ever-changing skies. Akbar's D., Hymn 4
Changeling Or sorrow such a c be ? In Mem. xvi 4
like a fairy c lay the mage ; Com. of Arthur 363
But only c out of Fairyland, Gareth and L. 203
Changest Who c not in any gale, In Mem. ii 10
And c, breathing it, the sullen wind, Prog. of Spring 110
Changeth old order c, yielding place to new, M. d'Arthur 240
old order c, yielding place to new ; Com. of Arthur 509
old order c, yielding place to new, Pass. of Arthur 408
Changing (*See also* **Chaängin'**, **Ever-changing**, **Never-changing**) In c, chime with never-changing Law. To Duke of Argyll 11
Channel (*See also* **Mid-channel**) Tho' every c of the State Should fill You ask me, why 23
the hoary C Tumbles a billow on chalk and sand ; To F. D. Maurice 23
brooks Are fashion'd by the c which they keep), Lover's Tale i 567
We seem'd like ships i' the C First Quarrel 42
may The fated c where thy motion lives De Prof. Two G. 19
Chant In the heart of the garden the merry bird c's. Poet's Mind 22
'C me now some wicked stave, Vision of Sin 151
c the history Of that great race, In Mem. ciii 34
From prime to vespers will I c thy praise Pelleas and E. 349
to the c of funeral hymns. Happy 48
Chanted C loudly, c lowly, L. of Shalott iv 29
C from an ill-used race of men that cleave Lotos-Eaters, C. S. 120
And c a melody loud and sweet, Poet's Song 6
c on the blanching bones of men ?' Princess ii 199
So they c : how shall Britain light Boädicea 45
So they c in the darkness, ,, 46
whose hymns Are c in the minster, Merlin and V. 766
She c snatches of mysterious hymns Lancelot and E. 1407
Had c on the smoky mountain-tops, Guinevere 282
and c the triumph of Finn, V. of Maeldune 48
And we c the songs of the Bards ,, 90
Chanter C of the Pollio, To Virgil 17
Chanting But mine own phantom c hymns ? In Mem. cviii 10
murmur of their temples c me, Me, me, Demeter and P. 72
Chaos C, Cosmos ! Cosmos, C ! (repeat) Locksley H., Sixty 103, 127
Chapel bore him to a c nigh the field, M. d'Arthur 8
To c : where a heated pulpiteer, Sea Dreams 20
The portal of King Pellam's c Balin and Balan 405
In the white rock a c and a hall Lancelot and E. 405
where the vale Was lowest, found a c, Holy Grail 442
bore him to a c nigh the field, Pass. of Arthur 176
Is it you, that preach'd in the c Despair 1
We have knelt in your know-all c ,, 94
Yonder in that c, slowly sinking Locksley H., Sixty 27
Chapel bell the c b's Call'd us : we left the walks ; Princess ii 470
when they toll the C b ! Locksley H., Sixty 261
Chapel-door and against the c d Laid lance, Holy Grail 459
I touch'd The c-d's at dawn I know ; ,, 536
meet you again tomorra,' says he, 'be the c-d.' Tomorrow 16
this body they foun' an the grass Be the c-d, ,, 74
Chapel-green she stept an the c-g, ,, 27
Chapel-yard in the precincts of the c-y, Merlin and V. 751
Then paced for coolness in the c-y ; ,, 757
Chap-fallen The c-f circle spreads : Vision of Sin 172
Chaplet And caught her c here— To Marq. of Dufferin 30
Char Nor ever lightning c thy grain, Talking Oak 277
Character'd laws of marriage c in gold Isabel 16
How dimly c and slight, In Mem. lxi 6

D*

Charade C's and riddles as at Christmas Princess, Pro. 189
Charge (imputation) Redeem'd it from the c of nothingness— M. d'Arthur, Ep. 7
Set up the c ye know, Merlin and V. 703
Merlin answer'd careless of her c, ,, 754
Charge (care) father left him gold, And in my c, Marr. of Geraint 452
And all in c of whom ? a girl : Geraint and E. 125
whom Uther left in c Long since, ,, 933
Modred whom he left in c of all, Guinevere 195
Charge (directions) he gave them c about the Queen, ,, 591
thy c Is an abounding pleasure to me. Gareth and L. 981
Charge (attack) surging c's foam'd themselves away ; Ode on Well. 126
O the wild c they made ! Light Brigade 51
Honour the c they made ! ,, 53
Plunged in the last fierce c at Waterloo, Sisters (E. and E.) 64
The crash of the c's, Batt. of Brunanburh 89
THE c of the gallant three hundred, Heavy Brigade 1
bad his trumpeter sound To the c, ,, 9
The trumpet, the gallop, the c, ,, 13
O mad for the c and the battle were we, ,, 41
Glory to each and to all, and the c that they made ! ,, 65
Charge (to enjoin) Come forth, I c thee, arise, Ode to Memory 46
I c thee, quickly go again M. d'Arthur 79
I c you now, When you shall see her, Enoch Arden 877
I c thee by my love,' Gareth and L. 55
'I c thee, ask not, but obey.' Marr. of Geraint 133
c the gardeners now To pick the faded creature ,, 670
I c thee ride before, Geraint and E. 14
I c thee, on thy duty as a wife, ,, 16
I c you, Enid, more especially, ,, 414
I count it of small use To c you) ,, 417
I c thee by that crown upon thy shield, Balin and Balan 481
I c you, follow me not.' Lancelot and E. 507
I c you that you get at once to horse. ,, 539
Leave me that, I c thee, my last hope. Guinevere 568
I c thee, quickly go again, Pass. of Arthur 247
I c you never to say that I laid him Rizpah 58
'Never surrender, I c you, Def. of Lucknow 10
Charge (to impute) if he did that wrong you c him with, Sea Dreams 279
Charge (to rush) C for the guns !' he said : Light Brigade 6
I myself beheld the King C at the head Lancelot and E. 304
Charge (to load) *See* **Double-charge**
Charged (ordered) Then Arthur c his warrior whom he loved Com. of Arthur 447
c by Valence to bring home the child. Merlin and V. 718
calling her three knights, she c them, Pelleas and E. 219
Charged (attacked) c Before the eyes of ladies and of kings. M. d'Arthur 224
down we swept and c and overthrew. Ode on Well. 130
c Before the eyes of ladies and of kings. Pass. of Arthur 392
Charged (filled) C both mine eyes with tears. D. of F. Women 13
and c the winds With spiced May-sweets Lover's Tale i 317
Charged (loaded) It is c and we fire, and they run. Def. of Lucknow 68
Charged (entrusted) so much wealth as God had c her with— Lover's Tale i 213
Charger When on my goodly c borne Sir Galahad 49
on my c's, trample them under us.' Boädicea 69
and take my c, fresh, Gareth and L. 1300
At once Sir Lancelot's c fiercely neigh'd, ,, 1400
cried, 'My c and her palfrey ;' Marr. of Geraint 126
His c trampling many a prickly star ,, 313
So Enid took his c to the stall ; ,, 382
Call the host and bid him bring C and palfrey.' Geraint and E. 401
Who saw the c's of the two that fell ,, 481
While the great c stood, grieved like a man. ,, 535
See ye take the c too, A noble one.' ,, 555
(His gentle c following him unled) ,, 571
fly, your c is without, ,, 749
When Edyrn rein'd his c at her side, ,, 820
found His c, mounted on him and away. Balin and Balan 418
glad, Knightlike, to find his c yet unlamed, ,, 428
so they overbore Sir Lancelot and his c, and a spear Down-glancing lamed the c, Lancelot and E. 487
from his c down he slid, and sat, ,, 510

Charger (*continued*) Full-arm'd upon his *c* all day long *Pelleas and E.* 216
Charging *C* an army, while All the world wonder'd: *Light Brigade* 30
at the midmost *c*, Prince Geraint Drave *Geraint and E.* 85
Charier *C* of sleep, and wine, and exercise, *Aylmer's Field* 448
Chariot to the lychgate, where his *c* stood, ,, 824
a sound arose of hoof And *c*, *Princess vi* 380
Up my Britons, on my *c*, *Boädicea* 69
her people all around the royal *c* agitated, ,, 73
each beside his *c* bound his own; *Spec. of Iliad* 3
The double tides of *c's* flow *In Mem. xcviii* 23
So those two brethren from the *c* took *Lancelot and E.* 1146
The prophet and the *c* and the steeds, *Lover's Tale i* 307
horses whirl'd The *c's* backward, *Achilles over the T.* 25
died Among their spears and *c's*. ,, 33
watch the *c* whirl About the goal *Tiresias* 176
Chariot-bier let there be prepared a *c-b* *Lancelot and E.* 1121
sad *c-b* Past like a shadow thro' the field, ,, 1139
Charioted Far in the East Boädicéa, standing loftily *c*, *Boädicea* 3
So the Queen Boädicéa, standing loftily *c*, ,, 70
Charioteer the *C* And starry Gemini hang *Maud III vi* 6
sheer-astounded were the *c's* To see the dread, *Achilles over the T.* 26
Charitable To save the offence of *c*, *Enoch Arden* 342
Charity summer calm of golden *c*, *Isabel* 8
And thou of God in thy great *c*) ,, 40
with shafts of gentle satire, kin to *c*, *Princess ii* 469
those fair *charities* Join'd at her side, ,, *vii* 65
A patron of some thirty *charities*, ,, *Con.* 88
Valour and *c* more and more. *To F. D. Maurice* 40
When one small touch of *C* Could lift *Lit. Squabbles* 13
In reverence and in *c*. *In Mem. cxiv* 28
C setting the martyr aflame; *Vastness* 9
Charlatan Defamed by every *c*, *In Mem. cxi* 23
Charles (the Second) Wherein the younger *C* abode *Talking Oak* 297
Charles (the First) From our first *C* by force we wrung our claims. *Third of Feb.* 26
Charles's Wain Till *C W* came out above *May Queen, N. Y's. E.* 12
Charley-Charlie and *C* ploughing the hill. *Grandmother* 80
And Harry and *C*, I hear them too— ,, 81
And little King *C* snarling, *Maud I xii* 30
but 'e leäved it to *C* 'is son, *Village Wife* 42
but *C* 'e cotch'd the pike, ,, 43
But *C* 'e sets back 'is ears, ,, 67
And Squire were at *C* ageän ,, 74
Ya wouldn't find *C's* likes— ,, 75
Theerabouts *C* joompt— ,, 81
thowt it wur *C's* ghoäst i' the derk, ,, 82
But Billy fell bakkuds o' *C*, an' *C* ,, 85
Charlock shone far-off as shines A field of *c* *Gareth and L.* 388
Charm (s) and the *c* of married brows.' *Œnone* 76
A heart that doats on truer *c's*. *L. C. V. de Vere* 14
all his life the *c* did talk About his path, *Day-Dm., Arrival* 21
A TOUCH, a kiss! the *c* was snapt ,, *Revival* 1
c have power to make New lifeblood *Will Water.* 21
Each, its own *c*; and Edith's everywhere; *Aylmer's Field* 165
loose A flying *c* of blushes o'er this cheek, *Princess ii* 430
nameless *c* That none has else for me?' ,, *v* 70
mar their *c* of stainless maidenhood.' *Balin and Balan* 268
For that small *c* of feature mine, pursued— *Merlin and V.* 76
Merlin once had told her of a *c*, ,, 205
see but him who wrought the *c* Coming and going, ,, 212
Vivien ever sought to work the *c*, ,, 215
make me wish still more to learn this *c* ,, 329
c so taught will charm us both to rest. ,, 332
when I told you first of such a *c*. ,, 359
I felt as tho' you knew this cursed *c*, ,, 435
I dreamt Of some vast *c* concluded in that star ,, 512
Giving you power upon me thro' this *c*, ,, 514
try this *c* on whom ye say ye love.' ,, 525
this fair *c* invented by yourself? ,, 540
I needed then no *c* to keep them mine ,, 547
wizard who might teach the King Some *c*, ,, 584
the *c* Of nature in her overbore their own: ,, 595
they found—his foragers for *c's*— ,, 619
save the King, who wrought the *c*, ,, 643
'Ye have the book: the *c* is written in it: ,, 652

Charm (s) (*continued*) To dig, pick, open, find and read the *c*: *Merlin and V.* 660
And every square of text an awful *c*, ,, 673
And in the comment did I find the *c*. ,, 683
mutter'd in himself, 'Tell *her* the *c*! ,, 809
told her all the *c*, and slept. ,, 966
in one moment, she put forth the *c* ,, 967
Wrought as a *c* upon them, *Guinevere* 144
haze to magnify The *c* of Edith— *Sisters (E. and E.)* 130
O they to be dumb'd by the *c*!— *V. of Maeldune* 25
She with all the *c* of woman, *Locksley H., Sixty* 48
Take the *c* 'For ever' from them, ,, 72
the *c* of all the Muses often flowering *To Virgil* 11
I hear a *c* of song thro' all the land. *Prog. of Spring* 47
What *c* in words, a *c* no words *Far-far-away* 16
Charm (verb) wish to *c* Pallas and Juno sitting by: *A Character* 14
seem'd to *c* from thence The wrath I nursed *Princess v* 436
Perchance, to *c* a vacant brain, *The Daisy* 106
bloom profuse and cedar arches *C*, *Milton* 12
c's Her secret from the latest moon?' *In Mem xxi* 19
red berries *c* the bird, *Gareth and L.* 85
charm so taught will *c* us both to rest. *Merlin and V.* 332
then he taught the King to *c* the Queen ,, 641
changing market frets or *c's* *Ancient Sage* 140
C us, Orator, till the Lion look *Locksley H., Sixty* 112
Do your best to *c* the worst, ,, 147
Charm-bound the eye Was riveted and *c-b*, *Lover's Tale ii* 188
Charm'd (*See also* **Anger-charm'd, Love-charm'd**) *c* and tied To where he stands,— *D. of F. Women* 193
C him thro' every labyrinth *Aylmer's Field* 479
the king her father *c* Her wounded soul with words: *Princess vi* 345
So much the gathering darkness *c*: ,, *Con.* 107
sitting round him, idle hands, *C*; *Gareth and L.* 513
golden mist *C* amid eddies of melodious airs, *Lover's Tale i* 450
Charming with a phosphorescence *c* even My Lady; *Aylmer's Field* 116
Charnel Ev'n in the *c's* of the dead, *Two Voices* 215
Charnel-cave When Lazarus left his *c-c*, *In Mem. xxxi* 1
Charr'd and *c* you thro' and thro' within, *Pelleas and E.* 467
sent him *c* and blasted to the deathless fire *Happy* 84
Chart (verb) *c's* us all in its coarse blacks *Walk. to the Mail* 107
Chartered craft seaworthy still, Have *c* this; *Pref. Son., 19th Cent.* 4
Chartist his bailiff brought A *C* pike. *Walk. to the Mail* 71
Chase (s) (*See also* **Chace**) and in the *c* grew wild, *Talking Oak* 126
Follow, follow the *c*! *Window. On the Hill* 11
sleek and shining creatures of the *c*, *Princess v* 155
And reason in the *c*: *Com. of Arthur* 168
And being ever foremost in the *c*, *Geraint and E.* 959
the tide within Red with free *c* *Last Tournament* 691
Chase (verb) rose To *c* the deer at five; *Talking Oak* 52
'*C*,' he said: the ship flew forward, *The Captain* 33
do I *c* The substance or the shadow? *Princess ii* 408
To *c* a creature that was current *Merlin and V.* 408
And bring or *c* the storm, *Mechanophilus* 14
Chased (engraved) hilt, How curiously and strangely *c*, *M. d'Arthur* 86
meadow gemlike *c* In the brown wild, *Geraint and E.* 198
hilt, How curiously and strangely *c*, *Pass of Arthur* 254
Chased (pursued) *c* away the still-recurring gnat, *Caress'd or Chidden* 7
So shape *c* shape as swift as, *D. of F. Women* 37
'A light wind *c* her on the wing, *Talking Oak* 125
but *c* The wisp that flickers where no foot can tread.' *Princess iv* 357
'I have seen the cuckoo *c* by lesser fowl, *Com. of Arthur* 167
c the flashes of his golden horns *Merlin and V.* 427
Who might have *c* and claspt Renown *To Marq. of Dufferin* 29
and *c* away That shadow of a likeness *Demeter and P.* 15
Chasing *C* itself at its own wild will, *Dying Swan* 17
C each other merrily. *The Merman* 20
Chasm (*See also* **Cavern-chasm**) 'Heaven opens inward, *c's* yawn, *Two Voices* 304
in the icy caves And barren *c's*, *M. d'Arthur* 187
lines of cliff breaking have left a *c*; And in the *c* are foam and yellow sands; *Enoch Arden* 1
till drawn thro' either *c*, ,, 670
from the gaps and *c's* of ruin left *Sea Dreams* 225

Chasm (*continued*) Thro' one wide *c* of time and frost *Princess, Pro.* 93
By every coppice-feather'd *c* and cleft, ,, *iv* 23
from the castle gateway by the *c* *Com. of Arthur* 370
little elves of *c* and cleft Made answer, *Guinevere* 248
clash'd his harness in the icy caves And barren *c's*, *Pass. of Arthur* 355
The yawning of an earthquake-cloven *c*. *Lover's Tale i* 377
Flies with a shatter'd foam along the *c*. ,, 383
Clove into perilous *c's* our walls *Def. of Lucknow* 55
black passes and foam-churning *c's*— *Sir J. Oldcastle* 9
blur of earth Left by that closing *c*, *Demeter and P.* 38
of the *c* between Work and Ideal? *Romney's R.* 63
Chasm-like With *c-l* portals open to the sea, *Holy Grail* 815
Chaste world's great bridals, *c* and calm: *Princess, vii* 294
All brave, and many generous, and some *c*. *Merlin and V.* 817
Chasten we love the Heaven that *c's* us. *Geraint and E.* 789
Chastisement brook the rod And *c* of human pride; *Supp. Confessions* 108
May not that earthly *c* suffice? *Aylmer's Field* 784
Chastity With the clear-pointed flame of *c*, *Isabel* 2
she rode forth, clothed on with *c*: *Godiva* 53
she rode back, clothed on with *c*: ,, 65
They bound to holy vows of *c*! *Merlin and V.* 695
To lead sweet lives in purest *c*, *Guinevere* 474
Chatelet The last wild thought of *C*, *Margaret* 37
Chattel Live *c's*, mincers of each other's fame, *Princess, iv* 515
Chatter Would *c* with the cold, and all my beard *St. S. Stylites* 31
I *c* over stony ways, *The Brook* 39
I *c*, *c*, as I flow To join the brimming river, ,, 47
crane,' I said, 'may *c* of the crane, *Princess iii* 104
then to hear a dead man *c* Is enough *Maud II v* 19
Chatter'd Philip *c* more than brook or bird; *The Brook* 51
They *c* trifles at the door: *In Mem. lxix* 4
Chatterer Begotten by enchantment—*c's* they, *Holy Grail* 145
Chattering (part.) *c* stony names Of shale and hornblende,' *Princess iii* 361
Chattering (s) Chafferings and *c's* at the market-cross, *Holy Grail* 558
Chaucer (Dan) *See* **Dan Chaucer**
Chaumber (chamber) i' my oän blue *c* to me. *Spinster's S's.* 80
Thou slep i' the *c* above us, *Owd Roä* 49
Roäver was theere i' the *c* ,, 88
Chaumber door (chamber door) thy *c d* wouldn't sneck; ,, 64
Chaunt (*See also* **Chant**) I would mock thy *c* anew; *The Owl ii* 8
And solemn *c's* resound between. *Sir Galahad* 36
Chaunteth *C* not the brooding bee *A Dirge* 16
Cheap had holden the power and glory of Spain so *c* *The Revenge* 106
Cheat (s) Yet, if she were not a *c*, (repeat) *Maud I vi* 35, 91
Scarcely, now, would I call him a *c*; ,, *xiii* 29
Cheat (verb) love to *c* yourself with words: *Princess vii* 334
C and be cheated, and die: *Maud I i* 32
Cheated (*See also* **Half-cheated**) Cheat and be *c*, and die: ,, 32
Cheating *c* the sick of a few last gasps, ,, 43
Check (s) 'Then comes the *c*, the change, *Two Voices* 163
With motions, *c's*, and counterchecks. ,, 300
Check (verb) too noble' he said 'to *c* at pies, *Merlin and V.* 126
the good nuns would *c* her gadding tongue *Guinevere* 313
c me too Nor let me shame my father's memory, ,, 317
pray you *c* me if I ask amiss— ,, 324
Check'd and *c* His power to shape: *Lucretius* 22
Here the King's calm eye Fell on, and *c*, *Gareth and L.* 548
there he *c* himself and paused. *Pelleas and E.* 527
Cheek (*See also* **Maiden-cheek**) The red *c* paling, The strong limbs failing; *All things will Die* 31
laughters dimple The baby-roses in her *c's*; *Lilian* 17
then the tears run down my *c*, *Oriana* 69
That dimples your transparent *c*, *Margaret* 15
Tie up the ringlets on your *c*: ,, 57
And your *c*, whose brilliant hue *Rosalind* 39
Leaning his *c* upon his hand, *Eleänore* 118
Returning with hot *c* and kindled eyes. *Alexander* 14
Tho' one should smite him on the *c*, *Two Voices* 251
c Flush'd like the coming of the day; *Miller's D.* 131
Her *c* had lost the rose, and round her neck *Œnone* 18
his *c* brighten'd as the foam-bow brightens ,, 61
eye Over her snow-cold breast and angry *c* Kept watch, ,, 142

Cheek (*continued*) His ruddy *c* upon my breast. *The Sisters* 20
with puff'd *c* the belted hunter blew *Palace of Art* 63
From *c* and throat and chin. ,, 140
along the brain, And flushes all the *c*. *D. of F. Women* 44
with swarthy *c's* and bold black eyes, ,, 127
A word could bring the colour to my *c*; *Gardener's D.* 196
clapt him on the hands and on the *c's*, *Dora* 133
laughter dimpled in his swarthy *c*; *Edwin Morris* 61
and pat The girls upon the *c*, *Talking Oak* 44
'Then flush'd her *c* with rosy light, ,, 165
Thy *c* begins to redden thro' the gloom, *Tithonus* 37
and thy tears are on my *c*. ,, 45
Then her *c* was pale and thinner *Locksley Hall* 21
On her pallid *c* and forehead came a colour ,, 25
the barking cur Made her *c* flame: *Godiva* 58
While, dreaming on your damask *c*, *Day-Dm., Pro.* 3
The blush is fix'd upon her *c*. *Day-Dm., Sleep. P.* 32
The colour flies into his *c's*: ,, *Arrival* 19
C by jowl, and knee by knee: *Vision of Sin* 84
Flamed in his *c*; and eager eyes, *Aylmer's Field* 66
Cooling her false *c* with a featherfan, ,, 289
yet her *c* Kept colour: wondrous! ,, 505
On glassy water drove his *c* in lines; *Princess i* 116
when the king Kiss'd her pale *c*, ,, *ii* 264
blew the swoll'n *c* of a trumpeter, ,, 364
flying charm of blushes o'er this *c*, ,, 430
but my *c* Began to burn and burn, ,, *iii* 45
till over brow And *c* and bosom brake ,, *iv* 383
my Sire, his rough *c* wet with tears, ,, *v* 23
And so belabour'd him on rib and *c* ,, 341
wan was her *c* With hollow watch, ,, *vi* 144
I love not hollow *c* or faded eye: ,, *vii* 7
wordless broodings on the wasted *c*— ,, 112
'The *c's* drop in; the body bows *In Mem. xxxv* 3
A touch of shame upon her *c*: ,, *xxxvii* 10
Come; let us go: your *c's* are pale; ,, *lvii* 5
To clap their *c's*, to call them mine. ,, *lxxxiv* 18
fan my brows and blow The fever from my *c*, ,, *lxxxvi* 9
beam of an eyelash dead on the *c*, *Maud I iii* 3
Roses are her *c's*, And a rose her mouth (repeat) *Maud I xvii* 7, 27
but speak Of my mother's faded *c* ,, *xix* 19
this was what had redden'd her *c* ,, 65
and a *c* of apple-blossom, Hawk-eyes; *Gareth and L.* 589
Struck at him with his whip, and cut his *c*. *Marr. of Geraint* 207
Whom first she kiss'd on either *c*, ,, 517
Made her *c* burn and either eyelid fall, ,, 775
Made her *c* burn and either eyelid fall. *Geraint and E.* 434
so there lived some colour in your *c*, ,, 621
spearman let his *c* Bulge with the unswallow'd piece, ,, 630
However lightly, smote her on the *c*. ,, 718
White was her *c*: sharp breaths of anger puff'd *Merlin and V.* 848
Seam'd with an ancient swordcut on the *c*, *Lancelot and E.* 258
c did catch the colour of her words. *Lover's Tale i* 569
bent above me, too; Wan was her *c*; ,, 694
c's as bright as when she climb'd the hill. ,, *iii* 47
As well as the plump *c*— *Sisters (E. and E.)* 184
kiss fell chill as a flake of snow on the *c*: *The Wreck* 32
to feel his breath Upon my *c*— *The Flight* 46
Yet tho' this *c* be gray, *Epilogue* 7
Each poor pale *c* a momentary rose— *The Ring* 315
rounder *c* had brighten'd into bloom. ,, 351
her lips Were warm upon my *c*, ,, 399
From off the rosy *c* of waking Day. *Akbar's Dream* 202
Cheek'd *See* **Apple-cheek'd**
Cheep *c* and twitter twenty million loves. *Princess iv* 101
Cheeping birds that circle round the tower Are *c* to each other *The Ring* 86
Cheer (s) flowers would faint at your cruel *c*. *Poet's Mind* 15
Died the sound of royal *c*; *L. of Shalott iv* 48
Naked I go, and void of *c*: *Two Voices* 239
A murmur, 'Be of better *c*.' ,, 429
Welcome her, thundering *c* of the street! *W. to Alexandra* 7
With festal *c*, With books and music, *In Mem. cvii* 21
And I make myself such evil *c*, *Maud I xv* 2

Cheer (s) (*continued*) With all good *c*, He spake and laugh'd, — Gareth and L. 301
Enid brought sweet cakes to make them *c*, — Marr. of Geraint 388
cried Geraint for wine and goodly *c* — Geraint and E. 283
lily maid had striven to make him *c*, — Lancelot and E. 327
Yet with good *c* he spake, — Pelleas and E. 240
Highlanders answer with conquering *c's*, — Def. of Lucknow 99
hard rocks, hard life, hard *c*, or none, — Sir J. Oldcastle 6
guest may make True *c* with honest wine— — Pro. to Gen. Hamley 16
men gallopt up with a *c* and a shout, — Heavy Brigade 61
Cheer (verb) Annie, come, *c* up before I go.' — Enoch Arden 200
'Annie, my girl, *c* up, be comforted, — ,, 218
Cheer'd And he *c* her soul with love. — L. of Burleigh 68
But he *c* me, my good man, — Grandmother 69
And we with singing *c* the way, — In Mem. xxii 5
Be *c* with tidings of the bride, — ,, xl 23
he spake and *c* his Table Round — Com. of Arthur 267
Nor ever *c* you with a kindly smile, — The Ring 388
Cheerful It wellnigh made her *c*; — Geraint and E. 443
grew so *c* that they deem'd her death — Lancelot and E. 1131
Cheerfully Enoch bore his weakness *c*. — Enoch Arden 827
Cheerful-minded Be *c-m*, talk and treat Of all things — In Mem. cvii 19
Cheerfulness hold out the lights of *c*; — Lover's Tale i 807
Cheque violates virgin Truth for a coin or a *c*. — The Dawn 15
Chequer-work A *c-w* of beam and shade — In Mem. lxxii 15
Cherish *c* that which bears but bitter fruit? — Locksley Hall 65
The love of all Thy daughters *c* Thee, — Ded. of Idylls 53
grace Thy climbing life, and *c* my prone year, — Gareth and L. 95
Cherish'd fed, and *c* him, and saved his life. — Lover's Tale iv 264
Cherry To catch a dragon in a *c* net, — Princess v 169
Cherub There is no being pure, My *c*; — Merlin and V. 52
Chess our wine and *c* beneath the planes, — Princess vi 246
Chest (part of body) like monstrous apes they crush'd my *c*: — St. S. Stylites 174
Live long, nor feel in head or *c* — Will Water. 237
big voice, big *c*, big merciless hands! — In the Child. Hosp. 4
The tiger spasms tear his *c*, — Ancient Sage 123
Chest (box) She took the little ivory *c*, — The Letters 17
For keep it like a puzzle *c* in *c*, With each *c* lock'd and padlock'd — Merlin and V. 654
—a *c* there, by which you knelt— — The Ring 112
There, the *c* was open—all The sacred relics — ,, 446
Chested *See* **Deep-chested**
Chestnut (tree) Or those three *c's* near, that hung — Miller's D. 55
I came and sat Below the *c's*, — ,, 60
While those full *c's* whisper by. — ,, 168
in the *c* shade I found the blue Forget-me-not. — ,, 201
Parks with oak and *c* shady, — L. of Burleigh 29
I see the slowly-thickening *c* towers — Prog. of Spring 42
Chestnut (fruit) *c*, when the shell Divides threefold (repeat) — The Brook 72, 207
The *c* pattering to the ground: — In Mem. xi 4
Chestnut-bloom that islet in the *c-b* Flamed in his cheek; — Aylmer's Field 65
Chestnut-bud drooping *c-b's* began To spread — Sir L. and Q. G. 16
Chew'd *c* The thrice-turn'd cud of wrath, — Princess i 65
Chick Sir *C*, that scarce hast broken shell — Balin and Balan 568
Or else Sir *C*—dismount and loose their casques — ,, 573
Chid be friends, like children being *c*! — Princess vi 289
C her, and forbid her to speak To me, — Maud I xix 63
Chidden Caress'd or *c* by the slender hand, — Caress'd or Chidden 1
Chief answer'd Lancelot, the *c* of knights: (repeat) — Lancelot and E. 140, 187
guess thee *c* of those, After the King, — ,, 183
heads of *c's* and princes fall so fast, — Aylmer's Field 763
an Eagle rising or, the Sun In dexter *c*; — Merlin and V. 476
she that seem'd the *c* among them said, — Pelleas and E. 62
Child (*See also* **Bairn, Childer, Children**) Fed thee, a *c*, lying alone, — Eleänore 25
A glorious *c*, dreaming alone, — ,, 27
One walk'd between his wife and *c*, — Two Voices 412
features of her *c* Ere it is born: her *c*! — Œnone 252
never *c* be born of me, Unblest, — ,, 254
You should not fret for me, mother, you have another *c*, — May Queen, N. Y's. E. 36
Child (*continued*) She'll be a better *c* to you than ever I have been. — May Queen, N. Y's. E. 44
dream of Fatherland, Of *c*, and wife, — Lotos-Eaters 40
With that fair *c* betwixt them born. — On a Mourner 25
Dora took the *c*, and went her way — Dora 71
none of all his men Dare tell him Dora waited with the *c*; — ,, 76
she rose and took The *c* once more, — ,, 81
Whose *c* is that? What are you doing here? — ,, 88
answer'd softly, 'This is William's *c*!' — ,, 90
take the *c*, And bless him for the sake of him that's gone!' — ,, 93
work for William's *c*, until he grows Of age — ,, 126
a-begging for myself, Or William, or this *c*; — ,, 142
three hours he sobb'd o'er William's *c* — ,, 167
cling About the darling *c*: — Talking Oak 128
O, the *c* too clothes the father — Locksley Hall 91
barbarian lower than the Christian *c*. — ,, 174
that *c's* heart within the man's Begins — Will Water. 31
'I speak the truth: you are my *c*. — Lady Clare 24
I buried her like my own sweet *c*, And put my *c* in her stead.' — ,, 27
'Nay now, my *c*,' said Alice the nurse, (repeat) — ,, 33, 41
Alas, my *c*, I sinn'd for thee.' — ,, 50
C, if it were thine error or thy crime — Come not, when, etc. 7
from the palace came a *c* of sin, — Vision of Sin 5
And give his *c* a better bringing-up — Enoch Arden 87
how should the *c* Remember this?' — ,, 233
the third *c* was sickly-born and grew Yet sicklier, — ,, 261
fears were common to her state, Being with *c*: but when her *c* was born, Then her new *c* — ,, 522
marriage, and the birth Of Philip's *c*: — ,, 709
darling Katie Willows, his one *c*! — The Brook 67
His only *c*, his Edith whom he loved — Aylmer's Field 23
Nursing a *c*, and turning to the warmth — ,, 185
—who could trust a *c*? — ,, 264
Their *c*.' 'Our *c*!' 'Our heiress!' — ,, 297
and because I love their *c* They hate me: — ,, 423
and read Writhing a letter from his *c*, — ,, 517
Of such a love as like a chidden *c*, — ,, 541
He seldom crost his *c* without a sneer; — ,, 562
praying him To speak before the people of her *c*, — ,, 608
The poor *c* of shame The common care — ,, 687
all the gentle attributes Of his lost *c*, — ,, 731
Is not our own *c* on the narrow way, — ,, 743
The childless mother went to seek her *c*; — ,, 829
in the narrow gloom By wife and *c*; — ,, 841
His wife, an unknown artist's orphan *c*— — Sea Dreams 2
Virgin Mother standing with her *c* — ,, 242
the *c* Clung to the mother, and sent out a cry — ,, 244
And mine but from the crying of a *c*.' — ,, 249
'*C*? No!' said he, 'but this tide's roar, — ,, 250
Good man, to please the *c*. — ,, 267
voice (You spoke so loud) has roused the *c* again. — ,, 281
flock'd at noon His tenants, wife and *c*, — Princess, Pro. 4
Half *c* half woman as she was, — ,, 101
they must lose the *c*, assume The woman: — ,, i 137
odes About this losing of the *c*; — ,, 141
when we came where lies the *c* We lost in other years, — ,, ii 10
Your language proves you still the *c*. — ,, 58
At her left, a *c*, In shining draperies, — ,, 108
turn'd to go, but Cyril took the *c*, — ,, 362
the *c* Push'd her flat hand against his face — ,, 365
call'd For Psyche's *c* to cast it from the doors; — ,, iv 238
on the purple footcloth, lay The lily-shining *c*; — ,, 287
For this lost lamb (she pointed to the *c*) — ,, 361
and a hope The *c* of regal compact, — ,, 421
live, dear lady, for your *c*!' — ,, v 80
my babe, my blossom, ah, my *c*, My one sweet *c*, whom I shall see no more! — ,, 82
when they say The *c* is hers—for every little fault, The *c* is hers; — ,, 87
My babe, my sweet Aglaïa, my one *c*: — ,, 101
Who gave me back my *c*?' — ,, 105
You have spoilt this *c*; she laughs at you — ,, 116
Our chiefest comfort is the little *c* — ,, 430
c shall grow To prize the authentic mother — ,, 432

Child (*continued*) the training of a *c* Is woman's wisdom.' *Princess v* 465
Set his *c* upon her knee— ,, *vi* 14
'Sweet my *c*, I live for thee.' ,, 16
Knelt on one knee,—the *c* on one,— ,, 91
She bow'd, she set the *c* on the earth; ,, 120
not yours, but mine: give me the *c*' ,, 141
The mother, me, the *c*; ,, 153
give her the *c*! (repeat) *Princess v* 168, 179, 183
twilight mellowing, dwelt Full on the *c*; *Princess v* 192
Ida spoke not, rapt upon the *c*. ,, 220
Blanche had gone, but left Her *c* among us, ,, *vii* 57
old world of ours is but a *c* Yet in the go-cart. ,, *Con.* 77
love not this French God, the *c* of Hell, *Third of Feb.* 7
But I wept like a *c* that day, *Grandmother* 64
wept like a *c* for the *c* that was dead ,, 68
King is happy In *c* and wife; *The Victim* 26
She cast her arms about the *c*. ,, 32
The *c* was only eight summers old, ,, 33
'They have taken the *c* To spill his blood ,, 43
Poor *c*, that waitest for thy love! *In Mem. vi* 28
They call'd me fool, they call me *c*: ,, *lxix* 13
find in *c* and wife An iron welcome ,, *xc* 7
Familiar to the stranger's *c*; ,, *ci* 20
c would twine A trustful hand, unask'd, in thine, ,, *cix* 18
Half-grown as yet, a *c*, and vain— ,, *cxiv* 9
With wisdom, like the younger *c*: ,, 20
No, like a *c* in doubt and fear: ,, *cxxiv* 17
Then was I as a *c* that cries, ,, 19
I play'd with the girl when a *c*; *Maud I i* 68
O *c*, you wrong your beauty, ,, *iv* 17
I have play'd with her when a *c*; ,, *vi* 87
For then, perhaps, as a *c* of deceit, ,, *xiii* 30
Made her only the *c* of her mother, ,, 40
desire that awoke in the heart of the *c*, ,, *xix* 48
one fair daughter, and none other *c*; *Com. of Arthur* 2
split the mother's heart Spitting the *c*, ,, 39
surely would have torn the *c* Piecemeal among them, ,, 217
Wherefore Merlin took the *c*, ,, 221
Or else the *c* of Anton, and no king, ,, 233
Arthur were the *c* of shamefulness, ,, 239
dried my tears, being a *c* with me. ,, 350
So that the *c* and he were clothed in fire. ,, 390
same *c*,' he said, 'Is he who reigns; ,, 392
The shining dragon and the naked *c* ,, 399
this King thine only *c*, Guinevere: ,, 413
the good mother holds me still a *c*! *Gareth and L.* 15
'Mother, tho' ye count me still the *c*, Sweet mother, do ye love the *c*?' ,, 34
'Then, mother, an ye love the *c*,' ,, 37
Hear the *c's* story.' ,, 39
'An ye hold me yet for *c*, Hear yet once more the story of the *c*. ,, 99
all day long hath rated at her *c*, ,, 1285
'My fair *c*, What madness made thee challenge ,, 1415
Had married Enid, Yniol's only *c*, *Marr. of Geraint* 4
dear *c* hath often heard me praise ,, 434
O noble host, For this dear *c*, ,, 497
'See here, my *c*, how fresh the colours ,, 680
Look on it, *c*, and tell me if ye know it.' ,, 684
worn My faded suit, as you, my *c*, ,, 706
my dear *c* is set forth at her best, ,, 728
your fair *c* shall wear your costly gift ,, 819
wail ye for him thus? ye seem a *c*. *Geraint and E.* 547
Make knight or churl or *c* or damsel seem *Balin and Balan* 162
plumed with green replied, 'Peace, *c*! *Merlin and V.* 90
neither eyes nor tongue—O stupid *c*! ,, 251
Your pardon, *c*. Your pretty sports have brighten'd all again. ,, 304
In you, that are no *c*, for still I find Your face ,, 366
a mere *c* Might use it to the harm of anyone, ,, 684
One *c* they had; it lived with her: ,, 716
charged by Valence to bring home the *c*. ,, 718
I ask you, is it clamour'd by the *c*, ,, 771
bitter weeping like a beaten *c*, ,, 855
moral *c* without the craft to rule, *Lancelot and E.* 146

Child (*continued*) 'True, my *c*. Well, I will wear it: *Lancelot and E.* 370
'Do me this grace, my *c*, to have my shield ,, 382
Sir Modred's brother, and the *c* of Lot, ,, 558
the diamond: wit ye well, my *c*, ,, 771
kiss the *c* That does the task assign'd, ,, 828
Meeker than any *c* to a rough nurse, ,, 857
Milder than any mother to a sick *c*, ,, 858
'O my *c*, ye seem Light-headed, ,, 1062
Yet, seeing you desire your *c* to live, ,, 1095
kiss'd me saying, "Thou are fair, my *c*, ,, 1409
I saw the fiery face as of a *c* *Holy Grail* 466
winding wall of rock Heard a *c* wail. *Last Tournament* 12
thro' the wind Pierced ever a *c's* cry: ,, 17
Vext her with plaintive memories of the *c*: ,, 29
that unhappy *c* Past in her barge: ,, 44
Queen White-robed in honour of the stainless *c*, ,, 147
whimpering of the spirit of the *c*, ,, 418
Arthur make me pure As any maiden *c*? ,, 693
'Will the *c* kill me with her innocent talk?' *Guinevere* 214
'Will the *c* kill me with her foolish prate?' ,, 225
They found a naked *c* upon the sands ,, 293
'The simple, fearful *c* Meant nothing, ,, 369
too-fearful guilt, Simpler than any *c*, ,, 371
'Liest thou here so low, the *c* of one I honour'd, ,, 422
Well is it that no *c* is born of thee. ,, 424
wife and *c* with wail Pass to new lords; *Pass. of Arthur* 44
Or Cowardice, the *c* of lust for gold, *To the Queen ii* 54
Which to the imprison'd spirit of the *c*, *Lover's Tale i* 204
Had thrust his wife and *c* and dash'd himself ,, 380
you may hear The moaning of the woman and the *c*, ,, 520
at last he freed himself From wife and *c*, ,, *iv* 380
I was a *c*, an' he was a *c*, an' he came *First Quarrel* 23
told it me all at once, as simple as any *c*, ,, 58
You'll have her to nurse my *c*, ,, 70
when he was but a *c*— *Rizpah* 25
The wind that 'ill wail like a *c* ,, 72
You never have borne a *c*— ,, 80
My father with a *c* on either knee, A hand upon the head of either *c*, *Sisters* (*E. and E.*) 54
Here's to your happy union with my *c*! ,, 68
widow with less guile than many a *c*. ,, 182
desire that her lost *c* Should earn ,, 250
here She bore a *c*, whom reverently we call'd Edith; ,, 268
gratefullest heart I have found in a *c* of her years— *In the Child. Hosp.* 32
the *c* didn't see I was there. ,, 44
I had sat three nights by the *c*— ,, 59
and we went to see to the *c*. ,, 68
I sorrow for that kindly *c* of Spain *Columbus* 212
OUT of the deep, my *c*, (repeat) *De Prof. Two G.* 1, 5, 26, 29
I am roused by the wail of a *c*, *The Wreck* 7
The *c* that I felt I could die for— ,, 36
That day my nurse had brought me the *c*. ,, 59
I thought of the *c* for a moment, ,, 84
I shall look on the *c* again. ,, 124
'O *c*, I am coming to thee.' ,, 134
I pray'd—'my *c*'—for I still could pray— ,, 138
Was it well with the *c*? ,, 141
Godless Jeptha vows his *c* . . . *The Flight* 26
that smiles at her sleepin' *c*— *Tomorrow* 26
Amy was a timid *c*; *Locksley H., Sixty* 19
dead the mother, dead the *c*. ,, 36
Edith but a *c* of six— ,, 258
wife and his *c* stood by him in tears, *Dead Prophet* 57
And warms the *c's* awakening world *Prin. Beatrice* 5
from her household orbit draws the *c* ,, 7
the *c* Is happy—ev'n in leaving *her*! ,, 11
can no more, thou camest, O my *c*, *Demeter and P.* 4
Queen of the dead no more—my *c*! ,, 18
C, those imperial, disimpassion'd eyes ,, 23
here, my *c*, tho' folded in thine arms, ,, 40
C, when thou wert gone, I envied human wives, ,, 52
do ye make your moaning for my *c*?' ,, 65
the *c* Of thee, the great Earth-Mother, ,, 96

Child (*continued*) *c*, Because I hear your Mother's voice in yours. *The Ring* 27
for we, my *c*, Have been till now each other's all-in-all. ,, 52
you the livelong guardian of the *c*. ,, 54
This ring bequeath'd you by your mother, *c*. ,, 75
C, I am happier in your happiness ,, 90
What chamber, *c*? Your nurse is here? ,, 95
but the *c* Is paler than before. ,, 326
forgotten it was your birthday, *c*— ,, 378
Kiss me *c* and go. ,, 489
Mother, dare you kill your *c*? *Forlorn* 37
I see the picture yet, Mother and *c*. *Romney's R.* 81
a *c* Had shamed me at it— ,, 111
and he loved to dandle the *c*, *Bandit's Death* 15
the birth of a baseborn *c*. *Charity* 28
For Babylon was a *c* new-born, *The Dawn* 9
Child-birth Lies my Amy dead in *c-b*, *Locksley H., Sixty* 36
Dying in *c-b* of dead sons. *Akbar's Dream* 12
Childer (children) thebbe all wi' the Lord my *c*, *Village Wife* 13
all es one, the *c* an' me, ,, 55
has now ten *c*, hansome an' tall, *Tomorrow* 85
Him an' his *c* wor keenin' ,, 86
But I niver not wish'd fur *c*, *Spinster's S's.* 84
Childhood when the dawn of rosy *c* past, *Enoch Arden* 37
Ere *c's* flaxen ringlet turn'd *In Mem. lxxix* 15
up from *c* shape His action like the greater ape, ,, *cxx* 10
One, that had loved him from his *c*, *Gareth and L.* 53
In the Maydews of *c*, *Lover's Tale i* 188
pillars which from earth uphold Our *c*, ,, 221
As was our *c*, so our infancy, ,, 249
A monument of *c* and of love; The poesy of *c*; ,, *ii* 183
Him the Mighty, Who taught me in *c*, *Merlin and the G.* 115
Childlike lose the *c* in the larger mind; *Princess vii* 284
Child-lover Lord of human tears; *C-l*; *To Victor Hugo* 4
Children (*See also* **Child, Childer, Men-children**)
May c *of our* c *say*, *To the Queen* 23
And *c* all seem full of Thee! *Supp. Confessions* 21
Two *c* in two neighbour villages *Circumstance* 1
Two *c* in one hamlet born and bred; ,, 8
I have been to blame. Kiss me, my *c*.' *Dora* 162
Not in our time, nor in our *c's* time, *Golden Year* 55
mothers brought Their *c*, clamouring, *Godiva* 15
Three fair *c* first she bore him, *L. of Burleigh* 87
Three *c* of three houses, *Enoch Arden* 11
In this the *c* play'd at keeping house. ,, 24
With *c*; first a daughter. ,, 84
To see his *c* leading evermore Low miserable lives ,, 115
When he was gone—the *c*—what to do? ,, 132
if he cared For her or his dear *c*, ,, 164
Her and her *c*, let her plead in vain; ,, 166
by the love you bear Him and his *c* ,, 308
yet he sent Gifts by the *c*, ,, 338
Philip was her *c's* all-in-all; ,, 348
Annie's *c* long'd To go with others, ,, 362
But when the *c* pluck'd at him to go, ,, 369
I fain would prove A father to your *c*; ,, 411
Up came the *c* laden with their spoil; ,, 445
And his own *c* tall and beautiful, ,, 762
Lord of his rights and of his *c's* love,— ,, 764
My *c* too! must I not speak to these? ,, 788
But if my *c* care to see me dead, ,, 888
A childly way with *c*, and a laugh Ringing *Aylmer's Field* 181
they talk'd, Poor *c*, for their comfort: ,, 427
Bodies, but souls—thy *c's*— ,, 672
Will there be *c's* laughter in their hall ,, 787
That love to keep us *c*! *Princess, Pro.* 133
they had but been, she thought, As *c*; ,, *i* 137
baser courses, *c* of despair.' ,, *iii* 213
every woman counts her due, Love, *c*, happiness?' ,, 245
c, would they grew Like field-flowers ,, 251
But *c* die; and let me tell you, girl, ,, 253
C—that men may pluck them from our hearts, ,, 257
O—*c*—there is nothing upon earth ,, 259
Whose name is yoked with *c's*, ,, *v* 418
Kiss and be friends, like *c* being chid! ,, *vi* 289

Children (*continued*) the *c* call, and I Thy shepherd pipe, *Princess vii* 217
Late the little *c* clung: *Ode on Well.* 237
But all my *c* have gone before me, *Grandmother* 18
But as to the *c*, Annie, they're all about me yet. ,, 76
Phantom wail of women and *c*, *Boädicea* 26
For by the hearth the *c* sit *In Mem. xx* 13
Who takes the *c* on his knee, ,, *lxvi* 11
Timour-Mammon grins on a pile of *c's* bones, *Maud I i* 46
wolf would steal The *c* and devour, *Com. of Arthur* 27
and the *c*, housed In her foul den, ,, 29
at tourney once, When both were *c*, *Gareth and L.* 533
And *c* of the King in cloth of gold *Marr. of Geraint* 664
all the *c* in their cloth of gold Ran to her, ,, 668
The cry of *c*, Enids and Geraints *Geraint and E.* 965
As *c* learn, be thou Wiser for falling! *Balin and Balan* 75
In *c* a great curiousness be well, *Merlin and V.* 364
Where *c* cast their pins and nails, ,, 430
To one at least, who hath not *c*, ,, 506
Lives for his *c*, ever at its best And fullest; *Lancelot and E.* 336
And mirthful sayings, *c* of the place, *Holy Grail* 555
Where *c* sat in white with cups of gold, *Last Tournament* 142
The *c* born of thee are sword and fire, *Guinevere* 425
Who either for his own or *c's* sake, ,, 513
When Harry an' I were *c*, *First Quarrel* 10
dogs of Seville, the *c* of the devil, *The Revenge* 30
'We have *c*, we have wives, ,, 92
God help the wrinkled *c* that are Christ's *Sisters (E. and E.)* 183
I am sure that some of our *c* would die *In the Child. Hosp.* 11
They are all his *c* here, ,, 19
we past to this ward where the younger *c* are laid: ,, 27
'Little *c* should come to me.' ,, 50
I find that it always can please Our *c*, the dear Lord Jesus with *c* about his knees.) ,, 52
Lord of the *c* had heard her, ,, 72
Women and *c* among us, God help them, our *c* *Def. of Lucknow* 8
'*C* and wives—if the tigers leap ,, 51
Grief for our perishing *c*, ,, 89
women and *c* come out, ,, 100
Their wives and *c* Spanish concubines, *Columbus* 175
they play'd with The *c* of Edward. *Batt. of Brunanburh* 92
clouds themselves are *c* of the Sun. *Ancient Sage* 242
Day and Night are *c* of the Sun, ,, 245
evil thought may soil thy *c's* blood; ,, 275
Happy *c* in a sunbeam sitting *Locksley H., Sixty* 14
City *c* soak and blacken soul ,, 218
laborious, Patient *c* of Albion, *On Jub. Q. Victoria* 59
Household happiness, gracious *c*, *Vastness* 24
Father's fault Visited on the *c*! *The Ring* 176
Innocent maidens, Garrulous *c*, *Merlin and the G.* 56
That wife and *c* drag an Artist down! *Romney's R.* 38
'Why left you wife and *c*? ,, 129
nurse my *c* on the milk of Truth, *Akbar's Dream* 162
Ah, that will *our c* be, *The Dawn* 24
Chill But he is *c* to praise or blame. *Two Voices* 258
Then fearing night and *c* for Annie, *Enoch Arden* 443
Bright was that afternoon, Sunny but *c*: ,, 670
As wan, as *c*, as wild as now: *In Mem. lxxii* 17
and dark the night and *c*! *Guinevere* 168
and dark and *c* the night! ,, 174
Whereof the *c*, to him who breathed it, *Pass. of Arthur* 96
'not even death Can *c* you all at once:' *Lover's Tale iv* 77
But he sent a *c* to my heart when I saw him *In the Child. Hosp.* 2
kiss fell *c* as a flake of snow on the cheek: *The Wreck* 32
His winter *c's* him to the root, *Ancient Sage* 119
Chill'd heavens Stifled and *c* at once; *Aylmer's Field* 613
Would that have *c* her bride-kiss? *Last Tournament* 590
He *c* the popular praises of the King *Guinevere* 13
The very fountains of her life were *c*; *Sisters (E. and E.)* 266
fell from that half-spiritual height *C*, *To E. Fitzgerald* 20
Chilling *c* his caresses By the coldness *Maud I xx* 12
like a phantom pass *C* the night: *Gareth and L.* 1336
Chillness Whose *c* would make visible *Supp. Confessions* 59
c of the sprinkled brook Smote on my brows, *Lover's Tale I* 635

Christian (*continued*) I shudder at the *C* and the stake ; *Akbar's Dream* 72
in praise of Whom The *C* bell, ,, 149
The *C's* own a Spiritual Head ; ,, 153
Call'd on the Power adored by the *C*, *Kapiolani* 32
Christian Church if it be a *C C*, people ring the bell for love to Thee. *Akbar's D. Inscrip.* 4
Christ Jesus of Him who died for men, *C J* !' *St. Telemachus* 64
Christless *C* code, That must have life *Maud II i* 26
Pellam, once A *C* foe of thine *Balin and Balan* 97
fury of peoples, and *C* frolic of kings, *The Dawn* 7
Christ-like The tenderest *C-l* creature *Charity* 32
Christmas (*See also* **Christmas day, Christmas-eve, Christmas-morn**) in the pits Which some green *C* crams with weary bones. *Wan Sculptor* 14
all the old honour had from *C* gone, *The Epic* 7
The cock crows ere the *C* morn, *Sir Galahad* 51
lastly there At *C* ; ever welcome at the Hall, *Aylmer's Field* 114
when the second *C* came, escaped His keepers, ,, 838
We seven stay'd at *C* up to read ; *Princess, Pro.* 178
play'd Charades and riddles as at *C* here, ,, 189
told a tale from mouth to mouth As here at *C*.' ,, 192
Chimeras, crotchets, *C* solecisms, ,, 203
The *C* bells from hill to hill *In Mem. xxviii* 3
weave The holly round the *C* hearth ; ,, *xxx* 2
Again at *C* did we weave The holly round the *C* hearth ; ,, *lxxviii* 1
where the winter thorn Blossoms at *C*, *Holy Grail* 53
Christmas day we were married o' *C d*, *First Quarrel* 39
Christmas Eäve Of a *C E*, an' as cowd as this, *Owd Roä* 31
goä that night to 'er foälk by cause o' the *C E* ; ,, 52
' be a-turnin' ma hout upo' *C E*' ? ,, 59
Christmas-eve (*See also* **Christmas Eäve**) At Francis Allen's on the *C-e*,— *The Epic* 1
How dare we keep our *C-e* ; *In Mem. xxix* 4
And sadly fell our *C-e*. ,, *xxx* 4
And calmly fell our *C-e* : ,, *lxxviii* 4
And strangely falls our *C-e*. ,, *cv* 4
Christmas-morn church-bells ring in the *C-m*. *M. d'Arthur, Ep.* 31
Christopher Colon (Columbus) ' Behold the bones of *C C*'— *Columbus* 210
Chronicle ran thro' all the coltish *c*, *The Brook* 159
dash'd Into the *c* of a deedful day, *Aylmer's Field* 196
we keep a *c* With all about him '— *Princess, Pro.* 27
So sang the gallant glorious *c* ; ,, 49
The total *c's* of man, the mind, ,, *ii* 381
Chronicler ask'd his *C* Of Akbar ' what has darken'd thee to-night ?' *Akbar's Dream* 2
Chrysalis This dull *c* Cracks into shining wings, *St. S. Stylites* 155
Or ruin'd *c* of one. *In Mem. lxxxii* 8
But she from out her death-like *c*, *Lover's Tale iii* 41
Chrysolite sardius, *C*, beryl, topaz, *Columbus* 85
Chrysoprase *c*, Jacynth, and amethyst— ,, 85
Chuch (church) the *c* weänt happen a fall. *Church-warden, etc.* 10
as long as I lives to the owd *c* now, ,, 15
Chuch-warden (church-warden) I beän *c-w* mysen i' the parish fur fifteen year. ,, 8
Well—sin ther beä *c-w's*, ,, 9
An' then I wur chose *C-w* ,, 38
plaäte fuller o' Soondays nor ony *c-w* afoor, ,, 40
Chuckle *c*, and grin at a brother's shame ; *Maud I iv* 29
Chuckled It clutter'd here, it *c* there ; *The Goose* 25
Church (*See also* **Chooch, Choorch, Christian Church, Chuch**) As homeward by the *c* I drew. *The Letters* 44
a moulder'd *c* ; and higher A long street *Enoch Arden* 4
c,—one night, except For greenish glimmerings *Aylmer's Field* 621
pious variers from the *c*, To chapel ; *Sea Dreams* 19
And in the dark *c* like a ghost *In Mem. lxvii* 15
A single *c* below the hill ,, *civ* 3
She came to the village *c*, *Maud I viii* 1
fragrant gloom Of foreign *c'es*— ,, *xix* 54
kill their *c*, As the *c'es* have kill'd ,, *II v* 28
Chief of the *c* in Britain, *Com. of Arthur* 454
walls Of that low *c* he built at Glastonbury. *Balin and Balan* 367
A little lonely *c* in days of yore, *Holy Grail* 64

Church (*continued*) first may be last—I have heard it in *c*— *Rizpah* 66
he calls to me now from the *c* ,, 84
To the deaf *c*—to be let in— *Sisters (E. and E.)* 238
Back to the pure and universal *c*, *Sir J. Oldcastle* 71
Tether'd to these dead pillars of the *C*— ,, 121
Authority of the *C*, Power of the keys !' ,, 161
Sylvester shed the venom of world-wealth Into the *c*, ,, 167
chiefly to my sorrow by the *C*, *Columbus* 56
Holy *C*, from whom I never swerved ,, 63
my Fathers belong'd to the *c* of old, *The Wreck* 1
Christian love among the *C's* *Locksley H., Sixty* 86
Break the State, the *C*, the Throne, ,, 138
Her spirit hovering by the *c*, *The Ring* 478
Touch'd at the golden Cross of the *c'es*, *Merlin and the G.* 68
all but sure I have—in Kendal *c*— *Romney's R.* 19
temple, neither Pagod, Mosque, nor *C*, *Akbar's Dream* 178
Church-bell The sweet *c-b's* began to peal. *Two Voices* 408
Toll ye the *c-b* sad and slow, *D. of the O. Year* 3
clear *c-b's* ring in the Christmas-morn. *M. d'Arthur, Ep.* 31
Church-commissioner Now harping on the *c-c's*, *The Epic* 15
Church-harpy scare *church-harpies* from the master's feast ; *To J. M. K.* 3
Churchmen Should all our *c* foam in spite *To F. D. Maurice* 9
the *c* fain would kill their church, *Maud II v* 28
Church-tower graves grass-green beside a gray *c-t*, *Circumstance* 6
morning grows apace, and lights the old *c-t*, *The Flight* 93
Churchwarden (*See also* **Chuch-warden**) Until the grave *c* doff'd, *The Goose* 19
Churchyard wall —in the night by the *c w*. *Rizpah* 56
Churl (*See also* **Village-churls**) low *c*, compact of thankless earth, *Godiva* 66
The *c* in spirit, up or down *In Mem. cxi* 1
The *c* in spirit, howe'er he veil ,, 5
Mark would sully the low state of *c* : *Gareth and L.* 427
Then riding close behind an ancient *c*, *Marr. of Geraint* 261
transitory word Made knight or *c* or child *Balin and Balan* 162
not worthy to be knight ; A *c*, a clown !' ,, 286
' *C*, thine axe !' he cried, ,, 295
said the *c*, ' our devil is a truth, ,, 302
' Old fabler, these be fancies of the *c*, ,, 307
laugh'd the father saying, ' Fie, Sir *C*, *Lancelot and E.* 200
A *c*, to whom indignantly the King, ' My *c*, *Last Tournament* 61
sawing the air, said the maim'd *c*, ,, 67
That doest right by gentle and by *c*, ,, 74
' Take thou my *c*, and tend him curiously ,, 90
Cicala At eve a dry *c* sung, *Mariana in the S.* 85
Cider flask of *c* from his father's vats, *Audley Court* 27
Cinder may make My scheming brain a *c*, *Merlin and V.* 933
Circle (s) (*See also* **Eagle-circle, Fairy-circle, Home-circle, Sea-circle, Water-circle**) round about the *c's* of the globes *The Poet* 43
In the same *c* we revolve. *Two Voices* 314
In lazy mood I watch'd the little *c's* die ; *Miller's D.* 74
The greensward into greener *c's*, *Gardener's D.* 134
in the *c* of his arms Enwound us both ; ,, 216
Sun will run his orbit, and the Moon Her *c*. *Love and Duty* 23
Thro' all the *c* of the golden year ?' *Golden Year* 51
music winding trembled, Wov'n in *c's* : *Vision of Sin* 18
Caught the sparkles, and in *c's*, ,, 30
mouldy dens The chap-fallen *c* spreads : ,, 172
yell'd and round me drove In narrowing *c's* *Lucretius* 57
a group of girls In *c* waited, *Princess, Pro.* 69
The *c* rounded under female hands ,, *ii* 372
Thro' *c's* of the bounding sky, *In Mem. xvii* 6
And in a *c* hand-in-hand Sat silent, ,, *xxx* 11
Against the *c* of the breast, ,, *xlv* 3
With all the *c* of the wise, ,, *lxi* 3
In *c* round the blessed gate, ,, *lxxxv* 23
O bliss, when all in *c* drawn About him, ,, *lxxxix* 21
memory fades From all the *c* of the hills. ,, *ci* 24
held All in a gap-mouth'd *c* his good mates *Gareth and L.* 511
remnant that were left Paynim amid their *c's*, *Holy Grail* 664
The *c* widens till it lip the marge, *Pelleas and E.* 94
The phantom *c* of a moaning sea. *Pass. of Arthur* 87
shower'd down Rays of a mighty *c* *Lover's Tale i* 418

Circle (s) (*continued*) Scarce housed within the *c* of this Earth, *Lover's Tale i* 479
caught and brought him in To their charm'd *c*, ,, *iv* 377
Whirling their sabres in *c's* of light! *Heavy Brigade* 34
Circle (verb) Make knowledge *c* with the winds; *Love thou thy land* 17
tho' I *c* in the grain Five hundred rings *Talking Oak* 83
We *c* with the seasons. *Will Water.* 64
full voice which *c's* round the grave, *Princess ii* 45
And *c* moaning in the air: *In Mem. xii* 15
It *c's* round, and fancy plays, ,, *Con.* 81
birds that *c* round the tower Are cheeping *The Ring* 85
Circled (*See also* **Azure-circled, Crimson-circled, Musky-circled, Ruby-circled**) *C* thro' all experiences, pure law, *Œnone* 166
I prosper, *c* with thy voice; *In Mem. cxxx* 15
c with her maids, The Lady Lyonors *Gareth and L.* 1374
and settling *c* all the lists. *Marr. of Geraint* 547
Circlet prize A golden *c* and a knightly sword, *Pelleas and E.* 12
Pelleas for his lady won The golden *c*, ,, 14
he will fight for me, And win the *c*: ,, 119
And win me this fine *c*, Pelleas, ,, 128
The sword and golden *c* were achieved. ,, 170
she caught the *c* from his lance, ,, 173
yea and he that won The *c*? ,, 321
their wills are hers For whom I won the *c*; ,, 325
the *c* of the jousts Bound on her brow, ,, 434
The *c* of the tourney round her brows, ,, 454
—on her head A diamond *c*, *Lover's Tale iv* 289
Circling past her feet the swallow *c* flies, *Prog. of Spring* 44
Circuit The *c's* of thine orbit round *In Mem. lxiii* 11
Circumstance strong Against the grief of *c* *Supp. Confessions* 92
saw The hollow orb of moving *C* *Palace of Art* 255
And breasts the blows of *c*, *In Mem. lxiv* 7
This ever-changing world of *c*, *To Duke of Argyll* 10
Cirque Within the magic *c* of memory, *Lover's Tale ii* 159
Citadel Troas and Ilion's column'd *c*, *Œnone* 13
Mast-throng'd beneath her shadowing *c* ,, 118
A moulder'd *c* on the coast, *The Daisy* 28
Fell the colony, city, and *c*, *Boädicea* 86
Past thro' into his *c*, the brain, *Lover's Tale i* 631
Citadel-crown'd Tempest-buffeted, *c-c*. *Will* 9
Cited Some *c* old Lactantius: *Columbus* 49
Citizen (*See also* **Fellow-citizen**) gravest *c* seems to lose his head, *Princess, Con.* 59
heart of the *c* hissing in war *Maud I i* 24
like a statue, rear'd To some great *c*, *Tiresias* 83
Citron-shadow clove The *c-s's* in the blue: *Arabian Nights* 15
City (*See also* **Mother-city, Queen-city, Soldier-city**) Full of the *c's* stilly sound, ,, 103
a *c* glorious—A great and distant *c*— *Deserted House* 19
Thro' the open gates of the *c* afar, *Dying Swan* 34
Below the *c's* eastern towers: *Fatima* 9
Or in a clear-wall'd *c* on the sea, *Palace of Art* 97
When I and Eustace from the *c* went *Gardener's D.* 2
grew The fable of the *c* where we dwelt. ,, 6
News from the humming *c* comes to it ,, 35
O'er the mute *c* stole with folded wings, ,, 186
in the dust and drouth Of *c* life! *Edwin Morris* 4
Beyond the lodge the *c* lies, *Talking Oak* 5
cities of men And manners, climates, *Ulysses* 13
I shaped The c's *ancient legend into this*:— *Godiva* 4
Mammon made The harlot of the *cities*: *Aylmer's Field* 375
A *C* clerk, but gently born and bred; *Sea Dreams* 1
There rose a shriek as of a *c* sack'd; *Princess iv* 165
we dash'd Your *cities* into shards with catapults, ,, *v* 138
cross of gold That shines over *c* and river, *Ode on Well.* 50
when the long-illumined *cities* flame, ,, 228
Flash, ye *cities*, in rivers of fire! *W. to Alexandra* 19
c Of little Monaco, basking, glow'd. *The Daisy* 7
the *c* glitter'd, Thro' cypress avenues, ,, 47
Yet here to-night in this dark *c*, ,, 95
The *c* sparkles like a grain of salt. *Will* 20
they rioted in the *c* of Cúnobelíne! *Boädicea* 60
Fell the colony, *c*, and citadel, ,, 86
And oxen from the *c*, and goodly sheep *Spec. of Iliad* 4
City (*continued*) breathed his latest breath, That *C*. *In Mem. xcviii* 6
I come once more: the *c* sleeps; ,, *cxix* 3
bubbles o'er like a *c*, with gossip, *Maud I iv* 8
For a tumult shakes the *c*, ,, *II iv* 50
vapours choke The great *c* sounding wide; ,, 64
paced a *c* all on fire With sun and cloth of gold, *Com. of Arthur* 479
At times the summit of the high *c* flash'd; *Gareth and L.* 192
the whole fair *c* had disappear'd. ,, 196
Here is a *c* of Enchanters, ,, 199
'Lord, there is no such *c* anywhere, ,, 206
Out of the *c* a blast of music peal'd. ,, 238
(Your *c* moved so weirdly in the mist) ,, 245
there be any *c* at all, Or all a vision: ,, 249
Fairy Queens have built the *c*, son; ,, 259
hold The King a shadow, and the *c* real: ,, 266
seeing the *c* is built To music, ,, 276
a *c* of shadowy palaces And stately, ,, 303
nay, the King's—Descend into the *c*:' ,, 540
thro' silent faces rode Down the slope *c*, ,, 735
Vivien, into Camelot stealing, lodged Low in the *c*, *Merlin and V.* 64
upon far-off *cities* while they dance— ,, 114
He saw two *cities* in a thousand boats ,, 561
heads should moulder on the *c* gates. ,, 594
arisen since With *cities* on their flanks— ,, 676
Past up the still rich *c* to his kin, *Lancelot and E.* 802
Far up the dim rich *c* to her kin; ,, 845
thro' the dim rich *c* to the fields, ,, 847
across the fields Far into the rich *c*, ,, 891
crown thee king Far in the spiritual *c*:' *Holy Grail* 162
all the dim rich *c*, roof by roof, ,, 228
And on the top, a *c* wall'd: ,, 422
I past Far thro' a ruinous *c*, ,, 429
crown me king Far in the spiritual *c*; ,, 483
I saw the spiritual *c* and all her spires ,, 526
from the star there shot A rose-red sparkle to the *c*, ,, 530
But when ye reach'd The *c*, ,, 708
O, when we reach'd The *c*, ,, 716
And follow'd to the *c*. *Pelleas and E.* 586
Down the slope *c* rode, and sharply turn'd *Last Tournament* 127
And down the *c* Dagonet danced away; ,, 359
and in it Far *cities* burnt, *Guinevere* 83
saw the King Ride toward her from the *c*, ,, 404
As of some lonely *c* sack'd by night, *Pass. of Arthur* 43
Sounds, as if some fair *c* were one voice ,, 460
the full *c* peal'd Thee and thy Prince! *To the Queen ii* 26
The *c* deck'd herself To meet me, *Columbus* 9
when a smoke from a *c* goes to heaven *Achilles over the T.* 7
men contend in grievous war From their own *c*, ,, 10
The madness of our *cities* and their kings. *Tiresias* 71
from within The *c* comes a murmur void of joy, ,, 101
All day long far-off in the cloud of the *c*, *The Wreck* 29
From out his ancient *c* came a Seer *Ancient Sage* 2
I am wearied of our *c*, son, ,, 15
But some in yonder *c* hold, my son, ,, 82
night enough is there In yon dark *c*: ,, 253
storms Of Autumn swept across the *c*, *Demeter and P.* 71
North to gain Her capital *c*, *The Ring* 482
ruin, this little *c* of sewers, *Happy* 34
To the *c* and palace Of Arthur the king; *Merlin and the G.* 65
passing it glanced upon Hamlet or *c*, ,, 104
BEAUTIFUL *c*, the centre and crater *Beautiful City* 1
at length he touch'd his goal, The Christian *c*. *St. Telemachus* 35
war dashing down upon *cities* and blazing farms, *The Dawn* 8
press of a thousand *cities* is prized ,, 14
Than a rotten fleet and a *c* in flames! *Riflemen, Form!* 18
City-gate before the *c-g's* Came on her brother *Lancelot and E.* 790
City-gloom Droopt in the giant-factoried *c-g*, *Sea Dreams* 5
City-house this pretty house, this *c-h* of ours? *City Child* 7
City-roar a shout More joyful than the *c-r* that hails Premier or king! *Princess, Con.* 101
Civility But keep a touch of sweet *c* *Geraint and E.* 312
Civilisation Or an infant *c* be ruled with rod *Maud I iv* 47
Claäy (clay) hoickt my feet wi' a flop fro' the *c*. *Spinster's S's.* 30
it wur clatted all ower wi' *c*. ,, 46

Clack'd-Clackt It *clack'd* and cackled louder. *The Goose* 24
The palace bang'd, and buzz'd and *clackt*, *Day-Dm., Revival* 14
Clad (*See also* **Ivy-clad, Lady-clad, Vine-clad, Winter-clad**) Or long-hair'd page in crimson *c*, *L. of Shalott ii* 22
She *c* herself in a russet gown, *Lady Clare* 57
looking hardly human, strangely *c*, *Enoch Arden* 638
c her like an April daffodilly *Princess ii* 324
Six hundred maidens *c* in purest white, ,, 472
c in iron burst the ranks of war, ,, *iv* 504
Mixt with myrtle and *c* with vine, *The Islet* 19
three were *c* like tillers of the soil. *Gareth and L.* 181
boat Become a living creature *c* with wings? *Holy Grail* 519
Leapt lightly *c* in bridal white— *Lover's Tale iii* 44
ere thy maiden birk be wholly *c*, *Prog. of Spring* 50
Claim (s) *A thousand* c's *to reverence closed* *To the Queen* 27
Smile at the *c's* of long descent. *L. C. V. de Vere* 52
she will not: waive your *c*: *Princess v* 296
To learn if Ida yet would cede our *c*, ,, 333
sware to combat for my *c* till death. ,, 360
With *c* on *c* from right to right, ,, 417
Nor did her father cease to press my *c*, ,, *vii* 87
asserts his *c* In that dread sound *Ode on Well.* 70
Attest their great commander's *c* ,, 148
From our first Charles by force we wrung our *c's*. *Third of Feb.* 26
Dispute the *c's*, arrange the chances; *To F. D. Maurice* 31
And each prefers his separate *c*, *In Mem cii* 18
crush'd in the clash of jarring *c's*, *Maud III vi* 44
Lays *c* to for the lady at his side, *Marr. of Geraint* 487
Who had a twofold *c* upon my heart, *Lover's Tale i* 210
their *c* to be thy peers; *To Victor Hugo* 6
I am bankrupt of all *c* On your obedience, *Romney's R.* 70
single star Should shriek its *c* *Akbar's Dream* 43
Claim (verb) Of sounder leaf than I can *c*; *You might have won* 4
in his walks with Edith, *c* A distant kinship *Aylmer's Field* 61
much that Ida *c's* as right Had ne'er been mooted, *Princess v* 202
Who but *c's* her as his due? *Maud I xx* 11
Came not to us, of us to *c* the prize, *Lancelot and E.* 544
Wilt spring to me, and *c* me thine, *Guinevere* 565
should this first master *c* His service, *Lover's Tale iv* 265
—one has come to *c* his bride, *Locksley H., Sixty* 263
I may *c* it without a lie. *Bandit's Death* 7
Claim'd So *c* the quest and rode away, *Balin and Balan* 138
Muriel *c* and open'd what I meant For Miriam, *The Ring* 242
Claiming *c* each This meed of fairest. *Œnone* 86
stood once more before her face, *C* her promise. *Enoch Arden* 458
Nay, but I am not *c* your pity: *Despair* 37
Clamber'd *c* half way up The counter side; *Golden Year* 6
narrow street that *c* toward the mill. *Enoch Arden* 60
I *c* o'er at top with pain, *Princess iv* 208
fall'n from off the crag we *c* up in play, *The Flight* 22
Clambering and *c* on a mast In harbour, *Enoch Arden* 105
vessel in mid-ocean, her heaved prow *C*, *Lover's Tale ii* 170
Clamour (s) And fill'd the house with *c*. *The Goose* 36
With peals of genial *c* sent *Will Water.* 187
and fill'd the shores With *c*. *Enoch Arden* 636
a herd of boys with *c* bowl'd and stump'd *Princess, Pro.* 81
To hear my father's *c* at our backs ,, *i* 105
A *c* thicken'd, mixt with inmost terms ,, *ii* 446
till a *c* grew As of a new-world Babel, ,, *iv* 486
trampling the flowers With *c*: ,, *v* 248
With blare of bugle, *c* of men, *Ode on Well.* 115
But that blind *c* made me wise; *In Mem cxxiv* 18
Far-off from the *c* of liars belied *Maud I iv* 51
C and rumble, and ringing and clatter, ,, *II v* 13
or like a *c* of the rooks At distance, *Marr. of Geraint* 249
And all the windy *c* of the daws *Geraint and E.* 255
Clamour (verb) and to *c*, mourn, and sob, *St. S. Stylites* 6
Yet cease I not to *c* and to cry, ,, 42
Nor ever ceased to *c* for the ring; *The Ring* 389
every splinter'd fraction of a sect Will *c* *Akbar's Dream* 34
Clamour'd 'Dead' *c* the good woman, *Enoch Arden* 840
and he *c* from a casement, 'Run' *The Brook* 85
'Take Lilia, then, for heroine,' *c* he, *Princess, Pro.* 223
Melissa *c* 'Flee the death;' ,, *iv* 166
And while the people *c* for a king *Com. of Arthur* 235
Clamour'd (*continued*) I ask you, is it *c* by the child, *Merlin and V.* 771
Clamouring *c*, 'If we pay, we starve!' *Godiva* 15
c etiquette to death, Unmeasured mirth; *Princess v* 17
but *c* out 'Mine—mine—not yours, ,, *vi* 140
c on, till Ida heard, Look'd up, ,, 150
pulses at the *c* of her enemy fainted *Boädicea* 82
the damsel *c* all the while, *Gareth and L.* 1134
Clan beyond the passions of the primal *c*? *Locksley H., Sixty* 93
Clang (s) overhead Begins the clash and *c* *In Mem., Con.* 61
Clang (verb) An eagle *c* an eagle to the sphere. *Princess iii* 106
wildswan in among the stars Would *c* it, ,, *iv* 435
the wood which grides and *c's* *In Mem. cvii* 11
C battleaxe, and clash brand! (repeat) *Com. of Arthur* 493, 496, 499
ring thy name To every hoof that *c's* it, *Tiresias* 138
Clang'd left and right The bare black cliff *c* round him, *M. d'Arthur* 188
knell to my desires, *C* on the bridge; *Princess iv* 175
left and right The bare black cliff *c* round him, *Pass. of Arthur* 356
again the bells Jangled and *c*: *Lover's Tale iii* 53
Clanging (*See also* **Iron-Clanging**) you hear The windy *c* of the minster clock; *Gardener's D.* 38
Clap (s) Dead *c's* of thunder from within *Sea Dreams* 55
stammering cracks and *c's* that follow'd, *Merlin and V.* 942
Clap (verb) *C's* her tiny hands above me, *Lilian* 4
crested bird That *c's* his wings at dawn. *D. of F. Women* 180
c their cheeks, to call them mine. *In Mem. lxxxiv* 18
The starling *c's* his tiny castanets. *Prog. of Spring* 56
Clapper Than in a *c* clapping in a garth, *Princess ii* 227
Clapping Laughing and *c* their hands between, *The Merman* 29
Than in a clapper *c* in a garth, *Princess ii* 227
all within was noise Of songs, and *c* hands, *In Mem. lxxxvii* 19
from distant walls There came a *c* as of phantom hands. *Marr. of Geraint* 566
Clapt and *c* her hands and cried, 'I marvel *Palace of Art* 189
c his hand On Everard's shoulder, *The Epic* 21
c him on the hands and on the cheeks, *Dora* 133
c his hand in mine and sang— *Audley Court* 39
And feet that ran, and doors that *c*, *Day-Dm., Revival* 3
c her hands and cried for war, *Princess iv* 590
Lancelot'—and she *c* her hands— *Gareth and L.* 1290
mused a little, and then *c* her hands *Merlin and V.* 866
Dagonet *c* his hands and shrill'd, *Last Tournament* 353
Sa I han't *c* eyes on 'im yit, *Village Wife* 123
I *c* my hands. *Happy* 83
Clara Vere de Vere (*See also* **Vere de Vere**) Lady *C V d V*, (repeat) *L. C. V. de Vere* 1, 9, 17, 25, 33, 41
Trust me, *C V d V*, *L. C. V. de Vere* 49
I know you, *C V d V* ,, 57
C, *C V d V*, ,, 65
Clare To give his cousin, Lady *C*. *Lady Clare* 4
And that is well,' said Lady *C*. ,, 12
'It was my cousin,' said Lady *C*, ,, 15
And you are *not* the Lady *C*.' ,, 20
Said Lady *C*, 'that ye speak so wild?' ,, 22
She was no longer Lady *C*: ,, 58
Lady *C*, you shame your worth! ,, 66
beggar born,' she said, 'And not the Lady *C*.' ,, 72
And you shall still be Lady *C*.' ,, 88
Clariance Claudias, and *C* of Northumberland, *Com. of Arthur* 113
Claribel Where *C* low-lieth (repeat) *Claribel* 1, 8, 21
Clarion shouts, and *c's* shrilling unto blood, *Com. of Arthur* 103
Clash (s) I heard the *c* so clearly. *Sea Dreams* 136
Roll of cannon and *c* of arms, *Ode on Well.* 116
overhead Begins the *c* and clang *In Mem., Con.* 61
crush'd in the *c* of jarring claims, *Maud III vi* 44
Shield-breakings, and the *c* of brands, *Pass. of Arthur* 109
long loud *c* of rapid marriage-bells. *Lover's Tale iii* 23
by their *c*, And prelude on the keys, *Sisters (E. and E.)* 1
And the *c* and boom of the bells *V. of Maeldune* 110
reasons had *He* to be glad of The *c* of the war-glaive— *Batt. of Brunanburh* 78
brightens at the *c* of 'Yes' and 'No,' *Ancient Sage* 71
struck from out the *c* of warring wills; *Prog. of Spring* 95
hear The *c* of tides that meet in narrow seas.— *Akbar's Dream* 58
and your fiery *c* of meteorites? *God and the Univ.* 3
Clash (verb) Fly on to *c* together again, *Lucretius* 41

Clash (verb) (*continued*) O hard, when love and duty *c* ! *Princess ii* 293
but you *c* them all in one, ,, *v* 180
C, ye bells, in the merry March air ! *W. to Alexandra* 18
C the darts and on the buckler *Boädicea* 79
Clang battleaxe, and *c* brand ! (repeat) *Com. of Arthur* 493, 496, 499
C like the coming and retiring wave, *Gareth and L.* 522
each would *c* the shield, and blow the horn. *Last Tournament* 436
at her girdle *c* The golden keys *To Marq. of Dufferin* 3
where the loyal bells *C* welcome— *The Ring* 483
And I *c* with an iron Truth, *The Dreamer* 6
Clash'd Dry *c* his harness in the icy caves *M. d'Arthur* 186
from them *c* The bells ; we listen'd ; *Gardener's D.* 220
shameless noon Was *c* and hammer'd *Godiva* 75
Touch'd, clink'd, and *c*, and vanish'd, *Sea Dreams* 135
and one, that *c* in arms, *Princess v* 5
they *c* their arms ; the drum Beat ; ,, 250
he *c* His iron palms together with a cry ; ,, 353
all silent, save When armour *c* or jingled, ,, *vi* 363
C with his fiery few and won ; *Ode on Well.* 100
As the music *c* in the hall ; *Maud I xxii* 34
his arms *C* ; and the sound was good *Gareth and L.* 312
Sir Gareth's brand *C* his, and brake it utterly ,, 1148
thrice They *c* together, and thrice they brake their spears. *Marr. of Geraint* 562
they sat, And cup *c* cup ; *Balin and Balan* 85
when they *c*, Rolling back upon Balin, ,, 561
table of our Arthur closed And *c* *Holy Grail* 330
And *c* with Pagan hordes, and bore them down ,, 479
meadow-grass Borne, *c* : *Pelleas and E.* 562
Dry *c* his harness in the icy caves *Pass. of Arthur* 354
slowly-ridging rollers on the cliffs *C*, *Lover's Tale i* 58
Two trains *c* : then and there he was crush'd *Charity* 21
Clashing (*See also* **Iron-clashing**) there were cries and *c's* in the nest, *Gareth and L.* 70
Enid heard the *c* of his fall, *Geraint and E.* 509
With all her golden thresholds *c*, *Lover's Tale i* 605
butted each other with *c* of bells, *V. of Maeldune* 108
Clasp (fastening) Buckled with golden *c's* before ; *Sir L. and Q. G.* 25
Clasp (embrace) In glance and smile, and *c* and kiss, *In Mem. lxxxiv* 7
Clasp (verb) I'd *c* it round so close and tight. *Miller's D.* 180
He *c's* the crag with crooked hands ; *The Eagle* 1
but everywhere Some must *c* Idols. *Supp. Confessions* 179
c These idols to herself ? *Lucretius* 164
c it once again, And call her Ida, *Princess vii* 95
C her window, trail and twine ! *Window. At the W.* 2
Trail and twine and *c* and kiss, ,, 4
Let Love *c* Grief lest both be drown'd, *In Mem. i* 9
Some landing-place, to *c* and say, ,, *xlvii* 15
Thy passion *c's* a secret joy : ,, *lxxxviii* 8
and *c* the hands and murmur, *Locksley H., Sixty* 192
Ah, *c* me in your arms, sister, *The Flight* 5
Clasp'd-Claspt (*See also* **Ivy-claspt**) *claspt* hand-in-hand with thee, *If I were loved* 9
Die, dying *clasp'd* in his embrace. *Fatima* 42
I saw her, who *clasp'd* in her last trance *D. of F. Women* 266
Are *clasp'd* the moral of thy life, *Day-Dm., L'Envoi* 55
But he *clasp'd* her like a lover, *L. of Burleigh* 67
Claspt hands and that petitionary grace *The Brook* 112
fell on him, *Clasp'd*, kiss'd him, wail'd : *Lucretius* 280
That *claspt* the feet of a Mnemosyne, *Princess iv* 269
in hands so lately *claspt* with yours, ,, *vi* 184
But he turn'd and *claspt* me in his arms, *Grandmother* 55
Claspt on her seal, my sweet ! *Window. The Answer* 2
A hand that can be *clasp'd* no more— *In Mem. vii* 5
And hands so often *clasp'd* in mine, ,, *x* 19
Of comfort *clasp'd* in truth reveal'd ; ,, *xxxvii* 22
land Where first he walk'd when *claspt* in clay ? ,, *xciii* 4
He is *claspt* by a passion-flower. *Maud I xiv* 8
ivy-stems *Claspt* the gray walls with hairy-fibred arms, *Marr. of Geraint* 323
claspt and kiss'd her, and they rode away. ,, 825
flinging round her neck, *Claspt* it, *Last Tournament* 750
but I *clasp'd* her without fear : *Lover's Tale ii* 202
And *claspt* her hand in his : ,, *iii* 52
Clasp'd-Claspt (*continued*) round him closed and *claspt* again. *Lover's Tale iv* 378
she that *clasp'd* my neck had flown ; *Locksley H., Sixty* 15
Here we stood and *claspt* each other, ,, 180
Who might have chased and *claspt* Renown *To Marq. of Dufferin* 29
You *claspt* our infant daughter, *Romney's R.* 77
Clasping That round me, *c* each in each, *Talking Oak* 143
I, *c* brother-hands, aver I could not, *In Mem. lxxxv* 102
Claspt *See* **Clasp'd**
Class Of Knowledge fusing *c* with *c*, *Freedom* 17
Clat (mess) But wa boäth was i' sich a *c* *Spinster's S's.* 33
their mucky bibs, an' the *c's* an' the clouts, ,, 87
Clatted (soiled) it wur *c* all ower wi' claäy. ,, 46
Clatter With cackle and with *c*. *The Goose* 12
Clamour and rumble, and ringing and *c*, *Maud II v* 13
and a *c* of hail on the glass, *In the Child. Hosp.* 62
c of arms, and voices, and men passing *Bandit's Death* 24
Claudias Urien, Cradlemont of Wales, *C*, *Com. of Arthur* 113
Claum (climb) I *c's* an' I mashes the winder hin, *Owd Roä* 83
Claumb'd (climbed) I *c* up ageän to the winder, ,, 99
Clause lead my Memmius in a train Of flowery *c's* *Lucretius* 120
the little *c* 'take not his life :' *Princess v* 470
Clave loved one only and who *c* to her—' *Ded. of Idylls* 11
c Like its own mists to all the mountain side ; *Lancelot and E.* 37
and all his kith and kin *C* to him, *Guinevere* 440
c To Modred, and a remnant stays with me. ,, 442
Claw Nature, red in tooth and *c* With ravine, *In Mem. lvi* 15
miss'd, and brought Her own *c* back, *Merlin and V.* 500
what evil beast Hath drawn his *c's* *Last Tournament* 63
Naäy, but the *c's* o' tha ! quiet ! *Spinster's S's.* 36
mun be fools to be hallus a-shawin' your *c's*, ,, 61
Clay (*See also* **Claäy**) grave Was deep, my mother, in the *c* ? *Supp. Confessions* 86
They should have trod me into *c*, *Oriana* 62
And on my *c* her darnel grow ; *My life is full* 22
Doing dishonour to my *c*.' *Two Voices* 102
common *c* ta'en from the common earth *To—— With Pal. of Art.* 17
growing coarse to sympathize with *c*. *Locksley Hall* 46
And the leaf is stamp'd in *c*. *Vision of Sin* 82
Rose from the *c* it work'd in as she past, *Aylmer's Field* 170
He shall not blind his soul with *c*.' *Princess vii* 331
Half-conscious of their dying *c*, *In Mem. lviii* 7
land Where first he walk'd when claspt in *c* ? ,, *xciii* 4
Not only cunning casts in *c* : ,, *cxx* 5
judge all nature from her feet of *c*, *Merlin and V.* 835
death, that seems to make us loveless *c*, *Lancelot and E.* 1014
From the same *c* came into light *Lover's Tale i* 194
make And break the vase of *c*, *Ancient Sage* 92
Claymore *C* and snowshoe, toys in lava, *Princess, Pro.* 18
Clean (*See also* **Cleän**) As *c* and white as privet when it flowers. *Walk. to the Mail* 56
whole, and *c*, and meet for Heaven, *St. S. Stylites* 213
will never make oneself *c*. *Grandmother* 36
make all *c*, and plant himself afresh. *Geraint and E.* 905
keep him bright and *c* as heretofore, ,, 937
As *c* as blood of babes, as white as milk : *Merlin and V.* 344
I decreed That even the dog was *c*, *Akbar's Dream* 53
Cleän *c* as a flower fro' 'eäd to feeät : *North. Cobbler* 44
an' I keeäps 'im *c* an' bright, ,, 97
but the cat mun be *c*. *Spinster's S's.* 34
es *c* Es a shillin' fresh fro' the mint ,, 75
An' thy farmin' es *c* es thysen,' ,, 77
Clean-cut There were some for the *c-c* stone, *V. of Maeldune* 112
Cleaner house with all its hateful needs no *c* than the beast, *Happy* 32
Cleaner-fashion'd fork of thine Is *c-f*— *Merlin and V.* 60
Cleaning *See* **A-cleanin'**
Cleanse working out his will, To *c* the world. *Gareth and L.* 25
c this common sewer of all his realm, *Marr. of Geraint* 39
c this common sewer of all my realm, *Geraint and E.* 895
Cleansed broke the bandit holds and *c* the land. ,, 944
Cleanser saved a life Worth somewhat as the *c* of this wood. *Gareth and L.* 828
Cleän-wud (clean-mad) An' I thowt as 'e'd goan *c-w*, *Owd Roä* 61
Clear (adj.) (*See also* **Silver-clear, Starry-clear**)
C, without heat, undying, *Isabel* 3

Clear (adj.) (*continued*) With chisell'd features *c* and sleek. *A Character* 30
C and bright it should be ever, *Poet's Mind* 5
Bright as light, and *c* as wind. ,, 7
so *c* and bold and free As you, *Rosalind* 17
C as the twanging of a harp, *Kate* 8
So healthy, sound, and *c* and whole, *Miller's D.* 15
Make Thou my spirit pure and *c* *St. Agnes' Eve* 9
O hark, O hear! how thin and *c*, *Princess iv* 7
nobbut a curate, an' weänt niver git hissen *c*, *N. Farmer, N. S.* 27
I feel so free and so *c* *Maud I xix* 98
world Was all so *c* about him, that he saw *Com. of Arthur* 98
C as a lark, high o'er me as a lark, *Holy Grail* 833
Name, surname, all as *c* as noon, *The Ring* 237
a faith as *c* as the heights of the June-blue heaven, *June-Bracken, etc.* 7
Clear (adv.) came A bitter wind, *c* from the North, *Pass. of Arthur* 124
That sings so delicately *c*, *Marr. of Geraint* 332
long es she lived she kep 'em all *c*, *Village Wife* 53
Clear (verb) Better to *c* prime forests, *Princess iii* 127
Will *c* away the parasitic forms ,, *vii* 269
balm May *c* the blood from poison, *Death of Œnone* 36
Clear-cut But a cold and *c-c* face, *Maud I ii* 3
Cold and *c-c* face, why come you so cruelly meek, ,, *iii* 1
Clear'd And a whirlwind *c* the larder: *The Goose* 52
flash of semi-jealousy *c* it to her. *Aylmer's Field* 189
moving everywhere *C* the dark places *Geraint and E.* 943
She *c* her sight, she arose, *Dead Prophet* 31
Clearer like a light that grows Larger and *c*, *Œnone* 109
The fires are all the *c*, *Window. Winter* 16
every turn and depth Between is *c* in my life *Lover's Tale i* 149
Clearest Yet *c* of ambitious crime, *Ode on Well.* 28
Clear-faced Until they found the *c-f* King, *Lancelot and E.* 432
Clear-featured that *c-f* face Was lovely, ,, 1159
Clear-headed *C-h* friend, whose joyful scorn, *Clear-headed friend* 1
Clearness 'are like the rest; No certain *c*, *Two Voices* 335
The starry *c* of the free? *In Mem. lxxxv* 86
The critic *c* of an eye, ,, *cix* 3
c of his fame hath gone Beneath the shadow *Lover's Tale i* 789
no shade of doubt, But utter *c*, *Ancient Sage* 236
Clear-pointed fed With the *c-p* flame of chastity, *Isabel* 2
Clear-stemm'd *c-s* platans guard The outlet, *Arabian Nights* 23
Clear-voiced The *c-v* mavis dwelleth, *Claribel* 16
Clear-wall'd Or in a *c-w* city on the sea, *Palace of Art* 97
Cleave (to adhere) love thee well and *c* to thee, *Œnone* 160
'The man will *c* unto his right.' *Lady Clare* 46
C to your contract: *Princess iv* 409
if I fall, *c* to the better man.' *Geraint and E.* 152
To love one maiden only, *c* to her, *Guinevere* 475
The shadow of another *c's* to me, ,, 618
c's to cairn and cromlech still; *To the Queen ii* 41
The lecher would *c* to his lusts, *Despair* 100
C ever to the sunnier side of doubt, *Ancient Sage* 68
C to one another still? *Open. I and C. Exhib.* 34
Cleave (to divide) Clear Love would pierce and *c*, *If I were loved* 6
ill-used race of men that *c* the soil, *Lotos-Eaters, C. S.* 120
To *c* the rift of difference deeper yet; *Princess v* 301
When mighty Love would *c* in twain *In Mem. xxv* 10
master-bowman, he, Would *c* the mark. ,, *lxxxvii* 30
To *c* a creed in sects and cries, ,, *cxxviii* 15
and so ye *c* His armour off him, *Gareth and L.* 1094
May this hard earth *c* to the Nadir hell *Merlin and V.* 349
Cleaved (For I *c* to a cause that I felt *Maud III vi* 31
ever like a loyal sister *c* To Arthur, *Com. of Arthur* 191
some she *c* to, but they died of her. *Gareth and L.* 113
So to this king I *c*: my friend was he, *Sir J. Oldcastle* 61
Cleaving The fruitful wit *C*, took root, *The Poet* 21
Cleft (s) (*See also* **Mountain-cleft**) Far-off the torrent call'd me from the *c*: *Œnone* 54
thro' mountain *c's* the dale Was seen *Lotos-Eaters* 20
every coppice-feather'd chasm and *c*, *Princess iv* 23
gather'd trickling dropwise from the *c*, *Merlin and V.* 274
little elves of chasm and *c* Made answer, *Guinevere* 248
saw The *c's* and openings in the mountains *Lover's Tale i* 330
Cleft (verb) He *c* me thro' the stomacher; *Princess ii* 407
spire of land that stands apart *C* from the main, ,, *iv* 282
Cleft (verb) (*continued*) Has risen and *c* the soil, and grown a bulk *Princess vi* 35
Which *c* and *c* again for evermore, *Ancient Sage* 43
Clelia *C*, Cornelia, with the Palmyrene *Princess ii* 83
Clematis O'erflourish'd with the hoary *c*: *Golden Year* 63
among the meadows, the clover and the *c*, *City Child* 9
Rose, rose and *c*, (repeat) *Window. At the W.* 3, 10
and the dark-blue *c*, clung, *V. of Maeldune* 39
Clemm'd (clutched) an' *c* owd Roä by the 'eäd, *Owd Roä* 99
Clench those, who *c* their nerves to rush *Love and Duty* 77
Clench'd (*See also* **Half-clench'd**) taunt that *c* his purpose like a blow! *Princess v* 306
c her fingers till they bit the palm, *Lancelot and E.* 611
c His hands, and madden'd with himself *Pelleas and E.* 459
Muriel *c* The hand that wore it, *The Ring* 261
Cleopatra-like *C-l* as of old To entangle me *Maud I vi* 27
Clergyman that good man, the *c*, has told me words of peace, *May Queen, Con.* 12
Clerk (*See also* **Parish-clerks**) worn-out *c* Browbeats his desk below. *To J. M. K.* 11
now we left The *c* behind us, I and he, *Edwin Morris* 97
That was a God, and is a lawyer's *c*, ,, 102
A CITY *c*, but gently born and bred; *Sea Dreams* 1
mitre-sanction'd harlot draws his *c's* Into the suburb— *Sir J. Oldcastle* 106
Cletch (brood of chickens) But Nelly, the last of the *c*, *Village Wife* 9
Cleverness not for all Aspasia's *c*, *Princess ii* 344
Click merry milkmaids *c* the latch, *The Owl I* 8
C with the pick, coming nearer *Def. of Lucknow* 28
Cliff (*See also* **Sea-cliff, Shore-cliff**) light upon the wall Of purple *c's*, *Ode to Memory* 54
mountain-shade Sloped downward to her seat from the upper *c*. *Œnone* 22
Along the *c* to fall and pause and fall *Lotos-Eaters* 9
bare black *c* clang'd round him, *M. d'Arthur* 188
Upon the *c's* that guard my native land, *Audley Court* 49
girt the region with high *c* and lawn: *Vision of Sin* 47
lines of *c* breaking have left a chasm: *Enoch Arden* 1
A narrow cave ran in beneath the *c*: ,, 23
sand and *c* and deep-inrunning cave, *Sea Dreams* 17
on sand they walk'd, and now on *c*, ,, 37
claps of thunder from within the *c's* ,, 55
enter'd one Of those dark caves that run beneath the *c's*. ,, 90
on those *c's* Broke, mixt with awful light ,, 214
those lines of *c's* were *c's* no more, ,, 217
we wound About the *c's*, the copses, *Princess iii* 360
O sweet and far from *c* and scar ,, *iv* 9
A stroke of cruel sunshine on the *c*, ,, 524
On capes of Afric as on *c's* of Kent, *W. to Marie Alex.* 17
And leave the *c's*, and haste away *In Mem. xii* 8
From scarped *c* and quarried stone ,, *lvi* 2
like a crag that tumbles from the *c*, *Marr. of Geraint* 318
Between the steep *c* and the coming wave; *Guinevere* 280
as a stream that spouting from a *c* Fails ,, 608
left and right The bare black *c* clang'd round him, *Pass. of Arthur* 356
HERE far away, seen from the topmast *c*, *Lover's Tale i* 1
slowly-ridging rollers on the *c's* Clash'd, ,, 57
the red passion-flower to the *c's*, *V. of Maeldune* 39
all round from the *c's* and the capes, ,, 55
And *c's* all robed in lianas that dropt *The Wreck* 73
blanch into spray At the feet of the *c*; ,, 138
I climb'd on all the *c's* of all the seas, *Demeter and P.* 63
Cliff-side broken rocks On some *c-s*, *Lancelot and E.* 1253
Climate manners, *c's*, councils, governments, *Ulysses* 14
Climax and he: 'The *c* of his age! *Princess ii* 50
Climb (*See also* **Claum**) Where he was wont to leap and *c*, *Supp. Confessions* 165
'Cry, faint not, *c*: the summits slope *Two Voices* 184
could she *c* Beyond her own material prime? ,, 377
You seem'd to hear them *c* and fall *Palace of Art* 70
'will you *c* the top of Art. *Gardener's D.* 169
long day wanes: the slow moon *c's*; *Ulysses* 55
I leave the plain, I *c* the height; *Sir Galahad*, 57
street *c's* to one tall-tower'd mill; *Enoch Arden* 5

Climb (*continued*) stairs That *c* into the windy halls of heaven: *Lucretius* 136
but we Set forth to *c*; *Princess iii* 354
as one that *c's* a peak to gaze O'er land and main, ,, *vii* 35
Be near us when we *c* or fall: *In Mem. li* 13
C thy thick noon, disastrous day; ,, *lxxii* 26
I *c* the hill: from end to end ,, *c* 1
I could *c* and lay my hand upon it, *Gareth and L.* 50
'*C* not lest thou break thy neck, ,, 54
felt the knot *C* in her throat, *Lancelot and E.* 741
C's to the mighty hall that Merlin built. *Holy Grail* 231
'There rose a hill that none but man could *c*, ,, 489
in a dream I seem'd to *c* For ever: ,, 836
I would not or I could not *c*— *Guinevere* 644
clomb Ev'n to the highest he could *c*, *Pass of Arthur* 463
C first and reach me down thy hand. *Sir J. Oldcastle* 204
sister of the sun Would *c* from out the dark, *Tiresias* 31
And *c* the Mount of Blessing, *Ancient Sage* 280
wounded warrior *c's* from Troy to thee. *Death of Œnone* 39
if ever a woman should *c* to the dwelling *Kapiolani* 22

Climb'd (*See also* **Claumb'd**) They *c* as quickly, for the rim Changed *The Voyage* 27
as he *c* the hill, Just where the prone edge *Enoch Arden* 66
he had *c* across the spikes, *Princess, Pro.* 111
we *c* The slope to Vivian-place, ,, *Con.* 39
I *c* to the top of the garth, *Grandmother* 38
I *c* the roofs at break of day; *Daisy* 61
And thither I *c* at dawn *Maud I xiv* 5
I have *c* nearer out of lonely Hell. ,, *xviii* 80
sweet son, had risk'd himself and *c*, *Gareth and L.* 60
And *c* upon a fair and even ridge, *Marr. of Geraint* 239
Guinevere had *c* The giant tower, ,, 826
on his foot She set her own and *c*; *Geraint and E.* 760
For one from out his village lately *c* *Balin and Balan* 167
c That eastern tower, and entering barr'd *Lancelot and E.* 14
Then to her tower she *c*, ,, 397
I *c* a thousand steps With pain: *Holy Grail* 835
came Arthur home, and while he *c*, *Last Tournament* 755
C to the high top of the garden-wall *Guinevere* 25
cheeks as bright as when she *c* the hill. *Lover's Tale iii* 47
heard a groaning overhead, and *c* The moulder'd stairs ,, *iv* 136
c one step beyond Our village *Ancient Sage* 206
I *c* on all the cliffs of all the seas, *Demeter and P.* 63
I *c* the hill with Hubert yesterday, *The Ring* 152
I have *c* to the snows of Age, *By an Evolution.* 17
c from the dens in the levels below, *The Dawn* 17

Climbing In ever *c* up the *c* wave? *Lotos-Eater's, C. S.* 50
And ever *c* higher; *D. of F. Women* 32
And *c* up into my airy home, *St. S. Stylites* 217
valleys underneath Came little copses *c*. *Amphion* 32
A lily-avenue *c* to the doors; *Aylmer's Field* 162
Was *c* up the valley; at whom he shot: ,, 228
then, *c*, Cyril kept With Psyche, *Princess iii* 354
turn'd his face And kiss'd her *c*, *Geraint and E.* 761
Cried to me *c*, 'Welcome, Percivale! *Holy Grail* 425
over all the great wood rioting And *c*, *Lover's Tale i* 404
set me *c* icy capes And glaciers, *To E. Fitzgerald* 25
Pallas Athene *c* from the bath In anger; *Tiresias* 40
Evolution ever *c* after some ideal good, *Locksley H., Sixty* 199
saw Him, *c* toward her with the golden *Death of Œnone* 15

Climbing (s) Maud with her venturous *c's* *Maud I i* 69

Clime THE poet in a golden *c* was born, *The Poet* 1
thro' mine ears in that unblissful *c*, *D. of F. Women* 82
Put forth and feel a gladder *c*.' *On a Mourner* 15
—what to me were sun or *c*? *Locksley Hall* 177
In divers seasons, divers *c's*; *Day-Dm., L'Envoi* 18
O hundred shores of happy *c's*, *The Voyage* 49
Again to colder *c's* we came, ,, 89
on the tables every *c* and age a Jumbled together; *Princess, Pro.* 16
For many a time in many a *c* *Ode on Well.* 64
And led him through the blissful *c's*, *In Mem. lxxxv* 25
who throve and branch'd from *c* to *c*, ,, *cxviii* 13
blown by the breeze of a softer *c*, *Maud I iv* 4
prayer of many a race and creed, and *c*— *To the Queen ii* 11

Clime (*continued*) arrowing light from *c* to *c*, *Akbar's D., Hymn* 5

Cling As close as might be would he *c* *Talking Oak* 127
They *c* together in the ghastly sack— *Aylmer's Field* 764
'My mother *c's* about my neck, *Sailor Boy* 17
flower that *c's* To the turrets and the walls; *Maud II iv* 33
all night long a cloud *c's* to the hill, *Geraint and E.* 691
voice *c's* to each blade of grass, *Lancelot and E.* 107
glory *c* To all high places like a golden cloud *Pass. of Arthur* 53
I *c* to the Catholic Cross once more, *The Wreck* 3
c to Faith beyond the forms of Faith! *Ancient Sage* 69
Who *c's* to earth, and once would dare ,, 115
That we might *c* together, *Happy* 92

Clinging Not *c* to some ancient saw; *Love thou thy land* 29
Unshaken, *c* to her purpose, *Princess v* 344
necks Of dragons *c* to the crazy walls, *Holy Grail* 347
C to the silent mother! *Locksley H., Sixty* 99

Clink (s) the tinsel *c* of compliment. *Princess ii* 55

Clink (verb) Thou hear'st the village hammer *c*, *In Mem. cxxi* 15

Clink'd Touch'd, *c*, and clash'd and vanish'd, *Sea Dreams* 135

Clinking Hammering and *c*, chattering stony names *Princess iii* 361

Clinkt blade flew Splintering in six, and *c* upon the stones. *Balin and Balan* 396

Clip And *c* your wings, and make you love: *Rosalind* 45
Tho' fortune *c* my wings, *Will Water.* 50

Clipt They read in arbours *c* and cut, *Amphion* 85
from her baby's forehead *c* A tiny curl, and gave it: *Enoch Arden* 235
many thousand days Were *c* by horror *Aylmer's Field* 603
Or keeps his wing'd affections *c* with crime: *Princess vii* 316
had *c* free manhood from the world— *Last Tournament* 446
a scrap, *c* out of the 'deaths' in a paper, fell. *The Wreck* 146

Cloak (s) And the red *c's* of market girls, *L. of Shalott ii* 17
Pitiful sight, wrapp'd in a soldier's *c*, *Princess v* 56
raised the *c* from brows as pale and smooth ,, 73
Wrapt in a *c*, as I saw him, *Maud I i* 59
Sir Gareth loosed A *c* that dropt *Gareth and L.* 682
wrapping her all over with the *c* He came in, *Lover's Tale iv* 86

Cloak (verb) wife-worship *c's* a secret shame? *Balin and Balan* 360
c's the scar of some repulse with lies; *Merlin and V.* 818

Cloak'd The Shadow *c* from head to foot, *In Mem. xxiii* 4

Cloäths (clothes) Sally she wesh'd foälks' *c* *North. Cobbler* 29
Look at the *c* on 'er back, ,, 109

Cloäthes (clothes) an' a-buyin' new *c*, *Village Wife* 37

Clock The slow *c* ticking, and the sound *Mariana* 74
The windy clanging of the minster *c*; *Gardener's D.* 38
The heavy *c's* knolling the drowsy hours. ,, 184
There rose a noise of striking *c's*, *Day-Dm., Revival* 2
speak for noise Of *c's* and chimes, *Princess i* 216
the dark, when *c's* Throbb'd thunder ,, *vii* 103
c Beats out the little lives of men. *In Mem. ii* 7
And hark the *c* within, *Maud I xviii* 64
lights the *c*! the hand points five— *The Flight* 94

Clock-work little *c-w* steamer paddling plied *Princess, Pro.* 71

Clod before the heavy *c* Weighs on me, *Supp. Confessions* 184
and the *c*, Less dull than thou, *Gareth and L.* 1391

Clog (s) A *c* of lead was round my feet, *The Letters* 5
To lighten this great *c* of thanks, *Princess vi* 126

Clog (verb) fulsome Pleasure *c* him, and drown *Maud I xvi* 4

Cloister (*See also* **Crag-cloister**) row Of *c's*, branch'd like mighty woods, *Palace of Art* 26
while our *c's* echo'd frosty feet, *Princess, Pro.* 183
world-old yew-tree, darkening half The *c's*, *Holy Grail* 14
Walk your dim *c*, and distribute dole *Guinevere* 683
Sometimes I frequent the Christian *c*, *Akbar's D., Inscrip.* 5

Clomb Imprisoning sweets, which, as they *c* *Arabian Nights* 40
C to the roofs, and gazed alone for hours *Princess vii* 32
neither *c*, nor brake his neck, *Gareth and L.* 56
And glad was I and *c*, but found at top *Holy Grail* 427
turn'd and slowly *c* The last hard footstep *Pass. of Arthur* 446
c Ev'n to the highest he could climb, ,, 462
C the mountain, and flung the bierries, *Kapiolani* 6

Close (an enclosure) I broke a *c* with force and arms: *Edwin Morris* 131
I lay Pent in a roofless *c* of ragged stones; *S. St. Stylites* 74
Are wither'd in the thorny *c*, *Day-Dm., Arrival* 11

Close (an end) sweet *c* of his delicious toils— *Palace of Art* 185

Close (an end) (*continued*) The *c*, 'Your Letty, only yours;' *Edwin Morris* 106
Of love that never found his earthly *c*, *Love and Duty* 1
Death dawning on him, and the *c* of all. *Enoch Arden* 832
At *c* of day; slept, woke, and went the next, *Sea Dreams* 18
Then comes the *c*.' ,, 29
and the bitter *c* of all, *Princess vi* 117
drove us, last to quite a solemn *c*— ,, *Con.* 17
all, they said, as earnest as the *c*? ,, 21
Such a war had such a *c*. *Ode on Well.* 118
Here; it is here, the *c* of the year, *Spiteful Letter* 1
Here is the golden *c* of love, *Window. Marr. Morn.* 3
To such a stern and iron-clashing *c*, *Merlin and V.* 419
Perchance, because we see not to the *c*;— *Pass. of Arthur* 21
Restrain'd himself quite to the *c*— *Lover's Tale iv* 10
Laud me not Before my time, but hear me to the *c*. ,, 243
My *c* of earth's experience May prove *Tiresias* 216
gloom of the evening, Life at a *c*; *Vastness* 15
were alone in the dell at the *c* of the day. *Bandit's Death* 19
Close (adj. and adv.) order'd all Almost as neat and *c* *Enoch Arden* 178
princedom lay *C* on the borders of a territory, *Marr. of Geraint* 33
So *c* are we, dear Mary, *To Mary Boyle* 59
but *c* to me to-day As this red rose, *Roses on the T.* 6
I was *c* on that hour of dishonour, *Charity* 28
my hot lips prest *C*, *c* to thine *Œnone* 204
I never can be *c* with her, *Balin and Balan* 186
c upon it peal'd A sharp quick thunder.' *Holy Grail* 695
C beneath the casement crimson *Locksley H., Sixty* 34
they stood So *c* together. *The Ring* 258
Now wraps her *c*, now arching leaves her bare *Prog. of Spring* 12
Close (verb) *C* the door, the shutters *c*, *Deserted House* 9
breathe it into earth and *c* it up *Wan Sculptor* 12
In love with thee forgets to *c* His curtains, *Adeline* 42
C up his eyes: tie up his chin: *D. of the O. Year* 48
With one wide Will that *c's* thine. *On a Mourner* 20
To *c* the interests of all. *Love thou thy land* 36
And this be true, till Time shall *c*, ,, 79
Death *c's* all: but something ere the end, *Ulysses* 51
till he heard the ponderous door *C*, *Aylmer's Field* 338
to *c* with Cyril's random wish: *Princess iii* 101
hearts So gentle, so employ'd, should *c* in love, ,, *vii* 67
before his journey *c's*, He shall find *Ode on Well.* 205
and the daisy *c* Her crimson fringes *In Mem. lxxii* 11
Until we *c* with all we loved, ,, *cxxxi* 11
'O dewy flowers that *c* when day is done, *Gareth and L.* 1067
To *c* with her lord's pleasure; *Geraint and E.* 214
—so that fate and craft and folly *c*, *Merlin and V.* 57
Down, down, and *c* again, and nip me flat, ,, 350
and *c* the hand Upon it; *Lancelot and E.* 1114
but he that *c's* both Is perfect, he is Lancelot— *Last Tournament* 708
And who shall escape if they *c*? *Heavy Brigade* 16
Both the days Now *c* in one. *The Ring* 79
closed her eyes, which would not *c*, ,, 299
Caught by the flower that *c's* on the fly, ,, 344
his fresh life may *c* as it began, *Prog. of Spring* 89
Close-bower'd Sir Balin sat *C-b* in that garden *Balin and Balan* 241
Close-button'd turned once more, *c-b* to the storm; *Edwin Morris* 136
Closed (*See also* **Half-closed**) *A thousand claims to reverence c* *To the Queen* 27
I *c* mine eyelids, lest the gems *M. d'Arthur* 152
all grace Summ'd up and *c* in little;— *Gardener's D.* 13
She turn'd, we *c*, we kiss'd, *Edwin Morris* 114
I had hoped that ere this period *c* *St. S. Stylites* 17
for the promise that it *c*: *Locksley Hall* 14
C in a golden ring. *Sir L. and Q. G.* 27
she *c* the Book and slept: *Enoch Arden* 499
when she *c* 'Enoch, poor man, was cast away ,, 712
Crept to the gate, and open'd it, and *c*, ,, 775
Until they *c* a bargain, hand in hand. *The Brook* 156
c her access to the wealthier farms, *Aylmer's Field* 503
fain had she *c* them now, ,, 805
c by those who mourn a friend in vain, *Lucretius* 142
And thus our conference *c*. *Princess ii* 367
until they *c* In conflict with the crash ,, *v* 490
darkness *c* me; and I fell. ,, 542

Closed (*continued*) My spirit *c* with Ida's at the lips; *Princess vii* 158
So *c* our tale, of which I give you all ,, *Con.* 1
the gates were *c* At sunset, ,, 36
few words and pithy, such as a *c* Welcome, farewell, ,, 94
where warm hands have prest and *c*, *In Mem. xiii* 7
such as *c* Grave doubts and answers ,, *xlviii* 2
whose dying eyes Were *c* with wail, ,, *xc* 6
pulses *c* their gates with a shock *Maud I i* 15
gates of Heaven are *c*, and she is gone. ,, *xviii* 12
now by this my love has *c* her sight ,, 67
C in her castle from the sound of arms. *Gareth and L* 163
But when they *c*—in a moment— ,, 1222
Dash'd on Geraint, who *c* with him, *Geraint and E.* 462
while he spoke *C* his death-drowsing eyes, *Balin and Balan* 631
C in the four walls of a hollow tower, (repeat) *Merlin and V.* 209, 543
and the thicket *c* Behind her, ,, 973
And *c* the hand upon it, and she died. *Lancelot and E.* 1135
great table of our Arthur *c* And clash'd *Holy Grail* 329
and then a fawn; and his eyes *c*. *Pelleas and E.* 39
Drew back a space, and when they *c*, ,, 573
'O *c* about by narrowing nunnery-walls, *Guinevere* 342
On the waste sand by the waste sea they *c*. *Pass. of Arthur* 92
'Sir King, I *c* mine eyelids, lest the gems ,, 320
Ideal manhood *c* in real man, *To the Queen ii* 38
round him *c* and claspt again. *Lover's Tale iv* 378
I *c* my heart to the gloom; *The Wreck* 38
If utter darkness *c* the day, *Ancient Sage* 199
c her eyes, which would not close, *The Ring* 299
Clouds and darkness *C* upon Camelot; *Merlin and the G.* 76
kiss'd his hand, another *c* his eyes, *Death of Œnone* 58
Close-latticed *C-l* to the brooding heat, *Mariana in the S.* 3
Close-lapt *c-l* in silken folds, *Lover's Tale i* 153
Closelier once mine, now thine, is *c* mine, *Merlin and V.* 446
Close-matted a wall of green *C-m*, *Day-Dm., Sleep P.* 46
Closeness such a *c*, but apart there grew, *Holy Grail* 884
Closer *C* is He than breathing, *High. Pantheism* 12
But thou art *c* to this noble prince, *Com. of Arthur* 314
C on the Sun, perhaps a world *Locksley H., Sixty* 184
Close-set wore A *c-s* robe of jasmine *Aylmer's Field* 158
Betwixt the *c-s* ivies came a broad *Lover's Tale ii* 172
Closet not to myself in the *c* alone, *Maud II v* 49
Closeted (*See also* **Long-closeted**) with that woman *c* for hours!' *Princess iii* 56
Closing (part) There—*c* like an individual life— *Love and Duty* 79
And *c* eaves of wearied eyes *In Mem. lxvii* 11
As *c* in himself the strength of ten, *Gareth and L.* 1339
c round him thro' the journey home, *Pelleas and E.* 202
Closing (s) And at the *c* of the day *L. of Shalott iv* 15
Clot Is a *c* of warmer dust, *Vision of Sin* 113
Cloth (*See also* **Altar-cloth**, **Cloth of Gold**, **Face-cloth**)
a *c* of palest gold, Which down he laid *Gareth and L.* 389
Arthur cried to rend the *c*, (repeat) ,, 400, 418
we should lap him up in *c* of lead, ,, 430
c of roughest web, and cast it down, ,, 683
sparkle of a *c* On fern and foxglove. *Sisters (E. and E.)* 117
What have I here in the *c*? *Bandit's Death* 8
Clothe That *c* the wold and meet the sky; *L. of Shalott i* 3
O, the child too *c's* the father *Locksley Hall* 91
C's and reclothes the happy plains, *Day-Dm., Sleep P.* 2
often toil'd to *c* your little ones; *Aylmer's Field* 699
lingereth she to *c* her heart with love, *Princess iv* 105
tender ash delays To *c* herself, ,, 107
Will *c* her for her bridals like the sun.' *Marr. of Geraint* 231
So *c* yourself in this, that better fits ,, 717
Herself would *c* her like the sun in Heaven. ,, 784
In this poor gown he bad me *c* myself, *Geraint and E.* 702
'And lo, I *c* myself with wisdom, *Merlin and V.* 255
her love did *c* itself in smiles About his lips! *Lover's Tale i* 658
earth-baldness *c's* itself afresh, *Demeter and P.* 49
Clothed river-sunder'd champaign *c* with corn, *Œnone* 114
C in white samite, mystic, wonderful, (repeat) *M. d'Arthur* 31, 144, 159
ridge to ridge, *C* with his breath, ,, 182
she rode forth, *c* on with chastity: *Godiva* 53

Cloud (s) (*continued*) All day long far-off in the *c* of the city, *The Wreck* 29
c of the mother's shame will enfold her ,, 100
only a *c* and a smoke who was once a pillar *Despair* 29
and higher, The *c* that hides it—higher still, the heavens Whereby the *c* was moulded, and whereout The *c* descended. *Ancient Sage* 12
beacon burn'd in vain, And now is lost in *c*: ,, 143
past into the Nameless, as a *c* Melts into Heaven. ,, 233
But still the *c's* remain;' The *c's* themselves are children of the Sun. ,, 241
A *c* between the Nameless and thyself, ,, 278
An' the sun kem out of a *c* *Tomorrow* 37
And roll'd them around like a *c*,— *Heavy Brigade* 40
One year without a storm, or even a *c*; *The Ring* 284
Would Earth tho' hid in *c* not be follow'd *Happy* 97
C's and darkness Closed upon Camelot; *Merlin and the G.* 75
Or does the gloom of Age And suffering *c* *Romney's R.* 65
my reign Was redden'd by that *c* of shame *Akbar's Dream* 64
methought The *c* was rifted by a purer gleam ,, 78
Cloud (verb) ever swarm about And *c* the highest heads, *Columbus* 120
Clouded So spake he, *c* with his own conceit, *M. d'Arthur* 110
(For all my mind is *c* with a doubt)— ,, 258
Being so *c* with his grief and love, *Holy Grail* 656
So spake he, *c* with his own conceit, *Pass. of Arthur* 278
(For all my mind is *c* with a doubt)— ,, 426
c with the grateful incense-fume *Tiresias* 183
all the Thrones are *c* by your loss, *D. of the Duke of C.* 6
Cloudier *c* on her knight—Linger'd Ettarre: *Pelleas and E.* 177
Cloudlet From little *c's* on the grass, *In Mem., Con.* 94
Cloud-pavilion'd The *c-p* element, the wood, *Lover's Tale ii* 108
Cloud-tower *C-t's* by ghostly masons wrought, *In Mem. lxx* 5
Cloud-weaver *C-w* of phantasmal hopes and fears, *To Victor Hugo* 2
Cloudy made him look so *c* and so cold; *Geraint and E.* 48
Clout an' the clats an' the *c's*, *Spinster's S's.* 87
Clove (s) nutmeg rocks and isles of *c*. *The Voyage* 40
Clove (verb) *c* The citron-shadows in the blue: *Arabian Nights* 14
the crowd dividing *c* An advent to the throne: *Princess iv* 283
Laid him that *c* it grovelling on the ground. *Gareth and L.* 972
with a stronger buffet he *c* the helm ,, 1406
said Mark, and *c* him thro' the brain. *Last Tournament* 754
C into perilous chasms our walls *Def. of Lucknow* 55
And *c* the Moslem crescent moon, *Happy* 44
Cloven (*See also* **Earthquake-cloven, Furrow-cloven**)
Was *c* with the million stars *Ode to Memory* 35
That not a worm is *c* in vain; *In Mem. liv* 9
Till Gareth's shield was *c*; *Gareth and L.* 971
earth beneath me yawning *c* With such a sound *Lover's Tale i* 602
My heart was *c* with pain; ,, *ii* 200
Clover Rare broidry of the purple *c*. *A Dirge* 38
among the meadows, the *c* and the clematis, *City Child* 9
Clover-hill with white bells the *c-h* swells *Sea-Fairies* 14
Clown thou art mated with a *c*, *Locksley Hall* 47
knave nor *c* Shall hold their orgies *You might have won* 11
Shakespeare's curse on *c* and knave ,, 27
this is proper to the *c*, Tho' smock'd, or furr'd and purpled, still the *c*, *Princess iv* 246
turnspits for the *c*, The drunkard's football, ,, 516
Glorifying *c* and satyr; ,, *v* 187
By blood a king, at heart a *c*; *In Mem. cxi* 4
Not all mismated with a yawning *c*, *Geraint and E.* 426
not worthy to be knight; A churl, a *c*!' *Balin and Balan* 286
Like a *c*—by chance he met me— *Locksley H., Sixty* 256
An' ya call'd 'im a *c*, ya did, *Church-warden, etc.* 30
Club (*See also* **Battle-club**) talk'd At wine, in *c's*, of art, *Princess, Pro.* 161
Clump (mend) I could fettle and *c* owd booöts *North. Cobbler* 13
Clung You should have *c* to Fulvia's waist, *D. of F. Women* 259
Then they *c* about The old man's neck, *Dora* 163
friendly mist of morn *C* to the lake. *Edwin Morris* 108
When I *c* to all the present *Locksley Hall* 14
evil fancies *c* Like serpent eggs together, *Enoch Arden* 479
from the beetling crag to which he *c* *Aylmer's Field* 229
sootflake of so many a summer still *C* to their fancies) *Sea Dreams* 36
and the child *C* to the mother, ,, 245
then, a moment after, *c* About him, *Princess ii* 312

Clung (*continued*) about his motion *c* The shadow of his sister, *Princess v* 257
Late the little children *c*: *Ode on Well.* 237
C to the shield that Lancelot lent him, *Gareth and L.* 1320
dawn ascending lets the day Strike where it *c*: *Geraint and E.* 693
but that other *c* to him, Fixt in her will, *Merlin and V.* 187
c about her lissome limbs, ,, 223
curved an arm about his neck, *C* like a snake; ,, 242
while the skin *C* but to crate and basket, ,, 625
c to him and hugg'd him close; ,, 945
to his crown the golden dragon *c*, *Lancelot and E.* 434
knightly in me twined and *c* Round that one sin, *Holy Grail* 774
fell thick rain, plume droopt and mantel *c*, *Last Tournament* 213
A voice *c* sobbing till he question'd it, ,, 759
C to the dead earth, and the land was still. *Guinevere* 8
for crest the golden dragon *c* Of Britain; ,, 594
c In utter silence for so long, *Sisters (E. and E.)* 216
from the ladders to which they had *c*, *Def. of Lucknow* 58
C closer to us for a longer term *Columbus* 197
and the dark-blue clematis, *c*, *V. of Maeldune* 39
I *c* to the sinking form, *The Wreck* 105
She *c* to me with such a hard embrace, *The Ring* 435
Cluster (s) (*See also* **Sun-cluster**) Below the starry *c's* bright, *L. of Shalott iii* 25
tropic shade and palms in *c*, *Locksley Hall* 160
red roofs about a narrow wharf In *c*; *Enoch Arden* 4
lithe reluctant boughs to tear away Their tawny *c's*, ,, 382
Came men and women in dark *c's* *Sea Dreams* 226
Cluster (verb) The foxglove *c* dappled bells.' *Two Voices* 72
Clustered sunny hair *C* about his temples *Œnone* 60
Clutch So I *c* it. Christ! 'Tis gone: *St. S. Stylites* 207
And lives to *c* the golden keys, *In Mem. lxiv* 10
Clutch'd (*See also* **Clemm'd**) *c* the sword, And strongly wheel'd and threw it. *M. d'Arthur* 135
stoop'd and *c* him, fair and good, *Will Water.* 133
So my mother *c* The truth at once, *Princess iii* 60
He, standing still, was *c*; ,, *iv* 260
wakening, fiercely *c* the shield; *Gareth and L.* 1304
C at the crag, and started thro' mid air *Last Tournament* 14
c the sword, And strongly wheel'd and threw it. *Pass. of Arthur* 303
Or *c* the sacred crown of Prester John, *Columbus* 110
Clutter'd It *c* here, it chuckled there; *The Goose* 25
Coal On the *c's* I lay, A vessel full of sin: *St. S. Stylites* 169
left his *c* all turn'd into gold *Maud I x* 11
c's of fire you heap upon my head *Romney's R.* 141
Coal-black flow'd His *c-b* curls as on he rode, *L. of Shalott iii* 31
Coämb (comb) raäke out Hell wi' a small-tooth *c*— *Village Wife* 76
Coämb'd (combed) theer an' then I *c* 'im down, *Church warden, etc.* 32
Coarse sense of touch is something *c*, *Talking Oak* 163
growing *c* to sympathise with clay. *Locksley Hall* 46
daughter of our meadows, yet not *c*; *The Brook* 69
thou, My lord, eat also, tho' the fare is *c*, *Geraint and E.* 208
I can well believe, for he look'd so *c* *In the Child. Hosp.* 7
Coarseness According to the *c* of their kind, *Princess iv* 346
Coast show'd an iron *c* and angry waves. *Palace of Art* 69
All round the *c* the languid air *Lotos-Eaters* 5
all in shade, Gloom'd the low *c* *The Voyage* 42
leagues along that breaker-beaten *c* *Enoch Arden* 51
Then moving up the *c* they landed him, ,, 665
seaward-bound for health they gain'd a *c*, *Sea Dreams* 16
she told it, having dream'd Of that same *c*. ,, 207
He bad you guard the sacred *c's*. *Ode on Well.* 172
left the last free race with naked *c's*! *Third of Feb.* 40
A moulder'd citadel on the *c*, *The Daisy* 28
A lucid veil from *c* to *c*, *In Mem. lxvii* 14
rolling brine That breaks the *c*. ,, *cvii* 15
shipwreck'd man on a *c* Of ancient fable and fear— *Maud II ii* 31
Back from the Breton *c*, ,, 43
province with a hundred miles of *c*, (repeat) *Merlin and V.* 588, 647
about a stone On the bare *c*. *Guinevere* 52
After the sunset, down the *c*, ,, 238
All down the lonely *c* of Lyonnesse, ,, 240
mountains ended in a *c* Of ever-shifting sand, *Pass. of Arthur* 85
while we roam'd along the dreary *c*, *Lover's Tale iv* 145
while I wander'd down the *c*, *Locksley H., Sixty* 53

College-time save for c-t's Or Temple-eaten terms, Alymer's Field 104
Colon (Columbus) See **Christopher Colon**
Colony near the c Cámulodúne, Boädicea 5
Lo their c half-defended ! lo their c, ,, 17
Then a phantom c smoulder'd on the refluent estuary ; ,, 28
Lo the c, there they rioted in the city of Cúnobelíne ! ,, 60
silent c hearing her tumultuous adversaries ,, 78
Fell the c, city and citadel, ,, 86
Colossal Let his great example stand C, Ode on Well. 221
Colosseum Gain'd their huge C. St. Telemachus 45
Colour (See also **Flame-colour**) sweet is the c of cove and cave, Sea-Fairies 30
I lose my c, I lose my breath, Eleänore 137
A magic web with c's gay. L. of Shalott ii 2
A word could bring the c to my cheek ; Gardener's D. 196
came a c and a light, Locksley Hall 25
The c flies into his cheeks : Day-Dm., Arrival 19
Then the Captain's c heighten'd, The Captain 29
the c flushes Her sweet face from brow to chin : L. of Burleigh 61
She wore the c's I approved. The Letters 16
a rough piece Of early rigid c, Aylmer's Field 281
yet her cheek Kept c : wondrous ! ,, 506
sense of wrong had touched her face With c) Princess, Pro. 220
April daffodilly (Her mother's c) ,, ii 325
In c's gayer than the morning mist, ,, 438
shook the woods, And danced the c, ,, iii 293
'Sir Ralph has got your c's : ,, iv 594
With Psyche's c round his helmet, ,, v 534
But such as gather'd c day by day. ,, vii 118
But distant c, happy hamlet, The Daisy 27
And with the thought her c burns ; In Mem. vi 34
Be all the c of the flower : ,, xliii 8
The c's of the crescent prime ? ,, cxvi 4
Saying in odour and c, 'Ah, be Among the roses Maud I xxi 12
O rainbow with three c's after rain, Gareth and L. 1160
my child, how fresh the c's look, How fast they hold like c's of a shell Marr. of Geraint 680
and play'd upon it, And made it of two c's ; Geraint and E. 292
And so there lived some c in your cheek, ,, 621
In c like the satin-shining palm Merlin and V. 224
With c's of the heart that are not theirs. ,, 822
Took gayer c's, like an opal warm'd. ,, 950
And lichen'd into c with the crags : Lancelot and E. 44
The low sun makes the c : ,, 134
The shape and c of a mind and life, ,, 335
let me bring your c back ; ,, 387
secret blazed itself In the heart's c's ,, 837
But did not love the c ; ,, 840
cell were dyed With rosy c's leaping on the wall ; Holy Grail 120
In c like the fingers of a hand Before a burning taper, ,, 693
Damsels in divers c's like the cloud Pelleas and E. 53
That ware their ladies' c's on the casque, Last Tournament 184
With all the kindlier c's of the field.' ,, 224
And glowing in all c's, the live grass, ,, 233
I yearn'd for warmth and c which I found In Lancelot— Guinevere 647
The c and the sweetness from the rose, Lover's Tale i 172
Her cheek did catch the c of her words. ,, 569
shadowing pencil's naked forms C and life : ,, ii 181
And blurr'd in c and form, Dead Prophet 22
concentrate into form And c all you are, Romney's R. 8
Colour'd See **Emerald-colour'd, Leaden-coloured, Vary-coloured**
Colourless for all his face was white And c, M. d'Arthur 213
for all his face was white And c, Pass. of Arthur 381
Colt 'Then ran she, gamesome as the c, Talking Oak 121
babes were running wild Like c's about the waste. Enoch Arden 305
He pointed out a pasturing c, The Brook 136
Squire had seen the c at grass, ,, 139
the c would fetch its price ; ,, 149
she's yet a c—Take, break her : Princess v 455
Ran like a c, and leapt at all he saw : Com. of Arthur 322
never c would more delight To roll Romney's R. 13
Colt-like c-l whinny and with hoggish whine St. S. Stylites 177
Columbus How young C seem'd to rove, The Daisy 17
Column Six c's, three on either side, Arabian Nights 144
So like a shatter'd c lay the King ; M. d'Arthur 221
people hum About the c's base, St. S. Stylites 39
The watcher on the c till the end ; ,, 163
And in we stream'd Among the c's, Princess ii 435
To left and right, of those tall c's ,, vi 354
bared the knotted c of his throat, Marr. of Geraint 74
massive c's, like a shorecliff cave, Lancelot and E. 406
So like a shatter'd c lay the King ; Pass. of Arthur 389
masses Of thundershaken c's indistinct, Lover's Tale ii 66
From c on to c, as in a wood, ,, iv 189
names, Graven on memorial c's, Tiresias 124
Co-mate one of my c-m's Own'd a rough dog, Gareth and L. 1010
true c-m's regather round the mast ; Pref. Son. 19th Cent. 5
Comb (s) See **Coämb, Comb of Pearl, Hornet-comb**
Comb (valley) they past a narrow c wherein Gareth and L. 1193
Comb (verb) With a comb of pearl I would c my hair ; The Mermaid 11
I would c my hair till my ringlets ,, 14
Combat (s) And when the tide of c stands, Sir Galahad 10
To prick us on to c 'Like to like ! Princess v 304
Not dare to watch the c, Geraint and E. 154
In c with the follower of Limours, ,, 501
Combat (verb) sware to c for my claim till death. Princess v 360
a knight To c for my sister, Lyonors, Gareth and L. 608
He needs must c might with might, Epilogue 23
Comb'd (See also **Coämb'd**) as I c I would sing and say, The Mermaid 12
I curl'd and c his comely head, The Sisters 31
Combing C her hair Under the sea, The Mermaid 4
c out her long black hair damp from the river ; Princess iv 276
Comb of Pearl With a c o p, On a throne ? The Mermaid 7
With a c o p I would comb my hair ; ,, 11
Made with her right a c o p Merlin and V. 244
Come (See also **Coom, To-come**) Spring will c never more. All Things will die 15
Ye will c never more, ,, 48
He will not c,' she said ; Mariana 82
When cats run home and light is c, The Owl i 1
C not as thou camest of late, Ode to Memory 8
C forth, I charge thee, arise, ,, 46
C from the woods that belt the gray hill-side, ,, 55
Dark-brow'd sophist, c not anear ; Poet's Mind 8
Hollow smile and frozen sneer C not here. ,, 11
O hither, c hither and furl your sails, Sea-Fairies 16
C hither to me and to me ; Hither, c hither and frolic and play ; ,, 17
Hither, c hither and see ; ,, 28
O hither, c hither, and be our lords, ,, 32
C away : no more of mirth Is here Deserted House 13
C away : for Life and Thought Here no longer dwell ; ,, 17
How could I rise and c away, Oriana 57
I dare not die and c to thee, ,, 96
Lull'd echoes of laborious day C to you, Margaret 30
C down, c down, and hear me speak : ,, 56
C down, c home, My Rosalind, Rosalind 33
C's out thy deep ambrosial smile. Eleänore 74
Thought seems to c and go In thy large eyes, ,, 96
C only, when the days are still, My life is full 23
Fresh-water springs c up through bitter brine. If I were loved 8
The knights c riding two and two ; L. of Shalott ii 25
'The curse is c upon me,' ,, iii 44
night c's on that knows not morn, Mariana in the S. 94
I saw the dragon-fly C from the wells Two Voices 9
'Then c's the check, the change, the fall, ,, 163
In days that never c again. ,, 324
Here c's to-day, Pallas and Aphroditè, Œnone 85
Should c most welcome, seeing men, ,, 129
(power of herself Would c uncall'd for) ,, 147
sounds at night c from the inmost hills, ,, 249
her child !—a shudder c's Across me : ,, 253
Lest their shrill happy laughter c to me ,, 258
the stars c forth Talk with the wild Cassandra, ,, 262
I made a feast ; I bad him c ; The Sisters 13
There c's no murmur of reply. Palace of Art 286

Come (*continued*) shepherd lads on every side 'ill c from far away, *May Queen* 27
The night-winds c and go, mother, ,, 33
I only wish to live till the snowdrops c again: *May Queen, N. Y's. E.* 14
and the sun c out on high: ,, ,, 15
And the swallow, 'ill c back again ,, ,, 19
When the flowers c again, mother, ,, ,, 25
And you'll c sometimes and see me ,, ,, 30
If I can I'll c again, mother, ,, ,, 37
Don't let Effie c to see me ,, ,, 43
sweet is the new violet, that c's beneath the skies, ,, *Con.* 5
if it c three times, I thought, ,, ,, 38
to wait a little while till you and Effie c— ,, ,, 58
we should c like ghosts to trouble joy. *Lotos-Eaters, C. S.* 74
'C here, That I may look on thee.' *D. of F. Women* 123
C's up to take his own. *D. of the O. Year* 36
And gently c's the world to those *To J. S.* 3
Nothing c's to thee new or strange. ,, 74
So let the change which c's be free *Love thou thy land* 45
The Spirit of the years to c ,, 55
keep a thing, its use will c. *The Epic* 42
Merlin sware that I should c again *M. d'Arthur* 23
land, where no one c's, Or hath c, ,, 202
'Arthur is c again: he cannot die.' ,, *Ep.* 24
'C again, and thrice as fair; ,, 26
'C With all good things, and war shall be no more.' ,, 27
News from the humming city c's to it In sound of funeral *Gardener's D.* 35
Nor heard us c, nor from her tendance ,, 144
Call'd to me from the years to c, ,, 180
the time Is c to raise the veil. ,, 274
for this orphan, I am c to you: *Dora* 64
His mother, he cried out to c to her: ,, 138
but now I c For Dora: take her back; ,, 142
I go to-night: I c to-morrow morn. *Audley Court* 70
And when does this c by? *Walk. to the Mail* 7
and here it c's With five at top: ,, 112
For that the evil ones c here, *St. S. Stylites* 98
That here c those that worship me? ,, 125
I do not say But that a time may c— ,, 190
C, blessed brother, c. ,, 204
And down the way you use to c, *Talking Oak* 115
Spun round in station, but the end had c. *Love and Duty* 76
O might it c like one that looks content, ,, 93
slow and sure c's up the golden year. *Golden Year* 31
The fatal byword of all years to c, *Godiva* 67
C, my friends, 'Tis not too late to seek *Ulysses* 56
Man c's and tills the field and lies *Tithonus* 3
there c's A glimpse of that dark world ,, 32
crimson c's upon the robin's breast; *Locksley Hall* 17
tho' my mortal summers to such length of years should c ,, 67
Slowly c's a hungry people, ,, 135
Knowledge c's, but wisdom lingers, (repeat) ,, 141, 143
Never c's the trader, never floats ,, 161
C's a vapour from the margin, ,, 191
Faint murmurs from the meadows c, *Day-Dm., Sleep P.* 6
C, Care and Pleasure, Hope and Pain, ,, 55
He c's, scarce knowing what he seeks: ,, *Arrival* 17
The flashes c and go; *St. Agnes' Eve* 26
'Love may c, and love may go, *Edward Gray* 29
Till Ellen Adair c back to me. ,, 32
she c's and dips Her laurel in the wine, *Will Water.* 17
earth of light and shade C's out a perfect round. ,, 68
To c and go, and c again, ,, 229
'That all c's round so just and fair: *Lady Clare* 18
Why c you drest like a village maid, ,, 67
'If I c drest like a village maid. ,, 69
When beneath his roof they c. *L. of Burleigh* 40
C not, when I am dead, *Come not, when, etc.* 1
There c's a sound of marriage bells. *The Letters* 48
Here is custom c your way; *Vision of Sin* 64
Therefore c's it we are wise. ,, 100

Come (*continued*) day that is dead Will never c back to me. *Break, break, etc.* 16
'Save them from this, whatever c's to me.' *Enoch Arden* 118
(Sure that all evil would c out of it) ,, 162
make him merry, when I c home again. ,, 199
C, Annie, c, cheer up before I go.' ,, 200
Look to the babes, and till I c again ,, 219
if he c again, vext will he be To find ,, 301
when Enoch c's again Why then he shall repay me— ,, 309
'C with us Father Philip' ,, 368
If Enoch c's—but Enoch will not c— ,, 431
C out and see.' But she—she put him off— ,, 460
when the dead man c to life beheld His wife ,, 758
let them c, I am their father; but she must not c, For my dead face would vex her after-life. ,, 889
'Whence c you?' and the brook, why not? replies. I c from haunts of coot and hern, *The Brook* 22
men may c and men may go, (repeat) *The Brook* 33, 49, 65, 184
Yes, men may c and go; and these are gone, *The Brook* 186
days That most she loves to talk of, c with me. ,, 226
you will be welcome—O, c in!' ,, 228
Cries 'C up hither,' as a prophet to us? *Aylmer's Field* 745
link'd their race with times to c— ,, 779
Then c's the close,' *Sea Dreams* 29
Too ripe, too late! they c too late for use. ,, 67
then c's what c's Hereafter: ,, 177
'His deeds yet live, the worst is yet to c. ,, 314
recollect the dreams that c Just ere the waking: *Lucretius* 35
'C out,' he said, 'To the Abbey: *Princess, Pro.* 50
'C, listen! here is proof that you were miss'd: ,, 177
No matter: we will say whatever c's. ,, 239
Should c to fight with shadows and to fall. ,, *i* 10
what, if these weird seizures c Upon you ,, 82
ye c, The first-fruits of the stranger: ,, *ii* 43
For Solomon may c to Sheba yet.' ,, 349
C from the dying moon, and blow, ,, *iii* 6
Father will c to thee soon; (repeat) ,, 10, 12
Father will c to his babe in the nest, ,, 13
Then c's the feebler heiress of your plan, ,, 237
Nor willing men should c among us, ,, 318
Would rather we had never c! ,, *iv* 243
there are those to avenge us and they c: ,, 501
Thy face across his fancy c's, ,, 579
in the night Had c on Psyche weeping: ,, *v* 50
c's With the air of the trumpet round him, ,, 161
You did but c as goblins in the night, ,, 220
(our royal word upon it, He c's back safe) ,, 225
As c's a pillar of electric cloud, ,, 524
'C hither, O Psyche,' she cried out, 'embrace me, c, Quick while I melt; ,, *vi* 284
C to the hollow heart they slander so! ,, 288
C down, O maid, from yonder mountain ,, *vii* 192
And c, for Love is of the valley, c, For Love is of the valley, c thou down And find him; ,, 198
but c; for all the vales Await thee; ,, 215
When c's another such? never, I think, ,, 244
Then c's the statelier Eden back to men: ,, 293
trust in all things high C's easy to him, ,, 330
the new day c's, the light Dearer for night, ,, 346
I love thee: c, Yield thyself up: ,, 363
But yonder, whiff! there c's a sudden heat, ,, *Con.* 58
To thee the greatest soldier c's; *Ode on Well.* 88
C to us, love us and make us your own: *W. to Alexandra* 30
Jenny, my cousin, had c to the place, *Grandmother* 25
she c's and goes at her will, ,, 79
Often they c to the door in a pleasant kind of a dream. They c and sit by my chair, ,, 82
neighbours c and laugh and gossip, ,, 91
summun 'ull c ater meä mayhap *N. Farmer, O. S.* 61
C, when no graver cares employ, Godfather, c and see your boy: *To F. D. Maurice* 1
(Take it and c) to the Isle of Wight; ,, 12
C, Maurice, c: the lawn as yet Is hoar with rime, ,, 41
Nor pay but one, but c for many, ,, 47
I c to the test, a tiny poem *Hendecasyllabics* 3

Come (*continued*) every height *c's* out, and jutting peak *Spec. of Iliad* 13
my heart is there before you are *c*, and gone, *Window. On the Hill* 14
Take my love, for love will *c*, Love will *c* but once a life. ,, *No Answer* 20
Sun *c's*, moon *c's*, Time slips away. ,, *When* 1
Flash, I am coming, I *c*, ,, *Marr. Morn.* 13
And yet we trust it *c's* from thee, *In Mem., Pro.* 23
From out waste places *c's* a cry, ,, *iii* 7
Or 'here to-morrow will he *c*.' ,, *vi* 24
A happy lover who has *c* ,, *viii* 1
saying; '*C's* he thus, my friend? ,, *xii* 13
C Time, and teach me, many years, ,, *xiii* 13
C stepping lightly down the plank, ,, *xiv* 7
c The man I held as half-divine; ,, 9
C quick, thou bringest all I love. ,, *xvii* 8
C then, pure hands, and bear the head ,, *xviii* 9
And *c*, whatever loves to weep, ,, 11
The praise that *c's* to constancy.' ,, *xxi* 12
To thee too *c's* the golden hour ,, *xxxix* 6
And hopes and light regrets that *c* ,, *xl* 7
The wonders that have *c* to thee, ,, *xli* 22
Peace; *c* away: the song of woe ,, *lvii* 1
Peace; *c* away: we do him wrong ,, 3
let us go. *C*; let us go: your cheeks are pale; ,, 5
With so much hope for years to *c*, ,, *lix* 14
The foolish neighbours *c* and go, ,, *lx* 13
There *c's* a glory on the walls: ,, *lxvii* 4
likeness, hardly seen before, *C's* out— ,, *lxxiv* 4
There cannot *c* a mellower change, ,, *lxxxi* 3
Ah dear, but *c* thou back to me: ,, *xc* 21
But he, the Spirit himself, may *c* ,, *xciii* 6
The violet *c's*, but we are gone. ,, *cv* 8
With thousand shocks that *c* and go, ,, *cxiii* 17
I *c* once more; the city sleeps; ,, *cxix* 3
Behind thee *c's* the greater light: ,, *cxxi* 12
With faith that *c's* of self-control, ,, *cxxxi* 9
And back we *c* at fall of dew. ,, *Con.* 100
can a sweeter chance ever *c* to me here? *Maud I i* 62
Cold and clear-cut face, why *c* you so cruelly meek ,, *iii* 1
C sliding out of her sacred glove, ,, *vi* 85
Then let *c* what *c* may, (repeat) ,, *xi* 5, 12
One is *c* to woo her. ,, *xii* 28
That old man never *c's* to his place: ,, *xiii* 24
shook my heart to think she *c's* once more; ,, *xviii* 10
her brother *c's*, like a blight On my fresh hope, ,, *xix* 102
And then, oh then, *c* out to me For a minute, ,, *xx* 44
C out to your own true lover, ,, 46
C into the garden, Maud, (repeat) ,, *xxii* 1, 3
C hither, the dances are done, ,, 54
But *c* to her waking, find her asleep, ,, *II ii* 81
Get thee hence, nor *c* again, ,, *iv* 56
The day *c's*, a dull red ball ,, 65
Has *c* to pass as foretold; ,, *v* 44
c's from another stiller world of the dead, ,, 70
he *c's* to the second corpse in the pit? ,, 88
some kind heart will *c* To bury me, ,, 102
I *c* to be grateful at last for a little thing: ,, *III vi* 3
Ye *c* from Arthur's court. *Com. of Arthur* 249
will not die, But pass, again to *c*; ,, 422
c to see The glories of our King: *Gareth and L.* 243
King be King at all, or *c* From Fairyland, ,, 246
Lest he should *c* to shame thy judging of him.' ,, 469
the seneschal, would *c* Blustering upon them, ,, 513
Now therefore have I *c* for Lancelot.' ,, 623
And therefore am I *c* for Lancelot.' ,, 644
And look who *c's* behind,' ,, 752
C, therefore, leave thy lady lightly ,, 957
Look, Who *c's* behind?' ,, 1211
and wherefore now *C* ye, not call'd? ,, 1248
I but *c* like you to see the hunt, *Marr. of Geraint* 179
To find, at some place I shall *c* at, ,, 219
C's flying over many a windy wave To Britain, ,, 337
Constrain'd us, but a better time has *c*; ,, 716
By the flat meadow, till she saw them *c*; ,, 832
Look, Here *c's* a laggard hanging down his head, *Geraint and E.* 60

Come (*continued*) *C*, we will slay him and will have his horse *Geraint and E.* 62
said the second, 'yonder *c's* a knight.' ,, 126
And if he want me, let him *c* to me. ,, 237
You *c* with no attendance, page or maid, ,, 322
c with morn, And snatch me from him as by violence; ,, 356
C slipping o'er their shadows on the sand, ,, 471
And now their hour has *c*; ,, 697
I *c* the mouthpiece of our King to Doorm ,, 796
'If he will not go To Arthur, then will Arthur *c* to you,' ,, 815
sometime you would *c* To these my lists ,, 839
now behold me *c* To cleanse this common sewer ,, 894
overthrowing ever knight who *c's*. *Balin and Balan* 13
My violence, and my villainy, *c* to shame.' ,, 492
Art yet half-yolk, not even *c* to down— ,, 569
and now The night has *c*. ,, 621
'*C* from the storm,' and having no reply, *Merlin and V.* 895
to have my shield In keeping till I *c*.' *Lancelot and E.* 383
who will *c* to all I am And overcome it; ,, 448
'Is it Lancelot who hath *c* Despite the wound ,, 565
This will he send or *c* for: ,, 635
when the ghostly man had *c* and gone, ,, 1101
Or *c* to take the King to Fairyland? ,, 1257
C, for you left me taking no farewell, ,, 1274
phantom of a cup that *c's* and goes?' *Holy Grail* 44
thought That now the Holy Grail would *c* again; But sin broke out. Ah, Christ, that it would *c*, ,, 92
might it *c* To me by prayer and fasting?' ,, 95
we know not whence they *c*; ,, 147
chance of noble deeds will *c* and go ,, 318
madness has *c* on us for our sins.' ,, 357
And hither am I *c*; ,, 468
fail'd from my side, nor *c* Cover'd, ,, 470
and in the strength of this *C* victor. ,, 481
and *c* thou too, For thou shalt see the vision ,, 483
and the vision had not *c*; ,, 572
C, as they will; and many a time they *c*, ,, 911
But lately *c* to his inheritance, *Pelleas and E.* 18
For out of the waste islands had he *c*, ,, 86
So that he could not *c* to speech with her. ,, 205
if he *c's* again'—there she brake short; ,, 295
C, ye know nothing: here I pledge my troth, ,, 341
Then, when I *c* within her counsels, ,, 348
they *c* no more Till the sweet heavens have fill'd it ,, 509
and say his hour is *c*, *Last Tournament* 86
C—let us gladden their sad eyes, ,, 222
Tristram, waiting for the quip to *c*, ,, 260
C, thou art crabb'd and sour: ,, 272
as the water Moab saw *C* round by the East, ,, 483
C, I am hunger'd and half-anger'd— ,, 719
And out beyond into the dream to *c*.' ,, 721
Traitor, *c* out, ye are trapt at last,' *Guinevere* 106
then she, 'The end is *c*, And I am shamed ,, 110
For if there ever *c* a grief to me ,, 200
knowest thou now from whence I *c*— ,, 433
think not that I *c* to urge thy crimes, ,, 532
I did not *c* to curse thee, Guinevere, ,, 533
But hither shall I never *c* again, ,, 578
Merlin sware that I should *c* again To rule *Pass. of Arthur* 191
waste land, where no one *c's*, Or hath *c*, ,, 370
He *c's* again; but—if he *c* no more— ,, 451
I *c*, great Mistress of the ear and eye: *Lover's Tale i* 22
O Love, O Hope! They *c*, ,, 47
Death gave back, and would no further *c*. ,, 115
thronging fancies *c* To boys and girls ,, 554
seas upon my head To *c* my way! ,, 661
should he not *c* my way if he would? ,, 667
why *should* he *c* my way Robed in those robes ,, 670
C like an angel to a damned soul, ,, 673
C like a careless and a greedy heir ,, 675
C's in upon him in the dead of night, ,, *ii* 154
thought His dreams had *c* again. ,, *iv* 78
Send! bid him *c*;' but Lionel was away— ,, 101
To *c* and revel for one hour with him ,, 182
'you are sure it 'll all *c* right,' *First Quarrel* 1

Come (*continued*) I'll *c* for an hour to-morrow, *First Quarrel* 46
C, c, little wife, let it rest ! ,, 62
I am sure it 'll all *c* right.' (repeat) ,, 74, 91
'O mother, *c* out to me !' *Rizpah* 2
what are *you* ? do you *c* as a spy ? ,, 11
C ! Here's to your happy union with my child ! *Sisters (E. and E.)* 67
Pray *c* and see my mother. ,, 191
'Pray *c* and see my mother, and farewell.' ,, 196
know they *c*, They smile upon me, ,, 278
when I saw him *c* in at the door, *In the Child. Hosp.* 2
Had ? has it *c* ? It has only dawn'd. It will *c* by and by. ,, 23
'Little children should *c* to me.' ,, 50
women and children *c* out, *Def. of Lucknow* 100
He might be kindlier : happily *c* the day ! *Sir J. Oldcastle* 23
might have *c* to learn Our Wiclif's learning : ,, 64
who will *c*, God willing, to outlearn the filthy friar. ,, 117
He that thirsteth, *c* and drink ! ,, 134
Who *c's* ? A thousand marks are set upon my head. ,, 194
he unchain'd for all the world to *c*.' *Columbus* 215
'*C* to us, O *c, c*' *V. of Maeldune* 98
that also has *c* from Thee ; *De Prof. Human C.* 7
from within The city *c's* a murmur void of joy, *Tiresias* 101
C from the brute, poor souls— *Despair* 36
When the bat *c's* out of his cave, ,, 89
'And idle gleams will *c* and go, *Ancient Sage* 240
C, speak a little comfort ! *The Flight* 17
he *c's*, and finds me dead. ,, 72
my own true sister, *c* forth ! the world is wide. ,, 96
That matters not : let *c* what will ; ,, 103
an' tould her to *c* away from the man, *Tomorrow* 20
whin Dan didn't *c* to the fore, ,, 43
av the bird 'ud *c* to me call, ,, 45
for a blessin' 'ud *c* wid the green !' ,, 64
to-morrow—you, you *c* so late, *Locksley H., Sixty* 214
one has *c* to claim his bride, ,, 263
I that loathed, have *c* to love him. ,, 280
On you will *c* the curse of all the land, *The Fleet* 3
C's at last to the bounteous *On Jub. Q. Victoria* 10
far-off friendship that he *c's* no more, *Demeter and P.* 90
She *c's* to dress me in my bridal veil. *The Ring* 98
My ring too when she *c's* of age, ,, 289
Let her *c* ! And we will feed her with our mountain air, ,, 318
There will *c* a witness soon *Forlorn* 25
Dreadful ! has it *c* to this, ,, 43
C back, nor let me know it ! *Happy* 5
wall of solid flesh that *c's* between your soul ,, 35
May I *c* a little nearer, ,, 55
'I *c* with your spring-flowers.' *To Mary Boyle* 17
C, Spring, for now from all the dripping eaves *Prog. of Spring* 5
She *c's* ! The loosen'd rivulets run ; ,, 9
C, Spring ! She *c's* on waste and wood, ,, 22
C, Spring ! She *c's*, and Earth is glad ,, 48
Will my Indian brother *c* ? *Romney's R.* 143
If my body *c* from brutes, (repeat) *By an Evolution.* 5, 13
ghostly murmur floated, '*C* to me, Œnone ! *Death of Œnone* 79
But *c*, My noble friend, *Akbar's Dream* 17
Or makes a friend where'er he *c*, *The Wanderer* 6
But seldom *c's* the poet here, *Poets and Critics* 15
c's a gleam of what is higher. *Faith* 6
Come-agains By-gones ma' be *c-a* ; *First Quarrel* 69
Comelier comely, yea, and *c* than myself. *Gareth and L.* 610
taller indeed, Rosier and *c*, thou— *Last Tournament* 710
Comeliness a broad-blown *c*, red and white, *Maud I xiii* 9
Comely '*C*, too, by all that's fair,' *Princess ii* 114
say she's *c* ; there's the fairer chance : ,, *v* 460
c, yea, and comelier than myself. *Gareth and L.* 610
Yet, since the face *is c*— *Geraint and E.* 551
Comer (*See also* **Chance-comer, New-comer**) But spring, a new *c*, A spring rich *Nothing will die* 21
Comest Thou *c* morning or even ; *Leonine Eleg.* 15
Thou *c* not with shows of flaunting vines *Ode to Memory* 48
Thou *c* atween me and the skies, *Oriana* 75
Thou *c*, much wept for : *In Mem. xvii* 1
'Whence *c* thou, my guest, *Lancelot and E.* 181

Comest (*continued*) thou *c*, darling boy ; (repeat) *De Prof. Two G.* 10, 34
Cometh At midnight the moon *c*, *Claribel* 13
she *c* not morning or even. *Leonine Eleg.* 15
He *c* not,' she said ; (repeat) *Mariana* 22, 34, 46, 58
I know He *c* quickly : *Fatima* 23
he that *c*, like an honour'd guest, *Ode on Well.* 80
and there *c* a victory now. *Boädicea* 46
Comfort (s) (*See also* **Coomfut**) The *c*, I have found in thee : *Miller's D.* 234
dreadful eternity, No *c* anywhere ; *Palace of Art* 268
Comfort thyself : what *c* is in me ? *M. d'Arthur* 243
Then follow'd counsel, *c*, *Love and Duty* 69
Where is *c* ? in division of the records of the mind ? *Locksley Hall* 69
C ? *c* scorned of devils ! ,, 75
'I may see her now, May be some little *c* ;' *Enoch Arden* 276
Why, that would be her *c* ;' ,, 809
but a voice Of *c* and an open hand of help, *Aylmer's Field* 174
they talk'd, Poor children, for their *c* : ,, 427
what *c* ? none for me !' *Princess v* 78
Take *c* : live, dear lady, ,, 80
I think Our chiefest *c* is the little child ,, 430
Sole *c* of my dark hour, ,, *vi* 194
That out of words a *c* win ; *In Mem. xx* 10
Of *c* clasp'd in truth reveal'd ; ,, *xxxvii* 22
And find his *c* in thy face ; ,, *cix* 20
take again That *c* from their converse *Geraint and E.* 950
saying in low tones, 'Have *c*,' *Lancelot and E.* 995
If here be *c*, and if ours be sin, *Last Tournament* 575
Comfort thyself : what *c* is in me ? *Pass. of Arthur* 411
Come, speak a little *c* ! *The Flight* 17
And yet no *c* came to me, ,, 18
'Take *c* you have won the Painter's fame,' *Romney's R.* 43
groans to see it, finds no *c* there. ,, 45
Comfort (verb) (*See also* **Coomfut**) They *c* him by night and day ; *Supp. Confessions* 45
But, Effie, you must *c her* *May Queen, Con.* 44
'It *c's* me in this one thought to dwell, *D. of F. Women* 233
C thyself : what comfort is in me ? *M. d'Arthur* 243
Take, give her this, for it may *c* her : *Enoch Arden* 899
said the kindly wife to *c* him, *Sea Dreams* 140
Reach out dead hands to *c* me. *In Mem. lxxx* 16
C her, *c* her, all things good, *Maud II ii* 75
And *c* her tho' I die. ,, 83
The love of all Thy people *c* Thee, *Ded. of Idylls* 54
'*C* thyself,' said Arthur, 'I nor mine Rest : *Gareth and L.* 601
Because I saw you sad, to *c* you. *Merlin and V.* 441
C your sorrows ; for they do not flow *Guinevere* 188
C thyself : what comfort is in me ? *Pass. of Arthur* 411
C yourself, for the heart of the father *The Wreck* 98
Comfortable Nor wholly *c*, I sit, *Will Water.* 158
Comforted 'Annie, my girl, cheer up, be *c*, *Enoch Arden* 218
look up : be *c* : Sweet is it to have done the thing *Princess v* 66
'Be *c* : have I not lost her too, ,, 69
'Be *c*,' Said Cyril, 'you shall have it :' ,, 105
and *c* my heart, And dried my tears, *Com. of Arthur* 349
let me go : be *c* : *Pelleas and E.* 355
He answer'd, 'O my soul, be *c* ! *Last Tournament* 573
after these had *c* the blood With meats ,, 724
Queen Smiles on me, saying, 'Be thou *c* ! *Columbus* 188
Let the weary be *c*, *On Jub. Q. Victoria* 34
Yet be *c* ; For if this earth be ruled *D. of the Duke of C.* 7
Comforting An image *c* the mind, *In Mem. lxxxv* 51
Comic Too *c* for the solemn things they are, *Princess, Con.* 67
Comin' remimbers wan night *c* down be the sthrame, *Tomorrow* 7
Coming (*See also* **Comin', Coomin'**) *C* in the scented breeze, *Eleänore* 24
heart Went forth to embrace him *c* ere he came. *Œnone* 63
C thro' Heaven, like a light that grows ,, 108
the New-year's *c* up, mother, *May Queen, N. Y's. E.* 7
A noise of some one *c* thro' the lawn, *D. of F. Women* 178
Each month, a birth-day *c* on, *Will Water.* 93
Philip *c* somewhat closer spoke. *Enoch Arden* 398
'Ay, ay, I mind him *c* down the street ; ,, 847
His wreck, his lonely life, his *c* back. ,, 862

Coming (*continued*) If James were *c*. '*C* every day,' *The Brook* 106
Leolin, *c* after he was gone, *Aylmer's Field* 234
and *c* fitfully Like broken music, ,, 476
A crippled lad, and *c* turn'd to fly, ,, 519
like swallows *c* out of time Will wonder *Princess ii* 431
Or at thy *c*, Princess, everywhere, *W. to Marie Alex.* 42
she to be *c* and slandering me, *Grandmother* 27
Flash, I am *c*, I come, *Window. Marr. Morn.* 13
they are *c* back from abroad; *Maud I i* 65
I see my Oread *c* down, ,, *xvi* 8
Her brother is *c* back to-night ,, *xix* 1
She is *c*, my dove, my dear; She is *c*, my life, my fate; ,, *xxii* 61
She is *c*, my own, my sweet; ,, 67
But *c* back he learns it, *Geraint and E.* 498
And *c* up close to her, said at last: ,, 670
c up quite close, and in his mood ,, 714
So *c* to the fountain-side beheld *Balin and Balan* 23
A STORM was *c*, but the winds were still, *Merlin and V.* 1
C and going, and he lay as dead ,, 213
Such trumpet-blowings in it, *c* down ,, 418
C and going, and she lay as dead, ,, 644
C upon me—O never harp nor horn, *Holy Grail* 113
and *c* out of gloom Was dazzled by the sudden light, *Pelleas and E.* 104
but a sound Of Gawain ever *c*, and this lay— ,, 396
feet Thro' the long gallery from the outer doors Rang *c*, *Guinevere* 414
To guard thee in the wild hour *c* on, ,, 446
for wasn't he *c* that day? *First Quarrel* 47
it is *c*—shaking the walls— *Rizpah* 85
c nearer and nearer again than before— *Def. of Lucknow* 28
c down on the still-shatter'd walls ,, 92
hands, when I heard him *c* would drop *The Wreck* 27
'I am *c* to thee in thine Ocean-grave.' ,, 132
'O child, I am *c* to thee.' ,, 134
light of a Sun that was *c* would scatter *Despair* 23
But a sun *c* up in his youth! *Dead Prophet* 42
Silver crescent-curve, *C* soon, *The Ring* 14
c home—And on your Mother's birthday— ,, 247
c nearer—Muriel had the ring— ,, 259
she sees Her maiden *c* like a Queen, ,, 480
he was *c* down the fell— *Happy* 82
C in the cold time, *The Snowdrop* 5
'SUMMER is *c*, summer is *c*. *The Throstle* 1
Summer is *c*, is *c*, my dear, ,, 15
in *c* near, Across the downward thunder *Death of Œnone* 22
Flush'd like the *c* of the day; *Miller's D.* 132
Narrow'd her goings out and *c's* in; *Aylmer's Field* 501
Half-blinded at the *c* of a light. *Com. of Arthur* 266
himself Had told her, and their *c* to the court. (repeat) *Marr. of Geraint* 144, 846
She look'd on ere the *c* of Geraint. ,, 614
'I will abide the *c* of my lord, *Geraint and E.* 131
And she abode his *c*, and said to him ,, 139
Would listen for her *c* and regret Her parting step, *Lancelot and E.* 866
ere the *c* of the Queen.' (repeat) *Guinevere* 223, 233
Before the *c* of the sinful Queen.' ,, 270
(My friend is long in *c*.) *Sir J. Oldcastle* 148
you have dared Somewhat perhaps in *c*? *Columbus* 242
kiss so sad, no, not since the *c* of man! *Despair* 60

Command (s) He, that ever following her *c's*, *Ode on Well.* 211
under whose *c* Is Earth and Earth's, *In Mem., Con.* 130
Thy life is thine at her *c*. *Gareth and L.* 983
gave *c* that all which once was ours *Marr. of Geraint* 696
one *c* I laid upon you, not to speak to me, *Geraint and E.* 77
Debating his *c* of silence given, ,, 366
Then breaking his *c* of silence given, ,, 390
Wroth that the King's *c* to sally forth *Lancelot and E.* 560
That only seems half-loyal to *c*,— *Last Tournament* 118
lifted up a voice Of shrill *c*, *Death of Œnone* 99

Command (verb) 'Will he obey when one *c's*? *Two Voices* 244
Man to *c* and woman to obey; *Princess v* 450
I cannot all *c* the strings; *In Mem. lxxxviii* 10
strength of the race to *c*, to obey, *Def. of Lucknow* 47

Commander Attest their great *c's* claim With honour; *Ode on Well.* 148

Commeasure *C* perfect freedom.' *Œnone* 167

Commenced However then *c* the dawn: *Princess ii* 138
c A to-and-fro, so pacing till she paused ,, 301

Comment thoughts in rubric thus For wholesale *c*,' ,, *iii* 51
and heard in thought Their lavish *c* *Merlin and V.* 151
crost, and cramm'd With *c*, ,, 678
And none can read the *c* but myself; And in the *c* did I find the charm. ,, 682
like the critic's blurring *c* make *Sisters (E. and E.)* 104
Six foot deep of burial mould Will dull their *c's*! *Romney's R.* 126

Commerce Saw the heavens fill with *c*, *Locksley Hall* 121
brought the stinted *c* of those days; *Enoch Arden* 817
two crowned twins, *C* and conquest, *Princess v* 421
From growing *c* loose her latest chain, *Ode Inter. Exhib.* 33
So hold I *c* with the dead, *In Mem. lxxxv* 93
No more shall *c* be all in all, *Maud III vi* 23
that *c* with the Queen, I ask you, *Merlin and V.* 770
Fifty years of ever-broadening *C*! *On Jub. Q. Victoria* 52

Commercing *c* with himself, He lost the sense *Walk. to the Mail* 21

Commingled *C* with the gloom of imminent war, *Ded. of Idylls* 13

Commission A bought *c*, a waxen face, *Maud I x* 30
c one of weight and worth To judge between *Columbus* 124

Commissioner *See* **Church-commissioner**

Common (adj.) and fears were *c* to her state, *Enoch Arden* 521
'Loss is *c* to the race'—And *c* is the commonplace, *In Mem. vi* 2
That loss is *c* would not make My own less bitter, ,, 5
Too *c*! Never morning wore To evening, ,, 7
Their *c* shout in chorus, mounting, *Balin and Balan* 87
but love's first flash in youth, Most *c*: *Lancelot and E.* 950

Common (s) crost the *c* into Darnley chase *The Brook* 132

Commonplace barren *c's* break In full and kindly blossom. *Will Water.* 23
And common is the *c*, And vacant chaff *In Mem. vi* 3
To lift us as it were from *c*, *Sisters (E. and E.)* 223
shrunk by usage into commonest *c*! *Locksley H., Sixty* 76

Common-sense Rich in saving *c-s*, *Ode on Well.* 32
crown'd Republic's crowning *c-s*, *To the Queen ii* 61
Priests Who fear the king's hard *c-s* *Sir J. Oldcastle* 66

Commonwealth from it sprang the *C*, which breaks *Lucretius* 241

Commune (s) For days of happy *c* dead; *In Mem. cxvi* 14
Held *c* with herself, *Geraint and E.* 368

Commune (verb) To *c* with that barren voice, *Two Voices* 461

Communed I *c* with a saintly man, *Holy Grail* 742
But *c* only with the little maid, *Guinevere* 150
And while I *c* with my truest self, *The Ring* 181

Communicate We two *c* no more.' *In Mem. lxxxv* 84

Communing *C* with herself: 'All these are mine, *Palace of Art* 181
C with his captains of the war. *Princess i* 67

Communion An hour's *c* with the dead. *In Mem. xciv* 4
was a very miracle Of fellow-feeling and *c*. *Lover's Tale i* 251

Como Remember how we came at last To *C*; *The Daisy* 70
past From *C*, when the light was gray, ,, 73

Compact (adj.) churl, *c* of thankless earth, *Godiva* 66
issued in a court *C* of lucid marbles, *Princess ii* 24

Compact (s) He said there was a *c*; ,, *i* 47
there did a *c* pass Long summers back, ,, 123
Our formal *c*, yet, not less ,, 165
and a hope The child of regal *c*, ,, *iv* 421
'that our *c* be fulfill'd: ,, *v* 115
she would not keep Her *c*.' ,, 324

Companion on her bridal morn before she past From all her old *c's*, ,, *ii* 263
Too harsh to your *c* yestermorn; ,, *iii* 199
When wine and free *c's* kindled him, *Geraint and E.* 293
Fled all the boon *c's* of the Earl, ,, 477
Meanwhile the new *c's* past away *Lancelot and E.* 399
My boon *c*, tavern-fellow— *Sir J. Oldcastle* 90
Kindly landlord, boon *c*— *Locksley H., Sixty* 240
Down to the haven, Call your *c's*, *Merlin and the G.* 125

Companionless I, the last, go forth *c*, *M. d'Arthur* 236
I, the last, go forth *c*, *Pass. of Arthur* 404

Companionship Who broke our fair *c*, *In Mem. xxii* 13

Company Where sat a *c* with heated eyes, *Vision of Sin* 7
The little wife would weep for *c*, *Enoch Arden* 34
yes !—but a *c* forges the wine. *Maud I i* 36
her brother lingers late With a roystering *c*) ,, *xiv* 15
twos and threes, or fuller *companies*, *Marr. of Geraint* 57
'Where is that goodly *c*,' said I, *Holy Grail* 432
Spread the slow smile thro' all her *c*. *Pelleas and E.* 95
'Belike for lack of wiser *c*; *Last Tournament* 245
A glorious *c*, the flower of men, *Guinevere* 464
in *companies* Troubled the track of the host *Batt. of Brunanburh* 39
Comparison And half asleep she made *c* *Marr. of Geraint* 651
Compass (s) And in the *c* of three little words, *Gardener's D.* 232
winds from all the *c* shift and blow, *Godiva* 33
Might lie within their *c*, *Aylmer's Field* 485
And his *c* is but of a single note, *The Islet* 28
sorrow of my spirit Was of so wide a *c* *Lover's Tale ii* 135
The *c*, like an old friend false *Columbus* 70
Compass (verb) To *c* our dear sisters' liberties.' *Princess iii* 288
To *c* her with sweet observances, *Geraint and E.* 39
you should only *c* her disgrace, *The Fleet* 17
made him leper to *c* him with scorn— *Happy* 16
Compass'd *And c by the inviolate sea.'* *To the Queen* 36
With what dull pain *C*, *D. of F. Women* 278
Then *c* round by the blind wall of night *Enoch Arden* 492
All beauty *c* in a female form, *Princess ii* 34
Sat *c* with professors: ,, 444
Tho' *c* by two armies and the noise ,, *v* 345
That, *c* round with turbulent sound, *Will* 7
And *c* by the fires of Hell; *In Mem. cxxvii* 17
So, *c* by the power of the King, *Com. of Arthur* 203
He *c* her with sweet observances *Marr. of Geraint* 48
Compassion 'Full of *c* and mercy—(repeat) *Rizpah* 62, 63
Compel I *c* all creatures to my will.' (repeat) *Geraint and E.* 629, 673
Compell'd such a breeze *C* thy canvas, *In Mem. xvii* 2
Compensated For often fineness *c* size: *Princess ii* 149
Compensating nor *c* the want By shrewdness, *Enoch Arden* 250
Competence Seven happy years of health and *c*, ,, 82
gracious children, debtless *c*, golden mean; *Vastness* 24
Complaining broad stream in his banks *c*, *L. of Shalott iv* 3
C, 'Mother, give me grace To help me *Mariana in the S.* 29
call'd him by his name, *c* loud, *M. d'Arthur* 210
call'd him by his name, *c* loud, *Pass. of Arthur* 378
Complaint Not whisper, any murmur of *c*. *St. S. Stylites* 22
What end is here to my *c*? *In Mem. lxxxi* 6
Completer gipsy bonnet Be the neater and *c*; *Maud I xx* 20
Completion awaits *C* in a painful school; *Love thou thy land* 58
fulfill'd itself, Merged in *c*? *Gardener's D.* 239
Complexity many-corridor'd *complexities* Of Arthur's palace: *Merlin and V.* 732
Complicated *See* **Tenfold-complicated**
Compliment Light coin, the tinsel clink of *c*. *Princess ii* 55
Composed All *c* in a metre of Catullus, *Hendecasyllabics* 4
Compound 'No *c* of this earthly ball *Two Voices* 35
Comprehensive *See* **All-comprehensive**
Comprest rais'd her head with lips *c*, *The Letters* 19
Comrade *C's*, leave me here a little, *Locksley Hall* 1
Hark, my merry *c's* call me, ,, 145
And Enoch's *c*, careless of himself, *Enoch Arden* 568
His *c's* having fought their last below, *Aylmer's Field* 227
till the *c* of his chambers woke, ,, 583
Which weep the *c* of my choice, *In Mem. xiii* 9
Is *c* of the lesser faith ,, *cxxviii* 3
labour him Beyond his *c* of the hearth, *Gareth and L.* 485
and then against his brace Of *c's*, *Geraint and E.* 88
His craven pair Of *c's* making slowlier ,, 167
To laughter and his *c's* to applause. ,, 296
—thy shame, and mine, Thy *c*— *Sir J. Oldcastle* 102
And some are wilder *c's*, sworn to seek *Pref. Son. 19th Cent.* 12
Gone the *c's* of my bivouac, *Locksley H., Sixty* 45
parted from his *c* in the boat, *The Ring* 308
Conceal she knows too, And she *c's* it.' *Princess iii* 60
And half *c* the Soul within. *In Mem. v* 4
Marriage will *c* it . . . *Forlorn* 10
Conceal'd it seem'd Better to leave Excalibur *c* *M. d'Arthur* 62
it seem'd Better to leave Excalibur *c* *Pass. of Arthur* 230
Concealment maiden-meek I pray'd *C*: *Princess iii* 135
Conceit (s) (*See also* **Self-conceit**) So spake he, clouded with his own *c*, *M. d'Arthur* 110
So spake he, clouded with his own *c*, *Pass. of Arthur* 278
Conceit (verb) *C's* himself as God that he can make *Last Tournament* 355
Conceive and in his agony *c's* A shameful sense *Lover's Tale i* 793
Conceived sinful man, *c* and born in sin: *St. S. Stylites* 122
Concentrate if I fail To conjure and *c* *Romney's R.* 7
Concession and the bounds Determining *c*; *To Duke of Argyll* 3
Conciliate so potent to coerce, And to *c*, *Tiresias* 121
Concluded At last a solemn grace *C*, *Princess ii* 453
dreamt Of some vast charm *c* in that star *Merlin and V.* 512
Conclusion To those *c's* when we saw *In Mem. lxxxvii* 35
a semi-smile As at a strong *c*— *Lover's Tale iv* 282
Concourse banquet, and *c* of knights and kings. *Lancelot and E.* 562
Concubine Sent like the twelve-divided *c* *Aylmer's Field* 759
wives and children Spanish *c's*, *Columbus* 175
Condemn'd prisoner at the bar, ever *c*: *Sea Dreams* 176
Condensation cramm'd With comment, densest *c*, *Merlin and V.* 678
Condition with sound of trumpet, all The hard *c*; *Godiva* 37
Hear my *c's*: promise (otherwise You perish) *Princess ii* 295
And these were the *c's* of the King: *Gareth and L.* 107
Conditioning ebb and flow *c* their march, *Golden Year* 30
Condole *See* **Condowl**
Condoned treacheries—wink'd at, and *c*— *Columbus* 226
Condowl (condole) frinds 'ud consowl an' *c* wid her, *Tomorrow* 47
Conduct (verb) *C* by paths of growing powers, *In Mem. lxxxiv* 31
Conduit Where the bloody *c* runs, *Vision of Sin* 144
Cone (*See also* **Cypress-cone, Mountain-cones**) In masses thick with milky *c's*. *Miller's D.* 56
Confederacy between her daughters o'er a wild *c*. *Boädicea* 6
Conference And thus our *c* closed. *Princess ii* 367
Confess I *c* with right) you think me bound ,, *i* 158
As I *c* it needs must be; *In Mem. lix* 4
Why wilt thou shame me to *c* to thee *Holy Grail* 567
I will find the Priest and *c*. *Bandit's Death* 18
Confessed thunders often have *c* Thy power, *To W. C. Macready* 2
Confidence In *c* of unabated strength, *Lover's Tale i* 511
Confined *C* on points of faith, ,, *ii* 150
Conflict *c* with the crash of shivering points, *Princess v* 491
Folk and his friends that had Fallen in *c*. *Batt. of Brunanburh* 71
Confluence A riotous *c* of watercourses *Lucretius* 30
Confound did all *c* Her sense; *Mariana* 76
Nor all Calamity's hugest waves *c*, *Will* 5
On whom the victor, to *c* them more, *Geraint and E.* 169
God the traitor's hope *c*! (repeat) *Hands all Round* 10, 22, 34
Confounded (*See also* **Worse-confounded**) Shame and wrath his heart *c*, *The Captain* 61
Saw them lie *c*, *The Tourney* 14
Confuse Nor thou with shadow'd hint *c* A life *In Mem. xxxiii* 7
pass on! the sight *c's*— *Parnassus* 15
Confused Makes thy memory *c*: *A Dirge* 45
Remaining utterly *c* with fears, *Palace of Art* 269
wicked broth *C* the chemic labour of the blood, *Lucretius* 20
Arriving all *c* among the rest *Princess iv* 224
C by brainless mobs and lawless Powers; *Ode on Well.* 153
C me like the unhappy bark *In Mem. xvi* 12
Thro' all that crowd *c* and loud, *Maud II iv* 71
'*C*, and illusion, and relation, *Gareth and L.* 287
Enid look'd, but all *c* at first, *Marr. of Geraint* 685
Those twelve sweet moons *c* his fatherhood.' *Merlin and V.* 712
Confusion The airy hand *c* wrought, *Palace of Art* 226
Is there *c* in the little isle? *Lotos-Eaters, C.S.* 79
There *is c* worse than death, ,, 83
Unsubject to *c*, Tho' soak'd and saturate, *Will Water.* 86
Man to command and woman to obey; All else *c*. *Princess v* 451
At first with all *c*: by and by Sweet order lived ,, *vii* 18
C's of a wasted youth; *In Mem., Pro.* 42
yet-loved sire would make *C* worse than death, ,, *xc* 19
Once for wrong done you by *c*, *Merlin and V.* 307
Thieves, bandits, leavings of *c*, *Last Tournament* 95
From flat *c* and brute violences, ,, 124
disloyal life Hath wrought *c* in the Table Round *Guinevere* 220
and ev'n on Arthur fell *C*, *Pass. of Arthur* 99

Confusion (*continued*) for on my heart hath fall'n *C*, *Pass. of Arthur* 144
centre and crater of European *c*, *Beautiful City* 1
Confuted come a witness soon Hard to be *c*, *Forlorn* 26
Conjecture (s) make *C* of the plumage and the form; *Marr. of Geraint* 333
Conjecture (verb) *C's* of the features of her child *Œnone* 252
count me all to blame if I *C* of a stiller guest, *In Mem., Con.* 86
Conjecturing *C* when and where: this cut is fresh; *Lancelot and E.* 21
Conjure if I fail To *c* and concentrate *Romney's R.* 7
Conquer From barren deeps to *c* all *Princess vii* 164
Is rack'd with pangs that *c* trust; *In Mem. l* 6
you are Lancelot; your great name, This *c's*: *Lancelot and E.* 151
Arise, go forth and *c* as of old,' *Pass. of Arthur* 64
lake and mountain *c's* all the day. *Sisters (E. and E.)* 100
Love will *c* at the last. *Locksley H., Sixty* 280
That only *c's* men to *c* peace, *Akbar's Dream* 15
Conquer'd (*See also* **Woman-conquer'd**) A cry above the *c* years *In Mem. cxxxi* 7
At last she let herself be *c* by him, *Merlin and V.* 900
knowing he was Lancelot; his great name *C*: *Lancelot and E.* 580
Conqueror (*See also* **Woman-conqueror**) Christian *c's* took and flung *Locksley H., Sixty* 84
Conquest two crowned twins, Commerce and *c*, *Princess v* 421
brag to his fellow rakes of his *c* *Charity* 18
Conscience A little grain of *c* made him sour.' *Vision of Sin* 218
'With all his *c* and one eye askew'—(repeat) *Sea Dreams* 180, 184
My *c* will not count me fleckless; *Princess ii* 294
'Who reverenced his *c* as his king; *Ded. of Idylls* 8
To whom a *c* never wakes; *In Mem. xxvii* 8
Without a *c* or an aim. ,, *xxxiv* 8
The *c* as a *c* at rest: ,, *xciv* 12
Their *c*, and their *c* as their King, *Guinevere* 469
as is the *c* of a saint Among his warring senses, ,, 639
Conscious (*See also* **Half-conscious**) nor *c* of a bar Between them, *Aylmer's Field* 134
Slowly and *c* of the rageful eye That watch'd him, ,, 336
c of ourselves, Perused the matting; *Princess ii* 67
And partly *c* of my own deserts, ,, *iv* 305
We, *c* of what temper you are built, ,, 400
am I *c*, more Than other Masters, *Romney's R.* 62
Consecrate I dedicate, I *c* with tears— *Ded. of Idylls* 4
be *c* to lead A new crusade against the Saracen. *Columbus* 102
Consent (*See also* **Half-consent**) To yield *c* to my desire: *Miller's D.* 138
his long wooing her, Her slow *c*, and marriage, *Enoch Arden* 708
Was handed over by *c* of all To one who had not spoken, *Lover's Tale iv* 271
Consequence Were wisdom in the scorn of *c*.' *Œnone* 150
And duty duty, clear of *c's*. *Princess iii* 152
can he tell Whether war be a cause or a *c*? *Maud I x* 45
Conservative That man's the true *C* *Hands all Round* 7
Consider '*C* well,' the voice replied, *Two Voices* 241
C, William: take a month to think, *Dora* 29
c them, and all Their bearing in their common bond *Balin and Balan* 149
Consider'd Again she *c* and said: *In the Child. Hosp.* 55
Considering *c* everywhere Her secret meaning *In Mem. lv* 9
Consistent liberal-minded, great, *C*; ,, *Con.* 39
Consol chances of dividend, *c*, and share— *The Wreck* 30
Consolable A long, long weeping, not *c*. *Merlin and V.* 856
Consolе *See* **Consowl**
Consolidate became *C* in mind and frame— *Two Voices* 366
Consort And a gentle *c* made he, *L. of Burleigh* 73
Consowl (console) 'ud *c* an' condowl wid her, *Tomorrow* 47
Constancy The praise that comes to *c*.' *In Mem. xxi* 12
may yours for ever be That old strength and *c* *Open. I. and C. Exhib.* 14
Constantinus Also the crafty one, *C*, *Batt. of Brunanburh* 63
Constellation Larger *c's* burning, mellow moons and happy skies, *Locksley Hall* 159
With *c* and with continent, *Princess i* 224
Sphere-music of stars and of *c's*. *Parnassus* 8
Constrain'd thro' that young traitor, cruel need *C* us, *Marr. of Geraint* 716
Constraining *C* it with kisses close and warm, *Lover's Tale i* 468
Consume Me only cruel immortality *C's*: *Tithonus* 6
Consumed utterly *c* with sharp distress, *Lotos-Eaters, C. S.* 13
Contained *See* **Self-contained**
Contemplate When I *c* all alone *In Mem. lxxxiv* 1
C all this work of Time, ,, *cxviii* 1
c The torment of the damn'd' *Akbar's Dream* 48
Contemplating no form of creed, But *c* all.' *Palace of Art* 212
but lay *C* her own unworthiness; *Marr. of Geraint* 533
Contemplation And luxury of *c*: *Eleänore* 107
Contempt (*See also* **Self-contempt**) touch'd on Mahomet With much *c*, *Princess ii* 135
Contend *C* for loving masterdom. *In Mem. cii* 8
Content (adj.) (*See also* **Ill-content, Well-content**) I had been *c* to perish, *Locksley Hall* 103
might it come like one that looks *c*, *Love and Duty* 93
'I am *c*' he answer'd 'to be loved *Enoch Arden* 428
Which left my after-morn *c*. *In Mem. ciii* 4
He rested well *c* that all was well. *Geraint and E.* 952
Nor rested thus *c*, but day by day, *Lancelot and E.* 13
'Queen, she would not be *c* Save that I wedded her, ,, 1314
Must be *c* to sit by little fires. *Holy Grail* 614
he well had been *c* Not to have seen, ,, 653
C am I so that I see thy face But once a day: *Pelleas and E.* 243
that had left her ill *c*; *The Revenge* 51
was I *c*? Ay—no, not quite; *Sisters (E. and E.)* 126
Not findable here—*c*, and not *c*, ,, 132
born of worldlings—father, mother—be *c* *Locksley H., Sixty* 25
I shall hardly be *c* Till I be leper *Happy* 87
He rests *c*, if his young music wakes *To Mary Boyle* 63
Content (s) (*See also* **Self-content**) breast That once had power to rob it of *c*. *The form, the form* 8
With meditative grunts of much *c*, *Walk. to the Mail* 87
found the sun of sweet *c* Re-risen *The Brook* 168
and break The low beginnings of *c*. *In Mem. lxxxiv* 48
nor more *c*, He told me, lives in any crowd, ,, *xcviii* 25
Contented (*See also* **Well-contented**) leapt into my arms, *C* there to die! *D. of F. Women* 152
Continent With constellation and with *c*, *Princess i* 224
Maoris and that Isle of *C*, *W. to Marie Alex.* 18
From isle and cape and *c*, *Open. I and C. Exhib.* 4
and sow The dust of *c's* to be; *In Mem. xxxv* 12
Continue you saw, As who should say '*C*.' *Lover's Tale iv* 5
Contradiction seem'd to live A *c* on the tongue, *In Mem. cxxv* 4
Contract Cleave to your *c*: *Princess iv* 409
Contracting Philip's rosy face *c* grew *Enoch Arden* 486
Contrast love will go by *c*, as by likes. *Sisters (E. and E.)* 42
Contrivance With great *c's* of Power. *Love thou thy land* 64
Contrived where the two *c* their daughter's good— *Aylmer's Field* 848
Contriving *c* their dear daughter's good— ,, 781
Control (s) (*See also* **Half-control, Self-control**) keep it ours, O God, from brute *c*; *Ode on Well.* 159
O friendship, equal-poised *c*, *In Mem. lxxxv* 33
Control (verb) changes should *c* Our being, *Love thou thy land* 41
Controll'd For they *c* me when a boy; *In Mem. xxviii* 18
Controlleth *C* all the soul and sense Of Passion *Eleänore* 115
Convent (*See also* **Hill-convent**) while I lived In the white *c* down the valley *St. S. Stylites* 62
Convention but *c* beats them down: *Princess, Pro.* 128
Dwell with these, and lose *C*, ,, *ii* 86
to-morrow morn We hold a great *c*: ,, *iv* 511
Convent-roof DEEP on the *c-r* the snows *St. Agnes' Eve* 1
Convent-tower shadows of the *c-t's* Slant down ,, 5
Converse (s) (*See also* **Honey-converse**) We may hold *c* with all forms *Ode to Memory* 115
War, who breaks the *c* of the wise; *Third of Feb.* 8
But open *c* is there none, *In Mem. xx* 17
Thy *c* drew us with delight, ,, *cx* 1
rode In *c* till she made her palfrey halt, *Gareth and L.* 1360
he suspends his *c* with a friend, *Marr. of Geraint* 340
told her all their *c* in the hall, ,, 520
Edyrn, whom he held In *c* for a little, *Geraint and E.* 882
That comfort from their *c* which he took ,, 950
c sweet and low—low *c* sweet, *Lover's Tale i* 541
Am not thyself in *c* with thyself, *Ancient Sage* 65

Converse (verb) Hears him lovingly *c*, *L. of Burleigh* 26
Convert That was a miracle to *c* the king. *Sir J. Oldcastle* 178
Convey'd *c* them on their way And left them *Gareth and L.* 889
Convict The noble and the *c* of Castile, *Columbus* 117
Convolution saturate, out and out, Thro' every *c*. *Will Water.* 88
Convolvulus The lustre of the long *c'es* *Enoch Arden* 576
with a myriad blossom the long *c* hung; *V. of Maeldune* 40
Cony Or *conies* from the down, *Enoch Arden* 340
Coo Deeply the wood-dove *c's*; *Leonine Eleg.* 6
Coodled (cuddled) An' coäx'd an' *c* me oop *North. Cobbler* 80
Coo'd it *c* to the Mother and smiled. *The Wreck* 60
Cook'd *c* his spleen, Communing with his captains *Princess i* 66
Cool (adj.) while she wept, and I strove to be *c*, *Maud II i* 15
fair days—not all as *c* as these, *Balin and Balan* 273
Is all as *c* and white as any flower.' *Last Tournament* 416
Cool (s) as we enter'd in the *c*. *Gardener's D.* 114
Cool (verb) 'Drink to lofty hopes that *c*— *Vision of Sin* 147
saw it and grieved—to slacken and to *c*; *Princess iv* 299
Cool'd placed upon the sick man's brow *C* it, *Aylmer's Field* 701
Or *c* within the glooming wave; *In Mem. lxxxix* 45
ere his cause Be *c* by fighting, *Gareth and L.* 703
Cooling *C* her false cheek with a featherfan, *Aylmer's Field* 289
Coolness paced for *c* in the chapel-yard; *Merlin and V.* 757
blew *C* and moisture and all smells of bud *Lover's Tale iii* 5
Coom (come) But Parson a *c's* an' a goäs, *N. Farmer, O. S.* 25
an' thy muther *c* to 'and, ,, *N. S.* 21
C's of a gentleman burn: ,, 38
Wrigglesby beck *c's* out by the 'ill! ,, 53
C oop, proputty, proputty— ,, 59
WAÄIT till our Sally *c's* in, *North. Cobbler* 1
one night I *c's* 'oäm like a bull ,, 33
'My lass, when I *c's* to die, ,, 103
C thou 'eer—yon laädy a-steppin' ,, 107
but 'e dosn' not *c* fro' the shere; *Village Wife* 23
sa I knaw'd es 'e'd *c* to be poor; ,, 46
C! *c*! feyther,' 'e says, ,, 69
fur they weänt niver *c* to naw good. ,, 96
When Molly *c's* in fro' the far-end close *Spinster's S's.* 2
Rob, *c* oop 'ere o' my knee. ,, 11
C give hoäver then, weant ye? ,, 63
let Steevie *c* oop o' my knee. ,, 67
Dick, when 'e *c's* to be deäd, *Owd Roä* 11
'ud *c* at the fall o' the year, ,, 23
I'll *c* an' I'll squench the light, ,, 117
an' 'e beal'd to ya 'Lad *c* hout' *Church-warden, etc.* 28
Coom'd (came) An' I hallus *c* to 's chooch *N. Farmer, O. S.* 17
said whot a owt to 'a said an' I *c* awaäy. ,, 20
afoor I *c* to the plaäce. ,, 34
sin fust a *c* to the 'All; ,, 55
afoor 'e *c* to the shere. ,, *N.S.* 28
'e *c* to the parish wi' lots o' Varsity debt, ,, 29
An' I *c* neck-an-crop soomtimes, *North. Cobbler* 20
An' when we *c* into Meeätin', ,, 53
fur New Squire *c* last night. *Village Wife* 1
new Squire's *c* wi' 'is taäil in 'is 'and, (repeat) ,, 14, 121
Thou's *c* oop by the beck; ,, 79
fur he *c* last night so laäte— ,, 123
But 'e c thruf the fire wi' my bairn *Owd Roä* 92
He *c* like a Hangel o' marcy ,, 93
An' 'is 'air *c* off i' my 'ands ,, 100
fur a lot on 'em *c* ta-year— *Church-warden, etc.* 13
They says 'at he *c* fra nowt— ,, 17
an' *c* to the top o' the tree, ,, 38
Coomfut (s) (comfort) But she wur a power o' *c*, *North. Cobbler* 79
Fur she hedn't naw *c* in 'er, *Village Wife* 12
Coomfut (verb) When I goäs fur to *c* the poor *Spinster's S's.* 108
Coomin' (coming) upo' *c* awaäy Sally gied me a kiss *North. Cobbler* 56
Fur I seed that Steevie wur *c*,' *Spinster's S's.* 40
but, O Lord, upo' *c* down— ,, 44
'cep' it wur at a dog *c* in, ,, 60
By a man *c* in wi' a hiccup ,, 98
Fur I seed the beck *c* down *Owd Roä* 40
an' the times 'at was *c* on; ,, 44
Coontryside (Countryside) booöts to be cobbled fro' hafe the *c*. *North. Cobbler* 94

E

Cooper *C* he was and carpenter, *Enoch Arden* 814
Cöoperant Is toil *c* to an end. *In Mem. cxxviii* 24
Coortin (courting) gied tha a raätin that sattled thy *c* o' me, *Spinster's S's.* 48
Coostom (custom) Foälks' *c* flitted awaäy *North. Cobbler* 28
An' *c* ageän draw'd in like a wind ,, 93
Coot I come from haunts of *c* and hern, *The Brook* 23
Cope *c* Of the half-attain'd futurity, *Ode to Memory* 32
Wrapt in dense cloud from base to *c*. *Two Voices* 186
one Not fit to *c* your quest. *Gareth and L.* 1174
slinks from what he fears To *c* with, *Pelleas and E.* 439
sound as when an iceberg splits From *c* to base— *Lover's Tale i* 604
the *c* and crown Of all I hoped and fear'd?— ,, *ii* 27
Cophetua came the beggar maid Before the king *C*. *Beggar Maid* 4
C sware a royal oath; ,, 15
Coppice in April suddenly Breaks from a *c* *Marr. of Geraint* 339
scour'd into the *c's* and was lost, *Geraint and E.* 534
from the fringe of *c* round them burst *Balin and Balan* 46
Coppice-feather'd every *c-f* chasm and cleft, *Princess iv* 23
Copse danced about the may-pole and in the hazel *c*, *May Queen, N. Y's. E.* 11
shadowy pine above the woven *c*. *Lotos-Eaters* 18
did we hear the *c's* ring, *Locksley Hall* 35
Came little *c's* climbing. *Amphion* 32
Then move the trees, the *c's* nod, *Sir Galahad* 77
In *c* and fern Twinkled the innumerable ear *The Brook* 133
firefly-like in *c* And linden alley: *Princess i* 208
we wound About the the cliffs, the *c's*, ,, *iii* 360
Here is the *c*, the fountain and— *Sir J. Oldcastle* 127
seas leaning on the mangrove *c*, *Prog. of Spring* 76
Coptic Lulling the brine against the *C* sands. *Buonaparte* 8
Coquette the slight *c*, she cannot love, *The form, the form* 12
Coquette-like or half *c-l* Maiden, *Hendecasyllabics* 20
Coquetting *C* with young beeches; *Amphion* 28
Cord The creaking *c's* which wound and eat *Supp. Confessions* 36
The wounding *c's* that bind and strain *Clear-headed friend* 4
We'll bind you fast in silken *c's*, *Rosalind* 49
Lower'd softly with a threefold *c* of love *D. of F. Women* 211
Bound by the golden *c* of their first love— *The Ring* 429
while she stared at those dead *c's* *Death of Œnone* 10
A silken *c* let down from Paradise, *Akbar's Dream* 139
Cordage coils of *c*, swarthy fishing-nets, *Enoch Arden* 17
Corded *See* **Sinew-corded**
Cordon draw The *c* close and closer *Aylmer's Field* 500
Core Else earth is darkness at the *c*, *In Mem. xxxiv* 3
To make a solid *c* of heat; ,, *cvii* 18
Corinna wrought With fair *C's* triumph; *Princess iii* 349
Coritanian hear *C*, Trinobant! (repeat) *Boädicea* 10, 34, 47
Gods have heard it, O Icenian, O *C*! *Boädicea* 21
Shout Icenian, Catieuchlanian, shout *C*, Trinobant, ,, 57
Corkscrew up the *c* stair With hand and rope *Walk. to the Mail* 90
Corn (*See also* **Curn**) river-sunder'd champaign clothed with *c*, *Œnone* 114
land of hops and poppy-mingled *c*, *Aylmer's Field* 31
Ruth among the fields of *c*, ,, 680
when a field of *c* Bows all its ears *Princess i* 236
glutted all night long breast-deep in *c*, ,, *ii* 387
Steel and gold, and *c* and wine, *Ode Inter. Exhib.* 17
sweating underneath a sack of *c*, *Marr. of Geraint* 263
Take him to stall, and give him *c*, ,, 371
fell Like flaws in Summer laying lusty *c*: ,, 764
spice and her vintage, her silk and her *c*; *Vastness* 13
A thousand squares of *c* and meadow, *The Ring* 149
Corn-bin horse That hears the *c-b* open, *The Epic* 45
Cornelia Clelia, *C*, with the Palmyrene *Princess ii* 83
Corner 'Sometimes a little *c* shines, *Two Voices* 187
From some odd *c* of the brain. *Miller's D.* 68
in dark *c's* of her palace stood Uncertain shapes; *Palace of Art* 237
crow shall tread The *c's* of thine eyes: *Will Water.* 236
sitting-room With shelf and *c* for the goods *Enoch Arden* 171
From distant *c's* of the street they ran ,, 349
or Ralph Who shines so in the *c*; *Princess, Pro.* 145
my own sad name in *c's* cried, *Maud I vi* 72
Found Enid with the *c* of his eye, *Geraint and E.* 281
A damsel drooping in a *c* of it. ,, 611
folded hands and downward eyes Of glancing *c*, *Merlin and V.* 70

Corner (*continued*) Or whisper'd in the *c*? do ye know it?' *Merlin and V.* 772
knelt Full lowly by the *c's* of his bed, *Lancelot and E.* 826
dragon, griffin, swan, At all the *c's*, *Holy Grail* 351
deal-box that was push'd in a *c* away, *First Quarrel* 48
Cornice Now watching high on mountain *c*, *The Daisy* 19
Stretch'd under all the *c* and upheld: *Gareth and L.* 219
Cornish held Tintagil castle by the *C* sea, *Com. of Arthur* 187
name of evil savour in the land, The *C* king. *Gareth and L.* 386
Mark her lord had past, The *C* King, *Last Tournament* 382
sands Of dark Tintagil by the *C* sea; *Guinevere* 294
Corn-laws And struck upon the *c-l*, *Audley Court* 35
Coronach Prevailing in weakness, the *c* stole *Dying Swan* 26
Coronal My *c* slowly disentwined itself *Lover's Tale i* 361
dost uphold Thy *c* of glory like a God, ,, 488
Coroner *c* doubtless will find it a felo-de-se, *Despair* 115
Coronet Kind hearts are more than *c's*, *L. C. V. de Vere* 55
Corp (corpse) a *c* lyin' undher groun'. *Tomorrow* 62
Corpse (*See also* **Corp**) On *c's* three-months-old at noon she came, *Palace of Art* 243
C's across the threshold; *D. of F. Women* 25
Step from the *c*, and let him in *D. of the O. Year* 49
he comes to the second *c* in the pit? *Maud II v* 88
A yet-warm *c*, and yet unburiable, *Gareth and L.* 80
My mother on his *c* in open field; (repeat) *Merlin and V.* 43, 73
night with its coffinless *c* to be laid *Def. of Lucknow* 80
I'd sooner fold an icy *c* dead of some *The Flight* 54
She tumbled his helpless *c* about. *Dead Prophet* 65
Pain, that has crawl'd from the *c* of Pleasure, *Vastness* 17
And found a *c* and silence, *The Ring* 217
lies, that blacken round The *c* of every man *Romney's R.* 123
Corpse-coffin end but in being our own *c-c's* at last, *Vastness* 33
Correspond Not for three years to *c* with home; *Princess ii* 70
Corridor Full of long-sounding *c's* it was, *Palace of Art* 53
Corridor'd *See* **Many-corridor'd**
Corrientes and flowers, From *C* to Japan, *To Ulysses* 4
Corrupt Plenty *c's* the melody That made thee famous once, *The Blackbird* 15
Lest one good custom should *c* the world. *M. d'Arthur* 242
C's the strength of heaven-descended *Will* 11
Lest one good custom should *c* the world. *Pass. of Arthur* 410
Corruption *c* crept among his knights, *Merlin and V.* 154
Corselet thro' the bulky bandit's *c* home, *Geraint and E.* 159
Cosmogony their *cosmogonies*, their astronomies: *Columbus* 42
Cosmopolite That man's the best *C* *Hands all Round* 3
Cosmos Chaos, *C*! *C*, Chaos! (repeat) *Locksley H., Sixty* 103, 127
Cossack *C* and Russian Reel'd *Light Brigade* 34
Cost (s) care not for the *c*; the *c* is mine.' *Geraint and E.* 288
Cost (verb) story that *c* me many a tear. *Grandmother* 22
it *c* me a world of woe, ,, 23
They still remember what it *c* them here, *The Ring* 201
Costliest. Black velvet of the *c*— *Aylmer's Field* 804
Costly the work To both appear'd so *c*, *Marr. of Geraint* 638
'Let her tomb Be *c*, *Lancelot and E.* 1340
Costly-broider'd Laid from her limbs the *c-b* gift, *Marr. of Geraint* 769
Costly-made half-cut-down, a pasty *c-m*, *Audley Court* 23
Costrel youth, that following with a *c* bore *Marr. of Geraint* 386
Cot and kiss'd him in his *c*. *Enoch Arden* 234
Here is the *c* of our orphan, *In the Child. Hosp.* 28
Softly she call'd from her *c* to the next, ,, 46
Thro' many a palace, many a *c*, *Demeter and P.* 55
Cotch'd (caught) but Charlie 'e *c* the pike, *Village Wife* 43
Thou'd niver 'a *c* ony mice *Spinster's S's.* 55
An' 'e *c* howd hard o' my hairm, *Owd Roä* 58
c 'er death o' cowd that night, ,, 114
I *c* tha wonst i' my garden, *Church-warden, etc.* 33
Coterie Came yews, a dismal *c*; *Amphion* 42
Cottage Or even a lowly *c* whence we see *Ode to Memory* 100
'Make me a *c* in the vale,' she said, *Palace of Art* 291
Love will make our *c* pleasant, *L. of Burleigh* 15
she seems to gaze On that *c* growing nearer, ,, 35
Fair is her *c* in its place, *Requiescat* 1
Served the poor, and built the *c*, *Locksley H., Sixty* 268
sound ran Thro' palace and *c* door, *Dead Prophet* 38
Cottager She was the daughter of a *c*, *Walk. to the Mail* 59
Cottage-walls robed your *c-w* with flowers *Aylmer's Field* 698
Cotter a *c's* babe is royal-born by right divine; *Locksley H., Sixty* 125
Cotton (s) Whose ear is cramm'd with his *c*, *Maud I x* 42
Cotton (verb) If tha *c's* down to thy betters, *Church-warden, etc.* 48
Cotton-spinner We are not *c-s's* all, *Third of Feb.* 45
Cotton-spinning Go' (shrill'd the *c-s* chorus); *Edwin Morris* 122
Co-twisted New things and old *c-t*, *Gareth and L.* 226
Couch Kings have no such *c* as thine, *Dirge* 40
She lying on her *c* alone, *Day-Dm., Sleep B.* 2
And flung her down upon a *c* of fire, *Aylmer's Field* 574
light of healing, glanced about the *c*, *Princess vii* 59
Rolling on their purple *c'es* *Boädicea* 62
And Enid woke and sat beside the *c*, *Marr. of Geraint* 79
which she laid Flat on the *c*, and spoke exultingly: ,, 679
left her maiden *c*, and robed herself, ,, 737
wearied out made for the *c* and slept, *Merlin and V.* 736
flung herself Down on the great King's *c*, *Lancelot and E.* 610
Low on the border of her *c* they sat *Guinevere* 101
And the crowded *c* of incest in the warrens *Locksley H., Sixty* 224
Couchant *c* with his eyes upon the throne, *Guinevere* 11
Couch'd (*See also* **Low-couch'd**) tame leopards *c* beside her throne, *Princess ii* 33
c behind a Judith, underneath The head ,, *iv* 226
The wine-flask lying *c* in moss, *In Mem. lxxxix* 44
c at ease, The white kine glimmer'd, (repeat) ,, *xcv* 14, 50
c at night with grimy kitchen-knaves. *Gareth and L.* 481
They *c* their spears and prick'd their steeds, *Lancelot and E.* 479
at her will they *c* their spears, Three against one: *Pelleas and E.* 273
Lancelot passing by Spied where he *c*, *Guinevere* 31
Cough *c's*, aches, stitches, ulcerous throes *St. S. Stylites* 13
Council (*See also* **College-council**) '*And statesmen at her c met* *To the Queen* 29
manners, climates, *c's*, governments, *Ulysses* 14
In iron gauntlets: break the *c* up.' *Princess i* 89
But when the *c* broke, I rose and past ,, 90
enter'd an old hostel, call'd mine host To *c*, ,, 174
'everywhere Two heads in *c*, ,, *ii* 173
Great in *c* and great in war, *Ode on Well.* 30
c's thinn'd, And armies waned, *Merlin and V.* 572
Council-hall The basest, far into that *c-h* *Lucretius* 171
His voice is silent in your *c-h* *Ode on Well.* 174
Counsel (advice) silver flow Of subtle-paced *c* *Isabel* 21
Then follow'd *c*, comfort, and the words *Love and Duty* 69
Her art, her hand, her *c* all had wrought *Aylmer's Field* 151
Nor dealing goodly *c* from a height ,, 172
You prized my *c*, lived upon my lips: *Princess iv* 293
In part It was ill *c* had misled the girl ,, *vii* 241
to whom He trusted all things, and of him required His *c*: *Com. of Arthur* 147
man of plots, Craft, poisonous *c's*, *Gareth and L.* 432
Abide: take *c*: for this lad is great ,, 730
thou begone, take *c*, and away, ,, 1002
take my *c*: let me know it at once: *Merlin and V.* 653
he turn'd Her *c* up and down within his mind, *Lancelot and E.* 369
Then, when I come within her *c's*, *Pelleas and E.* 348
I would not spurn Good *c* of good friends, *Sir J. Oldcastle* 146
My *c* that the tyranny of all Led backward *Tiresias* 75
And following thy true *c*, *Akbar's Dream* 154
mix the wines of heresy in the cup Of *c*— ,, 175
Counsel (advocate) a sound Like sleepy *c* pleading; *Amphion* 74
A man is likewise *c* for himself, *Sea Dreams* 182
Counsel (verb) Speak to me, sister; *c* me; *The Flight* 75
Counsell'd but old Merlin *c* him, *Com. of Arthur* 306
Counsellor He play'd at *c's* and kings, *In Mem. lxiv* 23
My noble friend, my faithful *c*, *Akbar's Dream* 18
and bravest soul for *c* and friend. ,, 69
Count (title) *c's* and kings Who laid about them *Princess, Pro.* 30
C, baron—whom he smote, he overthrew. *Lancelot and E.* 465
C who sought to snap the bond *Happy* 61
Count (reckoning) 'Heaven heads the *c* of crimes *D. of F. Women* 201
Count (verb) I can but *c* thee perfect gain, *Palace of Art* 198
or touch Of pension, neither *c* on praise: *Love thou thy land* 26
C's nothing that she meets with base, *On a Mourner* 4
but *c* not me the herd! *Golden Year* 13
But I *c* the gray barbarian lower *Locksley Hall* 174
Deep as Hell I *c* his error. *The Captain* 3

Court (*continued*) neither *c* nor country, though they sought *Marr. of Geraint* 729
I can scarcely ride with you to *c*, ,, 749
such a sense might make her long for *c* ,, 803
In this poor gown I rode with him to *c*, *Geraint and E.* 700
A knight of Arthur's *c*, who laid his lance In rest, ,, 775
Was but to rest awhile within her *c*; ,, 855
we be mightier men than all In Arthur's *c*; *Balin and Balan* 34
c and King And all the kindly warmth ,, 235
stall'd his horse, and strode across the *c*, ,, 341
He rose, descended, met The scorner in the castle *c*, ,, 387
from the castle a cry Sounded across the *c*, ,, 400
the mask of pure Worn by this *c*, *Merlin and V.* 36
because that foster'd at *thy c* I savour ,, 38
narrow *c* and lubber King, farewell! ,, 119
thro' the peaceful *c* she crept And whisper'd: ,, 139
wily Vivien stole from Arthur's *c*. ,, 149
leaving Arthur's *c* he gained the beach; ,, 197
I rose and fled from Arthur's *c* ,, 297
the thing was blazed about the *c*, ,, 743
the *c*, the king, dark in your light, ,, 875
Arthur, holding then his *c* Hard on the river *Lancelot and E.* 74
Moving to meet him in the castle *c*; ,, 175
great knight, the darling of the *c*, ,, 261
much they ask'd of *c* and Table Round, ,, 268
she heard Sir Lancelot cry in the *c*, ,, 344
Above her, graces of the *c*, and songs, Sighs, ,, 648
we two May meet at *c* hereafter: ,, 698
ye will learn the courtesies of the *c*, ,, 699
Thence to the *c* he past; ,, 706
So ran the tale like fire about the *c*, ,, 734
And all the gentle *c* will welcome me, ,, 1060
I go in state to *c*, to meet the Queen. ,, 1124
I hear of rumours flying thro' your *c*. ,, 1190
Nun as she was, the scandal of the *C*, *Holy Grail* 78
'Gawain am I, Gawain of Arthur's *c*, *Pelleas and E.* 371
Gawain of the *c*, Sir Gawain— ,, 379
Then he crost the *c*, And spied not any light ,, 418
Creep with his shadow thro' the *c* again, ,, 441
My tower is full of harlots, like his *c*, *Last Tournament* 81
tonguesters of the *c* she had not heard. ,, 393
QUEEN GUINEVERE had fled the *c*, *Guinevere* 1
one morn when all the *c*, Green-suited, ,, 21
lissome Vivien, of her *c* The wiliest and the worst; ,, 28
Lured by the crimes and frailties of the *c*, ,, 136
I came into *c* to the Judge and the lawyers. *Rizpah* 33
showing *c's* and kings a truth *Columbus* 37
Fonseca my main enemy at their *c*, ,, 126
Cast off, put by, scouted by *c* and king— ,, 165
Than any friend of ours at *C*? ,, 198
You move about the *C*, I pray you tell King Ferdinand ,, 222

Courted a well-worn pathway *c* us To one green wicket *Gardener's D.* 109

Courteous And mighty *c* in the main— *Aylmer's Field* 121
Sir, I was *c*, every phrase well oil'd, *Princess iii* 133
C or bestial from the moment, *Gareth and L.* 631
C—amends for gauntness— *Merlin and V.* 104
Gawain, surnamed The *C*, fair and strong, *Lancelot and E.* 555
'Too *c* truly! ye shall go no more ,, 716
Too *c* are ye, fair Lord Lancelot. ,, 972
some one thrice as *c* as thyself— *Last Tournament* 706

Courtesy To greet the sheriff, needless *c*! *Edwin Morris* 133
Then broke all bonds of *c*, *Aylmer's Field* 323
With garrulous ease and oily *courtesies* *Princess i* 164
in his coffin the Prince of *c* lay. *G. of Swainston* 10
men have I known In *c* like to thee: ,, 12
amends For a *c* not return'd. *Maud I vi* 14
stout knaves with foolish *courtesies*:' *Gareth and L.* 733
waving to him White hands, and *c*; ,, 1377
Geraint, from utter *c*, forbore. *Marr. of Geraint* 381
Host and Earl, I pray your *c*; ,, 403
'I pray you of your *c*, He being as he is, *Geraint and E.* 641
I see ye scorn my *courtesies*, ,, 671
such a grace Of tenderest *c*, ,, 862
To learn what Arthur meant by *c*, *Balin and Balan* 158

Courtesy (*continued*) high-set *courtesies* are not for me. *Balin and Balan* 227
Whom all men rate the king of *c*. ,, 257
'Is this thy *c*—to mock me, ha? ,, 495
wonted *c*, *C* with a touch of traitor in it, *Lancelot and E.* 638
ye will learn the *courtesies* of the court, ,, 699
Deeming our *c* is the truest law, ,, 712
Obedience is the *c* due to kings.' ,, 718
myself Would shun to break those bounds of *c* ,, 1220
And loved thy *courtesies* and thee, ,, 1363
such a *c* Spake thro' the limbs and in the voice— *Holy Grail* 22
one Murmuring, 'All *c* is dead,' *Last Tournament* 211
King by *c*, Or King by right— ,, 341
The greater man, the greater *c*. ,, 633
For *c* wins woman all as well As valour ,, 707
trustful *courtesies* of household life, *Guinevere* 86
And of the two first-famed for *c*— ,, 323
Had yet that grace of *c* in him left ,, 436
Yield thee full thanks for thy full *c* *To Victor Hugo* 13

Court-favour willing she should keep *C-f*: *Princess vii* 58

Court-Galen *c-G* poised his gilt-head cane, ,, *i* 19

Court-lady And should some great *c-l* say, *Marr. of Geraint* 723

Courtliness He moving up with pliant *c*, *Geraint and E.* 278
thought, and amiable words And *c*, *Guinevere* 482

Courting *See* **Coortin**

Courtly Not her, who is neither *c* nor kind, *Maud I v* 27
looking at her, Full *c*, yet not falsely, *Lancelot and E.* 236

Courtship Discussing how their *c* grew, *In Mem., Con.* 97

Cousin a silent *c* stole Upon us and departed: *Edwin Morris* 115
Trust me, *c*, all the current of my being *Locksley Hall* 24
Saying, 'Dost thou love me, *c*?' ,, 30
O my *c*, shallow-hearted! ,, 39
To give his *c*, Lady Clare. *Lady Clare* 4
'It was my *c*,' said Lady Clare, ,, 15
Her and her far-off *c* and betrothed, *The Brook* 75
My lady's *c*, Half-sickening of his pension'd *Aylmer's Field* 460
And had a *c* tumbled on the plain, *Princess vi* 319
Jenny, my *c*, had come to the place, *Grandmother* 25
Had made his goodly *c*, Tristram, knight, *Gareth and L.* 394
'O *c*, slay not him who gave you life.' *Geraint and E.* 783
'Fair and dear *c*, you that most had ,, 824
poor *c*, with your meek blue eyes, ,, 841
fear not, *c*; I am changed indeed.' ,, 873
My sister, and my *c*, and my love, *Lover's Tale iii* 43
c of his and hers—O God, so like!' ,, *iv* 327
'Take my free gift, my *c*, for your wife; ,, 363
And Muriel Erne—the two were *c's*— *The Ring* 147
I found these *c's* often by the brook, ,, 158

Cove dimple in the dark of rushy *c's*, *Ode to Memory* 60
sweet is the colour of *c* and cave, *Sea-Fairies* 30
And shadow'd *c's* on a sunny shore, *Eleänore* 18
waves that up a quiet *c* Rolling slide, ,, 108
And steering, now, from a purple *c*, *The Daisy* 20
curl'd Thro' all his eddying *c's*; *In Mem. lxxix* 10
The sailing moon in creek and *c*; ,, *ci* 16
then the two Dropt to the *c*, *Com. of Arthur* 378
Sat by the river in a *c*, and watch'd *Lancelot and E.* 1389

Covenant Breathed, like the *c* of a God, *Gardener's D.* 209

Coventry *I waited for the train at* C; *Godiva* 1
wife to that grim Earl, who ruled In *C*: ,, 13

Cover (s) I slide by hazel *c's*; *The Brook* 171

Cover (verb) Have mercy, mercy! *c* all my sin. *St. S. Stylites* 84
C the lions on thy shield, *Gareth and L.* 585

Cover'd His blue shield-lions *c*— ,, 1217
All over *c* with a luminous cloud, *Holy Grail* 189
fail'd from my side, nor come *C*, ,, 471
what I saw was veil'd And *c*; ,, 852

Coverlet Across the purple *c*, *Day-Dm., Sleep. B.* 3
Who, moving, cast the *c* aside, *Marr. of Geraint* 73

Coverlid The silk star-broider'd *c* *Day-Dm., Sleep. B.* 9
And all the *c* was cloth of gold *Lancelot and E.* 1157

Covert Rode thro' the *c's* of the deer, *Sir L. and Q. G.* 21
Here often they break *c* at our feet.' *Marr. of Geraint* 183

Coverture In closest *c* upsprung, *Arabian Nights* 68

Cow He praised his ploughs, his *c's*, his hogs, *The Brook* 125

Cow (*continued*) theer warn't not feeäd for a *c*; *N. Farmer, O. S.* 37
Wi' aäf the *c's* to cauve ,, 52
as big i' the mouth as a *c*, *Village Wife* 103
wi' her paäils fro' the *c*. *Spinsters S's.* 2
peasant *c* shall butt the 'Lion passant' *Locksley H., Sixty* 248
an' wa lost wer Haldeny *c*, *Church-warden, etc.* 5
an' I doubts they poison'd the *c*. ,, 16
an' it poison'd the *c*. ,, 54
Coward The fear of men, a *c* still. *Two Voices* 108
Where idle boys are *c's* to their shame, *Princess v* 309
dwell On doubts that drive the *c* back, *In Mem. xcv* 30
were he not crown'd King, *c*, and fool.' *Merlin and V.* 789
a *c* slinks from what he fears To cope with, *Pelleas and E.* 438
'Fore God I am no *c*: *The Revenge* 4
'I know you are no *c*; ,, 8
I should count myself the *c* if I left them, ,, 11
spared the flesh of thousands, the *c* and the base, *Happy* 17
Cowardice full of *c* and guilty shame, *Princess iv* 348
being thro' his *c* allow'd Her station, *Guinevere* 516
Or *c*, the child of lust for gold, *To the Queen II* 54
Cowd (cold) sa *c*!—hev another glass! Straänge an' *c* fur the time! *Village Wife* 20
Of a Christmas Eäve, an' as *c* as this, *Owd Roä* 31
but the barn was as *c* as owt, ,, 111
she cotch'd 'er death o' *c* that night, ,, 114
Cower'd A dwarf-like Cato *c*. *Princess vii* 126
Had often truckled and *c* When he rose *Dead Prophet* 62
Cowering *See* **Low-cowering**
Cowl And turn'd the *c's* adrift: *Talking Oak* 48
leaving for the *c* The helmet in an abbey *Holy Grail* 5
Cowl'd Some *c*, and some bare-headed, *Princess vi* 77
Beside that tower where Percivale was *c*, *Pelleas and E.* 501
Cowslip Spring Letters *c's* on the hill? *Adeline* 62
To stoop the *c* to the plains, *Rosalind* 16
c and the crowfoot are over all the hill, *May Queen* 38
As *c* unto oxlip is, *Talking Oak* 107
The little dells of *c*, fairy palms, *Aylmer's Field* 91
what joy can be got from a *c* out of the field; *In the Child. Hosp.* 36
Cowslip Ball he made me the *c b*, *First Quarrel* 13
Cowslip Wine hev a glass o' *c w*! *Village Wife* 5
Craädle (cradle) An' I tummled athurt the *c* *North. Cobbler* 35
Nelly wur up fro' the *c* *Village Wife* 103
bring tha down, an' thy *c* an' all; *Owd Roä* 50
Craäzed (crazed) Warn't I *c* fur the lasses mysén *N. Farmer, N. S.* 18
'Cushie wur *c* fur 'er cauf' *Spinster's S's.* 115
Crab like a butt, and harsh as *c's*. *Walk. to the Mail* 49
Crabb'd Thro' solid opposition *c* and gnarl'd. *Princess iii* 126
Come, thou are *c* and sour: *Last Tournament* 272
Crack (s) deafen'd with the stammering *c's* *Merlin and V.* 942
c of earthquake shivering to your base *Pelleas and E.* 465
Crack (verb) chrysalis *C's* into shining wings, *St. S. Stylites* 156
splinter'd spear-shafts *c* and fly, *Sir Galahad* 7
earthquake in one day *C's* all to pieces,— *Lucretius* 252
living hearts that *c* within the fire *Princess v* 379
and takes, and breaks, and *c's*, and splits, ,, 527
whelp to *c*; *C* them now for yourself, *Maud II v* 55
Burst vein, snap sinew, and *c* heart, *Sir J. Oldcastle* 123
Crack'd The mirror *c* from side to side; *L. of Shalott iii* 43
all her bonds *C*; and I saw the flaring atom-streams *Lucretius* 38
The forest *c*, the waters curl'd, *In Mem. xv* 5
And *c* the helmet thro', and bit the bone, *Marr. of Geraint* 573
And once the laces of a helmet *c*, *Last Tournament* 164
whin I *c* his skull for her sake, *Tomorrow* 41
Casques were *c* and hauberks hack'd *The Tourney* 7
Crackle The tempest *c's* on the leads, *Sir Galahad* 53
Crackling His hair as it were *c* into flames, *Aylmer's Field* 586
heard A *c* and a rising of the roofs, *Holy Grail* 183
Cradle (*See also* **Craädle**) To deck thy *c*, Eleänore. *Eleänore* 21
Then lightly rocking baby's *c* *Enoch Arden* 194
sway'd The *c*, while she sang this baby song. *Sea Dreams* 292
on my *c* shone the Northern star. *Princess i* 4
rock the snowy *c* till I died. ,, *iv* 104
Love, Warm in the heart, his *c*, *Lover's Tale i* 158
we slept In the same *c* always, ,, 259
place of burial Far lovelier than its *c*; ,, 530
Cradle (*continued*) bending by the *c* of her babe. *The Ring* 415
paler then Than ever you were in your *c*, moan'd, ,, 432
Cradled (*See also* **Lily-cradled**) Their Margaret *c* near them, *Sea Dreams* 57
Cradle-head half-embraced the basket *c-h* ,, 289
Cradle-time Familiar up from *c-t*, so wan, *Balin and Balan* 591
Cradlemont Urien, *C* of Wales, Claudias, *Com. of Arthur* 112
Craft (art, etc.) before we came, This *c* of healing. *Princess iii* 320
less from Indian *c* Than beelike instinct ,, *iv* 198
Yet Merlin thro' his *c*, *Com. of Arthur* 234
man of plots, *C*, poisonous counsels, *Gareth and L.* 432
answer'd with such *c* as women use, *Geraint and E.* 352
Nor left untold the *c* herself had used; ,, 393
moral child without the *c* to rule, *Lancelot and E.* 146
The *c* of kindred and the Godless hosts *Guinevere* 427
chance and *c* and strength in single fights, *Pass. of Arthur* 106
c and madness, lust and spite, *Locksley H., Sixty* 189
Had never served for *c* or fear, *To Marq. of Dufferin* 27
C with a bunch of all-heal in her hand, *Vastness* 12
O the flattery and the *c* *Forlorn* 3
Then you that drive, and know your *C*, *Politics* 5
Craft (vessel) I boated over, ran My *c* aground, *Edwin Morris* 109
At times a carven *c* would shoot *The Voyage* 53
Become the master of a larger *c*, *Enoch Arden* 144
pushing his black *c* among them all, *Merlin and V.* 563
seamen made mock at the mad little *c* *The Revenge* 38
Of others their old *c* seaworthy still, *Pref. Son. 19th Cent.* 3
Crag (*See also* **Island-crag**) And the *c* that fronts the Even, *Eleänore* 40
A gleaming *c* with belts of pines. *Two Voices* 189
barr'd with long white cloud the scornful *c's*, *Palace of Art* 83
All night the splinter'd *c's* that wall the dell *D. of F. Women* 187
And the wild water lapping on the *c*.' *M. d'Arthur* 71
'I heard the water lapping on the *c*, ,, 116
based His feet on juts of slippery *c* ,, 189
when the bracken rusted on their *c's*, *Edwin Morris* 100
The light cloud smoulders on the summer *c*. ,, 147
My right leg chain'd into the *c*, I lay *St. S. Stylites* 73
still hearth, among these barren *c's*, *Ulysses* 2
swings the trailer from the *c*; *Locksley Hall* 162
He clasps the *c* with crooked hands; *The Eagle* 1
At the foot of thy *c's*, O Sea! *Break, break, etc.* 14
from the beetling *c* to which he clung *Aylmer's Field* 229
came On flowery levels underneath the *c*, *Princess iii* 336
like a jewel set In the dark *c*: ,, 359
find the toppling *c's* of Duty scaled *Ode on Well.* 215
They tremble, the sustaining *c's*: *In Mem. cxxvii* 11
like a *c* that tumbles from the cliff, And like a *c* was gay with wilding flowers: *Marr. of Geraint* 318
And lichen'd into colour with the *c's*: *Lancelot and E.* 44
And found a people there among their *c's*, *Holy Grail* 662
Clutch'd at the *c*, and started thro' mid air *Last Tournament* 14
and *c* and tree Scaling, Sir Lancelot ,, 17
And the wild water lapping on the *c*.' *Pass. of Arthur* 239
'I heard the water lapping on the *c*, ,, 284
based His feet on juts of slippery *c* ,, 357
last hard footstep of that iron *c*; ,, 447
path was perilous, loosely strown with *c's*: *Lover's Tale i* 384
issuing from his portals in the *c* ,, 430
Revenge herself went down by the island *c's* *The Revenge* 118
the pine shot along from the *c* *V. of Maeldune* 16
down the *c's* and thro' the vales. *Montenegro* 8
The noonday *c* made the hand burn; *Tiresias* 35
When I had fall'n from off the *c* we clamber'd *The Flight* 22
Crag-carven left *c-c* o'er the streaming Gelt— *Gareth and L.* 1203
Crag-cloister *C-c*; Anatolian Ghost; *To Ulysses* 43
Crag-platform huge *c-p*, smooth as burnish'd brass *Palace of Art* 5
Crake (*See also* **Meadow-crake**) flood the haunts of hern and *c*; *In Mem. ci* 14
Cram green Christmas *c's* with weary bones. *Wan Sculptor* 14
'Give, *C* us with all,' *Golden Year* 13
c him with the fragments of the grave, *Princess iii* 311
Well needs it we should *c* our ears with wool ,, *iv* 65
Like any pigeon will I *c* his crop, *Gareth and L.* 459
Cramm'd (*See also* **Furze-cramm'd**) 'The Bull, the Fleece are *c*, *Audley Court* 1

Cramm'd (*continued*) And *c* a plumper crop; *Will Water.* 124
Not like your Princess *c* with erring pride, *Princess iii* 102
Titanic shapes, they *c* The forum, ,, *vii* 124
she was *c* with theories out of books, ,, *Con.* 35
Whose ear is *c* with his cotton, *Maud I x* 42
every margin scribbled, crost, and *c* With comment, *Merlin and V.* 677
When was age so *c* with menace? *Locksley H., Sixty* 108
Cramming *C* all the blast before it, *Locksley Hall* 192
Cramp (s) stitches, ulcerous throes and *c's*, *St. S. Stylites* 13
Cramp (verb) *c* its use, if I Should hook it *Day-Dm., Moral* 15
I will not *c* my heart, nor take Half-views *Will Water.* 51
To *c* the student at his desk, *In Mem. cxxviii* 18
Cramp'd (*See also* **Iron-cramp'd**) for women, up till this *C* under worse *Princess iii* 278
weakness or necessity have *c* Within themselves, *Tiresias* 87
Crane *c*,' I said, 'may chatter of the *c*, *Princess iii* 104
steaming marshes of the scarlet *c's*, *Prog. of Spring* 75
Crannied FLOWER in the *c* wall, *Flow. in Cran. wall* 1
Cranny I pluck you out of the *crannies*, ,, 2
In an ancient mansion's *crannies* and holes: *Maud II v* 61
A light was in the *crannies*, *Holy Grail* 838
Crape Nor wreathe thy cap with doleful *c*, *My life is full* 14
Crash (s) came The *c* of ruin, and the loss of all *Enoch Arden* 549
In conflict with the *c* of shivering points, *Princess v* 491
There at his right with a sudden *c*, *The Islet* 8
thro' the *c* of the near cataract hears *Geraint and E.* 172
c Of battleaxes on shatter'd helms, *Pass. of Arthur* 109
maim'd for life In the *c* of the cannonades *The Revenge* 78
The *c* of the charges, *Batt. of Brunanburh* 89
My brain is full of the *c* of wrecks, *The Wreck* 4
then came the *c* of the mast. ,, 92
the *c* was long and loud— *Happy* 80
Crash (verb) The fortress *c'es* from on high, *In Mem. cxxvii* 14
I thought the great tower would *c* *Balin and Balan* 515
hail of Arês *c* Along the sounding walls. *Tiresias* 96
Crash'd boys That *c* the glass and beat the floor; *In Mem. lxxxvii* 20
and so they *c* In onset, *Balin and Balan* 555
the stormy surf *C* in the shingle: *Lover's Tale iii* 54
as if she had struck and *c* on a rock; *The Wreck* 108
C like a hurricane, Broke thro' the mass *Heavy Brigade* 28
Crashing *C* went the boom, *The Captain* 44
c with long echoes thro' the land, *Aylmer's Field* 338
c thro' it, their shot and their shell, *Def. of Lucknow* 18
Crass (cross) as ye did—over yer *C*! *Tomorrow* 90
An shure, be the *C*, that's betther nor cuttin' ,, 94
Crasst (crossed) 'niver *c* over say to the Sassenach whate; ,, 48
Crate the skin Clung but to *c* and basket, *Merlin and V.* 625
Crater the centre and *c* of European confusion, *Beautiful City* 1
Broke the Taboo, Dipt to the *c*, *Kapiolani* 31
Crathur' (whisky) been takin' a dhrop o' the *c* *Tomorrow* 11
Crave household shelter *c* From winter rains *Two Voices* 260
I *c* your pardon, O my friend; *In Mem. lxxxv* 100
damsel back To *c* again Sir Lancelot of the King. *Gareth and L* 882
See thou *c* His pardon for thy breaking ,, 985
C pardon for that insult done the Queen, *Marr. of Geraint* 583
stay'd to *c* permission of the King, *Balin and Balan* 288
dazzled by the sudden light, and *c* Pardon: *Pelleas and E.* 105
Might I *c* One favour? *Romney's R.* 69
Craved He *c* a fair permission to depart, *Marr. of Geraint* 40
Lancelot at the palace *c* Audience of Guinevere, *Lancelot and E.* 1162
Craven Silenced for ever—*c*—a man of plots, *Gareth and L.* 431
'A *c*; how he hangs his head.' *Geraint and E.* 127
c, weakling, and thrice-beaten hound: *Pelleas and E.* 291
my *c* seeks To wreck thee villainously: *Last Tournament* 548
c shifts, and long crane legs of Mark— ,, 729
Craw (crow) theer's a *c* to pluck wi' tha, Sam: *N. Farmer, N. S.* 5
Crawin' (crowing) cocks kep a-crawin' an' *c*' *Owd Roä* 106
Crawl Why inch by inch to darkness *c*? *Two Voices* 200
The wrinkled sea beneath him *c's*; *The Eagle* 4
But into some low cave to *c*, *Merlin and V.* 884
Crawl'd (*See also* **Scaped**) *C* slowly with low moans to where he lay, *Balin and Balan* 592
Pain, that has *c* from the corpse of Pleasure, *Vastness* 17
But 'e creeäpt an' 'e *c* along, *Church-warden, etc.* 19
Crawling scorpion *c* over naked skulls;— *Demeter and P.* 78
Crayon Mary, my *c's*! if I can, I will. *Romney's R.* 88
Craze if the King awaken from his *c*, *Gareth and L.* 724
Crazed (*See also* **Craäzed, Half-crazed**) I saw her (and I thought him *c*, *Lover's Tale iv* 163
so *c* that at last There were some leap'd *V. of Maeldune* 75
arrogant opulence, fear'd myself turned *c*, *Despair* 78
I *c* myself over their horrible infidel writings? ,, 87
for War's own sake Is fool, or *c*, or worse; *Epilogue* 31
coals of fire you heap upon my head Have *c* me. *Romney's R.* 142
I was all but *c* With the grief *Bandit's Death* 38
Craziness such a *c* as needs A cell and keeper), *Lover's Tale iv* 164
For such a *c* as Julian's look'd ,, 168
Crazy when I were so *c* wi' spite, *First Quarrel* 73
Never a prophet so *c*! *The Throstle* 10
Creak but am led by the *c* of the chain, *Rizpah* 7
Creak'd The doors upon their hinges *c*; *Mariana* 62
Cream fruits and *c* Served in the weeping elm; *Gardener's D.* 194
robb'd the farmer of his bowl of *c*: *Princess v* 223
Cream-white Her *c-w* mule his pastern set: *Sir L. and Q. G.* 31
Crease (weapon) cursed Malayan *c*, and battle clubs *Princess, Pro.* 21
Create Life eminent *c's* the shade of death; *Love and Death* 13
Creation Yet could not all *c* pierce *A Character* 5
And all *c* in one act at once, *Princess iii* 325
serene *C* minted in the golden moods ,, *v* 194
And love *C's* final law— *In Mem. lvi* 14
To which the whole *c* moves. ,, *Con.* 144
Creature Did never *c* pass So slightly, *Talking Oak* 86
But not a *c* was in sight: ,, 167
happy as God grants To any of his *c's*. *Enoch Arden* 417
As hunters round a hunted *c* draw *Aylmer's Field* 499
the gentle *c* shut from all Her charitable use, ,, 565
The *c* laid his muzzle on your lap, *Princess ii* 272
Like some wild *c* newly-caged, ,, 301
So stood that same fair *c* at the door. ,, 329
The sleek and shining *c's* of the chase, ,, *v* 155
The lovely, lordly *c* floated on ,, *vi* 89
Like *c's* native unto gracious act, ,, *vii* 27
Thy *c*, whom I found so fair. *In Mem., Pro.* 38
leave at times to play As with the *c* of my love; ,, *lix* 12
O beautiful *c*, what am I *Maud I xvi* 10
A *c* wholly given to brawls and wine, *Marr. of Geraint* 441
To pick the faded *c* from the pool, ,, 671
they themselves, like *c's* gently born *Geraint and E.* 191
c's voiceless thro' the fault of birth, ,, 266
I compel all *c's* to my will.' (repeat) ,, 629, 673
To chase a *c* that was current then *Merlin and V.* 408
There sat the lifelong *c* of the house. *Lancelot and E.* 1143
or had the boat Become a living *c* clad with wings? *Holy Grail* 519
Are ye but *c's* of the board and bed, *Pelleas and E.* 267
His *c's* to the basement of the tower *Guinevere* 104
and his *c's* took and bare him off, ,, 109
Had I but loved thy highest *c* here? ,, 656
but the *c's* had worked their will. *Rizpah* 50
glorious *c* Sank to his setting. *Batt. of Brunanburh* 29
O unhappy *c*? *Forlorn* 44
diseaseful *c* which in Eden was divine, *Happy* 33
I worshipt all too well this *c* of decay, ,, 45
like a *c* frozen to the heart Beyond all hope *Death of Œnone* 73
tenderest Christ-like *c* that ever stept *Charity* 32
Credible I almost think That idiot legend *c*. *Princess v* 153
Credit (s) Hadst thou such *c* with the soul? *In Mem. lxxi* 5
His *c* thus shall set me free; ,, *lxxx* 13
Credit (verb) The world which *c's* what is done ,, *lxxv* 15
Credited *See* **Scarce-credited**
Creditor They set an ancient *c* to work: *Edwin Morris* 130
Credulous *c* Of what they long for, *Geraint and E.* 875
Credulousness darken, as he cursed his *c*, *Sea Dreams* 13
Creeäp (creep) But *c* along the hedge-bottoms, *Church-warden, etc.* 50
Creeäpt (crept) But 'e *c* an' 'e crawl'd along, ,, 19
Creed compare All *c's* till we have found the one, *Supp. Confessions* 176
The knots that tangle human *c's*, *Clear-headed friend* 3
And other than his form of *c*, *A Character* 29
cares to lisp in love's delicious *c's*: *Caress'd or Chidden* 11
A dust of systems and of *c's*. *Two Voices* 207

Creed (*continued*) I sit as God holding no form of *c*, *Palace of Art* 211
Against the scarlet woman and her *c* ; *Sea Dreams* 23
Who keeps the keys of all the *c's*, *In Mem. xxiii* 5
wrought With human hands the *c* of *c's* ,, *xxxvi* 10
shriek'd against his *c*— ,, *lvi* 16
Believe me, than in half the *c's*. ,, *xcvi* 12
To cleave a *c* in sects and cries, ,, *cxxviii* 15
The prayer of many a race and *c*, and clime— *To the Queen ii* 11
drear night-fold of your fatalist *c*, *Despair* 21
cramping *c's* that had madden'd the peoples ,, 24
Despite of very Faith and *C*, *To Mary Boyle* 51
I hate the rancour of their castes and *c's*, *Akbar's Dream* 65
when *c* and race Shall bear false witness, ,, 97
Like calming oil on all their stormy *c's*, ,, 160
Neither mourn if human *c's* be lower *Faith* 5
Creedless This *c* people will be brought to Christ *Columbus* 189
Creek marish-flowers that throng The desolate *c's* and pools among, *Dying Swan* 41
The Lotos blows by every winding *c*: *Lotos-Eaters, C. S.* 101
The sailing moon in *c* and cove ; *In Mem. ci* 16
Creep (*See also* **Creeäp**) Wind *c* ; dews fall chilly : *Leonine Eleg.* 7
These in every shower *c* *A Dirge* 33
a languid fire *c's* Thro' my veins *Eleänore* 130
c's from pine to pine, And loiters, *Œnone* 4
And thro' the moss the ivies *c*, *Lotos-Eaters C. S.* 9
lost their edges, and did *c* Roll'd on each other, *D. of F. Women* 50
C's to the garden water-pipes beneath, ,, 206
c's on, Barge-laden, to three arches of a bridge *Gardener's D.* 42
The slow-worm *c's*, and the thin weasel *Aylmer's Field* 852
Where never *c's* a cloud, or moves a wind, *Lucretius* 106
Could dead flesh *c*, or bits of roasting ox ,, 131
Some ship of battle slowly *c*, *To F. D. Maurice* 26
And like a guilty thing I *c* *In Mem. vii* 7
When the blood *c's*, and the nerves prick ,, *l* 2
Must *I* too *c* to the hollow and dash myself *Maud I i* 54
Felt a horror over me *c*, ,, *xiv* 35
Always I long to *c* Into some still cavern deep, ,, *II iv* 95
The slow tear *c* from her closed eyelid *Merlin and V.* 906
C with his shadow thro' the court again, *Pelleas and E.* 441
like a new disease, unknown to men, *C's*, *Guinevere* 519
down, down ! and *c* thro' the hole ! *Def. of Lucknow* 25
who *c* from thought to thought, *Ancient Sage* 103
he—some one— this way *c's* ! *The Flight* 70
fire of fever *c's* across the rotted floor, *Locksley H., Sixty* 223
c down to the river-shore, *Charity* 15
Creeper as falls A *c* when the prop is broken, *Aylmer's Field* 810
With *c's* crimsoning to the pinnacles, *The Ring* 82
Creeping (*See also* **A-creeäpin, Forward-creeping, Silent-creeping**) *C* thro' blossomy rushes and bowers *Leonine Eleg.* 3
And crystal silence *c* down, *Two Voices* 86
Upon the tortoise *c* to the wall ; *D. of F. Women* 27
c on from point to point : *Locksley Hall* 134
comes a hungry people, as a lion *c* nigher, ,, 135
Still *c* with the *c* hours *St. Agnes' Eve* 7
Crept (*See also* **Creeäpt**) The cluster'd marish-mosses *c*. *Mariana* 40
deep inlay Of braided blooms unmown, which *c* Adown *Arabian Nights* 29
' From grave to grave the shadow *c* : *Two Voices* 274
And out I stept, and up I *c* : *Edwin Morris* 111
And down my surface *c*. *Talking Oak* 162
C down into the hollows of the wood ; *Enoch Arden* 76
Another hand *c* too across his trade ,, 110
He *c* into the shadow : at last he said, ,, 387
c Still downward thinking ' dead ,, 688
C to the gate, and open'd it, ,, 775
With hooded brows I *c* into the hall, *Princess iv* 225
As on The Lariano *c* To that fair port *The Daisy* 78
a gentler feeling *c* Upon us : *In Mem. xxx* 17
till he *c* from a gutted mine *Maud I x* 9
My life has *c* so long on a broken wing ,, *III vi* 1
thro' the peaceful court she *c* And whisper'd : *Merlin and V.* 139
some corruption *c* among his knights, ,, 154
from the carven-work behind him *c* *Lancelot and E.* 436
C to her father, while he mused alone, ,, 748

Crept (*continued*) all that walk'd, or *c*, or perch'd, or flew. *Last Tournament* 367
in the pause she *c* an inch Nearer, *Guinevere* 527
my blood *C* like marsh drains thro' all my languid limbs ; *Lover's Tale ii* 53
the night has *c* into my heart, *Rizpah* 16
C to his North again, Hoar-headed hero ! *Batt. of Brunanburh* 64
Black was the night when we *c* away *Bandit's Death* 25
Crescent (adj.) (*See also* **De-crescent, In-crescent**) many a youth Now *c*, who will come *Lancelot and E.* 448
Crescent (s) Hundreds of *c's* on the roof *Arabian Nights* 129
And April's *c* glimmer'd cold, *Miller's D.* 107
beneath a moon, that, just In *c*, *Audley Court* 81
When down the stormy *c* goes, *Sir Galahad* 25
As when the sun, a *c* of eclipse, *Vision of Sin* 10
A downward *c* of her minion mouth, *Aylmer's Field* 533
To which thy *c* would have grown ; *In Mem. lxxxiv* 4
To yon hard *c*, as she hangs ,, *cvii* 10
Half-lost in the liquid azure bloom of a *c* of sea, *Maud I iv* 5
With this last moon, this *c*— *De Prof. Two G.* 9
red with blood the *C* reels from fight *Montenegro* 6
Crescent-bark range Of vapour buoy'd the *c-b*, *Day-Dm., Depart.* 22
Crescent-curve Set in a gleaming river's *c-c*, *Princess i* 171
Silver *c-c*, Coming soon, *The Ring* 13
Crescent-lit while the balmy glooming, *c-l*, *Gardener's D.* 263
Crescent-moon And clove the Moslem *c-m*, *Happy* 44
Crescent-wise thro' stately theatres Bench'd *c-w*. *Princess ii* 370
Cress brook that loves To purl o'er matted *c* *Ode to Memory* 59
I loiter round my *c'es* ; *The Brook* 181
Crest She watch'd my *c* among them all, *Oriana* 30
lapwing gets himself another *c* ; *Locksley Hall* 18
and light as the *c* Of a peacock, *Maud I xvi* 16
With but a drying evergreen for *c*, *Gareth and L.* 1116
The giant tower, from whose high *c*, they say, *Marr. of Geraint* 827
stormy *c's* that smoke against the skies, *Lancelot and E.* 484
And wearing but a holly-spray for *c*, *Last Tournament* 172
while he mutter'd, ' Craven *c's* ! O shame ! ,, 187
Fall, as the *c* of some slow-arching wave, ,, 462
To which for *c* the golden dragon clung *Guinevere* 594
c of the tides Plunged on the vessel *The Wreck* 89
' A warrior's *c* above the cloud of war '— *The Ring* 338
Crete Had rest by stony hills of *C*. *On a Mourner* 35
Crevice shriek'd, Or from the *c* peer'd about. *Mariana* 65
fretful as the wind Pent in a *c* : *Princess iii* 81
Crew (s) the seamen Made a gallant *c*, *The Captain* 6
beneath the water *C* and Captain lie ; ,, 68
And half the *c* are sick or dead, *The Voyage* 92
They sent a *c* that landing burst away *Enoch Arden* 634
And ever as he mingled with the *c*, ,, 643
a *c* that is neither rude nor rash, *The Islet* 10
mann'd the Revenge with a swarthier alien *c*, *The Revenge* 110
harass'd by the frights Of my first *c*, *Columbus* 68
ran into the hearts of my *c*, *V. of Maeldune* 33
the *c* should cast me into the deep, *The Wreck* 94
the *c* were gentle, the captain kind ; ,, 129
Crew (verb) sitting, as I said, The cock *c* loud ; *M. d'Arthur, Ep.* 10
Crichton I call'd him *C*, for he seem'd *Edwin Morris* 21
Cricket (*See also* **Balm-cricket**) The *c* chirps ; the light burns low : *D. of the O. Year* 40
not a *c* chirr'd : *In Mem. xcv* 6
As that gray *c* chirpt of at our hearth— *Merlin and V.* 110
Than of the myriad *c* of the mead, *Lancelot and E.* 106
And each was as dry as a *c*, *V. of Maeldune* 50
Cricketed They boated and they *c* ; *Princess, Pro.* 160
Cried he took the boy that *c* aloud *Dora* 101
when the boy beheld His mother he *c* out ,, 138
Leolin *c* out the more upon them— *Aylmer's Field* 367
mock'd him with returning calm, and *c* : *Lucretius* 25
c out upon herself As having fail'd in duty ,, 277
clapt her hands and *c* for war, *Princess iv* 590
So thrice they *c*, I likewise, ,, *Con.* 104
I *c* myself well-nigh blind, *Grandmother* 37
Like those who *c* Diana great : *Lit. Squabbles* 16
So thick they died the people *c*, *The Victim* 5
And *c* with joy, ' The Gods have answer'd : ,, 38

Cried (*continued*) my own sad name in corners *c*, *Maud I vi* 72
Arthur *c* to rend the cloth (repeat) *Gareth and L.* 400, 417
when mounted, *c* from o'er the bridge, *Gareth and L.* 951
Then *c* the fall'n, 'Take not my life: ,, 973
C out with a big voice, 'What, is he dead?' *Geraint and E.* 541
Here the huge Earl *c* out upon her talk, ,, 651
had you *c*, or knelt, or pray'd to me, ,, 844
more than one of us *C* out on Garlon, *Balin and Balan* 123
lost itself in darkness, till she *c*— ,, 514
I *c* because ye would not pass Beyond it, *Lancelot and E.* 1042
So many knights that all the people *c*, *Holy Grail* 335
'That so *c* out upon me?' ,, 433
left alone once more, and *c* in grief, ,, 437
'Queen of Beauty,' in the lists *C*— *Pelleas and E.* 117
his helpless heart Leapt, and he *c*, ,, 131
from the tower above him *c* Ettarre, ,, 231
'And oft in dying *c* upon your name.' ,, 385
And woke again in utter dark, and *c*, *Last Tournament* 623
We *c* when we were parted: *Lover's Tale i* 253
the bones that had laughed and had *c*— *Rizpah* 53
Sir Richard *c* in his English pride, *The Revenge* 82
An' I *c* along wi' the gells, *Village Wife* 96
Fur, lawks! 'ow I *c* when they went, ,, 111
Some *c* on Cobham, on the good Lord Cobham; *Sir J. Oldcastle* 43
a score of wild birds *C* from the topmost summit *V. of Maeldune* 28
Once in an hour they *c*, ,, 29
An' I could 'a *c* ammost, *Spinster's S's.* 47
c the king of sacred song; *Locksley H., Sixty* 201
And the Muses *c* with a stormy cry *Dead Prophet* 2
till I *c* again: 'O Miriam, if you love me *The Ring* 262
I *c* for nurse, and felt a gentle hand ,, 418
I *c* to the Saints to avenge me. *Bandit's Death* 14
that the boy never *c* again. ,, 28

Crime thorough-edged intellect to part Error from *c*; *Isabel* 15
And all alone in *c*: *Palace of Art* 272
'Heaven heads the count of *c's* *D. of F. Women* 201
When single thought is civil *c*, *'You ask me, why,* 19
if it were thine error or thy *c* *Come not, when, etc.* 7
it was a *c* Of sense avenged by sense *Vision of Sin* 213
'The *c* of sense became The *c* of malice, ,, 215
keeps his wing'd affections clipt with *c*: *Princess vii* 316
Yet clearest of ambitious *c*, *Ode on Well.* 28
to dodge and palter with a public *c*? *Third of Feb.* 24
And ever weaker grows thro' acted *c*, *Will* 12
Unfetter'd by the sense of *c*, *In Mem. xxvii* 7
Day, mark'd as with some hideous *c*, ,, *lxxii* 18
I count it *c* To mourn for any overmuch; ,, *lxxxv* 61
Perhaps from madness, perhaps from *c*, *Maud I xvi* 22
came to loathe His *c* of traitor, *Marr. of Geraint* 594
call him the main cause of all their *c*; *Merlin and V.* 788
that most impute a *c* Are pronest to it, ,, 825
all her *c*, All—all—the wish to prove him ,, 864
blaze the *c* of Lancelot and the Queen.' *Pelleas and E.* 570
Lured by the *c's* and frailties of the court, *Guinevere* 136
think not that I come to urge thy *c's*, ,, 532
A shameful sense as of a cleaving *c*— *Lover's Tale i* 794
or such *c's* As holy Paul— *Sir J. Oldcastle* 109
curbing *c's* that scandalised the Cross, *Columbus* 193
But the *c*, if a *c*, of her eldest-born, *Despair* 73
crown'd for a virtue, or hang'd for a *c*? ,, 76
C and hunger cast our maidens *Locksley H., Sixty* 220
'Who was witness of the *c*? *Forlorn* 7
His *c* was of the senses: *Romney's R.* 151
Whose *c* had half unpeopled Ilion, *Death of Œnone* 61
his kisses were red with his *c*, *Bandit's Death* 13

Crimson (adj.) (*See also* **Silvery-crimson**) above, *C*, a slender banneret fluttering. *Gareth and L.* 913
c in the belt of strange device, A *c* grail *Holy Grail* 154
All pall'd in *c* samite, ,, 847
We steer'd her toward a *c* cloud *In Mem. ciii* 55
c with battles, and hollow with graves, *The Dreamer* 12

Crimson (s) long-hair'd page in *c* clad, *L. of Shalott ii* 22
Till all the *c* changed, and past *Mariana in the S.* 25
In the Spring a fuller *c* comes *Locksley Hall* 17
add A *c* to the quaint Macaw, *Day-Dm., Pro.* 16

Crimson (s) (*continued*) rocket molten into flakes Of *c* *In Mem. xcviii* 32
Sunder the glooming *c* on the marge, *Gareth and L.* 1365
In *c's* and in purples and in gems. *Marr. of Geraint* 10
the *c* and scarlet of berries that flamed *V. of Maeldune* 61
Close beneath the casement *c* *Locksley H., Sixty* 34
Was all ablaze with *c* to the roof, *The Ring* 250
but—when now Bathed in that lurid *c*— *St. Telemachus* 18

Crimson (verb) *C's* over an inland mere, *Eleänore* 42
Crimson-circled Before the *c-c* star *In Mem. lxxxix* 47
Crimson'd glow that slowly *c* all Thy presence *Tithonus* 56
Crimson-hued *c-h* the stately palmwoods Whisper *Milton* 15
Crimson-rolling when the *c-r* eye Glares ruin, *Princess iv* 494
Crimson-threaded When from *c-t* lips Silver-treble laughter trilleth: *Lilian* 23

Cripple a story which in rougher shape Came from a grizzled *c*, *Aylmer's Field* 8
he met A *c*, one that held a hand for alms— *Pelleas and E.* 542

Crisp To make the sullen surface *c*. *In Mem. xlix* 8
Crispeth The babbling runnel *c*, *Claribel* 19
Critic No *c* I—would call them masterpieces: *Princess i* 145
Musician, painter, sculptor, *c*, ,, *ii* 178
And like the *c's* blurring comment *Sisters (E. and E.)* 104
And the *C's* rarer still. *Poets and Critics* 16
Critic-pen Unboding *c-p*. *Will Water.* 42

Croak *c* thee sister, or the meadow-crake *Princess iv* 124
When did a frog coarser *c* upon our Helicon? *Trans. of Homer* 4
For a raven ever *c's*, at my side, *Maud I vi* 57
Once at the *c* of a Raven who crost it, *Merlin and the G.* 24
Croak'd A blot in heaven, the Raven, flying high, *C*, *Guinevere* 134
Crocodile *C's* wept tears for thee: *A Dirge* 22

Crocus at their feet the *c* brake like fire, *Œnone* 96
From one hand droop'd a *c*: *Palace of Art* 119
C, anemone, violet, *To F. D. Maurice* 44
And we roll'd upon capes of *c* *V. of Maeldune* 47
in this roaring moon of daffodil And *c*, *Pref. Son. 19th Cent.* 8
groundflame of the *c* breaks the mould, *Prog. of Spring* 1

Croft Thro' *c's* and pastures wet with dew *Two Voices* 14
Started a green linnet Out of the *c*; *Minnie and Winnie* 18
an' thy windmill oop o' the *c*, *Spinster's S's.* 73
Cromlech And cleaves to cairn and *c* still; *To the Queen ii* 41
Crone rhymes and scraps of ancient *c's*, *Lover's Tale i* 289
Garrulous old *c*, *The Ring* 120
Crook *C* and turn upon itself *Locksley H., Sixty* 236
Crooked Lame, *c*, reeling, livid, *Death of Œnone* 27
Crop (of a bird) And cramm'd a plumper *c*; *Will Water.* 124
Like any pigeon will I cram his *c*, *Gareth and L.* 459
Crop (verb) call him overquick To *c* his own sweet rose *Merlin and V.* 725
Cropt They might have *c* the myriad flower of May, *Balin and Balan* 577

Cross (s) (*See also* **Catholic Cross, Crass, Market-Cross**)
A broken chancel with a broken *c*, *M. d'Arthur* 9
I lift the *c*, and strive and wrestle *St. S. Stylites* 118
I smote them with the *c*; ,, 173
Fly happy with the mission of the *C*; *Golden Year* 43
Made Him his catspaw and the *C* his tool, *Sea Dreams* 190
They mark'd it with the red *c* to the fall, *Princess vi* 41
Under the *c* of gold That shines *Ode on Well.* 49
roll'd Thro' the dome of the golden *c*; ,, 61
the *c* And those around it and the Crucified, *Com. of Arthur* 272
like the *c* her great and goodly arms Stretch'd *Gareth and L.* 218
Thorns of the crown and shivers of the *c*, *Balin and Balan* 111
beat the *c* to earth, and break the King ,, 458
lone woman, weeping near a *c*, Stay'd him. *Last Tournament* 493
A broken chancel with a broken *c*, *Pass. of Arthur* 177
the copse, the fountain and—a *C*! *Sir J. Oldcastle* 127
how I anger'd Arundel asking me To worship Holy *C*! ,, 136
I said, a *c* of flesh and blood And holier. ,, 137
we, who bore the *C* Thither, were excommunicated *Columbus* 191
curbing crimes that scandalised the *C*, ,, 193
He that has nail'd all flesh to the *C*, *Vastness* 28
My soldier of the *C*? it is he and he *Happy* 12
My warrior of the Holy *C* and of the conquering sword, ,, 21
yesterday They bore the *C* before you ,, 48
Touch'd at the golden *C* of the churches, *Merlin and the G.* 68
under the *C'es* The dead man's garden, ,, 105
sunset glared against a *c* *St. Telemachus* 5

Cross (verb) Nor any cloud would *c* the vault — *Mariana in the S.* 38
he was wrong to *c* his father thus: — *Dora* 148
Should my Shadow *c* thy thoughts Too sadly — *Love and Duty* 88
Should it *c* thy dreams, O might it come — ,, 92
the lonely seabird *c'es* With one waft of the wing. — *The Captain* 71
Not for three years to *c* the liberties; — *Princess ii* 71
It *c'es* here, it *c'es* there, — *Maud II iv* 70
never shadow of mistrust can *c* Between us. — *Marr. of Geraint* 815
shadow of mistrust should never *c* — *Geraint and E.* 248
Your leave, my lord, to *c* the room, — ,, 298
He shall not *c* us more; — ,, 342
I forbear you thus: *c* me no more. — ,, 678
To *c* our mighty Lancelot in his loves! — *Lancelot and E.* 688
To *c* between their happy star and them? — *Lover's Tale i* 730
Cross-bones carved *c-b*, the types of Death, — *Will Water.* 245
Cross'd-Crost (*See also* **Crasst**) And they *cross'd* themselves for fear, — *L. of Shalott iv* 49
Sometimes your shadow *cross'd* the blind. — *Miller's D.* 124
And *cross'd* the garden to the gardener's lodge, — *Audley Court* 17
then we *crost* Between the lakes, and clamber'd — *Golden Year* 5
And seldom *crost* her threshold, — *Enoch Arden* 337
Abhorrent of a calculation *crost*, — ,, 473
crost By that old bridge which, half in ruins — *The Brook* 78
where the waters marry—*crost*, Whistling a random bar — ,, 81
Then *crost* the common into Darnley chase — ,, 132
He seldom *crost* his child without a sneer; — *Aylmer's Field* 562
then we *crost* To a livelier land; — *Princess i* 109
back again we *crost* the court To Lady Psyche's: — ,, *ii* 100
We *cross'd* the street and gain'd a petty mound — ,, *iv* 557
But when we *crost* the Lombard plain — *The Daisy* 49
The shade by which my life was *crost*, — *In Mem. lxvi* 5
little thumb, That *crost* the trencher — *Marr. of Geraint* 396
Crost and came near, lifted adoring eyes, — *Geraint and E.* 304
A walk of lilies *crost* it to the bower: — *Balin and Balan* 243
every margin scribbled, *crost*, and cramm'd With comment, — *Merlin and V.* 677
was it earthly passion *crost*?' — *Holy Grail* 29
with the bones of men, Not to be *crost*, — ,, 501
every bridge as quickly as he *crost* Sprang into fire — ,, 505
crost the dimness of a cloud Floating, — *Pelleas and E.* 37
Then he *crost* the court, And spied not any light — ,, 418
her thin hands *crost* on her breast— — *In the Child. Hosp.* 39
Wiclif-preacher whom I *crost* In flying hither? — *Sir J. Oldcastle* 38
Cross'd! for once he sailed the sea — *Locksley H., Sixty* 29
at the croak of a Raven who *crost* it, — *Merlin and the G.* 24
shadowy fighters *crost* The disk, — *St. Telemachus* 23
When I have *crost* the bar. — *Crossing the Bar* 16
Crossing (part) And, *c*, oft we saw the glisten — *The Daisy* 35
I past him, I was *c* his lands; — *Maud I xiii* 6
Rivulet *c* my ground, — ,, *xxi* 1
Guinevere was *c* the great hall Cast herself down, — *Merlin and V.* 65
c her own picture as she came, — *Lover's Tale iv* 286
we saw your soldiers *c* the ridge, — *Bandit's Death* 21
Crossing (s) Who sweep the *c's*, wet or dry, — *Will Water.* 47
Cross-lightnings *c-l* of four chance-met eyes — *Aylmer's Field* 129
Cross-pipes carved *c-p*, and, underneath, — *Will Water.* 247
Cross-road stake and the *c-r*, fool, if you will, — *Despair* 116
Crost *See* **Cross'd**
Crotchet Chimeras, *c's*, Christmas solecisms, — *Princess, Pro.* 203
Crouch'd with playful tail *C* fawning in the weed. — *Œnone* 201
I *c* on one that rose Twenty by measure; — *St. S. Stylites* 88
I *c* upon deck— — *The Wreck* 120
She *c*, she tore him part from part, — *Dead Prophet* 69
heard as we *c* below, The clatter of arms, — *Bandit's Death* 23
Crow (s) (*See also* **Craw**) Perch'd like a *c* upon a three-legg'd stool, — *Audley Court* 45
many-winter'd *c* that leads — *Locksley Hall* 68
ere the hateful *c* shall tread The corners — *Will Water.* 235
a troop of carrion *c's* Hung like a cloud — *Merlin and V.* 598
sober rook And carrion *c* cry 'Mortgage.' — *The Ring* 174
Crow (verb) she heard the night-fowl *c*: — *Mariana* 26
Before the red cock *c's* from the farm — *May Queen, N. Y's. E.* 23
The cock *c's* ere the Christmas morn, — *Sir Galahad* 51
And the cock couldn't *c*, — *V. of Maeldune* 18
and *c's* to the sun and the moon, — *Despair* 90

E*

Crow (verb) *continued* he *c's* before his time; — *The Flight* 3
Crowd (s) I saw *c's* in columned sanctuaries: — *D. of F. Women* 22
The *c's*, the temples, waver'd, — ,, 114
To me, methought, who waited with a *c*, — *M. d'Arthur, Ep.* 20
A *c* of hopes, That sought to sow themselves — *Gardener's D.* 64
To tear his heart before the *c*! — *You might have won* 36
those that held their heads above the *c*, — *The Brook* 10
Among the honest shoulders of the *c*, — *Sea Dreams* 166
while none mark'd it, on the *c* Broke, — ,, 234
c's that in an hour Of civic tumult — *Lucretius* 168
they gave The park, the *c*, the house; — *Princess, Pro.* 94
preach'd An universal culture for the *c*, — ,, 109
as we came, the *c* dividing clove An advent — ,, *iv* 283
I know Your faces there in the *c*— — ,, 510
thereat the *c* Muttering, dissolved: — ,, 522
the *c* were swarming now, To take their leave, — ,, *Con.* 37
civic manhood firm against the *c*— — ,, 57
For me, the genial day, the happy *c*, — ,, 75
let the sorrowing *c* about it grow, — *Ode on Well.* 16
Till *c's* at length be sane and crowns be just. — ,, 169
dark *c* moves, and there are sobs and tears; — ,, 268
c's that stream from yawning doors, — *In Mem. lxx* 9
more content, He told me, lives in any *c*, — ,, *xcviii* 26
To fool the *c* with glorious lies, — ,, *cxxviii* 14
Thro' all that *c* confused and loud, — *Maud II iv* 71
turn thy wheel above the staring *c*; — *Marr. of Geraint* 356
such blows, that all the *c* Wonder'd, — ,, 564
and in this Are harlots like the *c*, — *Merlin and V.* 831
c Will murmur, 'Lo the shameless ones, — *Lancelot and E.* 99
Then of the *c* ye took no more account — ,, 105
And by the gateway stirr'd a *c*; — *Holy Grail* 424
rough *c*, Hearing he had a difference with their priests, — ,, 673
no precaution used, among the *c*, — *Guinevere* 519
But as a Latin Bible to the *c*; — *Sir J. Oldcastle* 18
And then in Latin to the Latin *c*, — ,, 31
a *c* Throng'd the waste field about the city gates: — ,, 39
I saw your face that morning in the *c*. — *Columbus* 7
the *c* would roar For blood, for war, — *Tiresias* 64
the heart of a listening *c*— — *The Wreck* 47
dark-muffled Russian *c* Folded its wings — *Heavy Brigade* 38
That all the *c* might stare. — *Dead Prophet* 16
lawless crown As of the lawless *c*; — *Freedom* 32
there past a *c* With shameless laughter, — *St. Telemachus* 38
draw The *c* from wallowing in the mire — *Akbar's Dream* 141
Crowd (verb) They come, they *c* upon me all at once— — *Lover's Tale i* 47
Launch your vessel, And *c* your canvas, — *Merlin and the G.* 127
Crowded *C* with driving atomies, — *Lover's Tale ii* 174
Crow'd *C* lustier late and early, — *Will Water.* 126
maid, That ever *c* for kisses.' — *Princess ii* 280
The cock has *c* already once, — *The Flight* 3
Crowfoot cowslip and the *c* are over all the hill, — *May Queen* 38
Crowing (*See also* **A-crawin', Crawin'**) At midnight the cock was *c*, — *Oriana* 12
Came *c* over Thames. — *Will Water.* 140
Crown (diadem, etc.) Revered Isabel, the *c* and head, — *Isabel* 10
better than to own A *c*, a sceptre, — *Ode to Memory* 121
With a *c* of gold, On a throne? — *The Merman* 6
under my starry sea-bud *c* Low adown — *The Mermaid* 16
Gliding with equal *c's* two serpents led — *Alexander* 6
his ample bound to some new *c*:— — *Poland* 8
from his cold *c* And crystal silence — *Two Voices* 85
Ilion's column'd citadel, The *c* of Troas. — *Œnone* 14
from all neighbour *c's* Alliance and allegiance, — ,, 124
rolling to and fro The heads and *c's* of kings; — *Palace of Art* 152
Last May we made a *c* of flowers: — *May Queen, N. Y's. E.* 9
only toil, the roof and *c* of things? — *Lotos-Eaters, C. S.* 24
soldier found Me lying dead, my *c* about my brows, — *D. of F. Women* 162
And, King-like, wears the *c*: — *Of old sat Freedom* 16
Three Queens with *c's* of gold— — *M. d'Arthur* 198
those moments when we met, The *c* of all, — *Edwin Morris* 70
the angel there That holds a *c*? — *St. S. Stylites* 204
'tis here again; the *c*! the *c*! — ,, 208
That a sorrow's *c* of sorrow is — *Locksley Hall* 76
The mountain stirr'd its bushy *c*, — *Amphion* 25
In robe and *c* the King stept down, — *Beggar Maid* 5

Crown (diadem, etc.) (*continued*) doom Of those that wear the Poet's c: *You might have won* 10
slender coco's drooping c of plumes, *Enoch Arden* 574
And so she wears her error like a c *Princess iii* 111
gold That veins the world were pack'd to make your c, ,, *iv* 543
one that sought but Duty's iron c *Ode on Well.* 122
crowds at length be sane and c's be just. ,, 169
he wears a truer c Than any wreath ,, 276
It wore a c of light, *The Flower* 10
And you my wren with a c of gold, *Window. Spring* 11
flit like the king of the wrens with a c of fire. ,, *Ay.* 16
I wore them like a civic c: *In Mem. lxix* 8
The fool that wears a c of thorns: ,, 12
He look'd upon my c and smiled: ,, 16
But ill for him that wears a c, ,, *cxxvii* 9
has past and leaves The C a lonely splendour. *Ded. of Idylls* 49
More like are we to reave him of his c *Gareth and L.* 419
Thorns of the c and shivers of the cross, *Balin and Balan* 111
'Thou shalt put the c to use. The c is but the shadow of the King, ,, 202
Balin bare the c, and all the knights Approved him, ,, 209
Before another wood, the royal c Sparkled, ,, 462
'Lo there' she cried—'a c— ,, 465
I charge thee by that c upon thy shield, ,, 481
Drove his mail'd heel athwart the royal c, ,, 540
Else never had he borne her c, ,, 566
Trampled ye thus on that which bare the C?' ,, 602
wreath of beauty thine the c of power, *Merlin and V.* 79
he, that once was king, had on a c Of diamonds, *Lancelot and E.* 45
from the skull the c Roll'd into light, ,, 50
he had the gems Pluck'd from the c, ,, 57
Since to his c the golden dragon clung, ,, 434
statue in the mould Of Arthur, made by Merlin, with a c, *Holy Grail* 239
the c And both the wings are made of gold, ,, 241
a c of gold About a casque all jewels; ,, 410
And from the c thereof a carcanet Of ruby *Last Tournament* 6
high on land, A c of towers. ,, 506
then this c of towers So shook to such a roar ,, 620
Three queens with c's of gold: *Pass. of Arthur* 366
The loyal to their c Are loyal to their own far sons, *To the Queen ii* 27
great c of beams about his brows— *Lover's Tale i* 672
the cope and c Of all I hoped and fear'd? ,, *ii* 27
clutch'd the sacred c of Prester John, *Columbus* 110
feed the rebels of the c, ,, 131
A c the Singer hopes may last, *Epilogue* 38
I should wear my c entire *Helen's Tower* 9
Thou loather of the lawless c *Freedom* 31
Wilt neither quit the widow'd C *Prin. Beatrice* 15
To wreathe a c not only for the king *Akbar's Dream* 23
The shadow of a c, that o'er him hung, *D. of the Duke of C.* 2

Crown (five shillings) (*See also* **Half-crown**) and he gave the ringers a c. *Grandmother* 58

Crown (verb) this high dial, which my sorrow c's— *St. S. Stylites* 95
C thyself, worm, and worship thine own lusts!— *Aylmer's Field* 650
you fair stars that c a happy day *Maud I xviii* 30
c thee king Far in the spiritual city:' *Holy Grail* 161
and one will c me king Far in the spiritual city; ,, 482
However they may c him otherwhere. ,, 902
To c it with herself. *Lover's Tale i* 63
who c's himself Above the naked poisons ,, 355
It still were right to c with song *Epilogue* 36

Crown'd (*See also* **Citadel-crown'd, Fire-crown'd, Glory-crown'd**) 'The simple senses c his head: *Two Voices* 277
night divine C dying day with stars, *Palace of Art* 184
A name for ever!—lying robed and c, *D. of F. Women* 163
I shall be saved; Yea, c a saint. *St. S. Stylites* 153
Catch me who can, and make the catcher c— *Golden Year* 18
reissuing, robed and c, To meet her lord, *Godiva* 77
Like Heavenly hope she c the sea, *The Voyage* 70
and true love C after trial; *Aylmer's Field* 100
two fair images, Both c with stars *Sea Dreams* 241
C with a flower or two, *Lucretius* 229
and c with all her flowers. *Ode Inter. Exhib.* 41
And, c with all the season lent, *In Mem. xxii* 6
c The purple brows of Olivet. ,, *xxxi* 11

Crown'd (*continued*) When c with blessing she doth rise *In Mem. xl* 5
I see thee sitting c with good, ,, *lxxxiv* 5
Or, c with attributes of woe ,, *cxviii* 18
for he heard of Arthur newly c, *Com. of Arthur* 41
clamour'd for a king, Had Arthur c; ,, 236
Arthur sat C on the daïs, ,, 258
the King stood out in heaven, C. ,, 444
And c with fleshless laughter— *Gareth and L.* 1383
he c A happy life with a fair death, *Geraint and E.* 967
had I c With my slain self the heaps *Balin and Balan* 177
were he not c King, coward, and fool.' *Merlin and V.* 789
Her godlike head c with spiritual fire, ,, 837
Arthur, long before they c him King, *Lancelot and E.* 34
Lancelot's azure lions, c with gold, ,, 663
the gilded parapets were c With faces, *Pelleas and E.* 165
there before the people c herself: ,, 174
c the state pavilion of the King, *Guinevere* 399
dying thus, C with her highest act *Lover's Tale i* 216
with my work thus C her clear forehead. ,, 345
where that day I c myself as king, ,, 592
Julian, who himself was c With roses, ,, *iv* 296
There c with worship— *Tiresias* 175
whether c for a virtue, or hang'd for a crime? *Despair* 76
Her shadow c with stars— *Ancient Sage* 201
songs in praise of death, and c with flowers! ,, 209
C with sunlight—over darkness— *Locksley H., Sixty* 92
C so long with a diadem Never worn by a worthier, *On Jub. Q. Victoria* 7
Love for the maiden, c with marriage, *Vastness* 23
maiden-Princess, c with flowers, *The Ring* 485
the c ones all disappearing! *Parnassus* 13
C her knights, and flush'd as red As poppies when she c it. *The Tourney* 16

Crowning Knighted by Arthur at his c— *Com. of Arthur* 175
And c's and dethronements: *To the Queen ii* 45

Crown-farm Sold the c-f's for all but nothing, *Columbus* 132

Crown-royal bear her own c-r upon shield, *Balin and Balan* 200
Why wear ye this c-r upon shield?' ,, 338
'Why wear ye that c-r?' ,, 348

Crown-scandalous wear ye still that same c-s?' ,, 390

Crowsfoot Made wet the crafty c round his eye; *Sea Dreams* 187

Crucified either they were stoned or c, *St. S. Stylites* 51
the cross And those around it and the C, *Com. of Arthur* 273

Crucifix Or the maid-mother by a c, *Palace of Art* 93

Cruel c as a schoolboy ere he grows To Pity— *Walk. to the Mail* 109
'C, c the words I said! *Edward Gray* 17
more harsh and c Seem'd the Captain's mood. *The Captain* 13
no tenderness—Too hard, too c: *Princess v* 516
O c, there was nothing wild or strange, *Merlin and V.* 860

Cruel-hearted They call me c-h, but I care not *May Queen* 19

Crueller C: as not passing thro' the fire *Aylmer's Field* 671
'O c than was ever told in tale, *Merlin and V.* 858
which was c? which was worse? *Locksley H., Sixty* 88

Cruelty Infinite c rather that made everlasting Hell, *Despair* 96

Cruet gentlemen, That trifle with the c. *Will Water.* 232

Crumble touch it, it will c into dust.' *Holy Grail* 439
and they c into dust. *Locksley H., Sixty* 72

Crumbled Till public wrong be c into dust, *Ode on Well.* 167
Fell into dust, and c in the dark— *Lover's Tale i* 95

Crumpled More c than a poppy from the sheath, *Princess v* 29
the rest Were c inwards. *The Ring* 454

Crupper Beyond his horse's c and the bridge, *Gareth and L.* 966
length of lance and arm beyond The c, *Geraint and E.* 464

Crusade to lead A new c against the Saracen, *Columbus* 103
lead One last c against the Saracen, ,, 239

Crush (s) great the c was, and each base, *Princess vi* 353

Crush (verb) Like a rose-leaf I will c thee, *Lilian* 29
Will c her pretty maiden fancies dead *Princess i* 88
Or c her, like a vice of blood, *In Mem. iii* 15
this Order lives to c All wrongers *Gareth and L.* 625
when I thought he meant To c me, *Holy Grail* 416
he sail'd the sea to c the Moslem in his pride; *Locksley H., Sixty* 29

Crush'd (*See also* **Half-crushed**) I c them on my breast, my mouth; *Fatima* 12
sin, that c My spirit flat before thee. *St. S. Stylites* 25
like monstrous apes they c my chest: ,, 174

Crush'd (*continued*) Lady Psyche will be *c*; *Princess iii* 63
she *c* The scrolls together, ,, *iv* 393
record of her wrongs, And *c* to death: ,, *v* 144
I found, tho' *c* to hard and dry, *The Daisy* 97
Had bruised the herb and *c* the grape, *In Mem. xxxv* 23
Mangled, and flatten'd, and *c*, *Maud I i* 7
c with a tap Of my finger-nail *Maud II ii* 21
c in the clash of jarring claims, ,, *III vi* 44
c The Idolaters, and made the people free? *Gareth and L.* 136
c the man Inward, and either fell, *Balin and Balan* 562
her feet unseen *C* the wild passion out *Lancelot and E.* 742
Then *c* the saddle with his thighs, *Pelleas and E.* 459
Caught in a mill and *c*— *In the Child. Hosp.* 14
he was *c* in a moment and died, *Charity* 21
Crushing Raw from the prime, and *c* down his mate; *Princess ii* 121
Crust one slough and *c* of sin, *St. S. Stylites* 2
saw Thee woman through the *c* of iron moods *Princess vii* 342
Crusted flower-plots Were thickly *c*, one and all: *Mariana* 2
Crutch Weak Truth a-leaning on her *c*, *Clear-headed friend* 18
Cry (s) (*See also* **Battle-cry, War-cry**) I cry aloud: none hear my *cries*, *Oriana* 73
one deep *c* Of great wild beasts; *Palace of Art* 282
the deep behind him, and a *c* Before. *M. d'Arthur* 184
A *c* that shiver'd to the tingling stars, ,, 199
the boy's *c* came to her from the field, *Dora* 104
lest a *c* Should break his sleep by night, *Walk. to the Mail* 73
In one blind *c* of passion and of pain, *Love and Duty* 80
Begins the scandal and the *c*: *You might have won* 16
In him woke, With his first babe's first *c*, *Enoch Arden* 85
Forward she started with a happy *c*, ,, 151
all the younger ones with jubilant *cries* Broke ,, 377
hard upon the *c* of 'breakers' came ,, 548
send abroad a shrill and terrible *c*, ,, 768
gave A half-incredulous, half-hysterical *c*. ,, 853
knew he wherefore he had made the *c*; *Aylmer's Field* 589
Clung to the mother, and sent out a *c* *Sea Dreams* 245
A music harmonizing our wild *cries*, ,, 255
The plaintive *c* jarr'd on her ire; *Princess iv* 393
To lag behind, scared by the *c* they made, ,, *v* 94
rose a *c* As if to greet the king; ,, 248
clash'd His iron palms together with a *c*; ,, 354
She nor swoon'd, nor utter'd *c*: ,, *vi* 2
went up a great *c*, The Prince is slain. ,, 25
piteous was the *c*: ,, 142
and out of languor leapt a *c*; ,, *vii* 155
Sent from a dewy breast a *c* for light: ,, 253
Whose crying is a *c* for gold: *The Daisy* 94
He heard a fierce mermaiden *c*, *Sailor Boy* 6
Greater than I—is that your *c*? *Spiteful Letter* 17
He caught her away with a sudden *c*; *The Victim* 69
Forgive these wild and wandering *cries*, *In Mem., Pro.* 41
From out waste places comes a *c*, ,, *iii* 7
And with no language but a *c*. ,, *liv* 20
To raise a *c* that lasts not long, ,, *lxxv* 10
strange Was love's dumb *c* defying change ,, *xcv* 27
The roofs, that heard our earliest *c*, ,, *cii* 3
With overthrowings, and with *cries*, ,, *cxiii* 19
To cleave a creed in sects and *cries*, ,, *cxxviii* 15
A *c* above the conquer'd years ,, *cxxxi* 7
A wounded thing with a rancorous *c*, *Maud I x* 34
And there rises ever a passionate *c* ,, *II i* 5
there rang on a sudden a passionate *c*, A *c* for a brother's blood: ,, 33
rings on a sudden a passionate *c*, ,, *iv* 47
loyal people shouting a battle *c*, ,, *III vi* 35
'Ay,' said the King, 'and hear ye such a *c*? *Com. of Arthur* 337
Died but of late, and sent his *c* to me, ,, 361
there were *cries* and clashings in the nest, *Gareth and L.* 70
Gareth crying prick'd against the *c*; ,, 1221
rose a *c* That Edyrn's men were on them, *Marr. of Geraint* 638
Sent forth a sudden sharp and bitter *c*, *Geraint and E.* 722
c of children, Enid's and Geraint's ,, 965
from the castle a *c* Sounded across the court, *Balin and Balan* 399
Pellam's feeble *c* 'Stay, stay him! ,, 420
Utter'd a little tender dolorous *c*. *Lancelot and E.* 817

Cry (s) (*continued*) overhead Thunder, and in the thunder was a *c*. *Holy Grail* 185
I saw the Holy Grail and heard a *c*— ,, 291
ye know the *cries* of all my realm Pass thro' this hall— ,, 315
Such was his *c*: for having heard the King *Pelleas and E.* 10
thro' the wind Pierced ever a child's *c*: *Last Tournament* 17
She ended, and the *c* of a great jousts ,, 51
mantle clung, And pettish *cries* awoke, ,, 214
Nor heard the King for their own *cries*, ,, 472
cities burnt, and with a *c* she woke. *Guinevere* 83
I cry my *c* in silence, and have done. ,, 201
Then on a sudden a *c*, 'The King.' ,, 411
but in going mingled with dim *cries* *Pass. of Arthur* 41
are these dim *cries* Thine? ,, 47
Nor any *c* of Christian heard thereon, ,, 128
King am I, whatsoever be their *c*: ,, 162
heard the deep behind him, and a *c* Before. ,, 352
A *c* that shiver'd to the tingling stars, ,, 367
Like the last echo born of a great *c*, ,, 459
witness, too, the silent *c*, *To the Queen ii* 10
sent my *c* Thro' the blank night to Him *Lover's Tale i* 751
I flung myself upon him In tears and *cries*: ,, *ii* 90
Cries of the partridge like a rusty key ,, 115
guests broke in upon him with meeting hands And *cries* ,, *iv* 239
Rush'd at each other with a *c*, ,, 373
hear that *c* of my boy that was dead, *Rizpah* 45
strangled vanity Utter'd a stifled *c*— *Sisters (E. and E.)* 200
there was a phantom *c* that I heard as I tost about, *In the Child. Hosp.* 63
and heard their musical *c*— *V. of Maeldune* 97
when the brazen *c* of Æakidês *Achilles over the T.* 22
Never a *c* so desolate, *Despair* 59
Gone the *c* of 'Forward, Forward,' *Locksley H., Sixty* 73
Let us hush this *c* of 'Forward' ,, 78
Cries of unprogressive dotage ,, 153
leave the dog too lame to follow with the *c*, ,, 226
the Muses cried with a stormy *c* *Dead Prophet* 2
O scorner of the party *c* *Freedom* 25
mighty was the mother's childless *c*, A *c* *Demeter and P.* 32
he, the God of dreams, who heard my *c*, ,, 91
lover thro' this ring Had sent his *c* for her forgiveness, *The Ring* 233
I myself was madden'd with her *c*, ,, 405
Nor lend an ear to random *cries*, *Politics* 7
from out the long ravine below, She heard a wailing *c*, *Death of Œnone* 20
following, as in trance, the silent *c*. ,, 86
the *c* from off the mosque, *Akbar's Dream* 149
on the sudden, and with a *c* 'Saleem' ,, 184
till the little one utter'd a *c*. *Bandit's Death* 26
Cry (verb) I *c* aloud: none hear my cries, *Oriana* 73
Call to each other and whoop and *c* *The Merman* 26
every smouldering town *Cries* to Thee, *Poland* 6
Cries to Thee, 'Lord, how long shall these things be? ,, 9
Than *c* for strength, remaining weak, *Two Voices* 95
'*C*, faint not: either Truth is born ,, 181
'*C*, faint not, climb: the summits slope ,, 184
We did so laugh and *c* with you, *D. of the O. Year* 25
Yet cease I not to clamour and to *c*, *St. S. Stylites* 42
for a tender voice will *c*. *Locksley Hall* 87
C down the past, not only we, *Godiva* 7
bade him *c*, with sound of trumpet, ,, 36
c For that which all deny them— *Will Water.* 45
let the wind sweep and the plover *c*; *Come not, when, etc.* 5
C to the summit, 'Is there any hope? *Vision of Sin* 220
I *c* to vacant chairs and widow'd walls, *Aylmer's Field* 720
Must *c* to these the last of theirs, ,, 792
I *c* to thee To kiss thy Mavors, *Lucretius* 81
Earth Reels, and the herdsmen *c*; *Princess v* 529
I cannot *c* for him, Annie: *Grandmother* 15
Than if the crowded Orb should *c* *Lit. Squabbles* 15
With morning wakes the will, and *cries*, *In Mem. iv* 15
thought That *cries* against my wish for thee. ,, *xc* 24
C thro' the sense to hearten trust ,, *cxvi* 7
Then was I as a child that *cries*, ,, *cxxiv* 19
I to *c* out on pride Who have won *Maud I xii* 17

Cry (verb) (*continued*) rose *cries*, 'She is near, she is near;' *Maud I xxii* 63
I will *c* to the steps above my head ,, *II v* 101
A *c* from out the dawning of my life, *Com. of Arthur* 333
Who will *c* shame? *Gareth and L.* 942
and *c*, 'Thou hast made us lords, ,, 1131
mother-maidenhood of Heaven, *C* out upon her. *Balin and Balan* 522
children cast their pins and nails, and *c*, *Merlin and V.* 430
she heard Sir Lancelot *c* in the court, *Lancelot and E.* 344
I *c* my cry in silence, *Guinevere* 201
'O mother!' I heard him *c*. *Rizpah* 42
an' saw she begins to *c*, *North. Cobbler* 71
I should *c* to the dear Lord Jesus to help me, *In the Child. Hosp.* 49
Before thy light, and *c* continually—*C* *Sir J. Oldcastle* 85
that men *C* out against thee: *Columbus* 153
So dark that men *c* out against the Heavens. *Ancient Sage* 172
weep my fill once more, and *c* myself to rest! *The Flight* 6
Cries to Weakest as to Strongest, *Locksley H., Sixty* 110
Nay, your pardon, *c* your 'forward,' ,, 225
Too many a voice may *c* That man *Epilogue* 72
Far off a phantom cuckoo *cries* *Pref. Poem Broth. S.* 19
sober rook And carrion crow *c* 'Mortgage.' *The Ring* 174
Nor even a Sir Joshua, some will *c*, *Romney's R.* 47
some *c* 'Quick' and some *c* 'Slow,' *Politics* 9
Shall the rose *C* to the lotus *Akbar's Dream* 37
And a beggar began to *c* 'Food, food *Voice spake, etc.* 5
Cryin' (part) an' *c* and teärin' 'er 'aäir, *North. Cobbler* 34
but we hard it *c*, 'Ochone!' *Tomorrow* 84
Crying (part) (*See also* **A-cryin'**, **Cryin'**, **Keenin'**) *c* to each other And calling, *Enoch Arden* 382
C with a loud voice 'A sail! ,, 913
And *c* upon the name of Leolin, *Aylmer's Field* 576
Some *c* there was an army in the land, *Princess iv* 484
An infant *c* in the night: An infant *c* for the light: *In Mem. liv* 18
But, *c*, knows his father near; ,, *cxxiv* 20
They were *c* and calling. *Maud I xii* 4
Were *c* and calling to her, ,, 26
many another suppliant *c* came With noise *Gareth and L.* 436
Then came a widow *c* to the King, ,, 333
Came yet another widow *c* to him, ,, 350
Gareth *c* prick'd against the cry; ,, 1221
flying back and *c* out, 'O Merlin, *Merlin and V.* 943
And all his legions *c* Christ and him, *Lancelot and E.* 305
c that his prize is death.' ,, 531
maiden sprang into the hall *C* on help: *Holy Grail* 209
c with full voice 'Traitor, come out, *Guinevere* 105
Whereat the novice *c*, with clasp'd hands, ,, 311
Two friars *c* that if Spain should oust *Columbus* 96
c after voices that have fled! *Locksley H., Sixty* 251
Crying (s) mine but from the *c* of a child.' *Sea Dreams* 249
Whose *c* is a cry for gold: *The Daisy* 94
and *c's* for the light, *Pass. of Arthur* 116
Or at my *c* 'Mother?' *The Ring* 141
Crypt My knees are bow'd in *c* and shrine: *Sir Galahad* 18
And fall'n into the dusty *c* *Will Water.* 183
those cold *c's* where they shall cease. *In Mem. lviii* 8
Crystal And down the streaming *c* dropt; *Princess vii* 165
In a shallop of *c* ivory-beak'd, *The Islet* 12
Became a *c*, and he saw them thro' it, *Merlin and V.* 630
c into which I braided Edwin's hair! *The Flight* 34
Cube hard-grain'd Muses of the *c* and square *Princess, Pro.* 180
Cubit lived upon a pillar, high Six *c's*, *St. S. Stylites* 87
numbers forty *c's* from the soil. ,, 91
Drave the long spear a *c* thro' his breast *Geraint and E.* 86
Cuckoo The *c* told his name to all the hills; *Gardener's D.* 93
I built the nest,' she said, 'To hatch the *c*. *Princess iv* 366
'*C*! *c*!' was ever a May so fine? *Window. Ay* 10
'I have seen the *c* chased by lesser fowl, *Com. of Arthur* 167
Than the gray *c* loves his name, *Lover's Tale i* 257
The *c* of a joyless June Is calling out of doors: *Pref Poem Broth. S.* 3
The *c* of a worse July Is calling thro' the dark: ,, 11
a phantom *c* cries From out a phantom hill; ,, 19
There! I heard Our *c* call. *To Mary Boyle* 6
A clamorous *c* stoops to meet her hand; *Prog. of Spring* 45
Cuckoo-flower As perfume of the *c-f*? *Margaret* 8
blow the faint sweet *c-f's*; *May Queen* 30
Cud chew'd The thrice-turn'd *c* of wrath, *Princess i* 66
Cuddle as good to *c* an' kiss as a lass as 'ant nowt? *N. Farmer, N. S.* 24
Cuddled (*See also* **Coodled**) An' we *c* and huddled togither, *Owd Roä* 112
Cuff'd Caught and *c* by the gale: *Maud I vi* 5
Cuirass on his *c* work our Lady's Head, *Lancelot and E.* 294
and a spear Prick'd sharply his own *c*, ,, 489
Cuisses and *c* dash'd with drops Of onset; *M. d'Arthur* 215
and *c* dash'd with drops Of onset; *Pass. of Arthur* 383
Cull I *c* from every faith and race *Akbar's Dream* 68
Cull'd whitest honey in fairy gardens *c*— *Eleänore* 26
Because all words, tho' *c* with choicest art, *D. of F. Women* 285
but one, by those fair fingers *c*, *Gardener's D.* 150
In mine own lady palms I *c* the spring *Merlin and V.* 273
Culminate lead The new light up, and *c* in peace, *Princess ii* 348
Culmination All starry *c* drop Balm-dews *Talking Oak* 267
Cultivation months of toil, And years of *c*, *Amphion* 98
Culture An universal *c* for the crowd, *Princess, Pro.* 109
whence they need More breadth of *c*: ,, *v* 188
Culver round her brows a woodland *c* flits, *Prog. of Spring* 18
Cunning-simple So innocent-arch, so *c-s*, *Lilian* 13
Cúnobelíne rioted in the city of *C*! *Boädicea* 60
Cup I drink the *c* of a costly death, *Eleänore* 138
I pledge her not in any cheerful *c*, *Wan Sculptor* 9
Three fingers round the old silver *c*— *Miller's D.* 10
incense of all odour steam'd From out a golden *c*. *Palace of Art* 40
That was the last drop in the *c* of gall. *Walk. to the Mail* 69
My little oakling from the *c*, *Talking Oak* 231
Will haunt the vacant *c*: *Will Water.* 172
'Fill the *c*, and fill the can: (repeat) *Vision of Sin* 95, 119, 203
'Fill the can, and fill the *c*: (repeat) ,, 131, 167
c's and silver on the burnish'd board Sparkled *Enoch Arden* 742
The magic *c* that fill'd itself anew. *Aylmer's Field* 143
Only such *c's* as left us friendly-warm, *Lucretius* 215
There they drank in *c's* of emerald, *Boädicea* 61
The crowning *c*, the three-times-three, *In Mem. Con.* 104
they sat, And *c* clash'd *c*; *Balin and Balan* 85
to hurl his *c* Straight at the speaker, *Merlin and V.* 30
Except indeed to drink: no *c* had we: ,, 272
made a pretty *c* of both my hands ,, 275
phantom of a *c* that comes and goes?' *Holy Grail* 44
'The *c*, the *c* itself, from which our Lord ,, 46
the holy *c* Was caught away to Heaven, ,, 57
Lancelot might have seen, The Holy *C* of healing; ,, 655
hast thou seen the Holy *C*, ,, 734
children sat in white with *c's* of gold, *Last Tournament* 142
And them that round it sat with golden *c's* ,, 289
white slips Handed her *c* and piped, ,, 296
the *c* was gold, the draught was mud.' ,, 298
c's Where nymph and god ran ever round *Lover's Tale iv* 196
Warm as the crocus *c*, *Early Spring* 29
wines of heresy in the *c* Of counsel— *Akbar's Dream* 174
Cupid The rentroll *C* of our rainy isles. *Edwin Morris* 103
The modish *C* of the day, *Talking Oak* 67
The seal was *C* bent above a scroll, *Princess i* 242
Cupid-boys By *C-b* of blooming hue— *Day-Dm., Ep.* 10
Cur yelp'd the *c*, and yawl'd the cat; *The Goose* 33
the barking *c* Made her cheek flame: *Godiva* 57
c Pluckt from the *c* he fights with, *Gareth and L.* 701
Curate and with Edward Bull The *c*; *Edwin Morris* 15
said the fat-faced *c* Edward Bull, (repeat) ,, 42, 90
'e's nobbut a *c*, an' weänt niver git hissen clear, *N. Farmer, N. S.* 27
An' thou'll be 'is *C* 'ere, *Church-warden, etc.* 45
Curb 'Wild natures need wise *c's*. *Princess v* 173
mine the voice to *c* The madness *Tiresias* 70
c the beast would cast thee in the mire, *Ancient Sage* 276
Curb'd strongly groom'd and straitly *c* *Princess v* 456
Curdled half the wolf's-milk *c* in their veins, ,, *vii* 130
Cure (curacy) The curate; he was fatter than his *c*. *Edwin Morris* 15
Cure (remedy) declined, And trusted any *c*. *Palace of Art* 156
Wonderful *c's* he had done, O yes, *In the Child. Hosp.* 5
Cured *C* lameness, palsies, cancers. *St. S. Stylites* 82
And *c* some halt and maim'd; ,, 137
could only be *c*, if *c*, by the surgeon's knife, *Despair* 80
Curious Hetairai, *c* in their art, *Lucretius* 52

Curious (*continued*) Too *c* Vivien, tho' you talk of trust, — *Merlin and V.* 358
Not ever be too *c* for a boon, — ,, 486
You are *c*. How should I tell? — *Despair* 3
Curiousness In children a great *c* be well, — *Merlin and V.* 364
Curl (s) his ridges are not *c's* And ripples — *Supp. Confessions* 130
In many a dark delicious *c*, — *Arabian Nights* 139
In a golden *c* With a comb of pearl, — *The Mermaid* 6
flow'd His coal-black *c's* as on he rode, — *L. of Shalott iii* 31
fingers drew Her streaming *c's* of deepest brown — *Mariana in the S.* 16
and the light and lustrous *c's*— — *M. d'Arthur* 216
dim *c's* kindle into sunny rings; — *Tithonus* 54
And moves not on the rounded *c*. — *Day-Dm., Sleep. B.* 8
took him by the *c's*, and led him in, — *Vision of Sin* 6
from her baby's forehead clipt A tiny *c*, and gave it: — *Enoch Arden* 236
The hand that play'd the patron with her *c's*. — *Princess, Pro.* 138
Melissa shook her doubtful *c's*, — ,, *iii* 75
From the flaxen *c* to the gray lock — ,, *iv* 426
on their *c's* From the high tree the blossom wavering fell, — ,, *vi* 79
And down dead-heavy sank her *c's*, — ,, 147
And winds their *c's* about his hand: — *In Mem. lxvi* 12
little head, sunning over with *c's*, — *Maud I xxii* 57
Perchance, one *c* of Arthur's golden beard. — *Merlin and V.* 58
and the light and lustrous *c's*— — *Pass. of Arthur* 384
One golden *c*, his golden gift, — *The Flight* 36
begun to gleam Thro' youthful *c's*, — *To Mary Boyle* 42
Curl (verb) *c* round my silver feet silently, — *The Mermaid* 50
May serve to *c* a maiden's locks, — *In Mem. lxxvii* 7
Began to move, seethe, twine and *c*: — *Gareth and L.* 234
Curl'd about His dusty forehead drily *c*, — *Miller's D.* 6
I *c* and comb'd his comely head, — *The Sisters* 31
on herself her serpent pride had *c*. — *Palace of Art* 257
the clouds are lightly *c* Round their golden houses, — *Lotos-Eaters, C. S.* 112
Faint shadows, vapours lightly *c*, — *Day-Dm., Sleep. P.* 5
All-graceful head, so richly *c*, — ,, *L'Envoi* 38
The forest crack'd, the waters *c*, — *In Mem. xv* 5
For us the same cold streamlet *c* — ,, *lxxix* 9
a mist Of incense *c* about her, — *Com. of Arthur* 288
breeze *c* over a peacefuller sea, — *The Wreck* 133
Curlew all around it, as of old, the *c's* call, — *Locksley Hall* 3
while I heard the *c's* call, — *Locksley H., Sixty* 3
Curn (Corn) Till I gied 'em Hinjian *c*, — *Village Wife* 118
Currency brooking not Exchange or *c*: — *Lover's Tale i* 448
Current (*See also* **Full-current, Main-current, Sea-current**) Till in its onward *c* it absorbs — *Isabel* 31
From those four jets four *c's* in one swell — *Palace of Art* 33
The ever-shifting *c's* of the blood — *D. of F. Women* 133
'all the *c* of my being sets to thee.' — *Locksley Hall* 24
upward runs The *c* of my days: — *Will Water.* 36
turn'd The *c* of his talk to graver things — *Enoch Arden* 203
Fast flow'd the *c* of her easy tears, — ,, 865
then the motion of the *c* ceased, — *Sea Dreams* 117
crystal *c's* of clear morning seas. — *Princess ii* 328
You turn'd your warmer *c's* all to her, — ,, *iv* 301
glowing in the broad Deep-dimpled *c* underneath, — *Gareth and L.* 1089
and driven My *c* to the fountain whence it sprang, — *Lover's Tale i* 503
But in the onward *c* of her speech, — ,, 565
Noises of a *c* narrowing, — *Locksley H., Sixty* 154
alchemise old hates into the gold Of Love, and make it *c*; — *Akbar's Dream* 164
Curse (s) A *c* is on her if she stay — *L. of Shalott ii* 4
She knows not what the *c* may be, — ,, 6
'The *c* is come upon me,' cried The Lady — ,, *iii* 44
I said, 'I toil beneath the *c*, — *Two Voices* 229
'My youth,' she said, 'was blasted with a *c*: — *D. of F. Women* 103
This is the *c* of time. — *To J. S.* 17
this world's *c*,—beloved but hated— — *Love and Duty* 47
My Shakespeare's *c* on clown and knave — *You might have won* 27
And left their memories a world's *c*— — *Aylmer's Field* 796
A *c* in his God-bless-you: — *Sea Dreams* 164
I remember'd that burnt sorcerer's *c* — *Princess v* 475
when she turn'd, the *c* Had fallen, — *In Mem. vi* 37
we have made them a *c*, — *Maud I i* 21

Curse (s) (*continued*) She may bring me a *c*. — *Maud I i* 73
the sparrow-hawk, My *c*, my nephew— — *Marr. of Geraint* 445
God's *c*, it makes me mad to see you weep. — *Geraint and E.* 616
Thy *c*, and darken'd all thy day; — *Balin and Balan* 620
'That is love's *c*; pass on, — *Lancelot and E.* 1353
woman-worshipper? Yea, God's *c*, and I! — *Last Tournament* 447
Until it came a kingdom's *c* with thee— — *Guinevere* 550
their *c's* and their groans. — *Columbus* 68
chain'd and coupled with the *c* Of blindness and their unbelief, — *Tiresias* 58
blunt the *c* Of Pallas, hear, — ,, 154
never gloom'd by the *c* Of a sin, — *The Wreck* 139
If a *c* meant ought, I would curse you — *Despair* 64
follies, furies, *c's*, passionate tears, — *Locksley H., Sixty* 39
man had coin'd himself a *c*: — ,, 87
And 'The *C* of the Prophet' in Heaven. — *Dead Prophet* 28
On you will come the *c* of all the land, — *The Fleet* 3
stings him back to the *c* of the light; — *Vastness* 18
My *c* upon the Master's apothegm, — *Romney's R.* 37
arose The shriek and *c* of trampled millions, — *Akbar's Dream* 190
I sent him a desolate wail and a *c*, — *Charity* 14
Curse (verb) I *c* not nature, no, nor death; — *In Mem. lxxiii* 7
c me the blabbing lip, And *c* me — *Maud II v* 57
I *c* the tongue that all thro' yesterday — *Gareth and L.* 1322
To *c* this hedgerow thief, — *Marr. of Geraint* 309
I did not come to *c* thee, Guinevere, — *Guinevere* 533
I would *c* you for not having let me be. — *Despair* 64
may the Great God *c* him and bring him — ,, 106
'*C* him!' *c* your fellow-victim? — *Locksley H., Sixty* 9
Cursed *c* and scorn'd, and bruised with stones: — *Two Voices* 222
And bless'd herself, and *c* herself, — *The Goose* 15
C be the social wants that sin against the strength of youth! *C* be the social lies that warp us from the living truth! *C* be the sickly forms that err from honest Nature's rule! *C* be the gold that gilds — *Locksley Hall* 59
face Would darken, as he *c* his credulousness, — *Sea Dreams* 13
C me and my flower. — *The Flower* 8
I have *c* him even to lifeless things) — *Maud I xix* 15
and *c* the tale, The told-of, and the teller. — *Balin and Balan* 542
c The dead babe and the follies, of the King; — *Last Tournament* 162
'I had sooner be *c* than kiss'd!'— — *First Quarrel* 83
I, Earth-Goddess, *c* the Gods of Heaven. — *Demeter and P.* 102
Snarl'd at and *c* me. — *Merlin and the G.* 28
he sobb'd and he wept, And *c* himself; — *Bandit's Death* 30
I had *c* the woman he married, — *Charity* 24
I had *c* her as woman and wife, — ,, 31
Cursing (part.) I stood With Florian, *c* Cyril, — *Princess iv* 171
I was *c* them and my doom, — *Maud I xix* 51
And *c* their lost time, and the dead man, — *Geraint and E.* 576
Cursing (s) she was deaf To blessing or to *c* — ,, 579
Curtain (*See also* **Casement-curtain**) In the white *c*, to and fro, She saw — *Mariana* 51
with thee forgets to close His *c's*, — *Adeline* 43
haunted with a jolly ghost, that shook The *c's*, — *Walk. to the Mail* 37
He had cast the *c's* of their seat aside— — *Aylmer's Field* 803
I beheld The death-white *c* drawn; — *Maud I xiv* 34
the death-white *c* meant but sleep, — ,, 37
By the *c's* of my bed — ,, *II iv* 54
at one end of the hall Two great funereal *c's*, — *Lover's Tale iv* 214
drama's closing *c* is the pall! — *Locksley H., Sixty* 62
Curtain-fold from out the silken *c-f's* — *Gareth and L.* 925
Curtsey made me a mocking *c* and went. — *Grandmother* 46
Curtseying *c* her obeisance, let us know The Princess Ida waited: — *Princess ii* 20
Curve (s) (*See also* **Crescent-curve**) the rainbow lives in the *c* of the sand; — *Sea-Fairies* 27
c's of mountain, bridge, Boat, island, — *Edwin Morris* 5
In *c's* the yellowing river ran, — *Sir L. and Q. G.* 15
With many a *c* my banks I fret — *The Brook* 43
To left and right thro' meadowy *c's*, — *In Mem. c* 15
Or the least little delicate aquiline *c* — *Maud I ii* 10
in kindly *c's*, with gentlest fall, — *De Prof., Two G.* 23
turn upon itself in many a backward streaming *c*. — *Locksley H., Sixty* 236

Curve (verb) And out again I *c* and flow *The Brook* 182
Curved (*See also* **Sudden-curved**) *c* an arm about his neck, *Merlin and V.* 241
Curvet Making a roan horse caper and *c* *Lancelot and E.* 792
Curving And *c* a contumelious lip, *Maud I xiii* 20
a procession, *c* round The silver-sheeted bay : *Lover's Tale ii* 75
Cushie '*C* wur craäzed fur 'er cauf ' *Spinster's S's.* 115
Cushion On silken *c's* half reclined ; *Eleänore* 126
The *c's* of whose touch may press *Talking Oak* 179
Tom, lig theere o' the *c*, *Spinster's S's.* 94
Custom (habit) one good *c* should corrupt the world. *M. d'Arthur* 242
Appraised the Lycian *c*, *Princess ii* 128
Disyoke their necks from *c*, ,, 143
And moved beyond his *c*, Gama said : ,, *vi* 229
For this was Arthur's *c* in his hall ; *Gareth and L.* 410
And reverencing the *c* of the house *Marr. of Geraint* 380
pick the vicious quitch Of blood and *c* *Geraint and E.* 904
I rode, Shattering all evil *c's* *Holy Grail* 477
one good *c* should corrupt the world. *Pass. of Arthur* 410
'There is a *c* in the Orient, friends— *Lover's Tale iv* 230
This *c*—' Pausing here a moment, ,, 236
This *c* steps yet further when the guest ,, 244
Cutsom (business) *See* **Coostom**
Here is *c* come your way ; *Vision of Sin* 64
Cut (s) this *c* is fresh ; That ten years back ; *Lancelot and E.* 21
Cut (verb) *c's* atwain The knots that tangle *Clear-headed friend* 2
they *c* away my tallest pines, *Œnone* 208
I was *c* off from hope in that sad place, *D. of F. Women* 105
C Prejudice against the grain : *Love thou thy land* 22
where the hedge-row *c's* the pathway, stood, *Gardener's D.* 86
some little cloud *C's* off the fiery highway *Enoch Arden* 130
C off the length of highway on before, ,, 673
This hair is his : she *c* it off and gave it, ,, 894
And *c* this epitaph above my bones ; *Princess ii* 207
C the Roman boy to pieces *Boädicea* 66
What is she, *c* from love and faith, *In Mem. cxiv* 11
c off from the mind The bitter springs *Maud I x* 48
Struck at him with his whip, and *c* his cheek. *Marr. of Geraint* 207
es he couldn't *c* down a tree ! *Village Wife* 30
'Lad, thou mun *c* off thy taäil, ,, 64
thou'll 'gree to *c* off thy taäil ,, 66
to git 'im to *c* off 'is taäil. ,, 74
an' 'e wouldn't *c* off the taäil. ,, 78
'Goin' to *c* the Sassenach whate ' *Tomorrow* 14
c his bit o' turf for the fire ? ,, 65
Cut *See also* **Clean-cut, Clear-cut**
Cuttin' betther nor *c* the Sassenach whate *Tomorrow* 94
Cutting (*See also* **Cuttin'**) *c* eights that day upon the pond, *The Epic* 10
Cycle (s) Young Nature thro' five *c's* ran, *Two Voices* 17
plann'd With *c's* of the human tale, *Palace of Art* 146
Better fifty years of Europe than a *c* of Cathay. *Locksley Hall* 184
together at her will Thro' all her *c's*— *Lucretius* 248
But when their *c* is o'er, *Voice and the P.* 26
lead The closing *c* rich in good. *In Mem. cv* 28
Cycle (verb) Falls off, but *c's* always round. *Two Voices* 348
Cycle-year Will mould him thro' the *c-y* *Epilogue* 77
Cygnet the swan's Is tawnier than her *c's* : *Lancelot and E.* 1185
Cymbal people rejoice With shawms, and with *c's*, *Dying Swan* 32
Cypress With *c* promenaded, *Amphion* 38
Nor waves the *c* in the palace walk ; *Princess vii* 177
watch'd awake A *c* in the moonlight shake, *The Daisy* 82
Made *c* of her orange flower, *In Mem. lxxxiv* 15
rise three dark, tall *c'es*,—Three *c'es*, *Lover's Tale i* 536
The mountain, the three *c'es*, the cave, ,, *ii* 109
Break thro' the yews and *c* of thy grave, *Ded. Poem Prin. Alice* 12
the poplar and *c* unshaken by storm *V. of Maeldune* 15
the palm Call to the *c* ' I alone am fair ? ' *Akbar's Dream* 38
Cypress-cone *c-c's* That spired above the wood ; *Lover's Tale ii* 38
Cyril I stood With *C* and with Florian, *Princess i* 52
C whisper'd : 'Take me with you too.' ,, 81
I stole from court With *C* and with Florian, ,, 103
'We of the court' said *C*. 'From the court ,, *ii* 48
'Comely, too, by all that's fair,' said *C*. ,, 115
'Let me die too,' said *C*, 'having seen ,, 210
Cyril (*continued*) 'You are that Psyche,' *C* said, (repeat) *Princess ii* 256, 278
Said *C*, 'Madam, he the wisest man ,, 350
C took the child, And held her round ,, 362
Said *C* : 'Pale one, blush again : ,, *iii* 67
As if to close with *C's* random wish : ,, 101
Hither came *C*, and yawning 'O hard task,' ,, 124
then, climbing, *C* kept With Psyche, ,, 354
C, with whom the bell-mouth'd glass had wrought ,, *iv* 155
I stood With Florian, cursing *C*, ,, 171
And where are Psyche, *C* ? both are fled : ,, 241
for *C*, howe'er He deal in frolic, as to-night— ,, 249
Go : *C* told us all.' ,, *v* 36
C met us. A little shy at first, ,, 44
To whom remorseful *C*, 'Yet I pray Take comfort : ,, 79
such as her ! if *C* spake her true, ,, 168
fiery-short was *C's* counter-scoff, ,, 307
and bore down a Prince, And *C*, one. ,, 519
C seeing it, push'd against the Prince, ,, 533
Beside us, *C*, batter'd as he was, ,, *vi* 154
When *C* pleaded, Ida came behind ,, *vii* 78
Cyrus And what she did to *C* after fight, ,, *v* 366
Czar Jack on his ale-house bench has as many lies as a *C* ; *Maud I iv* 9

D

Daäle (dale) (*See also* **Howlaby Daäle**) an' the *d* was all of a thaw, *Owd Roä* 39
Daäy (day) 'e shall stan to my dying *d* ; *North. Cobbler* 95
'e snifft up a box in a *d*, *Village Wife* 40
I'll tell tha some o' these *d's*. ,, 58
niver 'a liked tha sa well, as I did that *d*, *Spinster's S.'s* 29
I warrant ye soom fine *d*— ,, 63
Thaw thou was es soäber es *d*, ,, 75
an' belt long afoor my *d* *Owd Roä* 21
Eh ? good *d* ! good *d* ! thaw it bean't not mooch of a *d*, *Church-warden, etc.* 1
I minds when i' Howlaby beck won *d* ,, 27
Dabbled all *d* with the blood Of his own son, *Princess vi* 104
Its lips in the field above are *d* with blood-red heath, *Maud I i* 2
Dabbling *d* in the fount of fictive tears, *The Brook* 93
D a shameless hand with shameful jest, *Princess iii* 314
Daffodil (*See also* **Daffodilly**) and found The shining *d* dead, *Maud I iii* 14
On a bed of *d* sky, ,, *xxii* 10
And the shining *d* dies, ,, *III vi* 6
left us just before The *d* was blown ? *Lover's Tale i* 294
in this roaring moon of *d* And crocus, *Pref. Son. 19th Cent.* 7
Daffodilly That clad her like an April *d* *Princess ii* 324
Dagger I made my *d* sharp and bright. *The Sisters* 26
and thrust The *d* thro' her side.' *D. of F. Women* 260
With that gold *d* of thy bill *The Blackbird* 11
A *d*, in rich sheath with jewels on it *Aylmer's Field* 220
Tumbled the tawny rascal at his feet, This *d* with him, ,, 231
left alone he pluck'd her *d* forth ,, 470
and the *d* which himself Gave Edith, ,, 596
Shot sidelong *d's* at us, *Princess ii* 450
had she found a *d* there *Merlin and V.* 851
Sir, do you see this *d* ? *Bandit's Death* 5
one day He had left his *d* behind him. ,, 12
felt I could end myself too with the *d*— ,, 37
I with this *d* of his—do you doubt me ? ,, 42
Dagonet *D*, the fool, whom Gawain in his mood *Last Tournament* 1
And little *D* on the morrow morn, ,, 240
D replied, 'Belike for lack of wiser company ; ,, 244
while he twangled little *D* stood Quiet ,, 252
And little *D*, skipping, 'Arthur, the King's ; ,, 262
but lean me down, Sir *D*, ,, 273
D with one foot poised in his hand, ,, 285
And little *D* mincing with his feet, ,, 311
D, turning on the ball of his foot, ,, 329
D answer'd, 'Ay, and when the land Was freed, ,, 338
D, 'Nay, nor will : I see it and hear. ,, 348

Dagonet (*continued*) *D* clapt his hands and shrill'd, *Last Tournament* 353
And down the city *D* danced away; „ 359
Dahomey boats of *D* that float upon human blood! *The Dawn* 5
Daily *D* and hourly, more and more. *Eleänore* 71
Daily-dwindling With *d-d* profits held the house; *Enoch Arden* 696
Dainty Are but *dainties* drest again: *Window. No Answer* 26
Dainty-woeful thro' the dew Of *d-w* sympathies. *Margaret* 53
Daïs I hung The royal *d* round. *Palace of Art* 132
and Arthur sat Crown'd on the *d*, *Com. of Arthur* 258
Daïs-throne like a rising sun High from the *d-t*— *M. d'Arthur* 218
And there sat Arthur on the *d-t*, *Holy Grail* 721
like a rising sun High from the *d-t*— *Pass. of Arthur* 386
Daisy Touch'd by his feet the *d* slept. *Two Voices* 276
linger'd there Till every *d* slept, *Gardiner's D.* 165
I pluck'd a *d*, I gave it you. *The Daisy* 88
Daisies and kingcups and honeysuckle-flowers.' *City Child* 10
the *d* close Her crimson fringes *In Mem. lxxii* 11
And left the *daisies* rosy. *Maud I xii* 24
But I and the first *d* on his grave *Lover's Tale i* 193
The *d* will shut to the shadow, *The Wreck* 38
tiny fist Had graspt a *d* from your Mother's grave— *The Ring* 323
hardly a *d* as yet, little friend, See, there is hardly a *d*. *The Throstle* 11
Daisy Blossomed Wash'd with still rains and *d b*; *Circumstance* 7
Daisy-chain Made blossom-ball or *d-c*, *Aylmer's Field* 87
He workt me the *d c*— *First Quarrel* 13
Dale (*See also* **Daäle**) here are the blissful downs and *d's*, *Sea-Fairies* 22
And long purples of the *d*. *A Dirge* 31
And the rivulet in the flowery *d* *May Queen* 39
thro' mountain clefts the *d* Was seen far inland, *Lotos-Eaters* 20
She went by *d*, and she went by down, *Lady Clare* 59
moon like a rick on fire was rising over the *d*, *Grandmother* 39
Till over down and over *d* *In Mem., Con.* 110
all in loops and links among the *d's* *Lancelot and E.* 166
Beheld at noon in some delicious *d* *Guinevere* 393
Dalliance O the *d* and the wit, *D. of F. Women* 147
Dallied But *d* with his golden chain, *Day-Dm., Revival* 31
Dally That with the napkin *d*; *Will Water.* 118
'and meets And *dallies* with him in the Mouth of Hell.' *Balin and Balan* 615
For dare we *d* with the sphere *Epilogue* 44
Dallying In lieu of idly *d* with the truth, *Lancelot and E.* 590
Tristram, ever *d* with her hand, *Last Tournament* 626
Dam (obstruction) The sleepy pool above the *d*, *Miller's D.* 99
As waits a river level with the *d* *Princess iv* 473
Dam (mother) Sent out a bitter bleating for its *d*; „ 392
Damask-work sloping of the moon-lit sward Was *d-w*, *Arabian Nights* 28
Dame Knight and burgher, lord and *d*, *L. of Shalott iv* 43
To have a *d* indoors, that trims us up, *Edwin Morris* 46
no livelier than the *d* That whisper'd 'Asses' ears,' *Princess ii* 112
Like that great *d* of Lapidoth she sang. „ *vi* 32
When *d's* and heroines of the golden year „ 64
behind, A train of *d's*: „ *vii* 128
found an ancient *d* in dim brocade; *Marr. of Geraint* 363
But that old *d*, to whom full tenderly „ 508
'Yea, surely,' said the *d*, 'And gladly „ 690
no more avail, *D*, to be gentle than ungentle *Geraint and E.* 716
nor lets Or *d* or damsel enter at his gates *Balin and Balan* 107
lived there neither *d* nor damsel *Merlin and V.* 606
Sir Valence wedded with an outland *d*: „ 714
One old *d* Came suddenly on the Queen *Lancelot and E.* 729
ever in the reading, lords and *d's* Wept, „ 1284
when now the lords and *d's* And people, „ 1346
with her knights and *d's* was Guinevere. *Pelleas and E.* 588
D, damsel, each thro' worship of their Queen *Last Tournament* 146
So *d* and damsel glitter'd at the feast „ 225
So *d* and damsel cast the simple white, „ 232
What *d* or damsel have ye kneel'd to last?' „ 550
Damn (*See also* **Dangtha**) One truth will *d* me with the mindless mob, *Romney's R.* 120
Damn'd (*See also* **Dang'd**) I am *d* already by the Priest *Sir J. Oldcastle* 200
ay, why not, being *d* beyond hope of grace? *Despair* 109
contemplate The torrent of the *d*' *Akbar's Dream* 49
Damosel twelve small *d's* white as Innocence, *Last Tournament* 291
Damp (adj.) air is *d*, and hush'd, and close, *A spirit haunts* 13
combing out her long black hair *D* from the river; *Princess iv* 277
Damp (s) heat, hail, *d*, and sleet, and snow; *St. S. Stylites* 16
sometimes Sucking the *d's* for drink, „ 77
Damsel (*See also* **Damosel**) Sometimes a troop of *d's* glad, *L. of Shalott ii* 19
The prettiest little *d* in the port, *Enoch Arden* 12
Safe, *d*, as the centre of this hall. *Gareth and L.* 604
'*D*, ye know this Order lives to crush All wrongers „ 625
But on the *d's* forehead shame, „ 656
by this entry fled The *d* in her wrath, „ 675
Mutter'd the *d*, 'Wherefore did the King Scorn me? „ 737
'*D*, the quest is mine. „ 745
'*D*,' Sir Gareth answer'd gently, „ 772
And when the *d* spake contemptuously, „ 806
wilt thou yield this *d* harbourage?' „ 834
placed a peacock in his pride Before the *d*, „ 851
left The *d* by the peacock in his pride, „ 870
Whether thou wilt not with thy *d* back „ 881
and calling, '*D*, is this he, „ 915
Said Gareth, '*D*, whether knave or knight, „ 943
The *d* crying, 'Well-stricken, kitchen-knave!' „ 970
'So this *d* ask it of me Good— „ 974
'*D*, thy charge Is an abounding pleasure „ 981
Thy shield is mine—farewell; and, *d*, thou, „ 988
'Fair *d*, you should worship me the more, „ 1022
'Hath not the good wind, *d*, changed again?' „ 1054
have ye slain The *d's* champion?' and the *d* cried, 'No star of thine, „ 1099
'Old, *d*, old and hard, Old, with the might and breath „ 1105
grizzled *d* came, And arm'd him in old arms, „ 1114
the *d* clamouring all the while, „ 1134
But the *d* said, 'I lead no longer; „ 1156
'*D*,' he said, 'you be not all to blame, „ 1171
nor meet To fight for gentle *d*, he, „ 1177
At any gentle *d's* waywardness. „ 1179
Then turn'd the noble *d* smiling at him, „ 1188
The *d's* headlong error thro' the wood— „ 1215
'Nay, noble *d*, but that I, the son Of old King Lot „ 1230
O *d*, be you wise To call him shamed, „ 1259
wherefore, *d*? tell me all you know. „ 1328
thou thyself, with *d* and with dwarf, *Marr. of Geraint* 581
have his horse And armour, and his *d* shall be ours.' *Geraint and E.* 63
possess your horse And armour, and your *d* should be theirs.' „ 75
Friend, let her eat; the *d* is so faint.' „ 206
While your good *d* rests, return, „ 224
speak To your good *d* there who sits apart, „ 299
found A *d* drooping in a corner of it. „ 611
nor lets Or dame or *d* enter at his gates *Balin and Balan* 107
Make knight or churl or child or *d* seem „ 162
D and lover? hear not what I hear. „ 282
Then to her Squire mutter'd the *d* 'Fools! „ 564
that twice a wanton *d* came, „ 609
I well believe this *d*, and the one „ 612
and the *d* bidden rise arose And stood *Merlin and V.* 68
Queen Among her *d's* broidering sat, „ 138
lived there neither dame nor *d* then „ 606
And set it in this *d's* golden hair, *Lancelot and E.* 205
O *d*, in the light of your blue eyes; „ 660
And, *d*, for I deem you know full well „ 689
This will I do, dead *d*, for your sake, „ 962
rose And pointed to the *d*, and the doors. „ 1263
had I dreamt the *d* would have died, „ 1305
Ye loved me, *d*, surely with a love „ 1394
D's in divers colours like the cloud *Pelleas and E.* 53
And all the *d's* talk'd confusedly, „ 57
'O *d*,' answer'd he, 'I woke from dreams; „ 103
her knights And all her *d's* too were gracious „ 122
O *d*, wearing this unsunny face To him who won „ 180
But after, when her *d's*, and herself, „ 186
She that saw him cried, '*D's*— „ 189
This her *d's* heard, And mindful of her small „ 200
With all her *d's*, he was stricken mute; „ 251
Up ran a score of *d's* to the tower; „ 368

Damsel (*continued*) And down they ran, Her *d's*, crying to their lady, *Pelleas and E.* 376
Froz'n by sweet sleep, four of her *d's* lay: „ 433
Dame, *d*, each thro' worship of their Queen *Last Tournament* 146
'Fair *d's*, each to him who worships each „ 207
dame and *d* glitter'd at the feast Variously gay: „ 225
So dame and *d* cast the simple white, „ 232
dame or *d* have ye kneel'd to last?' „ 550
Damsel-errant A *d-e*, warbling, as she rode *Balin and Balan* 438
Youth, we are *d's-e*, and we ride, *Pelleas and E.* 64
Dan that had no likin' for *D*, *Tomorrow* 19
An' *D* stood there for a minute, „ 22
whin *D* didn't come to the fore, „ 43
Dan Chaucer *D C*, the first warbler, *D. of F. Women* 5
Danaë lies the Earth all *D* to the stars, *Princess vii* 182
Danaïd prove The *D* of a leaky vase, „ *ii* 340
Dance (s) (*See also* **Devil's-dances**) echoing *d* Of reboant whirlwinds, *Supp. Confessions* 96
Yet in the whirling *d's* as we went, *The form, the form* 5
star that with the choral starry *d* Join'd not, *Palace of Art* 253
Leaving the *d* and song, *D. of F. Women* 216
men and maids Arranged a country *d*, *Princess, Pro.* 84
d's broke and buzz'd in knots of talk; „ *i* 133
Like one that wishes at a *d* to change The music— „ *iv* 589
In *d* and song and game and jest? *In Mem. xxix* 8
And *d* and song and hoodman-blind. „ *lxxviii* 12
wheels the circled *d*, and breaks The rocket „ *xcviii* 30
No *d*, no motion, save alone What lightens „ *cv* 23
And last the *d*;—till I retire: „ *Con.* 105
A dinner and then a *d* For the maids and marriage-makers, *Maud I xx* 34
She is weary of *d* and play.' „ *xxii* 22
Come hither, the *d's* are done, „ 54
with *d* And revel and song, made merry over Death, *Gareth and L.* 1422
Rush'd into *d*, and like wild Bacchanals *Lover's Tale iii* 25
whirling rout Led by those two rush'd into *d*, „ 55
An' the fall of yer foot in the *d* *Tomorrow* 36
Dance (verb) About thee breaks and *d's*: *Madeline* 30
And the spangle *d's* in bight and bay, *Sea-Fairies* 24
but to *d* and sing, be gaily drest, *The form, the form* 3
for she says A fire *d's* before her, *Œnone* 264
And make her *d* attendance; *Amphion* 62
And the dead begin to *d*. *Vision of Sin* 166
I make the netted sunbeam *d* *The Brook* 176
But fit to flaunt, to dress, to *d*, to thrum, *Princess iv* 519
to *d* Its body, and reach its fatling innocent arms „ *vi* 137
let the torrent *d* thee down To find him in the valley; „ *vii* 209
To *d* with death, to beat the ground, *In Mem. i* 12
Now *d* the lights on lawn and lea, „ *cxv* 9
Till the red man *d* By his red cedar-tree, *Maud I xvii* 17
flickering in a grimly light *D* on the mere. *Gareth and L.* 827
Down upon far-off cities while they *d*— *Merlin and V.* 114
eating dry To *d* without a catch, a roundelay To *d* to.' *Last Tournament* 250
D to the pibroch!—saved! *Def. of Lucknow* 103
D in a fountain of flame with her devils, *Kapiolani* 10
Danced we *d* about the may-pole and in the hazel copse, *May Queen, N'Y's E.* 11
Till all the tables *d* again, *The Goose* 47
d The greensward into greener circles, *Gardener's D.* 133
D into light, and died into the shade; „ 203
And madly *d* our hearts with joy, *The Voyage* 3
the gilded ball *D* like a wisp: *Princess, Pro.* 64
O'er it shook the woods, And *d* the colour, „ *iii* 293
For I that *d* her on my knee, *In Mem., Con.* 45
Yniol's heart *D* in his bosom, *Marr. of Geraint* 505
and the sand *d* at the bottom of it. *Balin and Balan* 27
For all my blood *d* in me, and I knew *Holy Grail* 366
D like a wither'd leaf before the hall. (repeat) *Last Tournament* 4, 242
And down the city Dagonet *d* away; „ 359
as *d* in 'er pratty blue eye; *North. Cobbler* 50
Dancer To the *d's* dancing in tune; *Maud I xxii* 16
When will the *d's* leave her alone? „ 21
A wreath of airy *d's* hand-in-hand *Guinevere* 261
Dancing Tho' if, in *d* after Letty Hill, *Edwin Morris* 55
Dancing (*continued*) that keeps A thousand pulses *d*, *In Mem. cxxv* 16
To the dancers *d* in tune; *Maud I xxii* 16
burst in *d*, and the pearls were spilt; *Merlin and V.* 452
Till the *d* will be over; *Maud I xx* 43
d of Fairies In desolate hollows, *Merlin and the G.* 41
Dandle shall we *d* it amorously? *Boädicea* 33
I bore him a son, and he loved to *d* the child, *Bandit's Death* 15
Dandled nor pretty babes To be *d*, *Princess iv* 147
breast that fed or arm that *d* you, „ *vi* 181
Dandy-despot What if that *d-d*, he, *Maud I vi* 42
Dane Saxon and Norman and *D* are we, But all of us *D's* in our welcome of thee, *W. to Alexandra* 3
For Saxon or *D* or Norman we, „ 31
We are each all *D* in our welcome of thee, „ 33
Dang'd (damned) an' be *d* if I iver let goa! *Village Wife* 68
Danger like of shocks, *D's*, and deeds, *Œnone* 164
Her household fled the *d*, *The Goose* 54
I take my part Of *d* on the roaring sea, *Sailor Boy* 22
I see the *d* which you cannot see: *Geraint and E.* 421
Dangled *D* a length of ribbon and a ring *Enoch Arden* 750
when my father *d* the grapes, *Maud I i* 71
d a hundred fathom of grapes, *V. of Maeldune* 56
Dangling one with shatter'd fingers *d* lame, *Last Tournament* 60
Dangtha (damn you) Woä then, wiltha? *d*! *N. Farmer, N.S.* 40
Daniel great Books (see *D* seven and ten) *Sea Dreams* 152
Danish behind it a gray down With *D* barrows; *Enoch Arden* 7
Pass from the *D* barrow overhead; „ 442
Danny (*See also* **Danny O'Roon**) an' *D* says 'Troth, an' I been Dhrinkin' *Tomorrow* 11
for *D* was not to be foun', „ 28
For the Divil a *D* was there, „ 30
'Your *D*,' they says, 'niver crasst over „ 48
Danny O'Roon (*See also* **Danny**) Molly Magee wid her batchelor, *D O'R*— „ 10
meet your päärints agin an' yer *D O'R* afore God „ 57
young man *D O'R* wid his ould woman, „ 88
about Molly Magee an' her *D O'R*, „ 92
Dante there the world-worn *D* grasp'd his song, *Palace of Art* 135
Danube The *D* to the Severn gave *In Mem. xix* 1
Let her great *D* rolling fair Enwind her isles, „ *xcviii* 9
Dare why *d* Paths in the desert? *Supp. Confessions* 78
d to kiss Thy taper fingers amorously, *Madeline* 43
I *d* not think of thee, Oriana. *Oriana* 93
I *d* not die and come to thee, „ 96
'The doubt would rest, I *d* not solve. *Two Voices* 313
'You will not, boy! you *d* to answer thus! *Dora* 26
none of all his men *D* tell him Dora waited „ 76
Then not to *d* to see! *Love and Duty* 38
'I will speak out, for I *d* not lie. *Lady Clare* 38
But I must go: I *d* not tarry,' *Princess iii* 95
'*D* we dream of that,' I ask'd, „ 297
I d All these male thunderbolts: „ *iv* 499
he that does the thing they *d* not do, „ *v* 160
What *d's* not Ida do that she should prize „ 174
d not ev'n by silence sanction lies. *Third of Feb.* 10
How *d* we keep our Christmas-eve; *In Mem. xxix* 4
Nor *d* she trust a larger lay, „ *xlviii* 13
And *d* we to this fancy give, „ *liii* 5
By which we *d* to live or die. „ *lxxxv* 40
D I say No spirit ever brake the band „ *xciii* 1
That which we *d* invoke to bless; „ *cxxiv* 1
Who can rule and *d* not lie. *Maud I x* 66
That I *d* to look her way; „ *xvi* 11
D I bid her abide by her word? „ 25
Who *d's* foreshadow for an only son *Ded. of Idylls* 29
not once *d* to look him in the face.' *Gareth and L.* 782
I *am* the cause, because I *d* not speak *Marr. of Geraint* 89
yet not *d* to tell him what I think, „ 105
How should I *d* obey him to his harm? *Geraint and E.* 136
Not *d* to watch the combat, „ 154
Nor did I care or *d* to speak with you, „ 871
'What *d* the full-fed liars say of me? *Merlin and V.* 692
And no man there will *d* to mock at me; *Lancelot and E.* 1053
What rights are his that *d* not strike for them? *Last Tournament* 527
how *d* I call him mine? *Guinevere* 617

Dare (continued) They swore that he d not rob the mail, Rizpah 30
names who d For that sweet mother land Tiresias 122
but if thou d—Thou, one of these, „ 133
would d Hell-heat or Arctic cold, Ancient Sage 115
I d without your leave to head Pro. to Gen. Hamley 19
For d we dally with the sphere Epilogue 44
Mother, d you kill your child? Forlorn 37
crying 'I d her, let Peelè avenge herself'! Kapiolani 32
Dared 'He d not tarry,' men will say, Two Voices 101
But when at last I d to speak, Miller's D. 129
I had not d to flow In these words toward you, To J. S. 6
my word was law, and yet you d To slight it. Dora 98
Yet d not stir to do it, Aylmer's Field 806
d To leap the rotten pales of prejudice, Princess ii 141
You that have d to break our bound, „ iv 539
sorrowing in a pause I d not break; „ vii 249
D not to glance at her good mother's face, Marr. of Geraint 766
Nor d to waste a perilous pity on him: Geraint and E. 525
she thought, 'He had not d to do it, „ 720
'They d me to do it,' he said, Rizpah 24
'The farmer d me to do it,' he said; „ 26
But they d not touch us again, The Revenge 72
d her with one little ship and his English few; „ 107
you have d Somewhat perhaps in coming? Columbus 242
and flung the berries, and d the Goddess, Kapiolani 6
Darest Who scarcely d to inquire, In Mem. iv 7
How d thou, if lover, push me even In fancy Last Tournament 638
Daring But now it were too d. Guinevere 654
Not d yet to glance at Lionel. Lover's Tale iv 309
Dark (See also **Derk, Dewy-dark**) In the d we must lie. All Things will Die 22
drive Thro' utter d a full-sail'd skiff, Supp. Confessions 95
I am void, D, formless, „ 121
When thickest d did trance the sky, Mariana 18
Which upon the d afloat, The Owl ii 3
level lake with diamond-plots Of d and bright. Arabian Nights 86
twisted silvers look'd to shame The hollow-vaulted d, „ 126
Or dimple in the d of rushy coves, Ode to Memory 60
thro' the wreaths of floating d upcurl'd, The Poet 35
All within is d as night: Deserted House 5
Ere the light on d was growing, Oriana 10
Remaining betwixt d and bright: Margaret 28
shoot into the d Arrows of lightnings. To J. M. K. 14
If I make d my countenance, Two Voices 53
'If all be d, vague voice,' I said, „ 265
seem'd all d and red—a tract of sand, Palace of Art 65
moon was setting, and the d was over all; May Queen, Con. 26
brides of ancient song Peopled the hollow d, D. of F. Women 18
Morn broaden'd on the borders of the d, „ 265
The unnetted black-hearts ripen d, The Blackbird 7
Shot on the sudden into d. To J. S. 28
And round them sea and air are d Love thou thy land 63
A length of bright horizon rimm'd the d. Gardener's D. 181
the sun fell, and all the land was d. (repeat) Dora 79, 109
all the varied changes of the d, Edwin Morris 36
Till now the d was worn, Love and Duty 71
spirit deeply dawning in the d of hazel eyes— Locksley Hall 28
'Love, if thy tresses be so d, How d those hidden eyes must be!' Day-Dm., Arrival 31
The twilight died into the d. „ Depart. 24
As these white robes are soil'd and d, St Agnes' Eve 13
I float till all is d. Sir Galahad 40
But o'er the d a glory spreads, „ 55
With wakes of fire we tore the d; The Voyage 52
And d and true and tender is the North. Princess iv 98
I dread His wildness, and the chances of the d.' „ 244
Slipt round and in the d invested you, „ 404
That glitter burnish'd by the frosty d; „ v 261
little seed they laugh'd at in the d, „ vi 34
like night and evening mixt Their d and gray, „ 132
And watches in the dead, the d, „ vii 103
D in its funeral fold. Ode on Well. 57
D is the world to thee: High. Pantheism 7
My will is bondsman to the d; In Mem. iv 2
And all the place is d, and all The chambers „ viii 7
Dark (continued) For all is d where thou art not. In Mem. viii 12
balmy drops in summer d Slide from the bosom „ xvii 15
Thy marble bright in d appears, „ lxvii 5
Immantled in ambrosial d, „ lxxxix 14
A shade falls on us like the d „ Con. 93
For the drift of the Maker is d, Maud I iv 43
Thro' the livelong hours of the d „ vi 17
Then returns the d With no more hope of light. „ ix 15
For d my mother was in eyes and hair, And d in hair and eyes am I; and d Was Gorloïs, yea and d was Uther too, Com. of Arthur 327
And tho' she lay d in the pool, she knew Marr. of Geraint 657
All round her prest the d, Balin and Balan 262
D my doom was here, and d It will be there. „ 623
D in the glass of some presageful mood, Merlin and V. 295
the court, the King, d in your light, „ 875
Arthur to the banquet, d in mood, Lancelot and E. 564
Was I too d a prophet when I said Holy Grail 889
Sprang from the door into the d. Pelleas and E. 603
d in the golden grove Appearing, Last Tournament 379
The night was d; the true star set. Isolt! The name was ruler of the d—Isolt? „ 605
Mark's way to steal behind one in the d— „ 618
That here in utter d I swoon'd away, And woke again in utter d, and cried, „ 622
Out of the d, just as the lips had touch'd, „ 752
look'd and saw The great Queen's bower was d,— „ 758
so late! and d the night and chill! Guinevere 168
so late! and d and chill the night! „ 174
Fell into dust, and crumbled in the d— Lover's Tale i 95
in the d of mine Is traced with flame. „ 297
We past from light to d. „ 516
All thro' the livelong hours of utter d, „ 810
spray wind-driven Far thro' the dizzy d. „ ii 199
Down welter'd thro' the d ever and ever. „ 208
the nightingale's hymn in the d. First Quarrel 34
call'd in the d to me year after year— Rizpah 47
I have been with God in the d— „ 79
he used but to call in the d, „ 83
I came on lake Llanberris in the d, Sisters (E. and E.) 95
D thro' the smoke and the sulphur Def. of Lucknow 33
D with the smoke of human sacrifice, Sir J. Oldcastle 84
Breaking with laughter from the d; De Prof., Two G. 18
I cannot laud this life, it looks so d: To W. H. Brookfield 12
sister of the sun Would climb from out the d, Tiresias 31
till mine grew d For ever, „ 47
in the d of his wonderful eyes. The Wreck 55
thy world Might vanish like thy shadow in the d. Ancient Sage 52
When all is d as night.' „ 170
the world is d with griefs and graves, So d that men cry out against the Heavens. „ 171
an' thin wint into the d. Tomorrow 22
Bright and D have sworn that I, Demeter and P. 96
Voices of the day Are heard across the Voices of the d. The Ring 40
but one was fair, And one was d, „ 161
one betwixt the d and light had seen Her, „ 414
Stark and d in his funeral fire. To Master of B. 20
dead cords that ran D thro' the mist, Death of Œnone 11
festal hour D with the blood of man who murder'd man. St. Telemachus 80
Thro' a dream of the d? The Dreamer 16
D no more with human hatreds Faith 8
Must my day be d by reason, God and the Univ. 2
And after that the d! Crossing the Bar 10
Dark-blue D-b the deep sphere overhead, Arabian Nights 89
Hateful is the d-b sky, Vaulted o'er the d-b sea. Lotos-Eaters, C. S. 39
and the d-b clematis, clung, V. of Maeldune 39
Dark-brow'd D-b sophist, come not anear; Poet's Mind 8
Dark-dawning For my d-d youth, Darken'd watching Maud I xix 7
Darken the days d round me, and the years, M. d'Arthur 237
And never more d my doors again.' Dora 32
shores that d with the gathering wolf, Aylmer's Field 767
face Would d, as he cursed his credulousness, Sea Dreams 13
And sorrow d's hamlet and hall. Ode on Well. 7
it brightens and d's down on the plain. Window. On the Hill 2

Darken (*continued*) *d's* and brightens like my hope, And it *d's* and brightens and *d's* like my fear, *Window. On the Hill* 18
drifts that pass To *d* on the rolling brine *In Mem. cvii* 14
Not close and *d* above me *Maud I xi* 9
Tho' many a light shall *d*, „ *III vi* 43
I would not mine again should *d* thine, *Balin and Balan* 625
May yon just heaven, that *d's* o'er me, *Merlin and V.* 931
flash of youth, would *d* down To rise hereafter *Lancelot and E.* 1318
o'er the plain that then began To *d* under Camelot; *Holy Grail* 218
deed seem'd to be done in vain, *D*; „ 275
the days *d* round me, and the years, *Pass. of Arthur* 405
And why was I to *d* their pure love, *Lover's Tale i* 727
into my heart, and begun to *d* my eyes. *Rizpah* 16
as I saw the white sail run, And *d*, *The Flight* 40
lost in the gloom of doubts that *d* the schools; *Vastness* 11
Storm in the South that *d's* the day! *Riflemen form!* 2
His shadow *d's* earth: *D. of the Duke of C.* 13
Darken'd (*See also* **Derken'd, Self-darken'd**) And her eyes were *d* wholly, *L. of Shalott iv* 31
And all the casement *d* there. *Miller's D.* 128
pines That *d* all the northward of her Hall. *Aylmer's Field* 415
all the sails were *d* in the west, *Sea Dreams* 39
You stood in your own light and *d* mine. *Princess iv* 314
And *d* sanctities with song.' *In Mem. xxxvii* 24
And life is *d* in the brain. „ *cxxi* 8
D watching a mother decline *Maud I xix* 8
He had *d* into a frown, „ 62
And *d* from the high light in his eyes, *Marr. of Geraint* 100
Till his eye *d* and his helmet wagg'd; *Geraint and E.* 505
So when his moods were *d*, court and King *Balin and Balan* 235
Thy curse, and *d* all thy day; „ 620
his face *D*, as I have seen it more than once, *Holy Grail* 273
D the common path: *Pelleas and E.* 550
when the outer lights are *d* thus, *Lover's Tale i* 35
Because my own was *d*? „ 729
And all my life was *d*, *The Flight* 39
The landskip *d*, The melody deaden'd, *Merlin and the G.* 31
'what has *d* thee to-night?' *Akbar's Dream* 2
d with doubts of a Faith that saves, *The Dreamer* 11
Darkening *d* thine own To thine own likeness; *Aylmer's Field* 673
swarms of men *D* her female field: *Princess vii* 34
And *d* the dark graves of men,— *In Mem. xxxix* 9
shadow of His loss drew like eclipse, *D* the world. *Ded. of Idylls* 15
world-old yew-tree, *d* half The cloisters, *Holy Grail* 13
D the wreaths of all that would advance, *To Victor Hugo* 5
And, *d* in the light, *Ancient Sage* 151
Darker Your hair is *d*, and your eyes *Margaret* 49
made those eyes *D* than darkest pansies, *Gardener's D.* 27
lonelier, *d*, earthlier for my loss. *Aylmer's Field* 750
loved to make men *d* than they are, *Merlin and V.* 876
Dark-eyed She was dark-haired, *d-e*: *Lover's Tale i* 74
Dark-green spread his *d-g* layers of shade. *Gardener's D.* 116
Dark-hair'd She was *d-h*, dark-eyed: *Lover's Tale i* 74
Darkling name Went wandering somewhere *d* in his mind. *Last Tournament* 457
Darkness something in the *d* draws His forehead earthward, *Supp. Confessions* 167
something which possess'd The *d* of the world, *Arabian Nights* 72
and lashes like to rays Of *d*, „ 137
All night long on *d* blind. *Adeline* 44
When in the *d* over me The four-handed mole *My life is full* 11
Why inch by inch to *d* crawl? *Two Voices* 200
And *d* in the village yew. „ 273
on her threshold lie Howling in outer *d*. *To ——, With Pal. of Art* 16
Gross *d* of the inner sepulchre *D. of F. Women* 67
Had wink'd and threaten'd *d*, *M. d'Arthur, Ep.* 2
I would I were The pilot of the *d* *Audley Court* 72
shake the *d* from their loosen'd manes, *Tithonus* 41
were shrivell'd into *d* in his head, *Godiva* 70
Beyond the *d* and the cataract, *Vision of Sin* 49
as they kiss'd each other In *d*, *Aylmer's Field* 431
worshipt their own *d* in the Highest? „ 643
May Pharaoh's *d*, folds as dense „ 771
and I was heaved upon it In *d*: *Sea Dreams* 93
Darkness (*continued*) Muses' heads were touch'd Above the *d* *Princess iii* 22
d closed me; and I fell. „ *v* 542
So much the gathering *d* charm'd: „ *Con.* 107
There I heard them in the *d*, *Boädicea* 36
So they chanted in the *d*, „ 46
A beam in *d*: let it grow. *In Mem., Pro.* 24
Let *d* keep her raven gloss: „ *i* 10
Else earth is *d* at the core, „ *xxxiv* 3
drop head-foremost in the jaws Of vacant *d* „ 16
That slope thro' *d* up to God, „ *lv* 16
How blanch'd with *d* must I grow! „ *lxi* 8
Death has made His *d* beautiful with thee. „ *lxxiv* 12
matin songs, that woke The *d* of our planet, „ *lxxvi* 10
which makes the *d* and the light, „ *xcvi* 19
But in the *d* and the cloud, „ 21
A treble *d*, Evil haunts The birth, „ *xcviii* 13
Ring out the *d* of the land, „ *cvi* 31
The Power in *d* whom we guess; „ *cxxiv* 4
out of *d* came the hands That reach thro' nature, „ 23
over whom thy *d* must have spread *Maud I xviii* 25
many a *d* into the light shall leap, „ *III vi* 46
Swept bellowing thro' the *d* on to dawn, *Gareth and L.* 177
would she make My *d* blackness? *Balin and Balan* 193
mark'd not on his right a cavern-chasm Yawn over *d*, „ 313
And lost itself in *d*, till she cried— „ 514
He walk'd with dreams and *d*, *Merlin and V.* 190
And counterchanged with *d*? „ 466
Approaching thro' the *d*, call'd; *Lancelot and E.* 1000
After the day of *d*, when the dead *Holy Grail* 49
and lying bounden there In *d* „ 677
d falling, sought A priory not far off, *Pelleas and E.* 213
their own *d*, throng'd into the moon. „ 458
She made her face a *d* from the King: *Guinevere* 417
And in the *d* o'er her fallen head, „ 583
forego The *d* of that battle in the West, *To the Queen ii* 65
far on within its inmost halls, The home of *d*; *Lover's Tale i* 524
and the *d* of the grave, The *d* of the grave and utter night, „ 597
And vex them with my *d*? „ 732
in the end, Opening on *d*, „ *ii* 125
so those fair eyes Shone on my *d*, „ 158
Seem'd stepping out of *d* with a smile. „ *iv* 220
What end but *d* could ensue from this *Sisters (E. and E.)* 175
bleat of a lamb in the storm and the *d* without; *In the Child. Hosp.* 64
Bugles and drums in the *d*, *Def. of Lucknow* 76
he past away From the *d* of life— *To Prin. F. of H.* 2
world of sight, that lives Behind this *d*, *Tiresias* 52
Stood out before a *d*, crying, „ 115
not to plunge Thy torch of life in *d*, „ 159
and the master gone. Gone into *d*, „ 202
fountain pour'd From *d* into daylight, *Ancient Sage* 8
Who knows but that the *d* is in man? „ 173
and forget The *d* of the pall.' „ 198
If utter *d* closed the day, my son— „ 199
Crown'd with sunlight—over *d*— *Locksley H., Sixty* 92
Flare from Tel-el-Kebir Thro' *d*, *Pro. to Gen. Hamley* 29
and griefs, and deaths, Were utter *d*— *Prin. Beatrice* 3
Are there spectres moving in the *d*? *On Jub. Q. Victoria* 67
the *d* Dawns into the Jubilee of the Ages. „ 70
bird that flies All night across the *d*, *Demeter and P.* 2
following out A league of labyrinthine *d*, „ 82
and for evermore The Bride of *D*.' „ 100
Then He, the brother of this *D*, „ 116
Clouds and *d* Closed upon Camelot; *Merlin and the G.* 75
For out of the *d* Silent and slowly „ 81
bubble bursts above the abyss Of *D*, *Romney's R.* 53
Dark-purple lying in *d-p* spheres of sea. *Locksley Hall* 164
Dark-splendid the face before her lived, *D-s*, *Lancelot and E.* 338
Darlin' wid a heart and a half, me *d*, *Tomorrow* 39
Darling (*See also* **Darlin'**) The *d* of my manhood, and, alas! *Gardener's D.* 278
how pale she had look'd *D*, to-night! *Aylmer's Field* 380
Seventy years ago, my *d*, (repeat) *Grandmother* 24, 56
'Me, not my *d*, no!' *The Victim* 68
Her feet, my *d*, on the dead; *In Mem., Con.* 50

Darling (*continued*) the moon-faced *d* of all,— *Maud I i* 72
You are not her *d*. „ *xii* 32
and render All homage to his own *d*, „ *xx* 49
But shall it? answer, *d*, answer, no. *Merlin and V.* 397
Then the great knight, the *d* of the court, *Lancelot and E.* 261
our orphan, our *d*, our meek little maid; *In the Child. Hosp.* 28
not a mother's heart, when I left my *d* alone.' *The Wreck* 97
All very well just now to be calling me *d* *Charity* 7
Darnel And on my clay her *d* grow; *My life is full* 22
Darnley There is *D* bridge, It has more ivy; *The Brook* 36
Then crost the common into *D* chase „ 132
Dart (s) with their fires Love tipt his keenest *d's*; *D. of F. Women* 173
Brandishing in her hand a *d* *Boädicea* 71
Madly dash'd the *d's* together, „ 74
Clash the *d's* and on the buckler „ 79
dying now Pierced by a poison'd *d*. *Death of Œnone* 34
Dart (verb) forward *d* again, and play About the prow, *In Mem. xii* 17
Darted thro' his manful breast *d* the pang *Marr. of Geraint* 121
Darter (daughter) the Squire an' 'is *d's* an' me, *Village Wife* 7
talkt o' my *d* es died o' the fever at fall: „ 10
ivry *d* o' Squire's hed her awn ridin-erse „ 35
niver hed none of 'er *d's* 'ere; „ 54
'Er an' 'er blessed *d*— „ 60
Then 'e married a greät Yerl's *d*, *Church-warden, etc.* 20
Dash *D* them anew together at her will *Lucretius* 247
birds on the light *D* themselves dead. *Princess iv* 496
Waves on a diamond shingle *d*, *The Islet* 16
d the brains of the little one out, *Boädicea* 68
and *d* myself down and die *Maud I i* 54
upon all things base, and *d* them dead, *Gareth and L.* 23
each at either *d* from either end— „ 535
To *d* against mine enemy and to win. „ 1355
D back that ocean with a pier, *Mechanophilus* 5
Dash'd (rushed) *D* downward in a cataract. *Day-Dm., Revival* 16
Again we *d* into the dawn! *The Voyage* 24
d Into the chronicle of a deedful day, *Aylmer's Field* 195
uttering a dry shriek, *D* on Geraint, *Geraint and E.* 462
But, mad for strange adventure, *d* away, *Balin and Balan* 289
'he *d* across me—mad, And maddening what he rode; *Holy Grail* 641
Pelleas overthrew them as they *d* Against him one by one; *Pelleas and E.* 221
d up alone Thro' the great gray slope *Heavy Brigade* 16
Dash'd (flung, hurled) As *d* about the drunken leaves *Amphion* 55
D together in blinding dew: *Vision of Sin* 42
grief Bore down in flood, and *d* his angry heart *Aylmer's Field* 633
or into rhythm have *d* The passion of the prophetess; *Princess iv* 139
and *d* Unopen'd at her feet: „ 470
roll The torrents, *d* to the vale: „ *v* 350
Then came a postscript *d* across the rest. „ 424
D on every rocky square Their surging charges *Ode on Well.* 125
Roll as a ground-swell *d* on the strand, *W. to Alexandra* 23
And wildly *d* on tower and tree *In Mem. xv* 7
Christless foe of thine as ever *d* Horse against horse; *Balin and Balan* 97
He *d* the pummel at the foremost face, „ 402
with violence The sword was *d* from out my hand, *Holy Grail* 826
Isolt of Britain *d* Before Isolt *Last Tournament* 588
and *d* himself Into the dizzy depth below. *Lover's Tale i* 380
and *d* herself Dead in her rage: *Tiresias* 152
And *d* half dead on barren sands, *The Ring* 309
Into the flame-billow *d* the berries, *Kapiolani* 33
Dash'd (struck) Madly *d* the darts together, *Boädicea* 74
He *d* the rowel into his horse, *Pelleas and E.* 486
sudden fire from Heaven had *d* him dead, *Happy* 83
Dash'd (broke) we *d* Your cities into shards with catapults, *Princess v* 137
Dash'd (bespattered) his greaves and cuisses *d* with drops Of onset; *M. d'Arthur* 215
And where it *d* the reddening meadow, *Lucretius* 49
d with death He reddens what he kisses: *Princess v* 164
d with wandering isles of night. *In Mem. xxiv* 4
That life is *d* with flecks of sin. „ *lii* 14
Deep tulips *d* with fiery dew, „ *lxxxiii* 11
his greaves and cuisses *d* with drops Of onset; *Pass. of Arthur* 383
Dashing *d* down on a tall wayside flower, *Guinevere* 253
Dashing (*continued*) *D* the fires and the shadows of dawn *V. of Maeldune* 99
the bolt of war *d* down upon cities *The Dawn* 8
Date but when his *d* Doubled her own, *Aylmer's Field* 80
Beyond the common *d* of death— *The Ring* 108
Dating *d*, many a year ago, Has hit on this, *To E. Fitzgerald* 49
Daughter (*See also* **Darter**) His little *d*, whose sweet face He kiss'd, *Two Voices* 253
It is the miller's *d*, *Miller's D.* 169
I am the *d* of a River-God, *Œnone* 38
We were two *d's* of one race: *The Sisters* 1
The *d* of a hundred Earls, *L. C. V. de Vere* 7
A *d* of the gods, divinely tall, *D. of F. Women* 87
The *d* of the warrior Gileadite, „ 197
Eustace from the city went To see the Gardener's *D*; *Gardener's D.* 3
Go and see The Gardener's *d*: „ 30
Who had not heard Of Rose, the Gardener's *d*? „ 52
The *d's* of the year, One after one, „ 200
She is my brother's *d*: *Dora* 17
for his sake I bred His *d* Dora: „ 20
woo'd and wed A labourer's *d*, Mary Morrison. „ 40
d of a cottager, Out of her sphere, *Walk. to the Mail* 59
Cry, like the *d's* of the horseleech, 'Give, *Golden Year* 12
preaching down a *d's* heart. *Locksley Hall* 94
'The old Earl's *d* died at my breast; *Lady Clare* 25
With children; first a *d*. *Enoch Arden* 84
evermore the *d* prest upon her To wed the man „ 483
tell my *d* Annie, whom I saw So like her mother, „ 882
A *d* of our meadows, yet not coarse; *The Brook* 69
And how it was the thing his *d* wish'd, „ 140
sons of men *D's* of God; *Aylmer's Field* 45
Averill walk So freely with his *d*? „ 270
Pale as the Jephtha's *d*, „ 280
He never yet had set his *d* forth „ 347
Grossly contriving their dear *d's* good— „ 781
devising their own *d's* death! „ 783
where the two contrived their *d's* good, „ 848
knowledge, so my *d* held, Was all in all: *Princess i* 135
His *d* and his housemaid were the boys: „ 190
turning round we saw The Lady Blanche's *d* „ *ii* 321
d's of the plough, stronger than men, „ *iv* 278
A Niobëan *d*, one arm out, „ 371
'Fair *d*, when we sent the Prince your way „ 398
Then those eight mighty *d's* of the plough „ 550
I would he had our *d*: „ *v* 214
vainlier than a hen To her false *d's* in the pool; „ 329
those eight *d's* of the plough Came „ 339
Sea-kings' *d* from over the sea, *W. to Alexandra* 1
The sea-kings' *d* as happy as fair, „ 26
Yell'd and shriek'd between her *d's*, (repeat) *Boädicea* 6, 72
he loved A *d* of our house; *In Mem., Con.* 7
love of all Thy *d's* cherish Thee, *Ded. of Idylls* 53
Had one fair *d*, and none other child; *Com. of Arthur* 2
Give me thy *d* Guinevere to wife.' „ 139
Give my one *d* saving to a king, „ 143
And *d's* had she borne him,— „ 189
'*D* of Gorloïs and Ygerne am I;' „ 316
Then at his call, 'O *d's* of the Dawn, *Gareth and L.* 923
were she the *d* of a king, *Marr. of Geraint* 229
The voice of Enid, Yniol's *d*, rang Clear „ 327
fair Enid, all in faded silk, Her *d*. „ 367
after, turn'd her *d* round, and said, „ 740
I doubted whether *d's* tenderness, Or easy nature, „ 797
behind them stept the lily maid Elaine, his *d*: *Lancelot and E.* 177
But I, my sons, and little *d* fled „ 276
D, I know not what you call the highest; „ 1080
Isolt, the *d* of the King? *Last Tournament* 397
The mother fell about the *d's* neck, *Sister's (E. and E.)* 154
told the living *d* with what love „ 253
England's England-loving *d*—thou *Ded. Poem Prin. Alice* 15
He saw not his *d*—he blest her: *To Prin. F. of H.* 3
d yield her life, heart, soul to one— *The Flight* 28
hold the Present fatal *d* of the Past, *Locksley H., Sixty* 105
Her maiden *d's* marriage; *Prin. Beatrice* 10
True *d*, whose all-faithful, filial eyes „ 13

Daughter (*continued*) *D* of the seed of Cain, *Forlorn* 39
You claspt our infant *d*, *Romney's R.* 77
David King *D* call'd the heavens a hide, *Columbus* 47
Daw And haunted by the wrangling *d*; *In Mem. c* 12
And all the windy clamour of the *d's* *Geraint and E.* 255
the *d's* flew out of the Towers *V. of Maeldune* 109
Dawes (Jocky) *See* **Jocky Dawes**
Dawn (s) (*See also* **Summer-dawn**) WHEN the breeze of a joyful *d* blew free, *Arabian Nights* 1
Thou dewy *d* of memory. (repeat) *Ode to Memory* 7, 45, 124
dew-impearled winds of *d* have kiss'd, " 14
Vast images in glimmering *d*, *Two Voices* 305
white-breasted like a star Fronting the *d* he moved; *Œnone* 58
The tearful glimmer of the languid *d* *D. of F. Women* 74
crested bird That claps his wings at *d*. " 180
With that sharp sound the white *d's* creeping beams, " 261
He will not see the *d* of day. *D. of the O. Year* 11
A bridal *d* of thunder-peals, *Love thou thy land* 51
hull Look'd one black dot against the verge of *d*, *M. d'Arthur* 271
The lusty bird takes every hour for *d*: " *Ep.* 11
till on to *d*, when dreams Begin to feel the truth " 18
light of London flaring like a dreary *d*; *Locksley Hall* 114
Again we dash'd into the *d*! *The Voyage* 24
God made himself an awful rose of *d*, (repeat) *Vision of Sin* 50, 224
when the *d* of rosy childhood past, *Enoch Arden* 37
Faint as a figure seen in early *d* " 357
the chill November *d's* and dewy-glooming downs, " 610
since the mate had seen at early *d* " 631
follow Such dear familiarities of *d*? *Aylmer's Field* 131
as *d* Aroused the black republic on his elms, " 528
I gave the letter to be sent with *d*; *Princess i* 245
However then commenced the *d*: " *ii* 138
sad and strange as in dark summer *d's* " *iv* 49
at eve and *d* With Ida, Ida, Ida, rang the woods; " 432
HE rose at *d* and, fired with hope, *Sailor Boy* 1
Green-rushing from the rosy thrones of *d*! (repeat) *Voice and the P.* 4, 40
Fixt by their cars, waited the golden *d*. *Spec. of Iliad.* 22
In that deep *d* behind the tomb, *In Mem. xlvi* 6
Thy tablet glimmers to the *d*. " *lxvii* 16
Risest thou thus, dim *d*, " *lxxii* 1
said 'The *d*, the *d*,' and died away; " *xcv* 61
Risest thou thus, dim *d*, again, " *xcix* 1
A light-blue lane of early *d*, " *cxix* 7
And thither I climb'd at *d* And stood *Maud I xiv* 5
Now and then in the dim-gray *d*; " 32
They sigh'd for the *d* and thee. " *xxii* 52
O *d* of Eden bright over earth and sky, " *II i* 8
In the shuddering *d*, behold, " *iv* 52
Voice in the rich *d* of an ampler day— *Ded. of Idylls* 36
Swept bellowing thro' the darkness on to *d*, *Gareth and L.* 177
honour shining like the dewy star Of *d*, " 330
How once the wandering forester at *d*, " 498
Will there be *d* in West and eve in East? " 712
Then at his call, 'O daughters of the *D*, " 923
In the half-light—thro' the dim *d*— " 1384
As the gray *d* stole o'er the dewy world, *Geraint and E.* 385
with the *d* ascending lets the day Strike " 692
one fair *d*, The light-wing'd spirit *Balin and Balan* 20
thou rememberest well—one summer *d*— " 505
passing one, at the high peep of *d*, *Merlin and V.* 560
the high *d* piercing the royal rose " 739
woke with *d*, and past Down thro' the dim rich city *Lancelot and E.* 846
the blood-red light of *d* Flared on her face, " 1025
I touch'd The chapel-doors at *d* I know; *Holy Grail* 536
her bloom A rosy *d* kindled in stainless heavens, *Pelleas and E.* 72
Glanced from the rosy forehead of the *d*. " 502
Pure on the virgin forehead of the *d*!' " 505
hull Look'd one black dot against the verge of *d*, *Pass. of Arthur* 439
stillness of the dead world's winter *d* Amazed him, " 442
Then from the *d* it seem'd there came, " 457
kindled from within As 'twere with *d*. *Lover's Tale i* 74
opposite The flush and *d* of youth, " 189

Dawn (s) (*continued*) at *d* from the cloud glitter'd o'er us *V. of Maeldune* 84
and the sunbright hand of the *d*, " 92
Dashing the fires and the shadows of *d* " 99
Waste *d* of multitudinous-eddying light— *De Prof., Two G.* 4
mothers with their babblers of the *d*, *Tiresias* 103
And we turn'd to the growing *d*, we had hoped for a *d* indeed, *Despair* 22
Hoped for a *d* and it came, " 27
see The high-heaven *d* of more than mortal day *Ancient Sage* 284
light the glimmer of the *d*? *Locksley H., Sixty* 229
Sun of *d* That brightens thro' the Mother's *Prin. Beatrice* 3
Virgil who would write ten lines, they say, At *d*, *Poets and their B.* 3
at *d* Falls on the threshold of her native land, *Demeter and P.* 2
the reaper in the gleam of *d* Will see me " 123
Are calling to each other thro' a *d* *The Ring* 37
in the gleam of those mid-summer *d's*, " 183
In the night, and nigh the *d*, *Forlorn* 83
A whisper from his *d* of life? a breath From some fair *d* beyond *Far-far-away* 10
Her husband in the flush of youth and *d*, *Death of Œnone* 17
d Struck from him his own shadow on to Rome. *St. Telemachus* 32
and it laugh'd like a *d* in May. *Bandit's Death* 20
slept, Ay, till *d* stole into the cave, " 31
RED of the *D*! (repeat) *The Dawn* 1, 6, 21
D not Day! (repeat) " 11, 16
Dawn (verb) let your blue eyes *d* Upon me *Margaret* 67
such a one As *d's* but once a season. *Lover's Tale i* 300
Than our poor twilight *d* on earth— *Tiresias* 206
That *d's* behind the grave. *Epilogue* 78
darkness *D's* into the Jubilee of the Ages. *On Jub. Q. Victoria* 71
Dawn'd *D* sometime thro' the doorway? *Aylmer's Field* 685
twilight *d*; and morn by morn the lark *Princess vii* 45
Had? has it come? It has only *d*. *In the Child. Hosp.* 23
One from the Sunrise *D* on His people, *Kapiolani* 25
Dawning (part.) (*See also* **Dark-dawning**) clear Delight, the infant's *d* year. *Supp. Confessions* 67
All the spirit deeply *d* in the dark *Locksley Hall* 28
he saw Death *d* on him, and the close of all. *Enoch Arden* 832
Dawning (s) thro' that *d* gleam'd a kindlier hope " 833
A cry from out the *d* of my life, *Com. of Arthur* 333
All in a fiery *d* wild with wind *Lancelot and E.* 1020
days Of dewy *d* and the amber eves *Lover's Tale i* 52
brought out a broad sky Of *d* over— *Columbus* 78
Long before the *d*. *Forlorn* 54
Day (*See also* **After-days, Birth-day, Christmas Day, Daäy, Death-day, Easterday, Gaudy-day, Jidgement Day, Judgment Daäy, Judgment Day, Marriage Day, Mid-day, Middle-day, Nine-days', One-day-seen, To-daäy, To-day, Yisther-day**)
As noble till the latest d! *To the Queen* 22
a world of peace And confidence, *d* after *d*; *Supp. Confessions* 30
They comfort him by night and *d*; " 45
She only said, 'The *d* is dreary, *Mariana* 33
All *d* within the dreamy house, " 61
the *d* Was sloping toward his western bower. " 79
Wears all *d* a fainter tone. *The Owl ii* 7
Flinging the gloom of yesternight On the white *d*; *Ode to Memory* 10
the prime labour of thine early *d's*: " 94
All *d* and all night it is ever drawn *Poet's Mind* 28
D and night to the billow the fountain calls: *Sea-Fairies* 9
We will sing to you all the *d*: " 20
It was the middle of the *d*. *Dying Swan* 8
Now is done thy long *d's* work; *A Dirge* 1
How could I look upon the *d*? *Oriana* 59
I would sit and sing the whole of the *d*; *The Merman* 9
I would sing to myself the whole of the *d*; *The Mermaid* 10
Looking at the set of *d*, *Adeline* 17
Lull'd echoes of laborious *d* Come to you, *Margaret* 29
And gave you on your natal *d*. " 42
all *d* long you sit between Joy and woe, " 63
delight of frolic flight, by *d* or night, *Rosalind* 47
MY life is full of weary *d's*, *My life is full* 1
Come only, when the *d's* are still, " 23
THERE she weaves by night and *d* *L. of Shalott ii* 1
And at the closing of the *d* " *iv* 15
But *d* increased from heat to heat, *Mariana in the S.* 39

Day (*continued*) But sometimes in the falling *d* — *Mariana in the S.* 73
From heat to heat the *d* decreased, „ 78
'The *d* to night,' she made her moan, 'The d to night, the night to morn, And *d* and night I am left alone „ 81
Would sweep the tracts of *d* and night. *Two Voices* 69
How grows the *d* of human power?' „ 78
One hope that warm'd me in the *d's* „ 122
In *d's* that never come again. „ 324
Whose troubles number with his *d's*: „ 330
That we may die the self-same *d*. *Miller's D.* 24
Flush'd like the coming of the *d*; „ 132
song I gave you, Alice, on the *d* When, arm in arm, „ 162
For hid in ringlets *d* and night, „ 173
And all *d* long to fall and rise „ 182
The *d*, when in the chestnut shade I found „ 201
wheresoe'er I am by night and *d*, *Œnone* 267
And, while *d* sank or mounted higher, *Palace of Art.* 46
Thro' which the livelong *d* my soul did pass, „ 55
young night divine Crown'd dying *d* with stars, „ 184
Of all the glad New-year, mother, the maddest merriest *d*; *May Queen* 3
call me loud when the *d* begins to break: „ 10
many a bolder lad 'ill woo me any summer *d*, „ 23
drop of rain the whole of the livelong *d*, „ 35
To-morrow 'ill be of all the year the maddest merriest *d*, „ 43
we had a merry *d*; *May Queen, N.Y's. E.* 9
I long to see a flower so before the *d* I die. „ 16
Good-night, sweet mother: call me before the *d* is born. „ 49
ere this *d* is done The voice, that now is speaking, „ *Con.* 53
All its allotted length of *d's*, *Lotos-Eaters, C. S.* 35
Eating the Lotos *d* by *d*, „ 60
All *d* the wind breathes low with mellower tone: „ 102
eyes of anger'd Eleanor Do hunt me, *d* and night.' *D. of F. Women* 256
He will not see the dawn of *d*. *D. of the O. Year* 11
Make bright our *d's* and light our dreams, *Of old sat Freedom* 22
From those, not blind, who wait for *d*, *Love thou thy land* 15
cutting eights that *d* upon the pond, *The Epic* 10
Looks freshest in the fashion of the *d*: „ 32
So all *d* long the noise of battle roll'd *M. d'Arthur* 1
the halls Of Camelot, as in the *d's* that were. „ 21
In those old *d's*, one summer noon, „ 29
And the *d's* darken round me, and the years, „ 237
Rise like a fountain for me night and *d*. „ 249
Begin to feel the truth and stir of *d*, „ *Ep.* 19
THIS morning is the morning of the *d* *Gardener's D.* 1
memory folds For ever in itself the *d* we went To see her. „ 75
Sang loud, as tho' he were the bird of *d*. „ 96
But the full *d* dwelt on her brows, „ 136
I, that whole *d*, Saw her no more, „ 163
d by *d*, Like one that never can be wholly known, „ 205
chambers of the heart, Let in the *d*.' „ 250
May not be dwelt on by the common *d*. „ 271
came a *d* When Allan called his son, *Dora* 9
d's went on, and there was born a boy To William; „ 48
And *d* by *d* he pass'd his father's gate, „ 50
Remembering the *d* when first she came, „ 106
And either twilight and the *d* between; *Edwin Morris* 37
I spoke her name alone. Thrice-happy *d's*! „ 68
seems a part of those fresh *d's* to me; „ 142
leap'd and laugh'd The modish Cupid of the *d*, *Talking Oak* 67
ah! my friend, the *d's* were brief „ 185
'Tis little more: the *d* was warm; „ 205
Some happy future *d*. „ 252
staring eye glazed o'er with sapless *d's*, *Love and Duty* 16
we that *d* had been Up Snowdon; *Golden Year* 3
A tongue-tied Poet in the feverous *d's*, „ 10
Happy *d's* Roll onward, leading up the golden year. „ 40
The long *d* wanes: the slow moon climbs: *Ulysses* 55
strength which in old *d's* Moved earth and heaven; „ 66
a saying learnt, In *d's* far-off, *Tithonus* 48
with what another heart In *d's* far-off, „ 51
thou shalt lower to his level *d* by *d*, *Locksley Hall* 45

Day (*continued*) turn to, lighting upon *d's* like these? *Locksley Hall* 99
When I heard my *d's* before me, „ 110
island unto island at the gateways of the *d*. „ 158
we sweep into the younger *d*: „ 183
Stillness with love, and *d* with light. *Day-Dm., Sleep. B.* 16
That strove in other *d's* to pass, „ *Arrival* 10
And deep into the dying *d* „ *Depart.* 7
Beyond the night, across the *d*, „ 31
song was great In *d's* of old Amphion, *Amphion* 10
fountain upward runs The current of my *d's*: *Will Water.* 36
draws me down Into the common *d*? „ 154
Ere *d's*, that deal in ana, „ 199
Thy latter *d's* increased with pence „ 219
God's blessing on the *d*! *Lady Clare* 8
D by *d* more harsh and cruel *The Captain* 13
On a *d* when they were going O'er the lone expanse, „ 25
Where they twain will spend their *d's* *L. of Burleigh* 36
Down the waste waters *d* and night, *The Voyage* 58
'She is more beautiful than *d*.' *Beggar Maid* 8
When a blanket wraps the *d*, *Vision of Sin* 80
the tender grace of a *d* that is dead *Break, break, etc.* 15
Enoch was host one *d*, Philip the next, *Enoch Arden* 25
And pass his *d's* in peace among his own. „ 147
Many a sad kiss by *d* by night renew'd „ 161
So all *d* long till Enoch's last at home, „ 172
ship I sail in passes here (He named the *d*) „ 215
the *d*, that Enoch mention'd, came, „ 239
in *d's* of difficulty And pressure, „ 254
Beheld the dead flame of the fallen *d* „ 441
Thro' many a fair sea-circle, *d* by *d*, „ 542
or all *d* long Sat often in the seaward-gazing gorge, „ 588
No sail from *d* to *d*, but every *d* „ 591
There Enoch rested silent many *d's*. „ 699
the dull November *d* Was growing duller twilight, „ 721
brought the stinted commerce of those *d's*; „ 817
meet the *d* When Enoch had return'd, „ 822
I have not three *d's* more to live; „ 851
Coming every *d*,' She answer'd, *The Brook* 106
five *d's* after that He met the bailiff „ 145
if you knew her in her English *d's*, „ 224
the *d's* That most she loves to talk of, „ 225
Thinn'd, or would seem to thin her in a *d*, *Aylmer's Field* 76
dash'd Into the chronicle of a deedful *d*, „ 196
Slept thro' the stately minuet of those *d's*: „ 207
The next *d* came a neighbour. „ 251
second *d*, My lady's Indian kinsman rushing in, „ 592
many thousand *d's* Were clipt by horror „ 602
Darkly that *d* rose: „ 609
At close of *d*; slept, woke, *Sea Dreams* 18
birdie say, In her nest at peep of *d*? „ 294
baby say, In her bed at peep of *d*? „ 302
Was it the first beam of my latest *d*? *Lucretius* 59
Whether I mean this *d* to end myself, „ 146
Shatter'd into one earthquake in one *d* „ 251
all a summer's *d* Gave his broad lawns *Princess, Pro.* 1
Took this fair *d* for text, „ 108
On a sudden in the midst of men and *d*, „ *i* 15
the *d's* drew nigh that I should wed, „ 41
three *d's* he feasted us, And on the fourth „ 118
At break of *d* the College Portress came: „ *ii* 15
In gentler *d's*, your arrow-wounded fawn „ 270
then *d* droopt; the chapel bells Call'd „ 470
the *d* fled on thro' all Its range of duties „ *iii* 176
and mould The woman to the fuller *d*.' „ 332
thinking of the *d's* that are no more. „ *iv* 43
So sad, so fresh, the *d's* that are no more. „ 48
So sad, so strange, the *d's* that are no more. „ 53
O Death in Life, the *d's* that are no more.' „ 58
was not thus, O Princess, in old *d's*: „ 292
yet this *d* (tho' you should hate me for it) „ 341
won it with a *d* Blanch'd in our annals, „ *vi* 62
a *d* Rose from the distance on her memory, „ 111
With kisses, ere the *d's* of Lady Blanche: „ 114
while the *d*, Descending, struck athwart the hall, „ 363
till on a *d* When Cyril pleaded, „ *vii* 77

Day (*continued*) out of memories of her kindlier *d's*, *Princess vii* 106
But such as gather'd colour *d* by *d*. „ 118
shares with man His nights, his *d's*, „ 263
the new *d* comes, the light Dearer for night, „ 346
For me, the genial *d*, the happy crowd, „ *Con.* 75
another sun, Warring on a later *d*, *Ode on Well.* 102
A *d* of onsets of despair! „ 124
Peace, it is a *d* of pain (repeat) „ 235, 238
not been down to the farm for a week and a *d*; *Grandmother* 33
But I wept like a child that *d*, „ 64
I climb'd the roofs at break of *d*; *Daisy* 61
And in my head, for half the *d*; „ 74
passion that lasts but a *d*; *G. of Swainston* 9
the *d* that follow'd the *d* she was wed, *The Islet* 4
autumn into seeming-leafless *d's*— *A Dedication* 10
stars from the night and the sun from the *d*! *Window. Gone* 5
merry for ever and ever, and one *d* more. „ *Ay* 4
Sun sets, moon sets, Love, fix a *d*. „ *When* 4
wait a little, You shall fix a *d*.' „ 12
And honour all the *d*. „ 16
Our little systems have their *d*; *In Mem., Pro.* 17
They have their *d* and cease to be: „ 18
On the bald street breaks the blank *d*. „ *vii* 12
And roar from yonder dropping *d*: „ *xv* 2
Week after week: the *d's* go by: „ *xvii* 7
Is on the waters *d* and night, „ 11
There twice a *d* the Severn fills; „ *xix* 5
And was the *d* of my delight As pure „ *xxiv* 1
The very source and fount of *D* „ 3
the *d* prepared The daily burden for the back. „ *xxv* 3
Old sisters of a *d* gone by, „ *xxix* 13
Draw forth the cheerful *d* from night: „ *xxx* 30
'Where wert thou, brother, those four *d's*?' „ *xxxi* 5
A life that leads melodious *d's*. „ *xxxiii* 8
As on a maiden in the *d* When first she wears her orange-flower! „ *xl* 3
A link among the *d's*, to knit „ 15
But he forgets the *d's* before „ *xliv* 3
The *d's* have vanish'd, tone and tint, „ 5
D's order'd in a wealthy peace, „ *xlvi* 11
The twilight of eternal *d*. „ *l* 16
Of hearts that beat from *d* to *d*, „ *lviii* 6
She sighs amid her narrow *d's*, „ *lx* 10
And tease her till the *d* draws by: „ 14
His inner *d* can never die, „ *lxvi* 15
The *d's* that grow to something strange, „ *lxxi* 11
D, when my crown'd estate begun „ *lxxii* 5
D, mark'd as with some hideous crime, „ 18
Climb thy thick noon, disastrous *d*: „ 26
I care not in these fading *d's* „ *lxxv* 9
Can trouble live with April *d's*, „ *lxxxiii* 7
For now the *d* was drawing on, „ *lxxxiv* 10
sun by sun the happy *d's* Descend below „ 27
Whatever way my *d's* decline, „ *lxxxv* 41
And break the livelong summer *d* „ *lxxxix* 31
And will not yield them for a *d*. „ *xc* 16
cast Together in the *d's* behind, „ *xcii* 6
call The spirits from their golden *d*, „ *xciv* 6
To broaden into boundless *d*. „ *xcv* 64
The *d's* she never can forget „ *xcvii* 14
D, when I lost the flower of men; „ *xcix* 4
And each reflects a kindlier *d*; „ *c* 18
These two have striven half the *d*, „ *cii* 17
Nor landmark breathes of other *d's*, „ *civ* 11
It is the *d* when he was born, A bitter *d* that early sank „ *cvii* 1
We keep the *d*. With festal cheer, „ 21
For *d's* of happy commune dead; „ *cxvi* 14
O *d's* and hours, your work is this, „ *cxvii* 1
Are breathers of an ampler *d* „ *cxviii* 6
And think of early *d's* and thee, „ *cxix* 8
In that it is thy marriage *d* „ *Con.* 3
Since that dark *d* a *d* like this; „ 8
We wish them store of happy *d's*. „ 84
But these are the *d's* of advance, *Maud I i* 25
and slurring the *d's* gone by, „ 33

Day (*continued*) riding at set of *d* Over the dark moor land, *Maud I ix* 5
I shall have had my *d*. (repeat). „ *xi* 7, 14
But this is the *d* when I must speak, „ *xvi* 7
O this is the *d*! „ 9
Go not, happy *d*, (repeat) „ *xvii* 1, 3
And you fair stars that crown a happy *d* „ *xviii* 30
Among the fragments of the golden *d*. „ 70
On the *d* when Maud was born; „ *xix* 40
Sat with her, read to her, night and *d*, „ 75
And half to the rising *d*; „ *xxii* 24
The *d* comes, a dull red ball „ *II iv* 65
paid our tithes in the *d's* that are gone, „ *v* 23
To catch a friend of mine one stormy *d*; „ 85
Voice in the rich dawn of an ampler *d*— *Ded. of Idylls* 36
wolf and boar and bear Came night and *d*, *Com. of Arthur* 24
And even in high *d* the morning star. „ 100
lords Of that fierce *d* were as the lords „ 216
those first *d's* had golden hours for me, „ 357
Blow, for our Sun is mightier *d* by *d*! „ 498
So make thy manhood mightier *d* by *d*; *Gareth and L.* 92
thou shalt serve a twelvemonth and a *d*.' „ 157
ancient kings who did their *d's* in stone; „ 305
drink among thy kitchen-knaves A twelvemonth and a *d*, „ 446
some fine *d* Undo thee not— „ 476
My deeds will speak: it is but for a *d*.' „ 577
That same *d* there past into the hall „ 587
call themselves the *D*, Morning-Star, „ 633
towers where that *d* a feast had been Held „ 847
To fight the brotherhood of *D* and Night— „ 857
D and Night and Death and Hell.' „ 887
O dewy flowers that close when *d* is done, „ 1067
O birds that warble as the *d* goes by, „ 1076
As on the *d* when Arthur knighted him.' „ 1240
all *d* long hath rated at her child, And vext his *d*, but blesses him asleep— „ 1285
Seeing he never rides abroad by *d*; „ 1334
sprang the happier *d* from underground; „ 1421
To make her beauty vary *d* by *d*. *Marr. of Geraint* 9
And *d* by *d* she thought to tell Geraint, „ 65
There on a *d*, he sitting high in hall, „ 147
milky-white, First seen that *d*: „ 151
And on the third *d* will again be here, „ 222
this nephew, fight In next *d's* tourney „ 476
Danced in his bosom, seeing better *d's*. „ 505
the third *d* from the hunting-morn Made „ 597
So bent he seem'd on going the third *d*, „ 604
Bent as he seem'd on going this third *d*, „ 625
Yet if he could but tarry a *d* or two, „ 627
when the fourth part of the *d* was gone, *Geraint and E.* 55
In former *d's* you saw me favourably. „ 315
but overtoil'd By that *d's* grief and travel, „ 377
dawn ascending lets the *d* Strike where it clung: „ 692
hardest tyrants in their *d* of power, „ 695
So past the *d's*. „ 930
And clothed her in apparel like the *d*. „ 948
Proclaim'd him Victor, and the *d* was won. *Balin and Balan* 90
those fair *d's*—not all as cool as these, „ 273
The whole *d* died, but, dying, gleam'd „ 314
'Brother, I dwelt a *d* in Pellam's hall: „ 605
Thy curse, and darken'd all thy *d*; „ 620
on a festal *d* When Guinevere was crossing *Merlin and V.* 64
on a dull *d* in an Ocean cave The blind wave „ 231
Had I for three *d's* seen, ready to fall. „ 296
Sweet were the *d's* when I was all unknown, „ 501
Well, those were not our *d's*: „ 612
Nor rested thus content, but *d* by *d*, *Lancelot and E.* 13
Dull *d's* were those, till our good Arthur „ 279
in the fight which all *d* long Rang „ 287
when the next *d* broke from underground, „ 413
If any man that *d* were left afield, „ 459
But on that *d* when Lancelot fled the lists, „ 525
our knight, thro' whom we won the *d*, „ 529
after two *d's*' tarriance there, return'd. „ 569
so *d* by *d* she past In either twilight „ 848
and every *d* she tended him, „ 850

Day (*continued*) Alas for me then, my good *d's* are done.' *Lancelot and E.* 947
And in those *d's* she made a little song, " 1004
So that *d* there was dole in Astolat. " 1136
That *d* Sir Lancelot at the palace craved " 1162
After the *d* of darkness, when the dead *Holy Grail* 49
A little lonely church in *d's* of yore, " 64
For on a *d* she sent to speak with me. " 101
beam of light seven times more clear than *d*: " 187
ride A twelvemonth and a *d* in quest of it, " 197
early that same *d*, Scaped thro' a cavern " 206
'But when the next *d* brake from under ground— " 338
but moving with me night and *d*, Fainter by *d*, but always in the night " 471
when the *d* began to wane, we went. " 488
while I tarried, every *d* she set A banquet richer than the *d* before " 588
then came a night Still as the *d* was loud; " 683
twelvemonth and a *d* were pleasant to me.' " 750
Seven *d's* I drove along the dreary deep, " 808
Let visions of the night or of the *d* Come, " 910
Riding at noon, a *d* or twain before, *Pelleas and E.* 20
and slowly Pelleas drew To that dim *d*, " 30
all *d* long Sir Pelleas kept the field " 168
but rose With morning every *d*, " 215
Full-arm'd upon his charger all *d* long Sat by the walls, " 216
I see thy face But once a *d*: " 244
Give me three *d's* to melt her fancy, " 356
So those three *d's*, aimless about the land, " 391
risen against me in their blood At the last *d*? " 462
And each foresaw the dolorous *d* to be: " 606
Arm'd for a *d* of glory before the King. *Last Tournament* 55
behold This *d* my Queen of Beauty is not here.' " 209
wan *d* Went glooming down in wet and weariness: " 214
Our one white *d* of Innocence hath past, " 218
new life—the *d's* of frost are o'er: New life, new love, to suit the newer *d*: " 278
I have had my *d*. " 316
I have had my *d* and my philosophies— " 319
King Was victor wellnigh *d* by *d*, " 335
fool,' said Tristram, 'not in open *d*.' " 347
So on for all that *d* from lawn to lawn " 373
Built for a summer *d* with Queen Isolt " 378
Then pressing *d* by *d* thro' Lyonesse " 501
he went To-day for three *d's'* hunting,— " 530
There came a *d* as still as heaven, *Guinevere* 292
golden *d's* In which she saw him first, " 380
and every *d* Beheld at noon in some delicious dale " 392
in the golden *d's* before thy sin. " 500
The *d's* will grow to weeks, " 624
The sombre close of that voluptuous *d*, " 688
that *d* when the great light of heaven Burn'd *Pass. of Arthur* 90
when the dolorous *d* Grew drearier " 122
The voice of *d's* of old and *d's* to be. " 135
whiter than the mist that all *d* long " 137
So all *d* long the noise of battle roll'd " 170
the halls Of Camelot, as in the *d's* that were. " 189
In those old *d's*, one summer noon, " 197
the *d's* darken round me, and the years, " 405
Rise like a fountain for me night and *d*. " 417
the three whereat we gazed On that high *d*, " 454
Bear witness, that rememberable *d*, *To the Queen ii* 3
make it wholly thine on sunny *d's*. *Lover's Tale i* 14
d's Of dewy dawning and the amber eves " 51
when *d* hung From his mid-dome in Heaven's " 65
all her flowers, And length of *d's*, " 105
with the growths Of vigorous early *d's*, " 133
Before he saw my *d* my father died, " 191
I said to her, 'A *d* for Gods to stoop,' " 304
for that *d* Love, rising, shook his wings, " 316
d which did enwomb that happy hour, Thou art blessed in the years, divinest *d*! " 485
Then had he stemm'd my *d* with night, " 502
Yet bearing round about him his own *d*, " 510
come To boys and girls when summer *d's* are new, " 555
where that *d* I crown'd myself as king, " 592

Day (*continued*) for the *d* was as the night to me! The night to me was kinder than the *d*; The night in pity took away my *d*, *Lover's Tale* 610
All *d* I watch'd the floating isles of shade, " *ii* 5
All *d* I sat within the cavern-mouth, " 37
The *d* waned; Alone I sat with her: " 139
From the outer *d*, Betwixt the close-set ivies " 171
I CAME one *d* and sat among the stones " *iii* 1
what height The *d* had grown I know not. " 9
had lain three *d's* without a pulse: " *iv* 34
till the great *d* Peal'd on us with that music " 64
that *d* a boy was born, Heir to his face and land, " 128
for wasn't he coming that *d*? *First Quarrel* 47
For the down's are as bright as *d*, *Rizpah* 4
you were only made for the *d*. " 19
past away with five ships of war that *d*, *The Revenge* 13
drew away From the Spanish fleet that *d*, " 47
fought such a fight for a *d* and a night " 83
And a *d* less or more At sea or ashore, " 86
tho' I loiter'd there The full *d* after, *Sisters* (*E. and E.*) 98
lake and mountain conquers all the *d*. " 100
my crowning hour, my *d* of *d's*. " 124
Then came the *d* when I, Flattering myself " 139
Not I that *d* of Edith's love or mine— " 142
Edith would be bridesmaid on the *d*. But on that *d*, not being all at ease, " 208
Thro' dreams by night and trances of the *d*, " 274
but the good Lord Jesus has had his *d*.' *In the Child. Hosp.* 22
Say that His *d* is done! " 71
for fifteen *d's* or for twenty at most. *Def. of Lucknow* 9
it chanced on a *d* Soon as the blast " 31
we were every *d* fewer and fewer. " 49
to be a soldier all *d* and be sentinel " 74
Ever the *d* with its traitorous death " 79
Then *d* and night, *d* and night, " 92
'Hold it for fifteen *d's*!' " 105
might be kindlier: happily come the *d*! *Sir J. Oldcastle* 23
so spurn'd, so baited two whole *d's*— " 163
more than once in *d's* Of doubt and cloud *Columbus* 155
To whom I send my prayer by night and *d*— " 233
slain my father the *d* before I was born. *V. of Maeldune* 8
And we stay'd three *d's*, and we gorged " 67
till the labourless *d* dipt under the West; " 86
thunder of God peal'd over us all the *d*, " 113
I shall join you in a *d*. *To W. H. Brookfield* 14
arm'd by *d* and night Against the Turk; *Montenegro* 3
All *d* the men contend in grievous war *Achilles over the T.* 9
I, wearing but the garland of a *d*, *To Dante* 6
When, in our younger London *d's*, *To E. Fitzgerald* 54
A clearer *d* Than our poor twilight *Tiresias* 205
All *d* long far-off in the cloud of the city, *The Wreck* 29
the sun of the soul made *d* in the dark " 55
That *d* my nurse had brought me the child. " 59
Ten long sweet summer *d's* upon deck, " 64
the sons of a winterless *d*. " 74
Ten long *d's* of summer and sin—if it must be so— But *d's* of a larger light than I ever again shall know—*D's* that will glimmer, I fear, " 77
little one found me at sea on a *d*, " 86
the storm and the *d's* went by, but I knew no more— " 111
'Ten long sweet summer *d's*' of fever, " 147
And gone—that *d* of the storm— " 148
Three *d's* since, three more dark *d's* *Despair* 6
to the glare of a drearier *d*; " 28
What rulers but the *D's* and Hours *Ancient Sage* 95
The *d's* and hours are ever glancing by, " 99
But with the Nameless is nor *D* nor Hour; " 102
For man has overlived his *d* " 150
If utter darkness closed the *d*, " 199
sight and night to lose themselves in *d*. " 203
When only *D* should reign.' " 244
D and Night are children of the Sun, " 245
No night no *d*!—I touch thy world again— " 249
And send the *d* into the darken'd heart; " 261
dawn of more than mortal *d* Strike on the Mount of Vision! " 284

Day (*continued*) morning brings the *d* I hate and fear; *The Flight* 2
the morn is calm, and like another *d*; „ 10
on that summer *d* When I had fall'n „ 21
love that keeps his heart alive beats on it night and *d*— „ 35
an' yer eyes as bright as the *d*! *Tomorrow* 32
paäirints had inter'd glory, an' both in wan *d*, „ 53
sleeps the gleam of dying *d*. *Locksley H., Sixty* 42
watching till the *d* begun— „ 91
force to guide us thro' the *d's* I shall not see? „ 158
On this *d* and at this hour, „ 175
planets whirling round them, flash a million miles a *d*. „ 204
I shelter'd in this archway from a *d* of driving showers— „ 259
my Leonard, use and not abuse your *d*, „ 265
stood like a rock In the wave of a stormy *d*; *Heavy Brigade* 57
I that loved thee since my *d* began, *To Virgil* 38
The light of *d's* when life begun, The *d's* that seem to-day, *Pref. Poem Broth. S.* 23
now thy long *d's* work hath ceased, *Epit. on Stratford* 2
maintain The *d* against the moment, and the year Against the *d*; *To Duke of Argyll* 6
live With stronger life from *d* to *d*; *Hands all round* 6
Two Suns of Love make *d* of human life, *Prin. Beatrice* 1
light and genial warmth of double *d*. „ 22
Men that in a narrower *d*— *Open I. and C. Exhib.* 25
lavish all the golden *d* To make them wealthier *Poets and their B.* 3
Your viceregal *d's* Have added fulness *To Marq. of Dufferin* 10
My memories of his briefer *d* Will mix „ 51
that the *d*, When here thy hands let fall *Demeter and P.* 8
And robed thee in his *d* from head to feet— „ 21
a worm which writhes all *d*, *Vastness* 17
Voices of the *d* Are heard across the Voices of the dark. *The Ring* 39
when you came of age Or on the *d* you married. Both the *d's* Now close in one. „ 78
made The rosy twilight of a perfect *d*. „ 187
on her birthday, and that *d* His death-day, „ 212
one *d* came And saw you, shook her head, „ 312
I came, I went, was happier *d* by *d*; „ 348
on that *d* Two lovers parted by no scurrilous tale— „ 426
In summer if I reach my *d*— *To Ulysses* 9
When frost is keen and *d's* are brief— „ 19
years ago, In rick-fire *d's*, When Dives loathed the times, *To Mary Boyle* 28
O'er his uncertain shadow droops the *d*. *Prog. of Spring* 8
While the long *d* of knowledge grows and warms, „ 101
Thy scope of operation, *d* by *d*, „ 111
stumbled back again Into the common *d*, *Romney's R.* 33
To you my *d's* have been a life-long lie, „ 41
To flame along another dreary *d*. „ 58
And on this white midwinter *d*— *To Master of B.* 9
d long labour'd, hewing the pines, *Death of Œnone* 62
vanish'd like a ghost Before the *d*, „ 68
more than he that sang the Works and *D's*, *To Virgil* 6
d by *d*, thro' many a blood-red eve, *St. Telemachus* 3
off the rosy cheek of waking *D*. *Akbar's Dream* 202
one *d* He had left his dagger behind him. *Bandit's Death* 11
alone in the dell at the close of the *d*. „ 19
and the *d* I was born. *Charity* 24
she sat *d* and night by my bed, „ 33
Dawn not *D*! (repeat) *The Dawn* 11, 16
Storm in the South that darkens the *d*! *Riflemen, form!* 2
if Thou willest, let my *d* be brief, So Thou wilt strike Thy glory thro' the *d*. *Doubt and Prayer* 13
Must my *d* be dark by reason, *God and the Univ.* 2
after his brief range of blameless *d's*, *D. of the Duke of C.* 9

Daylight Ind to Ind, but in fair *d* woke, *Buonaparte* 4
Flood with full *d* glebe and town? *Two Voices* 87
Seems to the quiet *d* of your minds *Lover's Tale i* 296
Long as the *d* Lasted, *Batt. of Brunanburh* 38
d made itself Ruddy thro' both the roofs of sight, *Tiresias* 2
whence an affluent fountain pour'd From darkness into *d*, *Ancient Sage* 8
vapour in *d* Over the mountain Floats, *Kapiolani* 16

Daylong you caught His weary *d* chirping, *The Brook* 53

Dayshine Naked in open *d*?' 'Nay,' she cried, *Gareth and L.* 1092

Dazed the sudden light *D* me half-blind: *Princess v* 12
And *d* all eyes, till Arthur by main might, *Com. of Arthur* 109

Dazed (*continued*) Some flush'd, and others *d*, *Com. of Arthur* 265
nor lights nor feast *D* or amazed, *Lover's Tale iv* 311
d and dumb With passing thro' at once *Demeter and P.* 6
end myself too with the dagger—so deafen'd and *d*— *Bandit's Death* 37

Dazing from the lava-lake *D* the starlight, *Kapiolani* 15

Dazzle not shown To *d* all that see them? *The Ring* 144

Dazzled both his eyes were *d*, as he stood, *M. d'Arthur* 59
The rhymes are *d* from their place *Day-Dm., Pro.* 19
boyish dream involved and *d* down *Princess iv* 450
Be *d* by the wildfire Love to sloughs „ *v* 441
In either hand be bore What *d* all, *Gareth and L.* 387
And *d* by the livid-flickering fork, *Merlin and V.* 941
So that his eyes were *d* looking at it. *Pelleas and E.* 36
Was *d* by the sudden light, „ 105
both his eyes were *d* as he stood, *Pass. of Arthur* 227

Dazzling The sun came *d* thro' the leaves, *L. of Shalott iii* 3

Dead (adj.) (*See also* **Deäd**, **Half-dead**) All cold, and *d*, and corpse-like grown? *Supp. Confessions* 17
I would that I were *d*!' (repeat) *Mariana* 12, 24, 36, 48, 60, 72
Oh God, that I were *d*!' *Mariana* 84
Nor canst thou show the dead are *d*. *Two Voices* 267
like a shadow, and the winds are *d*. *Œnone* 28
He look'd so grand when he was *d*. *The Sisters* 32
Since I beheld young Laurence *d*. *L. C. V. de Vere* 28
Roman soldier found Me lying *d*, *D. of F. Women* 162
And the old year is *d*. „ 248
But he'll be *d* before. *D. of the O. Year* 32
I see the true old times are *d*, *M. d'Arthur* 229
who was *d*, Who married, who was like to be, *Audley Court* 29
I hope my end draws nigh: half *d* I am, *St. S. Stylites* 37
this wonder, *d*, become Mere highway dust? *Love and Duty* 10
Better thou wert *d* before me, *Locksley Hall* 56
Can I think of her as *d*, and love her „ 73
And half the crew are sick or *d*, *The Voyage* 92
Come not, when I am *d*, *Come not, when, etc.* 1
She talk'd as if her love were *d*, *The Letters* 27
tender grace of a day that is *d* *Break, break, etc.* 15
Still downward thinking '*d* or *d* to me!' *Enoch Arden* 689
If you could tell her you had seen him *d*, „ 808
Not to reveal it, till you see me *d*.' '*D*,' „ 839
But if my children care to see me *d*, „ 888
Were *d* to him already; bent as he was *Aylmer's Field* 445
D for two years before his death was he; „ 837
We *must* forgive the dead.' 'Dead! who is *d*?' *Sea Dreams* 270
He suddenly dropt *d* of heart-disease.' '*D*? he? of heart-disease? what heart had he To die of? *d*!' „ 274
crush her pretty maiden fancies *d* *Princess i* 88
Peace be with her. She is *d*. „ *iv* 136
And strikes him *d* for thine and thee. „ 584
cold reverence worse than were she *d*. „ *v* 92
I would the old God of war himself were *d*, „ 145
Home they brought her warrior *d*: „ *vi* 1
she said, 'he lives: he is not *d*: „ 122
he is *d*, Or all as *d*: „ 169
Till the Sun drop, *d*, from the signs.' „ *vii* 245
lift thine eyes; my doubts are *d*, „ 348
if to-night our greatness were struck *d*, *Third of Feb.* 17
was *d* before he was born, (repeat) *Grandmother* 59, 68
not always certain if they be alive or *d*. „ 84
And when I am there and *d* and gone, *Window. No Answer* 11
Where lies the master newly *d*; *In Mem. xx* 4
But, he was *d*, and there he sits, „ *xxxii* 3
'But brooding on the dear one *d*, *In Mem. xxxvii* 17
Nor can I dream of thee as *d*: „ *lxviii* 4
Regret is *d*, but love is more „ *Con.* 17
and found The shining daffodil *d*, *Maud I iii* 14
Had I lain for a century *d*; „ *xxii* 72
Strike *d* the whole weak race of venomous worms, „ *II i* 46
Who knows if he be *d*? „ *ii* 71
She is but *d*, and the time is at hand „ *iii* 8
There is some one dying or *d*, „ *iv* 48
D, long *d*, Long *d*! „ *v* 1
And wept, and wish'd that I were *d*; *Com. of Arthur* 345
Thrall'd in his castle, and hath starved him *d*; *Gareth and L.* 358
Emrys would have scourged thee *d*, „ 375

Dead (adj.) (*continued*) Fell, as if *d*; but quickly rose and drew, *Gareth and L.* 967
and all wing'd nothings peck him *d*! *Marr. of Geraint* 275
be he *d* I know not, but he past to the wild land. ,, 442
once without remorse to strike her *d*, *Geraint and E.* 109
and so left him stunn'd or *d*, ,, 464
'What, is he *d*?' 'No, no, not *d*!' ,, 541
sure am I, quite sure, he is not *d*.' ,, 545
if he be not *d*, Why wail ye for him thus? ,, 546
And be he *d*, I count you for a fool; Your wailing will not quicken him: *d* or not, ,, 548
yet lay still, and feign'd himself as *d*, ,, 588
were I *d* who is it would weep for me? ,, 618
Take warning: yonder man is surely *d*; ,, 672
Except he surely knew my lord was *d*,' ,, 721
died Earl Doorm by him be counted *d*. ,, 730
D, whom we buried; more than one of us *Balin and Balan* 122
yonder lies one *d* within the wood. Not *d*; ,, 468
like brainless bulls, *D* for one heifer!' ,, 579
Coming and going, and he lay as *d* *Merlin and V.* 213
Coming and going, and she lay as *d*, ,, 644
And in the hollow oak he lay as *d*, ,, 969
I fear me, that will strike my blossom *d*. *Lancelot and E.* 971
Give me good fortune, I will strike him *d*, ,, 1071
she did not seem as *d*, But fast asleep, ,, 1160
broken shed, And in it a *d* babe; *Holy Grail* 399
dry old trunks about us, *d*, Yea, rotten ,, 495
And one had wedded her, and he was *d*, ,, 586
'Lo! Pelleas is *d*—he told us— *Pelleas and E.* 377
'*D*, is it so?' she ask'd. 'Ay, ay,' said he, ,, 384
I to your *d* man have given my troth, ,, 389
one Murmuring, 'All courtesy is *d*,' *Last Tournament* 211
The leaf is *d*, the yearning past away: ,, 277
Is all the laughter gone *d* out of thee?— ,, 300
High on a grim *d* tree before the tower, ,, 430
Heard in *d* night along that table-shore, ,, 463
'my man Hath left me or is *d*;' ,, 495
child of one I honour'd, happy, *d* before thy shame? *Guinevere* 423
strike him *d*, and meet myself Death, ,, 575
strikes them *d* is as my death to me. *Pass. of Arthur* 74
That quick or *d* thou holdest me for King. ,, 161
I see the true old times are *d*, ,, 397
Hope was not wholly *d*, But breathing hard *Lover's Tale i* 584
I had lain as *d*, Mute, blind and motionless ,, 606
D, for henceforth there was no life for me! ,, 608
but mine was wholly *d*, ,, 724
Some one had told me she was *d*, ,, *ii* 70
low knell tolling his lady *d*— *D*— ,, *iv* 33
All that look'd on her had pronounced her *d*. ,, 35
but after my man was *d*; *First Quarrel* 6
an' I wish I was *d*— ,, 52
hear that cry of my boy that was *d*, *Rizpah* 45
bullet struck him that was dressing it suddenly *d*, *The Revenge* 67
nay, murder'd, doubtless *d*. *Sir J. Oldcastle* 60
Some *d* of hunger, some beneath the scourge, *Columbus* 177
he had stricken my father *d*— *V. of Maeldune* 1
men dropt *d* in the valleys ,, 31
D of some inward agony—is it so? *To W. H. Brookfield* 10
the winds were *d* for heat; *Tiresias* 34
and dash'd herself *D* in her rage: ,, 153
D to the death beside me, *The Wreck* 113
I would thank him, the other is *d*, *Despair* 70
From the *d* fossil skull that is left in the rocks of an earth that is *d*? ,, 86
Would fain that he were *d*; *Ancient Sage* 126
Found, fear'd me *d*, and groan'd, *The Flight* 23
an icy corpse *d* of some foul disease: ,, 54
he comes, and finds me *d*. ,, 72
'Ud 'a shot his own sowl *d* for a kiss *Tomorrow* 40
her wits wor *d*, an' her hair was as white ,, 60
an' dhropt down *d* an the dead. ,, 80
D the warrior, *d* his glory, *d* the cause *Locksley H., Sixty* 30
Lies my Amy *d* in child-birth, *d* the mother, *d* the child. *D*—and sixty years ago, and *d* her aged husband now— ,, 36

Dead (adj.) (*continued*) earth be *d* as yon *d* world the moon? *D* the new astronomy calls her. . . . *Locksley H., Sixty* 174
D, but now her living glory lights the hall, ,, 181
D! And the Muses cried with a stormy cry *Dead Prophet* 1
D! 'Is it *he* then brought so low?' ,, 5
D, who had served his time, ,, 9
somewhere *d* far in the waste Soudan, *Epit. on Gordon* 2
Tho' *d* in its Trinacrian Enna, *To Prof. Jebb* 11
The dead are not *d* but alive. *Vastness* 36
she my Miriam *d* within the year. *The Ring* 286
D! I took And chafed the freezing hand. ,, 451
D!—and maybe stung With some remorse, ,, 454
—but *d* so long, gone up so far, ,, 462
In fright, and fallen *d*. ,, 471
'He is fled—I wish him *d*— *Forlorn* 1
He is fled, or he is *d*, ,, 9
and when The Priest pronounced you *d*, *Happy* 50
fire from Heaven had dash'd him *d*, ,, 83
As *d* from all the human race as if beneath the mould; If you be *d*, then I am *d*, ,, 95
D with the dead? *To Mary Boyle* 14
mountain rolls into the plain, Fell headlong *d*; *Death of Œnone* 52
then a shower of stones that stoned him *d*, *St. Telemachus* 68
rabble in half-amaze Stared at him *d*, ,, 72
band will be scatter'd now their gallant captain is *d*, *Bandit's Death* 41
birthday came of a boy born happily *d*. *Charity* 34
when all but the winds were *d*, *The Dreamer* 1

Dead (s) (*See also* **Living-dead**). Ev'n in the charnels of the *d*, *Two Voices* 215
Nor canst thou show the *d* are dead. ,, 267
'We find no motion in the *d*.' ,, 279
And of the rising from the *d*, *Palace of Art* 206
Once heard at *d* of night to greet *On a Mourner* 32
As we bear blossom of the *d*; *Love thou thy land* 94
And grassy barrows of the happier *d*. *Tithonus* 71
He gazes on the silent *d*: *Day-Dm., Arrival* 13
'O love, thy kiss would wake the *d*!' ,, *Depart.* 20
was deadly wounded Falling on the *d*. *The Captain* 64
And the *d* begin to dance. *Vision of Sin* 166
Yes, as the *d* we weep for testify— *Aylmer's Field* 747
We *must* forgive the *d*.' '*D*! who is dead?' *Sea Dreams* 270
shine among the *d* Hereafter; tales! *Lucretius* 129
Sat watching like a watcher by the *d*. *Princess v* 62
And watches in the *d*, the dark, ,, *vii* 103
Thy living voice to me was as the voice of the *d*, *V. of Cauteretz* 8
voice of the *d* was a living voice to me. ,, 10
And scratch the very *d* for spite: *Lit. Squabbles* 8
That name the under-lying *d*, *In Mem. ii* 2
And hear the ritual of the *d*. ,, *xviii* 12
But Sorrow—fixt upon the *d*, ,, *xxxix* 8
How fares it with the happy *d*? ,, *xliv* 1
Do we indeed desire the *d* Should still be near ,, *li* 1
The *d* shall look me thro' and thro'. ,, *li* 12
Eternal greetings to the *d*; ,, *lvii* 14
So hold I commerce with the *d*; ,, *lxxxv* 93
Or so methinks the *d* would say; ,, 94
That could the *d*, whose dying eyes ,, *xc* 5
hold An hour's communion with the *d*. ,, *xciv* 4
The noble letters of the *d*: ,, *xcv* 24
And woodlands holy to the *d*; ,, *xcix* 8
I dream'd a vision of the *d*, ,, *ciii* 3
But trust that those we call the *d* ,, *cxviii* 5
Should pile her barricades with *d*. ,, *cxxvii* 8
Her feet, my darling, on the *d*; ,, *Con.* 50
I hear the *d* at midday moan, *Maud I vi* 70
For I thought the *d* had peace, ,, *II v* 15
which makes us loud in the world of the *d* ,, 25
For it is but a world of the *d*; ,, 40
comes from another stiller world of the *d*, ,, 70
the living quiet as the *d*, *Com. of Arthur* 123
I cannot brook to gaze upon the *d*.' *Balin and Balan* 586
Among the *d* and sown upon the wind— *Merlin and V.* 45
And by the cold Hic Jacets of the *d*!' ,, 753
and the *d*, Oar'd by the dumb, *Lancelot and E.* 1153

Dead (s) (*continued*) If one may judge the living by the *d*, — *Lancelot and E.* 1368
the *d* Went wandering o'er Moriah— — *Holy Grail* 49
Moans of the dying, and voices of the *d*. — *Pass. of Arthur* 117
beats upon the faces of the *d*, My *d*, — „ 141
Behold, I seem but King among the *d*.' — „ 146
and so the *d* have kings, — „ 148
'He passes to be King among the *d*, — „ 449
She is his no more: The *d* returns to me, and I go down To kiss the *d*.' — *Lover's Tale iv* 49
that great love they both had borne the *d*, — „ 181
drew back with her *d* and her shame. — *The Revenge* 60
they stared at the *d* that had been so valiant — „ 105
mother broke her promise to the *d*, — *Sisters (E. and E.)* 252
one of those who would break their jests on the *d*, — *In the Child. Hosp.* 8
Voice of the *d* whom we loved, — *Def. of Lucknow* 11
women in travail among the dying and *d*, — „ 88
God's Own voice to justify the *d*— — *Columbus* 203
And we left the *d* to the birds — *V. of Maeldune* 36
hours Now silent, and so many *d*, — *Tiresias* 211
lay like the *d* by the *d* on the cabin floor, — *The Wreck* 112
And wish the *d*, as happier than ourselves — *Ancient Sage* 205
an' dhropt down dead an the *d*. — *Tomorrow* 80
single sordid attic holds the living and the *d*. — *Locksley H., Sixty* 222
all my steps are on the *d*. — „ 252
stood stark by the *d*; — *Dead Prophet* 19
She gabbled, as she groped in the *d*, — „ 73
Persephone! Queen of the *d* no more— — *Demeter and P.* 18
as having risen from out the *d*, — „ 144
the *d* are not dead but alive — *Vastness* 36
Priest, who join'd you to the *d*, — *Happy* 93
Dead with the *d*? — *Mary Boyle* 14
would sound so mean That all the *d*, — *Romney's R.* 132
Thin as the batlike shrillings of the *D* — *Death of Œnone* 21
Silent Voices of the *d*, — *Silent Voices* 4
Deäd hallus coom'd to 's chooch afoor moy Sally wur *d*, — *N. Farmer, O.S.* 17
toäner 'ed shot 'um as *d* as a naäil. — „ 35
an' she weänt 'a nowt when 'e's *d*, — „ *N.S.* 25
But 'e tued an' moil'd 'issén *d*, — „ 52
boooks wur gone an' 'is boy wur *d*, — *Village Wife* 87
an' one o' ye *d* ye knaws! — *Spinster's S's.* 62
Dick, when 'e cooms to be *d*, — *Owd Roä* 11
an' I taäked 'im at fust fur *d*; — „ 100
Dead-blue And a lack-lustre *d-b* eye, — *A Character* 17
Deaden and learns to *d* Love of self, — *Ode on Well.* 204
Deaden'd landskip darken'd, The melody *d*, — *Merlin and the G.* 32
Dead-heavy down *d-h* sank her curls, — *Princess vi* 147
Dead Innocence call'd The Tournament of the *D I*, — *Last Tournament* 136
Dead March the *D M* wails in the people's ears: — *Ode on Well.* 267
Dead-pale *D-p* between the houses high, — *L. of Shalott iv* 40
Deaf (*See also* **Deäf**) 'Much less this dreamer, *d* and blind, — *Two Voices* 175
parch'd and wither'd, *d* and blind, — *Fatima* 6
my end draws nigh: half *d* I am, — *St. S. Stylites* 37
she was *d* To blessing or to cursing — *Geraint and E.* 578
mark'd not this, but blind and *d* — *Balin and Balan* 318
For wert thou born or blind or *d*, — *Ancient Sage* 175
no man halt, or *d* or blind; — *Locksley H., Sixty* 163
And *d* to the melody, — *Merlin and the G.* 27
all but *d* thro' age and weariness, — *St. Telemachus* 41
Be not *d* to the sound that warns, — *Riflemen form!* 8
Deäf an' maäkin' ma *d* wi' their shouts, — *Spinster's S's.* 88
Deafen'd *d* with the stammering cracks and claps — *Merlin and V.* 942
end myself too with the dagger—so *d* and dazed— — *Bandit's Death* 37
Deafer I will be *d* than the blue-eyed cat, — *Holy Grail* 865
'*D*,' said the blameless King, — „ 869
Deal You know so ill to *d* with time, — *L. C. V. de Vere* 63
Nor *d* in watch-words overmuch: — *Love thou thy land* 28
Ere days, that *d* in ana, swarm'd — *Will Water.* 199
Her answer was 'Leave me to *d* with that.' — *Princess iii* 149
nor *d's* in that Which men delight in, — „ 215
d's with the other distance and the hues — „ *iv* 86
for Cyril, howe'er He *d* in frolic, — „ 250
learn With whom they *d*, — „ 513
Shall we *d* with it as an infant? — *Boädicea* 33
Deal (*continued*) *d's* comfortable words To hearts wounded — *Lover's Tale i* 717
Deal-box An' I hit on an old *d-b* that was push'd — *First Quarrel* 48
Deal'd sa I hallus *d* wi' the Hall, — *Village Wife* 115
Dealing (part.) 'For memory *d* but with time, — *Two Voices* 376
Nor *d* goodly counsel from a height — *Aylmer's Field* 172
Dealing (s) And full of *d's* with the world? — *Miller's D.* 8
Thy elect have no *d's* with either heresy or orthodoxy; — *Akbar's D., Inscrip.* 7
Dealt Oh! deathful stabs were *d* apace, — *Oriana* 50
My nerves have *d* with stiffer. — *Will Water.* 78
hoard of tales that *d* with knights, — *Princess, Pro.* 29
For Wisdom *d* with mortal powers, — *In Mem. xxxvi* 5
this *d* him at Caerlyle; That at Caerleon; — *Lancelot and E.* 22
knight of Arthur's noblest *d* in scorn; — *Guinevere* 40
Our mutual mother *d* to both of us: — *Lover's Tale i* 246
Dean (forest) Before him came a forester of *D*, — *Marr. of Geraint* 148
Across the forest call'd of *D*, to find — *Pelleas and E.* 21
Dean (dignitary) prudes for proctors, dowagers for *d's*, — *Princess, Pro.* 141
they vext the souls of *d's*; — „ 162
Dear And she is grown so *d*, so *d*, — *Miller's D.* 170
D is the memory of our wedded lives, — *Lotos-Eaters, C.S.* 69
d the last embraces of our wives — „ 70
As thou are lief and *d*, and do the thing — *M. d'Arthur* 80
I hold thee *d* For this good pint of port. — *Will Water.* 211
I am not all as wrong As a bitter jest is *d*. — *Vision of Sin* 198
To wed the man so *d* to all of them — *Enoch Arden* 484
The discords *d* to the musician. — *Sea Dreams* 258
declared that ancient ties Would still be *d* — *Princess ii* 265
'*D* as remember'd kisses after death, — „ *iv* 54
there's no rose that's half so *d* to them — „ *v* 159
D to the man that is *d* to God; — *To F. D. Maurice* 36
For those are few we hold as *d*; — „ 46
Yet both are near, and both are *d*, — *The Victim* 59
D, near and true—no truer Time — *A Dedication* 1
follow them down to the window-pane of my *d*, — *Window. On the Hill* 17
frost is here, And fuel is *d*, — „ *Winter* 2
D as the mother to the son, — *In Mem. ix* 19
(And *d* to me as sacred wine To dying lips — „ *xxxvii* 19
Shall count new things as *d* as old: — „ *xl* 28
Knowing the primrose yet is *d*, — „ *lxxxv* 118
And this hath made them trebly *d*.' — „ *cii* 16
That if *I* be *d* to some one else, — *Maud I xv* 3
But If *I* be *d* to some one else, — „ 5
I should be to myself more *d*. — „ 6
If I be *d* If I be *d* to some one else — „ 9
With *d* Love's tie, makes Love himself more *d*.' — „ *xviii* 61
THESE to His Memory—since he held them *d*, — *Ded. of Idylls* 1
d to Science, *d* to Art, *D* to thy land and ours, — „ 40
d to Arthur was that hall of ours, — *Holy Grail* 222
As thou are lief and *d*, and do the thing — *Pass. of Arthur* 248
an' soa purr awaäy, my *d*, — *Spinster's S's.* 57
D! *d*! *d*! I mun part them Tommies— — „ 92
Dearer a little *d* than his horse. — *Locksley Hall* 50
All he shows her makes him *d* — *L. of Burleigh* 33
the light *D* for night, as *d* thou for faults — *Princess vii* 347
tho' he make you evermore *D* and nearer, — *A Dedication* 3
the fuel is all the *d*, — *Window. Winter* 15
Our wood, that is *d* than all; — *Maud I xxii* 38
therefore *d*; or if not so new, Yet therefore tenfold *d* — *Marr. of Geraint* 809
reverence, *D* to true young hearts — *Lancelot and E.* 419
by white bonds and warm, *D* than freedom. — *Pelleas and E.* 354
I held you at that moment even *d* than before; — *Happy* 90
fame with me To make it *d*. — *Romney's R.* 56
Dearest 'Never, *d*, never: here I brave the worst:' — *Edwin Morris* 117
Were it our nearest, Were it our *d*, — *The Victim* 14
Take you his *d*, Give us a life.' — „ 27
Is *he* your *d*? Or I, the wife?' — „ 51
And which the *d* I cannot tell!' — „ 60
'We have his *d*, His only son!' — „ 63
shrieking '*I* am his *d*, I—*I* am his *d*!' — „ 71
Which was his nearest? Who was his *d*? — „ 77
The beauty that is *d* to his heart— — *Lover's Tale iv* 249
To show you what is *d* to my heart, — „ 252

Dearest (*continued*) Of all things upon earth the *d* to me.' *Lover's Tale iv* 319
which of all things is the *d* to me, " 348
What sound was *d* in his native dells? *Far-far-away* 4
Dearness with a *d* not his due. *Locksley Hall* 91
A distant *d* in the hill, *In Mem. lxiv* 19
Death Oh! vanity! *D* waits at the door. *All Things will Die* 17
Hark! *d* is calling While I speak to ye, " 28
Patient of ill, and *d*, and scorn, *Supp. Confessions* 4
To hold a common scorn of *d*! " 34
He hath no care of life or *d*; " 48
stooping low Unto the *d*, not sunk! " 98
Shall we not look into the laws Of life and *d*, " 172
O weary life! O weary *d*! " 188
A gentler *d* shall Falsehood die, *Clear-headed friend* 16
Life, anguish, *d*, immortal love, *Arabian Nights* 73
when he taketh repose An hour before *d*; *A Spirit haunts* 15
He saw thro' life and *d*, *The Poet* 5
In your eye there is *d*, *Poet's Mind* 16
D, walking all alone beneath a yew, *Love and Death* 5
'You must begone,' said *D*, " 7
Life eminent creates the shade of *d*; " 13
I drink the cup of a costly *d*, *Eleänore* 138
With secret *d* for ever, in the pits *Wan Sculptor* 13
And range of evil between *d* and birth, *If I were loved* 3
wait for *d*—mute—careless of all ills, " 10
'Thou hadst not between *d* and birth *Two Voices* 169
Know I not *D*? the outward signs? " 270
Has ever truly long'd for *d*. " 396
Oh life, not *d*, for which we pant; " 398
That I should die an early *d*: *Miller's D.* 90
O *d*, *d*, *d*, thou ever-floating cloud, *Œnone* 238
Walking the cold and starless road of *D* " 259
And *d* and life she hated equally, *Palace of Art* 265
And sweeter far is *d* than life to me *May Queen, Con.* 8
D is the end of life; *Lotos-Eaters, C. S.* 41
Give us long rest or *d*, dark *d*, or dreamful ease. " 53
There *is* confusion worse than *d*, " 83
The downward slope to *d*. *D. of F. Women* 16
bright *d* quiver'd at the victim's throat; " 115
I was ripe for *d*. " 208
who knew that Love can vanquish *D*, " 269
Once thro' mine own doors *D* did pass; *To J. S.* 19
D is blown in every wind;' " 46
fluting a wild carol ere her *d*, *M. d'Arthur* 267
But Dora lived unmarried till her *d*. *Dora* 172
suit had wither'd, nipt to *d* by him *Edwin Morris* 101
did not all thy martyrs die one *d*? *St. S. Stylites* 50
and whole years long, a life of *d*. " 54
hope ere *d* Spreads more and more and more, " 156
Like *D* betwixt thy dear embrace and mine, *Love and Duty* 48
Like bitter accusation ev'n to *d*, " 81
every hour Must sweat her sixty minutes to the *d*, *Golden Year* 69
D closes all: but something ere the end, *Ulysses* 51
Till mellow *D*, like some late guest, *Will Water.* 239
No carved cross-bones, the types of *D*, " 245
Pale again as *d* did prove: *L. of Burleigh* 66
gray and gap-tooth'd man as lean as *d*, *Vision of Sin* 60
Let us hob-and-nob with *D*. " 74
'*D* is king, and Vivat Rex! " 179
Hob-and-nob with brother *D*! " 194
In those two *d's* he read God's warning *Enoch Arden* 571
His baby's *d*, her growing poverty, " 705
than he saw *D* dawning on him, " 832
peace which each had prick'd to *d*. *Aylmer's Field* 52
no force, Persuasion, no, nor *d* could alter her: " 418
cordon close and closer toward the *d*, " 500
a letter edged with *d* Beside him, " 595
Averill went and gazed upon his *d*. " 599
for the second *d* Scarce touch'd her " 604
hapless loves And double *d* were widely murmur'd, " 617
wounded to the *d* that cannot die; " 662
from the people's eyes Ere the great *d*, " 773
devising their own daughter's *d*! " 783
Stumbling across the market to his *d*, " 820
Dead for two years before his *d* was he; " 837

Death (*continued*) dark retinue reverencing *d* At golden thresholds; *Aylmer's Field* 842
Bound on a matter he of life and *d*: *Sea Dreams* 151
gout and stone, that break Body toward *d*, *Lucretius* 154
nor shunn'd a soldier's *d*, *Princess, Pro.* 38
I would make it *d* For any male thing " 151
As blank as *d* in marble; " *i* 177
LET NO MAN ENTER IN ON PAIN OF *D*? " *ii* 195
I give thee to *d* My brother! " 307
To give three gallant gentlemen to *d*.' " 335
I spoke of war to come and many *d's*, " *iii* 150
you will shock him ev'n to *d*, " 212
act Of immolation, any phase of *d*, " 285
Sun Grew broader toward his *d* and fell, " 364
'Dear as remember'd kisses after *d*, " *iv* 54
O *D* in Life, the days that are no more.' " 58
Melissa clamour'd 'Flee the *d*;' " 166
On all sides, clamouring etiquette to *d*, " *v* 17
those that mourn half-shrouded over *d* " 74
record of her wrongs, And crush'd to *d*: " 144
dash'd with *d* He reddens what he kisses: " 164
and had not shunn'd the *d*, " 178
sware to combat for my claim till *d*. " 360
trust that there is no one hurt to *d*, " *vi* 242
think that you might mix his draught with *d*, " 277
well-nigh close to *d* For weakness: " *vii* 119
Leapt fiery Passion from the brinks of *d*; " 156
nor cares to walk With *D* and Morning " 204
Or pines in sad experience worse than *d*, " 315
All in the valley of *D* Rode the six hundred. *Light Brigade* 3
Into the valley of *D* Rode the six hundred. (repeat) " 7, 16
Into the jaws of *D*, " 24
Came thro' the jaws of *D*, " 46
first time, too, that ever I thought of *d*. *Grandmother* 61
'*d* is sure To those that stay and those that roam, *Sailor Boy* 13
My father raves of *d* and wreck, " 19
Far worse than any *d* to me.' " 24
The wages of sin is *d*: *Wages* 6
Thou madest *D*; and lo, thy foot *In Mem., Pro.* 7
To dance with *d*, to beat the ground, " *i* 12
O Priestess in the vaults of *D*, " *iii* 2
No hint of *d* in all his frame, " *xiv* 18
Cold in that atmosphere of *D*, " *xx* 14
If *D* were seen At first as *D*, " *xxxv* 18
To that vague fear implied in *d*; " *xli* 14
If Sleep and *D* be truly one, " *xliii* 1
(If *D* so taste Lethean springs), " *xliv* 10
Beyond the second birth of *D*. " *xlv* 16
There must be wisdom with great *D*: " *li* 11
I bring to life, I bring to *d*: " *lvi* 6
Sleep, *D's* twin-brother, times my breath; Sleep, *D's* twin-brother, knows not *D*, " *lxviii* 2
Sleep, kinsman thou to *d* and trance " *lxxi* 1
I curse not nature, no, nor *d*; " *lxxiii* 7
knowing *D* has made His darkness beautiful " *lxxiv* 11
That holy *D* ere Arthur died " *lxxx* 2
But *D* returns an answer sweet: " *lxxxi* 9
I wage not any feud with *D* " *lxxxii* 1
Nor blame I *D*, because he bare " 9
For this alone on *D* I wreak " 13
till Doubt and *D*, Ill brethren, " *lxxxvi* 11
sire would make Confusion worse than *d*, " *xc* 19
shocks of Chance—The blows of *D*. " *xcv* 43
Mixt their dim lights, like life and *d*, " 63
gleams On Lethe in the eyes of *D*. " *xcviii* 8
And unto myriads more, of *d*. " *xcix* 16
As one would sing the *d* of war, " *ciii* 33
Or dive below the wells of *D*? " *cviii* 8
on the depths of *d* there swims The reflex " 11
She cannot fight the fear of *d*. " *cxiv* 10
Like Paul with beasts, I fought with *D*; " *cxx* 4
I slip the thoughts of life and *d*; " *cxxii* 16
Unpalsied when he met with *D*, " *cxxviii* 2
whatever is ask'd her, answers '*D*.' *Maud I i* 4
To the *d*, for their native land. " *v* 11

Death (*continued*) Singing of *D*, and of Honour that cannot die, *Maud I v* 16
thought like a fool of the sleep of *d*. „ *xiv* 38
for sullen-seeming *D* may give More life „ *I xviii* 46
Spice his fair banquet with the dust of *d*? „ 56
The dusky strand of *D* inwoven here „ 60
And given false *d* her hand, „ 68
mine by a right, from birth till *d*. „ *xix* 42
Far into the North, and battle, and seas of *d*. „ *III vi* 37
chance what will, I trust thee to the *d*.' *Com. of Arthur* 134
born the son of Gorloïs, after *d*, „ 240
thro' the strait and dreadful pass of *d*, „ 395
chance what will, I love thee to the *d*!' „ 468
'King and my lord, I love thee to the *d*!' „ 470
And Modred's blank as *d*; and Arthur cried *Gareth and L.* 417
names himself the Night and oftener *D* „ 638
Despite of Day and Night and *D* and Hell.' „ 887
white breast-bone, and barren ribs of *D*, „ 1382
doom'd to be the bride of Night and *D*; „ 1396
D's dark war-horse bounded forward with him. „ 1401
saw That *D* was cast to ground, and slowly rose. „ 1403
revel and song, made merry over *D*, „ 1423
maybe pierced to *d* before mine eyes, *Marr. of Geraint* 104
doubtless he would put me soon to *d*, „ 463
Long for my life, or hunger for my *d*, *Geraint and E.* 81
Leave me to-night: I am weary to the *d*.' „ 358
So pains him that he sickens nigh to *d*; „ 499
were himself nigh wounded to the *d*.' „ 919
he crown'd A happy life with a fair *d*, „ 968
His passion half had gauntleted to *d*, *Balin and Balan* 220
Balin's horse Was wearied to the *d*, „ 561
To save thy life, have brought thee to thy *d*. „ 600
bore me there, for born from *d* was I *Merlin and V.* 44
an enemy that has left *D* in the living waters, „ 148
D in all life and lying in all love, „ 194
Fame that follows *d* is nothing to us; „ 464
Flash'd the bare-grinning skeleton of *d*! „ 847
little daughter fled From bonds or *d*, *Lancelot and E.* 277
Prize me no prizes, for my prize is *d*! „ 506
crying that his prize is *d*.' „ 531
had died the *d* In any knightly fashion „ 870
'Him or *d*,' she mutter'd, '*d* or him,' Again and like a burthen, 'Him or *d*.' „ 902
Ev'n to the *d*,' as tho' ye were my blood, „ 960
D, like a friend's voice from a distant field „ 999
call'd her song 'The Song of Love and *D*,' „ 1005
sweet is *d* who puts an end to pain: „ 1008
'Love, art thou sweet? then bitter *d* must be: 'Love, thou art bitter; sweet is *d* to me. O Love, if *d* be sweeter, let me die. „ 1010
Sweet *d*, that seems to make us loveless clay, „ 1014
I needs must follow *d*, who calls for me; „ 1017
Phantom of the house That ever shrieks before a *d*,' „ 1023
I shall guard it even in *d*. „ 1115
her *d* Was rather in the fantasy than the blood. „ 1131
bruise and blow, With *d's* of others, „ 1166
therefore my true love has been my *d*. „ 1277
for this most gentle maiden's *d* „ 1291
as would have help'd her from her *d*.' „ 1311
after heaven, on our dull side of *d*, „ 1382
And I was thirsty even unto *d*; *Holy Grail* 377
storm Round us and *d*; „ 492
rotten with a hundred years of *d*, „ 496
Your sleep is *d*,' and drew the sword, *Pelleas and E.* 447
But here will I disedge it by thy *d*,' „ 578
this honour after *d*, Following thy will! *Last Tournament* 34
heart in one full shock With Tristram ev'n to *d*: „ 181
And stings itself to everlasting *d*, „ 452
hates thee, as I him—ev'n to the *d*. „ 518
and I will love thee to the *d*, „ 720
To help it from the *d* that cannot die, *Guinevere* 66
she thought 'He spies a field of *d*; „ 134
many a mystic lay of life and *d* „ 281
Fear not: thou shalt be guarded till my *d*. „ 448
The doom of treason and the flaming *d*, „ 538

Death (*continued*) strike him dead, and meet myself *D*, *Guinevere* 576
My God, thou hast forgotten me in my *d*: *Pass. of Arthur* 27
Light was Gawain in life, and light in *d* Is Gawain, „ 56
strikes them dead is as my *d* to me. „ 74
or thro' *d* Or deathlike swoon, „ 119
fluting a wild carol ere her *d*, „ 435
govern a whole life from birth to *d*, *Lover's Tale i* 76
Time and Grief did beckon unto *D*, And *D* drew nigh „ 110
wakeful portress, and didst parle with *D*,— „ 113
So *D* gave back, and would no further come. „ 115
and his spirit From bitterness of *d*. „ 143
Is to me daily life and daily *d*: „ 169
I died then, I had not known the *d*; „ 496
from whose left hand floweth The Shadow of *D*, „ 499
Which seeming for the moment due to *d*, „ 508
But breathing hard at the approach of *D*, „ 585
Smit with exceeding sorrow unto *D*. „ 601
from a dismal dream of my own *d*, „ 748
may *d* Awake them with heaven's music „ 760
So Love, arraign'd to judgment and to *d*, „ 785
vestibules To caves and shows of *D*: „ *ii* 126
A beauty which is *d*; „ 190
down-hung The jaws of *D*: „ 205
till helpless *d* And silence made him bold— „ *iv* 72
He reverenced his dear lady even in *d*; „ 74
'not even *d* Can chill you all at once:' „ 76
He falling sick, and seeming close on *d*, „ 258
For some new *d* than for a life renew'd; „ 374
which might Be *d* to one: *Sisters (E. and E.)* 35
And all her sweet self-sacrifice and *d*. „ 255
D from their rifle-bullets, and *d* from their cannon-balls, *D* in our innermost chamber, and *d* at our slight barricade, *D* while we stood with the musket, and *d* while we stoopt to the spade, *D* to the dying, and wounds to the wounded, *Def. of Lucknow* 14
D—for their spies were among us, „ 19
D at the glimpse of a finger „ 23
D from the heights of the mosque and the palace, and *d* in the ground! „ 24
Ever the *d* with its traitorous *d* „ 79
Lord of life Be by me in my *d*. *Sir J. Oldcastle* 174
I woke, and thought—*d*—I shall die— *Columbus* 87
That I am loyal to him till the *d*, „ 227
it was all of it as quiet as *d*, *V. of Maeldune* 20
I bad them remember my father's *d*, „ 70
From *d* to *d* thro' life and life, *De Prof., Two G.* 52
In seas of *D* and sunless gulfs of Doubt. *Pref. Son. 19th Cent.* 14
Fell the shipcrews Doom'd to the *d*. *Batt. of Brunanburh* 23
Drew to this island: Doom'd to the *d*, „ 51
storm and sin and *d* to the ancient fold, *The Wreck* 2
He helpt me with *d*, and he heal'd me with sorrow „ 58
'as in truest Love no *D*.' „ 80
'The wages of sin is *d*,' „ 93
Dead to the *d* beside me, „ 113
a scrap, clipt out of the '*d's*' in a paper, fell. „ 146
Glared on our way toward *d*, *Despair* 11
I am frighted at life not *d*.' „ 14
With songs in praise of *d*, *Ancient Sage* 209
on Edwin's ship, with Edwin, ev'n in *d*, *The Flight* 46
dhrame of a married man, *d* alive, is a mortial sin.' *Tomorrow* 51
I myself so close on *d*, and *d* *Locksley H., Sixty* 4
While she vows 'till *d* shall part us,' „ 24
that crowning barren *D* as lord of all, „ 61
Beautiful was *d* in him, who saw the *d*, „ 63
D and Silence hold their own. „ 237
That on dumb *d* had thriven; *Dead Prophet* 26
She tore the Prophet after *d*, „ 77
with all its pains, and griefs, and *d's*, *To Prin. Beatrice* 2
Gods against the fear Of *D* and Hell; *Demeter and P.* 142
thou that hast from men, As Queen of *D*, „ 143
D for the right cause, *d* for the wrong cause, *Vastness* 8
Beyond the common date of *d*— *The Ring* 108
theft were *d* or madness to the thief, „ 204
drew the ring From his dead finger, wore it till her *d*, „ 218
to laugh at love in *d*! „ 231

Death (*continued*) *D* and marriage, *D* and marriage! *Forlorn* 67
To share his living *d* with him, *Happy* 8
D will freeze the supplest limbs— „ 46
Too early blinded by the kiss of *d*— *Romney's R.* 103
beyond the doors of *d* Far-far-away? *Far-far-away* 11
My life and *d* are in thy hand. *Death of Œnone* 40
A silence follow'd as of *d*, and then A hiss *St. Telemachus* 65
And then once more a silence as of *d*. „ 69
Baths, the Forum gabbled of his *d*, „ 74
But *D* had ears and eyes; *Akbar's Dream* 187
I could make Sleep *D*, if I would— *Bandit's Death* 32
sod Draw from my *d* Thy living flower *Doubt and Prayer* 6
Wait till *D* has flung them open, *Faith* 7
Has vanish'd in the shadow cast by *D*. *D. of the Duke of C.* 3
face of *D* is toward the Sun of Life, „ 12
Deathbed Kind? but the *d* desire Spurn'd *Maud I xix* 77
as by some one *d* after wail Of suffering, *Pass. of Arthur* 118
I hear a *d-b* Angel whisper 'Hope.' *Romney's R.* 148
Death-blow *d-b* struck the dateless doom of kings, *Lucretius* 236
Death-day her birthday, and that day His *d-d*, *The Ring* 213
birthday, *d-d*, and betrothal ring, „ 276
Your birthday was her *d-d*. „ 301
Death-drowsing while he spoke Closed his *d-d* eyes, *Balin and Balan* 631
Death-dumb in a *d-d* autumn-dripping gloom, *Last Tournament* 756
Deathful-grinning *d-g* mouths of the fortress, *Maud III vi* 52
Death-hymn wild swan's *d-h* took the soul *Dying Swan* 21
Death-in-life Lay lingering out a five-years' *d-i-l*. *Enoch Arden* 565
and palsy, *d-i-l*, And wretched age— *Lucretius* 154
Deathless (*See also* **Seeming-deathless**) That Gods there are, and *d*. „ 121
magic cirque of memory, Invisible but *d*, *Lover's Tale ii* 160
Deathlike Luminous, gemlike, ghostlike, *d*, *Maud I iii* 8
Deathly-pale *d-p* Stood grasping what was nearest, *Lancelot and E.* 965
Death-pale *D-p*, for lack of gentle maiden's aid. „ 765
Deathruckle Vows that will last to the last *d*, *Vastness* 26
Death-scaffold seem'd to hear Her own *d-s* raising, *Enoch Arden* 175
Death's-head not a *d-h* at the wine.' *Princess iv* 87
Deathsong Some *d* for the Ghouls To make *Ancient Sage* 17
Death-watch dog howl, mother, or the *d-w* beat, *May Queen, Con.* 21
O the *d* beating! *Forlorn* 24
Death-white beheld The *d-w* curtain drawn; *Maud I xiv* 34
Knew that the *d-w* curtain meant but sleep, „ 37
Debased right arm *d* The throne of Persia, *Alexander* 1
Debate beat the floor; Where once we held *d*, *In Mem. lxxxvii* 21
Debated while the King *d* with himself If Arthur *Com. of Arthur* 238
Debating Leodogran in heart *D*— „ 141
D his command of silence given, *Geraint and E.* 366
Debt Love the gift is Love the *d*. *Miller's D.* 207
Deep, indeed, Their *d* of thanks to her *Princess ii* 141
my *d* to him, This nightmare weight of gratitude, „ *vi* 299
We have a voice, with which to pay the *d* *Ode on Well.* 156
coom'd to the parish wi' lots o' Varsity *d*, *N. Farmer, N. S.* 29
Vext with lawyers and harass'd with *d*: *Maud I xix* 22
I feel I shall owe you a *d*, „ 87
That I owe this *d* to you „ 90
the whole dear *d* of all you are. *Geraint and E.* 319
Fur I finds es I be that i' *d*, *Village Wife* 65
easy es leäves their *d's* to be paäid. „ 94
This father pays his *d* with me, *The Flight* 20
how dear a *d* We owed you, and are owing yet *To Marq. of Dufferin* 18
that ample woodland whisper'd '*d*,' The brook that feeds this lakelet murmur'd '*d*,' *The Ring* 170
Debtor *d's* for our lives to you, *Princess ii* 355
And the man said 'Am I your *d*?' *By an Evolution.* 2
Decad Thro' sunny *d's* new and strange, *Day-Dm., L'Envoi* 22
Averill was a *d* and a half his elder, *Aylmer's Field* 82
Old scandals buried now seven *d's* deep „ 442
Decay (s) Upon the general *d* of faith *The Epic* 18
And on one side a castle in *d*, *Marr. of Geraint* 245
worshipt all too well this creature of *d*, *Happy* 45
Decay (verb) The woods *d*, the woods *d* and fall, *Tithonus* 1
Decay'd and learn If his old prowess were in aught *d*; *Lancelot and E.* 584
and the Grail Past, and the beam *d*, *Holy Grail* 122
Decaying Stench of old offal *d*, *Def. of Lucknow* 82
Decease from the Queen's *d* she brought her up. *Princess iii* 86

Decease (*continued*) And chains regret to his *d*, *In Mem. xxix* 3
Deceased Nor will be when our summers have *d*. *Maud I xviii* 14
Deceit weave me a snare Of some coquettish *d*, „ *vi* 26
I *may* be beguiled By some coquettish *d*, „ 90
For then, perhaps, as a child of *d*, „ *xiii* 30
Deceive. *See* **Desave**
Deceived I never will be twice *d*. *The Letters* 30
Meet is it the good King be not *d*. *Balin and Balan* 533
One had *d* her an' left her *First Quarrel* 25
Is it I who have *d* thee or the world? *Columbus* 151
December The gloom of ten *D's*. *Will Water.* 104
Their meetings made *D* June *In Mem. xcvii* 11
Decent *d* not to fail In offices of tenderness, *Ulysses* 40
Decide '*D* not ere you pause. *Princess iii* 156
at once *D's* it, 'sdeath! against my father's will.' „ *v* 298
'*D* it here: why not? „ 310
Decided beardless apple-arbiter *D* fairest. *Lucretius* 92
Decision The intuitive *d* of a bright *Isabel* 13
Kept watch, waiting *d*, made reply. *Œnone* 143
Since, what *d*? if we fail, we fail, *Princess v* 322
Deck (s) *d's* were dense with stately forms *M. d'Arthur* 196
d's were shatter'd, Bullets fell like rain; *The Captain* 45
Over mast and *d* were scatter'd Blood and brains „ 47
Spars were splinter'd; *d's* were broken: „ 49
On the *d's* as they were lying, „ 53
and while he stood on *d* Waving, *Enoch Arden* 243
light Shall glimmer on the dewy *d's*. *In Mem. ix* 12
The man we loved was there on *d*, „ *ciii* 41
I stood on a giant *d* and mix'd *Maud III vi* 34
Bright with a shining people on the *d's*, *Com. of Arthur* 376
Loyal, the dumb old servitor, on *d*, *Lancelot and E.* 1144
on the black *d's* laid her in her bed, „ 1147
all the *d's* were dense with stately forms, *Pass. of Arthur* 364
With her hundred fighters on *d*, *The Revenge* 34
soldiers look'd down from their *d's* „ 37
wound to be drest he had left the *d*, „ 66
he rose upon their *d's*, and he cried: „ 100
he fell upon their *d's*, and he died. „ 104
Ten long sweet summer days upon *d*, *The Wreck* 64
every soul from the *d's* of The Falcon „ 109
that I Stumbled on *d*, half mad. „ 118
I crouch'd upon *d*— „ 120
who saw the death, but kept the *d*, *Locksley H., Sixty* 63
Deck (verb) To *d* thy cradle, Eleänore. *Eleänore* 21
flowers or leaves To *d* the banquet. *In Mem. cvii* 6
wherewithal *d* the boar's head? *Gareth and L.* 1073
d it like the Queen's For richness, *Lancelot and E.* 1118
add my diamonds to her pearls; *D* her with these; „ 1225
D your houses, illuminate All your towns *On Jub. Q. Victoria* 18
Deck'd—Deckt *deck'd* her out For worship without end; *Princess vii* 168
A life that all the Muses *deck'd* *In Mem. lxxxv* 45
and *deckt* in slowly-waning hues. *Gareth and L.* 1195
Array'd and *deck'd* her, as the loveliest, *Marr. of Geraint* 17
for he had *decked* them out As for a solemn sacrifice *Lover's Tale iv* 300
The city *deck'd* herself To meet me, *Columbus* 9
Declare Such as no language may *d*.' *Two Voices* 384
D when last Olivia came *Talking Oak* 99
Had braced my purpose to *d* myself: *Sisters (E. and E.)* 143
Declared *d* that ancient ties Would still *Princess ii* 264
Decline (s) Looks thro' in his sad *d*, *Adeline* 13
Decline (verb) sap dries up: the plant *d's*. *Two Voices* 268
to *d* On a range of lower feelings *Locksley Hall* 43
Whatever way my days *d*, *In Mem. lxxxv* 41
Darken'd watching a mother *d* *Maud I xix* 8
Declined once more like some sick man *d*, *Palace of Art* 155
And thou, as one that once *d*, *In Mem. lxii* 5
Decrease That now dilate, and now *d*, „ *xxviii* 10
Decreased From heat to heat the day *d*, *Mariana in the S.* 78
Decree '*By shaping some august* d, *To the Queen* 33
To mould a mighty state's *d's*, *In Mem. lxiv* 11
Decreed *d* that thou should'st dwell *Demeter and P.* 120
and *d* That Rome no more should wallow *St. Telemachus* 77
I *d* That even the dog was clean, *Akbar's Dream* 52
De-crescent Between the in-crescent and *d-c* moon, *Gareth and L.* 529
Dedicate I *d*, I *d*, I consecrate with tears— *Ded. of Idylls* 3

Dedicate (*continued*) Shut in from Time, and *d* to thee: *Lover's Tale i* 438
Dee Bala lake Fills all the sacred *D*. *Geraint and E.* 930
Deed Fruitful of further thought and *d*, *Two Voices* 144
Blowing a noise of tongues and *d's*, „ 206
a life of shocks, Dangers, and *d's*, *Œnone* 164
'I take possession of man's mind and *d*. *Palace of Art* 209
our great *d's*, as half-forgotten things. *Lotos-Eaters, C. S.* 78
Would serve his kind in *d* and word, *Love thou thy land* 86
Delight our souls with talk of knightly *d's*, *M. d'Arthur* 19
the Powers, who wait On noble *d's*, *Godiva* 72
'They perish'd in their daring *d's*.' *Day-Dm., Arrival* 14
I am yours in word and in *d*. *Lady Clare* 74
Divorce the Feeling from her mate the *D*. *The Brook* 95
Nor *d's* of gift, but gifts of grace *Sea Dreams* 192
'His *d's* yet live, the worst is yet to come. „ 314
and your great *d's* For issue, *Princess iii* 242
Howe'er you babble, great *d's* cannot die; „ 254
on the highest Foam of men's *d's*— „ *v* 320
Bright let it be with its blazon'd *d's*, *Ode on Well.* 56
thine the *d's* to be celebrated, *Boädicea* 41
In loveliness of perfect *d's*, *In Mem. xxxvi* 11
Her secret meaning in her *d's*, „ *lv* 10
What fame is left for human *d's* „ *lxxiii* 11
On songs, and *d's*, and lives, „ *lxxvii* 3
O true in word, and tried in *d*, „ *lxxxv* 5
Perplext in faith, but pure in *d's*, „ *xcvi* 9
Flow thro' our *d's* and make them pure, „ *cxxxi* 4
some good knight had done one noble *d*, *Gareth and L.* 411
And the *d's* sake my knighthood do the *d*, „ 572
My *d's* will speak: it is but for a day.' „ 577
for the *d's* sake have I done the *d*, „ 832
'Say thou thy say, and I will do my *d*. „ 901
said your say; Mine answer was my *d*. „ 1175
far-sounded among men For noble *d's*? *Marr. of Geraint* 428
So grateful is the noise of noble *d's* „ 437
Because I knew my *d's* were known, *Geraint and E.* 858
doubtless, all unearn'd by noble *d's*. *Balin and Balan* 471
love of God and men And noble *d's*, *Merlin and V.* 413
And each incited each to noble *d's*. „ 414
the great *d's* Of Lancelot, and his prowess *Lancelot and E.* 81
do and almost overdo the *d's* Of Lancelot; „ 469
some brave *d* seem'd to be done in vain, *Holy Grail* 274
This chance of noble *d's* will come and go „ 318
every evil *d* I ever did, Awoke and cried, „ 373
honour and all noble *d's* Flash'd, *Pelleas and E.* 278
flower Waits to be solid fruit of golden *d's*, *Last Tournament* 100
uprear'd By noble *d's* at one with noble vows, „ 123
Did mightier *d's* than elsewise he had done, „ 680
here and there a *d* Of prowess done *Guinevere* 458
And worship her by years of noble *d's*, „ 476
miss to hear high talk of noble *d's* „ 499
she, for her good *d's* and her pure life, „ 693
and in the mist Was many a noble *d*, *Pass. of Arthur* 105
Delight our souls with talk of knightly *d's*, „ 187
breathless body of her good *d's* past. *Lover's Tale i* 217
Love and Longing dress thy *d's* in light, *Ded. Poem Prin. Alice* 9
this ballad of the *d's* Of England, „ 20
Virtue must shape itself in *d*, *Tiresias* 86
light upon the ways of men As one great *d*. „ 162
crown with song The warrior's noble *d*— *Epilogue* 37
For so the *d* endures; „ 39
And *d* and song alike are swept Away, „ 67
nation's heart, Is in itself a *d*.' „ 82
His dream became a *d* that woke the world, *St. Telemachus* 70
prayers, That have no successor in *d*, *Akbar's Dream* 10
By *d's* a light to men? „ 111
Deem who *d* him not, Or will not *d* him, *Gareth and L.* 120
And *d's* it carrion of some woodland thing, „ 748
But *d* not I accept thee aught the more, „ 839
who *d* this maid Might wear as fair a jewel *Lancelot and E.* 239
d this prize of ours is rashly given: „ 541
damsel, for I *d* you know full well „ 689
I *d* As of the visions that he told— *Lover's Tale iv* 22
If I should *d* it over nice— *Tiresias* 191
And *d* me grateful, and farewell! *The Wanderer* 16
Deem'd she *d* no mist of earth could dull *Ode to Memory* 38
well had *d* he felt the tale Less than the teller: *Enoch Arden* 711
Things in an Aylmer *d* impossible, *Aylmer's Field* 305
the peace, that I *d* no peace, is over *Maud III vi* 50
Smile at him, as he *d*, presumptuously: *Balin and Balan* 222
wherein she *d* she look'd her best, *Lancelot and E.* 907
they *d* her death Was rather in the fantasy „ 1131
wellnigh *d* His wish by hers was echo'd; *Pelleas and E.* 120
I loved you and I *d* you beautiful, „ 297
I *d* him fool? yea so? „ 309
She *d* I wore a brother's mind: *Lover's Tale i* 740
Deeming Vivien, *d* Merlin overborne By instance, *Merlin and V.* 800
D our courtesy is the truest law, *Lancelot and E.* 712
Deem'st *D* thou that I accept thee *Gareth and L.* 766
Deep (adj. and adv.) (*See also* **Ankle-deep, Breast-deep, Elbow-deep, Fathom-deep, Knee-deep, Love-deep, Mellow-deep, Mid-thigh-deep, Waist-deep**)
Tho' *d* not fathomless, *Ode to Memory* 34
grow so full and *d* In thy large eyes *Eleänore* 85
So full, so *d*, so slow, „ 95
King Arthur: then, because his wound was *d*, *M. d'Arthur* 5
rain, That makes thee broad and *d*! *Talking Oak* 280
And *d* into the dying day *Day-Dm., Depart.* 7
One sabbath *d* and wide— *St. Agnes' Eve* 34
D as Hell I count his error. *The Captain* 3
King Arthur. Then, because his wound was *d*, *Pass. of Arthur* 174
Love lieth *d*: Love dwells not in lip-depths. *Lover's Tale i* 466
I can't dig *d*, I am old— *Rizpah* 56
look you here—the shadows are too *d*, *Sisters (E. and E.)* 103
I heard that voice,—as mellow and *d* As a psalm *The Wreck* 52
Six foot *d* of burial mould Will dull *Romney's R.* 125
thou knowest how *d* a well of love *Akbar's Dream* 170
Deep (s) (*See also* **Forest-deeps**) Below the thunders of the upper *d*; *The Kraken* 1
Until the latter fire shall heat the *d*; „ 13
drove The fragrant, glistening *d's*, *Arabian Nights* 14
Round thee blow, self-pleached *d*, *A Dirge* 29
From his coiled sleeps in the central *d's* *The Mermaid* 24
And drives them to the *d*.' *Palace of Art* 204
The abysmal *d's* of Personality, „ 223
roaring *d's* and fiery sands, *Lotos-Eaters, C. S.* 115
Nine years she wrought it, sitting in the *d's* *M. d'Arthur* 105
He heard the *d* behind him, „ 184
the *d* Moans round with many voices. *Ulysses* 55
Where either haven open'd on the *d's*, *Enoch Arden* 671
Trembled in perilous places o'er a *d*: *Sea Dreams* 11
I from out the boundless outer *d* „ 88
I thought the motion of the boundless *d* „ 91
motion of the great *d* bore me on, „ 111
To the waste *d's* together. „ 238
great black cloud Drag inward from the *d's*, *Princess vii* 37
From barren *d's* to conquer all with love; „ 164
Glimmer away to the lonely *d*, *To F. D. Maurice* 28
But they—they feel the desire of the *d*— *Voice and the P.* 19
The *d* has power on the height, And the height has power on the *d*; „ 21
A *d* below the *d*, „ 33
Which heaves but with the heaving *d*. *In Mem. xi* 20
That stir the spirit's inner *d's*, „ *xlii* 10
A higher height, a deeper *d*. „ *lxiii* 12
and we to draw From *d* to *d*, „ *ciii* 39
cloud That landlike slept along the *d*. „ 56
There rolls the *d* where grew the tree. „ *cxxiii* 1
That tumbled in the Godless *d*; „ *cxxiv* 12
To seek thee on the mystic *d's*, „ *cxxv* 14
Powers of the height, Powers of the *d*, *Maud II ii* 82
by the side of the Black and the Baltic *d*, „ *III vi* 51
high upon the dreary *d's* It seem'd in heaven, *Com. of Arthur* 373
gathering half the *d* And full of voices, „ 380
From the great *d* to the great *d* he goes.' „ 411
in the *d's* whereof a mere, *Gareth and L.* 798
by night to let the boundless *d* Down *Merlin and V.* 113
boat Drave with a sudden wind across the *d's*, „ 201
On some wild down above the windy *d*, „ 658
fell the floods of heaven drowning the *d*. *Holy Grail* 533

Delaying (*continued*) *D* long, delay no more. *In Mem. lxxxiii* 4
O thou, new-year, *d* long, „ 13
Delayingly And yet she held him on *d* *Enoch Arden* 468
Delegate she send her *d* to thrall These fighting hands *Pelleas and E.* 336
Delicacy But could not out of bashful *d*; *Marr. of Geraint* 66
Delicate (*See also* **Fairily-delicate**) Fair speech was his, and *d* of phrase. *Lover's Tale iv* 273
Delicate-handed dilettante, *D-h* priest intone; *Maud I viii* 11
Delicately Most *d* hour by hour He canvass'd *A Character* 19
And Enid took a little *d*, *Geraint and E.* 212
Delicious made the air Of Life *d*, *Gardener's D.* 70
Were not his words *d*, *Edwin Morris* 71
Delicto what's the Latin word ?—*D*: *Walk. to the Mail* 35
Delight (s) triple-mailèd trust, and clear *D*, *Supp. Confessions* 67
So took echo with *d*, (repeat) *The Owl ii* 4
d, Life, anguish, death, immortal love, *Arabian Nights* 72
and feedeth The senses with a still *d* *Margaret* 17
Whose free *d*, from any height of rapid flight, *Rosalind* 3
seeming-bitter From excess of swift *d*. „ 32
And that *d* of frolic flight, „ 47
Falling into a still *d*, *Eleänore* 106
I die with my *d*, before I hear what I would hear „ 140
'Some vague emotion of *d* *Two Voices* 361
My heart, pierced thro' with fierce *d*, *Fatima* 34
'I marvel if my still *d* *Palace of Art* 190
great *d* and shuddering took hold of all my mind, *May Queen, Con.* 35
When she made pause I knew not for *d*; *D. of F. Women* 169
The sole *d* is, sitting still, *The Blackbird* 10
The common mouth, So gross to express *d*, *Gardener's D.* 56
drunk *d* of battle with my peers, *Ulysses* 16
To shape the song for your *d* *Day-Dm., Ep.* 6
and all The chambers emptied of *d*: *In Mem. viii* 8
And was the day of my *d* As pure „ *xxiv* 1
With shower'd largess of *d* In dance „ *xxix* 7
And what *d's* can equal those „ *xlii* 9
Thy converse drew us with *d*, „ *cx* 1
when we meet, *D* a hundredfold accrue, „ *cxvii* 8
Maud the *d* of the village, *Maud I i* 70
and seems But an ashen-gray *d*. „ *vi* 22
echo of something Read with a boy's *d*, „ *vii* 10
and my *D* Had a sudden desire, „ *xiv* 19
darkness must have spread With such *d* as theirs „ *xviii* 26
My bride to be, my evermore *d*, „ 73
Breaking up my dream of *d*. „ *xix* 2
I sorrow after The *d* of early skies; „ *II iv* 25
The *d* of happy laughter, the *d* of low replies. „ 29
a dream, yet it yielded a dear *d* „ *III vi* 15
Guinevere, and in her his one *d*. *Com. of Arthur* 4
He, reddening in extremity of *d*, *Geraint and E.* 219
Inflate themselves with some insane *d*, *Merlin and V.* 834
Sprang to her face and fill'd her with *d*; *Lancelot and E.* 377
shrilling, 'Hollow, hollow all *d*! *Pass. of Arthur* 33
And hollow, hollow, hollow all *d*.' „ 37
She took the body of my past *d*, *Lover's Tale i* 681
without hope, without any *d* In anything *Despair* 7
Delight (verb) in her web she still *d's* To weave *L. of Shalott ii* 28
D our souls with talk of knightly deeds, *M. d'Arthur* 19
how the sun *d's* To glance and shift about *Lucretius* 188
nor deals in that Which men *d* in, *Princess iii* 216
D myself with gossip and old wives, *Holy Grail* 553
D our souls with talk of knightly deeds, *Pass. of Arthur* 187
and *d* thyself To make it wholly thine *Lover's Tale i* 13
never colt would more *d* To roll himself *Romney's R.* 13
Delighted *D* with the freshness and the sound. *Edwin Morris* 99
I am all as well *d*, *Maud I xx* 40
Delighteth nightingale *d* to prolong Her low preamble *Palace of Art* 173
Delirium I would catch Her hand in wild *d*, *Princess vii* 93
Delius the Sun, Apollo, *D*, or of older use *Lucretius* 125
Deliver *D* not the tasks of might To weakness, *Love thou thy land* 13
D me the blessed sacrament; *St. S. Stylites* 218
Thy tribute wave *d*: *A Farewell* 2
Ignorance *D's* brawling judgments, *Merlin and V.* 665
Rise and take This diamond, and *d* it, *Lancelot and E.* 546
Deliver'd *D* at a secret postern-gate *Com. of Arthur* 213
Deliverer and call'd them dear *d's*, *Princess vi* 92
Delivering *D*, that to me, by common voice *Œnone* 84
D seal'd dispatches which the Head *Princess iv* 379
D, that his lord, the vassal king, *Gareth and L.* 391
So she, *d* it to Arthur, said, *Last Tournament* 30
Dell Out of the live-green heart of the *d's* *Sea-Fairies* 12
We would call aloud in the dreamy *d's*, *The Merman* 25
diamond-ledges that jut from the *d's*; *The Mermaid* 40
The furzy prickle fire the *d's*, *Two Voices* 71
all night long, in falling thro' the *d*, *D. of F. Women* 183
the splinter'd crags that wall the *d* „ 187
The little *d's* of cowslip, fairy palms, *Aylmer's Field* 91
How richly down the rocky *d* *The Daisy* 9
And snowy *d's* in a golden air. „ 68
moved in the hollows under the *d's*, *V. of Maeldune* 107
What sound was dearest in his native *d's*? *Far-far-away* 4
were alone in the *d* at the close of the day. *Bandit's Death* 19
rang out all down thro' the *d*, „ 36
Deluge some new *d* from a thousand hills *If I were loved* 12
Pour with such sudden *d's* of light *Lover's Tale i* 315
or a *d* of cataract skies, *Def. of Lucknow* 81
In the common *d* drowning old political common-sense! *Locksley H., Sixty* 250
Delver careful robins eye the *d's* toil, *Marr. of Geraint* 774
careful robins eye the *d's* toil; *Geraint and E.* 431
Demand (s) *To make* d *of modern rhyme* *To the Queen* 11
obedience make *d* Of whom ye gave me to, *Gareth and L.* 558
Demand (verb) if a king *d* An act unprofitable, *M. d'Arthur* 95
The sense of human will *d's* *In Mem. lxxxv* 39
D not thou a marriage lay; „ *Con.* 2
thy love to me, Thy mother,—I *d*.' *Gareth and L.* 147
sent Her maiden to *d* it of the dwarf; *Marr. of Geraint* 193
Sent her own maiden to *d* the name, „ 411
Garlon, mine heir, Of him *d* it,' *Balin and Balan* 118
if a king *d* An act unprofitable, *Pass. of Arthur* 263
Demanded she *d* who we were, And why we came? *Princess iii* 135
And then, *d* if her mother knew, „ *iv* 233
Was this *d*—if he yearn'd To hear *In Mem. xxxi* 3
when the Queen *d* as by chance *Merlin and V.* 128
And when the King *d* how she knew, *Lancelot and E.* 575
Demanding And then to me *d* why? *The Epic* 29
D, so to bring relief *In Mem. lxxxv* 6
Demigod Elysian lawns, Where paced the *D's* of old, *Princess iii* 343
Democrat what care I, Aristocrat, *d*, *Maud I x* 65
Demon Pallas from the brain Of *D's*? *In Mem. cxiv* 13
some *d* in the woods Was once a man, *Balin and Balan* 124
who will hunt for me This *d* of the woods?' „ 137
Whereout the *D* issued up from Hell. „ 317
Celtic Demos rose a *D*, *Locksley H., Sixty* 90
A *d* vext me, *Merlin and the G.* 29
and drove the *d* from Hawa-i-ee. *Kapiolani* 33
Demon-god is the *d-g* Wroth at his fall?' *St. Telemachus* 19
Demonstration rounded under female hands With flawless *d*: *Princess ii* 373
Demos Celtic *D* rose a Demon, *Locksley H., Sixty* 90
D end in working its own doom. „ 114
Demur He yielded, wroth and red, with fierce *d*: *Princess v* 358
Demure The little maiden walk'd *d*, *Two Voices* 419
Den We heard the lion roaring from his *d*; *D. of F. Women* 222
'Trooping from their mouldy *d's* *Vision of Sin* 171
and the children, housed In her foul *d*, *Com. of Arthur* 29
climb'd from the *d's* in the levels below, *The Dawn* 17
Denial Or by *d* flush her babbling wells *Princess v* 334
Who will not *hear d*, vain and rude *Lover's Tale i* 628
Denied He oft *d* his heart his dearest wish, *Enoch Arden* 336
'Come with us Father Philip' he *d*; „ 368
at first Was silent; closer prest, *d* it not, *Princess iv* 232
she affirm'd not, or *d*: „ 234
'ye never yet *D* my fancies— *Lancelot and E.* 1112
d to him, Who finds the Saviour *Sir J. Oldcastle* 114
Denouncing like a Ghost's *D* judgment, *Guinevere* 421
Dense the decks were *d* with stately forms *M. d'Arthur* 196
folds as *d* as those Which hid the Holiest *Aylmer's Field* 771
race thro' many a mile Of *d* and open, *Balin and Balan* 424
But that these eyes of men are *d* and dim, *Pass. of Arthur* 19
all the decks were *d* with stately forms, „ 364

Deny What! *d* it now? Nay, draw, *St. S. Stylites* 206
and cry For that which all *d* them— *Will Water.* 46
And would if ask'd *d* it. *Enoch Arden* 44
To hold your own, *d* not hers to her *Princess vi* 178
father, tender and true, *D* me not,' *Lancelot and E.* 1111
you will not *d* my sultry throat *Romney's R.* 22
Denying *D* not these weather-beaten limbs *St. S. Stylites* 19
Denyingly How hard you look and how *d*! *Merlin and V.* 338
Depart He craved a fair permission to *d*, *Marr. of Geraint* 40
friend, too old to be so young, *d*, *Balin and Balan* 17
and still *d* From death to death *De Prof., Two G.* 51
Departed a silent cousin stole Upon us and *d*: *Edwin Morris* 116
She watch'd it, and *d* weeping for him; *Enoch Arden* 246
James *d* vext with him and her.' *The Brook* 110
then *d*, hot in haste to join Their luckier mates, *Geraint and E.* 574
So these *d*. Early, one fair dawn, *Balin and Balan* 20
And thence *d* every one his way. *Holy Grail* 360
Departest then before thine answer given *D*, *Tithonus* 45
Departing With frequent smile and nod *d* *Marr. of Geraint* 515
Deplore Where shall we lay the man whom we *d*? *Ode on Well.* 8
Such was he whom we *d*. " 40
Still mine, that cannot but *d*, *In Mem. lxxxv* 109
Depress'd With lips *d* as he were meek, *A Character* 25
Depth (*See also* **Love-depths**) The springs of life, the *d's* of awe, *Two Voices* 140
Tears from the *d* of some divine despair *Princess iv* 40
on the *d's* of death there swims The reflex *In Mem. cviii* 11
You cannot find their *d*; for they go back, *Lover's Tale i* 80
tho' every turn and *d* Between is clearer " 148
dash'd himself Into the dizzy *d* below. " 381
dwelling on the light and *d* of thine, " 492
There on the *d* of an unfathom'd woe " 746
Derive *D's* it not from what we have *In Mem. lv* 3
Derk (dark) thowt it wur Charlie's ghoäst i' the *d*, *Village Wife* 82
Derken'd (darkened) —they niver *d* my door. " 60
Desave (deceive) an' she didn't intind to *d*, *Tomorrow* 59
Descend *d*, and proffer these The brethren *Princess vi* 70
D below the golden hills *In Mem. lxxxiv* 28
D, and touch, and enter; " *xciii* 13
Why then my scorn might well *d* On you " *cxxviii* 21
Would the happy spirit *d*, *Maud II iv* 81
fire of God *D's* upon thee in the battle-field: *Com. of Arthur* 129
nay, the King's—*D* into the city:' *Gareth and L.* 540
The Holy Grail, *d* upon the shrine: *Holy Grail* 465
Descendant On him their last *d*, *Aylmer's Field* 834
Descended (*See also* **Heaven-descended**) tree by tree, The country-side *d*; *Amphion* 52
Then all *d* to the port, *Enoch Arden* 446
D to the court that lay three parts *Princess iii* 20
As we *d* following Hope, *In Mem. xxii* 11
his dream was changed, the haze *D*, *Com. of Arthur* 442
The Sun of May *d* on their King, " 462
the stream *D*, and the Sun was wash'd away. *Gareth and L.* 1047
robed them in her ancient suit again, And so *d*. *Marr. of Geraint* 771
finds himself *d* from the Saint Arimathæan Joseph; *Balin and Balan* 101
D, and disjointed it at a blow: " 296
He rose, *d*, met The scorner in the castle court, " 386
setting, when Even *d*, the very sunset *V. of Maeldune* 66
and whereout The cloud *d*. *Ancient Sage* 14
beheld The Life that had *d* re-arise, *Demeter and P.* 30
Descending angels rising and *d* met *Palace of Art* 143
d they were ware That all the decks *M. d'Arthur* 195
Once she lean'd on me, *D*; *Princess iv* 27
D, burst the great bronze valves, " *vi* 75
the day, *D*, struck athwart the hall, " 364
Phantom sound of blows *d*, *Boädicea* 25
D thro' the dismal night— *Com. of Arthur* 371
D in the glory of the seas— " 400
And then *d* met them at the gates, *Marr. of Geraint* 833
d they were ware That all the decks *Pass. of Arthur* 363
D from the point and standing both, *Lover's Tale i* 411
some, *d* from the sacred peak Of hoar *Pref. Son. 19th Cent.* 9
Self-darken'd in the sky, *d* slow! *Prog. of Spring* 28
Descent Smile at the claims of long *d*. *L. C. V. de Vere* 52

Descent (*continued*) She might by a true *d* be untrue; *Maud I xiii* 31
Fierce in the strength of far *d*, *Lover's Tale i* 382
farm can teach us there is something in *d*. *Locksley H., Sixty* 26
Descried wall Of purple cliffs, aloof *d*: *Ode to Memory* 54
Descry I could *d* The stern black-bearded kings *D. of F. Women* 110
Desenzano Row us out from *D*, *Frater Ave, etc.* 1
Desert (merit) *Royal grace To one of less* d *allows*, *To the Queen* 6
bowing at their own *d's*: *The Brook* 128
And partly conscious of my own *d's*, *Princess iv* 305
Desert (waste) why dare Paths in the *d*? *Supp. Confessions* 79
Of that long *d* to the south. *Fatima* 14
Which makes a *d* in the mind, *In Mem. lxvi* 6
every blazing *d* till'd, *Locksley H., Sixty* 168
science making toward Thy Perfectness Are blinding *d* sand; *Akbar's Dream* 30
the Star that lights a *d* pathway, *Locksley H., Sixty* 275
Deserve *d* That we this night should pluck *Princess iv* 413
what might that man not *d* of me, " *v* 104
Deserved Since we *d* the name of friends, *In Mem. lxv* 9
Design wherein were wrought Two grand *d's*; *Princess vii* 122
the vast *d's* Of his labour'd rampart-lines, *Ode on Well.* 104
giant aisles, Rich in model and *d*; *Ode Inter. Exhib.* 13
A miracle of *d*! *Maud II ii* 8
learnt and warn'd me of their fierce *d* *Lancelot and E.* 274
found The new *d* wherein they lost themselves, " 441
broke The vast *d* and purpose of the King. *Guinevere* 670
Design'd was there Not less than truth *d*. *Palace of Art* 92
Not less than life, *d*. " 128
Desire (s) oh, haste, Visit my low *d*! *Ode to Memory* 4
flow'd upon the soul in many dreams Of high *d*. *The Poet* 32
'Which did accomplish their *d*, *Two Voices* 217
To yield consent to my *d*: *Miller's D.* 138
The skies stoop down in their *d*; *Fatima* 32
my *d* is but to pass to Him that died for me. *May Queen, Con.* 20
things have ceased to be, with my *d* of life. " 48
Strength came to me that equall'd my *d*. *D. of F. Women* 230
vague *d's*, like fitful blasts of balm *Gardener's D.* 68
to say That my *d*, like all strongest hopes, " 237
this gray spirit yearning in *d* To follow *Ulysses* 30
The bird that pipes his lone *d* *You might have won* 31
thro' the smoke The blight of low *d's*— *Aylmer's Field* 673
thro' their own *d* accomplish'd, " 776
That lent my knee *d* to kneel, *Princess iii* 193
fail so far In high *d*, they know not, " 280
And every hoof a knell to my *d's*, " *iv* 174
Melt into stars for the land's *d*! *W. to Alexandra* 21
welcome her, welcome the land's *d*, " 25
But they—they feel the *d* of the deep— *Voice and the P.* 19
sparrow and throstle, and have your *d*! *Window, Ay* 14
That thou should'st fail from thy *d*, *In Mem. iv* 6
That not a moth with vain *d* Is shrivell'd " *liv* 10
The centre of a world's *d*; " *lxiv* 16
If any vague *d* should rise, " *lxxx* 1
I seem to meet their least *d*, " *lxxxiv* 17
born of love, the vague *d* That spurs " *cx* 19
Submitting all things to *d*. " *cxiv* 8
might ensue *D* of nearness doubly sweet; " *cxvii* 6
Dear friend, far off, my lost *d*, " *cxxix* 1
and my Delight Had a sudden *d*, *Maud I xiv* 20
A *d* that awoke in the heart of the child, " *xix* 48
but the deathbed *d* Spurn'd by this heir " 77
the heart of a people beat with one *d*; " *III vi* 49
d To close with her lord's pleasure; *Geraint and E.* 213
monk and nun, ye scorn the world's *d*, *Balin and Balan* 445
low *d* Not to feel lowest makes them level all; *Merlin and V.* 827
Suddenly flash'd on her a wild *d*, *Lancelot and E.* 357
but you work against your own *d*; " 1096
her hand is hot With ill *d's*, *Last Tournament* 415
when old and gray, And past *d*!' " 628
love me ev'n when old, Gray-hair'd, and past *d*, " 653
Ay, ay, O ay—a star was my *d*, " 733
words And courtliness, and the *d* of fame, *Guinevere* 482
or *d* that her lost child Should earn *Sisters (E. and E.)* 250
O therefore that the unfulfill'd *d*, *Tiresias* 79
sank with the body at times in the sloughs of a low *d*, *By an Evolution.* 18

Desire (s) (*continued*) Till, led by dream and vague *d*, *To Master of B.* 17
creeds be lower than the heart's *d*! *Faith* 5
and woke *D* in me to infuse my tale of love *Princess v* 240
save *my* soul, that is all your *d*: *Rizpah* 77
d to keep So skilled a nurse about you always— *The Ring* 373
Desire (verb) If I were loved, as I *d* to be, *If I were loved* 1
Her open eyes *d* the truth. *Of old sat Freedom* 17
Why should a man *d* in any way To vary *Tithonus* 28
And I *d* to rest. *Come not, when, etc.* 10
not of those that men *d*, Sleek Odalisques, *Princess ii* 76
d you more Than growing boys their manhood; „ *iv* 456
She *d's* no isles of the blest, *Wages* 8
Do we indeed *d* the dead *In Mem. li* 1
not to *d* or admire, if a man could learn *Maud I iv* 41
Rich in the grace all women *d*, „ *x* 13
save yourself *d* it, We will not touch *Marr. of Geraint* 310
Yet, seeing you *d* your child to live, *Lancelot and E.* 1095
now his chair *d's* him here in vain, *Holy Grail* 901
howsoever much they may *d* Silence, *Guinevere* 206
Who could *d* more beauty at a feast?' *Lover's Tale iv* 240
more than one Here sitting who *d's* it. „ 242
Wan, but as pretty as heart can *d*, *In the Child. Hosp.* 40
Desired You are not one to be *d*. *L. C. V. de Vere* 8
long *d* A certain miracle of symmetry, *Gardener's D.* 10
they hated, Had what they *d*: *The Captain* 38
broke the bond which they *d* to break, *Aylmer's Field* 778
—and many men *D* her; one, good lack, no man *d*. *Gareth and L.* 106
needs Must wed that other, whom no man *d*, „ 109
d his name, and sent Her maiden to demand it *Marr. of Geraint* 192
But now *d* the humbling of their best, *Geraint and E.* 637
Desiring *D* what is mingled with past years, *D. of F. Women* 282
D to be join'd with Guinevere; *Com. of Arthur* 77
Wasted and pined, *d* him in vain. *Pelleas and E.* 496
And I, *d* that diviner day, *To Victor Hugo* 12
Desk worn-out clerk Brow-beats his *d* below. *To J. M. K.* 12
'Oh! who would cast and balance at a *d*, *Audley Court* 44
Erect behind a *d* of satin-wood, *Princess ii* 105
To cramp the student at his *d*, *In Mem. cxxviii* 18
Deskwork a dozen years Of dust and *d*: *Sea Dreams* 78
Desolate O spirit and heart made *d*! *Supp. Confessions* 189
Your house is left unto you *d*!' (repeat) *Aylmer's Field* 629, 797
'My house is left unto me *d*.' „ 721
'Our house is left unto us *d*'? „ 737
became Imbecile; his one word was '*d*;' „ 836
D? yes! *D* as that sailor, *The Ring* 306
Desolation Against the *d's* of the world. *Aylmer's Field* 634
No *d* but by sword and fire? „ 748
and her *d* came Upon her, and she wept *Geraint and E.* 518
wind of the Night shrilling out *D* and wrong *The Dreamer* 15
Despair Plagued her with sore *d*. *Palace of Art* 224
And nothing saw, for her *d*, „ 266
must mix with action, lest I wither by *d*. *Locksley Hall* 98
Whisper'd 'Listen to my *d*: *Edward Gray* 22
shake The midriff of *d* with laughter, *Princess i* 201
Or baser courses, children of *d*.' „ *iii* 213
Tears from the depth of some divine *d* „ *iv* 40
hold That it becomes no man to nurse *d*, „ 464
A day of onsets of *d*! *Ode on Well.* 124
If any calm, a calm *d*: *In Mem. xi* 16
Can calm *d* and wild unrest Be tenants „ *xvi* 2
D of Hope, and earth of thee. „ *lxxxiv* 16
and ever wann'd with *d*, *Maud I i* 10
was but a dream, yet it lighten'd my *d* „ *III vi* 18
He half *d's*; so Gareth seem'd to strike *Gareth and L.* 1133
Gray-hair'd, and past desire, and in *d*.' *Last Tournament* 653
Despair'd approach To save the life *d* of, *Enoch Arden* 831
Despise my flesh, which I *d* and hate, *St. S. Stylites* 58
whom the strong sons of the world *d*; *The Brook* 3
But that his pride too much *d's* me: And I myself
sometimes *d* myself; *Marr. of Geraint* 464
Despised *See* **Half-despised**
Despite *D* of Day and Night and Death and Hell.' *Gareth and L.* 887
till he felt, *d* his mail, Strangled, „ 1151
Lancelot who hath come *D* the wound *Lancelot and E.* 566
many a year have done *d* and wrong To one „ 1209

Despite (*continued*) *d* All fast and penance. *Holy Grail* 630
the Gods, *d* of human prayer, Are slower to forgive *Tiresias* 9
D of every Faith and Creed, *To Mary Boyle* 51
Despondence Listless in all *d*,—read; *Aylmer's Field* 534
Despot (*See also* **Dandy-despot**) the fire Where smoulder
their dead *d's*; *Princess v* 380
Nothing of the lawless, of the *D*, *On Jub. Q. Victoria* 12
How can a *d* feel with the Free? *Riflemen form!* 11
Destined opposite Of all my heart had *d* *Guinevere* 492
Destiny No one can be more wise than *d*. *D. of F. Women* 94
hung their heavy hands, The weight of *d*: *Princess iv* 554
Destitute All the lowly, the *d*, *On Jub. Q. Victoria* 31
Destroyed void, Dark, formless, utterly *d*. *Supp. Confessions* 122
And this *d* him; for the wicked broth *Lucretius* 19
That not one life shall be *d*, *In Mem. liv* 6
Destructive was as a boy *D*, *Walk. to the Mail* 82
Detaching *d*, fold by fold, From those still heights *Vision of Sin* 51
Detail Another kind of beauty in *d* *Princess iv* 448
Detention for the rest, Our own *d*, why, „ *v* 215
Determined Thus Enoch in his heart *d* all: *Enoch Arden* 148
Detestable She might not rank with those *d* *Princess v* 457
Dethronement And crownings and *d's*: *To the Queen ii* 45
Develop'd (*See also* **Slow-developed**) Beyond all
grades *d*? *Gardener's D.* 241
Development present The world with some *d*. *Two Voices* 75
And new *d's*, whatever spark Be struck *Prog. of Spring* 94
Device our *d*; wrought to the life; *Princess iii* 303
Were Arthur's wars in weird *d's* done, *Gareth and L.* 225
by some *d* Full cowardly, or by mere unhappiness, „ 767
Or some *d*, hast foully overthrown), „ 998
D and sorcery and unhappiness— „ 1235
All the *d's* blazon'd on the shield *Lancelot and E.* 9
Blank, or at least with some *d* not mine.' „ 194
thread And crimson in the belt a strange *d*; *Holy Grail* 154
Among the strange *d's* of our kings; „ 730
Restrain'd him with all manner of *d*, *Pelleas and E.* 204
Devil (*See also* **Divil, Wood-devil**) What *D* had the
heart to scathe Flowers *Supp. Confessions* 83
That pride, the sin of *d's*, „ 109
A glorious *D*, large in heart and brain, *To ——, With Pal. of Art* 5
And oft some brainless *d* enters in, *Palace of Art* 203
Quoth she, 'The *D* take the goose, *The Goose* 55
Vex'd with a morbid *d* in his blood *Walk. to the Mail* 19
let him go; his *d* goes with him, „ 27
scarce meet For troops of *d's*, *St. S. Stylites* 4
D's pluck'd my sleeve, „ 171
Comfort? comfort scorn'd of *d's*! *Locksley Hall* 75
glaring, by his own stale *d* spurr'd, *Aylmer's Field* 290
True *D's* with no ear, they howl in tune With
nothing but the *D*!' *Sea Dreams* 260
if there be A *d* in man, there is an angel too, „ 278
A *d* rises in my heart, *Sailor Boy* 23
and the *D* may pipe to his own. *Maud I i* 76
thou could'st lay the *D* of these woods *Balin and Balan* 298
Balin cried 'Him, or the viler *d* who plays his part,
To lay that *d* would lay the *D* in me.' 'Nay,'
said the churl, 'our *d* is a truth, „ 300
Or *d* or man Guard thou thine head.' „ 552
Know well that Envy calls you *D's* son: *Merlin and V.* 467
And then did Envy call me *D's* son: „ 497
and stirs the pulse With *d's* leaps, *Guinevere* 522
dogs of Seville, the children of the *d*, *The Revenge* 30
I never turn'd my back upon Don or *d* yet.' „ 31
Was he *d* or man? He was *d* for aught they knew, „ 108
Are we *d's*? are we men? *Locksley H., Sixty* 99
Dance in a fountain of flame with her *d's*, *Kapiolani* 10
only the *D* can tell what he means. *Riflemen form!* 25
Devil-born You tell me, doubt is *D-b*. *In Mem. xcvi* 4
Devil's-dances bagpipes, revelling, *d-d*. *Sir J. Oldcastle* 149
Devised Besought Lavaine to write as she *d* *Lancelot and E.* 1103
Then he wrote The letter she *d*; „ 1109
her lips, Who had *d* the letter, moved again. „ 1288
Devising And moist and dry, *d* long, *Love thou thy land* 38
d their own daughter's death! *Aylmer's Field* 783
urged All the *d's* of their chivalry *Gareth and L.* 1349

Devising (*continued*) But bode his hour, *d* wretchedness. *Last Tournament* 386
Devoir Now weary of my service and *d*, *Lancelot and E.* 118
Devolved *D* his rounded periods. *A Character* 18
Devon A tributary prince of *D*, *Marr. of Geraint* 2
I am Geraint Of *D*— „ 410
'was it for him she wept In *D*?' *Geraint and E.* 398
Men of Bideford in *D*, *The Revenge* 17
Devotion gaze upon him With such a fixt *d*, *Merlin and V.* 183
Devour wolf would steal The children and *d*, *Com. of Arthur* 27
Devour'd bank that is daily *d* by the tide— *Def. of Lucknow* 39
Dew (*See also* **Balm-dew, Night-dew**) Winds creep; *d's* fall chilly: *Leonine Eleg.* 7
to brush the *d* From thine own lily, *Supp. Confessions* 84
Her tears fell with the *d's* at even; Her tears fell ere the *d's* were dried, *Mariana* 13
And *d* is cold upon the ground, *The Owl I* 2
woodbine and eglatere Drip sweeter *d's* *A Dirge* 24
violet woos To his heart the silver *d's*? *Adeline* 32
But ever trembling thro' the *d* *Margaret* 52
Some red heath-flower in the *d*, *Rosalind* 41
Thro' crofts and pastures wet with *d* *Two Voices* 14
And *d's*, that would have fall'n in tears, *Miller's D.* 151
as sunlight drinketh *d*. *Fatima* 21
slowly dropping fragrant *d*. *Œnone* 106
quick-falling *d* Of fruitful kisses, „ 204
fresh-wash'd in coolest *d* The maiden splendours *D. of F. Women* 54
dark wood-walks drench'd in *d*, „ 75
And tho' mine own eyes fill with *d*, *To J. S.* 37
A thought would fill my eyes with happy *d*; *Gardener's D.* 197
my thighs are rotted with the *d*; *St. S. Stylites* 41
I am wet With drenching *d's*, „ 115
And flung him in the *d*. *Talking Oak* 232
and there rain'd a ghastly *d* *Locksley Hall* 123
Dash'd together in blinding *d*: *Vision of Sin* 42
till the gracious *d's* Began to glisten *Princess ii* 316
blossom-fragrant slipt the heavy *d's* „ *v* 243
the *d* Dwelt in her eyes, „ *vii* 135
And on these *d's* that drench the furze, *In Mem. xi* 6
When all our path was fresh with *d*, „ *lxviii* 6
Deep tulips dash'd with fiery *d*, „ *lxxxiii* 11
The sweep of scythe in morning *d*, „ *lxxxix* 18
And back we come at fall of *d*. „ *Con.* 100
still The *d* of their great labour, *Marr. of Geraint* 568
than the sward with drops of *d*, *Geraint and E.* 690
The deer, the *d's*, the fern, the founts, *Last Tournament* 727
The *d* of tears is an unwholesome *d*, *Lover's Tale i* 765
fresh as a codlin wesh'd i' the *d*. *North. Cobbler* 110
my eyes are dim with *d*, *The Flight* 97
and fills The flower with *d*; *Early Spring* 46
scatters on her throat the sparks of *d*, *Prog. of Spring* 58
drank the *d's* and drizzle of the North, „ 81
Dew'd and, *d* with showery drops, *Lotos-Eaters* 17
Dewdrop when two *d's* on the petal shake *Princess vii* 68
And every *d-d* paints a bow, *In Mem. cxxii* 18
glanced with *d* or with gem Like sparkles *Gareth and L.* 929
Dew-fed and in the moon Nightly *d-f*; *Lotos-Eaters, C.S.* 30
Dew-impearled *d-i* winds of dawn have kiss'd, *Ode to Memory* 14
Dewless bearded grass Is dry and *d*. *Miller's D.* 246
Dew-lit And those *d-l* eyes of thine, *Adeline* 47
Dewy-dark lawn was *d-d*, And *d-d* aloft *Œnone* 48
Dewy-fresh The fields between Are *d-f*, *Gardener's D.* 46
Dewy-glooming November dawns and *d-g* downs, *Enoch Arden* 610
Dewy-tassell'd In the green gleam of *d-t* trees: *Princess i* 94
Thro' all the *d-t* wood, *In Mem. lxxxvi* 6
Dewy-warm eyelids, growing *d-w* With kisses *Tithonus* 58
Dexter Eagle rising or, the Sun In *d* chief; *Merlin and V.* 476
Dhrame (dream) like a bit of yisther-day in a *d*— *Tomorrow* 8
An' to *d* of a married man, death alive, „ 51
Dhrink (drink) give me a thrifle to *d* yer health „ 98
Dhrinkin' (drinking) an' I been *D* yer health „ 12
Dhrop (drop) been takin' a *d* o' the crathur' „ 11
Wid a diamond *d* in her eye, „ 28
Dhropt (dropt) an' *d* down dead an the dead. „ 80
Dhrownded (drowned) foun' *D* in black bog-wather „ 62

Diadem Crown'd so long with a *d* *On Jub. Q. Victoria* 7
Diagonal I moved as in a strange *d*, *Princess, Con.* 27
Dial this high *d*, which my sorrow crowns— *St. S. Stylites* 95
Nor take thy *d* for thy deity, *Ancient Sage* 109
Diamond Then fillip'd at the *d* in her ear; *Godiva* 25
With bracelets of the *d* bright: *Day-Dm., Sleep B.* 14
rode to tilt For the great *d* in the *d* jousts, *Lancelot and E.* 31
since a *d* was the prize. „ 33
king, had on a crown Of *d's*, one in front, „ 46
Lancelot won the *d* of the year, „ 68
Now for the central *d* and the last And largest, „ 73
my love is more Than many *d's*' „ 88
yearn'd to make complete The tale of *d's* „ 91
joust as one unknown At Camelot for the *d*, „ 191
maiden dreamt That some one put this *d* in her hand, „ 212
And you shall win this *d*,—as I hear It is a fair large *d*,— „ 227
'A fair large *d*,' added plain Sir Torre, „ 230
Blazed the last *d* of the nameless king. „ 444
'Advance and take thy prize The *d*;' but he answer'd, *D* me No *d's*! „ 504
Rise and take This *d*, and deliver it, „ 546
he took, And gave, the *d*: „ 551
Rode with his *d*, wearied of the quest, „ 616
leave My quest with you; the *d* also: here! „ 691
whether he love or not, A *d* is a *d*. „ 695
kiss'd the hand to which he gave, The *d*, „ 703
I gave the *d*: she will render it; „ 713
with mine own hand give his *d* to him, „ 760
'Ay, ay, the *d*: wit ye well, my child, „ 771
'Your prize the *d* sent you by the King:' „ 821
the tale Of King and Prince, the *d* sent, „ 824
And laid the *d* in his open hand. „ 827
The nine-years-fought-for *d's*: „ 1167
What are these? *D's* for me! „ 1212
pray you, add my *d's* to her pearls; „ 1224
once fair Was richer than these *d's*— „ 1229
flash'd, as it were, *D's* to meet them, „ 1237
Those *d's* that I rescued from the tarn, *Last Tournament* 37
'Io t'amo'—and these *d's*— *The Ring* 70
or to find My Mother's *d's* hidden „ 142
Diamond-drift showering wide Sleet of *d-d* *Vision of Sin* 22
Diamond-ledge *d-l's* that jut from the dells; *The Mermaid* 40
Diamond-plot *d-p's* Of dark and bright. *Arabian Nights* 85
Dian set a wrathful *D's* moon on flame, *Princess vi* 368
Diana Like those who cried *D* great: *Lit. Squabbles* 16
Diaper'd Engarlanded and *d* With inwrought flowers, *Arabian Nights* 148
Dice vows his child . . . . to one cast of the *d*. *The Flight* 26
Dick if thou marries a bad un, I'll leäve the land to *D*— *N. Farmer, N. S.* 58
D, when 'e cooms to be deäd, *Owd Roä* 11
'Ya mun saäve little *D*, an' be sharp about it „ 81
and soa little *D*, good-night. „ 118
Dicky Bedtime, *D*! but waäit till tha 'eärs „ 18
But *D*, the Ghoäst moästlins „ 38
An' I'd cleär forgot, little *D*, „ 64
Dictator The mulberry-faced *D's* orgies *Lucretius* 54
Dido wars, and filial faith, and *D's* pyre; *To Virgil* 4
Die (*See also* **Doy**) The breezes pause and *d*, *Claribel* 2
aweary of beating? And nature *d*? Never, oh! never, nothing will *d*; *Nothing will Die* 7
Nothing will *d*. Nothing will *d*; „ 13
Nothing was born; Nothing will *d*; „ 37
Yet all things must *d*. *All Things will Die* 8
For all things must *d*. (repeat) „ 13, 49
All things must *d*. „ 14
And the old earth must *d*. „ 41
Men say that Thou Didst *d* for me, for such as me, *Supp. Confessions* 3
draws His forehead earthward, and he *d's*. „ 168
he shall rise and on the surface *d*. *The Kraken* 15
A gentler death shall Falsehood *d*, *Clear-headed friend* 16
I dare not *d* and come to thee, *Oriana* 96
D in their hearts for the love of me. *The Mermaid* 30
I *d* with my delight, *Eleänore* 140
No tears of love, but tears that Love can *d*. *Wan Sculptor* 8
Live forgotten and *d* forlorn.' (repeat) *Mariana in the S.* 60, 72

Die (*continued*) I wept, 'Tho' I should *d*, I know *Two Voices* 58
Than once from dread of pain to *d*. „ 105
To flatter me that I may *d*? „ 204
Not simple as a thing that *d's*. „ 288
My own sweet Alice, we must *d*. *Miller's D.* 18
That we may *d* the self-same day. „ 24
I watch'd the little circles *d*; „ 74
I should *d* an early death: „ 90
I *will* possess him or will *d*. *Fatima* 39
Grow, live, *d* looking on his face, *D*, dying clasp'd in his embrace. „ 41
mother Ida, harken ere I *d*. (repeat) *Œnone* 24, 35, 46, 53, 64, 77, 91, 103, 120, 134, 151, 173, 183, 195
And I shall be alone until I *d*. „ 194
mother, hear me yet before I *d*. (repeat) „ 207, 220, 230, 245, 256
shadow all my soul, that I may *d*. „ 242
Weigh heavy on my eyelids: let me *d*. „ 244
I will not *d* alone, (repeat) „ 246, 257
'I have found A new land, but I *d*.' *Palace of Art* 284
And save me lest I *d*?' „ 288
I long to see a flower so before the day I *d*. *May Queen, N. Y.'s. E.* 16
To *d* before the snowdrop came, „ *Con.* 4
up to Heaven and *d* among the stars. „ 40
Waiting to see me *d*. *D. of F. Women* 112
leapt into my arms, Contented there to *d*! „ 152
a thousand times I would be born and *d*. „ 204
How beautiful a thing it was to *d* For God „ 231
Old year, you must not *d*; *D. of the O. Year* 6
Old year, you shall not die. (repeat) „ 9, 24
I've half a mind to *d* with you, Old year, if you must *d*. „ 26
To see him *d*, across the waste His son and heir „ 30
Shake hands, before you *d*. „ 42
Speak out before you *d*. „ 45
I will see before I *d* The palms and temples *You ask me, why* 27
Nor shall see, here or elsewhere, till I *d*, *M. d'Arthur* 154
I fear My wound hath taken cold, and I shall *d*.' „ 166
I fear it is too late, and I shall *d*.' „ 180
'Arthur is come again: he cannot *d*.' „ *Ep.* 24
see My grandchild on my knees before I *d*: *Dora* 13
did not all thy martyrs *d* one death? *St. S. Stylites* 50
I *d* here To-day, and whole years long, „ 53
strive and wrestle with thee till I *d*: „ 119
I prophesy that I shall *d* to-night, „ 220
Of all the western stars, until I *d*. *Ulysses* 61
after many a summer *d's* the swan. *Tithonus* 4
happy men that have the power to *d*, „ 70
'But I would *d*,' said she. *Godiva* 23
When will the hundred summers *d*, *Day-Dm., Sleep P.* 49
The thick-set hazel *d's*; *Will. Water* 234
the lady replied, 'Tho' I should *d* to-night.' *Lady Clare* 48
Every moment *d's* a man, (repeat) *Vision of Sin* 97, 121
Yet we will not *d* forlorn.' „ 206
For now the Poet cannot *d*, *You might have won* 13
And *d's* unheard within his tree, „ 32
But let me hold my purpose till I *d*. *Enoch Arden* 875
not to *d* a listener, I arose, *The Brook* 163
And left the living scandal that shall *d*— *Aylmer's Field* 444
wounded to the death that cannot *d*; „ 662
what heart had he To *d* of? dead!' *Sea Dreams* 276
the soul flies out and *d's* in the air.' *Lucretius* 274
gossip and spite And slander, *d*. *Princess ii* 93
'Let me *d* too,' said Cyril, „ 210
speak, and let the topic *d*.' „ *iii* 205
we like them well: But children *d*; and let me tell you, girl, Howe'er you babble, great deeds cannot *d*; „ 253
O love, they *d* in yon rich sky, „ *iv* 13
To follow up the worthiest till he *d*: „ 466
protomartyr of our cause, *D*: „ 506
wakes A lisping of the innumerous leaf and *d's*, „ *v* 14
And either she will *d* from want of care, „ 85
the question settled *d*.' „ 317
'She must weep or she will *d*.' „ *vi* 4
Let our girls flit, Till the storm *d*! „ 338
O my friend, I will not have thee *d*! „ *vii* 8

Die (*continued*) often she believed that I should *d*: *Princess vii* 100
Sweet dream, be perfect. I shall *d* to-night. „ 149
Stoop down and seem to kiss me ere I *d*.' „ 150
Their's but to do and *d*: *Light Brigade* 15
fairer she, but ah how soon to *d*! *Requiescat* 5
Echo on echo *D's* to the moon. *Minnie and Winnie* 12
Give her the wages of going on, and not to *d*. *Wages* 10
I may *d* but the grass will grow, *Window, No Answer* 4
He thinks he was not made to *d*; *In Mem., Pro.* 11
all the magic light *D's* off at once „ *viii* 6
Or dying, there at least may *d*. „ 24
impart The life that almost *d's* in me; That *d's* not, but endures with pain, „ *xviii* 16
Before their time? they too will *d*. „ *xxix* 16
do not *d* Nor lose their mortal sympathy, „ *xxx* 22
Which telling what it is to *d* „ *xxxi* 7
use A little patience ere I *d*; „ *xxxiv* 12
Man *d's*: nor is there hope in dust:' „ *xxxv* 4
Half-dead to know that I shall *d*.' „ 16
The purple from the distance *d's*, „ *xxxviii* 3
And weave their petty cells and *d*. „ *l* 12
Yet in these ears, till hearing *d's*, „ *lvii* 9
His other passion wholly *d's*, „ *lxii* 10
His inner day can never *d*, „ *lxvi* 15
From off my bed the moonlight *d's*; „ *lxvii* 10
O last regret, regret can *d*! „ *lxxviii* 17
demands By which we dare to live or *d*. „ *lxxxv* 40
Their every parting was to *d*. „ *xcvii* 12
I think once more he seems to *d*. „ *c* 20
Ring out, wild bells, and let him *d*. „ *cvi* 4
And let the ape and tiger *d*. „ *cxviii* 28
And ready, thou, to *d* with him, „ *cxxi* 2
Dear heavenly friend that canst not *d*, „ *cxxix* 7
I shall not lose thee tho' I *d*. „ *cxxx* 16
Cheat and be cheated, and *d*: *Maud I i* 32
and dash myself down and *d* „ 54
Singing of Death, and of Honour that cannot *d*, „ *v* 16
I must tell her, or *d*. „ *xvi* 34
And do accept my madness, and would *d* „ *xviii* 44
Would *d*; for sullen-seeming Death may give „ 46
Not *d*; but live a life of truest breath, „ 53
Yet so did I let my freshness *d*. „ *xix* 11
To faint in his light, and to *d*. „ *xxii* 12
ring in my heart and my ears, till I *d*, till I *d*. „ *II i* 35
And comfort her tho' I *d*. „ *ii* 83
When thou shalt more than *d*. „ *iii* 9
Crack them now for yourself, and howl, and *d*. „ *v* 56
And the shining daffodil *d's*, „ *III vi* 6
That old hysterical mock-disease should *d*.' „ 33
For here between the man and beast we *d*.' *Com. of Arthur* 45
there between the man and beast they *d*. „ 79
An old man's wit may wander ere he *d*. „ 405
he will not *d*, But pass again to come, „ 421
live the strength and *d* the lust! „ 492
'Strike for the King and *d*! „ 494
lived and died for men, the man shall *d*.' *Gareth and L.* 383
He passes and is heal'd and cannot *d*'— „ 503
I finish this fair quest, Or *d* therefore.' „ 775
'Then shall he *d*.' „ 978
marvel *d's*, and leaves me fool'd and trick'd, „ 1251
two things shalt thou *do*, or thou shalt *d*.' *Marr. of Geraint* 586
cast it on the mixen that it *d*.' „ 672
Far liefer by his dear hand had I *d*, *Geraint and E.* 68
if he *d*, why earth has earth enough To hide him. „ 554
I will not look at wine until I *d*.' „ 667
Henceforward I will rather *d* than doubt. „ 738
will henceforward rather *d* than doubt.' „ 745
here *d*—*D*: let the wolves' black maws *Balin and Balan* 486
I too could *d*, as now I live, for thee.' „ 583
and we *d* Together by one doom:' „ 629
'I dread me, if I draw it, you will *d*.' *Lancelot and E.* 513
But he, 'I *d* already with it: draw— „ 514
in daily doubt Whether to live or *d*, „ 521
added wound to wound, And ridd'n away to *d*?' „ 568
'Being so very wilful you must *d*.' „ 783

Die (*continued*) He will not love me: how then? must I *d*? *Lancelot and E.* 893
half the night repeating, 'Must I *d*?' " 899
I must *d* for want of one bold word.' " 927
I love you: let me *d*.' " 930
O Love, if death be sweeter, let me *d*. " 1012
Call and I follow, I follow! let me *d*.' " 1018
she shrilling, 'Let me *d*!' " 1026
I should but *d* the sooner; " 1098
and let me shrive me clean, and *d*.' " 1100
lay the letter in my hand A little ere I *d*, " 1114
some do hold our Arthur cannot *d*, " 1258
Not knowing he should *d* a holy man. " 1429
In moments when he feels he cannot *d*, *Holy Grail* 916
I *d* thro' mine unhappiness.' *Pelleas and E.* 332
One rose, my rose; a rose that will not *d*,— " 408
He *d's* who loves it,—if the worm be there.' " 409
but here, Here let me rest and *d*,' " 515
help it from the death that cannot *d*, *Guinevere* 66
I, whose vast pity almost makes me *d* " 534
I waged His wars, and now I pass and *d*. *Pass. of Arthur* 12
God my Christ—I pass but shall not *d*.' " 28
Nor shall see, here or elsewhere, till I *d*, " 322
I fear My wound hath taken cold, and I shall *d*.' " 334
I fear it is too late, and I shall *d*.' " 348
Where all of high and holy *d's* away. *To the Queen ii* 66
To *d* in gazing on that perfectness *Lover's Tale i* 88
And cannot *d*, and am, in having been— " 121
I died then, I had not seem'd to *d*, " 494
Love would *d* when Hope was gone, " 818
I seem'd to faint and fall, To fall and *d* away. " *ii* 97
What did he then? not *d*: he is here and hale— " *iv* 40
And leave him in the public way to *d*. " 261
if I *d* o' my lying in! *First Quarrel* 70
I kiss'd my boy in the prison, before he went out to *d*. *Rizpah* 23
'My lass, when I cooms to *d*, *North. Cobbler* 103
For to fight is but to *d*! *The Revenge* 27
We *d*—does it matter when? " 88
With a joyful spirit I Sir Richard Grenville *d*!' " 103
I am sure that some of our children would *d* *In the Child. Hosp.* 11
every man *d* at his post!' (repeat) *Def. of Lucknow* 10, 13, 52
Kill or be kill'd, live or *d*, " 41
I am not like to *d* for lack of bread. *Sir J. Oldcastle* 205
I woke, and thought—death—I shall *d*— *Columbus* 87
would rush on a thousand lances and *d*— *V. of Maeldune* 24
Nobly to do, nobly to *d*. *Tiresias* 123
The child that I felt I could *d* for— *The Wreck* 36
I would fling myself over and *d*! " 118
no souls—and to *d* with the brute— *Despair* 36
we were used to believe everlasting would *d*: " 54
If every man *d* for ever, " 82
With him, where summer never *d's*, with Love, *The Flight* 44
I will wander till I *d* about the barren moors. " 56
war will *d* out late then. *Locksley H., Sixty* 173
gallant three hundred whose glory will never *d*— *Heavy Brigade* 10
for evermore. Let the people *d*.' *Dead Prophet* 4
Catullus, whose dead songster never *d's*; *Poets and their B.* 8
Thine is it that our drama did not *d*, *To W. C. Macready* 9
why The sons before the fathers *d*, *To Marq. of Dufferin* 47
And all the Shadow *d* into the Light, *Demeter and P.* 138
Do not *d* with a lie in your mouth, *Forlorn* 57
No—you will not *d* before, " 61
Tell him all before you *d*, Lest you *d* for ever . . . " 75
would he live and *d* alone? *Happy* 5
d with him side by side? " 8
I will live and *d* with you. " 108
They lose themselves and *d* On that new life *Prog. of Spring* 35
king who loved me, And cannot *d*; *Merlin and the G.* 80
And can no longer, But *d* rejoicing, " 112
To win her back before I *d*— *Romney's R.* 118
Go back to thine adulteress and *d*!' *Death of Œnone* 48
his dying words, Which would not *d*, *St. Telemachus* 76
Form, be ready to do or *d*! *Riflemen form!* 22
beggar began to cry 'Food, food or I *d*'! *Voice spake, etc.* 6

Died *D* round the bulbul as he sung; *Arabian Nights* 70

Died (*continued*) Singing in her song she *d*, *L. of Shalott iv* 35
D the sound of royal cheer; " 48
'His face, that two hours since hath *d*; *Two Voices* 242
She *d*: she went to burning flame: *The Sisters* 7
desire is but to pass to Him that *d* for me. *May Queen, Con.* 20
The dim red morn had *d*, *D. of F. Women* 61
Many drew swords and *d*. " 95
Myself for such a face had boldly *d*,' " 98
Contented there to *d*! 'And there he *d*: " 152
'I *d* a Queen. The Roman soldier found Me " 161
her that *d* To save her father's vow; " 195
To whom the Egyptian; 'O, you tamely *d*! " 258
And when the zoning eve has *d* *On a Mourner* 21
And on the mere the wailing *d* away. *M. d'Arthur* 272
Danced into light, and *d* into the shade; *Gardener's D.* 203
Had once hard words, and parted, and he *d* *Dora* 18
and in harvest time he *d*. " 55
when William *d*, he *d* at peace With all men; " 144
like endless welcome, lived and *d*. *Love and Duty* 68
The twilight *d* into the dark. *Day-Dm., Depart.* 24
Or stow'd, when classic Canning *d*, *Will Water.* 101
old Earl's daughter *d* at my breast; *Lady Clare* 25
Then before her time she *d*. *L. of Burleigh* 88
Then the music touch'd the gates and *d*: *Vision of Sin* 23
When the years have *d* away.' *Poet's Song* 16
And that mysterious instinct wholly *d*. *Enoch Arden* 526
Surely the man had *d* of solitude. " 621
tell her that I *d* Blessing her, praying for her, " 878
And tell my son that I *d* blessing him. " 885
he *d* at Florence, quite worn out, *The Brook* 35
knolls That dimpling *d* into each other, *Aylmer's Field* 149
scandals that have lived and *d*, " 443
Remembering her dear Lord who *d* for all, *Sea Dreams* 47
(I thought I could have *d* to save it) " 134
a low musical note Swell'd up and *d*; " 211
the first embrace had *d* Between them, *Lucretius* 3
laid about them at their wills and *d*; *Princess, Pro.* 31
teaching him that *d* Of hemlock; our device; " *iii* 302
her heart Would rock the snowy cradle till I *d*. " *iv* 104
Better have *d* and spilt our bones in the flood— " 532
My dream had never *d* or lived again. " *vi* 17
Ida has a heart'—just ere she *d*— " 235
and *d* Of fright in far apartments. " 370
And he *d*, and I could not weep— *Grandmother* 72
God's will that I, too, then could have *d*: " 73
an' 'e *d* a good 'un, 'e did. *N. Farmer, N. S.* 52
So thick they *d* the people cried, *The Victim* 5
And cattle *d*, and deer in wood, " 18
That holy Death ere Arthur *d* *In Mem. lxxx* 2
And He that *d* in Holy Land " *lxxxiv* 42
'The dawn, the dawn,' and *d* away; " *xcv* 61
So many a summer since she *d*, *Maud I vi* 66
Whose old grandfather has lately *d*, " *x* 5
past in bridal white, And *d* to live, " *xviii* 66
Aurelius lived and fought and *d*, And after him King Uther fought and *d*, *Com. of Arthur* 13
King Uther *d* himself, Moaning and wailing " 206
the savage yells Of Uther's peerage *d*, " 257
D but of late, and sent his cry to me, " 361
served about the King, Uther, before he *d*; " 366
some she cleaved to, but they *d* of her. *Gareth and L.* 113
King Who lived and *d* for men, " 383
but, overtaken, *d* the death Themselves *Geraint and E.* 177
So *d* Earl Doorm by him he counted dead. " 730
and the spiteful whisper *d*: " 958
when he *d*, his soul Became a Fiend, *Balin and Balan* 128
The whole day *d*, but, dying, gleam'd " 314
'I hold them happy, so they *d* for love: " 581
I that fain had *d* To save thy life, " 599
My father *d* in battle against the King, *Merlin and V.* 42
My father *d* in battle for thy King, " 72
One child they had: it lived with her: she *d*: " 716
while his anger slowly *d* Within him, " 891
better have *d* Thrice than have ask'd it once— " 918
the living smile *D* from his lips, *Lancelot and E.* 324

Died (*continued*) *d* the death In any knightly fashion *Lancelot and E.* 870
Then take the little bed on which I *d* „ 1117
And closed the hand upon it, and she *d*. „ 1135
I dreamt the damsel would have *d*, „ 1305
this she would not, and she *d*.' „ 1325
From Camelot, there, and not long after, *d*. *Holy Grail* 7
ere the summer when he *d*, „ 16
The rosy quiverings *d* into the night. „ 123
And all talk *d*, as in a grove all song *Pelleas and E.* 607
'My churl, for whom Christ *d*, *Last Tournament* 62
and he *d*, Kill'd in a tilt, *Guinevere* 320
till in time their Abbess *d*. „ 692
My dead, as tho' they had not *d* for me?— *Pass. of Arthur* 142
And on the mere the wailing *d* away. „ 440
Trust me, long ago I should have *d*, *Lover's Tale i* 87
I had *d*, But from my farthest lapse, „ 89
Before he saw my day my father *d*, „ 191
Had I *d* then, I had not seem'd to die, „ 494
Had I *d* then, I had not known the death; „ 496
So *d* that hour, and fell into the abysm „ 796
So that hour *d* Like odour rapt „ 800
Had *d* almost to serve them any way, „ *iv* 124
His master would not wait until he *d*, „ 259
An' I almost *d* o' your going away, *First Quarrel* 54
And he fell upon their decks, and he *d*. *The Revenge* 104
She *d* and she was buried ere we knew. *Sisters (E. and E.)* 241
my darter es *d* o' the fever at fall: *Village Wife* 10
But arter she *d* we was all es one, „ 55
each of them liefer had *d* than have done *V. of Maeldune* 6
and the harvest *d* from the field, „ 30
twelve of their noblest *d* Among their spears *Achilles over the T.* 32
prayer for a soul that *d* in his sin, *The Wreck* 10
But it *d*, and I thought of the child „ 84
perhaps, perhaps, if we *d*, if we *d*; *Despair* 56
dead the cause in which he *d*. *Locksley H., Sixty* 30
Rain-rotten *d* the wheat, *Demeter and P.* 112
d in the doing it, flesh without mind; *Vastness* 27
till Self *d* out in the love of his kind; „ 28
she did not grow, she *d*. *Romney's R.* 105
happy had I *d* within thine arms, *Death of Œnone* 31
In the great name of Him who *d* for men, *St. Telemachus* 63
An' it beäts ma to knaw wot she *d* on, *Church-warden, etc.* 6
he was crush'd in a moment and *d*, *Charity* 21
She *d* of a fever caught when a nurse „ 41
Diest if thou *d*, The King is King, *Com. of Arthur* 494
two things shalt thou do, or else thou *d*. *Marr. of Geraint* 580
Diet *D* and seedling, jesses, leash and lure. *Merlin and V.* 125
As if they knew your *d* spares *To E. Fitzgerald* 10
Differ Or do my peptics *d*? *Will Water.* 80
men at most *d* as Heaven and earth, *Merlin and V.* 814
Difference When thy peculiar *d* Is cancell'd *Two Voices* 41
Might I not tell Of *d*, reconcilement, *Gardener's D.* 257
girl and boy, Sir, know their *d's*!' *Aylmer's Field* 274
when some heat of *d* sparkled out, „ 705
That have as many *d's* as we. *Princess v* 181
To cleave the rift of *d* deeper yet; „ 301
Not like to like, but like in *d*. „ *vii* 278
Ay me, the *d* I discern! *In Mem. xl* 21
Hearing he had a *d* with their priests, *Holy Grail* 674
Difficulty in days of *d* And pressure, had she sold *Enoch Arden* 254
With *d* in mild obedience Driving them on: *Geraint and E.* 104
Diffuse *D* thyself at will thro' all my blood, *Prog. of Spring* 24
Diffused Thy God is far *d* in noble groves *Aylmer's Field* 653
D the shock thro' all my life, *In Mem. lxxxv* 55
D and molten into flaky cloud. *Lover's Tale i* 641
Diffusing A central warmth *d* bliss *In Mem. lxxxiv* 6
Dig builds the house, or *d's* the grave, „ *xxxvi* 14
d, pick, open, find and read the charm: *Merlin and V.* 660
I can't *d* deep, I am old— *Rizpah* 56
Digg'd An' 'e *d* up a loomp i' the land *Village Wife* 48
Diggin' last month they wor *d* the bog, *Tomorrow* 61
Digging *See* **Diggin', Half-digging**
Dignity maiden *dignities* of Hope and Love— *Lover's Tale i* 580
Dilate in a day, A joyous to *d*, as toward the light. *Aylmer's Field* 77
That now *d*, and now decrease, *In Mem. xxviii* 10

Dilating wind of prophecy *D* on the future; *Princess ii* 172
Dilation her eye with slow *d* roll'd Dry flame, „ *vi* 189
Dilettante snowy-banded, *d*, Delicate-handed *Maud I viii* 10
Dim (adj.) eyes are *d* with glorious tears, *Two Voices* 151
About him broods the twilight *d*: „ 263
My heart is breaking, and my eyes are *d*, *Œnone* 32
eyes grown *d* with gazing on the pilot-stars. *Lotos-Eaters, C. S.* 87
Till all the paths were *d*, *Talking Oak* 298
He saw not far: his eyes were *d*: *The Voyage* 75
Perhaps her eye was *d*, hand tremulous; *Enoch Arden* 242
We sung, tho' every eye was *d*, *In Mem. xxx* 14
Is *d*, or will be *d*, with weeds: „ *lxxiii* 10
I remain'd, whose hopes were *d*, „ *lxxxv* 29
Thou watches't all things ever *d* And dimmer, „ *cxxi* 3
Myself would work eye *d*, *Marr. of Geraint* 628
the hall was *d* with steam of flesh: *Geraint and E.* 603
and *d* thro' leaves Blinkt the white morn, *Balin and Balan* 384
So strange, and rich, and *d*; *Holy Grail* 342
these eyes of men are dense and *d*, *Pass. of Arthur* 19
and mine Were *d* with floating tears, *Lover's Tale i* 442
Dim (verb) work in hues to *d* The Titianic Flora. *Gardener's D.* 170
Dim-gray Now and then in the *d-g* dawn; *Maud I xiv* 32
Diminutive In babyisms, and dear *d's*, *Aylmer's Field* 539
Dim-lit while he past the *d-l* woods, *Guinevere* 251
Dimm'd broad valley *d* in the gloaming: *Leonine Eleg.* 1
thro' the cloud that *d* her broke *Princess vi* 281
trust in things above Be *d* of sorrow, *In Mem. lxxxv* 10
and the sorrow *d* her sight, *Lancelot and E.* 889
Thy glorious eyes were *d* with pain *Freedom* 10
Dimmer all things ever dim And *d*, *In Mem. cxxi* 4
Dimness o'er it crost the *d* of a cloud Floating, *Pelleas and E.* 37
Dimple Till the lightning laughters *d* *Lilian* 16
Or *d* in the dark of rushy coves, *Ode to Memory* 60
That *d's* your transparent cheek, *Margaret* 15
Dimpled laughter *d* in his swarthy cheek; *Edwin Morris* 61
Dimpling knolls That *d* died into each other, *Aylmer's Field* 149
Upon the dappled *d's* of the wave, *Lover's Tale i* 44
Dim Saesneg with his hard '*D S*' passes, *Sir J. Oldcastle* 21
Dim-yellow With her fair head in the *d-y* light, *Marr. of Geraint* 600
Din From the groves within The wild-bird's *d*. *Poet's Mind* 21
The dust and *d* and steam of town: *In Mem. lxxxix* 8
But when the heart is full of *d*, „ *xciv* 13
for me that sicken at your lawless *d*, *Locksley H., Sixty* 149
Dine You'll have no scandal while you *d*, *To F. D. Maurice* 17
shall we fast, or *d*? *Geraint and E.* 490
an' we be a-goin to *d*, *North. Cobbler* 111
Dinner (*See also* **After-dinner**) with the steam Of thirty thousand *d's*. *Will Water.* 224
hark the bell For *d*, let us go!' *Princess ii* 433
A grand political *d* To half the squirelings *Maud I xx* 25
A grand political *d* To the men of many acres, „ 31
A *d* and then a dance For the maids „ 34
Man with his brotherless *d* *The Dawn* 3
Dinnerless when I left your mowers *d*. *Geraint and E.* 234
The lusty mowers labouring *d*, „ 251
Dint Sharp-smitten with the *d* of armed heels— *M. d'Arthur* 190
every *d* a sword had beaten in it, *Lancelot and E.* 19
Sharp-smitten with the *d* of armed heels— *Pass. of Arthur* 358
Dinted and crush'd, and *d* into the ground: *Maud I i* 7
his strong hands gript And *d* the gilt dragons *Last Tournament* 182
Diotima beneath an emerald plane Sits *D*, *Princess iii* 302
Dip (s) the last *d* of the vanishing sail *Enoch Arden* 245
The *d* of certain strata to the North. *Princess iii* 170
Dip (verb) the prime swallow *d's* his wing, *Edwin Morris* 145
and *d's* Her laurel in the wine, *Will Water.* 17
D forward under starry light, *Move eastward* 10
d Their wings in tears, and skim away. *In Mem. xlviii* 15
D down upon the northern shore, „ *lxxxiii* 1
and *d's* and springs For ever; *Gareth and L.* 1146
these low bushes *d* their twigs in foam, *Prog. of Spring* 51
Dippest And *d* toward the dreamless head, *In Mem. xxxix* 5
Dipping *d* his head low beneath the verge, *Lover's Tale i* 509
ships from out the West go *d* thro' the foam, *The Flight* 91
Dipt (*See also* **Half-dipt**) the sky *D* down to sea and sands. *Palace of Art* 32

Dipt (*continued*) But ere he *d* the surface, rose an arm *M. d'Arthur* 143
d, And mix'd with shadows of the common ground! *Gardener's D.* 134
one green sparkle ever and anon *D* by itself, *Audley Court* 89
d and rose, And turn'd to look at her. *Talking Oak* 131
When I *d* into the future (repeat) *Locksley Hall* 15, 119
with her *d* Against the rush of the air *Aylmer's Field* 85
d in all That treats of whatsoever is, *Princess ii* 379
and *d* Beneath the satin dome and enter'd in, „ *iv* 30
a dearer being, all *d* In Angel instincts, „ *vii* 320
I sleep till dusk is *d* in gray: *In Mem. lxvii* 12
And *d* in baths of hissing tears, „ *cxviii* 23
Beneath a low door *d*, and made his feet *Balin and Balan* 403
Sparkle, until they *d* below the downs. *Lancelot and E.* 396
But ere he *d* the surface, rose an arm *Pass. of Arthur* 311
till the labourless day *d* under the West; *V. of Maeldune* 86
son, who *d* In some forgotten book of mine *To E. Fitzgerald* 46
dark hull *d* under the smiling main, *The Wreck* 127
never yet hath *d* into the abysm, *Ancient Sage* 39
we *d* down under the bridge *Bandit's Death* 22
Broke the Taboo, *D* to the crater, *Kapiolani* 31
Dircê who found Beside the springs of *D*, *Tiresias* 14
and the springs Of *D* laving yonder battle-plain, „ 139
Direct Now over and now under, now *d*, *Lucretius* 62
Dirt these, tho' fed with careful *d*, *Amphion* 89
Disappear earth yawns: the mortal *d's*; *Ode on Well.* 269
and as the phantom *d's*, *Locksley H., Sixty* 253
Disappear'd the whole fair city had *d*. *Gareth and L.* 196
And up the rocky pathway *d*, *Geraint and E.* 243
cup Was caught away to Heaven, and *d*.' *Holy Grail* 58
as he spoke Fell into dust, and *d*, „ 436
Became a shadow, sank and *d*, *Death of Œnone* 50
Disarm'd The proud was half *d* of pride, *In Mem. cx* 6
Who let him into lodging and *d*. *Lancelot and E.* 171
Thither I made, and there was I *d*. *Holy Grail* 575
Disarray Drove it in wild *d*, *Heavy Brigade* 60
Disarray'd found, Half *d* as to her rest, *Marr. of Geraint* 516
Disaster all *d* unto thine and thee! *Gareth and L.* 1101
Disband bidding him *D* himself, and scatter *Geraint and E.* 798
Discaged Until she let me fly *d* to sweep *Gareth and L.* 20
Discern *d* The roofs Of Sumner-place! (repeat) *Talking Oak* 31, 95, 151
till thy bough *d* The front of Sumner-place. „ 247
Till a gateway she *d's* With armorial bearings *L. of Burleigh* 42
Ay me, the difference I *d*! *In Mem. xl* 21
I wake, and I *d* the truth; „ *lxviii* 14
Discerned into my inmost ring A pleasure I *d*, *Talking Oak* 174
Discerning *d* to fulfil This labour, *Ulysses* 35
Disciple and yet Was no *d*, richly garb'd, *Ancient Sage* 4
Disclaim'd each *D* all knowledge of us: *Princess iv* 229
Disclosed *D* a fruit of pure Hesperian gold, *Œnone* 66
Discomfort this *d* he hath done the house.' *Lancelot and E.* 1072
blew my merry maidens all about With all *d*; *Holy Grail* 749
Disconsolate On the nigh-naked tree the robin piped *D*, *Enoch Arden* 677
Discontent lent The pulse of hope to *d*. *Two Voices* 450
She look'd with *d*. *Talking Oak* 116
muttering *d* Cursed me and my flower. *The Flower* 7
Discord soul Of *D* race the rising wind; *Love thou thy land* 68
too like The *d's* dear to the musician. *Sea Dreams* 258
A monster then, a dream, A *d*. *In Mem. lvi* 22
Discordance no *d* in the roll And march *D. of the Duke of C.* 14
Discouraged I grew *d*, Sir; but since I knew *Princess iii* 153
Discourse In such *d* we gain'd the gàrden rails, „ *Con.* 80
Discourtesy 'Meseems, that here is much *d*, *Gareth and L.* 853
I pray you, use some rough *d* *Lancelot and E.* 973
This was the one *d* that he used. „ 988
some *d* Against my nature: „ 1302
Discover'd All precious things, *d* late, *Day-Dm., Arrival* 1
Discoverer The first *d* starves—his followers, *Columbus* 166
Discovery For the *d* And newness of thine art *Ode to Memory* 87
Discredit heaven, how much I shall *d* him! *Marr. of Geraint* 621
Far liefer than so much *d* him.' „ 629
Discuss We might *d* the Northern sin *To F. D. Maurice* 29
Discuss'd *d* the farm, The fourfield system, *Audley Court* 33
D his tutor, rough to common men, *Princess, Pro.* 114
D a doubt and tost it to and fro: „ *ii* 445
D the books to love or hate, *In Mem. lxxxix* 34
Discussing *D* how their courtship grew, *In Mem., Con.* 97
Discussion That from *D's* lip may fall With *Love thou thy land* 33
Disdain (*See also* **Half-disdain**) And my *d* is my reply. *L. C. V. de Vere* 22
with some *d* Answer'd the Princess, *Princess iv* 61
With some surprise and thrice as much *d* Turn'd, *Marr. of Geraint* 557
not with half *d* Hid under grace, *Lancelot and E.* 263
Sir Lancelot leant, in half *d* At love, „ 1238
Disdain'd if the Queen *d* to grant it! *Balin and Balan* 191
Tolerant of what he half *d*, and she, Perceiving that she was but half *d*, *Merlin and V.* 178
Disease (*See also* **Heart-disease, Mock-disease**) But sickening of a vague *d*, *L. C. V. de Vere* 62
wretched age—and worst *d* of all, *Lucretius* 155
Ring out old shapes of foul *d*; *In Mem. cvi* 25
A *d*, a hard mechanic ghost That never came *Maud II ii* 34
She like a new *d*, unknown to men, *Guinevere* 518
and the loathsome smells of *d* *In the Child. Hosp.* 25
I'd sooner fold an icy corpse dead of some foul *d*: *The Flight* 54
Some thro' age and slow *d's*, *Locksley H., Sixty* 46
All *d's* quench'd by Science, „ 163
mar the beauty of your bride with your *d*. *Happy* 24
Diseased (*See also* **Half-diseased**) But ours he swore were all *d*. *The Voyage* 76
The land is sick, the people *d*, *The Victim* 45
You thought my heart too far *d*; *In Mem. lxvi* 1
Disedge served a little to *d* The sharpness *Geraint and E.* 189
But here will I *d* it by thy death.' *Pelleas and E.* 578
Disembark'd touching Breton sands, they *d*. *Merlin and V.* 202
Disengage I strove to *d* myself, but fail'd, *Lover's Tale i* 692
Disentwined My coronal slowly *d* itself „ 361
Disfame *See* **Half-disfame.**
Disgraäced (disgraced) I'd feäl mysen cleän *d*. *North. Cobbler* 102
black Sal, es 'ed been *d*? *Spinster's S's.* 25
Disgrace Alone might hint of my *d*; *Two Voices* 360
lying, hidden from the heart's *d*, *Locksley Hall* 57
why, the greater their *d*! *Aylmer's Field* 384
Heap'd on her terms of *d*, *Maud II i* 14
an' often at home in *d*, *First Quarrel* 15
If you should only compass her *d*, *The Fleet* 17
Disgraced (*See also* **Disgraäced**) Memmian naphtha-pits, *d* For ever— *Alexander* 1
d, Dishonour'd all for trial of true love— *Pelleas and E.* 474
Disguise common light of smiles at our *d* *Princess v* 276
Disguised thou shalt go *d* to Arthur's hall, *Gareth and L.* 152
For hence will I, *d*, and hire myself „ 169
Thou art so well *d*, I knew thee not. *Sir J. Oldcastle* 197
Dish harpies miring every *d*, *Lucretius* 159
And those that hand the *d* across the bar. *Gareth and L.* 155
Think ye this fellow will poison the King's *d*? „ 471
thrust the *d* before her, crying, 'Eat.' *Geraint and E.* 655
Dishallow 'Ye, that so *d* the holy sleep, *Pelleas and E.* 446
Dishelm'd she saw me lying stark, *D* and mute, *Princess vi* 101
Dishonour Doing *d* to my clay.' *Two Voices* 102
Becomes *d* to her race— „ 255
So loathed the bright *d* of his love, *Com. of Arthur* 195
His honour rooted in *d* stood, *Lancelot and E.* 876
knights At that *d* done the gilded spur, *Last Tournament* 435
I was close on that hour of *d*, *Charity* 28
Dishonourable 'Ungenerous, *d*, base, *Aylmer's Field* 292
Dishonour'd *D* all for trial of true love— *Pelleas and E.* 477
Dishorsed each, *d* and drawing, lash'd at each *Marr. of Geraint* 563
D himself, and rose again, and fled *Balin and Balan* 330
Dish-washer *D-w* and broach-turner, loon!— *Gareth and L.* 770
Disjoint Nor wielded axe *d*, *Talking Oak* 262
Disjointed Descended, and *d* it at a blow: *Balin and Balan* 296
Disk studded wide With *d's* and tiars, *Arabian Nights* 64
Ray round with flames her *d* of seed, *In Mem. ci* 6
flight of shadowy fighters crost The *d*, *St. Telemachus* 24
Dislink'd *D* with shrieks and laughter: *Princess, Pro.* 70
But she *d* herself at once and rose, *Merlin and V.* 909
Dislodging heroes tall *D* pinnacle and parapet *D. of F. Women* 26
Dismay were the words Mutter'd in our *d*; *Heavy Brigade* 47
Dismay'd Was there a man *d*? *Light Brigade* 10
we turn'd to each other, whispering, all *d*, *Heavy Brigade* 44
Dismember May never saw *d* thee, *Talking Oak* 261

Dismiss *D* me, and I prophesy your plan, *Princess iv* 354
Your oath is broken: we *d* you: „ 360
Dismissal She spoke, and bowing waved *D*: „ *ii* 100
Dismiss'd *d* in shame to live No wiser than their mothers, „ *iv* 513
Dismount *d* and loose their casques *Balin and Balan* 573
Dismounting *d* like a man That skins the wild beast *Geraint and E.* 92
Geraint, *d*, pick'd the lance That pleased him „ 179
d on the sward They let the horses graze, „ 210
at his side all pale *D*, loosed the fastenings „ 511
Disobey deep harm to *d*, Seeing obedience is the bond of rule. *M. d'Arthur* 93
I needs must *d* him for his good; *Geraint and E.* 135
Then not to *d* her lord's behest, „ 450
Deep harm to *d*, Seeing obedience is the bond of rule. *Pass. of Arthur* 261
Disorderly *D* the women. Alone I stood *Princess iv* 170
from the high door streaming, brake *D*, *Lancelot and E.* 1348
Disparagement with some prelude of *d*, Read, *The Epic* 49
Flush'd slightly at the slight *d* *Lancelot and E.* 234
With silent smiles of slow *d*; *Guinevere* 14
Dispassionate Quiet, *d*, and cold, *A Character* 28
Dispatch Delivering sealed *d'es* which the Head *Princess iv* 379
Dispell'd I loved, and love *d* the fear *Miller's D.* 89
Dispense *D* with careful hands: *Mechanophilus* 34
Dispenser drowsy hours, *d's* of all good, *Gardener's D.* 185
Dispensing *D* harvest, sowing the To-be, *Princess vii* 289
Dispersed made a plunge To the bottom, and *d*, *Enoch Arden* 380
D his resolution like a cloud. *Lancelot and E.* 884
Displaced If this false traitor have *d* his lord, *Guinevere* 216
Display to *d* A tunic white as May! *Prog. of Spring* 64
Display'd *D* a splendid silk of foreign loom, *Geraint and E.* 687
Dispraise In praise and in *d* the same, *Ode on Well.* 73
hissing *d* Because their natures are little, *Maud I iv* 52
Dispread *See* **Wide-dispread**
Disprinced one rag, *d* from head to heel. *Princess v* 30
Disproof as he was To make *d* of scorn, *Aylmer's Field* 446
Disproven nothing worthy proving can be proven, Nor yet *d*: *Ancient Sage* 67
Dispute (s) breed *D* betwixt myself and mine: *Princess i* 157
for she took no part In our *d*: „ *Con.* 30
Or deep *d*, and graceful jest; *In Mem. lxxxiv* 24
Dispute (verb) *D* the claims, arrange the chances; *To F. D. Maurice* 31
Disquiet But long *d* merged in rest. *Two Voices* 249
Disrelish Why should I so *d* that short word? *Romney's R.* 11
Disrobed If gazing on divinity *d* *Œnone* 157
D the glimmering statue of Sir Ralph *Princess, Con.* 117
Disrooted (*See also* **Half-disrooted**) Whate'er I was *D*, what I am is grafted here. „ *ii* 220
Disruption sought To make *d* in the Table Round *Guinevere* 17
Dissecting wayward modern mind *D* passion. *Edwin Morris* 88
Dissembling Fright and foul *d*, *Forlorn* 32
Dissipated shrink For fear our solid aim be *d*, *Princess iii* 266
Dissoluble Gods Being atomic not be *d*, *Lucretius* 115
Dissolution clench their nerves to rush Upon their *d*, *Love and Duty* 78
Dissolve *d* the previous seal on a bond, *Maud I xix* 45
Dissolved *D* the riddle of the earth. *Two Voices* 170
d the mystery Of folded sleep. *D. of F. Women* 262
now the whole ROUND TABLE is *d* *M. d'Arthur* 234
thereat the crowd Muttering, *d*: *Princess iv* 523
now the whole Round Table is *d* *Pass. of Arthur* 402
Dissolving *See* **Half-dissolving**
Dissolvingly to all my frame, *D* and slowly: *Eleänore* 132
Distance mountain Which stands in the *d* yonder: *Poet's Mind* 30
Some blue peaks in the *d* rose, *Dying Swan* 11
such a *d* from his youth in grief, *Gardener's D.* 54
in the *d* overlooks the sandy tracts, *Locksley Hall* 5
And a song from out the *d* „ 84
Not in vain the *d* beacons. „ 181
and shows At *d* like a little wood; *Day-Dm., Sleep. P.* 42
A trumpet in the *d* pealing news Of better, *Princess iv* 81
deals with the other *d* and the hues Of promise; „ 86
but Blanche At *d* follow'd: „ *vi* 83
a day Rose from the *d* on her memory, „ 112
and broken system made No purple in the *d*, „ 196
And see the sails at *d* rise, *In Mem. xii* 11
Distance (*continued*) The purple from the *d* dies, *In Mem. xxxviii* 3
O, from the *d* of the abyss „ *xciii* 11
The *d* takes a lovelier hue, „ *cxv* 6
That out of *d* might ensue „ *cxvii* 5
or like a clamour of the rocks At *d*, *Marr. of Geraint* 250
drumming thunder of the huger fall At *d*, *Geraint and E.* 174
warmth of Arthur's hall Shadow'd an angry *d*: *Balin and Balan* 237
sound As from a *d* beyond *d* grew *Holy Grail* 112
and set me far In the gray *d*, *Last Tournament* 640
Heaven Will blow the tempest in the *d* back *To the Queen II* 47
And heralded the *d* of this time! *Lover's Tale i* 562
that same nearness Were father to this *d*, „ *ii* 29
in the *d*, From out the yellow woods upon the hill „ 79
And voices in the *d* calling to me „ 118
and murmur down Truth in the *d*— *Columbus* 120
Are there thunders moaning in the *d*? *On Jub. Q. Victoria* 66
Thro' the gates that bar the *d* comes a gleam *Faith* 6
Distant in her throat Her voice seem'd *d*, *To J. S.* 55
cry came to her from the field, More and more *d*. *Dora* 105
Distill'd *D* from some worm-canker'd homily; *To J. M. K.* 6
hoard of happiness *d* Some drops of solace; *Lover's Tale i* 714
Distilling *D* odours on me as they went *Gardener's D.* 187
Distinct *D* with vivid stars inlaid, *Arabian Nights* 90
D in individualities, *Princess vii* 291
Distress flow Of subtle-paced counsel in *d* *Isabel* 21
Small thought was there of life's *d*; *Ode to Memory* 37
And utterly consumed with sharp *d*, *Lotos-Eaters, C. S.* 13
then *d'es* came on him; *Dora* 49
Who show'd a token of *d*? *In Mem. lxxviii* 13
No limit to his *d*; *Maud II v* 31
Distribute Walk your dim cloister, and *d* dole *Guinevere* 683
Distrust *See* **Self-distrust**
Disturb 'Woman, *d* me not now at the last, *Enoch Arden* 874
Disturb'd *D* me with the doubt 'if this were she,' *Princess iv* 217
one glittering foot *d* The lucid well; *Tiresias* 41
Disyoke *D* their necks from custom, *Princess ii* 143
Ditch cannot see for slime, Slime of the *d*: *Holy Grail* 772
from the *d* where they shelter we drive them *Def. of Lucknow* 59
Dive they shall *d*, and they shall run, *Locksley Hall* 169
Or *d* below the wells of Death? *In Mem. cviii* 8
or *d's* In yonder greening gleam, „ *cxv* 13
made him quickly *d* Beneath the boughs, *Balin and Balan* 422
wilt *d* Into the Temple-cave of thine own self, *Ancient Sage* 31
Dived I *D* in a hoard of tales that dealt with knights, *Princess, Pro.* 29
Diver *See* **Marsh-diver**
Diverse woman is not undevelopt man, But *d*: „ *vii* 276
Dives When *D* loathed the times, *To Mary Boyle* 29
Divide God *d* the night with flying flame, *D. of F. Women* 225
these two parties still *d* the world— *Walk. to the Mail* 77
shell *D's* threefold to show the fruit (repeat) *The Brook* 73, 208
Eternal form shall still *d* The eternal soul *In Mem. xlvii* 6
D us not, be with me now, „ *cxxii* 10
shriek of a mother *d* the shuddering night. *Maud I i* 16
She seem'd to *d* in a dream „ *III vi* 10
Could scarce *d* it from her foolish dream: *Marr. of Geraint* 686
Divided *d* quite The kingdom of her thought. *Palace of Art* 227
D in a graceful quiet—paused, *Gardener's D.* 156
a walk Of shingle, and a walk *d* it: *Enoch Arden* 737
nor was his love the less Because it was *d*, *Lover's Tale i* 229
d as I am From either by the stillness *Sisters (E. and E.)* 281
The barrier that *d* beast from man *St. Telemachus* 60
Dividend chances of *d*, consol, and share— *The Wreck* 30
Dividing *d* the swift mind, In act to throw; *M. d'Arthur* 60
the crowd *d* clove An advent to the throne: *Princess iv* 283
d the swift mind, In act to throw; *Pass. of Arthur* 228
Divil (devil) blessed feälds wi' the *d's* oän teäm. *N. Farmer, O. S.* 62
an' 'e's the *D's* oän sen.' *North. Cobbler* 76
the *D's* in 'im,' said I. „ 104
'The *D* take all the black lan', *Tomorrow* 64
Divine (adj.) (*See also* **Half-divine**) Scarce of earth nor all *d*, *Adeline* 3
You are not less *d*, *Margaret* 46
Apart the Chamian Oracle *d* *Alexander* 10
I think, That my youth was half *d*. *Vision of Sin* 78
Left by the Teacher, whom he held *d*. *Lucretius* 13
Love by right *d* is deathless king, *W. to Marie Alex.* 29

Divine (adj.) (*continued*) Thou seemest human and *d*, *In Mem., Pro.* 13
To count their memories half *d*; „ *xc* 12
Known and unknown; human, *d*; „ *cxxix* 5
not learnable, *d*, Beyond *my* reach. *Balin and Balan* 175
see the highest Human Nature is *d*. *Locksley H., Sixty* 276
creature which in Eden was *d*, *Happy* 33
she the faultless, the *d*; *Locksley H., Sixty* 5
Divine (verb) A deeper tale my heart *d's*. *Two Voices* 269
Nor the meaning can *d*, *L. of Burleigh* 54
She is not *of* us, as I *d*; *Maud II v* 69
Divinely *D* thro' all hindrance finds the man *Lancelot and E.* 333
Some warning—sent *d*—as it seem'd *Lover's Tale iv* 21
Divinity the dull Saw no *d* in grass, *A Character* 8
If gazing on *d* disrobed Thy mortal eyes *Œnone* 157
lift the woman's fall'n *d* Upon an even pedestal *Princess iii* 223
Division in *d* of the records of the mind? *Locksley Hall* 69
'betwixt these two *D* smoulders hidden; *Princess iii* 79
Are they not sign and symbol of thy *d* from Him? *High. Pantheism* 6
Made strange *d* of its suffering With her, *Lover's Tale ii* 128
Divorce *D* the Feeling from her mate the Deed. *The Brook* 95
d thee not From earthly love and life— *Ded. Poem Prin. Alice* 3
Divorced I prophesy your plan, *D* from my experience, *Princess iv* 355
can I breathe *d* from the Past? *Despair* 113
Do 'Ye *d* it to me, when ye *d* it to these'? *In the Child. Hosp.* 26
Doat sisters That *d* upon each other, *To ——. With Pal. of Art* 11
A heart that *d's* on truer charms. *L. C. V. de Vere* 14
if the blossom can *d* on the blight, *The Wreck* 19
eye, that only *d's* On outward beauty, *The Ring* 163
and *d's* On this of yours.' „ 358
Dock'd For which his gains were *d*, *Sea Dreams* 7
Doctor lilted out By violet-hooded *D's*, *Princess ii* 376
then the *D's*! O to hear The *D's*! „ 421
'Here's a leg for a babe of a week!' says *d*; *Grandmother* 11
whoy, *D's* abeän an' agoän; *N. Farmer, O. S.* 2
D's, they knaws nowt, „ 5
D's a 'toättler, lass, „ 66
I weänt breäk rules fur *D*, „ 67
D, if *you* can wait, I'll tell you the tale *First Quarrel* 9
An' *D* 'e calls o' Sunday *North. Cobbler* 87
Our *d* had call'd in another, *In the Child. Hosp.* 1
—so quiet, our *d* said 'Poor little dear, „ 41
I walk'd with our kindly old *d* „ 43
And the *d* came at his hour, „ 68
Doctrine if we held the *d* sound *In Mem. liii* 9
Dodge to *d* and palter with a public crime? *Third of Feb.* 24
Dodged He *d* me with a long and loose account. *Sea Dreams* 149
Doe Lord Ronald brought a lily-white *d* *Lady Clare* 3
The lily-white *d* Lord Ronald had brought „ 61
And follow'd up by a hundred airy *d's*, *Princess vi* 87
Doff'd Until the grave churchwarden *d*, *The Goose* 19
cast his lance aside, And *d* his helm: *Geraint and E.* 596
Dog (*See also* **Shepherd-dog**) I did not hear the *d* howl, mother, *May Queen, Con.* 21
Not less, tho' *d's* of Faction bay, *Love thou thy land* 85
At first like dove and dove were cat and *d*. *Walk. to the Mail* 58
Something better than his *d*, *Locksley Hall* 50
Like a *d*, he hunts in dreams, „ 79
he strode About the hall, among his *d's*, *Godiva* 17
He parted, with great strides among his *d's*. „ 31
And barking *d's*, and crowing cocks; *Day-Dm., Revival* 4
He praised his ploughs, his cows, his hogs, his *d's*; *The Brook* 125
My men shall lash you from them like a *d*; *Aylmer's Field* 325
the *d* With inward yelp and restless forefoot *Lucretius* 44
he had breathed the Proctor's *d's*; *Princess, Pro.* 113
swine were sows, and all the *d's*'— „ *i* 193
wild *d*, and wolf and boar and bear Came *Com. of Arthur* 23
'*D*, thou liest. I spring from loftier lineage *Gareth and L.* 960
one of my co-mates Own'd a rough *d*, „ 1011
a *d* am I, To worry, and not to flee— „ 1014
advanced, Each growling like a *d*, *Geraint and E.* 559
Vivien, tho' ye beat me like your *d*, *Balin and Balan* 582
I better prize The living *d* than the dead lion: „ 585
There like a *d* before his master's door! *Pelleas and E.* 263
Trembled and quiver'd, as the *d*, „ 284
these Inquisition *d's* and the devildoms of Spain.' *The Revenge* 12

Dog (*continued*) Let us bang these *d's* of Seville, *The Revenge* 30
shook 'em off as a *d* that shakes his ears „ 54
And mangle the living *d* that had loved him *In the Child. Hosp.* 9
and the *d* couldn't bark. *V. of Maeldune* 18
they kep the cat an' the *d*, *Tomorrow* 71
sweär 'cep' it wur at a *d* coomin' in, *Spinster's S's.* 60
Eighty winters leave the *d* too lame *Locksley H., Sxty* 226
Fur the *d's* stoän-deäf, an' e's blind, *Owd Roä* 2
Roä was the *d* as knaw'd when an' wheere „ 8
An' the *d's* was a-yowlin' all round, „ 107
I decreed That even the *d* was clean, *Akbar's Dream* 53
He was loved at least by his *d*: *Bandit's Death* 35
Dogg'd and *d* us, and drew me to land? *Despair* 2
Dogwhip-weals From ear to ear with *d-w*, *Last Tournament* 58
Doing See here, my *d*: *Edwin Morris* 5
their own *d*; this is none of mine; *St. S. Stylites* 123
With all its *d's* had and had not been, *Princess iv* 566
No, no, you are *d* me wrong! *First Quarrel* 4
died in the *d* it, flesh without mind; *Vastness* 27
Dole (mourning) that day there was *d* in Astolat. *Lancelot and E.* 1136
Dole (gift) distribute *d* To poor sick people, *Guinevere* 683
hath not our great Queen My *d* of beauty trebled?' *Last Tournament* 558
Dole (verb) I mete and *d* Unequal laws *Ulysses* 3
Domain *See* **World-domain.**
Dome (s) (*See also* **Mid-dome**) stay'd beneath the *d* Of hollow boughs. *Arabian Nights* 41
stream'd Upon the mooned *d's* aloof „ 127
Arno, and the *d* Of Brunelleschi; *The Brook* 189
and dipt Beneath the satin *d* *Princess iv* 31
roll'd Thro' the *d* of the golden cross; *Ode on Well.* 61
Save that the *d* was purple, *Gareth and L.* 912
fallen every purple Cæsar's *d*— *To Virgil* 30
this bare *d* had not begun to gleam *To Mary Boyle* 41
roll her North below thy deepening *d*, *Prog. of Spring* 49
and men, below the *d* of azure Kneel *Akbar's D., Hymn* 7
Dome (verb) *d's* the red-plow'd hills With loving blue; *Early Spring* 3
Domed *See* **Deep-domed.**
Domestic Many a gallant gay *d* Bows *L. of Burleigh* 47
Domine 'Libera me, *D*!' you sang the Psalm, *Happy* 49
'Libera *nos*, *D*'—you knew not one was there „ 53
Dominion *D* in the head and breast.' *Two Voices* 21
Think I may hold *d* sweet, *Maud I xvi* 12
Thro' all the vast *d* which a sword, *Akbar's Dream* 14
Don I never turn'd my back upon *D* or devil yet.' *The Revenge* 31
Done *See* **Ill-done**
Donjon The ruinous *d* as a knoll of moss, *Balin and Balan* 334
And if thou keep me in thy *d* here, *Pelleas and E.* 242
Donn'd Then as he *d* the helm, *Gareth and L.* 690
Donovan's back wid the best he could give at ould *D's* wake— *Tomorrow* 42
Doom (s) chord which Hampden smote Will vibrate to the *d*. *England and Amer.* 20
Hard is my *d* and thine: *Love and Duty* 54
thunder Roaring out their *d*; *The Captain* 42
you have miss'd the irreverent *d* *You might have won* 9
in their eyes and faces read his *d*; *Enoch Arden* 73
his lonely *d* Came suddenly to an end. „ 626
like the blast of *d*, Would shatter all „ 769
the voice that calls *D* upon kings, *Aylmer's Field* 742
Announced the coming *d*, *Sea Dreams* 22
Boanerges with his threats of *d*, „ 251
death-blow struck the dateless *d* of kings, *Lucretius* 236
But lies and dreads his *d*. *Princess vii* 154
Bellowing victory, bellowing *d*: *Ode on Well.* 66
thou fulfillest thy *d* Making him *High. Pantheism* 9
Fall, and follow their *d*. *Voice and the P.* 20
On souls, the lesser lords of *d*. *In Mem. cxii* 8
And batter'd with the shocks of *d* „ *cxviii* 24
While I rose up against my *d*, „ *cxxii* 2
I was cursing them and my *d*, *Maud I xix* 51
I embrace the purpose of God, and the *d* assign'd. „ *III vi* 59
and striking found his *d*. *Com. of Arthur* 325
Arthur said, 'Behold thy *d* is mine. „ 467
the King Throned, and delivering *d*— *Gareth and L.* 321
own false *d*, That shadow of mistrust *Geraint and E.* 247
My madness all thy life has been thy *d*, *Balin and Balan* 619

Doom (s) *(continued)* Dark my *d* was here, and dark It will be — *Balin and Balan* 623
born together, and we die Together by one *d*:' — „ 630
A *d* that ever poised itself to fall, — *Merlin and V.* 191
loved him, with that love which was her *d*. — *Lancelot and E.* 260
Galahad, when he heard of Merlin's *d*, Cried, — *Holy Grail* 177
draw me into sanctuary, And bide my *d*.' — *Guinevere* 122
Pray for him that he scape the *d* of fire, And weep for her who drew him to his *d*.' — „ 347
that I march to meet my *d*. — „ 450
The *d* of treason and the flaming death, — „ 538
that my *d* is, I love thee still. — „ 559
I know not what mysterious *d*. — „ 576
became as mist Before her, moving ghostlike to his *d*. — „ 605
Ill *d* is mine To war against my people — *Pass. of Arthur* 70
'My house hath been my *d*. — „ 154
On that sharp ridge of utmost *d* ride — *Lover's Tale i* 805
whose issue was their *d*, — *Tiresias* 65
echo shall not tongue thy glorious *d*, — „ 136
uncall'd, between me and the deep and my *d*, — *Despair* 5
Demos end in working its own *d*. — *Locksley H., Sixty* 114
for man can half-control his *d* — „ 277
at the doubtful *d* of human kind; — *To Virgil* 24
the dead, who wait the *d* of Hell — *Romney's R.* 132

Doom (verb) King will *d* me when I speak.' — *Gareth and L.* 324

Doom'd *D* them to the lash. — *The Captain* 12
kings of old had *d* thee to the flames, — *Gareth and L.* 374
d to be the bride of Night and Death; — „ 1396
Who rose and *d* me to the fire. — *Sir J. Oldcastle* 172
And *d* to burn alive. — „ 183
Fell the shipcrews *D* to the death. — *Batt. of Brunanburh* 23
Drew to this island: *D* to the death. — „ 51

Doomsday as grand as *d* and as grave: — *Princess i* 187
To and thro' the *D* fire, — *Helen's Tower* 10

Doon (Bonny) *See* **Bonny Doon.**

Door (*See also* **Chamber-door, Chapel-door, Chaumber door, Dovecote-doors, Shrine-doors, Tavern-door**) Oh! vanity! Death waits at the *d*. — *All Things will Die* 17
The *d's* upon their hinges creak'd; — *Mariana* 62
Old faces glimmer'd thro' the *d's*, — „ 66
The costly *d's* flung open wide, — *Arabian Nights* 17
Right to the carven cedarn *d's*, — „ 115
poplars four That stand beside my father's *d*, — *Ode to Memory* 57
Leaving *d* and windows wide: — *Deserted House* 3
And no murmur at the *d*, — „ 7
Close the *d*, the shutters close, — „ 9
An image seem'd to pass the *d*, (repeat) — *Mariana in the S.* 65, 74
The very air about the *d* Made misty — *Miller's D.* 103
As near this *d* you sat apart, — „ 158
The guilt of blood is at your *d*: — *L. C. V. de Vere* 43
carried out from the threshold of the *d*; — *May Queen, N. Y's. E.* 42
thro' the *d* Hearing the holy organ — *D. of F. Women* 190
standeth there alone, And waiteth at the *d*. — *D. of the O. Year* 51
a new face at the *d*, my friend, A new face at the *d*. — „ 53
thro' mine own *d's* Death did pass; — *To J. S.* 19
There strode a stranger to the *d*, (repeat) — *The Goose* 3, 39
d's that bar The secret bridal chambers of the heart, — *Gardener's D.* 248
And never more darken my *d's* again.' — *Dora* 32
The *d* was off the latch: they peep'd, — „ 130
whined in lobbies, tapt at *d's*, — *Walk. to the Mail* 37
I say, that time is at the *d's* — *St. S. Stylites* 192
This same grand year is ever at the *d's*.' — *Golden Year* 74
Every *d* is barr'd with gold, — *Locksley Hall* 100
all Should keep within, *d* shut, — *Godiva* 41
And feet that ran, and *d's* that clapt, — *Day-Dm., Revival* 3
He lifts me to the golden *d's*; — *St. Agnes' Eve* 25
The stalls are void, the *d's* are wide, — *Sir Galahad* 31
One fix'd for ever at the *d*, — *Will Water.* 143
gay domestic Bows before him at the *d*. — *L. of Burleigh* 48
Paused for a moment at an inner *d*, — *Enoch Arden* 278
there At Annie's *d* he paused and gave his hand, — „ 447
when they follow'd us from Philip's *d*, — *The Brook* 167
A lily-avenue climbing to the *d's*; — *Aylmer's Field* 162
Withdrawing by the counter *d* — „ 282

Door *(continued)* should I find you by my *d's* again, — *Aylmer's Field* 324
till he heard the ponderous *d* Close, — „ 337
month by month the noise about their *d's*, — „ 488
oaken finials till he touch'd the *d*; — „ 823
jam the *d's*, and bear The keepers down, — *Lucretius* 169
stood that same fair creature at the *d*. — *Princess ii* 329
call'd For Psyche's child to cast it from the *d's*; — „ *iv* 238
came a little stir About the *d's*, — „ 374
I will go and sit beside the *d's*, — „ *v* 96
He batter'd at the *d's*; none came: — „ 337
one glance he caught Thro' open *d's* of Ida — „ 343
'Fling our *d's* wide! all, all, — „ *vi* 334
bare Straight to the *d's*: to them the *d's* — „ 349
long-laid galleries past a hundred *d's* — „ 375
roll the torrent out of dusky *d's*: — „ *vii* 208
Thy name was blest within the narrow *d*; — *W. to Marie Alex.* 38
Often they come to the *d* — *Grandmother* 82
D's, where my heart was used to beat — *In Mem. vii* 3
I creep At earliest morning to the *d*. — „ 8
as if a *d* Were shut between me and the sound: — „ *xxviii* 7
Shall enter in at lowly *d's*. — „ *xxxvi* 8
They chatter'd trifles at the *d*: — „ *lxix* 4
crowds that stream from yawning *d's*, — „ *lxx* 9
Another name was on the *d*: — „ *lxxxvii* 17
From out the *d's* where I was bred, — „ *ciii* 2
D's, where my heart was used to beat — „ *cxix* 1
Thou listenest to the closing *d*, — „ *cxxi* 7
And touch with shade the bridal *d's*, — „ *Con.* 117
Look, a horse at the *d*, — *Maud I xii* 29
even then I heard her close the *d*, — „ *xviii* 11
Did he stand at the diamond *d* — „ *II ii* 16
Modred laid his ear beside the *d's*, — *Com. of Arthnr* 323
shone the fields of May thro' open *d*, — „ 460
Ate with young lads his portion by the *d*, — *Gareth and L.* 480
saw without the *d* King Arthur's gift, — „ 676
so Sir Kay beside the *d* Mutter'd in scorn — „ 705
broken into Thro' open *d's* and hospitality; — *Marr. of Geraint* 456
Glanced at the *d's* or gambol'd down — „ 665
d, Push'd from without, drave backward — *Geraint and E.* 272
thought she heard the wild Earl at the *d*, — „ 381
A walk of roses ran from *d* to *d*; — *Balin and Balan* 242
And all in shadow from the counter *d* — „ 246
Beneath a low *d* dipt, and made his feet — „ 403
found a *d*, And darkling felt the sculptured ornament — *Merlin and V.* 733
and entering barr'd her *d*, — *Lancelot and E.* 15
guide me to that palace, to the *d's*.' — „ 1129
There two stood arm'd, and kept the *d*; — „ 1247
rose And pointed to the damsel, and the *d's*. — „ 1263
lords and dames And people, from the high *d* streaming, — „ 1347
behold a woman at a *d* Spinning; — *Holy Grail* 391
against the chapel *d* Laid lance, and enter'd, — „ 459
Pass not from *d* to *d* and out again, — „ 714
at the last I reach'd a *d*, — „ 837
in my madness I essay'd the *d*; — „ 841
the high *d's* Were softly sunder'd, — *Pelleas and E.* 3
Unbind him now, And thrust him out of *d's*; — „ 257
There like a dog before his master's *d*! — „ 263
but thrust him bounden out of *d*. — „ 314
straight on thro' open *d* Rode Gawain, — „ 382
Pelleas, leaping up, Ran thro' the *d's* — „ 539
Sprang from the *d* into the dark. — „ 603
And while they stood within the *d's*, — *Last Tournament* 113
machicolated tower That stood with open *d's*, — „ 425
but sprang Thro' open *d's*, — „ 473
Flush'd, started, met him at the *d's*, — „ 512
Like to some doubtful noise of creaking *d's*, — *Guinevere* 72
There rode an armed warrior to the *d's*. — „ 409
Thro' the long gallery from the outer *d's* Rang — „ 413
waiting by the *d's* the warhorse neigh'd — „ 530
lo, he sat on horseback at the *d*! — „ 589
open'd on the pines with *d's* of glass, — *Lover's Tale i* 41
Death drew nigh and beat the *d's* of Life; — „ 111
had Heaven from all her *d's*, — „ 604
To stand a shadow by their shining *d's*, — „ 731

Door (*continued*) bad his menials bear him from the *d*, *Lover's Tale iv* 260
There were our horses ready at the *d's*— „ 385
They had fasten'd the *d* of his cell. *Rizpah* 42
to keep the wolf fro' the *d*, *North. Cobbler* 29
our Sally as kep the wolf fro' the *d*, „ 59
They have left the *d's* ajar; *Sisters (E. and E)* 1
and a noise of welcome at the *d's*— „ 149
found her beating the hard Protestant *d's*. „ 240
they niver derken'd my *d*. *Village Wife* 60
when I saw him come in at the *d*, *In the Child. Hosp.* 2
Boardings and rafters and *d's*— *Def. of Lucknow* 67
what a *d* for scoundrel scum I open'd *Columbus* 170
The *d's* of Night may be the gates of Light; *Ancient Sage* 174
let them spurn me from the *d's*, *The Flight* 55
A *d* was open'd in the house— „ 69
but she put thim all to the *d*. *Tomorrow* 44
sound ran Thro' palace and cottage *d*, *Dead Prophet* 38
Opens a *d* in Heaven; *Early Spring* 7
cuckoo of a joyless June Is calling out of *d's*: *Pref. Poem Broth. S.* 4
Door-handles turn'd when none was at the *d*, And bolted *d's* that open'd of themselves: *The Ring* 412
The *d* is open. He! is he standing at the *d*, *Happy* 11
some fair dawn beyond the *d's* of death *Far-far-away* 11
—a widow came to my *d*: *Charity* 26
Door'd *See* **Open-door'd**
Door-handle *D-h's* turn'd when none was at the door, *The Ring* 412
Doorm *D*, whom his shaking vassals call'd the Bull, *Geraint and E.* 439
we may meet the horsemen of Earl *D*, „ 492
One took him for a victim of Earl *D*, „ 524
Another, flying from the wrath of *D* „ 530
at the point of noon the huge Earl *D*, „ 536
said Earl *D*: 'Well, if he be not dead, „ 546
And bore him to the naked hall of *D*, „ 570
return'd The huge Earl *D* with plunder to the hall. „ 592
Earl *D* Struck with a knife's haft hard „ 599
But when Earl *D* had eaten all he would, „ 609
So died Earl *D* by him he counted dead. „ 730
I took you for a bandit knight of *D*; „ 786
I come the mouthpiece of our King to *D* „ 796
'and lo, the powers of *D* Are scatter'd,' „ 801
Door-poorch (door-porch) my oän *d-p* wi' the woodbine *Spinster's S's.* 105
to pictur the *d-p* theere, *Owd Roä* 24
Doorwaäy (doorway) An' then as I stood i' the *d*, „ 42
Doorway (*See also* **Doorwaäy, Palace-doorway**) Dawn'd sometime thro' the *d*? *Aylmer's Field* 685
God shut the *d's* of his head. *In Mem. xliv* 4
out by this main *d* past the King. *Gareth and L.* 671
Doost (dust) Loovs 'im, an' roobs 'im, an' *d's* 'im, *North. Cobbler* 98
Dora at the farm abode William and *D*. *Dora* 2
Now *D* felt her uncle's will in all, „ 5
Thought not of *D*. „ 8
Now therefore look to *D*; „ 15
for his sake I bred His daughter *D*: „ 20
'I cannot marry *D*; by my life, I will not marry *D*.' „ 23
his ways were harsh; But *D* bore them meekly. „ 36
And *D* promised, being meek. „ 46
D stored what little she could save, „ 52
Then *D* went to Mary. „ 56
and thought Hard things of *D*. *D* came and said: „ 58
D took the child, and went her way „ 71
none of all his men Dare tell him *D* waited with the child; „ 76
D would have risen and gone to him, „ 77
D cast her eyes upon the ground, „ 89
'did I not Forbid you, *D*?' *D* said again: „ 92
The wreath of flowers fell At *D's* feet. „ 103
Then *D* went to Mary's house, „ 110
Mary saw the boy Was not with *D*. „ 112
D said, 'My uncle took the boy; „ 114
now I come For *D*: take her back; „ 143
take *D* back And let all this be as it was „ 154
and *D* hid her face By Mary. „ 156
But *D* lived unmarried till her death. „ 172
Dorhawk-whirr and *d-w* Awoke me not, *Lover's Tale ii* 116
Dormouse blue wood-louse, and the plump *d*, *Window, Winter* 9

Dorset-Dorsetshire There was a farmer in *Dorset* of Harry's kin, *First Quarrel* 17
So Harry was bound to the *Dorsetshire* farm „ 19
Dose fumes Of that dark opiate *d* you gave me,— *Romney's R.* 31
Dot hull Look'd one black *d* against the verge *M. d'Arthur* 271
hull Look'd one black *d* against the verge *Pass. of Arthur* 439
The fires that arch this dusky *d*— *Epilogue* 52
Dotage Cries of unprogressive *d* *Locksley H., Sixty* 153
Dotard call him *d* in your rage „ 9
ere the *d* fell asleep? „ 153
Dote *d* and pore on yonder cloud *In Mem. xv* 16
Double (adv.) And then we drank it *d*; *Will Water.* 96
Double (verb) wind And *d* in and out the boles, *Princess iv* 262
Double-charge Now *d-c* it with grape! *Def. of Lucknow* 68
Doubled *d* his own warmth against her lips, *Gardener's D.* 138
old man Was wroth, and *d* up his hands, *Dora* 25
but when his date *D* her own, *Aylmer's Field* 81
Double-dragon'd fill'd his *d-d* chair. *Last Tournament* 144
Doubling *d* all his master's vice of pride, *Marr. of Geraint* 195
Doubt (s) a special care Of God, to fortify from *d*, *Supp. Confessions* 64
Moved from beneath with *d* and fear. „ 138
If so be that from *d* at length, „ 143
Roof'd the world with *d* and fear, *Eleänore* 99
carve out Free space for every human *d*, *Two Voices* 137
These things are wrapt in *d* and dread, „ 266
There must be answer to his *d*. „ 309
'The *d* would rest, I dare not solve. „ 313
The *d* my mother would not see; *Miller's D.* 154
In *d* and great perplexity, *Palace of Art* 278
but empty breath And rumours of a *d*? *M. d'Arthur* 100
(For all my mind is clouded with a *d*) „ 258
lying thus inactive, *d* and gloom. *Enoch Arden* 113
Such *d's* and fears were common to her state, „ 521
One spiritual *d* she did not soothe? *Aylmer's Field* 704
Discuss'd a *d* and tost it to and fro: *Princess ii* 445
Disturb'd me with the *d* 'if this were she,' „ *iv* 217
came On a sudden the weird seizure and the *d*: „ 560
for spite of *d's* And sudden ghostly shadowings „ 571
Deeper than those weird *d's* could reach me, „ *vii* 51
I have heard Of your strange *d's*: „ 336
my *d's* are dead, My haunting sense of hollow shows: „ 348
In *d* if you be of our Barons' breed— *Third of Feb.* 32
A spectral *d* which makes me cold, *In Mem. xli* 19
O turn thee round, resolve the *d*; „ *xliv* 14
such as closed Grave *d's* and answers „ *xlviii* 3
What slender shade of *d* may flit, „ 7
Defects of *d*, and taints of blood; „ *liv* 4
Nor can my dream resolve the *d*: „ *lxviii* 12
D and Death, Ill brethren, let the fancy fly „ *lxxxvi* 11
And *d* beside the portal waits, „ *xciv* 14
bold to dwell On *d's* that drive the coward back, „ *xcv* 30
trance Was cancell'd, stricken thro' with *d*. „ 44
You tell me, *d* is Devil-born. „ *xcvi* 4
There lives more faith in honest *d*, „ 11
He fought his *d's* and gather'd strength, „ 13
To seize and throw the *d's* of man; „ *cix* 6
Our dearest faith; our ghastliest *d*; „ *cxxiv* 2
No, like a child in *d* and fear: „ 17
Mix not memory with *d*, *Maud II iv* 57
A *d* that ever smoulder'd in the hearts *Com. of Arthur* 64
in daily *d* Whether to live or die, *Lancelot and E.* 520
Lost in a *d*, Pelleas wandering Waited, *Pelleas and E.* 392
This tender rhyme, and evermore the *d*, „ 410
fault and *d*—no word of that fond tale— *Last Tournament* 578
but empty breath And rumours of a *d*? *Pass. of Arthur* 268
(For all my mind is clouded with a *d*)— „ 426
'But solve me first a *d*. *Lover's Tale iv* 254
Naw *d*: But I liked a bigger feller to fight *North. Cobbler* 99
fluttering in a *d* Between the two— *Sisters (E. and E.)* 33
raise the full High-tide of *d* „ 178
in days Of *d* and cloud and storm, *Columbus* 156
And *D* is the lord of this dunghill *Despair* 90
Cleave ever to the sunnier side of *d*, *Ancient Sage* 68
and yet no shade of *d*, But utter clearness, „ 235
lost in the gloom of *d's* that darken the schools; *Vastness* 11

Doubt (s) (*continued*) after hours of search and d and threats, The Ring 278
Still—at times A d, a fear,— Akbar's Dream 169
darken'd with d's of a Faith that saves, The Dreamer 11
Doubt (verb) It is man's privilege to d, Supp. Confessions 142
I fear All may not d, „ 178
evidence, By which he d's against the sense? Two Voices 285
I d not thro' the ages Locksley Hall 137
'True,' she said, 'We d not that. Princess, Pro. 169
'D my word again!' he said. „ 176
Until we d not that for one so true Ode on Well. 255
D not ye the Gods have answer'd, Boädicea 22
For can I d, who knew thee keen In Mem. cxiii 5
I d not what thou wouldst have been: „ cxiii 8
Who d's thee victor? Gareth and L. 1296
I do not d To find, at some place Marr. of Geraint 218
Henceforward I will rather die than d. Geraint and E. 738
And will henceforward rather die than d. „ 745
nor did he d her more, But rested in her fealty, „ 966
I d not that however changed, Lancelot and E. 1218
To d her fairness were to want an eye, To d her pureness were to want a heart— „ 1376
heard a voice, 'D not, go forward; if thou d, the beasts Will tear thee piecemeal.' Holy Grail 824
enow To make one d if ever the great Queen Last Tournament 564
never d each other more. Happy 92
I with this dagger of his—do you d me? Bandit's Death 42
an' I d's they poison'd the cow. Church-warden, etc. 16
D no longer that the Highest is the wisest Faith 1
Doubted D, and drowsed, nodded and slept, Com. of Arthur 427
and d him No more than he, himself; Gareth and L. 125
I d whether daughter's tenderness, Marr. of Geraint 797
Doubtful I answer'd nothing, d in myself Princess iii 272
the old man, Tho' d, felt the flattery, Merlin and V. 184
some were d how the law would hold, Lover's Tale iv 270
Doubting thought To sift his d's to the last, Com. of Arthur 311
Doubtless 'D—ay, but ever since In all the world The Ring 363
Dove (*See also* **Ringdove, Wood-dove**) Let Thy d Shadow me over, Supp. Confessions 180
And oft I heard the tender d Miller's D. 41
Came voices of the well-contented d's. Gardener's D. 89
Like d's about a dovecote, wheeling round „ 224
they that loved At first like d and d Walk. to the Mail 58
iris changes on the burnish'd d; Locksley Hall 19
I would not one of thine own d's, Lucretius 68
morning d's That sun their milky bosoms Princess ii 102
The d may murmur of the d, „ iii 105
A troop of snowy d's athwart the dusk, „ iv 168
The moan of d's in immemorial elms, „ vii 221
O merry the linnet and d, Window, Ay 13
O somewhere, meek, unconscious d, In Mem. vi 25
as a d when up she springs To bear „ xii 1
then flew in a d And brought a summons „ ciii 15
She is coming, my d, my dear; Maud I xxii 61
My own d with the tender eye? „ II iv 46
And while your d's about you flit, To E. Fitzgerald 7
round her forehead wheels the woodland d, Prog. of Spring 57
Dovecote Like doves about a d, wheeling round Gardener's D. 224
Dovecote-doors some one batters at the d-d, Princess iv 169
Dowager prudes for proctors, d's for deans, „ Pro. 141
Do-well D-w will follow thought, Ancient Sage 273
Dower lent you, love, your mortal d Of pensive thought Margaret 5
Dower'd D with the hate of hate, The Poet 3
Dowerless but both Were d, and myself, The Ring 167
Down (hill) here are the blissful d's and dales, Sea-Fairies 22
the yellow d Border'd with palm, Lotos-Eaters 21
Round and round the spicy d's „ C. S. 104
She went by dale, and she went by d, Lady Clare 59
behind it a gray d With Danish barrows; Enoch Arden 6
Green in a cuplike hollow of the d. „ 9
But in the leafy lanes behind the d, „ 97
early roses from his wall, Or conies from the d, „ 340
after scaling half the weary d, „ 372
November dawns and dewy-glooming d's, „ 610
Close to the ridge of a noble d. To F. D. Maurice 16
And on the d's a rising fire: In Mem., Con. 108
Down (hill) (*continued*) And rise, O moon, from yonder d, In Mem., Con. 109
Till over d and over dale „ 110
face of night is fair on the dewy d's, Maud III vi 5
some wild d above the windy deep, Merlin and V. 658
And there among the solitary d's, Lancelot and E. 163
O'er these waste d's whereon I lost myself, „ 225
Sparkle, until they dipt below the d's. „ 396
the long backs of the bushless d's, (repeat) „ 400, 789
For the d's are as bright as day, Rizpah 4
and the storm rushing over the d, „ 6
when the storm on the d's began, „ 71
lived With Muriel's mother on the d, The Ring 148
Among the quarried d's of Wight, To Ulysses 32
THERE on the top of the d, June Bracken, etc. 1
Down (feathery substance) silk-soft folds, upon yielding d, Eleänore 28
rosy thigh Half-buried in the Eagle's d, Palace of Art 122
wild hawk stood with the d on his beak, Poet's Song 11
in broider'd d we sank Our elbows: Princess iv 32
When in the d I sink my head, In Mem. lxviii 1
Art yet half-yolk, not even come to d— Balin and Balan 569
Down-carolling D-c to the crisped sea, The Winds, etc. 6
Downcast her eyes were d, not to be seen) Maud I ii 5
Down-deepening D-d from swoon to swoon, Fatima 27
Down-droop'd-Down-dropt EYES not down-dropt nor over-bright, Isabel 1
Down-droop'd, in many a floating fold, Arabian Nights 147
With down-dropt eyes I sat alone: Œnone 56
Downfall 'tween the spring and d of the light, St. S. Stylites 110
Down-glancing a spear D-g lamed the charger Lancelot and E. 488
Down-lapsing fancies, by d-l thought Stream'd onward, D. of F. Women 49
Down-streaming the dread sweep of the d-s seas: Enoch Arden 55
Down-way Pleasure who flaunts on her wide d-w Vastness 16
Dowry Large dowries doth the raptured eye Ode to Memory 72
Doy (die) But sin' I mun d I mun d, N. Farmer, O. S. 64
an' if I mun d I mun d. „ 68
Doze Fell in a d; and half-awake I heard The Epic 13
half in d I seem'd To float about Princess i 246
Did I hear it half in a d Long since, Maud I vii 1
In a wakeful d I sorrow For the hand, „ II iv 26
Dozed Miriam watch'd and d at intervals, Enoch Arden 909
As the pimpernel d on the lea; Maud I xxii 48
Then d awhile herself, but overtoil'd Geraint and E. 376
I d; I woke. An open landaulet Whirl'd Sisters (E. and E.) 85
Dozing Lay, d in the vale of Avalon, Palace of Art 107
Draäin (drain) Miss Annie she said it wur d's, Village Wife 11
Draff chaff and d, much better burnt.' The Epic 40
Drag will have weight to d thee down. Locksley Hall 48
And that d's down his life: Sea Dreams 177
poor Psyche whom she d's in tow.' Princess iii 103
Should d you down, and some great Nemesis „ vi 174
and d's me down From my fixt height „ 307
a great black cloud D inward from the deeps, „ vii 37
That seem to keep her up but d her down— „ 270
And onward d's a labouring breast, In Mem. xv 18
To d me down to seventy-nine. To Ulysses 8
wife and children d an Artist down! Romney's R. 38
if the rebel subject seek to d me from the throne, By an Evolution. 15
Dragg'd we d her to the college tower Walk. to the Mail 89
What Roman would be d in triumph thus? Lucretius 234
I d my brains for such a song, Princess iv 154
a madden'd beach d down by the wave, Maud I iii 12
D him, and struck, but from the castle Balin and Balan 399
so by force they d him to the King. Merlin and V. 640
He d his eyebrow bushes down, „ 807
d me up there to his cave in the mountain, Bandit's Death 11
and the weight that d at my hand; „ 39
Dragging Grimy nakedness d his trucks Maud I x 7
a dream Of d down his enemy made them move. Lancelot and E. 814
Reversion ever d Evolution in the mud. Locksley H., Sixty 200
Draggle An' Sally wur sloomy an' d North. Cobbler 41
Draggled Tho' somewhat d at the skirt. Last Tournament 219
Dragon The golden gorge of d's spouted forth Palace of Art 23
A gilded d, also, for the babes. Enoch Arden 540
To catch a d in a cherry net, Princess v 169
D's of the prime, That tare each other In Mem. lvi 22

Dragon (*continued*) the shape thereof A *d* wing'd, *Com. of Arthur* 375
The shining *d* and the naked child „ 399
Thro' twenty folds of twisted *d*, *Gareth and L.* 510
Since to his crown the golden *d* clung, And down his robe the *d* writhed in gold, *Lancelot and E.* 434
behind him crept Two *d's* gilded, „ 437
saw The golden *d* sparkling over all: *Holy Grail* 263
weigh'd the necks Of *d's* clinging „ 347
On wyvern, lion, *d*, griffin, swan, „ 350
dinted the gilt *d's* right and left, *Last Tournament* 182
his foot was on a stool Shaped as a *d*; „ 672
The *D* of the great Pendragonship, (repeat) *Guinevere* 398, 598
for crest the golden *d* clung Of Britain; „ 594
made West East, and sail'd the *D's* mouth, *Columbus* 25
the multitudinous beast, The *d*, *Tiresias* 16
D's cave, Half hid, they tell me, „ 143
rolling of *d's* By marble of water, *Merlin and the G.* 44
Dragon (inn sign) At the *D* on the heath! *Vision of Sin* 72
Dragon-boughts *d-b* and elvish emblemings *Gareth and L.* 233
Dragon'd *See* **Double-Dragon'd**
Dragon-fly 'To-day I saw the *d-f* *Two Voices* 8
glancing like a *d-f* In summer suit *Marr. of Geraint* 172
d Shot by me like a flash of purple fire. *Lover's Tale ii* 16
Drain (s) (*See also* **Draäin**) Flaying the roofs and sucking up the *d's*, *Princess v* 525
my blood Crept like marsh *d's* *Lover's Tale ii* 53
Send the *d* into the fountain, *Locksley H., Sixty* 144
Drain (verb) a lip to *d* thy trouble dry. *Locksley Hall* 88
d's The chalice of the grapes of God; *In Mem. x* 15
Drainage with the *d* of your sewer; *Locksley H., Sixty* 143
Drain'd (*See also* **Half-drain'd**) Ida stood nor spoke, *d* of her force *Princess vi* 266
love for him have *d* My capabilities of love; *In Mem. lxxxv* 11
scheme that had left us flaccid and *d*. *Maud I i* 20
blood Of their strong bodies, flowing, *d* their force. *Marr. of Geraint* 569
the hurt that *d* her dear lord's life. *Geraint and E.* 516
D of her force, again she sat, *Last Tournament* 540
raised the school, and *d* the fen. *Locksley H., Sixty* 268
Drake So witty that ye play'd at ducks and *d's* *Last Tournament* 344
Drama Victor in *D*, Victor in Romance, *To Victor Hugo* 1
Thine is it that our *d* did not die, *To W. C. Macready* 9
In some fifth Act what this wild *D* means. *The Play* 4
Drank 'We *d* the Libyan Sun to sleep, *D. of F. Women* 145
The butler *d*, the steward scrawl'd, *Day-Dm., Revival* 10
And then we *d* it double; *Will Water.* 96
and *d* The magic cup that fill'd itself *Aylmer's Field* 142
d and past it; till at length the two, „ 408
D the large air, and saw, *Sea Dreams* 34
Sat at his table: *d* his costly wines; „ 74
d the gale That blown about the foliage *Princess iii* 120
and *d* himself into his grave. *Grandmother* 6
And *d*, and loyally *d* to him. *The Daisy* 24
There they *d* in cups of emerald, *Boädicea* 61
Nor ever *d* the inviolate spring *In Mem. xc* 2
Sir Gareth *d* and ate, *Gareth and L.* 1280
Earl Limours *D* till he jested with all ease, *Geraint and E.* 290
they *d* and some one sang, *Balin and Balan* 85
then you *d* And knew no more, *Merlin and V.* 276
cup itself, from which our Lord *D* at the last sad supper *Holy Grail* 47
But even while I *d* the brook, „ 387
drink, Sir Fool,' and thereupon I *d*, *Last Tournament* 297
In that close kiss, and *d* her whisper'd tales. *Lover's Tale i* 817
And parted lips which *d* her breath, „ *ii* 204
Well then—our solemn feast—we ate and *d*, „ *iv* 221
show'd he *d* beyond his use; „ 228
d the dews and drizzle of the North, *Prog. of Spring* 81
Draped sweet sculpture *d* from head to foot, *Princess v* 57
grayly *d* With streaming grass, appear'd, *Balin and Balan* 332
Drapery At her left, a child, In shining *draperies*, *Princess ii* 109
Draught Brimm'd with delirious *d's* of warmest life. *Eleänore* 139
Some *d* of Lethe might await *Two Voices* 350
gather'd green From *d's* of balmy air. *Sir L. and Q. G.* 9
mix the foaming *d* Of fever, *Princess ii* 251
think that you might mix his *d* with death, „ *vi* 277

Draught (*continued*) A shot, ere half thy *d* be done, *In Mem. vi* 11
the cup was gold, the *d* was mud.' *Last Tournament* 298
keeps A *d* of that sweet fountain *Lover's Tale i* 141
Love pledge Hatred in her bitter *d's*, „ 776
deny my sultry throat One *d* of icy water. *Romney's R.* 23
Drave I *d* Among the thickest and bore down a Prince, *Princess v* 517
Then he *d* The heathen; *Com. of Arthur* 58
Who *d* the heathen hence by sorcery *Gareth and L.* 204
He *d* his enemy backward down the bridge, „ 969
D the long spear a cubit thro' his breast *Geraint and E.* 86
door, Push'd from without, *d* backward „ 273
the boat *D* with a sudden wind across the deeps, *Merlin and V.* 201
d his kith and kin, And all the Table Round *Lancelot and E.* 498
d her ere her time across the fields „ 890
'He took them and he *d* them to his tower— *Last Tournament* 68
Red Knight Brake in upon me and *d* them to his tower; „ 72
Draw *D* down into his vexed pools *Supp. Confessions* 133
something in the darkness *d's* His forehead „ 167
the mountain *d's* it from Heaven above, *Poet's Mind* 32
And *d* itself to what it was before; *Eleänore* 94
D's different threads, and late and soon *Two Voices* 179
plunging seas *d* backward from the land *Palace of Art* 251
To her full height her stately stature *d's*; *D. of F. Women* 102
Watch what main-currents *d* the years: *Love thou thy land* 21
'My end *d's* nigh; 'tis time that I were gone. *M. d'Arthur* 163
and *d's* The greater to the lesser, *Gardener's D.* 9
end *d's* nigh; I hope my end *d's* nigh: *St. S. Stylites* 36
deny it now? Nay, *d*, *d*, *d* nigh. „ 207
And *d's* the veil from hidden worth. *Day-Dm., Arrival* 4
D me, thy bride, a glittering star, *St Agnes' Eve* 23
what *d's* me down Into the common day? *Will Water.* 153
Some that she but held off to *d* him on; *Enoch Arden* 476
And *d* them all along, and flow *The Brook* 63
hunters round a hunted creature *d* The cordon *Aylmer's Field* 499
yet he *d's* Nearer and nearer, *Lucretius* 194
what mother's blood You *d* from, fight; *Princess v* 405
Ask me no more: the moon may *d* the sea; „ *vii* 1
and *d* The sting from pain; „ 63
D toward the long frost and longest night, *A Dedication* 11
So *d* him home to those that mourn *In Mem. ix* 5
And scarce endure to *d* the breath, „ *xx* 15
The time *d's* near the birth of Christ: „ *xxviii* 1
D forth the cheerful day from night: „ *xxx* 30
Like birds the charming serpent *d's*, „ *xxxiv* 14
D down Æonian hills, and sow The dust „ *xxxv* 11
d The deepest measure from the chords: „ *xlviii* 11
And tease her till the day *d's* by: „ *lx* 14
virtue such as *d's* A faithful answer „ *lxxxv* 13
and we to *d* From deep to deep, „ *ciii* 38
The time *d's* near the birth of Christ; „ *civ* 1
To *d*, to sheathe a useless sword, „ *cxxviii* 13
But they must go, the time *d's* on, „ *Con.* 89
A soul shall *d* from out the vast „ 123
dark undercurrent woe That seems to *d*— *Maud I xviii* 84
To turn the broach, *d* water, *Gareth and L.* 486
and ever fail'd to *d* The quiet night into her blood. *Marr. of Geraint* 531
as the worm *d's* in the wither'd leaf *Geraint and E.* 633
long have watch'd how Lancelot *d's* *Balin and Balan* 375
Gasping to Sir Lavaine, '*D* the lance-head:' *Lancelot and E.* 511
'I dread me, if I *d* it, you will die.' „ 513
'I die already with it: *d*—*D*,'— „ 514
For I will *d* me into sanctuary, *Guinevere* 121
'My end *d's* nigh; 'tis time that I were gone. *Pass. of Arthur* 331
sail Will *d* me to the rising of the sun, *Lover's Tale i* 27
Whereof to all that *d* the wholesome air, „ 500
mitre-sanction'd harlot *d's* his clerks *Sir J. Oldcastle* 106
In his own well, *d* solace as he may. *Tiresias* 89
but seem to *d* From yon dark cave, *Ancient Sage* 9
from her household orbit *d's* the child *To Prin. Beatrice* 7
serpent-wanded power *D* downward into Hades *Demeter and P.* 26
would fail, to *d* The crowd from wallowing *Akbar's Dream* 140
nor the sod *D* from my death Thy living flower *Doubt and Prayer* 6
Draw'd coostom ageän *d* in like a wind *North. Cobbler* 93

Drawing D into his narrow earthen urn, Ode to Memory 61
d nigh Half-whisper'd in his ear, Œnone 185
bright river d slowly His waters Lotos-Eaters, C. S. 92
And o'er him, d it, the winter moon, M. d'Arthur 53
Then spoke King Arthur, d thicker breath; „ 148
And newer knowledge, d nigh, Day-Dm., Sleep P. 51
slowly d near, A vapour heavy, hueless, Vision of Sin 52
For now the day was d on, In Mem. lxxxiv 10
each, dishorsed and d, lash'd at each So often Marr. of Geraint 563
And d down the dim disastrous brow Balin and Balan 597
And d somewhat backward she replied, Last Tournament 523
And d foul ensample from fair names, Guinevere 490
o'er him, d it, the winter moon, Pass. of Arthur 221
Then spoke King Arthur, d thicker breath: „ 316
d down from both The light and genial warmth To Prin. Beatrice 21
the star of eve was d light From the dead sun, Death of Œnone 64
Drawn Thence thro' the garden I was d— Arabian Nights 100
all which thou hast d of fairest Or boldest since, Ode to Memory 89
All day and all night it is ever d Poet's Mind 28
D from each other mellow-deep; Eleänore 67
creeps from pine to pine, And loiters, slowly d. Œnone 5
dew, D from the spirit thro' the brain, To J. S. 38
the dusky highway near and nearer d, Locksley Hall 113
But all my heart is d above, Sir Galahad 17
robe Of twilight slowly downward d, The Voyage 22
till d thro' either chasm, Enoch Arden 670
With reasons d from age and state, Princess v 357
all their foreheads d in Roman scowls, „ vii 129
sweet little body that never had d a breath. Grandmother 62
And then I know the mist is d In Mem. lxvii 13
It might have d from after-heat.' „ lxxxi 12
O bliss, when all in circle d „ lxxxix 21
The silvery haze of summer d; „ xcv 4
The boat is d upon the shore; „ cxxi 6
I beheld The death-white curtain d; Maud I xiv 34
Gareth overthrew him, lighted, drew, There met him d, Gareth and L. 1122
souls the old serpent long had d Down, Geraint and E. 632
coverlid was cloth of gold D to her waist, Lancelot and E. 1158
what evil beast Hath d his claws athwart thy face? Last Tournament 63
Irish eyes Had d him home—what marvel? „ 405
Had d herself from many thousand years, Lover's Tale i 550
As if 'twere d asunder by the rack. „ ii 57
the portrait of his friend D by an artist, Sisters (E. and E.) 135
living water, d By this good Wiclif mountain Sir J. Oldcastle 131
Sphinx, with wings d back, Folded her lion paws, Tiresias 148
magnet of Art to the which my nature was d, The Wreck 22
still d downward for an hour, The Ring 477
Dread (s) once from d of pain to die. Two Voices 105
'These things are wrapt in doubt and d, „ 266
Deep d and loathing of her solitude Palace of Art 229
and half in d To hear my father's clamour Princess i 104
Sick, am I sick of a jealous d? Maud I x 1
And dream of her beauty with tender d, „ xvi 14
But save for d of thee had beaten me, Last Tournament 525
Dread (verb) might I d that you, With only Fame Princess iii 241
I d His wildness, and the chances of the dark.' „ iv 243
But lies and d's his doom. „ vii 154
No inner vileness that we d? In Mem. li 4
but, so thou d to swear, Gareth and L. 272
I rather d the loss of use than fame; Merlin and V. 519
'I d me, if I draw it, you will die.' Lancelot and E. 513
if she knows And d's it we are fall'n.— To the Queen ii 33
I almost d to find her, dumb!' Lover's Tale iv 339
Dreaded he, she d most, bare down upon him. Geraint and E. 156
Dreadful D! has it come to this, Forlorn 43
Dreading d worse than shame Her warrior Tristram, Last Tournament 384
Dream (s) (See also **Dhrame, Half-dream**) sweet d's softer than unbroken rest Ode to Memory 29
Heaven flow'd upon the soul in many d's The Poet 31
a name to shake All evil d's of power— „ 47
To lapse far back in some confused d Sonnet To —— 3
Dreaming, she knew it was a d: Mariana in the S. 49
said the voice, 'thy d was good, Two Voices 157

Dream (s) (continued) And did not dream it was a d; Two Voices 213
men Forget the d that happens then, „ 353
Like glimpses of forgotten d's— „ 381
'I talk,' said he, 'Not with thy d's. „ 386
Before I dream'd that pleasant d— Miller's D. 46
Breathing like one that hath a weary d. Lotos-Eaters 6
my voice was thick with sighs As in a d. D. of F. Women 110
captain of my d's Ruled in the eastern sky. „ 263
Into that wondrous track of d's again! But no two d's are like. „ 279
Make bright our days and light our d's, Of old sat Freedom 22
Black-stoled, black-hooded, like a d— M. d'Arthur 197
on to dawn, when d's Begin to feel the truth „ Ep. 18
sweeter than the d Dream'd by a happy man, Gardener's D. 71
The pilot of the darkness and the d Audley Court 72
should one give to light on such a d?' Edwin Morris 58
Should it cross thy d's, Love and Duty 92
A white-hair'd shadow roaming like a d Tithonus 8
Like a dog, he hunts in d's, Locksley Hall 79
Fool, again the d, the fancy! „ 173
Whose odours haunt my d's; Sir Galahad 68
But, as in d's, I could not. Vision of Sin 57
Uncertain as a vision or a d, Enoch Arden 356
Who feels a glimmering strangeness in his d. The Brook 216
teeth that ground As in a dreadful d, Aylmer's Field 329
After an angry d this kindlier glow Faded „ 411
oft from out a despot d The father panting woke, „ 527
Had you ill d's?' Sea Dreams 85
'That was then your d,' she said, „ 105
Now I see My d was Life; „ 137
you made and broke your d: A trifle makes a d, a trifle breaks.' „ 143
I ask'd the woman in my d. „ 147
But will you hear my d, „ 203
and she grieved In her strange d, „ 230
d awed me:—well—but what are d's? „ 247
Went both to make your d: „ 254
what d's, ye holy Gods, what d's! For thrice I waken'd after d's. Lucretius 33
We do but recollect the d's that come Just ere the waking: „ 35
that was mine, my d, I knew it— „ 43
I thought my d would show to me, „ 51
Seven and yet one, like shadows in a d.— Princess, Pro. 229
truly, waking d's were, more or less, „ i 12
And feel myself the shadow of a d. „ 18
and read My sickness down to happy d's? „ ii 253
Intent on her, who rapt in glorious d's, „ 442
I myself the shadow of a d, „ iii 188
We had our d's: perhaps he mixt with them: „ 220
I found My boyish d involved and dazzled „ iv 450
To dream myself the shadow of a d: „ v 481
it seem'd a d, I dream'd Of fighting. „ 492
and in my d I glanced aside, and saw „ 507
let me make my d All that I would. „ 519
and d and truth Flow'd from me; „ 541
My d had never died or lived again. „ vi 17
lonely listenings to my mutter'd d, „ vii 110
'If you be, what I think you, some sweet d, „ 145
only, if a d, Sweet d, be perfect. „ 148
'A d That once was mine! „ 309
Princess with as wise a d As some of theirs— „ Con. 69
wildest d's Are but the needful preludes „ 73
all men else their nobler d's forget, Ode on Well. 152
Let us dream our d to-day. Ode Inter. Exhib. 31
come to the door in a pleasant kind of a d. Grandmother 82
Her quiet d of life this hour may cease. Requiescat 6
D's are true while they last, and do we not live in d's? High. Pantheism 4
So bring him: we have idle d's: In Mem. x 9
I do not suffer in a d; „ xiii 14
What vaster d can hit the mood Of Love „ xlvii 11
So runs my d: but what am I? „ liv 17
That Nature lends such evil d's? „ lv 6
A monster then, a d, A discord. „ lvi 21

Dream (s) (*continued*) Yet feels, as in a pensive *d*, *In Mem. lxiv* 17
Nor can my *d* resolve the doubt: „ *lxviii* 12
Or threaded some Socratic *d*; „ *lxxxix* 36
And dream my *d*, and hold it true; „ *cxxiii* 10
Behold, I dream a *d* of good, „ *cxxix* 11
What is she now? My *d's* are bad. *Maud I i* 73
Kept itself warm in the heart of my *d's*, „ *vi* 18
Even in *d's* to the chink of his pence, „ *x* 43
Breaking up my *d* of delight. „ *xix* 2
My *d*? do I dream of bliss? „ 3
Half in *d's* I sorrow after The delight „ *II iv* 24
And I wake, my *d* is fled; „ 51
divide in a *d* from a band of the blest, *Maud III vi* 10
it was but a *d*, yet it yielded a dear delight To have look'd, tho' but in a *d*, upon eyes so fair, „ 15
but a *d*, yet it lighten'd my despair „ 18
Vext with waste *d's*? *Com. of Arthur* 85
Till with a wink his *d* was changed, „ 441
O star, my morning *d* hath proven true, *Gareth and L.* 1000
And heated the strong warrior in his *d's*; *Marr. of Geraint* 72
lay late into the morn, Lost in sweet *d's*, „ 158
All overshadow'd by the foolish *d*, „ 675
Could scarce divide it from her foolish *d*; „ 686
And ears to hear you even in his *d's*.' *Geraint and E.* 429
D's ruling when wit sleeps! *Balin and Balan* 143
Let be: ye stand, fair lord, as in a *d*.' „ 258
Lancelot with his hand among the flowers 'Yea—for a *d*. „ 260
poisoning all his rest, Stung him in *d's*. „ 384
And now full loth am I to break thy *d*, „ 500
As one that labours with an evil *d*, *Merlin and V.* 101
ride, and dream The mortal *d* that never yet was mine— „ 117
He walk'd with *d's* and darkness, „ 190
Ev'n in the jumbled rubbish of a *d*, „ 347
tiny-trumpeting gnat can break our *d* *Lancelot and E.* 137
I behold him in my *d's* Gaunt „ 763
a *d* Of dragging down his enemy made them move. „ 813
plagued with *d's* of something sweet *Holy Grail* 625
in a *d* I seem'd to climb For ever: „ 836
damsel,' answer'd he, 'I woke from *d's*; *Pelleas and E.* 104
so lay, Till shaken by a *d*, „ 517
Or art thou mazed with *d's*? „ 525
The sudden trumpet sounded as in a *d* *Last Tournament* 151
Tristram waking, the red *d* Fled with a shout, „ 487
And out beyond into the *d* to come.' „ 721
if she slept, she dream'd An awful *d*; *Guinevere* 76
down the long wind the *d* Shrill'd; *Pass. of Arthur* 40
Arthur woke and call'd 'Who spake? A *d*. „ 46
And care not thou for *d's* from him, „ 58
Black-stoled, black-hooded, like a *d*— „ 365
they fall asleep Into delicious *d's*, *Lover's Tale i* 162
As from a dismal *d* of my own death, „ 748
One golden *d* of love, from which may death „ 760
Were wrought into the tissue of my *d*: „ *ii* 113
Like sounds without the twilight realm of *d's*, „ 120
thought His *d's* had come again. „ *iv* 78
Thro' *d's* by night and trances of the day, *Sisters (E. and E.)* 274
broken besides with *d's* of the dreadful knife *In the Child. Hosp.* 65
Not yet—not all—last night a *d*— *Columbus* 66
The Lord had sent this bright, strange *d* to me „ 91
wrought To mould the *d*; *To E. Fitzgerald* 30
Beyond all *d's* of Godlike womanhood, *Tiresias* 54
And mixt the *d* of classic times „ 194
And all the phantoms of the *d*, „ 195
With a dim *d*, now and then, *The Wreck* 114
quiet at length out of pleasant *d's*, *Despair* 66
words are like the babblings in a *d* Of nightmare, when the babblings break the *d*. *Ancient Sage* 106
brainless will May jar thy golden *d* *Freedom* 16
d's that scarce will let me be, *To Marq. of Dufferin* 41
Led upward by the God of ghosts and *d's*, *Demeter and P.* 5
he, the God of *d's*, who heard my cry, „ 91
saw the world fly by me like a *d*, *The Ring* 180
Or is it some half memory of a *d*? „ 422

Dream (s) (*continued*) O foolish *d's*, that you, that I, *Happy* 89
you were then a lover's fairy *d*, *To Mary Boyle* 43
Till, led by *d* and vague desire, *To Master of B.* 17
thro' her *d* A ghostly murmur floated, *Death of Œnone* 78
and the *d* Wail'd in her, „ 81
His *d* became a deed that woke the world, *St. Telemachus* 70
shadow of a *d*—an idle one It may be. *Akbar's Dream* 5
I pray'd against the *d*. „ 7
I vow'd Whate'er my *d's*, I still would do the right „ 13
And yet so wild and wayward that my *d*— „ 172
Desolation and wrong Thro' a *d* of the dark? *The Dreamer* 16
Brings the *D's* about my bed, *Silent Voices* 2
d of a shadow, go—God bless you. *To W. H. Brookfield* 13
Dream (verb) As a young lamb, who cannot *d*, *Supp. Confessions* 170
And did not *d* it was a dream; *Two Voices* 213
sweet it was to *d* of Fatherland, *Lotos-Eaters* 39
To *d* and *d*, like yonder amber light, „ *C. S.* 57
More things are wrought by prayer Than this world *d's* of. *M. d'Arthur* 248
Ellen Aubrey, sleep, and *d* of me: *Audley Court* 62
And sleeping, haply *d* her arm is mine. „ 64
Ellen Aubrey, love, and *d* of me.' „ 73
borne as much as this—Or else I *d*— *St. S. Stylites* 93
She sleeps, nor *d's*, but ever dwells *Day-Dm., Sleep B.* 23
D's over lake and lawn, and isles *Vision of Sin* 11
to *d* That love could bind them closer *Aylmer's Field* 40
Indeed, We *d* not of him: *Princess ii* 59
'Dare we *d* of that,' I ask'd, „ *iii* 297
We shudder but to *d* our maids should ape „ 309
To *d* myself the shadow of a dream: „ *v* 481
To *d* thy cause embraced in mine, „ *vi* 200
Let us *d* our dream to-day. *Ode Open. Exhib.* 31
Perchance, to *d* you still beside me, *The Daisy* 107
D in the sliding tides. *Requiescat* 4
That made me *d* I rank'd with him. *In Mem. xlii* 4
Nor can I *d* of thee as dead: „ *lxviii* 4
rather *d* that there, A treble darkness, „ *xcviii* 12
Nor *d* of human love and truth, „ *cxviii* 3
And *d* my dream, and hold it true; „ *cxxiii* 10
Behold, I *d* a dream of good, „ *cxxix* 11
Did I *d* it an hour ago, *Maud I vii* 3
And *d* of her beauty with tender dread, „ *xvi* 14
My dream? do I *d* of bliss? „ *xix* 3
And *d* he dropt from heaven: *Com. of Arthur* 183
what *d* ye when they utter forth May-music *Gareth and L.* 1079
d's Of goodly supper in the distant pool, „ 1186
To *d* she could be guilty of foul act, *Marr. of Geraint* 120
I full oft shall *d* I see my princess „ 751
d That any of these would wrong thee, *Balin and Balan* 143
Or *d*—of thee they dream'd not— *Merlin and V.* 115
ride, and *d* The mortal dream that never yet „ 116
Ride, ride and *d* until ye wake— „ 118
'Man *d's* of Fame while woman wakes to love.' „ 460
because ye *d* they babble of you.' „ 690
I cannot bear to *d* you so forsworn: *Pelleas and E.* 300
Too wholly true to *d* untruth in thee, *Guinevere* 541
Let no man *d* but that I love thee still. „ 560
Let no one *d* but that he loves me „ 674
More things are wrought by prayer Than this world *d's* of. *Pass. of Arthur* 416
Or if thou *d* aught farther, *d* but how *Lover's Tale i* 769
And in my vision bidding me *d* on, „ *ii* 119
But who could *d* that we, who bore the Cross *Columbus* 191
Indian warriors *d* of ampler hunting grounds *Locksley H., Sixty* 69
but *d* not that the hour will last. „ 106
Could we *d* of wars and carnage, „ 189
He *d's* of that long walk *To Mary Boyle* 55
Dreäm'd Till I *d* 'at Squire walkt in, *Owd Roä* 55
Dream'd-Dreamt (*See also* **Dreäm'd**) In midst of knowledge, *dream'd* not yet. *Two Voices* 90
Before I *dream'd* that pleasant dream— *Miller's D.* 46
sweeter than the dream *Dream'd* by a happy man, *Gardener's D.* 72
I too *dream'd*, until at last *Day-Dm., Pro.* 9
'I *dream'd* Of such a tide swelling *Sea Dreams* 86
I *dream'd* that still The motion of the great deep „ 110

Dream'd-Dreamt (*continued*) told it, having *dream'd* Of that same coast. *Sea Dreams* 206
Sphere-music such as that you *dream'd* about, „ 256
it seem'd a dream, I *dream'd* Of fighting. *Princess v* 492
I *dream'd* there would be Spring no more, *In Mem. lxix* 1
I *dream'd* a vision of the dead, „ *ciii* 3
And her smile were all that I *dream'd*, *Maud I vi* 37
her smile had all that I *dream'd*, „ 93
They never *dream'd* the passes would be past,' *Gareth and L.* 1413
They never *dream'd* the passes could be past.' „ 1420
dreamt herself was such a faded form *Marr. of Geraint* 654
Or dream—of thee they *dream'd* not— *Merlin and V.* 115
I *dreamt* Of some vast charm concluded „ 511
the maiden *dreamt* That some one put this diamond *Lancelot and E.* 211
He had not *dream'd* she was so beautiful. „ 353
Who *dream'd* my knight the greatest knight „ 667
'And if *I dream'd*,' said Gawain, „ 668
this night I *dream'd* That I was all alone „ 1045
I *dreamt* the damsel would have died, „ 1305
for he *dream'd* His lady loved him, *Pelleas and E.* 152
I *dream'd* the bearing of our knights *Last Tournament* 120
laid His brows upon the drifted leaf and *dream'd*. „ 406
He *dream'd*; but Arthur with a hundred spears „ 420
if she slept, she *dream'd* An awful dream; *Guinevere* 75
such a feast As never man had *dream'd*; „ 264
and as yet no sin was *dream'd*,) „ 388
Had I not *dream'd* I loved her yestermorn? *Sisters (E. and E.)* 169
I *dream'd* last night of that clear summer noon, *Romney's R.* 74
sphere-music as the Greek Had hardly *dream'd* of. *Akbar's Dream* 45
and yester afternoon I *dream'd*,— „ 170
I *dream'd* That stone by stone I rear'd „ 176
he *dream'd* that a Voice of the Earth went *The Dreamer* 3

Dreamer 'Much less this *d*, deaf and blind, *Two Voices* 175
fools they,—we forward: *d's* both: *Golden Year* 67
visions in the Northern *d's* heavens, *Aylmer's Field* 161
white-headed *d* stoopt and kiss'd her *Locksley H., Sixty* 38
heard an answer 'Wake Thou deedless *d*, *St. Telemachus* 21

Dreaming A glorious child, *d* alone, *Eleänore* 27
In *d* of my lady's eyes. *Kate* 28
D, she knew it was a dream: *Mariana in the S.* 49
While, *d* on your damask cheek, *Day-Dm., Pro.* 3
To see you *d*—and, behind, „ 7
wrathful, petulant, *D* some rival, *Lucretius* 15
'What are they *d* of? Who can tell?' *Minnie and Winnie* 15
For pastime, *d* of the sky; *In Mem. lxvi* 14
Or how should England *d* of *his* sons *Ded. of Idylls* 31
nodded and slept, and saw, *D*, *Com. of Arthur* 428
glance of Gareth *d* on his liege. *Gareth and L.* 1316
and *d* of her love For Lancelot, *Marr. of Geraint* 158
he pray'd for both he slept *D* of both: *Lover's Tale i* 228
D together (*d* of each other They should have added), „ 262
What is this you're *d*? *Forlorn* 14

Dreamlike *D*, should on the sudden vanish, *Holy Grail* 260

Dream-world thou be wise in this *d-w* of ours, *Ancient Sage* 108

Dreamt *See* **Dream'd**

Dreary She only said, 'My life is *d*, (repeat) *Mariana* 9, 45, 69
She only said, 'The night is *d*, (repeat) „ 21, 57
She only said, 'The day is *d*, „ 33
Then, said she, 'I am very *d*, „ 81

Dregs *D* of life, and lees of man: *Vision of Sin* 205

Drench stoop'd To *d* his dark locks *Princess iv* 187
And on these dews that *d* the furze, *In Mem. xi* 6
Thro' clouds that *d* the morning star, „ *lxxii* 22

Drench'd long, rank, dark wood-walks *d* in dew, *D. of F. Women* 75
For I was *d* with ooze, and torn with briers, *Princess v* 28
So *d* it is with tempest, to the sun, „ *vii* 142
I find myself *d* with the rain. *Rizpah* 8
D with the hellish oorali— *In the Child. Hosp.* 10

Dress (s) (*See also* **Hunting-dress**) This *d* and that by turns you tried, *Miller's D.* 147
'Bring the *d* and put it on her, *L. of Burleigh* 95
drest In the *d* that she was wed in, „ 99
'What do you here? and in this *d*? *Princess ii* 189
you look well too in your woman's *d*: „ *iv* 529
Nay, the plainness of her *d'es*? *Maud I xx* 14

Dress (s) (*continued*) all her *d* Wept from her sides *Gareth and L.* 216
put on thy worst and meanest *d* *Marr. of Geraint* 130
he came on her Drest in that *d*, (repeat) „ 141, 843
And all her foolish fears about the *d*, (repeat) „ 142, 844
(His *d* a suit of fray'd magnificence, „ 296
At this she cast her eyes upon her *d*, „ 609
The *d* that now she look'd on to the *d* „ 613
Enid fell in longing for a *d* „ 630
Put on your worst and meanest *d*,' „ 848
your wretched *d*, A wretched insult on you, *Geraint and E.* 327
there were books and *d'es*—left to me, *The Ring* 113
D'es and laces and jewels and never a ring *Charity* 6

Dress (verb) *d* the victim to the offering up. *Princess iv* 130
to flaunt, to *d*, to dance, to thrum, „ 519
d her beautifully and keep her true'— *Geraint and E.* 40
Love and Longing *d* thy deeds in light, *Ded. Poem Prin. Alice* 9
Pretty anew when ya *d'es* 'em oop, *Spinster's S's.* 85
She comes to *d* me in my bridal veil. *The Ring* 98

Dressed *See* **Drest**

Dressing (*See also* **A-dressin'**) *D* their hair with the white sea-flower; *The Merman* 13
flout and scorn By *d* it in rags? *Geraint and E.* 676
bullet struck him that was *d* it suddenly dead, *The Revenge* 67
I am *d* the grave of a woman with flowers. *Charity* 2
I am *d* her grave with flowers. „ 44

Drest-Dressed to dance and sing, be gaily *drest*, *The form, the form* 3
Why come you *drest* like a village maid, *Lady Clare* 67
'If I come *drest* like a village maid, „ 69
her body, *drest* In the dress that she was wed in, *L. of Burleigh* 98
each by other *drest* with care Descended *Princess iii* 19
'What, if you *drest* it up poetically!' „ *Con.* 6
Are but dainties *drest* again: *Window, No Answer* 26
he came on her *Drest* in that dress, (repeat) *Marr. of Geraint* 141, 843
A tribe of women, *dress'd* in many hues, *Geraint and E.* 598
With a grisly wound to be *drest* *The Revenge* 66

Drew She *d* her casement-curtain by, *Mariana* 19
Thro' rosy taper fingers *d* Her streaming curls *Mariana in the S.* 15
rising, from her bosom *d* Old letters, „ 61
once he *d* With one long kiss my whole soul *Fatima* 19
With rosy slender fingers backward *d* *Œnone* 176
As half-asleep his breath he *d*, *The Sisters* 28
as morn from Memnon, *d* Rivers of melodies. *Palace of Art* 171
Many *d* swords and died. *D. of F. Women* 95
they *d* into two burning rings All beams of Love, „ 174
D forth the poison with her balmy breath, „ 271
There *d* he forth the brand Excalibur, *M. d'Arthur* 52
and *d* him under in the mere. (repeat) „ 146, 161
O'er both his shoulders *d* the languid hands, „ 174
Came, *d* your pencil from you, *Gardener's D.* 26
as one large cloud *D* downward: „ 79
wave of such a breast As never pencil *d*. „ 140
Light pretexts *d* me; „ 192
and *d* My little oakling from the cup, *Talking Oak* 230
As homeward by the church I *d*. *The Letters* 44
as their faces *d* together, groan'd, *Enoch Arden* 74
thro' all his blood *D* in the dewy meadowy „ 660
talking from the point, he *d* him in, *The Brook* 154
What amulet *d* her down to that old oak, *Aylmer's Field* 507
the great ridge *d*, Lessening to the lessening music, *Sea Dreams* 220
One rear'd a font of stone And *d*, *Princess, Pro.* 60
the days *d* nigh that I should wed, „ *i* 41
I *d* near; I gazed. „ *iii* 182
the flood *d*; yet I caught her; „ *iv* 182
One reaching forward *d* My burthen from mine arms; „ 191
roll'd on the earth and rose again and *d*: „ *v* 497
D from my neck the painting and the tress, „ *vi* 110
he *d* Her robe to meet his lips, „ 155
Whence *d* you this steel temper? „ 232
D the great night into themselves, „ *vii* 49
voice from which their omens all men *d*, *Ode on Well.* 36
Round affrighted Lisbon *d* The treble works, „ 103
And up the snowy Splugen *d*, *The Daisy* 86
Thy converse *d* us with delight, *In Mem. cx* 1
D in the expression of an eye, „ *cxi* 19
The shadow of His loss *d* like eclipse, *Ded. of Idylls* 14

Drew (*continued*) D all their petty princedoms under him, — Com. of Arthur 18
those great lords D back in wrath, — „ 514
King D in the petty princedoms under him, — „ 517
To whom Sir Gareth d (And there were none — Gareth and L. 743
Fell, as if dead; but quickly rose and d, — „ 967
d him home; but he that fought no more, — „ 1049
lighted, d, There met him drawn, — „ 1121
softly d Behind the twain, and when he saw the star — „ 1217
d himself Bright from his old dark life, — Marr. of Geraint 594
d from those dead wolves Their three gay suits — Geraint and E. 180
Sweet lady, never since I first d breath — „ 619
these her emblems d mine eyes— — Balin and Balan 265
Balin d the shield from off his neck, — „ 429
D the vague glance of Vivien, — „ 464
and d down from out his night-black hair — „ 511
d The vast and shaggy mantle of his beard — Merlin and V. 255
magnet-like she d The rustiest iron — „ 573
d back, and let her eyes Speak for her, — „ 615
D the vast eyelid of an inky cloud, — „ 634
when the time d nigh Spake (for she had been sick) — Lancelot and E. 77
she d Nearer and stood. — „ 349
draw—Draw,'—and Lavaine d, — „ 515
D near, and sigh'd in passing, 'Lancelot, — „ 1350
D me, with power upon me, till I grew — Holy Grail 486
The heads of all her people d to me, — „ 601
There d my sword. — „ 820
slowly Pelleas d To that dim day, — Pelleas and E. 29
find a nest and feels a snake, he d: — „ 437
and d the sword, and thought, 'What! — „ 447
and either knight D back a space, — „ 573
D from before Sir Tristram to the bounds, — Last Tournament 185
and when she d No answer, by and by — Guinevere 161
weep for her who d him to his doom.' — „ 348
kings who d The knighthood-errant of this realm — „ 460
d Down with his blood, till all his heart — Pass. of Arthur 96
There d he forth the brand Excalibur, — „ 220
and d him under in the mere. (repeat) — „ 314, 329
O'er both his shoulders d the languid hands, — „ 342
Death d nigh and beat the doors of Life; — Lover's Tale i 111
ever d from thence The stream of life, — „ 238
and Love d in her breath In that close kiss, — „ 816
upon the sands Insensibly I d her name, — „ ii 7
fed we from one fountain? d one sun? — „ 24
from his brow d back His hand to push me — „ 92
She d it long ago Forthgazing on the waste — „ 176
Four galleons d away From the Spanish fleet — The Revenge 46
d back with her dead and her shame. — „ 60
one quick peal Of laughter d me thro' — Sisters (E. and E.) 116
But I d them the one from the other; — V. of Maeldune 35
every one d His sword on his fellow to slay him, — „ 67
D to this shore lit by the suns — De Prof., Two G. 38
D to this island: Doom'd to the death. — Batt. of Brunanburh 50
Omar d Full-handed plaudits from our best — To E. Fitzgerald 37
as we d to the land; — The Wreck 136
and dogg'd us, and d me to land? — Despair 2
horsemen, d to the valley—and stay'd; — Heavy Brigade 3
d The foe from the saddle and threw — „ 53
d perchance a happier lot Than ours, — Epilogue 50
out of his body she d The red 'Blood-eagle' — Dead Prophet 70
And d him over sea to you— — To Marq. of Dufferin 22
D from thyself the likeness of thyself — Demeter and P. 92
d down before his time Sickening, — „ 114
d the ring From his dead finger, — The Ring 217
Unclosed the hand, and from it d the ring, — „ 269
D to the valley Named of the shadow, — Merlin and the G. 86
that which d from out the boundless deep — Crossing the Bar 7

Dried Her tears fell ere the dews were d; — Mariana 14
'He d his wings: like gauze they grew; — Two Voices 13
all his juice is d, and all his joints — Audley Court 46
comforted my heart, And d my tears, — Com. of Arthur 350

Drier but felt his eyes Harder and d — Pelleas and E. 507

Drift (*See also* **Diamond-drift**) city lies, Beneath its d of smoke; — Talking Oak 6
Thro' scudding d's the rainy Hyades — Ulysses 10

Drift (*continued*) Together, in the d's that pass To darken — In Mem. cvii 13
For the d of the Maker is dark, — Maud I iv 43
Wrapt in d's of lurid smoke — „ II iv 66
In d's of smoke before a rolling wind, — Com. of Arthur 434
and sank Down on a d of foliage — Last Tournament 388
with his d Of flickering spectres, — Demeter and P. 26
a downy d against the brakes, — Prog. of Spring 27

Drifted These d, stranding on an isle — Enoch Arden 552

Drifting d up the stream In fancy, — Sea Dreams 108

Drill d the raw world for the march of mind, — Ode on Well. 168

Drink (s) sometimes Sucking the damps for d, — St. S. Stylites 77
this, at times, she mingled with his d, — Lucretius 18
Yea ev'n of wretched meat and d, — Maud I xv 8
hire thyself to serve for meats and d's — Gareth and L. 153
grant me to serve For meat and d — „ 445
Kay, The master of the meats and d's — „ 451
mellow master of the meats and d's! — „ 560
And mighty thro' thy meats and d's am I, (repeat) — „ 650, 862
with meats and d's And forage for the horse, — „ 1276
pinch a murderous dust into her d, — Merlin and V. 610
and then I taäkes to the d. — North. Cobbler 16
she druv me to d the moor, — „ 30
All along o' the d, fur I loov'd her — „ 60
'Pilgrimages?' 'D, bagpipes, — Sir J. Oldcastle 149

Drink (verb) (*See also* **Dhrink**) I d the cup of a costly death, — Eleänore 138
I will d Life to the lees: — Ulysses 6
We d defying trouble, — Will Water. 94
'I am old, but let me d; — Vision of Sin 75
'D, and let the parties rave; — „ 123
'D to lofty hopes that cool— — „ 147
D we, last, the public fool, — „ 149
'D to Fortune, d to Chance, — „ 191
D to heavy Ignorance! — „ 193
D deep, until the habits of the slave, — Princess ii 91
To d the cooler air, and mark — In Mem. lxxxix 15
Will d to him, whate'er he be, — „ cvii 23
'D, then,' he answer'd. 'Here!' — Geraint and E. 658
D therefore and the wine will change your will.' — „ 663
I will not d Till my dear lord arise and bid me do it, And d with me; — „ 664
Not eat nor d? And wherefore wail for one, — „ 674
you never open'd lip, Except indeed to d: — Merlin and V. 272
Forgot to d to Lancelot and the Queen, — Lancelot and E. 737
'D, d, Sir Fool,' and thereupon I drank, — Last Tournament 297
Nor d: and when thou passest any wood — „ 534
'Summat to d—sa' 'ot?' — North. Cobbler 5
He that thirsteth, come and d! — Sir J. Oldcastle 134
Then d to England, every guest; — Hands all Round 2
To this great cause of Freedom d, my friends, (repeat) — „ 11, 35
To this great name of England d, — „ 23
men may taste Swine-flesh, d wine; — Akbar's Dream 54

Drinketh as sunlight d dew. — Fatima 21

Drinkin' thaw theer's naw d i' Hell; — North. Cobbler 58

Drinking (*See also* **Dhrinkin', Drinkin'**) As d health to bride and groom — In Mem., Con. 83
Men were d together, D and talking of me; — Maud I vii 5

Drinking-song why should Love, like men in d-s's, — „ xviii 55

Drip woodbine and eglatere D sweeter dews — A Dirge 24
When the rotten woodland d's, — Vision of Sin 81
red-ribb'd ledges d with a silent horror of blood, — Maud I i 3
I feeäld it d o' my neck. — Owd Roä 42

Dripping (*See also* **Autumn-dripping**) D with Sabæan spice On thy pillow, — Adeline 53

Dript belike the lance hath d upon it— — Last Tournament 200

Drive (s) What d's about the fresh Cascinè, — The Daisy 43

Drive (verb) and seest me d Thro' utter dark — Supp. Confessions 94
And d's them to the deep.' — Palace of Art 204
Nature's evil star D men in manhood, — Love thou thy land 74
And shoals of pucker'd faces d; — In Mem. lxx 10
On doubts that d the coward back, — „ xcv 30
Is enough to d one mad. — Maud II v 20
sword, Whereby to d the heathen out: — Com. of Arthur 287
To d the heathen from your Roman wall, — „ 512
and d them all apart. — Gareth and L. 515

Drive (verb) *(continued)* '*D* them on Before you;' (repeat) *Geraint and E.* 99, 184
d The Heathen, who, some say, shall rule the land *Lancelot and E.* 64
'Out! And *d* him from the walls.' *Pelleas and E.* 220
And *d* him from my walls.' ,, 229
from the ditch where they shelter we *d* them *Def. of Lucknow* 59
and *d* Innocent cattle under thatch, *Locksley H., Sixty* 95
Then you that *d*, and know your Craft, *Politics* 5
Or you may *d* in vain, ,, 8
To *d* A people from their ancient fold *Akbar's Dream* 60
Driv'n-Driven (*See also* **O'er-driven, Wind-driven**)
morning *driv'n* her plow of pearl Far furrowing *Love and Duty* 99
the herd was *driven*, Fire glimpsed; *Com. of Arthur* 432
'O King, for thou hast *driven* the foe without, *Gareth and L.* 593
driven by evil tongues From all his fellows, *Balin and Balan* 125
Their plumes *driv'n* backward by the wind *Lancelot and E.* 480
Thy holy nun and thou have *driven* men mad, *Holy Grail* 862
camel, *driven* Far from the diamond fountain *Lover's Tale i* 136
driven My current to the fountain whence it sprang,— ,, 502
the wild brier had *driven* Its knotted thorns ,, 619
driven by one angel face, And all the Furies. *Sisters (E. and E.)* 158
I am *driven* by storm and sin and death *The Wreck* 2
she had never *driven* me wild. *Locksley H., Sixty* 20
the foe was *driven*, And Wolseley overthrew *Pro. to Gen. Hamley* 29
shrillings of the Dead When *driven* to Hades, *Death of Œnone* 22
Driveth Let us alone. Time *d* onward fast, *Lotos-Eaters, C. S.* 43
Driving The sunlight *d* down the lea, *Rosalind* 13
blood by Sylla shed Came *d* rainlike *Lucretius* 48
D, hurrying, marrying, burying, *Maud II v* 12
difficulty in mild obedience *D* them on: *Geraint and E.* 105
Drizzle Thicker the *d* grew, deeper the gloom; *Enoch Arden* 679
(A bill of sale gleam'd thro' the *d*) ,, 688
drank the dews and *d* of the North, *Prog. of Spring* 81
Drone *See* **Pulpit-drone**
Droned *d* her lurdane knights Slumbering, *Pelleas and E.* 430
Droonk (drunk) hallus as *d* as a king, *North. Cobbler* 27
D wi' the Quoloty's wine, an' *d* wi' the farmer's aäle, *Village Wife* 77
Droop Fair-fronted Truth shall *d* not now *Clear-headed friend* 12
I cannot veil, or *d* my sight, *Eleänore* 87
D's both his wings, regarding thee, ,, 119
D's blinded with his shining eye: *Fatima* 38
The purple flower *d's*: *Œnone* 29
D's the heavy-blossom'd bower, *Locksley Hall* 163
Here *d's* the banner on the tower, *Day-Dm., Sleep P.* 13
mantles from the golden pegs *D* sleepily: ,, 20
Where on the double rosebud *D's* ,, *L'Envoi* 47
his own head Began to *d*, to fall; *Aylmer's Field* 835
d's the milkwhite peacock like a ghost, *Princess vii* 180
left hand *D* from his mighty shoulder *Merlin and V.* 243
and seeing Pelleas *d*, Said Guinevere, *Pelleas and E.* 178
O'er his uncertain shadow *d's* the day. *Prog. of Spring* 8
Droop'd-Droopt a leopard-skin *Droop'd* from his shoulder, *Œnone* 59
From one hand *droop'd* a crocus: *Palace of Art* 119
So she *droop'd* and *droop'd* before him, *L. of Burleigh* 85
thinking that her clear germander eye *Droopt* *Sea Dreams* 5
then day *droopt*; the chapel bells Call'd *Princess ii* 470
The lilylike Melissa *droop'd* her brows; ,, *iv* 161
above her *droop'd* a lamp, And made ,, 272
And how my life had *droop'd* of late, *In Mem. xiv* 14
His age hath slowly *droopt*, and now lies *Gareth and L.* 79
he let them glance At Enid, where she *droopt*: *Geraint and E.* 247
plume *droopt* and mantle clung, *Last Tournament* 213
Drooping (*See also* **A-drooping, Half-drooping, Low-drooping**) found A damsel *d* in a corner of it. *Geraint and E.* 611
answer'd in low voice, her meek head yet *D*, ,, 641
D and beaten by the breeze, *Lover's Tale i* 700
Droopt *See* **Droop'd.**
Drop (s) (*See also* **Dhrop**) There will not be a *d* of rain *May Queen* 35
and, dew'd with showery *d's*, *Lotos-Eaters* 17
greaves and cuisses dash'd with *d's* Of onset; *M. d'Arthur* 215
That was the last *d* in the cup of gall. *Walk. to the Mail* 69
Thro' glittering *d's* on her sad friend. *Princess vi* 283
And balmy *d's* in summer dark *In Mem. xvii* 15
As *d* by *d* the water falls In vaults and catacombs, ,, *lviii* 3
than the sward with *d's* of dew, *Geraint and E.* 690
Drop (s) *(continued)* Thicker than *d's* from thunder, *Holy Grail* 348
greaves and cuisses dash'd with *d's* Of onset; *Pass. of Arthur* 383
Like water, *d* by *d*, upon my ear Fell; *Lover's Tale i* 576
few *d's* of that distressful rain Fell on my face, ,, 698
hoard of happiness distill'd Some *d's* of solace; ,, 715
I weänt shed a *d* on 'is blood, *North. Cobbler* 114
wi' hoffens a *d* in 'is eye. *Village Wife* 34
Taäste another *d* o' the wine— ,, 120
ye shant hev a *d* fro' the paäil. *Spinster's S.'s* 65
Like *d's* of blood in a dark-gray sea, *Heavy Brigade* 43
The falling *d* will make his name *Epilogue* 60
you spill The *d's* upon my forehead. *Romney's R.* 24
Drop (verb) that grace Would *d* from his o'er-brimming love, *Supp. Confessions* 113
o'er black brows *d's* down (repeat) *Madeline* 34, 46
D's in a silent autumn night. *Lotos-Eaters, C. S.* 34
Till all my limbs *d* piecemeal from the stone, *St. S. Stylites* 44
All starry culmination *d* Balm-dews *Talking Oak* 267
a larger egg Than modern poultry *d*, *Will Water.* 122
To *d* thy foolish tears upon my grave, *Come not, when, etc.* 2
And *d's* at Glory's temple-gates, *You might have won* 34
And the lark *d* down at his feet. *Poet's Song* 8
Till the Sun *d*, dead, from the signs.' *Princess vii* 245
d me a flower, *D* me a flower. *Window, At the W.* 6
D me a flower, a flower, to kiss, ,, 11
D's in his vast and wandering grave. *In Mem. vi* 16
To *d* head-foremost in the jaws ,, *xxxiv* 15
'The cheeks *d* in; the body bows Man dies: ,, *xxxv* 3
D's flat, and after the great waters break *Last Tournament* 464
would *d* from the chords or the keys, *The Wreck* 27
till I feäld mysen ready to *d*. *Owd Roä* 84
gold from each laburnum chain *D* to the grass. *To Mary Boyle* 11
Dropp'd-Dropt (*See also* **Dhropt, Down-drooped, Down-dropt, Half-dropt, Low-dropt**) before my eyelids *dropt* their shade, *D. of F. Women* 1
a tear *Dropt* on the letters as I wrote. *To J. S.* 56
She *dropt* the goose, and caught the pelf, *The Goose* 13
And *dropt* the branch she held, and turning *Gardener's D.* 157
tho' my teeth, which now are *dropt* away, *St. S. Stylites* 30
'Her eyelids *dropp'd* their silken eaves. *Talking Oak* 209
Dropt dews upon her golden head, ,, 227
shrivell'd into darkness in his head, And *dropt* before him. *Godiva* 71
Down they *dropt*—no word was spoken— *The Captain* 51
Nor anchor *dropt* at eve or morn; *The Voyage* 82
Dropt her head in the maiden's hand, *Lady Clare* 63
He suddenly *dropt* dead of heart-disease.' *Sea Dreams* 274
And *dropt* a fairy parachute and past: *Princess, Pro.* 76
Like threaded spiders, one by one, we *dropt*, ,, *i* 108
We *dropt* with evening on a rustic town ,, 170
Two plummets *dropt* for one to sound the abyss ,, *ii* 176
Dropt thro' the ambrosial gloom to where below ,, *iv* 24
I clamber'd o'er at top with pain, *Dropt* on the sward, ,, 209
And down the streaming crystal *dropt*; ,, *vii* 165
Nor find him *dropt* upon the firths of ice, ,, 206
a flower, a flower, *Dropt*, a flower. *Window, At the W.* 14
And *dropt* the dust on tearless eyes; *In Mem. lxxx* 4
Dropt off gorged from a scheme that had left *Maud I i* 20
And dream he *dropt* from heaven: *Com. of Arthur* 183
then the two *Dropt* to the cove, ,, 378
A cloak that *dropt* from collar-bone to heel, *Gareth and L.* 682
'And thence I *dropt* into a lowly vale, *Holy Grail* 440
Dropt down from heaven? *Last Tournament* 685
with his head below the surface *dropt* *Lover's Tale i* 636
And the men *dropt* dead in the valleys *V. of Maeldune* 31
it open'd and *dropt* at the side of each man, ,, 85
that *dropt* to the brink of his bay, *The Wreck* 73
She *dropt* the gracious mask of motherhood, *The Ring* 384
Dropping (*See also* **Slow-dropping**) Some *d* low their crimson bells *Arabian Nights* 62
lean'd Upon him, slowly *d* fragrant dew. *Œnone* 106
d bitter tears against his brow *M. d'Arthur* 211
d down with costly bales; *Locksley Hall* 122
D the too rough H in Hell and Heaven, *Sea Dreams* 196
a breadth Of Autumn, *d* fruits of power; *Princess vi* 55
d bitter tears against a brow *Pass. of Arthur* 379

Dropping-wells Laburnums, *d-w* of fire. *In Mem. lxxxiii* 12
Dropt *See* **Dropp'd**
Dropwise gather'd trickling *d* from the cleft, *Merlin and V.* 274
Dross scurf of salt, and scum of *d*, *Vision of Sin* 211
Drought On stony *d* and steaming salt; *Mariana in the S.* 40
Drouth (*See also* **Drowth**) I look'd athwart the burning *d* *Fatima* 13
My one Oasis in the dust and *d* Of city life! *Edwin Morris* 3
in the dust and *d* of London life She moves " 143
Drove (s) I watch the darkening *d's* of swine *Palace of Art* 199
Not one of all the *d* should touch me: swine!' *Merlin and V.* 699
Drove (verb) (*See also* **Druv**) foliage, *d* The fragrant, glistening deeps. *Arabian Nights* 13
His own thought *d* him, like a goad. *M. d'Arthur* 185
d his heel into the smoulder'd log, " *Ep.* 14
fear of change at home, that *d* him hence. *Walk. to the Mail* 68
Across the boundless east we *d*, *The Voyage* 38
But whence were those that *d* the sail " 86
Storm, such as *d* her under moonless heavens *Enoch Arden* 547
The horse he *d*, the boat he sold, " 609
thought Haunted and harass'd him, and *d* him forth, " 720
d The footstool from before him, and arose; *Aylmer's Field* 326
D in upon the student once or twice, " 462
and round me *d* In narrowing circles *Lucretius* 56
With that he *d* the knife into his side: " 275
tale of her That *d* her foes with slaughter *Princess, Pro.* 123
On glassy water *d* his cheek in lines; " *i* 116
Right on this we *d* and caught, " *iv* 188
And *d* us, last, to quite a solemn close— " *Con.* 17
We broke them on the land, we *d* them on the seas. *Third of Feb.* 30
and goodly sheep In haste they *d*, *Spec. of Iliad* 5
gold of the ruin'd woodlands *d* thro' the air. *Maud I i* 12
and she *d* them thro' the waste. *Geraint and E.* 100
and she *d* them thro' the wood. " 185
He *d* the dust against her veilless eyes: " 529
D his mail'd heel athwart the royal crown, *Balin and Balan* 540
Whom Pellam *d* away with holy heat. " 611
And *d* him into wastes and solitudes *Lancelot and E.* 252
Tell me, what *d* thee from the Table Round, *Holy Grail* 28
D me from all vainglories, rivalries, " 32
heapt in mounds and ridges all the sea *D* like a cataract, " 799
Seven days I *d* along the dreary deep, And with me *d* the moon and all the stars; " 808
His own thought *d* him like a goad. *Pass. of Arthur* 353
I flung him the letter that *d* me wild, *First Quarrel* 57
and *d* them, and smote them, and slew, *Def. of Lucknow* 71
D me and my good brothers home *Columbus* 134
D thro' the midst of the foe, *Heavy Brigade* 30
D it in wild disarray, " 60
D from out the mother's nest *Open. I. and C. Exhib.* 27
I *d* the blade that had slain my husband *Bandit's Death* 34
and *d* the demon from Hawa-i-ee. *Kapiolani* 33
Drown her sacred blood doth *d* The fields, *Poland* 4
Whose muffled motions blindly *d* *In Mem. xlix* 15
d His heart in the gross mud-honey *Maud I xvi* 4
they should burst and *d* with deluging storms " *II i* 42
Might *d* all life in the eye,— " *ii* 61
A stone about his neck to *d* him in it. *Gareth and L.* 812
and then like vermin here *D* him, " 823
melody That *d's* the nearer echoes. *Lover's Tale i* 533
Nor *d* thyself with flies *Ancient Sage* 268
Drowndid (drowned) Wheer the poor wench *d* hersen, *Spinster's S's.* 25
Drown'd (*See also* **Dhrownded, Drowndid**) I *d* the whoopings of the owl *St. S. Stylites* 33
part were *d* within the whirling brook: *Princess, Pro.* 47
the glens are *d* in azure gloom " *iv* 525
tall columns *d* In silken fluctuation " *vi* 354
Love clasp Grief lest both be *d*, *In Mem. i* 9
Was *d* in passing thro' the ford, " *vi* 39
And *d* in yonder living blue " *cxv* 7
in which all spleenful folly was *d*, *Maud I iii* 2
Would she had *d* me in it, *Lancelot and E.* 1412
rest of her *D* in the gloom and horror *Lover's Tale iv* 62
such a vehemence that it *d* The feebler motion " 82
d in the deeps of a meaningless Past? *Vastness* 34
Drowning I brim with sorrow *d* song, *In Mem. xix* 12
Drowning (*continued*) fell the floods of heaven *d* the deep. *Holy Grail* 533
and the transient trouble of *d*— *Despair* 67
d old political common-sense! *Locksley H., Sixty* 250
Thousands of voices *d* his own *Vastness* 6
Drowse Let not your prudence, dearest, *d*, *Princess ii* 339
heel against the pavement echoing, burst Their *d*; *Geraint and E.* 272
Drowsed Doubted, and *d*, nodded and slept, *Com. of Arthur* 427
ravine Which *d* in gloom, seld-darken'd *Death of Œnone* 76
Drowsing *See* **Death-drowsing**
Drowth (*See also* **Drouth**) Thro' the heat, the *d*, the dust, *Sisters (E. and E.)* 6
Drug (s) 'What *d* can make A wither'd palsy *Two Voices* 56
Drug (verb) *D* thy memories, lest thou learn it, *Locksley Hall* 77
D down the blindfold sense of wrong *In Mem. lxxi* 7
Druid Each was like a *D* rock; *Princess iv* 280
grove and altar of the *D* and Druidess, *Boädicea* 2
Druidess grove and altar of the Druid and *D*, " 2
Drum (*See also* **War-drum**) The murmurs of the *d* and fife *Talking Oak* 215
Thy voice is heard thro' rolling *d's* *Princess iv* 577
they clash'd their arms; the *d* Beat; " *v* 250
Now, to the roll of muffled *d's*, *Ode on Well.* 87
Bugles and *d's* in the darkness, *Def. of Lucknow* 76
Drunk (*See also* **Droonk, Sow-droonk**) And *d* delight of battle with my peers, *Ulysses* 16
Ah, sweeter to be *d* with loss, *In Mem. i* 11
D even when he woo'd; *Marr. of Geraint* 442
Till, *d* with its own wine, and overfull *Lover's Tale i* 271
Were *d* into the inmost blue, " 309
D in the largeness of the utterance Of Love; " 472
for my brain was *d* with the water, *Despair* 65
Drunkard Shaking a little like a *d's* hand, *Enoch Arden* 465
The *d's* football, laughing-stocks of Time, *Princess iv* 517
let the *d*, as he stretch'd from horse *Last Tournament* 459
Drunken (*See also* **Love-drunken**) Before I well have *d*, scarce can eat: *Geraint and E.* 662
Druv (drove) she *d* me to drink the moor, *North. Cobbler* 30
But the heät *d* hout i' my heyes *Owd Roä* 84
Dry (adj.) (*See also* **Dusty-dry**) Earth is *d* to the centre, *Nothing will Die* 20
the bearded grass Is *d* and dewless. *Miller's D.* 246
the silver tongue, Cold February loved, is *d*: *The Blackbird* 14
youth Keep *d* their light from tears; *Of old sat Freedom* 20
And moist and *d*, devising long, *Love thou thy land* 38
passion sweeping thro' me left me *d*, *Locksley Hall* 131
Full cold my greeting was and *d*; *The Letters* 13
Whose pious talk, when most his heart was *d*, *Sea Dreams* 186
I found, tho' crush'd to hard and *d*, *The Daisy* 97
Be near me when my faith is *d*, *In Mem. l* 9
But with long use her tears are *d*. " *lxxviii* 20
For underfoot the herb was *d*; " *xcv* 2
cells and chambers; all were fair and *d*; *Lancelot and E.* 407
and moist or *d*, Full-arm'd upon his charger *Pelleas and E.* 215
I never said 'on wi' the *d*,' *First Quarrel* 77
but thaw tha was iver sa *d*, *North. Cobbler* 9
And each was as *d* as a cricket, *V. of Maeldune* 50
Dry (verb) 'The sap *dries* up: the plant declines. *Two Voices* 268
if thou be'st Love, *d* up these tears *Lover's Tale i* 780
Dryad-like *D-l*, shall wear Alternate leaf *Talking Oak* 286
Dry-tongued the *d-t* laurels' pattering talk *Maud I xviii* 8
Dubb'd Said Arthur, when he *d* him knight; *Holy Grail* 137
Dubric To whom arrived, by *D* the high saint, *Com. of Arthur* 453
holy *D* spread his hands and spake, " 471
D said; but when they left the shrine " 476
For by the hands of *D*, the high saint, *Marr. of Geraint* 838
oft I talk'd with *D*, the high saint, *Geraint and E.* 865
Duck grew So witty that ye play'd at *d's* and drakes *Last Tournament* 344
Duct 'Before the little *d's* began *Two Voices* 325
Due (adj.) feud, with question unto whom 'twere *d*: *Œnone* 82
Up in one night and *d* to sudden sun: *Princess iv* 312
and *d* To languid limbs and sickness; " *vi* 376
one so saved was *d* All to the saver— *Lover's Tale iv* 279
Due (s) little *d's* of wheat, and wine and oil; *Lotos-Eaters, C. S.* 122
clothes the father with a dearness not his *d*. *Locksley Hall* 91
So many years from his *d*.' *Lady Clare* 32

Due (s) (*continued*) what every woman counts her *d*, Love, *Princess iii* 244
but as frankly theirs As *d's* of Nature. „ *v* 204
Who give the Fiend himself his *d*, *To F. D. Maurice* 6
they miss their yearly *d* Before their time? *In Mem. xxix* 15
And render human love his *d's*; „ *xxxvii* 16
Which else were fruitless of their *d*, „ *xlv* 14
lazy lover Who but claims her as his *d*? *Maud I xx* 11
and let the dark face have his *d*! *Def. of Lucknow* 69
Tho' a prophet should have his *d*, *Dead Prophet* 50
Dug (*See also* **New-dug**) falling prone he *d* His fingers into the wet earth, *Enoch Arden* 779
But iron *d* from central gloom, *In Mem. cxviii* 21
Duglas loud battles by the shore Of *D*; *Lancelot and E.* 290
Duke Bury the Great *D* With an empire's lamentation,
Let us bury the Great *D* *Ode on Well.* 1
Truth-lover was our English *D*; „ 189
King, *d*, earl, Count, baron— *Lancelot and E.* 464
Dull (adj.) the *d* Saw no divinity in grass, *A Character* 7
You never would hear it; your ears are so *d*; *Poet's Mind* 35
How *d* it is to pause, to make an end, *Ulysses* 22
And *d* the voyage was with long delays, *Enoch Arden* 655
d and self-involved, Tall and erect, *Aylmer's Field* 118
Dull (verb) *d* Those spirit-thrilling eyes *Ode to Memory* 38
'Weep, weeping *d's* the inward pain.' *To J. S.* 40
burial mould Will *d* their comments! *Romney's R.* 126
Dull'd And *d* the murmur on thy lip, *In Mem. xxii* 16
Duller something *d* than at first, *Will Water.* 157
Dumb (*See also* **Death-dumb**) And the far-off stream is *d*, *The Owl i* 3
in a little while our lips are *d*. *Lotos-Eaters, C. S.* 44
The streets are *d* with snow. *Sir Galahad* 52
Winds are loud and you are *d*, *Window, No Answer* 19
ran Thro' lands where not a leaf was *d*; *In Mem. xxiii* 10
lo, thy deepest lays are *d* „ *lxxvi* 7
D is that tower which spake so loud, „ *Con.* 106
Then I cannot be wholly *d*; *Maud II v* 100
and the dead, Oar'd by the *d*, went upward *Lancelot and E.* 1154
one hath sung and all the *d* will sing. *Holy Grail* 301
and cast her eyes down, and was *d*. *Lover's Tale iv* 329
I almost dread to find her, *d*!' „ 339
'She is but *d*, because in her you see „ 341
'Now all be *d*, and promise all of you „ 351
D on the winter heath he lay. *Dead Prophet* 13
dazed and *d* With passing thro' *Demeter and P.* 6
Dumb'd the wholesome music of the wood Was *d* *Balin and Balan* 437
O they to be *d* by the charm!— *V. of Maeldune* 25
Dune (*See also* **Sea-dune**) long low *d*, and lazy-plunging sea. *Last Tournament* 484
glory lights the hall, the *d*, the grass! *Locksley H., Sixty* 181
Dung round and round In *d* and nettles! *Pelleas and E.* 471
Dungeon histories Of battle, bold adventure, *d*, *Aylmer's Field* 98
In damp and dismal *d's* underground, *Lover's Tale ii* 149
airs of heaven After a *d's* closeness. *Sisters (E. and E.)* 198
rib-grated *d* of the holy human ghost, *Happy* 31
Dunghill Upon an ampler *d* trod, *Will Water.* 125
And Doubt is the lord of this *d* *Despair* 90
Duomo Of tower or *d*, sunny-sweet, *The Daisy* 46
Dupe Christ the bait to trap his *d* *Sea Dreams* 191
Dusk (s) Beam'd thro' the thicken'd cedar in the *d*. *Gardener's D.* 166
A troop of snowy doves athwart the *d*, *Princess iv* 168
And in the *d* of thee, the clock Beats out *In Mem. ii* 7
I sleep till *d* is dipt in gray: „ *lxvii* 12
this flat lawn with *d* and bright; „ *lxxxix* 2
shapes That haunt the *d*, with ermine capes „ *xcv* 11
now the doubtful *d* reveal'd The knolls „ 49
So till the *d* that follow'd evensong *Gareth and L.* 793
Till the points of the foam in the *d* came *Despair* 50
or seated in the *d* Of even, *Demeter and P.* 125
Dusk (verb) Little breezes *d* and shiver *L. of Shalott i* 11
Dusky-rafter'd The *d-r* many-cobweb'd hall, *Marr. of Geraint* 362
Dust (*See also* **Blossom-dust, Doost, Lotos-dust, Touch-wood-dust**) *tho' the faults were thick as* d *In vacant chambers,* *To the Queen* 18
right ear, that is fill'd with *d*, Hears little *Two Voices* 116
soil'd with noble *d*, he hears His country's war-song „ 152
A *d* of systems and of creeds. „ 207

Dust (*continued*) Two handfuls of white *d*, shut in an urn of brass! *Lotos-Eaters, C. S.* 68
I knew your brother: his mute *d* I honour *To J. S.* 29
Lie still, dry *d*, secure of change. „ 76
parch'd with *d*; Or, clotted into points *M. d'Arthur* 218
The pillar'd *d* of sounding sycamores, *Audley Court* 16
My one Oasis in the *d* and drouth Of city life! *Edwin Morris* 3
For in the *d* and drouth of London Life „ 143
you may carve a shrine about my *d*, *St. S. Stylites* 195
With anthers and with *d*: *Talking Oak* 184
dead, become Mere highway *d*? *Love and Duty* 11
And vex the unhappy *d* thou wouldst not save. *Come not, when, etc.* 4
Is a clot of warmer *d*, *Vision of Sin* 113
Are but *d* that rises up, (repeat) „ 133, 169
D are our frames; and, gilded *d*, *Aylmer's Field* 1
scrapings from a dozen years Of *d* and deskwork: *Sea Dreams* 78
Have fretted all to *d* and bitterness.' *Princess vi* 264
Till public wrong be crumbled into *d*, *Ode on Well.* 167
Ashes to ashes, *d* to *d*; „ 270
if the wages of Virtue be *d*, *Wages* 6
Thou wilt not leave us in the *d*: *In Mem., Pro.* 9
The *d* of him I shall not see „ *xvii* 19
Ye never knew the sacred *d*: „ *xxi* 22
And *d* and ashes all that is; „ *xxxiv* 4
Man dies: nor is there hope in *d*:' „ *xxxv* 4
sow The *d* of continents to be; „ 12
And Time, a maniac scattering *d*, „ *l* 7
grope, And gather *d* and chaff, „ *lv* 18
Be blown about the desert *d*, „ *lvi* 19
we talk'd Of men and minds, the *d* of change, „ *lxxi* 10
To stir a little *d* of praise. „ *lxxv* 12
And dropt the *d* on tearless eyes; „ *lxxx* 4
The *d* and din and steam of town: „ *lxxxix* 8
Our father's *d* is left alone „ *cv* 5
The life re-orient out of *d*, „ *cxvi* 6
That we may lift from out of *d* A voice „ *cxxxi* 5
who knows? we are ashes and *d*. *Maud I i* 32
Spice his fair banquet with the *d* of death? „ *xviii* 56
My *d* would hear her and beat, „ *xxii* 71
That sting each other here in the *d*; „ *II i* 47
And my heart is a handful of *d*, „ *v* 3
he will lift us from the *d*. *Com. of Arthur* 491
who swept the *d* of ruin'd Rome *Gareth and L.* 135
turning round she saw *D*, and the points of lances *Geraint and E.* 449
held Her finger up, and pointed to the *d*. „ 453
He drove the *d* against her veilless eyes: „ 529
Or pinch a murderous *d* into her drink, *Merlin and V.* 610
in the *d* of half-forgotten kings, *Lancelot and E.* 1338
Fell into *d*, and I was left alone, (repeat) *Holy Grail* 389, 400, 419
she, too, Fell into *d* and nothing, „ 397
Fell into *d*, and disappear'd, „ 436
And touch it, it will crumble into *d*.' „ 439
whirl the *d* of harlots round and round *Pelleas and E.* 470
he knew the Prince tho' marr'd with *d*, *Guinevere* 36
I saw One lying in the *d* at Almesbury, *Pass. of Arthur* 77
parch'd with *d*; Or, clotted into points „ 386
heart of Hope Fell into *d*, and crumbled *Lover's Tale i* 95
Down in the dreadful *d* that once was man, *D*, „ *iv* 67
Raving of dead men's *d* and beating hearts. „ 140
D to *d*—low down—let us hide! *Rizpah* 37
Thro' the heat, the drowth, the *d*, the glare, *Sisters (E. and E.)* 6
The guess of a worm in the *d* *Despair* 30
And changed her into *d*. *Ancient Sage* 162
Her *d* is greening in your leaf, „ 165
and burns the feet would trample it to *d*. *The Flight* 68
and they crumble into *d*. *Locksley H., Sixty* 72
Only '*d* to *d*' for me that sicken „ 149
D in wholesome old-world *d* „ 150
she swept The *d* of earth from her knee. *Dead Prophet* 32
may roll with the *d* of a vanish'd race. *Vastness* 2
Stampt into *d*—tremulous, all awry, *Romney's R.* 113
The *d* send up a steam of human blood, *St. Telemachus* 53
d of the rose-petal belongs to the heart *Akbar's D., Inscrip.* 9
Dusty-dry all but yester-eve was *d-d*. *Lucretius* 32
Dusty-white The river-bed was *d-w*; *Mariana in the S.* 54

Dutch sometimes a *D* love For tulips; — *Gardener's D.* 192
Duty for a man may fail in *d* twice, — *M. d'Arthur* 129
I must be taught my *d*, and by you! — *Dora* 97
and *D* loved of Love— — *Love and Duty* 46
centred in the sphere Of common *duties*, — *Ulysses* 40
Go to him: it is thy *d*: kiss him: — *Locksley Hall* 52
To all *duties* of her rank: — *L. of Burleigh* 72
Like one who does his *d* by his own, — *Enoch Arden* 333
Swerve from her *d* to herself and us— — *Aylmer's Field* 304
As having fail'd in *d* to him, — *Lucretius* 278
Thy *d*? What is *d*? Fare thee well!' — „ 281
O hard, when love and *d* clash! — *Princess ii* 293
My brother! it was *d* spoke, not I. — „ 308
she replied, her *d* was to speak, And *d d*, clear of consequences. — „ *iii* 151
day fled on thro' all Its range of *duties* — „ 177
they That love their voices more than *d*, — „ *iv* 512
Some sense of *d*, something of a faith, — „ *Con.* 54
Till one that sought but *D's* iron crown — *Ode on Well.* 122
path of *d* was the way to glory: (repeat) — „ 202, 210
find the toppling crags of *D* scaled — „ 215
The path of *d* be the way to glory: — „ 224
I done moy *d* boy 'um, (repeat) — *N. Farmer, O. S.* 12, 24
I done moy *d* by Squoire an' I done moy *d* — „ 56
As it were a *d* done to the tomb, — *Maud I xix* 49
I charge thee, on thy *d* as a wife, — *Geraint and E.* 16
It was my *d* to have loved the highest: — *Guinevere* 657
for a man may fail in *d* twice, — *Pass. of Arthur* 297
I have only done my *d* as a man is bound to do: — *The Revenge* 102
Dwarf (s) *D's* of the gynæceum, fail so far — *Princess iii* 279
after seen The *d's* of presage: — „ *iv* 447
there rode Full slowly by a knight, lady, and *d*; Whereof the *d* lagg'd latest, — *Marr. of Geraint* 187
sent Her maiden to demand it of the *d*; — „ 193
my faith, thou shalt not,' cried the *d*; — „ 198
Made sharply to the *d*, and ask'd it of him,' — „ 204
His *d*, a vicious under-shapen thing, — „ 412
thou thyself, with damsel and with *d*, — „ 581
Selfish, strange! What *d's* are men! — *Sisters (E. and E.)* 199
for all but a *d* was he, — *The Wreck* 42
Dwarf (verb) *d's* the petty love of one to one. — *Merlin and V.* 492
Dwarf'd rise or sink Together, *d* or godlike, — *Princess vii* 260
How *d* a growth of cold and night, — *In Mem. lxi* 7
their ever-rising life has *d* Or lost — *The Ring* 463
Dwarf-elm like an old *d-e* That turns its back — *Pelleas and E.* 543
Dwarf-like among the rest A *d-l* Cato cower'd. — *Princess vii* 126
Dwell Where she would ever wish to *d*, — *Supp. Confessions* 54
Life and Thought Here no longer *d*; — *Deserted House* 18
His light upon the letter *d's*, — *Miller's D.* 189
May those kind eyes for ever *d*! — „ 220
Wherein at ease for aye to *d*. — *Palace of Art* 2
My Gods, with whom I *d*! — „ 196
others in Elysian valleys *d*, — *Lotos-Eaters C. S.* 124
'It comforts me in this one thought to *d*, — *D. of F. Women* 233
thou may'st warble, eat and *d*. — *The Blackbird* 4
And *d's* in heaven half the night. — *To J. S.* 52
would *d* One earnest, earnest moment — *Love and Duty* 36
To *d* in presence of immortal youth, — *Tithonus* 21
d's A perfect form in perfect rest. — *Day-Dm., Sleep B.*, 23
Where the wealthy nobles *d*.' — *L. of Burleigh* 24
D with these, and lose Convention, — *Princess ii* 85
pretty home, the home where mother *d's*? — *City Child* 2
there—there—they *d* no more. — *Boädicea* 63
But more of reverence in us *d*; — *In Mem., Pro.* 26
the vigour, bold to *d* On doubts that drive — „ *xcv* 29
And *d's* not in the light alone, — „ *xcvi* 20
She *d's* on him with faithful eyes, — „ *xcvii* 35
But in my spirit will I *d*, — „ *cxxiii* 9
So dark a mind within me *d's*, — *Maud I xv* 1
wastes where footless fancies *d* — „ *xviii* 69
for she *d's* Down in a deep; calm, — *Com. of Arthur* 291
I *d* Savage among the savage woods, — *Balin and Balan* 485
'She *d's* among the woods' he said — „ 614
and in me there *d's* No greatness, — *Lancelot and E.* 449
As when we *d* upon a word we know, — „ 1027
Dwell (*continued*) Why did the King *d* on my name to me? — *Lancelot and E.* 1402
I must not *d* on that defeat of fame. — *Guinevere* 628
d with you; Wear black and white, — „ 676
Love *d's* not in lip-depths. — *Lover's Tale i* 466
Shakespeare's bland and universal eye *D's* pleased, — *To W. C. Macready* 14
thou should'st *d* For nine white moons — *Demeter and P.* 120
thou shalt *d* the whole bright year with me, — „ 139
noble Ulric *d's* forlorn, — *Happy* 10
Dweller some dark *d* by the coco-palm — *Prog. of Spring* 68
Dwelleth The clear-voiced mavis *d*, — *Claribel* 16
Dwelling *D* amid these yellowing bowers: — *A spirit haunts* 2
d on his boundless love, — *Marr. of Geraint* 63
Her fancy *d* in this dusky hall: — „ 802
thus he spake, his eye, *d* on mine, — *Holy Grail* 485
their eyes are dim With *d* on the light — *Lover's Tale i* 492
Unto the *d* she must sway. — *Ode to Memory* 79
Philip's *d* fronted on the street, — *Enoch Arden* 731
How mend the *d's*, of the poor; — *To F. D. Maurice* 38
With one great *d* in the middle of it; — *Holy Grail* 574
This is a charmed *d* which I hold;' — *Lover's Tale i* 114
the sweet *d* of her eyes Upon me — *Sisters (E. and E.)* 165
who sack'd My *d*, seized upon my papers, — *Columbus* 130
and the *d* broke into flame; — *V. of Maeldune* 32
Old Empires, *d's* of the kings of men; — *Prog. of Spring* 99
climb to the *d* of Peelè the Goddess! — *Kapiolani* 22
Dwelling-place So unproportion'd to the *d-p*,) — *Lover's Tale i* 187
Dwelt The fable of the city where we *d*. — *Gardener's D.* 6
But the full day *d* on her brows, — „ 136
keep me from that Eden where she *d*. — „ 191
May not be *d* on by the common day. — „ 271
And *d* a moment on his kindly face, — *Enoch Arden* 326
Ev'n as she *d* upon his latest words, — „ 454
Her hand *d* lingeringly on the latch, — „ 519
D with eternal summer, ill-content. — „ 562
best and brightest, when they *d* on hers, — *Aylmer's Field* 69
But when I *d* upon your old affiance, — *Princess iii* 139
There *d* an iron nature in the grain: — „ *vi* 50
mournful twilight mellowing, *d* Full on the child; — „ 191
A doubtful smile *d* like a clouded moon — „ 270
the dew *D* in her eyes, — „ *vii* 136
There they *d* and there they rioted; — *Boädicea* 63
I past To see the rooms in which he *d*. — *In Mem. lxxxvii* 16
These two—they *d* with eye on eye, — „ *xcvii* 9
Methought I *d* within a hall, — „ *ciii* 5
From which he sallies, and wherein he *d*. — *Balin and Balan* 132
they *d* Deep-tranced on hers, — „ 277
'Brother, I *d* a day in Pellam's hall: — „ 605
Lifted her eyes, and they *d* languidly On Lancelot, — *Lancelot and E.* 84
and *d* among the woods By the great river — „ 277
His own far blood, which *d* at Camelot; — „ 803
Yet larger thro' his leanness, *d* upon her, — „ 835
So *d* the father on her face, — „ 1030
happy as when we *d* among the woods, — „ 1036
I saw That man had once *d* there; — *Holy Grail* 430
shot A rose-red sparkle to the city, and there *D*, — „ 531
D with them, till in time their Abbess died. — *Guinevere* 692
to those With whom he *d*, new faces, — *Pass. of Arthur* 5
fragments of forgotten peoples *d*, — „ 84
Who hath but *d* beneath one roof with me. — „ 156
And heaven pass too, *d* on my heaven, — *Lover's Tale i* 72
the sudden wail his lady made *D* in his fancy: — „ *iv* 150
he *d* and whence he roll'd himself — *Tiresias* 145
while we *d* Together in this valley— — *Death of Œnone* 29
Love and Justice came and *d* therein; (repeat) — *Akbar's Dream* 181, 194
Dwindle Thou shalt wax and he shall *d*, — *Boädicea* 40
Science grows and Beauty *d's*— — *Locksley H., Sixty* 246
Dwindled *d* down to some odd games In some odd nooks — *The Epic* 8
Dwindling *See* **Daily-Dwindling**
Dyed walls of my cell were *d* With rosy colours leaping — *Holy Grail* 119
splash'd and *d* The strong White Horse — „ 311
Dyeing blood spirted upon the scarf, *D* it; — *Marr. of Geraint* 209
Dyflen Shaping their way toward *D* again, — *Batt. of Brunanburh* 98

Dying (*See also* **Slowly-dying**) I *would* be *d* evermore, So *d* ever, Eleänore 143
Then *d* of a mortal stroke, Two Voices 154
Die, *d* clasp'd in his embrace. Fatima 42
They say he's *d* all for love, May Queen 21
When Ellen Adair was *d* for me. Edward Gray 16
as they lay *d*, Did they smile on him. The Captain 55
foretold, *D*, that none of all our blood Princess i 8
He, *d* lately, left her, as I hear, " 78
Blow, bugle; answer, echoes, *d*, *d*, *d*. (repeat) " iv 6, 12
And answer, echoes, answer, *d*, *d*, *d*. " 18
Or *d*, there at least may die. In Mem. viii 24
The year is *d* in the night; " cvi 3
I felt she was slowly *d* Vext with lawyers Maud I xix 21
D abroad and it seems apart " 29
When he lay *d* there, " II ii 67
There is some one *d* or dead, " iv 48
d, gleam'd on rocks Roof-pendent, sharp; Balin and Balan 314
laughter *d* down as the great knight Approach'd Lancelot and E. 179
methought I spied A *d* fire of madness Holy Grail 768
'And oft in *d* cried upon your name.' Pelleas and E. 385
Moans of the *d*, and voices of the dead. Pass. of Arthur 117
d thus, Crown'd with her highest act Lover's Tale i 215
And the lion there lay *d*, The Revenge 96
D so English thou wouldst have her flag Ded. Poem Prin. Alice 16
Death to the *d*, and wounds to the wounded, Def. of Lucknow 17
women in travail among the *d* and dead, " 88
glory and shame *d* out for ever Despair 75
and *d* while they shout her name. Locksley H., Sixty 128
D, 'Unspeakable' he wrote 'Their kindness,' To Marq. of Dufferin 35
but then A kinsman, *d*, summon'd me to Rome— The Ring 178
And *d* rose, and rear'd her arms, " 222
I sat beside her *d*, and she gaspt: " 287
You that know you're *d* . . . Forlorn 58
I am Merlin, And *I* am *d*, Merlin and the G. 8
worn-out Reason *d* in her house May leave the windows Romney's R. 145
I am *d* now Pierced by a poison'd dart. Death of Œnone 33
D in childbirth of dead sons. Akbar's Dream 12
Dyke Adown the crystal *d's* at Camelot Geraint and E. 470
Ah little rat that borest in the *d* Merlin and V. 112
From wall to *d* he stept, he stood, Achilles over the T. 15
Thrice from the *d* he sent his mighty shout, " 30
Dynamite if *d* and revolver leave you courage Locksley H., Sixty 107

E

Each *E* month is various to present the world Two Voices 74
E morn my sleep was broken thro' Miller's D. 39
And steal you from *e* other! Aylmer's Field 707
Who hate *e* other for a song, Lit. Squabbles 5
scarce could hear *e* other speak for noise Of clocks and chimes, Princess i 215
with *e* light air On our mail'd heads: " v 244
while *e* ear was prick'd to attend A tempest, " vi 280
and *e* base, To left and right, " 353
Christmas bells from hill to hill Answer *e* other in the mist. In Mem. xxviii 4
E voice four changes on the wind, " 9
and prey By *e* cold hearth, " xcviii 18
That will not yield *e* other way. " cii 20
and join'd *E* office of the social hour " cxi 14
Where *e* man walks with his head in a cloud of poisonous flies. Maud I iv 54
hiss'd *e* at other's ear What shall not be recorded— Geraint and E. 634
With *e* chest lock'd and padlock'd thirty-fold, Merlin and V. 655
the knights, Glorying in *e* new glory, Last Tournament 336
Do *e* low office of your holy house; Guinevere 682
How like *e* other was the birth of *e*! Lover's Tale i 197
E way from verge to verge a Holy Land, " 337
No sisters ever prized *e* other more. Sisters (E. and E.) 43
Sway'd by *e* Love, and swaying to *e* Love, Prin. Beatrice 19
birds that circle round the tower Are cheeping to *e* other The Ring 86

'Eäd (head) bummin' awaäy loike a buzzard-clock ower my *'e*, N. Farmer, O. S. 18
Breäk me a bit o' the esh for his *'e* " N. S. 41
cleän as a flower fro' *'e* to feeät: North. Cobbler 44
'When theer's naw *'e* to a 'Ouse Village Wife 17
but 'e niver not lift oop 'is *'e*: " 88
fever 'ed baäked Jinny's *'e* as bald as one o' them heggs, " 102
wi' a bran-new *'e* o' the Queeän, Spinster's S's. 76
an' the mark o' 'is *'e* o' the chairs! " 100
an' the Freeä Traäde runn'd 'i my *'e*, Owd Roä 54
an' clemm'd owd Roä by the *'e*, " 99
Eager and arose *E* to bring them down, Enoch Arden 872
e eyes, that still Took joyful note of all things joyful, Aylmer's Field 66
But Edith's *e* fancy hurried with him " 208
rising race were half as *e* for the light. Locksley H., Sixty 228
they lifted up Their *e* faces, wondering at the strength, Merlin and V. 133
But *e* to follow, I saw, Merlin and the G. 101
Eager-hearted *E-h* as a boy when first he leaves his father's field, Locksley Hall 112
Eagerness in his heat and *e* Trembled and quiver'd, Pelleas and E. 283
Eagle (*See also* **Blood-eagle, Heagle**) Half-buried in the *E's* down, Palace of Art 122
Shall *e's* not be *e's*? wrens be wrens? Golden Year 37
wonder of the *e* were the less, But he not less the *e*. " 39
Unclasp'd the wedded *e's* of her belt, Godiva 43
An *e* clang an *e* to the sphere. Princess iii 106
a poising *e*, burns Above the unrisen morrow:' " iv 82
A train of dames: by axe and *e* sat, " vii 128
Lean-headed *E's* yelp alone, " 211
Till o'er the hills her *e's* flew Ode on Well. 112
Again their ravening *e* rose In anger, " 119
Must their ever-ravening *e's* beak and talon Boädicea 11
Tho' the Roman *e* shadow thee, " 39
Or *e's* wing, or insect's eye; In Mem. cxxiv 6
Roman legions here again, And Cæsar's *e*: Com. of Arthur 35
For this an *E*, a royal *E*, Gareth and L. 44
an *E* rising or, the Sun In dexter chief; Merlin and V. 475
and started thro' mid air Bearing an *e's* nest: Last Tournament 15
Follow'd a rush of *e's* wings, " 417
THEY rose to where their sovran *e* sails, Montenegro 1
Left for the white-tail'd *e* to tear it, Batt. of Brunanburh 107
rose as it were on the wings of an *e* The Wreck 69
That young *e* of the West To forage for herself Open. I. and C. Exhib. 28
Eagle-borne 'Peace to thine *e-b* Dead nestling, Last Tournament 33
Eagle-circle sweep In ever-highering *e-c's* Gareth and L. 21
Eagle-like *e-l* Stoop at thy will on Lancelot Balin and Balan 535
Eagle-owl Round as the red eye of an *E-o*, Gareth and L. 799
Eagle-peak I stared from every *e-p*, Demeter and P. 68
Eaglet Foster'd the callow *e*— Œnone 212
Ear (organ of hearing) (*See also* **Captain's-ear, Ear-stunning**) Pour round mine *e's* the livelong bleat Ode to Memory 65
You never would hear it; your *e's* are so dull; Poet's Mind 35
at first to the *e* The warble was low, Dying Swan 23
With dinning sound my *e's* are rife, Eleänore 135
The right *e*, that is fill'd with dust, Two Voices 116
His country's war-song thrill his *e's*: " 153
A second voice was at mine *e*, " 427
the jewel That trembles in her *e*: Miller's D. 172
drawing nigh Half-whisper'd in his *e*, Œnone 186
a sound Rings ever in her *e's* of armed men. " 265
Or hollowing one hand against his *e*, Palace of Art 109
Like Herod, when the shout was in his *e's*, " 219
music in his *e's* his beating heart did make. Lotos-Eaters 36
a clear under-tone Thrill'd thro' mine *e's* D. of F. Women 82
horse That hears the corn-bin open, prick'd my *e's*; The Epic 45
murmuring at his *e* 'Quick, Quick! M. d'Arthur 179
Rings in mine *e's*. The steer forgot to graze, Gardener's D. 85
my *e's* could hear Her lightest breath; Edwin Morris 64
pits of fire, that still Sing in mine *e's*. St. S. Stylites 185
(And hear me with thine *e's*,) Talking Oak 82

Ear (organ of hearing) (*continued*) If the sense is hard
To alien *e's*, *Love and Duty* 52
song from out the distance in the ringing of thine *e's*; *Locksley Hall* 84
Then fillip'd at the diamond in her *e*; *Godiva* 25
And whisper'd voices at his *e*. *Day-Dm., Arrival* 24
In her *e* he whispers gaily, *L. of Burleigh* 1
Worried his passive *e* with petty wrongs *Enoch Arden* 352
a whisper on her *e*, She knew not what; „ 515
likewise, in the ringing of his *e's*, „ 613
Twinkled the innumerable *e* and tail. *The Brook* 134
Call'd all her vital spirits into each *e* *Aylmer's Field* 201
And foam'd away his heart at Averill's *e*: „ 342
His message ringing in thine *e's*, „ 666
won mysterious way Thro' the seal'd *e* „ 696
True Devils with no *e*, they howl in tune *Sea Dreams* 260
Or lend an *e* to Plato where he says, *Lucretius* 147
twinn'd as horse's *e* and eye. *Princess i* 57
my very *e's* were hot To hear them: „ 134
no livelier than the dame That whisper'd 'Asses' *e's*,' „ *ii* 113
To dying *e's*, when unto dying eyes „ *iv* 51
we should cram our *e's* with wool And so pace by: „ 65
at mine *e* Bubbled the nightingale and heeded not, „ 265
Each hissing in his neighbour's *e*; „ *v* 15
infuse my tale of love In the old king's *e's*, „ 241
while each *e* was prick'd to attend A tempest, „ *vi* 280
the Dead March wails in the people's *e's*: *Ode on Well.* 267
And the *e* of man cannot hear, *High. Pantheism* 17
But I should turn mine *e's* and hear *In Mem. xxxv* 8
Not all ungrateful to thine *e*. „ *xxxviii* 12
Yet in these *e's*, till hearing dies, „ *lvii* 9
Till on mine *e* this message falls, „ *lxxxv* 18
A willing *e* We lent him. „ *lxxxvii* 30
heart and *e* were fed To hear him, „ *lxxxix* 22
words of life Breath'd in her *e*. „ *Con.* 53
centre-bits Grind on the wakeful *e* *Maud I i* 42
(Look at it) pricking a cockney *e*. „ *x* 22
Whose *e* is cramm'd with his cotton, „ 42
With the evil tongue and the evil *e*, „ 51
hope to win her With his chirrup at her *e*. „ *xx* 30
It will ring in my heart and my *e's*, till I die. „ *II i* 35
An old song vexes my *e*; „ *ii* 47
Modred laid his *e* beside the doors, *Com. of Arthur* 323
weary her *e's* with one continuous prayer, *Gareth and L.* 19
and the sound was good to Gareth's *e*. „ 312
felt his young heart hammering in his *e's*, „ 322
He sow'd a slander in the common *e*, *Marr. of Geraint* 450
she *could* speak whom his own *e* had heard *Geraint and E.* 113
prick'd their light *e's*, and felt Her low firm voice „ 193
And *e's* to hear you even in his dreams.' „ 429
a heavily-galloping hoof Smote on her *e*, „ 448
hiss'd each at other's *e* What shall not be recorded— „ 634
tho' mine own *e's* heard you yestermorn— „ 740
in the King's own *e* Speak what has chanced; „ 808
Then hand at *e*, and hearkening from what side *Balin and Balan* 415
Woods have tongues, As walls have *e's*: „ 531
And sowing one ill hint from *e* to *e*, *Merlin and V.* 143
That glorious roundel echoing in our *e's*, „ 426
All *e's* were prick'd at once, *Lancelot and E.* 724
Her father's latest word humm'd in her *e*, „ 780
till the *e* Wearies to hear it, „ 897
the world, the world, All *e* and eye; „ 941
a stupid heart To interpret *e* and eye, „ 942
And took both *e* and eye; *Holy Grail* 383
by mine eyes and by mine *e's* I swear, „ 864
From *e* to *e* with dogwhip-weals, *Last Tournament* 58
'A sound is in his *e's*'? „ 116
trumpet sounded as in a dream To *e's* but half-awaked. „ 152
one of thy long asses' *e's*, „ 273
Modred still in green, all *e* and eye, *Guinevere* 24
To vex an *e* too sad to listen to me, „ 315
and past his *e* Went shrilling, 'Hollow, *Pass. of Arthur* 32
murmuring at his *e*, 'Quick, Quick! „ 347
I come, great Mistress of the *e* and eye: *Lover's Tale i* 22
drop by drop, upon my *e* Fell; „ 576

Ear (organ of hearing) (*continued*) And thro' the hasty notice of the *e* *Lover's Tale i* 615
address'd More to the inward than the outward *e*, „ 721
marriage-bells, echoing in *e* and heart— „ *iv* 3
A crueller reason than a crazy *e*, „ 32
Flying by each fine *e*, an Eastern gauze „ 291
we shook 'em off as a dog that shakes his *e's* *The Revenge* 54
But Charlie 'e sets back 'is *e's*, *Village Wife* 67
pibroch of Europe is ringing again in our *e's*! *Def. of Lucknow* 97
lyre Is ever sounding in heroic *e's* Heroic hymns, *Tiresias* 181
Nor lend an *e* to random cries, *Politics* 7
at his *e* he heard a whisper 'Rome' *St. Telemachus* 26
But Death had *e's* and eyes; *Akbar's Dream* 187
The toll of funeral in an Angel *e* *D. of the Duke of C.* 10

Ear (as of corn) Bows all its *e's* before the roaring East; *Princess i* 237
And pluck'd the ripen'd *e's*, „ *ii* 2
For now is love mature in *e*.' *In Mem. lxxxi* 4
some scatter'd *e's*, Some *e's* for Christ *Sir J. Oldcastle* 12

'Ear (hear) Dosn't thou '*e* my 'erse's legs, *N. Farmer, N. S.* 1
that's what I '*e's* 'em saäy. „ 2
woä then woä—let ma '*e* mysén speäk. „ 8
that's what I '*e's* 'im saäy— „ 59
But I '*e's* es 'e'd gie fur a howry owd book *Village Wife* 45
An' I liked to '*e* it I did, *Spinster's S's* 18
ye knawed it wur pleasant to '*e*, „ 21
so es all that I '*e's* be true; „ 56
wait till tha '*e's* it be strikin' the hour. *Owd Roä* 18
thaw I didn't haäfe think as 'e'd '*e*, „ 91
an' I '*e's* 'em yit; „ 106
An' Parson '*e* '*e's* on it all, *Church-warden, etc.* 37

'Eärd (heard) An '*e* 'um a bummin' awaäy *N. Farmer, O. S.* 18
Theer wur a boggle in it, I often '*e* 'um mysen; Moäst like a butter-bump, fur I '*e* 'um about an' about, „ 30
we '*e* 'im a-mountin' oop 'igher an' 'igher, *North. Cobbler* 47
An' nawbody '*e* on 'er sin, *Village Wife* 98
Ye niver '*e* Steevie sweär *Spinster's S's.* 60
I '*e* 'er a maäkin' 'er moän, „ 115
we couldn't ha' '*e* tha call, *Owd Roä* 49
tummled up stairs, fur I '*e* 'im, „ 63
as soon as '*e* '*e* 'is naäme, „ 93
An' I '*e* the bricks an' the baulks „ 109

Earl (*See also* **Yerl**) O the *E* was fair to see! (repeat) *The Sisters* 6, 12, 18, 24, 30, 36
The daughter of a hundred *E's*, *L. C. V. de Vere* 7
that grim *E*, who ruled In Coventry: *Godiva* 12
eagles of her belt, The grim *E's* gift; „ 44
'The old *E's* daughter died at my breast; *Lady Clare* 25
Wherein were bandit *e's*, and caitiff knights, *Marr. of Geraint* 35
There musing sat the hoary-headed *E*, „ 295
Then sigh'd and smiled the hoary-headed *E*, „ 307
But none spake word except the hoary *E*: „ 369
while the Prince and *E* Yet spoke together, „ 384
Then suddenly addrest the hoary *E*: 'Fair Host and *E*, I pray your courtesy; „ 402
So spake the kindly-hearted *E*, „ 514
'*E*, entreat her by my love, „ 760
fetch Fresh victual for these mowers of our *E*; *Geraint and E.* 225
And into no *E's* palace will I go. „ 235
And feast with these in honour of their *E*; „ 287
'*E*, if you love me as in former years, „ 355
bow'd the all-amorous *E*, „ 360
thought she heard the wild *E* at the door, „ 381
To the waste earldom of another *e*, „ 438
Fled all the boon companions of the *E*, „ 477
Rode on a mission to the bandit *E*; „ 527
And their own *E*, and their own souls, „ 577
the huge *E* cried out upon her talk, „ 651
Then strode the brute *E* up and down his hall, „ 712
I knew this *E*, when I myself Was half a bandit „ 794
the huge *E* lay slain within his hall. „ 806
King, duke, *e*, Count, baron— *Lancelot and E.* 464
Athelstan King, Lord among *E's*, *Batt. of Brunanburh* 2
Seven strong *E's* of the army of Anlaf „ 53
E's that were lured by the Hunger „ 123

Earldom From mine own *e* foully ousted me; *Marr. of Geraint* 459
Thou shalt give back their *e* to thy kin. „ 585
'This noble prince who won our *e* back, „ 619
Because we have our *e* back again. „ 701
To the waste *e* of another earl, *Geraint and E.* 438
ye shall share my *e* with me, girl, „ 626
Earlier (*See also* **Season-earlier**) I will turn that *e* page. *Locksley Hall* 107
Break, happy land, into *e* flowers! *W. to Alexandra* 10
But that was in her *e* maidenhood, *Holy Grail* 73
Earliest Because they are the *e* of the year). *Ode to Memory* 27
The *e* pipe of half-awaken'd birds *Princess iv* 50
like a guilty thing I creep At *e* morning to the door. *In Mem. vii* 8
With one that was his *e* mate; „ *lxiv* 24
The roofs, that heard our *e* cry, „ *cii* 3
she placed where morning's *e* ray Might strike it, *Lancelot and E.* 5
So what was *e* mine in *e* life, *Lover's Tale i* 247
nor tell Of this our *e*, our closest-drawn, „ 278
with *e* violets And lavish carol of clear-throated larks „ 282
first gray streak of *e* summer-dawn, *Ancient Sage* 220
A soul that, watch'd from *e* youth, *To Marq. of Dufferin* 25
Early (*See also* **Rathe**) gaze On the prime labour of thine *e* days: *Ode to Memory* 94
Make thy grass hoar with *e* rime. *Two Voices* 66
love dispell'd the fear That I should die an *e* death: *Miller's D.* 90
His *e* rage Had force to make me rhyme in youth, „ 192
Whole weeks and months, and *e* and late, *The Sisters* 10
In the *e e* morning the summer sun 'ill shine, *May Queen, N. Y's. E.* 22
And once I ask'd him of his *e* life, *Edwin Morris* 23
leave me here a little, while as yet 'tis *e* morn: *Locksley Hall* 1
Faint as a figure seen in *e* dawn *Enoch Arden* 357
mate had seen at *e* dawn Across a break „ 631
a rough piece Of *e* rigid colour, *Aylmer's Field* 281
Some pleasure from thine *e* years. *In Mem. iv* 10
e light Shall glimmer on the dewy decks. „ *ix* 11
Her *e* Heaven, her happy views; „ *xxxiii* 6
to him she sings Of *e* faith and plighted vows; „ *xcvii* 30
A light-blue lane of *e* dawn, And think of *e* days and thee, „ *cxix* 7
Half in dreams I sorrow after The delight of *e* skies; *Maud II iv* 25
Enid, my *e* and my only love, *Geraint and E.* 307
soul twines and mingles with the growths Of vigorous *e* days, *Lover's Tale i* 133
I was then in *e* boyhood, Edith but a child of six— *Locksley H., Sixty* 258
When over the valley, In *e* summers, *Merlin and the G.* 18
Early-silvering Thus over Enoch's *e-s* head *Enoch Arden* 622
Earn (*See also* **Addle**) *E* well the thrifty months, *Love thou thy land* 95
lease Of life, shalt *e* no more; *Will Water.* 244
metaphysics! read and *e* our prize, *Princess iii* 300
popular name such manhood *e's*, *Merlin and V.* 787
child Should *e* from both the praise of heroism, *Sisters (E. and E.)* 251
Earn'd Thus *e* a scanty living for himself: *Enoch Arden* 818
Has *e* himself the name of sparrow-hawk. *Marr. of Geraint* 492
'Have I not *e* my cake in baking of it? *Gareth and L.* 575
Earnest (adj.) (*See also* **Too-earnest**) all, they said, as *e* as the close? *Princess, Con.* 21
her full and *e* eye Over her snow-cold breast *Œnone* 141
dwell One *e*, *e* moment upon mine, *Love and Duty* 37
Earnest (seriousness) words were half in *e*, half in jest,) *Gardener's D.* 23
take it—*e* wed with sport, *Day-Dm., Ep.* 11
jest and *e* working side by side, *Princess iv* 563
By these in *e* those in mockery call'd *Last Tournament* 135
Earnest (pledge) *e* of the things that they shall do: *Locksley Hall* 118
Are *e* that he loves her yet, *In Mem. xcvii* 15
blood Hath *e* in it of far springs to be. *Merlin and V.* 557
Earning save all *e's* to the uttermost *Enoch Arden* 86
Ear-stunning *e-s* hail of Arês crash Along the sounding walls.' *Tiresias* 96
Earth *O you that hold A nobler office upon* e *Than arms,* *To the Queen* 2
E is dry to the centre, *Nothing will Die* 20
The old *e* Had a birth, *All Things will Die* 37
And the old *e* must die. „ 41
in her first sleep *e* breathes stilly: *Leonine Eleg.* 7
And Thou and peace to *e* were born. *Supp. Confessions* 26
whene'er *E* goes to *e*, with grief, „ 38

Earth (*continued*) Hating to wander out on *e*, *Supp. Confessions* 57
To the *e*—until the ice would melt „ 81
Breathed low around the rolling *e* *The Winds, etc.* 3
star The black *e* with brilliance rare. *Ode to Memory* 20
sure she deem'd no mist of *e* could dull „ 38
Over the dark dewy *e* forlorn, „ 69
Over its grave i' the *e* so chilly; (repeat) *A spirit haunts* 10, 22
And said the *e* was beautiful. *A Character* 12
spirit of man, Making *e* wonder, *The Poet* 52
It would shrink to the *e* if you came in. *Poet's Mind* 37
The house was builded of the *e*, *Deserted House* 15
Adeline, Scarce of *e* nor all divine, *Adeline* 3
The choicest wealth of all the *e*, *Eleanore* 19
But breathe it into *e* and close it up *Wan Sculptor* 12
What is there in the great sphere of the *e*, *If I were loved* 2
true, To what is loveliest upon *e*.' *Mariana in the S.* 64
Dissolved the riddle of the *e*. *Two Voices* 170
To that last nothing under *e*!' „ 333
Have I not found a happy *e*? *Miller's D.* 25
Hear me, O *E*, hear me, O Hills, *Œnone* 36
O happy *e*, how canst thou bear my weight? „ 237
There are enough unhappy on this *e*, „ 239
All *e* and air seem only burning fire.' „ 268
common clay ta'en from the common *e* *To ——, With Pal. of Art* 17
Lord of the visible *e*, *Palace of Art* 179
oft the riddle of the painful *e* Flash'd thro' her „ 213
mouldering with the dull *e's* mouldering sod, „ 261
Was never born into the *e*. *To J. S.* 32
note, Should thus be lost for ever from the *e*, *M. d'Arthur* 90
round *e* is every way Bound by gold chains „ 254
Felt *e* as air beneath me, *Gardener's D.* 212
Unfit for *e*, unfit for heaven, *St. S. Stylites* 3
Heaven, and *E*, and Time are choked. „ 104
men on *e* House in the shade of comfortable roofs, „ 106
The fat *e* feed thy branchy root, *Talking Oak* 273
dark *E* follows wheel'd in her ellipse; *Golden Year* 24
strength which in old days Moved *e* and heaven; *Ulysses* 67
In days far-off, on that dark *e*, *Tithonus* 48
I *e* in *e* forget these empty courts, „ 75
And the kindly *e* shall slumber, *Locksley Hall* 130
perish one by one, Than that *e* should stand at gaze „ 180
one low churl, compact of thankless *e*, *Godiva* 66
For we are Ancients of the *e*, *Day-Dm., L'Envoi* 19
This *e* is rich in man and maid; *Will Water.* 65
This whole wise *e* of light and shade Comes out „ 67
Like all good things on *e*! „ 202
That are the flower of the *e*?' *Lady Clare* 68
Bore to *e* her body, drest In the dress *L. of Burleigh* 98
MOVE eastward, happy *e*, and leave *Move Eastward* 1
'Cold altar, Heaven and *e* shall meet *The Letters* 7
No public life was his on *e*, *You might have won* 23
he dug His fingers into the wet *e*, *Enoch Arden* 780
this, a milky-way on *e*, Like visions *Aylmer's Field* 160
one kiss Was Leolin's one strong rival upon *e*; „ 557
Never since our bad *e* became one sea, „ 635
e Lightens from her own central Hell— „ 760
All over earthy, like a piece of *e*, *Sea Dreams* 99
blood by Sylla shed Came driving rainlike down again on *e*, *Lucretius* 48
never yet on *e* Could dead flesh creep, „ 130
two sphere lamps blazon'd like Heaven and *E* *Princess i* 223
close upon the Sun, Than our man's *e*; „ *ii* 37
broad and bounteous *E* Should bear a double growth „ 179
there is nothing upon *e* More miserable „ *iii* 259
Leapt from the dewy shoulders of the *E*, „ *v* 43
sweet influences Of *e* and heaven? „ 192
fixt As are the roots of *e* and base of all; „ 446
Part roll'd on the *e* and rose again „ 497
twists the grain with such a roar that *E* Reels, „ 528
she set the child on the *e*; „ *vi* 120
lies the *E* all Danaë to the stars, „ *vii* 182
black *e* yawns: the mortal disappears; *Ode on Well.* 269
wide hall with *e's* invention stored, *Ode Inter. Exhib.* 2
And gathering all the fruits of *e* „ 41
The gloom that saddens Heaven and *E*, *The Daisy* 102
I cast to *e* a seed. *The Flower* 2

Earth (*continued*) To a sweet little Eden on *e* that I know, *The Islet* 14
E, these solid stars, this weight of body *High. Pantheism* 5
You have bitten into the heart of the *e*, *Window, Winter* 18
Be merry on *e* as you never were merry before, „ *Ay* 2
Light, so low upon *e*, „ *Marr. Morn.* 1
Where he in English *e* is laid, *In Mem. xviii* 2
This *e* had been the Paradise It never look'd „ *xxiv* 6
A rainy cloud possess'd the *e*, „ *xxx* 3
Else *e* is darkness at the core, „ *xxxiv* 3
The baby new to *e* and sky, „ *xlv* 1
The silent snow possess'd the *e*, „ *lxxviii* 3
No lower life that *e*'s embrace May breed „ *lxxxii* 3
he bare The use of virtue out of *e*: „ 10
To wander on a darken'd *e*, „ *lxxxv* 31
To myriads on the genial *e*, „ *xcix* 14
A lever to uplift the *e* And roll it „ *cxiii* 15
As dying Nature's *e* and lime; „ *cxviii* 4
They say, The solid *e* whereon we tread „ 8
O *e*, what changes hast thou seen! „ *cxxiii* 2
yet I keep Within his court on *e*, „ *cxxvi* 7
The brute *e* lightens to the sky, „ *cxxvii* 15
under whose command Is *E* and *E's*, „ *Con.* 131
eft was of old the Lord and Master of *E*, *Maud I iv* 31
Put down the passions that make *e* Hell! „ *x* 46
This lump of *e* has left his estate „ *xvi* 1
Has our whole *e* gone nearer to the glow „ *xviii* 78
Were it *e* in an earthy bed; „ *xxii* 70
dawn of Eden bright over *e* and sky, „ *II i* 8
kisses sweeter sweeter Than anything on *e*. „ *iv* 10
she was fairest of all flesh on *e*, *Com. of Arthur* 3
Reddening the sun with smoke and *e* with blood, „ 37
O *e* that soundest hollow under me, „ 84
the bounds of heaven and *e* were lost— „ 372
and the solid *e* became As nothing, „ 442
And loveliest of all women upon *e*. *Marr. of Geraint* 21
better were I laid in the dark *e*, „ 97
I will track this vermin to their *e's*: „ 217
'I have track'd him to his *e*.' „ 253
if he die, why *e* has *e* enough To hide him. *Geraint and E.* 554
draws in the wither'd leaf And makes it *e*, „ 634
Sir Lancelot with his eyes on *e*, *Balin and Balan* 253
Leapt in a semicircle, and lit on *e*; „ 414
beat the cross to *e*, and break the King „ 458
Tore from the branch, and cast on *e*, „ 539
O Merlin, may this *e*, if ever I, *Merlin and V.* 345
May this hard *e* cleave to the Nadir hell „ 349
men at most differ as Heaven and *e*, „ 814
spikes and splinters of the wood The dark *e* „ 938
who loves me must have a touch of *e*; *Lancelot and E.* 133
Might wear as fair a jewel as is on *e*, „ 240
hard *e* shake, and a low thunder of arms. „ 460
He bore a knight of old repute to the *e*, „ 492
An armlet for the roundest arm on *e*, „ 1183
for all her shining hair Was smear'd with *e*, *Holy Grail* 210
heaven appear'd so blue, nor *e* so green, „ 365
Which never eyes on *e* again shall see. „ 532
Cared not for her, nor anything upon *e*.' „ 612
But live like an old badger in his *e*, With *e* about him everywhere, „ 629
And felt the boat shock *e*, „ 812
Until this *e* he walks on seems not *e*, „ 912
At random looking over the brown *e* *Pelleas and E.* 32
One rose, a rose that gladden'd *e* and sky, „ 402
the one true knight on *e*, And only lover; „ 494
Clung to the dead *e*, and the land was still. *Guinevere* 8
seem'd the heavens upbreaking thro' the *e*, „ 391
note, Should thus be lost for ever from the *e*, *Pass. of Arthur* 258
round *e* is every way Bound by gold chains „ 422
will not pass, till *e* And heaven pass too, *Lover's Tale i* 71
My inward sap, the hold I have on *e*, „ 166
pillars which from *e* uphold Our childhood, „ 220
High over all the azure-circled *e*, „ 390
and the *e* They fell on became hallow'd evermore. „ 439
Scarce housed within the circle of this *E*, „ 479
Sooner *E* Might go round Heaven, „ 481

Earth (*continued*) all the separate Edens of this *e*, *Lover's Tale* 551
had the *e* beneath me yawning cloven „ 602
all from these to where she touch'd on *e*, „ *iv* 167
loved His master more than all on *e* beside. „ 257
Of all things upon *e* the dearest to me.' „ 319
Crazy with laughter and babble and *e's* new wine, *To A. Tennyson* 2
Turning my way, the loveliest face on *e*. *Sisters (E. and E.)* 87
sent Our Edith thro' the glories of the *e*, „ 225
gleam from our poor *e* May touch thee, *Ded. Poem Prin. Alice* 18
Twice do we hurl them to *e* from the ladders *Def. of Lucknow* 58
chains For him who gave a new heaven, a new *e*, *Columbus* 20
suck in with his milk hereafter—*e* A sphere. „ 38
a tent Spread over *e*, and so this *e* was flat: „ 48
half-assured this *e* might be a sphere. „ 60
Spain once the most chivalric race on *e*, Spain then the mightiest, wealthiest realm on *e*, „ 204
boasted he sprang from the oldest race upon *e*. *V. of Maeldune* 4
her dark orb Touch'd with *e's* light— *De Prof., Two G.* 10
Glode over *e* till the glorious creature *Batt. of Brunanburh* 29
One night when *e* was winter-black, *To E. Fitzgerald* 21
Two voices heard on *e* no more; „ 41
clearer day Than our poor twilight dawn on *e*— *Tiresias* 206
My close of *e's* experience May prove as peaceful „ 216
without any delight In anything here upon *e*? *Despair* 8
no soul on the *e* below, „ 19
own selves on an *e* that bore not a flower; „ 44
We never had found Him on *e*, this *e* is a fatherless Hell— „ 57
left in the rocks of an *e* that is dead? „ 86
And *e* as fair in hue! *Ancient Sage* 24
blue of sky and sea, the green of *e*, „ 41
'And since—from when this *e* began— „ 53
stir the sleeping *e*, and wake The bloom „ 93
Who clings to *e*, and once would dare Hell-heat „ 115
In vain you tell me '*E* is fair' „ 169
And we, the poor *e's* dying race, „ 178
e's dark forehead flings athwart the heavens „ 200
The lark has past from *e* to Heaven *The Flight* 62
gone as all on *e* will go. *Locksley H., Sixty* 46
E at last a warless world, „ 165
for is not *E* as yet so young?— „ 166
Can it, till this outworn *e* be dead „ 174
smiling downward at this earthlier *e* of ours, „ 183
Is there evil but on *e*? „ 197
Many an Æon moulded *e* before her highest, man, was born, Many an Æon too may pass when *e* is manless and forlorn, *E* so huge, and yet so bounded— „ 205
e will be Something other than the widest „ 231
E may reach her earthly-worst, „ 233
E would never touch her worst, „ 270
Ill To waste this *e* began— *Epilogue* 23
And so does *E*; for Homer's fame, „ 58
E passes, all is lost In what they prophesy, „ 64
unlaborious *e* and oarless sea; *To Virgil* 20
They call'd her 'Reverence' here upon *e*, *Dead Prophet* 27
she swept The dust of *e* from her knee. „ 32
angel eyes In *e's* recurring Paradise. *Helen's Tower* 12
This *e* has never borne a nobler man. *Epit. On Gordon* 4
His isle, the mightiest Ocean-power on *e*, *The Fleet* 6
cry that rang thro' Hades, *E*, and Heaven! *Demeter and P.* 33
one black blur of *e* Left by that closing chasm, „ 37
glancing from his height On *e* a fruitless fallow, „ 118
in the harvest hymns of *E* The worship „ 148
as this poor *e's* pale history runs,— *Vastness* 3
and all these old revolutions of *e*; „ 29
Stranger than *e* has ever seen; *The Ring* 38
An ever lessening *e*—and she perhaps, „ 46
Gleam'd for a moment in her own on *e*. „ 297
lost the moment of their past on *e*, „ 464
that poor link With *e* is broken, „ 476
E and Hell will brand your name, *Forlorn* 51
Would *E* tho' hid in cloud not be follow'd *Happy* 97
name that *e* will not forget Till *e* *To Ulysses* 27
She comes, and *E* is glad To roll her North *Prog. of Spring* 48
lured me from the household fire on *e*. *Romney's R.* 40

Earth (*continued*) throbs Thro' e, and all her graves, — Romney's R. 128
Sounding for ever and ever thro' E — Parnassus 7
e's green stole into heaven's own hue, — Far-far-away 2
all the bounds of e, Far-far-away? — „ 14
Act first, this E, a stage so gloom'd — The Play 1
In silence wept upon the flowerless e. — Death of Œnone 9
'Is e On fire to the West? — St. Telemachus 18
Yea, Alla here on e, who caught and held — Akbar's Dream 84
mists of e Fade in the noon of heaven, — „ 96
Let the Sun, Who heats our e to yield us grain — „ 105
draw The crowd from wallowing in the mire of e, — „ 141
'The meek shall inherit the e' — The Dreamer 2
dream'd that a Voice of the E went wailingly past — „ 3
Moaning your losses, O E, — „ 17
The Reign of the Meek upon e, — „ 25
Minds on this round e of ours — Poets and Critics 3
For if this e be ruled by Perfect Love, — D. of the Duke of C. 8
His shadow darkens e: — „ 13
Earth-angel O Heaven's own white E-a, — Merlin and V. 81
Earth-baldness e-b clothes itself afresh, — Demeter and P. 49
Earthen Drawing into his narrow e urn, — Ode to Memory 61
Earth-Goddess I, E-G, cursed the Gods of Heaven. — Demeter and P. 102
I, E-G, am but ill-content With them, — „ 128
Earthlier myself Am lonelier, darker, e for my loss — Aylmer's Field 750
your modern amourist is of easier, e make. — Locksley H., Sixty 18
smiling downward at this e earth of ours, — „ 183
Earthly Of love that never found his e close, — Love and Duty 1
As this pale taper's e spark, — St. Agnes' Eve 15
So in mine e house I am, — „ 19
May not that e chastisement suffice? — Aylmer's Field 784
Lay your e fancies down, — Ode on Well. 279
For I am but an e Muse, — In Mem. xxxvii 13
May some dim touch of e things Surprise thee — „ xliv 11
the song of woe Is after all an e song: — „ lvii 2
The head hath miss'd an e wreath: — „ lxxiii 6
Till slowly worn her e robe, — „ lxxxiv 33
For she is e of the mind, — „ cxiv 21
he defileth heavenly things With e uses '— — Balin and Balan 422
was it e passion crost?' — Holy Grail 29
e heats that spring and sparkle out — „ 33
how should E measure mete The Heavenly-unmeasured — Lover's Tale i 473
divorce thee not From e love and life— — Ded. Poem Prin. Alice 4
happier voyage now Toward no e pole. — Sir J. Franklin 4
Trusting no longer that e flower would be heavenly fruit— — Despair 35
filial eyes Have seen the loneliness of e thrones, — Prin. Beatrice 14
Miriam, breaks her latest e link With me to-day. — The Ring 47
Earthly-best or if she gain her e-b, — Locksley H., Sixty 233
Earthly-heavenliest Most loveliest, e-h harmony? — Lover's Tale i 279
Earthly-wise blessed Lord, I speak too e, — Holy Grail 627
Earthly-worst Earth may reach her e-w, — Locksley H., Sixty 233
Earth-Mother child Of thee, the great E-M, — Demeter and P. 97
reap with me, E-m, in the harvest hymns — „ 148
Earth-narrow whether this e-n life Be yet but yolk, — Ancient Sage 129
Earthquake (*See also* **World's-earthquake**) Blight and famine, plague and e, — Lotos-Eaters, C. S. 115
flood, fire, e, thunder, wrought Such waste — Aylmer's Field 639
wholly out of sight, and sink Past e— — Lucretius 153
Shatter'd into one e in one day — „ 251
like a bell Toll'd by an e in a trembling tower, — Princess vi 332
crack of e shivering to your base Split you, — Pelleas and E. 465
An e, my loud heart-beats, — Lover's Tale ii 193
a wave like the wave that is raised by an e grew, — The Revenge 115
another wild e out-tore Clean from our lines — Def. of Lucknow 61
an e always moved in the hollows under the dells, — V. of Maeldune 107
Shrine-shattering e, fire, flood, thunderbolt, — Tiresias 61
Gone like fires and floods and e's — Locksley H., Sixty 40
Thunder, or the rending e, or the famine, — Faith 4
Earthquake-cloven yawning of an e-c chasm. — Lover's Tale i 377
Earth-shock'd Above some fair metropolis, e-s,— — „ ii 62
Earth-sweeping upbare A broad e-s pall of whitest lawn — „ 78
Earthy Were it earth in an e bed; — Maud I xxii 70
All over e, like a piece of earth, — Sea Dreams 99
Earwig *See* **Battle-Twig**

Ease Two lives bound fast in one with golden e; — Circumstance 5
'Why, if man rot in dreamless e, — Two Voices 280
Alice, you were ill at e; — Miller's D. 146
Wherein at e for aye to dwell, — Palace of Art 2
long rest or death, dark death, or dreamful e. — Lotos-Eaters, C. S. 53
You ask me, why, tho' ill at e, — You ask me, why 1
control Our being, lest we rust in e. — Love thou thy land 42
Seeing with how great e Nature can smile, — Lucretius 174
With garrulous e and oily courtesies — Princess i 164
We break our laws with e, — „ vi 323
but your Highness breaks with e The law — „ 325
I would set their pains at e. — In Mem. lxiii 8
wrought All kind of service with a noble e — Gareth and L. 489
Drank till he jested with all e, — Geraint and E. 290
She lied with e; but horror-stricken he, — Balin and Balan 525
he let his wisdom go For e of heart, — Merlin and V. 893
Them surely I can silence with all e. — Lancelot and E. 109
they lost themselves, Yet with all e, — „ 442
And found no e in turning or in rest; — „ 901
Who read but on my breviary with e, — Holy Grail 545
ruffians at their e Among their harlot-brides, — Last Tournament 427
But on that day, not being all at e, — Sister's (E. and E.) 209
And yet my heart is ill at e, — The Flight 97
Eased And e her heart of madness . . . — Forlorn 82
Easeful wilt thou leave Thine e biding here, — Gareth and L. 128
Easier With fuller profits lead an e life, — Enoch Arden 145
But evermore it seem'd an e thing — Geraint and E. 108
your modern amourist is of e, earthlier make. — Locksley H., Sixty 18
East Till that o'ergrown Barbarian in the E — Poland 7
And slowly rounded to the e — Mariana in the S. 79
light increased With freshness in the dawning e. — Two Voices 405
Four courts I made, E, West and South and North, — Palace of Art 21
Smote by the fresh beam of the springing e; — M. d'Arthur 214
dark E, Unseen, is brightening to his bridal morn. — Gardener's D. 72
went To greet their fairer sisters of the E. — „ 188
The ever-silent spaces of the E, — Tithonus 9
Yet hold me not for ever in thine E: — „ 64
Across the boundless e we drove, — The Voyage 38
The blaze upon the waters to the e; — Enoch Arden 594
I to the E And he for Italy— — The Brook 1
darken'd in the west, And rosed in the e: — Sea Dreams 40
King of the E altho' he seem, — Lucretius 133
Bows all its ears before the roaring E; — Princess i 237
Nor stunted squaws of West or E; — „ ii 78
touch'd Above the darkness from their native E. — „ iii 22
'Alas your Highness breathes full E,' — „ 231
beam Of the E, that play'd upon them, — „ v 259
a feast Of wonder, out of West and E, — Ode Inter. Exhib. 21
The bitter e, the misty summer And gray metropolis — The Daisy 103
voices go To North, South, E, and West; — Voice and the P. 14
Far in the E Boädicéa, standing loftily charioted, — Boädicea 3
Flown to the e or the west, — Window, Gone 7
O Father, touch the e, and light — In Mem. xxx 31
heaved a windless flame Up the deep E, — „ lxxii 14
E and West, without a breath, — „ xcv 62
What lightens in the lucid e — „ cv 24
Fiercely flies The blast of North and E, — „ cvii 7
Blush from West to E, Blush from E to West, Till the West is E, — Maud I xvii 21
breeze that streams to thy delicious E, — „ xviii 16
there be dawn in West and eve in E? — Gareth and L. 712
pale and bloodless e began To quicken — Marr. of Geraint 534
There lived a king in the most Eastern E, — Merlin and V. 555
in her chamber up a tower to the e — Lancelot and E. 3
star Led on the gray-hair'd wisdom of the e; — Holy Grail 453
'One night my pathway swerving e, — „ 634
Let the fierce e scream thro' your eyelet-holes, — Pelleas and E. 469
water Moab saw Come round by the E, — Last Tournament 483
Smote by the fresh beam of the springing e; — Pass. of Arthur 382
deeds Of England, and her banner in the E? — Ded. Poem Prin. Alice 21
Or Amurath of the E? — Sir J. Oldcastle 97
made West E, and sail'd the Dragon's mouth, — Columbus 25
our most ancient E Moriah with Jerusalem; — „ 80
Up from the E hither Saxon and Angle — Batt. of Brunanburh 117
Who wert the voice of England in the E. — Epit. on Stratford 4

East (*continued*) clash The golden keys of *E* and West. — *To Marq. of Dufferin* 4
she lent The sceptres of her West, her *E*, — " 6
Easterday For it was past the time of *E*. — *Gareth and L.* 186
Eastern Below the city's *e* towers: — *Fatima* 9
captain of my dreams Ruled in the *e* sky. — *D. of F. Women* 264
Far up the porch there grew an *E* rose, — *Gardener's D.* 123
Beyond the fair green field and *e* sea. — *Love and Duty* 101
'There lived a king in the most *E* East, — *Merlin and V.* 555
an *E* gauze With seeds of gold— — *Lover's Tale iv* 291
Who reads your golden *E* lay, — *To E. Fitzgerald* 32
e flowers large, Some dropping low — *Arabian Nights* 61
But she was sharper than an *e* wind, — *Audley Court* 53
The foaming grape of *e* France. — *In Mem., Con.* 80
climb'd That *e* tower, and entering barr'd her door, — *Lancelot and E.* 15
at the *e* end, Wealthy with wandering lines — *Holy Grail* 251
Eastward Past *e* from the falling sun. — *Balin and Balan* 320
singing in the topmost tower To the *e*: — *Holy Grail* 835
East-wind In the stormy *e-w* straining, — *L. of Shalott iv* 1
Easy (*See also* **Eäsy**) For it's *e* to find a rhyme. (repeat) — *Window, Ay* 6, 12
sleepless nights Of my long life have made it *e* to me. — *Merlin and V.* 680
He will answer to the purpose, *e* things to understand— — *Locksley Hall* 55
Fast flow'd the current of her *e* tears, — *Enoch Arden* 865
Were no false passport to that *e* realm, — *Aylmer's Field* 183
I said no, Yet being an *e* man, gave it: — *Princess i* 149
winning *e* grace, No doubt, for slight delay, — " *iv* 330
If *e* patrons of their kin Have left the last free race — *Third of Feb.* 39
doubted whether daughter's tenderness, Or *e* nature, — *Marr. of Geraint* 798
down the highway moving on With *e* laughter — *Tiresias* 200
Flowing with *e* greatness and touching — *The Wreck* 50
Eäsy an' a says it *e* an' freeä — *N. Farmer, O. S.* 25
Lets them inter 'eaven *e* es leäves their debts to be paäid. — *Village Wife* 94
but they wasn't that *e* to pleäse, — " 117
Eat The creaking cords which wound and *e* — *Supp. Confessions* 36
princes over-bold Have *e* our substance, — *Lotos-Eaters, C. S.* 76
thou may'st warble, *e* and dwell. — *The Blackbird* 4
we sat and *e* And talk'd old matters over; — *Audley Court* 28
e wholesome food, And wear warm clothes, — *St. S. Stylites* 108
I will not *e* my heart alone, — *In Mem. cviii* 3
'A thousand pips *e* up your sparrow-hawk! — *Marr. of Geraint* 274
I will enter, I will *e* With all the passion — " 305
those That *e* in Arthur's hall at Camelot. — " 432
'Friend, let her *e*; the damsel is so faint.' — *Geraint and E.* 206
My lord, *e* also, tho' the fare is coarse, — " 208
And rising on the sudden he said, '*E*! — " 614
it makes me mad to see you weep. *E*! — " 617
E and be glad, for I account you mine.' — " 647
thrust the dish before her, crying, '*E*.' — " 655
'No, no,' said Enid, vext, 'I will not *e* — " 656
man upon the bier arise, And *e* with me.' — " 658
Before I well have drunken, scarce can *e*: — " 662
Not *e* nor drink? And wherefore wail for one, — " 674
E's scarce enow to keep his pulse abeat; — *Balin and Balan* 105
And one said '*E* in peace! a liar is he, — " 607
Who meant to *e* her up in that wild wood — *Merlin and V.* 260
e's And uses, careless of the rest; — " 462
After the king, who *e* in Arthur's halls. — *Lancelot and E.* 184
I knew For one of those who *e* in Arthur's hall; — *Holy Grail* 24
but *e* not thou with Mark, — *Last Tournament* 532
Is it worth his while to *e*, — *Voice spake, etc.* 7
'Eät (heat) What's the *'e* of this 'illside to the *'e* — *North. Cobbler* 6
Eaten (*See also* **Temple-eaten, Worm-eaten**) after all had *e*, then Geraint, — *Marr. of Geraint* 397
'Boy,' said he, 'I have *e* all, — *Geraint and E.* 217
when Earl Doorm had *e* all he would, — " 609
And myself, I had *e* but sparely, — *V. of Maeldune* 69
Eater *See* **Lotos-Eaters**
Eating *E* the Lotos day by day, — *Lotos-Eaters, C. S.* 60
Until the ulcer, *e* thro' my skin, — *St. S. Stylites* 67
and *e* not, Except the spare chance-gift — " 77
Eating (*continued*) And *e* hoary grain and pulse the steeds, — *Spec. of Iliad.* 21
And a morbid *e* lichen fixt On a heart — *Maud I vi* 77
the village boys Who love to vex him *e*, — *Geraint and E.* 561
'tis *e* dry To dance without a catch, — *Last Tournament* 249
Eavedrops Then I rise, the *e* fall, — *Maud II iv* 62
'Eaven (heaven) Lets them inter *'e* eäsy es leäves — *Village Wife* 94
Eaves (*See also* **Bower-eaves, Mountain-eaves**) Her eyelids dropp'd their silken *e*. — *Talking Oak* 209
One, almost to the martin-haunted *e* — *Aylmer's Field* 163
Fly to her, and fall upon her gilded *e*, — *Princess iv* 94
closing *e* of wearied eyes I sleep till dusk — *In Mem. lxvii* 11
Who murmurest in the foliaged *e* — " *xcix* 9
Makes daggers at the sharpen'd *e*, — " *cvii* 8
With hands for *e*, uplooking and almost Waiting — *Lover's Tale i* 311
And murmur at the low-dropt *e* of sleep, — " *ii* 122
now from all the dripping *e* The spear of ice — *Prog. of Spring* 5
Ebb (s) We left the dying *e* that faintly lipp'd — *Audley Court* 12
Have *e* and flow conditioning their march, — *Golden Year* 30
float or fall in endless *e* and flow; — *W. to Marie Alex.* 27
I could rest, a rock in *e's* and flows, — *Marr. of Geraint* 812
from my farthest lapse, my latest *e*, — *Lover's Tale i* 90
Sway'd by vaster *e's* and flows — *Locksley H., Sixty* 194
Ebb (verb) brood, And *e* into a former life, — *Sonnet To —* 2
According to my humour *e* and flow. — *D. of F. Women* 134
When the tide *e's* in sunshine, — *Princess vi* 162
Ebb'd sat round the wassail-bowl, Then half-way *e*: — *The Epic* 6
(possibly He flow'd and *e* uncertain, — *Aylmer's Field* 218
'O mine have *e* away for evermore, — *Merlin and V.* 439
Ebbing felt them slowly *e*, name and fame.' — " 437
Ebony brow of pearl Tress'd with redolent *e*, — *Arabian Nights* 138
cups of emerald, there at tables of *e* lay, — *Boädicea* 61
Echo (s) So took *e* with delight, (repeat) — *The Owl ii* 4
Lull'd *e's* of laborious day Come to you, — *Margaret* 29
An *e* from a measured strain, — *Miller's D.* 66
To hear the dewy *e's* calling From cave to cave — *Lotos-Eaters, C. S.* 94
Were faint Homeric *e's*, nothing-worth, — *The Epic* 39
the great *e* flap And buffet round the hills, — *Golden Year* 76
Like hints and *e's* of the world — *Day-Dm., Sleep. P.* 7
Like *e's* from beyond a hollow, — *Aylmer's Field* 298
crashing with long *e's* thro' the land, — " 338
E answer'd in her sleep From hollow fields: — *Princess, Pro.* 66
An *e* like a ghostly woodpecker, — " 217
Blow, bugle, blow, set the wild *e's* flying, (repeat) — " *iv* 5, 17
Blow, bugle; answer, *e's*, dying, dying, dying. (repeat) — " 6, 12
Our *e's* roll from soul to soul, — " 15
And answer, *e's*, answer, dying, dying, — " 18
A step Of lightest *e*, — " 215
barrier like a wild horn in a land Of *e's*, — " *v* 487
And now and then an *e* started up, — " *vi* 369
The proof and *e* of all human fame, — *Ode on Well.* 145
E on *e* Dies to the moon. — *Minnie and Winnie* 11
A hollow *e* of my own— — *In Mem. iii* 11
Like *e's* in sepulchral halls, — " *lviii* 2
As *e's* out of weaker times, — " *Con.* 22
E there, whatever is ask'd her, — *Maud I i* 4
an *e* of something Read with a boy's delight, — " *vii* 9
a million horrible bellowing *e's* broke — " *II i* 24
And the woodland *e* rings; — " *iv* 38
great Queen, In words whose *e* lasts, — *Marr. of Geraint* 782
old *e's* hidden in the wall Rang out — *Pelleas and E.* 366
Like the last *e* born of a great cry, — *Pass. of Arthur* 459
And mellow'd *e's* of the outer world— — *Lover's Tale i* 208
melody That drowns the nearer *e's*. — " 533
e's of the hollow-banked brooks Are fashion'd — " 566
If so be that the *e* of that name Ringing — " 644
Whose *e* shall not tongue thy glorious doom, — *Tiresias* 136
A dying *e* from a falling wall; — *Ancient Sage* 263
Silent *e's*! You, my Leonard, — *Locksley H., Sixty* 265
Echo (verb) Hear a song that *e's* clearly, — *L. of Shallot i* 30
The haunts of memory *e* not. — *Two Voices* 369
With sounds that *e* still. — *D. of F. Women* 8
'Hear how the bushes *e*! — *Gardener's D.* 98
Then made his pleasure *e*, hand to hand, — *Aylmer's Field* 257
E round his bones for evermore. — *Ode on Well.* 12

Edmund Atheling (*See also* **Atheling**) He with his brother, *E A*, *Batt. of Brunanburh* 6
Edward (the Elder, King of the English, 901-925)
Sons of *E* with hammer'd brands. " 14
they play'd with The children of *E*. " 92
Edward (III., King of England) Gray with distance *E's* fifty summers, *On Jub. Q. Victoria* 40
Edward (Christian name) Then, and here in *E's* time, *Locksley H., Sixty* 83
Edward Bull With Edwin Morris and with *E B* *Edwin Morris* 14
Then said the fat-faced curate *E B*, (repeat) " 42, 90
Edward Gray 'And are you married yet, *E G*?' *Edward Gray* 4
love no more Can touch the heart of *E G*. " 8
'To trouble the heart of *E G*' " 20
And here the heart of *E G*!' " 28
And there the heart of *E G*!' " 36
Edward Head Sir *E H's*: But he's abroad: *Walk. to the Mail* 15
Edwin (*See also* **Edwin Morris**) 'Friend *E*, do not think yourself alone *Edwin Morris* 77
And I and *E* laugh'd; " 93
So left the place, left *E*, " 137
crystal into which I braided *E's* hair! *The Flight* 34
follow *E* to those isles, those islands of the Blest! " 42
O would I were in *E's* arms— " 45
—on *E's* ship, with *E*, ev'n in death, " 46
My *E* loved to call us then " 80
flowers of the secret woods, when *E* found us there, " 82
sail at last which brings our *E* home. " 92
Edwin Morris (*See also* **Edwin**) With *E M* and with Edward Bull *Edwin Morris* 14
But *E M*, he that knew the names, " 16
Edyrn answer, groaning, '*E*, son of Nudd! *Marr. of Geraint* 576
'Then, *E*, son of Nudd,' replied Geraint, " 579
E answer'd, 'These things will I do, " 587
night of fire, when *E* sack'd their house, " 634
rose a cry That *E's* men were on them, " 639
E's men had caught them in their flight, " 642
Beholding it was *E* son of Nudd, *Geraint and E.* 781
E moving frankly forward spake: " 784
Till *E* crying, 'If ye will not go To Arthur, " 814
And one from *E*. Every now and then, When *E* rein'd his charger at her side, " 819
went apart with *E*, whom he held In converse " 881
E and with others: have ye look'd At E? " 896
E has done it, weeding all his heart " 906
This work of *E* wrought upon himself " 912
Eerie My people too were scared with *e* sounds, *The Ring* 408
Eery elfin prancer springs By night to *e* warblings, *Sir L. and Q. G.* 34
Effect (s) And thine *e* so lives in me, *In Mem. lxv* 10
Thro' manifold *e* of simple powers— *Prog. of Spring* 86
Effect (verb) tho' she herself *e* But little: *Princess iii* 264
Effeminacy Rolling on their purple couches in their tender *e*. *Boädicea* 62
all his force Is melted into mere *e*? *Marr. of Geraint* 107
Effeminate '*E* as I am, I will not fight my way *Geraint and E.* 20
Effie Little *E* shall go with me tomorrow *May Queen* 25
Don't let *E* come to see me *May Queen, N. Y's. E.* 43
And *E* on the other side, " *Con.* 24
I thought of you and *E* dear; " 29
But, *E*, you must comfort *her* " 44
there to wait a little while till you and *E* come— " 58
Effluence perennial *e's*, Whereof to all that draw *Lover's Tale i* 499
Effort I made one barren *e* to break it at the last. *Happy* 72
Eft A monstrous *e* was of old the Lord *Maud I iv* 31
A bedmate of the snail and *e* and snake, *Holy Grail* 570
Egalities That cursed France with her *e*! *Aylmer's Field* 265
Egbert doing nothing Since *E*—why, " 384
Egg (*See also* **Hegg**) The goose let fall a golden *e* *The Goose* 11
we stole his fruit, His hens, his *e's*; *Walk. to the Mail* 85
Roof-haunting martins warm their *e's*: *Day-Dm., Sleep. P.* 17
The Cock was of a larger *e* *Will Water.* 121
evil fancies clung Like serpent *e's* *Enoch Arden* 480
Sleeps in the plain *e's* of the nightingale. *Aylmer's Field* 103
lay their *e's*, and sting and sing *In Mem. l* 11
'twere but of the goose and golden *e's*.' *Gareth and L.* 40
Egg (*continued*) good mother, but this *e* of mine Was finer gold *Gareth and L.* 42
even in their hens and in their *e's*— *Holy Grail* 560
Nor bruised the wildbird's *e*. *Lover's Tale ii* 21
She hears the lark within the songless *e*, *Ancient Sage* 76
Egg-shell Nor cared a broken *e-s* for her lord. *Geraint and E.* 364
Eglantine Vine, vine and *e*, (repeat) *Window, At the W.* 1, 8
presently received in a sweet grave Of *e's*, *Lover's Tale i* 529
Beneath the bower of wreathed *e's*: " *ii* 43
Eglatere woodbine and *e* Drip sweeter dews *A Dirge* 23
Egypt (*See also* **Agypt**) O my life In *E*! *D. of F. Women* 147
the time When we made bricks in *E*. *Princess iv* 128
fierce Soldan of *E*, would break down *Columbus* 98
torpid mummy wheat Of *E* bore a grain as sweet *To Prof. Jebb* 6
Egyptian To whom the *E*: 'O, you tamely died! *D. of F. Women* 258
Egypt-plague our arms fail'd—this *E-p* of men! *Princess v* 427
Eight (adj.) (*See also* **Height**) Was proxy-wedded with a bootless calf At *e* years old; " *i* 35
close behind her stood *E* daughters of the plough, " *iv* 278
Then those *e* mighty daughters of the plough " 550
those *e* daughters of the plough Came sallying thro' " *v* 339
And *e* years past, *e* jousts had been, *Lancelot and E.* 67
E that were left to make a purer world— *Aylmer's Field* 638
The child was only *e* summers old, *The Victim* 33
Eight (s) cutting *e's* that day upon the pond, *The Epic* 10
Eighteen Pass me then A term of *e* years. *Lover's Tale i* 287
E long years of waste, seven in your Spain, *Columbus* 36
Eighty Whose *e* winters freeze with one rebuke *Ode on Well.* 186
Timur built his ghastly tower of *e* thousand human skulls, *Locksley H., Sixty* 82
E winters leave the dog too lame to follow " 226
Forward far and far from here is all the hope of *e* years. " 254
starved the wild beast that was linkt with thee *e* years back *By an Evolution.* 11
e thousand Christian faces watch Man murder man. *St. Telemachus* 55
Eighty-thousand Should *e-t* college-councils *To F. D. Maurice* 7
Eight-year-old *See* **Height-year-old**
Either *e* hand, Or voice, or else a motion of the mere. *M. d'Arthur* 76
On *e* side All round about the fragrant marge *Arabian Nights* 58
And *e* twilight and the day between; *Edwin Morris* 37
Powers of the House On *e* side the hearth, *Aylmer's Field* 288
with his hopes in *e* grave. " 624
familiar with her, Easily gather'd *e* guilt. *Princess iv* 236
seeing *e* sex alone Is half itself, " *vii* 301
For groves of pine on *e* hand, *To F. D. Maurice* 21
And drops of water fell from *e* hand; *Gareth and L.* 220
In *e* hand he bore What dazzled all, " 386
And each at either dash from *e* end— " 535
she lifted *e* arm, 'Fie on thee, King! " 657
and *e* spear Bent but not brake, and *e* knight at once, " 963
at *e* end whereof There swung an apple *Marr. of Geraint* 169
Whom first she kiss'd on *e* cheek, and then On *e* " 517
Made her cheek burn and *e* eyelid fall. " 775
day by day she past In *e* twilight ghost-like *Lancelot and E.* 849
at the base we found On *e* hand, *Holy Grail* 498
yell'd the youth, and *e* knight Drew back a space, *Pelleas and E.* 572
Wheel'd round on *e* heel, Dagonet replied, *Last Tournament* 244
At once from *e* side, with trumpet-blast, *Com. of Arthur* 102
e hand, Or voice, or else a motion of the mere. *Pass. of Arthur* 244
As tho' there beat a heart in *e* eye; *Lover's Tale i* 34
Love wraps his wings on *e* side the heart, " 467
My father with a child on *e* knee, A hand upon the head of *e* child, *Sisters (E. and E.)* 54
He joins us once again, to his *e* office true: *Happy* 106
Thy elect have no dealings with *e* heresy or orthodoxy; *Akbar's D., Inscrip.* 7
With all the Hells a-glare in *e* eye, *Akbar's Dream* 115
And each at *e* dash from either end— *Gareth and L.* 535
Elaborately Who read me rhymes *e* good, *Edwin Morris* 20
Elaine *E* the fair, *E* the loveable, *E*, the lily maid *Lancelot and E.* 1
behind them stept the lily maid *E*, " 177
E, and heard her name so tost about, " 233
lily maid *E*, Won by the mellow voice " 242

Elaine (*continued*) Who parted with his own to fair *E*: — *Lancelot and E.* 381
stay'd; and cast his eyes on fair *E*: — „ 640
'So be it,' cried *E*, And lifted her fair face — „ 681
'Torre and *E*! why here? — „ 796
Then rose *E* and glided thro' the fields, — „ 843
call her friend and sister, sweet *E*, — „ 865
I had been wedded earlier, sweet *E*: — „ 935
on her face, and thought 'Is this *E*?' — „ 1031
Elbow In every *e* and turn, — *Ode to Memory* 62
deep in broider'd down we sank Our *e's*: — *Princess iv* 33
Elbow-chair She shifted in her *e-c*, — *The Goose* 27
Elbow-deep Or *e-d* in sawdust, slept, — *Will Water.* 99
Elbowed *See* **Half-elbowed**
Elburz *E* and all the Caucasus have heard; — *W. to Marie Alex.* 13
Elder (s) led The holy *E's* with the gift of myrrh. — *M. d'Arthur* 233
Thine *e's* and thy betters. — *Will Water.* 192
with jubilant cries Broke from their *e's*, — *Enoch Arden* 378
passion of youth Toward greatness in its *e*, — *Lancelot and E.* 283
led The holy *E's* with the gift of myrrh — *Pass. of Arthur* 400
Elder (adj.) The Tory member's *e* son, — *Princess, Con.* 50
Elderly I knew them all as babies, and now they're *e* men. — *Grandmother* 88
Elder-thicket saw The white-flower'd *e-t* from the field — *Godiva* 63
Elder-tree *See* **Boor-tree**
Eldest-born Whatever *e-b* of rank or wealth — *Aylmer's Field* 484
And Willy, my *e-b*, is gone, you say, — *Grandmother* 1, 87
Willy, my beauty, my *e-b*, the flower of the flock; — „ 9
Willy, my *e-b*, at nigh threescore and ten; — „ 87
Willy has gone, my beauty, my *e-b*, my flower; — „ 101
her *e-b*, her glory, her boast, — *Despair* 73
Eleanor Those dragon eyes of anger'd *E* — *D. of F. Women* 255
Eleänore To deck thy cradle, *E*. — *Eleänore* 21
Crimsons over an inland mere, *E*! — „ 43
Of thy swan-like stateliness, *E*? — „ 48
Of thy floating gracefulness, *E*? — „ 51
Every lineament divine, *E*. — „ 54
Who may express thee, *E*? — „ 68
I stand before thee, *E*; — „ 69
Serene, imperial *E*! (repeat) — „ 81, 121
In thy large eyes, imperial *E*. — „ 97
So dying ever, *E*. — „ 144
Elect (chosen) Thy *e* have no dealings with either heresy or orthodoxy; — *Akbar's D., Inscrip.* 7
Elected by common voice *E* umpire, — *Œnone* 85
Election *E*, *E* and Reprobation— — *Rizpah* 73
Electric *e* shock Dislink'd with shrieks and laughter: — *Princess, Pro.* 69
E, chemic laws, and all the rest, — „ *ii* 384
came As comes a pillar of *e* cloud, — „ *v* 524
this *e* force, that keeps A thousand pulses dancing, — *In Mem. cxxv* 15
with some *e* thrill A cold air pass'd between us, — *The Ring* 379
Elegant *See* **Illigant**
Elegy *elegies* And quoted odes, — *Princess ii* 376
Element The *e's* were kindlier mix'd.' — *Two Voices* 228
may soul to soul Strike thro' a finer *e* — *Aylmer's Field* 579
And in their own clear *e*, they moved. — *Princess vii* 28
Large *e's* in order brought, — *In Mem. cxii* 13
One God, one law, one *e*, — „ *Con.* 142
I saw The holy *e's* alone; — *Holy Grail* 463
I am not made of so slight *e's*. — *Guinevere* 510
The cloud-pavilion'd *e*, the wood, — *Lover's Tale ii* 108
Elemental And learnt their *e* secrets, — *Merlin and V.* 632
Eleusis Who laid thee at *E*, dazed and dumb — *Demeter and P.* 6
Eleventh when the *e* moon After their marriage lit the lover's Bay, — *Lover's Tale iv* 27
Elf the little *elves* of chasm and cleft Made — *Guinevere* 248
Elves, and the harmless glamour of the field; — *Pass. of Arthur* 52
and glancing at *E* of the woodland, — *Merlin and the G.* 38
Elf-god 'I saw the little *e-g* eyeless once — *Merlin and V.* 249
Elfin rich With jewels, *e* Urim, on the hilt, — *Com. of Arthur* 298
whose *e* prancer springs By night — *Sir L. and Q. G.* 33
Elfland The horns of *E* faintly blowing! — *Princess iv* 10
Elizabeth (Queen) The spacious times of great *E* — *D. of F. Women* 7
in arts of government *E* and others; — *Princess ii* 162
Elizabeth (Aunt) there is Aunt *E* And sister Lilia — „ *Pro.* 51
And here we lit on Aunt *E* — „ 96

Elk the monstrous horns of *e* and deer, — *Princess, Pro.* 23
Ellen (*See also* **Ellen Adair, Ellen Aubrey**) Sleep, *E*, folded in thy sister's arm, — *Audley Court* 63
'Sleep, *E*, folded in Emilia's arm; — „ 65
By *E's* grave, on the windy hill. — *Edward Gray* 12
'You said that you hated me, *E*, — *First Quarrel* 79
Ellen Adair (*See also* **Ellen**) '*E A* she loved me well, — *Edward Gray* 9
When *E A* was dying for me. — „ 16
Speak a little, *E A*!' — „ 24
'Here lies the body of *E A*; — „ 27
Till *E A* come back to me. — „ 32
There lies the body of *E A*! — „ 35
Ellen Aubrey (*See also* **Ellen**) *E A*, sleep, and dream of me: — *Audley Court* 62
Sleep, *E A*, love, and dream of me.' — „ 73
Elle vous suit sent a note, the seal an *E v s*, — *Edwin Morris* 105
Ellipse Earth follows wheel'd in her *e*; — *Golden Year* 24
Elm (*See also* **Dwarf-elm, Witch-elm**) The seven *e's*, the poplars four — *Ode to Memory* 56
The mellow ouzel fluted in the *e*; — *Gardener's D.* 94
fruits and cream Served in the weeping *e*; — „ 195
Old *e's* came breaking from the vine, — *Amphion* 45
Aroused the black republic on his *e's*, — *Aylmer's Field* 529
always friends, none closer, *e* and vine: — *Princess ii* 337
varies from the lily as far As oak from *e*: — „ *v* 183
The moan of doves in immemorial *e's*, — „ *vii* 221
approaching rookery swerve From the *e's*, — „ *Con.* 97
Rock'd the full-foliaged *e's*, — *In Mem. xcv* 58
swaying upon a restless *e* Drew the vague glance — *Balin and Balan* 463
in Julian's land They never nail a dumb head up in *e*), — *Lover's Tale iv* 37
in yon arching avenue of old *e's*, — *The Ring* 172
Of leafless *e*, or naked lime, — *To Ulysses* 16
few lanes of *e* And whispering oak. — *To Mary Boyle* 67
Elm-tree rook 'ill caw from the windy tall *e-t*, — *May Queen, N.Y's. E.* 17
topmost *e-t* gather'd green From draughts — *Sir L. and Q. G.* 8
e's ruddy-hearted blossom-flake Is fluttering — *To Mary Boyle* 3
Elm-tree-boles Enormous *e-t-b* did stoop and lean — *D. of F. Women* 57
Eloquence A full-cell'd honeycomb of *e* — *Edwin Morris* 26
and golden *e* And amorous adulation, — *Lancelot and E.* 649
his *e* caught like a flame From zone to zone — *Dead Prophet* 34
Eloquent The form, the form alone is *e*! — *The form, the form* 1
her *e* eyes, (As I have seen them many a hundred times) — *Lover's Tale ii* 144
'Elp (help) es I oäps es thou'll '*e* me a bit, — *Village Wife* 65
Elsewise Did mightier deeds than *e* he had done, — *Last Tournament* 680
Elsinore when *E* Heard the war moan — *Buonaparte* 9
Elusion *E*, and occasion, and evasion'? — *Gareth and L.* 288
Elvish dragon-boughts and *e* emblemings Began to move, — „ 233
Elysian others in *E* valleys dwell, — *Lotos-Eaters, C. S.* 124
fields Are lovely, lovelier not the *E* lawns, — *Princess iii* 342
Elysium dimly-glimmering lawns Of that *E*, — *Demeter and P.* 151
Emancipation on whom The secular *e* turns — *Princess ii* 289
Embalm *e* In dying songs a dead regret, — *In Mem., Con.* 13
Embark 'I will *e* and I will lose myself, — *Holy Grail* 805
may there be no sadness of farewell, When I *e*; — *Crossing the Bar* 12
Embassage till their *e* return'd. — *Balin and Balan* 93
Embassy Such touches are but *embassies* of love, — *Gardener's D.* 18
Embathing *E* all with wild and woeful hues, — *Lover's Tale ii* 64
Embattail To *e* and to wall about thy cause — *To J. M. K.* 8
Embattled when we saw the *e* squares, — *Princess v* 246
Till this *e* wall of unbelief My prison, — *Doubt and Prayer* 11
Embellish overflowing revenue Wherewith to *e* state, — *Œnone* 113
Emblem Graven with *e's* of the time, — *Arabian Nights* 108
Like *e's* of infinity, — *Ode to Memory* 103
Caryatids, lifted up A weight of *e*, — *Princess iv* 202
rich in *e* and the work Of ancient kings — *Gareth and L.* 304
Half-tarnish'd and half-bright, his *e*, shone. — „ 1118
these her *e's* drew mine eyes—away: — *Balin and Balan* 265
Emblematic Amazon As *e* of a nobler age; — *Princess ii* 127
Embleming and elvish *e's* Began to move, — *Gareth and L.* 233
Embodied When truth *e* in a tale — *In Mem. xxxvi* 7
Emboss'd bronze valves, *e* with Tomyris — *Princess v* 365
Embower However deep you might *e* the nest, — „ *Pro.* 147
Embowering *See* **Oriel-embowering**

Enchantment (*continued*) Begotten by *e*—chatterers they, *Holy Grail* 145
all his guests Once more as by *e*; *Lover's Tale iv* 360
Enchantress A great *e* you may be; *L. C. V. de Vere* 30
Encircle *E's* all the heart, and feedeth *Margaret* 16
Enclosing hollow shades *e* hearts of flame, *Palace of Art* 241
every marge *e* in the midst A square of text *Merlin and V.* 670
Encompass love of all Thy sons *e* Thee, *Ded. of Idylls* 52
Encompass'd sleep *E* by his faithful guard, *In Mem. cxxvi* 8
Encounter A little in the late *e* strain'd, *Geraint and E.* 158
End (s) (*See also* **Gable-ends, Hend**) 'And cruel love,
whose *e* is scorn, Is this the *e* to be left alone, *Mariana in the S.* 70
apprehend A labour working to an *e*. *Two Voices* 297
'The *e* and the beginning vex His reason: ,, 298
'I see the *e*, and know the good.' ,, 432
'Which in all action is the *e* of all; *Œnone* 122
Death is the *e* of life; ah, why *Lotos-Eaters, C. S.* 41
wood is all thine own, Until the *e* of time.' *D. of F. Women* 84
Sleep till the *e*, true soul and sweet. *To J. S.* 73
Love, that endures not sordid *e's*, *Love thou thy land* 6
'My *e* draws nigh; 'tis time that I were gone. *M. d'Arthur* 163
Here, then, my words have *e*. *Gardener's D.* 250
my *e* draws nigh; I hope my *e* draws nigh: *St. S. Stylites* 36
The watcher on the column till the *e*; ,, 163
The *e*! the *e*! Surely the *e*! ,, 201
The set gray life, and apathetic *e*. *Love and Duty* 18
And that which shapes it to some perfect *e*. ,, 26
Spun round in station, but the *e* had come. ,, 76
How dull it is to pause, to make an *e*, *Ulysses* 22
something ere the *e*, Some work of noble note, ,, 51
if I Should hook it to some useful *e*. *Day-Dm., Moral* 16
Enough if at the *e* of all A little garden blossom. *Amphion* 103
For them I battle till the *e*, *Sir Galahad* 15
A life that moves to gracious *e's* *You might have won* 6
Down at the far *e* of an avenue, *Enoch Arden* 358
his lonely doom Came suddenly to an *e*, ,, 627
rioted his life out, and made an *e*. *Aylmer's Field* 391
thro' every labyrinth till he saw An *e*, ,, 480
nor wanted at his *e* The dark retinue ,, 841
Crown'd with a flower or two, and there an *e*— *Lucretius* 229
noise with bees and breeze from *e* to *e*. *Princess, Pro.* 88
from *e* to *e* With beauties every shade ,, *ii* 436
if our *e* were less achievable By slow approaches, ,, *iii* 283
I fight with iron laws, in the *e* Found golden: ,, *iv* 75
But great is song Used to great *e's*: ,, 138
some grand fight to kill and make an *e*: ,, 591
you failing, I abide What *e* soever: ,, *v* 406
at the further *e* Was Ida by the throne, ,, *vi* 356
For worship without *e*; nor *e* of mine, ,, *vii* 169
Yoked in all exercise of noble *e*, ,, 361
Gone, till the *e* of the year, *Window. Gone* 2
Over the world to the *e* of it *Window, Marr. Morn.* 23
O what to her shall be the *e*? *In Mem. vi* 41
'Is this the *e*? Is this the *e*?' ,, *xii* 16
And move thee on to noble *e's*. ,, *lxv* 12
Are sharpen'd to a needle's *e*; ,, *lxxvi* 4
What *e* is here to my complaint? ,, *lxxxi* 6
Now looking to some settled *e*, ,, *lxxxv* 97
I climb the hill: from *e* to *e* ,, *c* 1
breathers of an ampler day For ever nobler *e's*. ,, *cxviii* 7
Is toil coöperant to an *e*. ,, *cxxviii* 24
Calming itself to the long-wish'd-for *e*, *Maud I xviii* 5
never an *e* to the stream of passing feet, ,, *II v* 11
And each at either dash from either *e*— *Gareth and L.* 535
At one *e* one, that gave upon a range ,, 666
at either *e* whereof There swung an apple *Marr. of Geraint* 169
O to what *e*, except a jealous one, *Merlin and V.* 538
and to this *e* Had made the pretext *Lancelot and E.* 581
sweet is death who puts an *e* to pain: ,, 1008
An *e* to this! A strange one! ,, 1222
one there is, and at the eastern *e*, *Holy Grail* 251
When the hermit made an *e*, ,, 457
run itself All out like a long life to a sour *e*— *Last Tournament* 288
mystic babble about his *e* Amazed me; ,, 670
whitens ere his hour Woos his own *e*; ,, 698
Serving his traitorous *e* *Guinevere* 19

End (s) (*continued*) 'The *e* is come, And I am shamed for
ever;' *Guinevere* 110
'My *e* draws nigh; 'tis time that I were gone. *Pass. of Arthur* 331
Was this the *e*? Why grew we then together *Lover's Tale ii* 22
in the *e*, Opening on darkness, ,, 124
Then at the far *e* of the vault he saw ,, *iv* 56
And stranger yet, at one *e* of the hall ,, 213
And when the feast was near an *e*, ,, 229
an' I work an' I wait to the *e*. *First Quarrel* 7
It was full of old odds an *e's*, ,, 49
they watch'd what the *e* would be. *The Revenge* 73
What *e* but darkness could ensue *Sisters (E. and E.)* 175
if life's best *e* Be to end well! *Tiresias* 130
A less diffuse and opulent *e*, ,, 189
of a Hell without help, without *e*. *Despair* 26
at last the *e* is sure, *The Flight* 103
globe from *e* to *e* Might sow and reap in peace, *Epilogue* 12
An' sattle their *e's* upo stools *Owd Roä* 24
when he heard what an *e* was mine? *Charity* 17
And loves the world from *e* to *e*, *The Wanderer* 7
End (verb) That to begin implies to *e*; *Two Voices* 339
tho' they could not *e* me, left me maim'd *Tithonus* 20
Whether I mean this day to *e* myself, *Lucretius* 146
Not manlike *e* myself?—our privilege— ,, 232
how the strange betrothment was to *e*: *Princess v* 474
There will I hide thee, till my life shall *e*, *Guinevere* 114
if life's best end Be to *e* well! *Tiresias* 131
who can tell how all will *e*? *Locksley H., Sixty* 103
Demos *e* in working its own doom. ,, 114
e but in being our own corpse-coffins at last, *Vastness* 33
I felt I could *e* myself with the dagger— *Bandit's Death* 37
all's well that *e's* well, (repeat) *The Dreamer* 19, 23, 27, 31
The gleam of household sunshine *e's*, *The Wanderer* 1
End *See also* **Far-end**
Endear the falling out That all the more *e's*, *Princess ii* 7
Ended (*See also* **Never-ended**) Here *e* Hall, and our
last light, *M. d'Arthur, Ep.* 1
Thus far he flow'd, and *e*; *Golden Year* 52
When, ere his song was *e*, *Amphion* 50
Till this was *e*, and his careful hand,— *Enoch Arden* 176
E he had not, but she brook'd no more: *Aylmer's Field* 798
but when the wordy storm Had *e*, *Sea Dreams* 32
She *e* here, and beckon'd us: *Princess ii* 182
She *e* with such passion that the tear, ,, *iv* 59
For when the jousts were *e* yesterday, *Marr. of Geraint* 692
But *e* with apology so sweet, *Geraint and E.* 394
Half-wroth he had not *e*, *Balin and Balan* 427
She *e*, and the cry of a great jousts *Last Tournament* 51
But when the twangling *e*, skipt again; ,, 255
He *e*: Arthur knew the voice; ,, 455
mountains *e* in a coast Of ever-shifting sand, *Pass. of Arthur* 85
ever that evening *e* a great gale blew, *The Revenge* 114
Have *e* mortal foes; *Ancient Sage* 158
Ending She, *e*, waved her hands: *Princess iv* 522
the mocker *e* here Turn'd to the right, *Gareth and L.* 294
And *e* in a ruin—nothing left, *Merlin and V.* 883
e, he moved toward her, and she said, *Last Tournament* 704
Endless 'Let me not cast in *e* shade *Two Voices* 5
memory of the wither'd leaf In *e* time is scarce
more brief ,, 113
river winding slow By herds upon an *e* plain, *Palace of Art.* 74
down in hell Suffer *e* anguish, *Lotos-Eaters, C. S.* 124
Farewell, like *e* welcome, lived and died. *Love and Duty* 68
And float or fall, in *e* ebb and flow; *W. to Marie Alex.* 27
Paid with a voice flying by to be lost on an *e* sea— *Wages* 2
And we shall sit at *e* feast, *In Mem. xlvii* 9
What fame is left for human deeds In *e* age? ,, *lxxiii* 12
Slain by himself, shall enter *e* night. *Gareth and L.* 642
glory and shame dying out for ever in *e* time, *Despair* 75
poet whom his Age would quote As heir of *e* fame— *Ancient Sage* 147
border-races, holding, each its own By *e* war: ,, 252
Endow *E* you with broad land and territory *Lancelot and E.* 957
Endurance until *e* grow Sinew'd with action, *Œnone* 164
Endure A courage to *e* and to obey; *Isabel* 25
All force in bonds that might *e*, *Palace of Art* 154

Endure (*continued*) Love, that *e's* not sordid ends, *Love thou thy land* 6
But while the races of mankind *e*, *Ode on Well.* 219
I will nevermore *e* To sit with empty hands *Sailor Boy* 15
Would she have heart to *e* for the life of the worm *Wages* 7
That dies not, but *e's* with pain, *In Mem. xviii* 17
And scarce *e* to draw the breath, „ *xx* 15
Whose loves in higher love *e*; „ *xxxii* 14
O living will that shalt *e* „ *cxxxi* 1
Let the sweet heavens *e*, *Maud I xi* 8
As long as my life *e's* I feel I shall owe you „ *xix* 86
Break not, O woman's-heart, but still *e*; Break not, for thou art Royal, but *e*, *Ded. of Idylls* 44
E's not that her guest should serve *Marr. of Geraint* 379
But can *e* it all most patiently.' „ 473
canst *e* To mouth so huge a foulness— *Balin and Balan* 378
thought to do while he might yet *e*, *Lancelot and E.* 495
strength of the race to command, to obey, to *e*, *Def. of Lucknow* 47
E! thou hast done so well for men, *Columbus* 152
every heart that loves with truth is equal to *e*. *The Flight* 104
For so the deed *e's*; *Epilogue* 39
But while my life's late eve *e's*, *To Marq. of Dufferin* 49
vanish and give place to the beauty that *e's*, The beauty that *e's* on the Spiritual height, *Happy* 36
caught one gleam of the beauty which *e's*— „ 60
Endured Have all in all *e* as much, *St. S. Stylites* 130
Nor yet *e* to meet her opening eyes, *Princess iv* 195
they knew her; *they e*, Long-closeted with her „ 321
ye surely have *e* Strange chances here alone;' *Geraint and E.* 809
Nor yet *e* in presence of His eyes *Lover's Tale i* 423
while I mused nor yet *e* to take So rich a prize, „ *iii* 49
Enduring (*See also* **All-enduring, Long-enduring**) 'Yet hadst thou, thro' *e* pain, *Two Voices* 166
Sow the seed, and reap the harvest with *e* toil, *Lotos-Eaters, C. S.* 121
'Enemies (anemones) Down i' the woild *'e* *N. Farmer, O. S.* 34
Enemy (*See also* **Hennemy**) 'Our *enemies* have fall'n, but this shall grow *Princess vi* 53
'Our *enemies* have fall'n, have fall'n: (repeat) *Princess vi* 33, 38, 43, 48
moan of an *e* massacred, *Boädicea* 25
tho' the gathering *e* narrow thee, „ 39
pulses at the clamouring of her *e* fainted „ 82
I trust if an *e's* fleet came yonder *Maud I i* 49
'A boon, Sir King! Thine *e*, King, am I. *Gareth and L.* 351
He drave his *e* backward down the bridge, „ 969
being but knave, I throw thine *enemies*.' „ 1023
To dash against mine *e* and to win. „ 1355
arms, arms, arms to fight my *e*? *Marr. of Geraint* 282
down his *e* roll'd, And there lay still; *Geraint and E.* 160
an *e* that has left Death in the living waters, *Merlin and V.* 147
roll'd his *e* down, And saved him: *Lancelot and E.* 26
the knights Are half of them our *enemies*, „ 99
a dream Of dragging down his *e* made them move. „ 814
and said, 'Mine *enemies* Pursue me, *Guinevere* 139
Ev'n in the presence of an *e's* fleet, „ 279
on all the defences our myriad *e* fell. *Def. of Lucknow* 35
in a moment two mines by the *e* sprung „ 54
Fonseca my main *e* at their court, *Columbus* 126
For there was not an *e* near, *V. of Maeldune* 93
so often in Strife with their *enemies* *Batt. of Brunanburh* 18
Love your *e*, bless your haters, *Locksley H., Sixty* 85
'Kill your *e*, for you hate him,' still, 'your *e* „ 94
Energy spurr'd at heart with fieriest *e* *To J. M. K.* 7
By its own *e* fulfill'd itself, *Gardener's D.* 238
suit The full-grown *energies* of heaven. *In Mem. xl* 20
come and go, With agonies, with *energies*, „ *cxiii* 18
To those still-working *energies* I spy *Mechanophilus* 19
Enfold So dear a life your arms *e* *The Daisy* 93
that large grief which these *e* *In Mem. v* 11
mother's shame will *e* her and darken *The Wreck* 100
Enfolded Two mutually *e*; Love, the third, *Gardener's D.* 215
And in her veil *e*, manchet bread. *Marr. of Geraint* 389
Enfolding *E* that dark body which had lain *Death of Œnone* 93
Enforced *E* she was to wed him in her tears, *Com. of Arthur* 204
Engarlanded *E* and diaper'd With inwrought flowers, *Arabian Nights* 148
Engine Which only to one *e* bound Falls off, *Two Voices* 347
Enginery Loom and wheel and *e*, *Ode Inter. Exhib.* 15

Engirt *E* with many a florid maiden-cheek, *Princess iii* 350
England And more than *E* honours that, *Talking Oak* 295
show you slips of all that grows From *E* to Van Diemen. *Amphion* 84
dewy meadowy morning-breath Of *E*, *Enoch Arden* 661
thanks to the Giver, *E*, for thy son. *Ode on Well.* 45
For this is *E's* greatest son, „ 95
And *E* pouring on her foes. „ 117
keep our noble *E* whole, „ 161
Truth-teller was our *E's* Alfred named; „ 188
E's honest censure went too far; *Third of Feb.* 2
What *E* was, shall her true sons forget? „ 44
some love *E* and her honour yet. „ 46
Harold's *E* fell to Norman swords; *W. to Marie Alex.* 22
It told of *E* then to me, *The Daisy* 89
harsher sound ever heard, ye Muses, in *E*? *Trans. of Homer* 3
God-gifted organ-voice of *E*, *Milton* 3
freedom in her regal seat Of *E*; *In Mem. cix* 15
Or how should *E* dreaming of *his* sons *Ded. of Idylls* 31
boundless homes For ever-broadening *E*, *To the Queen ii* 30
Thou—*E's* England-loving daughter—thou *Ded. Poem Prin. Alice* 15
this ballad of the deeds Of *E*, „ 21
BANNER of *E*, not for a season, *Def. of Lucknow* 1
upon the topmost roof our banner of *E* blew. (repeat) *Def. of Lucknow* 6, 30, 45, 60, 94
the old banner of *E* blew. „ 106
appeal Once more to France or *E*; *Columbus* 58
Who dost not love our *E*— *To Victor Hugo* 9
E, France, all man to be Will make one people „ 10
To younger *E* in the boy my son. „ 14
E may go down in babble at last. *Locksley H., Sixty* 8
Yet know you, as your *E* knows *Pro. to Gen. Hamley* 23
Who wert the voice of *E* in the East. *Epit. on Stratford* 4
Then drink to *E*, every guest; *Hands all Round* 2
New *E* of the Southern Pole! „ 16
the great name of *E*, round and round. (repeat) „ 12, 36
To *E* under Indian skies, „ 17
To this great name of *E* drink, „ 23
if you shall fail to understand What *E* is, *The Fleet* 2
Should this old *E* fall Which Nelson left „ 4
The fleet of *E* is her all-in-all; „ 13
that which gilds the glebe of *E*, *To Prof. Jebb.* 7
a valorous weapon in olden *E*! *Kapiolani* 4
England-loving England's *E-l* daughter—thou *Ded. Poem Prin. Alice* 15
English (*See also* **Half-English**) first reveal'd themselves to *E* air, *Eleänore* 2
one, an *E* home—gray twilight pour'd *Palace of Art* 85
E natures, freemen, friends, *Love thou thy land* 7
Who sprang from *E* blood! *England and Amer.* 10
Gallant sons of *E* freemen, *The Captain* 7
if you knew her in her *E* days, *The Brook* 224
sweet as *E* air could make her, she: *Princess, Pro.* 155
Nor ever lost an *E* gun; *Ode on Well.* 97
Truth-lover was our *E* Duke; „ 189
since *E* Harold gave its throne a wife, *W. to Marie Alex.* 24
we may stand Where he in *E* earth is laid, *In Mem. xviii* 2
feet like sunny gems on an *E* green, *Maud I v* 14
I see her there, Bright *E* lily, „ *xix* 55
Sir Richard cried in his *E* pride, *The Revenge* 82
dared her with one little ship and his *E* few; „ 107
Dying so *E* thou wouldst have her flag *Ded. Poem Prin. Alice* 16
we were *E* in heart and in limb, *Def. of Lucknow* 46
When he coin'd into *E* gold some treasure *The Wreck* 67
no version done In *E* more divinely well; *To E. Fitzgerald* 34
an age of noblest *E* names, *Locksley H., Sixty* 83
who long To keep our *E* Empire whole! *Hands all Round* 14
Or marvel how in *E* air My yucca, *To Ulysses* 20
All flaming, made an *E* homestead Hell— *To Mary Boyle* 37
Englishman A great broad-shoulder'd genial *E*, *Princess, Con.* 85
The last great *E* is low. *Ode on Well.* 18
'We be all good *English men*. *The Revenge* 29
held his own Like an *E* there and then; *Heavy Brigade* 19
Engrail'd over hills with peaky tops *e*, *Palace of Art* 113
Engrain'd walk with vary-colour'd shells Wander'd *e*. *Arabian Nights* 58
Engrave I bad the man *e* 'From Walter' on the ring, *The Ring* 235
Engraven 'From Edith' was *e* on the blade. *Aylmer's Field* 598

Engraven (*continued*) Some younger hand must have *e* the ring— *The Ring* 238

Enid Had married *E*, Yniol's only child, *Marr. of Geraint* 4
E, but to please her husband's eye, „ 11
E loved the Queen, and with true heart „ 19
Allowing it, the Prince and *E* rode, „ 43
Told *E*, and they sadden'd her the more: „ 64
E woke, and sat beside the couch, „ 79
'If *E* errs, let *E* learn her fault.' „ 132
The voice of *E*, Yniol's daughter, rang „ 327
the sweet voice of *E* moved Geraint; „ 334
song that *E* sang was one Of Fortune and her wheel, and *E* sang: „ 345
Moved the fair *E*, all in faded silk, „ 366
'*E*, the good knight's horse stands in the court; „ 370
the Prince, as *E* past him, fain To follow, „ 375
E took his charger to the stall; „ 382
E brought sweet cakes to make them cheer, „ 388
rest On *E* at her lowly handmaid-work, „ 400
Raised my own town against me in the night Before my *E's* birthday, „ 458
looking round he saw not *E* there, „ 506
red and pale Across the face of *E* hearing her; „ 524
my pride Is broken down, for *E* sees my fall!' „ 590
E, for she lay With her fair head in the dim-yellow light, „ 599
And *E* fell in longing for a dress „ 630
And *E* started waking, with her heart „ 674
E look'd, but all confused at first, „ 685
E listen'd brightening as she lay; „ 733
call'd For *E*, and when Yniol made report Of that good mother making *E* gay „ 756
E, all abash'd she knew not why, „ 765
make your *E* burst Sunlike from cloud— „ 788
how can *E* find A nobler friend? „ 792
But *E* ever kept the faded silk, „ 841
No, not a word!' and *E* was aghast; *Geraint and E.* 18
So the last sight that *E* had of home „ 24
E leading down the tracks Thro' which he bad „ 28
E was aware of three tall knights On horseback, „ 56
E ponder'd in her heart, and said: (repeat) „ 64, 130
E waited pale and sorrowful, „ 83
E, keeping watch, behold In the first shallow shade „ 118
E stood aside to wait the event, „ 153
Geraint Had ruth again on *E* looking pale: „ 203
And *E* took a little delicately, „ 212
he let them glance At *E*, where she droopt: „ 247
Found *E* with the corner of his eye, „ 281
'*E*, the pilot star of my lone life, *E*, my early and my only love, *E*, the loss of whom hath turn'd me wild— „ 306
E, you and he, I see with joy, „ 320
E fear'd his eyes, Moist as they were, „ 350
How *E* never loved a man but him, „ 363
But *E* left alone with Prince Geraint, „ 365
He fell asleep, and *E* had no heart To wake him, „ 369
then to *E*, 'Forward! and to-day I charge you, *E*, „ 413
E answer'd, 'Yea, my lord, I know Your wish, „ 418
Went *E* with her sullen follower on. „ 440
And *E* heard the clashing of his fall, „ 509
So for long hours sat *E* by her lord, „ 580
Till *E* shrank far back into herself, „ 607
'No, no' said *E*, vext, 'I will not eat „ 656
But *E* answer'd, harder to be moved „ 694
E said: 'In this poor gown my dear lord „ 697
E, in her utter helplessness, „ 719
'*E*, I have used you worse than that dead man; „ 735
And *E* could not say one tender word, „ 746
'Then, *E*, shall you ride Behind me.' 'Yea,' said *E*, 'let us go.' „ 750
'The voice of *E*,' said the knight; „ 780
fear not, *E*, I should fall upon him, „ 787
But *E* in their going had two fears, „ 817
E easily believed, Like simple noble natures, „ 874
past to *E's* tent: and thither came The King's own leech „ 922

Enid (*continued*) And *E* tended on him there: *Geraint and E.* 924
E, whom her ladies loved to call *E* the Fair, a grateful people named *E* the Good; and in their halls arose The cry of children, *E's* and Geraint's „ 962
sat betwixt her best *E*, and lissome Vivien, *Guinevere* 28

Enjoy all the saints *E* themselves in heaven, *St. S. Stylites* 106

Enjoy'd all times I have *e* Greatly, have suffer'd greatly, *Ulysses* 7

Enjoying *E* each the other's good: *In Mem. xlvii* 10

Enjoyment There methinks would be *e* more *Locksley Hall* 165

Enlighten Strengthen me, *e* me! (repeat) *Ode to Memory* 5, 43, 122

Enna moved Like Proserpine in *E*, gathering flowers: *Edwin Morris* 112
in this pleasant vale we stand again, The field of *E*, *Demeter and P.* 35
Tho' dead in its Trinacrian *E*, *To Prof. Jebb* 11

Enoch (*See also* **Arden, Enoch Arden**) *E* was host one day, Philip the next, *Enoch Arden* 25
E would hold possession for a week: „ 27
if they quarrell'd, *E* stronger-made Was Master: „ 30
Shriek out 'I hate you, *E*,' „ 33
E spoke his love, But Philip loved in silence; „ 40
But she loved *E*; tho' she knew it not, „ 43
E set A purpose evermore before his eyes, „ 44
Than *E*. Likewise had he served a year „ 52
E and Annie, sitting hand-in-hand, „ 69
While *E* was abroad on wrathful seas, „ 91
E's white horse, and *E's* ocean spoil „ 93
Friday fare was *E's* ministering. „ 100
thither used *E* at times to go by land or sea; „ 104
the master of that ship *E* had served in, „ 120
Would *E* have the place? And *E* all at once assented to it, „ 125
Then *E* lay long-pondering on his plans; „ 133
Thus *E* in his heart determined all: „ 148
Whom *E* took, and handled all his limbs, „ 153
first since *E's* golden ring had girt Her finger, „ 157
For *E* parted with his old sea-friend, „ 168
So all day long till *E's* last at home, „ 172
E faced this morning of farewell Brightly „ 182
E as a brave God-fearing man Bow'd himself „ 185
O *E*, you are wise; And yet for all your wisdom „ 210
'Well then,' said *E*, 'I shall look on yours. „ 213
E rose, Cast his strong arms about his drooping wife, „ 227
when the day, that *E* mention'd, came, „ 239
still foreboding 'what would *E* say? „ 253
(Since *E* left he had not look'd upon her), „ 273
speak to you of what he wish'd, *E*, your husband: „ 292
For, if you will, when *E* comes again „ 309
But *E* lives; that is borne in on me. „ 319
Philip gain'd As *E* lost: for *E* seem'd „ 355
so ten years Since *E* left his hearth and native land, Fled forward, and no news of *E* came. „ 360
can you be ever loved As *E* was? „ 427
'I am content,' he answer'd, 'to be loved A little after *E*.' „ 429
If *E* comes—but *E* will not come— „ 431
Pray'd for a sign 'my *E* is he gone?' „ 491
E sitting on a height, Under a palm tree, „ 500
where was *E*? prosperously sail'd The ship „ 527
E traded for himself, and bought Quaint monsters „ 538
the loss of all But *E* and two others. „ 550
And *E's* comrade, careless of himself, „ 568
Thus over *E's* early-silvering head „ 622
There *E* spoke no word to any one, „ 667
There *E* rested silent many days. „ 699
E was so brown, so bow'd, So broken— „ 703
'*E*, poor man, was cast away and lost' „ 713
E yearn'd to see her face again; „ 717
E shunn'd the middle walk and stole Up by the wall, „ 738
griefs Like his have worse or better, *E* saw. „ 741
E set himself, Scorning an alms, „ 811
round again to meet the day When *E* had return'd, „ 823
And *E* bore his weakness cheerfully. „ 827
E thinking 'after I am gone, „ 834
'Swear' added *E* sternly 'on the book.' „ 842
Then *E* rolling his gray eyes upon her, „ 844
E said again, 'My God has bow'd me down „ 855
for *E* hung A moment on her words, „ 872
While *E* slumber'd motionless and pale, „ 908

Equal (s) The woman were an *e* to the man. *Princess i* 131
and this proud watchword rest Of *e*; „ *vii* 301
in true marriage lies Nor *e*, nor unequal: „ 303
'Ye are *e's*, equal-born.' *Locksley H., Sixty* 110
Each religion says, 'Thou art one, without *e*.' *Akbar's D., Inscrip.* 3
Equal (verb) what delights can *e* those *In Mem. xlii* 9
Equal-blowing Beneath a broad and *e-b* wind, *Gardener's D.* 77
Equal-born 'Ye are equals, *e-b*' *E-b*? *Locksley H., Sixty* 110
Equall'd Strength came to me that *e* my desire. *D. of F. Women* 230
Equal-poised O friendship, *e-p* control, *In Mem. lxxxv* 33
Equatorial Not such as here—an *e* one, *Lover's Tale iv* 190
Equinox feel in head or chest Our changeful *e'es*, *Will Water.* 238
Erased *See* **Sand-erased**
Erect Tall and *e*, but bending from his height *Aylmer's Field* 119
anger-charm'd from sorrow, soldierlike, *E*: „ 729
Tall and *e*, but in the middle aisle Reel'd, „ 818
Strode from the porch, tall, and *e* again. „ 825
E behind a desk of satin-wood, *Princess ii* 105
Lady Blanche *e* Stood up and spake, „ *iv* 290
E and silent, striking with her glance „ *vi* 152
Erin With Anguisant of *E*, Morganore, *Com. of Arthur* 115
Ermine with *e* capes And woolly-breasts and beaded eyes; *In Mem. xcv* 11
Erne (Miriam) *See* **Miriam, Miriam Erne**
Erne (Muriel) *See* **Muriel, Muriel Erne**
Eros a bevy of *E'es*, apple-cheek'd, *The Islet* 11
Err forms that *e* from honest Nature's rule! *Locksley Hall* 61
O my princess! true she *e's*, *Princess iii* 107
she that has a son And sees him *e*: „ 261
For nothing is that *e's* from law. *In Mem. lxxiii* 8
'If Enid *e's*, let Enid learn her fault.' *Marr. of Geraint* 132
Errant (*See also* **Damsel-errant, Knighthood-errant**)
and *e* knights And ladies came, *Marr. of Geraint* 545
To lead an *e* passion home again. *Lucretius* 17
Prince had brought his *e* eyes Home from the rock, *Geraint and E.* 245
Errantry *See* **Knight-errantry**
Err'd Aim'd at the helm, his lance *e*; *Geraint and E.* 157
if ancient prophecies Have *e* not, *Guinevere* 450
Errest 'Nay—but thou *e*, Lancelot: *Holy Grail* 881
Erring an *e* pearl Lost in her bosom: *Princess iv* 60
Error intellect to part *E* from crime; *Isabel* 15
Shall *E* in the round of time Still father Truth? *Love and Duty* 4
Deep as Hell I count his *e*. *The Captain* 3
Dismal *e*! fearful slaughter! „ 65
Child, if it were thine *e* or thy crime *Come not, when, etc.* 7
some gross *e* lies In this report, *Princess i* 69
so she wears her *e* like a crown „ *iii* 111
The damsel's headlong *e* thro' the wood— *Gareth and L.* 1215
When he flouted a statesman's *e*, *The Wreck* 68
Life with its anguish, and horrors, and *e's*— *Despair* 48
'Erse (horse) Dosn't thou 'ear my *'e's* legs, *N. Farmer, N. S.* 1
Fur he ca'd 'is *'e* Billy-rough-un, *Village Wife* 84
Esau a heart as rough as *E's* hand, *Godiva* 28
Escape (s) and tumbles and childish *e's*, *Maud I i* 69
From which was no *e* for evermore; *Merlin and V.* 210
From which is no *e* for evermore.' „ 544
Escape (verb) who scarce would *e* with her life; *In the Child. Hosp.* 66
if they be bold enough, who shall *e*? *Def. of Lucknow* 40
if I do not *e* you at last. *Despair* 114
And who shall *e* if they close? *Heavy Brigade* 16
can *e* From the lower world within him, *Making of Man* 1
Escaped (*See also* **'Scaped**) when the second Christmas came, *e* His keepers, *Aylmer's Field* 838
From which I *e* heart-free, *Maud I ii* 11
Escaping Like the caged bird *e* suddenly, *Enoch Arden* 269
Esh (ash) Breäk me a bit o' the *e* for his 'eäd, *N. Farmer, N. S.* 41
Eshcol vines with grapes Of *E* hugeness; *To E. Fitzgerald* 28
Espalier *e's* and the standards all Are thine; *The Blackbird* 5
Espied stood, Until the King *e* him, *Holy Grail* 755
Essay must thou dearly love thy first *e*, *Ode to Memory* 83
Essay'd *e*, by tenderest-touching terms, *Merlin and V.* 898
Then in my madness I *e* the door; *Holy Grail* 841
Essayist Authors—*e*, atheist, novelist, *Locksley H., Sixty* 139
Essence I floated free, As naked *e*, *Two Voices* 374
O sacred *e*, other form, *In Mem. lxxxv* 35

Essence (*continued*) his *e's* turn'd the live air sick, *Maud I xiii* 11
In thine own *e*, and delight thyself *Lover's Tale i* 13
Estate (condition) Whose life in low *e* began *In Mem. lxiv* 3
Day, when my crown'd *e* begun To pine „ *lxxii* 5
Beholding one so bright in dark *e*, *Marr. of Geraint* 786
Estate (lands) (*See also* **'Staäte**) now lord of the broad *e* and the Hall, *Maud I i* 19
This lump of earth has left his *e* „ *xvi* 1
an orphan with half a shire of *e*,— *Charity* 13
Estate (verb) *E* them with large land and territory *Lancelot and E.* 1322
Esteem talk kindlier: we *e* you for it— *Princess v* 212
Esteem'd we trust that you *e* us not Too harsh „ *iii* 198
Esther those of old That lighted on Queen *E*, *Marr. of Geraint* 731
Estuary colony smoulder'd on the refluent *e*; *Boädicea* 28
Ethereal over those *e* eyes The bar of Michael Angelo. *In Mem. lxxxvii* 39
Eternal (adj.) Lay there exiled from *e* God, *Palace of Art* 263
every hour is saved From that *e* silence, *Ulysses* 27
Pure lilies of *e* peace, *Sir Galahad* 67
Or that *e* want of pence, *Will Water.* 43
Dwelt with *e* summer, ill-content. *Enoch Arden* 562
center'd in *e* calm. *Lucretius* 79
E honour to his name. (repeat) *Ode on Well.* 150, 231
Nor palter'd with *E* God for power; „ 180
shall bloom The *e* landscape of the past; *In Mem. xlvi* 8
E form shall still divide The *e* soul from all beside; „ *xlvii* 6
on the low dark verge of life The twilight of *e* day. „ *l* 16
E greetings to the dead; „ *lvii* 14
E process moving on, „ *lxxxii* 5
Which masters Time indeed, and is *E*, „ *lxxxv* 66
To bare the *e* Heavens again, „ *cxxii* 4
Lo! I forgive thee, as *E* God Forgives: *Guinevere* 544
quiet fields of *e* sleep! *V. of Maeldune* 80
bawl'd the dark side of your faith and a God of *e* rage, *Despair* 39
pity for our own selves till we long'd for *e* sleep. „ 46
march of that *E* Harmony Whereto the worlds beat time, *D. of the Duke of C.* 15
Eternal (s) Shiah and Sunnee, Symbol the *E*! *Akbar's Dream* 108
Eternity All things will change Thro' *e*. *Nothing will Die* 16
even and morn Ever will be Thro' *e*. „ 35
even and morn Ye will never see Thro' *e*. *All Things will Die* 46
So in the light of great *e* *Love and Death* 12
He names the name *E*. *Two Voices* 291
But dreadful time, dreadful *e*, *Palace of Art* 267
The sabbaths of *E*, *St Agnes' Eve* 33
Music's golden sea Setting toward *e*, *Ode on Well.* 253
O skill'd to sing of Time or *E*, *Milton* 2
girth of Time Inswathe the fullness of *E*, *Lover's Tale i* 483
You that shape for *E*, *On Jub. Q. Victoria* 43
Seem'd nobler than their hard *Eternities*. *Demeter and P.* 107
Etiquette clamouring *e* to death, *Princess v* 17
Ettarre for the lady was *E*, And she was a great lady *Pelleas and E.* 97
Linger'd *E*: and seeing Pelleas droop, „ 178
from the tower above him cried *E*, „ 231
Then when he came before *E*, „ 237
Bound on her brow, were Gawain and *E*. „ 435
Eunuch-hearted art thou not that *e-h* King *Last Tournament* 445
whine And snivel, being *e-h* too, „ 450
Europa sweet *E's* mantle blew unclasp'd, *Palace of Art* 117
Europe Better fifty years of *E* than a cycle of Cathay. *Locksley Hall* 184
guard the eye, the soul Of *E*, *Ode on Well.* 161
Once the weight and fate of *E* hung. „ 240
Tho' all the storm of *E* on us break; *Third of Feb.* 14
But the one voice in *E*: we *must* speak; „ 16
avenging rod Shall lash all *E* into blood; *To F. D. Maurice* 34
Surely the pibroch of *E* is ringing *Def. of Lucknow* 97
gain'd a freedom known to *E*, known to all; *Locksley H., Sixty* 129
European never floats an *E* flag, *Locksley Hall* 161
the centre and crater of *E* confusion, *Beautiful City* 1
Europe-shadowing wheel'd on *E's* wings, *Ode on Well.* 120
Eustace I and *E* from the city went *Gardener's D.* 2
My *E* might have sat for Hercules; „ 7
E painted her, And said to me, „ 20
E turn'd, and smiling said to me, „ 97
'*E*,' I said, 'this wonder keeps the house.' „ 119
With solemn gibe did *E* banter me. „ 168

Eustace (*continued*) till Autumn brought an hour For *E*, *Gardener's D.* 208
Evangel Heaven-sweet *E*, ever-living word, *Sir J. Oldcastle* 28
Evangelist something seal'd The lips of that *E*. *In Mem. xxxi* 16
Evasion Elusion, and occasion, and *e*'? *Gareth and L.* 288
Eve (*See also* **Christmas Eäve, Christmas-eve, Yester-eve**)
At *e* the beetle boometh *Claribel* 9
At *e* a dry cicala sung, *Mariana in the S.* 85
And when the zoning *e* has died *On a Mourner* 21
Nor anchor dropt at *e* or morn; *The Voyage* 82
From fringes of the faded *e*, *Move eastward* 3
Except when for a breathing-while at *e*, *Aylmer's Field* 449
As thro' the land at *e* we went, *Princess ii* 1
at *e* and dawn With Ida, Ida, Ida, rang the woods; „ *iv* 432
sitting at home in my father's farm at *e*: *Grandmother* 90
Will there be dawn in West and *e* in East? *Gareth and L.* 712
No later than last *e* to Prince Geraint— *Marr. of Geraint* 603
Her seer, her bard, her silver star of *e*, *Merlin and V.* 954
Heard on the winding waters, *e* and morn *Lancelot and E.* 1408
days Of dewy dawning and the amber *e's* *Lover's Tale i* 52
while my life's late *e* endures, *To Marq. of Dufferin* 49
star of *e* was drawing light From the dead sun, *Death of Œnone* 64
day by day, thro' many a blood-red *e*, *St. Telemachus* 3
E after *e* that haggard anchorite Would haunt „ 12
Eve (proper name) since the time when Adam first Embraced his *E* *Day-Dm., L'Envoi* 42
Shadowing the snow-limb'd *E* *Maud I xviii* 28
Evelyn *E* begins it 'O diviner Air.' *Sisters (E. and E.)* 4
Now follows Edith echoing *E*. „ 15
graver than the other—Edith than *E*. „ 27
E is gayer, wittier, prettier, „ 36
The younger sister, *E*, enter'd— „ 152
told your wayside story to my mother And *E*. „ 190
For *E* knew not of my former suit, „ 205
round my *E* clung In utter silence for so long, „ 216
bright quick smile of *E*, that had sunn'd „ 243
this I named from her own self, *E*: „ 271
traitors to her; our quick *E*— „ 285
Even (adj.) Upon an *e* pedestal with man.' *Princess iii* 224
And climb'd upon a fair and *e* ridge, *Marr. of Geraint* 239
Even (s) (*See also* **Yester-even**) For *e* and morn Ever will be Thro' eternity. *Nothing will Die* 33
For *e* and morn Ye will never see Thro' eternity. *All Things will Die* 44
Thou comest morning or *e*; she cometh not morning or *e*. *Leonine Eleg.* 15
Her tears fell with the dews at *e*; *Mariana* 13
And the crag that fronts the *E*, *Eleänore* 40
Whisper in odorous heights of *e*. *Milton* 16
gave a shield whereon the Star of *E* *Gareth and L.* 1117
setting, when *E* descended, the very sunset *V. of Maeldune* 66
Light the fading gleam of *E*? *Locksley H., Sixty* 229
or seated in the dusk Of *e*, *Demeter and P.* 126
Evenfall. thro' the laurels At the quiet *e*, *Maud II iv* 78
Evening (adj.) (*See also* **Evening-Star**) And with the *e* cloud, *Ode to Memory* 22
To the shepherd who watcheth the *e* star. *Dying Swan* 35
You are the *e* star, *Margaret* 27
Floating thro' an *e* atmosphere, *Eleänore* 100
Eyed like the *e* star, with playful tail *Œnone* 200
same strength which threw the Morning Star Can throw the *E*,' *Gareth and L.* 1109
We should see the Globe we groan in, fairest of their *e* stars. *Locksley H., Sixty* 188
The mellow lin-lan-lone of *e* bells *Far-far-away* 5
SUNSET and *e* star, *Crossing the Bar* 1
Twilight and *e* bell, „ 9
Evening (s) in stillest *e's* With what voice *Adeline* 30
Many an *e* by the waters did we watch *Locksley Hall* 37
It chanced one *e* Annie's children long'd *Enoch Arden* 362
At *e* when the dull November day „ 721
We dropt with *e* on a rustic town *Princess i* 170
With brow to brow like night and *e* mixt „ *vi* 131
it was *e*: silent light Slept on the painted walls, „ *vii* 120
all of an *e* late I climb'd to the top *Grandmother* 37
Never morning wore To *e*, *In Mem. vi* 8
air, That rollest from the gorgeous gloom Of *e* „ *lxxxvi* 3
It leads me forth at *e*, *Maud II iv* 17
knight, That named himself the Star of *E*, *Gareth and L.* 1090
Evening (s) (*continued*) mixt Her fancies with the sallow-rifted glooms Of *e*, *Lancelot and E.* 1003
or ever that *e* ended a great gale blew, *The Revenge* 114
gloom of the *e*, Life at a close; *Vastness* 15
Evening-lighted From the *e-l* wood, *Margaret* 10
Evening-Star call themsleves the Day, Morning-Star, and Noon-Sun, and *E-S*, *Gareth and L.* 634
Evenness I lost myself and fell from *e*, *Sir J. Oldcastle* 164
Even-sloping Near him a mound of *e-s* side, *Pelleas and E.* 25
Evensong I know At matins and at *e*, *Supp. Confessions* 99
till the dusk that follow'd *e* *Gareth and L.* 793
Event such refraction of *e's* As often rises *In Mem. xcii* 15
And one far-off divine *e*, „ *Con.* 143
Enid stood aside to wait the *e*, *Geraint and E.* 153
thou remaining here wilt learn the *e*; *Guinevere* 577
Move with me to the *e*. *Lover's Tale i* 298
there, my latest vision—then the *e*! „ *iii* 59
HE flies the *e*: he leaves the *e* to me: „ *iv* 1
the *e* Glanced back upon them in his after life, „ 23
Eventide Either at morn or *e*. *Mariana* 16
For at *e*, listening earnestly, *A spirit haunts* 4
Then, on a golden autumn *e*, *Enoch Arden* 61
Everard (*See also* **Everard Hall, Hall**) clapt his hand On *E's* shoulder, and, 'I hold by him.' And I,' quoth *E*, *The Epic* 22
For I remember'd *E's* college fame „ 46
Everard Hall (*See also* **Everard, Hall**) parson Holmes, the poet *E H*, „ 4
Ever-breaking heard an *e-b* shore That tumbled *In Mem. cxxiv* 11
Ever-brightening Fifty years of *e-b* Science! *On Jub. Q. Victoria* 53
Ever-broadening Fifty years of *e-b* Commerce! „ 52
ocean-empire with her boundless homes For *e-b* England, *To the Queen ii* 30
Ever-changing a power to make This *e-c* world of circumstance, *To Duke of Argyll* 10
the never-changing One And *e-c* Many, *Akbar's Dream* 148
thee the changeless in thine *e-c* skies. *Akbar's D., Hymn* 4
Ever-climbing but that *e-c* wave, Hurl'd back again *Last Tournament* 92
Ever-deepen'd By the long torrent's *e-d* roar, *Death of Œnone* 85
Ever-echoing And *e-e* avenues of song. *Ode on Well.* 79
Ever-fancied Before an *e-f* arrow, made *Geraint and E.* 531
Ever-fleeting And rippled like an *e-f* wave, *Gareth and L.* 215
Ever-floating death, death, thou *e-f* cloud, *Œnone* 238
Evergreen (adj.) that *e* laurel is blasted by more than lightning! *Parnassus* 12
Evergreen (s) And in it throve an ancient *e*, *Enoch Arden* 735
O hollies and ivies and *e's*, *Spiteful Letter* 23
With but a drying *e* for crest, *Gareth and L.* 1116
Ever-growing Almost blind With *e-g* cataract, *Sisters (E. and E.)* 192
How long thine *e-g* mind Hath still'd *Freedom* 33
Ever-heightening And every phase of *e-h* life, *De Prof., Two G.* 7
Ever-highering In *e-h* eagle-circles up To the great Sun *Gareth and L.* 21
Everlasting The marvel of the *e* will, *The Poet* 7
she took the tax away And built herself an *e* name. *Godiva* 79
Nor sound of human sorrow mounts to mar Their sacred *e* calm! *Lucretius* 110
Lamp of the Lord God Lord *e*, *Batt. of Brunanburh* 28
Knowing the Love we were used to believe *e* would die: *Despair* 54
Infinite cruelty rather than make *e* Hell, „ 96
In the name Of the *e* God, I will live and die with you. *Happy* 108
Ever-living Heaven-sweet Evangel, *e-l* word, *Sir J. Oldcastle* 28
Ever-loyal Their *e-l* iron leader's fame, *Ode on Well.* 229
Ever-moaning An *e-m* battle in the mist, *Merlin and V.* 192
Evermore My bride to be, my *e* delight, *Maud I xviii* 73
Ever-murder'd *e-m* France, By shores that darken *Aylmer's Field* 766
Ever-ravening *e-r* eagle's beak and talon *Boädicea* 11
Ever-rising A hundred *e-r* mountain lines, *Ancient Sage* 282
now their *e-r* life has dwarf'd *The Ring* 463
Ever-scattering wearing but a holly-spray for crest, With *e-s* berries, *Last Tournament* 173
Ever-shifting *e-s* currents of the blood *D. of F. Women* 133
long mountains ended in a coast Of *e-s* sand, *Pass of Arthur* 86
Ever-showering And rode beneath an *e-s* leaf, *Last Tournament* 492
Ever-silent The *e-s* spaces of the East, *Tithonus* 9
passive sailor wrecks at last In *e-s* seas; *Ancient Sage* 137
Ever-tremulous falling showers, And *e-t* aspen-trees, *Lancelot and E.* 524

Eye (s) (*continued*) E's with idle tears are wet. Miller's D. 211
Look thro' mine e's with thine. " 215
May those kind e's for ever dwell! They have not shed a many tears, Dear e's, " 220
Droops blinded with his shining e: Fatima 38
My e's are full of tears, my heart of love, My heart is breaking, and my e's are dim, Œnone 31
With down-dropt e's I sat alone: " 56
The while, above, her full and earnest e " 141
Thy mortal e's are frail to judge of fair, " 158
She with a subtle smile in her mild e's, " 184
And I beheld great Herè's angry e's, " 190
to vex me with his father's e's! " 255
gaze upon My palace with unblinded e's, Palace of Art 42
hand and e's That said, We wait for thee. " 103
Flush'd in her temples and her e's, " 170
all things fair to sate my various e's! " 193
Oh your sweet e's, your low replies: L. C. V. de Vere 29
The languid light of your proud e's " 59
There's many a black e, they say, May Queen 5
Than tir'd eyelids upon tir'd e's; Lotos-Eaters, C. S. 6
With half-shut e's ever to seem Falling " 55
e's grown dim with gazing on the pilot-stars. " 87
Charged both mine e's with tears. D. of F. Women 13
The star-like sorrows of immortal e's, " 91
stern black-bearded kings with wolfish e's, " 111
with swarthy cheeks and bold black e's, " 127
nor tame and tutor with mine e " 138
Those dragon e's of anger'd Eleanor " 255
But tho' his e's are waxing dim, D. of the O. Year 21
Close up his e's: tie up his chin: " 48
And tho' mine own e's fill with dew, To J. S. 37
Memory standing near Cast down her e's, " 54
Her open e's desire the truth. Of old sat Freedom 17
broke From either side, nor veil his e's: Love thou thy land 90
both his e's were dazzled, as he stood, M. d'Arthur 59
might have pleased the e's of many men. " 91
Laid widow'd of the power in his e " 122
Valuing the giddy pleasure of the e's. " 128
'Now see I by thine e's that this is done. " 149
looking wistfully with wide blue e's As in a picture, " 169
charged Before the e's of ladies and of kings. " 225
shall I hide my forehead and my e's? " 228
made those e's Darker than darkest pansies, Gardener's D. 26
Her violet e's, and all her Hebe bloom, " 137
A thought would fill my e's with happy dew; " 197
following her dark e's Felt earth as air " 211
while I mused came Memory with sad e's, " 243
this whole hour your e's have been intent " 269
Make thine heart ready with thine e's: " 273
And I will set him in my uncle's e Dora 67
To make him pleasing in her uncle's e. " 84
Dora cast her e's upon the ground, " 89
like a pear In growing, modest e's, Walk. to the Mail 54
his nice e's Should see the raw mechanic's " 74
film made thick These heavy, horny e's. St. S. Stylites 201
with what delighted e's I turn to yonder oak. Talking Oak 7
I breathed upon her e's " 210
sunbeam slip, To light her shaded e; " 218
Streaming e's and breaking hearts? Love and Duty 2
staring e glazed o'er with sapless days, " 16
When e's, love-languid thro' half tears " 36
Gave utterance by the yearning of an e, " 62
With quiet e's unfaithful to the truth, " 94
Shines in those tremulous e's Tithonus 26
sweet e's brighten slowly close to mine, " 38
with what other e's I used to watch— " 51
I dipt into the future far as human e could see; (repeat) Locksley Hall 15, 119
And her e's on all my motions " 22
dawning in the dark of hazel e's— " 28
What is this? his e's are heavy: " 51
an e shall vex thee, looking ancient kindness " 85
and left me with the jaundiced e; E, to which all order festers, " 132

Eye (s) (*continued*) No e look down, she passing; Godiva 40
heads upon the spout Had cunning e's to see: " 57
but his e's, before they had their will, " 69
Nor look with that too-earnest e— Day-Dm., Pro. 18
A fairy Prince, with joyful e's, " Arrival 7
How dark those hidden e's must be!' " 32
'O e's long laid in happy sleep!' " Depart. 17
So much your e's my fancy take— " L'Envoi 26
That I might kiss those e's awake! " 28
What e's, like thine, have waken'd hopes, " 45
this heart and e's, Are touch'd, Sir Galahad 71
crow shall tread The corners of thine e's: Will Water. 236
She look'd into Lord Ronald's e's, Lady Clare 79
gladness lighten'd In the e's of each. The Captain 32
He saw not far: his e's were dim: The Voyage 75
One praised her ancles, one her e's, Beggar Maid 11
To glass herself in dewy e's That watch me Move eastward 7
I saw with half-unconscious e She wore the colours The Letters 15
Where sat a company with heated e's, Vision of Sin 7
Hair, and e's, and limbs, and faces, " 39
Glimmer in thy rheumy e's. " 154
I cannot praise the fire In your e— " 184
then would Philip, his blue e's All flooded Enoch Arden 31
Enoch set A purpose evermore before his e's, " 45
His large gray e's and weather-beaten face " 70
And in their e's and faces read his doom; " 73
She could not fix the glass to suit her e; Perhaps her e was dim, hand tremulous; " 241
rose, and fixt her swimming e's upon him, " 325
his e's Full of that lifelong hunger, " 463
His e's upon the stones, he reach'd " 684
Enoch rolling his gray e's upon her, " 844
That once again he roll'd his e's upon her " 904
Her e's a bashful azure, and her hair The Brook 71
Katie snatch'd her e's at once from mine, " 101
sweet content Re-risen in Katie's e's, " 169
he stared On e's a bashful azure, " 206
Whose e's from under a pyramidal head Aylmer's Field 20
eager e's, that still Took joyful note " 66
the cross-lightnings of four chance-met e's " 129
Till Leolin ever watchful of her e, " 210
conscious of the rageful e That watch'd him, " 336
With a weird bright e, sweating and trembling, " 585
her fresh and innocent e's Had such a star of morning " 691
hid the Holiest from the people's e's " 772
Then their e's vext her; " 802
And those fixt e's of painted ancestors " 832
thinking that her clear germander e Droopt Sea Dreams 4
night-light flickering in my e's Awoke me.' " 103
then my e's Pursued him down the street, " 164
all his conscience and one e askew'—(repeat) " 180, 184
Made wet the crafty crowsfoot round his e; " 187
Grave, florid, stern, as far as e could see, " 219
show'd their e's Glaring, and passionate looks, " 235
I fixt My wistful e's on two fair images, " 240
'Dead! who is dead?' 'The man your e pursued. " 272
And here he glances on an e new-born, Lucretius 137
her arm lifted, e's on fire— Princess, Pro. 41
turns Up thro' gilt wires a crafty loving e, " 172
twinn'd as horse's ear and e. " i 57
raised the blinding bandage from his e's: " 244
such e's were in her head, " ii 37
all her thoughts as fair within her e's, " 326
Abase those e's that ever loved to meet " 427
wander from his wits Pierced thro' with e's, " 441
glowing round her dewy e's The circled Iris " iii 26
her lynx e To fix and make me hotter, " 46
settled in her e's The green malignant light " 131
Up went the hush'd amaze of hand and e. " 138
we had limed ourselves With open e's, " 143
as she smote me with the light of e's " 192
She spake With kindled e's: " 334
Rise in the heart, and gather to the e's, " iv 41
unto dying e's The casement slowly grows " 51
Stared with great e's, and laugh'd with alien lips, " 119

Eye (s) (*continued*) She wept her true *e's* blind for such a one, *Princess iv* 134
with *e's* Of shining expectation fixt on mine. „ 152
Not yet endured to meet her opening *e's*, „ 195
an *e* like mine, A lidless watcher of the public weal, „ 324
Fear Stared in her *e's*, and chalk'd her face, „ 377
gems and gemlike *e's*, And gold and golden heads; „ 480
the crimson-rolling *e* Glares ruin, „ 494
slink From ferule and the trespass-chiding *e*, „ *v* 38
Alive with fluttering scarfs and ladies' *e's*, „ 509
loved me closer than his own right *e*, „ 531
old lion, glaring with his whelpless *e*, „ *vi* 99
grief and mother's hunger in her *e*, „ 146
her *e* with slow dilation roll'd Dry flame, „ 189
meet it, with an *e* that swum in thanks; „ 210
So she, and turn'd askance a wintry *e*: „ 330
The common men with rolling *e's*; „ 360
I love not hollow cheek or faded *e*: „ *vii* 7
Nor knew what *e* was on me, „ 53
the dew Dwelt in her *e's*, „ 136
I on her Fixt my faint *e's*, and utter'd „ 144
with shut *e's* I lay Listening; then look'd. „ 223
and mild the luminous *e's*, „ 226
yearlong poring on thy pictured *e's*, „ 340
lift thine *e's*; my doubts are dead, „ 348
guard the *e*, the soul Of Europe, *Ode on Well.* 160
he turn'd, and I saw his *e's* all wet, *Grandmother* 49
thank God that I keep my *e's*. „ 106
and the *e* of man cannot see; *High. Pantheism* 17
A jewel, a jewel dear to a lover's *e*! *Window, On the Hill* 3
fine little feet—Dewy blue *e*. „ *Letter* 4
Tell my wish to her dewy blue *e*: „ „ 14
lighten into my *e's* and my heart, „ *Marr. Morn.* 15
cross All night below the darken'd *e's*; *In Mem. iv* 14
But since it pleased a vanish'd *e*, „ *viii* 21
Mine *e's* have leisure for their tears; „ *xiii* 16
Paradise It never look'd to human *e's* „ *xxiv* 7
if that *e* which watches guilt And goodness, „ *xxvi* 5
Oh, if indeed that *e* foresee Or see „ 9
We sung, tho' every *e* was dim, „ *xxx* 14
Her *e's* are homes of silent prayer, „ *xxxii* 1
those wild *e's* that watch the wave „ *xxxvi* 15
Make April of her tender *e's*; „ *xl* 8
See with clear *e* some hidden shame „ *li* 7
With larger other *e's* than ours, „ 15
Such splendid purpose in his *e's*, „ *lvi* 10
That ever look'd with human *e's*. „ *lvii* 12
And if thou cast thine *e's* below, „ *lxi* 5
Tho' if an *e* that's downward cast „ *lxii* 1
Or in the light of deeper *e's* „ 11
And closing eaves of wearied *e's* „ *lxvii* 11
I find a trouble in thine *e*, „ *lxviii* 10
him, who turns a musing *e* On songs, „ *lxxvii* 2
And dropt the dust on tearless *e's*; „ *lxxx* 4
And over those ethereal *e's* „ *lxxxvii* 39
He brought an *e* for all he saw; „ *lxxxix* 9
dying *e's* Were closed with wail, „ *xc* 5
And woolly breasts and beaded *e's*; „ *xcv* 12
whose light-blue *e's* Are tender over drowning flies, „ *xcvi* 2
These two—they dwelt with *e* on *e*, „ *xcvii* 9
She dwells on him with faithful *e's*, „ *xcvii* 35
gleams On Lethe in the *e's* of Death. „ *xcviii* 8
But each has pleased a kindred *e*, „ *c* 17
The critic clearness of an *e*, „ *cix* 3
and thee mine *e's* Have look'd on: „ 21
Drew in the expression of an *e*, „ *cxi* 19
I, who gaze with temperate *e's* „ *cxii* 2
I seem to cast a careless *e* On souls, „ 7
And bright the friendship of thine *e*; „ *cxix* 10
Or eagle's wing, or insect's *e*; „ *cxxiv* 6
She did but look thro' dimmer *e's*; „ *cxxv* 6
Sweet human hand and lips and *e*; „ *cxxix* 6
On me she bends her blissful *e's* „ *Con.* 29
By village *e's* as yet unborn; „ 59
e to *e*, shall look On knowledge; „ 129

Eye (s) (*continued*) (for her *e's* were downcast, not to be seen) *Maud I ii* 5
An *e* well-practised in nature, „ *iv* 38
her *e* seem'd full Of a kind intent to me, „ *vi* 40
And a moist mirage in desert *e's*, „ 53
once, but once, she lifted her *e's*, „ *viii* 5
Let not my tongue be a thrall to my *e*, „ *xvi* 32
Innumerable, pitiless, passionless *e's*, „ *xviii* 38
often I caught her with *e's* all wet, „ *xix* 23
every *e* but mine will glance At Maud „ *xx* 36
In violets blue as your *e's*, „ *xxii* 42
Was it he lay there with a fading *e*? „ *II i* 29
But only moves with the moving *e*, „ *ii* 37
it well Might drown all life in the *e*,— „ 61
I sorrow For the hand, the lips, the *e's*, „ *iv* 27
My own dove with the tender *e*? „ 46
look'd, tho' but in a dream, upon *e's* so fair, „ *III vi* 16
O passionate heart and morbid *e*, „ 32
Felt the light of her *e's* into his life *Com. of Arthur* 56
And dazed all *e's*, till Arthur by main might, „ 109
From *e* to *e* thro' all their Order flash „ 270
Bewildering heart and *e*— „ 300
Fixing full *e's* of question on her face, „ 312
dark my mother was in *e's* and hair, And dark in hair and *e's* am I; „ 327
the Queen replied with drooping *e's*, „ 469
Gareth answer'd her with kindling *e's*, (repeat) *Gareth and L.* 41, 62
Nor fronted man or woman, *e* to *e*— „ 112
The mother's *e* Full of the wistful fear „ 172
Gareth likewise on them fixt his *e's* „ 236
shyly glanced *E's* of pure women, „ 314
the listening *e's* Of those tall knights, „ 327
the field was pleasant in our *e's*, „ 337
The field was pleasant in my husband's *e*.' „ 342
Return, and meet, and hold him from our *e's*, „ 429
the King's calm *e* Fell on, and check'd, „ 547
A head with kindling *e's* above the throng, „ 646
Round as the red *e* of an Eagle-owl, „ 799
Gareth's *e's* had flying blots Before them „ 1031
And Enid, but to please her husband's *e*, *Marr. of Geraint* 11
this she gather'd from the people's *e's*: „ 61
darken'd from the high light in his *e's*, „ 100
maybe pierced to death before mine *e's*, „ 104
with fixt *e* following the three. „ 237
Let his *e* rove in following, „ 399
To whom Geraint with *e's* all bright replied, „ 494
Nor did she lift an *e* nor speak a word, „ 528
At this she cast her *e's* upon her dress, „ 609
Myself would work *e* dim, and finger lame, „ 628
Help'd by the mother's careful hand and *e*, „ 738
the Prince had brought his errant *e's* *Geraint and E.* 245
Found Enid with the corner of his *e*, „ 281
Crost and came near, lifted adoring *e's*, „ 304
would not make them laughable in all *e's*, „ 326
Made his *e* moist; but Enid fear'd his *e's*, „ 350
With *e's* to find you out however far, „ 428
his *e* darken'd and his helmet wagg'd; „ 505
let her true hand falter, nor blue *e* Moisten, „ 512
drove the dust against her veilless *e's*: „ 529
Bound on a foray, rolling *e's* of prey, „ 538
Half-bold, half-frighted, with dilated *e's*, „ 597
He roll'd his *e's* about the hall, „ 610
o'er her meek blue *e's*, came a happy mist „ 769
Yet not so misty were her meek blue *e's* „ 772
with your meek *e's*, The truest *e's* „ 841
with your own true *e's* Beheld the man „ 846
having look'd too much thro' alien *e's*, „ 892
King went forth and cast his *e's* On each „ 932
Sent me a three-years' exile from thine *e's*. *Balin and Balan* 59
Sir Lancelot with his *e's* on earth, „ 253
Lo! these her emblems drew mine *e's*— „ 265
Then Lancelot lifted his large *e's*; „ 277
hast thou *e's*, or if, are these So far besotted „ 358
Then fiercely to Sir Garlon '*E's* have I That saw „ 372
E's too that long have watch'd how Lancelot „ 375
The longest lance his *e's* had ever seen, „ 411

Eye (s) *(continued)* *he* lifted faint *e's*; he felt One near him; *Balin and Balan* 594
Closed his death-drowsing *e's*, and slept ,, 631
stood with folded hands and downward *e's* Of glancing corner, *Merlin and V.* 69
her slow sweet *e's* Fear-tremulous, ,, 85
With reverent *e's* mock-loyal, ,, 157
neither *e's* nor tongue—O stupid child! ,, 251
sweetly gleam'd her *e's* behind her tears ,, 402
isle-nurtured *e's* Waged such unwilling tho' successful war ,, 570
lady never made *unwilling* war With those fine *e's*: ,, 604
Not one to flirt a venom at her *e's*, ,, 609
let her *e's* Speak for her, glowing on him, ,, 615
So lean his *e's* were monstrous; ,, 624
often o'er the sun's bright *e* Drew the vast eyelid ,, 633
densest condensation, hard To mind and *e*; ,, 679
A snowy penthouse for his hollow *e's*, ,, 808
Without the will to lift their *e's*, ,, 836
His *e* was calm, and suddenly she took To bitter weeping ,, 854
He raised his *e's* and saw The tree that shone ,, 938
Her *e's* and neck glittering went and came; ,, 960
Queen Lifted her *e's*, and they dwelt *Lancelot and E.* 84
gleam'd a vague suspicion in his *e's*: ,, 127
she, who held her *e's* upon the ground, ,, 232
Lifted her *e's*, and read his lineaments. ,, 244
And noblest, when she lifted up her *e's*. ,, 256
she lifted up her *e's* And loved him, ,, 259
let his *e's* Run thro' the peopled gallery ,, 429
stay'd; and cast his *e's* on fair Elaine: ,, 640
O damsel, in the light of your blue *e's*; ,, 660
he roll'd his *e's* Yet blank from sleep, ,, 819
His *e's* glisten'd: she fancied 'Is it for me?' ,, 822
his large black *e's*, Yet larger thro' his leanness, ,, 834
'Nay, the world, the world, All ear and *e*, with such a stupid heart To interpret ear and *e*, ,, 941
Speaking a still good-morrow with her *e's*. ,, 1033
old servitor, on deck, Winking his *e's*, ,, 1145
saw with a sidelong *e* The shadow of some piece ,, 1173
Close underneath his *e's*, and right across ,, 1240
and *e's* that ask'd 'What is it?' ,, 1249
men Shape to their fancy's *e* from broken rocks ,, 1252
From the half-face to the full *e*, ,, 1262
raised his head, their *e's* met and hers fell, ,, 1312
He answer'd with his *e's* upon the ground, ,, 1352
Seeing the homeless trouble in thine *e's*, ,, 1365
To doubt her fairness were to want an *e*, ,, 1376
lifted up his *e's* And saw the barge that brought ,, 1390
I trust We are green in Heaven's *e's*; *Holy Grail* 38
her *e's* Beyond my knowing of them, beautiful, ,, 102
His *e's* became so like her own, ,, 141
sent the deathless passion in her *e's* Thro' him, ,, 163
lifting up mine *e's*, I found myself Alone, ,, 375
And took both ear and *e*; ,, 383
And kind the woman's *e's* and innocent, ,, 393
'While thus he spake, his *e*, dwelling on mine, ,, 485
On either hand, as far as *e* could see, ,, 498
Which never *e's* on earth again shall see. ,, 532
like bright *e's* of familiar friends, ,, 688
his *e's*, An out-door sign of all the warmth ,, 703
'A welfare in thine *e* reproves Our fear ,, 726
I saw it;' and the tears were in his *e's*. ,, 759
A dying fire of madness in his *e's*— ,, 768
angels, awful shapes, and wings and *e's*. ,, 848
by mine *e's* and by mine ears I swear, ,, 864
light that strikes his *e* is not light, ,, 913
So that his *e's* were dazzled looking at it. *Pelleas and E.* 36
and his *e's* closed. And since he loved all maidens, ,, 39
For large her violet *e's* look'd, ,, 71
for those large *e's*, the haunts of scorn, ,, 75
while they rode, the meaning in his *e's*, ,, 109
green wood-ways, and *e's* among the leaves; ,, 139
in mid-banquet measuring with his *e's* ,, 150
tower fill'd with *e's* Up to the summit, ,, 166
glory fired her face; her *e* Sparkled, ,, 172
but felt his *e's* Harder and drier ,, 506

Eye (s) *(continued)* hard his *e's*; harder his heart Seem'd; *Peleas and E.* 512
Rolling his *e's*, a moment stood, then spake: ,, 581
Pelleas lifted up an *e* so fierce She quail'd; ,, 601
nose Bridge-broken, one *e* out, and one hand off, *Last Tournament* 59
He look'd but once, and vail'd his *e's* ,, 150
Come—let us gladden their sad *e's*, ,, 222
Made dull his inner, keen his outer *e* ,, 366
The black-blue Irish hair and Irish *e's* ,, 404
steel-blue *e's*, The golden beard that clothed ,, 667
Lay couchant with his *e's* upon the throne, *Guinevere* 11
Modred still in green, all ear and *e*, ,, 24
Heart-hiding smile, and gray persistent *e*: ,, 64
Hands in hands, and *e* to *e*. ,, 100
Makes wicked lightnings of her *e's*, ,, 520
her hand Grasp'd, made her vail her *e's*: ,, 663
richer in His *e's* Who ransom'd us, ,, 684
these *e's* of men are dense and dim, *Pass. of Arthur* 19
both his *e's* were dazzled as he stood, ,, 227
might have pleased the *e's* of many men. ,, 259
Laid widow'd of the power in his *e* ,, 290
Valuing the giddy pleasure of the *e's*. ,, 296
'Now see I by thine *e's* that this is done. ,, 317
looking wistfully with wide blue *e's* As in a picture. ,, 337
charged Before the *e's* of ladies and of kings. ,, 393
shall I hide my forehead and my *e's*? ,, 396
Straining his *e's* beneath an arch of hand, ,, 464
I come, great Mistress of the ear and *e*: *Lover's Tale i* 22
tho' there beat a heart in either *e*; ,, 34
Leapt like a passing thought across her *e's*; ,, 70
Oh, such dark *e's*! a single glance of them ,, 75
a common light of *e's* Was on us as we lay: ,, 236
Shading his *e's* till all the fiery cloud, ,, 306
down to sea, and far as *e* could ken, ,, 336
light methought broke from her dark, dark *e's*, ,, 368
endured in presence of His *e's* To indue his lustre; ,, 423
our *e's* met: hers were bright, ,, 441
gaze upon thee till their *e's* are dim ,, 491
still I kept my *e's* upon the sky. ,, 572
Of *e's* too weak to look upon the light; ,, 614
Leaning its roses on my faded *e's*. ,, 621
And what it has for *e's* as close to mine ,, 651
how her choice did leap forth from his *e's*! ,, 657
e's—I saw the moonlight glitter on their tears— ,, 696
And could I look upon her tearful *e's*? ,, 735
Fixing my *e's* on those three cypress-cones ,, *ii* 38
Flash'd thro' my *e's* into my innermost brain, ,, 95
Like morning from her *e's*—her eloquent *e's*, ,, 144
All unawares before his half-shut *e's*, ,, 153
so those fair *e's* Shone on my darkness, ,, 157
and the *e* Was riveted and charm-bound, ,, 187
over my dim *e's*, And parted lips which drank her breath, ,, 203
—her *e's* And cheeks as bright as when she climb'd ,, *iii* 46
she rais'd an *e* that ask'd 'Where?' ,, *iv* 94
dark *e's* of hers—Oh! such dark *e's*! and not her *e's* alone, ,, 165
Wonder'd at some strange light in Julian's *e's* ,, 205
Have jested also, but for Julian's *e's*, ,, 223
breast Hard-heaving, and her *e's* upon her feet, ,, 308
Dazed or amazed, nor *e's* of men; ,, 311
She shook, and cast her *e's* down, ,, 329
and begun to darken my *e's*. *Rizpah* 16
sun as danced in 'er pratty blue *e*; *North. Cobbler* 50
sweet *e's* frown: the lips Seem but a gash. *Sisters (E. and E.)* 106
the sweet dwelling of her *e's* Upon me ,, 165
her own true *e's* Are traitors to her; ,, 284
wi' hoffens a drop in 'is *e*. *Village Wife* 34
Sa I han't clapt *e's* on 'im yit, ,, 123
and the smile, and the comforting *e*— *In the Child. Hosp.* 12
and his *e's* were sweet, *V. of Maeldune* 117
YOU that were *e's* and light to the King *To Prin. F. of H.* 1
and woke, These *e's*, now dull, but then so keen *Tiresias* 4
And from her virgin breast, and virgin *e's* ,, 46
Menœceus, thou hast *e's*, and I can hear ,, 90
These eyeless *e's*, that cannot see thine own, ,, 108
these *e's* will find The men I knew, ,, 175

Eye (s) *continued*) in the dark of his wonderful *e's*. — *The Wreck* 55
sad *e's* fixt on the lost sea-home, — „ 126
When the rolling *e's* of the lighthouse — *Despair* 9
leave him, blind of heart and *e's*, — *Ancient Sage* 113
Nor care—for Hunger hath the Evil *e*— — „ 264
in the sidelong *e's* a gleam of all things ill— — *The Flight* 31
my *e's* are dim with dew, — „ 97
Wid a diamond dhrop in her *e*, — *Tomorrow* 28
an' yer *e's* as bright as the day ! — „ 32
An' ye'll niver set *e's* an the face — „ 50
the dhry *e* thin but was wet for the frinds — „ 83
E's that lured a doting boyhood — *Locksley H., Sixty* 10
kiss'd the miniature with those sweet *e's*. — „ 12
sphere of all the boundless Heavens within the human *e*, — „ 210
Aged *e's* may take the growing glimmer — „ 230
in the wars your own Crimean *e's* had seen; — *Pro. to Gen. Hamley* 12
Those *e's* the blue to-day, — *Epilogue* 9
be found of angel *e's* In earth's recurring Paradise. — *Helen's Tower* 11
Thy glorious *e's* were dimm'd with pain — *Freedom* 10
brightens thro' the Mother's tender *e's*, — *Prin. Beatrice* 4
True daughter, whose all-faithful, filial *e's* — „ 13
make them wealthier in his readers' *e's*; — *Poets and their B.* 4
Shakespeare's bland and universal *e* Dwells — *To W. C. Macready* 13
Thine *e's* Again were human-godlike, — *Demeter and P.* 18
e's Awed even me at first, thy mother—*e's* That oft had seen the serpent-wanded power — „ 23
who was he with such love-drunken *e's* — *The Ring* 21
landscape which your *e's* Have many a time — „ 150
surface *e*, that only doats On outward beauty, — „ 163
a ribald twinkle in his bleak *e's*— — „ 199
Beyond our burial and our buried *e's*, — „ 296
closed her *e's*, which would not close, — „ 299
the glazed *e* Glared at me as in horror. — „ 450
floated in with sad reproachful *e's*, — „ 469
I lifted up my *e's*, he was coming down the fell— — *Happy* 82
Whose *e's* have known this globe of ours, — *To Ulysses* 2
Watching her large light *e's* — *Prog. of Spring* 19
These will thine *e's* not brook in forest-paths, — „ 31
Her light makes rainbows in my closing *e's*, — „ 46
gray Magician With *e's* of wonder, — *Merlin and the G.* 6
Her sad *e's* plead for my own fame — *Romney's R.* 55
mine from your pretty blue *e's* to your feet, — „ 96
I blind your pretty blue *e's* with a kiss! — „ 101
One kiss'd his hand, another closed his *e's*, — *Death of Œnone* 58
lure those *e's* that only yearn'd to see, — *St. Telemachus* 36
had left His aged *e's*, he raised them, — „ 51
are faint And pale in Alla's *e's*, — *Akbar's Dream* 11
all the Hells a-glare in either *e*, — „ 115
But Death had ears and *e's*; — „ 187
gladdening human hearts and *e's*. — „ *Hymn* 2
Haven't you *e's*? I am dressing the grave — *Charity* 2
And the hard blue *e's* have it still, — „ 10

Eye (verb) careful robins *e* the delver's toil, — *Marr. of Geraint* 774
careful robin's *e* the delver's toil; — *Geraint and E.* 431

Eyeball warm blood mixing; The *e's* fixing. — *All Things will Die* 34

Eyebrow He dragg'd his *e* bushes down, — *Merlin and V.* 807
Still makes a hoary *e* for the gleam — *The Brook* 80

Eyed (adj.) (*See also* **Blue-eyed, Cock-eyed, Dark-eyed, False-eyed, Falcon-eyed, Gold-eyed, Gray-eyed, Mild-eyed, Still-eyed, White-eyed, Wild-eyed**) a wild and wanton pard, *E* like the evening star, — *Œnone* 200

Eyed (verb) And every follower *e* him as a God; — *Last Tournament* 678

Eyelash The lifting of whose *e* is my lord, — *Princess v* 140
golden beam of an *e* dead on the cheek, — *Maud I iii* 3
morn Has lifted the dark *e* of the Night — *Akbar's Dream* 201

Eyeless 'I saw the little elf-god *e* once — *Merlin and V.* 249
These *e* eyes, that cannot see thine own,— — *Tiresias* 108

Eyelet-holes fierce east scream thro' your *e-h*, — *Pelleas and E.* 469

Eyelid (*See also* **Sister-eyelids**) Ray-fringed *e's* of the morn Roof not a glance — *Clear-headed friend* 6
Pacing with downward *e's* pure. — *Two Voices* 420
Her *e* quiver'd as she spake. — *Miller's D.* 144
Weigh heavy on my *e's*: let me die. — *Œnone* 244
I kiss'd his *e's* into rest: — *The Sisters* 19
Than tir'd *e's* upon tir'd eyes; — *Lotos-Eaters, C. S.* 6

Eyelid (*continued*) With half-dropt *e* still, — *Lotos-Eaters, C. S.* 90
I READ, before my *e's* dropt their shade, — *D. of F. Women* 1
I closed mine *e's*, lest the gems Should blind — *M. d'Arthur* 152
'Her *e's* dropp'd their silken eaves. — *Talking Oak* 209
forehead, *e's*, growing dewy-warm With kisses — *Tithonus* 58
A little flutter'd, with her *e's* down, — *The Brook* 89
And here upon a yellow *e* fall'n — *Lucretius* 141
Beat balm upon our *e's*. — *Princess iii* 123
on my heavy *e's* My anguish hangs — *Maud II iv* 73
Made her cheek burn and either *e* fall, — *Marr. of Geraint* 775
Made her cheek burn and either *e* fall. — *Geraint and E.* 434
Made answer, either *e* wet with tears: — *Merlin and V.* 379
Drew the vast *e* of an inky cloud, — „ 634
saw The slow tear creep from her closed *e* — „ 906
I closed mine *e's*, lest the gems Should blind — *Pass. of Arthur* 320
Falling, unseal'd our *e's*, and we woke — *Lover's Tale i* 265
My heart paused—my raised *e's* would not fall, — „ 571
felt the blast Beat on my heated *e's*: — „ *iii* 28
Had caught her hand, her *e's* fell— — *Sisters (E. and E.)* 148
Vailing a sudden *e* with his hard — *Sir J. Oldcastle* 20

Eye-reach Eagle, laid Almost beyond *e-r*, — *Gareth and L.* 45

Eyesight Not with blinded *e* poring — *Locksley Hall* 172

Eye-witness would'st against thine own *e-w* fain — *Merlin and V.* 793

Eyry lured that falcon from his *e* on the fell, — *Happy* 59

F

Faäce (face) fun 'um theer a-laäid of 'is *f* — *N. Farmer, O. S.* 33
an' scratted my *f* like a cat, — *North. Cobbler* 22
An' the babby's *f* wurn't wesh'd — „ 42
I'll loöök my hennemy straït i' the *f*, — „ 74
Tommy's *f* be as fresh as a codlin — „ 110
call'd me afoor my awn foälks to my *f* — *Village Wife* 105
wi' a niced red *f*, an' es cleän Es a shillin' — *Spinster's S's.* 75
a-callin ma 'hugly' mayhap to my *f*, — „ 91
I seed at 'is *f* wur as red as the Yule-block — *Owd Roä* 56
an' ya thraw'd the fish i' 'is *f*, — *Church-warden, etc.* 30

Faäir (fair) like a bull gotten loose at a *f*, — *North. Cobbler* 33

Faäithful (faithful) '*F* an' True'—(repeat) — *Owd Roä* 15
'A *f* an' loovin' wife!' — *Spinster's S's.* 72

Fable (s) we grew The *f* of the city where we dwelt. — *Gardener's D.* 6
Read my little *f*: — *The Flower* 17
Like a shipwreck'd man on a coast Of ancient *f* and fear— — *Maud II ii* 32
Old milky *f's* of the wolf and sheep, — *Pelleas and E.* 196
Rare in *F* or History, — *On Jub. Q. Victoria* 5
my soul uncertain, or a *f*, — *By an Evolution.* 5

Fable (verb) aught they *f* of the quiet Gods. — *Lucretius* 55

Fabled why we came? I *f* nothing fair, — *Princess iii* 136

Fabler Balin answer'd him 'Old *f*, — *Balin and Balan* 307

Fabric *F* rough, or fairy-fine, — *Ode Inter. Exhib.* 18

Face (*See also* **Faäce, Fine-face, Half-face**) Old *f's* glimmer'd thro' the doors, — *Mariana* 66
Sweet *f's*, rounded arms, and bosoms — *Sea-Fairies* 3
I was down upon my *f*, — *Oriana* 53
O pale, pale *f* so sweet and meek, — „ 66
Breathing Light against thy *f*, — *Adeline* 56
and slowly grow To a full *f*, — *Eleänore* 92
While I muse upon thy *f*; — „ 129
So, friend, when first I look'd upon your *f*, — *Sonnet To* —— 9
He said, 'She has a lovely *f*; — *L. of Shalott iv* 52
glow'd The clear perfection of her *f*. — *Mariana in the S.* 32
God's glory smote him on the *f*.' — *Two Voices* 225
'His *f*, that two hours since hath died; — „ 242
little daughter, whose sweet *f* He kiss'd, — „ 253
Whose wrinkles gather'd on his *f*, — „ 329
And turning look'd upon your *f*, — *Miller's D.* 157
Grow, live, die looking on his *f*, — *Fatima* 41
tell her to her *f* how much I hate Her presence, — *Œnone* 228
O happy Heaven, how canst thou see my *f*? — „ 236
She was the fairest in the *f*: — *The Sisters* 2
Two godlike *f's* gazed below; — *Palace of Art* 162

Face (*continued*) O silent f's of the Great and Wise, *Palace of Art* 195
I shall look upon your f; *May Queen, N. Y's. E.* 38
round about the keel with f's pale, Dark f's pale
against that rosy flame, *Lotos-Eaters* 25
With those old f's of our infancy ,, *C. S.* 66
turning on my f The star-like sorrows *D. of F. Women* 90
Myself for such a f had boldly died,' ,, 98
My father held his hand upon his f; ,, 107
Here her f Glow'd, as I look'd at her. ,, 239
His f is growing sharp and thin. *D. of the O. Year* 46
a new f at the door, my friend, A new f at the door. ,, 53
Imitates God, and turns her f To every land *On a Mourner* 2
reveal'd The fullness of her f— *Of old sat Freedom* 12
Lift up thy rocky f, *England and Amer.* 12
all his f was white And colourless, *M. d'Arthur* 212
Among new men, strange f's, other minds.' ,, 238
If thou should'st never see my f again, ,, 246
Then he turn'd His f and pass'd— *Dora* 151
and Dora hid her f By Mary. ,, 156
came again together on the king With heated f's; *Audley Court* 37
hid his f From all men, *Walk. to the Mail* 20
A pretty f is well, and this is well, *Edwin Morris* 45
saw Their f's grow between me and my book; *St. S. Stylites* 176
I know thy glittering f. ,, 205
before my f I see the moulder'd Abbey-walls, *Talking Oak* 2
seen some score of those Fresh f's, ,, 50
Turn your f, Nor look with that too-earnest eye— *Day-Dm., Pro.* 17
Grave f's gather'd in a ring. ,, *Sleep. P.* 38
And yawn'd, and rubb'd his f, and spoke, ,, *Revival* 19
'There I put my f in the grass— *Edward Gray* 21
the dusty crypt Of darken'd forms and f's. *Will Water.* 184
Were their f's grim. *The Captain* 54
colour flushes Her sweet f from brow to chin: *L. of Burleigh* 62
Her f was evermore unseen, *The Voyage* 61
So sweet a f, such angel grace, *Beggar Maid* 13
Panted hand-in-hand with f's pale, *Vision of Sin* 19
Hair, and eyes, and limbs, and f's, ,, 39
Every f, however full, Padded round ,, 176
His large gray eyes and weather-beaten f *Enoch Arden* 70
And in their eyes and f's read his doom; Then, as
their f's drew together, groan'd, ,, 73
his f, Rough-redden'd with a thousand winter gales, ,, 94
I shall look upon your f no more.' ,, 212
Spy out my f, and laugh at all your fears.' ,, 216
Cared not to look on any human f, ,, 282
'I cannot look you in the f I seem so foolish ,, 315
And dwelt a moment on his kindly f, ,, 326
but her f had fall'n upon her hands; ,, 391
stood once more before her f, Claiming her promise. ,, 457
Philip's rosy f contracting grew Careworn and wan; ,, 486
He could not see, the kindly human f, ,, 581
Enoch yearn'd to see her f again; 'If I might look
on her sweet f again ,, 717
my dead f would vex her after-life. ,, 891
With half a score of swarthy f's came. *Aylmer's Field* 191
a hoary f Meet for the reverence of the hearth, ,, 332
her sweet f and faith Held him from that: ,, 392
mixt Upon their f's, as they kiss'd each other ,, 430
f to f With twenty months of silence, ,, 566
careless of the household f's near, ,, 575
His f magnetic to the hand from which ,, 626
the wife, who watch'd his f, Paled ,, 731
he veil'd His f with the other, ,, 809
pendent hands, and narrow meagre f ,, 813
The rabbit fondles his own harmless f, ,, 851
sitting all alone, his f Would darken, *Sea Dreams* 12
altho' his fire is on my f Blinding, *Lucretius* 144
sown With happy f's and with holiday. *Princess, Pro.* 56
(A little sense of wrong had touch'd her f ,, 219
prince I was, blue-eyed, and fair in f, ,, *i* 1
I saw my father's f Grow long and troubled ,, 58
keep your hoods about the f; ,, *ii* 358
Push'd her flat hand against his f ,, 366
She sent for Blanche to accuse her f to f; ,, *iv* 239
And falling on my f was caught and known. ,, 270

Face (*continued*) Half-drooping from her, turn'd her f, *Princess, iv.* 368
Stared in her eyes, and chalk'd her f, ,, 377
I know Your f's there in the crowd— ,, 510
Bent their broad f's toward us and address'd ,, 551
so from her f They push'd us, down the steps, ,, 554
Thy f across his fancy comes, ,, 579
And every f she look'd on justify it) ,, *v* 134
therefore I set my f Against all men, ,, 388
Took the face-cloth from the f; ,, *vi* 11
The haggard father's f and reverend beard ,, 103
then once more she look'd at my pale f: ,, 115
And turn'd each f her way: ,, 144
when she learnt his f, Remembering his ill-omen'd song, ,, 158
thro' the parted silks the tender f Peep'd, ,, *vii* 60
at which her f A little flush'd, ,, 80
Hortensia pleading: angry was her f. ,, 132
all for languor and self-pity ran Mine down my f, ,, 140
Pale was the perfect f; ,, 224
His dear little f was troubled, *Grandmother* 65
Before the stony f of Time, *Lit. Squabbles* 3
His f was ruddy, his hair was gold, *The Victim* 35
Till the f of Bel be brighten'd, *Boädicea* 16
they hide their f's, miserable in ignominy! ,, 51
are you flying over her sweet little f? *Window, On the Hill* 13
Ay or no, if ask'd to her f? ,, *Letter* 9
Whom we, that have not seen thy f, *In Mem., Pro.* 2
Roves from the living brother's f, ,, *xxxii* 7
And tears are on the mother's f, ,, *xl* 10
I strive to paint The f I know; ,, *lxx* 3
And shoals of pucker'd f's drive; ,, 10
Looks thy fair f and makes it still. ,, 16
As sometimes in a dead man's f, ,, *lxxiv* 1
And in a moment set thy f ,, *lxxvi* 2
For changes wrought on form and f; ,, *lxxxii* 2
I see their unborn f's shine ,, *lxxxiv* 19
saw The God within him light his f, ,, *lxxxvii* 36
swims The reflex of a human f. ,, *cviii* 12
And find his comfort in thy f; ,, *cix* 20
Not all regret: the f will shine Upon me, ,, *cxvi* 9
Many a merry f Salutes them— ,, *Con.* 66
And hearts are warm'd and f's bloom, ,, 82
make my heart as a millstone, set my f as a flint, *Maud I i* 31
But a cold and clear-cut f, ,, *ii* 3
Cold and clear-cut f, why come you so cruelly meek, ,, *iii* 1
Passionless, pale, cold f, star-sweet ,, 4
pride flash'd over her beautiful f. ,, *iv* 16
Maud with her exquisite f, ,, *v* 12
A f of tenderness might be feign'd, ,, *vi* 52
A bought commission, a waxen f, ,, *x* 30
His f, as I grant, in spite of spite, ,, *xiii* 8
Last year, I caught a glimpse of his f, ,, 27
And he struck me, madman, over the f, ,, *II i* 18
And the f's that one meets, ,, *iv* 93
the f of night is fair on the dewy downs, ,, *III vi* 5
One among many, tho' his f was bare. *Com. of Arthur* 54
find nor f nor bearing, limbs nor voice, ,, 71
And ere it left their f's, ,, 272
gazing on him, tall, with bright Sweet f's, ,, 279
her f Wellnigh was hidden in the minster ,, 288
And sad was Arthur's f Taking it, ,, 305
Fixing full eyes of question on her f, ,, 312
Southward they set their f's, *Gareth and L.* 182
on thro' silent f's rode Down the slope city, ,, 734
not once dare to look him in the f.' ,, 782
And cipher f of rounded foolishness, ,, 1039
Slab after slab, their f's forward all, ,, 1206
'Follow the f's, and we find it. ,, 1210
nor rough f, or voice, Brute bulk of limb, ,, 1329
'God wot, I never look'd upon the f, ,, 1333
Issued the bright f of a blooming boy ,, 1408
the sweet f of her Whom he loves most, *Marr. of Geraint* 122
knight Had vizor up, and show'd a youthful f, ,, 189
Guinevere, not mindful of his f ,, 191
kept her off and gazed upon her f, ,, 519
Across the f of Enid hearing her; ,, 524

Face (*continued*) all his *f* Glow'd like the heart of a great fire *Marr. of Geraint* 558
Dared not to glance at her good mother's *f*, „ 766
But rested with her sweet *f* satisfied; „ 776
to her own bright *f* Accuse her *Geraint and E.* 110
Greeted Geraint full *f*, but stealthily, „ 279
'Your sweet *f's* make good fellows fools „ 399
Ye mar a comely *f* with idiot tears. Yet, since the *f* is comely—some of you, „ 550
felt the warm tears falling on his *f*; „ 586
he turn'd his *f* And kiss'd her climbing, „ 760
Fearing the mild *f* of the blameless King, „ 812
His very *f* with change of heart is changed. „ 899
Came with slow steps, the morning on her *f*; *Balin and Balan* 245
all the light upon her silver *f* Flow'd „ 263
leaves Laid their green *f's* flat against the panes, „ 344
He dash'd the pummel at the foremost *f*, „ 402
Stumbled headlong, and cast him *f* to ground. „ 426
Balin first woke, and seeing that true *f*, „ 590
and they lifted up Their eager *f's*, *Merlin and V.* 133
she lifted up A *f* of sad appeal, „ 234
I find Your *f* is practised when I spell the lines, „ 367
So tender was her voice, so fair her *f*, „ 401
look upon his *f*!—but if he sinn'd, „ 761
harlots paint their talk as well as *f* „ 821
heaving shoulder, and the *f* Hand-hidden, „ 896
with what *f*, after my pretext made, *Lancelot and E.* 141
Had marr'd his *f*, and mark'd it ere his time. „ 247
all night long his *f* before her lived, As when a painter, poring on a *f*, „ 331
and so paints him that his *f*, „ 334
so the *f* before her lived, Dark-splendid, „ 337
Rapt on his *f* as if it were a God's. „ 356
blood Sprang to her *f* and fill'd her with delight; „ 377
Her bright hair blown about the serious *f* „ 392
with smiling *f* arose, With smiling *f* „ 552
sharply turn'd about to hide her *f*, „ 608
Where could be found *f* daintier? „ 641
And lifted her fair *f* and moved away: „ 682
Some read the King's *f*, some the Queen's, „ 727
Sat on his knee, stroked his gray *f* „ 749
Came on her brother with a happy *f* „ 791
Her *f* was near, and as we kiss the child That does the task assign'd, he kiss'd her *f*. „ 828
In the heart's colours on her simple *f*; „ 837
Full often the bright image of one *f*, „ 882
like a ghost she lifted up her *f*, „ 918
'Not to be with you, not to see your *f*— „ 946
the blood-red light of dawn Flared on her *f*, „ 1026
So dwelt the father on her *f*, and thought „ 1030
She with a *f*, bright as for sin forgiven, „ 1102
Winking his eyes, and twisted all his *f*. „ 1145
her *f*, and that clear-featured *f* Was lovely, „ 1159
but that oarsman's haggard *f*, As hard and still as is the *f* that men Shape to their fancy's eye „ 1250
looking often from his *f* who read „ 1285
By God for thee alone, and from her *f*, „ 1367
every knight beheld his fellow's *f* *Holy Grail* 191
bright *f's*, ours, Full of the vision, „ 266
his *f* Darken'd, as I have seen it more than once, „ 272
I saw the fiery *f* as of a child That smote itself „ 466
And knowing every honest *f* of theirs „ 550
And one hath had the vision *f* to *f*, „ 900
have the Heavens but given thee a fair *f*, *Pelleas and E.* 101
his *f* Shone like the countenance of a priest „ 143
gilded parapets were crown'd With *f's*, „ 166
the heat Of pride and glory fired her *f*; „ 172
O damsel, wearing this unsunny *f* „ 180
those three knights all set their *f's* home, „ 187
Content am I so that I see thy *f* „ 243
Thus to be bounden, so to see her *f*, „ 326
Let me be bounden, I shall see her *f*; „ 331
beast Hath drawn his claws athwart thy *f*? *Last Tournament* 63
Modred, a narrow *f*: „ 166
Before him fled the *f* of Queen Isolt „ 363

Face (*continued*) Anon the *f*, as, when a gust hath blown, *Last Tournament* 368
That sent the *f* of all the marsh aloft „ 439
the *f* Wellnigh was helmet-hidden, „ 455
trampled out his *f* from being known, „ 470
Men, women, on their sodden *f's*, „ 474
mist, like a face-cloth to the *f*, Clung *Guinevere* 7
Modred's narrow foxy *f*, „ 63
grim *f's* came and went Before her, „ 70
Till ev'n the clear *f* of the guileless King, „ 85
Fired all the pale *f* of the Queen, „ 357
grovell'd with her *f* against the floor: „ 415
She made her *f* a darkness from the King: „ 417
I might see his *f*, and not be seen.' „ 588
so she did not see the *f*, Which then was as an angel's, „ 595
those With whom he dwelt, new *f's*, other minds. *Pass. of Arthur* 5
some beheld the *f's* of old ghosts Look in „ 103
the wan wave Brake in among dead *f's*, „ 130
And beats upon the *f's* of the dead, „ 141
for all his *f* was white And colourless, „ 380
new men, strange *f's*, other minds.' „ 406
If thou should'st never see my *f* again, „ 414
dwelt on my heaven, a *f* Most starry-fair, *Lover's Tale i* 72
placid *f* And breathless body of her good deeds „ 216
slept In the same cradle always, *f* to *f*. „ 259
in the shuddering moonlight brought its *f* „ 650
drops of that distressful rain Fell on my *f*, „ 699
when their *f's* are forgot in the land— „ 759
the *f*, The very *f* and form of Lionel „ *ii* 93
those that held the bier before my *f*, „ *iii* 16
His lady with the moonlight on her *f*; „ *iv* 57
Heir of his *f* and land, to Lionel. „ 129
Sent such a flame into his *f*, „ 177
I, by Lionel sitting, saw his *f* Fire, „ 322
lifted up a *f* All over glowing with the sun „ 380
I had but to look in his *f*. *First Quarrel* 16
But I turn'd my *f* from *him*, an' he turn'd *his f* an' he went. „ 84
praised him to his *f* with their courtly *The Revenge* 99
Turning my way, the loveliest *f* on earth. The *f* of one there sitting opposite, *Sisters (E. and E.)* 87
and for a *f* Gone in a moment—strange. „ 93
Sun himself has limn'd the *f* for me. „ 101
So that bright *f* was flash'd thro' sense and soul „ 109
the *f* again, My Rosalind in this Arden— „ 118
There was the *f*, and altogether she. „ 153
driven by one angel *f*, And all the Furies. „ 158
but his voice and his *f* were not kind, *In the Child. Hosp.* 15
and let the dark *f* have his due! Thanks to the kindly dark *f's* who fought with us, *Def. of Lucknow* 69
white *f's* of Havelock's good fusileers, „ 101
I saw your *f* that morning in the crowd. *Columbus* 7
thought to turn my *f* from Spain, „ 57
f and form are hers and mine in one, *De Prof., Two G.* 13
flash The *f's* of the Gods— *Tiresias* 173
a ghastlier *f* than ever has haunted a grave *The Wreck* 8
I will hide my *f*, I will tell you all. „ 12
The small sweet *f* was flush'd, „ 60
Then his pale *f* twitch'd; 'O Stephen, „ 101
the *f* I had known, O Mother, was not the *f* „ 116
and away from your faith and your *f*! *Despair* 110
waken every morning to that *f* I loathe to see: *The Flight* 8
an the *f* of the thraithur agin in life! *Tomorrow* 50
pelt your offal at her *f*. *Locksley H., Sixty* 134
Peept the winsome *f* of Edith „ 260
Fled wavering o'er thy *f*, and chased away *Demeter and P.* 15
sighs after many a vanish'd *f*, *Vastness* 1
the *f* Of Miriam grew upon me, *The Ring* 184
as a man Who sees his *f* in water, „ 370
a sudden *f* Look'd in upon me like a gleam „ 419
And the *f*, The hand,—my Mother. „ 424
Among them Muriel lying on her *f*— „ 448
I will front him *f* to *f*. *Happy* 19
For Age will chink the *f*, „ 46
A beauty came upon your *f*, „ 51

Face (*continued*) and with Grief Sit *f* to *f*, *To Mary Boyle* 46
On human *f's*, And all around me, *Merlin and the G.* 20
And rough-ruddy *f's* Of lowly labour, „ 59
Less profile! turn to me—three-quarter *f*. *Romney's R.* 98
'*My* Rose' set all your *f* aglow, *Roses on the T.* 3
ghastlier than the Gorgon head, a *f*,—*His f* deform'd by lurid blotch and blain— *Death of Œnone* 71
saw The ring of *f's* redden'd by the flames „ 92
set his *f* By waste and field and town *St. Telemachus* 29
Christian *f's* watch Man murder man. „ 55
Glanced from our Presence on the *f* of one, *Akbar's Dream* 113
ray red as blood Glanced on the strangled *f*— *Bandit's Death* 32
So I turn'd my *f* to the wall, *Charity* 27
with a sudden glow On her patient *f* „ 36
she is *f* to *f* with her Lord, „ 42
The *f* of Death is toward the Sun of Life, *D. of the Duke of C.* 12
I hope to see my Pilot *f* to *f* *Crossing the Bar* 15
Face-cloth Took the *f-c* from the face; *Princess vi* 11
mist, like a *f-c* to the face, Clung *Guinevere* 7
Faced (*See also* **Babe-faced, Broad-faced, Clear-faced, Fat-faced, Free-faced, Full-faced, Moon-faced, Mulberry-faced, Plain-faced, Red-faced, Smooth-faced, White-faced**) Enoch *f* this morning of farewell Brightly *Enoch Arden* 182
He *f* the spectres of the mind *In Mem. xcvi* 15
Face-flatterer *F-f* and backbiter are the same. *Merlin and V.* 824
Facet The *f's* of the glorious mountain flash *The Islet* 22
glance and sparkle like a gem Of fifty *f's*; *Geraint and E.* 295
Fact that plain *f*, as taught by these, *Two Voices* 281
Wherever Thought hath wedded *F*. *Love thou thy land* 52
Taught them with *f's*. *Princess, Pro.* 59
A *f* within the coming year; *In Mem. xcii* 10
and, laughing sober *f* to scorn, *Locksley H., Sixty* 109
Faction Where *f* seldom gathers head, *You ask me, why* 13
Not less, tho' dogs of *F* bay, *Love thou thy land* 85
Not swaying to this *f* or to that; *Ded. of Idylls* 21
and counter-yells of feud And *f*, *To Duke of Argyll* 9
Faculty all my *faculties* are lamed. *Lucretius* 123
Fade It will change, but it will not *f* *Nothing will Die* 31
Fix'd—then as slowly *f* again, *Eleänore* 93
Ripens and *f's*, and falls, *Lotos-Eaters, C. S.* 37
Ay, ay, the blossom *f's*, *Walk. to the Mail* 57
whose margin *f's* For ever and for ever *Ulysses* 20
since the nobler pleasure seems to *f*, *Lucretius* 230
When can their glory *f*? *Light Brigade* 50
flower of poesy Which little cared for *f's* not yet. *In Mem. viii* 20
Before the spirits *f* away, „ *xlvii* 14
Be near me when I *f* away, „ *l* 13
F wholly, while the soul exults, „ *lxxiii* 14
And year by year our memory *f's* „ *ci* 23
Now *f's* the last long streak of snow, „ *cxv* 1
Let it flame or *f*, and the war roll down *Maud III vi* 54
'Sweet love, that seems not made to *f* *Lancelot and E.* 1013
Cast at thy feet one flower that *f's* away. *To Dante* 7
Shall *f* with him into the unknown, *Tiresias* 215
and wake The bloom that *f's* away? *Ancient Sage* 94
The phantom walls of this illusion *f*, „ 181
blackthorn-blossom *f's* and falls and leaves *The Flight* 15
we watch'd the sun *f* from us thro' the West, „ 41
glimpse and *f* Thro' some slight spell, *Early Spring* 31
FAIR things are slow to *f* away, *To Prof. Jebb.* 1
Moon, you *f* at times From the night. *The Ring* 9
mists of earth *F* in the noon of heaven, *Akbar's Dream* 97
but, while the races flower and *f*, *Making of Man* 5
Faded (adj.) *f* places, By squares of tropic summer *Amphion* 86
From fringes of the *f* eve, *Move eastward* 3
His wife a *f* beauty of the Baths, *Aylmer's Field* 27
then ensued A Martin's summer of his *f* love, „ 560
Autumn's mock sunshine of the *f* woods „ 610
Lady Blanche alone Of *f* form and haughtiest lineaments, *Princess ii* 448
f woman-slough To sheathing splendours „ *v* 40
I love not hollow cheek or *f* eye: „ *vii* 7
This *f* leaf, our names are as brief; *Spiteful Letter* 13
thro' the *f* leaf The chestnut pattering to the ground: *In Mem. xi* 3
I did but speak Of my mother's *f* cheek *Maud I xix* 19

Faded (adj.) (*continued*) Then she bethought her of a *f* silk, A *f* mantle and a *f* veil, *Marr. of Geraint* 134
That lightly breaks a *f* flower-sheath, Moved the fair Enid, all in *f* silk, „ 365
All staring at her in her *f* silk: „ 617
to her own *f* self And the gay court, „ 652
dreamt herself was such a *f* form „ 654
charge the gardeners now To pick the *f* creature from the pool, „ 671
I myself unwillingly have worn My *f* suit, „ 706
That she ride with me in her *f* silk.' „ 762
But Enid ever kept the *f* silk, „ 841
And tearing off her veil of *f* silk *Geraint and E.* 514
From Camelot in among the *f* fields To furthest towers; *Last Tournament* 53
as one Who sits and gazes on a *f* fire, „ 157
The *f* rhymes and scraps of ancient crones, *Lover's Tale i* 289
Leaning its roses on my *f* eyes. „ 621
Fainting flowers, *f* bowers, *Sisters (E. and E.)* 11
On icy fallow And *f* forest, *Merlin and the G.* 85
Faded (verb) the heart Faints, *f* by its heat. *D. of F. Women* 288
by Nature's law, Have *f* long ago; *Talking Oak* 74
this kindlier glow *F* with morning, *Aylmer's Field* 412
it *f*, and seems But an ashen-gray delight. *Maud I vi* 21
f from the presence into years Of exile— *Balin and Balan* 156
then the music *f*, and the Grail Past, *Holy Grail* 121
And the Quest *f* in my heart. „ 600
till they *f* like my love. *Lover's Tale ii* 10
but the promise had *f* away; *Despair* 27
FIFTY times the rose has flower'd and *f*, *On Jub. Q. Victoria* 1
form of Muriel *f*, and the face Of Miriam *The Ring* 184
Fading (*See also* **Slowly-fading**) breath Of the *f* edges of box beneath, *A spirit haunts* 19
The *f* politics of mortal Rome, *Princess ii* 286
And *f* legend of the past; *In Mem. lxii* 4
I care not in these *f* days To raise a cry „ *lxxv* 9
Was it he lay there with a *f* eye? *Maud II i* 29
Flatter'd the fancy of my *f* brain; *Lover's Tale ii* 107
Of her I loved, adorn'd with *f* flowers. „ *iii* 40
Closer on the Sun, perhaps a world of never *f* flowers. *Locksley H., Sixty* 184
Light the *f* gleam of Even? „ 229
F slowly from his side: *L. of Burleigh* 86
Growing and *f* and growing (repeat) *Maud I iii* 7, 9
Green Sussex *f* into blue With one gray glimpse *Pro. to Gen. Hamley* 7
Faggot we will make it *f's* for the hearth, *Princess vi* 45
Fail I shall not *f* to find her now. *Two Voices* 191
till thy hand *F* from the sceptre-staff. *Œnone* 126
So wrought, they will not *f*. *Palace of Art* 148
Lest she should *f* and perish utterly, „ 221
for a man may *f* in duty twice, *M. d'Arthur* 129
You scarce can *f* to match his masterpiece.' *Gardener's D.* 31
You cannot *f* but work in hues to dim „ 170
Who may be made a saint, if I *f* here? *St. S. Stylites* 48
Thy leaf shall never *f*, nor yet *Talking Oak* 259
decent not to *f* In offices of tenderness, *Ulysses* 40
'The many *f*: the one succeeds.' *Day-Dm., Arrival* 16
Her heart within her did not *f*: *Lady Clare* 78
Rose again from where it seem'd to *f*, *Vision of Sin* 24
it *f's* at last And perishes as I must; *Lucretius* 264
Who *f* to find thee, being as thou art „ 268
Ere half be done perchance your life may *f*; *Princess iii* 236
f so far In high desire, they know not, „ 279
if we *f*, we *f*, And if we win, we *f*: „ *v* 322
What end soever: *f* you will not. „ 406
She mental breadth, nor *f* in childward care, „ *vii* 283
Forgive them where they *f* in truth, *In Mem., Pro.* 43
I seem to *f* from out my blood „ *ii* 15
That thou should'st *f* from thy desire, „ *iv* 6
Swell out and *f*, as if a door „ *xxviii* 7
Thou *f* not in a world of sin, „ *xxxiii* 15
Where truth in closest words shall *f*, „ *xxxvi* 6
Lest life should *f* in looking back. „ *xlvi* 4
No life may *f* beyond the grave, „ *lv* 2
I shall pass; my work will *f*. „ *lvii* 8

Fail (*continued*) Could make thee somewhat blench or *f*, *In Mem. lxii* 2
Thy spirit should *f* from off the globe; „ *lxxxiv* 36
that keeps A thousand pulses dancing, *f*. „ *cxxv* 16
shall I shriek if a Hungary *f*? *Maud I iv* 46
solid ground Not *f* beneath my feet „ *xi* 2
fill up the gap where force might *f* *Gareth and L.* 1352
Like him who tries the bridge he fears may *f*, *Geraint and E.* 303
they *f* to see This fair wife-worship *Balin and Balan* 359
fine plots may *f*, Tho' harlots paint *Merlin and V.* 820
if ye *f*, Give ye the slave mine order *Pelleas and E.* 269
spouting from a cliff *F's* in mid air, *Guinevere* 609
for a man may *f* in duty twice, *Pass. of Arthur* 297
That saved her many times, not *f*— *To the Queen ii* 62
scales Their headlong passes, but his footstep *f's*, *Montenegro* 5
Pray God our greatness may not *f* *Hands all Round* 31
if you shall *f* to understand What England is, *The Fleet* 1
should those *f*, that hold the helm, *Prog. of Spring* 100
if I *f* To conjure and concentrate *Romney's R.* 6
When fine Philosophies would *f*, *Akbar's Dream* 140
And let not Reason *f* me, *Doubt and Prayer* 5
Fail'd sweet incense rose and never *f*, *Palace of Art* 45
her heart *f* her; and the reapers reap'd, *Dora* 78
She *f* and sadden'd knowing it; *Enoch Arden* 257
all her force *F* her; and sighing, „ 375
thought and nature *f* a little, „ 792
As having *f* in duty to him, *Lucretius* 278
the year in which our olives *f*. *Princess i* 125
none to trust Since our arms *f*— „ *v* 427
Old studies *f*: seldom she spoke: „ *vii* 31
she had *f* In sweet humility; had *f* in all; „ 228
for a vast speculation had *f*, *Maud I i* 9
either *f* to make the kingdom one. *Com. of Arthur* 15
ever *f* to draw The quiet night into her blood, *Marr. of Geraint* 531
f of late To send his tribute; *Balin and Balan* 3
But on all those who tried and *f*, *Merlin and V.* 590
many tried and *f*, because the charm „ 595
I well believe she tempted them and *f*, „ 819
f to find him, tho' I rode all round *Lancelot and E.* 709
yet thee She *f* to bind, tho' being, „ 1385
This Holy Thing, *f* from my side, nor come Cover'd, *Holy Grail* 470
'Hath Gawain *f* in any quest of thine? „ 859
the great heart of knighthood in thee *f* *Pelleas and E.* 596
They *f* to trace him thro' the flesh and blood *Last Tournament* 686
the purport of my throne hath *f*, *Pass. of Arthur* 160
strove to disengage myself, but *f*, Being so feeble: *Lover's Tale i* 692
But ever I *f* to please him, *The Wreck* 28
Amy loved me, Amy *f* me, *Locksley H., Sixty* 19
Britain *f*; and never more, *Open I. and C. Exhib.* 22
I *f* To send my life thro' olive-yard *Demeter and P.* 109
All her splendour *f* To lure those eyes *St. Telemachus* 35
wild horse, anger, plunged To fling me, and *f*. *Akbar's Dream* 119
Failing (part.) The strong limbs *f*; *All Things will Die* 32
F to give the bitter of the sweet, *D. of F. Women* 286
utterance *f* her, She whirl'd them on to me, *Princess iv* 395
you *f*, I abide What end soever: „ *v* 405
When the mind is *f*! *Forlorn* 36
Failing (s) that unnoticed *f* in herself, *Geraint and E.* 47
Fain how *f* was I To dream thy cause embraced *Princess vi* 199
'Sir,—and, good faith, I *f* had added—Knight, *Gareth and L.* 1162
'*F* would I still be loyal to the Queen.' *Balin and Balan* 254
and *f*, For hate and loathing, would have past „ 387
I *f* would know what manner of men they be.' „ 574
Balin, Balin, I that *f* had died To save thy life, „ 599
f Have all men true and leal, *Merlin and V.* 793
Lionel, who *f* had risen, but fell again, *Lover's Tale iv* 361
Would *f* that he were dead; *Ancient Sage* 126
one of those I *f* would meet again, *Pro. to Gen. Hamley* 22
Faint (adj.) Bramble roses, *f* and pale, *A Dirge* 30
Wherefore those *f* smiles of thine, *Adeline* 21
Wherefore that *f* smile of thine, „ 38
Thou *f* smiler, Adeline? „ 48
And *f*, rainy lights are seen, *Margaret* 60
by the meadow-trenches blow the *f* sweet cuckoo-flowers; *May Queen* 30
these twelve books of mine Were *f* Homeric echoes, *The Epic* 39
Faint (adj.) (*continued*) To whom replied King Arthur, *f* and pale: *M. d'Arthur* 72
with slow steps, With slow, *f* steps, *St. S. Stylites* 183
F shadows, vapours lightly curl'd, *F* murmurs from the meadows come, *Day-Dm., Sleep. P.* 5
sketches rude and *f*. *Aylmer's Field* 100
I on her Fixt my *f* eyes, *Princess vii* 144
F heart never won— *Window, Answer* 9
The *f* horizons, all the bounds of earth, *Far-far-away* 14
F she grew, and ever fainter, *L. of Burleigh* 81
The voice grew *f*: there came a further change: *Vision of Sin* 207
F as a figure seen in early dawn *Enoch Arden* 357
the hues are *f* And mix with hollow masks *In Mem. lxx* 3
This haunting whisper makes me *f*, „ *lxxxi* 7
let her eat; the damsel is so *f*.' *Geraint and E.* 206
chafing his *f* hands, and calling to him; „ 585
seem'd to change, and grow *F* and far-off. *Balin and Balan* 218
F in the low dark hall of banquet: „ 343
dying brother cast himself Dying; and *he* lifted *f* eyes; „ 594
I was *f* to swooning, and you lay Foot-gilt *Merlin and V.* 281
all too *f* and sick am I For anger: *Lancelot and E.* 1086
To whom replied King Arthur, *f* and pale: *Pass. of Arthur* 240
there came, but *f* As from beyond the limit of the world, „ 457
the heart—it beat: *F*—but it beat: *Lover's Tale iv* 81
faint-stomach'd! *f* as I am, *Sir J. Oldcastle* 192
F as a climate-changing bird that flies *Demeter and P.* 1
are *f* And pale in Alla's eyes, *Akbar's Dream* 10
Faint (verb) I *f*, I fall. Men say that thou *Supp. Confessions* 2
I *f* in this obscurity, (repeat) *Ode to Memory* 6, 44, 123
My very heart *f's* and my whole soul grieves *A spirit haunts* 16
flowers would *f* at your cruel cheer. *Poet's Mind* 15
'Cry, *f* not: either Truth is born *Two Voices* 181
'Cry, *f* not, climb: the summits slope „ 184
F's like a dazzled morning moon. *Fatima* 28
and the heart *F's*, faded by its heat. *D. of F. Women* 288
They *f* on hill or field or river: *Princess iv* 14
Beginning to *f* in the light that she loves *Maud I xxii* 9
To *f* in the light of the sun she loves, To *f* in his light, and to die. „ 11
my whole soul languishes And *f's*, *Lover's Tale i* 268
at his feet I seem'd to *f* and fall, „ *ii* 96
Faint-blue A *f-b* ridge upon the right, *Mariana in the S.* 5
Fainted at the clamouring of her enemy *f* *Boädicea* 82
sick with love, *F* at intervals, *Lover's Tale i* 546
Fainter Wears all day a *f* tone. *The Owl ii* 7
She replies, in accents *f*, *L. of Burleigh* 5
Faint she grew and ever *f*, „ 81
F by day, but always in the night Blood-red, *Holy Grail* 472
f onward, like wild birds that change *Pass. of Arthur* 38
Our voices were thinner and *f* *V. of Maeldune* 22
slower and *f*, Old and weary, *Merlin and the G.* 99
Is it turning a *f* red? *The Dawn* 22
Faintest *f* sunlights flee About his shadowy sides: *The Kraken* 4
The smallest rock far on the *f* hill, *Com. of Arthur* 99
Has push'd toward our *f* sun *To Ulysses* 23
Faint-heart'd *F-h*? tut!—faint-stomach'd! *Sir J. Oldcastle* 192
Fainting *F* flowers, faded bowers, *Sisters (E. and E.)* 11
Faintlier Then laugh'd again, but *f*, *Guinevere* 58
savour of thy kitchen came upon me A little *f*: *Gareth and L.* 994
Faintly Tho' *f*, merrily—far and far away— *Enoch Arden* 614
F smiling Adeline, *Adeline* 2
Faintly-flush'd How *f-f*, how phantom-fair, *The Daisy* 65
Faintly-shadow'd as he traced a *f-s* track, *Lancelot and E.* 165
Faintly-venom'd smiles, and *f-v* points Of slander, *Merlin and V.* 172
Faint-stomach'd '*f-s*! faint as I am, *Sir J. Oldcastle* 192
Fair (adj., s., adv.) (*See also* **Full-fair, Phantom-fair, Silver-fair, Starry-fair**) But beyond expression *f* *Adeline* 5
gleaming rind ingrav'n, 'For the most *f*,' *Œnone* 73
Thy mortal eyes are frail to judge of *f*, „ 158
Fairest—why fairest wife? am I not *f*? „ 196
Methinks I must be *f*, for yesterday, „ 198
uninvited came Into the *f* Peleïan banquet-hall, „ 225
O the Earl was *f* to see! (repeat) *The Sisters* 6, 12, 18, 24, 30, 36
divinely tall, And most divinely *f*. *D. of F. Women* 88

Fair (adj., s., adv.) (*continued*) in *f* field Myself for such a face had boldly died *D. of F. Women* 97
"No *f* Hebrew boy Shall smile away my maiden blame „ 213
I am that Rosamond, whom men call *f*, „ 251
'Come again, and thrice as *f*;' *M. d'Arthur, Ep.* 26
maid or spouse, As *f* as my Olivia, *Talking Oak* 35
f young beech That here beside me stands, „ 141
oak on lea Shall grow so *f* as this.' „ 244
What moral is in being *f*. *Day-Dm., Moral* 4
'What wonder, if he thinks me *f*?' „ *Ep.* 4
Sees whatever *f* and splendid *L. of Burleigh* 27
She was more *f* than words can say: *Beggar Maid* 2
Tomohrit, Athos, all things *f*, *To E. L.* 5
frequent interchange of foul and *f*, *Enoch Arden* 533
'Too happy, fresh, and *f*, Too fresh and *f* *The Brook* 217
a couple, *f* As ever painter painted, *Aylmer's Field* 105
Sear'd by the close ecliptic, was not *f*; „ 193
Should as by miracle, grow straight and *f*— „ 676
F as the Angel that said 'Hail!' „ 681
a fearful night!' 'Not fearful; *f*,' Said the good wife, 'if every star in heaven Can make it *f*: *Sea Dreams* 82
one that arm'd Her own *f* head, *Princess, Pro.* 33
then the maiden Aunt Took this *f* day for text, „ 108
A prince I was, blue-eyed, and *f* in face, „ *i* 1
'My sister.' 'Comely, too, by all that's *f*, „ *ii* 114
and pass With all *f* theories made to gild „ 233
all her thoughts as *f* within her eyes, „ 326
So stood that same *f* creature at the door. „ 329
beauties every shade of brown and *f* „ 437
And why we came? I fabled nothing *f*, „ *iii* 136
The head and heart of all our *f* she-world, „ 163
'or with *f* philosophies That lift the fancy; „ 340
elaborately wrought With *f* Corinna's triumph; „ 349
'*F* daughter, when we sent the Prince your way „ *iv* 398
From all high places, lived in all *f* lights, „ 430
All her *f* length upon the ground she lay: „ *v* 59
Upon the skirt and fringe of our *f* land, „ 219
'O *f* and strong and terrible! „ *vi* 163
So their *f* college turn'd to hospital; „ *vii* 17
till she not *f* began To gather light „ 23
And found *f* peace once more among the sick. „ 44
those *f* charities Join'd at her side; „ 65
Stays all the *f* young planet in her hands— „ 264
The sea-kings' daughter as happy as *f*, *W. to Alexandra* 26
Not once or twice in our *f* island-story, *Ode on Well.* 209
That one *f* planet can produce, *Ode Inter. Exhib.* 24
let the *f* white-wing'd peacemaker fly To happy havens „ 34
F empires branching, both, in lusty life!— *W. to Marie Alex.* 21
Lariano crept To that *f* port below the castle *The Daisy* 79
The fields are *f* beside them, *Voice and the P.* 17
F is her cottage in its place, *Requiescat* 1
Thy creature, whom I found so *f*. *In Mem., Pro.* 38
And glad to find thyself so *f*, „ *vi* 27
F ship, that from the Italian shore „ *ix* 1
Who broke our *f* companionship, „ *xxii* 13
And all we met was *f* and good, „ *xxiii* 17
If all was good and *f* we met, „ *xxiv* 5
Man, her last work, who seem'd so *f*, „ *lvi* 9
Looks thy *f* face and makes it still. „ *lxx* 16
With promise of a morn as *f*; „ *lxxxiv* 29
great Intelligences *f* That range above „ *lxxxv* 21
When one would aim an arrow *f*, „ *lxxxvii* 25
My Arthur found your shadows *f*, „ *lxxxix* 6
Imaginations calm and *f*, „ *xciv* 10
And those *f* hills I sail'd below, „ *xcviii* 2
Let her great Danube rolling *f* Enwind her isles, „ 9
Unloved, the sun-flower, shining *f*, „ *ci* 5
trust In that which made the world so *f*. „ *cxvi* 8
And in the setting thou art *f*. „ *cxxx* 4
she grows For ever, and as *f* as good. „ *Con.* 36
she promised then to be *f*. *Maud I i* 68
Man in his pride, and Beauty *f* in her flower; „ *iv* 25
I had fancied it would be *f*. „ *vi* 6
And *f* without, faithful within, „ *xiii* 37

Fair (adj., s., adv.) (*continued*) garden of roses And lilies *f* on a lawn; *Maud I xiv* 2
Upon a pastoral slope as *f*, „ *xviii* 19
And you *f* stars that crown a happy day „ 30
Spice his *f* banquet with the dust of death? „ 56
When the face of night is *f* on the dewy downs, „ *III vi* 5
To have look'd, tho' but in a dream, upon eyes so *f*, „ 16
Had one *f* daughter, and none other child; *Com. of Arthur* 2
One falling upon each of three *f* queens, „ 276
but this King is *f* Beyond the race of Britons „ 330
And hated this *f* world and all therein, „ 344
The *f* beginners of a nobler time, „ 457
And we that fight for our *f* father Christ, „ 510
One was *f*, strong, arm'd— *Gareth and L.* 104
the whole *f* city had disappear'd „ 196
Broad brows and *f*, a fluent hair and fine, High nose, a nostril large and fine, and hands Large, *f* and fine!— „ 464
f and fine, forsooth! „ 474
I leave not till I finish this *f* quest, „ 774
find My fortunes all as *f* as hers who lay „ 903
Bare-footed and bare-headed three *f* girls „ 926
F words were best for him who fights for thee; „ 946
'*F* damsel, you should worship me the more, „ 1022
And seeing now thy words are *f*, methinks „ 1181
'My *f* child, What madness made thee challenge the chief knight Of Arthur's hall?' '*F* Sir, they bad me do it. „ 1415
He craved a *f* permission to depart, *Marr. of Geraint* 40
'Farewell, *f* Prince,' answer'd the stately Queen. „ 224
And climb'd upon a *f* and even ridge, „ 239
'Whither, *f* son?' to whom Geraint replied, „ 298
Moved the *f* Enid, all in faded silk, „ 366
'*F* Host and Earl, I pray your courtesy; „ 403
Nor can see elsewhere, anything so *f*. „ 499
'Advance and take, as fairest of the *f*, „ 553
With her *f* head in the dim-yellow light, „ 600
For tho' ye won the prize of fairest *f*, And tho' I heard him call you fairest *f*, „ 719
however *f*, She is not fairer in new clothes „ 721
She never yet had seen her half so *f*; „ 741
I vow'd that could I gain her, our *f* Queen, „ 787
When your *f* child shall wear your costly gift „ 819
not to goodly hill or yellow sea Look'd the *f* Queen, „ 831
But hire us some *f* chamber for the night, *Geraint and E.* 238
Femininely *f* and dissolutely pale. „ 275
'*F* and dear cousin, you that most had cause „ 824
Did her mock-honour as the fairest *f*, „ 833
Before the Queen's *f* name was breathed upon, „ 951
her ladies loved to call Enid the *F*, „ 963
till he crown'd A happy life with a *f* death, „ 968
Early, one *f* dawn, The light-wing'd spirit *Balin and Balan* 20
'*F* Sirs,' said Arthur, 'wherefore sit ye here?' „ 31
And brought report of azure lands and *f*, „ 168
ye stand, *f* lord, as in a dream.' „ 258
we have ridd'n before among the flowers In those *f* days— „ 273
This *f* wife-worship cloaks a secret shame? „ 360
this *f* lord The flower of all their vestal knighthood, „ 507
'And is the *f* example follow'd, Sir, *Merlin and V.* 19
He hath given us a *f* falcon which he train'd; „ 96
Had met her, Vivien, being greeted *f*, „ 155
tender was her voice, so *f* her face, „ 401
Is like the *f* pearl-necklace of the Queen, „ 451
And found a *f* young squire who sat alone, „ 472
Was this *f* charm invented by yourself? „ 540
I mean, as noble, as their Queen was *f*? „ 608
kinsman left him watcher o'er his wife And two *f* babes, „ 707
What say ye then to *f* Sir Percivale „ 747
Sees what his *f* bride is and does, „ 782
Elaine the *f*, Elaine the loveable, *Lancelot and E.* 1
you cannot move To these *f* jousts?' „ 80
Why go ye not to these *f* jousts? „ 98
as I hear It is a *f* large diamond,— „ 228
'A *f* large diamond,' added plain Sir Torre, „ 230
'If what is *f* be but for what is *f*, „ 237

Fair (adj., s., adv.) (*continued*) who deem this maid
Might wear as f a jewel — *Lancelot and E.* 240
'Save your great self, f lord;' — „ 320
'F lord, whose name I know not— — „ 360
'F lady, since I never yet have worn — „ 363
Who parted with his own to f Elaine: — „ 381
cells and chambers: all were f and dry; — „ 407
Gawain, surnamed The Courteous, f and strong, — „ 555
And stay'd; and cast his eyes on f Elaine: — „ 640
And lifted her f face and moved away: — „ 682
'Nay, for near you, f lord, I am at rest.' — „ 833
a faith once f Was richer than these diamonds— — „ 1228
F lord, as would have help'd her from her death.' — „ 1311
Delicately pure and marvellously f, — „ 1369
'F she was, my King, Pure, — „ 1374
Farewell too—now at last—Farewell, f lily. — „ 1397
kiss'd me saying, 'Thou art f, my child, — „ 1409
and f the house whereby she sat, — *Holy Grail* 392
disarm'd By maidens each as f as any flower: — „ 576
till one f morn, I walking to and fro beside a stream — „ 591
For f thou art and pure as Guinevere, — *Pelleas and E.* 44
have the Heavens but given thee a f face, — „ 101
'Ay,' thought Gawain, 'and you be f enow: — „ 388
A rose, one rose, and this was wondrous f, — „ 401
Let be thy f Queen's fantasy. — *Last Tournament* 197
Be happy in thy f Queen as I in mine.' — „ 204
'F damsels, each to him who worships each — „ 207
In that f Order of my Table Round, — *Guinevere* 463
And be the f beginning of a time. — „ 466
And drawing foul ensample from f names, — „ 490
And so thou lean on our f father Christ, — „ 562
What might I not have made of thy f world, — „ 655
Or else as if the world were wholly f, — *Pass. of Arthur* 18
f with orchard-lawns And bowery hollows — „ 430
Sounds, as if some f city were one voice — „ 460
Ye cannot shape Fancy so f as is this memory. — *Lover's Tale i* 548
F speech was his and delicate of phrase, — „ 719
Above some f metropolis, earth-shock'd,— — „ *ii* 62
Oftentimes The vision has f prelude, — „ 124
so those f eyes Shone on my darkness, — „ 157
rare or f Was brought before the guest: — „ *iv* 203
F speech was his, and delicate of phrase. — „ 273
Making fresh and f All the bowers and the
flowers, — *Sisters (E. and E.)* 9
the great things of Nature and the f, — „ 222
what is f without Is often as foul within.' — *Dead Prophet* 67
all that is filthy with all that is f? — *Vastness* 32
one was f, And one was dark, — *The Ring* 160
Who would be A mermaid f, — *The Mermaid* 2
I would be a mermaid f; — „ 9
From Ind to Ind, but in f daylight woke, — *Buonaparte* 4
Not these alone, but every landscape f, — *Palace of Art* 89
In some f space of sloping greens Lay, — „ 106
but every legend f Which the supreme Caucasian mind — „ 126
Above, the f hall-ceiling stately-set — „ 141
'O all things f to sate my various eyes! — „ 193
none so f as little Alice in all the land they say, — *May Queen* 7
With that f child betwixt them born. — *On a Mourner* 25
That her f form may stand and shine, — *Of old sat Freedom* 21
happy, f with orchard-lawns And bowery hollows — *M. d'Arthur* 262
by those f fingers cull'd, — *Gardener's D.* 150
Pontius and Iscariot by my side Show'd like
f seraphs. — *St. S. Stylites* 169
Beyond the f green field and eastern sea. — *Love and Duty* 101
the f new forms, That float about the threshold — *Golden Year* 15
The maid-of-honour blooming f; — *Day-Dm., Sleep. P.* 28
He trusts to light on something f; — *Arrival* 20
So keep I f thro' faith and prayer A virgin heart — *Sir Galahad* 23
With f horizons bound: — *Will Water.* 66
Nor for my lands so broad and f; — *Lady Clare* 10
Lord of Burleigh, f and free, — *L. of Burleigh* 58
Three f children first she bore him, — „ 87
For one f Vision ever fled Down the waste waters — *The Voyage* 57
Like Virtue firm, like Knowledge f, — „ 68
Will bring f weather yet to all of us. — *Enoch Arden* 191

Fair (adj., s., adv.) (*continued*) Thro' many a f sea-circle,
day by day, — *Enoch Arden* 542
'Then I fixt My wistful eyes on two f images, — *Sea Dreams* 240
The marvel of that f new nature— — *Columbus* 79
It was all of it f as life, it was all of it quiet as
death, — *V. of Maeldune* 20
F Florence honouring thy nativity, — *To Dante* 3
And earth as f in hue! — *Ancient Sage* 24
'Earth is f' When all is dark as night.' — „ 169
And show us that the world is wholly f. — „ 182
O Thou so f in summers gone, — *Freedom* 1
So f in southern sunshine bathed, — „ 5
Our own f isle, the lord of every sea— — *The Fleet* 7
as honouring your f fame Of Statesman, — *To Marq. of Dufferin* 14
Hail the f Ceremonial Of this year — *On Jub. Q. Victoria* 23
F things are slow to fade away, — *To Prof. Jebb* 1
I loved you first when young and f, — *Happy* 29
F Spring slides hither o'er the Southern sea, — *Prog. of Spring* 2
a breath From some f dawn beyond the doors
of death — *Far-far-away* 11
f mothers they Dying in childbirth of dead sons. — *Akbar's Dream* 11
From each f plant the blossom choicest-grown — „ 22
palm Call to the cypress 'I alone am f'? — „ 38
F garments, plain or rich, and fitting close — „ 131
loosen, stone from stone, All my f work; — „ 189
Fair (s) (*See also* **Faäir**) the f Was holden at the town; — *Talking Oak* 101
Fairer guerdon could not alter me To f. — *Œnone* 154
Emilia, f than all else but thou, For thou art f
than all else that is. — *Audley Court* 66
F his talk, a tongue that ruled the hour, — *Aylmer's Field* 194
F than Rachel by the palmy well, F than Ruth
among the fields of corn, — „ 679
And f she, but ah how soon to die! — *Requiescat* 5
Stiller, not f than mine. — *Maud II v* 71
F than aught in the world beside, — „ 73
She is not f in new clothes than old. — *Marr. of Geraint* 722
O as much f—as a faith once fair — *Lancelot and E.* 1228
To greet their f sisters of the East. — *Gardener's D.* 188
Where f fruit of Love may rest Some happy
future day. — *Talking Oak* 251
there's the f chance: — *Princess v* 460
F thy fate than mine, if life's best end — *Tiresias* 130
She that finds a winter sunset f than a morn
of Spring — *Locksley H., Sixty* 22
Fairest That all which thou hast drawn of f — *Ode to Memory* 89
(Tho' all her f forms are types of thee, — *Isabel* 39
claiming each This meed of f. — *Œnone* 87
So shalt thou find me f. — „ 155
I promise thee The f and most loving wife in Greece,' — „ 187
F—why f wife? am I not fair? — „ 196
She was the f in the face: — *The Sisters* 2
rose the tallest of them all And f, — *M. d'Arthur* 208
beardless apple-arbiter Decided f. — *Lucretius* 92
her that is the f under heaven, — *Com. of Arthur* 86
The prize of beauty for the f there, — *Marr. of Geraint* 485
'Advance and take, as f of the fair, — „ 553
For tho' ye won the prize of f fair, And tho' I
heard him call you f fair, — „ 719
f and the best Of ladies living gave me — *Balin and Balan* 339
I, and all, As f, best and purest, — „ 350
'F I grant her: I have seen; — „ 356
rose the tallest of them all And f, — *Pass. of Arthur* 376
f of their evening stars. — *Locksley H., Sixty* 188
f flesh at last is filth on which the worm will feast; — *Happy* 30
Fairest-spoken That art the f-s tree — *Talking Oak* 263
Fair-fronted F-f Truth shall droop not now — *Clear-headed friend* 12
Fair-hair'd a loftier Annie Lee, F-h and tall, — *Enoch Arden* 749
F-h and redder than a windy morn; — *Princess, Con.* 91
came a f-h youth, that in his hand Bare — *Geraint and E.* 201
when the f-h youth came by him, said, — „ 205
Fair-hands Sir Fine-face, Sir F-h? — *Gareth and L.* 475
Fairily Made so f well With delicate spire — *Maud II ii* 5
Fairily-delicate F-d palaces shine — *The Islet* 18
Fair-maid many welcomes, February f-m, (repeat) — *The Snowdrop* 2, 10
Fairness To doubt her f were to want an eye, — *Lancelot and E.* 1376

Fairplay ask'd but space and f for her scheme; Princess v 282
Fair-spoken stranger that hath been To thee f-s?' Gareth and L. 284
Fairy (adj.) AIRY, f Lilian, Flitting, f Lilian, Lilian 1
Like a rose-leaf I will crush thee, F Lilian. „ 30
A f shield your Genius made Margaret 41
With whitest honey in f gardens cull'd— Eleänore 26
And woke her with a lay from f land. Caress'd or chidden 8
'Tis the f Lady of Shalott.' L. of Shalott i 35
heavens between their f fleeces pale Gardener's D. 261
With the f tales of science, Locksley Hall 12
And bring the fated f Prince. Day-Dm., Sleep P. 56
A f Prince, with joyful eyes, „ Arrival 7
As wild as aught of f lore; „ L'Envoi 12
From havens hid in f bowers, The Voyage 54
many a f foreland set With willow-weed The Brook 45
Show'd her the f footings on the grass, The little dells of cowslip, f palms, The petty marestail forest, f pines, Aylmer's Field 90
What look'd a flight of f arrows aim'd „ 94
And dropt a f parachute and past: Princess, Pro. 76
golden foot or a f horn Thro' his dim water-world? Maud II ii 19
Here is a city of Enchanters, built By f Kings.' Gareth and L. 200
whether this be built By magic, and by f Kings and Queens; „ 248
a F King And F Queens have built the city, „ 258
Shrunk like a f changeling lay the mage; Com. of Arthur 363
Until they vanish'd by the f well That laughs at iron— Merlin and V. 428
sharp breaths of anger puff'd Her f nostril out; „ 849
Look how she sleeps—the F Queen, so fair! Lancelot and E. 1255
we chanted the songs of the Bards and the glories of f kings; V. of Maeldune 90
The f fancies range, Early Spring 39
but now Your f Prince has found you, The Ring 69
And you were then a lover's f dream, To Mary Boyle 43
Fairy (s) The oriental f brought, Eleänore 14
'For as to fairies, that will flit Talking Oak 89
dancing of Fairies In desolate hollows, Merlin and the G. 41
Fairy-circle flickering f-c wheel'd and broke Guinevere 257
Fairy-fine Fabric rough, or f-f, Ode Inter. Exhib. 18
Fairyland (See also **Fairy**) But only changeling out of F, Gareth and L. 203
if the King be King at all, or come From F; „ 247
Or come to take the King to F? Lancelot and E. 1257
Fairy-tale (See also **Fairy**) told her f-t's, Show'd her the fairy Aylmer's Field 89
Faith (See also **Catholic Faith**) left to me, but Thou, And f in Thee? Supp. Confessions 19
How sweet to have a common f! „ 33
that knew The beauty and repose of f, „ 75
Great in f, and strong Against the grief „ 91
And simple f than Norman blood. L. C. V. de Vere 56
F from tracts no feet have trod, On a Mourner 29
settled down Upon the general decay of f The Epic 18
run My f beyond my practice into his: Edwin Morris 54
we closed, we kiss'd, swore f, „ 114
with a larger f appeal'd Than Papist unto Saint. Talking Oak 15
Wait: my f is large in Time, Love and Duty 25
So keep I fair thro' f and prayer Sir Galahad 23
I will know If there be any f in man.' 'Nay now, what f?' said Alice the nurse, Lady Clare 44
His resolve Upbore him, and firm f, Enoch Arden 800
her sweet face and f Held him from that: Aylmer's Field 392
Have f, have f! We live by f,' said he; Sea Dreams 157
why kept ye not your f? Princess v 77
their sinless f, A maiden moon that sparkles „ 185
f in womankind Beats with his blood, „ vii 328
Some sense of duty, something of a f, „ Con. 54
The sport half-science, fill me with a f, „ 76
honouring your sweet f in him, A Dedication 5
By f, and f alone, embrace, In Mem., Pro. 3
We have but f: we cannot know; „ 21
Whose f has centre everywhere, „ xxxiii 3
Her f thro' form is pure as thine, „ 9
This f has many a purer priest, „ xxxvii 3

Faith (continued) Is f as vague as all unsweet: In. Mem. xlvii 5
Be near me when my f is dry, „ l 9
Shall love be blamed for want of f? „ li 10
I stretch lame hands of f, and grope, „ lv 17
May breed with him, can fright my f. „ lxxxii 4
The f, the vigour, bold to dwell „ xcv 29
Perplext in f, but pure in deeds, „ xcvi 9
There lives more f in honest doubt, „ 11
To find a stronger f his own; „ 17
to him she sings Of early f and plighted vows; „ xcvii 30
Her f is fixt and cannot move, „ 33
What profit lies in barren f, „ cviii 5
What is she, cut from love and f, „ cxiv 11
Our dearest f; our ghastliest doubt; „ cxxiv 2
If e'er when f had fall'n asleep, „ cxxiv 9
all is well, tho' f and form Be sunder'd „ cxxvii 1
Is comrade of the lesser f „ cxxviii 3
With f that comes of self-control, „ cxxxi 9
have f in a tradesman's ware or his word? Maud I i 26
and f in their great King, Gareth and L. 330
good f, I fain had added—Knight, „ 1162
'Nay, by my f, thou shalt not,' cried Marr. of Geraint 198
a rock in ebbs and flows, Fixt on her f. „ 813
Brought the great f to Britain over seas; Balin and Balan 103
F and unfaith can ne'er be equal powers: Unfaith in aught is want of f in all. Merlin and V. 388
break f with one I may not name? Lancelot and E. 685
And f unfaithful kept him falsely true. „ 877
f once fair Was richer than these diamonds— „ 1228
heal'd at once, By f, of all his ills. Holy Grail 56
a maid, Who kept our holy f among her kin „ 697
those who love them, trials of our f. Pelleas and E. 210
all these pains are trials of my f, „ 246
'F of my body,' he said, 'and art thou not— „ 318
f have these in whom they sware to love? Last Tournament 188
here the f That made us rulers? To the Queen ii 18
fierce or careless looseners of the f, „ 52
Confined on points of f, Lover's Tale ii 150
'I have fought for Queen and F The Revenge 101
In matters of the f, alas the while! Sir J. Oldcastle 76
Lest the false f make merry over them! „ 82
'O soul of little f, slow to believe! Columbus 147
the sacred peak Of hoar high-templed F, Pref. Poem 19th Cent. 10
to the F that saves, The Wreck 3
Where you bawl'd the dark side of your f Despair 39
away from your f and your face! „ 110
cling to F beyond the forms of F! Ancient Sage 69
Bring the old dark ages back without the f, Locksley H., Sixty 137
wars and filial f, and Dido's pyre; To Virgil 4
F at her zenith, or all but lost Vastness 11
Despite of every F and Creed, To Mary Boyle 51
Whose F and Works were bells of full accord, In Mem. G. W. Ward 2
With a f as clear as the heights June Bracken, etc. 7
And mood of f may hold its own, Akbar's Dream 56
A people from their ancient fold of F, „ 61
I cull from every f and race the best „ 68
shook Those pillars of a moulder'd f, „ 81
and to spread the Divine F „ 159
darken'd with doubts of a F that saves, The Dreamer 11
Faithful (See also **Faäithful**) Lean'd on him, f, gentle, good, Two Voices 416
And shaping f record of the glance Gardener's D. 177
'O just and f knight of God! Sir Galahad 79
I, falling on his f heart, In Mem. xviii 14
Thrice blest whose lives are f prayers, „ xxxii 13
A f answer from the breast, „ lxxxv 14
She dwells on him with f eyes, „ xcvii 35
sleep Encompass'd by his f guard, „ cxxvi 8
And fair without, f within, Maud I xiii 37
She is not f to me, and I see her Weeping Marr of Geraint 117
Hath push'd aside his f wife, Balin and Balan 106
He had a f servant, one who loved His master Lover's Tale iv 256
in her you see That f servant whom we spoke about, „ 342
Thanks to the kindly dark faces who fought with us, f and few, Def. of Lucknow 70

Faithful (*continued*) Burnt too, my *f* preacher, Beverley! *Sir J. Oldcastle* 80
My noble friend, my *f* counsellor, *Akbar's Dream* 18
True we have got—*such* a *f* ally *Riflemen form!* 24
Faithfulness loving, utter *f* in love, *Gareth and L.* 554
Faithless Lest I be found as *f* in the quest *Lancelot and E.* 761
Whate'er the *f* people say. *In Mem. xcvii* 16
The *f* coldness of the times; „ *cvi* 18
Falcon (adj.) bold and free As you, my *f* Rosalind. *Rosalind* 18
Falcon (s) My frolic *f*, with bright eyes, „ 2
My bright-eyed, wild-eyed *f*, „ 6
If all the world were *f's*, what of that? *Golden Year* 38
Forgetful of the *f* and the hunt, *Marr. of Geraint* 51
given us a fair *f* which he train'd; *Merlin and V.* 96
unhooded casting off The goodly *f* free; „ 131
No surer than our *f* yesterday, *Lancelot and E.* 656
beauty lured that *f* from his eyry on the fell, *Happy* 59
Falcon (name of ship) every soul from the decks of The *F* but one; *The Wreck* 109
Falcon-eyed quick brunette, well-moulded, *f-e*, *Princess ii* 106
Fall (s) (*See also* **Foot-fall, Tourney-fall**) many a *f* Of diamond rillets musical, *Arabian Nights* 47
comes the check, the change, the *f*, *Two Voices* 163
Came in a sun-lit *f* of rain. *Sir L. and Q. G.* 4
Illyrian woodlands, echoing *f's* Of water, *To E. L.* 1
like the flakes In a *f* of snow, *Lucretius* 167
and the river made a *f* Out yonder: *Princess iii* 172
blossom'd branch Rapt to the horrible *f*: „ *iv* 180
They mark'd it with the red cross to the *f*, „ *vi* 41
That huddling slant in furrow-cloven *f's* „ *vii* 207
as the rapid of life Shoots to the *f*— *A Dedication* 4
These leaves that redden to the *f*; *In Mem. xi* 14
And back we come at *f* of dew. „ *Con.* 100
Here at the head of a tinkling *f*, *Maud I xxi* 6
My pride is broken: men have seen my *f*.' *Marr. of Geraint* 578
my pride Is broken down, for Enid sees my *f*!' „ 590
The drumming thunder of the huger *f* *Geraint and E.* 173
Enid heard the clashing of his *f*, „ 509
never woman yet, since man's first *f*, *Lancelot and E.* 859
hear the manner of thy fight and *f*; *Pelleas and E.* 347
bide, unfrowardly, A *f* from *him*?' „ 598
laugh'd Lightly, to think of Modred's dusty *f*, *Guinevere* 55
a *f* fro' a kiss to a kick like Saätan as fell *North. Cobbler* 57
we may happen a *f* o' snaw— *Village Wife* 21
kindly curves, with gentlest *f*, *De. Prof., Two G.* 23
Following a torrent till its myriad *f's* *Tiresias* 37
and mine was the deeper *f*; *The Wreck* 11
An' the *f* of yer foot in the dance *Tomorrow* 36
A *f* of water lull'd the noon asleep. *Romney's R.* 83
is the Demon-god Wroth at his *f*?' *St. Telemachus* 20
he, That other, prophet of their *f*, *Akbar's Dream* 82
Fall (autumn) an' I mean'd to 'a stubb'd it at *f*, *N. Farmer, O. S.* 41
we talkt o' my darter es died o' the fever at *f*: *Village Wife* 10
'ud coom at the *f* o' the year, *Owd Roä* 23
An' pigs didn't sell at *f*, *Church-warden, etc.* 5
Fall (verb) (*See also* **Fall out**) Letting the rose-leaves *f*: *Claribel* 3
Down by the poplar tall rivulets babble and *f*. *Leonine Eleg.* 4
Winds creep; dews *f* chilly; „ 7
I faint, I *f*, Men say that Thou Didst die *Supp. Confessions* 2
on his light there *f's* A shadow; „ 163
Place it, where sweetest sunlight *f's* *Ode to Memory* 85
It would *f* to the ground if you came in. *Poet's Mind* 23
And shall *f* again to ground. *Deserted House* 16
The shadow passeth when the tree shall *f*, *Love and Death* 14
my ringlets would *f* Low adown, *The Mermaid* 14
Then did my response clearer f: *Two Voices* 34
when a billow, blown against, *F's* back, „ 317
Which only to one engine bound *F's* off, „ 348
Until they *f* in trance again. „ 354
And all day long to *f* and rise *Miller's D.* 182
You seem'd to hear them climb and *f* *Palace of Art* 70
to hear the dully sound Of human footsteps *f*. „ 276
Along the cliff to *f* and pause and *f* did seem. *Lotos-Eaters* 9
There is sweet music here that softer *f's* „ *C. S.* 1
turning yellow *F's*, and floats adown the air. „ 31
Ripens and fades, and *f's*, and hath no toil, „ 37

Fall (verb) (*continued*) In silence: ripen, *f* and cease: *Lotos-Eaters* 52
thunder-drops *f* on a sleeping sea: *D. of F. Women* 122
f down and glance From tone to tone, „ 166
F into shadow, soonest lost: *To J. S.* 11
that on which it throve *F's* off, „ 16
That from Discussion's lip may *f* With Life, *Love thou thy land* 33
The goose let *f* a golden egg *The Goose* 11
Where *f's* not hail, or rain, or any snow, *M. d'Arthur* 260
'*F* down, O Simeon: thou hast suffer'd long *St. S. Stylites* 99
and oft I *f*, Maybe for months, „ 102
Once more the gate behind me *f's*; *Talking Oak* 1
And when my marriage morn may *f*, „ 285
not leap forth and *f* about thy neck, *Love and Duty* 41
The woods decay, the woods decay and *f*, *Tithonus* 1
and the shadows rise and *f*. *Locksley Hall* 80
now for me the roof-tree *f*. „ 190
Let it *f* on Locksley Hall, „ 193
I'll take the showers as they *f*, *Amphion* 101
Perfume and flowers *f* in showers, *Sir Galahad* 11
On whom their favours *f*! „ 14
Swells up, and shakes and *f's*. „ 76
F from his Ocean-lane of fire, *The Voyage* 19
And like a thunderbolt he *f's*. *The Eagle* 6
A footstep seem'd to *f* beside her path, *Enoch Arden* 514
F back upon a name! rest, rot in that! *Aylmer's Field* 385
heads of chiefs and princes *f* so fast, „ 763
as *f's* A creeper when the prop is broken, „ 809
and seem'd Always about to *f*, „ 822
his own head Began to droop, to *f*; „ 835
'Set them up! they shall not *f*!' *Sea Dreams* 227
ever *f's* the least white star of snow, *Lucretius* 107
She heard him raging, heard him *f*; „ 276
come to fight with shadows and to *f*. *Princess i* 10
but prepare: I speak; it *f's*.' „ *ii* 224
the gracious dews Began to glisten and to *f*: „ 317
The splendour *f's* on castle walls „ *iv* 1
Fly to her, and *f* upon her gilded eaves, „ 94
Bred will in me to overcome it or *f*. „ *v* 351
one should fight with shadows and should *f*; „ 476
Yea, let her see me *f*! „ 517
tho' he trip and *f* He shall not blind his soul „ *vii* 330
Mourning when their leaders *f*, *Ode on Well.* 5
float or *f*, in endless ebb and flow; *W. to Marie Alex.* 27
I roar and rave for I *f*. *Voice and the P.* 12
F, and follow their doom. „ 20
Bloodily, bloodily *f* the battle-axe, *Boädicea* 56
she felt the heart within her *f* „ 81
I *f* unawares before the people, *Hendecasyllabics* 7
Her place is empty, *f* like these; *In Mem xiii* 4
When fill'd with tears that cannot *f*, „ *xix* 11
My deeper anguish also *f's*, „ 15
If such a dreamy touch should *f*, „ *xliv* 13
should *f* Remerging in the general Soul, „ *xlvii* 3
Be near us when we climb or *f*: „ *li* 13
I can but trust that good shall *f* „ *liv* 14
As drop by drop the water *f's* „ *lviii* 3
When on my bed the moonlight *f's*, „ *lxvii* 1
Till on mine ear this message *f's*, „ *lxxxv* 18
And lightly does the whisper *f*; „ 89
And strangely *f's* our Christmas-eve. „ *cv* 4
A shade *f's* on us like the dark From little cloudlets „ *Con.* 93
And breaking let the splendour *f* „ 119
Shall I weep if a Poland *f*? *Maud I iv* 46
and *f* before Her feet on the meadow grass, „ *v* 25
For I heard your rivulet *f* „ *xxii* 36
the heavens *f* in a gentle rain, „ *II i* 41
a dewy splendour *f's* On the little flower „ *iv* 32
Then I rise, the eavedrops *f*, „ 62
and watch'd the great sea *f*, Wave after wave, *Com. of Arthur* 378
f battleaxe upon helm, *F* battleaxe, „ 486
See that he *f* not on thee suddenly, *Gareth and L.* 921
'Lo,' said Gareth, 'the foe *f's*!' „ 1317
And if I *f* her name will yet remain *Marr. of Geraint* 500
While slowly falling as a scale that *f's*, „ 525
Made her cheek burn and either eyelid *f*, „ 775
Before he turn to *f* seaward again, *Geraint and E.* 117

Fall (verb) (*continued*) Wait here, and when he passes *f* upon him.' *Geraint and E.* 129
And they will *f* upon him unawares. „ 134
they will *f* upon you while ye pass.' „ 145
And if I *f*, cleave to the better man.' „ 152
Made her cheek burn and either eyelid *f*. „ 434
a dreadful loss *F's* in a far land and he knows it not, „ 497
and made as if to *f* upon him. „ 776
fear not, Enid, I should *f* upon him, „ 787
see He do not *f* behind me: *Balin and Balan* 135
Deep-tranced on hers, and could not *f*: „ 278
A doom that ever poised itself to *f*, *Merlin and V.* 191
Had I for three days seen, ready to *f*. „ 296
Set up the charge ye know, to stand or *f*!' „ 703
the victim's flowers before he *f*.' *Lancelot and E.* 910
women watch Who wins, who *f's*; *Holy Grail* 35
all the light that *f's* upon the board „ 249
King himself had fears that it would *f*, „ 341
F on him all at once, And if ye slay him *Pelleas and E.* 268
'Would rather you had let them *f*,' *Last Tournament* 39
cold *F's* on the mountain in midsummer snows, „ 228
F, as the crest of some slow-arching wave, „ 462
Where *f's* not hail, or rain, or any snow, *Pass. of Arthur* 428
as anger *f's* aside And withers on the breast *Lover's Tale i* 9
Or as men know not when they *f* asleep „ 161
It *f* on its own thorns—if this be true— „ 273
my raised eyelids would not *f*, „ *i* 571
First *f's* asleep in swoon, wherefrom awaked, „ 791
faint and *f*, To *f* and die away. „ *ii* 96
nay—what was there left to *f*? *Rizpah* 9
F's? what *f's*? who knows? As the tree *f's* so must it lie. „ 12
the thunderbolt will *f* Long and loud, *The Revenge* 44
F into the hands of God, not into the hands of Spain!' „ 90
Better to *f* by the hands that they love, than to *f* *Def. of Lucknow* 53
Mark him—he *f's*! then another, „ 65
I knew we should *f* on each other, *V. of Maeldune* 104
Have heard this footstep *f*, *Tiresias* 27
Thy Thebes shall *f* and perish, „ 116
I felt one warm tear *f* upon it. „ 167
My Shelley would *f* from my hands *The Wreck* 25
She tastes the fruit before the blossom *f's*, *Ancient Sage* 75
The blackthorn-blossom fades and *f's* *The Flight* 15
thro' the tonguesters we may *f*. *Locksley H., Sixty* 130
Kingdoms and Republics *f*, „ 159
Jacob's ladder *f's* On greening grass, *Early Spring* 9
Should this old England *f* *The Fleet* 4
and at dawn *F's* on the threshold *Demeter and P.* 3
thy hands let *f* the gather'd flower, „ 9
flowers that brighten as thy footstep *f's*, „ 36
felt a gentle hand *F* on my forehead, *The Ring* 419
my strongest wish *F's* flat before your least unwillingness. *Romney's R.* 72
Thou, thou—I saw thee *f* before me, *Akbar's Dream* 185
the chuch weänt happen a *f*. *Church-warden, etc.* 10
your shadow *f's* on the grave. *Charity* 20
My prison, not my fortress, *f* away! *Doubt and Prayer* 12
The bridal garland *f's* upon the bier, *D. of the Duke of C.* 1

Fallen (*See also* **Chap-fallen, Half-fallen, New-fallen, Newly-fallen**) legend of a *f* race Alone might hint *Two Voices* 359
mournful light That broods above the *f* sun, *To J. S.* 51
To trample round my *f* head, *Come not, when* 3
Philip glancing up Beheld the dead flame of the *f* day *Enoch Arden* 441
The two remaining found a *f* stem; „ 567
To lift the woman's *f* divinity *Princess iii* 223
So those two foes above my *f* life, „ *vi* 130
O *f* nobility, that, overawed, *Third of Feb.* 35
In those *f* leaves which kept their green, *In Mem. xcv* 23
saw the chargers of the two that fell Start from their *f* lords, *Geraint and E.* 482
Arising wearily at a *f* oak, *Balin and Balan* 425
Then leapt her palfrey o'er the *f* oak, „ 587
And in the darkness o'er her *f* head, *Guinevere* 583
Or ev'n a *f* feather, vanish'd again. *Last Tournament* 372
My *f* forehead in their to and fro, *Lover's Tale i* 701

Fallen (*continued*) Were she . . . a *f* state? *The Fleet* 10
I saw the tiger in the ruin'd fane Spring from his *f* God, *Demeter and P.* 80
stem, which else had *f* quite With cluster'd flower-bells *Isabel* 35
F silver-chiming, seem'd to shake *Arabian Nights* 51
dews, that would have *f* in tears, *Miller's D.* 151
She ceased in tears, *f* from hope and trust: *D. of F. Women* 257
Had *f* in Lyonnesse about their Lord, *M. d'Arthur* 4
half has *f* and made a bridge; *Walk. to the Mail* 32
f into the dusty crypt Of darken'd forms *Will. Water* 183
The rain had *f*, the Poet arose, *Poet's Song* 1
but her face had *f* upon her hands; *Enoch Arden* 391
on her the thunders of the house Had *f* first *Aylmer's Field* 279
How low his brother's mood had *f*, „ 404
'Let them lie, for they have *f*.' *Sea Dreams* 228
And here upon a yellow eyelid *f* *Lucretius* 141
When *f* in darker ways.' *Princess v* 68
'Our enemies have *f*, have *f*: (repeat) *Princess vi* 33, 38, 43, 48
would have strown it, and are *f* themselves. *Princess vi* 42
Our enemies have *f*, but this shall grow „ 53
O *f* at length that tower of strength *Ode on Well.* 38
when she turn'd, the curse Had *f*, *In Mem. vi* 38
What words are these have *f* from me? „ *xvi* 1
And towers *f* as soon as built— „ *xxvi* 8
Had *f* into her father's grave, „ *lxxxix* 48
There has *f* a splendid tear From the passion-flower *Maud I xxii* 59
Then cried the *f*, 'Take not my life: *Gareth and L.* 973
I have not *f* so low as some would wish. *Marr. of Geraint* 129
So that I be not *f* in fight. Farewell.' „ 223
And here had *f* a great part of a tower, „ 317
now they saw their bulwark *f*, stood; *Geraint and E.* 168
creatures gently born But into bad hands *f*, „ 192
catch a loathly plume *f* from the wing *Merlin and V.* 727
Lay like a rainbow *f* upon the grass, *Lancelot and E.* 431
Where these had *f*, slowly past the barge „ 1241
apples by the brook *F*, and on the lawns. *Holy Grail* 385
Lancelot, with his heel upon the *f*, *Pelleas and E.* 580
A manner somewhat *f* from reverence— *Last Tournament* 119
And shouted and leapt down upon the *f*; „ 469
Ye twain had *f* out about the bride Of one— „ 545
wonders, what has *f* upon the realm? *Guinevere* 275
turn'd, and reel'd, and would have *f*, „ 304
Tumbling the hollow helmets of the *f*, *Pass. of Arthur* 132
for on my heart hath *f* Confusion, „ 143
Had *f* in Lyonnesse about their lord, „ 173
if she knows And dreads it we are *f*.— *To the Queen ii* 33
And *f* away from judgment. *Lover's Tale i* 103
pillars which from earth uphold Our childhood, one had *f* away, „ 221
that shock of gloom had *f* Unfelt, „ 505
and the rain Had *f* upon me, and the gilded snake „ 623
I had *f* Prone by the dashing runnel on the grass. „ *ii* 100
Anything *f* again? nay— *Rizpah* 9
and his friends that had *F* in conflict, *Batt. of Brunanburh* 71
When I had *f* from off the crag *The Flight* 22
but now to silent ashes *f* away. *Locksley H., Sixty* 41
f every purple Cæsar's dome— *To Virgil* 30
Fifty times the golden harvest *f*, *On Jub. Q. Victoria* 2
torn the ring In fright, and *f* dead. *The Ring* 471
All his leaves *F* at length, *The Oak* 12

Falling (*See also* **Fast-falling, Half-falling, Quick-falling, Slow-falling**) The jaw is *f*, The red cheek paling, *All Things will Die* 30
Long alleys *f* down to twilight grots, *Ode to Memory* 107
F into a still delight, And luxury *Eleänore* 106
The leaves upon her *f* light— *L. of Shalott iv* 21
Lo, *f* from my constant mind, *Fatima* 5
The long brook *f* thro' the clov'n ravine *Œnone* 8
watch the emerald-colour'd water *f* *Lotos-Eaters, C. S.* 96
Sound all night long, in *f* thro' the dell, *D. of F. Women* 183
content to perish, *f* on the foeman's ground, *Locksley Hall* 103
himself was deadly wounded *F* on the dead. *The Captain* 64
Rising, *f*, like a wave, *Vision of Sin* 125
Like moonlight on a *f* shower? *Margaret* 4
Just ere the *f* axe did part The burning brain „ 38

Fame (*continued*) And one—they call'd her *F*; and one,— *Gareth and L.* 113
And lost to life and use and name and *f*. (repeat) *Merlin and V.* 214, 970
such fire for *f*, Such trumpet-blowings in it, „ 417
My use and name and *f*. „ 304
Upon my life and use and name and *f*, „ 374
And into such a song, such fire for *f*, „ 417
felt them slowly ebbing, name and *f*.' „ 437
touching *f*, howe'er ye scorn my song, „ 444
For *f*, could *f* be mine, that *f* were thine, „ 447
'Man dreams of *F* while woman wakes to love.' „ 460
F, The *F* that follows death is nothing „ 463
what is *F* in life but half-disfame, „ 465
the scroll 'I follow *f*.' „ 476
this for motto, 'Rather use than *f*.' „ 480
F with men, Being but ampler means to serve „ 488
Use gave me *F* at first, and *F* again „ 493
Right well know I that *F* is half-disfame, „ 504
That other *f*, To one at least, who hath not children, „ 505
concluded in that star To make *f* nothing. „ 513
I rather dread the loss of use than *f*; „ 519
Born to the glory of thy name and *f*, *Lancelot and E.* 1372
May not your crescent fear for name and *f* „ 1400
'I am wrath and shame and hate and evil *f*, *Pelleas and E.* 568
courtliness, and the desire of *f*, *Guinevere* 482
I must not dwell on that defeat of *f*. „ 628
now much honour and much *f* were lost.' *Pass. of Arthur* 277
all the clearness of his *f* hath gone *Lover's Tale i* 789
As heir of endless *f*— *Ancient Sage* 147
patriot—soldier take His meed of *f* in verse; *Epilogue* 33
And so does Earth; for Homer's *f*, „ 58
Her ancient *f* of Free— *The Fleet* 9
honouring your fair *f* Of Statesman, *To Marq. of Dufferin* 14
F blowing out from her golden trumpet *Vastness* 21
'Take comfort you have won the Painter's *f*,' *Romney's R.* 43
What *f*? I am not Raphaël, „ 46
Wrong there! The painter's *f*? „ 48
Her sad eyes plead for my own *f* with me „ 55
thy *f* Is blown thro' all the Troad, *Death of Œnone* 36
Famed *See* **Far-famed, First-famed**
Fame-lit Bard whose *f-l* laurels glance *To Victor Hugo* 4
Familiar And pace the sacred old *f* fields, *Enoch Arden* 625
like bright eyes of *f* friends, *Holy Grail* 688
till the things *f* to her youth Had made a silent answer: *Lover's Tale iv* 95
Surely his King and most *f* friend *Lancelot and E.* 592
whence the Royal mind, *f* with her, *Princess iv* 235
bones were blest Among *f* names to rest *In Mem. xviii* 7
grow *F* to the stranger's child; „ *ci* 20
F up from cradle-time, so wan, *Balin and Balan* 591
Familiarity Such dear *familiarities* of dawn? *Aylmer's Field* 131
Family the *f* tree Sprang from the midriff of a prostrate king— „ 15
A fiery *f* passion for the name Of Lancelot, *Lancelot and E.* 477
Famine Blight and *f*, plague and earthquake, *Lotos-Eaters, C. S.* 115
A *f* after laid them low, *The Victim* 2
'Help us from *f* And plague and strife! „ 9
And blight and *f* on all the lea: „ 46
shipwrecks, *f's*, fevers, fights, Mutinies, *Columbus* 225
when I spake of *f*, plague, Shrine-shattering earthquake, *Tiresias* 60
to stay, Not spread the plague, the *f*; *Demeter and P.* 134
earthquake, or the *f*, or the pest! *Faith* 4
Famishing *f* populace, wharves forlorn; *Vastness* 14
Famous Plenty corrupts the melody That made thee *f* once, *Blackbird* 16
fellowship of *f* knights Whereof this world holds record. *M. d'Arthur* 15
Thy *f* brother-oak. *Talking Oak* 296
That many a *f* man and woman, *Princess iv* 445
Thine island loves thee well, thou *f* man, *Ode on Well.* 85
rather proven in his Paynim wars Than *f* jousts; *Balin and Balan* 39
the most *f* man of all those times, *Merlin and V.* 166
lance had beaten down the knights, So many and *f* names; *Holy Grail* 364
I will make thee with my spear and sword As *f*— *Pelleas and E.* 46

Famous (*continued*) fellowship of *f* knights Whereof this world holds record. *Pass. of Arthur* 183
And mingled with the *f* kings of old, *Tiresias* 171
Fan (s) To spread into the perfect *f*, *Sir L. and Q. G.* 17
toys in lava, *f's* Of sandal, amber, *Princess, Pro.* 18
Fan (verb) A soft air *f's* the cloud apart; *Tithonus* 32
f my brows and blow The fever from my cheek, *In Mem. lxxxvi* 8
Fancied (*See also* **Ever-fancied**) I had *f* it would be fair. *Maud I vi* 6
she *f* 'Is it for me?' *Lancelot and E.* 822
I *f* that my friend For this brief idyll *Tiresias* 187
In impotence of *f* power. *A Character* 24
Beneath all *f* hopes and fears Ay me, *In Mem. xlix* 13
And then was painting on it *f* arms, *Merlin and V.* 474
Fancy (s) And a *f* as summer-new As the green *June Bracken, etc.* 8
Would that my gloomed *f* were As thine, *Supp. Confessions* 68
With youthful *f* re-inspired, *Ode to Memory* 114
F came and at her pillow sat, *Caress'd or chidden* 5
F watches in the wilderness, Poor *F* sadder than a single star, „ 12
My *f* made me for a moment blest *The form, the form* 6
my life with *f* play'd Before I dream'd *Miller's D.* 45
I thought that it was *f*, and I listen'd *May Queen, Con.* 33
those sharp *fancies*, by down-lapsing thought *D. of F. Women* 49
And if I said that *F*, led by Love, *Gardener's D.* 59
In the Spring a young man's *f* lightly turns *Locksley Hall* 20
Falser than all *f* fathoms, „ 41
Soothe him with thy finer *fancies*, „ 54
I have but an angry *f*: „ 102
Fool, again the dream, the *f*! „ 173
founts of inspiration well thro' all my *f* yet. „ 188
Across my *f*, brooding warm, *Day-Dm., Pro.* 10
So much your eyes my *f* take— „ *L'Envoi* 26
My *f*, ranging thro' and thro', „ 34
But whither would my *f* go? *Will Water.* 145
she gleam'd Like *F* made of golden air, *The Voyage* 66
Set thy hoary *fancies* free; *Vision of Sin* 156
evil *fancies* clung Like serpent eggs together, *Enoch Arden* 479
His *f* fled before the lazy wind Returning, „ 657
Prattling the primrose *fancies* of the boy, *The Brook* 19
But Edith's eager *f* hurried with him *Aylmer's Field* 208
many a summer still Clung to their *fancies*) *Sea Dreams* 36
drifting up the stream In *f*, till I slept again, „ 109
maiden *fancies*; loved to live alone *Princess i* 49
crush her pretty maiden *fancies* dead „ 88
What were those *fancies*? „ 95
fair philosophies That lift the *f*; „ *iii* 341
sweet as those by hopeless *f* feign'd „ *iv* 55
thine are *fancies* hatch'd In silken-folded „ 66
Which melted Florian's *f* as she hung, „ 370
Thy face across his *f* comes, „ 579
understanding all the foolish work Of *F*, „ *vi* 117
fancies like the vermin in a nut Have fretted „ 263
Lay your earthly *fancies* down, *Ode on Well.* 279
My *f* fled to the South again. *The Daisy* 108
flatters thus Our home-bred *fancies*: *In Mem. x* 11
My *fancies* time to rise on wing, „ *xiii* 17
And but for *fancies*, which aver „ *xv* 9
delirious man Whose *f* fuses old and new, „ *xvi* 18
And *F* light from *F* caught, „ *xxiii* 14
I vex my heart with *fancies* dim: „ *xlii* 1
The *f's* tenderest eddy wreathe, „ *xlix* 6
And dare we to this *f* give, „ *liii* 5
I lull a *f* trouble-tost „ *lxv* 2
You wonder when my *fancies* play „ *lxvi* 2
Take wings of *f*, and ascend, „ *lxxvi* 1
Then *f* shapes, as *f* can, The grief my loss „ *lxxx* 5
backward *f*, wherefore wake The old bitterness again, „ *lxxxiv* 46
Ill brethren, let the *f* fly. „ *lxxxvi* 12
Or villain *f* fleeting by, „ *cxi* 18
And all the breeze of *F* blows, „ *cxxii* 17
It circles round, and *f* plays, „ *Con.* 81
The *f* flatter'd my mind, *Maud I xiv* 23
dreamful wastes where footless *fancies* dwell „ *xviii* 69
these be for the snare (So runs thy *f*) *Gareth and L.* 1082
Then let her *f* flit across the past, *Marr. of Geraint* 645

Fancy (s) (*continued*) Her *f* dwelling in this dusky hall; *Marr. of Geraint* 802
And sweet self-pity, or the *f* of it, *Geraint and E.* 349
fabler, these be *fancies* of the churl, *Balin and Balan* 307
mood as that, which lately gloom'd Your *f* *Merlin and V.* 326
So fixt her *f* on him: let them be. „ 777
what was once to me Mere matter of the *f*, „ 924
To snare her royal *f* with a boon *Lancelot and E.* 71
Rapt in this *f* of his Table Round, „ 129
Full often lost in *f*, lost his way; „ 164
that ghostly grace Beam'd on his *f*, „ 886
Her *fancies* with the sallow-rifted glooms „ 1002
'ye never yet Denied my *fancies*— „ 1112
Not for me! For her! for your new *f*. „ 1216
men Shape to their *f's* eye from broken rocks „ 1252
Give me three days to melt her *f*, *Pelleas and E.* 356
her ever-veering *f* turn'd To Pelleas, „ 493
Appearing, sent his *f* back to where *Last Tournament* 380
push me even In *f* from thy side, „ 639
Made all our tastes and *fancies* like, *Lover's Tale i* 242
graceful thought of hers Grav'n on my *f*! „ 358
Ye cannot shape *F* so fair as in this memory. „ 548
thronging *fancies* come To boys and girls „ 554
Ringing within the *f* had updrawn A fashion „ 645
Flatter'd the *f* of my fading brain; „ *ii* 107
The *f* stirr'd him so He rose and went, „ *iv* 51
the sudden wail his lady made Dwelt in his *f*: „ 150
And idle *fancies* flutter me, *The Flight* 74
Set the maiden *fancies* wallowing *Locksley H., Sixty* 145
All the chosen coin of *f* flashing out *To Virgil* 7
The fairy *fancies* range, *Early Spring* 39
till I believing that the girl's Lean *f*, *The Ring* 336
For one monotonous *f* madden'd her, „ 404
But chaining *f* now at home *To Ulysses* 31
Fancy (verb) I *f* her sweetness only due To the sweeter blood *Maud I xiii* 33
What thing soever ye may hear, or see, Or *f* *Geraint and E.* 416
Hope! O yes, I hope, or *f* that, *Romney's R.* 158
Fancy-borne Or *f-b* perhaps upon the rise *Lucretius* 10
Fancy-fed And pining life be *f-f*. *In Mem. lxxxv* 96
Fancy-flies we that love the mud, Rising to no *f-f*. *Vision of Sin* 102
Fancying *f* that her glory would be great *Merlin and V.* 217
Fane translucent *f* Of her still spirit; *Isabel* 4
hopes and hates, his homes and *f's*, *Lucretius* 255
wise humility As befits a solemn *f*: *Ode on Well.* 250
Who built him *f's* of fruitless prayer, *In Mem. lvi* 12
And heard once more in college *f's* „ *lxxxvii* 5
I saw the tiger in the ruin'd *f* *Demeter and P.* 79
an old *f* No longer sacred to the Sun, *St. Telemachus* 6
anchorite Would haunt the desolated *f*, „ 12
stone by stone, I rear'd a sacred *f*, *Akbar's Dream* 177
Fang the *f's* Shall move the stony bases *Princess vi* 57
Fann'd sudden flame, By veering passion *f*, *Madeline* 29
Thy bounteous forehead was not *f* *Eleänore* 9
A summer *f* with spice. *Palace of Art* 116
Low breezes *f* the belfry bars, *The Letters* 43
river-breeze, Which *f* the gardens of that rival rose *Aylmer's Field* 455
The woods with living airs How softly *f*, *Early Spring* 20
Fantastic overhead *F* gables, crowding, stared: *Godiva* 61
That lute and flute *f* tenderness, *Princess iv* 129
long *f* night With all its doings „ 565
round of green, this orb of flame, *F* beauty; *In Mem. xxxiv* 6
spreading made *F* plume or sable pine; *The Voyage* 44
Fantastical So *f* is the dainty metre. *Hendecasyllabics* 14
Albeit I know my knights *f*, *Lancelot and E.* 594
Fantasy Her gay-furr'd cats a painted *f*, *Princess iii* 186
Proud in their *f* call themselves the Day, *Gareth and L.* 633
Or whether it be the maiden's *f*, „ 874
A border *f* of branch and flower, *Lancelot and E.* 11
And saved him: so she lived in *f*. „ 27
There kept it, and so lived in *f*. „ 398
death Was rather in the *f* than the blood. „ 1132
Let be thy fair Queen's *f*. *Last Tournament* 197
Or prophets of them in his *f*, *Lover's Tale iv* 12
Far Thoro' the black-stemm'd pines only the *f* river shines. *Leonine Eleg.* 2
Far (*continued*) Sadly the *f* kine loweth: *Leonine Eleg.* 9
overtakes *F* thought with music that it makes: *Two Voices* 438
Going before to some *f* shrine, *On a Mourner* 17
I cannot sink So *f*—*f* down, *My life is full* 9
And fixt upon the *f* sea-line; *The Voyage* 62
Down at the *f* end of an avenue, *Enoch Arden* 358
phrases of the hearth, And *f* allusion, *Princess ii* 316
O sweet and *f* from cliff and scar „ *iv* 9
and died Of fright in *f* apartments. „ *vi* 371
Thro' the long gorge to the *f* light *Ode on Well.* 213
'*F* and *f* away,' said the dainty little maiden, (repeat) *City Child* 3, 8
He seems so near and yet so *f*, *In Mem. xcvii* 23
Falls in a *f* land and he knows it not, *Geraint and E.* 497
my blood Hath earnest in it of *f* springs *Merlin and V.* 557
His own *f* blood, which dwelt at Camelot; *Lancelot and E.* 803
flame At sunrise till the people in *f* fields, *Holy Grail* 243
loyal to their crown Are loyal to their own *f* sons, *To the Queen ii* 28
Fierce in the strength of *f* descent, *Lover's Tale i* 382
Then at the *f* end of the vault he saw His lady „ *iv* 56
On one *f* height in one far-shining fire, *Tiresias* 185
Some *f* blue fell, *Early Spring* 34
Watch'd my *f* meadow zoned with airy morn; *Prog. of Spring* 69
Desolate sweetness—*f* and *f* away— *Ancient Sage* 226
Far-blazing *F-b* from the rear of Philip's house, *Enoch Arden* 727
Far-brought love *f-b* From out the storied Past, *Love thou thy land* 1
Farce 'Ah fool, and made myself a Queen of *f*! *Princess vii* 243
For by and by she sicken'd of the *f*, *The Ring* 383
Fare (s) Friday *f* was Enoch's ministering. *Enoch Arden* 100
With store of rich apparel, sumptuous *f*, *Marr. of Geraint* 709
My lord, eat also, tho' the *f* is coarse, *Geraint and E.* 208
And serve thee costlier than with mowers' *f*.' Then said Geraint, 'I wish no better *f*: „ 231
That Lenten *f* makes Lenten thought, *To E. Fitzgerald* 31
Fare (verb) So *f's* it since the years began, *Will Water.* 169
F's richly, in fine linen, not a hair *Aylmer's Field* 659
Thy duty? What is duty? *F* thee well!' *Lucretius* 281
O heart, how *f's* it with thee now, *In Mem. iv* 5
How *f's* it with the happy dead? „ *xliv* 1
bring us where he is, and how he *f's*, *Lancelot and E.* 547
F you well A thousand times!— „ 695
How *f's* my lord Sir Lancelot?' „ 795
Fared so *f* she gazing there; *Princess vii* 41
Whereon with equal feet we *f*; *In Mem. xxv* 2
So *f* it with Geraint, who thought and said, *Marr. of Geraint* 343
So *f* it with Geraint, (repeat) *Geraint and E.* 8, 500
Then *f* it with Sir Pelleas as with one *Pelleas and E.* 528
Far-end When Molly cooms in fro' the *f-e* close *Spinster's S's.* 2
Farewell Ye merry souls, *f*. *All Things will Die* 36
But now *f*. I am going a long way With these thou seëst— *M. d'Arthur* 256
might I tell of meetings, of *f's*— *Gardener's D.* 251
F, like endless welcome, lived and died. *Love and Duty* 68
a long *f* to Locksley Hall! *Locksley Hall* 189
Enoch faced this morning of *f* Brightly *Enoch Arden* 182
she said: '*f*, Sir—and to you. *Princess ii* 235
he reach'd White hands of *f* to my sire, „ *v* 233
The wrath I nursed against the world: *f*.' „ 437
Pledge of a love not to be mine, *f*; „ *vi* 197
few words and pithy, such as closed Welcome, *f*, „ *Con.* 95
landing-place, to clasp and say '*F*! *In Mem. xlvii* 16
In those sad words I took *f*: „ *lviii* 1
I cannot think the thing *f*. „ *cxxiii* 12
F, we kiss, and they are gone. „ *Con.* 92
own heart's heart, my ownest own, *f*; *Maud I xviii* 74
Thy shield is mine—*f*; *Gareth and L.* 988
So that I be not fall'n in fight. *F*.' '*F*, fair Prince,' answer'd the stately Queen. *Marr. of Geraint* 223
narrow court and lubber King, *f*! *Merlin and V.* 119
F; think gently of me, for I fear My fate or folly, „ 926
She needs must bid *f* to sweet Lavaine. *Lancelot and E.* 341
A thousand times!—a thousand times *f*! „ 696
Nor bad *f*, but sadly rode away. „ 987
Gawain, who bad a thousand *f's* to me, „ 1056
'Sister, *f* for ever,' and again '*F*, „ 1151

Farewell (*continued*) Come, for you left me taking no *f*,
Hither, to take my last *f* of you. *Lancelot and E.* 1274
I left her and I bad her no *f*; " 1304
F too—now at last—*F*, fair lily. " 1396
Than to be loved again of you—*f*; *Pelleas and E.* 302
It was their last hour, A madness of *f's*. *Guinevere* 103
Nay, friend, for we have taken our *f's*. " 117
see thee no more—*F*!' " 580
F? I should have answer'd his *f*. " 615
F! there is an isle of rest for thee. *Pass. of Arthur* 35
But now *f*. I am going a long way With these thou seëst— " 424
And bad them to a banquet of *f's*. *Lover's Tale iv* 186
We bad them no *f*, but mounting these He past " 386
She remembers you. *F*. *Sisters (E. and E.)* 190
thinks She sees you when she hears. Again *f*.' " 193
'Pray come and see my mother, and *f*.' " 196
for ever and ever, for ever and ever *f*,' *Despair* 58
a whisper—some divine *f*— *Ancient Sage* 225
Strike on the Mount of Vision! So, *f*. " 286
F, Macready, since to-night we part; *To W. C. Macready* 1
F, Macready, since this night we part; " 5
F, Macready; moral, grave, sublime; " 12
Not there to bid my boy *f*, *To Marq. of Dufferin* 42
if so, Bid him *f* for me, *Romney's R.* 147
F, whose living like I shall not find, *In Mem. W. G. Ward* 1
F!—You will not speak, my friends, *The Wanderer* 3
deem me grateful, and *f*! " 16
And may there be no sadness of *f*, *Crossing the Bar* 11

Far-famed *F-f* for well-won enterprise, *Kate* 22
Far-fleeted *F-f* by the purple island-sides, *Princess vii* 166
Far-folded *F-f* mists, and gleaming halls of morn. *Tithonus* 10
Far-heard *F-h* beneath the moon. *D. of F. Women* 184

Farm (*See also* **Crown-farm**) red cock crows from the *f* upon the hill, *May Queen, N. Y's. E.* 23
WITH farmer Allan at the *f* abode *Dora* 1
and set out, and reach'd the *f*. " 129
discuss'd the *f*, The four-field system, *Audley Court* 33
Till last by Philip's *f* I flow *The Brook* 31
Philip's *f* where brook and river meet. " 38
and call'd old Philip out To show the *f*: " 121
how he sent the bailiff to the *f* To learn " 141
He found the bailiff riding by the *f*, " 153
ask'd her 'Are you from the *f*?' " 209
We bought the *f* we tenanted before. " 222
closed her access to the wealthier *f's*, *Aylmer's Field* 503
princely halls, and *f's*, and flowing lawns, " 654
the broad woodland parcell'd into *f's*; " 847
Willy had not been down to the *f* *Grandmother* 33
there past by the gate of the *f*, Willy,— " 41
sitting at home in my father's *f* at eve: " 90
Feyther run oop to the *f*, *N. Farmer, N. S.* 54
And crowded *f's* and lessening towers, *In Mem. xi* 11
To leave the pleasant fields and *f's*; " *cii* 22
had need Of a good stout lad at his *f*; *First Quarrel* 18
Harry was bound to the Dorsetshire *f* " 19
that workt with him up at the *f*, " 24
they does it at Willis's *f*, *Village Wife* 119
An' 'cos o' thy *f* by the beck, *Spinster's S's.* 73
Ev'n the homely *f* can teach us *Locksley H., Sixty* 26
Fur the gell o' the *f* 'at slep wi' tha *Owd Roä* 51
Moother 'ed beän a-naggin' about the gell o' the *f*, " 69
mine the hall, the *f*, the field; *The Ring* 169
on waste and wood, On *f* and field: *Prog. of Spring* 23
How be the *f* gittin on? noäways. *Church-warden, etc.* 3
war dashing down upon cities and blazing *f's*, *The Dawn* 8

Farmer WITH *f* Allan at the farm abode *Dora* 1
Far off the *f* came into the field And spied her not; " 74
when the *f* pass'd into the field He spied her, " 85
Francis Hale, The *f's* son, who lived across the bay, *Audley Court* 75
The *f* vext packs up his beds and chairs, *Walk. to the Mail* 39
robb'd the *f* of his bowl of cream: *Princess v* 223
There was a *f* in Dorset of Harry's kin, *First Quarrel* 17
'The *f* dared me to do it,' he said; *Rizpah* 26
Howiver was British *f's* to stan' ageän *Owd Roä* 46

Farmin' An' thy *f'* es cleän es thysen,' *Spinster's S's.* 77
Farmstead he, by *f*, thorpe and spire, *Will Water.* 137

Far-off And the *f-o* stream is dumb, *The Owl i* 3
F-o the torrent call'd me from the cleft: *Œnone* 54
I dimly see My *f-o* doubtful purpose, " 251
In those *f-o* seven happy years were born; *Enoch Arden* 686
her *f-o* cousin and betrothed, *The Brook* 75
sorcerer, whom a *f-o* grandsire burnt *Princess i* 6
to catch The *f-o* interest of tears? *In Mem. i* 8
The brook alone *f-o* was heard, " *xcv* 7
And one *f-o* divine event, " *Con.* 143
the *f-o* sail is blown by the breeze *Maud I iv* 4
some *f-o* touch Of greatness to know *Lancelot and E.* 450
The storm, you hear *F-o*, is Muriel— *The Ring* 139
Only to hear and see the *f-o* sparkling brine, *Lotos-Eaters, C. S.* 98
In days *f-o*, on that dark earth, be true? *Tithonus* 48
deep Down upon *f-o* cities while they dance— *Merlin and V.* 114
from him flits to warn A *f-o* friendship *Demeter and P.* 90
For have the *f-o* hymns of May, *To Master of B.* 10

Farran'd (fashioned) *See* Owd-farran'd
Far-renowned *f-r* brides of ancient song *D. of F. Women* 17
Far-rolling Seem'd those *f-r*, westward-smiling seas, *Last Tournament* 587
Far-seen Amid thy melancholy mates *f-s*, *Lover's Tale i* 489
Far-shadowing half in light, and half *F-s* *Princess, Con.* 42
Far-shining On one far height in one *f-s* fire. *Tiresias* 185
'One height and one *f-s* fire' " 186
Far-sighted *F-s* summoner of War and Waste *Ded. of Idylls* 37
Far-sounded Geraint, a name *f-s* among men *Marr. of Geraint* 427
Farther With *f* lookings on. *Miller's D.* 231
Farthest But from my *f* lapse, my latest ebb, *Lover's Tale i* 90
Far-welter'd (overthrown) Woorse nor a *f-w* yowe: *N. Farmer, N. S.* 32

Fashion (s) After the *f* of the time, *Arabian Nights* 119
Looks freshest in the *f* of the day: *The Epic* 32
I know your sex, From the *f* of your bones. *Vision of Sin* 182
In sailor *f* roughly sermonizing *Enoch Arden* 204
Fire-hollowing this in Indian *f*, " 569
No more in soldier *f* will he greet *Ode on Well.* 21
veil His want in forms for *f's* sake, *In Mem. cxi* 6
What the *f* of the men?' 'They be of foolish *f*, O Sir King, The *f* of that old knight-errantry *Gareth and L.* 627
and sumptuously According to his *f*, *Geraint and E.* 285
In any knightly *f* for her sake. *Lancelot and E.* 871
Knowest thou not the *f* of our speech? *Pelleas and E.* 100
had updrawn A *f* and a phantasm of the form *Lover's Tale i* 645
In some such *f* as a man may be *Sisters (E. and E.)* 133

Fashion (verb) skill To strive, to *f*, to fulfil— *In Mem. cxiii* 7

Fashion'd (*See also* **Altar-fashion'd, Cleaner-fashion'd, Noblier-fashion'd, Owd-farran'd**) holy hand hath *f* on the rock *Gareth and L.* 1197
f for it A case of silk, and braided *Lancelot and E.* 7
F by Merlin ere he past away, *Holy Grail* 168
brooks Are *f* by the channel which they keep), *Lover's Tale i* 567
a people have *f* and worship a Spirit *Kapiolani* 1
F after certain laws; *Poets and Critics* 5

Fast (adj.) my friend was he, Once my *f* friend: *Sir J. Oldcastle* 62
By changes all too fierce and *f* *Freedom* 22

Fast (s) all the passion of a twelve hours' *f*.' *Marr. of Geraint* 306
heard mass, broke *f*, and rode away: *Lancelot and E.* 415
life of prayer, Praise, *f* and alms; *Holy Grail* 5
She gave herself, to *f*, and alms. " 77
about him everywhere, despite All *f* and penance. " 631
Fast with your *f's*, not feasting *Guinevere* 678
Penance?' '*F*, Hairshirt and scourge— *Sir J. Oldcastle* 141

Fast (adv.) Two lives bound *f* in one *Circumstance* 5
And I believe, if you were *f* my wife, *Enoch Arden* 414
We must bind And keep you *f*, my Rosalind, *F*, *f*, my wild-eyed Rosalind, *Rosalind* 43
We'll bind you *f* in silken cords, " 49
'Lead, and I follow,' and *f* away she fled. (repeat) *Gareth and L.* 760, 990

Fast (verb) If it may be, *f* Whole Lents, *St. S. Stylites* 181
bear his armour? shall we *f*, or dine? *Geraint and E.* 490
brother, *f* thou too and pray, And tell thy brother knights to *f* and pray, *Holy Grail* 125

Father (s) (*continued*) O F, touch the east, and light — In Mem. xxx 31
And doubtful joys the f move, — „ xl 9
How many a f have I seen, — „ liii 1
star Had fall'n into her f's grave, — „ lxxxix 48
f's bend Above more graves, — „ xcviii 15
Our f's dust is left alone And silent — „ cv 5
But crying, knows his f near; — „ cxxiv 20
O f! O God! was it well?— — Maud I i 6
raging alone as my f raged in his mood? — „ 53
sweet purse-mouth when my f dangled the grapes, — „ 71
When have I bow'd to her f, — „ iv 13
Your f has wealth well-gotten, — „ 18
Your f is ever in London, — „ 59
Why sits he here in his f's chair? — „ xiii 23
Not touch on her f's sin: — „ xix 17
That Maud's dark f and mine Had bound — „ 37
Mine, mine—our f's have sworn. — „ 43
Thou noble F of her Kings to be, — Ded. of Idylls 34
'Her f said That there between the man — Com. of Arthur 78
we that fight for our fair f Christ, — „ 510
thy f Lot beside the hearth Lies like a log, — Gareth and L. 74
Thy f, Uther, reft From my dead lord — „ 334
who from the wrongs his f did Would shape — „ 347
Affirming that his f left him gold, — Marr. of Geraint 451
I thought, but that your f came between, — Geraint and E. 314
And loved me serving in my f's hall: — „ 699
I should have slain your f, seized yourself. — „ 838
My f hath begotten me in his wrath. — Balin and Balan 283
My f died in battle against the King, — Merlin and V. 42
My f died in battle for thy King, — „ 72
Leaving her household and good f, — Lancelot and E. 14
Here laugh'd the f saying 'Fie,' — „ 200
Nay, f, nay good f, shame me not — „ 207
But, f, give me leave, an if he will, — „ 219
Crept to her f, while he mused alone, — „ 748
'F, you call me wilful, and the fault Is yours — „ 750
Sweet f, will you let me lose my wits?' — „ 752
Sweet f, I behold him in my dreams — „ 763
My f, to be sweet and serviceable — „ 767
Then her f nodding said, 'Ay, ay, — „ 770
Her f's latest word humm'd in her ear, — „ 780
brother's love, And your good f's kindness.' — „ 945
her f: 'Ay, a flash, I fear me, — „ 970
Then came her f, saying in low tones, — „ 994
call'd The f, and all three in hurry — „ 1024
So dwelt the f on her face, and thought — „ 1030
'Peace,' said her f, 'O my child, — „ 1062
'Highest?' the f answer'd, echoing 'highest?' — „ 1078
'Sweet f, all too faint and sick am I — „ 1086
so let me pass, My f, howsoe'er I seem to you, — „ 1092
wherefore cease, Sweet f, and bid call — „ 1099
sweet f, tender and true, Deny me not,' — „ 1110
She ceased: her f promised; — „ 1130
Her f laid the letter in her hand, — „ 1134
in testimony, Her brethren, and her f, — „ 1300
'O F!' ask'd the maiden, — Holy Grail 95
A slender page about her f's hall, — „ 581
Fought in her f's battles? wounded — Last Tournament 592
So said my f, and himself was knight — Guinevere 234
So said my f—yea, and furthermore, — „ 250
Not even thy wise f with his signs — „ 274
one, a bard; of whom my f said, — „ 277
So said my f—and that night the bard — „ 285
and the tales Which my good f told me, check me too
Nor let me shame my f's memory, — „ 317
And so thou lean on our fair f Christ, — „ 562
Before he saw my day my f died, — Lover's Tale i 191
She was motherless And I without a f. — „ 219
what use To know her f left us just before — „ 293
that same nearness Were f to this distance, — „ ii 29
His other f you! Kiss him, — „ iv 174
he sent, an' the f agreed; — First Quarrel 18
You count the f of your fortune, — Sisters (E. and E.) 28
My f with a child on either knee, — „ 54
he had stricken my f dead— — V. of Maeldune 1

Father (s) (*continued*) slain my f the day before I was born. — V. of Maeldune 8
I bad them remember my f's death, — „ 70
His f's have slain thy f's in war or in single strife, Thy f's have slain his f's, each taken a life for a life, Thy f had slain his f, — „ 121
The man that had slain my f. — „ 128
trembling f's call'd The God's own son — Tiresias 16
my F's belong'd to the church of old, — The Wreck 1
the heart of the f will care for his own.' — „ 98
'The heart of the f will spurn her,' — „ 99
one son had forged on his f and fled, — Despair 69
Some say, the Light was f of the Night, And some, the Night was f of the Light, — Ancient Sage 247
This f pays his debt with me, — The Flight 20
What f, this or mine, was he, — „ 21
I loved him then; he *was* my f then. No f now, the tyrant vassal of a tyrant vice! — „ 24
My f's madness makes me mad— — „ 59
And tho' these f's will not hear, — „ 67
who? who? my f sleeps! — „ 69
she knew this f well; — „ 87
f, mother,—be content, — Locksley H., Sixty 25
Gone our sailor son thy f, — „ 55
constancy Which has made your f's great — Open I. and C. Exhib. 15
Shall we sin our f's sin, — „ 24
why The sons before the f's die, — To Marq. of Dufferin 47
No! f, Spain, but Hubert brings me home — The Ring 59
F's fault Visited on the children! — „ 175
you, poor desolate F, and poor me, — „ 303
'F and Mother will watch you grow'—(repeat) — Romney's R. 104, 106
and the murderous f at rest, . . . — Bandit's Death 33
As we surpass our f's skill, — Mechanophilus 21
My F, and my Brother, and my God! — Doubt and Prayer 8

Father (verb) in the round of time Still f Truth? — Love and Duty 5
Father'd *See* **Re-father'd**
Father-fool Thwarted by one of these old f-f's, — Aylmer's Field 390
Father-grape f-g grew fat On Lusitanian summers. — Will Water. 7
Fatherhood twelve sweet moons confused his f.' — Merlin and V. 712
Fatherland sweet it was to dream of F, — Lotos-Eaters 39
Fatherless this earth is a f Hell— — Despair 57
Fatherlike Appraised his weight and fondled f, — Enoch Arden 154
Fathom For thou canst not f it. — Poet's Mind 4
Falser than all fancy f's, — Locksley Hall 41
Philip did not f Annie's mind: — Enoch Arden 344
'Tis hard for thee to f this; — In Mem. lxxxv 90
dangled a hundred f of grapes, — V. of Maeldune 56
Fathom-deep Should gulf him f-d in brine; — In Mem. x 18
Fathom'd Which none have f. — Lover's Tale i 518
Fathomless half-attain'd futurity, Tho' deep not f, — Ode to Memory 34
Fatling reach its f innocent arms And lazy lingering fingers. — Princess vi 138
Fatten many streams to f lower lands, — Golden Year 34
Fatter he was f than his cure. — Edwin Morris 15
No, there is f game on the moor; — Maud I i 74
Fault *tho' the* f's *were thick as dust* — To the Queen 18
'Proclaim the f's he would not show: — You might have won 17
Nor mine the f, if losing both of these — Aylmer's Field 719
gentleman of broken means (His father's f) — Princess i 54
'My f' she wept 'my f! and yet not mine; — „ iii 30
The child is hers—for every little f, — „ v 87
her one f The tenderness, not yours, — „ vi 185
as dearer thou for f's Lived over: — „ vii 347
Not ours the f if we have feeble hosts— — Third of Feb. 38
Or seeming-genial venial f, — Will 13
let it be granted her: where is the f? — Maud I ii 4
blind To the f's of his heart and mind, — „ xix 68
'The f was mine, the f was mine'— — „ II i 1
'The f was mine,' he whisper'd, 'fly!' — „ 30
a little f Whereof I was not guilty; — Com. of Arthur 341
wayside ambushings—No f of thine: — Gareth and L. 433
'If Enid errs, let Enid learn her f.' — Marr. of Geraint 132
creatures voiceless thro' the f of birth, — Geraint and E. 266
and for her f she wept Of petulancy; — Merlin and V. 952
He is all f who hath no f at all: — Lancelot and E. 132
you call me wilful, and the f Is yours — „ 750

Fault (*continued*) Seeing it is no more Sir Lancelot's f — Lancelot and E. 1075
f and doubt—no word of that fond tale— — Last Tournament 578
change your name: no f of mine! — Sisters (E. and E.) 69
I care not for a name—no f of mine. — „ 77
beauties of the work appear The darkest f's: — „ 106
by the f o' that ere maäle— — Village Wife 17
wroth at things of old—No f of mine. — Sir J. Oldcastle 22
Blasphemy? whose is the f? — Despair 107
Father's f Visited on the children! — The Ring 175
be the f's your Poet makes Or many or few, — To Mary Boyle 61
the f is less In me than Art. — Romney's R. 8
You make our f's too gross, — To one who ran down Eng. 1
an' not the f's o' the Squire. — Church-warden, etc. 46
Some too high—no f of thine— — Poets and Critics 12
Faultful her great heart thro' all the f Past — Princess vii 248
Faultless Henceforth be truer to your f lord? — Lancelot and E. 119
'Arthur, my lord, Arthur, the f King, — „ 121
Faultily f, icily regular, — Maud I ii 6
she the f, the divine; — Locksley H., Sixty 5
Faun mountain quickens into Nymph and F; — Lucretius 187
Arise and fly The reeling F, — In Mem. cxviii 26
Faunus in the garden snared Picus and F, — Lucretius 182
Favour (*See also* **Court-favour**) On whom their f's fall! — Sir Galahad 14
I came to ask a f of you.' — Enoch Arden 285
'F from one so sad and so forlorn — „ 287
This is the f that I came to ask.' — „ 313
Else I withdraw f and countenance From you — Aylmer's Field 307
Arranged the f, and assumed the Prince. — Princess iv 602
Who have won her f! — Maud I xii 18
I bound to thee for any f ask'd!' — Gareth and L. 977
To seek a second f at his hands. — Marr. of Geraint 626
love or fear, or seeking f of us, — „ 700
That he should wear her f at the tilt. — Lancelot and E. 358
will you wear My f at this tourney?' — „ 362
worn F of any lady in the lists. (repeat) — „ 364, 474
find thy f changed and love thee not'— — Last Tournament 500
Black with bridal f's mixt! — Forlorn 69
Might I crave One f? — Romney's R. 70
Favourable a f speed Ruffle thy mirror'd mast, — In Mem. ix 6
Favour'd (*See also* **White-favour'd**) These f lips of mine; — Will Water. 20
Favourite I know the song, Their f— — Sisters (E. and E.) 3
Favouritism 'So puddled as it is with f.' — Princess iii 146
Fawn (s) your arrow-wounded f Came flying — „ ii 270
That was f's blood, not brother's, — „ 275
Ah Maud, you milkwhite f, — Maud I iv 57
shadow of a bird Flying, and then a f; — Pelleas and E. 39
Fawn (verb) And f at a victor's feet. — Maud I vi 30
Fawn'd dog that had loved him and f at his knee— — In the Child. Hosp. 9
Fawning Crouch'd f in the weed. — Œnone 201
Feäl (feel) I'd f mysen cleän disgraäced. — North. Cobbler 102
Feäld (field) Huzzin' an' maäzin' the blessed f's — N. Farmer, O. S. 62
nor a mortal beäst o' the f. — North. Cobbler 38
Feäld (felt) till I f mysen ready to drop. — Owd Roä 84
Fëalty rendering true answer, as beseem'd Thy f, — M. d'Arthur 75
In token of true heart and f. — Gareth and L. 399
doubt her more, But rested in her f, — Geraint and E. 967
Friends, thro' your manhood and your f,— — Last Tournament 97
Forgetful of their troth and f, — Guinevere 442
and saps The f of our friends, — „ 521
rendering true answer, as beseem'd Thy f, — Pass. of Arthur 243
and give His f to the halcyon hour! — The Wanderer 12
Fear (s) Earth goes to earth, with grief, not f, — Supp. Confessions 38
Moved from beneath with doubt and f. — „ 138
Whispering to each other half in f, — Sea-Fairies 5
What hope or f or joy is thine? — Adeline 23
Roof'd the world with doubt and f, — Eleänore 99
And they cross'd themselves for f, — L. of Shallott iv 49
'Think you this mould of hopes and f's — Two Voices 28
heaping on the f of ill The f of men, — „ 107
sitting, burnish'd without f The brand, — „ 128
love dispell'd the f That I should die — Miller's D. 89
I loved you better for your f's, — „ 149
Acting the law we live by without f; — Œnone 148
I shut my sight for f: — „ 188

Fear (s) (*continued*) Remaining utterly confused with f's, — Palace of Art 269
I would not brook my f Of the other: — D. of F. Women 154
f of change at home, that drove him hence. — Walk. to the Mail 68
the low wind hardly breathed for f. — Godiva 55
Boring a little auger-hole in f, — „ 68
to me is given Such hope, I know not f; — Sir Galahad 62
Nor yet the f of little books — Will Water. 195
Hush'd all the groves from f of wrong: — Sir L. and Q. G. 13
All his Annie's f's, Save, as his Annie's, — Enoch Arden 184
Spy out my face, and laugh at all your f's.' — „ 216
Such doubts and f's were common to her state, — „ 521
Has she no f that her first husband lives?' — „ 806
'Ay, ay, poor soul' said Miriam, 'f enow! — „ 807
hollow as the hopes and f's of men? — Lucretius 180
for f This whole foundation ruin, — Princess ii 340
nor shrink For f our solid aim be dissipated — „ iii 266
F Stared in her eyes, and chalk'd her face, — „ iv 376
yet I blame you not so much for f; — „ 506
Six thousand years of f have made you that — „ 507
Fatherly f's—you used us courteously— — „ v 216
Bow-back'd with f: — „ vi 359
Shall f's and jealous hatreds flame again? — W. to Marie Alex. 41
The King was shaken with holy f; — The Victim 57
it darkens and brightens and darkens like my f, — Window, On the Hill 19
but for f it is not so, The wild unrest — In Mem. xv 14
All subtle thought, all curious f's, — „ xxxii 9
yields To that vague f implied in death; — „ xli 14
Beneath all fancied hopes and f's — „ xlix 13
I wrong the grave with f's untrue: — „ li 9
For f divine Philosophy Should push beyond her mark, — „ liii 14
and is Eternal, separate from f's: — „ lxxxv 66
The feeble soul, a haunt of f's, — „ cx 3
She cannot fight the f of death. — „ cxiv 10
And heated hot with burning f's, — „ cxviii 22
No, like a child in doubt and f: — „ cxxiv 17
Be sunder'd in the night of f; — „ cxxvii 2
Wild Hours that fly with Hope and F, — „ cxxviii 9
I fled from the place and the pit and the f? — Maud I i 64
The bitter springs of anger and f; — „ x 49
she lay Sick once, with a f of worse, — „ xix 73
a coast Of ancient fable and f— — „ II ii 32
Sick of a nameless f, Back to the dark sea-line — „ 44
cells of madness, haunts of horror and f, — „ III vi 2
mother's eye Full of the wistful f — Gareth and L. 173
Yet pressing on, tho' all in f — „ 325
Thou shakest in thy f: there yet is time: — „ 940
the new knight Had f he might be shamed; — „ 1044
after all their foolish f's And horrors — „ 1424
all her foolish f's about the dress, (repeat) — Marr. of Geraint 142, 844
Rapt in the f and in the wonder of it; — „ 529
For love or f, or seeking favour of us, — „ 700
The long way smoke beneath him in his f; — Geraint and E. 532
Enid in their going had two f's, — „ 817
Truly save for f's, My f's for thee, — Balin and Balan 146
As Love, if Love be perfect, casts out f, So Hate, if Hate be perfect, casts out f. — Merlin and V. 40
She shook from f, and for her fault she wept — „ 952
First as in f, step after step, she stole — Lancelot and E. 342
Then came on him a sort of sacred f, — „ 354
For f our people call you lily maid — „ 386
So fine a f in our large Lancelot — „ 595
all three in hurry and f Ran to her, — „ 1024
May not your crescent f for name and fame Speak, — „ 1400
The King himself had f's that it would fall, — Holy Grail 341
Our f of some disastrous chance for thee — „ 727
whence the f lest this my realm, uprear'd, — Last Tournament 122
but how ye greet me—f And fault and doubt— — „ 577
or a vague spiritual f— — Guinevere 71
all his heart was cold With formless f; — Pass. of Arthur 98
their f's Are morning shadows huger than the shapes — To the Queen ii 62
over the deep graves of Hope and F, — Lover's Tale ii 58
Had I not known where Love, at first a f, — Sisters (E. and E.) 170

Fear (s) (*continued*) And f's for our delicate Emmie — *In the Child. Hosp.* 66
Cloud-weaver of phantasmal hopes and f's, — *To Victor Hugo* 2
fail Thro' craven f's of being great. — *Hands all Round* 32
Had never swerved for craft or f, — *To Marq. of Dufferin* 27
as Gods against the f Of Death and Hell; — *Demeter and P.* 141
that worship which is F, Henceforth, — " 143
and paced his land In f of worse, — *To Mary Boyle* 30
May your f's be vain! — *To one who ran down Eng.* 2
Still—at times A doubt, a f,— — *Akbar's Dream* 169
'Twere joy, not f, claspt hand-in-hand with thee, — *If I were loved* 9

Fear (verb) I f All may not doubt, — *Supp. Confessions* 177
I f to slide from bad to worse. — *Two Voices* 231
What is it that I may not f?' — " 240
That I should f,—if I were loved — *If I were loved* 4
I f My wound hath taken cold, — *M. d'Arthur* 165
I f it is too late, and I shall die.' — " 180
I f That we shall miss the mail: — *Walk. to the Mail* 111
'F not thou to loose thy tongue; — *Vision of Sin* 155
f no more for me; or if you f Cast all your cares — *Enoch Arden* 221
I f, If there were many Lilias in the brood, — *Princess, Pro.* 145
Let them not f: some said their heads were less: — " *ii* 147
I f My conscience will not count me fleckless; — " 293
But, dearest Lady, pray you f me not, — " 333
'Ah, f me not' Replied Melissa; — " 342
'What f ye, brawlers? am not I your Head? — " *iv* 498
what is it ye f? Peace! — " 500
'We f, indeed, you spent a stormy time — " *v* 121
f we not To break them more in their behoof, — " *vi* 60
Sighing she spoke 'I f They will not.' — " *vii* 297
Approach and f not; breathe upon my brows; — " 353
Shall we f *him*? our own we never fear'd. — *Third of Feb.* 25
I f you'll listen to tales, be jealous — *Grandmother* 54
'F not, isle of blowing woodland, — *Boädicea* 38
We mock thee when we do not f: — *In Mem., Pro.* 30
She f's not, or with thee beside — " *Con.* 43
And me behind her, will not f. — " 44
I f, the new strong wine of love, — *Maud I vi* 82
some one else may have much to f; — " *xv* 4
I should grow light-headed, I f, — " 100
Should I f to greet my friend — " *II iv* 85
I almost f they are not roses, but blood; — " *v* 78
F not to give this King thine only child, — *Com. of Arthur* 413
I f that I am no true wife.' — *Marr. of Geraint* 108
Like him who tries the bridge he f's may fail, — *Geraint and E.* 303
Yet f me not: I call mine own self wild, — " 311
he f's To lose his bone, and lays his foot — " 561
f not, Enid, I should fall upon him, — " 787
men may f Fresh fire and ruin. — " 822
you that most had cause To f me, f no longer, — " 825
f not, cousin; I am changed indeed.' — " 873
O Vivien, save ye f The monkish manhood, — *Merlin and V.* 34
Vivien answer'd, smiling scornfully, 'Why f? — " 38
I savour of thy—virtues? f them? no. — " 39
loathe, f—but honour me the more.' — " 122
make me f still more you are not mine, — " 327
Wherefore, if I f, Giving you power upon me — " 513
for I f My fate or folly, — " 926
a flash, I f me, that will strike my blossom dead, — *Lancelot and E.* 971
as a coward slinks from what he f's To cope with, — *Pelleas and E.* 438
'F God: honour the King— — *Last Tournament* 302
Because he hates thee even more than f's; — " 533
F not: thou shalt be guarded till my death. — *Guinevere* 448
I f My wound hath taken cold, — *Pass. of Arthur* 333
I f it is too late, and I shall die.' — " 348
tho' sometimes I f You may be flickering, — *Sisters (E. and E.)* 32
she'll never live thro' it, I f.' — *In the Child. Hosp.* 42
Priests Who f the king's hard common-sense — *Sir J. Oldcastle* 66
And a man men f is a man to be loved — *The Wreck* 18
Days that will glimmer, I f, — " 79
'Do you f?' and there came thro' the roar of the breaker a whisper, a breath, 'F? am I not with you? — *Despair* 13
morning brings the day I hate and f; — *The Flight* 2
lurks, listens, f's his victim may have fled— — " 71

Fear (verb) (*continued*) and what is it that you f? — *Happy* 1
an' thou'll git along, niver f, — *Church-warden, etc.* 7
F not thou the hidden purpose of that Power — *God and the Univ.* 5

Fear'd f To send abroad a shrill and terrible cry, — *Enoch Arden* 767
I f Lest the gay navy there should splinter — *Sea Dreams* 130
I f To meet a cold 'We thank you, — *Princess iv* 327
but f To incense the Head once more; — " *vii* 76
she f that I should lose my mind, — " 99
Shall we fear *him*? our own we never f. — *Third of Feb.* 25
I say, we *never* f! — " 29
There sat the Shadow f of man; — *In Mem. xxii* 12
And that she f she was not a true wife. — *Marr. of Geraint* 114
she f In every wavering brake an ambuscade. — *Geraint and E.* 50
Enid f his eyes, Moist as they were, — " 350
I ever f ye were not wholly mine; — *Merlin and V.* 315
ridd'n away to die?' So f the King, — *Lancelot and E.* 568
cope and crown Of all I hoped and f?— — *Lover's Tale ii* 27
he was f to look at me now. — *First Quarrel* 38
they f that we still could sting, — *The Revenge* 72
I f The very fountains of her life were chill'd; — *Sisters (E. and E.)* 265
I be f fur to tell tha 'ow much— — *Village Wife* 47
f myself turning crazed, — *Despair* 78
Found, f me dead, and groan'd, — *The Flight* 23
They was all on 'em f o' the Ghoäst — *Owd Roä* 37
She f I had forgotten her, — *The Ring* 102

Fearful (*See also* **Too-fearful**) Too f that you should not please. — *Miller's D.* 148
Half f that, with self at strife, — *Will Water.* 161
If you be f, then must we be bold. — *Third of Feb.* 19
Dismal error! f slaughter! — *The Captain* 65
the sea roars Ruin: a f night!' 'Not f; — *Sea Dreams* 81
'The simple, f child Meant nothing, — *Guinevere* 369

Fearing (*See also* **God-fearing**) hid my feelings, f they should do me wrong; — *Locksley Hall* 29
F the lazy gossip of the port, — *Enoch Arden* 335
Then f night and chill for Annie, — " 443
dwelt lingeringly on the latch, F to enter: — " 520
And f waved my arm to warn them off; — *Sea Dreams* 132
fling whate'er we felt, not f, into words. — *Third of Feb.* 6
F to lose, and all for a dead man, — *Geraint and E.* 564
Then, f for his hurt and loss of blood, — " 777
F the mild face of the blameless King, — " 812
But Vivien, f heaven had heard her oath, — *Merlin and V.* 940
f rust or soilure fashion'd for it — *Lancelot and E.* 7
Still hoping, f 'is it yet too late?' — *Guinevere* 691
f not to plunge Thy torch of life — *Tiresias* 158

Fear-tremulous her slow sweet eyes F-t, — *Merlin and V.* 86

Feast (s) Rise from the f of sorrow, lady, — *Margaret* 62
scare church-harpies from the master's f; — *To J. M. K.* 3
I made a f; I bad him come; — *The Sisters* 13
while Audley f Humm'd like a hive — *Audley Court* 4
No larger f than under plane or pine — *Lucretius* 213
near his tomb a f Shone, silver-set; — *Princess, Pro.* 105
Nymph, or Goddess, at high tide of f, — " *i* 197
Blanch'd in our annals, and perpetual f, — " *vi* 63
a f Of wonder, out of West and East, — *Ode Inter. Exhib.* 20
And we shall sit at endless f, — *In Mem. xlvii* 9
Be neither song, nor game, nor f; — " *cv* 21
The reeling Faun, the sensual f; — " *cxviii* 26
Who stay to share the morning f, — " *Con.* 75
Again the f, the speech, the glee, — " 101
the King Made f for, saying, as they sat at meat, — *Com. of Arthur* 247
that day a f had been Held in high hall, — *Gareth and L.* 847
suit of fray'd magnificence, Once fit for f's of ceremony) — *Marr. of Geraint* 297
eyes, Moist as they were, wine-heated from the f; — *Geraint and E.* 351
Till when at f Sir Garlon likewise ask'd — *Balin and Balan* 347
our knights at f Have pledged us in this union, — *Lancelot and E.* 114
So dame and damsel glitter'd at the f — *Last Tournament* 225
such a f As never man had dream'd; — *Guinevere* 263
Fast with your fasts, not feasting with your f's; — " 678
And Julian made a solemn f: — *Lover's Tale iv* 187
such a f, ill-suited as it seem'd To such a time, — " 207
such a f So rich, so strange, — " 210
our solemn f—we ate and drank, — " 221

Feast (s) (*continued*) And when the *f* was near an end, he said: *Lover's Tale iv* 229
Who could desire more beauty at a *f*?' „ 240
him nor lights nor *f* Dazed or amazed, „ 310
I would not mingle with their *f's*; *Demeter and P.* 103
mouthing a bloodless name at *her* cannibal *f*, *The Dawn* 12
Feast (verb) *f* with these in honour of their Earl; *Geraint and E.* 287
a man Will honour those who *f* with him, *Lover's Tale iv* 232
fairest flesh at last is filth on which the worm will *f*; *Happy* 30
Feasted three days he *f* us, And on the fourth *Princess i* 118
he the wisest man *F* the woman wisest then, „ *ii* 351
having there so oft with all his knights *F*, *Holy Grail* 224
Feastful Singing and murmuring in her *f* mirth, *Palace of Art* 177
Feasting Fast with your fasts, not *f* with your feasts; *Guinevere* 678
Feat often heard me praise Your *f's* of arms, *Marr. of Geraint* 435
Feather (s) (*See also* **Helmet-feather**) All grass of silky *f* grow— *Talking Oak* 269
I did but shear a *f*, and dream and truth *Princess v* 541
We'll be birds of a *f*, *Window, Spring* 14
ask me whether The habit, hat, and *f*, *Maud I xx* 18
Or ev'n a fall'n *f*, vanish'd again. *Last Tournament* 372
ready for their bridal-time By change of *f*: *Sisters (E. and E.)* 72
Feather (verb) all about the large lime *f's* low, *Gardener's D.* 47
wood began To *f* toward the hollow, (repeat) *Enoch Arden* 68, 374
Feather'd *See* **Coppice-feather'd**
Featherfan Cooling her false cheek with a *f*, *Aylmer's Field* 289
Feathering the ripple *f* from her bows: *Enoch Arden* 544
Feature chisell'd *f's* clear and sleek. *A Character* 30
Conjectures of the *f's* of her child *Œnone* 252
Reading her perfect *f's* in the gloom, *Gardener's D.* 175
I cannot see the *f's* right, *In Mem. lxx* 1
that small charm of *f* mine, pursued— *Merlin and V.* 76
Featured (*See also* **Clear-featured**) The mother *f* in the son; *Open I. and C. Exhib.* 12
February (adj.) Many many welcomes *F* fair-maid, (repeat) *The Snowdrop* 2, 10
February (s) silver tongue, Cold *F* loved, is dry; *The Blackbird* 14
Fed (*See also* **Dew-fed, Fancy-fed, Fountain-fed, Full-fed**) *f* With the clear-pointed flame of chastity, *Isabel* 1
f the time With odour *Arabian Nights* 64
F thee, a child, lying alone, *Eleänore* 25
these, tho' *f* with careful dirt, *Amphion* 89
By dancing rivulets *f* his flocks *To E. L.* 22
They *f* her theories, in and out of place *Princess i* 129
I *f* you with the milk of every Muse; „ *iv* 295
breast that *f* or arm that dandled you, „ *vi* 181
heart and ear were *f* To hear him, *In Mem. lxxxix* 22
distant hills From hidden summits *f* with rills „ *ciii* 7
You have but *f* on the roses *Maud I iv* 60
f With honey'd rain and delicate air, „ *xviii* 20
Memory *f* the soul of Love with tears. *Lover's Tale i* 822
Why *f* we from one fountain? „ *ii* 24
f and cherish'd him, and saved his life. „ *iv* 264
island-myriads *f* from alien lands— *The Fleet* 12
She watch'd me, she nursed me, she *f* me, *Charity* 33
Federation the *F* of the world. *Locksley Hall* 128
The *F's* and the Powers; *Day-Dm., L'Envoi* 16
Fee To hold the costliest love in *f*. *In Mem. lxxix* 4
Mammonite mother kills her babe for a burial *f*, *Maud I i* 45
Feeäd (feed) theer warn't not *f* for a cow; *N. Farmer, O. S.* 37
an' now theer's lots o' *f*, „ 39
Feeäl (feel) '*F* thou this! thou can't graw *North. Cobbler* 86
Feeäld (felt) I *f* it drip o' my neck. *Owd Roä* 42
till 'e *f* 'e could howd 'is oän, *Church-warden, etc.* 19
Feeät (feet) cleän as a flower fro' 'eäd to *f*: *North. Cobbler* 44
Wi' Roäver athurt my *f*, *Owd Roä* 30
British farmers to stan' ageän o' their *f*. „ 46
Feeble Now am I *f* grown; *St. S. Stylites* 36
And laid the *f* infant in his arms; *Enoch Arden* 152
his knees Were *f*, so that falling prone „ 779
frail at first And *f*, all unconscious of itself, *Princess vii* 117
disengage myself, but fail'd, Being so *f*: *Lover's Tale i* 693
wild hearts and *f* wings That every sophister can lime. *Love thou thy land* 11
Not ours the fault if we have *f* hosts— *Third of Feb.* 38
Feeble (*continued*) The *f* soul, a haunt of fears, *In Mem. cx* 3
f vassals of wine and anger and lust, *Maud II i* 43
thro' the *f* twilight of this world Groping, *Geraint and E.* 5
and Pellam's *f* cry, 'Stay, stay him!' *Balin and Balan* 420
Feebler Is *f* than his knees; *Ancient Sage* 135
Then comes the *f* heiress of your plan, *Princess iii* 237
it drown'd The *f* motion underneath his hand. *Lover's Tale iv* 83
Feed (*See also* **Feeäd**) For the Ox *F's* in the herb, *Supp. Confessions* 151
Thy kingly intellect shall *f*, *Clear-headed friend* 20
Upon himself himself did *f*: *A Character* 27
Some honey-converse *f's* thy mind, *Adeline* 40
little ducts began To *f* thy bones with lime, *Two Voices* 326
Nor *f* with crude imaginings The herd, *Love thou thy land* 10
The fat earth *f* thy branchy root, *Talking Oak* 273
That hoard, and sleep, and *f*, *Ulysses* 5
That early woke to *f* her little ones, *Princess vii* 252
The full new life that *f's* thy breath *In Mem. lxxxvi* 10
That *f* the mothers of the flock; „ *c* 16
a rose-carnation *f* With summer spice „ *ci* 7
Nor *f* with sighs a passing wind: „ *cviii* 4
goodly cheer To *f* the sudden guest, *Geraint and E.* 284
call'd for flesh and wine to *f* his spears. „ 601
Feeding like horses when you hear them *f*; „ 606
and *f's* their downward flow. *Lover's Tale i* 784
f the rebels of the crown, *Columbus* 131
F the budding rose of boyhood *Locksley H., Sixty* 143
brook that *f's* this lakelet murmur'd 'debt,' *The Ring* 171
we will *f* her with our mountain air, „ 319
Feedeth *f* The senses with a still delight *Margaret* 16
Feeding water-pipes beneath, *F* the flower; *D. of F. Women* 207
And *f* high, and living soft, *The Goose* 17
F like horses when you hear them feed; *Geraint and E.* 606
Feel (*See also* **Feäl, Feeäl**) and I *f* as thou hast felt? *Supp. Confessions* 82
I *f* the tears of blood arise *Oriana* 77
f their immortality Die in their hearts *The Mermaid* 29
For Kate no common love will *f*; *Kate* 14
To *f*, altho' no tongue can prove, *Two Voices* 445
Joying to *f* herself alive, *Palace of Art* 178
Put forth and *f* a gladder clime.' *On a Mourner* 15
Like one that *f's* a nightmare on his bed *M. d'Arthur* 177
Begin to *f* the truth and stir of day, „ *Ep.* 19
make a man *f* strong in speaking truth; *Love and Duty* 70
I *f* about my feet The berried briony *Talking Oak* 147
my heart so slow To *f* it! *Love and Duty* 35
unto him who works, and *f's* he works. *Golden Year* 73
guinea helps the hurt that Honour *f's*, *Locksley Hall* 105
Make me *f* the wild pulsation „ 109
the master-chord Of all I felt and *f*. *Will Water.* 28
Live long, nor *f* in head or chest „ 237
Their voices make me *f* so solitary.' *Enoch Arden* 397
f's a glimmering strangeness in his dream. *The Brook* 216
Were living nerves to *f* the rent; *Aylmer's Field* 536
And *f* myself the shadow of a dream. *Princess i* 18
f, at least, that silence here were sin, *Third of Feb.* 37
which has power to *f* 'I am I'? *High. Pantheism* 8
But they—they *f* the desire of the deep— *Voice and the P.* 19
As one who *f's* the immeasurable world, *A Dedication* 7
To put in words the grief I *f*; *In Mem. v* 2
and *f's* Her place is empty, „ *xiii* 3
I should not *f* it to be strange. „ *xiv* 20
reaches forth her arms To *f* from world to world, „ *xxi* 19
I *f* it, when I sorrow most; „ *xxvii* 14
and call To what I *f* is Lord of all, „ *lv* 19
Yet *f's*, as in a pensive dream, „ *lxiv* 17
I felt and *f*, tho' left alone, „ *lxxxv* 42
Canst thou *f* for me Some painless sympathy „ 87
My Ghost may *f* that thine is near. „ *xciii* 16
She darkly *f's* him great and wise, „ *xcvii* 34
To *f* once more, in placid awe, „ *cxxii* 5
I *f* There is a lower and a higher; „ *cxxix* 3
To *f* thee some diffusive power, „ *cxxx* 7
I *f* with thee the drowsy spell. *Maud I xviii* 72
I *f* I shall owe you a debt, „ *xix* 87
I *f* so free and so clear By the loss „ 98

Fell (verb) (*continued*) Heavy as it was, a great stone slipt and f, Holy Grail 680
stones Raw, that they f from, brought us to the hall. ,, 720
wind f, and on the seventh night I heard ,, 810
sword was dash'd from out my hand, and f. ,, 826
star Reel'd in the smoke, brake into flame, and f. Pelleas and E. 519
Then f thick rain, plume droopt Last Tournament 213
thus he f Head-heavy; then the knights, ,, 467
Her light feet f on our rough Lyonnesse, ,, 554
hurl'd him headlong, and he f Stunn'd, Guinevere 108
He falter'd, and his hand f from the harp, ,, 303
prone from off her seat she f, ,, 414
and ev'n on Arthur f Confusion, Pass. of Arthur 98
some whisper of the seething seas, A dead hush f; ,, 122
and all but slain himself, he f. ,, 169
So flash'd and f the brand Excalibur: ,, 310
silver-smiling Venus ere she f Would often loiter Lover's Tale i 61
heart of Hope F into dust, and crumbled ,, 95
My coronal slowly disentwined itself And f between us both; ,, 362
f about My footsteps on the mountains. ,, 371
and the earth They f on became hallow'd ,, 440
water, drop by drop, upon my ear F; ,, 577
Even the feet of her I loved, I f, ,, 600
wealth Flash'd from me a moment and I f Beggar'd for ever— ,, 669
few drops of that distressful rain F on my face, ,, 699
and f into the abysm Of forms outworn, ,, 796
till they f Half-digging their own graves) ,, ii 46
and f Slanting upon that picture, ,, 174
the surge f From thunder into whispers; ,, iii 30
Lionel, who fain had risen, but f again, ,, iv 361
Saätan as f Down out o' heaven North. Cobbler 57
And he f upon their decks, and he died. The Revenge 104
sea plunged and f on the shot-shatter'd navy ,, 117
Had caught her hand, her eyelids f— Sisters (E. and E.) 148
The mother f about the daughter's neck, ,, 154
But Billy f bakkuds o' Charlie, Village Wife 85
there f, Striking the hospital wall, Def. of Lucknow 17
on all the defences our myriad enemy f. ,, 35
I lost myself and f from evenness, Sir J. Oldcastle 164
The crowd's roar f as at the 'Peace, be still!' Columbus 13
trees grew downwards, rain f upward, ,, 50
The hurricane of the latitude on him f, ,, 138
They almost f on each other; V. of Maeldune 26
steer f down at the plow and the harvest died ,, 30
and his white beard f to his feet, ,, 118
F the shipcrews Doom'd to the death. Batt. of Brunanburh 22
Then f from that half-spiritual height Chill'd, To E. Fitzgerald 19
His formal kiss f chill as a flake of snow The Wreck 32
then f fluttering down at my feet; ,, 82
And I f—and the storm and the days went ,, 111
a scrap, clipt out of the 'deaths' in a paper, f. ,, 146
the tundher, an' rain that f, Tomorrow 23
F like a cannonshot, Heavy Brigade 26
When That within the coffin f, F— To Marq. of Dufferin 43
leaf f, and the sun, Pale at my grief, Demeter and P. 113
causer of that scandal, fought and f; The Ring 215
And then the tear f, the voice broke. ,, 367
hands F from each other, and were join'd again. ,, 381
A noise of falling weights that never f, ,, 410
fell'd the foes before you as the woodman f's the wood, Happy 42
F on the shadow, No longer a shadow, Merlin and the G. 92
mountain rolls into the plain, F headlong dead; Death of Œnone 52

Fell'd slew the beast, and f The forest, Com. of Arthur 59
And f him, and set foot upon his breast, Marr. of Geraint 574
hand Which f the foes before you Happy 42

Feller (fellow) I knaw'd a Quaäker f as often 'as N. Farmer, N. S. 19
I liked a bigger f to fight wi' North. Cobbler 100
I calls 'em arter the f's Spinster's S's 4
The f's as maäkes them picturs, Owd Roä 23
An' all along o' the f (Sir Robert Peel) as turn'd ,, 48

Fell out We f o, my wife and I, O we f o I know not why, Princess ii 3

Fellow (adj.) Or brag to his f rakes of his conquest Charity 18
Fellow (adj.) (*continued*) Let be thy wail and help thy f men, Ancient Sage 258

Fellow (s) (*See also* **Feller, Tavern-fellow**) if his f spake, His voice was thin, Lotos-Eaters 33
And lowing to his f's. Gardener's D. 88
he, Poor f, could he help it? The Brook 158
That great pock-pitten f had been caught? Aylmer's Field 256
wise To let that handsome f Averill walk ,, 269
'This f would make weakness weak, In Mem. xxi 7
This f hath broken from some Abbey, Gareth and L. 456
Think ye this f will poison the King's dish? ,, 471
a hart Taller than all his f's, milky-white, Marr. of Geraint 150
And heard one crying to his f, 'Look, Geraint and E. 59
'Your sweet faces make good f's fools ,, 399
From all his f's, lived alone, Balin and Balan 126
This f hath wrought some foulness with his Queen: ,, 565
would ye look On this proud f again, Lancelot and E. 1065
all was done He flung it among his f's— Rizpah 32
But I gather'd my f's together, V. of Maeldune 2
drew His sword on his f to slay him, ,, 68

Fellow-citizen Welcome f-c's, Hollow hearts Vision of Sin 173

Fellow-feeling a very miracle Of f-f and communion. Lover's Tale i 251

Fellow-monk one, a f-m among the rest, Holy Grail 8

Fellowship goodliest f of famous knights M. d'Arthur 15
O Sorrow, cruel f, In Mem. iii 1
Mere f of sluggish moods, ,, xxxv 21
To give him the grasp of f; Maud I xiii 16
'God bless the King, and all his f!' Gareth and L. 698
'What dost thou, scullion, in my f? ,, 765
so rich a f Would make me wholly blest: Balin and Balan 147
your f O'er these waste downs whereon I lost myself, Lancelot and E. 224
My brethren have been all my f; ,, 672
The goodliest f of famous knights Pass. of Arthur 183
They grew aweary of her f: Lover's Tale i 109

Fellow-victim 'Curse him!' curse your f-v? Locksley H., Sixty 9

Fellow-worker In which I might your f-w be, Princess iv 308

Felo-de-se coroner doubtless will find it a f-d-s, Despair 115

Felon (adj.) F talk! Let be! no more!' Balin and Balan 380
'Stay, f knight, I avenge me for my friend.' Gareth and L. 1220

Felon (s) that tall f there Whom thou by sorcery Gareth and L. 996
Else yon black f had not let me pass, ,, 1293

Felt (*See also* **Feäld, Feeäld, Feel'd**) and I feel as thou hast f? Supp. Confessions 82
She f he was and was not there. Mariana in the S. 50
'To search thro' all I f or saw, Two Voices 139
something f, like something here; ,, 382
I pray'd for both, and so I f resign'd, May Queen, Con. 31
She f her heart grow prouder: The Goose 22
F earth as air beneath me, till I reach'd Gardener's D. 212
Dora f her uncle's will in all, Dora 5
I f a pang within As when I see the woodman lift Talking Oak 234
f my blood Glow with the glow Tithonus 55
pulsation that I f before the strife, Locksley Hall 109
And round her waist she f it fold, Day-Dm., Depart. 2
I never f the kiss of love, Sir Galahad 19
touch upon the master-chord Of all I f and feel. Will Water. 28
We f the good ship shake and reel, The Voyage 15
I read and f that I was there: To E. L. 8
life's ascending sun Was f by either, Enoch Arden 39
well had deem'd he f the tale Less ,, 711
when he f the silence of his house About him, Aylmer's Field 830
escaped His keepers, and the silence which he f, ,, 839
I f My heart beat thick with passion Princess iii 189
f the blind wildbeast of force, ,, v 266
you have known the pangs we f, ,, 374
tender orphan hands F at my heart, ,, 436
I f my veins Stretch with fierce heat; ,, 537
I f Thy helpless warmth about my barren breast ,, vi 201
f it sound and whole from head to foot, ,, 211
and perhaps they f their power, ,, Con. 13
fling whate'er we f, not fearing, into words. Third of Feb. 6
she f the heart within her fall and flutter Boädicea 81
I f it, when I sorrow'd most, In Mem. lxxxv 2
I f and feel, tho' left alone, ,, 42

Felt (*continued*) transfer The whole I f for him to you. *In Mem. lxxxv* 104
and f The same, but not the same; „ *lxxxvii* 13
I f the thews of Anakim, „ *ciii* 31
A love of freedom rarely f, „ *cix* 13
And f thy triumph was as mine; „ *cx* 14
Stood up and answer'd, 'I have f.' „ *cxxiv* 16
Because he f so fix'd in truth: „ *cxxv* 8
Nor have I f so much of bliss „ *Con.* 5
f himself in his force to be Nature's crowning race. *Maud I iv* 33
F a horror over me creep, „ *xiv* 35
I f she was slowly dying Vext with lawyers „ *xix* 21
Strange, that I f so gay, „ *xx* 1
I cleaved to a cause that I f to be pure „ *III vi* 31
I have f with my native land, „ 58
His love, unseen but f, o'ershadow Thee, *Ded. of Idylls* 51
F the light of her eyes into his life *Com. of Arthur* 56
but f him more, Of closest kin to me: *Gareth and L.* 126
f his young heart hammering in his ears, „ 322
he f, despite his mail, Strangled, „ 1151
I f Thy manhood thro' that wearied lance „ 1265
Lancelot thro' his warm blood f Ice strike, „ 1398
F ye were somewhat, yea, and by your state *Marr. of Geraint* 430
He f, were she the prize of bodily force, „ 541
I f That I could rest, a rock in ebbs and flows, „ 811
f that tempest brooding round his heart, *Geraint and E.* 11
f Her low firm voice and tender government. „ 193
f the warm tears falling on his face; „ 586
She f so blunt and stupid at the heart: „ 747
And f him hers again: she did not weep, „ 768
f His work was neither great nor wonderful, „ 920
and he f his being move In music with his order, *Balin and Balan* 211
He f the hollow-beaten mosses thud „ 321
when their foreheads f the cooling air, „ 589
he lifted faint eyes; he f One near him; „ 594
old man, Tho' doubtful, f the flattery, *Merlin and V.* 184
I, feeling that you f me worthy trust, „ 334
I f as tho' you knew this cursed charm, „ 435
that I lay And f them slowing ebbing, „ 437
darkling f the sculptured ornament „ 734
Thro' her own side she f the sharp lance go; *Lancelot and E.* 624
f the knot Climb in her throat, „ 740
And f the boat shock earth, *Holy Grail* 812
f the sun Beat like a strong knight on his helm, *Pelleas and E.* 22
she, that f the cold touch on her throat, „ 488
but f his eyes Harder and drier than a fountain bed „ 506
and f the goodly hounds Yelp at his heart, *Last Tournament* 503
My soul, I f my hatred for my Mark Quicken „ 519
f the King's breath wander o'er her neck, *Guinevere* 582
f the blast Beat on my heated eyelids: *Lover's Tale iii* 27
Thrice in a second, f him tremble too, „ *iv* 324
I f that my heart was hard, *First Quarrel* 76
An' I f I had been to blame; „ 90
I f I could do it no more. *In the Child. Hosp.* 60
I f one warm tear fall upon it. *Tiresias* 167
The child that I f I could die for— *The Wreck* 36
till I f myself ready to weep „ 51
With the first great love I had f „ 76
Does it matter so much what I f? *Despair* 4
but f thro' what we feel *Ancient Sage* 87
F within us as ourselves, the Powers of Good, *Locksley H., Sixty* 273
I f On a sudden I know not what, *The Ring* 31
and f An icy breath play on me, „ 130
and f a gentle hand Fall on my forehead, „ 418
I f for what I could not find, the key, „ 440
And sanguine Lazarus f a vacant hand *To Mary Boyle* 31
I f I could end myself too with the dagger— *Bandit's Death* 37

Female The stately flower of f fortitude, *Isabel* 11
A random string Your finer f sense offends. *Day-Dm., L'Envoi* 2
We sent mine host to purchase f gear; *Princess i* 199
All beauty compass'd in a f form, „ *ii* 34
The circle rounded under f hands „ 372
tender ministries Of f hands and hospitality.' „ *vi* 73
and served With f hands and hospitality.' „ 96
and the swarm Of f whisperers: „ 356
swarms of men Darkening her f field: „ *vii* 34

Female (*continued*) manhood fused with f grace In such a sort, *In Mem. cix* 17
Which types all Nature's male and f plan, *On one who affec. E. M.* 3
then a loftier form Than f, *Princess iv* 216

Fen From the dark f the oxen's low Came *Mariana* 28
Fly o'er waste f's and windy fields. *Sir Galahad* 60
raised the school, and drain'd the f. *Locksley H., Sixty* 268
somewheers i' the Wowd or the F, *Church-warden, etc.* 47

Fence three horses that have broken f, *Princess ii* 386
Robins—a niver mended a f: *N. Farmer, O. S.* 50
Breäk me a bit o' the esh for his 'eäd, lad, out o' the f! „ *N. S.* 41
An' the f's all on 'em bolster'd oop *Owd Roä* 32

Fenced (fought) voice with which I f A little ceased, *Two Voices* 317

Fenced (hedged) I f it round with gallant institutes, *Princess v* 392

Ferdinand F Hath signed it and our Holy Catholic queen *Columbus* 29
I pray you tell King F who plays with me, „ 223

Fere And raceth freely with his f, *Supp. Confessions* 158

Fern (*See also* **Ice-ferns, Lady-fern, Tree-fern**) learned names of agaric, moss and f, *Edwin Morris* 17
Hail, hidden to the knees in f, *Talking Oak* 29
Oh, hide thy knotted knees in f, „ 93
O muffle round thy knees with f, „ 149
O flourish, hidden deep in f, „ 201
Step deeper yet in herb and f, „ 245
Among the palms and f's and precipices; *Enoch Arden* 593
And sparkle out among the f, *The Brook* 25
In copse and f Twinkled the innumerable „ 133
From slope to slope thro' distant f's, *Princess, Con.* 99
stood a shatter'd archway plumed with f; *Marr. of Geraint* 316
all round was open space, And f and heath: *Pelleas and E.* 29
f without Burnt as a living fire of emeralds, „ 34
The deer, the dews, the f, the founts, *Last Tournament* 727
sparkle of a cloth On f and foxglove. *Sisters (E. and E.)* 118

Ferreted I have f out their burrowings, *Merlin and V.* 55

Ferule As boys that slink From f *Princess v* 38

Fervent With such a f flame of human love, *Holy Grail* 74

Fescue Sweeping the frothfly from the f *Aylmer's Field* 530

Festal With music and sweet showers Of f flowers, *Ode to Memory* 78
On the hall-hearths the f fires, *Day-Dm., Sleep. P.* 14
With f cheer, With books and music, *In Mem. cvii* 21
on a f day When Guinevere was crossing *Merlin and V.* 64
'If I be loved, these are my f robes, *Lancelot and E.* 909
make her f hour Dark with the blood of man *St. Telemachus* 79

Fester Eye, to which all order f's, *Locksley Hall* 133

Festival Two strangers meeting at a f; *Circumstance* 3
illuminate All your towns for a f, *On Jub. Q. Victoria* 19

Festoon in many a wild f Ran riot, *Œnone* 100

Festooning Their humid arms f tree to tree, *D. of F. Women* 70

Fetch Go f your Alice here,' she said: *Miller's D.* 143
And down I went to f my bride: „ 145
Go f a pint of port: *Will Water.* 4
Eh, let me f 'em, Arden,' *Enoch Arden* 871
the colt would f its price; *The Brook* 149
with furs And jewels, gifts, to f her: *Princess i* 43
f the wine, Arrange the board and brim the glass; *In Mem. cvii* 15
f Fresh victual for these mowers of our Earl; *Geraint and E.* 224
I will f you forage from all fields, „ 628
Lancelot went ambassador, at first, To f her, *Merlin and V.* 775
Well, I will wear it: f it out to me: *Lancelot and E.* 371
Fur 'e'd f an' carry like owt, *Owd Roä* 6

Fetch'd-Fetcht *fetch'd* His richest beeswing from a binn *Aylmer's Field* 404
booöks *fetch'd* nigh to nowt at the saäle, *Village Wife* 73
I *fetcht* 'im a kick an' 'e went. *Owd Roä* 62

Fettle I could f and clump owd booöts *North. Cobbler* 13

Feud Rose f, with question unto whom 'twere due: *Œnone* 82
New and Old, disastrous f, *Love thou thy land* 77
how they mar this little by their f's. *Sea Dreams* 49
'How grew this f betwixt the right and left.' *Princess iii* 77
Then rose a little f betwixt the two, „ *Con.* 23
I wage not any f with Death *In Mem. lxxxii* 1
Ring out the f of rich and poor, „ *cvi* 11
And ever mourning over the f, *Maud I xix* 31
splinter it into f's Serving his traitorous end; *Guinevere* 18

Feud (*continued*) counter-yells of *f* And faction, *To Duke of Argyll* 8
Before the *f* of Gods had marr'd our peace, *Death of Œnone* 32
Feudal above their heads I saw The *f* warrior lady-clad; *Princess, Pro.* 119
A *f* knight in silken masquerade, " 234
And tuft with grass a *f* tower; *In Mem. cxxviii* 20
Fever till at last a *f* seized On William, *Dora* 54
In hungers and in thirsts, *f's* and cold, *St. S. Stylites* 12
some low *f* ranging round to spy The weakness *Aylmer's Field* 569
mix the foaming draught Of *f*, *Princess ii* 252
fan my brows and blow The *f* from my cheek, *In Mem. lxxxvi* 9
There *f* seized upon him: *Lover's Tale iv* 132
there from *f* and my care of him Sprang up " 143
we talkt o' my darter es died o' the *f* at fall: *Village Wife* 10
f 'ed baäked Jinny's 'eäd as bald as one o' them heggs, " 102
Cholera, scurvy, and *f*, *Def. of Lucknow* 84
f's, fights, Mutinies, treacheries— *Columbus* 225
summer days' of *f*, and want of care! *The Wreck* 147
fire of *f* creeps across the rotted floor, *Locksley H., Sixty* 223
born of *f*, or the fumes Of that dark opiate dose *Romney's R.* 30
She died of a *f* caught when a nurse *Charity* 41
Fever'd so hot, So *f*! never colt would more delight *Romney's R.* 13
Upon my *f* brows that shook and throbb'd *Lover's Tale iii* 7
Feverous (*See also* **Brain-feverous**) A tongue-tied Poet in the *f* days, *Golden Year* 10
who slept After a night of *f* wakefulness, *Enoch Arden* 231
or laid his *f* pillow smooth! *Aylmer's Field* 701
Fever-worn When, pale as yet, and *f-w*, *To the Queen ii* 4
Few (adj.) Sharp and *f*, but seeming-bitter *Rosalind* 31
'I found him when my years were *f*; *Two Voices* 271
Who spoke *f* words and pithy, *Princess, Con.* 94
For those are *f* we hold as dear; *To F. D. Maurice* 46
While another is cheating the sick of a *f* last gasps, *Maud I i* 43
f, *F*, but all brave, all of one mind with him; *Com. of Arthur* 254
so *f* words, and seem'd So justified *Geraint and E.* 395
That has but one plain passage of *f* notes, *Lancelot and E.* 895
Thanks to the kindly dark faces who fought with us, faithful and *f*, *Def. of Lucknow* 70
these *f* lanes of elm And whispering oak. *To Mary Boyle* 67
some *f* drops of that distressful rain Fell on my face, *Lover's Tale i* 698
Few (s) Clash'd with his fiery *f* and won; *Ode on Well.* 100
that honest *f*, Who give the Fiend *To F. D. Maurice* 5
F at first will place thee well; *Poets and Critics* 10
Fewer we were every day *f* and *f*. *Def. of Lucknow* 49
albeit their glorious names Were *f*, *Princess ii* 156
Fewmet But at the slot or *f's* of a deer, *Last Tournament* 371
Feyther (father) Them or thir *f's*, tha sees, *N. Farmer, N. S.* 49
F 'ad ammost nowt; " 51
F run oop to the farm, " 54
Coom! coom! *f*,' 'e says, *Village Wife* 69
Sa *f* an' son was buried togither, " 90
F 'ud saäy I wur ugly es sin, *Spinster's S's.* 15
Fur if iver thy *f* 'ed riled me *Church-Warden, etc.* 41
Fiat This *f* somewhat soothed himself *Aylmer's Field* 26
Fibre Thy *f's* net the dreamless head, *In Mem. ii* 3
Fibred *See* **Hairy-fibred**
Fibrous pale and *f* as a wither'd leaf, *Lover's Tale i* 422
Fickle 'You're too slight and *f*,' I said, *Edward Gray* 19
bright and fierce and *f* is the South, *Princess iv* 97
Whatever *f* tongues may say. *In Mem. xxvi* 4
'Rapt from the *f* and the frail " *xxx* 25
so *f* are men—the best! *The Ring* 392
Fictive Who dabbling in the fount of *f* tears, *The Brook* 93
Fiddle And ta'en my *f* to the gate, (repeat) *Amphion* 11, 15
Twang out, my *f*! shake the twigs! " 61
wa 'greed as well as a *f* i' tune: *North. Cobbler* 12
Fiddled And *f* in the timber! *Amphion* 16
Fie she lifted either arm, '*F* on thee, King! *Gareth and L.* 658
Field (adj.) (*See also* **Field-flower**) like the arrow-seeds of the *f* flower, *The Poet* 19
Field (s) (*See also* **Autumn-fields, Battle-field, Feäld, Field-of-battle, Four-field, Harvest-field, War-field, Winter-field**) the high *f* on the bushless Pike, *Ode to Memory* 96
Whither away from the high green *f*, *Sea-Fairies* 8
f and wood Grow green beneath the showery gray, *My life is full* 16
her sacred blood doth drown The *f's*, *Poland* 5

Field (s) (*continued*) Long *f's* of barley and of rye, *L. of Shalott i* 2
And thro' the *f* the road runs by " 4
That sparkled on the yellow *f*, " *iii* 8
The willowy hills and *f's* among, " *iv* 25
thy father play'd In his free *f*, *Two Voices* 320
And forth into the *f's* I went, " 448
see me more in the long gray *f's* at night; *May Queen, N. Y's. E.* 26
in the *f's* all round I hear the bleating of the lamb. " *Con.* 2
He shines upon a hundred *f's*, " 50
Weary the wandering *f's* of barren foam. *Lotos-Eaters* 42
in fair *f* Myself for such a face had boldly died,' *D. of F. Women* 97
Then stept she down thro' town and *f* *Of old sat Freedom* 9
And bore him to a chapel nigh the *f*, *M. d'Arthur* 8
The *f's* between Are dewy-fresh, *Gardener's D.* 45
Leaning his horns into the neighbour *f*, " 87
hired himself to work within the *f's*; *Dora* 38
Far off the farmer came into the *f* " 74
when the farmer pass'd into the *f* " 85
the boy's cry came to her from the *f*, " 104
And scarce can recognise the *f's* I know; *St. S. Stylites* 40
To yonder oak within the *f* I spoke *Talking Oak* 13
Beyond the fair green *f* and eastern sea. *Love and Duty* 101
Man comes and tills the *f* and lies beneath, *Tithonus* 3
the steam Floats up from those dim *f's* " 69
a boy when first he leaves his father's *f*, *Locksley Hall* 112
white-flower'd elder-thicket from the *f* *Godiva* 63
Fly o'er waste fens and windy *f's*. *Sir Galahad* 60
The houseless ocean's heaving *f*, *The Voyoge* 30
And pace the sacred old familiar *f's*, *Enoch Arden* 625
I fret By many a *f* and fallow, *The Brook* 44
all about the *f's* you caught His weary daylong chirping, " 52
Sunning himself in a waste *f* alone— *Aylmer's Field* 9
became in other *f's* A mockery to the yeomen " 496
Fairer than Ruth among the *f's* of corn, " 680
That all neglected places of the *f* " 693
Follows the mouse, and all is open *f*. " 853
woman heard his foot Return from pacings in the *f*, *Lucretius* 6
makes Thy glory fly along the Italian *f*, " 71
answer'd in her sleep From hollow *f's*: *Princess, Pro.* 67
when a *f* of corn Bows all its ears " *i* 236
First in the *f*: some ages had been lost; " *ii* 153
for indeed these *f's* Are lovely, " *iii* 341
They faint on hill or *f* or river: " *iv* 14
waive your claim: If not, the foughten *f*, " *v* 297
ran the *f* Flat to the garden-wall: " 361
Man for the *f* and woman for the hearth: " 447
Thro' open *f* into the lists they wound Timorously; " *vi* 84
swarms of men Darkening her female *f*: " *vii* 34
after that dark night among the *f's* " 73
'The *f's* are fair beside them, *Voice and the P.* 17
The *f*, the chamber and the street, *In Mem. viii* 11
beast that takes His license in the *f* of time, " *xxvii* 6
And loiter'd in the master's *f*, " *xxxvii* 23
My paths are in the *f's* I know, " *xl* 31
The howlings from forgotten *f's*; " *xli* 16
And those five years its richest *f*. " *xlvi* 12
A bounded *f*, nor stretching far; " 14
And hill and wood and *f* did print " *lxxix* 7
trees Laid their dark arms about the *f*. (repeat) " *xcv* 16, 52
set To leave the pleasant *f's* and farms; " *cii* 22
Its lips in the *f* above are dabbled *Maud I i* 2
Go not, happy day, From the shining *f's*, " *xvii* 2
Came night and day, and rooted in the *f's*, *Com. of Arthur* 24
Sware on the *f* of death a deathless love. " 132
from the foughten *f* he sent Ulfius, " 135
F after *f*, up to a height, the peak Haze-hidden, " 429
Far shone the *f's* of May thro' open door, " 460
mount That rose between the forest and the *f*. *Gareth and L.* 191
gate shone Only, that open'd on the *f* below: " 195
abide Without, among the cattle of the *f*. " 274
Uther, reft From my dead lord a *f* with violence: " 335
Yet, for the *f* was pleasant in our eyes, " 337
reft us of it Perforce, and left us neither gold nor *f*.' " 339
'Whether would ye? gold or *f*?' " 340

Field (s) (*continued*) The f was pleasant in my husband's eye.' And Arthur, 'Have thy pleasant f again, *Gareth and L.* 342
shone far-off as shines A f of charlock „ 388
paused without, beside The f of tourney, „ 664
But by the f of tourney lingering yet „ 736
Silent the silent f They traversed. „ 1313
pitch'd Beside the Castle Perilous on flat f, „ 1363
what knight soever be in f Lays claim *Marr. of Geraint* 486
Geraint Beheld her first in f, awaiting him, „ 540
For these are his, and all the f is his, *Geraint and E.* 226
I will fetch you forage from all f's, „ 628
Are scatter'd,' and he pointed to the f, „ 802
One from the bandit scatter'd in the f, „ 818
My mother on his corpse in open f; (repeat) *Merlin and V.* 43, 73
in the f were Lancelot's kith and kin, *Lancelot and E.* 466
spoke, and vanish'd suddenly from the f „ 508
So that he went sore wounded from the f: „ 600
crown'd with gold, Ramp in the f, „ 664
For pleasure all about a f of flowers: „ 793
Then rose Elaine and glided thro' the f's, „ 843
past Down thro' the dim rich city to the f's, „ 847
And drave her ere her time across the f's „ 890
Death, like a friend's voice from a distant f „ 999
Past like a shadow thro' the f, „ 1140
flame At sunrise till the people in far f's, *Holy Grail* 243
in one full f Of gracious pastime, „ 323
where it smote the plowshare in the f, „ 403
But found a silk pavilion in a f, „ 745
And whipt me into the waste f's far away; „ 788
I stinted stroke in foughten f? „ 860
Who may not wander from the allotted f „ 908
and the sweet smell of the f's Past, *Pelleas and E.* 5
the flat f by the shore of Usk Holden: „ 164
all day long Sir Pelleas kept the f With honour: „ 168
And he was left alone in open f. „ 208
flung His rider, who call'd out from the dark f, „ 575
Caught his unbroken limbs from the dark f, „ 585
in among the faded f's To furthest towers; *Last Tournament* 53
Enchair'd tomorrow, arbitrate the f; „ 104
With all the kindlier colours of the f.' „ 224
'Free love—free f—we love (repeat) „ 275, 281
Showing a shower of blood in a f noir, „ 433
she thought 'He spies a f of death; *Guinevere* 134
I mark'd Him in the flowering of His f's, *Pass. of Arthur* 10
and the harmless glamour of the f; „ 52
the pale King glanced across the f Of battle: „ 126
Had held the f of battle was the King: „ 138
And bore him to a chapel nigh the f. „ 176
For I heard it abroad in the f's *First Quarrel* 32
Hard was the frost in the f, „ 39
what joy can be got from a cowslip out of the f; *In the Child. Hosp.* 36
breezes of May blowing over an English f, *Def. of Lucknow* 83
ears for Christ in this wild f of Wales— *Sir J. Oldcastle* 13
a crowd Throng'd the waste f about the city gates: „ 40
and the harvest died from the f, *V. of Maeldune* 30
Silent palaces, quiet f's of eternal sleep! „ 80
By quiet f's, a slowly-dying power, *De Prof., Two G.* 24
the f with blood of the fighters Flow'd, *Batt. of Brunanburh* 24
hear the voices from the f. *Locksley H., Sixty* 116
cow shall butt the 'Lion passant' from his f. „ 248
out of the f, And over the brow and away. *Heavy Brigade* 63
a careless people flock'd from the f's *Dead Prophet* 7
Produce of your f and flood, *Open. I. and C. Exhib.* 5
in this pleasant vale we stand again, The f of Enna, *Demeter and P.* 35
Blessing his f, or seated in the dusk Of even, „ 125
glide Along the silent f of Asphodel. „ 153
mine the hall, the farm, the f; *The Ring* 169
She comes on waste and wood, On farm and f: *Prog. of Spring* 23
and I gaze at a f in the Past, *By an Evolution.* 17
WHAT sight so lured him thro' the f's *Far-far-away* 1
waste and f and town of alien tongue, *St. Telemachus* 30
I reap No revenue from the f of unbelief. *Akbar's Dream* 67
And laughs upon thy f as well as mine, „ 106
Nor in the f without were seen or heard „ 195
And plow the Present like a f, *Mechanophilus* 31

Field-flower (*See also* **Field (adj.)**) would they grew Like f-f's everywhere! *Princess iii* 252
Field-of-battle Arthur reach'd a f-o-b *Com. of Arthur* 96
Fiend Who give the F himself his due, *To F. D. Maurice* 6
the f best knows whether woman or man *Maud I i* 75
when he died, his soul Became a F, *Balin and Balan* 129
hold them outer f's, Who leap at thee to tear thee; „ 141
but in him His mood was often like a f, *Lancelot and E.* 251
drawn his claws athwart thy face? or f? *Last Tournament* 63
In fuming sulphur blue and green, a f— „ 617
like so many f's in their hell— *Def. of Lucknow* 33
we have sent them very f's from Hell; *Columbus* 184
The F would yell, the grave would yawn, *The Flight* 51
the night, While the F is prowling. *Forlorn* 66
Fierce Kate loves well the bold and f; *Kate* 29
My heart, pierced thro' with f delight, *Fatima* 34
Twisted hard in f embraces, *Vision of Sin* 40
f old man Follow'd, and under his own lintel *Aylmer's Field* 330
Methought I never saw so f a fork— *Lucretius* 28
I urged the f inscription on the gate, *Princess iii* 141
That bright and f and fickle is the South, „ *iv* 97
a tide of f Invective seem'd to wait „ 471
He yielded, wroth and red, with f demur: „ *v* 358
I felt my veins Stretch with f heat; „ 538
half the wolf's-milk curdled in their veins, The f triumvirs; „ *vii* 131
He heard a f mermaiden cry, *Sailor Boy* 6
Mad and maddening all that heard her in her f volubility, *Boädicea* 4
Yell'd and shriek'd between her daughters in her f volubility. „ 72
f extremes employ Thy spirits in the darkening leaf, *In Mem. lxxxviii* 5
Till I with as f an anger spoke, *Maud II i* 17
In that f light which beats upon a throne, *Ded. of Idylls* 27
Her own brood lost or dead, lent her f teat *Com. of Arthur* 28
the lords Of that f day were as the lords of this, „ 216
When I was kitchen-knave among the rest F was the hearth, *Gareth and L.* 1010
flash'd the f shield, All sun; „ 1030
When I that knew him f and turbulent Refused her *Marr. of Geraint* 447
Thy too f manhood would not let thee lie. *Balin and Balan* 74
In those f wars, struck hard— „ 177
Nor ever touch'd f wine, nor tasted flesh, *Merlin and V.* 627
'He learnt and warn'd me of their f design *Lancelot and E.* 274
So f a gale made havoc here of late *Holy Grail* 729
Let the f east scream thro' your eyelet-holes, *Pelleas and E.* 469
But Pelleas lifted up an eye so f She quail'd; „ 601
wrath which forced my thoughts on that f law, *Guinevere* 537
And f or careless looseners of the faith, *To the Queen ii* 52
Hued with the scarlet of a f sunrise, *Lover's Tale i* 353
F in the strength of far descent, „ 382
Plunged in the last f charge at Waterloo, *Sisters (E. and E.)* 64
he, the f Soldan of Egypt, *Columbus* 97
HAD the f ashes of some fiery peak Been hurl'd *St. Telemachus* 1
Blown by the f beleaguerers of a town, *Achilles over the T.* 20
because the f beast found A wiser than herself, *Tiresias* 151
By changes all too f and fast *Freedom* 22
Fierceness With such a f that I swoon'd *Holy Grail* 845
Fierier F and stormier from restraining, *Balin and Balan* 229
Fieriest But spurr'd at heart with f energy *To J. M. K.* 7
Fiery for f thoughts Do shape themselves within me, *Œnone* 246
roaring deeps and f sands, *Lotos-Eaters, C. S.* 115
To make my blood run quicker, Used all her f will, *Will Water.* 111
cloud Cuts off the f highway of the sun, *Enoch Arden* 130
chance-met eyes Flash into f life from nothing, *Aylmer's Field* 130
Or down the f gulf as talk of it, *Princess iii* 287
And as the f Sirius alters hue, „ *v* 262
shower the f grain Of freedom broadcast „ 421
And into f splinters leapt the lance, „ 494
Leapt f Passion from the brinks of death; „ *vii* 156
Clash'd with his f few and won; *Ode on Well.* 100
Not sting the f Frenchman into war. *Third of Feb.* 4
Deep tulips dash'd with f dew, *In Mem. lxxxiii* 11
here and there A f finger on the leaves; „ *xcix* 12
which outran The hearer in its f course; „ *cix* 8

Fiery (*continued*) all at *f* speed the two Shock'd on the central bridge, *Gareth and L.* 962
Sir Balin with a *f* 'Ha! *Balin and Balan* 393
But follow Vivien thro' the *f* flood! " 454
A *f* family passion for the name Of Lancelot, *Lancelot and E.* 477
All in a *f* dawning wild with wind " 1020
I saw the *f* face as of a child *Holy Grail* 466
For every *f* prophet in old times, " 876
Shading his eyes till all the *f* cloud, *Lover's Tale i* 306
Like to a low-hung and a *f* sky " *ii* 61
Brother-in-law—the *f* nearness of it— *Sisters (E. and E.)* 173
A *f* scroll written over with lamentation and woe. *Despair* 20
To vex the noon with *f* gems, *Ancient Sage* 265
and Suns along their *f* way, *Locksley H., Sixty* 203
While squirrels from our *f* beech Were bearing off the mast, *Pro. to Gen. Hamley* 3
Three that were next in their *f* course, *Heavy Brigade* 21
lighted from below By the red race of *f* Phlegethon; *Demeter and P.* 28
'A *f* phœnix rising from the smoke, *The Ring* 339
And you spurr'd your *f* horse, *Happy* 76
would wallow in *f* riot and revel On Kilauēä, *Kapiolani* 8
Quail not at the *f* mountain, *Faith* 3
and your *f* clash of meteorites? *God and the Univ.* 3
Fiery-hot *f-h* to burst All barriers *In Mem. cxiv* 13
Fiery-new yet unkept, Had relish *f-n*, *Will Water.* 98
Fiery-short *f-s* was Cyril's counter-scoff, *Princess v* 307
Fife The murmurs of the drum and *f* *Talking Oak* 215
merrily-blowing shrill'd the martial *f*; *Princess v* 251
March with banner and bugle and *f* *Maud I v* 10
Fifteen I ha' work'd for him *f* years, *First Quarrel* 7
and for *f* days or for twenty at most. *Def. of Lucknow* 9
'Hold it for *f* days!' " 105
and his winters were *f* score, *V. of Maeldune* 116
beän chuch-warden mysen i' the parish fur *f* year. *Church-warden, etc.* 8
mountain-like San Philip that, of *f* hundred tons, *The Revenge* 40
Fifth To slant the *f* autumnal slope, *In Mem. xxii* 10
Your *f* September birthday. *The Ring* 423
Our Playwright may show In some *f* Act. *The Play* 4
Fifty Better *f* years of Europe than a cycle of Cathay. *Locksley Hall* 184
Seam'd with the shallow cares of *f* years: *Aylmer's Field* 814
Her that talk'd down the *f* wisest men; *Princess v* 294
finding that of *f* seeds She often brings *In Mem. lv* 11
these have clothed their branchy bowers With *f* Mays, " *lxxvi* 14
And *f* knights rode with them, *Marr. of Geraint* 44
Was wont to glance and sparkle like a gem Of *f* facets; *Geraint and E.* 295
f knights rode with them to the shores Of Severn, " 954
I have not broken bread for *f* hours. *Sir J. Oldcastle* 199
F times the rose has flower'd and faded, *F* times the golden harvest fallen, *On Jub. Q. Victoria* 1
Henry's *f* years are all in shadow, Gray with distance Edward's *f* summers, " 39
F years of ever-broadening Commerce! *F* years of ever-brightening Science! *F* years of ever-widening Empire! " 52
Rose, on this terrace *f* years ago, *Roses on the T.* 1
That blush of *f* years ago, my dear, " 5
on our terrace here Glows in the blue of *f* miles away. " 8
Ah, what shall I be at *f* *Maud I vi* 31
Fifty-fold 'My lord, you overpay me *f-f*.' *Geraint and E.* 220
Fifty-three We are six ships of the line; can we fight with *f-t*?' *The Revenge* 7
Fig *F's* out of thistles, silk from bristles, *Last Tournament* 356
the *f* ran up from the beach and rioted over the land, *V. of Maeldune* 58
Are *f's* of thistles? or grapes of thorns? *Riflemen form!* 10
Fight (s) Ere I rode into the *f*, *Oriana* 21
Laid by the tumult of the *f*. *Margaret* 26
pierce The blackest files of clanging *f*, *Kate* 26
Clanging *f's*, and flaming towns, *Lotos-Eaters, C. S.* 116
He got it; for their captain after *f*, *Aylmer's Field* 226
Sun-shaded in the heat of dusty *f's*) *Princess ii* 241
some grand *f* to kill and make and end: " *iv* 591
And what she did to Cyrus after *f*, " *v* 366

Fight (s) (*continued*) something real, A gallant *f*, a noble princess— *Princess, Con.* 19
He that gain'd a hundred *f's*, *Ode on Well.* 96
For each had warded either in the *f*, *Com. of Arthur* 131
So that I be not fall'n in *f*. *Marr. of Geraint* 223
My lord is weary with the *f* before, *Geraint and E.* 133
pleased To find him yet unwounded after *f*, " 371
I, myself, when flush'd with *f*, " 660
free to stretch his limbs in lawful *f*, " 754
having been With Arthur in the *f* *Lancelot and E.* 287
hear the manner of thy *f* and fall; *Pelleas and E.* 347
Nor ever yet had Arthur fought a *f* Like this *Pass. of Arthur* 93
chance and craft and strength in single *f's*, " 106
But never a moment ceased the *f* *The Revenge* 57
fought such a *f* for a day and a night " 83
fevers, *f's*, Mutinies, treacheries— *Columbus* 225
Each was as brave in the *f* *V. of Maeldune* 5
red with blood the Crescent reels from *f* *Montenegro* 6
some in *f* against the foe, *Locksley H., Sixty* 45
the charge, and the might of the *f*! *Heavy Brigade* 13
Who were held for a while from the *f*, " 36
for he fought Thy *f* for Thee, *Happy* 15
Struck by a poison'd arrow in the *f*, *Death of Œnone* 26
The gladiators moving toward their *f*, *St. Telemachus* 54
Ralph went down like a fire to the *f* *The Tourney* 3
Fight (verb) She saw me *f*, she heard me call, *Oriana* 32
who would *f* and march and countermarch, *Audley Court* 40
brother, where two *f* The strongest wins, *Aylmer's Field* 364
one Should come to *f* with shadows and to fall. *Princess i* 10
Nor would I *f* with iron laws, " *iv* 75
I prove Your knight, and *f* your battle, " 595
'*F*' she said, 'And make us all we would be, " 598
make yourself a man to *f* with men. " *v* 35
I was pledged To *f* in tourney for my bride, " 353
what mother's blood You draw from, *f*; " 405
F and *f* well strike and strike home. " 409
one should *f* with shadows and should fall; " 476
she sees me *f*, Yea, let her see me fall! " 516
I would sooner *f* thrice o'er than see it.' " *vi* 226
king is scared, the soldier will not *f*, " *Con.* 60
a lie which is part a truth is a harder matter to *f*. *Grandmother* 32
Glory of Virtue, to *f*, to struggle, *Wages* 3
She cannot *f* the fear of death. *In Mem. cxiv* 10
teach true life to *f* with mortal wrongs. *Maud I xviii* 54
It is better to *f* for the good than to rail " *III vi* 57
we that *f* for our fair father Christ, *Com. of Arthur* 510
Hereafter I will *f*.' *Gareth and L.* 447
the cur Pluckt from the cur he *f's* with, " 702
F, an thou canst: I have missed the only way.' " 792
To *f* the brotherhood of Day and Night— " 857
Far liefer had I *f* a score of times " 944
Fair words were best for him who *f's* for thee; " 946
Such *f* not I, but answer scorn with scorn. " 953
nor meet To *f* for gentle damsel, " 1177
thou goest, he will *f* thee first; " 1295
yield him this again: 'tis he must *f*: " 1321
Said Gareth laughing, 'An he *f* for this, " 1345
will I *f* him, and will break his pride, *Marr. of Geraint* 221
arms, arms to *f* my enemy? " 282
And *f* and break his pride, and have it of him. " 416
this nephew, *f* In next day's tourney " 475
thou, that hast no lady, canst not *f*.' " 493
I will not *f* my way with gilded arms, *Geraint and E.* 21
he will *f* for me, And win the circlet: *Pelleas and E.* 118
look at mine! but wilt thou *f* for me, " 127
'*F* therefore,' yell'd the youth, " 572
The king who *f's* his people *f's* himself. *Pass. of Arthur* 72
I liked a bigger feller to *f* wi' *North. Cobbler* 100
can we *f* with fifty-three? *The Revenge* 7
fly them for a moment to *f* with them again. " 9
only a hundred seamen to work the ship and to *f*, " 22
'Shall we *f* or shall we fly? " 25
For to *f* is but to die! " 27
many were shatter'd, and so could *f* us no more— " 61
he said '*F* on! *f* on! (repeat) " 63, 69

Fine (*continued*) Cuck-oo!' was ever a May so *f*? *Window, Ay* 10
hair Is golden like thy Mother's, not so *f*.' *The Ring* 104
From head to ancle *f*, *Talking Oak* 224
in *f* linen, not a hair Ruffled upon the scarfskin, *Aylmer's Field* 659
In that *f* air I tremble, all the past *Princess vii* 354
This *f* old world of ours is but a child „ *Con.* 77
Broad brows and fair, a fluent hair and *f*, High nose, a nostril large and *f*, and hands Large, fair and *f*!— *Gareth and L.* 464
fair and *f*, forsooth! Sir Fine-face, Sir Fair-hands? but see thou to it That thine own fineness, Lancelot, some *f* day „ 474
Such *f* reserve and noble reticence, *Geraint and E.* 860
and your *f* epithet Is accurate too, *Merlin and V.* 532
lady never made *unwilling* war With those *f* eyes: „ 604
for *f* plots may fail, „ 820
Told him that her *f* care had saved his life. *Lancelot and E.* 863
But there the *f* Gawain will wonder at me, „ 1054
Then came the *f* Gawain and wonder'd at her, „ 1267
And win me this *f* circlet, Pelleas, *Pelleas and E.* 128
a wire as musically as thou Some such *f* song— *Last Tournament* 324
I thought I could not breathe in that *f* air *Guinevere* 645
Flying by each *f* ear, an Eastern gauze *Lover's Tale iv* 291
F an' meller 'e mun be by this, *North. Cobbler* 101
I warrant ye soom *f* daäy— *Spinster's S's.* 63
An' my oän *f* Jackman i' purple „ 106
'This model husband, this *f* Artist'! *Romney's R.* 124
When *f* Philosophies would fail, *Akbar's Dream* 140

Fine-face Sir *F-f*, Sir Fair-hands? *Gareth and L.* 475

Fineness some pretext of *f* in the meal *Enoch Arden* 341
For often *f* compensated size; *Princess ii* 149
That thine own *f*, Lancelot, *Gareth and L.* 476
force might fail With skill and *f*. „ 1352

Finer Soothe him with thy *f* fancies, *Locksley Hall* 54
A random string Your *f* female sense offends. *Day-Dm., L'Envoi* 2
may soul to soul Strike thro' a *f* element of her own? *Aylmer's Field* 579
And like a *f* light in light. *In Mem. xci* 16
Who wants the *f* politic sense To mask, *Maud I vi* 47
this egg of mine Was *f* gold than any goose can lay; *Gareth and L.* 43
I, the *f* brute rejoicing in my hounds, *By an Evolution.* 7
tho' somewhat *f* than their own, „ 13

Finest because he was The *f* on the tree. *Talking Oak* 238
Are touch'd, are turn'd to *f* air. *Sir Galahad* 72
Of *f* Gothic lighter than a fire, *Princess, Pro.* 92

Finger (adj.) seem'd All-perfect, finish'd to the *f* nail. *Edwin Morris* 22

Finger (s) lets his rosy *f's* play About his mother's neck, *Supp. Confessions* 42
weary with a *f's* touch Those writhed limbs *Clear-headed friend* 22
dare to kiss Thy taper *f's* amorously, *Madeline* 44
Kate snaps her *f's* at my vows; *Kate* 19
Thro' rosy taper *f's* drew Her streaming curls *Mariana in the S.* 15
Three *f's* round the old silver cup— *Miller's D.* 10
With rosy slender *f's* backward drew *Œnone* 176
And on thy heart a *f* lays, *On a Mourner* 11
One rose, but one, by those fair *f's* cull'd, *Gardener's D.* 150
And with a flying *f* swept my lips, „ 246
To save her little *f* from a scratch *Edwin Morris* 63
Baby *f's*, waxen touches, *Locksley Hall* 90
'You would not let your little *f* ache *Godiva* 22
f's steal And touch upon the master-chord *Will Water.* 26
Enoch's golden ring had girt Her *f*, *Enoch Arden* 158
Suddenly put her *f* on the text, „ 497
he dug His *f's* into the wet earth, „ 780
My lady with her *f's* interlock'd, *Aylmer's Field* 199
(I kept the book and had my *f* in it) *Princess, Pro.* 53
And takes a lady's *f* with all care, „ 173
now a pointed *f*, told them all; „ *v* 270
she laid A feeling *f* on my brows, „ *vi* 121
innocent arms And lazy lingering *f's*. „ 139
With trembling *f's* did we weave The holly *In Mem. xxx* 1
God's *f* touch'd him, and he slept. „ *lxxxv* 20
A fiery *f* on the leaves; „ *xcix* 12
With petulant thumb and *f*, shrilling, *Gareth and L.* 750

Finger (s) (*continued*) Myself would work eye dim, and *f* lame, *Marr. of Geraint* 628
He sits unarm'd; I hold a *f* up; *Geraint and E.* 337
moving back she held Her *f* up, „ 453
clench'd her *f's* till they bit the palm, *Lancelot and E.* 611
In colour like the *f's* of a hand Before a burning taper, *Holy Grail* 693
one with shatter'd *f's* dangling lame, *Last Tournament* 60
had let one *f* lightly touch The warm white apple „ 716
Touch'd by the adulterous *f* of a time *To the Queen ii* 43
placed My ring upon the *f* of my bride. *Sisters (E. and E.)* 214
Death at the glimpse of a *f* *Def. of Lucknow* 23
nor voice Nor *f* raised against him— *Sir J. Oldcastle* 45
drew the ring From his dead *f*, *The Ring* 218
His *f's* were so stiffen'd by the frost „ 239
mark ran All round one *f* pointed straight, „ 453
worn the ring—Then torn it from her *f*, „ 456

Finger-ache Who never knewest *f-a*, *Gareth and L.* 87

Fingering *f* at the hair about his lip, *Princess v* 303
F at his sword-handle until he stood *Pelleas and E.* 442

Finger-nail (*See also* **Finger (adj.)**) crush'd with a tap Of my *f-n* on the sand, *Maud II ii* 22

Fingers an' toäs (a disease in turnips) tonups was haäfe on 'em *f a t*, *Church-warden, etc.* 4

Finger-tips she sway'd The rein with dainty *f-t*, *Sir L. and Q. G.* 41

Finials grasping the pews And oaken *f* *Aylmer's Field* 823

Finish I leave not till I *f* this fair quest, *Gareth and L.* 774
'Ay, wilt thou *f* it? Sweet lord, „ 776

Finished when four years were wholly *f*, *Palace of Art* 289
Of such a *f* chasten'd purity. *Isabel* 41
seem'd All-perfect, *f* to the finger-nail. *Edwin Morris* 22
'It is *f*. Man is made.' *Making of Man* 8

Finite-infinite wrought Not Matter, nor the *f-i*, *De Prof., Two G.* 54
Sun, sun, and sun, thro' *f-i* space In *f-i* Time— „ 45

Finn and chanted the triumph of *F*, *V. of Maeldune* 48
And we sang of the triumphs of *F*, „ 88
Go back to the Isle of *F* „ 124
I landed again, with a tithe of my men, on the Isle of *F*. „ 130

Fir tall *f's* and our fast-falling burns; *Gareth and L.* 91
glories of the moon Below black *f's*, *Lover's Tale ii* 111

Fire (s) (*See also* **Afire, Altar-fire, Hell-fire, Idol-fires, Rick-fire**) a bolt of *f* Would rive the slumbrous summer noon *Supp. Confessions* 10
the storm Of running *f's* and fluid range „ 147
Until the latter *f* shall heat the deep; *The Kraken* 13
Thou who stealest *f*, From the fountains *Ode to Memory* 1
Tho' one did fling the *f*. *The Poet* 30
Losing his *f* and active might *Eleänore* 104
a languid *f* creeps Thro' my veins „ 130
with sudden *f's* Flamed over: *Buonaparte* 11
Like Stephen, an unquenched *f*. *Two Voices* 219
O Love, O *f*! once he drew With one long kiss *Fatima* 19
from beyond the noon a *f* Is pour'd upon the hills, „ 30
at their feet the crocus brake like *f*, *Œnone* 96
for she says A *f* dances before her, „ 264
All earth and air seem only burning *f*.' „ 268
Burnt like a fringe of *f*. *Palace of Art* 48
slow-flaming crimson *f's* From shadow'd grots „ 50
And highest, snow and *f*. „ 84
She howl'd aloud, 'I am on *f* within. „ 285
wild marsh-marigold shines like *f* *May Queen* 31
blasts That run before the fluttering tongues of *f*; *D. of F. Women* 30
their *f's* Love tipt his keenest darts; „ 173
The glass blew in, the *f* blew out, *The Goose* 49
hung From Allan's watch, and sparkled by the *f*. *Dora* 136
Or burn'd in *f*, or boil'd in oil, *St. S. Stylites* 52
Sit with their wives by *f's*, „ 108
Have scrambled past those pits of *f*, „ 184
beat the twilight into flakes of *f*. *Tithonus* 42
and winks behind a slowly-dying *f*. *Locksley Hall* 136
with rain or hail, or *f* or snow; „ 193
On the hall-hearths the festal *f's*, *Day-Dm., Sleep. P.* 14
The *f* shot up, the martin flew, „ *Revival* 11
But in my words were seeds of *f*. *The Letters* 28
Fall from his Ocean-lane of *f*, *The Voyage* 19

Fire (s) (*continued*) With wakes of *f* we tore the dark; *The Voyage* 52
'No, I cannot praise the *f* In your eye— *Vision of Sin* 183
All-kindled by a still and sacred *f*, *Enoch Arden* 71
Keep a clean hearth and a clear *f* for me, ” 192
And flung her down upon a couch of *f*, *Aylmer's Field* 574
flood, *f*, earthquake, thunder, wrought ” 639
as not passing thro' the *f* Bodies, but souls— ” 671
No desolation but by sword and *f*? ” 748
a *f*, The *f* that left a roofless Ilion, *Lucretius* 64
altho' his *f* is on my face Blinding, ” 144
her arm lifted, eyes on *f*— *Princess, Pro.* 41
Of finest Gothic lighter than a *f*, ” 92
made to kill Time by the *f* in winter.' ” 205
But chafing me on *f* to find my bride) ” *i* 166
Burnt like the mystic *f* on a mast-head, ” *iv* 274
bloom As of some *f* against a stormy cloud, ” 384
The next, like *f* he meets the foe, ” 583
red-faced war has rods of steel and *f*; ” *v* 118
living hearts that crack within the *f* ” 379
the *f's* of Hell Mix with his hearth: ” 454
out of stricken helmets sprang the *f*. ” 495
Break from a darken'd future, crown'd with *f*, ” *vi* 175
Flash, ye cities, in rivers of *f*! *W. to Alexander* 19
the tongue is a *f* as you know, my dear, the tongue is a *f*. *Grandmother* 28
moon like a rick on *f* was rising over the dale, ” 39
The giant windows' blazon'd *f's*, *The Daisy* 58
Then thorpe and byre arose in *f*, *The Victim* 3
At his highest with sunrise *f*; *Voice and the P.* 30
Thunder, a flying *f* in heaven, *Boädicea* 24
many a *f* before them blazed: *Spec. of Iliad* 10
many a *f* between the ships and stream ” 17
Sat fifty in the blaze of burning *f*; ” 20
And *f's* burn clear, And frost is here *Window, Winter* 4
The *f's* are all the clearer, ” 16
king of the wrens with a crown of *f*. ” *Ay* 16
A looming bastion fringed with *f*. *In Mem. xv* 20
Is shrivell'd in a fruitless *f*, ” *liv* 11
Laburnums, dropping-wells of *f*. ” *lxxxiii* 12
shine Beside the never-lighted *f*. ” *lxxxiv* 20
But on her forehead sits a *f*: ” *cxiv* 5
And compass'd by the *f's* of Hell; ” *cxxvii* 17
And on the downs a rising *f*: ” *Con.* 108
f of a foolish pride flash'd over *Maud I iv* 16
Cold *f's*, yet with power to burn and brand ” *xviii* 39
f's of Hell brake out of thy rising sun, The *f's* of Hell and of Hate; ” *II i* 9
blood-red blossom of war with a heart of *f*. ” *III vi* 53
f of God Descends upon thee in the battle-field: *Com. of Arthur* 128
And all at once all round him rose in *f*, ” 389
the child and he were clothed in *f*. ” 390
echo'd by old folk beside their *f's* For comfort ” 417
the herd was driven, *F* glimpsed; ” 433
a city all on *f* With sun and cloth of gold, ” 479
I will walk thro' *f*, Mother, to gain it— *Gareth and L.* 133
'Will ye walk thro' *f*? Who walks thro' *f* will hardly heed the smoke. ” 142
f, That lookt half-dead, brake bright, ” 684
For an your *f* be low ye kindle mine! ” 711
But up like *f* he started: ” 1123
forage for the horse, and flint for *f*. ” 1277
Glow'd like the heart of a great *f* at Yule, *Marr. of Geraint* 559
night of *f*, when Edyrn sack'd their house, ” 634
loosed in words of sudden *f* the wrath *Geraint and E.* 106
In a hollow land, From which old *f's* have broken, men may fear Fresh *f* and ruin. ” 822
f of Heaven has kill'd the barren cold, *Balin and Balan* 440
f of heaven is not the flame of Hell. (repeat) ” 443, 447, 451, 455
Yet in your frosty cells ye feel the *f*! ” 446
'The *f* of Heaven is on the dusty ways. ” 448
'The *f* of Heaven is lord of all things good, And starve not thou this *f* within thy blood, ” 452
'This *f* of heaven, This old sun-worship, ” 456
into such a song, such *f* for fame, *Merlin and V.* 417

Fire (s) (*continued*) Rage like a *f* among the noblest names, *Merlin and V.* 802
Her godlike head crown'd with spiritual *f*, ” 837
in this heathen war the *f* of God Fills him: *Lancelot and E.* 315
shot red *f* and shadows thro' the cave, ” 414
So ran the tale like *f* about the court, ” 734
F in dry stubble a nine-days' wonder flared: ” 735
wrapt In unremorseful folds of rolling *f*. *Holy Grail* 261
while ye follow wandering *f's* Lost in the quagmire! ” 319
most of us would follow wandering *f's*, (repeat) ” 369, 599
years of death, Sprang into *f*: ” 497
Sprang into *f* and vanish'd, ” 506
Must be content to sit by little *f's*. ” 614
A mocking *f*: 'what other *f* than he, ” 670
methought I spied A dying *f* of madness ” 768
most of them would follow wandering *f's*, ” 891
Burnt as a living *f* of emeralds, *Pelleas and E.* 35
A vision hovering on a sea of *f*, ” 52
a sacrifice Kindled by *f* from heaven; ” 146
thro' his heart The *f* of honour and all noble deeds Flash'd, ” 278
maiden snow mingled with sparks of *f*. *Last Tournament* 149
Who sits and gazes on a faded *f*, ” 157
Arthur's vows on the great lake of *f*. ” 345
one was water and one star was *f*, ” 736
Pray for him that he scape the doom of *f*, *Guinevere* 347
The children born of thee are sword and *f*, ” 425
making all the night a steam of *f*. ” 599
land of old unheaven from the abyss By *f*, *Pass. of Arthur* 83
and blew Fresh *f* into the sun, *Lover's Tale i* 319
Thy *f's* from heaven had touch'd it, ” 439
dragonfly Shot by me like a flash of purple *f*. ” *ii* 17
Fill'd all with pure clear *f*, ” 146
Had suck'd the *f* of some forgotten sun, ” *iv* 194
and all *f* again Thrice in a second, ” 323
if my boy be gone to the *f*? *Rizpah* 78
an' I seeäd 'im a-gittin' o' *f*; *North. Cobbler* 26
an' 'e shined like a sparkle o' *f*. ” 48
leaves i' the middle to kindle the *f*; *Village Wife* 72
F from ten thousand at once of the rebels *Def. of Lucknow* 22
Sharp is the *f* of assault, ” 57
thou bringest Not peace, a sword, a *f*. *Sir J. Oldcastle* 36
and life Pass in the *f* of Babylon! ” 124
Who rose and doom'd me to the *f*. ” 172
How now, my soul, we do not heed the *f*? ” 191
For I must live to testify by *f*.' ” 206
Thro' the *f* of the tulip and poppy, *V. of Maeldune* 43
And we came to the Isle of *F*: ” 71
For the peak sent up one league of *f* ” 72
There were some leap'd into the *f*; ” 76
Dashing the *f's* and the shadows of dawn ” 99
with set of sun Their *f's* flame thickly, *Achilles over the T.* 11
To see the dread, unweariable *f* ” 27
Shrine-shattering earthquake, *f*, flood, thunderbolt, *Tiresias* 61
On one far height in one far-shining *f*. ” 185
'One height and one far-shining *f*.' ” 186
Flashing with *f's* as of God, *Despair* 16
and a smoke who was once a pillar of *f*, ” 29
Love is *f*, and burns the feet *The Flight* 68
cut his bit o' turf for the *f*? *Tomorrow* 65
Gone the *f's* of youth, the follies, *Locksley H., Sixty* 39
Gone like *f's* and floods and earthquakes ” 40
F's that shook me once, but now to silent ashes ” 41
f of fever creeps across the rotted floor, ” 223
The *f's* that arch this dusky dot— *Epilogue* 52
Ilion's lofty temples robed in *f*, *To Virgil* 2
One shriek'd 'The *f's* of Hell!' *Dead Prophet* 80
To and thro' the Doomsday *f*, *Helen's Tower* 10
all the hateful *f's* Of torment, *Demeter and P.* 151
'e coom'd thruf the f *wi' my bairn i' 'is mouth* *Owd Roä* 92
the *f* was a-raägin' an' raävin' ” 110
Fur we moänt 'ev naw moor *f's*— ” 118
vows that are snapt in a moment of *f*; *Vastness* 26
f from Heaven had dash'd him dead, *Happy* 83
blasted to the deathless *f* of Hell. ” 84
lured me from the household *f* on earth. *Romney's R.* 40

Fire (s) (*continued*) The coals of *f* you heap upon my head *Romney's R.* 141
If the lips were touch'd with *f* *Parnassus* 17
the *f* within him would not falter; „ 19
Stark and dark in his funeral *f*. *To Master of B.* 20
mixt herself with *him* and past in *f*. *Death of Œnone* 106
'Is earth On *f* to the West? *St. Telemachus* 19
were seen or heard *F's* of Sűttee, *Akbar's Dream* 196
passing souls thro' *f* to the *f*, *The Dawn* 4
Ralph went down like a *f* to the fight *The Tourney* 3
in the glare of deathless *f*! *Faith* 8
f—thro' one that will not shame *Gareth and L.* 1310
Fire (verb) The furzy prickle *f* the dells, *Two Voices* 71
And *f's* your narrow casement glass, *Miller's D.* 243
I, by Lionel sitting, saw his face *F*, *Lover's Tale iv* 323
Now let it speak, and you *f*, *Def. of Lucknow* 29
It is charged and we *f*, and they run. „ 68
Fire-balloon a *f-b* Rose gem-like up *Princess, Pro.* 74
Firebrand this *f*—gentleness To such as her! „ *v* 167
Fire-crown'd The *f-c* king of the wrens, *Window, Ay.* 8
Fired Not a gun was *f*. *The Captain* 40
man with knobs and wires and vials *f* A cannon; *Princess, Pro.* 65
Now *f* an angry Pallas on the helm, „ *vi* 367
He rose at dawn and, *f* with hope, *Sailor Boy* 1
he saw *F* from the west, far on a hill, *Lancelot and E.* 168
the heat Of pride and glory *f* her face; *Pelleas and E.* 172
that Gawain *f* The hall of Merlin, „ 517
echoing yell with yell, they *f* the tower, *Last Tournament* 478
F all the pale face of the Queen, *Guinevere* 357
Fire-fly Glitter like a swarm of *fire-flies* *Locksley Hall* 10
The *f-f* wakens: waken thou with me. *Princess vii* 179
Firefly-like glitter *f-l* in copse And linden alley: „ *i* 208
Fire-hollowing *F-h* this in Indian fashion, fell *Enoch Arden* 569
Fireside her old *f* Be cheer'd with tidings of the bride, *In Mem. xl* 22
at your own *f*, With the evil tongue *Maud I x* 50
Firewood heap'd Their *f*, and the winds *Spec. of Iliad* 7
Firm (adj. and adv.) Not swift nor slow to change, but *f*: *Love thou thy land* 31
With measured footfall *f* and mild, *Two Voices* 413
Thereon I built it *f*. *Palace of Art* 9
Like Virtue *f*, like Knowledge fair, *Voyage* 68
His resolve Upbore him, and *f* faith, *Enoch Arden* 800
f upon his feet, And like an oaken stock *Golden Year* 61
Not one stroke *f*. *Romney's R.* 115
he stood *f*; and so the matter hung; (repeat) *The Brook* 144, 148
Her *f* will, her fix'd purpose. *The Ring* 293
f Tho' compass'd by two armies *Princess v* 344
Some civic manhood *f* against the crowd— „ *Con.* 57
keep the soldier *f*, the statesman pure: *Ode on Well.* 222
Met his full frown timidly *f*, and said; *Geraint and E.* 71
felt Her low *f* voice and tender government. „ 194
Firm (s) Head of all the golden-shafted *f*, *Princess ii* 405
Firmament Shoot your stars to the *f*, *On Jub. Q. Victoria* 17
Firm-based stand *F-b* with all her Gods. *Tiresias* 142
Firmer Stept forward on a *f* leg, *Will Water.* 123
And slowly forms the *f* mind, *In Mem. xviii* 18
mine is the *f* seat, *Lancelot and E.* 446
Firmly Will *f* hold the rein, *Politics* 6
Firmness and said to him With timid *f*, *Geraint and E.* 140
Firry heard the tender dove In *f* woodlands making moan; *Miller's D.* 42
First (adj.) (*See also* **Fust**) in her *f* sleep earth breathes stilly: *Leonine Eleg.* 7
When the *f* matin-song hath waken'd loud *Ode to Memory* 68
In setting round thy *f* experiment „ 81
Needs must thou dearly love thy *f* essay, „ 83
The *f* house by the water-side, *L. of Shalott iv* 34
From that *f* nothing ere his birth *Two Voices* 332
For is not our *f* year forgot? „ 368
foundation-stones were laid Since my *f* memory?' *Palace of Art* 236
Dan Chaucer, the *f* warbler, whose sweet breath *D. of F. Women* 5
Love at *f* sight, first-born, and heir to all, *Gardener's D.* 189
beheld her ere she knew my heart, My *f*, last love; „ 277
once I ask'd him of his early life, And his *f* passion; *Edwin Morris* 24
when the *f* low matin-chirp hath grown Full quire, *Love and Duty* 98
Or this *f* snowdrop of the year *St. Agnes' Eve* 11
'Tell me tales of thy *f* love— *Vision of Sin* 163
In him woke, With his *f* babe's *f* cry, *Enoch Arden* 85

First (adj.) (*continued*) Has she no fear that her *f* husband lives?' *Enoch Arden* 806
Leolin's *f* nurse was, five years after, hers: *Aylmer's Field* 79
and the *f* embrace has died Between them, *Lucretius* 3
Was it the *f* beam of my latest day? „ 59
Huge Ammonites, and the *f* bones of Time; *Princess, Pro.* 15
took advantage of his strength to be *F* in the field: „ *ii* 153
'Fresh as the *f* beam glittering on a sail, „ *iv* 44
Deep as *f* love, and wild with all regret; „ 57
lines of green that streak the white Of the *f* snowdrop's inner leaves; „ *v* 197
From our *f* Charles by force we wrung our claims. *Third of Feb.* 26
That was the *f* time, too, *Grandmother* 61
Since our *f* Sun arose and set. *In Mem. xxiv* 8
Where thy *f* form was made a man; „ *lxi* 10
F love, *f* friendship, equal powers, „ *lxxxv* 107
Seal'd her mine from her *f* sweet breath. *Maud I xix* 41
But those *f* days had golden hours for me, *Com. of Arthur* 357
let my name Be hidd'n, and give me the *f* quest, *Gareth and L.* 545
'I have given him the *f* quest: „ 582
In the *f* shallow shade of a deep wood, *Geraint and E.* 119
O'er the four rivers the *f* roses blew, „ 764
who held and lost with Lot In that *f* war, *Balin and Balan* 2
which ruin'd man Thro' woman the *f* hour: *Merlin and V.* 363
Hurt in his *f* tilt was my son, Sir Torre. *Lancelot and E.* 196
never woman yet, since man's *f* fall, „ 859
This is not love: but love's *f* flash in youth, „ 949
Embraced me, and so kiss'd me the *f* time, *Holy Grail* 596
O the pity To find thine own *f* love once more— „ 620
But I and the *f* daisy on his grave *Lover's Tale i* 193
should this *f* master claim His service, „ *iv* 265
As I of mine, and my *f* passion. *Sisters (E. and E.)* 67
Love at *f* sight May seem— „ 91
at *f* glimpse and for a face Gone in a moment— „ 93
I sail'd On my *f* voyage, harass'd by the frights Of my *f* crew, *Columbus* 67
scouted by court and king—The *f* discoverer starves— „ 166
Who fain had pledged her jewels on my *f* voyage, „ 229
With the *f* great love I had felt for the *f* and greatest of men; *The Wreck* 76
The *f* gray streak of earliest summer-dawn, *Ancient Sage* 220
Leave the Master in the *f* dark hour of his last sleep alone. *Locksley H., Sixty* 238
Bound by the golden cord of their *f* love— *The Ring* 429
First (s) And these had been together from the *f*; *Aylmer's Field* 713
First-born love thou bearest The *f-b* of thy genius. *Ode to Memory* 92
Love at first sight, *f-b*, and heir to all, *Gardener's D.* 189
meal she makes On the *f-b* of her sons. *Vision of Sin* 146
First-famed of the two *f-f* for courtesy— *Guinevere* 323
First-fruits The *f-f* of the stranger: *Princess ii* 44
Firstling And bring the *f* to the flock; *In Mem. ii* 6
Ever as of old time, Solitary *f*, *The Snowdrop* 4
Firth find him dropt upon the *f's* of ice, *Princess vii* 206
By *f* and loch thy silver sister grow, *Sir J. Oldcastle* 58
Fish *F* are we that love the mud, *Vision of Sin* 101
beast or bird or *f*, or opulent flower: *Lucretius* 249
the bird, the *f*, the shell, the flower, *Princess ii* 383
bird in air, and *f'es* turn'd And whiten'd *The Victim* 19
o'er her breast floated the sacred *f*; *Gareth and L.* 223
'If we have *f* at all Let them be gold; *Marr. of Geraint* 669
vanish'd panic-stricken, like a shoal Of darting *f*, *Geraint and E.* 469
an' ya thraw'd the *f* i' 'is faäce, *Church-warden, etc.* 30
Fish'd An' 'e niver not *f* 'is awn ponds, *Village Wife* 43
Fisherman O well for the *f's* boy, *Break, break, etc.* 5
A luckier or a bolder *f*, *Enoch Arden* 49
Fishing-nets coils of cordage, swarthy *f-n*, „ 17
and wrought To make the boatmen *f-n*, „ 815
Fist tiny *f* Had graspt a daisy from your Mother's grave— *The Ring* 322
Fit (adj.) I scarce am *f* for your great plans: *Princess vi* 218
Becoming as is meet and *f* A link *In Mem. xl* 14
asking, one Not *f* to cope your quest. *Gareth and L.* 1174
ye that scarce are *f* to touch, *Pelleas and E.* 292
O happy he, and *f* to live, *The Wanderer* 9
Fit (s) Gleam'd to the flying moon by *f's*. *Miller's D.* 116
in a *f* of frolic mirth She strove to span my waist: *Talking Oak* 137

Fit (s) (*continued*) Or breaking into song by *f's*, *In Mem. xxiii* 2
only breathe Short *f's* of prayer, *Geraint and E.* 155
Began to break her sports with graver *f's*, *Merlin and V.* 180
the riotous *f's* Of wine and harlotry— *Sir J. Oldcastle* 100
Fit (verb) *f* us like a nature second-hand; *Walk. to the Mail* 65
f their little streetward sitting-room *Enoch Arden* 170
sad and slow, As *f's* an universal woe, *Ode on Well.* 14
harden'd skins That *f* him like his own; *Gareth and L.* 1094
better *f's* Our mended fortunes and a Prince's bride: *Marr. of Geraint* 717
Fitful like *f* blasts of balm To one that travels quickly, *Gardener's D.* 68
Fitly yield your flower of life To one more *f* yours, *Lancelot and E.* 953
Fitted Power *f* to the season; wisdom-bred *Œnone* 123
Gown'd in pure white, that *f* to the shape— *Gardener's D.* 126
So now 'tis *f* on and grows to me, *St. S. Stylites* 209
old and formal, *f* to thy petty part, *Locksley Hall* 93
As his unlikeness *f* mine. *In Mem. lxxix* 20
No stone is *f* in yon marble girth *Tiresias* 135
Who *f* stone to stone again, *Akbar's Dream* 193
Fitter a villain *f* to stick swine Than ride abroad *Gareth and L.* 865
I am *f* for my bed, or for my grave, *The Ring* 433
Fitting expert In *f* aptest words to things, *In Mem. lxxv* 6
and *f* close Or flying looselier, *Akbar's Dream* 131
Whence shall she take a *f* mate? *Kate* 13
She cannot find a *f* mate. ,, 31
Fitz Old *F*, who from your suburb grange, *To E. Fitzgerald* 1
which you will take My *F*, and welcome, ,, 51
Five Alone and warming his *f* wits, (repeat) *The Owl i* 6, 13
Young Nature thro' *f* cycles ran, *Two Voices* 17
Lord of the senses *f*; *Palace of Art* 180
You know there has not been for these *f* years *Dora* 65
and here it comes With *f* at top: *Walk. to the Mail* 113
Leolin's first nurse was, *f* years after, hers: *Aylmer's Field* 79
son A Walter too,—with others of our set, *F* others: *Princess, Pro.* 9
And those *f* years its richest field. *In Mem. xlvi* 12
beneath *f* figures, armed men, *Gareth and L.* 1205
'Take *F* horses and their armours;' *Geraint and E.* 409
and hath overborne *F* knights at once, *Holy Grail* 303
f summers back, And left me; *Guinevere* 321
So Lord Howard past away with *f* ships of war *The Revenge* 13
swarm Of Turkish Islam for *f* hundred years, *Montenegro* 11
F young kings put asleep by the sword-stroke, *Batt. of Brunanburh* 52
Five-acre While Harry is in the *f-a* *Grandmother* 80
Five-beaded The tender pink *f-b* baby-soles, *Aylmer's Field* 186
Five-fold *f-f* thy term Of years, I lay; *Tiresias* 33
Five-words-long quoted odes, and jewels *f-w-l* *Princess ii* 377
Fix Holding the bush, to *f* it back, she stood, *Gardener's D.* 127
'Twere all as one to *f* our hopes on Heaven *Golden Year* 57
She could not *f* the glass to suit her eye; *Enoch Arden* 241
and her lynx eye To *f* and make me hotter, *Princess iii* 47
Sun sets, moon sets, Love, *f* a day. *Window, When* 4
wait a little, You shall *f* a day.' ,, 12
Nor cares to *f* itself to form, *In Mem. xxxiii* 4
And *f* my thoughts on all the glow ,, *lxxxiv* 3
Who shall *f* Her pillars? ,, *cxiv* 3
Fixed-Fixt there like a sun remain *Fix'd*— *Eleänore* 93
'Not that the grounds of hope were *fix'd*, *Two Voices* 227
Be *fix'd* and froz'n to permanence: ,, 237
And, last, you *fix'd* a vacant stare, *L. C. V. de Vere* 47
Counting the dewy pebbles, *fix'd* in thought; *M. d'Arthur* 84
The blush is *fix'd* upon her cheek. *Day-Dm., Sleep. P.* 32
One *fix'd* for ever at the door, *Will Water.* 143
And *fix't* upon the far sea-line; *The Voyage* 62
Were *fixed* shadows of thy *fixed* mood, *Isabel* 9
orb of moving Circumstance Roll'd round by one *fix'd* law. *Palace of Art* 256
True love turn'd round on *fixed* poles, *Love thou thy land* 5
my fresh but *fixt* resolve To pass away *Holy Grail* 737
either *fixt* his heart On that one girl; *Enoch Arden* 39
where he *fixt* his heart he set his hand ,, 294
and *fixt* her swimming eyes upon him, ,, 325
fixt the Sabbath. Darkly that day rose: *Aylmer's Field* 609
And those *fixt* eyes of painted ancestors ,, 832
I *fixt* My wistful eyes on two fair images, *Sea Dreams* 239

Fixed-Fixt (*continued*) eyes Of shining expectation *fixt* on mine. *Princess iv* 153
Fixt like a beacon-tower above the waves ,, 493
this is *fixt* As are the roots of earth ,, *v* 445
Fix'd in yourself, never in your own arms ,, *vi* 177
drags me down From my *fixt* height to mob me ,, 308
I on her *Fixt* my faint eyes, and utter'd whisperingly: ,, *vii* 144
she *fixt* A showery glance upon her aunt, ,, *Con.* 32
Fixt by their cars, waited the golden dawn. *Spec. of Iliad* 22
But Sorrow—*fixt* upon the dead, *In Mem. xxxix* 8
Her faith is *fixt* and cannot move, ,, *xcvii* 33
Because he felt so *fix'd* in truth: ,, *cxxv* 8
And a morbid eating lichen *fixt* On a heart *Maud I vi* 77
Gareth likewise on them *fixt* his eyes *Gareth and L.* 236
with *fixt* eye following the three. *Marr. of Geraint* 237
Two forks are *fixt* into the meadow ground, ,, 482
there they *fixt* the forks into the ground, ,, 548
a rock in ebbs and flows, *Fixt* on her faith. ,, 813
humbly hopeful, rose *Fixt* on her hearer's, *Merlin and V.* 87
or all-silent gaze upon him With such a *fixt* devotion, ,, 183
but that other clung to him, *Fixt* in her will, ,, 188
So *fixt* her fancy on him: let them be. ,, 777
ye *fixt* Your limit, oft returning with the tide. *Lancelot and E.* 1040
Counting the dewy pebbles, *fix'd* in thought; *Pass. of Arthur* 252
and virgin eyes Remaining *fixt* on mine, *Tiresias* 47
With sad eyes *fixt* on the lost sea-home, *The Wreck* 126
'*That* should be *fix'd*,' she said; *The Ring* 316
But after ten slow weeks her *fix'd* intent, ,, 345
Her firm will, her *fix'd* purpose. ,, 293
Fixing warm blood mixing; The eyeballs *f*. *All Things will Die* 34
F full eyes of question on her face, *Com. of Arthur* 312
F my eyes on those three cypress-cones *Lover's Tale ii* 38
Fixt *See* **Fixed**
Flaäme (**flame**) 'at summun seed i' the *f*, *Owd Roä* 94
Flaccid a scheme that had left us *f* and drain'd. *Maud I i* 20
Flag never floats an European *f*, *Locksley Hall* 161
F's, flutter out upon turrets and towers! *W. to Alexander* 15
their sails and their masts and their *f's*, *The Revenge* 116
thou would'st have her *f* Borne on thy coffin— *Ded. Poem Prin. Alice* 16
But one—he was waving a *f*— *The Wreck* 119
wherever her *f* fly, Glorying between sea and sky, *Open I. and C. Exhib.* 17
One life, one *f*, one fleet, one Throne!' ,, 39
Flag-flower tall *f-f's* when they sprung *Miller's D.* 53
Flagrante Caught *in f*—what's the Latin word?— *Walk. to the Mail* 34
Flagship stately Spanish men to their *f* bore him *The Revenge* 97
Flail From Arac's arm, as from a giant's *f*, *Princess v* 500
A thresher with his *f* had scatter'd them. *Gareth and L.* 842
Flake (*See also* **Blossom-flake, Foam-flakes**) sea-wind sang Shrill, chill, with *f's* of foam. *M. d'Arthur* 49
beat the twilight into *f's* of fire. *Tithonus* 42
here and there a foamy *f* Upon me, *The Brook* 59
thicker, like the *f's* In a fall of snow, *Lucretius* 166
Before me shower'd the rose in *f's*; *Princess iv* 264
This *f* of rainbow flying on the highest ,, *v* 319
rocket molten into *f's* Of crimson *In Mem. xcviii* 31
sea-wind sang Shrill, chill, with *f's* of foam. *Pass. of Arthur* 217
gladly see I thro' the wavering *f's* *Prog. of Spring* 29
Flaky Diffused and molten into *f* cloud. *Lover's Tale i* 641
Flame (s) (*See also* **Altar-flame, Flaäme, Martyr-flames, Sun-flame, Under-flame**) With the clear-pointed *f* of chastity, *Isabel* 2
A subtle, sudden *f*, By veering passion fann'd, *Madeline* 28
alight As with the quintessence of *f*, *Arabian Nights* 123
arrows of his thoughts were headed And wing'd with *f*, *The Poet* 12
in her raiment's hem was traced in *f* Wisdom, ,, 45
Burn'd like one burning *f* together, *L. of Shalott iii* 22
A thousand little shafts of *f* *Fatima* 17
She died: she went to burning *f*: *The Sisters* 7
thro' the topmost Oriels' coloured *f* *Palace of Art* 161
hollow shades enclosing hearts of *f*, ,, 241
Dark faces pale against that rosy *f*, *Lotos-Eaters* 26
'Saw God divide the night with flying *f*, *D. of F. Women* 225
Beheld the dead *f* of the fallen day *Enoch Arden* 441

Flame (s) (*continued*) His hair as it were crackling into *f's*, *Aylmer's Field* 586
and girt With song and *f* and fragrance, *Lucretius* 134
on a tripod in the midst A fragrant *f* rose, *Princess iv* 34
her eye with slow dilation roll'd Dry *f*, „ *vi* 190
Now set a wrathful Dian's moon on *f*, „ 368
F's, on the windy headland flare! *W. to Alexandra* 16
Or down in a furrow scathed with *f*: *The Victim* 22
Pierces the keen seraphic *f* *In Mem. xxx* 27
This round of green, this orb of *f*, „ *xxxiv* 5
And Life, a Fury slinging *f*. „ *l* 8
As slowly steals a silver *f* „ *lxvii* 6
Who might'st have heaved a windless *f* „ *lxxii* 13
Ray round with *f's* her disk of seed, „ *ci* 6
Ready to burst in a colour'd *f*; *Maud I vi* 19
and all the wave was in a *f*: And down the wave and in the *f* was borne A naked babe, *Com. of Arthur* 382
kings of old had doom'd thee to the *f's*, *Gareth and L.* 374
I spring Like *f* from ashes.' „ 546
sparkle in the blood Break into furious *f*; *Geraint and E.* 828
seems a *f* That rages in the woodland far below, *Balin and Balan* 233
fire of Heaven is not the *f* of Hell. (repeat) „ 443, 447, 451, 455
Touch flax with *f*—a glance will serve— *Merlin and V.* 111
darken down To rise hereafter in a stiller *f* *Lancelot and E.* 1319
such a fervent *f* of human love, *Holy Grail* 74
Against the *f* about a sacrifice Kindled *Pelleas and E.* 145
star Reel'd in the smoke, brake into *f*, and fell. „ 519
all their dewy hair blown back like *f*: *Guinevere* 284
in the dark of mine Is traced with *f*. *Lover's Tale i* 298
his high hills, with *f* Milder and purer. „ 322
his own Sent such a *f* into his face, „ *iv* 177
with her battle-thunder and *f*; *The Revenge* 59
Dooms our unlicensed preacher to the *f*, *Sir J. Oldcastle* 105
and the dwelling broke into *f*; *V. of Maeldune* 32
from it lighted an all-shining *f*. *Achilles over the T.* 6
The flight of birds, the *f* of sacrifice, *Tiresias* 6
flung the conquer'd Christian into *f's*. *Locksley H., Sixty* 84
eloquence caught like a *f* From zone to zone *Dead Prophet* 34
The *f* of life went wavering down; *To Marq. of Dufferin* 32
saw The ring of faces redden'd by the *f's* *Death of Œnone* 92
in the *f* that measures Time! *Akbar's D., Hymn* 8
Dance in a fountain of *f* with her devils, *Kapiolani* 10
Than a rotten fleet and a city in *f's*! *Riflemen form!* 18

Flame (verb) barking cur Made her cheek *f*: *Godiva* 58
wild peasant rights himself, the rick *F's*, *Princess iv* 386
when the long-illumined cities *f*, *Ode on Well.* 228
Shall fears and jealous hatreds *f* again? *W. to Marie Alex.* 41
For him did his high sun *f*, *Maud I iv* 32
f's The blood-red blossom of war „ *III vi* 52
Let it *f* or fade, and the war roll down „ 54
f At sunrise till the people in far fields, *Holy Grail* 242
He saw them—headland after headland *f* *Guinevere* 243
with set of sun Their fires *f* thickly, *Achilles over the T.* 11
sun has risen To *f* along another dreary day. *Romney's R.* 58

Flame-banner great *f-b* borne by Teneriffe, *Columbus* 69

Flame-billow Into the *f-b* dash'd the berries, *Kapiolani* 33

Flame-colour smote *F-c*, vert and azure, *Com. of Arthur* 274

Flamed with sudden fires *F* over: *Buonaparte* 12
And *f* upon the brazen greaves *L. of Shalott iii* 4
By peaks that *f*, or, all in shade, *The Voyage* 41
F in his cheek; and eager eyes, *Aylmer's Field* 66
Tho' Leolin *f* and fell again, „ 409
scarlet of berries that *f* upon bine and vine, *V. of Maeldune* 61
or *f* at a public wrong. *The Wreck* 68
and *f* On one huge slope beyond, *St. Telemachus* 7

Flamest Once again thou *f* heavenward, *Akbar's D., Hymn* 1

Flaming (*See also* **Slow-flaming**) *f* downward over all From heat to heat *Mariana in the S.* 77
Clanging fights, and *f* towns, *Lotos-Eaters, C. S.* 116
doom of treason and the *f* death, *Guinevere* 538
that red night When thirty ricks, All *f*, *To Mary Boyle* 37

Flank (adj.) better aimed are your *f* fusillades— *Def. of Lucknow* 57

Flank (s) arisen since With cities on their *f's*— *Merlin and V.* 676

Flap and the great echo *f* And buffet *Golden Year* 76

Flap (*continued*) dimpled flounce of the sea-furbelow *f*, *Sea Dreams* 266
a boat Tacks, and the slacken'd sail *f's*, *Princess ii* 186

Flapp'd-Flapt They *flapp'd* my light out as I read: *St. S. Stylites* 175
conquering battle or *flapt* to the battle-cry! *Def. of Lucknow* 2

Flare Flames, on the windy headland *f*! *W. to Alexandra* 16
F from Tel-el-Kebir Thro' darkness, *Pro. to Gen. Hamley* 28

Flar'd threaten'd darkness, *f* and fell: *M. d'Arthur, Ep.* 2
a great mist-blotted light *F* on him, *Enoch Arden* 681
Fire in dry stubble a nine-days' wonder *f*: *Lancelot and E.* 735
blood-red light of dawn *F* on her face, „ 1026

Flaring (*See also* **Sudden-flaring**) A million tapers *f* bright From twisted silvers *Arabian Nights* 124
Sees in heaven the light of London *f* *Locksley Hall* 114
I saw the *f* atom-streams And torrents *Lucretius* 38
Thro' blasted valley and *f* forest *Kapiolani* 12

Flash (s) The lightning *f* atween the rains, *Rosalind* 12
A living *f* of light he flew.' *Two Voices* 15
ran by him without speaking, like a *f* of light. *May Queen* 18
a shape, a shade, A *f* of light. *St. S. Stylites* 203
The *f's* come and go; *St. Agnes' Eve* 26
The lightning *f* of insect and of bird, *Enoch Arden* 575
A *f* of semi-jealousy clear'd it to her. *Aylmer's Field* 189
and once the *f* of a thunderbolt— *Lucretius* 27
I learnt more from her in a *f*, *Princess ii* 397
These *f'es* on the surface are not he. „ *iv* 253
And like a *f* the weird affection came: „ *v* 477
Down in the South is a *f* and a groan: *Window, Gone* 8
You send a *f* to the sun. *Window, Marr. Morn.* 2
A little *f*, a mystic hint; *In Mem. xliv* 8
As in the former *f* of joy, „ *cxxii* 15
at the *f* and motion of the man They vanish'd *Geraint and E.* 467
I saw the *f* of him but yestereven. *Balin and Balan* 303
And chased the *f'es* of his golden horns *Merlin and V.* 427
send One *f*, that, missing all things else, „ 932
free *f'es* from a height Above her, *Lancelot and E.* 647
but love's first *f* in youth, Most common: „ 949
'Ay, a *f*, I fear me, that will strike „ 970
I told her that her love Was but the *f* of youth, „ 1318
F upon *f* they lighten thro' me— *Lover's Tale i* 51
Shot by me like a *f* of purple fire. „ *ii* 17
The light was but a *f*, and went again. „ *iv* 55

Flash (verb) And *f'es* off a thousand ways, *Rosalind* 23
of tentimes they *f* and glitter Like sunshine „ 28
F in the pools of whirling Simois. *Œnone* 206
f the lightnings, weigh the Sun. *Locksley Hall* 186
This proverb *f'es* thro' his head, *Day-Dm., Arrival* 15
F into fiery life from nothing, *Aylmer's Field* 130
naked marriages *F* from the bridge, „ 766
F, ye cities, in rivers of fire! *W. to Alexandra* 19
The facets of the glorious mountain *f* *The Islet* 22
in the vale You *f* and lighten afar, *Window, Marr. Morn.* 10
F, I am coming, I come, „ 31
F for a million miles. „ 24
And *f'es* into false and true, *In Mem. xvi* 19
And *f* at once, my friend, to thee. „ *xli* 12
Will *f* along the chords and go. „ *lxxxviii* 12
f A momentary likeness of the King: *Com. of Arthur* 270
F brand and lance, fall battleaxe upon helm, „ 486
Fall battleaxe, and *f* brand! (repeat) „ 487, 490, 502
A light of armour by him *f*, and pass *Balin and Balan* 326
Re-makes itself, and *f'es* down the vale— *Guinevere* 610
if what we call The spirit *f* *Ded. Poem Prin. Alice* 5
I saw The glory of the Lord *f* up, *Columbus* 82
about their ocean-islets *f* The faces of the Gods— *Tiresias* 172
f a million miles a day. *Locksley H., Sixty* 204
shine the level lands, And *f* the floods; *Early Spring* 16
Shall *f* thro' one another in a moment *Happy* 40

Flash'd He *f* into the crystal mirror, *L. of Shalott iii* 34
The distant battle *f* and rung. *Two Voices* 126
F thro' her as she sat alone, *Palace of Art* 214
So *f* and fell the brand Excalibur: *M. d'Arthur* 142
He *f* his random speeches, *Will Water.* 198
That autumn into autumn *f* again, *Enoch Arden* 456
jests, that *f* about the pleader's room, *Aylmer's Field* 440
They *f* a saucy message to and fro *Princess, Pro.* 78

Flash'd (*continued*) A thought *f* thro' me which I clothed in act, *Princess i* 195
young captains *f* their glittering teeth, ,, *v* 20
Heaven *f* a sudden jubilant ray, *Ode on Well.* 129
F all their sabres bare, *F* as they turn'd *Light Brigade* 27
The living soul was *f* on mine, *In Mem. xcv* 36
pride *f* over her beautiful face. *Maud I iv* 16
Something *f* in the sun, ,, *ix* 10
Barons of his realm *F* forth and into war: *Com. of Arthur* 66
At times the summit of the high city *f*; *Gareth and L.* 192
and *f* as those Dull-coated things, ,, 685
So Gareth ere he parted *f* in arms. ,, 689
madden'd her, and away she *f* again ,, 784
f the fierçe shield, All sun; ,, 1030
Whereat Geraint *f* into sudden spleen: *Marr. of Geraint* 273
out he *f*, And into such a song, *Merlin and V.* 416
F the bare-grinning skeleton of death! ,, 847
Suddenly *f* on her a wild desire, *Lancelot and E.* 357
Then *f* into wild tears, and rose again, ,, 613
and down they *f*, and smote the stream. ,, 1235
f, as it were, Diamonds to meet them, ,, 1236
Then *f* a yellow gleam across the world, *Holy Grail* 402
a stream That *f* across her orchard underneath ,, 593
The fire of honour and all noble deeds *F*, *Pelleas and E.* 279
For so the words were *f* into his heart ,, 503
Then *f* a levin-brand; and near me stood, *Last Tournament* 616
So *f* and fell the brand Excalibur: *Pass. of Arthur* 310
A mystic light *f* ev'n from her white robe *Lover's Tale i* 370
all my wealth *F* from me in a moment ,, 669
face and form of Lionel *F* thro' my eyes ,, *ii* 95
jewels Of many generations of his house Sparkled and *f*, ,, *iv* 300
one lightning-fork *F* out the lake; *Sisters (E. and E.)* 97
bright face was *f* thro' sense and soul ,, 109
And all the heavens *f* in frost; *To E. Fitzgerald* 22
upon me *f* The power of prophesying— *Tiresias* 56
and *f* into the Red Sea, *To Marq. of Dufferin* 44
and *f* into a frolic of song And welcome; *Demeter and P.* 12
F on the Tournament, Flicker'd and bicker'd *Merlin and the G.* 69

Flashest All along the valley, stream that *f* white, *V. of Cauteretz* 1

Flashing She, *f* forth a haughty smile, began *D. of F. Women* 129
f round and round, and whirl'd in an arch, *M. d'Arthur* 138
The cataract *f* from the bridge, *In Mem. lxxi* 15
Came quickly *f* thro' the shallow ford *Marr. of Geraint* 167
Was all the marble threshold *f*, *Geraint and E.* 25
on the splendour came, *f* me blind; *Holy Grail* 413
f round and round, and whirl'd in an arch, *Pass. of Arthur* 306
the whole isle-side *f* down from the peak *V. of Maeldune* 45
F with fires as of God, *Despair* 16
Rode *f* blow upon blow, *Heavy Brigade* 32
coin of fancy *f* out from many a golden phrase; *To Virgil* 8

Flask (*See also* **Wine-flask**) A *f* of cider from his father's vats, *Audley Court* 27
Here sits the Butler with a *f* *Day-Dm., Sleep. P.* 25
I leave an empty *f*: *Will Water.* 164

Flat (adj. and adv.) and so this earth was *f*: *Columbus* 48
dying ebb that faintly lipp'd The *f* red granite; *Audley Court* 13
sin, that crush'd My spirit *f* before thee. *St. S. Stylites* 26
child Push'd her *f* hand against his face *Princess ii* 366
on this side the palace ran the field *F* ,, *v* 362
Of this *f* lawn with dusk and bright; *In Mem. lxxxix* 2
pitch'd Beside the Castle Perilous on *f* field, *Gareth and L.* 1363
up the vale of Usk, By the *f* meadow, *Marr. of Geraint* 832
Take my salute,' unknightly with *f* hand, *Geraint and E.* 717
Arthur had the jousts Down in the *f* field *Pelleas and E.* 164
From *f* confusion and brute violences, *Last Tournament* 124
in dead night along that table-shore, Drops *f*, ,, 464
A *f* malarian world of reed and rush! *Lover's Tale iv* 142
Strow yonder mountain *f*, *Mechanophilus* 6
leaves Laid their green faces *f* *Balin and Balan* 344
To lay the sudden heads of violence *f*, *Holy Grail* 310
teeth of Hell flay bare and gnash thee *f*!— *Last Tournament* 444
and my strongest wish Falls *f* *Romney's R.* 72

Flat (a level) And glanced athwart the glooming *f's*. *Mariana* 20
By sands and steaming *f's*, and floods *The Voyage* 45
here upon the *f* All that long morn *Princess v* 367

Flat (a level) (*continued*) all about The same gray *f's* again, *In Mem. lxxxvii* 13
Wide *f's*, where nothing but coarse grasses grew; *Holy Grail* 794
if yonder hill be level with the *f*. *Locksley H., Sixty* 111

Flat (note in music) run thro' every change of sharp and *f*; *Caress'd or chidden* 4

Flatten'd Mangled, and *f*, and crush'd, *Maud I i* 7

Flatter (*See also* **Face-flatter**) They would sue me, and woo me, and *f* me, *The Mermaid* 43
To *f* me that I may die? *Two Voices* 204
F myself that always everywhere I know *Princess ii* 412
This look of quiet *f's* thus Our home-bred fancies: *In Mem. x* 10
at times Would *f* his own wish in age for love, *Merlin and V.* 185
Softly laugh'd Isolt; '*F* me not, *Last Tournament* 557
F me rather, seeing me so weak, ,, 642
O you that can *f* your victims, *Charity* 29

Flatter'd Teach your *f* kings that only those *Locksley H., Sixty* 132
thought of power *F* his spirit; *Œnone* 137
Be *f* to the height. *Palace of Art* 192
snares them by the score *F* and fluster'd, *Princess v* 164
The fancy *f* my mind, *Maud I xiv* 23
therefore *f* him, Being so gracious, *Pelleas and E.* 119
F the fancy of my fading brain; *Lover's Tale ii* 107

Flattering But *f* the golden prime *Arabian Nights* 76
f thy childish thought The oriental fairy brought, *Eleänore* 13
A splendid presence *f* the poor roofs *Aylmer's Field* 175
I, that *f* my true passion, saw The knights, *Merlin and V.* 874
Half-envious of the *f* hand, *Lancelot and E.* 349
F myself that all my doubts were fools *Sisters (E. and E.)* 140

Flattery the wit, The *f* and the strife, *D. of F. Women* 148
Nor speak I now from foolish *f*; *Marr. of Geraint* 433
the old man, Tho' doubtful, felt the *f*, *Merlin and V.* 184
F gilding the rift in a throne; *Vastness* 20
O the *f* and the craft Which were my undoing . . . *Forlorn* 3

Flaunt Was this a time for these to *f* their pride? *Aylmer's Field* 770
and *f* With prudes for proctors, *Princess, Pro.* 140
to *f*, to dress, to dance, to thrum, ,, *iv* 519
Pleasure who *f's* on her wide downway *Vastness* 16

Flaunted took the ring, and *f* it Before that other *The Ring* 243

Flaunting Thou comest not with shows of *f* vines *Ode to Memory* 48

Flaw Like *f's* in summer laying lusty corn: *Marr. of Geraint* 764
heirless *f* In his throne's title make him feel so frail, *Sir J. Oldcastle* 72

Flawless circle rounded under female hands With *f* demonstration: *Princess ii* 373

Flax Touch *f* with flame—a glance will serve *Merlin and V.* 111

Flaxen With thy floating *f* hair; *Adeline* 6
From the *f* curl to the gray lock *Princess iv* 426
Ere childhood's *f* ringlet turn'd To black and brown *In Mem. lxxix* 15
on one arm The *f* ringlets of our infancies *Lover's Tale i* 234

Flay teeth of Hell *f* bare and gnash thee *Last Tournament* 444
f Captives whom they caught in battle— *Locksley H., Sixty* 79

Flayflint There lived a *f* near; we stole *Walk. to the Mail* 84

Flaying *F* the roofs and sucking up the drains, *Princess v* 525

Flea text no larger than the limbs of *f's*; *Merlin and V.* 672

Fleck slid, a sunny *f*, From head to ancle *Talking Oak* 223
That life is dash'd with *f's* of sin. *In Mem. lii* 14

Fleckless My conscience will not count me *f*; *Princess ii* 294

Fled *f* Beyond the Memmian naphtha-pits, *Alexander* 3
Her household *f* the danger, *The Goose* 54
Her voice *f* always thro' the summer land; *Edwin Morris* 67
I read, and *f* by night, and flying turn'd: ,, 134
Then *f* she to her inmost bower, *Godiva* 42
'O happy sleep, that lightly *f*!' *Day-Dm., Depart.* 18
Thought her proud, and *f* over the sea; *Edward Gray* 14
For one fair Vision ever *f* Down the waste waters *The Voyage* 57
As fast she *f* thro' sun and shade, *Sir L. and Q. G.* 37
F forward, and no news of Enoch came. *Enoch Arden* 361
His fancy *f* before the lazy wind Returning, ,, 657
For maidens, on the spur she *f*; *Princess i* 151
when he fell, And all else *f*? ,, *ii* 243
They *f*, who might have shamed us: ,, 299
As flies the shadow of a bird, she *f*. ,, *iii* 96
the day *f* on thro' all Its range of duties ,, 176
and *f*, as flies A troop of snowy doves ,, *iv* 167
Amazed he *f* away Thro' the dark land, ,, *v* 48

Flesh (*continued*) If man and wife be but one *f*, — *Happy* 94
Flesh'd *See* **Foul-flesh'd**
Fleshless crown'd with *f* laughter— — *Gareth and L.* 1383
like a barren ghost From out the *f* world of spirits, — *The Ring* 228
Fleshly this *f* sign That thou art thou— — *De Prof.: Two G.* 40
Fleurs-de-lys sink Thy *f-d-l* in slime again, — *Sir J. Oldcastle* 99
Flew Out *f* the web and floated wide; — *L. of Shalott iii* 42
That loosely *f* to left and right— — „ *iv* 20
A living flash of light he *f*.' — *Two Voices* 15
The goose *f* this way and *f* that, — *The Goose* 35
The fire shot up, the martin *f*, — *Day-Dm., Revival* 11
F over roof and casement: — *Will Water.* 134
'Chase,' he said: the ship *f* forward, — *The Captain* 33
the rim Changed every moment as we *f*. — *The Voyage* 28
till they *f*, Hair, and eyes, and limbs, — *Vision of Sin* 38
a country dance, and *f* thro' light And shadow, — *Princess, Pro.* 84
f kite, and raced the purple fly, — „ *ii* 248
Till o'er the hills her eagles *f* — *Ode on Well.* 112
The gust that round the garden *f*, — *In Mem. lxxxix* 19
then *f* in a dove And brought a summons — „ *ciii* 15
and the blade *f* Splintering in six, — *Balin and Balan* 395
all that walk'd, or crept, or perch'd, or *f*. — *Last Tournament* 367
its shadow *f* Before it, till it touch'd her, — *Guinevere* 79
And the daws *f* out of the Towers — *V. of Maeldune* 109
Flexile So youthful and so *f* then, — *Amphion* 59
Flicker The shadows *f* to and fro: — *D. of the O. Year* 39
Where the dying night-lamp *f's*, — *Locksley Hall* 80
wisp that *f's* where no foot can tread.' — *Princess iv* 358
To *f* with his double tongue. — *In Mem. cx* 8
seem to *f* past thro' sun and shade, — *Ancient Sage* 100
Nor *f* down to brainless pantomime, — *To W. C. Macready* 10
Flicker'd high masts *f* as they lay afloat; — *D. of F. Women* 113
F like doubtful smiles about her lips, — *Lover's Tale i* 68
in the heaven above it there *f* a songless lark, — *V. of Maeldune* 17
Lightnings *f* along the heath; — *Dead Prophet* 79
F and bicker'd From helmet to helmet, — *Merlin and the G.* 70
Flickering (*See also* **Livid-flickering**) night-light *f* in my eyes Awoke me.' — *Sea Dreams* 103
and *f* in a grimly light Dance on the mere. — *Gareth and L.* 826
lark Shot up and shrill'd in *f* gyres, — *Princess vii* 46
f fairy-circle wheel'd and broke — *Guinevere* 257
Draw downward into Hades with his drift Of *f* spectres, — *Demeter and P.* 27
Prince Who scarce had pluck'd his *f* life — *To the Queen ii* 5
Might find a *f* glimmer of relief In change of place. — *To Mary Boyle* 47
sometimes I fear You may be *f*, — *Sisters (E. and E.)* 33
Flight (flying) (*See also* **Swallow-flight**) And of so fierce a *f*, From Calpe unto Caucasus — *The Poet* 14
Love wept and spread his sheeny vans for *f*; — *Love and Death* 8
free delight, from any height of rapid *f*, — *Rosalind* 3
And that delight of frolic *f*, — „ 47
Rapt after heaven's starry *f*, — *Two Voices* 68
summits slope Beyond the furthest *f's* of hope, — „ 185
she led, In hope to gain upon her *f*. — *The Voyage* 60
What look'd a *f* of fairy arrows aim'd — *Aylmer's Field* 94
F's, terrors, sudden rescues, — „ 99
Your *f* from out your bookless wilds — *Princess ii* 56
Edyrn's men had caught them in their *f*, — *Marr. of Geraint* 642
she fled, her cause of *f* Sir Modred; — *Guinevere* 9
prone *f* By thousands down the crags — *Montenegro* 7
f of birds, the flame of sacrifice, — *Tiresias* 6
cheeping to each other of their *f* To summer lands! — *The Ring* 86
And over the *f* of the Ages! — *Parnassus* 3
once a *f* of shadowy fighters crost The disk, — *St. Telemachus* 23
Flight (of stairs) Broad-based *f's* of marble stairs — *Arabian Nights* 117
And up a *f* of stairs into the hall. — *Princess ii* 31
Fling (s) Give me my *f*, and let me say my say.' — *Aylmer's Field* 399
Fling (verb) to *f* The winged shafts of truth, — *The Poet* 25
Tho' one did *f* the fire. — „ 30
f on each side my low-flowing locks, — *The Mermaid* 32
take Excalibur, And *f* him far into the middle mere: — *M. d'Arthur* 37
But, if thou spare to *f* Excalibur, — „ 131
good luck Shall *f* her old shoe after. — *Will Water.* 216
And *f* the diamond necklace by.' — *Lady Clare* 40
'Can I not *f* this horror off me again, — *Lucretius* 173

Fling (verb) (*continued*) will she *f* herself, Shameless upon me? — *Lucretius* 202
f The tricks, which make us toys of men, — *Princess ii* 62
all prophetic pity, *f* Their pretty maids — „ *v* 381
'*F* our doors wide! all, all, not one, — „ *vi* 334
And *f* it like a viper off, and shriek — „ *vii* 94
f whate'er we felt, not fearing, into words. — *Third of Feb.* 6
Never a man could *f* him: — *Grandmother* 10
f This bitter seed among mankind; — *In Mem. xc* 3
sadness *f's* Her shadow on the blaze of kings: — „ *xcviii* 18
Did he *f* himself down? who knows? — *Maud I i* 9
I swear thou canst not *f* the fourth.' — *Gareth and L.* 1327
And *f* me deep in that forgotten mere, — *Lancelot and E.* 1426
an ye *f* those rubies round my neck In lieu of hers, — *Last Tournament* 312
take Excalibur, And *f* him far into the middle mere: — *Pass. of Arthur* 205
But, if thou spare to *f* Excalibur, — „ 299
That *f's* a mist behind it in the sun— — *Lover's Tale iv* 294
and *f* Thy royalty back into the riotous fits — *Sir J. Oldcastle* 99
I would *f* myself over and die! — *The Wreck* 118
earth's dark forehead *f's* athwart the heavens — *Ancient Sage* 200
And *f* free alms into the beggar's bowl, — „ 260
What? *f* them to you?—well— — *Happy* 103
Mussulman Who *f's* his bowstrung Harem — *Romney's R.* 135
horse, anger, plunged To *f* me, and fail'd. — *Akbar's Dream* 119
Flinging *F* the gloom of yesternight On the white day; — *Ode to Memory* 9
f round her neck, Claspt it, and cried — *Last Tournament* 749
like the wave *f* forward again, — *Def. of Lucknow* 43
Was *f* fruit to lions; — *Tiresias* 67
Flint shake The sparkling *f's* beneath the prow. — *Arabian Nights* 52
clattering *f's* batter'd with clanging hoofs; — *D. of F. Women* 21
Is there no stoning save with *f* and rock? — *Aylmer's Field* 746
own one port of sense not *f* to prayer, — *Princess vi* 182
out upon you, *f*! You love nor her, — „ 259
heart as a millstone, set my face as a *f*, — *Maud I i* 31
But then what a *f* is he! — „ *xix* 57
forage for the horse, and *f* for fire. — *Gareth and L.* 1277
Flippant The *f* put himself to school — *In Mem. cx* 10
Flirt Not one to *f* a venom at her eyes, — *Merlin and V.* 609
Flit will *f* To make the greensward fresh, — *Talking Oak* 89
Let our girls *f*, Till the storm die! — *Princess vi* 337
Look, look, how he *f's*, — *Window, Ay* 7
f like the king of the wrens with a crown of fire. — „ 16
Or like to noiseless phantoms *f*: — *In Mem. xx* 16
What slender shade of doubt may *f*, — „ *xlviii* 7
F's by the sea-blue bird of March; — „ *xci* 4
A shadow *f's* before me, — *Maud II iv* 11
shadow *f's* and fleets And will not let me be; — „ 90
Then let her fancy *f* across the past, — *Marr. of Geraint* 645
And while your doves about you *f*, — *To E. Fitzgerald* 7
from him *f's* to warn A far-off friendship — *Demeter and P.* 89
round her brows a woodland culver *f's*, — *Prog. of Spring* 18
Flitted *F* across into the night, — *Miller's D.* 127
The little innocent soul *f* away. — *Enoch Arden* 270
unawares they *f* off, Busying themselves about — *Aylmer's Field* 202
left me in shadow here! Gone—*f* away! — *Window, Gone* 4
f I know not where! — „ 7
Foälks' coostom *f* awaäy like a kite — *North. Cobbler* 28
music Of falling torrents, *F* The Gleam. — *Merlin and the G.* 48
Flittermouse-shriek fainter than any *f-s*; — *V. of Maeldune* 22
Flitteth The shallop *f* silken-sail'd — *L. of Shalott i* 22
Flitting (part.) 'What! You're *f*!' 'Yes, we're *f*,' — *Walk. to the Mail* 43
says he, 'you *f* with us too— — „ 45
F, fairy Lilian, — *Lilian* 2
And airy forms of *f* change. — *Madeline* 7
till all my *f* chance Were caught within the record — *Princess v* 142
Flitting (s) After the *f* of the bats, — *Mariana* 17
Plagued with a *f* to and fro, — *Maud II ii* 33
Float *F's* from his sick and filmed eyes, — *Supp. Confessions* 166
F by you on the verge of night. — *Margaret* 31
languors of thy love-deep eyes *F* on to me. — *Eleänore* 77
as the warm gulf-stream of Florida *F's* — *Mine be the strength* 13
Floated her hair or seem'd to *f* in rest. — *Œnone* 19
Falls, and *f's* adown the air. — *Lotos-Eaters, C. S.* 31

Float (*continued*) forms, That *f* about the threshold of an age, *Golden Year* 16
steam *F's* up from those dim fields about the homes *Tithonus* 69
never *f's* an European flag, *Locksley Hall* 161
f thro' Heaven, and cannot light? *Day-Dm., Ep.* 8
I *f* till all is dark. *Sir Galahad* 40
I seem'd To *f* about a glimmering night, *Princess i* 247
bottom agates seem to wave and *f* „ *ii* 327
the streams that *f* us each and all „ *iv* 70
And *f* or fall, in endless ebb and flow; *W. to Marie Alex.* 27
airy-light To *f* above the ways of men, *To E. Fitzgerald* 18
She *f's* across the hamlet. *Prog. of Spring* 40
May *f* awhile beneath the sun, *Romney's R.* 50
vapour in daylight Over the mountain *F's*, *Kapolani* 18
boats of Dahomey that *f* upon human blood! *The Dawn* 5
Floated Adown it *f* a dying swan, *Dying Swan* 6
Out flew the web and *f* wide; *L. of Shalott iii* 42
She *f* down to Camelot: „ *iv* 23
A gleaming shape she *f* by, „ 39
if first I *f* free, As naked essence, *Two Voices* 373
F her hair or seem'd to float in rest. *Œnone* 19
F the glowing sunlights, as she moved. „ 182
she *f* to us and said: 'You have done well *Princess iv* 526
lordly creature *f* on To where her wounded brethren lay; „ *vi* 89
And o'er her breast *f* the sacred fish; *Gareth and L.* 223
She might have risen and *f* when I saw her. *Holy Grail* 100
White as white clouds, *f* from sky to sky. *Lover's Tale i* 5
Waver'd and *f*—which was less than Hope, „ 452
And *f* on and parted round her neck, „ 704
about my brow Her warm breast *f* in the utterance „ *ii* 141
f in—While all the guests in mute amazement „ *iv* 304
F in conquering battle or flapt to the battle-cry! *Def. of Lucknow* 2
Had *f* in with sad reproachful eyes, *The Ring* 469
Moving to melody, *F* The Gleam. *Merlin and the G.* 23
and thro' her dream A ghostly murmur *f*, *Death of Œnone* 79
Floating (*See also* **Ever-floating**) And *f* about the under-sky, *Dying Swan* 25
F thro' an evening atmosphere, *Eleänore* 100
misty folds, that *f* as they fell Lit up *Palace of Art* 35
With thy *f* flaxen hair; *Adeline* 6
Down-droop'd, in many a *f* fold, *Arabian Nights* 147
Stays on her *f* locks the lovely freight *Ode to Memory* 16
thro' the wreaths of *f* dark upcurl'd, *The Poet* 35
land Of lavish lights, and *f* shades: *Eleänore* 12
luxuriant symmetry Of thy *f* gracefulness, „ 50
Made misty with the *f* meal. *Miller's D.* 104
Buoy'd upon *f* tackle and broken spars, *Enoch Arden* 551
Came *f* on for many a month and year, *Vision of Sin* 54
o'er it crost the dimness of a cloud *F*, *Pelleas and E.* 38
and mine Were dim with *f* tears, *Lover's Tale i* 442
All day I watch'd the *f* isles of shade, „ *ii* 5
in their *f* folds They past and were no more: „ 99
Flock And in the *f's* The lamb rejoiceth *Supp. Confessions* 156
By dancing rivulets fed his *f's* *To E. L.* 22
when he came again, his *f* believed— *Aylmer's Field* 600
half amazed half frighted all his *f*: „ 631
my eldest-born, the flower of the *f*; *Grandmother* 9
And bring the firstling to the *f*; *In Mem. ii* 6
meadowy curves, That feed the mothers of the *f*; „ *c* 16
The *f's* are whiter down the vale, „ *cxv* 10
Flock'd thither *f* at noon His tenants, *Princess, Pro.* 3
a careless people *f* from the fields *Dead Prophet* 7
Flood (s) (*See also* **Fountain-flood**) From the westward-winding *f*, *Margaret* 9
island queen who sways the *f's* and lands *Buonaparte* 3
They past into the level *f*, *Miller's D.* 75
dragons spouted forth A *f* of fountain-foam. *Palace of Art* 24
and takes the *f* With swarthy webs. *M. d'Arthur* 268
By sands and steaming flats, and *f's* *The Voyage* 45
his passions all in *f* And masters of his motion, *Aylmer's Field* 339
Bore down in *f*, and dash'd his angry heart „ 633
f, fire, earthquake, thunder, wrought Such waste „ 639
the *f* drew; yet I caught her; *Princess iv* 182
Better have died and spilt our bones in the *f*— „ 532
fling Their pretty maids in the running *f*, „ *v* 382
Flood (s) (*continued*) And whiten'd all the rolling *f*; *The Victim* 20
lead Thro' prosperous *f's* his holy urn. *In Mem. ix* 8
Summer on the steaming *f's*, „ *lxxxv* 69
shadowing down the horned *f* In ripples, „ *lxxxvi* 7
lay At anchor in the *f* below; „ *ciii* 20
And roll'd the *f's* in grander space, „ 26
And molten up, and roar in *f*; „ *cxxvii* 13
No doubt vast eddies in the *f* Of onward time „ *cxxviii* 5
have isled together, knave, In time of *f*. *Gareth and L.* 894
follow Vivien thro' the fiery *f*! *Balin and Balan* 454
when ye used to take me with the *f* *Lancelot and E.* 1037
far up the shining *f* Until we found the palace „ 1043
I was all alone upon the *f*, „ 1046
Beyond the poplar and far up the *f*, „ 1050
Oar'd by the dumb, went upward with the *f*— „ 1154
Then fell the *f's* of heaven drowning the deep. *Holy Grail* 533
and takes the *f* With swarthy webs. *Pass. of Arthur* 436
booming indistinct Of the confused *f's*, *Lover's Tale i* 638
Saving his life on the fallow *f*. *Batt. of Brunanburh* 61
Shrine-shattering earthquake, fire, *f*, thunderbolt, *Tiresias* 61
Gone like fires and *f's* and earthquakes *Locksley H., Sixty* 40
shine the level lands, And flash the *f's*; *Early Spring* 16
Produce of your field and *f*, *Open. I. and C. Exhib.* 5
From under rose a muffled moan of *f's*; *Prog. of Spring* 70
The *f* may bear me far, *Crossing the Bar* 14
Flood (verb) *F* with full daylight glebe and town? *Two Voices* 87
F's all the deep-blue gloom with beams *D. of F. Women* 186
Ready to burst and *f* the world with foam: *Princess iv* 474
And *f* a fresher throat with song. *In Mem. lxxxiii* 16
f the haunts of hern and crake; „ *ci* 14
poach'd filth that *f's* the middle street, *Merlin and V.* 798
f's with redundant life Her narrow portals. *Lover's Tale i* 84
Flooded Were *f* over with eddying song. *Dying Swan* 42
risen before his time And *f* at our nod. *D. of F. Women* 144
eyes All *f* with the helpless wrath of tears, *Enoch Arden* 32
Over all the woodland's *f* bowers, *Sisters (E. and E.)* 20
the lake beyond his limit, And all was *f*; *The Daisy* 72
Flooding *f*, leaves Low banks of yellow sand; *Lover's Tale i* 534
On hill, or plain, at sea, or *f* ford. *Holy Grail* 728
Floor Old footsteps trod the upper *f's*, *Mariana* 67
Flung inward over spangled *f's*, *Arabian Nights* 116
The meal-sacks on the whiten'd *f*, *Miller's D.* 101
find my garden-tools upon the granary *f*: *May Queen, N. Y's. E.* 45
rolling waves Of sound on roof and *f* Within, *D. of F. Women* 192
There's a new foot on the *f*, my friend, *D. of the O. Year* 52
As head and heels upon the *f* They flounder'd *The Goose* 37
All heaven bursts her starry *f's*, *St. Agnes' Eve* 27
thou shalt cease To pace the gritted *f*, *Will Water.* 242
shape it plank and beam for roof and *f*, *Princess vi* 46
Throbb'd thunder thro' the palace *f's*, „ *vii* 104
crash'd the glass and beat the *f*; *In Mem. lxxxvii* 20
Witch-elms that counterchange the *f* „ *lxxxix* 1
But let no footstep beat the *f*, „ *cv* 17
russet-bearded head roll'd on the *f*. *Geraint and E.* 729
others from the *f*, Tusklike, arising, *Balin and Balan* 315
Crush'd the wild passion out against the *f* *Lancelot and E.* 742
once she slipt like water to the *f*. „ 830
grovell'd with her face against the *f*: *Guinevere* 415
Parted a little ere they met the *f*, *Lover's Tale iv* 215
like the dead by the dead on the cabin *f*, *The Wreck* 112
as we was a-cleänin' the *f*, *Spinster's S's.* 49
fire of fever creeps across the rotted *f*, *Locksley H., Sixty* 223
wi' my hairm hingin' down to the *f*, *Owd Roä* 65
Found in a chink of that old moulder'd *f*!' *The Ring* 280
The sacred relics tost about the *f*— „ 447
Flop hoickt my feet wi' a *f* fro' the claäy. *Spinster's S's.* 30
Flora (Christian name) work in hues to dim The Titianic *F*. *Gardener's D.* 171
O, Lady *F*, let me speak: *Day-Dm., Pro.* 1
So, Lady *F*, take my lay, „ *Moral* 1
So, Lady *F*, take my lay, „ *Ep.* 1
Florence (town) 'Poor lad, he died at *F*, *The Brook* 35
At *F* too what golden hours, *The Daisy* 41
Abroad, at *F*, at Rome, *Maud I xix* 58
Fair *F* honouring thy nativity, Thy *F* now the crown of Italy, *To Dante* 3

Flores At *F* in the Azores Sir Richard Grenville lay, *The Revenge* 1
And he sailed away from *F* „ 23
Florian I stood With Cyril and with *F*, *Princess i* 52
F said: I have a sister at the foreign court, „ 74
I stole from court With Cyril and with *F*, „ 103
F, but no livelier than the dame „ *ii* 112
'The fifth in line from that old *F*, „ 238
The loyal warmth of *F* is not cold, „ 244
'Are you that Psyche,' *F* added; „ 246
'Are you that Psyche,' *F* ask'd, „ 269
so pacing till she paused By *F*; „ 303
I am sad and glad To see you, *F*. „ 307
'Ungracious!' answer'd *F*; 'have you learnt „ 392
What think you of it, *F*? „ 408
'Tell us,' *F* ask'd, 'How grew this feud „ *iii* 76
Then murmur'd *F* gazing after her, „ 97
Cyril kept With Psyche, with Melissa *F*, „ 355
F nodded at him, I frowning; „ *iv* 159
Alone I stood With *F*, cursing Cyril, „ 171
the doubt 'if this were she,' But it was *F*. „ 218
prayer, Which melted *F's* fancy as she hung, „ 370
Then *F* knelt, and 'Come' he whisper'd to her, „ *v* 63
F, he That loved me closer than his own right eye, „ 530
'Your brother, Lady,—*F*,—ask for him „ *vi* 313
But Psyche tended *F*: „ *vii* 55
Florid *f*, stern, as far as eye could see, *Sea Dreams* 219
Engirt with many a *f* maiden-cheek, *Princess iii* 350
Florida as the warm gulf-stream of *F* Floats *Mine be the strength* 12
Flounce dimpled *f* of the sea-furbelow flap, *Sea Dreams* 266
Flounder began to move, And *f* into hornpipes. *Amphion* 24
Should I *f* awhile without a tumble *Hendecasyllabics* 9
Floundered They *f* all together, *The Goose* 38
Floundering The weary steed of Pelleas *f* *Pelleas and E.* 574
Part stumbled mixt with *f* horses. *Princess v* 498
Flour *f* From his tall mill that whistled *Enoch Arden* 342
Flourish (s) In the mid might and *f* of his May, *Lancelot and E.* 554
Flourish (verb) O *f* high, with leafy towers, *Talking Oak* 197
O *f*, hidden deep in fern, „ 201
f'es Green in a cuplike hollow of the down. *Enoch Arden* 8
life in him Could scarce be said to *f*, *The Brook* 12
Out of evil evil *f'es*, *Boädicea* 83
She said, 'The evil *f* in the world.' *Lover's Tale i* 348
Flourish'd *F* a little garden square and wall'd: *Enoch Arden* 734
They *f* then or then; but life in him *The Brook* 11
From all a closer interest *f* up, *Princess vii* 113
poplar and cypress unshaken by storm *f* up beyond sight, *V. of Maeldune* 15
You should be jubilant that you *f* here *Poets and their B.* 12
Flourishing cave Of touchwood, with a single *f* spray. *Aylmer's Field* 512
thence they wasted all the *f* territory, *Boädicea* 54
Flout put your beauty to this *f* and scorn *Geraint and E.* 675
And all to *f* me, when they bring me in, *Pelleas and E.* 330
Flouted When he *f* a statesman's error, *The Wreck* 68
Flow (s) Low-tinkled with a bell-like *f* *The winds, etc.* 7
silver *f* Of subtle-paced counsel in distress, *Isabel* 20
Down from the central fountain's *f* *Arabian Nights* 50
sonorous *f* Of spouted fountain-floods. *Palace of Art* 27
that *f* Of music left the lips of her that died *D. of F. Women* 194
Have ebb and *f* conditioning their march, *Golden Year* 30
float or fall, in endless ebb and *f*; *W. to Marie Alex.* 27
a rock in ebbs and *f's*, Fixt on her faith. *Marr. of Geraint* 812
clearer in my life than all Its present *f*. *Lover's Tale i* 150
With its true-touch'd pulses in the *f* „ 205
source Of these sad tears, and feeds their downward *f*. „ 784
Sway'd by vaster ebbs and *f's* *Locksley H., Sixty* 194
Flow (verb) The stream *f's*, The wind blows, *Nothing will Die* 9
The stream will cease to *f*; *All Things will Die* 9
till his own blood *f's* About his hoof. *Supp. Confessions* 155
All night the silence seems to *f* *Oriana* 86
Motions *f* To one another, *Eleänore* 61
May into uncongenial spirits *f*; *Mine be the strength* 11
But now thy beauty *f's* away. *Mariana in the S.* 67
There's somewhat *f's* to us in life, *Miller's D.* 21
They saw the gleaming river seaward *f* *Lotos-Eaters* 14
According to my humour ebb and *f*. *D. of F. Women* 134

Flow (verb) (*continued*) I had not dared to *f* In these words toward you, *To J. S.* 6
thro' such tears As *f* but once a life. *Love and Duty* 64
F down, cold rivulet, to the sea, *A Farewell* 1
F, softly *f*, by lawn and lea, „ 5
Till last by Philip's farm I *f* *The Brook* 31
and *f* To join the brimming river, (repeat) „ 63, 182
your great name *f* on with broadening time *Princess iii* 164
let the turbid streams of rumour *f* *Ode on Well.* 181
All along the valley, where thy waters *f*, *V. of Cauteretz* 3
The tide *f's* down, the wave again Is vocal *In Mem. xix* 13
The double tides of chariots *f* „ *xcviii* 23
The hills are shadows, and they *f* „ *cxxiii* 5
F thro' our deeds and make them pure, „ *cxxxi* 4
And all we *f* from, soul in soul. „ 12
they do not *f* From evil done; *Guinevere* 188
F back again unto my slender spring *Lover's Tale i* 147
Flow'd tide of time *f* back with me, *Arabian Nights* 3
Heaven *f* upon the soul in many dreams *The Poet* 31
Rare sunrise *f*. „ 36
F forth on a carol free and bold; *Dying Swan* 30
From underneath his helmet *f* *L. of Shalott, iii* 30
o'er him *f* a golden cloud, and lean'd Upon him, *Œnone* 105
Thus far he *f*, and ended; *Golden Year* 52
Fast *f* the current of her easy tears, *Enoch Arden* 865
(possibly He *f* and ebb'd uncertain, *Aylmer's Field* 218
The mother *f* in shallower acrimonies: „ 563
but when the preacher's cadence *f* „ 729
and dream and truth *F* from me; *Princess v* 542
Bloodily *f* the Tamesa rolling phantom bodies *Boädicea* 27
ladies came, and by and by the town *F* in, *Marr. of Geraint* 547
light upon her silver face *F* from the spiritual lily *Balin and Balan* 264
in that hour A hope *f* round me, *Lover's Tale i* 449
that life I heeded not *F* from me, „ 597
Loosed from their simple thrall they had *f* abroad, „ 703
past and *f* away To those unreal billows: „ *ii* 195
the grape from whence it *f* Was blackening *Sisters (E. and E.)* 61
the field with blood of the fighters *F*, *Batt. of Brunanburh* 25
Flower (s) (*See also* **Cuckoo-flower, Field-flower, Flag-flower, Hearth-flower, Heather-flower, Honey-suckle-flower, Marish-flowers, Passion-flower, Poison-flowers, Orange-flower, Sea-flower, Spring-flowers, Wild-flower, Wildweed-flower**)
the heart to scathe *F's* thou hadst rear'd— *Supp. Confessions* 84
The stately *f* of female fortitude, *Isabel* 11
In order, eastern *f's* large, *Arabian Nights* 61
Engarlanded and diaper'd With inwrought *f's*, „ 149
(Those peerless *f's* which in the rudest wind *Ode to Memory* 24
and sweet showers Of festal *f's*, „ 78
the heavy stalks Of the mouldering *f's*: *A spirit haunts* 8
like the arrow-seeds of the field *f*, *The Poet* 19
mother plant in semblance, grew A *f* all gold, „ 24
water will I pour Into every spicy *f* *Poet's Mind* 13
The *f's* would faint at your cruel cheer. „ 15
With many a deep-hued bell-like *f* *Eleänore* 37
Overlook a space of *f's*, *L. of Shalott i* 16
About the opening of the *f*, *Two Voices* 161
You scarce could see the grass for *f's*. „ 453
and you were gay With bridal *f's*— *Miller's D.* 165
I roll'd among the tender *f's*: *Fatima* 11
meadow-ledges midway down Hang rich in *f's*, *Œnone* 7
purple *f* droops: the golden bee Is lily-cradled: „ 29
With bunch and berry and *f* thro' and thro'. „ 102
A simple maiden in her *f* Is worth *L. C. V. de Vere* 15
But I must gather knots of *f's*, *May Queen* 11
Last May we made a crown of *f's*: *May Queen, N. Y's. E.* 9
There's not a *f* on all the hills: „ 13
I long to see a *f* so before the day I die. „ 16
When the *f's* come again, mother, „ 25
the land about, and all the *f's* that blow, „ *Con.* 7
Wild *f's* in the valley for other hands „ 52
enchanted stem, Laden with *f* and fruit, *Lotos-Eaters* 29
in the stream the long-leaved *f's* weep, „ *C. S.* 10
The *f* ripens in its place, „ 36
I knew the *f's*, I knew the leaves, *D. of F. Women* 73

Flower (s) (*continued*) Feeding the *f*; but ere my *f* to fruit Changed, *D. of F. Women* 207
shadow of the *f's* Stole all the golden gloss, *Gardener's D.* 129
Each garlanded with her peculiar *f* „ 201
And made a little wreath of all the *f's* *Dora* 82
The wreath of *f's* fell At Dora's feet. „ 102
honeycomb of eloquence Stored from all *f's*? *Edwin Morris* 27
The *f* of each, those moments when we met, „ 69
Like Proserpine in Enna, gathering *f's*: „ 112
bring me offerings of fruit and *f's*: *St. S. Stylites* 128
The *f*, she touch'd on, dipt and rose, *Talking Oak* 131
The drooping *f* of knowledge changed to fruit *Love and Duty* 24
Live happy; tend thy *f's*; „ 87
we reap The *f* and quintessence of change. *Day-Dm., L'Envoi* 24
bird of Eden burst In carol, every bud to *f*, „ 44
Perfume and *f's* fall in showers, *Sir Galahad* 11
That are the *f* of the earth?' *Lady Clare* 68
With naked limbs and *f's* and fruit, *The Voyage* 55
But we nor paused for fruit nor *f's*. „ 56
What! the *f* of life is past: *Vision of Sin* 69
robed your cottage-walls with *f's* *Aylmer's Field* 698
Makes his heart voice amid the blaze of *f's*: *Lucretius* 101
Crown'd with a *f* or two, and there an end— „ 229
Or beast or bird or fish, or opulent *f*: „ 249
F's of all heavens, and lovelier than their names, *Princess, Pro.* 12
Laid it on *f's*, and watch'd it lying bathed „ *i* 93
and with great urns of *f's*. „ *ii* 26
the bird, the fish, the shell, the *f*, „ 383
long hall glitter'd like a bed of *f's*. „ 439
Fluctuated, as *f's* in storm, some red, „ *iv* 482
Remembering her mother: O my *f*! „ *v* 89
the household *f* Torn from the lintel— „ 128
squadrons of the Prince, trampling the *f's* „ 247
I take her for the *f* of womankind, „ 287
Their feet in *f's*, her loveliest: „ *vi* 78
With books, with *f's*, with Angel offices, „ *vii* 26
And like a *f* that cannot all unfold, „ 141
and crown'd with all her *f's*. *Ode Inter. Exhib.* 42
Break, happy land, into earlier *f's*! *W. to Alexandra* 10
Has given our Prince his own imperial *F*, *W. to Marie Alex.* 4
welcome Russian *f*, a people's pride, To Britain when her *f's* begin to blow! „ 6
my eldest-born, the *f* of the flock; *Grandmother* 9
Shadow and shine is life, little Annie, *f* and thorn. „ 60
my beauty, my eldest-born, my *f*; „ 101
—wot's a beauty?—the *f* as blaws. *N. Farmer, N. S.* 15
Up there came a *f*, The people said, *The Flower* 3
muttering discontent Cursed me and my *f*. „ 8
the people cried, 'Splendid is the *f*.' „ 16
Most can raise the *f's* now, „ 19
F in the crannied wall, *Flow. in cran. wall* 1
Little *f*—but *if* I could understand „ 4
fruit Which in our winter woodland looks a *f*. *A Dedication* 13
All of *f's*, and drop me a *f*, Drop me a *f*. *Window, At the W.* 6
Cannot a *f*, a *f*, be mine? „ 9
Drop me a *f*, a *f*, to kiss, „ 11
her bower All of *f's*, a *f*, a *f*, Dropt, a *f*. „ 13
The seasons bring the *f* again, *In Mem. ii* 5
may find A *f* beat with rain and wind, „ *viii* 15
And this poor *f* of poesy „ 19
From *f* to *f*, from snow to snow: „ *xxii* 4
When *f* is feeling after *f*; „ *xxxix* 7
traces of the past Be all the colour of the *f*: „ *xliii* 8
The path we came by, thorn and *f*, „ *xlvi* 2
The perfect *f* of human time; „ *lxi* 4
Made cypress of her orange *f*, „ *lxxxiv* 15
And brushing ankle-deep in *f's*, „ *lxxxix* 49
Day, when I lost the *f* of men; „ *xcix* 4
The time admits not *f's* or leaves „ *cvii* 5
the *f* And native growth of noble mind; „ *cxi* 15
But tho' I seem in star and *f* To feel thee „ *cxxx* 6
But where is she, the bridal *f*, „ *Con.* 25
weight Of learning lightly like a *f*. „ 40
That pelt us in the porch with *f's*. „ 68
is but seed Of what in them is *f* and fruit; „ 136

Flower (s) (*continued*) Man in his pride, and Beauty fair in her *f*; *Maud I iv* 25
To the *f's*, and be their sun. „ *xxii* 58
For a shell, or a *f*, little things „ *II ii* 64
splendour falls On the little *f* that clings „ *iv* 33
It is only *f's*, they had no fruits, „ *v* 77
Wearing the white *f* of a blameless life, *Ded. of Idylls* 25
Lancelot past away among the *f's*, *Com. of Arthur* 450
and return'd Among the *f's*, in May, „ 452
the live green had kindled into *f's*, *Gareth and L.* 185
nose Tip-tilted like the petal of a *f*; „ 591
As if the *f*, That blows a globe of after arrowlets, „ 1028
'O dewy *f's* that open to the sun, O dewy *f's* that close when day is done, „ 1066
'What knowest thou of *f's*, except, belike, „ 1069
Who lent me thee, the *f* of kitchendom, A foolish love for *f's*? „ 1071
F's? nay, the boar hath rosemaries and bay. „ 1074
Miss the full *f* of this accomplishment.' „ 1297
will hide with mantling *f's* As if for pity?' „ 1392
Fresh as a *f* new-born, and crying, „ 1409
like a crag was gay with wilding *f's*: *Marr. of Geraint* 319
Whom Gwydion made by glamour out of *f's*, „ 743
Betwixt the cressy islets white in *f*; *Geraint and E.* 475
wealth Of leaf, and gayest garlandage of *f's*, *Balin and Balan* 83
Lancelot with his hand among the *f's* „ 259
Prince, we have ridd'n before among the *f's* „ 272
The *f* of all their vestal knighthood, knelt „ 508
They might have cropt the myriad *f* of May, „ 577
As once—of old—among the *f's*—they rode. *Merlin and V.* 136
And noble deeds, the *f* of all the world. „ 413
'to pluck the *f* in season,' So says the song, „ 722
A border fantasy of branch and *f*, *Lancelot and E.* 11
Lancelot, the *f* of bravery, Guinevere, The pearl „ 113
The *f* of all the west and all the world, „ 249
So saying, from the carven *f* above, „ 549
if I bide, lo! this wild *f* for me!' „ 644
For pleasure all about a field of *f's*: „ 793
the victim's *f's* before he fall.' „ 910
Hereafter, when you yield your *f* of life „ 952
showers of *f's* Fell as we past; *Holy Grail* 348
disarm'd By maidens each as fair as any *f*: „ 576
the wholesome *f* And poisonous grew together, „ 775
see thou, that it may bear its *f*. „ 887
your *f* Waits to be solid fruit of golden deeds, *Last Tournament* 99
purple slopes of mountain *f's* Pass under white, till the warm hour returns With veer of wind, and all are *f's* again; „ 229
Is all as cool and white as any *f*.' „ 416
Come dashing down on a tall wayside *f*, *Guinevere* 253
A glorious company, the *f* of men, „ 464
To which my spirit leaneth all her *f's*, *Lover's Tale i* 104
broad and open *f* tell What sort of bud it was, „ 151
Can ye take off the sweetness from the *f*, „ 171
And then point out the *f* or the star? „ 175
mine made garlands of the selfsame *f*, „ 343
let grow The *f's* that run poison in their veins. „ 347
poppy-stem, 'whose *f*, Hued with the scarlet of a fierce sunrise, „ 352
no leaf, no *f*, no fruit for me. „ 725
Laden with thistledown and seeds of *f's*, „ *ii* 13
her I loved, adorn'd with fading *f's*. „ *iii* 40
the *f* of a year and a half is thine, *To A. Tennyson* 3
'Our Nelly's the *f* of 'em all.' *First Quarrel* 28
cleän as a *f* fro' 'eäd to feeät: *North. Cobbler* 44
All the bowers and the *f's*, Fainting *f's*, faded bowers, *Sisters (E. and E.)* 10
Over all the meadows drowning *f's*, „ 21
you used to send her the *f's*; *In the Child. Hosp.* 33
F's to these 'spirits in prison' „ 37
And she lay with a *f* in one hand „ 39
And we came to the Isle of *F's*: *V. of Maeldune* 37
we tore up the *f's* by the million „ 53
one carved all over with *f's*, „ 106
there were more for the carven *f's*, „ 112

Flower (s) (*continued*) Cast at thy feet one *f* that fades away. *To Dante* 7
one snowy knee was prest Against the margin *f's*; *Tiresias* 43
And him the last; and laying *f's*, " 212
speaking aloud To women, the *f* of the time, *The Wreck* 49
Who had borne my *f* on her hireling heart; " 143
Trusting no longer that earthly *f* *Despair* 35
on an earth that bore not a *f*; " 44
And wind the front of youth with *f's*, *Ancient Sage* 97
songs in praise of death, and crown'd with *f's*! " 209
a *f* Had murmurs 'Lost and gone and lost and gone!' " 223
'His two wild woodland *f's*.' Wild *f's* blowing side by side *The Flight* 80
Wild *f's* of the secret woods, " 82
May all the *f's* o' Jeroosilim blossom *Tomorrow* 89
An' the lark fly out o' the *f's* " 91
carpet es fresh es a midder o' *f's* i' Maäy— *Spinster's S's.* 45
used to call the very *f's* Sisters, *Locksley H., Sixty* 101
perhaps a world of never fading *f's*. " 184
face of Edith like a *f* among the *f's*. " 260
Or Love with wreaths of *f's*. " *Epilogue* 17
the laughing shepherd bound with *f's*; *To Virgil* 16
and fills The *f* with dew; *Early Spring* 46
where the purple *f's* grow, *Frater Ave, etc.* 4
here thy hands let fall the gather'd *f*, *Demeter and P.* 9
now once more ablaze With *f's* that brighten " 36
All *f's*—but for one black blur of earth " 37
My quick tears kill'd the *f*, " 108
Caught by the *f* that closes on the fly, *The Ring* 344
lonely maiden-Princess, crown'd with *f's*, " 485
Her tribes of men, and trees, and *f's*, *To Ulysses* 3
the bloodless heart of lowly *f's* *Prog. of Spring* 84
No louder than a bee among the *f's*, *Romney's R.* 82
the rose Cry to the lotus 'No *f* thou'? *Akbar's Dream* 37
Warble bird, and open *f*, and, men, " *Hymn* 7
I am dressing the grave of a woman with *f's*. *Charity* 2
I am dressing her grave with *f's*. " 44
Vary like the leaves and *f's*, *Poets and Critics* 4
Draw from my death Thy living *f* and grass, *Doubt and Prayer* 6
Flower (verb) white as privet when it *f's*. *Walk. to the Mail* 56
but as poets' seasons when they *f*, *Golden Year* 28
his followers, all *F* into fortune— *Columbus* 167
So blighted here, would *f* into full health *The Ring* 317
while the races *f* and fade, *Making of Man* 5
Flowerage Busying themselves about the *f* *Aylmer's Field* 203
Flower-bells cluster'd *f-b* and ambrosial orbs *Isabel* 36
Flower'd (*See also* **Freshly-flowered, White-flower'd**)
a dress All branch'd and *f* with gold, *Marr. of Geraint* 631
answers to his mother's calls From the *f* furrow. *Supp. Confessions* 160
Fifty times the rose has *f* and faded, *On Jub. Q. Victoria* 1
A rhyme that *f* betwixt the whitening sloe *To Mary Boyle* 25
Flowering (part. and adj.) A spacious garden full of *f* weeds, *To—— With Pal. of Art* 4
there grew an Eastern rose, That, *f* high, *Gardener's D.* 124
burgeons every maze of quick About the *f* squares, *In Mem. cxv* 3
The snowdrop only, *f* thro' the year, *Last Tournament* 220
f grove Of grasses Lancelot pluck'd him *Guinevere* 33
And we hated the *F* Isle, *V. of Maeldune* 52
charm of all the Muses often *F* in a lonely word; *To Virgil* 12
Flowering (s) I mark'd Him in the *f* of his fields, *Pass. of Arthur* 10
Flowerless In silence wept upon the *f* earth. *Death of Œnone* 9
Flower-plot With blackest moss the *f-p's* *Mariana* 1
Flower-sheath lightly breaks a faded *f-s*, *Marr of Geraint* 365
Flowery rivulet in the *f* dale 'll merrily glance and play. *May Queen* 39
I turning saw, throned on a *f* rise, *D. of F. Women* 125
All the land in *f* squares, *Gardener's D.* 76
lead my Memmius in a train Of *f* clauses *Lucretius* 120
came On *f* levels underneath the crag, *Princess iii* 336
Thy partner in the *f* walk Of letters, *In Mem. lxxxiv* 22
Witness their *f* welcome. *Balin and Balan* 145
course of life that seem'd so *f* to me *Merlin and V.* 880
Floweth From thy rose-red lips my name *F*; *Eleänore* 134
from whose left hand *f* The Shadow of Death, *Lover's Tale i* 498

Flowing (*See also* **Forward-flowing, Full-flowing, Low-flowing**) stream be aweary of *f* Under my eye? *Nothing will Die* 1
the blue river chimes in its *f* *All Things will Die* 1
A clear stream *f* with a muddy one, *Isabel* 30
f rapidly between Their interspaces, *Arabian Nights* 83
F beneath her rose-hued zone; " 140
lordly music *f* from The illimitable years. *Ode to Memory* 41
F like a crystal river; *Poet's Mind* 6
Winds were blowing, waters *f*, *Oriana* 14
My tears, no tears of love, are *f* *Wan Sculptor* 7
island in the river *F* down to Camelot *L. of Shalott i* 14
her canvas *f*, Rose a ship of France. *The Captain* 27
hung to hear The rapt oration *f* free *In Mem. lxxxvii* 32
the blood Of their strong bodies, *f*, *Marr. of Geraint* 569
F with easy greatness and touching *The Wreck* 50
A land of promise *f* with the milk And honey *Lover's Tale i* 334
Were stoled from head to foot in *f* black; " *ii* 85
And holding them back by their *f* locks *The Merman* 14
But pledge me in the *f* grape. *My life is full* 15
And o'er them many a *f* range *Day-Dm., Depart.* 21
The truth, that flies the *f* can, *Will Water.* 171
princely halls, and farms, and *f* lawns, *Aylmer's Field* 654
Dragon's cave Half hid, they tell me, now in *f* vines— *Tiresias* 144
Flown as tho' it were The hour just *f*, *Gardener's D.* 83
He rode a horse with wings, that would have *f*, *Vision of Sin* 3
Had tost his ball and *f* his kite, *Aylmer's Field* 84
tell her, Swallow, that thy brood is *f*: *Princess iv* 108
F to the east or the west, *Window, Gone* 7
love is more Than in the summers that are *f*, *In Mem., Con.* 18
For the black bat, night, has *f*, *Maud I xxii* 2
as the cageling newly *f* returns, *Merlin and V.* 901
life had *f*, we sware but by the shell— *Last Tournament* 270
she that clasp'd my neck had *f*; *Locksley H., Sixty* 15
Floy (fly) a knaws naw moor nor a *f*; *N. Farmer, O. S.* 67
Fluctuate And *f* all the still perfume, *In Mem. xcv* 56
Fluctuated *F*, as flowers in storm, some red, *Princess iv* 482
Fluctuation tall columns drown'd In silken *f* " *vi* 355
world-wide *f* sway'd In vassal tides *In Mem. cxii* 15
Flue sent a blast of sparkles up the *f*: *M. d'Arthur, Ep.* 15
Fluent In tracts of *f* heat began, *In Mem. cxviii* 9
Broad brows and fair, a *f* hair and fine, *Gareth and L.* 464
Fluid and *f* range Of lawless airs, *Supp. Confessions* 147
'This world was once a *f* haze of light, *Princess ii* 116
Fluke Anchors of rusty *f*, and boats updrawn; *Enoch Arden* 18
Flung (*See also* **Broad-flung**) The costly doors *f* open wide, *Arabian Nights* 17
F inward over spangled floors, " 116
F leagues of roaring foam into the gorge *If I were loved* 13
Backward the lattice-blind she *f*, *Mariana in the S.* 87
Then with both hands I *f* him, *M. d'Arthur* 157
And *f* him in the dew. *Talking Oak* 232
F the torrent rainbow round: *Vision of Sin* 32
And *f* her down upon a couch of fire, *Aylmer's Field* 574
His body half *f* forward in pursuit, " 587
F ball, flew kite, and raced the purple fly, *Princess ii* 248
She took it and she *f* it. 'Fight' she said, " *iv* 598
and *f* defiance down Gagelike to man, " *v* 177
She *f* it from her, thinking: " *Con.* 32
We *f* the burthen of the second James. *Third of Feb.* 28
and *f* A ballad to the brightening moon: *In Mem. lxxxix* 27
and *f* The lilies to and fro, and said " *xcv* 59
I ran And *f* myself down on a bank of heath, *Com. of Arthur* 343
here is glory enow In having *f* the three: *Gareth and L.* 1326
To which he *f* a wrathful answer back: *Geraint and E.* 146
f herself Down on the great King's couch, *Lancelot and E.* 609
Unclasping *f* the casement back, " 981
F them, and down they flash'd, " 1235
A stone is *f* into some sleeping tarn, *Pelleas and E.* 93
nipt the hand, and *f* it from her; " 133
And *f* them o'er the walls; " 316
steed of Pelleas floundering *f* His rider, " 574
I have *f* thee pearls and find thee swine.' *Last Tournament* 310
Then with both hands I *f* him, *Pass. of Arthur* 325
would have *f* himself From cloud to cloud, *Lover's Tale i* 301
I *f* myself upon him In tears and cries: " *ii* 89

Flung (*continued*) I, groaning, from me *f* Her empty phantom: *Lover's Tale ii* 205
This question, so *f* down before the guests, „ *iv* 268
I *f* him the letter that drove me wild, *First Quarrel* 57
when all was done He *f* it among his fellows— *Rizpah* 32
the Priest's pearl, *f* down to swine— *Sir J. Oldcastle* 116
and *f* them in bight and bay, *V. of Maeldune* 53
Pallas *f* Her fringed ægis, *Achilles over the T.* 3
I am *f* from the rushing tide of the world *The Wreck* 6
I caught the wreath that was *f*. „ 40
Till you *f* us back on ourselves, *Despair* 40
Christian conquerors took and *f* *Locksley H., Sixty* 84
from their hands *F* thro' the woods, *Early Spring* 18
f herself Against my heart, *The Ring* 397
and *f* the mould upon your feet, *Happy* 50
f himself between The gladiatorial swords, *St. Telemachus* 61
women shrieking 'Atheist' *f* Filth from the roof, *Akbar's Dream* 91
I *f* myself down at her feet, *Charity* 38
Clomb the mountain, and *f* the berries, *Kapiolani* 6
Wait till Death has *f* them open, *Faith* 7

Flur *F*, for whose love the Roman Cæsar *Marr. of Geraint* 745

Flurried the little fowl were *f* at it, *Gareth and L.* 69

Flush (s) *f* of anger'd shame O'erflows thy calmer glances, *Madeline* 32
for when the morning *f* Of passion *Lucretius* 2
As light a *f* As hardly tints the blossom *Balin and Balan* 266
For here a sudden *f* of wrathful heat *Guinevere* 356
opposite The *f* and dawn of youth, *Lover's Tale i* 189
Her husband in the *f* of youth and dawn, *Death of Œnone* 17

Flush (verb) strikes along the brain, And *f'es* all the cheek. *D. of F. Women* 44
colour *f'es* Her sweet face from brow to chin: *L. of Burleigh* 61
After his books, to *f* his blood with air, *Aylmer's Field* 459
Or by denial *f* her babbling wells *Princess v* 334
madness *f'es* up in the ruffian's head, *Maud I i* 37
and made him *f*, and bow Lowly, *Gareth and L.* 548

Flush'd (*See also* **Faintly-flushed, New-flush'd, Sun-flush'd**) *F* all the leaves with rich gold-green, *Arabian Nights* 82
F like the coming of the day; *Miller's D.* 132
f Ganymede, his rosy thigh Half-buried *Palace of Art* 121
F in her temples and her eyes, „ 170
'Then *f* her cheek with rosy light, *Talking Oak* 165
Psyche *f* and wann'd and shook; *Princess iv* 160
When first she came, all *f* you said to me „ *vi* 250
her face A little *f*, and she past on; „ *vii* 81
Where oleanders *f* the bed Of silent torrents, *The Daisy* 33
The Peak is high and *f* At his highest *Voice and the P.* 29
Some *f*, and others dazed, *Com. of Arthur* 265
when *f* with fight, or hot, God's curse, *Geraint and E.* 660
that other *f*, And hung his head, „ 810
Upright and *f* before him: *Merlin and V.* 912
F slightly at the slight disparagement *Lancelot and E.* 234
beyond them *f* The long low dune, *Last Tournament* 483
F, started, met him at the doors, „ 512
The small sweet face was *f*, *The Wreck* 60
and *f* as red As poppies when she crown'd it. *The Tourney* 16

Flushing rosy red *f* in the northern night. *Locksley Hall* 26
let my query pass Unclaim'd, in *f* silence, *The Brook* 105
f the guiltless air, Spout from the maiden fountain *Lucretius* 239

Fluster'd him that *f* his poor parish wits *Aylmer's Field* 521
snares them by the score Flatter'd and *f*, *Princess v* 164
But once in life was *f* with new wine, *Merlin and V.* 756
so *f* with anger were they, They almost fell *V. of Maeldune* 25

Flute (s) Blow, *f*, and stir the stiff-set sprigs, *Amphion* 63
thicket rang To many a *f* of Arcady. *In Mem. xxiii* 24
Nor harp be touch'd, nor *f* be blown; „ *cv* 22
the roses heard The *f*, violin, bassoon; *Maud I xxii* 14
To the sound of dancing music and *f's*: „ *II v* 76

Flute (verb) lute and *f* fantastic tenderness, *Princess iv* 129

Fluted The mellow ouzel *f* in the elm; *Gardener's D.* 94
From *f* vase, and brazen urn In order, *Arabian Nights* 60
And *f* to the morning sea. *To E. L.* 24

Flute-notes thy *f-n* are changed to coarse, *The Blackbird* 18

Fluting swan That, *f* a wild carol ere her death, *M. d'Arthur* 267
swan That, *f* a wild carol ere her death, *Pass. of Arthur* 435

Flutter His spirit *f's* like a lark, *Day-Dm., Arrival* 29

Flutter (*continued*) Wings *f*, voices hover clear: *Sir Galahad* 78
Flags, *f* out upon turrets and towers! *W. to Alexandra* 15
heart within her fall and *f* tremulously, *Boädicea* 81
There *f's* up a happy thought, *In Mem. lxv* 7
The tender blossom *f* down, „ *ci* 2
idle fancies *f* me, I know not where to turn; *The Flight* 74

Flutter'd *F* about my senses and my soul; *Gardener's D.* 67
A second *f* round her lip Like a golden butterfly; *Talking Oak* 219
melody *F* headlong from the sky. *Vision of Sin* 45
A little *f*, with her eyelids down, *The Brook* 89
there *f* in, Half-bold, half-frighted, *Geraint and E.* 596
And *f* adoration, and at last With dark sweet hints *Merlin and V.* 158
The footstep *f* me at first: *Last Tournament* 515
And a pinnace, like a *f* bird, *The Revenge* 2

Fluttering (part.) voice Faltering and *f* in her throat, *Princess ii* 187
Alive with *f* scarfs and ladies' eyes, „ *v* 509
above, Crimson, a slender banneret *f*. *Gareth and L.* 913
f in a doubt Between the two— *Sisters (E. and E.)* 33
F the hawks of this crown-lusting line— *Sir J. Oldcastle* 57
and then fell *f* down at my feet; *The Wreck* 82
elmtree's ruddy-hearted blossom-flake Is *f* down. *To Mary Boyle* 4
blasts That run before the *f* tongues of fire; *D. of F. Women* 30
And on the board the *f* urn: *In Mem. xcv* 8
With half a night's appliances, recall'd Her *f* life: *Lover's Tale iv* 94

Fluttering (s) I watch'd the little *f's*, *Miller's D.* 153

Fly (s) (*See also* **Dragon-fly, Fancy-flies, Fire-fly, Floy, Gad-fly**) The blue *f* sung in the pane; *Mariana* 63
Kate saith 'the men are gilded *flies*.' *Kate* 18
The swallow stopt as he hunted the *f*, *Poet's Song* 9
Like *flies* that haunt a wound, *Aylmer's Field* 571
flew kite, and raced the purple *f*, *Princess ii* 248
In lieu of many mortal *flies*, „ *iii* 268
endure for the life of the worm and the *f*? *Wages* 7
bees are still'd, and the *flies* are kill'd, *Window, Winter* 10
And men the *flies* of latter spring, *In Mem. l* 10
eyes Are tender over drowning *flies*, „ *xcvi* 3
his head in a cloud of poisonous *flies*. *Maud I iv* 54
And call'd herself a gilded summer *f* *Merlin and V.* 258
since you name yourself the summer *f*, „ 369
gape for *flies*—we know not whence they come; *Holy Grail* 147
and infinite torment of *flies*, *Def. of Lucknow* 82
men Walk'd like the *f* on ceilings? *Columbus* 51
for you know The *flies* at home, „ 119
Nor drown thyself with *flies* in honied wine; *Ancient Sage* 268
Miriam sketch'd and Muriel threw the *f*; *The Ring* 159
She threw the *f* for me; „ 355
black *f* upon the pane May seem the black ox *To one who ran down Eng.* 3

Fly (verb) Then away she *flies*. *Lilian* 18
whither away, whither away? *f* no more. *Sea-Fairies* 7
rainbow forms and *flies* on the land „ 25
mariner, mariner, *f* no more. „ 42
Whither *f* ye, what game spy ye, *Rosalind* 8
'Here sits he shaping wings to *f*: *Two Voices* 289
let her herald, Reverence, *f* Before her *Love thou thy land* 18
To ingroove itself with that which *flies*, „ 46
Sun *flies* forward to his brother Sun; *Golden Year* 23
'*F*, happy happy sails, and bear the Press; *F* happy with the mission of the Cross; „ 42
And order'd words asunder *f*. *Day-Dm., Pro.* 20
The colour *flies* into his cheeks: „ *Arrival* 19
splinter'd spear-shafts crack and *f*, *Sir Galahad* 7
F o'er waste fens and windy fields. „ 60
And *f*, like a bird, from tree to tree; *Edward Gray* 30
The truth, that *flies* the flowing can, *Will Water.* 171
We follow that which *flies* before: *The Voyage* 94
to *f* sublime Thro' the courts, the camps, *Vision of Sin* 103
A crippled lad, and coming turn'd to *f*, *Aylmer's Field* 519
Let me *f*, says little birdie, *Sea Dreams* 295
rests a little longer, Then she *flies* away. „ 300
Let me rise and *f* away. „ 304
Baby too shall *f* away. „ 308
F on to clash together again, *Lucretius* 41
Thy glory *f* along the Italian field, „ 71
do they *f* Now thinner, and now thicker, „ 165
the soul *flies* out and dies in the air.' „ 274

Fly (verb) *(continued)* baby loves F twanging headless arrows at the hearts, — Princess ii 402
f,' she cried, 'O f, while yet you may! — „ iii 28
But you may yet be saved, and therefore f: — „ 64
As flies the shadow of a bird, she fled. — „ 96
F to her, and fall upon her gilded eaves, — „ iv 94
F to her, and pipe and woo her, — „ 115
and fled, as flies A troop of snowy doves — „ 167
I grant in her some sense of shame, she flies; — „ 349
She flies too high, she flies too high! — „ v 281
I say she flies too high, 'sdeath! — „ 286
peacemaker f To happy havens under all the sky, — Ode Inter. Exhib. 34
The lights and shadows f! — Window, On the Hill 1
F; F to the light in the valley below— — „ Letter 12
As flies the lighter thro' the gross. — In Mem. xli 4
Ill brethren, let the fancy f — „ lxxxvi 12
Fiercely flies The blast of North and East, — „ cvii 6
and f The happy birds, that change their sky — „ cxv 14
Arise and f The reeling Faun, — „ cxviii 25
Wild Hours that f with Hope and Fear, — „ cxxviii 9
'The fault was mine,' he whisper'd, 'f!' — Maud II i 30
I saw the dreary phantom arise and f — „ III vi 36
Until she let me f discaged to sweep — Gareth and L. 20
A jewell'd harness, ere they pass and f. — „ 688
But after sod and shingle ceased to f — „ 761
'I f no more: I allow thee for an hour. — „ 892
Larded thy last, except thou turn and f. — „ 1084
all about it flies a honeysuckle. — „ 1278
and wildly f, Mixt with the flyers. — Geraint and E. 482
'F, they will return And slay you; f, your charger is without, — „ 748
Behold, I f from shame, A lustful King, — Balin and Balan 473
I f to thee. Save, save me thou— — Merlin and V. 77
When did not rumours f? — Lancelot and E. 1194
if he f us, Small matter! let him.' — Pelleas and E. 199
And f to my strong castle overseas: — Guinevere 113
yet rise now, and let us f, — „ 120
Stands in a wind, ready to break and f, — „ 365
And he that fled no further f the King; — Pass. of Arthur 89
stream Flies with a shatter'd foam — Lover's Tale i 383
He flies the event: he leaves the event — „ iv 1
I must f, but follow quick. — The Revenge 6
You f them for a moment to fight with them again. — „ 9
'Shall we fight or shall we f? — „ 25
and aloft the glare Flies streaming, — Achilles over the T. 12
shell must break before the bird can f. — Ancient Sage 154
and now I f from Hell, And you with me; — The Flight 88
An' the lark f out o' the flowers — Tomorrow 91
stormy moment f and mingle with the Past. — Locksley H., Sixty 279
And wherever her flag f, — Open I. and C. Exhib. 17
bird that flies All night across the darkness, — Demeter and P. 1
F—care not. Birds and brides must leave the nest. — The Ring 89
And saw the world f by me like a dream, — „ 180
And flies above the leper's hut, — Happy 4
Now past her feet the swallow circling flies, — Prog. of Spring 44
Flies back in fragrant breezes to display — „ 64

Flyer arms stretch'd as to grasp a f: — Aylmer's Field 588
and all f's from the hand Of Justice, — Marr. of Geraint 36
and wildly fly, Mixt with the f's. — Geraint and E. 483
brands That hack'd among the f's, — Com. of Arthur 121
Fiercely we hack'd at the f's before us. — Batt. of Brunanburh 42

Flyin' Molly Magee kem f acrass me, — Tomorrow 21

Flying (*See also* **A-Flyin', Flyin'**) fled by night, and f turn'd: — Edwin Morris 134
Dreary gleams about the moorland f — Locksley Hall 4
in the f of a wheel Cry down the past, — Godiva 6
Or f shone, the silver boss Of her own halo's dusky shield; — The Voyage 31
following up And f the white breaker, — Enoch Arden 21
And caught the blossom of the f terms, — Princess, Pro. 164
we dropt, And f reach'd the frontier: — „ i 109
your arrow-wounded fawn Came f — „ ii 271
and loose A f charm of blushes o'er this cheek, — „ 430
he could not see The bird of passage f south — „ iii 210
Blow, bugle, blow, set the wild echoes f, (repeat) — „ iv 5, 17

Flying *(continued)* 'O Swallow, Swallow, f, f South, — Princess iv 93
'O Swallow, f from the golden woods, — „ 114
A woman-post in f raiment. — „ 376
f on the highest Foam of men's deeds— — „ v 319
shot A f splendour out of brass and steel, — „ vi 365
f struck With showers of random sweet — „ vii 85
or call'd On f Time from all their silver tongues— — „ 105
Paid with a voice f by to be lost — Wages 2
are you f over her sweet little face? — Window, On the Hill 13
and birds' song F here and there, — „ Spring 2
f gold of the ruin'd woodlands drove thro' the air. — Maud I i 12
F along the land and the main— — „ II ii 38
they swerved and brake F, — Com. of Arthur 120
follow'd by his f hair Ran like a colt, — „ 321
servingman F from out of the black wood, — Gareth and L. 802
Gareth's eyes had f blots Before them — „ 1031
Comes f over many a windy wave To Britain, — Marr. of Geraint 337
And white sails f on the yellow sea; — „ 829
F, but, overtaken, died the death Themselves — Geraint and E. 177
Another, f from the wrath of Doorm — „ 530
f back and crying out, 'O Merlin, — Merlin and V. 943
I hear of rumours f thro' your court. — Lancelot and E. 1190
and once the shadow of a bird F, — Pelleas and E. 39
A blot in heaven, the Raven, f high, — Guinevere 133
wheel'd and broke F, and link'd again, and wheel'd and broke F, — „ 258
Quiver'd a f glory on her hair, — Lover's Tale i 69
F by each fine ear, an Eastern gauze — „ iv 291
pinnace, like a flutter'd bird, came f from far away: — The Revenge 2
F at top of the roofs in the ghastly siege — Def. of Lucknow 4
F and foil'd at the last by the handful — „ 44
Wiclif-preacher whom I crost In f hither? — Sir J. Oldcastle 39
Trade f over a thousand seas with her spice — Vastness 13
with her f robe and her poison'd rose; — „ 16
and brighter The Gleam f onward, — Merlin and the G. 96
and fitting close Or f looselier, — Akbar's Dream 132
Gleam'd to the f moon by fits. — Miller's D. 116
Sole as a f star shot thro' the sky — Palace of Art 123
'Saw God divide the night with f flame, — D. of F. Women 225
To follow f steps of Truth Across the brazen bridge of war— — Love thou thy land 75
Would play with f forms and images, — Gardener's D. 60
And with a f finger swept my lips, — „ 246
Thunder, a f fire in heaven, — Boädicea 24
Loosely robed in f raiment, — „ 37
Is matter for a f smile. — In Mem. lxii 12
And sow the sky with f boughs, — „ lxxii 24
The f cloud, the frosty light: — „ cvi 2
like a f star Led on the gray-hair'd wisdom — Holy Grail 452

Foälk (folk) F's coostom flitted awaäy — North. Cobbler 28
an' f stood a-gawmin' in, — „ 81
call'd me afoor my awn f's to my faäce — Village Wife 105
that the f be sa scared at, — Spinster's S's. 24
Fur to goä that night to 'er f by cause — Owd Roä 52

Foam (s) (*See also* **Fountain-foam, Ocean-foam, Sea-foam**) the green brink and the running f, — Sea-Fairies 2
Flung leagues of roaring f into the gorge — If I were loved 13
brightens When the wind blows the f, — Œnone 62
Aphroditè beautiful, Fresh as the f, — „ 175
Rolling a slumbrous sheet of f below. — Lotos-Eaters 13
Weary the wandering fields of barren f. — „ 42
I would the white cold heavy-plunging f, — D. of F. Women 118
sea-wind sang Shrill, chill, with flakes of f. — M. d'Arthur 49
in the chasm are f and yellow sands; — Enoch Arden 2
And scaled in sheets of wasteful f, — Sea Dreams 53
burst and flood the world with f: — Princess iv 474
flying on the highest F of men's deeds— — „ v 320
sang from the three-decker out of the f, — Maud I i 50
Hurl'd back again so often in empty f, — Last Tournament 93
As tremulously as f upon the beach — Guinevere 364
sea-wind sang Shrill, chill, with flakes of f. — Pass. of Arthur 217
Flies with a shatter'd f along the chasm. — Lover's Tale i 383
the points of the f in the dusk came playing — Despair 50
ships from out the West go dipping thro' the f, — The Flight 91
On broader zones beyond the f, — To Ulysses 30

Foam (s) (*continued*) And these low bushes dip their twigs in *f*, *Prog. of Spring* 51
Too full for sound and *f*, *Crossing the Bar* 6
Foam (verb) Should all our churchmen *f* in spite *To F. D. Maurice* 9
forward-creeping tides Began to *f*, *In Mem. ciii* 38
Foam-bow his cheek brighten'd as the *f-b* brightens *Œnone* 61
Foam-churning These wet black passes and *f-c* chasms— *Sir J. Oldcastle* 9
Foam'd *f* away his heart at Averill's ear: *Aylmer's Field* 342
Their surging charges *f* themselves away; *Ode on Well.* 126
raved And thus *f* over at a rival name: *Balin and Balan* 567
Foam-flakes Crisp *f-f* scud along the level sand, *D. of F. Women* 39
Foam-fountains monster spouted his *f-f* in the sea. *Lotos-Eaters, C. S.* 107
Foaming horse across the *f's* of the ford, *Gareth and L.* 1040
To smoothe my pillow, mix the *f* draught Of fever, *Princess ii* 251
The *f* grape of eastern France. *In Mem., Con.* 80
Foamy here and there a *f* flake Upon me, *The Brook* 59
Foe tho' his *f's* speak ill of him, He was a friend to me. *D. of the O. Year* 22
The land, where girt with friends or *f's* *You ask me, why* 7
Must ever shock, like armed *f's*, *Love thou thy land* 78
went she Norward, Till she near'd the *f*. *The Captain* 36
divine to warn them of their *f's*: *Sea Dreams* 69
Had beat her *f's* with slaughter *Princess, Pro.* 34
drove her *f's* with slaughter from her walls, " 123
The next, like fire he meets the *f*, " *iv* 583
The general *f*. More soluble is this knot, " *v* 135
Truest friend and noblest *f*; " *vi* 7
those two *f's* above my fallen life, " 130
friend or *f*, Shall enter, if he will. " 336
His *f's* were thine; he kept us free; *Ode on Well.* 91
And England pouring on her *f's*. " 117
Who never spoke against a *f*; " 185
For on them brake the sudden *f*; *The Victim* 4
Friend, to be struck by the public *f*, *Maud II v* 89
bright With pitch'd pavilions of his *f*, *Com. of Arthur* 97
thou hast driven the *f* without, See to the *f* within! *Gareth and L.* 593
thou hast wreak'd his justice on his *f's*, " 1268
'Lo,' said Gareth, 'the *f* falls!' " 1317
second was your *f*, the sparrow-hawk, *Marr. of Geraint* 444
what they long for, good in friend or *f*, *Geraint and E.* 876
Pellam, once A Christless *f* of thine *Balin and Balan* 97
He makes no friend who never made a *f*. *Lancelot and E.* 1089
I hold that man the worst of public *f's* *Guinevere* 512
friend and *f* were shadows in the mist, *Pass. of Arthur* 100
Revenge ran on sheer into the heart of the *f*, *The Revenge* 33
and they yielded to the *f*. " 96
the *f* sprung his mine many times, *Def. of Lucknow* 31
and the *f* may outlive us at last— " 52
Friend?—*f* perhaps—a tussle for it then! *Sir J. Oldcastle* 196
Far off from out an island girt by *f's*, *Achilles over the T.* 8
and a boundless panic shook the *f*. " 18
where'er they ran, Have ended mortal *f's*; *Ancient Sage* 158
some in fight against the *f*, *Locksley H., Sixty* 45
the *f* was driven, And Wolseley overthrew Arâbi, *Pro. to Gen. Hamley* 29
Drove thro' the midst of the *f*, *Heavy Brigade* 30
drew The *f* from the saddle and threw " 54
Warrior of God, man's friend, and tyrant's *f*, *Epit. on Gordon* 1
hand Which fell'd the *f's* before you *Happy* 42
Foeman forth there stept a *f* tall, *Oriana* 33
What time the *f's* line is broke, *Two Voices* 155
to perish, falling on the *f's* ground, *Locksley Hall* 103
But they heard the *f's* thunder *The Captain* 41
still the *f* spoil'd and burn'd, *The Victim* 17
body enow to hold his *foemen* down?' *Com. of Arthur* 253
and by this will beat his *foemen* down.' " 309
foemen scared, like that false pair who turn'd *Geraint and E.* 176
f surged, and waver'd, and reel'd Up the hill, *Heavy Brigade* 62
Fog the white *f* vanish'd like a ghost *Death of Œnone* 67
Foil'd Flying and *f* at the last by the handful *Def. of Lucknow* 44
Fold (thing folded) Down-droop'd, in many a floating *f*, *Arabian Nights* 147
In silk-soft *f's*, upon yielding down, *Eleänore* 28
Look up, the *f* is on her brow. *Two Voices* 192
Winds all the vale in rosy *f's*, *Miller's D.* 242
In misty *f's*, that floating as they fell *Palace of Art* 35

Fold (thing folded) (*continued*) detaching, *f* by *f*, From those still heights, *Vision of Sin* 51
f's as dense as those Which hid the Holiest *Aylmer's Field* 771
The drowsy *f's* of our great ensign shake *Princess v* 8
With *f* to *f*, of mountain or of cape; " *vii* 3
Dark in its funeral *f*. *Ode on Well.* 57
And wrapt thee formless in the *f*, *In Mem. xxii* 15
In *f* upon *f* of hueless cloud, *Maud I vi* 3
Thro' twenty *f's* of twisted dragon, *Gareth and L.* 510
sprigs of summer laid between the *f's*, *Marr. of Geraint* 138
Thro' knots and loops and *f's* innumerable *Lancelot and E.* 439
wrapt In unremorseful *f's* of rolling fire. *Holy Grail* 261
a streetway hung with *f's* of pure White samite, *Last Tournament* 140
Enwound him *f* by *f*, and made him gray And grayer, *Guinevere* 603
I wish that somewhere in the ruin'd *f's*, *Œnone* 221
Thro' all its *f's* the multitudinous beast, *Tiresias* 15
close-lapt in silken *f's*, *Lover's Tale i* 153
There is no shade or *f* of mystery " 182
I thought it was an adder's *f*, " 691
Hung round with ragged rims and burning *f's*,— " *ii* 63
in their floating *f's* They past and were no more: " 99
Fold (as for sheep) (*See also* **Night-fold**) 'Bring this lamb back into Thy *f*, *Supp. Confessions* 105
the thick-fleeced sheep from wattled *f's*, *Ode to Memory* 66
very whitest lamb in all my *f* Loves you: *Aylmer's Field* 361
who are these? a wolf within the *f*! *Princess ii* 190
Far off from men I built a *f* for them: " *v* 390
No gray old grange, or lonely *f*, *In Mem. c* 5
some black wether of St. Satan's *f*. *Merlin and V.* 750
brand us, after, of whose *f* we be: " 764
if the tigers leap into the *f* unawares— *Def. of Lucknow* 51
driven by storm and sin and death to the ancient *f*, *The Wreck* 2
ranged from the narrow warmth of your *f*, *Despair* 38
A people from their ancient *f* of Faith, *Akbar's Dream* 61
Fold (verb) *F* thy palms across thy breast, *F* thine arms, turn to thy rest. *A Dirge* 2
the green that *f's* thy grave. (repeat) *A Dirge* 6, 13, 20, 27, 34, 41, 48
'High up the vapours *f* and swim: *Two Voices* 262
f our wings, And cease from wanderings, *Lotos-Eaters, C. S.* 19
sure this orbit of the memory *f's* *Gardener's D.* 74
about my feet The berried briony *f*.' *Talking Oak* 148
round her waist she felt it *f*, *Day-Dm., Depart.* 2
Now *f's* the lily all her sweetness up, *Princess vii* 186
So *f* thyself, my dearest, thou, " 188
or *f* Thy presence in the silk of sumptuous *Ancient Sage* 265
ah, *f* me to your breast! *The Flight* 5
I'd sooner *f* an icy corpse dead of some foul disease: " 54
Fold *See also* **Five-fold, Hundred-fold, Fifty-fold, Ten-hundred-fold, Thousand-fold**
Folded (*See also* **Far-folded, Heavy-folded, Many-folded, Silken-folded**) Thought *f* over thought, smiling asleep, *Eleänore* 84
'His palms are *f* on his breast: *Two Voices* 247
Sleep, Ellen, *f* in thy sister's arm, *Audley Court* 63
'Sleep, Ellen, *f* in Emilia's arm; " 65
To spirits *f* in the womb. *Day-Dm., Sleep P.* 8
Bow'd on her palms and *f* up from wrong, *Princess iv* 288
She heard, she moved, She moan'd, a *f* voice; " *v* 72
And every spirit's *f* bloom *In Mem. xliii* 2
Is pealing, *f* in the mist. " *civ* 4
And yearn'd to burst the *f* gloom, " *cxxii* 3
Not to be *f* more in these dear arms, *Marr. of Geraint* 99
Wherein she kept them *f* reverently With sprigs of summer " 137
letter she devised; which being writ And *f*, *Lancelot and E.* 1110
Hath *f* in the passes of the world.' *Pass. of Arthur* 78
on the horizon of the mind Lies *f*, *Lover's Tale i* 50
the sweet figure *f* round with night " *iv* 219
F her lion paws, and look'd to Thebes. *Tiresias* 149
Russian crowd *F* its wings from the left *Heavy Brigade* 39
and I was *f* in thine arms. *Demeter and P.* 22
here, my child, tho' *f* in thine arms, " 40
The *f* leaf is woo'd from out the bud *Lotos-Eaters, C. S.* 26
dissolved the mystery Of *f* sleep. *D. of F. Women* 263
O'er the mute city stole with *f* wings, *Gardener's D.* 186

Folded (continued) Holding the f annals of my youth; Gardener's D. 244
With f feet, in stoles of white, Sir Galahad 43
Mute with f arms they waited— The Captain 39
stood with f hands and downward eyes Merlin and V. 69
Folding black f's, that which housed therein. Gareth and L. 1380
F each other, breathing on each other, Lover's Tale i 261
F his hands, deals comfortable words „ 717
Foliage rustling thro' The low and bloomed f, Arabian Nights 13
gale That blown about the f underneath, Princess iii 121
all thy breadth and height Of f, In Mem. lxxxix 4
sank Down on a drift of f random-blown; Last Tournament 389
moisture and all smells of bud And f Lover's Tale iii 6
Foliaged (See also **Full-foliaged**) Who murmurest in the f eaves In Mem. xcix 9
Folk (See also **Foälk**) f that knew not their own minds, Enoch Arden 478
And echo'd by old f beside their fires Com. of Arthur 417
mingle with our f; And knowing every honest face Holy Grail 549
slay the f, and spoil the land.' Guinevere 137
He that was reft of his F and his friends Batt. of Brunanburh 70
Foller (**follow**) tha'll f 'im slick into Hell.' North. Cobbler 66
Foller'd (**followed**) fur the 'turney's letters they f sa fast; Village Wife 62
Follow (See also **Foller**) lightning to the thunder Which f's it, The Poet 51
because right is right, to f right Œnone 149
To f flying steps of Truth Love thou thy land 75
What good should f this, if this were done? M. d'Arthur 92
dark Earth f's wheel'd in her ellipse; Golden Year 24
f knowledge like a sinking star, Ulysses 31
The vine stream'd out to f, Amphion 46
May my soul f soon! St. Agnes' Eve 4
I f till I make thee mine.' The Voyage 64
We f that which flies before: „ 94
f Such dear familiarities of dawn? Aylmer's Field 130
One who cried, 'Leave all and f me.' „ 664
the thin weasel there F's the mouse, „ 853
which all our greatest fain Would f, Lucretius 79
not be dissoluble, Not f the great law? „ 116
A satyr, a satyr, see, F's; „ 193
The rest would f, each in turn; Princess, Pro. 201
'Then f me, the Prince,' I answer'd, „ 227
Voice Went with it, 'F, f, thou shalt win.' „ i 100
falling in a land Of promise; fruit would f. „ ii 140
If more and acted on, what f's? „ 229
Whence f's many a vacant pang; „ 403
bird of passage flying south but long'd To f: „ iii 211
'O Swallow, Swallow, if I could f, „ iv 99
And tell her, tell her, that I f thee.' „ 116
I cannot cease to f you, „ 455
To f up the worthiest till he die: „ 466
F us: who knows? we four may build some plan „ v 230
And on the 'F, f, thou shalt win: „ 472
But f; let the torrent dance thee down „ vii 209
farewell, and welcome for the year To f: „ Con. 96
Fall, and f their doom. Voice and the P. 20
F, f the chase! Window, On the Hill 11
F them down the slope! And I f them down to the window-pane „ 16
Nor f, tho' I walk in haste, In Mem. xxii 18
'The King will f Christ, and we the King Com. of Arthur 599
f the deer By these tall firs and our fast-falling burns; Gareth and L. 90
F the deer? f the Christ, the King, Live pure, speak true, right wrong, f the King— „ 117
Thou get to horse and f him far away. „ 584
f's, being named, His owner, „ 703
Lead, and I f.' (repeat) Gareth and L. 746, 760, 807, 891, 990, 1053, 1155
'F, I lead!' so down among the pines He plunged; Gareth and L. 808
'Full pardon, but I f up the quest, „ 886
'F the faces, and we find it. „ 1210
the Prince, as Enid past him, fain To f, Marr. of Geraint 376
the knight besought him, 'F me, Geraint and E. 807
'Enough,' he said, 'I f,' and they went. „ 816
and crying 'Sirs, Rise, f! Balin and Balan 48

Follow (continued) But f Vivien thro' the fiery flood! Balin and Balan 454
Help, for he f's! take me to thyself! Merlin and V. 82
The Fame that f's death is nothing to us; „ 464
the scroll 'I f fame.' „ 476
I charge you, f me not.' Lancelot and E. 507
serve you, and to f you thro' the world.' „ 939
'I fain would f love, if that could be; I needs must f death, who calls for me; Call and I f, I f! let me die.' „ 1016
Then might she f me thro' the world, „ 1316
I sware a vow to f it till I saw.' Holy Grail 282
Galahad, and O Galahad, f me.' „ 292
But ye, that f but the leader's bell' „ 298
while ye f wandering fires Lost in the quagmire! „ 319
most of us would f wandering fires, (repeat) „ 369, 599
and vanish'd, tho' I yearn'd To f; „ 507
most of them would f wandering fires, „ 891
the gloom, That f's on the turning of the world, Pelleas and E. 549
after wail Of suffering, silence f's, Pass. of Arthur 119
What good should f this, if this were done? „ 260
I could not rise Albeit I strove to f. Lover's Tale ii 98
I must fly, but f quick. The Revenge 6
Now f's Edith echoing Evelyn. Sisters (E. and E.) 15
crying out: 'F me, f me!'— Def. of Lucknow 64
Do-well will f thought, Ancient Sage 273
f Edwin to those isles, those islands of the Blest! The Flight 42
these would feel and f Truth if only you and you, Locksley H., Sixty 119
leave the dog too lame to f with the cry, „ 226
know them, f him who led the way, „ 266
F you the Star that lights a desert pathway, „ 275
F Light, and do the Right— „ 277
'F,' and up the hill, up the hill, Heavy Brigade 11
bound to f, wherever she go Stark-naked, Dead Prophet 45
O f, leaping blood, Early Spring 25
poor Muriel when you hear What f's! The Ring 274
I am Merlin Who f The Gleam. Merlin and the G. 10
The Master whisper'd 'F the Gleam.' „ 34
But eager to f, I saw, „ 101
After it, f it, F the Gleam. „ 130
I whirl, and I f the Sun.' The Dreamer 14
Whirl, and f the Sun! (repeat) The Dreamer 20, 24, 28, 32
But what may f who can tell? The Wanderer 14
Follow'd (See also **Foller'd**) For surer sign had f, either hand, M. d'Arthur 76
Then f counsel, comfort, and the words Love and Duty 69
The happy princess f him. Day-Dm., Depart. 8
Thro' all the world she f him. „ 32
And f with acclaims, Will Water. 138
And f her all the way. Lady Clare 64
still we f where she led, (repeat) The Voyage 59, 90
Then f calms, and then winds variable, Enoch Arden 545
when they f us from Philip's door, The Brook 167
Where Aylmer f Aylmer at the Hall Aylmer's Field 36
the fierce old man F, and under his own lintel stood „ 331
Seconded, for my lady f suit, „ 558
f out Tall and erect, but in the middle aisle Reel'd, „ 817
I f: and at top She pointed seaward: Sea Dreams 121
I began, And the rest f: Princess, Pro. 244
We f up the river as we rode, „ i 206
f then A classic lecture, rich in sentiment, „ ii 373
resolder'd peace, whereon F his tale. „ v 48
but Blanche At distance f: so they came: „ vi 83
And f up by a hundred airy does, „ 87
Passionate tears F: the king replied not: „ 312
F up in valley and glen With blare of bugle, Ode on Well. 114
F by the brave of other lands, „ 194
the day that f the day she was wed, The Islet 4
And silence f, and we wept. In Mem. xxx 20
In vassal tides that f thought. „ cxii 16
f by his flying hair Ran like a colt, Com. of Arthur 321
thereafter f calm, Free sky and stars: „ 391
But in the weeks that f, the good Queen, Gareth and L. 526
The two that out of north had f him: „ 679
till the dusk that f evensong Rode on the two, „ 793

Follow'd (*continued*) He f nearer: ruth began to work — *Geraint and E.* 101
He f nearer still; the pain she had — „ 186
And overthrew the next that f him, — „ 465
His lusty spearmen f him with noise: — „ 593
ye be sent for by the King,' They f; — *Balin and Balan* 49
F the Queen; Sir Balin heard her — „ 250
and f this, But all so blind in rage — „ 327
'And is the fair example f, Sir, — *Merlin and V.* 19
Vivien f, but he mark'd her not. — „ 199
And then she f Merlin all the way, — „ 203
Dear feet, that I have f thro' the world, — „ 227
You f me unask'd; — „ 298
the stammering cracks and claps That f, — „ 943
F, and in among bright faces, ours, — *Holy Grail* 266
and she F Him down, and like a flying star — „ 452
Told him he f—almost Arthur's words— — „ 669
knights all set their faces home, Sir Pelleas f. — *Pelleas and E.* 188
And f to the city. — „ 586
Arthur rose and Lancelot f him, — *Last Tournament* 112
F a rush of eagle's wings, — „ 417
For surer sign had f, either hand, — *Pass. of Arthur* 244
in weeping and in praise Of her, we f: — *Lover's Tale ii* 88
it seem'd By that which f— — „ *iv* 22
F us too that night, and dogg'd us, — *Despair* 2
From wasteful living, f— — *Ancient Sage* 5
Good, for Good is Good, he f, — *Locksley H, Sixty* 60
up the hill, F the Heavy Brigade. — *Heavy Brigade* 12
All in a moment f with force — „ 20
f up by her vassal legion of fools; — *Vastness* 12
hid in cloud not be f by the Moon? — *Happy* 97
Thro' which I f line by line Your leading hand, — *To Ulysses* 45
A silence f as of death, — *St. Telemachus* 65
those that f, loosen, stone from stone, — *Akbar's Dream* 188

Follower tho' thou numberest with the f's — *Aylmer's Field* 663
And at her head a f of the camp, — *Princess v* 60
my f's ring him round: He sits unarm'd; — *Geraint and E.* 336
With all his rout of random f's, — „ 382
Went Enid with her sullen f on. — „ 440
prick'd In combat with the f of Limours, — „ 501
one true knight—Sole f of the vows'— — *Last Tournament* 303
And every f eyed him as a God; — „ 678
his f's, all Flower into fortune— — *Columbus* 166
O f of the Vision, still In motion to the distant gleam, — *Freedom* 13

Following f her dark eyes Felt earth as air — *Gardener's D.* 211
or f up And flying the white breaker, — *Enoch Arden* 20
f our own shadows thrice as long — *The Brook* 166
f thro' the porch that sang All round with laurel, — *Princess ii* 22
Went forth in long retinue f up The river — „ *iii* 195
ever f those two crowned twins, — „ *v* 420
He, that ever f her commands, — *Ode on Well.* 211
As we descended f Hope, — *In Mem. xxii* 11
Tho' f with an upward mind The wonders — „ *xli* 21
And Gareth f was again beknaved, — *Gareth and L.* 786
with fixt eye f the three. — *Marr. of Geraint* 237
A youth, that f with a costrel bore — „ 386
Let his eye rove in f, or rest On Enid — „ 399
(His gentle charger f him unled) — *Geraint and E.* 571
and Vivien f him, Turn'd to her: — *Merlin and V.* 32
And when I look'd, and saw you f still, — „ 299
gloom'd Your fancy when ye saw me f you, — „ 326
f you to this wild wood, Because I saw you sad, — „ 440
and this honour after death, F thy will! — *Last Tournament* 35
f these my mightiest knights, — *Guinevere* 489
Few were his f, Fled to his warship: — *Batt. of Brunanburh* 58
F a torrent till its myriad falls — *Tiresias* 37
and, f out A league of labyrinthine darkness, — *Demeter and P.* 81
So, f her old pastime of the brook, — *The Ring* 354
How loyal in the f of thy Lord! — *In Mem. W. G. Ward* 6
f lighted on him there, And shouted, — *Death of Œnone* 55
f, as in trance, the silent cry. — „ 86
F a hundred sunsets, and the sphere — *St. Telemachus* 31
And f thy true counsel, by thine aid, — *Akbar's Dream* 154

Folly 'Ah, f!' in mimic cadence answer'd James—
'Ah, f! for it lies so far away, — *Golden Year* 53
Fill'd I was with f and spite, — *Edward Gray* 15

Folly (*continued*) And others' follies teach us not, — *Will Water.* 173
f taking wings Slipt o'er those lazy limits — *Aylmer's Field* 494
brace Of twins may weed her of her f. — *Princess v* 464
How I hate the spites and the follies! — *Spiteful Letter* 24
Deep f! yet that this could be— — *In Mem. xli* 9
slumber in which all spleenful f was drown'd, — *Maud I iii* 2
heart of the poet is whirl'd into f and vice. — „ *iv* 39
perplext her With his worldly talk and f: — „ *xx* 7
thy much f hath sent thee here His kitchen-knave: — *Gareth and L.* 919
for I fear My fate or f, — *Merlin and V.* 927
I came All in my f to the naked shore, — *Holy Grail* 793
dead babe and the follies of the King; — *Last Tournament* 163
But then what f had sent him overseas — „ 394
Gone the fires of youth, the follies, — *Locksley H., Sixty* 39

Fond But O too f, when have I answer'd — *Princess vii* 4
no word of that f tale— — *Last Tournament* 578

Fonder man of science himself is f of glory, — *Maud I iv* 37

Fondle rabbit f's his own harmless face, — *Aylmer's Field* 851

Fondled Appraised his weight and f fatherlike, — *Enoch Arden* 154
Too ragged to be f on her lap, — *Aylmer's Field* 686
And all this morning when I f you: — *Merlin and V.* 286
we f it, Stephen and I, But it died, — *The Wreck* 83

Fondling f all her hand in his he said, — *Marr. of Geraint* 509
Tristram, f her light hands, replied, — *Last Tournament* 601

Fonseca F my main enemy at their court, — *Columbus* 126

Font One rear'd a f of stone And drew, — *Princess, Pro.* 59
Nor winks the gold fin in the porphyry f: — „ *vii* 178
Entwine the cold baptismal f, — *In Mem. xxix* 10

Food eat wholesome f, And wear warm clothes, — *St. S. Stylites* 108
wine and f were brought, and Earl Limours — *Geraint and E.* 289
a beggar began to cry 'F, f or I die'! — *Voice spake, etc.* 6

Fool (adj.) What, if she be fasten'd to this f lord, — *Maud I xvi* 24
'Beat little heart' on this f brain of mine. — *Romney's R.* 155

Fool (s) (*See also* **Father-fool**) an absent f, I cast me down, — *Miller's D.* 62
we should mimic this raw f the world, — *Walk. to the Mail* 106
while we stood like f's Embracing, — *Edwin Morris* 118
push'd the happy season back,—The more f's they,— — *Golden Year* 67
gilds the straiten'd forehead of the f! — *Locksley Hall* 62
F, again the dream, the fancy! — „ 173
'A ship of f's,' he shriek'd in spite, 'A ship of f's,' he sneer'd and wept. — *The Voyage* 77
Bandied by the hands of f's. — *Vision of Sin* 106
Drink we, last, the public f, — „ 149
April hopes, the f's of chance; — „ 164
f's, With such a vantage-ground for nobleness! — *Aylmer's Field* 386
Went further, f! and trusted him with all, — *Sea Dreams* 76
Christ the bait to trap his dupe and f; — „ 191
(God help her) she was wedded to a f; — *Princess iii* 83
slaves at home and f's abroad.' — „ *iv* 521
'Ah f, and made myself a Queen of farce! — „ *vii* 243
Ah, there's no f like the old one— — *Grandmother* 44
but I beänt a f: — *N. Farmer, O. S.* 3
'F,' he answer'd, 'death is sure To those that stay — *Sailor Boy* 13
Ah God! the petty f's of rhyme — *Lit. Squabbles* 1
no God at all, says the f; — *High. Pantheism* 15
We are f's and slight; — *In Mem., Pro.* 29
'Thou shalt not be the f of loss.' — „ *iv* 16
O to us, The f's of habit, — „ *x* 12
The f that wears a crown of thorns: — „ *lxix* 12
They call'd me f, they call'd me child: — „ 13
and the brazen f Was soften'd, — „ *cx* 11
who but a f would have faith in a tradesman's ware — *Maud I i* 26
angry pride Is cap and bells for a f. — „ *vi* 62
F that I am to be vext with his pride! — „ *xiii* 5
thought like a f of the sleep of death. — „ *xiv* 38
Struck me before the languid f, — „ *II i* 19
betraying His party-secret, f, to the press; — „ *v* 35
and Evening-Star, Being strong f's; — *Gareth and L.* 635
all these four be f's, but mighty men, — „ 643
Back wilt thou, f? For hard by here is one — „ 895
The second brother in their f's parable— — „ 1004
this strong f whom thou, Sir Knave, — „ 1058
There stands the third f of their allegory.' — „ 1085
yon four f's have suck'd their allegory — „ 1199

Fool (s) (*continued*) Knight, knave, prince and *f*, *Gareth and L.* 1255
'*F*, for thou hast, men say, the strength of ten, „ 1387
sweet faces make good fellows *f's* *Geraint and E.* 399
which a wanton *f*, Or hasty judger „ 432
And be he dead, I count you for a *f*; „ 548
F's prate, and perish traitors. *Balin and Balan* 530
to her Squire mutter'd the damsel '*F's*! „ 564
were he not crown'd King, coward, and *f*.' *Merlin and V.* 789
shrieking out 'O *f*!' the harlot leapt Adown the forest, and the thicket closed Behind her, and the forest echo'd '*f*.' „ 972
She mutter'd, 'I have lighted on a *f*, *Pelleas and E.* 113
'Thou *f*,' she said, 'I never heard his voice „ 255
F to the midmost marrow of his bones, „ 258
I deem'd him *f*? yea, so? „ 309
Pelleas whom she call'd her *f*? „ 474
F, beast—he, she, or I? myself most *f*; „ 475
the King Hath made us *f's* and liars. „ 479
DAGONET, the *f*, whom Gawain in his mood *Last Tournament* 1
Tristram, saying, 'Why skip ye so, Sir *F*?' (repeat) „ 9, 243
being *f*, and seeing too much wit Makes the world rotten, „ 246
'Ay, *f*,' said Tristram, 'but 'tis eating dry „ 249
ask'd, 'Why skipt ye not, Sir *F*?' „ 256
what music have I broken, *f*?' „ 261
Sir *f*,' said Tristram, 'I would break thy head. *F*, I came late, the heathen wars were o'er, „ 268
I am but a *f* to reason with a *f*— „ 271
'Drink, drink, Sir *F*,' and thereupon I drank, „ 297
marking how the knighthood mock thee, *f*— „ 301
but when the King Had made thee *f*, „ 306
frighted all free *f* from out thy heart: Which left thee less than *f*, „ 307
thank the Lord I am King Arthur's *f*. „ 320
Some such fine song—but never a king's *f*.' „ 324
goats, asses, geese The wiser *f's*, „ 326
Tristram, 'Ay, Sir *F*, for when our King Was victor „ 334
'Nay, *f*,' said Tristram, 'not in open day.' „ 347
'Lo, *f*,' he said, 'ye talk *F's* treason: is the King thy brother *f*?' „ 351
Ay, ay, my brother *f*, the king of *f's*! „ 354
Long live the king of *f's*! „ 358
Sent up an answer, sobbing, 'I am thy *f*, „ 761
all my doubts were *f's* Born of the *f* *Sisters (E. and E.)* 140
stake and the cross-road, *f*, if you will, *Despair* 116
But man to-day is fancy's *f* *Ancient Sage* 27
I beänt sich a *f* as ye thinks; *Spinster's S's.* 18
ye mun be *f's* to be hallus a-shawin' your claws, „ 61
tell them 'old experience is a *f*,' *Locksley H., Sixty* 131
Nor is he the wisest man who never proved himself a *f*. „ 244
for War's own sake Is *f*, or crazed, or worse; *Epilogue* 31
follow'd up by her vassal legion of *f's*; *Vastness* 12
'This model husband, this fine Artist'! *F*, *Romney's R.* 124
Fool (verb) my own weakness *f's* My judgment *Supp. Confessions* 136
To *f* the crowd with glorious lies, *In Mem. cxxviii* 14
being fool'd Of others, is to *f* one's self. *Gareth and L.* 1275
Fool'd Ah! let me not be *f*, sweet saints: *St. S. Stylites* 212
And were half *f* to let you tend our son, *Princess vi* 274
dies, and leaves me *f* and trick'd, *Gareth and L.* 1251
for worse than being *f* Of others, is to fool one's self. „ 1274
What shock has *f* her since, *To the Queen ii* 22
Fooleries 'Are these your pretty tricks and *f*, *Merlin and V.* 265
Fool-fury The red *f-f* of the Seine *In Mem. cxxvii* 7
Foolish but sing the *f* song I gave you, *Miller's D.* 161
And let the *f* yeoman go. *L. C. V. de Vere* 72
Aid all this *f* people; *St. S. Stylites* 223
They to whom my *f* passion were a target for their scorn: *Locksley Hall* 146
To drop thy *f* tears upon my grave, *Come not, when* 2
I seem so *f* and so broken down. *Enoch Arden* 316
Till understanding all the *f* work Of Fancy, *Princess vi* 116
But help thy *f* ones to bear; *In Mem. Pro.* 31
Whose youth was full of *f* noise, „ *liii* 3
The *f* neighbours come and go, „ *lx* 13
That *f* sleep transfers to thee. „ *lxviii* 16
But the fire of a *f* pride flash'd over *Maud I iv* 16

Foolish (*continued*) 'They be of *f* fashion, O Sir King, *Gareth and L.* 628
'ye are overfine To mar stout knaves with *f* courtesies:' „ 733
A *f* love for flowers? „ 1072
who lets His heart be stirr'd with any *f* heat „ 1178
As being after all their *f* fears „ 1424
And all her *f* fears about the dress, *Marr. of Geraint* 142
Nor speak I now from *f* flattery; „ 433
whether very wise Or very *f*; „ 470
with her heart All overshadow'd by the *f* dream, „ 675
Could scarce divide it from her *f* dream: „ 686
And all her *f* fears about the dress, „ 844
Brother, I need not tell thee *f* words,— *Holy Grail* 855
'Will the child kill me with her *f* prate?' *Guinevere* 225
I myself have often babbled doubtless of a *f* past; *Locksley H., Sixty* 7
O *f* dreams, that you, that I, *Happy* 89
Foolishness cipher face of rounded *f*, *Gareth and L.* 1039
Fool-like Nay, for he spake too *f-l*: mystery! „ 472
Foorty (forty) An' I've 'ed my quart ivry market-noight for *f* year. *N. Farmer, O. S.* 8
Foot (*See also* **Crow-foot, Feeät, Light-foot**) O! hither lead thy *feet*! *Ode to Memory* 64
with echoing *feet* he threaded The secretest walks *The Poet* 9
curl round my silver *feet* silently, *The Mermaid* 50
if you kiss'd her *feet* a thousand years, *The form, the form* 13
WITH one black shadow at its *feet*, *Mariana in the S.* 1
Thy *feet*, millenniums hence, be set *Two Voices* 89
Touch'd by his *feet* the daisy slept. „ 276
at their *feet* the crocus brake like fire, *Œnone* 96
from the violets her light *f* Shone rosy-white, „ 179
And laid him at his mother's *feet*. *The Sisters* 35
when you pass, With your *feet* above my head *May Queen, N. Y's. E.* 32
There's a new *f* on the floor, my friend, *D. of the O. Year* 52
Sleep full of rest from head to *feet*; *To J. S.* 75
Comes Faith from tracts no *feet* have trod, *On a Mourner* 29
The thunders breaking at her *feet*: *Of old sat Freedom* 2
he based His *feet* on juts of slippery crag *M. d'Arthur* 189
Bound by gold chains about the *feet* of God. „ 255
So light of *f*, so light of spirit— *Gardener's D.* 14
a *f*, that might have danced The greensward „ 133
The wreath of flowers fell At Dora's *feet*. *Dora* 103
a hand, a *f* Lessening in perfect cadence, *Walk. to the Mail* 54
But put your best *f* forward, „ 111
Or when I feel about my *feet* *Talking Oak* 147
And at my *feet* she lay. „ 208
drop Balm-dews to bathe thy *feet*! „ 268
full Of force and choler, and firm upon his *feet*, *Golden Year* 61
and cold my wrinkled *feet* *Tithonus* 67
His beard a *f* before him, and his hair A yard behind. *Godiva* 18
till noon no *f* should pace the street, „ 39
YEAR after year unto her *f*, *Day-Dm., Sleep B.* 1
feet that ran, and doors that clapt, „ *Revival* 3
And sixty *feet* the fountain leapt. „ 8
Each pluck'd his one *f* from the grave, *Amphion* 43
With folded *feet*, in stoles of white, *Sir Galahad* 43
A clog of lead was round my *feet*, *The Letters* 5
break, At the *f* of thy crags, O Sea! *Break, break, etc.* 14
And the lark drop down at his *feet*. *Poet's Song* 8
And stared, with his *f* on the prey, „ 12
sketching with her slender pointed *f* *The Brook* 102
Tumbled the tawny rascal at his *feet*, *Aylmer's Field* 230
therefore with His light about thy *feet*, „ 665
fell The woman shrieking at his *feet*, „ 811
she with her strong *feet* up the steep hill *Sea Dreams* 120
woman heard his *f* Return from pacings *Lucretius* 5
golden *feet* on those empurpled stairs „ 135
She tapt her tiny silken-sandal'd *f*: *Princess, Pro.* 150
our cloisters echo'd frosty *feet*, „ 183
make her some great Princess, six *feet* high, „ 224
he started on his *feet*, Tore the king's letter, „ *i* 60
tips of her long hands, And to her *feet*. „ *ii* 41
Woman, if I might sit beside your *feet*, „ 258
her *f* on one Of those tame leopards. „ *iii* 180
Many a light *f* shone like a jewel set „ 358
But when we planted level *feet*, „ *iv* 30

Foot (*continued*) push'd alone on *f* (For since her horse was lost *Princess iv* 196
fleet I was of *f*: Before we shower'd the rose „ 263
a vine, That claspt the *feet* of a Mnemosyne, „ 269
their mask was patent, and my *f* Was to you: „ 326
wisp that flickers where no *f* can tread.' „ 358
lost lamb at her *feet* Sent out a bitter bleating „ 391
and dash'd Unopen'd at her *feet*: „ 471
some sweet sculpture draped from head to *f*, „ *v* 57
lay my little blossom at my *feet*, „ 100
those that iron-cramp'd their women's *feet*; „ 376
We plant a solid *f* into the Time, „ 415
they came, Their *feet* in flowers, her loveliest: „ *vi* 78
Steps with a tender *f*, light as on air, „ 88
See, your *f* is on our necks, We vanquish'd, „ 166
felt it sound and whole from head to *f*, „ 211
on her *f* she hung A moment, and she heard, „ *vii* 79
She moved, and at her *feet* the volume fell. „ 254
And the *feet* of those he fought for, *Ode on Well.* 11
myriad horns of plenty at our *feet*. *Ode Inter. Exhib.* 6
Scatter the blossom under her *feet*. *W. to Alexandra* 9
Thro' cypress avenues, at our *feet*. *The Daisy* 48
and nearer than hands and *feet*. *High. Pantheism* 12
Fine little hands, fine little *feet*— *Window, Letter* 3
f Is on the skull which thou hast made. *In Mem., Pro.* 7
The Shadow cloak'd from head to *f*, „ *xxiii* 4
Whereon with equal *feet* we fared; „ *xxv* 2
She bows, she bathes the Saviour's *feet* „ *xxxii* 11
On thy Parnassus set thy *feet*, „ *xxxvii* 6
That nothing walks with aimless *feet*; „ *liv* 5
Whose *feet* are guided thro' the land, „ *lxvi* 9
Thy *feet* have stray'd in after hours „ *cii* 14
my *feet* are set To leave the pleasant fields „ 21
Her *feet*, my darling, on the dead; „ *Con.* 50
feet like sunny gems on an English green, *Maud I v* 14
fall before Her *feet* on the meadow grass, „ 26
And fawn at a victor's *feet*. „ *vi* 30
solid ground Not fail beneath my *feet* „ *xi* 2
For her *feet* have touch'd the meadows „ *xii* 23
Gorgonised me from head to *f* „ *xiii* 21
the delicate Arab arch of her *feet* „ *xvi* 15
her light *f* along the garden walk, „ *xviii* 9
He sets the jewel-print of your *feet* In violets „ *xxii* 41
Would start and tremble under her *feet*, „ 73
A shadow there at my *feet*, „ *II i* 39
Lying close to my *f*, Frail, but a work divine, „ *ii* 3
A golden *f* or a fairy horn „ 19
the rivulet at her *feet* Ripples on „ *iv* 41
never an end to the stream of passing *feet*, „ *v* 11
mock their foster-mother on four *feet*, *Com. of Arthur* 31
in the flame was borne A naked babe, and rode to Merlin's *feet*, „ 384
their *feet* were planted on the plain *Gareth and L.* 187
I leap from Satan's *f* to Peter's knee— „ 538
loosed his bonds and on free *feet* Set him, „ 817
their *feet* In dewy grasses glisten'd; „ 927
The gay pavilion and the naked *feet*, „ 937
do him further wrong Than set him on his *feet*, „ 955
often they break covert at our *feet*.' *Marr. of Geraint* 183
Worn by the *feet* that now were silent, „ 321
fell'd him, and set *f* upon his breast, „ 574
rose Limours, and looking at his *feet*, *Geraint and E.* 302
lays his *f* upon it, Gnawing and growling: „ 562
on his *f* She set her own and climb'd; „ 759
set his *f* upon me, and give me life. „ 850
Hath hardly scaled with help a hundred *feet* *Balin and Balan* 170
made his *feet* Wings thro' a glimmering gallery, „ 403
At Merlin's *feet* the wily Vivien lay. *Merlin and V.* 5
all the heathen lay at Arthur's *feet*, „ 144
kiss'd his *feet*, As if in deepest reverence „ 219
Dear *feet*, that I have follow'd thro' the world, „ 227
Behind his ankle twined her hollow *feet* Together, „ 240
Vivien bathed your *feet* before her own? „ 284
Scared by the noise upstarted at our *feet*, „ 422
The *feet* unmortised from their ankle-bones „ 552

Foot (*continued*) judge all nature from her *feet* of clay, *Merlin and V.* 835
the green path that show'd the rarer *f*, *Lancelot and E.* 162
her shape From forehead down to *f*, perfect—again From *f* to forehead exquisitely turn'd: „ 642
with her *feet* unseen Crush'd the wild passion „ 741
he wellnigh kiss'd her *feet* For loyal awe, „ 1172
let the shield of Lancelot at her *feet* Be carven, „ 1341
made a silken mat-work for her *feet*; *Holy Grail* 151
how my *feet* recrost the deathful ridge „ 534
—yea, his very hand and *f*— „ 915
one whose *f* is bitten by an ant, *Pelleas and E.* 184
there three squires across their *feet*: „ 431
The *f* that loiters, bidden go,— *Last Tournament* 117
Dagonet with one *f* poised in his hand, „ 285
little Dagonet mincing with his *feet*, „ 311
Dagonet, turning on the ball of his *f*, „ 329
when she heard the *feet* of Tristram grind „ 510
Her light *feet* fell on our rough Lyonnesse, „ 554
his *f* was on a stool Shaped as a dragon; „ 671
about his *feet* A voice clung sobbing till he question'd it, „ 758
voice about his *feet* Sent up an answer, „ 760
broadening from her *feet*, And blackening, *Guinevere* 81
let us in, tho' late, to kiss his *feet*! „ 178
with a wild sea-light about his *feet*, He saw them— „ 242
when armed *feet* Thro' the long gallery „ 412
in the darkness heard his armed *feet* Pause by her; „ 418
and laid her hands about his *feet*. „ 528
My pride in happier summers, at my *feet*. „ 536
And while she grovell'd at his *feet*, „ 581
based His *feet* on juts of slippery crag *Pass. of Arthur* 357
Bound by gold chains about the *feet* of God. „ 423
To stay his *feet* from falling, *Lover's Tale i* 142
she saw Beneath her *feet* the region far away, „ 395
at her *feet*, Ev'n the *feet* of her I loved, „ 599
Were stoled from head to *f* in flowing black; „ *ii* 85
at his *feet* I seem'd to faint and fall, „ 96
Hard-heaving, and her eyes upon her *feet*, „ *iv* 308
I lay At thy pale *feet* this ballad *Ded. Poem Prin. Alice* 20
and bullets would rain at our *feet*— *Def. of Lucknow* 21
was pollen'd from head to *feet* *V. of Maeldune* 49
and his white beard fell to his *feet*, „ 118
Cast at thy *feet* one flower that fades away. *To Dante* 7
Or on your head their rosy *feet*, *To E. Fitzgerald* 9
one glittering *f* disturb'd The lucid well; *Tiresias* 41
I will sit at your *feet*, I will hide my face, *The Wreck* 12
then fell fluttering down at my *feet*; „ 82
blanch into spray At the *feet* of the cliff; „ 138
foam in the dusk came playing about our *feet*. *Despair* 50
And Love is fire, and burns the *feet* *The Flight* 68
A stealthy *f* upon the stair! „ 70
fall of yer *f* in the dance was as light as snow *Tomorrow* 36
an' laid himself undher yer feet, „ 38
I plumpt *f* fust i' the pond; *Spinster's S's.* 28
tha' hoickt my *feet* wi' a flop fro' the claäy. „ 30
forefather, with his *feet* upon the hound. *Locksley H., Sixty* 28
and woman to her tender *feet*, „ 50
Set the *feet* above the brain and swear the brain is in the *feet*. „ 136
Progress halts on palsied *feet*, „ 219
We needs must scan him from head to *feet* *Dead Prophet* 55
wild mob's million *feet* Will kick you *The Fleet* 18
robed thee in his day from head to *feet*— *Demeter and P.* 21
For, see, thy *f* has touch'd it; „ 48
see beneath our *feet* The mist of autumn *The Ring* 328
and flung the mould upon your *feet*, *Happy* 50
past her *feet* the swallow circling flies, *Prog. of Spring* 44
f to *f* With your own shadow in the placid lake, *Romney's R.* 75
mine from your pretty blue eyes to your *feet*, „ 96
Six *f* deep of burial mould Will dull their comments! „ 125
vines Which on the touch of heavenly *feet* *Death of Œnone* 5
The mango spurn the melon at his *f*? *Akbar's Dream* 39
I flung myself down at her *feet*, *Charity* 38

Football drunkard's *f*, laughing-stocks of Time, *Princess iv* 517

Footcloth and tumbled on the purple *f*, „ 286

Footed *See* **Bare-footed, Cat-footed, Four-footed, Lighter-footed, Little-footed, Wind-footed**
Foot-fall With measured *f* firm and mild, *Two Voices* 413
list a *f-f*, ere he saw The wood-nymph, *Palace of Art* 110
her palfrey's *f* shot Light horrors *Godiva* 58
Or ghostly *f* echoing on the stair. *Guinevere* 507
Foot-gilt lay *F-g* with all the blossom-dust *Merlin and V.* 282
Footing Show'd her the fairy *f's* on the grass, *Aylmer's Field* 90
A slender-shafted Pine Lost *f*, fell, *Gareth and L.* 4
hath o'erstept The slippery *f* of his narrow wit, *Lover's Tale i* 102
Footless where *f* fancies dwell Among the fragments *Maud I xviii* 69
Foot-lights By the low *f-l* of the world— *The Wreck* 40
Footprint left The little *f* daily wash'd away. *Enoch Arden* 22
May only make that *f* upon sand *Princess iii* 239
watch The sandy *f* harden into stone.' „ 271
The kingcup fills her *f*, *Prog. of Spring* 59
Foot-sore Reel'd as a *f* ox in crowded ways *Aylmer's Field* 819
F-s, way-worn, at length he touch'd his goal, *St. Telemachus* 34
Footstep Old *f's* trod the upper floors, *Mariana* 67
night come from the inmost hills, Like *f's* upon wool. *Œnone* 250
hear the dully sound Of human *f's* fall. *Palace of Art* 276
his *f's* smite the threshold stairs Of life— *St. S. Stylites* 191
More close and close his *f's* wind: *Day-Dm., Arrival* 25
While he treads with *f* firmer, *L. of Burleigh* 51
A *f* seem'd to fall beside her path, *Enoch Arden* 514
I prest my *f's* into his, *Lucretius* 118
He seems as one whose *f's* halt, *Will* 15
The *f's* of his life in mine; *In Mem. lxxxv* 44
But at his *f* leaps no more, „ 112
But let no *f* beat the floor, „ *cv* 17
guide Her *f's*, moving side by side „ *cxiv* 19
The *f* flutter'd me at first: *Last Tournament* 515
clomb The last hard *f* of that iron crag; *Pass. of Arthur* 447
and fell about My *f's* on the mountains. *Lover's Tale i* 372
scales Their headlong passes, but his *f* fails, *Montenegro* 5
Have heard this *f* fall, *Tiresias* 27
flowers that brighten as thy *f* falls, *Demeter and P.* 36
A *f*, a low throbbing in the walls, *The Ring* 409
Footstool drove The *f* from before him, and arose; *Aylmer's Field* 327
Forage *f* for the horse, and flint for fire. *Gareth and L.* 1277
I will fetch you *f* from all fields, *Geraint and E.* 628
To *f* for herself alone; *Open I. and C. Exhib.* 29
Forager they found—his *f's* for charms— *Merlin and V.* 619
Foray Bound on a *f*, rolling eyes of prey, *Geraint and E.* 538
Such as they brought upon their *f's* out „ 567
Forbad *F* her first the house of Averill, *Aylmer's Field* 502
Forbear '*F*,' the Princess cried; '*F*, Sir' I; *Princess iv* 162
caught His purple scarf, and held, and said, '*F*! *Marr. of Geraint* 377
'*F*: there is a worthier,' „ 556
That I *f* you thus: cross me no more. *Geraint and E.* 678
'Nay,' said Pelleas, 'but *f*. *Pelleas and E.* 280
call'd '*F* In the great name of Him who died for men, *St. Telemachus* 62
Forbearance Arguing boundless *f*: *Aylmer's Field* 317
Forbid 'did I not *F* you, Dora?' *Dora* 92
Chid her, and *f* her to speak To me, *Maud I xix* 63
And batten on her poisons? Love *f*! *Lover's Tale i* 777
Forbore Bore and *f*, and did not tire, *Two Voices* 218
But awed and promise-bounden she *f*, *Enoch Arden* 869
Geraint, from utter courtesy, *f*. *Marr. of Geraint* 381
hurl his cup Straight at the speaker, but *f*: *Merlin and V.* 31
the meek maid Sweetly *f* him ever, *Lancelot and E.* 856
looking at the villainy done, *F*, *Pelleas and E.* 283
F his own advantage, (repeat) *Guinevere* 331, 333
Force (s) Had *f* to make me rhyme in youth, *Miller's D.* 193
All *f* in bonds that might endure, *Palace of Art* 154
I broke a close with *f* and arms: *Edwin Morris* 131
you know him,—old, but full Of *f* and choler, *Golden Year* 61
his passion shall have spent its novel *f*, *Locksley Hall* 49
Titanic *f's* taking birth In divers seasons, *Day-Dm., L'Envoi* 17
I spoke with heart, and heat and *f*, *The Letters* 37
toward the hollow, all her *f* Fail'd her; *Enoch Arden* 374
she promised that no *f*, Persuasion, no, *Aylmer's Field* 417
Is duer unto freedom, *f* and growth Of spirit *Princess iv* 141
felt the blind wildbeast of *f*, „ *v* 266

Force (s) (*continued*) Ida stood nor spoke, drain'd of her *f* *Princess vi* 266
Some patient *f* to change them when we will, „ *Con.* 56
can bereave him Of the *f* he made his own *Ode on Well.* 273
From our first Charles by *f* we wrung our claims. *Third of Feb.* 26
Who makes by *f* his merit known *In Mem. lxiv* 9
Of *f* that would have forged a name. „ *lxxiii* 16
I know thee of what *f* thou art „ *lxxix* 3
Seraphic intellect and *f* To seize and throw „ *cix* 5
with *f* and skill To strive, to fashion, „ *cxiii* 6
Should licensed boldness gather *f*, „ 13
this electric *f*, that keeps A thousand pulses dancing, „ *cxxv* 15
in his *f* to be Nature's crowning race. *Maud I iv* 33
but of *f* to withstand, Year upon year, „ *II ii* 24
That save he won the first by *f*, *Gareth and L.* 107
his great self, Hath *f* to quell me.' „ 1183
so fill up the gap where *f* might fail „ 1352
Reproach you, saying all your *f* is gone? *Marr. of Geraint* 88
all his *f* Is melted into mere effeminacy? „ 106
He felt, were she the prize of bodily *f*, „ 541
blood Of their strong bodies, flowing, drain'd their *f*. But either's *f* was match'd till Yniol's cry, „ 569
could I someway prove such *f* in her „ 805
elemental secrets, powers And *f's*; *Merlin and V.* 633
so by *f* they dragg'd him to the King. „ 640
I do not mean the *f* alone, *Lancelot and E.* 471
for what *f* is yours to go So far, „ 1063
Drain'd of her *f*, again she sat, *Last Tournament* 540
But had not *f* to shape it as he would, *Pass. of Arthur* 15
F is from the heights. *Ancient Sage* 14
f to guide us thro' the days I shall not see? *Locksley H., Sixty* 158
Howe'er blind *f* and brainless will May jar *Freedom* 15
my brothers, work, and wield The *f's* of to-day, *Mechanophilus* 30
Force (verb) cruel glee *F's* on the freer hour. *Vision of Sin* 130
this wild king to *f* her to his wish, *Princess, Pro.* 37
Forced I *f* a way Thro' solid opposition „ *iii* 125
f Sweet love on pranks of saucy boyhood: „ *vii* 343
brute world howling *f* them into bonds, *Merlin and V.* 744
wrath which *f* my thoughts on that fierce law, *Guinevere* 537
the jailer *f* me away. (repeat) *Rizpah* 41, 44
fur theere we was *f* to 'ide, *Spinster's S's.* 39
Forcing *f* far apart Those blind beginnings *Lucretius* 245
Ford By bridge and *f*, by park and pale, *Sir Galahad* 82
her future Lord Was drown'd in passing thro' the *f*, *In Mem. vi* 39
bridge, *f*, beset By bandits, *Gareth and L.* 594
hard by here is one that guards a *f*— „ 1003
Push'd horse across the foamings of the *f*, „ 1040
Gareth laid his lance athwart the *f*; „ 1048
There lies a ridge of slate across the *f*; „ 1056
And victor of the bridges and the *f*, „ 1232
quickly flashing thro' the shallow *f* *Marr. of Geraint* 167
hill, or plain, at sea, or flooding *f*. *Holy Grail* 728
Forded Took horse, and *f* Usk, and gain'd the wood; *Marr. of Geraint* 161
Fore when Dan didn't come to the *f*, *Tomorrow* 43
Forebode His heart *f's* a mystery: *Two Voices* 290
Foreboding *f* 'what would Enoch say?' *Enoch Arden* 253
Forecast But who shall so *f* the years *In Mem. i* 5
Foredoom'd Made us, foreknew us, *f* us, *Despair* 97
Foredooming *F* all his trouble was in vain, *Gareth and L.* 1127
Forefather His own *f's'* arms and armour hung. *Princess, Pro.* 24
thy great *F's* of the thornless garden, *Maud I xviii* 27
Lies the warrior, my *f*, with his feet upon the hound. *Locksley H., Sixty* 28
that same path our true *f's* trod; *Doubt and Prayer* 4
Forefinger on the stretch'd *f* of all Time Sparkle *Princess ii* 378
Forefoot With inward yelp and restless *f* plies *Lucretius* 45
Forego which *f* The darkness of that battle *To the Queen ii* 64
Foregoing *F* all her sweetness, like a weed. *Holy Grail* 623
Foregone 'But could I, as in times *f*, *Talking Oak* 189
have quite *f* All matters of this world: *Balin and Balan* 116
Foreground a *f* black with stones and slags, *Palace of Art* 81
Forehead (adj.) and his *f* veins Bloated, and branch'd; *Balin and Balan* 391
Forehead (s) draws His *f* earthward, and he dies. *Supp. Confessions* 168

Forehead (s) (*continued*) Thy bounteous *f* was not fann'd With breezes *Eleänore* 9
about His dusty *f* drily curl'd, *Miller's D.* 6
And, with dim fretted *f's* all, *Palace of Art* 242
curls—That made his *f* like a rising sun *M. d'Arthur* 217
Where shall I hide my *f* and my eyes? ,, 228
and opposed Free hearts, free *f's*— *Ulysses* 49
f, eyelids, growing dewy-warm With kisses *Tithonus* 58
On her pallid cheek and *f* came a colour *Locksley Hall* 25
gilds the straiten'd *f* of the fool! ,, 62
I, to herd with narrow *f's*, ,, 175
Annie from her baby's *f* clipt A tiny curl, *Enoch Arden* 235
at last he said, Lifting his honest *f*, ,, 388
We turn'd our *f's* from the falling sun, *The Brook* 165
With that she kiss'd His *f*, *Princess ii* 312
and o'er her *f* past A shadow, ,, *vi* 106
With all their *f's* drawn in Roman scowls, ,, *vii* 129
and her *f* sank upon her hands, ,, 247
But on her *f* sits a fire: *In Mem. cxiv* 5
But on the damsel's *f* shame, *Gareth and L.* 656
Had bared her *f* to the blistering sun, *Geraint and E.* 515
when their *f's* felt the cooling air, *Balin and Balan* 589
her shape From *f* down to foot, perfect—again From foot to *f* exquisitely turn'd: *Lancelot and E.* 642
Clean from her *f* all that wealth of hair *Holy Grail* 150
their *f's* grimed with smoke, and sear'd, ,, 265
Met *f's* all along the street of those Who watch'd us pass; ,, 344
This air that smites his *f* is not air ,, 914
Glanced from the rosy *f* of the dawn. *Pelleas and E.* 502
Pure on the virgin *f* of the dawn!' ,, 505
curls—That made his *f* like a rising sun *Pass. of Arthur* 385
Where shall I hide my *f* and my eyes? ,, 396
with my work thus Crown'd her clear *f*. *Lover's Tale i* 345
holdeth his undimmed *f* far Into a clearer zenith, ,, 513
brush'd My fallen *f* in their to and fro, ,, 701
Brow-high, did strike my *f* as I past; ,, *ii* 19
Bullets would sing by our *f's*, *Def. of Lucknow* 21
earth's dark *f* flings athwart the heavens *Ancient Sage* 200
f vapour-swathed In meadows ever green; *Freedom* 7
felt a gentle hand Fall on my *f*, *The Ring* 419
round her *f* wheels the woodland dove, *Prog. of Spring* 57
And last on the *f* Of Arthur the blameless *Merlin and the G.* 72
you spill The drops upon my *f*. *Romney's R.* 24
Foreign and he died In *f* lands; *Dora* 19
And I will tell him tales of *f* parts, *Enoch Arden* 198
'I have a sister at the *f* court, *Princess i* 75
And travell'd men from *f* lands; *In Mem. x* 6
often abroad in the fragrant gloom Of *f* churches— *Maud I xix* 54
Display'd a splendid silk of *f* loom, *Geraint and E.* 687
some other question'd if she came From *f* lands, *Lover's Tale iv* 331
they praised him to his face with their courtly *f* grace; *Revenge* 99
Urge him to *f* war. *Sir J. Oldcastle* 68
Foreigner (*See also* **Furriner**) A *f*, and I your country-woman, *Princess iv* 317
Foreknew Made us, *f* us, foredoom'd us, *Despair* 97
Foreland many a fairy *f* set With willow-weed *The Brook* 45
Forelock Are taken by the *f*. Let it be. *Golden Year* 19
Foremost (*See also* **Head-foremost**) *f* in thy various gallery Place it, *Ode to Memory* 84
And being ever *f* in the chase, *Geraint and E.* 959
I the heir of all the ages, in the *f* files of time— *Locksley Hall* 178
which, on the *f* rocks Touching, *Sea Dreams* 51
F captain of his time, *Ode on Well.* 31
He dash'd the pummel at the *f* face, *Balan and Balan* 402
Foreran So much the boy *f*; *Aylmer's Field* 80
Forerun *F* thy peers, thy time, and let Thy feet, *Two Voices* 88
in the cold wind that *f's* the morn *Guinevere* 132
Foresaw (*See also* **Half-foresaw**) The fame is quench'd that I *f*, *In Mem. lxxiii* 5
what doubt that he *f* This evil work *Guinevere* 306
And each *f* the dolorous day to be: *Pelleas and E.* 606
Foresee Oh, if indeed that eye *f* *In Mem. xxvi* 9
could none of them *f*, Not even thy wise father *Guinevere* 273
Foreseeing Howbeit ourself, *f* casualty, *Princess iii* 317
Foreshadow Who dares *f* for an only son A lovelier life, *Ded. of Idylls* 29
What omens may *f* fate to man And woman, *Tiresias* 7
Foreshadowing His heart *f* all calamity, *Enoch Arden* 683
Immersed in rich *f's* of the world, *Princess vii* 312
Foreshorten'd lie *F* in the tract of time? *In Mem. lxxvii* 4
Foresight Whose *f* preaches peace, *Love and Duty* 34
Take wings of *f*; lighten thro' The secular abyss *In Mem. lxxvi* 5
Forest (adj.) And armour'd all in *f* green, *Last Tournament* 170
his good warhorse left to graze Among the *f* greens, ,, 491
He burst his lance against a *f* bough, *Balin and Balan* 329
hurl'd it from him Among the *f* weeds, ,, 542
Forest (s) (*See also* **Mid-forest, New Forest**) so deadly still As that wide *f*. *D. of F. Women* 69
Between dark stems the *f* glows, *Sir Galahad* 27
The petty marestail *f*, fairy pines, *Aylmer's Field* 92
Better to clear prime *f's*, heave and thump *Princess iii* 127
While I roved about the *f*, *Boädicea* 35
The *f* crack'd, the waters curl'd, *In Mem. xv* 5
and pitch'd His tents beside the *f*. *Com. of Arthur* 58
slew the beast, and fell'd The *f*, ,, 60
mount That rose between the *f* and the field. *Gareth and L.* 191
A mile beneath the *f*, challenging And over-throwing *Balin and Balan* 12
the harlot leapt Adown the *f*, and the thicket closed Behind her, and the *f* echo'd 'fool.' *Merlin and V.* 973
the gloomy skirts Of Celidon the *f*; *Lancelot and E.* 292
Across the *f* call'd of Dean, to find Caerleon *Pelleas and E.* 21
Alone, and in the heart of the great *f*. *Lover's Tale ii* 3
moanings in the *f*, the loud brook, ,, 114
On icy fallow And faded *f*, *Merlin and the G.* 85
Thro' blasted valley and flaring *f* *Kapiolani* 12
Forest-deeps And far, in *f-d* unseen, *Sir L. and Q. G.* 7
Forester How once the wandering *f* at dawn, *Gareth and L.* 498
Down on a rout of craven *f's*. ,, 841
Before him came a *f* of Dean, *Marr. of Geraint* 148
Forest-path thine eyes not brook in *f-p's*, *Prog. of Spring* 31
Forest-shadow and through the *f-s* borne *Lover's Tale ii* 72
Forethought So dark a *f* roll'd about his brain, *Merlin and V.* 230
Foretold *f*, Dying, that none of all our blood *Princess i* 7
He too *f* the perfect rose. *In Mem., Con.* 34
Has come to pass as *f*; *Maud II v* 44
Forfeits game of *f* done—the girls all kiss'd *The Epic* 2
magic music, *f*, all the rest. *Princess, Pro.* 195
Forgave there the Queen *f* him easily. *Marr. of Geraint* 592
And he *f* me, and I could not speak. *Guinevere* 614
Forge yes!—but a company *f's* the wine. *Maud I i* 36
f a life-long trouble for ourselves, *Geraint and E.* 3
Forged 'Who *f* that other influence, *Two Voices* 283
f a thousand theories of the rocks, *Edwin Morris* 18
he *f*, But that was later, boyish histories *Aylmer's Field* 96
Nor deeds of gift, but gifts of grace he *f*, *Sea Dreams* 192
and so We *f* a sevenfold story. *Princess, Pro.* 202
thou hast *f* at last A night-long Present *In Mem. lxxi* 2
results Of force that would have *f* a name. ,, *lxxiii* 16
Whereof they *f* the brand Excalibur, *Gareth and L.* 67
one son had *f* on his father and fled, *Despair* 69
Forget rose In love with thee *f's* to close His curtains, *Adeline* 42
men *F* the dream that happens then, *Two Voices* 353
'I might *f* my weaker lot; ,, 367
who that knew him could *f* The busy wrinkles *Miller's D.* 3
Can he pass, and we *f*? ,, 204
What is love? for we *f*: ,, 213
I shall not *f* you, mother, *May Queen, N. Y's. E.* 31
And God *f* the stranger!' *The Goose* 56
Authority *f's* a dying king, *M. d'Arthur* 121
I earth in earth *f* these empty courts, *Tithonus* 75
Perplext her, made her half *f* herself, *Aylmer's Field* 303
Swear by St something—I *f* her name— *Princess v* 293
all men else their nobler dreams *f*, *Ode on Well.* 152
What England was, shall her true sons *f*? *Third of Feb.* 44
ten years back, or more, if I don't *f*: *Grandmother* 75
Could we *f* the widow'd hour *In Mem. xl* 1
But he *f's* the days before ,, *xliv* 3
Nor can it suit me to *f* The mighty hopes ,, *lxxxv* 59
The days she never can *f* ,, *xcvii* 14

Forget (*continued*) I should *f* That I owe this debt to you *Maud I xix* 89
shall I say?—If ever I *should f*, ,, 93
the lone hern *f's* his melancholy, *Gareth and L.* 1185
f My heats and violences? live afresh? *Balin and Balan* 189
ye *f* Obedience is the courtesy due to kings.' *Lancelot and E.* 717
Authority *f's* a dying king, *Pass. of Arthur* 289
Men will *f* what we suffer and not what we do. *Def. of Lucknow* 73
and *f* The darkness of the pall.' *Ancient Sage* 197
As we *f* our wail at being born. *The Ring* 465
A name that earth will not *f* *To Ulysses* 27
but thou forgive, *F* it. *Death of Œnone* 44
Forgetful *F* how my rich prœmion makes Thy glory fly *Lucretius* 70
F of Maud and me, *Maud I xxi* 4
F of his promise to the King, *Marr. of Geraint* 50
F of the falcon and the hunt, ,, 51
F of the tilt and tournament, *F* of his glory and his name, *F* of his princedom and its cares. ,, 52
'The sound of that *f* shore *In Mem. xxxv* 14
dreaming of her love For Lancelot, and *f* of the hunt; *Marr. of Geraint* 159
F of their troth and fealty, *Guinevere* 442
f of the man, Whose crime had half unpeopled Ilion, *Death of Œnone* 60
Forgetfulness falling into Lot's *f* I know not thee, *Gareth and L.* 96
And this *f* was hateful to her. *Marr. of Geraint* 55
Forget-me-not I found the blue *F-m-n.* *Miller's D.* 202
f-m-n's That grow for happy lovers. *The Brook* 172
Forgetteth The place he knew *f* him.' *Two Voices* 264
Forgetting *F* how to render beautiful Her countenance *Lover's Tale i* 96
O the night, Where there's no *f.* *Forlorn* 78
Forgive Us, O Just and Good, *F*, *Poland* 12
I have been wild and wayward, but you'll *f* me now; You'll kiss me, my own mother, and *f* me ere I go; *May Queen N. Y's. E.* 33
May God *f* me!—I have been to blame. *Dora* 161
And easily *f's* it as his own, *Aylmer's Field* 401
'Love, *f* him:' but he did not speak; *Sea Dreams* 45
'*F*! How many will say, '*f*,' ,, 60
neither God nor man can well *f*, ,, 63
Before you prove him, rogue, and proved, *f.* ,, 171
We *must f* the dead.' ,, 270
f him, dear, And I shall sleep the sounder!' ,, 311
I do *f* him!' 'Thanks, my love,' ,, 316
F me, I waste my heart in sighs: *Princess vii* 358
F what seem'd my sin in me; *In Mem., Pro.* 33
F my grief for one removed, ,, 37
F these wild and wandering cries, ,, 41
F them where they fail in truth, ,, 43
hearts that know not how to *f*: *Maud II i* 44
Or to say '*F* the wrong,' ,, *iv* 86
F me; mine was jealousy in love.' *Lancelot and E.* 1351
I *f* thee, as Eternal God *F's*: *Guinevere* 544
Kiss him, and then *F* him, *Lover's Tale iv* 175
Are slower to *f* than human kings. *Tiresias* 10
All his virtues—I *f* them— *Locksley H., Sixty* 44
For you *f* me, you are sure of that— *Romney's R.* 160
but thou *f*, Forget it. *Death of Œnone* 43
Forgiven not easily *f* Are those, who setting *Gardener's D.* 247
Say one soft word and let me part *f.*' *Princess vi* 219
Caress her! let her feel herself *f* *Merlin and V.* 381
She with a face, bright as for sin *f*, *Lancelot and E.* 1102
pass on, my Queen, *f.*' ,, 1353
blessed be the King, who hath *f* My wickedness *Guinevere* 634
'Yea, little maid, for am *I* not *f*?' ,, 665
And has he not *f* me yet, *Happy* 6
trust myself *f* by the God to whom I kneel. ,, 86
Reflected, sends a light on the *f.* *Romney's R.* 161
Forgiveness *I* seem no more: *I* want *f* too: *Princess vi* 290
we embrace you yet once more With all *f*, ,, 295
thro' this ring Had sent his cry for her *f*, *The Ring* 233
Could kneel for your *f.* *Romney's R.* 26
Human *f* touches heaven, and thence— ,, 159
Forgiving I had set my heart on your *f* him *Sea Dreams* 269
Forgot For is not our first year *f*? *Two Voices* 368
having seen, *f*? The common mouth, *Gardener's D.* 55

Forgot (*continued*) The steer *f* to graze, *Gardener's D.* 85
Philip sitting at her side *f* Her presence, *Enoch Arden* 384
might be May or April, he *f*, *The Brook* 151
Sir Aylmer half *f* his lazy smile *Aylmer's Field* 197
And I *f* the clouded Forth, *The Daisy* 101
F his weakness in thy sight. *In Mem. cx* 4
Nor yet *f* her practice in her fright, *Merlin and V.* 947
F to drink to Lancelot and the Queen, *Lancelot and E.* 737
And the sick man *f* her simple blush, ,, 864
so *f* herself A moment, and her cares; *Last Tournament* 25
when their faces are *f* in the land— *Lover's Tale i* 759
that I might ha' *f* him somehow— *First Quarrel* 37
The warrior hath *f* his arms, *Ancient Sage* 138
But I cleän *f* tha, my lad, *Owd Roä* 53
An' I'd cleär *f*, little Dicky, ,, 64
Forgotten (*See also* **Half-forgotten, Long-forgotten**)
To live *f*, and love forlorn.' (repeat) *Mariana in the S.* 24, 84, 96
I sleep *f*, I wake forlorn.' ,, 36
Walks *f*, and is forlorn.' ,, 48
Live *f* and die forlorn.' (repeat) ,, 60, 72
not to be *f*—not at once—Not all *f.* *Love and Duty* 91
I meant? I have *f* what I meant: *Lucretius* 122
F, rusting on his iron hills, *Princess v* 146
And doing battle with *f* ghosts, ,, 480
'I had *f* all in my strong joy To see thee— *Last Tournament* 582
My God, thou hast *f* me in my death: *Pass. of Arthur* 27
Where fragments of *f* peoples dwelt, ,, 84
Are you sleeping? have you *f*? *The Flight* 1
Ev'n her grandsire's fifty half *f.* *On Jub. Q. Victoria* 41
She fear'd I had *f* her, and I ask'd About my Mother, *The Ring* 102
I had *f* it was your birthday, child— ,, 378
f mine own rhyme By mine own self, As I shall be *f* by old Time, *To Mary Boyle* 21
Like glimpses of *f* dreams— *Two Voices* 381
wasting his *f* heart, *Aylmer's Field* 689
The howlings from *f* fields; *In Mem. xli* 16
And fling me deep in that *f* mere, *Lancelot and E.* 1426
Had suck'd the fire of some *f* sun, *Lover's Tale iv* 194
who dipt In some *f* book of mine *To E. Fitzgerald* 47
Fork (*See also* **Lightning-fork**) Who, God-like, grasps the triple *f's*, *Of old sat Freedom* 15
Ruin'd trunks on wither'd *f's*, *Vision of Sin* 93
I never saw so fierce a *f*— *Lucretius* 28
A double hill ran up his furrowy *f's* *Princess iii* 174
Two *f's* are fixt into the meadow ground, *Marr. of Geraint* 482
there they fixt the *f's* into the ground, ,, 548
To me this narrow grizzled *f* of thine *Merlin and V.* 59
And dazzled by the livid-flickering *f*, ,, 941
Forked things that are *f*, and horned, and soft, *The Mermaid* 53
f Of the near storm, and aiming at his head, *Aylmer's Field* 726
Forlorn In sleep she seem'd to walk *f*, *Mariana* 30
To live forgotten, and love *f.*' (repeat) *Mariana in the S.* 24, 84, 96
I sleep forgotten, I wake *f.*' ,, 36
Walks forgotten, and is *f.* ,, 48
Live forgotten and die *f.*' (repeat) ,, 60, 72
I am too *f*, Too shaken: *Supp. Confessions* 135
Over the dark dewy earth *f*, *Ode to Memory* 69
in a lonely grove He set up his *f* pipes, *Amphion* 22
I ceased, and sat as one *f.* *Two Voices* 400
Mournful Œnone, wandering *f* Of Paris, *Œnone* 16
Yet we will not die *f.*' *Vision of Sin* 206
'Favour from one so sad and so *f* *Enoch Arden* 287
A tonsured head in middle age *f*, *The Brook* 200
The little village looks *f*; *In Mem. lx* 9
I walk as ere I walk'd *f*, ,, *lxviii* 5
purple-frosty bank Of vapour, leaving night *f.* ,, *cvii* 4
Who am no more so all *f*, *Maud I xviii* 32
speak of the mother she loved As one scarce less *f*, ,, *xix* 28
The tiny cell is *f*, ,, *II ii* 13
thus in grief to wander forth *f*; *The Flight* 85
may pass when earth is manless and *f*, *Locksley H., Sixty* 206
tho', in this lean age *f*, *Epilogue* 71
And fled by many a waste, *f* of man, *Demeter and P.* 74
Where noble Ulric dwells *f*, *Happy* 10
To wait on one so broken, so *f*? *Romney's R.* 17

Form (s) This excellence and solid f Of constant beauty. *Supp. Confessions* 149
(Tho' all her fairest f's are types of thee, *Isabel* 39
And airy f's of flitting change. *Madeline* 7
converse with all f's Of the many-sided mind, *Ode to Memory* 115
And other than his f of creed, *A Character* 29
rites and f's before his burning eyes Melted *The Poet* 39
Fretteth thine enshrouded f. *A Dirge* 10
THE f, the f alone is eloquent! *The form, the form* 1
'Is this the f,' she made her moan, *Mariana in the S.* 33
The reflex of a beauteous f, *Miller's D.* 77
o'er her rounded f Between the shadows *Œnone* 180
I sit as God holding no f of creed, *Palace of Art* 211
f's that pass'd at windows and on roofs *D. of F. Women* 23
That her fair f may stand and shine, *Of old sat Freedom* 21
Matures the individual f. *Love thou thy land* 40
Phantoms of other f's of rule, " 59
all the decks were dense with stately f's *M. d'Arthur* 196
play with flying f's and images, *Gardener's D.* 60
fair new f's, That float about the threshold *Golden Year* 15
Cursed be the sickly f's that err *Locksley Hall* 61
And loosely settled into f. *Day-Dm., Pro.* 12
On either side her tranced f Forth streaming " *Sleep B.* 5
ever dwells A perfect f in perfect rest. " 24
But blessed f's in whistling storms *Sir Galahad* 59
dusty crypt Of darken'd f's and faces. *Will Water.* 184
And slowly quickening into lower f's; *Vision of Sin* 210
All beauty compass'd in a female f, *Princess ii* 34
since to look on noble f's Makes noble " 86
There sat along the f's, like morning doves " 102
Of faded f and haughtiest lineaments, " 448
then a loftier f Than female, " *iv* 215
I saw the f's: I knew not where I was: " *vii* 133
Will clear away the parasitic f's " 269
And other f's of life than ours, *Ode on Well.* 264
A hollow f with empty hands.' *In Mem. iii* 12
A late-lost f that sleep reveals, " *xiii* 2
But knows no more of transient f " *xvi* 7
Nor cares to fix itself to f, " *xxxiii* 4
Her faith thro' f is pure as thine, " 9
Eternal f shall still divide The eternal soul " *xlvii* 6
Where thy first f was made a man; " *lxi* 10
print The same sweet f's in either mind. " *lxxix* 8
For changes wrought on f and face; " *lxxxii* 2
O sacred essence, other f, " *lxxxv* 35
And seem to lift the f, and glow " *lxxxvii* 37
'And merge,' he said, 'in f and gloss " *lxxxix* 41
wear the f by which I know Thy spirit " *xci* 5
Come, beauteous in thine after f, " 15
frame In matter-moulded f's of speech, " *xcv* 46
For who would keep an ancient f " *cv* 19
And ancient f's of party strife; " *cvi* 14
he veil His want in f's for fashion's sake, " *cxi* 6
And grew to seeming-random f's, " *cxviii* 10
flow From f to f, and nothing stands; " *cxxiii* 6
tho' faith and f Be sunder'd in the night " *cxxvii* 1
these damp walls, and taken but the f. *Gareth and L.* 1200
Conjecture of the plumage and the f; *Marr. of Geraint* 333
And dreamt herself was such a faded f " 654
all her f shone forth with sudden light *Holy Grail* 450
O imperial-moulded f, *Guinevere* 548
all the decks were dense with stately f's, *Pass. of Arthur* 364
a phantasm of the f It should attach to? *Lover's Tale i* 646
Mantling her f halfway. " 705
fell into the abysm Of f's outworn, " 797
very face and f of Lionel Flash'd thro' my eyes " *ii* 94
f's which ever stood Within the magic cirque " 158
pencil's naked f's Colour and life: " 180
Grew after marriage to full height and f? *Sisters (E. and E.)* 171
face and f are hers and mine in one, *De Prof., Two G.* 13
I clung to the sinking f, *The Wreck* 105
and itself For ever changing f, *Ancient Sage* 193
And blurr'd in colour and f, *Dead Prophet* 22
The f of Muriel faded, and the face Of Miriam *The Ring* 184
concentrate into f And colour all you are, *Romney's R.* 7

Form (s) (*continued*) crown'd f's high over the sacred fountain? *Parnassus* 1
all else F, Ritual, varying with the tribes of men, *Akbar's Dream* 124
thou knowest I hold that f's Are needful: " 126
And what are f's? Fair garments, " 130
F's! The Spiritual in Nature's market-place— " 134
Who shaped the f's, obey them, " 143
And is a living f? *Mechanophilus* 16

Form (verb) the rainbow f's and flies on the land *Sea-Fairies* 25
slowly f's the firmer mind, *In Mem. xviii* 18
Storm, Storm, Riflemen f! (repeat) *Riflemen form!* 5, 19
Riflemen, Riflemen, Riflemen, f! (repeat) " 7, 14, 21, 28
F, F, Riflemen F! (repeat) " 12, 26
F, be ready to do or die! F in Freedom's name and the Queen's! " 22

Formal O the f mocking bow, *The Flight* 29
His f kiss fell chill as a flake of snow *The Wreck* 32
O, I see thee old and f, *Locksley Hall* 93

Formalism they blurt Their furious f's, *Akbar's Dream* 57

Former And ebb into a f life, *Sonnet, To ——* 2
remembering His f talks with Edith, *Aylmer's Field* 457
became Her f beauty treble; *Princess vii* 25
Makes f gladness loom so great? *In Mem. xxiv* 10
As in the f flash of joy, " *cxxii* 15
In f days you saw me favourably. *Geraint and E.* 315
'Earl, if you love me as in f years, " 355
that I began To glance behind me at my f life, " 863
Because his f madness, *Holy Grail* 649
For Evelyn knew not of my f suit, *Sisters (E. and E.)* 205

Forming The lucid outline f round thee; *Tithonus* 53
Be yet but yolk, and f in the shell? *Ancient Sage* 130

Formless I am void, Dark, f, utterly destroyed. *Supp. Confessions* 122
A vapour heavy, hueless, f, cold, *Vision of Sin* 53
And wrapt thee f in the fold, *In Mem. xxii* 15
till all his heart was cold With f fear; *Pass. of Arthur* 98

Forrards (forwards) if tha' wants to git f a bit, *Church-warden, etc.* 49

Forsake Ah yet, tho' all the world f, *Will Water.* 49
what a heart was mine to f her *The Wreck* 95
leech f the dying bed for terror *Happy* 98

Forsaken O my f heart, with thee And this poor flower *In Mem. viii* 18
We saw far off an old f house, *The Ring* 155

Forsaking See! our friends are all f *All Things will Die* 18

Forsworn I cannot bear to dream you so f: *Pelleas and E.* 300
I swore to the great King, and am f. *Last Tournament* 661
I swear and swear f To love him most, *The Flight* 49

Fort (*See also* **Hill-fort**) Welcome her, thunders of f and of fleet! *W. to Alexandra* 6
Built that new f to overawe my friends, *Marr. of Geraint* 460

Forth And I forgot the clouded F, *The Daisy* 101

Forthgazing F on the waste and open sea, *Lover's Tale ii* 177

Fortitude stately flower of female f, *Isabel* 11

Fortress The f, and the mountain ridge, *In Mem. lxxi* 14
The f crashes from on high, " *cxxvii* 14
deathful-grinning mouths of the f, *Maud III vi* 52
White from the mason's hand, a f rose; *Marr. of Geraint* 244
And onward to the f rode the three, " 251
Ride into that new f by your town, " 407
be thy heart a f to maintain The day *To Duke of Argyll* 5
My prison, not my f, fall away! *Doubt and Prayer* 12

Fortunate You, the Mighty, the F, *On Jub. Q. Victoria* 55

Fortune I rode sublime On F's neck: *D. of F. Women* 142
Tho' f clip my wings, I will not cramp my heart, *Will Water.* 50
I am but as my f's are: *Lady Clare* 70
'Drink to F, drink to Chance, *Vision of Sin* 191
mark me! for your f's are to make. *Aylmer's Field* 300
Name, f too: the world should ring of him " 395
Thro' which a few, by wit or f led, " 438
besides Their slender household f's *Sea Dreams* 9
ally Your f's, justlier balanced, *Princess ii* 66
affluent F emptied all her horn. *Ode on Well.* 197
Becomes on F's crowning slope, *In Mem. lxiv* 14
My f's all as fair as hers who lay *Gareth and L.* 903
loved her in a state Of broken f's, *Marr. of Geraint* 13
song that Enid sang was one Of F and her wheel, " 346
'Turn, F, turn thy wheel and lower the proud; " 347

Fortune (*continued*) 'Turn, *F*, turn thy wheel with smile or frown; *Marr. of Geraint* 350
since our *f* slipt from sun to shade, „ 714
that better fits Our mended *f's* „ 718
Give me good *f*, I will strike him dead, *Lancelot and E.* 1071
You count the father of your *f*, *Sisters (E. and E.)* 28
his followers, all Flower into *f*— *Columbus* 167
Forty (*See also* **Foorty**) That numbers *f* cubits from the soil. *St. S. Stylites* 91
And *f* blest one bless him, *Aylmer's Field* 372
for *f* years A hermit, who had pray'd, *Lancelot and E.* 402
Divil a Danny was there, yer Honour, for *f* year, *Tomorrow* 30
Gone with whom for *f* years my life in golden sequence ran, *Locksley H., Sixty* 47
Forum Titanic shapes, they cramm'd The *f*. *Princess vii* 125
Now thy *F* roars no longer, *To Virgil* 29
The Baths, the *F* gabbled of his death, *St. Telemachus* 74
Forward (*See also* **Forrards**) with increasing might doth *f* flee *Mine be the strength* 5
F, *f* let us range, *Locksley Hall* 181
'*F*, the Light Brigade! (repeat) *Light Brigade* 5, 9
She sets her *f* countenance *In Mem. cxiv* 6
To right? to left? straight *f*? *Pelleas and E.* 67
Then bounded *f* to the castle walls, „ 363
Gone the cry of '*F*, *F*,' *Locksley H., Sixty* 73
'*F*' rang the voices then, „ 77
Let us hush the cry of '*F*' „ 78
f—naked—let them stare. „ 142
F, *f*, ay and backward, „ 146
F, backward, backward, *f*, „ 193
Nay, your pardon, cry your '*f*,' „ 225
F then, but still remember how the course of Time will swerve, „ 235
F far and far from here is all the hope of eighty years. „ 254
F, till you see the highest Human Nature is divine. „ 276
F, let the stormy moment fly and mingle with the Past. „ 279
moving quickly *f* till the heat Smote on her brow, *Death of Œnone* 97
F to the starry track Glimmering up *Silent Voices* 8
Forward-creeping *f-c* tides Began to foam, *In Mem. ciii* 37
Forward-flowing The *f-f* tide of time; *Arabian Nights* 4
Fossil lark and leveret lay, Like *f's* of the rock, *Audley Court* 25
Foster guard and *f* her for evermore. *Guinevere* 592
Foster'd *F* the callow eaglet— *Œnone* 212
Which once she *f* up with care; *In Mem. viii* 16
because that *f* at *thy* court I savour of thy—virtues? *Merlin and V.* 38
that was Arthur; and they *f* him *Guinevere* 295
OLD poets *f* under friendlier skies, *Poets and their B.* 1
Foster-mother mock their *f-m* on four feet, *Com. of Arthur* 31
Foster-sister She was my *f-s*: *Lover's Tale i* 233
Fought (*See also* **Fowt**) And in thy spirit with thee *f*— *England and Amer.* 9
Annie *f* against his will: *Enoch Arden* 158
His comrades having *f* their last below, *Aylmer's Field* 227
F with what seem'd my own uncharity; *Sea Dreams* 73
with the Palmyrene That *f* Aurelian, *Princess ii* 84
And nursed by those for whom you *f*, „ *vi* 95
I and mine have *f* Your battle: „ 224
And the feet of those he *f* for, *Ode on Well.* 11
those great men who *f*, and kept it ours. „ 158
Than when he *f* at Waterloo, „ 257
have we *f* for Freedom from our prime, *Third of Feb.* 23
Were those your sires who *f* at Lewes? „ 33
They that had *f* so well Came thro' the jaws *Light Brigade* 45
may be met and *f* with outright, *Grandmother* 31
for the babe had *f* for his life. „ 64
He *f* his doubts and gather'd strength, *In Mem. xcvi* 13
Like Paul with beasts, I *f* with Death; „ *cxx* 4
Aurelius lived and *f* and died, And after him King Uther *f* and died, *Com. of Arthur* 13
F, and in twelve great battles overcame „ 518
He *f* against him in the Barons' war, *Gareth and L.* 77
Lot and many another rose and *f* Against thee, „ 354
but he that *f* no more, As being all bone-batter'd „ 1049
thy foul sayings *f* for me: „ 1180
twice they *f*, and twice they breathed, *Marr. of Geraint* 567

Fought (*continued*) *f* Hard with himself, and seem'd at length in peace, *Balin and Balan* 238
f in her name, Sware by her— *Merlin and V.* 13
two brothers, one a king, had met And *f* *Lancelot and E.* 40
if I went and *if* I *f* and won it „ 216
'you have *f*. O tell us—for we live apart— „ 283
it seem'd half-miracle To those he *f* with,— „ 498
name Of greatest knight? I *f* for it, „ 1414
'Have ye *f*?' She ask'd of Lancelot. *Pelleas and E.* 592
whatever knight of thine I *f* And tumbled. *Last Tournament* 453
F in her father's battles? wounded there? „ 592
Isolt?—I *f* his battles, for Isolt! „ 604
brake the petty kings, and *f* with Rome, *Pass. of Arthur* 68
Nor ever yet had Arthur *f* a fight Like this „ 93
fell Confusion, since he saw not whom he *f*. „ 99
shiver'd brands that once had *f* with Rome, „ 133
He *f* the boys that were rude, *First Quarrel* 14
and they *f* us hand to hand, *The Revenge* 52
And we had not *f* them in vain, „ 74
'We have *f* such a fight for a day and a night As may never be *f* again! „ 83
'I have *f* for Queen and Faith „ 101
Each of us *f* as if hope for the garrison *Def. of Lucknow* 48
Thanks to the kindly dark faces who *f* with us, faithful and few, *F* with the bravest among us, „ 70
and *f* till I sunder'd the fray, *V. of Maeldune* 69
F for their lives in the narrow gap *Heavy Brigade* 23
Britain *f* her sons of yore— *Open I. and C. Exhib.* 21
He wildly *f* a rival suitor, him The causer of that scandal, *f* and fell; *The Ring* 214
for he *f* Thy fight for Thee, *Happy* 15
Foughten the lords Have *f* like wild beasts *Com. of Arthur* 226
had I *f*—well—In those fierce wars, *Balin and Balan* 176
the *f* field, what else, at once Decides it, *Princess v* 297
Then quickly from the *f* field he sent *Com. of Arthur* 135
When have I stinted stroke in *f* field? *Holy Grail* 860
Foul (adj.) keep where you are: you are *f* with sin; *Poet's Mind* 36
Kill the *f* thief, and wreak me for my son.' *Gareth and L.* 363
But if their talk were *f*, „ 504
But truly *f* are better, „ 947
thy *f* sayings fought for me: „ 1180
F are their lives; *f* are their lips; *Balin and Balan* 616
Of that *f* bird of rapine whose whole prey *Merlin and V.* 728
as false and *f* As the poach'd filth „ 797
what is fair without Is often as *f* within.' *Dead Prophet* 68
You say your body is so *f*— *Happy* 25
Your body is not *f* to me, and body is *f* at best. „ 28
F! *f*! the word was yours not mine, „ 41
'I So *f* a traitor to myself and her, *Aylmer's Field* 319
nature crost Was mother of the *f* adulteries „ 376
Ring out old shapes of *f* disease; *In Mem. cvi* 25
housed In her *f* den, there at their meat would growl, *Com. of Arthur* 30
As one that let *f* wrong stagnate and be, *Geraint and E.* 891
And drawing *f* ensample from fair names, *Guinevere* 490
sucking The *f* steam of the grave to thicken by it, *Lover's Tale i* 649
I'd sooner fold an icy corpse dead of some *f* disease: *The Flight* 54
Fright and *f* dissembling, *Forlorn* 32
strip your own *f* passions bare; *Locksley H., Sixty* 141
Foul (s) frequent interchange of *f* and fair, *Enoch Arden* 533
Foul'd Experience, in her kind Hath *f* me— *Last Tournament* 318
Foulest Or the *f* sewer of the town— *Dead Prophet* 48
Foul-flesh'd as one That smells a *f-f* agaric in the holt, *Gareth and L.* 747
Foully phantom husks of something *f* done, *Lucretius* 160
Foulness canst endure To mouth so huge a *f*— *Balin and Balan* 379
This fellow hath wrought some *f* „ 565
And of the horrid *f* that he wrought, *Merlin and V.* 748
To all the *f* that they work. „ 785
Foun' for Dhanny was not to be *f*, *Tomorrow* 28
they *f* Dhrownded in black bog-wather „ 61
they laid this body they *f* an the grass „ 73
Found (find) (*See also* **Foun', Fun**) compare All creeds till we have *f* the one, *Supp. Confessions* 176
Down she came and *f* a boat *L. of Shalott iv* 6
'I *f* him when my years were few; *Two Voices* 271

Found (find) (*continued*) to be *f* Long after, as it seem'd, *Sisters (E. and E.)* 110
seen And lost and *f* again, „ 147
They *f* her beating the hard Protestant doors. „ 240
gratefullest heart I have *f* in a child *In the Child. Hosp.* 32
(Hath he been here—not *f* me—gone *Sir J. Oldcastle* 152
He would be *f* a heretic to Himself, „ 182
the harmless people whom we *f* *Columbus* 181
You *f* some merit in my rhymes, *To E. Fitzgerald* 55
who *f* Beside the springs of Dircê, smote, *Tiresias* 13
the fierce beast *f* A wiser than herself, „ 151
little one *f* me at sea on a day, *The Wreck* 86
I *f* myself moaning again 'O child, „ 134
We never had *f* Him on earth, *Despair* 57
F, fear'd me dead, and groan'd, *The Flight* 23
when Edwin *f* us there, „ 82
burnt at midnight *f* at morn, *Locksley H., Sixty* 97
Shepherds, have I *f*, and more than once, „ 121
poet, surely to be *f* When Truth is *f* again. *Pref. Poem Broth. S.* 15
be *f* of angel eyes In earth's recurring Paradise. *Helen's Tower* 11
now Your fairy Prince has *f* you, *The Ring* 69
I *f* these cousins often by the brook, „ 158
And *f* a corpse and silence, „ 217
F in a chink of that old moulder'd floor!' „ 280
laugh'd a little and *f* her two— „ 337
I *f* her not in house Or garden— „ 444
F yesterday—forgotten mine own rhyme *To Mary Boyle* 21
Wizard Who *f* me at sunrise Sleeping, *Merlin and the G* 12
and the same who first had *f* Paris, *Death of Œnone* 53
He had left his dagger behind him. I *f* it. *Bandit's Death* 12
She *f* my letter upon him, *Charity* 23
I *f* The tenderest Christ-like creature „ 31
Found (establish) All wild to *f* an University *Princess i* 150
ere he *f* Empire for life? *Gardener's D.* 19
Foundation-stone Whereof the strong *f-s's* were laid *Palace of Art* 235
Founded She had *f*; they must build. *Princess ii* 145
I Have *f* my Round Table in the North, *Last Tournament* 78
some Order, which our King Hath newly *f*, „ 742
Table Round Which good King Arthur *f*, *Guinevere* 221
We *f* many a mighty state; *Hands all Round* 30
Founder statues, king or saint, or *f* fell; *Sea Dreams* 224
on that *f* of our blood. *Locksley H., Sixty* 32
Founding About the *f* of a Table Round, *Merlin and V.* 411
knight Of the great Table—at the *f* of it; *Guinevere* 235
Foundress The *f* of the Babylonian wall, *Princess ii* 80
Some say the third—the authentic *f* you. „ *iii* 158
Fount he was thrown From his loud *f* *Mine be the strength* 4
Ancient *f's* of inspiration well *Locksley Hall* 188
burst away In search of stream or *f*, *Enoch Arden* 635
Who dabbling in the *f* of fictive tears, *The Brook* 93
Not past the living *f* of pity in Heaven. *Aylmer's Field* 752
There while we stood beside the *f*, *Princess iii* 23
The very source and *f* of Day *In Mem. xxiv* 3
deer, the dews, the fern, the *f's*, the lawns; *Last Tournament* 727
Fountain (adj.) Harder and drier than a *f* bed In summer: *Pelleas and E.* 507
Fountain (s) (*See also* **Foam-fountains**) Life of the *f* there, beneath Its salient springs, *Supp. Confessions* 55
from the central *f's* flow Fall'n silver-chiming, *Arabian Nights* 50
stealest fire, From the *f's* of the past, *Ode to Memory* 2
In the middle leaps a *f* *Poet's Mind* 24
Day and night to the billow the *f* calls: *Sea-Fairies* 9
I should look like a *f* of gold *The Mermaid* 18
let thy voice Rise like a *f* for me *M. d'Arthur* 249
The *f* to his place returns *Day-Dm., Sleep. P.* 11
And sixty feet the *f* leapt. „ *Revival* 8
runs to seed Beside its native *f*. *Amphion* 96
Against its *f* upward runs The current *Will Water.* 35
Expecting when a *f* should arise: *Vision of Sin* 8
Till the *f* spouted, showering wide „ 21
Like *f's* of sweet water in the sea, *Enoch Arden* 803
Spout from the maiden *f* in her heart. *Lucretius* 240
The *f* of the moment, playing, now *Princess, Pro.* 61
the splash and stir Of *f's* spouted up „ *i* 218
Enring'd a billowing *f* in the midst; „ *ii* 28

Fountain (s) (*continued*) Knowledge is now no more a *f* seal'd: *Princess ii* 90
and race By all the *f's*: fleet I was of foot: „ *iv* 263
And tears that at their *f* freeze; *In Mem. xx* 12
And show'd him in the *f* fresh „ *lxxxv* 26
From household *f's* never dry; „ *cix* 2
saw The *f* where they sat together, *Balin and Balan* 291
and by *f's* running wine, *Last Tournament* 141
'Friend, did ye mark that *f* yesterday „ 286
let thy voice Rise like a *f* for me *Pass. of Arthur* 417
springing from her *f's* in the brain, *Lover's Tale i* 83
from the diamond *f* by the palms, „ 137
A draught of that sweet *f* that he loves, „ 141
whate'er is *f* to the one Is *f* to the other; „ 179
My current to the *f* whence it sprang,— „ 503
Why fed we from one *f*? drew one sun? „ *ii* 24
I fear'd The very *f's* of her life were chill'd; *Sisters (E. and E.)* 266
Here is the copse, the *f* and—a Cross! *Sir J. Oldcastle* 127
f pour'd From darkness into daylight, *Ancient Sage* 7
She finds the *f* where they wail'd 'Mirage'! „ 77
Send the drain into the *f*, *Locksley H., Sixty* 144
shedding poison in the *f's* of the Will. „ 274
The *f* pulses high in sunnier jets, *Prog. of Spring* 54
What be those crown'd forms high over the sacred *f*? *Parnassus* 1
What be those two shapes high over the sacred *f*, „ 9
Dance in a *f* of flame with her devils, *Kapiolani* 10
Fountain'd *See* **Many-fountain'd**
Fountain-fed *f-f* Ammonian Oasis in the waste. *Alexander* 7
Fountain-flood sonorous flow Of spouted *f-f's*. *Palace of Art* 28
Fountain-foam dragons spouted forth A flood of *f-f*. „ 24
Fountain-head The murmur of the *f-h*— *Two Voices* 216
Full-welling *f-h's* of change, *Palace of Art* 166
Fountain-jets others tost a ball Above the *f-j*, *Princess ii* 461
Fountain-side sit near Camelot at a *f-s*, *Balin and Balan* 11
So coming to the *f-s* beheld Balin and Balan „ 23
Fountain-urns Gods at random thrown By *f-u*; *To E. L.* 16
Four The seven elms, the poplars *f* *Ode to Memory* 56
F gray walls, and *f* gray towers, *L. of Shalott i* 15
From those *f* jets *f* currents in one swell *Palace of Art* 33
From *f* wing'd horses dark against the stars; *Princess i* 211
Thro' *f* sweet years arose and fell, *In Mem. xxii* 3
F voices of *f* hamlets round, „ *xxviii* 5
Each voice *f* changes on the wind, „ 9
'Where wert thou, brother, these *f* days?' „ *xxxi* 5
And mock their foster-mother on *f* feet, *Com. of Arthur* 31
And all these *f* be fools, but mighty men, *Gareth and L.* 643
f strokes they struck With sword „ 1042
yon *f* fools have suck'd their allegory „ 1199
O'er the *f* rivers the first roses blew, *Geraint and E.* 764
Closed in the *f* walls of a hollow tower, (repeat) *Merlin and V.* 209, 543
in the *f* loud battles by the shore Of Duglas; *Lancelot and E.* 289
and strange knights From the *f* winds came in: *Pelleas and E.* 148
I thought *F* bells instead of one began to ring, *F* merry bells, *f* merry marriage-bells, *Lover's Tale iii* 20
F galleons drew away From the Spanish fleet *The Revenge* 46
a single piece Weigh'd nigh *f* thousand Castillanos *Columbus* 136
An' noän o' my *f* sweet-arts 'ud 'a let me 'a hed my oän waäy, *Spinster's S's.* 101
upo' *f* short legs ten times fur one upo' two. *Owd Roä* 16
bird that still is veering there Above his *f* gold letters) *The Ring* 333
Four-field The *f-f* system, and the price of grain; *Audley Court* 34
Four-footed no slaves of a *f-f* will? *The Dawn* 18
Four-handed The *f-h* mole shall scrape, *My life is full* 12
Four-hundredth In that *f-h* summer after Christ, *St. Telemachus* 4
Four-in-hand as quaint a *f-i-h* As you shall see— *Walk. to the Mail* 113
Foursquare build some plan *F* to opposition.' *Princess v* 231
stood *f* to all the winds that blew! *Ode on Well.* 39
Four-year-old 'That was the *f-y-o* I sold the Squire.' *The Brook* 137
Fowl (*See also* **Night-fowl, Ocean-fowl, Water-fowl**) To scare the *f* from fruit: *Princess ii* 228
I have seen the cuckoo chased by lesser *f*, *Com. of Arthur* 167
all the little *f* were flurried at it, *Gareth and L.* 69
and horrible *f's* of the air, *Rizpah* 39
Fowt (fought) An' once I *f* wi' the Taäilor— *North. Cobbler* 21
feller to fight wi' an' *f* it out. „ 100
'e'd fight wi' a will *when* 'e *f*; *Owd Roä* 7

Fox whole hill-side was redder than a *f*. *Walk. to the Mail* 3
And lighter-footed than the *f*. *Day-Dm., Arrival* 8
Then of the latest *f*—where started— *Aylmer's Field* 253
Let the *f* bark, let the wolf yell. *Pelleas and E.* 472
An' 'e niver runn'd arter the *f*, *Village Wife* 41
Foxglove The *f* cluster dappled bells.' *Two Voices* 72
Bring orchis, bring the *f* spire, *In Mem. lxxxiii* 9
snowlike sparkle of a cloth On fern and *f*. *Sisters (E. and E.)* 118
Foxlike Or *f* in the vine; *Princess vii* 203
Foxy Modred's narrow *f* face, *Guinevere* 63
Fraction Some niggard *f* of an hour, *Aylmer's Field* 450
For every splinter'd *f* of a sect Will clamour *Akbar's Dream* 33
Fragile pressure thrice as sweet As woodbine's *f* hold, *Talking Oak* 146
The *f* bindweed-bells and briony rings; *The Brook* 203
Fragment leaning on *f* twined with vine, *Œnone* 20
Among the *f's* tumbled from the glens, „ 222
But *f's* of her mighty voice Came *Of old sat Freedom* 7
The silver *f's* of a broken voice, *Gardener's D.* 234
cram him with the *f's* of the grave, *Princess iii* 311
Among the *f's* of the golden day. *Maud I xviii* 70
He heard but *f's* of her later words, *Marr. of Geraint* 113
Among the tumbled *f's* of the hills.' *Lancelot and E.* 1427
Where *f's* of forgotten peoples dwelt, *Pass. of Arthur* 84
And all the *f's* of the living rock *Lover's Tale ii* 44
Spurning a shatter'd *f* of the God, *St. Telemachus* 16
Fragrance girt With song and flame and *f*, *Lucretius* 134
f and the green Of the dead spring: *Lover's Tale i* 723
Fragrant (*See also* **All-fragrant, Blossom-fragrant**)
drove The *f*, glistening deeps, *Arabian Nights* 14
All round about the *f* marge „ 59
blinded With many a deep-hued bell-like flower Of *f* trailers, *Eleänore* 38
slowly dropping *f* dew. *Œnone* 106
mingled with her *f* toil, *Gardener's D.* 143
And burn a *f* lamp before my bones, *St. S. Stylites* 196
The *f* tresses are not stirr'd That lie *Day-Dm., Sleep B.* 19
Yet *f* in a heart remembering His former talks *Aylmer's Field* 456
on a tripod in the midst A *f* flame rose, *Princess iv* 34
And bats went round in *f* skies, *In Mem. xcv* 9
often abroad in the *f* gloom Of foreign churches— *Maud I xix* 53
mountain arose like a jewell'd throne thro' the *f* air, *V. of Maeldune* 59
Flies back in *f* breezes to display A tunic *Prog. of Spring* 64
With many a pendent bell and *f* star, *Death of Œnone* 13
Frail (adj.) Thy mortal eyes are *f* to judge of fair, *Œnone* 158
nor shrink For fear our solid aim be dissipated By *f* successors. *Princess iii* 267
f at first And feeble, all unconscious of itself, „ *vii* 116
O life as futile, then, as *f*! *In. Mem. lvi* 25
F, but a work divine, *Maud II ii* 4
F, but of force to withstand, „ 24
The *f* bluebell peereth over Rare broidry *A Dirge* 37
Your melancholy sweet and *f* As perfume *Margaret* 7
Friends, this *f* bark of ours, when sorely tried, *Aylmer's Field* 715
F Life was startled from the tender love *Lover's Tale i* 616
And sympathies, how *f*, In sound and smell! *Early Spring* 35
F were the works that defended the hold *Def. of Lucknow* 7
In his throne's title make him feel so *f*, *Sir J. Oldcastle* 73
Frail (s) 'Rapt from the fickle and the *f* *In Mem. xxx* 25
Frailer the *f* caravel, With what was mine, *Columbus* 140
Frailty Why not yet Anchor thy *f* there, *Supp. Confessions* 124
Nor human *f* do me wrong. *In Mem. lii* 8
Lured by the crimes and *frailties* of the court, *Guinevere* 136
Thy *f* counts most real, *Ancient Sage* 51
Frame (s) (*See also* **Broidery-frame**) creeps Thro my veins to all my *f*, *Eleänore* 131
A healthy *f*, a quiet mind.' *Two Voices* 99
Consolidate in mind and *f*— „ 366
shafts of flame Were shiver'd in my narrow *f*. *Fatima* 18
Pour'd back into my empty soul and *f* *D. of F. Women* 78
Dust are our *f's*; and, gilded dust, *Aylmer's Field* 1
Another and another *f* of things *Lucretius* 42
The morals, something of the *f*, the rock, *Princess ii* 382
woman wed is not as we, But suffers change of *f*. „ *v* 463
A man of well-attemper'd *f*. *Ode on Well.* 74
No hint of death in all his *f*, *In Mem. xiv* 18
Frame (s) (*continued*) Deep-seated in our mystic *f*. *In Mem. xxxvi* 2
As thro' the *f* that binds him in His isolation „ *xlv* 11
Be near me when the sensuous *f* Is rack'd „ *l* 5
No—mixt with all this mystic *f*, „ *lxxxviii* 18
new life that feeds thy breath Throughout my *f*, „ *lxxxvi* 11
That in this blindness of the *f* „ *xciii* 15
Remade the blood and changed the *f*, „ *Con.* 11
I steal, a wasted *f*, It crosses here, *Maud II iv* 69
my inmost *f* Was riven in twain: *Lover's Tale i* 595
shook me, that my *f* would shudder, „ *ii* 56
taken Some years before, and falling hid the *f*. „ *iv* 217
Frame (verb) Vague words! but ah, how hard to *f* *In Mem. xcv* 45
Framed Neither modell'd, glazed, nor *f*: *Vision of Sin* 188
Framework With royal *f-w* of wrought gold; *Ode to Memory* 82
yet with such a *f* scarce could be. *Princess, Con.* 22
And all the *f* of the land; *In Mem. lxxxvii* 24
speak His music by the *f* and the chord; *Holy Grail* 879
Framing (*See also* **Sea-framing**) *F* the mighty landscape to the west, *Lover's Tale i* 406
France Joan of Arc, A light of ancient *F*; *D. of F. Women* 268
Rose a ship of *F*. *The Captain* 28
That cursed *F* with her egalities! *Aylmer's Field* 265
Had golden hopes for *F* and all mankind, „ 464
ever-murder'd *F*, By shores that darken „ 766
Imagined more than seen, the skirts of *F*. *Princess, Con.* 48
Back to *F* her banded swarms, Back to *F* with countless blows, *Ode on Well.* 110
In which we went thro' summer *F*. *In Mem. lxxi* 4
The foaming grape of eastern *F*. „ *Con.* 80
Art with poisonous honey stol'n from *F*, *To the Queen ii* 56
Fresh from the surgery-schools of *F* *In the Child. Hosp.* 3
appeal Once more to *F* or England; *Columbus* 58
Stormy voice of *F*! Who dost not love our England— *To Victor Hugo* 8
England, *F*, all man to be Will wake one people „ 10
F had shown a light to all men, *Locksley H., Sixty* 89
Franchise Her fuller *f*—what would that be worth— *The Fleet* 8
Francis (*See also* **Francis Allen**) *F*, laughing, clapt his hand On Everard's shoulder, *The Epic* 21
'But I,' said *F*, 'pick'd the eleventh „ 41
F, muttering like a man ill-used, *M. d'Arthur, Ep.* 12
To *F*, with a basket on his arm, To *F* just alighted from the boat, *Audley Court* 6
'With all my heart,' Said *F*. „ 9
F laid A damask napkin wrought with horse and hound, „ 20
Francis Allen (*See also* **Francis**) At *F A's* on the Christmas-eve,— *The Epic* 1
Francis Hale *F H*, The farmer's son, *Audley Court* 74
Francis of Assisi Sweet St *F o A*, would that he *Locksley H., Sixty* 100
Frank 'You know,' said *F*, 'he burnt His Epic, *The Epic* 27
Frankincense sweet! spikenard, and balm, and *f*. *St. S. Stylites* 211
Frantic *F* love and *f* hate. *Vision of Sin* 150
For while the *f* rabble in half-amaze Stared at him dead, *St. Telemachus* 71
Frater Ave atque Vale '*F A a V*'—as we wander'd *Frater Ave, etc.* 7
Fraud whispers of this monstrous *f*! *Third of Feb.* 36
Fraught when *f* With a passion so intense *Maud II ii* 58
Fray and fought till I sunder'd the *f*, *V. of Maeldune* 69
and threw Underfoot there in the *f*— *Heavy Brigade* 55
Fray'd (His dress a suit of *f* magnificence, *Marr. of Geraint* 296
Free (adj.) (*See also* **Freeä, Heart-free**) With mellow preludes, 'We are *f*.' *The Winds, etc.* 4
Atween the blossoms, 'We are *f*.' „ 8
so clear and bold and *f* As you, *Rosalind* 17
to have been Joyful and *f* from blame. *D. of F. Women* 80
So let the change which comes be *f* *Love thou thy land* 45
I am always bound to you, but you are *f*.' *Enoch Arden* 450
clothes they gave him and *f* passage home; „ 650
—*f* of alms her hand— *Aylmer's Field* 697
'King, you are *f*! We did but keep you surety for our son, *Princess v* 24
Knowledge in our own land make her *f*, „ 419
yourself and yours shall have *F* adit; „ *vi* 302
dwarf'd or godlike, bond or *f*: „ *vii* 260
His foes were thine; he kept us *f*; *Ode on Well.* 91

Free (adj.) (*continued*) all too *f* For such a wise humility *Ode on Well.* 248
peace, so it be *f* from pain, *Grandmother* 97
Survive in spirits render'd *f*, *In Mem. xxxviii* 10
Whose jest among his friends is *f*, „ *lxvi* 10
Ring in the valiant man and *f*, „ *cvi* 29
I feel so *f* and so clear By the loss *Maud I xix* 98
unhooded casting off The goodly falcon *f*; *Merlin and V.* 131
Flow'd forth a carol *f* and bold; *Dying Swan* 30
Whose *f* delight, from any height of rapid flight, *Rosalind* 3
Like two streams of incense *f* *Eleänore* 58
Mine be the strength of spirit, full and *f*, *Mine be the strength* 1
'Where wert thou when thy father play'd In his *f* field, *Two Voices* 320
and opposed *F* hearts, *f* foreheads— *Ulysses* 49
Lord of Burleigh, fair and *f*, *L. of Burleigh* 58
Set thy hoary fancies *f*; *Vision of Sin* 156
That our *f* press should cease to brawl, *Third of Feb.* 3
Have left the last *f* race with naked coasts! „ 40
presently thereafter follow'd calm, *F* sky and stars; *Com. of Arthur* 392
crush'd The Idolaters, and made the people *f*? Who should be King save him who makes us *f*?' *Gareth and L.* 137
'The thrall in person may be *f* in soul, „ 165
Till ev'n the lonest hold were all as *f* „ 598
Gareth loosed his bonds and on *f* feet Set him, „ 817
'I take it as *f* gift, then,' said the boy. *Geraint and E.* 222
told *F* tales, and took the word and play'd upon it, „ 291
When wine and *f* companions kindled him, „ 293
'My *f* leave,' he said; 'Get her to speak: „ 300
But *f* to stretch his limbs in lawful fight, „ 754
f flashes from a height Above her, *Lancelot and E.* 647
but *f* love will not be bound.' '*F* love, so bound, were freëst,' said the King. 'Let love be *f*; *f* love is for the best: „ 1379
'*F* love—*f* field—we love but while we may: (repeat) *Last Tournament* 275, 281
It frighted all *f* fool from out thy heart; „ 307
King Who fain had clipt *f* manhood from the world— „ 446
tide within Red with *f* chase and heather-scented air, „ 691
Was not the land as *f* thro' all her ways *Lover's Tale i* 662
Bore her free-faced to the *f* airs of heaven, „ *iv* 38
'Take my *f* gift, my cousin, for your wife; „ 363
An' coäx'd an' coodled me oop till ageän I feel'd mysen *f*. *North. Cobbler* 80
Cold, but as welcome as *f* airs of heaven *Sisters (E. and E.)* 197
'What, will she never set her sister *f*?' „ 218
And God's *f* air, and hope of better things. *Sir J. Oldcastle* 10
gave All but *f* leave for all to work the mines, *Columbus* 133
when thou sendest thy *f* soul thro' heaven, *Ancient Sage* 47
And fling *f* alms into the beggar's bowl, „ 260
Wild flowers blowing side by side in God's *f* light and air, *The Flight* 81
But Moother was *f* of 'er tongue, *Owd Roä* 73
they know too that whene'er In our *f* Hall, *Akbar's Dream* 55
Till every Soul be *f*; *Freedom* 20
Her ancient fame of *F*— *The Fleet* 9
With earth is broken, and has left her *f*, *The Ring* 476
calls to them 'Set yourselves *f*!' *Kapiolani* 3
walking and haunting us yet, and be *f*? *The Dawn* 23
Free (s) The starry clearness of the *f*? *In Mem. lxxxv* 86
How can a despot feel with the *F*? *Riflemen form!* 11
Freeä (free) Parson a cooms an' a goäs, an' a says it eäsy an' *f* *N. Farmer, O. S.* 25
an' the *F* Traäde runn'd i' my 'ead, *Owd Roä* 54
Freed Well hast thou done; for all the stream is *f*, *Gareth and L.* 1267
the land Was *f*, and the Queen false, *Last Tournament* 339
he *f* himself From wife and child, *Lover's Tale iv* 379
and *f* the people Of Hawa-i-ee! *Kapiolani* 6
Freedom *and make The bounds of f wider yet* *To the Queen* 32
And *F* rear'd in that august sunrise *The Poet* 37
pure law, Commeasure perfect *f*.' *Œnone* 167
That sober-suited *F* chose, *You ask me, why, etc.* 6
F slowly broadens down From precedent to precedent: „ 11

Freedom (*continued*) And individual *f* mute; *You ask me, why, etc.* 20
Of old sat *F* on the heights, *Of old sat Freedom* 1
shout For some blind glimpse of *f* *Love and Duty* 6
F, gaily doth she tread; *Vision of Sin* 136
Embrace our aims: work out your *f*. *Princess ii* 89
for song Is duer unto *f*, „ *iv* 141
shower the fiery grain Of *f* broadcast „ *v* 422
bear the yoke, I wish it Gentle as *f*'— „ *vi* 206
And save the one true seed of *f* sown *Ode on Well.* 162
That sober *f* out of which there springs „ 164
we fought for *F* from our prime, *Third of Feb.* 23
A love of *f* rarely felt, *In Mem. cix* 13
Of *f* in her regal seat Of England; „ 14
white bonds and warm, Dearer than *f*. *Pelleas and E.* 354
For *f*, or the sake of those they loved, *Sir J. Oldcastle* 186
They kept their faith, their *f*, *Montenegro* 2
rough rock-throne Of *F*! „ 10
F, free to slay herself, *Locksley H., Sixty* 128
we gain'd a *f* known to Europe, „ 129
To this great cause of *F* drink, my friends, (repeat) *Hands all Round* 11, 35
Thraldom who walks with the banner of *F*, *Vastness* 10
Form in *F*'s name and the Queen's! *Riflemen form!* 23
Free-faced Bore her *f-f* to the free airs *Lover's Tale iv* 38
Freeing any knight Toward thy sister's *f*.' *Gareth and L.* 1018
Freeman It is the land that *freemen* till, *You ask me, why, etc.* 5
For English natures, *freemen*, friends, *Love thou thy land* 7
Gallant sons of English *freemen*, *The Captain* 7
and the Rome of *freemen* holds her place, *To Virgil* 34
To mark in many a *f's* home The slave, *Freedom* 11
Freër leave thee *f*, till thou wake refresh'd *Love and Duty* 97
But smit with *f* light shall slowly melt *Golden Year* 33
tyrant's cruel glee Forces on the *f* hour. *Vision of Sin* 130
noble thought be *f* under the sun, *Maud III vi* 48
Free-spoken or being one Of our *f-s* Table *Pelleas and E.* 526
Freëst 'Free love, so bound, were *f*,' *Lancelot and E.* 1380
Freewill joy I had in my *f* All cold, *Supp. Confessions* 16
Freeze eighty winters *f* with one rebuke *Ode on Well.* 186
tears that at their fountain *f*; *In Mem. xx* 12
tho' every pulse would *f*, *The Flight* 53
Death will *f* the supplest limbs— *Happy* 46
Freezing here he stays upon a *f* orb *Lucretius* 139
The *f* reason's colder part, *In Mem. cxxiv* 14
I took And chafed the *f* hand. *The Ring* 452
Freight lovely *f* Of overflowing blooms, *Ode to Memory* 16
And, thy dark *f*, a vanish'd life. *In Mem. x* 8
French We love not this *F* God, the child of Hell, *Third of Feb.* 7
F of the *F*, and Lord of human tears; *To Victor Hugo* 3
Frenchman Not sting the fiery *F* into war. *Third of Feb.* 4
Frenzied *See* **Half-frenzied**
Frequence Not in this *f* can I lend full tongue, *Princess iv* 442
Staled by *f*, shrunk by usage *Locksley H., Sixty* 76
Frequent (adj.) So *f* on its hinge before. *Deserted House* 8
I was *f* with him in my youth, *Gareth and L.* 124
Where from the *f* bridge, *Ode to Memory* 102
And *f* interchange of foul and fair, *Enoch Arden* 533
A *f* haunt of Edith, on low knolls *Aylmer's Field* 148
she With *f* smile and nod departing found, *Marr. of Geraint* 515
Frequent (verb) Sometimes I *f* the Christian cloister, *Akbar's D., Inscrip.* 5
Fresh (*See also* **Dewy-fresh, Frish, Sparkling-fresh**)
Keeps his blue waters *f* for many a mile. *Mine be the strength* 8
Aphroditè beautiful, *F* as the foam, *Œnone* 175
All the valley, mother, 'ill be *f* *May Queen* 37
How *f* the meadows look Above the river, *Walk. to the Mail* 1
I have seen some score of those *F* faces, *Talking Oak* 50
flit To make the greensward *f*, „ 90
Oh, nature first was *f* to men, *Amphion* 57
moon Smote by the *f* beam of the springing east; *M. d'Arthur* 214
My sweet, wild, *f* three quarters of a year, *Edwin Morris* 2
She seems a part of those *f* days to me; „ 142
her *f* and innocent eyes Had such a star *Aylmer's Field* 691
What drives about the *f* Cascinè, *The Daisy* 43
her brother comes, like a blight On my *f* hope, *Maud I xix* 103
take my charger, *f*, Not to be spurr'd, *Gareth and L.* 1300
and fetch *F* victual for these mowers of our Earl; *Geraint and E.* 225

Fresh (*continued*) men may fear *F* fire and ruin. *Geraint and E.* 823
my *f* but fixt resolve To pass away *Holy Grail* 737
moon Smote by the *f* beam of the springing east; *Pass. of Arthur* 382
evermore *F* springing from her fountains in the brain, *Lover's Tale i* 83
and blew *F* fire into the sun, " 319
an' es clean Es a shillin' *f* fro' the mint *Spinster's S's.* 76
While yet thy *f* and virgin soul *Freedom* 2
There no one came, the turf was *f*, *Prog. of Spring* 72
flowers To work old laws of Love to *f* results, " 85
That his *f* life may close as it began, " 89
How *f* was every sight and sound *The Voyage* 5
So *f* they rose in shadow'd swells *The Letters* 46
F from the burial of her little one, *Enoch Arden* 281
'Too happy, *f* and fair, Too *f* *The Brook* 217
Lady Psyche will harangue The *f* arrivals of the week *Princess ii* 96
F as the first beam glittering on a sail, " *iv* 44
So sad, so *f*, the days that are no more. " 48
f young captains flash'd their glittering teeth, " *v* 20
When all our path was *f* with dew, *In Mem. lxviii* 6
And show'd him in the fountain *f* " *lxxxv* 26
If not so *f*, with love as true, " 101
pleased him, *f* from brawling courts " *lxxxix* 11
from the garden and the wild A *f* association blow, " *ci* 18
daily fronted him In some *f* splendour; *Marr. of Geraint* 14
my child, how *f* the colours look, " 680
this cut is *f*; That ten years back; *Lancelot and E.* 21
Tommy's faäce be as *f* as a codlin *North. Cobbler* 110
Making *f* and fair All the bowers and the flowers, *Sisters (E. and E.)* 9

Freshen They *f* the silvery-crimson shells, *Sea-Fairies* 13
They *f* and sweeten the wards *In the Child. Hosp.* 38

Fresher And flood a *f* throat with song. *In Mem. lxxxiii* 16
Bright Phosphor, *f* for the night, " *cxxi* 9
She from her bier, as into *f* life, *Lover's Tale iii* 42

Freshest a truth Looks *f* in the fashion of the day: *The Epic* 32

Freshlier And gathering *f* overhead, *In Mem. xcv* 57

Freshly-flower'd and lay Upon the *f-f* slope. *Miller's D.* 112

Freshmen Everard's college fame When we were *F*: *The Epic* 47

Freshness The unsunn'd *f* of my strength, *Supp. Confessions* 140
increased With *f* in the dawning east. *Two Voices* 405
Delighted with the *f* and the sound. *Edwin Morris* 99
Yet so did I let my *f* die. *Maud I xix* 11
immortality Of thought, and *f* ever self-renew'd. *Lover's Tale i* 106

Fresh-wash'd *f-w* in coolest dew The maiden splendours *D. of F. Women* 54

Fresh-water *F-w* springs come up through bitter brine. *If I were loved* 8

Fret (s) busy *f* Of that sharp-headed worm *Supp. Confessions* 185
Love is hurt with jar and *f*. *Miller's D.* 209
(all *f's* But chafing me on fire to find *Princess i* 165

Fret (verb) rib and *f* The broad-imbased beach, *Supp. Confessions* 127
You should not *f* for me, mother, *May Queen, N. Y's. E.* 36
say to Robin a kind word, and tell him not to *f*; " *Con.* 45
The changing market *f's* or charms *Ancient Sage* 140
To *f* the summer jenneting. *The Blackbird* 12
We *f*, we fume, would shift our skins, *Will Water.* 225
With many a curve my banks I *f* *The Brook* 43
'So *f* not, like an idle girl, *In Mem. lii* 13
Is that a matter to make me *f*? *Maud I xiii* 2
'*F* not yourself, dear brother, *Lancelot and E.* 1074

Fretful *f* as the wind Pent in a crevice: *Princess iii* 80
common sense of most shall hold a *f* realm in awe, *Locksley Hall* 129

Fretted (adj.) By Bagdat's shrines of *f* gold, *Arabian Nights* 7
And, with dim *f* foreheads all, *Palace of Art* 242

Fretted (verb) Have *f* all to dust and bitterness.' *Princess vi* 264

Fretteth *F* thine enshrouded form. *A Dirge* 10

Fretwork holds a stately *f* to the Sun, *Princess vi* 86

Friar For I am emptier than a *f's* brains; *Sir J. Oldcastle* 7
at Pardoners, Summoners, *F's*, absolution-sellers, " 93
God willing, to outlearn the filthy *f*. " 118
poor man's money gone to fat the *f*. " 150
F's, bellringers, Parish-clerks— " 160
Two *f's* crying that if Spain should oust *Columbus* 96

Friday Whose *F* fare was Enoch's ministering. *Enoch Arden* 100
we sail'd on a *F* morn— *V. of Maeldune* 7

Friend (*See also* **Bosom-friend, Frind, Sea-friend**)
our *f's* are all forsaking The wine *All Things will Die* 18

Friend (*continued*) CLEAR-HEADED *f*, whose joyful scorn, *Clear-headed friend* 1
My *f*, with you to live alone, *Ode to Memory* 119
So, *f*, when first I look'd upon your face, *Sonnet To ——* 9
painting some dead *f* from memory? *Wan Sculptor* 4
'He seems to hear a Heavenly *F*, *Two Voices* 295
f's to man, Living together under the same roof, *To —— With Pal. of Art* 11
Prythee, *f*, Where is Mark Antony? *D. of F. Women* 139
He gave me a *f*, and a true true-love, *D. of the O. Year* 13
He was a *f* to me. " 23
The night is starry and cold, my *f*, And the New-Year blithe and bold, my *f*, " 34
Alack! our *f* is gone. " 47
There's a new foot on the floor, my *f*, And a new face at the door, my *f*, " 52
he too was a *f* to me: Both are my *f's*, *To J. S.* 61
The land, where girt with *f's* or foes *You ask me, why, etc.* 7
English natures, freemen, *f's*, *Love thou thy land* 7
Both for themselves and those who call them *f*? *M. d'Arthur* 253
who lived across the bay, My *f*; *Audley Court* 76
'*F* Edwin, do not think yourself alone *Edwin Morris* 77
Sets out, and meets a *f* who hails *Walk. to the Mail* 42
my *f*, the days were brief Whereof the poets talk, *Talking Oak* 185
Come, my *f's*, 'Tis not too late to seek *Ulysses* 56
In Art like Nature, dearest *f*; *Day-Dm., Moral* 14
To fall asleep with all one's *f's*; " *L'Envoi* 4
She told me all her *f's* had said; *The Letters* 25
Thro' troops of unrecording *f's*, *You might have won* 7
naming those, his *f's*, for whom they were: *The Brook* 131
'Good,' said his *f*, 'but watch!' *Aylmer's Field* 275
The man was his, had been his father's, *f*: " 344
his nearer *f* would say 'Screw not the chord " 468
F's, I was bid to speak of such a one " 677
F's, this frail bark of ours, " 715
their guest, their host, their ancient *f*, " 790
'My dearest *f*, Have faith, have faith! *Sea Dreams* 156
I found a hard *f* in his loose accounts, " 162
he that wrongs his *f* Wrongs himself " 172
closed by those who mourn a *f* in vain, *Lucretius* 142
and lady *f's* From neighbour seats: *Princess, Pro.* 97
They rode; they betted; made a hundred *f's*, " 163
Cyril and with Florian, my two *f's*: " *i* 52
Went forth again with both my *f's*. " 167
always *f's*, none closer, elm and vine: " *ii* 337
'O *f*, we trust that you esteem'd us not " *iii* 198
brings our *f's* up from the underworld, " *iv* 45
Nor found my *f's*; but push'd alone on foot " 196
Then came your new *f*: you began to change— " 298
I your old *f* and tried, she new in all? " 318
'Her,' she said, 'my *f*—Parted from her— " *v* 75
—and ours shall see us *f's*. " 228
Truest *f* and noblest foe; " *vi* 7
a world Of traitorous *f* and broken system " 195
'We two were *f's*: I go to mine own land " 216
had you got a *f* of your own age, " 251
glittering drops on her sad *f*. " 283
be *f's*, like children, being chid! " 289
Whatever man lies wounded, *f* or foe, " 336
O my *f*, I will not have thee die! " *vii* 8
hears his burial talk'd of by his *f's*, " 152
'Look there, a garden!' said my college *f*, " *Con.* 49
O *f's*, our chief state-oracle is mute: *Ode on Well.* 23
amoighty's a taäkin o' you to 'issén, my *f*,' (repeat) *N. Farmer, O. S.* 10, 26
Thunder 'Anathema,' *f*, at you; *To F. D. Maurice* 8
One writes, that 'Other *f's* remain,' *In Mem. vi* 1
And unto me no second *f*. " 44
My *f*, the brother of my love; " *ix* 16
saying; 'Comes he thus, my *f*? " *xii* 13
And flash at once, my *f*, to thee. " *xli* 12
Methinks my *f* is richly shrined; " *lvii* 7
'Does my old *f* remember me?' " *lxiv* 28
Since we deserved the name of *f's*, " *lxv* 9
Whose jest among his *f's* is free, " *lxvi* 10

Friend (*continued*) Thy blood, my *f*, and partly mine; *In Mem. lxxxiv* 9
For other *f's* that once I met; " *lxxxv* 58
I crave your pardon, O my *f*; " 100
held debate, a band Of youthful *f's*, " *lxxxvii* 22
f from *f* Is oftener parted, " *xcviii* 14
Some gracious memory of my *f*; " *c* 4
With thy lost *f* among the bowers, " *cii* 15
O, *f*, who camest to thy goal " *cxiv* 23
To hear the tidings of my *f*, " *cxxvi* 3
Dear *f*, far off, my lost desire, " *cxxix* 1
Dear heavenly *f* that canst not die, " 7
Strange *f*, past, present, and to be; " 9
That *f* of mine who lives in God, " *Con.* 140
I have led her home, my love, my only *f*. *Maud I xviii* 1
To be *f's* for her sake, to be reconciled; " *xix* 50
To be *f's*, to be reconciled! " 56
To me, her *f* of the years before; " 64
Should I fear to greet my *f* " *II iv* 85
To catch a *f* of mine one stormy day; " *v* 85
F, to be struck by the public foe, " 89
'O *f*, had I been holpen half as well *Com. of Arthur* 161
an old knight And ancient *f* of Uther; " 223
the *f's* Of Arthur, gazing on him, " 277
three Queens, the *f's* Of Arthur, *Gareth and L.* 229
a stalwart Baron, Arthur's *f*. " 818
'*F*, whether thou be kitchen-knave, or not, " 873
and now thy pardon, *f*, " 1166
felon, knight, I avenge me for my *f*.' " 1220
They hate the King, and Lancelot, the King's *f*, " 1418
'*F*, he that labours for the sparrow-hawk *Marr. of Geraint* 271
'O *f*, I seek a harbourage for the night.' " 299
'Thanks, venerable *f*,' replied Geraint; " 303
he suspends his converse with a *f*, " 340
Built that new fort to overawe my *f's*, " 460
how can Enid find A nobler *f*? " 793
Embraced her with all welcome as a *f*, " 834
'*F*, let her eat; the damsel is so faint.' *Geraint and E.* 206
Call in what men soever were his *f's*, " 286
'All of one mind and all right-honest *f's*! " 484
what they long for, good in *f* or foe, " 876
the great Queen once more embraced her *f*, " 947
'Old *f*, too old to be so young, depart, *Balin and Balan* 17
Poor wretch—no *f*!— *Merlin and V.* 75
Sir Lancelot, *f* Traitor or true? " 769
I know the Table Round, my *f's* of old; " 816
were I glad of you as guide and *f*: *Lancelot and E.* 226
'This shield, my *f*, where is it?' " 345
Surely his king and most familiar *f* " 592
Marr'd her *f's* aim with pale tranquillity. " 733
call her *f* and sister, sweet Elaine, " 865
Death, like a *f's* voice from a distant field " 999
He makes no *f* who never made a foe. " 1089
To this I call my *f's* in testimony, " 1299
to warm My cold heart with a *f*: *Holy Grail* 619
And these, like bright eyes of familiar *f's*, " 688
'Thou, too, my Lancelot,' ask'd the King, 'my *f*, " 764
King, my *f*, if *f* of thine I be, " 769
But as for thine, my good *f* Percivale, " 861
But hold me for your *f*: Come, ye know nothing: *Pelleas and E.* 340
F's, thro' your manhood and your fëalty,— *Last Tournament* 97
'*F*, did ye mark that fountain yesterday " 286
(what marvel—she could see)—Thine, *f*; " 548
Nay, *f*, for we have taken our farewells. *Guinevere* 117
The most disloyal *f* in all the world.' " 340
and saps The fealty of our *f's*, " 521
the warhorse neigh'd As at a *f's* voice, " 531
all whereon I lean'd in wife and *f* *Pass. of Arthur* 24
For *f* and foe were shadows in the mist, And *f* slew *f* not knowing whom he slew; " 100
Both for themselves and those who call them *f*? " 421
f's Of Arthur, who should help him at his need?' " 455
f's—your love Is but a burthen: *To the Queen ii* 16
Permit me, *f*, I prythee, To pass my hand *Lover's Tale i* 30
And, like all other *f's* i' the world, " 108
Ye ask me, *f's* When I began to love. " 144

Friend (*continued*) Life (like a wanton too-officious *f*, *Lover's Tale i* 627
f, the neighbour, Lionel, the beloved, " 653
Oh *f*, thoughts deep and heavy as these " 688
looking round upon his tearful *f's*, " 792
And then to *f's*—they were not many— " *iv* 184
'There is a custom in the Orient, *f's*— " 230
his *f* Replied, in half a whisper, " 335
sight of this So frighted our good *f*, " 383
an' you are my only *f*. *First Quarrel* 8
my best And oldest *f*, your uncle, wishes it, *Sisters (E. and E.)* 47
the portrait of his *f* Drawn by an artist, " 134
an' 'e smiled, fur 'e hedn't naw *f*, *Village Wife* 89
My *f* should meet me somewhere hereabout *Sir J. Oldcastle* 1
hang'd, poor *f's*, as rebels And burn'd alive " 47
my *f* was he, Once my fast *f*: " 61
led my *f* Back to the pure and universal church, " 70
Burnt—good Sir Roger Acton, my dear *f*! " 79
My *f* should meet me here—Here is the copse, " 126
(My good *f* By this time should be with me.) " 138
I would not spurn Good counsel of good *f's*, " 146
(My *f* is long in coming.) " 148
F?—foe perhaps—a tussle for it then! Nay, but my *f*. " 196
My *f's* await me yonder? " 202
The compass, like an old *f* false at last *Columbus* 70
Than any *f* of ours at Court? " 198
reft of his Folk and his *f's* *Batt. of Brunanburh* 70
Old *f's* outvaluing all the rest, *To E. Fitzgerald* 40
But we old *f's* are still alive, " 42
I fancied that my *f* For this brief idyll *Tiresias* 187
away from the Christ, our human brother and *f*, *Despair* 25
'Yet wine and laughter *f's*! *Ancient Sage* 195
would I were there, the *f*, the bride, the wife, *The Flight* 43
With breaking hearts, without a *f*, " 100
and take their wisdom for your *f*. *Locksley H., Sixty* 104
You wrong me, passionate little *f*. *Epilogue* 10
I count them all My *f's* and brother souls, " 19
His *f's* had stript him bare, *Dead Prophet* 14
Warrior of God, man's *f*, and tyrant's foe, *Epit. on Gordon* 1
To this great cause of Freedom drink, my *f's*, (repeat) *Hands all Round* 11, 35
To this great name of England drink, my *f's*, " 23
came, my *f*, To prize your various book, *To Ulysses* 46
You came not, *f*; *To Mary Boyle* 17
golden youth bewail the *f*, the wife, " 53
I once had *f's*—and many—none like you. *Romney's R.* 156
But, *f*, man-woman is not woman-man. *On one who effec. E. M.* 4
hardly a daisy as yet, little *f*, *The Throstle* 11
My *f*, the most unworldly of mankind, *In Mem. W. G. Ward* 3
My noble *f*, my faithful counsellor, *Akbar's Dream* 18
bravest soul for counsellor and *f*. " 69
my *f*, thou knowest I hold that forms Are needful: " 126
Fur Quoloty's hall my *f's*, *Church-warden, etc.* 39
You were his *f*—you—you— *Charity* 11
You will not speak, my *f's*, *The Wanderer* 3
O well for him that finds a *f*, " 5
Or makes a *f* where'er he come, " 6
Friendlier Old poets foster'd under *f* skies, *Poets and their B.* 1
Friendly (*See also* **Frindly**) The *f* mist of morn Clung to the lake. *Edwin Morris* 107
Friendly-warm Only such cups as left us *f-w*, *Lucretius* 215
Friendship a *f* so complete Portion'd in halves *Gardener's D.* 4
My college *f's* glimmer. *Will Water.* 40
'*F*!—to be two in one— *Vision of Sin* 107
O *f*, equal-poised control, *In Mem. lxxxv* 33
such A *f* as had master'd Time; " 64
seek A *f* for the years to come. " 80
First love, first *f*, equal powers, " 107
Less yearning for the *f* fled, " *cxvi* 15
And bright the *f* of thine eye; " *cxix* 10
So vanish *f's* only made in wine. *Geraint and E.* 479
it was a bond and seal Of *f*, *Lover's Tale ii* 182
Sprang up a *f* that may help us yet. " *iv* 144
Gone into darkness, that full light Of *f*! *Tiresias* 203
flits to warn A far-off *f* that he comes *Demeter and P.* 90
Frieze boss'd with lengths Of classic *f*, *Princess ii* 25

Fright (s) and died Of *f* in far apartments. *Princess vi* 371
dead weight trail'd, by a whisper'd *f*, *Maud I i* 14
F's to my heart; but stay: *Gareth and L.* 90
call'd him dear protector in her *f*, Nor yet forgot her practice in her *f*, *Merlin and V.* 946
and the bitter frost and the *f*? *Rizpah* 18
till 'e'd gotten a *f* at last, *Village Wife* 61
harass'd by the *f's* Of my first crew, *Columbus* 67
she had torn the ring In *f*, *The Ring* 471
F and foul dissembling, *Forlorn* 32
Frighted (verb) breed with him, can *f* my faith. *In Mem. lxxxii* 4
Frighted (*See also* **Half-frighted**) Queen had added Get thee hence,' Fled *f*. *Guinevere* 367
My *f* Wiclif-preacher whom I crost In flying hither? *Sir J. Oldcastle* 38
half amazed half *f* all his flock: *Aylmer's Field* 631
f all free fool from out thy heart; *Last Tournament* 307
the sight of this So *f* our good friend, *Lover's Tale iv* 383
I am *f* at life not death.' *Despair* 14
Frighten'd *See* **Half-frighten'd**
Frightful the bells Lapsed into *f* stillness; *Lover's Tale iii* 30
Frill door Of his house in a rainbow *f*? *Maud II ii* 17
Frind (friend) But shure we wor betther *f's* *Tomorrow* 41
An' her nabours an' *f's* 'ud consowl „ 47
dhry eye thin but was wet for the *f's* „ 83
Frindly an' she gev him a *f* nod, „ 58
Fringe (*See also* **Under-fringe**) Burnt like a *f* of fire. *Palace of Art* 48
Torn from the *f* of spray. *D. of F. Women* 40
beard Was tagg'd with icy *f's* in the moon, *St. S. Stylites* 32
From *f's* of the faded eve, *Move eastward* 3
Upon the skirt and *f* of our fair land, *Princess v* 219
daisy close Her crimson *f's* to the shower; *In Mem. lxxii* 12
f Of that great breaker, sweeping up the strand. *Com. of Arthur* 386
from the *f* of coppice round them burst *Balin and Balan* 46
and the narrow *f* Of curving beach— *Lover's Tale i* 38
we kiss'd the *f* of his beard. *V. of Maeldune* 125
Fringed (adj. and part.) (*See also* **Gold-fringed, Ray-fringed, Sun-fringed**) hollows of the *f* hills In summer heats, *Supp. Confessions* 153
A looming bastion *f* with fire. *In Mem. xv* 20
Pallas flung Her *f* ægis, *Achilles over the T.* 4
Fringed (verb) the knightly growth that *f* his lips. *M. d'Arthur* 220
the knightly growth that *f* his lips. *Pass. of Arthur* 388
Frish (fresh) But a *f* gineration had riz, *Tomorrow* 75
Frith o'er the *f's* that branch and spread *In Mem., Con.* 115
Frock Or the *f* and gipsy bonnet *Maud I xx* 19
Frog When did a *f* coarser croak *Trans. of Homer* 4
Frolic (adj.) My *f* falcon, with bright eyes, *Rosalind* 2
in a fit of *f* mirth She strove to span my waist: *Talking Oak* 137
with a *f* welcome took The thunder and the sunshine, *Ulysses* 47
Frolic (s) Cyril, howe'er He deal in *f*, *Princess iv* 250
fury of peoples, and Christless *f* of kings, *The Dawn* 7
Frolic (verb) come hither and *f* and play; *Sea-Fairies* 18
Front (adj.) all at once The *f* rank made a sudden halt; *Lover's Tale iii* 29
Front (s) (*See also* **Minster-front, Palace-front**) More black than ashbuds in the *f* of March.' *Gardener's D.* 28
but in *f* The gorges, opening wide apart, *Œnone* 11
In *f* they bound the sheaves. *Palace of Art* 78
discern The *f* of Sumner-place. *Talking Oak* 248
Past thro' the solitary room in *f*, *Enoch Arden* 277
A *f* of timber-crost antiquity, „ 692
But huge cathedral *f's* of every age, *Sea Dreams* 218
some inscription ran along the *f*, *Princess i* 212
terrace ranged along the Northern *f*, „ *iii* 118
riders *f* to *f*, until they closed In conflict „ *v* 490
Cannon in *f* of them Volley'd and thunder'd; *Light Brigade* 20
Betwixt the black *f's* long-withdrawn *In Mem. cxix* 6
For *f* to *f* in an hour we stood, *Maud II i* 23
whereof along the *f*, Some blazon'd, *Gareth and L.* 405
thicker down the *f* With jewels *Geraint and E.* 689
Kiss'd the white star upon his noble *f*, „ 757
in *f* of which Six stately virgins, all in white, *Lover's Tale ii* 76
in *f* of that ravine Which drowsed in gloom, *Death of Œnone* 75
Front (verb) And the crag that *f's* the Even, *Eleänore* 40
And eastward *f's* the statue, *Holy Grail* 241
Henceforward rarely could she *f* in hall, *Guinevere* 62
Front (verb) (*continued*) Shape your heart to *f* the hour, *Locksley H., Sixty* 106
I will *f* him face to face. *Happy* 19
Me they *f* With sullen brows. *Akbar's Dream* 51
Fronted (*See also* **Fair-fronted**) Philip's dwelling *f* on the street, *Enoch Arden* 731
when first I *f* him, Said, 'Trust him not;' *Sea Dreams* 70
daily *f* him In some fresh splendour; *Marr. of Geraint* 13
We *f* there the learning of all Spain, *Columbus* 41
Frontier And flying reach'd the *f*: *Princess i* 109
Hard by your father's *f*: „ 148
Fronting like a star *F* the dawn he moved; *Œnone* 58
Frontless Suddenly bawls this *f* kitchen-knave, *Gareth and L.* 860
Frost There is *f* in your breath *Poet's Mind* 17
the *f* is on the pane: *May Queen, N. Y's. E.* 13
sparkled keen with *f* against the hilt: *M. d'Arthur* 55
Rain, wind, *f*, heat, hail, *St. S. Stylites* 16
With drenching dews, or stiff with crackling *f*. „ 115
one wide chasm of time and *f* they gave *Princess, Pro.* 93
Draw toward the long *f* and longest night, *A Dedication* 11
The *f* is here, And fuel is dear, *Window, Winter* 1
And *f* is here And has bitten the heel „ 5
Bite, *f*, bite! (repeat) „ 7, 13
That grief hath shaken into *f*! *In Mem. iv* 12
The streets were black with smoke and *f*, „ *lxix* 3
The yule-log sparkled keen with *f*, „ *lxxviii* 5
'My sudden *f* was sudden gain, „ *lxxxi* 10
New leaf, new life—the days of *f* are o'er: *Last Tournament* 278
sparkled keen with *f* against the hilt: *Pass. of Arthur* 223
Hard was the *f* in the field, *First Quarrel* 39
and the bitter *f* and the fright? *Rizpah* 18
all the heavens flash'd in *f*; *To E. Fitzgerald* 22
leaf rejoice in the *f* that sears it at night; *The Wreck* 20
'No *f* there,' so he said, „ 80
Sun-flame or sunless *f*, *Epilogue* 66
His fingers were so stiffen'd by the *f* *The Ring* 239
When *f* is keen and days are brief— *To Ulysses* 19
Frost-bead *f-b* melts upon her golden hair; *Prog. of Spring* 10
Frost-like And tipt with *f-l* spires. *Palace of Art* 52
Frosty (*See also* **Purple-frosty**) Make thou my spirit pure and clear As are the *f* skies, *St. Agnes' Eve* 10
For while our cloisters echo'd *f* feet, *Princess, Pro.* 183
That glitter burnish'd by the *f* dark; „ *v* 261
Made the noise of *f* woodlands, *Boädicea* 75
The flying cloud, the *f* light: *In Mem. cvi* 2
Yet in your *f* cells ye feel the fire! *Balin and Balan* 446
Thaw once of a *f* night I slither'd *North. Cobbler* 19
Froth Upon the topmost *f* of thought. *In Mem. lii* 4
Froth'd He *f* his bumpers to the brim; *D. of the O. Year* 19
is your spleen *f* out, or have ye more? *Merlin and V.* 767
Frothfly Sweeping the *f* from the fescue *Aylmer's Field* 530
Frown (s) who may know Whether smile or *f* be fleeter? Whether smile or *f* be sweeter, *Madeline* 12
F's perfect-sweet along the brow „ 15
Thy smile and *f* are not aloof From one another, „ 19
black brows drops down A sudden-curved *f*. (repeat) „ 35, 47
other *f's* than those That knit themselves *Aylmer's Field* 723
He had darken'd into a *f*, *Maud I xix* 62
Fortune, turn thy wheel with smile or *f*; *Marr. of Geraint* 350
Met his full *f* timidly firm, and said; *Geraint and E.* 71
Frown (verb) *F* and we smile, the lords of our own hands; *Marr. of Geraint* 354
sweet eyes *f*: the lips Seem but a gash. *Sisters (E. and E.)* 106
Frown'd The seldom-frowning King *f*, *Lancelot and E.* 715
and you took them tho' you *f*; You *f* and yet you kiss'd them. *Happy* 74
Frowning (*See also* **Seldom-frowning**) Smiling, *f*, evermore, (repeat) *Madeline* 8, 25
Florian nodded at him, I *f*; *Princess iv* 160
Vivien, *f* in true anger, said: *Merlin and V.* 691
Vivien answer'd *f* wrathfully: „ 704
Vivien answer'd *f* yet in wrath: „ 768
With smiling face and *f* heart, *Lancelot and E.* 553
Froze with surprise *F* my swift speech: *D. of F. Women* 90
To me you *f*: this was my meed for all. *Princess iv* 302

Froze (*continued*) how it *f* you from your bride, *Happy* 71
Frozen Till her blood was *f* slowly, *L. of Shalott iv* 30
Hollow smile and *f* sneer Come not here. *Poet's Mind* 10
Be fix'd and *f* to permanence: *Two Voices* 237
My *f* heart began to beat, „ 422
Caught in the *f* palms of Spring. *The Blackbird* 24
Larger than human on the *f* hills. *M. d'Arthur* 183
That longs to burst a *f* bud *In Mem. lxxxiii* 15
Larger than human on the *f* hills. *Pass. of Arthur* 351
These be no rubies, this is *f* blood, *Last Tournament* 413
and stood Stiff as a viper *f*; *Merlin and V.* 845
the placid lip *F* by sweet sleep, *Pelleas and E.* 433
like a creature *f* to the heart *Death of Œnone* 73
Frugal *f*, savage, arm'd by day and night *Montenegro* 3
Fruit (*See also* **First-fruits**) shoots Of orient green giving safe pledge of *f's*, *Ode to Memory* 18
Disclosed a *f* of pure Hesperian gold, *Œnone* 66
Behold this *f*, whose gleaming rind ingrav'n „ 72
Paris held the costly *f* Out at arm's-length, „ 135
cast the golden *f* upon the board, „ 226
enchanted stem, Laden with flower and *f*, *Lotos-Eaters* 29
ere my flower to *f* Changed, I was ripe for death. *D. of F. Women* 207
f's and cream Served in the weeping elm; *Gardener's D.* 194
we stole his *f*, His hens, his eggs; *Walk. to the Mail* 84
bring me offerings of *f* and flowers: *St. S. Stylites* 128
This *f* of thine by Love is blest, *Talking Oak* 249
Where fairer *f* of Love may rest „ 251
flower of knowledge changed to *f* Of wisdom. *Love and Duty* 24
and *f's*, and spices, clear of toll, *Golden Year* 45
cherish that which bears but bitter *f*? *Locksley Hall* 65
With naked limbs and flowers and *f*, But we nor paused for *f* nor flowers. *The Voyage* 55
Gifts by the children, garden-herbs and *f*, *Enoch Arden* 338
Divides threefold to show the *f* within. (repeat) *The Brook* 73, 208
The red *f* of an old idolatry— *Aylmer's Field* 762
babies roll'd about Like tumbled *f* *Princess, Pro.* 83
falling in a land Of promise; *f* would follow. „ *ii* 140
To scare the fowl from *f*: „ 228
F, blossom, viand, amber wine, „ *iv* 35
breadth Of Autumn, dropping *f's* „ *vi* 55
And gathering all the *f's* of earth *Ode Inter. Exhib.* 41
Wearing his wisdom lightly, like the *f* *A Dedication* 12
A life that bears immortal *f* *In Mem. xl* 18
I'll rather take what *f* may be „ *cviii* 13
Of what in them is flower and *f*; „ *Con.* 136
It is only flowers, they had no *f's*, *Maud II v* 77
little pitted speck in garner'd *f*, *Merlin and V.* 394
sure I think this *f* is hung too high *Lancelot and E.* 774
your flower Waits to be solid *f* *Last Tournament* 100
the red *f* Grown on a magic oak-tree „ 744
manners are not idle, but the *f* Of loyal nature, *Guinevere* 335
said the maid, 'be manners such fair *f*? „ 337
no leaf, no flower, no *f* for me. *Lover's Tale i* 725
promise of blossom, but never a *f*! *V. of Maeldune* 51
And we came to the Isle of *F's*: „ 55
in every berry and *f* was the poisonous pleasure „ 62
giddy besides with the *f's* we had gorged, „ 75
Was flinging *f* to lions; *Tiresias* 67
earthly flower would be heavenly *f*— *Despair* 35
She tastes the *f* before the blossom falls, *Ancient Sage* 75
The kernel of the shrivell'd *f* „ 121
climbing toward her with the golden *f*, *Death of Œnone* 15
'Mine is the one *f* Alla made for man.' *Akbar's Dream* 40
heats our earth to yield us grain and *f*, „ 105
Fruitage *f* golden-rinded On golden salvers, *Eleänore* 33
Soft *f*, mighty nuts, and nourishing roots; *Enoch Arden* 555
Fruit-bunches rich *f-b* leaning on each other— *Isabel* 37
Fruited *See* **Heavy-fruited**
Fruitful like the arrow-seeds of the field flower, The *f* wit Cleaving, *The Poet* 20
F of further thought and deed, *Two Voices* 144
close to thine in that quick-falling dew Of *f* kisses, *Œnone* 205
Fast-rooted in the *f* soil. *Lotos-Eaters, C. S.* 38
I keep smooth plats of *f* ground, *The Blackbird* 3
When the centuries behind me like a *f* land reposed; *Locksley Hall* 13
Fruitful (*continued*) With *f* cloud and living smoke, *In Mem. xxxix* 3
The *f* hours of still increase; „ *xlvi* 10
To *f* strifes and rivalries of peace— *Ded. of Idylls* 38
Fruitless Which else were *f* of their due, *In Mem. xlv* 14
Is shrivell'd in a *f* fire, „ *liv* 11
Who built him fanes of *f* prayer, „ *lvi* 12
'Wherefore grieve Thy brethren with a *f* tear? „ *lviii* 10
glancing from his height On earth a *f* fallow, *Demeter and P.* 118
Gods Avenge on stony hearts a *f* prayer For pity. *Death of Œnone* 41
Frustration out of long *f* of her care, *Princess vii* 101
Fuel Secret wrath like smother'd *f* Burnt *The Captain* 15
The frost is here, and *f* is dear, *Window, Winter* 2
The *f* is all the dearer, „ 15
Fuel-smother'd And from it like a *f-s* fire, *Gareth and L.* 684
Fulfil *F's* him with beatitude. *Supp. Confessions* 62
God *f's* himself in many ways, *M. d'Arthur* 241
discerning to *f* This labour, *Ulysses* 35
I would but ask you to *f* yourself: *Princess vii* 146
each *f's* Defect in each, „ 303
To strive, to fashion, to *f*— *In Mem. cxiii* 7
F the boundless purpose of their King!' *Com. of Arthur* 475
God *f's* himself in many ways, *Pass. of Arthur* 409
Fulfill'd By its own energy *f* itself, *Gardener's D.* 238
For daily hope *f*, to rise again *Edwin Morris* 38
My father 'that our compact be *f*: *Princess v* 115
King was all *f* with gratefulness, *Last Tournament* 593
delightedly *f* All lovingkindnesses, *Lover's Tale i* 224
Fulfillest thou *f* thy doom Making him broken gleams, *High. Pantheism* 9
Fulfilling *See* **Still-fulfilling**
Fulfilment to rise again Revolving toward *f*, *Edwin Morris* 39
Full so *f* and deep In thy large eyes, *Eleänore* 85
and slowly grow To a *f* face, „ 92
So *f*, so deep, so slow, „ 95
Since in his absence *f* of light and joy, *Lover's Tale i* 425
that strove to rise From my *f* heart. „ 712
It was *f* of old odds an' ends, *First Quarrel* 49
and the *f* moon stares at the snow. *Rizpah* 4
'*F* of compassion and mercy—(repeat) *Rizpah* 62, 63
My brain is *f* of the crash of wrecks, *The Wreck* 4
I fun thy pockets as *f* o' my pippins *Church-warden, etc.* 34
Too *f* for sound and foam, *Crossing the Bar* 6
And yet, tho' its voice be so clear and *f*, *Poet's Mind* 34
The warble was low, and *f* and clear; *Dying Swan* 24
Thy rose-lips and *f* blue eyes *Adeline* 7
My life is *f* of weary days, *My life is full* 1
Mine be the strength of spirit, *f* and free, *Mine be the strength* 1
But my *f* heart, that work'd below, *Two Voices* 44
Flood with *f* daylight glebe and town? „ 87
They met with two so *f* and bright— *Miller's D.* 86
While those *f* chestnuts whisper by. „ 168
My eyes are *f* of tears, my heart of love, *Œnone* 31
her *f* and earnest eye Over her snow-cold breast „ 141
Her slow *f* words sank thro' the silence drear, *D. of F. Women* 121
He was *f* of joke and jest, *D. of the O. Year* 28
on one Lay a great water, and the moon was *f*. *M. d'Arthur* 12
But the *f* day dwelt on her brows, and sunn'd *Gardener's D.* 136
You know there has not been for these five years So *f* a harvest: *Dora* 66
that when his heart is glad Of the *f* harvest, „ 69
To some *f* music rose and sank the sun, And some *f* music seem'd to move and change *Edwin Morris* 34
Sneeze out a *f* God-bless-you right and left? „ 80
On the coals I lay, A vessel *f* of sin: *St. S. Stylites* 170
The *f* south-breeze around thee blow *Talking Oak* 271
when the first low matin-chirp hath grown *F* quire, *Love and Duty* 99
amid Her *f* black ringlets downward roll'd, *Day-Dm., Sleep. B.* 12
barren commonplaces break In *f* and kindly blossom. *Will Water.* 24
F cold my greeting was and dry; *The Letters* 13
and made himself *F* sailor; *Enoch Arden* 54
Out of *f* heart and boundless gratitude „ 346
his *f* tide of youth Broke with a phosphorescence *Aylmer's Field* 115
with all my heart, With my *f* heart: *Princess i* 127
and watch A *f* sea glazed with muffled moonlight, „ 248
that *f* voice which circles round the grave, „ *ii* 45
'Alas your Highness breathes *f* East,' „ *iii* 231

Full (*continued*) Not in this frequence can I lend *f* tongue, *Princess iv* 442
and meek Seem'd the *f* lips, „ *vii* 226
The two-cell'd heart beating, with one *f* stroke, „ 307
Not perfect, nay, but *f* of tender wants, „ 319
Uplift a thousand voices *f* and sweet, *Ode Inter. Exhib.* 1
Spread thy *f* wings, and waft him o'er. *In Mem. ix* 4
sigh The *f* new life that feeds thy breath „ *lxxxvi* 10
But when the heart is *f* of din, „ *xciv* 13
And if the song were *f* of care, „ *cxxv* 9
underlip, you may call it a little too ripe, too *f*, *Maud I ii* 9
love of a peace that was *f* of wrongs and shames, „ *III vi* 40
Fixing *f* eyes of question on her face, *Com. of Arthur* 312
gathering half the deep And *f* of voices, „ 381
Albeit neither loved with that *f* love *Gareth and L.* 83
your *f* leave to go. „ 134
When waken'd by the wind which with *f* voice „ 176
This railer, that hath mock'd thee in *f* hall— „ 369
The wood is nigh as *f* of thieves as leaves: „ 789
'*F* pardon, but I follow up the quest, „ 886
the stream, *F*, narrow; „ 908
knave that doth thee service as *f* knight „ 1016
so will my knight-knave Miss the *f* flower „ 1297
Met his *f* frown timidly firm, and said; *Geraint and E.* 71
The whole wood-world is one *f* peal of praise. *Balin and Balan* 450
for this *f* love of mine Without the *f* heart *Merlin and V.* 533
that *f* heart of yours Whereof ye prattle, „ 548
He is so *f* of lustihood, he will ride, *Lancelot and E.* 203
then turn'd the tongueless man From the half-face to the *f* eye, „ 1262
with *f* affection said, 'Lancelot, my Lancelot, „ 1355
let us meet The morrow morn once more in one *f* field *Holy Grail* 323
That kept the entry, and the moon was *f*. „ 818
My tower is *f* of harlots, like his court, *Last Tournament* 81
free chase and heather-scented air, Pulsing *f* man; „ 692
So then, when both were brought to *f* accord, „ 722
crying with *f* voice 'Traitor, come out, *Guinevere* 105
land was *f* of signs And wonders „ 232
for all the land was *f* of life. „ 259
on one Lay a great water, and the moon was *f*. *Pass. of Arthur* 180
when the *f* city peal'd Thee and thy Prince! *To the Queen ii* 26
and tho' I loiter'd there The *f* day after, *Sisters (E. and E.)* 98
Grew after marriage to *f* height and form? „ 171
Love and Honour join'd to raise the *f* High-tide „ 177
Back to that passionate answer of *f* heart „ 259
golden guess Is morning-star to the *f* round of truth. *Columbus* 44
then full-current thro' *f* man: *De Prof., Two G.* 22
Yield thee *f* thanks for thy *f* courtesy *To Victor Hugo* 13
I can hear Too plainly what *f* tides of onset *Tiresias* 91
that *f* light Of friendship! „ 202
One *f* voice of allegiance, *On Jub. Q. Victoria* 22
would flower into *f* health Among our heath *The Ring* 317
Not less would yield *f* thanks to you *To Ulysses* 33
Whose Faith and Work were bells of *f* accord, *In Mem., W. G. Ward* 2
And borne along by that *f* stream of men, *St. Telemachus* 43
Full-accomplished hers by right of *f-a* Fate; *Palace of Art* 207
Full-arm'd *F-a* upon his charger all day *Pelleas and E.* 216
Full-blown sail'd, *F-b*, before us into rooms *Princess i* 229
Full-brain All the *f-b*, half-brain races, *Locksley H., Sixty* 161
Full-breasted *f-b* swan That, fluting a wild carol *M. d'Arthur* 266
f-b swan That, fluting a wild carol *Pass. of Arthur* 434
Full-busted *f-b* figure-head Stared o'er the ripple *Enoch Arden* 543
Full-cell'd A *f-c* honeycomb of eloquence *Edwin Morris* 26
Full-current then *f-c* thro' full man: *De Prof., Two G.* 22
Fuller More life, and *f*, that I want.' *Two Voices* 399
In the Spring a *f* crimson comes upon the robin's breast; *Locksley Hall* 17
A *f* light illumined all, *Day-Dm., Revival* 5
with *f* sound In curves the yellowing river ran, *Sir L. and Q. G.* 14
With *f* profits lead an easier life, *Enoch Arden* 145
and mould The woman to the *f* day.' *Princess iii* 332
So now thy *f* life is in the west, *W. to Marie Alex.* 36
But ring the *f* minstrel in. *In Mem. cvi* 20
For *f* gain of after bliss; „ *cxvii* 4
Till all my blood, a *f* wave, „ *cxxii* 12
they met In twos and threes, or *f* companies, *Marr. of Geraint* 57

Fuller (*continued*) Her *f* franchise—what would that be worth— *The Fleet* 8
Larger and *f*, like the human mind! *Prog. of Spring* 112
When I gits the plaäte *f* o' Soondays *Church-warden, etc.* 40
Fullest his children, ever at its best And *f*; *Lancelot and E.* 337
'Taliessin is our *f* throat of song, *Holy Grail* 300
Full-faced all the *f-f* presence of the Gods *Œnone* 80
F-f above the valley stood the moon; *Lotos-Eaters* 7
glowing *f-f* welcome, she Began to address us, *Princess ii* 183
Full-fair All in a *f-f* manor and a rich, *Gareth and L.* 846
Full-fed a *f-f* river winding slow By herds *Palace of Art* 73
one warm gust, *f-f* with perfume, *Gardener's D.* 113
What dare the *f-f* liars say of me? *Merlin and V.* 692
Full-flowing *f-f* harmony Of thy swan-like stateliness, *Eleänore* 46
f-f river of speech Came down upon my heart. *Œnone* 68
Full-foliaged Rock'd the *f-f* elms, and swung *In Mem. xcv* 58
Full-grown *f-g* will, Circled thro' all experiences, *Œnone* 165
suit The *f-g* energies of heaven. *In Mem. xl* 20
Full-handed your Omar drew *F-h* plaudits from our best *To E. Fitzgerald* 38
F-h thunders often have confessed Thy power, *To W. C. Macready* 2
Full-juiced The *f-j* apple, waxing over-mellow, *Lotos-Eaters, C. S.* 33
Full-limb'd those whom God had made *f-l* and tall, *Guinevere* 42
Full-maned the *f-m* horses whirl'd The chariots backward, *Achilles over the T.* 24
Fullness (*See also* **Fulness**) But by degrees to *f* wrought, *You ask me, why, etc.* 14
part by part to men reveal'd The *f* of her face— *Of old sat Freedom* 12
Full-orb'd to this present My *f-o* love has waned not. *Lover's Tale i* 734
Full-sail'd How may *f-s* verse express, *Eleänore* 44
and seest me drive Thro' utter dark a *f-s* skiff, *Supp. Confessions* 95
Full-summ'd side by side, *f-s* in all their powers, *Princess vii* 288
Full-summer thro' the field, that shone *F-s*, *Lancelot and E.* 1141
Full-tided at Caerleon the *f-t* Usk, *Geraint and E.* 116
Full-toned swells High over the *f-t* sea: *Sea-Fairies* 15
The nightingale, *f-t* in middle May, *Balin and Balan* 213
Full-tuned break its syllables, to keep My own *f-t*,— *Love and Duty* 40
Full-welling *F-w* fountain-heads of change, *Palace of Art* 166
Fulminated *f* Against the scarlet woman *Sea Dreams* 22
Fulmined She *f* out her scorn of laws Salique *Princess ii* 133
Fulness (*See* also **After-fulness**) Have added *f* to the phrase *To Marq. of Dufferin* 11
throng'd my pulses with the *f* of the Spring. *Locksley Hall* 36
The *f* of the pensive mind; *Day-Dm., L'Envoi* 48
Lest of the *f* of my life I leave *Will Water.* 163
the note Had reach'd a thunderous *f*, *Sea Dreams* 214
And weep the *f* from the mind: *In Mem. xx* 6
Fulsome And *f* Pleasure clog him, and drown His heart *Maud I xvi* 4
Affronted with his *f* innocence? *Pelleas and E.* 266
Fulvia You should have clung to *F's* waist, *D. of F. Women* 259
Fume (s) (*See also* **Incense-fume**) For mockery is the *f* of little hearts. *Guinevere* 633
or the *f's* Of that dark opiate dose you gave me, *Romney's R.* 30
Fume (verb) We fret, we *f*, would shift our skins, *Will Water.* 225
Fuming and near me stood, In *f* sulphur blue and green, *Last Tournament* 617
Fun (found) *f* 'um theer a-laäid on 'is faäce *N. Farmer, O. S.* 33
Fur I *f*', when 'er back wur turn'd, *North. Cobbler* 31
Ull be *f*' upo' four short legs *Owd Roä* 16
Then I waäked an' I *f* it was Roäver „ 60
Till I *f* that it warn't not the gaäinist waäy *Church-warden, etc.* 12
I *f* thy pockets as full o' my pippins „ 34
Function plies His *f* of the woodland: *Lucretius* 46
Funeral (adj.) Dark as a *f* scarf from stem to stern, *M. d'Arthur* 194
In sound of *f* or of marriage bells; *Gardener's D.* 36
Dark in its *f* fold. *Ode on Well.* 57
Dark as a *f* scarf from stem to stern, *Pass. of Arthur* 362
tolling of his *f* bell Broke on my Pagan Paradise, *Tiresias* 192
F hearses rolling! *Forlorn* 68
They bore the Cross before you to the chant of *f* hymns. *Happy* 48
And built their shepherd-prince a *f* pile; *Death of Œnone* 63
crying 'Husband!' she leapt upon the *f* pile, „ 105
Find her warrior Stark and dark in his *f* fire. *To Master of B.* 20
Funeral (s) A *f*, with plumes and lights And music, *L. of Shalott ii* 31
the little port Had seldom seen a costlier *f*. *Enoch Arden* 917
Mother weeps At that white *f* of the single life, *Prin. Beatrice* 9

Funeral (s) (*continued*) toll of *f* in an Angel ear Sounds happier — *D. of the Duke of C.* 10
Funereal at one end of the hall Two great *f* curtains, — *Lover's Tale iv* 214
And lay on that *f* boat, — *To Marq. of Dufferin* 34
Fur My father sent ambassadors with *f's* — *Princess i* 42
Furbelow *See* **Sea-furbelow**
Furious nature's prideful sparkle in the blood Break into *f* flame; — *Geraint and E.* 828
As after *f* battle turfs the slain On some wild down — *Merlin and V.* 657
they blurt Their *f* formalisms, — *Akbar's Dream* 57
Furiously *f* Down thro' the bright lawns — *Aylmer's Field* 340
Furl come hither and *f* your sails, — *Sea-Fairies* 16
Mariner, mariner, *f* your sails, — „ 21
Furl'd battle-flags were *f* In the Parliament — *Locksley Hall* 127
And never sail of ours was *f*, — *The Voyage* 81
Furlough To yield us farther *f*:' — *Princess iii* 74
Furnace all the *f* of the light Struck up — *Mariana in the S.* 55
a heat, As from a seventimes-heated *f*, — *Holy Grail* 843
Furnished bravely *f* all abroad to fling — *The Poet* 25
Furnitur O' *f* 'ere i' the 'ouse, — *North. Cobbler* 36
Furr'd (*See also* **Gay-furr'd**) Tho' smock'd, or *f* and purpled, — *Princess iv* 247
Furriner (foreigner) gawin' to let in *f's'* wheät, — *Owd Roä* 45
Furrow to his mother's calls From the flower'd *f*. — *Supp. Confessions* 160
sitting well in order smite The sounding *f's*; — *Ulysses* 59
in the *f* broke the ploughman's head, — *Princess v* 221
reddening in the *f's* of his chin, — „ *vi* 228
meteor on, and leaves A shining *f*, — „ *vii* 185
down in a *f* scathed with flame: — *The Victim* 22
Or in the *f* musing stands; — *In Mem. lxiv* 27
leaving share in *f* come to see The glories — *Gareth and L.* 243
Furrow-cloven huddling slant in *f-c* falls — *Princess vii* 207
Furrowing *f* into light the mounded rack, — *Love and Duty* 100
Came *f* all the orient into gold. — *Princess iii* 18
F a giant oak, and javelining With darted spikes — *Merlin and V.* 936
Furrowy A double hill ran up his *f* forks — *Princess iii* 174
Further We brook no *f* insult but are gone.' — „ *vi* 342
at the *f* end Was Ida by the throne, — „ 356
Not ever to be question'd any more Save on the *f* side; — *Com. of Arthur* 397
and on the *f* side Arose a silk pavilion, — *Gareth and L.* 909
For this were shame to do him *f* wrong — „ 954
Furthest summits slope Beyond the *f* flights of hope, — *Two Voices* 185
From Camelot in among the faded fields To *f* towers; — *Last Tournament* 54
Fury (rage) (*See also* **Fool-fury**) struck such warbling *f* thro' the words; — *Princess iv* 586
Had often wrought some *f* on myself, — *Balin and Balan* 62
'How then? who then? a *f* seized them — *Lancelot and E.* 476
furies, curses, passionate tears, — *Locksley H., Sixty* 39
narrower The cage, the more their *f*. — *Akbar's Dream* 51
rememberest what a *f* shook Those pillars — „ 80
Godless *f* of peoples, and Christless frolic of kings, — *The Dawn* 7
Fury (a deity) Like to *Furies*, like to Graces, — *Vision of Sin* 41
numbs the *F's* ringlet-snake, and plucks — *Lucretius* 262
And Life, a *F* slinging flame. — *In Mem. l* 8
The household *F* sprinkled with blood — *Maud I xix* 32
one angel face, And all the *Furies*. — *Sisters (E. and E.)* 159
Furze (*See* also **Fuzz**) on these dews that drench the *f*, — *In Mem. xi* 6
Furze-cramm'd *F-c*, and bracken-rooft, — *Last Tournament* 377
Furzy The *f* prickle fire the dells, — *Two Voices* 71
Fuse Whose fancy *f's* old and new, — *In Mem. xvi* 18
They *f* themselves to little spicy baths, — *Prog. of Spring* 33
power to *f* My myriads into union under one; — *Akbar's Dream* 156
Fused manhood *f* with female grace — *In Mem. cix* 17
f together in the tyrannous light— — *Lover's Tale ii* 67
Fusileer faces of Havelocks good *f's*, — *Def. of Lucknow* 101
Fusillade better aimed are your flank *f's*— — „ 57
Hark cannonade, *f*! — „ 95
Fusing *f* all The skirts of self again, — *In Mem. xlvii* 2
Of Knowledge *f* class with class, — *Freedom* 17
Fust (first) then I minded the *f* kiss I gied 'er by Thursby thurn; — *North. Cobbler* 45
Futile O life as *f*, then, as frail! — *In Mem. lvi* 25
Future (adj.) transfused Thro' *f* time by power of thought. — *Love thou thy land* 4
I think that we Shall never more, at any *f* time, — *M. d'Arthur* 18
fruit of Love may rest Some happy *f* day. — *Talking Oak* 252
Some *f* time, if so indeed you will, — *Princess ii* 64
Perchance upon the *f* man: — „ *Con.* 109
her *f* Lord Was drown'd in passing thro' the ford, — *In Mem. vi* 38
And leaps into the *f* chance, — „ *cxiv* 7
I think that we Shall never more, at any *f* time, — *Pass. of Arthur* 186
Future (s) When I dipt into the *f*, — *Locksley Hall* 15
For I dipt into the *f*, — „ 119
this he kept Thro' all his *f*; — *Enoch Arden* 237
a wind of prophecy Dilating on the *f*; — *Princess ii* 172
Nemesis Break from a darken'd *f*, — „ *vi* 175
prescient of whate'er The *F* had in store: — *Lover's Tale ii* 133
And past and *f* mix'd in Heaven — *The Ring* 186
and thence maintain Our darker *f*. — *To one ran down Eng.* 2
Far as the *F* vaults her skies, — *Mechanophilus* 17
Futurity the cope Of the half-attain'd *f*, — *Ode to Memory* 33
Fuzz (furze) Nowt at all but bracken an' *f*, — *N. Farmer, O. S.* 38

G

Gaäinist (nearest) I fun' that it warn't not the *g* waäy to the narra Gaäte, — *Church-warden, etc.* 12
Gaäinsaäy (gainsay) I weänt *g* it, my lad, — *North. Cobbler* 17
Gaäpin' (gaping) tha be new to the plaäce—thou'rt *g*— — *Spinster's S's.* 3
Gaäte (gate) why didn't tha hesp the *g*? — *Village Wife* 124
an looök thruf Maddison's *g*! — *Spinster's S's.* 6
I fun that it warn't not the gaäinist waäy to the narra *G*. — *Church-warden, etc.* 12
Gabble Nothing but idiot *g*! — *Maud II v* 41
Gabbled She *g*, as she groped in the dead, — *Dead Prophet* 73
The Baths, the Forum *g* of his death, — *St. Telemachus* 74
Gable and half A score of *g's*. — *Walk. to the Mail* 14
overhead Fantastic *g's*, crowding, — *Godiva* 61
Gable-ends burn'd On the blossom'd *g-e* — *Maud I vi* 9
Gable-wall held the pear to the *g-w*. — *Mariana* 4
Gabriel Whose Titan angels, *G*, Abdiel, — *Milton* 5
Gad-fly sung to, when, this *g-f* brush'd aside, — *Princess v* 414
Gadding Said the good nuns would check her *g* tongue — *Guinevere* 313
Gaffer Ran *G*, stumbled Gammer. — *The Goose* 34
Gag the wholesome boon of gyve and *g*.' — *Gareth and L.* 370
Gagelike flung defiance down *G* to man, — *Princess v* 178
Gaiety *G* without eclipse Wearieth me, — *Lilian* 20
Gain (s) I can but count thee perfect *g*, — *Palace of Art* 198
But gentle words are always *g*: — *Love thou thy land* 23
foreheads, vacant of our glorious *g's*, — *Locksley Hall* 175
his *g's* were dock'd, however small: Small were his *g's*, and hard his work; — *Sea Dreams* 7
His *g* is loss; for he that wrongs his friend — „ 172
Who, never naming God except for *g*, — „ 188
Ours the pain, be his the *g*! — *Ode on Well.* 241
And find in loss a *g* to match? — *In Mem. i* 6
Or but subserves another's *g*. — „ *liv* 12
But turns his burthen into *g*. — „ *lxxx* 12
'My sudden frost was sudden *g*, — „ *lxxxi* 10
For fuller *g* of after bliss: — „ *cxvii* 4
And lust of *g*, in the spirit of Cain, — *Maud I i* 23
all for *g* Of glory, and hath added wound — *Lancelot and E.* 566
allow my pretext, as for *g* Of purer glory.' — „ 586
that make our griefs our *g's*. — *Sisters (E. and E.)* 231
The *g* of such large life as match'd — *Ancient Sage* 237
Gain (verb) And *g* her for my bride. — *Talking Oak* 284
In hope to *g* upon her flight. — *The Voyage* 60
man may *g* Letting his own life go. — *Lucretius* 112
help my prince to *g* His rightful bride, — *Princess iii* 160
And play the slave to *g* the tyranny. — „ *iv* 132
He *g* in sweetness and in moral height, — „ *vii* 281
How *g* in life, as life advances, — *To F. D. Maurice* 39
g The praise that comes to constancy.' — *In Mem. xxi* 11
I will walk thro' fire, Mother, to *g* it— — *Gareth and L.* 134
And glory gain'd, and evermore to *g*. — „ 332

Gain (verb) (*continued*) I vow'd that could I *g* her, our fair Queen, *Marr. of Geraint* 787
she set herself to *g* Him, the most famous man *Merlin and V.* 165
Woo her and *g* her then: no wavering, boy! *Sisters (E. and E.)* 39
or if she *g* her earthly-best, *Locksley H., Sixty* 233
Ere she *g* her Heavenly-best. „ 271
in the North to *g* Her capital city, *The Ring* 481
corpse of every man that *g's* a name; *Romney's R.* 123
As Wisdom hopes to *g*,' *Politics* 4
Gain'd 'Thou hast not *g* a real height, *Two Voices* 91
but even then she *g* Her bower; *Godiva* 76
And *g* a laurel for your brow *You might have won* 3
G for her own a scanty sustenance, *Enoch Arden* 259
Philip *g* As Enoch lost; „ 354
seaward-bound for health they *g* a coast, *Sea Dreams* 16
We *g* the mother-city thick with towers, *Princess i* 112
further on we *g* A little street half garden „ 213
and *g* The terrace ranged along the Northern front, „ *iii* 117
thus much, nor more I *g*.' „ 167
grasping down the boughs I *g* the shore. „ *iv* 189
We cross'd the street and *g* a petty mound „ 557
And on they moved and *g* the hall, „ *vi* 352
In such discourse we *g* the garden rails, „ *Con.* 80
He that *g* a hundred fights, *Ode on Well.* 96
A wretched vote may be *g*. *Maud I vi* 56
And glory *g*, and evermore to gain. *Gareth and L.* 332
Took horse, and forded Usk, and *g* the wood; *Marr. of Geraint* 161
fatal quest Of honour, where no honour can be *g*: *Geraint and E.* 704
leaving Arthur's court he *g* the beach; *Merlin and V.* 197
when they *g* the cell wherein he slept, *Lancelot and E.* 811
Storm at the top, and when we *g* it, *Holy Grail* 491
she *g* her castle, upsprang the bridge, *Pelleas and E.* 206
but turning, past and *g* Tintagil, *Last Tournament* 504
G in the service of His Highness, *Columbus* 236
Step by step we *g* a freedom *Locksley H., Sixty* 129
But when she *g* the broader vale, *Death of Œnone* 91
G their huge Colosseum. *St. Telemachus* 45
Gaining Yet oceans daily *g* on the land, *Golden Year* 29
worship woman as true wife beyond All hopes of *g*, *Merlin and V.* 24
G a lifelong Glory in battle, *Batt. of Brunanburh* 7
a glory slowly *g* on the shade, *Making of Man* 6
Gainsay *See* **Gaäinsaäy**
Galahad (a Knight of the Round Table) Not even Lancelot brave, nor *G* clean. *Merlin and V.* 805
Sir Percivale And pure Sir *G* to uplift the maid; *Lancelot and E.* 1265
ever moved Among us in white armour, *G*. *Holy Grail* 135
made a knight Till *G*; and this *G*, when he heard „ 139
G, when he heard of Merlin's doom, „ 177
G would sit down in Merlin's chair. „ 181
and *G* sware the vow, And good Sir Bors, „ 199
G on the sudden, and in a voice Shrilling „ 288
G, and O *G*, follow me.' 'Ah, *G*, *G*,' „ 292
What are ye? *G's*?—no, nor Percivales' (For thus it pleased the King to range me close After Sir *G*); „ 306
And I myself and *G*, for a strength Was in us „ 333
Shouting, 'Sir *G* and Sir Percivale!' „ 337
not lost thyself to save thyself As *G*.' „ 457
In silver armour suddenly *G* shone Before us, „ 458
I, *G*, saw the Grail, The Holy Grail, „ 464
G fled along them bridge by bridge, „ 504
O brother, saving this Sir *G*, „ 561
after I was join'd with *G* Cared not for her, „ 611
Galaxy Hung in the golden G. *L. of Shalott iii* 12
Gale And merrily, merrily carol the *g's*, *Sea-Fairies* 23
Sweet *g's*, as from deep gardens, blow *Fatima* 24
strong *g's* Hold swollen clouds from raining, *D. of F. Women* 10
last night's *g* had caught, And blown across *Gardener's D.* 124
Caught the shrill salt, and sheer'd the *g*. *The Voyage* 12
And to and thro' the counter *g*? „ 88
Storm'd in orbs of song, a growing *g*; *Vision of Sin* 25
Rough-redden'd with a thousand winter *g's*, *Enoch Arden* 95
drank the *g* That blown about the foliage *Princess iii* 120
Who changest not in any *g*, *In Mem. ii* 10
Caught and cuff'd by the *g*: *Maud I vi* 5
So fierce a *g* made havoc here of late *Holy Grail* 729
Gale (*continued*) this *g* Tore my pavilion from the tenting-pin, *Holy Grail* 746
ever that evening ended a great *g* blew, *The Revenge* 114
Galilæe often mutter low 'Vicisti *G*'; louder again Spurning a shatter'd fragment of the God, 'Vicisti *G*!' *St. Telemachus* 15
Galilee still'd the rolling wave of *G*! *Aylmer's Field* 709
Galingale meadow, set with slender *g*; *Lotos-Eaters* 23
Gall (bitterness) changed a wholesome heart to *g*. *L. C. V. de Vere* 44
That was the last drop in the cup of *g*. *Walk. to the Mail* 69
Unto me my maudlin *g* And my mockeries *Vision of Sin* 201
Gall (oak-gall) insects prick Each leaf into a *g*) *Talking Oak* 70
Gall (verb) Began to *g* the knighthood, asking *Last Tournament* 683
Gallant My woman-soldier, *g* Kate, *Kate* 15
the seamen Made a *g* crew, *G* sons of English freemen, *The Captain* 6
Many a *g* gay domestic Bows before him *L. of Burleigh* 47
So sang the *g* glorious chronicle; *Princess, Pro.* 49
To give three *g* gentlemen to death.' „ *ii* 335
He seems a gracious and a *g* Prince, „ *v* 213
I fenced it round with *g* institutes, „ 392
A *g* fight, a noble princess— „ *Con.* 19
Who pledgest now thy *g* son; *In Mem. vi* 10
A passionate ballad *g* and gay, *Maud I v* 4
The charge of the *g* three hundred, *Heavy Brigade* 1
he waved his blade To the *g* three hundred „ 10
up the hill, Gallopt the *g* three hundred, „ 25
'Lost are the *g* three hundred of Scarlett's Brigade!' „ 45
O great and *g* Scott, *Bandit's Death* 1
'*G* Sir Ralph,' said the king. *The Tourney* 6
Galleon Four *g's* drew away From the Spanish fleet *The Revenge* 46
their high-built *g's* came, „ 58
Galleried a minster there, A *g* palace, *The Ring* 246
Gallery foremost in thy various *g* Place it, *Ode to Memory* 84
By garden-wall and *g*, *L. of Shalott iv* 38
And round the roofs a gilded *g* *Palace of Art* 29
The light aërial *g*, golden-rail'd, „ 47
long-laid *galleries* past a hundred doors *Princess vi* 375
golden hours, In those long *galleries*, *The Daisy* 42
made his feet Wings thro' a glimmering *g*, *Balin and Balan* 404
let his eyes Run thro' the peopled *g* *Lancelot and E.* 430
Rich *galleries*, lady-laden, weigh'd the necks *Holy Grail* 346
He glanced and saw the stately *galleries*, *Last Tournament* 145
Tristram round the *g* made his horse Caracole; „ 205
armed feet Thro' the long *g* from the outer doors *Guinevere* 413
Gallop The trumpet, the *g*, the charge, *Heavy Brigade* 13
Gallopaded willows two and two By rivers *g*. *Amphion* 40
Gallop'd-Gallopt and so *gallop'd* up the knoll. *Marr. of Geraint* 168
as he *gallop'd* up To join them, „ 171
Gallopt the gallant three hundred, *Heavy Brigade* 25
our men *gallopt* up with a cheer and a shout, „ 61
Galloping (*See also* **Heavily-galloping**) *g* hoofs bare on the ridge of spears *Princess v* 489
Gallopt *See* **Gallop'd**
Gama His name was *G*; crack'd and small his voice, „ *i* 114
Then *G* turn'd to me: 'We fear, indeed, „ *v* 120
you spake but sense Said *G*. „ 207
This *G* swamp'd in lazy tolerance. „ 443
can this be he From *G's* dwarfish loins? „ 506
And moved beyond his custom, *G* said: „ *vi* 229
Gambol mother he had never known, In *g's*; *Aylmer's Field* 691
For these your dainty *g's*: wherefore ask; *Merlin and V.* 309
Nor ever let you *g* in her sight, *The Ring* 387
Gamboll'd-Gambol'd when she *gamboll'd* on the greens *Talking Oak* 77
We *gambol'd*, making vain pretence Of gladness, *In Mem. xxx* 6
Glanced at the doors or *gambol'd* down the walks; *Marr. of Geraint* 665
And a hundred *gamboll'd* and pranced on the wrecks *V. of Maeldune* 102
Gambolling Down shower the *g* waterfalls *Sea-Fairies* 10
Game (thing hunted) Stoops at all *g* that wing the skies, *Rosalind* 4
Whither fly ye, what *g* spy ye, „ 8
touch'd upon the *g*, how scarce it was *Audley Court* 32
Man is the hunter; woman is his *g*: *Princess v* 154
He bore but little *g* in hand; *The Victim* 42
No, there is fatter *g* on the moor; *Maud I i* 74
Royaller *g* is mine. *Merlin and V.* 108

Game (pastime) The *g* of forfeits done— *The Epic* 2
dwindled down to some odd *g's* In some odd nooks „ 8
She remember'd that: A pleasant *g*, *Princess, Pro.* 194
Quoit, tennis, ball—no *g's*? „ *iii* 215
At civil revel and pomp and *g*, (repeat) *Ode on Well.* 147, 227
In dance and song and *g* and jest? *In Mem. xxix* 8
Again our ancient *g's* had place, „ *lxxviii* 10
Poor rivals in a losing *g*, „ *cii* 19
Be neither song, nor *g*, nor feast; „ *cv* 21
moved by an unseen hand at a *g* That pushes *Maud I iv* 26
And play the *g* of the despot kings, „ *x* 39
once again the sickening *g*; *Locksley H., Sixty* 127
God must mingle with the *g*: „ 271
Romans brawling of their monstrous *g's*; *St. Telemachus* 40
Gamesome 'Then ran she, *g* as the colt, *Talking Oak* 121
Gammer Ran Gaffer, stumbled *G.* *The Goose* 34
Gamut their shrieks Ran highest up the *g*, *Sea Dreams* 233
Ganymede flush'd *G*, his rosy thigh Half-buried *Palace of Art* 121
I think he came like *G*, *Will Water.* 119
'They mounted, *G's*, To tumble, Vulcans, *Princess iii* 71
Gap from the *g's* and chasms of ruin left *Sea Dreams* 225
fill up the *g* where force might fail *Gareth and L.* 1352
thro' the *g* Glimmer'd the streaming scud: *Holy Grail* 681
thro' the *g* The seven clear stars of Arthur's Table Round— „ 683
new knights to fill the *g* Left by the Holy Quest; *Pelleas and E.* 1
In this *g* between the sandhills, *Locksley H., Sixty* 176
Fought for their lives in the narrow *g* they had made— *Heavy Brigade* 23
Gape A gulf that ever shuts and *g's*, *In Mem. lxx* 6
too high For any mouth to *g* for save a queen's— *Lancelot and E.* 775
g for flies—we know not whence they come; *Holy Grail* 147
Gaped Lavaine *g* upon him As on a thing miraculous, *Lancelot and E.* 452
tier over tier, Were added mouths that *g*, „ 1249
Gaping (*See also* **Gaäpin'**) The passive oxen *g*. *Amphion* 72
fool, Who was *g* and grinning by: *Maud II i* 20
Gap-mouth'd All in a *g-m* circle his good mates *Gareth and L.* 511
Gapp'd their masses are *g* with our grape— *Def. of Lucknow* 42
Gap-tooth'd A gray and *g-t* man as lean as death, *Vision of Sin* 60
Garbaging and Gave to the *g* war-hawk to gorge it, *Batt. of Brunanburh* 109
Garb'd richly *g*, but worn From wasteful living, *Ancient Sage* 4
Garda Lake Gazing at the Lydian laughter of the *G L* below *Frater Ave, etc.* 3
Garden (adj.) By *g* porches on the brim, *Arabian Nights* 16
whose root Creeps to the *g* water-pipes beneath, *D. of F. Women* 206
black-hearts ripen dark, All thine, against the *g* wall. *Blackbird* 8
There sat we down upon a *g* mound, *Gardener's D.* 214
fountain to his place returns Deep in the *g* lake withdrawn. *Day-Dm., Sleep P.* 12
Some figure like a wizard pentagram On *g* gravel, *The Brook* 104
all within The sward was trim as any *g* lawn: *Princess, Pro.* 95
found at length The *g* portals. „ *iv* 200
To take their leave, about the *g* rails, „ *Con.* 38
In such discourse we gain'd the *g* rails. „ 80
all by myself in my own dark *g* ground, *Maud I iii* 10
Seem'd her light foot along the *g* walk, „ *xviii* 9
And long by the *g* lake I stood, „ *xxii* 35
'this *g* rose Deep-hued and many-folded! *Balin and Balan* 269
And oft they met among the *g* yews, *Lancelot and E.* 645
one morn it chanced He found her in among the *g* yews, „ 923
Garden (s) (*See also* **Hall-garden, Olive-gardens, Rose-garden**) High-wall'd *g's* green and old; *Arabian Nights* 8
Thence thro' the *g* I was drawn— „ 100
When rooted in the *g* of the mind, *Ode to Memory* 26
a *g* bower'd close With plaited alleys „ 105
the world Like one great *g* show'd, *The Poet* 34
In the heart of the *g* the merry bird chants. *Poet's Mind* 22
whitest honey in fairy *g's* cull'd— *Eleänore* 26
Sweet gales, as from deep *g's*, blow *Fatima* 24
A spacious *g* full of flowering weeds, *To —— With Pal. of Art* 4
Walking about the *g's* and the halls Of Camelot, *M. d'Arthur* 20
blooms the *g* that I love. *Gardener's D.* 34
between it and the *g* lies A League of grass, „ 39

Garden (s) (*continued*) The *g* stretches southward. *Gardener's D.* 115
One after one, thro' that still *g* pass'd; „ 201
And cross'd the *g* to the gardener's lodge, *Audley Court* 17
A breeze thro' all the *g* swept, *Day-Dm., Revival* 6
A *g* too with scarce a tree, *Amphion* 3
at the end of all A little *g* blossom. „ 104
Parks and order'd *g's* great, *L. of Burleigh* 30
Flourished a little *g* square and wall'd: *Enoch Arden* 734
arranged Her *g*, sow'd her name and kept it green *Aylmer's Field* 88
Which fann'd the *g's* of that rival rose „ 455
Kept to the *g* now, and grove of pines, „ 550
that in the *g* snared Picus and Faunus, *Lucretius* 181
A little street half *g* and half house; *Princess i* 214
grace Concluded, and we sought the *g's*: „ *ii* 453
Above the *g's* glowing blossom-belts, „ *v* 363
'Look there, a *g*!' said my college friend, „ *Con.* 49
All round a careless-order'd *g* *To F. D. Maurice* 15
'All among the *g's*, auriculas, anemones, *City Child* 4
So that still *g* of the souls *In Mem. xliii* 10
The gust that round the *g* flew, „ *lxxxix* 19
Till from the *g* and the wild „ *ci* 17
like the sultan of old in a *g* of spice. *Maud I iv* 42
Maud has a *g* of roses And lilies „ *xiv* 1
great Forefathers of the thornless *g*, „ *xviii* 27
Come into the *g*, Maud, (repeat) „ *xxii* 1, 3
Queen rose of the rosebud *g* of girls, „ 53
g by the turrets Of the old manorial hall. „ *II iv* 79
But I know where a *g* grows, „ *v* 72
And wallow'd in the *g's* of the King. *Com. of Arthur* 25
But this was in the *g* of a king; *Marr. of Geraint* 656
Sir Balin sat Close-bower'd in that *g* *Balin and Balan* 241
a slope of *g*, all Of roses white and red, *Pelleas and E.* 421
Walking about the *g's* and the halls of Camelot, *Pass. of Arthur* 188
as tho' A man in some still *g* should infuse *Lover's Tale i* 269
the daily want Of Edith in the house, the *g*, *Sisters (E. and E.)* 246
Down we look'd: what a *g*! *V. of Maeldune* 78
Wi' my oän little *g* outside, *Spinster's S's.* 104
Every grim ravine a *g*, *Locksley H., Sixty* 168
I found her not in house Or *g*— *The Ring* 445
from every vale and plain And *g* pass, *To Mary Boyle* 10
Across my *g*! and the thicket stirs, *Prog. of Spring* 53
under the Crosses The dead man's *g*, *Merlin and the G.* 106
like a lonely man In the king's *g*, *Akbar's Dream* 21
I cotch'd tha wonst i' my *g*, *Church-warden, etc.* 33
Garden (verb) I shall never *g* more: *May Queen, N. Y's. E.* 46
Garden-bower Black the *g-b's* and grots *Arabian Nights* 78
To and fro they went Thro' my *g-b*, *The Flower* 6
Gardener The *g* Adam and his wife *L. C. V. de Vere* 51
I and Eustace from the city went To see the *G's* Daughter; *Gardener's D.* 3
'Go and see The *G's* daughter: „ 30
not heard Of Rose, the *G's* daughter? „ 52
And cross'd the garden to the *g's* lodge, *Audley Court* 17
charge the *g's* now To pick the faded creature *Marr. of Geraint* 670
And made a *G* putting in a graff, *Merlin and V.* 479
g's hand Picks from the colewort a green caterpillar, *Guinevere* 31
Garden-gate And push'd at Philip's *g-g*. *The Brook* 83
And stood by her *g-g*; *Maud I xiv* 6
looks Upon Maud's own *g-g*: „ 16
Garden-glass The *g-g'es* glanced, and momently *Gardener's D.* 117
Garden-herbs Gifts by the children, *g-h* and fruit, *Enoch Arden* 338
Gardening Botanic Treatises, And Works on *G* *Amphion* 78
Garden-isles meadowy holms And alders, *g-i*; *Edwin Morris* 96
Garden-lawn By grove and *g-l*, and rushing brook, *Holy Grail* 230
Garden-rose outredden All voluptuous *g-r's*. *Ode on Well.* 208
This *g-r* that I found, *Maud I xxi* 3
Garden-square And in the sultry *g-s's*, *The Blackbird* 17
Garden-squirt Half-conscious of the *g-s*, *Amphion* 91
Garden-tools find my *g-t* upon the granary floor: *May Queen, N. Y's. E.* 45
Garden-tree Beneath your sheltering *g-t*, *To E. Fitzgerald* 6
Garden-walks As down the *g-w* I move, *In Mem. cii* 6
Garden-wall By *g-w* and gallery, *L. of Shalott iv* 38
And feeling all along the *g-w*, *Enoch Arden* 773
this side the palace ran the field Flat to the *g-w*: *Princess v* 362

Garden-wall (*continued*) Climb'd to the high top of the *g-w* — *Guinevere* 25

Gareth (a knight of the Round Table) *G*, in a showerful spring Stared at the spate. — *Gareth and L.* 2
'How he went down,' said *G*, 'as a false knight ,, 5
And *G* went, and hovering round her chair ,, 33
G answer'd her with kindling eyes, (repeat) ,, 41, 62
G, 'An ye hold me yet for child, ,, 99
G answer'd quickly, 'Not an hour, ,, 132
G cried, 'A hard one, or a hundred, ,, 149
G was too princely-proud To pass thereby; ,, 161
Silent awhile was *G*, then replied, ,, 164
G awhile linger'd. ,, 172
Then those who went with *G* were amazed, ,, 197
G answer'd them With laughter, ,, 208
those with *G* for so long a space Stared at the figures, ,, 231
they call'd To *G*, 'Lord, the gateway is alive.' And *G* likewise on them fixt his eyes So long, ,, 235
Then *G*, 'We be tillers of the soil, ,, 242
G spake Anger'd, 'Old Master, ,, 279
Whom *G* looking after said, 'My men, ,, 296
and the sound was good to *G's* ear. ,, 312
Then into hall *G* ascending heard A voice, ,, 317
G saw The shield of Gawain blazon'd rich and bright, ,, 415
G leaning both hands heavily Down on the shoulders ,, 439
So *G* all for glory underwent The sooty yoke ,, 478
G bow'd himself With all obedience to the King, ,, 487
G was glad. (repeat) ,, 497, 504
G telling some prodigious tale Of knights, ,, 508
This, *G* hearing from a squire of Lot ,, 531
Shame never made girl redder than *G* joy. ,, 536
G, lightly springing from his knees, ,, 556
G ask'd, 'Have I not earn'd my cake in baking of it? ,, 574
with a kindly hand on *G's* arm Smiled the great King, ,, 578
Arthur mindful of Sir *G* ask'd, ,, 624
Sir *G* call'd from where he rose, ,, 645
on to this Sir *G* strode, and saw without the door ,, 676
Sir *G* loosed A cloak that dropt from collar-bone ,, 681
So *G* ere he parted flash'd in arms. ,, 689
thro' lanes of shouting *G* rode Down the slope street, ,, 699
So *G* past with joy; but as the cur Pluckt ,, 701
Mutter'd in scorn of *G* whom he used To harry ,, 706
To whom Sir *G* drew (And there were none ,, 743
G to him, 'Master no more! too well I know thee, ,, 755
G cried again, 'Lead, and I follow,' ,, 759
'Damsel,' Sir *G* answer'd gently, ,, 772
I shall assay,' said *G* with a smile. That madden'd her, ,, 783
And *G* following was again beknaved. ,, 786
G, 'Bound am I to right the wrong'd, ,, 804
'Lead, and I follow,' *G* cried again, ,, 807
G loosed the stone From off his neck, ,, 814
G loosed his bonds and on free feet Set him, ,, 817
G sharply spake, 'None! ,, 831
and the Baron set *G* beside her, ,, 852
seating *G* at another board, Sat down beside him, ,, 871
G said, 'Full pardon, but I follow up the quest, ,, 885
Sir *G* spake, 'Lead, and I follow.' ,, 890
To whom Sir *G* answer'd courteously, ,, 900
G silent gazed upon the knight, ,, 933
Said *G*, 'Damsel, whether knave or knight, ,, 943
G lash'd so fiercely with his brand ,, 968
Till *G's* shield was cloven: ,, 971
G, 'So this damsel ask it of me Good— ,, 974
G there unlaced His helmet as to slay him, ,, 978
Sir *G* answer'd, laughingly, 'Parables? ,, 1007
G's eyes had flying blots Before them ,, 1031
Whom *G* met midstream: ,, 1041
Then *G* laid his lance athwart the ford; ,, 1048
and *G* sent him to the King. ,, 1051
G, 'Wherefore waits the madman there ,, 1091
Said *G*, 'Old, and over-bold in brag! ,, 1107
And *G* overthrew him, lighted, drew, ,, 1121
G brought him grovelling on his knees, ,, 1124
Till *G* panted hard, and his great heart, ,, 1126
so *G* seem'd to strike Vainly, ,, 1133

Gareth (*continued*) And *G* hearing ever stronglier smote, — *Gareth and L.* 1141
Sir *G's* brand Clash'd his, and brake it utterly ,, 1147
G lookt and read—In letters like to those ,, 1201
star Gleam, on Sir *G's* turning to him, ,, 1219
G crying prick'd against the cry; ,, 1221
Lancelot answer'd, 'Prince, O *G*— ,, 1237
Then *G*, 'Thou—Lancelot!—thine the hand That threw me? ,, 1241
'Blessed be thou, Sir *G*! knight art thou ,, 1258
turning to Lynette he told The tale of *G*, ,, 1273
Sir *G* drank and ate, and all his life Past into sleep; ,, 1280
Let *G*, an he will, Change his for mine, ,, 1299
G, wakening, fiercely clutch'd the shield; ,, 1304
allured The glance of *G* dreaming on his liege. ,, 1316
'Lo,' said *G*, 'the foe falls!' ,, 1317
Said *G* laughing, 'An he fight for this, ,, 1345
Then *G*, 'Here he rules. I know but one— ,, 1354
which Sir *G* graspt, And so, before the two could hinder him, ,, 1367
But *G* spake and all indignantly, ,, 1386
Sir *G's* head prickled beneath his helm; ,, 1397
with one stroke Sir *G* split the skull. ,, 1404
Answer'd Sir *G* graciously to one Not many a moon his younger, ,, 1414
So large mirth lived and *G* won the quest. ,, 1426
tale in older times Says that Sir *G* wedded Lyonors, ,, 1428
Tristram, and Geraint And *G*, a good knight, — *Lancelot and E.* 557

Gargarus topmost *G* Stands up and takes the morning: — *Œnone* 10

Garland The *g* of new-wreathed emprise: — *Kate* 24
Do make a *g* for the heart: — *Miller's D.* 198
knots of flowers, and buds and *g's* gay, — *May Queen* 11
spears That soon should wear the *g*; — *Aylmer's Field* 112
made *g's* of the selfsame flower, — *Lover's Tale i* 343
a light Burst from the *g* I had wov'n, ,, 366
Wreathed round the bier with *g's*: ,, *ii* 79
Great *g's* swung and blossom'd; ,, *iv* 191
I, wearing but the *g* of a day, — *To Dante* 6
The bridal *g* falls upon the bier, — *D. of the Duke of C.* 1

Garlandage leaf, and gayest *g* of flowers, — *Balin and Balan* 83

Garlanded Each *g* with her peculiar flower — *Gardener's D.* 202

Garlanding *g* the gnarled boughs With bunch — *Œnone* 101

Garlon (a Knight of the Round Table) *G*, mine heir, Of him demand it,' which this *G* gave With much ado, — *Balin and Balan* 117
more than one of us Cried out on *G*, ,, 123
Sir *G* too Hath learn'd black magic, ,, 304
Till when at feast Sir *G* likewise ask'd ,, 347
Made *G*, hissing; then he sourly smiled. ,, 355
Then fiercely to Sir *G*, 'Eyes have I That saw to-day ,, 372
The scorn of *G*, poisoning all his rest, ,, 383
Sir *G* utter'd mocking-wise; ,, 389
Then *G*, reeling slowly backward, fell, ,, 397
This *G* mock'd me, but I heeded not. ,, 606
And sought for *G* at the castle-gates, ,, 610

Garment eddying of her *g's* caught from thee — *Ode to Memory* 31
The woman's *g* hid the woman's heart.' — *Princess v* 305
Fair *g's*, plain or rich, — *Akbar's Dream* 131

Garner The wrath that *g's* in my heart; — *In Mem. lxxxii* 14
And *g* all you may! — *Mechanophilus* 32

Garner'd (adj.) time is scarce more brief Than of the *g* Autumn-sheaf. — *Two Voices* 114
Or little pitted speck in *g* fruit, — *Merlin and V.* 394
and bless Their *g* Autumn also, — *Demeter and P.* 147

Garner'd (verb) long ago they had glean'd and *g* — *Lover's Tale i* 128

Garnet Each like a *g* or a turkis in it; — *Marr. of Geraint* 661

Garnet-headed hear the *g-h* yaffingale Mock them: — *Last Tournament* 700

Garnish flowers, except, belike, To *g* meats with? — *Gareth and L.* 1070

Garrick *G* and statelier Kemble, — *To W. C. Macready* 7

Garrison as if hope for the *g* hung but on him; — *Def. of Lucknow* 48
on a sudden the *g* utter a jubilant shout, ,, 98

Garrulity Shame on her own *g* garrulously, — *Guinevere* 312

Garrulous Miriam Lane was good and *g*, — *Enoch Arden* 700
G under a roof of pine: — *To F. D. Maurice* 20
With *g* ease and oily courtesies — *Princess i* 164

Gather'd (*continued*) Grave faces *g* in a ring.] *Day-Dm., Sleep P.* 38
Till they be *g* up; *Will Water.* 170
topmost elm-tree *g* green From draughts *Sir L. and Q. G.* 8
there again When burr and bine were *g*; *Aylmer's Field* 113
G the blossom that rebloom'd, „ 142
Easily *g* either guilt. *Princess iv* 236
rose A hubbub in the court of half the maids *G* together: „ 477
the heavy dews *G* by night and peace, „ *v* 244
But such as *g* colour day by day. „ *vii* 118
Abide: thy wealth is *g* in, *In Mem. lii* 15
He fought his doubts and *g* strength, „ *xcvi* 13
The maidens *g* strength and grace „ *ciii* 27
He has *g* the bones for his o'ergrown whelp *Maud II v* 55
this she *g* from the people's eyes: *Marr. of Geraint* 61
g trickling dropwise from the cleft, *Merlin and V.* 274
I stoop'd, I *g* the wild herbs, *Lover's Tale i* 342
I have *g* my baby together— *Rizpah* 20
But I *g* my fellows together, *V. of Maeldune* 2
I would that I were *g* to my rest, *Tiresias* 170
Thousands of horsemen had *g* there *Heavy Brigade* 14
The vast sun-clusters' *g* blaze, *Epilogue* 54
Gathering (adj. and part.) the mighty moon was *g* light *Love and Death* 1
Proserpine in Enna, *g* flowers: *Edwin Morris* 112
G up from all the lower ground; *Vision of Sin* 15
And *g* all the fruits of earth *Ode Inter. Exhib.* 41
And *g* freshlier overhead, *In Mem. xcv* 57
G woodland lilies, Myriads blow together. *Maud I xii* 7
By shores that darken with the *g* wolf, *Aylmer's Field* 767
So much the *g* darkness charm'd: *Princess, Con.* 107
tho' the *g* enemy narrow thee, *Boädicea* 39
g half the deep And full of voices, *Com. of Arthur* 380
Vivien, *g* somewhat of his mood, *Merlin and V.* 842
but *g* at the base Re-makes itself, and flashes *Guinevere* 609
And *g* ruthless gold— *Columbus* 135
g here and there From each fair plant *Akbar's Dream* 21
Gathering (s) A *g* of the Tory, *Maud I xx* 33
Gaud those gilt *g's* men-children swarm to see. *To W. C. Macready* 11
Gaudy Showing a *g* summer-morn, *Palace of Art* 62
Gaudy-day Amends hereafter by some *g-d*, *Marr. of Geraint* 818
Gaunt Lancelot? goodly—ay, but *g*: *Merlin and V.* 103
G as it were the skeleton of himself, (repeat) *Lancelot and E.* 764, 816
(The *g* old Baron with his beetle brow *Princess ii* 240
Gauntlet maiden fancies dead In iron *g's*: „ *i* 89
added fullness to the phrase Of '*G* in the velvet glove.' *To Marq. of Dufferin* 12
Gauntleted my hand Was *g*, half slew him; *Balin and Balan* 57
His passion half had *g* to death, „ 220
Gauntness Courteous—amends for *g*— *Merlin and V.* 104
Gauze 'He dried his wings: like *g* they grew; *Two Voices* 13
Purple *g's*, golden hazes, liquid mazes, *Vision of Sin* 31
Half-lapt in glowing *g* and golden brede, *Princess vi* 134
an Eastern *g* With seeds of gold— *Lover's Tale iv* 291
Gave (*See also* **Gied, Giv**) *God g her peace; her land reposed;* *To the Queen* 26
And *g* you on your natal day. *Margaret* 42
Our thought *g* answer each to each, *Sonnet To* —— 10
'She *g* him mind, the lordliest Proportion, *Two Voices* 19
sing the foolish song I *g* you, Alice, *Miller's D.* 162
thought of that sharp look, mother, I *g* him yesterday, *May Queen* 15
flower and fruit, whereof they *g* To each, *Lotos-Eaters* 29
my bliss of life, that Nature *g*, *D. of F. Women* 210
because the kiss he *g* me, ere I fell, „ 235
He *g* me a friend, and a true true-love, *D. of the O. Year* 13
'Hast thou perform'd my mission which I *g*? *M. d'Arthur* 67
This, yielding, *g* into a grassy walk *Gardener's D.* 111
Kissing the rose she *g* me o'er and o'er, „ 176
G utterance by the yearning of an eye, *Love and Duty* 62
The trance *g* way To those caresses, „ 65
And *g* my letters back to me. And *g* the trinkets and the rings, *The Letters* 20
He *g* the people of his best: His worst he kept, his best he *g*. *You might have won* 25
from her baby's forehead clipt A tiny curl, and *g* it: *Enoch Arden* 236
less Than what she *g* in buying what she sold: „ 256
At Annie's door he paused and *g* his hand, „ 447

Gave (*continued*) clothes they *g* him and free passage *Enoch Arden* 650
Pitying the lonely man, and *g* him it: „ 664
the woman *g* A half-incredulous, half-hysterical cry. „ 852
This hair is his: she cut it off and *g* it, „ 894
He *g* them line: (repeat) *The Brook* 145, 150
scared with threats of jail and halter *g* *Aylmer's Field* 520
the dagger which himself *G* Edith, „ 597
g the verse 'Behold, Your house is left unto you desolate!' „ 628
G his broad lawns until the set of sun *Princess, Pro.* 2
they *g* The park, the crowd, the house; „ 93
I said no, Yet being an easy man, *g* it: „ *i* 149
we *g* a costly bribe To guerdon silence, „ 203
rooms which *g* Upon a pillar'd porch, „ 229
I *g* the letter to be sent with dawn; „ 245
a glance I *g*, No more; „ *iv* 180
On one knee Kneeling, I *g* it, „ 470
Who *g* me back my child?' „ *v* 105
Let so much out as *g* us leave to go. „ 235
for everything *G* way before him: „ 530
Was it for this we *g* our palace up, „ *vi* 244
Refuse her proffer, lastly *g* his hand. „ 347
to them the doors *g* way Groaning, „ 349
pray'd the men, the women: I *g* assent: „ *Con.* 7
English Harold *g* its throne a wife, *W. to Marie Alex.* 24
and he *g* the ringers a crown. *Grandmother* 58
I pluck'd a daisy, I *g* it you. *The Daisy* 88
Hexameters no worse than daring Germany *g* us, *Trans. of Homer* 5
The Danube to the Severn *g* *In Mem. xix* 1
And *g* all ripeness to the grain, „ *lxxxi* 11
Received and *g* him welcome there; „ *lxxxv* 24
With him to whom her hand I *g*. „ *Con.* 70
He fiercely *g* me the lie, *Maud II i* 16
By the home that *g* me birth, „ *iv* 7
Merlin took the child, And *g* him to Sir Anton, *Com. of Arthur* 222
She *g* the King his huge cross-hilted sword, „ 286
Arthur *g* him back his territory, *Gareth and L.* 78
Of whom ye *g* me to, the Seneschal, „ 559
that *g* upon a range Of level pavement „ 666
blue arms, and *g* a shield Blue also, „ 931
and thee the King *G* me to guard, „ 1014
g a shield whereon the Star of Even „ 1117
good king *g* order to let blow His horns *Marr. of Geraint* 152
g command that all which once was ours „ 696
he but *g* a wrathful groan, Saying, *Geraint and E.* 398
cousin, slay not him who *g* you life.' „ 783
I rode all-shamed, hating the life He *g* me, „ 853
which this Garlon *g* With much ado, *Balin and Balan* 118
best Of ladies living *g* me this to bear.' „ 340
one that hath defamed The cognizance she *g* me: „ 485
knew no more, nor *g* me one poor word; *Merlin and V.* 277
Use *g* me Fame at first, and Fame again Increasing *g* me use. „ 493
His brother's; which he *g* to Lancelot, *Lancelot and E.* 380
Sir Lancelot *g* A marvellous great shriek „ 515
he took, And *g*, the diamond: „ 551
he *g*, And slightly kiss'd the hand to which he *g*, „ 701
I *g* the diamond: she will render it; „ 713
Stript off the case, and *g* the naked shield; „ 979
Then *g* a languid hand to each, and lay, „ 1032
I *g* No cause, not willingly, for such a love: „ 1297
G him an isle of marsh whereon to build; *Holy Grail* 62
to prayer and praise She *g* herself, „ 77
And *g* herself and all her wealth to me. „ 597
in my madness I essay'd the door; It *g*; „ 842
Then *g* it to his Queen to rear: *Last Tournament* 22
Tristram won, and Lancelot *g*, the gems, „ 190
and Innocence the King *G* for a prize— „ 295
this I *g* thee, look, Is all as cool and white „ 415
he *g* them charge about the Queen, *Guinevere* 591
'Hast thou perform'd my mission which I *g*? *Pass. of Arthur* 235
So Death *g* back, and would no further come. *Lover's Tale i* 115
He that *g* Her life, to me delightedly fulfill'd „ 223
Then playfully she *g* herself the lie— „ 349
'Kiss him,' she said. 'You *g* me life again. „ *iv* 172

Gave (*continued*) (Meaning the print that you g us, *In the Child. Hosp.* 51
chains For him who g a new heaven, *Columbus* 20
G glory and more empire to the kings „ 22
g All but free leave for all to work „ 132
G to the garbaging war-hawk to gorge it, *Batt. of Brunanburh* 109
sweet mother land which g them birth *Tiresias* 122
He that they g me to, mother, *The Wreck* 13
I refused the hand he g. *Locksley H., Sixty* 256
and g Thy breast to ailing infants *Demeter and P.* 55
g it me, who pass'd it down her own, *The Ring* 270
pardon, O my love, if I ever g you pain. *Happy* 68
fumes Of that dark opiate dose you g me, *Romney's R.* 31
I sent him back what he g,— *Charity* 19

Gaw (go) 'I mun g up ageän fur Roä.' 'G up ageän fur the varmint?' *Owd Roä* 97

Gawain (a knight of the Round Table) G and young Modred, her two sons, *Com. of Arthur* 244
G went, and breaking into song Sprang out, „ 320
G, when he came With Modred hither *Gareth and L.* 25
all in fear to find Sir G, or Sir Modred, „ 326
The shield of G blazon'd rich and bright, „ 416
'I have stagger'd thy strong G in a tilt „ 542
rise, O G, and ride forth and find the knight. *Lancelot and E.* 537
G, surnamed The Courteous, fair and strong, „ 555
G the while thro' all the region round „ 615
G saw Sir Lancelot's azure lions, „ 662
if I dream'd,' said G, 'that you love This greatest knight, „ 638
But there the fine G will wonder at me, „ 1054
G, who bad a thousand farewells to me, „ 1056
Then came the fine G and wonder'd at her, „ 1267
G sware, and louder then the rest.' *Holy Grail* 202
sharply turning, ask'd Of G, 'G, was this Quest for thee?' 'Nay, Lord,' said G, 'not for such as I. „ 740
left The hall long silent, till Sir G— „ 854
'Hath G fail'd in any quest of thine? „ 859
'G, and blinder unto holy things „ 870
Three against one: and G passing by, *Pelleas and E.* 274
G, looking at the villainy done, Forebore, „ 282
Forth sprang G, and loosed him from his bonds, „ 315
G answer'd kindly tho' in scorn, „ 333
and took G's, and said, 'Betray me not, „ 360
'Ay,' said G, 'for women be so light.' „ 362
But G lifting up his vizor said, 'G am I, G of Arthur's court, „ 370
G, G of the Court, Sir G— „ 379
straight on thro' open door Rode G, „ 383
'Ay,' thought G, 'and you be fair enow: „ 388
but a sound Of G ever coming, and this lay— „ 396
'Why lingers G with his golden news?' „ 411
Bound on her brow, were G and Ettarre. „ 435
turn'd herself To G: 'Liar, for thou hast not slain „ 490
that G fired The hall of Merlin, „ 517
shouting, 'False, And false with G!' „ 546
DAGONET, the fool, whom G in his mood *Last Tournament* 1
G kill'd In Lancelot's war, the ghost of G blown Along a wandering wind, *Pass. of Arthur* 30
Thine, G, was the voice— „ 47
Light was G in life, and light in death Is G, „ 56

Gawin' (going) g to let in furriners' wheät, *Owd Roä* 45
I wur g that waäy to the bad, „ 71

Gay you were g With bridal flowers— *Miller's D.* 164
Or g, or grave, or sweet, or stern, *Palace of Art* 91
many songs, But never a one so g, *Poet's Song* 14
statue propt against the wall, As g as any. *Princess, Pro.* 100
My g young hawk, my Rosalind: *Rosalind* 34
and buds and garlands g, *May Queen* 11
Or g quinquenniads would we reap *Day-Dm., L'Envoi* 23
'And, leg and arm with love-knots g, *Talking Oak* 65
With many kinsmen g, *Will Water.* 90
Many a gallant g domestic Bows before him *L. of Burleigh* 47
I fear'd Lest the g navy there should splinter on it, *Sea Dreams* 131
silk pavilion, g with gold In streaks and rays, *Gareth and L.* 910
The g pavilion and the naked feet, „ 937
Prophet of the g time, *The Snowdrop* 6
remembering the g playmate rear'd Among them, *Death of Œnone* 59

Gay (*continued*) one is glad; her note is g, *In Mem. xxi* 25
fancies play To find me g among the g, „ *lxvi* 3
all is g with lamps, and loud With sport „ *xcviii* 27
Like things of the season g, *Maud I iv* 3
if I cannot be g let a passionless peace „ 50
A passionate ballad gallant and g, „ *v* 4
Strange, that I felt so g, „ *xx* 1
one With whom she has heart to be g. „ *xxii* 20
I see her Weeping for some g knight in Arthur's hall.' *Marr. of Geraint* 118
And seeing one so g in purple silks, „ 284
like a crag was g with wilding flowers: „ 319
these to her own faded self And the g court, „ 653
Clothed with my gift, and g among the g.' „ 753
that good mother, making Enid g In such apparel „ 757
And all that week was old Caerleon g, „ 837
The three g suits of armour which they wore, *Geraint and E.* 95
drew from those dead wolves Their three g suits of armour, „ 181
How g, how suited to the house of one „ 683
and damsel glitter'd at the feast Variously g: *Last Tournament* 225
Thy g lent-lilies wave and put them by, *Prog. of Spring* 37
Bountiful, beautiful, apparell'd g, „ 62

Gayer But once were g than a dawning sky *Death of Œnone* 12
In colours g than the morning mist, *Princess ii* 438
My fate or folly, passing g youth For one so old, *Merlin and V.* 927
pale blood of the wizard at her touch Took g colours, „ 950
Evelyn is g, wittier, prettier, *Sisters (E. and E.)* 36

Gayest wealth Of leaf, and g garlandage of flowers, *Balin and Balan* 83

Gay-furr'd Her g-f cats a painted fantasy, *Princess iii* 186

Gaze (s) Than that earth should stand at g *Locksley Hall* 180
her ardent g Roves from the living brother's face, *In Mem. xxxii* 6
her hue Changed at his g: *Balin and Balan* 279
And were only standing at g, *Heavy Brigade* 37
The linnet's bosom blushes at her g, *Prog. of Spring* 17

Gaze (verb) Ever retiring thou dost g *Ode to Memory* 93
Ev'n while we g on it, *Eleänore* 90
g upon My palace with unblinded eyes, *Palace of Art* 41
He g's on the silent dead: *Day-Dm., Arrival* 13
Evermore she seems to g *L. of Burleigh* 34
orb That fain would g upon him to the last; *Lucretius* 140
climbs a peak to g O'er land and main, *Princess vii* 35
I, who g with temperate eyes *In Mem. cxii* 2
bear some token of his Queen Whereon to g, *Balin and Balan* 189
I cannot brook to g upon the dead.' „ 586
Sigh fully, or all-silent g upon him *Merlin and V.* 182
But who can g upon the Sun in heaven? *Lancelot and E.* 123
even while I g The crack of earthquake *Pelleas and E.* 464
as one Who sits and g's on a faded fire, *Last Tournament* 157
and we woke To g upon each other. *Lover's Tale i* 266
To g upon thee till their eyes are dim „ 491
and I g at a field in the Past, *By an Evolution.* 17
she used to g Down at the Troad; *Death of Œnone* 2
and there G at the ruin, often mutter low *St. Telemachus* 14
And g on this great miracle, the World, *Akbar's Dream* 122
and is, And is not, what I g on— „ 124

Gazed G on the Persian girl alone, *Arabian Nights* 134
Two godlike faces g below; *Palace of Art* 162
He g so long That both his eyes were dazzled, *M. d'Arthur* 58
Averill went and g upon his death. *Aylmer's Field* 599
long we g, but satiated at length Came to the ruins. *Princess, Pro.* 90
I drew near; I g. „ *iii* 183
She g awhile and said, 'As these rude bones „ 295
while We g upon her came a little stir „ *iv* 373
Clomb to the roofs, and g alone for hours „ *vii* 32
place Where first we g upon the sky; *In Mem. cii* 2
They g on all earth's beauty in their Queen, *Com. of Arthur* 463
Gareth silent g upon the knight, *Gareth and L.* 933
on whom the maiden g. „ 1281
And kept her off and g upon her face, *Marr. of Geraint* 519
King Had g upon her blankly and gone by: *Merlin and V.* 161
I never g upon it but I dreamt Of some vast charm „ 511
G at the heaving shoulder, and the face Hand-hidden, „ 896
while he g wonderingly at her, came *Lancelot and E.* 626

Gazed (*continued*) while he g The beauty of her flesh abash'd — *Pelleas and E.* 77
she g upon the man Of princely bearing, ,, 305
Full wonderingly she g on Lancelot ,, 589
He g so long That both his eyes were dazzled *Pass. of Arthur* 226
three whereat we g On that high day, ,, 453
for as that other g, Shading his eyes *Lover's Tale i* 305
While I g My coronal slowly disentwined itself ,, 360
while I g My spirit leap'd as with those thrills ,, 362
The other, like the sun I g upon, ,, 507
the stars Did tremble in their stations as I g; ,, 582
We g on it together In mute and glad remembrance, ,, *ii* 185
and the light Grew as I g, *Columbus* 77
And we g at the wandering wave *V. of Maeldune* 89
Her heart! I g into the mirror, *The Ring* 369
Gazer greet With lifted hand the g in the street. *Ode on Well.* 22
Gazest When thou g at the skies? *Adeline* 50
Gazing (*See also* **Seaward-gazing**) G on thee for evermore, *Eleänore* 80
Sometimes with most intensity G, I seem to see ,, 83
and sense Of Passion g upon thee. ,, 116
G where the lilies blow Round an island *L. of Shalott i* 7
In g up an Alpine height, *Two Voices* 362
If g on divinity disrobed Thy mortal eyes *Œnone* 157
eyes grown dim with g on the pilot-stars. *Lotos-Eaters, C. S.* 87
From her isle-altar g down, *Of old sat Freedom* 14
There he sat down g on all below; *Enoch Arden* 723
His g in on Annie, his resolve, ,, 863
They stood, so rapt, we g, came a voice, *Princess ii* 318
Then murmur'd Florian g after her, ,, *iii* 97
All open-mouth'd, all g to the light, ,, *iv* 483
Ida spoke not, g on the ground, ,, *vi* 227
so fared she g there; ,, *vii* 41
And g on thee, sullen tree, *In Mem. ii* 13
the friends Of Arthur, g on him, tall, *Com. of Arthur* 278
In scornful stillness g as they past; ,, 478
that men Were giddy g there; *Gareth and L.* 228
pace At sunrise, g over plain and wood; ,, 668
And sadly g on her bridle-reins, *Geraint and E.* 494
gone, And left me g at a barren board, *Holy Grail* 893
Pelleas g thought, 'Is Guinevere herself so beautiful?' *Pelleas and E.* 69
Peace at his heart, and g at a star ,, 559
To die in g on that perfectness *Lover's Tale i* 88
g like The Indian on a still-eyed snake, ,, *ii* 188
G for one pensive moment on that founder *Locksley H., Sixty* 32
And, g from this height alone, *Pro. to Gen. Hamley* 9
G at the Lydian laughter of the Garda Lake below *Frater Ave, etc.* 8
Gear We sent mine host to purchase female g; *Princess i* 199
for my ships are out of g, *The Revenge* 5
Gell (girl) an' soä is scoors o' g's, *N. Farmer, N. S.* 14
an' 'is g's as thaw was g's o' mine, *Village Wife* 6
The g's they counts for nowt, ,, 18
An' the g's, they hedn't naw taäils, ,, 29
or the g's 'ull goä to the 'Ouse, ,, 64
An' I cried along wi' the g's, ,, 96
an' 'is g's es belong'd to the land; ,, 112
a bouncin' boy an' a g. *Spinster's S's.* 82
g's bobs to ma hoffens es I be abroad i' the laänes, ,, 107
g o' the farm 'at slep wi' tha then *Owd Roä* 51
a-naggin' about the g o' the farm, ,, 69
the g was as howry a trollope ,, 72
Gelt left crag-carven o'er the streaming G— *Gareth and L.* 1203
Gem (s) In hollow'd moons of g's, *Palace of Art* 188
lest the g's Should blind my purpose, *M. d'Arthur* 152
Airing a snowy hand and signet g, *Princess i* 121
rainbow robes, and g's and gemlike eyes, ,, *iv* 480
How like a g, beneath, the city Of little Monaco, *The Daisy* 7
feet like sunny g's on an English green, *Maud I v* 14
All over glanced with dewdrop or with g *Gareth and L.* 929
In crimsons and in purples and in g's. *Marr. of Geraint* 10
wont to glance and sparkle like a g Of fifty facets; *Geraint and E.* 294
so thickly shone the g's. ,, 693
he had the g's Pluck'd from the crown, *Lancelot and E.* 56
Received at once and laid aside the g's ,, 1202

Gem (s) (*continued*) Tristram won, and Lancelot gave, the g's, *Last Tournament* 190
Who left the g's which Innocence the Queen ,, 293
lest the g's Should blind my purpose, *Pass. of Arthur* 320
Which are as g's set in my memory, *Lover's Tale i* 291
g's Moveable and resettable at will, ,, *iv* 198
after he hath shown him g's or gold, ,, 246
Swept like a torrent of g's from the sky *V. of Maeldune* 46
To vex the noon with fiery g's, *Ancient Sage* 265
Gem (verb) new life that g's the hawthorn line; *Prog. of Spring* 36
Gemini starry G hang like glorious crowns *Maud III vi* 7
Gem-like a fire-balloon Rose g-l up before the dusky groves *Princess, Pro.* 75
And rainbow robes, and gems and g eyes, ,, *iv* 480
Luminous, g, ghostlike, deathlike, *Maud I iii* 8
a meadow g chased In the brown wild, *Geraint and E.* 198
Gemm'd Breaks from a coppice g with green and red, *Marr. of Geraint* 339
Gemmy The g bridle glitter'd free, *L. of Shalott iii* 10
General Upon the g decay of faith Right thro' the world, *The Epic* 18
every face she look'd on justify it) The g foe. *Princess v* 135
should fall Remerging in the g Soul, *In Mem. xlvii* 4
whatsoe'er Our g mother meant for me alone, *Lover's Tale i* 245
Generating *See* **All-generating**
Generation (*See also* **Gineration**) And mould a g strong to move *Princess v* 416
to knit The g's each with each; *In Mem. xl* 16
jewels Of many g's of his house Sparkled *Lover's Tale iv* 299
National hatreds of whole g's, *Vastness* 25
Generous All brave, and many g, and some chaste. *Merlin and V.* 817
Most g of all Ultramontanes, Ward, *In Mem. W. G. Ward* 4
But, having sown some g seed, *Two Voices* 143
everywhere they meet And kindle g purpose, *Tiresias* 128
Genial (*See also* **Seeming-genial**) With peals of g clamour sent From many a tavern-door, *Will Water.* 187
so g was the hearth: *Enoch Arden* 743
all-generating powers and g heat Of Nature, *Lucretius* 97
The g giant, Arac, roll'd himself *Princess v* 274
broke A g warmth and light once more, ,, *vi* 282
For we, the g day, the happy crowd, ,, *Con.* 75
A great broad-shoulder'd g Englishman, ,, 85
partner in the flowery walk Of letters, g table-talk, *In Mem. lxxxiv* 23
And g warmth; and o'er the sky The silvery haze ,, *xcv* 3
To myriads on the g earth, ,, *xcix* 14
The g hour with mask and mime; ,, *cv* 10
Let all my g spirits advance To meet ,, *Con.* 77
Fill'd all the g courses of his blood *Geraint and E.* 926
The light and g warmth of double day. *Prin. Beatrice* 22
Genius thou bearest The first-born of thy g. *Ode to Memory* 92
A fairy shield your G made And gave you *Margaret* 41
G of that hour which dost uphold Thy coronal *Lover's Tale i* 487
Genovese The grave, severe G of old. *The Daisy* 40
Being but a G, I am handled worse than had I been a Moor, *Columbus* 106
I am but an alien and a G. ,, 243
Gentle (*See also* **Stately-gentle**) Lean'd on him, faithful, g, good, *Two Voices* 416
gently comes the world to those That are cast in g mould. *To J. S.* 4
By g words are always gain: *Love thou thy land* 23
A g sound, an awful light! *Sir Galahad* 41
And they speak in g murmur, *L. of Burleigh* 49
And a g consort made he, And her g mind was such That she grew a noble lady, ,, 73
The g shower, the smell of dying leaves, *Enoch Arden* 611
a languor came Upon him, g sickness, ,, 824
So that the g creature shut from all Her charitable use, *Aylmer's Field* 565
Softening thro' all the g attributes ,, 730
came Melissa hitting all we saw with shafts Of g satire, *Princess ii* 469
on my spirits Settled a g cloud of melancholy; ,, *iv* 570
the yoke, I wish it G as freedom '— ,, *vi* 206
nor stranger seem'd that hearts So g, ,, *vii* 67
Sleep, g heavens, before the prow; Sleep, g winds, as he sleeps now, *In Mem. ix* 14
My mother, who was so g and good? *Maud I vi* 67
Of her whose g will has changed my fate, ,, *xviii* 23
I trust that I did not talk To g Maud in our walk ,, *xix* 13

Gentle (*continued*) Was it g to reprove her For stealing — Maud I xx 8
nor meet To fight for g damsel, he, who lets His heart be stirr'd with any foolish heat At any g damsel's waywardness. — Gareth and L. 1177
there fell A horror on him, lest his g wife, — Marr. of Geraint 29
Am much too g, have not used my power: — ,, 467
Sank her sweet head upon her g breast; — ,, 527
That tho' her g presence at the lists — ,, 795
nor told his g wife What ail'd him, — Geraint and E. 503
(His g charger following him unled) — ,, 571
Pray you be g, pray you let me be: — ,, 708
Dame, to be g than ungentle with you; — ,, 716
'I will be g' he thought 'And passing g' caught his hand — Balin and Balan 370
Then the g Squire 'I hold them happy, — ,, 580
I thought that he was g, being great: — Merlin and V. 871
The g wizard cast a shielding arm. — ,, 908
Some g maiden's gift. — Lancelot and E. 605
Death-pale, for lack of g maiden's aid. — ,, 765
And all the g court will welcome me, — ,, 1060
To whom the g sister made reply, — ,, 1073
Know that for this most g maiden's death — ,, 1291
Unbound as yet, and g, as I know.' — ,, 1386
That doest right by g and by churl, — Last Tournament 74
Ah great and g lord, Who wast, — Guinevere 638
to which her gracious lips Did lend such g utterance, — Lover's Tale i 457
Then he patted my hand in his g way, — First Quarrel 67
the crew were g, the captain kind; — The Wreck 129
Our g mother, had *she* lived— — The Flight 77
All is gracious, g, great and Queenly. — On Jub. Q. Victoria 14
and felt a g hand Fall on my forehead, — The Ring 418
You that would not tread on a worm For your g nature . . . — Forlorn 46

Gentle-hearted The g-h wife Sat shuddering — Sea Dreams 29

Gentleman bore King Arthur, like a modern g — M. d'Arthur, Ep. 22
And watch'd by silent *gentlemen*, — Will Water. 231
first, a g of broken means (His father's fault) — Princess i 53
To give three gallant *gentlemen* to death.' — ,, ii 335
'You have done well and like a g, — ,, iv 527
Well have you done and like a g. — ,, 530
Cooms of a g burn: — N. Farmer, N. S. 38
G burn! what's g burn? — ,, 42
The grand old name of g, — In Mem. cxi 22
O selfless man and stainless g, — Merlin and V. 792
True g, heart, blood and bone, — Bandit's Death 2

Gentleness Winning its way with extreme g — Isabel 23
More soluble is this knot, By g than war. — Princess v 136
but this firebrand—g To such as her! — ,, 167
The g he seem'd to be, — In Mem. cxi 12
sworn to vows Of utter hardihood, utter g, — Gareth and L. 553
world were one Of utter peace, and love, and g! — ,, 1289
Yea, God, I pray you of your g, — Geraint and E. 710
Subdued me somewhat to that g, — ,, 867
what the King So prizes—overprizes—g. — Balin and Balan 184
airs of Heaven Should kiss with an unwonted g. — Lover's Tale i 739
With politic care, with utter g, — Akbar's Dream 128

Gentler A g death shall Falsehood die, — Clear-headed friend 16
In g days, your arrow-wounded fawn — Princess ii 270
We ceased: a g feeling crept Upon us: — In Mem. xxx 17
But golden earnest of a g life!' — Balin and Balan 208

Gentler-born The g-b the maiden, the more bound, — Lancelot and E. 766

Gentlest whom the g airs of Heaven Should kiss — Lover's Tale i 738
And last in kindly curves, with g fall, — De Prof., Two G. 23

Gentlewoman hammer at this reverend g. — Princess iii 129
Or sit beside a noble g.' — Gareth and L. 867
There is not one among my *gentlewomen* — Geraint and E. 622
see ye not my *gentlewomen* here, — ,, 682
one among his *gentlewomen* Display'd — ,, 686
and stood, A virtuous g deeply wrong'd, — Merlin and V. 911

Gentlier Music that g on the spirit lies, — Lotos-Eaters, C. S. 5

Geoffrey (of Monmouth) Of G's book, or him of Malleor's, — To the Queen ii 42

Geology Now hawking at G and schism; — The Epic 16
Astronomy and G, terrible Muses! — Parnassus 16

Geraint (a Knight of the Round Table) brave G, a knight of Arthur's court, — Marr. of Geraint 1
so loved G To make her beauty vary day by day, — ,, 8
Grateful to Prince G for service done, — ,, 15
Long in their common love rejoiced G. — ,, 23
Not less G believed it; — ,, 28
day by day she thought to tell G, — ,, 65
Prince G, Late also, wearing neither hunting-dress — ,, 164
G Exclaiming, 'Surely I will learn the name,' — ,, 202
Prince G, now thinking that he heard — ,, 232
came G, and underneath Beheld the long street — ,, 241
thought G, 'I have track'd him to his earth.' — ,, 253
Whereat G flash'd into sudden spleen: — ,, 273
Then rode G, a little spleenful yet, — ,, 293
Then rode G into the castle court, — ,, 312
So the sweet voice of Enid moved G; — ,, 334
So fared it with G, who thought and said, — ,, 343
thought G, 'Here by God's rood is the one maid — ,, 367
G, from utter courtesy, forbore. — ,, 381
G had longing in him evermore To stoop and kiss — ,, 394
But after all had eaten, then G, — ,, 397
—I am G Of Devon— — ,, 409
G, a name far-sounded among men For noble deeds? — ,, 427
'Well said, true heart,' replied G, — ,, 474
old And rusty, old and rusty, Prince G, Are mine, — ,, 478
To whom G with eyes all bright replied, — ,, 494
And waited there for Yniol and G. — ,, 538
when G Beheld her first in field awaiting him, — ,, 539
Increased G's, who heaved his blade aloft, — ,, 572
No later than last eve to Prince G— — ,, 603
She look'd on ere the coming of G. — ,, 614
G Woke where he slept in the high hall, — ,, 754
rejoiced More than G to greet her thus attired; — ,, 772
So fared it with G, (repeat) — Geraint and E. 8, 500
Prince G Drave the long spear a cubit thro' his breast — ,, 85
his lance err'd; but G's, A little in the late encounter — ,, 157
G, dismounting, pick'd the lance That pleased him best, — ,, 179
G had ruth again on Enid looking pale: — ,, 202
G Ate all the mowers' victual unawares, — ,, 214
Then said G, 'I wish no better fare: — ,, 232
Her suitor in old years before G, Enter'd, — ,, 276
Greeted G full face, but stealthily, — ,, 279
Then cried G for wine and goodly cheer — ,, 283
But Enid left alone with Prince G, — ,, 365
And G look'd and was not satisfied. — ,, 435
G Waving an angry hand as who should say — ,, 443
uttering a dry shriek, Dash'd on G, — ,, 462
Then like a stormy sunlight smiled G, — ,, 480
This heard G, and grasping at his sword, — ,, 725
then G upon the horse Mounted, and reach'd a hand, — ,, 758
'My lord G, I greet you with all love; — ,, 785
But while G lay healing of his hurt, — ,, 931
when G was whole again, they past With Arthur — ,, 945
tho' G could never take again That comfort — ,, 949
Enids and G's Of times to be; — ,, 965
after Lancelot, Tristram, and G And Gareth, — Lancelot and E. 556

Germ (*See also* **Baby-germ**) in it is the g of all That grows within the woodland. — Amphion 7

German No little G state are we, — Third of Feb. 15

Germander that her clear g eye Droopt — Sea Dreams 4

Germany worse than daring G gave us, — Trans. of Homer 5

Get (*See also* **Git**) g thee hence—Lest that rough humour — Gareth and L. 376
Thou g to horse and follow him far away. — ,, 584
Flee down the valley before he g to horse. — ,, 941
with Sir Pelleas as with one Who g's a wound in battle, — Pelleas and E. 529
I couldn't g back tho' I tried, — Rizpah 43
In yon dark city: g thee back: — Ancient Sage 253
Till Holy St. Pether g's up wid his kays — Tomorrow 93
Up, g up, and tell him all, — Forlorn 55
Up, g up, the time is short, — ,, 73
I have told you my tale. G you gone. — Charity 44

Gift (*continued*) we knew your g that way At college: The Epic 24
The holy Elders with the g of myrrh. M. d'Arthur 233
Requiring at her hand the greatest g, Gardener's D. 229
'And yet it was a graceful g— Talking Oak 233
Let me go: take back thy g: Tithonus 27
Gods themselves cannot recall their g's.' „ 49
eagles of her belt, The grim Earl's g; Godiva 44
g's, when g's of mine could please; The Letters 22
G's by the children, garden-herbs Enoch Arden 338
shower'd His oriental g's on everyone And most on Edith: Aylmer's Field 214
Among the g's he left her „ 217
'A gracious g to give a lady, this!' „ 240
'Were I to give this g of his to one „ 242
'Take it,' she added sweetly, 'tho' his g; „ 246
Nor deeds of g, but g's of grace he forged, Sea Dreams 192
And jewels, g's, to fetch her: Princess i 43
they saw the king: he took the g's; „ 46
g's of grace, that might express In Mem. lxxxv 46
Ah, take the imperfect g I bring, „ 117
She keeps the g of years before, „ xcvii 25
and saw without the door King Arthur's g, Gareth and L. 677
branch'd and flower'd with gold, a costly g Marr. of Geraint 631
'Yea, I know it; your good g, „ 688
Your own good g!' 'Yea, surely,' said the dame, „ 690
I see her now, Clothed with my g, and gay among the gay.' „ 753
Laid from her limbs the costly-broider'd g, „ 769
your fair child shall wear your costly g „ 819
Who knows? another g of the high God, „ 821
'I take it as free g, then,' said the boy, Geraint and E. 222
'These be g's, Born with the blood, Balin and Balan 174
A seven months' babe had been a truer g. Merlin and V. 711
broider'd with great pearls, Some gentle maiden's g.' Lancelot and E. 605
she should ask some goodly g of him „ 912
price of half a realm, his costly g, „ 1164
they had been thrice their worth Being your g, „ 1213
value of all g's Must vary as the giver's. „ 1214
this life of mine I guard as God's high g Guinevere 494
holy Elders with the g of myrrh. Pass. of Arthur 401
my rich g is wholly mine to give. Lover's Tale iv 350
'Take my free g, my cousin, for your wife; „ 363
One golden curl, his golden g, before The Flight 36
G's from every British zone; Open. I. and C. Exhib. 9
And golden grain, my g to helpless man. Demeter and P. 111
sacred those Ghost Lovers hold the g.' The Ring 205
full thanks to you For your rich g, To Ulysses 34
send A g of slenderer value, mine. „ 48
Gifted (*See also* **God-gifted**) As some divinely g man, In Mem. lxiv 2
Gigantesque The sort of mock-heroic g, Princess, Con. 11
Gigglesby we was shaämed to cross G Greeän, Spinster's S's. 33
out o' sight o' the winders o' G Hinn— „ 35
foälk be sa scared at, i' G wood. „ 24
Gild g's the straiten'd forehead of the fool! Locksley Hall 62
grain as sweet As that which g's the glebe of England, To Prof. Jebb 7
Gilded (adj. and part.) (*See also* **Lichen-gilded**) Kate saith 'the men are g flies.' Kate 18
And round the roofs a g gallery Palace of Art 29
Near g organ-pipes, her hair Wound with white roses, „ 98
The parrot in his g wires. Day-Dm., Sleep. P. 16
A g dragon, also, for the babes. Enoch Arden 540
DUST are our frames; and, g dust, our pride Aylmer's Field 1
Staring for ever from their g walls „ 833
steep-up spout whereon the g ball Danced like a wisp: Princess, Pro. 63
Fly to her, and fall upon her g eaves, „ iv 94
And slain with laughter roll'd the g Squire. „ v 22
let his coltish nature break At seasons thro' the g pale: In Mem. cxi 8
Sweet nature g by the gracious gleam Of letters, Ded. of Idylls 39
on such a palm As glitters g in thy Book of Hours. Gareth and L. 46
were birds Of sunny plume in g trellis-work; Marr. of Geraint 659
I will not fight my way with g arms, Geraint and E. 21
And call'd herself a g summer fly Merlin and V. 258
Set every g parapet shuddering; Lancelot and E. 299
Gilded (adj. and part.) (*continued*) from the carven-work behind him crept Two dragons g, Lancelot and E. 437
the g parapets were crown'd With faces, Pelleas and E. 165
inflamed the knights At that dishonour done the g spur, Last Tournament 435
G with broom or shatter'd into spires, Lover's Tale i 400
and the g snake Had nestled in this bosom-throne of Love, „ i 623
A veil, that seemed no more than g air, „ iv 290
I have broke their cage, no g one, I trow— Sir J. Oldcastle 3
and once we only saw Your g vane, The Ring 331
Gilded (verb) Would that have g me? Columbus 114
Gilden-peakt pavilions rear'd Above the bushes, g-p: Pelleas and E. 429
Gildest star that g yet this phantom shore; To Virgil 26
Gilding Flattery g the rift in a throne; Vastness 20
Gileadite The daughter of the warrior G, D. of F. Women 197
Gillyflowers a rosy sea of g About it; Aylmer's Field 159
Gilt (*See also* **Foot-gilt**) as a parrot turns Up thro' g wires a crafty loving eye, Princess, Pro. 172
dark old place will be g by the touch of a millionaire: Maud I i 66
his strong hands gript And dinted the g dragons right and left, Last Tournament 182
And those g gauds men-children swarm to see. To W. C. Macready 11
Gilt-head court-Galen poised his g-h cane, Princess i 19
Gin I'll tell tha. G. North. Cobbler 7
Thou gits naw g fro' the bottle theer, „ 10
seeäs stannin' theer, yon big black bottle o' g. „ 70
summat bewitch'd istead of a quart o' g; „ 82
Fur I couldn't 'owd 'ands off g, „ 84
An' 'e points to the bottle o' g, „ 90
Gineration (generation) But a frish g had riz, Tomorrow 75
Gipsy Or the frock and g bonnet Maud I xx 19
Gird minds did g their orbs with beams, The Poet 29
Uncared for, g the windy grove, In Mem. ci 13
Far liefer had I g his harness on him, Marr. of Geraint 93
many a mystic symbol, g the hall: Holy Grail 233
Girded *See* **Man-girded**
Girdle (*See also* **Vapour-girdle**) And I would be the g Miller's D. 175
twist his g tight, and pat The girls Talking Oak 43
She moving, at her g clash The golden keys To Marq. of Dufferin 3
Girdled g with the gleaming world: Lotos-Eaters, C. S. 113
and g her with music. Princess vii 327
the rebels that g us round— Def. of Lucknow 22
Girl (*See also* **Baby-girl, Gell, Market-girl, Orphan-girl**)
Gazed on the Persian g alone, Arabian Nights 134
And the red cloaks of market g's, L. of Shalott ii 17
the g's all kiss'd Beneath the sacred bush The Epic 2
like a g Valuing the giddy pleasure of the eyes. M. d'Arthur 127
'My g, I love you well; Dora 42
'Go!—G, get you in!' She went— Edwin Morris 125
and pat The g's upon the cheek, Talking Oak 44
This g, for whom your heart is sick, „ 71
either fixt his heart On that one g; Enoch Arden 40
the g Seem'd kinder unto Philip than to him; „ 41
I'll be back, my g, before you know it.' „ 193
as the village g, Who sets her pitcher „ 206
'Annie, my g, cheer up, be comforted, „ 218
let me put the boy and g to school: „ 312
Philip put the boy and g to school, „ 331
And o'er her second father stoopt a g, „ 747
the g So like her mother, and the boy, my son.' „ 790
Where once with Leolin at her side the g, Aylmer's Field 184
would it be more gracious' asked the g „ 241
The g might be entangled ere she knew. „ 272
g and boy, Sir, know their differences!' „ 274
twenty boys and g's should marry on it, „ 371
found the g And flung her down upon a couch of fire, „ 573
Born of a village g, carpenter's son, „ 668
But g's, Hetairai, curious in their art, Lucretius 52
a group of g's In circle waited, Princess, Pro. 68
like as many g's—Sick for the hollies „ 186
lengths of yellow ringlet, like a g, „ i 3
G's, Knowledge is now no more a fountain „ ii 89
G's?—more like men!' „ iii 43
Men! g's, like men! why, if they had been men „ 49

Girl (*continued*) To nurse a blind ideal like a g, Methinks he seems no better than a g; As g's were once, as we ourself have been: *Princess iii* 217
But children die; and let me tell you, g, „ 253
G after g was call'd to trial: „ *iv* 228
like enough, O g's, To unfurl the maiden banner „ 502
and they will beat my g Remembering her mother: „ *v* 88
you spent a stormy time With our strange g: „ 122
'Tut, you know them not, the g's. „ 151
Let our g's flit, Till the storm die! „ *vi* 337
ill counsel had mislead the g To vex true hearts: yet was she but a g— „ *vii* 241
'So fret not, like an idle g, *In Mem. lii* 13
Like some poor g whose heart is set „ *lx* 3
I play'd with the g when a child; *Maud I i* 68
'Well if it prove a g, the boy (repeat) „ *vii* 7, 15
And soften as if to a g, „ *x* 16
save from some slight shame one simple g. „ *xviii* 45
Queen rose of the rosebud garden of g's, „ *xxii* 53
Shame never made g redder than Gareth joy. *Gareth and L.* 536
three fair g's In gilt and rosy raiment came: „ 926
massacring Man, woman, lad and g— „ 1341
Half disarray'd as to her rest, the g; *Marr. of Geraint* 516
And all in charge of whom? a g: *Geraint and E.* 125
ye shall share my earldom with me, g, „ 626
'G, for I see ye scorn my courtesies, „ 671
Sir Lancelot worshipt no unmarried g *Merlin and V.* 12
beyond All hopes of gaining, than as maiden g. „ 24
came the village g's And linger'd talking, *Pelleas and E.* 508
like a g Valuing the giddy pleasure of the eyes. *Pass. of Arthur* 295
thronging fancies come To boys and g's *Lover's Tale i* 555
but Lionel and the g Were wedded, „ *iv* 13
Passionate g tho' I was, *First Quarrel* 15
There was a g, a hussy, that workt „ 24
the g was the most to blame. „ 26
It's the little g with her arms lying out *In the Child. Hosp.* 58
And so, when I bore him a g, *The Wreck* 33
he the knight for an amorous g's romance! „ 44
The g's of equal age, but one was fair, *The Ring* 160
you my g Rode on my shoulder home— „ 321
I believing that the g's Lean fancy, „ 335
lover's fairy dream, His g of g's; *To Mary Boyle* 44
Girl-graduates sweet g-g in their golden hair. *Princess, Pro.* 142
Girlish Is g talk at best; *Epilogue* 43
Girt Among the thorns that g Thy brow, *Supp. Confessions* 6
g round With blackness as a solid wall, *Palace of Art* 273
The land, where g with friends or foes *You ask me, why, etc.* 7
Tho' sitting g with doubtful light. *Love thou thy land* 16
g the region with high cliff and lawn: *Vision of Sin* 47
Enoch's golden ring had g Her finger, *Enoch Arden* 157
g With song and flame and fragrance, *Lucretius* 133
G by half the tribes of Britain, *Boädicea* 5
the King Came g with knights: *Lancelot and E.* 1261
Far off from out an island g by foes, *Achilles over the T.* 8
Girth Alas, I was so broad of g, *Talking Oak* 139
and grown a bulk Of spanless g, *Princess vi* 36
strait g of Time Inswathe the fulness of Eternity, *Lover's Tale i* 482
No stone is fitted in yon marble g *Tiresias* 135
Would my granite g were strong *Helen's Tower* 7
Git (get) G ma my ääle, (repeat) *N. Farmer, O. S.* 4, 68
nobbut a curate, an' weänt niver g hissen clear, „ *N. S.* 27
Squire were at Charlie ageän to g 'im to cut off 'is taäil. *Village Wife* 74
or she weänt g a maäte onyhow! „ 104
Robby, g down wi'tha, wilt tha? *Spinster's S's.* 67
Steevie g down. „ 92
An' I says 'G awaäy, ya beäst,' *Owd Roä* 62
G oop, if ya're onywaäys good for owt.' „ 77
when I g's to the top, „ 83
Too laäte, tha mun g tha to bed, „ 117
an' thou'll g along, niver fear, *Church-warden, etc.* 7
I g's the plaäte fuller o' Soondays „ 40
if iver tha meäns to g 'igher, „ 45
if tha wants to g forrards a bit, „ 49
Gittin' (getting) Fur work mun 'a gone to the g *N. Farmer, N. S.* 50
Gittin' (getting) (*continued*) allus afear'd of a man's g' ower fond, *Spinster's S's.* 27
How be the farm g on? noäways. G on i' deeäd! *Church-warden, etc.* 3
Giv (gave) I niver g it a thowt— *N. Farmer, N. S.* 23
Give (*See also* **Gev, Gie**) *Could* g *the warrior kings of old,* *To the Queen* 4
'Mother, g me grace To help me of my weary load.' *Mariana in the S.* 29
fill my glass: g me one kiss: *Miller's D.* 17
O would she g me vow for vow, „ 119
'O Paris, G it to Pallas!' *Œnone* 170
G us long rest or death, dark death, *Lotos-Eaters, C. S.* 53
Failing to g the bitter of the sweet, *D. of F. Women* 286
God g's us love. Something to love He lends us; *To J. S.* 13
What should one g to light on such a dream?' *Edwin Morris* 58
'G? G all thou art,' he answer'd, „ 59
like the daughters of the horseleech, 'G, *Golden Year* 12
I ask'd thee, 'G me immortality.' *Tithonus* 15
wealthy men who care not how they g. „ 17
in the rights that name may g, *Day-Dm., L'Envoi* 54
a lily-white doe To g his cousin, Lady Clare. *Lady Clare* 4
'Yet g one kiss to your mother dear! „ 49
Little can I g my wife. *L. of Burleigh* 14
And g his child a better bringing-up *Enoch Arden* 87
To g his babes a better bringing-up „ 299
—a month—G her a month— „ 462
aid me, g me strength Not to tell her, „ 785
Take, g her this, for it may comfort her: „ 899
'A gracious gift to g a lady, this!' *Aylmer's Field* 240
'Were I to g this gift of his to one „ 242
G me my fling, and let me say my say.' „ 399
G me your prayers, for he is past „ 751
or a song To g us breathing-space.' *Princess, Pro.* 242
And here I g the story and the songs. „ 247
I can g you letters to her; „ *i* 159
'We g you welcome: not without redound „ *ii* 42
I g thee to death My brother! „ 307
g three gallant gentlemen to death.' „ 335
we g you, being strange, A license: „ *iii* 204
If we could g them surer, quicker proof— „ 282
g's the manners of your countrywomen?' „ *iv* 151
g him your hand: Cleave to your contract: „ 408
And g's the battle to his hands: „ 580
G us, then, your mind at large: „ *v* 123
G's her harsh groom for bridal-gift a scourge; „ 378
It is not yours, but mine: g me the child.' „ *vi* 141
g her the child! (repeat) „ 168, 179, 183
G me it: I will g it her.' „ 187
what answer should I g? „ *vii* 6
let her make herself her own To g or keep, „ 273
of which I g you all The random scheme „ *Con.* 1
men required that I should g throughout „ 10
And yet to g the story as it rose, „ 26
G it time To learn its limbs: „ 78
these great Sirs G up their parks some dozen times a year „ 103
he kept us free; O g him welcome, *Ode on Well.* 92
a weänt niver g it to Joänes, *N. Farmer, O. S.* 59
Who g the Fiend himself his due, *To F. D. Maurice* 6
one lay-hearth would g you welcome „ 11
'We g you his life.' *The Victim* 16
Take you his dearest, G us a life.' „ 28
We g them the boy' „ 40
'O, Father Odin, We g you a life. „ 75
Gods have answer'd; We g them the wife!' „ 79
G her the glory of going on, *Wages* 5
G her the wages of going on, „ 10
To Sleep I g my powers away; *In Mem. iv* 1
No joy the blowing season g's, „ *xxxviii* 5
the hoarding sense G's out at times „ *xliv* 7
And dare we to this fancy g, „ *liii* 5
Hath power to g thee as thou wert? „ *lxxv* 8
meets the year, and g's and takes „ *cxvi* 3
Some bitter notes my harp would g, „ *cxxv* 2
And I must g away the bride; „ *Con.* 42

Give (*continued*) To *g* him the grasp of fellowship; *Maud I xiii* 16
sullen-seeming Death may *g* More life to Love ,, *xviii* 46
squire will *g* A grand political dinner ,, *xx* 24
A learned man Could *g* it a clumsy name. ,, *II ii* 10
G me thy daughter Guinevere to wife.' *Com. of Arthur* 139
G my one daughter saving to a king, ,, 143
Fear not to *g* this King thine only child, ,, 413
G me to right her wrong, and slay the man.' *Gareth and L.* 366
let my name Be hidd'n, and *g* me the first quest, ,, 545
and so *g's* the quest to him— ,, 864
g him back the shield.' ,, 1344
Take him to stall, and *g* him corn, *Marr. of Geraint* 371
Thou shalt *g* back their earldom to thy kin. ,, 585
Albeit I *g* no reason but my wish, ,, 761
Then not to *g* you warning, that seems hard; *Geraint and E.* 422
to *g* him warning, for he rode As if he heard not, ,, 451
set his foot upon me, and *g* me life. ,, 850
G's him the lie! There is no being pure, *Merlin and V.* 51
But since I will not yield to *g* you power ,, 373
But, father, *g* me leave, an if he will, *Lancelot and E.* 219
if you love, it will be sweet to *g* it; ,, 692
with mine own hand *g* his diamond to him, ,, 760
yea, and you must *g* it— ,, 773
G me good fortune, I will strike him dead, ,, 1071
g at last The price of half a realm, ,, 1163
if ye fail, *G* ye the slave mine order *Pelleas and E.* 270
G me three days to melt her fancy, ,, 356
'I will flee hence and *g* myself to God'— *Last Tournament* 624
G's birth to a brawling brook, *Lover's Tale i* 526
but you know that you must *g* me back: ,, *iv* 100
you shall *g* me back when he returns.' ,, 112
pronounced That my rich gift is wholly mine to *g*. ,, 350
would venture to *g* him the nay? *The Wreck* 17
he ped me back wid the best he could *g* *Tomorrow* 42
Yer Honour 'ill *g* me a thrifle to dhrink ,, 98
Coom *g* hoäver then, weant ye? *Spinster's S's.* 63
G your gold to the Hospital, *On Jub. Q. Victoria* 33
'And if you *g* the ring to any maid, *The Ring* 200
and *g* place to the beauty that endures, *Happy* 36
'Beat, little heart—I *g* you this and this' *Romney's R.* 1
For I *g* you this, and I *g* you this! ,, 100
a charm no words could *g*? *Far—far—away* 16
I whisper'd '*g* it to me,' but he would not *Bandit's Death* 27
and *g* His fealty to the halcyon hour! *The Wanderer* 11
G me a hand—and you—and you— ,, 15
Or mine to *g* him meat, *Voice spake, etc.* 8

Given Achieving calm, to whom was *g* *Two Voices* 209
difference, reconcilement, pledges *g*, *Gardener's D.* 257
I found him garrulously *g*, *Talking Oak* 23
then before thine answer *g* Departest, *Tithonus* 44
to me is *g* Such hope, I know not fear; *Sir Galahad* 61
A man had *g* all other bliss, *Sir G. and Q. G.* 42
Came, with a month's leave *g* them, *Sea Dreams* 6
but *g* to starts and bursts Of revel; *Princess i* 54
the king,' he said, 'Had *g* us letters, ,, 181
with mutual pardon ask'd and *g* For stroke and song, ,, *v* 46
G back to life, to life indeed, ,, *vii* 345
Is *g* in outline and no more. *In Mem. v* 12
the shock, so harshly *g*, Confused me ,, *xvi* 11
unto thee is *g* A life that bears immortal fruit ,, *xl* 17
His who had *g* me life— *Maud I i* 6
if she Had *g* her word to a thing so low? ,, *xvi* 27
And *g* false death her hand, ,, *xviii* 68
For the prophecy *g* of old And then not understood, ,, *II v* 42
'I have *g* him the first quest: *Gareth and L.* 582
thou hast *g* me but a kitchen-knave.' ,, 659
Canst thou not trust the limbs thy God hath *g*, ,, 1388
A creature wholly *g* to brawls and wine, *Marr. of Geraint* 441
Woke and bethought her of her promise *g* ,, 602
He would not leave her, till her promise *g*— ,, 605
g her on the night Before her birthday, ,, 632
'And gladly *g* again this happy morn. ,, 691
(No reason *g* her) she could cast aside ,, 807
Debating his command of silence *g*, *Geraint and E.* 366
breaking his command of silence *g*, ,, 390

Given (*continued*) sunshine that hath *g* the man A growth, *Balin and Balan* 181
but neither marry, nor are *g* In marriage, *Merlin and V.* 15
He hath *g* us a fair falcon which he train'd; ,, 96
no more thanks than might a goat have *g* ,, 278
I fain had *g* them greater wits: ,, 496
He promised more than ever king has *g*, ,, 586
deem this prize of ours is rashly *g*: *Lancelot and E.* 541
'Sweet is true love tho' *g* in vain, ,, 1007
a space of land is *g* to the plow. *Holy Grail* 907
have the Heavens but *g* thee a fair face, *Pelleas and E.* 101
And thou hast *g* thy promise, and I know ,, 245
And so, leave *g*, straight on thro' open door ,, 382
I to your dead man have *g* my troth, ,, 389
Not knowing they were lost as soon as *g*— *Last Tournament* 42
And if I do not there is penance *g*— *Guinevere* 187
For you have *g* me life and love again, *Lover's Tale iv* 110
I would have *g* my life To help his own *Sir J. Oldcastle* 62
G thee the keys of the great Ocean-sea? *Columbus* 149
one thing *g* me, to love and to live for, *The Wreck* 35
Was to be *g* you—such her dying wish—*G* on the morning when you came of age *The Ring* 76
Miriam! have you *g* your ring to her? ,, 260
for *him* who had *g* her the name. *Charity* 39

Giver Render thanks to the *G*, (repeat) *Ode on Well.* 44, 47
value of all gifts Must vary as the *g's*. *Lancelot and E.* 1215
And were it only for the *g's* sake, *Lover's Tale iv* 364

Giving *g* light To read those laws; *Isabel* 18
g safe pledge of fruits, *Ode to Memory* 18
record of the glance That graced the *g*— *Gardener's D.* 178
And part it, *g* half to him. *In Mem. xxv* 12
G you power upon me thro' this charm, *Merlin and V.* 514
In *g* so much beauty to the world, *Lover's Tale i* 212
And *g* light to others. ,, 426
g him That which of all things is the dearest ,, *iv* 347
of a hand *g* bread and wine, *The Wreck* 114

Glacier with tears By some cold morning *g*; *Princess vii* 116
And the lilies like *g's* winded down, *V. of Maeldune* 42
set me climbing icy capes And *g's*, *To E. Fitzgerald* 26

Glad (*See also* **Maäin-Glad**) So full of summer warmth, so *g*, *Miller's D.* 14
when his heart is *g* Of the full harvest, *Dora* 68
and we were *g* at heart. *Audley Court* 89
I'm *g* I walk'd. How fresh the meadows look *Walk. to the Mail* 1
I was *g* at first To think that in our often-ransack'd world *Sea Dreams* 128
light is large, and lambs are *g* *Lucretius* 99
I am sad and *g* To see you, Florian. *Princess ii* 306
Be *g*, because his bones are laid by thine! *Ode on Well.* 141
And *g* to find thyself so fair, *In Mem. vi* 27
And one is *g*; her note is gay, ,, *xxi* 25
And *g* at heart from May to May: ,, *xxii* 8
I read Of that *g* year which once had been, ,, *xcv* 22
'Yea, my kind lord,' said the *g* youth, and went, *Geraint and E.* 241
Eat and be *g*, for I account you mine.' ,, 647
'How should I be *g* Henceforth in all the world ,, 648
Kiss'd the white star upon his noble front, *G* also; ,, 758
Then were I *g* of you as guide and friend: *Lancelot and E.* 226
And *g* was I and clomb, but found at top *Holy Grail* 427
G that no phantom vext me more, ,, 538
so *g* were spirits and men Before the coming *Guinevere* 269
'Were they so *g*? ill prophets were they all, ,, 272
Sometimes a troop of damsels *g*, *L. of Shalott ii* 19
To-morrow 'ill be the happiest time of all the *g* New-year; (repeat) *May Queen* 2, 42
Of all the *g* New-year, mother, ,, 3
For I would see the sun rise upon the *g* New-year. ,, *N. Y's. E.* 2
Gareth was *g*. (repeat) *Gareth and L.* 497, 504
Lancelot, and all as *g* to find thee whole, ,, 1239
all *g*, Knightlike, to find his charger yet unlamed, *Balin and Balan* 427
so *g* was he. *Pelleas and E.* 146
April promise, *g* new-year Of Being, *Lover's Tale i* 281
We gazed on it together In mute and *g* remembrance, ,, *ii* 186
Let the maim'd in his heart rejoice At this *g* Ceremonial, *On Jub. Q. Victoria* 37

Glad (*continued*) pierce the *g* and songful air, *Demeter and P.* 45
g to seeä tha sa 'arty an' well. *North. Cobbler* 2
So *g*? no tear for him, who left you wealth, *The Ring* 188
She comes, and Earth is *g* To roll her North *Prog. of Spring* 48
Gladden the Shepherd *g's* in his heart: *Spec. of Iliad* 16
Come—let us *g* their sad eyes, *Last Tournament* 222
Gladden'd a rose that *g* earth and sky, *Pelleas and E.* 402
Gladder Put forth and feel a *g* clime.' *On a Mourner* 15
Glade (*See also* **Olive-glade**) With breezes from our oaken *g's*, *Eleänore* 10
winding *g's* high up like ways to Heaven, *Enoch Arden* 573
His wonted glebe, or lops the *g's*; *In Mem. ci* 22
thro' many a grassy *g* And valley, *Marr. of Geraint* 236
with droopt brow down the long *g's* he rode; *Balin and Balan* 311
Then they reach'd a *g*, „ 460
drew me thro' the glimmering *g's* *Sisters (E. and E.)* 116
Gladed *See* **Gloomy-gladed**
Gladiator *g's* moving toward their fight, *St. Telemachus* 54
Gladiatorial and flung himself between The *g* swords, „ 62
Gladlier For sure no *g* does the stranded wreck *Enoch Arden* 828
Gladly How *g*, were I one of those, *The Flight* 63
Gladness a cloudy *g* lighten'd In the eyes of each. *The Captain* 31
I grew in *g* till I found My spirits in the golden age. *To E. L.* 11
Makes former *g* loom so great? *In Mem. xxiv* 10
making vain pretence Of *g*, „ *xxx* 7
solemn *g* even crown'd The purple brows of Olivet. „ *xxxi* 11
Borne down by *g* so complete, „ *xxxii* 10
Neigh'd with all *g* as they came, *Geraint and E.* 755
Glaive *See* **War-glaive**
Glamour he had *g* enow In his own blood, *Gareth and L.* 209
Gwydion made by *g* out of flowers, *Marr. of Geraint* 743
and the harmless *g* of the field; *Pass. of Arthur* 52
Glance (s) (*See also* **Half-glance**) women smile with saint-like *g's* *Supp. Confessions* 22
Roof not a *g* so keen as thine: *Clear-headed friend* 7
Sudden *g's*, sweet and strange, *Madeline* 5
O'erflows thy calmer *g's*, „ 33
Every turn and *g* of thine, *Eleänore* 52
shaping faithful record of the *g* That graced *Gardener's D.* 177
cast back upon him A piteous *g*, and vanish'd. *Aylmer's Field* 284
a *g* I gave, No more; *Princess iv* 180
one *g* he caught Thro' open doors of Ida „ *v* 342
striking with her *g* The mother, me, the child; „ *vi* 152
And sidelong *g's* at my father's grief, „ *vii* 107
she fixt A showery *g* upon her aunt, „ *Con.* 33
and rolling *g's* lioness-like, *Boädicea* 71
In *g* and smile, and clasp and kiss, *In Mem. lxxxiv* 7
allured The *g* of Gareth dreaming on his liege. *Gareth and L.* 1316
Drew the vague *g* of Vivien, and her Squire; *Balin and Balan* 464
That *g* of theirs, but for the street, *Merlin and V.* 105
a *g* will serve—the liars! „ 111
made him at one *g* More bondsman in his heart *Pelleas and E.* 238
the *g* That only seems half-loyal to command,— *Last Tournament* 117
a single *g* of them Will govern a whole life *Lover's Tale i* 75
But cast a parting *g* at me, you saw, „ *iv* 4
at a *g* And as it were, perforce, *Tiresias* 55
when he cast a contemptuous *g* *The Wreck* 25
after one quick *g* upon the stars, *Akbar's Dream* 3
Glance (verb) Life shoots and *g's* thro' your veins, *Rosalind* 22
In crystal eddies *g* and poise, *Miller's D.* 52
rivulet in the flowery dale 'ill merrily *g* and play, *May Queen* 39
fall down and *g* From tone to tone, *D. of F. Women* 166
I slip, I slide, I gloom, I *g*, *The Brook* 174
And here he *g's* on an eye new-born, *Lucretius* 137
how the sun delights To *g* and shift about „ 189
made them *g* Like those three stars *Princess v* 259
And *g* about the approaching sails, *In Mem. xiii* 18
Let random influences *g*, „ *xlix* 2
And every eye but mine will *g* At Maud *Maud I xx* 36
Dared not to *g* at her good mother's face, *Marr. of Geraint* 766
sideways he let them *g* At Enid, *Geraint and E.* 246
stare at open space, nor *g* The one at other, „ 268
wont to *g* and sparkle like a gem Of fifty facets; „ 294
To *g* behind me at my former life, „ 863
speak Of the pure heart, nor seem to *g* at thee? *Guinevere* 502

Glance (verb) (*continued*) Not daring yet to *g* at Lionel. *Lover's Tale iv* 309
G at the wheeling Orb of change, *To E. Fitzgerald* 3
That *g's* from the bottom of the pool, *The Ring* 371
g the tits, and shriek the jays, *Prog. of Spring* 15
g's from the sun of our Islâm. *Akbar's Dream* 79
Glanced And *g* athwart the glooming flats. *Mariana* 20
The damned arrow *g* aside, *Oriana* 41
garden-glasses *g*, and momently The twinkling laurel *Gardener's D.* 117
She *g* across the plain; *Talking Oak* 166
We sat: the Lady *g*: *Princess ii* 111
G at the legendary Amazon As emblematic „ 126
G like a touch of sunshine on the rocks, „ *iii* 357
I *g* aside, and saw the palace-front „ *v* 508
I struck out and shouted; the blade *g*, „ 540
A light of healing, *g* about the couch, „ *vii* 59
mute she glided forth, Nor *g* behind her, „ 171
Whereat we *g* from theme to theme, *In Mem. lxxxix* 33
shyly *g* Eyes of pure women, *Gareth and L.* 313
the hair All over *g* with dewdrop or with gem „ 929
G at the doors or gambol'd down the walks; *Marr. of Geraint* 665
had *g* away From being knighted till he smote the thrall, *Balin and Balan* 154
g aside, and paced The long white walk of lilies „ 248
the King *G* first at him, then her, *Lancelot and E.* 95
But Lancelot, when they *g* at Guinevere, „ 270
maid *G* at, and cried, 'What news from Camelot, „ 620
yet he *g* not up, nor waved his hand, „ 986
g and shot Only to holy things; *Holy Grail* 75
And in he rode, and up I *g*, and saw „ 262
every moment *g* His silver arms and gloom'd: „ 492
Then *g* askew at those three knights of hers, *Pelleas and E.* 134
G down upon her, turn'd and went her way. „ 185
G from the rosy forehead of the dawn. „ 502
He *g* and saw the stately galleries, *Last Tournament* 145
bluebell, kingcup, poppy *g* About the revels, „ 234
g at him, thought him cold, High, *Guinevere* 405
pale King *g* across the field Of battle: *Pass. of Arthur* 126
the event *G* back upon them in his after life, *Lover's Tale iv* 24
G at the point of law, to pass it by, „ 276
to love and to live for, *g* at in scorn! *The Wreck* 35
She *g* at me, at Muriel, and was mute. *The Ring* 264
In passing it *g* upon Hamlet or city, *Merlin and the G.* 103
no such light *G* from our Presence *Akbar's Dream* 113
a ray red as blood *G* on the strangled face— *Bandit's Death* 32
Glancing (*See also* **Dawn-glancing**) *G* with black-beaded eyes, *Lilian* 15
g thence, discuss'd the farm, *Audley Court* 33
Philip *g* up Beheld the dead flame *Enoch Arden* 440
he saw The mother *g* often toward her babe, „ 754
The white-faced halls, the *g* rills, *In Mem., Con.* 113
Arthur *g* at him, Brought down a momentary brow. *Gareth and L.* 652
g like a dragon-fly In summer suit *Marr. of Geraint* 172
And *g* all at once as keenly at her „ 773
and *g* round the waste she fear'd *Geraint and E.* 50
g for a minute, till he saw her Pass into it, „ 886
And *g* on the window, when the gloom Of twilight *Balin and Balan* 232
stood with folded hands and downward eyes Of *g* corner, *Merlin and V.* 70
slander, *g* here and grazing there; „ 173
g thro' the hoary boles, he saw, *Pelleas and E.* 50
And many a *g* plash and sallowy isle, *Last Tournament* 422
g up beheld the holy nuns All round her, *Guinevere* 666
I from the altar *g* back upon her, *Sisters (E. and E.)* 210
The days and hours are ever *g* by, *Ancient Sage* 99
g heavenward on a star so silver-fair, *Locksley H., Sixty* 191
g downward on the kindly sphere *Poets and their B.* 9
g from his height On earth a fruitless fallow, *Demeter and P.* 117
g from the one To the other, *The Ring* 164
Whose mantle, every shade of *g* green, *Prog. of Spring* 63
and *g* at Elf of the woodland, *Merlin and the G.* 37
Glare (s) steady *g* Shrank one sick willow *Mariana in the S.* 52
No sun, but a wannish *g* In fold upon fold *Maud I vi* 2
in change of *g* and gloom Her eyes and neck *Merlin and V.* 959
and thro' a stormy *g*, a heat *Holy Grail* 842
Thro' the heat, the drowth, the dust, the *g*, *Sisters (E. and E.)* 6
Lured by the *g* and the blare, *V. of Maeldune* 73

Glean'd (verb) long ago they had *g* and garner'd *Lover's Tale i* 128
Gleaner Homestead and harvest, Reaper and *g*, *Merlin and the G.* 58
Glebe Flood with full daylight *g* and town? *Two Voices* 87
Sons of the *g*, with other frowns *Aylmer's Field* 723
those horn-handed breakers of the *g*, *Princess ii* 159
the labourer tills His wonted *g*, *In Mem. ci* 22
That grind the *g* to powder! *Tiresias* 95
sweet As that which gilds the *g* of England, *To Prof. Jebb.* 7
lest the naked *g* Should yawn once more *Demeter and P.* 42
Glee (joy) Love lighted down between them full of *g*, *Bridesmaid* 6
tyrant's cruel *g* Forces on the freer hour. *Vision of Sin* 129
Glee (part-music) The merry *g's* are still; *All Things will Die* 23
Again the feast, the speech, the *g*, *In Mem., Con.* 101
Glem Rang by the white mouth of the violent *G*; *Lancelot and E.* 288
Glen (*See also* **Glin**) And runlets babbling down the *g*. *Mariana in the S.* 44
The swimming vapour slopes athwart the *g*, *Œnone* 3
between the piney sides Of this long *g*. „ 94
Among the fragments tumbled from the *g's*, „ 222
from the darken *g*, 'Saw God divide the night *D. of F. Women* 224
That watch me from the *g* below. *Move eastward* 8
And snared the squirrel of the *g*? *Princess ii* 249
let us hear the purple *g's* replying: „ *iv* 11
all the *g's* are drown'd in azure gloom „ 525
Follow'd up in valley and *g* *Ode on Well.* 114
Had found a *g*, gray boulder and black tarn. *Lancelot and E.* 36
they fell and made the *g* abhorr'd: „ 42
Downward thunder in hollow and *g*, *To Master of B.* 16
Glide would she *g* between your wraths, *Aylmer's Field* 706
g a sunbeam by the blasted Pine, *Princess vii* 196
broad water sweetly slowly *g's*. *Requiescat* 2
g, Like a beam of the seventh Heaven, *Maud I xiv* 20
Thy shadow still would *g* from room to room, *Guinevere* 504
The sisters *g* about me hand in hand, *Sisters (E. and E.)* 275
and the shadowy warrior *g* Along *Demeter and P.* 152
Glided *g* thro' all change Of liveliest utterance. *D. of F. Women* 167
but mute she *g* forth, Nor glanced behind *Princess vii* 170
Above thee *g* the star. *Voice and the P.* 8
We *g* winding under ranks Of iris, *In Mem. ciii* 23
Then *g* out of the joyous wood *Maud II i* 31
she *g* out Among the heavy breathings *Geraint and E.* 401
Then rose Elaine and *g* thro' the fields, *Lancelot and E.* 843
the sweet Grail *G* and past, and close upon it *Holy Grail* 695
sad eyes fixt on the lost sea-home, as we *g* away, *The Wreck* 126
Then *g* a vulturous Beldam forth, *Dead Prophet* 25
he sprang, And *g* lightly down the stairs, *St. Telemachus* 59
Glidest How surely *g* thou from March to May, *Prog. of Spring* 109
Gliding *G* with equal crowns two serpents led *Alexander* 6
past In either twilight ghost-like to and fro *G*, *Lancelot and E.* 850
Over a wilderness *G*, *Merlin and the G.* 37
g thro' the branches over-bower'd *Death of Œnone* 6
The woman, *g* toward the pyre, *To Master of B.* 18
Glimmer (s) I knew The tearful *g* of the languid dawn *D. of F. Women* 74
Across a hazy *g* of the west, *Gardener's D.* 219
the old mysterious *g* steals From thy pure brows, *Tithonus* 34
Walk'd in a wintry wind by a ghastly *g*, *Maud I iii* 13
In gloss of satin and *g* of pearls, „ *xxii* 55
in the light's last *g* Tristram show'd And swung *Last Tournament* 739
I have had some *g*, at times, *Despair* 103
Awake! the creeping *g* steals, *The Flight* 4
light the *g* of the dawn? *Locksley H., Sixty* 229
eyes may take the growing *g* „ 230
Might find a flickering *g* of relief *To Mary Boyle* 47
Gleam, that had waned to a wintry *g* On icy fallow *Merlin and the G.* 83
And slowly brightening Out of the *g*, „ 89
Glimmer (verb) 'A third would *g* on her neck *Talking Oak* 221
My college friendships *g*. *Will Water.* 40
G in thy rheumy eyes. *Vision of Sin* 154
And like a ghost she *g's* on to me. *Princess vii* 181
G away to the lonely deep, *To F. D. Maurice* 28
early light Shall *g* on the dewy decks. *In Mem. ix* 12
Thy tablet *g's* to the dawn. „ *lxvii* 16
on the landward side, by a red rock, *g's* the Hall; *Maud I iv* 10
Days that will *g*, I fear, *The Wreck* 79
She sees the Best that *g's* thro' the Worst, *Ancient Sage* 72
light That *g's* on the marsh and on the grave.' *The Ring* 341

Glimmer'd Old faces *g* thro' the doors, *Mariana* 66
And April's crescent *g* cold, *Miller's D.* 107
Her taper *g* in the lake below: *Edwin Morris* 135
white kine *g*, and the trees Laid their dark arms (repeat) *In Mem. xcv* 15, 51
And *g* on his armour in the room. *Geraint and E.* 386
In Arthur's casement *g* chastely down, *Merlin and V.* 740
and thro' the gap *G* the streaming scud: *Holy Grail* 682
And God Hath more than *g* on me. *Columbus* 144
Glimmer-gowk (owl) sit like a greät *g-g* *Village Wife* 38
Glimmering (adj. and part.) (*See also* **Green-glimmering**)
the *g* water outfloweth: *Leonine Eleg.* 9
Vast images in *g* dawn, *Two Voices* 305
Who paced for ever in a *g* land, *Palace of Art* 67
Ranges of *g* vaults with iron grates, *D. of F. Women* 35
cold my wrinkled feet Upon thy *g* thresholds, *Tithonus* 68
When all the *g* moorland rings *Sir L. and Q. G.* 35
And on the *g* limit far withdrawn *Vision of Sin* 223
Naiads oar'd A *g* shoulder under gloom *To E. L.* 17
Who feels a *g* strangeness in his dream. *The Brook* 216
half in doze I seem'd To float about a *g* night, *Princess i* 247
The casement slowly grows a *g* square „ *iv* 52
By *g* lanes and walls of canvas led „ *v* 6
Disrobed the *g* statue of Sir Ralph From those rich silks, „ *Con.* 117
Came *g* thro' the laurels At the quiet evenfall, *Maud II iv* 77
and made his feet Wings thro' a *g* gallery, *Balin and Balan* 404
to Almesbury Fled all night long by *g* waste and weald, *Guinevere* 128
peal Of laughter drew me thro' the *g* glades *Sisters (E. and E.)* 116
G up the heights beyond me, *Silent Voices* 9
Glimmering (s) greenish *g's* thro' the lancets,— *Aylmer's Field* 622
There was a *g* of God's hand. *Columbus* 142
Glimpse (s) Like *g's* of forgotten dreams— *Two Voices* 381
shout For some blind *g* of freedom *Love and Duty* 6
A *g* of that dark world where I was born. *Tithonus* 33
Yet *g's* of the true. *Will Water.* 60
The shimmering *g's* of a stream; *Princess Con.* 46
And never a *g* of her window pane! *Window, No Answer* 3
Last year, I caught a *g* of his face, *Maud I xiii* 27
He never had a *g* of mine untruth, *Lancelot and E.* 125
Possible—at first *g*, and for a face Gone in a moment— *Sisters (E. and E.)* 93
Death at the *g* of a finger *Def. of Lucknow* 23
For larger *g's* of that more than man *Tiresias* 21
Green Sussex fading into blue With one gray *g* of sea; *Pro. to Gen. Hamley* 8
a *g* of a height that is higher. *By an Evolution.* 20
Glimpse (verb) lift the hidden ore That *g's*, *D. of F. Women* 275
Past, Future *g* and fade Thro' some slight spell, *Early Spring* 31
Glimpsed the herd was driven, Fire *g*; *Com. of Arthur* 433
Glimpsing And *g* over these, just seen, *Day-Dm., Sleep. P.* 47
Glin (glen) sthrames runnin' down at the back o' the *g* *Tomorrow* 24
Glisten (s) oft we saw the *g* Of ice, *The Daisy* 35
Glisten (verb) O listen, listen, your eyes shall *g* (repeat) *Sea-Fairies* 35, 37
gracious dews Began to *g* and to fall: *Princess ii* 317
Glisten'd the torrent ever pour'd And *g*— *To E. L.* 14
their feet In dewy grasses *g*; *Gareth and L.* 928
His eyes *g*: she fancied 'Is it for me?' *Lancelot and E.* 822
Glistening drove The fragrant, *g* deeps, *Arabian Nights* 14
fill'd With the blue valley and the *g* brooks, *Lover's Tale i* 331
buds Were *g* to the breezy blue; *Miller's D.* 61
Glitter flash and *g* Like sunshine on a dancing rill, *Rosalind* 28
G like a swarm of fire-flies *Locksley Hall* 10
His mantle *g's* on the rocks— *Day-Dm., Arrival* 6
Began to *g* firefly-like in copse *Princess i* 208
That *g* burnish'd by the frosty dark; „ *v* 261
on such a palm As *g's* gilded in thy Book of Hours. *Gareth and L.* 46
I saw the moonlight *g* on their tears— *Lover's Tale i* 697
Glitter'd The gemmy bridle *g* free, *L. of Shalott iii* 10
Large Hesper *g* on her tears, *Mariana in the S.* 90
The long hall *g* like a bed of flowers. *Princess ii* 439
the city *g*, Thro' cypress avenues, *The Daisy* 47
But when it *g* o'er the saddle-bow, *Gareth and L.* 1119
where it *g* on her pail, The milkmaid left *Holy Grail* 405
So dame and damsel *g* at the feast *Last Tournament* 225
brooks *g* on in the light without sound, *V. of Maeldune* 13

Glitter'd (*continued*) *g* o'er us a sunbright hand, *V. of Maldune* 84
Glittering (adj. and part.) Gold *g* thro' lamplight dim, *Arabian Nights* 18
Come, blessed brother, come. I know thy *g* face. *St. S. Stylites* 205
Draw me, thy bride, a *g* star, *St. Agnes' Eve* 23
'Fresh as the first beam *g* on a sail, *Princess iv* 44
goes, like *g* bergs of ice, „ 71
fresh young captains flash'd their *g* teeth, „ *v* 20
The *g* axe was broken in their arms, „ *vi* 51
shone Thro' *g* drops on her sad friend. „ 283
as the white and *g* star of morn Parts from a bank of snow, *Marr. of Geraint* 734
Queen who stood All *g* like May sunshine *Merlin and V.* 88
Her eyes and neck *g* went and came; „ 960
Fled like a *g* rivulet to the tarn: *Lancelot and E.* 52
Whom *g* in enamell'd arms the maid „ 619
yet one *g* foot disturb'd The lucid well; *Tiresias* 41
The *g* Capitol; *Freedom* 4
Glittering (s) Blown into *g* by the popular breath, *Romney's R.* 49
Globe circles of the *g's* Of her keen eyes *The Poet* 43
Thro' the shadow of the *g* we sweep *Locksley Hall* 183
As thro' the slumber of the *g* *The Voyage* 23
Thy spirit should fail from off the *g*; *In Mem. lxxxiv* 36
flower, That blows a *g* of after arrowlets, *Gareth and L.* 1029
We should see the *G* we groan in, *Locksley H., Sixty* 188
I would the *g* from end to end *Epilogue* 12
Since our Queen assumed the *g*, the sceptre. *On Jub. Q. Victoria* 3
Many a hearth upon our dark *g* *Vastness* 1
G again, and make Honey Moon. *The Ring* 15
eyes have known this *g* of ours, *To Ulysses* 2
hurl'd so high they ranged about the *g*? *St. Telemachus* 2
Globed stars that *g* themselves in Heaven, *Enoch Arden* 597
Globing *G* Honey Moons Bright as this. *The Ring* 7
Glode *G* over earth till the glorious creature *Batt. of Brunanburh* 29
Gloom (s) (*See also* **City-gloom, Thunder-gloom**) Flinging the *g* of yesternight On the white day; *Ode to Memory* 9
That over-vaulted grateful *g*, *Palace of Art* 54
Floods all the deep-blue *g* with beams *D. of F. Women* 186
A motion toiling in the *g*— *Love thou thy land* 54
Reading her perfect features in the *g*, *Gardener's D.* 175
Thy cheek begins to redden thro' the *g*, *Tithonus* 37
The *g* of ten Decembers. *Will Water.* 104
glimmering shoulder under *g* Of cavern pillars; *To E. L.* 17
lying thus inactive, doubt and *g*. *Enoch Arden* 113
Thicker the drizzle grew, deeper the *g*; „ 679
find a deeper in the narrow *g* By wife and child; *Aylmer's Field* 840
from utter *g* stood out the breasts, *Lucretius* 60
Dropt thro' the ambrosial *g* *Princess iv* 24
Out I sprang from glow to *g*: „ 178
moving thro' the uncertain *g*, „ 216
all the glens are drown'd in azure *g* „ 525
The height, the space, the *g*, *The Daisy* 59
The *g* that saddens Heaven and Earth, „ 102
and a stifled splendour and *g*. *High. Pantheism* 10
To touch thy thousand years of *g*: *In Mem. ii* 12
Thy *g* is kindled at the tips, „ *xxxix* 11
And passes into *g* again. „ 12
Thro' all its intervital *g* In some long trance „ *xliii* 3
When on the *g* I strive to paint The face „ *lxx* 2
Recalls, in change of light or *g*, „ *lxxxv* 74
rollest from the gorgeous *g* Of evening „ *lxxxvi* 2
And suck'd from out the distant *g* „ *xcv* 53
But touch'd with no ascetic *g*; „ *cix* 10
But iron dug from central *g*, „ *cxviii* 21
And yearn'd to burst the folded *g*, „ *cxxii* 3
With tender *g* the roof, the wall; „ *Con.* 118
cold face, star-sweet on a *g* profound; *Maud I iii* 4
And laying his trams in a poison'd *g* „ *x* 8
Set in the heart of the carven *g*, „ *xiv* 11
in the fragrant *g* Of foreign churches— „ *xix* 53
Commingled with the *g* of imminent war, *Ded. of Idylls* 13
Before a *g* of stubborn-shafted oaks, *Geraint and E.* 120
thro' the green *g* of the wood they past, „ 195
So bush'd about it is with *g*, *Balin and Balan* 95
the *g* Of twilight deepens round it, „ 232

Gloom (s) (*continued*) and in him *g* on *g* Deepen'd: *Balin and Balan* 286
there in *g* cast himself all along, Moaning „ 434
she will call That three-days-long presageful *g* *Merlin and V.* 320
The tree that shone white-listed thro' the *g*. „ 939
in change of glare and *g* Her eyes and neck „ 959
the sallow-rifted *g's* Of evening, *Lancelot and E.* 1002
Came like a driving *g* across my mind. *Holy Grail* 370
coming out of *g* Was dazzled by the sudden light, *Pelleas and E.* 104
the *g*, That follows on the turning of the world, „ 548
and yellowing leaf And *g* and gleam, *Last Tournament* 155
All in a death-dumb autumn-dripping *g*, „ 756
Filling with purple *g* the vacancies *Lover's Tale i* 2
that shock of *g* had fall'n Unfelt, „ 505
In battle with the *g's* of my dark will, „ 744
But these, their *g*, the mountains and the Bay, „ *iv* 16
Drown'd in the *g* and horror of the vault. „ 62
kept it thro' a hundred years of *g*, „ 195
nine long months of antenatal *g*, *De Prof., Two G.* 8
I closed my heart to the *g*; *The Wreck* 38
the Godless *g* Of a life without sun, *Despair* 6
last long stripe of waning crimson *g*, *Ancient Sage* 221
lost within a growing *g*; *Locksley H., Sixty* 73
lifts her buried life from *g* to bloom, *Demeter and P.* 98
g of the evening, Life at a close; *Vastness* 15
but a murmur of gnats in the *g*, „ 35
in the night, While the *g* is growing.' *Forlorn* 12
Or does the *g* of Age And suffering *Romney's R.* 64
the bracken amid the *g* of the heather. *June Bracken, etc.* 9
front of that ravine Which drowsed in *g*, *Death of Œnone* 76
the momentary *g*, Made by the noonday blaze *St. Telemachus* 49
Gloom (verb) There *g* the dark broad seas. *Ulysses* 45
I slip, I slide, I *g*, I glance, *The Brook* 174
That *g's* his valley, sighs to see the peak *Balin and Balan* 165
Gloom'd Would that my *g* fancy were As thine, *Supp. Confessions* 68
G the low coast and quivering brine *The Voyage* 42
A black yew *g* the stagnant air, *The Letters* 2
twilight *g*; and broader-grown the bowers *Princess vii* 48
mood as that, which lately *g* Your fancy *Merlin and V.* 325
every moment glanced His silver arms and *g*: *Holy Grail* 493
never *g* by the curse Of a sin, *The Wreck* 139
this Earth, a stage so *g* with woe *The Play* 1
Gloomier those *g* which forego The darkness *To the Queen ii* 64
Gloomiest I have had some glimmer, at times, in my *g* woe, *Despair* 103
Glooming (*See also* **Dewy-glooming, Green-glooming, Light-glooming**) And glanced athwart the *g* flats. *Mariana* 20
Or while the balmy *g*, crescent-lit, *Gardener's D.* 263
we sank From rock to rock upon the *g* quay, *Audley Court* 84
Or cool'd within the *g* wave; *In Mem. lxxxix* 45
Sunder the *g* crimson on the marge, *Gareth and L.* 1365
among the *g* alleys Progress halts on palsied feet, *Locksley H., Sixty* 219
Gloomy To anchor by one *g* thought; *Two Voices* 459
wind made work In which the *g* brewer's soul *Talking Oak* 55
Sailing along before a *g* cloud *Sea Dreams* 124
in and out the *g* skirts Of Celidon the forest; *Lancelot and E.* 291
rolling far along the *g* shores The voice of days *Pass. of Arthur* 134
Gloomy-gladed tops of many thousand pines A *g-g* hollow slowly sink *Gareth and L.* 797
Gloried I *g* in my knave, Who being still rebuked, „ 1248
Glorify fountains of the past, To *g* the present; *Ode to Memory* 3
Glorifying sparkles on a sty, *G* clown and satyr; *Princess v* 187
Glorious But in a city *g*— *Deserted House* 19
A *g* child, dreaming alone, *Eleänore* 27
'Whose eyes are dim with *g* tears, *Two Voices* 151
A *g* Devil, large in heart and brain, *To —— With Pal. of Art* 5
When I am gather'd to the *g* saints. *St. S. Stylites* 197
So *g* in his beauty and thy choice, *Tithonus* 12
vacant of our *g* gains, *Locksley Hall* 175
So sang the gallant *g* chronicle; *Princess, Pro.* 49
and albeit their *g* names Were fewer, „ *ii* 155
who rapt in *g* dreams, „ 442
facets of the *g* mountain flash Above the valleys *The Islet* 22
the leader in these *g* wars Now to *g* burial slowly borne, *Ode on Well.* 192
who gaze with temperate eyes On *g* insufficiences, *In Mem. cxii* 3
To fool the crowd with *g* lies, „ *cxxviii* 14

Glorious (*continued*) like a g ghost, to glide, Like a beam — Maud I xiv 20
starry Gemini hang like g crowns — „ III vi 7
That g roundel echoing in our ears, — Merlin and V. 426
—you know Of Arthur's g wars.' — Lancelot and E. 285
where the g King Had on his cuirass worn our Lady's Head, — „ 293
that night the bard Sang Arthur's g wars, — Guinevere 286
A g company, the flower of men, — „ 464
There came a g morning, such a one As dawns — Lover's Tale i 299
G poet who never hast written a line, — To A. Tennyson 5
Havelock's g Highlanders answer with conquering cheers, — Def. of Lucknow 99
till the g creature Sank to his setting. — Batt. of Brunanburh 29
around his head The g goddess wreath'd a golden cloud, — Achilles over the T. 5
Whose echo shall not tongue thy g doom, — Tiresias 136
Thy g eyes were dimm'd with pain — Freedom 10
And all her g empire, round and round. — Hands all Round 24
Sharers of our g past, — Open. I. and C. Exhib. 31
'Hail to the g Golden year of her Jubilee!' — On Jub. Q. Victoria 64
g annals of army and fleet, — Vastness 7

Glory (s) In marvel whence that g came — Arabian Nights 94
God's g smote him on the face.' — Two Voices 225
'G to God,' she sang, and past afar, — D. of F. Women 242
And the long glories of the winter moon. — M. d'Arthur 192
As down dark tides the g slides, — Sir Galahad 47
But o'er the dark a g spreads, — „ 55
things as they are, But thro' a kind of g. — Will Water. 72
Yet he hoped to purchase g, — The Captain 17
We lov'd the glories of the world, — The Voyage 83
And drops at G's temple-gates, — You might have won 34
glows And glories of the broad belt of the world, — Enoch Arden 579
between the less And greater g varying — Aylmer's Field 73
Thy g fly along the Italian field, — Lucretius 71
redound Of use and g to yourselves — Princess ii 43
And the wild cataract leaps in g. — „ iv 4
Like a Saint's g up in heaven: — „ v 514
The path of duty was the way to g: (repeat) — Ode on Well. 202, 210
The path of duty be the way to g: — „ 224
When can their g fade? — Light Brigade 50
The height, the space, the gloom, the g! — The Daisy 59
G of warrior, g of orator, g of song, — Wages 1
G of virtue, to fight, to struggle, to right the wrong—Nay, but she aim'd not at g, no lover of g she: Give her the g of going on, and still to be. — „ 3
G about thee, without thee; — High. Pantheism 9
Thine the liberty, thine the g, — Boädicea 41
win A g from its being far; — In Mem. xxiv 14
There comes a g on the walls: — „ lxvii 4
The mystic g swims away; — „ 9
He reach'd the g of a hand, — „ lxix 17
g of the sum of things Will flash along — „ lxxxviii 11
crown'd with attributes of woe Like glories, — „ cxviii 19
dim And dimmer, and a g done: — „ cxxi 4
The man of science himself is fonder of g, — Maud I iv 37
A g I shall not find. — „ v 22
every eye but mine will glance At Maud in all her g. — „ xx 37
your true lover may see Your g also, — „ 48
g of manhood stand on his ancient height, — „ III vi 21
Whose g was, redressing human wrong; — Ded. of Idylls 9
eagle-circles up To the great Sun of G, — Gareth and L. 22
her son Beheld his only way to g — „ 159
And g gain'd, and evermore to gain. — „ 332
Gareth all for g underwent The sooty yoke — „ 478
trusts to overthrow, Then wed, with g: — „ 620
tilt for lady's love and g here, — „ 740
here is g enow In having flung the three: — „ 1325
Forgetful of his g and his name, — Marr. of Geraint 53
court And all its perilous glories: — „ 804
Balan answer'd 'For the sake Of g; — Balin and Balan 33
As fancying that her g would be great — Merlin and V. 217
crying 'I have made his g mine,' — „ 971
your pretext, O my knight, As all for g; — Lancelot and E. 154
No keener hunter after g breathes. — „ 156
need to speak Of Lancelot in his g! — „ 464

Glory (s) (*continued*) the name Of Lancelot, and a g one with theirs. — Lancelot and E. 478
wound he spake of, all for gain Of g, — „ 567
allow my pretext, as for gain Of purer g.' — „ 587
it is my g to have loved One peerless, — „ 1090
sons Born to the g of thy name and fame, — „ 1372
beheld his fellow's face As in a g, — Holy Grail 192
Naked of g for His mortal change, — „ 448
spires And gateways in a g like one pearl— — „ 527
'G and joy and honour to our Lord — „ 839
the heat Of pride and g fired her face; — Pelleas and E. 172
unsunny face To him who won thee g! — „ 181
knights Arm'd for a day of g before the King. — Last Tournament 55
The g of our Round Table is no more.' (repeat) — „ 189, 212
the knights, Glorying in each new g, — „ 336
in their stead thy name and g cling — Pass. of Arthur 53
And the long glories of the winter moon. — „ 360
Quiver'd a flying g on her hair, — Lover's Tale i 69
A solid g on her bright black hair; — „ 367
And g of broad waters interfused, — „ 401
uphold Thy coronal of g like a God, — „ 488
in this g I had merged The other, — „ 506
sunset, glows and glories of the moon — „ ii 110
for the g of the Lord. — The Revenge 21
We have won great g, my men! — „ 85
had holden the power and g of Spain so cheap — „ 106
Better have sent Our Edith thro' the glories of the earth, — Sisters (E. and E.) 225
Never with mightier g than when we had rear'd — Def. of Lucknow 3
Gave g and more empire to the kings — Columbus 22
All g to the all-blessed Trinity, — „ 61
All g to the mother of our Lord, — „ 62
I saw The g of the Lord flash up, — „ 82
To walk within the g of the Lord — „ 89
and the glories of fairy kings; — V. of Maeldune 90
Gaining a lifelong G in battle, — Batt. of Brunanburh 8
King and Atheling, Each in his g, — „ 102
lured by the Hunger of g — „ 124
strive Again for g, while the golden lyre — Tiresias 180
of her eldest-born, her g, her boast, — Despair 73
g and shame dying out for ever in endless time, — „ 75
an' Hiven in its g smiled, As the Holy Mother o' G that smiles — Tomorrow 25
afther her paärints had inter'd g, — „ 53
Dead the warrior, dead his g, — Locksley H., Sixty 30
how her living g lights the hall, — „ 181
stars in heaven Paled, and the g grew. — Pro. to Gen. Hamley 32
three hundred whose g will never die— — Heavy Brigade 10
G to each and to all, and the charge that they made! G to all the three hundred, and all the Brigade! — „ 65
Thou sawest a g growing on the night, — Epit. on Caxton 2
Glorying in the glories of her people, — On Jub. Q. Victoria 26
once more in varnish'd g shine Thy stars — Prog. of Spring 38
plunging down Thro' that disastrous g, — St. Telemachus 29
'Thy g baffles wisdom. — Akbar's Dream 28
for no Mirage of g, but for power to fuse — „ 156
g of Kapiolani be mingled with either on Hawa-i-ee. — Kapiolani 18
Prophet-eyes may catch a g — Making of Man 6
Thou wilt strike Thy g thro' the day. — Doubt and Prayer 14

Glory (verb) how would'st thou g in all The splendours — Ancient Sage 176

Glory-circled A center'd, g-c memory, — Lover's Tale i 446

Glory-crown'd His own vast shadow g-c; — In Mem. xcvii 3

Glorying upon the bridge of war Sat g; — Spec. of Iliad 10
g in their vows and him, his knights Stood round him, — Com. of Arthur 458
stood a moment, ere his horse was brought, G; — Gareth and L. 935
the knights, G in each new glory, — Last Tournament 336
A low sea-sunset g round her hair — „ 508
g in the blissful years again to be, — To Virgil 17
G between sea and sky, — Open I. and C. Exhib. 18
G in the glories of her people, — On Jub. Q. Victoria 26

Gloss shadow of the flowers Stole all the golden g, — Gardener's D. 130
hair In g and hue the chestnut, (repeat) — The Brook 72, 207
Let darkness keep her raven g: — In Mem. i 10
merge' he said 'in form and g — „ lxxxix 41
In g of satin and glimmer of pearls, — Maud I xxii 55

Glossy find the stubborn thistle bursting Into g purples, *Ode on Well.* 207
then with a riding whip Leisurely tapping a g boot, *Maud I xiii* 19
and smooth'd The g shoulder, *Lancelot and E.* 348
Glossy-throated g-t grace, Isolt the Queen. *Last Tournament* 509
Glove With blots of it about them, ribbon, g *Aylmer's Field* 620
It chanced, her empty g upon the tomb *Princess iv* 596
Come sliding out of her sacred g, *Maud I vi* 85
fit to wear your slipper for a g. *Geraint and E.* 623
added fullness to the phrase Of 'Gauntlet in the velvet g.' *To Marq. of Dufferin* 12
Glow (s) steady sunset g That stays upon thee? *Eleänore* 55
sun begins to rise, the heavens are in a g; *May Queen, Con.* 49
felt my blood Glow with the g that slowly crimson'd *Tithonus* 56
and looks Had yet their native g: *Will Water.* 194
g's And glories of the broad belt of the world, *Enoch Arden* 578
this kindlier g Faded with morning, *Aylmer's Field* 411
Out I sprang from g to gloom: *Princess iv* 178
With a satin sail of a ruby g, *The Islet* 13
lone g and long roar Green-rushing (repeat) *Voice and the P.* 3, 39
not for thee the g, the bloom, *In Mem. ii* 9
And reach the g of southern skies, " *xii* 10
And fix my thoughts on all the g " *lxxxiv* 3
earth gone nearer to the g Of your soft splendours *Maud I xviii* 78
sunset, g's and glories of the moon *Lover's Tale ii* 110
wid all the light an' the g, *Tomorrow* 67
moon was falling greenish thro' a rosy g, *Locksley H., Sixty* 178
groves of olive in the summer g, *Frater Ave, etc.* 3
said with a sudden g On her patient face *Charity* 35
Glow (verb) vines that g Beneath the battled tower. *D. of F. Women* 219
felt my blood G with the glow that slowly crimson'd *Tithonus* 56
G's forth each softly-shadow'd arm *Day-Dm., Sleep B.* 13
Between dark stems the forest g's, *Sir Galahad* 27
over thy dark shoulder g Thy silver sister-world, *Move Eastward* 5
from his ivied nook G like a sunbeam: *Princess, Pro.* 105
now her father's chimney g's In expectation *In Mem. vi* 29
g In azure orbits heavenly-wise; " *lxxxvii* 37
The wizard lightnings deeply g, " *cxxii* 19
G's in the blue of fifty miles away. *Roses on the T.* 8
Glow'd His broad clear brow in sunlight g; *L. of Shalott iii* 28
And on the liquid mirror g *Mariana in the S.* 31
her face G, as I look'd at her. *D. of F. Women* 240
G for a moment as we past. *The Voyage* 48
before us g Fruit, blossom, viand, *Princess iv* 34
the city Of little Monaco, basking, g. *The Daisy* 8
As he g like a ruddy shield *Maud III vi* 14
his face G like the heart of a great fire *Marr. of Geraint* 559
A holy maid; tho' never maiden g, *Holy Grail* 72
G intermingling close beneath the sun. *Lover's Tale i* 436
Glowing g full-faced welcome, she Began *Princess ii* 183
g round her dewy eyes The circled Iris " *iii* 26
Above the garden's g blossom-belts, " *v* 363
Half-lapt in g gauze and golden brede, " *vi* 134
she rose G all over noble shame; " *vii* 160
She enters, g like the moon Of Eden *In Mem., Con.* 27
and g in the broad Deep-dimpled current *Gareth and L.* 1088
g on him, like a bride's On her new lord, *Merlin and V.* 616
g in all colours, the live grass, *Last Tournament* 233
Yet g in a heart of ruby— *Lover's Tale iv* 196
All over g with the sun of life, " 381
A g arm, a gleaming neck, *Miller's D.* 78
Between the shadows of the vine-bunches Floated the g sunlights, *Œnone* 182
In g health, with boundless wealth, *L. C. V. de Vere* 61
Love took up the glass of Time, and turn'd it in his g hands; *Locksley Hall* 31
delicate spark Of g and growing light *Maud I vi* 16
Pass and blush the news Over g ships; " *xvii* 12
above Broaden the g isles of vernal blue. *Prog. of Spring* 60
G with all-colour'd plums *V. of Maeldune* 60
Glowworm (adj.) lapt in wreaths of g light The mellow breaker *Princess iv* 435
Glow-worm (s) And the g-w of the grave Glimmer *Vision of Sin* 153
No bigger than a g-w shone the tent *Princess iv* 25
Now poring on the g, now the star, " 211
Glutted g all night long breast-deep in corn, " *ii* 387
Gnarl'd Thro' solid opposition crabb'd and g. *Princess iii* 126
All silver silver-green with g bark: *Mariana* 42
garlanding the g boughs With bunch and berry *Œnone* 101
Gnarr a thousand wants G at the heels *In Mem. xcviii* 17
Gnash teeth of Hell flay bare and g thee *Last Tournament* 444
Gnat (*See also* **Water-gnat**) chased away the still-recurring g, *Caress'd or Chidden* 7
Not even of a g that sings. *Day-Dm., Sleep P.* 21
I well could wish a cobweb for the g, *Merlin and V.* 370
tiny-trumpeting g can break our dream *Lancelot and E.* 137
but a murmur of g's in the gloom, *Vastness* 35
Gnaw'd g his under, now his upper lip, *Geraint and E.* 669
crazed With the grief that g at my heart, *Bandit's Death* 39
Gnawing lays his foot upon it, G and growling: *Geraint and E.* 563
Gnome G of the cavern, Griffin and Giant, *Merlin and the G.* 39
Go (*See also* **Gaw, Goä**) We are call'd—we must g. *All Things will Die* 20
Nine times goes the passing bell: " 35
whene'er Earth goes to earth, with grief, *Supp. Confessions* 38
the whirring sail goes round, (repeat) *The Owl i* 4
A weary, weary way I g, *Oriana* 89
Thought seems to come and g *Eleänore* 96
Of that deep grave to which I g: *My life is full* 7
And up and down the people g, *L. of Shalott i* 6
page in crimson clad, Goes by to tower'd Camelot; " *ii* 23
'G, vexed Spirit, sleep in trust; *Two Voices* 115
'I will g forward, sayest thou, " 190
I g, weak from suffering here: " 238
Naked I g, and void of cheer: " 239
grass Is dry and dewless. Let us g. *Miller's D.* 246
I will rise and g Down into Troy, *Œnone* 261
And let the foolish yeoman g. *L. C. V. de Vere* 72
Little Effie shall g with me to-morrow to the green, *May Queen* 25
The night-winds come and g, mother, " 33
and forgive me ere I g; *May Queen, N. Y's. E.* 34
sweeter far is death than life to me that long to g. *May Queen, Con.* 8
seem'd to g right up to Heaven and die " 40
music went that way my soul will have to g. " 42
I care not if I g to-day. " 43
Slow-dropping veils of thinnest lawn, did g; *Lotos-Eaters* 11
Old Year, you must not g; *D. of the O. Year* 15
Old Year, you shall not g. " 18
'G, take the goose, and wring her throat, *The Goose* 31
Yet now, I charge thee, quickly g again *M. d'Arthur* 79
'Ah! my lord Arthur, whither shall I g? " 227
I, the last, g forth companionless, " 236
these thou seëst—if indeed I g— " 257
But g you hence, and never see me more.' *Dora* 100
I will g, And I will have my boy, " 121
I g to-night: I come to-morrow morn. 'I g, but I return: I would I were The pilot *Audley Court* 70
let him g; his devil goes with him, *Walk. to the Mail* 27
G' (shrill'd the cotton-spinning chorus); *Edwin Morris* 122
'G!—Girl, get you in!' " 124
Power goes forth from me. *St. S. Stylites* 145
Let me g: take back thy gift: *Tithonus* 27
G to him: it is thy duty: *Locksley Hall* 52
wind arises, roaring seaward, and I g. " 194
G, look in any glass and say, *Day-Dm., Moral* 3
My breath to heaven like vapour goes: *St. Agnes' Eve* 3
The flashes come and g; " 26
When down the stormy crescent goes, *Sir Galahad* 25
Thro' dreaming towns I g, " 50
'Love may come, and love may g, *Edward Gray* 29
How goes the time? 'Tis five o'clock. *Will Water.* 3
And all the world g by them. " 48
But whither would my fancy g? " 145
'Tis gone, and let it g. " 180
G, therefore, thou! thy betters went " 185
Thy latter days increased with pence G down among the pots: " 220
To come and g, and come again, " 229
And bless me, mother, ere I g.' *Lady Clare* 56
So she goes by him attended, *L. of Burleigh* 25
O, happy planet, eastward g; *Move eastward* 4
But thou, g by. *Come not, when, etc.* 6

Go (*continued*) *G* by, *g* by. *Come not, when, etc.* 12
'Let her *g*! her thirst she slakes *Vision of Sin* 143
And the stately ships *g* on To their haven *Break, break, etc.* 9
used Enoch at times to *g* by land or sea; *Enoch Arden* 104
wanting yet a boatswain. Would he *g*? „ 123
g This voyage more than once? „ 141
cared For her or his dear children, not to *g*. „ 164
Annie, come, cheer up before I *g*.' „ 200
Keep everything shipshape, for I must *g*. „ 220
Can I *g* from Him? „ 225
wherefore did he *g* this weary way, „ 296
Annie's children long'd To *g* with others, nutting to the wood, And Annie would *g* with them; „ 363
the children pluck'd at him to *g*, „ 369
'See your bairns before you *g*! „ 870
such a time as *goes* before the leaf, *The Brook* 13
men may come and men may *g*, But I *g* on for ever. *The Brook* 33, 49, 65, 184
Yes, men may come and *g*; and these are gone, *The Brook* 186
would *g*, Labour for his own Edith, *Aylmer's Field* 419
'Let not the sun *g* down upon your wrath,' *Sea Dreams* 44
if I *g my* work is left Unfinish'd—*if* I *g*. *Lucretius* 103
man may gain Letting his own life *g*. „ 113
I spoke. 'My father, let me *g*. *Princess i* 68
against all rules For any man to *g*: „ 179
Leave us: you may *g*: „ *ii* 94
I shudder at the sequel, but I *g*.' „ 236
'Thanks,' she answer'd '*G*: we have been too long „ 357
We turn'd to *g*, but Cyril took the child, „ 362
hark the bell For dinner, let us *g*!' „ 433
Over the rolling waters *g*, „ *iii* 5
she *goes* to inform The Princess: „ 62
heal me with your pardon ere you *g*.' „ 65
I must *g*: I dare not tarry,' „ 95
Would we *g* with her? we should find the land „ 171
goes, like glittering bergs of ice, „ *iv* 71
Your oath is broken; we dismiss you: *g*. „ 360
'Stand, who *goes*?' 'Two from the palace' „ *v* 3
G: Cyril told us all.' „ 36
I will take her up and *g* my way, „ 102
A smoke *g* up thro' which I loom to her „ 130
Let so much out as gave us leave to *g*. „ 235
'All good *g* with thee! take it Sir,' „ *vi* 207
I *g* to mine own land For ever: „ 216
Let the long long procession *g*, *Ode on Well.* 15
From love to love, from home to home you *g*, *W. to Marie Alex.* 8
Patter she *goes*, my own little Annie, *Grandmother* 78
over the boards, she comes and *goes* at her will, „ 79
I, too, shall *g* in a minute. „ 104
O love, we two shall *g* no longer *The Daisy* 91
O whither, love, shall we *g*, (repeat) *The Islet* 1, 5
O thither, love, let us *g*.' „ 24
'Mock me not! mock me not! love, let us *g*.' „ 30
'A thousand voices *g* To North, *Voice and the P.* 13
Shall I write to her? shall I *g*? *Window, Letter* 5
G, little letter, apace, apace, Fly; „ 11
wet west wind and the world will *g* on. (repeat) *Window, No Answer* 6, 12
wet west wind and the world may *g* on. „ 18
I *g* to plant it on his tomb, *In Mem. viii* 22
Like her I *g*; I cannot stay; „ *xii* 5
Week after week: the days *g* by: „ *xvii* 7
The path by which we twain did *g*, „ *xxii* 1
Yet *g*, and while the holly boughs Entwine „ *xxix* 9
'*G* down beside thy native rill, „ *xxxvii* 5
And look thy look, and *g* thy way, „ *xlix* 9
I care for nothing, all shall *g*. „ *lvi* 4
let us *g*. Come; let us *g*: „ *lvii* 4
The foolish neighbours come and *g*, „ *lx* 13
Will flash along the chords and *g*. „ *lxxxviii* 12
g By summer belts of wheat and vine „ *xcviii* 3
We *g*, but ere we *g* from home, „ *cii* 5
I turn to *g*: my feet are set To leave the pleasant fields „ 21
when they learnt that I must *g* They wept „ *ciii* 17
'Enter likewise ye And *g* with us:' „ 52

Go (*continued*) The year is going, let him *g*; *In Mem. cvi* 7
With thousand shocks that come and *g*, „ *cxiii* 17
Like clouds they shape themselves and *g*. „ *cxxiii* 8
But they must *g*, the time draws on, „ *Con.* 89
nine months *g* to the shaping an infant *Maud I iv* 34
G not, happy day, (repeat) „ *xvii* 1, 3
G in and out as if at merry play, „ *xviii* 31
It is but for a little space I *g*: „ 75
brief night *goes* In babble and revel „ *xxii* 27
Let me and my passionate love *g* by, „ *II ii* 77
Me and my harmful love *g* by; „ 80
And the wheels *g* over my head, „ *v* 4
Ever about me the dead men *g*; „ 18
Let it *g* or stay, so I wake to the higher aims „ *III vi* 38
From the great deep to the great deep he *goes*.' *Com. of Arthur* 411
sent him from his senses: let me *g*.' *Gareth and L.* 71
Mother, to gain it—your full leave to *g*. „ 134
'A hard one, or a hundred, so I *g*. „ 149
Full of the wistful fear that he would *g*, „ 173
crying, 'Let us *g* no further, lord. „ 198
Thou that art her kin, *G* likewise; „ 379
Sir Kay nodded him leave to *g*, „ 520
G therefore,' and all hearers were amazed. „ 655
wherefore wilt thou *g* against the King, „ 727
'*G* therefore,' and so gives the quest to him— „ 864
O birds, that warble as the day *goes* by, „ 1076
Hence: let us *g*.' „ 1312
in, *g* in; for save yourself desire it, *Marr. of Geraint* 310
With that wild wheel we *g* not up or down; „ 351
G to the town and buy us flesh and wine; „ 372
G thou to rest, but ere thou *g* to rest Tell her, „ 512
But Yniol *goes*, and I full oft shall dream „ 751
'I will *g* back a little to my lord, *Geraint and E.* 65
And into no Earl's palace will I *g*. „ 235
I love that beauty should *g* beautifully: „ 681
Who loves that beauty should *g* beautifully? „ 684
'Yea,' said Enid, 'let us *g*.' „ 751
'If ye will not *g* To Arthur, then will Arthur come „ 814
I will weed this land before I *g*. „ 907
'*G* thou with him and him and bring it *Balin and Balan* 6
His Baron said 'We *g* but harken: „ 10
Arthur, 'Let who *goes* before me, „ 134
but thou shalt *g* with me, And we will speak „ 531
We *g* to prove it. Bide ye here the while.' She past; and Vivien murmur'd after '*G*! I bide the while.' *Merlin and V.* 97
Let *g* at last!—they ride away— „ 107
'It is not worth the keeping: let it *g*: „ 396
let his wisdom *g* For ease of heart, „ 892
Would reckon worth the taking? I will *g*. „ 917
Why *g* ye not to these fair jousts? *Lancelot and E.* 98
therefore hear my words: *g* to the jousts: „ 136
men *g* down before your spear at a touch, „ 149
hide it therefore; *g* unknown: „ 151
since I *g* to joust as one unknown At Camelot „ 190
He seem'd so sullen, vext he could not *g*: „ 210
Thro' her own side she felt the sharp lance *g*; „ 624
ye shall *g* no more On quest of mine, „ 716
Being so very wilful you must *g*,' (repeat) „ 777, 781
speak your wish, Seeing I *g* to-day:' „ 925
what force is yours to *g*, So far, „ 1063
I *g* in state to court, to meet the Queen. „ 1124
let our dumb old man alone *G* with me, „ 1128
phantom of a cup that comes and *goes*?' *Holy Grail* 44
G, since your vows are sacred, „ 314
noble deeds will come and *g* Unchallenged, „ 318
my time is hard at hand, And hence I *g*; „ 482
thou shalt see the vision when I *g*.' „ 484
g forth and pass Down to the little thorpe „ 546
entering, loosed and let him *g*.' „ 698
heard a voice, 'Doubt not, *g* forward; „ 824
but will ye to Caerleon? I *G* likewise: *Pelleas and E.* 106
Nay, let him *g*—and quickly,' „ 313
and thought, 'I will *g* back, and slay them „ 444
The foot that loiters, bidden *g*,— *Last Tournament* 117
From the great deep to the great deep he *goes*.' „ 133

Go (*continued*) Now—ere he *goes* to the great Battle? *Guinevere* 652
Arise, *g* forth and conquer as of old.' *Pass. of Arthur* 64
I charge thee, quickly *g* again, „ 247
my Lord Arthur, whither shall I *g*? „ 395
I, the last, *g* forth companionless, „ 404
With these thou seest—if indeed I *g* „ 425
'From the great deep to the great deep he *goes*.' „ 445
and *g* From less to less and vanish into light. „ 467
your love Is but a burthen: loose the bond, and *g*.' *To the Queen ii* 17
for they *g* back, And farther back, *Lover's Tale i* 80
If you *g* far in (The country people rumour) „ 518
he would *g*, Would leave the land for ever, „ *iv* 18
but for a whisper, '*G* not yet,' „ 20
Now, now, will I *g* down into the grave, „ 46
and I *g* down To kiss the dead.' „ 49
'He casts me out,' she wept, 'and *goes*' „ 103
But he was all the more resolved to *g*, „ 179
When Julian *goes*, the lord of all he saw. „ 315
saying, 'It is over: let us *g*'— „ 384
an' kiss you before I *g*.' *First Quarrel* 46
you'll kiss me before I *g*?' „ 80
an' *g* to-night by the boat.' „ 88
when he knows that I cannot *g*? *Rizpah* 3
and now you may *g* your way. „ 20
But I *g* to-night to my boy, „ 74
g, *g*, you may leave me alone— „ 79
make the Spaniard promise, if we yield, to let us *g*; *The Revenge* 94
love will *g* by contrast, as by likes. *Sisters (E. and E.)* 42
then another, and *him* too, and down *goes* he. *Def. of Lucknow* 65
G back to the Isle of Finn and suffer the Past *V. of Maeldune* 124
when a smoke from a city *goes* to heaven *Achilles over the T.* 7
g To spend my one last year among the hills. *Ancient Sage* 15
'And idle gleams will come and *g*, „ 240
this Hall at last will *g*—perhaps have gone, *The Flight* 27
ships from out the West *g* dripping thro' „ 91
gone as all on earth will *g*. *Locksley H., Sixty* 46
bound to follow, wherever she *g* *Dead Prophet* 45
G, take thine honours home; *To W. C. Macready* 6
I cannot *g*, *g* you.' *The Ring* 434
Kiss me child and *g*. „ 489
you wave me off—poor roses—must I *g*— *Happy* 101
find the white heather wherever you *g*, *Romney's R.* 108
G back to thine adulteress and die!' *Death of Œnone* 48
They sing it. Let us *g*.' *Akbar's Dream* 204
'My dear, I will tell you before I *g*.' *Charity* 36
bodies and souls *g* down in a common wreck, *The Dawn* 13
Deep under deep for ever *goes*, *Mechanophilus* 35
Let your reforms for a moment *g*! *Riflemen form!* 15

Goä (go) But Parson a cooms an' a *g's*, *N. Farmer, O. S.* 25
Seeä'd her to-daäy *g* by— „ *N. S.* 13
but *g* wheere munny is!' „ 20
Maakin' 'em *g* togither as they've good right to do. „ 34
Strange fur to *g* fur to think *North. Cobbler* 4
tha mun *g* fur it down to the inn. „ 8
Thou'll *g* sniffin' about the tap „ 64
I weänt *g* sniffin' about the tap.' „ 67
tha mun *g* fur it down to the Hinn, „ 113
I'll *g* wi' tha back: all right; *Village Wife* 2
'e bowt owd money, es wouldn't *g*, „ 49
or the gells 'ull *g* to the 'Ouse, „ 64
G to the laäne at the back, *Spinster's S's.* 6
an' they *g's* fur a walk, „ 85
When I *g's* fur to coomfut the poor „ 108
'e can naither stan' nor *g*. *Owd Roä* 2
Fur to *g* that night to 'er foälk „ 52
'Then hout to-night tha shall *g*.' „ 58
tell'd 'er, 'Yeäs I mun *g*.' „ 98

Goad prick'd with *g's* and stings; *Palace of Art* 150
His own thought drove him, like a *g*. *M. d'Arthur* 185
His own thought drove him like a *g*. *Pass. of Arthur* 353

Goal Making for one sure *g*. *Palace of Art* 248
pass beyond the *g* of ordinance *Tithonus* 30
make Our progress falter to the woman's *g*.' *Princess vi* 127
his days, moves with him to one *g*, „ *vii* 263
Is the *g* so far away? *Ode Inter. Exhib.* 29

Goal (*continued*) good Will be the final *g* of ill, *In Mem. liv* 2
Touch thy dull *g* of joyless gray, „ *lxxii* 27
Arrive at last the blessed *g*, „ *lxxxiv* 41
friend, who camest to thy *g* So early, „ *cxiv* 23
larger, tho' the *g* of all the saints— *Holy Grail* 528
g of this great world Lies beyond sight: *To the Queen ii* 59
No guess-work! I was certain of my *g*; *Columbus* 45
watch the chariot whirl About the *g* again, *Tiresias* 177
And if we move to such a *g* *Politics* 3
he touch'd his *g*, The Christian city. *St. Telemachus* 34

Goän (gone) *G* into mangles an' tonups, *Owd Roä* 28
An' 'ed *g* their waäys; „ 36
thowt o' the good owd times 'at was *g*, „ 43
an' I thowt as 'e'd *g* cleän-wud, „ 61

Goan Padre And when the *G P* quoting Him, *Akbar's Dream* 74

Goat Leading a jet-black *g* white-horn'd, *Œnone* 51
are men better than sheep or *g's* *M. d'Arthur* 250
Catch the wild *g* by the hair, *Locksley Hall* 170
the beard-blown *g* Hang on the shaft, *Princess iv* 78
no more thanks than might a *g* have given *Merlin and V.* 278
Swine, say ye? swine, *g's*, asses, *Last Tournament* 321
'Then were swine, *g's*, asses, geese The wiser fools, „ 325
are men better than sheep or *g's* *Pass. of Arthur* 418

Goatfoot Catch her, *g*: nay, Hide, hide *Lucretius* 203

Goatskin wear an undress'd *g* on my back; *St. S. Stylites* 116

Go-between To play their *g-b* as heretofore *Aylmer's Field* 523

Goblet A *g* on the board by Balin, *Balin and Balan* 362
priceless *g* with a priceless wine Arising, *Lover's Tale iv* 227

Goblin You did but come as *g's* in the night, *Princess v* 220

Go-cart is but a child Yet in the *g-c*. „ *Con.* 78

God *G gave her peace; her land reposed;* *To the Queen* 26
O *G*! my *G*! have mercy now. *Supp. Confessions* 1
sure it is a special care Of *G*, „ 64
strive To reconcile me with thy *G*. „ 102
stood Betwixt me and the light of *G*! That hitherto
I had defied And had rejected *G*— „ 110
I would pray—that *G* would move And strike „ 115
Yet, my *G*, Whom call I Idol? „ 179
And thou of *G* in thy great charity) *Isabel* 40
Oh *G*, that I were dead!' *Mariana* 84
not the *g's* More purely, when they wish to charm *A Character* 13
G's great gift of speech abused *A Dirge* 44
Half *G's* good sabbath, *To J. M. K.* 11
Warrior of *G*, whose strong right arm *Alexander* 1
How long, O *G*, shall men be ridden down, *Poland* 1
G in his mercy lend her grace, *L. of Shalott iv* 53
G's glory smote him on the face.' *Two Voices* 225
On to *G's* house the people prest: „ 409
Would *G* renew me from my birth *Miller's D.* 27
But that *G* bless thee, dear— „ 235
Cluster'd about his temples like a *G's*; *Œnone* 60
all the full-faced presence of the *G's* „ 80
see thy Paris judge of *G's*.' „ 90
the *G's* Rise up for reverence. „ 109
likest *g's*, who have attain'd Rest in a happy place „ 130
strike within thy pulses, like a *G's*, „ 162
Her presence, hated both of *G's* and men. „ 229
Moulded by *G*, and temper'd with the tears *To —— With Pal. of Art* 18
My *G's*, with whom I dwell! *Palace of Art* 196
I sit as *G* holding no form of creed, „ 211
G, before whom ever lie bare The abysmal deeps „ 222
Lay there exiled from eternal *G*, „ 263
To lie within the light of *G*, *May Queen, Con.* 59
The *G's* are hard to reconcile: *Lotos-Eaters, C. S.* 81
On the hills like *G's* together, „ 110
A daughter of the *g's*, divinely tall, *D. of F. Women* 87
we sat as *G* by *G*: „ 142
'My *G*, my land, my father— „ 209
'Saw *G* divide the night with flying flame, „ 225
beautiful a thing it was to die For *G* and for my sire! „ 232
'Glory to *G*,' she sang, and past afar, „ 242
G gives us love. Something to love He lends us; *To J. S.* 13
I will not say '*G's* ordinance Of Death „ 45
Imitates *G*, and turns her face To every land *On a Mourner* 2

God (continued) And Virtue, like a household g Promising empire; On a Mourner 30
And G forget the stranger!' The Goose 56
G knows: he has a mint of reasons: The Epic 33
G fulfils himself in many ways, M. d'Arthur 241
knowing G, they lift not hands of prayer „ 252
Bound by gold chains about the feet of G. „ 255
Breathed, like the covenant of a G, Gardener's D. 209
She broke out in praise To G, Dora 113
'G bless him!' he said, 'and may he never know „ 149
May G forgive me!—I have been to blame. „ 161
G made the woman for the man, (repeat) Edwin Morris 43, 50
'G made the woman for the use of man, „ 91
him That was a G, and is a lawyer's clerk, „ 102
Let this avail, just, dreadful, mighty G, St. S. Stylites 9
I had not stinted practice, O my G. „ 59
I bore, whereof, O G, thou knowest all. „ 70
Thou, O G, Knowest alone whether this was or no. „ 82
in your looking you may kneel to G. „ 141
G reaps a harvest in me. „ 148
G reaps a harvest in thee. „ 149
G hath now Sponged and made blank of crimeful record „ 157
G only thro' his bounty hath thought fit, „ 186
a priest, a man of G, Among you there, „ 214
for a man is not as G, Love and Duty 30
G love us, as if the seedsman, Golden Year 70
Meet adoration to my household g's, Ulysses 42
unbecoming men that strove with G's. „ 53
To his great heart none other than a G! Tithonus 14
'The G's themselves cannot recall their gifts.' „ 49
Would to G—for I had loved thee more Locksley Hall 64
Ah, blessed vision! blood of G! Sir Galahad 45
'O just and faithful knight of G! „ 79
Sipt wine from silver, praising G, Will Water. 127
G's blessing on the day! Lady Clare 8
G be thank'd!' said Alice the nurse, „ 17
'As G's above,' said Alice the nurse, „ 23
G made himself an awful rose of dawn, (repeat) Vision of Sin 50, 224
'Lo! G's likeness—the ground-plan— „ 187
broad-limb'd G's at random thrown By fountain-urns; To E. L. 15
'Annie, this voyage by the grace of G Enoch Arden 190
G bless him, he shall sit upon my knees „ 197
Cast all your cares on G; „ 222
We might be still as happy as G grants „ 416
'You have been as G's good angel in our house. G bless you for it, G reward you for it, „ 423
for G's sake,' he answer'd, 'both our sakes, „ 509
In those two deaths he read G's warning 'wait.' „ 571
O G Almighty, blessed Saviour, „ 782
'My G has bow'd me down to what I am; „ 856
that almighty man, The county G— Aylmer's Field 14
sons of men Daughters of G; „ 45
'Bless, G bless 'em: marriages are made in Heaven.' „ 188
all but those who knew the living G— „ 637
with thy worst self hast thou clothed thy G. „ 646
No coarse and blockish G of acreage „ 651
Thy G is far diffused in noble groves „ 653
In such a shape dost thou behold thy G. „ 657
Prince of Peace, the Mighty G, „ 669
'O pray G that he hold up' „ 733
A rushing tempest of the wrath of G „ 757
and made Their own traditions G, „ 795
sin That neither G nor man can well forgive, Hypocrisy, Sea Dreams 63
Who, never naming G except for gain, „ 188
what dreams, ye holy G's, what dreams! Lucretius 33
worse Than aught they fable of the quiet G's. „ 55
Rather, O ye G's, Poet-like, „ 92
Which things appear the work of mighty G's. The G's! and if I go my work is left Unfinish'd—if I go. The G's, who haunt The lucid interspace of world „ 102
The G's, the G's! If all be atoms, how then should the G's Being atomic „ 113
My master held That G's there are, „ 117
G's there are, and deathless. „ 121

God (continued) 'Look where another of our G's, the Sun, Lucretius 124
men like soldiers may not quit the post Allotted by the G's: but he that holds The G's are careless, „ 149
Picus and Faunus, rustic G's? „ 182
O ye G's, I know you careless, „ 207
(G help her) she was wedded to a fool; Princess iii 83
tho' your Prince's love were like a G's, „ 248
the old G of war himself were dead, „ v 145
Interpreter between the G's and men, „ vii 322
G bless the narrow sea which keeps her off, „ Con. 51
G bless the narrow seas! „ 70
keep it ours, O G, from brute control; Ode on Well. 159
palter'd with Eternal G for power; „ 180
To which our G himself is moon and sun. „ 217
On G and Godlike men we build our trust. „ 266
G accept him, Christ receive him. „ 281
We love not this French G, the child of Hell, Third of Feb. 7
I wish'd it had been G's will that I, Grandmother 73
G, not man, is the Judge of us all „ 95
thank G that I keep my eyes. „ 106
Dear to the man that is dear to G; To F. D. Maurice 36
'G help me! save I take my part Sailor Boy 21
Ah G! the petty fools of rhyme Lit. Squabbles 1
G's are moved against the land.' The Victim 6
'The G's have answer'd: We give them the boy.' „ 39
The holy G's, they must be appeased, „ 47
G's, he said, 'would have chosen well; „ 58
G's have answer'd; We give them the wife!' „ 78
G is law, say the wise; High. Pantheism 13
Law is G, say some: no G at all, says the fool; „ 15
I should know what G and man is. Flow. in cran. wall. 6
'Hear it, G's! the G's have heard it, Boädicea 21
Doubt not ye the G's have answer'd, „ 22
thine the battle-thunder of G,' „ 44
Strong Son of G, immortal Love, In Mem., Pro. 1
O mother, praying G will save Thy sailor,— „ vi 13
drains The chalice of the grapes of G; „ x 16
What then were G to such as I? „ xxxiv 9
G shut the doorways of his head. „ xliv 4
Ye watch, like G, the rolling hours „ li 14
When G hath made the pile complete; „ liv 8
The likest G within the soul? „ lv 4
Are G and Nature then at strife, „ 5
That slope thro' darkness up to G, „ 16
Who trusted G was love indeed „ lvi 13
In endless age? It rests with G. „ lxxiii 12
But stay'd in peace with G and man. „ lxxx 8
G's finger touch'd him, and he slept. „ lxxxv 20
saw The G within him light his face, „ lxxxvii 36
With g's in unconjectured bliss, „ xciii 10
Israel made their g's of gold, „ xcvi 23
Where G and Nature met in light; „ cxi 20
mix'd with G and Nature thou, „ cxxx 11
That friend of mine who lives in G, „ Con. 140
That G, which ever lives and loves, „ 141
One G, one law, one element, „ 142
O father! O G! was it well?— Maud I i 6
ah G, as he used to rave. „ 60
G grant I may find it at last! „ ii 1
how G will bring them about „ iv 44
Ah G, for a man with heart, head, hand, „ x 60
May G make me more wretched Than ever „ xix 94
Arise, my G, and strike, „ II i 45
as long, O G, as she Have a grain of love for me, „ ii 52
Britain's one sole G be the millionaire: „ III vi 22
G's just wrath shall be wreak'd on a giant liar; „ 45
I embrace the purpose of G, „ 59
G's love set Thee at his side again! Ded. of Idylls 55
'the fire of G Descends upon thee in the battle-field: Com. of Arthur 129
Arthur said, 'Man's word is G in man: „ 133
G hath told the King a secret word. „ 489
In whom high G hath breathed a secret thing. „ 501
G wot, he had not beef and brewis enow, Gareth and L. 457
as for love, G wot, I love not yet, But love I shall, G willing.' „ 561

God (*continued*) and cried, '*G* bless the King, and all his fellowship!' *Gareth and L.* 698
my lance Hold, by *G's* grace, he shall into the mire— „ 723
G wot, so thou wert nobly born, „ 1064
'*G* wot, I never look'd upon the face, „ 1333
Canst thou not trust the limbs thy *G* hath given, „ 1388
'Here, by *G's* grace, is the one voice for me.' *Marr. of Geraint* 344
'Here by *G's* rood is the one maid for me.' „ 368
Who knows? another gift of the high *G*, „ 821
I know, *G* knows, too much of palaces! *Geraint and E.* 236
G's curse, it makes me mad to see you „ 616
flush'd with fight, or hot, *G's* curse, with anger— „ 661
Yea, *G*, I pray you of your gentleness, „ 710
Man's word is *G* in man.' *Balin and Balan* 8
and yet—*G* guide them—young.' *Merlin and V.* 29
by *G's* rood, I trusted you too much.' „ 376
for love of *G* and men And noble deeds, „ 412
Her *G*, her Merlin, the one passionate love „ 955
O *G*, that I had loved a smaller man! „ 872
G's mercy, what a stroke was there! *Lancelot and E.* 24
but *G* Broke the strong lance, „ 25
rule the land Hereafter, which *G* hinder.' „ 66
honours his own word, As if it were his *G's*?' „ 144
G wot, his shield is blank enough. „ 197
in this heathen war the fire of *G* Fills him: „ 315
Rapt on his face as if it were a *G's*. „ 356
No diamonds! for *G's* love, a little air! „ 505
'Yea, by *G's* death,' said he, 'ye love him well, „ 679
Not all unhappy, having loved *G's* best And greatest, „ 1093
I would to *G*, Seeing the homeless trouble „ 1364
shaped, it seems, By *G* for thee alone, „ 1367
may *G*, I pray him, send a sudden Angel „ 1423
'*G* make thee good as thou are beautiful,' *Holy Grail* 136
named us each by name, Calling '*G* speed!' „ 352
seem'd Shoutings of all the sons of *G*: „ 509
If *G* would send the vision, well: „ 658
When *G* made music thro' them, „ 878
Nor the high *G* a vision, nor that One Who rose again: „ 918
I might have answer'd them Even before high *G*. *Pelleas and E.* 463
'Fear *G*: honour the King— *Last Tournament* 302
Conceits himself as *G* that he can make „ 355
woman-worshipper? Yea, *G's* curse, and I! „ 447
My *G*, the measure of my hate for Mark „ 537
Pale-blooded, she will yield herself to *G*.' „ 608
'I will flee hence and give myself to *G*'— „ 624
May *G* be with thee, sweet, (repeat) „ 627, 629
My *G*, the power Was once in vows „ 648
And every follower eyed him as a *G*; „ 678
those whom *G* had made full-limb'd and tall, *Guinevere* 42
Would *G* that thou could'st hide me „ 118
To honour his own word as if his *G's*, „ 473
I guard as *G's* high gift from scathe and wrong, „ 494
I forgive thee, as Eternal *G* Forgives: „ 544
We two may meet before high *G*, „ 564
hereafter in the heavens Before high *G*. „ 638
my *G*, What might I not have made of thy fair world, „ 654
As if some lesser *g* had made the world, *Pass. of Arthur* 14
Till the High *G* behold it from beyond, „ 16
My *G*, thou hast forgotten me in my death: Nay— *G* my Christ—I pass but shall not die.' „ 27
G fulfils himself in many ways, „ 409
knowing *G*, they lift not hands of prayer „ 420
Bound by gold chains about the feet of *G*. „ 423
G unknits the riddle of the one, *Lover's Tale i* 181
so much wealth as *G* had charged her with— „ 213
I said to her, 'A day for *G's* to stoop,' „ 304
uphold Thy coronal of glory like a *G*, „ 488
tell him of the bliss he had with *G*— „ 674
nymph and *g* ran ever round in gold— „ *iv* 197
Some cousin of his and hers—O *G*, so like!' „ 327
G bless you, my own little Nell.' *First Quarrel* 22
I told them my tale, *G's* own truth— *Rizpah* 34
G 'ill pardon the hell-black raven „ 39
I have been with *G* in the dark— „ 79
an' the loov o' *G* fur men, *North. Cobbler* 55

God (*continued*) 'Fore *G* I am no coward; *The Revenge* 4
G of battles, was ever a battle like this „ 62
Fall into the hands of *G*, „ 90
and lodged with Plato's *G*, *Sisters (E. and E.)* 131
G help the wrinkled children that are Christ's „ 183
My *G*, I would not live Save that I think „ 228
G help them, our children and wives! *Def. of Lucknow* 8
But *G* is with me in this wilderness, *Sir J. Oldcastle* 8
G's free air, and hope of better things. „ 10
So much *G's* cause was fluent in it— „ 17
Had he *G's* word in Welsh He might be kindlier: „ 22
come, *G* willing, to outlearn the filthy friar. „ 118
to thee, green boscage, work of *G*, „ 129
I spread mine arms, *G's* work, I said, „ 137
'Bury them as *G's* truer images Are daily buried.' „ 140
Do penance in his heart, *G* hears him.' „ 143
What profits an ill Priest Between me and my *G*? „ 145
'No bread, no bread. *G's* body!' „ 159
Then I, *G* help me, I So mock'd, „ 162
G pardon all—Me, them, and all the world— „ 168
the fourth Was like the Son of *G*! „ 176
G willing, I will burn for Him. „ 193
In praise to *G* who led me thro' the waste. *Columbus* 17
that was clean Against *G's* word: „ 55
There was a glimmering of *G's* hand. „ 142
And *G* Hath more than glimmer'd on me. „ 143
Ah *G*, the harmless people whom we found „ 181
Who took us for the very *G's* from Heaven, „ 183
in that flight of ages which are *G's* „ 202
thunder of *G* peal'd over us all the day, *V. of Maeldune* 113
Whereon the Spirit of *G* moves as he will— *De Prof., Two G.* 28
dream of a shadow, go—*G* bless you. *To W. H. Brookfield* 14
and the secret of the *G's*. My son the *G's*, despite of human prayer, *Tiresias* 8
great *G*, Arês, burns in anger still „ 11
trembling fathers call'd The *G's* own son. „ 17
some strange hope to see the nearer *G*. „ 29
angers of the *G's* for evil done „ 62
Falling about their shrines before their *G's*, „ 105
yesternight, To me, the great *G* Arês, „ 111
stand Firm-based with all her *G's*. „ 142
and quench The red *G's* anger, „ 158
flash The faces of the *G's*— „ 173
those who mix all odour to the *G's* „ 184
ah *G*, what a heart was mine to forsake her *The Wreck* 95
'would *G*, we had never met!' „ 102
but ah *G*, that night, that night *Despair* 8
Flashing with fires as of *G*, „ 16
your faith and a *G* of eternal rage, „ 39
taking the place of the pitying *G* that should be! „ 42
'Ah *G*' tho' I felt as I spoke I was taking the name in vain—'Ah *G*' and we turn'd to each other, „ 52
Ah *G*, should we find Him, perhaps, „ 56
And if I believed in a *G*, „ 70
but were there a *G* as you say, „ 101
Of a *G* behind all—after all—the great *G* for aught that I know; But the *G* of Love and of Hell together— „ 104
If there be such a *G*, may the great *G* „ 106
Or power as of the *G's* gone blind *Ancient Sage* 80
none but *G's* could build this house „ 83
To lie, to lie—in *G's* own house— *The Flight* 52
side by side in *G's* free light and air, „ 81
meet your paärints agin an' yer Danny O'Roon afore *G* *Tomorrow* 57
if soä pleäse *G*, to the hend. *Spinster's S's.* 112
'thank *G* that I hevn't naw cauf o' my oän.' „ 116
Sons of *G*, and kings of men *Locksley H., Sixty* 122
'Would to *G* that we were there'? „ 192
a *G* must mingle with the game: „ 271
Warrior of *G*, man's friend, and tyrant's foe, *Epit. on Gordon* 1
G the traitor's hope confound! (repeat) *Hands all Round* 10, 22, 34
Pray *G* our greatness may not fail „ 31
Led upward by the *G* of ghosts and dreams, *Demeter and P.* 5
when before have *G's* or men beheld The Life „ 29
Spring from his fallen *G*, „ 80
we spin the lives of men, And not of *G's*, „ 86

God (*continued*) he, the *G* of dreams, who heard my cry, *Demeter and P.* 91
I, Earth-Goddess, cursed the *G's* of Heaven. „ 102
But younger kindlier *G's* to bear us down, As we bore down the *G's* before us? *G's*, To quench, not hurl the thunderbolt, „ 131
G's indeed, To send the noon into the night „ 134
made themselves as *G's* against the fear Of Death „ 141
O *G*, I could blaspheme, *Happy* 15
That *G* would ever slant His bolt from falling „ 81
trust myself forgiven by the *G* to whom I kneel „ 86
Now *G* has made you leper in His loving care „ 91
In the name Of the everlasting *G*, I will live and die „ 108
G stay me there, if only for your sake, *Romney's R.* 34
happy to be chosen Judge of *G's*, *Death of Œnone* 16
Paris, himself as beauteous as a *G*. „ 18
Paris, no longer beauteous as a *G*, „ 25
Before the feud of *G's* had marr'd our peace, „ 32
Thou knowest, Taught by some *G*, „ 35
G's Avenge on stony hearts a fruitless prayer „ 40
Spurning a shatter'd fragment of the *G*, *St. Telemachus* 16
in his heart he cried 'The call of *G*!' „ 27
muttering to himself 'The call of *G*' „ 42
O *G* in every temple I see people that see thee, *Akbar's D., Inscrip.* 1
to be reconcil'd?—No, by the Mother of *G*, *Bandit's Death* 17
as *G's* own scriptures tell, *Charity* 3
a woman, *G* bless her, kept me from Hell. „ 4
Vanish'd shadow-like *G's* and Goddesses, *Kapiolani* 27
My Father, and my Brother, and my *G*! *Doubt and Prayer* 8

Godamoighty (God Almighty) *g* an' parson 'ud nobbut le ma aloän, *N. Farmer, O. S.* 43
Do *g* knaw what a's doing a-taäkin' o' meä? „ 45
But *g* a moost taäke meä an' taäke ma now „ 51

God-bless-you Sneeze out a full *G-b-y* right and left? *Edwin Morris* 80
Gript my hand hard, and with *G-b-y* went. *Sea Dreams* 160
A curse in his *G-b-y*: „ 164

Goddess (*See also* **Earth-goddess**) if thou canst, O *G*, like ourselves *Lucretius* 80
presented Maid Or Nymph, or G, *Princess i* 197
Even now the *G* of the Past, *Lover's Tale i* 16
The glorious *g* wreath'd a golden cloud, *Achilles over the T.* 5
for the bright-eyed *g* made it burn. „ 29
O *G'es*, help me up thither! *Parnassus* 3
flung the berries, and dared the *G*, *Kapiolani* 6
believing that Peelè the *G* would wallow „ 8
climb to the dwelling of Peelè the *G*! „ 22
Vanish'd shadow-like Gods and *G'es*, „ 27

Godfather *G*, come and see your boy: *To F. D. Maurice* 2

God-fearing Altho' a grave and staid *G-f* man, *Enoch Arden* 112
Enoch as a brave *G-f* man Bow'd himself down „ 185

God-gifted *G-g* organ-voice of England, *Milton* 3

God-in-man *G-i-m* is one with man-in-God, *Enoch Arden* 187

Godiva *G*, wife to that grim Earl, *Godiva* 12

Godless That tumbled in the *G* deep; *In Mem. cxxiv* 12
The craft of kindred and the *G* hosts *Guinevere* 427
three more dark days of the *G* gloom *Despair* 6
The *G* Jeptha vows his child . . . *The Flight* 26
G fury of peoples, and Christless frolic of kings, *The Dawn* 7

God-like (*See also* **Human-Godlike**) *G-l*, grasps the triple forks, *Of old sat Freedom* 15
But then most *G* being most a man. *Love and Duty* 31
Together, dwarf'd or *g*, bond or free: *Princess vii* 260
Her *g* head crown'd with spiritual fire, *Merlin and V.* 837
Thee the *G*, thee the changeless *Akbar's D., Hymn* 4
Two *g* faces gazed below; *Palace of Art* 162
'O *G-l* isolation which art mine, „ 197
On God and *G* men we build our trust. *Ode on Well.* 266
touch of Charity Could lift them nearer *G-l* state *Lit. Squabbles* 14
Beyond all dreams of *G* womanhood, *Tiresias* 54

God-speed And left them with *G-s*, *Gareth and L.* 890

Goest whither *g* thou, tell me where?' *Day-Dm., Depart.* 26
And now thou *g* up to mock the King, *Gareth and L.* 292
thou *g*, he will fight thee first; „ 1295

Goin' (going) an' gied to the tramps *g* by— *Village Wife* 33
'Ochone are ye *g'* away?' '*G*' to cut the Sassenach whate' *Tomorrow* 13
'An' whin are ye *g'* to lave me?' „ 17

Going (*See also* **A-Gawin', Gawin', Goin'**) We heard the steeds to battle *g*, *Oriana* 15
G before to some far shrine, *On a Mourner* 17
I am *g* a long way With these thou seëst— *M. d'Arthur* 256
On a day when they were *g* O'er the lone expanse, *The Captain* 25
They by parks and lodges *g* *L. of Burleigh* 17
far end of an avenue, *G* we know not where: *Enoch Arden* 359
Narrow'd her *g's* out and comings in; *Aylmer's Field* 501
And thinner, clearer, farther *g*! *Princess iv* 8
Give her the glory of *g* on, *Wages* 5
Give her the wages of *g* on, „ 10
And has bitten the heel of the *g* year. *Window, Winter* 6
The year is *g*, let him go; *In Mem. cvi* 7
g to the king, He made this pretext, *Marr. of Geraint* 32
bent he seem'd on *g* the third day, „ 604
Bent as he seem'd on *g* this third day, „ 625
Enid in their *g* had two fears, *Geraint and E.* 817
Coming and *g*, and he lay as dead *Merlin and V.* 213
Coming and *g*, and she lay as dead, „ 644
'*G*? and we shall never see you more. *Lancelot and E.* 926
but in *g* mingled with dim cries Far in the moonlit *Pass. of Arthur* 41
I am *g* a long way With these thou seëst— „ 424
Between the *g* light and growing night? *Lover's Tale i* 664
I am *g* to leave you a bit— *First Quarrel* 80
'*G*! you're *g* to her—kiss her— „ 81
Good-night. I am *g*. He calls. *Rizpah* 86
G? I am old and slighted: *Columbus* 241
I was not *g* to stab you, *Bandit's Death* 6

Gold (adj.) With that *g* dagger of thy bill *Blackbird* 11
Bound by *g* chains about the feet of God. *M. d'Arthur* 255
His face was ruddy, his hair was *g*, *The Victim* 35
'If we have fish at all Let them be *g*; *Marr. of Geraint* 670
true hearts be blazon'd on her tomb In letters *g* and azure!' *Lancelot and E.* 1345
the cup was *g*, the draught was mud.' *Last Tournament* 298
Bound by *g* chains about the feet of God. *Pass. of Arthur* 423
knew not that which pleased it most, The raven ringlet or the *g*; *The Ring* 166
bright bird that still is veering there Above his four *g* letters) „ 333

Gold (s) (*See also* **Cloth of Gold, Gowd**) laws of marriage character'd in *g* *Isabel* 16
By Bagdat's shrines of fretted *g*, *Arabian Nights* 7
G glittering thro' lamplight dim, „ 18
With royal frame-work of wrought *g*; *Ode to Memory* 82
plant in semblance, grew A flower all *g*, *The Poet* 24
bosoms prest To little harps of *g*; *Sea-Fairies* 4
with cymbals, and harps of *g*, *Dying Swan* 32
With a crown of *g* On a throne? *The Merman* 6
I should look like a fountain of *g* *The Mermaid* 18
Slowly, as from a cloud of *g*, *Eleänore* 73
Disclosed a fruit of pure Hesperian *g*, *Œnone* 66
Brow-bound with burning *g*. *D. of F. Women* 128
Either from lust of *g*, or like a girl *M. d'Arthur* 127
Three Queens with crowns of *g*— „ 198
Cursed be the *g* that gilds the straiten'd forehead *Locksley Hall* 62
Every door is barr'd with *g*, „ 100
trapt In purple blazon'd with armorial *g*. *Godiva* 52
Pull off, pull off, the brooch of *g*, *Lady Clare* 39
Beneath a manelike mass of rolling *g*, *Aylmer's Field* 68
g that branch'd itself Fine as ice-ferns „ 221
made pleasant by the baits Of *g* and beauty, „ 487
heaps of living *g* that daily grow, „ 655
swore Not by the temple but the *g*, „ 794
but a gulf of ruin, swallowing *g*, *Sea Dreams* 79
a long reef of *g*, Or what seem'd *g*: „ 127
Still so much *g* was left; „ 130
Wreck'd on a reef of visionary *g*.' „ 139
silken hood to each, And zoned with *g*; *Princess ii* 18
Came furrowing all the orient into *g*. „ *iii* 18
Fruit, blossom, viand, amber wine, and *g*. „ *iv* 35
gemlike eyes, And *g* and golden heads; „ 481

Gold (s) (*continued*) all the *g* That veins the world were pack'd *Princess iv* 542
A single band of *g* about her hair, „ *v* 513
Under the cross of *g* That shines over city and river, *Ode on Well.* 49
Steel and *g*, and corn and wine, *Ode Inter. Exhib.* 17
Whose crying is a cry for *g*: *The Daisy* 94
And you with *g* for hair! *Window, Spring* 4
And you my wren with a crown of *g*, „ 11
gossamers That twinkle into green and *g*: *In Mem. xi* 8
Israel made their gods of *g*, „ *xcvi* 23
Ring out the narrowing lust of *g*; „ *cvi* 26
the flying *g* of the ruin'd woodlands *Maud I i* 12
And left his coal all turn'd into *g* „ *x* 11
lost for a little her lust of *g*, „ *III vi* 39
egg of mine Was finer *g* than any goose can lay; *Gareth and L.* 43
'*G*? said I *g*?—ay then, why he, or she, „ 63
had the thing I spake of been Mere *g*— „ 66
howsoe'er at first he proffer'd *g*, „ 336
and left us neither *g* nor field.' „ 339
'Whether would ye? *g* or field?' „ 340
thrice the *g* for Uther's use thereof, „ 344
a cloth of palest *g*, Which down he laid „ 389
gay with *g* In streaks and rays, „ 910
There swung an apple of the purest *g*, *Marr. of Geraint* 170
Affirming that his father left him *g*, „ 451
a dress All branch'd and flower'd with *g*, „ 631
strown With *g* and scatter'd coinage, *Geraint and E.* 26
In green and *g*, and plumed with green *Merlin and V.* 89
A twist of *g* was round her hair; „ 221
The snake of *g* slid from her hair, „ 888
down his robe the dragon writhed in *g*, *Lancelot and E.* 435
Sir Lancelot's azure lions, crown'd with *g*, „ 663
both the wings were made of *g*, *Holy Grail* 242
a crown of *g* About a casque all jewels; „ 410
third night hence will bring thee news of *g*.' *Pelleas and E.* 357
children sat in white with cups of *g*, *Last Tournament* 142
heard it ring as true as tested *g*.' „ 284
Either from lust of *g*, or like a girl *Pass. of Arthur* 295
Three queens with crowns of *g*: „ 366
Or Cowardice, the child of lust for *g*, *To the Queen ii* 54
rose as it were breath and steam of *g*, *Lover's Tale i* 402
nymph and god ran ever round in *g*— „ *iv* 197
G, jewels, arms, whatever it may be. „ 235
after he had shown him gems or *g*, „ 246
an Eastern gauze With seeds of *g*, „ 292
We brought this iron from our isles of *g*. *Columbus* 3
G? I had brought your Princes *g* „ 105
all The *g* that Solomon's navies carried „ 113
And gathering ruthless *g*— „ 135
seas of our discovering over-roll Him and his *g*; „ 140
When he coin'd into English *g* *The Wreck* 67
and the miser would yearn for his *g*, *Despair* 100
make thy *g* thy vassal not thy king, *Ancient Sage* 259
From war with kindly links of *g*, *Epilogue* 16
I hold Mother's love in letter'd *g*, *Helen's Tower* 4
Give your *g* to the Hospital, *On Jub. Q. Victoria* 33
Mere want of *g*—and still for twenty years *The Ring* 428
g from each laburnum chain Drop to the grass. *To Mary Boyle* 11
Bright in spring, Living *g*; *The Oak* 5
Soberer-hued *G* again. „ 10
alchemise old hates into the *g* Of Love, *Akbar's Dream* 163
When I make for an Age of *g*, *The Dreamer* 7

Golden (*See also* **All-golden**) Her subtil, warm, and *g* breath, *Supp. Confessions* 60
The summer calm of *g* charity, *Isabel* 8
THOU art not steep'd in *g* languors, *Madeline* 1
the *g* prime Of good Haroun Alraschid. (repeat) *Arabian Nights* 10, 21, 32, 43, 54, 65, 76, 87, 98, 109, 120, 131, 142, 153
marble stairs Ran up with *g* balustrade, *Arabian Nights* 118
THE poet in a *g* clime was born, With *g* stars above; *The Poet* 1
sharp clear twang of the *g* chords Runs up the ridged sea. *Sea-Fairies* 38
Two lives bound fast in one with *g* ease; *Circumstance* 5

Golden (*continued*) In a *g* curl With a comb of pearl, *The Mermaid* 6
with fruitage golden-rinded On *g* salvers, *Eleänore* 34
Grow *g* all about the sky; „ 101
Nor *g* largess of thy praise. *My life is full* 5
branch of stars we see Hung in the *g* Galaxy. *L. of Shalott iii* 12
the *g* bee Is lily-cradled: *Œnone* 29
And o'er him flow'd a *g* cloud, „ 105
hair Ambrosial, *g* round her lucid throat And shoulder: „ 178
As she withdrew into the *g* cloud, „ 191
And cast the *g* fruit upon the board, „ 226
wherefrom The *g* gorge of dragons spouted forth *Palace of Art* 23
cloud of incense of all odour steam'd From out a *g* cup. „ 40
one hand grasp'd The mild bull's *g* horn. „ 120
the clouds are lightly curl'd Round their *g* houses, *Lotos-Eaters, C. S.* 113
A *g* bill! the silver tongue, *The Blackbird* 13
Should fill and choke with *g* sand— *You ask me, why, etc.* 24
The goose let fall a *g* egg *The Goose* 11
shadow of the flowers Stole all the *g* gloss, *Gardener's D.* 130
such a noise of life Swarm'd in the *g* present, „ 179
lad stretch'd out And babbled for the *g* seal, *Dora* 135
with *g* yolks Imbedded and injellied; *Audley Court* 25
A second flutter'd round her lip Like a *g* butterfly; *Talking Oak* 220
Dropt dews upon her *g* head, „ 227
themselves Move onward, leading up the *g* year. *Golden Year* 26
And slow and sure comes up the *g* year. „ 31
Thro' all the season of the *g* year. „ 36
Roll onward, leading up the *g* year. „ 41
Enrich the markets of the *g* year. „ 46
Thro' all the circle of the *g* year?' „ 51
Every moment, lightly shaken, ran itself in *g* sands. *Locksley Hall* 32
Every door is barr'd with gold, and opens but to *g* keys. „ 100
mantles from the *g* pegs Droop sleepily: *Day-Dm., Sleep. P.* 19
But dallied with his *g* chain, „ *Revival* 31
And, stream'd thro' many a *g* bar, „ *Depart.* 15
He lifts me to the *g* doors; *St. Agnes' Eve* 25
And raked in *g* barley. *Will Water.* 128
now she gleam'd Like Fancy made of *g* air, *The Voyage* 66
Buckled with *g* clasps before; A light-green tuft of plumes she bore Closed in a *g* ring. *Sir L. and Q. G.* 25
Purple gauzes, *g* hazes, liquid mazes, *Vision of Sin* 31
I grew in gladness till I found My spirits in the *g* age. *To E. L.* 12
Then, on a *g* autumn eventide, *Enoch Arden* 61
first since Enoch's *g* ring had girt Her finger, „ 157
And sent her sweetly by the *g* isles, „ 536
the *g* lizard on him paused, „ 601
many a silvery waterbreak Above the *g* gravel, *The Brook* 62
Ringing like proven *g* coinage true, *Aylmer's Field* 182
Had *g* hopes for France and all mankind, „ 464
dark retinue reverencing death At *g* thresholds; „ 843
great Sicilian called Calliope to grace his *g* verse— *Lucretius* 94
slowly lifts His *g* feet on those empurpled stairs „ 135
that hour, My *g* work in which I told a truth „ 260
And sweet girl-graduates in their *g* hair. *Princess, Pro.* 142
ere the silver sickle of that month Became her *g* shield, „ *i* 102
read and earn our prize, A *g* brooch: „ *iii* 301
fight with iron laws, in the end Found *g*: „ *iv* 76
'O Swallow, flying from the *g* woods, „ 114
But led by *g* wishes, and a hope „ 420
gems and gemlike eyes, And gold and *g* heads; „ 481
sheathing splendours and the *g* scale Of harness, „ *v* 41
Creation minted in the *g* moods Of sovereign artists; „ 194
When dames and heroines of the *g* year „ *vi* 64
Half-lapt in glowing gauze and *g* brede, „ 134
Reels, as the *g* Autumn woodland reels „ *vii* 357
anthem roll'd Thro' the dome of the *g* cross; *Ode on Well.* 61
we hear The tides of Music's *g* sea Setting „ 252
Mourn'd in this *g* hour of jubilee, *Ode Inter. Exhib.* 8
And mix the seasons and the *g* hours; „ 36
The *g* news along the steppes is blown, *W. to Marie Alex.* 11
At Florence too what *g* hours, *The Daisy* 41
And snowy dells in a *g* air. „ 68
ONCE in a *g* hour I cast to earth a seed. *The Flower* 1
To rest in a *g* grove, or to bask in a summer sky: *Wages* 9
Fixt by their cars, waited the *g* dawn. *Spec. of Iliad* 22

Golden (*continued*) Here is the *g* close of love, *Window, Marr. Morn.* 3
For this is the *g* morning of love, „ 11
That sittest ranging *g* hair; *In Mem. vi* 26
To thee too comes the *g* hour When flower „ *xxxix* 6
And lives to clutch the *g* keys, „ *lxiv* 10
sun by sun the happy days Descend below the *g* hills „ *lxxxiv* 28
The promise of the *g* hours? „ *lxxxv* 106
call The spirits from their *g* day, „ *xciv* 6
We glided winding under ranks Of iris, and the *g* reed; „ *ciii* 24
To him who grasps a *g* ball, „ *cxi* 3
I too may passively take the print Of the *g* age— *Maud I i* 30
Pale with the *g* beam of an eyelash dead on the cheek, „ *iii* 3
Among the fragments of the *g* day. „ *xviii* 70
A *g* foot or a fairy horn Thro' his dim water-world? „ *II ii* 19
The *g* symbol of his kinglihood, *Com. of Arthur* 50
But those first days had *g* hours for me, „ 357
An 'twere but of the goose and *g* eggs.' *Gareth and L.* 40
And handed down the *g* treasure to him.' „ 61
And over that a *g* sparrow-hawk. *Marr. of Geraint* 484
And over that the *g* sparrow-hawk, „ 550
Near that old home, a pool of *g* carp; „ 648
and by and by Slips into *g* cloud, „ 736
But *g* earnest of a gentler life!' *Balin and Balan* 208
Beheld before a *g* altar lie The longest lance „ 410
Had wander'd from her own King's *g* head, „ 513
Perchance, one curl of Arthur's *g* beard. *Merlin and V.* 58
Arriving at a time of *g* rest, „ 142
In these wild woods, the hart with *g* horns. „ 409
And chased the flashes of his *g* horns „ 427
To make her smile, her *g* ankle-bells. „ 579
A league of mountain full of *g* mines, „ 587
Made proffer of the league of *g* mines, „ 646
And set it in this damsel's *g* hair, *Lancelot and E.* 205
Since to his crown the *g* dragon clung, „ 434
and *g* eloquence And amorous adulation, „ 649
'Stay a little! One *g* minute's grace! „ 684
and saw The *g* dragon sparkling over all: *Holy Grail* 263
In *g* armour with a crown of gold „ 410
his horse In *g* armour jewell'd everywhere: „ 412
Merlin moulded for us Half-wrench'd a *g* wing; „ 733
the prize A *g* circlet and a knightly sword, Full fain
had Pelleas for his lady won The *g* circlet, *Pelleas and E.* 12
The sword and *g* circlet were achieved. „ 170
'Why lingers Gawain with his *g* news?' „ 411
your flower Waits to be solid fruit of *g* deeds, *Last Tournament* 100
them that round it sat with *g* cups To hand the wine „ 289
dark in the *g* grove Appearing, „ 379
The *g* beard that clothed his lips with light— „ 668
Went slipping back upon the *g* days *Guinevere* 380
As in the *g* days before thy sin. „ 500
makes me die To see thee, laying there thy *g* head, „ 535
O *g* hair, with which I used to play Not knowing! „ 547
To which for crest the *g* dragon clung Of Britain „ 594
glory cling To all high places like a *g* cloud For
ever: *Pass. of Arthur* 54
And some had visions out of *g* youth, „ 102
like a *g* mist Charm'd amid eddies of melodious airs, *Lover's Tale i* 449
And sitting down upon the *g* moss, „ 540
With all her *g* thresholds clashing, „ 605
One *g* dream of love, from which may death „ 760
Did I make bare of all the *g* moss, „ *ii* 48
Well he had One *g* hour—of triumph shall I say? „ *iv* 6
evermore Holding his *g* burthen in his arms, „ 89
(I told you that he had his *g* hour), „ 206
Smoothing their locks, as *g* as his own Were silver, *Sisters (E. and E.)* 56
The *g* gates would open at a word. „ 145
but the *g* guess Is morning-star to the full round of truth. *Columbus* 43
each like a *g* image was pollen'd from head to feet *V. of Maeldune* 49
Glowing with all-colour'd plums and with *g* masses
of pear, „ 60
sworn to seek If any *g* harbour be for men *Pref. Son 19th Cent.* 13
The glorious goddess wreath'd a *g* cloud, *Achilles over the T.* 5
Who reads your *g* Eastern lay, *To E. Fitzgerald* 32
a dreadful light Came from her *g* hair, her *g* helm
And all her *g* armour on the grass, *Tiresias* 44

Golden (*continued*) while the *g* lyre Is ever sounding in
heroic ears *Tiresias* 180
Remembering all the *g* hours Now silent, „ 210
and call For *g* music, *Ancient Sage* 197
One *g* curl, his *g* gift, before he past away. *The Flight* 36
She that holds the diamond necklace dearer than
the *g* ring, *Locksley H., Sixty* 21
Gone with whom for forty years my life in *g*
sequence ran, „ 47
From the *g* alms of Blessing man had coin'd
himself a curse: „ 87
flashing out from many a *g* phrase; *To Virgil* 8
G branch amid the shadows, „ 27
blind force and brainless will May jar the *g* dream *Freedom* 16
lavish all the *g* day To make them wealthier *Poets and their B.* 3
at her girdle clash The *g* keys of East and West. *To Marq. of Dufferin* 4
have I made the name A *g* portal to my rhyme: „ 16
Fifty times the *g* harvest fallen, *On Jub. Q. Victoria* 2
'Hail to the glorious *G* year of her Jubilee!' „ 65
To send my life thro' olive-yard and vine And
g grain, *Demeter and P.* 111
Fame blowing out from her *g* trumpet a jubilant
challenge *Vastness* 21
debtless competence, *g* mean; „ 24
'Thy hair Is *g* like thy Mother's, not so fine.' *The Ring* 104
for twenty years Bound by the *g* cord of their
first love— „ 429
Let *g* youth bewail the friend, the wife, *To Mary Boyle* 53
The frost-bead melts upon her *g* hair; *Prog. of Spring* 10
Touch'd at the *g* Cross of the churches, *Merlin and the G.* 67
Let the *g* Iliad vanish, Homer here is Homer there. *Parnassus* 20
she saw Him, climbing toward her with the *g* fruit, *Death of Œnone* 15
Golden Fleece (Inn sign) met the bailiff at the *G F*, *The Brook* 146
Golden-hair'd *G-h* Ally whose name is one with mine, *To A. Tennyson* 1
Golden-hilted Nor weapon, save a *g-h* brand, *Marr. of Geraint* 166
Golden-netted heart entanglest In a *g-n* smile; *Madeline* 41
Golden-rail'd The light aërial gallery, *g-r*, *Palace of Art* 47
Golden-rinded with fruitage *g-r* On golden salvers, *Eleänore* 33
Golden-shafted The Head of all the *g-s* firm, *Princess ii* 405
Gold-eyed The *g-e* kingcups fine; *A Dirge* 36
Gold-fringed upswells The *g-f* pillow lightly prest: *Day-Dm., Sleep. B.* 22
Gold-green Flush'd all the leaves with rich *g-g*, *Arabian Nights* 82
Gold-lily While the *g-l* blows, *Edwin Morris* 146
Gold-mine from the deep *G-m's* of thought *D. of F. Women* 274
Gone (*See also* **Agoän, Goän**) Autumn and Summer
Are *g* long ago; *Nothing will Die* 19
LIFE and Thought have *g* away *Deserted House* 1
I said, 'When I am *g* away, *Two Voices* 100
The dull and bitter voice was *g*. „ 426
And now those vivid hours are *g*, *Miller's D.* 195
tell her, when I'm *g*, to train the rose-bush *May Queen, N. Y's. E.* 47
Alack! our friend is *g*. *D. of the O. Year* 47
all the old honour had from Christmas *g*, Or *g*, *The Epic* 7
'My end draws nigh; 'tis time that I were *g*. *M. d'Arthur* 163
for the sake of him that's *g*, (repeat) *Dora* 62, 70, 94
Dora would have risen and *g* to him, „ 77
The troubles I have *g* thro'!' „ 150
prate Of penances I cannot have *g* thro', *St. S. Stylites* 101
Christ! 'Tis *g*: 'tis here again; „ 208
adoration to my household gods, When I am *g*. *Ulysses* 43
his spirit leaps within him to be *g* *Locksley Hall* 115
But for my pleasant hour, 'tis *g*; 'Tis *g*, and let it
go. 'Tis *g*: a thousand such have slipt Away *Will Water.* 179
Well I know, when I am *g*, *Vision of Sin* 109
the wife— When he was *g*—the children— *Enoch Arden* 132
So might she keep the house while he was *g*. „ 140
Pray'd for a sign 'my Enoch is he *g*?' „ 491
'He is *g*,' she thought 'he is happy, „ 502
After he was *g*, The two remaining found „ 566
He thought it must have *g*; but he was *g* „ 694
'after I am *g*, Then may she learn I lov'd „ 834
when I am *g*, Take, give her this, „ 898
and these are *g*, All *g*. *The Brook* 186
breathes in April autumns. All are *g*.' „ 196
Leolin, coming after he was *g*, *Aylmer's Field* 234

Gone (*continued*) you had *g* to her, She told, perforce; *Princess iv* 329
found that you had *g*, Ridd'n to the hills, „ 342
many a pleasant hour with her that's *g*, „ *vi* 247
We brook no further insult but are *g*.' „ 342
Blanche had *g*, but left Her child among us, „ *vii* 56
He is *g* who seem'd so great.—*G*; *Ode on Well.* 271
And Willy, my eldest-born, is *g*, *Grandmother* 1
and Willy, you say, is *g*. „ 8
I ought to have *g* before him: „ 14
But all my children have *g* before me, „ 18
laughing at things that have long *g* by. „ 92
So Willy has *g*, my beauty, „ 101
he has but *g* for an hour,—*G* for a minute, my son, „ 102
work mun 'a *g* to the gittin' whiniver *N. Farmer, N. S.* 50
there before you are come, and *g*, *Window, On the Hill* 14
G! *G*, till the end of the year, *G*, and the light *g* with her, „ *Gone* 1
G—flitted away, „ 4
G, and a cloud in my heart, „ 6
the grass will grow when I am *g*, „ *No Answer* 5
when I am there and dead and *g*, „ 11
Blow then, blow, and when I am *g*, „ 17
And learns her *g* and far from home; *In Mem. viii* 4
'How good! how kind! and he is *g*.' „ *xx* 20
Old sisters of a day *g* by, „ *xxix* 13
My prospect and horizon *g*. „ *xxxviii* 4
She cries, 'A thousand types are *g*: „ *lvi* 3
Quite in the love of what is *g*, „ *lxxxv* 114
The violet comes, but we are *g*. „ *cv* 8
Farewell, we kiss, and they are *g*. „ *Con.* 92
and slurring the days *g* by, *Maud I i* 33
So many a million of ages have *g* „ *iv* 35
In a moment they were *g*: „ *ix* 12
lately died, *G* to a blacker pit, „ *x* 6
Like some of the simple great ones *g* „ 61
He may stay for a year who has *g* for a week: „ *xvi* 6
gates of Heaven are closed, and she is *g*. „ *xviii* 12
our whole earth *g* nearer to the glow „ 78
Now half to the setting moon are *g*, „ *xxii* 23
Is it *g*? my pulses beat— „ *II i* 36
It is *g*; and the heavens fall in a gentle rain, „ 41
paid our tithes in the days that are *g*, „ *v* 23
We have lost him: he is *g*: *Ded. of Idylls* 15
So that the realm has *g* to wrack: *Com. of Arthur* 227
And *g* as soon as seen. „ 377
Arthur all at once *g* mad replies, *Gareth and L.* 863
younger brethren have *g* down Before this youth; „ 1102
a prince whose manhood was all *g*, *Marr. of Geraint* 59
Reproach you, saying all your force is *g*? „ 88
with the morning all the court were *g*. „ 156
when the fourth part of the day was *g*, *Geraint and E.* 55
For the man's love once *g* never returns. „ 333
when I am *g* Who used to lay them! *Balin and Balan* 140
King Had gazed upon her blankly and *g* by: *Merlin and V.* 161
lists of such a beard as youth *g* out „ 245
Writ in a language that has long *g* by. „ 674
Was one year *g*, and on returning found „ 708
No sooner *g* than suddenly she began: *Lancelot and E.* 96
take Their pastime now the trustful King is *g*!' „ 101
g sore wounded, and hath left his prize „ 530
I mean nothing: so then, get you *g*, „ 776
on his helm, from which her sleeve had *g*. „ 982
His very shield was *g*; only the case, „ 990
when the ghostly man had come and *g*, „ 1101
the heat is *g* from out my heart, „ 1116
those that had *g* out upon the Quest, *Holy Grail* 722
Lost in the quagmire?—lost to me and *g*, „ 892
g he is To wage grim war against Sir Lancelot *Guinevere* 192
By couriers *g* before; and on again, „ 396
listening till those armed steps were *g*, „ 585
'*G*—my lord! *G* thro' my sin to slay and to be slain! „ 612
G, my lord the King, My own true lord! „ 616
'My end draws nigh; 'tis time that I were *g*. *Pass. of Arthur* 331
and he groan'd, 'The King is *g*.' „ 443
had *g* Surely, but for a whisper, *Lover's Tale iv* 19

K

Gone (*continued*) he told me that so many years had *g* by, *First Quarrel* 36
Flesh of my flesh was *g*, *Rizpah* 51
if my boy be *g* to the fire? „ 78
half of the short summer night was *g*, *The Revenge* 65
for a face *G* in a moment—strange. *Sisters (E. and E.)* 94
Sa 'is taäil wur lost an' 'is boooks wur *g* *Village Wife* 87
sa o' coorse she be *g* to the bad! „ 98
(Hath he been here—not found me—*g* again? *Sir. J. Oldcastle* 152
She is *g*—but you will tell the King, *Columbus* 234
G! He will achieve his greatness. *Tiresias* 167
the master *g*. *G* into darkness, „ 201
And *g*—that day of the storm— *The Wreck* 148
Hence! she is *g*! can I stay? *Despair* 113
'Lost and *g* and lost and *g*!' *Ancient Sage* 224
this Hall at last will go—perhaps have *g*, *The Flight* 27
He's *g* to the States, aroon, *Tomorrow* 49
dhry eye thin but was wet for the frinds that was *g*! „ 83
G the fires of youth, the follies, *Locksley H., Sixty* 39
G like fires and floods and earthquakes „ 40
G the tyrant of my youth, „ 43
G the comrades of my bivouac, „ 45
g as all on earth will go. „ 46
G with whom for forty years my life „ 47
G our sailor son thy father, „ 55
G thy tender-natured mother, „ 57
G for ever! Ever? no— „ 65
G the cry of 'Forward, Forward,' „ 73
till ten thousand years have *g*. „ 78
G at eighty, mine own age, „ 281
Midnight—and joyless June *g* by, *Pref. Poem Broth. S.* 9
O thou so fair in summers *g*, *Freedom* 1
Child, when thou wert *g*, I envied human wives, *Demeter and P.* 52
an' screeäd like a Howl *g* wud— *Owd Roä* 76
So far *g* down, or so far up in life, *The Ring* 193
Laid on her table overnight, was *g*; „ 277
g! and *g* in that embrace! „ 443
but dead so long, *g* up so far, „ 462
Is memory with your Marian *g* to rest, *To Mary Boyle* 13
bewail the friend, the wife, For ever *g*. „ 54

Good (adj.) the golden prime Of *g* Haroun Alraschid. *Arabian Nights* 11, 22, 33, 44, 55, 66, 77, 88, 99, 110, 121, 132, 143, 154
But *g* things have not kept aloof, *My life is full* 2
humming of the drowsy pulpit-drone Half God's *g* sabbath, *To J. M. K.* 11
'In some *g* cause, not in mine own, *Two Voices* 148
'Yea!' said the voice, 'thy dream was *g*, „ 157
Lean'd on him, faithful, gentle, *g*, „ 416
he set and left behind The *g* old year, the dear old time, *May Queen, N. Y's. E.* 6
And that *g* man, the clergyman, has told me words of peace. „ *Con.* 12
'*The Legend of G Women*,' long ago Sung *D. of F. Women* 2
Lest one *g* custom should corrupt the world. *M. d'Arthur* 242
'Come With all *g* things, and war shall be no more.' „ *Ep.* 28
Who read me rhymes elaborately *g*, *Edwin Morris* 20
G people, you do ill to kneel to me. *St. S. Stylites* 133
The *g* old Summers, year by year *Talking Oak* 39
slow sweet hours that bring us all things *g*, *Love and Duty* 57
And all *g* things from evil, „ 59
It is not bad but *g* land, *Amphion* 6
My *g* blade carves the casques of men, *Sir Galahad* 1
Like all *g* things on earth! *Will Water.* 202
I hold it *g*, *g* things should pass: „ 205
I hold thee dear For this *g* pint of port. „ 212
We felt the *g* ship shake and reel, *The Voyage* 15
Wine is *g* for shrivell'd lips, *Vision of Sin* 79
Virtue!—to be *g* and just— „ 111
Then her *g* Philip was her all-in-all, *Enoch Arden* 525
But Miriam Lane was *g* and garrulous, „ 700
Heard the *g* mother softly whisper 'Bless, *Aylmer's Field* 187
Till after our *g* parents past away „ 358

Good **(adj.)** (*continued*) plagued themselves To sell her, those *g* parents, for her good. *Aylmer's Field* 483
And bad him with *g* heart sustain himself— „ 544
'Not fearful; fair,' Said the *g* wife, *Sea Dreams* 83
'Was he so bound, poor soul?' said the *g* wife; „ 169
old Sir Ralph's at Ascalon: A *g* knight he! *Princess, Pro.* 27
For which the *g* Sir Ralph had burnt them all— „ 236
But my *g* father thought a king a king; „ *i* 25
mounted our *g* steeds, And boldly ventured „ 204
As I might slay this child, if *g* need were, „ *ii* 287
Wasps in our *g* hive, „ *iv* 535
thus I won Your mother, a *g* mother, a *g* wife, „ *v* 166
Were we ourselves but half as *g*, as kind, „ 201
When the *g* Queen, her mother, shore the tress „ *vi* 113
and all the *g* knights maim'd, „ 241
She needs must wed him for her own *g* name; „ *vii* 74
O *g* gray head which all men knew, *Ode on Well.* 35
let all *g* things await Him who cares not to be great, „ 198
You cannot love me at all, if you love not my *g* name.' *Grandmother* 48
'Sweetheart, I love you so well that your *g* name is mine. „ 50
But he cheer'd me, my *g* man, „ 69
Maakin' 'em goä together as they've *g* right to do. *N. Farmer, N. S.* 34
an 'e died a *g* un, 'e did. „ 52
if thou marries a *g* un I'll leäve the land to thee. „ 56
'How *g*! how kind! and he is gone.' *In Mem. xx* 20
And all we met was fair and *g*, And all was *g* „ *xxiii* 17
If all was *g* and fair we met, „ *xxiv* 5
If thou wilt have me wise and *g*. „ *lix* 8
They sang of what is wise and *g* And graceful. „ *ciii* 10
for thee she grows For ever, and as fair as *g*. „ *Con.* 36
My mother, who was so gentle and *g*? *Maud I vi* 67
Comfort her, comfort her, all things *g*, „ *II ii* 75
lily and rose That blow by night, when the season is *g*, „ *v* 75
Have strength and wit, in my *g* mother's hall *Gareth and L.* 12
Since the *g* mother holds me still a child! *G* mother is bad mother unto me! „ 15
'Nay, nay, *g* mother, but this egg of mine „ 42
one, *g* lack, no man desired. „ 106
'Son, I have seen the *g* ship sail Keel upward, „ 253
With all *g* cheer He spake and laugh'd, „ 301
and the sound was *g* to Gareth's ear. „ 312
Then strode a *g* knight forward, „ 364
When some *g* knight had done one noble deed, „ 411
Truth-speaking, brave, *g* livers, them we enroll'd „ 424
All in a gap-mouth'd circle his *g* mates Lying „ 511
And the spear spring, and *g* horse reel, „ 523
g Queen, Repentant of the word she made him swear, „ 526
'Son, the *g* mother let me know thee here, „ 550
heart of her *g* horse Was nigh to burst with violence „ 762
Three with *g* blows he quieted, but three Fled „ 813
g cause is theirs To hate me, „ 820
G—I accord it easily as a grace.' „ 975
Is all as *g*, meseems, as any knight „ 1017
'Hath not the *g* wind, damsel, changed again?' „ 1054
hath not our *g* King Who lent me thee, „ 1070
O *g* knight-knave—O knave, „ 1135
'Sir,—and, *g* faith, I fain had added—Knight, „ 1162
Saving that you mistrusted our *g* King „ 1172
Where bread and baken meats and *g* red wine Of Southland, „ 1190
son Of old King Lot and *g* Queen Bellicent, „ 1231
and thy *g* horse And thou are weary; „ 1264
G lord, how sweetly smells the honeysuckle „ 1287
Care not, *g* beasts, so well I care for you. „ 1308
Then the *g* King gave order to let blow His horns *Marr. of Geraint* 152
There is *g* chance that we shall hear the hounds: „ 182
Harbourage? truth, *g* truth, I know not, save, „ 290
'Enid, the *g* knight's horse stands in the court; „ 370
Rest! the *g* house, tho' ruin'd, O my son, „ 378
His name? but no, *g* faith, I will not have it: „ 405
And tilts with my *g* nephew thereupon, „ 488
a costly gift Of her *g* mother, given her „ 632
'Yea, I know it; your *g* gift, „ 688
So sadly lost on that unhappy night; Your own *g* gift!' „ 690

Good **(adj.)** (*continued*) Yniol made report Of that *g* mother making Enid gay *Marr. of Geraint* 757
Dared not to glance at her *g* mother's face, „ 766
I charge thee ride before, Ever a *g* way on before; *Geraint and E.* 15
While your *g* damsel rests, return, and fetch „ 224
speak To your *g* damsel there who sits apart, „ 299
'Your sweet faces make *g* fellows fools And traitors. „ 399
like a dog, when his *g* bone Seems to be pluck'd „ 559
G luck had your *g* man, „ 617
Embracing Balin, '*G* my brother, hear! *Balin and Balan* 139
As pass without *g* morrow to thy Queen?' „ 252
'The fire of Heaven is lord of all things *g*, „ 452
Meet is it the *g* King be not deceived. „ 533
this *g* knight Told me, that twice a wanton damsel came, „ 608
And made her *g* man jealous with *g* cause. *Merlin and V.* 605
G: take my counsel: let me know it at once: „ 653
foul bird of rapine whose whole prey Is man's *g* name: „ 729
By which the *g* King means to blind himself, „ 783
Leaving her household and *g* father, *Lancelot and E.* 14
How came the lily maid by that *g* shield Of Lancelot, „ 28
That passionate perfection, my *g* lord— „ 122
'Nay, father, nay *g* father, shame me not „ 207
till our *g* Arthur broke The Pagan yet once more „ 279
Gareth, a *g* knight, but therewithal Sir Modred's brother, „ 557
he went sore wounded from the field: Yet *g* news too: „ 601
Then far away with *g* Sir Torre for guide „ 788
And your *g* father's kindness.' „ 945
Alas for me then, my *g* days are done.' „ 947
More specially should your *g* knight be poor, „ 956
Give me *g* fortune, I will strike him dead, „ 1071
for *g* she was and true, „ 1292
For *g* ye are and bad, and like to coins, *Holy Grail* 25
g saint Arimathæan Joseph, journeying brought „ 50
'God make thee *g* as thou art beautiful,' „ 136
And *g* Sir Bors, our Lancelot's cousin, sware, „ 200
Said *g* Sir Bors, 'beyond all hopes of mine, „ 690
But as for thine, my *g* friend Percivale, „ 861
then binding his *g* horse To a tree, *Pelleas and E.* 30
Yet with *g* cheer he spake, 'Behold me, Lady, „ 240
'Pity on him,' she answer'd, 'a *g* knight, „ 386
'*G* now, what music have I broken, fool?' *Last Tournament* 261
He whistled his *g* warhorse left to graze „ 490
'*G*: an I turn'd away my love for thee „ 705
(When the *g* King should not be there) *Guinevere* 97
they talk at Almesbury About the *g* King and his wicked Queen, „ 209
wrought confusion in the Table Round Which *g* King Arthur founded, „ 221
Said the *g* nuns would check her gadding tongue „ 313
tales Which my *g* father told me, „ 317
Then she, for her *g* deeds and her pure life, „ 693
Lest one *g* custom should corrupt the world. *Pass. of Arthur* 410
breathless body of her *g* deeds past. *Lover's Tale i* 217
There the *g* mother's kindly ministering, „ *iv* 92
So frighted our *g* friend, that turning to me „ 383
had need Of a *g* stout lad at his farm; *First Quarrel* 18
To make a *g* wife for Harry, „ 30
and they never would let him be *g*; *Rizpah* 29
we had always borne a *g* name— „ 35
read me a Bible verse of the Lord's *g* will toward men— „ 61
We could sing a *g* song at the Plow, (repeat) *North. Cobbler* 18
G Sir Richard, tell us now, *The Revenge* 26
'We be all *g* English men. „ 29
Your *g* Uncle, whom You count the father of your fortune, *Sisters (E. and E.)* 27
'*G*! very like! not altogether he.' „ 136
And not without *g* reason, my *g* son— „ 287
bowt owd money, es wouldn't goä, wi' *g* gowd o' the Queen, *Village Wife* 49
'Ay, *g* woman, can prayer set a broken bone?' *In the Child. Hosp.* 20
but the *g* Lord Jesus had had His day.' „ 22
Clean from our lines of defence ten or twelve *g* paces *Def. of Lucknow* 62
Blessing the wholesome white faces of Havelock's *g* fusileers, „ 101

Good (adj.) (*continued*) As *g* need was—thou hast come to talk our isle. *Sir J. Oldcastle* 32
Some cried on Cobham, on the *g* Lord Cobham; „ 43
Burnt—*g* Sir Roger Acton, my dear friend! „ 79
drawn By this *g* Wiclif mountain down from heaven, „ 132
(My *g* friend By this time should be with me.) „ 138
I would not spurn *G* counsel of *g* friends, „ 146
CHAINS, my *g* lord: in your raised brows I read *Columbus* 1
Drove me and my *g* brothers home in chains, „ 134
O never was time so *g*! *V. of Maeldune* 87
You needs must have *g* lynx-eyes if I do not escape you *Despair* 114
Steevie be right *g* manners bang thruf *Spinster's S's.* 66
Hesper, whom the poet call'd the Bringer home of all *g* things. All *g* things „ 185
G, this forward, you that preach it, „ 216
When our own *g* redcoats sank from sight, *Heavy Brigade* 42
'e was allus as *g* as gowd. *Owd Roä* 6
Fur 'e's moor *g* sense na the Parliament man 'at stans for us 'ere, „ 13
an' I thowt o' the *g* owd times 'at was goan, „ 43
An' I says 'I'd be *g* to tha, Bess, if tha'd onywaäys let ma be *g*,' „ 75
Git oop, if ya're onywaäys *g* for owt.' And I says 'If I beänt noäwaäys—not nowadaäys—*g* fur nowt— „ 77
An' Roä was as *g* as the Hangel i' saävin' a son fur me. „ 96
the *g* and brave! He sees me, waves me from him. *Happy* 18
G, I am never weary painting you. *Romney's R.* 3
EH? *g* daäy! *g* daäy! thaw it bean't not mooch of a daäy, *Church-warden, etc.* 1
Us, O Just and *G*, Forgive, *Poland* 11
such strange war with something *g*, *Two Voices* 302
'Tis only noble to be *g*. *L. C. V. de Vere* 54
waked with silence, grunted '*G*!' *M. d'Arthur, Ep.* 4
'*G*! my lady's kinsman! *g*!' *Aylmer's Field* 198
'*G*: Your oath is broken: we dismiss you: *Princess iv* 359
make us all we would be, great and *g*.' „ 599
Were we ourselves but half as *g*, as kind, „ *v* 201
Good (s) '*She wrought her people lasting* g; *To the Queen* 24
saw thro' life and death, thro' *g* and ill, *The Poet* 5
'And not to lose the *g* of life— *Two Voices* 132
'I see the end, and know the *g*.' „ 432
or if *G*, *G* only for its beauty, seeing not That Beauty, *G*, and Knowledge, are three sisters *To —— With Pal. of Art* 8
Would love the gleams of *g* that broke *Love thou thy land* 89
What *g* should follow this, if this were done? *M. d'Arthur* 92
The drowsy hours, dispensers of all *g*, *Gardener's D.* 185
the *g* and increase of the world. (repeat) *Edwin Morris* 44, 51, 92
some one say, Then why not ill for *g*? *Love and Duty* 27
when shall all men's *g* Be each man's rule, *Golden Year* 47
Subdue them to the useful and the *g*. *Ulysses* 38
But for some true result of *g* *Will Water.* 55
He never meant us anything but *g*. *Enoch Arden* 887
To sell her, those good parents, for her *g*. *Aylmer's Field* 483
contriving their dear daughter's *g*— „ 781
the two contrived their daughter's *g*— „ 848
all things work together for the *g* Of those '— *Sea Dreams* 158
All for the common g *of womankind.*' *Princess ii* 209
'All *g* go with thee! take it Sir,' „ *vi* 207
Whole in himself, a common *g*. *Ode on Well.* 26
Till each man find his own in all men's *g*, *Ode Inter. Exhib.* 37
Embrace her as my natural *g*; *In Mem. iii* 14
And what to me remains of *g*? „ *vi* 42
Her hands are quicker unto *g*: „ *xxxiii* 10
Enjoying each the other's *g*: „ *xlvii* 10
Hold thou the *g*: define it well: „ *liii* 13
g Will be the final goal of ill, „ *liv* 1
I can but trust that *g* shall fall „ 14
I see thee sitting crown'd with *g*, „ *lxxxiv* 5
lead The closing cycle rich in *g*. „ *cv* 28
Ring in the common love of *g*. „ *cvi* 24
High nature amorous of the *g*, „ *cix* 9
Yet O ye mysteries of *g*, „ *cxxviii* 8
Behold, I dream a dream of *g*, „ *cxxix* 11

Good (s) (*continued*) Full to the banks, close on the promised *g*. *Maud I xviii* 6
Nor let any man think for the public *g*, „ *II v* 45
It is better to fight for the *g* „ *III vi* 57
I needs must disobey him for his *g*; *Geraint and E.* 135
what they long for, *g* in friend or foe, „ 876
This *g* is in it, whatsoe'er of ill, *Lancelot and E.* 1207
as the base man, judging of the *g*, *Pelleas and E.* 80
None knows it, and my tears have brought me *g*: *Guinevere* 202
What *g* should follow this, if this were done? *Pass. of Arthur* 260
fur they weänt niver coom to naw *g*. *Village Wife* 96
power hath work'd no *g* to aught that lives, *Tiresias* 77
running after a shadow of *g*; *Despair* 92
No ill no *g*! such counter-terms, my son, *Ancient Sage* 250
G, for *G* is *G*, he follow'd, *Locksley H., Sixty* 60
Truth for truth, and *g* for *g*! The *G*, the True, the Pure, the Just— „ 71
preach'd a Gospel, all men's *g*; „ 89
Evolution ever climbing after some ideal *g*, „ 199
Powers of *G*, the Powers of Ill, „ 273
whatsoe'er He wrought of *g* or brave *Epilogue* 76
That wanders from the public *g*, *Freedom* 26
Shall we not thro' *g* and ill *Open I. and C. Exhib.* 33
Goodbye when he came to bid me *g*. *First Quarrel* 78
I had bid him my last *g*; *Rizpah* 41
Good Fortune prosperously sail'd The ship '*G F*,' *Enoch Arden* 528
blown by baffling winds, Like the *G F*, „ 629
Goodlier 'A goodly youth and worth a *g* boon! But so thou wilt no *g*, then must Kay, *Gareth and L.* 450
(And there were none but few *g* than he) „ 744
When all the *g* guests are past away, *Last Tournament* 158
Goodliest The *g* fellowship of famous knights *M. d'Arthur* 15
he seem'd the *g* man That ever among ladies *Lancelot and E.* 254
Reputed the best knight and *g* man, *Guinevere* 382
The *g* fellowship of famous knights *Pass. of Arthur* 183
Goodly In sooth it was a *g* time, *Arabian Nights* 20
A *g* place, a *g* time, (repeat) „ 31, 53
A *g* time, For it was in the golden prime „ 42
When on my *g* charger borne *Sir Galahad* 49
Nor dealing *g* counsel from a height *Aylmer's Field* 172
and *g* sheep In haste they drove, *Spec. of Iliad* 4
her great and *g* arms Stretch'd under all the cornice *Gareth and L.* 218
Had made his *g* cousin, Tristram, knight, „ 394
The *g* knight! What! „ 402
'A *g* youth and worth a goodlier boon! „ 449
For strong thou art and *g* therewithal, „ 878
dreams Of *g* supper in the distant pool, „ 1187
'Full merry am I to find my *g* knave „ 1291
following with a costrel bore The means of *g* welcome, *Marr. of Geraint* 387
And roam the *g* places that she knew; „ 646
Ah, dear, he took me from a *g* house, „ 708
Yea, and he brought me to a *g* house; „ 713
Men saw the *g* hills of Somerset, „ 828
But not to *g* hill or yellow sea „ 830
Three horses and three *g* suits of arms, *Geraint and E.* 124
Then cried Geraint for wine and *g* cheer „ 283
Some *g* cognizance of Guinevere, *Balin and Balan* 195
till his *g* horse, Arising wearily at a fallen oak, „ 424
tramples on the *g* shield to show His loathing „ 550
and unhooded casting off The *g* falcon free; *Merlin and V.* 131
for *g* hopes are mine That Lancelot is no more *Lancelot and E.* 601
she should ask some *g* gift of him For her own self „ 912
while I drank the brook, and ate The *g* apples, *Holy Grail* 388
'Where is that *g* company,' said I, „ 432
And then I chanced upon a *g* town „ 573
Saving the *g* sword, his prize, *Pelleas and E.* 359
A *g* brother of the Table Round Swung by the neck: *Last Tournament* 431
and felt the *g* hounds Yelp at his heart, „ 503
with *g* rhyme and reason for it— *Sisters (E. and E.)* 92
but the *g* view Was now one blank, *Death of Œnone* 3
Goodman her small *g* Shrinks in his arm-chair *Princess v* 453
Goodmorrow *G*—Dark my doom was here, *Balin and Balan* 623
'Goodnight, true brother here! *g* there! „ 628
Speaking a still *g-m* with her eyes. *Lancelot and E.* 1033

Goodness eye which watches guilt And g, In Mem. xxvi 6
Goodnight G, g, when I have said g for evermore, May Queen, N. Y's. E. 41
G, sweet mother: call me before the day is born. ,, 49
G! for we shall never bid again Good morrow— Balin and Balan 622
mine again should darken thine, G, true brother.' ,, 626
'G, true brother here! goodmorrow there! ,, 628
the stout Prince bad him a loud g-n. Geraint and E. 361
G-n. I am going. He calls. Rizpah 86
and soä little Dick, g-n. Owd Roä 118
Goods with what she brought Buy g and stores— Enoch Arden 138
Bought Annie g and stores, ,, 169
shelf and corner for the g and stores. ,, 171
Goodwill G to me as well as all— Supp. Confessions 27
Peace and g, g and peace, Peace and g, In Mem. xxviii 11
Bible verse of the Lord's g w toward men— Rizpah 61
Goose (See also **Wild-goose**) He held a g upon his arm, The Goose 5
take the g, and keep you warm, ,, 7
She caught the white g by the leg, A g— ,, 9
The g let fall a golden egg ,, 11
She dropt the g, and caught the pelf, ,, 13
more the white g laid It clack'd and cackled louder. ,, 23
'Go, take the g, and wring her throat, ,, 31
The g flew this way and flew that, ,, 35
He took the g upon his arm, ,, 41
Quoth she, 'The Devil take the g, ,, 55
He praised his hens, his geese, his guinea-hens; The Brook 126
From the long-neck'd geese of the world Maud I iv 52
'Being a g and rather tame than wild, Gareth and L. 38
'twere but of the g and golden eggs.' ,, 40
egg of mine Was finer gold than any g can lay; ,, 43
rams and geese Troop'd round a Paynim harper Last Tournament 321
swine, goats, asses, geese The wiser fools, ,, 325
Gorge (s) (See also **Mountain-gorge**) roaring foam into the g Below us, If I were loved 13
The g's, opening wide apart, reveal Œnone 12
craggy ledge High over the blue g, ,, 210
golden g of dragons spouted forth A flood Palace of Art 23
Sat often in the seaward-gazing g, Enoch Arden 589
Downward from his mountain g ,, 636
Thro' the long g to the far light Ode on Well. 213
Gorge (verb) Gave to the garbaging war-hawk to g it, Batt. of Brunanburh 109
Gorged snake-like slimed his victim ere he g; Sea Dreams 193
We issued g with knowledge, Princess ii 388
Dropt off g from a scheme that had left us flaccid Maud I i 20
we stay'd three days, and we g and we madden'd, V. of Maeldune 67
giddy besides with the fruits we had g, ,, 75
Gorgeous And title-scrolls and g heraldries. Aylmer's Field 656
this is he Worthy of our g rites, Ode on Well. 93
Starr'd from Jehovah's g armouries, Milton 6
That rollest from the g gloom Of evening In Mem. lxxxvi 2
Without a mirror, in the g gown; Marr. of Geraint 739
Nor meanly, but with g obsequies, Lancelot and E. 1335
Mixt with the g west the lighthouse shone, Lover's Tale i 60
Raise a stately memorial, Make it regally g, On Jub. Q. Victoria 45
Gorgon stared upon By ghastlier than the G head, Death. of Œnone 71
Gorgonised G me from head to foot Maud I xiii 21
Gorloïs This is the son of G, not the King; Com. of Arthur 73
Some calling Arthur born of G, Others of Anton? ,, 170
The prince and warrior G, he that held ,, 186
But she, a stainless wife to G, ,, 194
That G and King Uther went to war: And overthrown was G and slain. ,, 196
many hated Uther for the sake Of G. ,, 221
a son of G he, Or else the child of Anton, ,, 232
born the son of G, after death, ,, 240
'Daughter of G and Ygerne am I;' ,, 316
and dark Was G, yea and dark was Uther too, ,, 329
those Who call'd him the false son of G: Guinevere 288
Gorse blaze of g, and the blush Of millions V. of Maeldune 43
Gospel The G, the Priest's pearl, Sir J. Oldcastle 116
Ah rather, Lord than that thy G, ,, 119
preach'd a G, all men's good; Locksley H., Sixty 89
Gossamer (adj.) Had seem'd a g filament up in air, Lover's Tale i 413
Gossamer (s) To trip a tigress with a g, Princess v 170
Gossamer (s) (continued) all the silvery g's That twinkle into green and gold: In Mem. xi 7
Gossip (adj.) A hate of g parlance, and of sway, Isabel 26
Gossip (s) Fearing the lazy g of the port, Enoch Arden 335
By this the lazy g's of the port, ,, 472
The sins of emptiness, g and spite Princess ii 92
like a city, with g, scandal, and spite; Maud I iv 8
Delight myself with g and old wives, Holy Grail 553
Gossip (verb) neighbours come and laugh and g, Grandmother 91
hear the magpie g Garrulous under a roof of pine: To F. D. Maurice 19
Gossoon Thin a slip of a g call'd, Tomorrow 78
Got G up betwixt you and the woman there. Dora 96
storming a hill-fort of thieves He g it; Aylmer's Field 226
'Sir Ralph has g your colours: Princess iv 594
Now had you g a friend of your own age, ,, vi 251
Stook to his taaïl they did, an' 'e 'ant g shut on 'em yet. N. Farmer, N. S. 30
For all have g the seed. The Flower 20
At last he g his breath and answer'd, Lancelot and E. 422
up the side, sweating with agony, g, ,, 494
So Lancelot g her horse, Set her thereon, Guinevere 122
we g to the barn, fur the barn wouldn't burn Owd Roä 103
Up she g, and wrote him all, Forlorn 79
True we have g—such a faithful ally Riflemen form! 24
Gothic (adj.) Gleam thro' the G archway in the wall. Godiva 64
A G ruin and a Grecian house, Princess, Pro. 232
Gothic (s) Of finest G lighter than a fire, ,, 92
Gotten (See also **Well-gotten**) you have g the wings of love, Window, Ay 15
then 'ed g wer leäve, Owd Roä 51
when Moother 'ed g to bed, ,, 53
Gourd By heaps of g's, and skins of wine, Vision of Sin 13
In us true growth, in her a Jonah's g, Princess iv 311
Gout g and stone, that break Body toward death, Lucretius 153
that I, Rack'd as I am with g, Columbus 235
Gouty The g oak began to move, Amphion 23
Govern I have no men to g in this wood: D. of F. Women 135
g a whole life from birth to death, Lover's Tale i 76
Governance And own the holy g of Rome.' Columbus 190
Governed 'I g men by change, and so I sway'd D. of F. Women 130
Governess See **Guvness**
Government A land of settled g, You ask me, why, etc. 9
And manners, climates, councils, g's, Ulysses 14
in arts of g Elizabeth and others; Princess ii 161
felt Her low firm voice and tender g. Geraint and E. 194
Gowd (gold) es wouldn't goä, wi' good g o' the Queen, Village Wife 49
boooks mebbe worth their weight i' g.' ,, 70
'e was allus as good as g. Owd Roä 6
Gown Her cap blew off, her g blew up, The Goose 51
She clad herself in a russet g, Lady Clare 57
A g of grass-green silk she wore, Sir L. and Q. G. 24
they should not wear our rusty g's, Princess, Pro. 143
A rosy blonde, and in a college g, ,, ii 323
I wore a lilac g; Grandmother 57
In which of old I wore the g; In Mem. lxxxvii 2
Without a mirror, in the gorgeous g; Marr. of Geraint 739
At least put off to please me this poor g, Geraint and E. 679
'In this poor g my dear lord found me first, ,, 698
In this poor g I rode with him to court, ,, 700
In this poor g he bad me clothe myself, ,, 702
And this poor g I will not cast aside ,, 705
taäil'd in an owd turn g, North. Cobbler 41
all the while I wur chaängin' my g, Spinster's S's. 43
to my faäce or a teärin' my g— ,, 91
loved by all the younger g There at Balliol, To Master of B. 2
Gowned One arm aloft—G in pure white, Gardener's D. 126
Graäce (grace) an' the power ov 'is G, North. Cobbler 73
An' saw by the G o' the Lord, Church-warden, etc. 42
Graäte (grate) red as the Yule-block theer i' the g. Owd Roä 56
Graäter (greater) They maäkes ma a g Laädy nor 'er i' the mansion theer, Spinster's S's. 110
Grabb'd An' I g the munny she maäde, North. Cobbler 32
Grace (See also **Graäce**) Victoria—since your Royal g To the Queen 5
that g Would drop from his o'er-brimming love, Supp. Confessions 112
From all things outward you have won A tearful g, Margaret 12

Grace (*continued*) I watch thy *g*; and in its place My heart *Eleänore* 127
God in his mercy lend her *g*, *L. of Shalott iv* 53
Complaining, 'Mother, give me *g* *Mariana in the S.* 29
'But looking upward, full of *g*, He pray'd, *Two Voices* 223
and, with a silent *g* Approaching, *Miller's D.* 159
loveliest in all *g* Of movement, *Œnone* 75
all *g* Summ'd up and closed in little;— *Gardener's D.* 12
shelter'd here Whatever maiden *g* The good old Summers, *Talking Oak* 38
So sweet a face, such angel *g*, *Beggar Maid* 13
But the tender *g* of a day that is dead *Break, Break, etc.* 15
'Annie, this voyage by the *g* of God *Enoch Arden* 190
(Claspt hands and that petitionary *g* *The Brook* 112
Nor deeds of gift, but gifts of *g* he forged, *Sea Dreams* 192
And so much *g* and power, breathing down *Princess ii* 38
arts of *g* Sappho and others vied with any man: „ 163
At last a solemn *g* Concluded, „ 452
easy *g*, No doubt, for slight delay, „ *iv* 330
Come, a *g* to me! I am your warrior: „ *vi* 223
who love best have best the *g* to know *W. to Marie Alex.* 28
and there is *G* to be had; *Grandmother* 94
The mimic picture's breathing *g*, *In Mem. lxxviii* 11
With gifts of *g*, that might express „ *lxxxv* 46
with power and *g* And music in the bounds „ *lxxxvii* 33
The maidens gather'd strength and *g* „ *ciii* 27
manhood fused with female *g* In such a sort, „ *cix* 17
Maud in the light of her youth and her *g*, *Maud I v* 15
Rich in the *g* all women desire, „ *x* 13
Some peculiar mystic *g* Made her only the child „ *xiii* 39
g that, bright and light as the crest Of a peacock, „ *xvi* 16
May nothing there her maiden *g* affright! „ *xviii* 71
heard that Arthur of his *g* Had made *Gareth and L.* 393
Treat him with all *g*, Lest he should come to shame „ 468
so my lance Hold, by God's *g*, he shall into the mire— „ 723
I accord it easily as a *g*.' „ 975
and with all *g* Of womanhood and queenhood, *Marr. of Geraint* 175
'Here, by God's *g*, is the one voice for me.' „ 344
It were but little *g* in any of us, „ 624
I might amend it by the *g* of Heaven, *Geraint and E.* 53
such a *g* Of tenderest courtesy, „ 861
Both *g* and will to pick the vicious quitch „ 903
with how sweet *g* She greeted my return! *Balin and Balan* 193
To learn the *g's* of their Table, „ 238
Name, manhood, and a *g*, but scantly thine, „ 377
into that rude hall Stept with all *g*, and not with half disdain Hid under *g*, *Lancelot and E.* 263
'Do me this *g*, my child, to have my shield „ 382
'A *g* to me,' She answer'd, 'twice to-day. „ 383
The *g* and versatility of the man! „ 472
g's of the court, and songs, Sighs, „ 648
'Stay a little! One golden minute's *g*! „ 684
while that ghostly *g* Beam'd on his fancy, „ 885
'Ye might at least have done her so much *g*, „ 1310
the seven clear stars—O *g* to me— *Holy Grail* 692
mighty reverent at our *g* was he: „ 702
glossy-throated *g*, Isolt the Queen. *Last Tournament* 509
'*G*, Queen, for being loved: she loved me well. „ 602
to yield thee *g* beyond thy peers.' „ 743
beauty, *g* and power, Wrought as a charm *Guinevere* 143
Who see your tender *g* and stateliness. „ 190
Had yet that *g* of courtesy in him left „ 436
and—not one moment's *g*— *Lover's Tale i* 659
—so, with that *g* of hers, Slow-moving „ *iv* 292
praised him to his face with their courtly foreign *g*; *The Revenge* 99
being damn'd beyond hope of *g*? *Despair* 109
Art and *G* are less and less: *Locksley H., Sixty* 245
the branching *g* Of leafless elm, *To Ulysses* 15
they do me too much *g*—for me? *Romney's R.* 27

Grace (goddess) Like to Furies, like to *G's*, *Vision of Sin* 41
Muses and the *G's*, group'd in threes, *Princess ii* 27
meet her *G's*, where they deck'd her „ *vii* 168

Grace (verb) moss or musk, To *g* my city rooms; *Gardener's D.* 194
Calliope to *g* his golden verse— *Lucretius* 94
'So ye will *g* me,' answer'd Lancelot, *Lancelot and E.* 223

Graced the glance That *g* the giving— *Gardener's D.* 178

Graced (*continued*) ease That *g* the lowliest act in doing it. *Gareth and L.* 490

Graceful (*See also* **All-graceful**) 'And yet it was a *g* gift— *Talking Oak* 233
Divided in a *g* quiet—paused, *Gardener's D.* 156
What looks so little *g*: 'men' *Princess iii* 53
Or deep dispute, and *g* jest; *In Mem. lxxxiv* 24
They sang of what is wise and good And *g*. „ *ciii* 11
The *g* tact, the Christian art; „ *cx* 16
you keep So much of what is *g*: *Lancelot and E.* 1219
A *g* thought of her Grav'n on my fancy! *Lover's Tale i* 357

Gracefulness symmetry Of thy floating *g*, *Eleänore* 50

Graceless Loud laugh'd the *g* Mark. *Merlin and V.* 62

Gracious Maud could be *g* too, no doubt To a lord, *Maud I x* 28
G lessons thine And maxims of the mud! *Merlin and V.* 48
For Lancelot will be *g* to the rat, „ 120
thine is more to me—soft, *g*, kind— *Last Tournament* 560
thy Mark is kindled on thy lips Most *g*; „ 562
Was *g* to all ladies, and the same In open battle *Guinevere* 329
All is *g*, gentle, great and Queenly. *On Jub. Q. Victoria* 14
—well—that were hardly *g*. No! *Happy* 103
A life that moves to *g* ends *You might have won* 6
A distant kinship to the *g* blood *Aylmer's Field* 62
'A *g* gift to give a lady, this!' 'But would it be more *g*' ask'd the girl 'Were I to give this gift of his to one That is no lady?' '*G*? No' said he. „ 240
So *g* was her tact and tenderness: *Princess i* 24
the Lord be *g* to me! A plot, a plot, „ *ii* 191
till the *g* dews Began to glisten and to fall: „ 316
those were *g* times. „ *iv* 297
He seems a *g* and a gallant Prince, „ *v* 213
Like creatures native unto *g* act, „ *vii* 27
Not learned, save in *g* household ways, „ 318
Whose hand at home was *g* to the poor: *W. to Marie Alex.* 37
Some *g* memory of my friend; *In Mem. c* 4
Or Love but play'd with *g* lies, „ *cxxv* 7
Sweet nature gilded by the *g* gleam Of letters, *Ded. of Idylls* 39
As in the presence of a *g* king. *Gareth and L.* 316
or what had been those *g* things, *Geraint and E.* 636
meet The morrow morn once more in one full field Of *g* pastime, *Holy Grail* 324
woman's eyes and innocent, And all her bearing *g*; „ 394
therefore flatter'd him, Being so *g*, *Pelleas and E.* 120
And all her damsels too were *g* to him, „ 122
So for the last time she was *g* to him. „ 175
Warm with a *g* parting from the Queen, „ 558
this name to which her *g* lips Did lend such gentle utterance, *Lover's Tale i* 456
for the sake Of one recalling *g* times, *To E. Fitzgerald* 53
Household happiness, *g* children, *Vastness* 24
She dropt the *g* mask of motherhood, *The Ring* 384
Watching her large light eyes and *g* looks, *Prog. of Spring* 19

Gradation Regard *g*, lest the soul Of Discord *Love thou thy land* 67

Grade Tho' scaling slow from *g* to *g*; *Two Voices* 174
g's Beyond all *g's* develop'd? *Gardener's D.* 240
To leap the *g's* of life and light, *In Mem. xli* 11

Gradual Her *g* fingers steal And touch *Will Water.* 26
while I walk'd with these In Marvel at that *g* change, *Lover's Tale iii* 19
saner lesson might he learn Who reads thy *g* process, *Prog. of Spring* 106

Gradually And *g* the powers of the night, *Princess, Con.* 111

Graduate *See* **Girl-graduates**

Graff made a Gardener putting in a *g*, *Merlin and V.* 479

Grafted Disrooted, what I am is *g* here. *Princess ii* 220
my days have been a life-long lie, *G* on half a truth; *Romney's R.* 42

Grail (*See also* **Holy Grail**) and the *G* Past, and the beam decay'd, *Holy Grail* 121
A crimson *g* within a silver beam; „ 155
Because I had not seen the *G*, „ 196
'Art thou so bold and hast not seen the *G*?' „ 279
I, Galahad, saw the *G*, The Holy Grail, „ 464
Before a burning taper, the sweet *G* Glided and past, „ 694
Could see it, thou hast seen the *G*;' „ 757

Grail (*continued*) And to the Holy Vessel of the *G.*' *Holy Grail* 840
Grain (corn) four-field system, and the price of *g*; *Audley Court* 34
shower the fiery *g* Of freedom broadcast *Princess v* 421
A pamphleteer on guano and on *g*, „ *Con.* 89
eating hoary *g* and pulse the steeds, *Spec. of Iliad* 21
And vacant chaff well meant for *g*. *In Mem. vi* 4
grown The *g* by which a man may live? „ *liii* 8
And gave all ripeness to the *g*, „ *lxxxi* 11
g Storm-strengthen'd on a windy site, *Gareth and L.* 691
Smuttier than blasted *g*: *Last Tournament* 305
and of the *g* and husk, the grape And ivyberry, *De Prof., Two G.* 50
torpid mummy wheat Of Egypt bore a *g* as sweet As that *To Prof. Jebb.* 6
thro' olive-yard and vine And golden *g*, *Demeter and P.* 111
From buried *g* thro' springing blade, „ 146
heats our earth to yield us *g* and fruit, *Akbar's Dream* 105
Grain (fibre, etc.) Cut Prejudice against the *g*: *Love thou thy land* 22
tho' I circle in the *g* Five hundred rings *Talking Oak* 83
Nor ever lightning char thy *g*, „ 277
the stem Less *g* than touchwood, *Princess iv* 333
And twists the *g* with such a roar „ *v* 528
There dwelt an iron nature in the *g*: „ *vi* 50
Too prurient for a proof against the *g* *Merlin and V.* 487
Grain (particle) A little *g* of conscience made him sour.' *Vision of Sin* 218
The city sparkles like a *g* of salt. *Will* 20
A little *g* shall not be spilt.' *In Mem. lxv* 4
For every *g* of sand that runs, „ *cxvii* 9
Have a *g* of love for me, *Maud II ii* 53
When weight is added only *g* by *g*, *Marr. of Geraint* 526
Not a *g* of gratitude mine! *Despair* 62
in the million-millionth of a *g* *Ancient Sage* 42
chains of mountain, *g's* of sand *Locksley H., Sixty* 208
Grain (fast dye) one the Master, as a rogue in *g* *Princess, Pro.* 116
Grained *See* **Hard-grained**
Granary find my garden-tools upon the *g* floor: *May Queen, N. Y's. E.* 45
garner'd up Into the *granaries* of memory— *Lover's Tale i* 129
Grand He look'd so *g* when he was dead. *The Sisters* 32
This same *g* year is ever at the doors.' *Golden Year* 74
Princess, six feet high, *G*, epic, homicidal; *Princess, Pro.* 225
She look'd as *g* as doomsday and as grave: „ *i* 187
true she errs, But in her own *g* way: „ *iii* 108
strange Poet-princess with her *g* Imaginations „ 273
Or some *g* fight to kill and make an end: „ *iv* 591
wherein were wrought Two *g* designs; „ *vii* 122
he bore without abuse The *g* old name of gentleman, *In Mem. cxi* 22
A *g* political dinner To half the squirelings near; *Maud I xx* 25
A *g* political dinner To the men of many acres, „ 31
Grandchild I wish to see My *g* on my knees *Dora* 13
Grander And roll'd the floods in *g* space, *In Mem. ciii* 26
Grandfather I mean your *g*, Annie: *Grandmother* 23
Whose old *g* has lately died, *Maud I x* 5
Grandsire The boy set up betwixt his *g's* knees, *Dora* 131
sorcerer, whom a far-off *g* burnt *Princess i* 6
he bestrode my *G*, when he fell, „ *ii* 242
a greatness Got from their *G's*— *Batt. of Brunanburh* 16
Ev'n her *G's* fifty half forgotten. *On Jub. Q. Victoria* 41
Grandson To a *g*, first of his noble line, *Maud I x* 12
Late, my *g*! half the morning have I paced *Locksley H., Sixty* 1
Here is Locksley Hall, my *g*, „ 213
Not the Hall to-night, my *g*! „ 237
Grange Upon the lonely moated *g*. *Mariana* 8
About the lonely moated *g*. „ 32
So pass I hostel, hall, and *g*; *Sir Galahad* 81
so by tilth and *g*, And vines, *Princess i* 110
nail me like a weasel on a *g* For warning: „ *ii* 205
burnt the *g*, nor buss'd the milking-maid, „ *v* 222
That ripple round the lonely *g*; *In Mem. xci* 12
No gray old *g*, or lonely fold, „ *c* 5
Old Fitz, who from your suburb *g*, *To E. Fitzgerald* 1
A height, a broken *g*, a grove, *Ancient Sage* 223
Rejoicing in the harvest and the *g*. *Demeter and P.* 127
Granite shadowy *g*, in a gleaming pass; *Lotos-Eaters, C. S.* 4
ebb that faintly lipp'd The flat red *g*; *Audley Court* 13
Grant 'Good soul! suppose I *g* it thee, *Two Voices* 38
Grant (*continued*) 'But if I *g*, thou mightst defend The thesis *Two Voices* 337
didst thou *g* mine asking with a smile, *Tithonus* 16
We might be still as happy as God *g's* *Enoch Arden* 416
(Altho' I *g* but little music there) *Sea Dreams* 253
You *g* me license; might I use it? *Princess iii* 235
I *g* in her some sense of shame, „ *iv* 349
G me your son, to nurse, „ *vi* 298
g my prayer. Help, father, brother, „ 304
God *g* I may find it at last! *Maud I ii* 1
His face, as I *g*, in spite of spite, „ *xiii* 8
G me some knight to do the battle for me, *Gareth and L.* 362
ev'n that thou *g* her none, „ 368
g me to serve For meat and drink among thy kitchen-knaves „ 444
And pray'd the King would *g* me Lancelot „ 856
G me pardon for my thoughts: *Marr. of Geraint* 816
if the Queen disdain'd to *g* it! *Balin and Balan* 191
'Fairest I *g* her: I have seen; „ 356
g me some slight power upon your fate, *Merlin and V.* 333
And *g* my re-reiterated wish, „ 353
O *g* my worship of it Words, as we *g* grief tears. *Lancelot and E.* 1187
Only this *G* me, I pray you: „ 1217
Queen, if I *g* the jealousy as of love, „ 1399
Granted Nor yet refused the rose, but *g* it, *Gardener's D.* 160
Perfectly beautiful: let it be *g* her: *Maud I ii* 4
As fairest, best and purest, *g* me To bear it!' *Balin and Balan* 350
What should be *g* which your own gross heart *Merlin and V.* 916
But takes it all for *g*: *Lover's Tale i* 157
Sanctuary *g* To bandit, thief, assassin— *Sir J. Oldcastle* 112
Grape (fruit) (*See also* **Father-grape**) But pledge me in the flowing *g*. *My life is full* 15
And *g's* with bunches red as blood; *Day-Dm., Sleep P.* 44
Let there be thistles, there are *g's*; *Will Water.* 57
skins of wine, and piles of *g's*. *Vision of Sin* 13
drains The chalice of the *g's* of God; *In Mem. x* 16
bruised the herb and crush'd the *g*, „ *xxxv* 23
shun The foaming *g* of eastern France. „ *Con.* 80
when my father dangled the *g's*, *Maud I i* 71
this wine—the *g* from whence it flow'd *Sisters (E. and E.)* 61
dangled a hundred fathom of *g's*, *V. of Maeldune* 56
grain and husk, the *g* And ivyberry, choose; *De Prof., Two G.* 50
vines with *g's* Of Eshcol hugeness; *To E. Fitzgerald* 27
Are figs of thistles? or *g's* of thorns? *Riflemen form!* 10
Grape (shot) their masses are gapp'd with our *g*— *Def. of Lucknow* 42
Now double-charge it with *g*! „ 68
Grape-loaded valleys of *g-l* vines that glow *D. of F. Women* 219
Grape-thicken'd in a bower *G-t* from the light, *Eleänore* 36
Grapple And *g's* with his evil star; *In Mem. lxiv* 8
Grappling airy navies *g* in the central blue; *Locksley Hall* 124
Grasp (s) A *g* Having the warmth and muscle *Aylmer's Field* 179
To give him the *g* of fellowship; *Maud I xiii* 16
g of hopeless grief about my heart, *Lover's Tale i* 126
I clasp'd her without fear: her weight Shrank in my *g*, „ *ii* 203
Pity for all that aches in the *g* of an idiot power, *Despair* 43
Grasp (verb) God-like, *g's* the triple forks, *Of old sat Freedom* 15
I will not cease to *g* the hope I hold Of saintdom, *St. S. Stylites* 5
his long arms stretch'd as to *g* a flyer: *Aylmer's Field* 588
And *g's* the skirts of happy chance, *In Mem. lxiv* 6
To him who *g's* a golden ball, „ *cxi* 3
Than language *g* the infinite of Love. *Lover's Tale i* 484
Grasp'd-Graspt one hand *grasp'd* The mild bull's golden horn. *Palace of Art* 119
there the world-worn Dante *grasp'd* his song, „ 135
And mounted horse and *graspt* a spear, *Gareth and L.* 691
long black horn Beside it hanging; which Sir Gareth *graspt*, „ 1367
This Balin *graspt*, but while in act to hurl, *Balin and Balan* 368
Queen *Graspt* it so hard, that all her hand *Last Tournament* 411
her hand *Grasp'd*, made her vail her eyes: *Guinevere* 663
I loved her, *graspt* the hand she lov'd, *Lover's Tale i* 750
'Woman'—he *graspt* at my arm— *The Wreck* 120
tiny fist Had *graspt* a daisy from your Mother's grave— *The Ring* 323
Graspest Old Yew, which *g* at the stones *In Mem. ii* 1
Dark yew, that *g* at the stones „ *xxxix* 4

Grasping *g* the pews And oaken finials *Aylmer's Field* 822
g down the boughs I gain'd the shore. *Princess iv* 189
lo! it was her mother *g* her *Marr. of Geraint* 676
This heard Geraint, and *g* at his sword, *Geraint and E.* 725
deathly-pale Stood *g* what was nearest, *Lancelot and E.* 966
Graspt *See* **Grasp'd**
Grass (*See also* **Meadow-grass, Oat-grass, Sparrow-grass, Sword-grass**) the dull Saw no divinity in *g*, *A Character* 8
And seem'd knee-deep in mountain *g*, *Mariana in the S.* 42
Make thy *g* hoar with early rime. *Two Voices* 66
You scarce could see the *g* for flowers. „ 453
the bearded *g* Is dry and dewless. *Miller's D.* 245
The grasshopper is silent in the *g*: *Œnone* 26
From level meadow-bases of deep *g* *Palace of Art* 7
above my head in the long and pleasant *g*. *May Queen, N. Y's. E.* 32
petals from blown roses on the *g*, *Lotos-Eaters, C. S.* 2
Heap'd over with a mound of *g*, „ 67
thro' lush green *g'es* burn'd The red anemone. *D. of F. Women* 71
A league of *g*, wash'd by a slow broad stream, *Gardener's D.* 40
So light upon the *g*: *Talking Oak* 88
He lies beside thee on the *g*. „ 239
All *g* of silky feather grow— „ 269
Or scatter'd blanching on the *g*. *Day-Dm., Arrival* 12
'There I put my face in the *g*— *Edward Gray* 21
High-elbow'd grigs that leap in summer *g*. *The Brook* 54
the Squire had seen the colt at *g*, „ 139
Show'd her the fairy footings on the *g*, *Aylmer's Field* 90
With neighbours laid along the *g*, *Lucretius* 214
babies roll'd about Like tumbled fruit in *g*; *Princess, Pro.* 83
Grate her harsh kindred in the *g*: „ *iv* 125
Lay like a new-fall'n meteor on the *g*, „ *vi* 135
she sat, she pluck'd the *g*, She flung it „ *Con.* 31
I may die but the *g* will grow, And the *g* will grow when I am gone, *Window, No Answer* 4
Spring is here with leaf and *g*: „ 23
And, since the *g'es* round me wave, *In Mem. xxi* 2
I take the *g'es* of the grave, „ 3
And tuft with *g* a feudal tower; „ *cxxviii* 20
From little cloudlets on the *g*, „ *Con.* 94
fall before Her feet on the meadow *g*, *Maud I v* 26
A livelier emerald twinkles in the *g*, „ *xviii* 51
their feet In dewy *g'es* glisten'd; *Gareth and L.* 928
when he found the *g* within his hands He laugh'd; „ 1225
pluck'd the *g* There growing longest *Geraint and E.* 256
Tho' happily down on a bank of *g*, „ 507
grayly draped With streaming *g*, appear'd, *Balin and Balan* 333
'Here are snakes within the *g*; *Merlin and V.* 33
lived alone in a great wild on *g*; „ 621
Went back to his old wild, and lived on *g*, „ 649
its own voice clings to each blade of *g*, *Lancelot and E.* 107
Lay like a rainbow fall'n upon the *g*, „ 431
eft and snake, In *g* and burdock, *Holy Grail* 571
flats, where nothing but coarse *g'es* grew; „ 794
live *g*, Rose-campion, bluebell, kingcup, *Last Tournament* 233
O ay—the winds that bow the *g*! „ 735
the flowering grove Of *g'es* Lancelot pluck'd *Guinevere* 34
Prone by the dashing runnel on the *g*. *Lover's Tale ii* 101
an' they sucks the muck fro' the *g*. *Village Wife* 32
Who live on milk and meal and *g*; *To E. Fitzgerald* 13
And all her golden armour on the *g*, *Tiresias* 45
they laid this body they foun' an the *g* *Tomorrow* 73
blossom an' spring from the *g*, „ 89
glory lights the hall, the dune, the *g*! *Locksley H., Sixty* 181
Jacob's ladder falls On greening *g*, *Early Spring* 10
gold from each laburnum chain Drop to the *g*. *To Mary Boyle* 11
delight To roll himself in meadow *g* *Romney's R.* 14
Thy living flower and *g*, *Doubt and Prayer* 6
Grass-green graves *g-g* beside a gray church-tower, *Circumstance* 6
A gown of *g-g* silk she wore, *Sir L. and Q. G.* 24
Grasshopper the *g* carolleth clearly; *Leonine Eleg.* 5
The *g* is silent in the grass: *Œnone* 26
Grassy The plain was *g*, wild and bare, *Dying Swan* 1
gave into a *g* walk Thro' crowded lilac-ambush *Gardener's D.* 111
And *g* barrows of the happier dead. *Tithonus* 71
By *g* capes with fuller sound In curves *Sir L. and Q. G.* 14
Grassy (*continued*) I steal by lawns and *g* plots, *The Brook* 170
thro' many a *g* glade And valley, *Marr. of Geraint* 236
When we had reach'd The *g* platform on some hill, *Lover's Tale i* 341
Grate (s) (*See also* **Graäte**) glimmering vaults with iron *g's*, *D. of F. Women* 35
rang the *g* of iron thro' the groove, *Pelleas and E.* 207
Grate (verb) the harsh shingle should *g* underfoot, *Enoch Arden* 772
I *g* on rusty hinges here:' *Princess i* 86
G her harsh kindred in the grass: „ *iv* 125
Grated (*See also* **Rib-grated**) faces flat against the panes, Sprays *g*, *Balin and Balan* 345
Blinkt the white morn, sprays *g*, „ 385
grew So *g* down and filed away with thought, *Merlin and V.* 623
Grateful *g* at last for a little thing: *Maud III vi* 3
G to Prince Geraint for service done, *Marr. of Geraint* 15
So *g* is the noise of noble deeds „ 437
be *g* for the sounding watchword *Locksley H., Sixty* 198
And deem me *g*, and farewell! *The Wanderer* 16
That over-vaulted *g* gloom, *Palace of Art* 54
a *g* people named Enid the Good; *Geraint and E.* 963
clouded with the *g* incense-fume *Tiresias* 183
Gratefullest Hers was the *g* heart I have found *In the Child. Hosp.* 32
Gratefulness King was all fulfill'd with *g*, *Last Tournament* 593
By all the laws of love and *g*, *Lover's Tale iv* 278
Gratify We would do much to *g* your Prince— *Princess v* 217
Grating Across the iron *g* of her cell Beat, *Holy Grail* 81
Struck from an open *g* overhead High in the wall, *Lover's Tale iv* 60
As from the *g* of a sepulchre, *The Ring* 400
Gratitude Out of full heart and boundless *g* *Enoch Arden* 346
This nightmare weight of *g*, I know it; *Princess vi* 300
Not a grain of *g* mine! *Despair* 62
G—loneliness—desire to keep So skilled *The Ring* 373
Gratulation and was moving on In *g*, *Princess ii* 185
Grave (adj.) Or gay, or *g*, or sweet, or stern, *Palace of Art* 91
G, florid, stern, as far as eye could see, *Sea Dreams* 219
a hero lies beneath, *G*, solemn!' *Princess Pro.* 213
She look'd as grand as doomsday and as *g*: „ *i* 187
In each we sat, we heard The *g* Professor. „ *ii* 371
Farewell, Macready; moral, *g*, sublime, *To W. C. Macready* 12
And that has made you *g*? *The Ring* 88
G mother of majestic works, *Of old sat Freedom* 13
Until the *g* churchwarden doff'd, *The Goose* 19
G faces gather'd in a ring. *Day-Dm., Sleep. P.* 38
Altho' a *g* and staid God-fearing man, *Enoch Arden* 112
The *g*, severe Genovese of old. *The Daisy* 40
G doubts and answers here proposed, *In Mem. xlviii* 3
Grave (s) *See also* **Ocean-grave**) when thy *g* Was deep, *Supp. Confessions* 85
Over its *g* i' the earth so chilly; (repeat) *A spirit haunts* 10, 22
the green that folds thy *g*. (repeat) *A Dirge* 6, 13, 20, 27, 34, 41, 48
Two *g's* grass-green beside a gray church-tower, *Circumstance* 6
the brink Of that deep *g* to which I go: *My life is full* 7
From winter rains that beat his *g*. *Two Voices* 261
A shadow on the *g's* I knew, „ 272
'From *g* to *g* the shadow crept: „ 274
I shall lie alone, mother, within the mouldering *g*. *May Queen, N. Y's. E.* 20
and upon that *g* of mine, „ 21
see me till my *g* be growing green: „ 43
His voice was thin, as voices from the *g*; *Lotos-Eaters* 34
and ripen toward the *g* In silence; „ *C. S.* 51
cord of love Down to a silent *g*. *D. of F. Women* 212
Thou seëst all things, thou wilt see my *g*: *Tithonus* 73
Each pluck'd his one foot from the *g*, *Amphion* 43
By Ellen's *g*, on the windy hill. *Edward Gray* 12
The very *g's* appear'd to smile, *The Letters* 45
drop thy foolish tears upon my *g*, *Come not, when, etc.* 2
glow-worm of the *g* Glimmer in thy rheumy eyes. *Vision of Sin* 153
Till the *g's* begin to move, „ 165
tho' she mourn'd his absence as his *g*, *Enoch Arden* 247
it would vex him even in his *g*, „ 303
thought to bear it with me to my *g*; „ 896
shame these mouldy Aylmers in their *g's*: *Aylmer's Field* 396
Above them, with his hopes in either *g*. „ 624
bring Their own gray hairs with sorrow to the *g*— „ 777

Grave (s) (*continued*) Pity, the violet on the tyrant's *g*. *Aylmer's Field* 845
his bones long laid within the *g*, *Lucretius* 256
very sides of the *g* itself shall pass, „ 257
There above the little *g*, (repeat) *Princess ii* 12, 13
that full voice which circles round the *g*, „ 45
cram him with the fragments of the *g*, „ *iii* 311
and drank himself into his *g*. *Grandmother* 6
Drops in his vast and wandering *g*. *In Mem. vi* 16
I take the grasses of the *g*, „ *xxi* 3
yearn'd To hear her weeping by his *g*? „ *xxxi* 4
Or builds the house, or digs the *g*, „ *xxxvi* 14
And darkening the dark *g's* of men,— „ *xxxix* 9
I wrong the *g* with fears untrue: „ *li* 9
No life may fail beyond the *g*, „ *lv* 2
Unused example from the *g* „ *lxxx* 15
And my prime passion in the *g*: „ *lxxxv* 76
Had fall'n into her father's *g*, „ *lxxxix* 48
fathers bend Above more *g's*, „ *xcviii* 16
with me, and the *g* Divide us not, „ *cxxii* 9
the *g* That has to-day its sunny side. „ *Con.* 71
To-day the *g* is bright for me, „ 73
thing that had made false haste to the *g*— *Maud I i* 58
and Orion low in his *g*. „ *iii* 14
Your mother is mute in her *g* „ *iv* 58
Perhaps from a selfish *g*. „ *xvi* 23
into a shallow *g* they are thrust, „ *II v* 6
To have no peace in the *g*, is that not sad? „ 16
Is it kind to have made me a *g* so rough, „ 97
Orion's *g* low down in the west, „ *III vi* 8
The cackle of the unborn about the *g*, *Merlin and V.* 507
Among the knightly brasses of the *g's*, „ 752
'I shudder, some one steps across my *g*;' *Guinevere* 57
that his *g* should be a mystery From all men, „ 297
From halfway down the shadow of the *g*, *To the Queen ii* 6
to whom I made it o'er his *g* Sacred, „ 35
I and the first daisy on his *g* *Lover's Tale i* 193
received in a sweet *g* Of eglantines, „ 528
That men plant over *g's*. „ 538
the darkness of the *g*, (repeat) „ 597
The foul steam of the *g* to thicken by it, „ 649
till they fell Half-digging their own *g's*) „ *ii* 47
over the deep *g's* of Hope and Fear, „ 58
now, will I go down into the *g*, „ *iv* 46
she joined, In and beyond the *g*, *Sisters (E. and E.)* 272
From either by the stillness of the *g*— „ 282
Break thro' the yews and cypress of thy *g*, *Ded. Poem Prin. Alice* 12
we laid him that night in his *g*. *Def. of Lucknow* 12
I will have them buried in my *g*. *Columbus* 201
some one standing by my *g* will say, „ 209
a ghastlier face than ever has haunted a *g* *The Wreck* 8
vex you with wretched words, who is best in his *g*? *Despair* 108
the world is dark with griefs and *g's*, *Ancient Sage* 171
and weds me to my *g*. *The Flight* 20
Fiend would yell, the *g* would yawn, „ 51
I seem to see a new-dug *g* up yonder by the yew! „ 98
hair was as white as the snow an a *g*. *Tomorrow* 60
in wan *g* be the dead boor-tree, „ 87
yet he look'd beyond the *g*, *Locksley H., Sixty* 60
I repent it o'er his *g*— „ 255
cycle-year That dawns behind the *g*. *Epilogue* 78
raise a wind To sing thee to thy *g*, *Freedom* 36
sowing the nettle on all the laurel'd *g's* of the Great; *Vastness* 22
graspt a daisy from your Mother's *g*— *The Ring* 323
glimmers on the marsh and on the *g*.' „ 341
I am fitter for my bed, or for my *g*, „ 433
O the night, While the *g* is yawning. *Forlorn* 60
I would leap into your *g*. *Happy* 20
throbs Thro' earth, and all her *g's*, *Romney's R.* 128
Hush'd as the heart of the *g*, *Bandit's Death* 26
I am dressing the *g* of a woman with flowers. *Charity* 2
your shadow falls on the *g*. „ 20
I am dressing her *g* with flowers. „ 44
crimson with battles, and hollow with *g's*, *The Dreamer* 12

Gravel waterbreak Above the golden *g*, *The Brook* 62
like a wizard pentagram On garden *g*, „ 104

Gravel-spread bed Of silent torrents, *g-s*; *The Daisy* 34

Graven *G* with emblems of the time, *Arabian Nights* 108
underneath, A pint-pot neatly *g*. *Will Water.* 248
on one side, *G* in the oldest tongue *Com. of Arthur* 302
A graceful thought of hers *G* on my fancy! *Lover's Tale i* 358
Their names, *G* on memorial columns, *Tiresias* 124

Graver No *g* than as when some little cloud *Enoch Arden* 129
he turn'd The current of his talk to *g* things „ 203
No *g* than a schoolboys' barring out; *Princess, Con.* 66
one is somewhat *g* than the other— *Sisters (E. and E.)* 26
No! but the paler and the *g*, Edith. „ 38
The *g* is the one perhaps for you „ 40
Come, when no *g* cares employ, *To F. D. Maurice* 1
'*G* cause than yours is mine To curse this hedgerow thief, *Marr. of Geraint* 308
Began to break her sports with *g* fits, *Merlin and V.* 180

Gravest The *g* citizen seems to lose his head, *Princess, Con.* 59

Graw (grow) an' proputty, proputty *g's*. *N. Farmer, N. S.* 16
thou can't *g* this upo' watter!' *North. Cobbler* 86

Graw'd (grew) as *g* hall ower the brick; *Owd Roä* 26

Gray (Edward) *See* **Edward Gray**

Gray (adj.) my hope is *g*, and cold At heart, *Supp. Confessions* 103
Come from the woods that belt the *g* hill-side, *Ode to Memory* 55
Two graves grass-green beside a *g* church-tower, *Circumstance* 6
Four *g* walls, and four *g* towers, *L. of Shalott i* 15
I see his *g* eyes twinkle yet At his own jest—*g* eyes lit up *Miller's D.* 11
g twilight pour'd On dewy pastures, *Palace of Art* 85
wild marsh-marigold shines like fire in swamps and hollows *g*, *May Queen* 31
You'll never see me more in the long *g* fields at night; *May Queen, N. Y's. E.* 26
range Of waning lime the *g* cathedral towers, *Gardener's D.* 218
The set *g* life, and apathetic end. *Love and Duty* 18
And this *g* spirit yearning in desire *Ulysses* 30
for this *g* shadow, once a man— *Tithonus* 11
But I count the *g* barbarian lower than the Christian child. *Locksley Hall* 174
my hair Is *g* before I know it. *Will Water.* 168
A *g* and gap-tooth'd man as lean as death, *Vision of Sin* 60
On thy cold *g* stones, O Sea! *Break, break, etc.* 2
high in heaven behind it a *g* down With Danish barrows; *Enoch Arden* 6
His large *g* eyes and weather-beaten face „ 70
He, shaking his *g* head pathetically, „ 714
See thro' the *g* skirts of a lifting squall „ 829
Then Enoch rolling his *g* eyes upon her, „ 844
left Their own *g* tower, or plain-faced tabernacle, *Aylmer's Field* 618
bring Their own *g* hairs with sorrow to the grave— „ 777
a work To assail this *g* preëminence of man! *Princess iii* 234
From the flaxen curl to the *g* lock a life „ *iv* 426
and without Found the *g* kings at parle: „ *v* 114
Look you! the *g* mare Is ill to live with, „ 451
G halls alone among their massive groves; „ *Con.* 43
O good *g* head which all men knew, *Ode on Well.* 35
From Como, when the light was *g*, *The Daisy* 73
misty summer And *g* metropolis of the North. „ 104
'We shall both be *g*.' *Window, When* 6
G nurses, loving nothing new; *In Mem. xxix* 14
The same *g* flats again, and felt The same, „ *lxxxvii* 13
No *g* old grange, or lonely fold, „ *c* 5
A *g* old wolf and a lean. *Maud I xiii* 28
Not that *g* old wolf, for he came not back „ *II v* 53
Sleuth-hound thou knowest, and *g*, *Gareth and L.* 462
ivy-stems Claspt the *g* walls with hairy-fibred arms, *Marr. of Geraint* 323
G swamps and pools, waste places of the hern, *Geraint and E.* 31
As the *g* dawn stole o'er the dewy world, „ 385
This *g* King Show'd us a shrine wherein *Balin and Balan* 108
As that *g* cricket chirpt of at our hearth— *Merlin and V.* 110
seem'd a lovely baleful star Veil'd in *g* vapour; „ 263
Had found a glen, *g* boulder and black tarn. *Lancelot and E.* 36
Sat on his knee, stroked his *g* face and said, „ 749
'May God be with thee, sweet, when old and *g*, *Last Tournament* 627
and set me far In the *g* distance, „ 640

K*

Great (*continued*) Bury the G Duke With an empire's lamentation, Let us bury the G Duke To the noise *Ode on Well.* 1
The last g Englishman is low. „ 18
G in council and g in war, „ 30
g World-victor's victor will be seen no more. „ 42
In that dread sound to the g name, „ 71
Was g by land as thou by sea. (repeat) „ 84, 90
And ever g and greater grew, „ 108
So g a soldier taught us there, „ 131
Attest their g commander's claim With honour, „ 148
reverence and regret To those g men who fought, „ 158
All g self-seekers trampling on the right; „ 187
Let his g example stand Colossal, „ 220
watching here At this, our g solemnity. „ 244
He is gone who seem'd so g.— „ 271
Sounds of the g sea Wander'd about. *Minnie and Winnie* 7
Like those who cried Diana g: *Lit. Squabbles* 16
Heart, are you g enough For a love that never tires? O heart, are you g enough for love? *Window, Marr. Morn.* 17
Calm and still light on yon g plain *In Mem. xi* 9
In those g offices that suit The full-grown energies „ *xl* 19
There must be wisdom with g Death: „ *li* 11
Upon the g world's altar-stairs „ *lv* 15
Leaving g legacies of thought, „ *lxxxiv* 35
The g Intelligences fair That range above „ *lxxxv* 21
She darkly feels him g and wise, „ *xcvii* 34
Let her g Danube rolling fair Enwind her isles, „ *xcviii* 9
one would chant the history Of that g race, „ *ciii* 35
where we saw A g ship lift her shining sides. „ 40
Brings in g logs and let them lie, „ *cvii* 17
I would the g world grew like thee, „ *cxiv* 25
By thee the world's g work is heard Beginning, „ *cxxi* 10
And the g Æon sinks in blood, „ *cxxvii* 16
As gentle; liberal-minded, g, Consistent; „ *Con.* 38
She would not do herself this g wrong, *Maud I x* 57
Like some of the simple g ones gone For ever „ 61
yellow vapours choke The g city sounding wide; „ *II iv* 64
praying To his own g self, as I guess; „ *v* 33
And so there grew g tracts of wilderness, *Com. of Arthur* 10
Of those g Lords and Barons of his realm „ 65
Made lightnings and g thunders over him, „ 108
whatsoever Merlin did In one g annal-book, „ 158
after, the g lords Banded, and so brake out in open war.' „ 236
And simple words of g authority, „ 261
So this g brand the king Took, „ 308
watch'd the g sea fall, Wave after wave, „ 378
And the fringe Of that g breaker, „ 387
From the g deep to the g deep he goes.' „ 411
so g bards of him will sing Hereafter; „ 414
There at the banquet those g Lords from Rome, „ 504
so those g lords Drew back in wrath, „ 513
in twelve g battles overcame The heathen hordes, „ 518
eagle-circles up To the g Sun of Glory, *Gareth and L.* 22
at times the g gate shone Only, „ 194
like the cross her g and goodly arms Stretch'd „ 218
and faith in their g King, with pure Affection, „ 330
But Mark hath tarnish'd the g name of king, „ 426
Lyonors, A lady of high lineage, of g lands, „ 609
Now two g entries open'd from the hall, „ 665
take counsel; for this lad is g And lusty, „ 730
Till Gareth panted hard, and his g heart, „ 1126
hew'd g pieces of his armour off him, „ 1142
There rides no knight, not Lancelot, his g self, „ 1182
one Of that g Order of the Table Round, *Marr. of Geraint* 3
Thro' that g tenderness for Guinevere, „ 30
watch his mightful hand striking g blows „ 95
by g mischance He heard but fragments „ 112
And here had fall'n a g part of a tower, „ 317
Our hoard is little, but our hearts are g. (repeat) „ 352, 374
For the g wave that echoes round the world; „ 420
Avenging this g insult done the Queen.' „ 425
his face Glow'd like the heart of a g fire at Yule, „ 559
and still The dew of their g labour, „ 568
'Remember that great insult done the Queen,' „ 571

Great (*continued*) fell at last In the g battle fighting for the King. *Marr. of Geraint* 596
And should some g court-lady say, „ 723
As this g Prince invaded us, and we, „ 747
our g Queen, In words whose echo lasts, „ 781
Till the g plover's human whistle amazed Her heart, *Geraint and E.* 49
Saw once a g piece of a promontory, „ 162
I will tell him How g a man thou art: „ 228
While the g charger stood, grieved like a man. „ 535
This work of his is g and wonderful. „ 898
A thousand-fold more g and wonderful „ 914
His work was neither g nor wonderful, „ 921
There the g Queen once more embraced her friend, „ 947
They call'd him the g Prince and man of men. „ 961
him who first Brought the g faith to Britain *Balin and Balan* 103
down that range of roses the g Queen Came „ 244
And by the g Queen's name, arise and hence.' „ 482
By the g tower—Caerleon upon Usk— „ 506
I thought the g tower would crash down on both— „ 515
But the g Queen herself, fought in her name, *Merlin and V.* 13
G Nature thro' the flesh herself hath made „ 50
When Guinevere was crossing the g hall „ 65
Then fell on Merlin a g melancholy; „ 189
work the charm Upon the g Enchanter of the Time, „ 216
'G Master, do ye love me?' he was mute. „ 237
Caught in a g old tyrant spider's web, „ 259
And therefore be as g as ye are named, „ 336
The g proof of your love: „ 354
I heard the g Sir Lancelot sing it once, „ 385
Then the g Master merrily answer'd her: „ 545
Who lived alone in a g wild on grass; „ 621
I thought that he was gentle, being g: „ 871
he rode to tilt For the g diamond in the diamond jousts, *Lancelot and E.* 31
'Then will ye miss,' he answer'd, 'the g deeds Of Lancelot, „ 81
your g name This conquers: „ 150
With laughter dying down as the g knight „ 179
The g and guilty love he bare the Queen, „ 245
the g knight, the darling of the court, „ 261
By the g river in a boatman's hut. „ 278
'O there, g lord, doubtless,' Lavaine said, „ 281
And seeing me, with a g voice he cried, „ 309
'Save your g self, fair lord;' „ 320
And after muttering 'The g Lancelot,' „ 421
'Me you call g: mine is the firmer seat, „ 446
Of greatness to know well I am not g: „ 451
Lancelot gave A marvellous g shriek and ghastly groan, „ 516
Came round their g Pendragon, saying to him, „ 528
So g a knight as we have seen to-day— „ 533
knowing he was Lancelot; his g name Conquer'd; „ 579
A sleeve of scarlet, broider'd with g pearls, „ 604
flung herself Down on the g King's couch, „ 610
I deem you know full well Where your g knight is hidden, „ 690
Yet the g knight in his mid-sickness made „ 878
Up the g river in the boatman's boat. „ 1038
And there the g Sir Lancelot muse at me; „ 1055
My knight, the g Sir Lancelot of the Lake.' „ 1373
Or sin seem less, the sinning seeming g? „ 1418
In our g hall there stood a vacant chair, *Holy Grail* 167
While the g banquet lay along the hall, „ 180
roofs Of our g hall are roll'd in thunder-smoke! „ 220
four g zones of sculpture, set betwixt „ 232
Where twelve g windows blazon Arthur's wars, „ 248
Streams thro' the twelve g battles of our King. „ 250
Knights that in twelve g battles splash'd and dyed „ 311
All the g table of our Arthur closed „ 329
A g black swamp and of an evil smell, „ 499
A thousand piers ran into the g Sea. „ 503
first At once I saw him far on the g Sea, „ 510
With one g dwelling in the middle of it; „ 574
bound and plunged him into a cell Of g piled stones; „ 676
a g stone slipt and fell, Such as no wind could move: „ 680
words Of so g men as Lancelot and our King „ 713

Greatest (*continued*) 'that you love This *g* knight, your pardon! — *Lancelot and E.* 669
what profits me my name Of *g* knight? — „ 1414
Alas for Arthur's *g* knight, — „ 1419
'We have heard of thee: thou art our *g* knight, — *Holy Grail* 603
Chancellor, or what is *g* would he be— — *Aylmer's Field* 397
life which all our *g* fain Would follow, — *Lucretius* 78
Our *g* yet with least pretence, — *Ode on Well.* 29
as the *g* only are, In his simplicity — „ 33
grieving that their *g* are so small, — *Merlin and V.* 833
to learn this knight were whole, Being our *g*: — *Lancelot and E.* 773
Not all unhappy, having loved God's best And *g*, — „ 1094
And calling me the *g* of all knights, — *Holy Grail* 595
My *g* hardly will believe he saw; — „ 896
bless your haters, said the *G* of the great; — *Locksley H., Sixty* 85

Greatness *And should your g, and the care* — *To the Queen* 9
Remembering all his *g* in the Past. — *Ode on Well.* 20
if to-night our *g* were struck dead, — *Third of Feb.* 17
I leave thy *g* to be guess'd; — *In Mem. lxxv* 4
She knows not what his *g* is, — „ *xcvii* 27
According to his *g* whom she quench'd. — *Merlin and V.* 218
passion of youth Toward *g* in its elder, — *Lancelot and E.* 283
No *g*, save it be some far-off touch Of *g* — „ 450
one isle, That knows not her own *g*: — *To the Queen ii* 32
a *g* Got from their Grandsires— — *Batt. of Brunanburh* 15
Gone! He will achieve his *g*. — *Tiresias* 168
Flowing with easy *g* and touching on all things great, — *The Wreck* 50
Step by step we rose to *g*,— — *Locksley H., Sixty* 130
Pray God our *g* may not fail — *Hands all round* 31
increased Her *g* and her self-content. — *To Marq. of Dufferin* 8

Greaves flamed upon the brazen *g* Of bold Sir Lancelot. — *L. of Shalott iii* 4
g and cuisses dash'd with drops Of onset; — *M. d'Arthur* 215
g and cuisses dash'd with drops Of onset; — *Pass. of Arthur* 383

Grecian A Gothic ruin and a *G* house, — *Princess, Pro.* 232
Ran down the Persian, *G*, Roman lines — „ *ii* 130
And read a *G* tale re-told, Which, cast in later *G* mould, — *To Master of B.* 5

Greeän (green) (adj.) an' jessmine a-dressin' it *g*, — *Spinster's S's.* 105

Greeän (s) we was shaämed to cross Gigglesby *G*, — „ 33

Greece fairest and most loving wife in *G*.' — *Œnone* 187

Greed Blockish irreverence, brainless *g*— — *Columbus* 129

Greedy Come like a careless and a *g* heir — *Lover's Tale i* 675

Greek (adj.) my ancient love With the *G* woman. — *Œnone* 261
show'd the house, *G*, set with busts: — *Princess, Pro.* 11

Greek (s) whilome spakest to the South in *G* — *Sir J. Oldcastle* 29
sphere-music as the *G* Had hardly dream'd of. — *Akbar's Dream* 44

Green (adj.) *See also* **Dark-green, Grass-green, Greeän, Light-green, Live-green, Pale-green, Silver-green)**
tears of penitence Which would keep *g* — *Supp. Confessions* 119
Under the hollow-hung ocean *g*! — *The Merman* 38
Are neither *g* nor sappy; — *Amphion* 90
flourishes *G* in a cuplike hollow of the down. — *Enoch Arden* 9
sow'd her name and kept it *g* — *Aylmer's Field* 88
I trust We are *g* in Heaven's eyes; — *Holy Grail* 38
heaven appear'd so blue, nor earth so *g*, — „ 365
forehead vapour-swathed In meadows ever — *Freedom* 8
And see my cedar *g*, — *To Ulysses* 17
High-wall'd gardens *g* and old; — *Arabian Nights* 8
From the *g* rivage many a fall Of diamond rillets — „ 47
Betwixt the *g* brink and the running foam, — *Sea-Fairies* 2
Whither away from the high *g* field, — „ 8
Grow *g* beneath the showery *g*, — *My life is full* 17
And in the middle of the *g* salt sea — *Mine be the strength* 7
in the pits Which some *g* Christmas crams with weary bones. — *Wan Sculptor* 14
on the casement-edge A long *g* box of mignonette, — *Miller's D.* 83
In this *g* valley, under this *g* hill, — *Œnone* 232
round the cool *g* courts there ran a row Of cloisters, — *Palace of Art* 25
All the valley, mother, 'ill be fresh and *g* and still, — *May Queen* 37
Don't let Effie come to see me till my grave be growing *g*: — *May Queen, N. Y's. E.* 43
and there Grows *g* and broad, and takes no care, — *Lotos-Eaters, C. S.* 28
at the root thro' lush *g* grasses burn'd — *D. of F. Women* 71
'Single I grew, like some *g* plant, — „ 205

Green (adj.) (*continued*) To one *g* wicket in a privet hedge; — *Gardener's D.* 110
With one *g* sparkle ever and anon Dipt — *Audley Court* 88
Beyond the fair *g* field and eastern sea. — *Love and Duty* 101
And dewy Northern meadows *g*. — *The Voyage* 36
bathed In the *g* gleam of dewy-tassell'd trees: — *Princess i* 94
'Ye are *g* wood, see ye warp not. — „ *ii* 75
The *g* malignant light of coming storm. — „ *iii* 132
when all the woods are *g*? — „ *iv* 107
Started a *g* linnet Out of the croft; — *Minnie and Winnie* 17
Within the *g* the moulder'd tree, — *In Mem. xxvi* 7
Who wears his manhood hale and *g*: — „ *liii* 4
So thro' the *g* gloom of the wood they past, — *Geraint and E.* 195
mist Like that which kept the heart of Eden *g* — „ 770
leaves Laid their *g* faces flat against the panes, — *Balin and Balan* 344
Chose the *g* path that show'd the rarer foot, — *Lancelot and E.* 162
g light from the meadows underneath Struck up — „ 408
Till all the place whereon she stood was *g*; — „ 1200
And *g* wood-ways, and eyes among the leaves; — *Pelleas and E.* 139
In fuming sulphur blue and *g*, a fiend— — *Last Tournament* 617
gardener's hand Picks from the colewort a *g* caterpillar, — *Guinevere* 32
prest together In its *g* sheath, — *Lover's Tale i* 153
G prelude, April promise, glad new-year Of Being, — „ 281
Rather to thee, *g* boscage, work of God, — *Sir J. Oldcastle* 129
but the whole *g* Isle was our own, — *V. of Maeldune* 93
Or the young *g* leaf rejoice in the frost — *The Wreck* 20
G Sussex fading into blue — *Pro. to Gen. Hamley* 7
'sitting on *g* sofas contemplate The torment of the damn'd' — *Akbar's Dream* 48

Green (s) (*See also* **Chapel-green, Greeän, Gold-green)**
Winnow with giant arms the slumbering *g*. — *The Kraken* 10
and earliest shoots Of orient *g*, — *Ode to Memory* 18
Shot over with purple, and *g*, — *Dying Swan* 20
the *g* that folds thy grave. (repeat) — *A Dirge* 6, 13, 20, 27, 34, 41, 48
In some fair space of sloping *g's* — *Palace of Art* 106
Effie shall go with me to-morrow to the *g*, — *May Queen* 25
Beneath the hawthorn on the *g* — *May Queen, N. Y's. E.* 10
branches, fledges with clearest *g*, — *D. of F. Women* 59
The smell of violets, hidden in the *g*, — „ 77
like a purple beech among the *g's* — *Edwin Morris* 84
when she gamboll'd on the *g's* — *Talking Oak* 77
All creeping plants, a wall of *g* — *Day-Dm., Sleep P.* 45
The topmost elm-tree gather'd *g* — *Sir L. and Q. G.* 8
all the wood stands in a mist of *g*, — *The Brook* 14
pure as lines of *g* that streak the white — *Princess v* 196
That twinkle into *g* and gold: — *In Mem. xi* 8
This round of *g*, this orb of flame, — „ *xxxiv* 5
And on a simple village *g*; — „ *lxiv* 4
Thy leaf has perish'd in the *g*, — „ *lxxv* 13
those fall'n leaves which kept their *g*, — „ *xcv* 23
feet like sunny gems on an English *g*, — *Maud I v* 14
damp hill-slopes were quicken'd into *g*, — *Gareth and L.* 184
the live *g* had kindled into flowers, — „ 185
Breaks from a coppice gemm'd with *g* and red, — *Marr. of Geraint* 339
like a shoaling sea the lovely blue Play'd into *g*, — *Geraint and E.* 689
In *g* and gold, and plumed with *g* — *Merlin and V.* 89
And armour'd all in forest *g*, — *Last Tournament* 170
good warhorse left to graze Among the forest *g's*, — „ 491
Modred still in *g*, all ear and eye, — *Guinevere* 24
—its wreaths of dripping *g*— — *Lover's Tale i* 39
recalling fragrance and the *g* Of the dead spring: — „ 723
lies Behind the *g* and blue? — *Ancient Sage* 26
blue of sky and sea, the *g* of earth, — „ 41
for a blessin' 'ud come wid the *g*!' — *Tomorrow* 64
Shallow skin of *g* and azure— — *Locksley H., Sixty* 208
mantle, every shade of glancing *g*, — *Prog. of Spring* 63
earth's *g* stole into heaven's own hue, — *Far—far—away* 2
as summer-new As the *g* of the bracken — *June Bracken, etc.* 9

Green (verb) *g's* The swamp, where humm'd the dropping snipe, — *On a Mourner* 8

Greener *This laurel g from the brows Of him* — *To the Queen* 7
might have danced The greensward into *g* circles, — *Gardener's D.* 134
Yet the yellow leaf hates the *g* leaf, — *Spiteful Letter* 15

Green-glimmering *G-g* toward the summit, *Lancelot and E.* 483
Green-glooming *g-g* twilight of the grove, *Pelleas and E.* 33
Greening Her dust is *g* in your leaf, *Ancient Sage* 165
Her mantle, slowly *g* in the Sun, *Prog. of Spring* 11
or dives In yonder *g* gleam, *In Mem. cxv* 14
A Jacob's ladder falls On *g* grass, *Early Spring* 10
Greenish except For *g* glimmerings thro' the lancets, *Aylmer's Field* 622
the moon was falling *g* thro' a rosy glow, *Locksley H., Sixty* 178
Green-rushing *G-r* from the rosy thrones (repeat) *Voice and the P.* 4, 40
Green-suited *G-s*, but with plumes that mock'd *Guinevere* 22
Greensward danced The *g* into greener circles, *Gardener's D.* 134
flit To make the *g* fresh, *Talking Oak* 90
Greenwood Thou liest beneath the *g* tree, *Oriana* 95
Greet to *g* Troy's wandering prince, *On a Mourner* 32
g their fairer sisters of the East. *Gardener's D.* 188
To *g* the sheriff, needless courtesy! *Edwin Morris* 133
To meet and *g* her on her way; *Beggar Maid* 6
'*G* her with applausive breath, *Vision of Sin* 135
To *g* his hearty welcome heartily; *Enoch Arden* 350
g her, wasting his forgotten heart, *Aylmer's Field* 689
ran To *g* him with a kiss, *Lucretius* 7
rose a cry As if to *g* the king; *Princess v* 249
No more in soldier fashion will he *g* *Ode on Well.* 21
thrice as large as man he bent To *g* us. *In Mem ciii* 43
To meet and *g* a whiter sun; „ *Con.* 78
Should I fear to *g* my friend *Maud II iv* 85
rejoiced More than Geraint to *g* her thus attired; *Marr. of Geraint* 772
'My lord Geraint, I *g* you with all love; *Geraint and E.* 785
the King himself Advanced to *g* them, „ 879
but how ye *g* me—fear And fault and doubt— *Last Tournament* 577
So sweetly and so modestly she came To *g* us, *Lover's Tale iv* 171
rose from off his throne to *g* Before *Columbus* 5
And *g* it with a kindly smile; *To E. Fitzgerald* 4
Every morning here we *g* it, *Akbar's D., Hymn* 3
Greeted Maiden, not to be *g* unbenignly. *Hendecasyllabics* 21
G Geraint full face, but stealthily, *Geraint and E.* 279
The Lost one Found was *g* as in Heaven *Balin and Balan* 81
and with how sweet grace She *g* my return! „ 194
Vivien, being *g* fair, Would fain have wrought *Merlin and V.* 155
For silent, tho' he *g* her, she stood *Lancelot and E.* 355
'Have comfort,' whom she *g* quietly. „ 995
thro' open door Rode Gawain, whom she *g* courteously. *Pelleas and E.* 383
and then on Pelleas, him Who had not *g* her, „ 591
Passion-pale they met And *g*. *Guinevere* 100
If *g* by your classic smile, *To Prof. Jebb* 10
Greeting Full cold my *g* was and dry; *The Letters* 13
And gets for *g* but a wail of pain; *Lucretius* 138
Eternal *g's* to the dead; *In Mem. lvii* 14
found the *g's* both of knight and King *Balin and Balan* 342
I send a birthday line Of *g*; *To E. Fitzgerald* 46
Grenade *See* **Hand-grenade**
Grenville (Sir Richard) *See* **Richard, Richard Grenville**
Grew (*See also* **Graw'd**) *G* darker from that under-flame: *Arabian Nights* 91
mother plant in semblance, *g* A flower all gold, *The Poet* 23
She, as her carol sadder *g*, *Mariana in the S.* 13
'He dried his wings: like gauze they *g*; *Two Voices* 13
'Single I *g*, like some green plant, *D. of F. Women* 205
G plump and able-bodied; *The Goose* 18
we *g* The fable of the city where we dwelt. *Gardener's D.* 5
hoarded in herself, *G*, seldom seen; „ 50
in praise of her *G* oratory. „ 57
For up the porch there *g* an Eastern rose, „ 123
Her beauty *g*; till Autumn brought an hour For Eustace, „ 207
mound That was unsown, where many poppies *g*. *Dora* 73
wreath of all the flowers That *g* about, „ 83
Of different ages, like twin-sisters *g*, *Edwin Morris* 32
I *g* Twice ten long weary weary years *St. S. Stylites* 89
And in the chase *g* wild, *Talking Oak* 126
To look as if they *g* there. *Amphion* 80
But such whose father-grape *g* fat *Will Water.* 7
That she *g* a noble lady, *L. of Burleigh* 75
Faint she *g*, and ever fainter, „ 81
warn'd that madman ere it *g* too late: *Vision of Sin* 56

Grew (*continued*) The voice *g* faint: there came a further change: *Vision of Sin* 207
I *g* in gladness till I found My spirits *To E. L.* 11
third child was sickly-born and *g* Yet sicklier, *Enoch Arden* 261
Philip's rosy face contracting *g* Careworn and wan; „ 486
Thicker the drizzle *g*, deeper the gloom; „ 679
Heaven in lavish bounty moulded, *g*. *Aylmer's Field* 107
and still *G* with the growing note, *Sea Dreams* 213
g Tired of so much within our little life, *Lucretius* 225
lovelier than their names, *G* side by side; *Princess, Pro.* 13
the brain was like the hand, and *g* With using; „ *ii* 150
'How *g* this feud betwixt the right and left.' „ *iii* 77
they were still together, *g* (For so they said themselves) „ 88
I *g* discouraged, Sir; but since I knew No rock „ 153
they *g* Like field-flowers everywhere! „ 251
Sun *G* broader toward his death and fell, „ 364
Till all men *g* to rate us at our worth, „ *iv* 145
thus a noble scheme *G* up from seed „ 310
there *g* Another kind of beauty in detail „ 447
a clamour *g* As of a new-world Babel, „ 486
That all things *g* more tragic and more strange; „ *vi* 23
o'er him *g* Tall as a figure lengthen'd „ 160
And ever great and greater *g*, *Ode on Well.* 108
What slender campanili *g* *The Daisy* 13
it *g* so tall It wore a crown of light, *The Flower* 9
And still as vaster *g* the shore *In Mem. ciii* 25
I would the great world *g* like thee, „ *cxiv* 25
And *g* to seeming-random forms, „ *cxviii* 10
There rolls the deep where *g* the tree. „ *cxxiii* 1
For thee she *g*, for thee she grows „ *Con.* 35
Discussing how their courtship *g*, „ 97
When it slowly *g* so thin, *Maud I xix* 20
months ran on and rumour of battle *g*, „ *III vi* 29
so there *g* great tracts of wilderness, *Com. of Arthur* 10
they *g* up to wolf-like men, Worse than the wolves. „ 32
and evermore As I *g* greater *g* with me; „ 351
a slope of land that ever *g*, Field after field, „ 428
To break him from the intent to which he *g*, *Gareth and L.* 140
under cloud that *g* To thunder-gloom „ 1358
g Forgetful of his promise to the King, *Marr. of Geraint* 49
still she look'd, and still the terror *g* „ 615
lie still, and yet the sapling *g*: *Geraint and E.* 165
he *g* Tolerant of what he half disdain'd, *Merlin and V.* 177
g So grated down and filed away with thought, „ 622
the dark wood *g* darker toward the storm „ 890
g between her and the pictured wall. *Lancelot and E.* 993
g so cheerful that they deem'd her death „ 1131
then the times *G* to such evil that the holy cup *Holy Grail* 57
sound As from a distance beyond distance *g* „ 112
till I *g* One with him, to believe as he believed. „ 486
wholesome flower And poisonous *g* together, „ 776
flats, where nothing but coarse grasses *g*; „ 794
With such a closeness, but apart there *g*, „ 884
Whereon a hundred stately beeches *g*, *Pelleas and E.* 26
g So witty that ye play'd at ducks and drakes *Last Tournament* 343
all this trouble did not pass but *g*; *Guinevere* 84
And *g* half-guilty in her thoughts again, „ 408
dolorous day *G* drearier toward twilight falling, *Pass. of Arthur* 123
They *g* aweary of her fellowship: *Lover's Tale i* 109
that my love *G* with myself— „ 165
sustenance, which, still as thought, *g* large, „ 240
and *g* again To utterance of passion. „ 546
Why *g* we then together in one plot? „ *ii* 23
g at length Prophetical and prescient „ 131
and each heart *G* closer to the other, „ 187
a wave like the wave that is raised by an earthquake *g*, *The Revenge* 115
G after marriage to full height and form? *Sisters (E. and E.)* 171
could it be That trees *g* downward, *Columbus* 50
and the light *G* as I gazed, „ 77
they prest, as they *g*, on each other, *V. of Maeldune* 64
fixt on mine, till mine *g* dark For ever, *Tiresias* 47
the great storm *g* with a howl and a hoot *The Wreck* 91
stars in heaven Paled, and the glory *g*. *Pro. to Gen. Hamley* 32
souls of men, who *g* beyond their race, *Demeter and P.* 140

Grinning (*continued*) and tooth'd with *g* savagery.' *Balin and Balan* 197
Grip in the hard *g* of his hand, *Sea Dreams* 163
An' 'e ligs on 'is back i' the *g*, *N. Farmer, N. S.* 31
Gripe hand in wild delirium, *g* it hard, *Princess vii* 93
Gript *G* my hand hard, and with God-bless-you went. *Sea Dreams* 160
Each *g* a shoulder, and I stood between; *Holy Grail* 822
his strong hands *g* And dinted the gilt dragons *Last Tournament* 181
He *g* it so hard by the throat *Bandit's Death* 28
Grisly haggard father's face and reverend beard Of *g* twine, *Princess vi* 104
With a *g* wound to be drest he had left the deck, *The Revenge* 66
Gritted and thou shalt cease To pace the *g* floor, *Will Water.* 242
Grizzled a story which in rougher shape Came from a *g* cripple, *Aylmer's Field* 8
forth a *g* damsel came, *Gareth and L.* 1114
To me this narrow *g* fork of thine Is cleaner-fashion'd— *Merlin and V.* 59
Grizzlier Albeit *g* than a bear, to ride And jest with: *Pelleas and E.* 193
Groan (s) exprest By signs or *g's* or tears; *D. of F. Women* 284
Down in the south is a flash and a *g*: *Window, Gone* 8
he but gave a wrathful *g*, Saying, *Geraint and E.* 398
gave A marvellous great shriek and ghastly *g*, *Lancelot and E.* 516
'Our mightiest!' answer'd Lancelot, with a *g*; *Holy Grail* 766
Or Labour, with a *g* and not a voice, *To the Queen ii* 55
their curses and their *g's*. *Columbus* 68
trumpets of victory, *g's* of defeat; *Vastness* 8
Groan (verb) mother who never has heard us *g*! *Despair* 98
We should see the Globe we *g* in, *Locksley H., Sixty* 188
g's to see it, finds no comfort there. *Romney's R.* 45
Groan'd deep brook *g* beneath the mill; *Miller's D.* 113
as their faces drew together, *g*, *Enoch Arden* 74
'No trifle,' *g* the husband; *Sea Dreams* 145
King Leodogran *G* for the Roman legions *Com. of Arthur* 34
G, and at times would mutter, *Balin and Balan* 173
g Sir Lancelot in remorseful pain, *Lancelot and E.* 1428
'Black nest of rats,' he *g*, *Pelleas and E.* 555
Until he *g* for wrath—so many of those, *Last Tournament* 183
and he *g*, 'The King is gone.' *Pass. of Arthur* 443
Found, fear'd me dead, and *g*, *The Flight* 23
He *g*, he turn'd, and in the mist *Death of Œnone* 49
while I *g*, From out the sunset pour'd *Akbar's Dream* 191
Groänin' Moother was naggin' an' *g* *Owd Roä* 108
Groaning (*See also* **Groänin'**) turn'd, and *g* said, 'Forgive! *Sea Dreams* 59
organ almost burst his pipes, *G* for power, *Princess ii* 475
to them the doors gave way *G*, „ *vi* 350
With hand and rope we haled the *g* sow, *Walk. to the Mail* 91
Kay near him *g* like a wounded bull— *Gareth and L.* 648
the fallen man Made answer, *g*, 'Edyrn, *Marr. of Geraint* 576
g laid The naked sword athwart their naked throats, *Pelleas and E.* 451
I, *g*, from me flung Her empty phantom: *Lover's Tale, ii* 205
I heard a *g* overhead, and climb'd „ *iv* 136
Grog But if thou wants thy *g*, *North. Cobbler* 8
But if tha wants ony *g* tha mun goä fur it „ 113
Grog-shop *See* **Shebeen**
Groom (a servant) *hung with* g's *and porters on the bridge,* *Godiva* 2
An' they rampaged about wi' their *g's*, *Village Wife* 36
Groom (bridegroom) (*See also* **Bridegroom**) Gives her harsh *g* for bridal-gift *Princess v* 378
As drinking health to bride and *g* *In Mem., Con.* 83
Groom'd strongly *g* and straitly curb'd *Princess v* 456
and now so long By bandits *g*, *Geraint and E.* 193
Groove down the ringing *g's* of change. *Locksley Hall* 182
Down rang the grate of iron thro' the *g*, *Pelleas and E.* 207
Grope *g*, And gather dust and chaff, *In Mem. lv* 17
And grovel and *g* for my son *Rizpah* 8
Groped *g* as blind, and seem'd Always about to fall, *Aylmer's Field* 821
She gabbled, as she *g* in the dead, *Dead Prophet* 73
Groping feeble twilight of this world *G*, *Geraint and E.* 6
the girl's Lean fancy, *g* for it, *The Ring* 336
Gross (adj.) In the *g* blackness underneath. *Supp. Confessions* 187
G darkness of the inner sepulchre *D. of F. Women* 67
So *g* to express delight, in praise of her *Gardener's D.* 56
It cannot be but some *g* error lies In this report, *Princess i* 69
Gross (adj.) (*continued*) yet On tiptoe seem'd to touch upon a sphere Too *g* to tread, *Princess vii* 325
drown His heart in the *g* mud-honey of town, *Maud I xvi* 5
What should be granted which your own *g* heart *Merlin and V.* 916
For when had Lancelot utter'd aught so *g* *Last Tournament* 631
Save that I think this *g* hard-seeming world *Sisters (E. and E.)* 229
You make our faults too *g*, and thence maintain *To One who ran down Eng.* 1
Gross (s) As flies the lighter thro' the *g*. *In Mem. xli* 4
Grosser with a *g* film made thick These heavy, horny eyes. *St. S. Stylites* 200
song Might have been worse and sinn'd in *g* lips *Princess iv* 251
Barbarians, *g* than your native bears— „ 537
draw water, or hew wood, Or *g* tasks; *Gareth and L.* 487
but *g* grown Than heathen, *Pass. of Arthur* 61
Grossest Love, tho' Love were of the *g*, *Merlin and V.* 461
Grossness the *g* of his nature will have weight *Locksley Hall* 48
Grot The hollow *g* replieth *Claribel* 20
From many a wondrous *g* and secret cell *The Kraken* 8
Black the garden-bowers and *g's* *Arabian Nights* 78
alleys falling down to twilight *g's*, *Ode to Memory* 107
shadow'd *g's* of arches interlaced, *Palace of Art* 51
Grotesque raillery, or *g*, or false sublime— *Princess iv* 588
Groun' a corp lyin' undher *g*. *Tomorrow* 62
Ground (s) (*See also* **Groun', Mountain-ground**) Till the air And the *g* *Nothing will Die* 28
And dew is cold upon the *g*, *The Owl i* 2
All the place is holy *g*; *Poet's Mind* 9
It would fall to the *g* if you came in. „ 23
And shall fall again to *g*. *Deserted House* 16
Not that the *g's* of hope were fix'd, *Two Voices* 227
from the *g* She raised her piercing orbs, *D. of F. Women* 170
I keep smooth plats of fruitful *g*, *The Blackbird* 3
as he near'd His happy home, the *g*. *Gardener's D.* 92
And mix'd with shadows of the common *g*! „ 135
Dora cast her eyes upon the *g*, *Dora* 89
perish, falling on the foeman's *g*, *Locksley Hall* 103
O Lord!—'tis in my neighbour's *g*, *Amphion* 75
To yonder shining *g*; *St. Agnes' Eve* 14
vapours weep their burthen to the *g*, *Tithonus* 2
Release me, and restore me to the *g*; „ 72
perfect fan, Above the teeming *g*. *Sir L. and Q. G.* 18
Gathering up from all the lower *g*; *Vision of Sin* 15
And track'd you still on classic *g*, *To E. L.* 10
All her fair length upon the *g* she lay: *Princess v* 59
Ida spoke not, gazing on the *g*, „ *vi* 227
To dance with death, to beat the *g*, *In Mem. i* 12
The chestnut pattering to the *g*: „ *xi* 4
here upon the *g*, No more partaker „ *xli* 7
And hide thy shame beneath the *g*. „ *lxxii* 28
But all is new unhallow'd *g*. „ *civ* 12
flatten'd, and crush'd, and dinted into the *g*: *Maud I i* 7
all by myself in my own dark garden *g*, „ *iii* 10
O let the solid *g* Not fail beneath my feet „ *xi* 1
Rivulet crossing my *g*, „ *xxi* 1
Laid him that clove it grovelling on the *g*. *Gareth and L.* 972
Death was cast to *g*, and slowly rose. „ 1403
Two forks are fixt into the meadow *g*, *Marr. of Geraint* 482
Coursed one another more on open *g* „ 522
And there they fixt the forks into the *g*, „ 548
Then, moving downward to the meadow *g*, *Geraint and E.* 204
And hurl'd to *g* what knight soever spurr'd *Balin and Balan* 66
Shot from behind him, run along the *g*. „ 323
Shot from behind me, ran along the *g*; „ 374
Stumbled headlong, and cast him face to *g*. „ 426
I set thee high on vantage *g*, „ 534
Then she, who held her eyes upon the *g*, *Lancelot and E.* 232
He answer'd with his eyes upon the *g*, „ 1352
made the *g* Reel under us, and all at once, *Lover's Tale ii* 193
never to say that I laid him in holy *g*. *Rizpah* 58
and the palace, and death in the *g*! *Def. of Lucknow* 24
coffinless corpse to be laid in the *g*, „ 80
slowly sinking now into the *g*, *Locksley H., Sixty* 27
ampler hunting *g's* beyond the night; „ 69
and you hurl'd them to the *g*. *Happy* 76

Ground (s) (*continued*) Christ-like creature that ever stept on the *g*. *Charity* 32
vaults her skies, From this my vantage *g* *Mechanophilus* 18
Ground (verb) teeth that *g* As in a dreadful dream, *Aylmer's Field* 328
For '*g* in yonder social mill *In Mem. lxxxix* 39
He *g* his teeth together, sprang with a yell, *Balin and Balan* 538
Groundflame *g* of the crocus breaks the mould *Prog. of Spring* 1
Ground-plan 'Lo! God's likeness—the *g-p*- *Vision of Sin* 187
Ground-swell a full tide Rose with *g-s*, *Sea Dreams* 51
Roll as a *g-s* dash'd on the strand, *W. to Alexandra* 23
Group A *g* of Houris bow'd to see *Palace of Art* 102
I have shadow'd many a *g* Of beauties, *Talking Oak* 61
a *g* of girls In circle waited, *Princess, Pro.* 68
and in *g's* they stream'd away. „ *Con.* 105
Group'd Muses and the Graces, *g* in threes, „ *ii* 27
stood her maidens glimmeringly *g* „ *iv* 190
Grove (*See also* **Sea-Groves**) lemon *g* In closest coverture upsprung, *Arabian Nights* 67
From the *g's* within The wild-bird's *Poet's Mind* 20
'I, rooted here among the *g's* *Talking Oak* 181
Wherever in a lonely *g* He set up *Amphion* 21
Hush'd all the *g's* from fear of wrong: *Sir L. and Q. G.* 13
Kept to the garden now, and *g* of pines, *Aylmer's Field* 550
Thy God is far diffused in noble *g's* „ 653
Rose gem-like up before the dusky *g's* *Princess, Pro.* 75
in a poplar *g* when a light wind wakes „ *v* 13
Gray halls alone among their massive *g's*; „ *Con.* 43
Yet present in his natal *g*, *The Daisy* 18
For *g's* of pine on either hand, *To F. D. Maurice* 21
To rest in a golden *g*, or to bask in a summer sky: *Wages* 9
Burnt and broke the *g* and altar *Boädicea* 2
Uncared for, gird the windy *g*, *In Mem. ci* 13
In the little *g* where I sit— *Maud I iv* 2
A knot, beneath, of snakes, aloft, a *g*. *Marr. of Geraint* 325
It seems another voice in other *g's*; *Balin and Balan* 215
With young Lavaine into the poplar *g*. *Lancelot and E.* 509
Hid from the wide world's rumour by the *g* „ 522
Touch'd at all points, except the poplar *g*, „ 617
Lavaine across the poplar *g* Led to the caves: „ 804
By *g*, and garden-lawn, and rushing brook, *Holy Grail* 230
green-glooming twilight of the *g*, *Pelleas and E.* 33
And all talk died, as in a *g* all song „ 607
dark in the golden *g* Appearing, *Last Tournament* 379
from the high wall and the flowering *g* Of grasses *Guinevere* 33
Rode under *g's* that look'd a paradise „ 389
all the low dark *g's*, a land of love! *Lover's Tale i* 332
A height, a broken grange, a *g*, *Ancient Sage* 223
thro' all the *g's* of olive in the summer glow, *Frater Ave, etc.* 3
palm And orange *g* of Paraguay, *To Ulysses* 12
Grovel Stands at thy gate for thee to *g* to— *Aylmer's Field* 652
g and grope for my son till I find myself *Rizpah* 8
Grovelike Once *g*, each huge arm a tree, *Aylmer's Field* 510
Grovell'd unlaced my casque And *g* on my body, *Princess vi* 28
And *g* with her face against the floor: *Guinevere* 415
And while she *g* at his feet, „ 581
Grovelling Laid him that clove it *g* on the ground. *Gareth and L.* 972
Gareth brought him *g* on his knees, „ 1124
Grow (*See also* **Graw**) Think my belief would stronger *g*! *Supp. Confessions* 13
g awry From roots which strike so deep? „ 77
in the rudest wind Never *g* sere, *Ode to Memory* 25
g so full and deep In thy large eyes, *Eleänore* 85
and slowly *g* To a full face, „ 91
G golden all about the sky; „ 101
G green beneath the showery gray, *My life is full* 17
And on my clay her darnel *g*; „ 22
How *g's* the day of human power?' *Two Voices* 78
'His sons *g* up that bear his name, „ 256
Some *g* to honour, some to shame,— „ 257
I will *g* round him in his place, *G*, live, *Fatima* 40
a light that *g's* Larger and clearer, *Œnone* 108
until endurance *g* Sinew'd with action, „ 164
G's green and broad, and takes no care, *Lotos-Eaters, C.S.* 28
It *g's* to guerdon after-days: *Love thou thy land* 27
She felt her heart *g* prouder: *The Goose* 22

Grow (*continued*) until he *g's* Of age to help us.' *Dora* 126
cruel as a schoolboy ere he *g's* To Pity— *Walk. to the Mail* 109
that my soul might *g* to thee, *St. S. Stylites* 71
Their faces *g* between me and my book; „ 176
So now 'tis fitted on and *g's* to me, „ 209
Shall *g* so fair as this.' *Talking Oak* 244
All grass of silky feather *g*— „ 269
'But we *g* old. Ah! when shall all men's good *Golden Year* 47
The vast Republics that may *g*, *Day-Dm., L'Envoi* 15
That *g's* within the woodland. *Amphion* 8
g's From England to Van Diemen. „ 83
patch of soil To *g* my own plantation. „ 100
I *g* in worth, and wit, and sense, *Will Water.* 41
Till, where the street *g's* straiter, „ 142
forget-me-nots That *g* for happy lovers. *The Brook* 173
Watching your growth, I seem'd again to *g*. *Aylmer's Field* 359
And heaps of living gold that daily *g*, „ 655
as by miracle, *g* straight and fair— „ 676
I saw my father's face *G* long and troubled *Princess i* 59
might *g* To use and power on this Oasis, „ *ii* 166
And *g* for ever and for ever. „ *iv* 16
slowly *g's* a glimmering square, „ 52
the child shall *g* To prize the authentic mother „ *v* 432
this shall *g* A night of Summer from the heat, „ *vi* 53
slight-natured, miserable, How shall men *g*? „ *vii* 266
in the long years liker must they *g*; „ 279
Purpose in purpose, will in will, they *g*, „ 305
let the sorrowing crowd about it *g*, *Ode on Well.* 16
ever weaker *g's* thro' acted crime, *Will* 12
I may die but the grass will *g*, And the grass will *g* when I am gone, *Window, No Answer* 4
A beam in darkness: let it *g*. *In Mem., Pro.* 24
Let knowledge *g* from more to more, „ 25
And *g* incorporate into thee. „ *ii* 16
But as he *g's* he gathers much, „ *xlv* 5
His isolation *g's* defined. „ 12
How blanch'd with darkness must I *g*! „ *lxi* 8
The days that *g* to something strange, „ *lxxi* 11
And year by year the landscape *g* „ *ci* 19
For thee she grew, for thee she *g's* „ *Con.* 35
I should *g* light-headed, I fear, *Maud I xix* 100
and ever afresh they seem'd to *g*. „ *II i* 28
But I know where a garden *g's*, „ *v* 72
change, and *g* Faint and far-off. *Balin and Balan* 217
ourselves shall *g* In use of arms and manhood, *Lancelot and E.* 63
days will *g* to weeks, the weeks to months, *Guinevere* 624
It *g's* upon me now—the semicircle *Lover's Tale i* 37
let *g* The flowers that run poison in their veins. „ 346
By firth and lock thy silver sister *g*, *Sir J. Oldcastle* 58
But look, the morning *g's* apace, *The Flight* 93
Science *g's* and Beauty dwindles— *Locksley H., Sixty* 246
where the purple flowers *g*, *Frater Ave, etc.* 4
since your name will *g* with Time, *To Marq. of Dufferin* 13
Young again you *g* Out of sight. *The Ring* 11
the long day of knowledge *g's* and warms, *Prog. of Spring* 101
'Father and mother will watch you *g*'—(repeat) *Romney's R.* 104, 106
You watch'd not I, she did not *g*, she died. „ 105
there is time for the race to *g*. *The Dawn* 20
You, what the cultured surface *g's*, *Mechanophilus* 33
Growest ever thus thou *g* beautiful In silence, *Tithonus* 43
grown In power, and ever *g*, *To Dante* 2
Growing (adj. and part.) (*See also* **A-grawin', Ever-growing**) Ere the light on dark was *g*, *Oriana* 10
Don't let Effie come to see me till my grave be *g* green: *May Queen, N. Y's. E.* 43
His face is *g* sharp and thin. *D. of the O. Year* 46
g dewy-warm With kisses balmier *Tithonus* 58
g coarse to sympathise with clay. *Locksley Hall* 46
gaze On that cottage *g* nearer, *L. of Burleigh* 35
May-music *g* with the *g* light, *Gareth and L.* 1080
a promontory, That had a sapling *g* on it, *Geraint and E.* 163
grass There *g* longest by the meadow's edge, „ 257
And on the fourth are men with *g* wings, *Holy Grail* 237
And *g*, on her tomb, *Ancient Sage* 164
Thou sawest a glory *g* on the night, *Epit. on Caxton* 2

Guess'd (*continued*) presence might have *g* you one of those — *Marr. of Geraint* 431
Now *g* a hidden meaning in his arms, — *Lancelot and E.* 17
Guess-work *they g* it, — *Columbus* 43
Guess-work *G-w they* guess'd it, — „ 43
No *g-w*! I was certain of my goal; — „ 45
Guest Each enter'd like a welcome *g*. — *Two Voices* 411
Head-waiter, honour'd by the *g* Half-mused, — *Will Water.* 73
mellow Death, like some late *g*, — „ 239
g, their host, their ancient friend, — *Aylmer's Field* 790
Shone, silver-set; about it lay the *g's*, — *Princess, Pro.* 106
You, likewise, our late *g's*, — „ *v* 229
Who is he that cometh, like an honour'd *g*, — *Ode on Well.* 80
father's chimney glows In expectation of a *g*; — *In Mem. vi* 30
Which brings no more a welcome *g* — „ *xxix* 5
I see myself an honour'd *g*, — „ *lxxxiv* 21
A *g*, or happy sister, sung, — „ *lxxxix* 26
if I Conjecture of a stiller *g*, — „ *Con.* 86
Endures not that her *g* should serve himself.' — *Marr. of Geraint* 379
wine and goodly cheer To feed the sudden *g*, — *Geraint and E.* 284
to thy *g*, Me, me of Arthur's Table. — *Balin and Balan* 379
'Whence comest thou, my *g*, — *Lancelot and E.* 181
one of your own knights, a *g* of ours, — *Holy Grail* 40
all the goodlier *g's* are past away, — *Last Tournament* 158
Was brought before the *g*: and they the *g's*, — *Lover's Tale iv* 204
all The *g's* broke in upon him with meeting hands — „ 238
custom steps yet further when the *g* Is loved and honour'd — „ 244
This question, so flung down before the *g's*, — „ 268
While all the *g's* in mute amazement rose— — „ 305
'My *g's*,' said Julian: 'you are honour'd now — „ 316
a *g* So bound to me by common love and loss— — „ 344
rose up, and with him all his *g's* — „ 359
How oft the Cantab supper, host and *g*, — *To W. H. Brookfield* 4
Like would-be *g's* an hour too late, — *Tiresias* 198
therewithin a *g* may make True cheer — *Pro. to Gen. Hamley* 15
Then drink to England, every *g*; — *Hands all Round* 2
Unfriendly of your parted *g*. — *The Wanderer* 4
Guide (s) the silver star, thy *g*, Shines — *Tithonus* 25
'They were dangerous *g's* the feelings— — *Locksley Hall* 95
When each by turns was *g* to each, — *In Mem. xxiii* 13
With you for *g* and master, only you, — *Merlin and V.* 881
Then were I glad of you as *g* and friend: — *Lancelot and E.* 226
far away with good Sir Torre for *g* — „ 788
Alla be my *g*! But come, My noble friend, — *Akbar's Dream* 16
Guide (verb) there is a hand that *g's*.' — *Princess, Con.* 79
g Her footsteps, moving side by side — *In Mem. cxiv* 18
I have not made the world, and He that made it will *g*. — *Maud I iv* 48
thou, Sir Prince, Wilt surely *g* me — *Balin and Balan* 478
and clean! and yet—God *g* them—young.' — *Merlin and V.* 29
and he Will *g* me to that palace, to the doors.' — *Lancelot and E.* 1129
force to *g* us thro' the days I shall not see? — *Locksley H., Sixty* 158
Guided Whose feet are *g* thro' the land, — *In Mem. lxvi* 9
Which not alone had *g* me, — „ *cxiii* 3
Guile pure as he from taint of craven *g*, — *Ode on Well.* 135
A widow with less *g* than many a child. — *Sisters (E. and E.)* 182
Guileless Till ev'n the clear face of the *g* King, — *Guinevere* 85
Guilt When I have purged my *g*.' — *Palace of Art* 296
The *g* of blood is at your door: — *L. C. V. de Vere* 43
To hold his hope thro' shame and *g*, — *Love thou thy land* 82
May wreck itself without the pilot's *g*, — *Aylmer's Field* 716
Easily gather'd either *g*. — *Princess iv* 236
eye which watches *g* And goodness, — *In Mem. xxvi* 5
hasty judger would have call'd her *g*, — *Geraint and E.* 433
subtle beast, Would track her *g* until he found, — *Guinevere* 60
too-fearful *g*, Simpler than any child, — „ 370
without some *g* should such grief be? — *Lover's Tale i* 795
Guiltless Guilty or *g*, to stave off a chance — *Geraint and E.* 353
flushing the *g* air, — *Lucretius* 239
far away the maid in Astolat, Her *g* rival, — *Lancelot and E.* 746
Against the *g* heirs of him from Tyre, — *Tiresias* 12
Being *g*, as an innocent prisoner, — *Lover's Tale i* 787
Guilty (*See also* **Half-guilty**) a little fault Whereof I was not *g*; — *Com. of Arthur* 342
be he *g*, by that deathless King Who lived — *Gareth and L.* 382
Touching her *g* love for Lancelot, — *Marr. of Geraint* 25

Guilty (*continued*) To dream she could be *g* of foul act, — *Marr of Geraint* 120
G or guiltless, to stave off a chance — *Geraint and E.* 353
rooted out the slothful officer Or *g*, — „ 939
And full of cowardice and *g* shame, — *Princess iv* 348
like a *g* thing I creep At earliest morning — *In Mem. vii* 7
It is this *g* hand!— — *Maud II i* 4
Am I *g* of blood? — „ *ii* 73
The great and *g* love he bare the Queen, — *Lancelot and E.* 245
Guinea jingling of the *g* helps the hurt — *Locksley Hall* 105
Guinea-hens praised his hens, his geese, his *g-h*; — *The Brook* 126
Guinevere Sir Launcelot and Queen *G* Rode — *Sir L. and Q. G.* 20
G, and in her his one delight. — *Com. of Arthur* 4
G Stood by the castle walls to watch him — „ 47
Desiring to be join'd with *G*; — „ 77
Give me thy daughter *G* to wife.' — „ 139
Fear not to give this King thine only child, *G*: — „ 414
return'd Among the flowers, In May, with *G*. — „ 452
Thro' that great tenderness for *G*, — *Marr. of Geraint* 30
G lay late into the morn, Lost in sweet dreams, — „ 157
G, not mindful of his face In the King's hall, — „ 191
A stately queen whose name was *G*, — „ 667
thrice that morning *G* had climb'd The giant tower, — „ 826
Some goodly cognizance of *G*, — *Balin and Balan* 195
O me, that such a name as *G's*, — „ 489
day When *G* was crossing the great hall — *Merlin and V.* 65
Spake (for she had been sick) to *G*, — *Lancelot and E.* 78
G, The pearl of beauty: — „ 113
Lancelot, when they glanced at *G*, — „ 270
Sir Lancelot at the palace craved Audience of *G*, — „ 1163
And therefore to our Lady *G*, — „ 1278
For fair thou art and pure as *G*, — *Pelleas and E.* 44
O my Queen, my *G*, For I will be thine Arthur — „ 46
'Is *G* herself so beautiful?' — „ 70
Said *G*, 'We marvel at thee much, — „ 179
'False! and I held thee pure as *G*.' — „ 522
'Am I but false as *G* is pure? — „ 524
There with her knights and dames was *G*. — „ 588
G had sinn'd against the highest, — *Last Tournament* 570
Queen *G* had fled the court, — *Guinevere* 1
When that storm of anger brake From *G*, — „ 362
I did not come to curse thee, *G*, — „ 533
yet not less, O *G*, For I was ever virgin save for thee, — „ 556
Guise and sets before him in rich *g* — *Lover's Tale iv* 247
Gules Langued *g*, and tooth'd with grinning savagery.' — *Balin and Balan* 197
Gulf (s) and brought Into the *g's* of sleep. — *D. of F. Women* 52
Sow'd all their mystic *g's* with fleeting stars; — *Gardener's D.* 262
It may be that the *g's* will wash us down: — *Ulysses* 62
a *g* of ruin, swallowing gold, — *Sea Dreams* 79
Or down the fiery *g* as talk of it, — *Princess iii* 287
Nor shudders at the *g's* beneath, — *In Mem. xli* 15
A *g* that ever shuts and gapes, — „ *lxx* 6
in this stormy *g* have found a pearl — *Maud I xviii* 42
seas of Death and sunless *g's* of Doubt. — *Pref. Son. 19th Cent.* 14
naked glebe Should yawn once more into the *g*, — *Demeter and P.* 43
woods Plunged *g* on *g* thro' all their vales — *Prog. of Spring* 73
Gulf (verb) Should *g* him fathom-deep in brine; — *In Mem. x* 18
Gulf'd And *g* his griefs in inmost sleep; — *Pelleas and E.* 516
Gulf-stream warm *g-s* of Florida Floats far away — *Mine be the strength* 12
Gulistan any rose of *G* Shall burst her veil· — *Princess iv* 122
Gull laugh'd and scream'd against the *g's*, — *Pelleas and E.* 89
Gull'd break our bound, and *g* Our servants, — *Princess iv* 539
Be not *g* by a despot's plea! — *Riflemen form!* 9
Gun they waited—Not a *g* was fired. — *The Captain* 40
Each beside his *g*. — „ 52
Nor ever lost an English *g*; — *Ode on Well.* 97
'Charge for the *g's*!' he said: — *Light Brigade* 6
high above us with her yawning tiers of *g's*, — *The Revenge* 41
not arter the birds wi' 'is *g*, — *Village Wife* 41
make way for the *g*! Now double-charge it — *Def. of Lucknow* 67
Gunner Sabring the *g's* there, — *Light Brigade* 29
Sink me the ship, Master *G*— — *The Revenge* 89
g said 'Ay, ay,' but the seamen made reply: — „ 91
Gurgle (s) as we sat by the *g* of springs, — *V. of Maeldune* 89

Gurgle (verb) All throats that *g* sweet! *Talking Oak* 266
Gurgling To drench his dark locks in the *g* wave *Princess iv* 187
Gurnion By castle *G*, where the glorious King *Lancelot and E.* 293
Gush *g'es* from beneath a low-hung cloud. *Ode to Memory* 71
Gush'd between Whose interspaces *g* in *Lover's Tale i* 408
Gushing *g* of the wave Far far away did seem *Lotos-Eaters* 31
Gust one warm *g*, full-fed with perfume, *Gardener's D.* 113
will be chaff For every *g* of chance, *Princess iv* 356
The *g* that round the garden flew, *In Mem. lxxxix* 19
An angry *g* of wind Puff'd out his torch *Merlin and V.* 730
Anon the face, as, when a *g* hath blown, *Last Tournament* 368
Waved with a sudden *g* that sweeping down *Lover's Tale iii* 34
a rougher *g* might tumble a stormier wave, *The Wreck* 131
Gustful a *g* April morn That puff'd the swaying branches *Holy Grail* 14
Gusty She saw the *g* shadow sway. *Mariana* 52
Gutted till he crept from a *g* mine *Maud I x* 9
Guvness (governess) Mun be a *g*, lad, or summut, *N. Farmer, N. S.* 26
Guzzlin' *G* an' soäkin' an' smoäkin' *North. Cobbler* 24
Gwydion *G* made by glamour out of flowers, *Marr. of Geraint* 743
Gynæceum Dwarfs of the *g*, fail so far In high desire, *Princess iii* 279
Gyre Shot up and shrill'd in flickering *g's*, „ *vii* 46
mighty *g's* Rapid and vast, of hissing spray *Lover's Tale ii* 197
Gyve the wholesome boon of *g* and gag.' *Gareth and L.* 370
sight run over Upon his steely *g's*; *Lover's Tale ii* 157

H

H too rough *H* in Hell and Heaven, *Sea Dreams* 196
Haäche (ache) es be down wi' their *h's* an' their paäins: *Spinster's S's.* 108
Haäcre (acre) Warnt worth nowt a *h*, *N. Farmer, O. S.* 39
wi haäte hoonderd *h* o' Squoire's, „ 44
wi' a hoonderd *h* o' sense— *Church-warden, etc.* 22
Haäfe (half) an' mea *h* down wi' my haäy! „ 2
Sa I warrants 'e niver said *h* wot 'e thowt, „ 18
Wi' *h* o' the chimleys a-twizzen'd an' twined *Owd Roä* 22
Haäf-pot (half-pot) An' a *h-p* o' jam, *Spinster's S's.* 109
Haäte (eight) Meä, wi' *h* hoonderd haäcre o' Squoire's, *N. Farmer, O. S.* 44
Haäte (hate) an' we *h's* boooklarnin' ere. *Village Wife* 24
to be sewer I *h's* 'em, my lass, „ 31
a-preächin' *mea* down, they heve, an' I *h's* 'em now, *Church-warden, etc.* 53
Haäted (hated) a-flyin' an' seeädin' tha *h* to see; *Spinster's S's.* 79
Haäy (hay) an' twined like a band o' *h*. *Owd Roä* 22
an' mea haäfe down wi' my *h*! *Church-warden, etc.* 2
Habit (custom) Idle *h* links us yet. *Miller's D.* 212
Or to burst all links of *h*— *Locksley Hall* 157
Drink deep, until the *h's* of the slave, *Princess ii* 91
to us, The fools of *h*, sweeter seems *In Mem. x* 12
Her memory from old *h* of the mind Went slipping *Guinevere* 379
Habit (riding dress) whether The *h*, hat, and feather, *Maud I xx* 18
Hack yea to him Who *h's* his mother's throat— *Sir J. Oldcastle* 114
Hack'd stay the brands That *h* among the flyers, *Com. of Arthur* 121
their arms *H*, and their foreheads grimed with smoke, *Holy Grail* 265
H the battleshield, *Batt. of Brunanburh* 13
Fiercely we *h* at the flyers before us. „ 42
Casques were crack'd and hauberks *h* *The Tourney* 7
Hades or the enthroned Persephonè in *H*, *Princess iv* 439
seen the serpent-wanded power Draw downward into *H* *Demeter and P.* 26
A cry that rang thro' *H*, Earth, and Heaven! „ 33
break The sunless halls of *H* into Heaven? „ 136
shrillings of the Dead When driven to *H*, *Death of Œnone* 22
Haft all the *h* twinkled with diamond sparks, *M. d'Arthur* 56
Struck with a knife's *h* hard against the board, *Geraint and E.* 600
all the *h* twinkled with diamond sparks, *Pass. of Arthur* 224
Haggard And shot from crooked lips a *h* smile. *Princess iv* 364
when she saw The *h* father's face and reverend beard „ *vi* 103
An armlet for an arm to which the Queen's Is *h*, *Lancelot and E.* 1227
'What is it?' but that oarsman's *h* face, „ 1250
As a vision Unto a *h* prisoner, *Lover's Tale ii* 148
Master scrimps his *h* sempstress of her daily bread, *Locksley H., Sixty* 221
Eve after eve that *h* anchorite Would haunt *St. Telemachus* 12

Hail (s) Where falls not *h*, or rain, or any snow, *M. d'Arthur* 260
Rain, wind, frost, heat, *h*, damp, *St. S. Stylites* 16
with rain or *h*, or fire or snow; *Locksley Hall* 193
And gilds the driving *h*. *Sir Galahad* 56
Sleet of diamond-drift and pearly *h*; *Vision of Sin* 22
Where falls not *h*, or rain, or any snow, *Pass. of Arthur* 428
and a clatter of *h* on the glass, *In the Child. Hosp.* 62
h of Arês crash Along the sounding walls. *Tiresias* 96
Hail (verb) Sets out, and meets a friend who *h's* him, *Walk. to the Mail* 42
city-roar that *h's* Premier or king! *Princess, Con.* 101
And voices *h* it from the brink; *In Mem. cxxi* 14
and all men *h* him for their king.' *Com. of Arthur* 424
ere he came, like one that *h's* a ship, *Geraint and E.* 540
H the fair Ceremonial Of this year of her Jubilee. *On Jub. Q. Victoria* 23
Hear thy myriad laureates *h* thee monarch *Akbar's D., Hymn* 6
Hail (interj.) *H*, hidden to the knees in fern, *Talking Oak* 29
Fair as the Angel that said '*H*!' *Aylmer's Field* 681
h once more to the banner of battle unroll'd! *Maud III vi* 42
Prince, Knight, *H*, Knight and Prince, *Gareth and L.* 1271
I will speak. *H*, royal knight, *Balin and Balan* 470
King, Who, when he saw me, rose, and bade me *h*, *Holy Grail* 725
King espied him, saying to him, '*H*, Bors! „ 756
H, King! to-morrow thou shalt pass away. *Pass. of Arthur* 34
'*H* to the glorious Golden year of her Jubilee!' *On Jub. Q. Victoria* 64
H ample presence of a Queen, *Prog. of Spring* 61
Hail'd Walter *h* a score of names upon her, *Princess, Pro.* 156
And toward him spurr'd, and *h* him, *Holy Grail* 637
Who never *h* another—was there one? *Lover's Tale i* 798
and there *h* on our houses and halls *Def. of Lucknow* 13
Hair (*See also* **'Aäir, 'Air**) smooth'd his chin and sleek'd his *h*, *A Character* 11
Dressing their *h* with the white sea-flower; *The Merman* 13
Combing her *h* Under the sea, *The Mermaid* 4
With a comb of pearl I would comb my *h*; „ 11
I would comb my *h* till my ringlets would fall „ 14
With thy floating flaxen *h*; *Adeline* 6
Your *h* is darker, and your eyes Touch'd *Margaret* 49
bright black eyes, her bright black *h*, *Kate* 2
round her neck Floated her *h* *Œnone* 19
his sunny *h* Cluster'd about his temples „ 59
From her warm brows and bosom her deep *h* Ambrosial, „ 177
her *h* Wound with white roses, slept St. Cecily; *Palace of Art* 98
blessings on his kindly voice and on his silver *h*! *May Queen, Con.* 13
that *h* More black than ashbuds in the front of March.' *Gardener's D.* 27
A single stream of all her soft brown *h* „ 128
wound Her looser *h* in braid, „ 158
leaf and acorn-ball In wreath about her *h*. *Talking Oak* 288
Catch the wild goat by the *h*, *Locksley Hall* 170
His beard a foot before him, and his *h* A yard behind. *Godiva* 18
The maiden's jet-black *h* has grown, *Day-Dm., Sleep B.* 4
my *h* Is gray before I know it. *Will Water.* 167
With a single rose in her *h*. *Lady Clare* 60
One her dark *h* and lovesome mien. *Beggar Maid* 12
H, and eyes, and limbs, and faces, *Vision of Sin* 39
This *h* is his: she cut it off and gave it, *Enoch Arden* 894
h In gloss and hue the chestnut, (repeat) *The Brook* 71, 206
made The hoar *h* of the Baronet bristle up *Aylmer's Field* 42
His *h* as it were crackling into flames, „ 586
not a *h* Ruffled upon the scarfskin, „ 659
bring Their own gray *h's* with sorrow to the grave— „ 777
Beat breast, tore *h*, cried out upon herself *Lucretius* 277
sweet girl-graduates in their golden *h*. *Princess, Pro.* 142
combing out her long black *h* Damp from the river; „ *iv* 276
'You have our son: touch not a *h* of his head: „ 407
Robed in the long night of her deep *h*, „ 491
And fingering at the *h* about his lip, „ *v* 303
and caught his *h*, And so belabour'd him „ 340
A single band of gold about her *h*, „ 513
His face was ruddy, his *h* was gold, *The Victim* 35
And you with gold for *h*! *Window, Spring* 4
That sittest ranging golden *h*; *In Mem. vi* 26
From youth and babe and hoary *h's*: „ *lxix* 10
To reverence and the silver *h* „ *lxxxiv* 32

Hair (*continued*) the roots of my *h* were stirred By a shuffled step, *Maud I i* 13
What if with her sunny *h*, „ *vi* 23
and thought It is his mother's *h*. „ *II ii* 70
and follow'd by his flying *h* Ran like a colt, *Com. of Arthur* 321
dark my mother was in eyes and *h*, And dark in *h* and eyes am I; „ 327
Broad brows and fair, a fluent *h* and fine, *Gareth and L.* 464
the *h* All over glanced with dewdrop or with gem „ 928
broken wings, torn raiment, and loose *h*, „ 1208
and drew down from out his night-black *h* *Balin and Balan* 511
A twist of gold was round her *h*; *Merlin and V.* 221
The snake of gold slid from her *h*, „ 888
And set it in this damsel's golden *h*, *Lancelot and E.* 205
Her bright *h* blown about the serious face „ 392
Then shook his *h*, strode off, and buzz'd abroad „ 722
—all her bright *h* streaming down— „ 1156
To seize me by the *h* and bear me far, „ 1425
Clean from her forehead all that wealth of *h* *Holy Grail* 150
all her shining *h* Was smear'd with earth, „ 209
black-blue Irish *h* and Irish eyes Had drawn *Last Tournament* 404
A low sea-sunset glorying round her *h* „ 508
His *h*, a sun that ray'd from off a brow „ 666
all their dewy *h* blown back like flame: *Guinevere* 284
with her milkwhite arms and shadowy *h* „ 416
Lest but a *h* of this low head be harm'd. „ 447
O golden *h*, with which I used to play „ 547
Quiver'd a flying glory on her *h*, *Lover's Tale i* 69
A solid glory on her bright black *h*; „ 367
her *h* Studded with one rich Provence rose— „ *iii* 44
thaw niver a *h* wur awry; *Village Wife* 84
Harsh red *h*, big voice, big chest, *In the Child. Hosp.* 4
And his white *h* sank to his heels *V. of Maeldune* 118
a dreadful light Came from her golden *h*, *Tiresias* 44
crystal into which I braided Edwin's *h*! *The Flight* 34
An' yer *h* as black as the night, *Tomorrow* 32
h was as white as the snow an a grave. „ 60
And that bright *h* the modern sun, *Epilogue* 8
'Thy *h* Is golden like thy Mother's, *The Ring* 103
The frost-bead melts upon her golden *h*; *Prog. of Spring* 10
one sleek'd the squalid *h*, One kiss'd *Death of Œnone* 57

Hair'd *See* **Dark-hair'd, Fair-hair'd, Golden-hair'd, Gray-hair'd, Long-hair'd, White-hair'd**

Hairless A little glassy-headed *h* man, *Merlin and V.* 620

Hairm (arm) An' 'e cotch'd howd hard o' my *h*, *Owd Roä* 58
wi' my *h* hingin' down to the floor, „ 65

Hair's-breadth Not even by one *h-b* of heresy, *Columbus* 64

Hairshirt 'Fast, *H* and scourge— *Sir J. Oldcastle* 142

Hairy-fibred Claspt the gray walls with *h-f* arms, *Marr. of Geraint* 323

Haithen (heathen) *h* kings in the flesh for the Jidgemint day, *Tomorrow* 70

Halcyon (adj.) and give His fealty to the *h* hour! *The Wanderer* 12

Halcyon (s) in her open palm a *h* sits Patient— *Prog. of Spring* 20

Haldeny (Alderney) pigs didn't sell at fall, an' wa lost wer *H* cow, *Church-warden, etc.* 5

Hale (Francis) *See* **Francis Hale**

Hale I was strong and *h* of body then; *St. S. Stylites* 29
Who wears his manhood *h* and green: *In Mem. liii* 4
What did he then? not die: he is here and *h*— *Lover's Tale iv* 40

Haled With hand and rope we *h* the groaning sow, *Walk. to the Mail* 91
The rope that *h* the buckets from the well, *St. S. Stylites* 64
And fain had *h* him out into the world, *Aylmer's Field* 467
They *h* us to the Princess where she sat *Princess iv* 271
h the yellow-ringleted Britoness— *Boädicea* 55

Haler and *h* too than I; *Guinevere* 685

Half (*See also* **Haafe**) *H* shown, are broken and withdrawn. *Two Voices* 306
a friendship so complete Portioned in *halves* between us, *Gardener's D.* 5
My words were *h* in earnest, *h* in jest,) „ 23
H light, *h* shade, She stood, „ 140
And *h* in love, *h* spite, he woo'd and wed *Dora* 39
h stands up And bristles; *h* has fall'n and made a bridge; *Walk. to the Mail* 31
I hope my end draws nigh: *h* dead I am, *St. S. Stylites* 37
love-languid thro' *h* tears would dwell One earnest, *Love and Duty* 36

Half (*continued*) *H* is thine and *h* is his: it will be worthy of the two. *Locksley Hall* 92
shall we pass the bill I mention'd *h* an hour ago?' *Day-Dm., Revival* 28
That my youth was *h* divine. *Vision of Sin* 78
With *h* a score of swarthy faces came. *Aylmer's Field* 191
his mind *H* buried in some weightier argument, *Lucretius* 9
H child *h* woman as she was, *Princess, Pro.* 101
we gain'd A little street *h* garden and *h* house; „ *i* 214
then to bed, where *h* in doze I seem'd To float „ 246
we stroll'd For *h* the day thro' stately theatres „ *ii* 369
Hers more than *h* the students, all the love. „ *iii* 39
bearing in my left The weight of all the hopes of *h* the world, „ *iv* 184
but *h* Without you; with you, whole; and of those *halves* You worthiest; „ 460
H turning to the broken statue, said, „ 593
Lily of the vale! *h* open'd bell of the woods! „ *vi* 193
H a league, *h* a league, *H* a league onward, *Light Brigade* 1
a lie which is *h* a truth is ever the blackest of lies, *Grandmother* 30
Girt by *h* the tribes of Britain, *Boädicea* 5
or *h* coquette-like Maiden, *Hendecasyllabics* 20
I sometimes hold it *h* a sin To put in words *In Mem. v* 1
like Nature, *h* reveal And *h* conceal the Soul within. „ 3
A shot, ere *h* thy draught be done, „ *vi* 11
And part it, giving *h* to him. „ *xxv* 12
My bosom-friend and *h* of life; „ *lix* 3
H jealous of she knows not what, „ *lx* 7
h exprest And loyal unto kindly laws. „ *lxxxv* 15
I, the divided *h* of such A friendship as had master'd Time; „ 63
And tumbled *h* the mellowing pears! „ *lxxxix* 20
To count their memories *h* divine; „ *xc* 12
Believe me, than in *h* the creeds. „ *xcvi* 12
These two have striven *h* the day, „ *cii* 17
Now *h* to the setting moon are gone, And *h* to the rising day; *Maud I xxii* 23
H the night I waste in sighs, *H* in dreams I sorrow „ *II iv* 23
'Thou hast *h* prevail'd against me,' *Gareth and L.* 30
Or whosoe'er it was, or *h* the world Had ventured— „ 64
everyone that owns a tower The Lord for *h* a league. „ 596
King Arthur's gift, the worth of *h* a town, „ 677
H fell to right and *h* to left and lay. „ 1405
Spring after spring, for *h* a hundred years: *Holy Grail* 19
That have no meaning *h* a league away: „ 556
With *h* a night's appliances, recall'd *Lover's Tale iv* 93
But his friend Replied, in *h* a whisper, „ 336
And the *h* my men are sick. *The Revenge* 6
For *h* of their fleet to the right and *h* to the left „ 35
And *h* of the rest of us maim'd for life „ 77
the great waters break Whitening for *h* a league, *Last Tournament* 465
Not quite so quickly, no, nor *h* as well. *Sisters (E. and E.)* 102
For the one *h* slew the other, *V. of Maeldune* 114
and her tears Are *h* of pleasure, *h* of pain— *Prin. Beatrice* 11
He married an heiress, an orphan with *h* a shire of estate,— *Charity* 13

Half-accomplish'd A spike of *h-a* bells— *To Ulysses* 24

Half afraid I myself Am *h a* to wear it. *The Ring* 472

Half-aghast Leolin still Retreated *h-a*, *Aylmer's Field* 330

Half-akin No longer *h-a* to brute, *In Mem., Con.* 133

Half-a-league Yon summit *h-a-l* in air— *Ancient Sage* 11

Half-allowing *h-a* smiles for all the world, *Aylmer's Field* 120

Half-amaze rabble in *h-a* Stared at him dead, *St. Telemachus* 71

Half-amazed Whereat he stared, replying, *h-a*, *Godiva* 21
seal'd dispatches which the Head Took *h-a*, *Princess iv* 380
mirth so loud Beyond all use, that, *h-a*, the Queen, *Last Tournament* 236
that *h-a* I parted from her, *The Ring* 436

Half-anger'd *H-a* with my happy lot, *Miller's D.* 200
Come, I am hunger'd and *h-a*—meat, *Last Tournament* 719

Half-arisen came upon him *h-a* from sleep, *Aylmer's Field* 584

Half-ashamed Then *h-a* and part-amazed, *Gareth and L.* 868

Half-asleep As *h-a* his breath he drew, *The Sisters* 28
And on me, *h-a*, came back That wholesome heat *To E. Fitzgerald* 23

Half-assured their Highnesses Were *h-a* *Columbus* 60

Half-attain'd cope Of the *h-a* futurity, *Ode to Memory* 33

Half-awake *h-a* I heard The parson taking wide and wider sweeps, *The Epic* 13
h-a he whisper'd, 'Where? O where? *Pelleas and E.* 41
Half-awaked sounded as in a dream To ears but *h-a*, *Last Tournament* 152
Half-awaken'd earliest pipe of *h-a* birds *Princess iv* 50
Half-blind sudden light Dazed me *h-b*: „ *v* 12
Half-blinded *H-b* at the coming of a light. *Com. of Arthur* 266
Half-bold *H-b*, half-frighted, with dilated eyes, *Geraint and E.* 597
Half-brain All the full-brain, *h-b* races, *Locksley H., Sixty* 161
Half-bright Star of Even Half-tarnish'd and *h-b*, *Gareth and L.* 1118
Half-buried *H-b* in the Eagle's down, *Palace of Art* 122
Half-canonized *H-c* by all that look'd on her, *Princess i* 23
Half-cheated rathe she rose, *h-c* in the thought *Lancelot and E.* 340
Half-clench'd hand *h-c* Went faltering sideways *Merlin and V.* 849
Half-closed dropping low their crimson bells *H-c*, *Arabian Nights* 63
Half-conscious *H-c* of the garden-squirt, *Amphion* 91
H-c of their dying clay, *In Mem. lviii* 7
Half-consent Assumed from thence a *h-c* *Princess vii* 82
Half-control for man can *h-c* his doom *Locksley H., Sixty* 277
Half-crazed I, once *h-c* for larger light *To Ulysses* 29
Half-crown Is it the weight of that *h-c*, *Will Water.* 155
Half-crush'd *h-c* among the rest A dwarf-like Cato *Princess vii* 125
Half-cut-down *h-c-d*, a pasty costly-made, *Audley Court* 23
Half-dead And all things look'd *h-d*, *Grandmother* 34
H-d to know that I shall die.' *In Mem. xxxv* 16
Maybe still I am but *h-d*; *Maud II. v* 99
fire, That lookt *h-d*, brake bright, *Gareth and L.* 685
Under the *h-d* sunset glared; „ 800
A stump of oak *h-d*, From roots like some black coil *Last Tournament* 12
dash'd *h d* on barren sands, was I. *The Ring* 309
Half-deed shall descend On this *h-d*, and shape it *Ancient Sage* 89
Half-defended Lo their colony *h-d*! *Boädicea* 17
Half-despised not look up, or *h-d* the height *Guinevere* 643
Half-digging they fell *H-d* their own graves) *Lover's Tale ii* 47
Half-dipt a summer moon *H-d* in cloud: *Godiva* 46
Half-disdain *h-d* Perch'd on the pouted blossom *Princess, Pro.* 198
Half-diseased 'And the liver is *h-d*!' *Dead Prophet* 76
Half-disfame what is Fame in life but *h-d*, *Merlin and V.* 465
Right well know I that Fame is *h-d*, „ 504
Half-disrooted A tree Was *h-d* from his place *Princess iv* 186
Half-divine The man I held as *h-d*; *In Mem. xiv* 10
Half-drain'd a flask Between his knees, *h-d*; *Day-Dm., Sleep P.* 26
Half-dream Falling asleep in a *h-d*! *Lotos-Eaters, C. S.* 56
Half-drooping half on her mother propt, *H-d* *Princess iv* 368
Half-dropt With *h-d* eyelid still, *Lotos-Eaters, C. S.* 90
Half-embraced And *h-e* the basket cradle-head *Sea Dreams* 289
Half-English sweet *h-E* Neilgherry air I panted, *The Brook* 17
Half-entering *H-e* the portals. *Lover's Tale ii* 123
Half-envious *H-e* of the flattering hand, *Lancelot and E.* 349
Half-face From the *h-f* to the full eye, „ 1262
Half-fall'n *H-f* across the threshold of the sun, *D. of F. Women* 63
Half-falling *h-f* from his knees, Half-nestled at his heart, *Merlin and V.* 904
Half-foresaw She *h-f* that he, the subtle beast, *Guinevere* 59
Half-forgotten our great deeds, as *h-f* things. *Lotos-Eaters, C. S.* 78
random rhymes, Ere they be *h-f*; *Will Water.* 14
Vivien *h-f* of the Queen *Merlin and V.* 137
Low in the dust of *h-f* kings, *Lancelot and E.* 1338
Half-frenzied when, *h-f* by the ring, *The Ring* 213
Half-frighted on the book, *h-f*, Miriam swore. *Enoch Arden* 843
Half-bold, *h-f*, with dilated eyes, *Geraint and E.* 597
Half-frighten'd Look'd down, half-pleased, *h-f*, *Amphion* 54
Half-glance With a *h-g* upon the sky *A Character* 1
Half-grown *H-g* as yet, a child, and vain— *In Mem. cxiv* 9
Half-guilty grew *h-g* in her thoughts again, *Guinevere* 408
Half-heard laid his ear beside the doors, And there *h-h*; *Com. of Arthur* 324
Half-hid Here *h-h* in the gleaming wood, *Maud I vi* 69
Half-hidden and there, *h-h* by him, stood, *Holy Grail* 754
Half-historic dealt with knights, Half-legend, *h-h*, *Princess, Pro.* 30
Half-hour For one *h-h*, and let him talk to me!' *The Brook* 115
Half-hysterical A half-incredulous, *h-h* cry. *Enoch Arden* 853
Half-incredulous A *h-i*, half-hysterical cry. „ 853
Half-invisible *H-i* to the view, Wheeling *Vision of Sin* 36
Half-lapt *H-l* in glowing gauze and golden brede, *Princess vi* 134
Half-legend dealt with knights, *H-l*, half-historic, *Princess, Pro.* 30
Half-light In the *h-l*—thro' the dim dawn— *Gareth and L.* 1384
Half-lost *H-l* in belts of hop and breadths *Princess, Con.* 45
H-l in the liquid azure bloom *Maud I iv* 5
Owe you me nothing for a life *h-l*? *Geraint and E.* 318
Some third-rate isle *h-l* among her seas? *To the Queen ii* 25
O dear Spirit *h-l* In thine own shadow *De Prof., Two G.* 39
Half-loyal the glance That only seems *h-l* *Last Tournament* 118
Half-man He scarce is knight, yea but *h-m*, *Gareth and L.* 1176
Half-melted moon, *H-m* into thin blue air, *Lover's Tale i* 421
Half-miracle seem'd *h-m* To those he fought with, *Lancelot and E.* 497
Half-moulder'd Sweeps suddenly all its *h-m* chords *Lover's Tale i* 19
Half-muffled answer which, *h-m* in his beard, *Princess v* 234
Half-mused the guest *H-m*, or reeling ripe, *Will Water.* 74
Half-naked *H-n* as if caught at once from bed *Princess iv* 285
Half-nestled half-falling from his knees, *H-n* at his heart, *Merlin and V.* 905
Half-oblivious (For I was *h-o* of my mask) *Princess iii* 338
Half-open Thro' *h-o* lattices Coming in the scented breeze, *Eleänore* 23
Half-opening balmier than *h-o* buds Of April, *Tithonus* 59
Half-parted *H-p* from a weak and scolding hinge, *The Brook* 84
Half-pennyworth *See* **Aäpoth**.
Half-pleased Look'd down, *h-p*, half-frighten'd, *Amphion* 54
Half-possess'd Lilia sang: We thought her *h-p*, *Princess iv* 585
Half-pot *See* **Haäf-pot**.
Half-right I thought her *h-r* talking of her wrongs; *Princess v* 285
Half-sardonically I ask'd him *h-s*. *Edwin Morris* 59
Half-science The sport *h-s*, fill me with a faith, *Princess, Con.* 76
Half-self my other heart, And almost my *h-s*, *Princess i* 56
Half-shadow And thought, 'For this *h-s* of a lie *Gareth and L.* 323
Half-shrouded *h-s* over death In deathless marble. *Princess v* 74
Half-shut With *h-s* eyes ever to seem Falling *Lotos-Eaters, C. S.* 55
All unawares before his *h-s* eyes, *Lover's Tale ii* 153
Half-shy And so it was—half-sly, *h-s*, *Miller's D.* 133
Half-sick *h-s* at heart, return'd. *Princess iv* 223
Half-sickening *H-s* of his pension'd afternoon, *Aylmer's Field* 461
Half-sister Raw Haste, *h-s* to Delay. *Love thou thy land* 96
Half-sly And so it was—*h-s*, half-shy, *Miller's D.* 133
Half-spiritual Then fell from that *h-s* height *To E. Fitzgerald* 19
Half-suffocated till I yell'd again *H-s*, *Lucretius* 58
H-s in the hoary fell And many winter'd fleece *Merlin and V.* 840
Half-swallow'd sea-foam sway'd a boat, *H-s* in it, *Holy Grail* 803
Half-tarnish'd *H-t* and half-bright, *Gareth and L.* 1118
Half-thinking *h-t* that her lips, Who had devised *Lancelot and E.* 1287
Half-turn'd fixt On a heart *h-t* to stone. *Maud I vi* 78
Half-unconscious I saw with *h-u* eye *The Letters* 15
Half-uncut 'She left the novel *h-u* *Talking Oak* 117
Half-unwillingly *h-u* Loving his lusty youthhood *Gareth and L.* 579
Half-views nor take *H-v* of men and things. *Will Water.* 52
Halfway *h* down the shadow of the grave, *To the Queen ii* 6
h-w down rare sails, white as white clouds, *Lover's Tale i* 4
Half-whisper'd drawing nigh *H-w* in his ear, *Œnone* 186
Half-within Seem'd *h-w* and half-without, *Miller's D.* 7
Half-without Seem'd half-within and *h-w*, „ 7
Half-world yonder morning on the blind *h-w*; *Princess vii* 352
Half-wrench'd *H-w* a golden wing; but now— *Holy Grail* 733
Half-wroth *H-w* he had not ended, but all glad, *Balin and Balan* 427
Half-yolk hast broken shell, Art yet *h-y*, „ 569
Haling six tall men *h* a seventh along, *Gareth and L.* 811
Hall (surname) (*See also* **Everard, Everard Hall**) 'Nay, nay,' said *H*, 'Why take the style *The Epic* 34
Here ended *H*, and our last light, *M. d'Arthur, Ep.* 1
Hall (*See also* **'All, Banquet-hall, Council-hall, Sea-hall**) the throne In the midst of the *h*; *The Mermaid* 22
Round the *h* where I sate, „ 26
Gods Ranged in the *h's* of Peleus; *Œnone* 81
'No voice,' she shriek'd in that lone *h*, *Palace of Art* 258
There stands a spectre in your *h*: *L. C. V. de Vere* 42
You pine among your *h's* and towers: „ 58
Walking about the gardens and the *h's* *M. d'Arthur* 20
how The races went, and who would rent the *h*: *Audley Court* 31
Far-folded mists, and gleaming *h's* of morn. *Tithonus* 10
Dreary gleams about the moorland flying over Locksley *H*; *Locksley Hall* 4

Hall (*continued*) Locksley *H*, that in the distance overlooks the sandy tracts, *Locksley Hall* 5
a long farewell to Locksley *H*! „ 189
Let it fall on Locksley *H*, with rain or hail, „ 193
he strode About the *h*, among his dogs, *Godiva* 17
A sudden hubbub shook the *h*, *Day-Dm., Revival* 7
So pass I hostel, *h*, and grange; *Sir Galahad* 81
Leading on from *h* to *h*. *L. of Burleigh* 52
And peacock-yewtree of the lonely *H*, *Enoch Arden* 99
The peacock-yewtree and the lonely *H*, „ 608
The county God—in whose capacious *h*, *Aylmer's Field* 14
Where Aylmer followed Aylmer at the *H* „ 36
so that Rectory and *H*, Bound in an immemorial intimacy, „ 38
At Christmas; ever welcome at the *H*, „ 114
darken'd all the northward of her *H*. „ 415
groves And princely *h's*, and farms, „ 654
Will there be children's laughter in their *h* „ 787
the great *H* was wholly broken down, „ 846
stairs That climb into the windy *h's* of heaven: *Lucretius* 136
from vases in the *h* Flowers of all heavens, *Princess, Pro.* 11
If our old *h's* could change their sex, „ 140
And up a flight of stairs into the *h*. „ *ii* 31
'We scarcely thought in our own *h* to hear „ 53
Look, our *h*! Our statues!— „ 75
Yet hangs his portrait in my father's *h* „ 239
in *h's* Of Lebanonian cedar: „ 351
A thousand hearts lie fallow in these *h's*, And round these *h's* a thousand baby loves „ 400
The long *h* glitter'd like a bed of flowers. „ 439
With hooded brows I crept into the *h*, „ *iv* 225
haled us to the Princess where she sat High in the *h*: „ 272
from the illumined *h* Long lanes of splendour „ 477
A cap of Tyrol borrow'd from the *h*, „ 601
And on they moved and gain'd the *h*, „ *vi* 352
Descending, struck athwart the *h*, „ 364
Love in the sacred *h's* Held carnival „ *vii* 84
Gray *h's* alone among their massive groves; „ *Con.* 43
And sorrow darkens hamlet and *h*. *Ode on Well.* 7
In this wide *h* with earth's invention stored, *Ode Inter. Exhib.* 2
We loved that *h*, tho' white and cold, *The Daisy* 37
Dies off at once from bower and *h*, *In Mem. viii* 6
At our old pastimes in the *h* We gambol'd, „ *xxx* 5
Like echoes in sepulchral *h's*, „ *lviii* 2
And saw the tumult of the *h's*; „ *lxxxvii* 4
Imperial *h's*, or open plain; „ *xcviii* 29
Methought I dwelt within a *h*, „ *ciii* 5
The *h* with harp and carol rang. „ 9
The white-faced *h's*, the glancing rills, „ *Con.* 113
that old man, now lord of the broad estate and the *H*, *Maud I i* 19
I am sick of the *H* and the hill, „ 61
Workmen up at the *H*!— „ 65
Maud the delight of the village, the ringing joy of the *H*, „ 70
by a red rock, glimmers the *H*; „ *iv* 10
tree In the meadow under the *H*! „ *v* 2
Bound for the *H*, I am sure was he; Bound for the *H*, „ *x* 25
On my fresh hope, to the *H* to-night. „ *xix* 103
And bringing me down from the *H* „ *xxi* 2
O Rivulet, born at the *H*, „ 8
As the music clash'd in the *h*; „ *xxii* 34
by the turrets Of the old manorial *h*. „ *II iv* 80
and set him in the *h*, Proclaiming, *Com. of Arthur* 229
sang the knighthood, moving to their *h*. „ 503
strength and wit, in my good mother's *h* *Gareth and L.* 12
both thy brethren are in Arthur's *h*, „ 82
thou shalt go disguised to Arthur's *h*, „ 152
a knight would pass Outward, or inward to the *h*: „ 311
Then into *h* Gareth ascending heard A voice, „ 317
Far over heads in that long-vaulted *h* „ 319
This railer, that hath mock'd thee in full *h*— „ 369
Then came in *h* the messenger of Mark, „ 384
down the side of that long *h* A stately pile,— „ 404
this was Arthur's custom in his *h*; „ 410
and they sit within our *h*. „ 425
or from sheepcot or king's *h*, „ 467
Look therefore when he calls for this in *h*, „ 583

Hall (*continued*) past into the *h* A damsel of high lineage, *Gareth and L.* 587
She into *h* past with her page and cried, „ 592
Safe, damsel, as the centre of this *h*. „ 604
Then ere a man in *h* could stay her, „ 660
two great entries open'd from the *h*, „ 665
The most ungentle knight in Arthur's *h*.' „ 757
that day a feast had been Held in high *h*, „ 848
Hear me—this morn I stood in Arthur's *h*, „ 855
The champion thou hast brought from Arthur's *h*? „ 916
Arise And quickly pass to Arthur's *h*, „ 984
'Here is a kitchen-knave from Arthur's *h* „ 1036
Where should be truth if not in Arthur's *h*, In Arthur's presence? „ 1254
What madness made thee challenge the chief knight Of Arthur's *h*?' „ 1417
Weeping for some gay knight in Arthur's *h*.' *Marr. of Geraint* 118
on a day, he sitting high in *h*, „ 147
not mindful of his face In the King's *h*, „ 192
Clear thro' the open casement of the *h*, „ 328
The dusky-rafter'd many-cobweb'd *h*, „ 362
because their *h* must also serve For kitchen, „ 390
Now here, now there, about the dusky *h*; „ 401
those That eat in Arthur's *h* at Camelot. „ 432
And told her all their converse in the *h*, „ 520
Geraint Woke where he slept in the high *h*, „ 755
Thereafter, when I reach'd this ruin'd *h*, „ 785
overbore Her fancy dwelling in this dusky *h*; „ 802
she, remembering her old ruin'd *h*, *Geraint and E.* 254
take him up, and bear him to our *h*: „ 552
And bore him to the naked *h* of Doorm, „ 570
he lay Down on an oaken settle in the *h*, „ 573
There in the naked *h*, propping his head, „ 581
return'd The huge Earl Doorm with plunder to the *h*. „ 592
And all the *h* was dim with steam of flesh: „ 603
And ate with tumult in the naked *h*, „ 605
He roll'd his eyes about the *h*, „ 610
At this he turn'd all red and paced his *h*, „ 668
And loved me serving in my father's *h*: „ 699
strode the brute Earl up and down his *h*, „ 712
all the men and women in the *h* Rose „ 731
the huge Earl lay slain within his *h*. „ 806
and in their *h's* arose The cry of children, „ 964
'I too,' said Arthur, 'am of Arthur's *h*, *Balin and Balan* 37
A thrall of mine in open *h*, „ 56
Thereafter, when Sir Balin enter'd *h*, „ 80
the *h* Of him to whom ye sent us, Pellam, „ 95
warmth of Arthur's *h* Shadow'd an angry distance: „ 236
Close-bower'd in that garden nigh the *h*. „ 241
the castle of a King, the *h* Of Pellam, „ 331
Faint in the low dark *h* of banquet: „ 343
Arthur's knights Were hated strangers in the *h*) „ 352
thou from Arthur's *h*, and yet So simple! „ 357
Who, sitting in thine own *h*, canst endure To mouth „ 378
Was dumb'd by one from out the *h* of Mark „ 437
Borne by some high lord-prince of Arthur's *h*, „ 466
bounden art thou, if from Arthur's *h*, To help the weak. „ 472
'Brother, I dwelt a day in Pellam's *h*: „ 605
he rose To leave the *h*, and, Vivien following him, *Merlin and V.* 32
When Guinevere was crossing the great *h* „ 65
but all was joust and play, Leaven'd his *h*. „ 146
built the King his havens, ships, and *h's*, „ 168
In Arthur's arras *h* at Camelot: „ 250
After the King, who eat in Arthur's *h's*, *Lancelot and E.* 184
'Known am I, and of Arthur's *h*, „ 188
goodliest man That ever among ladies ate in *h*, „ 255
into that rude *h* Stept with all grace, „ 262
a chapel and a *h* On massive columns, „ 405
And reverently they bore her into *h*. „ 1266
I knew For one of those who eat in Arthur's *h*; *Holy Grail* 24
In our great *h* there stood a vacant chair, „ 167
the great banquet lay along the *h*, „ 180
in the blast there smote along the *h* A beam of light „ 186
said Percivale, 'the King, Was not in *h*: „ 206
Ah outraged maiden sprang into the *h* „ 208

Hall (*continued*) roofs Of our great *h* are roll'd in thunder-smoke! *Holy Grail* 220
For dear to Arthur was that *h* of ours, „ 222
'O brother, had you known our mighty *h*, „ 225
Climbs to the mighty *h* that Merlin built. „ 231
With many a mystic symbol, gird the *h*: „ 233
brother, had you known our *h* within, „ 246
So to this *h* full quickly rode the King, „ 258
(Because the *h* was all in tumult— „ 269
Shrilling along the *h* to Arthur, call'd, „ 289
cries of all my realm Pass thro' this *h*— „ 316
But when they led me into *h*, behold, „ 577
A slender page about her father's *h*, „ 581
that they fell from, brought us to the *h*. „ 720
Yea, shook this newer, stronger *h* of ours, „ 731
And up into the sounding *h* I past; But nothing in the sounding *h* I saw, „ 827
Lancelot left The *h* long silent, „ 854
and as he sat In *h* at old Caerleon, *Pelleas and E.* 3
And spied not any light in *h* or bower, „ 419
he Gasping, 'Of Arthur's *h* am I, but here, „ 514
that Gawain fired The *h* of Merlin, „ 518
High up in heaven the *h* that Merlin built, „ 553
It chanced that both Brake into *h* together, „ 587
Then a long silence came upon the *h*, „ 609
Danced like a wither'd leaf before the *h*. (repeat) *Last Tournament* 4, 242
And toward him from the *h*, with harp in hand, „ 5
Into the *h* stagger'd, his visage ribb'd „ 57
warrior-wise thou stridest thro' his *h's* Who hates thee, „ 517
beheld That victor of the Pagan throned in *h*— „ 665
stairway to the *h*, and look'd and saw „ 757
rarely could she front in *h*, Or elsewhere, *Guinevere* 62
Swung round the lighted lantern of the *h*; And in the *h* itself was such a feast „ 262
live To sit once more within his lonely *h*, „ 497
Walking about the gardens and the *h's* *Pass. of Arthur* 188
From his mid-dome in Heaven's airy *h's*; *Lover's Tale i* 66
Is scoop'd a cavern and a mountain *h*, „ 517
streams Running far on within its inmost *h's*, „ 523
round his *h* From column on to column, „ *iv* 188
at one end of the *h* Two great funereal curtains, „ 213
rose—And slowly pacing to the middle *h*, „ 306
this last strange hour in his own *h*; „ 358
hup to Harmsby and Hutterby *H*. *North. Cobbler* 14
people throng'd about them from the *h*, *Sisters (E. and E.)* 156
sa I hallus deal'd wi' the *H*, *Village Wife* 115
there hail'd on our houses and *h's* *Def. of Lucknow* 13
princelier looking man never stept thro' a Prince's *h*. *The Wreck* 16
this *H* at last will go—perhaps have gone, *The Flight* 27
I myself so close on death, and death itself in Locksley *H*. *Locksley H., Sixty* 4
In the *h* there hangs a painting— „ 13
how her living glory lights the *h*, „ 181
Here is Locksley *H*, my grandson, here the lion-guarded gate. Not to-night in Locksley *H*—to-morrow— „ 213
Not the *H* to-night, my grandson! „ 237
Here to-night, the *H* to-morrow, „ 261
Then I leave thee Lord and Master, latest Lord of Locksley *H*. „ 282
and break The sunless *h's* of Hades *Demeter and P.* 136
And yet not mine the *h*, the farm, the field; *The Ring* 169
they know too that whene'er In our free *H*, *Akbar's Dream* 55
Hall-ceiling the fair *h-c* stately-set *Palace of Art* 141
Halleluiah HALLOWED be Thy name—*H*! (repeat) *De Prof., Human C.* 1, 5, 9
Hallelujah blend in choric *H* to the Maker *Making of Man* 8
Hall-garden up in the high *H-g* I see her pass *Maud I iv* 11
Birds in the high *H-g* (repeat) „ *xii* 1, 25
Hall-hearths On the *h-h* the festal fires, *Day Dm., Sleep P.* 14
Halloo Shrilly the owlet *h's*; *Leonine Eleg.* 6
With a lengthen'd loud *h*, *The Owl ii* 13
in the *h* Will topple to the trumpet down, *Princess ii* 231
Hallow'd torrent brooks of *h* Israel *D. of F. Women* 181
earth They fell on became *h* evermore. *Lover's Tale i* 440
Hallow'd (*continued*) my name has been A *h* memory like the names of old, *Lover's Tale i* 445
Your very armour *h*, *Princess v* 413
H be Thy name—Halleluiah! (repeat) *De Prof., Human C.* 1, 5, 9
Halo hence this *h* lives about The waiter's hands, *Will Water.* 113
boss Of her own *h's* dusky shield; *The Voyage* 32
Halt (adj.) And cured some *h* and maim'd; *St. S. Stylites* 137
is there any of you *h* or maim'd? „ 142
But, if a man were *h* or hunch'd, *Guinevere* 41
no man *h*, or deaf or blind; *Locksley H., Sixty* 163
Halt (s) they made a *h*; The horses yell'd; *Princess v* 249
The front rank made a sudden *h*; *Lover's Tale iii* 29
Halt (verb) He seems as one whose footsteps *h*, *Will* 15
rode In converse till she made her palfrey *h*, *Gareth and L.* 1360
cry '*H*,' and to her own bright face Accuse her *Geraint and E.* 110
Progress *h's* on palsied feet, *Locksley H., Sixty* 219
Halted hung his head, and *h* in reply, *Geraint and E.* 811
And when we *h* at that other well, *Merlin and V.* 280
he look'd at the host that had *h* *Heavy Brigade* 7
Halter scared with threats of jail and *h* *Aylmer's Field* 520
Halting lookt So sweet, that *h*, in his past, *Last Tournament* 388
Halyard Shot thro' the staff or the *h*, *Def. of Lucknow* 5
Hamilton Who are you? What! the Lady *H*? *Romney's R.* 2
Hamlet Two children in one *h* born and bred; *Circumstance* 8
many too had known Edith among the *h's* round, *Aylmer's Field* 615
among their massive groves; Trim *h's*; *Princess, Con.* 44
And sorrow darkens *h* and hall. *Ode on Well.* 7
But distant colour, happy *h*, *The Daisy* 27
Or where the kneeling *h* drains The chalice *In Mem. x* 15
Four voices of four *h's* round, „ *xxviii* 5
She floats across the *h*. *Prog. of Spring* 40
passing it glanced upon *H* or city, *Merlin and the G.* 104
Hammer (s) Came to the *h* here in March— *Audley Court* 60
Shaking their pretty cabin, *h* and axe, Auger and saw, *Enoch Arden* 173
silver *h's* falling On silver anvils, *Princess i* 216
iron-clanging anvil bang'd With *h's*; „ *v* 505
Thou hear'st the village *h* clink, *In Mem. cxxi* 15
and everywhere Was *h* laid to hoof, *Marr. of Geraint* 256
Hammer (verb) *h* at this reverend gentlewoman. *Princess iii* 129
Hammer'd Sons of Edward with *h* brands. *Batt. of Brunanburh* 14
noon Was clash'd and *h* from a hundred towers, *Godiva* 75
All that long morn the lists were *h* up, *Princess v* 368
Hammergrate (emigrate) An' saw she mun *h*, lass, *Village Wife* 104
Hammering *H* and clinking, chattering stony names *Princess iii* 361
felt his young heart *h* in his ears, *Gareth and L.* 322
Hammock-shroud His heavy-shotted *h-s* *In Mem. vi* 15
Hampden deep chord which *H* smote Will vibrate *England and Amer.* 19
Han' (hand) Queen wid her sceptre in sich an illigant *h*,' *Tomorrow* 35
Father Molowny he tuk her in *h*,' „ 55
Hand (part of body) (*See also* **'And, Han', Hond**) *knew the seasons when to take Occasion by the* h, *To the Queen* 31
Propt on thy knees, my *h's* upheld In thine, *Supp. Confessions* 70
Claps her tiny *h's* above me, *Lilian* 4
When I would kiss thy *h*, *Madeline* 31
Thou leddest by the *h* thine infant Hope. *Ode to Memory* 30
O cursed *h*! O cursed blow! *Oriana* 82
Laughing and clapping their *h's* between, *The Merman* 29
Leaning his cheek upon his *h*, *Eleänore* 118
And now shake *h's* across the brink *My life is full* 6
Shake *h's* once more: I cannot sink So far— „ 8
her wooden walls,—lit by sure *h's*,— *Buonaparte* 5
CARESS'D or chidden by the slender *h*, *Caress'd or chidden* 1
And prest thy *h*, and knew the press return'd, *The Bridesmaid* 12
But who hath seen her wave her *h*? *L. of Shalott i* 24
Or answer should one press his *h's*? *Two Voices* 245
On either *h* The lawns and meadow-ledges *Œnone* 5
till thy *h* Fail from the sceptre-staff. „ 125
Ev'n on this *h*, and sitting on this stone? „ 233
h's and eyes That said, We wait for thee. *Palace of Art* 103
Or hollowing one *h* against his ear, „ 109
From one *h* droop'd a crocus: one *h* grasp'd „ 119
clapt her *h's* and cried, 'I marvel if my still delight „ 189

Hand (part of body) (*continued*) The airy *h* confusion wrought, *Palace of Art* 226
If time be heavy on your *h's*, *L. C. V. de Vere* 66
sit beside my bed, mother, and put your *h* in mine, *May Queen, Con.* 23
flowers in the valley for other *h's* than mine. „ 52
and sinking ships, and praying *h's*. *Lotos-Eaters, C. S.* 116
Beauty and anguish walking *h* in *h* *D. of F. Women* 15
My father held his *h* upon his face; „ 107
Shake *h's*, before you die. *D. of the O. Year* 42
But with his *h* against the hilt, *Love thou thy land* 83
laughing, clapt his *h* On Everard's shoulder, *The Epic* 21
either *h*, Or voice, or else a motion of the mere. *M. d'Arthur* 76
I will arise and slay thee with my *h's*.' „ 132
Then with both *h's* I flung him, „ 157
O'er both his shoulders drew the languid *h's*, „ 174
those three Queens Put forth their *h's*, „ 206
chafed his *h's*, And call'd him by his name, „ 209
knowing God, they lift not *h's* of prayer, „ 252
Requiring at her *h* the greatest gift, *Gardener's D.* 229
old man Was wroth, and doubled up his *h's*, *Dora* 25
She bow'd upon her *h's*, „ 103
clapt him on the *h's* and on the cheeks, „ 133
clapt his *h* in mine and sang— *Audley Court* 39
modest eyes, a *h*, a foot Lessening in perfect cadence, *Walk. to the Mail* 54
With *h* and rope we haled the groaning sow, „ 91
Again with *h's* of wild rejection 'Go!— *Edwin Morris* 124
She might have lock'd her *h's*. *Talking Oak* 144
kingdoms overset, Or lapse from *h* to *h*, „ 258
should not plunge His *h* into the bag: *Golden Year* 72
turn'd it in his glowing *h's*; *Locksley Hall* 31
kiss him: take his *h* in thine. „ 52
tho' I slew thee with my *h*! „ 56
Then a *h* shall pass before thee, „ 81
a heart as rough as Esau's *h*, *Godiva* 28
The page has caught her *h* in his: *Day-Dm., Sleep P.* 29
on either *h* upswells The gold-fringed pillow „ *Sleep B.* 21
That lightly rain from ladies' *h's*. *Sir Galahad* 12
Nor maiden's *h* in mine. „ 20
And, stricken by an angel's *h*, „ 69
Who hold their *h's* to all, and cry *Will Water.* 45
this halo lives about The waiter's *h's*, „ 114
And lay your *h* upon my head, *Lady Clare* 55
Dropt her head in the maiden's *h*, „ 63
He clasps the crag with crooked *h's*; *The Eagle* 1
Panted *h* in *h* with faces pale, *Vision of Sin* 19
Bandied by the *h's* of fools. „ 106
And the warmth of *h* in *h*. „ 162
But O for the touch of a vanish'd *h*, *Break, break, etc.* 11
Another *h* crept too across his trade *Enoch Arden* 110
set his *h* To fit their little streetward sitting-room „ 169
and his careful *h*,—The space was narrow,— „ 176
caught His bundle, waved his *h*, and went his way. „ 238
Perhaps her eye was dim, *h* tremulous; „ 242
For where he fixt his heart he set his *h* „ 294
Caught at his *h*, and wrung it passionately, „ 328
but her face had fall'n upon her *h's*; „ 391
At Annie's door he paused and gave his *h*, „ 447
Shaking a little like a drunkard's *h*, „ 465
Her *h* dwelt lingeringly on the latch, „ 519
on the right *h* of the hearth he saw Philip, „ 744
from her lifted *h* Dangled a length of ribbon „ 749
on the left *h* of the hearth he saw The mother „ 753
Almost to all things could he turn his *h*. „ 813
(Claspt *h's* and that petitionary grace *The Brook* 112
Until they closed a bargain, *h* in *h*. „ 156
Her art, her *h*, her counsel all had wrought *Aylmer's Field* 151
Queenly responsive when the loyal *h* Rose „ 169
voice Of comfort and an open *h* of help, „ 174
Then playing with the blade he prick'd his *h*, „ 239
Then made his pleasure echo, *h* to *h*, „ 257
under his own lintel stood Storming with lifted *h's*, „ 332
Is whiter even than her pretty *h*: „ 363
and the *h's* of power Were bloodier, „ 452

Hand (part of body) (*continued*) His face magnetic to the *h* from which Livid *Aylmer's Field* 626
free of alms her *h*—The *h* that robed your cottage-walls „ 697
laid, Wifelike, her *h* in one of his, „ 808
her own people bore along the nave Her pendent *h's*, „ 813
A pickaxe in her *h*: *Sea Dreams* 100
Gript my *h* hard, and with God-bless-you went. „ 160
A loose one in the hard grip of his *h*, „ 163
Left him one *h*, and reaching thro' the night „ 287
h's they mixt, and yell'd and round me drove *Lucretius* 56
unseen monster lays His vast and filthy *h's* upon my will, „ 220
that sport Went *h* in *h* with Science; *Princess, Pro.* 80
The *h* that play'd the patron with her curls. „ 138
with long arms and *h's* Reach'd out, „ *i* 28
Airing a snowy *h* and signet gem, „ 121
I sat down and wrote, In such a *h* as when „ 236
Lived thro' her to the tips of her long *h's*, „ *ii* 40
when we set our *h* To this great work, „ 59
Besides the brain was like the *h*, „ 150
Took both his *h's*, and smiling faintly said: „ 304
Melissa, with her *h* upon the lock, „ 322
Push'd her flat *h* against his face and laugh'd; „ 366
The circle rounded under female *h's* „ 372
one In this *h* held a volume as to read, „ 455
But Lady Psyche was the right *h* now, „ *iii* 37
Up went the hush'd amaze of *h* and eye. „ 138
Dabbing a shameless *h* with shameful jest, „ 314
Many a little *h* Glanced like a touch of sunshine „ 356
once or twice she lent her *h*, „ *iv* 27
her heart Palpitated, her *h* shook, „ 389
but fell Into his father's *h's*, „ 402
Render him up unscathed: give him your *h*: „ 408
Whose brains are in their *h's* and in their heels, „ 518
She, ending, waved her *h's*: „ 522
But on my shoulder hung their heavy *h's*, „ 553
And gives the battle to his *h's*: „ 580
clapt her *h's* and cried for war, „ 590
Lay by her like a model of her *h*. „ 597
'then we fell Into your father's *h*, „ *v* 51
push'd by rude *h's* from its pedestal, „ 58
reach'd White *h's* of farewell to my sire, „ 233
now a wandering *h* And now a pointed finger, „ 269
the tender orphan *h's* Felt at my heart, „ 435
sit Upon a king's right *h* in thunder-storms, „ 439
a moment *h* to *h*, And sword to sword, „ 538
tender ministries Of female *h's* and hospitality.' „ *vi* 73
and served With female *h's* and hospitality.' „ 96
prest Their *h's*, and call'd them dear deliverers, „ 92
in *h's* so lately claspt with yours, „ 184
Laid the soft babe in his hard-mailed *h's*. „ 208
kiss her; take her *h*, she weeps: „ 225
the rougher *h* Is safer: „ 278
Refuse her proffer, lastly gave his *h*. „ 347
Low voices with the ministering *h* Hung round the sick: „ *vii* 21
Nor knew what eye was on me, nor the *h* That nursed me, „ 53
sometimes I would catch Her *h* in wild delirium, „ 93
And often feeling of the helpless *h's*, „ 111
touch Came round my wrist and tears upon my *h* „ 138
Or *h* in *h* with Plenty in the maize, „ *vii* 201
And the voice trembled and the *h*. „ 227
and her forehead sank upon her *h's*, „ 247
Stays all the fair young planet in her *h's*— „ 264
Lay thy sweet *h's* in mine and trust to me.' „ 366
there is a *h* that guides.' „ *Con.* 79
Now shaking *h's* with him, now him, „ 92
will he greet With lifted *h* the gazer in the street. *Ode on Well.* 22
from both her open *h's* Lavish Honour shower'd „ 195
with toil of heart and knees and *h's*, „ 212
upon whose *h* and heart and brain „ 239
thou with thy young lover *h* in *h* *W. to Marie Alex.* 34
Whose *h* at home was gracious to the poor: „ 37
Strong of his *h's*, and strong on his legs, *Grandmother* 13
But marry me out of *h*: „ 52
For groves of pine on either *h*, *To F. D. Maurice* 21
To sit with empty *h's* at home. *Sailor Boy* 16

Hand (part of body) (*continued*) To Thor and Odin lifted a *h*: *The Victim* 8
He bore but little game in *h*; „ 42
The King bent low, with *h* on brow, „ 53
and nearer than *h's* and feet. *High. Pantheism* 12
I hold you here, root and all, in my *h*, *Flow. in cran. wall.* 3
Brandishing in her *h* a dart *Boädicea* 71
beat with rapid unanimous *h*, „ 79
Fine little *h's*, fine little feet— *Window, Letter* 3
Two little *h's* that meet, (repeat) *Window, The Answer* 1, 4
And loving *h's* must part— „ „ 6
Or reach a *h* thro' time to catch *In Mem. i* 7
A hollow form with empty *h's*.' „ *iii* 12
waiting for a *h*, A *h* that can be clasp'd „ *vii* 4
And letters unto trembling *h's*; „ *x* 7
And *h's* so often clasp'd in mine, „ 19
where warm *h's* have prest and closed, „ *xiii* 7
Should strike a sudden *h* in mine, „ *xiv* 11
Come then, pure *h's*, and bear the head „ *xviii* 9
Her *h's* are quicker unto good: „ *xxxiii* 10
wrought With human *h's* the creeds of creeds „ *xxxvi* 10
But thou and I have shaken *h's*, „ *xl* 29
I stretch lame *h's* of faith, and grope, „ *lv* 17
And reaps the labour of his *h's*, „ *lxiv* 26
And winds their curls about his *h*: „ *lxvi* 12
He reach'd the glory of a *h*, „ *lxix* 17
A *h* that points, and palled shapes „ *lxx* 7
When the dark *h* struck down thro' time, „ *lxxii* 19
Whate'er thy *h's* are set to do „ *lxxv* 19
Reach out dead *h's* to comfort me. „ *lxxx* 16
Would reach us out the shining *h*, *In Mem. lxxxiv* 43
How much of act at human *h's* „ *lxxxv* 38
all within was noise Of songs, and clapping *h's*, „ *lxxxvii* 19
Behold their brides in other *h's*; „ *xc* 14
The larger heart, the kindlier *h*; „ *cvi* 30
the child would twine A trustful *h*, „ *cix* 19
A higher *h* must make her mild, „ *cxiv* 17
I take the pressure of thine *h*. „ *cxix* 12
And out of darkness came the *h's* „ *cxxiv* 23
Sweet human *h* and lips and eye; „ *cxxix* 6
With him to whom her *h* I gave. „ *Con.* 70
in their *h* Is Nature like an open book; „ 131
Pickpockets, each *h* lusting for all that is not its own; *Maud I i* 22
or are moved by an unseen *h* at a game „ *iv* 26
Ready in heart and ready in *h*, „ *v* 9
she touch'd my *h* with a smile so sweet, „ *vi* 12
I saw the treasured splendour, her *h*, „ 84
She waved to me with her *h*. „ *ix* 8
Ah God, for a man with heart, head, *h*, „ *x* 60
I kiss'd her slender *h*, „ *xii* 13
Sunn'd itself on his breast and his *h's*. „ *xiii* 13
if a *h*, as white As ocean-foam in the moon, „ *xiv* 17
To labour and the mattock-harden'd *h*, „ *xviii* 34
And given false death her *h*, „ 68
It is this guilty *h*!— „ *II i* 4
I sorrow For the *h*, the lips, the eyes, „ *iv* 27
And mightier of his *h's* with every blow, *Com. of Arthur* 110
But sought to rule for his own self and *h*, „ 219
h's Of loyal vassals toiling for their liege. „ 281
holy Dubric spread his *h's* and spake, „ 471
I could climb and lay my *h* upon it, *Gareth and L.* 50
But ever when he reach'd a *h* to climb, „ 52
And drops of water fell from either *h*; „ 220
Toward the sunrise, each with harp in *h*, „ 261
Merlin's *h*, the Mage at Arthur's court, „ 306
With thine own *h* thou slewest my dear lord, „ 352
In either *h* he bore What dazzled all, „ 386
ye know we stay'd their *h's* From war „ 421
Accursed, who strikes nor lets the *h* be seen!' „ 435
Gareth leaning both *h's* heavily Down „ 439
a nostril large and fine, and *h's* Large, fair and fine!— „ 465
Lying or sitting round him, idle *h's*, Charm'd; „ 512
and bow Lowly, to kiss his *h*, „ 549
So with a kindly *h* on Gareth's arm „ 578
And told him of a cavern hard at *h*, „ 1189
h hath fashion'd on the rock The war of Time „ 1197

Hand (part of body) (*continued*) when he found the grass within his *h's* He laugh'd; *Gareth and L.* 1225
Lancelot!—thine the *h* That threw me? „ 1241
O Lancelot, Lancelot'—and she clapt her *h's*— „ 1290
waving to him White *h's*, and courtesy; „ 1377
Lady Lyonors wrung her *h's* and wept, „ 1395
with her own white *h's* Array'd and deck'd her, *Marr. of Geraint* 16
and all flyers from the *h* Of Justice, „ 36
watch his mightful *h* striking great blows „ 95
instinctive *h* Caught at the hilt, „ 209
White from the mason's *h*, (repeat) „ 244, 408
Came forward with the helmet yet in *h* „ 285
Or it may be the labour of his *h's*, „ 341
Frown and we smile, the lords of our own *h's*; „ 354
And fondling all her *h* in his he said, „ 509
On either shining shoulder laid a *h*, „ 518
and *h* in *h* they moved Down to the meadow „ 536
There came a clapping as of phantom *h's*. „ 566
To seek a second favour at his *h's*. „ 626
and in her *h* A suit of bright apparel, „ 677
Came one with this and laid it in my *h*, „ 699
Help'd by the mother's careful *h* and eye, „ 738
Her by both *h's* he caught, and sweetly said, „ 778
our fair Queen, No *h* but hers, should make „ 788
For by the *h's* of Dubric, the high saint, „ 838
Far liefer by his dear *h* had I die, *Geraint and E.* 68
creatures gently born But into bad *h's* fall'n. „ 192
in his *h* Bare victual for the mowers: „ 201
In the mid-warmth of welcome and graspt *h*, „ 280
Geraint Waving an angry *h* as who should say „ 444
But lift a shining *h* against the sun, „ 473
Nor let her true *h* falter, nor blue eye Moisten, „ 512
after all was done that *h* could do, She rested, „ 517
chafing his pale *h's*, and calling to him. „ 582
chafing his faint *h's*, and calling to him; „ 585
Take my salute,' unknightly with flat *h*, „ 717
reach'd a *h*, and on his foot She set her own and climb'd; „ 759
Put *h* to *h* beneath her husband's heart, „ 767
wrought too long with delegated *h's*, „ 893
set up a stronger race With hearts and *h's*, „ 941
my *h* Was gauntleted, half slew him; *Balin and Balan* 56
Lancelot with his *h* among the flowers „ 259
Saint who stands with lily in *h* In yonder shrine. „ 261
'And passing gentle' caught his *h* away „ 371
Then *h* at ear, and hearkening from what side „ 415
white *h* whose ring'd caress Had wander'd „ 512
The hearts of all this Order in mine *h*— *Merlin and V.* 56
damsel bidden rise arose And stood with folded *h's* „ 69
Courteous—amends for gauntness—takes her *h*— „ 104
how *h* lingers in *h*! Let go at last!— „ 106
her left *h* Droop from his mighty shoulder, „ 242
And make a pretty cup of both my *h's* „ 275
And Merlin lock'd his *h* in hers (repeat) „ 290, 470
charm Of woven paces and of waving *h's*, (repeat) „ 330, 968
Merlin loosed his *h* from hers and said, „ 356
It lives dispersedly in many *h's*, „ 457
The wrist is parted from the *h* that waved, „ 551
ringing with their serpent *h's*, „ 578
her *h* half-clench'd Went faltering sideways „ 849
clapt her *h's* Together with a wailing shriek, „ 866
some one put this diamond in her *h*, *Lancelot and E.* 212
Half-envious of the flattering *h*, „ 349
So kiss'd her, and Sir Lancelot his own *h*, „ 389
she smote her *h*: wellnigh she swoon'd: „ 625
it will be sweet to have it From your own *h*; „ 694
slightly kiss'd the *h* to which he gave, „ 702
with mine own *h* give his diamond to him, „ 760
His battle-writhen arms and mighty *h's* „ 812
And laid the diamond in his open *h*. „ 827
yet he glanced not up, nor waved his *h*, „ 986
Then gave a languid *h* to each, and lay, „ 1032
lay the letter in my *h* A little ere I die, and close the *h* Upon it; „ 1113
Her father laid the letter in her *h*, And closed the *h* upon it, and she died. „ 1134

Hand (part of body) (*continued*) Set in her *h* a lily, o'er her hung The silken case *Lancelot and E.* 1148
In her right *h* the lily, in her left The letter— „ 1155
in one cold passive *h* Received at once and laid aside „ 1201
Arthur spied the letter in her *h*, „ 1270
shield of Lancelot at her feet Be carven, and her lily in her *h*. „ 1342
we blow with breath, or touch with *h*, *Holy Grail* 114
and at the base we found On either *h*, „ 498
The Quest and he were in the *h's* of Heaven. „ 659
In colour like the fingers of a *h* Before a burning taper, „ 693
caught his *h*, Held it, and there, half-hidden „ 753
The sword was dash'd from out my *h*, and fell. „ 826
—yea, his very *h* and foot— „ 915
slender was her *h* and small her shape; *Pelleas and E.* 74
Taking his *h*, 'O the strong *h*,' she said, „ 126
straitly nipt the *h*, and flung it from her; „ 133
by that strong *h* of his The sword and golden circlet „ 169
And mindful of her small and cruel *h*, „ 201
strong *h*, which had overthrown Her minion-knights, „ 234
Shaking his *h's*, as from a lazar's rag, „ 317
delegate to thrall These fighting *h's* of mine— „ 337
tame thy jailing princess to thine *h*. „ 344
as a *h* that pushes thro' the leaf To find a nest „ 436
clench'd His *h's*, and madden'd with himself „ 460
Sent *h's* upon him, as to tear him, „ 521
A cripple, one that held a *h* for alms— „ 542
toward him from the hall, with harp in *h*, *Last Tournament* 5
Slid from my *h's*, when I was leaning out „ 43
Bridge-broken, one eye out, and one *h* off, „ 59
his strong *h's* gript And dinted the gilt dragons „ 181
See, the *h* Wherewith thou takest this, „ 192
My *h*—belike the lance hath dript upon it— „ 200
Dagonet with one foot poised in his *h*, „ 285
Dagonet clapt his *h's* and shrill'd, „ 353
'Isolt Of the white *h's*' they call'd her: „ 398
served him well with those white *h's* „ 400
Graspt it so hard, that all her *h* was red. Then cried the Breton, 'Look, her *h* is red! „ 411
melts within her *h*—her *h* is hot With ill desires, „ 414
Not lift a *h*—not, tho' he found me thus! „ 528
And she, my namesake of the *h's*, „ 594
Tristram, fondling her light *h's*, replied, „ 601
Tristram, ever dallying with her *h*, „ 626
gardener's *h* Picks from the colewort *Guinevere* 31
H's in *h's*, and eye to eye Low on the border „ 100
and bow'd down upon her *h's* Silent, „ 158
full passionately, Her head upon her *h's*, „ 181
meat he long'd for served By *h's* unseen; „ 266
He falter'd, and his *h* fell from the harp, „ 303
Whereat the novice crying, with clasp'd *h's*, „ 311
He spared to lift his *h* against the King „ 437
I made them lay their *h's* in mine and swear „ 467
and laid her *h's* about his feet. „ 528
I cannot take thy *h*; that too is flesh, „ 553
Perceived the waving of his *h's* that blest. „ 584
Here her *h* Grasp'd, made her vail her eyes: „ 662
to and fro Swaying the helpless *h's*, *Pass. of Arthur* 131
either *h*, Or voice, or else a motion of the mere. „ 244
I will arise and slay thee with my *h's*.' „ 300
Then with both *h's* I flung him, „ 325
O'er both his shoulders drew the languid *h's*, „ 342
those three Queens Put forth their *h's*, „ 374
chafed his *h's*, and call'd him by his name, „ 377
knowing God, they lift not *h's* of prayer „ 420
Straining his eyes beneath an arch of *h*, „ 464
To pass my *h* across my brows, *Lover's Tale i* 31
With *h's* for eaves, uplooking and almost „ 311
had the Power from whose right *h* the light „ 497
from whose left *h* floweth The Shadow of Death, „ 498
Folding his *h's*, deals comfortable words „ 717
I loved her, graspt the *h* she lov'd, „ 750
he Would hold the *h* of blessing over them, „ 754
with mad *h* Tearing the bright leaves of the ivy-screen, „ *ii* 39
drew back His *h* to push me from him; „ 93

Hand (part of body) (*continued*) Shrank in me, like a snowflake in the *h*, *Lover's Tale iii* 38
One *h* she reach'd to those that came behind, „ 48
And claspt her *h* in his: „ 52
And raised us *h* in *h*.' „ *iv* 66
But, placing his true *h* upon her heart, „ 75
drown'd The feebler motion underneath his *h*. „ 83
with meeting *h's* And cries about the banquet— „ 238
Then taking his dear lady by one *h*, „ 369
better ha' put my naked *h* in a hornets' nest. *First Quarrel* 50
he patted my *h* in his gentle way, „ 67
When I cannot see my own *h*, *Rizpah* 7
Sir Richard bore in *h* all his sick men *The Revenge* 15
and they fought us *h* to *h*. „ 52
Fall into the *h's* of God, not into the *h's* of Spain!' „ 90
A *h* upon the head of either child, *Sisters (E. and E.)* 55
Had caught her *h*, her eyelids fell— „ 148
But counterpressures of the yielded *h* „ 163
Put forth cold *h's* between us, „ 265
The sisters glide about me *h* in *h* „ 275
big chest, big merciless *h's*! *In the Child. Hosp.* 4
she lay with a flower in one *h* and her thin *h's* crost on her breast— „ 39
Keep the revolver in *h*! *Def. of Lucknow* 26
Better to fall by the *h's* that they love, „ 53
but be sure that your *h* be as true! „ 56
h of the Highlander wet with their tears! „ 102
Climb first and reach me down thy *h*. *Sir J. Oldcastle* 204
lifted *h* and heart and voice In praise to God *Columbus* 16
There was a glimmering of God's *h*. „ 142
I lead thee by the *h*, Fear not.' „ 158
Some over-labour'd, some by their own *h's*,— „ 178
glitter'd o'er us a sunbright *h*, *V. of Maeldune* 84
and the sunbright *h* of the dawn, „ 92
chariots backward, knowing griefs at *h*; *Achilles over the T.* 25
And plant on shoulder, *h* and knee, *To E. Fitzgerald* 8
The noonday crag made the *h* burn; *Tiresias* 35
these blind *h's* were useless in their wars. „ 78
if one of these By his own *h*— „ 118
examples reach a *h* Far thro' all years, „ 126
let thine own *h* strike Thy youthful pulses „ 156
This useless *h*! I felt one warm tear fall upon it. „ 166
My Shelley would fall from my *h's* *The Wreck* 25
My *h's*, when I heard him coming would drop „ 27
the *h* that would help me, would heal me— „ 56
Ten long sweet summer days upon deck, sitting *h* in *h*— „ 64
of a *h* giving bread and wine, „ 114
I knew that *h* too well— „ 145
And she laid her *h* in my own— *Despair* 49
books are scatter'd from *h* to *h*— „ 93
in his *h* A scroll of verse— *Ancient Sage* 5
But in the *h* of what is more than man, Or in man's *h* when man is more than man, „ 256
—rather than that *h* in mine, *The Flight* 53
Our dying mother join'd our *h's*; „ 87
but wander *h* in *h* With breaking hearts, „ 99
clasp the *h's* and murmur, *Locksley H., Sixty* 192
I refused the *h* he gave. „ 256
stars are from their *h's* Flung thro' the woods, *Early Spring* 17
H's all round! (repeat) *Hands all Round* 9, 21, 33
Her fleet is in your *h's*, *The Fleet* 14
Works of subtle brain and *h*, *Open I. and C. Exhib.* 7
Trust the *H* of light will lead her people, *On Jub. Q. Victoria* 68
thy *h's* let fall the gather'd flower, *Demeter and P.* 9
Craft with a bunch of all-heal in her *h*, *Vastness* 12
stretch'd my *h's* As if I saw her; *The Ring* 116
Some younger *h* must have engraven the ring— „ 238
What sparkled there? whose *h* was that? „ 257
Muriel clench'd The *h* that wore it, „ 262
Unclosed the *h*, and from it drew the ring, „ 269
and the *h's* Fell from each other, „ 380
bells that rang without a *h*, „ 411
and felt a gentle *h* Fall on my forehead, „ 418
And the face, The *h*,—my Mother. „ 425
I took And chafed the freezing *h*. „ 452

Happiness Spirit of h And perfect rest — Supp. Confessions 50
all the warmth, the peace, the h, — Enoch Arden 761
Would shatter all the h of the hearth. — " 770
woman counts her due, Love, children, h?' — Princess iii 245
What h to reign a lonely king, — Com. of Arthur 82
From his great hoard of h distill'd — Lover's Tale i 714
a life More living to some happier h, — " 762
One bloom of youth, health, beauty, h, — Sisters (E. and E.) 120
tho' the h of each in each Were not enough, — " 220
Household h, gracious children, — Vastness 24
I am happier in your h Than in mine own. — The Ring 90
Happt (wrapped) an' h wersens oop as we mowt. — Owd Roä 112
Happy (See also **'Appy, Thrice-happy**) Christians with h countenances— — Supp. Confessions 20
that h morn When angels spake to men aloud, — " 24
Thrice h state again to be The trustful infant — " 40
and the h blossoming shore? — Sea-Fairies 8
Who can light on as h a shore All the world o'er, — " 40
O h thou that liest low, — Oriana 84
Oh! what a h life were mine — The Merman 37
O BRIDESMAID, ere the h knot was tied, — Bridesmaid 1
A h bridesmaid makes a h bride.' — " 4
'O h bridesmaid, make a h bride.' (repeat) — " 8, 14
'Waiting to strive a h strife, — Two Voices 130
from a h place God's glory smote him on the face.' — " 224
Have I not found a h earth? — Miller's D. 25
She wish'd me h, but she thought — " 139
Rest in a h place and quiet seats — Œnone 131
O h tears, and how unlike to these! O h Heaven, how canst thou see my face? O h earth, how canst thou bear my weight? — " 235
Pass by the h souls, that love to live: — " 240
Lest their shrill h laughter come to me — " 258
h stars above them seem to brighten as they pass; — May Queen 34
many a worthier than I, would make him h yet. — " Con. 46
h fair with orchard-lawns And bowery hollows — M. d'Arthur 262
sweeter than the dream Dream'd by a h man, — Gardener's D. 72
shook his song together as he near'd His h home, — " 92
Ah, h shade—and still went wavering down, — " 132
A thought would fill my eyes with h dew; — " 197
Made me most h, faltering, — " 235
Might have been h: but what lot is pure? — Walk. to the Mail 97
do not think yourself alone Of all men h. — Edwin Morris 78
may rest Some h future day. — Talking Oak 252
Live h; tend thy flowers; be tended by My blessing! — Love and Duty 87
H days Roll onward, leading up the golden year. 'Fly, h h sails, and bear the Press; Fly h with the mission of the Cross; — Golden Year 40
Old writers push'd the h season back,— — " 66
It may be we shall touch the H Isles, — Ulysses 63
Of h men that have the power to die, — Tithonus 70
Is it well to wish thee h?— — Locksley Hall 43
Overlive it—lower yet—be h! — " 97
mellow moons and h skies, — " 159
Clothes and reclothes the h plains, — Day-Dm., Sleep. P. 2
The h princess follow'd him. — " Depart. 8
'O eyes long laid in h sleep!' 'O h sleep, that lightly fled!' 'O h kiss, that woke thy sleep!' — " 17
when Adam first Embraced his Eve in h hour, — L'Envoi 42
Such h intonation, — Amphion 18
With twisted quirks and h hits, — Will Water. 189
O hundred shores of h climes, — The Voyage 49
The h winds upon her play'd, — Sir L. and Q. G. 38
MOVE eastward, h earth, and leave Yon orange sunset — Move eastward 1
O, h planet, eastward go; — " 4
And round again to h night. — " 12
seven h years, Seven h years of health and competence, — Enoch Arden 81
Forward she started with a h cry, — " 151
We might be still as h as God grants — " 416
'he is h, he is singing Hosanna in the highest: — " 502
Whereof the h people strowing cried — " 505
In those far-off seven h years were born; — " 686

Happy (continued) And know that she is h.' — Enoch Arden 719
sweet forget-me-nots That grow for h lovers. — The Brook 173
'Too h, fresh and fair, Too fresh and fair — " 217
And you are h: let her parents be.' — Aylmer's Field 366
sown With h faces and with holiday. — Princess, Pro. 56
and read My sickness down to h dreams? — " ii 253
In looking on the h Autumn-fields, — " iv 42
And h warriors, and immortal names, — " vi 93
but at the h word 'he lives' My father stoop'd, — " 128
And at the h lovers heart in heart— — " vii 108
Fill'd thro' and thro' with Love, a h sleep. — " 172
And find him; by the h threshold, he, — " 200
H he With such a mother! — " 327
turning saw The h valleys, half in light, — " Con. 41
the h crowd, The sport half-science, — " 75
peacemaker fly To h havens under all the sky, — Ode Inter. Exhib. 35
Break, h land, into earlier flowers! — W. to Alexandra 10
The sea-kings' daughter as h as fair, — " 26
But marry me out of hand: we two shall be h still.' — Grandmother 52
Never jealous—not he: we had many a h year; — " 71
And h has been my life; but I would not live it again. — " 98
But distant colour, h hamlet, — The Daisy 27
Many and many a h year. — To F. D. Maurice 48
'The King is h In child and wife; — The Victim 25
But the Priest was h, His victim won: — " 61
And the Priest was h, — " 73
A h lover who has come To look on her that loves — In Mem. viii 1
The murmur of a h Pan: — " xxiii 12
Rise, h morn, rise, holy morn, — " xxx 29
Her early Heaven, her h views; — " xxxiii 6
How fares it with the h dead? — " xliv 1
And grasps the skirts of h chance, — " lxiv 6
There flutters up a h thought, — " lxv 7
sun by sun the h days Descend below the golden hills — " lxxxiv 27
A guest, or h sister, sung, — " lxxxix 26
Ring, h bells, across the snow: — " cvi 6
h birds, that change their sky To build and brood; — " cxv 15
For days of h commune dead; — " cxvi 14
While thou, dear spirit, h star, — " cxxvii 18
O h hour, and happier hours Await them. — " Con. 65
O h hour, behold the bride With him to whom — " 69
We wish them store of h days. — " 84
To spangle all the h shores By which they rest, — " 120
In the h morning of life and of May, — Maud I v 7
Go not, h day, (repeat) — " xvii 1, 3
Pass the h news, Blush it thro' the West; — " 15
And you fair stars that crown a h day — " xviii 30
It seems that I am h, that to me A livelier emerald — " 50
Beat, h stars, timing with things below, — " 81
The delight of h laughter, — " II iv 29
Would the h spirit descend, — " 81
'And gladly given again this h morn. — Marr. of Geraint 691
But o'er her meek eyes came a h mist — Geraint and E. 769
Tho' pale, yet h, ask'd her not a word, — " 880
till be crown'd A h life with a fair death, — " 968
'I hold them h, so they died for love: — Balin and Balan 581
What said the h sire? — Merlin and V. 710
And as it chanced they are h, being pure.' — " 745
But she was h enough and shook it off, — Lancelot and E. 784
Came on her brother with a h face — " 791
So that would make you h: furthermore, — " 959
As h as when we dwelt among the woods, — " 1036
make me h, making them An armlet for the roundest arm — " 1182
'In h time behold our pilot-star! — Pelleas and E. 63
'O h world,' thought Pelleas, 'all, meseems, Are h; — " 136
Be h in thy fair Queen as I in mine.' — Last Tournament 204
Crown'd warrant had we for the crowning sin That made us h: — " 577
the child of one I honour'd, h, dead before thy shame? — Guinevere 423
h, fair with orchard-lawns And bowery hollows — Pass. of Arthur 430
And he was h that he saw it not; — Lover's Tale i 192
O day which did enwomb that h hour, — " 485
It was so h an hour, so sweet a place, — " 558
The loved, the lover, the h Lionel, — " 654
Why was I To cross between their h star and them? — " 730

Happy (*continued*) Him who loving made The *h* and the unhappy love, *Lover's Tale i* 753
I was *h* when I was with him, *First Quarrel* 11
Often I seem'd unhappy, and often as *h* too, „ 31
He means me I'm sure to be *h* with Willy, *Rizpah* 76
Here's to your *h* union with my child! *Sister's (E. and E.)* 68
We left her, *h* each in each, and then, „ 219
Pour'd in on all those *h* naked isles— *Columbus* 174
Live, and be *h* in thyself, and serve This mortal race *De Prof., Two G.* 15
So—your *h* suit was blasted— *Locksley H., Sixty* 5
H children in a sunbeam sitting on the ribs of wreck. „ 14
Poet of the *h* Tityrus piping underneath *To Virgil* 13
the child Is *h*—ev'n in leaving *her*! *Prin. Beatrice* 12
We planted both together, *h* in our marriage morn? *Happy* 14
I am *h*, *h*. Kiss me. „ 107
Sing like a bird and be *h*, *Parnassus* 14
'Here again, here, here, here, *h* year! *The Throstle* 13
Him, *h* to be chosen Judge of Gods, *Death of Œnone* 16
while we dwelt Together in this valley—*h* then—Too *h* had I died within thine arms, „ 30
The morning light of *h* marriage broke „ 102
O *h* he, and fit to live, On whom a *h* home has power *The Wanderer* 9
Hapt *H* in this isle, since Up the East *Batt. of Brunanburh* 116
Harangue Lady Psyche will *h* The fresh arrivals *Princess ii* 95
Harass'd the thought Haunted and *h* him, *Enoch Arden* 720
Vext with lawyers and *h* with debt: *Maud I xix* 22
h by the frights Of my first crew, *Columbus* 67
Harbour and clambering on a mast In *h*, *Enoch Arden* 106
Ev'n in that *h* whence he sail'd before. „ 666
to seek If any golden *h* be for men *Pref. Son. 19th Cent.* 13
Desolate offing, sailorless *h's*, *Vastness* 14
Harbourage But wilt thou yield this damsel *h*?' *Gareth and L.* 834
But an this lord will yield us *h*, Well.' „ 844
Where can I get me *h* for the night? *Marr. of Geraint* 281
H? truth, good truth, I know not, „ 290
'O friend, I seek a *h* for the night.' „ 299
Harbour-bar Shot o'er the seething *h-b*, *Sailor Boy* 2
Harbour-buoy *h-b*, Sole star of phosphorescence *Audley Court* 86
Harbour-mouth Yet waft me from the *h-m*, *You ask me, why, etc.* 25
capes and islands, Many a *h-m*, *The Captain* 22
painted buoy That tosses at the *h-m*; *The Voyage* 2
Hard It seem'd so *h* at first, mother, to leave the blessed sun, And now it seems as *h* to stay, *May Queen, Con.* 9
The Gods are *h* to reconcile: *Lotos-Eaters, C. S.* 81
'Tis *h* to settle order once again. „ 82
How *h* he breathes! over the snow I heard *D. of the O. Year* 37
A saying, *h* to shape in act; *Love thou thy land* 49
But vague in vapour, *h* to mark; „ 62
The blast was *h* and harder. *The Goose* 50
For how *h* it seem'd to me, When eyes, *Love and Duty* 35
If the sense is *h* To alien ears, „ 51
H is my doom and thine: „ 54
'Your riddle is *h* to read.' *Lady Clare* 76
H coils of cordage, swarthy fishing-nets, *Enoch Arden* 17
was it *h* to take The helpless life „ 556
'Too *h* to bear! why did they take me „ 781
O *h*, when love and duty clash! *Princess ii* 293
all those *h* things That Sheba came to ask of Solomon.' „ 345
'O *h* task,' he cried; 'No fighting shadows here! „ *iii* 124
No rock so *h* but that a little wave „ 154
they will take her, they will make her *h*, „ *v* 90
Thus the *h* old King: I took my leave, „ 467
no tenderness—Too *h*, too cruel: „ 516
These men are *h* upon us as of old, „ *vi* 198
the woman is so *h* Upon the woman. „ 222
And call her *h* and cold which seem'd a truth: „ *vii* 98
you think I am *h* and cold; *Grandmother* 17
be jealous and *h* and unkind.' „ 54
I found, tho' crush'd to *h* and dry, *The Daisy* 97
O little bard, is your lot so *h*, *Spiteful Letter* 5
H, *h*, *h* is it, only not to tumble, *Hendecasyllabics* 13
'It will be *h*,' they say, 'to find *In Mem. xx* 7
The words were *h* to understand. „ *lxix* 20
'Tis *h* for thee to fathom this; „ *lxxxv* 90

Hard (*continued*) The *h* heir strides about their lands, *In Mem. xc* 15
how *h* to frame In matter-moulded forms „ *xcv* 45
'A *h* one, or a hundred, so I go. *Gareth and L.* 149
h by here is one will overthrow And slay thee: „ 896
'Old damsel, old and *h*, Old, „ 1105
blew A *h* and deadly note upon the horn. „ 1111
Then not to give you warning, that seems *h*; *Geraint and E.* 422
How *h* you look and how denyingly! *Merlin and V.* 338
May this *h* earth cleave to the Nadir hell „ 349
(Brother, the King was *h* upon his knights) *Holy Grail* 299
house of ours Where all the brethren are so *h*, „ 618
H was the frost in the field, *First Quarrel* 39
I felt that my heart was *h*, „ 76
So I knew my heart was *h*, „ 78
But say nothing *h* of my boy, *Rizpah* 22
you are just as *h* as a stone. „ 80
they tell me that the world is *h*, and harsh of mind, But can it be so *h*, so harsh, *The Flight* 101
come a witness soon *H* to be confuted, *Forlorn* 26
He gript it so *h* by the throat that the boy *Bandit's Death* 28
That God would move And strike the *h*, *h* rock, *Supp. Confessions* 116
'*H* task, to pluck resolve,' I cried, *Two Voices* 118
he and I Had once *h* words, and parted, *Dora* 18
and thought *H* things of Dora. „ 58
for you Will make him *h*, „ 153
H wood I am, and wrinkled rind, *Talking Oak* 171
bade him cry, with sound of trumpet, all The *h* condition; *Godiva* 37
The *h* brands shiver on the steel, *Sir Galahad* 6
Small were his gains, and *h* his work; *Sea Dreams* 8
last Gript my hand *h*, and with God-bless-you went. „ 160
I found a *h* friend in his loose accounts, A loose one in the *h* grip of his hand, „ 162
For us, we will not spare the tyrant one *h* word. *Third of Feb.* 42
That a calamity *h* to be borne? *Maud I xiii* 3
a *h* mechanic ghost That never came from on high „ *II ii* 34
Yniol with that *h* message went; *Marr. of Geraint* 763
The *h* earth shake, and a low thunder of arms. *Lancelot and E.* 460
As *h* and still as is the face that men „ 1251
over *h* and soft, striking the sod From out the soft, the spark from off the *h*, *Pelleas and E.* 498
h his eyes; harder his heart Seem'd; „ 512
Modred thought, 'The time is *h* at hand.' „ 610
H on that helm which many a heathen sword *Pass. of Arthur* 166
clomb The last *h* footstep of that iron crag; „ 447
They found her beating the *h* Protestant doors. *Sisters (E. and E.)* 240
I find *h* rocks, *h* life, *h* cheer, or none, *Sir J. Oldcastle* 6
Vailing a sudden eyelid with his *h* 'Dim Saesneg' „ 20
Priests Who fear the king's *h* common-sense „ 66
harlot draws his clerks Into the suburb—their *h* celibacy, „ 107
These *h* memorials of our truth to Spain *Columbus* 196
H was his hand-play, *Batt. of Brunanburh* 44
Beneath a *h* Arabian moon And alien stars. *To Marq. of Dufferin* 45
Seem'd nobler than their *h* Eternities. *Demeter and P.* 107
An' 'e cotch'd howd *h* o' my hairm, *Owd Roä* 58
she loves her own *h* self, Her firm will, *The Ring* 292
She clung to me with such a *h* embrace, „ 435
H Romans brawling of their monstrous games; *St. Telemachus* 40
And the *h* blue eyes have it still, *Charity* 10
Hard (heard) I *h* his Riverence say, *Tomorrow* 69
tould yer Honour whativer I *h* an' seen, „ 97
Hard-breathing cast himself Down on a bench, *h-b*. *Pelleas and E.* 592
Harden watch The sandy footprint *h* into stone.' *Princess iii* 271
Harden'd (*See also* **Mattock-harden'd, War-harden'd**)
only wrapt in *h* skins That fit him like his own; *Gareth and L.* 1093
His arms are old, he trusts the *h* skin— „ 1139
But lash'd in vain against the *h* skin, „ 1143
Harder The blast was hard and *h*. *The Goose* 50
H the times were, and the hands of power *Aylmer's Field* 452
the according hearts of men Seem'd *h* too; „ 454
Enid answer'd, *h* to be moved Than hardest tyrants *Geraint and E.* 694
but felt his eyes *H* and drier than a fountain bed *Pelleas and E.* 507
hard his eyes; *h* his heart Seem'd; „ 512
But a lie which is part a truth is a *h* matter to fight. *Grandmother* 32
Tho' carved in *h* stone— *Epilogue* 59
Hardest Than *h* tyrants in their day of power, *Geraint and E.* 695

Hate (verb) (*continued*) he thought—'What, if she *h* me now? *Last Tournament* 496
thou stridest thro' his halls Who *h's* thee, „ 518
Because he *h's* thee even more than fears; „ 533
I should *h* thee more than love.' „ 600
With what a hate the people and the King Must *h* me,' *Guinevere* 158
but who *h's* thee, he that brought The heathen *Pass. of Arthur* 151
I *h* her—an' I *h* you!' *First Quarrel* 71
Yet loves and *h's* with mortal hates and loves, *Tiresias* 23
I *h* the black negation of the bier, *Ancient Sage* 204
morning brings the day I *h* and fear; *The Flight* 2
'Kill your enemy, for you *h* him,' *Locksley H., Sixty* 94
I *h* the rancour of their castes and creeds, *Akbar's Dream* 65

Hated (adj. and part.) this world's curse,—beloved but *h*— *Love and Duty* 47
(for Arthur's Knights Were *h* strangers in the hall) *Balin and Balan* 352
with *h* warmth of apprehensiveness. *Lover's Tale i* 632
Her presence, *h* both of Gods and men. *Œnone* 229
Thro' madness, *h* by the wise, *Love and Duty* 7

Hated (verb) (*See also* **Haäted**) I *h* him with the hate of hell, *The Sisters* 22
And death and life she *h* equally, *Palace of Art* 265
But they *h* his oppression, *The Captain* 9
Then they look'd at him they *h*, „ 37
H him with a momentary hate. *Aylmer's Field* 211
Men *h* learned women: *Princess ii* 466
They *h* banter, wish'd for something real, „ *Con.* 18
many *h* Uther for the sake Of Gorlöis. *Com. of Arthur* 220
And *h* this fair world and all therein, „ 344
They *h* her, who took no thought of them, *Geraint and E.* 639
She *h* all the knights, and heard in thought *Merlin and V.* 150
and she *h* all who pledged. *Lancelot and E.* 744
wail'd and wept, and *h* mine own self, *Holy Grail* 609
'You said that you *h* me, Ellen, *First Quarrel* 79
And we *h* the beautiful Isle, *V. of Maeldune* 21
And we *h* the Flowering Isle, as we *h* the isle that was mute, „ 52
Till we *h* the Bounteous Isle „ 92
Troubled the track of the host that we *h*, *Batt. of Brunanburh* 40
he learnt that I *h* the ring I wore, *The Wreck* 57
tho' I think I *h* him less, *Bandit's Death* 17

Hateful *H* is the dark-blue sky, *Lotos-Eaters, C. S.* 39
Your falsehood and yourself are *h* to us: *Princess iv* 545
Horrible, *h*, monstrous, not to be told; *Maud III vi* 41
And this forgetfulness was *h* to her. *Marr. of Geraint* 55
Last night I wasted *h* hours *Fatima* 8
Long, ere the *h* crow shall tread The corners *Will Water.* 235
and when the beauteous *h* isle Return'd upon him, *Enoch Arden* 617
all the *h* fires Of torment, *Demeter and P.* 151
This house with all its *h* needs no cleaner than the beast, *Happy* 32
in the heart of this most ancient realm A *h* voice be utter'd, *Prog. of Spring* 103

Hater What room is left for a *h*? *Spiteful Letter* 14
Love your enemy, bless your *h's*, *Locksley H., Sixty* 85

Hating *H* to wander out on earth, *Supp. Confessions* 57
h to hark The humming of the drowsy pulpit-drone *To J. M. K.* 9
went *H* his own lean heart and miserable. *Aylmer's Field* 526
all-shamed, *h* the life He gave me, *Geraint and E.* 852

Hatred *h* of her weakness, blent with shame. *Princess vii* 30
Shall fears and jealous *h's* flame again? *W. to Marie Alex.* 41
No more of *h* than in Heaven itself, *Balin and Balan* 151
My soul, I felt my *h* for my Mark Quicken *Last Tournament* 519
Love pledge *H* in her bitter draughts, *Lover's Tale i* 776
National *h's* of whole generations, *Vastness* 25
Dark no more with human *h's* *Faith* 8

Hattics (attics) An' Hetty wur weak i' the *h*, *Village Wife* 101

Hauberk shield of Balan prick'd The *h* to the flesh; *Balin and Balan* 560
Casques were crack'd and *h's* hack'd *The Tourney* 7

Haughtier She paused, and added with a *h* smile *Princess iii* 225

Haughtiest Lady Blanche alone Of faded form and *h* lineaments, „ *ii* 448
Imperious, and of *h* lineaments. *Marr. of Geraint* 190

Haughty She, flashing forth a *h* smile, began: *D. of F. Women* 129
My *h* jousts, and took a paramour; *Geraint and E.* 832
but she, *h*, ev'n to him, Lancelot; *Last Tournament* 562

Haughty (*continued*) *H* war-workers who Harried the Welshman, *Batt. of Brunanburh* 121

Haunch On his *h'es* rose the steed, *Princess v* 493

Haunt (s) The *h's* of memory echo not. *Two Voices* 369
A *h* of ancient Peace. *Palace of Art* 88
battenest by the greasy gleam In *h's* of hungry sinners, *Will Water.* 222
A *h* of brawling seamen once, *Enoch Arden* 697
I come from *h's* of coot and hern, *The Brook* 23
A frequent *h* of Edith, *Aylmer's Field* 148
And flood the *h's* of hern and crake; *In Mem. ci* 14
The feeble soul, a *h* of fears, „ *cx* 3
cells of madness, *h's* of horror and fear, *Maud III vi* 2
in lonely *h's* Would scratch a ragged oval *Gareth and L.* 533
but for those large eyes, the *h's* of scorn, *Pelleas and E.* 75
there In *h's* of jungle-poison'd air *To Marq. of Dufferin* 31

Haunt (verb) A SPIRIT *h's* the year's last hours *A Spirit haunts* 1
than whatever Oread *h* The knolls of Ida, *Œnone* 74
Whose odours *h* my dreams; *Sir Galahad* 68
Will *h* the vacant cup: *Will Water.* 172
Like flies that *h* a wound, or deer, *Aylmer's Field* 571
Gods, who *h* The lucid interspace of world *Lucretius* 104
h About the moulder'd lodges of the Past *Princess iv* 62
They *h* the silence of the breast, *In Mem. xciv* 9
the filmy shapes That *h* the dusk, „ *xcv* 11
Evil *h's* The birth, the bridal; „ *xcviii* 13
'Look, He *h's* me—I cannot breathe— *Pelleas and E.* 227
all that *h's* the waste and wild Mourn, *Pass. of Arthur* 48
those three words would *h* him when a boy, *Far—far—away* 8
anchorite Would *h* the desolated fane, *St. Telemachus* 13

Haunted (adj. and part.) (*See also* **Bandit-haunted, Martin-haunted, Satan-haunted**) From old well-heads of *h* rills, *Eleänore* 16
Heard by the watcher in a *h* house, *Guinevere* 73
Was *h* with a jolly ghost, that shook The curtains, *Walk. to the Mail* 36
and a hazelwood, By autumn nutters *h*, *Enoch Arden* 8
And *h* by the wrangling daw; *In Mem. c* 12
h by the starry head Of her whose gentle will *Maud I xviii* 22

Haunted (verb) It *h* me, the morning long, *Miller's D.* 69
the thought *H* and harass'd him, *Enoch Arden* 720
still *H* us like her ghost; *Sisters (E. and E.)* 247
ghastlier face than ever has *h* a grave by night, *The Wreck* 8
she that had *h* his pathway still, *Dead Prophet* 61

Haunting (adj. and part.) (*See also* **Roof-haunting**) phantoms moved Before him *h* him, or he himself Moved *h* people, *Enoch Arden* 603
a tender Christian hope, *H* a holy text, *Sea Dreams* 42
My *h* sense of hollow shows: *Princess vii* 349
ever *h* round the palm A lusty youth, *Gareth and L.* 47
but shatter'd nerve, Yet *h* Julian, *Lover's Tale iv* 106
This *h* whisper makes me faint, *In Mem. lxxxi* 7
Brute that is walking and *h* us yet, *The Dawn* 23

Haunting (s) No ghostly *h's* like his Highness. *Princess ii* 411
And out of *h's* of my spoken love, „ *vii* 109

Havelock (Gen. Sir Henry) *H* baffled, or beaten, or butcher'd *Def. of Lucknow* 91
Outram and *H* breaking their way through „ 96
H's glorious Highlanders answer with conquering cheers, „ 99
Blessing the wholesome white faces of *H's* good fusileers, „ 101
Saved by the valour of *H*, „ 104

Haven From many an inland town and *h* large, *Œnone* 117
From *h's* hid in fairy bowers, *The Voyage* 54
ships go on To their *h* under the hill; *Break, break, etc.* 10
northward of the narrow port Open'd a larger *h*: *Enoch Arden* 103
Till silent in her oriental *h*. „ 537
Where either *h* open'd on the deeps, „ 671
To rush abroad all round the little *h*, „ 867
That all the houses in the *h* rang. „ 911
while I breathed in sight of *h*, he, Poor fellow, *The Brook* 157
peacemaker fly To happy *h's* under all the sky, *Ode Inter. Exhib.* 35
Had built the King his *h's*, *Merlin and V.* 168
You from the *h* Under the sea-cliff, *Merlin and the G.* 2
O young Mariner, Down to the *h*, „ 124

Havock-Havoc wrought Such waste and *havock* *Aylmer's Field* 640
Made *havock* among those tender cells, *Lucretius* 22
So fierce a gale made *havoc* here of late *Holy Grail* 729

Haw Nor hoary knoll of ash and *h* *In Mem. c* 9

Hawa-i-ee (one of the Sandwich Islands) and freed the people Of *H*! *Kapiolani* 7
be mingled with either on *H*. „ 18
and drove the demon from *H*. „ 33
Hawk (s) (*See also* **Sparrow-hawk, War-hawk**) My gay young *h*, my Rosalind: *Rosalind* 34
The wild *h* stood with the down on his beak, *Poet's Song* 11
Lies the *h's* cast, the mole has made his run, *Aylmer's Field* 849
And pastime both of *h* and hound, *Marr. of Geraint* 711
Fluttering the *h's* of this crown-lusting line— *Sir J. Oldcastle* 57
Hawk (verb) As when a hawker *h's* his wares. *The Blackbird* 20
they ride away—to *h* For waterfowl. *Merlin and V.* 107
Hawkard (awkward) An' a haxin' ma *h* questions, *Spinster's S's.* 90
Hawker As when a *h* hawks his wares. *The Blackbird* 20
This broad-brimm'd *h* of holy things, *Maud I x* 41
Hawk-eye Your *h-e's* are keen and bright, *Rosalind* 25
and a cheek of apple-blossom, *H-e's*; *Gareth and L.* 590
Hawking (*See also* **A-hawking**) Now *h* at Geology and schism; *The Epic* 16
Hawk-mad Speak, if ye be not like the rest, *h-m*, *Marr. of Geraint* 280
Hawl (awl) poonch'd my 'and wi' the *h*, *North. Cobbler* 78
Hawmin' (lounging) an' *h* about i' the laïnes, „ 24
Hawthorn (adj.) bury me, my mother, just beneath the *h* shade, *May Queen, N. Y's. E.* 29
that new life that gems the *h* line; *Prog. of Spring* 36
Hawthorn (s) Beneath the *h* on the green *May Queen, N. Y's. E.* 10
Hax'd (asked) An' they hallus paäid what I *h*, *Village Wife* 115
When summun 'ed *h* fur a son, *Owd Roä* 95
Haxin' (asking) An' a *h* ma hawkard questions, *Spinster's S's.* 90
Hay (*See also* **Haäy**) And rarely smells the new-mown *h*, *The Owl i* 9
Stuff his ribs with mouldy *h*. *Vision of Sin* 66
Haze (*See also* **Sea-haze**) Spread the light *h* along the river-shores, *Gardener's D.* 264
Purple gauzes, golden *h's*, *Vision of Sin* 31
thro' the dripping *h* The dead weight *Enoch Arden* 677
'This world was once a fluid *h* of light, *Princess ii* 116
And is it that the *h* of grief *In Mem. xxiv* 9
The silvery *h* of summer drawn; „ *xcv* 4
mingled with the *h* And made it thicker; *Com. of Arthur* 435
his dream was changed, the *h* Descended, „ 441
Far in the moonlit *h* among the hills, *Pass. of Arthur* 42
find or feel a way Thro' this blind *h*, „ 76
heated *h* to magnify The charm of Edith— *Sisters (E. and E.)* 129
Haze-hidden to a height, the peak *H-h*, *Com. of Arthur* 430
Hazel (adj.) about the may-pole and in the *h* copse, *May Queen, N. Y's. E.* 11
deeply dawning in the dark of *h* eyes— *Locksley Hall* 28
but as lissome as a *h* wand; *The Brook* 70
I slide by *h* covers; „ 171
Hazel (s) The thick-set *h* dies; *Will Water.* 234
great and small, Went nutting to the *h's*. *Enoch Arden* 64
Down thro' the whitening *h's* made a plunge „ 379
In native *h's* tassel-hung.' *In Mem. cii* 12
Hazel-tree on the bridge beneath the *h-t*? *May Queen* 14
Hazelwood a *h*, By autumn nutters haunted, *Enoch Arden* 7
Hazy Across a *h* glimmer of the west, *Gardener's D.* 219
Far over the blue tarns and *h* seas, *Gareth and L.* 499
Head (Edward) *See* **Edward Head**
Head (s) (*See also* **Boat-head, Cradle-head, Death's-head, 'Ead, Fountain-head, Hattics, Heäd, Lady's-head, Lance-head, Mast-head, Shock-head, Well-heads**)
Madonna-wise on either side her *h*; *Isabel* 6
Revered Isabel, the crown and *h*, „ 10
Thou wilt never raise thine *h* *A Dirge* 19
from *h* to tail Came out clear plates *Two Voices* 11
Dominion in the *h* and breast.' „ 21
'The simple senses crown'd his *h*: „ 277
Beat time to nothing in my *h* *Miller's D.* 67
Upon my lap he laid his *h*: *The Sisters* 17
I curl'd and comb'd his comely *h*, „ 31
The *h's* and crowns of kings; *Palace of Art* 152
You put strange memories in my *h*. *L. C. V. de Vere* 26
With your feet above my *h* *May Queen, N. Y's. E.* 32
on his kindly heart and on his silver *h*! „ *Con.* 15
one that from a casement leans his *h*, *D. of F. Women* 246

Head (s) (*continued*) Her murder'd father's *h*, *D. of F. Women* 267
Sleep full of rest from *h* to feet; *To J. S.* 75
Where faction seldom gathers *h*, *You ask me, why, etc.*, 13
And heap their ashes on the *h*; *Love thou thy land* 70
As *h* and heels upon the floor They flounder'd *The Goose* 37
laid his *h* upon her lap, *M. d'Arthur* 208
And May with me from *h* to heel. *Gardener's D.* 81
She bow'd down her *h*, Remembering the day *Dora* 105
Jack, turn the horses' *h's* and home again.' *Walk. to the Mail* 46
my stiff spine can hold my weary *h*, *St. S. Stylites* 43
She sank her *h* upon her arm *Talking Oak* 207
a sunny fleck, From *h* to ancle fine, „ 224
Dropt dews upon her golden *h*, „ 227
shook her *h*, And shower'd the rippled ringlets to her knee; *Godiva* 46
wide-mouth'd *h's* upon the spout Had cunning eyes „ 56
Were shrivell'd into darkness in his *h*, „ 70
This proverb flashes thro' his *h*, *Day-Dm., Arrival* 15
You shake your *h*. A random string „ *L'Envoi* 1
All-graceful *h*, so richly curl'd, „ 38
power to turn This wheel within my *h*, *Will Water.* 84
Live long, ere from thy topmost *h* „ 233
Live long, nor feel in *h* or chest „ 237
And lay your hand upon my *h*, *Lady Clare* 55
Dropt her *h* in the maiden's hand, „ 63
To trample round my fallen *h*, *Come not, when, etc.* 3
Then raised her *h* with lips compress, *The Letters* 19
I saw within my *h* A gray and gap-tooth'd man *Vision of Sin* 59
In her left a human *h*. „ 138
Hollow hearts and empty *h's*! „ 174
Then calling down a blessing on his *h* *Enoch Arden* 327
over Enoch's early-silvering *h* „ 622
He, shaking his gray *h* pathetically, „ 714
Held his *h* high, and cared for no man, „ 848
'His *h* is low, and no man cares for him. „ 850
As when she laid her *h* beside my own. „ 881
those that held their *h's* above the crowd, *The Brook* 10
and holds her *h* to other stars, „ 195
A tonsured *h* in middle age forlorn, „ 200
Whose eyes from under a pyramidal *h* *Aylmer's Field* 20
For heart, I think, help'd *h*: „ 475
made Still paler the pale *h* of him, „ 623
fork'd Of the near storm, and aiming at his *h*, „ 727
The *h's* of chiefs and princes fall so fast, „ 763
his own *h* Began to droop, to fall; „ 834
ask'd; but not a word; she shook her *h*. *Sea Dreams* 116
Like her, he shook his *h*. „ 148
one that arm'd Her own fair *h*, *Princess, Pro.* 33
moved the multitude, a thousand *h's*: „ 57
above their *h's* I saw The feudal warrior lady-clad; „ 118
'Where,' Ask'd Walter, patting Lilia's *h* „ 125
o'er his *h* Uranian Venus hung, „ *i* 243
such eyes were in her *h*, And so much grace and power, „ *ii* 37
some said their *h's* were less: Some men's were small; „ 147
'everywhere Two *h's* in council, „ 173
axelike edge unturnable, our *H*, The Princess.' „ 203
O by the bright *h* of my little niece, „ 276
The *H* of all the golden-shafted firm, „ 405
the Muses' *h's* were touch'd Above the darkness „ *iii* 21
says the Princess should have been the *H*, „ 34
The *h* and heart of all our fair she-world, „ 163
He ceasing, came a message from the *H*. „ 168
Among her maidens, higher by the *h*, „ 179
spoke and turn'd her sumptuous *h* with eyes, „ *iv* 152
'The *H*, the *H*, the Princess, O the *H*!' „ 176
underneath The *h* of Holofernes peep'd and saw. „ 227
And partly that you were my civil *h*, „ 306
seal'd dispatches which the *H* Took half-amazed, „ 379
You have our son: touch not a hair of his *h*: „ 407
after-beauty makes Such *h* from act to act, „ 452
gems and gemlike eyes, And gold and golden *h's*; „ 481
Not peace she look'd, the *H*: „ 490
'What fear ye, brawlers? am not I your *H*? „ 498
all one rag, disprinced from *h* to heel. „ *v* 30
Like some sweet sculpture draped from *h* to foot, „ 57
And at her *h* a follower of the camp, „ 60

Head (s) (*continued*) 'Lift up your *h*, sweet sister: *Princess v* 64
in the furrow broke the ploughman's *h*, „ 221
with each light air On our mail'd *h's*: „ 245
Man with the *h* and woman with the heart: „ 449
felt it sound and whole from *h* to foot, „ *vi* 211
Her *h* a little bent; „ 269
Lifting his grim *h* from my wounds. „ 272
ask for him Of your great *h*— „ 314
That o'er the statues leapt from *h* to *h*, „ 366
here and there the small bright *h*, A light of healing, „ *vii* 58
fear'd To incense the *H* once more; „ 77
The gravest citizen seems to lose his *h*, „ *Con.* 59
Among six boys, *h* under *h*, „ 83
O good gray *h* which all men knew, *Ode on Well.* 35
Hadn't a *h* to manage, and drank himself *Grandmother* 6
we saw the glisten Of ice, far up on a mountain *h*. *The Daisy* 36
And in my *h*, for half the day, „ 74
the singer shaking his curly *h* Turn'd as he sat, *The Islet* 6
Take the hoary Roman *h* and shatter it, *Boädicea* 65
Thy fibres net the dreamless *h*, *In Mem. ii* 3
save Thy sailor—while thy *h* is bow'd, „ *vi* 14
Come then, pure hands, and bear the *h* „ *xviii* 9
The Shadow cloak'd from *h* to foot, „ *xxiii* 4
And dippest toward the dreamless *h*, „ *xxxix* 5
God shut the doorways of his *h*. „ *xliv* 4
When in the down I sink my *h*, „ *lxviii* 1
The *h* hath miss'd an earthly wreath: „ *lxxiii* 6
How pure at heart and sound in *h*, „ *xciv* 1
Their pensive tablets round her *h*, „ *Con.* 51
And catch at every mountain *h*, „ 114
vitriol madness flushes up in the ruffian's *h*, *Maud I i* 37
I bow'd to her father, the wrinkled *h* of the race? „ *iv* 13
walks with his *h* in a cloud of poisonous flies. „ 54
At the *h* of the village street, „ *vi* 10
plucks The slavish hat from the villager's *h*? „ *x* 4
Ah God, for a man with heart, *h*, hand, „ 60
Gorgonised me from *h* to foot With a stony British stare. „ *xiii* 21
crest Of a peacock, sits on her shining *h*, „ *xvi* 17
haunted by the starry *h* Of her whose gentle will „ *xviii* 22
Shaking her *h* at her son and sighing „ *xix* 24
Here at the *h* of a tinkling fall, „ *xxi* 6
little *h*, sunning over with curls, „ *xxii* 57
My bird with the shining *h*, „ *II iv* 45
And the wheels go over my *h*, „ *v* 4
tickle the maggot born in an empty *h*, „ 38
she is standing here at my *h*; „ 65
I will cry to the steps above my *h* „ 101
king and *h*, and made a realm, and reign'd. *Com. of Arthur* 19
there be many rumours on this *h*: „ 178
beheld Far over *h's* in that long-vaulted hall *Gareth and L.* 319
A *h* with kindling eyes above the throng, „ 646
wherewithal deck the boar's *h*? „ 1073
Sir Gareth's *h* prickled beneath his helm; „ 1397
the women who attired her *h*, To please her, *Marr. of Geraint* 62
Sank her sweet *h* upon her gentle breast; „ 527
her fair *h* in the dim-yellow light, „ 600
break perforce Upon a *h* so dear in thunder, *Geraint and E.* 13
Here comes a laggard hanging down his *h*, „ 60
'A craven; how he hangs his *h*.' „ 127
Held his *h* high, and thought himself a knight, „ 242
But one with arms to guard his *h* and yours, „ 427
There in the naked hall, propping his *h*, „ 581
found his own dear bride propping his *h*, „ 584
answer'd in low voice, her meek *h* yet Drooping, „ 640
The russet-bearded *h* roll'd on the floor. „ 729
And hung his *h*, and halted in reply, „ 811
wander'd from her own King's golden *h*, *Balin and Balan* 513
Or devil or man Guard thou thine *h*.' „ 553
Their *h's* should moulder on the city gates. *Merlin and V.* 594
Her godlike *h* crown'd with spiritual fire, „ 837
she turn'd away, she hung her *h*, „ 887
plunged, and caught, And set it on his *h*, *Lancelot and E.* 54
King Had on his cuirass worn our Lady's *H*, „ 294
Charge at the *h* of all his Table Round, „ 304
and the *h* Pierced thro' his side, „ 489

Head (s) (*continued*) 'Nay, by mine *h*,' said he, 'I lose it, *Lancelot and E.* 658
by mine *h* she knows his hiding-place.' „ 714
He raised his *h*, their eyes met and hers fell, „ 1312
And mine, as *h* of all our Table Round, „ 1328
when the knights had laid her comely *h* Low „ 1337
power To lay the sudden *h's* of violence flat, *Holy Grail* 310
And o'er his *h* the Holy Vessel hung (repeat) „ 512, 520
on my breviary with ease, Till my *h* swims; „ 546
The *h's* of all her people drew to me, „ 601
Make their last *h* like Satan in the North. *Last Tournament* 98
Working a tapestry, lifted up her *h*, „ 129
Lancelot, Round whose sick *h* all night, „ 138
fool, said Tristram, 'I would break thy *h*. „ 268
sank his *h* in mire, and slimed themselves: „ 471
full passionately, Her *h* upon her hands, *Guinevere* 181
Each with a beacon-star upon his *h*, „ 241
and bow'd her *h* nor spake. „ 310
Lest but a hair of this low *h* be harm'd. „ 447
The realms together under me, their *H*, „ 462
die To see thee, laying there thy golden *h*, „ 535
And in the darkness o'er her fallen *h*, „ 583
laid his *h* upon her lap, *Pass. of Arthur* 376
And dipping his *h* low beneath the verge, *Lover's Tale i* 509
Who with his *h* below the surface dropt „ 636
and dimly knows His *h* shall rise no more: „ 639
When the effect weigh'd seas upon my *h* „ 660
stoled from *h* to foot in flowing black; „ *ii* 85
in Julian's land They never nail a dumb *h* up in elm), „ *iv* 37
on her *h* A diamond circlet, „ 288
for the name at the *h* of my verse is thine. *To A. Tennyson* 6
the boy can hold up his *h*, *First Quarrel* 5
I must ha' been light i' my *h*— „ 82
was wounded again in the side and the *h*, *The Revenge* 68
A hand upon the *h* of either child, *Sisters (E. and E.)* 55
as far as the *h* of the stair, *In the Child. Hosp.* 43
To thee, dead wood, I bow not *h* nor knees. *Sir J. Oldcastle* 128
A thousand marks are set upon my *h*. „ 195
that ever swarm about And cloud the highest *h's*, *Columbus* 120
I swore I would strike off his *h*. *V. of Maeldune* 2
like a golden image was pollen'd from *h* to feet „ 49
Plunged *h* down in the sea, „ 82
around his *h* The glorious goddess wreath'd *Achilles over the T.* 4
from his *h* the splendour went to heaven. „ 14
o'er the great Peleion's *h* Burn'd, „ 28
Or on your *h* their rosy feet, *To E. Fitzgerald* 9
This wreath, above his honour'd *h*, *Tiresias* 213
and there Lost, *h* and heart, in the chances *The Wreck* 30
She shook her *h*, And the Motherless Mother kiss'd it, „ 61
The palsy wags his *h*; *Ancient Sage* 124
she lifted her *h*—'He said he would meet me *Tomorrow* 79
Tumble Nature heel o'er *h*, *Locksley H., Sixty* 135
'The stars with *h* sublime,' *Epilogue* 47
We needs must scan him from *h* to feet *Dead Prophet* 55
And robed thee in his day from *h* to feet— *Demeter and P.* 21
came On three gray *h's* beneath a gleaming rift. „ 83
Those gray *h's*, What meant they „ 129
came And saw you, shook her *h*, and patted yours, *The Ring* 313
Who yearn to lay my loving *h* *Happy* 26
slant his bolt from falling on your *h*— „ 81
leper like yourself, my love, from *h* to heel. „ 88
The coals of fire you heap upon my *h* *Romney's R.* 141
let me lean my *h* upon your breast. „ 154
And stand with my *h* in the zenith, *Parnassus* 6
stared upon By ghastlier than the Gorgon *h*, *Death of Œnone* 71
Then her *h* sank, she slept, „ 78
And muffling up her comely *h*, „ 104
The Christians own a Spiritual *H*; *Akbar's Dream* 153
You have set a price on his *h*: *Bandit's Death* 7
do you doubt me? Here is his *h*! „ 42
was a Scripture that rang thro' his *h*, *The Dreamer* 2
Edith bow'd her stately *h*, *The Tourney* 13
Edith Montfort bow'd her *h*, „ 15

Heäd (s) An' 'e kep his *h* hoop like a king, *Owd Roä* 9
An' the Heagle 'as hed two *h's* „ 25

Head (verb) Heaven *h's* the count of crimes — *D. of F. Women* 201
to *h* These rhymings with your name, — *Pro. to Gen. Hamley* 19
Head-blow Some old *h-b* not heeded in his youth — *Gareth and L.* 714
Headed (*See also* **Bare-headed, Brazen-headed, Clear-headed, Glassy-headed, Hoar-headed, Hoary-headed, Lean-headed, Light-headed, Many-headed, Seven-headed, Sharp-headed, White-headed**) arrows of his thoughts were *h* And wing'd with flame, — *The Poet* 11
In shining draperies, *h* like a star, — *Princess ii* 109
Head-foremost To drop *h-f* in the jaws — *In Mem. xxxiv* 15
Not plunge *h* from the mountain there, — *Lover's Tale iv* 41
all ablaze too plunging in the lake *H-f*— — *The Ring* 252
Head-heavy thus he fell *H-h*; — *Last Tournament* 468
Head-hunter *H-h's* and boats of Dahomey — *The Dawn* 5
Headland Flames, on the windy *h* flare! — *W. to Alexandra* 16
He saw them—*h* after *h* flame — *Guinevere* 243
Headless Fly twanging *h* arrows at the hearts, — *Princess ii* 402
Headlong and so hurl'd him *h* o'er the bridge — *Gareth and L.* 1153
The damsel's *h* error thro' the wood— — „ 1215
whose inroad nowhere scales Their *h* passes, — *Montenegro* 5
Headstone About the moss'd *h*: — *Claribel* 12
And at my *h* whisper low, — *My life is full* 24
Head-waiter O PLUMP *h-w* at The Cock, — *Will Water.* 1
H-w, honour'd by the guest Half-mused, — „ 73
And one became *h-w*. — „ 144
H-w of the chop-house here, — „ 209
Heagle (eagle) An' the *H* 'as hed two heäds — *Owd Roä* 25
Heal (*See also* **All-heal**) I will *h* me of my grievous wound.' — *M. d'Arthur* 264
I can *h* him. Power goes forth from me. — *St. S. Stylites* 145
h me with your pardon ere you go.' — *Princess iii* 65
To spill his blood and *h* the land: — *The Victim* 44
a harm no preacher can *h*; — *Maud I iv* 22
h the world of all their wickedness! — *Holy Grail* 94
and harm'd where she would *h*; — *Guinevere* 355
treat their loathsome hurts and *h* mine own; — „ 686
I will *h* me of my grievous wound.' — *Pass. of Arthur* 432
the hand that would help me, would *h* me— — *The Wreck* 56
love which once was mine, Help, *h* me. — *Death of Œnone* 46
'He, whom thou wouldst not *h*!' — „ 101
Heal'd To touch my body and be *h*, — *St. S. Stylites* 79
They say that they are *h*. — „ 146
He passes and is *h* and cannot die'— — *Gareth and L.* 503
he was *h* at once, By faith, of all his ills. — *Holy Grail* 55
and all the world be *h*.' — „ 128
that *h* Thy hurt and heart with unguent and caress— — *Last Tournament* 594
the wound that *would* not be *h*, — *Def. of Lucknow* 84
he *h* me with sorrow for evermore. — *The Wreck* 58
blind or deaf, and then Suddenly *h*, — *Ancient Sage* 176
Healing before we came, This craft of *h*. — *Princess iii* 320
A light of *h*, glanced about the couch, — „ *vii* 59
while Geraint lay *h* of his hurt, — *Geraint and E.* 931
Lancelot might have seen, The Holy Cup of *h*; — *Holy Grail* 655
And after *h* of his grievous wound — *Pass. of Arthur* 450
Health In glowing *h*, with boundless wealth, — *L. C. V. de Vere* 61
breathing *h* and peace upon her breast: — *Audley Court* 68
Seven happy years of *h* and competence, — *Enoch Arden* 82
Now seaward-bound for *h* they gain'd a coast, — *Sea Dreams* 16
Huge women blowzed with *h*, — *Princess iv* 279
I that have wasted here *h*, wealth, and time, — „ 352
poor men wealth, Than sick men *h*— — „ 460
As drinking *h* to bride and groom — *In Mem., Con.* 83
double *h*, The crowning cup, the three-times-three, — „ 103
One bloom of youth, *h*, beauty, — *Sisters (E. and E.)* 120
Had set the blossom of her *h* again, — „ 151
redder than rosiest *h* or than utterest shame, — *V. of Maeldune* 65
life without sun, without *h*, without hope, — *Despair* 7
an' I been Dhrinkin' yer *h* — *Tomorrow* 12
give me a thrifle to dhrink yer *h* in potheen. — „ 98
I Had been abroad for my poor *h* — *The Ring* 101
would flower into full *h* Among our heath — „ 317
'Muriel's *h* Had weaken'd, — „ 356
Youth and *H*, and birth and wealth, — *By an Evolution.* 8
Healthful And all about a *h* people stept — *Gareth and L.* 315
Her countenance with quick and *h* blood— — *Lover's Tale i* 97
Healthfuller Make their neighbourhood *h*, — *On Jub. Q. Victoria* 32
Healthly A *h* frame, a quiet mind.' — *Two Voices* 99
So *h*, sound, and clear and whole, — *Miller's D.* 15
Heap (s) (*See also* **Heäp**) wealth no more shall rest in mounded *h's*, — *Golden Year* 32
By *h's* of gourds, and skins of wine, — *Vision of Sin* 13
And *h's* of living gold that daily grow, — *Aylmer's Field* 655
Each hurling down a *h* of things that rang — *Geraint and E.* 594
crown'd With my slain self the *h's* of whom I slew— — *Balin and Balan* 178
I saw him, after, stand High on a *h* of slain, — *Lancelot and E.* 307
horses stumbling as they trode On *h's* of ruin, — *Holy Grail* 717
Heäp (s) *H's* an' *h's* o' boooks, I ha' see'd 'em, — *Village Wife* 71
An I heärd greät *h's* o' the snaw — *Owd Roä* 41
Heap (verb) And *h* their ashes on the head; — *Love thou thy land* 70
coals of fire you *h* upon my head — *Romney's R.* 141
Heaped Of *h* hills that mound the sea, — *Ode to Memory* 98
Heap'd-Heapt *Heap'd* over with a mound of grass, — *Lotos-Eaters, C. S.* 67
Pain *heap'd* ten-hundred-fold to this, — *St. S. Stylites* 23
heap'd Their firewood, and the winds from off the plain — *Spec. of Iliad* 6
heap'd the whole inherited sin On that huge scapegoat — *Maud I xiii* 41
Heap'd on her terms of disgrace, — „ *II i* 14
heap'd The pieces of his armour in one place, — *Geraint and E.* 373
Tho' *heapt* in mounds and ridges all the sea — *Holy Grail* 798
Heaping Still *h* on the fear of ill — *Two Voices* 107
Heapt *See* **Heap'd**
Hear (*See also* **'Ear**) at a burial to *h* The creaking cords which wound — *Supp. Confessions* 35
you may *h* him sob and sigh — *A spirit haunts* 5
you cannot *h* From the groves within — *Poet's Mind* 19
never would *h* it: your ears are so dull; — „ 35
I cry aloud: none *h* my cries, — *Oriana* 73
I *h* the roaring of the sea, — „ 98
To *h* the murmur of the strife, — *Margaret* 23
Come down, come down, and *h* me speak: — „ 56
I *h* what I would *h* from thee; — *Eleänore* 141
Kate will not *h* of lovers' sighs. — *Kate* 20
H a song that echoes cheerly — *L. of Shalott i* 30
H's little of the false or just.' — *Two Voices* 117
he *h's* His country's war-song thrill his ears: — „ 152
'He will not *h* the north-wind rave, — „ 259
'He seems to *h* a Heavenly Friend, — „ 295
Or from the bridge I lean'd to *h* — *Miller's D.* 49
H me, O Earth, *h* me, O Hills, — *Œnone* 36
H me, for I will speak, — „ 39
unheard *H* all, and see thy Paris judge of Gods.' — „ 90
heard me not, Or hearing would not *h* me, — „ 171
mother, *h* me yet before I die. (repeat) — *Œnone* 207, 220, 230, 245, 256
as I *h* Dead sounds at night come from — *Œnone* 248
H me, O Earth. I will not die alone, — „ 257
You seem'd to *h* them climb and fall — *Palace of Art* 70
king to *h* Of wisdom and of law. — „ 111
my soul to *h* her echo'd song Throb thro' — „ 175
that *h's* all night The plunging seas — „ 250
h the dully sound Of human footsteps — „ 275
h's the low Moan of an unknown sea; — „ 279
word That scarce is fit for you to *h*; — *L. C. V. de Vere* 38
I shall *h* you when you pass, — *May Queen, N. Y's. E.* 31
I *h* the bleating of the lamb. — „ *Con.* 2
I did not *h* the dog howl, mother, — „ 21
To *h* each other's whisper'd speech; — *Lotos-Eaters, C. S.* 59
To *h* the dewy echoes calling From cave to cave — „ 94
to *h* and see the far-off sparkling brine, — „ 98
Only to *h* were sweet, — „ 99
I *h* thee not at all, or hoarse — *The Blackbird* 19
Ev'n now we *h* with inward strife — *Love thou thy land* 53
like a horse That *h's* the corn-bin open, — *The Epic* 45
h The windy clanging of the minster clock; — *Gardener's D.* 37
'*H* how the bushes echo! — „ 98
Yet for the pleasure that I took to *h*, — „ 228
blackbird on the pippin hung To *h* him, — *Audley Court* 39

Hear (*continued*) I do not *h* the bells upon my cap, *Edwin Morris* 56
my ears could *h* Her lightest breath; „ 64
About the windings of the marge to *h* „ 94
nor heard of her, nor cared to *h*. (repeat) „ 138
I scarce can *h* the people hum *St. S. Stylites* 38
(And *h* me with thine ears,) *Talking Oak* 82
And *h* me swear a solemn oath, „ 281
that paused Among her stars to *h* us; *Love and Duty* 74
h These measured words, my work of yestermorn. *Golden Year* 20
tremulous eyes that fill with tears To *h* me? *Tithonus* 27
and could *h* the lips that kiss'd Whispering „ 60
on the moorland did we *h* the copses ring, *Locksley Hall* 35
Thou shalt *h* the 'Never, never,' „ 83
'O wake for ever, love,' she *h's*, *Day-Dm., Depart.* 11
That lets thee neither *h* nor see: „ *L'Envoi* 52
But what is that I *h*? a sound *Amphion* 73
I *h* a noise of hymns: *Sir Galahad* 28
I *h* a voice but none are there; „ 30
Let him *h* my song. *The Captain* 4
H's him lovingly converse, *L. of Burleigh* 26
Before you *h* my marriage vow.' *The Letters* 8
Annie seem'd to *h* Her own death-scaffold *Enoch Arden* 174
H's and not *h's*, and lets it overflow. „ 209
Nor ever *h* a kindly voice, „ 582
'Dead,' clamour'd the good woman, '*h* him „ 840
left Their own gray tower, or plain-faced tabernacle
To *h* him; *Aylmer's Field* 619
you do but *h* the tide. *Sea Dreams* 84
But will you *h* *my* dream, „ 203
He, dying lately, left her, as I *h*, *Princess i* 78
To *h* my father's clamour at our backs „ 105
my very ears were hot To *h* them: „ 135
h each other speak for noise Of clocks „ 215
'We scarcely thought in our own hall to *h* „ *ii* 53
there was one to *h* And help them? „ 267
H my conditions: promise (otherwise You perish) „ 295
then the Doctors! O to *h* The Doctors! „ 421
O *h* me, pardon me. „ *iii* 31
O hark, O *h*! how thin and clear, „ *iv* 7
Blow, let us *h* the purple glens replying: „ 11
h A trumpet in the distance pealing news „ 80
tell her what they were, and she to *h*: „ 323
we shall *h* of it From Lady Psyche:' „ 328
For thus I *h*; and known at last (my work) „ 347
we *h* You hold the woman is the better man; „ 409
h me, for I bear, Tho' man, yet human, „ 424
I stood and seem'd to *h* As in a poplar grove „ *v* 12
they hate to *h* me like a wind Wailing „ 98
when I *h* you prate I almost think „ 152
'Amazed am I to *h* Your Highness: „ *vi* 324
h's his burial talk'd of by his friends, „ *vii* 152
h The tides of Music's golden sea *Ode on Well.* 251
Eh!—but he wouldn't *h* me— *Grandmother* 8
Harry and Charlie, I *h* them too— „ 81
And only *h* the magpie gossip *To F. D. Maurice* 19
That it makes one weary to *h*.' *The Islet* 29
I *h* the roll of the ages. *Spiteful Letter* 8
cannot *h* The sullen Lethe rolling doom *Lit. Squabbles* 10
Speak to Him thou for He *h's*, *High. Pantheism* 11
And the ear of man cannot *h*, „ 17
But if we could see and *h*, this Vision— „ 18
Did they *h* me, would they listen, *Boädicea* 8
H Icenian, Catieuchlanian, *h* (repeat) *Boädicea* 10, 34, 47
h it, Spirit of Cássivëlaún! '*H* it, Gods! the Gods
have heard it, „ 20
Till the victim *h* within and yearn to hurry „ 58
I *h* the noise about thy keel; *In Mem. x* 1
I *h* the bell struck in the night: „ 2
And *h* the ritual of the dead. „ *xviii* 12
The traveller *h's* me now and then, „ *xxi* 5
To *h* her weeping by his grave? „ *xxxi* 4
turn mine ears and *h* The moanings of the homeless sea, „ *xxxv* 8
And *h* thy laurel whisper sweet „ *xxxvii* 7
I *h* it now, and o'er and o'er, „ *lvii* 13
I *h* a wizard music roll, „ *lxx* 14

Hear (*continued*) I *h* the sentence that he speaks; *In Mem. lxxx* 10
We cannot *h* each other speak. „ *lxxxii* 16
hung to *h* The rapt oration flowing free „ *lxxxvii* 31
heart and ear were fed To *h* him, „ *lxxxix* 23
I *h* a wind Of memory murmuring the past. „ *xcii* 7
h The wish too strong for words to name; „ *xciii* 13
And *h* the household jar within. „ *xciv* 16
That *h's* the latest linnet trill, „ *c* 10
And sing the songs he loved to *h*. „ *cvii* 24
I *h* a chirp of birds; „ *cxix* 5
To *h* the tidings of my friend, „ *cxxvi* 3
And *h* at times a sentinel Who moves about „ 9
h A deeper voice across the storm, „ *cxxvii* 3
I *h* thee where the waters run; „ *cxxx* 2
A voice as unto him that *h's*, „ *cxxxi* 6
Still! I will *h* you no more, *Maud I v* 23
I *h* the dead at midday moan, „ *vi* 70
Did I *h* it half in a doze Long since, „ *vii* 1
Strange, that I *h* two men, „ 13
I wish I could *h* again The chivalrous battle-song „ *x* 53
The larkspur listens, 'I *h*, I *h*;' „ *xxii* 65
My heart would *h* her and beat, „ 69
My dust would *h* her and beat, „ 71
Do I *h* her sing as of old, „ *II iv* 44
to *h* a dead man chatter Is enough to drive one mad. „ *v* 19
I *h* A cry from out the dawning of my life, *Com. of Arthur* 332
A mother weeping, and I *h* her say, „ 334
said the King, 'and *h* ye such a cry? „ 337
To *h* him speak before he left his life. „ 362
H the child's story.' *Gareth and L.* 39
nor sees, nor *h's*, nor speaks, nor knows. „ 81
H yet once more the story of the child. „ 100
H me—this morn I stood in Arthur's hall, „ 855
Than *h* thee so missay me and revile. „ 945
H a parable of the knave. „ 1008
stay'd Waiting to *h* the hounds; *Marr. of Geraint* 163
There is good chance that we shall *h* the hounds: „ 182
They would not *h* me speak: „ 421
Hath ask'd again, and ever loved to *h*; „ 436
thro' the crash of the near cataract *h's* *Geraint and E.* 172
soldiers wont to *h* His voice in battle, „ 174
And *h* him breathing low and equally. „ 372
What thing soever ye may *h*, or see, „ 415
I *h* the violent threats you do not *h*, „ 420
And ears to *h* you even in his dreams.' „ 429
Feeding like horses when you *h* them feed; „ 606
Submit, and *h* the judgment of the King.' 'He *h's*
the judgment of the King of kings,' „ 799
Damsel and lover? *h* not what I *h*. *Balin and Balan* 282
swan-mother, sitting, when she *h's* A strange knee rustle „ 353
Ye scarce can overpraise, will *h* and know. *Merlin and V.* 92
By Heaven that *h's* I tell you the clean truth, „ 343
will ye *h* The legend as in guerdon for your rhyme? „ 553
And therefore *h* my words: go to the jousts: *Lancelot and E.* 136
we *h* it said That men go down before your spear „ 148
as I *h* It is a fair large diamond,— „ 227
'*H*, but hold my name Hidden, „ 416
we shall *h* anon, Needs must we *h*.' „ 636
'we needs must *h* anon Of him, „ 756
till the ear Wearies to *h* it, „ 898
'Speak: that I live to *h*,' he said, 'is yours.' „ 928
I *h* of rumours flying thro' your court. „ 1190
'My lord liege Arthur, and all ye that *h*, „ 1290
To *h* the manner of thy fight and fall; *Pelleas and E.* 347
'Nay, nor will: I see it and *h*. *Last Tournament* 348
I, and Arthur and the angels *h*, „ 350
lock up my tongue From uttering freely what I freely *h*? „ 694
h the garnet-headed yaffingale Mock them: „ 700
And miss to *h* high talk of noble deeds *Guinevere* 499
Thro' the thick night I *h* the trumpet „ 569
I *h* the steps of Modred in the west, *Pass. of Arthur* 59
you may *h* The moaning of the woman and the child, *Lover's Tale i* 519
I heard and trembled, yet I could but *h*; „ 570
and then I seem'd to *h* Its murmur, as the drowning
seaman *h's*, „ 634

Hear (*continued*) Paused in their course to *h* me, *Lover's Tale ii* 14
I say the bird That will not *h* my call, „ *iv* 160
Laud me not Before my time, but *h* me to the close. „ 243
h that cry of my boy that was dead, *Rizpah* 45
you know that I couldn't but *h*; „ 48
and mercy, the Lord '—let me *h* it again; „ 62
But I cannot *h* what you say „ 82
Nay—you can *h* it yourself— „ 85
yet she thinks She sees you when she *h's*. *Sisters (E. and E.)* 193
Not es I cares fur to *h* ony harm, *Village Wife* 22
I *h's* es soom o' thy booöks „ 70
you can *h* him—the murderous mole! *Def. of Lucknow* 26
they came to *h* their preacher. *Sir J. Oldcastle* 42
Do penance in his heart, God *h's* him.' „ 143
I shall *h* his voice again— *Columbus* 159
readier, if the King would *h*, to lead One last crusade „ 238
turn'd upon his heel to *h* My warning *Tiresias* 72
I can *h* Too plainly what full tides of onset sap „ 90
h, and tho' I speak the truth Believe I speak it, „ 155
the waters—you *h* them call! *Despair* 47
If thou would'st *h* the Nameless, *Ancient Sage* 31
She *h's* the lark within the songless egg, „ 76
And tho' these fathers will not *h*, *The Flight* 67
and *h* the waters roar, „ 90
h the voices from the field. *Locksley H., Sixty* 116
Shall I *h* in one dark room a wailing, „ 262
H's he now the Voice that wrong'd him? „ 269
Moon of married hearts, *H* me, you! *The Ring* 4
I *h* your Mother's voice in yours. „ 28
I *h* her yet—A sound of anger like a distant storm. „ 118
The storm, you *h* Far-off, is Muriel— „ 138
poor Muriel when you *h* What follows! „ 273
All the world will *h* a voice *Forlorn* 27
I *h* a charm of song thro' all the land. *Prog. of Spring* 47
and *h* their words On pathway'd plains; „ 82
I *h* a death-bed Angel whisper 'Hope.' *Romney's R.* 148
But I *h* no yelp of the beast, *By an Evolution.* 19
H my cataract's Downward thunder *To Master of B.* 15
h The clash of tides that meet in narrow seas.— *Akbar's Dream* 57
but we *h* Music: our palace is awake, „ 199
H thy myriad laureates hail thee „ *Hymn* 6

Heard (*See also* **'Eärd, Far-heard, Half-heard, Hard, Heärd**) voice of the bird Shall no more be *h*, *All Things will Die* 25
Waking she *h* the night-fowl crow: *Mariana* 26
We *h* the steeds to battle going, *Oriana* 15
She saw me fight, she *h* me call, „ 32
Hast thou *h* the butterflies What they say *Adeline* 28
Elsinore *H* the war moan along the distant sea, *Buonaparte* 10
I have *h* that, somewhere in the main, *If I were loved* 7
She has *h* a whisper say,. *L. of Shalott ii* 3
They *h* her singing her last song, „ *iv* 26
H a carol, mournful, holy, „ 28
And *h* her native breezes pass, *Mariana in the S.* 43
'But *h*, by secret transport led, *Two Voices* 214
And oft I *h* the tender dove In firry woodlands *Miller's D.* 41
Sometimes I *h* you sing within; „ 123
Then first I *h* the voice of her, *Œnone* 107
Give it to Pallas!' but he *h* me not, „ 170
Indeed I *h* one bitter word That scarce is fit *L. C. V. de Vere* 37
wild March-morning I *h* the angels call; *May Queen, Con.* 25
wild March-morning I *h* them call my soul. „ 28
who made His music *h* below; *D. of F. Women* 4
I *h* sounds of insult, shame, and wrong, „ 19
Sudden I *h* a voice that cried, „ 123
I *h* my name Sigh'd forth with life „ 153
h A noise of some one coming thro' the lawn, „ 177
We *h* the lion roaring from his den; „ 222
I *h* Him, for He spake, and grief became „ 227
I *h* just now the crowing cock. *D. of the O. Year* 38
Once *h* at dead of night to greet Troy's wandering prince, *On a Mourner* 32
She *h* the torrents meet. *Of old sat Freedom* 4
half-awake I *h* The parson taking wide and wider sweeps, *The Epic* 13
What is it thou hast seen? or what hast *h*? (repeat) *M. d'Arthur* 68, 114

Heard (*continued*) I *h* the ripple washing in the reeds, *M. d'Arthur* 70
'I *h* the water lapping on the crag, „ 116
Speak out: what is it thou hast *h*, or seen?' „ 150
He *h* the deep behind him, and a cry Before. „ 184
and *h* indeed The clear church-bells ring „ *Ep.* 30
Who had not *h* Of Rose, the Gardener's daughter? *Gardener's D.* 51
when I *h* her name My heart was like a prophet „ 62
Born out of everything I *h* and saw, „ 66
Nor *h* us come, nor from her tendance turn'd „ 144
all that night I *h* the watchman peal The sliding season: all that night I *h* The heavy clocks knolling „ 182
when I *h* his deep 'I will,' Breathed, „ 208
left *his* wife behind; for so I *h*. *Walk. to the Mail* 47
I had *h* it was this bill that past, „ 67
h with beating heart The Sweet-Gale rustle *Edwin Morris* 109
nor *h* of her, nor cared to hear. „ 138
since I *h* him make reply Is many a weary hour; *Talking Oak* 25
That oft hast *h* my vows, „ 98
I *h* them blast The steep slate-quarry, *Golden Year* 75
Like that strange song I *h* Apollo sing, *Tithonus* 62
When I *h* my days before me, *Locksley Hall* 110
H the heavens fill with shouting, „ 123
She sleeps: her breathings are not *h* *Day-Dm., Sleep B.* 17
But they *h* the foeman's thunder Roaring *The Captain* 41
Then methought I *h* a mellow sound, *Vision of Sin* 14
they that *h* it sigh'd, Panted hand-in-hand „ 18
At last I *h* a voice upon the slope Cry „ 219
Him running on thus hopefully she *h*, *Enoch Arden* 201
she *h*, *H* and not *h* him; „ 205
h The myriad shriek of wheeling ocean-fowl, „ 582
He *h* the pealing of his parish bells; „ 615
h them talking, his long-bounden tongue Was loosen'd, „ 644
Because things seen are mightier than things *h*, „ 766
As the woman *h*, Fast flow'd the current of her easy tears, „ 864
'Have you not *h*?' said Katie, *The Brook* 221
worse than had he *h* his priest Preach *Aylmer's Field* 43
H the good mother softly whisper 'Bless, „ 187
And neither loved nor liked the thing he *h*. „ 250
had Sir Aylmer *h*—Nay, but he must— „ 261
till he *h* the ponderous door Close, „ 337
thunder from within the cliffs *H* thro' the living roar. *Sea Dreams* 56
I woke, I *h* the clash so clearly. „ 136
often when the woman *h* his foot Return *Lucretius* 5
for thrice I *h* the rain Rushing; „ 26
She *h* him raging, *h* him fall; „ 276
he *h* her speak; She scared him; life! *Princess i* 185
'having seen And *h* the Lady Psyche.' „ *ii* 211
'Ah—Melissa—you! You *h* us?' „ 331
'O pardon me I *h*, I could not help it, „ 332
In each we sat, we *h* The grave Professor. „ 370
like parting hopes I *h* them passing from me: „ *iv* 173
behind I *h* the puff'd pursuer; „ 265
we *h* In the dead hush the papers that she held Rustle: „ 389
I *h* of, after seen The dwarfs of presage: „ 446
saw the lights and *h* The voices murmuring. „ 558
Thy voice is *h* thro' rolling drums, „ 577
we *h* The drowsy folds of our great ensign „ ***v* 7**
She *h*, she moved, She moan'd, „ **71**
prated peace, when first I *h* War-music, „ **265**
h Of those that iron-cramp'd their women's feet; „ **375**
Seeing I saw not, hearing not I *h*: „ ***vi* 19**
My father *h* and ran In on the lists, „ **26**
they *h* A noise of songs they would not understand: „ **39**
clamouring on, till Ida *h*, Look'd up, „ **150**
'I've *h* that there is iron in the blood, „ **230**
you had a heart—I *h* her say it— „ **234**
on her foot she hung A moment, and she *h*, „ ***vii* 80**
I *h* her turn the page; „ **190**
I have *h* Of your strange doubts: „ **335**
His captain's-ear has *h* them boom Bellowing victory, *Ode on Well.* **65**
My Lords, we *h* you speak: *Third of Feb.* **1**
Elburz and all the Caucasus have *h*; *W. to Marie Alex.* **13**
He *h* a fierce mermaiden cry, *Sailor Boy* **6**
All night have I *h* the voice Rave *Voice and the P.* **5**
Mad and maddening all that *h* her *Boädicea* **4**

Heard (*continued*) 'Hear it, Gods! the Gods have *h* it, *Boädicea* 21
a murmur *h* aërially, „ 24
There I *h* them in the darkness, „ 36
When was a harsher sound ever *h*, *Trans. of Homer* 3
I have *h* of thorns and briers. *Window, Marr. Morn.* 20
The words that are not *h* again. *In Mem. xviii* 20
Before I *h* those bells again: „ *xxviii* 16
We *h* them sweep the winter land; „ *xxx* 10
And *h* once more in college fanes „ *lxxxvii* 5
We *h* behind the woodbine veil „ *lxxxix* 50
The brook alone far-off was *h*, „ *xcv* 7
And yet myself have *h* him say, „ *xcviii* 20
The roofs, that *h* our earliest cry, „ *cii* 3
h The low love-language of the bird „ 10
The flippant put himself to school And *h* thee, „ *cx* 11
the world's great work is *h* Beginning, „ *cxxi* 10
I *h* a voice 'believe no more' And *h* an ever-breaking shore „ *cxxiv* 10
I *h* The shrill-edged shriek of a mother *Maud I i* 15
I have *h*, I know not whence, „ 67
I *h* no longer The snowy-banded, „ *viii* 9
I *h* no sound where I stood But the rivulet „ *xiv* 28
even then I *h* her close the door, „ *xviii* 11
All night have the roses *h* The flute, „ *xxii* 13
For I *h* your rivulet fall From the lake „ 36
That *h* me softly call, „ *II iv* 76
I *h* it shouted at once from the top „ *v* 50
for he *h* of Arthur newly crown'd, *Com. of Arthur* 41
But *h* the call, and came: and Guinevere „ 47
he *h*, Leodogran in heart Debating— „ 140
there was *h* among the holy hymns A voice „ 290
his knights have *h* That God hath told the King „ 488
h him Kingly speak, and doubted him No more *Gareth and L.* 125
Before the wakeful mother *h* him, went. „ 180
we have *h* from our wise men at home To Northward, „ 201
ascending *h* A voice, the voice of Arthur, „ 317
having *h* that Arthur of his grace Had made „ 393
For an ye *h* a music, „ 275
I *h* thee call thyself a knave,— „ 1163
nor have I *h* the voice. „ 1336
And muffled voices *h*, and shadows past; „ 1373
nor yet was *h* The world's loud whisper *Marr. of Geraint* 26
He *h* but fragments of her later words, „ 113
but *h* instead A sudden sound of hoofs, „ 163
thinking that he *h* The noble hart at bay, „ 232
H by the lander in a lonely isle, „ 330
this dear child hath often *h* me praise „ 434
And tho' I *h* him call you fairest fair, „ 720
And *h* one crying to his fellow, 'Look, *Geraint and E.* 59
h them boast That they would slay you, „ 73
his own ear had *h* Call herself false: „ 113
thought she *h* the wild Earl at the door, „ 381
for he rode As if he *h* not, „ 452
Enid *h* the clashing of his fall, „ 509
She spake so low he hardly *h* her speak, „ 643
This *h* Geraint, and grasping at his sword, „ 725
tho' mine own ears *h* you yestermorn— „ 740
I *h* you say, that you were no true wife: „ 742
for I *h* He had spoken evil of me; *Balin and Balan* 57
Follow'd the Queen; Sir Balin *h* her 'Prince, „ 250
in a moment *h* them pass like wolves Howling; „ 407
h and thought 'The scream of that Wood-devil „ 547
Mark The Cornish King, had *h* a wandering voice, *Merlin and V.* 8
sat, *h*, watch'd And whisper'd: „ 138
They *h* and let her be. „ 146
and *h* in thought Their lavish comment „ 150
I *h* the great Sir Lancelot sing it once, „ 385
other was the song that once I *h* By this huge oak, „ 405
And *h* their voices talk behind the wall, „ 631
spoke in words part *h*, in whispers part, „ 839
Vivien, fearing heaven had *h* her oath, „ 940
in his heart *H* murmurs 'Lo, thou likewise *Lancelot and E.* 55
Elaine, and *h* her name so tost about, „ 233
H from the Baron that, ten years before, „ 272
she *h* Sir Lancelot cry in the court, „ 344

Heard (*continued*) They rose, *h* mass, broke fast, and rode away: *Lancelot and E.* 415
She, that had *h* the noise of it before, „ 731
when she *h* his horse upon the stones, „ 980
still she *h* him, still his picture form'd „ 992
the brothers *h*, and thought With shuddering, „ 1021
chanted snatches of mysterious hymns *H* on the winding waters, „ 1408
We *h* not half of what he said. *Holy Grail* 43
I *h* a sound As of a silver horn „ 108
this Galahad, when he *h* My sister's vision, „ 139
Galahad, when he *h* of Merlin's doom, Cried, „ 177
we *h* A cracking and a riving of the roofs, „ 182
I *h* the sound, I saw the light, „ 280
I saw the Holy Grail and *h* a cry— „ 291
'We have *h* of thee: thou art our greatest knight, „ 603
He *h* the hollow-ringing heavens sweep Over him „ 678
I told him all thyself hast *h*, „ 736
I *h* the shingle grinding in the surge, „ 811
h a voice, 'Doubt not, go forward; „ 823
But always in the quiet house I *h*, „ 832
I *h*, 'Glory and joy and honour to our Lord „ 838
h the King Had let proclaim a tournament— *Pelleas and E.* 10
This her damsels *h*, „ 200
He *h* her voice; Then let the strong hand, „ 233
'Thou fool,' she said, 'I never *h* his voice „ 255
Pelleas had *h* sung before the Queen, „ 397
And *h* but his own steps, and his own heart Beating, „ 416
hast not *h* That Lancelot'—there he check'd himself „ 526
beneath a winding wall of rock *H* a child wail. *Last Tournament* 12
he *h* The voice that billow'd round the barriers „ 166
And *h* it ring as true as tested gold.' „ 284
tonguesters of the court she had not *h*. „ 393
the Red Knight *h*, and all, „ 441
and I that *h* her whine And snivel, „ 449
H in dead night along that table-shore, „ 463
Nor *h* the King for their own cries, „ 472
h The hounds of Mark, and felt the goodly hounds „ 502
h the feet of Tristram grind The spiring stone „ 510
Murmuring a light song I had *h* thee sing, „ 614
H by the watcher in a haunted house, *Guinevere* 73
Vivien, lurking, *h*. She told Sir Modred. „ 98
h the Spirits of the waste and weald Moan as she fled, or thought she *h* them moan: „ 129
when she *h*, the Queen look'd up, and said, „ 164
'Have we not *h* the bridegroom is so sweet? „ 177
down the coast, he *h* Strange music, „ 238
in the darkness *h* his armed feet Pause by her; „ 418
H in his tent the moanings of the King: *Pass. of Arthur* 8
This *h* the bold Sir Bedivere and spake: „ 50
Nor any cry of Christian *h* thereon, „ 128
What is it thou hast seen? or what hast *h*?' (repeat) „ 236, 282
I *h* the ripple washing in the reeds, „ 238
I *h* the water lapping on the crag, „ 284
Speak out: what is it thou hast *h*, or seen?' „ 318
He *h* the deep behind him, and a cry Before. „ 352
we lately *h* A strain to shame us *To the Queen ii* 14
and show us That we are surely *h*. *Lover's Tale i* 365
I too have *h* a sound—perchance of streams „ 522
I *h* and trembled, yet I could but hear; „ 570
now first *h* with any sense of pain, „ 709
The hollow caverns *h* me—the black brooks Of the midforest *h* me— „ *ii* 11
H yet once more the tolling bell, „ *iv* 29
I *h* a groaning overhead, and climb'd The moulder'd stairs „ 136
And *h* him muttering, 'So like, so like; „ 325
we *h* them a-ringing the bell, *First Quarrel* 21
For I *h* it abroad in the fields „ 32
you—and what have you *h*? *Rizpah* 13
'O mother!' I *h* him cry. „ 42
the first may be last—I have *h* it in church— „ 66
H, have you? what? they have told you „ 69
H! have you ever *h*! when the storm on the downs „ 71
I *h* Wheels, and a noise of welcome at the doors— *Sisters (E. and E.)* 148

Heard (continued) I h 'im a roomlin' by, Village Wife 122
but I know that I h him say ' All very well— In the Child. Hosp. 21
Emmie had h him. Softly she call'd from her cot „ 46
was a phantom cry that I h as I tost about, „ 63
The Lord of the children had h her, „ 72
I h his voice between The thunders Columbus 145
I h his voice, ' Be not cast down. „ 157
a hundred who h it would rush on a thousand lances V. of Maeldune 24
past to the Isle of Witches and h their musical cry— „ 97
and we pray'd as we h him pray, „ 125
oft we two have h St. Mary's chimes ! To W. H. Brookfield 3
cry of Æakidês Was h among the Trojans, Achilles over the T. 23
Two voices h on earth no more ; To E. Fitzgerald 41
Have h this footstep fall, Tiresias 27
I h a voice that said ' Henceforth be blind, „ 48
who h And h not, when I spake of famine, „ 59
are a song H in the future ; „ 125
H from the roofs by night, „ 140
My hands, when I h him coming would drop The Wreck 27
I knew not what, when I h that voice,— „ 52
brute mother who never has h us groan ! Despair 98
That nightingale is h ! Ancient Sage 20
Powers, that rule Were never h or seen.' „ 30
and h his passionate vow, The Flight 83
while I h the curlews call, Locksley H., Sixty 3
only h in silence from the silence of a tomb. „ 74
Because you h the lines I read Pro. to Gen. Hamley 17
for he spoke and the people h, Dead Prophet 33
breathing in his sleep, H by the land. Early Spring 24
thy voice, a music h Thro' all the yells and counter-yells To Duke of Argyll 7
And one drear sound I have not h, To Marq. of Dufferin 40
and h The murmurs of their temples chanting me, Demeter and P. 71
I h one voice from all the three ' We know not, „ 84
So he, the God of dreams, who h my cry, „ 91
Voices of the day Are h across the Voices The Ring 40
I h the sober rook And carrion crow cry ' Mortgage.' „ 173
I that h, and changed the prayer Happy 55
There ! I h Our cuckoo call. To Mary Boyle 5
My birds would sing, You h not. „ 19
long ravine below, She h a wailing cry, Death of Œnone 20
shouted, and the shepherds h and came. „ 56
she h The shriek of some lost life „ 89
h an answer ' Wake Thou deedless dreamer, St Telemachus 20
And at his ear he h a whisper ' Rome ' „ 26
on to reach Honorius, till he h them, „ 77
I h a mocking laugh ' the new Korân ! ' Akbar's Dream 183
field without were seen or h Fires of Sûttee, „ 195
To have seen thee, and h thee, and known. Bandit's Death 4
They h, they bided their time. „ 14
and h as we crouch'd below, The clatter of arms, „ 23
when he h what an end was mine ? Charity 17
tho' faintly h Until the great Hereafter. Death of the Duke of C. 16
Heärd An' I h greät heäps o' the snaw Owd Roä 41
Hearer While thus he spoke, his h's wept ; Aylmer's Field 722
outran The h in its fiery course ; In Mem. cix 8
and all h's were amazed. Gareth and L. 655
humbly hopeful, rose Fixt on her h's, Merlin and V. 87
Hear'st Thou h the village hammer clink, In Mem. cxxi 15
'H thou this great voice that shakes the world, Pass. of Arthur 139
Hearing (part.) Or h would not hear me, Œnone 171
How sweet it were, h the downward stream, Lotos-Eaters, C. S. 54
H the holy organ rolling waves Of sound D. of F. Women 191
h his mischance, Came, for he knew the man Enoch Arden 120
That shook the heart of Edith h him. Aylmer's Field 63
Seeing I saw not, h not I heard : Princess vi 19
h her tumultuous adversaries Boädicea 78
This, Gareth h from a squire of Lot Gareth and L. 531
And Gareth h ever stronglier smote, „ 1141
Not h any more his noble voice, Marr. of Geraint 98
(Who h her own name had stol'n away) „ 507
red and pale Across the face of Enid h her ; „ 524
crowd, H he had a difference with their priests, Holy Grail 674

Hearing (part.) (continued) And h ' harlot ' mutter'd twice or thrice, Merlin and V. 843
Hearing (s) Our h is not h, Voice and the P. 35
And in the h of the wave. In Mem. xix 4
Yet in these ears, till h dies, „ lvii 9
Within the h of cat or mouse, Maud II v 48
But since her mind was bent On h, Pelleas and E. 115
even into my inmost heart As to my outward h : Lover's Tale i 429
nor hope for a deathless h ! Parnassus 14
Hearsay blamed herself for telling h tales : Merlin and V. 951
Hearse Funeral h's rolling ! Forlorn 68
Heart (See also **'Art, Black-heart, Lion-heart, Woman's-heart**) When will the h be aweary of beating ? Nothing will Die 6
The cloud fleets, The h beats, „ 12
Every h this May morning in joyance is beating All Things will Die 6
The h will cease to beat ; „ 12
cords which wound and eat Into my human h, Supp. Confessions 37
And loveth so his innocent h, „ 52
What Devil had the h to scathe Flowers „ 83
Albeit, my hope is gray, and cold At h, „ 104
run short pains Thro' his warm h ; „ 162
O spirit and h made desolate ! „ 189
Thro' my very h it thrilleth Lilian 22
Upon the blanched tablets of her h ; Isabel 17
Right to the h and brain, „ 22
cords that bind and strain The h until it bleeds, Clear-headed Friend 5
my bounding h entanglest In a golden-netted smile ; Madeline 40
My very h faints and my whole soul grieves A spirit haunts 16
In the h of the garden the merry bird chants. Poet's Mind 22
Out of the live-green h of the dells Sea-Fairies 12
My h is wasted with my woe, Oriana 1
And pierced thy h, my love, my bride, „ 42
Thy h, my life, my love, my bride, „ 44
O breaking h that will not break, „ 64
Up from my h unto my eyes, „ 78
Within thy h my arrow lies, „ 80
Die in their h's for the love of me. The Mermaid 30
Take the h from out my breast. Adeline 8
Do beating h's of salient springs Keep measure „ 26
violet woos To his h the silver dews ? „ 32
Encircles all the h, and feedeth The senses Margaret 16
The burning brain from the true h, „ 39
And the h's of purple hills, Eleänore 17
My h a charmed slumber keeps, „ 128
Her h is like a throbbing star. Kate 9
And either lived in either's h and speech. Sonnet to —— 14
My hope and h is with thee— To J. M. K. 1
But spurr'd at h with fieriest energy „ 7
He thought to quell the stubborn h's of oak, Buonaparte 1
The h of Poland hath not ceased To quiver, Poland 3
To find my h so near the beauteous breast The form, the form 7
' O cruel h,' she changed her tone, Mariana in the S. 69
But my full h, that work'd below, Two Voices 44
Nor sold his h to idle moans, „ 221
A deeper tale my h divines. „ 269
His h forebodes a mystery : „ 290
My frozen h began to beat, „ 422
From out my sullen h a power Broke, „ 443
And full at h of trembling hope, Miller's D. 110
Approaching, press'd you h to h. „ 160
And her h would beat against me, „ 177
Do make a garland for the h : „ 198
Round my true h thine arms entwine „ 216
still affection of the h Became an outward breathing type, „ 225
My h, pierced thro' with fierce delight, Fatima 34
My eyes are full of tears, my h of love, My h is breaking, and my eyes are dim, Œnone 31
My h may wander from its deeper woe. „ 44
all my h Went forth to embrace him coming „ 62
full-flowing river of speech Came down upon my h. „ 69
Thou weighest heavy on the h within, „ 243
Devil, large in h and brain, To ——, With Pal. of Art 5
hollow shades enclosing h's of flame, Palace of Art 241
You thought to break a country h For pastime, L. C. V. de Vere 3
A h that doats on truer charms. „ 14

Heart (*continued*) You changed a wholesome h to gall. *L. C. V. de Vere* 44
Kind h's are more than coronets, „ 55
Pray Heaven for a human h, „ 71
They say his h is breaking, mother— *May Queen* 22
O blessings on his kindly h „ *Con.* 15
music in his ears his beating h did make. *Lotos-Eaters* 36
To lend our h's and spirits wholly „ *C. S.* 63
Sore task to h's worn out by many wars „ 86
tho' my h, Brimful of those wild tales, *D. of F. Women* 11
melting the mighty h's Of captains and of kings. „ 175
the h Faints, faded by its heat. „ 287
His memory long will live alone In all our h's, *To J. S.* 50
Sleep sweetly, tender h, in peace: „ 69
And on thy h a finger lays, *On a Mourner* 11
Teach that sick h the stronger choice, „ 18
wild h's the feeble wings That every sophister *Love thou thy land* 11
Not yet the wise of h would cease To hold his hope „ 81
She felt her h grow prouder: *The Goose* 22
The summer pilot of an empty h *Gardener's D.* 16
So blunt in memory, so old at h, „ 53
My h was like a prophet to my h, „ 63
we coursed about The subject most at h, „ 223
A woman's h, the h of her I loved; „ 230
doors that bar The secret bridal chambers of the h, „ 249
h on one wild leap Hung tranced from all pulsation, „ 259
Make thine h ready with thine eyes: „ 273
I beheld her ere she knew my h, „ 276
I have set my h upon a match. *Dora* 14
when his h is glad Of the full harvest, „ 68
gone to him, But her h fail'd her; „ 78
' With all my h,' Said Francis. *Audley Court* 8
And all my h turn'd from her, „ 54
Dipt by itself, and we were glad at h. „ 89
I would have hid her needle in my h, *Edwin Morris* 62
heard with beating h The Sweet-Gale rustle „ 109
Until he plagiarised a h, *Talking Oak* 19
This girl, for whom your h is sick, „ 71
with throbbing h I came To rest beneath thy boughs? „ 155
Streaming eyes and breaking h's? *Love and Duty* 2
Better the narrow brain, the stony h, „ 15
Whose foresight preaches peace, my h so slow To feel it! „ 34
And to the want, that hollow'd all the h, „ 61
seem to lift a burthen from thy h And leave thee freër, „ 96
For always roaming with a hungry h *Ulysses* 12
and opposed Free h's, free foreheads— „ 49
One equal temper of heroic h's, „ 68
To his great h none other than a God! *Tithonus* 14
And bosom beating with a h renew'd. „ 36
with what another h In days far-off, „ 50
lower feelings and a narrower h than mine! *Locksley Hall* 44
hidden from the h's disgrace, „ 57
tho' my h be at the root. „ 66
lest thy h be put to proof, „ 77
hoard of maxims preaching down a daughter's h. „ 94
Left me with the palsied h, „ 132
deep h of existence beat for ever like a boy's? „ 140
And from a h as rough as Esau's hand, *Godiva* 28
That lie upon her charmed h. *Day-Dm., Sleep. B.* 20
Magic Music in his h Beats quick and quicker, „ *Arrival* 26
strength of ten, Because my h is pure. *Sir Galahad* 4
But all my h is drawn above, „ 17
A virgin h in work and will. „ 24
This weight and size, this h and eyes, „ 71
' And have you lost your h?' she said; *Edward Gray* 3
Can touch the h of Edward Gray. „ 8
' To trouble the h of Edward Gray.' „ 20
And here the h of Edward Gray!' „ 28
And there the h of Edward Gray!' „ 36
that child's h within the man's Begins to move *Will Water.* 31
I will not cramp my h, „ 51
But, all his vast h sherris-warm'd, „ 197
Her h within her did not fail: *Lady Clare* 78
Shame and wrath his h confounded, *The Captain* 61
' If my h by signs can tell, *L. of Burleigh* 2
Thus her h rejoices greatly, „ 41

Heart (*continued*) Shaped her h with woman's meekness *L. of Burleigh* 71
Which did win my h from me!' „ 84
And madly danced our h's with joy, *The Voyage* 3
Across the whirlwind's h of peace, „ 87
To waste his whole h in one kiss *Sir L. and Q. G.* 44
Pass on, weak h, and leave me where I lie: *Come not, when, etc.* 11
That mock'd the wholesome human h, *The Letters* 10
I spoke with h, and heat and force, „ 37
Every h, when sifted well, *Vision of Sin* 112
Hollow h's and empty heads! „ 174
vulture waits To tear his h before the crowd! *You might have won* 36
either fixt his h On that one girl; *Enoch Arden* 39
Bearing a lifelong hunger in his h. „ 79
Enoch in his h determined all: „ 148
But had no h to break his purposes To Annie, „ 155
Philip's true h, which hunger'd for her peace „ 272
For where he fixt his h he set his hand „ 294
He oft denied his h his dearest wish, „ 336
Out of full h and boundless gratitude „ 346
Brook'd not the expectant terror of her h, „ 493
But never merrily beat Annie's h. „ 513
Then the new mother came about her h, „ 524
had not his poor h Spoken with That, „ 618
His h foreshadowing all calamity, „ 683
While in her h she yearn'd incessantly „ 866
James Willows, of one name and h with her. *The Brook* 76
there he mellow'd all his h with ale, „ 155
That shook the h of Edith hearing him. *Aylmer's Field* 63
So these young h's not knowing that they loved, „ 133
Having the warmth and muscle of the h, „ 180
And foam'd away his h at Averill's ear: „ 342
the according h's of men Seem'd harder too; „ 453
fragrant in a h remembering His former talks „ 456
where his worldless h had kept it warm, „ 471
For h, I think, help'd head: „ 475
Hating his own lean h and miserable. „ 526
And bad him with good h sustain himself— „ 544
down in flood, and dash'd his angry h „ 633
To greet her, wasting his forgotten h, „ 689
Long since her h had beat remorselessly, „ 799
from tender h's, And those who sorrow'd „ 843
Whose pious talk, when most his h was dry, *Sea Dreams* 186
' I loathe it: he had never kindly h, „ 200
I had set my h on your forgiving him „ 269
what h had he To die of? dead!' „ 275
His angel broke his h. „ 280
bird Makes his h voice amid the blaze of flowers: *Lucretius* 101
What beast has h to do it? „ 233
Spout from the maiden fountain in her h. „ 240
' O noble h who, being strait-besieged *Princess, Pro.* 36
And bites it for true h and not for harm, „ 174
And still I wore her picture by my h, „ *i* 38
my other h, And almost my half-self, „ 55
with all my h, With my full h: „ 126
think I bear that h within my breast, „ *ii* 334
A thousand h's lie fallow in these halls, „ 400
Fly twanging headless arrows at the h's, „ 402
And dear is sister Psyche to my h, „ 418
when your sister came she won the h Of Ida; „ *iii* 87
I tried the mother's h. „ 147
head and h of all our fair she-world, „ 163
My h beat thick with passion and with awe; „ 190
that men may pluck them from our h's, „ 257
Or in the dark dissolving human h, „ 312
Rise in the h, and gather to the eyes, „ *iv* 41
her h Would rock the snowy cradle till I died. „ 103
cursing Cyril, vext at h, „ 171
To whom none spake, half-sick at h, return'd. „ 223
Beaten with some great passion at her h, „ 388
block and bar Your h with system out from mine, „ 463
Bursts of great h and slips in sensual mire, „ *v* 199
The woman's garment hid the woman's h.' „ 305
Suck'd from the dark h of the long hills „ 349
living h's that crack within the fire „ 379
at the h Made for all noble motion: „ 383

Heart (*continued*) the tender orphan hands Felt at my *h*, *Princess v* 436
Man with the head and woman with the *h*: „ 449
Her noble *h* was molten in her breast; „ *vi* 119
Win you the *h's* of women; „ 171
She said You had a *h*—I heard her say it—" Our Ida has a *h* "—just ere she died— „ 234
You will not? well—no *h* have you, „ 262
Come to the hollow *h* they slander so! „ 288
I cannot keep My *h* an eddy from the brawling hour: „ 322
nor stranger seem'd that *h's* So gentle, „ *vii* 66
And at the happy lovers *h* in *h*— „ 108
And all thy *h* lies open unto me. „ 183
ill counsel had misled the girl To vex true *h's*: „ 242
her great *h* thro' all the faultful Past „ 248
two-cell'd *h* beating, with one full stroke, „ 307
I waste my *h* in signs: let be. „ 359
And a deeper knell in the *h* be knoll'd; *Ode on Well.* 59
What long-enduring *h's* could do In that world-earthquake, „ 132
On with toil of *h* and knees and hands, „ 212
upon whose hand and *h* and brain „ 239
Uplifted high in *h* and hope are we, „ 254
and change the *h's* of men, *W. to Marie Alex.* 44
But *h's* that change not, „ 46
And in thy *h* the scrawl shall play.' *Sailor Boy* 12
A devil rises in my *h*, „ 23
h to endure for the life of the worm and the fly? *Wages* 7
Tear the noble *h* of Britain, *Boädicea* 12
Till she felt the *h* within her fall and flutter „ 81
and the Shepherd gladdens in his *h*: *Spec. of Iliad* 16
my *h* is there before you are come, *Window, On the Hill* 14
Gone, and a cloud in my *h*, „ *Gone* 6
you bite far into the *h* of the house, „ *Winter* 11
You have bitten into the *h* of the earth, „ 18
Break—you may break my *h*. Faint *h* never won— *The Answer* 8
O merry my *h*, you have gotten the wings of love, *Ay* 15
lighten into my eyes and my *h*, Into my *h* and my blood! *Marr. Morn.* 15
H, are you great enough (repeat) „ 17, 19
And with my *h* I muse and say: *In Mem. iv* 4
O *h*, how fares it with thee now, „ 5
But, for the unquiet *h* and brain, „ *v* 5
but some *h* did break. „ *vi* 8
Doors, where my *h* was used to beat So quickly „ *vii* 3
O my forsaken *h*, with thee And this poor flower „ *viii* 18
And in my *h*, if calm at all, „ *xi* 15
A void where *h* on *h* reposed; „ *xiii* 6
I, falling on his faithful *h*, „ *xviii* 14
The darken'd *h* that beat no more; „ *xix* 2
And melt the waxen *h's* of men.' „ *xxi* 8
And glad at *h* from May to May: „ *xxii* 8
Nor could I weary, *h* or limb, „ *xxv* 9
The *h* that never plighted troth „ *xxvii* 10
To lull with song an aching *h*, „ *xxxvii* 15
I vex my *h* with fancies dim: „ *xlii* 1
the *h* is sick, And all the wheels of Being slow. „ *l* 3
broke the peace Of *h's* that beat from day to day, „ *lviii* 6
Like some poor girl whose *h* is set On one „ *lx* 3
On some unworthy *h* with joy, „ *lxii* 7
Can hang no weight upon my *h* „ *lxiii* 3
You thought my *h* too far diseased; „ *lxvi* 1
Let this not vex thee, noble *h*! „ *lxxix* 2
The wrath that garners in my *h*; „ *lxxxii* 14
O *h*, with kindliest motion warm, „ *lxxxv* 34
That marry with the virgin *h*. „ 108
My *h*, tho' widow'd, may not rest Quite in the love „ 113
in the midmost *h* of grief Thy passion clasps „ *lxxxviii* 7
h and ear were fed To hear him, „ *lxxxix* 22
How pure at *h* and sound in head, „ *xciv* 1
But when the *h* is full of din, „ 13
A hunger seized my *h*; I read Of that glad year „ *xcv* 21
Their *h's* of old have beat in tune, „ *xcvii* 10
He seems to slight her simple *h*. „ 20
The pulses of a Titan's *h*; „ *ciii* 32
The larger *h*, the kindlier hand; „ *cvi* 30

Heart (*continued*) I will not eat my *h* alone, *In Mem. cviii* 3
By blood a king, at *h* a clown; „ *cxi* 4
Doors, where my *h* was used to beat So quickly, „ *cxix* 1
the *h* Stood up and answer'd 'I have felt.' „ *cxxiv* 15
And *h's* are warm'd and faces bloom, „ *Con.* 82
closed their gates with a shock on my *h* *Maud I i* 15
Than the *h* of the citizen hissing in war „ 24
May make my *h* as a millstone, „ 31
passionate *h* of the poet is whirl'd into folly „ *iv* 39
Ready in *h* and ready in hand, „ *v* 9
Kept itself warm in the *h* of my dreams, „ *vi* 18
On a *h* half-turn'd to stone. „ 78
O *h* of stone, are you flesh, „ 79
suddenly, sweetly, my *h* beat stronger „ *viii* 8
Sick, sick to the *h* of life, am I. „ *x* 36
Ah God, for a man with *h*, head, hand, „ 60
Set in the *h* of the carven gloom, „ *xiv* 11
drown His *h* in the gross mud-honey of town, „ *xvi* 5
Catch not my breath, O clamorous *h*, „ 31
shook my *h* to think she comes once more; „ *xviii* 10
Dear *h*, I feel with thee the drowsy spell. „ 72
My own *h's* *h*, my ownest own, farewell; „ 74
Beat with my *h* more blest than *h* can tell, „ 82
And that dead man at her *h* and mine: „ *xix* 9
From him who had ceased to share her *h*, „ 30
A desire that awoke in the *h* of the child, „ 48
To the faults of his *h* and mind, „ 68
There is but one With whom she has *h* to be gay. „ *xxii* 20
My *h* would hear her and beat, „ 69
It will ring in my *h* and my ears, „ *II i* 35
little *h's* that know not how to forgive: „ 44
Shall I nurse in my dark *h*, „ *ii* 55
Courage, poor *h* of stone! „ *II iii* 1
Courage, poor stupid *h* of stone.— „ 5
H's with no love for me: „ *iv* 94
And my *h* is a handful of dust, „ *v* 3
surely, some kind *h* will come To bury me, „ 102
it is time, O passionate *h*,' said I „ *III vi* 30
'It is time, O passionate *h* and morbid eye, „ 32
the *h* of a people beat with one desire; „ 49
flames The blood-red blossom of war with a *h* of fire. „ 53
We have proved we have *h's* in a cause, „ 55
inheritance Of such a life, a *h*, *Ded. of Idylls* 33
the spike that split the mother's *h* *Com. of Arthur* 38
A doubt that ever smoulder'd in the *h's* „ 64
And in the *h* of Arthur joy was lord. „ 124
when he heard, Leodogran in *h* Debating— „ 140
bold in *h* and act and word was he, „ 176
there be those who hate him in their *h's*, „ 179
Bewildering *h* and eye— „ 300
comforted my *h*, And dried my tears, „ 349
But brake his very *h* in pining for it, *Gareth and L.* 57
and tourney-falls, Frights to my *h*; „ 90
Albeit in mine own *h* I knew him King, „ 123
felt his young *h* hammering in his ears, „ 322
In token of true *h* and feälty. „ 399
h of her good horse Was nigh to burst with violence „ 762
Gareth panted hard, and his great *h*, „ 1126
lets His *h* be stirr'd with any foolish heat „ 1178
Sent all his *h* and breath thro' all the horn. „ 1369
with true *h* Adored her, as the stateliest *Marr. of Geraint* 19
Low to her own *h* piteously she said: „ 85
Our hoard is little, but our *h's* are great. (repeat) „ 352, 374
grateful is the noise of noble deeds To noble *h's* „ 438
I seem to suffer nothing *h* or limb, „ 472
'Well said, true *h*,' replied Geraint, „ 474
Yniol's *h* Danced in his bosom, „ 504
Tell her, and prove her *h* toward the Prince.' „ 513
their converse in the hall, Proving her *h*: „ 521
Glow'd like the *h* of a great fire at Yule, „ 559
softly to her own sweet *h* she said: „ 618
her *h* All overshadow'd by the foolish dream, „ 674
felt that tempest brooding round his *h*, *Geraint and E.* 11
there he broke the sentence in his *h* Abruptly, „ 41
great plover's human whistle amazed Her *h*, „ 50

Heart (*continued*) Enid ponder'd in her *h*, and said: (repeat) *Geraint and E.* 64, 130
disedge The sharpness of that pain about her *h*: „ 190
Here in the *h* of waste and wilderness. „ 313
fell asleep, and Enid had no *h* To wake him, „ 369
sadden'd all her *h* again. „ 445
has your palfrey *h* enough To bear his armour? „ 489
to his own *h*, 'She weeps for me:' (repeat) „ 587, 590
As all but empty *h* and weariness „ 652
She felt so blunt and stupid at the *h*: „ 747
hand to hand beneath her husband's *h*, „ 767
mist Like that which kept the *h* of Eden green „ 770
(With one main purpose ever at my *h*) „ 831
His very face with change of *h* is changed. „ 899
Edyrn has done it, weeding all his *h* „ 906
set up a stronger race With *h's* and hands, „ 941
vigorously yet mildly, that all *h's* Applauded, „ 957
spirit of his youth return'd On Arthur's *h*; *Balin and Balan* 22
maidens often laugh When sick at *h*, „ 498
Brave *h's* and clean! and yet— *Merlin and V.* 29
Mark was half in *h* to hurl his cup „ 30
The *h's* of all this Order in mine hand— „ 56
Who feels no *h* to ask another boon. „ 382
Lo now, what *h's* have men! „ 442
brought Her own claw back, and wounded her own *h*. „ 500
Without the full *h* back may merit well „ 534
that full *h* of yours Whereof ye prattle, „ 548
The rustiest iron of old fighters' *h's*; „ 574
Merlin to his own *h*, loathing, said: „ 790
colours of the *h* that are not theirs. „ 822
'Stabb'd through the *h's* affections to the *h*! „ 868
I should have found in him a greater *h*. „ 873
he let his wisdom go For ease of *h*, „ 893
from his knees, Half-nestled at his *h*, „ 905
own gross *h* Would reckon worth the taking? „ 916
The vast necessity of *h* and life. „ 925
in his *h* Heard murmurs 'Lo, thou likewise *Lancelot and E.* 54
a *h* Love-loyal to the least wish of the Queen „ 88
Low to her own *h* said the lily maid, „ 319
She braved a riotous *h* in asking for it. „ 359
reverence, Dearer to true young *h's* „ 419
To which it made a restless *h*, „ 550
With smiling face and frowning *h*, „ 553
That Lancelot is no more a lonely *h*. „ 602
kept The one-day-seen Sir Lancelot in her *h*, „ 747
And changed itself and echo'd in her *h*, „ 782
And in her *h* she answer'd it and said, „ 786
and in her *h* she laugh'd, Because he had not loosed it „ 808
her *h's* sad secret blazed itself In the *h's* colours „ 836
Making a treacherous quiet in his *h*, „ 883
speak the wish most near to your true *h*; „ 914
a stupid *h* To interpret ear and eye, „ 941
the heat is gone from out my *h*, „ 1116
And parted, laughing in his courtly *h*. „ 1176
in my *h* of *h's* I did acknowledge nobler. „ 1210
To loyal *h's* the value of all gifts Must vary „ 1214
For all true *h's* be blazon'd on her tomb „ 1344
To doubt her pureness were to want a *h*— „ 1377
'Ah simple *h* and sweet, Ye loved me, damsel, „ 1393
Arthur's greatest knight, a man Not after Arthur's *h*! „ 1420
and wrought into his *h* A way by love *Holy Grail* 10
men's *h's* became Clean for a season, „ 90
'I know not, for thy *h* is pure as snow.' „ 97
I was lifted up in *h*, and thought „ 361
And every homely secret in their *h's*, „ 552
that one only, who had ever Made my *h* leap; „ 580
maiden, all my *h* Went after her with longing: „ 582
And the Quest faded in my *h*. „ 600
to warm My cold *h* with a friend: „ 619
Small *h* was his after the Holy Quest: „ 657
strove To tear the twain asunder in my *h*, „ 786
and in her *h* She mutter'd, 'I have lighted on a fool, *Pelleas and E.* 112
his helpless *h* Leapt, and he cried, „ 130
More bondsman in his *h* than in his bonds. „ 239
thro' his *h* The fire of honour and all noble deeds „ 277

Heart (*continued*) vext his *h*, And marr'd his rest— *Pelleas and E.* 398
heard but his own steps, and his own *h* Beating, „ 416
Black as the harlot's *h*—hollow as a skull! „ 468
the words were flash'd into his *h* „ 503
hard his eyes; harder his *h* Seem'd; „ 512
Peace at his *h*, and gazing at a star „ 559
Hath the great *h* of knighthood in thee fail'd „ 596
yearn'd to shake The burthen off his *h* *Last Tournament* 180
Strength of *h* And might of limb, „ 197
It frighted all free fool from out thy *h*; „ 307
But in the *h* of Arthur pain was lord. „ 486
and felt the goodly hounds Yelp at his *h*, „ 504
heal'd Thy hurt and *h* with unguent and caress— „ 595
meats and wines, and satiated their *h's*— „ 725
Rankled in him and ruffled all his *h*, *Guinevere* 49
Sing, and unbind my *h* that I may weep.' „ 166
Then to her own sad *h* mutter'd the Queen, „ 213
Far on into the rich *h* of the west: „ 244
Sigh'd, and began to gather *h* again, „ 368
loathsome opposite Of all my *h* had destined did obtain „ 492
could speak Of the pure *h*, nor seem to glance „ 502
Better the King's waste hearth and aching *h* „ 524
while I weigh'd thy *h* with one Too wholly true „ 540
For mockery is the fume of little *h's*. „ 633
left me hope That in mine own *h* I can live down sin „ 636
and her *h* was loosed Within her, and she wept „ 667
Right well in *h* they know thee for the King. *Pass. of Arthur* 63
till all his *h* was cold With formless fear; „ 97
O Bedivere, for on my *h* hath fall'n Confusion, „ 143
that takes The *h*, and sometimes touches *Lover's Tale i* 17
As tho' there beat a *h* in either eye; „ 34
deep vault where the *h* of Hope Fell into dust, „ 94
The grasp of hopeless grief about my *h*, „ 126
Or from the after-fulness of my *h*, „ 146
neither Love, Warm in the *h*, his cradle, „ 158
Camilla close beneath her beating *h*, „ 203
Who had a twofold claim upon my *h*, „ 210
H beating time to *h*, lip pressing lip, „ 260
More warmly on the *h* than on the brow. „ 328
the naked poisons of his *h* In his old age.' „ 356
my inmost *h* As to my outward hearing: „ 428
(A visible link into the home of my *h*), „ 431
love, soul, spirit, and *h* and strength. „ 460
Love wraps his wings on either side the *h*, „ 467
words stole with most prevailing sweetness Into my *h*, „ 554
And soul and *h* and body are all at ease: „ 556
My *h* paused—my raised eyelids would not fall, „ 571
For all the secret of her inmost *h*, „ 588
For in the sudden anguish of her *h* Loosed „ 702
syllables, that strove to rise From my full *h*. „ 712
deals comfortable words To *h's* wounded for ever; „ 718
let my *h* Break rather— „ 737
There be some *h's* so airily built, „ 803
Alone, and in the *h* of the great forest. „ *ii* 3
motions of my *h* seem'd far within me, „ 54
Makes the *h* tremble, and the sight run over „ 156
and each *h* Grew closer to the other, „ 186
My *h* was cloven with pain; „ 200
I turn'd: my *h* Shrank in me, „ *iii* 37
the bells, Those marriage-bells, echoing in ear and *h*— „ *iv* 3
as he said, that once was loving *h's*, *H's* that had beat with such a love „ 68
placing his true hand upon her *h*, 'O, you warm *h*,' he moaned, „ 75
It beat—the *h*—it beat: Faint—but it beat: „ 80
Raving of dead men's dust and beating *h's*. „ 140
Talk of lost hopes and broken *h*! „ 176
Yet glowing in a *h* of ruby— „ 196
The beauty that is dearest to his *h*— „ 249
'O my *h's* lord, would I could show you,' he says, 'Ev'n my *h* too.' „ 250
To show you what is dearest to my *h*, And my *h* too. „ 252
while I show you all my *h*.' „ 353
I felt that my *h* was hard, *First Quarrel* 76
So I knew my *h* was hard, „ 78

Heart (*continued*) But the night has crept into my *h*, *Rizpah* 16
But not the black *h* of the lawyer who kill'd him „ 40
Revenge ran on sheer into the *h* of the foe, *The Revenge* 33
I could stamp my image on her *h*! *Sisters (E. and E)* 195
cold *h* or none—No bride for me. „ 201
answer of full *h* I had from her at first. „ 259
But he sent a chill to my *h* when I saw him *In the Child. Hosp.* 2
gratefullest *h* I have found in a child of her years— „ 32
Wan, but as pretty as *h* can desire, „ 40
we were English in *h* and in limb, *Def. of Lucknow* 46
Rifleman, true is your *h*, „ 56
Burst vein, snap sinew, and crack *h*, *Sir J. Oldcastle* 123
Do penance in his *h*, God hears him.' „ 143
lifted hand and *h* and voice In praise to God *Columbus* 16
ran into the *h's* of my crew, *V. of Maeldune* 33
rang into the *h* and the brain, „ 110
all their *h's* Were troubled, *Achilles over the T.* 23
The boundless yearning of the Prophet's *h*— *Tiresias* 81
I never have wrong'd his *h*, *The Wreck* 14
and there Lost, head and *h*, in the chances of dividend, „ 30
I closed my *h* to the gloom; „ 38
the *h* of a listening crowd— „ 47
the *h* that was wise! „ 56
what a *h* was mine to forsake her even for you.' 'Never the *h* among women,' he said, „ 95
'The *h*! not a mother's *h*, „ 97
for the *h* of the father will care for his own.' 'The *h* of the father will spurn her,' „ 98
'The *h*, the *h*!' I kiss'd him, „ 105
Who had borne my flower on her hireling *h*; „ 143
and the human *h*, and the Age. *Despair* 40
Struck hard at the tender *h* of the mother, „ 74
And Hope will have broken her *h*, „ 92
And leave him, blind of *h* and eyes, *Ancient Sage* 113
that world-prophet in the *h* of man. „ 213
send the day into the darken'd *h*; „ 261
daughter yield her life, *h*, soul to one— *The Flight* 28
love that keeps this *h* alive beats on it „ 35
And yet my *h* is ill at ease, „ 97
With breaking *h's*, without a friend, „ 100
every *h* that loves with truth is equal to endure. „ 104
set me *h* batin' to music wid ivery word! *Tomorrow* 34
wid a *h* and a half, me darlin', „ 39
She that in her *h* is brooding *Locksley H., Sixty* 23
Woman to her inmost *h*, and woman to her tender feet, „ 50
Pining for the stronger *h* that once had beat „ 58
Shape your *h* to front the hour, „ 106
men Were soldiers to her *h's* desire, *Pro. to Gen. Hamley* 25
In the *h* of the Russian hordes, *Heavy Brigade* 50
'The song that nerves a nation's *h*, *Epilogue* 81
The red 'Blood-eagle' of liver and *h*; *Dead Prophet* 71
'See, what a little *h*,' she said, „ 75
O *h*, look down and up Serene, *Early Spring* 27
Thou livest in all *h's*, *Epit. on Gordon* 3
be thy *h* a fortress to maintain The day *To Duke of Argyll* 5
To all the loyal *h's* who long To keep *Hands all Round* 13
One with Britain, *h* and soul! *Open I. and C. Exhib.* 38
thank thee with our voice, and from the *h*. *To W. C. Macready* 4
a multitude Loyal, each, to the *h* of it, *On Jub. Q. Victoria* 21
Let the maim'd in his *h* rejoice „ 36
All your *h's* be in harmony, „ 62
I feel the deathless *h* of motherhood *Demeter and P.* 41
I thridded the black *h* of all the woods, „ 69
Stirs up again in the *h* of the sleeper, *Vastness* 18
Moon of married *h's*, Hear me, you! *The Ring* 3
Hubert weds in you The *h* of Love, „ 62
No voice for either spoke within my *h* „ 162
Shrined him within the temple of her *h*, „ 219
call thro' this 'Io t'amo' to the *h* Of Miriam; „ 234
she makes Her *h* a mirror that reflects but you.' „ 366
Her h! I gazed into the mirror, „ 368
flung herself Against my *h*, „ 398
And eased her *h* of madness . . . *Forlorn* 82

Heart (*continued*) leper plague may scale my skin but never taint my *h*; *Happy* 27
Within the bloodless *h* of lowly flowers *Prog. of Spring* 84
in the *h* of this most ancient realm „ 102
'Beat, little *h*—I give you this and this' *Romney's R.* 1
claspt our infant daughter, *h* to *h*. „ 77
'Beat upon mine, little *h*! „ 94
'Beat little *h*' on this fool brain of mine. „ 155
The Gods Avenge on stony *h's* *Death of Œnone* 41
I am poison'd to the *h*.' „ 46
There, like a creature frozen to the *h* „ 73
in his *h* he cried 'The call of God!' *St. Telemachus* 27
thro' all the nobler *h's* In that vast Oval „ 72
belongs to the *h* of the perfume seller. *Akbar's D., Incrip.* 9
Still I raised my *h* to heaven, *Akbar's Dream* 6
warm'd but by the *h* Within them, „ 132
how deep a well of love My *h* is for my son, „ 171
gladdening human *h's* and eyes. „ *Hymn* 2
True gentleman, *h*, blood and bone, *Bandit's Death* 2
Hush'd as the *h* of the grave, „ 26
crazed With the grief that gnaw'd at my *h*, „ 39
Men, with a *h* and a soul, *The Dawn* 18
creeds be lower than the *h's* desire! *Faith* 5
Heart-affluence *H-a* in discursive talk *In Mem. cix* 1
Heart-beat An earthquake, my loud *h-b's*, *Lover's Tale ii* 193
Heart-broken he pass'd his father's gate, *H-b*, *Dora* 51
Heart-disease He suddenly dropt dead of *h-d*.' *Sea Dreams* 274
'Dead? he? of *h-d*? what heart had he To die of? „ 275
Hearted *See* **Cruel-hearted, Eager-hearted, Eunuch-hearted, Evil-hearted, Faint-hearted, Gentle-hearted, Honey-hearted, Human-hearted, Icy-hearted, Iron-hearted, Kindly-hearted, Loyal-hearted, Noblest-hearted, Open-hearted, Ruddy-hearted, Simple-hearted, Shallow-hearted, Sweet-hearted, Tenderest-hearted, Traitor-hearted, Truer-hearted**
Hearten Cry thro' the sense to *h* trust *In Mem. cxvi* 7
Heart-free From which I escaped *h-f*, *Maud I ii* 11
Hearth (*See also* **Hall-hearth, Lay-hearth**) For surely now our household *h's* are cold: *Lotos-Eaters, C. S.* 72
'pick'd the eleventh from this *h* *The Epic* 41
an idle king, By this still *h*, *Ulysses* 2
Keep a clean *h* and a clear fire for me, *Enoch Arden* 192
ten years, Since Enoch left his *h* and native land, „ 360
so genial was the *h*: And on the right hand of the *h* he saw „ 743
on the left hand of the *h* he saw The mother „ 753
Would shatter all the happiness of the *h*. „ 770
warm-blue breathings of a hidden *h* *Aylmer's Field* 155
On either side the *h*, indignant; „ 288
face Meet for the reverence of the *h*, „ 333
who beside your *h's* Can take her place— „ 735
strangers at my *h* Not welcome, *Lucretius* 158
Two heads in council, two beside the *h*, *Princess ii* 173
household talk, and phrases of the *h*, „ 315
Man for the field and woman for the *h*; „ *v* 447
the fires of Hell Mix with his *h*: „ 455
we will make it faggots for the *h*, „ *vi* 45
Till happier times each to her proper *h*: „ 303
azure pillars of the *h* Arise to thee; „ *vii* 216
land whose *h's* he saved from shame *Ode on Well.* 225
For by the *h* the children sit *In Mem. xx* 13
weave The holly round the Christmas *h*; „ *xxx* 2
weave The holly round the Christmas *h*; „ *lxxviii* 2
and prey By each cold *h*, „ *xcviii* 18
father Lot beside the *h* Lies like a log, *Gareth and L.* 74
rend In pieces, and so cast it on the *h*. „ 401
Rose, and high-arching over-brow'd the *h*. „ 408
rend the cloth and cast it on the *h*. „ 418
labour him Beyond his comrade of the *h*, „ 485
But one was counter to the *h*, „ 672
We lack thee by the *h*.' „ 754
My champion from the ashes of his *h*.' „ 899
kitchen-knave among the rest Fierce was the *h*, „ 1010
wear your costly gift Beside your own warm *h*, *Marr. of Geraint* 820
Thus, as a *h* lit in a mountain home, *Balin and Balan* 231

Hearth (*continued*) that gray cricket chirpt of at our *h*— *Merlin and V.* 110
Better the King's waste *h* and aching heart *Guinevere* 524
And the roof sank in on the *h*, *V. of Maeldune* 32
their hoards and their *h's* and their homes. *Batt. of Brunanburh* 19
The jungle rooted in his shatter'd *h*, *Demeter and P.* 76
MANY a *h* upon our dark globe sighs *Vastness* 1
Make all true *h's* thy home. *Prog. of Spring* 52
Hearth-flower The little *h-f* Lilia. *Princess, Pro.* 166
Heart-hiding *H-h* smile, and gray persistent eye: *Guinevere* 64
Hearthstone hissing in war on his own *h*? *Maud I i* 24
Heartily they ran To greet his hearty welcome *h*; *Enoch Arden* 350
Heartless Insolent, brainless, *h*! *Aylmer's Field* 368
Heart-weary *H-w* and overdone! *The Dreamer* 18
Hearty (*See also* **'Arty**) they ran To greet his *h* welcome heartily; *Enoch Arden* 350
Heart-yearning deep *h-y's*, thy sweet memories *Last Tournament* 579
Heat (s) (*See also* **After-heat, 'Eat, Heät, Hell-heat**)
hollows of the fringed hills In summer *h's*, *Supp. Confessions* 154
Clear, without *h*, undying, *Isabel* 3
Close-latticed to the brooding *h*, *Mariana in the S.* 3
But day increased from *h* to *h*, „ 39
From *h* to *h* the day decreased, „ 78
That *h* of inward evidence, *Two Voices* 284
Remembering its ancient *h*. „ 423
Throbbing thro' all thy *h* and light, *Fatima* 4
and the heart Faints, faded by its *h*. *D. of F. Women* 288
if in noble *h* Those men thine arms withstood, *England and Amer.* 6
Rain, wind, frost, *h*, hail, damp, *St. S. Stylites* 16
Then added, all in *h*: 'What stuff is this! *Golden Year* 64
I spoke with heart, and *h* and force, *The Letters* 37
Or when some *h* of difference sparkled out, *Aylmer's Field* 705
all-generating powers and genial *h* Of Nature, *Lucretius* 97
With animal *h* and dire insanity? „ 163
Sun-shaded in the *h* of dusty fights) *Princess ii* 241
under arches of the marble bridge Hung, shadow'd from the *h*: „ 459
while my honest *h* Were all miscounted „ *iv* 333
many a bold knight started up in *h*, „ *v* 359
What *h's* of indignation when we heard „ 375
I felt my veins Stretch with fierce *h*; „ 538
A night of Summer from the *h*, „ *vi* 54
Where we withdrew from summer *h's* and state, „ 245
But yonder, whiff! there comes a sudden *h*, „ *Con.* 58
For life outliving *h's* of youth, *In Mem. liii* 10
mark The landscape winking thro' the *h*: „ *lxxxix* 16
To make a solid core of *h*; „ *cvii* 18
not the schoolboy *h*, The blind hysterics „ *cix* 15
tread In tracts of fluent *h* began, „ *cxviii* 9
true blood spilt had in it a *h* To dissolve *Maud I xix* 44
Then Uther in his wrath and *h* besieged *Com. of Arthur* 198
His heart be stirr'd with any foolish *h* *Gareth and L.* 1178
And after nodded sleepily in the *h*. *Geraint and E.* 253
Who, with mild *h* of holy oratory, „ 866
Took, as in rival *h*, to holy things; *Balin and Balan* 100
forget My *h's* and violences? „ 190
Whom Pellam drove away with holy *h*. „ 611
Brain-feverous in his *h* and agony, *Lancelot and E.* 854
And when the *h* is gone from out my heart, „ 1116
thro' the casement standing wide for *h*, „ 1234
And earthly *h's* that spring and sparkle out *Holy Grail* 33
And almost burst the barriers in their *h*, „ 336
and thro' a stormy glare, a *h* „ 842
the *h* Of pride and glory fired her face; *Pelleas and E.* 171
in his *h* and eagerness Trembled and quiver'd, „ 283
a sudden flush of wrathful *h* Fired all the pale face *Guinevere* 356
the white *h's* of the blinding noons Beat *Lover's Tale i* 139
Thro' the *h*, the drowth, the dust, the glare, *Sisters (E. and E.)* 6
H like the mouth of a hell, *Def. of Lucknow* 81
none could breathe Within the zone of *h*; *Columbus* 53
with thirst in the middle-day *h*. *V. of Maeldune* 50
That wholesome *h* the blood had lost, *To E. Fitzgerald* 24
the winds were dead for *h*; *Tiresias* 34
Of the hellish *h* of a wretched life *Despair* 68
Sunn'd with a summer of milder *h*. *To Prof. Jebb.* 8
Heat (s) (*continued*) till the *h* Smote on her brow, *Death of Œnone* 97
Heät (s) But the *h* druv hout i' my heyes *Owd Roä* 84
Heat (verb) the latter fire shall *h* the deep; *The Kraken* 13
Let the Sun, Who *h's* our earth to yield *Akbar's Dream* 105
Heated (*See also* **Seventimes-heated, Wine-heated**) high shrine-doors burst thro' with *h* blasts *D. of F. Women* 29
came again together on the king With *h* faces; *Audley Court* 37
Where sat a company with *h* eyes, *Vision of Sin* 7
To chapel; where a *h* pulpiteer, *Sea Dreams* 20
and from within Burst thro' the *h* buds, *Lover's Tale i* 320
and felt the blast Beat on my *h* eyelids: „ *iii* 28
Had made a *h* haze to magnify The charm of Edith— *Sisters (E. and E.)* 129
h thro' and thro' with wrath and love, *Princess iv* 163
And *h* hot with burning fears, *In Mem. cxviii* 22
And *h* the strong warrior in his dreams; *Marr. of Geraint* 72
H am I? you—you wonder— *Locksley H., Sixty* 151
Heath (barren country) blackening over *h* and holt, *Locksley Hall* 191
Who slowly rode across a wither'd *h*, *Vision of Sin* 61
At the Dragon on the *h*! „ 72
The Priest went out by *h* and hill; *The Victim* 29
Arise in open prospect—*h* and hill, *Lover's Tale i* 397
Dumb on the winter *h* he lay. *Dead Prophet* 13
Lightnings flicker'd along the *h*; „ 79
Heath (heather) (*See also* **Heather**) lips in the field above are dabbled with blood-red *h*, *Maud I i* 2
And flung myself down on a bank of *h*, *Com. of Arthur* 342
all round was open space, And fern and *h*: *Pelleas and E.* 29
Among our *h* and bracken. *The Ring* 318
Heathen (adj.) from time to time the *h* host Swarm'd overseas, *Com. of Arthur* 8
last a *h* horde, Reddening the sun with smoke „ 36
in twelve great battles overcame The *h* hordes, „ 519
Red as the rising sun with *h* blood, *Lancelot and E.* 308
Yet in this *h* war the fire of God Fills him: „ 315
Wasted so often by the *h* hordes, *Holy Grail* 244
splash'd and dyed The strong White Horse in his own *h* blood— „ 312
Fool, I came late, the *h* wars were o'er, *Last Tournament* 269
Hard on that helm which many a *h* sword *Pass. of Arthur* 166
Burn? *h* men have borne as much as this, *Sir J. Oldcastle* 185
Christian love among the Churches look'd the twin of *h* hate. *Locksley H., Sixty* 86
Heathen (s) (*See also* **Haithen**) Then he drave The *h*; after, slew the beast, *Com. of Arthur* 59
cross-hilted sword, Whereby to drive the *h* out: „ 287
then or now Utterly smite the *h* underfoot, „ 423
'Shall Rome or *H* rule in Arthur's realm? „ 485
To drive the *h* from your Roman wall, „ 512
Who drave the *h* hence by sorcery *Gareth and L.* 204
and fell Against the *h* of the Northern Sea *Geraint and E.* 969
While all the *h* lay at Arthur's feet, *Merlin and V.* 144
till we drive The *h*, who, some say, *Lancelot and E.* 65
The *h* caught and reft him of his tongue. „ 273
sand-shores of Trath Treroit, Where many a *h* fell; „ 302
The *h* are upon him, his long lance Broken, *Last Tournament* 87
The *h*—but that ever-climbing wave, „ 92
H, the brood by Hengist left; *Guinevere* 16
For now the *H* of the Northern Sea, „ 135
And leagued with him the *h*, „ 155
Godless hosts Of *h* swarming o'er the Northern Sea; „ 428
To break the *h* and uphold the Christ, „ 470
Lords of the White Horse, *h*, and knights, „ 574
but grosser grown Than *h*, *Pass. of Arthur* 62
Or thrust the *h* from the Roman wall, „ 69
shouts of *h* and the traitor knights, „ 113
Nor any cry of Christian heard thereon, Nor yet of *h*; „ 129
he that brought The *h* back among us, „ 152
a shame to speak of them—Among the *h*— *Sir J. Oldcastle* 111
Heather find the white *h* wherever you go, *Romney's R.* 108
my white *h* only blooms in heaven „ 110
wild *h* round me and over me June's high blue, *June Bracken, etc.* 2
the bracken so bright and the *h* so brown, „ 3
green of the bracken amid the gloom of the *h*. „ 9
Heather-scented and *h-s* air, Pulsing full man; *Last Tournament* 691

Heather-scented (*continued*) on that clear and *h-s* height The rounder cheek — The Ring 350
Heath-flower Some red *h-f* in the dew, — Rosalind 41
Heathy Playing mad pranks along the *h* leas, — Circumstance 2
Heave *h* and thump A league of street — Princess iii 127
For tho' the Giant Ages *h* the hill — Ode on Well. 259
Which *h's* but with the heaving deep. — In Mem. xi 20
Then the rough Torre began to *h* and move, — Lancelot and E. 1066
Began to *h* upon that painted sea; — Lover's Tale ii 192
water began to *h* and the weather to moan, — The Revenge 113
ocean on every side Plunges and *h's* at a bank — Def. of Lucknow 39
Heaved (adj.) With a *h* shoulder and a saucy smile, — Aylmer's Field 466
vessel in mid-ocean, her *h* prow Clambering, — Lover's Tale ii 169
Heaved (verb) The silver lily *h* and fell; — To E. L. 19
I was *h* upon it In darkness: — Sea Dreams 92
huge bush-bearded Barons *h* and blew, — Princess v 21
That only *h* with a summer swell. — The Daisy 12
Who might'st have *h* a windless flame — In Mem. lxxii 13
the Sun *H* up a ponderous arm to strike — Gareth and L. 1045
h his blade aloft, And crack'd the helmet — Marr. of Geraint 572
Heaven (*See also* **'Eaven, High-heaven, Hiven, Mid-heaven**) And then one *H* receive us all. — Supp. Confessions 32
that blue *h* which hues and paves The other? — „ 134
She could not look on the sweet *h*, — Mariana 15
h's mazed signs stood still In the dim tract — Clear-headed friend 28
Sure she was nigher to *h's* spheres, — Ode to Memory 40
H flow'd upon the soul in many dreams — The Poet 31
the mountain draws it from *H* above, — Poet's Mind 32
the air Sleepeth over all the *h*, — Eleänore 39
As tho' a star, in inmost *h* set, — „ 89
Thou from a throne Mounted in *h* wilt shoot — To J. M. K. 13
H over *H* rose the night. — Mariana in the S. 92
Rapt after *h's* starry flight, — Two Voices 68
The joy that mixes man with *H*: — „ 210
'H opens inward, chasms yawn, — „ 304
Coming thro' *H*, like a light that grows — Œnone 108
From me, *H's* Queen, Paris, to thee king-born, — „ 127
O happy *H*, how canst thou see my face? — „ 236
hollow'd moons of gems, To mimic *h*; — Palace of Art 189
From yon blue *h's* above us bent — L. C. V. de Vere 50
Pray *H* for a human heart, — „ 71
seem'd to go right up to *H* and die among the stars. — May Queen, Con. 40
sun begins to rise, the *h's* are in a glow; — „ 49
Beneath a *h* dark and holy, — Lotos-Eaters, C. S. 91
'*H* heads the count of crimes With that wild oath.' — D. of F. Women 201
Rose with you thro' a little arc Of *h*, — To J. S. 27
And dwells in *h* half the night. — „ 52
all else of *h* was pure Up to the Sun, — Gardener's D. 79
praise the *h's* for what they have?' — „ 102
For which to praise the *h's* but only love, — „ 104
h's between their fairy fleeces pale — „ 261
—*H* knows—as much within; — Edwin Morris 82
Unfit for earth, unfit for *h*, — St. S. Stylites 3
Battering the gates of *h* with storms — „ 7
H, and Earth, and Time are choked. — „ 104
the saints Enjoy themselves in *h*, — „ 106
I think you know I have some power with *H* — „ 143
I am whole, and clean, and meek for *H*. — „ 213
whisper'd under *H* None else could understand; — Talking Oak 21
'Twere all as one to fix our hopes on *H* — Golden Year 57
which in old days Moved earth and *h*; — Ulysses 67
Sees in *h* the light of London — Locksley Hall 114
Saw the *h's* fill with commerce, — „ 121
Heard the *h's* fill with shouting, — „ 123
birds of Paradise That float thro' *H*, and cannot light? — Day-Dm., Ep. 8
My breath to *h* like vapour goes: — St. Agnes' Eve 3
Break up the *h's*, O Lord! — „ 21
All *h* bursts her starry floors, — „ 27
I yearn to breathe the airs of *h* — Sir Galahad 63
And set in *H's* third story, — Will Water. 70
Shall show thee past to *H*: — „ 246
With tears and smiles from *h* again — Sir L. and Q. G. 2

Heaven (*continued*) Blue isles of *h* laugh'd between, — Sir L. and Q. G. 6
'Cold altar, *H* and earth shall meet — The Letters 7
high in *h* behind it a gray down With Danish barrows; — Enoch Arden 6
sermonizing On providence and trust in *H*, — „ 205
The breath of *h* came continually — „ 535
such as drove her under moonless *h's* — „ 547
lawns And winding glades high up like ways to *H*, — „ 573
great stars that globed themselves in *H*, — „ 597
Which at a touch of light, an air of *h*, — Aylmer's Field 5
Or *H* in lavish bounty moulded, — „ 107
Like visions in the Northern dreamer's *h's*, — „ 161
God bless 'em: marriages are made in *H*.' — „ 188
The rain of *h*, and their own bitter tears, Tears, and the careless rain of *h*, — „ 428
breathless burthen of low-folded *h's* — „ 612
Shot up their shadows to the *H* of *H's*, — „ 642
thy brother man, the Lord from *H*, — „ 667
roof so lowly but that beam of *H* Dawn'd — „ 684
past the living fount of pity in H. — „ 752
if every star in *h* Can make it fair: — Sea Dreams 83
trees As high as *h*, and every bird that sings: — „ 102
Dropping the too rough *H* in Hell and *H*, — „ 196
One shriek of hate would jar all the hymns of *h*: — „ 259
Slide from that quiet *h* of hers, — Lucretius 87
stairs That climb into the windy halls of *h*: — „ 136
vases in the hall Flowers of all *h's*, — Princess, Pro. 12
Myself too had weird seizures, *H* knows what: — „ i 14
two sphere lamps blazon'd like *H* and Earth — „ 223
to call down from *H* A blessing on her labours — „ ii 478
let us breathe for one hour more in *H*' — „ iii 69
Appealing to the bolts of *H*; — „ iv 372
and his anger reddens in the *h's*; — „ 386
sweet influences Of earth and *h*? — „ v 192
Like a Saint's glory up in *h*: — „ 514
And right ascension, *H* knows what; — „ vi 257
cloud may stoop from *h* and take the shape — „ vii 2
H, Star after star, arose and fell; — „ 49
But cease to move so near the *H's*, — „ 195
Beyond all thought into the *H* of *H's*. — „ Con. 115
H flash'd a sudden jubilant ray, — Ode on Well. 129
The blue *h* break, and some diviner air — W. to Marie Alex. 43
The gloom that saddens *H* and Earth, — The Daisy 102
But thou wert silent in *h*, — Voice and the P. 7
voice and the Peak Far into *h* withdrawn. — „ 38
Thunder, a flying fire in *h*, — Boädicea 24
Roll'd the rich vapour far into the *h*. — Spec. of Iliad 8
when in *h* the stars about the moon Look beautiful, — „ 11
immeasurable *h's* Break open to their highest, — „ 14
Be merry in *h*, O larks, and far away, — Window, Ay 3
Sleep, gentle *h's*, before the prow; — In Mem. ix 14
To bear thro' *H* a tale of woe, — „ xii 2
Hung in the shadow of a *h*? — „ xvi 10
Her early *H*, her happy views; — „ xxxiii 6
suit The full-grown energies of *h*. — „ xl 20
In its assumptions up to *h*; — „ lxiii 4
starry *h's* of space Are sharpen'd to a needle's end; — „ lxxvi 3
drank the inviolate spring Where nighest *h*, — „ xc 3
To scale the *h's* highest height, — „ cviii 7
To bare the eternal *H's* again, — „ cxxii 4
And high in *h* the streaming cloud, — „ Con. 107
Let the sweet *h's* endure, — Maud I xi 8
O Maud were sure of *H* If lowliness could save her. — „ xii 19
to glide, Like a beam of the seventh *H*, — „ xiv 21
gates of *H* are closed, and she is gone. — „ xviii 12
thunder'd up into *H* the Christless code, — „ II i 26
and the *h's* fall in a gentle rain, — „ 41
To her that is the fairest under *h*, — Com. of Arthur 86
And dream he dropt from *h*: — „ 183
In which the bounds of *h* and earth were lost— — „ 372
It seem'd in *h*, a ship, the shape thereof — „ 374
but the King stood out in *h*, Crown'd. — „ 443
H yield her for it, but in me put force — Gareth and L. 18
And there was no gate like it under *h*. — „ 213
Keel upward, and mast downward, in the *h's*, — „ 254

Heaven (*continued*) peak And pinnacle, and had made it spire to *h*. *Gareth and L.* 309
Rather than—O sweet *h*! O fie upon him— " 741
Immingled with *H's* azure waveringly, " 936
'No star of thine, but shot from Arthur's *h* " 1100
'*H* help thee,' sigh'd Lynette. " 1357
And loved her, as he loved the light of *H*. And as the light of *H* varies, *Marr. of Geraint* 5
So aid me *H* when at mine uttermost, " 502
on open ground Beneath a troubled *h*, " 523
Sweet *h*, how much I shall discredit him! " 621
Herself would clothe her like the sun in *H*. " 784
she was ever praying the sweet *h's* *Geraint and E.* 44
I might amend it by the grace of *H*, " 53
issuing under open *h's* beheld A little town " 196
she cried, 'by *H*, I will not drink " 664
we love the *H* that chastens us. " 789
The truest eyes that ever answer'd *H*, " 842
Lost one Found was greeted as in *H* With joy *Balin and Balan* 81
No more of hatred than in *H* " 151
fire of *H* has kill'd the barren cold, " 440
fire of *H* is not the flame of Hell. (repeat) " 443, 447, 451, 455
'The fire of *H* is on the dusty ways. " 448
'The fire of *H* is lord of all things good, " 452
'This fire of *h*, This old sun-worship, " 456
The deathless mother-maidenhood of *H*, " 521
vows like theirs, that high in *h* Love most, *Merlin and V.* 14
O *H's* own white Earth-angel, " 80
Was also Bard, and knew the starry *h's*; " 169
By *H* that hears I tell you the clean truth, " 343
For men at most differ as *H* and earth, But women, worst and best, as *H* and Hell. " 814
May yon just *h*, that darkens o'er me, " 931
Scarce had she ceased, when out of *h* a bolt " 934
Vivien, fearing *h* had heard her oath, " 940
But who can gaze upon the Sun in *h*? *Lancelot and E.* 123
'*H* hinder,' said the King, 'that such an one, " 532
'I lose it, as we lose the lark in *h*, " 659
And, after *h*, on our dull side of death, " 1382
strength Within us, better offer'd up to *H*.' *Holy Grail* 36
I trust We are green in *H's* eyes; " 38
the holy cup Was caught away to *H*, " 58
'My knight, my love, my knight of *h*, " 157
Pray *H*, they be not smitten by the bolt.' " 221
Feasted, and as the stateliest under *h*. " 224
and never yet Had *h* appear'd so blue, " 365
Prick'd with incredible pinnacles into *h*. " 423
the *h's* Open'd and blazed with thunder " 507
the *h's* open'd and blazed again Roaring, " 516
Then fell the floods of *h* drowning the deep. " 533
and blest be *H* That brought thee here " 616
Quest and he were in the hands of *H*. " 659
and the stones They pitch up straight to *h*: " 665
heard the hollow-ringing *h's* sweep Over him " 678
they roll Thro' such a round in *h*, " 686
But *h* had meant it for a sunny one: " 706
clouded *h's* Were shaken with the motion and the sound. " 800
But if indeed there came a sign from *h*, " 873
A rosy dawn kindled in stainless *h's*, *Pelleas and E.* 72
Or have the *H's* but given thee a fair face, " 101
a sacrifice Kindled by fire from *h*: " 146
Till the sweet *h's* have fill'd it " 510
but when he saw High up in *h* the hall " 553
that young life Being smitten in mid *h* *Last Tournament* 27
Man was it who marr'd *h's* image in thee thus?' " 64
We call the harp of Arthur up in *h*?' " 333
High on all hills, and in the signs of *h*.' " 337
It makes a silent music up in *h*, " 349
sun that ray'd from off a brow Like hillsnow high in *h*, " 667
Dropt down from *h*? wash'd up from out the deep? " 685
A star in *h*, a star within the mere! " 732
A blot in *h*, the Raven, flying high, *Guinevere* 133
There came a day as still as *h*, " 292
But help me, *h*, for surely I repent. " 372

Heaven (*continued*) seem'd the *h's* upbreaking thro' the earth, *Guinevere* 391
I knew Of no more subtle master under *h* " 478
be his mate hereafter in the *h's* Before high God. " 637
the great light of *H* Burn'd at his lowest *Pass. of Arthur* 90
those who falling down Look'd up for *h*, " 112
mightiest of all peoples under *h*? *To the Queen ii* 21
trust that *H* Will blow the tempest " 46
From his mid-dome in *H's* airy halls; *Lover's Tale i* 66
till earth And *h* pass too, dwelt on my *h*, " 72
Waiting to see some blessed shape in *h*, " 312
and joy In breathing nearer *h*; " 389
To breathe with her as if in *h* itself; " 391
Thy fires from *h* had touch'd it, " 439
Sooner Earth Might go round *H*, " 482
bliss stood round me like the light of *H*,— " 495
Steppeth from *H* to *H*, from light to light, " 512
had *H* from all her doors, With all her golden thresholds " 604
whom the gentlest airs of *H* Should kiss " 738
may death Awake them with *h's* music " 761
Bore her free-faced to the free airs of *H*, " *iv* 38
wines that, *H* knows when, Had suck'd the fire " 193
Ah *h's*! Why need I tell you all?— " 200
Down out o' *h* i' Hell-fire— *North. Cobbler* 58
melted like a cloud in the silent summer *h*; *The Revenge* 14
a man's ideal Is high in *H*, *Sisters (E. and E.)* 131
Cold, but as welcome as free airs of *h* " 197
saved by the blessing of *H*! *Def. of Lucknow* 104
this good Wiclif mountain down from *h*, *Sir J. Oldcastle* 132
the great 'Laudamus' rose to *h*. *Columbus* 18
chains For him who gave a new *h*, " 20
King David call'd the *h's* a hide, " 47
Who took us for the very Gods from *H*, " 183
Queen of *H* who seest the souls in Hell " 216
high in the *h* above it there flicker'd *V. of Maeldune* 17
where the *h's* lean low on the land, " 83
For a wild witch naked as *h* " 100
when a smoke from a city goes to *h* *Achilles over the T.* 7
from his head the splendour went to *h*. " 14
all the *h's* flash'd in frost; *To E. Fitzgerald* 22
more than man Which rolls the *h's*, *Tiresias* 22
voice rang out in the thunders of Ocean and *H* *The Wreck* 88
No soul in the *h* above, *Despair* 19
higher still, the *h's* Whereby the cloud *Ancient Sage* 12
thou sendest thy free soul thro' *h*, " 47
So dark that men cry out against the *H's*. " 172
earth's dark forehead flings athwart the *h's* " 200
past into the Nameless, as a cloud Melts into *H*. " 234
The lark has past from earth to *H* *The Flight* 62
the blessed *H's* are just, " 67
She bad us love, like souls in *H*, " 88
While the silent *H's* roll, *Locksley H., Sixty* 203
sphere of all the boundless *H's* " 210
the stars in *h* Paled, and the glory grew. *Pro. to Gen. Hamley* 31
Whole *h's* within themselves, amaze *Epilogue* 56
And 'The Curse of the Prophet' in *H*. *Dead Prophet* 28
Opens a door in *H*; *Early Spring* 7
Like some conjectured planet in mid *h* *To Prin. Beatrice* 20
cry that rang thro' Hades, Earth, and *H*! *Demeter and P.* 33
I, Earth-Goddess, cursed the Gods of *H*. " 102
break The sunless halls of Hades into *H*? " 136
MELLOW moon of *h*, Bright in blue, *The Ring* 1
No sudden *h*, nor sudden hell, for man, " 41
past and future mix'd in *H* and made The rosy twilight " 186
sudden fire from *H* had dash'd him dead, *Happy* 83
to trace On paler *h's* the branching grace *To Ulysses* 15
For his clear *h*, and these few lanes *To Mary Boyle* 67
H lours, But in the tearful splendour *Prog. of Spring* 40
all but in *H* Hovers The Gleam. *Merlin and the G.* 118
This seem'd my lodestar in the *H* of Art, *Romney's R.* 39
roll The rainbow hues of *h* about it— " 51
my white heather only blooms in *h* " 110
the shout Of His descending peals from *H*, " 127
Human forgiveness touches *h*, " 159
earth's green stole in *h's* own hue, *Far—far—away* 2

Heaven (*continued*) as the heights of the June-blue *h*, *June Bracken, etc.* 7
topmost pine Spired into bluest *h*, *Death of Œnone* 69
A sudden strength from *h*, *St. Telemachus* 56
Still I raised my heart to *h*, *Akbar's Dream* 6
Well spake thy brother in his hymn to *h* „ 27
star Should shriek its claim 'I only am in *h*' „ 43
mists of earth Fade in the noon of *h*, „ 97
'hast *thou* brought us down a new Korân From *h*? „ 117
always open-door'd To every breath from *h*, „ 180
fur owt but the Kingdom o' *H*; *Church-warden, etc.* 44
~~She~~ is high in the *H* of *H's*, *Charity* 42
He is racing from *h* to *h* And less will be lost *The Dreamer* 21
H over *h* expands. *Mechanophilus* 36
O ye *H's*, of your boundless nights, *God and the Univ.* 2
Heaven-descended Corrupts the strength of *h-d* Will, *Will* 11
Heavenliest *See* **Earthly-heavenliest**
Heavenly 'He seems to hear a *H* Friend, *Two Voices* 295
For me the *H* Bridegroom waits, *St. Agnes' Eve* 31
Like *H* Hope she crown'd the sea, *The Voyage* 70
But Wisdom *h* of the soul. *In Mem. cxiv* 22
Dear *h* friend that canst not die, „ *cxxix* 7
he defileth *h* things With earthly uses '— *Balin and Balan* 421
Trusting no longer that earthly flower would be *h* fruit— *Despair* 35
ONCE more the *H* Power Makes all things new, *Early Spring* 1
For now the *H* Power Makes all things new, „ 43
Which on the touch of *h* feet had risen, *Death of Œnone* 5
Heavenly-best Ere she gain her *H-b*, *Locksley H., Sixty* 271
Heavenly-toned So *h-t*, that in that hour *Two Voices* 442
Heavenly-unmeasured *H-u* or unlimited Love, *Lover's Tale i* 474
Heavenly-wise glow In azure orbits *h-w*; *In Mem. lxxxvii* 38
Heaven-sweet *H-s* Evangel, ever-living word, *Sir J. Oldcastle* 28
Heavenward glancing *h* on a star so silver-fair, *Locksley H., Sixty* 191
As mounts the *h* altar-fire, *In Mem. xli* 3
Once again thou flamest *h*, *Akbar's D., Hymn* 1
Heavier tougher, *h*, stronger, he that smote *Princess v* 536
Heaviest roll'd Her *h* thunder— *Lover's Tale i* 606
Heavily-galloping sound of many a *h-g* hoof *Geraint and E.* 447
Heaviness Why are we weigh'd upon with *h*, *Lotos-Eaters, C. S.* 12
Heaving (*See also* **Hard-heaving**) Which heaves but with the *h* deep. *In Mem. xi* 20
Gazed at the *h* shoulder, and the face Hand-hidden, *Merlin and V.* 896
With his huge sea-castles *h* upon the weather bow. *The Revenge* 24
Heavy (*See also* **Dead-heavy, Head-heavy**) If time be *h* on your hands, *L. C. V. de Vere* 66
What is this? his eyes are *h*: *Locksley Hall* 51
for this most gentle maiden's death Right *h* am I; *Lancelot and E.* 1292
H as it was, a great stone slipt and fell, *Holy Grail* 680
teach me yet Somewhat before the *h* clod Weighs on me, *Supp. Confessions* 184
Earthward he boweth the *h* stalks *A spirit haunts* 7
Slide the *h* barges trail'd By slow horses; *L. of Shalott i* 20
The *h* clocks knolling the drowsy hours. *Gardener's D.* 184
with a grosser film made thick These *h*, horny eyes. *St. S. Stylites* 201
Rain out the *h* mist of tears, *Love and Duty* 43
But that his *h* rider kept him down. *Vision of Sin* 4
A vapour *h*, hueless, formless, cold, „ 53
Drink to *h* Ignorance! „ 193
But on my shoulder hung their *h* hands, *Princess iv* 553
And blossom-fragrant slipt the *h* dews „ *v* 243
on my *h* eyelids My anguish hangs like shame. *Maud II iv* 73
Among the *h* breathings of the house, *Geraint and E.* 402
thoughts deep and *h* as these well-nigh *Lover's Tale i* 688
Heavy-blosssom'd Droops the *h-b* bower, *Locksley Hall* 163
Heavy Brigade charge of the gallant three hundred, the *H B*! *Heavy Brigade* 1
up the hill, up the hill, Follow'd the *H B*. „ 12
Gallopt the gallant three hundred, the *H B*. „ 25
Heavy-folded and swung The *h-f* rose, *In Mem. xcv* 59
Heavy-fruited hangs the *h-f* tree— *Locksley Hall* 163
Heavy-plunging 'I would the white cold *h-p* foam, *D. of F. Women* 118
Heavy-shotted His *h-s* hammock-shroud *In Mem. vi* 15
Hebe (adj.) violet eyes, and all her *H* bloom, *Gardener's D.* 137
Hebe (s) *H's* are they to hand ambrosia, *Princess iii* 113
Hebe (s) (*continued*) Cassandra, *H*, Joan, *Romney's R.* 4
Hebrew 'No fair *H* boy Shall smile away my maiden blame among The *H* mothers'— *D. of F. Women* 213
Hector So *H* spake; the Trojans roar'd *Spec. of Iliad* 1
Hedge (s) To one green wicket in a privet *h*; *Gardener's D.* 110
All round a *h* upshoots, *Day-Dm., Sleep. P.* 41
He breaks the *h*: he enters there: „ *Arrival* 18
The *h* broke in, the banner blew, „ *Revival* 9
The very sparrows in the *h* Scarce answer *Amphion* 67
Lawrence Aylmer, seated on a stile In the long *h*, *The Brook* 198
breath Of tender air made tremble in the *h* „ 202
tho' she were a beggar from the *h*, *Marr. of Geraint* 230
pick'd a ragged-robin from the *h*, „ 724
sputtering thro' the *h* of splinter'd teeth, *Last Tournament* 65
Hedge (verb) laurel-shrubs that *h* it around. *Poet's Mind* 14
Hedge-bottoms But creeäp along the *h-b*, *Church-warden, etc.* 50
Hedgehog *h* underneath the plantain bores, *Aylmer's Field* 850
Hedgerow Not sowing *h* texts and passing by, „ 171
'Graver cause than yours is mine To curse this *h* thief, *Marr. of Geraint* 309
Hedge-row (s) where the *h-r* cuts the pathway, *Gardener's D.* 86
Heed (s) Yet take thou *h* of him, for, so thou pass *Gareth and L.* 267
And being found take *h* of Vivien. *Merlin and V.* 529
I didn't take *h* o' *them*, *First Quarrel* 29
Heed (verb) Why pray To one who *h's* not, *Supp. Confessions* 90
Shall I *h* them in their anguish? *Boädicea* 9
whether he *h* it or not, *Maud I iv* 53
How now, my soul, we do not *h* the fire? *Sir J. Oldcastle* 191
What are men that He should *h* us? *Locksley H., Sixty* 201
Heeded 'He *h* not reviling tones, *Two Voices* 220
All would be well—the lover *h* not, *Aylmer's Field* 545
Bubbled the nightingale and *h* not, *Princess iv* 266
Some old head-blow not *h* in his youth *Gareth and L.* 714
Garlon mock'd me, but I *h* not. *Balin and Balan* 606
that life I *h* not Flow'd from me, *Lover's Tale i* 596
Heedless a *h* and innocent bride— *The Wreck* 13
Heedlessness pleased her with a babbling *h* *Guinevere* 151
Heehaw A jackass *h's* from the rick, *Amphion* 71
Heel As head and *h's* upon the floor *The Goose* 37
Sharp-smitten with the dint of armed *h's*— *M. d'Arthur* 190
And drove his *h* into the smoulder'd log, „ *Ep.* 14
May with me from head to *h*. *Gardener's D.* 81
snarling at each other's *h's*. *Locksley Hall* 106
a precipitate *h*, Fledged as it were *Lucretius* 200
She trampled some beneath her horses' *h's*, *Princess, Pro.* 44
brains are in their hands and in their *h's*, „ *iv* 518
one rag, disprinced from head to *h*. „ *v* 30
The virgin marble under iron *h's*: „ *vi* 351
And has bitten the *h* of the going year. *Window, Winter* 6
a thousand wants Gnarr at the *h's* of men, *In Mem. xcviii* 17
A cloak that dropt from collar-bone to *h*, *Gareth and L.* 682
And *h* against the pavement echoing, *Geraint and E.* 271
At which her palfrey whinnying lifted *h*, „ 533
Drove his mail'd *h* athwart the royal crown, *Balin and Balan* 540
And lissome Vivien, holding by his *h*, *Merlin and V.* 238
The men who met him rounded on their *h's* *Pelleas and E.* 142
Lancelot, with his *h* upon the fall'n, „ 580
Wheel'd round on either *h*, Dagonet replied, *Last Tournament* 244
Lancelot pluck'd him by the *h*, *Guinevere* 34
Sharp-smitten with the dint of armed *h's*— *Pass. of Arthur* 358
And his white hair sank to his *h's*, *V. of Maeldune* 118
turn'd upon his *h* to hear My warning *Tiresias* 72
Tumble Nature *h* o'er head, *Locksley H., Sixty* 135
I be leper like yourself, my love, from head to *h*. *Happy* 88
Year will graze the *h* of year, *Poets and Critics* 14
Hegg (egg) Butter an' *h's*—yis—yis. *Village Wife* 2
an' I warrants the *h's* be as well, „ 3
fever 'ed baäked Jinny's 'eäd as bald as one o' them *h's*, „ 102
But I sarved 'em wi' butter an' *h's* „ 114
an' they knaw'd what a *h* wur an' all; „ 116
an' they laäid big *h's* es tha seeas; „ 118
Heifer brainless bulls, Dead for one *h*!' *Balin and Balan* 579
Height sponges of millennial growth and *h*; *The Kraken* 6
free delight, from any *h* of rapid flight, *Rosalind* 3
'Thou hast not gain'd a real *h*, *Two Voices* 91

Height (*continued*) In gazing up an Alpine *h*, *Two Voices* 362
O sun, that from thy noonday *h* Shudderest *Fatima* 2
Beyond, a line of *h's*, and higher *Palace of Art* 82
Be flatter'd to the *h*. „ 192
Which will not leave the myrrh-bush on the *h*; *Lotos-Eaters, C. S.* 58
To her full *h* her stately stature draws; *D. of F. Women* 102
Of old sat Freedom on the *h's*, *Of old sat Freedom* 1
I leave the plain, I climb the *h*; *Sir Galahad* 57
fold by fold, From those still *h's*, *Vision of Sin* 52
When lo! her Enoch sitting on a *h*, *Enoch Arden* 500
bending from his *h* With half-allowing smiles *Aylmer's Field* 119
Nor dealing goodly counsel from a *h* „ 172
from his *h* and loneliness of grief „ 632
She rose her *h*, and said: *Princess ii* 41
The rosy *h's* came out above the lawns. „ *iii* 365
When storm is on the *h's*, „ *v* 348
song, arose Once more thro' all her *h*, „ *vi* 160
drags me down From my fixt *h* to mob me „ 308
O maid, from yonder mountain *h*: „ *vii* 192
What pleasure lives in *h* (the shepherd sang) In *h* and cold, the splendour of the hills? „ 193
He gain in sweetness and in moral *h*, „ 281
The *h*, the space, the gloom, the glory! *The Daisy* 59
They leave the *h's* and are troubled, *Voice and the P.* 15
'The deep has power on the *h*, And the *h* has power on the deep; „ 21
And a *h* beyond the *h*! „ 34
Whisper in odorous *h's* of even. *Milton* 16
every *h* comes out, and jutting peak And valley, *Spec. of Iliad* 13
On Argive's *h's* divinely sang, *In Mem. xxiii* 22
Upon the last and sharpest *h*, „ *xlvii* 13
A higher *h*, a deeper deep. „ *lxiii* 12
all thy breadth and *h* Of foliage, „ *lxxxix* 3
About empyreal *h's* of thought, „ *xcv* 38
To scale the heaven's highest *h*, „ *cviii* 7
Powers of the *h*, Powers of the deep, *Maud II ii* 82
glory of manhood stand on his ancient *h*, „ *III vi* 21
up to a *h*, the peak Haze-hidden, *Com. of Arthur* 429
Sigh'd, as a boy lame-born beneath a *h*, *Balin and Balan* 164
Another sinning on such *h's* with one, *Lancelot and E.* 248
free flashes from a *h* Above her, „ 647
heavens have fill'd it from the *h's* *Pelleas and E.* 510
For once—ev'n to the *h*—I honour'd him. *Last Tournament* 662
not look up, or half-despised the *h* *Guinevere* 643
To what *h* The day had gown I know not. *Lover's Tale iii* 8
Grew after marriage to full *h* and form? *Sisters (E. and E.)* 171
Death from the *h's* of the mosque and the palace, *Def. of Lucknow* 24
from the crag to an unbelievable *h*, *V. of Maeldune* 16
kept their faith, their freedom, on the *h*, *Montenegro* 2
fell from that half-spiritual *h* Chill'd, *To E. Fitzgerald* 19
to scale the highest of the *h's* *Tiresias* 28
In *h* and prowess more than human, „ 179
On one far *h* in one far-shining fire. 'One *h* and one far-shining fire' „ 185
Force is from the *h's*. *Ancient Sage* 14
A *h*, a broken grange, a grove, „ 223
And, gazing from this *h* alone, *Pro. to Gen. Hamley* 9
horsemen had gather'd there on the *h*, *Heavy Brigade* 14
glancing from his *h* On earth a fruitless fallow, *Demeter and P.* 117
an ever opening *h*, An ever lessening earth— *The Ring* 45
on that clear and heather-scented *h* „ 350
beauty that endures on the Spiritual *h*, *Happy* 37
madden'd to the *h* By tonguester tricks, *To Mary Boyle* 33
And suffering cloud the *h* I stand upon *Romney's R.* 65
Muses have raised to the *h's* of the mountain, *Parnassus* 2
As he stands on the *h's* of his life with a glimpse of a *h* that is higher. *By an Evolution.* 20
as the *h's* of the June-blue heaven, *June Bracken, etc.* 7
Glimmering up the *h's* beyond me, *Silent Voices* 9
vanish in your deeps and *h's*? *God and the Univ.* 1

Height (eight) an' theere—it be strikin' *h*— *Spinster's S's.* 114

Heighten'd Then the Captain's colour *h*, *The Captain* 29

Heightening (*See also* **Ever-heightening**) peaks they stand ever spreading and *h*; *Parnassus* 11

Height-year-howd (eight-year-old) thou was a *h-y-h*, *Church-warden, etc.* 33

Heir His son and *h* doth ride post-haste, *D. of the Old Year* 31
first sight, first-born, and *h* to all, *Gardener's D.* 189
I the *h* of all the ages, *Locksley Hall* 178
Lord Ronald is *h* of all your lands, *Lady Clare* 19
And I,' said he, 'the lawful *h*, „ 86
loved As heiress and not *h* regretfully? *Aylmer's Field* 24
Blissful bride of a blissful *h*, Bride of the *h* of the kings of the sea— *W. to Alexandra* 27
The hard *h* strides about their lands, *In Mem. xc* 15
Spurn'd by this *h* of the liar— *Maud I xix* 78
Moaning and wailing for an *h* to rule After him, *Com. of Arthur* 207
'Here is Uther's *h*, your king.' „ 230
Moaning and wailing for an *h*, „ 368
cried 'The King! Here is an *h* for Uther!' „ 386
prince his *h*, when tall and marriageable, *Gareth and L.* 102
Garlon, mine *h*, Of him demand it,' *Balin and Balan* 117
dead love's harsh *h*, jealous pride? *Lancelot and E.* 1398
and tend him curiously Like a king's *h*, *Last Tournament* 91
greedy *h* That scarce can wait the reading *Lover's Tale i* 675
H of his face and land, to Lionel. „ *iv* 129
Against the guiltless *h's* of him from Tyre, *Tiresias* 12
quote As *h* of endless fame— *Ancient Sage* 147
I am *h*, and this my kingdom. *By an Evolution.* 14
My heart is for my son, Saleem, my *h*,— *Akbar's Dream* 171

Heiress 'If you are not the *h* born, (repeat) *Lady Clare* 83, 85
loved As *h* and not heir regretfully? *Aylmer's Field* 24
Their child.' 'Our child!' 'Our *h*!' „ 297
h, wealth, Their wealth, their *h*! „ 368
Then comes the feebler *h* of your plan, *Princess iii* 237
He married an *h*, an orphan with half a shire *Charity* 13

Heirless now a lonely man Wifeless and *h*, *Lancelot and E.* 1371
whether that *h* flaw In his throne's title *Sir J. Oldcastle* 72

Heirloom *H's*, and ancient miracles of Art, *Lover's Tale iv* 192

Held That *h* the pear to the gable-wall. *Mariana* 4
Paris *h* the costly fruit Out at arm's-length, *Œnone* 135
not the less *h* she her solemn mirth, *Palace of Art* 215
You *h* your course without remorse, *L. C. V. de Vere* 45
H me above the subject, as strong gales *D. of F. Women* 10
My father *h* his hand upon his face; „ 107
Her rags scarce *h* together; *The Goose* 2
He *h* a goose upon his arm, „ 5
there we *h* a talk, How all the old honour *The Epic* 6
I mean of verse (for so we *h* it then), „ 26
dropt the branch she *h*, and turning, *Gardener's D.* 157
h it better men should perish one by one, *Locksley Hall* 179
grieving *h* his will, and bore it thro'. *Enoch Arden* 167
And yet she *h* him on delayingly „ 468
Some that she but *h* off to draw him on; „ 476
With daily-dwindling profits *h* the house; „ 696
H his head high, and cared for no man, „ 848
those that *h* their heads above the crowd, *The Brook* 10
sweet face and faith *H* him from that: *Aylmer's Field* 393
Faded with morning, but his purpose *h*. „ 412
as if he *h* The Apocalyptic millstone, *Sea Dreams* 25
My master *h* That Gods there are, *Lucretius* 116
She *h* it out; and as a parrot turns *Princess, Pro.* 171
He *h* his sceptre like a pedant's wand „ *i* 27
knowledge, so my daughter *h*, Was all in all: „ 135
And *h* her round the knees against his waist, „ *ii* 363
In this hand *h* a volume as to read, „ 455
heard In the dead hush the papers that she *h* Rustle: „ *iv* 390
some pretext *h* Of baby troth, invalid, „ *v* 397
I poring upon her letter which I *h*, „ 469
painting and the tress, And *h* them up: „ *vi* 111
Love in the sacred halls *H* carnival at will, „ *vii* 85
h A volume of the Poets of her land: „ 173
I *H* it truth, with him who sings *In Mem. i* 1
The man I *h* as half-divine; „ *xiv* 10
if we *h* the doctrine sound For life outliving „ *liii* 9
Where once we *h* debate, a band Of youthful friends, „ *lxxxvii* 21
'Tis *h* that sorrow makes us wise, „ *cviii* 15
'Tis *h* that sorrow makes us wise; „ *cxiii* 1
These to His Memory—since he *h* them dear, *Ded. of Idylls* 1
h Tintagil castle by the Cornish sea, *Com. of Arthur* 187

Held (*continued*) I *h* with these, and loathe to ask thee aught. — *Gareth and L.* 356
h All in a gap-mouth'd circle his good mates „ 510
a casque; that *h* The horse, the spear; „ 680
that day a feast had been *H* in high hall, „ 848
H court at old Caerleon upon Usk. *Marr. of Geraint* 146
caught His purple scarf, and *h*, and said, „ 377
Down to the meadow where the jousts were *h*, „ 537
H his head high, and thought himself a knight, *Geraint and E.* 242
H commune with herself, and while she *h* „ 368
moving back she *h* Her finger up, „ 452
(And fill'd a horn with wine and *h* it to her,) „ 659
Edyrn, whom he *h* In converse for a little, „ 881
who *h* and lost with Lot In that first war, *Balin and Balan* 1
Flow'd from the spiritual lily that she *h*. „ 264
one had watch'd, and had not *h* his peace: *Merlin and V.* 162
And that it was too slippery to be *h*, *Lancelot and E.* 213
she, who *h* her eyes upon the ground, „ 232
noble things, and *h* her from her sleep. „ 339
They that assail'd, and they that *h* the lists, „ 455
Ranged with the Table Round that *h* the lists, „ 467
And all the Table Round that *h* the lists, „ 499
h her tenderly, And loved her with all love „ 867
Her all but utter whiteness *h* for sin, *Holy Grail* 84
caught his hand, *H* it, and there, „ 754
h, that if the King Had seen the sight „ 903
she said, 'Had ye not *h* your Lancelot *Pelleas and E.* 182
'False! and I *h* thee pure as Guinevere.' „ 522
'Have any of our Round Table *h* their vows?' „ 533
met A cripple, one that *h* a hand for alms— „ 542
had *h* sometime with pain His own against him, *Last Tournament* 178
H her awake: or if she slept, she dream'd *Guinevere* 75
Had *h* the field of battle was the King: *Pass. of Arthur* 138
H for a space 'twixt cloud and wave, *Lover's Tale i* 417
H converse sweet and low—low converse sweet, „ 541
Long time entrancement *h* me. „ 626
And those that *h* the bier before my face, „ *iii* 16
our house has *h* Three hundred years— *Sisters (E. and E.)* 52
defended the hold that we *h* with our lives— *Def. of Lucknow* 7
we have *h* it for eighty-seven! „ 105
when I *h* it aloft in my joy, *The Wreck* 33
But pity—the Pagan *h* it a vice— *Despair* 41
and *h* his own Like an Englishman *Heavy Brigade* 18
were *h* for a while from the fight, „ 36
She *h* them up to the view; *Dead Prophet* 72
I *h* you at that moment even dearer than before; *Happy* 90
caught and *h* His people by the bridle-rein of Truth. *Akbar's Dream* 84

Helen the breasts, The breasts of *H*, *Lucretius* 61
H's Tower, here I stand, *Helen's Tower* 1

Helicon frog coarser croak upon our *H*? *Trans. of Homer* 4

Heliconian *H* honey in living words, *Lucretius* 224
lands that lie Subjected to the *H* ridge *Tiresias* 26

Hell I hated him with the hate of *h*, *The Sisters* 22
Struck thro' with pangs of *h*. *Palace of Art* 220
some, 'tis whisper'd—down in *h* Suffer endless anguish, *Lotos-Eaters, C. S.* 123
all *h* beneath Made me boil over. *St. S. Stylites* 170
Deep as *H* I count his error. *The Captain* 3
'Thro' slander, meanest spawn of *H*— *The Letters* 33
Mix'd with cunning sparks of *h*. *Vision of Sin* 114
Lightens from her own central *H*— *Aylmer's Field* 761
Dropping the too rough H in *H* and Heaven, *Sea Dreams* 196
The mortal soul from out immortal *h*, *Lucretius* 263
paints the gates of *H* with Paradise, *Princess iv* 131
the fires of *H* Mix with his hearth: „ *v* 454
this French God, the child of *H*, *Third of Feb.* 7
Into the mouth of *H* Rode the six hundred. *Light Brigade* 25
Back from the mouth of *H*, „ 47
Procuress to the Lords of *H*. *In Mem. liii* 16
And compass'd by the fires of *H*; „ *cxxvii* 17
the passions that make earth *H*! *Maud I x* 46
I have climb'd nearer out of lonely *H*. „ *xviii* 80
fires of *H* brake out of thy rising sun, „ *II i* 9
The fires of *H* and of Hate; „ 10
Despite of Day and Night and Death and *H*.' *Gareth and L.* 887

Hell (*continued*) I was halfway down the slope to *H*, *Geraint and E.* 791
Whereout the Demon issued up from *H*. *Balin and Balan* 317
fire of Heaven is not the flame of *H*. (repeat) „ 443, 447, 451, 455
And dallies with him in the Mouth of *H*.' „ 615
May this hard earth cleave to the Nadir *h* *Merlin and V.* 349
women, worst and best, as Heaven and *H*. „ 815
H burst up your harlot roofs Bellowing, *Pelleas and E.* 466
'Thou art false as H: slay me: „ 576
he could harp his wife up out of *h*.' *Last Tournament* 328
'The teeth of *H* flay bare and gnash thee „ 444
the scorpion-worm that twists in *h*, „ 451
leave me all alone with Mark and *h*. „ 536
and I shall not find him in *H*. *Rizpah* 74
thaw theer's naw drinkin' i' *H*; *North. Cobbler* 58
tha'll foller 'im slick into *H*.' „ 66
raäke out *H* wi' a small-tooth coämb— *Village Wife* 76
sulphur like so many fiends in their *h*— *Def. of Lucknow* 33
Heat like the mouth of a *h*, „ 81
we have sent them very fiends from *H*; *Columbus* 184
seest the souls in *H* And purgatory, „ 216
In the rigging, voices of *h*— *The Wreck* 92
spoke, of a *H* without help, without end. *Despair* 26
this earth is a fatherless *H*— „ 57
Infinite cruelty rather that made everlasting *H*, „ 96
H! if the souls of men were immortal, „ 99
And so there were *H* for ever! „ 101
His Love would have power over *H* „ 102
But the God of Love and of *H* together— „ 105
and now I fly from *H*, And you with me; *The Flight* 88
sthrames runnin' down at the back o' the glin 'ud 'a dhrownded *H*. *Tomorrow* 24
One shriek'd 'The fires of *H*!' *Dead Prophet* 80
thence The shrilly whinnyings of the team of *H*, *Demeter and P.* 44
Gods against the fear Of Death and *H*; „ 142
No sudden heaven, nor sudden *h*, for man, *The Ring* 41
There is laughter down in *H* *Forlorn* 15
Earth and *H* will brand your name, „ 51
blasted to the deathless fire of *H*. *Happy* 84
made an English homestead *H*— *To Mary Boyle* 37
the dead, who wait the doom of *H* *Romney's R.* 132
all the *H's* a-glare in either eye, *Akbar's Dream* 115
an' the tongue's sit afire o' *H*, *Church-warden, etc.* 24
a woman, God bless her, kept me from *H*. *Charity* 4

Hell-black God 'ill pardon the *h-b* raven *Rizpah* 39

Hell-fire An' Muggins 'e preäch'd o' *H-f* *North. Cobbler* 55
Down out o' heaven i' *H-f*— „ 58

Hell-heat would dare *H-h* or Arctic cold, *Ancient Sage* 116

Hellish Drench'd with the *h* oorali— *In the Child. Hosp.* 10
Of the *h* heat of a wretched life *Despair* 68

Helm (helmet) I am so deeply smitten thro' the *h* *M. d'Arthur* 25
Aidless, alone, and smitten thro' the *h*. „ 41
A scarf of orange round the stony *h*, *Princess, Pro.* 102
fired an angry Pallas on the *h*, „ *vi* 367
he neither wore on *h* or shield The golden symbol *Com. of Arthur* 49
fall battleaxe upon *h*, Fall battleaxe, „ 486
h could ride Therethro' nor graze: *Gareth and L.* 673
Then as he donn'd the *h*, and took the shield „ 690
brought a *h* With but a drying evergreen „ 1115
Sir Gareth's head prickled beneath his *h*; „ 1397
he clove the *h* As throughly as the skull; „ 1406
Aim'd at the *h*, his lance err'd; *Geraint and E.* 157
cast his lance aside, And doff'd his *h*: „ 596
Hard upon *h* smote him, and the blade flew *Balin and Balan* 395
Balin by the banneret of his *h* Dragg'd him, „ 398
upon his *h* A sleeve of scarlet, *Lancelot and E.* 603
he had not loosed it from his *h*, „ 809
look'd Down on his *h*, from which her sleeve had gone. „ 982
Beat like a strong knight on his *h*, *Pelleas and E.* 23
Even to tipmost lance and topmost *h*, *Last Tournament* 442
he spake to these his *h* was lower'd, *Guinevere* 593
the crash Of battleaxes on shatter'd *h's*, *Pass. of Arthur* 110
Hard on that *h* which many a heathen sword „ 166
I am so deeply smitten thro' the *h* „ 193
Aidless, alone, and smitten through the *h*.— „ 209

Helm (helmet) (*continued*) her golden *h* And all her golden armour on the grass, — *Tiresias* 44
Helm (as of a boat) She took the *h* and he the sail; — *Merlin and V.* 200
but the man that was lash'd to the *h* had gone; — *The Wreck* 110
Whatever statesman hold the *h*. — *Hands all Round* 20
Or should those fail, that hold the *h*, — *Prog. of Spring* 100
Helm (verb) overbears the bark, And him that *h's* it, — *Lancelot and E.* 486
Helmet The *h* and the helmet-feather Burn'd — *L. of Shalott iii* 21
From underneath his *h* flow'd His coal-black curls — „ 30
She saw the *h* and the plume, — „ 40
out of stricken *h's* sprang the fire. — *Princess v* 495
With Psyche's colour round his *h*, — „ 534
And wears a *h* mounted with a skull, — *Gareth and L.* 639
Gareth there unlaced His *h* as to slay him, — „ 979
Sat riveting a *h* on his knee, — *Marr. of Geraint* 268
Came forward with the *h* yet in hand — „ 285
crack'd the *h* thro', and bit the bone, — „ 573
Till his eye darken'd and his *h* wagg'd; — *Geraint and E.* 505
then he bound Her token on his *h*, — *Lancelot and E.* 374
leaving for the cowl The *h* in an abbey far away — *Holy Grail* 6
And once the laces of a *h* crack'd, — *Last Tournament* 164
Tumbling the hollow *h's* of the fallen, — *Pass. of Arthur* 132
spear and *h* tipt With stormy light — *Tiresias* 113
Flicker'd and bicker'd From *h* to *h*, — *Merlin and the G.* 71
Helmet-feather The helmet and the *h-f* Burn'd — *L. of Shalott iii* 21
Helmet-hidden the face Wellnigh was *h-h*, — *Last Tournament* 456
Helmless I sit within a *h* bark, — *In Mem. iv* 3
Helmsman I leap on board: no *h* steers: — *Sir Galahad* 39
Help (s) without *h* I cannot last till morn. — *M. d'Arthur* 26
I grieve to see you poor and wanting *h*: — *Enoch Arden* 406
a voice Of comfort and an open hand of *h*, — *Aylmer's Field* 174
who promised *h*, and oozed All o'er with honey'd answer — *Princess v* 241
Because it needed *h* of Love: — *In Mem. xxv* 8
For *h* and shelter to the hermit's cave. — *Gareth and L.* 1209
scaled with *h* a hundred feet Up from the base: — *Balin and Balan* 170
maiden sprang into the hall Crying on *h*: — *Holy Grail* 209
shall I kill myself? What *h* in that? — *Guinevere* 621
without *h* I cannot last till morn. — *Pass. of Arthur* 194
of a Hell without *h*, without end. — *Despair* 26
they maäkes ma a *h* to the poor, — *Church-warden, etc.* 39
Help (verb) (*See also* **'Elp**) grace To *h* me of my weary load.' — *Mariana in the S.* 30
until he grows Of age to *h* us.' — *Dora* 127
h's the hurt that Honour feels, — *Locksley Hall* 105
h me as when life begun: — „ 185
I cannot *h* you as I wish to do Unless— — *Enoch Arden* 407
H me not to break in upon her peace. — „ 787
How could I *h* her? 'Would I— — *The Brook* 111
Poor fellow, could he *h* it? — „ 158
there was one to hear And *h* them? — *Princess ii* 268
I heard, I could not *h* it, — „ 332
oh, Sirs, could I *h* it, but my cheek — „ *iii* 45
(God *h* her) she was wedded to a fool; — „ 83
h my prince to gain His rightful bride, — „ 160
H, father, brother, *h*; speak to the king: — „ *vi* 305
one That wholly scorn'd to *h* their equal rights — „ *vii* 233
For, saving that, ye *h* to save mankind — *Ode on Well.* 166
How best to *h* the slender store, — *To F. D. Maurice* 37
'God *h* me! save I take my part Of danger — *Sailor Boy* 21
'*H* us from famine And plague and strife! — *The Victim* 9
But *h* thy foolish ones to bear; — *In Mem., Pro.* 31
H thy vain worlds to bear thy light. — „ 32
Sent to him, saying 'Arise, and *h* us thou! — *Com. of Arthur* 44
Sweet faces, who will *h* him at his need. — „ 279
friends Of Arthur, who should *h* him at his need, — *Gareth and L.* 230
'We sit King, to *h* the wrong'd Thro' all our realm. — „ 371
unhappiness Of one who came to *h* thee, — „ 1238
'Heaven *h* thee,' sigh'd Lynette. — „ 1357
name Slip from my lips if I can *h* it— — *Marr. of Geraint* 446
So this will *h* him of his violences!' — *Balin and Balan* 205
bounden art thou, if from Arthur's hall, To *h* the weak. — „ 473
H, for he follows! take me to thyself! — *Merlin and V.* 82
The sick weak beast seeking to *h* herself — „ 498

Help (verb) (*continued*) 'What matter, so I *h* him back to life?' — *Lancelot and E.* 787
and said, 'Betray me not, but *h*— — *Pelleas and E.* 360
If I, the Queen, May *h* them, loose thy tongue, — „ 600
To *h* it from the death that cannot die, — *Guinevere* 66
But *h* me, heaven, for surely I repent. — „ 372
friends Of Arthur, who should *h* him at his need?' — *Pass. of Arthur* 456
Sprang up a friendship that may *h* us yet. — *Lover's Tale iv* 144
And *h* us to our joy. — *Sisters (E. and E.)* 224
I should cry to the dear Lord Jesus to *h* me, — *In the Child. Hosp.* 49
given my life To *h* his own from scathe, — *Sir J. Oldcastle* 63
Then I, God *h* me, I So mock'd, — „ 162
but Thou wilt *h* us to be. — *De Prof., Human C.* 8
and sail to *h* him in the war; — *Achilles over the T.* 13
hand that would *h* me, would heal me— — *The Wreck* 56
Let be thy wail and *h* thy fellow men, — *Ancient Sage* 258
to *h* his homelier brother men, — *Locksley H., Sixty* 267
O Goddesses, *h* me up thither! — *Parnassus* 3
you will *h* me to overcome it, — „ 5
by thy love which once was mine, *H*, heal me. — *Death of Œnone* 46
Help'd-Helpt and his father *help'd* him not. — *Dora* 51
God, that *help'd* her in her widowhood. — „ 113
or *help'd* At lading and unlading the tall barks, — *Enoch Arden* 815
For heart, I think, *help'd* head: — *Aylmer's Field* 475
Came running at the call, and *help'd* us down. — *Princess i* 227
Help'd by the mother's careful hand and eye, — *Marr. of Geraint* 738
Yea, would have *help'd* him to it: — *Geraint and E.* 638
And at Caerleon had he *help'd* his lord, — *Lancelot and E.* 297
some rough use, And *help'd* her from herself.' — „ 1307
as would have *help'd* her from her death.' — „ 1311
He *helpt* me with death, and he heal'd — *The Wreck* 58
hands of mine Have *helpt* to pass a bucket — *To Mary Boyle* 39
Helper Henceforth thou hast a *h*, me, — *Princess vii* 258
Helpful a *h* harper thou, That harpest downward! — *Last Tournament* 331
Helping *h* back the dislocated Kay To Camelot, — *Gareth and L.* 1213
Her mother silent too, nor *h* her, — *Marr. of Geraint* 768
Helpless his blue eyes All flooded with the *h* wrath of tears, — *Enoch Arden* 32
The *h* life so wild that it was tame. — „ 557
I felt Thy *h* warmth about my barren breast — *Princess vi* 202
And often feeling of the *h* hands, — „ *vii* 111
Than as a little *h* innocent bird, — *Lancelot and E.* 894
Then his *h* heart Leapt, and he cried, — *Pelleas and E.* 130
to and fro Swaying the *h* hands, — *Pass. of Arthur* 131
till *h* death And silence made him bold— — *Lover's Tale iv* 72
H, taking the place of the pitying God — *Despair* 42
Would echo *h* laughter to your jest! — *To W. H. Brookfield* 5
peasants maim the *h* horse, and drive Innocent cattle — *Locksley H., Sixty* 95
She tumbled his *h* corpse about. — *Dead Prophet* 65
And golden grain, my gift to *h* man. — *Demeter and P.* 111
Helplessness Enid, in her utter *h*, — *Geraint and E.* 719
Helpmate 'lo mine *h*, one to feel My purpose — *Guinevere* 485
Helpt *See* **Help'd**
Helter-skelter *H-s* runs the age; — *Poets and Critics* 2
Hem (s) in her raiment's *h* was traced in flame — *The Poet* 45
Hem (verb) one but speaks or *h's* or stirs his chair, — *Sonnet To* —— 5
Hemlock Diotima, teaching him that died Of *h*; — *Princess iii* 303
the *h*, Brow-high, did strike my forehead — *Lover's Tale ii* 18
Their nectar smack'd of *h* on the lips, — *Demeter and P.* 104
Hen (*See also* **Guinea-hens**) we stole his fruit, His *h's*, his eggs; — *Walk. to the Mail* 85
praised his *h's*, his geese, his guinea-hens; — *The Brook* 126
a *h* To her false daughters in the pool; — *Princess v* 328
even in their *h's* and in their eggs— — *Holy Grail* 560
Pluksh!!! the *h's* i' the peäs! — *Village Wife* 124
Hend (end) theer wur a *h* o' the taäil, — „ 86
buried togither, an' this wur the *h*. — „ 90
if soä please God, to the *h*. — *Spinster's S's.* 112
Hengist Heathen, the brood by *H* left; — *Guinevere* 16
Hennemy (enemy) Theer's thy *h*, man, an' I knaws, — *North. Cobbler* 65
I'll looök my *h* straït i' the faäce, — „ 74
Henry (the Third) *H's* fifty years are all in shadow, — *On Jub. Q. Victoria* 39
Hepitaph (epitaph) Nor her wi' the *h* yonder! — *Spinster's S's.* 72
Herald (adj.) The *h* melodies of spring, — *In Mem. xxxviii* 6

Hid (*continued*) an Isis *h* by the veil. *Maud I iv* 43
more exprest Than *h* her, clung about her lissome limbs, *Merlin and V.* 223
and not with half disdain *H* under grace, *Lancelot and E.* 264
H from the wide world's rumour by the grove „ 522
And *h* Excalibur the second time, *Pass. of Arthur* 279
and falling *h* the frame. *Lover's Tale iv* 217
She feels the Sun is *h* but for a night, *Ancient Sage* 73
Would Earth tho' *h* in cloud *Happy* 97
left his dagger behind him. I found it. I *h* it away. *Bandit's Death* 12

Hidalgo and his *H's*—shipwrecks, famines, *Columbus* 225

Hidden (*See also* **Half-hidden, Haze-hidden, Helmet-hidden**) place with joy *H* in sorrow: *Dying Swan* 23
The smell of violets, *h* in the green, *D. of F. Women* 77
Gold-mines of thought to lift the *h* ore „ 274
Hail, *h* to the knees in fern, *Talking Oak* 29
h from the heart's disgrace, *Locksley Hall* 57
Lay *h* as the music of the moon *Aylmer's Field* 102
warm-blue breathings of a *h* hearth „ 155
'betwixt these two Division smoulders *h*; *Princess iii* 79
her face Wellnigh was *h* in the minster gloom; *Com. of Arthur* 289
let my name Be *h*, and give me the first quest, *Gareth and L.* 545
Nay, truly we were *h*: this fair lord, *Balin and Balan* 507
and bottom of the well, Where Truth is *h*. *Merlin and V.* 48
Now guess'd a *h* meaning in his arms, *Lancelot and E.* 17
Lancelot saying, 'Hear, but hold my name *H*, „ 417
know full well Where your great knight is *h*, „ 690
echoes *h* in the wall Rang out like hollow woods *Pelleas and E.* 366
(When first I learnt thee *h* here) *Guinevere* 539
number'd the bones, I have *h* them all. *Rizpah* 10
h there from the light of the sun— *Def. of Lucknow* 63
Mother's diamonds *h* from her there, *The Ring* 142
And all the winters are *h*. *The Throstle* 16
A thousand things are *h* still *Mechanophilus* 23
'Some *h* principle to move, *Two Voices* 133
'A *h* hope,' the voice replied: „ 441
sitting in the deeps Upon the *h* bases of the hills.' *M. d'Arthur* 106
And draws the veil from *h* worth. *Day-Dm., Arrival* 4
How dark those *h* eyes must be!' „ 32
See with clear eye some *h* shame *In Mem. li* 7
distant hills From *h* summits fed with rills „ *ciii* 7
sitting in the deeps Upon the *h* bases of the hills.' *Pass. of Arthur* 274
that sends the *h* sun Down yon dark sea, *De Prof., Two G.* 33
Son, in the *h* world of sight, that lives *Tiresias* 51
Fear not thou the *h* purpose of that Power *God and the Univ.* 5

Hide (*See also* **'Ide**) run to and fro, and *h* and seek, *The Mermaid* 35
for the tear thou couldst not *h*, *The Bridesmaid* 11
'I cannot *h* that some have striven, *Two Voices* 208
neither *h* the ray From those, not blind, *Love thou thy land* 14
Where shall I *h* my forehead and my eyes? *M. d'Arthur* 228
Oh, *h* thy knotted knees in fern, *Talking Oak* 93
H me from my deep emotion, *Locksley Hall* 108
H, *h* them, million-myrtled wilderness, *Lucretius* 204
And cavern-shadowing laurels, *h*! „ 205
See they sit, they *h* their faces, *Boädicea* 51
Is there no baseness we would *h*? *In Mem. li* 3
And *h* thy shame beneath the ground. „ *lxxii* 28
That evermore she long'd to *h* herself, *Gareth and L.* 111
will *h* with mantling flowers As if for pity?' „ 1392
if he die, why earth has earth enough To *h* him. *Geraint and E.* 555
Well, *h* it, *h* it; I shall find it out; *Merlin and V.* 528
h it therefore; go unknown: Win! *Lancelot and E.* 151
therefore would he *h* his name From all men, „ 580
And sharply turn'd about to *h* her face, „ 608
There will I *h* thee, till my life shall end, *Guinevere* 114
Would God that thou could'st *h* me from myself! „ 118
Where shall I *h* my forehead and my eyes? *Pass. of Arthur* 396
Dust to dust—low down—let us *h*! *Rizpah* 37
H me, Mother! my Fathers belong'd to the church of old, *The Wreck* 1
I would *h* from the storm without, „ 9
I will *h* my face, I will tell you all. „ 12
and higher, The cloud that *h's* it— *Ancient Sage* 12
Marriage will not *h* it, *Forlorn* 50

Hideous Day, mark'd as with some *h* crime, *In Mem. lxxii* 18

Hideousness roofs of slated *h*! *Locksley H., Sixty* 246

Hiding (*See also* **Heart-hiding**) To take me to that *h* in the hills. *Sir J. Oldcastle* 2

Hiding-place by mine head she knows his *h-p.*' *Lancelot and E.* 714

High (*See also* **Breast-high, Brow-high**) either babbling world of *h* and low; *Ode on Well.* 182
Peak, That standest *h* above all? *Voice and the P.* 10
The Peak is *h* and flush'd „ 29
The Peak is *h*, and the stars are *h*, „ 31
they set him on *h* That all the ships *Rizpah* 37
She is *h* in the Heaven of Heavens, *Charity* 42
Some too *h*—no fault of thine— *Poets and Critics* 12
Whether the *h* field on the bushless Pike, *Ode to Memory* 96
Heaven flow'd upon the soul in many dreams Of *h* desire. *The Poet* 32
Whither away from the *h* green field, *Sea-Fairies* 8
To the pale-green sea-groves straight and *h*, *The Merman* 19
H things were spoken there, unhanded down; *Alexander* 12
live alone unto herself In her *h* palace there. *Palace of Art* 12
h shrine-doors burst thro' with heated blasts *D. of F. Women* 29
'The *h* masts flicker'd as they lay afloat; „ 113
his forehead like a rising sun *H* from the daïs-throne— *M. d'Arthur* 218
Three years I lived upon a pillar, *h* Six cubits, *St. S. Stylites* 86
this *h* dial, which my sorrow crowns— „ 95
From my *h* nest of penance here proclaim „ 167
H towns on hills were dimly seen, *The Voyage* 34
That girt the region with *h* cliff and lawn: *Vision of Sin* 47
trees As *h* as heaven, and every bird that sings: *Sea Dreams* 102
Both crown'd with stars and *h* among the stars,— „ 241
'And make her some great Princess, six feet *h*, *Princess, Pro.* 224
Or Nymph, or Goddess, at *h* tide of feast, „ *i* 197
At those *h* words, we conscious of ourselves, „ *ii* 67
fail so far In *h* desire, they know not, „ *iii* 280
They haled us to the Princess where she sat *H* in the hall: „ *iv* 272
when a boy, you stoop'd to me From all *h* places, „ 430
From the *h* tree the blossom wavering fell, „ *vi* 80
trust in all things *h* Comes easy to him, „ *vii* 329
Or tower, or *h* hill-convent, seen *The Daisy* 29
With many a rivulet *h* against the Sun *The Islet* 21
Calm and deep peace on this *h* wold, *In Mem. xi* 5
Did ever rise from *h* to higher; „ *xli* 2
My guardian angel will speak out In that *h* place, „ *xliv* 16
The *h* Muse answer'd: 'Wherefore grieve „ *lviii* 9
And moving up from *h* to higher, „ *lxiv* 13
H nature amorous of the good, „ *cix* 9
up in the *h* Hall-garden I see her pass like a light; *Maud I iv* 11
For him did his *h* sun flame, „ 32
Not making his *h* place the lawless perch *Ded. of Idylls* 22
And even in *h* day the morning star. *Com. of Arthur* 100
Beheld, so *h* upon the dreary deeps „ 373
To whom arrived, by Dubric the *h* saint, „ 453
In whom *h* God hath breathed a secret thing. „ 501
At times the summit of the *h* city flash'd; *Gareth and L.* 192
over all *H* on the top were those three Queens, „ 229
H nose, a nostril large and fine, „ 465
there past into the hall A damsel of *h* lineage, „ 588
Lyonors, A lady of *h* lineage, of great lands, „ 609
rose *H* that the highest-crested helm could ride „ 673
that day a feast had been Held in *h* hall, „ 848
Till *h* above him, circled with her maids, „ 1374
darken'd from the *h* light in his eyes, *Marr. of Geraint* 100
lords and ladies of the *h* court went In silver tissue „ 662
Geraint Woke where he slept in the *h* hall, „ 755
another gift of the *h* God, Which, maybe, „ 821
giant tower, from whose *h* crest, they say, „ 827
For by the hands of Dubric, the *h* saint, „ 838
Held his head *h*, and thought himself a knight, *Geraint and E.* 242
For once, when I was up so *h* in pride „ 790
And oft I talk'd with Dubric, the *h* saint, „ 865
but when he mark'd his *h* sweet smile In passing, *Balin and Balan* 160
'Too *h* this mount of Camelot for me: „ 226
Borne by some *h* Lord-prince of Arthur's hall, „ 466
See now, I set thee *h* on vantage ground, „ 534
And the *h* purpose broken by the worm. *Merlin and V.* 196
passing one, at the *h* peep of dawn, „ 560

High (*continued*) Till the *h* dawn piercing the royal rose — *Merlin and V.* 739
Because of that *h* pleasure which I had — „ 877
If this be *h*, what is it to be low?' — *Lancelot and E.* 1084
from the *h* door streaming, brake Disorderly, — „ 1347
and watch'd The *h* reed wave, — „ 1390
Low as the hill was *h*, and where the vale — *Holy Grail* 441
And this *h* Quest as at a simple thing: — „ 668
Clear as a lark, *h* o'er me as a lark, — „ 833
Nor the *h* God a vision, nor that One Who rose again: — „ 918
h doors Were softly sunder'd, and thro' these — *Pelleas and E.* 3
I might have answer'd them Even before *h* God. — „ 463
he saw *H* up in heaven the hall that Merlin built, — „ 553
At Camelot, *h* above the yellowing woods, — *Last Tournament* 3
In her *h* bower the Queen, Working a tapestry, — „ 128
set his name *H* on all hills, — „ 337
Like hillsnow *h* in heaven, the steel-blue eyes, — „ 667
Climb'd to the *h* top of the garden-wall — *Guinevere* 25
So from the *h* wall and the flowering grove — „ 33
H, self-contain'd, and passionless, — „ 406
But teach *h* thought, and amiable words — „ 481
I guard as God's *h* gift from scathe and wrong, — „ 494
And miss to hear *h* talk of noble deeds — „ 499
We two may meet before *h* God, and thou — „ 564
And likewise for the *h* rank she had borne, — „ 695
Till the *H* God behold it from beyond, — *Pass. of Arthur* 16
To all *h* places like a golden cloud For ever: — „ 54
three whereat we gazed On that *h* day, — „ 454
his *h* hills, with flame Milder and purer. — *Lover's Tale i* 322
Who scarce can tune his *h* majestic sense — „ 475
I was the *H* Priest in her holiest place, — „ 686
from an open grating overhead *H* in the wall, — „ *iv* 61
that a man's ideal Is *h* in Heaven, — *Sisters (E. and E.)* 131
thaw the banks o' the beck be sa *h*, — *Village Wife* 83
Rifleman, *h* on the roof, hidden there — *Def. of Lucknow* 63
what full tides of onset sap Our seven *h* gates, — *Tiresias* 92
Thro' her *h* hill-passes of stainless snow, — *Dead Prophet* 47
wild heather round me and over me June's *h* blue, — *June Bracken, etc.* 2
Been hurl'd so *h* they ranged about the globe? — *St. Telemachus* 2

High-arch'd *H-a* and ivy-claspt, Of finest Gothic — *Princess, Pro.* 91

High-built storm their *h-b* organs make, — *In Mem. lxxxvii* 6
their *h-b* galleons came, Ship after ship, — *The Revenge* 58

High-elbow'd *H-e* grigs that leap in summer grass. — *The Brook* 54

Higher (*See also* **'Igher**) Up *h* with the yew-tree by it, — *Walk. to the Mail* 13
As never sow was *h* in this world— — „ 96
the sensuous organism That which is *h*. — *Princess ii* 88
stood Among her maidens, *h* by the head, — „ *iii* 179
And the thought of a man is *h*. — *Voice and the P.* 32
shine ye here so low? Thy ward is *h* up: — *Gareth and L.* 1098
Which set the horror *h*: — „ 1394
Broader and *h* than any in all the lands! — *Holy Grail* 247
But angled in the *h* pool. — *Miller's D.* 64
I might have look'd a little *h*; — „ 140
sure he was a foot *H* than you be.' — *Enoch Arden* 855
yet, my Lords, not well: there is a *h* law. — *Third of Feb.* 12
Of their dead selves to *h* things. — *In Mem. i* 4
That rises upward always *h*, — „ *xv* 17
Our voices took a *h* range; — „ *xxx* 21
Whose loves in *h* love endure; — „ *xxxii* 14
Did ever rise from high to *h*; — „ *xli* 2
A *h* height, a deeper deep. — „ *lxiii* 12
And moving up from high to *h*, — „ *lxiv* 13
A *h* hand must make her mild, — „ *cxiv* 17
The herald of a *h* race, And of himself in *h* place, — „ *cxviii* 14
There is a lower and a *h*; — „ *cxxix* 4
I wake to the *h* aims Of a land that has lost — *Maud III vi* 38
If I lose it and myself in the *h* beauty, — *Happy* 58
raising her Still *h*, past all peril, — *Lover's Tale i* 394
which was more and *h* than all Hope, — „ 454
but, son, the source is *h*, Yon summit half-a-league in air—and *h*, The cloud that hides it—*h* still, the heavens Whereby the cloud was moulded, — *Ancient Sage* 10
dead, as happier than ourselves And *h*, — „ 206

Higher (*continued*) if thou Look *h*, then—perchance—thou mayest— — *Ancient Sage* 281
So the *H* wields the Lower, while the Lower is the *H*. — *Locksley H., Sixty* 124
Something kindlier, *h*, holier— — „ 160
a glimpse of a height that is *h*. — *By an Evolution.* 20
comes a gleam of what is *h*. — *Faith* 6

Highering *See* **Ever-highering**

Highest And *h*, snow and fire. — *Palace of Art* 84
And clouds are *h* up in air, — *Lady Clare* 2
he is singing Hosanna in the *h*: — *Enoch Arden* 503
people strowing cried 'Hosanna in the *h*!' — „ 506
worshipt their own darkness in the *H*? — *Aylmer's Field* 643
The *h* is the measure of the man, — *Princess ii* 157
This flake of rainbow flying on the *h* — „ *v* 319
the midmost and the *h* Was Arac: — „ 256
flush'd At his *h* with sunrise fire; — *Voice and the P.* 30
immeasurable heavens Break open to their *h*, — *Spec. of Iliad* 15
The King is King, and ever wills the *h*. — *Com. of Arthur* 495
On Caer-Eryri's *h* found the King, — *Gareth and L.* 500
Arthur in the *h* Leaven'd the world, — *Merlin and V.* 140
The meanest having power upon the *h*, — „ 195
Him of all men who seems to me the *h*.' '*H*?' the father answer'd, echoing '*h*?' — *Lancelot and E.* 1077
Daughter, I know not what you call the *h*; — „ 1080
Guinevere had sinn'd against the *h*, — *Last Tournament* 570
Thou art the *h* and most human too, — *Guinevere* 649
It was my duty to have loved the *h*: — „ 657
We needs must love the *h* when we see it, — „ 660
thro' what we feel Within ourselves is *h*, — *Ancient Sage* 88
According to the *H* in the *H*. — „ 90
'The Bright one in the *h* Is brother of the Dark — *Demeter and P.* 94
He Who still is *h*, glancing from his height — „ 117
ill-content With them, who still are *h*. — „ 129
the *H* is the wisest and the best, — *Faith* 1
ere we reach'd the *h* summit I pluck'd a daisy, — *The Daisy* 87
The *h*, holiest manhood, thou: — *In Mem., Pro.* 14
To scale the heaven's *h* height, — „ *cviii* 7
What find I in the *h* place, — „ 9
A soul on *h* mission sent, — „ *cxiii* 10
The *h* virtue, mother of them all; — *Holy Grail* 446
Crown'd with her *h* act the placid face — *Lover's Tale i* 216
that ever swarm about And cloud the *h* heads, — *Co umbus* 120
Forward, till you see the *h* Human Nature is divine. — *Locksley H., Sixty* 276

Highest-crested rose High that the *h-c* helm could ride — *Gareth and L.* 673

Highest-mounted 'The *h-m* mind,' he said, — *Two Voices* 79

High-heaven see The *h-h* dawn of more than mortal day — *Ancient Sage* 284

Highlander Havelock's glorious *H's* answer — *Def. of Lucknow* 99
war-harden'd hand of the *H* wet with their tears! — „ 102

Highlands Sailing under palmy *h* — *The Captain* 23

Highness Your *H* would enroll them with your own, — *Princess i* 239
One rose in all the world, your *H* — „ *ii* 51
No ghostly hauntings like his *H*. — „ 411
Your *H* might have seem'd the thing you say.' — „ *iii* 202
surely, if your *H* keep Your purport, — „ 211
'Alas your *H* breathes full East,' — „ 231
'pass on; His *H* wakes:' — „ *v* 5
'Amazed am I to hear Your *H*: but your *H* breaks with ease The law your *H* did not make: — „ *vi* 325
these men came to woo Your *H*— — „ 329

High-set *h-s* courtesies are not for me. — *Balin and Balan* 227

High-tempted Of hoar *h-t* Faith, have leagued again — *Pref. Son. 19th Cent.* 10

High-tide raise the full *H-t* of doubt — *Sisters (E. and E.)* 178

High-walled *H-w* gardens green and old; — *Arabian Nights* 8

Highway (adj.) dead, become Mere *h* dust? — *Love and Duty* 11

Highway (s) There she sees the *h* near — *L. of Shalott ii* 13
at night along the dusky *h* near — *Locksley Hall* 113
Cuts off the fiery *h* of the sun, — *Enoch Arden* 130
Cut off the length of *h* on before, — „ 673
went harping down The black king's *h*, — *Last Tournament* 343
The *h* running by it leaves a breadth — *Sisters (E. and E.)* 80
down the *h* moving on With easy laughte — *Tiresias* 199
I scaled the buoyant *h* of the birds, — *Prog. of Spring* 80

Hill (*continued*) we shall stand transfigured, like Christ on Hermon *h*, *Happy* 38
Where am I? snow on all the *h's*! *Romney's R.* 12
To wallow in that winter of the *h's*. „ 15
I had been among the *h's*, and brought you down „ 78
But, while the *h's* remain, Up *h* 'Too-slow' will need the whip, Down *h* 'Too-quick,' the chain. *Politics* 10
Hill-convent Or tower, or high *h-c*, seen *The Daisy* 29
Hill-fort storming a *h-f* of thieves He got it; *Aylmer's Field* 225
Hillock Peace Pipe on her pastoral *h* *Maud III vi* 24
The mortal *h*, Would break into blossom; *Merlin and the G.* 107
Hill-pass high *h-p'es* of stainless snow, *Dead Prophet* 47
Hill-side (*See also* **'Ill-Side**) woods that belt the gray *h-s*, *Ode to Memory* 55
The whole *h-s* was redder than a fox. *Walk. to the Mail* 3
Hill-slope damp *h-s's* were quickened into green, *Gareth and L.* 184
Hillsnow a brow Like *h* high in heaven, *Last Tournament* 667
Hilt But with his hand against the *h*, *Love thou thy land* 83
sparkled keen with frost against the *h*: *M. d' Arthur* 55
But when he saw the wonder of the *h*, „ 85
Thou would'st betray me for the precious *h*; „ 126
caught him by the *h*, and branish'd him (repeat) „ 145, 160
So great a miracle as yonder *h*. „ 156
rich With jewels, elfin Urim, on the *h*, *Com. of Arthur* 299
Clash'd his, and brake it utterly to the *h*. *Gareth and L.* 1148
Caught at the *h*, as to abolish him: *Marr. of Geraint* 210
sparkled keen with frost against the *h*: *Pass. of Arthur* 223
But when he saw the wonder of the *h*, „ 253
Thou would'st betray me for the precious *h*; „ 294
caught him by the *h*, and branish'd him (repeat) „ 313, 328
So great a miracle as yonder *h*. „ 324
Hilted *See* **Golden-Hilted**
Hind the *h* fell, the herd was driven, Fire glimpsed; *Com. of Arthur* 432
the *h* To whom a space of land is given to plow. *Holy Grail* 906
Calling me thy white *h*, and saying to me *Last Tournament* 569
Hinder Came all in haste to *h* wrong, *Princess iv* 401
What *h's* me To take such bloody vengeance „ 533
And so, before the two could *h* him, *Gareth and L.* 1368
rule the land Hereafter, which God *h*.' *Lancelot and E.* 66
'Heaven *h*,' said the King, „ 532
Hindering (*See also* **Marriage-hindering**) Had made the pretext of a *h* wound, „ 582
Hindrance Divinely thro' all *h* finds the man „ 333
Hindustan Thro' all the warring world of *H* *Akbar's Dream* 26
Hinge The doors upon their *h's* creak'd; *Mariana* 62
So frequent on its *h* before. *Deserted House* 8
Half-parted from a weak and scolding *h*, *The Brook* 84
I grate on rusty *h's* here:' *Princess i* 86
Hingin' (hanging) wi' my hairm *h* down to the floor, *Owd Roä* 65
Hinjian (Indian) Till I gied 'em *H* curn, *Village Wife* 118
Hinn (Inn) I started awaäy like a shot, an' down to the *H*, *North. Cobbler* 69
tha mun göa fur it down to the *H*, „ 113
out o' sight o' the winders o' Gigglesby *H*— *Spinsters S's.* 35
Hint (s) A little *h* to solace woe, A *h*, *Two Voices* 433
Like *h's* and echoes of the world *Day-Dm., Sleep. P.* 7
No *h* of death in all his frame, *In Mem. xiv* 18
with shadow'd *h* confuse A life that leads „ *xxxiii* 7
A little flash, a mystic *h*; „ *xliv* 8
And sowing one ill *h* from ear to ear, *Merlin and V.* 143
dark sweet *h's* of some who prized him „ 159
Hint (verb) Ah pity—*h* it not in human tones, *Wan Sculptor* 11
Alone might *h* of my disgrace; *Two Voices* 360
laughingly Would *h* at worse in either. *Enoch Arden* 481
We whisper, and *h*, and chuckle, *Maud I iv* 29
Hinted matron saw That *h* love was only wasted bait, *The Ring* 360
Hip *See* **Huck**
Hip and Thigh my race Hew'd Ammon, *h a t*, *D. of F. Women* 238
Hire (s) Money—my *h*—*his* money— *Charity* 19
Hire (verb) And *h* thyself to serve for meats *Gareth and L.* 153
h myself To serve with scullions and with kitchen knaves; „ 169
But *h* us some fair chamber for the night, *Geraint and E.* 238
Hired *h* himself to work within the fields; *Dora* 38
Nurse, were you *h*? *Romney's R.* 16
O yes! I *h* you for a season there, „ 20
Hireling Who had borne my flower on her *h* heart, *The Wreck* 143
Hispaniola Howl'd me from *H*; *Columbus* 118
harmless people whom we found In *H's* island-Paradise! „ 182
Hiss the hot *h* And bustling whistle of the youth *Marr. of Geraint* 256
h, snake—I saw him there—Let the fox bark, *Pelleas and E.* 471
A *h* as from a wilderness of snakes, *St. Telemachus* 66
Hiss'd *h* each at other's ear What shall not be *Geraint and E.* 634
wedded her,' he said, Not said, but *h* it: *Last Tournament* 620
He *h*, 'Let us revenge ourselves, *Happy* 63
Hissing Each *h* in his neighbour's ear; *Princess v* 15
And dipt in baths of *h* tears, *In Mem. cxviii* 23
h in war on his own hearthstone? *Maud I i* 24
geese of the world that are ever *h* dispraise „ *iv* 52
h spray wind-driven Far thro' the dizzy dark. *Lover's Tale ii* 198
Garlon, *h*; then he sourly smiled. *Balin and Balin* 355
he, *h* 'I have no sword,' Sprang from the door *Pelleas and E.* 602
roused a snake that *h* writhed away; *Death of Œnone* 88
Hist *H O H*,' he said, 'They seek us: *Princess iv* 218
Historic *See* **Half-Historic**
History boyish *histories* Of battle, *Aylmer's Field* 97
would chant the *h* Of that great race, *In Mem. ciii* 34
Now made a pretty *h* to herself *Lancelot and E.* 18
old writers Have writ of in *histories*— *Batt. of Brunanburh* 115
Poor old Heraldry, poor old *H*, *Locksley H., Sixty* 249
kindliness Rare in Fable or *H*, *On Jub. Q. Victoria* 5
as this poor earth's pale *h* runs,— *Vastness* 3
Hit (s) With twisted quirks and happy *h's*, *Will Water.* 189
Hit (verb) He scarcely *h* my humour, *Edwin Morris* 76
And *h* the Northern hills. *Princess v* 44
dream can *h* the mood Of Love on earth? *In Mem. xlvii* 11
Some sudden vivid pleasure *h* him there. *Lover's Tale iv* 178
An' I *h* on an old deal-box *First Quarrel* 48
Has *h* on this, which you will take My Fitz, *To E. Fitzgerald* 50
Hither And on the *h* side, or so she look'd, *Princess ii* 107
But on the *h* side of that loud morn *Last Tournament* 56
Hitting aim'd All at one mark, all *h*: *Aylmer's Field* 95
h all we saw with shafts Of gentle satire, *Princess ii* 468
Hive Audley feast Humm'd like a *h* all round *Audley Court* 5
from all the provinces, And fill the *h*.' *Princess ii* 98
—Wasps in our good *h*, „ *iv* 535
There the *h* of Roman liars worship *Boädicea* 19
h of those wild bees That made such honey *Holy Grail* 214
vineyard, *h* and horse and herd; *To Virgil* 10
moment's anger of bees in their *h*? *Vastness* 35
Hiven (heaven) an' *H* in its glory smiled, *Tomorrow* 25
An' sorra the bog that's in *H* „ 67
An' tell thim in *H* about Molly Magee „ 92
Hoälm (Holm) an' Thurnaby *h's* to plow! *N. Farmer, O. S.* 52
Hoam (home) I walk'd wi' tha all the way *h* *Spinster's S's.* 32
Hoar Make thy grass *h* with early rime. *Two Voices* 66
brows in silent hours become Unnaturally *h* with rime, *St. S. Stylites* 166
the lawn as yet Is *h* with rime, *To F. D. Maurice* 42
And the willow-branches *h* and dank, *Dying Swan* 37
made The *h* hair of the Baronet bristle up *Aylmer's Field* 42
descending from the sacred peak Of *h* high-templed Faith, *Pref. Son. 19th Cent.* 10
Hoard (s) With a little *h* of maxims preaching *Locksley Hall* 94
a *h* of tales that dealt with knights, *Princess, Pro.* 29
Our *h* is little, but our hearts are great. (repeat) *Marr. of Geraint* 352, 374
From his great *h* of happiness distill'd *Lover's Tale i* 714
Struck for their *h's* and their hearths *Batt. of Brunanburh* 19
Hoard (verb) I *h* it as a sugar-plum for Holmes.' *The Epic* 43
That *h*, and sleep, and feed, *Ulysses* 5
some three suns to store and *h* myself, „ 29
To *h* all savings to the uttermost, *Enoch Arden* 46
I *h* in thought The faded rhymes and scraps *Lover's Tale i* 288
Hoarded *h* in herself, Grew, seldom seen: *Gardener's D* 1 9
Hoarding perhaps the *h* sense Gives out at times *In Mem. xliv* 6
Hoarhead Came on the *h* woodman at a bough *Balin and Balan* 294
Hoar-headed Crept to his North again, *H-h* hero! *Batt. of Brunanburh* 65
Hoarse I hear thee not at all, or *h* *The Blackbird* 19
Hoary And *h* to the wind. *Palace of Art* 80

Hoary (*continued*) O'erflourish'd with the *h* clematis : *Golden Year* 63
Set thy *h* fancies free ; *Vision of Sin* 156
Still makes a *h* eyebrow for the gleam *The Brook* 80
a *h* face Meet for the reverence of the hearth, *Aylmer's Field* 332
h Channel Tumbles a billow on chalk and sand ; *To F. D. Maurice* 23
Take the *h* Roman head and shatter it, *Boädicea* 65
And eating *h* grain and pulse the steeds, *Spec. of Iliad* 21
From youth and babe and *h* hairs : *In Mem. lxix* 10
Nor *h* knoll of ash and haw „ *c* 9
lifted his voice, and call'd A *h* man, *Com. of Arthur* 145
Then spake the *h* chamberlain and said, „ 148
But none spake word except the *h* Earl : *Marr. of Geraint* 369
Then suddenly addrest the *h* Earl : „ 402
Half-suffocated in the *h* fell *Merlin and V.* 840
And glancing thro' the *h* boles, *Pelleas and E.* 50
From *h* deeps that belt the changeful West, *Prog. of Spring* 98
h Sheik, On whom the women shrieking ' Atheist ' *Akbar's Dream* 90
Hoary-headed There musing sat the *h-h* Earl, *Marr. of Geraint* 295
Then sigh'd and smiled the *h-h* Earl, „ 307
Hob wi' my oän kettle theere o' the *h*, *Spinster's S's.* 9
Hob-and-nob Let us *h-a-n* with Death. *Vision of Sin* 74
H-a-n with brother Death ! „ 194
Hobble *See* **Hopple**
Hoed *See* **Stubb'd**
Hofficer (officer) she walkt awaäy wi' a *h* lad, *Village Wife* 97
Hog his ploughs, his cows, his *h's*, his dogs ; *The Brook* 125
And sleeker shall he shine than any *h*.' *Gareth and L.* 460
men brought in whole *h's* and quarter beeves, *Geraint and E.* 602
Hoggish With colt-like whinny and with *h* whine *St. S. Stylites* 177
Hold (grasp) shuddering took *h* of all my mind, *May Queen, Con.* 35
thrice as sweet As woodbine's fragile *h*, *Talking Oak* 146
Nor greatly cared to lose, her *h* on life. *Aylmer's Field* 568
And that my *h* on life would break *In Mem. xxviii* 15
from my *h* on these Streams virtue—fire— *Gareth and L.* 1309
of that token on the shield Relax'd his *h* : *Balin and Balan* 370
And sweep me from my *h* upon the world, *Merlin and V.* 303
and their law Relax'd its *h* upon us, *Guinevere* 457
My inward sap, the *h* I have on earth, *Lover's Tale i* 166
Hunger of glory gat *H* of the land. *Batt. of Brunanburh* 125
Would loose him from his *h* ; *Ancient Sage* 118
Hold (stronghold) new-comers in an ancient *h*, *Edwin Morris* 9
calmer hours to Memory's darkest *h*, *Love and Duty* 90
ev'n the lonest *h* were all as free *Gareth and L.* 598
I would track this caitiff to his *h*, *Marr. of Geraint* 415
by bandit-haunted *h's*, Gray swamps and pools, *Geraint and E.* 30
Right in the gateway of the bandit *h*, „ 774
broke the bandit *h's* and cleansed the land. „ 944
Scaped thro' a cavern from a bandit *h*, *Holy Grail* 207
And many of those who burnt the *h*, „ 264
defended the *h* that we held with our lives— *Def. of Lucknow* 7
Hold (of a ship) And the sick men down in the *h* *The Revenge* 79
Hold (verb) (*See also* **Howd, 'Owd**) *you that* h *A nobler office upon earth* *To the Queen* 1
in mild unrest *h's* him beneath in her breast. *Leonine Eleg.* 12
To *h* a common scorn of death ! *Supp. Confessions* 34
We may *h* converse with all forms *Ode to Memory* 115
' Yet how should I for certain *h*, *Two Voices* 340
For now the noonday quiet *h's* the hill : *Œnone* 25
H swollen clouds from raining, *D. of F. Women* 11
To *h* his hope thro' shame and guilt, *Love thou thy land* 82
there was no anchor, none, To *h* by.' *The Epic* 21
hand On Everard's shoulder, with ' I *h* by him.' „ 22
Whereof this world's *h's* record. *M. d'Arthur* 16
He, by some law that *h's* in love, *Gardener's D.* 9
h From thence thro' all the worlds : „ 209
what it *h's* May not be dwelt on by the common day. „ 270
I will not cease to grasp the hope I *h* *St. S. Stylites* 5
my stiff spine can *h* my weary head, „ 43
Is that the angel there That *h's* a crown ? „ 204
I *h* them exquisitely knit, *Talking Oak* 91
h passion in a leash, And not leap forth *Love and Duty* 40
my purpose *h's* To sail beyond the sunset, *Ulysses* 59
Yet *h* me met not for ever in thine East : *Tithonus* 64
h thee, when his passion shall have spent *Locksley Hall* 49
common sense of most shall *h* a fretful realm in awe, „ 129

Hold (verb) (*continued*) Who *h* their hands to all, and cry *Will Water.* 45
I *h* it good, good things shall pass : „ 205
I *h* thee dear For this good pint of port. „ 211
Shall *h* their orgies at your tomb. *You might have won* 12
Enoch would *h* possession for a week : *Enoch Arden* 27
Cast all your cares on God ; that anchor *h's*. „ 222
But let me *h* my purpose till I die. „ 875
and *h's* her head to other stars, *The Brook* 195
' O pray God that he *h* up ' *Aylmer's Field* 733
but he that *h's* The Gods are careless, *Lucretius* 149
h Your promise : all, I trust, may yet be well.' *Princess ii* 360
substance or the shadow ? will it *h* ? „ 409
such, my friend, We *h* them slight : „ *iv* 127
I *h* These flashes on the surface are not „ 252
You *h* the woman is the better man ; „ 410
I *h* That it becomes no man to nurse despair, „ 463
to-morrow morn We *h* a great convention : „ 511
yet I *h* her, king, True woman : *Princess, v* 179
That *h's* a stately fretwork to the Sun, „ *vi* 86
never in your own arms To *h* your own, „ 178
h against the world this honour of the land. *Third of Feb.* 48
For those are few we *h* as dear ; *To F. D. Maurice* 46
I *h* you here, root and all, in my hand, *Flow. in cran. wall* 3
Take the hoary Roman head and shatter it, *h* it abominable, *Boädicea* 65
I sometimes *h* it half a sin *In Mem. v* 1
lake That *h's* the shadow of a lark „ *xvi* 9
I *h* it true, whate'er befall ; „ *xxvii* 13
And *h's* it sin and shame to draw „ *xlviii* 11
H thou the good : define it well : „ *liii* 13
To *h* the costliest love in fee. „ *lxxix* 4
So *h* I commerce with the dead ; „ *lxxxv* 93
they that *h* apart The promise of the golden hours ? „ 105
h An hour's communion with the dead. „ *xciv* 3
And *h* it solemn to the past. „ *cv* 16
High wisdom *h's* my wisdom less, „ *cxii* 1
To *h* me from my proper place, „ *cxvii* 2
And dream my dream, and *h* it true ; „ *cxxiii* 10
Rather than *h* by the law that I made, *Maud I i* 55
h Awe-stricken breaths at a work divine, „ *x* 16
Think I may *h* dominion sweet, „ *xvi* 12
Arise, my God, and strike, for we *h* Thee just, „ *II i* 45
Whatever the Quaker *h's*, from sin ; „ *v* 92
theirs are bestial, *h* him less than man : *Com. of Arthur* 181
Hath body enow to *h* his foemen down ? ' „ 253
the good mother *h's* me still a child ! *Gareth and L.* 15
' An ye *h* me yet for child, „ 99
h The King a shadow, and the city real : „ 265
Return, and meet, and *h* him from our eyes, „ 429
the mightiest, *h's* her stay'd In her own castle, „ 615
and so my lance *H*, by God's grace, „ 723
I *h* He scarce is knight, yea but half-man, „ 1175
Some *h* that he hath swallow'd infant flesh, „ 1342
We *h* a tourney here to-morrow morn, *Marr. of Geraint* 287
How fast they *h* like colours of a shell „ 681
I *h* a finger up ; They understand : *Geraint and E.* 337
h them outer fiends, Who leap at thee to tear thee ; *Balin and Balan* 141
That honour too wherein she *h's* him— „ 180
' I *h* them happy, so they died for love : „ 581
some few—ay, truly—youths that *h* *Merlin and V.* 21
Lancelot saying, ' Hear, but *h* my name Hidden, *Lancelot and E.* 416
Yet, if he love, and his love *h*, „ 697
some do *h* our Arthur cannot die, „ 1258
Not at my years, however it *h* in youth. „ 1296
Unproven, *h's* himself as Lancelot, *Holy Grail* 304
to *h*, *H* her a wealthy bride within thine arms, „ 620
Or all but *h*, and then—cast her aside, „ 622
But *h* me for your friend : *Pelleas and E.* 340
Some *h* he was a table-knight of thine— *Last Tournament* 69
A naked aught—yet swine I *h* thee still, „ 309
I'll *h* thou hast some touch Of music, „ 313
There *h* thee with my life against the world.' She answer'd, ' Lancelot, wilt thou *h* me so ? *Guinevere* 115
that strong castle where he *h's* the Queen ; „ 194
I *h* that man the worst of public foes „ 512

Hollow-hung Under the *h-h* ocean green! *The Merman* 38
Hollowing (*See also* **Fire-hollowing**) Or *h* one hand against his ear, *Palace of Art* 109
Hollow-ringing He heard the *h-r* heavens sweep Over him *Holy Grail* 678
Hollow-vaulted look'd to shame The *h-v* dark, *Arabian Nights* 126
Holly (adj.) while the *h* boughs Entwine the cold baptismal font, *In Mem. xxix* 9
Holly (s) Sick for the *hollies* and the yews *Princess, Pro.* 187
But this is the time of *hollies*. *Spiteful Letter* 22
O *hollies* and ivies and evergreens, „ 23
weave The *h* round the Christmas hearth; *In Mem. xxx* 2
weave The *h* round the Christmas hearth; „ *lxxviii* 2
let us leave This laurel, let this *h* stand: „ *cv* 2
here and there great *hollies* under them; *Pelleas and E.* 27
Black *h*, and white-flower'd wayfaring-tree! *Sir J. Oldcastle* 130
Holly-hoak Before a tower of crimson *h-h's*, *Princess, Con.* 82
Hollyhock Heavily hangs the *h*, (repeat) *A spirit haunts* 11, 23
A summer burial deep in *h's*; *Aylmer's Field* 164
Holly-spray And wearing but a *h-s* for crest, *Last Tournament* 172
Holm (*See also* **Hoälm**) soft wind blowing over meadowy *h's* *Edwin Morris* 95
Holmes The parson *H*, the poet Everard Hall, *The Epic* 4
I hoard it as a sugar-plum for *H*.' „ 43
Holofernes underneath The head of *H* peep'd *Princess iv* 227
Holp *h* To lace us up, till, each, in maiden plumes „ *i* 201
However much he *h* me at my need, *Com. of Arthur* 142
Sir Lancelot *h* To raise the Prince, *Guinevere* 45
Holpen had I been *h* half as well By this King Arthur *Com. of Arthur* 161
And being lustily *h* by the rest, *Lancelot and E.* 496
Holt thro' damp *h's* new-flush'd with may, *My life is full* 19
She sent her voice thro' all the *h* *Talking Oak* 123
blackening over heath and *h*, *Locksley Hall* 191
Of wither'd *h* or tilth or pasturage. *Enoch Arden* 675
smells a foul-flesh'd agaric in the *h*, *Gareth and L.* 747
Holy (*See also* **Holy Ghost, Holy Grail**) All the place is *h* ground; *Poet's Mind* 9
H water will I pour Into every spicy flower „ 12
Heard a carol, mournful, *h*, *L. of Shalott iv* 28
Nor steep our brows in slumber's *h* balm; *Lotos-Eaters, C. S.* 21
Beneath a heaven dark and *h*, „ 91
h organ rolling waves Of sound on roof *D. of F. Women* 191
invade Even with a verse your *h* woe. *To J. S.* 8
Sleep, *h* spirit, blessed soul, „ 70
light that led The *h* Elders with the gift of myrrh. *M. d'Arthur* 233
more Than many just and *h* men, *St. S. Stylites* 131
'By *h* rood, a royal beard! *Day-Dm., Revival* 20
Then desperately seized the *h* Book, *Enoch Arden* 495
Haunting a *h* text, and still to that Returning, *Sea Dreams* 42
o'er the rest Arising, did his *h* oily best, „ 195
'Storm, and what dreams, ye *h* Gods, what dreams! *Lucretius* 33
'Is this thy vengeance, *h* Venus, thine, „ 67
And *h* secrets of this microcosm. *Princess iii* 313
The *h* Gods, they must be appeased, *The Victim* 47
The King was shaken with *h* fear; „ 57
lead Thro' prosperous floods his *h* urn. *In Mem. ix* 8
Rise, happy morn, rise, *h* morn, „ *xxx* 29
That *h* Death ere Arthur died „ *lxxx* 2
And He that died in *H* Land „ *lxxxiv* 42
And woodlands *h* to the dead; „ *xcix* 8
This broad-brimm'd hawker of *h* things, *Maud I x* 41
But speak to her all things *h* and high, „ *II ii* 78
But there was heard among the *h* hymns *Com. of Arthur* 290
And *h* Dubric spread his hands and spake, „ 471
Save whom she loveth, or a *h* life. *Gareth and L.* 622
Whose *h* hand hath fashion'd on the rock „ 1197
Who, with mild heat of *h* oratory, *Geraint and E.* 866
King Took, as in rival heat, to *h* things; *Balin and Balan* 100
brought By *h* Joseph hither, „ 113
boss'd With *h* Joseph's legend, „ 363
King Pellam's *h* spear, Reputed to be red with sinless blood, „ 556
Whom Pellam drove away with *h* heat. „ 611
saith not *H* Writ the same?'— *M rlin and V.* 52
They bound to *h* vows of chastity! „ 695
Or else were he, the *h* king, whose hymns „ 765
Holy (*continued*) Full many a *h* vow and pure resolve. *Lancelot and E.* 879
Not knowing he should die a *h* man. „ 1429
times Grew to such evil that the *h* cup Was caught away to Heaven, *Holy Grail* 57
But who first saw the *h* thing to-day?' „ 67
if ever *h* maid With knees of adoration wore the stone, A *h* maid; „ 70
glanced and shot Only to *h* things; „ 76
Thy *h* nun and thou have seen a sign— „ 295
thereby A *h* hermit in a hermitage, „ 443
at the sacring of the mass I saw The *h* elements alone; „ 463
This *H* Thing, fail'd from my side, „ 470
And o'er his head the *H* Vessel hung (repeat) „ 512, 520
thence Taking my war-horse from the *h* man, „ 537
And ev'n the *H* Quest, and all but her; „ 610
'Ridest thou then so hotly on a quest So *h*,' „ 643
so Lancelot might have seen, The *H* Cup of healing; „ 655
Small heart was his after the *H* Quest: „ 657
a maid, Who kept our *h* faith among her kin „ 697
This vision—hast thou seen the *H* Cup, „ 734
Perhaps, like him of Cana in *H* Writ, „ 762
Then I spake To one most *h* saint, „ 781
And to the *H* Vessel of the Grail.' „ 840
Thy *h* nun and thou have driven men mad, „ 862
To *h* virgins in their ecstasies, „ 867
'Gawain, and blinder unto *h* things „ 870
To those who went upon the *H* Quest, „ 890
King Arthur made new knights to fill the gap Left by the *H* Quest; *Pelleas and E.* 2
'Ye, that so dishallow the *h* sleep, „ 446
sat There in the *h* house at Almesbury Weeping, *Guinevere* 2
Then glancing up beheld the *h* nuns All round her, „ 666
Do each low office of your *h* house; „ 682
light that led The *h* Elders with the gift of myrrh. *Pass. of Arthur* 401
Each way from verge to verge a *H* Land, *Lover's Tale i* 337
I charge you never to say that I laid him in *h* ground. *Rizpah* 58
Now reddest with the blood of *h* men, *Sir J. Oldcastle* 54
or such crimes As *h* Paul— „ 110
how I anger'd Arundel asking me To worship *H* Cross! „ 136
As *h* John had prophesied of me, *Columbus* 21
Ferdinand Hath sign'd it and our *H* Catholic queen— „ 30
All glory to the mother of our Lord, And *H* Church, „ 63
And free the *H* Sepulchre from thrall. „ 104
And own the *h* governance of Rome.' „ 190
And ready—tho' our *H* Catholic Queen, „ 228
And save the *H* Sepulchre from thrall. „ 240
the *H* man he assoil'd us, and sadly we sail'd away. *V. of Maeldune* 126
As the *H* Mother o' Glory that smiles at her sleepin' child— *Tomorrow* 26
Till *H* St. Pether gets up wid his kays „ 93
Near us Edith's *h* shadow, smiling *Locksley H., Sixty* 54
My warrior of the *H* Cross and of the conquering sword, *Happy* 21
This poor rib-grated dungeon of the *h* human ghost, „ 31
sway'd the sword that lighten'd back the sun of *H* land, „ 43
You parted for the *H* War without a word to me, „ 77
Who reads thy gradual process, *H* Spring. *Prog. of Spring* 106
If it be a mosque people murmur the *h* prayer, *Akbar's D., Inscrip.* 4
Holy Ghost the warning of the *H G*, I prophesy *St. S. Stylites* 219
Holy Grail (*See also* **Grail**) Three angels bear the *h G*: *Sir Galahad* 42
Until I find the *h G*. „ 84
sweet vision of the *H G* Drove me from all vainglories, *Holy Grail* 31
To whom the monk: 'The *H G*!—I trust „ 37
Spake often with her of the *H G*, „ 86
thought That now the *H G* would come again; „ 92
'Sweet brother, I have seen the *H G*: „ 107
And down the long beam stole the *H G*, (repeat) „ 117, 188
I, Sir Arthur, saw the *H G*, I saw the *H G* „ 290
I knew That I should light upon the *H G*. „ 367
if I find the *H G* itself And touch it, „ 438
saw the Grail, The *H G*, descend upon the shrine: „ 465
and there Dwelt, and I knew it was the *H G*, „ 531
I find not there this *H G*, „ 542
the hope That could I touch or see the *H G* „ 779
I saw the *H G*, All pall'd in crimson samite, „ 846
Homage Honour,' she said, 'and *h*, tax and toll, *Œnone* 116

Honest (*continued*) Among the h shoulders of the crowd, *Sea Dreams* 166
while my h heat Were all miscounted *Princess iv* 333
And there's a downright h meaning in her; „ *v* 280
That England's h censure went too far; *Third of Feb.* 2
For, being of that h few, *To F. D. Maurice* 5
But h talk and wholesome wine, „ 18
The lips of men with h praise, *In Mem. lxxxiv* 26
There lives more faith in h doubt, „ *xcvi* 11
his h fame should at least by me be maintained: *Maud I i* 18
Worthier soul was he than I am, sound and h, *Locksley H., Sixty* 239
True cheer with h wine— *Pro. to Gen. Hamley* 16
h Poverty, bare to the bone; *Vastness* 19
Like an h woman's, *Forlorn* 20

Honey (adj.) (*See also* **Honeymoon**) Globing H Moons Bright as this. *The Ring* 7
Globe again, and make H Moon. „ 16
They made a thousand h moons of one? „ 22

Honey (s) (*See also* **Mud-honey**) whitest h in fairy gardens cull'd— *Eleänore* 26
Or Heliconian h in living words, *Lucretius* 224
madness of love, The h of poison-flowers *Maud I iv* 56
'I sit and gather h; yet, methinks *Merlin and V.* 601
wild bees That made such h in his realm. *Holy Grail* 215
h from hornet-combs, And men from beasts— *Last Tournament* 357
Art with poisonous h stol'n from France, *To the Queen ii* 56
land of promise flowing with the milk And h *Lover's Tale i* 335
'Sleep, little blossom, my h, my bliss! *Romney's R.* 99

Honeycomb A full-cell'd h of eloquence *Edwin Morris* 26

Honey-converse Some h-c feeds thy mind, *Adeline* 40

Honey'd oozed All o'er with h answer as we rode *Princess v* 242
Would lisp in h whispers of this monstrous fraud! *Third of Feb.* 36
fed With h rain and delicate air, *Maud I xviii* 21

Honey-hearted h-h wine And bread from out the houses *Spec. of Iliad* 5

Honeying But h at the whisper of a lord; *Princess, Pro.* 115

Honeymoon But thirty moons, one h to that, *Edwin Morris* 29
Globing H M's Bright as this. *The Ring* 7
Globe again, and make H M. „ 16
They made a thousand h m's of one? „ 22
No second cloudless h was mine. „ 382

Honeysuckle The h round the porch has wov'n *May Queen* 29
Broke from a bower of vine and h: *Aylmer's Field* 156
But all about it flies a h. *Gareth and L.* 1278
how sweetly smells the h In the hush'd night, „ 1287

Honeysuckle-flower kingcups and h-f's.' *City Child* 10

Hong-Kong H-K, Karnac, and all the rest. *To Ulysses* 44

Honied And buzzings of the h hours. *In Mem. lxxxix* 52
Nor drown thyself with flies in h wine; *Ancient Sage* 268

Honorius to reach H, till he heard them, *St. Telemachus* 77

Honour (s) (*See also* **Mock-honour**) In h of the golden prime *Arabian Nights* 109
Some grow to h, some to shame,— *Two Voices* 257
H,' she said, 'and homage, tax and toll, *Œnone* 116
all the old h had from Christmas gone, *The Epic* 7
But now much h and much fame were lost.' *M. d'Arthur* 109
Old age hath yet his h and his toil; *Ulysses* 50
helps the hurt that H feels, *Locksley Hall* 105
an h Unto which she was not born. *L. of Burleigh* 79
a snowy hand and signet gem, 'All h. *Princess i* 122
I lose My h, these their lives.' „ *ii* 342
for h: every captain waits Hungry for h, „ *v* 313
this h, if ye will. It needs must be for h „ 320
since you think me touch'd In h— „ 402
h, h, h, h to him, Eternal h to his name. (repeat) *Ode on Well.* 149, 230
Lavish H shower'd all her stars, „ 196
But some love England and her h yet. *Third of Feb.* 46
hold against the world this h of the land. „ 48
Singing of Death, and of H that cannot die, *Maud I v* 16
Clear h shining like the dewy star *Gareth and L.* 329
yield him this large h all the more; „ 397
And did her h as the Prince's bride, *Marr. of Geraint* 835
And feast with these in h of their Earl; *Geraint and E.* 287
we rode upon this fatal quest Of h, where no h „ 704
That h too wherein she holds him—this, *Balin and Balan* 180
We will do him No customary h: *Lancelot and E.* 543
His h rooted in dishonour stood, „ 876

Honour (s) (*continued*) To win his h and to make his name, *Lancelot and E.* 1362
'Glory and joy and h to our Lord *Holy Grail* 839
Sir Pelleas kept the field With h: *Pelleas and E.* 169
and thro' his heart The fire of h „ 278
by the h of the Table Round, I will be leal to thee „ 342
this h after death, Following thy will! *Last Tournament* 34
White-robed in h of the stainless child, „ 147
In h of poor Innocence the babe, „ 292
But now much h and much fame were lost.' *Pass. of Arthur* 277
sank his body with h down into the deep, *The Revenge* 109
I could not free myself in h— *Sisters (E. and E.)* 161
Love and H jarr'd Tho' Love and H join'd „ 176
Go, take thine h's home; *To W. C. Macready* 6

Honour (verb) his mute dust I h and his living worth: *To J. S.* 30
And more than England h's that, *Talking Oak* 295
and h thy brute Baäl, *Aylmer's Field* 644
And h all the day. *Window, When* 16
H the charge they made! H the Light Brigade, *Light Brigade* 53
loathe, fear—but h me the more.' *Merlin and V.* 122
Before a king who h's his own word, *Lancelot and E.* 143
'Fear God: h the King— *Last Tournament* 302
To h his own word as if his God's, *Guinevere* 473
whom most I loathe, to h whom I scorn? *The Flight* 50

Honourable And mutual love and h toil; *Enoch Arden* 83

Honour'd To perish, wept for, h, known, *Two Voices* 149
bard has h beech or lime, *Talking Oak* 291
Myself not least, but h of them all; *Ulysses* 15
Head-waiter, h by the guest Half-mused, *Will Water.* 73
laugh'd upon his warrior whom he loved And h *Com. of Arthur* 125
warrior whom he loved And h most, Sir Lancelot, „ 448
beyond the rest, And h him, and wrought *Holy Grail* 10
For once—ev'n to the height—I h him. *Last Tournament* 662
the child of one I h, happy, dead before *Guinevere* 423
And, tho' he loved and h Lionel, *Lover's Tale iv* 148
when the guest Is loved and h to the uttermost. „ 245
'you are h now Ev'n to the uttermost: „ 316
one that loved, and h him, *Ancient Sage* 3
Who is he that cometh, like an h guest, *Ode on Well.* 80
I see myself an h guest, *In Mem. lxxxiv* 21
This wreath, above his h head, *Tiresias* 213

Honouring h your sweet faith in him, *A Dedication* 5
h his wise mother's word— *Achilles over the T.* 16
Florence h thy nativity, *To Dante* 3
h your fair fame Of Statesman, *To Marq. of Dufferin* 14

Hood we must h your random eyes, *Rosalind* 37
born In teacup-times of h and hoop, *Talking Oak* 63
in hue The lilac, with a silken h to each, *Princess ii* 17
keep your h's about the face; „ 358
Those cobras ever setting up their h's— *Akbar's Dream* 166

Hooded (*See also* **Black-hooded, Violet-hooded**) With h brows I crept into the hall, *Princess iv* 225

Hoodman-blind dance and song and h-b. *In Mem. lxxviii* 12

Hoof his own blood flows About his h. *Supp. Confessions* 156
On burnish'd hooves his war-horse trode; *L. of Shalott iii* 29
clattering flints batter'd with clanging h's; *D. of F. Women* 21
h by h And every h a knell to my desires, *Princess iv* 173
galloping h's bare on the ridge of spears „ *v* 489
That afternoon a sound arose of h And chariot, „ *vi* 379
the h's of the horses beat, (repeat) *Maud II v* 8
The h of his horse slipt in the stream, *Gareth and L.* 1046
heard instead A sudden sound of h's, *Marr. of Geraint* 164
and everywhere Was hammer laid to h, „ 256
The sound of many a heavily-galloping h *Geraint and E.* 447
Not a h left: and I methinks till now Was honest— „ 485
ring thy name To every h that clangs it, *Tiresias* 138

Hoof-print We saw the h-p of a horse, no more.' *Balin and Balan* 133

Hook if I Should h it to some useful end. *Day-Dm., Moral* 16
milky arm Red-rent with h's of bramble, *Holy Grail* 211

Hook'd At last I h my ankle in a vine, *Princess iv* 268

Hoonderd (hundred) Mëa, wi' haäte h haäcre o' Squoire's *N. Farmer, O. S.* 44
thou be a big scholard now wi' a h haäcre o' sense— *Church-warden, etc.* 22

Hoop born In teacup-times of hood and h, *Talking Oak* 63

Hoop (*continued*) and roll'd His *h* to pleasure Edith, *Aylmer's Field* 85
Hoot storm grew with a howl and a *h* of the blast *The Wreck* 91
Hooved *See* **White-hooved**
Hop A land of *h's* and poppy-mingled corn, *Aylmer's Field* 31
tower Half-lost in belts of *h* and breadths of wheat; *Princess, Con.* 45
Hope (s) (*See also* '**Oäp**) my *h* is gray, and cold At heart, *Supp. Confessions* 103
Shall man live thus, in joy and *h* „ 169
without *h* of change, In sleep she seem'd to walk *Mariana* 29
Thou leddest by the hand thine infant *H.* *Ode to Memory* 30
the breathing spring Of *H* and Youth. *The Poet* 28
What *h* or fear or joy is thine? *Adeline* 23
My *h* and heart is with thee— *To J. M. K.* 1
Light *H* at Beauty's call would perch and stand, *Caress'd or chidden* 3
H is other *H* and wanders far, „ 10
'Think you this mould of *h's* and fears *Two Voices* 28
raise One *h* that warm'd me in the days „ 122
summits slope Beyond the furthest flights of *h*, „ 185
'Not that the grounds of *h* were fix'd, „ 227
'A hidden *h*,' the voice replied: „ 441
Nature's living motion lent The pulse of *h* to discontent. „ 450
And full at heart of trembling *h*, *Miller's D.* 110
With blessings beyond *h* or thought, „ 237
'I was cut off from *h* in that sad place, *D. of F. Women* 105
She ceased in tears, fallen from *h* and trust: „ 257
Come *H* and Memory, spouse and bride, *On a Mourner* 23
To hold his *h* thro' shame and guilt, *Love thou thy land* 82
A crowd of *h's*, That sought to sow themselves *Gardener's D.* 64
say That my desire, like all strongest *h's*, „ 237
For daily *h* fulfill'd, to rise again *Edwin Morris* 38
I will not cease to grasp the *h* I hold *St. S. Stylites* 5
and *h* ere death Spreads more and more „ 156
'Twere all as one to fix our *h's* on Heaven *Golden Year* 57
Care and Pleasure, *H* and Pain, *Day-Dm., Sleep. P.* 55
What eyes, like thine, have waken'd *h's*, „ *L'Envoi* 45
to me is given Such *h*, I know not fear; *Sir Galahad* 62
And phantom *h's* assemble; *Will Water.* 30
For I had *h*, by something rare To prove myself „ 165
In *h* to gain upon her flight. *The Voyage* 60
Like Heavenly *H* she crown'd the sea, „ 70
'Drink to lofty *h's* that cool— *Vision of Sin* 147
April *h's*, the fools of chance; „ 164
'Youthful *h's*, by scores, to all, „ 199
Cry to the summit, 'Is there any *h*?' „ 220
It is beyond all *h*, against all chance, *Enoch Arden* 403
His *h's* to see his own, And pace the sacred old familiar fields, „ 624
but labour for himself, Work without *h*, „ 820
boat that bears the *h* of life approach „ 830
thro' that dawning gleam'd a kindlier *h* On Enoch „ 833
strong in *h's*, And prodigal of all brain-labour *Aylmer's Field* 446
Had golden *h's* for France and all mankind, „ 464
saw An end, a *h*, a light breaking upon him. „ 480
Seem'd *h's* returning rose: „ 559
tower'd Above them, with his *h's* in either grave. „ 624
Where she, who kept a tender Christian *h*, *Sea Dreams* 41
within As hollow as the *h's* and fears of men? *Lucretius* 180
his *h's* and hates, his homes and fanes, „ 255
hills, that look'd across a land of *h*, *Princess i* 169
H, a poising eagle, burns Above the unrisen morrow:' „ *iv* 82
like parting *h's* I heard them passing from me: „ 172
weight of all the *h's* of half the world, „ 184
I bore up in *h* she would be known: „ 320
and a *h* The child of regal compact, „ 420
my *h's* and thine are one: „ *vii* 364
Uplifted high in heart and *h* are we, *Ode on Well.* 254
He rose at dawn and, fired with *h*, *Sailor Boy* 1
and darkens and brightens like my *h*, *Window, On the Hill* 18
As we descended following *H*, *In Mem. xxii* 11
The light that shone when *H* was born. „ *xxx* 32
Man dies: nor is there *h* in dust:' „ *xxxv* 4
And *h's* and light regrets that come „ *xl* 7
Beneath all fancied *h's* and fears „ *xlix* 13
And faintly trust the larger *h*. „ *lv* 20
What *h* of answer, or redress? „ *lvi* 27
With so much *h* for years to come, „ *lix* 14

Hope (s) *continued*) The pillar of a people's *h*, *In Mem. lxiv* 15
What *h* is here for modern rhyme „ *lxxvii* 1
Love, then, had *h* of richer store: „ *lxxxi* 5
Despair of *H*, and earth of thee. „ *lxxxiv* 16
I remain'd, whose *h's* were dim, „ *lxxxv* 29
The mighty *h's* that make us men. „ 60
The *h* of unaccomplish'd years „ *xci* 7
And *h* could never hope too much, „ *cxii* 11
Yet *H* had never lost her youth; „ *cxxv* 5
Wild Hours that fly with *H* and Fear, „ *cxxviii* 9
why not. I have neither *h* nor trust; *Maud I i* 30
returns the dark With no more *h* of light. „ *ix* 16
brother comes, like a blight On my fresh *h*, „ *xix* 103
a *h* for the world in the coming wars— „ *III vi* 11
in that *h*, dear soul, let trouble have rest, „ 12
his own blood, his princedom, youth and *h's*, *Gareth and L.* 210
I lived in *h* that sometime you would come *Geraint and E.* 839
worship woman as true wife beyond All *h's* of gaining, *Merlin and V.* 24
goodly *h's* are mine That Lancelot is no more *Lancelot and E.* 601
'Yea, lord,' she said, 'Thy *h's* are mine,' „ 607
Said good Sir Bors, 'beyond all *h's* of mine, *Holy Grail* 690
in the *h* That could I touch or see the Holy Grail „ 778
tho' ye kill my *h*, not yet my love, *Pelleas and E.* 303
Leave me that, I charge thee, my last *h*. *Guinevere* 568
what *h*? I think there was a *h*, Except he mock'd me when he spoke of *h*; His *h* he call'd it; „ 630
left me *h* That in mine own heart I can live „ 635
O Love, O *H*! They come, they crowd upon me *Lover's Tale i* 46
deep vault where the heart of *H* Fell into dust, „ 94
swathe thyself all round *H's* quiet urn For ever? „ 100
in that hour A *h* flow'd round me, „ 449
which was less than *H*, Because it lack'd the power of perfect *H*; But which was more and higher than all *H*, Because all other *H* had lower aim; „ 452
'let this be call'd henceforth The Hill of *H*;' and I replied, 'O sister, My will is one with thine; the Hill of *H*.' „ 462
Her maiden dignities of *H* and Love— „ 580
No wish—no *h*. *H* was not wholly dead, „ 584
Love could walk with banish'd *H* no more? „ 813
Love's arms were wreath'd about the neck of *H*, And *H* „ 815
Love would die when *H* was gone, And Love mourn'd long, and sorrow'd after *H*; „ 818
trod The same old paths where Love had walk'd with *H*, „ 821
But over the deep graves of *H* and Fear, „ *ii* 58
Talk of lost *h's* and broken heart! „ *iv* 176
if the *h* of the world were a lie? *In the Child. Hosp.* 24
as if *h* for the garrison hung but on him; *Def. of Lucknow* 48
faltering *h's* of relief, Havelock baffled, „ 90
God's free air, and *h* of better things. *Sir J. Oldcastle* 10
drowning *h* Sank all but out of sight, *Columbus* 156
h was mine to spread the Catholic Faith, „ 230
Cloud-weaver of phantasmal *h's* and fears, *To Victor Hugo* 2
some strange *h* to see the nearer God. *Tiresias* 29
'We are sinking, and yet there's *h*: *The Wreck* 121
life without sun, without health, without *h*, *Despair* 7
Bright as with deathless *h*— „ 17
And *H* will have broken her heart, „ 92
being damn'd beyond *h* of grace? „ 109
market frets or charms The merchant's *h* no more; *Ancient Sage* 141
Without their *h* of wings!' „ 211
h I catch at vanishes and youth is turn'd *The Flight* 16
H was ever on her mountain, *Locksley H., Sixty* 91
without the faith, without the *h*, „ 137
yours are *h* and youth, but I Eighty winters leave the dog „ 225
far from here is all the *h* of eighty years. „ 254
As all my *h's* were thine— *Pref. Poem Broth. S.* 26
God the traitor's *h* confound! (repeat) *Hands all Round* 10, 22, 34
Star of the morning, *H* in the sunrise; *Vastness* 15
Yes, for some wild *h* was mine That, *The Ring* 135
men have *h's*, which race the restless blood, *Prog. of Spring* 115
'The miserable have no medicine But only *H*!' *Romney's R.* 150
Beyond all *h* of warmth, Œnone sat Not moving, *Death of Œnone* 74

Horse (*continued*) like a *h* That hears the corn-bin open, *The Epic* 44
Francis laid A damask napkin wrought with *h* and hound, *Audley Court* 21
turn the *h's'* heads and home again.' *Walk. to the Mail* 46
a little dearer than his *h*. *Locksley Hall* 50
The *h* and rider reel: *Sir Galahad* 8
He rode a *h* with wings, that would have flown, *Vision of Sin* 3
Below were men and *h's* pierced with worms, „ 209
Enoch's white *h*, and Enoch's ocean-spoil *Enoch Arden* 93
He knew her, as a horseman knows his *h*— „ 136
The *h* he drove, the boat he sold, „ 609
praised his land, his *h's*, his machines; *The Brook* 124
She trampled some beneath her *h's'* heels, *Princess, Pro.* 44
twinn'd as *h's* ear and eye. „ *i* 57
four wing'd *h's* dark against the stars; „ 211
Till like three *h's* that have broken fence, „ *ii* 386
shook My pulses, till to *h* we got, „ *iii* 194
'To *h*' Said Ida; 'home! to *h*!' „ *iv* 166
(For since her *h* was lost I left her mine) „ 197
The *h's* yell'd; they clash'd their arms; „ *v* 250
Part stumbled mixt with floundering *h's*. „ 498
With stroke on stroke the *h* and horseman, „ 523
And sword to sword, and *h* to *h* we hung, „ 539
While *h* and hero fell, *Light Brigade* 44
rolling phantom bodies of *h's* and men; *Boädicea* 27
loosed their sweating *h's* from the yoke, *Spec. of Iliad* 2
Or kill'd in falling from his *h*. *In Mem. vi* 40
Yet pity for a *h* o'er-driven, „ *lxiii* 1
And those white-favour'd *h's* wait; „ *Con.* 90
Look, a *h* at the door, *Maud I xii* 29
That he left his wine and *h's* and play, „ *xix* 74
the hoofs of the *h's* beat, (repeat) „ *II v* 8
long-lanced battle let their *h's* run. *Com. of Arthur* 104
A *h* thou knowest, a man thou dost not know: *Gareth and L.* 463
he had ask'd For *h* and armour: „ 474
And the spear spring, the good *h* reel, „ 523
Thou get to *h* and follow him far away. „ 584
Took *h*, descended the slope street, „ 662
that held The *h*, the spear; „ 681
took the shield And mounted *h* and graspt a spear, „ 691
'Bound upon a quest With *h* and arms— „ 709
heart of her good *h* Was nigh to burst „ 762
Who stood a moment, ere his *h* was brought, „ 934
Flee down the valley before he get to *h*. „ 941
take his *h* And arms, and so return him to the King. „ 955
Beyond his *h's* crupper and the bridge, „ 966
Huge on a huge red *h*, and all in mail „ 1026
Push'd *h* across the foamings of the ford, „ 1040
hoof of his *h* slipt in the stream, „ 1046
His *h* thereon stumbled—ay, for I saw it. „ 1057
knights on *h* Sculptured, and deckt in slowly-waning hues. „ 1194
and thy good *h* And thou are weary; „ 1264
And forage for the *h*, and flint for fire. „ 1277
Lancelot now To lend thee *h* and shield: „ 1324
How best to manage *h*, lance, sword and shield, „ 1351
High on a nightblack *h*, in nightblack arms, „ 1381
Took *h*, and forded Usk, and gain'd the wood; *Marr. of Geraint* 161
when she put her *h* toward the knight, „ 200
Prince Had put his *h* in motion toward the knight, „ 206
the good knight's *h* stands in the court; „ 370
That morning, when they both had got to *h*, *Geraint and E.* 9
Come, we will slay him and will have his *h* „ 62
they would slay you, and possess your *h* „ 74
bound the suits Of armour on their *h's*, „ 97
Three *h's* and three goodly suit of arms, „ 124
bound them on their *h's*, each on each, „ 182
They let the *h's* graze, and ate themselves. „ 211
but take A *h* and arms for guerdon; „ 218
stalling for the *h's*, and return With victual „ 239
up the rocky pathway disappear'd, Leading the *h*, „ 244
'Take Five *h's* and their armours;' „ 409
wild Limours, Borne on a black *h*, „ 458
'*H* and man,' he said, 'All of one mind and all right-honest friends! „ 483
Was honest—paid with *h's* and with arms; „ 486

Horse (*continued*) Prince, without a word, from his *h* fell. *Geraint and E.* 508
Feeding like *h's* when you hear them feed; „ 606
moving out they found the stately *h*, „ 752
then Geraint upon the *h* Mounted, „ 758
And, gravely smiling, lifted her from *h*, „ 883
Men weed the white *h* on the Berkshire hills „ 936
on the right of Balin Balin's *h* Was fast *Balin and Balan* 28
Christless foe of thine as ever dash'd *H* against *h*; „ 98
We saw the hoof-print of a *h*, no more.' „ 133
stall'd his *h*, and strode across the court, „ 341
till his goodly *h*, Arising wearily at a fallen oak, „ 424
And there a *h*! the rider? where is he? „ 467
vaulted on his *h*, and so they crash'd In onset, „ 555
Balin's *h* Was wearied to the death, „ 560
Beheld the Queen and Lancelot get to *h*. *Merlin and V.* 102
Then got Sir Lancelot suddenly to *h*, *Lancelot and E.* 159
strong neighings of the wild white *H* „ 298
There to his proud *h* Lancelot turn'd, „ 347
And brought his *h* to Lancelot where he lay. „ 493
I charge you that you get at once to *h*. „ 539
So all in wrath he got to *h* and went; „ 563
all wearied of the quest Leapt on his *h*, „ 704
Making a roan *h* caper and curvet For pleasure „ 792
when she heard his *h* upon the stones, „ 980
splash'd and dyed The strong White *H* *Holy Grail* 312
his *h* In golden armour jewell'd everywhere: „ 411
our *h's* stumbling as they trode On heaps of ruin, „ 716
reel'd Almost to falling from his *h*; *Pelleas and E.* 24
binding his good *h* To a tree, cast himself down; „ 30
all of them On *h's*, and the *h's* richly trapt „ 55
Pelleas rose, And loosed his *h*, „ 61
Lend me thine *h* and arms, and I will say „ 345
Wherefore now thy *h* And armour: „ 354
Behold his *h* and armour. „ 373
he told us—he that hath His *h* and armour: „ 378
and bound his *h* Hard by the gates. „ 413
And forth he past, and mounting on his *h* „ 456
He dash'd the rowel into his *h*, „ 486
Ran thro' the doors and vaulted on his *h* And fled: „ 539
small pity upon his *h* had he, Or on himself, „ 540
Tristram round the gallery made his *h* Caracole; *Last Tournament* 205
as he stretch'd from *h* To strike him, „ 459
And tamper'd with the Lords of the White *H*, *Guinevere* 15
So Lancelot got her *h*, Set her thereon, „ 122
And still at evenings on before his *h* „ 256
who leagues With Lords of the White *H*, „ 574
There were our *h's* ready at the doors— *Lover's Tale iv* 385
h's whirl'd The chariots backward, *Achilles over the T.* 24
tramp of the hornfooted *h* That grind the glebe *Tiresias* 94
peasants maim the helpless *h*, *Locksley H., Sixty* 95
Wedged themselves in between *h* and *h*, *Heavy Brigade* 22
vineyard, hive and *h* and herd; *To Virgil* 10
And you spurr'd your fiery *h*, *Happy* 76
wild *h*, anger, plunged To fling me, *Akbar's Dream* 118
Bring me my *h*—my *h*? my wings That I may soar the sky, *Mechanophilus* 9
Horseback Enid was aware of three tall knights On *h*, *Geraint and E.* 57
lo, he sat on *h* at the door! *Guinevere* 589
Horseleech like the daughters of the *h*, 'Give, *Golden Year* 12
Horseman He knew her, as a *h* knows his horse— *Enoch Arden* 136
With stroke on stroke the horse and *h*. *Princess v* 523
Three other *horsemen* waiting, *Geraint and E.* 121
we may meet the *horsemen* of Earl Doorm, „ 492
Thousands of *horsemen*, drew to the valley— *Heavy Brigade* 3
Thousands of *horsemen* had gather'd „ 14
Hortensia On the other side *H* spoke against the tax; *Princess vii* 127
and before them paused *H* pleading: „ 132
Horticultural a piece of inmost *H* art, *Hendecasyllabics* 20
Hosanna he is singing *H* in the highest: *Enoch Arden* 503
people strowing cried '*H* in the highest!' „ 506
Hospitable Whom all men rate as kind and *h*: *Princess i* 71
Hospital their fair college turn'd to *h*; „ *vii* 17
She died of a fever caught when a nurse in a *h* ward. *Charity* 41
Striking the *h* wall, crashing thro' it, *Def. of Lucknow* 18

Hospital (*continued*) delicate women who tended the *h* bed, *Def. of Lucknow* 87
Sick from the *h* echo them, „ 100
Give your gold to the *H*, *On Jub. Q. Victoria* 33
Hospitality tender ministries Of female hands and *h*.' *Princess vi* 73
and served With female hands and *h*.' „ 96
broken into Thro' open doors and *h*; *Marr. of Geraint* 456
innocent *hospitalities* quench'd in blood, *Columbus* 176
Host (**entertainer of guests**) The *h* and I sat round the wassail-bowl, *The Epic* 5
Enoch was *h* one day, Philip the next, *Enoch Arden* 25
I, their guest, their *h*, their ancient friend, *Aylmer's Field* 790
enter'd an old hostel, call'd mine *h* To council, *Princess i* 173
We sent mine *h* to purchase female gear; „ 199
'Fair *H* and Earl, I pray you courtesy; *Marr. of Geraint* 403
Let *me* lay lance in rest, O noble *h*, „ 496
bad the *h* Call in what men soever *Geraint and E.* 285
Call the *h* and bid him bring Charger and palfrey.' „ 400
Till issuing arm'd he found the *h* and cried, „ 407
the *h*, Suddenly honest, answer'd in amaze, „ 409
How oft the Cantab supper, *h* and guest, *To W. H. Brookfield* 4
Host (**array of men**) two *h's* that lay beside the walls, *Princess vi* 383
Remember him who led your *h's*; *Ode on Well.* 171
Not ours the fault if we have feeble *h's*— *Third of Feb.* 38
from time to time the heathen *h* Swarm'd overseas, *Com. of Arthur* 8
Arthur's *h* Proclaim'd him Victor, *Balin and Balan* 89
craft of kindred and the Godless *h's* *Guinevere* 427
They summon me their King to lead mine *h's* „ 570
Who slowly paced among the slumbering *h*, *Pass. of Arthur* 7
Then rose the King and moved his *h* by night, „ 79
ever and anon with *h* to *h* Shocks, „ 107
king was on them suddenly with a *h*. *Sir J. Oldcastle* 41
Troubled the track of the *h* that we hated, *Batt. of Brunanburh* 40
he look'd at the *h* that had halted *Heavy Brigade* 7
Hostage And here he keeps me *h* for his son.' *Princess iv* 405
Hostel So pass I *h*, hall, and grange; *Sir Galahad* 81
enter'd an old *h*, call'd mine host To council, *Princess i* 173
riding wearily, Found every *h* full, *Marr. of Geraint* 255
And pausing at a *h* in a marsh, *Lover's Tale iv* 131
A dismal *h* in a dismal land, „ 141
There is one old *H* left us *Locksley H., Sixty* 247
In this *H*—I remember—I repent it „ 255
Hostess Then stept a buxom *h* forth, *Princess i* 228
Hot (*See also* **Fiery-hot, 'Ot, Red-hot**) my very ears were *h* To hear them: „ 134
And heated *h* with burning fears, *In Mem. cxviii* 22
h in haste to join Their luckier mates, *Geraint and E.* 574
flush'd with fight, or *h*, God's curse, with anger— „ 660
H was the night and silent; *Pelleas and E.* 395
snow on all the hills! so *h*, So fever'd! *Romney's R.* 12
Returning with *h* cheek and kindled eyes. *Alexander* 14
and my *h* lips prest Close, *Œnone* 203
Or rosy blossom in *h* ravine, *The Daisy* 32
h hiss And bustling whistle of the youth *Marr. of Geraint* 256
her hand is *h* With ill desires, *Last Tournament* 414
And leave the *h* swamp of voluptuousness *Ancient Sage* 277
Hot-and-hot To serve the *h-a-h*; *Will Water.* 228
Hottentot And not the Kaffir, *H*, Malay, *Princess ii* 158
Hotter her lynx eye To fix and make me *h*, „ *iii* 47
Hougoumont roar of *H* Left mightiest of all peoples *To the Queen ii.* 20
Hound (*See also* **Sleuth-hound**) Francis laid A damask napkin wrought with horse and *h*, *Audley Court* 21
monstrous males that carve the living *h*, *Princess iii* 310
And love in which my *h* has part, *In Mem. lxiii* 2
thou knowest, and gray, and all the *h's*; *Gareth and L.* 462
stay'd Waiting to hear the *h's*; *Marr. of Geraint* 163
There is good chance that we shall hear the *h's*: „ 182
Cavall, King Arthur's *h* of deepest mouth, „ 186
And pastime both of hawk and *h*, „ 711
Who seems no bolder than a beaten *h*; *Geraint and E.* 61
weakling, and thrice-beaten *h*: *Pelleas and E.* 291
or a traitor proven, or *h* Beaten, „ 439
Like a dry bone cast to some hungry *h*? *Last Tournament* 196
heard The *h's* of Mark, and felt the goodly *h's* „ 503
Hound (*continued*) my forefather, with his feet upon the *h*. *Locksley H., Sixty* 28
I, the finer brute rejoicing in my *h's*, *By an Evolution.* 7
Hour (*See also* **Half-hour, Tavern-hour**) THE winds, as at their *h* of birth, *The winds, etc.* 1
The cock sung out an *h* ere light: *Mariana* 27
but most she loathed the *h* „ 77
A SPIRIT haunts the year's last *h's* *A spirit haunts* 1
sick man's room when he taketh repose An *h* before death; „ 15
Most delicately *h* by *h* He canvass'd *A Character* 19
ere he parted said, 'This *h* is thine: *Love and Death* 9
So runs the round of life from *h* to *h*. *Circumstance* 9
a phantom two *h's* old Of a maiden past away, *Adeline* 18
'Were this not well, to bide mine *h*, *Two Voices* 76
Who is it that could live an *h*? „ 162
'His face, that two *h's* since hath died; „ 242
So heavenly-toned, that in that *h* „ 442
I wonder'd at the bounteous *h's*, „ 451
But, Alice, what an *h* was that, *Miller's D.* 57
And now those vivid *h's* are gone, „ 195
Last night I wasted hateful *h's* *Fatima* 8
Is wearied of the rolling *h's*. *L.C.V. de Vere* 60
The warders of the growing *h*, *Love thou thy land* 61
The lusty bird takes every *h* for dawn: *M. d'Arthur, Ep.* 11
as tho' it were The *h* just flown, *Gardener's D.* 83
ere an *h* had pass'd, We reach'd a meadow „ 107
heavy clocks knolling the drowsy *h's*. „ 184
till Autumn brought an *h* For Eustace, „ 207
this whole *h* your eyes have been intent „ 269
for three *h's* he sobb'd o'er William's child *Dora* 167
we met; one *h* I had, no more: *Edwin Morris* 104
I, whose bald brows in silent *h's* become *St. S. Stylites* 165
make reply Is many a weary *h*; *Talking Oak* 26
'An *h* had past—and, sitting straight „ 109
slow sweet *h's* that bring us all things good, The slow sad *h's* that bring us all things ill, *Love and Duty* 57
calmer *h's* to Memory's darkest hold, „ 90
every *h* Must sweat her sixty minutes *Golden Year* 68
every *h* is saved From that eternal silence, *Ulysses* 26
thy strong *H's* indignant work'd their wills, *Tithonus* 18
Made war upon each other for an *h*, *Godiva* 34
A pleasant *h* has passed away *Day-Dm., Pro.* 2
shall we pass the bill I mention'd half an *h* ago?' „ *Revival* 28
The Poet-forms of stronger *h's*, „ *L'Envoi* 14
Embraced his Eve in happy *h*, „ 42
Still creeping with the creeping *h's* *St. Agnes' Eve* 7
To-day I sat for an *h* and wept, *Edward Gray* 11
Thro' many an *h* of summer suns, *Will Water.* 33
But for my pleasant *h*, 'tis gone; „ 179
H's, when the Poet's words and looks „ 193
Let us have a quiet *h*, *Vision of Sin* 73
tyrant's cruel glee Forces on the freer *h*. „ 130
An *h* behind; but as he climb'd the hill, *Enoch Arden* 66
Had his dark *h* unseen, and rose and past „ 78
To find the precious morning *h's* were lost. „ 302
remember'd one dark *h* Here in this wood, „ 385
That was your *h* of weakness. I was wrong, „ 449
'O would I take her father for one *h*, *The Brook* 114
He wasted *h's* with Averill; *Aylmer's Field* 109
but so they wander'd, *h* by *h* Gathered the blossom „ 141
Fairer his talk, a tongue that ruled the *h*, „ 194
Lightning of the *h*, the pun, „ 441
Some niggard fraction of an *h*, „ 450
Thro' weary and yet ever wearier *h's*, „ 828
but later by an *h* Here than ourselves, *Sea Dreams* 263
crowds that in an *h* Of civic tumult jam the doors, *Lucretius* 168
that *h* perhaps Is not so far when momentary man „ 252
till that *h*, My golden work in which I told a truth „ 259
And with that woman closeted for *h's*!' *Princess iii* 56
Yet let us breathe for one *h* more in Heaven' „ 69
Its range of duties to the appointed *h*. „ 177
Such head from act to act, from *h* to *h*, „ *iv* 452
O would I had his sceptre for one *h*! „ 538
I took it for an *h* to mine own bed This morning: „ *v* 434
Sole comfort of my dark *h*, „ *vi* 194

Hour (*continued*) many a pleasant *h* with her that's gone, *Princess vi* 247
With one that cannot keep her mind an *h*: " 287
My heart an eddy from the brawling *h*: " 322
Clomb to the roofs, and gazed alone for *h's* " *vii* 32
To wile the length from languorous *h's*, " 63
Melts mist-like into this bright *h*, " 355
Who never sold the truth to serve the *h*, *Ode on Well.* 179
Mourn'd in this golden *h* of jubilee, *Ode Inter. Exhib.* 8
mix the seasons and the golden *h's*; " 36
he has but gone for an *h*,— *Grandmother* 102
O LOVE, what *h's* were thine and mine, *The Daisy* 1
At Florence too what golden *h's*, " 41
ONCE in a golden *h* I cast to earth *The Flower* 1
Her quiet dream of life this *h* may cease. *Requiescat* 6
that the victor *H's* should scorn The long result of love, *In Mem. i* 13
wrought At that last *h* to please him well; " *vi* 18
learn That I have been an *h* away. " *xii* 20
an *h* For private sorrow's barren song, " *xxi* 13
But for one *h*, O Love, I strive " *xxxv* 6
To thee too comes the golden *h* When " *xxxix* 6
Could we forget the widow'd *h* " *xl* 1
Unconscious of the sliding *h*, " *xliii* 5
Is shadow'd by the growing *h*, " *xlvi* 3
The fruitful *h's* of still increase; " 10
Ye watch, like God, the rolling *h's* " *li* 14
Who usherest in the dolorous *h* " *lxxii* 9
But that remorseless iron *h* " *lxxxiv* 14
And all the train of bounteous *h's* " 30
The promise of the golden *h's*? " *lxxxv* 106
And buzzings of the honied *h's*. " *lxxxix* 52
An *h's* communion with the dead. " *xciv* 4
Thy feet have stray'd in after *h's* " *cii* 14
That wakens at this *h* of rest " *civ* 6
No more shall wayward grief abuse The genial *h* " *cv* 10
and join'd Each office of the social *h* " *cxi* 14
In watching thee from *h* to *h*, " *cxii* 12
O days and *h's*, your work is this " *cxvii* 1
Which every *h* his couriers bring. " *cxxvi* 4
Wild *H's* that fly with Hope and Fear, " *cxxviii* 9
O happy *h*, and happier *h's* Await them. " *Con.* 65
O happy *h*, behold the bride With him " 69
cannot be kind to each other here for an *h*; *Maud I iv* 28
Thro' the livelong *h's* of the dark " *vi* 17
Did I dream it an *h* ago, " *vii* 3
twelve sweet *h's* that past in bridal white, " *xviii* 65
For front to front in an *h* we stood, " *II i* 23
For one short *h* to see The souls we loved, " *iv* 14
holden far apart Until his *h* should come; *Com. of Arthur* 215
when Merlin (for his *h* had come) Brought Arthur " 228
those first days had golden *h's* for me, " 357
As glitters gilded in thy Book of *H's*. *Gareth and L.* 46
'Not an *h*, So that ye yield me— " 132
till an *h*, When waken'd by the wind " 175
'I fly no more: I allow thee for an *h*. " 892
Allow me for mine *h*, and thou wilt find My fortunes " 902
that *h* When the lone hern forgets his melancholy, " 1184
I will eat With all the passion of a twelve *h's*' fast.' *Marr. of Geraint* 306
How many among us at this very *h* Do forge *Geraint and E.* 2
O pardon me! the madness of that *h*, " 346
So for long *h's* sat Enid by her lord, " 580
And now their *h* has come; and Enid said: " 697
in that perilous *h* Put hand to hand " 766
Was half a bandit in my lawless *h*, " 795
but this *h* We ride a-hawking with Sir Lancelot. *Merlin and V.* 94
you which ruin'd man Thro' woman the first *h*; " 363
lay the reckling, one But one *h* old! " 710
To crop his own sweet rose before the *h*?' " 725
And not the one dark *h* which brings remorse, " 763
Joust for it, and win, and bring it in an *h*, *Lancelot and E.* 204
In darkness thro' innumerable *h's* *Holy Grail* 677
But never let me bide one *h* at peace. *Pelleas and E.* 387
and say his *h* is come, The heathen are upon him, *Last Tournament* 86
as when an *h* of cold Falls on the mountain " 227
the warm *h* returns With veer of wind, " 230
spake not any word, But bode his *h*, " 386

Hour (*continued*) And so returns belike within an *h*. *Last Tournament* 531
To see thee—yearnings?—ay! for, *h* by *h*, " 583
O ay—the wholesome madness of an *h*— " 675
ptarmigan that whitens ere this *h* Woos his own end; " 697
Many a time for *h's*, Beside the placid breathings *Guinevere* 68
It was their last *h*, A madness of farewells. " 102
'Late! so late! What *h*, I wonder, now?' " 161
an *h* or maybe twain After the sunset, " 237
To guard thee in the wild *h* coming on, " 446
And well for thee, saying in my dark *h*, *Pass. of Arthur* 159
wealthier—wealthier—*h* by *h*! *To the Queen ii* 23
And wordy trucklings to the transient *h*, " 51
On the same morning, almost the same *h*, *Lover's Tale i* 198
that little *h* was bound Shut in from Time, " 437
and in that *h* A hope flow'd round me, " 448
Else had the life of that delighted *h* " 471
O day which did enwomb that happy *h*, " 485
Genius of that *h* which dost uphold " 487
Thy name is ever worshipp'd among *h's*! " 493
It was so happy an *h*, so sweet a place, " 558
So died that *h*, and fell into the abysm " 796
So that *h* died Like odour rapt into the winged wind " 800
All thro' the livelong *h's* of utter dark, " 810
Well he had One golden *h*— " *iv* 6
Would you had seen him in that *h* of his! " 8
I may not stay, No, not an *h*; " 116
after this, An *h* or two, Camilla's travail came Upon her, " 127
Travelling that land, and meant to rest an *h*; " 133
To come and revel for one *h* with him " 182
(I told you that he had his golden *h*), " 206
Down to this last strange *h* in his own hall; " 358
I'll come for an *h* to-morrow, *First Quarrel* 46
I have only an *h* of life. *Rizpah* 22
I spent What seem'd my crowning *h*, *Sisters (E. and E.)* 124
talk to 'em *h's* after *h's*! *In the Child. Hosp.* 34
And the doctor came at his *h*, " 68
when the wild *h* and the wine Had set the wits aflame. *Sir J. Oldcastle* 94
I have not broken bread for fifty *h's*. " 199
Once in an *h* they cried, *V. of Maeldune* 29
nor, in *h's* Of civil outbreak, *Tiresias* 67
Like would-be guests an *h* too late, " 198
Remembering all the golden *h's* Now silent, " 210
Why should we bear with an *h* of torture, *Despair* 81
What rulers but the Days and *H's* *Ancient Sage* 95
The days and *h's* are ever glancing by, " 99
But with the Nameless is nor Day nor *H*; " 102
hands point five—O me—it strikes the *h*— *The Flight* 94
a hiccup at ony *h* o' the night! *Spinster's S's.* 98
Shape your heart to front the *h*, but dream not that the *h* will last. *Locksley H., Sixty* 106
On this day and at this *h*, " 175
Insects of an *h*, that hourly work their brother insect wrong, " 202
the first dark *h* of his last sleep alone. " 238
Expecting all things in an *h*— *Freedom* 39
breaks into the crocus-purple *h* That saw thee vanish. *Demeter and P.* 50
The man, that only lives and loves an *h*, " 106
waäit till tha 'eärs it be strikin' the *h*. *Owd Roä* 18
after *h's* of search and doubt and threats, *The Ring* 278
still drawn downward for an *h*, " 477
And *h* by *h* unfolding woodbine leaves *Prog. of Spring* 7
Beyond the darker *h* to see the bright, " 88
and make her festal *h* Dark with the blood *St. Telemachus* 79
'wasting the sweet summer *h's*'? *Charity* 1
I was close on that *h* of dishonour, " 28
give His fealty to the halcyon *h*! *The Wanderer* 12
WHEN the dumb *H*, clothed in black, *Silent Voices* 1

Houri A group of *H's* bow'd to see The dying Islamite, *Palace of Art* 102

Hourly Daily and *h*, more and more. *Eleänore* 71
And *h* visitation of the blood, *Lover's Tale i* 206

Hourly-mellowing summer's *h-m* change May breathe, *In Mem. xci* 9

House (s) (*See also* **Ale-house, Chop-house, City-house, 'Ouse, Pleasure-house**) All day within the dreamy *h*, *Mariana* 61
and vacancy Of the dark deserted *h*. *Deserted House* 12

House (s) (*continued*) The *h* was builded of the earth, *Deserted House* 15
The first *h* by the water-side, *L. of Shalott iv* 34
Dead-pale between the *h's* high, „ 40
The *h* thro' all the level shines, *Mariana in the S.* 2
On to God's *h* the people prest: *Two Voices* 409
To move about the *h* with joy, *Miller's D.* 95
In this great *h* so royal-rich, *Palace of Art* 191
I saw you sitting in the *h*, *May Queen, Con.* 30
lightly curl'd Round their golden *h's*, *Lotos-Eaters, C. S.* 113
And fill'd the *h* with clamour. *The Goose* 36
nightmare on his bed When all the *h* is mute. *M. d'Arthur* 178
' this wonder keeps the *h*.' He nodded, *Gardener's D.* 119
So rapt, we near'd the *h*; „ 142
He had been always with her in the *h*, *Dora* 7
he left his father's *h*, And hired himself to work „ 37
Then Dora went to Mary's *h*, „ 110
Then thou and I will live within one *h*, „ 125
So those four abode Within one *h* together; „ 170
Whose *h* is that I see? *Walk. to the Mail* 11
but his *h*, for so they say, Was haunted „ 35
So in mine earthly *h* I am, *St. Agnes' Eve* 19
For I am of a numerous *h*, *Will Water.* 89
' Let us see these handsome *h's* *L. of Burleigh* 23
She is of an ancient *h*: *Vision of Sin* 140
Three children of three *h's*, *Enoch Arden* 11
the children play'd at keeping *h*. „ 24
' This is my *h* and this my little wife.' „ 28
So might she keep the *h* while he was gone. „ 140
Lords of his *h* and of his mill were they; „ 351
' You have been as God's good angel in our *h*. „ 423
The babes, their babble, Annie, the small *h*, „ 606
With daily-dwindling profits held the *h*; „ 696
So broken—all the story of his *h*. „ 704
Far-blazing from the rear of Philip's *h*, „ 727
The latest *h* to landward; „ 732
But kept the *h*, his chair, and last his bed. „ 826
That all the *h's* in the haven rang. „ 911
like a storm he came, And shook the *h*, *Aylmer's Field* 216
the thunders of the *h* Had fallen first, „ 278
beheld the Powers of the *H* On either side the hearth, „ 287
The last remaining pillar of their *h*, „ 295
Forbad her first the *h* of Averill, „ 502
to spy The weakness of a people or a *h*, „ 570
Your *h* is left unto you desolate!' (repeat) „ 629, 797
' My *h* is left unto me desolate.' „ 721
' Our *h* is left unto us desolate'? „ 737
The deathless ruler of thy dying *h* „ 661
Who entering fill'd the *h* with sudden light. „ 682
when he felt the silence of his *h* About him, „ 830
Walter show'd the *h*, Greek, set with busts: *Princess, Pro.* 10
they gave The park, the crowd, the *h*; „ 94
A Gothic ruin and a Grecian *h*, „ 232
There lived an ancient legend in our *h*. „ *i* 5
An old and strange affection of the *h*. „ 13
He cared not for the affection of the *h*; „ 26
A little street half garden and half *h*; „ 214
wish'd to marry; they could rule a *h*; „ *ii* 465
came Upon me, the weird vision of our *h*: „ *iii* 184
Still in the *h* in his coffin the Prince *G. of Swainston* 10
this pretty *h*, this city-house of ours? *City Child* 7
And bread from out the *h's* brought, *Spec. of Iliad* 6
you bite far into the heart of the *h*, *Window, Winter* 11
Dark *h*, by which once more I stand *In Mem. vii* 1
Are but as servants in a *h* „ *xx* 3
That guard the portals of the *h*; „ *xxix* 12
And home to Mary's *h* return'd, „ *xxxi* 2
From every *h* the neighbours met, „ 9
Should murmur from the narrow *h*, „ *xxxv* 2
Or builds the *h*, or digs the grave, „ *xxxvi* 14
In that dark *h* where she was born. „ *lx* 12
link thy life with one Of mine own *h*, „ *lxxxiv* 12
And in the *h* light after light Went out, „ *xcv* 19
She knows but matters of the *h*, „ *xcvii* 31
he told me that he loved A daughter of our *h*; „ *Con.* 7
Living alone in an empty *h*, *Maud I. vi* 68

House (s) (*continued*) all round the *h* I beheld The death-white curtain *Maud I xiv* 33
sprinkled with blood By which our *h's* are torn: „ *xix* 33
Wrought for his *h* an irredeemable woe; „ *II i* 22
stand at the diamond door Of his *h* in a rainbow frill? „ *ii* 17
shouted at once from the top of the *h*; „ *v* 50
To make a horror all about the *h*, *Gareth and L.* 1411
Lady Lyonors and her *h*, with dance And revel „ 1422
slender entertainment of a *h* Once rich, *Marr. of Geraint* 301
Rest! the good *h*, tho' ruin'd, „ 378
reverencing the custom of the *h* Geraint, „ 380
Before my Enid's birthday, sack'd my *h*; „ 458
when Edyrn sack'd their *h*, And scatter'd all they had „ 634
He found the sack and plunder of our *h* All scatter'd thro' the *h's* of the town; „ 694
Ah, dear, he took me from a goodly *h*, „ 708
Yea, and he brought me to a goodly *h*; „ 713
Call for the woman of the *h*,' *Geraint and E.* 263
Among the heavy breathings of the *h*, „ 402
how suited to the *h* of one Who loves that beauty „ 683
mother of the *h* There was not: *Lancelot and E.* 177
warn'd me of their fierce design Against my *h*, „ 275
shuddering, ' Hark the Phantom of the *h* „ 1022
this discomfort he hath done the *h*.' „ 1072
There sat the lifelong creature of the *h*, „ 1143
saw One of her *h*, and sent him to the Queen „ 1168
and fair the *h* whereby she sat, *Holy Grail* 392
h Became no better than a broken shed, „ 397
brought thee here to this poor *h* of ours „ 617
and out again, But sit within the *h*. „ 715
But always in the quiet *h* I heard, „ 832
sat There in the holy *h* at Almesbury *Guinevere* 2
Heard by the watcher in a haunted *h*, „ 73
Whom he knows false, abide and rule the *h*: „ 515
Do each low office of your holy *h*; „ 682
Modred, unharm'd, the traitor of thine *h*.' *Pass. of Arthur* 153
spake the King: ' My *h* hath been my doom. „ 154
But call not thou this traitor of my *h* „ 155
My *h* are rather they who sware my vows, „ 157
nightmare on his bed When all the *h* is mute. „ 346
But thou didst sit alone in the inner *h*, *Lover's Tale i* 112
Still larger moulding all the *h* of thought, „ 241
O blossom'd portal of the lonely *h*, „ 280
Back to his mother's *h* among the pines. „ *iv* 15
to the mother's *h* where she was born. „ 91
But all their *h* was old and loved them both, And all the *h* had known the loves of both; „ 122
such a *h* as his, And his was old, „ 202
jewels Of many generations of his *h* Sparkled and flash'd, „ 299
my *h* an' my man were my pride, *First Quarrel* 41
So I set to righting the *h*, „ 47
our *h* has held Three hundred years— *Sisters (E. and E.)* 52
thick of question and reply I fled the *h*, „ 158
want Of Edith in the *h*, the garden, „ 246
there hail'd on our *h's* and halls *Def. of Lucknow* 13
none but Gods could build this *h* of ours, *Ancient Sage* 83
To lie, to lie—in God's own *h*— *The Flight* 52
A door was open'd in the *h*— „ 69
To both our *H's*, may they see Beyond *Hands all Round* 27
Deck your *h's*, illuminate All your towns *On Jub. Q. Victoria* 18
Theere, when the 'ouse wur a *h*, *Owd Roä* 29
the *h* is afire,' she said. „ 68
We saw far off an old forsaken *h*, *The Ring* 155
being waked By noises in the *h*— „ 417
I found her not in *h* Or garden— „ 444
O the night, While the *h* is sleeping. *Forlorn* 42
This *h* with all its hateful needs *Happy* 32
This worn-out Reason dying in her *h* *Romney's R.* 145
Lord let the *h* of a brute *By an Evolution.* 1

House (verb) That *h* the cold crown'd snake! *Œnone* 37
H in the shade of comfortable roofs, *St. S. Stylites* 107

Housed the children, *h* In her foul den, *Com. of Arthur* 29
those black foldings, that which *h* therein. *Gareth and L.* 1380
Scarce *h* within the circle of this Earth, *Lover's Tale i* 479

Household (adj.) *h* shelter crave From winter rains *Two Voices* 260

Household (adj.) (*continued*) For surely now our *h* hearths are cold: *Lotos-Eaters, C. S.* 72
Virtue, like a *h* god Promising empire; *On a Mourner* 30
Meet adoration to my *h* gods, *Ulysses* 42
farmer vext packs up his beds and chairs, And all his *h* stuff; *Walk. to the Mail* 40
While yet she went about her *h* ways, *Enoch Arden* 453
Their slender *h* fortunes (for the man *Sea Dreams* 9
common vein of memory Sweet *h* talk, *Princess ii* 315
and the *h* flower Torn from the lintel— „ *v* 128
As daily vexes *h* peace, *In Mem. xxix* 2
Moving about the *h* ways, „ *lx* 11
And hear the *h* jar within. „ *xciv* 16
From *h* fountains never dry; „ *cix* 2
The *h* Fury sprinkled with blood *Maud I xix* 32
Beyond all titles, and a *h* name, *Ded. of Idylls* 42
And like a *h* Spirit at the walls Beat, *Geraint and E.* 403
And trustful courtesies of *h* life, *Guinevere* 86
Red in thy birth, redder with *h* war, *Sir J. Oldcastle* 53
Which from her *h* orbit draws the child *Prin. Beatrice* 7
H happiness, gracious children, *Vastness* 24
And lured me from the *h* fire on earth. *Romney's R.* 40
THE gleam of *h* sunshine ends, *The Wanderer* 1
Household (s) Her *h* fled the danger, *The Goose* 54
And lift the *h* out of poverty; *Enoch Arden* 485
example follow'd, Sir, In Arthur's *h*?'— *Merlin and V.* 20
Leaving her *h* and good father, *Lancelot and E.* 14
Housel nor sought, Wrapt in her grief, for *h* *Guinevere* 149
Houseless The *h* ocean's heaving field, *The Voyage* 30
Housemaid His daughter and his *h* were the boys: *Princess i* 190
Hove Then saw they how there *h* a dusky barge, *M. d'Arthur* 193
Then saw they how there *h* a dusky barge, *Pass. of Arthur* 361
Hovell'd the poor are *h* and hustled together, *Maud I i* 34
Hover (*See also* **Wind-hover**) all his life the charm did talk About his path, and *h* near *Day-Dm., Arrival* 22
Wings flutter, voices *h* clear: *Sir Galahad* 78
They come and sit by my chair, they *h* about my bed— *Grandmother* 83
And the bird of prey will *h*, *Maud I xx* 28
Hover'd wherefore *h* round Lancelot, but when he mark'd *Balin and Balan* 159
That *h* between war and wantonness, *To the Queen ii* 44
Hovering *h* o'er the dolorous strait To the other shore, *In Mem. lxxxiv* 39
and *h* round her chair Ask'd, 'Mother, *Gareth and L.* 33
breath Of her sweet tendance *h* over him, *Geraint and E.* 926
Whenever in her *h* to and fro The lily maid *Lancelot and E.* 326
A vision *h* on a sea of fire, *Pelleas and E.* 52
Her spirit *h* by the church, *The Ring* 478
Hoveringly *h* a sword Now over and now under, *Lucretius* 61
How setting the *how much* before the *h*, *Golden Year* 11
Howard (*See also* **Thomas Howard**) I should count myself the coward if I left them, my Lord *H*, *The Revenge* 11
Lord *H* past away with five ships of war „ 13
Howd (hold) whoä's to *h* the lond ater meä *N. Farmer, O. S.* 58
'e could *h* 'is oan, *Owd Roä* 7
An' 'e cotch'd *h* hard o' my hairm, „ 58
till 'e feeäld 'e could *h* 'is oän, *Church-warden, etc.* 19
Howd (old) hes now be a-grawin' sa *h*, *Village Wife* 107
Howdin' (holding) Thy Moother was *h* the lether, *Owd Roä* 85
Howl (verb) I did not hear the dog *h*, mother, *May Queen, Con.* 21
h in tune With nothing but the Devil!' *Sea Dreams* 260
Crack them now for yourself, and *h*, *Maud II v* 56
H as he may. But hold me for your friend: *Pelleas and E.* 340
Howl (s) rose the *h* of all the cassock'd wolves, *Sir J. Oldcastle* 158
the great storm grew with a *h* and a hoot *The Wreck* 91
Howl (owl) an' screeäd like a *H* gone wud— *Owd Roä* 76
Howlaby Beck But I minds when i' *H B* won daäy *Church-warden, etc.* 27
Howlaby Daäle when we was i' *H D.* *Owd Roä* 10
I wants to tell tha o' Roä when we lived i' *H D.* „ 19
Howl'd She *h* aloud, 'I am on fire within. *Palace of Art* 285
In blood-red armour sallying, *h* to the King, *Last Tournament* 443
whereat He shrank and *h*, and from his brow *Lover's Tale ii* 92
H me from Hispaniola; *Columbus* 118
Howlest And *h*, issuing out of night, *In Mem. lxxii* 2
Howling The wind is *h* in turret and tree. *The Sisters* 9
Howling (*continued*) on her threshold lie *H* in outer darkness. *To——, With Pal. of Art* 16
The *h's* from forgotten fields; *In Mem. xli* 16
heard them pass like wolves *H*; *Balin and Balan* 408
The brute world *h* forced them into bonds, *Merlin and V.* 744
When the wolves are *h*. *Forlorn* 72
How much setting the *h m* before the *how*, *Golden Year* 11
Howry (dirty) the gell was as *h* a trollope *Owd Roä* 72
I eärs es 'e'd gie fur a *h* owd book *Village Wife* 45
Hubbub A sudden *h* shook the hall, *Day-Dm., Revival* 7
A *h* in the court of half the maids *Princess iv* 476
for those That stir this *h*—you and you— „ 509
clamour of liars belied in the *h* of lies; *Maud I iv* 51
Thro' the *h* of the market I steal, „ *II iv* 68
Ask'd yet once more what meant the *h* here? *Marr. of Geraint* 264
search and doubt and threats, And *h*, *The Ring* 279
Hubert The prophet of his own, my *H*— „ 23
'Air and Words,' Said *H*, „ 25
H brings me home With April and of swallow. „ 59
What need to wish when *H* weds in you The heart of Love, and you the soul of Truth In *H*? „ 61
I climb'd the hill with *H* yesterday, „ 152
Huck (hip) I slither'd and hurted my *h*, *North. Cobbler* 19
Huckster This *h* put down war! *Maud I x* 44
Huddled The cattle *h* on the lea; *In Mem. xv* 6
h here and there on mound and knoll, *Geraint and E.* 803
An' we cuddled and *h* togither, *Owd Roä* 112
Huddling *h* slant in furrow-cloven falls *Princess vii* 207
Hue (verb) blue heaven which *h's* and paves The other? *Supp. Confessions* 134
Hue (s) *H's* of the silken sheeny woof *Madeline* 22
Touch'd with a somewhat darker *h*, *Margaret* 50
And your cheek, whose brilliant *h* *Rosalind* 39
shapes and *h's* that please me well! *Palace of Art* 194
cannot fail but work in *h's* to dim The Titianic Flora. *Gardener's D.* 170
By Cupid-boys of blooming *h*— *Day-Dm., Ep.* 10
Moved with violence, changed in *h*, *Vision of Sin* 34
we know the *h* Of that cap upon her brows. „ 141
hair In gloss and *h* the chestnut, (repeat) *The Brook* 72, 207
a but less vivid *h* Than of that islet *Aylmer's Field* 64
Academic silks, in *h* The lilac, *Princess ii* 16
the other distance and the *h's* Of promise; „ *iv* 86
thoughts that changed from *h* to *h*, „ 210
And as the fiery Sirius alters *h*, „ *v* 262
o'er her forehead past A shadow, and her *h* changed, „ *vi* 107
And shapes and *h's* of Art divine! *Ode Inter. Exhib.* 22
bays, the peacock's neck in *h*; *The Daisy* 14
h's are faint And mix with hollow masks *In Mem. lxx* 3
The distance takes a lovelier *h*, „ *cxv* 6
and all Lent-lily in *h*, Save that the dome was purple, *Gareth and L.* 911
Sculptured, and deckt in slowly-waning *h's*. „ 1195
A tribe of women, dress'd in many *h's*, *Geraint and E.* 598
her *h* Changed at his gaze: *Balin and Balan* 278
Embathing all with wild and woful *h's*, *Lover's Tale ii* 64
And earth as fair in *h*! *Ancient Sage* 24
with the living *h's* of Art. *Locksley H., Sixty* 140
may roll The rainbow *h's* of heaven about it— *Romney's R.* 51
heaven's own *h*, Far—far—away? *Far—far—away* 2
Hued (*See also* **Crimson-hued, Deep-hued, Rose-hued, Soberer-hued**) 'whose flower, *H* with the scarlet of a fierce sunrise, *Lover's Tale i* 353
Hueless In the *h* mosses under the sea *The Mermaid* 49
In fold upon fold of *h* cloud, *Maud I vi* 3
Nor settles into *h* gray, *To Marq. of Dufferin* 50
Huge above him swell *H* sponges of millennial growth *The Kraken* 6
lie Battening upon *h* seaworms in his sleep, „ 12
A *h* crag-platform, smooth as burnish'd brass *Palace of Art* 5
whisper of *h* trees that branch'd And blossom'd *Enoch Arden* 585
Once grovelike, each *h* arm a tree, *Aylmer's Field* 510
Now striking on *h* stumbling-blocks of scorn „ 538
But *h* cathedral fronts of every age, *Sea Dreams* 218
H Ammonites, and the first bones of Time; *Princess, Pro.* 15
H women blowzed with health, and wind, „ *iv* 279
The *h* bush-bearded Barons heaved and blew, „ *v* 21

Huge (*continued*) rode we with the old king across the lawns Beneath *h* trees, *Princess v* 237
A raiser of *h* melons and of pine, „ *Con.* 87
On that *h* scapegoat of the race, *Maud I xiii* 42
She gave the King his *h* cross-hilted sword, *Com. of Arthur* 286
A *h* man-beast of boundless savagery. *Gareth and L.* 637
H on a *h* red horse, and all in mail „ 1026
A *h* pavilion like a mountain peak „ 1364
The *h* pavilion slowly yielded up, „ 1379
At this he hurl'd his *h* limbs out of bed, *Marr. of Geraint* 124
h Earl Doorm, Broad-faced with under-fringe of russet beard, *Geraint and E.* 536
return'd The *h* Earl Doorm with plunder to the hall. „ 592
Here the *h* Earl cried out upon her talk, „ 651
told How the *h* Earl lay slain within his hall. „ 806
canst endure To mouth so *h* a foulness— *Balin and Balan* 379
Before an oak, so hollow, *h* and old *Merlin and V.* 3
other was the song that once I heard By this *h* oak, „ 406
seem'd to me the Lord of all the world, Being so *h*. *Holy Grail* 415
O towers so strong, *H*, solid, *Pelleas and E.* 464
Glared on a *h* machicolated tower *Last Tournament* 424
(*H* blocks, which some old trembling of the world *Lover's Tale ii* 45
With his *h* sea-castles heaving upon the weather bow. *The Revenge* 24
For a *h* sea smote every soul from the decks *The Wreck* 109
Earth so *h*, and yet so bounded— *Locksley H., Sixty* 207
and flamed On one *h* slope beyond, *St Telemachus* 8
Gain'd their *h* Colosseum. „ 45
Huger drumming thunder of the *h* fall At distance, *Geraint and E.* 173
Well—can I wish her any *h* wrong *Last Tournament* 596
their fears Are morning shadows *h* than the shapes *To the Queen ii* 63
Taller than all the Muses, and *h* than all the mountain? *Parnassus* 10
Hugest Nor all Calamity's *h* waves confound, *Will* 5
place which now Is this world's *h*, *Lancelot and E.* 76
apples, the *h* that ever were seen, *V. of Maeldune* 63
Hugg'd And *h* and never *h* it close enough, *Princess vi* 212
clung to him and *h* him close; *Merlin and V.* 945
wrought upon his mood and *h* him close. „ 948
Hugger-mugger (untidy) *H-m* they lived, but they wasn't that eäsy to pleäse, *Village Wife* 117
Hugh 'this,' he said, 'was *H's* at Agincourt; *Princess, Pro.* 25
Hugly (ugly) But I niver wur downright *h*, *Spinster's S's.* 16
An' a-callin' ma '*h*' mayhap to my faäce „ 91
Hull *h* Look'd one black dot against the verge of dawn, *M. d'Arthur* 270
Than if my brainpan were an empty *h*, *Princess ii* 398
h Look'd one black dot against the verge of dawn, *Pass. of Arthur* 438
mark'd the black *h* moving yet, and cried, „ 448
Till it smote on their *h's* and their sails *The Revenge* 116
the low dark *h* dipt under the smiling main, *The Wreck* 127
Hum (s) With the *h* of swarming bees *Eleänore* 29
Hum (verb) scarce can hear the people *h* About the column's base, *St. S. Stylites* 38
And here by thee will *h* the bee, *A Farewell* 11
all the lavish hills would *h* The murmur of a happy Pan: *In Mem. xxiii* 11
by and by began to *h* An air the nuns *Guinevere* 162
Human Is not my *h* pride brought low? *Supp. Confessions* 14
cords that wound and eat Into my *h* heart, „ 37
brook the rod And chastisement of *h* pride; „ 108
cuts atwain The knots that tangle *h* creeds, *Clear-headed friend* 3
hour by hour He canvass'd *h* mysteries, *A Character* 20
But more *h* in your moods, *Margaret* 47
Far off from *h* neighbourhood, *Eleänore* 6
Ah pity—hint it not in *h* tones, *Wan Sculptor* 11
How grows the day of *h* power?' *Two Voices* 78
While still I yearn'd for *h* praise. „ 123
Free space for every *h* doubt, „ 137
That I first was in *h* mould? „ 342
No life that breathes with *h* breath „ 395
With cycles of the *h* tale Of this wide world, *Palace of Art* 146
hear the dully sound Of *h* footsteps fall. „ 276
Pray Heaven for a *h* heart, *L. C. V. de Vere* 71
To mingle with the *h* race, *Of old sat Freedom* 10
h things returning on themselves Move onward, *Golden Year* 25
Beyond the utmost bound of *h* thought. *Ulysses* 32

Human (*continued*) I dipt into the future far as *h* eye could see; (repeat) *Locksley Hall* 15, 119
song That mock'd the wholesome *h* heart, *The Letters* 10
In her left a *h* head. *Vision of Sin* 138
Cared not to look on any *h* face, *Enoch Arden* 282
No want was there of *h* sustenance, „ 554
He could not see, the kindly *h* face, „ 581
Brown, looking hardly *h*, strangely clad, „ 638
Nor sound of *h* sorrow mounts to mar *Lucretius* 109
Or in the dark dissolving *h* heart, *Princess iii* 312
Tho' man, yet *h*, whatsoe'er your wrongs, „ *iv* 425
Then springs the crowning race of *h* kind. „ *vii* 295
The proof and echo of all *h* fame, *Ode on Well.* 145
Till in all lands and thro' all *h* story „ 223
What would you have of us? *H* life? *The Victim* 12
Thou seemest *h* and divine, *In Mem., Pro.* 13
It never look'd to *h* eyes Since our first Sun „ *xxiv* 7
wrought With *h* hands the creed of creeds „ *xxxvi* 10
And render *h* love his dues; „ *xxxvii* 16
To point the term of *h* strife, „ *l* 14
Nor *h* frailty do me wrong. „ *lii* 8
sweetest soul That ever look'd with *h* eyes. „ *lvii* 12
The perfect flower of *h* time; „ *lxi* 4
What fame is left for *h* deeds In endless age? „ *lxxiii* 11
But somewhere, out of *h* view, „ *lxxv* 18
I know transplanted *h* worth Will bloom „ *lxxxii* 11
How much of act at *h* hands The sense of *h* will „ *lxxxv* 38
But in dear words of *h* speech „ 83
there swims The reflex of a *h* face. „ *cviii* 12
take what fruit may be Of sorrow under *h* skies: „ 14
Nor dream of *h* love and truth, „ *cxviii* 3
That sees the course of *h* things. „ *cxxviii* 4
Known and unknown; *h*, divine; Sweet *h* hand and lips and eye; „ *cxxix* 5
Whose glory was, redressing *h* wrong; *Ded. of Idylls* 9
lent her fierce teat To *h* sucklings; *Com. of Arthur* 29
Till the great plover's *h* whistle amazed *Geraint and E.* 49
They ride abroad redressing *h* wrongs! *Merlin and V.* 693
With such a fervent flame of *h* love, *Holy Grail* 74
And leaving *h* wrongs to right themselves, „ 898
Beast too, as lacking *h* wit—disgraced, *Pelleas and E.* 476
To ride abroad redressing *h* wrongs, *Guinevere* 471
Thou art the highest and most *h* too, „ 649
Dark with the smoke of *h* sacrifice, *Sir J. Oldcastle* 84
Cried from the topmost summit with *h* voices and words; *V. of Maeldune* 28
French of the French, and Lord of *h* tears; *To Victor Hugo* 3
My son, the Gods, despite of *h* prayer, Are slower to forgive than *h* kings. *Tiresias* 9
whose one bliss Is war, and *h* sacrifice— „ 112
In height and prowess more than *h*, „ 179
we broke away from the Christ, our *h* brother *Despair* 25
and the *h* heart, and the Age. „ 40
Set the sphere of all the boundless Heavens within the *h* eye, Sent the shadow of Himself, the boundless, thro' the *h* soul; *Locksley H., Sixty* 210
Would she find her *h* offspring this ideal man at rest? „ 234
Forward, till you see the highest *H* Nature is divine. „ 276
As a lord of the *H* soul, *Dead Prophet* 54
at the doubtful doom of *h* kind; *To Virgil* 24
sunder'd once from all the *h* race, „ 36
too fierce and fast This order of Her *H* Star, *Freedom* 23
Two Suns of Love make day of *h* life, *Prin. Beatrice* 1
You see your Art still shrined in *h* shelves, *Poets and their B.* 11
I envied *h* wives, and nested birds, *Demeter and P.* 53
This poor rib-grated dungeon of the holy *h* ghost, *Happy* 31
As dead from all the *h* race as if beneath the mould; „ 95
Larger and fuller, like the *h* mind! *Prog. of Spring* 112
On *h* faces, And all around me, *Merlin and the G.* 20
H forgiveness touches heaven, and thence— *Romney's R.* 159
Hold the sceptre, *H* Soul, *By an Evolution.* 16
The dust send up a steam of *h* blood, *St. Telemachus* 53
Every morning is thy birthday gladdening *h* hearts and eyes. *Akbar's D., Hymn* 2

Hung (*continued*) Once the weight and fate of Europe *h*. *Ode on Well.* 240
and Jenny *h* on his arm. *Grandmother* 42
H in the shadow of a heaven? *In Mem. xvi* 10
h to hear The rapt oration flowing free „ *lxxxvii* 31
On thee the loyal-hearted *h*, „ *cx* 5
H over her dying bed— *Maud I xix* 36
And down from one a sword was *h*, *Gareth and L.* 221
he loosed a mighty purse, *H* at his belt, *Geraint and E.* 23
Enid had no heart To wake him, but *h* o'er him, „ 370
And *h* his head, and halted in reply, „ 811
high on a branch *H* it, and turn'd aside *Balin and Balan* 433
drawing down the dim disastrous brow That o'er him *h*, „ 598
a troop of carrion crows *H* like a cloud *Merlin and V.* 599
She paused, she turn'd away, she *h* her head, „ 887
sure I think this fruit is *h* too high *Lancelot and E.* 774
o'er her *h* The silken case with braided blazonings, „ 1148
o'er his head the Holy Vessel *h* (repeat) *Holy Grail* 512, 520
down a streetway *h* with folds of pure White samite, *Last Tournament* 140
the sloping seas *H* in mid-heaven, *Lover's Tale i* 4
day *h* From his mid-dome in Heaven's airy halls; „ 65
H round with ragged rims and burning folds,— „ *ii* 63
H round with paintings of the sea, „ 168
Took the edges of the pall, and blew it far Until it *h*, „ *iii* 36
the great San Philip *h* above us like a cloud *The Revenge* 43
as if hope for the garrison *h* but on him; *Def. of Lucknow* 48
I have *h* them by my bed, *Columbus* 200
the long convolvulus *h*; *V. of Maeldune* 40
The sun *h* over the gates of Night, *Dead Prophet* 23
The shadow of a crown, that o'er him *h*, *D. of the Duke of C.* 2
Hungary shall I shriek if a *H* fail? *Maud I iv* 46
Hunger (s) In *h's* and in thirsts, fevers and cold, *St. S. Stylites* 12
Bearing a lifelong *h* in his heart. *Enoch Arden* 79
Philip with eyes Full of that lifelong *h*, „ 464
Red grief and mother's *h* in her eye, *Princess vi* 146
And in her *h* mouth'd and mumbled it, „ 213
A *h* seized my heart; I read *In Mem. xcv* 21
Some dead of *h*, some beneath the scourge, *Columbus* 177
for *H* hath the Evil eye— *Ancient Sage* 264
Crime and *h* cast our maidens *Locksley H., Sixty* 220
Hunger (verb) Long for my life, or *h* for my death, *Geraint and E.* 81
Hunger'd true heart, which *h* for her peace *Enoch Arden* 272
Come, I am *h* and half-anger'd— *Last Tournament* 719
Hungering staring wide And *h* for the gilt *Lover's Tale iv* 313
Hungerworn how weak and *h* I seem—leaning on these? *Gareth and L.* 443
Hungry For always roaming with a *h* heart *Ulysses* 12
Slowly comes a *h* people, as a lion creeping nigher, *Locksley Hall* 135
greasy gleam In haunts of *h* sinners, *Will Water.* 222
every captain waits *H* for honour, *Princess v* 314
Like a dry bone cast to some *h* hound? *Last Tournament* 196
Hunt (s) Forgetful of the falcon and the *h*, *Marr. of Geraint* 51
petition'd for his leave To see the *h*, „ 155
her love For Lancelot, and forgetful of the *h*; „ 159
I but come like you to see the *h*, „ 179
And while they listen'd for the distant *h*, „ 184
A little vext at losing of the *h*, „ 234
Hunt (verb) Do *h* me, day and night.' *D. of F. Women* 256
Like a dog, he *h's* in dreams, *Locksley Hall* 79
'They *h* old trails,' said Cyril *Princess ii* 390
We *h* them for the beauty of their skins; „ *v* 156
who will *h* for me This demon of the woods? *Balin and Balan* 136
not Arthur's use To *h* by moonlight;' *Holy Grail* 111
To *h* the tiger of oppression out From office; *Akbar's Dream* 158
Hunted (adj.) As hunters round a *h* creature draw *Aylmer's Field* 499
Hunted (verb) The swallow stopt as he *h* the fly, *Poet's Song* 9
Hunter (huntsman) (*See also* **Head-Hunter**) with puff'd cheek the belted *h* blew *Palace of Art* 63
As *h's* round a hunted creature draw *Aylmer's Field* 499
Nor her that o'er her wounded *h* wept *Lucretius* 89
the *h* rued His rash intrusion, manlike, *Princess iv* 203
Man is the *h*; woman is his game: „ *v* 154
made Broad pathways for the *h* and the knight *Com. of Arthur* 61
No keener *h* after glory breathes. *Lancelot and E.* 156
'O *h*, and O blower of the horn, Harper, *Last Tournament* 542
'Ah then, false *h* and false harper, „ 567
and *h's* race The shadowy lion, *Tiresias* 177

Hunter (horse) And rode his *h* down. *Talking Oak* 104
Hunting (*See also* **'Untin', Wife-hunting**) The King was *h* in the wild; *The Victim* 30
gave order to let blow His horns for *h* *Marr. of Geraint* 153
he went To-day for three days' *h*— *Last Tournament* 530
Hunting-dress wearing neither *h-d* Nor weapon, *Marr. of Geraint* 165
Hunting-morn the third day from the *h-m* „ 597
Hunting-tide Rang out like hollow woods at *h-t.* *Pelleas and E.* 367
Hup-on-end (up-on-end) An' I slep i' my chair *h-o-e*, *Owd Roä* 54
Hupside (upside) an' the 'ole 'ouse *h* down. *North Cobbler* 43
Hurl *h* their lances in the sun; *Locksley Hall* 170
Balin graspt, but while in act to *h*, *Balin and Balan* 368
Mark was half in heart to *h* his cup *Merlin and V.* 30
when he stopt we long'd to *h* together, „ 420
Twice do we *h* them to earth *Def. of Lucknow* 58
Gods, To quench, not *h* the thunderbolt, *Demeter and P.* 133
Hurl'd the bolts are *h* Far below them *Lotos-Eaters, C. S.* 111
And *h* the pan and kettle. *The Goose* 28
H as a stone from out of a catapult *Gareth and L.* 965
They madly *h* together on the bridge; „ 1120
h him headlong o'er the bridge Down to the river, „ 1153
At this he *h* his huge limbs out of bed, *Marr. of Geraint* 124
Hung at his belt, and *h* it toward the squire. *Geraint and E.* 23
h to ground what knight soever spurr'd Against us, *Balin and Balan* 66
h it from him Among the forest weeds, „ 541
he *h* into it Against the stronger: *Lancelot and E.* 462
H back again so often in empty foam, *Last Tournament* 93
h The tables over and the wines, „ 474
Leapt on him, and *h* him headlong, *Guinevere* 108
you *h* them to the ground. *Happy* 76
Been *h* so high they ranged about the globe? *St. Telemachus* 2
when she *h* a plaäte at the cat *Church-warden, etc.* 25
Noble the Saxon who *h* at his Idol *Kapiolani* 4
Hurling Each *h* down a heap of things that rang *Geraint and E.* 594
Hurrah we roar'd a *h*, and so The little Revenge *The Revenge* 32
Hurricane like the smoke in a *h* whirl'd. *Boädicea* 59
The *h* of the latitude on him fell, *Columbus* 138
Crash'd like a *h*, Broke thro' the mass *Heavy Brigade* 28
Hurried Edith's eager fancy *h* with him *Aylmer's Field* 208
Hurry (s) (*See also* **'Urry**) all three in *h* and fear Ran to her, *Lancelot and E.* 1024
Hurry (verb) By thirty hills I *h* down, *The Brook* 27
and yearn to *h* precipitously *Boädicea* 58
Hurrying Myriads of rivulets *h* thro' the lawn, *Princess vii* 220
Driving, *h*, marrying, burying, *Maud II v* 12
Another *h* past, a man-at-arms, *Geraint and E.* 526
Then, *h* home, I found her not in house *The Ring* 444
Hurt (s) helps the *h* that Honour feels, *Locksley Hall* 105
swathed the *h* that drain'd her dear lord's life. *Geraint and E.* 516
Then, fearing for his *h* and loss of blood, „ 777
came The King's own leech to look into his *h*; „ 923
But while Geraint lay healing of his *h*, „ 931
tho' he call'd his wound a little *h* *Lancelot and E.* 852
when Sir Lancelot's deadly *h* was whole, „ 904
Like a king's heir, till all his *h's* be whole. *Last Tournament* 91
heal'd Thy *h* and heart with unguent and caress— „ 595
treat their loathsome *h's* and heal mine own; *Guinevere* 686
Hurt (verb and part.) Love is *h* with jar and fret. *Miller's D.* 209
H in that night of sudden ruin and wreck, *Enoch Arden* 564
There by a keeper shot at, slightly *h*, *Aylmer's Field* 548
almost all that is, hurting the *h*— „ 572
With their own blows they *h* themselves, *Princess vi* 49
I trust that there is no one *h* to death, „ 242
H in his first tilt was my son, Sir Torre. *Lancelot and E.* 196
'But parted from the jousts *H* in the side,' „ 623
h Whom she would soothe, and harm'd *Guinevere* 354
Hurted I slither'd and *h* my huck, *North. Cobbler* 19
Hurting almost all that is, *h* the hurt— *Aylmer's Field* 572
Husban' at yer wake like *h* an' wife. *Tomorrow* 82
Husband (*See also* **Husban'**) As the *h* is, the wife is: *Locksley Hall* 47
of what he wish'd, Enoch, your *h*: *Enoch Arden* 292
Has she no fear that her first *h* lives? „ 806
only near'd Her *h* inch by inch, *Aylmer's Field* 807
'No trifle,' groan'd the *h*; *Sea Dreams* 145
The field was pleasant in my *h's* eye.' *Gareth and L.* 342

Husband (*continued*) my *h's* brother had my son Thrall'd in his castle, *Gareth and L.* 357
Enid, but to please her *h's* eye, *Marr. of Geraint* 11
Put hand to hand beneath her *h's* heart, *Geraint and E.* 767
I am thine *h*—not a smaller soul, *Guinevere* 566
the widower *h* and dead wife Rush'd each at each *Lover's Tale iv* 372
and dead her aged *h* now— *Locksley H., Sixty* 37
'This model *h*, this fine Artist'! *Romney's R.* 124
Her *h* in the flush of youth and dawn, *Death of Œnone* 17
crying '*H*!' she leapt upon the funeral pile, „ 105
blade that had slain my *h* thrice thro' *Bandit's Death* 34
Husbandry with equal *h* The woman were an equal to the man. *Princess i* 130
Harvest-tool and *h*, Loom and wheel *Ode Inter. Exhib.* 14
Hush (s) we heard In the dead *h* the papers *Princess iv* 390
in the *h* of the moonless nights, *Maud I i* 42
And a *h* with the setting moon. „ *xxii* 18
had blown—after long *h*—at last— *Gareth and L.* 1378
A dead *h* fell; but when the dolorous day *Pass. of Arthur* 122
Hush (verb) If prayers will not *h* thee, *Lilian* 27
'O *h*, *h*!' and she began. *Princess ii* 115
H, the Dead March wails in the people's ears: *Ode on Well.* 267
And *h'es* half the babbling Wye, *In Mem. xix* 7
Let us *h* this cry of 'Forward' *Locksley H., Sixty* 78
Hush'd air is damp, and *h*, and close, *A spirit haunts* 13
The town was *h* beneath us: *Audley Court* 85
Ranges of glimmering vaults with iron grates, And *h* seraglios *D. of F. Women* 36
Up went the *h* amaze of hand and eye. *Princess iii* 138
how sweetly smells the honeysuckle In the *h* night, *Gareth and L.* 1288
H all the groves from fear of wrong: *Sir L. and Q. G.* 13
h itself at last Hopeless of answer: *Aylmer's Field* 542
The Wye is *h* nor moved along, And *h* my deepest grief of all, *In Mem. xix* 9
all was *h* within, Till when at feast Sir Garlon *Balin and Balan* 346
Here too, all *h* below the mellow moon, *Pelleas and E.* 424
woods are *h*, their music is no more: *Last Tournament* 276
'Bygones! you kept yours *h*,' I said, *First Quarrel* 68
my ravings *h* The bird, *Demeter and P.* 108
Stood round it, *h*, or calling on his name. *Death of Œnone* 66
H as the heart of the grave, *Bandit's Death* 26
Husk rent the veil Of his old *h*: *Two Voices* 11
phantom *h's* of something foully done, *Lucretius* 160
and of the grain and *h*, the grape *De Prof., Two G.* 50
Husk'd *See* **Hollow-Husk'd**
Hussy There was a girl, a *h*, that workt with him *First Quarrel* 24
Hustle Would *h* and harry him, and labour him *Gareth and L.* 484
Gareth whom he used To harry and *h*. „ 707
Hustings That so, when the rotten *h* shake *Maud I vi* 54
Hustings-liar looking upward to the practised *h-l*; *Locksley H., Sixty* 123
Hustled *h* together, each sex, like swine. *Maud I i* 34
Hut a *h*, Half *h*, half native cavern. *Enoch Arden* 559
h's At random scatter'd, each a nest in bloom, *Aylmer's Field* 149
By the great river in a boatman's *h*. *Lancelot and E.* 278
And flies above the leper's *h*, *Happy* 4
Is that the leper's *h* on the solitary moor, „ 9
Hutterby Hall hup to Harmsby and *H H*. *North. Cobbler* 14
Huzzin' (humming) *H* an' maäzin' the blessed feälds *N. Farmer, O. S.* 62
Hyacinth sweeter still The wild-wood *h* *Balin and Balan* 271
over sheets of *h* That seem'd the heavens *Guinevere* 390
Hyades Thro' scudding drifts the rainy *H* *Ulysses* 10
Hyaline pine slope to the dark *h*. *Leonine Eleg.* 10
Hymen *See* **Mock-Hymen**
Hymn (*See also* **Death-Hymn, 'Ymn**) sound Of pious *h's* and psalms, *St. S. Stylites* 34
Roundhead rode, And humm'd a surly *h*. *Talking Oak* 300
I hear a noise of *h's*: *Sir Galahad* 28
shriek of hate would jar all the *h's* of heaven: *Sea Dreams* 259
The bearded Victor of ten-thousand *h's*, *Princess iii* 352
ourself have often tried Valkyrian *h's*, „ *iv* 139
mine own phantom chanting *h's*? *In Mem. cviii* 10
But there was heard among the holy *h's* *Com. of Arthur* 290
there past along the *h's* A voice as of the waters, „ 464
king, whose *h's* Are chanted in the minster, *Merlin and V.* 765
She chanted snatches of mysterious *h's* *Lancelot and E.* 1407

Hymn (*continued*) the nightingale's *h* in the dark. *First Quarrel* 34
sounding in heroic ears Heroic *h's*, *Tiresias* 182
in the harvest *h's* of Earth The worship which is Love, *Demeter and P.* 148
bore the Cross before you to the chant of funeral *h's*. *Happy* 48
For have the far-off *h's* of May, *To Master of B.* 10
spake thy brother in his *h* to heaven *Akbar's Dream* 27
Our *h* to the sun. They sing it. „ 203
Hymn'd *h* from hence With songs in praise *Ancient Sage* 208
Hyperion or of older use All-seeing *H*— *Lucretius* 126
Hypocrisy *H*, I saw it in him at once. *Sea Dreams* 64
Hypothesis If that *h* of theirs be sound' *Princess iv* 20
Hysterical (*See also* **Half-hysterical**) That old *h* mock-disease should die.' *Maud III vi* 33
Hysterics The blind *h* of the Celt: *In Mem. cix* 16

I

I learns the use of '*I*' and 'me,' *In Mem. xlv* 6
Ice *I* with the warm blood mixing; *All Things will Die* 33
To the earth—until the *i* would melt *Supp. Confessions* 81
I bump'd the *i* into three several stars, *The Epic* 12
goes, like glittering bergs of *i*, *Princess iv* 71
an old-world mammoth bulk'd in *i*, „ *v* 148
find him dropt upon the firths of *i*, „ *vii* 206
oft we saw the glisten Of *i*, *The Daisy* 36
skater on *i* that hardly bears him, *Hendecasyllabics* 6
i Makes daggers at the sharpen'd eaves, *In Mem cvii* 7
The spires of *i* are toppled down, „ *cxxvii* 12
'A doubtful throne is *i* on summer seas. *Com. of Arthur* 248
Sworn to be veriest *i* of pureness, *Sir J. Oldcastle* 108
The spear of *i* has wept itself away, *Prog. of Spring* 6
Iceberg sound as when an *i* splits From cope to base— *Lover's Tale i* 603
Ice-ferns Fine as *i-f* on January panes *Aylmer's Field* 222
Icenian Hear *I*, Catieuchlanian, (repeat) *Boädicea* 10, 34, 47
the Gods have heard it, O *I*, „ 21
Shout *I*, Catieuchlanian, „ 57
Icicle lance that splinter'd like an *i*, *Geraint and E.* 89
Icy Day clash'd his harness in the *i* caves *M. d'Arthur* 186
Was tagg'd with *i* fringes in the moon, *St. S. Stylites* 32
Day clash'd his harness in the *i* caves *Pass. of Arthur* 354
And set me climbing *i* capes And glaciers, *To E. Fitzgerald* 25
I'd sooner fold an *i* corpse dead of some foul disease: *The Flight* 54
and felt An *i* breath play on me, *The Ring* 131
an *i* breath, As from the grating of a sepulchre, „ 399
up the tower—an *i* air Fled by me, „ 445
That *i* winter silence—how it froze you *Happy* 71
On *i* fallow And faded forest, *Merlin and the G.* 84
you will not deny my sultry throat One draught of *i* water. *Romney's R.* 23
Icy-hearted How long this *i-h* Muscovite Oppress the region?' *Poland* 10
'Id (hid) wheer Sally's owd stockin' wur '*i*, *North. Cobbler* 31
Ida (mountain of Phrygia) THERE lies a vale in *I*, *Œnone* 1
'O mother *I*, many-fountain'd *I*, (repeat) *Œnone* 23, 34, 45, 172
mother *I*, hearken ere I die. (repeat) *Œnone* 24, 35, 46, 53, 64, 77, 91, 103, 120, 134, 151, 173, 183, 195
whatever Oread haunt The knolls of *I*, *Œnone* 75
Whom all the pines of *I* shook to see *Lucretius* 86
found Paris, a naked babe, among the woods Of *I*, *Death of Œnone* 55
Ida (heroine of 'The Princess') let us know The Princess *I* waited: *Princess ii* 21
affianced years ago To the Lady *I*: „ 216
and silver litanies, The work of *I*, „ 478
She had the care of Lady *I's* youth, „ *iii* 85
your sister came she won the heart Of *I*: „ 88
Princess *I* seem'd a hollow show, „ 185
Said *I*: 'let us down and rest;' „ *iv* 21
'To horse' Said *I*; 'home! to horse!' „ 167
turn'd her face, and cast A liquid look on *I*, „ 369
at eve and dawn With *I*, *I*, *I*, rang the words; „ 433
The mellow breaker murmur'd *I*. „ 436
I lend full tongue, O noble *I*, „ 443

Ida (heroine of "The Princess") (*continued*) For now will cruel *I* keep her back; *Princess v* 84
What dares not *I* do that she should prize The soldier? „ 174
is not *I* right? They worth it? „ 188
much that *I* claims as right Had ne'er been mooted, „ 202
You talk almost like *I*: *she* can talk; „ 210
Arac's word is thrice As ours with *I*: „ 227
To learn if *I* yet would cede our claim, „ 333
one glance he caught Thro' open doors of *I* „ 343
I's answer, in a royal hand, „ 371
With Psyche's babe, was *I* watching us, „ 512
high upon the palace *I* stood With Psyche's babe in arm: „ *vi* 30
clamouring on, till *I* heard, Look'd up, „ 150
But *I* spoke not, rapt upon the child. „ 220
'*I*— 'sdeath! you blame the man; You wrong yourselves— „ 221
But *I* spoke not, gazing on the ground, „ 227
I heard her say it—' Our *I* has a heart'— „ 235
But *I* stood nor spoke, drain'd of her force „ 266
'Ay so,' said *I* with a bitter smile, „ 316
I with a voice, that like a bell Toll'd by an earthquake „ 331
at the further end Was I by the throne, „ 357
Then the voice Of *I* sounded, „ 373
But sadness on the soul of *I* fell, „ *vii* 29
When Cyril pleaded, *I* came behind Seen but of Psyche: „ 78
and shriek 'You are not *I*;' clasp it once again, And call her *I*, tho' I knew her not, „ 95
look like hollow shows; nor more Sweet *I*: „ 135
But if you be that *I* whom I knew, „ 147
My spirit closed with *I's* at the lips; „ 158
'But I,' Said *I*, tremulously, „ 333

Idalian *I* Aphroditè beautiful, *Œnone* 174

'Ide (hide) fur theere we was forced to *'i*, *Spinster's S's.* 39

Ideal (adj.) A more *i* Artist be than all (repeat) *Gardener's D.* 25, 173
Scarce other than my king's *i* knight, *Ded. of Idylls* 7
I manhood closed in real man, *To the Queen ii* 38
Evolution ever climbing after some *i* good, *Locksley H., Sixty* 199
Would she find her human offspring this *i* man at rest? „ 234

Ideal (s) He worships your *i*:' she replied: *Princess ii* 52
To nurse a blind *i* like a girl, „ *iii* 217
spirit wholly true To that *i* which he bears? *In Mem. lii* 10
a man's *i* Is high in Heaven, *Sisters (E. and E.)* 130
of the chasm between Work and *I*? *Romney's R.* 64

Ideality Infinite *I*! Immeasurable Reality! *De Prof., Human C.* 2

Idiot (adj.) Nothing but *i* gabble! *Maud II v* 41
Ye mar a comely face with *i* tears. *Geraint and E.* 550
Pity for all that aches in the grasp of an *i* power, *Despair* 43

Idiot (s) (*See also* **Emperor-idiot**) No pliable *i* I to break my vow; *The Ring* 402

Idioted being much befool'd and *i* *Aylmer's Field* 590

Idiotlike mumbling, *i* it seem'd, *Enoch Arden* 639

Idle Nor sold his heart to *i* moans, *Two Voices* 221
Eyes with *i* tears are wet. *I* habit links us yet. *Miller's D.* 211
It little profits that an *i* king, *Ulysses* 1
They are fill'd with *i* spleen; *Vision of Sin* 124
An *i* signal, for the brittle feet *Sea Dreams* 133
'Tears, *i* tears, I know not what they mean, *Princess iv* 39
Where *i* boys are cowards to their shame, „ *v* 309
So bring him: we have *i* dreams: *In Mem. x* 9
Behold, ye speak an *i* thing: „ *xxi* 21
O me, what profits it to put An *i* case? „ *xxxv* 18
'So fret not, like an *i* girl, „ *lii* 13
Then be my love, an *i* tale, „ *lxii* 3
and show That life is not as *i* ore, „ *cxviii* 20
As half but *i* brawling rhymes, „ *Con.* 23
Lying or sitting round him, *i* hands, *Gareth and L.* 512
Has little time for *i* questioners.' *Marr. of Geraint* 272
Hope not to make thyself by *i* vows, *Holy Grail* 871
For manners are not *i*, but the fruit *Guinevere* 335
And *i*—and couldn't be *i*—my Willy— *Rizpah* 27
'And *i* gleams will come and go, *Ancient Sage* 240
And *i* gleams to thee are light to me. „ 246
And *i* fancies flutter me, I know not where to turn; *The Flight* 74
Down, you *i* tools, Stampt into dust— *Romney's R.* 112
shadow of a dream—an *i* one It may be. *Akbar's Dream* 5

Idleness hatch'd In silken-folded *i*; *Princess iv* 67

Idly In lieu of *i* dallying with the truth, *Lancelot and E.* 590

Idol but everywhere Some must clasp *I's*. *Supp. Confessions* 179
Yet, my God, Whom call I *I*? „ 180
the *i* of my youth, The darling of my manhood, *Gardener's D.* 277
The rosy *i* of her solitudes, *Enoch Arden* 90
clasp These *i's* to herself? *Lucretius* 165
the wild figtree split Their monstrous *i's*, *Princess iv* 80
nations rear on high Their *i* smear'd with blood, *Freedom* 28
And when they roll their *i* down— „ 29
Noble the Saxon who hurl'd at his *I* *Kapiolani* 4

Idolater Count the more base *i* of the two; *Aylmer's Field* 670
and crush'd The *I's*, and made the people free? *Gareth and L.* 137

Idolatry waste and havock as the *idolatries*, *Aylmer's Field* 640
The red fruit of an old *i*— „ 762

Idol-fires A wind to puff your *i-f*, *Love thou thy land* 69

Idris pushing could move The chair of *I*. *Marr. of Geraint* 543

Idyll she found a small Sweet *Idyl*, *Princess vii* 191
I consecrate with tears—These *I's*. *Ded. of Idylls* 5
For this brief *i* would require *Tiresias* 188

'Igher (higher) we 'eärd 'im a-mountin' oop *'i* an' *'i*, *North. Cobbler* 47
if iver tha meäns to git *'i*, *Church-warden, etc.* 45

Ignoble And soil'd with all *i* use. *In Mem. cxi* 24
Was noble man but made *i* talk. *Lancelot and E.* 1088

Ignominy hide their faces, miserable in *i*! *Boädicea* 51

Ignorance In this extremest misery Of *i*, *Supp. Confessions* 8
he grows To Pity—more from *i* than will. *Walk. to the Mail* 110
Drink to heavy *I*! *Vision of Sin* 193
where blind and naked *I* Delivers brawling judgments, *Merlin and V.* 664
You lose yourself in utter *i*; *Lover's Tale i* 79

Ignorant (*See also* **Hignorant**) *I*, devising their own daughter's death! *Aylmer's Field* 783
As *i* and impolitic as a beast— *Columbus* 128

Ilex and there My giant *i* keeping leaf *To Ulysses* 18

Iliad Let the golden *I* vanish, *Parnassus* 20

Ilion Troas and *I's* column'd citadel, *Œnone* 13
While *I* like a mist rose into towers. *Tithonus* 63
The fire that left a roofless *I*, *Lucretius* 65
I's lofty temples robed in fire, *I* falling, Rome arising, *To Virgil* 2
Whose crime had half unpeopled *I*, *Death of Œnone* 61
What star could burn so low? not *I* yet. „ 83

Ill (adj. and adv.) But, Alice, you were *i* at ease; *Miller's D.* 146
You know so *i* to deal with time, *L. C. V. de Vere* 63
You ask me, why, tho' *i* at ease, *You ask me, why, etc.* 1
Good people, you do *i* to kneel to me. *St. S. Stylites* 133
The slow sad hours that bring us all things *i*, *Love and Duty* 58
Had you *i* dreams?' *Sea Dreams* 85
'You jest: *i* jesting with edge-tools! *Princess ii* 201
I mother that I was to leave her there, „ *v* 93
the gray mare Is *i* to live with, „ 452
Let them not lie in the tents with coarse mankind, *I* nurses; „ *vi* 70
In part It was *i* counsel had misled the girl „ *vii* 241
When *i* and weary, alone and cold, *The Daisy* 96
But *i* for him who, bettering not with time, *Will* 10
I brethren, let the fancy fly From belt to belt *In Mem. lxxxvi* 12
But *i* for him that wears a crown, „ *cxxvii* 9
sadder age begins To war against *i* uses of a life, *Gareth and L.* 1130
And sowing one *i* hint from ear to ear, *Merlin and V.* 143
I news, my Queen, for all who love him, *Lancelot and E.* 598
her hand is hot With *i* desires, *Last Tournament* 415
i prophets were they all, Spirits and men: *Guinevere* 272
I doom is mine To war against my people *Pass. of Arthur* 70
that within her womb that had left her *i* content; *The Revenge* 51
'are you *i*?' (so ran The letter) *Sisters (E. and E.)* 185
'What profits an *i* Priest Between me and my God? *Sir J. Oldcastle* 144
But often in the sidelong eyes a gleam of all things *i*— *The Flight* 31
And yet my heart is *i* at ease, „ 97

Ill (s) Patient of *i*, and death, and scorn, *Supp. Confessions* 4
saw thro' life and death, thro' good and *i*, *The Poet* 5
heaping on the fear of *i* The fear of men, *Two Voices* 107
death—mute—careless of all *i's*, *If I were loved* 10
and grief became A solemn scorn of *i's*. *D. of F. Women* 228

Inane Ruining along the illimitable *i*, *Lucretius* 40
Inarticulate idiotlike it seem'd, With *i* rage, *Enoch Arden* 640
Inaudible Alway the *i* invisible thought, *Lover's Tale ii* 102
Incense (s) Like two streams of *i* free *Eleänore* 58
A cloud of *i* of all odour steam'd *Palace of Art* 39
And that sweet *i* rise?' For that sweet *i* rose and never fail'd, „ 44
a mist Of *i* curl'd about her, and her face *Com. of Arthur* 288
Roll'd *i*, and there past along the hymns „ 464
Absorbing all the *i* of sweet thoughts *Lover's Tale i* 469
Incense (verb) fear'd To *i* the Head once more; *Princess vii* 77
Incense-fume clouded with the grateful *i-f* *Tiresias* 183
Incest crowded couch of *i* in the warrens of the poor. *Locksley H., Sixty* 224
Inch Why *i* by *i* to darkness crawl? *Two Voices* 200
only near'd Her husband *i* by *i*, *Aylmer's Field* 807
strain to make an *i* of room For their sweet selves *Lit. Squabbles* 9
in the pause she crept an *i* Nearer, *Guinevere* 527
Incited each *i* each to noble deeds. *Merlin and V.* 414
Incline over rainy mist *i's* A gleaming crag *Two Voices* 188
Till all thy life one way *i* With one wide Will *On a Mourner* 19
Incompetent must I be *I* of memory: *Two Voices* 375
Incomplete While man and woman are still *i*, *On one who effec. E. M.* 1
Inconsiderate And like an *i* boy, *In Mem. cxxii* 14
Incorporate And grow *i* into thee. „ *ii* 16
The *i* blaze of sun and sea. *Lover's Tale i* 409
Incorruptible have bought A mansion *i*. *Deserted H.* 21
Increase (s) for the good and *i* of the world. (repeat) *Edwin Morris* 44, 51, 92
The fruitful hours of still *i*; *In Mem. xlvi* 10
Increase (verb) While the stars burn, the moons *i*, *To J. S.* 71
watch her harvest ripen, her herd *i*, *Maud III vi* 25
Increased lest brute Power be *i*, *Poland* 6
But day *i* from heat to heat, *Mariana in the S.* 39
light *i* With freshness in the dawning east. *Two Voices* 404
and with each The year *i*. *Gardener's D.* 199
Thy latter days *i* with pence *Will Water.* 219
His beauty still with his years *i*, *The Victim* 34
For them the light of life *i*, *In Mem., Con.* 74
i, Upon a pastoral slope as fair, *Maud I xviii* 18
I Geraint's, who heaved his blade aloft, *Marr. of Geraint* 572
that ruling has *i* Her greatness and her self-content. *To Marq. of Dufferin* 7
Increasing Which with *i* might doth forward flee *Mine be the strength* 5
I doubt not thro' the ages one *i* purpose runs, *Locksley Hall* 137
and Fame again *I* gave me use. *Merlin and V.* 494
Incredible spires Prick'd with *i* pinnacles into heaven. *Holy Grail* 423
Incredulous *See* **Half-incredulous**
In-crescent Between the *i-c* and de-crescent moon, *Gareth and L.* 529
Ind sways the floods and lands From *I* to *I*, *Buonaparte* 4
Indecent *See* **Ondecent**
Indeed soldier of the Cross? it is he and he *i*! *Happy* 12
Life, which is Life *i*. *Prog. of Spring* 117
India all the sultry palms of *I* known, *W. to Marie Alex.* 14
Where some refulgent sunset of *I* *Milton* 13
upon the topmost roof our banner in *I* blew. *Def. of Lucknow* 72
For he—your *I* was his Fate, *To Marq. of Dufferin* 21
Queen, and Empress of *I*, *On Jub. Q. Victoria* 6
Indian (*See also* **Hinjian, West-Indian**) *I* reeds blown from his silver tongue, *The Poet* 13
The throne of *I* Cama slowly sail'd *Palace of Art* 115
Fire-hollowing this in *I* fashion, *Enoch Arden* 569
My lady's *I* kinsman unannounced *Aylmer's Field* 190
My lady's *I* kinsman rushing in, „ 593
less from *I* craft Than beelike instinct hiveward, *Princess iv* 198
yet the morn Breaks hither over *I* seas, *In Mem. xxvi* 14
gazing like The *I* on a still-eyed snake, *Lover's Tale ii* 189
Praise to our *I* brothers, *Def. of Lucknow* 69
not That *I* isle, but our most ancient East *Columbus* 80
I warriors dream of ampler hunting grounds *Locksley H., Sixty* 69
To England under *I* skies, *Hands all Round* 17
I, Australasian, African, *On Jub. Q. Victoria* 60
Will my *I* brother come? *Romney's R.* 143
wail of baby-wife, Or *I* widow; *Akbar's Dream* 197
Indies Of the Ocean—of the *I*—Admirals we— *Columbus* 31
Indies (*continued*) Rome's Vicar in our *I*? *Columbus* 195
Indifference Attain the wise *i* of the wise; *A Dedication* 8
And Love the *i* to be, *In Mem. xxvi* 12
Indignant But thy strong Hours *i* work'd their wills, *Tithonus* 18
On either side the hearth, *i*; *Aylmer's Field* 288
and she returned *I* to the Queen; (repeat) *Marr. of Geraint* 202, 414
Indignantly Gareth spake and all *i*, *Gareth and L.* 1386
And yet he answer'd half *i*: *Merlin and V.* 404
Indignation What heats of *i* when we heard *Princess v* 375
her white neck Was rosed with *i*: „ *vi* 344
Indistinct muffled booming *i* Of the confused floods, *Lover's Tale i* 637
masses Of thundershaken columns *i*, „ *ii* 66
Individual (adj.) And *i* freedom mute; *You ask me why, etc.* 20
Matures the *i* form. *Love thou thy land* 40
There—closing like an *i* life— *Love and Duty* 79
Individual (s) And the *i* withers, *Locksley Hall* 142
Individuality Distinct in *individualities*, *Princess vii* 291
Indolent O you chorus of *i* reviewers, Irresponsible, *i* reviewers, *Hendecasyllabics* 1
Waking laughter in *i* reviewers. „ 8
All that chorus of *i* reviewers. „ 12
believe me Too presumptuous, *i* reviewers. „ 16
Indoor an' a trouble an' plague wi' *i*. *Spinster's S's.* 50
Indrawing Like some old wreck on some *i* sea, *St. Telemachus* 44
Induce persecute Opinion, and *i* a time *You ask me why, etc.* 18
Indue His eyes To *i* his lustre; *Lover's Tale i* 424
my love should ne'er *i* the front And mask of Hate, „ 774
Ineffable Toil and *i* weariness, *Def. of Lucknow* 90
Beyond all dreams of Godlike womanhood, *I* beauty, *Tiresias* 55
Inexorable No saint—*i*—no tenderness— *Princess v* 515
fall the battle-axe, unexhausted, *i*. *Boädicea* 56
Infancy In the silken sail of *i*, *Arabian Nights* 2
O'er the deep mind of dauntless *i*. *Ode to Memory* 36
With those old faces of our *i* *Lotos-Eaters, C. S.* 66
To ailing wife or wailing *i* *Aylmer's Field* 177
flaxen ringlets of our *infancies* Wander'd, *Lover's Tale i* 234
As was our childhood, so our *i*, „ 249
Infant (adj.) Or an *i* civilisation be ruled with rod or with knout? *Maud I iv* 47
Some hold that he hath swallow'd *i* flesh, *Gareth and L.* 1342
You claspt our *i* daughter, heart to heart. *Romney's R.* 77
Infant (s) The trustful *i* on the knee! *Supp. Confessions* 41
Which mixing with the *i's* blood. „ 61
clear Delight, the *i's* dawning year. „ 67
Thou leddest by the hand thine *i* Hope. *Ode to Memory* 30
And laid the feeble *i* in his arms; *Enoch Arden* 152
more than *i's* in their sleep. *Princess vii* 54
Shall we deal with it as an *i*? *Boädicea* 53
An *i* crying in the night: An *i* crying for the light: *In Mem. liv* 18
shaping an *i* ripe for his birth, *Maud I iv* 34
gave Thy breast to ailing *i's* in the night, *Demeter and P.* 56
Infidel (adj.) Have I crazed myself over their horrible *i* writings? *Despair* 87
Infidel (s) that large *i* Your Omar; *To E. Fitzgerald* 36
I loathe the very name of *i*. *Akbar's Dream* 70
Infinite (*See also* **Finite-infinite**) Because the scale is *i*. *Two Voices* 93
and serve that *I* Within us, as without, *Akbar's Dream* 145
'Mid onward-sloping motions *i* *Palace of Art* 247
and *i* torment of flies, *Def. of Lucknow* 82
And shatter'd phantom of that *i* One, *De Prof., Two G.* 47
I Ideality! Immeasurable Reality! *I* Personality! „ *Human C.* 2
I should call on that *I* Love that has served us so well? *I* cruelty rather that made everlasting Hell, *Despair* 95
Infinity Like emblems of *i*, The trenched *Ode to Memory* 103
In flagrante Caught *i f*—what's the Latin word?— *Walk. to the Mail* 34
Inflame twelve-divided concubine To *i* the tribes: *Aylmer's Field* 760
Inflamed like a rising moon, *I* with wrath: *Princess i* 60
a horn, *i* the knights At that dishonour *Last Tournament* 434
Inflate *I* themselves with some insane delight, *Merlin and V.* 834
Influence self-same *i* Controlleth all the soul *Eleänore* 114
'Who forged that other *i*, *Two Voices* 283
To the *i* of mild-minded melancholy; *Lotos-Eaters, C. S.* 64
and use Her *i* on the mind, *Will Water.* 12
sacred from the blight Of ancient *i* and scorn. *Princess ii* 169
Twice as magnetic to sweet *i's* Of earth „ *v* 191

Influence (*continued*) By many a varying *i* and so long. *Princess vi* 267
A kindlier *i* reign'd ; „ *vii* 20
Or in their silent *i* as they sat, „ *Con.* 15
Mourn for the man of amplest *i*, *Ode on Well.* 27
Let random *i's* glance, *In Mem. xlix* 2
Influence-rich *i-r* to soothe and save, „ *lxxx* 14
Infold *See* **Self-infold**
Inform beauty doth *i* Stillness with love, *Day-Dm., Sleep B.* 15
early risen she goes to *i* The Princess: *Princess iii* 62
Inform'd *I* the pillar'd Parthenon, *Freedom* 3
Infuse Desire in me to *i* my tale of love *Princess v* 240
Should *i* Rich atar in the bosom of the rose, *Lover's Tale i* 269
Ingrav'n (*See also* **Engraven**) rind *i* 'For the most fair,' *Œnone* 72
Ingress for your *i* here Upon the skirt *Princess v* 218
Ingroove be free To *i* itself with that which flies, *Love thou thy land* 46
Inhabitant liker to the *i* Of some clear planet *Princess ii* 35
Inherit Our sons *i* us: our looks are strange: *Lotos-Eaters, C. S.* 73
'The meek shall *i* the earth' *The Dreamer* 2
Inheritance some *i* Of such a life, a heart, *Ded. of Idylls* 32
And standeth seized of that *i* *Gareth and L.* 359
But lately come to his *i*, *Pelleas and E.* 18
Inherited (adj.) heap'd the whole *i* sin On that huge scapegoat *Maud I xiii* 41
But if sin be sin, not *i* fate, *The Wreck* 85
Inherited (verb) And he that next *i* the tale *Princess iv* 592
Injellied golden yolks Imbedded and *i*; *Audley Court* 26
Injured *See* **Seeming-injured**
Injuries life-long *i* burning unavenged, *Geraint and E.* 696
Inky Draw the vast eyelid of an *i* cloud, *Merlin and V.* 634
Inlaid Distinct with vivid stars *i*, *Arabian Nights* 90
Inland And ripples on an *i* mere? *Supp. Confessions* 131
Crimsons over an *i* mere, *Eleänore* 42
From many an *i* town and haven large, *Œnone* 117
thro' mountain clefts the dale Was seen far *i*, *Lotos-Eaters* 21
Inlay deep *i* Of braided blooms unmown, *Arabian Nights* 28
Inlet In glaring sand and *i's* bright. *Mariana in the S.* 8
Inmingled *I* with Heaven's azure waveringly, *Gareth and L.* 936
Inmost Upon the mooned domes aloof In *i* Bagdat, *Arabian Nights* 128
As tho' a star, in *i* heaven set, *Eleänore* 89
Dead sounds at night come from the *i* hills, *Œnone* 249
'And even into my *i* ring A pleasure *Talking Oak* 173
Then fled she to her *i* bower, *Godiva* 42
clamour thicken'd, mixt with *i* terms *Princess ii* 446
Came in long breezes rapt from *i* south And blown to *i* north; „ *iv* 431
As some rare little rose, a piece of *i* Horticultural art, *Hendecasyllabics* 19
wordy snares to track Suggestion to her *i* cell. *In Mem. xcv* 32
And gulf'd his griefs in *i* sleep; *Pelleas and E.* 516
Not ev'n in *i* thought to think again *Guinevere* 374
like a little star Were drunk into the *i* blue, *Lover's Tale i* 309
Spoke loudly even into my *i* heart „ 428
streams Running far on within its *i* halls, „ 523
For all the secret of her *i* heart, „ 588
tight chain within my *i* frame Was riven in twain: „ 595
Woman to her *i* heart, and woman to her tender feet, *Locksley H., Sixty* 50
Inn (*See also* **Hinn**) And lighted at a ruin'd *i*, and said: *Vision of Sin* 62
tha mun goä fur it down to the *i*. *North. Cobbler* 8
like old-world *i's* that take Some warrior *Pro. to Gen. Hamley* 13
Inner with shows of flaunting vines Unto mine *i* eye, *Ode to Memory* 49
With an *i* voice the river ran, *Dying Swan* 5
Springing alone With a shrill *i* sound, *Mermaid* 20
All the *i*, all the outer world of pain *If I were loved* 5
'An *i* impulse rent the veil Of his old husk: *Two Voices* 10
river seaward flow From the *i* land: *Lotos-Eaters* 14
Nor harken what the *i* spirit sings, „ *C. S.* 22
Gross darkness of the *i* sepulchre Is not so deadly still *D. of F. Women* 67
green that streak the white Of the first snowdrop's *i* leaves; *Princess v* 197
when sundown skirts the moor An *i* trouble I behold, *In Mem. xli* 18
That stir the spirit's *i* deeps, „ *xlii* 10
No *i* vileness that we dread? „ *li* 4
His *i* day can never die, „ *lxvi* 15
Inner (*continued*) Made dull his *i*, keen his outer eye *Last Tournament* 366
But thou didst sit alone in the *i* house, *Lover's Tale i* 112
vessel, as with *i* life, Began to heave „ *ii* 191
Innermost Flash'd thro' my eyes into my *i* brain, „ 95
Death in our *i* chamber, *Def. of Lucknow* 15
Inniskillens Brave *I* and Greys *Heavy Brigade* 33
Innocence Affronted with his fulsome *i*? *Pelleas and E.* 266
'Take thou the jewels of this dead *i*, *Last Tournament* 31
Our one white day of *I* hath past, „ 218
small damosels white as *I*, In honour of poor *I* „ 291
left the gems with *I* the Queen Lent to the King, and *I* „ 293
Which lives with blindness, or plain *i* Of nature, *Sisters (E. and E.)* 249
I seethed in her mother's milk, *Vastness* 9
Innocency O yield me shelter for mine *i* *Merlin and V.* 83
Innocent (adj.) And loveth so his *i* heart, *Supp. Confessions* 52
The little *i* soul flitted away. *Enoch Arden* 270
nightly wirer of their *i* hare Falter *Aylmer's Field* 490
for her fresh and *i* eyes Had such a star „ 691
and reach its fatling *i* arms And lazy lingering fingers. *Princess vi* 138
Then as a little helpless *i* bird, *Lancelot and E.* 894
And kind the woman's eyes and *i*, *Holy Grail* 393
'Will the child kill me with her *i* talk?' *Guinevere* 214
Why should *she* weep? O *i* of spirit— *Lover's Tale i* 737
Being guiltless, as an *i* prisoner, „ 787
Their *i* hospitalities quench'd in blood, *Columbus* 176
a heedless and *i* bride— *The Wreck* 13
and drive *I* cattle under thatch, *Locksley H., Sixty* 96
I maidens, Garrulous children, *Merlin and the G.* 55
Innocent (s) Themselves had wrought on many an *i*. *Geraint and E.* 178
Innocent-arch So *i-a*, so cunning-simple, *Lilian* 13
Innumerable (*See also* **Numerable-innumerable**) In copse and fern Twinkled the *i* ear and tail. *The Brook* 134
And sated with the *i* rose, *Princess iii* 122
And murmuring of *i* bees.' „ *vii* 222
bark and blacken *i*, *Boädicea* 13
I, pitiless, passionless eyes, *Maud I xviii* 38
Thro' knots and loops and folds *i* *Lancelot and E.* 439
lying bounden there In darkness thro' *i* hours *Holy Grail* 677
are these but symbols of *i* man, *Locksley H., Sixty* 195
Innumerous A lisping of the *i* leaf and dies, *Princess v* 14
Inosculated (For so they said themselves) *i*; „ *iii* 89
Inquire Who scarcely darest to *i*, *In Mem. iv* 7
Inquisition To these *I* dogs and the devildoms of Spain.' *The Revenge* 12
Inrunning (*See also* **Deep-inrunning**) And at the *i* of a little brook Sat by the river *Lancelot and E.* 1388
Insane Inflate themselves with some *i* delight, *Merlin and V.* 834
Insanity With animal heat and dire *i*? *Lucretius* 163
Roll'd again back on itself in the tides of a civic *i*! *Beautiful City* 4
Inscription And some *i* ran along the front, *Princess i* 212
How saw you not the *i* on the gate, „ *ii* 194
'for that *i* there, I think no more of deadly lurks „ 225
I urged the fierce *i* on the gate, „ *iii* 141
Insect *i's* prick Each leaf into a gall) *Talking Oak* 69
The lightning flash of *i* and of bird, *Enoch Arden* 575
Or eagle's wing, or *i's* eye; *In Mem. cxxiv* 6
I's of an hour, that hourly work their brother *i* wrong, *Locksley H., Sixty* 202
Insipid *I* as the Queen upon a card; *Aylmer's Field* 28
Insolence blustering I know not what Of *i* *Princess v* 397
Smelling of musk and of *i*, *Maud I vi* 45
Insolent *I*, brainless, heartless! *Aylmer's Field* 368
'*I* scullion: *I* of thee? *Gareth and L.* 976
Inspiration Ancient founts of *i* well *Locksley Hall* 188
Instance That wilderness of single *i's*, *Aylmer's Field* 437
But Vivien, deeming Merlin overborne By *i*, *Merlin and V.* 801
Instant *I* were his words. *Gareth and L.* 1353
Abash'd Lavaine, whose *i* reverence, *Lancelot and E.* 418
Instep brandish'd plume Brushing his *i*, *Geraint and E.* 360
Instinct of the moral *i* would she prate *Palace of Art* 205
And that mysterious *i* wholly died. *Enoch Arden* 526
less from Indian craft Than beelike *i* *Princess iv* 199
a dearer being, all dipt In Angel *i's*, „ *vii* 321

Instinctive his quick *i* hand Caught at the hilt, — *Marr. of Geraint* 209
Institute their *I* Of which he was the patron. — *Princess, Pro.* 5
The patient leaders of their *I* Taught them — „ 58
I fenced it round with gallant *i's*, — „ *v* 392
Some Imperial *I*, Rich in symbol, — *On Jub. Q. Victoria* 46
Insufficiencies temperate eyes On glorious *i*, — *In Mem. cxii* 3
Insult I heard sounds of *i*, shame, and wrong, — *D. of F. Women* 19
We brook no further *i* but are gone.' — *Princess vi* 342
'I will avenge this *i*, noble Queen, — *Marr. of Geraint* 215
Avenging this great *i* done the Queen.' — „ 425
'Remember that great *i* done the Queen,' — „ 571
Crave pardon for that *i* done the Queen, — „ 583
your wretched dress, A wretched *i* on you, — *Geraint and E.* 328
Oaths, *i*, filth, and monstrous blasphemies, — *Pass. of Arthur* 114
Inswathe *I* the fulness of Eternity, — *Lover's Tale i* 483
Inswathed *I* sometimes in wandering mist, — *St. S. Stylites* 75
Intellect thorough-edged *i* to part Error from crime; — *Isabel* 14
Thy kingly *i* shall feed, — *Clear-headed friend* 20
All-subtilising *i*: — *In Mem. lxxxv* 48
Or ev'n for *i* to reach Thro' memory — „ *xcv* 47
Seraphic *i* and force To seize and throw — „ *cix* 5
For can I doubt, who knew thee keen In *i*, — „ *cxiii* 6
Intellectual And *i* throne. — *Palace of Art* 216
bow'd myself down as a slave to his *i* throne. — *The Wreck* 66
Intelligence The great *I's* fair That range — *In Mem. lxxxv* 21
Intelligible From over-fineness not *i* — *Merlin and V.* 796
Intend (*See also* **Intind**) The thesis which thy words *i*— — *Two Voices* 338
Intense 'Or will one beam be less *i*, — „ 40
when fraught With a passion so *i* — *Maud II ii* 59
Intensity Sometimes, with most *i* Gazing, — *Eleänore* 82
Intent (adj.) have been *i* On that veil'd picture— — *Gardener's D.* 269
I kept mine own *I* on her, — *Princess ii* 442
Intent (s) almost ere I knew mine own *i*, — *Gardener's D.* 146
eye seem'd full Of a kind *i* to me, — *Maud I vi* 41
But after ten slow weeks her fix'd *i*, — *The Ring* 345
fur I noäwaäys knaw'd 'is *i*; — *Owd Roä* 61
Interchange angels rising and descending met With *i* of gift. — *Palace of Art* 144
And frequent *i* of foul and fair, — *Enoch Arden* 533
Interest To close the *i's* of all. — *Love thou thy land* 36
From all a closer *i* flourish'd up, — *Princess vii* 113
catch The far-off *i* of tears? — *In Mem. i* 8
Interfused And glory of broad waters *i*, — *Lover's Tale i* 401
Interlaced shadow'd grots of arches *i*, — *Palace of Art* 51
Interlock'd My lady with her fingers *i*, — *Aylmer's Field* 199
Intermitted tenfold dearer by the power Of *i* usage; — *Marr. of Geraint* 811
Interpret True love *i's*—right alone. — *Miller's D.* 188
with such a stupid heart To *i* ear and eye, — *Lancelot and E.* 942
Interpretation a tongue To blare its own *i*— — „ 943
Interpreter *I* between the Gods and men, — *Princess vii* 322
How, in the mouths of base *i's*, — *Merlin and V.* 795
Interpreting she broke out *i* my thoughts: — *Princess iii* 275
Interspace flowing rapidly between Their *i's*, — *Arabian Nights* 84
The lucid *i* of world and world, — *Lucretius* 105
between Whose *i's* gush'd in blinding bursts — *Lover's Tale i* 408
Intertwisted A lodge of *i* beechen-boughs — *Last Tournament* 376
Interval fill'd with light The *i* of sound. — *D. of F. Women* 172
Miriam watch'd and dozed at *i's*, — *Enoch Arden* 909
streak'd or starr'd at *i's* With falling brook — *Lover's Tale i* 404
sick with love, Fainted at *i's*, — „ 546
thence at *i's* A low bell tolling. — „ *ii* 82
Intervital spirit's folded bloom Thro' all its *i* gloom — *In Mem. xliii* 3
Intimacy Bound in an immemorial *i*, — *Aylmer's Field* 39
Bound, but an immemorial *i*, — „ 136
Intind (intend) an' she didn't *i* to desave, — *Tomorrow* 59
Intolerable became Anguish *i*. — *Lover's Tale ii* 138
Intolerant The menacing poison of *i* priests, — *Akbar's Dream* 165
Intonation a tuneful tongue, Such happy *i*, — *Amphion* 18
Intone Delicate-handed priest *i*; — *Maud I viii* 11
Intricate wanderings Of this most *i* Universe — *A Character* 3
Intrusion hunter rued His rash *i*, manlike, — *Princess iv* 204
Intuitive *i* decision of a bright And thorough-edged intellect — *Isabel* 13
Inutterable Kill'd with *i* unkindliness.' — *Merlin and V.* 886
Invade *i* Even with a verse your holy woe. — *To J. S.* 7
Invaded 'Our land *i*, 'sdeath! — *Princess v* 276
Invaded (*continued*) for whose love the Roman Cæsar first *I* Britain, But we beat him back, As this great Prince *i* us, — *Marr. of Geraint* 746
Was mine a mood To be *i* rudely, — *Lover's Tale i* 678
Invalid *i*, since my will Seal'd not the bond— — *Princess v* 398
Invective a tide of fierce *I* seem'd to wait — „ *iv* 472
Invent the years *i*; Each month is various — *Two Voices* 73
But when did woman ever yet *i*?' — *Princess ii* 391
Invented Was this fair charm *i* by yourself? — *Merlin and V.* 540
Inventor O MIGHTY-MOUTH'D *i* of harmonies, — *Milton* 1
Inverted he heard his priest Preach an *i* scripture, — *Aylmer's Field* 44
Invested Slipt round, and in the dark *i* you, — *Princess iv* 404
Inveterately Time Were nothing, so *i*, — *Gareth and L.* 227
Invidious Who breaks his birth's *i* bar, — *In Mem. lxiv* 5
Inviolable a doubtful lord To bind them by *i* vows, — *Last Tournament* 688
Inviolate *And compass'd by the i sea.'* — *To the Queen* 36
Nor ever drank the *i* spring — *In Mem. xc* 2
Invisible And praise the *i* universal Lord, — *Ode Inter. Exhib.* 3
Alway the inaudible *i* thought, — *Lover's Tale ii* 102
I but deathless, waiting still The edict — „ 160
Invited For I am not *i*, But, with the Sultan's pardon, — *Maud I xx* 38
Invoke That which we dare *i* to bless; — *In Mem. cxxiv* 1
Involuntary from my breast the *i* sigh Brake, — *Princess iii* 191
Involve My love *i's* the love before; — *In Mem. cxxx* 9
Involved (*See also* **Self-involved**) but in you I found My boyish dream *i* — *Princess iv* 450
Assumed from thence a half-consent *i* In stillness, — „ *vii* 82
To the other shore, *i* in thee, — *In Mem. lxxxiv* 40
My mind *i* yourself the nearest thing — *Merlin and V.* 300
Involving worlds before the man *I* ours— — *Epilogue* 26
Inward from the outward to the *i* brought, — *Eleänore* 4
More *i* than at night or morn, — *Mariana in the S.* 58
a knight would pass Outward, or *i* to the hall: — *Gareth and L.* 311
portal of King Pellam's chapel wide And *i* to the wall; — *Balin and Balan* 406
the rest Were crumpled *i's*. Dead!— — *The Ring* 454
With an ancient melody Of an *i* agony, — *Claribel* 7
That heat of *i* evidence, — *Two Voices* 284
'Weep, weeping dulls the *i* pain.' — *To J. S.* 40
Ev'n now we hear with *i* strife — *Love thou thy land* 53
Again in deeper *i* whispers 'lost!' — *Enoch Arden* 716
With *i* yelp and restless forefoot plies — *Lucretius* 45
My *i* sap, the hold I have on earth, — *Lover's Tale i* 166
address'd More to the *i* than the outward ear, — „ 721
Dead of some *i* agony—is it so? — *To W. H. Brookfield* 10
Inwoven dusky strand of Death *i* here — *Maud I xviii* 60
Inwrapt *I* tenfold in slothful shame, — *Palace of Art* 262
Inwreathe *i* (How lovelier, nobler then!) — *Lover's Tale i* 458
Inwrought diaper'd With *i* flowers, — *Arabian Nights* 149
Ionian Than all the valleys of *I* hills. — *Œnone* 2
And there the *I* father of the rest; — *Palace of Art* 137
Io t'amo '*I t*'—and these diamonds— — *The Ring* 70
This very ring *I t*? — „ 134
sent This ring '*I t*' to his best beloved, — „ 210
and cried 'I see him, *I t, I t*.' — „ 223
call thro' this '*I t*' to the heart Of Miriam; — „ 234
'*I t*, all is well then.' Muriel fled. — „ 271
You love me still '*I t*.' — „ 291
No! '*I t, I t*'! flung herself Against my heart, — „ 397
even that '*I t*,' those three sweet Italian words, — „ 406
Irân Alla call'd In old *I* the Sun of Love? — *Akbar's Dream* 87
A voice from old *I*! Nay, but I know it— — „ 89
Ire The plaintive cry jarr'd on her *i*; — *Princess iv* 393
Ireland Sailing from *I*.' — *Last Tournament* 555
Iris (prismatic colours) *i* changes on the burnish'd dove; — *Locksley Hall* 19
The circled *I* of a night of tears; — *Princess iii* 27
Iris (flag-flower) glided winding under ranks Of *i*, — *In Mem. ciii* 24
Iris (messenger of the Gods) But light-foot *I* brought it yester-eve, — *Œnone* 83
So saying, light-foot *I* pass'd away. — *Achilles over the T.* 1
Irish The black-blue *I* hair and *I* eyes Had drawn — *Last Tournament* 404
Irish Bog aisier work av they lived be an *I b*. — *Tomorrow* 72
Iron (adj.) One show'd an *i* coast and angry waves. — *Palace of Art* 69
Ranges of glimmering vaults with *i* grates, — *D. of F. Women* 35
Which men call'd Aulis in those *i* years: — „ 106

Iron (adj.) (*continued*) A grazing *i* collar grinds my neck; — St. S. Stylites 117
I jointed, supple-sinew'd, they shall dive, — Locksley Hall 169
Paled at a sudden twitch of his *i* mouth; — Aylmer's Field 732
crush her pretty maiden fancies dead In *i* gauntlets: — Princess i 89
Binds me to speak, and O that *i* will, — „ ii 202
Nor would I fight with *i* laws, — „ iv 75
Forgotten, rusting on his *i* hills, — „ v 146
he clash'd His *i* palms together with a cry; — „ 354
There dwelt an *i* nature in the grain: — „ vi 50
Her *i* will was broken in her mind; — „ 118
in the Vestal entry shriek'd The virgin marble under *i* heels; — „ 351
and saw Thee woman thro' the crust of *i* moods — „ vii 342
O *i* nerve to true occasion true, — Ode on Well. 37
Till one that sought but Duty's *i* crown — „ 122
Their ever-loyal *i* leader's fame, — „ 229
Or seal'd within the *i* hills? — In Mem. lvi 20
But that remorseless *i* hour Made cypress — „ lxxxiv 14
An *i* welcome when they rise: — „ xc 8
and clangs Its leafless ribs and *i* horns — „ cvii 12
That makes you tyrants in your *i* skies, — Maud I xviii 37
That an *i* tyranny now should bend or cease, — „ III vi 20
Across the *i* grating of her cell Beat, — Holy Grail 81
The last hard footstep of that *i* crag; — Pass. of Arthur 447
butted with the shuddering War-thunder of *i* rams; — Tiresias 100
Brass mouths and *i* lungs! — Freedom 40
And I clash with an *i* Truth, — The Dreamer 6
Iron (s) clad in *i* burst the ranks of war, — Princess iv 504
This red-hot *i* to be shaped with blows. — „ v 209
'I've heard that there is *i* in the blood, — „ vi 230
But *i* dug from central gloom, — In Mem. cxviii 21
fight my way with gilded arms, All shall be *i*;' — Geraint and E. 22
That laughs at *i*—as our warriors did— — Merlin and V. 429
drew The rustiest *i* of old fighters' hearts; — „ 574
We brought this *i* from our isles of gold. — Columbus 3
Iron-clanging an *i-c* anvil bang'd With hammers; — Princess v 504
Iron-clashing such a stern and *i-c* close, — Merlin and V. 419
Iron-cramp'd those that *i-c* their women's feet; — Princess v 376
Iron-hearted *i-h* victors they. — Locksley H., Sixty 80
Iron-stay'd *i-s* In damp and dismal dungeons — Lover's Tale ii 148
Iron-worded wall about thy cause With *i-w* proof, — To J. M. K. 9
Irony call her sweet, as if in *i*, — Princess vii 97
Irredeemable Wrought for his house an *i* woe; — Maud II i 22
Irrepressible cloud of thought Keen, *i*. — Lover's Tale ii 165
Irresponsible *I*, indolent reviewers, — Hendecasyllabics 2
Irreverence Blockish *i*, brainless greed— — Columbus 129
Irreverent you have miss'd the *i* doom — You might have won 9
A reckless and *i* knight was he, — Holy Grail 856
Irritable being vicious, old and *i*, — Marr. of Geraint 194
Is For was, and *i*, and will be, are but *i*; — Princess iii 324
Isabel Revered *I*, the crown and head, — Isabel 10
Crown'd *I*, thro' all her placid life, — „ 27
Iscariot Pontius and *I* by my side — St. S. Stylites 168
Isis an *I* hid by the veil. — Maud I iv 43
Islam beating back the swarms Of Turkish *I* — Montenegro 11
Islám Polytheism and *I* feel after thee. — Akbar's D., Inscrip. 2
gleam Than glances from the sun of our *I*. — Akbar's Dream 79
Myself am such in our *I*, — „ 155
Islamite Houris bow'd to see The dying *I*, — Palace of Art 103
Island (adj.) 'Our *i* home Is far beyond the wave; — Lotos-Eaters 44
Or else the *i* princes over-bold — „ C. S. 75
bind with bands That *i* queen who sways — Buonaparte 3
Not once or twice in our rough *i* story, — Ode on Well. 201
Revenge herself went down by the *i* crags — The Revenge 118
made your fathers great In our ancient *i* State, — Open. I. and C. Exhib. 16
greatest of women, *i* heroine, Kapiolani — Kapiolani 5
Island (s) on the land Over the *i's* free; — Sea-Fairies 26
Round an *i* there below, The *i* of Shalott. — L. of Shalott i 8
By the *i* in the river Flowing down to Camelot. — „ 13
Boat, *i*, ruins of a castle, — Edwin Morris 6
On from *i* unto *i* at the gateways of the day. — Locksley Hall 158
So they past by capes and *i's*, — The Captain 21
The blaze upon his *i* overhead; — Enoch Arden 595
Island (s) (*continued*) Thine *i* loves thee well, — Ode on Well. 85
For out of the waste *i's* had he come, — Pelleas and E. 86
Drew to this *i*: Doom'd to the death. — Batt. of Brunanburh 50
Far off from out an *i* girt by foes, — Achilles over the T. 8
follow Edwin to those isles, those *i's* of the Blest! — The Flight 42
I, from out the Northern *I* sunder'd once — To Virgil 35
shake with her thunders and shatter her *i*, — Kapiolani 10
'Woe to this *i* if ever a woman (repeat) — „ 20, 22
Island-crag Set in a cataract on an *i-c*, — Princess v 347
Island-myriads Her *i-m* fed from alien lands— — The Fleet 12
Island-Paradise In Hispaniola's *i-P*! — Columbus 182
Island-sides Far-fleeted by the purple *i-s*, — Princess vii 166
Island-story once or twice in our rough *i-s*, — Ode on Well. 201
Not once or twice in our fair *i-s*, — „ 209
Island-valley To the *i-v* of Avilion; — M. d'Arthur 259
To the *i-v* of Avilion; — Pass. of Arthur 427
Isle (s) (*See also* **Bounteous Isle, Eden-isle, Garden-isles, South-sea-isle, World-isle**) flee By town, and tower, and hill, and cape, and *i*, — Mine be the strength 6
the silent *i* imbowers The Lady of Shalott. — L. of Shalott i 17
Is there confusion in the little *i*? — Lotos-Eaters, C. S. 79
where the moving *i's* of winter shock By night, — M. d'Arthur 140
mellow brickwork on an *i* of bowers. — Edwin Morris 12
The rentroll Cupid of our rainy *i's*. — „ 103
To whom I leave the sceptre and the *i*— — Ulysses 34
It may be we shall touch the Happy *I's*, — „ 63
Summer *i's* of Eden lying in dark-purple — Locksley Hall 164
breaker sweep The nutmeg rocks and *i's* of clove. — The Voyage 40
Blue *i's* of heaven laugh'd between, — Sir L. and Q. G. 6
over lake and lawn, and *i's* and capes— — Vision of Sin 11
And sent her sweetly by the golden *i's*, — Enoch Arden 536
stranding on an *i* at morn Rich, — „ 552
Far in a darker *i* beyond the line; — „ 605
beauteous hateful *i* Return'd upon him, — „ 617
Stay'd by this *i*, not knowing where she lay: — „ 630
Across a break on the mist-wreathen *i* — „ 632
Thou That didst uphold me on my lonely *i*, — „ 783
and battle-clubs From the *i's* of palm: — Princess, Pro. 22
As yet we find in barbarous *i's*, — „ ii 122
over them the tremulous *i's* of light Slided, — „ vi 81
O saviour of the silver-coasted *i*, — Ode on Well. 136
Maoris and that *I* of Continent, — W. to Marie Alex. 18
(Take it and come) to the *I* of Wight; — To F. D. Maurice 12
For in all that exquisite *i*, my dear, — The Islet 26
She desires no *i's* of the blest, — Wages 8
'Fear not, *i* of blowing woodland, *i* of silvery parapets! — Boädicea 38
Streams o'er a rich ambrosial ocean *i*, — Milton 14
Is dash'd with wandering *i's* of night. — In Mem. xxiv 4
Danube rolling fair Enwind her *i's*, — „ xcviii 10
over all whose realms to their last *i*, — Ded. of Idylls 12
a petty king ere Arthur came Ruled in this *i*, — Com. of Arthur 6
'He passes to the *I* Avilion, — Gareth and L. 502
Heard by the lander in a lonely *i*, — Marr. of Geraint 330
Whose bark had plunder'd twenty nameless *i's*; — Merlin and V. 559
Lords of waste marches, kings of desolate *i's*, — Lancelot and E. 527
Gave him an *i* of marsh whereon to build; — Holy Grail 62
And this new knight, Sir Pelleas of the *i's*— — Pelleas and E. 17
And lord of many a barren *i* was he— — „ 19
Scarce any but the women of his *i's*, — „ 88
many a glancing plash and sallowy *i*, — Last Tournament 422
Farewell! there is an *i* of rest for thee. — Pass. of Arthur 35
where the moving *i's* of winter shock By night, — „ 308
third-rate *i* half-lost among her seas? — To the Queen ii 25
throne In our vast Orient, and one *i*, one *i*, — „ 31
All day I watch'd the floating *i's* of shade, — Lover's Tale ii 5
But work was scant in the *I*, — First Quarrel 43
thou hast come to talk our *i*. — Sir J. Oldcastle 32
not That Indian *i*, but our most ancient East — Columbus 80
Pour'd in on all those happy naked *i's*— — „ 173
He lived on an *i* in the ocean— — V. of Maeldune 7
And we came to the *i* in the ocean, — „ 9
And we came to the Silent *I* — „ 11
And we hated the beautiful *I*, — „ 21
And we came to the *I* of Shouting, — „ 27
And we came to the *I* of Flowers: — „ 37

J

Jacquerie after massacre, Jacobinism and *J*, *Locksley H., Sixty* 157
Jacynth chrysoprase, *J*, and amethyst— *Columbus* 86
Jael a cymbal'd Miriam and a *J*, *Princess v* 511
Jail scared with threats of *j* and halter *Aylmer's Field* 520
Jailer And the *j* forced me away. (repeat) *Rizpah* 41, 44
Jailing And tame thy *j* princess to thine hand. *Pelleas and E.* 344
Jam (s) An' a haäf-pot o' *j*, or a mossel o' meät *Spinster's S's.* 109
Jam (verb) *j* the doors, and bear The keepers *Lucretius* 169
James (*See also* **James Willows, Willows**) Old *J* was with me: we that day had been Up Snowdon; *Golden Year* 3
in mimic cadence answer'd *J*—'Ah, folly! „ 53
J,—you know him,—old, but full Of force „ 60
She and *J* had quarrell'd. Why? *The Brook* 96
she said, no cause; *J* had no cause: but when I prest the cause, I learnt that *J* had flickering jealousies which anger'd her. Who anger'd *J*? I said. „ 98
till I ask'd If *J* were coming. 'Coming every day,' „ 106
J departed vext with him and her.' „ 110
I saw where *J* Made toward us, „ 116
My brother *J* is in the harvest-field: „ 227
James (II.) We flung the burthen of the second *J*. *Third of Feb.* 28
James Willows (*See also* **James, Willows**) *J W*, of one name and heart with her. *The Brook* 76
Jane And what do I care for *J*, *Grandmother* 51
Jangled again the bells *J* and clang'd: *Lover's Tale iii* 53
daws flew out of the Towers and *j* and wrangled in vain, *V. of Maeldune* 109
Jangling *j*, the casque Fell, and he started up *Geraint and E.* 388
In clanging cadence *j* peal on peal— *Lover's Tale iii* 22
January (adj.) Fine as ice-ferns on *J* panes *Aylmer's Field* 222
January (s) woodlands, when they shiver in *J*, *Boädicea* 75
Japan From Corrientes to *J*, *To Ulysses* 4
Japed —him Who gibed and *j*—in many a merry tale *Sir J. Oldcastle* 91
Jaques Our kindlier, trustier *J*, past away! *To W. H. Brookfield* 11
Jar (s) Love is hurt with *j* and fret. *Miller's D.* 209
And hear the household *j* within. *In Mem. xciv* 16
Jar (verb) no mortal motion *j's* The blackness *On a Mourner* 26
shriek of hate would *j* all the hymns of heaven: *Sea Dreams* 259
May *j* thy golden dream Of Knowledge *Freedom* 16
Jarr'd something *j*; Whether he spoke too largely; *Edwin Morris* 72
The plaintive cry *j* on her ire; *Princess iv* 393
He laugh'd; the laughter *j* upon Lynette: *Gareth and L.* 1226
Love and Honour *j* Tho' Love and Honour *Sisters (E. and E.)* 176
Jarring Who touch'd a *j* lyre at first, *In Mem. xcvi* 7
For those that are crush'd in the clash of *j* claims, *Maud III vi* 44
relic of Javelins over The *j* breaker, *Batt. of Brunanburh* 97
Jasmine (*See also* **Jessamine, Jessmine**) Growths of *j* turn'd Their humid arms *D. of F. Women* 69
close-set robe of *j* sown with stars: *Aylmer's Field* 158
In meshes of the *j* and the rose: *Princess i* 219
Jasmine-leaves dawn Upon me thro' the *j-l*. *Margaret* 68
Jasper In the branching *j's* under the sea; *The Mermaid* 47
j, sapphire, Chalcedony, emerald, *Columbus* 83
Jaundice That veil'd the world with *j*, *Walk. to the Mail* 20
Jaundiced and left me with the *j* eye; *Locksley Hall* 132
Javelin lay many a man Marr'd by the *j*, *Batt. of Brunanburh* 32
rush of the *j's*, The crash of the charges, „ 88
Blood-redden'd relic of *J's* over The jarring breaker, „ 96
Javelining *j* With darted spikes and splinters *Merlin and V.* 936
Jaw The *j* is falling, The red cheek paling, *All Things will Die* 30
Into the *j's* of Death, *Light Brigade* 24
Came thro' the *j's* of Death, „ 46
in the *j's* Of vacant darkness *In Mem. xxxiv* 15
down-hung The *j's* of Death: *Lover's Tale ii* 205
Jay Ring sudden scritches of the *j*, *My life is full* 20
glance the tits, and shriek the *j's*, *Prog. of Spring* 15
Jealous (*See also* **Over-jealous**) be *j* and hard and unkind.' *Grandmother* 54
Never *j*—not he: we had many a happy year; „ 71
Half *j* of she knows not what, *In Mem. lx* 7
O to what end, except a *j* one, And one to make me *j* if I love, *Merlin and V.* 538
What wonder, being *j*, that he sent His horns „ 580
And made her good man *j* with good cause. „ 605
I was *j*, anger'd, vain, *Happy* 66
I meant to make *you j*. Are you *j* of me now? „ 67

Jealous (*continued*) But yet your mother's *j* temperament— *Princess ii* 338
'tis my mother, Too *j*, „ *iii* 80
Shall fears and *j* hatreds flame again? *W. to Marie Alex.* 41
Sick, am I sick of a *j* dread? *Maud I x* 1
Not rather dead love's harsh heir, *j* pride? *Lancelot and E.* 1398
Jealousy (*See also* **Semi-jealousy**) James had flickering *jealousies* *The Brook* 99
Down with ambition, avarice, pride, *J*, down! *Maud I x* 48
all narrow *jealousies* Are silent; *Ded. of Idylls* 16
No more of *j* than in Paradise.' *Balin and Balan* 152
A sudden spurt of woman's *j*,— *Merlin and V.* 524
And as to woman's *j*, O why not? „ 537
Forgive me; mine was *j* in love.' *Lancelot and E.* 1351
'*J* in love?' Not rather dead love's harsh heir, „ 1397
Queen, if I grant the *j* as of love, „ 1399
youthful *j* is a liar. *Locksley H., Sixty* 240
Jeer Began to scoff and *j* and babble of him *Marr. of Geraint* 58
point and *j*, And gibber at the worm, *Romney's R.* 136
Jehovah Starr'd from *J's* gorgeous armouries, *Milton* 6
Jenneting To fret the summer *j*. *The Blackbird* 12
Jenny *J*, my cousin, had come to the place, and I knew right well That *J* had tript in her time: *Grandmother* 25
J, to slander me, who knew what *J* had been! „ 35
and *J* hung on his arm. „ 42
J, the viper, made me a mocking curtsey „ 46
Jephtha Pale as the *J's* daughter, *Aylmer's Field* 280
The Godless *J* vows his child . . . *The Flight* 26
Jeroosilim (Jerusalem) May all the flowers o' *J* *Tomorrow* 89
Jersey I ha' six weeks' work in *J* *First Quarrel* 88
Jerusalem (*See also* **Jeroosilim**) but our most ancient East Moriah with *J*; *Columbus* 81
Jess Diet and seedling, *j'es*, leash and lure. *Merlin and V.* 125
Jessamine (*See also* **Jasmine, Jessmine**) All night has the casement *j* stirr'd *Maud I xxii* 15
Jessmine (*See also* **Jasmine, Jessamine**) door-porch wi' the woodbine an' *j* *Spinster's S's.* 105
Jest (s) eyes twinkle yet At his own *j*— *Miller's D.* 12
He was full of joke and *j*, *D. of the O. Year* 28
My words were half in earnest, half in *j*,) *Gardener's D.* 23
I am not all as wrong As a bitter *j* is dear. *Vision of Sin* 198
The *j's*, that flash'd about the pleader's room, *Aylmer's Field* 440
Dabbling a shameless hand with shameful *j*, *Princess iii* 314
The *j* and earnest working side by side, „ *iv* 563
beneath his vaulted palm A whisper'd *j* „ *v* 32
and ere the windy *j* Had labour'd down „ 272
In dance and song and game and *j*? *In Mem. xxix* 8
Whose *j* among his friends is free, „ *lxvi* 10
Or deep dispute, and graceful *j*; „ *lxxxiv* 24
Merlin in our time Hath spoken also, not in *j*, *Com. of Arthur* 420
We will not touch upon him ev'n in *j*.' *Marr. of Geraint* 311
some light *j* among them rose With laughter dying *Lancelot and E.* 178
vext he could not go: A *j*, no more! „ 211
(But all was *j* and joke among ourselves) Then must she keep it safelier. All was *j*. „ 217
moved to merriment at a passing *j*. *Sisters (E. and E.)* 121
he was one of those who would break their *j's* on the dead, *In the Child. Hosp.* 8
Would echo helpless laughter to your *j*! *To W. H. Brookfield* 5
As he did half in *j*, Old Horace? *Epilogue* 45
shameless laughter, Pagan oath, and *j*, *St. Telemachus* 39
Jest (verb) 'You *j*: ill jesting with edge-tools! *Princess ii* 201
grizzlier than a bear, to ride And *j* with: *Pelleas and E.* 194
Who *j* and laugh so easily and so well. *Sisters (E. and E.)* 41
Jested while he *j* thus, A thought flash'd *Princess i* 194
Drank till he *j* with all ease, *Geraint and E.* 290
Have *j* also, but for Julian's eyes, *Lover's Tale iv* 223
Jesting 'You jest: ill *j* with edge-tools! *Princess ii* 201
Jesus (*See also* **Christ, Christ Jesus, Lord Jesus**) O *J*, if thou wilt not save my soul, *St. S. Stylites* 46
Jet (s) (*See also* **Fountain-jets**) From those four *j's* four currents in one swell *Palace of Art* 33
The fountain pulses high in sunnier *j's*, *Prog. of Spring* 54
Jet (verb) *J* upward thro' the mid-day blossom. *Demeter and P.* 47
Jet-black Leading a *j-b* goat white-horn'd, *Œnone* 51
The maiden's *j-b* hair has grown, *Day-Dm., Sleep. B.* 4

Jetted A dozen angry models *j* steam : *Princess, Pro.* 73
Jew Spain in his blood and the *J*— *The Wreck* 15
Jewel *J* or shell, or starry ore, *Eleänore* 20
the *j* That trembles in her ear : *Miller's D.* 171
A dagger, in rich sheath with *j's* *Aylmer's Field* 220
That seem'd a fleet of *j's* under me, *Sea Dreams* 123
furs And *j's*, gifts, to fetch her : *Princess i* 43
quoted odes, and *j's* five-words-long „ *ii* 377
shone like a *j* set In the dark crag : „ *iii* 358
made the single *j* on her brow Burn „ *iv* 273
A *j*, a *j* dear to a lover's eye ! *Window, On the Hill* 3
What, has he found my *j* out ? *Maud I x* 23
And Maud will wear her *j's*, „ *xx* 27
rich With *j's*, elfin Urim, on the hilt, *Com. of Arthur* 299
fled With little save the *j's* they had on, *Marr. of Geraint* 640
and thicker down the front With *j's* *Geraint and E.* 690
' These *j's*, whereupon I chanced Divinely, *Lancelot and E.* 58
maid Might wear as fair a *j* as is on earth, „ 240
I had not won except for you, These *j's*, „ 1182
a crown of gold About a casque all *j's* ; *Holy Grail* 411
' Take thou the *j's* of this dead innocence, *Last Tournament* 31
luck will go With these rich *j's*, „ 46
And some with scatter'd *j's*, „ 148
what he brought to adorn her with, The *j's*, „ 716
The value of that *j* he had to guard ? *Lover's Tale iv* 153
Gold, *j's*, arms, whatever it may be. „ 235
j's Of many generations of his house Sparkled „ 298
Who fain had pledged her *j's* on my first voyage, *Columbus* 229
Dresses and laces and *j's* *Charity* 6
Jewell'd (*See also* **Thick-jewell'd**) That *j* mass of millinery, *Maud I vi* 43
all beneath there burns A *j* harness, *Gareth and L.* 688
his horse In golden armour *j* everywhere : *Holy Grail* 412
But, while he bow'd to kiss the *j* throat, *Last Tournament* 751
hungering for the gilt and *j* world About him, *Lover's Tale iv* 313
the mountain arose like a *j* throne thro' the fragrant air, *V. of Maeldune* 59
Jeweller Venice, where a *j*, So far gone down, *The Ring* 192
Jewellery and jacinth-work Of subtlest *j*. *M. d'Arthur* 58
and jacinth-work Of subtlest *j*. *Pass. of Arthur* 226
Jewel-print He sets the *j-p* of your feet In violets *Maud I xxii* 41
Jewel-thick barbarous opulence *j-t* „ *xiii* 12
Jidgemint Day (**Judgment Day**) kings in the flesh for the *J d*, *Tomorrow* 70
Jilt White Rose, Bellerophon, the *J*, *The Brook* 161
Jilted their pretty saying ? *j*, is it ? *J* I was : *Aylmer's Field* 353
J for a wealthier ! wealthier ? *Locksley H., Sixty* 11
Jingle *j* of bits, Shouts, arrows, *Tiresias* 93
Jingled When armour clash'd or *j*, *Princess vi* 363
Jingling (**adj.**) moorland rings With *j* bridle-reins. *Sir L. and Q. G.* 36
Two sets of three laden with *j* arms, *Geraint and E.* 188
Jingling (**s**) the *j* of the guinea helps the hurt *Locksley Hall* 105
Jinny fever 'ed baäked *J's* 'eäd as bald *Village Wife* 102
Joan (*See also* **Joan of Arc**) arts of war The peasant *J* and others ; *Princess ii* 163
Cassandra, Hebe, *J*, Or spinning at your wheel *Romney's R.* 4
Joan of Arc *J o A*, A light of ancient France ; *D. of F. Women* 267
Joänes *J*, as 'ant not a 'aäpoth o' sense, *N. Farmer, O. S.* 49
thot a weänt niver give it to *J*, „ 59
Jocky Dawes as with his tenant, *J D.* *Walk. to the Mail* 28
John Falling had let appear the brand of *J*— *Aylmer's Field* 509
As holy *J* had prophesied of me, *Columbus* 21
John (**Prester**) *See* **Prester John**
Join this byway *j's* The turnpike ? *Walk. to the Mail* 4
flow To *j* the brimming river, (repeat) *The Brook* 32, 48, 64, 183
Tho' truths in manhood darkly *j*, *In Mem. xxxvi* 1
as he gallop'd up To *j* them, *Marr. of Geraint* 172
come like you to see the hunt, Not *j* it.' „ 180
hot in haste to *j* Their luckier mates, *Geraint and E.* 574
knowing me Call'd me to *j* them ; *Sisters* (*E. and E.*) 123
I shall *j* you in a day. *To W. H. Brookfield* 14
He *j's* us once again, to his either office true : *Happy* 106
Join'd with the choral starry dance *J* not, *Palace of Art* 254
Of many changes, aptly *j*, *Love thou thy land* 65
What lips, like thine, so sweetly *j* ? *Day-Dm., L'Envoi* 46
lay the guests, And there we *j* them : *Princess, Pro.* 107
those fair charities *J* at her side ; „ *vii* 66

Join'd (*continued*) and *j* Each office of the social hour *In Mem. cxi* 13
Desiring to be *j* with Guinevere ; *Com. of Arthur* 77
for saving I be *j* To her that is the fairest „ 85
were I *j* with her, Then might we live together „ 90
Then after I was *j* with Galahad *Holy Grail* 611
Love and Honour *j* to raise the full High-tide *Sisters* (*E. and E.*) 177
she *j*, In and beyond the grave, „ 271
he stept, he stood, nor *j* The Achæans— *Achilles over the T.* 15
Our dying mother *j* our hands ; *The Flight* 87
Fell from each other, and were *j* again. *The Ring* 381
j you to the dead, has *j* our hands of old ; *Happy* 93
Joining And suck'd the *j* of the stones, *Marr. of Geraint* 324
Joint And work, a *j* of state, *Love thou thy land* 47
and all his *j's* Are full of chalk ? *Audley Court* 46
all things here are out of *j* : *Locksley Hall* 133
My *j's* are somewhat stiff or so. *Day-Dm., Revival* 26
I admire *J's* of cunning workmanship. *Vision of Sin* 186
Jointed Iron *j*, supple-sinew'd, they shall dive, *Locksley Hall* 169
Joke He was full of *j* and jest, *D. of the O. Year* 28
(But all was jest and *j* among ourselves) *Lancelot and E.* 217
Jollier A *j* year we shall not see. *D. of the O. Year* 20
Jolly his house, for so they say, Was haunted with a *j* ghost, *Walk. to the Mail* 36
Jonah In us true growth, in her a *J's* gourd, *Princess iv* 311
' I am the *J*, the crew should cast me into the deep, *The Wreck* 94
Joomp (**jump**) ' Billy,' says 'e, ' hev a *j* ! '— *Village Wife* 83
Joompt (**jumped**) Theerabouts Charlie *j*— „ 81
Fur tha *j* in thysen, *Spinster's S's.* 30
Joseph descended from the Saint Arimathæan *J*, *Balin and Balan* 102
brought By holy *J* hither, that same spear „ 113
boss'd With holy *J's* legend, „ 363
Arimathæan *J*, journeying brought To Glastonbury, *Holy Grail* 51
I know That *J* came of old to Glastonbury, „ 60
That *J* brought of old to Glastonbury ? ' „ 735
Joshua at gaze like *J's* moon in Ajalon ! *Locksley Hall* 180
Nor even a Sir *J*, some will cry. *Romney's R.* 47
Journey dim red morn had died, her *j* done, *D. of F. Women* 61
before his *j* closes, He shall find the stubborn thistle *Ode on Well.* 205
And all his *j* to her, as himself Had told her (repeat) *Marr. of Geraint* 143, 845
' Be prosperous in this *j*, as in all ; „ 225
They, closing round him thro' the *j* home, *Pelleas and E.* 202
sigh'd to find Her *j* done, glanced at him, *Guinevere* 405
Journey'd while I *j* hence, And saw the world fly *The Ring* 179
Journeying Or often *j* landward ; *Enoch Arden* 92
A body *j* onward, sick with toil. *Lover's Tale i* 124
Joust-Jousts (**s**) one might show it at a *j* of arms, *M. d'Arthur* 102
And thee, mine innocent, the *j's*, the wars, *Gareth and L.* 86
And I shall see the *j's*. Thy son am I, „ 166
if there chanced a *j*, So that Sir Kay nodded „ 519
Yet have I watch'd thee victor in the *j*, „ 1356
moved Down to the meadow where the *j's* were held, *Marr. of Geraint* 537
For when the *j's* were ended yesterday, „ 692
My haughty *j's*, and took a paramour ; *Geraint and E.* 832
And, but for my main purpose in these *j's*, „ 837
proven in his Paynim wars Than famous *j's* ; *Balin and Balan* 39
no quest came, but all was *j* and play, *Merlin and V.* 145
diamond *j's*, Which Arthur had ordain'd, *Lancelot and E.* 31
Once every year, a *j* for one of these : „ 61
And eight years past, eight *j's* had been, „ 67
let proclaim a *j* At Camelot, „ 76
you cannot move To these fair *j's* ? ' „ 80
Why go ye not to these fair *j's* ? „ 98
therefore hear my words : go to the *j's* : „ 136
nor cares For triumph in our mimic wars, the *j's*— „ 312
parted from the *j's* Hurt in the side,' „ 622
and sparkle out Among us in the *j's*, *Holy Grail* 34
blush'd and brake the morning of the *j's*, *Pelleas and E.* 157
Arthur had the *j's* Down in the flat field „ 163
the circlet of the *j's* Bound on her brow, „ 434
the prize Of Tristram in the *j's* of yesterday, *Last Tournament* 8
She ended, and the cry of a great *j's* „ 51
one low roll Of Autumn thunder, and the *j's* began : „ 153
wroth at Tristram and the lawless *j's*, „ 237
one might show it at a *j* of arms, *Pass. of Arthur* 270

Joust (verb) For pastime; yea, he said it: *j* can I. *Gareth and L.* 543
For here be mighty men to *j* with, „ 880
since I go to *j* as one unknown At Camelot *Lancelot and E.* 190
he will ride, *J* for it, and win, „ 204
That he might *j* unknown of all, „ 583
Jovial He must have been a *j* king. *Day-Dm., Sleep. P.* 40
Jowl Cheek by *j*, and knee by knee: *Vision of Sin* 84
Joy The *j* I had in my freewill All cold, *Supp. Confessions* 16
Scarce outward signs of *j* arise, „ 49
Shall man live thus, in *j* „ 169
wild swan's death-hymn took the soul Of that waste place with *j* *Dying Swan* 22
What hope or fear or *j* is thine? *Adeline* 23
all day long you sit between *J* and woe, *Margaret* 64
Because you are the soul of *j*, *Rosalind* 20
'Twere *j*, not fear, claspt hand-in-hand *If I were loved* 9
The *j* that mixes man with Heaven: *Two Voices* 210
To move about the house with *j*, *Miller's D.* 95
'There is no *j* but calm!' *Lotos-Eaters, C. S.* 23
we should come like ghosts to trouble *j*. „ 74
emptied of all *j*, Leaving the dance and song, *D. of F. Women* 215
Such *j* as you have seen with us, *D. of the O. Year* 17
But Thou rejoice with liberal *j*, *England and Amer.* 11
lark could scarce get out his notes for *j*, *Gardener's D.* 90
So home I went, but could not sleep for *j*, „ 174
perfect *J*, perplex'd for utterance, „ 255
I look'd at him with *j*: *Talking Oak* 106
reaps not harvest of his youthful *j's*, *Locksley Hall* 139
I muse on *j* that will not cease, *Sir Galahad* 65
A private life was all his *j*, *Will Water.* 129
And madly danced our hearts with *j*, *The Voyage* 3
LIKE souls that balance *j* and pain, *Sir L. and Q. G.* 1
O *j* to the people and *j* to the throne, *W. to Alexandra* 29
Making the little one leap for *j*. *To F. D. Maurice* 4
The Priest beheld him, And cried with *j*, *The Victim* 38
They bring me sorrow touch'd with *j*, *In Mem. xxviii* 19
And doubtful *j's* the father move, „ *xl* 9
On some unworthy heart with *j*, „ *lxii* 7
Thy passion clasps a secret *j*: „ *lxxxviii* 8
O *j* to him in this retreat, „ *lxxxix* 13
As in the former flash of *j*, „ *cxxii* 15
tells The *j* To every wandering breeze; „ *Con.* 62
And, tho' in silence, wishing *j*. „ 88
the ringing *j* of the Hall, *Maud I i* 70
With a *j* in which I cannot rejoice, „ *v* 21
That she warbled alone in her *j*! „ *x* 55
in the heart of Arthur *j* was lord. *Com. of Arthur* 124
Stood round him, and rejoicing in his *j*. „ 459
Shame never made girl redder than Gareth *j*. *Gareth and L.* 536
So Gareth past with *j*; but as the cur Pluckt „ 701
Not beat him back, but welcomed him with *j*. *Marr. of Geraint* 748
Lost one Found was greeted as in Heaven With *j* *Balin and Balan* 82
Lady, my liege, in whom I have my *j*, *Lancelot and E.* 1180
I pray you: have your *j's* apart. „ 1217
thou in whom I have Most *j* and most affiance, „ 1357
Redder than any rose, a *j* to me, *Holy Grail* 521
And each made *j* of either; then he ask'd, „ 638
'Glory and *j* and honour to our Lord „ 839
'I had forgotten all in my strong *j* To see thee— *Last Tournament* 582
Himself beheld three spirits mad with *j* *Guinevere* 252
feel My purpose and rejoicing in my *j*.' „ 486
not grieving at your *j's*, But not rejoicing; „ 679
London roll'd one tide of *j* thro' all Her trebled millions, *To the Queen ii* 8
great pine shook with lonely sounds of *j* *Lover's Tale i* 325
to both there came The *j* of life in steepness overcome, „ 386
and *j* In breathing nearer heaven; and *j* to me, „ 388
more than *j* that I to her became Her guardian „ 392
Since in his absence full of light and *j*, „ 425
All *j*, to whom my agony was a *j*. „ 656
from commonplace, And help us to our *j*. *Sisters (E. and E.)* 224
Little guess what *j* can be got from a cowslip *In the Child. Hosp.* 36
within The city comes a murmur void of *j*, *Tiresias* 101
when I held it aloft in my *j*, *The Wreck* 33
is it well to wish you *j*? *Locksley H., Sixty* 216

Joy *(continued)* Wish me *j*! *The Ring* 60
this life of mingled pains And *j's* to me, *To Mary Boyle* 50
world-whisper, mystic pain or *j*, *Far—far—away* 7
Joyance this May morning in *j* is beating Full merrily; *All Things will Die* 6
To keep them in all *j*: more than this I could not; *Lancelot and E.* 1324
Joyful led *J* to that palm-planted fountain-fed *Alexander* 7
to have been *J* and free from blame. *D. of F. Women* 80
J came his speech: *The Captain* 30
Took *j* note of all things *j*, *Aylmer's Field* 67
a shout More *j* than the city-roar that hails *Princess, Con.* 101
WHEN the breeze of a *j* dawn blew free *Arabian Nights* 1
CLEAR-HEADED friend, whose *j* scorn, *Clear-headed friend* 1
'I sung the *j* Pæan clear, *Two Voices* 127
by my life, These birds have *j* thoughts. *Gardener's D.* 99
A fairy Prince, with *j* eyes, *Day-Dm., Arrival* 7
The streets were fill'd with *j* sound, *In Mem. xxxi* 10
Mute symbols of a *j* morn, „ *Con.* 58
With a *j* spirit I Sir Richard Grenville die!' *The Revenge* 103
Joyfully You then *j*, all of you, *On Jub. Q. Victoria* 15
Joying *J* to feel herself alive, *Palace of Art* 178
Joyless Touch thy dull goal of *j* gray, *In Mem. lxxii* 27
cuckoo of a *j* June Is calling out of doors: *Pref. Poem Broth. S.* 3
Midnight—and *j* June gone by, „ 9
Till the *j* birthday came of a boy born happily dead. *Charity* 34
Joyous She seem'd a part of *j* Spring: *Sir L. and Q. G.* 23
A *j* to **dilate**, as toward the light. *Aylmer's Field* 77
Then glided out of the *j* wood *Maud II i* 31
Jubilant But anon her awful *j* voice, *Dying Swan* 28
While all the younger ones with *j* cries *Enoch Arden* 377
Heaven flash'd a sudden *j* ray, *Ode on Well.* 129
Roll and rejoice, *j* voice, *W. to Alexandra* 22
All on a sudden the garrison utter a *j* shout, *Def. of Lucknow* 98
a *j* challenge to Time and to Fate; *Vastness* 21
Before her skims the *j* woodpecker, *Prog. of Spring* 16
You should be *j* that you flourish'd here *Poets and their B.* 12
Jubilee With pleasure and love and *j*: *Sea-Fairies* 36
Mourn'd in this golden hour of *j*, *Ode Inter. Exhib.* 8
Utter your *j*, steeple and spire! *W. to Alexandra* 17
Crowning year of her *J*. *On Jub. Q. Victoria* 11
Ceremonial Of this year of her *J*. „ 24
And this year of her *J*. (repeat) „ 38, 51
'Hail to the glorious Golden year of her *J*!' „ 65
darkness Dawns into the *J* of the Ages. „ 71
Judah Not least art thou, thou little Bethlehem In *J*, *Sir J. Oldcastle* 25
Judge (s) Himself the *j* and jury, *Sea Dreams* 175
God, not man, is the *J* of us all *Grandmother* 95
Modred for want of worthier was the *j*. *Gareth and L.* 28
I came into court to the *J* and the lawyers. *Rizpah* 33
Him, happy to be chosen *J* of Gods, *Death of Œnone* 16
Judge (verb) and see thy Paris *j* of Gods.' *Œnone* 90
J thou me by what I am, „ 154
Thy mortal eyes are frail to *j* of fair, „ 158
'Let the Princess *j* Of that' *Princess ii* 234
pray'd me not to *j* their cause from her „ *vii* 235
bring him here, that I may *j* the right, *Gareth and L.* 380
And *j* all nature from her feet of clay, *Merlin and V.* 835
If one may *j* the living by the dead, *Lancelot and E.* 1368
To *j* between my slander'd self and me— *Columbus* 125
Judged now the Priest has *j* for me.' *The Victim* 56
Judger hasty *j* would have call'd her guilt, *Geraint and E.* 433
Judging he should come to shame thy *j* of him.' *Gareth and L.* 469
as the base man, *j* of the good, *Pelleas and E.* 80
Judgment my own weakness fools My *j*, *Supp. Confessions* 137
pick'd offenders from the mass For *j*. *Princess i* 30
You shame your mother's *j* too. „ *vi* 261
He would not make his *j* blind, *In Mem. xcvi* 14
And shalt abide her *j* on it; *Marr. of Geraint* 584
Submit, and hear the *j* of the King.' 'He hears the *j* of the King of kings,' *Geraint and E.* 799
naked Ignorance Delivers brawling *j's*, *Merlin and V.* 665
Rash were my *j* then, who deem this maid *Lancelot and E.* 239
and hollow like a Ghost's Denouncing *j*, *Guinevere* 421

Judgment (*continued*) And fall'n away from *j*. *Lover's Tale i* 103
Love, arraign'd to *j* and to death, „ 785
when the trumpet of *j* 'ill sound, *Rizpah* 57
And would defend his *j* well, *Tiresias* 190
Judgment daäy an roarin' like *j d*. *Owd Roä* 110
Judgment-day (*See also* **Jidgemint day, Judgment daäy**)
the loud world's bastard *j-d*, *Romney's R.* 119
Judith couch'd behind a *J*, underneath The head of Holofernes *Princess iv* 226
But your *J*—but your worldling— *Locksley H., Sixty* 20
Juggle Is a *j* born of the brain? *Maud II ii* 42
and *j*, and lie and cajole, *Charity* 29
Juice Till all his *j* is dried, *Audley Court* 46
Juiced *See* **Full-juiced**
Julian Poor *J*—how he rush'd away; *Lover's Tale iv* 2
J came again Back to his mother's house „ 14
(for in *J's* land They never nail a dumb head „ 36
but shatter'd nerve, Yet haunting *J*, „ 106
'Stay then a little,' answer'd *J*, „ 113
For such a craziness as *J's* look'd „ 168
Forgive him, if his name be *J* too.' „ 175
And *J* made a solemn feast: „ 187
Wonder'd at some strange light in *J's* eyes „ 205
Have jested also, but for *J's* eyes, „ 223
Then *J* made a secret sign to me „ 284
younger *J*, who himself was crown'd With roses, „ 296
When *J* goes, the lord of all he saw. „ 315
'My guests,' said *J*: 'you are honour'd now „ 316
But *J*, sitting by her, answer'd all: „ 340
I with him, my *J*, back to mine. „ 388
Juliet *J*, she So light of foot, *Gardener's D.* 13
J answer'd laughing, 'Go and see The Gardener's daughter: „ 29
Will you match My *J*? you, not you,— „ 172
July The cuckoo of a worse *J* Is calling *Pref. Poem Broth. S.* 11
Jumbled Ev'n in the *j* rubbish of a dream, *Merlin and V.* 347
every clime and age *J* together; *Princess, Pro.* 17
Jump *See* **Joomp**
Jumped *See* **Joompt**
Jumping *See* **A-Joompin'**
June Their meetings made December *J* *In Mem. xcvii* 11
married, when wur it? back-end o' *J*, *North. Cobbler* 11
The cuckoo of a joyless *J* Is calling *Pref. Poem Broth. S.* 3
Midnight—and joyless *J* gone by, „ 9
When I was in my *J*, you in your May, *Roses on the T.* 2
round me and over me *J's* high blue, *June Bracken, etc.* 2
June-blue clear as the heights of the *J-b* heaven, „ 7
Jungle-poison'd In haunts of *j-p* air *To Marq. of Dufferin* 31
Junketing growth Of spirit than to *j* and love. *Princess iv* 142
Juno to charm Pallas and *J* sitting by: *A Character* 15
Jury Himself the judge and *j*, *Sea Dreams* 175
Just Us, O *J* and Good, Forgive, *Poland* 11
Hears little of the false or *j*.' *Two Voices* 117
A man more pure and bold and *j* Was never born *To J. S.* 31
'That all comes round so *j* and fair: *Lady Clare* 18
'Virtue!—to be good and *j*— *Vision of Sin* 111
'tis but *j* The many-headed beast should know.' *You might have won* 19
woman's state in each, How far from *j*; *Princess ii* 132
crowds at length be sane and crowns be *j*. *Ode on Well.* 169
desires no isles of the blest, no quiet seats of the *j*, *Wages* 8
And thou hast made him: thou art *j*. *In Mem., Pro.* 12
Who battled for the True, the *J*, „ *lvi* 18
Arise, my God, and strike, for we hold Thee *j*, *Maud II i* 45
the blessed Heavens are *j*, *The Flight* 67
For ever and for ever with those *j* souls and true— *May Queen, Con.* 55
A man more pure and bold and *j* *To J. S.* 31
A land of *j* and old renown, *You ask me, why, etc.* 10
Let this avail, *j*, dreadful, mighty God, *St. S. Stylites* 9
and more Than many *j* and holy men, „ 131
'O *j* and faithful knight of God! *Sir Galahad* 79
Yet God's *j* wrath shall be wreak'd on a giant liar; *Maud III vi* 45
thy *j* wrath Sent me a three-years' exile *Balin and Balan* 58
To a *j* man and a wise— *Voice spake, etc.* 2
The Good, the True, the Pure, the *J*— *Locksley H., Sixty* 71
Juster A *j* epoch has begun. *Epilogue* 6
Justice A silent court of *j* in his breast, *Sea Dreams* 174
social truth shall spread, And *j*, *In Mem. cxxvii* 6
No boon is here, But *j*, *Gareth and L.* 346
According to the *j* of the King: „ 381
thou hast wreak'd his *j* on his foes, „ 1268
and all flyers from the hand Of *J*, *Marr. of Geraint* 37
to guard the *j* of the King: *Geraint and E.* 934
And there he kept the *j* of the King „ 956
Him, who should bear the sword Of *J*— *Sir J. Oldcastle* 88
led by *J*, Love, and Truth; *Locksley H., Sixty* 161
Love and *J* came and dwelt therein; (repeat) *Akbar's Dream* 181, 194
Justified seem'd So *j* by that necessity, *Geraint and E.* 396
Justify ever face she look'd on *j* it) *Princess v* 134
Justly How *j*, after that vile term of yours, *Merlin and V.* 921
Jut (s) By zig-zag paths, and *j's* of pointed rock, *M. d'Arthur* 50
based His feet on *j's* of slippery crag „ 189
By zigzag paths, and *j's* of pointed rock, *Pass. of Arthur* 218
based His feet on *j's* of slippery crag „ 357
Jut (verb) diamond-ledges that *j* from the dells; *The Mermaid* 40
Jutting Is *j* thro' the rind; *Ancient Sage* 122
every height comes out, and *j* peak And valley, *Spec. of Iliad* 13

K

Kaffir And not the *K*, Hottentot, Malay, *Princess ii* 158
Kalifa One Alla! one *K*! *Akbar's Dream* 167
Kapiolani (Chieftainess, Sandwich Islands) greatest of women, island heroine, *K* *Kapiolani* 5
will the glory of *K* be mingled with either on Hawa-i-ee. „ 18
Peelè remaining as *K* ascended her mountain, „ 28
Karnac Hong-Kong, *K*, and all the rest. *To Ulysses* 44
Kate 'Tis *K*—she sayeth what she will: For *K* hath an unbridled tongue, *Kate* 6
K hath a spirit ever strung Like a new bow, „ 10
For *K* no common love will feel; My woman-soldier, gallant *K*, „ 14
K saith 'the world is void of might.' *K* saith 'the men are gilded flies.' *K* snaps her fingers at my vows; *K* will not hear of lovers' sighs. „ 17
K loves well the bold and fierce; But none are bold enough for *K* „ 29
Margaret and Mary, there's *K* and Caroline: *May Queen* 6
Katie (*See also* **Katie Willows, Willows**) 'Sweet *K*, once I did her a good turn, *The Brook* 74
'Run' To *K* somewhere in the walks below, 'Run, *K*!' *K* never ran: she moved To meet me, „ 86
less of sentiment than sense Had *K*; „ 92
But *K* snatch'd her eyes at once from mine, „ 101
'O *K*, what I suffer'd for your sake! „ 119
sun of sweet content Re-risen in *K's* eyes, „ 169
K walks By the long wash of Australasian seas „ 193
What do they call you?' '*K*.' „ 211
That *K* laugh'd, and laughing blush'd, „ 214
'Have you not heard?' said *K*, „ 221
Katie Willows 'O darling *K W*, his one child! „ 67
Katty wid Shamus O'Shea at *K's* shebeen; *Tomorrow* 12
says to me wanst, at *K's* shebeen, „ 63
Kay (a Knight of the Round Table) Then came Sir *K*, the seneschal, and cried, *Gareth and L.* 367
let *K* the seneschal Look to thy wants, „ 433
K, The master of the meats and drinks, „ 450
then *K*, a man of mien Wan-sallow as the plant „ 452
K, 'What murmurest thou of mystery? „ 470
But *K* the seneschal, who loved him not, „ 483
Sir *K*, the seneschal, would come Blustering „ 513
So that Sir *K* nodded him leave to go, „ 520
for he mark'd *K* near him groaning like a wounded bull— „ 648
so Sir *K* beside the door Mutter'd in scorn „ 705
'*K*, wherefore wilt thou go against the King, „ 727
'Tut, tell me not,' said *K*, 'ye are overfine „ 732
look who comes behind,' for there was *K*. „ 752

Keep (verb) (*continued*) yet in him *k's* A draught of that sweet fountain *Lover's Tale i* 140
It seem'd to *k* its sweetness to itself, „ 154
Are fashion'd by the channel which they *k*), „ 567
And *k* yourself, none knowing, to yourself; „ *iv* 114
Sally she wesh'd foälks' cloäths to *k* the wolf fro' the door, *North. Cobbler* 29
K the revolver in hand! *Def. of Lucknow* 26
The love that *k's* this heart alive *The Flight* 35
Could *k* their haithen kings in the flesh *Tomorrow* 70
To *k* our English Empire whole! *Hands all Round* 14
I bad her *k*, Like a seal'd book, *The Ring* 122
desire to *k* So skilled a nurse about you always— „ 373
How bright you *k* your marriage-ring! *Romney's R.* 59

Keeper (*See also* **Keäper, Keeäper**) There by a *k* shot at, slightly hurt, *Aylmer's Field* 548
escaped His *k's*, and the silence which he felt, „ 839
jam the doors, and bear The *k's* down, *Lucretius* 170
the *k* was one, so full of pride, *Maud II v* 79
not with such a craziness as needs A cell and *k*), *Lover's Tale iv* 164

Keeping the children play'd at *k* house. *Enoch Arden* 24
did Enid, *k* watch, behold In the first shallow *Geraint and E.* 118
'It is not worth the *k*: let it go: *Merlin and V.* 396
to have my shield In *k* till I come.' *Lancelot and E.* 383
I said 'You were *k* with her, *First Quarrel* 64
My giant ilex *k* leaf When frost is keen *To Ulysses* 18

Kelt (*See also* **Celt**) Slav, Teuton, *K*, I count them all *Epilogue* 18

Kem (came) An' the sun *k* out of a cloud *Tomorrow* 37

Kemble Garrick and statelier *K*, and the rest *To W. C. Macready* 7

Ken to sea, as far as eye could *k*, *Lover's Tale i* 336

Kendal I am all but sure I have—in *K* church— *Romney's R.* 19

Kent lands in *K* and messuages in York, *Edwin Morris* 127
On capes of Afric as on cliffs of *K*, *W. to Marie Alex.* 17

Kep (kept) 'Siver, I *k* 'um, I *k* 'um, my lass, *N. Farmer, O. S.* 23
fur to kick our Sally as *k* the wolf fro' the door, *North. Cobbler* 59
I 'a *k*' thruf thick an' thin *Spinster's S's.* 12
boäth on us *k* out o' sight o' the winders „ 35
fur, Steevie, tha *k*' it sa neät „ 77
An' 'e *k* his heäd hoop like a king, *Owd Roä* 9
Sa I *k* i' my chair, fur I thowt she was nobbut a-rilin' „ 74
k a-callin' o' Roä till 'e waggled 'is taäil fur a bit, But the cocks *k* a-crawin' an' crawin' „ 105
I *k*' mysen meeäk as a lamb, *Churchwarden, etc.* 41

Kept (*See also* **Kep**) *Which* k *her throne unshaken still, To the Queen* 34
But good things have not *k* aloof, *My life is full* 2
K watch, waiting decision, *Œnone* 143
this *k*, Stored in some treasure-house *M. d'Arthur* 100
on the leads we *k* her till she pigg'd. *Walk. to the Mail* 92
But that his heavy rider *k* him down. *Vision of Sin* 4
His worst he *k*, his best he gave. *You might have won* 26
this he *k* Thro' all his future; *Enoch Arden* 236
Smote him, as having *k* aloof so long. „ 274
but he was gone Who *k* it; „ 695
put her little ones to school, And *k* them in it, „ 707
K him a living soul. „ 804
But *k* the house, his chair, and last his bed. „ 826
His gazing in on Annie, his resolve, And how he *k* it. „ 864
sow'd her name and *k* it green In living letters, *Aylmer's Field* 88
where his worldless heart had *k* it warm, „ 471
yet her cheek *K* colour: wondrous! „ 506
K to the garden now, and grove of pines, „ 550
she, who *k* a tender Christian hope, *Sea Dreams* 41
(I *k* the book and had my finger in it) *Princess, Pro.* 53
I *k* mine own Intent on her, „ *ii* 441
She *k* her state, and left the drunken king „ *iii* 229
then, climbing, Cyril *k* With Psyche, „ 354
Saw that they *k* apart, no mischief done; „ *iv* 340
why *k* ye not your faith? O base and bad! „ *v* 77
Part sat like rocks: part reel'd but *k* their seats: „ 496
His foes were thine; he *k* us free; *Ode on Well.* 91
great men who fought, and *k* it ours. „ 158
Like ballad-burthen music, *k*, *The Daisy* 77
My blood an even tenor *k*, *In Mem. lxxxv* 17
In those fall'n leaves which *k* their green, „ *xcv* 23
K itself warm in the heart of my dreams, *Maud I vi* 18

Kept (*continued*) and *k* and coax'd and whistled to— *Gareth and L.* 14
Wherein she *k* them folded reverently *Marr. of Geraint* 137
And *k* her off and gazed upon her face, „ 519
But *k* it for a sweet surprise at morn. „ 703
But Enid ever *k* the faded silk, „ 841
Because she *k* the letter of his word, *Geraint and E.* 455
Like that which *k* the heart of Eden green „ 770
But *k* myself aloof till I was changed; „ 872
And there he *k* the justice of the King „ 956
Some lost, some stolen, some as relics *k*. *Merlin and V.* 453
since he *k* his mind on one sole aim, „ 626
Some cause had *k* him sunder'd from his wife: „ 715
and took the shield, There *k* it, *Lancelot and E.* 398
friend Might have well *k* his secret. „ 593
k The one-day-seen Sir Lancelot in her heart, „ 746
And faith unfaithful *k* him falsely true. „ 877
There two stood arm'd, and *k* the door; „ 1247
a maid, Who *k* our holy faith among her kin *Holy Grail* 697
Arthur *k* his best until the last; „ 763
a lion on each side That *k* the entry, „ 818
Sir Pelleas *k* the field With honour: *Pelleas and E.* 168
still he *k* his watch beneath the wall. „ 223
Wide open were the gates, And no watch *k*; „ 415
this *k*, Stored in some treasure-house *Pass. of Arthur* 268
But still I *k* my eyes upon the sky. *Lover's Tale i* 572
And *k* it thro' a hundred years of gloom, „ *iv* 195
'Bygones! you *k* yours hush'd,' I said, *First Quarrel* 68
They *k* their faith, their freedom, *Montenegro* 2
saw the death, but *k* the deck, *Locksley H., Sixty* 63
and Ætna *k* her winter snow. *Demeter and P.* 115
you—you loved me, *k* your word. *The Ring* 290
k their watch upon the ring and you. „ 300
I *k* it as a sacred amulet About me,— „ 442
a woman, God bless her, *k* me from Hell. *Charity* 4

Kerchief about them, ribbon, glove Or *k*; *Aylmer's Field* 621

Kernel trash' he said, 'but with a *k* in it. *Princess ii* 395
The *k* of the shrivell'd fruit *Ancient Sage* 121

Kestrel Kite and *k*, wolf and wolfkin, *Boädicea* 15

Kettle (*See also* **Kittle**) And hurl'd the pan and *k*. *The Goose* 28
wi' my oän *k* theere o' the hob, *Spinster's S's.* 9

Kex tho' the rough *k* break The starr'd mosaic, *Princess iv* 77

Key (*See also* **Kays**) and opens but to golden *k's*. *Locksley Hall* 100
With half a sigh she turn'd the *k*, *The Letters* 18
Who keeps the *k's* of all the creeds, *In Mem. xxiii* 5
That Shadow waiting with the *k's*, „ *xxvi* 15
And lives to clutch the golden *k's*, „ *lxiv* 10
Cries of the partridge, like a rusty *k* Turn'd in a lock, *Lover's Tale ii* 115
'Authority of the Church, Power of the *k's*!'— *Sir J. Oldcastle* 162
Given thee the *k's* of the great Ocean-sea? *Columbus* 149
and since The *k* to that weird casket, *Ancient Sage* 254
The golden *k's* of East and West. *To Marq. of Dufferin* 4
I felt for what I could not find, the *k*, *The Ring* 440

Keys (of a piano) Turn'd as he sat, and struck the *k* *The Islet* 7
and by their clash, And prelude on the *k*, *Sisters (E. and E.)* 2
would drop from the chords or the *k*, *The Wreck* 27

Keystone For barefoot on the *k*, *Gareth and L.* 214

Khan given the Great *K's* palaces to the Moor, *Columbus* 109

Kick all women *k* against their Lords *Princess iv* 412
an' I gied our Sally a *k*, *North. Cobbler* 36
I seeäd that our Sally went laämed Cos' o' the *k* as I gied 'er, „ 40
Heer wur a fall fro' a kiss to a *k* „ 57
fur to *k* our Sally as kep the wolf fro' the door, „ 59
mob's million feet Will *k* you from your place, *The Fleet* 19
I fetcht 'im a *k* an' 'e went. *Owd Roä* 62

Kick'd *K*, he returns: do ye not hate him, *Pelleas and E.* 264
An' I thowt 'at I *k* 'im ageän, but I *k* thy Moother istead. *Owd Roä* 67

Kid Seethed like the *k* in its own mother's milk! *Merlin and V.* 869

Kilauēā wallow in fiery riot and revel On *K*, *Kapiolani* 9

Kill eyes, That care not whom they *k*, *Rosalind* 37
why should you *k* yourself And make them orphans *Enoch Arden* 394
monsters only made to *k* Time by the fire in winter.' *Princess, Pro.* 204

Kill (*continued*) ' *K* him now, The tyrant! *k* him — *Princess, Pro.* 206
K us with pity, break us with ourselves— „ *iii* 258
some grand fight to *k* and make an end: „ *iv* 591
tenderness, not yours, that could not *k*, „ *vi* 186
that Which *k's* me with myself, and drags „ 307
Mammonite mother *k's* her babe for a burial fee, *Maud I i* 45
the churchmen fain would *k* their church, „ *II v* 28
K the foul thief, and wreak me for my son.' *Gareth and L.* 363
I speak, and tho' he *k* me for it, *Geraint and E.* 137
shivers, ere he springs and *k's*. *Pelleas and E.* 286
tho' ye *k* my hope, not yet my love, „ 303
Christ *k* me then But I will slice him „ 337
' Will the child *k* me with her innocent talk?' *Guinevere* 214
' Will the child *k* me with her foolish prate?' „ 225
shall I *k* myself? What help in that? I cannot *k* my sin, If soul be soul; nor can I *k* my shame; „ 620
K or be kill'd, live or die, *Def. of Lucknow* 41
k Their babies at the breast for hate of Spain— *Columbus* 179
'*K* you enemy, for you hate him,' *Locksley H., Sixty* 94
Mother, dare you *k* your child? *Forlorn* 37

Kill'd I have *k* my son. I have *k* him— *Dora* 159
Till, *k* with some luxurious agony, *Vision of Sin* 43
latest fox—where started—*k* In such a bottom: *Aylmer's Field* 253
This truthful change in thee has *k* it. *Princess vii* 350
bees are still'd, and the flies are *k*, *Window, Winter* 10
Or *k* in falling from his horse. *In Mem. vi* 40
As the churches have *k* their Christ. *Maud II v* 29
I should not less have *k* him. *Geraint and E.* 845
fire of Heaven has *k* the barren cold, *Balin and Balan* 440
K with a word worse than a life of blows! *Merlin and V.* 870
K with unutterable unkindliness.' „ 886
And here a thrust that might have *k*, *Lancelot and E.* 25
K in a tilt, come next, five summers back, *Guinevere* 321
Gawain *k* In Lancelot's war, *Pass. of Arthur* 30
they *k* him, they *k* him for robbing the mail. *Rizpah* 34
lawyer who *k* him and hang'd him there. „ 40
Kill or be *k*, live or die, *Def. of Lucknow* 41
Those that in barbarian burials *k* the slave, *Locksley H., Sixty* 67
tiger madness muzzled, every serpent passion *k*, „ 167
My quick tears *k* the flower, *Demeter and P.* 108
' She has *k* him, has *k* him, has *k* him ' *Bandit's Death* 36

Killest O thou that *k*, hads't thou known, *Aylmer's Field* 738

Killing and, half *k* him With kisses, *Lover's Tale iv* 377

Kin lift His axe to slay my *k*. *Talking Oak* 236
I am well-to-do—no *k*, no care, *Enoch Arden* 418
shafts Of gentle satire, *k* to charity, *Princess ii* 469
If easy patrons of their *k* *Third of Feb.* 39
but felt him mine, Of closest *k* to me: *Gareth and L.* 127
Thou that art her *k*, Go likewise; „ 378
Thou shalt give back their earldom to thy *k*. *Marr. of Geraint* 585
in the field were Lancelot's kith and *k*, *Lancelot and E.* 466
drave his kith and *k*, And all the Table Round „ 498
little cause for laughter: his own *k*— „ 597
His kith and *k*, not knowing, set upon him; „ 599
Past up the still rich city to his *k*, „ 802
Far up the dim rich city to her *k*; „ 845
Lancelot's kith and *k* so worship him *Holy Grail* 651
kept our holy faith among her *k* In secret, „ 697
and all his kith and *k* Clave to him, *Guinevere* 439
call My sister's son—no *k* of mine, „ 573
laid her in the vault of her own *k*. *Lover's Tale iv* 39
There was a farmer in Dorset of Harry's *k*, *First Quarrel* 17
are *they* his mother? are *you* of his *k*? *Rizpah* 70
noä, not fur Sally's oän *k*. *North. Cobbler* 114
and vaulted our kith and our *k*, *V. of Maeldune* 47
serve This mortal race thy *k* so well, *De Prof., Two G.* 16
Amy's *k* and mine are left to me. *Locksley H., Sixty* 56

Kind (adj.) a nature never *k*! *Walk. to the Mail* 62
K nature is the best: „ 64
' Her kisses were so close and *k*, *Talking Oak* 169
love her, as I knew her, *k*? *Locksley Hall* 70
But may she still be *k*, *Will Water.* 10
Whom all men rate as *k* and hospitable: *Princess i* 71
we ourselves but half as good, as *k*, „ *v* 201
Is it *k*? Speak to her I say: „ *vi* 248

Kind (adj.) (*continued*) *K*, like a man, was he; like a man, *Grandmother* 70
Stiles where we stay'd to be *k*, *Window, Marr. Morn.* 7
So *k* an office hath been done, *In Mem. xvii* 17
' How good! how *k*! and he is gone.' „ *xx* 20
He looks so cold: she thinks him *k*. „ *xcvii* 24
we cannot be *k* to each other here for an hour; *Maud I iv* 28
Nor her, who is neither courtly nor *k*, „ *v* 27
her eye seem'd full Of a *k* intent to me, „ *vi* 41
Now I thought she was *k* „ *xiv* 26
And says he is rough but *k*, „ *xix* 70
K? but the deathbed desire Spurn'd by this heir „ 77
Rough but *k*? yet I know He had plotted against me „ 79
K to Maud? that were not amiss. „ 82
Well, rough but *k*; why let it be so: „ 83
Not beautiful now, not even *k*; „ *II v* 66
Is it *k* to have made me a grave so rough, „ 97
surely, some *k* heart will come To bury me, „ 102
such a silence is more wise than *k*.' *Merlin and V.* 289
And *k* the woman's eyes and innocent, *Holy Grail* 393
thine is more to me—soft, gracious, *k*— *Last Tournament* 560
May those *k* eyes for ever dwell! *Miller's D.* 220
K hearts are more than coronets, *L. C. V. de Vere* 55
And say to Robin a *k* word, *May Queen, Con.* 45
But though we love *k* Peace so well, *Third of Feb.* 9
' Yea, my *k* lord,' said the glad youth, *Geraint and E.* 241
' Would some of your *k* people take him up, „ 543
Manners so *k*, yet stately, such a grace „ 861
but his voice and his face were not *k*, *In the Child. Hosp.* 15
the crew were gentle, the captain *k*; *The Wreck* 129
yer Honour's the thrue ould blood that always manes to be *k*, *Tomorrow* 5
Than ha' spoken as *k* as you did, *First Quarrel* 73
he was always *k* to me. „ 90
for it's *k* of you, Madam, to sit by an old dying wife. *Rizpah* 21
I think that you mean to be *k*, „ 81
so harsh, as those that should be *k*? *The Flight* 102
you look so *k* That you will not deny *Romney's R.* 21
I count you *k*, I hold you true; *The Wanderer* 13

Kind (s) (*See also* **Human-kind**) Yet is there plenty of the *k*.' *Two Voices* 33
She had the passions of her *k*, *L. C. V. de Vere* 35
Would serve his *k* in deed and word, *Love thou thy land* 86
all *k's* of thought, That verged upon them, *Gardener's D.* 70
ever cared to better his own *k*, *Sea Dreams* 201
Beastlier than any phantom of his *k* *Lucretius* 196
Lucius Junius Brutus of my *k*? *Princess ii* 284
According to the coarseness of their *k*, „ *iv* 346
there grew Another *k* of beauty in detail „ 448
in a pleasant *k* of a dream. *Grandmother* 82
Has made me kindly with my *k*, *In Mem. lxvi* 7
But thou and I are one in *k*, „ *lxxix* 5
What *k* of life is that I lead; „ *lxxxv* 8
I will not shut me from my *k*, „ *cviii* 1
and that of a *k* The viler, as underhand, *Maud I i* 27
I am one with my *k*, „ *III vi* 58
think what *k* of bird it is That sings *Marr. of Geraint* 331
Came purer pleasure unto mortal *k* *Geraint and E.* 765
and to hate his *k* With such a hate, *Balin and Balan* 127
But kindly man moving among his *k*: *Lancelot and E.* 265
Being mirthful he, but in a stately *k*— „ 322
in me lived a sin, So strange, of such a *k*, *Holy Grail* 773
Seem'd my reproach? He is not of my *k*. *Pelleas and E.* 311
Experience, in her *k* Hath foul'd me— *Last Tournament* 317
chain that bound me to my *k*. *Locksley H., Sixty* 52
sadness at the doubtful doom of human *k*; *To Virgil* 24
till Self died out in the love of his *k*; *Vastness* 28
Some half remorseful *k* of pity too— *The Ring* 375

Kinder girl Seem'd *k* unto Philip than to him; *Enoch Arden* 42
The night to me was *k* than the day; *Lover's Tale i* 611

Kindle The dim curls *k* into sunny rings; *Tithonus* 54
For an your fire be low ye *k* mine! *Gareth and L.* 711
leaves i' the middle to *k* the fire; *Village Wife* 72
they meet And *k* generous purpose, *Tiresias* 128

Kindled (adj. and part) (*See also* **All-kindled, Rosy-kindled**) Returning with hot cheek and *k* eyes. *Alexander* 14
She spake With *k* eyes : *Princess iii* 334
Thy gloom is *k* at the tips, *In Mem. xxxix* 11
And the live green had *k* into flowers, *Gareth and L.* 185
hear His voice in battle, and be *k* by it, *Geraint and E.* 175
her bloom A rosy dawn *k* in stainless heavens, *Pelleas and E.* 72
a sacrifice *K* by fire from heaven : „ 146
but *k* from within As 'twere with dawn. *Lover's Tale i* 73
Mark is *k* on thy lips Most gracious ; *Last Tournament* 561
And, who, when his anger was *k*, *The Wreck* 17
Kindled (verb) When wine and free companions *k* him, *Geraint and E.* 293
And *k* all the plain and all the wold. *Balin and Balan* 441
k the pyre, and all Stood round it, *Death of Œnone* 65
Kindlier since man's first fall, Did *k* unto man, *Lancelot and E.* 860
He might be *k* : happily come the day ! *Sir J. Oldcastle* 23
For thro' that dawning gleam'd a *k* hope *Enoch Arden* 833
but *k* than themselves To ailing wife *Aylmer's Field* 176
After an angry dream this *k* glow „ 411
A *k* influence reign'd ; *Princess vii* 20
And out of memories of her *k* days, „ 106
And each reflects a *k* day ; *In Mem. c* 18
The larger heart, the *k* hand ; „ *cvi* 30
And yielding to his *k* moods, *Merlin and V.* 174
With all the *k* colours of the field.' *Last Tournament* 224
Our *k*, trustier Jaques, past away ! *To W. H. Brookfield* 11
and burn the *k* brutes alive. *Locksley H., Sixty* 96
Something *k*, higher, holier— „ 160
But younger *k* Gods to bear us down, *Demeter and P.* 131
Kindliest O heart, with *k* motion warm, *In Mem. lxxxv* 34
The truest, *k*, noblest-hearted wife *Romney's R.* 35
Kindliness She beloved for a *k* Rare in Fable *On Jub. Q. Victoria* 4
Kindling And Gareth answer'd her with *k* eyes, (repeat) *Gareth and L.* 41, 62
A head with *k* eyes above the throng, „ 646
Kindly O blessings on his *k* voice and on his silver hair ! *May Queen, Con.* 13
O blessings on his *k* heart and on his silver head ! „ 15
But you can talk ! yours is a *k* vein : *Edwin Morris* 81
break In full and *k* blossom. *Will Water.* 24
To vary from the *k* race of men, *Tithonus* 29
And the *k* earth shall slumber, *Locksley Hall* 130
Proudly turns he round and *k*, *L. of Burleigh* 55
And dwelt a moment on his *k* face, *Enoch Arden* 326
He could not see, the *k* human face, Nor ever hear a *k* voice, „ 581
officers and men Levied a *k* tax upon themselves, „ 663
Never one *k* smile, one *k* word : *Aylmer's Field* 564
' Nay,' said the *k* wife to comfort him, *Sea Dreams* 140
' I loathe it : he had never *k* heart, „ 200
A word, but one, one little *k* word, *Princess vi* 258
Has made me *k* with my kind, *In Mem. lxvi* 7
half exprest And loyal unto *k* laws. „ *lxxxv* 16
To pledge them with a *k* tear, „ *xc* 10
How modest, *k*, all-accomplish'd, wise, *Ded. of Idylls* 18
So with a *k* hand on Gareth's arm *Gareth and L.* 578
Here ceased the *k* mother out of breath ; *Marr. of Geraint* 732
And all the *k* warmth of Arthur's hall *Balin and Balan* 236
But *k* man moving among his kind : *Lancelot and E.* 265
There the good mother's *k* ministering, *Lover's Tale iv* 92
bear the sword Of Justice—what ! the kingly *k* boy ; *Sir J. Oldcastle* 88
Their *k* native princes slain or slaved, *Columbus* 174
I sorrow for that *k* child of Spain „ 212
Thanks to the *k* dark faces who fought with us, *Def. of Lucknow* 70
And last in *k* curves, with gentlest fall, *De Prof., Two G.* 23
And greet it with a *k* smile ; *To E. Fitzgerald* 4
And at home if I sought for a *k* caress, *The Wreck* 31
K landlord, boon companion— *Locksley H., Sixty* 240
From war with *k* links of gold, *Epilogue* 16
If, glancing downward on the *k* sphere *Poets and their B.* 9
smiled, and making with a *k* pinch *The Ring* 314
Nor ever cheer'd you with a *k* smile, „ 388
Kindly-hearted So spake the *k-h* Earl, *Marr. of Geraint* 514
Kindness *I could trust Your* k. *To the Queen* 20
looking ancient *k* on thy pain. *Locksley Hall* 85
I think your *k* breaks me down; *Enoch Arden* 318
Kindness (*continued*) money can be repaid ; Not *k* such as yours.' *Enoch Arden* 321
Soul-stricken at their *k* to him, *Aylmer's Field* 525
summer of his faded love, Or ordeal by *k* ; „ 561
more in *k* than in love, *Merlin and V.* 907
your brother's love, And your good father's *k*.' *Lancelot and E.* 945
he wrote ' Their *k*,' and he wrote no more ; *To Marq. of Dufferin* 36
Kindred (adj.) But branches current yet in *k* veins.' *Princess ii* 245
To black and brown on *k* brows. *In Mem. lxxix* 16
To-day they count as *k* souls ; „ *xcix* 19
But each has pleased a *k* eye, „ *c* 17
Kindred (s) Grate her harsh *k* in the grass : *Princess iv* 125
Thy *k* with the great of old. *In Mem. lxxiv* 8
craft of *k* and the Godless hosts Of heathen *Guinevere* 427
Kine Sadly the far *k* loweth : *Leonine Eleg.* 9
fields between Are dewy-fresh, browsed by deep-udder'd *k*, *Gardener's D.* 46
white *k* glimmer'd, and the trees (repeat) *In Mem. xcv* 15, 51
King (*See also* **Sea-king, Warrior-king**) *Could give the warrior* k's *of old*, *To the Queen* 4
K's have no such couch as thine, *A Dirge* 40
But the *k* of them all would carry me, *The Mermaid* 45
' Reign thou apart, a quiet *k*, *Palace of Art* 14
stay'd the Ausonian *k* to hear Of wisdom and of law. „ 111
The heads and crowns of *k's* ; „ 152
black-bearded *k's* with wolfish eyes, *D. of F. Women* 111
the mighty hearts Of captains and of *k's*. „ 176
kneeling, with one arm about her *k*, „ 270
took it, and have worn it, like a *k* : *M. d'Arthur* 33
' It is not meet, Sir *K*, to leave thee thus, „ 40
So strode he back slow to the wounded *K*. (repeat) „ 65, 112
if a *k* demand An act unprofitable, „ 95
K is sick, and knows not what he does. „ 97
Stored in some treasure-house of mighty *k's*, „ 101
Authority forgets a dying *k*, „ 121
And lightly went the other to the *K*. „ 147
So sigh'd the *K*, Muttering and murmuring „ 178
three Queens Put forth their hands, and took the *K*, „ 206
So like a shatter'd column lay the *K* ; „ 221
charged Before the eyes of ladies and of *k's*. „ 225
And came again together on the *k* *Audley Court* 36
There came a mystic token from the *k* *Edwin Morris* 132
It little profits that an idle *k*, *Ulysses* 1
Than those old portraits of old *k's*, [*Day-Dm., Sleep. P.* 23
His state the *k* reposing keeps. He must have been a jovial *k*. „ 39
And last with these the *k* awoke, „ *Revival* 17
' Pardy,' return'd the *k*, ' but still My joints „ 25
In robe and crown the *k* stept down, *Beggar Maid* 5
' Death is *k*, and Vivat Rex ! *Vision of Sin* 179
No blazon'd statesman he, nor *k*. *You might have won* 24
Like that long-buried body of the *k*, *Aylmer's Field* 3
Sprang from the midriff of a prostrate *k*— „ 16
the voice that calls Doom upon *k's*, „ 742
broke The statues, *k* or saint, or founder fell ; *Sea Dreams* 224
K of the East altho' he seem, *Lucretius* 133
Whose death-blow struck the dateless doom of *k's*, „ 236
counts and *k's* Who laid about them at their wills *Princess, Pro.* 30
being strait-besieged By this wild *k* „ 37
my good father thought a *k* a *k* ; „ *i* 25
they saw the *k* ; he took the gifts ; „ 46
Tore the *k's* letter, snow'd it down, „ 61
In this report, this answer of a *k*, „ 70
' No ! ' Roar'd the rough *k*, ' you shall not ; „ 87
And in the imperial palace found the *k*. „ 113
without a star, Not like a *k* : „ 118
Thus the *k* ; And I, tho' nettled „ 162
show'd the late-writ letters of the *k*. „ 175
' If the *k*,' he said, ' Had given us letters, „ 180
The *k* would bear him out : ' „ 182
when the *k* Kiss'd her pale cheek, „ *ii* 263
' Our *k* expects—was there no precontract ? „ *iii* 207
kept her state, and left the drunken *k* „ 229
the tumult and the *k's* Were shadows ; „ *iv* 564
old *k's* Began to wag their baldness „ *v* 18

King (*continued*) '*K*, you are free ! We did but keep you surety — *Princess v* 24
(thus the *K* Roar'd) make yourself a man to fight — „ 34
and without Found the gray *K's* at parle : — „ 114
' Not war, if possible, O *k*,' I said, — „ 126
I hold her, *k*, True woman : — „ 179
Then rode we with the old *k* across the lawns — „ 236
infuse my tale of love In the old *k's* ears, — „ 241
then rose a cry As if to greet the *k* ; — „ 249
then took the *k* His three broad sons ; — „ 268
Hungry for honour, angry for his *k*. — „ 314
' Boys ! ' shriek'd the old *k*, — „ 328
I told the *k* that I was pledged To fight in tourney — „ 352
sit Upon a *k's* right hand in thunder-storms, — „ 439
the spindling *k*, This Gama swamp'd in lazy tolerance. — „ 442
Thus the hard old *k* : I took my leave, — „ 467
I thought on all the wrathful *k* had said, — „ 473
K, camp and college turned to hollow shows ; — „ 478
k in bitter scorn Drew from my neck the painting — „ *vi* 109
the small *k* moved beyond his wont. — „ 265
Before these *k's* we embrace you yet once more — „ 294
Help, father, brother, help ; speak to the *k* : — „ 305
Passionate tears Follow'd : the *k* replied not : — „ 312
the *k* her father charm'd Her wounded soul — „ 345
The *k* is scared, the soldier will not fight, — „ *Con.* 60
More joyful than the city-roar that hails Premier or *k* ! — „ 102
Guarding realms and *k's* from shame ; — *Ode on Well.* 68
And barking for the thrones of *k's* ; — „ 121
Our loyal passion for our temperate *k's* ; — „ 165
O silent father of our *K's* to be — *Ode Inter. Exhib.* 7
Bride of the heir of the *k's* of the sea— — *W. to Alexandra* 28
Love by right divine is deathless *k*, — *W. to Marie Alex.* 29
' The *K* is happy In child and wife ; — *The Victim* 25
The *K* was hunting in the wild ; — „ 30
The *K* return'd from out the wild, — „ 41
The *K* bent low, with hand on brow, — „ 53
The *K* was shaken with holy fear ; — „ 57
I'll be *K* of the Queen of the wrens, — *Window, Spring* 15
The fire-crown'd *k* of the wrens, — „ *Ay* 8
flit like the *k* of the wrens with a crown of fire. — „ 16
He play'd at counsellors and *k's*, — *In Mem. lxiv* 23
flings Her shadow on the blaze of *k's* : — „ *xcviii* 19
By blood a *k*, at heart a clown ; — „ *cxi* 4
Love is and was my Lord and *K*, — „ *cxxvi* 1
Love is and was my *K* and Lord, — „ 5
And play the game of the despot *k's*, — *Maud I x* 39
' Who reverenced his conscience as his *k* ; — *Ded. of Idylls* 8
Thou noble Father of her *K's* to be, — „ 34
Leodogran, the *K* of Cameliard, — *Com. of Arthur* 1
many a petty *k* ere Arthur came Ruled in this isle, — „ 5
Their *k* and head, and made a realm, and reign'd. — „ 19
And wallow'd in the gardens of the *K*. — „ 25
then his brother *k*, Urien, assail'd him : — „ 35
the *K* Sent to him, saying, ' Arise, and help us — „ 43
these, Colleaguing with a score of petty *k's*, — „ 67
This is the son of Gorloïs, not the *K* ; This is the son of Anton, not the *K*.' — „ 73
What happiness to reign a lonely *k*, — „ 82
when the *K* had set his banner broad, — „ 101
now the Barons and the *k's* prevail'd, And now the *K*, — „ 105
leading all his knighthood threw the *k's* — „ 111
' Thou dost not doubt me *K*, — „ 126
I know thee for my *K* ! ' — „ 130
Debating—' How should I that am a *k*, — „ 141
Give my one daughter saving to a *k*, And a *k's* son ? '— — „ 143
' Sir *K*, there be but two old men that know : — „ 149
when they came before him, the *K* said, — „ 166
Whenever slander breathed against the *K*— — „ 177
So, compass'd by the power of the *K*, — „ 203
' Here is Uther's heir, your *k*,' A hundred voices cried ' Away with him ! No *k* of ours ! a son of Gorloïs he, Or else the child of Anton, and no *k*, — „ 230
And while the people clamour'd for a *k*, — „ 235

King (*continued*) Then while the *K* debated with himself — *Com. of Arthur* 238
K Made feast for, saying, as they sat at meat, — „ 246
Yea, but ye—think ye this *k*— — „ 250
' O *K*,' she cried, ' and I will tell thee : — „ 254
' Be thou the *k*, and we will work thy will — „ 259
Then the *K* in low deep tones, — „ 260
flash A momentary likeness of the *K* : — „ 271
She gave the *K* his huge cross-hilted sword, — „ 286
So this great brand the *k* Took, — „ 308
therefore Arthur's sister ? ' asked the *K*. — „ 317
this *K* is fair Beyond the race of Britons — „ 330
' Ay,' said the *K*, ' and hear ye such a cry ? — „ 337
K ! ' she cried, ' and I will tell thee true : — „ 339
I surely thought he would be *k*. — „ 358
Merlin ever served about the *K*, Uther, before he died — „ 365
two Left the still *K*, and passing forth to breathe, — „ 369
cried ' The *K* ! Here is an heir for Uther ! ' — „ 385
Fear not to give this *K* thine only child, — „ 413
Speak of the *K* ; and Merlin in our time Hath spoken — „ 419
Till these and all men hail him for their *k*.' — „ 424
a phantom *k*, Now looming, and now lost ; — „ 430
while the phantom *k* Sent out at times a voice ; — „ 436
crying ' No *k* of ours, No son of Uther, and no *k* of ours ; ' — „ 439
but the *K* stood out in heaven, Crown'd. — „ 443
the *K* That morn was married, — „ 455
The Sun of May descended on their *K*, — „ 462
' *K* and my lord, I love thee to the death ! ' — „ 470
Fulfil the boundless purpose of their *K* ! ' — „ 475
Arthur's knighthood sang before the *K* :— — „ 481
' Let the *K* reign.' (repeat) — *Com. of Arthur* 484, 487, 490, 493, 496, 499, 502
' Strike for the *K* and live ! his knights have heard That God hath told the *K* a secret word. — *Com. of Arthur* 488
' Strike for the *K* and die ! and if thou diest, The *K* is *K*, — „ 494
' The *K* will follow Christ, and we the *K* — „ 500
To wage my wars, and worship me their *K* ; — „ 508
the *K* Drew in the petty princedoms under him, — „ 516
as a false knight Or evil *k* before my lance — *Gareth and L.* 6
Then were I wealthier than a leash of *k's*.' — „ 51
ever since when traitor to the *K* He fought — „ 76
mother, there was once a *K*, like ours. — „ 101
the *K* Set two before him. One was fair, — „ 103
And these were the conditions of the *K* : — „ 107
follow the Christ, the *K*, Live pure, speak true, right wrong, follow the *K*— — „ 117
Or will not deem him, wholly proven *K*—Albeit in mine own heart I knew him *K*, — „ 122
Life, limbs, for one that is not proven *K* ? — „ 129
Who should be *K* save him who makes us free ? ' — „ 138
Before you ask the *K* to make thee knight, — „ 145
Nor tell my name to any—no, not the *K*.' — „ 171
city of Enchanters, built By fairy *K's*.' — „ 200
this *K* is not the *K*, But only changeling out of Fairyland, — „ 202
come to see The glories of our *K* : — „ 244
Doubt if the *K* be *K* at all, or come From Fairyland ; and whether this be built By magic, and by fairy *K's* and Queens ; — „ 246
a Fairy *K* And Fairy Queens have built the city, — „ 258
For there is nothing in it as it seems Saving the *K* ; tho' some there be that hold The *K* a shadow, and the city real : — „ 265
for the *K* Will bind thee by such vows, — „ 269
And now thou goest up to mock the *K*, — „ 292
ancient *k's* who did their days in stone ; — „ 305
As in the presence of a gracious *k*. — „ 316
K Throned, and delivering doom— — „ 320
The truthful *K* will doom me when I speak.' — „ 324
and faith in their great *K*, with pure Affection, — „ 330
a widow crying to the *K*, ' A boon, Sir *K* ! — „ 333
' A boon, Sir *K* ! Thine enemy *K*, am I. — „ 351
' A boon, Sir *K* ! I am her kinsman, I. — „ 365

King (*continued*) came Sir Kay, the seneschal, and cried, ' A boon, Sir *K* ! *Gareth and L.* 368
Arthur, ' We sit *K*, to help the wrong'd Thro' all our realm. „ 371
k's of old had doom'd thee to the flames, „ 374
that rough humour of the *k's* of old Return „ 377
According to the justice of the *K* : Then, be he guilty, by that deathless *K* Who lived and died „ 381
name of evil savour in the land, The Cornish *k*. „ 386
Delivering, that his lord, the vassal *k*, „ 391
Being a *k*, he trusted his liege-lord „ 396
made him knight because men call him *k*. „ 420
The *k's* we found, ye know we stay'd their hands From war among themselves, but left them *k's* ; „ 422
Mark hath tarnish'd the great name of *k*, „ 426
Approach'd between them toward the *K*, „ 441
' A boon, Sir *K* (his voice was all ashamed), „ 442
To him the *K*, ' A goodly youth and worth a goodlier boon ! „ 448
Think ye this fellow will poison the *K's* dish ? „ 471
Gareth bow'd himself With all obedience to the *K*, „ 488
one would praise the love that linkt the *K* And Lancelot—how the *K* had saved his life In battle twice, and Lancelot once the *K's*— „ 492
On Caer-Eryri's highest found the *K*, A naked babe, „ 500
nay, the *K's*—Descend into the city : ' „ 539
whereon he sought The *K* alone, and found, „ 541
the *K's* calm eye Fell on, and check'd, „ 547
And uttermost obedience to the *K*.' „ 555
' My *K*, for hardihood I can promise thee. „ 557
K—' Make thee my knight in secret ? „ 563
Let Lancelot know, my *K*, let Lancelot know, „ 567
K—' But wherefore would ye men should wonder at you ? „ 569
rather for the sake of me, their *K*, „ 571
on Gareth's arm Smiled the great *K*, „ 579
' O *K*, for thou hast driven the foe without, „ 593
Rest would I not, Sir *K*, an I were *k*, „ 597
' They be of foolish fashion, O Sir *K*, „ 628
such As have nor law nor *k* ; „ 632
' A boon, Sir *K*—this quest ! ' „ 647
K, thou knowest thy kitchen-knave am I, „ 649
Thy promise, *K*,' and Arthur glancing at him, „ 652
she lifted either arm, ' Fie on thee, *K* ! „ 658
Fled down the lane of access to the *K*, „ 661
pavement where the *K* would pace At sunrise, „ 667
And out by this main doorway past the *K*. „ 671
and cried, ' God bless the *K*, and all his fellowship ! ' „ 698
the *K* hath past his time—My scullion knave ! „ 709
Thence, if the *K* awaken from his craze, „ 724
' Kay, wherefore wilt thou go against the *K*, „ 727
But ever meekly served the *K* in thee ? „ 729
' Wherefore did the *K* Scorn me ? „ 737
In uttermost obedience to the *K*. „ 833
And pray'd the *K* would grant me Lancelot „ 856
whether she be mad, or else the *K*, „ 875
To crave again Sir Lancelot of the *K*. „ 882
shame the *K* for only yielding me My champion „ 898
lay Among the ashes and wedded the *K's* son.' „ 904
The *K* in utter scorn Of thee and thy much folly „ 918
take his horse And arms, and so return him to the *K*. „ 956
and thee the *K* Gave me to guard, „ 1013
and Gareth sent him to the *K*. „ 1051
hath not our good *K* Who lent me thee, „ 1070
thought the *K* Scorn'd me and mine ; „ 1165
Saving that you mistrusted our good *K* „ 1172
knight art thou To the *K's* best wish. „ 1259
They hate the *K*, and Lancelot, the *K's* friend, „ 1418
going to the *k*, He made this pretext, *Marr. of Geraint* 32
K himself should please To cleanse this common sewer „ 38
and the *k* Mused for a little on his plea, „ 41
Forgetful of his promise to the *K*, „ 50
these things he told the *K*. Then the good *K* gave order to let blow His horns „ 151
not mindful of his face In the *K's* hall, „ 192

King (*continued*) were she the daughter of a *k*, *Marr. of Geraint* 229
In the great battle fighting for the *K*. „ 596
But this was in the garden of a *k* ; „ 656
children of the *K* in cloth of gold Glanced „ 664
I come the mouthpiece of our *K* to Doorm (The *K* is close behind me) *Geraint and E.* 796
Submit, and hear the judgment of the *K*.' „ 799
' He hears the judgment of the *K* of *k's*,' „ 800
in the *K's* own ear Speak what has chanced ; „ 808
Fearing the mild face of the blameless *K*, „ 812
the *K* himself Advanced to greet them, „ 878
So spake the *K* ; low bow'd the Prince, „ 920
came The *K's* own leech to look into his hurt ; „ 923
blameless *K* went forth and cast his eyes „ 932
to guard the justice of the *K* : „ 934
there he kept the justice of the *K* „ 956
In battle, fighting for the blameless *K*. „ 970
PELLAM the *K*, who held and lost with Lot *Balin and Balan* 1
ye be sent for by the *K*,' They follow'd ; „ 48
K, Methought that if we sat beside the well, „ 64
move To music with thine Order and the *K*. „ 77
' Sir *K* ' they brought report ' we hardly found, „ 94
the *K* Took, as in rival heat, to holy things ; „ 99
This gray *K* Show'd us a shrine wherein were wonders— „ 108
the *K* So prizes—overprizes—gentleness. „ 183
I pray the *K* To let me bear some token of his Queen „ 187
she smiled and turn'd her to the *K*, „ 201
The crown is but the shadow of the *K*, „ 203
But light to me ! no shadow, O my *K*, „ 207
move In music with his Order, and the *K*. „ 212
court and *K* And all the kindly warmth of Arthur's hall „ 235
Whom all men rate the *k* of courtesy. „ 257
Our noble *K* will send thee his own leech— „ 275
stay'd to crave permission of the *K*, „ 288
the castle of a *K*, the hall Of Pellam, „ 331
found the greetings both of knight and *K* „ 342
and break the *K* And all his Table.' „ 458
Behold, I fly from shame, A lustful *K*, „ 474
Wilt surely guide me to the warrior *K*, „ 478
wander'd from her own *K's* golden head, „ 513
' Rise, my sweet *K*, and kiss me on the lips, „ 516
Meet is it the good *K* be not deceived. „ 533
Mark The Cornish *K*, had heard a wandering voice, *Merlin and V.* 8
My father died in battle against the *K*, „ 42
Thy blessing, stainless *K* ! „ 54
My father died in battle for thy *K*, „ 72
Poor wretch—no friend !—and now by Mark the *K* „ 75
stainless bride of stainless *K*— „ 81
narrow court and lubber *K*, farewell ! „ 119
the *K* Had gazed upon her blankly and gone by : „ 160
Vivien should attempt the blameless *K*. „ 164
Had built the *K* his havens, ships, and halls, „ 168
(As sons of *k's* loving in pupilage „ 517
' There lived a *k* in the most Eastern East, „ 555
The *K* impaled him for his piracy ; „ 569
brutes of mountain back That carry *k's* in castles, „ 577
a wizard who might teach the *K* Some charm, „ 583
He promised more than ever *k* has given, „ 586
the *K* Pronounced a dismal sentence, „ 590
Or like a *k*, not to be trifled with— „ 593
And so by force they dragg'd him to the *K*. And then he taught the *K* to charm the Queen In such-wise, that no man could see her more, Nor saw she save the *K*, who wrought the charm, „ 640
K Made proffer of the league of golden mines, „ 645
holy *k*, whose hymns Are chanted in the minster, „ 765
A rumour runs, she took him for the *K*, „ 776
Arthur, blameless *K* and stainless man ? ' „ 779
the good *k* means to blind himself, „ 783
were he not crown'd *K*, coward, and fool.' „ 789
' O true and tender ! O my liege and *K* ! „ 791
the court, the *K*, dark in your light, „ 875
Arthur, long before they crown'd him *K*, *Lancelot and E.* 34
two brothers, one a *k*, had met And fought „ 39
he, that once was *k*, had on a crown Of diamonds, „ 45

King (*continued*) Lancelot or our lord the *K*?' *Guinevere* 326
the *K* In open battle or the tilting-field „ 331
Sir Lancelot's, were as noble as the *K's*, „ 351
That crown'd the state pavilion of the *K*, „ 399
point where first she saw the *K* Ride toward her „ 403
Then on a sudden a cry, 'The *K*.' „ 411
She made her face a darkness from the *K*: „ 417
but tho' changed, the *K's*: „ 421
He spared to lift his hand against the *K* „ 437
That I the *K* should greatly care to live; „ 452
I was first of all the *k's* who drew The knighthood-errant „ 460
and swear To reverence the *K*, as if he were Their
conscience, and their conscience as their *K*, „ 468
Better the *K's* waste hearth and aching heart „ 524
nay, they never were the *K's*. „ 552
They summon me their *K* to lead mine hosts „ 570
She felt the *K's* breath wander o'er her neck, „ 582
The moony vapour rolling round the *K*, „ 601
Gone, my lord the *K*, My own true lord! „ 616
he, the *K*, Call'd me polluted: „ 619
blessed be the *K*, who hath forgiven My wickedness „ 634
Is there none Will tell the *K* I love him „ 651
broke The vast design and purpose of the *K*. „ 670
wrought the ruin of my lord the *K*.' „ 689
Heard in his tent the moanings of the *K*: *Pass. of Arthur* 8
Hail, *K*! to-morrow thou shalt pass away. „ 34
'O me, my *K*, let pass whatever will, „ 51
Right well in heart they know thee for the *K*. „ 63
brake the petty *k's*, and fought with Rome, „ 68
k who fights his people fights himself. „ 72
rose the *K* and moved his host by night, „ 79
he that fled no further fly the *K*; „ 89
pale *K* glanced across the field Of battle: „ 126
Had held the field of battle was the *K*: „ 138
Nor whence I am, nor whether I be *K*. Behold,
I seem but *K* among the dead.' „ 145
'My *K*, *K* everywhere! and so the dead have *k's*,
There also will I worship thee as *K*. „ 147
Then spake the *K*: 'My house hath been my doom. „ 154
even while they brake them, own'd me *K*. „ 158
That quick or dead thou holdest me for *K*. *K* am
I, whatsoever be their cry; „ 161
And uttering this the *K* Made at the man: „ 164
And took it, and have worn it, like a *k*; „ 201
'It is not meet, Sir *K*, to leave thee thus, „ 208
So strode he back slow to the wounded *K*. (repeat) „ 233, 280
if a *k* demand An act unprofitable, „ 263
The *K* is sick, and knows not what he does. „ 265
Stored in some treasure-house of mighty *k's*, „ 269
Authority forgets a dying *k*, „ 289
And lightly went the other to the *K*. „ 315
sigh'd the *K*, Muttering and murmuring at his ear, „ 346
three Queens Put forth their hands, and took the *K*, „ 374
So like a shatter'd column lay the *K*; „ 389
charged Before the eyes of ladies and of *k's*. „ 393
and he groan'd, 'The *K* is gone.' „ 443
'He passes to be *K* among the dead, „ 449
Around a *k* returning from his wars. „ 461
thought he saw, the speck that bare the *K*, „ 465
Rather than that gray *k*, whose name, a ghost, *To the Queen ii* 39
where I hoped myself to reign as *k*, There, where
that day I crown'd myself as *k*, *Lover's Tale i* 591
But rich as for the nuptials of a *k*. „ *iv* 212
The *K* should have made him a soldier, *Rizpah* 28
an' hallus as droonk as a *k*, *North. Cobbler* 27
The *k* was on them suddenly with a host. *Sir J. Oldcastle* 41
but the *k*—nor voice Nor finger raised „ 44
to take the *k* along with him— „ 49
So to this *k* I cleaved: „ 61
Priests Who fear the *k's* hard common-sense „ 66
That was a miracle to convert the *k*. „ 178
Does the *k* know you deign to visit him *Columbus* 4
Before his people, like his brother *k*? „ 6
the *k*, the queen Bad me be seated, speak, „ 10
he *k*, the queen, Sank from their thrones, „ 14

King (*continued*) showing courts and *k's* a truth the babe *Columbus* 37
outbuzz'd me so That even our proudest *k*, „ 122
put by, scouted by court and *k*— „ 165
tell the *K*, that I, Rack'd as I am with gout, „ 234
And readier, if the *K* would hear, „ 238
Each of them look'd like a *k*, *V. of Maeldune* 3
and the glories of fairy *k's*; „ 90
Five young *k's* put asleep by the sword-stroke, *Batt. of Brunanburh* 52
Fleeted his vessel to sea with the *k* in it, „ 60
Also the brethren, *K* and Atheling, „ 101
O YOU that were eyes and light to the *K* *To Prin. F. of H.* 1
the blind *K* sees you to-day, „ 3
K, that hast reign'd six hundred years, *To Dante* 1
Are slower to forgive than human *k's*. *Tiresias* 10
The madness of our cities and their *k's*. „ 71
And mingled with the famous *k's* of old, „ 171
make thy gold thy vassal not thy *k*, *Ancient Sage* 259
Could keep their haithen *k's* in the flesh *Tomorrow* 70
a cat may looök at a *k* thou knaws *Spinster's S's.* 34
Assyrian *k's* would flay Captives *Locksley H., Sixty* 79
Sons of God, and *k's* of men in utter nobleness „ 122
Teach your flatter'd *k's* that only those who cannot read „ 132
perfect peoples, perfect *k's*. „ 186
cried the *k* of sacred song; „ 201
k's and realms that pass to rise no more; *To Virgil* 28
Was one of the people's *k's*, *Dead Prophet* 10
The *k's* and the rich and the poor; „ 40
shadow of a likeness to the *k* Of shadows, *Demeter and P.* 16
Three dark ones in the shadow with thy *K*. „ 122
An' 'e kep his heäd hoop like a *k*, *Owd Roä* 9
Old Empires, dwellings of the *k's* of men; *Prog. of Spring* 99
city and palace Of Arthur the *k*; *Merlin and the G.* 66
The *k* who loved me, And cannot die: „ 79
like a lonely man In the *k's* garden, *Akbar's Dream* 21
To wreathe a crown not only for the *k* „ 23
may not *k's* Express Him also by their warmth „ 108
fury of peoples, and Christless frolic of *k's*, *The Dawn* 7
'Gallant Sir Ralph,' said the *k*. *The Tourney* 6
'O what an arm,' said the *k*. „ 12
'Take her Sir Ralph,' said the *k*. „ 18
King-born *k-b*, A shepherd all thy life but yet *k-b*, *Œnone* 127
Kingcup (adj.) betwixt the whitening sloe And *k* blaze, *To Mary Boyle* 26
Kingcup (s) The gold-eyed *k's* fine; *A Dirge* 36
Daisies and *k's* and honeysuckle-flowers.' *City Child* 10
Rose-campion, bluebell, *k*, poppy, *Last Tournament* 234
The *k* fills her footprint, *Prog. of Spring* 59
Kingdom (*See also* **Under-kingdom**) divided quite
The *k* of her thought. *Palace of Art* 228
But thou, while *k's* overset, *Talking Oak* 257
A *k* topples over with a shriek Like an old
woman, *Princess, Con.* 62
But either fail'd to make the *k* one. *Com. of Arthur* 15
are the *k's*, not the King's— *Lancelot and E.* 59
Until it came a *k's* curse with thee— *Guinevere* 550
More worth than all the *k's* of this world, *Sir J. Oldcastle* 77
K's and Republics fall, *Locksley H., Sixty* 159
I am heir, and this my *k*. *By an Evolution.* 14
fur owt but the *K* o' Heaven; *Church-warden, etc.* 44
Kinghood one last act of *k* shalt thou see *Pass. of Arthur* 163
Kingless those three *k* years Have past— *Balin and Balan* 63
Kingliest Thou art the *k* of all kitchen-knaves. *Gareth and L.* 1158
Kinglihood The golden symbol of his *k*, *Com. of Arthur* 50
King-like *K-l*, wears the crown: *Of old sat Freedom* 16
Kingly Thy *k* intellect shall feed, *Clear-headed friend* 20
With merriment of *k* pride, *Arabian Nights* 151
bear the sword Of Justice—what! the *k*, kindly boy; *Sir J. Oldcastle* 88
Kinship A distant *k* to the gracious blood *Aylmer's Field* 62
Kinsman With many *kinsmen* gay, *Will Water.* 90
My lady's Indian *k* unannounced *Aylmer's Field* 190
'Good! my lady's *k*! good!' „ 198
she, Once with this *k*, ah so long ago, „ 206
My lady's Indian *k* rushing in, „ 593
Sleep, *k* thou to death and trance *In Mem. lxxi* 1
'A boon, Sir King! I am her *k*, I. *Gareth and L.* 365
him Whose *k* left him watcher o'er his wife *Merlin and V.* 706

Kinsman (*continued*) His *k* travelling on his own affair — *Merlin and V.* 717
but then A *k*, dying, summon'd me to Rome— — *The Ring* 178
him, who left you wealth, Your *k*? — „ 189
Kirtle blood Was sprinkled on your *k*, — *Princess ii* 274
Kiss (s) (*See also* **Bride-kiss**) kiss sweet *k'es*, and speak sweet words: — *Sea-Fairies* 34
Yet fill my glass: give me one *k*: — *Miller's D.* 17
The *k*, The woven arms, seem but to be Weak symbols — „ 231
once he drew With one long *k* my whole soul — *Fatima* 20
that quick-falling dew Of fruitful *k'es*, — *Œnone* 205
Seal'd it with *k'es*? water'd it with tears? — „ 234
the wild *k*, when fresh from war's alarms, — *D. of F. Women* 149
Because the *k* he gave me, ere I fell, — „ 235
worth a hundred *k'es* press'd on lips — *Gardener's D.* 151
k'es, where the heart on one wild leap — „ 259
'Her *k'es* were so close and kind, — *Talking Oak* 169
I would have paid her *k* for *k*, — „ 195
that last *k*, which never was the last, — *Love and Duty* 67
k'es balmier than half-opening buds Of April, — *Tithonus* 59
His own are pouted to a *k*: — *Day-Dm., Sleep. P.* 31
A TOUCH, a *k*! the charm was snapt. — „ *Revival* 1
O love, for such another *k*;' — „ *Depart.* 10
'O happy *k*, that woke thy sleep!' 'O love, thy *k* would wake the dead!' — „ 19
evermore a costly *k* The prelude to some brighter world. — „ *L'Envoi* 39
A sleep by *k'es* undissolved, — „ 51
I never felt the *k* of love, — *Sir Galahad* 19
'Yet give one *k* to your mother dear! — *Lady Clare* 49
'Yet here's a *k* for my mother dear, — „ 53
To waste his whole heart in one *k* — *Sir L. and Q. G.* 44
Many a sad *k* by day by night renew'd — *Enoch Arden* 161
Never: no father's *k* for me— — „ 790
that one *k* Was Leolin's one strong rival — *Aylmer's Field* 556
and ran To greet him with a *k*, — *Lucretius* 7
little maid, That ever crow'd for *k'es*.' — *Princess ii* 280
'Dear as remember'd *k'es* after death, — „ *iv* 54
her mother, shore the tress With *k'es*, — „ *vi* 114
In glance and smile, and clasp and *k*, — *In Mem. lxxxiv* 7
And every *k* of toothed wheels, — „ *cxvii* 11
She took the *k* sedately; — *Maud I xii* 14
made my Maud by that long loving *k*, — „ *xviii* 58
embraces Mixt with *k'es* sweeter sweeter — „ *II iv* 9
had been A clinging *k*— — *Merlin and V.* 106
I am silent then, And ask no *k*:' — „ 254
Win! by this *k* you will: — *Lancelot and E.* 152
Yet rosy-kindled with her brother's *k*— — „ 393
we twain Had never kiss'd a *k*, or vow'd a vow. — *Holy Grail* 584
Constraining it with *k'es* close and warm, — *Lover's Tale i* 468
answering lisp'd To *k'es* of the wind, — „ 545
Love drew in her breath In that close *k*, — „ 817
and, half killing him With *k'es*, — „ *iv* 378
then I minded the fust *k* I gied 'er — *North. Cobbler* 45
An' I says 'I mun gie tha a *k*,' — „ 51
I gied 'er a *k*, an' then anoother, — „ 52
Sally gied me a *k* ov 'ersen. — „ 56
Heer wur a fall fro' a *k* to a kick — „ 57
fatal *k*, Born of true life and love, — *Ded. Poem Prin. Alice* 2
k fell chill as a flake of snow on the cheek: — *The Wreck* 32
Never a *k* so sad, no, not since the coming of man! — *Despair* 60
sowl dead for a *k* of ye, Molly Magee. — *Tomorrow* 40
tha may gie ma a *k*, — *Spinster's S's.* 31
Before a *k* should wake her. — *The Ring* 67
then with my latest *k* Upon them, — „ 298
That trembles not to *k'es* of the bee: — *Prog. of Spring* 4
I blind your pretty blue eyes with a *k*! — *Romney's R.* 101
Too early blinded by the *k* of death— — „ 103
his *k'es* were red with his crime, — *Bandit's Death* 13
Kiss (verb) When I would *k* thy hand, — *Madeline* 31
If my lips should dare to *k* Thy taper fingers — „ 43
k sweet kisses, and speak sweet words: — *Sea-Fairies* 34
I would *k* them often under the sea, And *k* them again till they kiss'd me (repeat) — *The Merman* 15, 34
And *k* away the bitter words From off your rosy mouth. — *Rosalind* 50
Kiss (verb) (*continued*) You'll *k* me, my own mother, — *May Queen, N. Y.'s E.* 34
I have been to blame. *K* me, my children.' — *Dora* 162
O *k* him once for me. — *Talking Oak* 240
'O *k* him twice and thrice for me, That have no lips to *k*, — „ 241
I *k* it twice, I *k* it thrice, — „ 253
Go to him: it is thy duty: *k* him: — *Locksley Hall* 52
He stoops—to *k* her—on his knee. — *Day-Dm., Arrival* 30
That I might *k* those eyes awake! — „ *L'Envoi* 28
I *k* the lips I once have kiss'd; — *Will Water.* 37
I cry to thee To *k* thy Mavors, — *Lucretius* 82
And *k* again with tears! — *Princess ii* 9
He reddens what he *k'es*: — „ *v* 165
k her; take her hand, she weeps: — „ *vi* 225
K and be friends, like children being chid! — „ 289
Stoop down and seem to *k* me ere I die.' — „ *vii* 150
as good to cuddle an' *k* as a lass as 'ant nowt? — *N. Farmer, N. S.* 24
Trail and twine and clasp and *k*, *K*, *k*; — *Window, At the Wind.* 4
Drop me a flower, a flower, to *k*, *K*, *k*— — „ 11
Farewell, we *k*, and they are gone. — *In Mem., Con.* 92
flush, and bow Lowly, to *k* his hand, — *Gareth and L.* 549
To stoop and *k* the tender little thumb, — *Marr. of Geraint* 395
'Rise, my sweet King, and *k* me on the lips, — *Balin and Balan* 516
tread me down And I will *k* you for it;' — *Merlin and V.* 229
pearls Ran down the silken thread to *k* each other — „ 455
we *k* the child That does the task assign'd, — *Lancelot and E.* 828
he bow'd to *k* the jewell'd throat, — *Last Tournament* 751
let us in, tho' late, to *k* his feet! — *Guinevere* 178
airs of Heaven Should *k* with an unwonted gentleness. — *Lover's Tale i* 739
And *k* her on the lips. She is his no more: — „ *iv* 48
and I go down To *k* the dead.' — „ 50
'*K* him,' she said. 'You gave me life again. — „ 172
K him, and then Forgive him, — „ 174
an' *k* you before I go.' — *First Quarrel* 46
Didn't you *k* me an' promise? — „ 53
—you'll *k* me before I go?' — „ 80
k her—if you will,' I said— — „ 81
You wouldn't *k* me, my lass, — „ 86
and he call'd to me '*K* me!' — *The Wreck* 104
I stoopt To take and *k* the ring. — *The Ring* 132
nurse is waiting. *K* me child and go. — „ 489
when I let him *k* my brow; — *Happy* 65
I am happy, happy. *K* me. — „ 107
Kiss'd dew-impearl'd winds of dawn have *k*, — *Ode to Memory* 14
And kiss them again till they *k* me (repeat) — *The Merman* 16, 35
I would not be *k* by all who would list, — *The Mermaid* 41
And if you *k* her feet a thousand years, — *The form, the form* 13
'His little daughter, whose sweet face He *k*, — *Two Voices* 254
I *k* away before they fell. — *Miller's D.* 152
I *k* his eyelids into rest: — *The Sisters* 19
girls all *k* Beneath the sacred bush — *The Epic* 2
So the women *k* Each other, — *Dora* 128
clung about The old man's neck, and *k* him many times. — „ 164
She turn'd, we closed, we *k*, swore faith, — *Edwin Morris* 114
And found, and *k* the name she found, — *Talking Oak* 159
She *k* me once again. — „ 168
could hear the lips that *k* Whispering — *Tithonus* 60
I kiss the lips I once have *k*; — *Will Water.* 37
He turn'd and *k* her where she stood: — *Lady Clare* 82
And *k* his wonder-stricken little ones; — *Enoch Arden* 229
and *k* him in his cot. — „ 234
as they *k* each other In darkness, — *Aylmer's Field* 430
She look'd so sweet, he *k* her tenderly — „ 555
Clasp'd, *k* him, wail'd: he answer'd, — *Lucretius* 280
And *k* again with tears. — *Princess ii* 5
We *k* again with tears. — „ 14
when the king *K* her pale cheek, — „ 264
With that she *k* His forehead, — „ 311
I *k* it and I read. 'O brother, — „ *v* 373
here she *k* it: then—'All good go with thee! — „ *vi* 206
I *k* her slender hand, — *Maud I xii* 13
Whom first she *k* on either cheek, — *Marr. of Geraint* 517
claspt and *k* her, and they rode away. — „ 825
K the white star upon his noble front, — *Geraint and E.* 757

Kiss'd (*continued*) he turn'd his face And *k* her climbing, *Geraint and E.* 761
And *k* her with all pureness, brother-like, „ 884
brow That o'er him hung, he *k* it, moan'd, and spake; *Balin and Balan* 598
lay she all her length and *k* his feet, *Merlin and V.* 219
she *k* them, crying, 'Trample me, Dear feet, „ 226
k her, and Sir Lancelot his own hand, *Lancelot and E.* 389
k the hand to which he gave, The diamond, „ 702
does the task assign'd, he *k* her face. „ 829
And *k* her quiet brows, and saying to her „ 1150
he wellnigh *k* her feet For loyal awe, „ 1172
She *k* me saying, 'Thou art fair, my child, „ 1409
we twain Had never *k* a kiss, or vow'd a vow. *Holy Grail* 584
Embraced me, and so *k* me the first time, „ 596
There *k*, and parted weeping: *Guinevere* 125
And Hope *k* Love, and Love drew in her breath *Lover's Tale i* 816
And *k* her more than once, „ *iv* 72
'I had sooner be cursed than *k*!'— *First Quarrel* 83
I *k* my boy in the prison, *Rizpah* 23
I *k* 'em, I buried 'em all— „ 55
Cold were his brows when we *k* him— *Def. of Lucknow* 12
And we *k* the fringe of his beard *V. of Maeldune* 125
And the Motherless Mother *k* it, *The Wreck* 62
'The heart, the heart!' I *k* him, „ 105
we *k*, we embraced, she and I, *Despair* 53
took and *k* me, and again He *k* me; *The Flight* 23
I remember how you *k* the miniature *Locksley H., Sixty* 12
dreamer stoopt and *k* her marble brow. „ 38
A ring too which you *k*, and I, she said, *The Ring* 114
You frown'd and yet you *k* them. *Happy* 75
One *k* his hand, another closed his eyes, *Death of Œnone* 58
I wept, and I *k* her hands, *Charity* 38
Kissin' Imbrashin' an' *k* aich other— *Tomorrow* 90
Kissing (*See also* **Kissin'**) *K* the rose she gave me o'er and o'er, *Gardener's D.* 176
K his vows upon it like a knight. *Aylmer's Field* 472
And satisfy my soul with *k* her: *Princess v* 103
our baby lips, *K* one bosom, *Lover's Tale i* 238
K the war-harden'd hand of the Highlander *Def. of Lucknow* 102
Kitchen (adj.) The *k* brewis that was ever supt *Gareth and L.* 781
Kitchen (s) out of *k* came The thralls in throng, „ 694
Thou smellest all of *k* as before.' „ 771
Nay—for thou smellest of the *k* still. „ 843
The savour of thy *k* came upon me „ 993
because their hall must also serve For *k*, *Marr. of Geraint* 391
in the Divil's *k* below. *Tomorrow* 68
Kitchendom lent me thee, the flower of *k*, *Gareth and L.* 1071
Kitchen-grease thou smellest all of *k-g*. „ 751
Kitchen-knave Among the scullions and the *k-k's*, „ 154
To serve with scullions and with *k-k's*; „ 170
among thy *k-k's* A twelvemonth and a day, „ 445
And couch'd at night with grimy *k-k's*. „ 481
'Yea, King, thou knowest thy *k-k* am I, „ 649
And thou hast given me but a *k-k*.' „ 659
beside The field of tourney, murmuring '*k-k*.' „ 664
Nor shamed to bawl himself a *k-k*. „ 717
O fie upon him—His *k-k*.' „ 742
'Sir *K-k*, I have miss'd the only way „ 787
And in a sort, being Arthur's *k-k*!— „ 838
bawls this frontless *k-k*, 'The quest is mine; thy *k-k* am I, „ 860
'Friend, whether thou be *k-k*, or not, „ 873
thy much folly hath sent thee here His *k-k*: „ 920
'A *k-k*, and sent in scorn of me: „ 952
The damsel crying, 'Well-stricken, *k-k*!' „ 970
and say His *k-k* hath sent thee. „ 985
When I was *k-k* among the rest Fierce was the hearth, „ 1009
'Here is a *k-k* from Arthur's hall „ 1036
Thou art the kingliest of all *k-k's*. „ 1158
And tumbled back into the *k-k*, „ 1228
Kitchen-vassalage Low down thro' villain *k-v*, „ 160
Gareth all for glory underwent The sooty yoke of *k-v*; „ 479
Kite (bird) *K* and kestrel, wolf and wolfkin, *Boädicea* 15
Kite (toy) Had tost his ball and flown his *k*, *Aylmer's Field* 84

Kite (toy) (*continued*) Flung ball, flew *k*, and raced the purple fly, *Princess ii* 248
coostom flitted awaäy like a *k* wi' a brokken string. *North. Cobbler* 28
Kith in the field were Lancelot's *k* and kin, *Lancelot and E.* 466
drave his *k* and kin, And all the Table Round „ 498
His *k* and kin, not knowing, set upon him; „ 599
Lancelot's *k* and kin so worship him *Holy Grail* 651
and all his *k* and kin Clave to him, *Guinevere* 439
and vaunted our *k* and our kin, *V. of Maeldune* 47
Kitten laugh As those that watch a *k*; *Merlin and V.* 177
Kittenlike *K* he roll'd And paw'd about her sandal. *Princess iii* 181
Kittle (kettle) ater meä mayhap wi' 'is *k* o' steäm *N. Farmer, O. S.* 61
Knave (*See also* **Kitchen-knave**) neither *k* nor clown Shall hold their orgies *You might have won* 11
My Shakespeare's curse on clown and *k* „ 27
K's are men, That lute and flute fantastic tenderness, *Princess iv* 128
The King hath past his time—My scullion *k*! *Gareth and L.* 710
Begone! my *k*!—belike and like enow „ 713
Well—I will after my loud *k*, „ 720
overfine To mar stout *k's* with foolish courtesies:' „ 733
But, *k*, anon thou shalt be met with, *k*, „ 779
Setting this *k*, Lord Baron, at my side. „ 854
Lion and stoat have isled together, *k*, In time of flood. „ 893
slay thee unarm'd; he is not knight but *k*.' „ 922
Thou art not knight but *k*.' Said Gareth, 'Damsel, whether *k* or knight, „ 942
Come, therefore, leave thy lady lightly, *k*. Avoid: for it beseemeth not a *k* To ride with such a lady.' „ 957
K, when I watch'd thee striking on the bridge „ 992
thou art not knight but *k*.' „ 1006
'Parables? Hear a parable of the *k*. „ 1008
knight or *k*—The *k* that doth thee service „ 1015
'Ay, Sir *K*! Ay, *k*, because thou strikest as a knight, Being but *k*, I hate thee all the more.' „ 1019
being but *k*, I throw thine enemies.' „ 1023
this strong fool whom thou, Sir *K*, „ 1058
O *k*, as noble as any of all the knights— „ 1136
I heard thee call thyself a *k*,— „ 1163
but, being *k*, Hast mazed my wit: „ 1169
'Sir *K*, my knight, a hermit once was here, „ 1196
I gloried in my *k*, Who being still rebuked, „ 1248
Knight, *k*, prince and fool, I hate thee and for ever.' „ 1255
find my goodly *k* Is knight and noble. „ 1291
teeming with liars, and madmen, and *k's*, *The Dreamer* 9
Knave-knight 'Well done, *k-k*, well stricken, *Gareth and L.* 1135
Knaw (know) Doctors, they *k's* nowt, *N. Farmer, O. S.* 5
Thaw a *k's* I hallus voäted wi' Squoire „ 15
Bessy Marris's barne! thaw *k's* she laäid it to meä. „ 21
Do godamoighty *k* what a's doing „ 45
Fur they *k's* what I beän to Squoire „ 55
a *k's* naw moor nor a floy; „ 67
Dosn't thou *k* that a man mun be eäther „ *N. S.* 6
I *k's* what maäkes tha sa mad. „ 17
it's them as niver *k's* wheer a meäls to be 'ad. „ 47
I *k's*, as *k's* tha sa well, *North. Cobbler* 65
Doesn't tha *k* 'er—sa pratty, „ 108
tha dosn *k* what that be? But I *k's* the law, I does, *Village Wife* 15
Not es I cares to hear ony harm, but I likes to *k*. „ 22
thou *k's* thebbe naither 'ere nor theer. „ 28
an' booöks, as thou *k's*, beänt nowt. „ 52
I *k's* that mooch o' sheä, „ 108
a cat may looök at a king thou *k's* *Spinster's S's.* 34
an' I *k's* it be all fur the best. „ 52
an' one o' ye deäd ye *k's*! „ 62
I *k's* I 'ed led tha a quieter life „ 71
but I *k's* they runs upo' four,— *Owd Roä* 17
An' it beäts ma to *k* wot she died on, *Church-warden, etc.* 6
ya tell'd 'im to *k* his awn plaäce „ 29
Knaw'd (knew) An' I niver *k* whot a meän'd *N. Farmer, O. S.* 19
I *k* a Quaäker feller as often 'as towd ma this: „ *N. S.* 19
Fur I *k* naw moor what I did *North. Cobbler* 38
sa I *k* es 'e'd coom to be poor; *Village Wife* 46
An' 'e niver *k* nowt but booöks, „ 52
An' they *k* what butter wur, an' they *k* what a hegg wur an' all; „ 116

Knaw'd (knew) (*continued*) ye *k* it wur pleasant to 'ear, *Spinster's S's.* 21
Roä was the dog as *k* when an' wheere *Owd Roä* 8
fur I noäwaäys *k* 'is intent; „ 61
Knee The trustful infant on the *k*! *Supp. Confessions* 41
when with brows Propt on thy *k's*, „ 70
Low on her *k's* herself she cast, *Mariana in the S.* 27
He sat upon the *k's* of men In days that never come again. *Two Voices* 323
took with care, and kneeling on one *k*, *M. d'Arthur* 173
I would wish to see My grandchild on my *k's* before I die: *Dora* 13
The boy set up betwixt his grandsire's *k's*, „ 131
with his boy Betwixt his *k's*, his wife upon the tilt, *Walk. to the Mail* 41
Hail, hidden to the *k's* in fern, *Talking Oak* 29
Oh, hide thy knotted *k's* in fern, „ 93
O muffle round thy *k's* with fern, „ 149
she wander'd round and round These knotted *k's* of mine, „ 158
shower'd the rippled ringlets to her *k*; *Godiva* 47
a flask Between his *k's*, half-drain'd; *Day-Dm., Sleep P.* 26
He stoops—to kiss her—on his *k*. „ *Arrival* 30
My *k's* are bow'd in crypt and shrine: *Sir Galahad* 18
Cheek by jowl, and *k* by *k*: *Vision of Sin* 84
God bless him, he shall sit upon my *k's* *Enoch Arden* 197
Stout, rosy, with his babe across his *k's*; „ 746
Hers, yet not his, upon the father's *k*, „ 760
knelt, but that his *k's* Were feeble, „ 778
And rotatory thumbs on silken *k's*, *Aylmer's Field* 200
And scoundrel in the supple-sliding *k*.' *Sea Dreams* 168
And rosy *k's* and supple roundedness, *Lucretius* 190
held her round the *k's* against his waist, *Princess ii* 363
That lent my *k* desire to kneel, „ *iii* 193
On one *k* Kneeling, I gave it, „ *iv* 469
He sees his brood about thy *k*; „ 582
Set his child upon her *k*— „ *vi* 14
Knelt on one *k*,—the child on one,— „ 91
Trail'd himself up on one *k*: „ 155
On with toil of heart and *k's* and hands, *Ode on Well.* 212
one about whose patriarchal *k* Late the little children clung: „ 236
He stay'd his arms upon his *k*: *The Victim* 54
Who takes the children on his *k*, *In Mem. lxvi* 11
At one dear *k* we proffer'd vows, „ *lxxix* 13
boys of thine Had babbled 'Uncle' on my *k*; „ *lxxxiv* 13
For I that danced her on my *k*, „ *Con.* 45
I leap from Satan's foot to Peter's *k*— *Gareth and L.* 538
Gareth, lightly springing from his *k's*, „ 556
Gareth brought him grovelling on his *k's*, „ 1124
Sat riveting a helmet on his *k*, *Marr. of Geraint* 268
on her *k's*, Who knows? another gift of the high God, „ 820
A strange *k* rustle thro' her secret reeds, *Balin and Balan* 354
Writhed toward him, slided up his *k* and sat, *Merlin and V.* 239
Across her neck and bosom to her *k*, „ 257
bow'd black *k's* Of homage, „ 577
she sat, half-falling from his *k's*, Half-nestled „ 904
Sat on his *k*, stroked his gray face *Lancelot and E.* 749
holy maid With *k's* of adoration wore the stone, *Holy Grail* 71
With supplication both of *k's* and tongue: „ 602
Full sharply smote his *k's*, and smiled, *Guinevere* 47
took with care, and kneeling on one *k*, *Pass. of Arthur* 341
an' sattled 'ersen o' my *k*, *North. Cobbler* 79
My father with a child on either *k*, *Sisters (E. and E.)* 54
dog that had loved him and fawn'd at his *k*— *In the Child. Hosp.* 9
dear Lord Jesus with children about his *k's*.) „ 52
To thee, dead wood, I bow not head nor *k's*. *Sir J. Oldcastle* 128
plant on shoulder, hand and *k*, *To E. Fitzgerald* 8
k was prest Against the margin flowers; *Tiresias* 42
Is feebler than his *k's*; *Ancient Sage* 135
wid her stick, she was lamed iv a *k*, *Tomorrow* 77
Rob, coom oop 'ere o' my *k*. *Spinster's S's.* 11
let Steevie coom oop o' my *k*. „ 67
swept The dust of earth from her *k*. *Dead Prophet* 32
Nor ever cared to set you on her *k*, *The Ring* 386
Knee-deep seem'd *k-d* in mountain grass, *Mariana in the S.* 42
Full *k-d* lies the winter snow, *D. of the O. Year* 1
Kneel Good people, you do ill to *k* to me. *St. S. Stylites* 133

Kneel (*continued*) in your looking you may *k* to God. *St. S. Stylites* 141
That lent my knee desire to *k*, *Princess iii* 193
'Why *k* ye there? What evil have ye wrought? *Merlin and V.* 67
Will ye not lie? not swear, as there ye *k*, *Last Tournament* 646
Shall I take *him*? I *k* with *him*? *The Flight* 49
Who saw you *k* beside your bier, *Happy* 54
trust myself forgiven by the God to whom I *k*. „ 86
I am a trouble to you, Could *k* for your forgiveness. *Romney's R.* 26
below the dome of azure *K* adoring Him the Timeless *Akbar's D., Hymn* 8
Kneel'd A red-cross knight for ever *k* *L. of Shalott iii* 6
What dame or damsel have ye *k* to last? *Last Tournament* 550
Kneeler I loved you like this *k*, *Princess iv* 296
Kneeling Who *k*, with one arm about her king, *D. of F. Women* 270
took with care, and *k* on one knee, *M. d'Arthur* 173
On one knee *K*, I gave it, *Princess iv* 470
Or where the *k* hamlet drains The chalice *In Mem. x* 15
when they rose, knighted from *k*, some Were pale *Com. of Arthur* 263
And offer'd you it *k*: *Merlin and V.* 276
Lancelot *k* utter'd, 'Queen, Lady, my liege, *Lancelot and E.* 1179
took with care, and *k* on one knee, *Pass. of Arthur* 341
And *k* there Down in the dreadful dust *Lover's Tale iv* 66
Knell every hoof a *k* to my desires, *Princess iv* 174
a deeper *k* in the heart be knoll'd; *Ode on Well.* 59
the silver *k* Of twelve sweet hours that past *Maud I xviii* 64
that low *k* tolling his lady dead— *Lover's Tale iv* 33
Knelt Bow myself down, where thou hast *k*, *Supp. Confessions* 80
I blest him, as he *k* beside my bed. *May Queen, Con.* 16
he would have *k*, but that his knees Were feeble, *Enoch Arden* 778
shaken with her sobs, Melissa *k*; *Princess iv* 290
Florian *k*, and 'Come' he whisper'd to her, „ *v* 63
K on one knee,—the child on one,— „ *vi* 91
he laid before the throne, and *k*, Delivering, *Gareth and L.* 390
had you cried, or *k*, or pray'd to me, *Geraint and E.* 844
k In amorous homage—*k*—what else? *Balin and Balan* 508
K, and drew from out his night-black hair „ 511
Cast herself down, *k* to the Queen, *Merlin and V.* 66
camels *k* Unbidden, and the brutes of mountain back „ 575
she *k* Full lowly by the corners of his bed, *Lancelot and E.* 825
and enter'd, and we *k* in prayer. *Holy Grail* 460
and spake To Tristram, as he *k* before her, *Last Tournament* 541
And *k*, and lifted hand and heart and voice *Columbus* 16
We have *k* in your know-all chapel *Despair* 94
where of old we *k* in prayer, *Locksley H., Sixty* 33
She *k*—'We worship him'—all but wept— *Dead Prophet* 29
The topmost—a chest there, by which you *k*— *The Ring* 112
Knew (*See also* **Knaw'd**) *Who* k *the seasons when to take Occasion* *To the Queen* 30
that *k* The beauty and repose of faith, *Supp Confessions* 74
tho' I *k* not in what time or place, *Sonnet To ——* 12
prest thy hand, and *k* the press return'd, *The Bridesmaid* 12
Dreaming, she *k* it was a dream: *Mariana in the S.* 49
The place he *k* forgetteth him.' *Two Voices* 264
A shadow on the graves I *k*, „ 272
And who that *k* him could forget *Miller's D.* 3
I *k* your taper far away, „ 109
I *k* you could not look but well; „ 150
Dear eyes, since first I *k* them well. „ 222
I *k* the flowers, I *k* the leaves, I *k* *D. of F. Women* 73
Touch'd; and I *k* no more.' „ 116
When she made pause I *k* not for delight; „ 169
her who *k* that Love can vanquish Death, „ 269
I *k* your brother: his mute dust I honour *To J. S.* 29
I *k* an old wife lean and poor, *The Goose* 1
'we *k* your gift that way At college: *The Epic* 24
And almost ere I *k* mine own intent, *Gardener's D.* 146
Requiring, tho' I *k* it was mine own, „ 227
I beheld her ere she *k* my heart, „ 276
You *k* my word was law, and yet you dared *Dora* 98
from his father's vats, Prime, which I *k*; *Audley Court* 28
I set the words, and added names I *k*. „ 61
built When men *k* how to build, *Edwin Morris* 7
he that *k* the names, Long learned names „ 16
since I *k* the right And did it; *Love and Duty* 29
And see the great Achilles, whom we *k*, *Ulysses* 64

Knew (*continued*) Whispering I *k* not what of wild and sweet, *Tithonus* 61
and love her, as I *k* her, kind? *Locksley Hall* 70
Mother-Age (for mine I *k* not) help me „ 185
And she, that *k* not, pass'd: *Godiva* 73
We *k* the merry world was round, *The Voyage* 7
she loved Enoch; tho' she *k* it not, *Enoch Arden* 43
for he *k* the man and valued him, „ 121
He *k* her, as a horseman knows his horse— „ 136
he had loved her longer than she *k*, „ 455
she *k* that she was bound— „ 462
simple folk that *k* not their own minds, „ 478
fall beside her path, She *k* not whence; a whisper on her ear, She *k* not what; „ 515
Philip thought he *k*: Such doubts and fears „ 520
tho' he *k* not wherefore, started up Shuddering, „ 616
and making signs They *k* not what: „ 641
Seeking a tavern which of old he *k*, „ 691
'Know him?' she said 'I *k* him far away. „ 846
see me dead, Who hardly *k* me living, „ 889
He *k* the man; the colt would fetch its price; *The Brook* 149
Sir, if you *k* her in her English days, „ 224
one they *k*—Raw from the nursery— *Aylmer's Field* 263
The girl might be entangled ere she *k*. „ 272
but he had powers, he *k* it: „ 393
Nor *k* he wherefore he had made the cry; „ 589
And all but those who *k* the living God— „ 637
Was always with her, whom you also *k*. „ 711
Poor souls, and *k* not what they did, „ 782
I lost it, *k* him less; *Sea Dreams* 72
In her strange dream, she *k* not why, „ 230
I had set my heart on your forgiving him Before you *k*. „ 270
that was mine, my dream, I *k* it— *Lucretius* 43
'I *k* you at the first: tho' you have grown *Princess ii* 305
I never *k* my father, but she says „ *iii* 82
Melissa, knowing, saying not she *k*: „ 148
since I *k* No rock so hard but that a little wave „ 153
I stammer'd that I *k* him—could have wish'd „ 206
laugh'd with alien lips, And *k* not what they meant; „ *iv* 120
She, question'd if she *k* us men, „ 231
And then, demanded if her mother *k*, „ 233
Then came these wolves; *they k* her: „ *iv* 321
We *k* not your ungracious laws, „ 399
nor *k* There dwelt an iron nature in the grain: „ *vi* 49
she nor cared Nor *k* it, clamouring on, „ 150
I had been wedded wife, I *k* mankind, „ 327
Nor *k* what eye was on me, nor the hand That nursed me, „ *vii* 53
call her Ida, tho' I *k* her not, „ 96
I saw the forms: I *k* not where I was: „ 133
But if you be that Ida whom I *k*, „ 147
she *k* it, she had fail'd In sweet humility; „ 228
O good gray head which all men *k*, *Ode on Well.* 35
He *k* their voices of old. „ 63
They *k* the precious things they had to guard: *Third of Feb.* 41
the soldier *k* Some one had blunder'd: *Light Brigade* 11
I *k* right well That Jenny had tript in her time: I *k*, but I would not tell. *Grandmother* 25
who *k* what Jenny has been! „ 35
I started, and spoke I scarce *k* how; „ 43
I *k* them all as babies, „ 88
Nor *k* we well what pleased us most, *The Daisy* 25
Ye never *k* the sacred dust: *In Mem. xxi* 22
That never *k* the summer woods: „ *xxvii* 4
I know not: one indeed I *k* „ *xcvi* 5
fool Was soften'd, and he *k* not why; „ *cx* 12
can I doubt, who *k* thee keen In intellect, „ *cxiii* 5
K that the death-white curtain meant *Maud I xiv* 32
O, if she *k* it, To know her beauty „ *xvi* 18
He *k* not whither he should turn for aid. *Com. of Arthur* 40
Are like to those of Uther whom we *k*. „ 72
A red-faced bride who *k* herself so vile, *Gareth and L.* 109
Albeit in mine own heart I *k* him King, „ 123
I that *k* him fierce and turbulent Refused her *Marr. of Geraint* 447
And roam the goodly places that she *k*; „ 646
she *k* That all was bright; „ 657
Then suddenly she *k* it and rejoiced, „ 687

Knew (*continued*) Enid, all abash'd she knew not why, *Marr. of Geraint* 765
And *k* her sitting sad and solitary. *Geraint and E.* 282
Except he surely *k* my lord was dead.' „ 721
And since I *k* this Earl, when I myself Was half „ 794
Because I *k* my deeds were known, I found, „ 858
lightly so return'd, and no man *k*. *Balin and Balan* 42
I *k* thee wrong'd. I brake upon thy rest, „ 499
Why had ye not the shield I *k*? „ 601
Merlin, who *k* the range of all their arts, *Merlin and V.* 167
Was also Bard, and *k* the starry heavens; „ 169
then you drank And *k* no more, „ 277
I felt as tho' you *k* this cursed charm, „ 435
And either slept, nor *k* of other there; „ 738
she that *k* not ev'n his name? *Lancelot and E.* 29
Sir Lancelot *k* there lived a knight Not far from Camelot, „ 401
sally forth In quest of whom he *k* not, „ 561
when the King demanded how she *k*, „ 575
'He won.' 'I *k* it,' she said. „ 622
they talk'd, Meseem'd, of what they *k* not; „ 675
k ye what all others know, And whom he loves.' „ 680
there told the King What the King *k*, „ 707
she *k* right well What the rough sickness meant, but what this meant She *k* not, „ 887
And Lancelot *k* the little clinking sound; „ 983
Lancelot *k* that she was looking at him. „ 985
I *k* For one of those who eat in Arthur's hall; *Holy Grail* 23
I *k* That I should light upon the Holy Grail. „ 366
and fell down Before it, and I *k* not why, „ 407
I *k* the veil had been withdrawn. „ 522
and I *k* it was the Holy Grail, „ 531
As well as ever shepherd *k* his sheep, „ 551
'So spake the King: I *k* not all he meant.' „ 920
there were those who *k* him near the King, *Pelleas and E.* 15
and he *k* himself Loved of the King: „ 153
Some rough old knight who *k* the wordly way, „ 192
Awaking *k* the sword, and turn'd herself To Gawain: „ 489
He *k* not whence or wherefore: „ 504
made his beast that better *k* it, swerve „ 551
Watch'd her lord pass, and *k* not that she sigh'd. *Last Tournament* 130
Lancelot *k*, had held sometime with pain „ 178
Who *k* thee swine enow before I came, „ 304
He ended: Arthur *k* the voice; „ 455
and *k* that thou wert nigh.' „ 520
he *k* the Prince tho' marr'd with dust, *Guinevere* 36
no man *k* from whence he came; „ 289
indeed I *k* Of no more subtle master „ 477
merry linnet *k* me, The squirrel *k* me, *Lover's Tale ii* 15
And partly made them—tho' he *k* it not. „ *iv* 25
He *k* the meaning of the whisper now, Thought that he *k* it. „ 43
Stung by his loss had vanish'd, none *k* where. „ 102
I *k* Some sudden vivid pleasure hit him „ 177
I *k* a man, not many years ago; „ 255
I *k* another, not so long ago, „ 262
She never had a sister. I *k* none. „ 326
So I *k* my heart was hard, *First Quarrel* 78
He was devil for aught they *k*, *The Revenge* 108
Evelyn *k* not of my former suit, *Sisters (E. and E.)* 205
She died and she was buried ere we *k*. „ 241
or butcher'd for all that we *k*— *Def. of Lucknow* 91
I would I *k* their speech; *Sir J. Oldcastle* 11
Thou art so well disguised, I *k* thee not. „ 198
I *k* we should fall on each other, *V. of Maeldune* 104
As if they *k* your diet spares *To E. Fitzgerald* 10
I *k* the twain Would each waste each, *Tiresias* 68
these eyes will find The men I *k*, „ 176
I *k* not what, when I keard that voice,— *The Wreck* 52
the days went by, but I *k* no more— „ 111
O Mother, was not the face that I *k*. „ 116
I *k* that hand too well— „ 145
we *k* that their light was a lie— *Despair* 16
Nature who *k* not that which she bore! „ 34
Who *k* no books and no philosophies, *Ancient Sage* 218
she *k* this father well; *The Flight* 87

Knew (*continued*) an' none of the parish *k*. *Tomorrow* 76
at the host that had halted he *k* not why, *Heavy Brigade* 7
There is a Fate beyond us.' Nothing *k*. *Demeter and P.* 87
k not that which pleased it most, *The Ring* 165
the face Of Miriam grew upon me, till I *k*; „ 185
you *k* not one was there Who saw you kneel *Happy* 53
I *k* that you were near me when I let him kiss my brow; „ 65
I *k* You were parting for the war, „ 73
Arthur had vanish'd I *k* not whither, *Merlin and the G.* 78
WHAT sight so lured him thro' the fields he *k* *Far—far—away* 1
you *k* that he meant to betray me—you *k*—you *k* that he lied. *Charity* 12

Knewest if thou *k*, tho' thou canst not know; *Ancient Sage* 36

Knife (*See also* **War-knife**) To war with falsehood to the *k*, *Two Voices* 131
he drove the *k* into his side: *Lucretius* 275
The *k* uprising toward the blow *The Victim* 66
I am his dearest!' rush'd on the *k*. „ 72
Struck with a *k's* haft hard against the board, *Geraint and E.* 600
They sit with *k* in meat and wine in horn! *Merlin and V.* 694
He was happier using the *k* *In the Child. Hosp.* 6
broken besides with dreams of the dreadful *k* „ 65
by the pitiful-pitiless *k*,— *Def. of Lucknow* 85
if cured, by the surgeon's *k*,— *Despair* 80
For I used to play with the *k*, *Charity* 15

Knight (*See also* **Boy-knight, Brother-knight, Knave-knight, Minion-knight, Mock-knight, Table-knight**) I would I were an armèd *k*, *Kate* 21
The *k's* come riding two and two She hath no loyal *k* and true, *L. of Shalott ii* 25
A red-cross *k* for ever kneel'd To a lady „ *iii* 6
K and burgher, lord and dame, „ *iv* 43
they cross'd themselves for fear, All the *k's* at Camelot: „ 50
Sir Bedivere, the last of all his *k's*, *M. d'Arthur* 7
The goodliest fellowship of famous *k's* „ 15
the mighty bones of ancient men, Old *k's*, „ 48
beseem'd Thy fëalty, nor like a noble *k*: „ 75
thou, the latest-left of all my *k's* „ 124
every chance brought out a noble *k*. „ 231
A maiden *k*—to me is given Such hope, *Sir Galahad* 61
'O just and faithful *k* of God! „ 79
Kissing his vows upon it like a *k*. *Aylmer's Field* 472
A good *k* he! we keep a chronicle With all about him'— *Princess, Pro.* 27
and I Dived in a hoard of tales that dealt with *k's*, „ 29
A feudal *k* in silken masquerade, „ 234
if I prove Your *k*, and fight your battle, „ *iv* 595
many a bold *k* started up in heat, „ *v* 359
and all the good *k's* maim'd, „ *vi* 241
Scarce other than my king's ideal *k*, *Ded. of Idylls* 7
But rode a simple *k* among his *k's*, *Com. of Arthur* 51
Broad pathways for the hunter and the *k* „ 61
His new-made *k's*, to King Leodogran, „ 137
Bedivere, the first of all his *k's* Knighted „ 174
an old *k* And ancient friend of Uther; „ 222
So few his *k's*, however brave they be— „ 252
his *k's* Stood round him, and rejoicing in his joy. „ 458
his *k's* have heard That God hath told the King „ 488
'as a false *k* Or evil king before my lance *Gareth and L.* 5
A *k* of Arthur, working out his will, „ 24
Ask'd me to tilt with him, the proven *k*. „ 27
Before thou ask the King to make thee *k*, „ 145
And ever and anon a *k* would pass Outward, „ 310
those tall *k's*, that ranged about the throne, „ 328
A *k* of Uther in the Barons' war, „ 353
Grant me some *k* to do the battle for me, „ 362
Then strode a good *k* forward, crying „ 364
Had made his goodly cousin, Tristram, *k*, „ 394
'The goodly *k*! What! shall the shield of Mark „ 402
And under every shield a *k* was named: „ 409
When some good *k* had done one noble deed, „ 411
make him *k* because men call him king. „ 420
And evermore a *k* would ride away. „ 438
Gareth telling some prodigious tale Of *k's*, „ 509
saw the *k's* Clash like the coming and retiring wave, „ 521

Knight (*continued*) Make me thy *k*—in secret! *Gareth and L.* 544
Made thee my *k*? my *k's* are sworn to vows „ 552
'Make thee my *k* in secret? „ 564
my need, a *k* To combat for my sister, Lyonors, „ 607
three *k's* Defend the passings, brethren, „ 613
And pardonable, worthy to be *k*— „ 654
I ask'd for thy chief *k*, And thou hast given me „ 658
The most ungentle *k* in Arthur's hall.' „ 757
Sweet lord, how like a noble *k* he talks! „ 777
he is not *k* but knave.' „ 922
And Gareth silent gazed upon the *k*, „ 933
Thou art not *k* but knave.' Said Gareth, 'Damsel, whether knave or *k*, „ 942
and either *k* at once, Hurl'd as a stone „ 964
K, Thy life is thine at her command. „ 982
thou art not *k* but knave.' „ 1006
k or knave—The knave that doth thee service as full *k* Is all as good, meseems, as any *k* Toward thy sister's freeing.' „ 1015
knave, because thou strikest as a *k*, „ 1020
the new *k* Had fear he might be shamed; „ 1043
the *k*, That named himself the Star of Evening, „ 1089
O knave, as noble as any of all the *k's*— „ 1136
and, good faith, I fain had added—*K*, „ 1162
He scarce is *k*, yea but half-man, „ 1176
methinks There rides no *k*, not Lancelot, his great self, „ 1182
k's on horse Sculptured, and deckt in slowly-waning hues. „ 1194
'Sir Knave, my *k*, a hermit once was here, „ 1196
'Stay, felon *k*, I avenge me for my friend.' „ 1220
And *k* of Arthur, here lie thrown by whom I know not, „ 1233
Courteous as any *k*—but now, if *k*, „ 1250
K, knave, prince and fool, I hate thee and for ever.' „ 1255
k art thou To the King's best wish. „ 1258
Prince, *K*, Hail, *K* and Prince, „ 1270
merry am I to find my goodly knave Is *k* and noble. „ 1292
'*K*, Slay me not: my three brethren bad me do it, „ 1409
What madness made thee challenge the chief *k* „ 1416
brave Geraint, a *k* of Arthur's court, *Marr. of Geraint* 1
bandit earls, and caitiff *k's*, Assassins, „ 35
Enid rode, And fifty *k's* rode with them, „ 44
Weeping for some gay *k* in Arthur's hall.' „ 118
rode Full slowly by a *k*, lady, and dwarf; „ 187
the *k* Had vizor up, and show'd a youthful face, „ 188
when she put her horse toward the *k*, „ 200
Had put his horse in motion toward the *k*, „ 206
'Pardon me, O stranger *k*; „ 286
the good *k's* horse stands in the court; „ 370
if he be the *k* whom late I saw Ride into that new fortress „ 406
what *k* soever be in field Lays claim to „ 486
errant *k's* And ladies came, and by and by the town Flow'd in, „ 545
the *k* With some surprise and thrice as much disdain „ 556
Enid was aware of three tall *k's* On horseback, *Geraint and E.* 56
said the second, 'yonder comes a *k*.' „ 126
Held his head high, and thought himself a *k*, „ 242
A *k* of Arthur's court, who laid his lance In rest, „ 775
'The voice of Enid,' said the *k*; „ 780
I took you for a bandit *k* of Doorm; „ 786
Now, made a *k* of Arthur's Table Round, „ 793
when the *k* besought him, 'Follow me, „ 807
Than if some *k* of mine, risking his life, „ 915
And fifty *k's* rode with them to the shores Of Severn, „ 954
two strange *k's* Who sit near Camelot *Balin and Balan* 10
challenging And overthrowing every *k* who comes. „ 13
For whatsoever *k* against us came „ 35
hurl'd to ground what *k* soever spurr'd Against us, „ 66
worthier to be thine Than twenty Balins, Balan *k*. „ 69
Rise, my true *k*. „ 75
in those deep woods we found A *k* „ 121
and a transitory word Make *k* or churl or child „ 162
Balin bare the crown, and all the *k's* Approved him, „ 209
not worthy to be *k*; A churl, a clown!' „ 285
found the greetings both of *k* and King „ 342
(for Arthur's *k's* Were hated strangers in the hall) „ 351

Knight (*continued*) Hail, royal *k*, we break on thy sweet rest, *Balin and Balan* 470
the *k*, with whom I rode, Hath suffer'd misadventure, „ 475
nor Prince Nor *k* am I, but one that hath defamed „ 484
this good *k* Told me, that twice a wanton damsel came, „ 608
It more beseems the perfect virgin *k* *Merlin and V.* 22
She hated all the *k's*, and heard in thought „ 150
some corruption crept among his *k's*, „ 154
but afterwards He made a stalwart *k*. „ 482
saw The *k's*, the court, the King, „ 875
and show'd them to his *k's*, Saying, *Lancelot and E.* 57
the *k's* Are half of them our enemies, „ 98
As to *k's*, Them surely can I silence with all ease. „ 108
our *k's* at feast Have pledged us in this union, „ 114
Then answer'd Lancelot, the chief of *k's*: (repeat) „ 140, 187
allow your pretext, O my *k*, As all for glory; „ 153
He loves it in his *k's* more than himself: „ 157
dying down as the great *k* Approach'd them: „ 179
Is that an answer for a noble *k*? „ 201
shame me not Before this noble *k*,' „ 208
for, *k*, the maiden dreamt That some one put this diamond „ 211
To ride to Camelot with this noble *k*: „ 220
slight disparagement Before the stranger *k*, „ 235
the great *k*, the darling of the court, „ 261
For if his own *k* cast him down, he laughs Saying, his *k's* are better men than he— „ 313
knew there lived a *k* Not far from Camelot, „ 401
wrathful that a stranger *k* Should do and almost overdo „ 468
He bore a *k* of old repute to the earth, „ 492
all the *k's*, His party, cried 'Advance „ 502
His party, *k's* of utmost North and West, „ 526
'Lo, Sire, our *k*, thro' whom we won the day, „ 529
So great a *k* as we have seen to-day— „ 533
O Gawain, and ride forth and find the *k*. „ 537
k's and kings, there breathes not one of you „ 540
since the *k* Came not to us, of us to claim the prize, „ 543
a good *k*, but therewithal Sir Modred's brother, „ 557
banquet, and concourse of *k's* and kings. „ 562
Albeit I know my *k's* fantastical, „ 594
What of the *k* with the red sleeve? „ 621
Here was the *k*, and here he left a shield; „ 634
Who dream'd my *k* the greatest *k* of all.' „ 667
'that you love This greatest *k*, your pardon! „ 669
know full well Where your great *k* is hidden, „ 690
the King knew 'Sir Lancelot is the *k*.' „ 707
the *k's* at banquet twice or thrice Forgot to drink „ 736
sweet and serviceable To noble *k's* in sickness, „ 768
Right fain were I to learn this *k* were whole, „ 772
Woke the sick *k*, and while he roll'd his eyes „ 819
the great *k* in his mid-sickness made „ 878
More specially should your good *k* be poor, „ 956
In all your quarrels will I be your *k*, „ 961
the King Came girt with *k's*: „ 1261
Sir Lancelot, As thou art a *k* peerless.' „ 1282
'O my *k*, It will be to thy worship, as my *k*, „ 1326
when the *k's* had laid her comely head „ 1337
Strike down the lusty and long practised *k*, „ 1360
My *k*, the great Sir Lancelot of the Lake.' „ 1373
Pure, as you ever wish your *k's* to be. „ 1375
what profits me my name Of greatest *k*? „ 1414
Alas for Arthur's greatest *k*, „ 1419
'Nay,' said the *k*; 'for no such earthly passion mine. *Holy Grail* 30
one of your own *k's*, a guest of ours, „ 40
And tell thy brother *k's* to fast and pray, „ 126
Said Arthur, when he dubb'd him *k*; and none, In so young youth, was ever made a *k* Till Galahad; „ 137
'My *k*, my love, my *k* of heaven, „ 157
every *k* beheld his fellow's face As in a glory, and all the *k's* arose, „ 191
Lancelot sware, and many among the *k's*, „ 201
there so oft with all his *k's* Feasted, „ 223

Knight (*continued*) 'Woe is me, my *k's*,' he cried, *Holy Grail* 275
he ask'd us, *k* by *k*, if any Had seen it, „ 283
(Brother, the King was hard upon his *k's*) „ 299
hath overborne Five *k's* at once, and every younger *k*, Unproven, „ 303
K's that in twelve great battles splash'd „ 311
how often, O my *k's* Your places being vacant „ 316
The yet-unbroken strength of all his *k's*, „ 326
overthrew So many *k's* that all the people cried, „ 335
k's and ladies wept, and rich and poor Wept, „ 353
my strong lance had beaten down the *k's*, „ 363
calling me the greatest of all *k's*, „ 595
thou art our greatest *k*, Our Lady says it, „ 603
Saw ye none beside, None of your *k's*?' „ 632
found ye all your *k's* return'd, „ 708
and when thy *k's* Sware, I swear with them „ 777
Mean *k's*, to whom the moving of my sword „ 790
painting on the wall Or shield of *k*; „ 830
A reckless and irreverent *k* was he, „ 856
Could all of true and noble in *k* and man „ 882
'And spake I not too truly, O my *k's*? „ 888
KING ARTHUR made new *k's* to fill the gap *Pelleas and E.* 1
'Make me thy *k*, because I know, „ 7
and Arthur made him *k*. And this new *k*, Sir Pelleas of the isles— „ 16
Beat like a strong *k* on his helm, „ 23
Arm'd as ye see, to tilt against the *k's* There at Caerleon, „ 65
Three *k's* were thereamong; and they too smiled, „ 96
her *k's* And all her damsels too were gracious „ 121
Then glanced askew at those three *k's* „ 134
and strange *k's* From the four winds came in: „ 147
and him his new-made *k* Worshipt, „ 154
For Arthur, loving his young *k*, „ 159
her look Bright for all others, cloudier on her *k*— „ 177
those three *k's* all set their faces home, „ 187
Some rough old *k* who knew the worldly way, „ 192
Then calling her three *k's*, she charged them „ 219
walking on the walls With her three *k's*, „ 226
Yield me thy love and know me for thy *k*.' „ 249
her anger, leaving Pelleas, burn'd Full on her *k's* „ 290
her *k's* Laugh'd not, but thrust him bounden out of door. „ 313
whom late our Arthur made *K* of his table; „ 320
I chant thy praise As prowest *k* and truest lover, „ 350
'Pity on him,' she answer'd, 'a good *k*, „ 386
droned her lurdane *k's* Slumbering, „ 430
and thought, 'What! slay a sleeping *k*? „ 448
'Alas that ever a *k* should be so false.' „ 450
as the one true *k* on earth, And only lover; „ 494
either *k* Drew back a space, and when they closed, „ 572
there with her *k's* and dames was Guinevere. „ 588
she, turning to Pelleas, 'O young *k*, „ 595
the purest of thy *k's* May win them for the purest *Last Tournament* 49
everywhere the *k's* Arm'd for a day of glory „ 54
A hundred goodly ones—the Red *K*, he— „ 70
Red *K* Brake in upon me and drave them „ 71
whatsoever his own *k's* have sworn My *k's* have sworn the counter to it— „ 79
My *k's* are all adulterers like his own, „ 84
My younger *k's*, new-made, in whom your flower „ 99
leave The leading of his younger *k's* to me. „ 110
Or have I dream'd the bearing of our *k's* „ 120
He spoke, and taking all his younger *k's*, „ 126
a *k* cast down Before his throne of arbitration „ 161
An ocean-sounding welcome to one *k*, „ 168
O chief *k*, Right arm of Arthur in the battlefield, „ 201
know myself the wisest *k* of all.' „ 248
one true *k*—Sole follower of the vows'— „ 302
'*K*, an ye fling those rubies round my neck „ 312
the *k's*, Glorying in each new glory, „ 335
And therebeside a horn, inflamed the *k's* „ 434
the Red *K* heard, and all, „ 441
Slain was the brother of my paramour By a *k* of thine, „ 449
To hang whatever *k* of thine I fought And tumbled. „ 453
k's, who watch'd him, roar'd And shouted „ 468
O Sir *K*, What dame or damsel have ye kneel'd to last?' „ 549

Knight (*continued*) Far other was the Tristram, Arthur's *k* ! *Last Tournament* 634
every *k* Believed himself a greater than himself, „ 676
I loved This knightliest of all *k's*, „ 711
No *k* of Arthur's noblest dealt in scorn ; *Guinevere* 40
said my father, and himself was *k* „ 234
every *k* Had whatsoever meat he long'd for „ 264
' Sir Lancelot, as became a noble *k*, „ 328
If ever Lancelot, that most noble *k*, „ 345
Reputed the best *k* and goodliest man, „ 382
my right arm The mightiest of my *k's*, „ 430
hand against the King Who made him *k* : but many a *k* was slain ; „ 438
Then others, following these my mightiest *k's*, „ 489
And miss the wonted number of my *k's*, „ 498
Lords of the White Horse, heathen, and *k's*, „ 574
Among his warring senses, to thy *k's*— „ 640
First made and latest left of all the *k's*, *Pass. of Arthur* 2
and *k's* Once thine, whom thou hast loved, „ 60
To war against my people and my *k's*. „ 71
And they my *k's*, who loved me once, „ 73
shouts of heathen and the traitor *k's*, „ 113
The goodliest fellowship of famous *k's* „ 183
the mighty bones of ancient men, Old *k's*, „ 216
beseem'd Thy fëalty, nor like a noble *k* : „ 243
thou, the latest-left of all my *k's*, „ 292
every chance brought out a noble *k*. „ 399
he the *k* for an amorous girl's romance ! *The Wreck* 44
K's were thwack'd and riven, *The Tourney* 10
Crown'd her *k's*, and flush'd as red As poppies „ 16

Knighted *K* by Arthur at his crowning, *Com. of Arthur* 174
when they rose, *k* from kneeling, some Were pale „ 263
As on the day when Arthur *k* him.' *Gareth and L.* 1240
three brief morns had glanced away From being *k* till he smote the thrall, *Balin and Balan* 155
Then being on the morrow *k*, *Pelleas and E.* 140

Knight-errantry old *k-e* Who ride abroad, *Gareth and L.* 629

Knighthood leading all his *k* threw the kings *Com. of Arthur* 111
And Arthur's *k* sang before the King :— „ 481
So sang the *k*, moving to their hall. „ 503
Arthur and his *k* for a space Were all one will, „ 515
And the deed's sake my *k* do the deed, *Gareth and L.* 572
so my *k* keep the vows they swore, „ 602
what Arthur meant by courtesy, Manhood, and *k* ; *Balin and Balan* 159
The flower of all their vestal *k*, „ 508
Boldness and royal *k* of the bird *Merlin and V.* 134
I swear by truth and *k* that I gave No cause, *Lancelot and E.* 1297
Arthur and his *k* call'd The Pure, *Holy Grail* 3
Some root of *k* and pure nobleness ; „ 886
All that belongs to *k*, and I love.' *Pelleas and E.* 9
Hath the great heart of *k* in thee fail'd „ 596
marking how the *k* mock thee, fool— *Last Tournament* 301
My *k* taught me this—ay, being snapt— „ 658
Began to gall the *k*, asking whence Had Arthur „ 683

Knighthood-errant drew The *k-e* of this realm *Guinevere* 461

Knight-knave well stricken, O good *k-k*— *Gareth and L.* 1135
so will my *k-k* Miss the full flower „ 1296

Knightlike He *k* in his cap instead of casque, *Princess iv* 600
all glad, *K*, to find his charger yet unlamed, *Balin and Balan* 428
say That out of naked *k* purity Sir Lancelot worshipt *Merlin and V.* 11

Knightly all of pure Noble, and *k* in me *Holy Grail* 774
and these Full *k* without scorn ; *Guinevere* 39
Delight our souls with talk of *k* deeds, *M. d'Arthur* 19
Mix'd with the *k* growth that fringed his lips. „ 220
Had carved himself a *k* shield of wood, *Merlin and V.* 473
Among the *k* brasses of the graves, „ 752
In any *k* fashion for her sake. *Lancelot and E.* 871
the prize A golden circlet and a *k* sword, *Pelleas and E.* 12
Delight our souls with talk of *k* deeds, *Pass. of Arthur* 187
Mix'd with the *k* growth that fringed his lips, „ 388

Knit I *k* a hundred others new : *Two Voices* 234
while I mused, Love with *k* brows went by, *Gardener's D.* 245
I hold them exquisitely *k*, *Talking Oak* 91
K land to land, and blowing havenward *Golden Year* 44

Knit (*continued*) those That *k* themselves for summer shadow, *Aylmer's Field* 724
Some dolorous message *k* below *In Mem. xii* 3
k The generations each with each ; „ *xl* 15
K to some dismal sandbank far at sea, *Lover's Tale i* 809

Knitted with such a chain Of *k* purport, *Two Voices* 168

Knob man with *k's* and wires and vials *Princess, Pro.* 65

Knock'd volume, all of songs, *K* down to me, *Audley Court* 58
I *k* and, bidden, enter'd ; *Princess iii* 130

Knocking Someone *k* there without ? No ! *Romney's R.* 142

Knoll Oread haunt The *k's* of Ida, *Œnone* 75
k's That dimpling died into each other, *Aylmer's Field* 148
perch'd about the *k's* A dozen angry models *Princess, Pro.* 72
From *k* to *k*, where, couch'd at ease, *In Mem. xcv* 14
dusk reveal'd The *k's* once more where, „ 50
Nor hoary *k* of ash and haw That hears „ *c* 9
There, on a little *k* beside it, stay'd *Marr. of Geraint* 162
ford Behind them, and so gallop'd up the *k*. „ 168
' For on this little *k*, if anywhere, „ 181
huddled here and there on mound and *k*, *Geraint and E.* 803
The ruinous donjon as a *k* of moss, *Balin and Balan* 334

Knoll'd a deeper knell in the heart be *k* ; *Ode on Well.* 59

Knolling heavy clocks *k* the drowsy hours. *Gardener's D.* 184

Knot (s) (*See also* **Love-Knots**) rusted nails fell from the *k's* *Mariana* 3
The *k's* that tangle human creeds, *Clear-headed friend* 3
Bridesmaid, ere the happy *k* was tied, *The Bridesmaid* 1
I must gather *k's* of flowers, *May Queen* 11
palms in cluster, *k's* of Paradise. *Locksley Hall* 160
Our dances broke and buzz'd in *k's* of talk ; *Princess i* 133
More soluble is this *k*, By gentleness „ *v* 135
look'd A *k*, beneath, of snakes, aloft, a grove. *Marr. of Geraint* 325
Thro' *k's* and loops and folds innumerable *Lancelot and E.* 439
felt the *k* Climb in her throat, „ 740

Knot (verb) as tight as I could *k* the noose ; *St. S. Stylites* 65

Knotted (*See also* **Many-knotted**) These *k* knees of mine, *Talking Oak* 158
And bared the *k* column of his throat, *Marr. of Geraint* 74
wild brier had driven Its *k* thorns thro' *Lover's Tale i* 620

Knout be ruled with rod or with *k* ? *Maud I iv* 47

Know (*See also* **Knaw**) As all men *k*, Long ago. *All Things will Die* 39
k's Nothing beyond his mother's eyes. *Supp. Confessions* 43
I *k* At matins and at evensong, „ 98
and then, from whence He *k's* not, „ 163
who may *k* Whether smile or frown be fleeter ? *Madeline* 11
I *K* her by her angry air, *Kate* 1
far down, but I shall *k* Thy voice, and answer *My life is full* 9
All this hath been, I *k* not when or where.' *Sonnet To* —— 8
She *k's* not what the curse may be, *L. of Shalott ii* 6
The night comes on that *k's* not morn, *Mariana in the S.* 94
I would have said, ' Thou canst not *k*,' *Two Voices* 43
I wept, ' Tho' I should die, I *k* „ 58
' I *k* that age to age succeeds, „ 205
K I not Death ? the outward signs ? „ 270
' He *k's* a baseness in his blood „ 301
Of something done, I *k* not where ; „ 383
' I see the end, and *k* the good.' „ 432
' I may not speak of what I *k*.' „ 435
The lanes, you *k*, were white with may, *Miller's D.* 130
I should *k* if it beat right, „ 179
I *k* He cometh quickly : *Fatima* 22
What this may be I *k* not, but I *k* *Œnone* 266
Verulam, The first of those who *k*. *Palace of Art* 164
And *k's* not if it be thunder, „ 281
I *k* you proud to bear your name, *L. C. V. de Vere* 10
I *k* you, Clara Vere de Vere, „ 57
You *k* so ill to deal with time, „ 63
I *k* not what was said ; *May Queen, Con.* 34
I *k* The blessed music went that way „ 41
a hundred fields, and all of them I *k*. „ 50
I *k* not how, All those sharp fancies, *D. of F. Women* 48
I wrote I *k* not what. *To J. S.* 57
' You *k*,' said Frank, ' he burnt His epic, *The Epic* 27
God *k's* ; he has a mint of reasons : „ 33
King is sick, and *k's* not what he does. *M. d'Arthur* 97

Know (*continued*) I *k* not: but we sitting, as I said, *M. d'Arthur, Ep.* 9
K you not Such touches are but embassies of love, *Gardener's D.* 17
nor did they *k* Who sent it; *Dora* 53
You *k* there has not been for these five years „ 65
may he never *k* The troubles I have gone thro'!' „ 149
shovell'd up into some bloody trench Where no one *k's*? *Audley Court* 43
Nay, who *k's*? he's here and there. *Walk. to the Mail* 26
What *k* we of the secret of a man? „ 104
Heaven *k's*—as much within; *Edwin Morris* 82
scarce can recognise the fields I *k*; *St. S. Stylites* 40
I *k* not well, For that the evil ones come here, „ 97
I think you *k* I have some power with Heaven „ 143
I *k* thy glittering face. „ 205
yesterday, you *k*, the fair Was holden at the town; *Talking Oak* 101
James,—you *k* him,—old, but full Of force *Golden Year* 60
but well I *k* That unto him who works, „ 72
That hoard, and sleep, and feed, and *k* not me. *Ulysses* 5
but I *k* my words are wild, *Locksley Hall* 173
Such hope, I *k* not fear; *Sir Galahad* 62
my hair Is gray before I *k* it. *Will Water.* 168
We *k* not what we *k*. „ 178
I will *k* If there be any faith in man.' *Lady Clare* 43
We *k* the merry world is round, *The Voyage* 95
Well I *k*, when I am gone, *Vision of Sin* 109
For they *k* not what they mean. „ 126
we *k* the hue Of that cap upon her brows. „ 141
Madam—if I *k* your sex, „ 181
The many-headed beast should *k*.' *You might have won* 20
knew her, as a horseman *k's* his horse— *Enoch Arden* 136
I'll be back, my girl, before you *k* it.' „ 193
And yet for all your wisdom well *k* I „ 211
If he could *k* his babes were running wild „ 304
end of an avenue, Going we *k* not where: „ 359
I *k* not why—Their voices make me feel so solitary.' „ 396
I *k* not when it first came there, I *k* that it will out at last. „ 401
Perhaps you *k* what I would have you *k*— „ 409
I have loved you longer than you *k*.' „ 421
If question'd, aught of what he cared to *k*. „ 654
look on her sweet face again And *k* that she is happy.' „ 719
Not to tell her, never to let her *k*. (repeat) „ 786, 798
must I not speak to these? They *k* me not. „ 789
' After the Lord has call'd me she shall *k*, „ 810
' Did you *k* Enoch Arden of this town?' ' *K* him?' she said ' I knew him far away. „ 845
Nevertheless, *k* you that I am he Who married— „ 858
glory varying to and fro, We *k* not wherefore; *Aylmer's Field* 74
other, save for Leolin's—Who *k's*? „ 141
I *k* not, for he spoke not, only shower'd „ 213
I *k* not whence at first, Nor of what race, „ 223
did Sir Aylmer *k* That great pock-pitten fellow „ 255
' The girl and boy, Sir, *k* their differences!' „ 274
indeed you *k* That you meant nothing. „ 313
I *k* her: the worst thought she has Is whiter „ 362
Nor let them *k* themselves betray'd; „ 524
when I came To *k* him more, I lost it, *Sea Dreams* 72
—nor *k's* he what he sees; *Lucretius* 132
O ye Gods, I *k* you careless, „ 208
Howbeit I *k* thou surely must be mine „ 270
none of all our blood should *k* The shadow from the substance, *Princess i* 8
Myself too had weird seizures, Heaven *k's* what: „ 14
she, you *k*, Who wedded with a nobleman „ 76
they that *k* such things—I sought but peace; „ 144
and more We *k* not,—only this: „ 152
O we fell out I *k* not why, „ *ii* 4
let us *k* The Princess Ida waited: „ 20
She answer'd, ' then ye *k* the Prince?' „ 49
I *k* the substance when I see it. „ 413
fly, while yet you may! My mother *k's*: „ *iii* 29
' Why—these—*are*—men:' I shudder'd: ' and you *k* it.' „ 58
And she *k's* too, And she conceals it.' „ 59
She calls her plagiarist; I *k* not what: „ 94
At no man's beck, but *k* ourself and thee, „ 227

Know (*continued*) I *k* the Prince, I prize his truth: *Princess iii* 232
fail so far In high desire, they *k* not, „ 280
yet we *k* Knowledge is knowledge, „ 315
' Tears, idle tears, I *k* not what they mean, „ *iv* 39
' *K* you no song of your own land,' „ 84
K you no song, the true growth of your soil, „ 150
I—you *k* it—I will not boast: „ 353
We did not *k* the real light, „ 357
I *k* Your faces there in the crowd— „ 509
' Tut, you *k* them not, the girls. „ *v* 151
something may be done—I *k* not what— „ 228
who *k's*? we four may build some plan „ 230
—I myself, What *k* I of these things? „ 284
blustering I *k* not what Of insolence and love, „ 396
and whereas I *k* Your prowess, Arac, „ 403
name is yoked with children's, *k* herself; „ 418
And right ascension, Heaven *k's* what; „ *vi* 257
This nightmare weight of gratitude, I *k* it; „ 300
that *k* The woman's cause is man's: „ *vii* 258
' Alone,' I said, ' from earlier than I *k*, „ 311
dark gates across the wild That no man *k's*. „ 363
What *k* we greater than the soul? *Ode on Well.* 265
who love best have best the grace to *k* *W. to Marie Alex.* 28
I *k* for a truth, there's none of them left *Grandmother* 85
To a sweet little Eden on earth that I *k*, *The Islet* 14
Well—if it be so, so it is, you *k*; *Spiteful Letter* 19
I should *k* what God and man is. *Flow. in cran. wall* 6
Flown to the east or the west, flitted I *k* not where! *Window, Gone* 7
Somebody *k's* that she'll say ay! (repeat) „ *Letter* 8, 15
Thou madest man, he *k's* not why, *In Mem., Pro.* 10
Our wills are ours, we *k* not how; „ 15
We have but faith: we cannot *k*; „ 21
Ye *k* no more than I who wrought „ *vi* 17
And beckoning unto those they *k*; „ *xiv* 8
But *k's* no more of transient form „ *xvi* 7
I *k* that this was Life,— „ *xxv* 1
Half-dead to *k* that I shall die.' „ *xxxv* 16
My paths are in the fields I *k*, „ *xl* 31
When one that loves but *k's* not, reaps A truth from one that loves and *k's*? „ *xlii* 11
(he *k's* not whence) A little flash, „ *xliv* 7
I shall *k* him when we meet: „ *xlvii* 8
Behold, we *k* not anything; „ *liv* 13
spirit does but mean the breath I *k* no more.' „ *lvi* 8
howsoe'er I *k* thee, some Could hardly tell „ *lix* 15
Half jealous of she *k's* not what, „ *lx* 7
I *k* that in thy place of rest „ *lxvii* 2
And then I *k* the mist is drawn „ 13
Death's twin-brother, *k's* not Death, „ *lxviii* 3
Which makes me sad I *k* not why „ 11
I strive to paint The face I *k*; „ *lxx* 3
How *k* I what had need of thee, „ *lxxiii* 3
and *k* Thy likeness to the wise below, „ *lxxiv* 6
I *k* thee of what force thou art „ *lxxix* 3
I *k* transplanted human worth Will bloom to profit, „ *lxxxii* 11
Yet none could better *k* than I, „ *lxxxv* 37
wear the form by which I *k* Thy spirit „ *xci* 5
tell me, doubt is Devil-born. I *k* not: „ *xcvi* 5
She *k's* not what his greatness is, „ *xcvii* 27
She *k's* but matters of the house, And he, he *k's* a thousand things. „ 31
They *k* me not, but mourn with me. „ *xcix* 20
That these are not the bells I *k*. „ *civ* 8
Let her *k* her place; „ *cxiv* 15
But, crying, *k's* his father near; „ *cxxiv* 20
Did he fling himself down? who *k's*? *Maud I i* 9
who *k's*? we are ashes and dust. „ 32
I have heard, I *k* not whence, „ 67
the fiend best *k's* whether woman or man be the worse „ 75
I *k* it, and smile a hard-set smile, „ *iv* 20
Who *k's* the ways of the world, „ 44
Did I hear in half a doze Long since, I *k* not where? „ *vii* 2
I *k* the way she went Home with her maiden posy, „ *xii* 21
And she *k's* it not: O, if she knew it, „ *xvi* 18
To *k* her beauty might half undo it. „ 19

Know (*continued*) I *k* it the one bright thing to save *Maud xvi* 20
I *k* He has plotted against me „ *xix* 79
Now I *k* her but in two, „ *xx* 15
I *k* her own rose-garden, „ 41
The ghastly Wraith of one that I *k*; „ *II i* 32
little hearts that *k* not how to forgive: „ 44
k Is a juggle born of the brain? „ *ii* 41
Who *k's* if he be dead? „ 71
I *k* not whether he came in the Hanover ship, But I *k* that he lies and listens mute „ *v* 59
But I *k* where a garden grows, „ 72
he is gone: We *k* him now: *Ded. of Idylls* 16
I *k* thee for my King!' *Com. of Arthur* 130
'Sir King, there be but two old men that *k*: „ 149
for ye *k* that in King Uther's time „ 185
Who *k's* a subtler magic than his own— „ 284
then the Queen made answer, 'What *k* I? „ 326
I *k* not whether of himself he came, „ 346
rain, and sun! and where is he who *k's*? „ 410
and I that *k*, Have strength and wit, *Gareth and L.* 11
sees, nor hears, nor speaks, nor *k's*. „ 81
I *k* not thee, myself, nor anything. „ 97
'*K* ye not then the Riddling of the Bards? „ 286
but I *k* thee who thou art. „ 291
ye *k* we stay'd their hands From war „ 421
A horse thou knowest, a man thou dost not *k*: „ 463
'Son, the good mother let me *k* thee here, „ 550
And one with me in all, he needs must *k*.' „ 566
'Let Lancelot *k*, my King, let Lancelot *k*, „ 567
ye *k* this Order lives to crush All wrongers „ 625
Whether he *k* me for his master yet. „ 721
'Master no more! too well I *k* thee, „ 756
I *k* That I shall overthrow him.' „ 948
knight of Arthur, here lie thrown by whom I *k* not, „ 1234
'Peradventure he, you name, May *k* my shield. „ 1299
'And wherefore, damsel? tell me all ye *k*. „ 1328
I *k* but one—To dash against mine enemy „ 1354
Made answer sharply that she should not *k*. *Marr. of Geraint* 196
Arms? truth! I *k* not: all are wanted here. „ 289
Harbourage? truth, good truth, I *k* not, „ 290
if ye *k* Where I can light on arms, „ 421
be he dead I *k* not, but he past to the wild land. „ 443
Nor *k* I whether I be very base Or very manful, „ 468
this I *k*, That whatsoever evil happen to me, „ 470
Look on it, child, and tell me if ye *k* it.' „ 684
'Yea, I *k* it; your good gift, „ 688
I *k*, When my dear child is set forth at her best, „ 727
Who *k's*? another gift of the high God, „ 821
he loves to *k* When men of mark are in his territory: *Geraint and E.* 228
I *k*, God *k's*, too much of palaces! „ 236
return With victual for these men, and let us *k*.' „ 240
Make me a little happier: let me *k* it: „ 317
I *k* Tho' men may bicker with the things they love, „ 324
well I *k* it—pall'd—For I *k* men: „ 331
'Yea, my lord, I *k* Your wish, „ 418
Falls in a far land and he *k's* it not, „ 497
I suffer from the things before me, *k*, Learn nothing; *Balin and Balan* 284
I fain would *k* what manner of men they be.' „ 574
Ye scarce can overpraise, will hear and *k*. *Merlin and V.* 92
knowing that I *k*, Will hate, loathe, fear— „ 121
'*K* ye the stranger woman?' „ 129
did you *k* That Vivien bathed your feet „ 283
However wise, ye hardly *k* me yet.' „ 355
I think ye hardly *k* the tender rhyme „ 383
K well that Envy calls you Devil's son, „ 467
Right well *k* I that Fame is half-disfame, „ 504
take my counsel; let me *k* it at once: ' „ 653
If ye *k*, Set up the charge ye *k*, „ 702
answer'd Merlin 'Nay, I *k* the tale. „ 713
he never wrong'd his bride. I *k* the tale. „ 730
Or whisper'd in the corner? do ye *k* it? To which he answer'd sadly, 'Yea, I *k* it. „ 772
is he man at all, who *k's* and winks? „ 781

Know (*continued*) I *k* the Table Round, my friends of old; *Merlin and V.* 816
I will not let her *k*: „ 823
believe you then, Who *k's*? once more. „ 923
'Yea, lord,' she said, 'ye *k* it.' *Lancelot and E.* 80
I am yours, Not Arthur's, as ye *k*, „ 135
Ye *k* right well, how meek soe'er he seem, „ 155
Hereafter ye shall *k* me—and the shield— „ 192
you *k* Of Arthur's glorious wars.' „ 284
'Fair lord, whose name I *k* not— „ 360
Such is my wont, as those, who *k* me, *k*.' „ 365
That those who *k* should *k* you.' „ 368
touch Of greatness to *k* well I am not great: „ 451
such his wont, as we, that *k* him, *k*.' „ 475
Albeit I *k* my knights fantastical, „ 594
your pardon! lo, ye *k* it! „ 669
Full simple was her answer, 'What *k* I? „ 671
I *k* not if I *k* what true love is, But if I *k*, then, if I love not him, I *k* there is none other I can love.' „ 676
knew ye what all others *k*, „ 680
you *k* full well Where your great knight „ 689
We two shall *k* each other.' „ 700
by mine head she *k's* his hiding-place.' „ 714
ye *k* When these have worn their tokens: „ 768
How *k* ye my lord's name is Lancelot?' „ 797
yea, I *k* it of mine own self: „ 950
I *k* not which is sweeter, no, not I. (repeat) „ 1009, 1015
As when we dwell upon a word we *k*, Repeating, till the word we *k* so well Becomes a wonder, and we *k* not why, „ 1027
And there the King will *k* me and my love, „ 1058
Daughter, I *k* not what you call the highest; But this I *k*, for all the people *k* it, „ 1080
K that for this most gentle maiden's death „ 1291
I *k* What thou hast been in battle by my side, „ 1357
Unbound as yet, and gentle, as I *k*.' „ 1386
if she will'd it? nay, Who *k's*? „ 1423
'From our old books I *k* That Joseph came of old *Holy Grail* 59
'I *k* not, for thy heart is pure as snow.' „ 97
—we *k* not whence they come; „ 147
ye *k* the cries of all my realm Pass thro' this hall— „ 315
I touch'd The chapel-doors at dawn I *k*; „ 536
And *k's* himself no vision to himself, „ 917
'Make me thy knight, because I *k*, *Pelleas and E.* 7
I love thee, tho' I *k* thee not. „ 43
I *k* That all these pains are trials of my faith, „ 245
Yield me thy love and *k* me for thy knight.' „ 249
Ye *k* yourselves: how can ye bide at peace, „ 265
He could not love me, did he *k* me well. „ 312
Come, ye *k* nothing: here I pledge my troth, „ 341
loose thy tongue, and let me *k*.' „ 600
Perchance—who *k's*?—the purest of thy knights *Last Tournament* 49
'Where is he who *k's*? „ 132
belike I skip To *k* myself the wisest knight of all.' „ 248
Dost thou *k* the star We call the harp of Arthur „ 332
I *k* not what I would'—but said to her, „ 498
k The ptarmigan that whitens ere his hour „ 696
Who knowing nothing *k's* but to obey, *Guinevere* 186
None *k's* it, and my tears have brought me good: „ 202
What can'st thou *k* of Kings and Tables Round, „ 228
'Yea, but I *k*: the land was full of signs „ 232
Howbeit I *k*, if ancient prophecies Have err'd not, „ 449
the wife Whom he *k's* false, abide and rule „ 515
claim me thine, and *k* I am thine husband— „ 565
I *k* not what mysterious doom. „ 576
'Ye *k* me then, that wicked one, „ 669
Right well in heart they *k* thee for the King. *Pass. of Arthur* 63
Confusion, till I *k* not what I am, „ 144
King is sick, and *k's* not what he does. „ 265
isle, one isle, That *k's* not her own greatness: if she *k's* And dreads it we are fall'n.— *To the Queen II* 32
that which *k's*, but careful for itself, And that which *k's* not, ruling that which *k's* „ 57
Ye *k* not what ye ask. *Lover's Tale i* 150
young Life *k's* not when young Life was born, „ 156

Knowledge (*See also* **Self-knowledge**) In midst of *k*, dream'd not yet. *Two Voices* 90
'That men with *k* merely play'd, „ 172
In *k* of their own supremacy.' *Œnone* 133
And *K* for its beauty; *To ——, With Pal. of Art* 8
Beauty, Good, and *K*, are three sisters „ 10
the *k* of his art Held me above the subject, *D. of F. Women* 9
And me this *k* bolder made, *To J. S.* 5
Make *k* circle with the winds; *Love thou thy land* 17
Certain, if *k* bring the sword, That *k* takes the sword away— „ 87
flower of *k* changed to fruit Of wisdom. *Love and Duty* 24
yearning in desire To follow *k* like a sinking star, *Ulysses* 31
K comes, but wisdom lingers, (repeat) *Locksley Hall* 141, 143
And newer *k*, drawing nigh, *Day-Dm., Sleep P.* 51
Like Virtue firm, like *K* fair, *The Voyage* 68
Without the captain's *k*: hope with me. *Aylmer's Field* 717
k, so my daughter held, Was all in all: *Princess i* 135
As arguing love of *k* and of power; „ *ii* 57
K is now no more a fountain seal'd: „ 90
We issued gorged with *k*, and I spoke: „ 388
yet we know *K* is *k*, and this matter hangs: „ *iii* 316
each Disclaim'd all *k* of us: „ *iv* 229
K in our own land make her free, „ *v* 419
sought far less for truth than power In *k*: „ *vii* 237
A greater than all *k*, beat her down. „ 238
For *k* is of things we see; *In Mem., Pro.* 22
Let *k* grow from more to more, „ 25
power to think And all my *k* of myself; „ *xvi* 16
All *k* that the sons of flesh Shall gather „ *lxxxv* 27
Who loves not *K*? Who shall rail Against her beauty? „ *cxiv* 1
grewest not alone in power And *k*, „ 27
eye to eye, shall look On *k*; „ *Con.* 130
behold, Without *k*, without pity, *Maud II iv* 53
This is my sum of *k*—that my love Grew with myself— *Lover's Tale i* 164
For *K* is the swallow on the lake *Ancient Sage* 37
Of *K* fusing class with class, *Freedom* 17
Without his *k*, from him flits to warn *Demeter and P.* 89
likeness of thyself Without thy *k*, „ 93
And utter *k* is but utter love— *The Ring* 43
While the long day of *k* grows and warms, *Prog. of Spring* 101

Known (*See also* **Long-known, Well-known**) Or is she *k* in all the land, *L. of Shalott i* 26
To perish, wept for, honour'd, *k*, *Two Voices* 149
In aftertime, this also shall be *k*: *M. d'Arthur* 35
Like one that never can be wholly *k*, *Gardener's D.* 206
Much have I seen and *k*; *Ulysses* 13
having *k* me—to decline On a range of lower feelings *Locksley Hall* 43
'No more of love; your sex is *k*: *The Letters* 29
Not only to the market-cross were *k*, *Enoch Arden* 96
Have we not *k* each other all our lives? (repeat) „ 306, 420
k Far in a darker isle beyond the line; „ 604
He must have *k*, himself had *k*: *Aylmer's Field* 346
He had *k* a man, a quintessence of man, „ 388
learn a language *k* but smatteringly „ 433
many too had *k* Edith among the hamlets round, „ 614
As with the mother he had never *k*, „ 690
O thou that killest, hadst thou *k*, „ 738
And whatsoever can be taught and *k*; *Princess ii* 385
falling on my face was caught and *k*. „ *iv* 270
I bore up in hope she would be *k*: „ 320
public use required she should be *k*; „ 336
and *k* at last (my work) And full of cowardice. „ 347
when *k*, there grew Another kind of beauty „ 447
'O brother, you have *k* the pangs we felt, „ 374
And all the sultry palms of India *k*, *W. to Marie Alex.* 14
Two dead men have I *k* In courtesy like to thee: *G. of Swainston* 11
Who makes by force his merit *k* *In Mem. lxiv* 9
And which, tho' veil'd, was *k* to me, „ *ciii* 13
And that dear voice, I once have *k*, „ *cxvi* 11
K and unknown; human, divine; „ *cxxix* 5
She is singing an air that is *k* to me, *Maud I v* 3
Everything came to be *k*. „ *II v* 51

Known (*continued*) And there be made *k* to the stately Queen, *Marr. of Geraint* 607
Because I knew my deeds were *k*, I found, *Geraint and E.* 858
Not willing to be *k*, He left the barren-beaten thoroughfare, *Lancelot and E.* 160
K as they are, to me they are unknown.' „ 186
'*K* am I, and of Arthur's hall, and *k*, „ 188
Robed in red samite, easily to be *k*, „ 433
love In women, whomsoever I have *k*. „ 1294
make men worse by making my sin *k*? „ 1417
never have I *k* the world without, *Holy Grail* 20
'O brother, had you *k* our mighty hall, „ 225
'And, brother, had you *k* our hall within, „ 246
O brother, had you *k* our Camelot, „ 339
But her thou hast not *k*: „ 454
he had *k* Scarce any but the women of his isles, *Pelleas and E.* 87
trampled out his face from being *k*, *Last Tournament* 470
wish her any huger wrong Than having *k* thee? „ 597
It surely was my profit had I *k*: *Guinevere* 658
In aftertime, this also shall be *k*: *Pass. of Arthur* 203
Never yet Before or after have I *k* the spring *Lover's Tale i* 314
I died then, I had not *k* the death; „ 496
love Shall ripen to a proverb, unto all *K*, „ 759
Not know? with such a secret to be *k*. „ *iv* 121
all the house had *k* the loves of both; „ 123
Had I not *k* where Love, at first a fear, *Sisters (E. and E.)* 170
that hast never *k* the embrace of love, *Tiresias* 164
But the face I had *k*, O Mother, *The Wreck* 116
That which knows, And is not *k*, but felt *Ancient Sage* 86
gain'd a freedom *k* to Europe, *k* to all; *Locksley H., Sixty* 129
and flows that can be *k* to you or me. „ 194
k By those who love thee best. *Pref. Poem Broth. S.* 7
Makes the might of Britain *k*; *Open. I. and C. Exhib.* 19
one other whom you have not *k*. *The Ring* 55
Whose eyes have *k* this globe of ours, *To Ulysses* 2
Had I but *k* you as I know you now— *Romney's R.* 90
On those two *k* peaks they stand *Parnassus* 11
To have seen thee, and heard thee, and *k*. *Bandit's Death* 4
thousand things are hidden still, And not a hundred *k*. *Mechanophilus* 24

Know-nothing We had read their *k-n* books *Despair* 55
For their knowing and *k-n* books „ 93

Knuckled boy That *k* at the taw: *Will Water.* 132

Korân I stagger at the *K* and the sword. *Akbar's Dream* 71
'hast *thou* brought us down a new *K* From heaven? „ 116
I heard a mocking laugh 'the new *K*!' „ 183

Kraken uninvaded sleep The *K* sleepeth: *The Kraken* 4

Kypris Ay, and this *K* also—did I take That popular name *Lucretius* 95

L

Laädy (lady) yon *l* a-steppin' along the streeät, *North. Cobbler* 107
But owd Squire's *l* es long es she lived *Village Wife* 53
They maäkes ma a graäter *L* *Spinster's S's.* 110

Laäid (laid) tha knaws she *l* it to meä. *N. Farmer, O. S.* 21
Wi' lots o' munny *l* by, „ *N. S.* 22
Could'n I luvv thy muther by cause o' 'er munny *l* by? „ 35
an' they *l* big heggs es tha seeas, *Village Wife* 118

Laäme (lame) An' Lucy wur *l* o' one leg, „ 99

Laämed (lamed) I seeäd that our Sally went *l* *North. Cobbler* 39

Laäne (lane) an' hawmin' about i' the *l's*, „ 24
Goä to the *l* at the back, *Spinster's S's.* 6
by the brokken shed i' the *l* at the back, „ 37
es I be abroad i' the *l's* „ 107

Laäte (late) fur he coom'd last night sa *l*— *Village Wife* 123
What maäkes 'er sa *l*? *Spinster's S's.* 5
what ha maäde our Molly sa *l*? „ 113
I says to him 'Squire, ya're *l*,' *Owd Roä* 55
Too *l*—but it's all ower now— „ 116
Too *l*—tha mun git tha to bed, „ 117

Laäy (lay) says Parson, and *l's* down 'is 'at, *North. Cobbler* 89

Laäzy (lazy) Them or thir feythers, tha sees, mun 'a beän a *l* lot, — *N. Farmer, N. S.* 49
Laborious *L* orient ivory sphere in sphere, — *Princess, Pro.* 20
And, lo! the long *l* miles Of Palace; — *Ode Inter. Exhib.* 11
L for her people and her poor— — *Ded. of Idylls* 35
You, the hardy, *l*, Patient children of Albion, — *On Jub. Q. Victoria* 58
Labour (s) (*See also* **Brain-labour**) gaze On the prime *l* of thine early days: — *Ode to Memory* 94
So were thy *l* little-worth. — *Two Voices* 171
A *l* working to an end. — „ 297
why Should life all *l* be? Let us alone. — *Lotos-Eaters, C. S.* 42
Long *l* unto aged breath, — „ 85
the shore Than *l* in the deep mid-ocean, — „ 127
And rested from her *l's*. — *The Goose* 16
discerning to fulfil This *l*, — *Ulysses* 36
Confused the chemic *l* of the blood, — *Lucretius* 20
A present, a great *l* of the loom; — *Princess i* 44
A blessing on her *l's* for the world. — „ *ii* 479
health, and wind, and rain, And *l*. — „ *iv* 280
That all her *l* was but as a block — „ *vii* 230
Science, Art, and *L* have outpour'd — *Ode Inter. Exhib.* 5
And reaps the *l* of his hands, — *In Mem. lxiv* 26
thy prosperous *l* fills The lips of men — „ *lxxxiv* 25
band Of youthful friends, on mind and art, And *l*, — „ *lxxxvii* 23
To *l* and the mattock-harden'd hand, — *Maud I xviii* 34
Or it may be the *l* of his hands, — *Marr. of Geraint* 341
dew of their great *l*, and the blood Of their strong bodies, — „ 568
Her own poor work, her empty *l*, left. — *Lancelot and E.* 991
Or *L*, with a groan and not a voice, — *To the Queen ii* 55
the *l* of fifty that had to be done by five, — *Def. of Lucknow* 77
And rough-ruddy faces Of lowly *l*, — *Merlin and the G.* 60
Labour (verb) No memory *l's* longer from the deep Gold-mines — *D. of F. Women* 273
Yet since he did but *l* for himself, — *Enoch Arden* 819
would go, *L* for his own Edith, — *Aylmer's Field* 420
and *l* him Beyond his comrade of the hearth, — *Gareth and L.* 484
'Friend, he that *l's* for the sparrow-hawk — *Marr. of Geraint* 271
As one that *l's* with an evil dream, — *Merlin and V.* 101
Labour'd (adj. and part) Or *l* mine undrainable of ore. — *Œnone* 115
Had *l* down within his ample lungs, — *Princess v* 273
vast designs Of his *l* rampart-lines, — *Ode on Well.* 105
A hermit, who had pray'd, *l* and pray'd, — *Lancelot and E.* 403
Had *l* in lifting them out of slime, — *Dead Prophet* 11
Labour'd (verb) *l* thro' His brief prayer-prelude, — *Aylmer's Field* 627
The bosom with long sighs *l*; — *Princess vii* 225
L with him, for he seem'd as one That all in later, — *Gareth and L.* 1128
All that day long *l*, hewing the pines, — *Death of Œnone* 62
Labourer woo'd and wed A *l's* daughter, — *Dora* 40
By sallowy rims, arose the *l's'* homes, — *Aylmer's Field* 147
year by year the *l* tills His wonted glebe, — *In Mem. ci* 21
Labouring And onward drags a *l* breast, — „ *xv* 18
The giant *l* in his youth; — „ *cxviii* 2
The lusty mowers *l* dinnerless, — *Geraint and E.* 251
Arthur came, and *l* up the pass, — *Lancelot and E.* 47
ever *l* had scoop'd himself In the white rock — „ 404
Labourless till the *l* day dipt under the West; — *V. of Maeldune* 86
Laburnum (adj.) all the gold from each *l* chain Drop to the grass. — *To Mary Boyle* 11
Laburnum (s) *L's*, dropping-wells of fire. — *In Mem. lxxxiii* 12
Labyrinth Charm'd him thro' every *l* — *Aylmer's Field* 479
He thrids the *l* of the mind, — *In Mem. xcvii* 21
Labyrinthine following out A league of *l* darkness, — *Demeter and P.* 82
Lace (fabric) The shadow of some piece of pointed *l*, — *Lancelot and E.*1174
books, the miniature, the *l* are hers, — *The Ring* 288
Dresses and *l's* and jewels and never a ring — *Charity* 6
Lace (a cord) burst The *l's* toward her babe; — *Princess vi* 149
And once the *l's* of a helmet crack'd, — *Last Tournament* 164
Lace (verb) holp To *l* us up, till, each, — *Princess i* 202
Laced *See* **Strait-laced**
Lack (s) tinged with wan from *l* of sleep, — *Princess iii* 25
Death-pale, for *l* of gentle maiden's aid. — *Lancelot and E.* 765
'Belike for *l* of wiser company; — *Last Tournament* 245
Lack (verb) We *l* not rhymes and reasons, — *Will Water.* 62
We *l* thee by the hearth.' — *Gareth and L.* 754
Lack'd-lackt I have not *lack'd* thy mild reproof, — *My life is full* 4
for, were Sir Lancelot *lackt*, at least — *Gareth and L.* 738
Because it *lack'd* the power of perfect Hope; — *Lover's Tale i* 453
angers of the Gods for evil done And expiation *lack'd* — *Tiresias* 63
Lackest Asks what thou *l*, thought resign'd, — *Two Voices* 98
Lacking given thee a fair face, *L* a tongue?' — *Pelleas and E.* 102
Beast too, as *l* human wit—disgraced, — „ 476
Lack-lustre And a *l-l* dead-blue eye, — *A Character* 17
Lackt *See* **Lack'd**
Lactantius Some cited old *L*: — *Columbus* 49
Lad (*See also* **Shepherd-lad**) There's many a bolder *l* 'ill woo me — *May Queen* 23
the shepherd *l's* on every side 'ill come — „ 27
the *l* stretch'd out And babbled for the golden seal, — *Dora* 134
O well for the sailor *l*, That he sings in his boat — *Break, break, etc.* 7
Enoch Arden, a rough sailor's *l* — *Enoch Arden* 14
'Poor *l*, he died at Florence, — *The Brook* 35
Leolin's emissary, A crippled *l*, — *Aylmer's Field* 519
long-limb'd *l* that had a Psyche too; — *Princess ii* 406
Himself would tilt it out among the *l's*: — „ *v* 355
Warn't I craäzed fur the lasses mysén when wur a *l*? — *N. Farmer, N. S.* 18
Mun be a guvness, *l*, or summut, and addle her breäd: — „ 26
Breäk me a bit o' the esh for his 'eäd, *l*, — „ 41
fair and fine!—Some young *l's* mystery— — *Gareth and L.* 466
an the *l* were noble, he had ask'd For horse and armour: — „ 473
Ate with young *l's* his portion by the door, — „ 480
take counsel; for this *l* is great And lusty, — „ 730
massacring Man, woman, *l* and girl— — „ 1341
This *l*, whose lightest word Is mere white truth — *Balin and Balan* 517
had need Of a good stout *l* at his farm; — *First Quarrel* 18
poor *l*, an' we parted in tears. — „ 20
For he thought—there were other *l's*— — „ 38
you haven't done it, my *l*, — „ 53
I weänt gaäinsaäy it, my *l*, — *North. Cobbler* 17
not hafe ov a man, my *l*— — „ 21
Proud on 'im, like, my *l*, an' I keeäps — „ 97
But I moänt, my *l*, and I weänt, — „ 102
'*L*, thou mun cut off thy taäil, — *Village Wife* 64
she walkt awaäy wi' a hofficer *l*, — „ 97
l will need little more of your care.' — *In the Child. Hosp.* 17
Steevie, my *l*, thou 'ed very nigh been — *Spinster's S's.* 68
But I cleän forgot tha, my *l*, — *Owd Roä* 53
wheere thou was a-liggin, my *l*, — „ 87
But sich an obstropulous *l*— — *Churchwarden, etc.* 23
an' 'e beal'd to ya '*L* coom hout' — „ 28
fur thou was the Parson's *l*. — „ 36
Ladder (*See also* **Lether**) lean a *l* on the shaft, — *St. S. Stylites* 216
hurl them to earth from the *l's* — *Def. of Lucknow* 58
shifting *l's* of shadow and light, — *Dead Prophet* 21
A Jacob's *l* falls On greening grass, — *Early Spring* 9
Ladder-of-heaven the *l-o-h* that hangs on a star. — *By an Evolution.* 12
Laddie *See* **Soldier-laddie**
Laden (*See also* **Barge-laden, Lady-laden**) enchanted stem, *L* with flower and fruit, — *Lotos-Eaters* 29
Knowledge comes, but wisdom lingers, and he bears a *l* breast, — *Locksley Hall* 143
came the children *l* with their spoil; — *Enoch Arden* 445
Two sets of three *l* with jingling arms, — *Geraint and E.* 188
Boughs on each side, *l* with wholesome shade, — *Lover's Tale i* 230
soft winds, *L* with thistledown and seeds — „ *ii* 13
Lading *l* and unlading the tall barks, — *Enoch Arden* 816
The *l* of a single pain, — *In Mem. xxv* 11
Lady (adj.) and *l* friends From neighbour seats: — *Princess, Pro.* 97
In mine own *l* palms I cull'd the spring — *Merlin and V.* 273
Lady (s) (*See also* **Court-lady, Laädy, Liege-lady**) The sweetest *l* of the time, — *Arabian Nights* 141
Rise from the feast of sorrow, *l*, — *Margaret* 62
In dreaming of my *l's* eyes. — *Kate* 28
knight for ever kneel'd To a *l* in his shield, — *L. of Shalott iii* 7
Before Our *L* murmur'd she; — *Mariana in the S.* 28
bore a *l* from a leaguer'd town; — *D. of F. Women* 47
At length I saw a *l* within call, — „ 85
'No marvel, sovereign *l*: in fair field — „ 97

Lady (s) (*continued*) charged Before the eyes of *ladies* and of kings. *M. d'Arthur* 225
I met my *l* once: A woman like a butt, *Walk. to the Mail* 48
lightly rain from *ladies'* hands. *Sir Galahad* 12
How sweet are looks that *ladies* bend „ 13
'And he shall have it,' the *l* replied, *Lady Clare* 47
Ancient homes of lord and *l*, *L. of Burleigh* 31
That she grew a noble *l*, „ 75
a phosphorescence charming even My *l*; *Aylmer's Field* 117
My *l's* Indian kinsman unannounced „ 190
'Good! my *l's* kinsman! good!' „ 198
My *l* with her fingers interlock'd, „ 199
'A gracious gift to give a *l*, this!' „ 240
give this gift of his to one That is no *l*?' „ 243
My *l's* cousin, Half-sickening of his pension'd afternoon, „ 460
Seized it, took home, and to my *l*,— „ 532
Seconded, for my *l* follow'd suit, „ 558
My *l's* Indian kinsman rushing in, „ 593
with these, a *l*, one that arm'd Her own fair head, *Princess, Pro.* 32
And takes a *l's* finger with all care, „ 173
A talk of college and of *ladies'* rights, „ 233
let the *ladies* sing us, if they will, „ 240
The *l* of three castles in that land: „ *i* 79
'Three *ladies* of the Northern empire „ 238
are the *ladies* of your land so tall?' „ *ii* 47
will do well, *Ladies*, in entering here, „ 62
We sat: the *L* glanced: Then Florian, „ 111
But, dearest *L*, pray you fear me not, „ 333
I ceased, and all the *ladies*, each at each, „ *iv* 117
strange experiences Unmeet for *ladies*. „ 159
Thereat the *L* stretch'd a vulture throat, „ 363
Take comfort: live, dear *l*, for your child!' „ *v* 80
Alive with fluttering scarfs and *ladies'* eyes, „ 509
'Your brother, *L*,—Florian,—ask for him „ *vi* 313
Sleep, little *ladies*! And they slept well. *Minnie and Winnie* 3
Wake, little *ladies*, The sun is aloft! „ 19
And never a line from my *l* yet! *Window, No Answer* 15
'And near him stood the *L* of the Lake, *Com. of Arthur* 283
A *l* of high lineage, of great lands, *Gareth and L.* 609
Who tilt for *l's* love and glory here, „ 740
Come, therefore, leave thy *l* lightly, knave. „ 957
it beseemeth not a knave To ride with such a *l*.' „ 959
rode Full slowly by a knight, *l*, and dwarf; *Marr. of Geraint* 187
Except the *l* he loves best be there. „ 481
Lays claim to for the *l* at his side, „ 487
Has ever won it for the *l* with him, „ 490
thou, that hast no *l*, canst not fight.' „ 493
errant-knights And *ladies* came, and by and by the town Flow'd in, „ 546
Spake to the *l* with him and proclaim'd, „ 552
lords and *ladies* of the high court went „ 662
Sweet *l*, never since I first drew breath *Geraint and E.* 619
her *ladies* loved to call Enid the Fair, „ 962
the fairest and the best Of *ladies* living *Balin and Balan* 340
Take one verse more—the *l* speaks it— *Merlin and V.* 445
The *l* never made *unwilling* war With those fine eyes: „ 603
man That ever among *ladies* ate in hall, *Lancelot and E.* 255
King Had on his cuirass worn our *L's* Head, „ 294
'Fair *l*, since I never yet have worn „ 363
Favour of any *l* in the lists. (repeat) „ 364, 474
L, my liege, in whom I have my joy, „ 1180
And to all other *ladies*, I make moan: „ 1279
Lancelot, whom the *L* of the Lake Caught „ 1404
The knights and *ladies* wept, *Holy Grail* 353
Our *L* says it, and we well believe: Wed thou our *L*, and rule over us, „ 604
Pelleas for his *l* won The golden circlet, *Pelleas and E.* 13
turn'd the *l* round And look'd upon her people; „ 91
for the *l* was Ettarre, And she was a great *l* in her land. „ 97
gracious to him, For she was a great *l*. „ 123
her *ladies* laugh'd along with her. „ 135
for he dream'd His *l* loved him, „ 153
Pelleas might obtain his *l's* love, „ 161
Then rang the shout his *l* loved: „ 171
'These be the ways of *ladies*,' Pelleas thought, „ 209

Lady (s) (*continued*) 'Behold me, *L*, A prisoner, *Pelleas and E.* 240
'For pity of thine own self, Peace, *L*, peace: „ 254
He needs no aid who doth his *l's* will.' „ 281
'*L*, for indeed I loved you and I deem'd you beautiful, „ 296
'Why, let my *l* bind me if she will, And let my *l* beat me if she will: „ 334
let my *l* sear the stump for him, „ 339
they cried, 'our *l* loves thee not.' „ 369
crying to their *l*, 'Lo! Pelleas is dead— „ 376
ware their *ladies'* colours on the casque, *Last Tournament* 184
'O pray you, noble *l*, weep no more; *Guinevere* 184
Ah sweet *l*, the King's grief For his own self, „ 196
sweet *l*, if I seem To vex an ear too sad „ 314
a noble knight, Was gracious to all *ladies*, „ 329
I could think, sweet *l*, yours would be „ 352
charged Before the eyes of *ladies* and of kings. *Pass. of Arthur* 393
Whether they *were* his *l's* marriage-bells, *Lover's Tale iv* 11
For that low knell tolling his *l* dead— „ 33
saw His *l* with the moonlight on her face; „ 57
He reverenced his dear *l* even in death; „ 74
sudden wail his *l* made Dwelt in his fancy: „ 149
About a picture of his *l*, taken Some years „ 216
Led his dear *l* to a chair of state. „ 321
Then taking his dear *l* by one hand, „ 369
yes—a *l*—none of their spies— *Rizpah* 15
Lady-clad I saw The feudal warrior *l-c*; *Princess, Pro.* 119
Lady-fern underneath a plume of *l-f*, Sang, *Balin and Balan* 26
Lady-laden long Rich galleries, *l-l*, *Holy Grail* 346
Lady of Shalott *See* **Shalott**
Lady's-head The *L-h* upon the prow *The Voyage* 11
Lady-sister I bow'd to his *l-s* as she rode *Maud I iv* 15
Lag To *l* behind, scared by the cry they made, *Princess v* 94
Laggard Here comes a *l* hanging down his head, *Geraint and E.* 60
Lagg'd I *l* in answer loth to render up *Princess v* 299
Whereof the dwarf *l* latest, and the knight Had vizor up, *Marr. of Geraint* 188
Laid (*See also* **Laäid, Long-laid**) *L* low, very low, In the dark we must lie. *All Things will Die* 21
L by the tumult of the fight. *Margaret* 26
Upon my lap he *l* his head: *The Sisters* 17
And *l* him at his mother's feet. „ 35
the strong foundation-stones were *l* *Palace of Art* 235
and see me where I am lowly *l*. *May Queen, N. Y's. E.* 30
argent of her breast to sight *L* bare. *D. of F. Women* 159
more the white goose *l* It clack'd and cackled louder. *The Goose* 23
L widow'd of the power in his eye *M. d'Arthur* 122
l his head upon her lap, And loosed „ 208
Francis *l* A damask napkin wrought with horse *Audley Court* 20
and the winds are *l* with sound. *Locksley Hall* 104
for when he *l* a tax Upon his town, *Godiva* 13
'O eyes long *l* in happy sleep!' *Day-Dm., Depart.* 17
HER arms across her breast she *l*; *Beggar Maid* 1
rises up, And is lightly *l* again. (repeat) *Vision of Sin* 134, 170
And *l* the feeble infant in his arms; *Enoch Arden* 152
when she *l* her head beside my own. „ 881
the Baronet yet had *l* No bar between them: *Aylmer's Field* 117
or *l* his feverous pillow smooth! „ 701
she *l*, Wifelike, her hand in one of his, „ 807
With neighbours *l* along the grass, *Lucretius* 214
his bones long *l* within the grave, „ 256
l about them at their wills and died; *Princess, Pro.* 31
pluck'd her likeness out; *L* it on flowers, „ *i* 93
The creature *l* his muzzle on your lap, „ *ii* 272
Mock-Hymen were *l* up like winter bats, „ *iv* 144
she *l* A feeling finger on my brows, „ *vi* 120
L the soft babe in his hard-mailed hands. „ 208
And others otherwhere they *l*; „ 378
And worthy to be *l* by thee; *Ode on Well.* 94
Be glad, because his bones are *l* by thine! „ 141
And where you tenderly *l* it by: *The Daisy* 100
A famine after *l* them low, *The Victim* 2
beautiful, when all the winds are *l*, *Spec. of Iliad* 12
Where he in English earth is *l*, *In Mem. xviii* 2
They *l* him by the pleasant shore, „ *xix* 3
L their dark arms about the field. (repeat) „ *xcv* 16, 52

Lamech But that of *L* is mine. *Maud II ii* 48
Lamed (*See also* **Laämed**) my mind Stumbles, and all my faculties are *l*. *Lucretius* 123
and a spear Down-glancing *l* the charger, *Lancelot and E.* 488
she was *l* iv a knee, *Tomorrow* 77
Lameness Cured *l*, palsies, cancers. *St. S. Stylites* 82
Lament floated a dying swan, And loudly did *l*. *Dying Swan* 7
a soul *l's*, which hath been blest, *D. of F. Women* 281
Lamentation a *l* and an ancient tale of wrong, *Lotos-Eaters, C. S.* 118
as it were one voice an agony Of *l*, *M. d'Arthur* 201
Bury the Great Duke With an empire's *l*, *Ode on Well.* 2
as it were one voice, an agony Of *l*, *Pass. of Arthur* 369
scroll written over with *l* and woe. *Despair* 20
Laming And caught the *l* bullet. *Sisters (E. and E.)* 65
Lamp (*See also* **Night-lamp**) Some yearning toward the *l's* of night; *Two Voices* 363
'by that *l*,' I thought, 'she sits!' *Miller's D.* 114
tho' my *l* was lighted late, *May Queen, Con.* 18
and lit *L's* which out-burn'd Canopus. *D. of F. Women* 146
burn a fragrant *l* before my bones, *St. S. Stylites* 196
two sphere *l's* blazon'd like Heaven and Earth *Princess i* 223
above her droop'd a *l*, And made the single jewel „ *iv* 272
When all is gay with *l's*, *In Mem. xcviii* 27
And just above the parting was a *l*: *Lover's Tale iv* 218
L of the Lord God Lord everlasting, *Batt. of Brunanburh* 27
set The *l's* alight, and call For golden music, *Ancient Sage* 196
Lamplight Gold glittering thro' *l* dim, *Arabian Nights* 18
Lamp-lit shone the tent *L-l* from the inner. *Princess iv* 26
Lan' (land) was as light as snow an the *l'*, *Tomorrow* 36
'The Divil take all the black *l'*, „ 64
Lancaster (*See also* **Rose of Lancaster**) York's white rose as red as *L's*, *Aylmer's Field* 51
Lance *L's* in ambush set; *D. of F. Women* 28
Not like that Arthur who, with *l* in rest, *M. d'Arthur* 222
and hurl their *l's* in the sun; *Locksley Hall* 170
My tough *l* thrusteth sure, *Sir Galahad* 2
some were push'd with *l's* from the rock, *Princess, Pro.* 46
And into fiery splinters leapt the *l*, „ *v* 494
Like light in many a shiver'd *l* *In Mem. xlix* 3
Flash brand and *l*, fall battleaxe upon helm, *Com. of Arthur* 486
before my *l* if *l* Were mine to use— *Gareth and L.* 6
my *l* Hold, by God's grace, he shall into the mire— „ 722
and knowing both of *l* and sword.' „ 731
no room was there For *l* or tourney-skill: „ 1042
Gareth laid his *l* athwart the ford; „ 1048
felt Thy manhood thro' that wearied *l* of thine. „ 1266
How best to manage horse, *l*, sword and shield, „ 1351
Let *me* lay *l* in rest, O noble host, *Marr. of Geraint* 496
A *l* that splinter'd like an icicle, *Geraint and E.* 89
Aim'd at the helm, his *l* err'd; „ 157
pick'd the *l* That pleased him best, „ 179
and the points of *l's* bicker in it. „ 449
Down by the length of *l* and arm beyond The crupper, „ 463
Came riding with a hundred *l's* up; „ 539
cast his *l* aside, And doff'd his helm: „ 595
l In rest, and made as if to fall upon him. „ 775
he sharply caught his *l* and shield, *Balin and Balan* 287
With pointed *l* as if to pierce, a shape, „ 325
He burst his *l* against a forest bough, „ 329
A score with pointed *l's*, making at him— „ 401
The longest *l* his eyes had ever seen, „ 411
And every scratch a *l* had made upon it, *Lancelot and E.* 20
God Broke the strong *l*, and roll'd his enemy down, „ 26
mine is the firmer seat, The truer *l*: „ 447
Set *l* in rest, strike spur, suddenly move, „ 456
Thro' her own side she felt the sharp *l* go; „ 624
such a tonurey and so full, So many *l's* broken— *Holy Grail* 331
my strong *l* had beaten down the knights, „ 363
against the chapel door Laid *l*, and enter'd, „ 460
she caught the circlet from his *l*, *Pelleas and E.* 173
his long *l* Broken, and his Excalibur a straw.' *Last Tournament* 87
My hand—belike the *l* hath dript upon it— „ 200
Even to tipmost *l* and topmost helm, „ 442
tilt with a *l* Becomes thee well— „ 636
Not like that Arthur who, with *l* in rest, *Pass. of Arthur* 390

N*

Lance (*continued*) would rush on a thousand *l's* and die— *V. of Maeldune* 24
the points of the Russian *l's* arose in the sky; *Heavy Brigade* 5
Thro' the forest of *l's* and swords „ 49
L's snapt in sunder, *The Tourney* 8
Lanced *See* **Long-lanced**
Lance-head Gasping to Sir Lavaine, 'Draw the *l-h*:' *Lancelot and E.* 511
Lancelot (a knight of the Round Table) (*See also* **Launcelot, Lancelot-like**) brazen greaves Of bold Sir *L*. *L. of Shalott iii* 5
'Tirra lirra,' by the river Sang Sir *L*. „ 36
But *L* mused a little space; „ *iv* 51
whom he loved And honour'd most, Sir *L*, *Com. of Arthur* 448
And *L* past away among the flowers, „ 450
Then *L* standing near,' Sir Seneschal, *Gareth and L.* 461
thine own fineness, *L*, some fine day Undo thee not— „ 476
L ever spake him pleasantly, „ 482
the love that linkt the King And *L*— „ 492
King had saved his life In battle twice, and *L* once the King's—For *L* was the first in Tournament, „ 494
'Let *L* know, my King, let *L* know, „ 567
Then, after summoning *L* privily, „ 581
thy chief man Sir *L* whom he trusts to overthrow, „ 619
Now therefore have I come for *L*.' „ 623
And therefore am I come for *L*.' „ 644
Till peacock'd up with *L's* noticing. „ 719
L said, 'Kay, wherefore wilt thou go against the King, „ 726
for, were Sir *L* lackt, at least He might have yielded „ 738
pray'd the King would grant me *L* To fight „ 856
To crave again Sir *L* of the King. „ 882
methinks There rides no knight, not *L*, „ 1182
Sir *L*, having swum the river-loops— „ 1216
L answer'd, 'Prince, O Gareth— „ 1236
one who came to help thee, not to harm, *L*, „ 1239
Then Gareth, 'Thou—*L*!—thine the hand That threw me? „ 1241
Shamed had I been, and sad—O *L*—thou!' „ 1245
'*L*, Why came ye not, when call'd? „ 1246
L said, 'Blessed be thou, Sir Gareth! „ 1257
Sir *L*, is hard by, with meats and drinks „ 1276
O *L*, *L*'—and she clapt her hands— „ 1290
Said *L*, 'Peradventure he, your name, „ 1293
'Courteous in this, Lord *L*, as in all.' „ 1303
L, from my hold on these Streams virtue— „ 1309
not shame Even the shadow of *L* under shield. „ 1311
Clung to the shield that *L* lent him, „ 1320
hath wrought on *L* now To lend thee horse „ 1323
O Prince, I went for *L* first, „ 1343
The quest is *L's*: give him back the shield.' „ 1344
L on him urged All the devisings of their chivalry „ 1348
ev'n Sir *L* thro' his warm blood felt Ice strike, „ 1398
At once Sir *L's* charger fiercely neigh'd, „ 1400
They hate the King, and *L*, the King's friend, „ 1418
Touching her guilty love for *L*, *Marr. of Geraint* 25
and dreaming of her love For *L*, „ 159
wherefore hover'd round *L*, but when he mark'd *Balin and Balan* 160
How far beyond him *L* seem'd to move, „ 172
Sir *L* as to meet her, then at once, „ 247
To whom Sir *L* with his eyes on earth, „ 253
Then *L* with his hand among the flowers „ 259
Then *L* lifted his large eyes; „ 277
'The Queen we worship, *L*, I, and all, „ 349
Eyes too that long have watch'd how *L* draws From homage „ 375
Which our high *L* hath so lifted up, „ 490
Stoop at thy will on *L* and the Queen.' „ 536
Sir *L* worshipt no unmarried girl *Merlin and V.* 12
They place their pride in *L* and the Queen. „ 25
We ride a-hawking with Sir *L*. „ 95
Beheld the Queen and *L* get to horse. „ 102
'Is that the *L*? goodly—ay, but gaunt: „ 103
L will be gracious to the rat, „ 120
'Let her be,' Said *L* and unhooded casting off „ 130
I heard the great Sir *L* sing it once, „ 385
what say ye to Sir *L*, friend Traitor or true? „ 769
Sir *L* went ambassador, at first, „ 774

Lancelot (a knight of the Round Table) (*continued*) Sir *L* told This matter to the Queen, *Guinevere* 53
'O *L*, get thee hence to thine own land, „ 88
And *L* ever promised, but remain'd, „ 93
'O *L*, if thou love me get thee hence.' „ 95
L, who rushing outward lionlike Leapt on him, „ 107
She answer'd, '*L*, wilt thou hold me so? „ 116
So *L* got her horse, Set her thereon, „ 122
while the King Was waging war on L: „ 156
gone is he To wage grim war against Sir *L* „ 193
he foresaw This evil work of *L* and the Queen?' „ 307
himself would say Sir *L* had the noblest; „ 320
you moved Among them, *L* or our lord the King?' „ 326
'Sir *L*, as became a noble knight, „ 328
L's needs must be a thousand-fold Less noble, „ 338
If ever *L*, that most noble knight, „ 345
Sir *L's*, were as noble as the King's, „ 351
L came, Reputed the best knight „ 381
not like him, 'Not like my *L*'— „ 407
Sir *L*, my right arm The mightiest of my knights, „ 429
Then came thy shameful sin with L; „ 487
touch thy lips, they are not mine, But *L's*: „ 552
not a smaller soul, Nor *L*, nor another. „ 567
yearn'd for warmth and colour which I found In *L*— „ 648
and most human too, Not *L*, nor another. „ 650
when we see it, Not *L*, nor another.' „ 661
Gawain kill'd In *L's* war, *Pass. of Arthur* 31

Lancelot-like '*L-l*, she said 'Courteous is this, *Gareth and L.* 1302

Lance-splintering 'Ramp ye *l-s* lions, on whom all spears Are rotten sticks! „ 1305

Lancets greenish glimmerings thro' the *l*, *Aylmer's Field* 622

Land (*See also* **Lan', Lond, Lotos-land, West-Saxon-land**)
God gave her peace; her l *reposed;* *To the Queen* 26
the rainbow forms and flies on the *l* *Sea-Fairies* 25
thou wert nursed in some delicious *l* *Eleänore* 11
Pressing up against the *l*, „ 112
who sways the floods and *l's* From Ind to Ind, *Buonaparte* 3
And woke her with a lay from fairy *l*. *Caress'd or chidden* 8
That sets at twilight in a *l* of reeds. „ 14
Or is she known in all the *l*, *L. of Shalott i* 26
Just breaking over *l* and main? *Two Voices* 84
gallery That lend broad verge to distant *l's*, *Palace of Art* 30
Who paced for ever in a glimmering *l*, „ 67
the times of every *l* So wrought, „ 147
plunging seas draw backward from the *l* „ 251
in strange *l's* a traveller walking slow, „ 277
I have found A new *l*, but I die.' „ 284
Nor any poor about your *l's*? *L. C. V. de Vere* 68
fair as little Alice in all the *l* they say, *May Queen* 7
And sweet is all the *l* about, „ *Con.* 7
'Courage!' he said, and pointed toward the *l*, *Lotos-Eaters* 1
In the afternoon they came unto a *l* „ 3
A *l* of streams! some, like a downward smoke, „ 10
river seaward flow From the inner *l*: „ 15
A *l* where all things always seem'd the same! „ 24
smile in secret, looking over wasted *l's*, „ *C. S.* 114
In every *l* I saw, wherever light illumineth, *D. of F. Women* 13
when to *l* Bluster the winds and tides „ 37
'My God, my *l*, my father— „ 209
To every *l* beneath the skies, *On a Mourner* 3
It is the *l* that freemen till, *You ask me, why, etc.* 5
The *l*, where girt with friends or foes „ 7
A *l* of settled government, A *l* of just and old renown, „ 9
Tho' Power should make from *l* to *l* „ 21
Love thou thy *l*, with love far-brought *Love thou thy land* 1
Would pace the troubled *l*, like Peace; „ 84
that sendest out the man To rule by *l* and sea, *England and Amer.* 2
stood on a dark strait of barren *l*. *M. d'Arthur* 10
shrills All night in a waste *l*, where no one comes, „ 202
All the *l* in flowery squares, *Gardener's D.* 76
and parted, and he died In foreign *l's*; *Dora* 19
the sun fell, and all the *l* was dark. (repeat) *Dora* 79, 109
the cliffs that guard my native *l*, *Audley Court* 49
Her voice fled always thro' the summer *l*; *Edwin Morris* 67

Land (*continued*) To *l's* in Kent and messuages in York, *Edwin Morris* 127
I will leave my relics in your *l*, *St. S. Stylites* 194
A babbler in the *l*. *Talking Oak* 24
nor yet Thine acorn in the *l*. „ 260
Yet oceans daily gaining on the *l*, *Golden Year* 29
In many streams to fatten lower *l's*, „ 34
Knit *l* to *l*, and blowing havenward „ 44
Lie like a shaft of light across the *l*, „ 49
like a fruitful *l* reposed; *Locksley Hall* 13
It is not bad but good *l*, *Amphion* 6
Nor for my *l's* so broad and fair; *Lady Clare* 10
Lord Ronald is heir of all your *l's*, „ 19
Made a murmur in the *l*. *L. of Burleigh* 20
In all that *l* had never been: *Beggar Maid* 14
Close to the sun in lonely *l's*, *The Eagle* 2
To which an answer peal'd from that high *l*, *Vision of Sin* 221
Enoch at times to go by *l* or sea; *Enoch Arden* 104
Enoch left his hearth and native *l*, „ 360
and ran Ev'n to the limit of the *l*, „ 578
He praised his *l*, his horses, his machines; *The Brook* 124
A *l* of hops and poppy-mingled corn, *Aylmer's Field* 31
A sleepy *l*, where under the same wheel „ 33
so sleepy was the *l*. „ 45
but he must—the *l* was ringing of it— „ 262
sole succeeder to their wealth, their *l's*, „ 294
crashing with long echoes thro' the *l*, „ 338
The *l* all shambles—naked marriages Flash „ 765
dream'd Of such a tide swelling toward the *l*, *Sea Dreams* 87
I slipt Into a *l* all sun and blossom, „ 101
sit the best and stateliest of the *l*? *Lucretius* 172
The lady of three castles in that *l*: *Princess i* 79
seizures come Upon you in those *l's*, „ 83
then we crost To a livelier *l*; „ 110
From hills, that look'd across a *l* of hope, „ 169
l, he understood, for miles about Was till'd „ 191
As thro' the *l* at eve we went, „ *ii* 1
are the ladies of your *l* so tall?' „ 47
beam Had slanted forward, falling in a *l* Of promise; „ 139
I promise you Some palace in our *l*, „ *iii* 162
we should find the *l* Worth seeing; „ 171
'Know you no song of your own *l*,' „ *iv* 84
swallow winging south From mine own *l*, „ 90
Strove to buffet to *l* in vain. „ 185
Or like a spire of *l* that stands apart „ 281
Some crying there was an army in the *l*, „ 484
Amazed he fled away Thro' the dark *l*, „ *v* 49
Upon the skirt and fringe of our fair *l*, „ 219
'Our *l* invaded, 'sdeath! and he himself Your captive, „ 276
Of *l's* in which at the altar the poor bride „ 377
Knowledge in our own *l* make her free, „ 419
like a wild horn in a *l* Of echoes, „ 486
I go to mine own *l* For ever: „ *vi* 216
climbs a peak to gaze O'er *l* and main, „ *vii* 36
held A volume of the Poets of her *l*: „ 174
Far-shadowing from the west, a *l* of peace; „ *Con.* 42
Was great by *l* as thou by sea. (repeat) *Ode on Well.* 84, 90
Follow'd by the brave of other *l's* „ 194
stand Colossal, seen of every *l*, „ 221
Till in all *l's* and thro' all human story „ 223
let the *l* whose hearths he saved from shame „ 225
We broke them on the *l*, we drove them on the seas. *Third of Feb.* 30
hold against the world this honour of the *l*. „ 48
Break, happy *l*, into earlier flowers! *W. to Alexandra* 10
Melt into stars for the *l's* desire! „ 21
Roar as the sea when he welcomes the *l*, And welcome her, welcome the *l's* desire, „ 24
thine own *l* has bow'd to Tartar hordes *W. to Marie Alex.* 23
Love has led thee to the stranger *l*, „ 31
an' a nicetish bit o' *l*. *N. Farmer, N. S.* 22
if thou marries a good un I'll leäve the *l* to thee. „ 56
if thou marries a bad un, I'll leäve the *l* to Dick.— „ 58
In *l's* of palm and southern pine; In *l's* of palm, of orange-blossom, *The Daisy* 2
To *l's* of summer across the sea; „ 92

Land (*continued*) And o'er a weary sultry l, *Will* 17
'The Gods are moved against the l.' *The Victim* 6
To spill his blood and heal the l: „ 44
The l is sick, the people diseased, „ 45
Thine the l's of lasting summer, *Boädicea* 43
Ran the l with Roman slaughter, „ 84
And travell'd men from foreign l's; *In Mem. x* 6
That thou hadst touch'd the l to-day, „ *xiv* 2
The violet of his native l. „ *xviii* 4
Thro' l's where not a leaf was dumb; „ *xxiii* 10
We heard them sweep the winter l; „ *xxx* 10
And thine in undiscover'd l's. „ *xl* 32
Whose feet are guided thro' the l, „ *lxvi* 9
And He that died in Holy L „ *lxxxiv* 42
And all the framework of the l; „ *lxxxvii* 24
The hard heir strides about their l's, „ *xc* 15
That stays him from the native l „ *xciii* 3
In l's where not a memory strays, „ *civ* 10
We live within the stranger's l, „ *cv* 3
Ring out the darkness of the l, „ *cvi* 31
that live their lives From l to l; „ *cxv* 17
They melt like mist, the solid l's, „ *cxxiii* 7
better war! loud war by l and by sea, *Maud I i* 47
sapphire-spangled marriage ring of the l? „ *iv* 6
To the death, for their native l. „ *v* 11
riding at set of day Over the dark moor l, „ *ix* 6
One still strong man in a blatant l, „ *x* 63
I past him, I was crossing his l's; „ *xiii* 6
From underneath in the darkening l— „ *II i* 6
High over the shadowy l. „ 40
Flying along the l and the main— „ *ii* 38
a l that has lost for a little her lust „ *III vi* 39
I have felt with my native l, „ 58
Dear to thy l and ours, a Prince indeed, *Ded. of Idylls* 41
waging war Each upon other, wasted all the l; *Com. of Arthur* 7
And thus the l of Cameliard was waste, „ 20
Shall I not lift her from this l of beasts Up to my throne, „ 80
power on this dark l to lighten it, „ 93
a slope of l that ever grew, Field after field, „ 428
and all the l from roof and rick, „ 433
name of evil savour in the l, The Cornish king. *Gareth and L.* 385
lady of high lineage, of great l's, „ 609
and they past to their own l; *Marr. of Geraint* 45
and we smile, the lords of many l's; „ 353
I know not, but he past to the wild l. „ 443
a dreadful loss Falls in a far l *Geraint and E.* 497
In a hollow l, From which old fires have broken, „ 821
pray'd me for my leave To move to your own l, „ 889
I will weed this l before I go. „ 907
broke the bandit holds and cleansed the l. „ 944
and they past to their own l. „ 955
And brought report of azure l's and fair, *Balin and Balan* 168
a silver shadow slipt away Thro' the dim l; and all day long we rode Thro' the dim l *Merlin and V.* 424
two fair babes, and went to distant l's; „ 707
Moaning and calling out of other l's, „ 962
The heathen, who, some say, shall rule the l *Lancelot and E.* 65
and Prince and Lord am I In mine own l, „ 917
Endow you with broad l and territory „ 957
Estate them with large l and territory „ 1322
This, from the blessed l of Aromat— *Holy Grail* 48
and higher than any in all the l's! „ 247
in a l of sand and thorns, (repeat) „ 376, 390
wearying in a l of sand and thorns. „ 420
his l and wealth and state were hers. „ 587
thou shalt be as Arthur in our l.' „ 606
the hind To whom a space of l is given to plow. „ 907
And she was a great lady in her l. *Pelleas and E.* 98
served with choice from air, l, stream, and sea, „ 149
So those three days, aimless about the l, „ 391
l Was freed, and the Queen false, *Last Tournament* 338
Tintagil, half in sea, and high on l, „ 505
Clung to the dead earth, and the l was still. *Guinevere* 8
And blackening, swallow'd all the l, „ 82
'O Lancelot, get thee hence to thine own l, „ 88

Land (*continued*) Back to his l; but she to Almesbury Fled *Guinevere* 127
Began to slay the folk, and spoil the l.' „ 137
the l was full of signs And wonders „ 232
sent a deep sea-voice thro' all the l, „ 247
for all the l was full of life. „ 259
Have everywhere about this l of Christ „ 431
Clave to him, and abode in his own l. „ 440
A l of old upheaven from the abyss *Pass. of Arthur* 82
That stood on a dark strait of barren l: „ 178
All night in a waste l, where no one comes, „ 370
And loyal to thy l, as this to thee— *To the Queen ii* 2
The voice of Britain, or a sinking l, „ 24
Betwixt the native l of Love and me, *Lover's Tale i* 25
And all the low dark groves, a l of love! A l of promise, a l of memory, A l of promise flowing with the milk And honey „ 332
Each way from verge to verge a Holy L, „ 337
Was not the l as free thro' all her ways „ 662
when their faces are forgot in the l— „ 759
Borne into alien l's and far away. „ 802
whole l weigh'd him down as Ætna does The Giant of Mythology: he would go, Would leave the l for ever, „ *iv* 17
(for in Julian's l They never nail a dumb head „ 36
So bore her thro' the solitary l „ 90
And all the l was waste and solitary: „ 125
Heir of his face and l, to Lionel. „ 129
myself was then Travelling that l, „ 133
A dismal hostel in a dismal l, „ 141
Before he left the l for evermore; „ 183
Scatteringly about that lonely l of his, „ 185
self-exile from a l He never would revisit, „ 209
question'd if she came From foreign l's, „ 331
I leave this l for ever.' „ 368
He past for ever from his native l; „ 387
wailing, wailing, the wind over l and sea— *Rizpah* 1
'Cast awaäy on a disolut l wi' a vartical soon!' *North. Cobbler* 3
sick men from the l Very carefully and slow, *The Revenge* 15
When he leaps from the water to the l. „ 55
When a wind from the l's they had ruin'd „ 112
all the broad l's in your view *Sisters (E. and E.)* 51
an niver lookt arter the l— *Village Wife* 25
Fur we puts the muck o' the l „ 32
For 'e warn't not burn to the l, „ 44
An' 'e digg'd up a loomp i' the l „ 48
an' 'is gells es belong'd to the l; „ 112
Fresh from the surgery-schools of France and of other l's— *In the Child. Hosp.* 3
from the beach and rioted over the l, *V. of Maeldune* 58
Isle, where the heavens lean low on the l, „ 83
Hunger of glory gat Hold of the l. *Batt. of Brunanburh* 124
in my wanderings all the l's that lie *Tiresias* 25
For that sweet mother l which gave them birth „ 122
Having l's at home and abroad *The Wreck* 46
warm winds had gently breathed us away from the l— „ 63
Rich was the rose of sunset there, as we drew to the l; „ 136
and dogg'd us, and drew me to l? *Despair* 2
fatal neck Of l running out into rock— „ 10
all that suffers on l or in air or the deep, „ 45
I am left alone on the l, „ 63
down the rocks he went, how loth to quit the l! *The Flight* 38
without a friend, and in a distant l. „ 100
pools of salt, and plots of l— *Locksley H., Sixty* 207
And shine the level l's, *Early Spring* 15
Heard by the l. „ 24
Dominant over sea and l. *Helen's Tower* 2
True leaders of the l's desire! *Hands all Round* 26
On you will come the curse of all the l, *The Fleet* 3
island-myriads fed from alien l's— „ 12
And splendours of the morning l, *Open I. and C. Exhib.* 8
Falls on the threshold of her native l, *Demeter and P.* 3
of their flight To summer l's! *The Ring* 87
sword that lighten'd back the sun of Holy l, *Happy* 43
your tale of l's I know not, *To Ulysses* 34
paced his l In fear of worse, *To Mary Boyle* 29

Land (*continued*) I hear a charm of song thro' all the *l*. — *Prog. of Spring* 47
basking in the sultry plains About a *l* of canes; — „ 78
so to the *l's* Last limit I came— — *Merlin and the G.* 109
Landaulet An open *l* Whirl'd by, which, — *Sisters (E. and E.)* 85
phantom of the whirling *l* For ever past me by: — „ 114
Landbird at length The *l*, and the branch — *Columbus* 73
Landed moving up the coast they *l* him, — *Enoch Arden* 665
we came to the Isle of Shouting, we *l*, — *V. of Maeldune* 27
When I *l* again, with a tithe of my men, — „ 130
So they row'd, and there we *l*— — *Frater Ave, etc.* 2
Lander Heard by the *l* in a lonely isle, — *Marr. of Geraint* 330
Landing sent a crew that *l* burst away — *Enoch Arden* 634
Landing-place Some *l-p*, to clasp and say, 'Farewell!' — *In Mem. xlvii* 15
Landlike cloud That *l* slept along the deep. — „ *ciii* 56
Landlord Kindly *l*, boon companion— — *Locksley H., Sixty* 240
Landmark Nor *l* breathes of other days, — *In Mem. civ* 11
Will see me by the *l* far away, — *Demeter and P.* 124
Landscape Nor these alone, but every *l* fair, — *Palace of Art* 89
And her the Lord of all the *l* round — *Aylmer's Field* 815
The eternal *l* of the past; — *In Mem. xlvi* 8
The *l* winking thro' the heat: — „ *lxxxix* 16
from end to end Of all the *l* underneath, — „ *c* 2
l grow Familiar to the stranger's child; — „ *ci* 19
Framing the mighty *l* to the west, — *Lover's Tale i* 406
a *l* which your eyes Have many a time ranged over — *The Ring* 150
Landscape-lover *L-l*, lord of language — *To Virgil* 5
Landscape-painter He is but a *l-p*, — *L. of Burleigh* 7
that he Were once more than *l-p*, — „ 83
Landskip man and woman, town And *l*, — *Princess iv* 446
The light retreated, The *l* darken'd, — *Merlin and the G.* 31
Blurr'd like a *l* in a ruffled pool,— — *Romney's R.* 114
Landslip Like some great *l*, tree by tree, — *Amphion* 51
Landward Or often journeying *l*; — *Enoch Arden* 92
The latest house to *l*; — „ 732
I found Only the *l* exit of the cave, — *Sea Dreams* 96
And here on the *l* side, by a red rock, glimmers the Hall; — *Maud I iv* 10
Lane (Miriam) *See* **Miriam, Miriam Lane**
Lane (*See also* **By-lane, Laäne, Ocean-lane, Sea-lane**)
The *l's*, you know, were white with may, — *Miller's D.* 130
like a *l* of beams athwart the sea, — *Golden Year* 50
in the leafy *l's* behind the down, — *Enoch Arden* 97
climbing street, the mill, the leafy *l's*, — „ 607
He led me thro' the short sweet-smelling *l's* — *The Brook* 122
Long *l's* of splendour slanted — *Princess iv* 478
By glimmering *l's* and walls of canvas — „ *v* 6
A light-blue *l* of early dawn, — *In Mem. cxix* 7
Fled down the *l* of access to the King, — *Gareth and L.* 661
thro' *l's* of shouting Gareth rode Down the slope street, — „ 699
Where under one long *l* of cloudless air — *Balin and Balan* 461
up that *l* of light into the setting sun. — *The Flight* 40
few *l's* of elm And whispering oak. — *To Mary Boyle* 67
Language (*See also* **Love-language**) In the *l* wherewith Spring Letters cowslips — *Adeline* 61
Such as no *l* may declare.' — *Two Voices* 384
To learn a *l* known but smatteringly — *Aylmer's Field* 433
Your *l* proves you still the child. — *Princess ii* 58
whose *l* rife With rugged maxims hewn from life; — *Ode on Well.* 183
A use in measured *l* lies; — *In Mem. v* 6
And with no *l* but a cry. — „ *liv* 20
Writ in a *l* that has long gone by. — *Merlin and V.* 674
Than *l* grasp the infinite of Love. — *Lover's Tale i* 484
The music that robes it in *l* — *The Wreck* 24
thro' that mirage of overheated *l* — *Locksley H., Sixty* 113
lord of *l* more than he that sang the Works — *To Virgil* 5
in every *l* I hear spoken, people praise thee. — *Akbar's D., Inscrip.* 1
Langued *L* gules, and tooth'd with grinning savagery.' — *Balin and Balan* 197
Languid (*See also* **Love-languid**) His bow-string slacken'd, *l* Love, — *Eleänore* 117
a *l* fire creeps Thro' my veins — „ 130
The *l* light of your proud eyes — *L. C. V. de Vere* 59
All round the coast the *l* air did swoon, — *Lotos-Eaters* 5
tearful glimmer of the *l* dawn On those long, — *D. of F. Women* 74
O'er both his shoulders drew the *l* hands, — *M. d'Arthur* 174

Languid (*continued*) That, stirr'd with *l* pulses of the oar, — *Gardener's D.* 41
Suffused them, sitting, lying, *l* shapes, — *Vision of Sin* 12
and due To *l* limbs and sickness; — *Princess vi* 377
And myself so *l* and base. — *Maud I v* 18
Struck me before the *l* fool, — „ *II i* 19
Pipe on her pastoral hillock a *l* note, — „ *III vi* 24
Then gave a *l* hand to each, and lay, — *Lancelot and E.* 1032
O'er both his shoulders drew the *l* hands, — *Pass. of Arthur* 342
my blood Crept like marsh drains thro' all my *l* limbs; — *Lover's Tale ii* 53
Languish And so would *l* evermore, — *Eleänore* 120
And *l* for the purple seas. — *You ask me, why, etc.* 4
thought of which my whole soul *l'es* And faints, — *Lover's Tale i* 267
Languor Thou art not steep'd in golden *l's*, — *Madeline* 1
The *l's* of thy love-deep eyes — *Eleänore* 76
a *l* came Upon him, gentle sickness, — *Enoch Arden* 823
thro' her limbs a drooping *l* wept: — *Princess vi* 268
all for *l* and self-pity ran Mine down my face, — „ *vii* 139
and out of *l* leapt a cry; — „ 155
Languorous To wile the length from *l* hours, — „ *vii* 63
half plagued by Lancelot's *l* mood, — *Last Tournament* 194
Lank 'Slip-shod waiter, *l* and sour, — *Vision of Sin* 71
Lantern Swung round the lighted *l* of the hall; — *Guinevere* 262
Lap (knees, etc.) Upon my *l* he laid his head: — *The Sisters* 17
Those in whose *l's* our limbs are nursed, — *To J. S.* 10
And fairest, laid his head upon her *l*, — *M. d'Arthur* 208
My beard has grown into my *l*.' — *Day-Dm., Revival* 22
Too ragged to be fondled on her *l*, — *Aylmer's Field* 686
creature laid his muzzle on your *l*, — *Princess ii* 272
Leapt from her session on his *l*, — *Merlin and V.* 844
And fairest, laid his head upon her *l*, — *Pass. of Arthur* 376
one soft *l* Pillow'd us both: — *Lover's Tale i* 235
sat each on the *l* of the breeze; — *V. of Maeldune* 38
Lap (drink) Till Robby an' Steevie 'es 'ed their *l* — *Spinster's S's.* 121
Lap (verb) Lest we should *l* him up in cloth of lead, — *Gareth and L.* 430
Lapidoth Like that great dame of *L* — *Princess vi* 32
Lapping And the wild water *l* on the crag.' — *M. d'Arthur* 71
I heard the water *l* on the crag, — „ 116
And the wild water *l* on the crag.' — *Pass. of Arthur* 239
I heard the water *l* on the crag, — „ 284
Lapse (s) No *l* of moons can canker Love, — *In. Mem. xxvi* 3
But from my farthest *l*, my latest ebb, — *Lover's Tale i* 90
Lapse (verb) or seem To *l* far back in some confused dream — *Sonnet To ——* 3
kingdoms overset, Or *l* from hand to hand, — *Talking Oak* 258
Lapsed 'But, if I *l* from nobler place, — *Two Voices* 358
But *l* into so long a pause again — *Aylmer's Field* 630
the bells *L* into frightful stillness; — *Lover's Tale iii* 30
Lapsing *See* **Down-lapsing**
Lapt (*See also* **Close-lapt Half-lapt**) earth shall slumber, *l* in universal law. — *Locksley Hall* 130
l In the arms of leisure, — *Princess ii* 167
l in wreaths of glowworm light The mellow breaker — „ *iv* 435
Lapwing (*See also* **Pewit**) *l* gets himself another crest; — *Locksley Hall* 18
Lar lay at wine with *L* and Lucumo; — *Princess ii* 129
Larboard Roll'd to starboard, roll'd to *l*, — *Lotos-Eaters, C. S.* 106
two upon the *l* and two upon the starboard — *The Revenge* 48
Larch When rosy plumelets tuft the *l*, — *In. Mem. xci* 1
There amid perky *l'es* and pine, — *Maud I. x* 20
Lard *See* **Saäme**
Larded Old boxes, *l* with the steam — *Will Water.* 223
See thou have not *L* thy last, — *Gareth and L.* 1084
Larder And a whirlwind clear'd the *l*: — *The Goose* 52
Larding these be for the spit, *L* and basting. — *Gareth and L.* 1082
Large brazen urn In order, eastern flowers *l*, — *Arabian Nights* 61
L dowries doth the raptured eye — *Ode to Memory* 72
With his *l* calm eyes for the love of me. — *The Mermaid* 27
grow so full and deep In thy *l* eyes, — *Eleänore* 86
Thought seems to come and go In thy *l* eyes, — „ 97
L Hesper glitter'd on her tears, — *Mariana in the S.* 90
From many an inland town and haven *l*, — *Œnone* 117
A glorious Devil, *l* in heart and brain, — *To ——, With Pal. of Art* 5
Lit with a low *l* moon. — *Palace of Art* 68
We saw the *l* white stars rise one by one, — *D. of F. Women* 223

Large (*continued*) And all about the *l* lime feathers low, — Gardener's D. 47
L range of prospect had the mother sow, — Walk. to the Mail 93
Wait: my faith is *l* in Time, — Love and Duty 25
Yearning for the *l* excitement that the coming years would yield, — Locksley Hall 111
His *l* gray eyes and weather-beaten face — Enoch Arden 70
Drank the *l* air, and saw, but scarce believed — Sea Dreams 34
and light is *l*, and lambs are glad — Lucretius 99
The *l* blows rain'd, as here and everywhere He rode — Princess v 501
But that *l* grief which these enfold — In. Mem. v 11
A lord of *l* experience, train To riper growth — „ xlii 7
O Love, thy province were not *l*, — „ xlvi 13
Nor dare she trust a *l* lay, — „ xlviii 13
self-infolds the *l* results Of force that would have forged a name. — „ lxxiii 15
Be *l* and lucid round thy brow. — „ xci 8
breeze began to tremble o'er The *l* leaves of the sycamore, — „ xcv 55
But thrice as *l* as man he bent To greet us. — „ ciii 42
L elements in order brought, — „ cxii 13
With *l*, divine, and comfortable words, — Com. of Arthur 268
Would yield him this *l* honour all the more; — Gareth and L. 397
High nose, a nostril *l* and fine, and hands *L*, fair and fine!— — „ 465
So *l* mirth lived and Gareth won the quest. — „ 1426
Bribed with *l* promises the men who served — Marr. of Geraint 453
Then Lancelot lifted his *l* eyes; — Balin and Balan 277
as I hear It is a fair *l* diamond,— — Lancelot and E. 228
'A fair *l* diamond,' added plain Sir Torre, — „ 230
So fine a fear in our *l* Lancelot Must needs have moved my laughter: — „ 595
his *l* black eyes Yet larger thro' his leanness, — „ 834
Estate them with *l* land and territory — „ 1322
For *l* her violet eyes look'd, and her bloom A rosy dawn — Pelleas and E. 71
And but for those *l* eyes, the haunts of scorn, — „ 75
a moon With promise of *l* light on woods and ways. — „ 394
And therefore is my love so *l* for thee, — Last Tournament 702
that *l* infidel Your Omar; — To E. Fitzgerald 36
The gain of such *l* life as match'd with ours — Ancient Sage 237
that *l* phrase of yours 'A Star among the stars.' — Epilogue 41
Watching her *l* light eyes and gracious looks, — Prog. of Spring 19
She spoke at *l* of many things, — Miller's D. 155

Large-brow'd Plato the wise, and *l-b* Verulam, — Palace of Art 163

Large-moulded that *l-m* man, His visage all agrin — Princess v 520

Larger like a light that grows *L* and clearer, — Œnone 109
L than human on the frozen hills. — M. d'Arthur 183
with a *l* faith appeal'd Than Papist unto Saint. — Talking Oak 15
L constellations burning, — Locksley Hall 159
Cock was of a *l* egg Than modern poultry drop, — Will Water. 121
Ten miles to northward of the narrow port Open'd a *l* haven: — Enoch Arden 103
Become the master of a *l* craft, — „ 144
then I saw one lovely star *L* and *l*. — Sea Dreams 94
No *l* feast than under plane or pine — Lucretius 213
Nor lose the childlike in the *l* mind; — Princess vii 284
rolling hours With *l* other eyes that ours, — In. Mem. li 15
And faintly trust the *l* hope. — „ lv 20
The *l* heart, the kindlier hand; — „ cvi 30
Whereof one seem'd far *l* than her lord, — Geraint and E. 122
But work as vassal to the *l* love, — Merlin and V. 491
The text no *l* than the limbs of fleas; — „ 672
Yet *l* thro' his leanness, dwelt upon her, — Lancelot and E. 835
l than themselves In their own darkness, — Pelleas and E. 457
Mine is the *l* need, who am not meek, — Last Tournament 610
For *l* glimpses of that more than man — Tiresias 21
But days of a *l* light than I ever again shall know— — The Wreck 78
Charm us, Orator, till the Lion look no *l* than the Cat, Till the Cat thro' that mirage of overheated language loom *L* than the Lion,— — Locksley H., Sixty 112
Stronger ever born of weaker, lustier body, *l* mind? — „ 164
Has enter'd on the *l* woman-world Of wives — The Ring 486
I, once half-crazed for *l* light — To Ulysses 29

Larger (*continued*) *L* and fuller, like the human mind! — Prog. of Spring 112
But find their limits by that *l* light, — Akbar's Dream 99

Larger-limb'd and one Is *l-l* than you are, — Geraint and E. 144
And every man were *l-l* than I, — „ 148

Largess Nor golden *l* of thy praise. — My life is full 5
With shower'd *l* of delight In dance and song — In. Mem. xxix 7

Largest Await the last and *l* sense to make — Ancient Sage 180

Lariano The *L* crept To that fair port — The Daisy 78

Lari Maxume Virgilian rustic measure Of *L M*, — „ 76

Lark The quick *l's* closest-caroll'd strains, — Rosalind 10
The *l* could scarce get out his notes — Gardener's D. 90
quail and pigeon, *l* and leveret lay, — Audley Court 24
livelier than a *l* She sent her voice — Talking Oak 122
His spirit flutters like a *l*, — Day-Dm., Arrival 29
And the *l* drop down at his feet. — Poet's Song 8
morn by morn the *l* Shot up and shrill'd — Princess vii 45
merry in heaven, O *l's*, and far away, — Window, Ay 3
That holds the shadow of a *l* — In Mem. xvi 9
But ere the *l* hath left the lea — „ lxviii 13
The *l* becomes a sightless song. — „ cxv 8
Then would he whistle rapid as any *l*, — Gareth and L. 505
'What knowest thou of birds, *l*, mavis, merle, — „ 1078
lose it, as we lose the *l* in heaven, — Lancelot and E. 659
Clear as a *l*, high o'er me as a *l*, — Holy Grail 833
carol of clear-throated *l's* Fill'd all the March of life!— — Lover's Tale i 283
the morning song of the *l*, — First Quarrel 33
Theer wur a *l* a-singin' 'is best — North. Cobbler 46
heaven above it there flicker'd a songless *l*, — V. of Maeldune 17
hears the *l* within the songless egg, — Ancient Sage 76
The *l* has past from earth to Heaven — The Flight 62
Molly Magee kem flyin' acrass me, as light as a *l*, — Tomorrow 21
An' the *l* fly out o' the flowers — „ 91
Up leaps the *l*, gone wild to welcome — Prog. of Spring 14

Larkspur The *l* listens, 'I hear, I hear;' — Maud I xxii 65

Larn (learn) I reckons I 'annot sa mooch to *l*. — N. Farmer, O. S. 13

Larn'd (learned) *L* a ma' beä. — „ 13
hignorant village wife as 'ud hev to be *l* her awn plaäce,' — Village Wife 106

Lash (eyelash) and *l'es* like to rays Of darkness, — Arabian Nights 136

Lash (whip) Doom'd them to the *l*. — The Captain 12

Lash (verb) My men shall *l* you from them like a dog; — Aylmer's Field 325
like a pedant's wand To *l* offence, — Princess i 28
war's avenging rod Shall *l* all Europe into blood; — To F. D. Maurice 34
L the maiden into swooning, — Boädicea 67
l with storm the streaming pane? — In Mem. lxxii 4
l the treasons of the Table Round.' — Pelleas and E. 566
The breakers *l* the shores: — Pref. Poem Broth. S. 2

Lash'd me they *l* and humiliated, (repeat) — Boädicea 49, 67
L at the wizard as he spake the word, — Com. of Arthur 388
Gareth *l* so fiercely with his brand — Gareth and L. 968
But *l* in vain against the harden'd skin, — „ 1143
dishorsed and drawing, *l* at each So often — Marr. of Geraint 563
And *l* it at the base with slanting storm; — Merlin and V. 635
but the man that was *l* to the helm had gone; — The Wreck 110

Lass 'Siver, I kep 'um, I kep 'um, my *l*, — N. Farmer, O. S. 23
D'ya moind the waäste, my *l*? — „ 29
Doctor's a 'toättler, *l*, — „ 66
thou's sweet upo' parson's *l*— — „ N. S. 11
Warn't I craäzed fur the *l'es* mysén when I wur a lad? — „ 18
as good to cuddle an' kiss as a *l* as 'ant nowt? — „ 24
Parson's *l* 'ant nowt, an she weänt — „ 25
thou can luvv thy *l* an' 'er munny too, — „ 33
thy muther says thou wants to marry the *l*, — „ 37
'What can it matter, my *l*, — First Quarrel 59
'Wait a little, my *l*, (repeat) — „ 74, 91
You wouldn't kiss me, my *l*, — „ 86
'My *l*, when I cooms to die, — North. Cobbler 103
'Ouse-keeper sent tha my *l*, — Village Wife 1
Fur 'staäte be i' taäle, my *l*: — „ 15
can tha tell ony harm on 'im *l*?— — „ 19
to be sewer I haätes 'em, my *l*, — „ 31
I laugh'd when the *l'es* 'ud talk o' their Missis's waäys, An' the Missis talk'd o' the *l'es*.— — „ 57

Lass (*continued*) *l'es* 'ed teärd out leaves i' the middle — *Village Wife* 72
Mad wi' the *l'es* an' all— „ 78
An' saw she mun hammergrate, *l*, „ 104
call'd me es pretty es ony *l* i' the Shere; *Spinster's S's.* 13
an' sarved by my oän little *l*, „ 103

Last A SPIRIT haunts the year's *l* hours — *A spirit haunts* 1
And the year's *l* rose. „ 20
The *l* wild thought of Chatelet, *Margaret* 37
trampled under by the *l* and least Of men? *Poland* 2
whose sweet face He kiss'd, taking his *l* embrace, *Two Voices* 254
To that *l* nothing under earth!' „ 333
L night, when some one spoke his name, *Fatima* 15
It is the *l* New-year that I shall ever see, *May Queen, N. Y's. E.* 3
dear the *l* embraces of our wives And their warm tears: *Lotos-Eaters, C. S.* 70
Sir Bedivere, the *l* of all his knights, *M. d'Arthur* 7
And I, the *l*, go forth companionless, „ 236
HERE ended Hall, and our *l* light, „ *Ep.* 1
l night's gale had caught, And blown across the walk. *Gardener's D.* 124
I beheld her ere she knew my heart, My first, *l* love; „ 277
That was the *l* drop in the cup of gall. *Walk. to the Mail* 69
Declare when *l* Olivia came To sport *Talking Oak* 99
In that *l* kiss, which never was the *l*, *Love and Duty* 67
It was *l* summer on a tour in Wales: *Golden Year* 2
Roll'd in one another's arms, and silent in a *l* embrace. *Locksley Hall* 58
So all day long till Enoch's *l* at home, *Enoch Arden* 172
But when the *l* of those *l* moments came, „ 217
Ev'n to the *l* dip of the vanishing sail She watch'd it, „ 245
But kept the house, his chair, and *l* his bed. „ 826
The *l* remaining pillar of their house, *Aylmer's Field* 295
They might have been together till the *l*. „ 714
I made by these the *l* of all my race, „ 791
Ev'n to its *l* horizon, „ 816
On him their *l* descendant, „ 834
And so *l* night she fell to canvass you: *Princess iii* 40
L night, their mask was patent, and my foot „ *iv* 326
The *l* great Englishman is low. *Ode on Well.* 18
Mourn, for to us he seems the *l*, „ 19
Have left the *l* free race with naked coasts! *Third of Feb.* 40
What more? we took our *l* adieu, *The Daisy* 85
At that *l* hour to please him well; *In Mem. vi* 18
The *l* red leaf is whirl'd away, „ *xv* 3
A merry song we sang with him *L* year: „ *xxx* 16
Upon the *l* and sharpest height, „ *xlvii* 13
Man, her *l* work, who seem'd so fair, „ *lvi* 9
O *l* regret, regret can die! „ *lxxviii* 17
On that *l* night before we went „ *ciii* 1
Now fades the *l* long streak of snow, „ *cxv* 1
While another is cheating the sick of a few *l* gasps, *Maud I i* 43
He now is first, but is he the *l*? „ *iv* 36
Whom but Maud should I meet *L* night, „ *vi* 8
L week came one to the county town, „ *x* 37
L year, I caught a glimpse of his face, „ *xiii* 27
loud on the stone The *l* wheel echoes away. „ *xxii* 26
Her—over all whose realms to their *l* isle, *Ded. of Idylls* 12
THE *l* tall son of Lot and Bellicent, *Gareth and L.* 1
No later than *l* eve to Prince Geraint— *Marr. of Geraint* 603
And this was on the *l* year's Whitsuntide. „ 840
So the *l* sight that Enid had of home *Geraint and E.* 24
L night methought I saw That maiden Saint *Balin and Balan* 260
Blazed the *l* diamond of the nameless king. *Lancelot and E.* 444
And came the *l*, tho' late, to Astolat: „ 618
High with the *l* line scaled her voice, „ 1019
Hither, to take my *l* farewell of you. „ 1275
our Lord Drank at the *l* sad supper with his own. *Holy Grail* 47
So for the *l* time she was gracious to him. *Pelleas and E.* 175
Would they have risen against me in their blood At the *l* day? „ 462
Make their *l* head like Satan in the North. *Last Tournament* 98
Then in the light's *l* glimmer Tristram show'd „ 739
hither brought by Tristram for his *l* Love-offering „ 747
It was their *l* hour, A madness of farewells. *Guinevere* 102
Bear with me for the *l* time while I show, „ 454
Leave me that, I charge thee, my *l* hope. „ 568

Last (*continued*) Then, ere that *l* weird battle in the west, *Pass. of Arthur* 29
one *l* act of knighthood shalt thou see Yet, „ 163
Striking the *l* stroke with Excalibur. „ 168
And I, the *l*, go forth companionless, „ 404
slowly clomb The *l* hard footstep of that iron crag; „ 447
Like the *l* echo born of a great cry, „ 459
Down to this *l* strange hour in his own hall; *Lover's Tale iv* 358
—*my* quarrel—the first an' the *l*. *First Quarrel* 56
I had bid him my *l* goodbye; *Rizpah* 41
Plunged in the *l* fierce charge at Waterloo, *Sister's (E. and E.)* 64
fur he coom'd *l* night sa laäte— *Village Wife* 123
l night a dream—I sail'd On my first voyage, *Columbus* 66
You will not. One *l* word. „ 221
yet Am ready to sail forth on one *l* voyage. „ 237
With this *l* moon, this crescent—her dark orb *De Prof., Two G.* 9
To that *l* deep where we and thou are still. „ 25
When the worm shall have writhed its *l*, and its *l* brother-worm will have fled *Despair* 85
go To spend my one *l* year among the hills. *Ancient Sage* 16
Await the *l* and largest sense to make „ 180
The *l* long stripe of waning crimson gloom, „ 221
and so many dead, And him the *l*; *Tiresias* 212
l year—Standin' here be the bridge, when *l* *Tomorrow* 1
here *l* month they wor diggin' the bog, „ 61
Leave the Master in the first dark hour of his *l* sleep alone. *Locksley H., Sixty* 238
Vows that will last to the *l* deathruckle, *Vastness* 26
I dream'd *l* night of that clear summer noon, *Romney's R.* 74
L year you sang it as gladly. *The Throstle* 6
And at the *l* she said: *Palace of Art* 208
oft as needed—*l*, returning rich, *Enoch Arden* 143
would work for Annie to the *l*, „ 180
I know that it will out at *l*. O Annie, „ 402
At *l* one night it chanced That Annie could not sleep, „ 489
may she learn I lov'd her to the *l*,' „ 835
'Woman, disturb me not now at the *l*, „ 874
and thou art *l* of the three. *G. of Swainston* 15
at *l*—The huge pavilion slowly yielded up, *Gareth and L.* 1378
of overpraise and overblame We choose the *l*. *Merlin and V.* 91
Let go at *l*!—they ride away—to hawk „ 107
at *l* With dark sweet hints of some who prized him „ 158
Thanks at *l*! But yesterday you never open'd lip, „ 270
At *l* they found—his foragers for charms— „ 619
At *l* she let herself be conquer'd by him, „ 900
Arthur kept his best until the *l*; *Holy Grail* 763
at the *l* I reach'd a door, A light was in the crannies, „ 837
at *l* They grew aweary of her fellowship: *Lover's Tale i* 108
But when at *l* his doubts were satisfied, „ *iv* 84
Lionel, when at *l* he freed himself „ 379
And Harry came home at *l*, *First Quarrel* 35
old Sir Richard caught at *l*, *The Revenge* 98
At *l* I go On that long-promised visit *Sisters (E. and E.)* 187
at *l* their Highnesses Were half-assured *Columbus* 59
we are all of us wreck'd at *l*— *Despair* 12
creeds that had madden'd the peoples would vanish at *l*, „ 24
shape it at the *l* According to the Highest *Ancient Sage* 89
this Hall at *l* will go— *The Flight* 27
Brothers, must we part at *l*? *Open I. and C. Exhib.* 32
yet at *l*, Gratitude—loneliness— *The Ring* 372
Man is quiet at *l* as he stands on the heights of his life *By an Evolution.* 19

Last (**verb**) Weep on: beyond his object Love can *l*: *Wan Sculptor* 5
What is it that will *l*? *Lotos-Eaters, C. S.* 45
without help I cannot *l* till morn. *M. d'Arthur* 26
should I prize thee, couldst thou *l*, *Will Water.* 203
a passion that *l's* but a day; *G. of Swainston* 9
I *l* but a moment longer. *Spiteful Letter* 12
Dreams are true while they *l*, *High. Pantheism* 4
Bare of the body, might it *l*, *In Mem. xliii* 6
And love will *l* as pure and whole „ 13
there no shade can *l* In that deep dawn „ *xlvi* 5
To raise a cry that *l's* not long, „ *lxxv* 10
matin songs, that woke The darkness of our planet, *l*, „ *lxxvi* 10
In words whose echo *l's*, *Marr. of Geraint* 782

Last (verb) (*continued*) without help I cannot *l* till morn. *Pass. of Arthur* 194
Obedient to her second master now; Which will not *l*. *Lover's Tale iv* 344
A crown the Singer hopes may *l*, *Epilogue* 38
a name may *l* for a thousand years, *Dead Prophet* 59
As either love, to *l* as long! *Helen's Tower* 8
'Light—more Light—while Time shall *l*!' *Epit. on Caxton* 1
Vows that will *l* to the last deathruckle, *Vastness* 26
world and all within it Will only *l* a minute!' *Voice spake, etc.* 4
but, *l*, Allowing it, the Prince and Enid rode, *Marr. of Geraint* 42
L in a roky hollow, belling, heard *Last Tournament* 502
L, as by some one deathbed often wail *Pass. of Arthur* 118
L we came To what our people call *Lover's Tale i* 373
and *l*, Framing the mighty landscape to the west, „ 405
And *l* on the forehead Of Arthur the blameless *Merlin and the G.* 72
Laste (least) yer *l* little whishper was sweet as the lilt of a bird! *Tomorrow* 33
Lasted Long as the daylight *L*, *Batt. of Brunanburh* 39
Lasting '*She wrought her people* l *good*; *To the Queen* 24
Thine the lands of *l* summer, *Boädicea* 43
Latangor King Brandagoras of *L*, *Com. of Arthur* 114
Latch (*See also* **Sneck**) Unlifted was the clinking *l*; *Mariana* 6
When merry milkmaids click the *l*, *The Owl i* 8
The door was off the *l*: they peep'd *Dora* 130
Her hand dwelt lingeringly on the *l*, *Enoch Arden* 519
Late (*See also* **Laäte**) *l* he learned humility Perforce, *Buonaparte* 13
I fear it is too *l*, and I shall die.' *M. d'Arthur* 180
'But I was born too *l*: *Golden Year* 15
not too *l* to seek a newer world. *Ulysses* 57
And he for Italy—too *l*—too *l*: *The Brook* 2
Too ripe, too *l*! they come too *l* for use. *Sea Dreams* 67
Or soon or *l*, yet out of season, *Lucretius* 271
'They seek us: out so *l* is out of rules. *Princess iv* 219
You, likewise, our *l* guests, if so you will, „ *v* 229
They rise, but linger; it is *l*; *In Mem., Con.* 91
the white rose weeps, 'She is *l*;' *Maud I xxii* 64
And now of *l* I see him less and less, *Com. of Arthur* 356
for Prince Geraint, *L* also, *Marr. of Geraint* 165
'*L*, *l*, Sir Prince,' she said, „ 177
so *l* That I but come like you to see the hunt, „ 178
And came at last, tho' *l*, to Astolat: *Lancelot and E.* 618
So fierce a gale made havoc here of *l* *Holy Grail* 729
in herself she moaned 'Too *l*, too *l*!' *Guinevere* 131
'*L*! so *l*! What hour, I wonder, now?' „ 160
air the nuns had taught her; '*L*, so *l*!' „ 163
L, *l*, so *l*! and dark the night and chill! *L*, *l*, so *l*! but we can enter still. „ 168
Too *l*, too *l*! ye cannot enter now. (repeat) *Guinevere* 170, 173, 176
'No light: so *l*! and dark and chill the night! *Guinevere* 174
O let us in, tho' *l*, to kiss his feet! No, no, too *l*! ye cannot enter now.' „ 178
Will tell the King I love him tho' so *l*? „ 651
Still hoping, fearing 'is it yet too *l*?' „ 691
I fear it is too *l*, and I shall die.' *Pass. of Arthur* 348
'you have not been here of *l*. *Sisters (E. and E.)* 186
Like would-be guests an hour too *l*, *Tiresias* 198
As if the *l* and early were but one— *Ancient Sage* 222
some of *l* would raise a wind To sing thee to thy grave, *Freedom* 35
But then too *l*, too *l*. *The Fleet* 20
Whole weeks and months, and early and *l*, *The Sisters* 10
Now, tho' my lamp was lighted *l*, there's One will let me in: *May Queen, Con.* 18
Till mellow Death, like some *l* guest, *Will Water.* 239
The *l* and early roses from his wall, *Enoch Arden* 339
all of an evening *l* I climb'd to the top of the garth, *Grandmother* 37
L, my grandson! half the morning have I paced these sandy tracts, *Locksley H., Sixty* 1
Warless? war will die out *l* then. Will it ever? *l* or soon? „ 173
Not to-night in Locksley Hall—to-morrow—you, you come so *l*. „ 214
But while my life's *l* eve endures, *To Marq. of Dufferin* 49
she that came to part them all too *l*, *The Ring* 216
Late-left *L-l* an orphan of the squire, *Miller's D.* 34
Late-lost A *l-l* form that sleep reveals, *In Mem. xiii* 2
Later A *l* but a loftier Annie Lee, *Enoch Arden* 748
But that was *l*, boyish histories Of battle, *Aylmer's Field* 97
One of our town, but *l* by an hour *Sea Dreams* 263
Warring on a *l* day, *Ode on Well.* 102
For it hangs one moment *l*. *Spiteful Letter* 16
The primrose of the *l* year, *In Mem. lxxxv* 119
for he seem'd as one That all in *l*, *Gareth and L.* 1129
by great mischance He heard but fragments of her *l* words, *Marr. of Geraint* 113
'Late, late, Sir Prince,' she said,' *l* than we! „ 177
This *l* light of Love have risen in vain, *Prin. Beatrice* 16
Which, cast in *l* Grecian mould, *To Master of B.* 6
Later-rising and one The *l-r* Sun of spousal Love, *Prin. Beatrice* 6
Late-shown thought Of all my *l-s* prowess *Holy Grail* 362
Latest *As noble till the* l *day!* *To the Queen* 22
To where the bay runs up its *l* horn. *Audley Court* 11
my *l* rival brings thee rest. *Locksley Hall* 89
Not only we, the *l* seed of Time, *Godiva* 5
Ev'n as she dwelt upon his *l* words, *Enoch Arden* 454
The *l* house to landward; but behind, „ 732
my *l* breath Was spent in blessing her „ 883
Then of the *l* fox—where started— *Aylmer's Field* 253
Was it the first beam of my *l* day? *Lucretius* 59
From growing commerce loose her *l* chain, *Ode Inter. Exhib.* 33
charms Her secret from the *l* moon?' *In Mem. xxi* 20
To take her *l* leave of home, „ *xl* 6
To where he breathed his *l* breath, „ *xcviii* 5
That hears the *l* linnet trill, „ *c* 10
Her father's *l* word humm'd in her ear, *Lancelot and E.* 780
But from my farthest lapse, my *l* ebb, *Lover's Tale i* 90
There, there, my *l* vision—then the event! *iii* 59
Days that will glimmer, I fear, thro' life to my *l* breath; *The Wreck* 79
Here we met, our *l* meeting—Amy—sixty years ago— *Locksley H., Sixty* 177
Then I leave thee Lord and Master, *l* Lord of Locksley Hall. „ 282
And sacred is the *l* word; *To Marq. of Dufferin* 37
Miriam, breaks her *l* earthly link With me to-day. *The Ring* 47
then with my *l* kiss Upon them, „ 298
Till earth has roll'd her *l* year— *To Ulysses* 28
Latest-born Nursing the sickly babe, her *l-b*. *Enoch Arden* 150
Latest-left For thou, the *l-l* of all my knights *M. d'Arthur* 124
For thou, the *l-l* of all my knights, *Pass. of Arthur* 292
Late-writ show'd the *l-w* letters of the king. *Princess i* 175
Latin (adj.) *in flagrante*—what's the *L* word?— *Walk. to the Mail* 34
As in the *L* song I learnt at school, *Edwin Morris* 79
But as a *L* Bible to the crowd; *Sir J. Oldcastle* 18
And then in Latin to the *L* crowd, „ 31
Latin (s) And then in *L* to the Latin crowd, „ 31
speaking clearly in thy native tongue—No L— „ 134
Latitude hurricane of the *l* on him fell, *Columbus* 138
Latter Until the *l* fire shall heat the deep; *The Kraken* 13
thou wilt be A *l* Luther, and a soldier-priest *To J. M. K.* 2
But in these *l* springs I saw *Talking Oak* 75
Thy *l* days increased with pence Go down among the pots: *Will Water.* 219
And men the flies of *l* spring, *In Mem. l* 10
(For then was *l* April) and return'd *Com. of Arthur* 451
Lattice (adj.) here and there on *l* edges Lay Or book or lute; *Princess ii* 29
Lattice (s) Thro' half-open *l's* Coming in the scented breeze, *Eleänore* 23
As by the *l* you reclined, *Day-Dm., Pro.* 5
if I could follow, and light Upon her *l*, *Princess iv* 100
thro' a *l* on the soul Looks thy fair face *In Mem. lxx* 15
Lattice-blind Backward the *l-b* she flung, *Mariana in the S.* 87
Latticed (*See also* **Close-latticed**) From the long alley's *l* shade Emerged, *Arabian Nights* 112
Laud *L* me not Before my time, *Lover's Tale iv* 242
I cannot *l* this life, it looks so dark: *To W. H. Brookfield* 12
Laudamus then the great '*L*' rose to heaven. *Columbus* 18
Laugh (s) Thereto she pointed with a *l*, *D. of F. Women* 159
He laugh'd a *l* of merry scorn: *Lady Clare* 81

Laugh (s) (*continued*) a *l* Ringing like proven golden coinage true, *Aylmer's Field* 181
a light *l* Broke from Lynette, *Gareth and L.* 836
answer'd with a low and chuckling *l*: *Merlin and V.* 780
She broke into a little scornful *l*: *Lancelot and E.* 120
I heard a mocking *l* 'the new Korân!' *Akbar's Dream* 183
Laugh (verb) We did so *l* and cry with you, *D. of the O. Year* 25
Baby lips will *l* me down: *Locksley Hall* 89
Spy out my face, and *l* at all your fears.' *Enoch Arden* 216
a tale To *l* at—more to *l* at in myself— *Lucretius* 183
she *l's* at you and man: *Princess v* 116
the neighbours come and *l* and gossip, *Grandmother* 91
Why *l* ye? that ye blew your boast *Gareth and L.* 1229
we maidens often *l* When sick at heart, *Balin and Balan* 497
l As those that watch a kitten; *Merlin and V.* 176
vanish'd by the fairy well That *l's* at iron— „ 429
and cry, '*L*, little well!' „ 431
l's Saying, his knights are better men *Lancelot and E.* 313
The wide world *l's* at it. *Last Tournament* 695
Ye would but *l*, If I should tell you *Lover's Tale i* 287
L, for the name at the head of my verse *To A. Tennyson* 6
Who jest and *l* so easily and so well. *Sisters (E. and E.)* 41
For all that *l*, and all that weep *Ancient Sage* 187
to *l* at love in death! *The Ring* 231
l's upon thy field as well as mine, *Akbar's Dream* 106
Laughable They would not make them *l* in all eyes, *Geraint and E.* 326
Laugh'd over his left shoulder *l* at thee, *The Bridesmaid* 7
The still voice *l*. 'I talk,' said he, *Two Voices* 385
She spoke and *l*: I shut my sight for fear: *Œnone* 188
He *l*, and I, tho' sleepy, *The Epic* 44
Lightly he *l*, as one that read my thought, *Gardener's D.* 106
With heated faces; till he *l* aloud; *Audley Court* 37
And I and Edwin *l*; *Edwin Morris* 93
About me leap'd and *l* The modish Cupid *Talking Oak* 66
l, and swore by Peter and by Paul: *Godiva* 24
He *l* a laugh of merry scorn: *Lady Clare* 81
Blue isles of heaven *l* between, *Sir L. and Q. G.* 6
He *l*, and yielded readily to their wish, *Enoch Arden* 370
And others *l* at her and Philip too, „ 477
Caught at and ever miss'd it, and they *l*; „ 752
Katie *l*, and laughing blush'd, till he *L* also, *The Brook* 214
easily forgives it as his own, He *l*; *Aylmer's Field* 402
Petulant she spoke, and at herself she *l*; *Princess, Pro.* 153
something so mock-solemn, that I *l* And Lilia woke „ 215
Push'd her flat hand against his face and *l*; „ *ii* 366
eye To fix and make me hotter, till she *l*: „ *iii* 47
Stared with great eyes, and *l* with alien lips, „ *iv* 119
The little seed they *l* at in the dark, „ *vi* 34
This brother had *l* her down, *Maud I xix* 60
He *l* upon his warrior whom he loved *Com. of Arthur* 125
He *l* as is his wont, and answer'd me „ 401
With all good cheer He spake and *l*, *Gareth and L.* 302
He *l*; he sprang. „ 537
when he found the grass within his hands He *l*; „ 1226
Arthur *l* upon him. *Balin and Balan* 16
Thereat she suddenly *l* and shrill, „ 493
Loud *l* the graceless Mark. *Merlin and V.* 62
l the father saying, 'Fie, Sir Churl, *Lancelot and E.* 200
and in her heart she *l*, „ 808
wives, that *l* and scream'd against the gulls, *Pelleas and E.* 89
'Ay, that will I,' she answer'd, and she *l*, „ 132
Till all her ladies *l* along with her. „ 135
L, and unbound, and thrust him from the gate. „ 260
And her knights *L* not, but thrust him bounden out of door. „ 314
under her black brows a swarthy one *L* shrilly, *Last Tournament* 217
Softly *l* Isolt; 'Flatter me not, „ 556
When Sir Lancelot told This matter to the Queen, at first she *l* Lightly, *Guinevere* 54
Then *l* again, but faintlier, „ 58
bones that had *l* and had cried— *Rizpah* 53
Sir Richard spoke and he *l*, *The Revenge* 32
soldiers look'd down from their decks and *l*, „ 37
'ow I *l* when the lasses 'ud talk *Village Wife* 57
sold This ring to me, then *l* 'the ring is weird.' *The Ring* 195
fleshless world of spirits, *l*: A hollow laughter! „ 228
Laugh'd (*continued*) *l* a little and found her two— *The Ring* 337
and it *l* like a dawn in May. *Bandit's Death* 20
Laughing *L* all she can; *Lilian* 5
L and clapping their hands between, *The Merman* 29
Francis, *l*, clapt his hand On Everard's shoulder, *The Epic* 21
Juliet answer'd *l*, 'Go and see The Gardener's daughter: *Gardener's D.* 29
Katie laugh'd, and *l* blush'd, *The Brook* 214
Then *l* 'what, if these weird seizures *Princess i* 82
l at things that have long gone by. *Grandmother* 92
Gareth *l*, 'An' he fight for this, *Gareth and L.* 1345
He answer'd *l*, 'Nay, not like to me. *Merlin and V.* 618
Whereat Lavaine said, *l*, 'Lily maid, *Lancelot and E.* 385
And parted, *l* in his courtly heart. „ 1176
And *l* back the light, *Ancient Sage* 168
Then Tristram *l* caught the harp, *Last Tournament* 730
l sober fact to scorn, *Locksley H., Sixty* 109
whom the *l* shepherd bound with flowers; *To Virgil* 15
Laughingly till they kiss'd me *L*, *l*; (repeat) *The Merman* 17, 36
Laughing-stock drunkard's football, *l-s's* of Time, *Princess iv* 517
Laughter Till the lightning *l's* dimple *Lilian* 16
crimson-threaded lips Silver-treble *l* trilleth: „ 24
whose joyful scorn, Edged with sharp *l*, *Clear-headed friend* 2
Her rapid *l's* wild and shrill, As *l's* of the woodpecker *Kate* 3
With her *l* or her sighs, *Miller's D.* 184
Lest their shrill happy *l* come to me *Œnone* 258
from out that mood *L* at her self-scorn. *Palace of Art* 232
light Of *l* dimpled in his swarthy cheek; *Edwin Morris* 61
Marrow of mirth and *l*; *Will Water.* 214
Save, as his Annie's, were a *l* to him. *Enoch Arden* 184
And *l* to their lords: *Aylmer's Field* 498
Will there be children's *l* in their hall „ 787
Dislink'd with shrieks and *l*: *Princess, Pro.* 70
a sight to shake The midriff of despair with *l*, „ *i* 201
and back again With *l*: „ *ii* 462
And secret *l* tickled all my soul. „ *iv* 267
with grim *l* thrust us out at gates. „ 556
slain with *l* roll'd the gilded Squire. „ *v* 22
spied its mother and began A blind and babbling *l*, „ *vi* 137
Waking *l* in indolent reviewers. *Hendecasyllabics* 8
The delight of happy *l*, *Maud II iv* 29
Gareth answer'd them With *l*, *Gareth and L.* 209
He laugh'd; the *l* jarr'd upon Lynette: „ 1226
And crown'd with fleshless *l*— „ 1383
he moved the Prince To *l* and his comrades to applause. *Geraint and E.* 296
It made the *l* of an afternoon *Merlin and V.* 163
some light jest among them rose With *l* *Lancelot and E.* 179
Must needs have moved my *l*: now remains But little cause for *l*: „ 596
And *l* at the limit of the wood, *Pelleas and E.* 49
Is all the *l* gone dead out of thee?— *Last Tournament* 300
With shrieks and ringing *l* on the sand *Lover's Tale iii* 32
Crazy with *l* and babble and earth's new wine, *To A. Tennyson* 2
one quick peal Of *l* drew me thro' the glimmering glades *Sisters (E. and E.)* 116
Breaking with *l* from the dark; *De Prof., Two G.* 18
echo helpless *l* to your jest! *To W. H. Brookfield* 5
moving on With easy *l* find the gate *Tiresias* 200
As *l* over wine, And vain the *l* as the tears, *Ancient Sage* 184
'Yet wine and *l* friends! „ 195
Gazing at the Lydian *l* of the Garda Lake *Frater Ave, etc.* 8
fleshless world of spirits, laugh'd: A hollow *l*! *The Ring* 229
There is *l* down in Hell *Forlorn* 15
there past a crowd With shameless *l*, *St. Telemachus* 39
Laughter-stirr'd his deep eye *l-s* With merriment *Arabian Nights* 150
Launcelot Sir *L* and Queen Guinevere Rode *Sir L. and Q. G.* 20
Launch *L* your vessel, And crowd your canvas, *Merlin and the G.* 126
Laureate Hear thy myriad *l's* hail thee monarch *Akbar's D., Hymn* 6
Laurel There in a silent shade of *l* brown *Alexander* 9
The peacock in his *l* bower, *Day-Dm., Sleep. P.* 15
This l *greener from the brows* *To the Queen* 7
The twinkling *l* scatter'd silver lights. *Gardener's D.* 118
she comes and dips Her *l* in the wine, *Will Water.* 18
gain'd a *l* for your brow Of sounder leaf *You might have won* 3
And cavern-shadowing *l's*, hide! *Lucretius* 205

Laurel (*continued*) Upon a pillar'd porch, the bases lost In *l*: *Princess i* 231
the porch that sang All round with *l*, „ *ii* 23
And hear thy *l* whisper sweet *In Mem. xxxvii* 7
To-night ungather'd let us leave This *l*, „ *cv* 2
Just now the dry-tongued *l's'* pattering talk *Maud I xviii* 8
Came glimmering thro' the *l's* At the quiet evenfall, „ *II iv* 77
Bard whose fame-lit *l's* glance *To Victor Hugo* 4
Lightning may shrivel the *l* of Cæsar, *Parnassus* 4
evergreen *l* is blasted by more than lightning! „ 12
Laurel'd sowing the nettle on all the *l* graves of the Great; *Vastness* 22
Laurel-shrubs the *l-s* that hedge it around. *Poet's Mind* 14
Laurence Since I beheld young *L* dead. *L. C. V. de Vere* 28
Lava Claymore and snowshoe, toys in *l*, *Princess, Pro.* 18
Lavaine (a knight of the Round Table) two strong sons, Sir Torre and Sir *L*, *Lancelot and E.* 174
L, my younger here, He is so full of lustihood, „ 202
Before this noble knight,' said young *L*, „ 208
'O there, great lord, doubtless,' *L* said, „ 281
needs must bid farewell to sweet *L*. „ 341
L Past inward, as she came from out the tower. „ 345
L Returning brought the yet-unblazon'd shield, „ 378
Whereat *L* said, laughing, 'Lily maid, „ 385
Abash'd *L*, whose instant reverence, „ 418
So spake *L*, and when they reach'd the lists „ 428
Lancelot answer'd young *L* and said, „ 445
L gaped upon him As on a thing miraculous, „ 452
Sir *L* did well and worshipfully; „ 491
With young *L* into the poplar grove. „ 509
Gasping to Sir *L*, 'Draw the lance-head: „ 511
'Ah my sweet lord Sir Lancelot,' said *L*, „ 512
L drew, and Sir Lancelot gave A marvellous great shriek „ 515
'and find out our dear *L*.' 'Ye will not lose your wits for dear *L*: „ 754
'*L*,' she cried '*L*, How fares my lord Sir Lancelot?' „ 794
L across the poplar grove Led to the caves: „ 804
Besought *L* to write as she devised A letter, „ 1103
Lava-lake lava-light Glares from the *l-l* *Kapiolani* 14
Lava-light *l-l* Glares from the lava-lake „ 13
Lave (to bathe) sunshine *l's* The lawn by some cathedral, *D. of F. Women* 189
Lave (leave) 'An' whin are ye goin' to *l* me?' *Tomorrow* 17
Lavender standing near Purple-spiked *l*: *Ode to Memory* 110
Lavin' (leaving) But I must be *l* ye soon.' *Tomorrow* 13
Laving springs Of Dircê *l* yonder battle-plain, *Tiresias* 139
Lavish (adj.) But thou wert nursed in some delicious land Of *l* lights, *Eleänore* 12
The *l* growths of southern Mexico. *Mine be the strength* 14
of all his *l* waste of words Remains the lean P. W. *The Brook* 191
Or Heaven in *l* bounty moulded, grew. *Aylmer's Field* 107
L Honour shower'd all her stars, *Ode on Well.* 196
But all the *l* hills would hum The murmur of a happy Pan: *In Mem. xxiii* 11
Her *l* mission richly wrought, „ *lxxxiv* 34
heard in thought Their *l* comment when her name was named. *Merlin and V.* 151
And *l* carol of clear-throated larks Fill'd all the March of life!— *Lover's Tale i* 283
Lavish (verb) *l* all the golden day To make them wealthier *Poets and their B.* 3
Lavish'd O vainly *l* love! *Merlin and V.* 859
Law (*See also* **Corn-laws**) Shall we not look into the *l's* *Supp. Confessions* 172
l's of marriage character'd in gold *Isabel* 16
giving light To read those *l's*; „ 19
live by *l*, Acting the *l* we live by without fear; *Œnone* 147
Circled thro' all experiences, pure *l*, „ 166
And reach the *l* within the *l*: *Two Voices* 141
stay'd the Ausonian king to hear Of wisdom and of *l*. *Palace of Art* 112
Roll'd round by one fix'd *l*. „ 256
And in its season bring the *l*; *Love thou thy land* 32
harmonies of *l* The growing world assume, *England and Amer.* 16
He, by some *l* that holds in love, *Gardener's D.* 9
in my time a father's word was *l*, *Dora* 27

Law (*continued*) My home is none of yours. My will is *l*.' *Dora* 45
You knew my word was *l*, and yet you dared „ 98
But there was *l* for *us*; *Walk. to the Mail* 85
by Nature's *l*, Have faded long ago; *Talking Oak* 73
hated by the wise, to *l* System and empire? *Love and Duty* 7
dole Unequal *l's* unto a savage race, *Ulysses* 4
slumber, lapt in universal *l*. *Locksley Hall* 130
But *l's* of nature were our scorn. *The Voyage* 84
Mastering the lawless science of our *l*, *Aylmer's Field* 435
Not follow the great *l*? *Lucretius* 116
fulmined out her scorn of *l's* Salique *Princess ii* 133
Electric, chemic *l's*, and all the rest, „ 384
Nor would I fight with iron *l's*, „ *iv* 75
We knew not your ungracious *l's*, „ 399
truer to the *l* within? „ *v* 189
biting *l's* to scare the beasts of prey „ 393
our sanctuary Is violate, our *l's* broken: „ *vi* 60
'Our *l's* are broken: let him enter too.' „ 317
We break our *l's* with ease, but let it be.' „ 323
your Highness breaks with ease The *l* your Highness did not make: „ 326
Sweet order lived again with other *l's*: „ *vii* 19
and storm'd At the Oppian *l*. „ 124
sons of men, and barbarous *l's*. (repeat) „ 234, 256
reverence for the *l's* ourselves have made, „ *Con.* 55
my Lords, not well: there is a higher *l*. *Third of Feb.* 12
God is *l*, say the wise; *High. Pantheism* 13
For if He thunder by *l* the thunder is yet His voice. „ 14
L is God, say some: no God at all, says the fool; „ 15
In holding by the *l* within, *In Mem. xxxiii* 14
But better serves a wholesome *l*, „ *xlviii* 10
And love Creation's final *l*— „ *lvi* 14
For nothing is that errs from *l*. „ *lxxiii* 8
And loyal unto kindly *l's*. „ *lxxxv* 16
And music in the bounds of *l*, „ *lxxxvii* 34
And dusty purlieus of the *l*. „ *lxxxix* 12
With sweeter manners, purer *l's*. „ *cvi* 16
In all her motion one with *l*; „ *cxxii* 8
One God, one *l*, one element, „ *Con.* 142
Rather than hold by the *l* that I made, *Maud I i* 55
such As have nor *l* nor king; *Gareth and L.* 632
crave His pardon for thy breaking of his *l's*. „ 986
and whatever loathes a *l*: *Marr. of Geraint* 37
Clear'd the dark places and let in the *l*, *Geraint and E.* 943
Deeming our courtesy is the truest *l*, *Lancelot and E.* 712
own no lust because they have no *l*! *Pelleas and E.* 481
He saw the *l's* that ruled the tournament *Last Tournament* 160
Red ruin, and the breaking up of *l's*, *Guinevere* 426
and their *l* Relax'd its hold upon us, „ 456
wrath which forced my thoughts on that fierce *l*, „ 537
some were doubtful how the *l* would hold, *Lover's Tale iv* 270
Glanced at the point of *l*, to pass it by, „ 276
By all the *l's* of love and gratefulness, „ 278
But I knaws the *l*, I does, *Village Wife* 16
this changing world of changeless *l*, *De Prof., Two G.* 6
chime with never-changing *L*. *To Duke of Argyll* 11
To work old *l's* of Love to fresh results, *Prog. of Spring* 85
For all they rule—by equal *l* for all? *Akbar's Dream* 110
Fashion'd after certain *l's*; *Poets and Critics* 5
Lawful And I,' said he, 'the *l* heir, *Lady Clare* 86
l and lawless war Are scarcely even akin. *Maud II v* 94
But free to stretch his limbs in *l* fight, *Geraint and E.* 754
Lawk *L*! 'ow I laugh'd when the lasses *Village Wife* 57
Lawless (adj.) running fires and fluid range Of *l* airs, *Supp. Confessions* 148
Mastering the *l* science of our law, *Aylmer's Field* 435
Confused by brainless mobs and *l* Powers; *Ode on Well.* 153
lawful and *l* war Are scarcely even akin. *Maud II v* 94
Not making his high place the *l* perch Of wing'd ambitions, *Ded. of Idylls* 22
therebefore the *l* warrior paced Unarm'd, *Gareth and L.* 914
For in that realm of *l* turbulence, *Geraint and E.* 521
To shun the wild ways of the *l* tribe. „ 608
when I myself Was half a bandit in my *l* hour, „ 795
And wroth at Tristram and the *l* jousts, *Last Tournament* 237
for me that sicken at your *l* din, *Locksley H., Sixty* 149

Lawless (adj.) (*continued*) Thou loather of the *l* crown As of the *l* crowd; *Freedom* 31
Lawless (s) Nothing of the *l*, of the Despot, *On Jub. Q. Victoria* 12
Lawn (grassy level) (*See also* **Garden-lawn, Orchard-lawns, Terrace-lawn**) And many a shadow-chequer'd *l* *Arabian Nights* 102
It springs on a level of bowery *l*, *Poet's Mind* 31
Or only look across the *l*, *Margaret* 65
The *l's* and meadow-ledges midway down *Œnone* 6
Aloft the mountain *l* was dewy-dark, „ 48
In each a squared *l*, *Palace of Art* 22
Leading from *l* to *l*. *D. of F. Women* 76
A noise of some one coming thro' the *l*, „ 178
broad sunshine laves The *l* by some cathedral, „ 190
the range of *l* and park: *The Blackbird* 6
Flow, softly flow, by *l* and lea, *A Farewell* 5
Dreams over lake and *l*, *Vision of Sin* 11
girt the region with high cliff and *l*: „ 47
l's And winding glades high up like ways to Heaven, *Enoch Arden* 572
I steal by *l's* and grassy plots, *The Brook* 170
thro' the bright *l's* to his brother's ran, *Aylmer's Field* 341
princely halls, and farms, and flowing *l's*, „ 654
Gave his broad *l's* until the set of sun *Princess, Pro.* 2
The sward was trim as any garden *l*: „ 95
others lay about the *l's*, Of the older sort, „ *ii* 462
fields Are lovely, lovelier not the Elysian *l's*, „ *iii* 342
rosy heights came out above the *l's*. „ 365
rode we with the old king across the *l's* „ *v* 236
Myriads of rivulets hurrying thro' the *l*, „ *vii* 220
the *l* as yet Is hoar with rime, or spongy-wet; *To F. D. Maurice* 41
voice and the Peak Far over summit and *l*, *Voice and the P.* 2
counterchange the floor Of this flat *l* *In Mem. lxxxix* 2
lay and read The Tuscan poets on the *l*: „ 24
By night we linger'd on the *l*, „ *xcv* 1
Now dance the lights on *l* and lea, „ *cxv* 9
And lilies fair on a *l*; *Maud I xiv* 2
But the rivulet on from the *l* „ 29
saw deep *l's*, and then a brook, *Holy Grail* 380
apples by the brook Fallen, and on the *l's*. „ 385
So on for all that day from *l* to *l* *Last Tournament* 373
the dews, the fern, the founts, the *l's*; „ 727
dimly-glimmering *l's* Of that Elysium, *Demeter and P.* 150
Lawn (linen) Slow-dropping veils of thinnest *l*, *Lotos-Eaters* 11
broad earth-sweeping pall of whitest *l*, *Lover's Tale ii* 78
Lawrence (Sir Henry) our *L* the best of the brave: *Def. of Lucknow* 11
Lawrence Aylmer (*See also* **Aylmer**) So *L A*, seated on a stile In the long hedge, *The Brook* 197
Lawyer was a God, and is a *l's* clerk, *Edwin Morris* 102
Vext with *l's* and harass'd with debt: *Maud I xix* 22
I came into court to the Judge and the *l's*. *Rizpah* 33
But not the black heart of the *l* who kill'd him „ 40
I stole them all from the *l's*— „ 52
For the *l* is born but to murder— „ 64
I knaws the law, I does, for the *l* ha towd it me. *Village Wife* 16
the *l* he towd it me That 'is taäil were soä tied up „ 29
Lay (s) woke her with a *l* from fairy land. *Caress'd or chidden* 8
So, Lady Flora, take my *l*, *Day-Dm., Moral* 1
So, Lady Flora, take my *l*, „ *Ep.* 1
In *l's* that will outlast thy Deity? *Lucretius* 72
If these brief *l's*, of Sorrow born, *In Mem. xlviii* 1
Nor dare she trust a larger *l*, „ 13
And lo, thy deepest *l's* are dumb „ *lxxvi* 7
Demand not thou a marriage *l*; „ *Con.* 2
Has link'd our names together in his *l*, *Lancelot and E.* 112
this *l*—Which Pelleas had heard sung before the Queen, *Pelleas and E.* 396
many a mystic *l* of life and death *Guinevere* 281
Adviser of the nine-years-ponder'd *l*, *Poets and their B.* 6
Lay (verb) (*See also* **Laäy**) thick-moted sunbeam *l* Athwart the chambers, *Mariana* 78
An open scroll, Before him *l*: *The Poet* 9
They should have stabb'd me where I *l*, (repeat) *Oriana* 55, 60
She loosed the chain, and down she *l*; *L. of Shalott iv* 16
and *l* Upon the freshly-flower'd slope. *Miller's D.* 111
To win his love I *l* in wait: *The Sisters* 11
Lay (verb) (*continued*) *L*, dozing in the vale of Avalon, *Palace of Art* 107
L there exiled from eternal God, „ 263
you may *l* me low i' the mould and think no more of me. *May Queen, N. Y's. E.* 4
high masts flicker'd as they *l* afloat; *D. of F. Women* 113
And on thy heart a finger *l's*, *On a Mourner* 11
On one side *l* the Ocean, and on one *L* a great water, *M. d'Arthur* 11
Where *l* the mighty bones of ancient men, „ 47
So like a shatter'd column *l* the King; „ 221
Where quail and pigeon, lark and leveret *l*, *Audley Court* 24
L great with pig, wallowing in sun and mud. *Walk. to the Mail* 88
I *l* Pent in a roofless close of ragged stones; *St. S. Stylites* 73
this is none of mine; *L* it not to me. „ 124
On the coals I *l*, A vessel full of sin: „ 169
And at my feet she *l*. *Talking Oak* 208
but a moment *l* Where fairer fruit of Love „ 250
I *l*, Mouth, forehead, eyelids, *Tithonus* 57
The dewy sister-eyelids *l*. *Day-Dm., Pro.* 4
On the mossy stone, as I *l*, *Edward Gray* 26
And *l's* it thrice upon my lips, *Will Water.* 19
And *l* your hand upon my head, *Lady Clare* 55
Leapt up from where she *l*, „ 62
In their blood, as they *l* dying, *The Captain* 55
L betwixt his home and hers; *L. of Burleigh* 28
And while he *l* recovering there, *Enoch Arden* 108
Enoch *l* long-pondering on his plans; „ 133
L lingering out a five-years' death-in-life. „ 565
Stay'd by this isle, not knowing where she *l*: „ 630
fail'd a little, And he *l* tranced; „ 793
L hidden as the music of the moon *Aylmer's Field* 102
L deeper than to wear it as his ring— „ 122
silenced by that silence *l* the wife, *Sea Dreams* 46
I *l*,' said he, 'And mused upon it, „ 107
right across its track there *l*, „ 126
belt, it seem'd, of luminous vapour, *l*, „ 209
l's His vast and filthy hands upon my will, *Lucretius* 219
on the pavement *l* Carved stones of the Abbey-ruin *Princess, Pro.* 13
about it *l* the guests, And there we join'd them: „ 106
patting Lilia's head (she *l* Beside him) „ 125
there on lattice edges *l* Or book or lute; „ *ii* 29
spoke of those That *l* at wine with Lar and Lucumo; „ 129
others *l* about the lawns, „ 462
court that *l* three parts In shadow, „ *iii* 20
L out the viands.' „ 347
And *l* me on her bosom, and her heart „ *iv* 103
on the purple footcloth, *l* The lily-shining child; „ 286
glove upon the tomb *L* by her like a model „ 597
All her fair length upon the ground she *l*: „ *v* 59
And *l* my little blossom at my feet, „ 100
As in some mystic middle state I *l*; „ *vi* 18
l's on every side A thousand arms and rushes „ 36
To where her wounded brethren *l*; „ 90
L like a new-fall'n meteor on the grass, „ 135
but he that *l* Beside us, Cyril, „ 153
or if you scorn to *l* it, Yourself, „ 183
those two hosts that *l* beside the walls, „ 383
L silent in the muffled cage of life: „ *vii* 47
l Quite sunder'd from the moving Universe, „ 51
I *l* still, and with me oft she sat: „ 91
I could no more, but *l* like one in trance, „ 151
while with shut eyes I *l* Listening; „ 223
L thy sweet hands in mine and trust in me.' „ 366
Where shall we *l* the man whom we deplore? *Ode on Well.* 8
L your earthly fancies down, „ 279
There *l* the sweet little body *Grandmother* 62
Sun-smitten Alps before me *l*. *The Daisy* 62
in his coffin the Prince of courtesy *l*. *G. of Swainston* 10
And dead men *l* all over the way, *The Victim* 21
there at tables of ebony *l*, *Boädicea* 61
Till growing winters *l* me low; *In Mem. xl* 30
That *l* their eggs, and sting and sing „ *l* 11
l and read The Tuscan poets on the lawn. „ *lxxxix* 23
little shallop *l* At anchor in the flood below; „ *ciii* 19
l Sick once, with a fear of worse, *Maud I xix* 72
Was it he *l* there with a fading eye? „ *II i* 29

Lead (verb) (*continued*) *l* Thro' prosperous floods his holy urn. *In Mem. ix* 7
Or on to where the pathway *l's*; „ *xxiii* 8
A life that *l's* melodious days. „ *xxxiii* 8
What kind of life is that I *l*; „ *lxxxv* 8
and *l* The closing cycle rich in good. „ *cv* 27
It *l's* me forth at evening, *Maud II iv* 17
way to glory *l* Low down thro' villain kitchen-vassalage, *Gareth and L.* 159
L, and I follow.' (repeat) *Gareth and L.* 746, 760, 807, 891, 990, 1053, 1155
'Follow, I *l*!' so down among the pines He plunged; *Gareth and L.* 808
'I *l* no longer; ride thou at my side; „ 1157
Thro' which he bad her *l* him on, *Geraint and E.* 29
Go likewise: shall I *l* you to the King?' '*L* then,' she said; and thro' the woods they went. *Pelleas and E.* 107
to *l* her to his lord Arthur, *Guinevere* 383
To *l* sweet lives in purest chastity, „ 474
They summon me their King to *l* mine hosts „ 570
that way my wish *l's* me evermore Still to believe it— *Lover's Tale i* 274
Yes. *L* on them. *Up* the mountain? *Sir J. Oldcastle* 203
be consecrate to *l* A new crusade against the Saracen, *Columbus* 102
I *l* thee by the hand, Fear not.' „ 158
to *l* One last crusade against the Saracen, „ 238
short, or long, as Pleasure *l's*, or Pain; *Ancient Sage* 101
two that love thee, *l* a summer life, *To Prin. Beatrice* 18
Hand of Light will *l* her people, *On Jub. Q. Victoria* 68

Leaden-colour'd the low moan of *l-c* seas. *Enoch Arden* 612

Leader patient *l's* of their Institute *Princess, Pro.* 58
The *l* wildswan in among the stars „ *iv* 434
as the *l* of the herd That holds a stately fretwork „ *vi* 85
Mourning when their *l's* fall, *Ode on Well.* 5
Lo, the *l* in these glorious wars „ 192
Their ever-loyal iron *l's* fame, „ 229
For a man and *l* of men. *Maud I x* 59
there lives No greater *l*.' *Lancelot and E.* 317
But ye, that follow but the *l's* bell' *Holy Grail* 298
Ready! take aim at their *l's*— *Def. of Lucknow* 42
Then the Norse *l*, Dire was his need of it, *Batt. of Brunanburh* 56
True *l's* of the land's desire! *Hands all Round* 26

Leading *L* a jet-black goat white-horn'd, *Œnone* 51
L from lawn to lawn. *D. of F. Women* 76
onward, *l* up the golden year. (repeat) *Golden Year* 26, 41
L on from hall to hall. *L. of Burleigh* 52
children *l* evermore Low miserable lives *Enoch Arden* 115
But sorrow seize me if ever that light be my *l* star! *Maud I iv* 12
And *l* all his knighthood threw the kings *Com. of Arthur* 111
Enid *l* down the tracks Thro' which he bad her lead *Geraint and E.* 28
up the rocky pathway disappear'd, *L* the horse, „ 244
Arthur *l*, slowly went The marshall'd Order *Lancelot and E.* 1331
The *l* of his younger knights to me. *Last Tournament* 110
Ever, ever, and for ever was the *l* light of man. *Locksley H., Sixty* 66
Thro' which I follow'd line by line Your *l* hand, *To Ulysses* 46

Leading-strings be sweet, to sin in *l-s*, *Last Tournament* 574
all the rest are as yet but in *l-s*. *The Dawn* 10

Lead-like those *l-l* tons of sin, *St. S. Stylites* 25

Leaf (*See also* **Jasmine-leaves, Rose-leaf**) Flush'd all the *leaves* with rich gold-green, *Arabian Nights* 82
moist rich smell of the rotting *leaves*, *A spirit haunts* 17
The sun came dazzling thro' the *leaves*, *L. of Shalott iii* 3
The *leaves* upon her falling light— „ *iv* 21
'The memory of the wither'd *l* *Two Voices* 112
I whirl like *leaves* in roaring wind. *Fatima* 7
blossom on the blackthorn, the *l* upon the tree. *May Queen, N. Y's. E.* 8
folded *l* is woo'd from out the bud *Lotos-Eaters, C. S.* 26
I knew the flowers, I knew the *leaves*, *D. of F. Women* 73
Shall sing for want, ere *leaves* are new, *The Blackbird* 23
And, sitting muffled in dark *leaves*, *Gardener's D.* 37
In whispers, like the whispers of the *leaves* „ 253
dimly rain'd about the *l* Twilights of airy silver, *Audley Court* 81
else may insects prick Each *l* into a gall) *Talking Oak* 70
'I swear, by *l*, and wind, and rain, „ 81
When that, which breathes within the *l*, „ 187
Thro' all the summer of my *leaves* „ 211
Thy *l* shall never fail, nor yet Thine acorn „ 259

Leaf (*continued*) shall wear Alternate *l* and acorn-ball *Talking Oak* 287
Here rests the sap within the *l*, *Day-Dm., Sleep P.* 3
As dash'd about the drunken *leaves* *Amphion* 55
And the *l* is stamp'd in clay. *Vision of Sin* 82
Of sounder *l* than I can claim; *You might have won* 4
and thatch'd with *leaves* of palm, a hut, *Enoch Arden* 559
gentle shower, the smell of dying *leaves*, „ 611
dead weight of the dead *l* bore it down: „ 678
touch'd On such a time as goes before the *l*, *The Brook* 13
A lisping of the innumerous *l* and dies, *Princess v* 14
Of the first snowdrop's inner *leaves*; „ 197
leaves were wet with women's tears: „ *vi* 39
This faded *l*, our names are as brief; *Spiteful Letter* 13
Yet the yellow *l* hates the greener *l*, „ 15
Brief, brief is a summer *l*, „ 21
Like the *l* in a roaring whirlwind, *Boädicea* 59
Spring is here with *l* and grass: *Window, No Answer* 23
And only thro' the faded *l* The chestnut *In Mem. xi* 3
These *leaves* that redden to the fall; „ 14
The last red *l* is whirl'd away, „ *xv* 3
Thro' lands where not a *l* was dumb; „ *xxiii* 10
In many a figured *l* enrolls The total world „ *xliii* 11
That seem'd to touch it into *l*: „ *lxix* 18
Thy *l* has perish'd in the green, „ *lxxv* 13
Thy spirits in the darkening *l*, „ *lxxxviii* 6
In those fall'n *leaves* which kept their green, „ *xcv* 23
The large *leaves* of the sycamore, „ 55
park and suburb under brown Of lustier *leaves*; „ *xcviii* 25
A fiery finger on the *leaves*; „ *xcix* 12
The time admits not flowers or *leaves* „ *cvii* 5
The dead *l* trembles to the bells. „ *Con.* 64
When the shiver of dancing *leaves* is thrown *Maud I vi* 73
like a sudden wind Among dead *leaves*, *Gareth and L.* 515
wood is nigh as full of thieves as *leaves*: „ 789
For as a *l* in mid-November is To what *Marr. of Geraint* 611
as the worm draws in the wither'd *l* *Geraint and E.* 633
wealth Of *l*, and gayest garlandage of flowers, *Balin and Balan* 83
leaves Laid their green faces flat „ 343
dim thro' *leaves* Blinkt the white morn, „ 384
The new *l* ever pushes off the old. „ 442
glittering like May sunshine on May *leaves* *Merlin and V.* 88
left hand Droop from his mighty shoulder, as a *l*, „ 243
Must our true man change like a *l* at last? *Lancelot and E.* 686
L after *l*, and tore, and cast them off, „ 1199
green wood-ways, and eyes among the *leaves*; *Pelleas and E.* 139
as a hand that pushes thro' the *l* „ 436
Danced like a wither'd *l* before the hall. (repeat) *Last Tournament* 4, 242
and yellowing *l* And gloom and gleam, „ 154
l is dead, the yearning past away: New *l*, „ 277
laid His brows upon the drifted *l* and dream'd. „ 406
And rode beneath an ever-showering *l*, „ 492
And pale and fibrous as a wither'd *l*, *Lover's Tale i* 422
No bud, no *l*, no flower, no fruit „ 725
Tearing the bright *leaves* of the ivy-screen, „ *ii* 40
All crisped sounds of wave and *l* and wind, „ 106
lasses 'ed teärd out *leaves* i' the middle *Village Wife* 72
without *l* or a thorn from the bush; *V. of Maeldune* 44
Or the young green *l* rejoice in the frost *The Wreck* 20
Her dust is greening in your *l*, *Ancient Sage* 165
and from each The light *l* falling fast, *Pro. to Gen. Hamley* 2
l fell, and the sun, Pale at my grief, *Demeter and P.* 113
and there My giant ilex keeping *l* *To Ulysses* 18
by hour unfolding woodbine *leaves* *Prog. of Spring* 7
leaves possess the season in their turn, „ 107
Light again, *l* again, life again, love again,' *The Throstle* 3
All his *leaves* Fall'n at length, *The Oak* 11
Vary like the *leaves* and flowers, *Poets and Critics* 4

Leafless (*See also* **Seeming-leafless**) What?—that the bush were *l*? *Lucretius* 206
wood which grides and clangs Its *l* ribs and iron horns *In Mem. cvii* 12
the branching grace Of *l* elm, or naked lime, *To Ulysses* 16

Leaflet with hardly a *l* between, *V. of Maeldune* 64

Leafy its walls And chimneys muffled in the *l* vine. *Audley Court* 19
O flourish high, with *l* towers, *Talking Oak* 197
But in the *l* lanes behind the down, *Enoch Arden* 97

Leafy (*continued*) The climbing street, the mill, the *l* lanes, *Enoch Arden* 607
Till they were swallow'd in the *l* bowers, *Lover's Tale iii* 57
League (s) (*See also* **Half-a-league**) For *l's* no other tree did mark The level waste, *Mariana* 43
Flung *l's* of roaring foam into the gorge *If I were loved* 13
A *l* of grass, wash'd by a slow broad stream, *Gardener's D.* 40
l's along that breaker-beaten coast *Enoch Arden* 51
Many a long *l* back to the North. *Princess i* 168
heave and thump A *l* of street in summer solstice „ *iii* 128
we rode a *l* beyond, And, o'er a bridge of pinewood „ 334
HALF a *l*, half a *l*, Half a *l* onward, *Light Brigade* 1
On *l's* of odour streaming far, *In Mem. lxxxvi* 14
At the shouts, the *l's* of lights, *Maud II iv* 21
everyone that owns a tower The Lord for half a *l*. *Gareth and L.* 596
A *l* beyond the wood, All in a full-fair manor „ 845
A *l* of mountain full of golden mines, *Merlin and V.* 587
King Made proffer of the *l* of golden mines, „ 646
That have no meaning half a *l* away: *Holy Grail* 556
great waters break Whitening for half a *l*, *Last Tournament* 465
And ever push'd Sir Modred, *l* by *l*, *Pass. of Arthur* 80
and loud *l's* of man And welcome! *To the Queen ii* 9
following out A *l* of labyrinthine darkness, *Demeter and P.* 82
League (verb) who *l's* With Lords of the White Horse, *Guinevere* 573
Leagued And *l* him with the heathen, „ 155
l again Their lot with ours to rove the world *Pref. Son. 19th Cent.* 10
League-long *l-l* roller thundering on the reef, *Enoch Arden* 584
Thro' many a *l-l* bower he rode. *Last Tournament* 374
You saw the *l-l* rampart-fire Flare from Tel-el-Kebir *Pro. to Gen. Hamley* 27
Leaguer for hours On that disastrous *l*, *Princess vii* 33
Leaguer'd That bore a lady from a *l* town; *D. of F. Women* 47
Leaky or prove The Danaïd of a *l* vase, *Princess ii* 340
Leal fain Have all men true and *l*, *Merlin and V.* 794
I will be *l* to thee and work thy work, *Pelleas and E.* 343
Lean (adj.) I KNEW an old wife *l* and poor, *The Goose* 1
And in my weak, *l* arms I lift the cross, *St. S. Stylites* 118
A gray and gap-tooth'd man as *l* as death, *Vision of Sin* 60
Remains the *l* P. W. on his tomb: *The Brook* 193
All over with the fat affectionate smile That makes the widow *l*. *Sea Dreams* 156
went Hating his own *l* heart and miserable. *Aylmer's Field* 526
Down from the *l* and wrinkled precipices, *Princess iv* 22
But still her lists were swell'd and mine were *l*; „ 319
A gray old wolf and a *l*. *Maud I xiii* 28
So *l* his eyes were monstrous; *Merlin and V.* 624
And a *l* Order—scarce return'd a tithe— *Holy Grail* 894
Her dear, long, *l*, little arms lying out *In the Child. Hosp.* 70
And tho', in this *l* age forlorn, *Epilogue* 71
Opulent Avarice, *l* as Poverty; *Vastness* 20
till I believing that the girl's *L* fancy, *The Ring* 336
Lean (verb) *l* out from the hollow sphere of the sea, *The Mermaid* 54
And a rose-bush *l's* upon, *Adeline* 14
Enormous elm-tree-boles did stoop and *l* *D. of F. Women* 57
that from a casement *l's* his head, „ 246
'Tis strange that those we *l* on most, *To J. S.* 9
and *l* a ladder on the shaft, *St. S. Stylites* 216
' On that which *l's* to you. *Princess iii* 232
but *l* me down, Sir Dagonet, *Last Tournament* 272
And so thou *l* on our fair father Christ, *Guinevere* 562
He *l's* on Antichrist; *Sir J. Oldcastle* 74
let me *l* my head upon your breast. *Romney's R.* 154
Lean'd-Leant And *lean'd* upon the balcony. *Mariana in the S.* 88
prudent partner of his blood *Lean'd* on him, *Two Voices* 416
Or from the bridge I *lean'd* to hear *Miller's D.* 49
o'er him flow'd a golden cloud, and *lean'd* Upon him, *Œnone* 105
And on her lover's arm she *leant*, *Day-Dm., Depart.* 1
He *lean'd* not on his fathers but himself. *Aylmer's Field* 56
Once she *lean'd* on me, Descending; *Princess iv* 26
What reed was that on which I *leant*? *In Mem. lxxxiv* 45
Push'd thro' an open casement down, *lean'd* on it, *Balin and Balan* 413
Sir Lancelot *leant*, in half disdain At love, *Lancelot and E.* 1238
all whereon I *lean'd* in wife and friend *Pass. of Arthur* 24
As I *lean'd* away from his arms— *The Wreck* 102
and we *lean'd* to the darker side— *Despair* 55

Lean'd-Leant (*continued*) She *lean'd* to from her Spiritual sphere, *The Ring* 484
Leaneth Thou art light, To which my spirit *l* *Lover's Tale i* 104
Lean-headed *L-h* Eagles yelp alone, *Princess vii* 211
Leaning (*See also* **A-leanin'**) *L* upon the ridged sea, *The Winds, etc.* 2
A *l* and upbearing parasite, *Isabel* 34
rich fruit-bunches *l* on each other— „ 37
L his cheek upon his hand, *Eleänore* 118
And you were *l* from the ledge *Miller's D.* 84
She, *l* on a fragrant twined with vine, *Œnone* 20
Upon her pearly shoulder *l* cold, „ 140
Robin *l* on the bridge beneath the hazel-tree? *May Queen* 14
L his horns into the neighbour field, *Gardener's D.* 87
And *l* there on those balusters, *Princess iii* 119
There *l* deep in broider'd down we sank „ *iv* 32
Gareth *l* both hands heavily *Gareth and L.* 439
and hungerworn I seem—*l* on these? „ 444
eyes all bright replied, *L* a little toward him, *Marr. of Geraint* 495
And speaking not, but *l* over him, *Merlin and V.* 477
when I was *l* out Above the river— *Last Tournament* 43
L its roses on my faded eyes. *Lover's Tale i* 621
The slant seas *l* on the mangrove copse, *Prog. of Spring* 76
Leanness black eyes, Yet larger thro' his *l*, *Lancelot and E.* 835
Leant *See* **Lean'd**
Leap (s) heart on one wild *l* Hung tranced from all pulsation, *Gardener's D.* 259
this a bridge of single arc Took at a *l*; *Gareth and L.* 909
and stirs the pulse With devil's *l's*, *Guinevere* 522
And leave the name of Lover's *L*: *Lover's Tale iv* 42
Leap (verb) Where he was wont to *l* and climb, *Supp. Confessions* 165
In the middle *l's* a fountain *Poet's Mind* 24
like a wave I would *l* From the diamond-ledges *The Mermaid* 39
And not *l* forth and fall about thy neck, *Love and Duty* 41
his spirit *l's* within him to be gone *Locksley Hall* 115
and *l* the rainbows of the brooks, „ 171
Be still the first to *l* to light *Day-Dm., L'Envoi* 27
I *l* on board: no helmsman steers: *Sir Galahad* 39
High-elbow'd grigs that *l* in summer grass. *The Brook* 54
To *l* the rotten pales of prejudice, *Princess ii* 142
And the wild cataract *l's* in glory. „ *iv* 4
l's in Among the women, snares them by the score „ *v* 162
Whatever record *l* to light He never shall be shamed. *Ode on Well.* 190
Making the little one *l* for joy. *To F. D. Maurice* 4
To *l* the grades of life and light, *In Mem. xli* 11
But at his footstep *l's* no more, „ *lxxxv* 112
And *l's* into the future chance, „ *cxiv* 7
snubnosed rogue would *l* from his counter and till, *Maud I i* 51
the red man's babe *L*, beyond the sea. „ *xvii* 20
many a darkness into the light shall *l*, „ *III vi* 46
I *l* from Satan's foot to Peter's knee— *Gareth and L.* 538
Who *l* at thee to tear thee; *Balin and Balan* 142
who had ever Made my heart *l*; *Holy Grail* 580
how her choice did *l* forth from his eyes! *Lover's Tale i* 657
When he *l's* from the water to the land. *The Revenge* 55
if the tigers *l* into the fold unawares— *Def. of Lucknow* 51
I would *l* into your grave. *Happy* 20
Up *l's* the lark, gone wild to welcome *Prog. of Spring* 14
Leap'd-Leapt Then *leapt* a trout. In lazy mood *Miller's D.* 73
My mailed Bacchus *leapt* into my arms, *D. of F. Women* 151
My words *leapt* forth: ' Heaven heads the count of crimes „ 201
About me *leap'd* and laugh'd The modish Cupid *Talking Oak* 66
And sixty feet the fountain *leapt*. *Day-Dm., Revival* 8
doe Lord Ronald had brought *Leapt* up from where she lay, *Lady Clare* 62
no one cared for, *leapt* To greet her, *Aylmer's Field* 688
Two Proctors *leapt* upon us, crying, ' Names: ' *Princess iv* 259
Leapt from the dewy shoulders of the Earth, „ *v* 43
And into fiery splinters *leapt* the lance, „ 494
o'er the statues *leapt* from head to head, „ *vi* 366
out of languor *leapt* a cry; *Leapt* fiery Passion „ *vii* 155
Thought *leapt* out to wed with Thought *In Mem. xxiii* 15
Ran like a colt, and *leapt* at all he saw: *Com. of Arthur* 322
Leapt in a semicircle, and lit on earth; *Balin and Balan* 414
his evil spirit upon him *leapt*, „ 537

Leap'd-Leapt (*continued*) Then *leapt* her palfrey o'er the fallen oak, — Balin and Balan 587
Leapt from her session on his lap, — Merlin and V. 844
the harlot *leapt* Adown the forest, — ,, 972
Leapt on his horse, and carolling as he went — Lancelot and E. 704
from the boat I *leapt*, and up the stairs. — Holy Grail 819
his helpless heart *Leapt*, and he cried, — Pelleas and E. 131
shouted and *leapt* down upon the fall'n; — Last Tournament 469
Leapt on him, and hurl'd him headlong, — Guinevere 108
Leapt like a passing thought across her eyes; — Lover's Tale i 70
My spirit *leap'd* as with those thrills of bliss — ,, 363
Leapt lightly clad in bridal white— — ,, iii 44
One has *leapt* up on the breach, — Def. of Lucknow 64
There were some *leap'd* into the fire; — V. of Maeldune 76
she *leapt* upon the funeral pile, — Death of Œnone 105

Leaping So, *l* lightly from the boat, — Arabian Nights 92
The *l* stream, the very wind, — Rosalind 14
O follow, *l* blood, — Early Spring 25
Then *l* out upon them unseen — The Merman 33
And, *l* down the ridges lightly, — M. d'Arthur 134
Pelleas, *l* up, Ran thro' the doors — Pelleas and E. 538
walls of my cell were dyed With rosy colours *l* on the wall; — Holy Grail 120
And, *l* down the ridges lightly, — Pass. of Arthur 302

Leapt *See* **Leap'd**

Learn (*See also* **Larn**) Will *l* new things when I am not.' — Two Voices 63
l at full How passion rose thro' circumstantial — Gardener's D. 239
he will *l* to slight His father's memory; — Dora 153
A thousand thanks for what I *l* — Talking Oak 203
Drug thy memories, lest thou *l* it, — Locksley Hall 77
And *l* the world, and sleep again; — Day-Dm., L'Envoi 8
For since I came to live and *l*, — Will Water. 81
Then may she *l* I lov'd her to the last.' — Enoch Arden 835
sent the bailliff to the farm To *l* the price, — The Brook 142
I am grieved to *l* your grief— — Aylmer's Field 398
and as we task ourselves To *l* a language — ,, 433
l A man is likewise counsel for himself, — Sea Dreams 181
Here might they *l* whatever men were taught: — Princess ii 146
women were too barbarous, would not *l*; — ,, 298
Who *l's* the one POU STO whence after-hands — ,, iii 263
l With whom they deal, — ,, iv 512
To *l* if Ida yet would cede our claim, — ,, v 333
To give or keep, to live and *l* and be All that — ,, vii 273
Give it time To *l* its limbs: — ,, Con. 79
and *l's* to deaden Love of self, — Ode on Well. 204
And *l's* her gone and far from home; — In Mem. viii 4
and *l* That I have been an hour away. — ,, xii 19
And *l's* the use of 'I' and 'me,' — ,, xlv 6
Had man to *l* himself anew — ,, 15
desire or admire, if a man could *l* it, — Maud I iv 41
after-years Will *l* the secret of our Arthur's birth.' — Com. of Arthur 159
and *l* Whether he know me for his master — Gareth and L. 720
'If Enid errs, let Enid *l* her fault.' — Marr. of Geraint 132
'Surely I will *l* the name,' — ,, 203
by the bird's song ye may *l* the nest,' — ,, 359
I will break his pride and *l* his name, — ,, 424
But coming back he *l's* it, — Geraint and E. 498
As children *l*, be thou Wiser for falling! — Balin and Balan 75
and came To *l* black magic, — ,, 127
To *l* what Arthur meant by courtesy, — ,, 158
To *l* the graces of their Table, — ,, 238
suffer from the things before me, know, L nothing; — ,, 285
make me wish still more to *l* this charm — Merlin and V. 329
Who have to *l* themselves and all the world, — ,, 365
we needs must *l* Which is our mightiest, — Lancelot and E. 62
l If his old prowess were in aught decay'd; And added, 'Our true Arthur, when he *l's*, — ,, 583
Whence you might *l* his name? — ,, 654
So ye will *l* the courtesies of the court, — ,, 699
fain were I to *l* this knight were whole, — ,, 772
bode among them yet a little space Till he should *l* it; — ,, 922
Till overborne by one, he *l's*— — Holy Grail 305
thou remaining here wilt *l* the event; — Guinevere 577
Must *l* to use the tongues of all the world. — Sir J. Oldcastle 34
He might have come to *l* Our Wiclif's learning: — ,, 64

Learn (*continued*) haply *l* the Nameless hath a voice, — Ancient Sage 34
simpler, saner lesson might he *l* — Prog. of Spring 105
Before I *l* that Love, which is, — Doubt and Prayer 7

Learnable not *l*, divine, Beyond *my* reach. — Balin and Balan 175

Learned (adj.) Long *l* names of agaric, moss and fern, — Edwin Morris 17
Men hated *l* women: — Princess ii 466
Not *l*, save in gracious household ways, — ,, vii 318
a *l* man Could give it a clumsy name. — Maud II ii 9

Learned (s) The *L* all his lore; — Ancient Sage 139

Learned-Learnt (verb) (*See also* **Larn'd**) late he *learned* humility Perforce, — Buonaparte 13
all at once a pleasant truth I *learn'd*, — The Bridesmaid 9
As in the Latin song I *learnt* at school, — Edwin Morris 79
a saying *learnt*, In days far-off, — Tithonus 47
I *learnt* that James had flickering jealousies — The Brook 99
'have you *learnt* No more from Psyche's lecture, — Princess ii 392
And *learnt*? I *learnt* more from her in a flash, — ,, 397
since we *learnt* our meaning here, — ,, iii 222
learnt, For many weary moons before we came, — ,, 318
We knew not your ungracious laws, which *learnt*, — ,, iv 399
but when she *learnt* his face, Remembering — ,, vi 158
Much had she *learnt* in little time. — vii 240
One lesson from one book we *learn'd*, — In Mem. lxxix 14
when they *learnt* that I must go They wept — ,, ciii 17
shall have *learn'd* to lisp you thanks.' — Marr. of Geraint 822
ere he *learnt* it, 'Take Five horses and their armours;' — Geraint and E. 408
Sir Garlon too Hath *learn'd* black magic, — Balin and Balan 305
And *learnt* their elemental secrets, — Merlin and V. 632
'He *learnt* and warn'd me of their fierce design — Lancelot and E. 274
'Sire, my liege, so much I *learnt*; — ,, 708
Lied, say ye? Nay, but *learnt*, — Last Tournament 656
(When first I *learnt* thee hidden here) — Guinevere 539
and *learn'd* To lisp in tune together; — Lover's Tale i 257
Because she *learnt* them with me; — ,, 292
Had I not *learnt* my loss before he came? — Lover's Tale i 665
I *learnt* the drearier story of his life; — ,, iv 147
I *learnt* it first. I had to speak. — Sisters (E. and E.) 242
he *learnt* that I hated the ring I wore, — The Wreck 57
I scarce have *learnt* the title of your book, — The Ring 126
and woke me And *learn'd* me Magic! — Merlin and the G. 14
when I *learn'd* my fate. — Charity 14
when I *learnt* it at last, I shriek'd, — ,, 37

Learning (part.) *l* this, the bridegroom will relent. — Guinevere 172
l it (They told her somewhat rashly as I think) — Lover's Tale iv 97

Learning (s) what was *l* unto them? — Princess ii 464
wearing all that weight Of *l* lightly — In Mem., Con. 40
He might have come to learn Our Wiclif's *l*: — Sir J. Oldcastle 65
We fronted there the *l* of all Spain, — Columbus 41

Learnt *See* **Learn'd**

Lease laying down an unctuous *l* Of life, — Will Water. 243
brooding on his briefer *l* of life, — Locksley H., Sixty 23

Leash hold passion in a *l*, — Love and Duty 40
Diet and seeling, jesses, *l* and lure. — Merlin and V. 125

Least (*See also* **Laste**) And trampled under by the last and *l* Of men? — Poland 2
her *l* remark was worth The experience of the wise. — Edwin Morris 65
Nor ever falls the *l* white star of snow, — Lucretius 107
In whose *l* act abides the nameless charm — Princess v 70
Our greatest yet with *l* pretence, — Ode on Well. 29
I seem to meet their *l* desire, — In Mem. lxxxiv 17
Or the *l* little delicate aquiline curve in a sensitive nose, From which I escaped heart-free, with the *l* little touch of spleen. — Maud I ii 10
to her own bright face Accuse her of the *l* immodesty: — Geraint and E. 111
Love-loyal to the *l* wish of the Queen — Lancelot and E. 89
Love-loyal to the *l* wish of the Queen, — Guinevere 126
my strongest wish Falls flat before your *l* unwillingness. — Romney's R. 72
Myself not *l*, but honour'd of them — Ulysses 15
Some men's were small; not they the *l* of men; — Princess ii 148
feel, at *l*, that silence here were sin, — Third of Feb. 37
'Thou pratest here where thou art *l*; — In Mem. xxxvii 2
I saw the *l* of little stars Down on the waste, — Holy Grail 524
made our mightiest madder than our *l*. — ,, 863

Leather *See* **Saddle-leather**
Leave-Leäve (holiday) with a month's *leave* given them, *Sea Dreams* 6
then 'ed gotten wer *leäve*, *Owd Roä* 51
Leave (permission) so much out as gave us *l* to go. *Princess v* 235
I'll have *l* at times to play *In Mem. lix* 11
to gain it—your full *l* to go. *Gareth and L.* 134
Sir Kay nodded him *l* to go, „ 520
Queen petition'd for his *l* To see the hunt, *Marr. of Geraint* 154
'Thy *l*! Let *me* lay lance in rest, „ 495
'Have I *l* to speak?' *Geraint and E.* 140
'Your *l*, my lord, to cross the room, „ 298
free *l*,' he said; 'Get her to speak: „ 300
my *l* To move to your own land, „ 888
But, father, give me *l*, an if he will, *Lancelot and E.* 219
But left him *l* to stammer,' Is it indeed? „ 420
And so, *l* given, straight on thro' open door *Pelleas and E.* 382
dare without your *l* to head These rhymings *Pro. to Gen. Hamley* 19
saying gently: 'Muriel, by your *l*,' *The Ring* 268
Leave (farewell)—took my *l*, for it was nearly noon: *Princess v* 468
crowd were swarming now, To take their *l*, „ *Con.* 38
To take her latest *l* of home, *In Mem. xl* 6
And thou shalt take a nobler *l*.' „ *lviii* 12
But how to take last *l* of all I loved? *Guinevere* 546
you still delay to take Your *l* of Town, *To Mary Boyle* 2
Leave (verb) (*See also* **Lave, Leäve**) *And* l *us rulers of your blood* *To the Queen* 21
hard at first, mother, to *l* the blessed sun, *May Queen, Con.* 9
Which will not *l* the myrrh-bush on the height; *Lotos-Eaters, C. S.* 58
'It is not meet, Sir King, to *l* thee thus, *M. d'Arthur* 40
it seem'd Better to *l* Excalibur conceal'd „ 62
'*L*,' she cried 'O *l* me!' 'Never, *Edwin Morris* 116
I will *l* my relics in your land, *St. S. Stylites* 194
But *l* thou mine to me. *Talking Oak* 200
And *l* thee freër, till thou wake refresh'd *Love and Duty* 97
To whom I *l* the sceptre and the isle— *Ulysses* 34
Comrades, *l* me here a little, *Locksley Hall* 1
L me here, and when you want me, „ 2
Eager-hearted as boy when first he *l's* his father's field, „ 112
I *l* the plain, I climb the height; *Sir Galahad* 57
I *l* an empty flask: *Will Water.* 164
And they *l* her father's roof. *L. of Burleigh* 12
and *l* Yon orange sunset waning slow: *Move eastward* 1
Pass on, weak heart, and *l* me where I lie: *Come not, when, etc.* 11
Nor *l* his music as of old, *You might have won* 14
go this weary way, And *l* you lonely? *Enoch Arden* 297
five years' death-in-life. They could not *l* him. „ 566
One who cried, '*L* all and follow me.' *Aylmer's Field* 664
L us: you may go: *Princess ii* 94
'*L* me to deal with that.' „ *iii* 149
Ill mother that I was to *l* her there, „ *v* 93
meteor on, and *l's* A shining furrow, „ *vii* 184
l The monstrous ledges there to slope, „ 211
Will *l* her space to burgeon out of all „ 271
And in the vast cathedral *l* him *Ode on Well.* 280
They *l* the heights and are troubled, *Voice and the P.* 15
l it gorily quivering? *Boädicea* 12
Thou wilt not *l* us in the dust: *In Mem., Pro.* 9
I *l* this mortal ark behind, „ *xii* 6
And *l* the cliffs, and haste away „ 8
L thou thy sister when she prays, „ *xxxiii* 5
But half my life I *l* behind: „ *lvii* 6
And what I see I *l* unsaid, „ *lxxiv* 10
I *l* thy praises unexpress'd „ *lxxv* 1
I *l* thy greatness to be guess'd; „ 4
You *l* us: you will see the Rhine, „ *xcviii* 1
We *l* the well-beloved place „ *cii* 1
To *l* the pleasant fields and farms; „ 22
And wilt thou *l* us now behind?' „ *ciii* 48
To-night ungather'd let us *l* This laurel, „ *cv* 1
They *l* the porch, they pass the grave „ *Con.* 71
your sweetness hardly *l's* me a choice *Maud I v* 24
When will the dancers *l* her alone? „ *xxii* 21
past and *l's* The Crown a lonely splendour. *Ded. of Idylls* 48
wilt thou *l* Thine easeful biding here, *Gareth and L.* 127
and *l* my man to me.' „ 477
Leave (verb) (*continued*) I *l* not till I finish this fair quest, *Gareth and L.* 774
Come, therefore, *l* thy lady lightly, knave. „ 957
and *l's* me fool'd and trick'd, „ 1251
not *l* her, till her promise given— *Marr. of Geraint* 605
L me to-night: I am weary to the death.' *Geraint and E.* 358
bounding forward '*L* them to the wolves.' *Balin and Balan* 588
he rose To *l* the hall, and, Vivien following *Merlin and V.* 32
To *l* an equal baseness; „ 830
ere I *l* thee let me swear once more „ 929
made him *l* The banquet, *Lancelot and E.* 561
let me *l* My quest with you; „ 690
Before ye *l* him for this Quest, *Holy Grail* 325
l The leading of his younger knights to me. *Last Tournament* 109
an arrow from the bush Should *l* me all alone „ 536
And of this remnant will I *l* a part, *Guinevere* 444
Yet must I *l* thee, woman, to thy shame. „ 511
L me that, I charge thee, my last hope. „ 567
'It is not meet, Sir King, to *l* thee thus, *Pass. of Arthur* 208
it seem'd Better to *l* Excalibur conceal'd „ 230
lake, that, flooding, *l's* Low banks of yellow sand; *Lover's Tale i* 534
He flies the event: he *l's* the event to me: „ *iv* 1
Would *l* the land for ever, „ 19
And *l* the name of Lover's Leap: „ 42
And *l* him in the public way to die. „ 261
I *l* this land for ever.' „ 368
I am going to *l* you a bit— *First Quarrel* 80
go, go, you may *l* me alone— *Rizpah* 79
highway running by it *l's* a breadth Of sward *Sisters (E. and E.)* 80
you *l* 'em outside on the bed— *In the Child. Hosp.* 56
Or in that vaster Spain I *l* to Spain. *Columbus* 208
And *l* him, blind of heart and eyes, *Ancient Sage* 113
And *l* the hot swamp of voluptuousness „ 277
blackthorn-blossom fades and falls and *l's* the bitter sloe, *The Flight* 15
You will not *l* me thus in grief „ 85
if dynamite and revolver *l* you courage *Locksley H., Sixty* 107
Eighty winters *l* the dog too lame „ 226
L the Master in the first dark hour „ 238
Then I *l* thee Lord and Master, „ 282
Birds and brides must *l* the nest. *The Ring* 89
Queen, who *l's* Some colder province in the North „ 480
shadow *l* the Substance in the brooding light of noon? *Happy* 99
now arching *l's* her bare To breaths of balmier air; *Prog. of Spring* 12
l's me harlot-like, Who love her still, *Romney's R.* 116
May *l* the windows blinded, „ 146
Leäve (verb) if thou marries a good un I'll *l* the land to thee. *N. Farmer, N. S.* 56
if thou marries a bad 'un, I'll *l* the land to Dick.— „ 58
Let's them inter 'eaven eäsy es *l's* *Village Wife* 94
Leäved (left) but 'e *l* it to Charlie 'is son, „ 42
they *l* their nasty sins i' *my* pond, *Churchwarden, etc.* 54
Leaved *See* **Long-leaved, Thick-leaved**
Leaven (s) the old *l* leaven'd all: *Princess v* 386
Leaven (verb) But now to *l* play with profit, „ *iv* 149
Of Love to *l* all the mass, *Freedom* 19
Leaven'd the old leaven *l* all: *Princess v* 386
then as Arthur in the highest *L* the world, *Merlin and V.* 141
but all was joust and play, *L* his hall. „ 146
Leave-taking Low at *l-t*, with his brandish'd plume *Geraint and E.* 359
Leaving (*See also* **Lavin'**) *L* door and windows wide: *Deserted House* 3
l my ancient love With the Greek woman. *Œnone* 260
L the dance and song, '*L* the olive-gardens far below, *L* the promise of my bridal bower, *D. of F. Women* 216
L great legacies of thought, *In Mem. lxxxiv* 35
And, *l* these, to pass away, „ *c* 19
l night forlorn. „ *cvii* 4
who camest to thy goal So early, *l* me behind, „ *cxiv* 24
Who *l* share in furrow come to see The glories *Gareth and L.* 243
ramp and roar at *l* of your lord!— „ 1307
never *l* her, and grew Forgetful of his promise *Marr. of Geraint* 49
so *l* him, Now with slack rein and careless *Balin and Balan* 308
So *l* Arthur's court he gain'd the beach; *Merlin and V.* 197

Leaving (*continued*) *L* her household and good father, *Lancelot and E.* 14
l for the cowl The helmet in an abbey *Holy Grail* 5
l the pale nun, I spake of this To all men ; „ 129
And *l* human wrongs to right themselves, „ 898
her anger, *l* Pelleas, burn'd Full on her knights *Pelleas and E.* 289
Thieves, bandits, *l's* of confusion, *Last Tournament* 95
now *l* to the skill Of others their old craft *Pref. Son. 19th Cent.* 2
L his son too Lost in the carnage, *Batt. of Brunanburh* 72
the child Is happy—ev'n in *l her* ! *To Prin. Beatrice* 12
Leavy Moving in the *l* beech. *Margaret* 61
Lebanon O, art thou sighing for *L* *Maud I xviii* 15
Sighing for *L*, Dark cedar, „ 17
Lebanonian in halls Of *L* cedar : *Princess ii* 352
Lecher The *l* would cleave to his lusts, *Despair* 100
Lecture (adj.) On the *l* slate The circle rounded *Princess ii* 371
Lecture (s) A classic *l*, rich in sentiment, „ 374
' have you learnt No more from Psyche's *l*, „ 393
Led (*See also* **Moon-led**) And like a bride of old In triumph *l*, *Ode to Memory* 76
Gliding with equal crowns two serpents *l* *Alexander* 6
' But heard, by secret transport *l*, *Two Voices* 214
light that *l* The holy Elders with the gift of myrrh. *M. d'Arthur* 232
Fancy, *l* by Love, Would play with flying forms *Gardener's D.* 59
still we follow'd where she *l*, (repeat) *The Voyage* 59, 90
took him by the curls, and *l* him in, *Vision of Sin* 6
l the way To where the rivulets of sweet water ran ; *Enoch Arden* 641
l me thro' the short sweet-smelling lanes *The Brook* 122
Thro' which a few, by wit or fortune *l*, *Aylmer's Field* 438
I *l* you then to all the Castalies ; *Princess iv* 294
But *l* by golden wishes, „ 420
l Threading the soldier-city, „ *v* 6
l A hundred maids in train across the Park. „ *vi* 75
Remember him who *l* your hosts ; *Ode on Well.* 171
Love has *l* thee to the stranger land, *W. to Marie Alex.* 31
Which *l* by tracts that pleased us well, *In Mem. xxii* 2
And *l* him thro' the blissful climes, „ *lxxxv* 25
They wept and wail'd, but *l* the way „ *ciii* 18
I have *l* her home, my love, *Maud I xviii* 1
' Lead and I follow.' Quietly she *l*. *Gareth and L.* 1053
L from the territory of false Limours *Geraint and E.* 437
answering not one word, she *l* the way. „ 495
across the poplar grove *L* to the caves : *Lancelot and E.* 805
like a flying star *L* on the gray-hair'd wisdom *Holy Grail* 453
But when they *l* me into hall, behold, „ 577
loosed his horse, and *l* him to the light. *Pelleas and E.* 61
l her forth, and far ahead Of his and her retinue *Guinevere* 384
light that *l* The holy Elders with the gift of myrrh. *Pass. of Arthur* 400
l on with light In trances and in visions : *Lover's Tale i* 77
I was *l* mute Into her temple like a sacrifice ; „ 684
Then those who *l* the van, and those in rear, „ *iii* 24
whirling rout *L* by those two rush'd into dance, „ 55
L his dear lady to a chair of state. „ *iv* 321
am *l* by the creak of the chain, *Rizpah* 7
far liever *l* my friend Back to the pure *Sir J. Oldcastle* 70
In praise of God who *l* me thro' the waste. *Columbus* 17
I know that he has *l* me all my life, „ 160
sometimes wish I had never *l* the way. „ 186
L backward to the tyranny of one ? *Tiresias* 76
I knaws I 'ed *l* tha a quieter life *Spinster's S's.* 71
Ages after, while in Asia, he that *l* the wild Moguls, *Locksley H., Sixty* 81
half-brain races, *l* by Justice, Love, and Truth ; „ 161
know them, follow him who *l* the way, „ 266
L upward by the God of ghosts and dreams, *Demeter and P.* 5
L me at length To the city and palace *Merlin and the G.* 64
Till, *l* by dream and vague desire, *To Master of B.* 17
And the Vision that *l* me of old, *The Dreamer* 5
Leddest *l* by the hand thine infant Hope. *Ode to Memory* 30
Ledge (*See also* **Diamond-ledge, Meadow-ledges**) And you were leaning from the *l* *Miller's D.* 84
tall dark pines, that plumed the craggy *l* *Œnone* 209
Of *l* or shelf The rock rose clear, *Palace of Art* 9
from the craggy *l* the poppy hangs in sleep. *Lotos-Eaters, C. S.* 11
leave The monstrous *l's* there to slope, *Princess vii* 212
About the *l's* of the hill.' *In Mem. xxxvii* 8

Ledge (*continued*) red-ribb'd *l's* drip with a silent horror of blood, *Maud I i* 3
Athwart the *l's* of rock, „ *II ii* 28
on the window *l*, Close underneath his eyes, *Lancelot and E.* 1239
And a hundred splash'd from the *l's*, *V. of Maeldune* 103
Ledger When only the *l* lives, *Maud I i* 35
Lee (Annie) *See* **Annie, Annie Lee**
Leech (blood-sucker) swarm'd His literary *l'es.* *Will Water.* 200
Leech (physician) King's own *l* to look into his hurt ; *Geraint and E.* 923
King will send thee his own *l*— *Balin and Balan* 275
l forsake the dying bed for terror of his life ? *Happy* 98
Leering *L* at his neighbour's wife. *Vision of Sin* 118
Lees I will drink Life to the *l* : *Ulysses* 7
Dregs of life, and *l* of man : *Vision of Sin* 205
Left (adj.) And over his *l* shoulder laugh'd at thee, *Bridesmaid* 7
And on the *l* hand of the hearth he saw *Enoch Arden* 753
letting her *l* hand Droop from his mighty shoulder, *Merlin and V.* 242
from whose *l* hand floweth The Shadow of Death, *Lover's Tale i* 498
And he call'd ' *L* wheel into line ! ' *Heavy Brigade* 6
Left (s) In her *l* a human head. *Vision of Sin* 138
left but narrow breadth to *l* and right *Enoch Arden* 674
And she the *l*, or not, or seldom used ; *Princess iii* 38
' How grew this feud betwixt the right and *l*.' „ 77
Oaring one arm, and bearing in my *l* „ *iv* 183
here and there to *l* and right Struck, *Holy Grail* 494
To right ? to *l* ? straight forward ? *Pelleas and E.* 67
Left (verb) (*See also* **Leaved**) And what is *l* to me, but Thou, *Supp. Confessions* 18
With silver anchor *l* afloat, *Arabian Nights* 93
She *l* the web, she *l* the loom, *L. of Shalott iii* 37
Beneath a willow *l* afloat, „ *iv* 7
Is this the end to be *l* alone, *Mariana in the S.* 71
And day and night I am *l* alone „ 83
And *l* a want unknown before ; *Miller's D.* 228
And I was *l* alone within the bower ; *Œnone* 192
lock'd in with bars of sand, *L* on the shore ; *Palace of Art* 250
he set and *l* behind The good old year, *May Queen, N. Y's. E.* 5
Then when I *l* my home.' *D. of F. Women* 120
What else was *l* ? look here ! ' „ 156
flow Of music *l* the lips of her that died „ 195
She lock'd her lips : she *l* me where I stood : „ 241
Falls off, and love is *l* alone. *To J. S.* 16
' at home was little *l*, And none abroad : *The Epic* 19
moved away, and *l* me, statue-like, *Gardener's D.* 161
l his father's house, And hired himself to work *Dora* 37
He spied her, and he *l* his men at work, „ 86
We *l* the dying ebb that faintly lipp'd *Audley Court* 12
He l his wife behind ; for so I heard. *Walk. to the Mail* 47
He *l* her, yes. I met my lady once : „ 48
till she was *l* alone Upon her tower, „ 98
and now we *l* The clerk behind us, *Edwin Morris* 96
So *l* the place, *l* Edwin, nor have seen Him since, „ 137
Yet this way was *l*, And by this way *St. S. Stylites* 178
Her father *l* his good arm-chair, *Talking Oak* 103
' She *l* the novel half-uncut Upon the rosewood shelf ; She *l* the new piano shut : „ 117
tho' they could not end me, *l* me maim'd *Tithonus* 20
my passion sweeping thro' me *l* me dry, *L* me with the palsied heart, and *l* me with the jaundiced eye ; *Locksley Hall* 131
I was *l* a trampled orphan, „ 156
So *l* alone, the passions of her mind. *Godiva* 32
My father *l* a park to me, *Amphion* 1
He *l* a small plantation ; „ 20
We *l* behind the painted buoy *The Voyage* 1
Long lines of cliff breaking have *l* a chasm ; *Enoch Arden* 1
daily *l* The little footprint daily wash'd away. „ 21
(Since Enoch *l* he had not look'd upon her), „ 273
ten years Since Enoch *l* his hearth „ 360
he who *l* you ten long years ago Should still be living ; „ 404
nor loved she to be *l* Alone at home, „ 516
l but narrow breadth to left and right „ 674
Among the gifts he *l* her (possibly He flow'd *Aylmer's Field* 217
And *l* the living scandal that shall die— „ 444
Then *l* alone he pluck'd her dagger forth „ 470

Left (verb) (*continued*) l Their own gray tower, or plain-faced tabernacle, *Aylmer's Field* 617
Your house is l unto you desolate!' (repeat) „ 629, 797
Eight that were l to make a purer world— „ 638
'My house is l unto me desolate.' „ 721
'Our house is l unto us desolate'? „ 737
Have not our love and reverence l them bare? „ 785
or one stone L on another, „ 789
And l their memories a world's curse— „ 796
Still so much gold was l; *Sea Dreams* 130
from the gaps and chasms of ruin l „ 225
L him one hand, and reaching thro' the night „ 287
scrolls L by the Teacher, whom he held divine. *Lucretius* 13
The fire that l a roofless Ilion, „ 65
if I go *my* work is l Unfinish'd—*if* I go. „ 103
to take Only such cups as l us friendly-warm, „ 215
He, dying lately, l her, as I hear, *Princess i* 78
last not least, she who had l her place, „ *ii* 165
(what other way was l) I came.' „ 217
chapel bells Call'd us: we l the walks; „ 471
l the drunken king To brawl at Shushan „ *iii* 229
(For since her horse was lost I l her mine) „ *iv* 197
With many thousand matters l to do, „ 458
what was l of faded woman-slough „ *v* 40
We l her by the woman, „ 113
which she l: She shall not have it back: „ 431
Pharos from his base Had l us rock. „ *vi* 340
l me in it; And others otherwise they laid; „ 377
but some were l of those Held sagest, „ 381
Blanche had gone, but l Her child among us, „ *vii* 56
And l her woman, lovelier in her mood „ 162
her labour was but as a block L in the quarry; „ 231
might be l some record of the things we said. *Third of Feb.* 18
Have l the last free race with naked coasts! „ 40
All that was l of them, L of six hundred. *Light Brigade* 48
my Annie who l me at two, *Grandmother* 77
there's none of them l alive; „ 85
There is but a trifle l you, „ 107
Nobbut a bit on it's l, *N. Farmer, O. S.* 41
What room is l for a hater? *Spiteful Letter* 14
if l to pass His autumn into seeming-leafless days— *A Dedication* 9
light gone with her, and l me in shadow here! *Window, Gone* 3
And, having l the glass, she turns *In Mem. vi* 35
When Lazarus l his charnel-cave, „ *xxxi* 1
soil, l barren, scarce had grown The grain „ *liii* 7
But ere the lark hath l the lea I wake, „ *lxviii* 13
What fame is l for human deeds In endless age? „ *lxxiii* 11
As in the winters l behind, „ *lxxviii* 9
I felt and feel, tho' l alone, „ *lxxxv* 42
Which l my after-morn content. „ *ciii* 4
Our father's dust is l alone „ *cv* 5
a scheme that had l us flaccid and drain'd. *Maud I i* 20
l his coal all turn'd into gold To a grandson, „ *x* 11
And l the daisies rosy. „ *xii* 24
This lump of earth has l his estate „ *xvi* 1
For who was l to watch her but I? „ *xix* 10
That, if l uncancell'd, had been so sweet: „ 46
That he l his wine and horses and play, „ 74
From the meadow your walks have l so sweet „ *xxii* 39
That thou art l for ever alone: „ *II iii* 4
L her and fled, and Uther enter'd in, *Com. of Arthur* 201
And ere it l their faces, „ 272
To hear him speak before he l his life. „ 362
the two L the still King, and passing forth to breathe, „ 369
but when they l the shrine Great Lords from Rome „ 476
and l us neither gold nor field.' *Gareth and L.* 339
thou that slewest the sire hast l the son. „ 360
war among themselves, but l them kings; „ 422
many a viand l, And many a costly cate, „ 848
l The damsel by the peacock in his pride, „ 869
And l them with God-speed, „ 890
l crag-carven o'er the streaming Gelt— „ 1203
Affirming that his father l him gold, *Marr. of Geraint* 451
And l her maiden couch, and robed herself, „ 737
When late l Caerleon, our great Queen, „ 781

Left (verb) (*continued*) Than when I l your mowers dinnerless. *Geraint and E.* 234
Leading the horse, and they were l alone. „ 244
Enid l alone with Prince Geraint, „ 365
Nor l untold the craft herself had used; „ 393
and so l him stunn'd or dead, „ 464
There is not l the twinkle of a fin „ 474
And l him lying in the public way; „ 478
Not a hoof l: and I methinks till now „ 485
But l two brawny spearmen, who advanced, „ 558
and the two Were l alone together, „ 734
That trouble which has l me thrice your own: „ 737
whom Uther l in charge Long since, „ 933
when we l, in those deep woods we found *Balin and Balan* 120
an enemy that has l Death in the living waters, *Merlin and V.* 147
lists of such a beard as youth gone out Had l in ashes: „ 246
Whose kinsman l him watcher o'er his wife „ 706
l Not even Lancelot brave, nor Galahad clean. „ 804
And ending in a ruin—nothing l, „ 883
Had l the ravaged woodland yet once more To peace; „ 963
He l it with her, when he rode to tilt *Lancelot and E.* 30
He l the barren-beaten thoroughfare, „ 161
But l her all the paler, „ 378
But l him leave to stammer 'Is it indeed?' „ 420
If any man that day were l afield, „ 459
and hath l his prize Untaken, „ 530
Here was the knight, and here he l a shield; „ 634
Why ask you not to see the shield he l, „ 653
As yon proud Prince who l the quest to me. „ 762
and being in his moods L them, „ 800
Her own poor work, her empty labour, l. „ 991
But when they l her to herself again, „ 998
Come, for you l me taking no farewell, „ 1274
I l her and I bad her no farewell; „ 1304
Fell into dust, and I was l alone, (repeat) *Holy Grail* 389, 400, 419
plowman l his plowing, and fell down Before it; „ 404
milkmaid l her milking, and fell down Before it, „ 406
Was l alone once more, and cried in grief, „ 437
a remnant that were l Paynim amid their circles, „ 663
shattered talbots, which had l the stones Raw, „ 719
Lancelot l The hall long silent, „ 853
And l me gazing at a barren board, „ 893
new knights to fill the gap L by the Holy Quest; *Pelleas and E.* 2
And he was l alone in open field. „ 208
There l it, and them sleeping; „ 453
so l him bruised And batter'd, and fled on, „ 546
Who l the gems which Innocence the Queen *Last Tournament* 293
Which l thee less than fool, „ 308
After she l him lonely here? „ 395
But l her all as easily, and return'd. „ 403
warhorse l to graze Among the forest greens, „ 490
'my man Hath l me or is dead;' „ 495
her too hast thou l To pine and waste „ 597
Heathen, the brood by Hengist l; *Guinevere* 16
Modred whom he l in charge of all, „ 195
come next, five summers back, And l me; „ 322
Then that other l alone Sigh'd, „ 367
Had yet that grace of courtesy in him l „ 436
For when the Roman l us, and their law „ 456
For which of us, who might be l, could speak „ 501
l me hope That in mine own heart I can live down sin „ 635
roar of Hougoumont L mightiest of all peoples *To the Queen ii* 21
L her own life with it; *Lover's Tale i* 215
To know her father l us just before „ 293
Before he l the land for evermore; „ *iv* 183
Lest there be none l here to bring her back: „ 367
One had deceived her an' l her alone *First Quarrel* 25
nay—what was there l to fall? *Rizpah* 9
but bone of my bone was l— „ 51
an' if Sally be l aloän, *North. Cobbler* 105
should count myself the coward if I l them, *The Revenge* 11
blest him in their pain, that they were not l to Spain, „ 20
be little of us l by the time this sun be set.' „ 28
within her womb that had l her ill content; „ 51
wound to be drest he had l the deck, „ 66

Left (verb) (*continued*) THEY have *l* the doors ajar; *Sisters (E. and E.)* 1
l me this, Which yet retains a memory of its youth, „ 65
We *l* her, happy each in each, „ 219
'Bread—Bread *l* after the blessing?' *Sir J. Oldcastle* 154
brought your Princes gold enough If *l* alone! *Columbus* 106
And we *l* the dead to the birds *V. of Maeldune* 36
And we *l* but a naked rock, „ 54
Many a carcase they *l* to be carrion, *Batt. of Brunanburh* 105
L for the white-tail'd eagle to tear it, and *L* for the horny-ribb'd raven to rend it, „ 107
when I *l* my darling alone.' *The Wreck* 97
the one man *l* on the wreck— „ 119
fossil skull that is *l* in the rocks *Despair* 86
He *l* us weeping in the woods; *The Flight* 37
That other *l* us to ourselves; „ 78
but 'a *l* me the work to do, *Spinster's S's.* 55
I was *l* within the shadow sitting on the wreck *Locksley H., Sixty* 16
Amy's kin and mine are *l* to me. „ 56
Gone thy tender-natured mother, wearying to be *l* alone, „ 57
But ere he *l* your fatal shore, *To Marq. of Dufferin* 33
For Naples which we only *l* in May? *The Ring* 58
l to me, A ring too which you kiss'd, „ 113
He *l* me wealth—and while I journey'd hence, „ 179
no tear for him, who *l* you wealth, „ 188
I took, I *l* you there; „ 347
oftener *l* That angling to the mother. „ 355
With earth is broken, and has *l* her free, „ 476
if *I* had been the leper would you have *l* the wife? *Happy* 100
For ere she *l* us, when we met, *To Mary Boyle* 15
'Why *l* you wife and children? *Romney's R.* 129
had *l* His aged eyes, he raised them, *St. Telemachus* 50
one day He had *l* his dagger behind him. *Bandit's Death* 12
She has *l* me enough to live on. *Charity* 40
Left *See also* **Late-left, Latest-left.**
Leg She caught the white goose by the *l*, *The Goose* 9
My right *l* chain'd into the crag, *St. S. Stylites* 73
'And, *l* and arm with love-knots gay, *Talking Oak* 65
And *l's* of trees were limber, *Amphion* 14
Stept forward on a firmer *l*, *Will Water.* 123
Callest thou that thing a *l*? *Vision of Sin* 89
and white, and strong on his *l's*, *Grandmother* 2
'Here's a *l* for a babe of a week!' „ 11
Strong of his hands, and strong on his *l's*, „ 13
DOSN'T thou 'ear my 'erse's *l's*, *N. Farmer, N. S.* 1
moor sense i' one o' 'is *l's* nor in all thy braaïns. „ 4
Lets down his other *l*, and stretching, *Gareth and L.* 1186
craven shifts, and long crane *l's* of Mark— *Last Tournament* 729
An' Lucy wur laäme o' one *l*, *Village Wife* 99
wi'out ony harm i' the *l's*, „ 101
Ull be fun' opo' four short *l's* *Owd Roä* 16
Legacy Leaving great *legacies* of thought, *In Mem. lxxxiv* 35
Some *l* of a fallen race Alone might hint *Two Voices* 359
Legend (*See also* **Half-legend**) Nor these alone: but every *l* fair *Palace of Art* 125
'*The L of Good Women*,' long ago Sung *D. of F. Women* 2
I shaped The city's ancient l *into this*:— *Godiva* 4
The reflex of a *l* past, *Day-Dm., Pro.* 11
The violet of a *l* blow *Will Water.* 147
There lived an ancient *l* in our house. *Princess i* 5
I almost think That idiot *l* credible. „ *v* 153
And fading *l* of the past; *In Mem. lxii* 4
boss'd With holy Joseph's *l*, *Balin and Balan* 363
The *l* as in guerdon for your rhyme? *Merlin and V.* 554
A *l* handed down thro' five or six, *Holy Grail* 87
Moreover, that weird *l* of his birth, *Last Tournament* 669
So may this *l* for awhile, *To Prof. Jebb* 9
And then he told their *l*: *The Ring* 206
L or true? so tender should be true! „ 224
Legendary Glanced at the *l* Amazon *Princess ii* 126
Legion King Leodogran Groan'd for the Roman *l's* *Com. of Arthur* 33
And all his *l's* crying Christ and him, *Lancelot and E.* 305
follow'd up by her vassal *l* of fools; *Vastness* 12
Legionary those Neronian *legionaries* Burnt and broke *Boädicea* 1
Perish'd many a maid and matron, many a valorous *l*, „ 85

Leisure And in the fallow *l* of my life *Audley Court* 77
lapt In the arms of *l*, *Princess ii* 168
Mine eyes have *l* for their tears; *In Mem. xiii* 16
Leman wert lying in thy new *l's* arms.' *Last Tournament* 625
Lemon *l* grove In closest coverture upsprung, *Arabian Nights* 67
Lend God in his mercy *l* her grace, *L. of Shalott iv* 53
To *l* our hearts and spirits wholly *Lotos-Eaters, C. S.* 63
Something to love He *l's* us; *To J. S.* 14
Or *l* an ear to Plato where he says, *Lucretius* 147
in this frequence can I *l* full tongue, *Princess iv* 442
wi' noän to *l* 'im a shuvv, *N. Farmer, N. S.* 31
That Nature *l's* such evil dreams? *In Mem. lv* 6
To *l* thee horse and shield: *Gareth and L.* 1324
I pray you *l* me one, if such you have, Blank, *Lancelot and E.* 193
so did Pelleas *l* All the young beauty of his own soul *Pelleas and E.* 82
L me thine horse and arms, „ 345
her gracious lips Did *l* such gentle utterance, *Lover's Tale i* 457
Nor *l* an ear to random cries, *Politics* 7
Length (*See also* **Arm's-length**) All its allotted *l* of days, *Lotos-Eaters, C. S.* 35
l of bright horizon rimm'd the dark. *Gardener's D.* 181
to such *l* of years should come *Locksley Hall* 67
Cut off the *l* of highway on before, *Enoch Arden* 673
Dangled a *l* of ribbon and a ring To tempt „ 750
With *l's* of yellow ringlet, like a girl, *Princess i* 3
boss'd with *l's* Of classic frieze, „ *ii* 24
All her fair *l* upon the ground she lay: „ *v* 59
To wile the *l* from languorous hours, „ *vii* 63
And lazy *l's* on boundless shores; *In Mem. lxx* 12
till at *l* Sir Gareth's brand Clash'd his, *Gareth and L.* 1147
Down by the *l* of lance and arm beyond *Geraint and E.* 463
and seem'd at *l* in peace. *Balin and Balan* 239
At *l*, and dim thro' leaves Blinkt the white morn, „ 384
lay she all her *l* and kiss'd his feet, *Merlin and V.* 219
Pall'd all its *l* in blackest samite, *Lancelot and E.* 1142
wilt at *l* Yield me thy love and know me *Pelleas and E* 248
At *l* A lodge of intertwisted beechen-boughs *Last Tournament* 375
At *l* Descending from the point and standing *Lover's Tale i* 410
grew at *l* Prophetical and prescient „ *ii* 131
at *l* When some were doubtful how the law „ *iv* 269
But at *l* we began to be weary, *V. of Maeldune* 91
All the millions one at *l* *Locksley H., Sixty* 162
Led me at *l* To the city and palace Of Arthur *Merlin and the G.* 64
brought you down A *l* of staghorn-moss, *Romney's R.* 79
All his leaves Fall'n at *l*, *The Oak* 12
at *l* he touch'd his goal, The Christian city. *St. Telemachus* 34
Lengthen'd Tall as a figure *l* on the sand *Princess vi* 161
With a *l* loud halloo, *The Owl ii* 13
Lent (fast) If it may be, fast Whole *L's*, *St. S. Stylites* 182
Lent (verb) Who *l* you, love, your mortal dower *Margaret* 5
motion *l* The pulse of hope to discontent. *Two Voices* 449
That *l* broad verge to distant lands, *Palace of Art* 30
That *l* my knee desire to kneel, *Princess iii* 193
once or twice she *l* her hand, „ *iv* 27
I, that have *l* my life to build up yours, „ 351
Still in the little book you *l* me, *The Daisy* 99
And, crown'd with all the season *l*, *In Mem. xxii* 6
A willing ear We *l* him. „ *lxxxvii* 31
l her fierce teat To human sucklings; *Com. of Arthur* 28
hath not our good King Who *l* me thee, *Gareth and L.* 1071
Clung to the shield that Lancelot *l* him, „ 1320
Pelleas *l* his horse and all his arms, *Pelleas and E.* 358
which Innocence the Queen *L* to the King, *Last Tournament* 294
l The sceptres of her West, her East, *To Marq. of Dufferin* 5
Lenten That *L* fare makes *L* thought, *To E. Fitzgerald* 31
Lent-lily and all *L-l* in hue, *Gareth and L.* 911
Thy gay *lent-lilies* wave and put them by, *Prog. of Spring* 37
Leodogran *L*, the King of Cameliard, *Com. of Arthur* 1
King *L* Groan'd for the Roman legions „ 33
His new-made knights, to King *L*, „ 137
L in heart Debating—'How should I that am a king, „ 140
To whom the King *L* replied, „ 160
Thereat *L* rejoiced, but thought „ 310
She spake and King *L* rejoiced, „ 425
L awoke, and sent Ulfius, and Brastias and Bedivere, „ 444

Leolin L, his brother, living oft With Averill, *Aylmer's Field* 57
L's first nurse was, five years after, „ 79
Would care no more for L's walking with her „ 124
Might have been other, save for L's— „ 140
Where once with L at her side the girl, „ 184
Till L ever watchful of her eye, „ 210
And L, coming after he was gone, „ 234
by the counter door to that Which L open'd, „ 283
And L's horror-stricken answer, „ 318
while L still Retreated half-aghast, „ 329
Went L; then, his passion all in flood „ 339
Some one, he thought, had slander'd L to him. „ 350
L, I almost sin in envying you: „ 360
But L cried out the more upon them— „ 367
Tho' L flamed and fell again, „ 409
So L went: and as we task ourselves „ 432
return'd L's rejected rivals from their suit „ 493
Came at the moment L's emissary, „ 518
Was L's one strong rival upon earth; „ 557
And crying upon the name of L, „ 576
Leonard you shall have that song which L wrote: *Golden Year* 1
been Up Snowdon; and I wish'd for L there, „ 4
L early lost at sea; *Locksley H., Sixty* 55
my L, use and not abuse your day, „ 265
Leopard (adj.) a l skin Droop'd from his shoulder, *Œnone* 58
Leopard (s) two tame l's couch'd beside her throne, *Princess ii* 33
her foot on one Of those tame l's. „ *iii* 181
I tamed my l's: shall I not tame these? „ *v* 400
Leper l plague may scale my skin but never taint my heart; *Happy* 27
'Last of the train, a moral l, I, *Princess iv* 222
And flies above the l's hut, *Happy* 4
Is that the l's hut on the solitary moor, Where noble Ulric dwells forlorn, and wears the l's weed? „ 9
made him l to compass him with scorn— „ 16
be content Till I be l like yourself, „ 88
Now God has made you l in His loving care „ 91
Or if I had been the l would you have left the wife? „ 100
Leprous Who yearn to lay my loving head upon your l breast. „ 26
let mine be l too, „ 94
Less (adj. and adv.) *To one of* l *desert allows* *To the Queen* 6
But now they live with Beauty l and l, *Caress'd or chidden* 9
some said their heads were l: *Princess ii* 147
L welcome find among us, „ 354
Not being l but more than all *In Mem. cxi* 11
And yet is love not l, but more; „ *Con.* 12
And theirs are bestial, hold him l than man: *Com. of Arthur* 181
And now of late I see him l and l, „ 356
Tells of a manhood ever l and lower? *Last Tournament* 121
Art and Grace are l and l: *Locksley H., Sixty* 245
L weight now for the ladder-of-heaven *By an Evolution.* 12
Less (s) O grief, can grief be changed to l? *In Mem. lxxviii* 16
From l and l to nothing; *Last Tournament* 467
From l to l and vanish into light. *Pass. of Arthur* 468
And l will be lost than won, *The Dreamer* 22
Lessen Nor will it l from to-day; *In Mem. lix* 10
Lessen'd And I be l in his love? „ *li* 8
great as Edith's power of love, Had l, *Sisters (E. and E.)* 262
Lessening a foot L in perfect cadence, *Walk. to the Mail* 55
L to the l music, back, *Sea Dreams* 221
And crowded farms and l towers, *In Mem. xi* 11
At Arthur's ordinance, tipt with l peak And pinnacle, *Gareth and L.* 308
an ever opening height, An ever l earth— *The Ring* 46
Lesser (adj.) Woman is the l man, and all thy passions, *Locksley Hall* 151
The l griefs that may be said, *In Mem. xx* 1
At noon or when the l wain Is twisting „ *ci* 11
to cast a careless eye On souls, the l lords of doom. „ *cxii* 8
Is comrade of the l faith That sees the course of human things. „ *cxxviii* 3
'I have seen the cuckoo chased by l fowl, *Com. of Arthur* 167
Had sent thee down before a l spear, *Gareth and L.* 1244
'then in wearing mine Needs must be l likelihood, *Lancelot and E.* 367
As if some l god had made the world, *Pass. of Arthur* 14
Lesser (s) draws The greater to the l, *Gardener's D.* 10
Lesson Retaught the l thou hadst taught, *England and Amer.* 8
Shall we teach it a Roman l? *Boädicea* 32
One l from one book we learn'd, *In Mem. lxxix* 14
Gracious l's thine And maxims of the mud! *Merlin and V.* 48
A simpler, saner l might he learn *Prog. of Spring* 105
Let And l's me from the saddle;' *Lancelot and E.* 94
L's them inter 'eaven eäsy es leäves *Village Wife* 94
Lethargy for months, in such blind *lethargies* *St. S. Stylites* 103
Lethe Some draught of L might await *Two Voices* 350
For she that out of L scales with man *Princess vii* 261
cannot hear The sullen L rolling doom *Lit. Squabbles* 11
gleams On L in the eyes of Death. *Im Mem. xcviii* 8
the abyss Of Darkness, utter L. *Romney's R.* 53
Lethean (If Death so taste L springs), *In Mem. xliv* 10
Lether (ladder) 'Ya mun run fur the l. *Owd Roä* 77
Sa I runs to the yard fur a l, „ 82
Thy Moother was howdin' the l, „ 85
Letter (epistle) from her bosom drew Old l's, *Mariana in the S.* 62
And gave my l's back to me. *The Letters* 20
her l's too, Tho' far between, *Aylmer's Field* 475
and read Writhing a l from his child, „ 517
The l which he brought, and swore „ 522
Found a dead man, a l edged with death Beside him, „ 595
Tore the king's l, snow'd it down, *Princess i* 61
I can give you l's to her; „ 159
show'd the late-writ l's of the king. „ 175
the king,' he said, 'Had given us l's, „ 181
I gave the l to be sent with dawn; „ 245
I read—two l's—one her sire's. „ *iv* 397
Behold your father's l.' „ 468
I pored upon her l which I held, „ *v* 469
And with it a spiteful l. *Spiteful Letter* 2
Go, little l, apace, apace, Fly; *Window, Letter* 11
And l's unto trembling hands; *In Mem. x* 7
The noble l's of the dead: „ *xcv* 24
to write as she devised A l, word for word; *Lancelot and E.* 1104
Then he wrote The l she devised; „ 1109
lay the l in my hand A little ere I die, „ 1113
Her father laid the l in her hand, „ 1134
In her right the lily, in her left The l— „ 1156
Arthur spied the l in her hand, „ 1270
her lips, Who had devised the l, moved again. „ 1288
an' a l along wi' the rest, *First Quarrel* 49
—this was the l—this was the l I read— „ 51
I flung him the l that drove me wild, „ 57
And then he sent me a l, „ 85
'are you ill?' (so ran The l) *Sisters (E. and E.)* 186
fur the 'turney's l's they foller'd sa fast; *Village Wife* 62
I shook as I open'd the l— *The Wreck* 145
She found my l upon him, *Charity* 23
Letter (character) a tear Dropt on the l's as I wrote. *To J. S.* 56
sow'd her name and kept it green In living l's, *Aylmer's Field* 89
Along the l's of thy name, *In Mem. lxvii* 7
In l's like to those the vexillary *Gareth and L.* 1202
on her tomb In l's gold and azure!' *Lancelot and E.* 1345
scroll Of l's in a tongue no man could read. *Holy Grail* 171
Not by the sounded l of the word, *Sisters (E. and E.)* 162
until The meaning of the l's shot into My brain; *Lover's Tale ii* 8
is veering there Above his four gold l's) *The Ring* 333
Letter (literal meaning) His light upon the l dwells, *Miller's D.* 189
I broke the l of it to keep the sense. *Princess iv* 338
Because she kept the l of his word, *Geraint and E.* 455
Letter (verb) Spring L's cowslips on the hill? *Adeline* 62
Letter'd I hold Mother's love in l gold. *Helen's Tower* 4
Letters (literature) From misty men of l's; *Will Water.* 190
Thy partner in the flowery walk Of l's, *In Mem. lxxxiv* 23
gilded by the gracious gleam Of l's, *Ded. of Idylls* 40
plaudits from our best In modern l's, *To E. Fitzgerald* 39
Before the Love of L's, overdone, *Poets and their B.* 13
Letting fell'd The forest, l in the sun, *Com. of Arthur* 60
l her left hand Droop from his mighty shoulder, *Merlin and V.* 242
Letty (*See also* **Hill, Letty Hill**) The close, 'Your L, only yours;' *Edwin Morris* 106
I have pardon'd little L; „ 140

Lie (verb) (*continued*) Man comes and tills the field and *l's* beneath, *Tithonus* 3
That *l* upon her charmed heart. *Day-Dm., Sleep. B.* 20
liberal applications *l* In Art like Nature, „ *Moral* 13
That in my bosom *l's*. *St. Agnes' Eve* 12
'Here *l's* the body of Ellen Adair; *Edward Gray* 27
There *l's* the body of Ellen Adair! „ 35
Crew and Captain *l*; *The Captain* 68
Pass on, weak heart, and leave me where I *l*: *Come not, when, etc.* 11
rank or wealth Might *l* within their compass, *Aylmer's Field* 485
L's the hawk's cast, the mole has made his run, „ 849
'Let them *l*, for they have fall'n.' *Sea Dreams* 228
Heroic, for a hero *l's* beneath, *Princess, Pro.* 212
some gross error *l's* In this report, „ *i* 69
when we came where *l's* the child We lost „ *ii* 10
Here l's *a brother by a sister slain*, „ 208
thousand hearts *l* fallow in these halls, „ 400
there she *l's*, But will not speak, nor stir.' „ *v* 51
'Lift up your head, sweet sister: *l* not thus. „ 64
Let them not *l* in the tents with coarse mankind, „ *vi* 69
that there *L* bruised and maim'd, „ 72
'You shall not *l* in the tents but here, „ 94
Whatever man *l's* wounded, friend or foe, „ 336
But *l's* and dreads his doom. „ *vii* 154
Now *l's* the Earth all Danaë to the stars, And all thy heart *l's* open unto me. „ 182
as far as in us *l's* We two will serve „ 267
in true marriage *l's* Nor equal, nor unequal; „ 302
I see the place where thou wilt *l*. *Sailor Boy* 8
A use in measured language *l's*; *In Mem. v.* 6
Where *l's* the master newly dead; „ *xx* 4
This use may *l* in blood and breath, „ *xlv* 13
l Foreshorten'd in the tract of time? „ *lxxvii* 3
Bring in great logs and let them *l*, „ *cvii* 17
What profit *l's* in barren faith, „ *cviii* 5
There yet *l's* the rock that fell *Maud I i* 8
And Sleep must *l* down arm'd, „ 41
Here will I *l*, while these long branches sway, „ *xviii* 29
wilderness, full of wolves, where he used to *l*; „ *II v* 54
I know that he *l's* and listens mute „ 60
Lot beside the hearth *L's* like a log, *Gareth and L.* 75
and now *l's* there A yet-warm corpse, „ 79
under this wan water many of them *L* „ 825
There *l's* a ridge of slate across the ford; „ 1056
let the bodies *l*, but bound the suits *Geraint and E.* 96
there *l* still, and yet the sapling grew: „ 165
Beheld before a golden altar *l* *Balin and Balan* 410
yonder *l's* one dead within the wood. „ 468
to *l* Closed in the four walls of a hollow tower, *Merlin and V.* 208
O did ye never *l* upon the shore, „ 291
Down to the little thorpe that *l's* so close, *Holy Grail* 547
go back, and slay them where they *l*.' *Pelleas and E.* 444
Never *l* by thy side; see thee no more— *Guinevere* 579
l before your shrines; „ 681
but it *l's* Deep-meadow'd, happy, *Pass. of Arthur* 429
goal of this great world *L's* beyond sight: *To the Queen II* 60
on the horizon of the mind *L's* folded, *Lover's Tale i* 50
As the tree falls so must it *l*. *Rizpah* 12
But if there *l* a preference eitherway, *Sisters (E. and E.)* 290
in my wanderings all the lands that *l* *Tiresias* 25
in thy virtue *l's* The saving of our Thebes; „ 109
l's all in the way that you walk. *Despair* 112
l's Behind the green and blue? *Ancient Sage* 25
L's the warrior, my forefather, *Locksley H., Sixty* 28
L's my Amy dead in child-birth, „ 36
Yonder *l's* our young sea-village— „ 245
You that *l* with wasted lungs Waiting *Forlorn* 21
'Who *l's* on yonder pyre?' *Death of Œnone* 95
Saw them *l* confounded, *The Tourney* 14

Lie (speak falsely) This is a shameful thing for men to *l*. *M. d'Arthur* 78
'I will speak out, for I dare not *l*. *Lady Clare* 38
and when only not all men *l*; *Maud I i* 35
Who can rule and dare not *l*. „ *x* 66
My scheming brain a cinder, if I *l*.' *Merlin and V.* 933
l to me: I believe. Will ye not *l*? *Last Tournament* 645
This is a shameful thing for men to *l*. *Pass. of Arthur* 246

Lie (speak falsely) (*continued*) fierce manhood would not let thee *l*. *Balin and Balan* 74
To *l*, to *l*—in God's own house—the blackest of all lies! *The Flight* 52
and juggle, and *l* and cajole, *Charity* 29

Lied wrong'd and *l* and thwarted us— *Princess iv* 540
l with ease; but horror-stricken he, *Balin and Balan* 525
foul are their lips; they *l*. „ 616
Lancelot vext at having *l* in vain: *Lancelot and E.* 102
They *l* not then, who sware, *Last Tournament* 650
L, say ye? Nay, but learnt, „ 656
you knew—you knew that he *l*. *Charity* 12

Lief go again As thou art *l* and dear, *M. d'Arthur* 80
go again, As thou art *l* and dear, *Pass. of Arthur* 248

Liefer-Liever Far *liefer* had I fight a score of times *Gareth and L.* 944
Far *liefer* had I gird his harness *Marr of Geraint* 93
Far *liefer* than so much discredit him.' „ 629
Far *liefer* by his dear hand had I die, *Geraint and E.* 68
I had *liefer* ye were worthy of my love, *Pelleas and E.* 301
Made answer, 'I had *liefer* twenty years *Last Tournament* 257
far *liever* led my friend Back to the pure *Sir J. Oldcastle* 70
And each of them *liefer* had died *V. of Maeldune* 6

Liege 'Sir and my *l*,' he cried, *Com. of Arthur* 128
loyal vassals toiling for their *l*. „ 282
Gareth dreaming on his *l*. *Gareth and L.* 1316
'O true and tender! O my *l* and King! *Merlin and V.* 791
she call'd him lord and *l*, Her seer, „ 953
'Sire, my *l*, so much I learnt; *Lancelot and E.* 708
Lady, my *l*, in whom I have my joy, „ 1180
'O King, my *l*,' he said, *Holy Grail* 858
Modred smote his *l* Hard on that helm *Pass. of Arthur* 165

Liege-lady he, he reverenced his *l-l* there; *Princess i* 188

Liege-lord trusted his *l-l* Would yield him *Gareth and L.* 396

Liest O happy thou that *l* low, *Oriana* 84
Thou *l* beneath the greenwood tree, „ 95
'*L* thou here so low, the child of one I honour'd, *Guinevere* 422

Liest (speakest falsely) 'Dog, thou *l*. I spring from loftier lineage *Gareth and L.* 960

Lieth (*See also* **Low-lieth**) He *l* still: he doth not move: *D. of the O. Year* 10
Love *l* deep: Love dwells not in lip-depths. *Lover's Tale i* 466

Lieu In *l* of many mortal flies, *Princess iii* 268
In *l* of idly dallying with the truth, *Lancelot and E.* 590

Liever *See* **Liefer**

Life (*See also* **After-life, Loife**) '*Her court was pure; her* l *serene*; *To the Queen* 25
the ground Shall be fill'd with *l* anew. *Nothing will Die* 29
They light his little *l* alway; *Supp. Confessions* 46
He hath no care of *l* or death; „ 48
L of the fountain there, „ 55
Which would keep green hope's *l*. „ 119
Shall we not look into the laws Of *l* and death, „ 173
O weary *l*! O weary death! „ 188
Crown'd Isabel, thro' all her placid *l*, *Isabel* 27
She only said 'My *l* is dreary, (repeat) *Mariana* 9, 45, 69
L, anguish, death, immortal love, *Arabian Nights* 73
Small thought was there of *l's* distress; *Ode to Memory* 37
in after *l* retired From brawling storms, „ 111
L in dead stones, or spirit in air; *A Character* 9
He saw thro' *l* and death, *The Poet* 5
L and Thought have gone away *Deserted House* 1
L and Thought Here no longer dwell; „ 17
Thou art the shadow of *l*, *Love and Death* 10
L eminent creates the shade of death; „ 13
Thy heart, my *l*, my love, my bride, *Oriana* 44
Two *lives* bound fast in one *Circumstance* 5
So runs the round of *l* from hour to hour. „ 9
Oh! what a happy *l* were mine *The Merman* 37
But enter not the toil of *l*. *Margaret* 24
L shoots and glances thro' your veins, *Rosalind* 22
Brimm'd with delirious draughts of warmest *l*. *Eleänore* 139
My *l* is full of weary days, *My life is full* 1
ebb into a former *l*, or seem To lapse *Sonnet to ——* 2
'My *l* is sick of single sleep: *The Bridesmaid* 13
I shut my *l* from happier chance. *Two Voices* 54
And not to lose the good of *l*— „ 132

Life (continued) The springs of l, the depths of awe, Two Voices 140
' To pass, when L her light withdraws, " 145
' A l of nothings, nothing-worth, " 331
' It may be that no l is found, " 346
' Or if thro' lower lives I came— " 364
No l that breathes with human breath " 395
' Tis l, whereof our nerves are scant, Oh l, not death, for which we pant; More l, and fuller, that I want.' " 397
There's somewhat flows to us in l, Miller's D. 21
I'd almost live my l again. " 28
For scarce my l with fancy play'd " 45
Like mine own l to me thou art, " 196
My other dearer l in l, " 217
I am all aweary of my l. Œnone 33
A shepherd all thy l but yet king-born, " 128
These three alone lead l to sovereign power. " 145
push thee forward thro' a l of shocks, " 163
I pray thee, pass before my light of l, " 241
Not less than l, design'd. Palace of Art 128
And death and l she hated equally, " 265
And sweeter far is death than l to me May Queen, Con. 8
And blessings on his whole l long, " 14
things have ceased to be, with my desire of l. " 48
And what is l, that we should moan? " 56
Death is the end of l; ah, why Should l all labour be? Lotos-Eaters, C. S. 41
Dear is the memory of our wedded lives, " 69
O my l In Egypt! D. of F. Women 146
I heard my name Sigh'd forth with l " 154
these did move Me from my bliss of l, " 210
He hath no other l above. D. of the O. Year 12
Without whose l I had not been. To J. S. 24
Till all thy l one way incline On a Mourner 19
With L, that, working strongly, binds— Love thou thy land 34
Yearning to mix himself with L. " 56
I live three lives of mortal men, M. d'Arthur 155
I have lived my l, and that which I have done " 244
That nourish a blind l within the brain, " 251
ere he found Empire for l? Gardener's D. 20
made the air Of L delicious, " 70
(For those old Mays had thrice the l of these,) " 84
by my l, These birds have joyful thoughts. " 98
such a noise of l Swarm'd in the golden present, " 178
Love trebled l within me, " 198
by my l, I will not marry Dora.' Dora 23
but let me live my l. (repeat) Audley Court 43, 47, 51, 55
And in the fallow leisure of my l " 77
He lost the sense that handles daily l— Walk. to the Mail 22
in the dust and drouth Of city l! Edwin Morris 4
once I ask'd him of his early l, " 23
in the dust and drouth of London l " 143
and whole years long, a l of death. St. S. Stylites 54
footsteps smite the threshold stairs Of l— " 192
The l that spreads in them, Talking Oak 192
' I took the swarming sound of l— " 213
To riper l may magnetise The baby-oak within. " 255
Sit brooding in the ruins of a l, Love and Duty 12
The set gray l, and apathetic end. " 18
such tears As flow but once a l. " 64
—closing like an individual l— " 79
knowing all L needs for l is possible to will— " 86
I will drink L to the lees: Ulysses 7
As tho' to breathe were l. L piled on l " 24
Love took up the harp of L, Locksley Hall 33[?]
'Tis a purer l than thine; " 88
and the tumult of my l; " 110
Orient, where my l began to beat; " 154
help me as when l begun: " 185
In these, in those the l is stay'd. Day-Dm., Sleep. P. 18
all his l the charm did talk About his path, " Arrival 21
all the long-pent stream of l Dash'd downward " Revival 15
Are clasp'd the moral of thy l, " L'Envoi 55
and smote Her l into the liquor. Will Water. 112
A private l was all his joy, " 129
Lest of the fulness of my l " 163

Life (continued) laying down an unctuous lease Of l, Will Water. 244
' But keep the secret for your l, Lady Clare 34
And I love thee more than l.' L. of Burleigh 16
Thro' you, my l will be accurst.' The Letters 36
What! the flower of l is past: Vision of Sin 69
Whited thought and cleanly l As the priest, " 116
Dregs of l, and lees of man: " 205
A l that moves to gracious ends You might have won 6
A deedful l, a silent voice: " 8
No public l was his on earth, " 23
The little l of bank and brier, " 30
new warmth of l's ascending sun Enoch Arden 38
he thrice had pluck'd a l From the dread sweep " 54
like a wounded l Crept down into the hollows " 75
Low miserable lives of hand-to-mouth, " 116
With fuller profits lead an easier l, " 145
And lived a l of silent melancholy. " 260
known each other all our lives? (repeat) " 306, 420
like a wounded l He crept into the shadow: " 386
' Annie, as I have waited all my l " 435
The helpless l so wild that it was tame. " 557
and beats out his weary l. " 730
when the dead man come to l beheld His wife " 758
not l in it Whereby the man could live; " 820
The boat that bears the hope of l approach To save the l despair'd of, " 830
His wreck, his lonely l, his coming back, " 862
l in him Could scarce be said to flourish, The Brook 11
Flash into fiery l from nothing, Aylmer's Field 130
thro' the perilous passes of his l: " 209
I lived for years a stunted sunless l; " 357
quintessence of man, The l of all— " 389
Had rioted his l out, and made an end. " 391
Nor greatly cared to lose, her hold on l. " 568
days Were clipt by horror from his term of l. " 603
sunshine of the faded woods Was all the l of it; " 611
sense Of meanness in her unresisting l. " 801
And musing on the little lives of men, Sea Dreams 48
Now I see My dream was L; " 137
Bound on a matter he of l and death: " 151
And that drags down his l: " 177
Live the great l which all our greatest fain Lucretius 78
man may gain Letting his own l go. " 113
sober majesties Of settled, sweet, Epicurean l. " 218
Tired of so much within our little l, Or of so little in our little l—Poor little l that toddles half an hour " 226
While l was yet in bud and blade, Princess i 32
l! he never saw the like; " 186
woman ripen'd earlier, and her l Was longer; " ii 154
Two in the liberal offices of l, " 175
' Well then, Psyche, take my l, " 204
I lose My honour, these their lives.' " 342
debtors for our lives to you, " 355
better blush our lives away. " iii 68
our three lives. True—we had limed ourselves " 142
Ere half be done perchance your l may fail; " 236
our device; wrought to the l; " 303
O Death in L, the days that are no more.' " iv 58
tell her, brief is l but love is long, " 111
that have lent my l to build up yours, " 351
a l Less mine than yours: " 426
thousand matters left to do, The breath of l; " 459
You saved our l: we owe you bitter thanks: " 531
Severer in the logic of a l? " v 190
l and soul! I thought her half-right " 284
babbling wells With her own people's l: " 335
Still Take not his l: " 407
And on the little clause ' take not his l:' " 470
' He saved my l: my brother slew him for it.' " vi 108
So those two foes above my fallen l, " 130
Lay silent in the muffled cage of l: " vii 47
with what l I had, And like a flower " 140
but let us type them now In our own lives, " 300
heart beating, with one full stroke, L.' " 308
A drowning l, besotted in sweet self, " 314

Life (*continued*) Giv'n back to *l*, to *l* indeed, thro' thee, *Princess vii* 345
My bride, My wife, my *l*. „ 360
The long self-sacrifice of *l* is o'er. *Ode on Well.* 41
Whose *l* was work, whose language rife With rugged maxims hewn from *l*; „ 183
And other forms of *l* than ours, „ 264
And mixt, as *l* is mixt with pain, *Ode Inter. Exhib.* 27
empires branching, both, in lusty *l* !— *W. to Marie Alex.* 21
now thy fuller *l* is in the west, „ 36
Shadow and shine is *l*, *Grandmother* 60
for the babe had fought for his *l*. „ 64
Judge of us all when *l* shall cease; „ 95
And happy has been my *l*; „ 98
So dear a *l* your arms enfold *The Daisy* 93
How gain in *l*, as *l* advances, *To F. D. Maurice* 39
Her quiet dream of *l* this hour may cease. *Requiescat* 6
What would you have of us? Human *l*? *The Victim* 12
'We give you his *l*.' „ 16
Take you his dearest, Give us a *l*.' „ 28
They have taken our son, They will have his *l*. „ 50
'O, Father Odin, We give you a *l*. „ 75
for the *l* of the worm and the fly? *Wages* 7
the rapid of *l* Shoots to the fall— *Dedication* 3
Ay is *l* for a hundred years, *Window, No Answer* 9
Love will come but once a *l*, „ 21
Love can love but once a *l*. „ 28
Thou madest *L* in man and brute; *In Mem., Pro.* 6
Beats out the little *lives* of men. „ *ii* 8
Hath still'd the *l* that beat from thee. „ *vi* 12
The noise of *l* begins again, „ *vii* 10
And, thy dark freight, a vanish'd *l*. „ *x* 8
An awful thought, a *l* removed, „ *xiii* 10
And how my *l* had droop'd of late, „ *xiv* 14
The *l* that almost dies in me; „ *xviii* 16
I know that this was *L*,— „ *xxv* 1
In more of *l* true *l* no more „ *xxvi* 11
that my hold on *l* would break Before I heard „ *xxviii* 15
And rests upon the *L* indeed. „ *xxxii* 8
blest whose *lives* are faithful prayers, „ 13
A *l* that leads melodious days. „ *xxxiii* 8
My own dim *l* should teach me this, „ *xxxiv* 1
That *l* shall live for evermore, „ 2
A *l* that bears immortal fruit „ *xl* 18
To leap the grades of *l* and light, „ *xli* 11
But evermore a *l* behind. „ 24
The total world since *l* began; „ *xliii* 12
Lest *l* should fail in looking back. „ *xlvi* 4
drown The bases of my *l* in tears. „ *xlix* 16
And *L*, a Fury slinging flame. „ *l* 8
And on the low dark verge of *l* „ 15
That *l* is dash'd with flecks of sin. „ *lii* 14
For *l* outliving heats of youth, „ *liii* 10
That not one *l* shall be destroy'd, „ *liv* 6
No *l* may fail beyond the grave, „ *lv* 2
So careless of the single *l*; „ 8
I bring to *l*, I bring to death: „ *lvi* 6
O *l* as futile, then, as frail! „ 25
But half my *l* I leave behind: „ *lvii* 6
My bosom-friend and half of *l*; „ *lix* 3
Whose *l* in low estate began „ *lxiv* 3
The shade by which my *l* was crost, „ *lxvi* 5
On songs, and deeds, and *lives*, „ *lxxvii* 3
A grief as deep as *l* or thought, „ *lxxx* 7
No lower *l* that earth's embrace „ *lxxxii* 3
He put our *lives* so far apart „ 15
The *l* that had been thine below, „ *lxxxiv* 2
should'st link thy *l* with one Of mine own house, „ 11
What kind of *l* is that I lead; „ *lxxxv* 8
Whose *l*, whose thoughts were little worth, „ 30
The footsteps of his *l* in mine; „ 44
A *l* that all the Muses deck'd „ 45
Diffused the shock thro' all my *l*, „ 55
And pining *l* be fancy-fed. „ 96
The full new *l* that feeds thy breath „ *lxxxvi* 10
Were closed with wail, resume their *l*, „ *xc* 6

Life (*continued*) Mix their dim lights, like *l* and death, *In Mem. xcv* 63
Two partners of a married *l*— „ *xcvii* 5
Her *l* is lone, he sits apart, „ 17
By which our *lives* are chiefly proved, „ *cv* 14
Ring in the nobler modes of *l*, „ *cvi* 15
A *l* in civic action warm, „ *cxiii* 9
live their *lives* From land to land; „ *cxv* 16
The *l* re-orient out of dust, „ *cxvi* 6
and show That *l* is not as idle ore, „ *cxviii* 20
And *l* is darken'd in the brain. „ *cxxi* 8
I slip the thoughts of *l* and death; „ *cxxii* 16
O when her *l* was yet in bud, „ *Con.* 33
That shielded all her *l* from harm „ 47
living words of *l* Breathed in her ear. „ 52
For them the light of *l* increased, „ 74
And, moved thro' *l* of lower phase, „ 125
His who had given me *l*—O father! O God! *Maud I i* 6
spirit of murder works in the very means of *l*, „ 40
Be mine a philosopher's *l* „ *iv* 49
fed on the roses and lain in the lilies of *l*. „ 60
Singing alone in the morning of *l*, „ *v* 6
In the happy morning of *l* and of May, „ 7
Sick, sick to the heart of *l*, am I. „ *x* 36
Before my *l* has found What some have found „ *xi* 3
To a *l* that has been so sad, „ 13
My yet young *l* in the wilds of Time, „ *xvi* 21
And made my *l* a perfumed altar-flame; „ *xviii* 24
More *l* to Love than is or ever was „ 47
but live a *l* of truest breath, And teach true *l* to fight with mortal wrongs. „ 53
L of my *l*, wilt thou not answer this? „ 59
As long as my *l* endures I feel I shall owe „ *xix* 86
She is coming, my *l*, my fate; „ *xxii* 62
That must have *l* for a blow. „ *II i* 27
Might drown all *l* in the eye,— „ *ii* 61
But the red *l* spilt for a private blow— „ *v* 93
My *l* has crept so long on a broken wing „ *III vi* 1
Wearing the white flower of a blameless *l*. *Ded. of Idylls* 25
A lovelier *l*, a more unstain'd, than his! „ 30
inheritance Of such a *l*, a heart, „ 33
light of her eyes into his *l* Smite on the sudden, *Com. of Arthur* 56
Travail, and throes and agonies of the *l*, „ 76
Then might we live together as one *l*, „ 91
A cry from out the dawning of my *l*, „ 333
hear him speak before he left his *l*. „ 362
to grace Thy climbing *l*, and cherish my prone year, *Gareth and L.* 95
and risk thine all, *L*, limbs, „ 129
how the King had saved his *l* In battle twice, „ 493
Save whom she loveth, or a holy *l*. „ 622
Good now, ye have saved a *l* Worth somewhat „ 827
And saver of my *l*; „ 879
The saver of my *l*.' „ 884
lord whose *l* he saved Had, some brief space, „ 888
'Take not my *l*: I yield.' „ 973
Thy *l* is thine at her command. „ 983
To war against ill uses of a *l*, But these from all his *l* arise, and cry, „ 1130
and all his *l* Past unto sleep; „ 1280
imageries Of that which *L* hath done with, „ 1391
drew himself Bright from his old dark *l*, *Marr. of Geraint* 595
Long for my *l*, or hunger for my death, *Geraint and E.* 81
I save a *l* dearer to me than mine.' „ 138
'Enid, the pilot star of my lone *l*, „ 306
Owe you me nothing for a *l* half-lost? „ 318
swathed the hurt that drain'd her dear lord's *l*. „ 516
'O cousin, slay not him who gave you *l*.' „ 783
set his foot upon me, and give me *l*. „ 850
hating the *l* He gave me, meaning to be rid of it. „ 852
To glance behind me at my former *l*, „ 863
wrought upon himself After a *l* of violence, „ 913
some knight of mine, risking his *l*, „ 915
crown'd A happy *l* with a fair death, „ 968
I have not lived my *l* delightsomely: *Balin and Balan* 60
lived A wealthier *l* than heretofore „ 92
He boasts his *l* as purer than thine own; „ 104

Life (*continued*) as the man in *l* Was wounded by blind tongues *Balin and Balan* 129
But golden earnest of a gentler *l* !' „ 208
I that fain had died To save thy *l*, „ 600
Foul are their *lives* ; foul are their lips ; „ 616
My madness all thy *l* has been thy doom, „ 619
World-war of dying flesh against the *l*, *Merlin and V.* 193
Death in all *l* and lying in all love, „ 194
lost to *l* and use and name and fame. (repeat) „ 214, 970
Upon my *l* and use and name and fame, „ 374
what is Fame in *l* but half-disfame, „ 465
lay as dead, And lost all use of *l* : „ 645
long sleepless nights Of my long *l* „ 680
once in *l* was fluster'd with new wine, „ 756
How from the rosy lips of *l* and love, „ 846
Kill'd with a word worse than a *l* of blows ! „ 870
course of *l* that seem'd so flowery to me „ 880
If the wolf spare me, weep my *l* away, „ 885
The vast necessity of heart and *l*. „ 925
the one passionate love Of her whole *l* „ 956
The shape and colour of a mind and *l*, *Lancelot and E.* 335
'What matter, so I help him back to *l* ?' „ 787
Told him that her fine care had saved his *l*. „ 863
when you yield your flower of *l* To one more fitly yours, „ 952
half disdain At love, *l*, all things, „ 1239
Had pass'd into the silent *l* of prayer, *Holy Grail* 4
we that want the warmth of double *l*, „ 624
Beyond all sweetness in a *l* so rich,— „ 626
To pass away into the quiet *l*, „ 738
Cares but to pass into silent *l*. „ 899
To have thee back in lusty *l* again, *Pelleas and E.* 352
thro' her love her *l* Wasted and pined, „ 495
that young *l* Being smitten in mid heaven *Last Tournament* 26
l had flown, we sware but by the shell— „ 270
New leaf, new *l*—the days of frost are o'er : New *l*, „ 278
All out like a long *l* to a sour end— „ 288
Art thou King ?—Look to thy *l* !' „ 454
half a *l* away, Her to be loved no more ? „ 640
And trustful courtesies of household *l*, *Guinevere* 86
There will I hide thee, till my *l* shall end, There hold thee with my *l* against the world.' „ 114
whose disloyal *l* Hath wrought confusion „ 219
for all the land was full of *l*. „ 259
And many a mystic lay of *l* and death „ 281
Thou hast not made my *l* so sweet to me, „ 451
For thou hast spoilt the purpose of my *l*. „ 453
To lead sweet *lives* in purest chastity, „ 474
this *l* of mine I guard as God's high gift „ 493
love thro' flesh hath wrought into my *l* „ 558
Myself must tell him in that purer *l*, „ 653
for her good deeds and her pure *l*, „ 693
Light was Gawain in *l*, and light in death *Pass. of Arthur* 56
Yet still my *l* is whole, and still I live „ 150
tho' I live three *lives* of mortal men, „ 323
I have lived my *l*, and that which I have done „ 412
nourish a blind *l* within the brain, „ 419
pluck'd his flickering *l* again From halfway *To the Queen ii* 5
Softness breeding scorn of simple *l*, „ 53
chambers of the morning star, And East of *L*. *Lover's Tale i* 29
govern a whole *l* from birth to death, „ 76
floods with redundant *l* Her narrow portals. „ 84
On these deserted sands of barren *l*. „ 93
Time and Grief abode too long with *L*, „ 107
Death drew nigh and beat the doors of *L* ; „ 111
Yet is my *l* nor in the present time, „ 116
Between is clearer in my *l* than all „ 149
young *L* knows not when young *L* was born, „ 156
Into delicious dreams, our other *l*, „ 162
Which yet upholds my *l*, and evermore Is to me daily *l* and daily death : „ 168
Or build a wall betwixt my *l* and love, „ 176
(For they seem many and my most of *l*, „ 185
for ever, Left her own *l* with it ; „ 215
He that gave Her *l*, to me delightedly fulfill'd „ 224

Life (*continued*) And sang aloud the matin-song of *l*. *Lover's Tale i* 232
The stream of *l*, one stream, one *l*, „ 239
So what was earliest mine in earliest *l*, „ 247
larks Fill'd all the March of *l* !— „ 284
The joy of *l* in steepness overcome, „ 386
her *l*, her love, With my *l*, love, soul, spirit, „ 459
Else had the *l* of that delighted hour „ 471
whose right hand the light Of *L* issueth, „ 498
that *l* I heeded not Flow'd from me, „ 596
henceforth there was no *l* for me ! „ 608
L was startled from the tender love „ 616
L (like a wanton too-officious friend, „ 627
As it had taken *l* away before, „ 710
with heaven's music in a *l* More living „ 761
worth the *l* That made it sensible. „ 799
Ruins, the ruin of all my *l* and me ! „ *ii* 68
Now the light Which was their *l*, „ 164
shadowing pencil's naked forms Colour and *l* : „ 181
That painted vessel, as with inner *l*, „ 191
all at once, soul, *l* And breath and motion, „ 194
She from her bier, as into fresher *l*, „ *iii* 42
Glanced back upon them in his after *l*, „ *iv* 24
Would you could toll me out of *l*, „ 30
recall'd Her fluttering *l* : „ 94
For you have given me *l* and love again, „ 110
I learnt the drearier story of his *l* ; „ 147
'Kiss him,' she said. 'You gave me *l* again. „ 172
fed, and cherish'd him, and saved his *l*. „ 264
Who thrust him out, or him who saved his *l* ?' „ 267
'body and soul And *l* and limbs, „ 283
some new death than for a *l* renew'd ; „ 374
All over glowing with the sun of *l*, „ 381
I'll tell you the tale o' my *l*. *First Quarrel* 9
what I did wi' my single *l* ? „ 59
I have only an hour of *l*. *Rizpah* 22
he took no *l*, but he took one purse, „ 31
wur it nobbut to saäve my *l* ; *North. Cobbler* 84
half of the rest of us maim'd for *l* *The Revenge* 77
And the Lord hath spared our *lives*. „ 93
very fountains of her *l* were chill'd ; *Sisters (E. and E.)* 266
Now in this quiet of declining *l*, „ 273
who scarce would escape with her *l* ; *In the Child. Hosp.* 66
which lived True *l*, live on—and if the fatal kiss, Born of true *l* and love, divorce thee not From earthly love and *l*— *Ded. Poem Prin. Alice* 2
Frail were the works that defended the hold that we held with our *lives*— *Def. of Lucknow* 7
for it never could save us a *l*. „ 86
I find hard rocks, hard *l*, hard cheer, *Sir J. Oldcastle* 6
I would have given my *l* To help his own from scathe, a thousand *lives* To save his soul. „ 62
and *l* Pass in the fire of Babylon ! „ 123
Lord of *l* Be by me in my death. „ 173
The vast occasion of our stronger *l*— *Columbus* 35
I am written in the Lamb's own Book of *L* „ 88
I know that he has led me all my *l*, „ 160
one, Whose *l* has been no play with him „ 224
It was all of it fair as *l*, *V. of Maeldune* 20
each taken a *l* for a *l*, „ 122
every phase of ever-heightening *l*, *De Prof., Two G.* 7
young *l* Breaking with laughter from the dark ; „ 17
From death to death thro' *l* and *l*, „ 52
I cannot laud this *l*, it looks so dark : *To W. H. Brookfield* 12
Saving his *l* on the fallow flood. *Batt. of Brunanburh* 61
From the darkness of *l*— *To Prin. F. of H.* 2
if *l's* best end Be to end well ! *Tiresias* 130
not to plunge Thy torch of *l* in darkness, „ 159
Offer thy maiden *l*. „ 165
What *l*, so maim'd by night, „ 208
My *l* itself is a wreck,' *The Wreck* 5
I would make my *l* one prayer „ 10
I had lived a wild-flower *l*, „ 37
thro' *l* to my latest breath ; „ 79
mother's shame will enfold her and darken her *l*.' „ 100
'May her *l* be as blissfully calm, „ 139

O

Life (*continued*) Godless gloom Of a *l* without sun, *Despair* 7
I am frighted at *l* not death.' „ 14
L with its anguish, and horrors, „ 48
and you saved me, a valueless *l*. „ 61
Of the hellish heat of a wretched *l* „ 68
whether this earth-narrow *l* Be yet but yolk, *Ancient Sage* 129
gain of such large *l* as match'd with ours „ 237
lose thy *l* by usage of thy sting; „ 270
daughter yield her *l*, heart, soul to one— *The Flight* 28
And all my *l* was darken'd, „ 39
where summer never dies, with Love, the Sun of *l*! „ 44
an the face of the thraithur agin in *l*! *Tomorrow* 50
ye would start back agin into *l*, „ 81
I knaws i 'ed led tha a quieter *l* *Spinster's S's*. 71
In my *l* there was a picture, *Locksley H., Sixty* 15
brooding on his briefer lease of *l*, „ 23
my *l* in golden sequence ran, „ 47
the sacred passion of the second *l*. „ 68
Fought for their *lives* in the narrow gap *Heavy Brigade* 23
The light of days when *l* begun, *Pref. Poem Broth. S.* 23
With stronger *l* from day to day; *Hands all Round* 6
Two Suns of Love make day of human *l*, *To Prin. Beatrice* 1
Mother weeps At that white funeral of the single *l*, „ 9
two that love thee, lead a summer *l*, „ 18
One *l*, one flag, one fleet, one Throne!' *Open. I. and C. Exhib.* 39
flame of *l* went wavering down; *To Marq. of Dufferin* 32
while my *l's* late eve endures, „ 49
The *L* that had descended re-arise, *Demeter and P.* 30
we spin the *lives* of men, And not of Gods, „ 85
Power That lifts her buried *l* from gloom to bloom, „ 98
I fail'd To send my *l* thro' olive-yard „ 110
Shalt ever send thy *l* along with mine „ 145
gloom of the evening, *L* at a close; *Vastness* 15
in the misery of my married *l*, *The Ring* 136
So far gone down, or so far up in *l*, „ 193
Made every moment of her after *l* „ 220
And there the light of other *l*, „ 295
Saved when your *l* was wreck'd! „ 305
That now their ever-rising *l* has dwarf'd „ 463
silent brow when *l* had ceased to beat. *Happy* 52
snap the bond that link'd us *l* to *l*, „ 61
leech forsake the dying bed for terror of his *l*? „ 98
this *l* of mingled pains And joys to me, *To Mary Boyle* 49
long walk thro' desert *l* Without the one. „ 55
new *l* that gems the hawthorn line; *Prog. of Spring* 36
his fresh *l* may close as it began, „ 89
L, which is *L* indeed. „ 117
As he stands on the heights of his *l* *By an Evolution.* 20
A whisper from his dawn of *l*? *Far—far—away* 10
Light again, leaf again, *l* again, love again,' *The Throstle* 3
LIVE thy *L*, Young and old, *The Oak* 1
My *l* and death are in thy hand. *Death of Œnone* 40
Let me owe my *l* to thee. „ 42
she heard The shriek of some lost *l* „ 90
lazying out a *l* Of self-suppression, *St. Telemachus* 21
Reason in the dusky cave of *L*, *Akbar's Dream* 121
on this bank in *some* way live the *l* Beyond the bridge, „ 144
To make him trust his *l*, *The Wanderer* 11
The face of Death is toward the Sun of *L*, *D. of the Duke of C.* 12
Lifeblood New *l* warm the bosom, *Will Water.* 22
Life-bubbling who sliced a red *l-b* way *Gareth and L.* 509
Lifeless I have cursed him even to *l* things) *Maud I xix* 15
Lifelong rose and past Bearing a *l* hunger in his heart. *Enoch Arden* 79
Then Philip with his eyes Full of that *l* hunger, „ 464
A *l* tract of time reveal'd; *In Mem. xlvi* 9
Do forge a *l-l* trouble of ourselves, *Geraint and E.* 3
With *l-l* injuries burning unavenged, „ 696
There sat the *l* creature of the house, *Lancelot and E.* 1143
Gaining a *l* Glory in battle, *Batt. of Brunanburh* 7
And you the *l* guardian of the child. *The Ring* 54
To you my days have been a *l-l* lie, *Romney's R.* 41
Lifetime Ere half the *l* of an oak. *In Mem. lxxvi* 12
Lift Many an arch high up did *l*, *Palace of Art* 142
to *l* the hidden ore That glimpses, *D. of F. Women* 274
L up thy rocky face, *England and Amer.* 12

Lift (*continued*) knowing God, they *l* not hands of prayer *M. d'Arthur* 252
in my weak, lean arms I *l* the cross, *St. S. Stylites* 118
when I see the woodman *l* His axe to slay my kin. *Talking Oak* 235
seem to *l* a burthen from thy heart *Love and Duty* 96
He *l's* me to the golden doors; *St. Agnes' Eve* 25
And *l* the household out of poverty; *Enoch Arden* 485
slowly *l's* His golden feet on those empurpled stairs *Lucretius* 134
l your natures up: Embrace our aims: *Princess ii* 88
To *l* the woman's fall'n divinity „ *iii* 223
fair philosophies That *l* the fancy; „ 341
'*L* up your head, sweet sister: „ *v* 64
l thine eyes; my doubts are dead, „ *vii* 348
Could *l* them nearer God-like state *Lit. Squabbles* 14
L as thou may'st thy burthen'd brows *In Mem. lxxii* 21
And seem to *l* the form, and glow „ *lxxxvii* 37
A great ship *l* her shining sides. „ *ciii* 40
That we may *l* from out of dust „ *cxxxi* 5
Shall I not *l* her from this land of beasts *Com. of Arthur* 80
'Blow trumpet! he will *l* us from the dust. „ 491
Nor did she *l* an eye nor speak a word, *Marr. of Geraint* 528
But *l* a shining hand against the sun, *Geraint and E.* 473
Without the will to *l* their eyes, *Merlin and V.* 836
Not *l* a hand—not, tho' he found me thus! *Last Tournament* 528
He spared to *l* his hand against the King *Guinevere* 437
knowing God, they *l* not hands of prayer *Pass. of Arthur* 420
To *l* us as it were from commonplace, *Sisters (E. and E.)* 223
but 'e niver not *l* oop 'is 'eäd: *Village Wife* 88
and *l's*, and lays the deep, *Tiresias* 22
Power That *l's* her buried life *Demeter and P.* 98
To thoughts that *l* the soul of men, *To Master of B.* 14
I can but *l* the torch Of Reason *Akbar's Dream* 120
Lifted (adj. and part.) And once my arm was *l* to hew down *D. of F. Women* 45
So *l* up in spirit he moved away. *Enoch Arden* 330
from her *l* hand Dangled a length of ribbon „ 749
under his own lintel stood Storming with *l* hands, *Aylmer's Field* 332
her arm *l*, eyes on fire— *Princess, Pro.* 41
With *l* hand the gazer in the street. *Ode on Well.* 22
till the cloud that settles round his birth Hath *l* but a little. *Gareth and L.* 131
Which our high Lancelot hath so *l* up, *Balin and Balan* 490
But when my name was *l* up, the storm Brake *Merlin and V.* 502
'And I was *l* up in heart, and thought *Holy Grail* 361
Till he, being *l* up beyond himself, *Last Tournament* 679
and morn Has *l* the dark eyelash of the Night *Akbar's Dream* 201
Lifted (verb) A limb was broken when they *l* him; *Enoch Arden* 107
l up A weight of emblem, *Princess iv* 201
At which she *l* up her voice and cried. „ *v* 81
Then us they *l* up, dead weights, „ *vi* 348
To Thor and Odin *l* a hand: *The Victim* 8
And once, but once, she *l* her eyes, *Maud I viii* 5
l his voice, and call'd A hoary man, *Com. of Arthur* 144
she *l* either arm, 'Fie on thee, King! *Gareth and L.* 657
How the villain *l* up his voice, „ 716
L an arm, and softly whisper'd, „ 1361
Crost and came near, *l* adoring eyes, *Geraint and E.* 304
At which her palfrey whinnying *l* heel, „ 533
gravely smiling, *l* her from horse, „ 883
Then Lancelot *l* his large eyes; *Balin and Balan* 277
and *he l* faint eyes; he felt One near him; „ 594
and they *l* up Their eager faces, *Merlin and V.* 132
when she *l* up A face of sad appeal, „ 233
And the Queen *L* her eyes, *Lancelot and E.* 84
L her eyes, and read his lineaments. „ 244
And noblest, when she *l* up her eyes. „ 256
she *l* up her eyes And loved him, „ 259
And *l* her fair face and moved away: „ 682
Then like a ghost she *l* up her face, „ 918
and *l* up his eyes And saw the barge „ 1390
Pelleas *l* up an eye so fierce She quail'd; *Pelleas and E.* 601
Working a tapestry, *l* up her head, *Last Tournament* 129
l up a face All over glowing with the sun *Lover's Tale iv* 380
and *l* hand and heart and voice In praise to God *Columbus* 16
she *l* her head— *Tomorrow* 79
Then I *l* up my eyes, *Happy* 82

Lifted (verb) (*continued*) she *l* up a voice Of shrill command, — Death of Œnone 98
Lifting (adj. and part.) at last he said, *L* his honest forehead, — Enoch Arden 388
See thro' the gray skirts of a *l* squall — „ 829
L his grim head from my wounds. — Princess vi 272
But Gawain *l* up his vizor said, — Pelleas and E. 370
l up mine eyes, I found myself Alone, — Holy Grail 375
Lifting (s) *l* of whose eyelash is my lord, — Princess v 140
labour'd in *l* them out of slime, — Dead Prophet 11
Lig (lie) An' 'e maäde the bed as 'e *l's* on — N. Farmer, N. S. 28
An' 'e *l's* on 'is back i' the grip, — „ 31
Theere, *l* down—I shall hev to gie one or tother awaäy. — Spinster's S's. 64
Tom, *l* theere o' the cushion, — „ 94
Liggin' (lying) and meä *l* 'ere aloän? — N. Farmer, O. S. 1
Light (adj. and adv.) *L* Hope at Beauty's call would perch and stand, — Caress'd or chidden 3
from the violets her *l* foot Shone rosy-white, — Œnone 179
The *l* aërial gallery, golden-rail'd, — Palace of Art 47
'The *l* white cloud swam over us. — D. of F. Women 221
Make bright our days and *l* our dreams, — Of old sat Freedom 22
and the *l* and lustrous curls— — M. d'Arthur 216
Juliet, she So *l* of foot, so *l* of spirit— — Gardener's D. 14
L pretexts drew me; — „ 192
Spread the *l* haze along the river shores, — „ 264
overhead The *l* cloud smoulders on the summer crag. — Edwin Morris 147
So *l* upon the grass: — Talking Oak 88
'A *l* wind chased her on the wing, — „ 125
'But *l* as any wind that blows — „ 129
her palfrey's footfall shot *L* horrors thro' her pulses: — Godiva 59
So for every *l* transgression Doom'd them to the lash. — The Captain 11
A *l* wind blew from the gates of the sun, — Poet's Song 3
Wearing the *l* yoke of that Lord of love, — Aylmer's Field 708
or is it a *l* thing That I, their guest, their host, — „ 789
'That's your *l* way; but I would make it death — Princess, Pro. 151
L coin, the tinsel clink of compliment. — „ ii 55
Many a *l* foot shone like a jewel set In the dark crag: — „ iii 358
As in a poplar grove when a *l* wind wakes — „ v 13
with each *l* air On our mail'd heads: — „ 244
Steps with a tender foot, *l* as on air, — „ vi 88
made me move As *l* as carrier-birds in air; — In Mem. xxv 6
And hopes and *l* regrets that come Make April — „ xl 7
Thro' *l* reproaches, half exprest And loyal — „ lxxxv 15
and *l* as the crest Of a peacock, — Maud I xvi 16
Seem'd her *l* foot along the garden walk, — „ xviii 9
a *l* laugh Broke from Lynette, — Gareth and L. 836
By bandits groom'd, prick'd their *l* ears, — Geraint and E. 193
some *l* jest among them rose With laughter — Lancelot and E. 178
and like to coins, Some true, some *l*, — Holy Grail 26
'Ay,' said Gawain, 'for women be so *l*.' — Pelleas and E. 362
Her *l* feet fell on our rough Lyonnesse, — Last Tournament 554
And Tristram, fondling her *l* hands, — „ 601
Murmuring a *l* song I had heard thee sing, — „ 614
L was Gawain in life, and *l* in death Is Gawain, — Pass. of Arthur 56
and the *l* and lustrous curls— — „ 384
all the while The *l* soul twines and mingles — Lover's Tale i 132
The leaves upon her falling *l*— — L. of Shalott iv 21
I must ha' been *l* i' my head— — First Quarrel 82
And idle gleams to thee are *l* to me. — Ancient Sage 246
Molly Magee kem flyin' acrass me, as *l* as a lark, — Tomorrow 21
all of yer foot in the dance was as *l* as snow an the lan', — „ 36
and from each The *l* leaf falling fast, — Pro. to Gen. Hamley 2
L airs from where the deep, — Early Spring 21
Watching her large *l* eyes and gracious looks, — Prog. of Spring 19
Light (s) (*See also* **Candle-light, Foot-lights, Gas-light, Half-light, Lava-light, Night-light, Sea-light, Topaz-lights**) They light his little *l* alway; — Supp. Confessions 46
stood Betwixt me and the *l* of God! — „ 110
on his *l* there falls A shadow; — „ 163
And far away in the sickly *l*, — The Kraken 7
giving *l* To read those laws; — Isabel 18
With swifter movement and in purer *l* — „ 32
The cock sung out an hour ere *l*: — Mariana 27

Light (s) (*continued*) Until the breaking of the *l*, — Clear-headed friend 25
Thro' *l* and shadow thou dost range, — Madeline 4
WHEN cats run home and *l* is come, — The Owl i 1
I enter'd, from the clearer *l*, — Arabian Nights 38
robed in soften'd *l* Of orient state. — Ode to Memory 10
The *l* of thy great presence; — „ 32
A pillar of white *l* upon the wall — „ 53
Filling with *l* And vagrant melodies — The Poet 16
Bright as *l*, and clear as wind. — Poet's Mind 7
In the windows is no *l*; — Deserted House 6
L and shadow ever wander — A Dirge 12
WHAT time the mighty moon was gathering *l* — Love and Death 1
So in the *l* of great eternity — „ 12
Ere the *l* on dark was growing, — Oriana 10
Low thunder and *l* in the magic night— — The Merman 23
Breathing *L* against thy face, — Adeline 56
gleams of mellow *l* Float by you on the verge of night. — Margaret 30
And faint, rainy *l's* are seen, — „ 60
To pierce me thro' with pointed *l*; — Rosalind 27
Of lavish *l's*, and floating shades: — Eleänore 12
in a bower Grape-thicken'd from the *l*, — „ 36
But am as nothing in its *l*: — „ 88
A funeral, with plumes and *l's* And music, — L. of Shalott ii 31
Some bearded meteor, trailing *l*, — „ iii 26
And all the furnace of the *l* — Mariana in the S. 55
A living flash of *l* he flew.' — Two Voices 15
'Not less swift souls that yearn for *l*, — „ 67
Those lonely *l's* that still remain, — „ 83
Nor art thou nearer to the *l*, — „ 92
'To pass, when Life her *l* withdraws, — „ 145
l increased With freshness in the dawning east. — „ 404
That these have never lost their *l*. — Miller's D. 88
I saw the village *l's* below; — „ 108
At last you rose and moved the *l*, — „ 125
His *l* upon the letter dwells, — „ 189
Throbbing thro' all thy heat and *l*, — Fatima 4
And, isled in sudden seas of *l*, — „ 33
like a *l* that grows Larger and clearer, — Œnone 108
I pray thee, pass before my *l* of life, — „ 241
Suddenly scaled the *l*. — Palace of Art 8
the *l's*, rose, amber, emerald, blue, — „ 169
Lit *l* in wreaths and anadems, — „ 186
spot of dull stagnation, without *l* Or power — „ 245
The languid *l* of your proud eyes — L. C. V. de Vere 59
I ran by him without speaking, like a flash of *l*. — May Queen 18
beneath the waning *l* You'll never see me more — May Queen, N. Y's. E. 25
and there his *l* may shine— — „ Con. 51
To lie within the *l* of God, — „ 59
thro' wavering *l's* and shadows broke, — Lotos-Eaters 12
Lo! sweeten'd with the summer *l*, — „ C. S. 32
To dream and dream, like yonder amber *l*, — „ 57
In every land I saw, wherever *l* illumineth, — D. of F. Women 14
fill'd with *l* The interval of sound. — „ 171
with welcome *l*, With timbrel and with song. — „ 199
O me, that I should ever see the *l*! — „ 254
Joan of Arc, A *l* of ancient France; — „ 268
The cricket chirps: the *l* burns low: — D. of the O. Year 40
mournful *l* That broods above the fallen sun, — To J. S. 50
Above her shook the starry *l's*: — Of old sat Freedom 3
Keep dry their *l* from tears; — „ 20
Tho' sitting girt with doubtful *l*. — Love thou thy land 16
Set in all *l's* by many minds, — „ 35
l that led The holy Elders with the gift of myrrh. — M. d'Arthur 232
and our last *l*, that long Had wink'd — „ Ep. 1
twinkling laurel scatter'd silver *l's*, — Gardener's D. 118
Half *l*, half shade, She stood, — „ 140
Danced into *l*, and died into the shade; — „ 203
a *l* Of laughter dimpled in his swarthy cheek; — Edwin Morris 60
If I may measure time by yon slow *l*, — St. S. Stylites 94
'tween the spring and downfall of the *l*, — „ 110
They flapp'd my *l* out as I read: — „ 175
What's here? a shape, a shade, A flash of *l*. — „ 203
take Example, pattern: lead them to thy *l*. — „ 224

Light (s) (*continued*) ' Then flush'd her cheek with rosy *l*, *Talking Oak* 165
l's of sunset and of sunrise mix'd *Love and Duty* 72
And point thee forward to a distant *l*, „ 95
furrowing into *l* the mounded rack, „ 100
smit with freër *l* shall slowly melt *Golden Year* 33
And *l* shall spread, and man be liker man „ 35
Lie like a shaft of *l* across the land, „ 49
l's begin to twinkle from the rocks: *Ulysses* 54
cold Are all thy *l's*, and cold my wrinkled feet *Tithonus* 67
came a colour and a *l*, *Locksley Hall* 25
Sees in heaven the *l* of London „ 114
Underneath the *l* he looks at, „ 116
The slumbrous *l* is rich and warm, *Day-Dm., Sleep. B.* 7
Stillness with love, and day with *l*. „ 16
A fuller *l* illumined all, „ *Revival* 5
Be still the first to leap to *l* „ *L'Envoi* 27
And strows her *l's* below, *St. Agnes' Eve* 28
A *l* upon the shining sea— „ 35
A *l* before me swims, *Sir Galahad* 26
A gentle sound, an awful *l*! „ 41
Ten thousand broken *l's* and shapes, *Will Water.* 59
This whole wide earth of *l* and shade „ 67
And sleep beneath his pillar'd *l*! *The Voyage* 20
Dip forward under starry *l*, *Move eastward, etc.* 10
A sleepy *l* upon their brows and lips— *Vision of Sin* 9
And isles a *l* in the offing: *Enoch Arden* 131
Started from bed, and struck herself a *l*, „ 494
a great mist-blotted *l* Flared on him, „ 680
But finding neither *l* nor murmur there „ 687
The ruddy square of comfortable *l*, „ 726
Which at a touch of *l*, an air of heaven, *Aylmer's Field* 5
A joyous to dilate, as toward the *l*. „ 77
An end, a hope, a *l* breaking upon him. „ 480
Star to star vibrates *l*: „ 578
Which from the low *l* of mortality „ 641
Thee therefore with His *l* about thy feet, „ 665
entering fill'd the house with sudden *l*. „ 682
And near the *l* a giant woman sat, *Sea Dreams* 98
—But round the North, a *l*, „ 208
on those cliffs Broke, mixt with awful *l* „ 215
on the crowd Broke, mixt with awful *l*, „ 235
and *l* is large, and lambs are glad *Lucretius* 99
dance, and flew thro' *l* And shadow, *Princess, Pro.* 84
when the college *l's* Began to glitter „ *i* 207
' This world was once a fluid haze of *l*, „ *ii* 116
' that we still may lead The new *l* up, „ 348
Before two streams of *l* from wall to wall, „ 473
green malignant *l* of coming storm. „ *iii* 132
as she smote me with the *l* of eyes „ 192
with the sun and moon renew their *l* For ever, „ 255
Let there be *l* and there was *l*: „ 323
all creation is one act at once, The birth of *l*: „ 326
The long *l* shakes across the lakes, „ *iv* 3
stood in your own *l* and darken'd mine. „ 314
We did not know the real *l*, „ 357
lived in all fair *l's*, „ 430
lapt in wreaths of glowworm *l* The mellow breaker „ 435
All open-mouth'd, all gazing to the *l*, „ 483
wild birds on the *l* Dash themselves dead. „ 495
You would-be quenchers of the *l* to be, „ 536
we saw the *l's*, and heard The voices murmuring. „ 558
the sudden *l* Dazed me half-blind: „ *v* 11
A common *l* of smiles at our disguise „ 271
over them the tremulous isles of *l* Slided, „ *vi* 81
A genial warmth and *l* once more, „ 282
till she not fair began To gather *l*, „ *vii* 24
small bright head, A *l* of healing, „ 59
silent *l* Slept on the painted walls, „ 120
Naked, a double *l* in air and wave, „ 167
Sent from a dewy breast a cry for *l*: „ 253
new day comes, the *l* Dearer for night, „ 346
The happy valleys, half in *l*, „ *Con.* 41
Whatever record leap to *l* *Ode on Well.* 190
Thro' the long gorge to the far *l* „ 213
A *l* amid its olives green; *The Daisy* 30

Light (s) (*continued*) From Como,-when the *l* was gray, *The Daisy* 73
And on thro' zones of *l* and shadow *To F. D. Maurice* 27
it grew so tall It wore a crown of *l*, *The Flower* 10
l and shadow illimitable, *Boädicea* 42
THE *l's* and shadows fly! *Window, On the Hill* 1
l's and shadows that cannot be still, „ 7
O *l's*, are you flying over her sweet little face? „ 13
Gone, and the *l* gone with her, „ *Gone* 3
You roll up away from the *l* The blue wood-louse, „ *Winter* 8
Fly; Fly to the *l* in the valley below— „ *Letter* 12
L, so low upon earth, „ *Marr. Morn.* 1
L, so low in the vale You flash and lighten „ 9
Thine are these orbs of *l* and shade; *In Mem., Pro.* 5
They are but broken *l's* of thee, „ 19
Help thy vain words to bear thy *l*. „ 32
magic *l* Dies off at once from bower and hall, „ *viii* 5
thro' early *l* Shall glimmer on the dewy decks. „ *ix* 11
Sphere all your *l's* around, above; „ 13
Calm and still *l* on yon great plain „ *xi* 9
My blessing, like a line of *l*, „ *xvii* 10
And Fancy *l* from Fancy caught, „ *xxiii* 14
light The *l* that shone when Hope was born. „ *xxx* 32
To leap the grades of life and *l*, „ *xli* 11
' Farewell! We lose ourselves in *l*.' „ *xlvii* 16
Like *l* in many a shiver'd lance „ *xlix* 3
Be near me when my *l* is low, „ *l* 1
An infant crying for the *l*: „ *liv* 19
Or in the *l* of deeper eyes „ *lxii* 11
Recalls, in change of *l* or gloom, „ *lxxxv* 74
And like a finer *l* in *l*. „ *xci* 16
in the house *l* after *l* Went out, „ *xcv* 19
Mixt their dim *l's*, like life and death, „ 63
Which makes the darkness and the *l*, „ *xcvi* 19
And dwells not in the *l* alone, „ 20
The flying cloud, the frosty *l*: „ *cvi* 2
Where God and Nature met in *l*; „ *cxi* 20
Now dance the *l's* on lawn and lea, „ *cxv* 9
Behind thee comes the greater *l*: „ *cxxi* 12
For them the *l* of life increased, „ *Con.* 74
To pestle a poison'd poison behind his crimson *l's*. *Maud I i* 44
in the high Hall-garden I see her pass like a *l*; „ *iv* 11
sorrow seize me if ever that *l* be my leading-star! „ 12
Maud in the *l* of her youth and her grace, „ *v* 15
delicate spark Of glowing and growing *l* „ *vi* 16
returns the dark With no more hope of *l*. „ *ix* 16
Beginning to faint in the *l* that she loves „ *xxii* 9
To faint in the *l* of the sun she loves, To faint in his *l*, and to die. „ 11
At the shouts, the leagues of *l's*, „ *II iv* 21
And the *l* and shadow fleet; „ 36
rivulet at her feet Ripples on in *l* and shadow „ 42
From the realms of *l* and song, „ 82
But the broad *l* glares and beats, „ 89
Tho' many a *l* shall darken, „ *III vi* 43
many a darkness into the *l* shall leap, „ 46
In that fierce *l* which beats upon a throne, *Ded. of Idylls* 27
shone so close beside Thee that ye made One *l* together, „ 48
Half-blinded at the coming of a *l*. *Com. of Arthur* 266
Affection, and the *l* of victory, *Gareth and L.* 331
flickering in a grimly *l* Dance on the mere. „ 826
May-music growing with the growing *l*, „ 1080
Echo'd the walls; a *l* twinkled; anon Came *l's* and *l's*, „ 1370
Beautiful among *l's*, and waving to him „ 1376
loved her, as he loved the *l* of Heaven. And as the *l* of Heaven varies, *Marr. of Geraint* 5
And darken'd from the high *l* in his eyes, „ 100
never *l* and shade Coursed one another more „ 521
her fair head in the dim-yellow *l*, „ 600
the red cock shouting to the *l*, *Geraint and E.* 384
But *l* to me! no shadow, O my King, *Balin and Balan* 207
all the *l* upon her silver face Flow'd „ 263
A *l* of armour by him flash, „ 326
They said a *l* came from her when she moved: *Merlin and V.* 567
the court, the King, dark in your *l*, „ 875
from the skull the crown Roll'd into *l*, *Lancelot and E.* 51

Light (s) (*continued*) The maiden standing in the dewy l. — *Lancelot and E.* 352
The green l from the meadows underneath „ 408
O damsel, in the l of your blue eyes; „ 660
the blood-red l of dawn Flared on her face, „ 1025
I heard the sound, I saw the l, *Holy Grail* 280
all her form shone forth with sudden l „ 450
A l was in the crannies, „ 838
This l that strikes his eyeball is not l, „ 913
loosed his horse, and led him to the l. *Pelleas and E.* 61
Was dazzled by the sudden l, „ 105
a moon With promise of large l on woods „ 394
And spied not any l in hall or bower, „ 419
golden beard that clothed his lips with l— *Last Tournament* 668
Then in the l's last glimmer Tristram show'd „ 739
one low l betwixt them burn'd *Guinevere* 4
'No l had we: for that we do repent; „ 171
'No l: so late! and dark and chill the night! O let us in, that we may find the l! „ 174
in the l the white mermaiden swam, „ 245
What knowest thou of the world, and all its l's And shadows, „ 343
thou reseated in thy place of l, „ 525
near him the sad nuns with each a l Stood, „ 590
Wet with the mists and smitten by the l's, „ 597
That pure severity of perfect l— „ 646
O l upon the wind, *Pass. of Arthur* 46
great l of heaven Burn'd at his lowest „ 90
cryings for the l, Moans of the dying, „ 116
the l that led The holy Elders with the gift of myrrh. „ 400
when, clothed with living l, They stood before his throne „ 454
From less to less and vanish into l. „ 468
For when the outer l's are darken'd thus, *Lover's Tale i* 35
led on with l In trances and in visions: „ 77
image, like a charm of l and strength „ 91
Thou art l, To which my spirit leaneth „ 103
Looking on her that brought him to the l: „ 160
From the same clay came into l at once. „ 194
a common l of eyes Was on us as we lay: „ 236
till the morning l Sloped thro' the pines, „ 263
Pour with such sudden deluges of l „ 315
Methought a l Burst from the garland I had wov'n, „ 365
A l methought broke from her dark, „ 368
mystic l flash'd ev'n from her white robe „ 370
a tissue of l Unparallel'd. „ 419
Since in his absence full of l and joy, And giving l to others. „ 425
dwelling on the l and depth of thine, „ 492
bliss stood round me like the l of Heaven,— „ 495
whose right hand the l Of Life issueth, „ 497
Steppeth from Heaven to Heaven, from l to l, „ 512
We past from l to dark. „ 516
eyes too weak to look upon the l; „ 614
The white l of the weary moon above, „ 640
Between the going l and growing night? „ 664
Robed in those robes of l I must not wear, „ 671
hold out the l's of cheerfulness; „ 807
Showers slanting l upon the dolorous wave. „ 811
what l, what gleam on those black ways „ 812
fused together in the tyrannous l— „ *ii* 67
bliss, which broke in l Like morning „ 143
Now the l Which was their life, „ 163
And solid beam of isolated l, „ 173
l Of smiling welcome round her lips— „ *iii* 45
And, making there a sudden l, „ *iv* 53
The l was but a flash, and went again. „ 55
Wonder'd at some strange l in Julian's eyes „ 205
him nor l's nor feast Dazed or amazed, „ 310
an' puts 'im back i' the l. *North. Cobbler* 98
O diviner l, *Sisters (E. and E.)* 16
Break, diviner l! „ 23
dress thy deeds in l, Ascends to thee; *Ded. Poem Prin. Alice* 9
hidden there from the l of the sun— *Def. of Lucknow* 63
Before thy l, and cry continually— *Sir J. Oldcastle* 85
Her love of l quenching her fear of pain— „ 190

Light (s) (*continued*) last the l, the l On Guanahani! *Columbus* 74
and the l Grew as I gazed, „ 76
Sunless and moonless, utter l— „ 90
Set thee in l till time shall be no more? „ 150
brooks glitter'd on in the l without sound, *V. of Maeldune* 13
we were lured by the l from afar, „ 71
Waste dawn of multitudinous-eddying l— *De Prof., Two G.* 4
—her dark orb Touch'd with earth's l— „ 10
that one l no man can look upon, „ 37
the lost l of those dawn-golden times, *To W. H. Brookfield* 7
O YOU that were eyes and l to the King *To Prin. F. of H.* 1
dreadful l Came from her golden hair, *Tiresias* 43
spear and helmet tipt With stormy l „ 114
Send no such l upon the ways of men „ 161
Gone into darkness, that full l Of friendship! „ 202
and awake to a livid l, *The Wreck* 7
in the l of a dowerless smile, „ 45
days of a larger l than I ever again shall know— „ 78
we knew that their l was a lie— *Despair* 16
When the l of a Sun that was coming „ 23
baby-girl, that had never look'd on the l: „ 71
And, darkening in the l, *Ancient Sage* 151
And laughing back the l, „ 168
doors of Night may be the gates of L; „ 174
Some say, the L was father of the Night, And some, the Night was father of the L, „ 247
up that lane of l into the setting sun. *The Flight* 40
side by side in God's free l and air, „ 81
wid all the l an' the glow, *Tomorrow* 67
when Molly 'd put out the l, *Spinster's S's.* 97
for ever was the leading l of man. *Locksley H., Sixty* 66
France had shown a l to all men, „ 89
shriek'd and slaked the l with blood. „ 90
in that point of peaceful l? „ 190
were half as eager for the l. „ 228
L the fading gleam of Even? l the glimmer of the dawn? „ 229
Follow L, and do the Right— „ 277
Whirling their sabres in circles of l! *Heavy Brigade* 34
L among the vanish'd ages; *To Virgil* 25
shifting ladders of shadow and l, *Dead Prophet* 21
The l of days when life begun, *Pref. Poem Broth. S.* 23
THY prayer was 'L—more L— *Epit. on Caxton* 1
shadows which that l would cast, Till shadows vanish in the L of L. „ 3
This later l of Love have risen in rain, *To Prin. Beatrice* 16
l and genial warmth of double day. „ 22
Trust the Hand of L will lead her people, *On Jub. Q. Victoria* 68
And the L is Victor, „ 70
And all the Shadow die into the L, *Demeter and P.* 138
I'll coom an' I'll squench the l, *Owd Roä* 117
stings him back to the curse of the l; *Vastness* 18
A l shot upward on them from the lake. *The Ring* 256
And there the l of other life, „ 295
saw Your gilded vane, a l above the mist'— „ 331
'and the l,' She said, 'was like that l'— „ 333
l That glimmers on the marsh and on the grave.' „ 340
one betwixt the dark and l had seen Her, „ 414
soul in soul and l in l, *Happy* 39
in the brooding l of noon? „ 99
I, once half-crazed for larger l *To Ulysses* 29
Her l makes rainbows in my closing eyes, *Prog. of Spring* 46
still-fulfilling promise of a l „ 90
l retreated, The landskip darken'd, *Merlin and the G.* 30
Could make pure l live on the canvas? *Romney's R.* 10
Reflected, sends a l on the forgiven. „ 161
L again, leaf again, life again, love again,' *The Throstle* 3
star of eve was drawing l From the dead sun, *Death of Œnone* 64
What l was there? „ 84
The morning l of happy marriage broke „ 102
'L of the nations' ask'd his Chronicler Of Akbar *Akbar's Dream* 1
There is l in all, And l, „ 45
But find their limits by that larger l, „ 99
By deeds a l to men? „ 111
But no such l Glanced from our Presence „ 112

Light (s) (*continued*) arrowing *l* from clime to clime, *Akbar's Dream, Hymn* 5
'I am losing the *l* of my Youth *The Dreamer* 4
Light (come upon, etc.) Who can *l* on as happy a shore *Sea-Fairies* 40
You could not *l* upon a sweeter thing: *Walk. to the Mail* 52
What should you give to *l* on such a dream?' *Edwin Morris* 58
He trusts to *l* on something fair; *Day-Dm., Arrival* 20
L on a broken word to thank him with. *Enoch Arden* 347
if I could follow, and *l* Upon her lattice, *Princess iv* 99
Britain *l* upon auguries happier? *Boädicea* 45
may you *l* on all things that you love, *Marr. of Geraint* 226
but if ye know Where I can *l* on arms, „ 422
I should *l* upon the Holy Grail. *Holy Grail* 367
tha'll *l* of a livin' somewheers i' the Wowd *Church-warden, etc.* 47
we shall *l* upon some lonely shore, *The Flight* 89
Light (kindle) *l* The light that shone when Hope was born. *In Mem. xxx* 31
Light (to illuminate) They *l* his little life alway; *Supp. Confessions* 46
I let a sunbeam slip, To *l* her shaded eye; *Talking Oak* 218
God within him *l* his face, *In Mem. lxxxvii* 36
L's with herself, when alone She sits *Maud I xiv* 12
and *l's* the old church-tower, And *l's* the clock! *The Flight* 93
'Light (to alight) Who *'l's* and rings the gateway bell, *In Mem. viii* 3
That float thro' Heaven, and cannot *l*? *Day-Dm., Ep.* 8
Light-blue Sweet-hearted, you, whose *l-b* eyes *In Mem. xcvi* 2
A *l-b* lane of early dawn, „ *cxix* 7
Light Brigade Forward, the *L B*! (repeat) *Light Brigade* 5, 9
Honour the *L B*, „ 54
Lighted (adj.) (*See also* **Evening-lighted, Never-lighted, Silent-lighted, Still-lighted**) And in the *l* palace near *L. of Shalott iv* 47
Swung round the *l* lantern of the hall; *Guinevere* 262
Lighted (kindled) tho' my lamp was *l* late, *May Queen, Con.* 18
Lighted (shone) from it *l* an all-shining flame. *Achilles over the T.* 6
Lighted (illuminated) *l* from below By the red race of fiery Phlegethon; *Demeter and P.* 27
And *l* from above him by the Sun? „ 31
Lighted (alighted) Love *l* down between them *The Bridesmaid* 6
And *l* at a ruin'd inn, *Vision of Sin* 62
Gareth overthrew him, *l*, drew, *Gareth and L.* 1121
Molly belike may 'a *l* to-night upo' one. *Spinster's S's.* 7
following *l* on him there, And shouted, *Death of Œnone* 55
Lighted on those of old That *l o* Queen Esther, *Marr. of Geraint* 731
till she had *l o* his wound, *Geraint and E.* 513
I *l o* the maid, Whose sleeve he wore; *Lancelot and E.* 710
mutter'd, 'I have *l o* a fool, *Pelleas and E.* 113
and the great King, *L o* words: „ 253
Lighten (illuminate) Have power on this dark land to *l* it, *Com. of Arthur* 93
Lighten (to flash) *L's* from her own central Hell— *Aylmer's Field* 761
now she *l's* scorn At him that mars her plan, *Princess v* 131
You flash and *l* afar, *Window, Marr. Morn.* 10
O, *l* into my eyes and my heart, „ 15
l thro' The secular abyss to come, *In Mem. lxxvi* 5
What *l's* in the lucid east „ *cv* 24
The brute earth *l's* to the sky, „ *cxxvii* 15
Flash upon flash they *l* thro' me— *Lover's Tale i* 51
Lighten (to make lighter) One burthen and she would not *l* it? *Aylmer's Field* 703
To *l* this great clog of thanks, *Princess vi* 126
Lighten'd (flashed) The random sunshine *l*! *Amphion* 56
a cloudy gladness *l* In the eyes of each. *The Captain* 31
stars all night above the brim Of waters *l* into view; *The Voyage* 26
silver rays, that *l* as he breathed; *Lancelot and E.* 296
sword that *l* back the sun of Holy land, *Happy* 43
Lighten'd (made lighter) but a dream, yet it *l* my despair *Maud III vi* 18
Lightening Came *l* downward, and so spilt itself *Pelleas and E.* 426
Lighter (adj.) touch him with thy *l* thought. *Locksley Hall* 54
Of finest Gothic *l* than a fire, *Princess, Pro.* 92
My *l* moods are like to these, *In Mem. xx* 9
The *l* by the loss of his weight; *Maud I xvi* 2
Lighter (s) As flies the *l* thro' the gross. *In Mem. xli* 4
Lighter-footed And *l-f* than the fox. *Day-Dm., Arrival* 8
Lightest my ears could hear Her *l* breath; *Edwin Morris* 65
Of *l* echo, then a loftier form Than female, *Princess iv* 215
The *l* wave of thought shall lisp, *In Mem. xlix* 5
This lad, whose *l* word Is mere white truth *Balin and Balan* 517
Lightest (*continued*) whose *l* whisper moved him more *Pelleas and E.* 155
Light-foot *l-f* Iris brought it yester-eve, *Œnone* 83
So saying, *l-f* Iris pass'd away. *Achilles over the T.* 1
Light-glooming *L-g* over eyes divine, *Madeline* 16
Light-green A *l-g* tuft of plumes she bore *Sir L. and Q. G.* 26
L-g with its own shadow, keel to keel, *Lover's Tale i* 43
Light-headed I should grow *l-h*, I fear, *Maud I xix* 100
'O my child, ye seem *L-h*, *Lancelot and E.* 1063
Lighthouse with the gorgeous west the *l* shone, *Lover's Tale i* 60
that night When the rolling eyes of the *l* *Despair* 9
Lighting *l* upon days like these? *Locksley Hall* 99
Lightning (adj.) Till the *l* laughters dimple *Lilian* 16
Those writhed limbs of *l* speed; *Clear-headed friend* 23
The *l* flash atween the rains, *Rosalind* 12
The *l* flash of insect and of bird, *Enoch Arden* 574
Lightning (s) (*See also* **Cross-lightnings, Sheet-lightnings**)
as the *l* to the thunder Which follows it, *The Poet* 50
In the middle leaps a fountain Like sheet *l*, *Poet's Mind* 25
wilt shoot into the dark Arrows of *l's*. *To J. M. K.* 14
With thunders, and with *l's*, *Buonaparte* 6
With summer *l's* of a soul *Miller's D.* 13
great brand Made *l's* in the splendour of the moon, *M. d'Arthur* 137
Nor ever *l* char thy grain, *Talking Oak* 277
flash the *l's*, weigh the Sun. *Locksley Hall* 186
L of the hour, the pun, *Aylmer's Field* 441
The wizard *l's* deeply glow, *In Mem. cxxii* 19
That like a silent *l* under the stars *Maud III vi* 9
Made *l's* and great thunders over him, *Com. of Arthur* 108
And *l's* play'd about it in the storm, *Gareth and L.* 68
so quick and thick The *l's* here and there *Holy Grail* 494
Makes wicked *l's* of her eyes, *Guinevere* 520
great brand Made *l's* in the splendour of the moon, *Pass. of Arthur* 305
Thunderless *l's* striking under sea *To the Queen ii* 12
tears, that shot the sunset In *l's* round me; *Lover's Tale i* 443
L's flicker'd along the heath; *Dead Prophet* 79
L may shrivel the laurel of Cæsar, *Parnassus* 4
evergreen laurel is blasted by more than *l*! „ 12
Lightning-fork one *l-f* Flash'd out the lake; *Sisters (E. and E.)* 96
Light-of-love he whom men call *l-o-l*?' *Pelleas and E.* 361
Lightsome Self-balanced on a *l* wing: *In Mem. lxv* 8
Light-wing'd *l-w* spirit of his youth return'd *Balin and Balan* 21
Like (adj., adv., s.) Her heart is *l* a throbbing star. *Kate* 9
L men, *l* manners: *l* breeds *l*, they say: *Walk. to the Mail* 63
L to Furies, *l* to Graces, *Vision of Sin* 41
Am I so *l* her? so they said on board. *The Brook* 223
and *l* a gentleman, And *l* a prince: *Princess iv* 527
Not *l* to *l*, but *l* in difference. „ *vii* 278
L the leaf in a roaring whirlwind, *l* *Boädicea* 59
For words, *l* Nature, half reveal And half conceal *In Mem. v* 3
l a stoic, or *l* A wise epicurean, *Maud I iv* 20
There is none *l* her, none. (repeat) *Maud I. xviii* 2, 13
Not thou, but *l* to thee: „ *II iv* 12
Tell me, was he *l* to thee?' *Merlin and V.* 613
But up *l* fire he started: *Gareth and L.* 1123
but one *l* him.' 'Why that *l* was he.' *Lancelot and E.* 574
Not *l* him, 'Not *l* my Lancelot'— *Guinevere* 406
And *l* the all-enduring camel, *Lover's Tale i* 136
Made all our tastes and fancies *l*, „ 242
L to a low-hung and a fiery sky „ *ii* 61
And heard him muttering, 'So *l*, so *l*; „ *iv* 325
cousin of his and hers—O God, so *l*!' „ 327
says, 'Good! very *l*! not altogether he.' *Sisters (E. and E.)* 136
What be the next un *l*? can tha tell *Village Wife* 19
Those three! the fourth Was *l* the Son of God! *Sir J. Oldcastle* 176
those two *l's* might meet and touch. *Two Voices* 357
life! he never saw the *l*; *Princess i* 186
To prick us on to combat '*L* to *l*! „ *v* 304
Pass, and mingle with your *l's*. „ *vi* 341
There was not his *l* that year in twenty parishes *Grandmother* 12
Not violating the bond of *l* to *l*.' *Lancelot and E.* 241
I never saw his *l*; there lives No greater leader.' „ 316
Camelot seen the *l*, since Arthur came; *Holy Grail* 332
love will go by contrast, as by *l's*. *Sisters (E. and E.)* 42
Like (verb) How *l* you this old satire?' *Sea Dreams* 198

Like (verb) (*continued*) we *l* them well: But children die; *Princess iii* 252
I l her none the less for rating at her! „ *v* 461
Not es I cares fur to hear ony harm, but I *l's* to knaw. *Village Wife* 22
Like *See also* **Artist-like, Beastlike, Bell-like, Brother-like, Catlike, Chasm-like, Childlike, Christ-like, Cleopatra-like, Colt-like, Coquette-like, Deathlike, Dreamlike, Dryad-like, Dwarf-like, Eagle-like, Echo-like, Fatherlike, Firefly-like, Fool-like, Frost-like, Gem-like, Ghostlike, God-like, Grovelike, Harlot-like, Idiotlike, Ixion-like, King-like, Knightlike, Lancelot-like, Landlike, Lead-like, Lilylike, Lioness-like, Lionlike, Loike, Magnet-like, Maidenlike, Manlike, Mist-like, Moonlike, Mountain-like, Nestlike, Oration-like, Poet-like, Princelike, Saint-like, Shadow-like, Snowlike, Soldierlike, Star-like, Statue-like, Sun-like, Swanlike, Tusklike, Unking-like, Unknightlike, Wizard-like, Womanlike**
Liked more he look'd at her The less he *l* her; *Dora* 35
neither loved nor *l* the thing he heard. *Aylmer's Field* 250
she *l* it more Than magic music, *Princess, Pro.* 194
Nor tho' she *l* him, yielded she, „ *vii* 76
But I *l* a bigger feller to fight *North. Cobbler* 100
I *l* the owd Squire an' 'is gells *Village Wife* 6
I *l* 'er the fust on 'em all, „ 9
Likelihood Needs must be lesser *l*, *Lancelot and E.* 367
Likely 'O ay,' said Vivien, 'that were *l* too. *Merlin and V.* 746
Liken'd he that tells the tale *L* them, *Last Tournament* 227
Likeness 'Lo! God's *l*—the ground-plan— *Vision of Sin* 187
darkening thine own To thine own *l*; *Aylmer's Field* 674
Found a still place, and pluck'd her *l* out; *Princess i* 92
A *l*, hardly seen before, Comes out— *In Mem. lxxiv* 3
Thy *l* to the wise below, „ 7
If any vision should reveal Thy *l*, „ *xcii* 2
A momentary *l* of the King: *Com. of Arthur* 271
That shadow of a *l* to the king *Demeter and P.* 16
Last as the *l* of a dying man, „ 88
the *l* of thyself Without thy knowledge, „ 92
groping for it, could not find One *l*, *The Ring* 337
Liker light shall spread, and man be *l* man *Golden Year* 35
The Princess; *l* to the inhabitant Of some clear planet *Princess ii* 35
Yet in the long years *l* must they grow; „ *vii* 279
Likest seeing men, in power Only, are *l* gods, *Œnone* 130
The *l* God within the soul? *In Mem. lv* 4
Lilac (adj.) So Willy and I were wedded: I wore a *l* gown; *Grandmother* 57
Lilac (s) And makes the purple *l* ripe, *On a Mourner* 7
Academic silks, in hue The *l*, *Princess ii* 17
Lilac-ambush Thro' crowded *l-a* trimly pruned; *Gardener's D.* 112
Lilia And sister *L* with the rest.' *Princess. Pro.* 52
And *L* with the rest, and lady friends „ 97
L, wild with sport, Half child half woman „ 100
'Where,' Ask'd Walter, patting *L's* head „ 125
Quick answer'd *L* 'There are thousands now „ 127
If there were many *L's* in the brood, „ 146
The little hearth-flower *L*. „ 166
and not for harm, So he with *L's*. „ 175
As many little trifling *L's*— „ 188
Said *L*; 'Why not now?' the maiden Aunt. „ 208
L woke with sudden-shrilling mirth „ 216
'Take *L* then, for heroine,' clamour'd he, „ 223
So *L* sang: we thought her half-possess'd, „ *iv* 585
With which we banter'd little *L* first: „ *Con.* 12
L pleased me, for she took no part In our dispute: „ 29
L, rising quietly, Disrobed the glimmering statue „ 116
Lilian (*See also* **May Lilian**) Airy, fairy *L*, Flitting, fairy *L*, *Lilian* 1
Cruel little *L*. „ 7
Lilied The streams through many a *l* row *The winds, etc.* 5
Lilt whishper was sweet as the *l* of a bird! *Tomorrow* 33
Lilted scraps of thundrous Epic *l* out *Princess ii* 375
Lilting I was *l* a song to the babe, *Bandit's Death* 20
Lily (adj.) holding out her *l* arms Took both his hands, *Princess ii* 303
Lily (s) (*See also* **Gold-lily, Lent-lily, Tiger-lily, Water-lily**) to brush the dew From thine own *l*, *Supp. Confessions* 85
Lily (s) (*continued*) Or opening upon level plots Of crowned *lilies*, *Ode to Memory* 109
Like a *l* which the sun Looks thro' *Adeline* 12
breath Of the *lilies* at sunrise? „ 37
Gazing where the *lilies* blow *L. of Shalott i* 7
amaracus, and asphodel, Lotos and *lilies*: *Œnone* 98
Waves all its lazy *lilies*, *Gardener's D.* 42
Pure *lilies* of eternal peace, *Sir Galahad* 67
It was the time when *lilies* blow, *Lady Clare* 1
The silver *l* heaved and fell; *To E. L.* 19
steamer paddling plied And shook the *lilies*: *Princess, Pro.* 72
than wear Those *lilies*, better blush „ *iii* 68
violet varies from the *l* as far As oak from elm: „ *v* 182
'Pretty bud! *L* of the vale! „ *vi* 193
Now folds the *l* all her sweetness up, „ *vii* 186
Roses and *lilies* and Canterbury-bells.' *City Child* 5
and flung The *lilies* to and fro, *In Mem. xcv* 60
fed on the roses and lain in the *lilies* of life. *Maud I iv* 60
Gathering woodland *lilies*, „ *xii* 7
Maud is here, here, here In among the *lilies*. „ 12
And *lilies* fair on a lawn; „ *xiv* 2
Bright English *l*, breathing a prayer To be friends, „ *xix* 55
I said to the *l*, 'There is but one „ *xxii* 19
The *lilies* and roses were all awake, „ 51
Queen *l* and rose in one; „ 56
And the *l* whispers, 'I wait.' „ 66
All made up of the *l* and rose That blow „ *II v* 74
Have I beheld a *l* like yourself. *Geraint and E.* 620
A walk of *lilies* crost it to the bower: *Balin and Balan* 243
white walk of *lilies* toward the bower. „ 249
Saint who stands with *l* in hand In yonder shrine. „ 261
Flow'd from the spiritual *l* that she held. „ 264
Set in her hand a *l*, o'er her hung The silken case *Lancelot and E* 1148
In her right hand the *l*, in her left The letter— „ 1155
Be carven, and her *l* in her hand. „ 1342
Farewell too—now at last—Farewell, fair *l*. „ 1397
spire of the mountain was *lilies* in lieu of snow, And the *lilies* like glaciers winded down, *V. of Maeldune* 41
And we wallow'd in beds of *lilies*, „ 48
Had set the *l* and rose By all my ways *Ancient Sage* 156
My *l* of truth and trust— „ 160
They made her *l* and rose in one, „ 161
O slender *l* waving there, „ 167
Lily-avenue A *l-a* climbing to the doors; *Aylmer's Field* 162
Lily-cradled the golden bee Is *l-c*: *Œnone* 30
Lily-handed No little *l-h* Baronet he, *Princess, Con.* 84
Lilylike The *l* Melissa droop'd her brows; „ *iv* 161
Lily maid Elaine, the *l m* of Astolat, *Lancelot and E.* 2
How came the *l m* by that good shield of Lancelot, „ 28
close behind them stept the *l m* Elaine, „ 176
l m Elaine, Won by the mellow voice „ 242
Low to her own heart said the *l m*, „ 319
The *l m* had striven to make him cheer, „ 327
'*L m*, For fear our people call you *l m* In earnest, „ 385
Lancelot and the *l m* Smiled at each other, „ 738
Then spake the *l m* of Astolat: „ 1085
barge Whereon the *l m* of Astolat Lay smiling, „ 1242
Lily-shining lay The *l-s* child; *Princess iv* 287
Lily-white Lord Ronald brought a *l-w* doe *Lady Clare* 3
The *l-w* doe Lord Ronald had brought „ 61
Limb The strong *l's* failing; *All Things will Die* 32
profulgent brows, And perfect *l's*, *Supp. Confessions* 146
Those writhed *l's* of lightning speed; *Clear-headed friend* 23
her clear and bared *l's* O'erthwarted *Œnone* 138
Resting weary *l's* at last on beds of asphodel. *Lotos-Eaters, C. S.* 125
Those in whose lap our *l's* are nursed, *To J. S.* 10
Denying not these weather-beaten *l's* *St. S. Stylites* 19
Till all my *l's* drop piecemeal from the stone, „ 44
coverlid Unto her *l's* itself doth mould *Day-Dm., Sleep. B.* 10
With naked *l's* and flowers and fruit, *The Voyage* 55
Hair, and eyes, and *l's*, and faces, *Vision of Sin* 39
A *l* was broken when they lifted him; *Enoch Arden* 107
Enoch took, and handled all his *l's*, „ 153
Till the little *l's* are stronger. *Sea Dreams* 306

Limb (*continued*) Down thro' her *l's* a drooping languor wept: *Princess vi* 268
and due To languid *l's* and sickness; „ 377
Give it time To learn its *l's*: „ *Con.* 79
this weight of body and *l*, *High. Pantheism* 5
Nor could I weary, heart or *l*, *In Mem. xxv* 9
And watch'd them, wax'd in every *l*; „ *ciii* 30
brood On a horror of shatter'd *l's* *Maud I i* 56
Dark cedar, tho' thy *l's* have here increased, „ *xviii* 18
find nor face nor bearing, *l's* nor voice, *Com. of Arthur* 71
nor pang Of wrench'd or broken *l*— *Gareth and L.* 88
and risk thine all, Life, *l's*, „ 129
Brute bulk of *l*, or boundless savagery „ 1330
not trust the *l's* thy God hath given, „ 1388
At this he hurl'd his huge *l's* out of bed, *Marr. of Geraint* 124
I seem to suffer nothing heart or *l*, „ 472
Laid from her *l's* the costly-broider'd gift, „ 769
strongly striking out her *l's* awoke; *Geraint and E.* 380
free to stretch his *l's* in lawful fight, „ 754
clung about her lissome *l's*, In colour *Merlin and V.* 223
The text no larger than the *l's* of fleas; „ 672
Spake thro' the *l's* and in the voice— *Holy Grail* 23
round her *l's*, mature in womanhood; *Pelleas and E.* 73
but so weary were his *l's*, „ 513
his unbroken *l's* from the dark field, „ 585
Strength of heart And might of *l*, *Last Tournament* 198
The weight as if of age upon my *l's*, *Lover's Tale i* 125
ivy-tress had wound Round my worn *l's*, „ 619
blood Crept like marsh drains thro' all my languid *l's*; „ *ii* 53
' body and soul And life and *l's*, „ *iv* 283
happier using the knife than in trying to save the *l*, *In the Child. Hosp.* 6
we were English in heart and in *l*, *Def. of Lucknow* 46
Lobbing away of the *l* by the pitiful-pitiless knife,— „ 85
a babe in lineament and *l* Perfect, *De Prof., Two G.* 11
I touch'd my *l's*, the *l's* Were strange *Ancient Sage* 234
Death will freeze the supplest *l's*— *Happy* 46
great shock may wake a palsied *l*, *St. Telemachus* 57
moved but by the living *l*, *Akbar's Dream* 133
Limbed *See* **Broad-limbed, Full-limbed, large-limbed, Long-limb'd, Snow-limbed**
Limber And legs of trees were *l*, *Amphion* 14
Lime (tree) arching *l's* are tall and shady, *Margaret* 59
Not thrice your branching *l's* have blown *L. C. V. de Vere* 27
beech and *l* Put forth and feel a gladder clime.' *On a Mourner* 14
all about the large *l* feathers low, The *l* *Gardener's D.* 47
and over many a range Of waning *l* „ 218
bard has honour'd beech or *l*, *Talking Oak* 291
overhead The broad ambrosial aisles of lofty *l* *Princess, Pro.* 87
Up that long walk of *l's* I past *In Mem. lxxxvii* 15
million emeralds break from the ruby-budded *l* *Maud I iv* 1
Of leafless elm, or naked *l*, *To Ulysses* 16
Lime (earth) To feed thy bones with *l*, *Two Voices* 326
As dying Nature's earth and *l*; *In Mem. cxviii* 4
I am mortal stone and *l*. *Helen's Tower* 6
Lime (verb) That every sophister can *l*. *Love thou thy land* 12
Limed True—we had *l* ourselves With open eyes, *Princess iii* 142
Limit till we reach'd The *l* of the hills; *Audley Court* 83
Here at the quiet *l* of the world, *Tithonus* 7
on the glimmering *l* far withdrawn *Vision of Sin* 223
and ran Ev'n to the *l* of the land, *Enoch Arden* 578
Twofooted at the *l* of his chain, *Aylmer's Field* 127
Slipt o'er those lazy *l's* down the wind „ 495
love-whispers may not breathe Within this vestal *l*, *Princess ii* 222
storm and blast Had blown the lake beyond his *l*, *The Daisy* 71
The *l* of his narrower fate, *In Mem. lxiv* 21
No *l* to his distress; *Maud II v* 31
And in what *l's*, and how tenderly; *Ded. of Idylls* 20
utter purity Beyond the *l* of their bond, *Merlin and V.* 27
there ye fixt Your *l*, oft returning with the tide. *Lancelot and E.* 1041
And laughter at the *l* of the wood, *Pelleas and E.* 49
As from beyond the *l* of the world, *Pass. of Arthur* 458
O'erbore the *l's* of my brain: *Lover's Tale i* 689

Limit (*continued*) Spain should oust The Moslem from her *l*, *Columbus* 97
mortal *l* of the Self was loosed, *Ancient Sage* 232
to know The *l's* of resistance, *To Duke of Argyll* 2
so to the land's Last *l* I came— *Merlin and the G.* 110
find their *l's* by that larger light, *Akbar's Dream* 99
at the *l* of thy human state, *God and the Univ.* 4
Limitless suns of the *l* Universe sparkled and shone in the sky, *Despair* 15
Limn'd Sun himself has *l* the face for me. *Sisters (E. and E.)* 101
Limours suitors as this maiden; first *L.* *Marr. of Geraint* 440
Enter'd, the wild lord of the place, *L.* *Geraint and E.* 277
Earl *L* Drank till he jested with all ease, „ 289
when the Prince was merry, ask'd *L*, „ 297
Then rose *L*, and looking at his feet, „ 302
told him all that Earl *L* had said, „ 391
Led from the territory of false *L* „ 437
moment after, wild *L*, Borne on a black horse, „ 457
In combat with the follower of *L*, „ 501
Limpet And on thy ribs the *l* sticks, *Sailor Boy* 11
Limpin' Molly kem *l* up wid her stick, *Tomorrow* 77
Linden (adj.) firefly-like in copse And *l* alley: *Princess i* 209
on the sward, and up the *l* walks, „ *iv* 209
Linden (s) The *l* broke her ranks and rent *Amphion* 33
Lindenwood Hew'd the *l*, Hack'd the battleshield, *Batt. of Brunanburh* 12
Line (s) (*See also* **Lion-line, Sea-line**) What time the foeman's *l* is broke, *Two Voices* 155
Beyond, a *l* of heights, and higher *Palace of Art* 82
tender curving *l's* of creamy spray; *Lotos-Eaters, C. S.* 62
We past long *l's* of Northern capes *The Voyage* 35
Long *l's* of cliff breaking have left a chasm; *Enoch Arden* 1
known Far in a darker isle beyond the *l*; „ 605
He gave them *l*: (repeat) *The Brook* 145, 150
Love, let me quote these *l's*, *Sea Dreams* 181
those *l's* of cliffs were cliffs no more, „ 217
On glassy water drove his cheek in *l's*; *Princess i* 116
the Persian, Grecian, Roman *l's* Of empire, „ *ii* 130
' The fifth in *l* from that old Florian, „ 238
L's of green that streak the white „ *v* 196
ride with us to our *l's*, And speak with Arac: „ 225
long *l* of the approaching rookery swerve „ *Con.* 97
Right thro' the *l* they broke; *Light Brigade* 33
Sunny tokens of the *L*, *Ode Inter. Exhib.* 19
And never a *l* from my lady yet! *Window, No Answer* 15
My blessing, like a *l* of light, *In Mem. xvii* 10
So word by word, and *l* by *l*, „ *xcv* 33
a grandson, first of his noble *l*, *Maud I x* 12
face is practised when I spell the *l's*, *Merlin and V.* 367
Yet is there one true *l*, the pearl of pearls: „ 459
Which is the second in a *l* of stars „ 509
High with the last *l* scaled her voice, *Lancelot and E.* 1019
with wandering *l's* of mount and mere, *Holy Grail* 252
Breast-high in that bright *l* of bracken stood: *Pelleas and E.* 56
Glorious poet who never hast written a *l*, *To A. Tennyson* 5
to the 'eät o' the *l*? *North. Cobbler* 6
We are six ships of the *l*; *The Revenge* 7
Clean from our *l's* of defence *Def. of Lucknow* 62
Fluttering the hawks of this crown-lusting *l*— *Sir J. Oldcastle* 57
I send a birthday *l* Of greeting; *To E. Fitzgerald* 45
A hundred ever-rising mountain *l's*, *Ancient Sage* 282
Because you heard the *l's* I read *Pro. to Gen. Hamley* 17
call'd ' Left wheel into *l*! ' *Heavy Brigade* 6
Virgil who would write ten *l's*, *Poets and their B.* 2
To you that bask below the *L*, *To Ulysses* 5
follow'd *l* by *l* Your leading hand, „ 45
bucket from the well Along the *l*, *To Mary Boyle* 40
new life that gems the hawthorn *l*; *Prog. of Spring* 36
Line (verb) May bind a book, may *l* a box, *In Mem. lxxvii* 6
Lineage past into the hall A damsel of high *l*, *Gereth and L.* 588
A lady of high *l*, of great lands, „ 609
I spring from loftier *l* than thine own.' „ 961
Lineament Every *l* divine, *Eleänore* 53
to take the cast Of those dead *l's* *Wan Sculptor* 2
Of faded form and haughtiest *l's*, *Princess ii* 448
writhing barbarous *l's*, *Boädicea* 74

Lineament (*continued*) Imperious, and of haughtiest *l's*. *Marr. of Geraint* 190
Lifted her eyes, and read his *l's*. *Lancelot and E.* 244
a babe in *l* and limb Perfect, *De Prof., Two G.* 11
Lined *l* And rippled like an ever-fleeting wave, *Gareth and L.* 214
And hollow *l* and wooded to the lips, *Lover's Tale i* 398
Linen Fares richly, in fine *l*, *Aylmer's Field* 659
Linger Knowledge comes, but wisdom *l's*, and I *l* on the shore, *Locksley Hall* 141
Knowledge comes, but wisdom *l's*, „ 143
I *l* by my shingly bars; *The Brook* 180
To *l* here with one that loved us.' *Princess iii* 339
And *l* weeping on the marge, *In Mem. xii* 12
They rise, but *l*; it is late; „ *Con.* 91
brother *l's* late With a roystering company) *Maud I xiv* 14
rose-garden, And mean to *l* in it „ *xx* 42
L with vacillating obedience, *Gareth and L.* 13
I hate that he should *l* here; *Marr. of Geraint* 91
how hand *l's* in hand! Let go at last! *Merlin and V.* 106
'Why *l's* Gawain with his golden news?' *Pelleas and E.* 411
and *l* there To silver all the valleys *Tiresias* 31
may *l*, till she sees Her maiden coming *The Ring* 479
l, till her own, the babe She lean'd „ 483
Linger'd charmed sunset *l* low adown *Lotos-Eaters* 19
altho' I *l* there Till every daisy slept, *Gardener's D.* 164
but ever at a breath She *l*, *Godiva* 45
Long o'er his bent brows *l* Averill, *Aylmer's Field* 625
I *l*; all within was noise Of songs, *In Mem. lxxxvii* 18
By night we *l* on the lawn, „ *xcv* 1
For while he *l* there, *Com. of Arthur* 63
Gareth awhile *l*. *Gareth and L.* 172
L that other, staring after him; *Lancelot and E.* 721
L Ettarre: and seeing Pelleas droop, *Pelleas and E.* 178
came the village girls And *l* talking, „ 509
well I could have *l* in that porch, *Lover's Tale i* 186
As if perpetual sunset *l* there, *The Ring* 83
preacher's *l* o'er his dying words, *St. Telemachus* 75
Lingereth 'Why *l* she to clothe her heart *Princess iv* 105
Lingering After a *l*,—ere she was aware,— *Enoch Arden* 268
l out a five-years' death-in-life. „ 565
L about the thymy promontories, *Sea Dreams* 38
and reach its fatling innocent arms And lazy *l* fingers. *Princess vi* 139
by the field of tourney *l* yet *Gareth and L.* 736
Lingeringly So *l* long, that half-amazed *The Ring* 436
Link (s) Or to burst all *l's* of habit— *Locksley Hall* 157
maids, That have no *l's* with men. *Princess vi* 292
A *l* among the days, to knit The generations *In Mem. xl* 15
lost the *l's* that bound Thy changes; „ *xli* 6
closer *l* Betwixt us and the crowning race „ *Con.* 127
all in loops and *l's* among the dales *Lancelot and E.* 166
(A visible *l* unto the home of my heart), *Lover's Tale i* 431
seem'd as tho' a *l* Of some tight chain „ 594
From war with kindly *l's* of gold, *Epilogue* 16
breaks her latest earthy *l* With me to-day. *The Ring* 47
is making a new *l* Breaking an old one? „ 50
that poor *l* With earth is broken, „ 475
And that was a *l* between us; *Bandit's Death* 16
We return'd to his cave—the *l* was broken— „ 29
Link (verb) Idle habit *l's* us yet. *Miller's D.* 212
To which she *l's* a truth divine! *In Mem. xxxiii* 12
thou should'st *l* thy life with one „ *lxxxiv* 11
Seems but a cobweb filament to *l* The yawning *Lover's Tale i* 376
Link'd-Linkt *Link'd* month to month with such a chain *Two Voices* 167
vapour touch'd the palace gate, And *link'd* again. *Vision of Sin* 59
Which else had *link'd* their race with times to come— *Aylmer's Field* 779
As *link'd* with thine in love and fate, *In Mem. lxxxiv* 38
He *linkt* a dead man there to a spectral bride; *Maud II v* 80
love that *linkt* the King And Lancelot— *Gareth and L.* 492
force in her *Link'd* with such love for me, *Marr. of Geraint* 806
Has *link'd* our names together in his lay, *Lancelot and E.* 112
built a way, where, *link'd* with many a bridge, *Holy Grail* 502
broke Flying, and *link'd* again, *Guinevere* 258
She that *link'd* again the broken chain *Locksley H., Sixty* 52

O*

Link'd-Linkt (*continued*) snap the bond that *link'd* us life to life, *Happy* 61
starved the wild beast that was *linkt* with thee *By an Evolution.* 11
Linking and *l* tree to tree, *Death of Œnone* 11
Linkt *See* **Link'd**
Lin-lan-lone mellow *l-l-l* of evening bells *Far—far—away* 5
Linnet (*See also* **Lintwhite**) Sometimes the *l* piped his song: *Sir L. and Q. G.* 10
Like *l's* in the pauses of the wind: *Princess, Pro.* 246
Started a green *l* Out of the croft; *Minnie and Winnie* 17
O merry the *l* and dove, *Window, Ay* 13
And pipe but as the *l's* sing: *In Mem. xxi* 24
The *l* born within the cage, „ *xxvii* 3
That hears the latest *l* trill, „ *c* 10
'What knowest thou of birds, lark, mavis, merle, *L*? *Gareth and L.* 1079
three gray *l's* wrangle for the seed: *Guinevere* 255
merry *l* knew me, The squirrel knew me, *Lover's Tale ii* 15
The *l's* bosom blushes at her gaze, *Prog. of Spring* 17
Lintel and under his own *l* stood Storming *Aylmer's Field* 331
the household flower Torn from the *l*— *Princess v* 129
Lintwhite (*See also* **Linnet**) Her song the *l* swelleth, *Claribel* 15
Lion (adj.) Folded her *l* paws, and look'd to Thebes. *Tiresias* 149
Lion (s) (*See also* **Shield-lion**) The *l* on your old stone gates *L. C. V. de Vere* 23
We heard the *l* roaring from his den; *D. of F. Women* 222
comes a hungry people, as a *l* *Locksley Hall* 135
The babe shall lead the *l*. *Aylmer's Field* 648
and in her *l's* mood Tore open, *Princess iv* 380
blazon'd *l's* o'er the imperial tent „ *v* 9
old *l*, glaring with his whelpless eye, „ *vi* 99
your long locks play the *L's* mane! „ 164
Porch-pillars on the *l* resting, *The Daisy* 55
To have her *l* roll in a silken net *Maud I vi* 29
A *l* ramps at the top, „ *xiv* 7
glow'd like a ruddy shield on the *L's* breast. „ *III vi* 14
Cover the *l's* on thy shield, *Gareth and L.* 585
L and stoat have isled together, „ 893
'Ramp ye lance-splintering *l's*, „ 1305
prize The living dog than the dead *l*: *Balin and Balan* 585
Gawain saw Sir Lancelot's azure *l's*, *Lancelot and E.* 663
On wyvern, *l*, dragon, griffin, swan, *Holy Grail* 350
For now there is a *l* in the way.' „ 645
none Stood near it but a *l* on each side „ 817
And the *l* there lay dying, *The Revenge* 96
Was flinging fruit to *l's*; *Tiresias* 67
and hunters race The shadowy *l*, „ 178
till the *L* look no larger than the Cat, Till the Cat thro' that mirage of overheated language loom Larger than the *L*,— *Locksley H., Sixty* 112
peasant cow shall butt the '*L* passant' „ 248
trailing a dead *l* away, One, a dead man. *St. Telemachus* 47
Lionel The friend, the neighbour, *L*, the beloved, The loved, the lover, the happy *L*, The low-voiced, tender-spirited *L*, *Lover's Tale i* 653
L, the happy, and her, and her, his bride! „ 755
very face and form of *L* Flash'd „ *ii* 94
but *L* and the girl Were wedded, „ *iv* 13
bid him come;' but *L* was away— „ 101
Heir of his face and land, to *L*. „ 129
And, tho' he loved and honour'd *L*, „ 148
And sent at once to *L*, praying him „ 180
to *L's* loss and his And that resolved self-exile „ 208
To one who had not spoken, *L*. „ 272
Not daring yet to glance at *L*. „ 309
I, by *L* sitting, saw his face Fire, „ 322
all but he, *L*, who fain had risen, „ 361
He slowly brought them both to *L*. „ 371
L, when at last he freed himself From wife and child, „ 379
Lioness *L* That with your long locks play *Princess vi* 163
Yea, the cubb'd *l*; *Demeter and P.* 54
Lioness-like and rolling glances *l-l*, *Boädicea* 71
Lion-guarded Here is Locksley Hall, my grandson, here the *l-g* gate. *Locksley H., Sixty* 213
Lion-heart The *l-h*, Plantagenet, *Margaret* 34
Lionlike rushing outward *l* Leapt on him, *Guinevere* 107

Lion-line Strong mother of a *L-l*, *England and Amer.* 3
Lion-whelp Far as the portal-warding *l-w*, *Enoch Arden* 98
Lip (s) (*See also* **Rose-lips**) When from crimson-threaded *l's* *Lilian* 23
Sweet *l's* whereon perpetually did reign *Isabel* 7
If my *l's* should dare to kiss Thy taper fingers *Madeline* 43
With *l's* depress'd as he were meek, *A Character* 25
Ere the placid *l's* be cold ? *Adeline* 20
Thro' *l's* and eyes in subtle rays. *Rosalind* 24
From thy rose-red *l-s* MY name Floweth ; *Eleänore* 133
'His *l's* are very mild and meek : *Two Voices* 250
Your ripe *l's* moved not, *Miller's D.* 131
With one long kiss my whole soul thro' My *l's*, *Fatima* 21
prest the blossom of his *l's* to mine, *Œnone* 78
and my hot *l's* prest Close, „ 203
And from her *l's*, as morn from Memnon, *Palace of Art* 171
And in a little while our *l's* are dumb. *Lotos-Eaters, C. S.* 44
with dead *l's* smiled at the twilight plain, *D. of F. Women* 62
music left the *l's* of her that died „ 195
She lock'd her *l's* : she left me where I stood : „ 241
Turning to scorn with *l's* divine *Of old sat Freedom* 23
from Discussion's *l* may fall With Life, *Love thou thy land* 33
knightly growth that fringed his *l's*. *M. d'Arthur* 220
among us lived Her fame from *l* to *l*. *Gardener's D.* 51
doubled his own warmth against her *l's*, „ 138
kisses press'd on *l's* Less exquisite than thine.' „ 151
stirr'd her *l's* For some sweet answer, „ 158
And with a flying finger swept my *l's*, „ 246
answer'd madly ; bit his *l's*, And broke away. *Dora* 33
breathing love and trust against her *l* : *Audley Court* 69
A second flutter'd round her *l* *Talking Oak* 219
me, That have no *l's* to kiss, „ 242
could hear the *l's* that kiss'd Whispering *Tithonus* 60
at the touching of the *l's*. *Locksley Hall* 38
a *l* to drain thy trouble dry. „ 88
Baby *l's* will laugh me down : „ 89
Her *l's* are sever'd as to speak : *Day-Dm., Sleep. P.* 30
What *l's*, like thine, so sweetly join'd ? „ *L'Envoi* 46
lays it thrice upon my *l's*, These favour'd *l's* of mine ; *Will Water.* 19
I kiss the *l's* I once have kiss'd ; „ 37
He to *l's*, that fondly falter, *L. of Burleigh* 9
one kiss Upon her perfect *l's*. *Sir L. and Q. G.* 45
Then raised her head with *l's* compress, *The Letters* 19
A sleepy light upon their brows and *l's*— *Vision of Sin* 9
Wine is good for shrivell'd *l's*, „ 79
I cannot praise the fire In your eye—nor yet your *l* : „ 184
Perch'd on the pouted blossom of her *l's* : *Princess, Pro.* 199
Proud look'd the *l's* : „ *i* 96
with her *l's* apart, And all her thoughts „ *ii* 325
fancy feign'd On *l's* that are for others ; „ *iv* 56
Stared with great eyes, and laugh'd with alien *l's*, „ 119
sinn'd in grosser *l's* Beyond all pardon— „ 251
You prized my counsel, lived upon my *l's* : „ 293
shot from crooked *l's* a haggard smile. „ 364
dying *l's*, With many thousand matters left to do, „ 457
Invective seem'd to wait behind her *l's*, „ 472
smiles at our disguise Broke from their *l's*, „ *v* 272
fingering at the hair about his *l*, „ 303
then he drew Her robe to meet his *l's*, „ *vi* 156
My spirit closed with Ida's at the *l's* ; „ *vii* 158
and meek Seem'd the full *l's*, „ 226
What whispers from thy lying *l* ? *In Mem. iii* 4
Would breathing thro' his *l's* impart „ *xviii* 15
And dull'd the murmur on thy *l*, „ *xxii* 16
seal'd The *l's* of that Evangelist. „ *xxxi* 16
dear to me as sacred wine To dying *l's* „ *xxxvii* 20
What whisper'd from her lying *l's* ? „ *xxxix* 10
loosens from the *l* Short swallow-flights of song, „ *xlviii* 14
fills The *l's* of men with honest praise, „ *lxxxiv* 26
could not win An answer from my *l's*, „ *ciii* 50
And bless thee, for thy *l's* are bland, „ *cxix* 9
For tho' my *l's* may breathe adieu, „ *cxxiii* 11
Sweet human hand and *l's* and eye ; „ *cxxix* 6
Its *l's* in the field above are dabbled *Maud I i* 2
And the sunlight broke from her *l* ? „ *vi* 86
And curving a contumelious *l*, „ *xiii* 20

Lip (s) (*continued*) When the happy Yes Falters from her *l's*, *Maud I xvii* 10
For the hand, the *l's*, the eyes, „ *II iv* 27
Prophet, curse me the blabbing *l*, „ *v* 57
Modred biting his thin *l's* was mute, *Gareth and L.* 31
have I sworn From his own *l's* to have it— *Marr. of Geraint* 409
Slip from my *l's* if I can help it— „ 446
Now gnaw'd his under, now his upper *l*, *Geraint and E.* 669
Rise, my sweet King, and kiss me on the *l's*, *Balin and Balan* 516
Foul are their lives ; foul are their *l's* ; „ 616
But yesterday you never open'd *l*, *Merlin and V.* 271
How from the rosy *l's* of life and love, „ 846
by what name Livest between the *l's* ? *Lancelot and E.* 182
the living smile Died from his *l's*, „ 324
Queen, who sat With *l's* severely placid, „ 740
her *l's*, Who had devised the letter, „ 1287
Smiled with his *l's*—a smile beneath a cloud, *Holy Grail* 705
In one, their malice on the placid *l* *Pelleas and E.* 432
'Yea, between thy *l's*—and sharp ; „ 577
Mark is kindled on thy *l's* Most gracious ; *Last Tournament* 561
golden beard that clothed his *l's* with light— „ 668
Out of the dark, just as the *l's* had touch'd, „ 752
I cannot touch thy *l's*, they are not mine, *Guinevere* 551
Mix'd with the knightly growth that fringed his *l's*. *Pass. of Arthur* 388
Flicker'd like doubtful smiles about her *l's*, *Lover's Tale i* 68
our baby *l's*, Kissing one bosom, „ 237
Heart beating time to heart, *l* pressing *l*, „ 260
And hollow lined and wooded to the *l's*, „ 398
gracious *l's* Did lend such gentle utterance, „ 456
clothe itself in smiles About his *l's* ! „ 659
her *l's* were sunder'd With smiles of tranquil bliss, „ *ii* 142
And parted *l's* which drank her breath, „ 204
light Of smiling welcome round her *l's*— „ *iii* 46
And kiss her on the *l's*. „ *iv* 48
eyes frown : the *l's* Seem but a gash. *Sisters (E. and E.)* 106
While men shall move the *l's* : *Tiresias* 133
Or if *l* were laid to *l* on the pillows *The Flight* 48
ever moulded by the *l's* of man. *To Virgil* 40
nectar smack'd of hemlock on the *l's*, *Demeter and P.* 104
while her *l's* Were warm upon my cheek, *The Ring* 398
Did he touch me on the *l's* ? *Happy* 66
If the *l's* were touch'd with fire *Parnassus* 17
Lip (verb) circle widens till it *l* the marge, *Pelleas and E.* 94
Lip-depths Love dwells not in *l-d*. *Lover's Tale i* 466
Lipp'd faintly *l* The flat red granite ; *Audley Court* 12
Liquid on the *l* mirror glow'd The clear perfection *Mariana in the S.* 31
Purple gauzes, golden hazes, *l* mazes, *Vision of Sin* 31
Make *l* treble of that bassoon, my throat ; *Princess ii* 426
and cast A *l* look on Ida, full of prayer, „ *iv* 369
Half-lost in the *l* azure bloom of a crescent of sea, *Maud I iv* 5
When first the *l* note beloved of men *Marr. of Geraint* 336
Liquor smote Her life into the *l*. *Will Water.* 112
But sin' I wur hallus i' *l* *North. Cobbler* 27
I weär'd it o' *l*, I did. „ 32
Lisbon Round affrighted *L* drew The treble works, *Ode on Well.* 103
Lisp Nor cares to *l* in love's delicious creeds ; *Caress'd or chidden* 11
Would *l* in honey'd whispers of this monstrous fraud ! *Third of Feb.* 36
lightest wave of thought shall *l*, *In Mem. xlix* 5
shall have learn'd to *l* you thanks.' *Marr. of Geraint* 822
learn'd To *l* in tune together ; *Lover's Tale i* 258
Lisp'd-lispt Was *lispt* about the acacias, *Princess vii* 251
waters answering *lisp'd* To kisses of the wind, *Lover's Tale i* 544
Lispeth The callow throstle *l*, *Claribel* 17
Lisping ran By ripply shallows of the *l* lake, *Edwin Morris* 98
A *l* of the innumerous leaf and dies, *Princess v* 14
Lispt *See* **Lisp'd**
Lissome Straight, but as *l* as a hazel wand ; *The Brook* 70
clung about her *l* limbs, In colour *Merlin and V.* 223
And *l* Vivien, holding by his heel, „ 238
Queen who sat betwixt her best Enid, and *l* Vivien, *Guinevere* 28
List (desire) not be kiss'd by all who would *l*, *The Mermaid* 41
O maiden, if indeed ye *l* to sing, *Guinevere* 165
List (roll of names) But still her *l's* were swell'd *Princess iv* 319
meaning by it To keep the *l* low *Merlin and V.* 592

List (strip, division) a comb of pearl to part The *l's* of such a beard *Merlin and V.* 245
List (to hear) To *l* a foot-fall, ere he saw *Palace of Art* 110
Listed *See* **White-listed**
Listen (*See also* **Listhen**) O *l*, *l*, your eyes shall glisten (repeat) *Sea-Fairies* 35, 37
Whither away? *l* and stay: " 42
stars that hung Love-charm'd to *l*: *Love and Duty* 75
But if you care indeed to *l*, hear *Golden Year* 20
Whisper'd '*L* to my despair: *Edward Gray* 22
'*L*, Annie, How merry they are down yonder *Enoch Arden* 388
Sit, *l*.' Then he told her of his voyage, " 861
Call'd all her vital spirits into each ear To *l*: *Aylmer's Field* 202
l! here is proof that you were miss'd: *Princess, Pro.* 177
I fear you'll *l* to tales, *Grandmother* 54
Did they hear me, would they *l*, *Boädicea* 8
They can but *l* at the gates, *In Mem. xciv* 15
The larkspur *l's*, 'I hear, I hear;' *Maud I xxii* 65
I know that he lies and *l's* mute " *II v* 60
That *l's* near a torrent mountain-brook, *Geraint and E.* 171
But *l* to me, and by me be ruled, " 624
And it shall answer for me. *L* to it. *Merlin and V.* 386
while the King Would *l* smiling. *Lancelot and E.* 116
but *l* to me, If I must find you wit: " 147
Would *l* for her coming and regret " 866
To vex an ear too sad to *l* to me, *Guinevere* 315
To speak no slander, no, nor *l* to it, " 472
L's the muffled booming indistinct *Lover's Tale i* 637
l how the birds Begin to warble *The Flight* 60
'If he? yes, he . . . lurks, *l's*, " 71
Your song—Sit, *l*! *Romney's R.* 92
L! we three were alone in the dell *Bandit's Death* 19
Listen'd my hands upheld In thine, I *l* to thy vows, *Supp. Confessions* 71
I look'd And *l*, the full-flowing river of speech *Œnone* 68
thought that it was fancy, and I *l* in my bed, *May Queen, Con.* 33
from them clash'd The bells; we *l*; *Gardener's D.* 221
The deep air *l* round her as she rode, *Godiva* 54
Amazed and melted all who *l* to it: *Enoch Arden* 649
While I *l*, came On a sudden the weird seizure *Princess iv* 559
Who spake no slander, no, nor *l* to it; *Ded. of Idylls* 10
And while they *l* for the distant hunt, *Marr. of Geraint* 184
Enid *l* brightening as she lay; " 733
I *l*, And her words stole with most prevailing sweetness *Lover's Tale i* 552
that I niver not *l* to noän! *Spinster's S's.* 8
Listener not to die a *l*, I arose, *The Brook* 163
but every roof Sent out a *l*: *Aylmer's Field* 614
Listenest Thou *l* to the closing door, *In Mem. cxxi* 7
Listening (adj. and part.) *L* the lordly music flowing *Ode to Memory* 41
For at eventide, *l* earnestly, *A spirit haunts* 4
L, whispers ''Tis the fairy Lady of Shallot.' *L. of Shalott i* 35
slow dilation roll'd Dry flame, she *l*; *Princess vi* 190
with shut eyes I lay *L*; then look'd. " *vii* 224
L now to the tide in its broad-flung *Maud I iii* 11
And seen her sadden *l*—vext his heart, *Pelleas and E.* 398
She sat Stiff-stricken, *l*; *Guinevere* 412
l till those armed steps were gone, " 585
but in all the *l* eyes Of those tall knights, *Gareth and L.* 327
The *l* rogue hath caught the manner of it. " 778
I came on him once at a ball, the heart of a *l* crowd— *The Wreck* 47
Sounding for ever and ever thro' Earth and her *l* nations, *Parnassus* 7
Listening (s) lonely *l's* to my mutter'd dream, *Princess vii* 110
Listhen (listen) 'ud *l* to naither at all, at all. *Tomorrow* 46
Listless To be the long and *l* boy *Miller's D.* 33
L in all despondence,—read; *Aylmer's Field* 534
And into many a *l* annulet, *Geraint and E.* 258
Lists Shot thro' the *l* at Camelot, *M. d'Arthur* 224
They reel, they roll in clanging *l*, *Sir Galahad* 9
All that long morn the *l* were hammer'd up, *Princess v* 368
woke it was the point of noon, The *l* were ready. " 483
He rode the mellay, lord of the ringing *l*, " 502
father heard and ran In on the *l*, " *vi* 27
Thro' open field into the *l* they wound Timorously; " 84
and settling circled all the *l*. *Marr. of Geraint* 547
Lists (*continued*) tho' her gentle presence at the *l* *Marr. of Geraint* 795
hope that sometime you would come To these my *l* with him *Geraint and E.* 840
Lancelot, and his prowess in the *l*, *Lancelot and E.* 82
Favour of any lady in the *l*. (repeat) " 364, 474
when they reach'd the *l* By Camelot in the meadow, " 428
They that assail'd, and they that held the *l*, " 455
the Table Round that held the *l*, (repeat) " 467, 499
on that day when Lancelot fled the *l*, " 525
Of all my late-shown prowess in the *l*, *Holy Grail* 362
'Queen of Beauty,' in the *l* Cried— *Pelleas and E.* 116
withheld His older and his mightier from the *l*, " 160
with cups of gold, Moved to the *l*, *Last Tournament* 143
Sat their great umpire, looking o'er the *l*. " 159
Shot thro' the *l* at Camelot, *Pass. of Arthur* 392
Lit (came upon, etc.) bore Them earthward till they *l*; *The Poet* 18
On the tree-tops a crested peacock *l*, *Œnone* 104
And here we *l* on Aunt Elizabeth, *Princess, Pro.* 96
And wheel'd or *l* the filmy shapes *In Mem. xcv* 10
Leapt in a semicircle, and *l* on earth; *Balin and Balan* 414
Lit (kindled, etc.) *l* your eyes with tearful power, *Margaret* 3
from her wooden walls,—*l* by sure hands,— *Buonaparte* 5
gray eyes *l* up With summer lightnings *Miller's D.* 12
L up a torrent-bow. *Palace of Art* 36
L with a low large moon. " 68
L light in wreaths and anadems, " 186
and *l* Lamps which out-burn'd Canopus. *D. of F. Women* 145
She *l* the spark within my throat, *Will Water.* 109
Thus, as a hearth *l* in a mountain home, *Balin and Balan* 231
Her smile *l* up the rainbow on my tears, *Lover's Tale i* 254
itself *l* up There on the depth of an unfathom'd woe " 745
After their marriage *l* the lover's Bay, " *iv* 28
an' just as candles was *l*, *North. Cobbler* 87
this shore *l* by the suns and moons *De Prof., Two G.* 38
Lit *See also* **Crescent-lit, Dew-lit, Dim-lit, Fame-lit, Lamp-lit, Moon-lit**
Litany solemn psalms, and silver *litanies*, *Princess ii* 477
Literary swarm'd His *l* leeches. *Will Water.* 200
Lithe bent or broke The *l* reluctant boughs *Enoch Arden* 381
and made her *l* arm round his neck Tighten, *Merlin and V.* 614
Litter-bier Yet raised and laid him on a *l-b*, *Geraint and E.* 566
Little They light his *l* life alway; *Supp. Confessions* 46
Had I So *l* love for thee? " 88
Cruel *l* Lilian. *Lilian* 7
Like *l* clouds sun-fringed, are thine, *Madeline* 17
and bosoms prest To *l* harps of gold; *Sea-Fairies* 4
Or when *l* airs arise, *Adeline* 33
L breezes dusk and shiver *L. of Shalott i* 11
And *l* other care hath she, " *ii* 8
'His *l* daughter, whose sweet face He kiss'd, *Two Voices* 253
'Before the *l* ducts began To feed thy bones with lime, " 325
The *l* maiden walk'd demure, " 419
A *l* whisper silver-clear, " 428
A *l* hint to solace woe, " 433
You would, and would not, *l* one! *Miller's D.* 134
but she thought I might have look'd a *l* higher; " 140
A thousand *l* shafts of flame Were shiver'd *Fatima* 17
And in a *l* while our lips are dumb. *Lotos-Eaters, C. S.* 44
Like a tale of *l* meaning tho' the words are strong; " 119
Storing yearly *l* dues of wheat, and wine and oil; " 122
Each *l* sound and sight. *D. of F. Women* 277
for this star Rose with you thro' a *l* arc *To J. S.* 26
A *l* thing may harm a wounded man. *M. d'Arthur* 42
And in the compass of three *l* words, *Gardener's D.* 232
And made a *l* wreath of all the flowers That grew about, *Dora* 82
To save her *l* finger from a scratch *Edwin Morris* 63
yet long ago I have pardon'd *l* Letty; " 140
Or in the night, after a *l* sleep, I wake: *St. S. Stylites* 113
'Tis *l* more: the day was warm; *Talking Oak* 205
and drew My *l* oakling from the cup, " 231
Life piled on life Were all too *l*, *Ulysses* 25
COMRADES, leave me here a *l*, *Locksley Hall* 1
With a *l* hoard of maxims preaching down a daughter's heart. " 94
'You would not let your *l* finger ache For such as *these*?'— *Godiva* 22

Little (*continued*) The *l* wide-mouth'd heads upon the spout *Godiva* 56
Boring a *l* auger-hole in fear, Peep'd— " 68
and shows At distance like a *l* wood ; *Day-Dm., Sleep. P.* 42
from the valleys underneath Came *l* copses climbing. *Amphion* 32
Nor yet the fear of *l* books Had made him talk for show ; *Will Water.* 195
She took the *l* ivory chest, *The Letters* 17
While we keep a *l* breath ! *Vision of Sin* 192
A *l* grain of conscience made him sour.' " 218
The *l* life of bank and brier, *You might have won* 30
Annie Lee, The prettiest *l* damsel in the port, *Enoch Arden* 12
daily left The *l* footprint daily wash'd away. " 22
' This is my house and this my *l* wife,' " 28
at this The *l* wife would weep for company, " 34
And say she would be *l* wife to both. " 36
No graver than as when some *l* cloud " 129
set his hand To fit their *l* streetward sitting-room " 170
This pretty, puny, weakly *l* one,— " 195
And kiss'd his wonder-stricken *l* ones ; " 229
The *l* innocent soul flitted away. " 270
' I may see her now, May be some *l* comfort ; ' " 276
Fresh from the burial of her *l* one, " 281
And past into the *l* garth beyond. " 329
How Philip put her *l* ones to school, " 706
Flourish'd a *l* garden square and wall'd : " 734
Uphold me, Father, in my loneliness A *l* longer ! " 785
To rush abroad all round the *l* haven, " 867
the *l* port Had seldom seen a costlier funeral. " 916
By twenty thorps, a *l* town, *The Brook* 29
The *l* dells of cowslip, fairy palms, *Aylmer's Field* 91
Has often toil'd to clothe your *l* ones ; " 699
(for the man Had risk'd his *l*) like the *l* thrift, *Sea Dreams* 10
And musing on the *l* lives of men, " 48
A sort of absolution in the sound To hate a *l* longer ! " 62
broke The glass with *l* Margaret's medicine in it ; " 142
(Altho' I grant but *l* music there) " 253
Sleep, *l* birdie, sleep ! will she not sleep Without her " *l* birdie " ? " 282
What does *l* birdie say In her nest at peep of day ? " 293
Let me fly, says *l* birdie, " 295
Birdie, rest a *l* longer, Till the *l* wings are stronger. " 297
So she rests a *l* longer, Then she flies away. " 299
What does *l* baby say, In her bed at peep of day ? " 301
Baby says, like *l* birdie, Let me rise and fly away. " 303
Baby, sleep a *l* longer, Till the *l* limbs are stronger. " 305
If she sleeps a *l* longer, Baby too shall fly away. " 307
Tired of so much within our *l* life, Or of so *l* in our *l* life— *Lucretius* 226
Poor *l* life that toddles half an hour " 228
round the lake A *l* clock-work steamer paddling plied *Princess, Pro.* 71
A rosebud set with *l* wilful thorns, " 154
The *l* hearth-flower Lilia. " 166
As many *l* trifling Lilias—play'd Charades " 188
(A *l* sense of wrong had touch'd her face With colour) " 219
A *l* dry old man, without a star, " *i* 117
A *l* street half garden and half house ; " 214
There above the *l* grave, O there above the *l* grave, " *ii* 12
O by the bright head of my *l* niece, " 276
' The mother of the sweetest *l* maid, " 279
While my *l* one, while my pretty one, sleeps. " *iii* 8
Sleep, my *l* one, sleep, my pretty one, sleep. " 16
What looks so *l* graceful : ' men ' " 53
Many a *l* hand Glanced like a touch of sunshine on the rocks, " 356
A *l* space was left between the horns, " *iv* 207
Upon the level in *l* puffs of wind, " 256
while We gazed upon her came a *l* stir About the doors, " 373
A *l* shy at first, but by and by We twain, " *v* 45
The child is hers—for every *l* fault, " 87
And lay my *l* blossom at my feet, " 100
indeed I think Our chiefest comfort is the *l* child " 430
And on the *l* clause ' take not his life : ' " 470
The *l* seed they laugh'd at in the dark, " *vi* 34
while Psyche ever stole A *l* nearer, " 133

Little (*continued*) and now A word, but one, one *l* kindly word, *Princess vi* 258
Her head a *l* bent ; and on her mouth A doubtful smile " 269
bird, That early woke to feed her *l* ones, " *vii* 252
With which we banter'd *l* Lilia first : " *Con.* 12
Then rose a *l* feud betwixt the two, " 23
The *l* boys begin to shoot and stab, " 61
and look'd No *l* lily-handed Baronet he, " 84
Last *l* Lilia, rising quietly, " 116
For one about whose patriarchal knee Late the *l* children clung : *Ode on Well.* 237
No *l* German state are we, *Third of Feb.* 15
AND Willy, my eldest-born, is gone, you say, *l* Annie ? *Grandmother* 1
And she to be coming and slandering me, the base *l* liar ! " 27
Shadow and shine is life, *l* Annie, flower and thorn. " 60
There lay the sweet *l* body that never had drawn a breath. " 62
I had not wept, *l* Annie, not since I had been a wife ; " 63
His dear *l* face was troubled, as if with anger or pain : " 65
I look'd at the still *l* body—his trouble had all been in vain. " 66
Patter she goes, my own *l* Annie, an Annie like you : " 78
And in this Book, *l* Annie, the message is one of Peace. " 96
the city Of *l* Monaco, basking, glow'd. *The Daisy* 8
Still in the *l* book you lent me, " 99
Making the *l* one leap for joy. *To F. D. Maurice* 4
Read my *l* fable : He that runs may read. *The Flower* 17
For a score of sweet *l* summers or so ? ' *The Islet* 2
The sweet *l* wife of the singer said, " 3
To a sweet *l* Eden on earth that I know, " 14
DAINTY *l* maiden, whither would you wander ? (repeat) *City Child* 1, 6
' Far and far away,' said the dainty *l* maiden, (repeat) " 3, 8
Sleep, *l* ladies ! And they slept well. *Minnie and Winnie* 3
Sleep, *l* ladies ! Wake not soon ! " 9
Wake, *l* ladies, The sun is aloft ! " 19
O *l* bard, is your lot so hard, *Spiteful Letter* 5
And do their *l* best to bite *Lit. Squabbles* 6
He bore but *l* game in hand ; *Victim* 42
I hold you here, root and all, in my hand, *L* flower— *Flow. in cran. wall* 4
dash the brains of the *l* one out, *Boädicea* 68
As some rare *l* rose, a piece of inmost Horticultural art, *Hendecasyllabics* 19
O lights, are you flying over her sweet *l* face ? *Window, On the Hill* 13
Go, *l* letter, apace, apace, *The Letter* 11
Two *l* hands that meet, (repeat) *Answer* 1, 4
Look how they tumble the blossom, the mad *l* tits ! *Ay* 9
Our *l* systems have their day ; *In Mem., Pro.* 17
the clock Beats out the *l* lives of men. " *ii* 8
'Tis *l* ; but it looks in truth As if the quiet bones " *xviii* 5
For now her *l* ones have ranged ; " *xxi* 26
or to use A *l* patience ere I die ; " *xxxiv* 12
And owning but a *l* art To lull with song an aching heart, " *xxxvii* 14
A *l* flash, a mystic hint ; " *xliv* 8
Abide a *l* longer here, " *lviii* 11
The *l* village looks forlorn ; " *lx* 9
When he was *l* more than boy, " *lxii* 6
A *l* grain shall not be spilt.' " *lxv* 4
breeze of song To stir a *l* dust of praise. " *lxxv* 12
The *l* speedwell's darling blue, " *lxxxiii* 10
Whose life, whose thoughts were *l* worth, " *lxxxv* 30
but led the way To where a *l* shallop lay " *ciii* 19
A *l* spare the night I loved, " *cv* 15
A *l* while from his embrace, " *cxvii* 3
From *l* cloudlets on the grass, " *Con.* 94
I HATE the dreadful hollow behind the *l* wood, *Maud I i* 1
Or the least *l* delicate aquiline curve in a sensitive nose, From which I escaped heart-free, with the least *l* touch of spleen. " *ii* 10
In the *l* grove where I sit—ah, " *iv* 2
whole *l* wood where I sit is a world of plunder and prey. " 24
However we brave it out, we men are a *l* breed. " 30
Because their natures are *l*, and, whether he heed it or not, " 53

Little (*continued*) *L* can I give my wife. *L. of Burleigh* 14
And how they mar this *l* by their feuds. *Sea Dreams* 49
Or of so *l* in our *l* life— *Lucretius* 227
So *l* done, such things to be, *In Mem. lxxiii* 2
And Enid took a *l* delicately, *Geraint and E.* 212
' Wait a *l*,' you say, ' you are sure it 'll all come right,' *First Quarrel* 1
' Wait a *l*, my lass, I am sure it 'ill all come right '— „ 91
Little-footed laws Salique And *l-f* China, *Princess ii* 134
Littleness a thousand peering *l'es*, *Ded. of Idylls* 26
Little-worth So were thy labour *l-w*. *Two Voices* 171
Live (adj.) *L* chattels, mincers of each other's fame, *Princess iv* 515
But his essences turn'd the *l* air sick, *Maud I xiii* 11
And the *l* green had kindled into flowers, *Gareth and L.* 185
And glowing in all colours, the *l* grass, *Last Tournament* 233
Which half that autumn night, like the *l* North, „ 479
Live (verb) Shall man *l* thus, in joy and hope *Supp. Confessions* 169
Living, but that he shall *l* on? „ 171
Thou wilt not *l* in vain. *Clear-headed friend* 9
My friend, with you to *l* alone, *Ode to Memory* 119
the rainbow *l's* in the curve of the sand; *Sea-Fairies* 27
unheard melody, Which *l's* about thee, *Eleänore* 65
We would *l* merrily, merrily. *The Merman* 40
now they *l* with Beauty less and less, *Caress'd or chidden* 9
His object *l's*: more cause to weep have I: *Wan Sculptor* 6
To *l* forgotten, and love forlorn.' (repeat) *Mariana in the S.* 12, 24, 84, 96
L forgotten and die forlorn.' (repeat) „ 60, 72
' To breathe and loathe, to *l* and sigh, *Two Voices* 104
Who is it that could *l* an hour? „ 162
I'd almost *l* my life again. *Miller's D.* 28
Grow, *l*, die looking on his face, *Fatima* 41
l by law, Acting the law we *l* by without fear; *Œnone* 147
Pass by the happy souls, that love to *l*: „ 240
My soul would *l* alone unto herself *Palace of Art* 11
I only wish to *l* till the snowdrops come again: *May Queen, N. Y's. E.* 14
To muse and brood and *l* again in memory, *Lotos-Eaters, C. S.* 65
In the hollow Lotos-land to *l* and lie „ 109
His memory long will *l* alone In all our hearts, *To J. S.* 49
But *l's* and loves in every place; *On a Mourner* 5
I *l* three lives of mortal men, *M. d'Arthur* 155
Mary, let me *l* and work with you: *Dora* 115
Then thou and I will *l* within one house, „ 125
but let me *l* my life. (repeat) *Audley Court* 43, 47, 51, 55
touch my body and be heal'd, and *l*: *St. S. Stylites* 79
L—yet *l*—Shall sharpest pathos blight us, *Love and Duty* 84
L happy; tend thy flowers; „ 87
'Tis like the second world to us that *l*; *Golden Year* 56
L on, God love us, as if the seedsman, „ 70
And that for which I care to *l*. *Day-Dm., L'Envoi* 56
For since I came to *l* and learn, *Will Water.* 81
hence this halo *l's* about The waiter's hands, „ 113
L long, ere from thy topmost head „ 233
L long, nor feel in head or chest „ 237
I speak the truth, as I *l* by bread! *Lady Clare* 26
Here he *l's* in state and bounty, *L. of Burleigh* 57
Enoch *l's*; that is borne in on me. *Enoch Arden* 319
Has she no fear that her first husband *l's*?' „ 806
Scorning an alms, to work whereby to *l*. „ 812
life in it Whereby the man could *l*; „ 821
I have not three days more to *l*; „ 851
there surely *l's* in man and beast Something divine *Sea Dreams* 68
' What a world,' I thought, ' To *l* in!' „ 95
' Have faith, have faith! We *l* by faith,' „ 157
' His deeds yet *l*, the worst is yet to come. „ 314
L the great life which all our greatest fain *Lucretius* 78
' *l's* there such a woman now?' *Princess, Pro.* 126
loved to *l* alone Among her women; „ *i* 49
Who am not mine, say, *l*: „ *ii* 223
yet may *l* in vain, and miss, Meanwhile, „ *iii* 243
And *l*, perforce, from thought to thought, „ 328
they cried ' she *l's*:' „ *iv* 192
dismiss'd in shame to *l* No wiser than their mothers, „ 513
l, dear lady, for your child!' „ *v* 80
risk'd it for my own; His mother *l's*: „ 408

Live (verb) (*continued*) the gray mare Is ill to *l* with, *Princess v* 452
' Sweet my child, I *l* for thee.' „ *vi* 16
' he *l's*: he is not dead: „ 122
at the happy word ' he *l's* ' My father stoop'd, „ 128
Ask me no more, lest I should bid thee *l*; „ *vii* 9
What pleasure *l's* in height (the shepherd sang) „ 193
to *l* and learn and be All that not harms „ 273
he, that doth not, *l's* A drowning life, „ 313
but I would not *l* it again. *Grandmother* 98
run oop to the brig, an' that thou'll *l* to see; *N. Farmer, N. S.* 55
And men will *l* to see it. *Spiteful Letter* 18
Dreams are true while they last, and do we not *l* in dreams? *High. Pantheism* 4
For merit *l's* from man to man, *In Mem., Pro.* 35
I trust he *l's* in thee, „ 39
The wild unrest that *l's* in woe „ *xv* 15
There *l's* no record of reply, „ *xxxi* 6
That life shall *l* for evermore, „ *xxxiv* 2
A doubtful gleam of solace *l's*. „ *xxxviii* 8
The grain by which a man may *l*? „ *liii* 8
O Sorrow, wilt thou *l* with me „ *lix* 1
But *l's* to wed an equal mind; „ *lxii* 8
And *l's* to clutch the golden keys, „ *lxiv* 10
And thine effect so *l's* in me, „ *lxv* 10
A part of mine may *l* in thee „ 11
Can trouble *l* with April days, „ *lxxxiii* 7
By which we dare to *l* or die. „ *lxxxv* 40
There *l's* more faith in honest doubt, „ *xcvi* 11
He told me, *l's* in any crowd, „ *xcviii* 26
We *l* within the stranger's land, „ *cv* 3
that *l* their lives From land to land; „ *cxv* 16
Yet less of sorrow *l's* in me „ *cxvi* 13
seem'd to *l* A contradiction on the tongue, „ *cxxv* 3
That friend of mine who *l's* in God, „ *Con.* 140
That God, which ever *l's* and loves, „ 141
When only the ledger *l's*, *Maud I i* 35
Well, he may *l* to hate me yet. „ *xiii* 4
In our low world, where yet 'tis sweet to *l*. „ *xviii* 48
Not die; but *l* a life of truest breath, „ 53
And died to *l*, long as my pulses play; „ 66
But to-morrow, if we *l*, „ *xx* 23
We are not worthy to *l*. „ *II i* 48
Then might we *l* together as one life, *Com. of Arthur* 91
power on this dead world to make it *l*.' „ 94
' Reign ye, and *l* and love, „ 472
' Strike for the King and *l*! „ 488
l the strength and die the lust! „ 492
L pure, speak true, right wrong, *Gareth and L.* 118
She *l's* in Castle Perilous: „ 611
ye know this Order *l's* to crush All wrongers „ 625
l to wed with her whom first you love: *Marr. of Geraint* 227
if I *l*, So aid me Heaven when at mine uttermost, „ 501
if he *l*, we will have him of our band; *Geraint and E.* 553
we will *l* like two birds in one nest, „ 627
l A wealthier life than heretofore *Balin and Balan* 91
From all his fellows, *l* alone, „ 126
forget My heats and violences? *l* afresh? „ 190
I too could die, as now I *l*, for thee.' „ 583
' *L* on, Sir Boy,' she cried. „ 584
It *l's* dispersedly in many hands, *Merlin and V.* 457
may now assure you mine; So *l* uncharm'd. „ 550
O tell us—for we *l* apart— *Lancelot and E.* 284
I never saw his like: there *l's* No greater leader.' „ 316
L's for his children, ever at its best And fullest; „ 336
in daily doubt Whether to *l* or die, „ 521
as but born of sickness, could not *l*: „ 880
' Speak: that I *l* to hear,' he said, ' is yours.' „ 928
Yet, seeing you desire your child to *l*, „ 1095
No memory in me *l's*; *Holy Grail* 535
But *l* like an old badger in his earth, „ 629
Long *l* the king of fools!' *Last Tournament* 358
True men who love me still, for whom I *l*, *Guinevere* 445
I the King should greatly care to *l*; „ 452
How sad it were for Arthur, should he *l*, „ 496
No, nor by living can I *l* it down. „ 623

Live (verb) (*continued*) in mine own heart I can *l* down sin — *Guinevere* 636
and still I *l* Who love thee ; — *Pass. of Arthur* 150
Not tho' I *l* three lives of mortal men, — „ 323
In that I *l* I love ; because I love I *l* : — *Lover's Tale i* 178
blight *L's* in the dewy touch of pity — „ 695
mask of Hate, who *l's* on others' moans. — „ 775
the Saviour *l's* but to bless. — *Rizpah* 64
l to fight again and to strike another blow.' — *The Revenge* 95
My God, I would not *l* Save that I think — *Sisters (E. and E.)* 228
necessity for talk Which *l's* with blindness, — „ 249
she'll never *l* thro' it, I fear.' — *In the Child. Hosp.* 42
' He says I shall never *l* thro' it, — „ 47
that, which lived True life, *l* on— — *Ded. Poem Prin. Alice* 2
Kill or be kill'd, *l* or die, — *Def. of Lucknow* 41
For I must *l* to testify by fire. — *Sir J. Oldcastle* 206
L, and be happy in thyself, — *De Prof., Two G.* 15
channel where thy motion *l's* Be prosperously shaped, — „ 19
L thou ! and of the grain and husk, — „ 50
Who *l* on milk and meal and grass ; — *To E. Fitzgerald* 13
that *l's* Behind this darkness, — *Tiresias* 51
work'd no good to aught that *l's*, — „ 77
one thing given me, to love and to *l* for, — *The Wreck* 35
Why should I *l* ? — *Despair* 69
Let it *l* then—ay, till when ? — *Epilogue* 63
May freedom's oak for ever *l* — *Hands all Round* 5
man, that only *l's* and loves an hour, — *Demeter and P.* 106
which *l's* Beyond our burial and our buried eyes, — *The Ring* 295
You will *l* till *that* is born, — *Forlorn* 63
leper's hut, where *l's* the living-dead. — *Happy* 4
would he *l* and die alone ? — „ 5
then I am dead, who only *l* for you. — „ 96
I will *l* and die with you. — „ 108
Could make pure light *l* on the canvas ? — *Romney's R.* 10
can Music make you *l* Far—far—away ? — *Far—far—away* 17
L thy Life, Young and old, — *The Oak* 1
l the life Beyond the bridge, — *Akbar's Dream* 144
I sticks like the ivin as long as I *l's* — *Church-warden, etc.* 15
She has left me enough to *l* on. — *Charity* 40
O happy he, and fit to *l*, — *The Wanderer* 9

Lived *l* in either's heart and speech. — *Sonnet To* —— 14
Have *l* and loved alone so long, — *Miller's D.* 38
If I had *l*—I cannot tell— — *May Queen, Con.* 47
You *l* with us so steadily, — *D. of the O. Year* 8
I have *l* my life, and that which I have done — *M. d'Arthur* 244
nor less among us *l* Her fame from lip to lip. — *Gardener's D.* 50
Dora *l* unmarried till her death. — *Dora* 172
The farmer's son, who *l* across the bay, — *Audley Court* 75
There *l* a flayflint near ; — *Walk. to the Mail* 84
Here *l* the Hills— — *Edwin Morris* 11
while I *l* In the white convent down the valley — *St. S. Stylites* 61
I *l* up there on yonder mountain side. — „ 72
Three years I *l* upon a pillar, — „ 86
Farewell, like endless welcome, *l* and died. — *Love and Duty* 68
They said he *l* shut up within himself, — *Golden Year* 9
O had I *l* when song was great — *Amphion* 9
And *l* a life of silent melancholy. — *Enoch Arden* 260
fell Sun-stricken, and that other *l* alone. — „ 570
Where Annie *l* and loved him, — „ 685
O had he *l* ! In our schoolbooks we say, — *The Brook* 9
I *l* for years a stunted sunless life ; — *Aylmer's Field* 357
In other scandals that have *l* and died, — „ 443
I thought I *l* securely as yourselves— — *Lucretius* 210
There *l* an ancient legend in our house. — *Princess i* 5
L thro' her to the tips of her long hands, — „ *ii* 40
bones of some vast bulk that *l* and roar'd — „ *iii* 294
You prized my counsel, *l* upon my lips : — „ *iv* 293
l in all fair lights, — „ 430
equal baseness *l* in sleeker times — „ *v* 385
and *l* but for mine own. — „ 389
My dream had never died or *l* again. — „ *vi* 17
Sweet order *l* again with other laws : — „ *vii* 19
as dearer thou for faults *L* over : — „ 348
the sooner, for he *l* far away. — *Grandmother* 16
Aurelius *l* and fought and died, — *Com. of Arthur* 13

Lived (*continued*) King Who *l* and died for men, — *Gareth and L.* 383
So large mirth *l* and Gareth won the quest. — „ 1426
Tho' yet there *l* no proof, — *Marr. of Geraint* 26
so there *l* some colour in your cheek, — *Geraint and E.* 621
l thro' her, who in that perilous hour — „ 766
l in hope that sometime you would come — „ 839
I have not *l* my life delightsomely : — *Balin and Balan* 60
There *l* a king in the most Eastern East, — *Merlin and V.* 555
And *l* there neither dame nor damsel — „ 606
Who *l* alone in a great wild on grass ; — „ 621
back to his old wild, and *l* on grass, — „ 649
One child they had : it *l* with her ; she died : — „ 716
And saved him : so she *l* in fantasy. — *Lancelot and E.* 27
A horror *l* about the tarn, — „ 37
all night long his face before her *l*, — „ 331
the face before her *l*, Dark-splendid, — „ 337
There kept it, and so *l* in fantasy. — „ 398
Sir Lancelot knew there *l* a knight — „ 401
Struck up and *l* along the milky roofs ; — „ 409
in me *l* a sin So strange, of such a kind, — *Holy Grail* 772
She *l* a moon in that low lodge with him : — *Last Tournament* 381
an Abbess, *l* For three brief years, — *Guinevere* 696
I have *l* my life, and that which I have done — *Pass. of Arthur* 412
So that, in that I *have l*, do I live, — *Lover's Tale i* 120
how should I have *l* and not have loved ? — „ 170
we *l* together, Apart, alone together on those hills. — „ 189
But many weary moons I *l* alone— — „ *ii* 2
l Scatteringly about that lonely land — „ *iv* 184
Affirming that as long as either *l*, — „ 277
Ah—you, that have *l* so soft, — *Rizpah* 17
he *l* with a lot of wild mates, — „ 29
Squire's laädy es long es she *l* — *Village Wife* 53
long es she *l* I niver hed none of 'er darters 'ere ; — „ 54
Hugger-mugger they *l*, but they wasn't — „ 117
which *l* True life, live on— — *Ded. Poem Prin. Alice* 1
He l on an isle in the ocean— — *V. of Maeldune* 7
He had *l* ever since on the Isle — „ 116
I had *l* a wild-flower life, — *The Wreck* 37
Our gentle mother, had *she l*— — *The Flight* 77
aisier work av they *l* be an Irish bog. — *Tomorrow* 72
But I couldn't 'a *l* wi' a man — *Spinster's S's.* 52
that you have not *l* in vain. — *Locksley H., Sixty* 242
An' 'e sarved me sa well when 'e *l*, — *Owd Roä* 11
when we *l* i' Howlaby Däale, — „ 19
He that has *l* for the lust of the minute, — *Vastness* 27
l With Muriel's mother on the down, — *The Ring* 147

Live-green Out of the *l-g* heart of the dells — *Sea-Fairies* 12

Livelier And *l* than a lark She sent her voice — *Talking Oak* 122
In the Spring a *l* iris changes on the burnish'd dove ; — *Locksley Hall* 19
then we crost To a *l* land ; — *Princess i* 110
Then Florian, but no *l* than the dame — „ *ii* 112
Nor less it pleased in *l* moods, — *In Mem. lxxxix* 29
No *l* than the wisp that gleams On Lethe — „ *xcviii* 7
Be quicken'd with a *l* breath, — „ *cxxii* 13
that to me A *l* emerald twinkles in the grass, — *Maud I xviii* 51

Liveliest glided thro' all change Of *l* utterance. — *D. of F. Women* 168

Livelong Pour round mine ears the *l* bleat — *Ode to Memory* 65
Past Yabbok brook the *l* night, — *Clear-headed friend* 27
Thro' which the *l* day my soul did pass, — *Palace of Art* 55
There will not be a drop of rain the whole of the *l* day, — *May Queen* 35
all the *l* way With solemn gibe did Eustace — *Gardener's D.* 167
break the *l* summer day With banquet — *In Mem. lxxxix* 31
light Thro' the *l* hours of the dark — *Maud I vi* 17
All thro' the *l* hours of utter dark, — *Lover's Tale i* 810

Lively Rapt in sweet talk or *l*, all on love — *Guinevere* 386

Liver (one who lives) Truth-speaking, brave, good *l's*, — *Gareth and L.* 424

Liver (organ of the body) pierces the *l* and blackens the blood ; — *The Islet* 35
red ' Blood-eagle ' of *l* and heart ; — *Dead Prophet* 71
' And the *l* is half-diseased ! ' — „ 76

Liveried dashing runnel in the spring Had *l* — *Lover's Tale ii* 50

Livest by what name *L* between the lips ? — *Lancelot and E.* 182
Thou *l* in all hearts, — *Epit. on Gordon* 3

Livid *L* he pluck'd it forth, — *Aylmer's Field* 627
Many a *l* one, many a sallow-skin— — *Batt. of Brunanburh* 106
I am roused by the wail of a child, and awake to a *l* light, — *The Wreck* 7

Loathsome (*continued*) till the *l* opposite Of all my heart had destined did obtain, *Guinevere* 490
And treat their *l* hurts and heal mine own; „ 686
and stood Stiff as a viper frozen; *l* sight, *Merlin and V.* 845
How could I bear with the sights and the *l* smells of disease *In the Child. Hosp.* 25
Lobby whined in *lobbies*, tapt at doors, *Walk. to the Mail* 37
Loch By firth and *l* thy silver sister grow, *Sir J. Oldcastle* 58
Lock (fastening) Break *l* and seal: *You might have won* 18
Melissa, with her hand upon the *l*, *Princess ii* 322
Cries of the partridge like a rusty key Turn'd in a *l*, *Lover's Tale ii* 116
Lock (of tresses) *l's* not wide-dispread, *Isabel* 5
Stays on her floating *l's* the lovely freight *Ode to Memory* 16
holding them back by their flowing *l's* *The Merman* 14
I would fling on each side my low-flowing *l's*, *The Mermaid* 32
While his *l's* a-drooping twined *Adeline* 57
When the *l's* are crisp and curl'd; *Vision of Sin* 200
To drench his dark *l's* in the gurgling wave *Princess iv* 187
From the flaxen curl to the gray *l* „ 426
with your long *l's* play the Lion's mane! „ *vi* 164
May serve to curl a maiden's *l's*, *In Mem. lxxvii* 7
Smoothing their *l's*, as golden as his own *Sisters (E. and E.)* 56
Lock (verb) *l* up my tongue From uttering freely *Last Tournament* 693
Lock'd salt pool, *l* in with bars of sand, *Palace of Art* 249
She *l* her lips: she left me where I stood: *D. of F. Women* 241
She might have *l* her hands. *Talking Oak* 144
slept the sleep With Balin, either *l* in either's arm. *Balin and Balan* 632
And Merlin *l* his hand in hers (repeat) *Merlin and V.* 290, 470
a puzzle chest in chest, With each chest *l* „ 655
Locket pluck from this true breast the *l* that I wear, *The Flight* 33
Locksley Dreary gleams about the moorland flying over *L* Hall; *Locksley Hall* 4
L Hall, that in the distance overlooks the sandy tracts, „ 5
a long farewell to *L* Hall! „ 189
Let it fall on *L* Hall, with rain or hail, „ 193
I myself so close on death, and death itself in *L* Hall. *Locksley H., Sixty* 4
Close beneath the casement crimson with the shield of *L*— „ 34
In this gap between the sandhills, whence you see the *L* tower, „ 176
Here is *L* Hall, my grandson, here the lion-guarded gate. Not to-night in *L* Hall—to-morrow— „ 213
one old Hostel left us where they swing the *L* shield, „ 247
Then I leave thee Lord and Master, latest Lord of *L* Hall. „ 282
Lodestar seem'd my *l* in the Heaven of Art, *Romney's R.* 39
Lodge (s) cross'd the garden to the gardener's *l*, *Audley Court* 17
Beyond the *l* the city lies, *Talking Oak* 5
They by parks and *l's* going *L. of Burleigh* 17
beyond her *l's*, where the brook Vocal, *Aylmer's Field* 145
haunt About the moulder'd *l's* of the Past *Princess iv* 63
A *l* of intertwisted beechen-boughs *Last Tournament* 376
She lived a moon in that low *l* with him: „ 381
that desert *l* to Tristram lookt So sweet, „ 387
that low *l* return'd, Mid-forest, „ 488
Some *l* within the waste sea-dunes, *The Flight* 90
Lodge (verb) *L* with me all the year! *Prog. of Spring* 26
Lodged Vivien, into Camelot stealing, *l* Low in the city, *Merlin and V.* 63
A priory not far off, there *l*, *Pelleas and E.* 214
and *l* with Plato's God, *Sisters (E. and E.)* 131
Lodging let him into *l* and disarm'd. *Lancelot and E.* 171
ere they past to *l*, she, Taking his hand, *Pelleas and E.* 125
Lodi At *L*, rain, Piacenza, rain. *The Daisy* 52
Loft in a *l*, with none to wait on him, *Lover's Tale iv* 138
Loftier A later but a *l* Annie Lee, *Enoch Arden* 748
then a *l* form Than female, *Princess iv* 215
I spring from *l* lineage than thine own.' *Gareth and L.* 961
A temple, neither Pagod, Mosque, nor Church, But *l*, simpler, *Akbar's Dream* 179
Loftiest a wild witch naked as heaven stood on each of the *l* capes, *V. of Maeldune* 100
Lofty 'Drink to *l* hopes that cool— *Vision of Sin* 147
Lofty (*continued*) broad ambrosial aisles of *l* lime Made noise with bees *Princess, Pro.* 87
Ilion's *l* temples robed in fire, *To Virgil* 2
Log (*See also* **Yule-log**) drove his heel into the smoulder'd *l*, *M. d'Arthur, Ep.* 14
Bring in great *l's* and let them lie, *In Mem. cvii* 17
Lies like a *l*, and all but smoulder'd out! *Gareth and L.* 75
Dagonet stood Quiet as any water-sodden *l* *Last Tournament* 253
Logic Severer in the *l* of a life? *Princess v* 190
Impassion'd *l*, which outran *In Mem. cix* 7
Loiar (liar) I weänt saäy men be *l's*, *N. Farmer, O. S.* 27
Loife (life) thaw *l* they says is sweet, „ 63
Loike (like) Moäst *l* a butter-bump, „ 31
Loins For many weeks about my *l* I wore *St. S. Stylites* 63
can this be he From Gama's dwarfish *l*? *Princess v* 506
Loiter from pine to pine, And *l's*, slowly drawn. *Œnone* 5
I *l* round my cresses; *The Brook* 181
With weary steps I *l* on, *In Mem. xxxviii* 1
The foot that *l's*, bidden go,— *Last Tournament* 117
Would often *l* in her balmy blue, *Lover's Tale i* 62
Loiter'd And *l* in the master's field, *In Mem. xxxvii* 23
and tho' I *l* there The full day after, *Sisters (E. and E.)* 97
Lombard But when we crost the *L* plain *The Daisy* 49
look'd the *L* piles; „ 54
You see yon *L* poplar on the plain. *Sisters (E. and E.)* 79
Lond (land) as I 'a done boy the *l*. (repeat) *N. Farmer, O. S.* 12, 24
an' *l* o' my oän. „ 44
whoä's to howd the *l* ater meä „ 58
London (adj.) For in the dust and drouth of *L* life *Edwin Morris* 143
When, in our younger *L* days, *To E. Fitzgerald* 54
London (s) (*See also* **Lunnon**) Sees in heaven the light of *L* flaring *Locksley Hall* 114
Here, in streaming *L's* central roar. *Ode on Well.* 9
L, Verulam, Cámulodúne. *Boädicea* 86
Your father is ever in *L*, *Maud I iv* 59
And *L* roll'd one tide of joy *To the Queen ii* 8
Roaring *L*, raving Paris, *Locksley H., Sixty* 190
And *L* and Paris and all the rest *The Dawn* 10
Lone At eve the beetle boometh Athwart the thicket *l*: *Claribel* 10
never more Shall *l* Œnone see the morning mist *Œnone* 216
'No voice,' she shriek'd in that *l* hall, *Palace of Art* 258
Thro' every hollow cave and alley *l* *Lotos-Eaters, C. S.* 103
On a day when they were going O'er the *l* expanse, *The Captain* 26
The bird that pipes his *l* desire *You might have won* 31
The *l* glow and long roar (repeat) *Voice and the P.* 3, 39
Her life is *l*, he sits apart, *In Mem. xcvii* 17
When the *l* hern forgets his melancholy, *Gareth and L.* 1185
'Enid, the pilot star of my *l* life, *Geraint and E.* 306
'And even in this *l* wood, Sweet lord, *Balin and Balan* 528
Perchance in *l* Tintagil far from all *Last Tournament* 392
Till one *l* woman, weeping near a cross, „ 493
And those *l* rites I have not seen, *To Marq. of Dufferin* 39
Lonelier *l*, darker, earthlier for my loss. *Aylmer's Field* 750
Loneliest but the *l* in a lonely sea. *Enoch Arden* 553
The *l* ways are safe from shore to shore. *Last Tournament* 102
Loneliness Uphold me, Father, in my *l* *Enoch Arden* 784
from his height and *l* of grief Bore down in flood, *Aylmer's Field* 632
Me rather all that bowery *l*, *Milton* 9
'Hast thou no pity upon my *l*? *Gareth and L.* 73
Gratitude—*l*—desire to keep So skilled a nurse *The Ring* 373
Lonely ancient thatch Upon the *l* moated grange. *Mariana* 8
winds woke the gray-eyed morn About the *l* moated grange. „ 32
Those *l* lights that still remain, *Two Voices* 83
Wrought by the *l* maiden of the Lake. *M. d'Arthur* 104
Wherever in a *l* grove He set up his forlorn pipes, *Amphion* 21
Sometimes on *l* mountain-meres I find a magic bark; *Sir Galahad* 37
l seabird crosses With one waft of the wing. *The Captain* 71
Close to the sun in *l* lands, *The Eagle* 2
And he sat him down in a *l* place, *Poet's Song* 5
And peacock-yewtree of the *l* Hall, *Enoch Arden* 99
And leave you *l*? not to see the world— „ 297
but the loneliest in a *l* sea. „ 553
The peacock-yewtree and the *l* Hall, „ 608
when his *l* doom Came suddenly to an end. „ 626
Pitying the *l* man, and gave him it: „ 664

Lonely (*continued*) Thou That didst uphold me on my *l* isle, *Enoch Arden* 783
His wreck, his *l* life, his coming back, „ 862
And *l* listenings to my mutter'd dream, *Princess vii* 110
zones of light and shadow Glimmer away to the *l* deep, *To F. D. Maurice* 28
And a storm never wakes on the *l* sea, *The Islet* 33
To breathe thee over *l* seas. *In Mem. xvii* 4
That beats within a *l* place, „ *lxxxv* 110
I find not yet one *l* thought That cries „ *xc* 23
That ripple round the *l* grange; „ *xci* 12
No gray old grange, or *l* fold, „ *c* 5
I have climb'd nearer out of *l* Hell. *Maud I xviii* 80
(For often in *l* wanderings I have cursed him „ *xix* 14
has past and leaves The Crown a *l* splendour. *Ded. of Idylls* 49
What happiness to reign a *l* king, *Com. of Arthur* 82
in *l* haunts Would scratch a ragged oval on the sand, *Gareth and L.* 533
Whom he loves most, *l* and miserable. *Marr. of Geraint* 123
Heard by the lander in a *l* isle, „ 330
good damsel there who sits apart, And seems so *l*?' *Geraint and E.* 300
That Lancelot is no more a *l* heart. *Lancelot and E.* 602
Who might have brought thee, now a *l* man „ 1370
built with wattles from the marsh A little *l* church *Holy Grail* 64
Here one black, mute midsummer night I sat, *L*, *Last Tournament* 613
All down the *l* coast of Lyonnesse, *Guinevere* 240
To sit once more within his *l* hall, „ 497
As of some *l* city sack'd by night, *Pass. of Arthur* 43
Wrought by the *l* maiden of the Lake. „ 272
O blossom'd portal of the *l* house, *Lover's Tale i* 280
great pine shook with *l* sounds of joy „ 325
And thus our *l* lover rode away, „ *iv* 130
who lived Scatteringly about that *l* land of his, „ 185
But *I* was the *l* slave of an often-wandering mind; *The Wreck* 130
O we poor orphans of nothing—alone on that *l* shore— *Despair* 33
and we shall light upon some *l* shore, *The Flight* 89
World-isles in *l* skies, *Epilogue* 55
charm of all the Muses often flowering in a *l* word; *To Virgil* 12
seated in the dusk Of even, by the *l* threshing-floor, *Demeter and P.* 126
The *l* maiden-Princess of the wood, *The Ring* 65
Her *l* maiden-Princess, crown'd with flowers, „ 485
you, that now are *l*, and with Grief Sit face to face, *To Mary Boyle* 45
I seem no longer like a *l* man In the king's garden, *Akbar's Dream* 20

Lonest Till ev'n the *l* hold were all as free *Gareth and L.* 598
Sir Bors Rode to the *l* tract of all the realm, *Holy Grail* 661

Long (adj. and adv.) (*See also* **Life-long**) From the *l* alley's latticed shade Emerged, *Arabian Nights* 112
L alleys falling down to twilight grots, *Ode to Memory* 107
Now is done thy *l* day's work; *A Dirge* 1
And *l* purples of the dale. „ 31
When the *l* dun wolds are ribb'd with snow, *Oriana* 5
How *l*, O God, shall men be ridden down, *Poland* 1
How *l* this icy-hearted Muscovite Oppress the region?' „ 10
L fields of barley and of rye, *L. of Shalott i* 2
Still moving after truth *l* sought, *Two Voices* 62
But *l* disquiet merged in rest. „ 249
To be the *l* and listless boy Late-left an orphan *Miller's D.* 33
Like those *l* mosses in the stream. „ 48
on the casement-edge A *l* green box of mignonette, „ 83
l shadow of the chair Flitted across into the night, „ 126
burning drouth Of that *l* desert to the south. *Fatima* 14
once he drew With one *l* kiss my whole soul thro' My lips, „ 20
roars The *l* brook falling thro' the clov'n ravine *Œnone* 8
between the piney sides Of this *l* glen. „ 94
higher All barr'd with *l* white cloud the scornful crags, *Palace of Art* 83
Smile at the claims of *l* descent. *L. C. V. de Vere* 52
You'll never see me more in the *l* gray fields at night; *May Queen, N. Y's. E.* 26
With your feet above my head in the *l* and pleasant grass. „ 32
Give us *l* rest or death, dark death, *Lotos-Eaters, C. S.* 53
L labour unto aged breath, „ 85
To watch the *l* bright river drawing slowly „ 92
glimmer of the languid dawn On those *l*, rank, *D. of F. Women* 75

Long (adj. and adv.) (*continued*) So *l* as you have been with us, *D. of the O. Year* 16
Brightening the skirts of a *l* cloud, *M. d'Arthur* 54
And the *l* ripple washing in the reeds.' „ 117
And the *l* glories of the winter moon. „ 192
I am going a *l* way With these thou seëst— „ 256
whispering rain Night slid down one *l* stream *Gardener's D.* 267
L learned names of agaric, moss and fern, *Edwin Morris* 17
Twice ten *l* weary weary years to this, *St. S. Stylites* 90
Or else I dream—and for so *l* a time, „ 93
thou hast suffer'd *l* For ages and for ages!' „ 99
I have some power with Heaven From my *l* penance: „ 144
The *l* mechanic pacings to and fro, *Love and Duty* 17
The *l* day wanes: *Ulysses* 55
With the fairy tales of science, and the *l* result of Time; *Locksley Hall* 12
'Dost thou love me, cousin?' weeping, 'I have loved thee *l*.' „ 30
a *l* farewell to Locksley Hall! „ 189
The poplars, in *l* order due, *Amphion* 37
We past *l* lines of Northern capes *The Voyage* 35
Where those *l* swells of breaker sweep „ 39
'Thou art mazed, the night is *l*, *Vision of Sin* 195
The *l* divine Peneïan pass, *To E. L.* 3
L lines of cliff breaking have left a chasm; *Enoch Arden* 1
higher A *l* street climbs to one tall-tower'd mill; „ 5
That he who left you ten *l* years ago „ 404
Then after a *l* tumble about the Cape „ 532
then winds variable, Then baffling, a *l* course of them; „ 546
lustre of the *l* convolvuluses That coil'd around „ 576
And dull the voyage was with *l* delays, „ 655
Then down the *l* street having slowly stolen, „ 682
his *l* wooing her, Her slow consent, and marriage, „ 707
All down the *l* and narrow street he went „ 795
And there he told a *l* long-winded tale *The Brook* 138
Katie walks By the *l* wash of Australasian seas „ 194
seated on a stile In the *l* hedge, „ 198
L since, a bygone Rector of the place, *Aylmer's Field* 11
crashing with *l* echoes thro' the land, „ 338
And his *l* arms stretch'd as to grasp a flyer: „ 588
But lapsed into so *l* a pause again „ 630
Ran in and out the *l* sea-framing caves, *Sea Dreams* 33
a *l* reef of gold, Or what seem'd gold: „ 127
He dodged me with a *l* and loose account. „ 149
rise And *l* roll of the Hexameter— *Lucretius* 11
And blasting the *l* quiet of my breast „ 162
And our *l* walks were stript as bare as brooms, *Princess, Pro.* 184
and with *l* arms and hands Reach'd out, „ *i* 28
Grow *l* and troubled like a rising moon, „ 59
there did a compact pass *L* summers back, „ 124
We rode Many a *l* league back to the North. „ 168
He with a *l* low sibilation, stared As blank as death „ 176
every turn Lived thro' her to the tips of her *l* hands, „ *ii* 40
And glutted all night *l* breast-deep in corn, „ 387
The *l* hall glitter'd like a bed of flowers. „ 439
A *l* melodious thunder to the sound Of solemn psalms, „ 476
'O *l* ago,' she said, 'betwixt these two „ *iii* 78
so Went forth in *l* retinue following up „ 195
The *l* light shakes across the lakes, „ *iv* 3
'O tell her, brief is life but love is *l*, „ 111
combing out her *l* black hair Damp from the river; „ 276
Came in *l* breezes rapt from inmost south „ 431
L lanes of splendour slanted o'er a press „ 478
rising up Robed in the *l* night of her deep hair, „ 491
l fantastic night With all its doings „ 565
blast and bray of the *l* horn And serpent-throated bugle, „ *v* 252
Suck'd from the dark heart of the *l* hills roll „ 349
All that *l* morn the lists were hammer'd up, „ 368
Lioness That with your *l* locks play the Lion's mane! „ *vi* 164
Till out of *l* frustration of her care, „ *vii* 101
The bosom with *l* sighs labour'd; „ 225
Yet in the *l* years liker must they grow; „ 279
made The *l* line of the approaching rookery swerve „ *Con.* 97
Let the *l l* procession go, **Ode on Well.** 15

Look (verb) *(continued)* *l* who comes behind,' (repeat) *Gareth and L.* 752, 1210
Shalt not once dare to *l* him in the face.' „ 782
and *l* thou to thyself: „ 920
L on it, child, and tell me if ye know it.' *Marr. of Geraint* 684
And once again she rose to *l* at it, *Geraint and E.* 387
Eat! *L* yourself. Good luck had your good man, „ 617
Until my lord arise and *l* upon me?' „ 650
I will not *l* at wine until I die.' „ 667
came The King's own leech to *l* into his hurt; „ 923
L to the cave.' *Balin and Balan* 306
these be fancies of the churl, *L* to thy woodcraft,' „ 308
Squire had loosed them, 'Goodly!—*l*! „ 576
How hard you *l* and how denyingly! *Merlin and V.* 338
A square of text that *l's* a little blot, „ 671
For *l* upon his face!—but if he sinn'd, „ 761
A sight ye love to *l* on.' *Lancelot and E.* 83
wherefore would ye *l* On this proud fellow again, „ 1064
and she, *L* how she sleeps— „ 1255
'See! *l* at mine! but wilt thou fight *Pelleas and E.* 127
'*L*, He haunts me—I cannot breathe— „ 226
ye *l* amazed, Not knowing they were lost *Last Tournament* 41
cried the Breton, '*L*, her hand is red! „ 412
this I gave thee, *l*, Is all as cool and white „ 415
Art thou King?—*L* to thy life!' „ 454
not *l* up, or half-despised the height *Guinevere* 643
face of old ghosts *L* in upon the battle; *Pass. of Arthur* 104
l at them, You lose yourself in utter ignorance; *Lover's Tale i* 78
Of eyes too weak to *l* upon the light; „ 614
And could I *l* upon her tearful eyes? „ 735
would not *l* at her—No not for months: „ *iv* 26
an' *l's* so wan an' so white: *First Quarrel* 2
I had but to *l* in his face. „ 16
he was fear'd to *l* at me now. „ 38
L at the cloäths on 'er back, *North. Cobbler* 109
For *l* you here—the shadows are too deep, *Sisters (E. and E.)* 103
l's at it, and says, 'Good! very like! „ 135
that one light no man can *l* upon, *De Prof., Two G.* 37
I cannot laud this life, it *l's* so dark: *To W. H. Brookfield* 12
l yonder,' he cried, 'a sail' *The Wreck* 121
I shall *l* on the child again. „ 124
whence, if thou *L* higher, *Ancient Sage* 281
But *l*, the morning grows apace, *The Flight* 93
till the Lion *l* no larger than the Cat, *Locksley H., Sixty* 112
O heart, *l* down and up Serene, *Early Spring* 27
from thine own To that which *l's* like rest, *Pref. Poem Broth. S.* 6
Why do you *l* so gravely at the tower? *The Ring* 80
but you *l* so kind That you will *Romney's R.* 21
L, the sun has risen To flame along another dreary day. „ 57
L, in their deep double shadow *Parnassus* 13
morning that *l's* so bright from afar! *By an Evolution.* 10
L, he stands, Trunk and bough, *The Oak* 13
L how the living pulse of Alla beats *Akbar's Dream* 41
L to your butts, and take good aims! *Riflemen form!* 16

Look'd-Lookt (*See also* **Looök'd-Looökt**) broken sheds *look'd* sad and strange: *Mariana* 5
look'd to shame The hollow-vaulted dark, *Arabian Nights* 125
Hast thou *look'd* upon the breath Of the lilies *Adeline* 36
when first I *look'd* upon your face, *Sonnet To* —— 9
She *look'd* down to Camelot. *L. of Shalott iii* 41
I might have *look'd* a little higher; *Miller's D.* 140
And turning *look'd* upon your face, „ 157
I *look'd* athwart the burning drouth *Fatima* 13
I *look'd* And listen'd, the full-flowing river *Œnone* 67
when I *look'd*, Paris had raised his arm, „ 189
He *look'd* so grand when he was dead. *The Sisters* 32
slept St. Cecily; An angel *look'd* at her. *Palace of Art* 100
her face Glow'd, as I *look'd* at her. *D. of F. Women* 240
I have not *look'd* upon you nigh, *To J. S.* 33
when I *look'd* again, behold an arm, *M. d'Arthur* 158
this is also true, that, long before I *look'd* upon her, *Gardener's D.* 62
She *look'd*: but all Suffused with blushes— „ 153
He often *look'd* at them, And often thought, *Dora* 3
more he *look'd* at her The less he liked her; „ 34

Look'd-Lookt *(continued)* Mary sat And *look'd* with tears upon her boy, *Dora* 57
I *look'd* at him with joy: *Talking Oak* 106
She *look'd* with discontent. „ 116
Look'd down, half-pleased, half-frighten'd, *Amphion* 54
She *look'd* into Lord Ronald's eyes, *Lady Clare* 79
Then they *look'd* at him they hated, *The Captain* 37
And he *look'd* at her and said, *L. of Burleigh* 94
She *look'd* so lovely, as she sway'd *Sir L. and Q. G.* 40
things Of his dead son, I *look'd* on these. *The Letters* 24
then I *look'd* up toward a mountain-tract, *Vision of Sin* 46
And all men *look'd* upon him favourably: *Enoch Arden* 56
Philip *look'd*, And in their eyes and faces „ 72
(Since Enoch left he had not *look'd* upon her), „ 273
silent, tho' he often *look'd* his wish; „ 482
he *look'd* up. There stood a maiden near, *The Brook* 204
and here he *look'd* so self-perplext, „ 213
What *look'd* a flight of fairy arrows *Aylmer's Field* 94
One *look'd* all rosetree, and another wore „ 157
And after *look'd* into yourself, „ 312
Half-canonized by all that *look'd* on her, *Princess i* 23
hills, that *look'd* across a land of hope, „ 169
And every face she *look'd* on justify it) „ *v* 134
then once more she *look'd* at my pale face: „ *vi* 115
Look'd up, and rising slowly from me, „ 151
down she *look'd* At the arm'd man sideways, „ 156
with shut eyes I lay Listening; then *look'd*. „ *vii* 224
Who *look'd* all native to her place, „ 323
and *look'd* the thing that he meant; *Grandmother* 45
I *look'd* at the still little body— „ 66
look'd the Lombard piles; *The Daisy* 54
And *look'd* at by the silent stars: *Lit. Squabbles* 4
That ever *look'd* with human eyes. *In Mem. lvii* 12
He *look'd* upon my crown and smiled: „ *lxix* 16
I *look'd* on these and thought of thee „ *xcvii* 6
and thee mine eyes Have *look'd* on: if they *look'd* in vain, „ *cix* 22
And how she *look'd*, and what he said, „ *Con.* 99
The sun *look'd* out with a smile *Maud I ix* 3
I *look'd*, and round, all round the house „ *xiv* 33
To have *look'd*, tho' but in a dream, upon eyes „ *III vi* 16
and *look'd* no more—But felt his young heart *Gareth and L.* 321
fire, That *lookt* half-dead, brake bright, „ 685
lord Now *look'd* at one and now at other, „ 869
and Gareth *lookt* and read—In letters „ 1201
'God wot, I never *look'd* upon the face, „ 1333
He *look'd* and saw that all was ruinous. *Marr. of Geraint* 315
dress that now she *look'd* on to the dress She *look'd* on ere the coming of Geraint. „ 613
still she *look'd*, and still the terror grew „ 615
Enid *look'd*, but all confused at first, „ 685
not to goodly hill or yellow sea *Look'd* the fair Queen, „ 831
They rode so slowly and they *look'd* so pale, *Geraint and E.* 35
he turn'd and *look'd* as keenly at her „ 430
And Geraint *look'd* and was not satisfied. „ 435
Once she *look'd* back, and when she saw him ride „ 441
By having *look'd* too much thro' alien eyes, „ 892
have ye *look'd* At Edyrn? have ye seen how nobly changed? „ 896
He *look'd* and found them wanting; „ 935
It *look'd* a tower of ivied masonwork, *Merlin and V.* 4
when I *look'd*, and saw you following still, „ 299
Merlin *look'd* and half believed her true, „ 400
Won by the mellow voice before she *look'd*, *Lancelot and E.* 243
He *look'd*, and more amazed Than if seven men „ 350
Lancelot *look'd* and was perplext in mind, „ 838
wherein she deem'd she *look'd* her best, „ 907
and *look'd* Down on his helm, „ 981
whence the King *Look'd* up, calling aloud, *Holy Grail* 219
large her violet eyes *look'd*, and her bloom A rosy dawn *Pelleas and E.* 71
turn'd the lady round And *look'd* upon her people; „ 92
Pelleas *look'd* Noble among the noble, „ 151
The Queen *Look'd* hard upon her lover, „ 605

Look'd-Lookt (*continued*) He *look'd* but once, and vail'd his eyes — *Last Tournament* 150
that desert lodge to Tristram *lookt* So sweet, „ 387
look'd and saw The great Queen's bower was dark,— „ 757
Which when she heard, the Queen *look'd* up, *Guinevere* 164
the pale Queen *look'd* up and answer'd her, „ 327
she *look'd* and saw The novice, weeping, „ 663
of those who falling down *Look'd* up for heaven, *Pass. of Arthur* 112
But when I *look'd* again, behold an arm, „ 326
A stately mountain nymph she *look'd*! *Lover's Tale i* 359
bridge is there, that, *look'd* at from beneath Seems „ 375
looking down On all that had *look'd* down on us; „ 388
Look'd forth the summit and the pinnacles „ *ii* 81
All that *look'd* on her had pronounced her dead. „ *iv* 35
look'd No less than one divine apology. „ 168
look'd, as he is like to prove, „ 314
but he *look'd* at me sidelong and shy, *First Quarrel* 35
the Lord has *look'd* into my care, *Rizpah* 75
soldiers *look'd* down from their decks and laugh'd, *The Revenge* 37
an niver *lookt* arter the land— *Village Wife* 25
can well believe, for he *look'd* so coarse and so red, *In the Child. Hosp.* 7
Each of them *look'd* like a king, *V. of Maeldune* 3
Down we *look'd*: what a garden! „ 78
Folded her lion paws, and *look'd* to Thebes. *Tiresias* 149
He *look'd* at it coldly, and said *The Wreck* 34
and I *look'd* at him, first, askance, With pity— „ 43
baby-girl, that had never *look'd* on the light: *Despair* 71
yet he *look'd* beyond the grave, *Locksley H., Sixty* 60
look'd the twin of heathen hate. „ 86
You came, and *look'd* and loved the view *Pro. to Gen. Hamley* 5
Then he *look'd* at the host that had halted *Heavy Brigade* 7
and a sudden face *Look'd* in upon me *The Ring* 420
When I *look'd* at the bracken so bright *June Bracken, etc.* 3

Looketh moon cometh, And *l* down alone. *Claribel* 14

Looking She, *l* thro' and thro' me *Lilian* 10
But, *l* fixedly the while, *Madeline* 39
Then *l* as 'twere in a glass, *A Character* 10
All *l* up for the love of me. *The Mermaid* 51
All *l* down for the love of me. „ 55
As a Naiad in a well, *L* at the set of day, *Adeline* 17
Sang *l* thro' his prison bars? *Margaret* 35
'But *l* upward, full of grace, *Two Voices* 223
Grow, live, die *l* on his face, *Fatima* 41
l over wasted lands, *Lotos-Eaters, C. S.* 114
And *l* wistfully with wide blue eyes *M. d'Arthur* 169
And in your *l* you may kneel to God. *St. S. Stylites* 141
l ancient kindness on thy pain. *Locksley Hall* 85
Brown, *l* hardly human, *Enoch Arden* 638
Then *l* at her; 'Too happy, fresh and fair, *The Brook* 217
In *l* on the happy Autumn-fields, *Princess iv* 42
stood The placid marble Muses, *l* peace. „ 489
And *l* back to whence I came, *In Mem. xxiii* 7
Sat silent, *l* each at each. „ *xxx* 12
Lest life should fail in *l* back. „ *xlvi* 4
Now *l* to some settled end, „ *lxxxv* 97
And *l* to the South, and fed With honey'd rain *Maud I xviii* 20
L, thinking of all I have lost; „ *II ii* 46
Arthur, *l* downward as he past, *Com. of Arthur* 55
slowly spake the mother *l* at him, *Gareth and L.* 151
Gareth *l* after said, 'My men, „ 296
Not turning round, nor *l* at him, *Marr. of Geraint* 270
And *l* round he saw not Enid there, „ 506
Then rose Limours, and *l* at his feet, *Geraint and E.* 302
then he spoke and said, Not *l* at her, *Merlin and V.* 247
'I once was *l* for a magic weed, „ 471
l at her, Full courtly, yet not falsely, *Lancelot and E.* 235
Lancelot knew that she was *l* at him. „ 985
l often from his face who read „ 1285
l up, Behold, the enchanted towers of Carbonek, *Holy Grail* 812
as he lay At random *l* over the brown earth *Pelleas and E.* 32
So that his eyes were dazzled *l* at it. „ 36
Gawain, *l* at the villainy done, „ 282
Sat their grea umpire, *l* o'er the lists. *Last Tournament* 159

Looking (*continued*) Here *l* down on thine polluted, *Guinevere* 555
And *l* wistfully with wide blue eyes *Pass. of Arthur* 337
L on her that brought him to the light: *Lover's Tale i* 160
We often paused, and, *l* back, „ 329
l down On all that had look'd down on us; „ 387
l round upon his tearful friends, „ 792
And *l* as much lovelier as herself „ *iv* 287
in the chapel there *l* over the sand? *Despair* 1
your know-all chapel too *l* over the sand. „ 94
l still as if she smiled, *Locksley H., Sixty* 35
l upward to the practised hustings-liar; „ 123
but wool's *l* oop ony how. *Church-warden, etc.* 6
With farther *l's* on. *Miller's D.* 231

Lookt See **Look'd**

Loom (s) She left the web, she left the *l*, *L. of Shalott iii* 37
A present, a great labour of the *l*; *Princess i* 44
rent The wonder of the *l* thro' warp and woof „ 62
L and wheel and enginery, *Ode Inter. Exhib.* 15
Display'd a splendid silk of foreign *l*, *Geraint and E.* 687
Thy presence in the silk of sumptuous *l's*; *Ancient Sage* 266

Loom (verb) smoke go up thro' which I *l* to her *Princess v* 130
Makes former gladness *l* so great? *In Mem. xxiv* 10
overheated language *l* Larger than the Lion,— *Locksley H., Sixty* 113

Looming To sail with Arthur under *l* shores, *M. d'Arthur, Ep.* 17
A *l* bastion fringed with fire. *In Mem. xv* 20
a phantom king, Now *l*, and now lost; *Com. of Arthur* 431

Loomp (lump) the poor in a *l* is bad. *N. Farmer, N. S.* 48
An' 'e digg'd up a *l* i' the land *Village Wife* 48

Loon Dish-washer and broach-turner, *l*!— *Gareth and L.* 770

Looök (look) Dubbut *l* at the waäste: *N. Farmer, O. S.* 37
an' fuzz, an' *l* at it now— „ 38
L 'ow quoloty smoiles „ 53
L thou theer wheer Wrigglesby beck cooms out „ *N. S.* 53
I'll *l* my hennemy straït i' the faäce, *North. Cobbler* 74
an' let ma *l* at 'im then, „ 75
and *l* thruf Maddison's gaäte' *Spinster's S's.* 6
Fur a cat may *l* at a king „ 34

Looök'd-Looökt (look'd-lookt) I *looök'd* cock-eyed at my noäse *North. Cobbler* 26
an' Sally *looökt* up an' she said, „ 62
But 'e niver *looökt* ower a bill, *Village Wife* 51
ghoäst i' the derk, fur it *looökt* sa white. „ 82
But whiniver I *looöked* i' the glass *Spinster's S's.* 20
An' I *looökt* out wonst at the night, *Owd Roä* 39

Loop (See also **River-loop**) a river Runs in three *l's* about her living-place; *Gareth and L.* 612
Then to the shore of one of those long *l's* „ 905
all in *l's* and links among the dales *Lancelot and E.* 166
Thro' knots and *l's* and folds innumerable „ 439

Loophole death from the *l's* around, *Def. of Lucknow* 79

Looping great funereal curtains, *l* down, *Lover's Tale iv* 214

Loose (adj.) He dodged me with a long and *l* account. *Sea Dreams* 149
I found a hard friend in his *l* accounts, A *l* one „ 162
torn raiment and *l* hair, *Gareth and L.* 1208
one night I cooms 'oäm like a bull gotten *l* at a faäir, *North. Cobbler* 33

Loose (verb) that she would *l* The people: *Godiva* 37
Let me *l* thy tongue with wine: *Vision of Sin* 88
'Fear not thou to *l* thy tongue; „ 155
when they ran To *l* him at the stables, *Aylmer's Field* 126
l A flying charm of blushes o'er this cheek, *Princess ii* 429
growing commerce *l* her latest chain, *Ode Inter. Exhib.* 33
—dismount and *l* their casques *Balin and Balan* 573
l thy tongue, and let me know.' *Pelleas and E.* 600
l the bond, and go.' *To the Queen ii* 17
Would *l* him from his hold; *Ancient Sage* 118
Shall we hold them? shall we *l* them? *Locksley H., Sixty* 118

Loosed She *l* the chain, and down she lay; *L. of Shalott iv* 16
And *l* the shatter'd casque, *M. d'Arthur* 209
l their sweating horses from the yoke, *Spec. of Iliad* 2
and *l* him from his vow. *Gareth and L.* 530
Sir Gareth *l* A cloak that dropt „ 681
Gareth *l* the stone From off his neck, „ 814
l his bonds and on free feet Set him, „ 817
he *l* a mighty purse, Hung at his belt, *Geraint and E.* 22

Loosed (*continued*) *l* in words of sudden fire the wrath *Geraint and E.* 106
l the fastenings of his arms, „ 511
And when the Squire had *l* them, *Balin and Balan* 575
our bond Had best be *l* for ever: *Merlin and V.* 342
Merlin *l* his hand from hers and said, „ 356
All ears were prick'd at once, all tongues were *l*: *Lancelot and E.* 724
Because he had not *l* it from his helm, „ 809
entering, *l* and let him go.' *Holy Grail* 698
Pelleas rose, And *l* his horse, *Pelleas and E.* 61
Forth sprang Gawain, and *l* him from his bonds, „ 315
and her heart was *l* Within her, *Guinevere* 667
And *l* the shatter'd casque, *Pass. of Arthur* 377
L from their simple thrall they had flow'd abroad, *Lover's Tale i* 703
l My captives, feed the rebels of the crown, *Columbus* 130
mortal limit of the Self was *l*, *Ancient Sage* 232
Loosen *l's* from the lip Short swallow-flights *In Mem. xlviii* 14
l, stone from stone, All my fair work; *Akbar's Dream* 188
Loosen'd his long-bounden tongue Was *l*, *Enoch Arden* 645
And shake the darkness from their *l* manes, *Tithonus* 41
The team is *l* from the wain, *In Mem. cxxi* 5
skirts are *l* by the breaking storm, *Geraint and E.* 459
Had *l* from the mountain, *Lover's Tale ii* 46
She comes! The *l* rivulets run; *Prog. of Spring* 9
Loosener fierce or careless *l's* of the faith, *To the Queen ii* 52
Looser and turning, wound Her *l* hair in braid, *Gardener's D.* 158
Loov (love) an' the *l* o' God fur men, *North. Cobbler* 55
I 'a gotten to *l* 'im ageän „ 96
L's 'im, an' roobs 'im, an' doosts 'im, „ 98
I *l's* tha to maäke thysen 'appy, *Spinster's S's.* 57
Loove (love) To *l* an' obaäy the Tommies! „ 96
Loov'd (loved) fur I *l* 'er as well as afoor. *North. Cobbler* 60
Loovin' (loving) 'A faäithful an' *l* wife!' *Spinster's S's.* 72
Lop His wonted glebe, or *l's* the glades; *In Mem. ci* 22
Who *l's* the moulder'd branch away. *Hands all Round* 8
Lopping *L* away of the limb by the pitiful-pitiless knife,— *Def. of Lucknow* 85
Lord (s) (*See also* **Liege-lord, Pheasant-lord**) My *L*, if so it be Thy will.' *Supp. Confessions* 106
O hither, come hither, and be our *l's*, *Sea-Fairies* 32
'*L*, how long shall these things be? *Poland* 9
Knight and burgher, *l* and dame, *L. of Shalott iv* 43
'Omega! thou art *L*,' they said, *Two Voices* 278
L over Nature, *L* of the visible earth, *L* of the senses five; *Palace of Art* 179
fall'n in Lyonnesse about their *L*, *M. d'Arthur* 4
What record, or what relic of my *l* „ 98
Such a *l* is Love, *Gardener's D.* 57
by the *L* that made me, you shall pack, *Dora* 31
Have mercy, *L*, and take away my sin. *St. S. Stylites* 8
O take the meaning, *L*: „ 21
O *L*, *L*, Thou knowest I bore this better „ 27
Bethink thee, *L*, while thou and all the saints „ 105
L, thou knowest what a man I am; „ 121
O *L*, Aid all this foolish people; „ 222
It may be my *l* is weary, *Locksley Hall* 53
She sought her *l*, and found him, *Godiva* 16
robed and crown'd, To meet her *l*, „ 78
How say you? we have slept, my *l's*. *Day-Dm., Revival* 21
My *l*, and shall we pass the bill „ 27
That lead me to my *L*: *St. Agnes' Eve* 8
Break up the heavens, O *L*! „ 21
Ancient homes of *l* and lady, *L. of Burleigh* 31
Not a *l* in all the country Is so great a *l* „ 59
'It is no wonder,' said the *l's*, *Beggar Maid* 7
L's of his house and of his mill *Enoch Arden* 351
reigning in his place, *L* of his rights „ 764
'After the *L* has call'd me she shall know, „ 810
Were he *l* of this, Why twenty boys and girls *Aylmer's Field* 370
And laughter to their *l's*: „ 498
There the manorial *l* too curiously Raking „ 513
came a *L* in no wise like to Baäl. „ 647
thy brother man, the *L* from Heaven, „ 667
the light yoke of that *L* of love, „ 708
scowl'd At their great *l*. „ 725
made Their own traditions God, and slew the *L*, „ 795

Lord (s) (*continued*) And her the *L* of all the landscape round *Aylmer's Field* 815
Remembering her dear *L* who died for all, *Sea Dreams* 47
But honeying at the whisper of a *l*; *Princess, Pro.* 115
with those self-styled our *l's* ally Your fortunes, „ *ii* 65
the *L* be gracious to me! A plot, „ 191
make all women kick against their *L's* „ *iv* 412
The lifting of whose eyelash is my *l*, „ *v* 140
But overborne by all his bearded *l's* „ 356
l of the ringing lists, „ 502
and the great *l's* out and in, „ *vi* 382
A *l* of fat prize-oxen and of sheep, „ *Con.* 86
My *L's*, we heard you speak: *Third of Feb.* 1
It was our ancient privilege, my *L's*, „ 5
my *L's*, not well: there is a higher law. „ 12
my *L's*, you make the people muse „ 31
And praise the invisible universal *L*, *Ode Inter. Exhib.* 3
thou, O *L*, art more than they. *In Mem., Pro.* 20
And not from man, O *L*, to thee. „ 36
her future *L* Was drown'd in passing thro' the ford, „ *vi* 38
A *l* of large experience, „ *xli* 7
Procuress to the *L's* of Hell. „ *liii* 16
To what I feel is *L* of all, „ *lv* 19
On souls, the lesser *l's* of doom. „ *cxii* 8
Love is and was my *L* and King, „ *cxxvi* 1
Love is and was my King and *L*, „ 5
old man, now *l* of the broad estate and the Hall, *Maud I i* 19
eft was of old the *L* and Master of Earth, „ *iv* 31
This new-made *l*, whose splendour plucks „ *x* 3
To a *l*, a captain, a padded shape, „ 29
Go back, my *l*, across the moor, „ *xii* 31
L of the pulse that is *l* of her breast, „ *xvi* 13
What, if she be fasten'd to this fool *l*, „ 24
He came with the babe-faced *l*; „ *II i* 13
And another, a *l* of all things, praying „ *v* 32
L's and Barons of his realm Flash'd forth *Com. of Arthur* 65
make myself in mine own realm Victor and *l*. „ 90
your *l's* stir up the heat of war, „ 169
l's Of that fierce day were as the *l's* „ 215
the *l's* Have foughten like wild beasts „ 225
but after, the great *l's* Banded, „ 236
Hath power to walk the waters like our *L*. „ 294
'King and my *l*, I love thee to the death!' „ 470
L's from Rome before the portal stood, „ 477
at the banquet those great *L's* from Rome, „ 504
so those great *l's* Drew back in wrath, „ 513
crying 'Let us go no further, *l*. *Gareth and L.* 198
'*L*, we have heard from our wise man „ 201
'*L*, there is no such city anywhere, „ 206
'*L*, the gateway is alive.' „ 235
reft From my dead *l* a field with violence: „ 335
my *l*, The field was pleasant in my husband's eye.' „ 341
thine own hand thou slewest my dear *l*, „ 352
The woman loves her *l*. „ 372
Delivering, that his *l*, the vassal king, „ 391
The *L* for half a league. „ 596
Sweet *l*, how like a noble knight he talks! „ 777
'They have bound my *l* to cast him in the mere.' „ 803
But an this *l* will yield us harbourage, „ 844
the *l* Now look'd at one and now at other, „ 868
the *l* whose life he saved Had, „ 888
'Thou hast made us *l's*, and canst not put us down!' „ 1132
Good *l*, how sweetly smells the honeysuckle „ 1287
ramp and roar at leaving of your *l*!— „ 1307
ever yet was wife True to her *l*, *Marr. of Geraint* 47
I cannot love my *l* and not his name. „ 92
Than that my *l* thro' me should suffer shame. „ 101
see my dear *l* wounded in the strife, „ 103
'Smile and we smile, the *l's* of many lands; Frown and we smile, the *l's* of our own hands; „ 353
l's and ladies of the high court went „ 662
save her dear *l* whole from any wound. *Geraint and E.* 45
'I will go back a little to my *l*, „ 65
That that my *l* should suffer loss or shame.' „ 69
'My *l*, I saw three bandits by the rock „ 72

Lord (s) (*continued*) Whereof one seem'd far larger than her l, Geraint and E. 122
'I will abide the coming of my l, „ 131
My l is weary with the fight before, „ 133
My l, eat also, tho' the fare is coarse, „ 208
To close with her l's pleasure; „ 214
'My l, you overpay me fifty-fold.' „ 220
'Yea, my kind l,' said the glad youth, „ 241
to which She answer'd, 'Thanks, my l;' „ 264
the wild l of the place, Limours. „ 277
Nor cared a broken egg-shell for her l. „ 364
tending her rough l, tho' all unask'd, „ 405
'My l, I scarce have spent the worth of one!' „ 411
'Yea, my l, I know Your wish, „ 418
Then not to disobey her l's behest, „ 450
Start from their fallen l's, and wildly fly, „ 482
swathed the hurt that drain'd her dear l's life. „ 516
So for long hours sat Enid by her l, „ 580
Until my l arise and look upon me?' „ 650
I will not drink Till my dear l arise and bid me do it, „ 665
'In this poor gown my dear l found me first, „ 698
Except he surely knew my l was dead,' „ 721
Let be: ye stand, fair l, as in a dream.' Balin and Balan 258
'L, thou couldst lay the Devil of these woods „ 298
'L, Why wear ye this crown-royal upon shield?' „ 337
fire of Heaven is l of all things good, „ 452
Their brother beast, whose anger was his l. „ 488
Again she sigh'd 'Pardon, sweet l! „ 497
this fair l, The flower of all their vestal knighthood, „ 507
in this lone wood, Sweet l, ye do right well „ 529
angels of our L's report. Merlin and V. 16
like a bride's On her new l, her own, „ 617
she call'd him l and liege, „ 953
'Yea, l,' she said, 'ye know it.' Lancelot and E. 80
Henceforth be truer to your faultless l?' „ 119
That passionate perfection, my good l— „ 122
In battle with the love he bare his l, „ 246
'O there, great l, doubtless,' Lavaine said, „ 281
at Caerleon had he help'd his l, „ 297
'Save your great self, fair l;' „ 320
'Fair l, whose name I know not— „ 360
Needs must be lesser likelihood, noble l, „ 367
our liege l, The dread Pendragon, „ 423
L's of waste marches, kings of desolate isles, „ 527
'L, no sooner had ye parted from us, „ 576
'Yea, l,' she said, 'Thy hopes are mine,' „ 606
'What news from Camelot, l? „ 620
Nay, for near you, fair l, I am at rest.' „ 833
Prince and L am I In mine own land, „ 916
'Is it for Lancelot, is it for my dear l? „ 1105
Nay, by the mother of our L himself, „ 1230
ever in the reading, l's and dames Wept, „ 1284
Fair l, as would have help'd her from her death.' „ 1311
when now the l's and dames And people, „ 1346
cup itself from which our L Drank at the last sad supper Holy Grail 46
thorn Blossoms at Christmas, mindful of our L. „ 53
a hundred winters old, From our L's time. „ 89
'Nay, for my l,' said Percivale, „ 205
l, I heard the sound, I saw the light, „ 280
l, and therefore have we sworn our vows.' „ 285
seem'd to me the L of all the world, „ 414
when the L of all things made Himself „ 447
blessed L, I speak too earthlywise, „ 627
'Nay, l,' said Gawain, 'not for such as I. „ 741
'Glory and joy and honour to our L „ 839
And l of many a barren isle was he— Pelleas and E. 19
and remain L of the tourney. „ 163
L, I was tending swine, Last Tournament 71
Watch'd her l pass, and knew not that she sigh'd. „ 130
and in her bosom pain was l. „ 239
thank the L I am King Arthur's fool. „ 320
Mark her l had past, the Cornish King, „ 382
in the heart of Arthur pain was l. „ 486
'Why weep ye?' 'L,' she said, „ 494
a doubtful l To bind them by inviolable vows, „ 687

Lord (s) (*continued*) tamper'd with the L's of the White Horse, Guinevere 15
false traitor have displaced his l, „ 216
to lead her to his l Arthur, „ 383
tho' thou wouldst not love thy l, Thy l has wholly lost his love for thee. „ 508
leagues With L's of the White Horse, „ 574
'Gone—my l! Gone thro' my sin to slay and to be slain! „ 612
Gone, my l the King, My own true l! „ 616
Ah great and gentle l, Who wast, „ 638
wife and child with wail Pass to new l's; Pass. of Arthur 45
fall'n in Lyonnesse about their l, „ 173
What record, or what relic of my l „ 266
Artificer and subject, l and slave, Lover's Tale ii 103
'O my heart's l, would I could show you,' „ iv 250
Julian goes, the l of all he saw. „ 315
Bible verse of the L's good will toward men— Rizpah 61
'Full of compassion and mercy, the L' „ 62
yes, as the L must know, „ 67
the L has look'd into my care, „ 75
'Stan' 'im theer i' the naäme o' the L North. Cobbler 73
for the glory of the L. The Revenge 21
And the L hath spared our lives. „ 93
An' I thowt 'twur the will o' the L, Village Wife 11
thebbe all wi' the L my childer, „ 13
But I beänt that sewer es the L, „ 93
where the works of the L are reveal'd In the Child. Hosp. 35
'but then if I call to the L, „ 53
The L has so *much* to see to! „ 57
L of the children had heard her, „ 72
Judah, for in thee the L was born; Sir J. Oldcastle 25
L give thou power to thy two witnesses! „ 81
than to persecute the L, And play the Saul „ 102
Ah rather, L, than that thy Gospel, „ 119
but how long, O L, how long! „ 125
L of life Be by me in my death. „ 173
CHAINS, my good l: in your raised brows Columbus 1
All glory to the mother of our L, „ 62
I saw The glory of the L flash up, „ 82
walk within the glory of the L „ 89
The L had sent this bright, strange dream „ 91
O my l, I swear to you I heard his voice „ 144
Still for all that, my l, „ 163
Remember the words of the L when he told us V. of Maeldune 120
L of human tears; Child-lover; To Victor Hugo 3
ATHELSTAN King, L among Earls, Batt. of Brunanburh 2
Lamp of the L God L everlasting, „ 27
thanks to the L that I niver not listen'd to noän! Spinster's S's. 8
but, O L, upo' coomin' down— „ 44
my l is lower than his oxen or his swine. Locksley H., Sixty 126
Then I leave thee L and Master, latest L of Locksley Hall. „ 282
they rode like Victors and L's Heavy Brigade 48
As a l of the human soul, Dead Prophet 54
Our own fair isle, the l of every sea— The Fleet 7
thy dark l accept and love the Sun, Demeter and P. 137
do you scorn me when you tell me, O my l, Happy 23
I replied 'Nay, L, for *Art*,' Romney's R. 131
L let the house of a brute to the soul of a man, By an Evolution. 1
And the L—'Not yet: but make it as clean „ 3
How loyal in the following of thy L! In Mem., W. H. Ward 6
when these behold their L, Akbar's Dream 142
An' saw by the Graäce o' the L, Church-warden, etc. 42
she is face to face with her L, Charity 42
Priests in the name of the L The Dawn 4

Lord (verb) every spoken tongue should l you. Princess iv 544

Lord Jesus (*See also* **Christ, Christ Jesus, Jesus**) 'to seek the L J in prayer; In the Child. Hosp. 18
but the good L J has had his day.' „ 22
I should cry to the dear L J to help me, „ 49
dear L J with children about his knees.) „ 52

Lordlier assert None l than themselves Princess ii 144
grace And presence, l than before; In Mem. ciii 28

Lordliest 'She gave him mind, the l Proportion, Two Voices 19

Lord-lover young l-l, what sighs are those, Maud I xxii 29

Lordly Listening the l music flowing Ode to Memory 41

Lordly (*continued*) I BUILT my soul a *l* pleasure-house, *Palace of Art* 1
They by parks and lodges going See the *l* castles stand: *L. of Burleigh* 18
The lovely, *l* creature floated on *Princess vi* 89
down from this a *l* stairway sloped *Gareth and L.* 669
They past on, The *l* Phantasms! *Lover's Tale ii* 99
Lord-manufacturer You, the *L-m*, *On Jub. Q. Victoria* 57
Lord of Astolat) (*See also* **Astolat**) And issuing found the *L o A* *Lancelot and E.* 173
then the *L o A*: 'Whence comest thou, „ 180
said the *L o A*, 'Here is Torre's: „ 195
came The *L o A* out, to whom the Prince „ 627
To whom the *L o A* 'Bide with us, „ 632
Lord of Burleigh *L o B*, fair and free, *L. of Burleigh* 58
Deeply mourn'd the *L o B*, „ 91
Lord-prince high *l-p* of Arthur's hall, *Balin and Balan* 466
Lord-territorial You, the *L-t*, *On Jub. Q. Victoria* 56
Lore (*See also* **Love-lore**) As wild as aught of fairy *l*; *Day-Dm., L'Envoi* 12
The Learned all his *l*; *Ancient Sage* 139
Lose I *l* my colour, I *l* my breath, *Eleänore* 137
And not to *l* the good of life— *Two Voices* 132
Oft *l* whole years of darker mind. „ 372
Nor greatly cared to *l*, her hold on life. *Aylmer's Field* 568
they must *l* the child, assume The woman: *Princess i* 137
Dwell with these, and *l* Convention, „ *ii* 85
I *l* My honour, these their lives.' „ 341
To our point: not war: Lest I *l* all.' „ *v* 205
she fear'd that I should *l* my mind, „ *vii* 99
Nor *l* the wrestling thews that throw the world; „ 282
Nor *l* the childlike in the larger mind; „ 284
The gravest citizen seems to *l* his head, „ *Con.* 59
I too, talk, and *l* the touch I talk of. *Lit. Squabbles* 17
Nor *l* their mortal sympathy, *In Mem. xxx* 23
We *l* ourselves in light.' „ *xlvii* 16
I shall not *l* thee tho' I die. „ *cxxx* 16
and he fears To *l* his bone, and lays his foot upon it, *Geraint and E.* 562
Fearing to *l*, and all for a dead man, „ 564
And *l* the quest he sent you on, *Lancelot and E.* 655
'I *l* it, as we *l* the lark in heaven, „ 659
Sweet father, will you let me *l* my wits?' „ 752
not *l* your wits for dear Lavaine: „ 755
Pleasure to have it, none; to *l* it, pain: „ 1415
'No man could sit but he should *l* himself:' *Holy Grail* 174
'If I *l* myself, I save myself!' „ 178
'I will embark and I will *l* myself, „ 805
Not greatly care to *l*; *Guinevere* 495
You *l* yourself in utter ignorance; *Lover's Tale i* 79
And *l* thy life by usage of thy sting; *Ancient Sage* 270
say 'that those who *l* can find.' *The Ring* 282
All is well If I *l* it and myself *Happy* 58
They *l* themselves and die *Prog. of Spring* 35
And yet The world would *l*, *Romney's R.* 68
Losing *L* his fire and active might *Eleänore* 104
L her carol I stood pensively, *D. of F. Women* 245
Nor mine the fault, if *l* both of these *Aylmer's Field* 719
odes About this *l* of the child; *Princess i* 141
Poor rivals in a *l* game, *In Mem. cii* 19
A little vext at *l* of the hunt, *Marr. of Geraint* 234
'I am *l* the light of my Youth *The Dreamer* 4
Loss Although the *l* had brought us pain, That *l* *Miller's D.* 229
Your *l* is rarer; for this star Rose *To J. S.* 25
And but for daily *l* of one she loved *Walk. to the Mail* 94
l of all But Enoch and two others. *Enoch Arden* 549
Am lonelier, darker, earthlier for my *l*. *Aylmer's Field* 750
His gain is *l*; for he that wrongs his friend *Sea Dreams* 172
And the volleying cannon thunder his *l*; *Ode on Well.* 62
And find in *l* a gain to match? *In Mem. i* 6
Ah, sweeter to be drunk with *l*, „ 11
'Thou shalt not be the fool of *l*.' „ *iv* 16
'*L* is common to the race'— „ *vi* 2
That *l* is common would not make „ 5
Which weep a *l* for ever new, „ *xiii* 5
Thy spirit ere our fatal *l* „ *xli* 1

Loss (*continued*) His night of *l* is always there. *In Mem. lxvi* 16
To breathe my *l* is more than fame, „ *lxxvii* 15
The grief my *l* in him had wrought, „ *lxxx* 6
The lighter by the *l* of his weight; *Maud I xvi* 2
By the *l* of that dead weight, „ *xix* 99
shadow of His *l* drew like eclipse, *Ded. of Idylls* 14
Than that my lord should suffer *l* or shame.' *Geraint and E.* 69
Enid, the *l* of whom hath turn'd me wild— „ 308
as a man to whom a dreadful *l* Falls in a far land „ 496
l So pains him that he sickens nigh to death; „ 498
Then, fearing for his hurt and *l* of blood, „ 777
I rather dread the *l* of use than fame; *Merlin and V.* 519
With *l* of half his people arrow-slain; „ 565
dame nor damsel then Wroth at a lover's *l*? „ 607
Had I not learnt my *l* before he came? *Lover's Tale i* 665
Stung by his *l* had vanish'd, none knew where. „ *iv* 102
ill-suited as it seem'd To such a time, to Lionel's *l* „ 208
—his *l* Weigh'd on him yet— „ 274
guest So bound to me by common love and *l*— „ 345
away she sail'd with her *l* and long'd for her own; *The Revenge* 111
lost to the *l* that was mine, *The Wreck* 113
and thro' *l* of Self The gain of such large life *Ancient Sage* 236
Moaning your *l'es*, O Earth, *The Dreamer* 17
Thrones are clouded by your *l*, *D. of the Duke of C.* 6
Lost (*See also* **Half-lost, Late-lost**) That these have never *l* their light. *Miller's D.* 88
Her cheek had *l* the rose, *Œnone* 18
one silvery cloud Had *l* his way „ 93
L to her place and name; *Palace of Art* 264
Stream'd onward, *l* their edges, *D. of F. Women* 50
Fall into shadow, soonest *l*: *To J. S.* 11
thus be *l* for ever from the earth, *M. d'Arthur* 90
much honour and much fame were *l*.' „ 109
l the sense that handles daily life— *Walk. to the Mail* 22
have you *l* your heart?' she said; *Edward Gray* 3
And now we *l* her, now she gleam'd *The Voyage* 65
the precious morning hours were *l*. *Enoch Arden* 302
Philip gain'd As Enoch *l*; „ 355
'The ship was *l*,' he said 'the ship was *l*! „ 393
Enoch, poor man, was cast away and *l*.' „ 713
Repeated muttering 'cast away and *l*;' Again in deeper inward whispers '*l*!' „ 715
slowly *l* Nor greatly cared to lose, *Aylmer's Field* 567
Softening thro' all the gentle attributes Of his *l* child, „ 731
I came To know him more, I *l* it, *Sea Dreams* 72
But now when all was *l* or seem'd as *l*— *Princess, Pro.* 39
They *l* their weeks; they vext the souls of deans; „ 162
a pillar'd porch, the bases *l* In laurel: „ *i* 230
the child We *l* in other years, „ *ii* 11
some ages had been *l*; „ 153
an erring pearl *L* in her bosom: „ *iv* 61
Wiser to weep a true occasion *l*, „ 68
(For since her horse was *l* I left her mine) „ 197
For this *l* lamb (she pointed to the child) „ 361
at once the *l* lamb at her feet Sent out a bitter bleating „ 391
'Be comforted: have I not *l* her too, „ *v* 69
our side was vanquish'd and my cause For ever *l*, „ *vi* 25
slip Into my bosom and be *l* in me.' „ *vii* 189
Nor ever *l* an English gun; *Ode on Well.* 97
flying by to be *l* on an endless sea— *Wages* 2
'Behold the man that loved and *l*, *In Mem. i* 15
Something it is which thou hast *l*, „ *iv* 9
With my *l* Arthur's loved remains, „ *ix* 3
'Tis better to have loved and *l* „ *xxvii* 15
l the links that bound Thy changes; „ *xli* 6
So then were nothing *l* to man; „ *xliii* 9
'Love's too precious to be *l*, „ *lxv* 3
And like to him whose sight is *l*; „ *lxvi* 8
That Nature's ancient power was *l*: „ *lxix* 2
The quiet sense of something *l*. „ *lxxviii* 8
'Tis better to have loved and *l*, „ *lxxxv* 3
No visual shade of some one *l*, „ *xciii* 5
Day, when I *l* the flower of men; „ *xcix* 4

Loud (*continued*) Altho' the trumpet blew so l. — In Mem. xcvi 24
and l With sport and song, in booth and tent, — „ xcviii 27
So l with voices of the birds, — „ xcix 2
Now rings the woodland l and long, — „ cxv 5
Is it peace or war? better, war! l war by land and by sea, — Maud I i 47
Low on the sand and l on the stone — „ xxii 25
makes us l in the world of the dead; — „ II v 25
and so l That first they mock'd, — Gareth and L. 507
Well—I will after my l knave, and learn — „ 720
more Than l Southwesterns, rolling ridge on ridge, — „ 1145
heard The world's l whisper breaking into storm, — Marr. of Geraint 27
And the stout Prince bad him a l good-night. — Geraint and E. 361
And in the four l battles by the shore Of Duglas; — Lancelot and E. 289
then came a night Still as the day was l; — Holy Grail 683
So l a blast along the shore and sea, — „ 796
But on the hither side of that l morn — Last Tournament 56
and with mirth so l Beyond all use, — „ 235
and l leagues of man And welcome! — To the Queen ii 9
Like to a quiet mind in the l world, — Lover's Tale i 7
and thro' the arch Down those l waters, — „ 59
And thence one night, when all the winds were l, — „ 378
for the sound Of the l stream was pleasant, — „ ii 35
The moanings in the forest, the l brook, — „ 114
An earthquake, my l heart-beats, — „ 193
A long l clash of rapid marriage-bells. — „ iii 23
The l black nights for us, — Rizpah 6
Whence the thunderbolt will fall Long and l, — The Revenge 45
Men l against all forms of power— — Freedom 37
When I was praying in a storm—the crash was long and l— — Happy 80
Then, in the l world's bastard judgment-day, — Romney's R. 119
Sing thou low or l or sweet, — Poets and Critics 6

Louder a l one Was all but silence— — Aylmer's Field 696
It clack'd and cackled l. — The Goose 24
Gawain sware, and l than the rest.' — Holy Grail 202
breakers on the shore Sloped into l surf: — Lover's Tale iii 15
l than thy rhyme the silent Word — Ancient Sage 212
No l than a bee among the flowers, — Romney's R. 82

Loud-lung'd And l-l Antibabylonianisms — Sea Dreams 252

Lounging *See* **Hawmin'**

Lour whatever tempests l For ever silent; — Ode on Well. 175
Heaven l's, But in the tearful splendour — Prog. of Spring 40

Louse *See* **Wood-louse**

Love (s) (*See also* **After-love, Boy-love, Loov, Luvv, Mock-love, True-love**) bring me my l, Rosalind. — Leonine Eleg. 14
Had I So little l for thee? — Supp. Confessions 88
grace Would drop from his o'er-brimming l, — „ 113
and Thy l Enlighten me. — „ 182
A l still burning upward, — Isabel 18
Life, anguish, death, immortal l, — Arabian Nights 73
l thou bearest The first-born of thy genius. — Ode to Memory 91
the scorn of scorn, The l of l. — The Poet 4
And it sings a song of undying l; — Poet's Mind 33
eyes shall glisten With pleasure and l and jubilee: — Sea-Fairies 36
L paced the thymy plots of Paradise, — Love and Death 2
L wept and spread his sheeny vans — „ 8
pierced thy heart, my l, my bride, — Oriana 42
Thy heart, my life, my l, my bride, — „ 44
With his large calm eyes for the l of me. — The Mermaid 27
Die in their hearts for the l of me. — „ 30
All looking up for the l of me. — „ 51
All looking down for the l of me. — „ 55
In l with thee forgets to close His curtains, — Adeline 42
Who lent you, l, your mortal dower — Margaret 5
languid L, Leaning his cheek upon his hand, — Eleänore 117
For Kate no common l will feel; — Kate 14
Nor cares to lisp in l's delicious creeds; — Caress'd or chidden 11
Weep on: beyond his object L can last: — Wan Sculptor 5
My tears, no tears of l, are flowing fast, No tears of l, but tears that L can die. — „ 7
Clear L would pierce and cleave, — If I were loved 6
L lighted down between them full of glee, — The Bridesmaid 6
'L,' they said, 'must needs be true, — Mariana in the S. 63
'And cruel l, whose end is scorn, — „ 70
And mete the bounds of hate and l— — Two Voices 135
And in their double l secure, — „ 418

Love (s) (*continued*) spreads above And veileth l, itself is l. — Two Voices 447
But ere I saw your eyes, my l, — Miller's D. 43
Such eyes! I swear to you, my l, — „ 87
I loved, and l dispell'd the fear — „ 89
For l possess'd the atmosphere, — „ 91
which true l spells—True l interprets— — „ 187
in truth You must blame L. — „ 192
L that hath us in the net, — „ 203
L the gift is L the debt. — „ 207
L is hurt with jar and fret. — „ 209
L is made a vague regret. — „ 210
What is l? for we forget: — „ 213
O L, L, L! O withering might! — Fatima 1
O L, O fire! once he drew With one long kiss — „ 19
My eyes are full of tears, my heart of l, — Œnone 31
My l hath told me so a thousand times. — „ 197
Hath he not sworn his l a thousand times, — „ 231
leaving my ancient l With the Greek woman. — „ 260
To win his l I lay in wait: — The Sisters 11
I won his l, I brought him home. — „ 14
he that shuts L out, in turn shall be Shut out from L, — To ——, With Pal. of Art. 14
They say he's dying all for l, — May Queen 21
Still with their fires L tipt his keenest darts; — D. of F. Women 173
beams of L, melting the mighty hearts Of captains — „ 175
softly with a threefold cord of l — „ 211
her who knew that L can vanquish Death, — „ 269
God gives us l. Something to love He lends us; but when l is grown To ripeness, — To J. S. 13
Falls off, and l is left alone. — „ 16
Love thou thy land, with l far-brought, — Love thou thy land 1
True l turn'd round on fixed poles, L, that endures not sordid ends, — „ 5
He, by some law that holds in l, — Gardener's D. 9
Such touches are but embassies of l, — „ 18
not your work, but L's. L, unperceived, — „ 24
Such a lord is L, — „ 57
Fancy, led by L, Would play with flying forms — „ 59
For which to praise the heavens but only l, That only l were cause enough for praise.' — „ 104
L's white star Beam'd thro' the thicken'd cedar — „ 165
the Master, L, A more ideal Artist he than all.' — „ 172
L at first sight, first-born, — „ 189
sometimes a Dutch l For tulips: — „ 192
L trebled life within me, — „ 198
L, the third, Between us, — „ 215
while I mused, L with knit brows went by, — „ 245
My first, last l; the idol of my youth, — „ 277
half in l, half spite, he woo'd and wed — Dora 39
all his l came back a hundredfold; — „ 166
and not a room For l or money. — Audley Court 2
breathing l and trust against her lip: — „ 69
'My l for Nature is as old as I; — Edwin Morris 28
three rich sennights more, my l for her. — „ 30
My l for Nature and my l for her, — „ 31
L to me As in the Latin song I learnt at school, — „ 78
The l, that makes me thrice a man, — Talking Oak 11
languidly adjust My vapid vegetable l's — „ 183
Pursue thy l's among the bowers — „ 199
This fruit of thine by L is blest, — „ 249
Where fairer fruit of L may rest — „ 251
Of l that never found his earthly close, — Love and Duty 1
But am I not the nobler thro' thy l? — „ 19
likewise thou Art more thro' L, — „ 21
Wait, and L himself will bring The drooping flower — „ 23
For L himself took part against himself To warn us off, and Duty loved of L—O this world's curse, — „ 45
Could L part thus? — „ 55
Caught up the whole of l and utter'd it, — „ 82
Can thy l, Thy beauty, make amends, — Tithonus 23
fancy lightly turns to thoughts of l. — Locksley Hall 20
L took up the glass of Time, — „ 31
L took up the harp of Life, — „ 33
and love her for the l she bore? — „ 73

Love (s) (*continued*) *l* is *l* for evermore. — *Locksley Hall* 74
beauty doth inform Stillness with *l*, — *Day-Dm., Sleep. B.* 16
For *l* in sequel works with fate, — " *Arrival* 3
O *l*, for such another kiss ; ' — " *Depart.* 10
' O wake for ever, *l*,' she hears. — " 11
' O *l*, 'twas such as this and this.' — " 12
' O *l*, thy kiss would wake the dead ! — " 20
I never felt the kiss of *l*, — *Sir Galahad* 19
l no more Can touch the heart of Edward Gray. — *Edward Gray* 7
' *L* may come, and *l* may go, — " 29
L will make our cottage pleasant, — *L. of Burleigh* 15
And he cheer'd her soul with *l*. — " 68
She talk'd as if her *l* were dead, — *The Letters* 27
' No more of *l* ; your sex is known : — " 29
Frantic *l* and frantic hate. — *Vision of Sin* 150
' Tell me tales of thy first *l*— — " 163
and Enoch spoke his *l*, — *Enoch Arden* 40
And mutual *l* and honourable toil ; — " 83
I do beseech you by the *l* you bear Him — " 307
Lord of his rights and of his children's *l*,— — " 764
dream That *L* could bind them closer — *Aylmer's Field* 41
and true *l* Crown'd after trial ; — " 99
how should *L*, Whom the cross-lightnings — " 128
his, a brother's *l*, that hung With wings — " 138
and truth and *l* are strength, — " 365
Of such a *l* as like a chidden child, — " 541
A Martin's summer of his faded *l*, — " 560
the hapless *l's* And double death — " 616
Wearing the light yoke of that Lord of *l*, — " 708
you loved, for he was worthy *l*. — " 712
our *l* and reverence left them bare ? — " 785
Ah *l*, there surely lives in man and beast — *Sea Dreams* 68
We remember *l* ourselves In our sweet youth : — *Princess i* 122
As arguing *l* of knowledge and of power ; — " *ii* 57
O hard, when *l* and duty clash ! — " 293
a thousand baby *l's* Fly twanging headless arrows — " 401
half the students, all the *l*. — " *iii* 39
angled with them for her pupil's *l* : — " 93
every woman counts her due, *L*, children, happiness ? ' — " 245
tho' your Prince's *l* were like a God's, — " 248
O *l*, they die in yon rich sky, — " *iv* 13
deep as *l*, Deep as first *l*, — " 56
cheep and twitter twenty million *l's*. — " 101
Why lingereth she to clothe her heart with *l*, — " 105
tell her, brief is life but *l* is long, — " 111
to junketing and *l*. *L* is it ? — " 142
heated thro' and thro' with wrath and *l*, — " 163
I bore up in part from ancient *l*, — " 303
I want her *l*. — " *v* 136
' We remember *l* ourself In our sweet youth ; — " 207
infuse my tale of *l* In the old king's ears, — " 240
I know not what Of insolence and *l*, — " 397
Be dazzled by the wildfire *L* to sloughs — " 441
L and Nature, these are two more terrible — " *vi* 165
where you seek the common *l* of these, — " 172
Pledge of a *l* not to be mine, — " 197
Two women faster welded in one *l* — " 253
so employ'd, should close in *l*, — " *vii* 67
L in the sacred halls Held carnival at will, — " 84
And out of hauntings of my spoken *l*, — " 109
L, like an Alpine harebell hung with tears — " 115
From barren deeps to conquer all with *l* ; — " 164
Fill'd thro' and thro' with *L*, — " 172
come, for *L* is of the valley, come, For *L* is of the valley, come thou down — " 198
make her as the man, Sweet *L* were slain : — " 277
Sweet *l* on pranks of saucy boyhood : — " 344
l of country move thee there at all, — *Ode on Well.* 140
debt Of boundless *l* and reverence and regret — " 157
and learns to deaden *L* of self, — " 205
From *l* to *l*, from home to home you go, — *W. to Marie Alex.* 8
L by right divine is deathless king, — " 29
L has led thee to the stranger land, — " 31
hearts that change not, *l* that cannot cease, — " 46
With a *l* that ever will be : — *G. of Swainston* 14

Love (s) (*continued*) running on one way to the home of my *l*, — *Window, On the Hill* 8
Birds' *l* and birds' song — " *Spring* 1
Birds' song and birds' *l*, (repeat) — " 3, 5
Men's song and men's *l*, — " 7
And women's *l* and men's ! — " 10
Take my *l*, for *l* will come, *L* will come but once a life. — " *No Answer* 20
Take my *l* and be my wife. — " 24
L can love but once a life. — " 28
you have gotten the wings of *l*, — " *Ay* 15
Sun sets, moon sets, *L*, fix a day. — " *When* 4
Here is the golden close of *l*, — " *Marr. Morn.* 3
For this is the golden morning of *l*, — " 11
For a *l* that never tires ? — " 18
O heart, are you great enough for *l* ? — " 19
Strong Son of God, immortal *L*, — *In Mem., Pro.* 1
Let *L* clasp Grief lest both be drown'd, — " *i* 9
victor Hours should scorn The long result of *l*, — " 14
Poor child, that waitest for thy *l* ! — " *vi* 28
Phosphor, bright As our pure *l*, — " *ix* 11
My friend, the brother of my *l* ; — " 16
Because it needed help of *L* : — " *xxv* 8
L would cleave in twain The lading of a single pain, — " 10
No lapse of moons can canker *L*, — " *xxvi* 3
And *L* the indifference to be, — " 12
Then one deep *l* doth supersede — " *xxxii* 5
Whose *l's* in higher *l* endure ; — " 14
But for one hour, O *L*, I strive — " *xxxv* 6
L would answer with a sigh, — " 13
At first as Death, *L* had not been, — " 19
And render human *l* his dues ; — " *xxxvii* 16
She enters other realms of *l* ; — " *xl* 12
And *l* will last as pure and whole — " *xliii* 13
O *L*, thy province were not large, — " *xlvi* 13
Look also, *L*, a brooding star, — " 15
dream can hit the mood Of *L* on earth ? — " *xlvii* 12
And makes it vassal unto *l* : — " *xlviii* 8
And I be lessen'd in his *l* ? — " *li* 8
Shall *l* be blamed for want of faith ? — " 10
For *l* reflects the thing beloved ; — " *lii* 2
The Spirit of true *l* replied ; — " 6
Who trusted God was *l* indeed — " *lvi* 13
And *l* Creation's final law— — " 14
play As with the creature of my *l* ; — " *lix* 12
Then be my *l* an idle tale, — " *lxii* 3
And *l* in which my hound has part, — " *lxiii* 2
' *L's* too precious to be lost, — " *lxv* 3
To utter *l* more sweet than praise. — " *lxxvii* 16
To hold the costliest *l* in fee. — " *lxxix* 4
' My *l* shall now no further range ; — " *lxxxi* 2
For now is *l* mature in ear.' — " 4
L, then, had hope of richer store : — " 5
As link'd with thine in *l* and fate, — " *lxxxiv* 38
l for him have drain'd My capabilities of *l* ; — " *lxxxv* 11
I woo your *l* : I count it crime To mourn — " 61
A meeting somewhere, *l* with *l*, — " 99
If not so fresh, with *l* as true, — " 101
First *l*, first friendship, equal powers, — " 107
Quite in the *l* of what is gone, — " 114
He tasted *l* with half his mind, — " *xc* 1
l's dumb cry defying change To test his worth ; — " *xcv* 27
My *l* has talk'd with rocks and trees ; — " *xcvii* 1
Their *l* has never past away ; — " 13
Two spirits of a diverse *l* Contend — " *cii* 7
Ring in the *l* of truth and right, — " *cvi* 23
Ring in the common *l* of good. — " 24
A *l* of freedom rarely felt, — " *cix* 13
But mine the *l* that will not tire, And, born of *l*, the vague desire — " *cx* 18
fillest all the room Of all my *l*, — " *cxii* 6
What is she, cut from *l* and faith, — " *cxiv* 11
Nor dream of human *l* and truth, — " *cxviii* 3
Or *L* but play'd with gracious lies, — " *cxxv* 7
L is and was my Lord and King, — " *cxxvi* 1

Love (s) (*continued*) *L* is and was my King and Lord, *In Mem. cxxvi* 5
The *l* that rose on stronger wings, „ *cxxviii* 1
My *l* involves the *l* before; „ *cxxx* 9
My *l* is vaster passion now; „ 10
And yet is *l* not less, but more; „ *Con.* 12
Regret is dead, but *l* is more „ 17
there was *l* in the passionate shriek, *L* for the silent thing that had made false haste *Maud I i* 57
I flee from the cruel madness of *l*, „ *iv* 55
I fear, the new strong wine of *l*, „ *vi* 82
I have led her home, my *l*, „ *xviii* 1
Death may give More life to *L* than is or ever was „ 47
L, like men in drinking-songs, „ 55
With dear *L's* tie, makes *L* himself more dear.' „ 61
now by this my *l* has closed her sight „ 67
And the planet of *L* is on high, „ *xxii* 8
Have a grain of *l* for me, „ *II ii* 53
Let me and my passionate *l* go by, „ 77
Me and my harmful *l* go by; „ 80
To find the arms of my true *l* Round me „ *iv* 3
Hearts with no *l* for me: „ 94
l of a peace that was full of wrongs and shames, „ *III vi* 40
May all *l*, His *l*, unseen but felt, *Ded. of Idylls* 50
The *l* of all Thy sons encompass Thee, The *l* of all Thy daughters cherish Thee, The *l* of all Thy people comfort Thee, Till God's *l* set Thee at his side again! „ 52, 53, 54
Sware on the field of death a deathless *l*. *Com. of Arthur* 132
Uther cast upon her eyes of *l*: „ 193
loathed the bright dishonour of his *l*, „ 195
Sware at the shrine of Christ a deathless *l*: „ 466
I charge thee by my *l*,' *Gareth and L.* 55
' True *l*, sweet son, had risk'd himself „ 60
l I feel for thee, nor worthy such a *l*: „ 83
thy *l* to me, Thy Mother,—I demand.' „ 146
l be blamed for it, not she, nor I: „ 299
Eyes of pure women, wholesome stars of *l*; „ 314
Peace to thee, woman, with thy *l's* and hates! „ 373
one would praise the *l* that linkt the King „ 492
And, loving, utter faithfulness in *l*, „ 554
And as for *l*, God wot, I love not yet, „ 561
Who tilt for lady's *l* and glory here, „ 740
Smile sweetly, thou! my *l* hath smiled on me.' „ 1001
twice my *l* hath smiled on me.' (repeat) „ 1062, 1077
What knowest thou of lovesong or of *l*? „ 1063
A foolish *l* for flowers? „ 1072
thrice my *l* hath smiled on me.' „ 1161
Of utter peace, and *l*, and gentleness! „ 1289
Long in their common *l* rejoiced Geraint. *Marr. of Geraint* 23
Touching her guilty *l* for Lancelot, „ 25
dwelling on his boundless *l*, „ 63
and dreaming of her *l* For Lancelot, „ 158
l or fear, or seeking favour of us, „ 700
for whose *l* the Roman Cæsar first Invaded Britain, „ 745
' Earl, entreat her by my *l*, „ 760
force in her Link'd with such *l* for me, „ 806
Enid, my early and my only *l*, *Geraint and E.* 307
For the man's *l* once gone never returns. „ 333
lord Geraint, I greet you with all *l*; „ 785
love you, Prince, with something of the *l* „ 788
With deeper and with ever deeper *l*, „ 928
bearing in their common bond of *l*, *Balin and Balan* 150
sought to win my *l* Thro' evil ways: „ 474
And yet hast often pleaded for my *l*— „ 571
' I hold them happy, so they died for *l*: „ 581
L, if *L* be perfect, casts out fear, *Merlin and V.* 40
flatter his own wish in age for *l*, „ 185
Death in all life and lying in all *l*, „ 194
As if in deepest reverence and in *l*. „ 220
wise in *l* Love most, say least,' „ 247
ask'd again: for see you not, dear *l*, „ 324
The great proof of your *l*: „ 354
' In *L*, if *L* be *L*, if *L* be ours, „ 387
for *l* of God and men And noble deeds, „ 412
L, tho' *L* were of the grossest, carves „ 461

Love (s) (*continued*) rest: and *L* Should have some rest and pleasure *Merlin and V.* 484
But work as vassal to the larger *l*, That dwarfs the petty *l* of one to one. „ 491
this full *l* of mine Without the full heart back „ 533
Full many a *l* in loving youth was mine; „ 546
charm to keep them mine But youth and *l*; „ 548
How from the rosy lips of life and *l*, „ 846
(For in a wink the false *l* turns to hate) „ 852
O vainly lavish'd *l*! „ 859
for what shame in *l*, So *l* be true, „ 861
more in kindness than in *l*, „ 907
' There must be now no passages of *l* „ 913
Merlin, the one passionate *l* Of her whole life; „ 955
my *l* is more Than many diamonds,' *Lancelot and E.* 87
great and guilty *l* he bare the Queen, „ 245
In battle with the *l* he bare his lord, „ 246
loved him, with that *l* which was her doom. „ 260
'*L*, are you yet so sick?' „ 571
And I, when often they have talk'd of *l*, „ 673
I know not if I know what true *l* is, „ 676
cross our mighty Lancelot in his *l's*! „ 688
Yet, if he love, and his *l* hold, „ 697
About the maid of Astolat, and her *l*. „ 723
woman's *l*, Save one, he not regarded, „ 840
but her deep *l* Upbore her; „ 860
loved her with all *l* except the *l* Of man and woman „ 868
shackles of an old *l* straiten'd him, „ 875
' Your *l*,' she said, ' your *l*—to be your wife.' „ 933
ill then should I quit your brother's *l*, „ 944
This is not *l*: but *l's* first flash in youth, „ 949
she by tact of *l* was well aware That Lancelot „ 984
her song, ' The Song of *L* and Death,' „ 1005
' Sweet is true *l* tho' given in vain, „ 1007
'*L*, art thou sweet? then bitter death must be: *L*, thou art bitter; sweet is death to me. O *L*, if death be sweeter, let me die. „ 1010
' Sweet *l*, that seems not made to fade away, „ 1013
' I fain would follow *l*, if that could be; „ 1016
there the King will know me and my *l*, „ 1058
she returns his *l* in open shame; „ 1083
And greatest, tho' my *l* had no return: „ 1094
take the little bed on which I died For Lancelot's *l*, „ 1118
in half disdain At *l*, life, all things, „ 1239
I loved you, and my *l* had no return, And therefore my true *l* has been my death. „ 1276
loved me with a *l* beyond all *l* In women, „ 1293
No cause, not willingly, for such a *l*: „ 1298
I told her that her *l* Was but the flash of youth, „ 1317
Forgive me; mine was jealousy in *l*.' „ 1351
' That is *l's* curse; pass on, my Queen, „ 1353
if what is worthy *l* Could bind him, but free *l* will not be bound.' „ 1378
' Free *l*, so bound, were freëst,' said the King. „ 1380
' Let *l* be free; free *l* is for the best: „ 1381
What should be best, if not so pure a *l* „ 1383
with a *l* Far tenderer than my Queen's. „ 1394
' Jealousy in *l*?' Not rather dead *l's* harsh heir, „ 1397
Queen, if I grant the jealousy as of *l*, „ 1399
Speak, as it waxes, of a *l* that wanes? „ 1401
A way by *l* that waken'd *l* within, *Holy Grail* 11
With such a fervent flame of human *l*, „ 74
' My knight, my *l*, my knight of heaven, O thou, my *l*, whose *l* is one with mine, „ 157
To find thine own first *l* once more— „ 620
Being so clouded with his grief and *l*, „ 656
That Pelleas might obtain his lady's *l*, *Pelleas and E.* 161
wilt at length Yield me thy *l* and know me „ 249
I had liefer ye were worthy of my *l*, „ 301
tho' ye kill my hope, not yet my *l*, „ 303
this man loves, If *l* there be: „ 308
Dishonour'd all for trial of true *l*—*L*?—we be all alike: „ 477
thro' her *l* her life Wasted and pined, „ 495
Sole Queen of Beauty and of *l*, *Last Tournament* 208
' Free *l*—free field—we love (repeat) „ 275, 281

Love (s) (*continued*) New life, new *l*, to suit the newer day: New *l's* — *Last Tournament* 279
Is as the measure of my *l* for thee.' „ 538
pluck'd one way by hate and one by *l*, „ 539
my Queen Paramount of *l* And loveliness— „ 552
Queen Have yielded him her *l*.' „ 565
therefore is my *l* so large for thee, Seeing it is not bounded save by *l*.' „ 702
an I turn'd away my *l* for thee „ 705
Rapt in sweet talk or lively, all on *l* And sport — *Guinevere* 386
the desire of fame, And *l* of truth, „ 483
Thy lord has wholly lost his *l* for thee. „ 509
My *l* thro' flesh hath wrought into my life „ 558
Past with thee thro' thy people and their *l*, — *To the Queen ii* 7
friends—your *l* Is but a burthen: „ 16
Not for itself, but thro' thy living *l* „ 34
withers on the breast of peaceful *l*; — *Lover's Tale i* 10
hills that watch'd thee, as *L* watcheth *L*, „ 12
Betwixt the native land of *L* and me, „ 25
O *L*, O Hope! They come, they crowd upon me „ 46
Here, too, my *l* Waver'd at anchor with me, „ 64
Flow back again into my slender spring And first of *l*, „ 148
neither *L*, Warm in the heart, his cradle, can remember *L* in the womb, „ 157
that my *l* Grew with myself— „ 164
Or build a wall betwixt my life and *l*, „ 176
As *L* and I do number equal years, So she, my *l*, is of an age with me. „ 195
My mother's sister, mother of my *l*, „ 209
nor was his *l* the less Because it was divided, „ 228
for that day, *L*, rising, shook his wings, „ 317
all the low dark groves, a land of *l*! „ 332
Spirit of *L*! that little hour was bound „ 437
her life, her *l*, With my life, *l*, soul, spirit, „ 459
I could not speak my *l*. *L* lieth deep: *L* dwells not in lip-depths. *L* wraps his wings on either side the heart, „ 465
Drunk in the largeness of the utterance Of *L*; but how should Earthly measure mete The Heavenly-unmeasured or unlimited *L*, „ 473
Than language grasp the infinite of *L*. „ 484
sick with *l*, Fainted at intervals, „ 545
Her maiden dignities of Hope and *L*— „ 580
the tender *l* Of him she brooded over. „ 616
nestled in this bosom-throne of *L*, „ 624
how her *l* did clothe itself in smiles „ 658
And why was I to darken their pure *l*, „ 727
to this present My full-orb'd *l* had waned not. „ 734
Her *l* did murder mine? What then? „ 740
She told me all her *l*: she shall not weep. „ 742
for I loved her, lost my *l* in *L*; „ 749
till their *l* Shall ripen to a proverb, „ 757
One golden dream of *l*, from which „ 760
sure my *l* should ne'er indue the front „ 774
Shall *L* pledge Hatred in her bitter draughts, And batten on her poisons? *L* forbid! „ 776
L passeth not the threshold of cold Hate, And Hate is strange beneath the roof of *L*. „ 778
O *L*, if thou be'st *L*, dry up these tears Shed for the *l* of *L*; „ 780
So *L*, arraign'd to judgment and to death, „ 785
when their *l* is wreck'd—if *L* can wreck— „ 804
Where *L* could walk with banish'd Hope „ 813
L's arms were wreath'd about the neck of Hope, and Hope kiss'd *L*, and *L* „ 815
They said that *L* would die when Hope was gone, And *L* mourn'd long, „ 818
trod The same old paths where *L* had walk'd with Hope, And Memory fed the soul of *L* with tears. „ 821
till they faded like my *l*. „ *ii* 10
if Affection Living slew *L*, and Sympathy hew'd out „ 31
I told him all my *l*, How I had loved her „ 90
A monument of childhood and of *l*; The poesy of childhood; my lost *l* Symbol'd in storm. „ 183
My sister, and my cousin, and my *l*, „ *iii* 43

Love (s) (*continued*) O *l*, I have not seen you for so long. — *Lover's Tale iv* 45
Hearts that had beat with such a *l* as mine— „ 69
am I made immortal, or my *l* Mortal once more?' „ 79
you have given me life and *l* again, „ 110
the house had known the *l's* of both; „ 123
This *l* is of the brain, the mind, the soul: „ 156
that great *l* they both had borne the dead, „ 181
By all the laws of *l* and gratefulness, „ 278
As for a solemn sacrifice of *l*— „ 301
guest So bound to me by common *l* and loss— „ 345
And then began the story of his *l* „ 354
And *l*, and boundless thanks— „ 382
An' he smiled at me, 'Ain't you, my *l*? — *First Quarrel* 62
For *l* will go by contrast, as by likes. — *Sisters (E. and E.)* 42
L at first sight May seem— „ 91
Not I that day of Edith's *l* or mine— „ 142
Had I not known where *L*, at first a fear, „ 170
So *L* and Honour jarr'd Tho' *L* and Honour „ 176
L Were not his own imperial all-in-all. „ 226
with what *l* Edith had welcomed my brief wooing „ 253
Not that her *l*, Tho' scarce as great as Edith's power of *l*, „ 260
remembering all The *l* they both have borne me, and the *l* I bore them both— „ 280
in the rich vocabulary of *L* 'Most dearest' „ 291
would die But for the voice of *L*, — *In the Child. Hosp.* 12
fatal kiss, Born of true life and *l*, divorce thee not From earthly *l* and life— — *Ded. Poem Prin. Alice* 3
Where *L* and Longing dress thy deeds in light, „ 9
Indissolubly married like our *l*; — *De Prof., Two G.* 14
Yet loves and hates with mortal hates and *l's* — *Tiresias* 23
that hast never known the embrace of *l*, „ 164
With the first great *l* I had felt — *The Wreck* 76
'as in truest *L* no Death.' „ 80
Knowing the *L* we were used to believe — *Despair* 54
'Dear *L*, for ever and ever, „ 58
Infinite *L* that has served us so well? „ 95
His *L* would have power over Hell „ 102
God of *L* and of Hell together— „ 105
My rose of *l* for ever gone, — *Ancient Sage* 159
not *L* but Hate that weds a bride against her will; — *The Flight* 32
The *l* that keeps this heart alive „ 35
where summer never dies, with *L*, the Sun of life! „ 44
And *L* is fire, and burns the feet „ 68
Christian *l* among the Churches — *Locksley H., Sixty* 86
Envy wears the mask of *L*, „ 109
half-brain races, led by Justice, *L*, and Truth; „ 161
Or *L* with wreaths of flowers. — *Epilogue* 17
Son's *l* built me, and I hold Mother's *l* in letter'd gold. — *Helen's Tower* 3
L is in and out of time, „ 5
granite girth were strong As either *l*, „ 8
Of *L* to leaven all the mass, — *Freedom* 19
Two Suns of *L* make day of human life, — *To Prin. Beatrice* 1
The later-rising Sun of spousal *L*, „ 6
This later light of *L* have risen in vain, „ 16
Sway'd by each *L*, and swaying to each *L*, „ 19
Will mix with *l* for you and yours. — *To Marq. of Dufferin* 52
harvest hymns of Earth The worship which is *L*, — *Demeter and P.* 149
L for the maiden, crown'd with marriage, — *Vastness* 23
till Self died out in the *l* of his kind; „ 28
Shall not *my l* last, Moon, with you, — *The Ring* 17
And utter knowledge is but utter *l*— „ 43
Hubert weds in you The heart of *L*, „ 62
to laugh at *l* in death! „ 231
matron saw That hinted *l* was only wasted bait, „ 360
but now my *l* was hers again, „ 393
Bound by the golden cord of their first *l*— „ 429
pardon, O my *l*, if I ever gave you pain. — *Happy* 68
be content Till I be leper like yourself, my *l*, „ 88
work old laws of *L* to fresh results, — *Prog. of Spring* 85
Light again, leaf again, life again, *l* again,' — *The Throstle* 3
'*L* again, song again, nest again, „ 9
This, and my *l* together, — *June Bracken, etc.* 5
by thy *l* which once was mine, — *Death of Œnone* 45

Love (verb) (*continued*) For truly there are those who *l* me yet; *Marr. of Geraint* 461
Except the lady he *l's* best be there. „ 481
I would the two Should *l* each other: „ 792
he *l's* to know When men of mark are in his territory: *Geraint and E.* 228
doth he *l* you as of old? „ 323
men may bicker with the things they *l*, „ 325
that this man *l's* you no more. „ 329
But here is one who *l's* you as of old; „ 334
'Earl, if you *l* me as in former years, „ 355
village boys Who *l* to vex him eating, „ 561
I *l* that beauty should go beautifully: „ 681
I never loved, can never *l* but him: „ 709
Who *l* you, Prince, with something of the love Wherewith we *l* the Heaven that chastens us. „ 788
A year ago—nay, then I *l* thee not— *Balin and Balan* 504
vows like theirs, that high in heaven *L* most, *Merlin and V.* 15
'O Merlin, do ye *l* me?' (repeat) „ 235, 236
'Great Master, do ye *l* me? „ 237
'Who are wise in love *L* most, say least,' „ 248
Master, do ye *l* my tender rhyme?' „ 399
methinks you think you *l* me well; For me, I *l* you somewhat; rest: „ 483
'Man dreams of Fame while woman wakes to *l*.' „ 460
proof against the grain Of him ye say ye *l*: „ 488
However well ye think ye *l* me now „ 516
try this charm on whom ye say ye *l*.' „ 525
My daily wonder is, I *l* at all. „ 536
And one to make me jealous if I *l*, „ 539
must be to *l* thee still. „ 928
'O Merlin, tho' you do not *l* me, save, Yet save me!' „ 944
A sight ye *l* to look on.' *Lancelot and E.* 83
who *l's* me must have a touch of earth; „ 133
He *l's* it in his knights more than himself: „ 157
Ill news, my Queen, for all who *l* him, „ 598
'that you *l* This greatest knight, „ 668
But if I know, then, if I *l* not him, I know there is none other I can *l*.' „ 677
'Yea, by God's death,' said he, 'ye *l* him well, „ 679
knew ye what all others know, And whom he *l's*.' „ 681
For if you *l*, it will be sweet to give it; And if he *l*, it will be sweet to have it „ 692
whether he *l* or not, A diamond is a diamond. „ 694
Yet, if he *l*, and his love hold, „ 697
Whose sleeve he wore; she *l's* him; „ 711
'The maid of Astolat *l's* Sir Lancelot, Sir Lancelot *l's* the maid of Astolat.' „ 725
But did not *l* the colour; „ 840
love Of man and woman when they *l* their best, „ 869
He will not *l* me: how then? „ 893
'I have gone mad. I *l* you: „ 930
Sir Lancelot's fault Not to *l* me, than it is mine to *l* Him „ 1076
He *l's* the Queen, and in an open shame: „ 1082
Yet to be loved makes not to *l* again; „ 1295
All that belongs to knighthood, and I *l*.' *Pelleas and E.* 9
I *l* thee, tho' I know thee not. „ 43
win me this fine circlet, Pelleas, That I may *l* thee?' „ 129
on the morrow knighted, sware To *l* one only. „ 141
'To those who *l* them, trials of our faith. „ 210
and if ye *l* me not, I cannot bear to dream „ 299
this man *l's*, If love there be: „ 307
He could not *l* me, did he know me well. „ 312
'Avaunt,' they cried, 'our lady *l's* thee not.' „ 369
That whom ye loathe, him will I make you *l*.' „ 390
He dies who *l's* it,—if the worm be there.' „ 409
What faith have these in whom they sware to *l*? *Last Tournament* 188
'Free love—free field—we *l* (repeat) „ 275, 281
What, if she *l* me still? „ 497
He find thy favour changed and *l* thee not'— „ 500
I should hate thee more than *l*.' „ 600
Did I *l* her? the name at least I loved. „ 603
I say, Swear to me thou wilt *l* me ev'n when old, „ 652
my soul, we *l* but while we may; „ 701

Love (verb) (*continued*) 'We *l* but while we may.' Well then, *Last Tournament* 712
and I will *l* thee to the death, „ 720
'O Lancelot, if thou *l* me get thee hence.' *Guinevere* 95
True men who *l* me still, for whom I live, „ 445
To *l* one maiden only, cleave to her, „ 475
tho' thou wouldst not *l* thy lord, „ 508
that my doom is, I *l* thee still. „ 559
Let no man dream but that I *l* thee „ 560
tell the King I *l* him tho' so late? „ 651
I must not scorn myself: he *l's* me still. „ 673
Let no one dream but that he *l's* me still. „ 674
thy life is whole, and still I live Who *l* thee; *Pass. of Arthur* 151
sons, who *l* Our ocean-empire *To the Queen ii* 28
draught of that sweet fountain that he *l's*, *Lover's Tale i* 141
Ye ask me, friends, When I began to *l*. „ 145
So know I not when I began to *l*. „ 163
In that I live I *l*; because I *l* I live: „ 178
Than the gray cuckoo *l's* his name, „ 257
I found, they two did *l* each other, „ 728
Did I *l* her? Ye know that I did *l* her; „ 732
Did I *l* her, And could I look upon her „ 735
Let them so *l* that men and boys may say, 'Lo! how they *l* each other!' „ 756
Deem that I *l* thee but as brothers do, So shalt thou *l* me still as sisters do; „ 767
had there been none else To *l* as lovers, „ 771
I will be alone with all I *l*, „ *iv* 47
solemn offering of you To him you *l*.' „ 119
I'll never *l* any but you, (repeat) *First Quarrel* 22, 32, 33, 34
I loved Edith, made Edith *l me*. *Sisters* (*E. and E.*) 139
I know not which of these I *l* the best. „ 283
But *you l* Edith; and her own true eyes „ 284
I think *I* likewise *l* your Edith most. „ 293
Better to fall by the hands that they *l*, *Def. of Lucknow* 53
Ay, for they *l* me! *Sir J. Oldcastle* 44
Who dost not *l* our England— *To Victor Hugo* 9
Yet *l's* and hates with mortal hates and loves, *Tiresias* 23
thou art wise enough, Tho' young, to *l* thy wiser, „ 154
one thing given me, to *l* and to live for, *The Wreck* 35
Stephen, I *l* you, I *l* you, and yet'— „ 101
The wife, the sons, who *l* him best *Ancient Sage* 125
I swear and swear forsworn To *l* him most, *The Flight* 50
They *l* their mates, to whom they sing; „ 65
She bad us *l*, like souls in Heaven, „ 88
every heart that *l's* with truth is equal to endure. „ 104
L your enemy, bless your haters, *Locksley H., Sixty* 85
I that loathed, have come to *l* him. „ 280
who *l's* War for War's own sake Is fool, *Epilogue* 30
only to be known By those who *l* thee best. *Pref. Poem Broth. S.* 8
Who *l's* his native country best. *Hands all Round* 4
To Canada whom we *l* and prize, „ 19
between The two that *l* thee, *To Prin. Beatrice* 18
Your rule has made the people *l* Their ruler. *To Marq. of Dufferin* 9
man, that only lives and *l's* an hour, *Demeter and P.* 106
Till thy dark lord accept and *l* the Sun, „ 137
for I loved him, and *l* him for ever: *Vastness* 36
And bind the maid to *l* you by the ring; *The Ring* 202
flaunted it Before that other whom I loved and *l*. „ 244
Miriam, if you *l* me take the ring!' „ 263
if you cannot *l* me, let it be.' „ 265
You *l* me still 'Io t'amo.'—Muriel—no—She cannot *l*; she *l's* her own hard self, „ 291
Why had I made her *l* me thro' the ring, „ 391
'That weak and watery nature *l* you? „ 396
but now I *l* you most; *Happy* 29
whisper'd me 'your Ulric *l's*' „ 62
Who *l* the winter woods, *To Ulysses* 14
Who *l* her still, and whimper, *Romney's R.* 117
I *l* you more than when we married. „ 157
cried '*L* one another little ones' *Akbar's Dream* 76
L me? O yes, no doubt—how long— *Charity* 5
And *l's* the world from end to end, *The Wanderer* 7

Loveable Elaine the fair, Elaine the *l*, *Lancelot and E.* 1

Love-charm'd stars that hung *L-c* to listen: *Love and Duty* 75

Loved (*See also* **Loov'd, Luvv'd, Well-loved, Yet-loved**) Ev'n in her sight he *l* so well? *Margaret* 40
IF I were *l*, as I desire to be, *If I were loved* 1
—if I were *l* by thee? „ 4
I *l* thee for the tear thou couldst not hide, *The Bridesmaid* 11
Have lived and *l* alone so long, *Miller's D.* 38
I *l*, and love dispell'd the fear „ 89
I *l* the brimming wave that swam Thro' quiet meadows „ 97
I *l* you better for your fears, „ 149
But I *l* his beauty passing well. *The Sisters* 23
silver tongue, Cold February *l*, is dry: *The Blackbird* 14
a sleep They sleep—the men I *l*. *M. d'Arthur* 17
we *l* the man, and prized his work; „ *Ep.* 8
woman's heart, the heart of her I *l*; *Gardener's D.* 230
on the cheeks, Like one that *l* him: *Dora* 134
I have kill'd him—but I *l* him— „ 160
l At first like dove and dove were cat and dog *Walk. to the Mail* 57
but for daily loss of one she *l* „ 94
and Duty *l* of Love— *Love and Duty* 46
both with those That *l* me, and alone; *Ulysses* 9
weeping, 'I have *l* thee long.' *Locksley Hall* 30
I had *l* thee more than ever wife was *l*. „ 64
No—she never *l* me truly: „ 74
to have *l* so slight a thing. „ 148
l the people well, And loathed to see them overtax'd; *Godiva* 8
therefore, as they *l* her well, „ 38
'Ellen Adair she *l* me well, *Edward Gray* 9
And the people *l* her much. *L. of Burleigh* 76
We *l* the glories of the world, *The Voyage* 83
And you, whom once I *l* so well, *The Letters* 35
But Philip *l* in silence; *Enoch Arden* 41
But she *l* Enoch; tho' she knew it not, „ 43
And her, he *l*, a beggar: „ 117
To sell the boat—and yet he *l* her well— „ 134
I have *l* you longer than you know.' „ 421
can you be ever *l* As Enoch was? „ 426
to be *l* A little after Enoch.' „ 428
he had *l* her longer than she knew, „ 455
nor *l* she to be left Alone at home, „ 516
home Where Annie lived and *l* him, „ 685
Then may she learn I *l* her to the last.' „ 835
yet the brook he *l*, For which, *The Brook* 15
fancies of the boy, To me that *l* him; „ 20
he *l* As heiress and not heir regretfully? *Aylmer's Field* 23
young hearts not knowing that they *l*, „ 133
He but less *l* than Edith, of her poor: „ 167
He, *l* for her and for himself. „ 179
neither *l* nor liked the thing he heard. „ 250
for I have *l* you more as son Than brother, „ 351
The life of all—who madly *l*—and he, „ 389
They *l* me, and because I love their child „ 423
Him too you *l*, for he was worthy love. „ 712
woman half turn'd round from him she *l*, *Sea Dreams* 286
tho' he *l* her none the less, *Lucretius* 4
the mind, except it *l* them, clasp These idols „ 164
l to live alone Among her women; *Princess i* 49
eyes that ever *l* to meet Star-sisters „ *ii* 427
'To linger here with one that *l* us.' „ *iii* 339
I *l* her. Peace be with her. „ *iv* 136
I *l* you like this kneeler, „ 296
he That *l* me closer than his own right eye, „ *v* 531
Call'd him worthy to be *l*, „ *vi* 6
if you *l* The breast that fed or arm that dandled you, „ 180
Dear traitor, too much *l*, why?—why?— „ 293
I *l* the woman: he, that doth not, „ *vii* 313
there was one thro' whom I *l* her, „ 317
Ere seen I *l*, and *l* thee seen, „ 341
We *l* the hall, tho' white and cold, *The Daisy* 37
I walk'd with one I *l* two and thirty years ago. *V. of Cauteretz* 4
Two dead men have I *l* With a love *G. of Swainston* 13
Three dead men have I *l* and thou art last of the three. „ 15
I find him worthier to be *l*. *In Mem., Pro.* 40
'Behold the man that *l* and lost, „ *i* 15
With my lost Arthur's *l* remains, „ *ix* 3
The human-hearted man I *l*, „ *xiii* 11

Loved (*continued*) I *l* the weight I had to bear, *In Mem. xxv* 7
'Tis better to have *l* and lost Than never to have *l* at all. „ *xxvii* 15
As when he *l* me here in Time, „ *xliii* 14
Who *l*, who suffer'd countless ills, „ *lvi* 17
My spirit *l* and loves him yet, „ *lx* 2
I *l* thee, Spirit, and love, „ *lxi* 11
'Tis better to have *l* and lost, Than never to have *l* at all— „ *lxxxv* 3
That *l* to handle spiritual strife, „ 54
He *l* to rail against it still, „ *lxxxix* 38
The shape of him I *l*, and love For ever: „ *ciii* 14
The man we *l* was there on deck, „ 41
A little spare the night I *l*, „ *cv* 15
And sing the songs he *l* to hear. „ *cvii* 24
And *l* them more, that they were thine, „ *cx* 15
O *l* the most, when most I feel „ *cxxix* 3
L deeplier, darklier understood; „ 10
Until we close with all we *l*, „ *cxxxi* 11
told me that he *l* A daughter of our house; „ *Con.* 6
For all we thought and *l* and did, „ 134
To speak of the mother she *l* *Maud I xix* 27
one short hour to see The souls we *l*, „ *II iv* 15
l one only and who clave to her—' *Ded. of Idylls* 11
He laugh'd upon his warrior whom he *l* And honour'd most. *Com. of Arthur* 125
Stern too at times, and then I *l* him not, But sweet again, and then I *l* him well. „ 354
Arthur charged his warrior, whom he *l* And honour'd most, „ 447
One, that had *l* him from his childhood, *Gareth and L.* 53
l with that full love I feel for thee, „ 83
Kay the seneschal, who *l* him not, „ 483
And *l* her, as he *l* the light of Heaven. *Marr. of Geraint* 5
so *l* Geraint To make her beauty vary „ 8
and *l* her in a state Of broken fortunes, „ 12
L her, and often with her own white hands „ 16
And Enid *l* the Queen, and with true heart „ 19
tho' he *l* and reverenced her too much „ 119
that dress, and how he *l* her in it, (repeat) „ 141, 843
Hath ask'd again, and ever *l* to hear; „ 436
Might well have served for proof that I was *l*, „ 796
Perhaps because he *l* her passionately, *Geraint and E.* 10
The being he *l* best in all the world, „ 103
Not while they *l* them; „ 327
Enid never *l* a man but him, „ 363
Except the passage that he *l* her not; „ 392
And *l* me serving in my father's hall: „ 699
I never *l*, can never love but him: „ 709
To these my lists with him whom best you *l*; „ 840
with your own true eyes Beheld the man you *l* „ 847
her ladies *l* to call Enid the Fair, „ 962
I *l* thee first, That warps the wit.' *Merlin and V.* 60
O God, that I had *l* a smaller man! „ 872
Who *l* to make men darker than they are, „ 876
My Queen, that summer, when ye *l* me first. *Lancelot and E.* 104
she lifted up her eyes And *l* him, „ 260
darling of the court, *L* of the loveliest, „ 262
l her with all love except the love „ 868
'If I be *l*, these are my festal robes, „ 909
'I never *l* him: an I meet with him, „ 1068
it is my glory to have *l* One peerless, „ 1090
having *l* God's best And greatest, „ 1093
I *l* you, and my love had no return, „ 1276
l me with a love beyond all love In women, „ 1293
Yet to be *l* makes not to love again; „ 1295
And *l* thy courtesies and thee, a man Made to be *l*; „ 1363
Thou couldst have *l* this maiden, „ 1366
to be *l*, if what is worthy love Could bind him, „ 1378
Ye *l* me, damsel, surely with a love „ 1394
l him much beyond the rest, And honour'd him, *Holy Grail* 9
And since he *l* all maidens, *Pelleas and E.* 40
for he dream'd His lady *l* him, and he knew himself *L* of the King: „ 153

Loved (*continued*) Then rang the shout his lady l: *Pelleas and E.* 171
I l you and I deem'd you beautiful, „ 297
Than to be l again of you—farewell; „ 302
yet him I l not. Why? I deem'd him fool? „ 308
For why should I have l her to my shame? I loathe her, as I l her to my shame. „ 482
I never l her, I but lusted for her— „ 484
l it tenderly, And named it Nestling; *Last Tournament* 24
And l him well, until himself had thought He l her also, „ 401
'Grace, Queen, for being l: she l me well. „ 602
Did I love her? the name at least I l. „ 603
Her to be l no more? „ 641
I l This knightliest of all knights, „ 710
how to take last leave of all I l? *Guinevere* 546
Had I but l thy highest creatures here? It was my duty to have l the highest: „ 656
We needs must l the highest when we see it, „ 660
knights Once thine, whom thou hast l, *Pass. of Arthur* 61
And they my knights, who l me once, „ 73
Such a sleep They sleep—the men I l. „ 185
how should I have lived and not have l? *Lover's Tale i* 170
we l The sound of one-another's voices „ 255
Next to her presence whom I l so well, „ 427
Parting my own l mountains was received, „ 433
Even the feet of her I l, I fell, „ 600
The l, the lover, the happy Lionel, „ 654
for I l her, lost my love in Love; I, for I l her, graspt the hand she l, „ 749
dream but how I could have l thee, had there been none else To love as lovers, l again by thee. „ 770
How I had l her from the first; „ *ii* 91
my spirit Was of so wide a compass it took in All I had l, „ 136
the settled countenance Of her I l, „ *iii* 40
all their house was old and l them both, „ *iv* 122
And, tho' he l and honour'd Lionel, „ 148
when the guest Is l and honour'd to the uttermost. „ 245
one who l His master more than all on earth „ 256
I l him better than play; *First Quarrel* 12
an' I l him better than all. „ 14
an' I never l any but you; „ 86
mother and her sister l More passionately still. *Sisters (E. and E.)* 44
Only, believing I l Edith, „ 138
Had I not dream'd I l her yestermorn? „ 169
she That L me—our true Edith— „ 235
In and beyond the grave, that one she l. „ 272
dog that had l him and fawn'd at his knee— *In the Child. Hosp.* 9
We have lost her who l her so much— „ 29
Voice of the dead whom we l, *Def. of Lucknow* 11
freedom, or the sake of those they l, *Sir J. Oldcastle* 186
Old Brooks, who l so well to mouth my rhymes, *To W. H. Brookfield* 2
those dawn-golden times, Who l you well! „ 8
a man men fear is a man to be l by the women they say. And I could have l him too, *The Wreck* 18
Seer Whom one that l, and honour'd him, *Ancient Sage* 3
What had he l, what had he lost, „ 227
I l him then; he *was* my father then. *The Flight* 24
My Edwin l to call us then „ 80
I l ye meself wid a heart and a half, *Tomorrow* 39
Amy l me, Amy fail'd me, *Locksley H., Sixty* 19
All I l are vanish'd voices, „ 252
a wailing, 'I have l thee well.' „ 262
You came, and look'd and l the view Long-known and l by me, *Pro. to Gen. Hamley* 5
I that l thee since my day began, *To Virgil* 38
cried 'Where is my l one? *Demeter and P.* 60
for I l him, and love him for ever: *Vastness* 36
He l my name not me; *The Ring* 191
flaunted it Before that other whom I l and love. „ 244
Miriam l me from the first, „ 274
you—you l me, kept your word. „ 290
all her talk was of the babe she l; „ 353
I l you first when young and fair, *Happy* 29
The king who l me, And cannot die; *Merlin and the G.* 79

Loved (*continued*) l by all the younger gown There at Balliol, *To Master of B.* 2
and he l to dandle the child, *Bandit's Death* 15
He was l at least by his dog: „ 35

Love-deep languors of thy l-d eyes *Eleänore* 76
Love-drunken who was he with such l-d eyes *The Ring* 21
Love-knots leg and arm with l-k gay, *Talking Oak* 65
Love-language heard The low l-l of the bird *In Mem. cii* 11
Love-languid eyes, l-l thro' half tears *Love and Duty* 36
Loveless Sweet death, that seems to make us l clay, *Lancelot and E.* 1014
Lovelier l Than all the valleys of Ionian hills. *Œnone* 1
As l than whatever Oread haunt The knolls of Ida, „ 74
What l of his own had he than her, *Aylmer's Field* 22
Flowers of all heavens, and l than their names, *Princess, Pro.* 12
these fields Are lovely, l not the Elysian lawns, „ *iii* 342
And left her woman, l in her mood „ *vii* 162
The distance takes a l hue, *In Mem. cxv* 6
A l life, a more unstain'd, than his! *Ded. of Idylls* 30
'Far l in our Lancelot had it been, *Lancelot and E.* 589
l than when first Her light feet fell *Last Tournament* 553
might inwreathe (How l, nobler then!) *Lover's Tale i* 459
Far l than its cradle; „ 530
l as herself Is l than all others— „ *iv* 287
Loveliest true To what is l upon earth.' *Mariana in the S.* 64
l in all grace Of movement, *Œnone* 75
Their feet in flowers, her l: *Princess vi* 78
Array'd and deck'd her, as the l, *Marr. of Geraint* 17
And l of all women upon earth. „ 21
darling of the court, Loved of the l, *Lancelot and E.* 262
Most l, earthly-heavenliest harmony? *Lover's Tale i* 279
Turning my way, the l face on earth. *Sisters (E. and E.)* 87
Loveliness Her l with shame and with surprise *D. of F. Women* 89
A miniature of l, all grace Summ'd up *Gardener's D.* 12
In l of perfect deeds, *In Mem. xxxvi* 11
so pure a love Clothed in so pure a l? *Lancelot and E.* 1384
Queen Paramount of love And l— *Last Tournament* 553
Love-longing I thought Laziness, vague l-l's, *Sisters (E. and E.)* 128
Love-lore Thou art perfect in l-l. (repeat) *Madeline* 9, 26
Lovelorn With melodious airs l, *Adeline* 55
Love-loyal L-l to the least wish of the Queen *Lancelot and E.* 89
L-l to the least wish of the Queen, *Guinevere* 126
Lovely (*See also* **Lowly-lovely**) A l time, For it was in the golden prime *Arabian Nights* 86
Stays on her floating locks the l freight *Ode to Memory* 16
He said, 'She has a l face; *L. of Shalott iv* 52
And whisper l words, and use Her influence *Will Water.* 11
She look'd so l, as she sway'd The rein *Sir L. and Q. G.* 40
'Look what a l piece of workmanship!' *Aylmer's Field* 237
then I saw one l star Larger and larger. *Sea Dreams* 93
these fields Are l, lovelier not the Elysian lawns, *Princess iii* 342
The l, lordly creature floated on „ *vi* 89
Be sometimes l like a bride, *In Mem. lix* 6
See what a l shell, Small and pure as a pearl, *Maud II ii* 1
Where like a shoaling sea the l blue *Geraint and E.* 688
But rather seem'd a l baleful star Veil'd *Merlin and V.* 262
and that clear-featured face Was l, *Lancelot and E.* 1160
Love-offering last L-o and peace-offering *Last Tournament* 748
Love-poem and this A mere l-p! *Princess iv* 126
Lover (*See also* **Landscape-lover, Truth-lover**) Two l's whispering by an orchard wall; *Circumstance* 4
Came two young l's lately wed; *L. of Shalott ii* 34
my l, with whom I rode sublime On Fortune's neck: *D. of F. Women* 141
AND on her l's arm she leant, *Day-Dm., Depart.* 1
L's long-betroth'd were they: *Lady Clare* 6
But he clasp'd her like a l, *L. of Burleigh* 67
He like a l down thro' all his blood *Enoch Arden* 659
That grow for happy l's. *The Brook* 173
Yet once by night again the l's met, *Aylmer's Field* 413
l heeded not, But passionately restless „ 545
And at the happy l's heart in heart— *Princess vii* 108
As thou with thy young l hand in hand *W. to Marie Alex.* 34
she aim'd not at glory, no l of glory she: *Wages* 4
me the l of liberty, *Boädicea* 48
A jewel, a jewel dear to a l's eye! *Window, On the Hill* 3

Lover (*continued*) A happy *l* who has come To look on her *In Mem. viii* 1
From a little lazy *l* Who but claims *Maud I xx* 10
Come out to your own true *l*, That your true *l* may see Your glory also, „ 46
For, call it *l's'* quarrels, yet I know *Geraint and E.* 324
one true *l* whom you ever own'd, „ 344
shall we strip him there Your *l*? „ 489
' The little rift within the *l's* lute *Merlin and V.* 393
neither dame nor damsel then Wroth at a *l's* loss? „ 607
chant thy praise As prowest knight and truest *l*, *Pelleas and E.* 350
as the one true knight on earth, And only *l*; „ 495
The Queen Look'd hard upon her *l*, „ 605
How darest thou, if *l*, push me *Last Tournament* 638
The loved, the *l*, the happy Lionel, *Lover's Tale i* 654
The blissful *l*, too, From his great hoard „ 713
had there been none else To love as *l's*, „ 771
And leave the name of *L's* Leap: „ *iv* 42
And thus our lonely *l* rode away, „ 130
I with our *l* to his native Bay. „ 155
What was it? for our *l* seldom spoke, „ 225
The *l* answer'd, ' There is more than one „ 241
For man is a *l* of Truth, *Dead Prophet* 44
souls Of two repentant *L's* guard the ring;' *The Ring* 198
sacred those Ghost *L's* hold the gift.' „ 205
Two *l's* parted by a scurrilous tale „ 208
as the bygone *l* thro' this ring Had sent his cry „ 232
on that day Two *l's* parted „ 427
As if—those two Ghost *l's*— „ 459
L's yet— *Miriam.* Yes, yes! „ 460
you were than a *l's* fairy dream, *To Mary Boyle* 43
For Ralph was Edith's *l*, *The Tourney* 2
Lover's Bay Keep thou thy name of '*L B.*' *Lover's Tale i* 15
Love-sighs passion seeks Pleasance in *l-s*, *Lilian* 9
Lovesome One her dark hair and *l* mien. *Beggar Maid* 12
Love-song A *l-s* I had somewhere read, *Miller's D.* 65
What knowest thou of *l* or of love? *Gareth and L.* 1063
Lovest *L* thou the doleful wind *Adeline* 49
I think thou *l* me well.' *L. of Burleigh* 4
Lovetale The wind Told a *l* beside us, *Lover's Tale i* 543
Loveth And *l* so his innocent heart, *Supp. Confessions* 52
She *l* her own anguish deep *To J. S.* 42
she will not wed Save whom she *l*, *Gareth and L.* 622
Love-whispers Affianced, Sir? *l-w* may not breathe *Princess ii* 221
Loving (*See also* **A-loving, England-loving, Loovin'**) ' I promise thee The fairest and most *l* wife in Greece,' *Œnone* 187
Most *l* is she? „ 201
When thy nerves could understand What there is in *l* tears, *Vision of Sin* 161
Blessing her, praying for her, *l* her; *Enoch Arden* 879
l her As when she laid her head beside my own. „ 880
For she—so lowly-lovely and so *l*. *Aylmer's Field* 168
Up thro' gilt wires a crafty *l* eye, *Princess, Pro.* 172
And *l* hands must part— *Window, Answer* 6
Gray nurses, *l* nothing new; *In Mem. xxix* 14
Two spirits of a diverse love Contend for *l* masterdom. „ *cii* 8
Maud made my Maud by that long *l* kiss, *Maud I xviii* 58
And, *l*, utter faithfulness in love, *Gareth and L.* 554
L his lusty youthhood yielded to him. „ 580
l the battle as well As he that rides him.' „ 1301
(As sons of kings *l* in pupilage *Merlin and V.* 517
For Arthur, *l* his young knight, *Pelleas and E.* 159
Dust, as he said, that once was *l* hearts, *Lover's Tale iv* 68
nay, but could I wed her *L* the other? *Sisters (E. and E.)* 168
Who yearn to lay my *l* head upon your leprous breast. *Happy* 26
Now God has made you leper in His *l* care for both, „ 91
domes the red-plow'd hills With *l* blue; *Early Spring* 4
Lovingkindness delightedly fulfill'd All *l'es*, *Lover's Tale i* 225
Low (adj. and adv.) Is not my human pride brought *l*? *Supp. Confessions* 14
stooping *l* Unto the death, not sunk! „ 97
Breathed *l* around the rolling earth *The winds, etc.* 3
an accent very *l* In blandishment, *Isabel* 19
And ever when the moon was *l*, *Mariana* 49
But when the moon was very *l*, „ 53
The *l* and bloomed foliage, *Arabian Nights* 13
oh, haste, Visit my *l* desire! *Ode to Memory* 4

Low (adj. and adv.) (*continued*) at first to the ear The warble was *l*, *Dying Swan* 24
L thunder and light in the magic night— *The Merman* 23
my ringlets would fall *L* adown, *l* adown, From under my starry sea-bud crown *L* adown *The Mermaid* 15
And at my headstone whisper *l*, *My life is full* 24
Heavily the *l* sky raining Over tower'd Camelot; *L. of Shalott iv* 4
L on her knees herself she cast, *Mariana in the S.* 27
Oh your sweet eyes, your *l* replies: *L. C. V. de Vere* 29
Lit with a *l* large moon. *Palace of Art* 68
Her *l* preamble all alone, „ 174
hears the *l* Moan of an unknown sea; „ 279
Then *l* and sweet I whistled thrice; *Edwin Morris* 113
Then when the first *l* matin-chirp hath grown *Love and Duty* 98
L thunders bring the mellow rain, *Talking Oak* 279
And all the *l* wind hardly breathed for fear. *Godiva* 55
And one *l* churl, compact of thankless earth, „ 66
Gloom'd the *l* coast and quivering brine *The Voyage* 42
L breezes fann'd the belfry bars, *The Letters* 43
Ever brightening With a *l* melodious thunder; *Poet's Mind* 27
L voluptuous music winding trembled, *Vision of Sin* 17
Swung themselves, and in *l* tones replied; „ 20
children leading evermore *L* miserable lives of hand-to-mouth, *Enoch Arden* 116
And the *l* moan of leaden-colour'd seas. „ 612
' His head is *l*, and no man cares for him. „ 850
On a sudden a *l* breath Of tender air *The Brook* 201
Somewhere beneath his own *l* range of roofs, *Aylmer's Field* 47
call'd away By one *l* voice to one dear neighbourhood, „ 60
on *l* knolls That dimpling died into each other, „ 148
Averill seeing How *l* his brother's mood had fallen, „ 405
Last, some *l* fever ranging round to spy „ 569
Which from the *l* light of mortality „ 641
thro' the smoke The blight of *l* desires— „ 673
L was her voice, but won mysterious way „ 695
ever in it a *l* musical note Swell'd up and died; *Sea Dreams* 210
He with a long *l* sibilation, stared As blank *Princess i* 176
Some to a *l* song oar'd a shallop by, „ *ii* 457
Sweet and *l*, sweet and *l*, „ *iii* 1
L, *l*, breathe and blow, „ 3
everywhere *L* voices with the ministering hand „ *vii* 21
There to herself, all in *l* tones, she read. „ 175
The last great Englishman is *l*. *Ode on Well.* 18
Thro' either babbling world of high and *l*; „ 182
Light, so *l* upon earth, *Window, Marr. Morn* 1
Light, so *l* in the vale You flash and lighten afar, „ 9
' What is it makes me beat so *l*?' *In Mem. iv* 8
Till growing winters lay me *l*; „ *xl* 30
Be near me when my light is *l*, „ *l* 1
on the *l* dark verge of life The twilight of eternal day. „ 15
How should he love a thing so *l*?' „ *lx* 16
Whose life in *l* estate began „ *lxiv* 3
The voice was *l*, the look was bright; „ *lxix* 15
and break The *l* beginnings of content. „ *lxxxiv* 48
Or *l* morass and whispering reed, „ *c* 6
and heard The *l* love-language of the bird „ *cii* 11
shining daffodil dead, and Orion *l* in his grave. *Maud I iii* 14
Had given her word to a thing so *l*? „ *xvi* 27
More life to Love than is or ever was In our *l* world, „ *xviii* 48
L on the sand and loud on the stone „ *xxii* 25
The delight of *l* replies. „ *II iv* 30
Then to strike him and lay him *l*, „ *v* 90
Over Orion's grave *l* down in the west, „ *III vi* 8
Then the King in *l* deep tones, *Com. of Arthur* 260
Go likewise; lay him *l* and slay him not, *Gareth and L.* 379
As Mark would sully the *l* state of churl: „ 427
For an your fire be *l* ye kindle mine! „ 711
I have not fall'n so *l* as some would wish. *Marr. of Geraint* 129
Made a *l* splendour in the world, „ 598
felt Her *l* firm voice and tender government. *Geraint and E.* 194
L at leave-taking, with his brandish'd plume „ 359
But answer'd in *l* voice, her meek head yet Drooping, „ 640
Faint in the *l* dark hall of banquet: *Balin and Balan* 343
walls Of that *l* church he built at Glastonbury. „ 367
Beneath a *l* door dipt, and made his feet „ 403

Low (adj. and adv.) (*continued*) Crawl'd slowly with *l* moans to where he lay, *Balin and Balan* 592
She answer'd with a *l* and chuckling laugh : *Merlin and V.* 780
we scarce can sink as *l* : „ 813
or *l* desire Not to feel lowest makes them level all ; „ 827
But into some *l* cave to crawl, and there, „ 884
The *l* sun makes the colour : I am yours, *Lancelot and E.* 134
The hard earth shake, and a *l* thunder of arms. „ 460
Then came her father, saying in *l* tones, „ 994
If this be high, what is it to be *l* ? ' „ 1084
But spake with such a sadness and so *l* *Holy Grail* 42
L as the hill was high, and where the vale Was lowest, „ 441
then one *l* roll Of Autumn thunder, *Last Tournament* 152
She lived a moon in that *l* lodge with him : „ 381
out beyond them flush'd The long *l* dune, „ 484
that *l* lodge return'd, Mid-forest, „ 488
A *l* sea-sunset glorying round her hair „ 508
one *l* light betwixt them burn'd *Guinevere* 4
' Liest thou here so *l*, the child of one I honour'd, „ 422
Lest but a hair of this *l* head be harm'd. „ 447
Do each *l* office of your holy house ; „ 682
And all the *l* dark groves, a land of love ! *Lover's Tale i* 332
lake, that, flooding, leaves *L* banks of yellow sand ; „ 535
Held converse sweet and *l*—*l* converse sweet, „ 541
At first her voice was very sweet and *l*, „ 563
for the sound Of that dear voice so musically *l*, „ 708
Unfrequent, *l*, as tho' it told its pulses ; „ *ii* 55
thence at intervals A *l* bell tolling. „ 83
For that *l* knell tolling his lady dead— „ *iv* 33
l down in a rainbow deep Silent palaces, *V. of Maeldune* 79
And his voice was *l* as from other worlds, „ 117
By the *l* foot-lights of the world— *The Wreck* 40
L warm winds had gently breathed us away from the land— „ 63
I sigh'd, as the *l* dark hull dipt under the smiling main, „ 127
' Is it *he* then brought so *l* ? ' *Dead Prophet* 6
And behind him, *l* in the West, „ 20
You speak so *l*, what is it ? *The Ring* 49
A footstep, a *l* throbbing in the walls, „ 409
And these *l* bushes dipt their twigs in foam, *Prog. of Spring* 51
Where I sank with the body at times in the sloughs of a *l* desire, *By an Evolution.* 18
Sing thou *l* or loud or sweet, *Poets and Critics* 6
Some too *l* would have thee shine, „ 11

Low (s) In summer heats, with placid *l's* Unfearing, *Supp. Confessions* 154
From the dark fen the oxen's *l* *Mariana* 28

Low (verb) and the bull couldn't *l*, *V. of Maeldune* 18

Low-brow'd or safely moor'd Beneath a *l-b* cavern, *Lover's Tale i* 55

Low-built appear'd, *l-b* but strong ; *Balin and Balan* 333

Low-couch'd Indian on a still-eyed snake, *l-c*— *Lover's Tale ii* 189

Low-cowering *L-c* shall the Sophist sit ; *Clear-headed friend* 10

Low-drooping *L-d* till he well-nigh kiss'd her feet *Lancelot and E.* 1172

Low-dropt murmur at the *l-d* eaves of sleep, *Lover's Tale ii* 122

Lower She breathed in sleep a *l* moan, *Mariana in the S.* 45
Calling thyself a little *l* ' Than angels. *Two Voices* 198
' Or if thro' *l* lives I came— „ 364
And *l* voices saint me from above. *St. S. Stylites* 154
On a range of *l* feelings and a narrower heart *Locksley Hall* 44
But I count the gray barbarian *l* than the Christian child. „ 174
Like a beast with *l* pleasures, like a beast with *l* pains ? „ 176
Gathering up from all the *l* ground ; *Vision of Sin* 15
And slowly quickening into *l* forms ; „ 210
We ranging down this *l* track, *In Mem. xlvi* 1
No *l* life that earth's embrace May breed with him, „ *lxxxii* 3
when most I feel There is a *l* and a higher ; „ *cxxix* 4
And, moved thro' life of *l* phase, „ *Con.* 125
Tells of a manhood ever less and *l* ? *Last Tournament* 121
Because all other Hope had *l* aim ; *Lover's Tale i* 455
my lord is *l* than his oxen or his swine. *Locksley H., Sixty* 126
youth and age are scholars yet but in the *l* school, „ 243
altogether can escape From the *l* world within him, *Making of Man* 2
Neither mourn if human creeds be *l* *Faith* 5

Lower (*continued*) So the Higher wields the *L*, while the *L* is the Higher. *Locksley H., Sixty* 124

Lower (verb) shalt *l* to his level day by day, *Locksley Hall* 45
Fortune, turn thy wheel and *l* the proud ; *Marr. of Geraint* 347

Lower'd *L* softly with a threefold cord of love *D. of F. Women* 211
he spake to these his helm was *l*, *Guinevere* 593
They *l* me down the side, *The Wreck* 125
(deferentially With nearing chair and *l* accent) *Aylmer's Field* 267

Lowest from a height That makes the *l* hate it, „ 173
Nor ever *l* roll of thunder moans, *Lucreiius* 108
barbarous isles, and here Among the *l*.' *Princess ii* 123
so Vivien in the *l*, Arriving at a time *Merlin and V.* 141
low desire Not to feel *l* makes them level all ; „ 828
And in the *l* beasts are slaying men, *Holy Grail* 234
where the vale Was *l*, found a chapel, „ 442
I could hardly sin against the *l*.' *Last Tournament* 572
Sorrowing with the sorrows of the *l* ! *On Jub. Q. Victoria* 27
Is brother of the Dark one in the *l*, *Demeter and P.* 95

Low-flowing fling on each side my *l-f* locks, *The Mermaid* 32
L-F breezes are roaming the broad valley *Leonine Eleg.* 1

Low-folded breathless burthen of *l-f* heavens *Aylmer's Field* 612

Low-hung gushes from beneath a *l-h* cloud. *Ode to Memory* 71
Like to a *l-h* and a fiery sky *Lover's Tale ii* 61

Lowing (part.) And *l* to his fellows. *Gardener's D.* 88

Lowing (s) So thick with *l's* of the herds, *In Mem. xcix* 3

Lowland Toward the *l* ways behind me, *Silent Voices* 5

Lowlier We taught him *l* moods, when Elsinore *Buonaparte* 9

Low-lieth WHERE Claribel *l-l* (repeat) *Claribel* 1, 8, 21

Lowlihead perfect wifehood and pure *l*. *Isabel* 12

Lowliness sure of Heaven If *l* could save her. *Maud I xii* 20

Lowly (adj.) Or even a *l* cottage whence we see *Ode to Memory* 100
When truth embodied in a tale Shall enter in at *l* doors. *In Mem. xxxvi* 8
or rest On Enid at her *l* handmaid-work, *Marr. of Geraint* 400
' And thence I dropt into a *l* vale, *Holy Grail* 440
For *l* minds were madden'd to the height *To Mary Boyle* 33
Within the bloodless heart of *l* flowers *Prog. of Spring* 84
And rough-ruddy faces Of *l* labour, *Merlin and the G.* 60

Lowly (s) All the *l*, the destitute, *On Jub. Q. Victoria* 31

Lowly-lovely she—so *l-l* and so loving, *Aylmer's Field* 168

Lowly-sweet Edith, yet so *l-s*, *Locksley H., Sixty* 49

Lowness The *l* of the present state, *In Mem. xxiv* 11

Low-spoken *L-s*, and of so few words, *Geraint and E.* 395

Low-throned *L-t* Hesper is stayed between the two peaks ; *Leonine Eleg.* 11

Low-tinkled *L-t* with a bell-like flow *The winds, etc.* 7

Low-toned So she *l-t* ; while with shut eyes I lay *Princess vii* 223

Low-tongued Doth the *l-t* Orient Wander *Adeline* 51

Low-voiced The *l-v*, tender-spirited Lionel, *Lover's Tale i* 655

Low-wheel'd Within the *l-w* chaise, *Talking Oak* 110

Loyal (*See also* **Ever-loyal, Half-loyal, Love-loyal, Mock-loyal**) She hath no *l* knight and true, *L. of Shalott ii* 25
' The slight she-slips of *l* blood, *Talking Oak* 57
Queenly responsive when the *l* hand *Aylmer's Field* 169
The *l* warmth of Florian is not cold, *Princess ii* 244
The *l* pines of Canada murmur thee, *W. to Marie Alex.* 19
Our *l* passion for our temperate kings ; *Ode on Well.* 165
And *l* unto kindly laws. *In Mem. lxxxv* 16
With a *l* people shouting a battle cry, *Maud III vi* 35
Hath ever like a *l* sister cleaved To Arthur,— *Com. of Arthur* 191
Of *l* vassals toiling for their liege. „ 282
Art thou so little *l* to thy Queen, *Balin and Balan* 251
' Fain would I still be *l* to the Queen.' „ 254
So *l* scarce is *l* to thyself, „ 256
But have ye no one word of *l* praise For Arthur, *Merlin and V.* 778
But now my *l* worship is allow'd Of all men : *Lancelot and E.* 110
Nor often *l* to his word, and now Wroth „ 559
' Prince, O *l* nephew of our noble King, „ 652
L, the dumb old servitor, on deck, „ 1144
Low-drooping till he wellnigh kiss'd her feet For *l* awe, „ 1173
To *l* hearts the value of all gifts Must vary „ 1214
' Hail, Bors ! if every *l* man and true Could see it, *Holy Grail* 756
For *l* to the uttermost am I.' *Pelleas and E.* 212
but the fruit Of *l* nature, and of noble mind.' *Guinevere* 336

Loyal (*continued*) O *L* to the royal in thyself, And *l* to thy land, *To the Queen ii* 1
So *l* is too costly! friends— „ 16
The *l* to their crown Are *l* to their own own far sons, „ 27
That I am *l* to him till the death, *Columbus* 227
she was always *l* and sweet— *Despair* 49
To all the *l* hearts who long To keep *Hands all Round* 13
multitude *L*, each, to the heart of it, *On Jub. Q. Victoria* 21
where the *l* bells Clash welcome— *The Ring* 482
How *l* in the following of thy Lord! *In Mem. W. G. Ward* 6
Loyal-hearted On thee the *l-h* hung, *In Mem. cx* 5
Lubber Then, narrow court and *l* King, farewell! *Merlin and V.* 119
Lucid golden round her *l* throat And shoulder: *Œnone* 178
The *l* outline forming round thee; *Tithonus* 53
Gods, who haunt The *l* interspace of world and world, *Lucretius* 105
issued in a court Compact of *l* marbles, *Princess ii* 24
the mist is drawn A *l* veil from coast to coast, *In Mem. lxvii* 14
Be large and *l* round thy brow. „ *xci* 8
What lightens in the *l* east Of rising worlds „ *cv* 24
The *l* chambers of the morning star, *Lover's Tale i* 28
yet one glittering foot disturb'd The *l* well; *Tiresias* 42
Lucilia *L*, wedded to Lucretius, found *Lucretius* 1
Lucius Junius Brutus The *L J B* of my kind? *Princess ii* 284
Luck good *l* Shall fling her old shoe after. *Will Water.* 215
Good *l* had your good man, *Geraint and E.* 617
but rosier *l* will go With these rich jewels, *Last Tournament* 45
Luckier so prosper'd that at last A *l* or a bolder fisherman, *Enoch Arden* 49
hot in haste to join Their *l* mates, *Geraint and E.* 575
Lucknow in the ghastly siege of *L*— *Def. of Lucknow* 4
Lucky Less *l* her home-voyage: *Enoch Arden* 541
For *l* rhymes to him were scrip and share, *The Brook* 4
Lucretius Lucilia, wedded to *L*, found *Lucretius* 1
Lucumo lay at wine with Lar and *L*; *Princess ii* 129
Lucy An' *L* wur laäme o' one leg, *Village Wife* 99
Straänge an' unheppen Miss *L*! „ 100
Lull (while warm airs *l* us, blowing lowly) *Lotos-Eaters, C. S.* 89
Perchance, to *l* the throbs of pain, *The Daisy* 105
To *l* with song an aching heart, *In Mem. xxxvii* 15
I *l* a fancy trouble-tost „ *lxv* 2
Lullabies These mortal *l* of pain May bind a book, „ *lxxvii* 5
Lull'd Thy tuwhits are *l*, I wot, *The Owl ii* 1
hum of swarming bees Into dreamful slumber *l*. *Eleänore* 30
L echoes of laborious day Come to you, *Margaret* 29
And *l* them in my own. *Talking Oak* 216
A fall of water *l* the noon asleep. *Romney's R.* 83
Lulling *L* the brine against the Coptic sands. *Buonaparte* 8
l random squabbles when they rise, *Holy Grail* 557
Lumber the waste and *l* of the shore, *Enoch Arden* 16
Luminous his stedfast shade Sleeps on his *l* ring.' *Palace of Art* 16
A belt, it seem'd, of *l* vapour, lay, *Sea Dreams* 209
meek Seem'd the full lips, and mild the *l* eyes, *Princess vii* 226
L, gemlike, ghostlike, deathlike, *Maud I iii* 8
Holy Grail All over cover'd with a *l* cloud, *Holy Grail* 189
Holy Vessel hung Clothed in white samite or a *l* cloud. „ 513
Lump (*See also* **Loomp**) This *l* of earth has left his estate *Maud I xvi* 1
Lungs labour'd down within his ample *l*, *Princess v* 273
writhings, anguish, labouring of the *l* *Pass. of Arthur* 115
Brass mouths and iron *l*! *Freedom* 40
You that lie with wasted *l* *Forlorn* 21
Lunnon (**London**) Squoire's i' *L*, an' summun *N. Farmer, O. S.* 57
Lurdane droned her *l* knights Slumbering, *Pelleas and E.* 430
Lure (s) Diet and seeling, jesses, leash, and *l*. *Merlin and V.* 125
follow, leaping blood, The season's *l*! *Early Spring* 26
Lure (verb) splendour fail'd To *l* those eyes *St. Telemachus* 36
Lured When we have *l* you from above, *Rosalind* 46
him they *l* Into their net made pleasant *Aylmer's Field* 485
one unctuous mouth which *l* him, *Sea Dreams* 14
L by the crimes and frailties of the court, *Guinevere* 136
Which often *l* her from herself; „ 152
we were *l* by the light from afar, *V. of Maeldune* 71
L by the glare and the blare, „ 73
Earls that were *l* by the Hunger of glory *Batt. of Brunanburh* 123
Eyes that *l* a doting boyhood *Locksley H., Sixty* 10
My beauty *l* that falcon from his eyry *Happy* 59

Lured (*continued*) What sight so *l* him thro 'the fields *Far—far—away* 1
l me from the household fire on earth. *Romney's R.* 40
Lurid Wrapt in drifts of *l* smoke *Maud II iv* 66
when now Bathed in that *l* crimson— *St. Telemachus* 18
His face deform'd by *l* blotch and blain— *Death of Œnone* 72
Lurk I think no more of deadly *l's* therein, *Princess ii* 226
such as *l's* In some wild Poet, *In Mem. xxxiv* 6
'There *l* three villains yonder in the wood, *Geraint and E.* 142
If he? yes, he . . . *l's*, listens, *The Flight* 71
Lurking Balan *l* there (His quest was unaccomplish'd) *Balin and Balan* 546
Vivien, *l*, heard. She told Sir Modred. *Guinevere* 98
Luscious Nor roll thy viands on a *l* tongue, *Ancient Sage* 267
Lush at the root thro' *l* green grasses burn'd *D. of F. Women* 71
Lusitanian father-grape grew fat On *L* summers. *Will Water.* 8
Lust Either from *l* of gold, or like a girl *M. d'Arthur* 127
Crown thyself, worm, and worship thine own *l's*!— *Aylmer's Field* 650
and keep him from the *l* of blood *Lucretius* 83
And twisted shapes of *l*, unspeakable, „ 157
For *l* or lusty blood or provender: „ 198
in his *l* and voluptuousness, *Boädicea* 66
Ring out the narrowing *l* of gold; *In Mem. cvi* 26
And *l* of gain, in the spirit of Cain, *Maud I. i* 23
feeble vassals of wine and anger and *l*, „ *II i* 43
land that has lost for a little her *l* of gold, „ *III vi* 39
live the strength and die the *l*! *Com. of Arthur* 492
own no *l* because they have no law! *Pelleas and E.* 481
Either from *l* of gold, or like a girl *Pass. of Arthur* 295
thro' which the *l*, Villany, violence, *Columbus* 171
The lecher would cleave to his *l's*, *Despair* 100
craft and madness, *l* and spite, *Locksley H., Sixty* 189
He that has lived for the *l* of the minute, *Vastness* 27
wallow in this old *l* Of Paganism, *St. Telemachus* 78
Lusted I never loved her, I but *l* for her— *Pelleas and E.* 484
ghastliest That ever *l* for a body, *Lover's Tale i* 648
Lustful A *l* King, who sought to win my love *Balin and Balan* 474
Lustier By park and suburb under brown Of *l* leaves; *In Mem. xcviii* 25
Until they find a *l* than themselves.' *Balin and Balan* 19
Stronger ever born of weaker, *l* body, larger mind? *Locksley H., Sixty* 164
Lustihood He is so full of *l*, he will ride, *Lancelot and E.* 203
Lusting *l* for all that is not its own; *Maud I i* 22
Lustre (*See also* **Lace-lustre**) Soft *l* bathes the range of urns *Day-Dm., Sleep. P.* 9
The *l* of the long convolvuluses *Enoch Arden* 576
His eyes To indue his *l*; *Lover's Tale i* 424
Lustreless one was patch'd and blurr'd and *l* *Marr. of Geraint* 649
Lustrous and the light and *l* curls— *M. d'Arthur* 216
And all about him roll'd his *l* eyes; *Love and Death* 3
Slides the bird o'er *l* woodland, *Locksley Hall* 162
and the light and *l* curls— *Pass. of Arthur* 384
Lusty The *l* bird takes every hour for dawn: *M. d'Arthur, Ep.* 11
And here and there a *l* trout, *The Brook* 57
For lust or *l* blood or provender: *Lucretius* 198
A *l* brace Of twins may weed her of her folly. *Princess v* 463
Fair empires branching, both, in *l* life!— *W. to Marie Alex.* 21
A *l* youth, but poor, who often saw *Gareth and L.* 48
Loving his *l* youthhood yielded to him. „ 580
for this lad is great And *l*, „ 731
it fell Like flaws in summer laying *l* corn: *Marr. of Geraint* 764
The *l* mowers labouring dinnerless, *Geraint and E.* 251
His *l* spearmen follow'd him with noise: „ 593
Strike down the *l* and long practised knight, *Lancelot and E.* 1361
till she long To have thee back in *l* life again, *Pelleas and E.* 352
I might have stricken a *l* stroke for him, *Sir J. Oldcastle* 69
Lute (s) on lattice edges lay Or book or *l*; *Princess ii* 30
'It is the little rift within the *l*, *Merlin and V.* 390
'The little rift within the lover's *l* „ 393
Lute (verb) That *l* and flute fantastic tenderness, *Princess iv* 129
Luther thou wilt be A latter *L*, *To J. M. K.* 2
Lutterworth Nor thou in Britain, little *L*, *Sir J. Oldcastle* 26
Luvv (love) (s) Noä—thou'll marry for *l*— *N. Farmer, N. S.* 12
fur, Sammy, 'e married fur *l*. „ 32
L? what's *l*? thou can luvv thy lass an' 'er munny too, „ 33

Luvv (love) (verb) Luvv? what's luvv? thou can *l* thy lass an' 'er munny too, — *N. Farmer, N. S.* 33
Could'n I *l* thy muther by cause o' 'er munny laäid by? — „ 35
Luvv'd (loved) fur I *l* 'er a vast sight moor fur it: — „ 36
Luxuriant The *l* symmetry Of thy floating gracefulness, — *Eleänore* 49
Luxurious Till, kill'd with some *l* agony, — *Vision of Sin* 43
Luxury And *l* of contemplation: — *Eleänore* 107
Lychgate to the *l*, where his chariot stood, — *Aylmer's Field* 824
By the *l-g* was Muriel. — *The Ring* 324
Lycian Appraised the *L* custom, — *Princess ii* 128
Lydian Gazing at the *L* laughter of the Garda Lake below — *Frater Ave, etc.* 8
Lying (adj. and part.) *See also* **A-laäid, A-liggin', Liggin', Under-lying)** Fed thee, a child, *l* alone, — *Eleänore* 25
l still Shadow forth the banks at will: — „ 109
L, robed in snowy white That loosely flew — *L. of Shalott iv* 19
Will vex thee *l* underground? — *Two Voices* 111
For *l* broad awake I thought of you — *May Queen, Con.* 29
The Roman soldier found Me *l* dead, — *D. of F. Women* 162
l robed and crown'd, Worthy a Roman spouse.' — „ 163
l, hidden from the heart's disgrace, — *Locksley Hall* 57
Summer isles of Eden *l* in dark-purple spheres — „ 164
She *l* on her couch alone, — *Day-Dm., Sleep. B.* 2
On the decks as they were *l*, — *The Captain* 53
Suffused them, sitting, *l*, languid shapes, — *Vision of Sin* 12
(His father *l* sick and needing him) — *Enoch Arden* 65
l thus inactive, doubt and gloom. — „ 113
Found *l* with his urns and ornaments, — *Aylmer's Field* 4
l bathed In the green gleam of dewy-tassell'd trees: — *Princess i* 93
You *l* close upon his territory, — „ *iv* 403
but when she saw me *l* stark, — „ *vi* 100
What whispers from thy *l* lip? — *In Mem. iii* 4
And found thee *l* in the port; — „ *xiv* 4
What whisper'd from her *l* lips? — „ *xxxix* 10
The wine-flask *l* couch'd in moss, — „ *lxxxix* 44
What was it? a *l* trick of the brain? — *Maud II i* 37
L close to my foot, Frail, — „ *ii* 3
his good mates *L* or sitting round him, — *Gareth and L.* 512
And left him *l* in the public way; — *Geraint and E.* 478
she that saw him *l* unsleek, unshorn, — *Lancelot and E.* 815
l bounden there In darkness thro' innumerable hours — *Holy Grail* 676
thou wert *l* in thy new leman's arms.' — *Last Tournament* 625
saw One *l* in the dust at Almesbury, — *Pass. of Arthur* 77
Ever the mine and assault, our sallies, their *l* alarms, — *Def. of Lucknow* 75
I've ninety men and more that are *l* sick ashore. — *The Revenge* 10
little girl with her arms *l* out on the counterpane.' — *In the Child. Hosp.* 58
little arms *l* out on the counterpane; — „ 70
I *l* here bedridden and alone, — *Columbus* 164
Among them Muriel *l* on her face— — *The Ring* 448
Tell him you were *l*! — *Forlorn* 56
Lying (s) Death in all life and *l* in all love, — *Merlin and V.* 194
Lyings-in aches, and teethings, *l-i*, — *Holy Grail* 554
Lynette 'My name?' she said—'*L* my name; — *Gareth and L.* 607
a light laugh Broke from *L*, — „ 837
He laugh'd; the laughter jarr'd upon *L*: — „ 1226
turning to *L* he told The tale of Gareth, — „ 1272
'Heaven help thee,' sigh'd *L*. — „ 1357
But he, that told it later, says *L*. — „ 1429
Lynx her *l* eye To fix and make me hotter, — *Princess iii* 46
Lynx-eyes You needs must have good *l-e* — *Despair* 114
Lyonesse sea-sounding wastes of *L*— — *Merlin and V.* 74
Lyonnesse Had fallen in *L* about their Lord, — *M. d'Arthur* 4
Roving the trackless realms of *L*, — *Lancelot and E.* 35
Rode Tristram toward *L* and the west. — *Last Tournament* 362
Then pressing day by day thro' *L* — „ 501
light feet fell on our rough *L*, — „ 554
when first I rode from our rough *L*, — „ 664
And rode thereto from *L*, and he said — *Guinevere* 236
All down the lonely coast of *L*, — „ 240
Back to the sunset bound of *L*— — *Pass. of Arthur* 81
Had fall'n in *L* about their lord, — „ 173
Lyonors a knight To combat for my sister, *L*, — *Gareth and L.* 608
the Lady *L* Had sent her coming champion, — „ 1191
Lyonors (*continued*) The Lady *L* at a window stood, — *Gareth and L.* 1375
The Lady *L* wrung her hands and wept, — „ 1395
And stay the world from Lady *L*. — „ 1412
And Lady *L* and her house, with dance — „ 1422
Says that Sir Gareth wedded *L*, — „ 1428
Lyre voice, a *l* of widest range Struck by all passion, — *D. of F. Women* 165
Who touch'd a jarring *l* at first, — *In Mem. xcvi* 7
golden *l* Is ever sounding in heroic ears — *Tiresias* 180
Lyrics dismal *l*, prophesying change — *Princess i* 142

M

Maäde (made) An' 'e *m* the bed as 'e ligs on — *N. Farmer, N. S.* 28
scratted my faäce like a cat, an' it *m* 'er sa mad — *North. Cobbler* 22
I grabb'd the munny she *m*, — „ 32
what ha *m* our Molly sa laäte? — *Spinster's S's.* 113
An' the munney they *m* by the war, — *Owd Roä* 44
An' soä they've *m* tha a parson, — *Church-warden, etc.* 7
peärky as owt, an' tha *m* me as mad as mad, — „ 35
Maäin-glad (main glad) but I be *m g* to seeä tha so 'arty — *North. Cobbler* 2
Naay—fur I be *m-g*, — „ 9
Maäke (make) I knaws what *m's* tha sa mad. — *N. Farmer, N. S.* 17
What *m's* 'er sa laäte? — *Spinster's S's.* 5
till I *m's* tha es smooth es silk, — „ 53
I loovs tha to *m* thysen 'appy, — „ 57
They *m's* ma a graäter Laädy — „ 110
meäns fur to *m* 'is owd aäge as 'appy — *Owd Roä* 3
The fellers as *m's* them picturs, — „ 23
Doänt *m* thysen sick wi' the caäke. — „ 34
an' they *m's* ma a help to the poor, — *Church-warden, etc.* 39
Maakin' (making) *M* 'em goä togither as they've good right to do. — *N. Farmer, N. S.* 34
an' *m* ma deäf wi' their shouts, — *Spinster's S's.* 88
I 'eärd 'er a *m* 'er moän, — „ 115
Maäle (male) by the fault o' that ere *m*— — *Village Wife* 17
Maäte (mate) or she weänt git a *m* onyhow! — „ 104
Maäy (hawthorn-bloom) niver ha seed it sa white wi' the *M* — „ 80
Maäy (month) carpet es fresh es a midder o' flowers i' *M* — *Spinster's S's.* 45
Maäzin' (bewildering) Huzzin' an' *m* the blessed feälds — *N. Farmer, O. S.* 62
Macaw add A crimson to the quaint *M*, — *Day-Dm., Pro.* 16
Mace brand, *m*, and shaft, shield— — *Princess v* 503
Machicolated Glared on a huge *m* tower — *Last Tournament* 424
Machine praised his land, his horses, his *m's*; — *The Brook* 124
Machree 'Tomorra, tomorra, *M*!' — *Tomorrow* 18
Macready FAREWELL, *M*, since to-night we part; — *To W. C. Macready* 1
Farewell, *M*, since this night we part, — „ 5
Farewell, *M*; moral, grave, sublime; — „ 12
Mad (*See also* **Cleän-wud, Hawk-mad, Wud**) troops of devils, *m* with blasphemy, — *St. S. Stylites* 4
Am I *m*, that I should cherish that which bears but bitter fruit? — *Locksley Hall* 65
the bailiff swore that he was *m*, — *The Brook* 143
Squoire 'ull be sa *m* an' all— — *N. Farmer, O. S.* 47
I knaws what maäkes tha sa *m*. — „ *N. S.* 17
M and maddening all that heard her — *Boädicea* 4
What matter if I go *m*, — *Maud I xi* 6
to hear a dead man chatter Is enough to drive one *m*. — „ *II v* 20
Then Arthur all at once gone *m* replies, — *Gareth and L.* 863
whether she be *m*, or else the King, Or both or neither, or thyself be *m*, I ask not: — „ 875
your town, where all the men are *m*; — *Marr. of Geraint* 418
it makes me *m* to see you weep. — *Geraint and E.* 616
for I was wellnigh *m*: — „ 836
m for strange adventure, dash'd away. — *Balin and Balan* 289
'I have gone *m*. I love you: — *Lancelot and E.* 930
'he dash'd across me—*m*, — *Holy Grail* 640
holy nun and thou have driven men *m*, — „ 862
What! art thou *m*?' — *Pelleas and E.* 537
beheld three spirits *m* with joy — *Guinevere* 252
Playing *m* pranks along the heathy leas; — *Circumstance* 2
Look how they tumble the blossom, the *m* little tits! — *Window, Ay* 9

Mad (*continued*) with m hand Tearing the bright leaves of the ivy-screen, *Lover's Tale ii* 39
their seamen made mock at the m little craft *The Revenge* 38
an' it maäde 'er sa m *North. Cobbler* 22
M wi' the lasses an' all— *Village Wife* 78
I Stumbled on deck, half m. *The Wreck* 118
m bride who stabb'd her bridegroom on her bridal night— *The Flight* 57
If m, then I am m, but sane, " 58
My father's madness makes me m— " 59
I am not m, not yet, not quite— " 60
m for the charge and the battle were we, *Heavy Brigade* 41
a-yowlin' an' yaupin' like m; *Owd Roä* 88
peärky as owt, an' tha maäde me as m as m, *Church-warden, etc.* 35
I was m, I was raving-wild, *Charity* 27

Madam *Take*, M, *this poor book of song;* *To the Queen* 17
M—if I know your sex, *Vision of Sin* 181
so mask'd, M, I love the truth; Receive it; *Princess ii* 213
not to answer, M, all those hard things " 345
'M, he the wisest man Feasted the women " 350
M, *you* should answer, *we* would ask) " 353
Nay—for it's kind of you, M, *Rizpah* 21
M, I beg your pardon! " 81

Madden Is this a time to m madness *Aylmer's Field* 769

Madden'd (adj. and part.) Now to the scream of a m beach dragg'd down by the wave, *Maud I iii* 12
cramping creeds that had m the peoples *Despair* 24
Till I myself was m with her cry, *The Ring* 405
For lowly minds were m to the height *To Mary Boyle* 33

Madden'd (verb) And ever he mutter'd and m, *Maud I i* 10
'I shall assay,' said Gareth with a smile That m her, *Gareth and L.* 784
and m with himself and moan'd: *Pelleas and E.* 460
and we gorged and we m, *V. of Maeldune* 67
For one monotonous fancy m her, *The Ring* 404

Maddening Mad and m all that heard her *Boädicea* 4
And m what he rode: *Holy Grail* 641

Madder made our mightiest m than our least. " 863

Maddest Of all the glad New-Year, mother, the m merriest day; *May Queen* 3
To-morrow 'ill be of all the year the m merriest day, " 43

Maddison's an' looök thruf M gaäte! *Spinster's S's.* 6

Made (*See also* **Costly-made, Maäde, New-made, Stronger-made**) The world was never m; *Nothing will Die* 30
O spirit and heart m desolate! *Supp. Confessions* 189
A fairy shield your Genius m *Margaret* 41
My fancy m me for a moment blest *The form, the form* 6
while the tender service m thee weep, *The Bridesmaid* 10
She m three paces thro' the room, *L. of Shalott iii* 38
'Is this the form,' she m her moan, *Mariana in the S.* 33
'The day to night,' she m her moan, " 81
And weeping then she m her moan, " 93
What is so wonderfully m.' *Two Voices* 6
'This is more vile,' he m reply, " 103
I told thee—hardly nigher m, " 173
play'd In his free field, and pastime m, " 320
These three m unity so sweet, " 421
wherefore rather I m choice To commune " 460
So sing that other song I m, *Miller's D.* 199
Love is m a vague regret. " 210
That loss but m us love the more, " 230
She to Paris m Proffer of royal power, *Œnone* 110
Kept watch, waiting decision, m reply. " 143
I m a feast; I bad him come; *The Sisters* 13
I m my dagger sharp and bright. " 26
To which my soul m answer readily: *Palace of Art* 17
Four courts I m, East, West and South and North, " 21
you'll be there, too, mother, to see me m the Queen; *May Queen* 26
Last May we m a crown of flowers: " *N. Y's. E.* 9
Beneath the hawthorn on the green they m me Queen of May; " 10
morning star of song, who m His music heard below; *D. of F. Women* 3
I m The ever-shifting currents of the blood " 132
And me this knowledge bolder m, *To J. S.* 5
To shame the boast so often m, *Love thou thy land* 71

Made (*continued*) I perish by this people which I m,— *M. d'Arthur* 22
great brand M lightnings in the splendour of the moon, " 137
M me most happy, faltering, *Gardener's D.* 235
m a little wreath of all the flowers *Dora* 82
half has fall'n and m a bridge; *Walk. to the Mail* 32
m it sweet To walk, to sit, to sleep, *Edwin Morris* 39
Man is m of solid stuff. " 49
God m the woman for the man, " 50
'God m the woman for the use of man, " 91
all hell beneath M me boil over. *St. S. Stylites* 171
So slightly, musically m, *Talking Oak* 87
M weak by time and fate, *Ulysses* 69
the barking cur M her cheek flame: *Godiva* 58
no sound is m, Not even of a gnat that sings. *Day Dm., Sleep. P.* 20
Had m him talk for show; *Will Water.* 196
the seamen M a gallant crew, *The Captain* 6
M a murmur in the land. *L. of Burleigh* 20
And a gentle consort m he, " 73
Like fancy m of golden air, *The Voyage* 66
But you have m the wiser choice, *You might have won* 5
That m the wild-swan pause in her cloud, *Poet's Song* 7
sailor's lad M orphan by a winter shipwreck, *Enoch Arden* 15
and m himself Full sailor; " 53
and m a home For Annie, neat and nestlike, " 58
The sea is His: He m it.' " 226
his duty by his own, M himself theirs; " 334
Down thro' the whitening hazels m a plunge " 379
tongue Was loosen'd, till he m them understand; " 645
M such a voluble answer promising all, " 903
I saw where James M toward us, *The Brook* 117
m The hoar hair of the Baronet bristle up *Aylmer's Field* 41
bounteously m And yet so finely, " 74
M blossom-ball or daisy-chain, " 87
'God bless 'em: marriages are m in Heaven.' " 188
Fine as ice-ferns on January panes M by a breath. " 223
Then m his pleasure echo, hand to hand, " 257
Perplext her, m her half forget herself, " 303
much allowance must be m for men. " 410
knew he wherefore he had m the cry; " 589
m Still paler the pale head of him, " 622
I m by these the last of all my race, " 791
and m Their own traditions God, " 794
M more and more allowance for his talk; *Sea Dreams* 75
breaking that, you m and broke your dream: " 143
M Him his catspaw and the Cross his tool, " 190
m The dimpled flounce of the sea-furbelow flap, " 265
M havock among those tender cells, *Lucretius* 22
it seem'd A void was m in Nature; " 37
blind beginnings that have m me man, " 246
M noise with bees and breeze from end to end. *Princess, Pro.* 88
m the old warrior from his ivied nook Glow " 104
They rode; they betted; m a hundred friends, " 163
My mother pitying m a thousand prayers; " *i* 21
He always m a point to post with mares; " 189
but that which m Woman and man. " *ii* 144
Have we not m ourself the sacrifice? " *iii* 249
I remember'd one myself had m, " *iv* 88
part m long since, and part Now while I sang, " 90
in the North long since my nest is m. " 110
beauty in detail M them worth knowing; " 449
M at me thro' the press, and staggering back " *v* 522
reverence for the laws ourselves have m, " *Con.* 55
O the wild charge they m! *Light Brigade* 51
Honour the charge they m! " 53
Who m the serf a man, and burst his chain— *W. to Marie Alex.* 3
the parson m it his text that week, *Grandmother* 29
Is on the skull which thou hast m. *In Mem., Pro.* 8
He thinks he was not m to die; And thou hast m him: thou art just. " 11
And m me that delirious man " *xvi* 17
m me move As light as carrier-birds in air; " *xxv* 5
Him that m them current coin; " *xxxvi* 4
When God hath m the pile complete; " *liv* 8
Where thy first form was m a man; " *lxi* 10
Has m me kindly with my kind, " *lxvi* 7

Made (*continued*) 'More years had *m* me love thee more. *In Mem. lxxxi* 8
I *m* a picture in the brain ; „ *lxxx* 9
And tracts of calm from tempest *m*, „ *cxii* 14
In that which *m* the world so fair. „ *cxvi* 8
flood Of onward time shall yet be *m*, „ *cxxviii* 6
Her sweet 'I will' has *m* you one. „ *Con.* 56
Rather than hold by the law that I *m*, *Maud I i* 55
I have not *m* the world, and He that *m* it „ *iv* 48
She *m* me divine amends For a courtesy „ *vi* 13
M her only the child of her mother, „ *xiii* 40
There were but a step to be *m*. „ *xiv* 22
And *m* my life a perfumed altar-flame ; „ *xviii* 24
Maud *m* my Maud by that long loving kiss, „ 58
M so fairily well With delicate spire and whorl, „ *II ii* 5
living will That *m* it stir on the shore. „ 15
All *m* up of the lily and rose That blow by night, „ *v* 74
star Which shone so close beside Thee that ye *m* One light together, *Ded. of Idylls* 47
and *m* a realm, and reign'd. (repeat) *Com. of Arthur* 19, 519
m Broad pathways for the hunter and the knight „ 60
M head against him, crying, „ 68
M lightnings and great thunders over him, „ 108
the King *M* feast for, saying, „ 247
the Queen *m* answer, 'What know I ? „ 326
mingled with the haze And *m* it thicker ; „ 436
crush'd The Idolators, and *m* the people free ? *Gareth and L.* 137
The birds *m* Melody on branch, „ 183
that old Seer *m* answer playing on him „ 252
and had *m* it spire to heaven. „ 309
m his goodly cousin, Tristram, knight, „ 394
Repentant of the word she *m* him swear, „ 527
Shame never *m* girl redder than Gareth joy. „ 536
and *m* him flush, and bow Lowly, „ 548
M thee my knight ? my knights are sworn „ 552
'Thou hast *m* us lords, and canst not put us down !' „ 1132
Always he *m* his mouthpiece of a page „ 1337
rode In converse till she *m* her palfrey halt, „ 1360
What madness *m* thee challenge the chief knight „ 1416
dance And revel and song, *m* merry over Death, „ 1423
wherefore going to the King, He *m* this pretext, *Marr. of Geraint* 33
Was ever man so grandly *m* as he ? „ 81
the strong passion in her *m* her weep „ 110
M answer sharply that she should not know. „ 196
M sharply to the dwarf, and ask'd it of him, „ 204
And *m* him like a man abroad at morn „ 335
M a low splendour in the world, „ 598
M her cheek burn and either eyelid fall, „ 775
Which *m* him look so cloudy and so cold ; *Geraint and E.* 48
and suffering thus he *m* Minutes an age : „ 114
And *m* it of two colours ; „ 292
Him that *m* me The one true lover whom you ever own'd, „ 343
M her cheek burn and either eyelid fall. „ 434
It wellnigh *m* her cheerful ; „ 443
m The long way smoke beneath him in his fear ; „ 531
M but a single bound, and with a sweep of it „ 727
and *m* as if to fall upon him. „ 776
I, therefore, *m* him of our Table Round, „ 908
m Those banners of twelve battles overhead Stir, *Balin and Balan* 87
and the Queen, and all the world *M* music, „ 211
m that mouth of night Whereout the Demon „ 316
M Garlon, hissing ; then he sourly smiled. „ 355
m his feet Wings thro' a glimmering gallery, „ 403
m him quickly dive Beneath the boughs, „ 422
Nature through the flesh herself hath *m* *Merlin and V.* 50
It *m* the laughter of an afternoon „ 163
M with her right a comb of pearl to part The lists „ 244
And *m* a pretty cup of both my hands „ 275
M answer, either eyelid wet with tears : „ 379
And *m* a Gardener putting in a graff, „ 479
but afterwards He *m* a stalwart knight. „ 482
Then *m* her Queen : but those isle-nurtured eyes „ 570
lady never *m* *unwilling* war With those fine eyes : „ 603
And *m* her good man jealous with good cause. „ 605
and *m* her lithe arm round his neck Tignten, „ 614

Made (*continued*) King *M* proffer of the league of golden mines, *Merlin and V.* 646
sleepless nights Of my long life have *m* it easy „ 680
That wreathen round it *m* it seem his own ; „ 735
And wearied out *m* for the couch and slept, „ 736
and *m* A snowy penthouse for his hollow eyes, „ 807
crying 'I have *m* his glory mine,' „ 971
Now *m* a pretty history to herself *Lancelot and E.* 18
every scratch a lance had *m* upon it, „ 20
down they fell and *m* the glen abhorr'd : „ 42
Thither he *m*, and blew the gateway horn. „ 169
m a sudden step to the gate, and there— „ 391
backward by the wind they *m* In moving, „ 480
'Sweet love, that seems not *m* to fade away, „ 1013
He makes no friend who never *m* a foe. „ 1089
and *m* him hers, and laid her mind On him, *Holy Grail* 164
wild bees That *m* such honey in his realm. „ 215
mould Of Arthur, *m* by Merlin, with a crown, „ 239
crown And both the wings are *m* of gold, „ 242
A sign to maim this Order which I *m*. „ 297
since your vows are sacred, being *m* : „ 314
Rejoicing in that Order which he *m*.' „ 327
Lord of all things *m* Himself Naked of glory „ 447
When the hermit *m* an end, „ 457
past thro' Pagan realms, and *m* them mine, „ 478
Thither I *m*, and there was I disarm'd „ 575
that one only, who had ever *M* my heart leap ; „ 580
And each *m* joy of either ; „ 638
So fierce a gale *m* havoc here of late „ 729
Who *m* me sure the Quest was not for me ; „ 743
m our mightier madder than our least. „ 863
When God *m* music thro' them, „ 878
King Arthur *m* new knights to fill the gap *Pelleas and E.* 1
and Arthur *m* him knight. „ 16
Then Arthur *m* vast banquets, „ 147
So *m* his moan ; and, darkness falling, „ 213
sight Of her rich beauty *m* him at one glance „ 238
whom late our Arthur *m* Knight of his table ; „ 319
only the King Hath *m* us fools and liars. „ 479
sword That *m* it plunges thro' the wound again, „ 530
And Percivale *m* answer not a word. „ 534
he twitch'd the reins, And *m* his beast „ 551
Had *m* mock-knight of Arthur's Table Round, *Last Tournament* 2
M answer, 'Ay, but wherefore toss me this „ 195
Great brother, thou nor I have *m* the world ; „ 203
Tristram round the gallery *m* his horse Caracole ; „ 205
M answer, 'I had liefer twenty years „ 257
I *m* it in the woods, And heard it ring as true „ 283
did ye mark that fountain yesterday *M* to run wine ?— „ 287
but when the King Had *m* thee fool, „ 306
M dull his inner, keen his outer eye „ 366
up thro' Alioth and Alcor, *M* all above it, „ 481
the crowning sin That *m* us happy : „ 577
The King prevailing *m* his realm :— „ 651
did you keep the vow you *m* to Mark „ 655
And so the realm was *m* ; but then their vows— „ 681
M such excuses as he might, *Guinevere* 38
And from the sun there swiftly *m* at her „ 78
To which a mournful answer *m* the Queen : „ 341
sins that *m* the past so pleasant to us : „ 375
m her face a darkness from the King : „ 417
He spared to lift his hand against the King Who *m* him knight : „ 438
Thou hast not *m* my life so sweet to me, „ 451
I *m* them lay their hands in mine and swear „ 467
I am not *m* of so slight elements. „ 510
Enwound him fold by fold, and *m* him gray And grayer, „ 603
What might I not have *m* of thy fair world, „ 655
First *m* and latest left of all the knights, *Pass. of Arthur* 2
As if some lesser god had *m* the world, „ 14
uttering this the King *M* at the man : „ 165
I perish by this people which I *m*,— „ 190
great brand *M* lightnings in the splendour of the moon, „ 305
here the faith That *m* us rulers ? *To the Queen ii* 19

Made (*continued*) to whom I *m* it o'er his grave Sacred, *To the Queen ii* 35
attracted, won, Married, *m* one with, *Lover's Tale i* 134
M all our tastes and fancies like, „ 242
m garlands of the selfsame flower, „ 343
had *m* The red rose there a pale one— „ 695
m The happy and the unhappy love, „ 752
one other, worth the life That *m* it sensible— „ 800
M strange division of its suffering „ *ii* 128
m the ground Reel under us, „ 193
The front rank *m* a sudden halt; „ *iii* 29
And partly *m* them—tho' he knew it not. „ *iv* 25
till helpless death And silence *m* him bold— „ 73
Or am I *m* immortal, or my love Mortal once more?' „ 79
things familiar to her youth Had *m* a silent answer: „ 96
sudden wail his lady *m* Dwelt in his fancy: „ 149
And Julian *m* a solemn feast: „ 187
Then Julian *m* a secret sign to me „ 284
answer'd not a word, Which *m* the amazement more, „ 334
he *m* me the cowslip ball, *First Quarrel* 13
you were only *m* for the day. *Rizpah* 19
The King should have *m* him a soldier, „ 28
seamen *m* mock at the mad little craft *The Revenge* 38
gunner said 'Ay, ay,' but the seamen *m* reply: „ 91
Had *m* a heated haze to magnify The charm of Edith— *Sisters (E. and E.)* 129
he had seen it and *m* up his mind, *In the Child. Hosp.* 16
m West East, and sail'd the Dragon's mouth, *Columbus* 25
vow I *m* When Spain was waging war against the Moor— „ 92
m by me, may seek to unbury me, „ 206
Who *m* thee unconceivably Thyself *De Prof., Two G.* 48
for the bright-eyed goddess *m* it burn. *Achilles over the T.* 29
but *m* me yearn For larger glimpses *Tiresias* 20
The noonday crag *m* the hand burn; „ 35
With present grief, and *m* the rhymes, „ 196
I took it, he *m* it a cage, *The Wreck* 83
M us, foreknew us, foredoom'd us, *Despair* 97
'The years that *m* the stripling wise *Ancient Sage* 111
They *m* her lily and rose in one, „ 161
Only That which *m* us, meant us to be mightier *Locksley H., Sixty* 209
Fought for their lives in the narrow gap they had *m*— *Heavy Brigade* 23
Glory to each and to all, and the charge that they *m*! „ 65
Which has *m* your fathers great *Open. I. and C. Exhib.* 15
Who *m* a nation purer through their art. *To W. C. Macready* 8
Your rule has *m* the people love Their ruler. *To Marq. of Dufferin* 9
have I *m* the name A golden portal to my rhyme: „ 15
m themselves as Gods against the fear *Demeter and P.* 141
They *m* a thousand honey moons of one? *The Ring* 22
And that has *m* you grave? „ 88
and *m* The rosy twilight of a perfect day. „ 186
M every moment of her after life A virgin victim „ 220
Why had I *m* her love me thro' the ring, „ 391
But still she *m* her outcry for the ring; „ 403
m him leper to compass him with scorn— *Happy* 16
I *m* one barren effort to break it at the last. „ 72
Now God has *m* you leper in His loving care „ 91
m an English homestead Hell— *To Mary Boyle* 37
I might have *m* you once, *Romney's R.* 89
m The wife of wives a widow-bride, „ 137
M by the noonday blaze without, *St. Telemachus* 50
'Mine is the one fruit Alla *m* for man.' *Akbar's Dream* 40
Adoring That who *m*, and makes, „ 123
Alphabet-of-heaven-in-man *M* vocal— „ 137
Man as yet is being *m*, *Making of Man* 3
'It is finish'd. Man is *m*.' „ 8
Madeline Ever varying *M*. (repeat) *Madeline* 3, 18, 27
Madest Who *m* him thy chosen, *Tithonus* 13
Thou *m* Life in man and brute; Thou *m* Death; *In Mem., Pro.* 6
Thou *m* man, he knows not why, „ 10
Madhouse I would not be mock'd in a *m*! *Despair* 79
Madly That you should carol so *m*? *The Throstle* 8
Madman *M*!—to chain with chains, *Buonaparte* 2
warn'd that *m* ere it grew too late: *Vision of Sin* 56
he struck me, *m*, over the face, *Maud II i* 18
'Wherefore waits the *m* there Naked *Gareth and L.* 1091

Madman (*continued*) And like a *m* brought her to the court, *Marr. of Geraint* 725
A *m* to vex you with wretched words, *Despair* 108
teeming with liars, and *madmen*, and knaves, *The Dreamer* 9
Madness Then in *m* and in bliss, *Madeline* 42
From cells of *m* unconfined, *Two Voices* 371
Thro' *m*, hated by the wise, *Love and Duty* 7
Mingle *m*, mingle scorn! *Vision of Sin* 204
Vext with unworthy *m*, and deform'd. *Aylmer's Field* 335
Is this a time to madden *m* then? „ 769
No *m* of ambition, avarice, none: *Lucretius* 212
The accomplice of your *m* unforgiven, *Princess vi* 276
kinsman thou to death and trance And *m*, *In Mem. lxxi* 2
the vitriol *m* flushes up in the ruffian's head, *Maud I i* 37
I flee from the cruel *m* of love, „ *iv* 55
Perhaps from *m*, perhaps from crime, „ *xvi* 22
And do accept my *m*, and would die „ *xviii* 44
Thro' cells of *m*, haunts of horror and fear, „ *III vi* 2
What *m* made thee challenge the chief knight *Gareth and L.* 1416
O pardon me! the *m* of that hour, *Geraint and E.* 346
And after *m* acted question ask'd: „ 813
break Into some *m* ev'n before the Queen?' *Balin and Balan* 230
My *m* all thy life has been thy doom, „ 619
'This *m* has come on us for our sins.' *Holy Grail* 357
former *m*, once the talk And scandal of our table, „ 649
A dying fire of *m* in his eyes— „ 768
My *m* came upon me as of old, „ 787
And in my *m* to myself I said, „ 804
Then in my *m* I essay'd the door; „ 841
And but for all my *m* and my sin, „ 849
And all the sacred *m* of the bard, „ 877
—the wholesome *m* of an hour— *Last Tournament* 675
It was their last hour, A *m* of farewells. *Guinevere* 103
curb The *m* of our cities and their kings. *Tiresias* 71
My father's *m* makes me mad— *The Flight* 59
age so cramm'd with menace? *m*? written, spoken lies? *Locksley H., Sixty* 108
After *m*, after massacre, Jacobinism and Jacquerie, „ 157
Every tiger *m* muzzled, every serpent passion kill'd, „ 167
dream of wars and carnage, craft and *m*, lust and spite, „ 189
Cast the poison from your bosom, oust the *m* from your brain. „ 241
The theft were death or *m* to the thief, *The Ring* 204
And eased her heart of *m*. . . . *Forlorn* 82
Madonna '*M*, sad is night and morn,' *Mariana in the S.* 22
Madonna-masterpieces *M-m* Of ancient Art in Paris, *Romney's R.* 86
Madonna-wise *M-w* on either side her head; *Isabel* 6
Maeldune 'O *M*, let be this purpose of thine! *V. of Maeldune* 119
Magazine O blatant *M's*, regard me rather— *Hendecasyllabics* 17
Mage 'And there I saw *m* Merlin, *Com. of Arthur* 280
like a fairy changeling lay the *m*; „ 363
Merlin's hand, the *M* at Arthur's court, *Gareth and L.* 306
Magee (Molly) *See* **Molly, Molly Magee**
Maggot tickle the *m* born in an empty head, *Maud II v* 38
'O worms and *m's* of to-day *Ancient Sage* 210
Magic (adj.) Low thunder and light in the *m* night— *The Merman* 23
A *m* web with colours gay. *L. of Shalott ii* 2
To weave the mirror's *m* sights, „ 29
Saw the heavens fill with commerce, argosies of *m* sails, *Locksley Hall* 121
The *M* Music in his heart Beats quick and quicker, *Day-Dm., Arrival* 26
on lonely mountain-meres I find a *m* bark; *Sir Galahad* 38
drank The *m* cup that fill'd itself anew. *Aylmer's Field* 143
she liked it more Than *m* music, forfeits, *Princess, Pro.* 195
all the *m* light Dies off at once *In Mem. viii* 5
wise man that ever served King Uther thro' his *m* art; *Com. of Arthur* 152
'I once was looking for a *m* weed, *Merlin and V.* 471
red fruit Grown on a *m* oak-tree in mid-heaven, *Last Tournament* 745
forms which ever stood Within the *m* cirque of memory, *Lover's Tale ii* 159
Magic (s) Is there some *m* in the place? *Will Water.* 79
Bleys, Who taught him *m*; *Com. of Arthur* 154
Bleys Laid *m* by, and sat him down, „ 156

Maiden (adj.) (*continued*) nor yet to the wife—to her *m* name ! *The Wreck* 144
Set the *m* fancies wallowing in the troughs of Zolaism,— *Locksley H., Sixty* 145
Her *m* daughter's marriage ; *Prin. Beatrice* 10
But ere thy *m* birk be wholly clad, *Prog. of Spring* 50
Maiden (s) phantom two hours old Of a *m* past away, *Adeline* 19
The little *m* walk'd demure, *Two Voices* 419
A simple *m* in her flower *L. C. V. de Vere* 15
of the warrior Gileadite, A *m* pure ; *D. of F. Women* 198
'Would I had been some *m* coarse and poor ! „ 253
Wrought by the lonely *m* of the Lake. *M. d'Arthur* 104
whose touch may press The *m's* tender palm. *Talking Oak* 180
The *m's* jet-black hair has grown, *Day-Dm., Sleep. B.* 4
Nor *m's* hand in mine. *Sir Galahad* 20
Dropt her head in the *m's* hand, *Lady Clare* 63
M, I have watch'd thee daily, *L. of Burleigh* 3
And a village *m* she. „ 8
A *m* of our century, yet most meek ; *The Brook* 68
There stood a *m* near, Waiting to pass. „ 204
more and more, the *m* woman-grown, *Aylmer's Field* 108
All wild to found an University For *m's*, *Princess i* 151
Six hundred *m's* clad in purest white, „ *ii* 472
'O marvellously modest *m*, you ! „ *iii* 48
'An open-hearted *m*, true and pure. „ 98
Among her *m's*, higher by the head, „ 179
Her college and her *m's*, empty masks, „ 187
There stood her *m's* glimmeringly group'd „ *iv* 190
All her *m's*, watching, said, „ *vi* 3
Stole a *m* from her place, „ 9
many a *m* passing home Till happier times ; „ 380
m's came, they talk'd, They sang, „ *vii* 22
m, whither would you wander ? (repeat) *City Child* 1, 6
far away,' said the dainty little *m*, (repeat) „ 3, 8
Lash the *m* into swooning, *Boädicea* 67
or half coquette-like *M*, *Hendecasyllabics* 21
As on a *m* in the day When first she wears *In Mem. xl* 3
May serve to curl a *m's* locks, „ *lxxvii* 7
I dwelt within a hall, And *m's* with me : „ *ciii* 6
The *m's* gather'd strength and grace „ 27
m's with one mind Bewail'd their lot ; „ 45
m's of the place, That pelt us in the porch „ *Con.* 67
Go not, happy day, Till the *m* yields. *Maud I xvii* 4
Or whether it be the *m's* fantasy, *Gareth and L.* 874
Whereat the *m*, petulant, 'Lancelot, „ 1246
on whom the *m* gazed. „ 1281
set the horror higher : a *m* swoon'd ; „ 1394
But rose at last, a single *m* with her, Took horse, *Marr. of Geraint* 160
sent Her *m* to demand it of the dwarf ; „ 193
Done in your *m's* person to yourself : „ 216
Sent her own *m* to demand the name, „ 411
never yet had woman such a pair Of suitors as this *m* ; „ 440
'Mother, a *m* is a tender thing, „ 510
Let never *m* think, however fair, „ 721
the *m* rose, And left her maiden couch, „ 736
call'd her like that *m* in the tale, „ 742
we *m's* often laugh When sick at heart, *Balin and Balan* 497
shelter for mine innocency Among thy *m's* !' *Merlin and V.* 84
m dreamt That some one put this diamond *Lancelot and E.* 211
And yield it to this *m*, if ye will.' „ 229
saw The *m* standing in the dewy light. „ 352
never yet have done so much For any *m* living,' „ 376
broider'd with great pearls, Some gentle *m's* gift.' „ 605
for lack of gentle *m's* aid. The gentler-born the *m*, „ 765
m, while that ghostly grace Beam'd on his fancy, „ 885
So in her tower alone the *m* sat : „ 989
'Is this Elaine ?' till back the *m* fell, „ 1031
Know that for this most gentle *m's* death „ 1291
to see The *m* buried, not as one unknown, „ 1334
Thou could'st have loved this *m*, „ 1366
A holy maid ; tho' never *m* glow'd, *Holy Grail* 72
'O Father !' ask'd the *m*, „ 95
sweet *m*, shore away Clean from her forehead „ 149
I, *m*, round thee, *m*, bind my belt. „ 159
An outraged *m* sprang into the hall „ 208

Maiden (s) (*continued*) By *m's* each as fair as any flower : *Holy Grail* 576
she a slender *m*, all my heart Went after her „ 582
And merry *m's* in it ; „ 746
blew my merry *m's* all about With all discomfort ; „ 748
And since he loved all *m's*, *Pelleas and E.* 40
'O *m*, if indeed ye list to sing, *Guinevere* 165
'Such as thou art be never *m* more „ 358
aghast the *m* rose, White as her veil, „ 362
love one *m* only, cleave to her, „ 475
Meek *m's*, from the voices crying "shame." „ 672
Wrought by the lonely *m* of the Lake. *Pass. of Arthur* 272
m's, wives, And mothers with their babblers *Tiresias* 102
Crime and hunger cast our *m's* by the thousand on the street. *Locksley H., Sixty* 220
Love for the *m*, crown'd with marriage, *Vastness* 23
Her *m* coming like a Queen, *The Ring* 480
Innocent *m's*, Garrulous children, *Merlin and the G.* 55
Maiden-cheek Engirt with many a florid *m-c*, *Princess iii* 350
Maidenhood (*See also* **Mother-maidenhood**) To her, perpetual *m*, *In Mem. vi* 43
Would mar their charm of stainless *m*.' *Balin and Balan* 268
To get me shelter for my *m*. „ 480
But that was in her earlier *m*, *Holy Grail* 73
Maidenlike *m* as far As I could ape their treble, *Princess iv* 91
Maiden-meek *m-m* I pray'd Concealment : „ *iii* 134
Maid-mother Or the *m-m* by a crucifix, *Palace of Art* 93
Maiden-Princess lonely *m-P* of the wood, *The Ring* 65
Her lonely *m-P*, crown'd with flowers, „ 485
Maid of Astolat (*See also* **Astolat**) Elaine, the lily *m o A*, *Lancelot and E.* 2
About the *m o A*, and her love. „ 723
'The *m o A* loves Sir Lancelot, Sir Lancelot loves the *m o A*.' „ 725
Then spake the lily *m o A* : „ 1085
past the barge Whereon the lily *m o A* Lay smiling, „ 1242
I, sometime call'd the *m o A*, „ 1273
Maid-of-honour The *m-o-h* blooming fair ; *Day-Dm., Sleep. P.* 28
Poor soul ! I had a *m o h* once ; *Princess iv* 133
Mail (armour) from head to tail Came out clear plates of sapphire *m*. *Two Voices* 12
And, ringing, springs from brand and *m* ; *Sir Galahad* 54
and all in *m* Burnish'd to blinding, *Gareth and L.* 1026
till he felt, despite his *m*, Strangled, „ 1151
splintering spear, the hard *m* hewn, *Pass. of Arthur* 108
Mail (coach) The *m* ? At one o'clock. *Walk. to the Mail* 8
I fear That we shall miss the *m* : „ 112
They swore he dare not rob the *m*, *Rizpah* 30
they kill'd him for robbing the *m*. „ 34
Mailed (*See also* **Hard-mailed, Triple-mailèd**) My *m* Bacchus leapt into my arms, *D. of F. Women* 151
with each light air On our *m* heads : *Princess v* 245
Breaking their *m* fleets and armed towers, *Ode Inter. Exhib.* 39
Drove his *m* heel athwart the royal crown, *Balin and Balan* 540
Maim A sign to *m* this Order, which I made. *Holy Grail* 297
Maim'd (adj. and part.) left me *m* To dwell in presence of immortal youth, *Tithonus* 20
Speak ! is there any of you halt or *m* ? *St. S. Stylites* 142
that there Lie bruised and *m*, *Princess vi* 72
and all the good knights *m*, „ 241
I see thee *m*, Mangled : *Gareth and L.* 1326
with blunt stump Pitch-blacken'd sawing the air, said the *m* churl, *Last Tournament* 67
And half of the rest of us *m* for life *The Revenge* 77
What life, so *m* by night, were worth Our living out ? *Tiresias* 208
Maim'd (s) And cured some halt and *m* ; *St. S. Stylites* 137
Let the *m* in his heart rejoice *On Jub. Q. Victoria* 36
Maim'd (verb) and him they caught and *m* ; *Lancelot and E.* 275
M me and maul'd, and would outright have slain, *Last Tournament* 75
Main (adj.) (*See* also **Maäin-glad**) till Arthur by *m* might, *Com. of Arthur* 109
And out by this *m* doorway past the King. *Gareth and L.* 671
And bare her by *m* violence to the board, *Geraint and E.* 654
(With one *m* purpose ever at my heart) „ 831
but for my *m* purpose in these jousts, „ 837
Could call him the *m* cause of all their crime ; *Merlin and V.* 788
That was their *m* test-question— *Sir J. Oldcastle* 155

Main (adj.) (*continued*) Fonseca my *m* enemy at their court, *Columbus* 126
Main (s) heard that, somewhere in the *m*, *If I were loved* 7
Just breaking over land and *m*? *Two Voices* 84
On open *m* or winding shore! *The Voyage* 6
And mighty courteous in the *m*— *Aylmer's Field* 121
spire of land that stands apart Cleft from the *m*, *Princess iv* 282
Let the great river take me to the *m*: „ *vii* 13
climbs a peak to gaze O'er land and *m*, „ 36
Blown from over every *m*, *Ode Inter. Exhib.* 26
To mingle with the bounding *m*: *In Mem. xi* 12
I am sick of the moor and the *m*. *Maud I i* 61
Flying along the land and the *m*— „ *II ii* 38
out to open *m* Glow'd intermingling close beneath the sun. *Lover's Tale i* 435
To be lost evermore in the *m*. *The Revenge* 119
hull dipt under the smiling *m*, *The Wreck* 127
sea-current would sweep us out to the *m*. *Despair* 51
O will she, moonlike, sway the *m*, *Mechanophilus* 13
Main-current Watch what *m-c's* draw the years: *Love thou thy land* 21
Main-miracle But this *m-m*, that thou art thou, *De Prof., Two G.* 55
Maintain thy heart a fortress to *m* The day *To Duke of Argyll* 5
and thence *m* Our darker future. *To one who ran down Eng.* 1
Maintained should at least by me be *m*: *Maud I i* 18
Maintaining *M* that with equal husbandry *Princess i* 130
Maintenance all That appertains to noble *m*. *Marr. of Geraint* 712
Maize hand in hand with Plenty in the *m*, *Princess vii* 201
Of olive, aloe, and *m* and vine. *The Daisy* 4
Majestic Grave mother of *m* works, *Of old sat Freedom* 13
Sees a mansion more *m* Than all those *L. of Burleigh* 45
Who scarce can tune his high *m* sense *Lover's Tale i* 475
Thou *m* in thy sadness at the doubtful doom of human kind; *To Virgil* 23
But scarce of such *m* mien *Freedom* 6
Majesty New *Majesties* of mighty states— *Love thou thy land* 60
Nothing to mar the sober *majesties* *Lucretius* 217
and so unmoved a *m* She might have seem'd her statue, *Lancelot and E.* 1170
Make (*See also* **Maäke, May, Re-make**) *yield you time To* m *demand of modern rhyme* *To the Queen* 11
and m *The bounds of freedom wider* „ 31
Shall *m* the winds blow Round and round, *Nothing will Die* 23
Whose chillness would *m* visible *Supp. Confessions* 59
Rain *m's* music in the tree *A Dirge* 26
M's thy memory confused: „ 45
the wave would *m* music above us afar— *The Merman* 22
M a carcanet of rays, *Adeline* 59
clip your wings, and *m* you love: *Rosalind* 45
happy bridesmaid *m's* a happy bride.' *The Bridesmaid* 4
happy bridesmaid, *m* a happy bride.' (repeat) „ 8, 14
'What drug can *m* A wither'd palsy cease to shake?' *Two Voices* 56
M thy grass hoar with early rime. „ 66
'Or *m* that morn, from his cold crown „ 85
'Wilt thou *m* everything a lie, „ 203
Not *m* him sure that he should cease? „ 282
'I cannot *m* this matter plain, „ 343
Far thought with music that it *m's*: „ 438
His memory scarce can *m* me sad. *Miller's D.* 16
And *m's* me talk too much in age. „ 194
Do *m* a garland for the heart: „ 198
'*M* me a cottage in the vale,' *Palace of Art* 291
To *m* him trust his modest worth, *L. C. V. de Vere* 46
many a worthier than I, would *m* him happy yet. *May Queen, Con.* 46
what is life, that we should moan? why *m* we such ado? „ 56
music in his ears his beating heart did *m*. *Lotos-Eaters* 36
And *m* perpetual moan, „ *C. S.* 17
That *m's* my only woe. *D. of F. Women* 136
Words weaker than your grief would *m* Grief more. *To J. S.* 65
And *m's* the purple lilac ripe, *On a Mourner* 7
Power should *m* from land to land *You ask me, why, etc.* 21
M bright our days and light our dreams, *Of old sat Freedom* 22
She stood, a sight to *m* an old man young. *Gardener's D.* 141
M thine heart ready with thine eyes: „ 273
'I'll *m* them man and wife.' *Dora* 4

Make (*continued*) To *m* him pleasing in her uncle's eye. *Dora* 84
let me have my boy, for you Will *m* him hard, „ 153
To *m* me an example of mankind, *St. S. Stylites* 188
The love, that *m's* me thrice a man, *Talking Oak* 11
But since I heard him *m* reply „ 25
To *m* the necklace shine; „ 222
mellow rain, That *m's* thee broad and deep! „ 280
words That *m* a man feel strong in speaking truth; *Love and Duty* 70
How dull it is to pause, to *m* an end, *Ulysses* 22
by slow prudence to *m* mild A rugged people, „ 36
Can thy love, Thy beauty, *m* amends, *Tithonus* 24
And *m* me tremble lest a saying learnt, „ 47
M me feel the wild pulsation *Locksley Hall* 109
M prisms in every carven glass, *Day-Dm., Sleep. P.* 35
And *m* her dance attendance; *Amphion* 62
M Thou thy spirit pure and clear *St. Agnes' Eve* 9
Heavenly Bridegroom waits, To *m* me pure of sin. „ 32
To *m* me write my random rhymes, *Will Water.* 13
Until the charm have power to *m* New lifeblood „ 21
To *m* my blood run quicker, „ 110
How out of place she *m's* The violet of a legend blow „ 146
empty glass That *m's* me maudlin-moral. „ 208
Hoped to *m* the name Of his vessel great in story, *The Captain* 18
'I can *m* no marriage present: *L. of Burleigh* 13
Love will *m* our cottage pleasant, „ 15
All he shows her *m's* him dearer „ 33
I follow till I *m* thee mine.' *The Voyage* 64
sweetest meal she *m's* On the first-born *Vision of Sin* 145
Who *m* it seem more sweet to be *You might have won* 29
purchase his own boat, and *m* a home For Annie: *Enoch Arden* 47
m him merry, when I come home again. „ 199
kill yourself And *m* them orphans quite?' „ 395
Their voices *m* me feel so solitary.' „ 397
To *m* the boatmen fishing-nets, „ 815
himself could *m* The thing that is not as the thing *The Brook* 7
I *m* a sudden sally, „ 24
Still *m's* a hoary eyebrow for the gleam „ 80
I *m* the netted sunbeam dance „ 176
Roaring to *m* a third: *Aylmer's Field* 128
counsel from a height That *m's* the lowest hate it, „ 173
for your fortunes are to *m*. I swear you shall not *m* them out of mine. „ 300
every star in heaven Can *m* it fair: *Sea Dreams* 84
A trifle *m's* a dream, a trifle breaks.' „ 144
fat affectionate smile That *m's* the widow lean. „ 156
—it *m's* me sick to quote him— „ 159
Went both to *m* your dream: „ 254
m our passions far too like The discords „ 257
m Another and another frame of things *Lucretius* 41
my rich procemion *m's* Thy glory fly „ 70
blood That *m's* a steaming slaughter-house of Rome. „ 84
bird *M's* his heart voice amid the blaze of flowers: „ 101
To *m* a truth less harsh, „ 225
I would *m* it death For any male thing *Princess, Pro.* 151
And sweet as English air could *m* her, „ 155
'And *m* her some great Princess, „ 224
doubt that we might *m* it worth his while. „ *i* 184
her lynx eye To fix and *m* me hotter, „ *iii* 47
your pains May only *m* that footprint „ 239
and *m* One act a phantom of succession: „ 328
pipe and woo her, and *m* her mine, „ *iv* 115
Would *m* all women kick against their Lords „ 412
'And *m* us all we should be, great and good.' „ 599
will take her, they will *m* her hard, „ *v* 90
Knowledge in our own land *m* her free, „ 419
The mother *m's* us most—and in my dream „ 507
let me *m* my dream All that I would. „ 519
let her *m* herself her own To give or keep, „ *vii* 272
—why Not *m* her true-heroic— „ *Con.* 20
break the shore, and evermore *M* and break, *Ode on Well.* 261
And you, my Lords, you *m* the people muse *Third of Feb.* 31
Come to us, love us and *m* us your own: *W. to Alexandra* 30
Annie, will never *m* oneself clean. *Grandmother* 36
it *m's* me angry now. „ 44

Make (*continued*) preacher says, our sins should *m* us sad : *Grandmother* 93
That it *m's* one weary to hear.' *The Islet* 29
And *m's* it a sorrow to be.' " 36
strain to *m* an inch of room For their sweet selves, *Lit. Squabbles* 9
m you evermore Dearer and nearer, *A Dedication* 2
m the carcase a skeleton, *Boädicea* 14
and *m* her a bower All of flowers, *Window, At the W.* 5
Our wills are ours, to *m* them thine. *In Mem., Pro.* 16
May *m* one music as before, " 28
And in thy wisdom *m* me wise. " 44
' What is it *m's* me beat so low ? ' " *iv* 8
That *m's* the barren branches loud ; " *xv* 13
And *m's* a silence in the hills. " *xix* 8
And *m* them pipes whereon to blow. " *xxi* 4
M April of her tender eyes ; " *xl* 8
A spectral doubt that *m's* me cold, " *xli* 19
And *m's* it vassal unto love : " *xlviii* 8
winds that *m* The seeming-wanton ripple break, " *xlix* 10
To *m* allowance for us all. " *li* 16
Could *m* thee somewhat blench or fail, " *lxii* 2
Who *m's* by force his merit known " *lxiv* 9
Which *m's* a desert in the mind, " *lxvi* 6
Which *m's* me sad I know not why " *lxviii* 11
Looks thy fair face and *m's* it still. " *lxx* 16
sire would *m* Confusion worse than death, " *xc* 18
But ever strove to *m* it true : " *xcvi* 8
He would not *m* his judgment blind, " 14
Which *m's* the darkness and the light, " 19
To *m* a solid core of heat ; " *cvii* 18
'Tis held that sorrow *m's* us wise, " *cviii* 15
'Tis held that sorrow *m's* us wise ; " *cxiii* 1
To *m* old bareness picturesque " *cxxviii* 19
Is that a matter to *m* me fret ? *Maud I xiii* 2
And I *m* myself such evil cheer, " *xv* 2
boundless plan That *m's* you tyrants " *xviii* 37
M answer, Maud my bliss, " 57
m's Love himself more dear.' " 61
May God *m* me more wretched Than ever " *xix* 94
But either fail'd to *m* the kingdom one. *Com. of Arthur* 15
nor *m* myself in mine own realm Victor " 89
power on this dead world to *m* it live.' " 94
live and love, and *m* the world Other, " 472
should be King save him who *m's* us free ? ' *Gareth and L.* 137
one proof, Before thou ask the King to *m* thee knight, " 145
Well, we will *m* amends.' " 300
m him knight because men call him king. " 420
M me thy knight—in secret ! (repeat) " 544, 564
m demand Of whom ye gave me to, the Seneschal, " 558
Let be my name until I *m* my name ! " 576
To break her will, and *m* her wed with him : " 617
mar the boast Thy brethren of thee *m*— " 1243
to *m* the terror of thee more, " 1389
To *m* a horror all about the house, " 1411
To *m* her beauty vary day by day. *Marr. of Geraint* 9
thro' his manful breast darted the pang That *m's* a man, " 122
And we will *m* us merry as we may. " 373
I will *m* her truly my true wife.' " 503
for my strange petition I will *m* Amends " 817
M me a little happier : let me know it : *Geraint and E.* 317
They would not *m* them laughable in all eyes, " 326
' Your sweet faces *m* good fellows fools " 399
God's curse, it *m's* me mad to see you weep. " 616
when it weds with manhood, *m's* a man. " 868
m all clean, and plant himself afresh. " 905
Should *m* an onslaught single on a realm " 917
And *m*, as ten-times worthier to be thine *Balin and Balan* 68
so rich a fellowship Would *m* me wholly blest : " 148
a transitory word *M* knight or churl " 162
would she *m* My darkness blackness ? " 192
as *m's* The white swan-mother, sitting, " 352
So thou be shadow, here I *m* thee ghost,' " 394
same mistrustful mood That *m's* you seem less noble *Merlin and V.* 322

Make (*continued*) Must *m* me fear still more you are not mine, Must *m* me yearn still more to prove you mine, And *m* me wish still more to learn *Merlin and V.* 327
That *m's* me passing wrathful ; " 341
That by and by will *m* the music mute, " 391
fain would *m* you Master of all vice.' " 469
charm concluded in that star To *m* fame nothing. " 513
And one to *m* me jealous if I love, " 539
ringing with their serpent hands, To *m* her smile, " 579
Or *m* her paler with a poison'd rose ? " 611
Not to feel lowest *m's* them level all ; " 828
Who loved to *m* men darker than they are, " 876
could *m* me stay—That proof of trust— " 919
may *m* My scheming brain a cinder, " 932
To *m* them like himself : *Lancelot and E.* 131
The low sun *m's* the colour : " 134
To *m* her thrice as wilful as before.' " 206
lily maid had striven to *m* him cheer, " 327
sloping down to *m* Arms for his chair, " 437
that I *m* My will of yours, " 915
So that would *m* you happy : " 959
sweetly could she *m* and sing. " 1006
Sweet death, that seems to *m* us loveless clay, " 1014
He *m's* no friend who never made a foe. " 1089
and *m* me happy, making them An armlet " 1182
Yet to be loved *m's* not to love again ; " 1295
' God *m* thee good as thou art beautiful,' *Holy Grail* 136
Hope not to *m* thyself by idle vows, " 871
' *M* me thy knight, because I know, *Pelleas and E.* 7
I will *m* thee with my spear and sword " 45
Stammer'd and could not *m* her a reply. " 85
His neighbour's *m* and might : " 151
Open gates, And I will *m* you merry.' " 374
whom ye loathe, him will I *m* you love.' " 390
And *m* them, an thou wilt a tourney-prize.' *Last Tournament* 32
M their last head like Satan in the North. " 98
Would *m* the world as blank as Winter-tide. " 221
too much wit *M's* the world rotten, " 247
Than any broken music thou canst *m*.' " 259
It *m's* a silent music up in heaven, " 349
he can *m* Figs out of thistles, " 355
Arthur *m* me pure As any maiden child ? " 692
I shall never *m* thee smile again.' " 762
chance Will *m* the smouldering scandal *Guinevere* 91
love of truth, and all that *m's* a man. " 483
M's wicked lightnings of her eyes, " 520
whose vast pity almost *m's* me die To see thee, " 534
And *m's* me one pollution : " 619
And enter it, and *m* it beautiful ? *Pass of Arthur* 17
To *m* it wholly thine on sunny days. *Lover's Tale i* 14
It *m's* a constant bubbling melody " 532
I *m* bare of all the golden moss, " *ii* 48
M's the heart tremble, and the sight run over " 156
I will *m* a solemn offering of you " *iv* 118
It *m's* me angry yet to speak of it— " 135
the soul : *That m's* the sequel pure ; " 157
To *m* a good wife for Harry, *First Quarrel* 30
no need to *m* such a stir.' " 63
You'll *m* her its second mother ! " 71
We will *m* the Spaniard promise, *The Revenge* 94
birds *m* ready for their bridal-time *Sisters (E. and E.)* 71
m The veriest beauties of the work appear " 104
that *m* our griefs our gains. " 231
call men traitors May *m* men traitors. *Sir J. Oldcastle* 51
Lest the false faith *m* merry over them ! " 82
They said ' Let us *m* man ' *De Prof., Two G.* 36
That Lenten fare *m's* Lenten thought, *To E. Fitzgerald* 31
I would *m* my life one prayer *The Wreck* 10
To *m* their banquet relish ? *Ancient Sage* 18
What power but the bird's could *m* This music in the bird ? " 21
' What Power but the Years that *m* And break the vase of clay, " 91
m the passing shadow serve thy will. " 110
to *m* The phantom walls of this illusion fade, " 180
m thy gold thy vassal not thy king, " 259
Nor *m* a snail's horn shrink for wantonness ; " 272

Man (*continued*) A *m* more pure and bold and just — *To J. S.* 31
A *m* may speak the thing he will; — *You ask me, why, etc.* 8
part by part to *men* reveal'd The fullness — *Of old sat Freedom* 11
Bear seed of *men* and growth of minds. — *Love thou thy land* 20
if Nature's evil star Drive *men* in manhood, — „ 74
O THOU, that sendest out the *m* — *England and Amer.* 1
in noble heat Those *men* thine arms withstood, — „ 7
So sitting, served by *m* and maid, — *The Goose* 21
and why should any *m* Remodel models? — *The Epic* 37
Until King Arthur's table, *m* by *m*, — *M. d'Arthur* 3
They sleep—the *men* I loved. — „ 17
A little thing may harm a wounded *m*. — „ 42
mighty bones of ancient *men*, Old knights, — „ 47
is a shameful thing for *men* to lie. — „ 78
Which might have pleased the eyes of many *men*. — „ 91
some old *m* speak in the aftertime — „ 107
for a *m* may fail in duty twice, — „ 129
I live three lives of mortal *men*, — „ 155
Among new *men*, strange faces, — „ 238
are *men* better than sheep or goats — „ 250
we loved the *m*, and prized his work; — „ *Ep.* 8
Francis, muttering, like a *m* ill-used, — „ 12
sweeter than the dream Dream'd by a happy *m*, — *Gardener's D.* 72
She stood, a sight to make an old *m* young. — „ 141
thought, 'I'll make them *m* and wife.' — *Dora* 4
Then the old *m* Was wroth, — „ 24
none of all his *men* Dare tell him Dora waited — „ 75
He spied her, and he left his *men* at work, — „ 86
when William died, he died at peace With all *men*; — „ 145
at once the old *m* burst in sobs:— — „ 158
they clung about The old *m's* neck, — „ 164
And all the *m* was broken with remorse; — „ 165
hid his face From all *men*, — *Walk. to the Mail* 21
You saw the *m*—on Monday, was it?— — „ 30
Like *men*, like manners: — „ 63
What know we of the secret of a *m*? — „ 104
built When *men* knew how to build, — *Edwin Morris* 7
God made the woman for the *m*, (repeat) — „ 43, 50
M is made of solid stuff. — „ 49
do not think yourself alone Of all *men* happy. — „ 78
'God made the woman for the use of *m*, — „ 91
Show me the *m* hath suffer'd more than I. — *St. S. Stylites* 49
and *men* on earth House in the shade — „ 106
Lord, thou knowest what a *m* I am; A sinful *m*, — „ 121
and more Than many just and holy *men*, — „ 131
by surname Stylites, among *men*; — „ 162
Speak, if there be a priest, a *m* of God, — „ 214
That love, that makes me thrice a *m*, — *Talking Oak* 11
To that *m* My work shall answer, — *Love and Duty* 28
for a *m* is not as God, — „ 30
But then most Godlike being most a *m*. — „ 31
words That make a *m* feel strong in speaking truth; — „ 70
light shall spread, and *m* be liker *m* — *Golden Year* 35
when shall all *men's* good Be each *m's* rule, — „ 47
cities of *men* And manners, climates, — *Ulysses* 13
unbecoming *men* that strove with Gods. — „ 53
M comes and tills the field and lies beneath, — *Tithonus* 3
Alas! for this gray shadow, once a *m*— — „ 11
wealthy *men* who care not how they give. — „ 17
Why should a *m* desire in any way To vary from the kindly race of *men*, — „ 28
happy *men* that have the power to die, — „ 70
In the Spring a young *m's* fancy — *Locksley Hall* 20
in among the throngs of *men*: — „ 116
Men, my brothers, *men* the workers, — „ 117
battle-flags were furl'd In the Parliament of *m*, — „ 128
thoughts of *men* are widen'd with the process of the suns. — „ 138
Woman is the lesser *m*, — „ 151
held it better *men* should perish one by one, — „ 179
New *men*, that in the flying of a wheel — *Godiva* 6
Bring truth that sways the soul of *men*? — *Day-Dm., Sleep. P.* 52
But any *m* that walks the mead, — „ *Moral* 9
To silence from the paths of *men*; — „ *L'Envoi* 6
Oh, nature first was fresh to *men*, — *Amphion* 57

Man (*continued*) My good blade carves the casques of *men*, — *Sir Galahad* 1
child's heart within the *m's* Begins to move — *Will Water.* 31
Which vexes public *men*, — „ 44
nor take Half-views of *men* and things. — „ 52
This earth is rich in *m* and maid; — „ 65
From misty *men* of letters; — „ 190
To keep the best *m* under the sun — *Lady Clare* 31
Lord Ronald's, When you are *m* and wife.' — „ 36
If there be any faith in *m*.' — „ 44
'The *m* will cleave unto his right.' — „ 46
Burnt in each *m's* blood. — *The Captain* 16
Blood and brains of *men*. — „ 48
each *m* murmur'd, 'O my Queen, I follow — *The Voyage* 63
A *m* had given all other bliss, — *Sir L. and Q. G.* 42
Henceforth I trust the *m* alone, — *The Letters* 31
gray and gap-tooth'd *m* as lean as death, — *Vision of Sin* 60
Every moment dies a *m*, (repeat) — „ 97, 121
'We are *men* of ruin'd blood; — „ 99
All the windy ways of *men* (repeat) — „ 132, 168
Buss me, thou rough sketch of *m*, — „ 189
Dregs of life, and lees of *m*: — „ 205
Below were *men* and horses pierced with worms, — „ 209
But in a tongue no *m* could understand; — „ 222
You shadow forth to distant *men*, — *To E. L.* 7
And all *men* look'd upon him favourably: — *Enoch Arden* 56
Altho' a grave and staid God-fearing *m*, — „ 112
he knew the *m* and valued him, — „ 121
Enoch as a brave God-fearing *m* — „ 185
You chose the best among us—a strong *m*: — „ 293
To wed the *m* so dear to all of them — „ 484
Surely the *m* had died of solitude. — „ 621
officers and *men* Levied a kindly tax upon themselves, Pitying the lonely *m*, and gave him it: — „ 662
with yet a bed for wandering *men*. — „ 698
'Enoch, poor *m*, was cast away and lost.' — „ 713
when the dead *m* come to life beheld His wife — „ 758
As lightly as a sick *m's* chamber-door, — „ 776
life in it Whereby the *m* could live; — „ 821
gentle sickness, gradually Weakening the *m*, — „ 825
'hear him talk! I warrant, *m*, — „ 841
Held his head high, and cared for no *m*, he.' — „ 848
'His head is low, and no *m* cares for him. — „ 850
I am the *m*.' — „ 852
For *men* may come and *men* may go, (repeat) — *The Brook* 33, 49, 65, 184
He knew the *m*; the colt would fetch its price; — „ 149
Yes, *men* may come and go; and these are gone, — „ 186
SIR AYLMER AYLMER, that almighty *m*, — *Aylmer's Field* 13
sons of *men* Daughters of God; — „ 44
My *men* shall lash you from them like a dog; — „ 325
the fierce old *m* Follow'd, — „ 330
m was his, had been his father's, friend: — „ 344
He had known a *m*, a quintessence of *m*, — „ 388
agreed That much allowance must be made for *men*. — „ 410
hearts of *men* Seem'd harder too; — „ 453
Like flies that haunt a wound, or deer, or *men*, — „ 571
a dead *m*, a letter edged with death Beside him, — „ 595
thy brother *m*, the Lord from Heaven, — „ 667
often placed upon the sick *m's* brow — „ 700
the *m* became Imbecile; his one word was 'desolate;' — „ 835
(for the *m* Had risk'd his little) — *Sea Dreams* 9
Not preaching simple Christ to simple *men*, — „ 21
And musing on the little lives of *men*, — „ 48
neither God nor *m* can well forgive, — „ 63
there surely lives in *m* and beast — „ 68
m is likewise counsel for himself, — „ 182
Came *men* and women in dark clusters round, — „ 226
men of flesh and blood, and men of stone, — „ 237
Good *m*, to please the child. — „ 267
who is dead?' 'The *m* your eye pursued. — „ 272
if there be A devil in *m*, there is an angel too, — „ 278
Then the *m*, 'His deeds yet live, — „ 313
tickling the brute brain within the *m's* — *Lucretius* 21
m may gain Letting his own life go. — „ 112
Gods there are, for all *men* so believe. — „ 117
his wrath were wreak'd on wretched *m*. — „ 128

Man (*continued*) *men* like soldiers may not quit the post *Lucretius* 148
hollow as the hopes and fears of *men* ? „ 180
what *m*, What Roman would be dragg'd in triumph „ 233
Those blind beginnings that have made me *m*, „ 246
into *m* once more, Or beast, or bird or fish, „ 248
that hour perhaps Is not so far when momentary *m* „ 253
carest not How roughly *men* may woo thee so they win— „ 273
A *m* with knobs and wires and vials fired *Princess, Pro.* 65
men and maids Arranged a country dance, „ 83
Discuss'd his tutor, rough to common *men*, „ 114
men have done it : how I hate you all ! „ 130
build Far off from *men* a college like a *m's*, And I would teach them all that *men* are taught ; „ 135
never *m*, I think, So moulder'd in a sinecure „ 181
what kind of tales did *men* tell *men*, „ 196
Between the rougher voices of the *men*, „ 245
On a sudden in the midst of *men* and day, „ *i* 15
he would send a hundred thousand *men*, „ 64
Whom all *men* rate as kind and hospitable : „ 71
A little dry old *m*, without a star, „ 117
The woman were an equal to the *m*. „ 131
Yet being an easy *m*, gave it : „ 149
see no *men*, Not ev'n her brother Arac, „ 152
it was clear against all rules For any *m* to go : „ 179
planet close upon the Sun, Than our *m's* earth ; „ *ii* 37
This barren verbiage, current among *men*, „ 54
tricks, which make us toys of *men*, „ 63
Not for three years to speak with any *men* ; „ 72
not of those that *men* desire, „ 76
then the monster, then the *m* ; „ 119
but that which made Woman and *m*. „ 145
Here might they learn whatever *men* were taught : „ 146
Some *men's* were small : not they the least of *men* ; „ 148
thence the *m's*, if more was more ; „ 151
The highest is the measure of the *m*, „ 157
Sappho and others vied with any *m* : „ 164
LET NO *M* ENTER IN ON PAIN OF DEATH ? „ 195
chanted on the blanching bones of *men* ? ' „ 199
the wisest *m* Feasted the woman wisest then, „ 350
The total chronicles of *m*, the mind, „ 381
Abate the stride, which speaks of *m*, „ 429
might a *m* not wander from his wits „ 440
Men hated learned women : „ 466
Girls ?—more like *men* ! ' „ *iii* 43
Men ! girls, like *men* ! why, if they had been *men* „ 49
' *men* ' (for still My mother went revolving on the word) „ 53
' And so they are—very like *men* indeed— „ 55
' Why—these—*are*—*men* : ' I shudder'd : „ 58
Three times more noble than three score of *men*, „ 109
every phrase well-oil'd, As *m's* could be ; „ 134
nor deals in that Which *men* delight in, „ 216
Upon an even pedestal with *m*.' „ 224
we move, my friend, At no *m's* beck, „ 227
To assail this gray preëminence of *m* ! „ 234
that *men* may pluck them from our hearts, „ 257
bones of some vast bulk that lived and roar'd Before *m* was. „ 295
Nor willing *men* should come among us, „ 318
And all the *men* mourn'd at his side : „ 353
So sweet a voice and vague, fatal to *men*, „ *iv* 64
Knaves are *men*, That lute and flute „ 128
Till all *men* grew to rate us at our worth, „ 145
She, question'd if she knew us *men*, „ 231
stronger than *men*, Huge women blowzed with health, „ 278
men will say We did not know the real light, „ 356
You hold the woman is the better *m* ; „ 410
I bear, Tho' *m*, yet human, „ 425
A *m* I came to see you : but, indeed, „ 441
That many a famous *m* and woman, „ 445
more than poor *men* wealth, Than sick *men* health— „ 459
That it becomes no *m* to nurse despair, „ 464
some that *men* were in the very walls, „ 485
Then *men* had said—but now— „ 533
make yourself a *m* to fight with *men*. „ *v* 35

Man (*continued*) what might that *m* not deserve of me *Princess v* 104
she laughs at you and *m* : „ 116
M is the hunter ; woman is his game : „ 154
fling defiance down Gagelike to *m*, „ 178
Not like the piebald miscellany, *m*, „ 198
nor ever had I seen Such thews of *men* : „ 256
home is in the sinews of a *m*, „ 267
Her that talk'd down the fifty wisest *men* ; „ 294
rainbow flying on the highest Foam of *men's* deeds— „ 320
lived in sleeker times With smoother *men* : „ 386
I set my face Against all *men*, „ 389
Far off from *men* I built a fold „ 390
sole *men* to be mingled with our cause, The sole *men* we shall prize in the aftertime, „ 411
this Egypt-plague of *men* ! „ 427
When the *m* wants weight, the woman takes it up, „ 444
M for the field and woman for the hearth : *M* for the sword and for the needle she. *M* with the head and woman with the heart : *M* to command and woman to obey ; „ 447
large-moulded *m*, His visage all agrin as at a wake, „ 520
boats and bridges for the use of *men*. „ *vi* 47
down she look'd At the arm'd *m* sideways, „ 157
These *men* are hard upon us as of old, „ 198
Ida—'sdeath ! you blame the *m* ; „ 221
men see Two women faster welded in one love „ 252
maids, That have no links with *men*. „ 292
these *men* came to woo Your Highness— „ 328
Whatever *m* lies wounded, friend or foe, „ 336
The common *men* with rolling eyes ; „ 360
swarms of *men* Darkening her female field ; „ *vii* 33
face Peep'd, shining in upon the wounded *m* „ 61
showers of random sweet on maid and *m*. „ 86
sons of *men*, and barbarous laws. (repeat) „ 234, 256
that know The woman's cause is *m's* : „ 259
For she that out of Lethe scales with *m* „ 261
shares with *m* His nights, his days, „ 262
slight-natured, miserable, How shall *men* grow ? „ 266
For woman is not undevelopt *m*, But diverse : could we make her as the *m*, Sweet love were slain : „ 275
The *m* be more of woman, she of *m* ; „ 280
Till at the last she set herself to *m*, „ 285
comes the statelier Eden back to *men* : „ 293
Interpreter between the Gods and *men*, „ 322
mask'd thee from *men's* reverence up, „ 343
dark gates across the wild That no *m* knows. „ 363
So pray'd the *men*, the women : „ *Con.* 7
men required that I should give throughout „ 10
Perchance upon the future *m* : „ 109
Where shall we lay the *m* whom we deplore ? *Ode on Well.* 8
Mourn for the *m* of long-enduring blood, „ 24
Mourn for the *m* of amplest influence, „ 27
O good gray head which all *men* knew, „ 35
O voice from which their omens all *men* drew, „ 36
A *m* of well-attemper'd frame. „ 74
Thine island loves thee well, thou famous *m*, „ 85
With blare of bugle, clamour of *men*, „ 115
all *men* else their nobler dreams forget, „ 152
great *men* who fought, and kept it ours. „ 158
spoke among you, and the *M* who spoke ; „ 178
More than is of *m's* degree Must be with us, „ 242
On God and Godlike *men* we build our trust. „ 266
any wreath that *m* can weave him. „ 277
Was there a *m* dismay'd ? *Light Brigade* 10
Till each *m* find his own in all *men's* good, *Ode Inter. Exhib.* 37
And all *men* work in noble brotherhood, „ 38
made the serf a *m*, and burst his chain— *W. to Marie Alex.* 3
Where *men* are bold and strongly say their say ;— „ 32
and change the hearts of *men*, „ 44
strong on his legs, he looks like a *m*. *Grandmother* 2
her father was not the *m* to save, „ 5
Never a *m* could fling him : „ 10
Willy stood up like a *m*, „ 45
But he cheer'd me, my good *m*, „ 69
Kind, like a *m*, was he ; like a *m*, too, „ 70

Man (*continued*) a *m* of plots, Craft, poisonous counsels, *Gareth and L.* 431
noise of ravage wrought by beast and *m*, „ 437
Down on the shoulders of the twain, his *men*, „ 440
then Kay, a *m* of mien Wan-sallow as the plant „ 452
A horse thou knowest, a *m* thou dost not know: „ 463
and leave my *m* to me.' „ 477
Our noblest brother, and our truest *m*, „ 565
would ye *men* should wonder at you? „ 570
do the battle with him, thy chief *m* Sir Lancelot „ 619
What the fashion of the *men*?' „ 627
these four be fools, but mighty *men*, „ 643
ere a *m* in hall could stay her, turn'd, „ 660
Arthur's *men* are set along the wood; „ 788
Saw six tall *men* haling a seventh along, „ 811
For here be mighty *m* to joust with, „ 880
The war of Time against the soul of *m*. „ 1198
beneath five figures, armed *men*, „ 1205
massacring *M*, woman, lad and girl— „ 1341
Belike he wins it as the better *m*: „ 1346
'Fool, for thou hast, *men* say, the strength of ten, „ 1387
Was ever *m* so grandly made as he? *Marr. of Geraint* 81
I the poor cause that *men* Reproach you, „ 87
And how *men* slur him, saying all his force „ 106
For all my pains, poor *m*, for all my pains, „ 116
pang That makes a *m*, in the sweet face of her „ 122
the *m* Not turning round, nor looking at him, „ 269
And made him like a *m* abroad at morn „ 335
the liquid note beloved of *men* Came flying „ 336
For *m* is *m* and master of his fate. „ 355
your town, where all the *men* are mad; „ 418
a name far-sounded among *men* For noble deeds? „ 427
since the proud *m* often is the mean, „ 449
Bribed with large promises the *men* who served About my person, „ 453
I have let *m* be, and have their way; „ 466
But in this tournament can no *m* tilt, „ 480
the fallen *m* Made answer, groaning, „ 575
men have seen my fall.' „ 578
rose a cry That Edyrn's *men* were on them, „ 639
Edyrn's *men* had caught them in their flight, „ 642
Never *m* rejoiced More than Geraint „ 771
Men saw the goodly hills of Somerset, „ 828
O PURBLIND race of miserable *men*, *Geraint and E.* 1
as a *m* upon his tongue May break it, „ 42
like a *m* That skins the wild beast after slaying him, „ 92
And every *m* were larger-limb'd than I, „ 148
And if I fall, cleave to the better *m*.' „ 152
yet the sapling grew: So lay the *m* transfixt. „ 166
I will tell him How great a *m* thou art: he loves to know When *men* of mark are in his territory: „ 228
and return With victual for these *men*, „ 240
Or two wild *men* supporters of a shield, „ 267
bad the host Call in what *men* soever were his friends, „ 286
men may bicker with the things they love, „ 325
that this *m* loves you no more. „ 329
the *m's* love once gone never returns. „ 333
He moving homeward babbled to his *men*, How Enid never loved a *m* but him, „ 362
Seeing that ye are wedded to a *m*, „ 425
But at the flash and motion of the *m* „ 467
But if a *m* who stands upon the brink „ 472
scared but at the motion of the *m*, „ 476
'Horse and *m*,' he said, 'All of one mind „ 483
But as a *m* to whom a dreadful loss Falls „ 496
great charger stood, grieved like a *m*. „ 535
Fearing to lose, and all for a dead *m*, „ 564
cursing their lost time, and the dead *m*, „ 576
men brought in whole hogs and quarter beeves, „ 602
Good luck had your good *m*, „ 617
'I will not eat Till yonder *m* upon the bier arise, „ 657
Take warning: yonder *m* is surely dead; „ 672
Until himself arise a living *m*, „ 706
all the *men* and women in the hall Rose when they saw the dead *m* rise, „ 731
I have used you worse than that dead *m*; „ 735

Man (*continued*) Shriek'd to the stranger 'Slay not a dead *m*!' *Geraint and E.* 779
Were *men* and women staring and aghast, „ 804
men may fear Fresh fire and ruin. „ 822
with your own true eyes Beheld the *m* you loved „ 847
when it weds with manhood, makes a *m*. „ 868
The world will not believe a *m* repents: „ 900
Full seldom doth a *m* repent, „ 902
as now *Men* weed the white horse on the Berkshire hills „ 936
sent a thousand *men* To till the wastes, „ 941
call'd him the great Prince and *m* of *men*. „ 961
M's word is God in *man*.' *Balin and Balan* 8
mightier *men* than all In Arthur's court; „ 33
And lightly so return'd, and no *m* knew. „ 42
My brother and my better, this *m* here, Balan. „ 54
A *m* of thine to-day Abash'd us both, „ 70
Reported of some demon in the woods Was once a *m*, „ 125
as the *m* in life Was wounded by blind tongues „ 129
This was the sunshine that hath given the *m* A growth, „ 181
Whom all *men* rate the king of courtesy. „ 257
Then spake the *men* of Pellam crying „ 337
Truly, ye *men* of Arthur be but babes.' „ 361
But thou art *m*, and canst abide a truth, „ 501
Or devil or *m* Guard thou thine head.' „ 552
crush'd the *m* Inward, and either fell, „ 562
I fain would know what manner of *men* „ 574
the most famous *m* of all those times, *Merlin and V.* 166
old *m*, Tho' doubtful, felt the flattery, „ 183
The *m* so wrought on ever seem'd to lie „ 208
none could find that *m* for evermore, „ 211
ruin'd *m* Thro' woman the first hour; „ 362
was to be, for love of God and *men* And noble deeds, „ 412
Lo now, what hearts have *men*! „ 442
'*M* dreams of Fame while woman wakes to love.' „ 460
Fame with *men*, Being but ampler means „ 488
for *men* sought to prove me vile, „ 495
made her good *m* jealous with good cause. „ 605
new lord, her own, the first of *men*. „ 617
A little glassy-headed hairless *m*, „ 620
sunders ghosts and shadow-casting *men* „ 629
here was the *m*. And so by force they dragg'd him „ 639
In such-wise, that no *m* could see her more, „ 642
that old *m* Went back to his old wild, „ 648
But you are *m*, you well can understand „ 697
sweet Sir Sagramore, That ardent *m*? „ 722
whose whole prey Is *m's* good name: „ 729
stainless *m* beside a stainless maid; „ 737
'A sober *m* is Percivale and pure; „ 755
Arthur, blameless King and stainless *m*?' „ 779
'*M*! is he *m* at all, who knows and winks? „ 781
O selfless *m* and stainless gentleman, „ 792
fain Have all *men* true and leal, all women pure; „ 794
For *men* at most differ as Heaven and earth, „ 814
O God, that I had loved a smaller *m*! „ 872
Who loved to make *men* darker than they are, „ 876
loyal worship is allow'd Of all *men*: *Lancelot and E.* 111
And swearing *men* to vows impossible, „ 130
men go down before your spear at a touch, „ 149
Then came an old, dumb, myriad-wrinkled *m*, „ 170
Lancelot marvell'd at the worldless *m*; „ 172
he seem'd the goodliest *m* That ever among ladies „ 254
But kindly *m* moving among his kind: „ 265
Suddenly speaking of the worldless *m*, „ 271
his knights are better *men* than he— „ 314
thro' all hindrance finds the *m* Behind it, „ 333
more amazed Than if seven *men* had set upon him, „ 351
I am not great: There is the *m*.' „ 452
that a *m* far-off might well perceive, „ 458
If any *m* that day were left afield, „ 459
Strong *men*, and wrathful that a stranger knight „ 468
The grace and versatility of the *m*! „ 472
men went down before his spear at a touch, „ 578
would he hide his name From all *men*, „ 581
our Lancelot! that true *m*!' „ 665

Man (*continued*) sick *men* down in the hold were most of them stark and cold, *The Revenge* 79
We have won great glory, my *men* ! „ 85
stately Spanish *men* to their flagship bore him then, „ 97
fought for Queen and Faith like a valiant *m* and true ; „ 101
only done my duty as a *m* is bound to do : „ 102
Was he devil or *m* ? He was devil for aught „ 108
a *m's* ideal Is high in Heaven, *Sisters (E. and E.)* 130
In some such fashion as a *m* may be „ 133
Selfish, strange ! What dwarfs are *men* ! „ 199
an' was 'untin' arter the *men*, *Village Wife* 36
every *m* die at his post ! ' (repeat) *Def. of Lucknow* 10, 13, 52
Handful of *men* as we were, „ 46
Men will forget what we suffer and not what we do. „ 73
to call *men* traitors May make *men* traitors. *Sir J. Oldcastle* 50
reddest with the blood of holy *men*, „ 54
nay, let a *m* repent, Do penance in his heart, „ 142
poor *m's* money gone to fat the friar. „ 150
heathen *men* have borne as much as this, „ 185
men Walk'd like the fly on ceilings ? *Columbus* 50
thou hast done so well for *men*, that *men* „ 152
the *men* that were mighty of tongue *V. of Maeldune* 23
the *men* dropt dead in the valleys „ 31
shook like a *m* in a mortal affright ; „ 74
it open'd and dropt at the side of each *m*, „ 85
And the Holy *m* he assoil'd us, „ 126
The *m* that had slain my father. „ 128
landed again, with a tithe of my *men*, „ 130
and prophet of the perfect *m* ; *De Prof., Two G.* 12
that *men* May bless thee as we bless thee, „ 16
then full-current thro' full *m* : „ 22
' Let us make *m* ' and that which should be *m*, From that one light no *m* can look upon, „ 36
seek If any golden harbour be for *men* *Pref. Son. 19th Cent.* 13
You *m* of humorous-melancholy mark, *To W. H. Brookfield* 9
England, France, all *m* to be Will make one people ere *m's* race be run : *To Victor Hugo* 10
lay many a *m* Marr'd by the javelin, *Batt. of Brunanburh* 31
Men of the Northland Shot over shield. „ 33
All day the *men* contend in grievous war *Achilles over the T.* 9
airy-light To float above the ways of *men*, *To E. Fitzgerald* 18
What omens may foreshadow fate to *m* And woman, *Tiresias* 7
more than *m* Which rolls the heavens, „ 21
moves unseen among the ways of *men*. „ 24
speak the truth that no *m* may believe.' „ 50
While *men* shall move the lips : „ 133
light upon the ways of *men* As one great deed. „ 161
wise *m's* word, Here trampled by the populace „ 173
these eyes will find The *men* I knew, „ 176
princelier looking *m* never stept thro' a Prince's hall. *The Wreck* 16
And a *m* *men* fear is a *m* to be loved „ 18
and *men* at the helm of state— „ 49
he, poor *m*, when he learnt that I hated the ring „ 57
felt for the first and greatest of *men* ; „ 76
all but the *m* that was lash'd to the helm had gone ; „ 110
the one *m* left on the wreck— „ 119
kiss so sad, no, not since the coming of *m* ! *Despair* 60
You have parted the *m* from the wife. „ 62
If every *m* die for ever, „ 82
if the souls of *men* were immortal, as *men* have been told, „ 99
till that old *m* before A cavern *Ancient Sage* 6
m to-day is fancy's fool As *m* hath ever been. „ 27
never spake with *m*, And never named the Name '— „ 55
beyond All work of *m*, yet, like the work of *m*, „ 85
The last and least of *men* ; „ 114
For *m* has overlived his day „ 150
So dark that *men* cry out against the Heavens. „ 172
Who knows but that the darkness is in *m* ? „ 173
Word Of that world-prophet in the heart of *m*. „ 213
But in the hand of what is more than *m*, Or in *m's* hand when *m* is more than *m*, Let be thy wail and help thy fellow *men*, „ 256
Nor list for guerdon in the voice of *men*, „ 262
tould her to come away from the *m*, *Tomorrow* 20
an' a dhrame of a married *m*, death alive, „ 51

Man (*continued*) An' where 'ud the poor *m*, thin, *Tomorrow* 65
bogs whin they swallies the *m* intire ! „ 66
Thou sees that i' spite o' the *men* *Spinster's S's.* 11
allus afear'd of a *m's* gittin' ower fond, „ 27
That a *m* be a durty thing an' a trouble „ 50
But I couldn't 'a lived wi' a *m* „ 52
By a *m* coomin' in wi' a hiccup „ 98
'es hallus to hax of a *m* how much to spare „ 111
she with all the breadth of *m*, *Locksley H., Sixty* 48
for ever was the leading light of *m*. „ 66
alms of Blessing *m* had coin'd himself a curse : „ 87
France had shown a light to all *men*, preach'd a Gospel, all *men's* good ; „ 89
still, ' your enemy ' was a *m*. „ 94
Are we devils ? are we *men* ? „ 99
Sons of God, and kings of *men* „ 122
to lower the rising race of *men* ; „ 147
no *m* halt, or deaf or blind ; „ 163
who can fancy warless *men* ? „ 172
are these but symbols of innumerable *m*, *M* or Mind that sees a shadow „ 195
What are *men* that He should heed us ? „ 201
before her highest, *m*, was born, „ 205
offspring this ideal *m* at rest ? „ 234
Nor is he the wisest *m*, who never proved „ 244
to help his homelier brother *men*, „ 267
—for *m* can half-control his doom „ 277
you and all your *men* Were soldiers *Pro. to Gen. Hamley* 24
Thro' the great gray slope of *men*, *Heavy Brigade* 17
our *men* gallopt up with a cheer and a shout, „ 61
In worlds before the *m* Involving ours— *Epilogue* 25
now we see, The *m* in Space and Time, „ 49
what they prophesy, our wise *men*, „ 65
all in vain As far as *m* can see, except The *m* himself remain ; „ 69
That *m* can have no after-morn, „ 73
The *m* remains, and whatsoe'er He wrought „ 75
measure ever moulded by the lips of *m*. *To Virgil* 40
touch'd on the whole sad planet of *m*, *Dead Prophet* 39
For *m* is a lover of Truth, „ 44
Was he noblier-fashion'd than other *men* ? „ 51
Warrior of God, *m's* friend, *Epit. on Gordon* 1
for all *men* know This earth has never borne a nobler *m*. „ 3
That *m's* the best Cosmopolite *Hands all Round* 3
That *m's* the true Conservative „ 7
Men loud against all forms of power— *Freedom* 37
When all *men* starve, the wild mob's million feet *The Fleet* 18
Men that in a narrower day— *Open. I. and C. Exhib.* 25
when before have Gods or *men* beheld *Demeter and P.* 29
fled by many a waste, forlorn of *m*, And grieved for *m* thro' all my grief for thee,— „ 74
we spin the lives of *men*, And not of Gods, „ 85
Last as the likeness of a dying *m*, „ 88
m, that only lives and loves an hour, „ 106
vine And golden grain, my gift to helpless *m*. „ 111
the praise And prayer of *men*, „ 120
souls of *men*, who grew beyond their race, „ 140
thou that hast from *men*, As Queen of Death, „ 142
nor I iver owäd mottal *m*. *Owd Roä* 4
moor good sense na the Parliament *m* 'at stans fur us 'ere, „ 13
men ater supper 'ed sung their songs „ 35
Howiver was I fur to find my rent an' to paäy my *men* ? „ 47
Ghost in *M*, the Ghost that once was *M*, But cannot wholly free itself from *M*, *The Ring* 35
No sudden heaven, nor sudden hell, for *m*, „ 41
I had seen the *m* but once ; „ 190
till the *m* repenting sent This ring „ 209
bad the *m* engrave ' From Walter ' on the ring, „ 235
as a *m* Who sees his face in water, „ 369
so fickle are *men*—the best ! „ 392
beauty came upon your face, not that of living *men*, *Happy* 51
If *m* and wife be but one flesh, „ 94
Ulysses, much-experienced *m*, *To Ulysses* 1

Man (*continued*) Her tribes of *men*, and trees, and flowers, *To Ulysses* 3
Where *m*, nor only Nature smiles ; „ 39
That I might mix with *men*, and hear their words *Prog. of Spring* 82
I too would teach the *m* „ 87
dwellings of the kings of *men* ; „ 99
men have hopes, which race the restless blood, „ 115
under the Crosses The dead *m's* garden, *Merlin and the G.* 106
blacken round The copse of every *m* *Romney's R.* 123
Should I know the *m* ? „ 144
And the *m* said ' Am I your debtor ? ' *By an Evolution.* 2
M is quiet at last As he stands on the heights „ 19
WHILE *m* and woman are still incomplete, I prize that soul where *m* and woman meet, *On one who affec. E. M.* 1
thoughts that lift the soul of *men*, *To Master of B.* 14
M is but the slave of Fate. *Death of Œnone* 44
and forgetful of the *m*, „ 60
But every *m* was mute for reverence. „ 96
The *m*, whose pious hand had built the cross, A *m* who never changed a word with *men*, *St. Telemachus* 9
borne along by that full stream of *men*, „ 43
trailing a dead lion away, One, a dead *m*. „ 48
Christian faces watch *M* murder *m*. „ 56
barrier that divided beast from *m* Slipt, „ 60
In the great name of Him who died for *men*, „ 63
Dark with the blood of *m* who murder'd *m*. „ 80
only conquers *men* to conquer peace, *Akbar's Dream* 15
I seem no longer like a lonely *m* „ 20
knows Himself, *men* nor themselves nor Him, „ 32
' Mine is the one fruit Alla made for *m*.' „ 40
men may taste Swine-flesh, drink wine ; „ 53
I let *men* worship as they will, „ 66
By deeds a light to *men* ? „ 111
Ritual, varying with the tribes of *men*. „ 125
and *men*, below the dome of azure Kneel „ *Hymn* 7
and voices, and *men* passing to and fro. *Bandit's Death* 24
And a *m* ruin'd mine, *Charity* 4
Would the *m* have a touch of remorse „ 17
M, can you even guess at the love of a soul for a soul ? „ 30
M with his brotherless dinner on *m* *The Dawn* 3
Men, with a heart and a soul, „ 18
We are far from the noon of *m*, „ 20
The *men* of a hundred thousand, „ 25
M as yet is being made, *Making of Man* 3
' It is finish'd. *M* is made.' „ 8
That no *m* would believe. *Mechanophilus* 28
To a just *m* and a wise— *Voice spake, etc.* 2
when the *m* will make the Maker *Faith* 7

Manage Hadn't a head to *m*, *Grandmother* 6
How best to *m* horse, lance, sword and shield, *Gareth and L.* 1351

Managed I 'a *m* for Squoire coom Michaelmas *N. Farmer, O. S.* 48

Man-at-arms Another hurrying past, a *m-a-a*, *Geraint and E.* 526

Man-beast *m-b* of boundless savagery. *Gareth and L.* 637

Man-breasted strong *m-b* things stood from the sea, *Guinevere* 246

Manchester throats of *M* may bawl, *Third of Feb.* 43

Manchet And in her veil enfolded, *m* bread. *Marr. of Geraint* 389

Mander (manner) noä *m* o' use to be callin' 'im Roä, *Owd Roä* 1

Mane shake the darkness from their loosen'd *m's*, *Tithonus* 41
To break my chain, to shake my *m* : *Princess ii* 424
with your long locks play the Lion's *m* ! „ *vi* 164
With sudden-flaring *m's* Those two great beasts *Holy Grail* 820

Maned *See* **Full-maned, Midnight-maned**

Manelike Beneath a *m* mass of rolling gold, *Aylmer's Field* 68

Manes (mean) An' yer Honour's the thrue ould blood that always *m* to be kind, *Tomorrow* 5

Manful Between your peoples truth and *m* peace, *W. to Marie Alex.* 49
Right thro' his *m* breast darted the pang *Marr. of Geraint* 121
Nor know I whether I be very base Or very *m*, „ 469

Manfulness he, from his exceeding *m* „ 211

Man-girdled Than thus *m-g* here : *Princess v* 429

Mangle And *m* the living dog that had loved him *In the Child. Hosp.* 9

Mangle (mangold) Goan into *m's* an' tonups, *Owd Roä* 28

Mangled *M*, and flatten'd, and crush'd, *Maud I i* 7
I see thee maim'd, *M* : *Gareth and L.* 1327
M to morsels, A youngster in war ! *Batt. of Brunanburh* 74

Mango The *m* spurn the melon at his foot ? *Akbar's Dream* 39

Mangold *See* **Mangle**

Mangrove The slant seas leaning on the *m* copse, *Prog. of Spring* 76

Manhood Nature's evil star Drive men in *m*, *Love thou thy land* 74
The darling of my *m*, and, alas ! *Gardener's D.* 278
who desire you more Than growing boys their *m* ; *Princess iv* 457
Accomplish thou my *m* and thyself ; „ *vii* 365
Some civic *m* firm against the crowd— „ *Con.* 57
The highest, holiest *m*, thou : *In Mem., Pro.* 14
Tho' truths in *m* darkly join, „ *xxxvi* 1
Who wears his *m* hale and green : „ *liii* 4
m fused with female grace In such a sort, „ *cix* 17
glory of *m* stand on his ancient height, *Maud III vi* 21
So make thy *m* mightier day by day ; *Gareth and L.* 92
I felt Thy *m* thro' that wearied lance of thine. „ 1266
a prince whose *m* was all gone, *Marr. of Geraint* 59
when it weds with *m*, makes a man. *Geraint and E.* 868
Thy too fierce *m* would not let thee lie. *Balin and Balan* 74
To learn what Arthur meant by courtesy, *M*, and knighthood ; „ 159
Name, *m*, and a grace, but scantly thine, „ 377
Vivien, save ye fear The monkish *m*, *Merlin and V.* 35
The pretty, popular name such *m* earns, „ 787
ourselves shall grow In use of arms and *m*, *Lancelot and E.* 64
Friends, thro' your *m* and your fëalty,— *Last Tournament* 97
Tells of a *m* ever less and lower ? „ 121
Who fain had clipt free *m* from the world— „ 446
as great As he was in his *m*, *Guinevere* 300
Ideal *m* closed in real man, *To the Queen ii* 38
Yet you in your mid *m*— *Happy* 47

Maniac Time, a *m* scattering dust, *In Mem. l* 7

Manifold With a music strange and *m*, *Dying Swan* 29
But *m* entreaties, many a tear, *Enoch Arden* 160
Thro' *m* effect of simple powers— *Prog. of Spring* 86
Sent notes of preparation *m*, *Lover's Tale i* 207

Man-in-God God-in-man is one with *m-i-G*, *Enoch Arden* 187

Mankind like Gods together, careless of *m*. *Lotos-Eaters, C. S.* 110
ALTHO' I be the basest of *m*, *St. S. Stylites* 1
Whereof my fame is loud amongst *m*, „ 81
To make me an example to *m*, „ 188
in the thoughts that shake *m*. *Locksley Hall* 166
Had golden hopes for France and all *m*, *Aylmer's Field* 464
Let them not lie in the tents with coarse *m*, *Princess vi* 69
I had been wedded wife, I knew *m*, „ 327
For, saving that, ye help to save *m* *Ode on Well.* 166
But while the races of *m* endure, „ 219
Peace and goodwill, to all *m*. *In Mem. xxviii* 12
This bitter seed among *m* ; „ *xc* 4
Ring in redress to all *m*. „ *cvi* 12
For each is at war with *m*. *Maud I x* 52
Being but ampler means to serve *m*, *Merlin and V.* 489
so might there be Two Adams, two *m's*, *Columbus* 54
My friend, the most unworldly of *m*, *In Mem., W. G. Ward* 3

Manless when earth is *m* and forlorn, *Locksley H., Sixty* 206

Manlike *m* end myself ?—our privilege— *Lucretius* 232
open-work in which the hunter rued His rash intrusion, *m*, *Princess iv* 204

Manly Is this the *m* strain of Runnymede ? *Third of Feb.* 34

Man-minded When his *m-m* offset rose *Talking Oak* 51

Man-mode in all *M-m's* of worship ; *Akbar's Dream* 47

Manna As *m* on my wilderness, *Supp. Confessions* 114

Mann'd *m* the Revenge with a swarthier alien crew, *The Revenge* 110

Manner (*See also* **Mander**) listening rogue hath caught the *m* of it. *Gareth and L.* 778
I fain would know what *m* of men they be.' *Balin and Balan* 574
His tenderness of *m*, and chaste awe, *Pelleas and E.* 110
Restrain'd him with all *m* of device, „ 204
To hear the *m* of thy fight and fall ; „ 347
A *m* somewhat fall'n from reverence— *Last Tournament* 119

Manner'd *See* **Nobly-manner'd**

Manners Her *m* had not that repose *L. C. V. de Vere* 39
Like men, like *m* : like breeds like, they say : Kind nature is the best : those *m* next *Walk. to the Mail* 63
What are indeed the *m* of the great. „ 66
cities of men And *m*, climates, councils, *Ulysses* 14
That gives the *m* of your countrywomen ? *Princess iv* 151

Margin (s) (*continued*) Comes a vapour from the *m*, — *Locksley Hall* 191
every *m* scribbled, crost, and cramm'd — *Merlin and V.* 677
And bear me to the *m*; — *Pass. of Arthur* 333
ere it vanishes Over the *m*, — *Merlin and the G.* 129
Mariam *See* **Issa Ben Mariam**
Marian Is memory with your *M* gone to rest, — *To Mary Boyle* 13
Marie (*See also* **Alexandrovna, Marie Alexandrovna**)
Here also *M*, shall thy name be blest, — *W. to Marie Alex.* 39
Marie Alexandrovna (*See also* **Alexandrovna, Marie**)
From mother unto mother, stately bride, *M A*! — „ 10
loyal pines of Canada murmur thee, *M A* — „ 20
Love by right divine is deathless king, *M A*! — „ 30
Here also, Marie, shall thy name be blest, *M A*! — „ 40
Marigold *See* **Marsh-marigold**
Mariner Slow sail'd the weary *m's* and saw, — *Sea Fairies* 1
M, *m*, furl your sails, — „ 21
listen and stay: *m*, *m*, fly no more. — „ 42
Oh rest ye, brother *m's*, — *Lotos-Eaters, C. S.* 128
My *m's*, Souls that have toil'd, — *Ulysses* 45
O young *M*, Down to the haven, — *Merlin and the G.* 123
Marish thro' the *m* green and still — *Dying Swan* 18
Marish-flowers the silvery *m-f* that throng — „ 40
Marish-mosses The cluster'd *m-m* crept. — *Mariana* 40
Marish-pipe With moss and braided *m-p*; — *On a Mourner* 10
Mark (coin) A thousand *m's* are set upon my head. — *Sir J. Oldcastle* 195
Mark (s) (*See also* **Merk**) thou,' said I, 'hast missed thy *m*, — *Two Voices* 388
he thought himself A *m* for all, — *Walk. to the Mail* 73
arrows aim'd All at one *m*, all hitting: — *Aylmer's Field* 95
push beyond her *m*, and be Procuress — *In Mem. liii* 15
No single tear, no *m* of pain: — „ *lxxviii* 14
master-bowman, he, Would cleave the *m*. — „ *lxxxvii* 30
loves to know When men of *m* are in his territory: — *Geraint and E.* 229
meant to stamp him with her master's *m*; — *Merlin and V.* 759
Yon man of humorous-melancholy *m*, — *To W. H. Brookfield* 9
an' the *m* o' 'is 'eäd o' the chairs! — *Spinster's S's.* 100
In aiming at an all but hopeless *m* — *The Ring* 346
A red *m* ran All round one finger — „ 452
And set a crueller *m* than Cain's on him, — *Happy* 18
Mark (Christian Name) came in hall the messenger of *M*, — *Gareth and L.* 384
shall the shield of *M* stand among these?' — „ 403
M hath tarnish'd the great name of king, — „ 426
M would sully the low state of churl: — „ 427
dumb'd by one from out the hall of *M* — *Balin and Balan* 437
M The Cornish King, had heard a wandering voice, — *Merlin and V.* 7
(She sat beside the banquet nearest *M*), — „ 18
M was half in heart to hurl his cup — „ 30
Loud laugh'd the graceless *M*. — „ 62
Poor wretch—no friend!—and now by *M* the King — „ 75
Nay—we believe all evil of thy *M*— — „ 93
M her lord had past, the Cornish King, — *Last Tournament* 382
heard The hounds of *M*, and felt the goodly hounds — „ 503
Crying aloud, 'Not *M*—not *M*, my soul! — „ 514
Catlike thro' his own castle steals my *M*, — „ 516
my hatred for my *M* Quicken within me, — „ 519
Let be thy *M*, seeing he is not thine.' — „ 522
bitten, blinded, marr'd me somehow—*M*? — „ 526
M's way, my soul!—but eat not thou with *M*, — „ 532
Should leave me all alone with *M* and hell. My God, the measure of my hate for *M* — „ 536
M is kindled on thy lips Most gracious; — „ 561
my *M's*, by whom all men Are noble, — „ 599
M's way to steal behind one in the dark—For there was *M*: — „ 618
Broken with *M* and hate and solitude, — „ 643
'Vows! did you keep the vow you made to *M* — „ 655
craven shifts, and long crane legs of *M*— — „ 729
'*M's* way,' said *M*, and clove him thro' the brain. — „ 754
Mark (verb) no other tree did *m* The level waste, — *Mariana* 43
I will stand and *m*. — *To J. M. K.* 14
But vague in vapour, hard to *m*; — *Love thou thy land* 62
m me and understand, While I have power to speak. — *Enoch Arden* 876
m me! for your fortunes are to make. — *Aylmer's Field* 300
and *m* The landscape winking thro' the heat: — *In Mem. lxxxix* 15
Hither, boy—and *m* me well. — *Balin and Balan* 502
Mark (verb) (*continued*) Friend, did ye *m* that fountain yesterday — *Last Tournament* 286
for some are scared, who *m*, Or wisely or unwisely, — *To the Queen ii* 48
M him—he falls! then another, — *Def. of Lucknow* 65
To *m* in many a freeman's home — *Freedom* 11
I may *m* The coming year's great good — *Prog. of Spring* 92
Mark Antony Prythee, friend, Where is *M A*? — *D. of F. Women* 140
Mark'd wave Returning, while none *m* it, — *Sea Dreams* 234
They *m* it with the red cross to the fall, — *Princess vi* 41
Day, *m* as with some hideous crime, — *In Mem. lxxii* 18
saw him not, or *m* not, if she saw, — *Com. of Arthur* 53
for he *m* Kay near him groaning like a wounded bull— — *Gareth and L.* 647
and all that *m* him were aghast. — „ 1399
saw me not, or *m* not if you saw; — *Geraint and E.* 870
he *m* his high sweet smile In passing, — *Balin and Balan* 160
So *m* not on his right a cavern-chasm — „ 312
He *m* not this, but blind and deaf — „ 318
he *m* The portal of King Pellam's chapel — „ 404
Vivien follow'd, but he *m* her not. — *Merlin and V.* 199
Had marr'd his face, and *m* it ere his time. — *Lancelot and E.* 247
Who *m* Sir Lancelot where he moved apart, — „ 1349
I *m* Him in the flowering of His fields, — *Pass. of Arthur* 10
Thence *m* the black hull moving yet, — „ 448
Market (adj.) The *m* boat is on the stream, — *In Mem. cxxi* 13
Market (s) (*See also* **Woman-markets**) Enrich the *m's* of the golden year. — *Golden Year* 46
Every gate is throng'd with suitors, all the *m's* overflow. — *Locksley Hall* 101
and bought Quaint monsters for the *m* — *Enoch Arden* 539
Stumbling across the *m* to his death, — *Aylmer's Field* 820
Thro' the hubbub of the *m* I steal, — *Maud II iv* 68
The changing *m* frets or charms — *Ancient Sage* 140
Pillory Wisdom in your *m's*, — *Locksley H., Sixty* 134
Market-cross Not only to the *m-c* were known, — *Enoch Arden* 96
Chafferings and chatterings at the *m-c*, — *Holy Grail* 558
Market-girl the red cloaks of *m-g's*, — *L. of Shalott ii* 17
Market-noight (night) 'ed my quart ivry *m-n* — *N. Farmer, O. S.* 8
Market-place Spiritual in Nature's *m-p*— — *Akbar's Dream* 135
Marking *m* how the knighthood mock thee, — *Last Tournament* 301
Marksmen their *m* were told of our best, — *Def. of Lucknow* 19
Marr'd beat me down and *m* and wasted me, — *Tithonus* 19
what follows! war; Your own work *m*: — *Princess ii* 230
Brake on us at our books, and *m* our peace, — „ *v* 395
Had *m* his face, and mark'd it ere his time. — *Lancelot and E.* 247
M as he was, he seem'd the goodliest man — „ 254
However *m*, of more than twice her years, — „ 257
M her friend's aim with pale tranquillity. — „ 733
I cannot brook to see your beauty *m* — *Pelleas and E.* 298
M tho' it be with spite and mockery now, — „ 327
vext his heart, And *m* his rest— — „ 399
Man was it who *m* heaven's image in thee thus?' — *Last Tournament* 64
Scratch'd, bitten, blinded, *m* me somehow— — „ 526
he knew the Prince tho' *m* with dust, — *Guinevere* 36
lay many a man *M* by the javelin, — *Batt. of Brunanburh* 32
My beauty *m* by you? by you! — *Happy* 57
Before the feud of Gods had *m* our peace, — *Death of Œnone* 32
Marriage (adj.) In sound of funeral or of *m* bells; — *Gardener's D.* 36
And when my *m* morn may fall, — *Talking Oak* 285
'I can make no *m* present: — *L. of Burleigh* 13
Heaven and earth shall meet Before you hear my *m* vow.' — *The Letters* 8
There comes a sound of *m* bells. — „ 48
Demand not thou a *m* lay: In that it is thy *m* day — *In Mem., Con.* 2
silent sapphire-spangled *m* ring of the land? — *Maud I iv* 6
Now over, now beneath her *m* ring, — *Gareth and E.* 259
We planted both together, happy in our *m* morn, — *Happy* 14
that you, that I, would slight our *m* oath: — „ 89
Marriage (s) (*See also* **Border-marriage**) laws of *m* character'd in gold — *Isabel* 16
The queen of *m*, a most perfect wife. — „ 28
I have wish'd this *m*, night and day, — *Dora* 21
Her slow consent, and *m*, — *Enoch Arden* 708
There was an Aylmer-Averill *m* once. — *Aylmer's Field* 49

Marriage (s) (*continued,* *m's* are made in Heaven.' — *Aylmer's Field* 188
naked *m's* Flash from the bridge, — „ 765
in true *m* lies Nor equal, nor unequal: — *Princess vii* 302
neither marry, nor are given In *m*, — *Merlin and V.* 16
And *m* with a princess of that realm, — *Last Tournament* 176
And sleek his *m* over to the Queen. — „ 391
Thy *m* and mine own, that I should suck — „ 644
eleventh moon After their *m* lit the lover's Bay, — *Lover's Tale iv* 28
Once more—a happier *m* than my own! — *Sisters (E. and E.)* 78
Grew after *m* to full height and form? Yet after *m*, that mock-sister there— — „ 171
that had sunn'd The morning of our *m*, — „ 244
counsel me; this *m* must not be. — *The Flight* 75
Her maiden daughter's *m*; — *To Prin. Beatrice* 10
Love for the maiden, crown'd with *m*, — *Vastness* 23
Had ask'd us to their *m*, and to share — *The Ring* 430
M will conceal it . . . — *Forlorn* 10
Shame and *m*, Shame and *m*, — „ 31
M will not hide it, — „ 50
Death and *m*, Death and *m*! — „ 67
The morning light of happy *m* broke — *Death of Œnone* 102
Marriageable prince his heir, when tall and *m*, — *Gareth and L.* 102
Marriage-banquet and to share Their *m-b*. — *The Ring* 431
Marriage-bell (*See also* **Marriage (adj.)**) Four merry bells, four merry *m-b's* — *Lover's Tale iii* 21
A long loud crash of rapid *m-b's*. — „ 23
the bells, Those *m-b's*, echoing in ear and heart— — „ *iv* 3
Whether they *were* his lady's *m-b's*, — „ 11
Sounds happier than the merriest *m-b*. — *D. of the Duke of C.* 11
Marriage-day on the dark night of our *m-d* The great Tragedian, — *Sisters (E. and E.)* 232
Marriage-hindering filthy *m-h* Mammon made The harlot — *Aylmer's Field* 374
Marriage-maker For the maids and *m-m's*, — *Maud I xx* 35
Marriage-morn And move me to my *m-m*, — *Move eastward* 11
but on her *m-m* This birthday, — *The Ring* 275
Marriage-pillow To thy widow'd *m-p's*, — *Locksley Hall* 82
Marriage-ring (*See also* **Marriage (adj.)**) That ever wore a Christian *m-r*. — *Romney's R.* 36
How bright you keep your *m-r*! — „ 59
Married I *m* late, but I would wish to see — *Dora* 12
Who *m*, who was like to be, — *Audley Court* 30
'And are you *m* yet, Edward Gray?' — *Edward Gray* 4
Nevertheless, know you that I am he Who *m*— — *Enoch Arden* 859
I *m* her who *m* Philip Ray. — „ 860
fur, Sammy, 'e *m* fur luvv. — *N. Farmer, N. S.* 32
the King That morn was *m*, — *Com. of Arthur* 456
Had *m* Enid, Yniol's only child, — *Marr. of Geraint* 4
attracted, won, *M*, made one with, — *Lover's Tale i* 134
Harry and I were *m*: — *First Quarrel* 5
we were *m* o' Christmas day, *M* among the red berries, — „ 39
kept yours hush'd,' I said, 'when you *m* me! — „ 68
Meä and thy sister was *m*, — *North. Cobbler* 11
Indissolubly *m* like our love; — *De Prof., Two G.* 14
an' he's *m* another wife, — *Tomorrow* 49
But if I 'ed *m* tha, Robby, — *Spinster's S's.* 54
Hed I *m* the Tommies—O Lord, — „ 95
and the charm of *m* brows.' — *Œnone* 76
Two partners of a *m* life- — *In Mem. xcvii* 5
Moon of *m* hearts, Hear me, you! — *The Ring* 3
came of age Or on the day you *m*. — „ 78
That, in the misery of my *m* life, — „ 136
Then I and she were *m* for a year, — „ 283
well, you know I *m* Muriel Erne. — „ 376
hovering by the church, where she Was *m* too, — „ 479
sang the *m* 'nos' for the solitary 'me.' — *Happy* 56
I love you more than when we *m*. — *Romney's R.* 157
Then 'e *m* a greät Yerl's darter, — *Church-warden, etc.* 20
He *m* an heiress, an orphan — *Charity* 13
I had cursed the woman he *m*, — „ 24
Marris (Bessy) *See* **Bessy Marris.**
Marrow *M* of mirth and laughter; — *Will Water.* 214
Fool to the midmost *m* of his bones, — *Pelleas and E.* 258
He withers *m* and mind; — *Ancient Sage* 120
Marry Woo me, and win me, and *m* me, — *The Mermaid* 46
'I cannot *m* Dora; by my life, I will not *m* Dora.' — *Dora* 23
where the waters *m*—crost, — *The Brook* 81
'he that *marries* her *marries* her name' — *Aylmer's Field* 25
twenty boys and girls should *m* on it, — „ 371
learning unto them? They wish'd to *m*; — *Princess ii* 465
But *m* me out of hand: — *Grandmother* 52
'*M* you, Willy!' said I, — „ 53
Thou'll not *m* for munny— — *N. Farmer, N. S.* 11
Noä—thou'll *m* for luvv— — „ 12
'Doänt thou *m* for munny, — „ 20
thy muther says thou wants to *m* the lass, — „ 37
if thou *marries* a good un I'll leäve the land to thee. — „ 56
But if thou *marries* a bad un, I'll leäve the land to Dick.— — „ 58
Ask her to *m* me by and by? — *Window, Letter* 6
That *m* with the virgin heart. — *In Mem. lxxxv* 108
but neither *m*, nor are given In marriage, — *Merlin and V.* 15
and yet one Should *m*, or all the broad lands — *Sister's (E. and E.)* 51
Tha thowt tha would *m* ma, did tha? — *Spinster's S's.* 74
when she comes of age, or when She *marries*; — *The Ring* 290
Marrying could not ever rue his *m* me— — *Dora* 146
Driving, hurrying, *m*, burying, — *Maud II v* 12
Mars pointed to *M* As he glow'd like a ruddy shield — „ *III vi* 13
native to that splendour or in *M*, — *Locksley H., Sixty* 187
Marsh (adj.) my blood Crept like *m* drains thro' all my languid limbs; — *Lover's Tale ii* 53
Marsh (s) wide and wild the waste enormous *m*, — *Ode to Memory* 101
Gave him an isle of *m* whereon to build; And there he built with wattles from the *m* — *Holy Grail* 62
and sliding down the blacken'd *m* Blood-red, — „ 473
The wide-wing'd sunset of the misty *m* — *Last Tournament* 423
as from men secure Amid their *m'es*, — „ 427
That sent the face of all the *m* aloft — „ 439
And pausing at a hostel in a *m*, — *Lover's Tale iv* 131
light That glimmers on the *m* and on the grave.' — *The Ring* 341
steaming *m'es* of the scarlet cranes, — *Prog. of Spring* 75
Marshall'd slowly went The *m* Order of their Table Round, — *Lancelot and E.* 1332
Marsh-diver *m-d's*, rather, maid, Shall croak — *Princess iv* 123
Marsh-marigold the wild *m-m* shines like fire — *May Queen* 31
Mart labour, and the changing *m*, — *In Mem. lxxxvii* 23
Marthyr (Martyr) Wid his blessed *M's* an' Saints;' — *Tomorrow* 58
an' Saints an' *M's* galore, — „ 95
Martial Which men delight in, *m* exercise? — *Princess iii* 216
merrily-blowing shrill'd the *m* fife; — „ *v* 251
And let the mournful *m* music blow; — *Ode on Well.* 17
A *m* song like a trumpet's call! — *Maud I v* 5
Martin Roof-haunting *m's* warm their eggs: — *Day-Dm., Sleep P.* 17
The fire shot up, the *m* flew, — „ *Revival* 11
A *M's* summer of his faded love, — *Aylmer's Field* 560
plaster'd like a *m's* nest To these old walls— — *Holy Grail* 548
Martin-haunted almost to the *m-h* eaves — *Aylmer's Field* 163
Martyr (*See also* **Marthyr**) did not all thy *m's* die one death? — *St. S. Stylites* 50
Charity setting the *m* aflame; — *Vastness* 9
Martyrdom arks with priceless bones of *m*, — *Balin and Balan* 110
Martyr-flames *m-f*, nor trenchant swords Can do — *Clear-headed friend* 14
Marvel (s) In *m* whence that glory came Upon me, — *Arabian Nights* 94
The *m* of the everlasting will, — *The Poet* 7
'No *m*, sovereign lady: — *D. of F. Women* 97
The *m* dies, and leaves me fool'd and trick'd, — *Gareth and L.* 1251
and all Had *m* what the maid might be, — *Lancelot and E.* 728
Some little of this *m* he too saw, — *Holy Grail* 216
With miracles and *m's* like to these, — „ 543
Had drawn him home—what *m*? — *Last Tournament* 405
(what *m*—she could see)— — „ 547
What *m* my Camilla told me all? (repeat) — *Lover's Tale i* 557, 579
In *m* at that gradual change, — „ *iii* 19
m among us that one should be left alive, — *Def. of Lucknow* 78
The *m* of that fair new nature— — *Columbus* 79
Half the *m's* of my morning, — *Locksley H., Sixty* 75
Marvel (verb) 'I *m* if my still delight — *Palace of Art* 190
And *m* what possess'd my brain; — *In Mem. xiv* 16
I would not *m* at either, — *Maud I iv* 40
mazed my wit: I *m* what thou art, — *Gareth and L.* 1170

Marvel (verb) (*continued*) Said Guinevere, 'We *m* at thee much, *Pelleas and E.* 179
Or *m* how in English air My yucca, *To Ulysses* 20
Marvell'd I *m* how the mind was brought *Two Voices* 458
so that all My brethren *m* greatly. *St. S. Stylites* 69
Lancelot *m* at the wordless man; *Lancelot and E.* 172
Marvelling Balin *m* oft How far beyond *Balin and Balan* 171
gazing at a star And *m* what it was: *Pelleas and E.* 560
Marvellous that *m* time To celebrate the golden prime *Arabian Nights* 130
Sir Lancelot gave A *m* great shriek and ghastly groan, *Lancelot and E.* 516
Most *m* in the wars your own Crimean eyes *Pro. to Gen. Hamley* 11
Mary (Virgin) But 'Ave *M*,' made she moan, And 'Ave *M*,' night and morn, *Mariana in the S.* 9
And 'Ave *M*,' was her moan, " 21
Mary (*See also* **Mary Morrison**) There's Margaret and *M*, there's Kate *May Queen* 6
Then Dora went to *M*. *M* sat And look'd *Dora* 56
M, for the sake of him that's gone, " 62
Then Dora went to *M's* house, " 110
M saw the boy Was not with Dora. " 111
But, *M*, let me live and work with you: " 115
Then answer'd *M*, 'This shall never be, " 117
And Allan set him down, and *M* said: " 139
So *M* said, and Dora hid her face By *M*. " 156
as years Went forward, *M* took another mate; " 171
And home to *M's* house return'd, *In Mem. xxxi* 2
So close are we, dear *M*, *To Mary Boyle* 59
O *M*, *M*! Vexing you with words! *Romney's R.* 28
M, my crayons! if I can, I will. " 88
Mary Morrison (*See also* **Mary**) A labourer's daughter, *M M*. *Dora* 40
Mash (smash) I claums an' I *m'es* the winder hin, *Owd Roä* 83
Mash'd (smashed) I *m* the taäbles an' chairs, *North. Cobbler* 37
Mashin' (smashing) An' their *m* their toys to pieäces *Spinster's S's.* 88
Mask (s) college and her maidens, empty *m's*, *Princess iii* 187
(For I was half-oblivious of my *m*) " 338
Last night, their *m* was patent, " *iv* 326
head That sleeps or wears the *m* of sleep, *In Mem. xviii* 10
And mix with hollow *m's* of night; " *lxx* 4
The genial hour with *m* and mime; " *cv* 10
and the *m* of pure Worn by this court, *Merlin and V.* 35
misfeaturing *m* that I saw so amazed me, *The Wreck* 117
Envy wears the *m* of Love, *Locksley H., Sixty* 109
dropt the gracious *m* of motherhood, *The Ring* 384
Mask (verb) *m*, tho' but in his own behoof, *Maud I vi* 48
courtly phrase that *m's* his malice now— *The Flight* 30
Mask'd 'Albeit so *m*, Madam, I love the truth; *Princess ii* 213
M like our maids, blustering I know not what " *v* 396
That *m* thee from men's reverence up, " *vii* 343
Mason Cloud-towers by ghostly *m's* wrought, *In Mem. lxx* 5
White from the *m's* hand, (repeat) *Marr. of Geraint* 244, 408
Masonwork It look'd a tower of ivied *m*, *Merlin and V.* 4
What rotten piles uphold their *m*, *Sir J. Oldcastle* 67
Masque *m* or pageant at my father's court. *Princess i* 198
Masquerade A feudal knight in silken *m*, " *Pro.* 234
Mass (eucharist) heard *m*, broke fast, and rode away: *Lancelot and E.* 415
but with gorgeous obsequies, And *m*, " 1336
at the sacring of the *m* I saw The holy elements *Holy Grail* 462
many's the time that I watch'd her at *m* *Tomorrow* 29
people 'ud see it that wint in to *m*— " 74
Mass (aggregation) In *m'es* thick with milky cones. *Miller's D.* 56
Beneath a manelike *m* of rolling gold, *Aylmer's Field* 68
pick'd offenders from the *m* For judgment. *Princess i* 29
That jewell'd *m* of millinery, *Maud I vi* 43
collapsed *m'es* Of thundershaken columns *Lover's Tale ii* 65
their *m'es* are gapp'd with our grape— *Def. of Lucknow* 42
and with golden *m'es* of pear, *V. of Maeldune* 60
Broke thro' the *m* from below, *Heavy Brigade* 29
Stagger'd the *m* from without, " 59
Of Love to leaven all the *m*, *Freedom* 19
Massacre or to whelm All of them in one *m*? *Lucretius* 207
all the pavement stream'd with *m*: *Last Tournament* 477
dying worm in a world, all *m*, murder, and wrong. *Despair* 32
After madness, after *m*, *Locksley H., Sixty* 157
Massacred moan of an enemy *m*, *Boädicea* 25
Massacring *m* Man, woman, lad and girl— *Gareth and L.* 1340
Massiest on his right Stood, all of *m* bronze: *Balin and Balan* 364
Massive underpropt a rich Throne of *m* ore, *Arabian Nights* 146
Gray halls alone among their *m* groves; *Princess, Con.* 43
The *m* square of his heroic breast, *Marr. of Geraint* 75
white rock a chapel and a hall On *m* columns, *Lancelot and E.* 406
Mast surf wind-scatter'd over sails and *m's*, *D. of F. Women* 31
'The high *m's* flicker'd as they lay afloat; " 113
Over *m* and deck were scatter'd Blood and brains of men. *The Captain* 47
and clambering on a *m* In harbour, *Enoch Arden* 105
Ruffle thy mirror'd *m*, *In Mem. ix* 7
Keel upward, and *m* downward, *Gareth and L.* 254
Ev'n to the swineherd's malkin in the *m*? *Last Tournament* 632
m bent and the ravin wind In her sail roaring. *Lover's Tale ii* 170
m's and the rigging were lying over the side; *The Revenge* 81
Where they laid him by the *m*, " 98
their sails and their *m's* and their flags, " 116
co-mates regather round the *m*; *Pref. Son. 19th Cent.* 5
With stormy light as on a *m* at sea, *Tiresias* 114
then came the crash of the *m*. *The Wreck* 92
fiery beech Were bearing off the *m*, *Pro. to Gen. Hamley* 4
Master (s) church-harpies from the *m's* feast; *To J. M. K.* 3
you, not you,—the *M*, Love, *Gardener's D.* 172
if they quarell'd, Enoch stronger-made Was *m*: *Enoch Arden* 31
the *m* of that ship Enoch had served in, " 119
Become the *m* of a larger craft, " 144
Seldom, but when he does, *M* of all. *Aylmer's Field* 132
all in flood And *m's* of his motion, " 340
Lucilia, wedded to Lucretius, found Her *m* cold; *Lucretius* 2
the *m* took Small notice, or austerely, " 7
My *m* held That Gods there are, " 116
And one the *M*, as a rogue in grain *Princess, Pro.* 116
The *M* was far away: *G. of Swainston* 7
Where lies the *m* newly dead; *In Mem. xx* 4
And loiter'd in the *m's* field, " *xxxvii* 23
eft was of old the Lord and *M* of Earth, *Maud I iv* 31
M of half a servile shire, " *x* 10
one Is Merlin's *m* (so they call him) Bleys, *Com. of Arthur* 153
but the scholar ran Before the *m*, " 155
For Bleys, our Merlin's *m*, as they say, " 360
'Old *M*, reverence thine own beard *Gareth and L.* 280
Kay, The *m* of the meats and drinks, " 451
No mellow *m* of the meats and drinks! " 560
Whether he know me for his *m* yet. " 721
Knowest thou not me? thy *m*? I am Kay. " 753
'*M* no more! too well I know thee, " 756
Thou hast overthrown and slain thy *m*— " 769
And doubling all his *m's* vice of pride, *Marr. of Geraint* 195
whistle of the youth who scour'd His *m's* armour; " 258
For man is man and *m* of his fate. " 355
'Great *M*, do ye love me?' *Merlin and V.* 237
O my *M*, have ye found your voice? " 269
M, be not wrathful with your maid; " 380
O *M*, do ye love my tender rhyme?' " 399
Since ye seem the *M* of all Art, They fain would make you *M* of all vice.' " 468
the great *M* merrily answer'd her: " 545
smiling as a *m* smiles at one That is not of his school, " 662
O *M*, shall we call him overquick " 724
meant to stamp him with her *m's* mark; " 759
With you for guide and *m*, only you, " 881
There like a dog before his *m's* door! *Pelleas and E.* 263
I knew Of no more subtle *m* under heaven *Guinevere* 478
loved His *m* more than all on earth beside. *Lover's Tale iv* 257
His *m* would not wait until he died, " 259
should this first *m* claim His service, " 265
Obedient to her second *m* now; " 343
gate Is bolted, and the *m* gone. *Tiresias* 201
As a psalm by a mighty *m* *The Wreck* 53
M scrimps his haggard sempstress *Locksley H., Sixty* 221
Leave the *M* in the first dark hour " 238
Then I leave thee Lord and *M*, " 282
had yielded her will To the *m*, *Dead Prophet* 64
Great the *M*, And sweet the Magic, *Merlin and the G.* 15

Maud (*continued*) And *M* too, *M* was moved To speak of the mother — *Maud I xix* 26
When only *M* and the brother Hung over her dying bed— „ 35
That *M's* dark father and mine Had bound us „ 37
On the day when *M* was born; „ 40
Yet *M*, altho' not blind To the faults „ 67
Kind to *M*? that were not amiss. „ 82
For shall not *M* have her will? „ 84
For, *M*, so tender and true, „ 85
nothing can be sweeter Than maiden *M* in either. „ *xx* 22
And *M* will wear her jewels, „ 27
every eye but mine will glance At *M* in all her glory. „ 37
Queen *M* in all her splendour. „ 50
Forgetful of *M* and me, „ *xxi* 4
My *M* has sent it by thee (If I read her sweet will right) „ 9
Come into the garden, *M*, (repeat) „ *xxii* 1, 3
Why should it look like *M*? „ *II ii* 39
Maudlin-moral empty glass That makes me *m-m*. — *Will Water.* 208
Maul'd Maim'd me and *m*, — *Last Tournament* 75
Maurice Come, *M*, come: the lawn as yet — *To F. D. Maurice* 41
Mavis (*See also* **Thrush**) The clear-voiced *m* dwelleth, — *Claribel* 16
'What knowest thou of birds, lark, *m*, merle, — *Gareth and L.* 1078
Mavors cry to thee To kiss thy *M*, — *Lucretius* 82
Maw let the wolves' black *m's* ensepulchre — *Balin and Balan* 487
Mawkin (*See also* **Malkin**) or a draggled *m*, thou, — *Princess, v* 26
Maxim With a little hoard of *m's* — *Locksley Hall* 94
With rugged *m's* hewn from life; — *Ode on Well.* 184
Gracious lessons thine And *m's* of the mud! — *Merlin and V.* 49
Maxume *See* **Lari Maxume**
May (hawthorn-bloom) (*See also* **Maäy**) thro' damp holts new-flush'd with *m*, — *My life is full* 19
lanes, you know, were white with *m*, — *Miller's D.* 130
but with plumes that mock'd the *m*, — *Guinevere* 22
wid the red o' the rose an' the white o' the *M*, — *Tomorrow* 31
May (month) (*See also* **Maäy**) Every heart this *M* morning in joyance is beating — *All Things will Die* 6
I'm to be Queen o' the *M*, (repeat) — *May Queen* 4, 8, 12, 16, 20, 24, 28, 32, 36, 40, 44
Last *M* we made a crown of flowers: — *May Queen N. Y's. E.* 9
Beneath the hawthorn on the green they made me Queen of *M*; „ 10
and *M* from verge to verge, And *M* with me from head to heel. — *Gardener's D.* 80
(For those old *M's* had thrice the life of these,) „ 84
he touch'd his one-and-twentieth *M* — *Enoch Arden* 57
(It might be *M* or April, he forgot, The last of April or the first of *M*) — *The Brook* 151
temper amorous, as the first of *M*, — *Princess i* 2
murmur'd that their *M* Was passing: „ *ii* 463
tho' it was the middle of *M*. — *Grandmother* 34
Cuck-oo!' was ever a *M* so fine? — *Window, Ay* 10
And glad at heart from *M* to *M*: — *In Mem. xxii* 8
clothed their branchy bowers With fifty *M's*, „ *lxxvi* 14
In the happy morning of life and of *M*, — *Maud I v* 7
Among the flowers, in *M*, with Guinevere. — *Com. of Arthur* 452
Far shone the fields of *M* thro' open door, „ 460
The sacred altar blossom'd white with *M*, „ 461
for the world is white with *M*; „ 482
'Blow, for our Sun is mighty in his *M*! „ 497
nightingale, full-toned in middle *M*, — *Balin and Balan* 213
wild-wood hyacinth and the bloom of *M*. „ 271
They might have cropt the myriad flower of *M*, „ 577
glittering like *M* sunshine on *M* leaves — *Merlin and V.* 88
the mid might and flourish of his *M*, — *Lancelot and E.* 554
an' all as merry as *M*— — *First Quarrel* 40
long ago, One bright *M* morning in a world of song, — *Sisters (E. and E.)* 82
vague love-longings, the bright *M*, „ 128
Thoughts of the breezes of *M* — *Def. of Lucknow* 83
shall we find a changeless *M*? — *Locksley H., Sixty* 156
For Naples which we only left in *M*? — *The Ring* 58
glidest thou from March to *M*, — *Prog. of Spring* 109
When I was in my June, you in your *M*, — *Roses on the T.* 2
Prophet of the *M* time, — *The Snowdrop* 7
display A tunic white as *M*! — *Prog. of Spring* 65

May (month) (*continued*) For have the far-off hymns of *M*, — *To Master of B.* 10
and it laugh'd like a dawn in *M*. — *Bandit's Death* 20
May (makes) —an ass as near as *m's* nowt— — *N. Farmer, N. S.* 39
May-blossom a brow *M-b*, and cheek of apple-blossom, — *Gareth and L* 589
and like *M-b's* in mid autumn— — *The Ring* 255
Maydew In the *M's* of childhood, — *Lover's Tale i* 188
Mayfly The *M* is torn by the swallow, — *Maud I iv* 23
Maying *See* **A-maying**
May Lilian (*See also* **Lilian**) Prythee weep, *M L*! (repeat) — *Lilian* 19, 25
May-music when they utter forth *M-m* — *Gareth and L.* 1080
May-pole And we danced about the *m-p* — *May Queen, N. Y's. E.* 11
May-sweet charged the winds With spiced *M-s's* — *Lover's Tale i* 318
Maytime (for the time Was *m*, and as yet no sin — *Guinevere* 388
May-white pride, wrath Slew the *M-w*: — *Gareth and L.* 657
Maze gauzes, golden hazes, liquid *m's*, — *Vision of Sin* 31
To thrid the musky-circled *m's*, — *Princess iv* 261
Now burgeons every *m* of quick — *In Mem. cxv* 2
Mazed 'Thou art *m*, the night is long, — *Vision of Sin* 195
heaven's *m* signs stood still In the dim tract of Penuel. — *Clear-headed friend* 28
but, being knave, Hast *m* my wit: — *Gareth and L.* 1170
Or art thou *m* with dreams? — *Pelleas and E.* 525
Mazing *See* **Maäzin'**
Me And learns the use of 'I,' and '*m*,' — *In Mem. xlv* 6
Mead But any man that walks the *m*, — *Day-Dm., Moral* 9
From far and near, on *m* and moor, — *In Mem. xxviii* 6
Or simple stile from *m* to *m*, „ *c* 7
And on by many a level *m*, „ *ciii* 21
Than of the myriad cricket of the *m*, — *Lancelot and E.* 106
Meadow (adj.) and fall before Her feet on the *m* grass, — *Maud I v* 26
Two forks are fixt into the *m* ground, — *Marr. of Geraint* 482
Then, moving downward to the *m* ground, — *Geraint and E.* 204
delight To roll himself in *m* grass — *Romney's R.* 14
Meadow (s) (*See also* **Midder**) Thro' quiet *m's* round the mill, — *Miller's D.* 98
vale And *m*, set with slender galingale; — *Lotos-Eaters* 23
reach'd a *m* slanting to the North; — *Gardener's D.* 108
sweep Of *m* smooth from aftermath — *Audley Court* 14
How fresh the *m's* look Above the river, — *Walk. to the Mail* 1
A sign betwixt the *m* and the cloud, — *St. S. Stylites* 14
Faint murmurs from the *m's* come, — *Day-Dm., Sleep P.* 6
And dewy Northern *m's* green. — *The Voyage* 36
daughter of our *m's*, yet not coarse; — *The Brook* 69
ghost of one who bore your name About these *m's*, „ 220
the dim *m* toward his treasure-trove, — *Aylmer's Field* 531
where it dash'd the reddening *m*, — *Lucretius* 49
'All among the *m's*, the clover and the clematis, — *City Child* 9
Oh, the woods and the *m's*, — *Window, Marr. Morn.* 5
M's in which we met! „ 8
I come, By *m* and stile and wood, „ 14
Over the *m's* and stiles, „ 22
over brake and bloom And *m*, — *In Mem. lxxxvi* 4
By *m's* breathing of the past, „ *xcix* 7
I smell the *m* in the street; „ *cxix* 4
voice by the cedar tree In the *m* under the Hall! — *Maud I v* 2
move to the *m* and fall before Her feet on the meadow grass, „ 25
For her feet have touch'd the *m's* „ *xii* 23
From the lake to the *m* and on to the wood, „ *xxii* 37
From the *m* your walks have left so sweet „ 39
She is walking in the *m*, „ *II iv* 37
She is singing in the *m* „ 40
Down to the *m* where the jousts were held, — *Marr. of Geraint* 537
up the vale of Usk, By the flat *m*, „ 832
a *m* gemlike chased In the brown wild, — *Geraint and E.* 198
grass There growing longest by the *m's* edge, „ 257
blossom-dust of those Deep *m's* we had traversed, — *Merlin and V.* 283
The green light from the *m's* underneath — *Lancelot and E.* 408
in the *m's* tremulous aspen-trees And poplars „ 410
reach'd the lists By Camelot in the *m*, „ 429
Over all the *m* baked and bare, — *Sisters (E. and E.)* 8
Over all the *m's* drowning flowers, „ 21
Summers of the snakeless *m*, — *To Virgil* 19
forehead vapour-swathed In *m's* ever green; — *Freedom* 8
A thousand squares of corn and *m*, — *The Ring* 149
my far *m* zoned with airy morn; — *Prog. of Spring* 69
Meadow-bases From level *m-b* of deep grass — *Palace of Art* 7

Meadow-crake the *m-c* Grate her harsh kindred — *Princess iv* 124
Meadow'd *See* **Deep-meadow'd**
Meadow-grass (*See also* **Meadow (adj.)**) come and go, mother, upon the *m-g*, — *May Queen* 33
Across the silent seeded *m-g* — *Pelleas and E.* 561
Meadow-ledges *m-l* midway down Hang rich in flowers, — *Œnone* 6
Meadow-sweet waist-deep in *m-s.* — *The Brook* 118
Meadow-trenches by the *m-t* blow the faint sweet cuckoo-flowers; — *May Queen* 30
Meadowy soft wind blowing over *m* holms And alders, — *Edwin Morris* 95
Drew in the dewy *m* morning-breath Of England, — *Enoch Arden* 660
rivulet that swerves To left and right thro' *m* curves, — *In Mem. c* 15
Meagre Her pendent hands, and narrow *m* face — *Aylmer's Field* 813
I was changed to wan And *m*, — *Holy Grail* 572
Meal (ground corn) Made misty with the floating *m.* — *Miller's D.* 104
With some pretext of fineness in the *m* — *Enoch Arden* 341
Who live on milk and *m* and grass; — *To E. Fitzgerald* 13
Meal (repast) (*See also* **Meäl**) sweetest *m* she makes On the first-born — *Vision of Sin* 145
scarce a coin to buy a *m* withal, — *Columbus* 169
Meäl (repast) an' taäkes their regular *m's.* — *N. Farmer, N. S.* 46
it's them as niver knaws wheer a *m's* to be 'ad. — „ 47
Meal-sacks The *m-s* on the whiten'd floor, — *Miller's D.* 101
Mealy-mouth'd nursed by *m-m* philanthropies, — *The Brook* 94
Mean (adj.) weep for a time so sordid and *m*, — *Maud I v* 17
since the proud man often is the *m*, — *Marr. of Geraint* 449
thought it never yet had look'd so *m*. — „ 610
M knights, to whom the moving of my sword — *Holy Grail* 790
that would sound so *m* That all the dead, — *Romney's R.* 131
Mean (s) debtless competence, golden *m*; — *Vastness* 24
Mean (verb) (*See also* **Manes, Meän Meäns**) another which you had, I *m* of verse — *The Epic* 26
For they know not what they *m*. — *Vision of Sin* 126
and *m* Vileness, we are grown so proud— — *Aylmer's Field* 755
Whether I *m* this day to end myself, — *Lucretius* 146
'Tears, idle tears, I know not what they *m*, — *Princess iv* 39
I *m* your grandfather, Annie: — *Grandmother* 23
my noätions, Sammy, wheerby I *m's* to stick; — *N. Farmer, N. S.* 57
The spirit does but *m* the breath: — *In Mem. lvi* 7
her own rose-garden, And *m* to linger in it — *Maud I xx* 42
'What *m's* the tumult in the town?' — *Marr. of Geraint* 259
They understand: nay; I do not *m* blood: — *Geraint and E.* 338
were all as tame, I *m*, as noble, — *Merlin and V.* 608
the good king *m's* to blind himself, — „ 783
I do not *m* the force alone— — *Lancelot and E.* 471
Nay, I *m* nothing: so then, get you gone, — „ 776
What might she *m* by that? — „ 834
He *m's* me I'm sure to be happy — *Rizpah* 76
I think that you *m* to be kind, — „ 81
show In some fifth Act what this wild Drama *m's.* — *The Play* 4
only the Devil can tell what he *m's.* — *Riflemen form!* 25
Meän (verb) she didn't not solidly *m* I wur gawin' — *Owd Roä* 71
Meän'd (meant) An' I niver knaw'd whot a *m* — *N. Farmer, O. S.* 19
an' I *m* to 'a stubb'd it at fall, Done it ta-year I *m*, — „ 41
Meanest (adj.) Better to me the *m* weed That blows upon its mountain, — *Amphion* 93
'Thro' slander, *m* spawn of Hell— — *The Letters* 33
put on thy worst and *m* dress And ride with me.' — *Marr. of Geraint* 130
Put on your worst and *m* dress,' — „ 848
Meanest (s) *m* having power upon the highest, — *Merlin and V.* 195
Meaning (part.) life He gave me, *m* to be rid of it. — *Geraint and E.* 853
m by it To keep the list low and pretenders back, — *Merlin and V.* 591
(*M* the print that you gave us, — *In the Child. Hosp.* 51
Meaning (s) So was their *m* to her words. — *The Poet* 53
Like a tale of little *m* tho' the words — *Lotos-Eaters, C. S.* 119
O take the *m*, Lord: — *St. S. Stylites* 21
A *m* suited to his mind. — *Day-Dm., Moral* 12
To search a *m* for the song, — „ *L'Envoi* 35
And, if you find a *m* there, — „ *Ep.* 2
Nor the *m* can divine, — *L. of Burleigh* 54
That was nothing to her: No *m* there: — *Enoch Arden* 499
Being other—since we learnt our *m* here, — *Princess iii* 222
there's a downright honest *m* in her; — „ *v* 280
Her secret *m* in her deeds, — *In Mem. lv* 10
I will not ask your *m* in it: — *Geraint and E.* 743
Meaning (s) (*continued*) this, indeed, her voice And *m*, — *To the Queen ii* 20
Now guess'd a hidden *m* in his arms, — *Lancelot and E.* 17
He thinking that he read her *m* there, — „ 86
That have no *m* half a league away: — *Holy Grail* 556
while they rode, the *m* in his eyes, — *Pelleas and E.* 109
Her words did of their *m* borrow sound, — *Lover's Tale i* 568
until The *m* of the letters shot into My brain; — „ *ii* 8
He knew the *m* of the whisper now, — „ *iv* 43
to seek The *m's* ambush'd — *Tiresias* 5
Meaningless drown'd in the deeps of a *m* Past? — *Vastness* 34
Meanness sense Of *m* in her unresisting life. — *Aylmer's Field* 801
Means Or *m* to pay the voice who best could tell — *Enoch Arden* 266
The first, a gentleman of broken *m* — *Princess i* 53
spirit of murder works in the very *m* of life, — *Maud I i* 40
following with a costrel bore The *m* of goodly welcome, — *Marr. of Geraint* 387
Because my *m* were somewhat broken into — „ 455
Being but ampler *m* to serve mankind, — *Merlin and V.* 489
should strike upon a sudden *m* To dig, — „ 659
Meäns *m's* fur to maäke 'is owd aäge — *Owd Roä* 3
if iver tha *m's* to git 'igher, — *Church-warden, etc.* 45
Meant (*See also* **Meän'd**) We met, but only *m* to part. — *The Letters* 12
He never *m* us anything but good. — *Enoch Arden* 887
you find That you *m* nothing—us indeed you know That you *m* nothing. — *Aylmer's Field* 313
I should find he *m* me well; — *Sea Dreams* 153
he *m*, he said he *m*, Perhaps he *m*, or partly *m*, you well.' — „ 178
'Ay, but I *m* not thee; I *m* not her, — *Lucretius* 85
and *m* Surely to lead my Memmius in a train — „ 118
M? I *m*? I have fogotten what I *m*: — „ 121
That she but *m* to win him back, — „ 279
alien lips, And knew not what they *m*; — *Princess iv* 120
And vacant chaff well *m* for grain. — *In Mem. vi* 4
She *m* to weave me a snare Of some coquettish deceit, — *Maud I vi* 25
Knew that the death-white curtain *m* but sleep, — „ *xiv* 37
Ask'd yet once more what *m* the hubbub here? — *Marr. of Geraint* 264
To learn what Arthur *m* by courtesy, — *Balin and Balan* 158
m to eat her up in that wild wood — *Merlin and V.* 260
m to stamp him with her master's mark; — „ 759
m once more perchance to tourney in it. — *Lancelot and E.* 810
rough sickness *m*, but what this *m* — „ 888
(He *m* to break the passion in her) — „ 1079
But when I thought he *m* To crush me, — *Holy Grail* 415
But heaven had *m* it for a sunny one: — „ 706
spake the King: I knew not all he *m*.' — „ 920
'The simple, fearful child *M* nothing, — *Guinevere* 370
Our general mother *m* for me alone, — *Lover's Tale i* 245
and *m* to rest an hour; — „ *iv* 133
I didn't know well what I *m*, — *First Quarrel* 83
If a curse *m* ought, I would curse — *Despair* 64
m us to be mightier by and by, — *Locksley H., Sixty* 209
Those gray heads, What *m* they — *Demeter and P.* 130
Muriel claim'd and open'd what I *m* For Miriam, — *The Ring* 242
And I *m* to make *you* jealous. — *Happy* 67
you knew that he *m* to betray me— — *Charity* 12
Measure (s) (*See also* **Slow-measure**) hearts of salient springs Keep *m* — *Adeline* 27
I crouch'd on one that rose Twenty by *m*; — *St. S. Stylites* 89
fresh to men, And wanton without *m*; — *Amphion* 58
Tread a *m* on the stones, — *Vision of Sin* 180
As meted by his *m* of himself, — *Aylmer's Field* 316
The highest is the *m* of the man, — *Princess ii* 157
rich Virgilian rustic *m* Of Lari Maxume, — *The Daisy* 75
draw The deepest *m* from the chords: — *In Mem. xlviii* 12
by the *m* of my grief I leave thy greatness — „ *lxxv* 3
God, the *m* of my hate for Mark Is as the *m* — *Last Tournament* 537
how should Earthly *m* mete The Heavenly-unmeasured — *Lover's Tale i* 473
Wielder of the stateliest *m* ever moulded — *To Virgil* 39
Measure (verb) *m* time by yon slow light, — *St. S. Stylites* 94
in the flame that *m's* Time! — *Akbar's D., Hymn* 8
Measured How many *m* words adore The full-flowing harmony — *Eleänore* 45
With *m* footfall firm and mild, — *Two Voices* 413

Measured (*continued*) An echo from a *m* strain, — Miller's D. 66
hear These *m* words, my work of yestermorn. — Golden Year 21
A use in *m* language lies; — In Mem. v 6
The *m* pulse of racing oars Among the willows; — „ lxxxvii 10
Run out your *m* arcs, and lead The closing cycle — „ cv 27
three paces *m* from the mound, — Princess v 1
Measureless honey of poison-flowers and all the *m* ill. — Maud I iv 56
For years, a *m* ill, — „ II ii 49
Measuring Æonian music *m* out The steps — In Mem. xcv 41
Oft in mid-banquet *m* with his eyes — Pelleas and E. 150
Meat (*See also* **Meät**) Yea ev'n of wretched *m* and drink, — Maud I xv 8
In her foul den, there at their *m* would growl, — Com. of Arthur 30
King Made feast for, saying, as they sat at *m*, — „ 247
hire thyself to serve for *m's* and drinks — Gareth and L. 153
grant me to serve For *m* and drink — „ 445
Kay, The master of the *m's* and drinks, — „ 451
No mellow master of the *m's* and drinks! — „ 560
mighty thro' thy *m's* and drinks (repeat) — „ 650, 862
except, belike, To garnish *m's* with? — „ 1070
Where bread and baken *m's* and good red wine — „ 1190
Sir Lancelot, is hard by, with *m's* and drinks — „ 1276
sit with knife in *m* and wine in horn! — Merlin and V. 694
with *m's* and vintage of their best — Lancelot and E. 266
where the *m's* became As wormwood, — „ 743
m, Wine, wine,—and I will love thee — Last Tournament 719
had comforted the blood With *m's* and wines, — „ 725
Had whatsoever *m* he long'd for served — Guinevere 265
our lover seldom spoke, Scarce touch'd the *m's*; — Lover's Tale iv 226
Or mine to give him *m*, — Voice spake, etc. 8
Meät or a mossel o' *m* when it beänt too dear, — Spinster's S's. 109
Mechanic (adj.) The long *m* pacings to and fro, — Love and Duty 17
The sad *m* exercise, — In Mem. v 7
A disease, a hard *m* ghost That never came from on high, — Maud II ii 34
Mechanic (s) see the raw *m's* bloody thumbs — Walk. to the Mail 75
Meddle and there was none to *m* with it. — Gareth and L. 1012
Meddling Some *m* rogue has tamper'd with him— — Lancelot and E. 128
Medicine glass with little Margaret's *m* in it; — Sea Dreams 142
blush and smile, a *m* in themselves — Princess vii 62
'The miserable have no *m* But only Hope!' — Romney's R. 149
Meditated while I *m* A wind arose and rush'd — Princess i 96
Meditating long and bitterly *m*, — Boädicea 35
Meditation In a silent *m*, — Eleänore 105
Meditative With *m* grunts of much content, — Walk. to the Mail 87
Mediterranean About the soft *M* shores, — Sir J. Oldcastle 30
Medley This *were* a *m*! we should have him — Princess, Pro. 237
Meeäk (meek) I kep' mysen *m* as a lamb, — Church-warden, etc. 41
Meeätin' (meeting) An' when we coom'd into *M*, — North. Cobbler 53
Meed claiming each This *m* of fairest. — Œnone 87
The *m* of saints, the white robe and the palm. — St. S. Stylites 20
this was my *m* for all. — Princess iv 302
Meek (adj.) (*See also* **Maiden-meek, Meeäk, Mock-meek**)
With lips depress'd as he were *m*, — A Character 25
'His lips are very mild and *m*: — Two Voices 250
And Dora promised, being *m*. — Dora 46
maiden of our century, yet most *m*; — The Brook 68
Him, to her *m* and modest bosom prest In agony, — Aylmer's Field 416
thought myself long-suffering, *m*, — „ 753
m Seem'd the full lips, and mild the luminous eyes. — Princess vii 225
why come you so cruelly *m*, — Maud I iii 1
Tut: he was tame and *m* enow with me, — Gareth and L. 718
and *m* withal As any of Arthur's best, — „ 1168
O pale, pale face so sweet and *m*, — Oriana 66
O somewhere, *m*, unconscious dove, — In Mem. vi 25
But answer'd in low voice, her *m* head yet Drooping, — Geraint and E. 640
But o'er her *m* eyes came a happy mist — „ 769
Yet not so misty were her *m* blue eyes — „ 772
And there, poor cousin, with your *m* blue eyes, — „ 841
Ye know right well, how *m* soe'er he seem, — Lancelot and E. 155
but the *m* maid Sweetly forbore him ever, — „ 855
So Arthur bad the *m* Sir Percivale — „ 1264
M maidens, from the voices crying "shame." — Guinevere 672
an' 'e says to 'im, *m* as a mouse, — Village Wife 63
our darling, our *m* little maid; — In the Child. Hosp. 28
Except his own *m* daughter yield her life, — The Flight 28
but set no *m* ones in their place; — Locksley H., Sixty 133

Meek (adj.) (*continued*) patient, and prayerful, *m*, Pale-blooded, — Last Tournament 607
who am not *m*, Pale-blooded, prayerful. — „ 610
Meek (s) 'The *m* shall inherit the earth' — The Dreamer 2
The Reign of the *M* upon earth, — „ 25
Meeker *M* than any child to a rough nurse, — Lancelot and E. 857
Some *m* pupil you must find, — L. C. V. de Vere 18
Meekness Shaped her heart with woman's *m* — L. of Burleigh 71
Meet (adj.) *M* is it changes should control Our being, — Love thou thy land 41
'It is not *m*, Sir King, to leave thee thus, — M. d'Arthur 40
scarce *m* For troops of devils, — St. S. Stylites 3
I am whole, and clean, and *m* for Heaven. — „ 213
pay *M* adoration to my household gods, — Ulysses 42
should pause, as is most *m* for all? — Tithonus 31
M for the reverence of the hearth, — Aylmer's Field 333
surely rest is *m*: 'They rest,' we said, — In Mem. xxx 18
Becoming as is *m* and fit A link among the days, — „ xl 14
nor *m* To fight for gentle damsel, — Gareth and L. 1176
fare is coarse, And only *m* for mowers;' — Geraint and E. 209
M is it the good King be not deceived. — Balin and Balan 533
'It is not *m*, Sir King, to leave thee thus, — Pass. of Arthur 207
Meet (verb) That clothe the wold and *m* the sky; — L. of Shalott i 3
For those two likes might *m* and touch. — Two Voices 357
I could *m* with her The Abominable, — Œnone 223
blessings on his whole life long, until he *m* me there! — May Queen, Con. 14
token when the night and morning *m*: — „ 22
Counts nothing that she *m's* with base, — On a Mourner 4
She heard the torrents *m*. — Of old sat Freedom 4
In whom should *m* the offices of all, — M. d'Arthur 125
Sets out, and *m's* a friend who hails him, — Walk. to the Mail 42
robed and crown'd, To *m* her lord, — Godiva 78
airs of heaven That often *m* me here. — Sir Galahad 64
sometimes two would *m* in one, — Will Water. 95
broad seas swell'd to *m* the keel, — The Voyage 13
To *m* and greet her on her way; — Beggar Maid 6
'Cold altar, Heaven and earth shall *m* — The Letters 7
year Roll'd itself round again to *m* the day When Enoch — Enoch Arden 822
Stands Philip's farm where brook and river *m*. — The Brook 38
Katie never ran: she moved To *m* me, — „ 88
Abase those eyes that ever loved to *m* Star-sisters — Princess ii 427
Not yet endured to *m* her opening eyes, — „ iv 195
I fear'd To *m* a cold 'We thank you, — „ 328
The next, like fire he *m's* the foe, — „ 583
to *m* us lightly pranced Three captains out; — „ v 254
then he drew Her robe to *m* his lips, — „ vi 156
turn'd half-round to Psyche as she sprang To *m* it, — „ 210
To *m* her Graces, where they deck'd her — „ vii 168
Who lets once more in peace the nations *m*, — Ode Inter. Exhib. 4
To *m* the sun and sunny waters, — The Daisy 11
In middle ocean *m's* the surging shock, — Will 8
and Spirit with Spirit can *m*— — High. Pantheism 11
Two little hands that *m*, (repeat) — Window, The Answer 1, 4
In which we two were wont to *m*, — In Mem. viii 10
I shall know him when we *m*: — „ xlvii 8
And envying all that *m* him there. — „ lx 8
I seem to *m* their least desire, — „ lxxxiv 17
O tell me where the passions *m*, — „ lxxxviii 4
And *m's* the year, and gives and takes — „ cxvi 3
And unto meeting when we *m*, — „ cxvii 7
they *m* thy look And brighten like the star — „ Con. 30
advance To *m* and greet a whiter sun; — „ 78
Whom but Maud should I *m*? (repeat) — Maud I vi 7, 11
She remembers it now we *m*. — „ 88
To the woody hollows in which we *m* — „ xxii 43
When I was wont to *m* her In the silent woody places — „ II iv 5
In a moment we shall *m*; — „ 39
And the faces that one *m's*, — „ 93
Return, and *m*, and hold him from our eyes, — Gareth and L. 429
'but thou shalt *m* thy match.' — „ 1024
one might *m* a mightier than himself; — „ 1350
pray That we may *m* the horsemen of Earl Doorm, — Geraint and E. 492
shadow from the counter door Sir Lancelot as to *m* her, — Balin and Balan 247

Melody (*continued*) Gleam flying onward, Wed to
the *m*, *Merlin and the G.* 97
All her *melodies*, All her harmonies *To Master of B.* 11
Melon A raiser of huge *m's* and of pine, *Princess, Con.* 87
m lay like a little sun on the tawny sand, *V. of Maeldune* 57
The mango spurn the *m* at his foot ? *Akbar's Dream* 39
Melpomene And my *M* replies, *In Mem. xxxvii* 9
Melt To the earth—until the ice would *m* *Supp. Confessions* 81
I wish the snow would *m* *May Queen, N. Y's. E.* 15
And from it *m* the dews of Paradise *St. S. Stylites* 210
light shall slowly *m* In many streams *Golden Year* 33
I will *m* this marble into wax *Princess iii* 73
'embrace me, come, Quick while I *m* ; „ *vi* 286
M's mist-like into this bright hour, „ *vii* 355
M into stars for the land's desire ! *W. to Alexandra* 21
And *m* the waxen hearts of men.' *In Mem. xxi* 8
They *m* like mist, the solid lands, „ *cxxiii* 7
A warmth within the breast would *m* „ *cxxiv* 13
A purer sapphire *m's* into the sea. *Maud I xviii* 52
Give me three days to *m* her fancy, *Pelleas and E.* 356
And *m's* within her hand—her hand is hot *Last Tournament* 414
as a cloud *M's* into Heaven. *Ancient Sage* 234
frost-bead *m's* upon her golden hair ; *Prog. of Spring* 10
Melted (*See also* **Half-melted**) rites and forms before
his burning eyes *M* like snow. *The Poet* 40
The twilight *m* into morn. *Day-Dm., Depart.* 16
Amazed and *m* all who listen'd to it : *Enoch Arden* 649
Which *m* Florian's fancy as she hung, *Princess iv* 370
all his force Is *m* into mere effeminacy ? *Marr. of Geraint* 107
Till he *m* like a cloud in the silent summer heaven ; *The Revenge* 14
Sank from their thrones, and *m* into tears, *Columbus* 15
Melteth *m* in the source Of these sad tears, *Lover's Tale i* 783
Melting *m* the mighty hearts Of captains *D. of F. Women* 175
Member (M.P.) (*See also* **County Member**) The Tory
m's elder son, *Princess, Con.* 50
Memmian Beyond the *M* naphtha-pits, *Alexander* 4
Memmius Surely to lead my *M* in a train *Lucretius* 119
Memnon from *M*, drew Rivers of melodies. *Palace of Art* 171
M smitten with the morning Sun.' *Princess iii* 116
Memorial (adj.) I seem'd to move in old *m* tilts, „ *v* 479
Their names, Graven on *m* columns, *Tiresias* 124
Memorial (s) I stored it full of rich *m* : *Princess v* 391
My sole *m* Of Edith—no, the other,— *Sisters (E. and E.)* 107
These hard *m's* of our truth to Spain *Columbus* 196
Raise a stately *m*, *On Jub. Q. Victoria* 44
Memory Thou dewy dawn of *m*. (repeat) *Ode to Memory* 7, 45, 124
Unto mine inner eye, Divinest *M* ! „ 50
Well hast thou done, great artist *M*, „ 80
Makes thy *m* confused : *A Dirge* 45
In painting some dead friend from *m* ? *Wan Sculptor* 4
'The *m* of the wither'd leaf *Two Voices* 112
Because my *m* is so cold, „ 341
The haunts of *m* echo not. „ 369
must I be Incompetent of *m* : 'For *m* dealing but with
time, „ 375
His *m* scarce can make me sad. *Miller's D.* 16
foundation-stones were laid Since my first *m* ?' *Palace of Art* 236
put strange *memories* in my head. *L. C. V. de Vere* 26
To muse and brood and live again in *m*, *Lotos-Eaters, C. S.* 65
Dear is the *m* of our wedded lives, „ 69
No *m* labours longer from the deep *D. of F. Women* 273
His *m* long will live alone In all our hearts, *To J. S.* 49
M standing near Cast down her eyes, „ 53
Come Hope and *M*, spouse and bride, *On a Mourner* 23
Sir Bedivere Revolving many *memories*, *M. d'Arthur* 270
So blunt in *m*, so old at heart, *Gardener's D.* 53
And sure this orbit of the *m* folds „ 74
while I mused came *M* with sad eyes, „ 243
Now the most blessed *m* of mine age. „ 279
he will learn to slight His father's *m* ; *Dora* 154
For calmer hours to *M's* darkest hold, *Love and Duty* 90
Drug thy *memories*, lest thou learn it, *Locksley Hall* 77
a thousand *memories* roll upon him, *Enoch Arden* 724
Old, and a mine of *memories*— *Aylmer's Field* 10
left their *memories* a world's curse— „ 796

Memory (*continued*) From out a common vein of *m*
Sweet household talk, *Princess ii* 314
Rose from the distance on her *m*, „ *vi* 112
And out of *memories* of her kindlier days, *vii* 106
brawling *memories* all too free *Ode on Well.* 248
From whence clear *m* may begin, *In Mem. xlv* 10
To count their *memories* half divine ; „ *xc* 12
I hear a wind Of *m* murmuring the past. „ *xcii* 8
The *m* like a cloudless air, „ *xciv* 11
Or ev'n for intellect to reach Thro' *m* „ *xcv* 48
Memories of bridal, or of birth, „ *xcix* 15
Some gracious *m* of my friend ; „ *c* 4
year by year our *m* fades From all the circle of the hills. „ *ci* 23
In lands where not a *m* strays, „ *civ* 10
To whom a thousand *memories* call, „ *cxi* 10
My drooping *m* will not shun The foaming grape „ *Con.* 79
Mix not *m* with doubt, *Maud II iv* 57
These to His *M*—since he held them dear, *Ded. of Idylls* 1
m of that cognizance on shield Weighted *Balin and Balan* 224
m of that token on the shield Relax'd his hold : „ 369
No *m* in me lives ; *Holy Grail* 535
Vext her with plaintive *memories* of the child : *Last Tournament* 29
Then ran across her *m* the strange rhyme „ 131
sweet *memories* Of Tristram in that year he was
away.' „ 579
O sweeter than all *memories* of thee, „ 585
pine and waste in those sweet *memories*. „ 598
Nor let me shame my father's *m*, *Guinevere* 318
Her *m* from old habit of the mind Went slipping back „ 379
Sir Bedivere Revolving many *memories*, *Pass. of Arthur* 438
The *m's* vision hath a keener edge. *Lover's Tale i* 36
garner'd up Into the granaries of *m*— „ 129
Doth question'd *m* answer not, „ 277
Which are as gems set in my *m*, „ 291
A land of promise, a land of *m*, „ 333
milk And honey of delicious *memories* ! „ 335
my name has been A hallow'd *m* like the names of old,
A center'd, glory-circled *m*, „ 445
Ye cannot shape Fancy so fair as is this *m*. „ 548
At last she sought out *M*, and they trod „ 820
And *M* fed the soul of Love with tears. „ 822
Within the magic cirque of *m*, „ *ii* 159
Which yet retains a *m* of its youth, *Sisters (E. and E.)* 66
Unvenerable will thy *m* be While men *Tiresias* 132
My *memories* of his briefer day *To Marq. of Dufferin* 51
break thro' clouded *memories* once again *Demeter and P.* 10
A virgin victim to his *m*, *The Ring* 221
Or is it some half *m* of a dream ? „ 422
Is *m* with your Marian gone to rest, *To Mary Boyle* 13
Menace When was age so cramm'd with *m* ? *Locksley H., Sixty* 108
Menacing beat back The *m* poison of intolerant
priests, *Akbar's Dream* 165
Men-at-arms *m-a-a*, A score with pointed lances, *Balin and Balan* 400
Men-children gauds *m-c* swarm to see. *To W. C. Macready* 11
Mend (*See also* **Clump**) How *m* the dwellings, of the
poor ; *To F. D. Maurice* 38
Mended (adj.) Our *m* fortunes and a Prince's
bride : *Marr. of Geraint* 718
Mended (verb) Robins—a niver *m* a fence : *N. Farmer, O. S.* 50
Mene Wrote '*M, m*,' and divided quite *Palace of Art* 227
Menial bad his *m's* bear him from the door, *Lover's Tale iv* 260
Menœceus *M*, thou hast eyes, and I can hear *Tiresias* 90
Mental Wanting the *m* range ; *Merlin and V.* 827
Mention seal'd book, all *m* of the ring, *The Ring* 123
Mention'd bill I *m* half an hour ago ?' *Day-Dm., Revival* 28
when the day, that Enoch *m*, came, *Enoch Arden* 239
Men-tommies Ye be wuss nor the *m-t*, *Spinster's S's.* 93
Merchant As tho' they brought but *m's'* bales, *In Mem. xiii* 19
market frets or charms The *m's* hope no more ; *Ancient Sage* 141
Merchantman served a year On board a *m*, *Enoch Arden* 53
Mercian Mighty the *M*, Hard was his hand-play, *Batt. of Brunanburh* 43
Merciful were any bounteous, *m*, *Gareth and L.* 423
Merciless big voice, big chest, big *m* hands ! *In the Child. Hosp.* 4
Mercury as it were with *M's* ankle-wing, *Lucretius* 201
M On such a morning would have flung himself *Lover's Tale i* 300

Merriment (*continued*) And moved to *m* at a passing jest. *Sisters E. and E.* 121
Merry The *m* glees are still; *All Things will Die* 23
Ye *m* souls, farewell. „ 36
When *m* milkmaids click the latch, *The Owl i* 8
In the heart of the garden the *m* bird chants. *Poet's Mind* 22
For *m* brides are we: *Sea-Fairies* 33
Of the bold *m* mermen under the sea; *The Mermaid* 42
How the *m* bluebell rings *Adeline* 34
A *m* boy in sun and shade? 'A *m* boy they call'd him then, *Two Voices* 321
I said, 'O Soul, make *m* and carouse, *Palace of Art* 3
Last May we made a crown of flowers: we had a *m* day; *May Queen, N. Y's. E.* 9
But all his *m* quips are o'er. *D. of the O. Year* 29
Hark, my *m* comrades call me, *Locksley Hall* 145
And many a *m* wind was borne, *Day-Dm., Depart.* 14
He laugh'd a laugh of *m* scorn: *Lady Clare* 81
We knew the *m* world was round, *The Voyage* 7
We know the *m* world is round, „ 95
And make him *m*, when I come home again. *Enoch Arden* 199
How *m* they are down yonder in the wood. „ 389
Clash, ye bells, in the *m* March air! *W. to Alexandra* 18
Be *m*, all birds, to-day, Be *m* on earth as you never were *m* before, Be *m* in heaven, O larks, and far away, And *m* for ever and ever, and one day more. *Window, Ay* 1
O *m* the linnet and dove, „ 13
O *m* my heart, you have gotten the wings of love, „ 15
The *m m* bells of Yule. *In Mem. xxviii* 20
A *m* song we sang with him Last year: „ *xxx* 15
Many a *m* face Salutes them— „ *Con.* 66
Go in and out as if at *m* play, *Maud I xviii* 31
I fear, Fantastically *m*; „ *xix* 101
'Full *m* am I to find my goodly knave *Gareth and L.* 1291
And we will make us *m* as we may. *Marr. of Geraint* 373
Then, when the Prince was *m*, ask'd Limours, *Geraint and E.* 297
And *m* maidens in it; *Holy Grail* 746
And blew my *m* maidens all about „ 748
should ye try him with a *m* one To find his mettle, *Pelleas and E.* 198
Open gates, And I will make you *m*.' „ 374
Down in the cellars *m* bloated things *Guinevere* 267
m linnet knew me, The squirrel knew me, *Lover's Tale ii* 15
Four *m* bells, four *m* marriage-bells, „ *iii* 21
Married among the red berries, an' all as *m* as May— *First Quarrel* 40
Lest the false faith make *m* over them! *Sir J. Oldcastle* 82
in many a *m* tale That shook our sides— „ 91
Merrymaking our friends are all forsaking The wine and the *m*. *All Things will Die* 19
no more of mirth Is here or *m-m* sound. *Deserted House* 14
while the rest were loud in *m-m*, *Enoch Arden* 77
Mersey New-comers from the *M*, *Edwin Morris* 10
Meseems '*M*, that here is much discourtesy, *Gareth and L.* 853
Is all as good, *m*, as any knight „ 1017
My quest, *m*, is here. *Balin and Balan* 552
Mesh In *m's* of the jasmine and the rose: *Princess i* 219
Message with His *m* ringing in thine ears, *Aylmer's Field* 666
They flash'd a saucy *m* to and fro *Princess, Pro.* 78
I brought a *m* here from Lady Blanche.' „ *ii* 319
He ceasing, came a *m* from the Head. „ *iii* 168
With *m* and defiance, went and came; „ *v* 370
in this Book, little Annie, the *m* is one of Peace. *Grandmother* 96
Some dolorous *m* knit below *In Mem. xii* 3
Till on mine ear this *m* falls, „ *lxxxv* 18
Yniol with that hard *m* went; *Marr. of Geraint* 763
Save that he sware me to a *m*, saying, *Last Tournament* 76
And waited for her *m*, piece by piece *Lover's Tale iv* 146
Messenger Then came in hall the *m* of Mark, *Gareth and L.* 384
Messuage lands in Kent and *m's* in York, *Edwin Morris* 127
Met (*See also* **Chance-met**) '*And statesmen at her council* m *To the Queen* 29
talking to himself, first *m* his sight: *Love and Death* 6
Methought that I had often *m* with you, *Sonnet To ——* 13
They *m* with two so full and bright— *Miller's D.* 86
And angels rising and descending *m* *Palace of Art* 143

Met (*continued*) When thus he *m* his mother's view, *L. C. V. de Vere* 34
or as once we *m* Unheedful, *Gardener's D.* 265
I *m* my lady once: *Walk. to the Mail* 48
those moments when we *m*, The crown of all, we *m* to part no more.' *Edwin Morris* 69
we *m*; one hour I had, no more: „ 104
I am a part of all that I have *m*; *Ulysses* 18
M me walking on yonder way, *Edward Gray* 2
then we *m* in wrath and wrong, We *m*, but only meant to part. *The Letters* 11
He *m* the bailiff at the Golden Fleece, *The Brook* 146
Yet once by night again the lovers *m*, *Aylmer's Field* 413
I *m* him suddenly in the street, *Sea Dreams* 146
Here Cyril *m* us. A little shy at first, *Princess v* 44
a lie which is all a lie may be *m* and fought with outright, *Grandmother* 31
Meadows in which we *m*! *Window, Marr. Morn.* 8
And ever *m* him on his way *In Mem. vi* 22
And all we *m* was fair and good, „ *xxiii* 17
If all was good and fair we *m*, „ *xxiv* 5
From every house the neighbours *m*, „ *xxxi* 9
I *m* with scoffs, I *m* with scorns „ *lxix* 9
For other friends that once I *m*; „ *lxxxv* 58
Where God and Nature *m* in light; „ *cxi* 20
Unpalsied when he *m* with Death, „ *cxxviii* 2
I *m* her to-day with her brother, *Maud I iv* 14
To entangle me when we *m*, „ *vi* 28
blush'd To find they were *m* by my own; „ *viii* 7
Alas for her that *m* me, „ *II iv* 75
I *m* Merlin, and ask'd him if these things *Com. of Arthur* 397
knave, anon thou shalt be *m* with, knave, *Gareth and L.* 779
Whom Gareth *m* midstream: no room was there „ 1041
Gareth overthrew him, lighted, drew, There *m* him drawn, „ 1122
when they *m* In twos and threes, *Marr. of Geraint* 56
then descending *m* them at the gates, „ 833
M his full frown timidly firm, *Geraint and E.* 71
m The scorner in the castle court, *Balin and Balan* 386
Had *m* her, Vivien, being greeted fair, *Merlin and V.* 155
would often when they *m* Sigh fully, „ 181
here we *m*, some ten or twelve of us, „ 407
two brothers, one a king, had *m* And fought *Lancelot and E* 39
And oft they *m* among the garden yews, „ 645
They *m*, and Lancelot kneeling utter'd, „ 1179
He raised his head, their eyes *m* and hers fell, „ 1312
M foreheads all along the street *Holy Grail* 344
'And then, with small adventure *m*, „ 660
And steps that *m* the breaker! „ 816
The men who *m* him rounded on their heels *Pelleas and E.* 142
he *m* A cripple, one that held a hand for alms— „ 541
Flush'd, started, *m* him at the doors, *Last Tournament* 512
But harken! have ye met him? „ 529
And still they *m* and *m*. Again she said, *Guinevere* 94
Passion-pale they *m* And greeted. „ 99
We turn'd; our eyes *m*: hers were bright, *Lover's Tale i* 441
Parted a little ere they *m* the floor, „ *iv* 215
their breath *m* us out on the seas, *V. of Maeldune* 37
'would God, we had never *m*!' *The Wreck* 102
Here we *m*, our latest meeting— *Locksley H., Sixty* 177
Like a clown—by chance he *m* me— „ 256
century's three strong eights have *m* *To Ulysses* 7
For ere she left us, when we *m*, *To Mary Boyle* 15
Have I not *m* you somewhere long ago? *Romney's R.* 18
when I *m* you first—when *he* brought you!— *Charity* 9
Metal Bright *m* all without alloy. *Rosalind* 21
Metaphysics she cried, 'you love The *m*! *Princess iii* 300
Mete And *m* the bounds of hate and love— *Two Voices* 135
I *m* and dole Unequal laws unto a savage race, *Ulysses* 3
Meted As *m* by his measure of himself, *Aylmer's Field* 316
Meteor Some bearded *m*, trailing light, *L. of Shalott iii* 26
The *m* of a splendid season, she, *Aylmer's Field* 205
like a new-fall'n *m* on the grass, *Princess vi* 135
Now slides the silent *m* on, „ *vii* 184
While thou, a *m* of the sepulchre, *Lover's Tale i* 99
Meteorite and your fiery clash of *m's*? *God and the Univ.* 3

Methinks *m* Some ruth is mine for thee. *Gareth and L.* 894
m There rides no knight, not Lancelot, „ 1181
Method *M's* of transplanting trees *Amphion* 79
Methody-man 'Thou'rt but a *M-m*,' says Parson, *North. Cobbler* 89
Methought yet *m* I saw the Holy Grail, *Holy Grail* 846
m The cloud was rifted by a purer gleam *Akbar's Dream* 77
Metre mellow *m's* more than cent for cent; *The Brook* 5
All composed in a *m* of Catullus, *Hendecasyllabics* 4
So fantastical is the dainty *m*. „ 14
Metrification Thro' this *m* of Catullus, „ 10
Metropolis And gray *m* of the North. *The Daisy* 104
Above some fair *m*, earth-shock'd,— *Lover's Tale ii* 62
Mettle It stirr'd the old wife's *m*: *The Goose* 26
try him with a merry one To find his *m*, good: *Pelleas and E.* 199
Mew (sea-gull) Here it is only the *m* that wails; *Sea-Fairies* 19
and wail'd about with *m's*. *Princess iv* 282
Mew (cry of a cat) *M*! *m*!—Bess wi' the milk! *Spinster's S's.* 113
Mewin (mewing) what art'a *m* at, Steevie? „ 41
Mexico lavish growths of southern *M*. *Mine be thy strength* 14
Michaël But *M* trampling Satan; *Last Tournament* 673
Michael Angelo The bar of *M A*. *In Mem. lxxxvii* 40
Michaelmas for Squoire coom *M* thutty year. *N. Farmer, O. S.* 48
Microcosm holy secrets of this *m*. *Princess iii* 313
Mid birds made Melody on branch, and melody in *m* air. *Gareth and L.* 183
In the *m* might and flourish of his May, *Lancelot and E.* 554
and started thro' *m* air Bearing an eagle's nest: *Last Tournament* 14
life Being smitten in *m* heaven with mortal cold „ 27
as a stream that spouting from a cliff Fails in *m* air, *Guinevere* 609
Like some conjectured planet in *m* heaven *Prin. Beatrice* 20
and like May-blossoms in *m* autumn— *The Ring* 255
Yet you in your *m* manhood— *Happy* 47
Mid-banquet in *m-b* measuring with his eyes *Pelleas and E.* 150
Mid-channel in the gurgling wave *M-c*. *Princess iv* 188
Mid-day Jet upward thro' the *m-d* blossom. *Demeter and P.* 47
Midder (meadow) an' the *m's* as white, *Owd Roä* 31
Middle (adj.) The living airs of *m* night Died round *Arabian Nights* 69
Shrill music reach'd them on the *m* sea. *Sea-Fairies* 6
And fling him far into the *m* mere: *M. d'Arthur* 37
But Enoch shunn'd the *m* walk and stole Up by the wall, *Enoch Arden* 738
but in the *m* aisle Reel'd, *Aylmer's Field* 818
As in some mystic *m* state I lay; *Princess vi* 18
In *m* ocean meets the surging shock, *Will* 8
The nightingale, full-toned in *m* May, *Balin and Balan* 213
As the poach'd filth that floods the *m* street, *Merlin and V.* 798
all in *m* street the Queen Who rode by Lancelot, *Holy Grail* 355
And fling him far into the *m* mere: *Pass. of Arthur* 205
Who toils across the *m* moonlit nights, *Lover's Tale i* 138
with such sudden deluges of light Into the *m* summer; „ 316
All the west And ev'n unto the *m* south was ribb'd „ 415
And slowly pacing to the *m* hall, „ *iv* 306
For the Spring and the *m* Summer sat *V. of Maeldune* 38
Middle (s) It was the *m* of the day. *Dying Swan* 8
And in the *m* of the green salt sea *Mine be the strength* 7
one great dwelling in the *m* of it; *Holy Grail* 574
All in the *m* of the rising moon: „ 636
Middle-day each was as dry as a cricket, with thirst in the *m-d* heat. *V. of Maeldune* 50
Mid-dome day hung From his *m-d* in Heaven's *Lover's Tale i* 66
Mid-forest that low lodge return'd, *M-f*, *Last Tournament* 489
black brooks Of the *m* heard me— *Lover's Tale ii* 12
Mid-heaven Grown on a magic oak-tree in *m-h*, *Last Tournament* 745
the sloping seas Hung in *m-h*, *Lover's Tale i* 4
Midmost (adj.) in the *m* heart of grief Thy passion clasps a secret joy: *In Mem. lxxxviii* 7
for save he be Fool to the *m* marrow of his bones, *Pelleas and E.* 258
Midmost (s) the *m* and the highest Was Arac: *Princess v* 256
And at the *m* charging, Prince Geraint *Geraint and E.* 85
Midnight At *m* the moon cometh, *Claribel* 13
Ask the sea At *m*, *Supp. Confessions* 126
At *m* the cock was crowing, *Oriana* 12
When *m* bells cease ringing suddenly, *D. of F. Women* 247
rode till *m* when the college lights *Princess i* 207
sitting on a hill Sees the midsummer, *m*, „ *iv* 575
Midnight (*continued*) but rode Ere *m* to her walls, *Pelleas and E.* 413
As rain of the midsummer *m* soft, *Lover's Tale i* 722
burnt at *m*, found at morn, *Locksley H., Sixty* 97
M—in no midsummer tune The breakers *Pref. Poem Broth. S.* 1
M—and joyless June gone by, „ 9
And thro' this *m* breaks the sun „ 21
forth again Among the wail of *m* winds, *Demeter and P.* 59
On a *m* in midwinter when all but the winds *The Dreamer* 1
Midnight-maned their arch'd necks, *m-m*, *Demeter and P.* 46
Midnoon It was the deep *m*: *Œnone* 92
Mid-November For as a leaf in *m-N* is *Marr. of Geraint* 611
Mid-ocean Than labour in the deep *m-o*, *Lotos-Eaters, C. S.* 127
whatever tempest mars *M-o*, spare thee, *In Mem. xvii* 14
one A vessel in *m-o*, her heaved prow Clambering, *Lover's Tale ii* 169
Mid-October To what it was in m-*O*, *Marr. of Geraint* 612
Midriff Sprang from the *m* of a prostrate king— *Aylmer's Field* 16
shake The *m* of despair with laughter, *Princess i* 201
Mid-sickness great knight in this *m-s* made *Lancelot and E.* 878
Midst Over the throne In the *m* of the hall; *The Mermaid* 22
And every marge enclosing in the *m* *Merlin and V.* 670
Midstream Whom Gareth met *m*: *Gareth and L.* 1041
Midsummer sitting on a hill Sees the *m*, midnight, *Princess iv* 575
As rain of the *m* midnight soft, *Lover's Tale i* 722
in the gleam of those *m-s* dawns, *The Ring* 183
as when an hour of cold Falls on the mountain in *m* snows, *Last Tournament* 228
Here one, black, mute *m* night I sat, Lonely, „ 612
Midnight—in no *m* tune The breakers lash the shores: *Pref. Poem. Broth. S.* 1
Mid-thigh-deep *m-t-d* in bulrushes and reed, *Gareth and L.* 810
Mid-warmth In the *m-w* of welcome and graspt *Geraint and E.* 280
Midway *m* down the side of that long hall *Gareth and L.* 404
Midwinter (adj.) And on this white *m* day— *To Master of B.* 9
Midwinter (s) On a midnight in *m* when all but the winds *The Dreamer* 1
Mien One her dark hair and lovesome *m*. *Beggar Maid* 12
then Kay, a man of *m* Wan-sallow *Gareth and L.* 452
But scarce of such majestic *m* *Freedom* 6
Might (*See also* **Mowt**) Losing his fire and active *m* *Eleänore* 104
with increasing *m* doth forward flee *Mine be the strength* 5
O Love, Love, Love! O withering *m*! *Fatima* 1
Deliver not the tasks of *m* To weakness, *Love thou thy land* 13
smote on all the chords with *m*; *Locksley Hall* 33
Toward that great year of equal *m's* and rights, *Princess iv* 74
That I could wing my will with *m* *In Mem. xli* 10
with *m* To scale the heaven's highest height, „ *cviii* 6
Her likewise would I worship an I *m*. *Balin and Balan* 185
m, Name, manhood, and a grace, but scantly thine, „ 376
In the mid *m* and flourish of his May, *Lancelot and E.* 554
His neighbour's make and *m*: *Pelleas and E.* 151
Strength of heart And *m* of limb, *Last Tournament* 198
Mightful And watch his *m* hand striking great blows *Marr. of Geraint* 95
Mightier Because things seen are *m* than things heard, *Enoch Arden* 766
And *m* of his hands with every blow, *Com. of Arthur* 110
Wave after wave, each *m* than the last, „ 379
Blow, for our Sun is *m* day by day! „ 498
So make thy manhood *m* day by day; *Gareth and L.* 92
we be *m* men than all In Arthur's court; *Balin and Balan* 33
Did *m* deeds than elsewise he had done, *Last Tournament* 680
One twofold *m* than the other was, *Lover's Tale i* 211
Never with *m* glory than when we had rear'd thee on high *Def. of Lucknow* 3
Has breathed a race of *m* mountaineers. *Montenegro* 14
Only That which made us, meant us to be *m* by and by, *Locksley H., Sixty* 209
When one might meet a *m* than himself; *Gareth and L.* 1350
withheld His older and his *m* from the lists, *Pelleas and E.* 160
Mightiest But Arthur *m* on the battle-field— *Gareth and L.* 496
and a fourth And of that four the *m*, „ 615
Then others, following these my *m* knights, *Guinevere* 489
Spain then the *m*, wealthiest realm on earth, *Columbus* 205
His isle, the *m* Ocean-power on earth, *The Fleet* 6
we needs must learn Which is our *m*, *Lancelot and E.* 63
Thou *m* and thou purest among men!' *Holy Grail* 426

Mightiest (*continued*) 'my friend, Our *m*, hath this Quest avail'd for thee?' 'Our *m*!' answer'd Lancelot, with a groan; *Holy Grail* 765
Yea, made our *m* madder than our least. „ 863
my right arm The *m* of my knights, *Guinevere* 430
Mighty As when a *m* people rejoice With shawms, *Dying Swan* 31
WHAT time the *m* moon was gathering light *Love and Death* 1
A *m* silver bugle hung, *L. of Shalott iii* 16
row Of cloisters, branch'd like *m* woods, *Palace of Art* 26
melting the *m* hearts Of captains and of kings. *D. of F. Women* 175
fragments of her *m* voice Came rolling on the wind. *Of old sat Freedom* 7
New Majesties of *m* States— *Love thou thy land* 60
Where lay the *m* bones of ancient men, *M. d'Arthur* 47
Stored in some treasure-house of *m* kings, „ 101
Which was an image of the *m* world; „ 235
Let this avail, just, dreadful, *m* God, *St. S. Stylites* 9
For the *m* wind arises, roaring seaward, and I go. *Locksley Hall* 194
To sleep thro' terms of *m* wars, *Day-Dm., L'Envoi* 9
The tavern-hours of *m* wits— *Will Water.* 191
and floods Of *m* mouth, we scudded fast, *The Voyage* 46
Soft fruitage, *m* nuts, and nourishing roots; *Enoch Arden* 555
And *m* courteous in the main— *Aylmer's Field* 121
Which things appear the work of *m* Gods. *Lucretius* 102
I wish I were Some *m* poetess, *Princess, Pro.* 132
Then those eight *m* daughters of the plough „ *iv* 550
To the noise of the mourning of a *m* nation, *Ode on Well.* 4
M Seaman, this is he Was great by land „ 83
M Seaman, tender and true, „ 134
thou shalt be the *m* one yet! *Boädicea* 40
When *m* Love would cleave in twain *In Mem. xxv* 10
To mould a *m* state's decrees, „ *lxiv* 11
The *m* hopes that make us men. „ *lxxxv* 60
I seem as nothing in the *m* world, *Com. of Arthur* 87
Seeing the *m* swarm about their walls, „ 200
'Blow, for our Sun is *m* in his May! „ 497
And all these four be fools, but *m* men, *Gareth and L.* 643
And *m* thro' thy meats and drinks am I, (repeat) „ 650, 862
For here be *m* men to joust with, „ 880
four strokes they struck With sword, and these were *m*; „ 1043
he loosed a *m* purse, Hung at his belt, *Geraint and E.* 22
But like a *m* patron, satisfied „ 644
letting her left hand Droop from his *m* shoulder, *Merlin and V.* 243
To cross our *m* Lancelot in his loves! *Lancelot and E.* 688
His battle-writhen arms and *m* hands „ 812
'O brother, had you known our *m* hall, *Holy Grail* 225
Climbs to the *m* hall that Merlin built. „ 231
'And I rode on and found a *m* hill, „ 421
Where lay the *m* bones of ancient men, *Pass. of Arthur* 215
Stored in some treasure-house of *m* kings, „ 269
Framing the *m* landscape to the west, *Lover's Tale i* 406
shower'd down Rays of a *m* circle, „ 418
m gyres Rapid and vast, of hissing spray wind-driven „ *ii* 197
And bearing high in arms the *m* babe, „ *iv* 295
And the men that were *m* of tongue *V. of Maeldune* 23
M the Mercian, Hard was his hand-play, *Batt. of Brunanburh* 43
Thrice from the dyke he sent his *m* shout, *Achilles over the T.* 30
as mellow and deep As a psalm by a *m* master *The Wreck* 53
We founded many a *m* state; *Hands all Round* 30
M the Wizard Who found me at sunrise *Merlin and the G.* 11
Bards, that the *m* Muses have raised *Parnassus* 2
You, the *m*, the Fortunate, *On Jub. Q. Victoria* 55
For thro' the Magic Of Him the *M*, *Merlin and the G.* 114
Mighty-mouth'd O *m-m* inventor of harmonies, *Milton* 1
Mignonette A long green box of *m*, *Miller's D.* 83
parlour-window and the box of *m*. *May Queen, N. Y's. E.* 48
But miss'd the *m* of Vivian-place, *Princess, Pro.* 165
Milan O *M*, O the chanting quires, *The Daisy* 57
Mild Throbbing in *m* unrest holds him beneath *Leonine Eleg.* 12
beheld Thy *m* deep eyes upraised, *Supp. Confessions* 74
I have not lack'd thy *m* reproof, *My life is full* 4
'His lips are very *m* and meek: *Two Voices* 250
With measured footfall firm and *m*, „ 413
She with a subtle smile in her *m* eyes, *Œnone* 184
one hand grasp'd The *m* bull's golden horn. *Palace of Art* 120
Mild (*continued*) Beside him Shakespeare bland and *m*; *Palace of Art* 134
by slow prudence to make *m* A rugged people, *Ulysses* 36
My mother was as *m* as any saint, *Princess i* 22
meek Seem'd the full lips, and *m* the luminous eyes, „ *vii* 226
The stern were *m* when thou wert by, *In Mem. cx* 9
A higher hand must make her *m*, „ *cxiv* 17
With difficulty in *m* obedience Driving them on: *Geraint and E.* 104
Fearing the *m* face of the blameless King, „ 812
Who, with *m* heat of holy oratory, „ 866
However *m* he seems at home, nor cares *Lancelot and E.* 311
Milder *M* than any mother to a sick child, „ 858
with flame *M* and purer. *Lover's Tale i* 323
Sunn'd with a summer of *m* heat. *To Prof. Jebb* 8
Mildew'd Who had *m* in their thousands, *Aylmer's Field* 383
Mild-eyed The *m-e* melancholy Lotos-eaters *Lotos-Eaters* 27
Mild-minded the influence of *m-m* melancholy; *Lotos-Eaters, C. S.* 64
Mile A *m* beneath the cedar-wood. *Eleänore* 8
Keeps his blue waters fresh for many a *m*. *Mine be the strength* 8
Ten *m's* to northward of the narrow port *Enoch Arden* 102
the long laborious *m's* Of Palace; *Ode Inter. Exhib.* 11
Flash for a million *m's*. *Window, Marr. Morn.* 24
I was walking a *m*, More than a *m* *Maud I ix* 1
A *m* beneath the forest, *Balin and Balan* 12
race thro' many a *m* Of dense and open, „ 423
province with a hundred *m's* of coast, (repeat) *Merlin and V.* 588, 647
But for a *m* all round was open space, *Pelleas and E.* 28
flash a million *m's* a day. *Locksley H., Sixty* 204
Glows in the blue of fifty *m's* away. *Roses on the T.* 8
Milk (*See also* **Wolf's-milk**) I fed you with the *m* of every Muse; *Princess iv* 295
The *m* that bubbled in the pail, *In Mem. lxxxix* 51
clean as blood of babes, as white as *m*: *Merlin and V.* 344
Seethed like the kid in its own mother's *m*! „ 869
m From burning spurge, honey from hornet-combs, *Last Tournament* 356
land of promise flowing with the *m* And honey *Lover's Tale i* 334
Hafe a pint o' *m* runs out *Village Wife* 4
the babe Will suck in with his *m* hereafter— *Columbus* 38
Who live on *m* and meal and grass; *To E. Fitzgerald* 13
M for my sweet-arts, Bess! *Spinster's S's.* 1
thou'd not 'a been worth thy *m*, „ 54
Mew! mew!—Bess wi' the *m*! „ 113
Innocence seethed in her mother's *m*, *Vastness* 9
nurse my children on the *m* of Truth, *Akbar's Dream* 162
Milk-bloom One long *m-b* on the tree; *Maud I xxii* 46
Milkier And *m* every milky sail *In Mem. cxv* 11
Milking The milkmaid left her *m*, and fell *Holy Grail* 406
Milking-maid burnt the grange, nor buss'd the *m-m*, *Princess v* 222
Milkmaid When merry *m's* click the latch, *The Owl i* 8
The *m* left her milking, and fell down *Holy Grail* 406
Milk-white opening out his *m-w* palm Disclosed a fruit *Œnone* 65
Now droops the *m* peacock like a ghost, *Princess vii* 180
Ah Maud, you *m* fawn, you are all unmeet for a wife. *Maud I iv* 57
There with her *m* arms and shadowy hair *Guinevere* 416
Milky like morning doves That sun their *m* bosoms *Princess ii* 103
The soft and *m* rabble of womankind, „ *vi* 309
if below the *m* steep Some ship of battle *To F. D. Maurice* 25
And milkier every *m* sail On winding stream *In Mem. cxv* 11
Struck up and lived along the *m* roofs; *Lancelot and E.* 409
either *m* arm Red-rent with hooks of bramble, *Holy Grail* 210
Old *m* fables of the wolf and sheep, *Pelleas and E.* 196
Milky-bell'd A *m-b* amaryllis blew. *The Daisy* 16
Milky-way this, a *m-w* on earth, *Aylmer's Field* 160
Milky-white Taller than all his fellows, *m-w*, *Marr. of Geraint* 150
Mill Thro' quiet meadows round the *m*, *Miller's D.* 98
The deep brook groan'd beneath the *m*; „ 113
To yon old *m* across the wolds; „ 240
long street climbs to one tall-tower'd *m*; *Enoch Arden* 5
narrow street that clamber'd toward the *m*. „ 60
flour From his tall *m* that whistled on the waste. „ 343
Lords of his house and of his *m* were they; „ 351
Blanch'd with his *m*, they found; „ 367
climbing street, the *m*, the leafy lanes, „ 607
an' I runs oop to the *m*; *N. Farmer, N. S.* 54
'ground in yonder social *m* We rub each other's angles down, *In Mem. lxxxix* 39

Mind (s) (*continued*) those maidens with one *m* Bewail'd their lot; *In Mem. ciii* 45
Ring out the grief that saps the *m*, „ *cvi* 9
And native growth of noble *m*; „ *cxi* 16
For she is earthly of the *m*, „ *cxiv* 21
these are the days of advance, the works of the men of *m*, *Maud I i* 25
Be still, for you only trouble the *m* „ *v* 20
cut off from the *m* The bitter springs of anger and fear; „ *x* 48
The fancy flatter'd my *m*, „ *xiv* 23
So dark a *m* within me dwells, „ *xv* 1
To the faults of his heart and *m*, „ *xix* 68
Strange, that the *m*, when fraught With a passion „ *II ii* 58
for she never speaks her *m*, „ *v* 67
awaked, as it seems, to the better *m*; „ *III vi* 56
inheritance Of such a life, a heart, a *m* as thine, *Ded. of Idylls* 33
but all brave, all of one *m* with him; *Com. of Arthur* 255
in my *m* I hear A cry from out the dawning „ 332
Ranging and ringing thro' the *m's* of men, „ 416
Across her *m*, and bowing over him, *Marr. of Grraint* 84
And ever in her *m* she cast about *Geraint and E.* 46
of one *m* and all right-honest friends! „ 484
with her *m* all full of what had chanced, „ 778
My *m* involved yourself the nearest thing *Merlin and V.* 300
since he kept his *m* on one sole aim, „ 626
densest condensation, hard To *m* and eye; „ 679
To sleek her ruffled peace of *m*, „ 899
The shape and colour of a *m* and life, *Lancelot and E.* 335
he turn'd Her counsel up and down within his *m*, „ 369
Lancelot look'd and was perplext in *m*, „ 838
So cannot speak my *m*. An end to this! „ 1222
made him hers, and laid her *m* On him, *Holy Grail* 164
Came like a driving gloom across my *m*. „ 370
since her *m* was bent On hearing, *Pelleas and E.* 114
Went wandering somewhere darkling in his *m*. *Last Tournament* 457
loyal nature, and of noble *m*.' *Guinevere* 336
Her memory from old habit of the *m* „ 379
With whom he dwelt, new faces, other *m's*. *Pass. of Arthur* 5
dividing the swift *m*, In act to throw: „ 228
Among new men, strange faces, other *m's*.' „ 406
(For all my *m* is clouded with a doubt)— „ 426
Like to a quiet *m* in the loud world, *Lover's Tale i* 7
sometimes on the horizon of the *m* Lies folded, „ 49
daylight of your *m's* But cloud and smoke, „ 296
And all the maiden empire of her *m*, „ 589
She deem'd I wore a brother's *m*: „ 741
whether the *m*, With some revenge— „ *ii* 126
born Not from believing *m*, but shatter'd nerve, „ *iv* 105
This love is of the brain, the *m*, the soul: „ 156
But arter I chaänged my *m*, *North. Cobbler* 105
he had seen it and made up his *m*, *In the Child. Hosp.* 16
his *m*, So quick, so capable in soldiership, *Sir J. Oldcastle* 74
When he clothed a naked *m* with the wisdom *The Wreck* 65
I was the lonely slave of an often-wandering *m*; „ 130
the blasphemy to *my m* lies all in the way *Despair* 112
'What Power? aught akin to *M*, The *m* *Ancient Sage* 78
thin *m's*, who creep from thought to thought, „ 103
He withers marrow and *m*; „ 120
the world is hard, and harsh of *m*, *The Flight* 101
for Molly was out of her *m*. *Tomorrow* 6
nurse of ailing body and *m*, *Locksley H., Sixty* 51
kings of men in utter nobleness of *m*, „ 122
lustier body, larger *m*? „ 164
Man or *M* that sees a shadow of the planner or the plan? „ 196
Universal Nature moved by Universal *M*; *To Virgil* 22
How long thine ever-growing *m* *Freedom* 33
died in the doing it, flesh without *m*; *Vastness* 27
When the *m* is failing! *Forlorn* 36
For lowly *m's* were madden'd to the height *To Mary Boyle* 33
Larger and fuller, like the human *m*! *Prog. of Spring* 112
of the *m* Mine; worse, cold, calculated. *Romney's R.* 151
How subtle at tierce and quart of *m* with *m*, *In Mem. W. G. Ward* 5
Now I'll gie tha a bit o' my *m* *Church-warden, etc.* 21
M's on this round earth of ours *Poets and Critics* 3

Mind (verb) (*See also* **Moind**) I *m* him coming down the street; *Enoch Arden* 847
m us of the time When we made bricks in Egypt. *Princess iv* 127
To *m* me of the secret vow I made *Columbus* 92
fur I *m* tha sa well, *Church-warden, etc.* 23
But I *m* when i' Howlaby beck won daäy „ 27
Minded *See* **Cheerful-minded, Liberal-minded, Man-minded, Mild-minded, Myriad-minded**
Mindful Guinevere, not *m* of his face *Marr. of Geraint* 191
And *m* of her small and cruel hand, *Pelleas and E.* 201
Mindless One truth will damn me with the *m* mob, *Romney's R.* 120
Mind-mist yourself the nearest thing In that *m-m*: *Merlin and V.* 301
Mine (*See also* **Gold-mine**) Or labour'd *m* undrainable of ore. *Œnone* 115
Old, and a *m* of memories— *Aylmer's Field* 10
To buy strange shares in some Peruvian *m*. *Sea Dreams* 15
there is no such *m*, None; but a gulf of ruin, „ 78
she said, 'by working in the *m's*:' „ 114
Secrets of the sullen *m*, *Ode Inter. Exhib.* 16
till he crept from a gutted *m* *Maud I x* 9
A league of mountain full of golden *m's*, *Merlin and V.* 587
Made proffer of the league of golden *m's*, „ 646
M? yes, a *m*! Countermine! *Def. of Lucknow* 25
but the foe sprung his *m* many times, „ 31
in a moment two *m's* by the enemy sprung „ 54
Ever the *m* and assault, our sallies, „ 75
All but free leave for all to work the *m's*, *Columbus* 133
Mount and *m*, and primal wood; *Open. I. and C. Exhib.* 6
Mingle Thought and motion *m*, *M* ever. *Eleänore* 60
To *m* with the human race, *Of old sat Freedom* 10
And star-like *m's* with the stars. *Sir Galahad* 48
M madness, *m* scorn! *Vision of Sin* 204
Pass, and *m* with your likes. *Princess vi* 341
To *m* with the bounding main: *In Mem. xi* 12
And *m's* all without a plan? „ *xvi* 20
And *m* all the world with thee. „ *cxxix* 12
and *m* with our folk; *Holy Grail* 549
wherefore shouldst thou care to *m* with it, *Last Tournament* 105
m with your rites; Pray and be pray'd for; *Guinevere* 680
soul twines and *m's* with the growths *Lover's Tale i* 132
God must *m* with the game: *Locksley H., Sixty* 271
let the stormy moment fly and *m* with the Past. „ 279
I would not *m* with their feasts; *Demeter and P.* 103
Mingled (*See also* **Poppy-mingled, Scarlet-mingled**)
Ceasing not, *m*, unrepress'd, *Arabian Nights* 74
Desiring what is *m* with past years, *D. of F. Women* 282
a Rose In roses, *m* with her fragrant toil, *Gardener's D.* 143
And ever as he *m* with the crew, *Enoch Arden* 643
this, at times, she *m* with his drink, *Lucretius* 18
Will rank you nobly, *m* up with me. *Princess ii* 46
The sole men to be *m* with our cause, „ *v* 411
m with the haze And made it thicker; *Com. of Arthur* 434
And *m* with the spearmen: *Geraint and E.* 599
bank Of maiden snow *m* with sparks of fire. *Last Tournament* 149
m with dim cries Far in the moonlit haze *Pass. of Arthur* 41
m with the famous kings of old, *Tiresias* 171
will the glory of Kapiolani be *m* *Kapiolani* 18
this life of *m* pains And joys to me, *To Mary Boyle* 49
Miniature A *m* of loveliness, *Gardener's D.* 12
I remember how you kiss'd the *m* *Locksley H., Sixty* 12
'The books, the *m*, the lace are hers, *The Ring* 288
Minion A downward crescent of her *m* mouth, *Aylmer's Field* 533
Minion-knight had overthrown Her *m-k's*, *Pelleas and E.* 235
Minister Who may *m* to thee? Summer herself should *m* *Eleänore* 31
Ministering Friday fare was Enoch's *m*. *Enoch Arden* 100
There the good mother's kindly *m*, *Lover's Tale iv* 92
everywhere Low voices with the *m* hand *Princess vii* 21
Ministration for the power of *m* in her, *Guinevere* 694
Ministries tender *m* Of female hands and hospitality.' *Princess vi* 72
Minneth from Aroer On Arnon unto *M*.' *D. of F. Women* 239
Minnie *M* and Winnie Slept in a shell. *Minnie and Winnie* 1
Minnow And see the *m's* everywhere *Miller's D.* 51
Minster (adj.) windy clanging of the *m* clock; *Gardener's D.* 38
south-breeze around thee blow The sound of *m* bells. *Talking Oak* 272

Mix (*continued*) while the fires of Hell *M* with his hearth : *Princess v* 455
think that you might *m* his draught with death, „ *vi* 277
And *m* the seasons and the golden hours ; *Ode Inter. Exhib.* 36
' The sands and yeasty surges *m* *Sailor Boy* 9
And *m* with hollow masks of night ; *In Mem. lxx* 4
O tell me where the senses *m*, „ *lxxxviii* 3
They *m* in one another's arms „ *cii* 23
May she *m* With men and prosper ! „ *cxiv* 2
M not memory with doubt, *Maud II iv* 57
Of those who *m* all odour to the Gods *Tiresias* 184
To *m* with what he plow'd ; *Ancient Sage* 145
senses break away To *m* with ancient Night.' „ 153
Will *m* with love for you and yours. *To Marq. of Dufferin* 52
That I might *m* with men, and hear their words *Prog. of Spring* 82
one of those Who *m* the wines of heresy *Akbar's Dream* 174
M me this Zone with that ! *Mechanophilus* 8

Mix'd-Mixt The elements were kindlier *mix'd.' Two Voices* 228
She *mix'd* her ancient blood with shame. *The Sisters* 8
Mix'd with the knightly growth that fringed his lips. *M. d'Arthur* 220
mix'd with shadows of the common ground ! *Gardener's D.* 135
A welcome *mix'd* with sighs. *Talking Oak* 212
lights of sunset and of sunrise *mix'd* *Love and Duty* 72
In mosses *mixt* with violet *Sir L. and Q. G.* 30
Mix'd with cunning sparks of hell. *Vision of Sin* 114
rain of heaven, *mixt* Upon their faces, *Aylmer's Field* 429
on those cliffs Broke, *mixt* with awful light *Sea Dreams* 215
on the crowd Broke, *mixt* with awful light, „ 235
cry Which *mixt* with little Margaret's, „ 246
And hands they *mixt*, and yell'd *Lucretius* 56
And *mixt* with these, a lady, *Princess, Pro.* 32
mixt with inmost terms Of art and science : „ *ii* 446
we *mixt* with those Six hundred maidens „ 471
our dreams ; perhaps he *mixt* with them : „ *iii* 220
Part stumbled *mixt* with floundering horses. „ *v* 498
like night and evening *mixt* Their dark and gray, „ *vi* 131
And *mixt*, as life is *mixt* with pain, *Ode Inter. Exhib.* 27
Mixt with myrtle and clad with vine, *The Islet* 19
No—*mixt* with all this mystic frame, *In Mem. lxxviii* 18
He *mixt* in all our simple sports ; „ *lxxxix* 10
Mixt their dim lights, like life and death, „ *xcv* 63
Tho' *mix'd* with God and Nature thou, „ *cxxx* 11
a world in which I have hardly *mixt*, *Maud I vi* 76
Mixt with kisses sweeter sweeter „ *II iv* 9
mix'd my breath With a loyal people shouting „ *III vi* 34
wildly fly, *Mixt* with the flyers. *Geraint and E.* 483
she *mixt* Her fancies with the sallow-rifted glooms *Lancelot and E.* 1001
brambles *mixt* And overgrowing them, *Pelleas and E.* 422
Nor with them *mix'd*, nor told her name, *Guinevere* 148
Mix'd with the knightly growth that fringed his lips. *Pass. of Arthur* 388
Mixt with the gorgeous west the lighthouse shone, *Lover's Tale i* 60
and these *Mixt* with her own, because the fierce beast *Tiresias* 151
And *mixt* the dream of classic times „ 194
past and future *mix'd* in Heaven *The Ring* 186
Black with bridal favours *mixt* ! *Forlorn* 69
mixt with the great Sphere-music of stars *Parnassus* 8
mixt herself with *him* and past in fire. *Death of Œnone* 106

Mixen cast it on the *m* that it die.' *Marr. of Geraint* 672

Mixing Ice with the warm blood *m* ; *All Things will Die* 33
Which *m* with the infant's blood, *Supp. Confessions* 61
He *m* with his proper sphere, *In Mem. lx* 5

Mixt *See* **Mix'd**

Mizpeh she went along From *M's* tower'd gate *D. of F. Women* 199

Mnemosyne That claspt the feet of a *M*, *Princess iv* 269

Moab water *M* saw Come round by the East, *Last Tournament* 482

Moan (s) (*See also* **Moän**) Heard the war *m* along the distant sea, *Buonaparte* 10
But ' Ave Mary,' made she *m*, *Mariana in the S.* 9
And ' Ave Mary,' was her *m*, „ 21
' Is this the form,' she made her *m*, „ 33
She breathed in sleep a lower *m*, „ 45
She whisper'd, with a stifled *m* „ 57
' The day to night,' she made her *m*, „ 81
And weeping then she made her *m*, „ 93

Moan (s) (*continued*) Nor sold his heart to idle *m's*, *Two Voices* 221
In firry woodlands making *m* ; *Miller's D.* 42
hears the low *M* of an unknown sea ; *Palace of Art* 280
And make perpetual *m*, *Lotos-Eaters, C. S.* 17
And the low *m* of leaden-colour'd seas. *Enoch Arden* 612
The *m* of doves in immemorial elms, *Princess vii* 221
m of an enemy massacred, *Boädicea* 25
Is that enchanted *m* only the swell *Maud I xviii* 62
Crawl'd slowly with low *m's* to where he lay, *Balin and Balan* 592
And to all other ladies, I make *m* : *Lancelot and E.* 1279
So made his *m*, and, darkness falling, *Pelleas and E.* 213
M's of the dying, and voices of the dead. *Pass. of Arthur* 117
But when that *m* had past for evermore, „ 441
mask of Hate, who lives on others' *m's*. *Lover's Tale i* 775
From under rose a muffled *m* of floods ; *Prog. of Spring* 70
and the *m* of my waves I whirl, *The Dreamer* 13
For *m's* will have grown sphere-music „ 29

Moän (s) I 'eärd 'er a maäkin' 'er *m*, *Spinster's S's.* 115

Moan (verb) what is life, that we should *m* ? *May Queen, Con.* 56
the deep *M's* round with many voices. *Ulysses* 56
Nor ever lowest roll of thunder *m's*, *Lucretius* 108
or bits of roasting ox *M* round the spit— „ 132
' Not such as *m's* about the retrospect, *Princess iv* 85
And *m* and sink to their rest. *Voice and the P.* 16
I hear the dead at midday *m*, *Maud I vi* 70
heard the Spirits of the waste and weald *M* as she fled, or thought she heard them *m* : *Guinevere* 130
and the sea that 'ill *m* like a man ? *Rizpah* 72
water began to heave and the weather to *m*, *The Revenge* 113
ask'd the waves that *m* about the world *Demeter and P.* 64
' We know not, and we know not why we *m*.' „ 67
M to myself ' one plunge— *Charity* 16

Moan'd the passion in her *m* reply *Enoch Arden* 286
She heard, she moved, She *m*, *Princess v* 72
And ever and aye the Priesthood *m*, *The Victim* 23
Weighted it down, but in himself he *m* : *Balin and Balan* 225
he kiss'd it, *m* and spake ; „ 598
All that had chanced, and Balan *m* again. „ 604
and madden'd with himself and *m* : *Pelleas and E.* 460
And in herself she *m* ' Too late, too late ! ' *Guinevere* 131
' O, you warm heart,' he *m*, *Lover's Tale iv* 76
' O Stephen,' I *m*, ' I am coming to thee *The Wreck* 132
m, I am fitter for my bed, or for my grave, *The Ring* 432
and *m* ' Œnone, *my* Œnone, *Death of Œnone* 28

Moaneth Wherefore he *m* thus, *Supp. Confessions* 132

Moänin' an' *m* an' naggin' ageän ; *Owd Roä* 108

Moaning (adj. and part.) (*See also* **Ever-moaning, Moänin'**) Nor, *m*, household shelter crave *Two Voices* 260
And circle *m* in the air : *In Mem. xii* 15
Uther died himself, *M* and wailing for an heir *Com. of Arthur* 207
Uther in Tintagil past away *M* and wailing for an heir, „ 368
M ' My violences, my violences ! ' *Balin and Balan* 435
M and calling out of other lands, *Merlin and V.* 962
The phantom circle of a *m* sea. *Pass. of Arthur* 87
stones Strewn in the entry of the *m* cave ; *Lover's Tale iii* 2
But I could wish yon *m* sea would rise *The Flight* 11
I found myself *m* again *The Wreck* 134
Are there thunders *m* in the distance ? *On Jub. Q. Victoria* 66
M your losses, O Earth, *The Dreamer* 17

Moaning (s) Yes, as your *m's* witness, *Aylmer's Field* 749
The *m's* of the homeless sea, *In Mem. xxxv* 9
glooms Of evening, and the *m's* of the wind. *Lancelot and E.* 1003
Heard in his tent the *m's* of the King : *Pass. of Arthur* 8
The *m* of the woman and the child, *Lover's Tale i* 520
The *m's* in the forest, the loud brook, „ *ii* 114
do ye make your *m* for my child ? ' *Demeter and P.* 65
And may there be no *m* of the bar, *Crossing the Bar* 3

Moat My malice is no deeper than a *m*, *Geraint and E.* 340

Moated Upon the lonely *m* grange. *Mariana* 8
About the lonely *m* grange. „ 32

Mob (s) Confused by brainless *m's* *Ode on Well.* 153
m's million feet Will kick you from your place, *The Fleet* 18
One truth will damn me with the mindless *m*, *Romney's R.* 120

Mob (verb) From my fixt height to *m* me up *Princess vi* 308

Molly (*continued*) when *M* 'd put out the light, *Spinster's S's.* 97
what ha maäde our *M* sa laäte ? „ 113
Molly Magee (*See also* **Molly**) They call'd her *M M.* *Tomorrow* 4
M M wid her batchelor, Danny O'Roon— „ 10
M M kem flyin' acrass me, as light as a lark, „ 21
M M, wid the red o' the rose an' the white o' the May, „ 31
'Ud 'a shot his own sowl dead for a kiss of ye, *M M.* „ 40
' Div ye know him, *M M* ? ' „ 78
Danny O'Roon wid his ould woman, *M M.* „ 88
tell thim in Hiven about *M M* an' her Danny O'Roon, „ 92
Moloch red-hot palms of a *M* of Tyre, *The Dawn* 2
Molowny an' Father *M* he tuk her in han', *Tomorrow* 55
Molten *m* on the waste Becomes a cloud : *Princess iv* 72
Her noble heart was *m* in her breast ; „ *vi* 119
Athwart a plane of *m* glass, *In Mem. xv* 11
The rocket *m* into flakes Of crimson „ *xcviii* 31
And *m* up, and roar in flood ; „ *cxxvii* 13
And *m* down in mere uxoriousness. *Marr. of Geraint* 60
m into all The beautiful in Past of act or place, *Lover's Tale i* 134
Diffused and *m* into flaky cloud. „ 641
m Into adulterous living, *Sir J. Oldcastle* 108
Moly propt on beds of amaranth and *m*, *Lotos-Eaters, C. S.* 88
Moment brought, At the *m* of thy birth, *Eleänore* 15
in a *m* I would pierce The blackest files *Kate* 25
A *m* came the tenderness of tears, *The form, the form* 9
flower of each, those *m's* when we met, *Edwin Morris* 69
One earnest, earnest *m* upon mine, *Love and Duty* 37
Every *m*, lightly shaken, ran itself *Locksley Hall* 32
Changed every *m* as we flew. *The Voyage* 28
Glow'd for a *m* as we past. „ 48
Every *m* dies a man, Every *m* one is born. *Vision of Sin* 97, 121
when the last of those last *m's* came, *Enoch Arden* 217
stood on deck Waving, the *m* and the vessel past. „ 244
Paused for a *m* at an inner door, „ 278
And dwelt a *m* on his kindly face, „ 326
She spoke ; and in one *m* as it were, „ 452
Which in one *m*, like the blast of doom, „ 769
Enoch hung A *m* on her words, „ 873
our pride Looks only for a *m* whole and sound ; *Aylmer's Field* 2
Between his palms a *m* up and down— „ 259
That night, that *m*, when she named „ 581
The fountain of the *m*, playing, *Princess, Pro.* 61
and a *m*, and once more The trumpet, „ *v* 487
on her foot she hung A *m*, and she heard, „ *vii* 80
Are mine for the *m* stronger ? *Spiteful Letter* 10
I last but a *m* longer. „ 12
I blush to belaud myself a *m*— *Hendecasyllabics* 18
In a *m* we shall meet ; *Maud II iv* 39
Courteous or bestial from the *m*, *Gareth and L.* 631
Who stood a *m*, ere his horse was brought, „ 934
But when they closed—in a *m*— „ 1222
in a *m* heard them pass like wolves Howling ; *Balin and Balan* 407
Then, in one *m*, she put forth the charm *Merlin and V.* 967
every *m* glanced His silver arms and gloom'd : *Holy Grail* 492
in a *m* when they blazed again Opening, „ 523
In *m's* when he feels he cannot die, „ 916
withheld A *m* from the vermin *Pelleas and E.* 285
Rolling his eyes, a *m* stood, „ 581
so forgot herself A *m*, and her cares ; *Last Tournament* 26
A *m*, ere the onward whirlwind shatter it, *Lover's Tale i* 451
Which seeming for the *m* due to death, „ 508
wealth Flash'd from me in a *m* and I fell „ 669
This custom——' Pausing here a *m*, „ *iv* 237
The passionate *m* would not suffer that— „ 356
fly them for a *m* to fight with them again. *The Revenge* 9
But never a *m* ceased the fight of the one and the fifty-three. „ 57
and for a face Gone in a *m*—strange. *Sisters (E. and E.)* 94
Roar upon roar in a *m* two mines by the enemy sprung *Def. of Lucknow* 54
and never a *m* for grief, „ 89
I suffer all as much As they do—for the *m*. *Columbus* 218
I thought of the child for a *m*, *The Wreck* 84
bear with an hour of torture, a *m* of pain, *Despair* 81
Gazing for one pensive *m* *Locksley H., Sixty* 32
Moment (*continued*) *m* fly and mingle with the Past. *Locksley H., Sixty* 279
All in a *m* follow'd with force *Heavy Brigade* 20
to maintain The day against the *m*, *To Duke of Argyll* 6
Made every *m* of her after life A virgin victim *The Ring* 220
Gleam'd for a *m* in her own on earth. „ 297
Or lost the *m* of their past on earth, „ 464
Shall flash thro' one another in a *m* *Happy* 40
See, I sinn'd but for a *m*. „ 85
held you at that *m* even dearer than before ; „ 90
still'd it for the *m* with a song *Romney's R.* 84
For one *m* afterward A silence follow'd *St. Telemachus* 64
then and there he was crush'd in a *m* and died, *Charity* 21
Let your reforms for a *m* go ! *Riflemen form!* 15
Momentary Hated him with a *m* hate. *Aylmer's Field* 211
that hour perhaps Is not so far when *m* man *Lucretius* 253
A *m* likeness of the King : *Com. of Arthur* 271
Brought down a *m* brow. *Gareth and L.* 653
That less than *m* thunder-sketch *Sisters (E. and E.)* 99
Each poor pale cheek a *m* rose— *The Ring* 315
when the *m* gloom, Made by the noonday blaze *St. Telemachus* 49
Mona WHILE about the shore of *M* *Boädicea* 1
Monaco city Of little *M*, basking, glow'd. *The Daisy* 8
Monarch *m* in their woodland rhyme. *Akbar's D., Hymn* 6
Monday saw the man—on *M*, was it ?— *Walk. to the Mail* 30
' O' *M* mornin' ' says he ; *Tomorrow* 17
Money (*See also* **Mooney, Munney, Munny**) and not a room For love or *m*. *Audley Court* 2
m can be repaid ; Not kindness such as yours.' *Enoch Arden* 320
Nor could he understand how *m* breeds, *The Brook* 6
An' 'e bowt owd *m*, es wouldn't goä, *Village Wife* 49
The poor man's *m* gone to fat the friar. *Sir J. Oldcastle* 150
M—my hire—*his m*— *Charity* 19
Monk (*See also* **Fellow-monk**) ' Old Summers, when the *m* was fat, *Talking Oak* 41
m and nun, ye scorn the world's desire, *Balin and Balan* 445
The *m* Ambrosius question'd Percivale : *Holy Grail* 17
To whom the *m* : ' The Holy Grail !—I trust „ 37
' Nay, *m* ! what phantom ? ' answer'd Percivale. „ 45
the *m* : ' From our old books I know That Joseph „ 59
Then spake the *m* Ambrosius, asking him, „ 203
Then said the *m*, ' Poor men, when yule is cold, „ 613
the *m* : ' And I remember now That pelican on the casque : „ 699
Monkeries absolution-sellers, *m* And nunneries, *Sir J. Oldcastle* 93
Monkey-spite No lewdness, narrowing envy, *m-s*, *Lucretius* 211
Monkish save ye fear The *m* manhood, *Merlin and V.* 35
Monmouth (Harry of) *See* **Harry of Monmouth**
Monotonous *M* and hollow like a Ghost's *Guinevere* 420
For one *m* fancy madden'd her, *The Ring* 404
Monster wallowing *m* spouted his foam-fountains *Lotos-Eaters, C. S.* 107
bought Quaint *m's* for the market of those times, *Enoch Arden* 539
m lays His vast and filthy hands upon my will, *Lucretius* 219
Seven-headed *m's* only made to kill Time *Princess, Pro.* 204
then the *m*, then the man ; Tattoo'd or woaded, „ *ii* 119
' No doubt we seem a kind of *m* to you ; „ *iii* 276
These *m's* blazon'd what they were, „ *iv* 345
I loom to her Three times a *m* : „ *v* 131
A *m* then, a dream, A discord. *In Mem. lvi* 21
The last a *m* unsubduable Of any save of him *Gareth and L.* 858
M ! O Prince, I went for Lancelot first, „ 1343
advanced The *m*, and then paused, „ 1385
Monstrous In bed like *m* apes they crush'd my chest : *St. S. Stylites* 174
Betwixt the *m* horns of elk and deer, *Princess, Pro.* 23
Those *m* males that carve the living hound, „ *iii* 310
and the wild figtree split Their *m* idols, „ *iv* 80
The Princess with her *m* woman-guard, „ 562
and leave The *m* ledges there to slope, „ *vii* 212
Would lisp in honey'd whispers of this *m* fraud ! *Third of Feb.* 36
Sown in a wrinkle of the *m* hill, *Will* 19
A *m* eft was of old the Lord and Master of Earth, *Maud I iv* 31
Horrible, hateful, *m*, not to be told ; „ *III vi* 41
m ivy-stems Claspt the gray walls *Marr. of Geraint* 322
So lean his eyes were *m* ; *Merlin and V.* 624

Monstrous (*continued*) *m* blasphemies, Sweat, writhings, anguish, *Pass. of Arthur* 114
Hard Romans brawling of their *m* games ; *St. Telemachus* 40
Monte Rosa how phantom-fair, Was *M R*, *The Daisy* 66
Montfort (Edith) *See* **Edith, Edith Montfort**
Month (*See also* **Seven-months'**) Each *m* is various to present The world *Two Voices* 74
Link'd *m* to *m* with such a chain Of knitted purport, „ 167
Whole weeks and *m's*, and early and late, *The Sisters* 10
Earn well the thrifty *m's*, *Love thou thy land* 95
Consider, William : take a *m* to think, *Dora* 29
before The *m* was out he left his father's house, „ 37
Above the river, and, but a *m* ago, *Walk. to the Mail* 2
in one *m* They wedded her to sixty thousand pounds, *Edwin Morris* 125
and oft I fall, Maybe for *m's*, *St. S. Stylites* 103
I must work thro' *m's* of toil, *Amphion* 97
Each *m*, a birth-day coming on, *Will Water.* 93
Came floating on for many a *m* and year, *Vision of Sin* 54
a *m*—Give her a *m*—she knew that she was bound—A *m*— *Enoch Arden* 461
So *m* by *m* the noise about their doors, *Aylmer's Field* 488
face to face With twenty *m's* of silence, „ 567
In one *m*, Thro' weary and yet ever wearier hours, „ 827
Came, with a *m's* leave given them, *Sea Dreams* 6
ere the silver sickle of that *m* *Princess i* 101
' A *m* hence, a *m* hence. *Window, When* 7
The all-assuming *m's* and years *In Mem. lxxxv* 67
And tho' the *m's*, revolving near, „ *xcii* 11
As nine *m's* go to the shaping an infant *Maud I iv* 34
In another *m* to his brazen lies, „ *vi* 55
as *m's* ran on and rumour of battle grew, „ *III vi* 29
So for a *m* he wrought among the thralls ; *Gareth and L.* 525
weeks to *m's*, The *m's* will add themselves *Guinevere* 624
would not look at her—No not for *m's* : *Lover's Tale iv* 27
nine long *m's* of antenatal gloom, *De Prof., Two G.* 8
last *m* they wor diggin' the bog, *Tomorrow* 61
Altho' the *m's* have scarce begun, *To Ulysses* 22
Monument A *m* of childhood and of love ; *Lover's Tale ii* 183
Mood Were fixed shadows of thy fixed *m*, *Isabel* 9
But more human in your *m's*, *Margaret* 47
We taught him lowlier *m's*, *Buonaparte* 9
In lazy *m* I watch'd the little circles die ; *Miller's D.* 73
fit for every *m* And change of my still soul. *Palace of Art* 59
As fit for every *m* of mind, „ 90
from which *m* was born Scorn of herself ; again, from out that *m* Laughter at her self-scorn. „ 230
' I govern'd men by change, and so I sway'd All *m's*. *D. of F. Women* 131
but betwixt this *m* and that, *Gardener's D.* 155
I went thro' many wayward *m's* *Day-Dm., Pro.* 6
She changes with that *m* or this, *Will Water.* 107
cruel Seem'd the Captain's *m*. *The Captain* 14
But subject to the season or the *m*, *Aylmer's Field* 71
How low his brother's *m* had fallen, „ 404
and in her lion's *m* Tore open, *Princess iv* 380
Creation minted in the golden *m's* Of sovereign artists ; „ *v* 194
And left her woman, lovelier in her *m* „ *vii* 162
saw Thee woman thro' the crust of iron *m's* „ 342
My lighter *m's* are like to these, *In Mem. xx* 9
I envy not in any *m's* The captive void „ *xxvii* 1
Mere fellowship of sluggish *m's*, „ *xxxv* 21
What vaster dream can hit the *m* Of Love on earth ? „ *xlvii* 11
She takes, when harsher *m's* remit, „ *xlviii* 6
And put thy harsher *m's* aside, „ *lix* 7
Nor less it pleased in livelier *m's*, „ *lxxxix* 29
am I raging alone as my father raged in his *m* ? *Maud I i* 53
My *m* is changed, for it fell at a time of year „ *III vi* 4
coming up quite close, and in his *m* *Geraint and E.* 714
Let not thy *m's* prevail, when I am gone *Balin and Balan* 140
So when his *m's* were darken'd, „ 235
fain have wrought upon his cloudy *m* *Merlin and V.* 156
And yielding to his kindlier *m's*, „ 174
Dark in the glass of some presageful *m*, „ 295

Mood (*continued*) fled from Arthur's court To break the *m*. *Merlin and V.* 298
Not half so strange as that dark *m* of yours. „ 314
same mistrustful *m* That makes you seem less noble „ 321
such a *m* as that, which lately gloom'd „ 325
As high as woman in her selfless *m*. „ 443
or a *m* Of overstrain'd affection, „ 521
Vivien, gathering somewhat of his *m*, „ 842
wrought upon his *m* and hugg'd him close. „ 948
but in him His *m* was often like a fiend, *Lancelot and E.* 251
Arthur to the banquet, dark in *m*, Past, „ 564
turn'd Sir Torre, being in his *m's* Left them, „ 799
Gawain in his *m* Had made mock-knight *Last Tournament* 1
Tristram, half plagued by Lancelot's languorous *m*, „ 194
Was mine a *m* To be invaded rudely, *Lover's Tale i* 677
At times too shrilling in her angrier *m's*, *The Ring* 395
your opiate then Bred this black *m* ? *Romney's R.* 62
each philosophy And *m* of faith *Akbar's Dream* 56
m's of tiger, or of ape ? *Making of Man* 2
Moon (*See also* **Crescent-moon, Honeymoon**) At midnight the *m* cometh, *Claribel* 13
The mellow'd reflex of a winter *m* ; *Isabel* 29
And ever when the *m* was low, *Mariana* 49
But when the *m* was very low, „ 53
WHAT time the mighty *m* was gathering light *Love and Death* 1
There would be neither *m* nor star ; *The Merman* 21
Neither *m* nor star. „ 24
Which the *m* about her spreadeth, *Margaret* 20
Breathes low between the sunset and the *m* ; *Eleänore* 124
And by the *m* the reaper weary, *L. of Shalott i* 33
Or when the *m* was overhead, „ *ii* 33
' For every worm beneath the *m* *Two Voices* 178
Gleam'd to the flying *m* by fits. *Miller's D.* 116
Faints like a dazzled morning *m*. *Fatima* 28
Lit with a low large *m*. *Palace of Art* 68
In hollow'd *m's* of gems, „ 188
It was when the *m* was setting, *May Queen, Con.* 26
Full-faced above the valley stood the *m* ; *Lotos-Eaters* 7
Between the sun and *m* upon the shore ; „ 38
and in the *m* Nightly dew-fed ; „ *C. S.* 29
Once, like the *m*, I made The ever-shifting currents *D. of F. Women* 132
Far-heard beneath the *m*. „ 184
balmy *m* of blessed Israel Floods all the deep-blue gloom „ 185
the next *m* was roll'd into the sky, „ 229
While the stars burn, the *m's* increase, *To J. S.* 71
Lay a great water, and the *m* was full. *M. d'Arthur* 12
And in the *m* athwart the place of tombs, „ 46
the winter *m* Brightening the skirts of a long cloud, „ 53
great brand Made lightnings in the splendour of the *m*, „ 137
And the long glories of the winter *m*. „ 192
colourless, and like the wither'd *m* „ 213
for some three careless *m's*, *Gardener's D.* 15
rose And saunter'd home beneath a *m*, that, just In crescent, *Audley Court* 80
But thirty *m's*, one honeymoon to that, *Edwin Morris* 29
my beard Was tagg'd with icy fringes in the *m*, *St. S. Stylites* 32
Sun will run his orbit, and the *M* Her circle. *Love and Duty* 22
long day wanes : the slow *m* climbs : *Ulysses* 55
mellow *m's* and happy skies, *Locksley Hall* 159
stand at gaze like Joshua's *m* in Ajalon ! „ 180
like a summer *m* Half-dipt in cloud : *Godiva* 45
the snows Are sparkling to the *m* : *St. Agnes' Eve* 2
Far ran the naked *m* across The houseless ocean's *The Voyage* 29
A thousand *m's* will quiver ; *A Farewell* 14
As shines the *m* in clouded skies, *Beggar Maid* 9
beneath a clouded *m* He like a lover *Enoch Arden* 658
I murmur under *m* and stars In brambly wildernesses ; *The Brook* 178
music of the *m* Sleeps in the plain eggs *Aylmer's Field* 102
Beneath a pale and unimpassion'd *m*, „ 334
father's face Grow long and troubled like a rising *m*, *Princess i* 59
Come from the dying *m*, and blow, „ *iii* 6
out of the west Under the silver *m* : „ 15
with the sun and *m* renew their light For ever, „ 255

Moon (*continued*) For many weary *m's* before we came, *Princess iii* 319
And brief the *m* of beauty in the South. „ *iv* 113
I babbled for you, as babies for the *m*, „ 428
A maiden *m* that sparkles on a sty, „ *v* 186
like a clouded *m* In a still water: „ *vi* 270
Now set a wrathful Dian's *m* on flame, „ 368
Ask me no more: the *m* may draw the sea; „ *vii* 1
our God Himself is *m* and sun. *Ode on Well.* 217
The *m* like a rick on fire was rising *Grandmother* 39
Echo on echo Dies to the *m*. *Minnie and Winnie* 12
The sun, the *m*, the stars, *High. Pantheism* 1
when in heaven the stars about the *m* *Spec. of Iliad* 11
Sun comes, *m* comes, Time slips away. Sun sets, *m* sets, Love, fix a day. *Window, When* 1
charms Her secret from the latest *m*?' *In Mem. xxi* 20
No lapse of *m's* can canker Love, „ *xxvi* 3
The *m* is hid; the night is still; „ *xxviii* 2
Or when a thousand *m's* shall wane „ *lxxvii* 8
Or sadness in the summer *m's*? „ *lxxxiii* 8
flung A ballad to the brightening *m*: „ *lxxxix* 28
The sailing *m* in creek and cove; „ *ci* 16
The *m* is hid, the night is still; „ *civ* 2
glowing like the *m* Of Eden on its bridal bower: „ *Con.* 27
And rise, O *m*, from yonder down, „ 109
hand, as white As ocean-foam in the *m*, *Maud I xiv* 18
And a hush with the setting *m*. „ *xxii* 18
Now half to the setting *m* are gone, „ 23
Not many *m's*, King Uther died himself, *Com. of Arthur* 206
Between the in-crescent and de-crescent *m*, *Gareth and L.* 529
O *m*, that layest all to sleep again, „ 1061
Answer'd Sir Gareth graciously to one Not many a *m* his younger, „ 1415
by night With *m* and trembling stars, *Marr. of Geraint* 8
but three brief *m's* had glanced away *Balin and Balan* 154
Those twelve sweet *m's* confused his fatherhood.' *Merlin and V.* 712
All in the middle of the rising *m*: *Holy Grail* 636
And with me drove the *m* and all the stars; „ 809
That kept the entry, and the *m* was full. „ 818
the rounded *m* Thro' the tall oriel on the rolling sea. „ 830
until the third night brought a *m* *Pelleas and E.* 393
Here too, all hush'd below the mellow *m*, „ 424
their own darkness, throng'd into the *m*. „ 458
She lived a *m* in that low lodge with him: *Last Tournament* 381
Far over sands marbled with *m* and cloud, „ 466
Beneath a *m* unseen albeit at full, *Guinevere* 6
on one Lay a great water, and the *m* was full, *Pass of Arthur* 180
in the *m* athwart the place of tombs, „ 214
winter *m*, Brightening the skirts of a long cloud, „ 221
great brand Made lightnings in the splendour of the *m*, „ 305
And the long glories of the winter *m*. „ 360
face was white And colourless, and like the wither'd *m* „ 381
the *m*, Half-melted into thin blue air, *Lover's Tale i* 420
came in The white light of the weary *m* above, „ 640
But many weary *m's* I lived alone— „ *ii* 2
glows and glories of the *m* Below black firs, „ 110
eleventh *m* After their marriage lit the lover's Bay, „ *iv* 27
m Struck from an open grating overhead „ 59
and the full *m* stares at the snow. *Rizpah* 4
Willy—the *m's* in a cloud— „ 86
With this last *m*, this crescent— *De Prof., Two G.* 9
ninth *m*, that sends the hidden sun Down yon dark sea, „ 33
Drew to this shore lit by the suns and *m's* „ 38
this roaring *m* of daffodil And crocus, *Pref. Son., 19th Cent.* 7
Rejoicing that the sun, the *m*, the stars *Tiresias* 160
and crows to the sun and the *m*, *Despair* 90
Till the Sun and the *M* of our science „ 91
there was but a slip of a *m*, *Tomorrow* 9
wid his song to the Sun an' the *M*, „ 91
dead as yon dead world the *m*? *Locksley H., Sixty* 174
m was falling greenish thro' a rosy glow, „ 178
Beneath a hard Arabian *m* And alien stars. *To Marq. of Dufferin* 45
gleam as of the *m*, When first she peers along *Demeter and P.* 13
dwell For nine white *m's* of each whole year „ 120
To send the *m* into the night and break „ 135

Moon (*continued*) Mellow *m* of heaven, Bright in blue, *M* of married hearts, Hear me, you! *The Ring* 1
Globing Honey *M's* Bright as this. „ 7
M, you fade at times From the night. „ 9
Globe again, and make Honey *M*. „ 16
Shall not *my* love last, *M*, with you, „ 18
They made a thousand honey *m's* of one? „ 22
And while the *m* was setting. *Forlorn* 84
not be follow'd by the *M*? *Happy* 97

Mooned Upon the *m* domes aloof In inmost Bagdat, *Arabian Nights* 127
Mooney (money) Parson as hesn't the call, nor the *m*, *Village Wife* 91
Moon-faced Maud the beloved of my mother, the *m-f* darling of all,— *Maud I i* 72
Moon-led Their *m-l* waters white. *Palace of Art* 252
Moonless Storm, such as drove her under *m* heavens *Enoch Arden* 547
Grind on the wakeful ear in the hush of the *m* nights, *Maud I i* 42
A *m* night with storm— *Sisters (E. and E.)* 96
Sunless and *m*, utter light—but no! *Columbus* 90
Moonlight By star-shine and by *m*, *Oriana* 24
Like *m* on a falling shower? *Margaret* 4
Are as *m* unto sunlight, *Locksley Hall* 152
A full sea glazed with muffled *m*, *Princess i* 248
A cypress in the *m* shake, *The Daisy* 82
m touching o'er a terrace One tall Agavè „ 83
When on my bed the *m* falls, *In Mem. lxvii* 1
From off my bed the *m* dies; „ 10
'It is not Arthur's use To hunt by *m*;' *Holy Grail* 111
There in the shuddering *m* brought its face *Lover's Tale i* 650
I saw the *m* glitter on their tears— „ 697
As *m* wandering thro' a mist: „ *ii* 52
His lady with the *m* on her face; „ *iv* 57
Yet the *m* is the sunlight, *Locksley H., Sixty* 182
Not of the *m*, Not of the starlight! *Merlin and the G.* 121
Moonlike glooms of my dark will, *M* emerged, *Lover's Tale i* 745
O will she, *m*, sway the main, *Mechanophilus* 13
Moon-lit The sloping of the *m-l* sward *Arabian Nights* 27
With narrow *m-l* slips of silver cloud, *Œnone* 218
Far in the *m* haze among the hills, *Pass. of Arthur* 42
Who toils across the middle *m* nights, *Lover's Tale i* 138
Moon-rise little before *m-r* hears the low Moan *Palace of Art* 279
Moonshine eyes all wet, in the sweet *m*: *Grandmother* 49
labouring up the pass, All in a misty *m*, *Lancelot and E.* 48
Moony The *m* vapour rolling round the King, *Guinevere* 601
Moor (adj.) Over the dark *m* land, *Maud I ix* 6
Moor (land) From far and near, on mead and *m*, *In Mem. xxviii* 6
Yet oft when sundown skirts the *m* „ *xli* 17
I am sick of the *m* and the main. *Maud I i* 61
No, there is fatter game on the *m*; „ 74
I bow'd to his lady-sister as she rode by on the *m*; „ *iv* 15
Betwixt the cloud and the *m* „ *ix* 4
And over the sullen-purple *m* (Look at it) „ *x* 21
Go back, my lord, across the *m*, „ *xii* 31
ye meanwhile far over *m* and fell „ *xviii* 76
When I bow'd to her on the *m*. „ *xix* 66
I will wander till I die about the barren *m's*. *The Flight* 56
Is that the leper's hut on the solitary *m*, *Happy* 9
Moor (more) Says that I moänt 'a naw *m* aäle: *N. Farmer, O. S.* 3
Moor (race of people) When Spain was waging war against the *M*—I strove myself with Spain against the *M*. *Columbus* 93
I am handled worse than had I been a *M*, „ 107
given the Great Khan's palaces to the *M*, Or clutch'd the sacred crown of Prester John, And cast it to the *M*: „ 109
Moor'd where man Hath *m* and rested? *Supp. Confessions* 124
Were borne about the bay or safely *m* *Lover's Tale i* 54
Moorland (*See also* **Moor (adj.)**) Dreary gleams about the *m* *Locksley Hall* 4
Many a morning on the *m* „ 35
O the dreary, dreary *m*! „ 40
glimmering *m* rings With jingling bridle-reins. *Sir L. and Q. G.* 35
wastest *m* of our realm shall be Safe, *Gareth and L.* 603
Mooted ne'er been *m*, but as frankly theirs *Princess v* 203
Moother (mother) *M* 'ed tell'd ma to bring tha down, *Owd Roä* 50
when *M* 'ed gotten to bed, „ 53
I kick'd 'im ageän, but I kick'd thy *M* istead. „ 67
M 'ed beän a-naggin' about the gell o' the farm, „ 69
But *M* was free of 'er tongue, „ 73

Moother (mother) (*continued*) Thy *M* was howdin' the lether, *Owd Roä* 85
M was naggin' an' groänin' an' moänin' „ 108
M 'ed beän sa soäk'd wi' the thaw „ 113

Moral (adj.) (*See also* **Maudlin-moral**) Then of the *m* instinct would she prate *Palace of Art* 205
'Last of the train, a *m* leper, I, *Princess iv* 222
He gain in sweetness and in *m* height, „ *vii* 281
'A *m* child without the craft to rule, *Lancelot and E.* 146
Farewell, Macready; *m*, grave, sublime; *To W. C. Macready* 12

Moral (s) And if you find no *m* there, *Day-Dm., Moral* 2
What *m* is in being fair. „ 4
is there any *m* shut Within the bosom „ 7
You'd have *my m* from the song, „ *L'Envoi* 31
Are clasp'd the *m* of thy life, „ 55
The *m's*, something of the frame, *Princess ii* 382

Morass Or low *m* and whispering reed, *In Mem. c* 6

Morbid Vex'd with a *m* devil in his blood *Walk. to the Mail* 19
Till a *m* hate and horror have grown *Maud I vi* 75
And a *m* eating lichen fixt On a heart „ 77
'It is time, O passionate heart and *m* eye, „ *III vi* 32
I used to walk This Terrace—*m*, melancholy; *The Ring* 168

More *See* **Moor**

Moreland (Emma) *See* **Emma Moreland**

Morganore *M*, And Lot of Orkney. *Com. of Arthur* 115

Moriah the dead Went wandering o'er *M*— *Holy Grail* 50
our most ancient East *M* with Jerusalem; *Columbus* 81

Morion shone Their *m's*, wash'd with morning, *Princess v* 264

Morn (*See also* **After-morn, Christmas-morn, Hunting-morn, Marriage-morn, Murn, Summer-morn, Yestermorn**) For even and *m* Ever will be Thro' eternity. *Nothing will Die* 33
For even and *m* Ye will never see Thro' eternity. *All Things will Die* 44
she bow'd Above Thee, on that happy *m* *Supp. Confessions* 24
'Yet,' said I, in my *m* of youth, „ 139
Either at *m* or eventide. *Mariana* 16
Till cold winds woke the gray-eyed *m* „ 31
Ray-fringed eyelids of the *m* *Clear-headed friend* 6
amber *m* Forth gushes from beneath a low-hung cloud. *Ode to Memory* 70
Wander from the side of the *m*, *Adeline* 52
Thou wert born, on a summer *m*, *Eleänore* 7
And 'Ave Mary,' night and *m*, *Mariana in the S.* 10
'Madonna, sad is night and *m*,' „ 22
'That won his praises night and *m*?' „ 34
And murmuring, as at night and *m*, „ 46
More inward than at night or *m*, „ 58
'The day to night, the night to *m*, „ 82
'The night comes on that knows not *m*, „ 94
'Or make that *m*, from his cold crown *Two Voices* 85
Or in the gateways of the *m*. „ 183
'Behold, it is the Sabbath *m*.' „ 402
Each *m* my sleep was broken thro' *Miller's D.* 39
in the dark *m* The panther's roar came muffled, *Œnone* 213
from her lips, as *m* from Memnon, drew Rivers *Palace of Art* 171
All night I lie awake, but I fall asleep at *m*; *May Queen, N. Y's. E.* 50
The dim red *m* had died, *D. of F. Women* 61
M broaden'd on the borders of the dark, „ 265
From out the borders of the *m*, *On a Mourner* 24
without help I cannot last till *m*. *M. d'Arthur* 26
Shot like a streamer of the northern *m*, „ 139
dark East, Unseen, is brightening to his bridal *m*. *Gardener'sD.* 73
hour just flown, that *m* with all its sound, „ 83
I come to-morrow *m*. I go, *Audley Court* 70
friendly mist of *m* Clung to the lake. *Edwin Morris* 107
And when my marriage *m* may fall, *Talking Oak* 285
Far-folded mists, and gleaming halls of *m*. *Tithonus* 10
Thou wilt renew thy beauty *m* by *m*; „ 74
leave me here a little, while as yet 'tis early *m*: *Locksley Hall* 1
The twilight melted into *m*. *Day-Dm., Depart.* 16
The cock crows ere the Christmas *m*, *Sir Galahad* 51
They two will wed the morrow *m*: *Lady Clare* 7
We two will wed to-morrow *m*, „ 87
And perplex'd her, night and *m*, *L. of Burleigh* 78

Morn (*continued*) Nor anchor dropt at eve or *m*; *The Voyage* 82
Have a rouse before the *m*: (repeat) *Vision of Sin* 96, 120
Ascending tired, heavily slept till *m*. *Enoch Arden* 181
drifted, stranding on an isle at *m* Rich, „ 552
m That mock'd him with returning calm, *Lucretius* 24
'That on her bridal *m* before she past *Princess ii* 262
M in the white wake of the morning star „ *iii* 17
To tumble, Vulcans, on the second *m*.' „ 72
to-morrow *m* We hold a great convention: „ *iv* 510
so here upon the flat All that long *m* „ *v* 368
all that *m* the heralds to and fro, „ 369
Between the Northern and the Southern *m*.' „ 423
m by *m* the lark Shot up and shrill'd „ *vii* 45
this Is *m* to more, and all the rich to-come Reels, „ 356
Fair-hair'd and redder than a windy *m*; „ *Con.* 91
I shall see him another *m*: *Grandmother* 67
Calm in the *m* without a sound, *In Mem. xi* 1
ere yet the *m* Breaks hither over Indian seas, „ *xxvi* 13
Rise, happy *m*, rise, holy *m*, „ *xxx* 29
Reveillée to the breaking *m*. „ *lxviii* 8
With promise of a *m* as fair; „ *lxxxiv* 29
Mute symbols of a joyful *m*, „ *Con.* 58
the King That *m* was married, *Com. of Arthur* 456
Far off they saw the silver-misty *m* *Gareth and L.* 189
Hear me—this *m* I stood in Arthur's hall, „ 855
next *m*, the lord whose life he saved Had, „ 888
At last, it chanced that on a summer *m* *Marr. of Geraint* 69
blow His horns for hunting on the morrow *m*. „ 153
But Guinevere lay late into the *m*, „ 157
We hold a tourney here to-morrow *m*, „ 287
made him like a man abroad at *m* „ 335
'And gladly given again this happy *m*. „ 691
kept it for a sweet surprise at *m*. „ 703
as the white and glittering star of *m* „ 734
like a shoal Of darting fish, that on a summer *m* *Geraint and E.* 469
Blinkt the white *m*, sprays grated, *Balin and Balan* 385
There *m* by *m*, arraying her sweet self *Lancelot and E.* 906
eve and *m* She kiss'd me saying, „ 1408
gustful April *m* That puff'd the swaying branches *Holy Grail* 14
let us meet The morrow *m* once more in one full field „ 323
till one fair *m*, I walking to and fro „ 591
But on the hither side of that loud *m* *Last Tournament* 56
And little Dagonet on the morrow *m*, „ 240
it chanced one *m* when all the court, *Guinevere* 21
Till in the cold wind that foreruns the *m*, „ 132
without help I cannot last till *m*. *Pass. of Arthur* 194
Shot like a streamer of the northern *m*, „ 307
this March *m* that sees Thy Soldier-brother's *Ded. Poem Prin. Alice* 10
we sail'd on a Friday *m*— *V. of Maeldune* 7
The night was calm, the *m* is calm, *The Flight* 10
and now the *m* appears, „ 18
burnt at midnight, found at *m*, *Locksley H., Sixty* 97
planted both together, happy in our marriage *m*? *Happy* 14
my fair meadow zoned with airy *m*; *Prog. of Spring* 69
m Has lifted the dark eyelash of the Night *Akbar's Dream* 200

Mornin' yer Honour ye gev her the top of the *m*, *Tomorrow* 3
whin are ye goin' to lave me?' 'O' Monday *m*' says he; „ 17
But airth was at pace nixt *m*, „ 25

Morning (adj.) Whilome thou camest with the *m* mist, (repeat) *Ode to Memory* 12, 21
never more Shall lone Œnone see the *m* mist *Œnone* 216
long ago Sung by the *m* star of song, *D. of F. Women* 3
The maiden splendours of the *m* star „ 55
And fluted to the *m* sea. *To E. L.* 24
To find the precious *m* hours were lost. *Enoch Arden* 302
when the *m* flush Of passion and the first embrace *Lucretius* 2
like *m* doves That sun their milky bosoms *Princess ii* 102
With whom I sang about the *m* hills, „ 247
In crystal currents of clear *m* seas. „ 328
In colours gayer than the *m* mist, „ 438
Morn in the white wake of the *m* star „ *iii* 17
A Memnon smitten with the *m* Sun.' „ 116
Alpine harebell hung with tears By some cold *m* glacier; „ *vii* 116

Morning (adj.) (*continued*) And whistled to the *m* star. *Sailor Boy* 4
And you are his *m* star. *Window, Marr. Morn.* 12
Thro' clouds that drench the *m* star, *In Mem. lxxii* 22
The sweep of scythe in *m* dew, „ *lxxxix* 18
Who stay to share the *m* feast, „ *Con.* 75
And even in high day the *m* star. *Com. of Arthur* 100
thereon the *m* star, And Gareth silent gazed *Gareth and L.* 932
And then she sang, ' O *m* star ' „ 996
' O *m* star that smilest in the blue, O star, my *m* dream hath proven true, „ 999
' O birds, that warble to the *m* sky, „ 1075
But that same strength which threw the *M* Star „ 1108
and the *m* star Reel'd in the smoke, *Pelleas and E.* 518
their fears Are *m* shadows huger than the shapes *To the Queen ii* 63
The lucid chambers of the *m* star, *Lover's Tale i* 28
A *m* air, sweet after rain, ran over „ *iii* 3
the *m* song of the lark, *First Quarrel* 33
lark has past from earth to Heaven upon the *m* breeze ! *The Flight* 62
And splendours of the *m* land, *Open. I. and C. Exhib.* 8
till the mortal *m* mists of earth Fade *Akbar's Dream* 96
The *m* light of happy marriage broke *Death of Œnone* 102
Morning (s) (*See also* **March-morning, Mornin' Murnin'**)
Every heart this May *m* in joyance is beating *All Things will Die* 6
Thou comest *m* or even ; she cometh not *m* or even. *Leonine Eleg.* 15
' Still sees the sacred *m* spread *Two Voices* 80
In her still place the *m* wept : „ 275
It haunted me, the *m* long, *Miller's D.* 69
you had set, That *m*, on the casement-edge „ 82
Gargarus Stands up and takes the *m* : *Œnone* 11
Far up the solitary *m* smote The streaks „ 55
In the early early *m* the summer sun *May Queen, N. Y's. E.* 22
How sadly, I remember, rose the *m* of the year ! „ *Con.* 3
came a sweeter token when the night and *m* meet : „ 22
It is a stormy *m*.' *The Goose* 44
every *m* brought a noble chance, *M. d'Arthur* 230
THIS *m* is the *m* of the day, *Gardener's D.* 1
The northern *m* o'er thee shoot, *Talking Oak* 275
m driv'n her plow of pearl Far furrowing *Love and Duty* 99
Many a *m* on the moorland *Locksley Hall* 35
And in the *m* of the times. *Day-Dm., L'Envoi* 20
I saw that every *m*, far withdrawn *Vision of Sin* 48
Enoch faced this *m* of farewell Brightly *Enoch Arden* 182
in those uttermost Parts of the *m* ? „ 224
that same *m* officers and men Levied a kindly tax „ 662
this kindlier glow Faded with *m*, *Aylmer's Field* 412
eyes Had such a star of *m* in their blue, „ 692
And me that *m* Walter show'd the house, *Princess, Pro.* 10
That *m* in the presence room I stood „ *i* 51
shone Their morions, wash'd with *m*, „ *v* 264
I took it for an hour in mine own bed This *m* : „ 435
I mused on that wild *m* in the woods, „ 471
Death and *M* on the silver horns, „ *vii* 204
Like yonder *m* on the blind half-world ; „ 352
the winds are up in the *m* ? (repeat) *Window, On the Hill* 5, 10, 15, 20
For this is the golden *m* of love, „ *Marr. Morn.* 11
With *m* wakes the will, and cries, *In Mem. iv* 15
Never *m* wore To evening, but some heart „ *vi* 7
I creep At earliest *m* to the door. „ *vii* 8
Singing alone in the *m* of life, In the happy *m* of life and of May, *Maud I v* 6
M arises stormy and pale, „ *vi* 1
Till at last when the *m* came In a cloud, „ 20
O when did a *m* shine So rich in atonement „ *xix* 5
For a breeze of *m* moves, „ *xxii* 7
'Tis a *m* pure and sweet, (repeat) *Maud II iv* 31, 35
So with the *m* all the court were gone. *Marr. of Geraint* 156
To ride with him this *m* to the court, „ 606
And now this *m* when he said to her, „ 847
Geraint, who issuing forth That *m*, *Geraint and E.* 9
Their chance of booty from the *m's* raid, „ 565
Then chanced, one *m*, that Sir Balin sat *Balin and Balan* 240
Came with slow steps, the *m* on her face ; „ 245
And all this *m* when I fondled you : *Merlin and V.* 286
she placed where *m's* earliest ray Might strike it, *Lancelot and E.* 5

Morning (s) (*continued*) o'er and o'er For all an April *m*, *Lancelot and E.* 897
ten slow *m's* past, and on the eleventh „ 1133
blush'd and brake the *m* of the jousts, *Pelleas and E.* 157
but rose With *m* every day, and, moist or dry, „ 215
But when the *m* of a tournament, *Last Tournament* 134
every *m* brought a noble chance, *Pass. of Arthur* 398
On the same *m*, almost the same hour, *Lover's Tale i* 198
There came a glorious *m*, such a one „ 299
Mercury On such a *m* would have flung „ 301
broke in light Like *m* from her eyes— „ *ii* 144
One *m* when the upblown billow ran Shoreward „ 178
One bright May *m* in a world of song, *Sisters (E. and E.)* 82
had sunn'd The *m* of our marriage, „ 244
Then in the gray of the *m* it seem'd *In the Child. Hosp.* 67
on another wild *m* another wild earthquake *Def. of Lucknow* 61
I saw your face that *m* in the crowd. *Columbus* 7
one *m* a bird with a warble *The Wreck* 81
the *m* brings the day I hate and fear ; *The Flight* 2
waken every *m* to that face I loathe to see : „ 8
their songs, that meet The *m* with such music, „ 66
But look, the *m* grows apace, „ 93
half the *m* have I paced these sandy tracts, *Locksley H., Sixty* 1
Half the marvels of my *m*, „ 75
Star of the *m*, Hope in the sunrise ; *Vastness* 15
Given on the *m* when you came of age *The Ring* 77
Why not bask amid the senses while the sun of *m* shines, *By an Evolution.* 6
Would I had past in the *m* that looks so bright „ 10
m of my reign Was redden'd by that cloud *Akbar's Dream* 63
Every *m* is thy birthday „ *Hymn* 2
Every *m* here we greet it, „ 3
Morning-breath dewy meadowy *m-b* Of England, *Enoch Arden* 660
Morning-mist thro' the sunless winter *m-m* In silence *Death of Œnone* 8
Morning-star (*See also* **Morning (adj.)**) Sung by the *m s* of song, *D. of F. Women* 3
maiden splendours of the *m s* Shook „ 55
Toward the *m-s*. „ 244
And whistled to the *m s*. *Sailor Boy* 4
M-S, and Noon-Sun, and Evening-Star, *Gareth and L.* 634
' Nay, nay,' she said, ' Sir *M-S*. „ 918
And servants of the *M-S*, approach, „ 924
golden guess Is *m-s* to the full round of truth. *Columbus* 44
Morningtide great Sun-star of *m*, *Batt. of Brunanburh* 26
Morris (Edwin) *See* **Edwin, Edwin Morris**
Morrison (Mary) *See* **Mary, Mary Morrison**
Morrow (adj.) (*See also* **To-morrow**) They two will wed the *m* morn : *Lady Clare* 7
blow His horns for hunting on the *m* morn. *Marr. of Geraint* 153
let us meet The *m* morn once more in one full field *Holy Grail* 323
And little Dagonet on the *m* morn, *Last Tournament* 240
Morrow (s) (*See also* **Goodmorrow, Tomorra, To-morrow**)
when the *m* came, she rose and took The child *Dora* 80
till the *m*, when he spoke. *Enoch Arden* 156
a poising eagle, burns Above the unrisen *m* : ' *Princess iv* 83
For the meeting of the *m*, *Maud II iv* 28
As pass without good *m* to thy Queen ? ' *Balin and Balan* 252
Then being on the *m* knighted, sware *Pelleas and E.* 140
and expectancy of worse Upon the *m*, *Lover's Tale ii* 152
Mors ' MERIDIES '—' HESPERUS '—' NOX '—' *M*,' *Gareth and L.* 1205
Morsel (*See also* **Mossel**) Mangled to *m's*, A youngster in war ! *Batt. of Brunanburh* 74
Mortal (adj.) (*See also* **Mortial, Mottal**) your *m* dower Of pensive thought *Margaret* 5
' Then dying of a *m* stroke, *Two Voices* 154
Who sought'st to wreck my *m* ark, „ 389
Thy *m* eyes are frail to judge of fair,— *Œnone* 158
And when no *m* motion jars The blackness *On a Mourner* 26
Not tho' I live three lives of *m* men, *M. d'Arthur* 155
made blank of crimeful record all My *m* archives. *St. S. Stylites* 159
tho' my *m* summers to such length of years *Locksley Hall* 67
My spirit beats her *m* bars, *Sir Galahad* 46
This *m* armour that I wear, „ 70
plucks The *m* soul from out immortal hell, *Lucretius* 263
Her stature more than *m* in the burst Of sunrise, *Princess, Pro.* 40
The fading politics of *m* Rome, „ *ii* 286

Mortal (adj.) (*continued*) In lieu of many *m* flies, a race Of giants living, *Princess iii* 268
I leave this *m* ark behind, *In Mem. xii* 6
'They do not die Nor lose their *m* sympathy, „ *xxx* 23
hardly worth my while to choose Of things all *m*, „ *xxxiv* 11
For Widsom dealt with *m* powers, „ *xxxvi* 5
These *m* lullabies of pain May bind a book, „ *lxxvii* 5
Intelligencies fair That range above our *m* state, „ *lxxxv* 22
And teach true life to fight with *m* wrongs. *Maud I xviii* 54
Came purer pleasure unto *m* kind *Geraint and E.* 765
ride, and dream The *m* dream that never yet was mine— *Merlin and V.* 117
Naked of glory for His *m* change, *Holy Grail* 448
Being smitten in mid heaven with *m* cold *Last Tournament* 27
Not tho' I live three lives of *m* men, *Pass. of Arthur* 323
Three cypresses, symbols of *m* woe, *Lover's Tale i* 537
forest-shadow borne With more than *m* swiftness, „ *ii* 73
or my love *M* once more?' „ *iv* 80
I knaw'd naw moor what I did nor a *m* beäst o' the feäld. *North. Cobbler* 38
and shook like a man in a *m* affright; *V. of Maeldune* 74
serve This *m* race thy kin so well, *De Prof., Two G.* 16
our *m* veil And shatter'd phantom of that infinite One, „ 46
Yet loves and hates with *m* hates and loves, *Tiresias* 23
no Nor yet that thou art *m*— *Ancient Sage* 63
Have ended *m* foes; „ 158
some have gleams or so they say Of more than *m* things.' „ 215
The *m* limit of the Self was loosed, „ 232
high-heaven dawn of more than *m* day „ 284
Twisted hard in *m* agony with their offspring, *Locksley H., Sixty* 98
Paint the *m* shame of nature with the living hues of Art. „ 140
But since, our *m* shadow, *Epilogue* 22
will make his name As *m* as my own. „ 61
I am *m* stone and lime. *Helen's Tower* 6
The dead man's garden, The *m* hillock, *Merlin and the G.* 107
Tho' their music here be *m* need the singer greatly care? *Parnassus* 18
till the *m* morning mists of earth Fade *Akbar's Dream* 96

Mortal (s) black earth yawns: the *m* disappears; *Ode on Well.* 269

Mortality from the low light of *m* Shot up their shadows *Aylmer's Field* 641

Mortgage sober rook And carrion crow cry '*M.*' *The Ring* 174

Mortial (mortal) to dhrame of a married man, death alive, is a *m* sin.' *Tomorrow* 51

Mortify *M* Your flesh, like me, *St. S. Stylites* 179

Mosaic Below was all *m* choicely plann'd *Palace of Art* 145
the rough kex break The starr'd *m*, *Princess iv* 78

Moses An', faix, be the piper o' *M*, *Tomorrow* 71

Moslem (adj.) clove the *M* crescent moon, and changed it into blood. *Happy* 44

Moslem (s) Spain should oust The *M* from her limit, *Columbus* 97
he sail'd the sea to crush the *M* in his pride; *Locksley H., Sixty* 29

Mosque Death from the heights of the *m* and the palace, *Def. of Lucknow* 24
If it be a *m* people murmur the holy prayer, *Akbar's D., Inscrip.* 4
Sometimes I frequent the Christian cloister, and sometimes the *m*. „ 5
Christian bell, the cry from off the *m*, *Akbar's Dream* 149
temple, neither Pagod, *M*, nor Church, „ 178

Moss (*See also* **Marish-mosses, Staghorn-moss**) WITH blackest *m* the flower-pots *Mariana* 1
creeping *m'es* and clambering weeds, *Dying Swan* 36
In the hueless *m'es* under the sea *The Mermaid* 49
bluebell rings To the *m'es* underneath? *Adeline* 35
Like those long *m'es* in the stream. *Miller's D.* 48
cool *m'es* deep, And thro' the *m* the ivies *Lotos-Eaters, C. S.* 8
then for roses, *m* or musk, To grace my city rooms; *Gardener's D.* 193
With *m* and braided marish-pipe; *On a Mourner* 10
Long learned names of agaric, *m* and fern, *Edwin Morris* 17
In *m'es* mixt with violet Her cream-white mule *Sir L. and Q. G.* 30
plash of rains, and refuse patch'd with *m*. *Vision of Sin* 212
The wine-flask lying couch'd in *m*, *In Mem. lxxxix* 44
He felt the hollow-beaten *m'es* thud *Balin and Balan* 321

Moss (*continued*) The ruinous donjon as a knoll of *m*, *Balin and Balan* 334
And sitting down upon the golden *m*, *Lover's Tale i* 540
I make bare of all the golden *m*, „ *ii* 48

Moss-bed Soft are the *m-b's* under the sea; *The Merman* 39

Moss'd wild bee hummeth About the *m* headstone: *Claribel* 12

Mossel (morsel) there warn't not a *m* o' harm; *Owd Roä* 70

Mossy and wrote On the *m* stone, as I lay, *Edward Gray* 26

Mostly The words are *m* mine; *Princess, Con.* 3

Moted *See* **Thick-moted**

Moth (*See also* **Emperor-moth**) we as rich as *m's* from dusk cocoons, *Princess ii* 19
That not a *m* with vain desire *In Mem. liv* 10
The *m* will singe her wings, *Sir J. Oldcastle* 189

Mother (adj.) That not in any *m* town With statelier progress *In Mem. xcviii* 21
Who finds the Saviour in his *m* tongue. *Sir J. Oldcastle* 115
For that sweet *m* land which gave them birth *Tiresias* 122

Mother (s) (*See also* **Earth-mother, Foster-mother, Maid-mother, Moother, Muther, Stepmother, Swan-mother**) *In her as* M, *Wife, and Queen;* *To the Queen* 28
Like Thine own *m's* when she bow'd *Supp. Confessions* 23
rosy fingers play About his *m's* neck, and knows Nothing beyond his *m's* eyes. „ 43
my gloomed fancy were As thine, my *m*, „ 69
grave Was deep, my *m*, in the clay? „ 86
answers to his *m's* calls From the flower'd furrow. „ 159
'*M*, give me grace To help me of my weary load.' *Mariana in the S.* 29
'Sweet *M*, let me not here alone „ 59
My *m* thought, What ails the boy? *Miller's D.* 93
slowly was my *m* brought To yield consent „ 137
The doubt my *m* would not see; „ 154
'O *m* Ida, many-fountain'd Ida, (repeat) *Œnone* 23, 34, 45, 172
m Ida, harken ere I die. (repeat) *Œnone* 24, 35, 46, 53, 64, 77, 91 103, 120, 134, 151, 173, 183, 195
'O *m*, hear me yet before I die. (repeat) *Œnone* 207, 220, 230, 245, 256
as a *m* Conjectures of the features of her child *Œnone* 251
And laid him at his *m's* feet. *The Sisters* 35
When thus he met his *m's* view, *L. C. V. de Vere* 34
must wake and call me early, call me early, *m* dear; (repeat) *May Queen* 1, 41
Of all the glad New-year, *m*, „ 3
I'm to be the Queen o' the May, *m*, (repeat) *May Queen* 4, 8, 12, 16, 20, 24, 28, 32, 36, 40, 44
I sleep so sound all night, *m*, *May Queen* 9
He thought of that sharp look, *m*, „ 15
He thought I was a ghost, *m*, „ 17
They say his heart is breaking, *m*— „ 22
And you'll be there, too, *m*, „ 26
The night-winds come and go, *m*, „ 33
All the valley, *m*, 'ill be fresh and green „ 37
IF you're waking call me early, call me early, *m* dear, (repeat) *May Queen, N. Y's. E.* 1, 52
And the New-year's coming up, *m*, „ 7
But I shall lie alone, *m*, „ 20
When you are warm-asleep, *m*, „ 24
When the flowers come again, *m*, „ 25
You'll bury me, my *m*, just beneath the hawthorn shade, „ 29
I shall not forget you, *m*, „ 31
You'll kiss me, my own *m*, „ 34
You should not fret for me, *m*, „ 36
If I can I'll come again, *m*, „ 37
Tho' you'll not see me, *m*, „ 38
Goodnight, sweet *m*: call me before the day is born. „ 49
It seem'd so hard at first, *m*, „ *Con.* 9
Nor would I now be well, *m*, „ 19
I did not hear the dog howl, *m*, „ 21
But sit beside my bed, *m*, „ 23
smile away my maiden blame among The Hebrew *m's*'— *D. of F. Women* 215
Grave *m* of majestic works, *Of old sat Freedom* 13
Strong *m* of a Lion-line, *England and Amer.* 3
he will teach him hardness, and to slight His *m*; *Dora* 121

Mother (s) (*continued*) but when the boy beheld His *m*, *Dora* 138
Christ, the Virgin *M*, and the saints ; *St. S. Stylites* 112
Her *m* trundled to the gate Behind the dappled grays. *Talking Oak* 111
press me from the *m's* breast. *Locksley Hall* 90
m's brought Their children, clamouring, *Godiva* 14
Against her father's and *m's* will : *Edward Gray* 10
O *m*,' she said, ' if this be true, *Lady Clare* 30
' Yet give one kiss to your *m* dear ! " 49
' O *m*, *m*, *m*,' she said, " 51
' Yet here's a kiss for my *m* dear, My *m* dear, if this be so, " 53
And bless me, *m*, ere I go.' " 56
Every *m's* son—Down they dropt— *The Captain* 50
m cared for it With all a *m's* care : *Enoch Arden* 262
Then the new *m* came about her heart, " 524
saw The *m* glancing often toward her babe, " 754
the girl So like her *m*, " 791
Annie, whom I saw So like her *m*, " 883
from the plaintive *m's* teat he took *The Brook* 129
My *m*, as it seems you did, " 225
Heard the good *m* softly whisper ' Bless, *Aylmer's Field* 187
nature crost Was *m* of the foul adulteries " 376
The *m* flow'd in shallower acrimonies : " 563
Yet the sad *m*, for the second death " 604
As with the *m* he had never known, " 690
The childless *m* went to seek her child ; " 829
wail'd and woke The *m*, and the father suddenly cried, *Sea Dreams* 58
The Virgin *M* standing with her child " 242
the child Clung to the *m*, and sent out a cry " 245
M, let me fly away. " 296
lambs are glad Nosing the *m's* udder, *Lucretius* 100
For so, my *m* said, the story ran. *Princess i* 11
My *m* pitying made a thousand prayers ; " 21
My *m* was as mild as any saint, " 22
' The *m* of the sweetest little maid, " *ii* 279
why should I not play The Spartan *M* with emotion, " 283
Our *m*, is she well ? ' " 310
clad her like an April daffodilly (Her *m's* colour) " 325
But yet your *m's* jealous temperament— " 338
Rest, rest, on *m's* breast, " *iii* 11
' O fly, while yet you may ! My *m* knows : ' " 29
My *m*, 'tis her wont from night to night " 32
(for still My *m* went revolving on the word) " 54
So my *m* clutch'd The truth at once, " 60
'tis my *m*, Too jealous, often fretful as the wind " 79
my *m* still Affirms your Psyche thieved her theories, " 91
I tried the *m's* heart. " 147
And then, demanded if her *m* knew, " *iv* 233
and you me Your second *m* : " 297
she, half on her *m* propt, Half-drooping from her, " 367
dismiss'd in shame to live No wiser than their *m's*, " 514
they will beat my girl Remembering her *m* : " *v* 89
Ill *m* that I was to leave her there, " 93
I won Your *m*, a good *m*, a good wife, " 166
and she of whom you speak, My *m*, " 193
M's—that, all prophetic pity, " 381
and what *m's* blood You draw from, fight ; " 404
risk'd it for your own ; His *m* lives : " 408
chiefest comfort is the little child Of one unworthy *m* ; " 431
prize the authentic *m* of her mind. " 433
The *m* makes us most— " 507
good Queen, her *m*, shore the tress With kisses, " *vi* 113
spied its *m* and began A blind and babbling laughter, " 136
So stood the unhappy *m* open-mouth'd, " 143
Red grief and *m's* hunger in her eye, " 146
half The sacred *m's* bosom, panting, " 148
striking with her glance, The *m*, me, the child ; " 153
thy *m* prove As true to thee as false, " 203
Not from your *m*, now a saint with saints. " 233
You shame your *m's* judgment too. " 261
Not only he, but by my *m's* soul, " 335
Happy he With such a *m* ! " *vii* 328
This *m* is your model. " 335
From *m* unto *m*, stately bride, *W. to Marie Alex.* 9

Mother (s) (*continued*) ' My *m* clings about my neck, *Sailor Boy* 17
this pretty home, the home where *m* dwells ? *City Child* 2
They found the *m* sitting still ; *The Victim* 31
The *m* said, ' They have taken the child " 43
Chop the breasts from off the *m*, *Boädicea* 68
O *m*, praying God will save Thy sailor,— *In Mem. vi* 13
Dear as the *m* to the son, " *ix* 19
And tears are on the *m's* face, " *xl* 10
That feed the *m's* of the flock ; " *c* 16
The shrill-edged shriek of a *m* *Maud I i* 16
a Mammonite *m* kills her babe for a burial fee, " 45
Maud the beloved of my *m*, " 72
Your *m* is mute in her grave as her image in marble above ; " *iv* 58
My *m*, who was so gentle and good ? " *vi* 67
Her *m* has been a thing complete, " *xiii* 35
Made her only the child of her *m*, " 40
Darken'd watching a *m* decline " *xix* 8
I did not speak Of my *m's* faded cheek " 19
Maud was moved To speak of the *m* she loved " 27
and thought It is his *m's* hair. " *II ii* 70
spike that split the *m's* heart Spitting the child, *Com. of Arthur* 38
the bitterness and grief That vext his *m*, " 211
For dark my *m* was in eyes and hair, " 327
A *m* weeping, and I hear her say, " 334
in my good *m's* hall Linger with vacillating obedience, *Gareth and L.* 12
Since the good *m* holds me still a child ! " 15
Good *m* is bad *m* unto me ! " 16
' *M*, tho' ye count me still the child, Sweet *m*, do ye love the child ? ' " 34
' Then, *m*, an ye love the child,' " 37
good *m*, but this egg of mine Was finer gold " 42
so the boy, Sweet *m*, neither clomb, " 56
m said, ' True love, sweet son, had risk'd himself " 59
m, there was once a King, like ours. " 101
M, How can ye keep me tether'd to you— " 114
To whom the *m* said, ' Sweet son, " 120
I will walk thro' fire, *M*, to gain it— " 134
obedience and thy love to me, Thy *m*,—I demand.' " 147
slowly spake the *m* looking at him, " 151
And since thou art my *m*, must obey. " 167
The *m's* eye Full of the wistful fear " 172
Before the wakeful *m* heard him, went. " 180
' Son, the good *m* let me know thee here, " 550
Seem I not as tender to him As any *m* ? " 1284
' *M*, a maiden is a tender thing, *Marr. of Geraint* 510
arose, and raised Her *m* too, " 536
a costly gift Of her good *m*, " 632
For while the *m* show'd it, and the two " 636
it was her *m* grasping her To get her well awake ; " 676
Here ceased the kindly *m* out of breath ; " 732
Help'd by the *m's* careful hand and eye, " 738
Yniol made report Of that good *m* making Enid gay " 757
Dared not to glance at her good *m's* face, " 766
Her *m* silent too, nor helping her, " 768
Then seeing cloud upon the *m's* brow, " 777
' O my new *m*, be not wroth or grieved " 779
He spoke : the *m* smiled, but half in tears, " 823
Pure as our own true *M* is our Queen.' *Balin and Balan* 617
My *m* on his corpse in open field ; (repeat) *Merlin and V.* 43, 73
Seethed like the kid in its own *m's* milk ! " 869
m of the house There was not : *Lancelot and E.* 177
Wish'd it had been my *m*, for they talk'd, " 674
Milder than any *m* to a sick child, " 858
Nay, by the *m* of our Lord himself, " 1230
Lady of the Lake Caught from his *m's* arms— " 1405
The highest virtue, *m* of them all ; *Holy Grail* 446
Such as the wholesome *m's* tell their boys. *Pelleas and E.* 197
sister of my *m*—she that bore Camilla *Lover's Tale i* 202
My *m's* sister, *m* of my love, " 209
whatsoe'er Our general *m* meant for me alone, Our mutual *m* dealt to both of us : " 245
Why were our *m's*' branches of one stem ? " *ii* 25
Back to his *m's* house among the pines. " *iv* 15

Mother (s) (*continued*) All softly as his *m* broke it to him— *Lover's Tale iv* 31
Back to the *m's* house where she was born. „ 91
Then the good *m's* kindly ministering, „ 92
You'll make her its second *m* ! *First Quarrel* 71
' O *m*, come out to me.' *Rizpah* 2
' O *m* ! ' I heard him cry. „ 42
' *M*, O *m* ! '—he call'd in the dark „ 47
How do they know it ? are *they* his *m* ? „ 70
their *m* and her sister loved More passionately still. *Sisters (E. and E.)* 44
The *m* fell about the daughter's neck, „ 154
Edith wrote : ' My *m* bids me ask ' „ 181
I told your wayside story to my *m* „ 189
' Pray come and see my *m*. „ 191
' Pray come and see my *m*, and farewell.' „ 196
the simple *m* work'd upon By Edith „ 206
The *m* broke her promise to the dead, „ 252
m's garrulous wail For ever woke the unhappy Past „ 262
Miss Annie were saw stuck oop, like 'er *m* afoor— *Village Wife* 59
And thine Imperial *m* smile again, *Ded. Poem Prin. Alice* 13
yea to him Who hacks his *m's* throat—denied to him, Who finds the Saviour in his mother tongue. *Sir J. Oldcastle* 114
All glory to the *m* of our Lord, *Columbus* 62
dear *m's*, crazing Nature, kill Their babies „ 179
—honouring his wise *m's* word— *Achilles over the T.* 16
maidens, wives, And *m's* with their babblers *Tiresias* 103
Hide me, *M* ! my Fathers belong'd to the church *The Wreck* 1
I was the tempter, *M*, „ 11
He that they gave me to, *M*, „ 13
M, I have not—however their tongues may have babbled „ 41
for *M*, the voice was the voice of the soul ; „ 54
but it coo'd to the *M* and smiled. „ 60
And the Motherless *M* kiss'd it, „ 62
M, one morning a bird with a warble „ 81
' The heart ! not a *m's* heart, „ 97
cloud of the *m's* shame will enfold her „ 100
M, the ship stagger'd under a thunderous shock, „ 107
the face I had known, O *M*, was not the face „ 116
O *M*, she came to me there. „ 148
Struck hard at the tender heart of the *m*, *Despair* 74
Better our dead brute *m* who never „ 98
grave would yawn, my *m's* ghost would rise— *The Flight* 51
Our gentle *m*, had *she* lived— „ 77
Our dying *m* join'd our hands ; „ 87
Thin Molly's ould *m*, yer Honour, *Tomorrow* 19
As the Holy *M* o' Glory that smiles „ 26
To be there wid the Blessed *M*, „ 95
—father, *m*,—be content, *Locksley H., Sixty* 25
dead the *m*, dead the child. „ 36
Gone thy tender-natured *m*, „ 57
Clinging to the silent *m* ! „ 99
Sun of dawn That brightens thro' the *M's* tender eyes, *To Prin. Beatrice* 4
M weeps At that white funeral of the single life, „ 8
But moving thro' the *M's* home, „ 17
The *m* featured in the son ; *Open. I. and C. Exhib.* 12
Drove from out the *m's* nest That young eagle „ 27
' *M* ! ' and I was folded in thine arms. *Demeter and P.* 22
disimpassion'd eyes Awed even me at first, thy *m*— „ 24
So mighty was the *m's* childless cry, „ 32
And set the *m* waking in amaze „ 57
chanting me, Me, me, the desolate *M* ! „ 73
Because I hear your *M's* voice in yours. *The Ring* 28
ring bequeath'd you by your *m*, child, „ 75
My *M's* nurse and mine. „ 97
I ask'd About my *M*, and she said, Thy hair Is golden like thy *M's*, not so fine.' „ 103
Of my dear *M* on your bracket here— „ 110
and I, she said, I babbled, *M*, *M*— „ 115
Miriam your *M* might appear to me. „ 137
Vext, that you thought my *M* came to me ? Or at my crying ' *M* ? ' or to find My *M's* diamonds hidden „ 140

Mother (s) (*continued*) Your *M* and step-mother— *The Ring* 146
lived With Muriel's *m* on the down, „ 148
And on your *M's* birthday— „ 248
poor *M* ! And you, poor desolate Father, „ 302
Muriel's *m* sent, And sure am I, „ 311
Had graspt a daisy from your *M's* grave— „ 323
You scorn my *M's* warning, „ 326
For Muriel nursed you with a *m's* care ; „ 349
but oftener left That angling to the *m*. „ 356
And the face, The hand,—my *M*. „ 425
larger woman-world Of wives and *m's*. „ 487
M, dare you kill your child ? *Forlorn* 37
I see the picture yet, *M* and child. *Romney's R.* 81
' Father and *M* will watch you grow '—(repeat) „ 104, 106
fair *m's* they Dying in childbirth of dead sons. *Akbar's Dream* 11
to be reconciled ?—No, by the *M* of God, *Bandit's Death* 17
Mother-age O thou wondrous *M-A* ! *Locksley Hall* 108
M-A (for mine I knew not) „ 185
Mother-city gain'd the *m-c* thick with towers, *Princess i* 112
Motherhood heart of *m* Within me shudder, *Demeter and P.* 41
She dropt the gracious mask of *m*, *The Ring* 384
Motherless She was *m* And I without a father. *Lover's Tale i* 218
M evermore of an ever-vanishing race, *Despair* 84
The *m* bleat of a lamb in the storm *In the Child. Hosp.* 64
And the *M* Mother kiss'd it, *The Wreck* 62
Mother-maidenhood deathless *m-m* of Heaven, *Balin and Balan* 521
Motion A *m* from the river won Ridged the smooth level, *Arabian Nights* 34
Thought and *m* mingle, Mingle ever. *M's* flow To one another, *Eleänore* 60
With *m's* of the outer sea : „ 113
' We find no *m* in the dead.' *Two Voices* 279
With *m's*, checks, and counterchecks. „ 300
Nature's living *m* lent The pulse of hope „ 449
I had no *m* of my own. *Miller's D.* 44
all those names, that in their *m* were *Palace of Art* 165
'Mid onward-sloping *m's* infinite „ 247
We have had enough of action, and of *m* we, *Lotos-Eaters, C. S.* 105
There was no *m* in the dumb dead air, *D. of F. Women* 65
Because with sudden *m* from the ground „ 170
when no mortal *m* jars The blackness *On a Mourner* 26
A *m* toiling in the gloom— *Love thou thy land* 54
Or voice, or else a *m* of the mere. *M. d'Arthur* 77
Like those blind *m's* of the Spring, *Talking Oak* 175
And her eyes on all my *m's* *Locksley Hall* 22
Nature made them blinder *m's* „ 150
No shadow past, nor *m* : *Enoch Arden* 710
his passions all in flood And masters of his *m*, *Aylmer's Field* 340
I thought the *m* of the boundless deep *Sea Dreams* 91
The *m* of the great deep bore me on, „ 111
And then the *m* of the current ceased, „ 117
Read rascal in the *m's* of his back, „ 167
faces toward us and address'd Their *m* : *Princess iv* 552
about his *m* clung The shadow of his sister, „ *v* 257
the heart Made for all noble *m* : „ 384
All in quantity, careful of my *m*, *Hendecasyllabics* 5
That all thy *m's* gently pass *In Mem. xv* 10
Whose muffled *m's* blindly drown „ *xlix* 15
As, unto vaster *m's* bound, „ *lxiii* 10
O heart, with kindliest *m* warm, „ *lxxxv* 34
No dance, no *m*, save alone What lightens „ *cv* 23
In all her *m* one with law ; „ *cxxii* 8
having the nerves of *m* as well as the nerves of pain, *Maud I i* 63
In counter *m* to the clouds, *Gareth and L.* 1315
put his horse in *m* toward the knight, *Marr. of Geraint* 206
But at the flash and *m* of the man *Geraint and E.* 467
So, scared but at the *m* of the man, „ 476
heavens Were shaken with the *m* and the sound. *Holy Grail* 801
Or voice, or else a *m* of the mere. *Pass. of Arthur* 245
or set apart Their *m's* and their brightness *Lover's Tale i* 174
And saw the *m* of all other things ; „ 574
m's of my heart seem'd far within me, „ *ii* 54
soul, life And breath and *m*, past and flow'd away „ 195
The feebler *m* underneath his hand. „ *iv* 83
fated channel where thy *m* lives *De Prof., Two G.* 19

Motion (*continued*) the boundless *m* of the deep. *Ancient Sage* 194
still In *m* to the distant gleam, *Freedom* 14
Motionless Enoch slumber'd *m* and pale, *Enoch Arden* 908
Mute, blind and *m* as then I lay; *Lover's Tale i* 607
Mottal (mortal) I owäs owd Roäver moor nor I iver owäd *m* man. *Owd Roä* 4
Motto Blazon your *m'es* of blessing *W. to Alexandra* 12
this for *m*, 'Rather use than fame.' *Merlin and V.* 480
Mould (earth) you may lay me low i' the *m* *May Queen, N. Y's. E.* 4
And render him to the *m*. *Ode on Well.* 48
and flung the *m* upon your feet, *Happy* 50
dead from all the human race as if beneath the *m*; „ 95
groundflame of the crocus breaks the *m*, *Prog. of Spring* 1
Six foot deep of burial *m* Will dull their comments! *Romney's R.* 125
Mould (form) 'Think you this *m* of hopes and fears *Two Voices* 28
That I was first in human *m*? „ 342
(Beauty seen In all varieties of *m* and mind) *To ——, With Pal. of Art* 7
those That are cast in gentle *m*. *To J. S.* 4
lovelier in her mood Than in her *m* that other, *Princess vii* 163
Those niched shapes of noble *m*, *The Daisy* 38
over all one statue in the *m* Of Arthur, *Holy Grail* 238
Which, cast in later Grecian *m*, *To Master of B.* 6
Mould (verb) Unto her limbs itself doth *m* *Day-Dm., Sleep. B.* 10
and *m* The woman to the fuller day.' *Princess iii* 331
And *m* a generation strong to move „ *v* 416
To *m* a mighty state's decrees, *In Mem. lxiv* 11
wrought To *m* the dream; *To E. Fitzgerald* 30
and the strength To *m* it into action *Tiresias* 129
Will *m* him thro' the cycle-year That dawns *Epilogue* 77
M them for all his people. *Akbar's Dream* 129
Moulded (*See also* **Imperial-moulded, Large-moulded, Master-moulded, Well-moulded**) *M* thy baby thought. *Eleänore* 5
And in the sixth she *m* man. *Two Voices* 18
M by God, and temper'd with the tears *To ——, With Pal. of Art* 18
Heaven in lavish bounty *m*, *Aylmer's Field* 107
As *m* like in Nature's mint; *In Mem. lxxix* 6
And *m* in colossal calm. „ *Con.* 16
Be *m* by your wishes for her weal; *Marr. of Geraint* 799
from the statue Merlin *m* for us *Holy Grail* 732
M the audible and visible; *Lover's Tale ii* 105
the heavens Whereby the cloud was *m*, *Ancient Sage* 13
stateliest measure ever *m* by the lips of man. *To Virgil* 40
Moulder cannons *m* on the seaward wall; *Ode on Well.* 173
That rotting inward slowly *m's* all. *Merlin and V.* 395
Their heads should *m* on the city gates. „ 594
but here too much We *m*— *Holy Grail* 39
Moulder'd (*See also* **Half-moulder'd**) I see the *m* Abbey-walls, *Talking Oak* 3
Shall it not be scorn to me to harp on such a *m* string? *Locksley Hall* 147
red roofs about a narrow wharf In cluster; then a *m* church; *Enoch Arden* 4
never man, I think, So *m* in a sinecure as he: *Princess, Pro.* 182
About the *m* lodges of the Past „ *iv* 63
A *m* citadel on the coast, *The Daisy* 28
hath power to see Within the green the *m* tree, *In Mem. xxvi* 7
I heard a groaning overhead, and climb'd The *m* stairs *Lover's Tale iv* 137
And a tree with a *m* nest On its barkless bones, *Dead Prophet* 18
Who lops the *m* branch away. *Hands all Round* 8
Found in a chink of that old *m* floor!' *The Ring* 280
what a fury shook Those pillars of a *m* faith, *Akbar's Dream* 81
Mouldering mouse Behind the *m* wainscot shriek'd, *Mariana* 64
Earthward he boweth the heavy stalks Of the *m* flowers: *A spirit haunts* 8
But I shall lie alone, mother, within the *m* grave. *May Queen, N. Y's. E.* 20
Yet how often I and Amy in the *m* aisle have stood, *Locksley H., Sixty* 31
From that casement where the trailer mantles all the *m* bricks— „ 257
m with the dull earth's *m* sod, *Palace of Art* 261
sunlit ocean tosses O'er them *m*, *The Captain* 70
Mouldering (*continued*) Before the *m* of a yew; *In Mem. lxxvi* 8
Still larger *m* all the house of thought, *Lover's Tale i* 241
Moulding reach thro' nature, *m* men. *In Mem. cxxiv* 24
Mouldy To shame these *m* Aylmers in their graves: *Aylmer's Field* 396
Stuff his ribs with *m* hay. *Vision of Sin* 66
'Trooping from their *m* dens The chap-fallen circle spreads: „ 171
Moult Some birds are sick and sullen when they *m*. *Sisters (E. and E.)* 73
Mound (s) A realm of pleasance, many a *m*, *Arabian Nights* 101
Heap'd over with a *m* of grass, *Lotos-Eaters, C. S.* 67
There sat we down upon a garden *m*, *Gardener's D.* 214
and sat upon a *m* That was unsown, *Dora* 72
took The child once more, and sat upon the *m*; „ 81
and gain'd a petty *m* Beyond it, *Princess iv* 557
scarce three paces measured from the *m*, „ *v* 1
huddled here and there on *m* and knoll, *Geraint and E.* 803
whelm all this beneath as vast a *m* *Merlin and V.* 656
Tho' heapt in *m's* and ridges all the sea *Holy Grail* 798
Near him a *m* of even-sloping side, *Pelleas amd E.* 25
Mound (verb) heaped hills that *m* the sea, *Ode to Memory* 98
Mounded Far furrowing into light the *m* rack, *Love and Duty* 100
'When wealth no more shall rest in *m* heaps, *Golden Year* 32
Mount (s) A *m* of marble, a hundred spires! *The Daisy* 60
Rolling her smoke about the Royal *m*, *Gareth and L.* 190
Right o'er a *m* of newly-fallen stones, *Marr. of Geraint* 361
'Too high this *m* of Camelot for me: *Balin and Balan* 226
on the *m* Of Badon I myself beheld the King *Lancelot and E.* 302
For all the sacred *m* of Camelot, *Holy Grail* 227
Wealthy with wandering lines of *m* and mere, „ 252
Strike on the *M* of Vision! *Ancient Sage* 285
M and mine, and primal wood; *Open. I. and C. Exhib.* 6
Mount (verb) Before he *m's* the hill, I know *Fatima* 22
Nor sound of human sorrow *m's* to mar *Lucretius* 109
As *m's* the heavenward altar-fire, *In Mem. xli* 3
never *m* As high as woman in her selfless mood. *Merlin and V.* 442
What did the wanton say? 'Not *m* as high;' „ 813
Mountain (adj.) why he Slumbers not like a *m* tarn? *Supp. Confessions* 129
And seem'd knee-deep in *m* grass, *Mariana in the S.* 42
O *m* brooks, I am the daughter of a River-God, *Œnone* 37
Aloft the *m* lawn was dewy-dark, And dewy dark aloft the *m* pine: „ 48
Ah me, my *m* shepherd, that my arms „ 202
thro' *m* clefts the dale Was seen far inland, *Lotos-Eaters* 20
I lived up there on yonder *m* side. *St. S. Stylites* 72
He watches from his *m* walls, *The Eagle* 5
Like torrents from a *m* source We rush'd *The Letters* 39
From him that on the *m* lea *To E. L.* 21
Downward from his *m* gorge Stept the long-hair'd long-bearded solitary, *Enoch Arden* 636
Turbia show'd In ruin, by the *m* road; *The Daisy* 6
Now watching high on *m* cornice, „ 19
oft we saw the glisten Of ice, far up on a *m* head. „ 36
A *m* islet pointed and peak'd; *The Islet* 15
The fortress, and the *m* ridge, *In Mem. lxxi* 14
And catch at every *m* head, „ *Con.* 114
A huge pavilion like a *m* peak *Gareth and L.* 1364
Thus, as a hearth lit in a *m* home, *Balin and Balan* 231
brutes of *m* back That carry kings in castles, *Merlin and V.* 576
Like its own mists to all the *m* side: *Lancelot and E.* 38
and on the naked *m* top Blood-red, *Holy Grail* 474
all the purple slopes of *m* flowers Pass under white, *Last Tournament* 229
Streams like a cloud, man-shaped, from *m* peak, *To the Queen ii* 40
A *m* nest—the pleasure-boat that rock'd, *Lover's Tale i* 42
As *m* streams Our bloods ran free: „ 326
A stately *m* nymph she look'd! „ 359
On the other side Is scoop'd a cavern and a *m* hall, „ 517
waterfalls Pour'd in a thunderless plunge to the base of the *m* walls, *V. of Maeldune* 14
beyond A hundred ever-rising *m* lines, *Ancient Sage* 282
And we will feed her with our *m* air, *The Ring* 319
Mountain (s) From the brain of the purple *m* *Poet's Mind* 29
And the *m* draws it from Heaven above, „ 32
Apart upon a *m*, tho' the surge *If I were loved* 11

Mouse (*continued*) Thou'd niver 'a cotch'd ony *mice* *Spinster's S's.* 55
thou be es 'ansom a tabby es iver patted a *m*. „ 70
Ghoäst moästlins was nobbut a rat or a *m*. *Owd Roä* 38
Mouth (s) (*See also* **Cavern-mouth, Harbour-mouth, Purse-mouth**) bitter words From off your rosy *m*. *Rosalind* 51
smite him on the cheek, And on the *m*, *Two Voices* 252
I crush'd them on my breast, my *m*; *Fatima* 12
common *m*, So gross to express delight, *Gardener's D.* 55
M, forehead, eyelids, growing dewy-warm *Tithonus* 58
steaming flats, and floods Of mighty *m*, *The Voyage* 46
A downward crescent of her minion *m*, *Aylmer's Field* 533
Paled at a sudden twitch of his iron *m*; „ 732
that one unctuous *m* which lured him, *Sea Dreams* 14
And often told a tale from *m* to *m* *Princess, Pro.* 191
Walter warp'd his *m* at this To something „ 214
a twitch of pain Tortured her *m*, „ *vi* 106
on her *m* A doubtful smile dwelt „ 269
Into the *m* of Hell Rode the six hundred. *Light Brigade* 25
Back from the *m* of Hell, „ 47
A rabbit *m* that is ever agape— *Maud I x* 31
And a rose her *m* (repeat) „ *xvii* 8, 28
deathful-grinning *m's* of the fortress, „ *III vi* 52
King Arthur's hound of deepest *m*, *Marr. of Geraint* 186
made that *m* of night Whereout the Demon *Balin and Balan* 316
meets And dallies with him in the *M* of Hell.' „ 615
How, in the *m's* of base interpreters, *Merlin and V.* 795
Rang by the white *m* of the violent Glem; *Lancelot and E.* 288
too high For any *m* to gape for save a queen's— „ 775
Were added *m's* that gaped, and eyes that ask'd „ 1249
An' I wur down i' tha *m*, *North. Cobbler* 77
as big i' the *m* as a cow, *Village Wife* 103
Heat like the *m* of a hell, *Def. of Lucknow* 81
That mock-meek *m* of utter Antichrist, *Sir J. Oldcastle* 170
and sail'd the Dragon's *m*, *Columbus* 25
Brass *m's* and iron lungs! *Freedom* 40
wi' my bairn i' 'is m *to the winder* *Owd Roä* 92
Do not die with a lie in your *m*, *Forlorn* 57
Whose ivy-matted *m* she used to gaze *Death of Œnone* 2
Mouth (verb) How she *m's* behind my back. *Vision of Sin* 110
endure To *m* so huge a foulness— *Balin and Balan* 379
actor *m* his last upon the stage. *Locksley H., Sixty* 152
Mouth'd (*See also* **Bell-mouthed, Gap-mouth'd, Mealy-mouth'd, Mighty-mouthed, Open-mouth'd, Wide-mouthed**) in her hunger *m* and mumbled it, *Princess vi* 213
Mouthing *m* out his hollow oes and aes, *The Epic* 50
While scandal is *m* a bloodless name *The Dawn* 12
Mouthpiece he made his *m* of a page Who came and went, *Gareth and L.* 1337
I come the *m* of our King to Doorm *Geraint and E.* 796
Move pray—that God would *m* And strike *Supp. Confessions* 115
You *m* not in such solitudes, *Margaret* 45
Or sometimes they swell and *m*, *Eleänore* 111
phantom of a wish that once could *m*, *The form, the form* 10
trailing light, *M's* over still Shalott. *L. of Shalott iii* 27
'Some hidden principle to *m*, *Two Voices* 133
To *m* about the house with joy, *Miller's D.* 95
And there I *m* no longer now, *May Queen, Con.* 51
these did *m* Me from my bliss of life, *D. of F. Women* 209
He lieth still: he doth not *m*: *D. of the O. Year* 10
some full music seem'd to *m* and change *Edwin Morris* 35
She *m's* among my visions of the lake, „ 144
wake and sleep, but all things *m*; *Golden Year* 22
M onward, leading up the golden year. „ 26
For ever and for ever when I *m*. *Ulysses* 21
sweetly did she speak and *m*: *Locksley Hall* 71
Science *m's*, but slowly slowly, „ 134
And *m's* not on the rounded curl. *Day-Dm., Sleep. B.* 8
The gouty oak began to *m*, *Amphion* 23
I could not *m* a thistle; „ 66
Me mightier transports *m* and thrill; *Sir Galahad* 22
Then *m* the trees, the copses nod, „ 77
Begins to *m* and tremble. *Will Water.* 32
And wheresoe'er thou *m*, good luck „ 215
But thou wilt never *m* from hence, „ 217
M eastward, happy earth, *Move eastward* 1

Move (*continued*) And *m* me to my marriage-morn, *Move Eastward* 11
Till the graves begin to *m*, *Vision of Sin* 165
A life that *m's* to gracious ends *You might have won* 6
I *m* the sweet forget-me-nots That grow *The Brook* 172
bough That moving *m's* the nest and nestling, *Sea Dreams* 291
never creeps a cloud, or *m's* a wind, *Lucretius* 106
But *m* as rich as Emperer-moths, *Princess, Pro.* 144
I seem'd to *m* among a world of ghosts, „ *i* 17
Who *m's* about the Princess; „ 76
whene'er she *m's* The Samian Herè rises „ *iii* 114
enter'd; found her there At point to *m*, „ 131
we *m*, my friend, At no man's beck, „ 226
whence after-hands May *m* the world, „ 264
lightlier *m* The minutes fledged with music:' „ *iv* 36
I seem'd to *m* among a world of ghosts; „ 561
And mould a generation strong to *m* „ *v* 416
I seem'd to *m* in old memorial tilts, „ 479
fangs Shall *m* the stony bases of the world. „ *vi* 58
cannot speak, nor *m*, nor make one sign, „ *vii* 153
But cease to *m* so near the Heavens, „ 195
m's with him to one goal, „ 263
If love of country *m* thee there *Ode on Well.* 140
The dark crowd *m's*, and there are sobs „ 268
For him nor *m's* the loud world's random mock, *Will* 4
And *m's* his doubtful arms, and feels *In Mem. xiii* 3
For I in spirit saw thee *m* „ *xvii* 5
But this it was that made me *m* „ *xxv* 5
And doubtful joys the father *m*, „ *xl* 9
Should *m* his rounds, and fusing all „ *xlvii* 2
'Thou canst not *m* me from thy side, „ *lii* 7
My centred passion cannot *m*. „ *lix* 9
And *m* thee on to noble ends. „ *lxv* 12
Her faith is fixt and cannot *m*, „ *xcvii* 33
As down the garden-walks I *m*, „ *cii* 6
m his course, and show That life is not an idle ore, „ *cxviii* 19
M upward, working out the beast, „ 27
a sentinel Who *m's* about from place to place, „ *cxxvi* 10
To which the whole creation *m's*. „ *Con.* 144
Do we *m* ourselves, or are moved *Maud I iv* 26
But to *m* to the meadow and fall before „ *v* 25
For a breeze of morning *m's*, „ *xxii* 7
But only *m's* with the moving eye, „ *II ii* 37
Pass and cease to *m* about! „ *iv* 59
Began to *m*, seethe, twine and curl: *Gareth and L.* 234
that ev'n to him they seem'd to *m*. „ 237
M's him to think what kind of bird it is *Marr. of Geraint* 331
pushing could *m* The chair of Idris. „ 542
When first I parted from thee, *m's* me yet.' *Geraint and E.* 347
my leave To *m* to your own land, „ 889
walk with me, and *m* To music with thine Order *Balin and Balan* 76
How far beyond him Lancelot seem'd to *m*, „ 172
he felt his being *m* In music with his Order, „ 211
you cannot *m* To these fair jousts?' *Lancelot and E.* 79
strike spur, suddenly *m*, Meet in the midst, „ 456
dream Of dragging down his enemy made them *m*. „ 814
the rough Torre began to heave and *m*, „ 1066
In which as Arthur's Queen I *m* and rule: „ 1221
Such as no wind could *m*: *Holy Grail* 681
M with me toward their quelling, *Last Tournament* 101
O ay—the winds that *m* the mere.' „ 738
in this battle in the west Whereto we *m*, *Pass. of Arthur* 67
wastes the narrow realm whereon we *m*, „ 140
M with me to the event. *Lover's Tale i* 298
The boat was beginning to *m*, *First Quarrel* 21
You *m* about the Court, I pray you tell *Columbus* 222
Whereon the Spirit of God *m's* as he will— *De Prof., Two G.* 28
And *m's* unseen among the ways of men. *Tiresias* 24
While men shall *m* the lips: „ 133
boundless deep That *m's*, and all is gone.' *Ancient Sage* 190
All good things may *m* in Hesper, *Locksley H., Sixty* 186
M among your people, know them, „ 266
draws the child To *m* in other spheres. *To Prin. Beatrice* 8
Thy power, well-used to *m* the public breast. *To W. C. Macready* 3
WE *m*, the wheel must always *m*, *Politics* 1
And if we *m* to such a goal As Wisdom „ 3

Move (*continued*) Will you *m* a little that way ? *Charity* 20
Moveable some with gems *M* and resettable at will, *Lover's Tale iv* 199
Moved *M* from beneath with doubt and fear. *Supp. Confessions* 138
At last you rose and *m* the light, *Miller's D.* 125
Your ripe lips *m* not, but your cheek Flush'd „ 131
Fronting the dawn he *m* ; *Œnone* 58
Floated the glowing sunlights, as she *m*. „ 182
bells that swung, *M* of themselves, *Palace of Art* 130
Its office, *m* with sympathy. *Love thou thy land* 48
barge with oar and sail *M* from the brink, *M. d'Arthur* 266
And *m* away, and left me, statue-like, *Gardener's D.* 161
she *m*, Like Proserpine in Enna, *Edwin Morris* 111
strength which in old days *M* earth and heaven ; *Ulysses* 67
You *m* her at your pleasure. *Amphion* 60
She faintly smiled, she hardly *m* ; *The Letters* 14
M with violence, changed in hue, *Vision of Sin* 34
So lifted up in spirit he *m* away. *Enoch Arden* 330
A phantom made of many phantoms *m* Before him haunting him, or he himself *M* haunting people, „ 602
Katie never ran : she *m* To meet me, *The Brook* 87
There *m* the multitude a thousand heads : *Princess, Pro.* 57
for still we *m* Together, „ *i* 56
so To the open window *m*, „ *iv* 492
Set into sunrise ; then we *m* away. „ 576
She heard, she *m*, She moan'd, „ *v* 72
Yet she neither spoke nor *m*. „ *vi* 8
Yet she neither *m* nor wept. „ 12
whether *m* by this, or was it chance, „ 97
And *m* beyond his custom, Gama said : „ 229
So said the small king *m* beyond his wont. „ 265
on they *m* and gain'd the hall, and there Rested : „ 352
And in their own clear element, they *m*. „ *vii* 28
I *m* : I sigh'd : a touch Came round my wrist, „ 137
She *m*, and at her feet the volume fell. „ 254
Sway'd to her from their orbits as they *m*, „ 326
I *m* as in a strange diagonal, „ *Con.* 27
'The Gods are *m* against the land.' *The Victim* 6
The Wye is hush'd nor *m* along, *In Mem. xix* 9
M in the chambers of the blood ; „ *xxiii* 20
We saw not, when we *m* therein ? „ *xxiv* 16
and *m* Upon the topmost froth of thought. „ *lii* 3
Had *m* me kindly from his side, „ *lxxx* 3
And, *m* thro' life of lower phase, „ *Con.* 125
m by an unseen hand at a game That pushes *Maud I iv* 26
Maud was *m* To speak of the mother she loved „ *xix* 26
and we see him as he *m*, *Ded. of Idylls* 17
(Your city *m* so weirdly in the mist) *Gareth and L.* 245
So the sweet voice of Enid *m* Geraint ; *Marr. of Geraint* 334
M the fair Enid, all in faded silk, „ 366
they *m* Down to the meadow where the jousts „ 536
and wings *M* in her ivy, „ 599
thus he *m* the Prince To laughter *Geraint and E.* 295
harder to be *m* Than hardest tyrants „ 694
Was *m* so much the more, and shriek'd again, „ 782
They said a light came from her when she *m* : *Merlin and V.* 567
Thus they *m* away : she stay'd a minute, *Lancelot and E.* 390
Must needs have *m* my laughter : „ 596
And *m* about her palace, proud and pale. „ 614
And lifted her fair face and *m* away : „ 682
Who had devised the letter, *m* again. „ 1288
mark'd Sir Lancelot where he *m* apart, „ 1349
m Among us in white armour, Galahad. *Holy Grail* 134
on me *m* In golden armour with a crown of gold „ 409
when I *m* of old A slender page about her father's hall, „ 580
whose lightest whisper *m* him more *Pelleas and E.* 155
for nothing *m* but his own self, „ 417
with cups of gold, *M* to the lists, *Last Tournament* 143
might have *m* slow-measure to my tune, „ 282
ending, he *m* toward her, and she said, „ 704
which had noblest, while you *m* Among them, *Guinevere* 325
rose the King and *m* his host by night, *Pass. of Arthur* 79
barge with oar and sail *M* from the brink, „ 434
Thereat once more he *m* about, „ 462
M from the cloud of unforgotten things, *Lover's Tale i* 48

Moved (*continued*) By that name I *m* upon her breath ; *Lover's Tale i* 560
rain Fell on my face, and her long ringlets *m*, „ 699
M with one spirit round about the bay, „ *iii* 17
He *m* thro' all of it majestically— „ *iv* 9
they are mine—not theirs—they had *m* in my side. *Rizpah* 54
And *m* to merriment at a passing jest. *Sisters (E. and E.)* 121
it often *m* me to tears, *In the Child. Hosp.* 31
an earthquake always *m* in the hollows *V. of Maeldune* 107
Whatever *m* in that full sheet Let down to Peter *To E. Fitzgerald* 11
Universal Nature *m* by Universal Mind ; *To Virgil* 22
m but by the living limb, *Akbar's Dream* 133
Movement in its onward current it absorbs With swifter *m* *Isabel* 32
loveliest in all grace Of *m*, *Œnone* 76
without light Or power of *m*, *Palace of Art* 246
Movest Nor canst thou prove the world thou *m* in, *Ancient Sage* 58
Moving (*See also* **Slow-moving**) *M* thro' a fleecy night. *Margaret* 21
M in the leavy beech. „ 61
m thro' a mirror clear That hangs before her *L. of Shalott ii* 10
Still *m* after truth long sought, *Two Voices* 62
lift the hidden ore That glimpses, *m* up, *D. of F. Women* 275
Seen where the *m* isles of winter shock By night, *M. d'Arthur* 140
m toward the stillness of his rest. *Locksley Hall* 144
Then *m* homeward came on Annie pale, *Enoch Arden* 149
The *m* whisper of huge trees that branch'd „ 585
Then *m* up the coast they landed him, „ 665
in *m* on I found Only the landward exit of the cave, *Sea Dreams* 95
bough That *m* moves the nest and nestling, „ 291
and was *m* on In gratulation, *Princess ii* 184
m thro' the uncertain gloom, „ *iv* 216
isles of light Slided, they *m* under shade : „ *vi* 82
lay Quite sunder'd from the *m* Universe, „ *vii* 52
M about the household ways, *In Mem. lx* 11
And *m* up from high to higher, „ *lxiv* 13
Eternal process *m* on, „ *lxxxii* 5
m side by side With wisdom, „ *cxiv* 19
And see'st the *m* of the team. „ *cxxi* 16
lost in trouble and *m* round Here at the head *Maud I xxi* 5
But only moves with the *m* eye, „ *II ii* 37
sang the knighthood, *m* to their hall. *Com. of Arthur* 503
Who, *m*, cast the coverlet aside, *Marr. of Geraint* 73
And *m* toward a cedarn cabinet, „ 136
I saw you *m* by me on the bridge, „ 429
So *m* without answer to her rest She found no rest, „ 530
Then, *m* downward to the meadow ground, *Geraint and E.* 204
He *m* up with pliant courtliness, „ 278
He *m* homeward babbled to his men, „ 362
m back she held Her finger up, „ 452
And *m* out they found the stately horse, „ 752
And Edyrn *m* frankly forward spake : „ 784
m everywhere Clear'd the dark places „ 942
M to meet him in the castle court ; *Lancelot and E.* 175
But kindly man *m* among his kind : „ 265
plumes driv'n backward by the wind they made In *m*, „ 481
saw the barge that brought her *m* down, „ 1391
thought he meant To crush me, *m* on me, *Holy Grail* 416
but *m* with me night and day, „ 471
Mean knights, to whom the *m* of my sword „ 790
and far ahead Of his and her retinue *m*, *Guinevere* 385
And *m* thro' the past unconsciously, „ 402
m ghostlike to his doom. „ 605
but no man was *m* there ; *Pass. of Arthur* 127
Seen where the *m* isles of winter shock By night, „ 308
Thence mark'd the black hull *m* yet, „ 448
down the highway *m* on With easy laughter *Tiresias* 199
But *m* thro' the Mother's home, *To Prin. Beatrice* 17
She *m*, at her girdle clash The golden keys *To Marq. of Dufferin* 3
Are there spectres *m* in the darkness ? *On Jub. Q. Victoria* 67
And *m* each to music, soul in soul *Happy* 39
M to melody, Floated The Gleam. *Merlin and the G.* 22
slowly *m* again to a melody Yearningly tender, „ 90
Œnone sat Not *m*, till in front of that ravine *th of Œnone* 75
Then *m* quickly forward till the heat „ 97
The gladiators *m* toward their fight, *St. Telemachus* 54
m easily Thro' after-ages in the love of Truth, *Akbar's Dream* 100
But such a tide as *m* seems asleep, *Crossing the Bar* 5

Mower and *m's* mowing in it: *Geraint and E.* 199
in his hand Bare victual for the *m's*: „ 202
fare is coarse, And only meet for *m's*;' „ 209
Ate all the *m's'* victual unawares, „ 215
Fresh victual for these *m's* of our Earl; „ 225
serve thee costlier than with *m's'* fare.' „ 231
Than when I left your *m's* dinnerless. „ 234
The lusty *m's* labouring dinnerless, „ 251
Mowing and mowers *m* in it: „ 199
Mown *See* **New-mown**
Mowt (might) *M* a beän, mayhap, for she wur a bad un, *N. Farmer, O. S.* 22
or I *m* 'a liked tha as well. *Spinster's S's.* 43
Much After *m* wailing, hush'd itself at last *Aylmer's Field* 542
Still so *m* gold was left; *Sea Dreams* 130
touch'd on Mahomet With *m* contempt, *Princess ii* 135
m profit! Not one word; No! „ *vi* 239
For himself has done *m* better. *Spiteful Letter* 4
thy *m* folly hath sent thee here His kitchen-knave: *Gareth and L.* 919
Much-beloved And he the *m-b* again, *In Mem. xlii* 6
Much-experienced ULYSSES, *m-e* man, *To Ulysses* 1
Muck slaäpe down i' the squad an' the *m*: *North. Cobbler* 20
Fur we puts the *m* o' the land an' they sucks the *m* fro' the grass. *Village Wife* 32
Mucky an' their *m* bibs, an' the clats an' the clouts, *Spinster's S's.* 87
Mud (*See also* **Squad**) Lay great with pig, wallowing in sun and *m*. *Walk. to the Mail.* 88
Fish are we that love the *m*, *Vision of Sin* 101
Gracious lessons thine And maxims of the *m*! *Merlin and V.* 49
Swine in the *m*, that cannot see for slime, *Holy Grail* 771
the cup was gold, the draught was *m*.' *Last Tournament* 298
an' the *m* o' 'is boots o' the stairs, *Spinster's S's.* 99
Reversion ever dragging Evolution in the *m*. *Locksley H., Sixty* 200
Muddier 'Was it *m* than thy gibes? *Last Tournament* 299
Muddle lond ater meä thot *m's* ma quoit; *N. Farmer, O. S.* 58
Muddy clear stream flowing with a *m* one, *Isabel* 30
Mud-honey His heart in the gross *m-h* of town, *Maud I xvi* 5
Muffle O *m* round thy knees with fern, *Talking Oak* 149
Muffled (*See also* **Half-muffled**) The panther's roar came *m*, *Œnone* 214
And, sitting *m* in dark leaves, *Gardener's D.* 37
And chimneys *m* in the leafy vine. *Audley Court* 19
watch A full sea glazed with *m* moonlight, *Princess i* 248
but we three Sat *m* like the Fates; „ *ii* 467
but I Lay silent in the *m* cage of life: „ *vii* 47
Now, to the roll of *m* drums, *Ode on Well.* 87
And standing, *m* round with woe, *In Mem. xiv* 5
Whose *m* motions blindly drown The bases of my life in tears. „ *xlix* 15
Whereon were hollow tramplings up and down And *m* voices heard, *Gareth and L.* 1373
Not *m* round with selfish reticence. *Merlin and V.* 337
Listens the *m* booming indistinct Of the confused floods, *Lover's Tale i* 637
From under rose a *m* moan of floods; *Prog. of Spring* 70
Muffling And *m* up her comely head, *Death of Œnone* 104
Muggins An' *M* 'e preäch'd o' Hell-fire *North. Cobbler* 55
Mulberry-faced made The *m-f* Dictator's orgies worse *Lucretius* 54
Mule Her cream-white *m* his pastern set: *Sir L. and Q. G.* 31
Multiplied Thus truth was *m* on truth, *The Poet* 33
Thrice *m* by superhuman pangs, *St. S. Stylites* 11
Multitude and so press in, perforce Of *m*, *Lucretius* 168
There moved the *m*, a thousand heads: *Princess, Pro.* 57
To cast wise words among the *m* *Tiresias* 66
And in each let a *m* Loyal, *On Jub. Q. Victoria* 20
Multitudinous Phantom wail of women and children, *m* agonies. *Boädicea* 26
Ran the land with Roman slaughter, *m* agonies. „ 84
still'd Thro' all its folds the *m* beast, *Tiresias* 15
Multitudinous-eddying Waste down of *m-e* light— *De Prof., Two G.* 4
Mumble priest, who *m* worship in your quire— *Balin and Balan* 444
Mumbled in her hunger mouth'd and *m* it, *Princess vi* 213
m that white hand whose ring'd caress *Balin and Balan* 512
'She too might speak to-day,' she *m*. *The Ring* 125
Mumbling Muttering and *m*, idiotlike *Enoch Arden* 639
Mummy That here the torpid *m* wheat Of Egypt *To Prof. Jebb* 5
Munney (money) An' the *m* they maäde by the war, *Owd Roä* 44
Munny (money) Thou'll not marry for *m*— *N. Farmer, N. S.* 11
soä is scoors o' gells, Them as 'as *m* an' all— „ 15
'Doänt thou marry for *m*, but goä wheer *m* is!' „ 20
An' I went wheer *m* war: an' thy muther coom to 'and, Wi' lots o' *m* laaïd by, „ 21
thou can luvv thy lass an' 'er *m* too. „ 33
Could'n I luvv thy muther by cause o' 'er *m* laaïd by? „ 35
Tis'n them as 'as *m* as breäks into 'ouses an' steäls, „ 45
work mun 'a gone to the gittin' whiniver *m* was got. „ 50
Feyther 'ad ammost nowt; leästways 'is *m* was 'id. „ 51
I grabb'd the *m* she maäde, *North. Cobbler* 32
Murder (*See also* **Wife-murder**) spirit of *m* works in the very means of life, *Maud I i* 40
That keeps the rust of *m* on the walls— *Guinevere* 74
Her love did *m* mine? What then? *Lover's Tale i* 740
For the lawyer is born but to *m*— *Rizpah* 64
how long shall the *m* last? *V. of Maeldune* 123
dying worm in a world, all massacre, *m*, and wrong. *Despair* 32
M would not veil your sin, *Forlorn* 49
Murder'd (*See also* **Ever-murder'd**) A woman weeping for her *m* mate *Geraint and E.* 522
Self-starved, they say—nay, *m*, doubtless dead. *Sir J. Oldcastle* 60
Glared on at the *m* son, and the murderous father at rest, . . . *Bandit's Death* 33
Murderer prov'n themselves Poisoners, *m's*. *Sir J. Oldcastle* 168
Murderous Or pinch a *m* dust into her drink, *Merlin and V.* 610
you can hear him—the *m* mole! *Def. of Lucknow* 26
and the *m* father at rest, . . . *Bandit's Death* 33
Muriel (*See also* **Muriel Erne**) Far-off, is *M*—your stepmother's voice. *The Ring* 139
lived With *M's* mother on the down, „ 148
Miriam sketch'd and *M* threw the fly; „ 159
The form of *M* faded, and the face Of Miriam „ 184
A 'Miriam' that might seem a '*M*'; „ 241
M claim'd and open'd what I meant For Miriam, „ 242
M and Miriam, each in white, „ 254
But coming nearer—*M* had the ring— „ 259
M clench'd The hand that wore it, „ 261
She glanced at me, at *M*, and was mute. „ 264
Then—*M* standing ever statue-like— „ 266
And saying gently: '*M*, by your leave,' „ 268
M fled. Poor *M*! Ay, poor *M* „ 271
M enter'd with it, 'See!—Found in a chink „ 279
M—no—She cannot love; she loves her own hard self, „ 291
Promise me, Miriam not *M*—she shall have the ring.' „ 294
M's mother sent, And sure am I, by *M*, „ 311
By the lych-gate was *M*. „ 324
For *M* nursed you with a mother's care; „ 349
'*M's* health Had weaken'd, nursing little Miriam. „ 356
'I take thee *M* for my wedded wife'— „ 377
M, paler then Than ever you were in your cradle, „ 431
Among them *M* lying on her face—I raised her, call'd her '*M*, *M* wake!' „ 448
Muriel Erne (*See also* **Muriel**) Miriam Erne And *M E*— „ 147
well, you know I married *M E*. „ 376
Murmur (s) Overblown with *m's* harsh, *Ode to Memory* 99
And no *m* at the door, *Deserted House* 7
To hear the *m* of the strife, *Margaret* 23
The *m* of the fountain-head— *Two Voices* 216
A *m* 'Be of better cheer.' „ 429
There comes no *m* of reply. *Palace of Art* 286
And *m's* of a deeper voice, *On a Mourner* 16
This *m* broke the stillness of that air *Gardener's D.* 147
Not whisper, any *m* of complaint. *St. S. Stylites* 22
The *m's* of the drum and fife *Talking Oak* 215
Faint *m's* from the meadows come, *Day-Dm., Sleep. P.* 6
Made a *m* in the land. *L. of Burleigh* 20
And they speak in gentle *m*, „ 49
But finding neither light nor *m* there *Enoch Arden* 687
Came *m's* of her beauty from the South, *Princess i* 36
By this a *m* ran Thro' all the camp „ *v* 110
a *m* heard aërially, *Boädicea* 24
And *m's* from the dying sun: *In Mem. iii* 8
And dull'd the *m* on thy lip, „ *xxii* 16

Murmur (s) (*continued*) lavish hills would hum The *m* of a happy Pan: *In Mem. xxiii* 12
A single *m* in the breast, „ *civ* 7
cackle of your bourg The *m* of the world! *Marr. of Geraint* 277
They take the rustic *m* of their bourg „ 419
m's 'Lo, thou likewise shalt be King.' *Lancelot and E.* 55
and then I seem'd to hear Its *m*, *Lover's Tale i* 635
mellow'd *m* of the people's praise *Ded. Poem Prin. Alice* 7
but never a *m*, a breath— *V. of Maeldune* 19
from within The city comes a *m* void of joy, *Tiresias* 101
a flower Had *m's* 'Lost and gone *Ancient Sage* 224
but a *m* of gnats in the gloom, *Vastness* 35
thro' her dream A ghostly *m* floated, *Death of Œnone* 79
Murmur (verb) in the burn water-gnats *m* and mourn. *Leonine Eleg.* 8
At heart, thou wouldest *m* still— *Supp. Confessions* 104
And the nations do but *m*, *Locksley Hall* 106
I *m* under moon and stars In brambly wildernesses; *The Brook* 178
The dove may *m* of the dove, *Princess iii* 105
loyal pines of Canada *m* thee, *W. to Marie Alex.* 19
Should *m* from the narrow house, *In Mem. xxxv.* 2
the crowd Will *m*, 'Lo the shameless ones, *Lancelot and E.* 100
And *m* at the low-dropt eaves of sleep, *Lover's Tale ii* 122
and *m* down Truth in the distance— *Columbus* 120
will *m* thee To thine own Thebes, *Tiresias* 140
clasp the hands and *m*, 'Would to God *Locksley H., Sixty* 192
If it be a mosque people *m* the holy prayer, *Akbar's D., Inscrip.* 4
Murmur'd Before Our Lady *m* she; *Mariana in the S.* 28
low voice, full of care, *M* beside me: *D. of F. Women* 250
m Arthur, 'Place me in the barge,' *M. d'Arthur* 204
And sweetly *m* thine. *Talking Oak* 160
m 'Oh, that he Were once more that landscape-painter, *L. of Burleigh* 82
But each man *m*, 'O my Queen, *The Voyage* 63
And double death were widely *m*, *Aylmer's Field* 617
For all the sloping pasture *m*, *Princess, Pro.* 55
and *m* that their May Was passing: „ *ii* 463
Then *m* Florian gazing after her, „ *iii* 97
The mellow breaker *m* Ida. „ *iv* 436
'I *m*, as I came along, *In Mem. xxxvii* 21
She past; and Vivien *m* after 'Go! *Merlin and V.* 98
She *m*, 'Vain, in vain: it cannot be. *Lancelot and E.* 892
m Arthur, 'Place me in the barge.' *Pass. of Arthur* 372
when the bridegroom *m*, 'With this ring,' *The Ring* 438
Murmurest Who *m* in the foliaged eaves *In Mem. xcix* 9
Then Kay, 'What *m* thou of mystery? *Gareth and L.* 470
Murmuring And *m*, as at night and morn, *Mariana in the S.* 46
Singing and *m* in her feastful mirth, *Palace of Art* 177
Muttering and *m* at his ear 'Quick, *M. d'Arthur* 179
we saw the lights and heard The voices *m*. *Princess iv* 559
And *m* of innumerable bees.' „ *vii* 222
The brooks of Eden mazily *m*, *Milton* 10
a wind Of memory *m* the past. *In Mem. xcii* 8
field of tourney, *m* 'kitchen-knave.' *Gareth and L.* 664
one *M*, 'All courtesy is dead,' *Last Tournament* 211
M a light song I had heard thee sing, „ 614
A *m* whisper thro' the nunnery ran, *Guinevere* 410
Muttering and *m* at his ear, 'Quick, *Pass. of Arthur* 347
Murmurous lime a summer home of *m* wings. *Gardener's D.* 48
Murn (morn) lark a-singin' 'is best of a Sunday at *m*, *North. Cobbler* 46
Murnin' (morning) An' when I waäk'd i' the *m* „ 39
D'ya mind the *m* when we was a-walkin' togither, *Spinster's S's.* 23
Muscle Having the warmth and *m* of the heart, *Aylmer's Field* 180
arms on which the standing *m* sloped, *Marr. of Geraint* 76
Muscovite How long this icy-hearted *M* *Poland* 10
Muscular So *m* he spread, so broad of breast. *Gardener's D.* 8
Muse (s) The modern *M's* reading. *Amphion* 76
No vain libation to the *M*, *Will Water.* 9
The *M*, the jolly *M*, it is! „ 105
hard-grain'd *M's* of the cube and square *Princess, Pro.* 180
M's and the Graces, group'd in threes, „ *ii* 27
And every *M* tumbled a science in. „ 399
the *M's'* heads were touch'd Above the darkness „ *iii* 21
So they blaspheme the *m*! „ *iv* 137
I fed you with the milk of every *M* „ 295

Muse (s) (*continued*) above them stood The placid marble *M's*, looking peace. *Princess iv* 489
O civic *m*, to such a name, *Ode on Well.* 75
sound ever heard, ye *M's*, in England? *Trans. of Homer* 3
'For I am but an earthly *M*, *In Mem. xxxvii* 13
high *M* answer'd: 'Wherefore grieve Thy brethren „ *lviii* 9
A life that all the *M's* deck'd With gifts of grace, „ *lxxxv* 45
That saw thro' all the *M's'* walk, „ *cix* 4
charm of all the *M's* often flowering *To Virgil* 11
the *M's* cried with a stormy cry *Dead Prophet* 2
M's have raised to the heights of the mountain, *Parnassus* 2
Taller than all the *M's*, „ 10
Astronomy and Geology, terrible *M's*! „ 16
Muse (verb) I *m*, as in a trance, *Eleänore* 75
While I *m* upon thy face; „ 129
with downcast eyes we *m* and brood, *Sonnet To* —— 1
To *m* and brood and live again in memory, *Lotos-Eaters, C. S.* 65
I *m* on joy that will not cease, *Sir Galahad* 65
my Lords, you make the people *m* *Third of Feb.* 31
And with my heart I *m* and say: *In Mem. iv* 4
face shine Upon me, while I *m* alone; „ *cxvi* 10
And there the great Sir Lancelot *m* at me; *Lancelot and E.* 1055
O my Queen, I *m* Why ye not wear on arm, *Last Tournament* 35
and *m* On those dear hills, *Lover's Tale i* 31
Mused (*See also* **Half-mused**) while they *m* Whispering to each other half in fear, *Sea-Fairies* 4
But Lancelot *m* a little space; *L. of Shalott iv* 51
But while I *m* came Memory with sad eyes, *Gardener's D.* 243
while I *m*, Love with knit brows went by, „ 245
M, and was mute. *The Brook* 201
And *m* upon it, drifting up the stream *Sea Dreams* 108
I *m* on that wild morning in the woods, *Princess v* 471
Who *m* on all I had to tell, *In Mem. vi* 19
is it pride, and *m* and sigh'd 'No surely, *Maud I viii* 12
the King *M* for a little on his plea, *Marr. of Geraint* 42
She *m* a little, and then clapt her hands *Merlin and V.* 866
Crept to her father, while he *m* alone, *Lancelot and E.* 748
Lancelot later came and *m* at her, „ 1268
while I *m* nor yet endured to take So rich a prize, *Lover's Tale iii* 49
Museth *m* where broad sunshine laves The lawn *D. of F. Women* 189
Music (*See also* **Bridal-music, May-music, Sphere-music, Thunder-music, War-music**) *Then—while a sweeter* m *wakes*, *To the Queen* 13
m flowing from The illimitable years. *Ode to Memory* 41
led, With *m* and sweet showers Of festal flowers, „ 77
Shrill *m* reach'd them on the middle sea. *Sea-Fairies* 6
With a *m* strange and manifold, *Dying Swan* 29
Rain makes *m* in the tree *A Dirge* 26
the wave would make *m* above us afar— *The Merman* 22
A funeral, with plumes, and lights And *m*, *L. of Shalott ii* 32
overtakes Far thought with *m* that it makes: *Two Voices* 438
Rose slowly to a *m* slowly breathed, *Œnone* 41
up the valley came a swell of *m* on the wind. *May Queen, Con.* 32
up the valley came again the *m* on the wind. „ 36
The blessed *m* went that way my soul „ 42
m in his ears his beating heart did make. *Lotos-Eaters* 36
THERE is sweet *m* here that softer falls „ *C. S.* 1
M that gentlier on the spirit lies, „ 5
M that brings sweet sleep down from the blissful skies. „ 7
they find a *m* centred in a doleful song „ 117
who made His *m* heard below; *D. of F. Women* 4
that flow Of *m* left the lips of her that died „ 195
Deep-chested *m*, and to this result. *The Epic* 51
To some full *m* rose and sank the sun, *Edwin Morris* 34
full *m* seem'd to move and change „ 35
I scarce have other *m*: yet say on. „ 57
The *m* from the town— *Talking Oak* 214
pass'd in *m* out of sight. *Locksley Hall* 34
The Magic *M* in his heart Beats quick *Day-Dm., Arrival* 26
Low voluptuous *m* winding trembled, *Vision of Sin* 17
Then the *m* touch'd the gates and died; „ 23
Nor leave his *m* as of old, *You might have won* 14
Lay hidden as the *m* of the moon Sleeps *Aylmer's Field* 102
and coming fitfully Like broken *m*, „ 477
Broke into nature's *m* when they saw her. „ 694

Music (*continued*) I had one That altogether went to *m* ? *Sea Dreams* 204
Lessening to the lessening *m*, back, And past into the belt and swell'd again Slowly to *m* : „ 221
(Altho' I grant but little *m* there) „ 253
A *m* harmonizing our wild cries, „ 255
she liked it more Than magic *m*, forfeits, all the rest. *Princess, Pro.* 195
lightlier move The minutes fledged with *m* :' *Princess iv* 37
as they say The seal does *m* ; „ 456
Like one that wishes at a dance to change The *m*— „ 590
With *m* in the growing breeze of Time, „ *vi* 56
Like perfect *m* unto noble words ; „ *vii* 286
And girdled her with *m*. „ 327
let the mournful martial *m* blow ; *Ode on Well.* 17
With banner and with *m*, „ 81
we hear The tides of *M's* golden sea „ 252
Make *m*, O bird, in the new-budded bowers ! *W. to Alexandra* 11
Like ballad-burthen *m*, kept, *The Daisy* 77
THESE lame hexameters the strong-wing'd *m* of Homer ! *Trans. of Homer* 1
May make one *m* as before, *In Mem., Pro.* 28
With all the *m* in her tone, „ *iii* 10
Were mellow *m* match'd with him. „ *lvi* 24
I hear a wizard *m* roll, „ *lxx* 14
Shall ring with *m* all the same ; „ *lxxvii* 14
And *m* in the bounds of law, „ *lxxxvii* 34
Æonian *m* measuring out The steps of Time— „ *xcv* 41
At last he beat his *m* out. „ *xcvi* 10
sweep A *m* out of sheet and shroud, „ *ciii* 54
With festal cheer, With books and *m*, „ *cvii* 22
Is *m* more than any song. „ *Con.* 4
when alone She sits by her *m* and books *Maud I xiv* 13
Beat to the noiseless *m* of the night ! „ *xviii* 77
As the *m* clash'd in the hall ; „ *xxii* 34
To the sound of dancing *m* and flutes : „ *II v* 76
Out of the city a blast of *m* peal'd. *Gareth and L.* 238
and this *m* now Hath scared them both, „ 250
And built it to the *m* of their harps. „ 262
For an ye heard a *m*, „ 275
seeing the city is built To *m*, „ 277
move To *m* with thine Order and the King. *Balin and Balan* 77
Queen, and all the world Made *m*, and he felt his being move In *m* with his Order, and the King. „ 211
The *m* in him seem'd to change, „ 217
the wholesome *m* of the wood Was dumb'd „ 436
That by and by will make the *m* mute, *Merlin and V.* 391
And mass, and rolling *m*, like a queen. *Lancelot and E.* 1336
Was like that *m* as it came ; *Holy Grail* 115
then the *m* faded, and the Grail Past, „ 121
When God made *m* thro' them, could but speak His *m* by the framework and the chord ; „ 878
Skip to the broken *m* of my brains Than any broken *m* *Last Tournament* 258
' Good now, what *m* have I broken, fool ? ' „ 261
Thou makest broken *m* with thy bride, „ 264
so thou breakest Arthur's *m* too.' ' Save for that broken *m* „ 266
And harken if my *m* be not true. „ 274
woods are hush'd, their *m* is no more : „ 276
I'll hold thou hast some touch Of *m*, „ 314
It makes a silent *m* up in heaven, „ 349
he heard Strange *m*, and he paused, *Guinevere* 239
with heaven's *m* in a life More living *Lover's Tale i* 761
day Peal'd on us with that *m* which rights all, „ *iv* 65
The *m* that robes it in language *The Wreck* 24
What power but the bird's could make This *m* in the bird ? *Ancient Sage* 22
set The lamps alight, and call For golden *m*, „ 197
their songs, that meet The morning with such *m*, *The Flight* 66
heart batin' to *m* wid ivery word ! *Tomorrow* 34
not the *m* of a deep ? *Locksley H., Sixty* 154
thy voice, a *m* heard Thro' all the yells *To Duke of Argyll* 7
And moving each to *m*, soul in soul *Happy* 39
if his young *m* wakes A wish in you. *To Mary Boyle* 63
Or cataract *m* Of falling torrents, *Merlin and the G.* 46

Music (*continued*) Tho' their *m* here be mortal *Parnassus* 18
can *M* make you live Far—far—away ? *Far—far—away* 17
Make but one *m*, harmonising ' Pray.' *Akbar's Dream* 151
but we hear *M* : our palace is awake, „ 200
Musical many a fall Of diamond rillets *m*, *Arabian Nights* 48
More *m* than ever came in one, *Gardener's D.* 233
ever in it a low *m* note Swell'd up and died ; *Sea Dreams* 210
There is but one bird with a *m* throat, *The Islet* 27
we past to the Isle of Witches and heard their *m* cry— *V. of Maeldune* 97
Musically winded it, and that so *m* *Pelleas and E.* 365
Musician The discords dear to the *m*. *Sea Dreams* 258
M, painter, sculptor, critic, *Princess ii* 178
Musing *M* on him that used to fill it for her, *Enoch Arden* 208
And *m* on the little lives of men, *Sea Dreams* 48
Or in the furrow *m* stands ; *In Mem. lxiv* 27
who turns a *m* eye On songs, and deeds, „ *lxxvii* 2
But *m* ' Shall I answer yea or nay ? ' *Com. of Arthur* 426
There *m* sat the hoary-headed Earl, *Marr. of Geraint* 295
could not rest for *m* how to smoothe And sleek *Last Tournament* 390
I sat, Lonely, but *m* on thee, wondering where, „ 613
Musk moss or *m*, To grace my city rooms ; *Gardener's D.* 193
Smelling of *m* and of insolence, *Maud I vi* 45
And the *m* of the rose is blown. „ *xxii* 6
Musket Death while we stood with the *m*, *Def. of Lucknow* 16
Musket-bullet Millions of *m-b's*, „ 93
Musket-shot Cannon-shot, *m-s*, „ 34
Musky-circled began To thrid the *m-c* mazes, *Princess iv* 261
Musqueteer came with their pikes and *m's*, *The Revenge* 53
Mussulman True *M* was I and sworn, *Arabian Nights* 9
M Who flings his bowstrung Harem in the sea, *Romney's R.* 134
But in due time for every *M*, *Akbar's Dream* 24
Musty In *m* bins and chambers, *Will Water.* 102
Mute wait for death—*m*—careless of all ills, *If I were loved* 10
When all the house is *m*. *M. d'Arthur* 178
M with folded arms they waited— *The Captain* 39
Here both were *m*, till Philip glancing up *Enoch Arden* 440
Mused, and was *m*. *The Brook* 201
He laugh'd ; and then was *m* ; *Aylmer's Field* 402
his *m* dust I honour and his living worth : *To J. S.* 29
And individual freedom *m* ; *You ask me, why, etc.* 20
O'er the *m* city stole with folded wings, *Gardener's D.* 186
her eyes on all my motions with a *m* observance hung. *Locksley Hall* 22
she would answer us to-day, Meantime be *m* : *Princess, iii* 167
she saw me lying stark, Dishelm'd and *m*, „ *vi* 101
but *m* she glided forth, Nor glanced behind her, „ *vii* 170
O friends, our chief state-oracle is *m* : *Ode on Well.* 23
And statued pinnacles, *m* as they. *The Daisy* 64
Your mother is *m* in her grave *Maud I iv* 58
Modred biting his thin lips was *m*, *Gareth and L.* 31
m As creatures voiceless thro' the fault of birth, *Geraint and E.* 265
I will kiss you for it : ' he was *m* : *Merlin and V.* 229
' Great Master, do ye love me ? ' he was *m*. „ 237
by and by will make the music *m*, „ 391
With all her damsels, he was stricken *m* ; *Pelleas and E.* 251
' Is the Queen false ? ' and Percivale was *m*. „ 532
And most of these were *m*, *Last Tournament* 210
Here one black, *m* midsummer night I sat, „ 612
When all the house is *m*. *Pass. of Arthur* 346
with an awful sense Of one *m* Shadow watching all. *In Mem. xxx* 8
M symbols of a joyful morn, „ *Con.* 58
but seem *M* of this miracle, far as I have read. *Holy Grail* 66
M, blind and motionless as then I lay ; *Lover's Tale i* 607
M, for henceforth what use were words to me ! „ 609
I was led *m* Into her temple like a sacrifice ; „ 684
We gazed on it together In *m* and glad remembrance, „ *ii* 186
While all the guests in *m* amazement rose— „ *iv* 305
I read no more the prisoner's *m* wail *Sir J. Oldcastle* 4
as we hated the isle that was *m*, *V. of Maeldune* 52
m below the chancel stones, *Locksley H., Sixty* 43
She glanced at me, at Muriel, and was *m*. *The Ring* 264
Shall the royal voice be *m* ? *By an Evolution.* 14
But every man was *m* for reverence. *Death of Œnone* 96

N

Naäil (nail) toäner 'ed shot 'um as deäd as a *n*. *N. Farmer, O. S.* 35
Naäkt (naked) An' ya stood oop *n* i' the beck, *Church-warden, etc.* 29
Naäme (name) 'Stan' 'im theer i' the *n* o' the Lord *North. Cobbler* 73
coom'd like a Hangel o' marcy as soon as 'e 'eärd 'is *n*, *Owd Roä* 93
Naämed (named) we *n* her 'Dot an' gaw one!' *Village Wife* 100
Nabour (neighbour) An' her *n's* an frinds 'ud consowl and condowl wid her, *Tomorrow* 47
Nadir hard earth cleave to the *N* hell *Merlin and V.* 349
Nager (nigger) Thim ould blind *n's* in Agypt, *Tomorrow* 69
Naggin' Moother was *n* an' groänin' an' moänin' an' *n* ageän; *Owd Roä* 108
Nagging *See* **A-naggin', Naggin'**
Naiad but the *N* Throbbing in mild unrest *Leonine Eleg.* 11
faintly smilest still, As a *N* in a well, *Adeline* 16
and *N's* oar'd A glimmering shoulder *To E. L.* 16
Nail (s) (*See also* **Finger-nail, Naäil**) The rusted *n's* fell from the knots *Mariana* 3
seem'd All-perfect, finish'd to the finger *n*. *Edwin Morris* 22
children cast their pins and *n's*, *Merlin and V.* 430
Nail (verb) *n* me like a weasel on a grange *Princess ii* 205
They never *n* a dumb head up in elm), *Lover's Tale iv* 37
Nail'd (adj.) Then with their *n* prows Parted the Norsemen, *Batt. of Brunanburh* 93
Nail'd (verb) He that has *n* all flesh to the Cross, *Vastness* 28
Naked (*See also* **Half-naked, Naäkt, Nigh-naked**) *N* I go, and void of cheer: *Two Voices* 239
As *n* essence, must I be Incompetent of memory: „ 374
All *n* in a sultry sky, *Fatima* 37
N they came to that smooth-swarded bower, *Œnone* 95
'Ride you *n* thro' the town, *Godiva* 29
Far too *n* to be shamed! *Vision of Sin* 190
I rate your chance Almost at *n* nothing.' *Princess i* 161
N, a double light in air and wave, „ *vii* 167
mighty hands Lay *n* on the wolfskin, *Lancelot and E.* 813
Far ran the *n* moon across The houseless ocean's *The Voyage* 29
With *n* limbs and flowers and fruit, „ 55
n marriages Flash from the bridge, *Aylmer's Field* 765
Have left the last free race with *n* coasts! *Third of Feb.* 40
down the wave and in the flame was borne A *n* babe, *Com. of Arthur* 384
The shining dragon and the *n* child „ 399
And truth or clothed or *n* let it be. „ 408
A *n* babe, of whom the Prophet spake, *Gareth and L.* 501
The gay pavilion and the *n* feet, „ 937
rose-red from the west, and all *N* it seem'd, „ 1088
'Wherefore waits the madman there *N* in open dayshine?' „ 1092
'Not *n*, only wrapt in harden'd skins „ 1093
weep True tears upon his broad and *n* breast, *Marr. of Geraint* 111
And bore him to the *n* hall of Doorm, *Geraint and E.* 570
There in the *n* hall, propping his head, „ 581
And ate with tumult in the *n* hall, „ 605
I smote upon the *n* skull A thrall of thine *Balin and Balan* 55
say That out of *n* knightlike purity *Merlin and V.* 11
But that where blind and *n* Ignorance „ 664
Stript off the case, and read the *n* shield, *Lancelot and E.* 16
battle-writhen arms and mighty hands Lay *n* on the wolfskin, „ 813
Stript off the case, and gave the *n* shield; „ 979
Himself *N* of glory for His mortal change, *Holy Grail* 448
and on the *n* mountain top Blood-red, „ 474
then I came All in my folly to the *n* shore, „ 793
laid The *n* sword athwart their *n* throats, *Pelleas and E.* 452
A *n* aught—yet swine I hold thee still, *Last Tournament* 309
then They found a *n* child upon the sands *Guinevere* 293
Above the *n* poisons of his heart In his old age.' *Lover's Tale i* 356
pour'd Into the shadowing pencil's *n* forms „ *ii* 180
I had better ha' put my *n* hand in a hornets' nest. *First Quarrel* 50
Pour'd in on all those happy *n* isles— *Columbus* 173

Naked (*continued*) And we left but a *n* rock, *V. of Maeldune* 54
For a wild witch *n* as heaven stood „ 100
One *n* peak—the sister of the sun *Tiresias* 30
When he clothed a *n* mind with the wisdom *The Wreck* 65
lest the *n* glebe Should yawn once more *Demeter and P.* 42
The scorpion crawling over *n* skulls;— „ 78
Of leafless elm, or *n* lime, *To Ulysses* 16
Trunk and bough, *N* strength. *The Oak* 15
gliding thro' the branches over-bower'd The *n* Three, *Death of Œnone* 7
same who first had found Paris, a *n* babe, „ 54
I stood there, *n*, amazed *Despair* 77
forward—*n*—let them stare. *Locksley H., Sixty* 142
Nakedness we shall see The *n* and vacancy *Deserted House* 11
These prodigies of myriad *n'es*, *Lucretius* 156
Grimy *n* dragging his trucks And laying *Maud I x* 7
Is mere white truth in simple *n*, *Balin and Balan* 518
roll'd his *n* everyway That all the crowd *Dead Prophet* 15
Name (s) (*See also* **Naäme**) WISDOM, a *n* to shake All evil dreams of power—a sacred *n*. *The Poet* 46
From thy rose-red lips MY *n* Floweth; *Eleänore* 133
Yet tell my *n* again to me, „ 142
round the prow they read her *n*, *L. of Shalott iv* 44
how thy *n* may sound Will vex thee lying underground? *Two Voices* 110
'His sons grow up that bear his *n*, „ 256
He names the *n* Eternity. „ 291
Last night, when some one spoke his *n*, *Fatima* 15
all those *n's*, that in their motion were *Palace of Art* 165
Lost to her place and *n*; „ 264
I know you proud to bear your *n*, *L. C. V. de Vere* 10
'I had great beauty: ask thou not my *n*: *D. of F. Women* 93
when I heard my *n* Sigh'd forth with life „ 153
my crown about my brows, A *n* for ever!— „ 163
The *n* of Britain trebly great— *You ask me, why, etc.* 22
'Thou hast betray'd thy nature and thy *n*, *M. d'Arthur* 73
call'd him by his *n*, complaining loud, „ 210
when I heard her *n* My heart was like a prophet *Gardener's D.* 62
The cuckoo told his *n* to all the hills; „ 93
if I carved my *n* Upon the cliffs that guard *Audley Court* 48
set the words, and added *n's* I knew. „ 61
he that knew the *n's*, Long learned *n's* *Edwin Morris* 16
I spoke her *n* alone. „ 68
n's Are register'd and calendar'd for saints. *St. S. Stylites* 131
thou, whereon I carved her *n*, (repeat) *Talking Oak* 33, 97
tell me, did she read the *n* „ 153
found, and kiss'd the *n* she found, „ 159
I am become a *n*; *Ulysses* 11
And built herself an everlasting *n*. *Godiva* 79
n of wife, And in the rights that *n* may give, *Day-Dm., L'Envoi* 53
Hoped to make the *n* Of his vessel great in story, *The Captain* 18
in whom he had reliance For his noble *n*, „ 58
What care I for any *n*? *Vision of Sin* 85
'*N* and fame! to fly sublime Thro' the courts, „ 103
YOU might have won the Poet's *n*, *You might have won* 1
but that *n* has twice been changed— *Enoch Arden* 859
James Willows, of one *n* and heart with her. *The Brook* 76
'Willows.' 'No!' 'That is my *n*.' „ 212
ghost of one who bore your *n* About these meadows, „ 219
'he that marries her marries her *n*' *Aylmer's Field* 25
almost all the village had one *n*; „ 35
sow'd her *n* and kept it green In living letters, „ 88
The one transmitter of their ancient *n*, „ 296
N, too, *n*! Their ancient *n*! „ 377
Fall back upon a *n*! rest, rot in that! „ 385
make a *n*, *N*, fortune too: „ 394
And crying upon the *n* of Leolin, „ 576
that moment, when she named his *n*, „ 581
So never took that useful *n* in vain, *Sea Dreams* 189
did I take That popular *n* of thine to shadow forth *Lucretius* 96
bears one *n* with her Whose death-blow struck „ 235
and lovelier than their *n's*, *Princess, Pro.* 12
Walter hail'd a score of *n's* upon her, „ 156
His *n* was Gama; crack'd and small his voice, „ *i* 114
albeit their glorious *n's* Were fewer, „ *ii* 155

Name (s) (*continued*) great *n* flow on with broadening time For ever.' *Princess iii* 164
chattering stony *n's* Of shale and hornblende, „ 361
Proctor's leapt upon us, crying '*N's*:' „ *iv* 259
Swear by St. something—I forget her *n*— „ *v* 293
Whose *n* is yoked with children's, „ 418
happy warrior's, and immortal *n's*, „ *vi* 93
She needs must wed him for her own good *n*; „ *vii* 74
In that dread sound to the great *n*, *Ode on Well.* 71
O civic muse, to such a *n*, To such a *n* for ages long, To such a *n*, „ 75
Eternal honour to his *n*. (repeat) „ 150, 231
at thy *n* the Tartar tents are stirr'd; *W to Marie Alex.* 12
Thy *n* was blest within the narrow door; „ 38
Here also, Marie, shall thy *n* be blest, „ 39
You cannot love me at all, if you love not my good *n*.' *Grandmother* 48
I love you so well that your good *n* is mine. „ 50
My *n* in song has done him much wrong, *Spiteful Letter* 3
This faded leaf, our *n's* are as brief; „ 13
Milton, a *n* to resound for ages; *Milton* 4
quiet bones were blest Among familiar *n's* to rest *In Mem. xviii* 7
We yield all blessing to the *n* „ *xxxvi* 3
Could hardly tell what *n* were thine. „ *lix* 16
Since we deserved the *n* of friends, „ *lxv* 9
Along the letters of thy *n*, „ *lxvii* 7
force that would have forged a *n*. „ *lxxiii* 16
Another *n* was on the door: „ *lxxxvii* 17
The grand old *n* of gentleman, „ *cxi* 22
Sweet Hesper-Phosphor, double *n* „ *cxxi* 17
sign your *n's*, which shall be read, „ *Con.* 57
The *n's* are signed, and overhead Begins the clash „ 60
And my own sad *n* in corners cried, *Maud I vi* 72
a learned man Could give it a clumsy *n*. „ *II ii* 10
the sudden making of splendid *n's*, „ *III vi* 47
a household *n*, Hereafter, thro' all times, *Ded. of Idylls* 42
Nor shalt thou tell thy *n* to anyone. *Gareth and L.* 156
Not tell my *n* to any—no, not the King.' „ 171
A *n* of evil savour in the land, „ 385
without a sign Saving the *n* beneath; „ 415
Mark hath tarnish'd the great *n* of king, „ 426
A twelvemonth and a day, nor seek my *n*. „ 446
let my *n* Be hidd'n, and give me the first quest, „ 544
Let be my *n* until I make my *n*! „ 576
What is thy *n*? thy need?' 'My *n*?' she said—'Lynette my *n*; „ 605
Forgetful of his glory and his *n*, *Marr. of Geraint* 53
I cannot love my lord and not his *n*. „ 92
desired his *n*, and sent Her maiden to demand it of the dwarf; „ 192
'Surely I will learn the *n*,' „ 203
His *n*? but no, good faith, I will not have it: „ 405
Sent her own maiden to demand the *n*, „ 411
I will break his pride and learn his *n*, „ 424
Geraint, a *n* far-sounded among men „ 427
I will not let his *n* Slip from my lips „ 445
earn'd himself the *n* of sparrow-hawk. „ 492
her *n* will yet remain Untarnish'd as before; „ 500
(Who hearing her own *n* had stol'n away) „ 507
'Thy *n*!' To whom the fallen man Made answer, „ 575
A stately queen whose *n* was Guinevere, „ 667
the Queen's fair *n* was breathed upon, *Geraint and E.* 951
Arthur seeing ask'd 'Tell me your *n's*; *Balin and Balan* 50
Saying 'An unmelodious *n* to thee, „ 52
realm Hath prosper'd in the *n* of Christ, „ 99
a *n* that branches o'er the rest, „ 182
might, *N*, manhood, and a grace, „ 377
by the great Queen's *n*, arise and hence.' „ 482
O me, that such a *n* as Guinevere's, „ 489
And thus foam'd over at a rival *n*: „ 567
fought in her *n*, Sware by her— *Merlin and V.* 13
Their lavish comment when her *n* was named. „ 151
lost to life and use and *n* and fame. (repeat) „ 214, 970
My use and *n* and fame. „ 304
Upon my life and use and *n* and fame, „ 374
felt them slowly ebbing, *n* and fame.' „ 437

Name (s) (*continued*) My *n*, once mine, now thine, *Merlin and V.* 446
But when my *n* was lifted up, „ 502
whose whole prey Is man's good *n*: „ 729
The pretty, popular *n* such manhood earns, „ 787
Rage like a fire among the noblest *n's*, „ 802
Some stain or blemish in a *n* of note, „ 832
she that knew not ev'n his *n*? *Lancelot and E.* 29
and by that *n* Had named them, „ 32
fought together; but their *n's* were lost; „ 40
Has link'd our *n's* together in his lay, „ 112
your great *n*, This conquers: „ 150
and by what *n* Livest between the lips? „ 181
Elaine, and heard her *n* so tost about, „ 233
'Fair lord, whose *n* I know not— „ 360
'Hear, but hold my *n* Hidden, „ 416
fiery family passion for the *n* Of Lancelot, „ 477
his great *n* Conquer'd; and therefore would he hide his *n* „ 579
Whence you might learn his *n*? „ 654
How know ye my lord's *n* is Lancelot?' „ 797
To win his honour and to make his *n*, „ 1362
sons Born to the glory of thy *n* and fame, „ 1372
Why did the King dwell on my *n* to me? „ 1402
Mine own *n* shames me, „ 1403
profits me my *n* Of greatest knight? „ 1413
named us each by *n*, Calling 'God speed!' *Holy Grail* 351
the knights, So many and famous *n's*; „ 364
after trumpet blown, her *n* And title, *Pelleas and E.* 115
Full on her knights in many an evil *n* „ 290
'And oft in dying cried upon your *n*.' „ 385
Lancelot, saying, 'What *n* hast thou That ridest „ 563
'No *n*, no *n*,' he shouted, 'a scourge am I „ 565
but thy *n*?' 'I have many *n's*,' he cried: „ 567
And when I call'd upon thy *n* *Last Tournament* 73
set his *n* High on all hills, „ 336
a *n*? Was it the *n* of one in Brittany, „ 395
the sweet *n* Allured him first, „ 398
n Went wandering somewhere darkling in his mind. „ 456
Of one—his *n* is out of me—the prize, „ 546
Did I love her? the *n* at least I loved. „ 603
The *n* was ruler of the dark—Isolt? „ 606
And once or twice I spake thy *n* aloud. „ 615
hers Would be for evermore a *n* of scorn. *Guinevere* 61
and yield me sanctuary, nor ask Her *n* „ 142
Nor with them mix'd, nor told her *n*, „ 148
And drawing foul ensample from fair *n's*, „ 490
And mine will ever be a *n* of scorn. „ 627
in their stead thy *n* and glory cling *Pass. of Arthur* 53
'Thou hast betrayed thy nature and thy *n*, „ 241
call'd him by his *n*, complaining loud, „ 378
Rather than that gray king, whose *n*, a ghost, *To the Queen, ii* 39
Keep thou thy *n* of 'Lover's Bay.' *Lover's Tale i* 15
more Than the gray cuckoo loves his *n*, „ 257
and my *n* was borne Upon her breath. „ 443
Henceforth my *n* has been A hallow'd memory like the *n's* of old, „ 444
this *n* to which her gracious lips Did lend such gentle utterance, this one *n*, In such obscure hereafter, „ 456
Nevertheless, we did not change the *n*. „ 464
Thy *n* is ever worshipp'd among hours! „ 493
And by that *n* I moved upon her breath; Dear *n*, which had too much of nearness in it „ 560
Him who should own that *n*? „ 643
If so be that the echo of that *n* „ 644
upon the sands Insensibly I drew her *n*, „ *ii* 7
And leave the *n* of Lover's Leap: „ *iv* 42
Forgive him, if his *n* be Julian too.' „ 175
GOLDEN-HAIR'D Ally whose *n* is one with mine, *To A. Tennyson,* 1
the *n* at the head of my verse is thine. „ 6
May'st thou never be wrong'd by the *n* that is mine! „ 7
we had always borne a good *n*— *Rizpath* 35
Yet must you change your *n*: *Sisters (E. and E.)* 69
An old and worthy *n*! „ 74
care not for a *n*—no fault of mine. „ 77
city deck'd herself To meet me, roar'd my *n*; *Columbus* 10

Name (s) (*continued*) I changed the *n*; San Salvador I call'd it; *Columbus* 75
Hallowed be Thy *n*—Halleluiah! (repeat) *De Prof., Human C.* 1, 5, 9
n's who dare For that sweet mother land *Tiresias* 121
Their *n's*, Graven on memorial columns, „ 123
ring thy *n* To every hoof that clangs it, „ 137
I have sullied a noble *n*, *The Wreck* 5
—to her maiden *n*! „ 144
felt as I spoke I was taking the *n* in vain— *Despair* 52
seest the Nameless of the hundred *n's*. *Ancient Sage* 49
And never named the *N*'— „ 56
Not even his own *n*. „ 149
an age of noblest English *n's*, *Locksley H. Sixty* 83
and dying while they shout her *n*. „ 128
leave to head These rhymings with your *n*, *Pro. to Gen. Hamley* 20
will you set your *n* A star among the stars. *Epilogue* 1
falling drop will make his *n* As mortal „ 60
till his Word Had won him a noble *n*. *Dead Prophet* 36
a *n* may last for a thousand years, „ 59
great *n* of England, round and round. (repeat) *Hands all Round* 12, 36
To this great *n* of England drink, my friends, „ 23
But since your *n* will grow with Time, *To Marq. of Dufferin* 13
have I made the *n* A golden portal to my rhyme: „ 15
and recks not to ruin a realm in her *n*. *Vastness* 10
He loved my *n* not me; *The Ring* 191
wrote *N*, Surname, all as clear as noon, „ 237
Earth and Hell will brand your *n*, *Forlorn* 51
In the *n* Of the everlasting God, *Happy* 107
A *n* that earth will not forget *To Ulysses* 27
corpse of every man that gains a *n*; *Romney's R.* 123
all Stood round it, hush'd, or calling on his *n*. *Death of Œnone* 66
In the great *n* of Him who died for men, *St. Telemachus* 63
I loathe the very *n* of infidel. *Akbar's Dream* 70
her *n*? what was it? I asked her. *Charity* 35
for *him* who had given her the *n*. „ 39
Priests in the *n* of the Lord *The Dawn* 4
scandal is mouthing a bloodless *n* „ 12
Form in Freedom's *n* and the Queen's! *Riflemen form!* 23
his truer *n* Is 'Onward,' *D. of the Duke of C.* 13

Name (verb) He *n's* the name Eternity. *Two Voices* 291
That *n* the under-lying dead, *In Mem. ii* 2
The wish too strong for words to *n*; *xciii* 14
The Sultan, as we *n* him,— *Maud I xx* 4
Let him *n* it who can, „ *II ii* 11
He *n's* himself the Night and oftener Death, *Gareth and L.* 638
'Peradventure he, you *n*, May know my shield. „ 1298
since you *n* yourself the summer fly, *Merlin and V.* 369
break faith with one I may not *n*? *Lancelot and E.* 685
she spake on, for I did *n* no wish, (repeat) *Lover's Tale i* 578, 583
those about us whom we neither see nor *n*, *Locksley H., Sixty* 272

Named (*See also* **Naämed**) dreamer, deaf and blind, *N* man, *Two Voices* 176
ship I sail in passes here (He *n* the day) *Enoch Arden* 215
that moment, when she *n* his name, *Aylmer's Field* 581
would bawl for civil rights, No woman *n*: *Princess v* 388
Truth-teller was our England's Alfred *n*; *Ode on Well.* 188
under every shield a knight was *n*: *Gareth and L.* 409
follows, being *n*, His owner, but remembers all, „ 703
That *n* himself the Star of Evening, „ 1090
a grateful people *n* Enid the Good; *Geraint and E.* 963
lavish comment when her name was *n*. *Merlin and V.* 151
therefore be as great as you are *n*, „ 336
n them, since a diamond was the prize. *Lancelot and E.* 33
n us each by name, Calling 'God speed!' *Holy Grail* 351
Thro' such a round in heaven, we *n* the stars, „ 686
loved it tenderly, And *n* it Nestling; *Last Tournament* 25
this I *n* from her own self, Evelyn; *Sisters (E. and E.)* 270
And never *n* the Name'— *Ancient Sage* 56
Drew to the valley *N* of the shadow, *Merlin and the G.* 87

Nameless (adj.) In whose least act abides the *n* charm *Princess v* 70
But spoke not, rapt in *n* reverie, „ *Con.* 108
Such clouds of *n* trouble cross All night *In Mem. iv* 13
Your father has wealth well-gotten, and I am *n* and poor. *Maud I iv* 18

Nameless (adj.) (*continued*) Sick of a *n* fear, *Maud II ii* 44
Whose bark had plunder'd twenty *n* isles; *Merlin and V.* 559
Blazed the last diamond of the *n* king. *Lancelot and E.* 444
The *n* Power, or Powers, that rule *Ancient Sage* 29

Nameless (s) If thou would'st hear the *N*, „ 31
thou May'st haply learn the *N* hath a voice, „ 34
Or even than the *N* is to me. „ 46
Thou seest the *N* of the hundred names. And if the *N* should withdraw from all „ 49
The *N* never came Among us, „ 54
Thou canst not prove the *N*, O my son, „ 57
But with the *N* is nor Day nor Hour; „ 102
past into the *N*, as a cloud Melts into Heaven. „ 233
A cloud between the *N* and thyself, „ 278

Namesake Her daintier *n* down in Brittany— *Last Tournament* 265
And she, my *n* of the hands, „ 594

Naming *n* each, And *n* those, his friends, *The Brook* 130
Who, never *n* God except for gain, *Sea Dreams* 188

Nap 'Twas but an after-dinner's *n*. *Day-Dm., Revival* 24

Nape the very *n* of her white neck Was rosed *Princess vi* 343
and the skull Brake from the *n*, *Lancelot and E.* 50

Naphtha-pits Beyond the Memmian *n-p*, *Alexander* 4

Napkin *n* wrought with horse and hound, *Audley Court* 21
like the common breed That with the *n* dally; *Will Water.* 118

Naples quite worn out, Travelling to *N*. *The Brook* 36
For *N* which we only left in May? *The Ring* 58

Narcotics Like dull *n's*, numbing pain. *In Mem. v* 8

Narded *N* and swathed and balm'd it *Lover's Tale i* 682

Narra (narrow) I fun that it warn't not the gaäinist waäy to the *n* Gaäte. *Church-warden, etc.* 12

Narrow (adj.) (*See also* **Earth-narrow, Narra**) Oh! *n*, *n* was the space, *Oriana* 46
Drawing into his *n* earthen urn, *Ode to Memory* 61
And fires your *n* casement glass, *Miller's D.* 243
Were shiver'd in my *n* frame. *Fatima* 18
With *n* moon-lit slips of silver cloud, *Œnone* 218
Better the *n* brain, the stony heart, *Love and Duty* 15
Humm'd like a hive all round the *n* quay, *Audley Court* 5
I, to herd with *n* foreheads, *Locksley Hall* 175
red roofs about a *n* wharf In cluster; *Enoch Arden* 3
A *n* cave ran in beneath the cliff: „ 23
halfway up The *n* street that clamber'd „ 60
Ten miles to northward of the *n* port „ 102
and his careful hand,—The space was *n*,— „ 177
And left but *n* breadth to left and right „ 674
Down to the pool and *n* wharf he went, „ 690
All down the long and *n* street he went „ 795
Doubtless our *n* world must canvass it: *Aylmer's Field* 774
n meagre face Seam'd with the shallow cares „ 813
To find a deeper in the *n* gloom „ 840
God bless the *n* sea which keeps her off, *Princess, Con.* 51
God bless the *n* seas! „ 70
Thy name was blest within the *n* door; *W. to Marie Alex.* 38
Till, in a *n* street and dim, *The Daisy* 22
Should murmur from the *n* house, *In Mem. xxxv* 2
She sighs amid her *n* days, „ *lx* 10
And Spring that swells the *n* brooks, „ *lxxxv* 70
all *n* jealousies Are silent; *Ded. of Idylls* 16
the stream Full, *n*; *Gareth and L.* 908
Anon they past a *n* comb wherein „ 1193
To me this *n* grizzled fork of thine *Merlin and V.* 59
Then, *n* court and lubber King, farewell! „ 119
In mine own realm beyond the *n* seas, *Lancelot and E.* 1323
like a vermin in its hole, Modred, a *n* face: *Last Tournament* 166
Or elsewhere, Modred's *n* foxy face, *Guinevere* 63
And wastes the *n* realm whereon we move, *Pass. of Arthur* 140
and the *n* fringe Of curving beach— *Lover's Tale i* 38
floods with redundant life Her *n* portals. „ 85
o'erstept The slippery footing of his *n* wit, „ 102
Small pity for those that have ranged from the *n* warmth of your fold, *Despair* 38
Fought for their lives in the *n* gap they had made— *Heavy Brigade* 23
The clash of tides that meet in *n* seas.— *Akbar's Dream* 58

Narrow (verb) tho' the gathering enemy *n* thee, *Boädicea* 39

Narrow'd *N* her goings out and comings in; *Aylmer's Field* 501
The river as it *n* to the hills. *Princess iii* 196
Narrower On a range of lower feelings and a *n* heart than mine! *Locksley Hall* 44
The limit of his *n* fate, *In Mem. lxiv* 21
Set light by *n* perfectness. „ *cxii* 4
Men that in a *n* day— *Open I. and C. Exhib.* 25
the *n* The cage, the more their fury. *Akbar's Dream* 50
Narrowest Or been in *n* working shut, *In Mem. xxxv* 20
Narrowing *N* in to where they sat assembled *Vision of Sin* 16
round me drove In *n* circles till I yell'd again *Lucretius* 57
No lewdness, *n* envy, monkey-spite, „ 211
Ring out the *n* lust of gold; *In Mem. cvi* 26
'O closed about by *n* nunnery-walls, *Guinevere* 342
O shut me round with *n* nunnery-walls, „ 671
Noises of a current *n*, not the music of a deep? *Locksley H., Sixty* 154
N the bounds of night.' *Prog. of Spring* 91
Narrowness Nor ever *n* or spite, *In Mem. cxi* 17
Nasty *N* an' snaggy an' shaäky, *North. Cobbler* 78
N, casselty weather! *Church-warden, etc.* 2
they leäved their *n* sins i' my pond, „ 54
Natal And gave you on your *n* day. *Margaret* 42
Yet present in his *n* grove, *The Daisy* 18
Nation And the *n's* do but murmur, *Locksley Hall* 106
From the *n's'* airy navies grappling „ 124
A *n* yet, the rulers and the ruled— *Princess, Con.* 53
To the noise of the mourning of a mighty *n*, *Ode on Well.* 4
a *n* weeping, and breaking on my rest? „ 82
Who lets once more in peace the *n's* meet, *Ode Inter. Exhib.* 4
'The song that nerves a *n's* heart, *Epilogue* 81
when the *n's* rear on high Their idol *Freedom* 27
Who made a *n* purer through their art. *To W. C. Macready* 8
thro' Earth and her listening *n's*, *Parnassus* 7
'Light of the *n's'* ask'd his Chronicler *Akbar's Dream* 1
National *N* hatreds of whole generations, *Vastness* 25
Native on his light there falls A shadow; and his *n* slope, *Supp. Confessions* 164
And heard her *n* breezes pass, *Mariana in the S.* 43
Upon the cliffs that guard my *n* land, *Audley Court* 49
herb that runs to seed Beside its *n* fountain. *Amphion* 96
Poet's words and looks Had yet their *n* glow: *Will Water.* 194
ten years, Since Enoch left his hearth and *n* land, *Enoch Arden* 360
a hut, Half hut, half *n* cavern. „ 560
Above the darkness from their *n* East. *Princess iii* 22
Barbarians, grosser than your *n* bears— „ *iv* 537
Who look'd all *n* to her place, „ *vii* 323
The violet of his *n* land. *In Mem. xviii* 4
Go down beside thy *n* rill, „ *xxxvii* 5
Who ploughs with pain his *n* lea „ *lxiv* 25
That stays him from the *n* land „ *xciii* 3
love-language of the bird In *n* hazels tassel hung.' „ *cii* 12
And *n* growth of noble mind; „ *cxi* 16
To the death, for their *n* land. *Maud I v* 11
I have felt with my *n* land, „ *III vi* 58
Betwixt the *n* land of Love and me, *Lover's Tale i* 25
how *n* Unto the hills she trod on! „ 359
I with our lover to his *n* Bay. „ *iv* 155
He past for ever from his *n* land; „ 387
And speaking clearly in thy *n* tongue— *Sir J. Oldcastle* 133
Their kindly *n* princes slain or slaved, *Columbus* 174
were we *n* to that splendour or in Mars, *Locksley H., Sixty* 187
Who loves his *n* country best. *Hands all Round* 4
at dawn Falls on the threshold of her *n* land, *Demeter and P.* 3
What sound was dearest in his *n* dells? *Far—far—away* 4
Nativity Fair Florence honouring thy *n*, *To Dante* 3
Natural Embrace her as my *n* good; *In Mem. iii* 14
Adown a *n* stair of tangled roots, *Lover's Tale i* 527
Nature heart be aweary of beating? And *n* die? *Nothing will Die* 7
analyse Our double *n*, and compare All creeds *Supp. Confessions* 175
Then let wise *N* work her will, *My life is full* 21
Young *N* thro' five cycles ran, *Two Voices* 17
'If *N* put not forth her power About the opening „ 160
In *N* can he nowhere find. „ 293
N's living motion lent The pulse of hope „ 449
each a perfect whole From living *N*, *Palace of Art* 58

Nature (*continued*) Carved out of *N* for itself, *Palace of Art* 127
Lord over *N*, Lord of the visible earth, „ 179
my bliss of life, that *N* gave, *D. of F. Women* 210
Great *N* is more wise than I: *To J. S.* 35
N, so far as in her lies, *On a Mourner* 1
English *n's*, freemen, friends, *Love thou thy land* 7
For *N* also, cold and warm, „ 37
if *N's* evil star Drive men in manhood, „ 73
For *n* brings not back the Mastodon, *The Epic* 36
'Thou hast betray'd thy *n* and thy name, *M. d'Arthur* 73
To what she is: a *n* never kind! *Walk. to the Mail* 62
Kind *n* is the best: those manners next That fit us like a *n* second-hand; „ 64
'My love for *N* is as old as I; *Edwin Morris* 28
My love for *N* and my love for her, „ 31
For those and theirs, by *N's* law, *Talking Oak* 73
How can my *n* longer mix with thine? *Tithonus* 65
the grossness of his *n* will have weight *Locksley Hall* 48
Cursed be the sickly forms that err from honest *N's* rule! „ 61
Nay, but *N* brings thee solace; „ 87
I am shamed thro' all my *n* „ 148
N made them blinder motions „ 150
Here at least, where *n* sickens, nothing. „ 153
liberal applications lie In Art like *N*, *Day-Dm., Moral* 14
Oh, *n* first was fresh to men, *Amphion* 57
But laws of *n* were our scorn. *The Voyage* 84
as neat and close as *N* packs Her blossom *Enoch Arden* 178
speech and thought and *n* fail'd a little, „ 792
n crost Was mother of the foul adulteries *Aylmer's Field* 375
Broke into *n's* music when they saw her. „ 694
for it seem'd A void was made in *N*; *Lucretius* 37
all-generating powers and genial heat Of *N*, „ 98
Seeing with how great ease *N* can smile, „ 174
Twy-natured is no *n*: „ 194
the womb and tomb of all, Great *N*, „ 245
lift your *n's* up: Embrace our aims: *Princess ii* 88
'Wild *n's* need wise curbs. „ *v* 173
but as frankly theirs As dues of *N*. „ 204
There dwelt an iron *n* in the grain: „ *vi* 50
Love and *N*, these are two more terrible „ 165
Thaw this male *n* to some touch of that Which kills „ 306
scales with man The shining steps of *N*, „ *vii* 262
and let thy *n* strike on mine, „ 351
And ruling by obeying *N's* powers, *Ode Inter. Exhib.* 40
'And all the phantom, *N*, stands— *In Mem. iii* 9
words, like *N*, half reveal And half conceal „ *v* 3
For tho' my *n* rarely yields „ *xli* 13
From art, from *n*, from the schools, „ *xlix* 1
To pangs of *n*, sins of will, „ *liv* 3
Are God and *N* then at strife, „ *lv* 5
That *N* lends such evil dreams? „ 6
Tho' *N*, red in tooth and claw With ravine, „ *lvi* 15
That *N's* ancient power was lost: „ *lxix* 2
And cancell'd *n's* best: but thou, „ *lxxii* 20
I curse not *n*, no, nor death; „ *lxxiii* 7
As moulded like in *N's* mint; „ *lxxix* 6
Thou doest expectant *n* wrong; „ *lxxxiii* 3
'Can clouds of *n* stain The starry clearness „ *lxxxv* 85
High *n* amorous of the good, „ *cix* 9
Will let his coltish *n* break At seasons „ *cxi* 7
Where God and *N* met in light; „ 20
As dying *N's* earth and lime; „ *cxviii* 4
hands That reach thro' *n*, moulding men. „ *cxxiv* 24
Tho' mix'd with God and *N* thou, „ *cxxx* 11
Is *N* like an open book; „ *Con.* 132
For *n* is one with rapine, *Maud I iv* 22
in his force to be *N's* crowning race. „ 33
An eye well-practised in *n*, „ 38
Because their *n's* are little, „ 53
Should *N* keep me alive, „ *vi* 32
Sweet *n* gilded by the gracious gleam *Ded of Idylls* 39
Had suffer'd, or should suffer any taint In *n*: *Marr. of Geraint* 32
Suspicious that her *n* had a taint. „ 68
doubted whether daughter's tenderness, Or easy *n*, „ 798
n's prideful sparkle in the blood *Geraint and E.* 827

Neck (*continued*) an' Charlie 'e brok 'is *n*, *Village Wife* 85
on the fatal *n* Of land running out into rock— *Despair* 9
Amy's arms about my *n*— *Locksley H., Sixty* 13
she that clasp'd my *n* had flown; „ 15
their arch'd *n's*, midnight-maned, *Demeter and P.* 46
I feeäld it drip o' my *n*. *Owd Roä* 42
as if 'e'd 'a brokken 'is *n*, „ 63
Neck-an-crop I coom'd *n-a-c* soomtimes *North. Cobbler* 20
Neck'd *See* **Long-neck'd**
Necklace (*See also* **Pearl-necklace**) And I would be the *n*, *Miller's D.* 181
To make the *n* shine; *Talking Oak* 222
And fling the diamond *n* by.' *Lady Clare* 40
Or *n* for a neck to which the swan's *Lancelot and E.* 1184
or a *n* for a neck O as much fairer— „ 1227
This ruby *n* thrice around her neck, *Last Tournament* 19
diamond *n* dearer than the golden ring, *Locksley H., Sixty* 21
Nectar For they lie beside their *n*, *Lotos-Eaters, C. S.* 111
Hebes are they to hand ambrosia, mix The *n*; *Princess iii* 114
n smack'd of hemlock on the lips, *Demeter and P.* 104
Need (s) wasted Truth in her utmost *n*. *Clear-headed friend* 19
Our dusted velvets have much *n* of thee: *To J. M. K.* 4
And if some dreadful *n* should rise *Love thou thy land* 91
vows, where there was never *n* of vows, *Gardener's D.* 258
As I might slay this child, if good *n* were, *Princess ii* 287
How know I what had *n* of thee, *In Mem. lxxiii* 3
What is thy name? thy *n*?' *Gareth and L.* 605
my *n*, a knight To combat for my sister, „ 607
cruel *n* Constrain'd us, *Marr. of Geraint* 715
All to be there against a sudden *n*; *Geraint and E.* 375
Mine is the larger *n*, who am not meek, *Last Tournament* 610
friends Of Arthur, who should help him at his *n*?' *Pass. of Arthur* 456
had *n* Of a good stout lad at his farm; *First Quarrel* 17
no *n* to make such a stir.' „ 63
'All the more *n*,' I told him, *In the Child. Hosp.* 18
As good *n* was—thou hast come to talk *Sir J. Oldcastle* 32
false at last In our most *n*, appall'd them, *Columbus* 71
Bread enough for his *n* till the labourless day *V. of Maeldune* 86
Then the Norse leader, Dire was his *n* of it, *Batt. of Brunanburh* 56
What *n* to wish when Hubert weds in you *The Ring* 61
house with all its hateful *n's* *Happy* 32
Need (verb) all Life *n's* for life is possible *Love and Duty* 86
'Wild natures *n* wise curbs. *Princess v* 173
whence they *n* More breadth of culture: „ 187
Whether I *n* have fled? *Maud II ii* 72
I *n* not tell thee foolish words,— *Holy Grail* 855
He *n's* no aid who doth his lady's will.' *Pelleas and E.* 281
I *n* Him now. *Last Tournament* 630
such a craziness as *n's* A cell and keeper), *Lover's Tale iv* 164
Ah heavens! Why *n* I tell you all?— „ 201
'The lad will *n* little more of your care.' *In the Child. Hosp.* 17
You *n* not wave me from you. *Happy* 20
music here be mortal *n* the singer greatly care? *Parnassus* 18
Up hill 'Too-slow' will *n* the whip, *Politics* 11
I *n* no wages of shame. *Charity* 40
Needed With all that seamen *n* or their wives— *Enoch Arden* 139
yea twice or thrice—As oft as *n*— „ 143
Or thro' the want of what it *n* most, „ 265
voice who best could tell What most it *n*— „ 267
Because it *n* help of Love: *In Mem. xxv* 8
I *n* then no charm to keep them mine *Merlin and V.* 547
Needful And bought them *n* books, and everyway, *Enoch Arden* 332
My *n* seeming harshness, pardon it. *Princess ii* 309
Are but the *n* preludes of the truth: „ *Con.* 74
thou knowest I hold that forms Are *n*: *Akbar's Dream* 127
Needing (His father lying sick and *n* him) *Enoch Arden* 65
Needle 'I would have hid her *n* in my heart, *Edwin Morris* 62
Man for the sword and for the *n* she: *Princess v* 448
Are sharpen'd to a *n's* end; *In Mem. lxxvi* 4
Be *n* to the magnet of your word, *To Mary Boyle* 7
Needless To greet the sheriff, *n* courtesy! *Edwin Morris* 133
Needs (adv.) he *n* Must wed that other, whom no man desired, *Gareth and L.* 108
one with me in all, he *n* must know.' „ 566
I *n* must disobey him for his good; *Geraint and E.* 135
You *n* must work my work. *Merlin and V.* 505
Needy Let the *n* be banqueted, *On Jub. Q. Victoria* 35
Negation I hate the black *n* of the bier, *Ancient Sage* 204
Neglect If men *n* your pages? *Spiteful Letter* 6
Neglected That all *n* places of the field *Aylmer's Field* 693
For thanks it seems till now *n*, *Merlin and V.* 308
Neighbour (adj.) from all *n* crowns Alliance and allegiance, *Œnone* 124
Leaning his horns into the *n* field, *Gardener's D.* 87
and lady friends From *n* seats: *Princess, Pro.* 98
But if my *n* whistle answers him— *Lover's Tale iv* 161
Neighbour (s) (*See also* **Nabour**) While all the *n's* shoot thee round, *The Blackbird* 2
And ran to tell her *n's*; *The Goose* 14
Yet say the *n's* when they call, *Amphion* 5
O Lord!—'tis in my *n's* ground, „ 75
Leering at his *n's* wife. *Vision of Sin* 118
The next day came a *n*. *Aylmer's Field* 251
With *n's* laid along the grass, *Lucretius* 214
Each hissing in his *n's* ear; *Princess v* 15
the *n's* come and laugh and gossip, *Grandmother* 91
From every house the *n's* met, *In Mem. xxxi* 9
The foolish *n's* come and go, „ *lx* 13
measuring with his eyes His *n's* make and might: *Pelleas and E.* 151
friend, the *n*, Lionel, the beloved, *Lover's Tale i* 653
if perchance the *n's* round May see, *Achilles over the T.* 12
Neighbourhood Far off from human *n*, *Eleänore* 6
As from some blissful *n*, *Two Voices* 430
By one low voice to one dear *n*, *Aylmer's Field* 60
Make their *n* healthfuller, *On Jub. Q. Victoria* 32
Neighbouring half The *n* borough with their Institute *Princess, Pro.* 5
betroth'd To one, a *n* Princess: „ *i* 33
Neigh'd Lancelot's charger fiercely *n*, *Gareth and L.* 1400
N with all gladness as they came, *Geraint and E.* 755
the warhorse *n* As at a friend's voice, *Guinevere* 530
Neighing strong *n's* of the wild white Horse *Lancelot and E.* 298
Neilgherry the sweet half-English *N* air *The Brook* 17
Nell God bless you, my own little *N*.' *First Quarrel* 22
Nelly 'Our *N's* the flower of 'em all.' „ 28
But *N*, the last of the cletch, *Village Wife* 9
N wur up fro' the craädle as big i' the mouth „ 103
an' our *N* she gied me 'er 'and, „ 111
Nelson old England fall Which *N* left so great. *The Fleet* 5
Nemesis great *N* Break from a darken'd future, *Princess vi* 174
Nephew sparrow-hawk, My curse, my *n*— *Marr. of Geraint* 445
if the sparrow-hawk, this *n*, fight „ 475
And tilts with my good *n* thereupon, „ 488
Then Yniol's *n*, after trumpet blown, „ 551
O loyal *n* of our noble King, *Lancelot and E.* 652
Neronian those *N* legionaries *Boädicea* 1
Nerve (s) 'Tis life, whereof our *n's* are scant, *Two Voices* 397
His *n's* were wrong. What ails us, *Walk. to the Mail* 105
like those, who clench their *n's* to rush *Love and Duty* 77
My *n's* have dealt with stiffer. *Will Water.* 78
When thy *n's* could understand *Vision of Sin* 160
Were living *n's* to feel the rent; *Aylmer's Field* 536
O iron *n* to true occasion true, *Ode on Well.* 37
A weight of *n's* without a mind, *In Mem. xii* 7
blood creeps, and the *n's* prick And tingle; „ *l* 2
Where all the *n* of sense is numb; „ *xciii* 7
O, having the *n's* of motion as well as the *n's* *Maud I i* 63
believing mind, but shatter'd *n*, *Lover's Tale iv* 105
Nerve (verb) 'The song that *n's* a nation's heart, *Epilogue* 81
Nerve-dissolving The *n-d* melody *Vision of Sin* 44
Nest From my high *n* of penance here proclaim *St. S. Stylites* 167
huts At random scatter'd, each a *n* in bloom. *Aylmer's Field* 150
bough That moving moves the *n* and nestling, *Sea Dreams* 291
birdie say In her *n* at peep of day? „ 294
However deep you might embower the *n*, *Princess, Pro.* 147
Father will come to his babe in the *n*, „ *iii* 13
in the North long since my *n* is made. „ *iv* 110
built the *n*' she said, 'To hatch the cuckoo. „ 365
We seem a *n* of traitors— „ *v* 426
And all in a *n* together. *Window, Spring* 16
there were cries and clashings in the *n*, *Gareth and L.* 70
by the bird's song ye may learn the *n*,' *Marr. of Geraint* 359

Nest (*continued*) we will live like two birds in one *n*, *Geraint and E.* 627
And yellow-throated nestling in the *n*. *Lancelot and E.* 12
almost plaster'd like a martin's *n* *Holy Grail* 548
find a *n* and feels a snake, he drew: *Pelleas and E.* 437
'Black *n* of rats,' he groan'd, „ 555
started thro' mid air Bearing an eagle's *n*: *Last Tournament* 15
Sir Lancelot from the perilous *n*, „ 18
A mountain *n*—the pleasure-boat that rock'd, *Lover's Tale i* 42
better ha' put my naked hand in a hornets' *n*. *First Quarrel* 50
And a tree with a moulder'd *n* *Dead Prophet* 18
Drove from out the mother's *n* *Open. I. and C. Exhib.* 27
Birds and brides must leave the *n*. *The Ring* 89
song again, *n* again, young again,' *The Throstle* 9
Nested (adj.) (*See also* **Half-nested**) I envied human wives, and *n* birds, *Demeter and P.* 53
Nested (verb) Wherein we *n* sleeping or awake, *Lover's Tale i* 231
Nestled and the gilded snake Had *n* „ 624
Nestlike a home For Annie, neat and *n*, *Enoch Arden* 59
Nestling bough That moving moves the nest and *n*, *Sea Dreams* 291
And yellow-throated *n* in the nest. *Lancelot and E.* 12
loved it tenderly, And named it *N*; *Last Tournament* 25
'Peace to thine eagle-borne Dead *n*, „ 34
Net (s) (*See also* **Ivy-net, Fishing-nets**) Love that hath us in the *n*, *Miller's D.* 203
n made pleasant by the baits Of gold *Aylmer's Field* 486
To catch a dragon in a cherry *n*, *Princess v* 169
To have her lion roll in a silken *n* *Maud I vi* 29
Makers of *n's*, and living from the sea. *Pelleas and E.* 90
and Love The *n* of truth?' *Abkar's Dream* 88
Net (verb) fibres *n* the dreamless head, *In Mem. ii* 3
Netted (*See also* **Golden-netted**) I make the *n* sunbeam dance *The Brook* 176
Nettle round and round In dung and *n's*! *Pelleas and E.* 471
sowing the *n* on all the laurel'd graves *Vastness* 22
Nettled tho' *n* that he seem'd to slur *Princess i* 163
Never Thou shalt hear the '*N*, *n*,' *Locksley Hall* 83
Never-changing In changing, chime with *n-c* Law. *To Duke of Argyll* 11
And over all, the *n-c* One *Akbar's Dream* 147
Never-ended Here in the *n-e* afternoon, *Last Tournament* 584
Never-lighted Beside the *n-l* fire. *In Mem. lxxxiv* 20
New (*See also* **Fiery-new, Spick-span-new**) Kate hath a spirit ever strung like a *n* bow, *Kate* 11
Transgress his ample bound to some *n* crown:— *Poland* 8
tho' the surge Of some *n* deluge from a thousand hills *If I were loved* 12
Will learn *n* things when I am not.' *Two Voices* 63
I knit a hundred others *n*: „ 234
With this old soul in organs *n*? „ 393
'I have found A *n* land, but I die.' *Palace of Art* 284
N from its silken sheath. *D. of F. Women* 60
Sweet as *n* buds in Spring. „ 272
Shall sing for want, ere leaves are *n*, *The Blackbird* 23
There's a *n* foot on the floor, my friend, And a *n* face at the door, my friend, A *n* face at the door. *D. of the O. Year* 52
Nothing comes to thee *n* or strange. *To J. S.* 74
N Majesties of mighty States— *Love thou thy land* 60
He thought that nothing *n* was said, *The Epic* 30
Among *n* men, strange faces, other minds.' *M. d'Arthur* 238
each in passing touch'd with some *n* grace *Gardener's D.* 204
N things and old, himself and her, she sour'd *Walk. to the Mail* 61
I breathed In some *n* planet: *Edwin Morris* 115
She left the *n* piano shut: *Talking Oak* 119
fair *n* forms, That float about the threshold of an age, *Golden Year* 15
something more, A bringer of *n* things; *Ulysses* 28
In that *n* world which is the old: *Day-Dm., Depart.* 4
Thro' sunny decades *n* and strange, *L'Envoi* 22
If old things, there are *n*; *Will Water.* 58
N stars all night above the brim Of waters *Voyage* 25
'No, I love not what is *n*; *Vision of Sin* 139
And the *n* warmth of life's ascending sun *Enoch Arden* 38
Then her *n* child was as herself renew'd, Then the *n* mother came about her heart, 523
'that we still may lead The *n* light up, *Princess ii* 348
those were gracious times. Then came your *n* friend: „ *iv* 298

New (*continued*) I your old friend and tried, she *n* in all? *Princess iv* 318
n day comes, the light Dearer for night, „ *vii* 346
Gray nurses, loving nothing *n*; *In Mem. xxix* 14
Shall count *n* things as dear as old: „ *xl* 28
The baby *n* to earth and sky, „ *xlv* 1
The full *n* life that feeds thy breath „ *lxxxvi* 10
But all is *n* unhallow'd ground. „ *civ* 12
With old results that look like *n*: „ *cxxviii* 11
But, I fear, the *n* strong wine of love, *Maud I vi* 82
N as his title, built last year, „ *x* 19
And that same night, the night of the *n* year, *Com. of Arthur* 209
N things and old co-twisted, as if Time Were nothing, *Gareth and L.* 226
the *n* knight Had fear he might be shamed; „ 1043
n sun Beat thro' the blindless casement of the room, *Marr. of Geraint* 70
Ride into that *n* fortress by your town, „ 407
Built that *n* fort to overawe my friends, „ 460
She is not fairer in *n* clothes than old. „ 722
'O my *n* mother, be not wroth or grieved At thy *n* son, „ 779
A splendour dear to women, *n* to her, And therefore dearer; or if not so *n*, „ 808
The *n* leaf ever pushes off the old. *Balin and Balan* 442
like a bride's On her *n* lord, her own, *Merlin and V.* 617
But once in life was fluster'd with *n* wine, „ 756
Meanwhile the *n* companions past away *Lancelot and E.* 399
till they found The *n* design wherein they lost themselves, „ 441
Not for me! For her! for your *n* fancy. „ 1216
King Arthur made *n* knights to fill the gap *Pelleas and E.* 1
And this *n* knight, Sir Pelleas of the isles— „ 17
N leaf, *n* life—the days of frost are o'er: *N* life, *n* love, to suit the newer day: *N* loves are sweet as those that went before: *Last Tournament* 278
the knights, Glorying in each *n* glory, „ 336
And thou wert lying in thy *n* leman's arms.' „ 625
She like a *n* disease, unknown to men, *Guinevere* 518
to those With whom he dwelt, *n* faces, other minds. *Pass. of Arthur* 5
wife and child with wail Pass to *n* lords; „ 45
Among *n* men, strange faces, other minds.' „ 406
And the *n* sun rose bringing the *n* year. „ 469
rather seem'd For some *n* death than for a life renew'd; *Lover's Tale iv* 374
Crazy with laughter and babble and earth's *n* wine, *To A. Tennyson* 2
those long-sweeping beechen boughs Of our *N* Forest. *Sisters (E. and E.)* 113
fur *N* Squire coom'd last night. *Village Wife* 1
Sa *n* Squire's coom'd wi' 'is taäil in 'is 'and, (repeat) „ 14, 121
an' dizen'd out, an' a-buyin' *n* cloäthes, „ 37
chains For him who gave a *n* heaven, a *n* earth, *Columbus* 20
The marvel of that fair *n* nature— „ 79
Whatever wealth I bought from that *n* world „ 101
be consecrate to lead A *n* crusade against the Saracen, „ 103
For these are the *n* dark ages, you see, *Despair* 88
Eh! tha be *n* to the plaäce— *Spinster's S's.* 3
Dead the *n* astronomy calls her. . . . *Locksley H., Sixty* 175
And some *n* Spirit o'erbear the old, *Epilogue* 14
Once more the Heavenly Power Makes all things *n*, *Early Spring* 2
For now the Heavenly Power Makes all things *n*, „ 44
N England of the Southern Pole! *Hands all Round* 16
For ten thousand years Old and *n*? *The Ring* 20
—is making a *n* link Breaking an old one? „ 50
On that *n* life that gems the hawthorn line; *Prog. of Spring* 36
And *n* developments, whatever spark „ 94
Sing the *n* year in under the blue. *The Throstle* 5
'*N*, *n*, *n*, *n*! Is it then *so n* „ 7
'hast *thou* brought us down a *n* Korân From heaven? *Akbar's Dream* 116
I heard a mocking laugh 'the *n* Korân!' „ 183
The wonders were so wildly *n*, *Mechanophilus* 27
If *N* and Old, disastrous feud, *Love thou thy land* 77
'The old order changeth, yielding place to *n*, *M. d'Arthur* 240
Whose fancy fuses old and *n*, *In Mem. xvi* 18

New (*continued*) Ring out the old, ring in the *n*, *In Mem. cvi* 5
'The old order changeth, yielding place to *n*, *Pass. of Arthur* 408
New-born here he glances on an eye *n-b*, *Lucretius* 137
face of a blooming boy Fresh as a flower *n-b*, *Gareth and L.* 1409
New-budded music, O bird, in the *n-b* bowers! *W. to Alexandra* 11
New-caged first as sullen as a beast *n-c*, *Geraint and E.* 856
these Are like wild brutes *n-c*— *Akbar's Dream* 50
New-comer *n-c's* in an ancient hold, *Edwin Morris* 9
N-c's from the Mersey, millionaires, „ 10
New-dug I seem to see a *n-d* grave up yonder *The Flight* 97
Newer 'Tis not too late to seek a *n* world. *Ulysses* 57
Yea, shook this *n*, stronger hall of ours, *Holy Grail* 731
New life, new love, to suit the *n* day: *Last Tournament* 279
Dust in wholesome old-world dust before the *n* world begin. *Locksley H. Sixty* 150
And cast aside, when old, for *n*,— *Akbar's Dream* 134
New-fall'n Lay like a *n-f* meteor on the grass, *Princess vi* 135
New-flush'd thro' damp holts *n-f* with may, *My life is full* 19
New Forest beechen boughs Of our *N F.* *Sisters (E. and E.)* 113
Newfoundland Than for his old *N's*, *Aylmer's Field* 125
Newly-caged Like some wild creature *n-c*, *Princess ii* 301
Newly-enter'd But *n-e*, taller than the rest, *Last Tournament* 169
Newly-fallen Right o'er a mount of *n-f* stones, *Marr. of Geraint* 361
New-made one of the two at her side This *n-m* lord, *Maud I x* 3
sent Ulfius, and Brastias, and Bedivere, His *n-m* knights, *Com. of Arthur* 137
and him his *n-m* knight Worshipt, *Pelleas and E.* 154
My younger knights, *n-m*, *Last Tournament* 99
New-mown rarely smells the *n-m* hay, *The Owl i* 9
Newness the discovery And *n* of thine art *Ode to Memory* 88
New-old accept this old imperfect tale, *N-o*, *To the Queen ii* 37
All *n-o* revolutions of Empire— *Vastness* 30
New-risen on the roof Of night *n-r*, *Arabian Nights* 130
News *N* from the humming city comes to it *Gardener's D.* 35
Expectant of that *n* which never came, *Enoch Arden* 258
and no *n* of Enoch came. „ 361
breaker of the bitter *n* from home, *Aylmer's Field* 594
She brought strange *n*. *Sea Dreams* 267
in the distance pealing *n* Of better, *Princess iv* 81
golden *n* along the steppes is blown, *W. to Marie Alex.* 11
Pass and blush the *n* Over glowing ships; *Maud I xvii* 11
Pass the happy *n*, Blush it thro' the West; „ 15
These *n* be mine, none other's— *Gareth and L.* 539
Ill *n*, my Queen, for all who love him, *Lancelot and E.* 598
Yet good *n* too; for goodly hopes are mine „ 601
'What *n* from Camelot, lord? „ 620
Came suddenly on the Queen with the sharp *n*. „ 730
third night hence will bring thee *n* of gold.' *Pelleas and E.* 357
'Why lingers Gawain with his golden *n*?' „ 411
New-wedded But the *n-w* wife was unharm'd, *Charity* 22
New-world clamour grew As of a *n-w* Babel, *Princess iv* 487
New-wreathed The garland of *n-w* emprise: *Kate* 24
New-year To-morrow 'ill be the happiest time of all the glad *N-y*; (repeat) *May Queen* 2, 42
Of all the glad *N-y*, mother, the maddest merriest day; „ 3
I would see the sun rise upon the glad *N-y*. (repeat) *May Queen N. Y's. E.* 2, 51
It is the last *N-y* that I shall ever see, „ 3
And the *N-y's* coming up, mother, „ 7
And the *N-y* will take 'em away. *D. of the O. Year* 14
And the *N-y* blithe and bold, my friend, „ 35
O sweet *n-y* delaying long; *In Mem. lxxxiii* 2
O thou, *n-y*, delaying long, „ 13
that same night, the night of the *n y*, *Com. of Arthur* 209
And the new sun rose bringing the *n y*. *Pass. of Arthur* 469
April promise, glad *n-y* Of Being, *Lover's Tale i* 281
Sing the *n y* in under the blue. *The Throstle* 5
Next 'When the *n* moon was roll'd into the sky, *D. of F. Women* 229
'So when, *n* morn, the lord whose life he saved *Gareth and L.* 888
fight In *n* day's tourney I may break his pride.' *Marr. of Geraint* 476
But when the *n* sun brake from underground, *Lancelot and E.* 1137
'But when the *n* day brake from under ground— *Holy Grail* 338
What be the *n* un like? *Village Wife* 19
Were nothing the *n* minute? *Voice spake, etc*, 10

R

Nibb'd *See* **Horny-nibb'd**
Nice his *n* eyes Should see the raw mechanic's bloody thumbs *Walk to the Mail* 74
If I should deem it over *n*— *Tiresias* 191
Nicetish Wi' lots o' munny laäid by, an' a *n* bit o' land. *N. Farmer, N. S.* 22
Niched Those *n* shapes of noble mould, *The Daisy* 38
Niece William was his son, And she his *n*. *Dora* 3
Allan call'd His *n* and said: „ 42
by the bright head of my little *n*, *Princess ii* 276
Niggard Some *n* fraction of an hour, *Aylmer's Field* 450
Tho' *n* throats of Manchester may bawl, *Third of Feb.* 43
Nigger *See* **Nager**
Nigh Far off thou art, but ever *n*; *In Mem. cxxx* 13
In the night, and *n* the dawn, *Forlorn* 83
'My end draws *n*; 'tis time that I were gone. *M. d' Arthur* 163
'My end draws *n*; 'tis time that I were gone. *Pass. of Arthur* 332
Nigher Sure she was *n* to heaven's spheres, *Ode to Memory* 40
Nigh-naked On the *n-n* tree the robin piped *Enoch Arden* 676
Night (*See also* **Goodnight, Market-noight, Noight, Sleeping-night, Yesternight**) They comfort him by *n* and day; *Supp. Confessions* 45
She only said, 'The *n* is dreary (repeat) *Mariana* 21, 57
Upon the middle of the *n*, „ 25
Past Yabbok brook the livelong *n*, *Clear-headed friend* 27
Until another *n* in *n* I enter'd, *Arabian Nights* 37
living airs of middle *n* Died round the bulbul „ 69
crescents on the roof Of *n* new-risen, „ 130
Nor was the *n* thy shroud. *Ode to Memory* 28
WITH a half-glance upon the sky At *n* *A Character* 2
All day and all *n* it is ever drawn *Poet's Mind* 28
Day and *n* to the billow the fountain calls: *Sea-Fairies* 9
All within is dark as *n*: *Deserted House* 5
In the yew-wood black as *n*, *Oriana* 19
All *n* the silence seems to flow „ 86
But at *n* I would roam abroad and play *The Merman* 11
Low thunder and light in the magic *n*— „ 23
whoop and cry All *n*, merrily, merrily; „ 27
But at *n* I would wander away, away, *The Mermaid* 31
wasting odorous sighs All *n* long *Adeline* 44
Moving thro' a fleecy *n*. *Margaret* 21
Float by you on the verge of *n*. „ 31
delight of frolic flight, by day or *n*, *Rosalind* 47
THERE she weaves by *n* and day A magic web *L. of Shalott ii* 1
For often thro' the silent *n's* A funeral, „ 30
As often thro' the purple *n*, „ *iii* 24
Thro' the noises of the *n* „ *iv* 22
And 'Ave Mary,' *n* and morn, *Mariana in the S.* 10
'Madonna, sad is *n* and morn,' „ 22
'That won his praises *n* and morn?' „ 34
And murmuring, as at *n* and morn, „ 46
More inward than at *n* or morn, „ 58
'The day to *n*,' she made her moan, 'The day to *n*, the *n* to morn, And day and *n* I am left alone „ 81
Heaven over Heaven rose the *n*. „ 92
'The *n* comes on that knows not morn, „ 94
Look up thro' *n*: the world is wide. *Two Voices* 24
Would sweep the tracts of day and *n*. „ 69
Some yearning toward the lamps of *n*; „ 363
When April *n's* began to blow, *Miller's D.* 106
Flitted across into the *n*, „ 127
I may seem, As in the *n's* of old, „ 166
For hid in ringlets day and *n*, „ 173
I scarce should be unclasp'd at *n*. „ 186
Last *n* I wasted hateful hours *Fatima* 8
Last *n*, when some one spoke his name, „ 15
I hear Dead sounds at *n* come from the inmost hills, *Œnone* 249
wheresoe'er I am by *n* and day, „ 267
I rose up in the silent *n*: *The Sisters* 25
Echoing all *n* to that sonorous flow *Palace of Art* 27
young *n* divine Crown'd dying day with stars, „ 183
that hears all *n* The plunging seas „ 250
I sleep so sound all *n*, mother, *May Queen* 9
never see me more in the long gray fields at *n*; *May Queen, N. Y's. E.* 26

Night (continued) All n I lie awake, but I fall asleep at morn; May Queen, N. Y's. E. 50
came a sweeter token when the n and morning meet: " Con. 22
Drops in a silent autumn n. Lotos-Eaters, C. S. 34
Sound all n long, in falling thro' the dell, D of F. Women 183
All n the splinter'd crags that wall the dell " 187
'Saw God divide the n with flying flame, " 225
Do hunt me, day and n.' " 256
The n is starry and cold, my friend, D. of the O. Year 34
And dwells in heaven half the n. To J. S. 52
heard at dead of n to greet Troy's wandering prince, On a Mourner 32
the moving isles of winter shock By n, M. d'Arthur 141
like a wind, that shrills All n in a waste land, " 202
voice Rise like a fountain for me n and day. " 249
last n's gale had caught, And blown Gardener's D. 124
all that n I heard the watchman peal The sliding season: all that n I heard The heavy clocks knolling " 182
and heir to all, Made this n thus. " 190
N slid down one long stream of sighing wind, " 267
ere the n we rose And saunter'd home Audley Court 79
a cry Should break his sleep by n, Walk. to the Mail 74
By n we dragg'd her to the college tower " 89
I read, and fled by n, and flying turn'd: Edwin Morris 134
in the n, after a little sleep, I wake: St. S. Stylites 113
brought the n In which we sat together Love and Duty 59
and of sunrise mix'd In that brief n; the summer n, " 73
Many a n from yonder ivied casement, Locksley Hall 7
Many a n I saw the Pleiads, " 9
rosy red flushing in the northern n. " 26
In the dead unhappy n, and when the rain " 78
at n along the dusky highway near and nearer drawn, " 113
Beyond the n, across the day, Day-Dm., Depart. 31
And perplex'd her, n and morn, L. of Burleigh 78
And burn the threshold of the n, The Voyage 18
New stars all n above the brim Of waters " 25
Down the waste waters day and n, " 58
overboard one stormy n He cast his body, " 79
elfin prancer springs By n to eery warblings, Sir L. and Q. G. 34
And round again to happy n. Move eastward 12
I HAD a vision when the n was late: Vision of Sin 1
'Thou art mazed, the n is long, " 195
And the longer n is near: " 196
seem'd, as in a nightmare of the n, Enoch Arden 114
Many a sad kiss by day by n renew'd " 161
After a n of feverous wakefulness, " 231
Then fearing n and chill for Annie, " 443
one n it chanced That Annie could not sleep, " 489
compass'd round by the blind wall of n " 492
Half the n, Buoy'd upon floating tackle " 550
Hurt in that n of sudden ruin and wreck, " 564
third n after this, While Enoch slumber'd " 907
was Edith that same n; Aylmer's Field 279
Yet once by n again the lovers met, " 413
rustling once at n about the place, " 547
That n, that moment, when she named his name, " 581
one n, except For greenish glimmerings " 621
Returning, as the bird returns, at n, Sea Dreams 43
the sea roars Ruin: a fearful n!' " 81
Left him one hand, and reaching thro' the n Her other, " 287
your sleep for this one n be sound: " 315
'Storm in the n! for thrice I heard the rain Lucretius 26
from some bay-window shake the n; Princess i 106
To float about a glimmering n, " 247
The circled Iris of a n of tears; " iii 27
My mother, 'tis her wont from n to n " 32
And so last n she fell to canvass you: " 40
Up in one n and due to sudden sun: " iv 312
Robed in the long n of her deep hair, " 491
the long fantastic n With all its doings " 565
came As n to him that sitting on a hill " 574
later in the n Had come on Psyche weeping: " v 49
You did but come as goblins in the n, " 220
heavy dews Gathered by n and peace, " 244

Night (continued) A n of Summer from the heat, Princess vi 54
like n and evening mixt Their dark and gray, " 131
whole n's long, up in the tower, " 255
cloud Drag inward from the deeps, a wall of n, " vii 37
Drew the great n into themselves, " 49
Blanche had sworn That after that dark n among the fields " 73
Deep in the n I woke: " 173
shares with man His n's, his days, " 263
the new day comes, the light Dearer for n, " 347
And gradually the powers of the n, " Con 111
Deepening thy voice with the deepening of the n, V. of Cauteretz 2
Stole the seed by n. The Flower 12
All n have I heard the voice Rave Voice and the P. 5
Draw toward the long frost and longest n, A Dedication 11
all n upon the bridge of war Sat glorying; Spec. of Iliad 9
Taken the stars from the n Window, Gone 5
All n below the darken'd eyes; In Mem. iv 14
All n no ruder air perplex " ix 9
I hear the bell struck in the n; " x 2
That strikes by n a craggy shelf, " xvi 13
Is on the waters day and n, " xvii 11
Is dash'd with wandering isles of n. " xxiv 4
The moon is hid; the n is still; " xxviii 2
To enrich the threshold of the n " xxix 6
Draw forth the cheerful day from n: " xxx 30
An infant crying in the n: " liv 18
At n she weeps, 'How vain am I! " lx 15
How dwarf'd a growth of cold and n, " lxi 7
His n of loss is always there. " lxvi 16
I found an angel of the n; " lxix 14
And mix with hollow masks of n; " lxx 4
And howlest, issuing out of n, " lxxii 2
Come: not in watches of the n, " xci 13
By n we linger'd on the lawn, " xcv 1
Withdrew themselves from me and n, " 18
Power was with him in the n, " xcvi 18
On that last n before we went " ciii 1
The moon is hid, the n is still; " civ 2
A little spare the n I loved, " cv 15
The year is dying in the n; " cvi 3
bank Of vapour, leaving n forlorn. " cvii 4
Bright Phosphor, fresher for the n, " cxxi 9
In the deep n, that all is well. " cxxvi 12
tho' faith and form Be sunder'd in the n of fear; " cxxvii 2
All n the shining vapour sail " Con 111
shriek of a mother divide the shuddering n. Maud I i 16
in the hush of the moonless n's, " 42
ghostlike, deathlike, half the n long " iii 8
Last n, when the sunset burn'd " vi 8
nodding together In some Arabian n? " vii 12
Like a sudden spark Struck vainly in the n, " ix 14
Beat to the noiseless music of the n! " xviii 77
Sat with her, read to her, n and day, " xix 75
For the black bat, n, has flown, " xxii 2
All n have the roses heard The flute, " 13
All n has the casement jessamine stirr'd " 15
brief n goes In babble and revel and wine. " 27
the rose was awake all n for your sake, " 49
Half the n I waste in sighs, " II iv 23
the lily and rose That blow by n, " v 75
face of n is fair on the dewy downs, " III vi 5
wolf and boar and bear Came n and day, Com. of Arthur 24
that same n, the n of the new year, " 209
on the n When Uther in Tintagil past away " 366
Descending thro' the dismal n—a n " 371
'Blow trumpet, the long n hath roll'd away! " 483
couch'd at n with grimy kitchen-knaves. Gareth and L. 481
names himself the N and oftener Death, " 638
Slain by himself, shall enter endless n. " 642
but at n let go the stone, And rise, " 825
To fight the brotherhood of Day and N— " 857
Despite of Day and N and Death and Hell.' " 887
smells the honeysuckle In the hush'd n, " 1288
like a phantom pass Chilling the n: " 1336
doom'd to be the bride of N and Death; " 1396

Night (continued) now by n With moon and trembling stars, Marr. of Geraint 7
At distance, ere they settle for the n. „ 250
Where can I get me harbourage for the n? „ 281
I seek a harbourage for the n.' „ 299
the n Before my Enid's birthday, „ 457
draw The quiet n into her blood, „ 532
given her on the n Before her birthday, „ 632
n of fire, when Edyrn sack'd their house, „ 634
So sadly lost on that unhappy n; „ 689
But hire us some fair chamber for the n, Geraint and E. 238
or touch at n the northern star; Balin and Balan 166
Last n methought I saw That maiden Saint „ 260
made that mouth of n Whereout the Demon „ 316
not the less by n The scorn of Garlon, „ 382
and now The n has come. „ 621
rat that borest in the dyke Thy hole by n Merlin and V. 113
sleepless n's Of my long life have made it easy „ 679
thither wending there that n they bode. Lancelot and E. 412
There bode the n: but woke with dawn, „ 846
she tended him, And likewise many a n: „ 851
so the simple maid Went half the n repeating, „ 899
this n I dream'd That I was all alone „ 1045
lily maid of Astolat Lay smiling, like a star in blackest n. „ 1243
Who passes thro' the vision of the n— „ 1406
waked at dead of n, I heard a sound Holy Grail 108
The rosy quiverings died into the n. „ 123
'Then on a summer n it came to pass, „ 179
but moving with me n and day, Fainter by day, but always in the n Blood-red, „ 471
For after I had lain so many n's, „ 569
but one n my vow Burnt me within, „ 607
'One n my pathway swerving east, „ 634
came a n Still as the day was loud; „ 682
For, brother, so one n, because they roll „ 685
on the seventh n I heard the shingle grinding „ 810
Let visions of the n or of the day Come, „ 910
Nor slept that n for pleasure in his blood, Pelleas and E. 138
The third n hence will bring thee news of gold.' „ 357
third n brought a moon With promise of large light „ 393
Hot was the n and silent; „ 395
Here in the still sweet summer n, „ 473
bounded forth and vanish'd thro' the n. „ 487
by wild and way, for half the n, „ 497
Round whose sick head all n, like birds of prey, Last Tournament 138
And Lancelot's, at this n's solemnity „ 223
Heard in dead n along that table-shore, „ 463
that autumn n, like the live North, „ 479
The n was dark; the true star set. „ 605
One black, mute midsummer n I sat, „ 612
That n came Arthur home, „ 755
In the dead n, grim faces came and went Guinevere 70
And then they were agreed upon a n „ 96
Fled all n long by glimmering waste and weald, „ 128
This n, a rumour wildly blown about Came, „ 153
and dark the n and chill! „ 168
and dark and chill the n! „ 174
that n the bard Sang Arthur's glorious wars, „ 285
Thro' the thick n I hear the trumpet blow: „ 569
making all the n a steam of fire. „ 599
like wild birds that change Their season in the n Pass. of Arthur 39
As of some lonely city sack'd by n, „ 43
rose the King and moved his host by n, „ 79
moving isles of winter shock By n, „ 309
like a wind that shrills All n in a waste land, „ 370
Rise like a fountain for me n and day. „ 417
toils across the middle moonlit n's, Lover's Tale i 138
thence one n, when all the winds were loud, „ 378
Then had he stemm'd my day with n, „ 502
darkness of the grave and utter n, „ 598
day was as the n to me! The n to me was kinder than the day; The n „ 610
Between the going light and growing n? „ 664
sent my cry Thro' the blank n to Him „ 752
winds Laid the long n in silver streaks „ ii 112

Night (continued) Comes in upon him in the dead of n, Lover's Tale ii 154
With half a n's appliances, „ iv 93
So the sweet figure folded round with n „ 219
the boat went down that n—(repeat) First Quarrel 92
The loud black n's for us, Rizpah 6
But the n has crept into my heart, „ 16
what should you know of the n, „ 17
in the n by the churchyard wall. „ 56
once of a frosty n I slither'd North. Cobbler 19
one n I cooms 'oäm like a bull gotten loose at a faäir, „ 33
Ship after ship, the whole n long, (repeat) The Revenge 58, 59, 60
half of the short summer n was gone, „ 65
the n went down, and the sun smiled „ 70
fought such a fight for a day and a n „ 83
cloud that roofs our noon with n, Sisters (E. and E.) 17
A moonless n with storm— „ 96
For on the dark n of our marriage-day „ 232
Thro' dreams by n and trances of the day, „ 274
fur New Squire coom'd last n. Village Wife 1
and it gied me a scare tother n, „ 81
fur he coom'd last n sa laäte— „ 123
I had sat three n's by the child— In the Child. Hosp. 59
we laid him that n in his grave. Def. of Lucknow 12
to be soldier all day and be sentinel all thro' the n— „ 74
Ever the n with its coffinless corpse „ 80
Then day and n, day and n, „ 92
that one n a crowd Throng'd the waste field Sir J. Oldcastle 39
Not yet—not all—last n a dream— Columbus 66
thunders in the black Veragua n's, „ 146
I send my prayer by n and day— „ 233
arm'd by day and n Against the Turk; Montenegro 3
One n when earth was winter-black, To E. Fitzgerald 21
And oldest age in shadow from the n, Tiresias 104
Heard from the roofs by n, „ 140
he roll'd himself At dead of n— „ 146
By n, into the deeper n! The deeper n? „ 204
If n, what barren toil to be! „ 207
What life, so maim'd by n, „ 208
ghastlier face than ever has haunted a grave by n, The Wreck 8
leaf rejoice in the frost that sears it at n; „ 20
Follow'd us too that n, and dogg'd us, Despair 2
What did I feel that n? „ 3
but ah God, that n, that n „ 8
We had past from a cheerless n „ 28
for she past from the n to the n. „ 72
She feels the Sun is hid but for a n, Ancient Sage 73
senses break away To mix with ancient N." „ 153
When all is dark as n.' „ 170
doors of N may be the gates of Light; „ 174
pass From sight and n to lose themselves „ 203
'And N and Shadow rule below „ 243
Day and N are children of the Sun, „ 245
Some say, the Light was father of the N, And some, the N was father of the Light, No n no day!— „ 247
but n enough is there In yon dark city: „ 252
And past the range of N and Shadow— „ 283
all n so calm you lay, The n was calm, the morn is calm, The Flight 9
all n I pray'd with tears, „ 17
love that keeps this heart alive beats on it n and day— „ 35
bride who stabb'd her bridegroom on her bridal n— „ 57
an' meself remimbers wan n Tomorrow 7
But wirrah! the storm that n— „ 23
An' yer hair as black as the n, „ 32
a hiccup at ony hour o' the n! Spinster's S's. 98
hunting grounds beyond the n; Locksley H., Sixty 69
and passing now into the n; „ 227
sun hung over the gates of N, Dead Prophet 23
Thou sawest a glory growing on the n, Epit. on Caxton 2
First pledge our Queen this solemn n, Hands all Round 1
Macready, since this n we part, To W. C. Macready 5
bird that flies All n across the darkness, Demeter and P. 2
gave Thy breast to ailing infants in the n, „ 56
out from all the n an answer shrill'd, „ 61

Night (*continued*) To send the moon into the *n* — *Demeter and P.* 135
An' theere i' the 'ouse one *n*— — *Owd Roä* 27
one *n* I wur sittin' aloän, — „ 29
oop wi' the windle that *n*; — „ 32
I looökt out wonst at the *n*, — „ 39
goä that *n* to 'er foälk by cause o' the Christmas Eäve; — „ 52
cocks kep a-crawin' an' crawin' all *n*, — „ 106
she cotch'd 'er death o' cowd that *n*, — „ 114
at *n* Stirs up again in the heart of the sleeper, — *Vastness* 17
Moon, you fade at times From the *n*. — *The Ring* 10
In the *n*, in the *n*, (repeat) — *Forlorn* 5, 11, 17
Catherine, Catherine, in the *n*, — „ 13
In the *n*, O the *n*! (repeat) — *Forlorn* 23, 29, 35, 41, 47, 53, 59, 65, 71, 77
O the *n* of weeping! — *Forlorn* 48
In the *n*, and nigh the dawn, — „ 83
remember that red *n* When thirty ricks, — *To Mary Boyle* 35
Narrowing the bounds of *n*.' — *Prog. of Spring* 91
I dream'd last *n* of that clear summer noon, — *Romney's R.* 74
morn Has lifted the dark eyelash of the *N* — *Akbar's Dream* 201
And—well, if I sinn'd last *n*, — *Bandit's Death* 18
Black was the *n* when we crept away— — „ 25
she sat day and *n* by my bed, — *Charity* 33
Was it only the wind of the *N* — *The Dreamer* 15
O ye Heavens, of your boundless *n's*, — *God and the Univ.* 2

Nightblack High on a *n* horse, in *n* arms, — *Gareth and L.* 1381
drew down from out his *n-b* hair — *Balin and Balan* 511

Nightcap but arter my *n* wur on; — *Village Wife* 122

Night-dew Or *n-d's* on still waters — *Lotos-Eaters, C. S.* 3

Night-fold we were nursed in the drear *n-f* — *Despair* 21

Night-fowl Waking she heard the *n-f* crow: — *Mariana* 26

Nightingale No *n* delighteth to prolong — *Palace of Art* 173
n Sang loud, as tho' he were the bird — *Gardener's D.* 95
whisper of the leaves That tremble round a *n*— — „ 254
As 'twere a hundred-throated *n*, — *Vision of Sin* 27
n thought, 'I have sung many songs, — *Poet's Song* 13
Sleeps in the plain eggs of the *n*. — *Aylmer's Field* 103
And all about us peal'd the *n*, — *Princess i* 220
at mine ear Bubbled the *n* and heeded not, — „ *iv* 266
in the bush beside me chirrupt the *n*. — *Grandmother* 40
N's warbled without, — *G. of Swainston* 1
N's sang in his woods: — „ 6
N's warbled and sang Of a passion — „ 8
To think or say, 'There is the *n*;' — *Marr. of Geraint* 342
The *n*, full-toned in middle May, — *Balin and Balan* 213
the *n's* hymn in the dark. — *First Quarrel* 34
That *n* is heard! — *Ancient Sage* 20
n Saw thee, and flash'd into a frolic — *Demeter and P.* 11

Night-lamp Where the dying *n-l* flickers, — *Locksley Hall* 80

Night-light *n-l* flickering in my eyes Awoke me.' — *Sea Dreams* 103

Night-long A *n-l* Present of the Past — *In Mem. lxxi* 3

Nightly made The *n* wirer of their innocent hare — *Aylmer's Field* 490

Nightmare (adj.) This *n* weight of gratitude, — *Princess vi* 300

Nightmare (s) And horrible *n's*, And hollow shades — *Palace of Art* 240
Like one that feels a *n* on his bed — *M. d'Arthur* 177
N of youth, the spectre of himself? — *Love and Duty* 13
He seem'd, as in a *n* of the night, — *Enoch Arden* 114
Like one that feels a *n* on his bed — *Pass. of Arthur* 345
the babblings in a dream Of *n*, — *Ancient Sage* 107

Night-wind The *n-w's* come and go, mother, — *May Queen* 33

Nile shaker of the Baltic and the *N*, — *Ode on Well.* 137

Nilus *N* would have risen before his time — *D. of F. Women* 143

Nine *N* times goes the passing bell: — *All Things will Die* 35
N years she wrought it, sitting in the deeps — *M. d'Arthur* 105
As *n* months go to the shaping an infant — *Maud I iv* 34
n tithes of times Face-flatterer and backbiter — *Merlin and V.* 823
For so by *n* years' proof we needs must learn — *Lancelot and E.* 62
N years she wrought it, sitting in the deeps — *Pass. of Arthur* 273
And *n* long months of antenatal gloom, — *De Prof., Two G.* 8
For *n* white moons of each whole year with me, — *Demeter and P.* 121

Nine-days' Fire in dry stubble a *n-d* wonder flared: — *Lancelot and E.* 735

Nineteen-hundred Tenderest of Roman poets *n-h* years ago, — *Frater Ave, etc.* 6

Ninety Rose a nurse of *n* years, — *Princess vi* 13

Ninety (*continued*) But I've *n* men and more that are lying sick — *The Revenge* 10
With her hundred fighters on deck, and her *n* sick below; — „ 34
fingers were so stiffen'd by the frost Of seven and *n* winters, — *The Ring* 240

Nine-years-fought-for The *n-y-f-f* diamonds: — *Lancelot and E.* 1167

Nine-years-ponder'd Adviser of the *n-y-p* lay, — *Poets and their B.* 6

Ninth Till last, a *n* one, gathering half the deep — *Com. of Arthur* 380
With this *n* moon, that sends the hidden sun — *De Prof., Two G.* 33

Niobe Upon her tower, the *N* of swine, — *Walk. to the Mail* 99

Niobëan A *N* daughter, one arm out, — *Princess iv* 371

Nip close again, and *n* me flat, — *Merlin and V.* 350

Nipt *n* to death by him That was a God, — *Edwin Morris* 101
n her slender nose With petulant thumb — *Gareth and L.* 749
n the hand, and flung it from her; — *Pelleas and E.* 133

No brightens at the clash of 'Yes' and '*N*,' — *Ancient Sage* 71

Noäks *N* or Thimbleby—toäner 'ed shot 'um — *N. Farmer, O. S.* 35
N wur 'ang'd for it oop at 'soize— — „ 36

Noäse (nose) I looök'd cock-eyed at my *n* — *North. Cobbler* 26
wi' 'is glasses athurt 'is *n*, — *Village Wife* 38
An' 'is *n* sa grufted wi' snuff — „ 39
An' anoother ageän my *n*. — *Church-warden, etc.* 26

Noätion (notion) Thim's my *n's*, Sammy, wheerby I means to stick; — *N. Farmer, N. S.* 57

Nobility O fall'n *n*, that, overawed, — *Third of Feb.* 35
And pure *n* of temperament, — *Marr. of Geraint* 212

Noble (adj.) *As n till the latest day!* — *To the Queen* 22
When, soil'd with *n* dust, he hears — *Two Voices* 152
And slew him with your *n* birth. — *L. C. V. de Vere* 48
'Tis only *n* to be good. — „ 54
Resolved on *n* things, and strove to speak, — *D. of F. Women* 42
That takes away a *n* mind. — *To J. S.* 48
What wonder, if in *n* heat Those men — *England and Amer.* 6
as beseem'd Thy fëalty, nor like a *n* knight: — *M. d'Arthur* 75
When every morning brought a *n* chance, And every chance brought out a *n* knight. — „ 230
Some work of *n* note, may yet be done, — *Ulysses* 52
So the Powers, who wait On *n* deeds, — *Godiva* 72
And beaker brimm'd with *n* wine. — *Day-Dm., Sleep P.* 36
in whom he had reliance For his *n* name, — *The Captain* 58
That she grew a *n* lady, — *L. of Burleigh* 74
n wish To save all earnings to the uttermost, — *Enoch Arden* 85
Not *keep* it *n*, make it nobler? fools, — *Aylmer's Field* 386
Thy God is far diffused in *n* groves — „ 653
'O *n* heart who, being strait-besieged — *Princess, Pro.* 36
O miracle of *n* womanhood!' — „ 48
since to look on *n* forms Makes *n* — „ *ii* 86
Better not be at all Than not be *n*. — „ 94
O Vashti, *n* Vashti! Summon'd out She kept her state, — „ *iii* 228
She bow'd as if to veil a *n* tear; — „ 289
thus a *n* scheme Grew up from seed — „ *iv* 309
O *n* Ida, to those thoughts that wait — „ 443
No more, and in our *n* sister's cause? — „ *v* 312
at the heart Made for all *n* motion: — „ 384
Her *n* heart was molten in her breast; — „ *vi* 119
she rose Glowing all over *n* shame; — „ *vii* 160
Like perfect music unto *n* words; — „ 286
Yoked in all exercise of *n* end, — „ 361
A gallant fight, a *n* princess— — „ *Con.* 19
keep our *n* England whole, — *Ode on Well.* 161
And all men work in *n* brotherhood, — *Ode Inter. Exhib.* 38
Those niched shapes of *n* mould, — *The Daisy* 38
Close to the ridge of a *n* down. — *To F. D. Maurice* 16
Tear the *n* heart of Britain, — *Boädicea* 12
And dead calm in that *n* breast — *In Mem. xi* 19
The captive void of *n* rage, — „ *xxvii* 2
And move thee on to *n* ends. — „ *lxv* 12
Let this not vex thee, *n* heart! — „ *lxxix* 2
The *n* letters of the dead: — „ *xcv* 24
join'd Each office of the social hour To *n* manners, as the flower And native growth of *n* mind; — „ *cxi* 15
was a *n* type Appearing ere the times — „ *Con.* 138
To a grandson, first of his *n* line, — *Maud I x* 12
And *n* thought be freër under the sun, — „ *III vi* 48

Noble (adj.) (*continued*) We have proved we have hearts in a cause, we are *n* still, *Maud III vi* 55
Thou *n* Father of her Kings to be, *Ded. of Idylls* 34
But thou art closer to this *n* prince, *Com. of Arthur* 314
When some good knight had done one *n* deed, *Gareth and L.* 411
Tut, an the lad were *n*, „ 473
All kind of service with a *n* ease „ 489
'Lynette my name; *n*; my need, a knight „ 607
Sweet lord, how like a *n* knight he talks! „ 777
Or sit beside a *n* gentlewoman.' „ 867
O knave, as *n* as any of all the knights— „ 1136
Missaid thee: *n* I am; and thought the King „ 1165
Then turn'd the *n* damsel smiling at him, „ 1188
'Nay, *n* damsel, but that I, the son „ 1230
merry am I to find my goodly knave Is knight and *n*. „ 1292
O *n* Lancelot, from my hold on these Streams virtue— „ 1309
'O *n* breast and all-puissant arms, *Marr. of Geraint* 86
Not hearing any more his *n* voice, „ 98
'Yea, *n* Queen,' he answer'd, „ 178
now thinking that he heard The *n* hart at bay, „ 233
Geraint, a name far-sounded among men For *n* deeds? „ 428
So grateful is the noise of *n* deeds To *n* hearts „ 437
Let *me* lay lance in rest, O *n* host, „ 496
'This *n* prince who won our earldom back, „ 619
all That appertains to *n* maintenance. „ 712
See ye take the charger too, A *n* one.' *Geraint and E.* 556
she Kiss'd the white star upon his *n* front, „ 757
Such fine reserve and *n* reticence, „ 860
Like simple *n* natures, credulous „ 875
Our *n* King will send thee his own leech— *Balin and Balan* 275
Not, doubtless, all unearn'd by *n* deeds. „ 471
Our *n* Arthur, him Ye scarce can overpraise, *Merlin and V.* 91
'She is too *n*' he said 'to check at pies, „ 126
That makes you seem less *n* than yourself, „ 322
for love of God and men And *n* deeds, the flower of all the world. And each incited each to *n* deeds. „ 413
such a *n* song was that. „ 433
were all as tame, I mean, as *n*, as their Queen „ 608
Is that an answer for a *n* knight? *Lancelot and E.* 201
shame me not Before this *n* knight,' „ 208
To ride to Camelot with this *n* knight: „ 220
full Of *n* things, and held her from her sleep. „ 339
'Fair lord, whose name I know not—*n* it is, „ 360
Needs must be lesser likelihood, *n* lord, „ 367
And ride no more at random, *n* Prince! „ 633
O loyal nephew of our *n* King, „ 652
to be sweet and serviceable To *n* knights in sickness, „ 768
'Nay, *n* maid,' he answer'd, 'ten times nay! „ 948
Was *n* man but made ignoble talk. „ 1088
'Most *n* lord, Sir Lancelot of the Lake, „ 1272
Wifeless and heirless, *n* issue, sons Born „ 1371
This chance of *n* deeds will come and go Unchallenged, *Holy Grail* 318
So strange, of such a kind, that all of pure *N*, „ 774
All of true and *n* in knight and man „ 882
and Pelleas look'd *N* among the *n*, *Pelleas and E.* 152
fire of honour and all *n* deeds Flash'd, „ 278
O *n* vows! O great and sane and simple race „ 479
By *n* deeds at one with *n* vows, *Last Tournament* 123
by whom all men Are *n*, „ 600
'O pray you, *n* lady, weep no more; *Guinevere* 184
Full many a *n* war-song had he sung, „ 278
'Sir Lancelot, as became a *n* knight, „ 328
fruit Of loyal nature, and of *n* mind.' „ 336
Less *n*, being, as all rumour runs, „ 339
If ever Lancelot, that most *n* knight, Were for one hour less *n* than himself, „ 345
Sir Lancelot's, were as *n* as the King's, „ 351
And worship her by years of *n* deeds, „ 476
And miss to hear high talk of *n* deeds „ 499
and in the mist Was many a *n* deed, *Pass. of Arthur* 105
as beseem'd Thy fëalty, nor like a *n* knight: „ 243
When every morning brought a *n* chance, And every chance brought out a *n* knight. „ 398
And bearing on one arm the *n* babe, *Lover's Tale iv* 370

Noble (adj.) (*continued*) and was *n* in birth as in worth, *V. of Maeldune* 3
I have sullied a *n* name, *The Wreck* 5
to crown with song The warrior's *n* deed— *Epilogue* 37
'So great so *n* was he!' *Dead Prophet* 30
till his Word Had won him a *n* name. *N*! he sung, „ 36
Great and *n*—O yes—but yet— „ 43
N and great—O ay—but then, „ 49
To all our *n* sons, the strong New England *Hands all Round* 15
Where *n* Ulric dwells forlorn, *Happy* 10
But come, My *n* friend, my faithful counsellor, *Akbar's Dream* 18
N the Saxon who hurl'd at his Idol *Kapiolani* 4
Noble (s) Where the wealthy *n*'s dwell.' *L. of Burleigh* 24
The *n* and the convict of Castile, *Columbus* 117
Nobleman she, you know, Who wedded with a *n* from thence: *Princess i* 77
Noble-natured the boy Is *n-n*. *Gareth and L.* 468
Nobleness With such a vantage-ground for *n*! *Aylmer's Field* 387
And much I praised her *n*, *Princess, Pro.* 124
That you trust me in your own *n*, *Lancelot and E.* 1195
Some root of knighthood and pure *n*; *Holy Grail* 886
the wines being of such *n*— *Lover's Tale iv* 222
kings of men in utter *n* of mind, *Locksley H., Sixty* 122
Nobler am I not the *n* thro' thy love? *Love and Duty* 19
Not *keep* it noble, make it *n*? *Aylmer's Field* 386
Balmier and *n* from her bath of storm, *Lucretius* 175
And since the *n* pleasure seems to fade. „ 230
as to slay One *n* than thyself.' *Gareth and L.* 981
A something—was it *n* than myself?— *Pelleas and E.* 310
might inwreathe (How lovelier, *n* then!) *Lover's Tale i* 459
Seem'd *n* than their hard Eternities. *Demeter and P.* 107
O you that hold A n *office upon earth* *To the Queen* 2
A *n* yearning never broke her rest *The form, the form* 2
'But, if I lapsed from *n* place, *Two Voices* 358
As emblematic of a *n* age; *Princess ii* 127
Tho' all men else their *n* dreams forget, *Ode on Well.* 152
There must be other *n* work to do „ 256
And thou shalt take a *n* leave.' *In Mem. lviii* 12
He past; a soul of *n* tone: *In Mem. lx* 1
Ring in the *n* modes of life, „ *cvi* 15
Are breathers of an ampler day For ever *n* ends. „ *cxviii* 7
The fair beginners of a *n* time, *Com. of Arthur* 457
how can Enid find A *n* friend? *Marr. of Geraint* 793
in my heart of hearts I did acknowledge *n*. *Lancelot and E.* 1211
This earth has never borne a *n* man. *Epit. on Gordon* 4
thro' all the *n* hearts In that vast Oval *St. Telemachus* 72
Noblest Truest friend and *n* foe; *Princess vi* 7
The *n* answer unto such Is perfect stillness *Lit. Squabbles* 19
but he, Our *n* brother, and our truest man, *Gareth and L.* 565
let Lancelot know, Thy *n* and thy truest!' „ 568
let her tongue Rage like a fire among the *n* names, *Merlin and V.* 802
goodliest man That ever among ladies ate in hall, And *n*, *Lancelot and E.* 256
one Of *n* manners, tho' himself would say Sir Lancelot had the noblest; *Guinevere* 319
But pray you, which had *n*, while you moved „ 325
here in Edward's time, an age of *n* English names, *Locksley H., Sixty* 83
All that is *n*, all that is basest, *Vastness* 32
One of our *n*, our most valorous, *Geraint and E.* 910
noble it is, I well believe, the *n*— *Lancelot and E.* 361
knight of Arthur's *n* dealt in scorn; *Guinevere* 40
would say Sir Lancelot had the *n*; „ 320
Noblest-hearted truest, kindliest, *n-h* wife *Romney's R.* 35
Noblier-fashion'd Was he *n-f* than other men? *Dead Prophet* 51
Nobly have ye seen how *n* changed? *Geraint and E.* 897
Nobly-manner'd Were the most *n-m* men of all; *Guinevere* 334
Nod (s) And flooded at our *n*. *D. of F. Women* 144
With frequent smile and *n* departing *Marr. of Geraint* 515
an' she gev him a frindly *n*, *Tomorrow* 58
Nod (verb) Glares at one that *n*'s and winks *Locksley Hall* 136
Then moves the trees, the copses *n*, *Sir Galahad* 77
Nodded The parson smirk'd and *n*. *The Goose* 20
He *n*, but a moment afterwards He cried, *Gardener's D.* 120
And Walter *n* at me; '*He* began, *Princess, Pro.* 200
Florian *n* at him, I frowning; „ *iv* 159

Nodded (*continued*) Doubted, and drowsed, n and slept, Com. of Arthur 427
Sir Kay n him leave to go, Gareth and L. 520
And after n sleepily in the heat. Geraint and E. 253
Miriam n with a pitying smile, The Ring 281
Nodding n, as in scorn, He parted, Godiva 30
Viziers n together In some Arabian night? Maud I vii 11
Then her father n said, 'Ay, ay, Lancelot and E. 770
Noight (night) I've 'ed my point o' äale ivry n N. Farmer, O. S. 7
Noir Showing a shower of blood in a field n, Last Tournament 433
Noise Thro' the n's of the night L. of Shalott iv 22
Blowing a n of tongues and deeds, Two Voices 206
The milldam rushing down with n, Miller's D. 50
n of some one coming thro' the lawn, D. of F. Women 178
So all day long the n of battle roll'd M. d'Arthur 1
with n's of the northern sea. „ 141
such a n of life Swarm'd in the golden present, Gardener's D. 178
There rose a n of striking clocks, Day-Dm., Revival 2
I hear a n of hymns: Sir Galahad 28
month by month the n about their doors, Aylmer's Field 488
Made n with bees and breeze from end to end. Princess, Pro. 88
scarce could hear each other speak for n Of clocks and chimes, „ i 215
compass'd by two armies and the n Of arms; „ v 345
A n of songs they would not understand: „ vi 40
To the n of the mourning of a mighty nation, Ode on Well. 4
far from n and smoke of town, To F. D. Maurice 13
Made the n of frosty woodlands, Boädicea 75
The n of life begins again, In Mem. vii 10
I hear the n about thy keel; „ x 1
Whose youth was full of foolish n, „ liii 3
Autumn, with a n of rooks, „ lxxxv 71
all within was n Of songs, and clapping hands, „ lxxxvii 18
n of ravage wrought by beast and man, Gareth and L. 437
out of town and valley came a n Marr. of Geraint 247
So grateful is the n of noble deeds „ 437
lusty spearmen follow'd him with n: Geraint and E. 593
Scared by the n upstarted at our feet, Merlin and V. 422
poplars made a n of falling showers. Lancelot and E. 411
poplars with their n of falling showers, „ 523
She, that had heard the n of it before, „ 731
some doubtful n of creaking doors, Guinevere 72
So all day long the n of battle roll'd Pass. of Arthur 170
with n's of the Northern Sea. „ 309
N's of a current narrowing, Locksley H., Sixty 154
n of falling weights that never fell, The Ring 410
being waked By n's in the house— „ 417
Noised do the deed, Than to be n of.' Gareth and L. 573
Noiseful From n arms, and acts of prowess Holy Grail 1
Noiseless a n riot underneath Strikes through the wood, Lucretius 185
Or like to n phantoms flit: In Mem. xx 16
Beat to the n music of the night! Maud I xviii 77
Noisy I wander'd from the n town, In Mem. lxix 5
I cast them in the n brook beneath, Lover's Tale ii 41
None There is n like her, n. (repeat) Maud I xviii 2, 13
N like her, n. „ 7
Nook odd games In some odd n's like this; The Epic 9
he made the old warrior from his ivied n Princess, Pro. 104
Noon At n the wild bee hummeth Claribel 11
fire Would rive the slumbrous summer n Supp. Confessions 11
Till now at n she slept again, Mariana in the S. 41
from beyond the n a fire Is pour'd upon the hills, Fatima 30
Hither came at n Mournful Œnone, Œnone 15
On corpses three-months-old at n she came, Palace of Art 243
Sun-steep'd at n, and in the moon Lotos-Eaters, C. S. 29
In those old days, one summer n, M. d'Arthur 29
till n no foot should pace the street, Godiva 39
the shameless n Was clash'd and hammer'd „ 74
I took my leave, for it was nearly n: Princess v 468
ere I woke it was the point of n, „ 482
pensive tendance in the all-weary n's, „ vii 102
Climb thy thick n, disastrous day; In Mem. lxxii 26
What stays thee from the clouded n's, „ lxxxiii 5
At n or when the lesser wain „ ci 11
That must be made a wife ere n? „ Con. 26
But now set out: the n is near, „ 41
Noon (*continued*) at the point of n the huge Earl Doorm, Geraint and E. 536
Or in the n of mist and driving rain, Merlin and V. 636
Riding at n, a day or twain before, Pelleas and E. 20
Beheld at n in some delicious dale Guinevere 393
In those old days, one summer n, Pass. of Arthur 197
the white heats of the blinding n's Lover's Tale i 139
When first we came from out the pines at n, „ 310
cloud that roofs our n with night, Sisters (E. and E.) 17
and the owls are whooping at n, Despair 89
To vex the n with fiery gems, Ancient Sage 265
Name, surname, all as clear as n, The Ring 237
in the brooding light of n? Happy 99
I dream'd last night of that clear summer n, Romney's R. 74
A fall of water lull'd the n asleep. „ 83
mists of earth Fade in the n of heaven, Akbar's Dream 97
We are far from the n of man, The Dawn 20
Noonday now the n quiet holds the hill: Œnone 25
Made by the n blaze without, St. Telemachus 50
O sun, that from thy n height Fatima 2
shone the N Sun Beyond a raging shallow. Gareth and L. 1027
And thrice as blind as any n owl, Holy Grail 866
The n crag made the hand burn; Tiresias 35
Noon-Sun Morning-Star, and N-S, and Evening-Star, Gareth and L. 634
Noorse (nurse) N? thourt nowt o' a n: N. Farmer, O. S. 2
Noose Twisted as tight as I could knot the n; St. S. Stylites 65
Norland loud the N whirlwinds blow, Oriana 6
When N winds pipe down the sea, „ 91
Norman (adj.) And simple faith than N blood. L. C. V. de Vere 56
Harold's England fell to N swords; W. to Marie Alex. 22
Norman (s) Saxon and N and Dane are we, W. to Alexandra 3
For Saxon or Dane or N we, „ 31
Norse Then the N leader, Dire was his need of it, Batt. of Brunanburh 56
Norsemen nail'd prows Parted the N, „ 94
North by day or night, From N to South, Rosalind 48
For look, the sunset, south and n, Miller's D. 241
Four courts I made, East, West and South and N, Palace of Art 21
In the n, her canvas flowing, The Captain 27
But round the N, a light, A belt, Sea Dreams 208
Many a long league back to the N. Princess i 168
Princess rode to take The dip of certain strata to the N. „ iii 170
And dark and true and tender is the N. „ iv 98
But in the N long since my nest is made. „ 110
And brief the sun of summer in the N, „ 112
And blown to inmost n; „ 432
And gray metropolis of the N. The Daisy 104
To N, South, East, and West; Voice and the P. 14
Thine the N and thine the South Boädicea 44
Fiercely flies The blast of N In Mem. cvii 7
and fly Far into the N, and battle, Maud III vi 37
two that out of n had follow'd him: Gareth and L. 679
knights of utmost N and West, Lancelot and E. 526
founded my Round Table in the N, Last Tournament 78
Make their last head like Satan in the N. „ 98
and sharply turn'd N by the gate. „ 128
half that autumn night, like the live N, „ 479
And shook him thro' the n. Pass. of Arthur 70
came A bitter wind, clear from the N, „ 124
that true N, whereof we lately heard To the Queen ii 14
I go On that long-promised visit to the N. Sisters (E. and E.) 188
somewhere in the N, as Rumour sang Sir J. Oldcastle 56
Crept to his N again, Hoar-headed hero! Batt. of Brunanburh 64
Not here! the white N has thy bones; Sir J. Franklin 1
leaves Some colder province in the N The Ring 481
roll her N below thy deepening dome, Prog. of Spring 49
drank the dews and drizzle of the N, „ 81
Northern Floats far away into the N seas Mine be the strength 13
Shot like a streamer of the n morn, M. d'Arthur 139
isles of winter shock By night, with noises of the n sea. „ 141
The n morning o'er thee shoot, Talking Oak 275
Like visions in the N dreamer's heavens, Aylmer's Field 161
seen the rosy red flushing in the n night. Locksley Hall 26
We past long lines of N capes And dewy N meadows green. The Voyage 35

Northern (*continued*) For on my cradle shone the *N* star. — *Princess i* 4
Three ladies of the *N* empire pray Your Highness — „ 238
The terrace ranged along the *N* front, — „ *iii* 118
'Peace, you young savage of the *N* wild! — „ 247
And hit the *N* hills. — „ *v* 44
Between the *N* and the Southern morn.' — „ 423
We might discuss the *N* sin — *To F. D. Maurice* 29
Dip down upon the *n* shore, — *In Mem. lxxxiii* 1
fell Against the heathen of the *N* Sea — *Geraint and E.* 969
or touch at night the *n* star; — *Balin and Balan* 166
And peak'd wings pointed to the *N* Star. — *Holy Grail* 240
For now the Heathen of the *N* Sea, — *Guinevere* 135
Godless hosts Of heathen swarming o'er the *N* Sea; — „ 428
Shot like a streamer of the *n* morn, — *Pass. of Arthur* 307
isles of winter shock By night, with noises of the *N* Sea. — „ 309
I, from out the *N* Island sunder'd once — *To Virgil* 35
peak sent up one league of fire to the *N* Star; — *V. of Maeldune* 72
Northland Men of the *N* Shot over shield. — *Batt. of Brunanburh* 33
North-sea as a wild wave in the wide *N-s*, — *Lancelot and E.* 482
Northumberland Claudias, and Clariance of *N*, — *Com. of Arthur* 113
Northward Ten miles to *n* of the narrow port — *Enoch Arden* 102
pines That darken'd all the *n* of her Hall. — *Aylmer's Field* 415
heard from our wise man at home To *N*, — *Gareth and L.* 202
and yonder—out To *n*— — *Ancient Sage* 202
North-wind 'He will not hear the *n-w* rave, — *Two Voices* 259
Norward Stately, lightly, went she *N*, — *The Captain* 35
Norway *N* sun Set into sunrise; — *Princess iv* 575
Nose (*See also* **Noäse**) aquiline curve in a sensitive *n*, — *Maud I ii* 10
High *n*, a nostril large and fine, — *Gareth and L.* 465
and lightly was her slender *n* Tip-tilted — „ 590
nipt her slender *n* With petulant thumb — „ 749
his *n* Bridge-broken, one eye out, — *Last Tournament* 58
Nosing *N* the mother's udder, — *Lucretius* 100
Nostril High nose, a *n* large and fine, — *Gareth and L.* 465
breaths of anger puff'd Her fairy *n* out; — *Merlin and V.* 849
Note (billet) sent a *n*, the seal an *Elle vous suit*, — *Edwin Morris* 105
Note (notice) a precious thing, one worthy *n*, — *M. d'Arthur* 89
Took joyful *n* of all things joyful, — *Aylmer's Field* 67
took *n* that when his living smile Died — *Lancelot and E.* 323
Surely a precious thing, one worthy *n*, — *Pass. of Arthur* 257
Note (as of music) (*See also* **Flute-notes**) The single *n* From that deep chord — *England and Amer.* 18
'A quinsy choke thy cursed *n*!' — *The Goose* 29
lark scarce get out his *n's* for joy, — *Gardener's D.* 90
a low musical *n* Swell'd up and died; — *Sea Dreams* 210
still Grew with the growing *n*, and when the *n* Had reach'd — „ 213
never out of tune With that sweet *n*; — „ 232
Consonant chords that shiver to one *n*; — *Princess iii* 90
And his compass is but of a single *n*, — *The Islet* 28
And one is glad; her *n* is gay, — *In Mem. xxi* 25
And one is sad; her *n* is changed, — „ 27
Some bitter *n's* my harp would give, — „ *cxxv* 2
Peace Pipe on her pastoral hillock a languid *n*, — *Maud III vi* 24
blew A hard and deadly *n* upon the horn. — *Gareth and L.* 1111
liquid *n* beloved of men Comes flying — *Marr. of Geraint* 336
a *n* so thin It seems another voice — *Balin and Balan* 214
but one plain passage of few *n's*, — *Lancelot and E.* 895
Sent *n's* of preparation manifold, — *Lover's Tale i* 207
Till at thy chuckled *n*, — *Early Spring* 37
Note (distinction) Some work of noble *n*, may yet be done, — *Ulysses* 52
Some stain or blemish in a name of *n*, — *Merlin and V.* 832
Nothing (*See also* **Know-nothing, Nowt**) *Of him that utter'd* n *base*; — *To the Queen* 8
Never, oh! never, *n* will die; — *Nothing will Die* 8
N will die. *N* will die; — „ 13
N was born; *N* will die; — „ 36
and knows *N* beyond his mother's eyes. — *Supp. Confessions* 44
n here, Which, from the outward to the inward brought, — *Eleänore* 3
For in thee Is *n* sudden, *n* single; — „ 57
But am as *n* in its light: — „ 88
From that first *n* ere his birth To that last *n* under earth!' — *Two Voices* 332
Beat time to *n* in my head — *Miller's D.* 67

Nothing (*continued*) *N* comes to thee new or strange. — *To J. S.* 74
Counts *n* that she meets with base, — *On a Mourner* 4
He thought that *n* new was said, or else Something so said 'twas *n*— — *The Epic* 30
'There now—that's *n*!' — *M d'Arthur, Ep.* 13
pilot of an empty heart Unto the shores of *n*! — *Gardener's D.* 17
n else For which to praise the heavens — „ 103
where nature sickens, *n*. — *Locksley Hall* 153
That was *n* to her: — *Enoch Arden* 498
wood stands in a mist of green, And *n* perfect: — *The Brook* 15
Saw from his windows *n* save his own— — *Aylmer's Field* 21
Flash into fiery life from *n*, — „ 130
howl in tune With *n* but the Devil!' — *Sea Dreams* 261
N to mar the sober majesties — *Lucretius* 217
N but this; my very ears were hot To hear them: — *Princess i* 134
I rate your chance Almost at naked *n*.' — „ 161
there is *n* upon earth More miserable — „ *iii* 259
n can bereave him Of the force he made his own — *Ode on Well.* 272
So then were *n* lost to man; — *In Mem. xliii* 9
That *n* walks with aimless feet; — „ *liv* 5
I care for *n*, all shall go. — „ *lvi* 4
For *n* is that errs from law. — „ *lxxiii* 8
From form to form, and *n* stands; — *cxxiii* 6
May *n* there her maiden grace affright! — *Maud I xviii* 71
n can be sweeter Than maiden Maud in either. — „ *xx* 21
N but idiot gabble! — „ *II v* 41
I seem as *n* in the mighty world, — *Com. of Arthur* 87
and the solid earth became As *n*, — „ 443
For there is *n* in it as it seems Saving the King; — *Gareth and L.* 264
and all wing'd *n's* peck him dead! — *Marr. of Geraint* 275
Who pipe of *n* but of sparrow-hawks! — „ 279
Owe you me *n* for a life half-lost? — *Geraint and E.* 318
empty heart and weariness And sickly *n*; — „ 653
Fame that follows death is *n* to us; — *Merlin and V.* 464
charm concluded in that star To make fame *n*. — „ 513
there was *n* wild or strange, — „ 860
n Poor Vivien had not done to win his trust — „ 862
And ending in a ruin—*n* left, — „ 883
And every voice is *n*. — *Lancelot and E.* 108
'Of all this will I *n*;' and so fell, — „ 967
she, too, Fell into dust and *n*, — *Holy Grail* 397
'*N* in nature is unbeautiful; — *Lover's Tale i* 350
That seeming something, yet was *n*, — „ *iv* 104
But say *n* hard of my boy, — *Rizpah* 22
We feel we are *n*— — *De Prof., Human C.* 6
We know we are *n*— — „ 8
Nothingness Teach me the *n* of things. — *A Character* 4
Redeem'd it from the charge of *n*— — *M. d'Arthur, Ep.* 7
to burn and brand His *n* into man. — *Maud I xviii* 40
Nothing-worth 'A life of nothings, *n-w*, — *Two Voices* 331
Were faint Homeric echoes, *n-w*, — *The Epic* 39
Notice A *n* faintly understood, — *Two Voices* 431
master took Small *n*, or austerely, — *Lucretius* 8
Till *n* of a change in the dark world — *Princess vii* 250
n of a hart Taller than all his fellows, — *Marr. of Geraint* 149
thro' the hasty *n* of the ear Frail life — *Lover's Tale i* 615
but send me *n* of him When he returns, — „ *iv* 116
Suddenly came her *n* and we past, — „ 154
Noticed I *n* one of his many rings — *Maud II ii* 68
Noticing peacock'd up with Lancelot's *n*. — *Gareth and L.* 719
Notion (*See also* **Noätion**) The boy might get a *n* into him; — *Aylmer's Field* 271
Nourish That *n* a blind life within the brain, — *M. d'Arthur* 251
That *n* a blind life within the brain, — *Pass. of Arthur* 419
Nourishing Here about the beach I wander'd, *n* a youth sublime — *Locksley Hall* 11
Soft fruitage, mighty nuts, and *n* roots; — *Enoch Arden* 555
Novel (adj.) 'And men, thro' *n* spheres of thought — *Two Voices* 61
when his passion shall have spent its *n* force, — *Locksley Hall* 49
And breathes a *n* world, the while — *In Mem. lxii* 9
some *n* power Sprang up for ever at a touch, — „ *cxii* 9
Novel (s) 'She left the *n* half-uncut — *Talking Oak* 117
Novelist *n*, realist, rhymester, — *Locksley H., Sixty* 139

O

Oak (*continued*) I turn to yonder *o*. *Talking Oak* 8
To yonder *o* within the field I spoke „ 13
Broad *O* of Sumner-chace, „ 30
Old *o*, I love thee well; „ 202
For never yet was *o* on lea „ 243
The gouty *o* began to move, *Amphion* 23
Parks with *o* and chestnut shady, *L. of Burleigh* 29
What amulet drew her down to that old *o*, *Aylmer's Field* 507
violet varies from the lily as far As *o* from elm: *Princess v* 183
when the winds of winter tear an *o* *Boädicea* 77
Ere half the lifetime of an *o*. *In Mem. lxxvi* 12
Before a gloom of stubborn-shafted *o's*, *Geraint and E.* 120
Arising wearily at a fallen *o*, *Balin and Balan* 425
Then leapt her palfrey o'er the fallen *o*, „ 587
Before an *o*, so hollow, huge and old *Merlin and V.* 3
song that once I heard By this huge *o*, „ 406
Call'd her to shelter in the hollow *o*, „ 894
struck, Furrowing a giant *o*, „ 936
And in the hollow *o* he lay as dead, „ 969
A stump of *o* half-dead, *Last Tournament* 12
May freedom's *o* for ever live *Hands all Round* 5
few lanes of elm And whispering *o*. *To Mary Boyle* 68
Young and old, Like yon *o*, *The Oak* 3
hew'd Like broad *o's* with thunder. *The Tourney* 11

Oaken With breezes from our *o* glades, *Eleänore* 10
And like an *o* stock in winter woods, *Golden Year* 62
And *o* finials till he touch'd the door; *Aylmer's Field* 823
The three decker's *o* spine *Maud II ii* 27
he lay Down on an *o* settle in the hall, *Geraint and E.* 573

Oakling drew My little *o* from the cup, *Talking Oak* 231

Oak-room Maud's own little *o-r* *Maud I xiv* 9

Oak-tree But the solemn *o-t* sigheth, *Claribel* 4
An *o-t* smoulder'd there. *Gareth and L.* 402
red fruit Grown on a magic *o-t* in mid-heaven, *Last Tournament* 745

'Oäm (home) one night I cooms *'o* like a bull *North. Cobbler* 33
'e were that outdacious at *'o*, *Village Wife* 75
boäth slinkt *'o* by the brokken shed *Spinster's S's.* 37

Oän (own) wi' the Divil's *o* teäm. *N. Farmer, O. S.* 62
an' 'e's the Divil's *o* sen.' *North. Cobbler* 76
An' Squire, his *o* very sen, „ 91
noa, not fur Sally's *o* kin. „ 114
So I sits i' my *o* armchair wi' my *o* kettle *Spinster's S's.* 9
fro' my *o* two 'oonderd a-year. „ 58
'ere i' my *o* blue chaumber to me. „ 80
'ud 'a let me 'a hed my *o* waäy, „ 101
An' I sits i' my *o* little parlour, an' sarved by my *o* little lass, Wi' my *o* little garden outside, an' my *o* bed o' sparrow-grass, An' my *o* door-poorch wi' the woodbine „ 103
'thank God that I hevn't naw cauf o' my *o*.' „ 117
An' I'd voät fur 'im, my *o* sen, *Owd Roä* 14

Oäp (hope) An' I *'o's* es 'e beänt boooklarn'd: *Village Wife* 23
es I *o's* es thou'll 'elp me a bit, „ 65
sewer an' sartin *'o* o' the tother side; „ 92

Oar weary seem'd the sea, weary the *o*, *Lotos-Eaters* 41
wind and wave and *o*; „ *C. S.* 127
barge with *o* and sail Moved from the brink, *M. d'Arthur* 265
stirr'd with languid pulses of the *o*, *Gardener's D.* 41
The measured pulse of racing *o's* *In Mem. lxxxvii* 10
barge with *o* and sail Moved from the brink, *Pass. of Arthur* 433

Oar'd Naiads *o* A glimmering shoulder *To E. L.* 16
Some to a low song *o* a shallop by, *Princess ii* 457
the dead, *O* by the dumb, went upward *Lancelot and E.* 1154

Oaring *O* one arm, and bearing in my left *Princess iv* 183

Oarless unlaborious earth and *o* sea; *To Virgil* 20

Oarsman *o's* haggard face, As hard and still *Lancelot and E.* 1250

Oasis fountain-fed Ammonian *O* in the waste. *Alexander* 8
My one *O* in the dust and drouth Of city life! *Edwin Morris* 3
they might grow To use and power on this *O*, *Princess ii* 167

Oat (*See also* **Whoats**) had the wild *o* not been sown, *In Mem. liii* 6

Oat-grass On the *o-g* and the sword-grass, *May Queen, N. Y's. E.* 28

Oath Let us swear an *o*, and keep it *Lotos-Eaters, C. S.* 108
Heaven heads the count of crimes With that wild *o*.' *D. of F. Women* 202

R*

Oath (*continued*) And hear me swear a solemn *o*, *Talking Oak* 281
Cophetua sware a royal *o*: *Beggar Maid* 15
since my *o* was ta'en for public use, *Princess iv* 337
Your *o* is broken: we dismiss you: „ 360
But keep that *o* ye sware, *Merlin and V.* 688
Vivien, fearing heaven had heard her *o*, „ 940
O's, insult, filth, and monstrous blasphemies, *Pass. of Arthur* 114
that you, that I, would slight our marriage *o*: *Happy* 89
laughter, Pagan *o*, and jest, *St. Telemachus* 39

Obaäy (obey) To loove an' *o* the Tommies! *Spinster's S's.* 96

Obedience Seeing *o* is the bond of rule. *M. d'Arthur* 94
Linger with vacillating *o*, *Gareth and L.* 13
Of thine *o* and thy love to me, „ 146
bow'd himself With all *o* to the King, „ 488
And uttermost *o* to the King.' „ 555
For uttermost *o* to make demand „ 558
In uttermost *o* to the King. „ 833
But silently, in all *o*, *Marr. of Geraint* 767
With difficulty in mild *o* Driving them on: *Geraint and E.* 104
O is the courtesy due to kings.' *Lancelot and E.* 718
Seeing *o* is the bond of rule. *Pass of Arthur* 262
bankrupt of all claim On your *o*, *Romney's R.* 71

Obedient most valorous, Sanest and most *o*: *Geraint and E.* 911
O to her second master now; *Lover's Tale iv* 343

Obeisance curtseying her *o*, let us know *Princess ii* 20

Obelisk *o's* Graven with emblems of the time, *Arabian Nights* 107

Obey (*See also* **Obaäy**) A courage to endure and to *o*; *Isabel* 25
'Will be *o* when one commands? *Two Voices* 244
well to *o* then, if a king demand An act unprofitable, *M. d'Arthur* 95
Man to command and woman to *o*; *Princess v* 450
And since thou art my mother, must *o*. *Gareth and L.* 167
'I charge thee, ask not, but *o*.' *Marr. of Geraint.* 133
How should I dare *o* him to his harm? *Geraint and E.* 136
I swear it would not ruffle me so much As you that not *o* me. „ 151
that ye speak not but *o*.' „ 417
I know Your wish, and would *o*; „ 419
Almost beyond me: yet I would *o*.' „ 423
Rise therefore; robe yourself in this: *o*.' „ 685
Who knowing nothing knows but to *o*, *Guinevere* 186
well to *o* then, if a king demand An act unprofitable, *Pass. of Arthur* 263
race to command, to *o*, to endure, *Def. of Lucknow* 47
Who shaped the forms, *o* them, *Akbar's Dream* 143

Obey'd 'I have *o* my uncle until now, *Dora* 59
and they wheel'd and *o*. *Heavy Brigade* 6

Object beyond his *o* Love can last: His *o* lives: *Wan Sculptor* 5
burn'd upon its *o* thro' such tears *Love and Duty* 63

Oblique 'If straight thy track, or if *o*, *Two Voices* 193

Oblivion With all forgiveness, all *o*, *Princess vi* 295

Oblivious *See* **Half-oblivious**

Obscure In some *o* hereafter, might inwreathe *Lover's Tale i* 458

Obscurity I faint in this *o*, (repeat) *Ode to Memory* 6, 44, 123

Obsequies Nor meanly, but with gorgeous *o*, *Lancelot and E.* 1335

Observance with a mute *o* hung. *Locksley Hall* 22
He compass'd her with sweet *o's* *Marr. of Geraint* 48
To compass her with sweet *o's*, *Geraint and E.* 39

Obstinacy At which the warrior in his *o*, „ 454

Obstinate *See* **Stunt**

Obstreperous *See* **Obstropulous**

Obstropulous (obstreperous) But sich an *o* lad— *Church-warden, etc.* 23

Obtain Pelleas might *o* his lady's love, *Pelleas and E.* 161
all my heart had destined did *o*, *Guinevere* 492

Obtain'd second suit *o* At first with Psyche. *Princess vii* 71

Occasion *seasons when to take O by the hand,* *To the Queen* 31
written as she found Or made *o*, *Aylmer's Field* 478
Wiser to weep a true *o* lost, *Princess iv* 68
O iron nerve to true *o* true, *Ode on Well.* 37
Elusion, and *o*, and evasion'? *Gareth and L.* 288
A little at the vile *o*, rode, *Marr. of Geraint* 235
The vast *o* of our stronger life— *Columbus* 35

Ocean (*See also* **Mid-ocean**) Under the hollow-hung *o* green! *The Merman* 38
On one side lay the *O*, *M. d'Arthur* 11

Ocean (*continued*) Yet *o's* daily gaining on the land, *Golden Year* 29
There the sunlit *o* tosses *The Captain* 69
The houseless *o's* heaving field, *The Voyage* 30
The hollower-bellowing *o*, *Enoch Arden* 598
Now pacing mute by *o's* rim; *The Daisy* 21
Or olive-hoary cape in *o*; „ 31
In middle *o* meets the surging shock, *Will.* 8
Cataract brooks to the *o* run, *The Islet* 17
Thine the myriad-rolling *o*, *Boädicea* 42
Charm, as a wanderer out in *o*, *Milton* 12
Streams o'er a rich ambrosial *o* isle, „ 14
By which they rest, and *o* sounds, *In Mem., Con.* 121
As on a dull day in an *O* cave *Merlin and V.* 231
On one side lay the *O*, *Pass. of Arthur* 179
as *o* on every side Plunges and heaves *Def. of Lucknow* 38
Chains for the Admiral of the *O*! *Columbus* 19
Chains! we are Admirals of the *O*, „ 28
Of the *O*—of the Indies—Admirals we— „ 31
He lived on an isle in the *o*— *V. of Maeldune* 7
And we came to the isle in the *o*, „ 9
silent *o* always broke on a silent shore, „ 12
voice rang out in the thunders of *O* and Heaven *The Wreck* 88
Universal *o* softly washing all her warless Isles. *Locksley H., Sixty* 170
There on the border Of boundless *O*, *Merlin and the G.* 117
Dash back that *o* with a pier, *Mechanophilus* 5
Ocean-empire who love Our *o-e* with her boundless homes *To the Queen ii* 29
Ocean-foam as white As *o-f* in the moon, *Maud I xiv* 18
Ocean-fowl myriad shriek of wheeling *o-f*, *Enoch Arden* 583
Ocean-grave 'I am coming to thee in thine *O-g*.' *The Wreck* 132
Ocean-islet about their *o-i's* flash The faces *Tiresias* 172
Ocean-lane Fall from his *O-l* of fire, *The Voyage* 19
Ocean-mirror O'er *o-m's* rounded large, *In Mem. xii* 9
Ocean-plain Sailest the placid *o-p's* „ *ix* 2
Ocean-power the mightiest *O-p* on earth, *The Fleet* 6
Ocean-ridge hollow *o-r's* roaring into cataracts. *Locksley Hall* 6
Ocean-roll Tho' thine *o-r* of rhythm sound *To Virgil* 31
Ocean-sea Given thee the keys of the great *O-s*? *Columbus* 149
Ocean-smelling ocean-spoil In *o-s* osier, *Enoch Arden* 94
Ocean-sounding *o-s* welcome to one knight, *Last Tournament* 168
Ocean-spoil *o-s* In ocean-smelling osier, *Enoch Arden* 94
Ochone but we hard it cryin' 'O!' *Tomorrow* 84
O'clock 'Tis nearly twelve *o*. *D. of the O. Year* 41
The mail? At one *o*. *Walk. to the Mail* 8
How goes the time? 'Tis five *o*. *Will Water.* 3
October *See* **Mid-October**
Odalisque Sleek *O's*, or oracles of mode, *Princess ii* 77
Odd (adj.) From some *o* corner of the brain. *Miller's D.* 68
or dwindled down to some *o* games In some *o* nooks like this; *The Epic* 8
Odd (s) And strength against all *o's*, *Balin and Balan* 183
It was full of old *o's* an' ends, *First Quarrel* 49
Ode then, Sir, awful *o's* she wrote, *Princess i* 138
o's About this losing of the child; „ 140
quoted *o's*, and jewels five-words-long „ *ii* 377
Odin To Thor and *O* lifted a hand: *The Victim* 8
'O, Father *O*, We give you a life. „ 74
Odorous wasting *o* sighs All night long *Adeline* 43
the amorous, *o* wind Breathes low *Eleänore* 123
Whisper in *o* heights of even. *Milton* 16
Odour fed the time With *o* *Arabian Nights* 65
A cloud of incense of all *o* steam'd *Palace of Art* 39
Distilling *o's* on me as they went *Gardener's D.* 187
Whose *o's* haunt my dreams; *Sir Galahad* 68
On leagues of *o* streaming far, *In Mem. lxxxvi* 14
Saying in *o* and colour, 'Ah, be Among the roses *Maud I xxi* 12
And flowing *o* of the spacious air, *Lover's Tale i* 478
that hour died Like *o* rapt into the winged wind „ 801
those who mix all *o* to the Gods *Tiresias* 184
Œnone Mournful *Œ*, wandering forlorn *Œnone* 16
'My own *Œ*, Beautiful-brow'd *Œ*, „ 70
never more Shall lone *Œ* see the morning mist „ 216
Œ sat within the cave from out *Death of Œnone* 1
downward thunder of the brook Sounded '*Œ*'; „ 24
and moan'd '*Œ, my Œ*, „ 29

Œnone (*continued*) *Œ*, by thy love which once was mine, *Death of Œnone* 45
Œ sat Not moving, „ 74
ghostly murmur floated, 'Come to me, *Œ*! „ 80
I can wrong thee now no more, *Œ*, my *Œ*,' „ 81
O'er-brimming Would drop from his *o-b* love, *Supp. Confessions* 113
O'er-driven Yet pity for a horse *o-d*, *In Mem. lxiii* 1
O'erflourish'd *O* with the hoary clematis: *Golden Year* 63
O'erflow *O's* thy calmer glances, *Madeline* 33
O'er-grown Till that *o-g* Barbarian in the East *Poland* 7
He has gather'd the bones for his *o-g* whelp to crack; *Maud II v* 55
O'erlook'st *O* the tumult from afar, *In Mem. cxxvii* 19
O'ershadow His love, unseen but felt, *o* Thee, *Ded. of Idylls* 51
O'erstept hath *o* The slippery footing *Lover's Tale i* 101
O'erthwarted *O* with the brazen-headed spear *Œnone* 139
Offal Stench of old *o* decaying, *Def. of Lucknow* 82
pelt your *o* at her face. *Locksley H., Sixty* 134
Offence To save the *o* of charitable, *Enoch Arden* 342
like a pedant's wand To lash *o*, *Princess i* 28
without *o*, Has link'd our names together *Lancelot and E.* 111
an' tha weant be taakin' *o*, *Church-warden, etc.* 21
Offend Your finer female sense *o's*. *Day-Dm., L'Envoi* 2
Offender pick'd *o's* from the mass For judgment. *Princess i* 29
Offer (s) I trample on your *o's* and on you: „ *iv* 546
Offer (verb) I *o* boldly: we will seat you highest: „ *iii* 159
I would *o* this book to you, *June Bracken, etc.* 4
Offer'd then and there had *o* something more, *The Brook* 147
Not ev'n a rose, were *o* to thee? *Lucretius* 69
cup of both my hands And *o* you it kneeling: *Merlin and V.* 276
better *o* up to Heaven.' *Holy Grail* 36
Offering (*See also* **Love-offering, Peace-offering**) bring me *o's* of fruit and flowers: *St. S. Stylites* 128
dress the victim to the *o* up. *Princess iv* 130
I will make a solemn *o* of you *Lover's Tale iv* 118
Office *O you that hold A nobler* o *upon earth* *To the Queen* 2
a joint of state, that plies Its *o*, *Love thou thy land* 48
In whom should meet the *o's* of all, *M. d'Arthur* 125
decent not to fail In *o's* of tenderness, *Ulysses* 41
Two in the liberal *o's* of life, *Princess ii* 175
With books, with flowers, with Angel o's, „ *vii* 26
So kind an *o* hath been done, *In Mem. xvii* 17
Her *o* there to rear, to teach, „ *xl* 13
In those great *o's* that suit The full-grown energies „ 19
join'd Each *o* of the social hour To noble manners, „ *cxi* 14
If all your *o* had to do With old results „ *cxxviii* 10
touch of their *o* might have sufficed, *Maud II v* 27
Do each low *o* of your holy house; *Guinevere* 682
In whom should meet the *o's* of all, *Pass. of Arthur* 293
all *o's* Of watchful care and trembling tenderness. *Lover's Tale i* 225
joins us once again, to his either *o* true: *Happy* 106
hunt the tiger of oppression out From *o*; *Akbar's Dream* 159
Officer (*See also* **Hofficer**) *o's* and men Levied a kindly tax *Enoch Arden* 662
an *o* Rose up, and read the statutes, *Princess ii* 68
He rooted out the slothful *o* *Geraint and E.* 938
Officious *See* **Too-officious**
Offing And isles a light in the *o*: *Enoch Arden* 131
Desolate *o*, sailorless harbours, *Vastness* 14
Offset man-minded *o* rose To chase the deer *Talking Oak* 51
Offspring with their *o*, born-unborn, *Locksley H., Sixty* 98
Would she find her human *o* „ 234
Often-ransack'd To think that in our *o-r* world *Sea Dreams* 129
Often-wandering *I* was the lonely slave of an *o-w* mind; *The Wreck* 130
Ogress 'petty *O*,' and 'ungrateful Puss,' *Princess, Pro.* 157
Oil realms of upland, prodigal in *o*, *Palace of Art* 79
pure quintessences of precious *o's* „ 187
little dues of wheat, and wine and *o*; *Lotos-Eaters, C. S.* 122
Or burn'd in fire, or boil'd in *o*, *St. S. Stylites* 52
Like calming *o* on all their stony creeds, *Akbar's Dream* 160
Oil'd (*See also* **Well-oiled**) That *o* and curl'd Assyrian Bull *Maud I vi* 44
Oilily *o* bubbled up the mere. *Gareth and L.* 816
Oily lower down The bay was *o* calm; *Audley Court* 86
o'er the rest Arising, did his holy *o* best, *Sea Dreams* 195
and *o* courtesies Our formal compact, *Princess i* 164

Old (*See also* **Howd, New-old, Ould, Owd, World-old**) The *o* earth Had a birth, *All Things will Die* 37
And the *o* earth must die. „ 41
O faces glimmer'd thro' the doors, *O* footsteps trod the upper floors, *O* voices called her from without. *Mariana* 66
High-walled gardens green and *o*; *Arabian Nights* 8
From *o* well-heads of haunted rills, *Eleänore* 16
rising, from her bosom drew *O* letters, *Mariana in the S.* 62
'An inner impulse rent the veil Of his *o* husk: *Two Voices* 11
Pain rises up, *o* pleasures pall. „ 164
'As *o* mythologies relate, „ 349
With this *o* soul in organs new? „ 393
Three fingers round the *o* silver cup— *Miller's D.* 10
Where this *o* mansion mounted high „ 35
To yon *o* mill across the wolds; „ 240
The lion on your *o* stone gates *L. C. V. de Vere* 23
The good *o* year, the dear *o* time, *May Queen, N. Y's. E.* 6
With those *o* faces of our infancy *Lotos-Eaters, C. S.* 66
methought that I had wander'd far In an *o* wood: *D. of F. Women* 54
And the *o* year is dead. „ 248
For the *o* year lies a-dying. *D. of the O. Year* 5
O year, you must not die; „ 6
O year, you shall not die. (repeat) „ 9, 24
O year, you must not go; „ 15
O year, you shall not go. „ 18
O year, if you must die. „ 27
O year, we'll dearly rue for you: „ 43
A land of just and *o* renown, *You ask me, why, etc.* 10
If New and *O*, disastrous feud, *Love thou thy land* 77
I KNEW an *o* wife lean and poor, *The Goose* 1
It stirr'd the *o* wife's mettle: „ 26
How all the *o* honour had from Christmas gone, *The Epic* 7
In those *o* days, one summer noon, *M. d'Arthur* 29
and mighty bones of ancient men, *O* knights, „ 48
So might some *o* man speak in the aftertime „ 107
For now I see the true *o* times are dead, „ 229
'The *o* order changeth, yielding place to new, „ 240
So blunt in memory, so *o* at heart, *Gardener's D.* 53
She stood, a sight to make an *o* man young. „ 141
Then they clung about The *o* man's neck, *Dora* 164
New things and *o*, himself and her, *Walk. to the Mail* 61
still The same *o* sore breaks out „ 79
'My love for Nature is as *o* as I; *Edwin Morris* 28
The good *o* Summers, year by year *Talking Oak* 39
'*O* Summers, when the monk was fat, „ 41
'But we grow *o*. Ah! when shall all men's good *Golden Year* 47
—*o*, but full Of force and choler, „ 60
O writers push'd the happy season back,— „ 66
you and I are *o*; *O* age hath yet his honour *Ulysses* 49
We are not now that strength which in *o* days „ 66
Once more the *o* mysterious glimmer steals *Tithonus* 34
O, I see thee *o* and formal, *Locksley Hall* 93
Than those *o* portraits of *o* kings, *Day-Dm., Sleep P.* 23
In that new world which is the *o*: „ *Depart.* 4
O wishes, ghosts of broken plans, *Will Water.* 29
If *o* things, there are new; „ 58
Shall fling her *o* shoe after. „ 216
In there came *o* Alice the nurse, *Lady Clare* 13
'The *o* Earl's daughter died at my breast; „ 25
'I am *o*, but let me drink; *Vision of Sin* 75
O plash of rains, and refuse patch'd with moss. „ 212
For Enoch parted with his *o* sea-friend, *Enoch Arden* 168
And pace the sacred *o* familiar fields, „ 625
So propt, worm-eaten, ruinously *o*, „ 693
O Philip; all about the fields you caught *The Brook* 52
crost By that *o* bridge which, half in ruins „ 79
and rolling in his mind *O* waifs of rhyme, „ 199
O, and a mine of memories—who had served, *Aylmer's Field* 10
The same *o* rut would deepen year by year; „ 34
Than for his *o* Newfoundland's, „ 125
These *o* pheasant-lords, These partridge-breeders „ 381
Thwarted by one of these *o* father-fools, „ 390
What amulet drew her down to that *o* oak, So *o*, „ 507
O there The red fruit of an *o* idolatry— „ 763

Old (*continued*) One babe was theirs, a Margaret, three years *o*: *Sea Dreams* 3
How like you this *o* satire?' „ 198
And that was *o* Sir Ralph's at Ascalon: *Princess, Pro.* 26
That made the *o* warrior from his ivied nook „ 104
I read Of *o* Sir Ralph a page or two that rang „ 121
If our *o* halls could change their sex, „ 140
An *o* and strange affection of the house. „ *i* 13
A little dry *o* man, without a star, „ 117
There, enter'd an *o* hostel, call'd mine host „ 173
'The fifth in line from that *o* Florian, „ *ii* 238
(The gaunt *o* Baron with his beetle brow „ 240
she past From all her *o* companions, „ 263
They hunt *o* trails' said Cyril 'very well; „ 390
But when I dwelt upon your *o* affiance, „ *iii* 139
trim our sails, and let *o* bygones be, „ *iv* 69
'It was not thus, O Princess, in *o* days: „ 292
I your *o* friend and tried, she new in all? „ 318
while now the two *o* kings Began to wag „ *v* 18
'Satan take The *o* women and their shadows! „ 34
I would the *o* God of war himself were dead, „ 145
Then rode we with the *o* king across the lawns „ 236
infuse my tale of love In the *o* king's ears, „ 241
'Boys!' shriek'd the *o* king, but vainlier „ 328
the *o* leaven leaven'd all: „ 386
Thus the hard *o* king: I took my leave, „ 467
I seem'd to move in *o* memorial tilts, „ 479
Up started from my side The *o* lion, „ *vi* 99
O studies fail'd; seldom she spoke: „ *vii* 31
kingdom topples over with a shriek Like an *o* woman, „ *Con.* 63
This fine *o* world of ours is but a child „ 77
And sombre, *o*, colonnaded aisles. *The Daisy* 56
all my children have gone before me, I am so *o*: *Grandmother* 18
Ah, there's no fool like the *o* one— „ 44
But stay with the *o* woman now: „ 108
O Yew, which graspest at the stones *In Mem. ii* 1
Whose fancy fuses *o* and new, „ *xvi* 18
And many an *o* philosophy On Argive heights „ *xxiii* 21
O sisters of a day gone by, „ *xxix* 13
At our *o* pastimes in the hall We gambol'd, „ *xxx* 5
O warder of these buried bones, „ *xxxix* 1
How often shall her *o* fireside „ *xl* 22
Shall count new things as dear as *o*: „ 28
'Does my *o* friend remember me?' „ *lxiv* 28
wherefore wake The *o* bitterness again, „ *lxxxiv* 47
My *o* affection of the tomb, (repeat) *In Mem. lxxxv* 75, 77
While now we sang *o* songs that peal'd *In Mem. xcv* 13
No gray *o* grange, or lonely fold, „ *c* 5
Ring out *o* shapes of foul disease; „ *cvi* 25
The grand *o* name of gentleman, „ *cxi* 22
With *o* results that look like new; „ *cxxviii* 11
To make *o* bareness picturesque „ 19
But that *o* man, now lord of the broad estate *Maud I i* 19
dark *o* place will be gilt by the touch of a millionaire: „ 66
Whose *o* grandfather has lately died, „ *x* 5
That *o* man never comes to his place: „ *xiii* 24
A gray *o* wolf and a lean. „ 28
An *o* song vexes my ear; „ *II ii* 47
In the garden by the turrets Of the *o* manorial hall. „ *iv* 80
Not that gray *o* wolf, for he came not back „ *v* 53
But what will the *o* man say? „ 83
For what will the *o* man say „ 87
That *o* hysterical mock-disease should die.' „ *III vi* 33
Sir King, there be but two *o* men that know: And each is twice as *o* as I; *Com. of Arthur* 149
And gave him to Sir Anton, an *o* knight „ 222
but *o* Merlin counsell'd him, 'Take thou and strike! „ 306
An *o* man's wit may wander ere he die. „ 405
And echo'd by *o* folk beside their fires „ 417
The *o* order changeth, yielding place to new; „ 509
Seeing that ye be grown too weak and *o* „ 511
To plunge *o* Merlin in the Arabian sea; *Gareth and L.* 211
New things and *o* co-twisted, „ 226
Then that *o* Seer made answer playing on him „ 252
'*O* Master, reverence thine own beard That looks „ 280

Old (*continued*) Or carol some *o* roundelay, and so loud *Gareth and L.* 506
The fashion of that *o* knight-errantry Who ride abroad, „ 629
Some *o* head-blow not heeded in his youth „ 714
Art thou not *o*?' '*O*, damsel, *o* and hard, *O*, with the might and breath „ 1105
'*O*, and over-bold in brag! „ 1107
An *o* storm-beaten, russet, many-stain'd Pavilion, „ 1113
And arm'd him in *o* arms, and brought a helm „ 1115
His arms are *o*, he trusts the harden'd skin— „ 1139
son Of *o* King Lot and good Queen Bellicent, „ 1231
Held court at *o* Caerleon upon Usk. *Marr. of Geraint* 146
Who being vicious, *o* and irritable, „ 194
'Arms, indeed, but *o* And rusty, *o* and rusty, „ 477
But that *o* dame, to whom full tenderly „ 508
slowly drew himself Bright from his *o* dark life, „ 595
Near that *o* home, a pool of golden carp; „ 648
She is not fairer in new clothes than *o*. „ 722
For *o* am I, and rough the ways and wild; „ 750
And all that week was *o* Caerleon gay, „ 837
But she, remembering her *o* ruin'd hall, *Geraint and E.* 254
Her suitor in *o* years before Geraint, „ 276
some, whose souls the *o* serpent long had drawn Down, „ 632
From which *o* fires have broken, men may fear „ 822
'*O* friend, too *o* to be so young, depart, *Balin and Balan* 17
'*O* fabler, these be fancies of the churl, „ 307
and *o* boughs Whined in the wood. „ 385
'*O* priest, who mumble worship in your buire—O monk and nun, „ 444
This *o* sun-worship, boy, will rise again, „ 457
Before an oak, so hollow, huge and *o* *Merlin and V.* 3
That *o* true filth, and bottom of the well, „ 47
With such a fixt devotion, that the *o* man, „ 183
Caught in a great *o* tyrant spider's web, „ 259
Less *o* than I, yet older, for my blood „ 556
drew The rustiest iron of *o* fighters' hearts; „ 574
that *o* man Went back to his *o* wild, „ 648
Came to her *o* perch back, and settled there. „ 903
passing gayer youth For one so *o*, „ 928
Then came an *o*, dumb, myriad-wrinkled man, *Lancelot and E.* 170
He bore a knight of *o* repute to the earth, „ 492
learn If his *o* prowess were in aught decay'd; „ 584
The shackles of an *o* love straiten'd him, „ 875
Beyond mine *o* belief in womanhood, „ 955
therefore let our dumb *o* man alone Go with me, „ 1127
Loyal, the dumb *o* servitor, on deck, „ 1144
Then rose the dumb *o* servitor, and the dead, „ 1153
'From our *o* books I know That Joseph came of old *Holy Grail* 59
had you known our Camelot, Built by *o* kings, age after age, so *o* „ 340
till the dry *o* trunks about us, dead, „ 495
plaster'd like a martin's nest To these *o* walls— „ 549
Delight myself with gossip and *o* wives, „ 553
But live like an *o* badger in his earth, „ 629
Were strong in that *o* magic which can trace „ 666
For every fiery prophet in *o* times, „ 876
as he sat In hall at *o* Caerleon, the high doors *Pelleas and E.* 3
Strange as to some *o* prophet might have seem'd „ 51
Some rough *o* knight who knew the worldly way, „ 192
O milky fables of the wolf and sheep, „ 196
That all the *o* echoes hidden in the wall „ 366
like an *o* dwarf-elm That turns its back on the salt blast, „ 543
'May God be with thee, sweet, when *o* and gray, *Last Tournament* 627
'May God be with thee, sweet, when thou art *o*, „ 629
Swear to me thou wilt love me ev'n when *o*, „ 652
fail'd to trace him thro' the flesh and blood Of our *o* kings: „ 687
Her memory from *o* habit of the mind *Guinevere* 379
some beheld the faces of *o* ghosts Look in *Pass. of Arthur* 103
In those *o* days, one summer noon, „ 197
O knights, and over them the sea-wind sang Shrill, „ 216
So might some *o* man speak in the aftertime „ 275
For now I see the true *o* times are dead, „ 397
'The *o* order changeth, yielding place to new, „ 407
accept this *o* imperfect tale, New-old, *To the Queen, ii* 36
half-moulder'd chords To some *o* melody, *Lover's Tale i* 20
Above the naked poisons of his heart In his *o* age.' „ 357

Old (*continued*) they trod The same *o* paths where Love had walk'd *Lover's Tale i* 821
(Huge blocks, which some *o* trembling of the world „ *ii* 45
But all their house was *o* and loved them both, „ *iv* 122
And his was *o*, has in it rare or fair „ 203
An' I hit on an *o* deal-box that was push'd *First Quarrel* 48
it's kind of you, Madam, to sit by an *o* dying wife. *Rizpah* 21
I can't dig deep, I am *o*— „ 56
o Sir Richard caught at last, *The Revenge* 98
An *o* and worthy name! *Sisters (E. and E.)* 74
I walked with our kindly *o* doctor as far *In the Child Hosp.* 43
Stench of *o* offal decaying, *Def. of Lucknow* 82
on the palace roof the *o* banner of England blew. „ 106
Some cited *o* Lactantius: *Columbus* 49
like an *o* friend false at last In our most need, „ 70
I am not yet too *o* to work his will— „ 161
To lay me in some shrine of this *o* Spain, „ 207
Going? I am *o* and slighted: „ 241
Of others their *o* craft seaworthy still, *Pref. Son 19th Cent.* 3
Such as *o* writers Have writ of in histories— *Batt. of Brunanburh* 114
O Fitz, who from your suburb grange, *To E. Fitzgerald* 1
O friends outvaluing all the rest, „ 40
But we *o* friends are still alive, „ 42
till that *o* man before A cavern *Ancient Sage* 6
and lights the *o* church-tower, And lights the clock! *The Flight* 93
our *o* England may go down in babble at last. *Locksley H., Sixty* 8
I this *o* white-headed dreamer stoopt and kiss'd „ 38
o Assyrian kings would flay Captives whom they caught in battle— „ 79
tell them '*o* experience is a fool,' „ 131
Bring the *o* dark ages back without the faith, „ 137
I am *o*, and think gray thoughts, for I am gray: „ 155
Lame and *o*, and past his time, „ 227
There is one *o* Hostel left us „ 247
Poor *o* Heraldry, poor *o* History, poor *o* Poetry, „ 249
In the common deluge drowning *o* political common-sense! „ 250
Poor *o* voice of eighty crying after voices „ 251
O Horace? 'I will strike' said he *Epilogue* 46
And he sung not alone of an *o* sun set, *Dead Prophet* 41
Should this *o* England fall *The Fleet* 4
That *o* strength and constancy *Open I. and C. Exhib.* 14
O poets foster'd under friendlier skies, *O* Virgil who would write ten lines, *Poets and their B.* 1
And you, *o* popular Horace, you the wise „ 5
and all these *o* revolutions of earth; *Vastness* 29
For ten thousand years *O* and new? *The Ring* 20
is making a new link Breaking an *o* one? „ 51
Garrulous *o* crone. „ 120
We saw far off an *o* forsaken house, „ 155
And in yon arching avenue of *o* elms, „ 172
Found in a chink of that *o* moulder'd floor!' „ 280
(Our *o* bright bird that still is veering there „ 332
So, following her *o* pastime of the brook, „ 354
forgotten mine own rhyme By mine *o* self, As I shall be forgotten by *o* Time, *To Mary Boyle* 22
To work *o* laws of Love to fresh results, *Prog. of Spring* 85
O Empires, dwellings of the kings of men; „ 99
slower and fainter, *O* and weary, *Merlin and the G.* 100
What hast thou done for me, grim *O* Age, *By an Evolution.* 9
Ever as of *o* time, *The Snowdrop* 3
Live thy Life, Young and *o*, *The Oak* 2
Rear'd on the tumbled ruins of an *o* fane *St. Telemachus* 6
Like some *o* wreck on some indrawing sea, „ 44
Rome no more should wallow in this *o* lust „ 78
was not Alla call'd In *o* Irân the Sun of Love? *Akbar's Dream* 87
A voice from *o* Irân! Nay, but I know it— „ 89
And cast aside, when *o*, for newer,— „ 134
alchemise *o* hates into the gold Of Love, „ 163
Could give the warrior kings of o, *To the Queen* 4
Seeking a tavern which of *o* he knew, *Enoch Arden* 691
Ring out the *o*, ring in the new, *In Mem. cvi* 5
sayings from of *o* Ranging and ringing *Com. of Arthur* 415
kings of *o* had doom'd thee to the flames, *Gareth and L.* 374
humour of the kings of *o* Return upon me! „ 377

Old (*continued*) Stir, as they stirr'd of *o*, *Balin and Balan* 89
The new leaf ever pushes off the *o*. „ 442
Many a time As once—of *o*— *Merlin and V.* 136
I know the Table Round, my friends of *o*; „ 816
I know That Joseph came of *o* to Glastonbury, *Holy Grail* 60
every evil thought I had thought of *o*, „ 372
when I moved of *o* A slender page about her father's hall, „ 580
her longing and her will Was toward me as of *o*; „ 591
Joseph brought of *o* to Glastonbury?' „ 735
My madness came upon me as of *o*, „ 787
Shone like the countenance of a priest of *o* *Pelleas and E.* 144
Arise, go forth and conquer as of *o*.' *Pass. of Arthur* 64
A land of *o* upheaven from the abyss „ 82
my name has been A hallow'd memory like the names of *o*, *Lover's Tale i* 445
I WISH I were as in the years of *o*, *Tiresias* 1
mingled with the famous kings of *o*, „ 171
my Fathers belong'd to the church of *o*, *The Wreck* 1
not claiming your pity: I know you of *o*— *Despair* 37
has join'd our hands of *o*; *Happy* 93
body which had lain Of *o* in her embrace, *Death of Œnone* 94
And the Vision that led me of *o*, *The Dreamer* 5

Olden a valorous weapon in *o* England! *Kapiolani* 4

Older others lay about the lawns, Of the *o* sort, *Princess ii* 463
And he that told the tale in *o* times *Gareth and L.* 1427
Less old than I, yet *o*, for my blood *Merlin and V.* 556
withheld His *o* and his mightier from the lists, *Pelleas and E.* 160

Oldest Behind yon whispering tuft of *o* pine, *Œnone* 88
Graven in the *o* tongue of all this world, *Com. of Arthur* 302
And *o* friend, your Uncle, wishes it, *Sisters (E. and E.)* 47
each of them boasted he sprang from the *o* race upon earth. *V. of Maeldune* 4
And *o* age in shadow from the night, *Tiresias* 104
one Their *o*, and the same who first *Death of Œnone* 53
Whereon their *o* and their boldest said, „ 100

Old-fashion'd *See* **owd-farran'd**

Old-recurring *o-r* waves of prejudice Resmooth *Princess iii* 240

Old-world *o-w* trains, upheld at court *Day-Dm., Ep.* 9
like an *o-w* mammoth bulk'd in ice, *Princess v* 148
Dust in wholesome *o-w* dust *Locksley H., Sixty* 150
And now—like *o-w* inns that take *Pro. to Gen. Hamley* 13

Old Year And the *o y* is dead. *D. of F. Women* 248
For the *o y* lies a-dying. *D. of the O. Year* 5
O y, you must not die; „ 6
O y, you shall not die. (repeat) „ 9, 24
O y, you must not go; „ 15
O y, you shall not go. „ 18
O y, if you must die. „ 27
O y, we'll dearly rue for you: „ 43

'Ole (whole) an' the '*o* 'ouse hupside down. *North. Cobbler* 42

Oleander Where *o's* flush'd the bed *The Daisy* 33

Olive (a girl's name) Will I to *O* plight my troth, *Talking Oak* 283

Olive (tree) the year in which our *o's* fail'd. *Princess i* 125
Of *o*, aloe, and maize and vine. *The Daisy* 4
A light amid its *o's* green; „ 30
Peace sitting under her *o*, *Maud I i* 33
to me thro' all the groves of *o* *Frater Ave, etc.* 3

Olive-gardens 'Leaving the *o-g* far below, *D. of F. Women* 217

Olive-glade There in a secret *o-g* I saw *Tiresias* 39

Olive-hoary Or *o-h* cape in ocean; *The Daisy* 31

Olive-silvery Sweet Catullus's all-but-island, *o-s* Sirmio! *Frater Ave, etc.* 9

Olivet crown'd The purple brows of *O*. *In Mem. xxxi* 12

Olive-yard *o-y* and vine And golden grain, *Demeter and P.* 110

Olivia maid or spouse, As fair as my *O*, *Talking Oak* 35
I saw Your own *O* blow, „ 76
Declare when last *O* came To sport „ 99

Olympian Ghost of Pindar in you Roll'd an *O*; *To Prof. Jebb.* 4

Omar that large infidel Your *O*; and your *O* drew Full-handed plaudits *To E. Fitzgerald* 37

Omega '*O*! thou art Lord,' they said, *Two Voices* 278

Omen from which their *o's* all men drew, *Ode on Well.* 36
What *o's* may foreshadow fate to man And woman, *Tiresias* 7

Omen'd *See* **Ill-omen'd**

Ondecent (indecent) an' saäyin' *o* things, *Spinster's S's.* 90

One (*See also* **Wan, Won, Wonn**) WE were two daughters of *o* race: *The Sisters* 1
By *o* low voice to *o* dear neighbourhood, *Aylmer's Field* 60
The *o* transmitter of their ancient name, „ 296
that *o* kiss Was Leolin's *o* strong rival „ 556
Never *o* kindly smile, *o* kindly word: „ 564
Never since our bad earth became *o* sea, „ 635
or *o* stone Left on another, „ 788
his *o* word was 'desolate;' „ 836
then I saw *o* lovely star Larger and larger. *Sea Dreams* 93
'With all his conscience and *o* eye askew'— „ 180
Without *o* pleasure and without *o* pain, *Lucretius* 269
And there we took *o* tutor as to read: *Princess, Pro.* 179
Yet let us breathe for *o* hour more in Heaven' „ *iii* 69
On *o* knee Kneeling, I gave it, which she caught, „ *iv* 469
My *o* sweet child, whom I shall see no more! „ *v* 83
My babe, my sweet Aglaïa, my *o* child: „ 101
her *o* fault The tenderness, not yours, „ *vi* 185
To *o* deep chamber shut from sound, „ 376
for on *o* side arose The women up in wild revolt, „ *vii* 122
His nights, his days, moves with him to *o* goal, „ 263
And save the *o* true seed of freedom sown *Ode on Well.* 162
But the *o* voice in Europe: we *must* speak; *Third of Feb.* 16
For us, we will not spare the tyrant *o* hard word. „ 42
That *o* fair planet can produce, *Ode Inter. Exhib.* 24
O tall Agavè above the lake. *The Daisy* 84
Yet *o* lay-hearth would give you welcome *To F. D. Maurice* 11
Or later, pay *o* visit here, „ 45
There is but *o* bird with a musical throat, *The Islet* 27
May make *o* music as before, *In Mem., Pro.* 28
Make *o* wreath more for Use and Wont, „ *xxix* 11
Of *o* mute Shadow watching all. „ *xxx* 8
Then *o* deep love doth supersede „ *xxxii* 5
But for *o* hour, *O* Love, I strive „ *xxxv* 6
That not *o* life shall be destroy'd, „ *liv* 6
At *o* dear knee we proffer'd vows, *O* lesson from *o* book we learn'd, „ *lxxix* 13
They mix in *o* another's arms „ *cii* 23
Whereat those maidens with *o* mind „ *ciii* 45
O God, *o* law, *o* element, And *o* far-off divine event, „ *Con.* 142
I know it the *o* bright thing to save *Maud I xvi* 20
To save from some slight shame *o* simple girl. „ *xviii* 45
O long milk-bloom on the tree; „ *xxii* 46
For *o* short hour to see The souls we loved, „ *II iv* 14
But is ever the *o* thing silent here. „ *v* 68
To catch a friend of mine *o* stormy day; „ 85
And the heart of a people beat with *o* desire; „ *III vi* 49
O light together, but has past and leaves *Ded. of Idylls* 48
Then might we live together as *o* life, And reigning with *o* will in everything *Com. of Arthur* 91
Give my *o* daughter saving to a king, „ 143
In *o* great annal-book, where after-years „ 158
'Few, but all brave, all of *o* mind with him; „ 255
That men are blinded by it—on *o* side, „ 301
Arthur and his knighthood for a space Were all *o* will, „ 516
only *o* proof, Before thou ask the King *Gareth and L.* 144
Our *o* white lie sits like a little ghost „ 297
When some good knight had done *o* noble deed, „ 411
At *o* end *o*, that gave upon a range Of level pavement „ 666
Then after *o* long slope was mounted, saw, „ 795
in a moment—at *o* touch Of that skill'd spear, „ 1222
But with *o* stroke Sir Gareth split the skull. „ 1404
In a long valley, on *o* side whereof, *Marr. of Geraint* 243
And on *o* side a castle in decay, „ 245
'Here, by God's grace, is the *o* voice for me.' „ 344
'Here by God's rood is the *o* maid for me.' „ 368
o command I laid upon you, not to speak to me, *Geraint and E.* 77
The *o* true lover whom you ever own'd, „ 344
The pieces of his armour in *o* place, „ 374
answering not *o* word, she led the way. „ 495
(With *o* main purpose ever at my heart) „ 831
o side had sea And ship and sail and angels *Balin and Balan* 364
The whole wood-world is *o* full peal of praise. „ 450
Where under *o* long lane of cloudless air „ 461
And sowing *o* ill hint from ear to ear, *Merlin and V.* 143

One (*continued*) And knew no more, nor gave me o poor word; *Merlin and V.* 277
Take o verse more—the lady speaks it—this: „ 445
Yet is there o true line, the pearl of pearls: „ 459
Read but o book, and ever reading grew „ 622
And since he kept his mind on o sole aim, „ 626
Was o year gone, and on returning found Not two but three? there lay the reckling, o But o hour old! „ 708
And not the o dark hour which brings remorse, „ 763
But have ye no o word of loyal praise For Arthur, „ 778
I will go. In truth, but o thing now— „ 918
send O flash, that, missing all things else, „ 932
the o passionate love Of her whole life; „ 955
in o moment, she put forth the charm „ 967
Carved of o emerald center'd in a sun Of silver rays, *Lancelot and E.* 295
'Stay a little! O golden minute's grace! „ 684
Full often the bright image of o face, „ 882
and o morn it chanced He found her in among „ 922
And I must die for want of o bold word.' „ 927
This was the o discourtesy that he used. „ 988
in o cold passive hand Received at once „ 1201
With o sharp rapid, where the crisping white *Holy Grail* 381
there I found Only o man of an exceeding age. „ 431
And gateways in a glory like o pearl— „ 527
With o great dwelling in the middle of it; „ 574
till o fair morn, I walking to and fro „ 591
'O night my pathway swerving east, I saw „ 634
For, brother, so o night, because they roll „ 685
knightly in me twined and clung Round that o sin, „ 775
But never let me bide o hour at peace. *Pelleas and E.* 387
A rose, o rose, and this was wondrous fair, O rose, a rose that gladden'd earth and sky, O rose, my rose, that sweeten'd all mine air— „ 401
'O rose, a rose to gather by and by, O rose, a rose, to gather and to wear, „ 405
O rose, my rose; a rose that will not die,— „ 408
Save that o rivulet from a tiny cave „ 425
turn'd To Pelleas, as the o true knight on earth, „ 494
his nose Bridge-broken, o eye out, and o hand off, *Last Tournament* 59
then o low roll Of Autumn thunder, „ 152
An ocean-sounding welcome to o knight, „ 168
Our o white day of Innocence hath past, „ 218
But Dagonet with o foot poised in his hand, „ 285
'Fear God: honour the King—his o true knight— „ 302
Till o lone woman, weeping near a cross, „ 493
So, pluck'd o way by hate and o by love, „ 539
Here o black, mute midsummer night I sat, „ 612
had let o finger lightly touch The warm white apple „ 716
o low light betwixt them burn'd *Guinevere* 4
For thus it chanced o morn when all the court, „ 21
To love o maiden only, cleave to her, „ 475
And makes me o pollution: he, the King, „ 619
as by some o deathbed after wail Of suffering, *Pass. of Arthur* 118
Who hath but dwelt beneath o roof with me. „ 156
o last act of kinghood shalt thou see Yet, „ 163
In those old days, o summer noon, „ 197
Then took with care, and kneeling on o knee, „ 341
Lest o good custom should corrupt the world. „ 410
hull Look'd o black dot against the verge of dawn, „ 439
Sounds, as if some fair city were o voice „ 460
And London roll'd o tide of joy thro' *To the Queen ii* 8
her throne In our vast Orient, and o isle, o isle, „ 31
sometimes touches but o string That quivers, *Lover's Tale i* 17
The stream of life, o stream, o life, o blood, O sustenance, „ 239
this o name, In some obscure hereafter, „ 457
O golden dream of love, from which may death „ 760
Why grew we then together in o plot? Why fed we from o fountain? drew o sun? Why were our mothers' branches of o stem, „ *ii* 23
Brooded o master-passion evermore, „ 60
O morning when the upblown billow ran „ 178
Moved with o spirit round about the bay, „ *iii* 17

One (*continued*) her hair Studded with o rich Provence rose— *Lover's Tale iii* 45
O hand she reach'd to those that came behind, „ 48
Well he had O golden hour—of triumph shall I say? „ *iv* 6
at o end of the hall Two great funereal curtains, „ 213
And bearing on o arm the noble babe, „ 370
he took no life, but he took o purse, *Rizpah* 31
An' o night I cooms 'oäm like a bull *North. Cobbler* 33
he dared her with o little ship and his English few; *The Revenge* 107
when o quick peal Of laughter drew me *Sisters (E. and E.)* 115
all O bloom of youth, health, beauty, happiness, „ 120
An' Lucy wur läame o' o leg, *Village Wife* 99
And she lay with a flower in o hand *In the Child. Hosp.* 39
that o night a crowd Throng'd the waste field *Sir J. Oldcastle* 39
Not even by o hair's-breadth of heresy, *Columbus* 64
Am ready to sail forth on o last voyage. „ 237
to lead O last crusade against the Saracen, „ 239
May send o ray to thee! *Ded. Poem Prin. Alice* 14
For the peak sent up o league of fire *V. of Maeldune* 72
For the o half slew the other, „ 114
From that o light no man can look upon, *De Prof., Two G.* 37
Will make o people ere man's race be run: *To Victor Hugo* 11
Cast at thy feet o flower that fades away. *To Dante* 7
O night when earth was winter-black, *To E. Fitzgerald* 21
—not o bush was near— *Tiresias* 36
o snowy knee was prest Against the margin flowers; „ 42
great God Arês, whose o bliss Is war, „ 111
Send no such light upon the ways of men As o great deed. „ 162
On o far height in o far-shining fire. „ 185
'O height and o far-shining fire' „ 186
I would make my life o prayer for a soul *The Wreck* 10
go To spend my o last year among the hills. *Ancient Sage* 16
having climb'd o step beyond Our village miseries, „ 206
Those three hundred millions under o Imperial sceptre now, *Locksley H., Sixty* 117
There is o old Hostel left us „ 247
With o gray glimpse of sea; *Pro. to Gen. Hamley* 8
Welcome, welcome with o voice! *Open. I. and C. Exhib.* 1
O life, o flag, o fleet, o Throne!' „ 39
By o side-path, from simple truth; *To Marq. of Dufferin* 28
And o drear sound I have not heard, „ 40
O full voice of allegiance, *On Jub. Q. Victoria* 22
and I heard o voice from all the three *Demeter and P.* 84
tha mun nobbut hev' o glass of äale. *Owd Roä* 20
An' theere i' the 'ouse o night— „ 27
Well, O way for Miriam. *The Ring* 73
o silent voice Came on the wind, „ 153
O year without a storm, or even a cloud; „ 284
Nay, you were my o solace; only— „ 310
o day came And saw you, shook her head, „ 312
groping for it, could not find O likeness, „ 337
For o monotonous fancy madden'd her, „ 404
A red mark ran All round o finger pointed straight, „ 453
Who never caught o gleam of the beauty *Happy* 60
If man and wife be but o flesh, „ 94
Might I crave O favour? *Romney's R.* 70
Lay your Plato for o minute down, *To Master of B.* 4
but the goodly view Was now o blank, *Death of Œnone* 4
flamed On o huge slope beyond, *St. Telemachus* 8
For o moment afterward A silence follow'd „ 64
Then o deep roar as of a breaking sea, „ 67
'Mine is the o fruit Alla made for man.' *Akbar's Dream* 40
Make but o music, harmonising "Pray." „ 151
O Alla! o Kalifa! „ 167
I had o brief summer of bliss. *Bandit's Death* 9
there o day He had left his dagger behind him. „ 11
Moan to myself 'o plunge—then quiet for evermore.' *Charity* 16
And o clear call for me! *Crossing the Bar* 2
For that the evil o's come here, and say, *St. S. Stylites* 98
'A rose, but o, none other rose had I, *Pelleas and E.* 400
No rose but o—what other rose had I? „ 407
the never-changing O And ever-changing Many, *Akbar's Dream* 147
But o was counter to the hearth, *Gareth and L.* 672
But never a o so gay, *Poet's Song* 14

One (*continued*) Why were we *o* in all things, save in that Where to have been *o* had been the cope and crown *Lover's Tale ii* 26
O with Britain, heart and soul! *Open. I. and C. Exhib.* 38
One-day-seen The *o-d-s* Sir Lancelot in her heart, *Lancelot and E.* 747
One-sided 'O dull, *o-s* voice,' said I, *Two Voices* 202
Only (adj.) His *o* child, his Edith, whom he loved *Aylmer's Field* 23
'We have his dearest, His *o* son!' *The Victim* 64
Fear not to give this King thine *o* child, *Com. of Arthur* 413
when her son Beheld his *o* way to glory *Gareth and L.* 159
I have miss'd the *o* way (repeat) „ 787, 792
Had married Enid, Yniol's *o* child, *Marr. of Geraint* 4
Onset greaves and cuisses dash'd with drops Of *o*; *M. d'Arthur* 216
A day of *o's* of despair! *Ode on Well.* 124
Rings to the roar of an angel *o*— *Milton* 8
and so they crash'd In *o*, *Balin and Balan* 556
greaves and cuisses dash'd with drops Of *o*; *Pass. of Arthur* 384
Onslaught make an *o* single on a realm *Geraint and E* 917
Onward (adj. and adv.) Still *o*; and the clear canal Is rounded *Arabian Nights* 45
Till in its *o* current it absorbs *Isabel* 31
fiery-hot to burst All barriers in her *o* race For power. *In Mem. cxiv* 14
vast eddies in the flood Of *o* time „ *cxxviii* 6
A moment, ere the *o* whirlwind shatter it, *Lover's Tale i* 451
But in the *o* current of her speech, „ 565
Onward (s) his truer name Is '*O*,' *D. of the Duke of C.* 14
Onward-sloping 'Mid *o-s* motions infinite *Palace of Art* 247
'Oonderd (hundred) an' thin my two *'o* a-year *Spinster's S's.* 12
wellnigh purr'd ma awaäy fro' my oän two *'o* a-year. „ 58
Oorali Drench'd with the hellish *o*— *In the Child. Hosp.* 10
Ooze (s) For I was drench'd with *o*, *Princess v* 28
Ooze (verb) bloat himself, and *o* All over *Sea Dreams* 154
Oozed *o* All o'er with honey'd answer *Princess v* 241
Opal gayer colours, like an *o* warm'd. *Merlin and V.* 950
Open (adj) The costly doors flung *o* wide, *Arabian Nights* 17
Showering thy gleaned wealth into my *o* breast *Ode to Memory* 23
An *o* scroll, Before him lay: *The Poet* 8
Wide, wild, and *o* to the air, *Dying Swan* 2
Thro' the *o* gates of the city afar, „ 34
Her *o* eyes desire the truth. *Of old sat Freedom* 17
More softly round the *o* wold, *To J. S.* 2
On *o* main or winding shore! *The Voyage* 6
Were *o* to each other; *Aylmer's Field* 40
voice Of comfort and an *o* hand of help, „ 174
Follows the mouse, and all is *o* field. „ 853
we had limed ourselves With *o* eyes, *Princess iii* 143
and in her lion's mood Tore *o*, „ *iv* 381
so To the *o* window moved, „ 492
one glance he caught Thro' *o* doors of Ida „ *v* 343
Thro' *o* field into the lists they wound „ *vi* 84
And all thy heart lies *o* unto me. „ *vii* 183
He, on whom from both her *o* hands *Ode on Well.* 195
immeasurable heavens Break *o* to their highest, *Spec. of Iliad* 15
But *o* converse is there none, *In Mem. xx* 17
Imperial halls, or *o* plain; „ *xcviii* 29
in their hand Is Nature like an *o* book; „ *Con.* 132
lords Banded, and so brake out in *o* war.' *Com. of Arthur* 237
'Wherefore waits the madman there Naked in *o* dayshine?' *Gareth and L.* 1092
rang Clear thro' the *o* casement of the hall, *Marr. of Geraint* 328
Thro' *o* doors and hospitality; „ 456
Coursed one another more on *o* ground „ 522
And issuing under *o* heavens beheld *Geraint and E.* 196
Painted, who stare at *o* space, nor glance „ 268
I smote upon the naked skull A thrall of thine in *o* hall, *Balin and Balan* 56
under *o* blue Came on the hoarhead woodman „ 293
Push'd thro' an *o* casement down, „ 413
My mother on his corpse in *o* field; (repeat) *Merlin and V.* 43, 73
And laid the diamond in his *o* hand. *Lancelot and E.* 827
He loves the Queen, and in an *o* shame: And she returns his love in *o* shame; „ 1082
But for a mile all round was *o* space, *Pelleas and E.* 28
And he was left alone in *o* field. „ 208
straight on thro' *o* door Rode Gawain, „ 382

Open (adj.) (*continued*) Wide *o* were the gates, And no watch kept; *Pelleas and E.* 414
'Nay, fool,' said Tristram, 'not in *o* day.' *Last Tournament* 347
huge machicolated tower That stood with *o* doors, „ 425
but sprang Thro' *o* doors, and swording right and left „ 473
In *o* battle or the tilting-field (repeat) *Guinevere* 330, 332
o flower tell What sort of bud it was, *Lover's Tale i* 151
Arise in *o* prospect—heath and hill, „ 397
Forthgazing on the waste and *o* sea, „ *ii* 177
moon Struck from an *o* grating overhead „ *iv* 60
An *o* landaulet Whirl'd by, which, after it had past me, *Sisters (E. and E.)* 85
Rip your brothers' vices *o*, *Locksley H., Sixty* 141
We often walk In *o* sun, *The Ring* 328
There, the chest was *o*—all The sacred relics „ 446
The door is *o*. He! is he standing at the door, *Happy* 11
And in her *o* palm a halcyon sits Patient— *Prog. of Spring* 20
Wait till Death has flung them *o*, *Faith* 7
Open (s) race thro' many a mile Of dense and *o*, *Balin and Balan* 424
Open (verb) Heaven *o's* inward, chasms yawn, *Two Voices* 304
like a horse That hears the corn-bin *o*, *The Epic* 45
and *o's* but to golden keys. *Locksley Hall* 100
o to me, And lay my little blossom at my feet, *Princess v* 99
'*O* dewy flowers that *o* to the sun, *Gareth and L.* 1066
The wayside blossoms *o* to the blaze. *Balin and Balan* 449
To dig, pick, *o*, find and read the charm: *Merlin and V.* 660
O gates, And I will make you merry.' *Pelleas and E.* 373
The golden gates would *o* at a word. *Sisters (E. and E.)* 145
He would *o* the books that I prized, *The Wreck* 21
Till Holy St. Pether gets up wid his kays an' *o's* the gate! *Tomorrow* 93
O's a door in Heaven; *Early Spring* 7
Open-door'd Once rich, now poor, but ever *o-d.*' *Marr. of Geraint* 302
always *o-d* To every breath from heaven, *Akbar's Dream* 179
Open'd (adj.) Lily of the vale! half *o* bell of the woods! *Princess vi* 193
Open'd (verb) Thy dark eyes *o* not, *Eleänore* 1
northward of the narrow port *O* a larger haven: *Enoch Arden* 103
Where either haven *o* on the deeps, „ 671
With one small gate that *o* on the waste, „ 733
Crept to the gate, and *o* it, „ 775
counter door to that Which Leolin *o*, *Aylmer's Field* 283
Books (see Daniel seven and ten) Were *o*, *Sea Dreams* 153
gate shone Only, that *o* on the field below: *Gareth and L.* 195
Now two great entries *o* from the hall, „ 665
But yesterday you never *o* lip, *Merlin and V.* 271
O his arms to embrace me as he came, *Holy Grail* 417
all the heavens *O* and blazed with thunder „ 508
the heavens *o* and blazed again Roaring, „ 516
Sat by the walls, and no one *o* to him. *Pelleas and E.* 217
o on the pines with doors of glass, *Lover's Tale i* 41
door for scoundrel scum I *o* to the West, *Columbus* 171
it *o* and dropt at the side of each man, *V. of Maeldune* 85
I shook as I *o* the letter— *The Wreck* 145
A door was *o* in the house— *The Flight* 69
Muriel claim'd and *o* what I meant For Miriam, *The Ring* 242
And bolted doors that *o* of themselves: „ 413
Opener nor the silent *O* of the Gate.' *God and the Univ.* 6
Open-hearted 'An *o-h* maiden, true and pure. *Princess iii* 98
Opening (adj. and part.) (*See also* **Half-opening**) *o* upon level plots Of crowned lilies, *Ode to Memory* 108
in front The gorges, *o* wide apart, *Œnone* 12
and *o* out his milk-white palm „ 65
The cloudy porch oft *o* on the Sun? *Love and Duty* 9
struck it thrice, and, no one *o*, Enter'd; *Enoch Arden* 279
o this I read Of old Sir Ralph a page or two *Princess, Pro.* 120
Not yet endured to meet her *o* eyes, „ *iv* 195
and she rose *O* her arms to meet me, *Holy Grail* 395
in a moment when they blazed again *O*, „ 524
long water *o* on the deep Somewhere *Pass. of Arthur* 466
in the end, *O* on darkness, *Lover's Tale ii* 125
an ever *o* height, An ever lessening earth— *The Ring* 45
Opening (s) About the *o* of the flower, *Two Voices* 161
we saw The clefts and *o's* in the mountains *Lover's Tale i* 330
Open-mouth'd All *o-m*, all gazing to the light, *Princess iv* 483
So stood the unhappy mother *o-m*, „ *vi* 143

Openness Till taken with her seeming *o* *Princess iv* 300
Open-work *o-w* in which the hunter rued „ 203
Operation Thy scope of *o*, day by day, *Prog. of Spring* 111
Ophir brought From Solomon's now-recover'd *O* *Columbus* 112
Opiate Then bring an *o* trebly strong, *In Mem. lxxi* 6
fumes Of that dark *o* dose you gave me, *Romney's R.* 31
Has your *o* then Bred this black mood? „ 61
Opinion banded unions persecute *O*, *You ask me, why, etc.* 18
Oppian and storm'd At the *O* law. *Princess vii* 124
Opposed *O* mirrors each reflecting each— *Sonnet To* —— 11
and *o* Free hearts, free foreheads— *Ulysses* 48
fifty there *O* to fifty, *Princess v* 484
Opposite loathsome *o* Of all my heart *Guinevere* 491
Opposition Yet not with brawling *o* she, *Enoch Arden* 159
Thro' solid *o* crabb'd and gnarl'd. *Princess iii* 126
we four may build some plan Foursquare to *o*.' „ *v* 231
Oppress icy-hearted Muscovite *O* the region?' *Poland* 11
Oppression But they hated his *o*, *The Captain* 9
hunt the tiger of *o* out From office; *Akbar's Dream* 158
Opulence barbarous *o* jewel-thick Sunn'd itself *Maud I xiii* 12
In a world of arrogant *o*, *Despair* 78
Opulent Or beast or bird or fish, or *o* flower: *Lucretius* 249
A less diffuse and *o* end, *Tiresias* 189
O Avarice, lean as Poverty; *Vastness* 20
Oracle (*See also* **State-oracle**) Sleek Odalisques, or *o's* of mode, *Princess ii* 77
Apart the Chamian *O* divine *Alexander* 10
Orange (adj.) leave Yon *o* sunset waning slow: *Move eastward* 2
some hid and sought In the *o* thickets: *Princess ii* 460
Made cypress of her *o* flower, *In Mem. lxxxiv* 15
And *o* grove of Paraguay, *To Ulysses* 12
Orange (s) past Into deep *o* o'er the sea, *Mariana in the S.* 26
A scarf of *o* round the stony helm, *Princess, Pro.* 102
Orange-bloom Soldier-brother's bridal *o-b* *Ded. Poem Prin. Alice* 11
Orange-blossom In lands of palm, of *o-b*, *The Daisy* 3
Orange-flower (*See also* **Orange (adj.)**) When first she wears her *o-f*! *In Mem. xl* 4
Oration hung to hear The rapt *o* „ *lxxxvii* 32
Oration-like and rolling words *O-l*. *Princess v* 373
Orator Stood up and spake, an affluent *o*. „ *iv* 291
Glory of warrior, glory of *o*, *Wages* 1
Charm us, *O*, till the Lion look *Locksley H., Sixty* 112
Oratory in praise of her Grew *o*. *Gardener's D.* 57
Who, with mild heat of holy *o*, *Geraint and E.* 866
Orb (s) ambrosial *o's* Of rich fruit-bunches *Isabel* 36
So many minds did gird their *o's* with beams, *The Poet* 29
Should slowly round his *o*, *Eleänore* 91
saw The hollow *o* of moving Circumstance *Palace of Art* 255
She raised her piercing *o's*, *D. of F. Women* 171
Storm'd in *o's* of song, *Vision of Sin* 25
And here he stays upon a freezing *o* *Lucretius* 139
Than if the crowded *O* should cry *Lit. Squabbles* 15
Thine are these *o's* of light and shade; *In Mem., Pro.* 5
From *o* to *o*, from veil to veil.' „ *xxx* 28
This round of green, this *o* of flame, „ *xxxiv* 5
her dark *o* Touch'd with earth's light— *De Prof., Two G.* 9
Glance at the wheeling *O* of change, *To E. Fitzgerald* 3
Orb (verb) That the whole mind might *o* about— *Two Voices* 138
o's Between the Northern and the Southern morn.' *Princess v* 422
And *o* into the perfect star We saw not, *In Mem. xxiv* 15
Orb'd (*See also* **Full-orb'd**) remain *O* in your isolation: *Princess vi* 169
Orbit this *o* of the memory folds For ever *Gardener's D.* 74
The Sun will run his *o*, *Love and Duty* 22
Sway'd to her from their *o's* as they moved, *Princess vii* 326
circuits of thine *o* round A higher height, *In Mem. lxiii* 11
In azure *o's* heavenly-wise; „ *lxxxvii* 38
from her household *o* draws the child *To Prin. Beatrice* 7
Orchard (adj.) Two lovers whispering by an *o* wall; *Circumstance* 4
birds Begin to warble yonder in the budding *o* trees! *The Flight* 61
Orchard (s) on a slope of *o*, Francis laid A damask napkin *Audley Court* 20
a stream That flash'd across her *o* *Holy Grail* 593
I whipt him for robbing an *o* once *Rizpah* 25
Orchard-lawns happy fair with *o-l* And bowery hollows *M. d'Arthur* 262
happy, fair with *o-l* And bowery hollows *Pass. of Arthur* 430
Orchis Bring *o*, bring the foxglove spire, *In Mem. lxxxiii* 9
Ordain'd diamond jousts, Which Arthur had *o*, *Lancelot and E.* 32
Ordeal faded love, Or *o* by kindness; *Aylmer's Field* 561
Order (arrangement, etc.) fluted vase, and brazen urn In *o*, *Arabian Nights* 61
all things in *o* stored, *Palace of Art* 87
'Tis hard to settle *o* once again. *Lotos-Eaters, C. S.* 82
old *o* changeth, yielding place to new, *M. d'Arthur* 240
That keeps us all in *o* more or less— *Walk. to the Mail* 23
sitting well in *o* smite The sounding furrows; *Ulysses* 58
Eye, to which all *o* festers, *Locksley Hall* 133
The poplars, in long *o* due, *Amphion* 37
What for *o* or degree? *Vision of Sin* 86
But till this cosmic *o* everywhere *Lucretius* 250
Sweet *o* lived again with other laws: *Princess vii* 19
Large elements in *o* brought, *In Mem. cxii* 13
Order (fraternity) I beheld From eye to eye thro' all their *O* *Com. of Arthur* 270
And all this *O* of thy Table Round „ 474
ye know this *O* lives to crush All wrongers *Gareth and L.* 625
Of that great *O* of the Table Round, *Marr. of Geraint* 3
move To music with thine *O* and the King. *Balin and Balan* 77
Then Balan added to their *O* lived „ 91
move In music with his *O*, and the King. „ 212
to show His loathing of our *O* and the Queen. „ 551
hearts of all this *O* in mine hand— *Merlin and V.* 56
marshall'd *O* of their Table Round, *Lancelot and E.* 1332
A sign to maim this *O* which I made. *Holy Grail* 297
Rejoicing in that *O* which he made.' „ 327
And a lean *O*—scarce return'd a tithe— „ 894
collar of some *O*, which our King Hath newly founded, *Last Tournament* 741
Claspt it, and cried 'Thine *O*, O my Queen!' „ 750
In that fair *O* of my Table Round, *Guinevere* 463
old *o* changeth, yielding place to new, *Pass. of Arthur* 408
This *o* of Her Human Star, *Freedom* 23
Order (command) King gave *o* to let blow His horns *Marr. of Geraint* 152
Give ye the slave mine *o* to be bound, *Pelleas and E.* 270
Order (verb) She will *o* all things duly, *L. of Burleigh* 39
Order'd (*See also* **Careless-order'd, Horder'd**) And *o* words asunder fly. *Day-Dm., Pro.* 20
Parks and *o* gardens great, *L. of Burleigh* 30
As all were *o*, ages since. *Day Dm., Sleep. P.* 54
having *o* all Almost as neat and close *Enoch Arden* 177
Days *o* in a wealthy peace, *In Mem. xlvi* 11
Ordering you, that have the *o* of her fleet, *The Fleet* 16
Ordinance 'God's *o* Of Death is blown in every wind;' *To J. S.* 45
Or pass beyond the goal of *o* *Tithonus* 30
voice Of Ida sounded, issuing *o*: *Princess vi* 373
and everywhere At Arthur's *o*, *Gareth and L.* 308
Ore a rich Throne of the massive *o*, *Arabian Nights* 146
Jewel or shell, or starry *o*, *Eleänore* 20
Or labour'd mine undrainable of *o*. *Œnone* 115
to lift the hidden *o* That glimpses, *D. of F. Women* 274
and show That life is not as idle *o*, *In Mem. cxviii* 20
Oread whatever *O* haunt The knolls of Ida, *Œnone* 74
here an *O*, how the sun delights To glance *Lucretius* 188
And I see my *O* coming down, *Maud I xvi* 8
Organ With this old soul in *o's* new? *Two Voices* 393
Hearing the holy *o* rolling waves Of sound *D. of F. Women* 191
While the great *o* almost burst his pipes, *Princess ii* 474
The storm their high-built *o's* make, *In Mem. lxxxvii* 6
psalm by a mighty master and peal'd from an *o*,—roll *The Wreck* 53
Organ-harmony A rolling *o-h* Swells up, *Sir Galahad* 75
Organism Makes noble thro' the sensuous *o* *Princess ii* 87
Organ-pipes Near gilded *o-p*, her hair *Palace of Art* 98
Organ-voice God-gifted *o-v* of England, *Milton* 3
Orgies Shall hold their *o* at your tomb. *You might have won* 12
The mulberry-faced Dictator's *o* *Lucretius* 54

Oriana My heart is wasted with my woe, *O.* (repeat) *Oriana* 2, 4, 7, 9, 11, 13, 16, 18, 20, 22, 25, 27, 29, 31, 34, 36, 38, 40, 43, 45, 47, 49, 52, 54, 56, 58, 61, 63, 65, 67, 70, 72, 74, 76, 79, 81, 83, 85, 88, 90, 92, 94, 97, 99
Oriel She sat betwixt the shining *O's*, *Palace of Art* 159
thro' the topmost *O's'* coloured flame „ 161
The beams, that thro' the *O* shine, *Day-Dm., Sleep. P.* 34
All in an *o* on the summer side, *Lancelot and E.* 1177
moon Thro' the tall *o* on the rolling sea. *Holy Grail* 831
Oriel-embowering Brake from the vast *o-e* vine *Lancelot and E.* 1198
Orient (adj.) (*See also* **Re-orient**) Tall *o* shrubs, and obelisks *Arabian Nights* 107
but robed in soften'd light Of *o* state. *Ode to Memory* 11
and earliest shoots Of *o* green, „ 18
Sunn'd by those *o* skies; *The Poet* 42
Laborious *o* ivory sphere in sphere, *Princess, Pro.* 20
To where in yonder *o* star *In Mem. lxxxvi* 15
Orient (s) Doth the low-tongued *O* Wander from the side of the morn, *Adeline* 51
Deep in yonder shining *O*, *Locksley Hall* 154
Came furrowing all the *o* into gold. *Princess iii* 18
and her throne In our vast *O*, *To the Queen ii* 31
There is a custom in the *O*, friends— *Lover's Tale iv* 230
Oriental Till silent in her *o* haven. *Enoch Arden* 537
flattering thy childish thought The *o* fairy brought, *Eleänore* 14
shower'd His *o* gifts on everyone And most on Edith: *Aylmer's Field* 214
Your *O* Eden-isles, *To Ulysses* 38
Orion great *O* sloping slowly to the West. *Locksley Hall* 8
shining daffodil dead, and *O* low in his grave. *Maud I iii* 14
Over *O's* grave low down in the west, „ *III vi* 8
Orkney Morganore, And Lot of *O.* *Com. of Arthur* 116
Lot's wife, the Queen of *O*, (repeat) „ 190, 245
Ornament Found lying with his urns and *o's*, *Aylmer's Field* 4
And darkling felt the sculptured *o* *Merlin and V.* 734
In hanging robe or vacant *o*, *Guinevere* 506
read Some wonder at our chamber *o's*. *Columbus* 2
Institute, Rich in symbol, in *o*, *On Jub. Q. Victoria* 47
Orphan (adj.) His wife, an unknown artist's *o* child— *Sea Dreams* 2
Made *o* by a winter shipwreck, *Enoch Arden* 15
there the tender *o* hands Felt at my heart, *Princess v* 435
'None wrought, but suffer'd much, an *o* maid! *Merlin and V.* 71
When her *o* wail came borne in the shriek *The Wreck* 87
Orphan (s) Late-left an *o* of the squire, *Miller's D.* 34
And for this *o*, I am come to you: *Dora* 64
I was left a trampled *o*, *Locksley Hall* 156
kill yourself And make them *o's* quite?' *Enoch Arden* 395
Here is the cot of our *o*, *In the Child. Hosp.* 28
O we poor *o's* of nothing— *Despair* 33
an *o* with half a shire of estate,— *Charity* 13
Orphan-boy Oh! teach the *o-b* to read, *L. C. V. de Vere* 69
Orphan'd So were we born, so *o.* *Lover's Tale i* 218
Orphan-girl Or teach the *o-g* to sew, *L. C. V. de Vere* 70
O'Roon (Danny) *See* **Danny, Danny O'Roon**
Orthodox Our *o* coroner doubtless will find it a felo-de-se, *Despair* 115
Heresy to the heretic, and religion to the *o*, *Akbar's D., Inscrip.* 8
Orthodoxy Thy elect have no dealings with either heresy or *o*; „ 7
O'Shea (Shamus) *See* **Shamus, Shamus O'Shea**
Osier ocean-spoil In ocean-smelling *o*, *Enoch Arden* 94
Ostler 'Wrinkled *o*, grim and thin! *Vision of Sin* 63
Ostleress A plump-arm'd *O* and a stable wench *Princess i* 226
'Ot (hot) 'Summat to drink—sa' *'o*?' *North. Cobbler* 5
Other (*See also* **Tother**) And little *o* care hath she, *L. of Shalott ii* 8
There is no *o* thing express'd *Two Voices* 248
'Who forged that *o* influence, „ 283
He hath no *o* life above. *D. of the O. Year* 12
Among new men, strange faces, *o* minds.' *M. d'Arthur* 238
and with what *o* eyes I used to watch— *Tithonus* 51
'Some *o* race of Averills'—prov'n or no, *Aylmer's Field* 54
became in *o* fields A mockery to the yeomen „ 496

Other (*continued*) *o* frowns than those That knit themselves *Aylmer's Field* 723
last, my *o* heart, And almost my half-self, *Princess i* 55
And thus (what *o* way was left) I came.' „ *ii* 217
Sweet order lived again with *o* laws: „ *vii* 19
On the *o* side Hortensia spoke against the tax; „ 126
Follow'd by the brave of *o* lands, *Ode on Well.* 194
One writes, that '*O* friends remain,' *In Mem. vi* 1
But there are *o* griefs within, „ *xx* 11
Nor *o* thought her mind admits „ *xxxii* 2
She enters *o* realms of love; „ *xl* 12
With larger *o* eyes than ours, „ *li* 15
the while His *o* passion wholly dies, „ *lxii* 10
To the *o* shore, involved in thee, „ *lxxxiv* 40
O sacred essence, *o* form, „ *lxxxv* 35
For *o* friends that once I met; „ 58
Behold their brides in *o* hands; „ *xc* 14
Nor landmark breathes of *o* days, „ *civ* 11
And silent under *o* snows: „ *cv* 6
But I was *born* to *o* things. „ *cxx* 12
Had one fair daughter, and none *o* child; *Com. of Arthur* 2
Lets down his *o* leg, and stretching, *Gareth and L.* 1186
Three *o* horsemen waiting, wholly arm'd, *Geraint and E.* 121
It seems another voice in *o* groves; *Balin and Balan* 215
And when we halted at that *o* well, *Merlin and V.* 280
Why will ye never ask some *o* boon? „ 375
That *o* fame, To one at least, „ 505
Moaning and calling out of *o* lands, „ 962
She might have made this and that *o* world *Lancelot and E.* 873
A mocking fire: 'what *o* fire than he, *Holy Grail* 670
'Or hast thou *o* griefs? *Pelleas and E.* 599
Among new men, strange faces, *o* minds.' *Pass. of Arthur* 406
And, like all *o* friends i' the world, *Lover's Tale i* 108
fall asleep Into delicious dreams, our *o* life, „ 162
On the *o* side Is scoop'd a cavern „ 516
And saw the motion of all *o* things; „ 574
had never seen it once. His *o* father you! „ *iv* 174
For he thought—there were *o* lads— *First Quarrel* 38
Fresh from the surgery-schools of France and of *o* lands— *In the Child. Hosp.* 3
For every *o* cause is less than mine. *Sir J. Oldcastle* 188
And his voice was low as from *o* worlds, *V. of Maeldune* 117
Was he noblier-fashion'd than *o* men? *Dead Prophet* 51
And there the light of *o* life, which lives *The Ring* 295
O songs for *o* worlds! *Parnassus* 19
Ottoman Emperor, *O*, which shall win: *To F. D. Maurice* 32
Ought Sweet is it to have done the thing one *o*, *Princess v* 67
I cannot love thee as I *o*, *In Mem. lii* 1
Ould (old) yer Honour's the thrue *o* blood *Tomorrow* 5
Thin Molly's *o* mother, yer Honour, „ 19
best he could give at *o* Donovan's wake— „ 42
Thim *o* blind nagers in Agypt, „ 69
Danny O'Roon wid his *o* woman, Molly Magee. „ 88
'Ouse (house) theer's a craw to pluck wi' tha, Sam: yon's parson's *'o*— *N. Farmer, N. S.* 5
Tis'n them as 'as munny as breäks into *'o's* an' steäls, „ 45
sweär'd as I'd breäk ivry stick O' furnitur 'ere i' the *'o*, *North. Cobbler* 36
an' the 'ole *'o* hupside down. „ 42
'When theer's naw 'eäd to a *'O* *Village Wife* 17
or the gells 'ull goä to the *'O*, „ 64
'e wur burn an' bred i' the *'o*, *Spinster's S's.* 69
An' the stink o' 'is pipe i' the *'o*, „ 100
a roäbin' the *'o* like a Queeän, „ 106
Straänge an' owd-farran'd the *'o*, *Owd Roä* 21
An' theere i' the *'o* one night— „ 27
Theere, when the *'o* wur a house, „ 29
an' dussn't not sleeäp i' the *'o*, „ 37
'Ouse-keeper (housekeeper) *'O-k* sent tha my lass, *Village Wife* 1
Oust *o* the madness from your brain. *Locksley H., Sixty* 241
Ousted From mine own earldom foully *o* me; *Marr. of Geraint* 459
Outbreak nor, in hours Of civil *o*, *Tiresias* 68
Outburn'd lit Lamps which *o* Canopus. *D. of F. Women* 146
Outbuzz'd *o* me so That even our prudent king, *Columbus* 121

Outcry still she made her *o* for the ring; *The Ring* 403
Outdacious (audacious) 'e were that *o* at 'oäm, *Village Wife* 75
Out-door eyes, An *o-d* sign of all *Holy Grail* 704
Outer With motions of the *o* sea: *Eleänore* 113
All the inner, all the *o* world of pain *If I were loved* 5
on her threshold lie Howling in *o* darkness. *To——, With Pal. of Art* 16
Where, three times slipping from the *o* edge, *The Epic* 11
And I from out the boundless *o* deep *Sea Dreams* 88
And one would pierce an *o* ring, *In Mem. lxxxvii* 27
hold them *o* fiends, Who leap at thee to tear thee; *Balin and Balan* 141
Made dull his inner, keen his *o* eye *Last Tournament* 366
feet Thro' the long gallery from the *o* doors *Guinevere* 413
chafed breakers of the *o* sea Sank powerless, *Lover's Tale i* 8
For when the *o* lights are darken'd thus, „ 35
And mellow'd echoes of the *o* world— „ 208
From the *o* day, Betwixt the close-set ivies „ *ii* 171
Outfloweth the glimmering water *o*: *Leonine Eleg.* 9
Outland Sir Valence wedded with an *o* dame: *Merlin and V.* 714
Outlast lays that will *o* thy Deity? *Lucretius* 72
Outlearn to *o* the filthy friar. *Sir J. Oldcastle* 118
Outlet clear-stemm'd platans guard The *o*, *Arabian Nights* 24
Outline The lucid *o* forming round thee; *Tithonus* 53
Is given in *o* and no more. *In Mem. v* 12
Outlive and the foe may *o* us at last— *Def. of Lucknow* 52
Outliving For life *o* heats of youth, *In Mem. liii* 10
Outpour'd *o* Their myriad horns of plenty *Ode Inter. Exhib.* 5
Outraged An *o* maiden sprang into the hall *Holy Grail* 208
Outrageous And pelted with *o* epithets, *Aylmer's Field* 286
Outram (Sir James) *O* and Havelock breaking their way *Def. of Lucknow* 96
Outran *o* The hearer in its fiery course; *In Mem. cix* 7
Outredden *o* All voluptuous garden-roses. *Ode on Well.* 207
Outside you leave 'em *o* on the bed— *In the Child. Hosp.* 56
Outstript He still *o* me in the race; *In Mem. xlii* 2
Out-tore another wild earthquake *o-t* *Def. of Lucknow* 61
Outward (adj.) Scarce *o* signs of joy arise, *Supp. Confessions* 49
Know I not Death? the *o* signs? *Two Voices* 270
Became an *o* breathing type, *Miller's D.* 226
Perplext his *o* purpose, till an hour, *Gareth and L.* 175
My *o* circling air wherewith I breathe, *Lover's Tale i* 167
even into my inmost heart As to my *o* hearing: „ 429
More to the inward than the *o* ear, „ 721
that only doats On *o* beauty, *The Ring* 164
Outward (adv.) a knight would pass *O*, or inward to the hall: *Gareth and L.* 311
Outward (s) from the *o* to the inward brought. *Eleänore* 4
Outwelleth The slumbrous wave *o*, *Claribel* 18
Outworks Thro' all the *o* of suspicious pride; *Isabel* 24
Outworn Of forms *o*, but not to me *o*, *Lover's Tale i* 797
till this *o* earth be dead as yon dead world the moon? *Locksley H., Sixty* 174
Ouzel The mellow *o* fluted in the elm; *Gardener's D.* 94
Oval the nobler hearts In that vast *O* *St. Telemachus* 73
Ovation To rain an April of *o* *Princess vi* 66
Over-acting her brain broke With *o-a*, *Sisters (E. and E.)* 236
Overawe Built that new fort to *o* my friends. *Marr. of Geraint* 460
Overawed O fall'n nobility, that, *o*, *Third of Feb.* 35
Am I to be *o* By what I cannot but know *Maud II ii* 40
Overbalancing strike him, *o* his bulk, *Last Tournament* 460
Overbear *o's* the bark, And him that helms it, *Lancelot and E.* 485
Overblame of overpraise and *o* We choose the last. *Merlin and V.* 90
Overblown *O* with murmurs harsh, *Ode to Memory* 99
Overboard *o* one stormy night He cast his body, *The Voyage* 79
Over-bold island princes *o-b* Have eat our substance, *Lotos-Eaters, C. S.* 75
And again seem'd *o*; *Maud I xiv* 24
'Old, and *o-b* in brag! *Gareth and L.* 1107
Overbore contrasting brightness, *o* Her fancy *Marr. of Geraint* 801
charm Of nature in her *o* their own: *Merlin and V.* 596
they *o* Sir Lancelot and his charger, *Lancelot and E.* 486
Overborne *o* by all his bearded lords *Princess v* 356
Vivien, deeming Merlin *o* By instance, *Merlin and V.* 800
and hath *o* Five knights at once, *Holy Grail* 302
Till *o* by one, he learns—and ye, „ 305
Overbower'd gliding thro' the branches *o* The naked Three, *Death of Œnone* 6
Over-bright Eyes not down-dropt nor *o-b*, *Isabel* 1
Overbrow'd high-arching *o* the hearth. *Gareth and L.* 408
Overcame Did more, and underwent, and *o*, *Godiva* 10
in twelve great battles *o* The heathen hordes, *Com. of Arthur* 518
and then Me too the black-wing'd Azrael *o*, *Akbar's Dream* 186
Overcome Bred will in me to *o* it or fall. *Princess v* 351
who will come to all I am And *o* it; *Lancelot and E.* 449
but you, you will help me to *o* it, *Parnassus* 5
Overdo almost *o* the deeds Of Lancelot; *Lancelot and E.* 469
Overdone Heart-weary and *o*! *The Dreamer* 18
Overdrest *See* **A-Dallackt.**
Overfine 'ye are *o* To mar stout knaves *Gareth and L.* 732
Overfineness From *o-f* not intelligible *Merlin and V.* 796
Overflow (s) Rain'd thro' my sight its *o*. *Two Voices* 45
Overflow (verb) all the markets *o*. *Locksley Hall* 101
Hears and not hears, and lets it *o*. *Enoch Arden* 209
Somewhile the one must *o* the other; *Lover's Tale i* 501
Overflow'd dissolving sand To watch them *o*, *Enoch Arden* 20
Overflowing the lovely freight Of *o* blooms, *Ode to Memory* 17
o revenue Wherewith to embellish state, *Œnone* 112
Over-full and *o-f* Of sweetness, *Lover's Tale i* 271
Overgrowing brambles mixt And *o* them, *Pelleas and E.* 423
Overhead Or when the moon was *o*, *L. of Shalott ii* 33
Those banners of twelve battles *o* *Balin and Balan* 88
arrow whizz'd to the right, one to the left, One *o*; „ 420
moon Struck from an open grating *o* *Lover's Tale iv* 60
watching *o* The aërial poplar wave, *Sisters (E. and E.)* 83
beheld A blood-red awning waver *o*, *St. Telemachus* 52
Overheated Cat thro' that mirage of *o* language *Locksley H., Sixty* 113
Over-jealous has he not forgiven me yet, his *o-j* bride, *Happy* 6
Over-labour'd Some *o-l*, some by their own hands,— *Columbus* 178
Overlaid *o* With narrow moon-lit slips *Œnone* 217
Overlive *O* it—lower yet—be happy! *Locksley Hall* 97
Overlived For man has *o* his day And, *Ancient Sage* 150
Overlook *O* a space of flowers, *L. of Shalott i* 16
And *o* the chace; *Talking Oak* 94
And *o* the lea, „ 198
in the distance *o's* the sandy tracts, *Locksley Hall* 5
Over-mellow full-juiced apple, waxing *o-m*, *Lotos-Eaters, C. S.* 33
Overmuch Nor asking *o* and taking less, *Enoch Arden* 252
I count it crime To mourn for any *o*; *In Mem. lxxxv* 62
Overnight Laid on her table *o*, was gone; *The Ring* 277
Overpay 'My Lord, you *o* me fifty-fold.' *Geraint and E.* 220
Overpower'd *o* quite, I cannot veil, or droop *Eleänore* 86
and had yielded her will To the master, as *o*, *Dead Prophet* 64
Overpraise of *o* and overblame We choose the last. *Merlin and V.* 90
Our noble Arthur, him Ye scarce can *o*, „ 92
Overprize King So prizes—*o's*—gentleness. *Balin and Balan* 184
Overquick *o* To crop his own sweet rose *Merlin and V.* 724
'*O* art thou To catch a loathly plume fall'n „ 726
Overrode boy Paused not, but *o* him, *Pelleas and E.* 545
Over-roll *o-r* Him and his gold; *Columbus* 139
Overseas sick of home went *o* for change. *Walk. to the Mail* 24
late From *o* in Brittany return'd, *Last Tournament* 175
But then what folly had sent him *o* „ 394
And fly to my strong castle *o*: *Guinevere* 113
Overset But thou, while kingdoms *o*, *Talking Oak* 257
Overshadow'd All *o* by the foolish dream, *Marr. of Geraint* 675
Over-smoothness some self-conceit, Or *o-s*: *Edwin Morris* 75
Overstep by that larger light, And *o* them, *Akbar's Dream* 100
Overstrain'd or a mood Of *o* affection, *Merlin and V.* 522
may merit well Your term of *o*. „ 535
Overstream'd And *o* and silvery-streak'd *The Islet* 20
Overtake *o's* Far thought with music *Two Voices* 437
Overtaken she stay'd, and *o* spoke. *Gareth and L.* 764
Flying, but, *o*, died the death Themselves *Geraint and E.* 177
Overtalk'd Merlin, *o* and overworn, Had yielded, *Merlin and V.* 965
Overtax'd And loathed to see them *o*; *Godiva* 9
Overthrew down we swept and charged and *o*. *Ode on Well.* 130
Gareth *o* him, lighted, drew, There met him drawn, and *o* him again, *Gareth and L.* 1121
And *o* the next that follow'd him, *Geraint and E.* 465
King, duke, earl, Count, baron—whom he smote, he *o*. *Lancelot and E.* 465

Overthrew (*continued*) *o* So many knights that all the people cried, *Holy Grail* 334
Pelleas *o* them as they dash'd Against him *Pelleas and E.* 221
down they went, And Pelleas *o* them „ 230
by those he *o* Be bounden straight, „ 235
Pelleas *o* them, one to three; „ 287
Overthrow (s) quick! by *o* Of these or those, *Princess v* 316
Overthrow (verb) Lancelot whom he trusts to *o*, *Gareth and L.* 620
hard by here is one will *o* And slay thee: „ 896
I know That I shall *o* him.' „ 949
o My proud self, and my purpose three years old, *Geraint and E.* 848
Whether me likewise ye can *o*.' *Balin and Balan* 40
Overthrower And *o* from being overthrown. *Gareth and L.* 1263
Overthrowing (part.) challenging And *o* every knight *Balin and Balan* 13
Overthrowing (s) With *o's*, and with cries, *In Mem. cxiii* 19
By *o* me you threw me higher. *Geraint and E.* 792
Overthrown And like a warrior *o*; *Two Voices* 150
And *o* was Gorloïs and slain. *Com. of Arthur* 197
Thou hast *o* and slain thy master— *Gareth and L.* 769
Or some device, hast foully *o*), „ 998
Hath *o* thy brother, and hath his arms.' „ 1037
Hast *o* thro' mere unhappiness), „ 1059
'Shamed and *o*, And tumbled back „ 1227
To call him shamed, who is but *o*? „ 1260
And overthrower from being *o*. „ 1263
And makest merry when *o*. „ 1270
I have never yet been *o*, And thou hast *o* me, *Marr. of Geraint* 588
Or I or he have easily *o*.' *Balin and Balan* 36
strong hand, which had *o* Her minion-knights, *Pelleas and E.* 234
'And thou hast *o* him?' 'Ay, my Queen.' „ 594
In twelve great battles ruining *o*. *Guinevere* 432
Overtoil'd *o* By that day's grief and travel, *Geraint and E.* 376
Overtopt The battlement *o* with ivytods, *Balin and Balan* 335
Over-tragic Deem this *o-t* drama's closing curtain is the pall! *Locksley H., Sixty* 62
Overtrailed Half *o* with a wanton weed, *Lover's Tale i* 525
Overtrue 'O ay,' said Vivien, '*o* a tale. *Merlin and V.* 720
Overtrust wink no more in slothful *o*. *Ode on Well.* 170
Overturn Behold me *o* and trample on him. *Geraint and E.* 843
Overturn'd (*See also* **Skelpt**) schemed and wrought Until I *o* him; „ 830
Over-vaulted That *o-v* grateful gloom, *Palace of Art* 54
Overwhelm'd shook And almost *o* her, *Enoch Arden* 530
Over-wise has written: she never was *o-w*, (repeat) *Grandmother* 3, 105
Overworn But all he was is *o*.' *In Mem. i* 16
Merlin, overtalk'd and *o*, Had yielded, *Merlin and V.* 965
Overwrought that his brain is *o*: *Locksley Hall* 53
being so *o*, Suddenly strike on a sharper sense *Maud II ii* 62
Owä (owe) Fur I *o's* owd Roäver moor *Owd Roä* 4
Owäd (owed) nor I iver *o* mottal man. „ 4
Owd (old) A mowt 'a taäen *o* Joänes, *N. Farmer, O. S.* 49
Doctor's a 'toättler, lass, an a's hallus i' the *o* taäle; „ 66
I could fettle and clump *o* booöts *North. Cobbler* 13
wheer Sally's *o* stockin' wur 'id, „ 31
an' draggle taäil'd in an *o* turn gown, „ 41
I liked the *o* Squire an' 'is gells *Village Wife* 6
new Squire's coom'd wi' 'is taäil in 'is 'and, an' *o* Squire's gone. (repeat) „ 14, 121
'e'd gie fur a howry *o* book thutty pound an' moor, „ 45
An' 'e'd wrote an *o* book, his awn sen, „ 46
fur an *o* scratted stoän, „ 47
An' 'e bowt *o* money, es wouldn't goä, „ 49
But *o* Squire's laädy es long es she lived „ 53
moäst on 'is *o* big booöks fetch'd nigh to nowt at the saäle, „ 73
Siver the mou'ds rattled down upo' poor *o* Squire i' the wood, „ 95
I didn't not taäke it kindly ov *o* Miss Annie „ 109
I meäns fur to maäke 'is *o* aäge as 'appy as iver I can, *Owd Roä* 3
I owäs *o* Roäver moor nor I iver owäd mottal man. „ 4
afoor thou was gotten too *o*, „ 5
an' I thowt o' the good *o* times 'at was goan, „ 43
an' clemm'd *o* Roä by the 'eäd, „ 99
Sa I sticks like the ivin as long as I lives to the *o* chuch now, *Church-warden, etc.* 15
'Owd (hold) Fur I couldn't '*o* 'ands off gin, *North. Cobbler* 84
pockets as full o' my pippins as iver they'd '*o*, *Church-warden, etc.* 34
Owd-farran'd (old-fashioned) Straänge an' *o-f* the 'ouse, *Owd Roä* 21
Owe (*See also* **Owä**) we *o* you bitter thanks: *Princess iv* 531
I feel I shall *o* you a debt, *Maud I xix* 87
forget That I *o* this debt to you „ 90
O you me nothing for a life half-lost? *Geraint and E.* 318
ask your boon, for boon I *o* you thrice, *Merlin and V.* 306
To you and yours, and still would *o*. *To Marq. of Dufferin* 20
Let me *o* my life to thee. *Death of Œnone* 42
Owed (*See also* **Owäd**) Whole in ourselves and *o* to none. *Princess iv* 148
how dear a debt We *o* you, and are owing yet *To Marq. of Dufferin* 19
Owing and are *o* yet To you and yours, „ 19
Owl (*See also* **Eagle-owl, Glimmer-gowk, Howl**) The white *o* in the belfry sits. (repeat) *The Owl i* 7, 14
I drown'd the whoopings of the *o* *St. S. Stylites* 33
bats wheel'd, and *o's* whoop'd, *Princess, Con.* 110
An *o* whoopt: 'Hark the victor pealing there!' *Gareth and L.* 1318
A home of bats, in every tower an *o*. *Balin and Balan* 336
the *o's* Wailing had power upon her, *Lancelot and E.* 1000
thrice as blind as any noonday *o*, *Holy Grail* 866
and the *o's* are whooping at noon, *Despair* 89
O the night, When the *o's* are wailing! *Forlorn* 30
Owlby He'll niver swap *O* an' Scratby *Church-warden, etc.* 44
Owlet shrilly the *o* halloos; *Leonine Eleg.* 6
Owl-whoop *o-w* and dorhawk-whirr Awoke me not, *Lover's Tale ii* 116
Own (adj.) (*See also* **Oän**) to brush the dew From thine *o* lily, *Supp. Confessions* 85
till his *o* blood flows About his hoof. „ 155
I see his gray eyes twinkle yet At his *o* jest— *Miller's D.* 12
My *o* sweet Alice, we must die. „ 18
You'll kiss me, my *o* mother, and forgive me ere I go; *May Queen, N. Y's. E.* 34
Once thro' mine *o* doors Death did pass; *To J. S.* 19
And tho' mine *o* eyes fill with dew, „ 37
She loveth her *o* anguish deep „ 42
So spake he, clouded with his *o* conceit, *M. d'Arthur* 110
His *o* thought drove him, like a goad. „ 185
It may be, for her *o* dear sake but this, *Edwin Morris* 141
But in these latter springs I saw Your *o* Olivia blow, *Talking Oak* 76
This is my son, mine *o* Telemachus, *Ulysses* 33
Upon my proper patch of soil To grow my *o* plantation. *Amphion* 100
He loves me for my *o* true worth, *Lady Clare* 11
I buried her like my *o* sweet child, „ 27
He not for his *o* self caring but her, *Enoch Arden* 165
while Annie seem'd to hear Her *o* death-scaffold rising, „ 175
'Take your *o* time, Annie, take your *o* time.' „ 466
Her *o* son Was silent, tho' he often look'd his wish; „ 481
And his *o* children tall and beautiful, „ 762
And following our *o* shadows thrice as long *The Brook* 166
bearing hardly more Than his *o* shadow in a sickly sun. *Aylmer's Field* 30
Somewhere beneath his *o* low range of roofs, „ 47
Him, glaring, by his *o* stale devil spurr'd, „ 290
under his *o* lintel stood Storming with lifted hands, „ 331
would go, Labour for his *o* Edith, and return „ 420
Burst his *o* wyvern on the seal, and read „ 516
went Hating his *o* lean heart and miserable „ 526
Now chafing at his *o* great self defied, „ 537
left Their *o* gray tower, or plain-faced tabernacle, „ 618
And worshipt their *o* darkness in the Highest? „ 643
Crown thyself, worm, and worship thine *o* lusts!— „ 650
darkening thine own To thine *o* likeness; „ 674
Is not our *o* child on the narrow way, „ 743
earth Lightens from her *o* central Hell— „ 761
Who, thro' their *o* desire accomplish'd, bring Their *o* gray hairs with sorrow to the grave— „ 776
but sat Ignorant, devising their *o* daughter's death! „ 783
and made Their *o* traditions God, and slew the Lord, „ 795
Then her *o* people bore along the nave Her pendent hands, „ 812
Fought with what seem'd my *o* uncharity; *Sea Dreams* 73
Nor ever cared to better his *o* kind, „ 201
His *o* forefathers' arms and armour hung. *Princess, Pro.* 24

Own (adj.) (*continued*) a lady, one that arm'd Her *o* fair head, *Princess Pro.* 33
‘We scarcely thought in our *o* hall to hear ,, *ii* 53
what follows? war; Your *o* work marr'd: ,, 230
true she errs, But in her *o* grand way: ,, *iii* 108
That we might see our *o* work out, ,, 270
‘Know you no song of your *o* land,’ she said, ,, *iv* 84
What time I watch'd the swallow winging south From mine *o* land, ,, 90
And partly conscious of my *o* deserts, ,, 305
You stood in your *o* light and darken'd mine. ,, 314
Our *o* detention, why, the causes weigh'd, ,, *v* 215
Or by denial flush her babbling wells With her *o* people's life: ,, 335
And Knowledge in our *o* land make her free, ,, 419
he That loved me closer than his *o* right eye, ,, 531
With their *o* blows they hurt themselves, ,, *vi* 49
all dabbled with the blood Of his *o* son, ,, 105
O let me have him with my brethren here In our *o* palace: ,, 124
never in your *o* arms To hold your own, ,, 177
I go to mine *o* land For ever: ,, 216
Now had you got a friend of your *o* age, ,, 251
to wait upon him, Like mine *o* brother. ,, 299
And in their *o* clear element, they moved. ,, *vii* 28
She needs must wed him for her *o* good name; ,, 74
‘Dear, but let us type them now In our *o* lives, ,, 300
I seem A mockery to my *o* self. ,, 337
Has given our Prince his *o* imperial Flower, *W. to Marie Alex.* 4
Yet thine *o* land has bow'd to Tartar hordes ,, 23
And he died, and I could not weep—my *o* time seem'd so near. *Grandmother* 72
Patter she goes, my *o* little Annie, an Annie like you: ,, 78
My *o* dim life should teach me this, *In Mem. xxxiv* 1
When thou should'st link thy life with one Of mine *o* house, ,, *lxxxiv* 12
His *o* vast shadow glory-crown'd; ,, *xcvii* 3
But mine *o* phantom chanting hymns? ,, *cviii* 10
heart of the citizen hissing in war on his *o* hearthstone? *Maud I i* 24
But arose, and all by myself in my *o* dark garden ground, ,, *iii* 10
finer politic sense To mask, tho' but in his *o* behoof, ,, *vi* 48
How prettily for his *o* sweet sake ,, 51
For often a man's *o* angry pride Is cap and bells for a fool. ,, 62
And my *o* sad name in corners cried, ,, 72
Down too, down at your *o* fireside, ,, *x* 50
Maud's *o* little oak-room ,, *xiv* 9
looks Upon Maud's *o* garden-gate: ,, 16
Running down to my *o* dark wood; ,, 30
My *o* heart's heart, my ownest own, farewell; ,, *xviii* 74
For I know her *o* rose-garden, ,, *xx* 41
Come out to your *o* true lover, ,, 46
and render All homage to his *o* darling, ,, 49
My *o* dove with the tender eye? ,, *II iv* 46
praying To his *o* great self, as I guess; ,, *v* 33
Her *o* brood lost or dead, lent her fierce teat *Com. of Arthur* 28
nor make myself in mine *o* realm Victor and lord. ,, 89
for each But sought to rule for his *o* self and hand, ,, 219
Bound them by so strait vows to his *o* self, ,, 262
But thou art closer to this noble prince, Being his *o* dear sister;’ ,, 315
Albeit in mine *o* heart I knew him King, *Gareth and L.* 123
Her *o* true Gareth was too princely-proud ,, 161
swearing he had glamour enow In his *o* blood, ,, 210
‘Old Master, reverence thine *o* beard That looks as white ,, 280
With thine *o* hand thou slewest my dear lord, ,, 352
see thou to it That thine *o* fineness, Lancelot, ,, 476
holds her stay'd In her *o* castle, ,, 616
often with her *o* white hands Array'd and deck'd her, as the loveliest, Next after her *o* self, *Marr. of Geraint* 16
and they past to their *o* land; ,, 45
Low of her *o* heart piteously she said: ,, 85
Frown and we smile, the lords of our *o* hands; ,, 354
then have I sworn From his *o* lips to have it— ,, 409
Queen Sent her *o* maiden to demand the name, ,, 411
Raised my *o* town against me in the night ,, 457

Own (adj.) (*continued*) From mine *o* earldom foully ousted me; *Marr. of Geraint* 459
(Who hearing her *o* name had stol'n away) ,, 507
but lay Contemplating her *o* unworthiness; ,, 533
And softly to her *o* sweet heart she said: ,, 618
made comparison Of that and these to her *o* faded self ,, 652
So sadly lost on that unhappy night; Your *o* good gift!’ ,, 690
Or whether some false sense in her *o* self ,, 800
child shall wear your costly gift Beside your *o* warm hearth, ,, 820
to her *o* bright face Accuse her of the least immodesty: *Geraint and E.* 110
That she *could* speak whom his *o* ear had heard ,, 113
I call mine *o* self wild, But keep a touch of sweet civility ,, 311
At this the tender sound of his *o* voice ,, 348
And their *o* Earl, and their *o* souls, and her. ,, 577
And found his *o* dear bride propping his head, ,, 584
And said to his *o* heart, ‘She weeps for me:’ ,, 587
And say to his *o* heart, ‘She weeps for me.’ ,, 590
Not, tho' mine *o* ears heard you yestermorn— ,, 740
in the King's *o* ear Speak what has chanced; ,, 808
with your *o* true eyes Beheld the man you loved ,, 846
ye pray'd me for my leave To move to your *o* land, ,, 889
came The King's *o* leech to look into his hurt; ,, 923
and they past to their *o* land. ,, 955
ask'd To bear her *o* crown-royal upon shield, *Balin and Balan* 200
Our noble King will send thee his *o* leech— ,, 274
Who, sitting in thine *o* hall, canst endure ,, 378
Had wander'd from her *o* King's golden head, ,, 513
Pure as our *o* true Mother is our Queen.’ ,, 617
Be thine the balm of pity, O Heaven's *o* white Earth-angel, *Merlin and V.* 80
at times Would flatter his *o* wish in age for love, ,, 185
In mine *o* lady palms I cull'd the spring ,, 273
brought Her *o* claw back, and wounded her *o* heart. ,, 500
His kinsman travelling on his *o* affair ,, 717
To crop his *o* sweet rose before the hour? ,, 725
Then Merlin to his *o* heart, loathing, said: ,, 790
Who wouldst against thine *o* eye-witness fain ,, 793
Seethed like the kid in its *o* mother's milk! ,, 869
What should be granted which your *o* gross heart ,, 916
All the devices blazon'd on the shield In their *o* tinct, *Lancelot and E.* 10
clave Like its *o* mists to all the mountain side: ,, 38
When its *o* voice clings to each blade of grass, ,, 107
I Before a King who honours his *o* word, ,, 144
For if his *o* knight cast him down, he laughs ,, 313
Low to her *o* heart said the lily maid, ,, 319
So kiss'd her, and Sir Lancelot his *o* hand, ,, 389
Dearer to true young hearts than their *o* praise, ,, 419
and a spear Prick'd sharply his *o* cuirass, ,, 489
his *o* kin—Ill news, my Queen, ,, 597
it will be sweet to have it From your *o* hand; ,, 694
And with mine *o* hand give his diamond to him, ,, 760
His *o* far blood, which dwelt at Camelot; ,, 803
she should ask some goodly gift of him For her *o* self or hers; ,, 913
and Prince and Lord am I In mine *o* land, ,, 917
and such a tongue To blare its *o* interpretation— ,, 943
Most common: yea, I know it of mine *o* self: And you yourself will smile at your *o* self Hereafter, ,, 950
only the case, Her *o* poor work, her empty labour, left. ,, 991
There surely I shall speak for mine *o* self, ,, 1125
these, as I trust That you trust me in your *o* nobleness, ,, 1195
In mine *o* realm beyond the narrow seas, ,, 1323
Mine *o* name shames me, seeming a reproach, ,, 1403
Yet one of your *o* knights, a guest of ours, *Holy Grail* 40
And once by misadvertence Merlin sat In his *o* chair, ,, 176
dyed The strong White Horse in his *o* heathen blood— ,, 312
But wail'd and wept, and hated mine *o* self, ,, 609
but O the pity To find thine *o* first love once more— ,, 620
Where saving his *o* sisters he had known *Pelleas and E.* 87
‘For pity of thine *o* self, Peace, Lady, peace: ,, 253
And heard but his *o* steps, and his *o* heart Beating, for nothing moved but his *o* self, And his *o* shadow. ,, 416

Own (adj.) (*continued*) towers that, larger than themselves In their *o* darkness, *Pelleas and E.* 458
And whatsoever his *o* knights have sworn *Last Tournament* 79
Nor heard the King for their *o* cries, „ 472
Catlike thro' his *o* castle steals my Mark, „ 516
ptarmigan that whitens ere his hour Woos his *o* end; „ 698
and cast thee back Thine *o* small saw, „ 712
'O Lancelot, get thee hence to thine *o* land, *Guinevere* 88
the King's grief For his *o* self, and his *o* Queen, „ 197
Then to her *o* sad heart mutter'd the Queen, „ 213
Shame on her *o* garrulity garrulously, „ 312
In open battle or the tilting-field Forbore his *o* advantage, and the King In open battle or the tilting-field Forbore his *o* advantage, „ 331
fearful child Meant nothing, but my *o* too-fearful guilt, „ 370
kith and kin Clave to him, and abode in his *o* land. „ 440
To honour his *o* word as if his God's, „ 473
do thou for thine *o* soul the rest. „ 545
and mine *o* flesh, Here looking down on thine polluted, „ 555
Gone, my lord the King, My *o* true lord! „ 617
That in mine *o* heart I can live down sin „ 636
So spake he, clouded with his *o* conceit, *Pass. of Arthur* 278
His *o* thought drove him like a goad. „ 353
The loyal to their crown Are loyal to their *o* far sons, *To the Queen ii* 28
That knows not her *o* greatness: „ 32
ruling that which knows To its *o* harm: „ 59
In thine *o* essence, and delight thyself *Lover's Tale i* 13
pleasure-boat that rock'd, Light-green with its *o* shadow, „ 43
Loathing to put it from herself for ever, Left her *o* life with it; „ 215
Till, drunk with its *o* wine, and over-full Of sweetness, and in smelling of itself, It fall on its *o* thorns— „ 271
Parting my *o* loved mountains was received, „ 433
Yet bearing round about him his *o* day, „ 510
As from a dismal dream of my *o* death, „ 748
till they fell Half-digging their *o* graves) „ *ii* 47
And laid her in the vault of her *o* kin. „ *iv* 39
as her *o* reproof At some precipitance in her burial. „ 106
Then, when her *o* true spirit had return'd, „ 108
And crossing her *o* picture as she came, „ 286
thence Down to this last strange hour in his *o* hall; „ 358
When Harry an' I were children, he call'd me his *o* little wife; *First Quarrel* 10
God bless you, my *o* little Nell.' „ 22
When I cannot see my *o* hand, but am led by the creak of the chain, *Rizpah* 7
I told them my tale, God's *o* truth— „ 34
if true Love Were not his *o* imperial all-in-all. *Sisters (E. and E.)* 227
A second—this I named from her *o* self, Evelyn; „ 270
mellow'd murmur of the people's praise From thine *o* State, *Ded. Poem Prin. Alice* 8
Yet art thou thine *o* witness that thou bringest Not peace, *Sir J. Oldcastle* 35
I am written in the Lamb's *o* Book of Life *Columbus* 88
Tho' quartering your *o* royal arms of Spain, „ 115
Some over-labour'd, some by their *o* hands,— „ 178
in that flight of ages which are God's *O* voice to justify the dead— „ 203
O dear Spirit half-lost In thine *o* shadow *De Prof., Two G.* 40
With power on thine *o* act and on the world. „ 56
never since thine *o* Black ridges drew the cloud *Montenegro* 12
Went to his own in his *o* West-Saxon-land, *Batt. of Brunanburh* 103
All day the men contend in grievous war From their *o* city, *Achilles over the T.* 10
which our trembling fathers call'd The God's *o* son. *Tiresias* 17
immerging, each, his urn In his *o* well, „ 89
yet if one of these By his *o* hand— „ 118
will murmur thee To thine *o* Thebes, „ 141
let thine *o* hand strike Thy youthful pulses into rest „ 156
And pity for our *o* selves on an earth that bore not a flower; *Despair* 44
And pity for our *o* selves till we long'd for eternal sleep. „ 46
wilt dive Into the Temple-cave of thine *o* self, *Ancient Sage* 32

Own (adj.) (*continued*) Except his *o* meek daughter yield her life, *The Flight* 28
To lie, to lie—in God's *o* house—the blackest of all lies! „ 52
Arise, my *o* true sister, come forth! the world is wide. „ 96
'Ud 'a shot his *o* sowl dead for a kiss of ye, Molly Magee. *Tomorrow* 40
Yer Honour's *o* agint, he says to me wanst, „ 63
Demos end in working its *o* doom. *Locksley H., Sixty* 114
strip your *o* foul passions bare; „ 141
Gone at eighty, mine *o* age, „ 281
When our *o* good redcoats sank from sight, *Heavy Brigade* 42
And who loves War for War's *o* sake Is fool, *Epilogue* 30
Our *o* fair isle, the lord of every sea— *The Fleet* 7
What is it all, if we all of us end but in being our *o* corpse-coffins at last, *Vastness* 33
That he was nearing his *o* hundred, *The Ring* 194
She cannot love; she loves her *o* hard self, „ 292
Till from her *o* hand she had torn the ring „ 470
forgotten mine *o* rhyme By mine old self, *To Mary Boyle* 21
or came of your *o* will To wait on one so broken, *Romney's R.* 16
Her sad eyes plead for my *o* fame with me „ 55
With your *o* shadow in the placid lake, „ 76
As where earth's green stole into heaven's *o* hue, *Far—far—away* 2
For a woman ruin'd the world, as God's *o* scriptures tell, *Charity* 3
every dawn Struck from him his *o* shadow on to Rome. *St. Telemachus* 33
Issa Ben Mariam, his *o* prophet, cried *Akbar's Dream* 75

Own (s) darkening thine *o* To thine own likeness; *Aylmer's Field* 673
never in your own arms To hold your *o*, *Princess vi* 178
My own heart's heart, my ownest *o*, farewell; *Maud I xviii* 74
at which his *o* began To pulse with such a vehemence *Lover's Tale iv* 81
Went to his *o* in his own West-Saxon-land, *Batt. of Brunanburh* 103
and will be his, his *o* and only *o*, *Happy* 7

Own (verb) better than to *o* A crown, a sceptre, *Ode to Memory* 120
'He *o's* the fatal gift of eyes, *Two Voices* 286
o one port of sense not flint to prayer, *Princess vi* 182
everyone that *o's* a tower The Lord for half a league. *Gareth and L.* 595
That *o* no lust because they have no law! *Pelleas and E.* 481
The Christians *o* a Spiritual Head; *Akbar's Dream* 153

Own'd one of my co-mates *O* a rough dog, *Gareth and L.* 1011
The one true lover whom you ever *o*, *Geraint and E.* 344
yourself have *o* ye did me wrong. *Merlin and V.* 316
nor tasted flesh, Nor *o* a sensual wish, „ 628
while they brake them, *o* me King. *Pass. of Arthur* 158

Owner follows, being named, His *o*, *Gareth and L.* 704

Ownest My own heart's heart, my *o* own, *Maud I xviii* 74

Owning *o* but a little more Than beasts, *Two Voices* 196
earthly Muse, And *o* but a little art *In Mem. xxxvii* 14

Ox For the *O* Feeds in the herb, *Supp. Confessions* 150
From the dark fen the *oxen's* low Came *Mariana* 28
The passive *oxen* gaping. *Amphion* 72
Reel'd, as a footsore *o* in crowded ways *Aylmer's Field* 819
roasting *o* Moan round the spit— *Lucretius* 131
oxen from the city, and goodly sheep *Spec. of Iliad* 4
my lord is lower than his *oxen* or his swine. *Locksley H., Sixty* 126
May seem the black *o* of the distant plain. *To one ran down Eng.* 4

Oxlip As cowslip unto *o* is, *Talking Oak* 107

P

Paäid (paid) eäsy es leäves their debts to be *p*. *Village Wife* 94
An' they hallus *p* what I hax'd, „ 115

Paäil (pail) wi' her *p's* fro' the cow. *Spinster's S's.* 2
ye shant hev a drop fro' the *p*. „ 65

Paäin (pain) Sam, thou's an ass for thy *p's*: *N. Farmer, N. S.* 3
an arn'd naw thanks fur 'er *p's*. *Village Wife* 12
es be down wi' their haäches an' their *p's*: *Spinster's S's.* 108

Paärint (parent) afther her *p's* had inter'd glory, *Tomorrow* 53
That ye'll meet your *p's* agin „ 57

Paäy (pay) find my rent an' to *p* my men? *Owd Roä* 47
'can ya *p* me the rent to-night?' „ 57

Pace (s) She made three p's thro' the room, *L. of Shalott iii* 38
Wheeling with precipitate p's To the melody, *Vision of Sin* 37
scarce three p's measured from the mound, *Princess v* 1
forth they rode, but scarce three p's on, *Geraint and E.* 19
Round was their p at first, but slacken'd soon: „ 33
she went back some p's of return, „ 70
With woven p's and with waving arms, *Merlin and V.* 207
Of woven p's and of waving hands, (repeat) „ 330, 968
ten or twelve good p's or more. *Def. of Lucknow* 62
Pace (verb) Would p the troubled land, *Love thou thy land* 84
till noon no foot should p the street, *Godiva* 39
thou shalt cease To p the gritted floor, *Will Water.* 242
p the sacred old familiar fields, *Enoch Arden* 625
cram our ears with wool And so p by: *Princess iv* 66
pavement where the King would p At sunrise, *Gareth and L.* 667
He seem'd to p the strand of Brittany *Last Tournament* 407
Paced (*See also* **Subtle-paced**) Love p the thymy plots of Paradise, *Love and Death* 2
I wonder'd, while I p along: *Two Voices* 454
Who p for ever in a glimmering land, *Palace of Art* 67
and p beside the mere, *M. d'Arthur* 83
he rose and p Back toward his solitary home *Enoch Arden* 793
forth they came and p the shore, *Sea Dreams* 32
out we p, I first, and following thro' the porch *Princess ii* 21
So saying from the court we p, „ *iii* 117
Where p the Demigods of old, „ 343
I p the terrace, till the Bear had wheel'd „ *iv* 212
p the shores And many a bridge, *In Mem. lxxxvii* 11
p a city all on fire With sun and cloth of gold, *Com. of Arthur* 479
the lawless warrior p Unarm'd, *Gareth and L.* 914
he turn'd all red and p his hall, *Geraint and E.* 668
and p The long white walk of lilies *Balin and Balan* 248
feet unmortised from their ankle-bones Who p it, ages back: *Merlin and V.* 553
Then p for coolness in the chapel-yard; „ 757
Bedivere, Who slowly p among the slumbering host, *Pass. of Arthur* 7
and p beside the mere, „ 251
How oft with him we p that walk of limes, *To W. H. Brookfield* 6
half the morning have I p these sandy tracts, *Locksley H., Sixty* 1
and p his land In fear of worse, *To Mary Boyle* 29
By the long torrent's ever-deepen'd roar, P, *Death of Œnone* 86
Pacing (part.) P with downward eyelids pure. *Two Voices* 420
And some one p there alone, *Palace of Art* 66
Walking up and p down, *L. of Burleigh* 90
so p till she paused By Florian; *Princess ii* 302
p staid and still By twos and threes, „ 435
Now p mute by ocean's rim; *The Daisy* 21
in her arms She bare me, p on the dusky mere. *Lancelot and E.* 1411
Tristram, p moodily up and down, *Last Tournament* 654
And slowly p to the middle hall, *Lover's Tale iv* 306
Pacing (s) long mechanic p's to and fro, *Love and Duty* 17
his foot Return from p's in the field, *Lucretius* 6
Pack (s) wolf within the fold! A p of wolves! *Princess ii* 191
Pack (verb) by the Lord that made me, you shall p, *Dora* 31
farmer vext p's up his beds and chairs, *Walk. to the Mail* 39
Let the canting liar p! *Vision of Sin* 108
neat and close as Nature p's Her blossom *Enoch Arden* 178
Pack'd (For they had p the thing among the beds,) *Walk. to the Mail* 44
were p to make your crown, *Princess iv* 543
Pad An abbot on an ambling p, *L. of Shalott ii* 20
Padded P round with flesh and fat, *Vision of Sin* 177
To a lord, a captain, a p shape, *Maud I x* 29
Paddling round the lake A little clock-work steamer p plied *Princess, Pro.* 71
Padlock'd each chest lock'd and p thirty-fold, *Merlin and V.* 655
Padre And when the Goan P quoting Him, *Akbar's Dream* 74
Pæan 'I sung the joyful P clear, *Two Voices* 127
Pagan (adj.) past thro' P realms, and made them mine, And clash'd with P hordes, *Holy Grail* 478
funeral bell Broke on my P Paradise, *Tiresias* 193
P oath, and jest, Hard Romans brawling *St. Telemachus* 39
Pagan (s) till our good Arthur broke The P *Lancelot and E.* 280
But pity—the P held it a vice— *Despair* 41
beheld That victor of the P throned in hall— *Last Tournament* 665
Paganism wallow in this old lust Of P, *St. Telemachus* 79
Page (boy) Or long-hair'd p in crimson clad, *L. of Shalott ii* 22
The p has caught her hand in his: *Day-Dm., Sleep P.* 29
The maid and p renew'd their strife, „ *Revival* 13
She into hall past with her p and cried, *Gareth and L.* 592
he made his mouthpiece of a p Who came and went, „ 1337
And p, and maid, and squire, *Marr. of Geraint* 710
You come with no attendance, p or maid, *Geraint and E.* 322
A slender p about her father's hall, *Holy Grail* 581
Page (of a book) I will turn that earlier p. *Locksley Hall* 107
And trust me while I turn'd the p, *To E. L.* 9
a p or two that rang With tilt and tourney; *Princess, Pro.* 121
I heard her turn the p; „ *vii* 190
If men neglect your p's? *Spiteful Letter* 6
passing, turn the p that tells A grief, *In Mem. lxxvii* 10
O ay, it is but twenty p's long, But every p having an ample marge, *Merlin and V.* 668
But you will turn the p's. *The Ring* 127
Pageant masque or p at my father's court. *Princess i* 198
Lead out the p: sad and slow, *Ode on Well.* 13
Pageantry All the p, Save those six virgins *Lover's Tale ii* 83
Pagod temple, neither P, Mosque, nor Church, *Akbar's Dream* 178
Paid (*See also* **Paäid, Ped**) there was law for *us*; We p in person. *Walk. to the Mail* 86
I would have p her kiss for kiss, *Talking Oak* 195
respect, however slight, was p To woman, *Princess ii* 136
P with a voice flying by to be lost *Wages* 2
p our tithes in the days that are gone, *Maud II v* 23
—p with horses and with arms; *Geraint and E.* 486
And the people p her well. *Dead Prophet* 78
Pail (*See also* **Paäil**) The milk that bubbled in the p, *In Mem. lxxxix* 51
where it glitter'd on her p, *Holy Grail* 405
Pain (s) (*See also* **Paäin**) run short p's Thro' his warm heart; *Supp. Confessions* 161
You care not for another's p's, *Rosalind* 19
All the inner, all the outer world of p *If I were loved* 5
Than once from dread of p to die. *Two Voices* 105
P rises up, old pleasures pall. „ 164
'Yet hadst thou, thro' enduring p, „ 166
Wilt thou find passion, p or pride? „ 243
Thy p is a reality.' „ 387
I least should breathe a thought of p. *Miller's D.* 26
Although the loss had brought us p, „ 229
Trouble on trouble, p on p, *Lotos-Eaters, C. S.* 84
I started once, or seem'd to start in p, *D. of F. Women* 41
With what dull p Compass'd, „ 277
'Weep, weeping dulls the inward p.' *To J. S.* 40
rose, Slowly, with p, reclining on his arm, *M. d'Arthur* 168
P heap'd ten-hundred-fold to this, *St. S. Stylites* 23
May match his p's with mine; „ 139
With slow, faint steps, and much exceeding p, „ 183
sting of shrewdest p Ran shrivelling thro' me, „ 198
one blind cry of passion and of p, *Love and Duty* 80
looking ancient kindness on thy p. *Locksley Hall* 85
woman's pleasure, woman's p— „ 149
like a beast with lower p's! „ 176
Care and Pleasure, Hope and P, *Day-Dm., Sleep. P.* 55
LIKE souls that balance joy and p, *Sir L. and Q. G.* 1
A band of p across my brow; *The Letters* 6
And gets for greeting but a wail of p; *Lucretius* 138
Without one pleasure and without one p, „ 269
LET NO MAN ENTER IN ON P OF DEATH?' *Princess ii* 195
your p's May only make that footprint upon sand „ *iii* 238
I clamber'd o'er at top with p, „ *iv* 208
a twitch of p Tortured her mouth, „ *vi* 105
and draw The sting from p; „ *vii* 64
Peace, it is a day of p (repeat) *Ode on Well.* 235, 238
Ours the p, be his the gain! „ 241
And mixt, as life is mixt with p, *Ode Inter. Exhib.* 27
troubled, as if with anger or p: *Grandmother* 65
peace, so it be free from p, „ 97
Perchance, to lull the throbs of p, *The Daisy* 105
Like dull narcotics, numbing p. *In Mem. v* 8
And I should tell him all my p, „ *xiv* 13
That dies not, but endures with p, „ *xviii* 17
He loves to make parade of p, „ *xxi* 10

Pain (s) (*continued*) The lading of a single *p*, — *In Mem. xxv* 11
This year I slept and woke with *p*, — „ *xxviii* 13
I would set their *p's* at ease. — „ *lxiii* 8
Who ploughs with *p* his native lea — „ *lxiv* 25
These mortal lullabies of *p* — „ *lxxvii* 5
No single tear, no mark of *p*: — „ *lxxviii* 14
Some painless sympathy with *p*?' — „ *lxxxv* 88
nerves of motion as well as the nerves of *p*, — *Maud I i* 63
possible After long grief and *p* To find the arms — „ *II iv* 2
Pass, thou deathlike type of *p*, — „ 58
And my bones are shaken with *p*, — „ *v* 5
Sun, that wakenest all to bliss or *p*, — *Gareth and L.* 1060
all my *p's*, poor man, for all my *p's*, — *Marr. of Geraint* 116
p she had To keep them in the wild ways — *Geraint and E.* 186
sharpness of that *p* about her heart: — „ 190
and down he sank For the pure *p*, — *Lancelot and E.* 518
sweet is death who puts an end to *p*: — „ 1008
Pleasure to have it, none; to lose it, *p*; — „ 1415
So groan'd Sir Lancelot in remorseful *p*, — „ 1428
I climb'd a thousand steps With *p*: — *Holy Grail* 836
I know That all these *p's* are trials of my faith, — *Pelleas and E.* 246
had held sometime with *p* His own against him, — *Last Tournament* 178
and in her bosom *p* was lord. — „ 239
in the heart of Arthur *p* was lord. — „ 486
rose, Slowly, with *p*, reclining on his arm, — *Pass. of Arthur* 336
now first heard with any sense of *p*, — *Lover's Tale i* 709
suffering view'd had been Extremest *p*; — „ *ii* 130
My heart was cloven with *p*; — „ 200
And they blest him in their *p*, — *The Revenge* 20
Patient of *p* tho' as quick as a sensitive plant — *In the Child. Hosp.* 30
Her love of light quenching her fear of *p*— — *Sir J. Oldcastle* 190
I am rack'd with *p's*. — *Columbus* 199
and wrench'd with *p's* Gain'd in the service — „ 235
p Of this divisible-indivisible world — *De Prof., Two G.* 42
I had now—with *him*—been out of my *p*.' — *The Wreck* 128
match'd with the *p's* Of the hellish heat — *Despair* 67
hour of torture, a moment of *p*, — „ 81
short, or long, as Pleasure leads, or *P*; — *Ancient Sage* 101
The plowman passes, bent with *p*, — „ 144
whose *p's* are hardly less than ours! — *Locksley H., Sixty* 102
or *p* in every peopled sphere? — „ 197
Thy glorious eyes were dimm'd with *p* — *Freedom* 10
with all its *p's*, and griefs, and deaths, — *To Prin. Beatrice* 2
her tears Are half of pleasure, half of *p*— — „ 11
P, that has crawl'd from the corpse of Pleasure, — *Vastness* 17
pardon, O my love, if I ever gave you *p*. — *Happy* 68
life of mingled *p's* And joys to me, — *To Mary Boyle* 49
world-whisper, mystic *p* or joy, — *Far—far—away* 7
Pain (verb) (*See also* **Paäin**) *p's* him that he sickens nigh to death; — *Geraint and E.* 499
Pain'd *P*, and, as bearing in myself the shame — *Aylmer's Field* 355
Her crampt-up sorrow *p* her, — „ 800
Painful (*See also* **Slowly-painful**) Full oft the riddle of the *p* earth — *Palace of Art* 213
Completion in a *p* school; — *Love thou thy land* 58
Till out of *p* phases wrought — *In Mem. lxv* 6
Painless Some *p* sympathy with pain?' — „ *lxxxv* 88
Paint 'When will *you p* like this?' — *Gardener's D.* 22
And *p* the gates of Hell with Paradise, — *Princess iv* 131
I strive to *p* The face I know; — *In Mem. lxx* 2
And every dew-drop *p's* a bow, — „ *cxxii* 18
harlots *p* their talk as well as face — *Merlin and V.* 821
Behind it, and so *p's* him that his face, — *Lancelot and E.* 334
P the mortal shame of nature — *Locksley H., Sixty* 140
Painted (adj.) (*See also* **Point-painted**) We left behind the *p* buoy — *The Voyage* 1
those fixt eyes of *p* ancestors Staring for ever — *Aylmer's Field* 832
Her gay-furr'd cats a *p* fantasy, — *Princess iii* 186
silent light Slept on the *p* walls, — „ *vii* 121
So like a *p* battle the war stood Silenced, — *Com. of Arthur* 122
Or two wild men supporters of a shield, *P*, — *Geraint and E.* 268
when all at once That *p* vessel, as with inner life, Began to heave upon that *p* sea; — *Lover's Tale ii* 191
Painted (verb) Eustace *p* her, And said to me, — *Gardener's D.* 20
a couple, fair As ever painter *p*, — *Aylmer's Field* 106
Painter (*See also* **Landscape-painter**) sorrowest thou, pale *P*, for the past, — *Wan Sculptor* 3
a couple, fair As ever *p* painted, — *Aylmer's Field* 106
Musician, *p*, sculptor, critic, — *Princess ii* 178
As when a *p*, poring on a face, — *Lancelot and E.* 332
'Take comfort you have won the *P's* fame,' — *Romney's R.* 43
Wrong there! The *p's* fame? — „ 48
Painting (part) *p* some dead friend from memory? — *Wan Sculptor* 4
And then was *p* on it fancied arms, — *Merlin and V.* 474
Good, I am never weary *p* you. — *Romney's R.* 3
Painting (s) with choice *p's* of wise men I hung — *Palace of Art* 131
Drew from my neck the *p* and the tress, — *Princess vi* 110
p on the wall Or shield of knight; — *Holy Grail* 829
Hung round with *p's* of the sea, — *Lover's Tale ii* 168
In the hall there hangs a *p*— — *Locksley H., Sixty* 13
Pair we went along, A pensive *p*, — *Miller's D.* 164
saw the *p*, Enoch and Annie, sitting — *Enoch Arden* 68
welded in one love Than *p's* of wedlock; — *Princess vi* 254
His craven *p* Of comrades making slowlier — *Geraint and E.* 166
like that false *p* who turn'd Flying, — „ 176
With a low whinny toward the *p*: — „ 756
Palace (adj.) 'Yet pull not down my *p* towers, — *Palace of Art* 293
High up, the topmost *p* spire. — *Day-Dm., Sleep P.* 48
In *p* chambers far apart. — „ *Sleep B.* 18
When that cold vapour touch'd the *p* gate, — *Vision of Sin* 58
clocks Throbb'd thunder thro' the *p* floors, — *Princess vii* 104
Nor waves the cypress in the *p* walk; — „ 177
sound ran Thro' *p* and cottage door, — *Dead Prophet* 38
Palace (s) (*See also* **Summer-palace**) And in the lighted *p* near — *L. of Shalott iv* 47
unto herself In her high *p* there. — *Palace of Art* 12
gaze upon My *p* with unblinded eyes, — „ 42
Full of great rooms and small the *p* stood, — „ 57
in dark corners of her *p* stood Uncertain shapes; — „ 237
forms that pass'd at windows and on roofs Of marble *p's*; — *D. of F. Women* 24
The *p* bang'd, and buzz'd and clackt, — *Day-Dm., Revival* 14
And from the *p* came a child of sin, — *Vision of Sin* 5
Which rolling o'er the *p's* of the proud, — *Aylmer's Field* 636
And in the imperial *p* found the king. — *Princess i* 113
I promise you Some *p* in our land, — „ *iii* 162
took this *p*; but even from the first — „ *iv* 313
we this night should pluck your *p* down; — „ 414
who goes?' 'Two from the *p*' I. — „ *v* 3
All on this side the *p* ran the field — „ 361
high upon the *p* Ida stood With Psyche's babe — „ *vi* 30
with my brethren here In our own *p*: — „ 124
Was it for this we gave our *p* up, — „ 244
the long laborious miles Of *P*; — *Ode Inter. Exhib.* 12
Or *p*, how the city glitter'd, — *The Daisy* 47
Fairily-delicate *p's* shine Mixt with myrtle — *The Islet* 18
Lo the *p's* and the temple, — *Boädicea* 53
Burst the gates, and burn the *p's*, — „ 64
Camelot, a city of shadowy *p's* And stately, — *Gareth and L.* 303
And he will have thee to his *p* here, — *Geraint and E.* 230
And into no Earl's *p* will I go. — „ 235
I know, God knows, too much of *p's*! — „ 236
hundred miles of coast, A *p* and a princess, — *Merlin and V.* 589
hundred miles of coast, The *p* and the princess, — „ 648
many corridor'd complexities Of Arthur's *p*: — „ 733
moved about her *p*, proud and pale. — *Lancelot and E.* 614
Until we found the *p* of the King. — „ 1044
Until I find the *p* of the King. — „ 1051
he Will guide me to that *p*, to the doors.' — „ 1129
Sir Lancelot at the *p* craved Audience of Guinevere, — „ 1162
of Arthur's *p* toward the stream, — „ 1178
And all the broken *p's* of the Past, — *Lover's Tale ii* 59
Death from the heights of the mosque and the *p*, — *Def. of Lucknow* 24
given the Great Khan's *p's* to the Moor, — *Columbus* 109
down in a rainbow deep Silent *p's*, — *V. of Maeldune* 80
Thro' many a *p*, many a cot, — *Demeter and P.* 55
A galleried *p*, or a battlefield, — *The Ring* 246
To the city and *p* Of Arthur the king; — *Merlin and the G.* 65
our *p* is awake, and morn Has lifted — *Akbar's Dream* 200
Palace-doorway On to the *p-d* sliding, paused. — *Lancelot and E.* 1246

Palace-front *p-f* Alive with flattering scarfs *Princess v* 508
Palace-gate (*See also* **Palace (adj.)**) youth came riding toward a *p-g*, *Vision of Sin* 2
Palace-walls *Where all about your* p-w *To the Queen* 15
Fleeting betwixt her column'd *p-w*, *St. Telemachus* 37
Palate Whither beneath the *p*, *D. of F. Women* 287
Pale (adj.) (*See also* **Dead-pale, Deathly-pale, Death-pale, Passion-pale**) Then her cheek was *p* and thinner *Locksley Hall* 21
P he turn'd and red, *The Captain* 62
P again as death did prove: *L. of Burleigh* 66
Then moving homeward came on Annie *p*, *Enoch Arden* 149
Enoch slumber'd motionless and *p*, „ 908
P, for on her the thunders of the house *Aylmer's Field* 278
P as the Jephtha's daughter, „ 280
Beneath a *p* and unimpassion'd moon, „ 334
how *p* she had look'd Darling, to-night! „ 379
made Still paler the *p* head of him, „ 623
seem'd he saw no *p* sheet-lightnings from afar, „ 726
when the king Kiss'd her *p* cheek, *Princess ii* 264
'*P* one, blush again: „ *iii* 67
some red, some *p*, All open-mouth'd, „ *iv* 482
raised the cloak from brows as *p* and smooth „ *v* 73
Dishelm'd and mute, and motionlessly *p*, „ *vi* 101
And then once more she look'd at my *p* face: „ 115
P was the perfect face; „ *vii* 224
Come; let us go: your cheeks are *p*; *In Mem. lvii* 5
P with the golden beam of an eyelash dead on the cheek, Passionless, *p*, *Maud I iii* 3
ever as *p* as before Growing and fading „ 6
Morning arises stormy and *p*, „ *vi* 1
some Were *p* as at the passing of a ghost, *Com. of Arthur* 264
red and *p* Across the face of Enid hearing her; *Marr. of Geraint* 523
when the *p* and bloodless east began To quicken „ 534
They rode so slowly and they look'd so *p*, *Geraint and E.* 35
Had ruth again on Enid looking *p*: „ 203
Femininely fair and dissolutely *p*. „ 275
and at his side all *p* Dismounting, „ 510
And chafing his *p* hands, and calling to him. „ 582
I never yet beheld a thing so *p*. „ 615
and beholding her Tho' *p*, yet happy, „ 880
break her sports with graver fits, Turn red or *p*, *Merlin and V.* 181
The *p* blood of the wizard at her touch Took gayer colours, „ 949
moved about her palace, proud and *p*. *Lancelot and E.* 614
Marr'd her friend's aim with *p* tranquillity. „ 733
how *p*! what are they? flesh and blood? „ 1256
Brake into hall together, worn and *p*. *Pelleas and E.* 587
When, *p* as yet, and fever-worn, *To the Queen ii* 4
sun, *P* at my grief, drew down before his time *Demeter and P.* 114
are faint And *p* in Alla's eyes, *Akbar's Dream* 11
Bramble roses, faint and *p*, *A Dirge* 30
O *p*, *p* face so sweet and meek, *Oriana* 66
O SWEET *p* Margaret, O rare *p* Margaret, (repeat) *Margaret* 1, 54
Of pensive thought and aspect *p*, „ 6
O sorrowest thou, *p* Painter, for the past, *Wan Sculptor* 3
The *p* yellow woods were waning, *L. of Shalott iv* 2
And round about the keel with faces *p*, Dark faces *p* against that rosy flame, *Lotos Eaters* 25
To whom replied King Arthur, faint and *p*: *M. d'Arthur* 72
At this *p* taper's earthly spark, *St. Agnes' Eve* 15
Panted hand-in-hand with faces *p*, *Vision of Sin* 19
'Then leaving the *p* nun, I spake of this *Holy Grail* 129
And *p* he turn'd, and reel'd, and would have fall'n, *Guinevere* 304
Then the *p* Queen look'd up and answer'd her, „ 327
wrathful heat Fired all the *p* face of the Queen, „ 357
Rose the *p* Queen, and in her anguish found „ 586
the *p* King glanced across the field Of battle: *Pass. of Arthur* 126
To whom replied King Arthur, faint and *p*: „ 240
its wreaths of dripping green—Its *p* pink shells— *Lover's Tale i* 40
And *p* and fibrous as a wither'd leaf, „ 422
dewy touch of pity had made The red rose there a *p* one— „ 696
The bridesmaid *p*, statutelike, passionless— *Sisters (E. and E.)* 212
I lay At thy *p* feet this ballad of the deeds *Ded. Poem Prin. Alice* 20
Then his *p* face twitch'd; 'O Stephen, *The Wreck* 101
I have scared you *p* with my scandalous talk, *Despair* 111

Pale (adj.) (*continued*) as this poor earth's *p* history runs,— *Vastness* 3
Each poor *p* cheek a momentary rose— *The Ring* 315
Pale (s) By bridge and ford, by park and *p*, *Sir Galahad* 82
To leap the rotten *p's* of prejudice, *Princess ii* 142
break At seasons thro' the gilded *p*: *In Mem. cxi* 8
Nor ever stray'd beyond the *p*: *Holy Grail* 21
Pale-blooded patient, and prayerful, meek, *P-b*, *Last Tournament* 608
who am not meek, *P-b*, prayerful. „ 611
Paled *P* at a sudden twitch of his iron mouth; *Aylmer's Field* 732
stars in heaven *P*, and the glory grew. *Pro. to Gen. Hamley* 32
Pale-green *p-g* sea-groves straight and high, *The Merman* 19
Paleness a *p*, an hour's defect of the rose, *Maud I ii* 8
Paler made Still *p* the pale head of him, *Aylmer's Field* 623
Or made her *p* with a poison'd rose? *Merlin and V.* 611
But left her all the *p*, when Lavaine *Lancelot and E.* 378
but the child Is *p* than before. *The Ring* 327
Muriel, *p* then Than ever you were in your cradle, „ 431
No! but the *p* and the graver, Edith. *Sisters (E. and E.)* 38
to trace On *p* heavens the branching grace *To Ulysses* 15
Palest Between two showers, a cloth of *p* gold, *Gareth and L.* 389
Palfrey there she found her *p* trapt *Godiva* 51
her *p's* footfall shot Light horrors „ 58
In converse till she made her *p* halt, *Gareth and L.* 1360
and cried, 'My charger and her *p*; *Marr. of Geraint* 126
Call the host and bid him bring Charger and *p*.' *Geraint and E.* 401
has your *p* heart enough To bear his armour? „ 489
At which her *p* whinnying lifted heel, „ 533
your charger is without, My *p* lost.' „ 750
Then leapt her *p* o'er the fallen oak, *Balin and Balan* 587
Palisade our walls and our poor *p's*. *Def. of Lucknow* 55
Pall (s) pass the gate Save under *p* with bearers. *Aylmer's Field* 827
Warriors carry the warrior's *p*, *Ode on Well.* 6
This truth came borne with bier and *p*, *In Mem. lxxxv* 1
upbare A broad earth-sweeping *p* of whitest lawn, *Lover's Tale ii* 78
Took the edges of the *p*, and blew it far „ *iii* 35
and forget The darkness of the *p*.' *Ancient Sage* 198
drama's closing curtain is the *p*! *Locksley H., Sixty* 62
and I and you will bear the *p*; „ 281
Pall (verb) Pain rises up, old pleasures *p*. *Two Voices* 164
Pallas (*See also* **Pallas Athene**) when they wish to charm *P* and Juno sitting by: *A Character* 15
Herè comes to-day, *P* and Aphroditè, *Œnone* 86
P where she stood, Somewhat apart, „ 137
'O Paris, Give it to *P*!' „ 170
There stood a bust of *P* for a sign, *Princess i* 222
Now fired an angry *P* on the helm, „ *vi* 367
some wild *P* from the brain Of Demons? *In Mem. cxiv* 12
P flung Her fringed ægis, *Achilles over the T.* 3
and *P* far away Call'd; „ 17
blunt the curse Of *P*, hear, *Tiresias* 155
Pallas Athene saw *P A* climbing from the bath „ 40
Palled (adj.) *p* shapes In shadowy thoroughfares of thought; *In Mem. lxx* 7
Pall'd (draped) *P* all its length in blackest samite, *Lancelot and E.* 1142
All *p* in crimson samite, *Holy Grail* 847
Pall'd (stale) well I know it—*p*—For I know men: *Geraint and E.* 331
Pallid On her *p* cheek and forehead came a colour *Locksley Hall* 25
Palling grew To thunder-gloom *p* all stars, *Gareth and L.* 1359
Palm (of the hand) Fold thy *p's* across thy breast, *A Dirge* 2
'His *p's* are folded on his breast: *Two Voices* 247
opening out his milk-white *p* Disclosed *Œnone* 65
Caught in the frozen *p's* of Spring. *The Blackbird* 24
he smote His *p's* together, and he cried *M. d'Arthur* 87
may press The maiden's tender *p*. *Talking Oak* 180
Between his *p's* a moment up and down— *Aylmer's Field* 259
Bow'd on her *p's* and folded up from wrong, *Princess iv* 288
some one sent beneath his vaulted *p* A whisper'd jest „ *v* 31
he clash'd His iron *p's* together with a cry; „ 354
nor more Sweet Ida: *p* to *p* she sat: „ *vii* 135
What time his tender *p* is prest *In Mem. xlv* 2
In mine own lady *p's* I cull'd the spring *Merlin and V.* 273
clench'd her fingers till they bit the *p*, *Lancelot and E.* 611
he smote His *p's* together, and he cried *Pass. of Arthur* 255
The rough brier tore my bleeding *p's*; *Lover's Tale ii* 18
Screams of a babe in the red-hot *p's* of a Moloch of Tyre, *The Dawn* 2

Palm (of the hand) (*continued*) in her open *p* a halcyon sits Patient— *Prog. of Spring* 20
Palm (sallow-bloom) In colour like the satin-shining *p* *Merlin and V.* 224
Palm (tree) (*See also* **Coco-palm**) Imbower'd vaults of pillar'd *p*, *Arabian Nights* 39
the solemn *p's* were ranged Above, „ 79
And many a tract of *p* and rice, *Palace of Art* 114
and the yellow down Border'd with *p*, *Lotos-Eaters* 22
The *p's* and temples of the South. *You ask me, why, etc.* 28
the white robe and the *p*. *St. S. Stylites* 20
Breadths of tropic shade and *p's* *Locksley Hall* 160
these be *p's* Whereof the happy people *Enoch Arden* 504
built, and thatch'd with leaves of *p*, a hut, „ 559
Among the *p's* and ferns and precipices; „ 593
little dells of cowslip, fairy *p's*, *Aylmer's Field* 91
battle-clubs From the isles of *p*: *Princess, Pro.* 22
To brawl at Shushan underneath the *p's*.' „ *iii* 230
all the sultry *p's* of India known, *W. to Marie Alex.* 14
In lands of *p* and southern pine; In lands of *p*, of orange-blossom, *The Daisy* 2
Not the clipt *p* of which they boast; „ 26
Above the valleys of *p* and pine.' *The Islet* 23
Betwixt the *p's* of paradise. *In Mem., Con.* 32
a *p* As glitters gilded in thy Book of Hours. *Gareth and L.* 45
was ever haunting round the *p* A lusty youth, „ 47
from the diamond fountain by the *p's*, *Lover's Tale i* 137
not those alien *p's*, *Columbus* 78
the high star-crowns of his *p's* *The Wreck* 72
by the *p* And orange grove of Paraguay, *To Ulysses* 11
Your cane, your *p*, tree-fern, bamboo, „ 36
p Call to the cypress 'I alone am fair'? *Akbar's Dream* 37
Palm-planted *p-p* fountain-fed Ammonian Oasis *Alexander* 7
Palm-tree 'Under the *p-t*.' That was nothing to her: *Enoch Arden* 498
Under a *p-t*, over him the Sun: „ 501
Palmwood crimson-hued the stately *p's* *Milton* 15
Palmy Sailing under *p* highlands *The Captain* 23
Fairer than Rachel by the *p* well, *Aylmer's Field* 679
Palmyrene with the *P* That fought Aurelian, *Princess ii* 83
Palpitated tempestuous treble throbb'd and *p*; *Vision of Sin* 28
P, her hand shook, and we heard In the dead hush *Princess iv* 389
Palpitation blissful *p's* in the blood, „ 28
Palsied Left me with the *p* heart, *Locksley Hall* 132
among the glooming alleys Progress halts on *p* feet, *Locksley H., Sixty* 219
As some great shock may wake a *p* limb, *St. Telemachus* 57
Palsy A wither'd *p* cease to shake?' *Two Voices* 57
Cured lameness, *palsies*, cancers. *St. S. Stylites* 82
wife or wailing infancy Or old bedridden *p*,— *Aylmer's Field* 178
p, death-in-life, And wretched age— *Lucretius* 154
The *p* wags his head; *Ancient Sage* 124
Palter to dodge and *p* with a public crime? *Third of Feb.* 24
Palter'd Nor *p* with Eternal God for power; *Ode on Well.* 180
Pamper But *p* not a hasty time, *Love thou thy land* 9
And *p* him with papmeat, if ye will, *Pelleas and E.* 195
Pamphleteer A *p* on guano and on grain, *Princess, Con.* 89
Pan (a god) The murmur of a happy *P*: *In Mem. xxiii* 12
Pan (a vessel) And hurl'd the *p* and kettle. *The Goose* 28
Pane (*See also* **Window-pane**) The blue fly sung in the *p*; *Mariana* 63
the frost is on the *p*: *May Queen, N. Y's. E.* 13
I peer'd athwart the chancel *p* *The Letters* 3
Fine as ice-ferns on January *p's* *Aylmer's Field* 222
Oh is it the brook, or a pool, or her window *p*, *Window, On the Hill* 4
And never a glimpse of her window *p*! *No Answer* 3
And lash with storm the streaming *p*? *In Mem. lxxii* 4
The prophet blazon'd on the *p's*; „ *lxxxvii* 8
Laid their green faces flat against the *p's*, *Balin and Balan* 344
thro' the pines, upon the dewy *p* Falling, *Lover's Tale i* 264
stars went down across the gleaming *p*, *The Flight* 13
small black fly upon the *p* *To one who ran down Eng.* 3
Pang Struck thro' with *p's* of hell. *Palace of Art* 220
Thrice multiplied by superhuman *p's*, *St. S. Stylites* 11
I felt a *p* within *Talking Oak* 234
Whence follows many a vacant *p*; *Princess ii* 403
brother, you have known the *p's* we felt, „ *v* 374
rack'd with *p's* that conquer trust; *In Mem. l* 6
To *p's* of nature, sins of will, „ *liv* 3
Pang (*continued*) nor *p* Of wrench'd or broken limb— *Gareth and L.* 87
Right thro' his manful breast darted the *p* *Marr. of Geraint* 121
The *p*—which while I weigh'd thy heart *Guinevere* 540
Panic and a boundless *p* shook the foe. *Achilles over the T.* 18
Panic-stricken *p-s*, like a shoal Of darting fish, *Geraint and E.* 468
Pansy eyes Darker than darkest *pansies*, *Gardener's D.* 27
Pant life, not death, for which we *p*; *Two Voices* 398
Panted as he walk'd, King Arthur *p* hard, *M. d'Arthur* 176
P hand-in-hand with faces pale, *Vision of Sin* 19
sweet half-English Neilgherry air I *p*, *The Brook* 18
P from weary sides 'King, you are free! *Princess v* 24
Gareth *p* hard, and his great heart, *Gareth and L.* 1126
as he walk'd, King Arthur *p* hard, *Pass. of Arthur* 344
Panther The *p's* roar came muffled, *Œnone* 214
A *p* sprang across her path, *Death of Œnone* 89
Panting *p*, burst The laces toward her babe; *Princess vi* 148
Pantomime Nor flicker down to brainless *p*, *To W. C. Macready* 10
Pap their bottles o' *p*, an' their mucky bibs, *Spinster's S's.* 87
Papal Prick'd by the *P* spur, we rear'd, *Third of Feb.* 27
Paper There at a board by tome and *p* sat, *Princess ii* 32
heard In the dead hush the *p's* that she held Rustle: „ *iv* 390
sack'd My dwelling, seized upon my *p's*, *Columbus* 130
a scrap, clipt out of the 'deaths' in a *p*, fell. *The Wreck* 146
Paphian new-bathed in *P* wells, *Œnone* 175
Papist Than *P* unto Saint. *Talking Oak* 16
Papmeat And pamper him with *p*, if ye will, *Pelleas and E.* 195
Parable second brother in their fool's *p*— *Gareth and L.* 1004
P's? Hear a *p* of the knave. „ 1008
Parachute And dropt a fairy *p* and past: *Princess, Pro.* 76
Parade He loves to make *p* of pain, *In Mem. xxi* 10
Paradise (*See also* **Island-Paradise**) Love paced the thymy plots of *P*, *Love and Death* 2
Or thronging all one porch of *P* *Palace of Art* 101
And from it melt the dews of *P*, *St. S. Stylites* 210
palms in cluster, knots of *P*. *Locksley Hall* 160
Like long-tail'd birds of *P* *Day-Dm., Ep.* 7
And paint the gates of Hell with *P*, *Princess iv* 131
dipt In Angel instincts, breathing *P*, „ *vii* 321
many-blossoming *P's*, *Boädicea* 43
This earth had been the *P* *In Mem. xxiv* 6
shook Betwixt the palms of *p*. „ *Con.* 32
And the valleys of *P*. *Maud I xxii* 44
since high in *P* O'er the four rivers *Geraint and E.* 763
No more of jealousy than in *P*.' *Balin and Balan* 152
Now talking of their woodland *p*, *Last Tournament* 726
groves that look'd a *p* Of blossom, *Guinevere* 389
I stood upon the stairs of *P*. *Sisters (E. and E.)* 144
And saw the rivers roll from *P*! *Columbus* 27
O bliss, what a *P* there! *V. of Maeldune* 78
and the *P* trembled away. „ 82
Broken on my Pagan *P*, *Tiresias* 193
'*P* there!' so he said, but I seem'd in *P* then *The Wreck* 75
In earth's recurring *P*. *Helen's Tower* 12
A silken cord let down from *P*, *Akbar's Dream* 139
Paragon look upon her As on a kind of *p*; *Princess i* 155
Paraguay palm And orange grove of *P*, *To Ulysses* 12
Paramount Tristram, 'Last to my Queen *P*, Here now to my Queen *P* *Last Tournament* 551
Paramour My haughty jousts, and took a *p*; *Geraint and E.* 832
Slain was the brother of my *p* *Last Tournament* 448
Parapet heroes tall Dislodging pinnacle and *p* *D. of F. Women* 26
isle of silvery *p's*! *Boädicea* 38
Set every gilded *p* shuddering; *Lancelot and E.* 299
gilded *p's* were crown'd With faces, *Pelleas and E.* 165
Parasite A leaning and upbearing *p*, *Isabel* 34
Parasitic Will clear away the *p* forms *Princess vii* 269
Parcel Portions and *p's* of the dreadful Past. *Lotos-Eaters, C. S.* 47
Parcel-bearded *p-b* with the traveller's-joy In Autumn, *Aylmer's Field* 153
Parcell'd the broad woodland *p* into farms; „ 847
Parch'd *p* and wither'd, deaf and blind, *Fatima* 6
p with dust; Or, clotted into points *M. d'Arthur* 218
p with dust; Or, clotted into points *Pass. of Arthur* 386
Pard a wild and wanton *p*, Eyed like the evening star, *Œnone* 199
Pardon (s) heal me with your *p* ere you go.' *Princess iii* 65
'What *p*, sweet Melissa, for a blush?' „ 66

Pardon (s) (*continued*) and sinn'd in grosser lips Beyond all *p*— *Princess iv* 252
with mutual *p* ask'd and given For stroke „ *v* 46
I crave your *p*, O my friend; *In Mem. lxxxv* 100
with the Sultan's *p*, I am all as well delighted, *Maud I xx* 39
Thy *p*; I but speak for thine avail, *Gareth and L.* 883
'Full *p*, but I follow up the quest, „ 886
crave His *p* for thy breaking of his laws. „ 986
and now thy *p*, friend, „ 1166
Crave *p* for that insult done the Queen, *Marr. of Geraint* 583
Grant me *p* for my thoughts: „ 816
Your *p*, child. Your pretty sports have brighten'd *Merlin and V.* 304
your *p*! lo, ye know it! Speak therefore: *Lancelot and E.* 669
dazzled by the sudden light, and crave *P*: *Pelleas and E.* 106
Madam, I beg your *p*! *Rizpah* 81
Nay, your *p*, cry your 'forward,' *Locksley H., Sixty* 225
Your *p*, O my love, if I ever gave you pain. *Happy* 68
Pardon (verb) 'Pray stay a little: *p* me; *The Brook* 210
I cared not for it. O *p* me, *Aylmer's Field* 244
and I (*P* me saying it) were much loth to breed *Princess i* 156
My needful seeming harshness, *p* it. „ *ii* 309
'O *p* me I heard, I could not help it, „ 331
Yet mine in part. O hear me, *p* me. „ *iii* 31
P, I am shamed That I must needs repeat „ 51
We *p* it; and for your ingress here „ *v* 218
'*P* me, O stranger knight; *Marr. of Geraint* 286
O *p* me! the madness of that hour, *Geraint and E.* 346
Again she sigh'd '*P*, sweet lord! *Balin and Balan* 497
sin in words Perchance, we both can *p*: *Lancelot and E.* 1189
God 'ill *p* the hell-black raven *Rizpah* 39
God *p* all—Me, them, and all the world— *Sir J. Oldcastle* 168
and yet *P*—too harsh, unjust. *Columbus* 199
Pardonable 'Rough, sudden, And *p*, *Gareth and L.* 654
Pardon'd I have *p* little Letty; *Edwin Morris* 140
Pardoner at *P's*, Summoners, Friars, *Sir J. Oldcastle* 92
Pare would *p* the mountain to the plain, *Merlin and V.* 829
Parent (*See also* **Päärint**) and their *p's* underground) *Aylmer's Field* 83
Till after our good *p's* past away „ 358
And you are happy: let her *p's* be.' „ 366
sell her, those good *p's*, for her good. „ 483
The *p's'* harshness and the hapless loves „ 616
do not doubt Being a watchful *p*, *Sisters* (*E. and E.*) 31
Paris (city of) Roaring London, raving *P*, *Locksley H., Sixty* 190
Madonna-masterpieces Of ancient Art in *P*, or in Rome. *Romney's R.* 87
And London and *P* and all the rest *The Dawn* 10
Paris (son of Priam) Œnone, wandering forlorn Of *P*, *Œnone* 17
Beautiful *P*, evil-hearted *P*, „ 50
Hear all, and see thy *P* judge of Gods.' „ 90
She to *P* made Proffer of royal power, „ 110
From me, Heaven's Queen, *P*, to thee king-born, „ 127
P held the costly fruit Out at arm's-length, „ 135
And *P* ponder'd, and I cried, 'O *P*, Give it to Pallas!' „ 169
when I look'd, *P* had raised his arm, „ 189
P, himself as beauteous as a God. *Death of Œnone* 18
on a sudden he, *P*, no longer beauteous as a God, „ 25
who first had found *P*, a naked babe, „ 54
Parish (adj.) He heard the pealing of his *p* bells; *Enoch Arden* 615
To him that fluster'd his poor *p* wits *Aylmer's Field* 521
Parish (s) like that year in twenty *p'es* round. *Grandmother* 12
'e coom'd to the *p* wi' lots o' Varsity debt, *N. Farmer, N. S.* 29
An' all o' the wust i' the *p*— *Village Wife* 34
an' nōne of the *p* knew. *Tomorrow* 76
Haäfe of the *p* runn'd oop *Owd Roä* 115
I beän chuch-warden i' the *p* fur fifteen year. *Church-warden, etc.* 8
Parish-clerks Friars, bellringers, *P-c*— *Sir J. Oldcastle* 160
Park the range of lawn and *p*: *The Blackbird* 6
The wild wind rang from *p* and plain, *The Goose* 45
voice thro' all the holt Before her, and the *p*. *Talking Oak* 124
My father left a *p* to me, *Amphion* 1
By bridge and ford, by *p* and pale, *Sir Galahad* 82
They by *p's* and lodges going *L. of Burleigh* 17
P's with oak and chestnut shady, „ 29
P's and order'd gardens great, „ 30
lay Carved stones of the Abbey-ruin in the *p*, *Princess, Pro.* 14
Down thro' the *p*: strange was the sight „ 54

Park (*continued*) they gave The *p*, the crowd, the house; *Princess, Pro.* 94
A hundred maids in train across the *P*. „ *vi* 76
Give up their *p's* some dozen times a year „ *Con.* 103
tides of chariots flow By *p* and suburb *In Mem. xcviii* 24
To range the woods, to roam the *p*, „ *Con.* 96
from the deluged *p* The cuckoo of a worse July *Pref. Poem Broth. S.* 10
Parlance A hate of gossip *p*, *Isabel* 26
Parle (s) Found the gray kings at *p*: *Princess v* 114
Parle (verb) wakeful portress, and didst *p* with Death,— *Lover's Tale i* 113
Parliament (adj.) moor good sense na the *p* man 'at stans fur us 'ere, *Owd Roä* 13
Parliament (s) furl'd In the *P* of man, *Locksley Hall* 128
A potent voice of *P*, *In Mem. cxiii* 11
Parlour I sits i' my oän little *p*, *Spinster's S's.* 103
Parlour-window rosebush that I set About the *p-w* *May Queen, N. Y's. E.* 48
Parma Of rain at Reggio, rain at *P*; *The Daisy* 51
Parnassus On thy *P* set thy feet, *In Mem. xxxvii* 6
Parrot Whistle back the *p's* call, *Locksley Hall* 171
The *p* in his gilded wires. *Day-Dm., Sleep. P.* 16
The *p* scream'd, the peacock squall'd, „ *Revival* 12
p turns Up thro' gilt wires a crafty loving eye, *Princess, Pro.* 171
Parsee Buddhist, Christian, and *P*, *Akbar's Dream* 25
Parson The *p* smirk'd and nodded. *The Goose* 20
The *p* Holmes, the poet Everard Hall, *The Epic* 4
The *p* taking wide and wider sweeps, „ 14
At which the *P*, sent to sleep with sound, *M. d'Arthur, Ep.* 3
'*P*,' said I, 'you pitch the pipe too low: *Edwin Morris* 52
the *p* made it his text that week, *Grandmother* 29
P's a beän loikewoise, *N. Farmer, O. S.* 9
But *P* a cooms an' a goäs, „ 25
p 'ud nobbut let ma aloän, „ 43
yon's *p's* 'ouse—Dosn't thou knaw „ *N. S.* 5
thou's sweet upo' *p's* lass— „ 11
P's lass 'ant nowt, „ 25
'Thou'rt but a Methody-man,' says *P*, *North. Cobbler* 89
An' *P* as hesn't the call, nor the mooney, *Village Wife* 91
An' soä they've maäde tha a *p*, *Church-warden, etc.* 7
ther mun be *p's* an' all, „ 9
fur thou was the *P's* lad. „ 36
An' *P* 'e 'ears on it all, „ 37
But *P* 'e *will* speäk out, „ 43
Part (adv.) a lie which is *p* a truth *Grandmother* 32
spoke in words *p* heard, in whispers *p*, *Merlin and V.* 839
P black, *p* whiten'd with the bones of men, *Holy Grail* 500
Part (s) they had their *p* Of sorrow: *Miller's D.* 223
seems a *p* of those fresh days to me; *Edwin Morris* 142
Love himself took *p* against himself *Love and Duty* 45
I am a *p* of all that I have met; *Ulysses* 18
fitted to thy petty *p*, *Locksley Hall* 93
She seem'd a *p* of joyous Spring: *Sir L. and Q. G.* 23
I will tell him tales of foreign *p's*, *Enoch Arden* 198
in those uttermost *P's* of the morning? „ 224
And been himself a *p* of what he told. *Aylmer's Field* 12
a *p* Falling had let appear the brand of John— „ 508
p were drown'd within the whirling brook: *Princess, Pro.* 47
As *p's*, can see but *p's*, now this, now that, „ *iii* 327
p made long since, and *p* Now while I sang, „ *iv* 90
P sat like rocks: *p* reel'd but kept their seats: „ *v* 496
P roll'd on the earth and rose again and drew: „ 497
P stumbled mixt with floundering horses. „ 498
for she took no *p* In our dispute: „ *Con.* 29
'God help me! save I take my *p* Of danger *Sailor Boy* 21
And love in which my hound has *p*, *In Mem. lxiii* 2
A *p* of mine may live in thee „ *lxv* 11
Can take no *p* away from this: „ *lxxxv* 68
A *p* of stillness, yearns to speak: „ 78
The freezing reason's colder *p*, „ *cxxiv* 14
when the fourth *p* of the day was gone, *Geraint and E.* 55
'Him, or the viler devil who plays his *p*, *Balin and Balan* 300
Now grown a *p* of me: *Lancelot and E.* 1416
of this remnant will I leave a *p*, *Guinevere* 444
is also past—*p*. And all is past, „ 542
low converse sweet, In which our voices bore least *p*. *Lover's Tale i* 542
I seem'd the only *p* of Time stood still; „ 573
but were a *p* of sleep, „ *ii* 117

Part (s) (*continued*) I would play my *p* with the young — *The Wreck* 39
realist, rhymester, play your *p*, — *Locksley H., Sixty* 139
She crouch'd, she tore him *p* from *p*, — *Dead Prophet* 69
Part (to part company) The crown of all, we met to *p* no more.' — *Edwin Morris* 70
I too must *p*: I hold thee dear — *Will Water.* 211
I trow they did not *p* in scorn: — *Lady Clare* 5
We met, but only meant to *p*. — *The Letters* 12
We too must *p*: and yet how fain — *Princess vi* 199
one soft word and let me *p* forgiven.' — „ 219
'Let us *p*: in a hundred years — *Grandmother* 47
At last must *p* with her to thee; — *In Mem., Con.* 48
I must tell her before we *p*, — *Maud I xvi* 33
For years, for ever, to *p*— — „ *II ii* 50
nor could I *p* in peace Till this were told.' — *Com. of Arthur* 393
to meet And *p* for ever. — *Guinevere* 98
Brothers, must we *p* at last? — *Open I. and C. Exhib.* 32
for a season there, And then we *p*; — *Romney's R.* 21
FAREWELL, Macready, since to-night we *p*; — *To W. C. Macready* 1
Farewell, Macready, since this night we *p*, — „ 5
Could Love *p* thus? — *Love and Duty* 55
And loving hands must *p*— — *Window, The Answer* 6
star of morn *P's* from a bank of snow, — *Marr. of Geraint* 735
No—We could not *p*. — *The Ring* 321
Part (to divide) thorough-edged intellect to *p* Error from crime; — *Isabel* 14
ere the falling axe did *p* The burning brain — *Margaret* 38
To put together, *p* and prove, — *Two Voices* 134
Can I *p* her from herself, — *Locksley Hall* 70
And *p* it, giving half to him. — *In Mem. xxv* 12
Her care is not to *p* and prove; — „ *xlviii* 5
a comb of pearl to *p* The lists of such a beard — *Merlin and V.* 244
It was ill-done to *p* you, Sisters fair; — *Lover's Tale i* 814
be loath To *p* them, or *p* from them: — *Sisters (E. and E.)* 50
I mun *p* them Tommies— — *Spinster's S's.* 92
While she vows 'till death shall *p* us,' — *Locksley H., Sixty* 24
she that came to *p* them all too late, — *The Ring* 216
Partake Then Yniol, 'Enter therefore and *p* — *Marr. of Geraint* 300
Partaker No more *p* of thy change. — *In Mem. xli* 8
Part-amazed Then half-ashamed and *p-a*, — *Gareth and L.* 868
Parted (adj.) Or thro' the *p* silks the tender face — *Princess vii* 60
And *p* lips which drank her breath, — *Lover's Tale ii* 204
Unfriendly of your *p* guest. — *The Wanderer* 4
Parted (parted company) ere he *p* said, 'This hour is thine: — *Love and Death* 9
Had once hard words, and *p*, — *Dora* 18
p, with great strides among his dogs. — *Godiva* 31
We *p*: sweetly gleam'd the stars, — *The Letters* 41
Enoch *p* with his old sea-friend, — *Enoch Arden* 168
'HERE, by this brook, we *p*; — *The Brook* 1
the week Before I *p* with poor Edmund; — „ 78
They *p*, and Sir Aylmer Aylmer watch'd. — *Aylmer's Field* 277
A little after you had *p* with him, — *Sea Dreams* 273
and beckon'd us: the rest *P*; — *Princess ii* 183
Gareth ere he *p* flash'd in arms. — *Gareth and L.* 689
madness of that hour, When first I *p* from thee, — *Geraint and E.* 347
rose without a word and *p* from her: — *Merlin and V.* 742
Who *p* with his own to fair Elaine: — *Lancelot and E.* 381
'Lord, no sooner had ye *p* from us, — „ 576
'But *p* from the jousts Hurt in the side,' — „ 622
He spake and *p*. Wroth, but all in awe, — „ 719
'Farewell, sweet sister,' *p* all in tears. — „ 1152
And *p*, laughing in his courtly heart. — „ 1176
then slowly to her bower *P*, — *Last Tournament* 239
rode to the divided way, There kiss'd, and *p* weeping: — *Guinevere* 125
poor lad, an' we *p* in tears. — *First Quarrel* 20
when we *p*, Edith spoke no word, — *Sisters (E. and E.)* 215
I *p* from her, and I went alone. — *The Ring* 437
You *p* for the Holy War without a word to me, — *Happy* 77
Parted (divided) 'my friend—*P* from her— — *Princess v* 76
friend from friend Is oftener *p*, — *In Mem. xcviii* 15
one at other, *p* by the shield. — *Geraint and E.* 269
The wrist is *p* from the hand that waved, — *Merlin and V.* 551
We cried when we were *p*; — *Lover's Tale i* 253
And floated on and *p* round her neck, — „ 704
P a little ere they met the floor, — „ *iv* 215
with their nail'd prows *P* the Norsemen, — *Batt. of Brunanburh* 94

Parted (divided) (*continued*) You have *p* the man from the wife. — *Despair* 62
rove no more, if we be *p* now! — *The Flight* 84
Two lovers *p* by a scurrilous tale — *The Ring* 208
storm Had *p* from his comrade in the boat, — „ 308
on that day Two lovers *p* by no scurrilous tale— — „ 427
Parthenon Inform'd the pillar'd *P*, — *Freedom* 3
Parting (adj. and part.) As *p* with a long embrace — *In Mem. xl* 11
nigh the sea *P* my own loved mountains — *Lover's Tale i* 433
But cast a *p* glance at me, you saw, — „ *iv* 4
I knew You were *p* for the war, — *Happy* 74
like *p* hopes I heard them passing from me: — *Princess iv* 172
and regret Her *p* step, and held her tenderly, — *Lancelot and E.* 867
Parting (s) Their every *p* was to die. — *In Mem. xcvii* 12
Warm with a gracious *p* from the Queen, — *Pelleas and E.* 558
And just above the *p* was a lamp: — *Lover's Tale iv* 218
Partner prudent *p* of his blood Lean'd on him, — *Two Voices* 415
Thy *p* in the flowery walk Of letters, — *In Mem. lxxxiv* 22
Two *p's* of a married life— — „ *xcvii* 5
Partridge Cries of the *p* like a rusty key — *Lover's Tale ii* 115
Partridge-breeder These *p-b's* of a thousand years, — *Aylmer's Field* 382
Party (adj.) And ancient forms of *p* strife; — *In Mem. cvi* 14
O scorner of the *p* cry That wanders — *Freedom* 25
Party (s) two *parties* still divide the world— — *Walk. to the Mail* 77
All *parties* work together. — *Will Water.* 56
'Drink, and let the *parties* rave: — *Vision of Sin* 123
being lustily holpen by the rest, His *p*,— — *Lancelot and E.* 497
knights, His *p*, cried 'Advance and take thy prize — „ 503
His *p*, knights of utmost North and West, — „ 526
Rivals of realm-ruining *p*, — *Locksley H., Sixty* 120
Party-secret betraying His *p-s*, fool, to the press; — *Maud II v* 35
Pass (s) (*See also* **Hill-pass**) shadowy granite, in a gleaming *p*; — *Lotos-Eaters, C. S.* 4
The long divine Peneïan *p*, — *To E. L.* 3
Snatch'd thro' the perilous *p'es* of his life: — *Aylmer's Field* 209
the strait and dreadful *p* of death, — *Com. of Arthur* 395
never dream'd the *p'es* would be past' — *Gareth and L.* 1413
never dream'd the *p'es* could be past.' — „ 1420
Arthur came, and labouring up the *p*, — *Lancelot and E.* 47
And solitary *p'es* of the wood — *Last Tournament* 361
Hath folded in the *p'es* of the world.' — *Pass. of Arthur* 78
wet black *p'es* and foam-churning chasms— — *Sir J. Oldcastle* 9
inroad nowhere scales Their headlong *p'es*, — *Montenegro* 5
from every vale and plain And garden *p*, — *To Mary Boyle* 10
Pass (verb) Men *p* me by; — *Supp. Confessions* 19
red cloaks of market girls, *P* onward from Shalott. — *L. of Shalott ii* 18
And heard her native breezes *p*, — *Mariana in the S.* 43
An image seem'd to *p* the door, (repeat) — „ 65, 74
To *p*, when Life her light withdraws, — *Two Voices* 145
Can he *p*, and we forget? — *Miller's D.* 204
P by the happy souls, that love to live: — *Œnone* 240
I pray thee, *p* before my light of life, — „ 241
the livelong day my soul did *p*, — *Palace of Art* 55
stars above them seem to brighten as they *p*: — *May Queen* 34
I shall hear you when you *p*, — *May Queen, N. Y's. E.* 31
I THOUGHT to *p* away before, — „ *Con.* 1
my desire is but to *p* to Him that died for me. — „ 20
'*P* freely thro': the wood is all thine own, — *D. of F. Women* 83
Once thro' mine own doors Death did *p*; — *To J. S.* 19
Did never creature *p* So slightly, — *Talking Oak* 86
Or *p* beyond the goal of ordinance — *Tithonus* 30
Then a hand shall *p* before thee, — *Locksley Hall* 81
Till all the hundred summers *p*, — *Day-Dm., Sleep. P.* 33
That strove in other days to *p*, — „ *Arrival* 10
My lord, and shall we *p* the bill — „ *Revival* 27
To *p* with all our social ties — „ *L'Envoi* 5
So *p* I hostel, hall, and grange; — *Sir Galahad* 81
I hold it good, good things should *p*: — *Will Water.* 205
P on, weak heart, and leave me where I lie: — *Come not, when, etc.* 11
And *p* his days in peace among his own. — *Enoch Arden* 147
Annie, the ship I sail in *p'es* here — „ 214
P from the Danish barrow overhead; — „ 442
let my query *p* Unclaim'd, — *The Brook* 104
There stood a maiden, near Waiting to *p*. — „ 205
But nevermore did either *p* the gate — *Aylmer's Field* 826
sides of the grave itself shall *p*, — *Lucretius* 257

Pass (verb) (continued) there did a compact p Long summers back, Princess i 123
and p With all fair theories only made to gild „ ii 232
he said, 'p on; His Highness wakes:' „ v 4
she will p me by in after-life „ 91
P, and mingle with your likes. „ vi 341
Her peaceful being slowly p'es by Requiescat 7
the voice, the peak, the star P, Voice and the P. 28
if left to p His autumn into seeming-leafless days— A Dedication 9
Winds are loud and winds will p! Window, No Answer 22
That all thy motions gently p In Mem. xv 10
The salt sea-water p'es by, „ xix 6
And p'es into gloom again. „ xxxix 12
I shall p; my work will fail. „ lvii 8
We p: the path that each man trod „ lxxiii 9
That these things p, and I shall prove „ lxxxv 98
And, leaving these, to p away, „ c 19
in the drifts that p To darken on the rolling brine „ cvii 13
They leave the porch, they p the grave „ Con. 71
But sweeps away as out we p „ 95
And p the silent-lighted town, „ 112
I see her p like a light; Maud I iv 11
P and blush the news Over glowing ships; „ xvii 11
P the happy news, Blush it thro' the West; „ 15
And trying to p to the sea; „ xxi 7
P, thou deathlike type of pain, „ II iv 58
P and cease to move about! „ 59
Guinevere Stood by the castle walls to watch him p; Com. of Arthur 48
and sign'd To those two sons to p, „ 319
he will not die, But p, again to come; „ 422
Gareth was too princely-proud To p thereby; Gareth and L. 162
so thou p Beneath this archway, „ 267
P not beneath this gateway, „ 273
a knight would p Outward, or inward to the hall: „ 310
'He p'es to the Isle Avilion, „ 502
He p'es and is heal'd and cannot die'— „ 503
jewell'd harness, ere they p and fly. „ 688
For whom we let thee p.' „ 917
And quickly p to Arthur's hall, „ 984
Else yon black felon had not let me p, „ 1293
like a phantom p Chilling the night: „ 1335
until we p and reach That other, Geraint and E. 6
Wait here, and when he p'es fall upon him.' „ 129
they will fall upon you while ye p.' „ 145
glancing for a minute, till he saw her P into it, „ 887
Wilt thou undertake them as we p, Balin and Balan 14
As p without good morrow to thy Queen?' „ 252
'Yea so' she said, 'but so to p me by— „ 255
and p And vanish in the woods; „ 326
heard them p like wolves Howling; „ 407
He must not p uncared for. Lancelot and E. 536
Only ye would not p beyond the cape „ 1039
I cried because ye would not p Beyond it, „ 1042
that I may p at last Beyond the poplar „ 1049
so let me p, My father, howsoe'er I seem to you, „ 1091
But that he p'es into Fairyland.' „ 1259
'That is love's curse; p on, my Queen, forgiven.' „ 1353
Who p'es thro' the vision of the night— „ 1406
'Then on a summer night it came to p, Holy Grail 179
cries of all my realm P thro' this hall— „ 316
the street of those Who watch'd us p; „ 345
go forth and p Down to the little thorpe „ 546
P not from door to door and out again, „ 714
resolve To p away into the quiet life, „ 738
Cares but to p into the silent life. „ 899
And p and care no more. Pelleas and E. 77
like a poisonous wind I p to blast „ 569
'First over me,' said Lancelot, 'shalt thou p.' „ 571
Watch'd her lord p, and knew not that she sigh'd. Last Tournament 130
purple slopes of mountain flowers P under white, „ 230
one will ever shine and one will p. „ 737
all this trouble did not p but grew; Guinevere 84
I waged His wars, and now I p and die. Pass. of Arthur 12
God my Christ—I p but shall not die.' „ 28

Pass (verb) (continued) King! To-morrow tnou shalt p away. Pass. of Arthur 34
wife and child with wail P to new lords; „ 45
'O me, my King, let p whatever will, „ 51
but as yet thou shalt not p. „ 55
one last act of knighthood shalt thou see Yet, ere I p.' „ 164
'He p'es to be King among the dead, „ 449
Somewhere far off, p on and on, „ 467
To p my hand across my brows, Lover's Tale i 31
And mine with one that will not p, till earth And heaven p too, „ 71
P we then A term of eighteen years. „ 286
So that they p not to the shrine of sound „ 470
Which p with that which breathes them? „ 481
'It was my wish,' he said, 'to p, to sleep, „ iv 63
Glanced at the point of law, to p it by, „ 276
Three hundred years—will p collaterally: Sisters (E. and E.) 53
but I thought that it never would p. In the Child. Hosp. 61
with his hard 'Dim Saesneg' p'es, Sir J. Oldcastle 21
and life P in the fire of Babylon! „ 124
The plowman p'es, bent with pain, Ancient Sage 144
but p From sight and night to lose themselves „ 202
and the sun himself will p. Locksley H., Sixty 182
Many an Æon too may p „ 206
Earth p'es, all is lost In what they prophesy, Epilogue 64
kings and realms that p to rise no more; To Virgil 28
o'er the mountain-walls Young angels p. Early Spring 12
Till the thunders p, the spectres vanish, On Jub. Q. Victoria 69
Your plague but p'es by the touch. Happy 104
helpt to p a bucket from the well To Mary Boyle 39
p on! the sight confuses— Parnassus 15
æon after æon p and touch him into shape? Making of Man 4
Some will p and some will pause. Poets and Critics 8
From sin thro' sorrow into Thee we p Doubt and Prayer 3
Passage clothes they gave him and free p home; Enoch Arden 650
Except the p that he loved her not; Geraint and E. 392
There must be now no p'es of love Merlin and V. 913
That has but one plain p of few notes, Lancelot and E. 895
Will sing the simple p o'er and o'er „ 896
Passant cow shall butt the 'Lion p' Locksley H., Sixty 248
Pass'd See **Past**
Passenger Should see thy p's in rank In Mem. xiv 6
Passest thou p any wood Close vizor, Last Tournament 534
Passeth shadow p when the tree shall fall, Love and Death 14
Love p not the threshold of cold Hate, Lover's Tale i 778
Passin' when they seeäs ma a p boy, N. Farmer, O. S. 53
Passing (See also **Passin'**) P the place where each must rest, Two Voices 410
each in p touch'd with some new grace Gardener's D. 204
In p, with a grosser film made thick St. S. Stylites 200
No eye look down, she p; Godiva 40
She p thro' the summer world again, Enoch Arden 534
Not sowing hedgerow texts and p by, Aylmer's Field 171
as not p thro' the fire Bodies, but souls— „ 671
and murmur'd that their May Was p: Princess ii 464
like parting hopes I heard them p „ iv 173
many a maiden p home Till happier times; „ vi 380
Nine times goes the p bell: All Things will Die 35
P with the weather, Window, Spring 6
Was drown'd in p thro' the ford, In Mem. vi 39
p, turn the page that tells A grief, „ lxxvii 10
Nor feed with sighs a p wind: „ cviii 4
The shade of p thought, the wealth Of words „ Con. 102
With never an end to the stream of p feet, Maud II v 11
Arthur, p thence to battle, felt Travail, Com. of Arthur 75
and p forth to breathe, „ 369
'And p gentle' caught his hand away Balin and Balan 371
That makes me p wrathful; Merlin and V. 341
And p one, at the high peep of dawn, „ 560
I fear My fate or folly, p gayer youth For one so old, „ 927
sigh'd in p 'Lancelot, Forgive me; Lancelot and E. 1350
Three against one: and Gawain p by, Pelleas and E. 274
He saw not, for Sir Lancelot p by Guinevere 30
Leapt like a p thought across her eyes; Lover's Tale i 70
that p lightly Adown a natural stair „ 526

Passing (*continued*) ships of the world could stare at him, p by. — Rizpah 83
And moved to merriment at a p jest. — Sisters (E. and E.) 121
Art p on thine happier voyage now — Sir J. Franklin 3
But make the p shadow serve thy will. — Ancient Sage 110
and p now into the night; — Locksley H., Sixty 227
poor old Poetry, p hence, — „ 249
p thro' at once from state to state, — Demeter and P. 7
clatter of arms, and voices, and men p to and fro. — Bandit's Death 24
p souls thro' fire to the fire, — The Dawn 4
The p of the sweetest soul — In Mem. lvii 11
some Were pale as at the p of a ghost, — Com. of Arthur 264
And o'er it are three p's, and three knights Defend the p's, — Gareth and L. 613
he mark'd his high sweet smile In p, — Balin and Balan 161
In p it glanced upon Hamlet or city, — Merlin and the G. 103

Passion (*See also* **Master-passion**) When my p seeks Pleasance — Lilian 8
By veering p fann'd, — Madeline 29
And those whom p hath not blinded, — Ode to Memory 117
In thee all p becomes passionless, — Eleänore 102
the soul and sense Of P gazing upon thee. — „ 116
A ghost of p that no smiles restore— — The form, the form 11
Wilt thou find p, pain or pride? — Two Voices 243
She had the p's of her kind, — L. C. V. de Vere 35
lyre of widest range Struck by all p, — D. of F. Women 166
How p rose thro' circumstantial grades — Gardener's D. 240
I ask'd him of his early life, And his first p; — Edwin Morris 24
something of a wayward modern mind Dissecting p. — „ 88
For when my p first began, — Talking Oak 9
hold p in a leash, And not leap forth — Love and Duty 40
In one blind cry of p and of pain, — „ 80
p shall have spent its novel force, — Locksley Hall 49
I triumph'd ere my p sweeping thro' me — „ 131
my foolish p were a target for their scorn: — „ 146
and all thy p's, match'd with mine, — „ 151
There the p's cramp'd no longer — „ 167
p's of her mind. As winds from all the compass — Godiva 32
He spoke; the p in her moan'd reply — Enoch Arden 286
where a p yet unborn perhaps Lay hidden — Aylmer's Field 101
his p's all in flood And masters of his motion, — „ 339
living p symbol'd there Were living nerves — „ 535
make our p's far too like The discords — Sea Dreams 257
flush Of p and the first embrace had died — Lucretius 3
To lead an errant p home again. — „ 17
My heart beat thick with p and with awe; — Princess iii 190
How much their welfare is a p to us. — „ 281
She ended with such p that the tear, — „ iv 59
rhythm have dash'd The p of the prophetess; — „ 140
Beaten with some great p at her heart, — „ 388
Leapt fiery P from the brinks of death; — „ vii 156
loyal p for our temperate kings; — Ode on Well. 165
sang Of a p that lasts but a day; — G. of Swainston 9
My centred p cannot move, — In Mem lix 9
His other p wholly dies, — „ lxii 10
my p hath not swerved To works of weakness, — „ lxxxv 49
And my prime p in the grave: — „ 76
O tell me where the p's meet, — „ lxxxviii 4
Thy p clasps a secret joy: — „ 8
And p pure in snowy bloom Thro' all the years — „ cix 11
My love is vaster p now; — „ cxxx 10
Put down the p's that make earth Hell! — Maud I x 46
mind, when fraught With a p so intense — „ II ii 59
the strong p in her made her weep — Marr. of Geraint 110
all the p of a twelve hours' fast.' — „ 306
So burnt he was with p, crying out, — „ 560
break it, when his p masters him. — Geraint and E. 43
With more exceeding p than of old: — „ 335
And all in p uttering a dry shriek, — „ 461
His p half had gauntleted to death, — Balin and Balan 220
I, that flattering my true p, saw The knights, — Merlin and V. 874
Till now the storm, its burst of p spent, — „ 961
sweet and sudden p of youth Toward greatness — Lancelot and E. 282
A fiery family p for the name Of Lancelot, — „ 477
Crush'd the wild p out against the floor — „ 742

Passion (*continued*) To blunt or break her p.' — Lancelot and E. 974
(He meant to break the p in her) — „ 1079
To break her p, some discourtesy — „ 1302
My brother? was it earthly p crost?' — Holy Grail 29
'Nay,' said the knight; 'for no such p mine. — „ 30
sent the deathless p in her eyes Thro' him, — „ 163
Than is the maiden p for a maid, — Guinevere 479
and grew again To utterance of p. — Lover's Tale i 547
As I of mine, and my first p. — Sisters (E. and E.) 67
I spoke it—told her of my p, — „ 146
For the p of battle was in us, — V. of Maeldune 96
Till the p of battle was on us, — „ 111
my boy-phrase 'The P of the Past.' — Ancient Sage 219
the sacred p of the second life. — Locksley H., Sixty 68
at last beyond the p's of the primal clan? — „ 93
strip your own foul p's bare; — „ 141
every serpent p kill'd, — „ 167

Passionate and show'd their eyes Glaring, and p looks, — Sea Dreams 236
P tears Follow'd: — Princess vi 311
there was love in the p shriek, — Maud I i 57
p heart of the poet is whirl'd into folly and vice. — „ iv 39
A p ballad gallant and gay, — „ v 4
there rises ever a p cry From underneath — „ II i 5
And there rang on a sudden a p cry, — „ 33
Let me and my p love go by, — „ ii 77
But there rings on a sudden a p cry, — „ iv 47
'It is time, it is time, O p heart,' — „ III vi 30
'It is time, O p heart and morbid eye, — „ 32
So p for an utter purity Beyond the limit of their bond, — Merlin and V. 26
Her God, her Merlin, the one p love — „ 955
That p perfection, my good lord— — Lancelot and E. 122
Went on in p utterance: — Guinevere 611
The p moment would not suffer that— — Lover's Tale iv 356
P girl tho' I was, an' often at home in disgrace, — First Quarrel 15
Back to that p answer of full heart — Sisters (E and E.) 259
tone so rough that I broke into p tears, — The Wreck 122
and heard his p vow, — The Flight 83
the follies, furies, curses, p tears, — Locksley H., Sixty 39
You wrong me, p little friend. — Epilogue 10
O you with your p shriek for the rights — Beautiful City 2

Passionately Then suddenly and p she spoke: — Lancelot and E. 929
while full p, Her head upon her hands, — Guinevere 180

Passion-flower He is claspt by a p-f. — Maud I xiv 8
splendid tear From the p-f at the gate. — „ xxii 60
And the red p-f to the cliffs, — V. of Maeldune 39

Passionless In thee all passion becomes p, — Eleänore 102
P bride, divine Tranquillity, — Lucretius 266
P, pale, cold face, star-sweet — Maud I iii 4
Where if I cannot be gay let a p peace be my lot, — „ iv 50
Innumerable, pitiless, p eyes, — „ xviii 38
The bridesmaid pale, statuelike, p— — Sisters (E. and E.) 212
High, self-contain'd, and p, — Guinevere 406

Passion-pale P-p they met And greeted. — „ 99

Passive The p oxen gaping. — Amphion 72
Worried his p ear with petty wrongs — Enoch Arden 352
when he ceased, in one cold p hand — Lancelot and E. 1201
p sailor wrecks at last In ever-silent seas; — Ancient Sage 136

Passport no false p to that easy realm, — Aylmer's Field 183

Past (adj.) (*See also* **Past (verb)** Strange friend, p, present, and to be; — In Mem. cxxix 9
all experience p became Consolidate in mind — Two Voices 365
Desiring what is mingled with p years, — D. of F. Women 282
She took the body of my p delight, — Lover's Tale i 681

Past (adv.) seem to flicker p thro' sun and shade, — Ancient Sage 100

Past (prep.) Lame and old, and p his time, — Locksley H., Sixty 227
Give me your prayers, for he is *past* your prayers, — Aylmer's Field 751
Not *past* the living fount of pity in Heaven. — „ 752
For it was *past* the time of Easterday. — Gareth and L. 186
when old and gray, And *past* desire!' — Last Tournament 628
old, Gray-hair'd, and *past* desire, — „ 653
wind, and *past* his ear Went shrilling, — Pass of Arthur 32
raising her Still higher, *past* all peril, — Lover's Tale i 394
to be sewer it be *past* 'er time. — Spinster's S's. 5
Then home, and *past* the ruin'd mill. — The Ring 156
Now *past* her feet the swallow circling flies, — Prog. of Spring 44

Past (prep.) (*continued*) Voice of the Earth went wailingly *past* him — *The Dreamer* 3

Past (s) fire, From the fountains of the *p*, — *Ode to Memory* 2
sorrowest thou, pale Painter, for the *p*, — *Wan Sculptor* 3
P and Present, wound in one, — *Miller's D.* 197
far-brought From out the storied *P*, — *Love thou thy land* 2
For all the *p* of Time reveals — „ 50
in the flying of a wheel Cry down the *p*, — *Godiva* 7
So mix for ever with the *p*, — *Will Water.* 201
bird's-eye-view of all the ungracious *p*; — *Princess ii* 125
haunt About the moulder'd lodges of the *P* — „ *iv* 63
let the *p* be *p*; — „ 76
great heart thro' all the faultful *P* — *Princess vii* 248
all the *p* Melts mist-like into this bright hour, — „ 354
Remembering all his greatness in the *P*. — *Ode on Well.* 20
That sets the *p* in this relief? — *In Mem. xxiv* 12
Or that the *p* will always win A glory — „ 13
And silent traces of the *p* — „ *xliii* 7
The eternal landscape of the *p*; — „ *xlvi* 8
And fading legend of the *p*; — „ *lxii* 4
A night-long Present of the *P* — „ *lxxi* 3
wind Of memory murmuring the *p*. — „ *xcii* 8
The dead man touch'd me from the *p*, — „ *xcv* 34
By meadows breathing of the *p*, — „ *xcix* 7
And hold it solemn to the *p*. — „ *cv* 16
Thou, like my present and my *p*, — „ *cxxi* 19
Then let her fancy flit across the *p*, — *Marr. of Geraint* 645
sins that made the *p* so pleasant to us: — *Guinevere* 375
And moving thro' the *p* unconsciously, — „ 402
Even now the Goddess of the *P*, — *Lover's Tale i* 16
The Present is the vassal of the *P*: — „ 119
The beautiful in *P* of act or place, — „ 135
And all the broken palaces of the *P*, — „ *ii* 59
mother's garrulous wail For ever woke the unhappy *P* again, — *Sisters (E. and E.)* 263
and suffer the *P* to be *P*.' — *V. of Maeldune* 124
mindful of the *p*, Our true co-mates regather — *Pref. Son. 19th Cent.* 4
would scatter the ghosts of the *P*, — *Despair* 23
can I breathe divorced from the *P*? — „ 113
statesman's brain that sway'd the *p* — *Ancient Sage* 134
In my boy-phrase 'The Passion of the *P*.' — „ 219
doubtless of a foolish *p*; — *Locksley H., Sixty* 7
hold the Present fatal daughter of the *P*, — „ 105
moment fly and mingle with the *P*. — „ 279
This heritage of the *p*; — *Freedom* 24
Sharers of our glorious *p*, — *Open. I. and C. Exhib.* 31
drown'd in the deeps of a meaningless *P*? — *Vastness* 34
And *p* and future mix'd in Heaven — *The Ring* 186
lost the moment of their *p* on earth, — „ 464
winter of the Present for the summer of the *P*; — *Happy* 70
I gaze at a field in the *P*, — *By an Evolution.* 17
Blooms in the *P*, but close to me to-day — *Roses on the T.* 6
Her *P* became her Present, — *Death of Œnone* 14

Past-Pass'd (verb) Of a maiden *past* away, — *Adeline* 19
and *past* Into deep orange o'er the sea, — *Mariana in the S.* 25
They *past* into the level flood, — *Miller's D.* 75
That into stillness *past* again, — „ 227
When I *past* by, a wild and wanton pard, — *Œnone* 199
you must comfort *her* when I am *past* away. — *May Queen, Con.* 44
forms that *pass'd* at windows and on roofs — *D. of F. Women* 23
'Glory to God,' she sang, and *past* afar, — „ 242
Beneath the sacred bush and *past* away— — *The Epic* 3
an hour had *pass'd*, We reach'd a meadow — *Gardener's D.* 107
One after one, thro' that still garden *pass'd*; — „ 201
he *pass'd* his father's gate, Heart-broken, — *Dora* 50
when the farmer *pass'd* into the field — „ 85
Then he turn'd His face and *pass'd*— — „ 151
pass'd thro' all The pillar'd dusk of sounding sycamores, — *Audley Court* 15
I had heard it was this bill that *past*, — *Walk. to the Mail* 67
'An hour had *past*—and, sitting straight — *Talking Oak* 109
trembling, *pass'd* in music out of sight. — *Locksley Hall* 34
And she, that knew not, *pass'd*: — *Godiva* 73
A pleasant hour has *passed* away — *Day-Dm., Pro.* 2

Past-Pass'd (verb) (*continued*) The reflex of a legend *past*, — *Day-Dm., Pro.* 11
Shall show thee *past* to Heaven: — *Will Water.* 246
So they *past* by capes and islands, — *The Captain* 21
We *past* long lines of Northern capes — *The Voyage* 35
Glow'd for a moment as we *past*. — „ 48
What! the flower of life is *past*: — *Vision of Sin* 69
He *pass'd* by the town and out of the street, — *Poet's Song* 2
when the dawn of rosy childhood *past*, — *Enoch Arden* 37
past Bearing a lifelong hunger in his heart. — „ 78
the moment and the vessel *past*. — „ 244
Past thro' the solitary room in front, — „ 277
And *past* into the little garth beyond. — „ 329
o'er his countenance No shadow *past*, — *Enoch Arden* 710
So *past* the strong heroic soul away. — „ 915
Rose from the clay it work'd in as she *past*, — *Aylmer's Field* 170
Sir Aylmer *past*, And neither loved nor liked — „ 249
Till after our good parents *past* away — „ 358
Then drank and *past* it; till at length — „ 408
and with her the race of Aylmer, *past*. — „ 577
past In sunshine: right across its track — *Sea Dreams* 125
And *past* into the belt and swell'd again — „ 222
he *past* To turn and ponder those three hundred scrolls — *Lucretius* 11
And dropt a fairy parachute and *past*, — *Princess, Pro.* 76
I rose and *past* Thro' the wild woods — „ *i* 90
She once had *past* that way; — „ 185
we *past* an arch, Whereon a woman-statue rose — „ 209
hastily we *past*, And up a flight of stairs — „ *ii* 30
she *past* From all her old companions, — „ 262
was it chance, She *past* my way. — „ *vi* 98
o'er her forehead *past* A shadow, — „ 106
her face A little flush'd, and she *past* on; — „ *vii* 81
there *past* by the gate of the farm, Willy,— — *Grandmother* 41
trifle left you, when I shall have *past* away. — „ 107
we *past* From Como, when the light was gray, — *The Daisy* 72
And after Autumn *past* — *A Dedication* 9
He *past*; a soul of nobler tone: — *In Mem. lx* 1
I *past* beside the reverend walls — „ *lxxxvii* 1
Up that long walk of limes I *past* — „ 15
But if they came who *past* away, — „ *xc* 13
Their love has never *past* away; — „ *xcvii* 13
as I found when her carriage *past*, — *Maud I ii* 3
I *past* him, I was crossing his lands; — „ *xiii* 6
But while I *past* he was humming an air, — „ 17
Of twelve sweet hours that *past* in bridal white, — „ *xviii* 65
Which else would have been *past* by! — „ *II ii* 65
has *past* and leaves The Crown a lonely splendour. — *Ded. of Idylls* 48
But Arthur, looking downward as he *past*, — *Com. of Arthur* 55
And Lancelot *past* away among the flowers, — „ 450
there *past* along the hymns A voice as of the waters, — „ 464
In scornful stillness gazing as they *past*; — „ 478
break his very heart in pining for it, And *past* away.' — *Gareth and L.* 58
Turn'd to the right, and *past* along the plain; — „ 295
while she *past*, Came yet another widow — „ 349
He rose and *past*; then Kay, a man of mien — „ 452
past into the hall A damsel of high lineage, — „ 587
She into hall *past* with her page and cried, — „ 592
past The weird white gate, and paused without, — „ 662
And out by this main doorway *past* the King. — „ 671
Gareth rode Down the slope street, and *past* without the gate. — „ 700
So Gareth *past* with joy; — „ 701
the King hath *past* his time— — „ 709
Anon they *past* a narrow comb wherein — „ 1193
and all his life *Past* into sleep; — „ 1281
muffled voices heard, and shadows *past*; — „ 1373
They never dream'd the passes would be *past*.' — „ 1413
They never dream'd the passes could be *past*.' — „ 1420
and they *past* to their own land; — *Marr. of Geraint* 45
like a shadow, *past* the people's talk — „ 82
Prince, as Enid *past* him, fain To follow, — „ 375
I know not, but he *past* to the wild land. — „ 443
they *past* The marches, and by bandit-haunted holds, — *Geraint and E.* 29
thro' the green gloom of the wood they *past*, — „ 195
And many *past*, but none regarded her, — „ 520
and *past* away, But left two brawny spearmen, — „ 557

Past-Pass'd (verb) (*continued*) And *past* to Enid's tent; *Geraint and E.* 922
So *past* the days. „ 930
they *past* With Arthur to Caerleon upon Usk. „ 945
and they *past* to their own land. „ 955
those three kingless years Have *past*— *Balin and Balan* 64
so turning side by side They past, „ 280
Past eastward from the falling sun. „ 320
For hate and loathing, would have *past* him by; „ 388
She *past*; and Vivien murmur'd after 'Go! *Merlin and V.* 98
eight years *past*, eight jousts had been, *Lancelot and E.* 67
Past inward, as she came from out the tower. „ 346
Meanwhile the new companions *past* away „ 399
Arthur to the banquet, dark in mood, *Past*, „ 565
Past to her chamber, and there flung herself „ 609
Thence to the court he *past*; „ 706
Past up the still rich city to his kin, „ 802
past beneath the weirdly-sculptured gates „ 844
and *past* Down thro' the dim rich city to the fields, „ 846
past In either twilight ghost-like to and fro „ 848
ten slow mornings *past*, and on the eleventh „ 1133
Past like a shadow thro' the field, „ 1140
Diamonds to meet them, and they *past* away. „ 1237
slowly *past* the barge Whereon the lily maid „ 1241
Had *pass'd* into the silent life of prayer, *Holy Grail* 4
the Grail *Past*, and the beam decay'd, „ 122
Fashion'd by Merlin ere he *past* away, „ 168
none might see who bare it, and it *past*. „ 190
showers of flowers Fell as we *past*; „ 349
thence I *past* Far thro' a ruinous city, „ 428
past thro' Pagan realms, and made them mine, „ 478
the sweet Grail Glided and *past*, „ 695
And up into the sounding hall I *past*; „ 827
and the sweet smell of the fields *Past*, *Pelleas and E.* 6
reach'd Caerleon, ere they *past* to lodging, she, „ 125
he *past*, And heard but his own steps, „ 415
forth he *past*, and mounting on his horse „ 456
with mortal cold *Past* from her; *Last Tournament* 28
that unhappy child *Past* in her barge: „ 45
When all the goodlier guests are *past* away, „ 158
Our one white day of Innocence hath *past*, „ 218
The leaf is dead, the yearning *past* away: „ 277
Isolt With ruby-circled neck, but evermore *Past*, „ 365
Mark her lord had *past*, the Cornish King, „ 382
lookt So sweet, that halting, in he *past*, „ 388
but turning, *past* and gain'd Tintagil, „ 504
he *past*, Love-loyal to the least wish *Guinevere* 125
while he *past* the dim-lit woods, „ 251
(When first I learnt thee hidden here) is *past*. „ 539
is also *past*—in part. And all is *past*, the sin „ 542
past To where beyond these voices there is peace. „ 697
when that moan had *past* for evermore, „ 441
Past with thee thro' thy people and their love, *To the Queen ii* 7
breathless body of her good deeds *past*. *Lover's Tale i* 217
We *past* from light to dark. „ 516
Past thro' into his citadel, the brain, „ 631
when the woful sentence hath been *past*, „ 788
did strike my forehead as I *past*; „ *ii* 19
They *past* on, The lordly Phantasms! in their floating folds They *past* „ 98
past and flow'd away To those unreal billows: „ 195
Suddenly came her notice and we *past*, „ *iv* 154
Past thro' his visions to the burial; „ 357
mounting these He *past* for ever from his native land; „ 387
in the pleasant times that had *past*, *First Quarrel* 55
Lord Howard *past* away with five ships of war *The Revenge* 13
Whirl'd by, which, after it had *past* me, *Sisters (E. and E.)* 86
whirling landaulet For ever *past* me by: „ 115
The morning of our marriage, *past* away: „ 244
past to this ward where the younger children are laid: *In the Child. Hosp.* 27
and Emmie had *past* away. „ 72
but only a whisper that *past*: *Def. of Lucknow* 50
On *them* the smell of burning had not *past*. *Sir J. Oldcastle* 177
and we *past* Over that undersea isle, *V. of Maeldune* 76
And we *past* to the Isle of Witches „ 97

Past-Pass'd (verb) (*continued*) So saying, light-foot Iris *pass'd* away. *Achilles over the T.* 1
light to the King till he *past* away *To Prin. F. of H.* 1
win all praise from all Who *past* it, *Tiresias* 84
past, in sleep, away By night, „ 203
and *past* Over the range and the change *The Wreck* 69
I remember I thought, as we *past*, *Despair* 11
We had *past* from a cheerless night „ 28
I had *past* into perfect quiet at length „ 66
for she *past* from the night to the night. „ 72
past into the Nameless, as a cloud Melts into Heaven. *Ancient Sage* 233
And *past* the range of Night and Shadow— „ 283
One golden curl, his golden gift, before he *past* away. *The Flight* 36
The lark has *past* from earth to Heaven „ 62
and thy shadow *past* Before me, crying *Demeter and P.* 93
breath that *past* With all the cold of winter. *The Ring* 32
then I *pass'd* Home, and thro' Venice, „ 191
And gave it me, who *pass'd* it down her own, „ 270
spoke no more, but turn'd and *pass'd* away. „ 342
A cold air *pass'd* between us, „ 380
the grating of a sepulchre, *Past* over both. „ 401
face Look'd in upon me like a gleam and *pass'd*, „ 420
Would I had *past* in the morning *By an Evolution.* 10
She waked a bird of prey that scream'd and *past*; *Death of Œnone* 87
mixt herself with *him* and *past* in fire. „ 106
there *past* a crowd With shameless laughter, *St. Telemachus* 38

Pastern cream-white mule his *p* set: *Sir L. and Q. G.* 31

Pastime play'd In his free field, and *p* made, *Two Voices* 320
You thought to break a country heart For *p*, *L. C. V. de Vere* 4
Why took ye not your *p*? *Love and Duty* 28
At our old *p's* in the hall *In Mem. xxx* 5
he beats his chair For *p*, „ *lxvi* 14
in a tilt For *p*; yea, he said it: *Gareth and L.* 543
And *p* both of hawk and hound, *Marr. of Geraint* 711
who take Their *p* now the trustful King is gone!' *Lancelot and E.* 101
in one full field Of gracious *p*, *Holy Grail* 324
Are winners in this *p* of our King. *Last Tournament* 199
following her old *p* of the brook, *The Ring* 354

Pastor being used to find her *p* texts, *Aylmer's Field* 606

Pastoral Nor *p* rivulet that swerves To left and right *In Mem. c.* 14
Upon a *p* slope as fair, *Maud I xviii* 19
and Peace Pipe on her *p* hillock a languid note, „ *III vi* 24

Pasturage wither'd holt or tilth or *p*. *Enoch Arden* 675

Pasture Thro' crofts and *p's* wet with dew *Two Voices* 14
gray twilight pour'd On dewy *p's*, dewy trees, *Palace of Art* 86
In tracts of *p* sunny-warm, „ 94
For all the sloping *p* murmur'd, *Princess, Pro.* 55
Silvery willow, *P* and plowland, *Merlin and the G.* 54

Pasturing He pointed out a *p* colt, and said: *The Brook* 136

Pasty half-cut-down, a *p* costly-made, *Audley Court* 23
what stick ye round The *p*? *Gareth and L.* 1073

Pat *p* The girls upon the cheek, *Talking Oak* 43

Patch (s) Or while the *p* was worn; „ 64
Upon my proper *p* of soil *Amphion* 99

Patch (verb) three castles *p* my tatter'd coat? *Princess ii* 416

Patch'd and refuse *p* with moss. *Vision of Sin* 212
one was *p* and blurr'd and lustreless *Marr. of Geraint* 649

Patent Last night, their mask was *p*, *Princess iv* 326

Paternoster *See* **Pather**

Path (*See also* **Forest-path, Side-path**) why dare *P's* in the desert? *Supp. Confessions* 79
He, stepping down By zig-zag *p's*, *M. d'Arthur* 50
Till all the *p's* were dim, *Talking Oak* 298
the charm did talk About his *p*, *Day-Dm., Arrival* 22
To silence from the *p's* of men; *L'Envoi* 6
footstep seem'd to fall beside her *p*, *Enoch Arden* 514
up the steep hill Trod out a *p*: *Sea Dreams* 121
you planed her *p* To Lady Psyche, *Princess iv* 315
The *p* of duty was the way to glory: (repeat) *Ode on Well.* 202, 210
has won His *p* upward, and prevail'd, „ 214
The *p* of duty be the way to glory: „ 224
The *p* by which we twain did go, *In Mem. xxii* 1
where the *p* we walk'd began To slant „ 9
My *p's* are in the fields I know, „ *xl* 31
The *p* we came by, thorn and flower, „ *xlvi* 2

Path (*continued*) When all our *p* was fresh with dew, *In Mem. lxviii* 6
the *p* that each man trod Is dim, „ *lxxiii* 9
Conduct by *p's* of growing powers, *In Mem. lxxxiv* 31
He stood on the *p* a little aside; *Maud I xiii* 7
And wildernesses, perilous *p's*, *Geraint and E.* 32
As not to see before them on the *p*, „ 773
Sideways he started from the *p*, and saw, *Balin and Balan* 324
ran the counter *p*, and found His charger, „ 417
Chose the green *p* that show'd the rarer foot, *Lancelot and E.* 162
Darken'd the common *p*: *Pelleas and E.* 550
He, stepping down By zigzag *p's*, *Pass. of Arthur* 218
The *p* was perilous, loosely strown with crags: *Lover's Tale i* 384
they trod The same old *p's* where Love „ 821
Yet trod I not the wildflower in my *p*, „ *ii* 20
my *p* was clear To win the sister. *Sisters (E. and E.)* 202
A panther sprang across her *p*, *Death of Œnone* 89
same *p* our true forefathers trod; *Doubt and Prayer* 4
Pather (Paternoster) singin' yer 'Aves' an' '*P's*' *Tomorrow* 96
Pathos Shall sharpest *p* blight us, *Love and Duty* 85
Pathway disgraced For ever—thee (by *p* sand-erased) *Alexander* 5
where the hedge-row cuts the *p*, stood, *Gardener's D.* 86
a well-worn *p* courted us To one green wicket „ 109
May beat a *p* out to wealth and fame. *Aylmer's Field* 439
Or on to where the *p* leads; *In Mem. xxiii* 8
made Broad *p's* for the hunter and the knight *Com. of Arthur* 61
And down a rocky *p* from the place *Geraint and E.* 200
And up the rocky *p* disappear'd, „ 243
Becomes the sea-cliff *p* broken short, *Merlin and V.* 882
'One night my *p* swerving east, *Holy Grail* 634
Follow you the Star that lights a desert *p*, *Locksley H., Sixty* 275
she that had haunted his *p* still, *Dead Prophet* 61
Pathway'd and hear their words On *p* plains; *Prog. of Spring* 83
Patience 'Have *p*,' I replied, 'ourselves are full *Princess, Con.* 72
P! Give it time To learn its limbs: „ 78
use A little *p* ere I die; *In Mem. xxxiv* 12
P—let the dying actor mouth his last *Locksley H., Sixty* 152
Steel me with *p*! *Doubt and Prayer* 9
Patient (adj.) *P* of ill, and death, and scorn, *Supp. Confessions* 4
I had been a *p* wife: *Dora* 147
P on this tall pillar I have borne *St. S. Stylites* 15
p leaders of their Institute Taught them *Princess, Pro.* 58
A *p* range of pupils; „ *ii* 104
howsoever *p*, Yniol's heart Danced in his bosom, *Marr. of Geraint* 504
And howsoever *p*, Yniol his. „ 707
crying, 'Praise the *p* saints, *Last Tournament* 217
p, and prayerful, meek, Pale-blooded, „ 607
P of pain tho' as quick as a sensitive plant *In the Child. Hosp.* 30
in her open palm a halcyon sits *P*— *Prog. of Spring* 21
P children of Albion, *On Jub. Q. Victoria* 59
She said with a sudden glow On her *p* face *Charity* 36
And yet be *p*—Our Playwright may show *The Play* 3
Patient (s) blabbing The case of his *p*— *Maud II v* 37
Patriarchal For one about whose *p* knee *Ode on Well.* 236
Patriot O *P* Statesman, be thou wise to know *To Duke of Argyll* 1
Patriot-soldier let the *p-s* take His meed *Epilogue* 32
Patron Sir Aylmer half forgot his lazy smile Of *p* *Aylmer's Field* 198
Institute Of which he was the *p*. *Princess, Pro.* 6
hand that play'd the *p* with her curls. „ 138
A *p* of some thirty charities, „ *Con.* 88
If easy *p's* of their kin Have left the last free race *Third of Feb.* 39
like a mighty *p*, satisfied With what himself *Geraint and E.* 644
Patted he *p* my hand in his gentle way, *First Quarrel* 67
thou be es 'ansom a tabby es iver *p* a mouse. *Spinster's S's.* 70
shook her head, and *p* yours, *The Ring* 313
Patter *P* she goes, my own little Annie, *Grandmother* 78
Pattering *P* over the boards, (repeat) „ 77, 79
The chestnut *p* to the ground: *In Mem. xi* 4
Just now the dry-tongued laurels' *p* talk *Maud I xviii* 8
Pattern let them take Example, *p*: *St. S. Stylites* 224
Can't ye taäke *p* by Steevie? *Spinster's S's.* 65
Patting Ask'd Walter, *p* Lilia's head *Princess, Pro.* 125
Paul (Saint) laugh'd, and swore by Peter and by *P*: *Godiva* 24
Like *P* with beasts, I fought with Death; *In Mem. cxx* 4
play the Saul that never will be *P*. *Sir J. Oldcastle* 103
or such crimes As holy *P*—a shame to speak „ 110
Paul's (Cathedral) down by smoky *P's* they bore, *Will Water.* 141
Pause (s) and a sweep Of richest *p's*, *Eleänore* 66
And, in the *p's* of the wind, *Miller's D.* 122
When she made *p* I knew not for delight; *D. of F. Women* 169
But lapsed into so long a *p* again *Aylmer's Field* 630
Like linnets in the *p's* of the wind: *Princess, Pro.* 246
Went sorrowing in a *p* I dared not break; „ *vii* 249
There came a minute's *p*, and Walter said, „ *Con.* 4
He paused, and in the *p* she crept an inch Nearer, *Guinevere* 527
Pause (verb) The breezes *p* and die, *Claribel* 2
stream Along the cliff to fall and *p* and fall did seem. *Lotos-Eaters* 9
How dull it is to *p*, to make an end, *Ulysses* 22
goal of ordinance Where all should *p*, *Tithonus* 31
That made the wild-swan *p* in her cloud, *Poet's Song* 7
'Yet *p*,' I said: 'for that inscription *Princess ii* 225
'Decide not ere you *p*. „ *iii* 156
turn to fall seaward again, *P's*, *Geraint and E.* 118
in the darkness heard his armed feet *P* by her; *Guinevere* 419
P! before you sound the trumpet, *Locksley H., Sixty* 116
Some will pass and some will *p*. *Poets and Critics* 8
Paused Among the tents I *p* and sung, *Two Voices* 125
p, And dropt the branch she held, *Gardener's D.* 156
we *p* About the windings of the marge *Edwin Morris* 93
that *p* Among her stars to hear us; *Love and Duty* 73
But we nor *p* for fruit nor flowers. *The Voyage* 56
p; and he, Who needs would work for Annie *Enoch Arden* 179
P for a moment at an inner door, „ 278
At Annie's door he *p* and gave his hand, „ 447
So still, the golden lizard on him *p*, „ 601
p Sir Aylmer reddening from the storm *Aylmer's Field* 321
so pacing till she *p* By Florian; *Princess ii* 302
She *p*, and added with a haughtier smile „ *iii* 225
before them *p* Hortensia pleading: „ *vii* 131
She turn'd; she *p*; She stoop'd; „ 154
We *p*: the winds were in the beech: *In Mem. xxx* 9
past The weird white gate, and *p* without, *Gareth and L.* 663
advanced The monster, and then *p*, „ 1385
often when I *p* Hath ask'd again, *Marr. of Geraint* 435
She *p*, she turn'd away, she hung her head, *Merlin and V.* 887
P by the gateway, standing near the shield *Lancelot and E.* 394
On to the palace-doorway sliding, *p*. „ 1246
'O King!'—and when he *p*, *Holy Grail* 767
—there he check'd himself and *p*. *Pelleas and E.* 527
the boy *P* not, but overrode him, „ 545
he heard Strange music, and he *p*, *Guinevere* 239
He *p*, and in the pause she crept an inch Nearer, „ 527
We often *p*, and, looking back, *Lover's Tale i* 329
We *p* amid the splendour. „ 414
My heart *p*—my raised eyelids would not fall, „ 571
P in their course to hear me, „ *ii* 14
Before the board, there *p* and stood, „ *iv* 307
and there she *p*, And long; *The Ring* 334
p—and then ask'd Falteringly, *Death of Œnone* 94
Pausing He *p*, Arthur answer'd, 'O my knight, *Lancelot and E.* 1326
And *p* at a hostel in a marsh, *Lover's Tale iv* 131
This custom——' *P* here a moment, „ 237
Pave blue heaven which hues and *p's* *Supp. Confessions* 134
Pavement from the *p* he half rose, Slowly, *M. d'Arthur* 167
on the *p* lay Carved stones of the Abbey-ruin *Princess, Pro.* 13
p where the King would pace At sunrise, *Gareth and L.* 667
And heel against the *p* echoing, *Geraint and E.* 271
heap of things that rang Against the *p*, „ 595
all the *p* stream'd with massacre: *Last Tournament* 477
from the *p* he half rose, Slowly, *Pass. of Arthur* 335
Nor in this *p* but shall ring thy name *Tiresias* 137
Pavilion I came upon the great *P* of the Caliphat. *Arabian Nights* 114
'Pitch our *p* here upon the sward; *Princess iii* 346
I stood With Florian, cursing Cyril, vext at heart, In the *p*: „ *iv* 172
bright With pitch'd *p's* of his foe, *Com. of Arthur* 97
on the further side Arose a silk *p*, *Gareth and L.* 910
The gay *p* and the naked feet, „ 937
old storm-beaten, russet, many-stain'd *P*, „ 1114
A huge *p* like a mountain peak „ 1364
at last—The huge *p* slowly yielded up, „ 1379
But found a silk *p* in a field, *Holy Grail* 745

Pavilion (*continued*) then this gale Tore my *p* from the tenting-pin, *Holy Grail* 747
three *p's* rear'd Above the bushes, gilden-peakt: *Pelleas and E.* 428
The silk *p's* of King Arthur raised *Guinevere* 394
That crown'd the state *p* of the King, „ 399
Pavilion'd *See* **Cloud-pavilion'd**
Paw Folded her lion *p's*, and look'd to Thebes. *Tiresias* 149
Paw'd *p* his beard, and mutter'd 'catalepsy.' *Princess i* 20
Kittenlike he roll'd And *p* about her sandal. „ *iii* 182
Pay (*See also* **Paäy**) *p* Meet adoration to my household gods, *Ulysses* 41
clamouring, 'If we *p*, we starve!' *Godiva* 15
'If they *p* this tax, they starve.' „ 20
half-crown, Which I shall have to *p*? *Will Water.* 156
Or means to *p* the voice who best could tell *Enoch Arden* 266
a voice, with which to *p* the debt Of boundless love *Ode on Well.* 156
Or later, *p* one visit here, *To F. D. Maurice* 45
Nor *p* but one, but come for many, „ 47
a debt, That I never can hope to *p*; *Maud I xix* 88
No tribute will we *p*:' *Com. of Arthur* 513
Will *p* thee all thy wages, and to boot. *Gareth and L.* 1005
And I will *p* you worship; *Merlin and V.* 228
This father *p's* his debt with me, *The Flight* 20
With a purse to *p* for the show. *Dead Prophet* 8
Paynim But rather proven in his *P* wars *Balin and Balan* 38
a remnant that were left *P* amid their circles, *Holy Grail* 664
Troop'd round a *P* harper once, *Last Tournament* 322
thy *P* bard Had such a mastery of his mystery „ 326
Peä 'ere a beän an' yonder a *p*; *N. Farmer, O. S.* 46
Pluksh! ! ! the hens i' the *p's*! *Village Wife* 124
Peace *God gave her* p; *her land reposed; To the Queen* 26
And Thou and *p* to earth were born. *Supp. Confessions* 26
a world of *p* And confidence, day after day; „ 29
A haunt of ancient *P*. *Palace of Art* 88
And let the world have *p* or wars, „ 182
the dear old time, and all my *p* of mind; *May Queen, N. Y's. E.* 6
good man, the clergyman, has told me words of *p*. „ *Con.* 12
Is there any *p* In ever climbing up *Lotos-Eaters, C. S.* 49
The place of him that sleeps in *p*. *To J. S.* 68
Sleep sweetly, tender heart, in *p*: „ 69
Would pace the troubled land, like *P*; *Love thou thy land* 84
when William died, he died at *p* With all men; *Dora* 144
breathing health and *p* upon her breast: *Audley Court* 68
Whose foresight preaches *p*, *Love and Duty* 34
cross thy thoughts Too sadly for their *p*, „ 89
universal *P* Lie like a shaft of light *Golden Year* 48
Pure lilies of eternal *p*, *Sir Galahad* 67
Across the whirlwind's heart of *p*, *The Voyage* 87
And pass his days in *p* among his own. *Enoch Arden* 147
Philip's true heart, which hunger'd for her *p* „ 272
all the warmth, the *p*, the happiness, „ 761
Help me not to break in upon her *p*. „ 787
sleeps in *p*: and he, poor Philip, *The Brook* 190
wounded *p* which each had prick'd to death. *Aylmer's Field* 52
hung With wings of brooding shelter o'er her *p*, „ 139
Jilted I was: I say it for your *p*. „ 354
Prince of *p*, the Mighty God, „ 669
The things belonging to thy *p* and ours! „ 740
I sought but *p*; No critic I— *Princess i* 144
'*p*! and why should I not play The Spartan Mother „ *ii* 282
lead The new light up, and culminate in *p*, „ 348
'*P*, you young savage of the Northern wild! „ *iii* 247
P be with her. She is dead. „ *iv* 136
marble Muses, looking *p*. Not *p* she look'd, „ 489
P! there are those to avenge us and they come: „ 501
resolder'd *p*, whereon Follow'd his tale. „ *v* 47
one The silken priest of *p*, one this, „ 184
heavy dews Gather'd by night and *p*, „ 244
but other thoughts than *P* Burnt in us, „ 245
I that prated *p*, when first I heard War-music, „ 265
boys Brake on us at our books, and marr'd our *p*, „ 395
found fair *p* once more among the sick. „ *vii* 44
plighted troth, and were at *p*. „ 83
Far-shadowing from the west, a land of *p*; „ *Con.* 42
P, his triumph will be sung *Ode on Well.* 232
P, it is a day of pain (repeat) „ 235, 238

Peace (*continued*) But though we love kind *P* so well, *Third of Feb.* 9
Who lets once more in *p* the nations meet, *Ode Inter. Exhib.* 4
The works of *p* with works of war. „ 28
And *p* be yours, the *p* of soul in soul! *W. to Marie Alex.* 47
Between your peoples truth and manful *p*, „ 49
mine in a time of *p*, (repeat) *Grandmother* 89, 94
in this Book, little Annie, the message is one of *P*. „ 96
And age is a time of *p*, so it be free from pain, „ 97
passes by To some more perfect *p*. *Requiescat* 8
Calm and deep *p* on this high wold, *In Mem. xi* 5
Calm and deep *p* in this wide air, „ 13
P and goodwill, goodwill and *p*, *P* and goodwill, „ *xxviii* 11
As daily vexes household *p*, „ *xxix* 2
'Twere best at once to sink to *p*, „ *xxxiv* 13
Days order'd in a wealthy *p*, „ *xlvi* 11
P; come away: the song of woe „ *lvii* 1
P; come away: we do him wrong To sing so wildly: „ 3
idly broke the *p* Of hearts that beat from day to day, „ *lviii* 5
But stay'd in *p* with God and man. „ *lxxx* 8
A hundred spirits whisper '*P*.' „ *lxxxvi* 16
and shake The pillars of domestic *p*. „ *xc* 20
My spirit is at *p* with all. „ *xciv* 8
Ring in the thousand years of *p*. „ *cvi* 28
Why do they prate of the blessings of *P*? *Maud I i* 21
Is it *p* or war? Civil war, as I think, „ 27
P sitting under her olive, „ 33
P in her vineyard—yes!— „ 36
Is it *p* or war? better, war! „ 47
if I cannot be gay let a passionless *p* be my lot, „ *iv* 50
P, angry spirit, and let him be! „ *xiii* 44
For I thought the dead had *p*, „ *II v* 15
To have no *p* in the grave, „ 16
and *P* Pipe on her pastoral hillock „ *III vi* 23
love of a *p* that was full of wrongs „ 40
For the *p*, that I deem'd no *p*, is over and done, „ 50
fruitful strifes and rivalries of *p*— *Ded. of Idylls* 38
nor could I part in *p* Till this were told.' *Com. of Arthur* 393
P to thee, woman, with thy loves and hates! *Gareth and L.* 373
as if the world were one Of utter *p*, and love, „ 1289
fought Hard with himself, and seem'd at length in *p*. *Balin and Balan* 239
one said 'Eat in *p*! a liar is he, „ 607
'*P*, child! of overpraise and overblame *Merlin and V.* 90
one had watch'd, and had not held his *p*: „ 162
sunn'd The world to *p* again: „ 639
To sleek her ruffled *p* of mind, „ 899
if I schemed against thy *p* in this, „ 930
ravaged woodland yet once more To *p*; „ 964
saying, '*P* to thee, Sweet sister,' *Lancelot and E.* 996
'*P*,' said her father, 'O my child, „ 1062
For pity of thine own self, *P*, Lady, *p*: *Pelleas and E.* 254
Ye know yourselves: how can ye bide at *p*, „ 265
But never let me bide one hour at *p*.' „ 387
P at his heart, and gazing at a star „ 559
'*P* to thine eagle-borne Dead nestling, *Last Tournament* 33
past To where beyond these voices there is *p*. *Guinevere* 698
wife and friend Is traitor to my *p*, *Pass. of Arthur* 25
thou bringest Not *p*, a sword, a fire. *Sir J. Oldcastle* 36
crowd's roar fell as at the '*P*, be still!' *Columbus* 13
Might sow and reap in *p*, *Epilogue* 13
must fight To make true *p* his own, „ 27
P, let it be! for I loved him, *Vastness* 36
Where stood the sheaf of *P*: *The Ring* 247
Before the feud of Gods had marr'd our *p*, *Death of Œnone* 32
only conquers men to conquer *p*, *Akbar's Dream* 15
Truth and *P* And Love and Justice came „ 180
Truth, *P*, Love and Justice came and dwelt therein, „ 193
Peaceful Her *p* being slowly passes by *Requiescat* 7
thro' the *p* court she crept And whisper'd: *Merlin and V.* 139
'Mine enemies Pursue me, but, O *p* Sisterhood, *Guinevere* 140
And withers on the breast of *p* love; *Lover's Tale i* 10
My close of earth's experience May prove as *p* as his own. *Tiresias* 217
in that point of *p* light? *Locksley H., Sixty* 190
Peacefuller when a balmier breeze curl'd over a *p* sea, *The Wreck* 133
Peacemaker let the fair white-wing'd *p* fly *Ode Inter. Exhib.* 34
Peace-offering last Love-offering and *p-o* *Last Tournament* 748

Peach Solved in the tender blushes of the *p*; *Prog. of Spring* 34
Peacock On the tree-tops a crested *p* lit, *Œnone* 104
The *p* in his laurel bower, *Day-Dm., Sleep. P.* 15
The parrot scream'd, the *p* squall'd, „ *Revival* 12
And smooth'd a petted *p* down with that: *Princess ii* 456
Now droops the milkwhite *p* like a ghost, „ *vii* 180
campanili grew By bays, the *p's* neck in hue; *The Daisy* 14
bright and light as the crest Of a *p*, *Maud I xvi* 17
placed a *p* in his pride Before the damsel, *Gareth and L.* 850
left The damsel by the *p* in his pride, „ 870
Peacock'd *p* up with Lancelot's noticing. „ 719
Peacock-yewtree And *p-y* of the lonely Hall, *Enoch Arden* 99
The *p-y* and the lonely Hall, „ 608
Peak (*See also* **Bosom-peak, Eagle-peak**) Twin *p's* shadow'd with pine slope *Leonine Eleg.* 10
Hesper is stayed between the two *p's*; „ 11
Some blue *p's* in the distance rose, *Dying Swan* 11
between The snowy *p* and snow-white cataract *Œnone* 211
high on every *p* a statue seem'd To hang *Palace of Art* 37
Lotos blooms below the barren *p*: *Lotos-Eaters, C. S.* 100
By *p's* that flamed, or, all in shade, *The Voyage* 41
The mountain wooded to the *p*, *Enoch Arden* 572
climbs a *p* to gaze O'er land and main, *Princess vii* 35
THE voice and the *P* (repeat) *Voice and the P.* 1, 37
Hast thou no voice, O *P*, „ 9
'I am the voice of the *P*, „ 11
The valley, the voice, the *p*, the star Pass, „ 27
P is high and flush'd At his highest „ 29
P is high, and the stars are high, „ 31
every height comes out, and jutting *p* *Spec. of Iliad.* 13
As over Sinaï's *p's* of old, *In Mem. xcvi* 22
the budded *p's* of the wood are bow'd *Maud I vi* 4
up to a height, the *p* Haze-hidden, *Com. of Arthur* 429
Stream'd to the *p*, and mingled with the haze „ 435
tipt with lessening *p* And pinnacle, *Gareth and L.* 308
A huge pavilion like a mountain *p* „ 1364
sighs to see the *p* Sun-flush'd, *Balin and Balan* 165
a cloud, man-shaped, from mountain *p*, *To the Queen ii* 40
isle-side flashing down from the *p* *V. of Maeldune* 45
the *p* of the mountain was apples, „ 63
p sent up one league of fire to the Northern Star; „ 72
For some, descending from the sacred *p* *Pref. Son. 19th Cent.* 9
One naked *p*—the sister of the sun *Tiresias* 30
two known *p's* they stand ever spreading *Parnassus* 11
HAD the fierce ashes of some fiery *p* *St. Telemachus* 1
Peak'd A mountain islet pointed and *p*; *The Islet* 15
Peakt *See* **Gilden-peakt**
Peaky Or over hills with *p* tops engrail'd, *Palace of Art* 113
The *p* islet shifted shapes, *The Voyage* 33
Peal (s) *P* after *p*, the British battle broke, *Buonaparte* 7
With *p's* of genial clamour sent *Will Water.* 187
A single *p* of bells below, *In Mem. civ* 5
whole wood-world is one full *p* of praise. *Balin and Balan* 450
In clanging cadence jangling *p* on *p*— *Lover's Tale iii* 22
p Of laughter drew me thro' the glimmering glades *Sisters (E. and E.)* 115
Then a *p* that shakes the portal— *Locksley H., Sixty* 263
Peal (verb) sweet church bells began to *p*. *Two Voices* 408
At this a hundred bells began to *p*, *M. d'Arthur, Ep.* 29
the watchman *p* The sliding season: *Gardener's D.* 182
shout Of His descending *p's* from Heaven, *Romney's R.* 127
Peal'd an answer *p* from that high land, *Vision of Sin* 221
And all about us *p* the nightingale, *Princess i* 220
old songs that *p* From knoll to knoll, *In Mem. xcv* 13
Out of the city a blast of music *p*. *Gareth and L.* 238
close upon it *p* A sharp quick thunder.' *Holy Grail* 695
the full city *p* Thee and thy Prince! *To the Queen ii* 26
till the great day *P* on us with that music *Lover's Tale iv* 65
and whenever their voices *p* *V. of Maeldune* 29
thunder of God *p* over us all the day, „ 113
and *p* from an organ,— *The Wreck* 53
Pealing He heard the *p* of his parish bells; *Enoch Arden* 615
trumpet in the distance *p* news Of better, *Princess iv* 81
single church below the hill Is *p*, *In Mem. civ* 4
wild voice *p* up to the sunny sky, *Maud I v* 13
'Hark the victor *p* there!' *Gareth and L.* 1318
Pear That held the *p* to the gable-wall. *Mariana* 4
body slight and round, and like a *p* In growing, *Walk. to the Mail* 53
tumbled half the mellowing *p's*! *In Mem. lxxxix* 20
and with golden masses of *p*, *V. of Maeldune* 60
Peärky (pert) An' thou was as *p* as owt, *Church-warden, etc.* 35
Pearl a brow of *p* Tress'd with redolent ebony, *Arabian Nights* 137
In a golden curl With a comb of *p*, *The Mermaid* 7
With a comb of *p* I would comb my hair; „ 10
morning driv'n her plow of *p* Far furrowing *Love and Duty* 99
Forth streaming from a braid of *p*: *Day-Dm., Sleep B.* 6
now a rain of *p's*, Or steep-up spout *Princess, Pro.* 62
shook and fell, an erring *p* Lost in her bosom: „ *iv* 60
When Time hath sunder'd shell from *p*.' *In Mem. lii* 16
in this stormy gulf have found a *p* *Maud I xviii* 42
In gloss of satin and glimmer of *p's*, „ *xxii* 55
Small and pure as a *p*, „ *II ii* 2
Made with her right a comb of *p* to part The lists *Merlin and V.* 244
burst in dancing, and the *p's* were spilt; „ 452
But nevermore the same two sister *p's* „ 454
Yet is there one true line, the *p* of *p's*: „ 459
Guinevere, The *p* of beauty: *Lancelot and E.* 114
'A red sleeve Broider'd with *p's*,' „ 373
wore the sleeve Of scarlet, and the *p's*; „ 502
sleeve of scarlet, broider'd with great *p's*, „ 604
carved and cut, and half the *p's* away, „ 807
So pray you, add my diamonds to her *p's*; „ 1224
gateways in a glory like one *p*— *Holy Grail* 527
For I have flung thee *p's* and find thee swine.' *Last Tournament* 310
since I care not for thy *p's*. Swine? „ 314
The Gospel, the Priest's *p*, flung down to swine— *Sir J. Oldcastle* 116
and those twelve gates, *P*— *Columbus* 87
Pearl-necklace Is like the fair *p-n* of the Queen, *Merlin and V.* 451
Pearly Upon her *p* shoulder leaning cold, *Œnone* 140
Sleet of diamond-drift and *p* hail; *Vision of Sin* 22
Peasant (adj.) Till the *p* cow shall butt the 'Lion passant' *Locksley H., Sixty* 248
Peasant (s) arts of war The *p* Joan and others; *Princess ii* 163
When the wild *p* rights himself, „ *iv* 385
p's maim the helpless horse, and drive *Locksley H., Sixty* 95
Pebble Counting the dewy *p's*, fix'd in thought; *M. d'Arthur* 84
I babble on the *p's*. *The Brook* 42
Counting the dewy *p's*, fix'd in thought; *Pass. of Arthur* 252
Peck all wing'd nothings *p* him dead! *Marr. of Geraint* 275
Peculiar When thy *p* difference Is cancell'd *Two Voices* 41
Each garlanded with her *p* flower *Gardener's D.* 202
Some *p* mystic grace Made her *Maud I xiii* 39
And a *p* treasure, brooking not Exchange *Lover's Tale i* 447
Ped (paid) he *p* me back wid the best *Tomorrow* 42
Pedant held his sceptre like a *p's* wand *Princess i* 27
Pedestal Upon an even *p* with man.' „ *iii* 224
push'd by rude hands from its *p*, „ *v* 58
seat you sole upon my *p* Of worship— *Merlin and V.* 878
Peelè that *P* the Goddess would wallow *Kapiolani* 8
handle or gather the berries of *P*! „ 20
climb to the dwelling of *P* the Goddess! „ 22
None but the terrible *P* remaining „ 28
crying 'I dare her, let *P* avenge herself'! „ 32
Peep (s) birdie say In her nest at *p* of day? *Sea Dreams* 294
baby say, In her bed at *p* of day? „ 302
passing one, at the high *p* of dawn, *Merlin and V.* 560
Peep (verb) For any male thing but to *p* at us.' *Princess, Pro.* 152
Peep'd-peept *peep'd*, and saw The boy set up betwixt *Dora* 130
Peep'd,—but his eyes, before they had their will, *Godiva* 69
underneath The head of Holofernes *peep'd* *Princess iv* 227
thro' the parted silks the tender face *Peep'd*, „ *vii* 61
Two bright stars *Peep'd* into the shell. *Minnie and Winnie* 14
Peept the winsome face of Edith *Locksley H., Sixty* 260
Peer (s) Could find no statelier than his *p's* *Two Voices* 29
'Forerun thy *p's*, thy time, „ 88
Regard the weakness of thy *p's*: *Love thou thy land* 24
drunk delight of battle with my *p's*, *Ulysses* 16
in sight of Collatine And all his *p's*, *Lucretius* 239
Surprise thee ranging with thy *p's*. *In Mem. xliv* 12
Thy spirit in time among thy *p's*; „ *xci* 6
to yield thee grace beyond thy *p's*.' *Last Tournament* 743

Peer (s) (*continued*) their claim to be thy *p's*; *To Victor Hugo* 6
Peer (verb) not to pry and *p* on your reserve, *Princess iv* 419
she *p's* along the tremulous deep, *Demeter and P.* 14
Peerage the savage yells Of Uther's *p* died, *Com. of Arthur* 257
Peer'd Or from the crevice *p* about. *Mariana* 65
I *p* athwart the chancel pane And saw the altar *The Letters* 3
and of all Who *p* at him so keenly, *Aylmer's Field* 817
I *p* thro' tomb and cave, *Demeter and P.* 70
Peereth The frail bluebell *p* over *A Dirge* 37
Peering thro' the portal-arch *P* askance, *Merlin and V.* 100
Before a thousand *p* littlenesses, *Ded. of Idylls* 26
Peerless my glory to have loved One *p*, *Lancelot and E.* 1091
As thou art a knight *p*.' „ 1282
(Those *p* flowers which in the rudest wind *Ode to Memory* 24
Peewit *See* **Pewit**
Peg The mantles from the golden *p's* *Day-Dm., Sleep P.* 19
'Let me screw thee up a *p*: *Vision of Sin* 87
Peleïan came Into the fair *P* banquet-hall, *Œnone* 225
Peleion o'er the great *P's* head Burn'd, *Achilles over the T.* 28
Peleus Gods Ranged in the halls of *P*; *Œnone* 81
Pelf dropt the goose, and caught the *p*, *The Goose* 13
Pelican I saw The *p* on the casque *Holy Grail* 635
I remember now That *p* on the casque: „ 700
Pellam *P* the King, who held and lost with Lot *Balin and Balan* 1
P, once A Christless foe of thine „ 96
till castle of a King, the hall Of *P*, „ 332
Then spake the men of *P* crying „ 337
mark'd The portal of King *P's* chapel „ 405
P's feeble cry 'Stay, stay him! „ 420
King *P's* holy spear, Reputed to be red with sinless blood, „ 556
'Brother, I dwelt a day in *P's* hall: „ 605
Whom *P* drove away with holy heat. „ 611
Pelleas (a Knight of the Round Table) and thro' these a youth, *P*, *Pelleas and E.* 5
had *P* for his lady won The golden circlet, „ 13
this new knight, Sir *P* of the isles— „ 17
and slowly *P* drew To that dim day, „ 29
It seem'd to *P* that the fern without Burnt „ 34
P rose, And loosed his horse, „ 60
P gazing thought, 'Is Guinevere herself so beautiful?' „ 69
so did *P* lend All the young beauty of his own soul „ 82
And win me this fine circlet, *P*, „ 128
'O happy world,' thought *P*, „ 136
P look'd Noble among the noble, „ 151
P might obtain his lady's love, „ 161
all day long Sir *P* kept the field With honour: „ 168
and seeing *P* droop, Said Guinevere, „ 178
knights all set their faces home, Sir *P* follow'd. „ 188
'These be the ways of ladies,' *P* thought, „ 209
P overthrew them as they dash'd Against him „ 221
they went, And *P* overthrew them one by one; „ 230
'Nay,' said *P*, 'but forbear; „ 280
And *P* overthrew them, one to three; „ 287
first her anger, leaving *P*, burn'd Full „ 289
P answer'd, 'Lady, for indeed I loved you „ 296
P answer'd, 'O, their wills are hers „ 324
P lent his horse and all his arms, „ 358
I have slain this *P* whom ye hate: „ 372
'Lo! *P* is dead—he told us— „ 377
Lost in a doubt, *P* wandering Waited, „ 392
this lay—Which *P* had heard sung before the Queen, „ 397
did *P* in an utter shame Creep with his shadow „ 440
the poor *P* whom she call'd her fool? „ 474
'Liar, for thou hast not slain This *P*! „ 491
her ever-veering fancy turn'd To *P*, „ 494
fared it with Sir *P* as with one Who gets a wound „ 528
P, leaping up, Ran thro' the doors and vaulted „ 538
weary steed of *P* floundering flung His rider, „ 574
Sir *P* in brief while Caught his unbroken limbs „ 584
then on *P*, him Who had not greeted her, „ 590
Then she, turning to *P*, 'O young knight, „ 595
P lifted up an eye so fierce She quail'd; „ 601
Pelt *p* me with starry spangles and shells, *The Merman* 28
That *p* us in the porch with flowers. *In Mem., Con.* 68
Pelt (*continued*) *p* your offal at her face. *Locksley H., Sixty* 134
Pelted And *p* with outrageous epithets, *Aylmer's Field* 286
Pen With such a pencil, such a *p*, *To E. L.* 6
Penance Betray'd my secret *p*, *St. S. Stylites* 68
prate Of *p's* I cannot have gone thro', „ 101
power with Heaven From my long *p*: „ 144
From my high nest of *p* here proclaim „ 167
And here I lay this *p* on myself, *Geraint and E.* 739
And all the *p* the Queen laid upon me „ 854
earth about him everywhere, despite All fast and *p*. *Holy Grail* 631
if I do not there is *p* given— *Guinevere* 187
'Heresy.—*P*?' 'Fast, Hairshirt *Sir J. Oldcastle* 141
Do *p* in his heart, God hears him.' „ 143
Pence (*See also* **Peter's-pence**) Or that eternal want of *p*, *Will Water.* 43
Thy latter days increased with *p* „ 219
is it shillins an' *p*? *N. Farmer, N. S.* 42
Even in dreams to the chink of his *p*, *Maud I x* 43
Pencil Came, drew your *p* from you, *Gardener's D.* 26
wave of such a breast As never *p* drew. „ 140
'Then I took a *p*, and wrote On the mossy stone, *Edward Gray* 25
With such a *p*, such a pen, *To E. L.* 6
Into the shadowing *p's* naked forms *Lover's Tale ii* 180
Pencill'd *See* **Shadowy-pencill'd, Tender-pencill'd**
Pendent (*See also* **Roof-pendent**) Her *p* hands, and narrow meagre face *Aylmer's Field* 813
With many a *p* bell and fragrant star, *Death of Œnone* 13
Pendragon The dread *P*, Britain's King of kings, *Lancelot and E.* 424
Came round their great *P*, saying „ 528
Pendragonship The Dragon of the great *P*, (repeat) *Guinevere* 398, 598
Peneïan The long divine *P* pass, *To E. L.* 3
Pension title, place, or touch Of *p*, *Love thou thy land* 26
Pension'd Half-sickening of his *p* afternoon, *Aylmer's Field* 461
Pensive Of *p* thought and aspect pale, *Margaret* 6
A *p* pair, and you were gay *Miller's D.* 164
The fulness of the *p* mind; *Day-Dm., L'Envoi* 48
Edith, whose *p* beauty, perfect else, *Aylmer's Field* 70
And *p* tendance in the all-weary noons, *Princess vii* 102
Yet feels, as in a *p* dream, *In Mem. lxiv* 17
Their *p* tablets round her head, „ *Con.* 51
Gazing for one *p* moment on that founder *Locksley H., Sixty* 32
Pent (*See also* **Long-pent**) I lay *P* in a roofless close *St. S. Stylites* 74
fretful as the wind *P* in a crevice: *Princess iii* 81
Pentagram Some figure like a wizard *p* *The Brook* 103
Pentecost Hereafter thou, fulfilling *P*, *Sir J. Oldcastle* 33
Penthouse A snowy *p* for his hollow eyes, *Merlin and V.* 808
Penuel In the dim tract of *P*. *Clear-headed friend* 29
People '*She wrought her* p *lasting good*; *To the Queen* 24
Broad-based upon her p*'s will*, „ 35
As when a mighty *p* rejoice With shawms, *Dying Swan* 31
And up and down the *p* go, *L. of Shalott i* 6
On to God's house the *p* prest: *Two Voices* 409
The *p* here, a beast of burden slow, *Palace of Art* 149
I perish by this *p* which I made,— *M. d'Arthur* 22
speak in the aftertime To all the *p*, „ 108
all the *p* cried, 'Arthur is come again: „ *Ep.* 23
scarce can hear the *p* hum About the column's base, *St. S. Stylites* 38
The silly *p* take me for a saint, „ 127
Good *p*, you do ill to kneel to me. „ 133
O Lord, Aid all this foolish *p*; „ 223
by slow prudence to make mild A rugged *p*, *Ulysses* 37
With the standards of the *p's* *Locksley Hall* 126
Slowly comes a hungry *p*, „ 135
loved the *p* well, And loathed to see them overtax'd; *Godiva* 8
but that she would loose The *p*: „ 38
And the *p* loved her much. *L. of Burleigh* 76
Then her *p*, softly treading, „ 97
He gave the *p* of his best: *You might have won* 25
The younger *p* making holiday, *Enoch Arden* 62
happy *p* strowing cried 'Hosanna „ 505
or he himself Moved haunting *p*, „ 604
p talk'd—that it was wholly wise *Aylmer's Field* 268
p talk'd—The boy might get a notion „ 270
The weakness of a *p* or a house, „ 570
To speak before the *p* of her child, „ 608
bid the Holiest from the *p's* eyes „ 772

People (*continued*) her own *p* bore along the nave Her pendent hands, *Aylmer's Field* 812
until the set of sun Up to the *p*: *Princess, Pro.* 3
were there any of our *p* there In want of peril, „ *ii* 266
babbling wells With her own *p's* life: „ *v* 335
All *p* said she had authority— „ *vi* 238
To let the *p* breathe? „ *Con.* 104
And a reverent *p* behold The towering car, *Ode on Well.* 54
thro' the centuries let a *p's* voice In full acclaim, A *p's* voice, The proof and echo of all human fame, A *p's* voice, when they rejoice „ 142
A *p's* voice! we are a *p* yet. „ 151
Betwixt a *p* and their ancient throne, „ 163
the Dead March wails in the *p's* ears: „ 267
you, my Lords, you make the *p* muse *Third of Feb.* 31
O joy to the *p* and joy to the throne, *W. to Alexandra* 29
thrones and *p's* are as waifs that swing, *W. to Marie Alex.* 26
Between your *p's* truth and manful peace, „ 49
A princely *p's* awful princes, *The Daisy* 39
came a flower, The *p* said, a weed. *The Flower* 4
all the *p* cried, 'Splendid is the flower.' „ 16
again the *p* Call it but a weed. „ 23
A PLAGUE upon the *p* fell, *The Victim* 1
So thick they died the *p* cried, „ 5
The land is sick, the *p* diseased, „ 45
her *p* all around the royal chariot *Boädicea* 73
Lest I fall unawares before the *p*, *Hendecasyllabics* 7
more and more the *p* throng The chairs *In Mem. xxi* 15
The pillar of a *p's* hope, „ *lxiv* 15
Whate'er the faithless *p* say. „ *xcvii* 16
a loyal *p* shouting a battle cry, *Maud III vi* 35
heart of a *p* beat with one desire; „ 49
Laborious for her *p* and her poor— *Ded. of Idylls* 35
The love of all Thy *p* comfort Thee, „ 54
And while the *p* clamour'd for a king, *Com. of Arthur* 235
Bright with a shining *p* on the decks, „ 376
crush'd The Idolaters, and made the *p* free? *Gareth and L.* 137
p stept As in the presence of a gracious king. „ 315
around him slowly prest The *p*, „ 694
by and by the *p*, when they met In twos and threes, *Marr. of Geraint* 56
this she gather'd from the *p's* eyes: „ 61
Then, like a shadow, past the *p's* talk „ 82
'Would some of your kind *p* take him up, *Geraint and E.* 543
a grateful *p* named Enid the Good; „ 963
The *p* call'd him Wizard; *Merlin and V.* 170
The *p* call you prophet: let it be: „ 317
With loss of half his *p* arrow-slain; „ 565
For fear our *p* call you lily maid *Lancelot and E.* 386
Of whom the *p* talk mysteriously, „ 425
this I know, for all the *p* know it, „ 1081
when now the lords and dames And *p*, „ 1347
till the *p* in far fields, Wasted so often *Holy Grail* 243
overthrew So many knights that all the *p* cried. „ 335
The heads of all her *p* drew to me, „ 601
And found a *p* there among their crags, „ 662
turn'd the lady round And look'd upon her *p*; *Pelleas and E.* 92
there before the *p* crown'd herself: „ 174
scandal break and blaze Before the *p*, *Guinevere* 92
'With what a hate the *p* and the King „ 157
The mockery of my *p*, and their bane.' „ 526
To poor sick *p*, richer in His eyes Who ransom'd us, „ 684
And with him many of thy *p*, *Pass. of Arthur* 60
To war against my *p* and my knights. „ 71
The king who fights his *p* fights himself. „ 72
Where fragments of forgotten *p's* dwelt, „ 84
I perish by this *p* which I made,— „ 190
speak in the aftertime To all the *p*, „ 276
Past with thee thro' thy *p* and their love, *To the Queen ii* 7
Left mightiest of all *p's* under heaven? „ 21
To what our *p* call 'The Hill of Woe.' *Lover's Tale i* 374
If you go far in (The country *p* rumour) „ 519
p throng'd about them from the hall, *Sisters (E. and E.)* 156
p's praise From thine own State, *Ded. Poem Prin. Alice* 7
rose from off his throne to greet Before his *p*, *Columbus* 6
harmless *p* whom we found In Hispaniola's „ 181

People (*continued*) This creedless *p* will be brought to Christ *Columbus* 189
three of the gentlest and best of my *p*, *V. of Maeldune* 81
O smallest among *p's*! *Montenegro* 9
make one *p* ere man's race be run: *To Victor Hugo* 11
creeds that had madden'd the *p's* *Despair* 24
p 'ud see it that wint in to mass— *Tomorrow* 74
perfect *p's*, perfect kings. *Locksley H., Sixty* 186
Move among your *p*, know them, „ 266
With all the *p's*, great and small, *Epilogue* 20
for evermore. Let the *p* die.' *Dead Prophet* 4
a careless *p* flock'd from the fields „ 7
Was one of the *p's* kings, „ 10
for he spoke and the *p* heard, „ 33
And all the *p* were pleased; „ 74
And the *p* paid her well. „ 78
Your rule has made the *p* love Their ruler. *To Marq. of Dufferin* 9
Glorying in the glories of her *p*, *On Jub. Q. Victoria* 26
Hand of Light will lead her *p*, „ 68
My *p* too were scared with eerie sounds, *The Ring* 408
A barbarous *p*, Blind to the magic, *Merlin and the G.* 25
O God in every temple I see *p* that see thee, and in every language I hear spoken, *p* praise thee. *Akbar's D., Inscrip.* 1
If it be a mosque *p* murmur the holy prayer, and if it be a Christian Church, *p* ring the bell from love to Thee. „ 4
drive A *p* from their ancient fold *Akbar's Dream* 61
held His *p* by the bridle-rein of Truth. „ 85
Mould them for all his *p*. „ 129
a *p* have fashion'd and worship a Spirit of Evil, *Kapiolani* 1
and freed the *p* Of Hawa-i-ee! „ 6
A *p* believing that Peelè the Goddess „ 8
One from the Sunrise Dawn'd on His *p*, „ 25
Godless fury of *p's*, *The Dawn* 7
Till the *p's* all are one, *Making of Man* 7

Peopled (adj.) eyes Run thro' the *p* gallery which half round *Lancelot and E.* 430
Is there evil but on earth? or pain in every *p* sphere? *Locksley H., Sixty* 197

Peopled (verb) *P* the hollow dark, like burning stars, *D. of F. Women* 18

Peptics Or do my *p* differ? *Will Water.* 80

Peradventure '*P* he, you name, May know *Gareth and L.* 1298

Perceive a man far-off might well *p*, *Lancelot and E.* 458

Perceived And I *p* no touch of change, *In Mem. xiv* 17
P the waving of the hands that blest. *Guinevere* 584

Perceiving He, *p*, said: 'Fair and dear cousin, *Geraint and E.* 823
P that she was but half disdain'd, *Merlin and V.* 179

Perch (s) lawless *p* Of wing'd ambitions, *Ded. of Idylls* 22
Came to her old *p* back, and settled *Merlin and V.* 903

Perch (verb) Light Hope at Beauty's call would *p* *Caress'd or chidden* 3

Perch'd *P* like a crow upon a three-legg'd stool, *Audley Court* 45
p about the knolls A dozen angry models *Princess, Pro.* 72
P on the pouted blossom of her lips: „ 199
all that walk'd, or crept, or *p*, or flew. *Last Tournament* 367
P on the shrouds, and then fell fluttering *The Wreck* 82

Percivale (a Knight of the Round Table) What say ye then to fair Sir *P* *Merlin and V.* 747
'A sober man is *P* and pure; „ 755
So Arthur bad the meek Sir *P* *Lancelot and E.* 1264
acts of prowess done In tournament or tilt, Sir *P*, *Holy Grail* 2
The monk Ambrosius question'd *P*: „ 17
'Nay, monk! what phantom?' answer'd *P*. „ 45
'A woman,' answer'd *P*, 'a nun, „ 68
'O my brother *P*,' she said, 'Sweet brother, „ 106
my lord,' said *P*, 'the King, Was not in hall: „ 205
the King Spake to me, being nearest, '*P*,' „ 268
Holier is none, my *P*, than she— „ 296
What are ye? Galahads?—no, nor *P's*' „ 306
Shouting, 'Sir Galahad and Sir *P*!' „ 337
these Cried to me climbing, 'Welcome, *P*! „ 425
Sir *P*: All men, to one so bound by such a vow, „ 564
'Yea so,' said *P*: 'One night my pathway swerving east, „ 633
answer'd *P*: 'And that can I, Brother, „ 711
But as for thine, my good friend *P*, „ 861
Blessed are Bors, Lancelot and *P*, „ 874
Beside that tower where *P* was cowl'd, *Pelleas and E.* 501
But *P* stood near him and replied, „ 523

Percivale (*continued*) 'Is the Queen false?' and *P* was mute. — *Pelleas and E.* 532
And *P* made answer not a word. — „ 534
'Is the King true?' 'The King!' said *P*. — „ 535
Perdition '*I* am on the Perfect Way, All else is to *p*.' — *Akbar's Dream* 35
Perennial *p* effluences, Whereof to all that draw the wholesome air, — *Lover's Tale i* 499
Perfect (adj.) (*See also* **All-perfect**) And *p* rest so inward is; — *Supp. Confessions* 51
An image with profulgent brows, And *p* limbs, — „ 146
Of *p* wifehood and pure lowlihead. — *Isabel* 12
The queen of marriage, a most *p* wife. — „ 28
Thou art *p* in love-lore. (repeat) — *Madeline* 9, 26
pure law, Commeasure *p* freedom.' — *Œnone* 167
temper'd with the tears Of angels to the *p* shape of man. — *To——, With Pal. of Art* 19
each a *p* whole From living Nature, — *Palace of Art* 58
I can but count thee *p* gain, — „ 198
Reading her *p* features in the gloom, — *Gardener's D.* 175
in sighs With *p* Joy, perplex'd for utterance, — „ 255
a hand, a foot Lessening in *p* cadence, — *Walk. to the Mail* 55
And that which shapes it to some *p* end. — *Love and Duty* 26
but ever dwells A *p* form in *p* rest. — *Day-Dm., Sleep. B.* 24
wide earth of light and shade Comes out a *p* round. — *Will Water.* 68
that reach To each his *p* pint of stout, — „ 115
drooping chestnut-buds began To spread into the *p* fan, — *Sir L. and Q. G.* 17
To waste his whole heart in one kiss Upon her *p* lips. — „ 45
Visions of a *p* State: — *Vision of Sin* 148
When all the wood stands in a mist of green, And nothing *p*: — *The Brook* 15
Edith, whose pensive beauty, *p* else, — *Aylmer's Field* 70
only, if a dream, Sweet dream, be *p*. — *Princess vii* 149
Pale was the *p* face; — „ 224
Like *p* music unto noble words; — „ 286
they grow, The single pure and *p* animal, — „ 306
Not *p*, nay, but full of tender wants, — „ 319
Her peaceful being slowly passes by To some more *p* peace. — *Requiescat* 8
Is *p* stillness when they brawl. — *Lit. Squabbles* 20
As pure and *p* as I say? — *In Mem. xxiv* 2
And orb into the *p* star We saw not, — „ 15
human hands the creed of ⌐.eeds In loveliness of *p* deeds, — „ *xxxvi* 11
The *p* flower of human time; — „ *lxi* 4
He too foretold the *p* rose. — „ *Con.* 34
It more beseems the *p* virgin knight — *Merlin and V.* 22
As Love, if Love be *p*, casts out fear, So Hate, if Hate be *p*, casts out fear. — „ 40
then her shape From forehead down to foot, *p*— — *Lancelot and E.* 642
And on the third are warriors, *p* men, — *Holy Grail* 236
but he that closes both Is *p*, he is Lancelot— — *Last Tournament* 709
That pure severity of *p* light— — *Guinevere* 646
Because it lack'd the power of *p* Hope; — *Lover's Tale i* 453
a babe in lineament and limb *P*, — *De Prof., Two G.* 12
I had past into *p* quiet at length — *Despair* 66
All good things may move in Hesper, *p* peoples, *p* kings. — *Locksley H., Sixty* 186
and made The rosy twilight of a *p* day. — *The Ring* 187
'*I* am on the *P* Way, All else is to perdition.' — *Akbar's Dream* 34
For if this earth be ruled by *P* Love, — *D. of the Duke of C.* 8
Perfect (s) 'That type of *P* in his mind In Nature — *Two Voices* 292
Perfection The clear *p* of her face. — *Mariana in the S.* 32
Dead *p*, no more; nothing more, — *Maud I ii* 7
That passionate *p*, my good lord— — *Lancelot and E.* 122
Perfectly *P* beautiful: let it be granted her: — *Maud I ii* 4
Perfectness Set light by narrower *p*. — *In Mem. cxii* 4
To die in gazing on that *p* Which I do bear — *Lover's Tale i* 88
science making toward Thy *P* Are blinding desert sand; — *Akbar's Dream* 29
Perfect-pure For see, how *p-p*! — *Balin and Balan* 266
Perfect-sweet Frowns *p-s* along the brow — *Madeline* 15
Perform Yet I thy hest will all *p* at full, — *M. d'Arthur* 43
Yet I thy hest will all *p* at full, — *Pass. of Arthur* 211
Perform'd 'Hast thou *p* my mission which I gave? — *M. d'Arthur* 67
'Hast thou *p* my mission which I gave? — *Pass. of Arthur* 235
Perfume (adj.) belongs to the heart of the *p* seller. — *Akbar's D., Inscrip.* 9
Perfume (s) As *p* of the cuckoo-flower? — *Margaret* 8
one warm gust, full-fed with *p*, — *Gardener's D.* 113
P and flowers fall in showers, — *Sir Galahad* 11
And fluctuate all the still *p*, — *In Mem. xcv* 56
Perfumed And made my life a *p* altar-flame; — *Maud I xviii* 24
Peril A carefuller in *p*, did not breathe — *Enoch Arden* 50
any of our people there In want or *p*, — *Princess ii* 267
the rest Spake but of sundry *p's* in the storm; — *Holy Grail* 761
raising her Still higher, past all *p*, — *Lover's Tale i* 394
That they had the better In *p's* of battle — *Batt. of Brunanburh* 85
Perilous Snatch'd thro' the *p* passes of his life: — *Aylmer's Field* 209
A *p* meeting under the tall pines — „ 414
Trembled in *p* places o'er a deep: — *Sea Dreams* 11
make her long for court And all its *p* glories: — *Marr. of Geraint* 804
And wildernesses, *p* paths, they rode: — *Geraint and E.* 32
Nor dared to waste a *p* pity on him: — „ 525
who in that *p* hour Put hand to hand — „ 766
And Merlin call'd it 'The Siege *p*,' *P* for good and ill; — *Holy Grail* 172
The path was *p*, loosely strown with crags: — *Lover's Tale i* 384
Above the *p* seas of Change and Chance; — „ 806
But in *p* plight were we, — *The Revenge* 75
Clove into *p* chasms our walls — *Def. of Lucknow* 55
we took to playing at battle, but that was a *p* play, — *V. of Maeldune* 95
Period Devolved his rounded *p's*. — *A Character* 18
I had hoped that ere this *p* closed — *St. S. Stylites* 17
Perish To *p*, wept for, honour'd, known, — *Two Voices* 149
Lest she should fail and *p* utterly, — *Palace of Art* 221
Till they *p* and they suffer— — *Lotos-Eaters, C. S.* 123
I *p* by this people which I made,— — *M. d'Arthur* 22
P in thy self-contempt! — *Locksley Hall* 96
I had been content to *p*, — „ 103
better men should *p* one by one, — „ 179
then it fails at last And *p'es* as I must; — *Lucretius* 265
promise (otherwise You *p*) as you came, — *Princess ii* 296
Fools prate, and *p* traitors. — *Balin and Balan* 530
I *p* by this people which I made,— — *Pass. of Arthur* 190
could I *p* While thou, a meteor of the sepulchre, — *Lover's Tale i* 98
Thy Thebes shall fall and *p*, — *Tiresias* 116
Perish'd I remember one that *p*: — *Locksley Hall* 71
'They *p* in their daring deeds.' — *Day-Dm., Arrival* 14
Not yet had *p*, when his lonely doom — *Enoch Arden* 626
P many a maid and matron, — *Boädicea* 85
Thy leaf has *p* in the green, — *In Mem. lxxv* 13
Now the Rome of slaves hath *p*, — *To Virgil* 33
Perishing Grief for our *p* children, — *Def. of Lucknow* 89
Perky (*See also* **Peärky**) There amid *p* larches and pine, — *Maud I x* 20
Permanence Be fix'd and froz'n to *p*: — *Two Voices* 237
Permission He craved a fair *p* to depart, — *Marr. of Geraint* 40
Nor stay'd to crave *p* of the King, — *Balin and Balan* 288
Permit *P* me, friend, I prythee, — *Lover's Tale i* 30
Perpetual And make *p* moan, — *Lotos-Eaters, C. S.* 17
May *p* youth Keep dry their light from tears; — *Of old sat Freedom* 19
Blanch'd in our annals, and *p* feast, — *Princess vi* 63
To her, *p* maidenhood, — *In Mem. vi* 43
As if *p* sunset linger'd there, — *The Ring* 83
On their *p* pine, nor round the beech; — *Prog. of Spring* 32
Perplex many things *p*, With motions, — *Two Voices* 299
no ruder air *p* Thy sliding keel, — *In Mem. ix* 9
Perplex'd-Perplext (*See also* **Self-perplext**) perfect Joy, *perplex'd* for utterance, — *Gardener's D.* 255
And *perplex'd* her, night and morn, — *L. of Burleigh* 78
Perplext her, made her half forget herself, — *Aylmer's Field* 303
Perplext in faith, but pure in deeds, — *In Mem. xcvi* 9
But he vext her and *perplext* her — *Maud I xx* 6
Perplext his outward purpose, till an hour, — *Gareth and L.* 175
Lancelot look'd and was *perplext* in mind, — *Lancelot and E.* 838
Perplexing *P* me with lies; — *St. S. Stylites* 102
Perplexity In doubt and great *p*, — *Palace of Art* 278
Perplext *See* **Perplex'd**
Persecute Should banded union *p* Opinion, — *You ask me, why, etc.* 17
than to *p* the Lord, And play the Saul — *Sir J. Oldcastle* 102
Persecutor 'bless' Whom? even 'your *p's*'! — *Akbar's Dream* 77
Persephonè or the enthroned *P* in Hades, — *Princess iv* 439
P! Queen of the dead no more— — *Demeter and P.* 17
Persia arm debased The throne of *P*, — *Alexander* 2

Persia (*continued*) a custom in the Orient, friends,—I read of it in *P*— *Lover's Tale iv* 231
Persian (adj.) Gazed on the *P* girl alone, *Arabian Nights* 134
Ran down the *P*, Grecian, Roman lines *Princess ii* 130
Persian (s) in his behalf Shall I exceed the *P*, *Lover's Tale iv* 347
Persistence *p* turn'd her scorn to wrath. *Pelleas and E.* 218
Persistent Heart-hiding smile, and gray *p* eye: *Guinevere* 64
Person law for *us*; We paid in *p*. *Walk. to the Mail* 86
'The thrall in *p* may be free in soul, *Gareth and L.* 165
Done in your maiden's *p* to yourself: *Marr. of Geraint* 216
promises the men who served About my *p*, „ 454
Yniol's rusted arms Were on his princely *p*, „ 544
Personal And therefore splenetic, *p*, base, *Maud I x* 33
Began to chafe as at a *p* wrong. *Enoch Arden* 474
Personality The abysmal deeps of *P*, *Palace of Art* 223
Immeasurable Reality! Infinite *P*! *De Prof., Human C.* 4
Pert *See* **Peärky**
Pest rending earthquake, or the famine, or the *p*! *Faith* 4
Persuade I might *p* myself then *Maud I x* 56
Persuasion *P*, no, nor death could alter her: *Aylmer's Field* 418
Perused conscious of ourselves, *P* the matting; *Princess ii* 68
Peruvian To buy strange shares in some *P* mine. *Sea Dreams* 15
Pestle To *p* a poison'd poison *Maud I i* 44
Pet (fit of peevishness) 'But in a *p* she started up, *Talking Oak* 229
Petal (*See also* **Rose-petal**) *p's* from blown roses on the grass, *Lotos-Eaters, C. S.* 2
two dewdrops on the *p* shake To the same sweet air, *Princess vii* 68
'Now sleeps the crimson *p*, „ 176
Tip-tilted like the *p* of a flower; *Gareth and L.* 591
Peter (*See also* **Pether**) laugh'd, and swore by *P* and by Paul: *Godiva* 24
'*P* had the brush, My *P*, first:' *Aylmer's Field* 254
I leap from Satan's foot to *P's* knee— *Gareth and L.* 538
sheet Let down to *P* at his prayers; *To E. Fitzgerald* 12
Rome of Cæsar, Rome of *P*, *Locksley H., Sixty* 88
Peter's-pence 'Ere yet, in scorn of *P-p*, *Talking Oak* 45
Pether (Peter) Till Holy St. *P* gets up wid his kays *Tomorrow* 93
Petition make a wild *p* night and day, *Princess v* 97
At thy new son, for my *p* to her. *Marr. of Geraint* 780
for my strange *p* I will make Amends „ 817
Petitionary (Claspt hands and that *p* grace *The Brook* 112
Petition'd *P* too for him. *Princess vi* 320
Queen *p* for his leave To see the hunt, *Marr. of Geraint* 154
Petted And smoothed a *p* peacock down with that: *Princess ii* 456
Pettish And *p* cries awoke, and the wan day *Last Tournament* 214
Petty O, I see thee old and formal, fitted to thy *p* part, *Locksley Hall* 93
Worried his passive ear with *p* wrongs *Enoch Arden* 352
The *p* marestail forest, fairy pines, *Aylmer's Field* 92
A *p* railway ran: a fire-balloon *Princess, Pro.* 74
And '*p* Ogress,' and 'ungrateful Puss,' „ 157
We cross'd the street and gain'd a *p* mound „ *iv* 557
AH God! the *p* fools of rhyme *Lit Squabbles* 1
And weave their *p* cells and die. *In Mem. l* 12
Let cares that *p* shadows cast, „ *cv* 13
The *p* cobwebs we have spun: „ *cxxiv* 8
For many a *p* king ere Arthur came *Com. of Arthur* 5
Drew all their *p* princedoms under him, „ 18
Colleaguing with a score of *p* kings, „ 67
Drew in the *p* princedoms under him, „ 517
That dwarfs the *p* love of one to one. *Merlin and V.* 492
And brake the *p* kings, and fought with Rome, *Pass. of Arthur* 68
Petulance Seer Would watch her at her *p*, *Merlin and V.* 175
Petulancy for her fault she wept Of *p*; „ 953
Petulant She brook'd it not; but wrathful, *p*, *Lucretius* 14
nipt her slender nose With *p* thumb *Gareth and L.* 750
Whereat the maiden, *p*, 'Lancelot, „ 1246
Petulantly *p* she said, 'Ay well— „ 1273
Pew grasping the p's And oaken finials *Aylmer's Field* 822
Pewit (*See also* **Lapwing**) Returning like the *p*, *Will Water.* 230
Phalanx Into that *p* of the summer spears *Aylmer's Field* 111
Phantasm white-eyed *p's* weeping tears of blood, *Palace of Art* 239
updrawn A fashion and a *p* of the form *Lover's Tale i* 646
They past on, The lordly *P's*! „ *ii* 99
Phantasmal Cloud-weaver of *p* hopes and fears, *To Victor Hugo* 2
Phantom (adj.) Thou shalt hear the 'Never, never,' whisper'd by the *p* years, *Locksley Hall* 83
Phantom (adj.) (*continued*) And *p* hopes assemble; *Will Water.* 30
The *p* husks of something foully done, *Lucretius* 160
P sound of blows descending, moan of an enemy massacred, *P* wail of women and children, multitudinous agonies. *Boädicea* 25
Bloodily flow'd the Tamesa rolling *p* bodies of horses and men; Then a *p* colony smoulder'd on the refluent estuary; „ 27
a *p* king, Now looming, and now lost; *Com. of Arthur* 430
while the *p* king Sent out at times a voice; „ 436
There came a clapping as of *p* hands. *Marr. of Geraint* 566
far away The *p* circle of a moaning sea. *Pass. of Arthur* 87
there was a *p* cry that I heard as I tost about, *In the Child. Hosp.* 63
yet No phantoms, watching from a *p* shore *Ancient Sage* 179
The *p* walls of this illusion fade, „ 181
star that gildest yet this *p* shore; *To Virgil* 26
Far off a *p* cuckoo cries From out a *p* hill; *Pref Poem, Broth. Son.* 19
Phantom (s) a *p* two hours old Of a maiden past away, *Adeline* 18
The *p* of a wish that once could move, *The form, the form* 10
The *p* of a silent song, *Miller's D.* 71
P's of other forms of rule, *Love thou thy land* 59
A *p* made of many *p's* moved Before him *Enoch Arden* 602
Beastlier than any *p* of his kind *Lucretius* 196
and make One act a *p* of succession: *Princess iii* 329
'And all the *p*, Nature, stands— *In Mem. iii* 9
Or like to noiseless *p's* flit: „ *xx* 16
But mine own *p* chanting hymns? „ *cviii* 10
That abiding *p* cold. *Maud II iv* 55
Till I saw the dreary *p* arise and fly „ *III vi* 36
But watch'd him have I like a *p* pass *Gareth and L.* 1335
'Hark the *P* of the house That ever shrieks *Lancelot and E.* 1022
The *p* of a cup that comes and goes?' *Holy Grail* 44
'Nay, monk! what *p*?' answer'd Percivale. „ 45
To whom I told my *p's*, and he said: „ 444
Glad that no *p* vext me more, „ 538
Came ye on none but *p's* in your quest, „ 562
And women were as *p's*. „ 566
Who seem'd the *p* of a Giant in it, *Guinevere* 602
P!—had the ghastliest That ever lusted for a body, *Lover's Tale i* 647
I, groaning, from me flung Her empty *p*: „ *ii* 206
The *p* of the whirling landaulet *Sisters (E. and E.)* 114
shatter'd *p* of that infinite One, *De Prof., Two G.* 47
And all the *p's* of the dream, *Tiresias* 195
and yet No *p's*, watching from a phanton shore *Ancient Sage* 179
and as the *p* disappears, *Locksley H., Sixty* 253
and that rich *p* of the tower? *The Ring* 253
Phantom-fair How faintly-flush'd, how *p-f*, *The Daisy* 65
Phantom-warning Should prove the *p-w* true. *In Mem. xcii* 12
Pharaoh May *P's* darkness, folds as dense *Aylmer's Field* 771
Pharisee These *P's*, this Caiaphas-Arundel *Sir J. Oldcastle* 179
Pharos roar that breaks the *P* from his base *Princess vi* 339
Phase act Of immolation, any *p* of death, „ *iii* 285
out of painful *p's* wrought There flutters *In Mem. lxv* 6
And, moved thro' life of lower *p*, „ *Con.* 125
every *p* of ever-heightening life, *De Prof., Two G.* 7
Pheasant-lord old *p-l's*, These partridge-breeders *Aylmer's Field* 381
Phenomenon Arbaces, and *P*, and the rest, *The Brook* 162
Philanthropies And nursed by mealy-mouth'd *p*, „ 94
Philip (*See also* **Philip Ray**) Enoch was host one day, *P* the next, *Enoch Arden* 25
then would *P*, his blue eyes All flooded „ 31
But *P* loved in silence; and the girl Seem'd kinder unto *P* „ 41
P stay'd (His father lying sick and needing him) „ 64
P look'd, And in their eyes and faces read his doom; „ 72
P's true heart, which hunger'd for her peace „ 272
P standing up said falteringly 'Annie, „ 284
P ask'd 'Then you will let me, Annie?' „ 322
P put the boy and girl to school, „ 331
P did not fathom Annie's mind: „ 344
P was her children's all-in-all; „ 348
call'd him Father *P*. *P* gain'd As Enoch lost; „ 354
they begg'd For Father *P* (as they call'd him) „ 365
'Come with us Father *P*' he denied; „ 368
So *P* rested with her well-content; „ 376
P sitting at her side forgot Her presence, „ 384
P coming somewhat closer spoke. „ 398
God reward you for it, *P*, „ 425

Philip (*continued*) 'dear *P*, wait a while: If Enoch comes— *Enoch Arden* 430
P sadly said 'Annie, as I have waited all my life „ 434
till *P* glancing up Beheld the dead flame „ 440
P with his eyes Full of that lifelong hunger, „ 463
Some thought that *P* did but trifle with her: „ 475
And others laugh'd at her and *P* too, „ 477
P's rosy face contracting grew Careworn and wan; „ 486
P thought he knew: „ 520
Then her good *P* was her all-in-all, „ 525
How *P* put her little ones to school, „ 706
and marriage, and the birth Of *P's* child: „ 709
Far-blazing from the rear of *P's* house, „ 727
P's dwelling fronted on the street, „ 731
P, the slighted suitor of old times, „ 745
And say to *P* that I blest him too; „ 886
Till last by *P's* farm I flow *The Brook* 31
P's farm where brook and river meet. „ 38
P chatter'd more than brook or bird; Old *P*; „ 51
And push'd at *P's* garden-gate. „ 83
in I went, and call'd old P out To show the farm: „ 120
And with me *P*, talking still; „ 164
when they follow'd us from *P's* door, „ 167
Poor *P*, of all his lavish waste of words „ 191
Philip Ray (*See also* **Philip**) *P R* the miller's only son, *Enoch Arden* 13
I married her who married *P R*. „ 860
Philosopher Be mine a *p's* life *Maud I iv* 49
Philosophy Affirming each his own *p*— *Lucretius* 216
fair *philosophies* That lift the fancy; *Princess iii* 340
And many an old *p* On Argive heights *In Mem. xxiii* 21
For fear divine *P* Should push beyond her mark, „ *liii* 14
I have had my day and my *philosophies*— *Last Tournament* 319
Science, *p*, song— *The Wreck* 51
knew no books and no *philosophies*, *Ancient Sage* 218
What the *philosophies*, all the sciences, *Vastness* 31
each *p* And mood of faith may hold *Akbar's Dream* 55
When fine *Philosophies* would fail, „ 140
Philtre brew'd the *p* which had power, *Lucretius* 16
Phlegethon By the red race of fiery *P*; *Demeter and P.* 28
Phœnix A fiery *p* rising from the smoke, *The Ring* 339
Phosphor till *P*, bright As our pure love, *In Mem. ix* 10
Bright *P*, fresher for the night, „ *cxxi* 9
Phosphorescence star of *p* in the calm, *Audley Court* 87
Broke with a *p* charming even My lady; *Aylmer's Field* 116
Phosphorus '*P*,' then 'MERIDIES'—'HESPERUS'— *Gareth and L.* 1204
Phra-bat *P-b* the step; your Pontic coast; *To Ulysses* 42
Phra-Chai *P-C*, the Shadow of the Best, „ 41
Phrase (*See also* **Boy-phrase**) In *p's* here and there at random, *Aylmer's Field* 434
household talk, and *p's* of the hearth, *Princess ii* 315
every *p* well-oil'd, As man's could be; „ *iii* 133
Fair speech was his and delicate of *p*, *Lover's Tale i* 719
Fair speech was his, and delicate of *p*. „ *iv* 273
courtly *p* that masks his malice now— *The Flight* 30
that large *p* of yours 'A Star among the stars,' *Epilogue* 41
flashing out from many a golden *p*; *To Virgil* 8
Have added fulness to the *p* *To Marq. of Dufferin* 11
Physician a vile *p*, blabbing The case of his patient— *Maud II v* 36
Piacenza At Lodi, rain, *P*, rain. *The Daisy* 52
Piano She left the new *p* shut: *Talking Oak* 119
Pibroch Dance to the *p*!—saved! *Def. of Lucknow* 103
Pick (s) Click with the *p*, coming nearer and nearer *Def. of Lucknow* 28
Pick (verb) *p* the faded creature from the pool, *Marr. of Geraint* 671
p the vicious quitch Of blood and custom *Geraint and E.* 903
To dig, *p*, open, find and read the charm: *Merlin and V.* 660
P's from the colewort a green caterpillar, *Guinevere* 32
Pickaxe A *p* in her hand: *Sea Dreams* 100
wait till the point of the *p* be thro'! *Def. of Lucknow* 27
Pick'd '*p* the eleventh from this hearth *The Epic* 41
p offenders from the mass For judgment. *Princess i* 29
Hath *p* a ragged-robin from the hedge, *Marr. of Geraint* 724
p the lance That pleased him best, *Geraint and E.* 179
Pickpocket *P's*, each hand lusting for all *Maud I i* 22
Picnic Let us *p* there At Audley Court.' *Audley Court* 2
Pictur (s) The fellers as maäkes them *p's*, *Owd Roä* 23
Pictur (verb) to *p* the door-poorch theere, *Owd Roä* 24
Picture (*See also* **Pictur**) with wide blue eyes As in a *p*. *M. d'Arthur* 170
eyes have been intent On that veil'd *p*— *Gardener's D.* 270
More like a *p* seemeth all Than those old portraits *Day-Dm., Sleep. P.* 22
still I wore her *p* by my heart, *Princess i* 38
The mimic *p's* breathing grace, *In Mem. lxxviii* 11
I make a *p* in the brain; „ *lxxx* 9
still his *p* form'd And grew between her *Lancelot and E.* 992
with wide blue eyes As in a *p*. *Pass. of Arthur* 338
and fell Slanting upon that *p*, *Lover's Tale ii* 175
About a *p* of his lady, taken Some years before, „ *iv* 216
And crossing her own *p* as she came, „ 286
for Emmie, you see, It's all in the *p* there: *In the Child. Hosp.* 50
In my life there was a *p*, *Locksley H., Sixty* 15
I used To prattle to her *p*— *The Ring* 116
I see the *p* yet, Mother and child. *Romney's R.* 80
Pictured From yearlong poring on thy *p* eyes, *Princess vii* 340
And grew between her and the *p* wall. *Lancelot and E.* 993
Picturesque The *p* of man and man.' *In Mem. lxxxix* 42
To make old bareness *p* And tuft with grass „ *cxxviii* 19
Picus snared *P* and Faunus, rustic Gods? *Lucretius* 182
Pie too noble' he said 'to check at *p's*, *Merlin and V.* 126
Pieäce (piece) An' their mashin' their toys to *p's* *Spinster's S's.* 88
Piebald Not like the *p* miscellany, man, *Princess v* 198
Piece (*See also* **Pieäce**) Look what a lovely *p* of workmanship!' *Aylmer's Field* 237
a rough *p* Of early rigid colour, „ 280
All over earthy, like a *p* of earth, *Sea Dreams* 99
earthquake in one day Cracks all to *p's*,— *Lucretius* 252
charr'd and wrinkled *p* of womanhood, *Princess v* 61
Cut the Roman boy to *p's* *Boädicea* 66
a *p* of inmost Horticultural art, *Hendecasyllabics* 19
I see in part That all, as in some *p* of art, *In Mem. cxxviii* 23
to rend the cloth, to rend In *p's*, *Gareth and L.* 401
hew'd great *p's* of his armour off him, „ 1142
And high above a *p* of turret stair, *Marr. of Geraint* 320
Saw once a great *p* of a promontory, *Geraint and E.* 162
heap'd The *p's* of his armour in one place, „ 374
his cheek Bulge with the unswallow'd *p*, „ 631
shadow of some *p* of pointed lace, *Lancelot and E.* 1174
p by *p* I learnt the drearier story *Lover's Tale iv* 146
a single *p* Weigh'd nigh four thousand Castillanos *Columbus* 135
Pieced I slept again, and *p* The broken vision; *Sea Dreams* 109
Piecemeal Till all my limbs drop *p* *St. S. Stylites* 44
surely would have torn the child *P* among them, *Com. of Arthur* 218
if thou doubt, the beasts Will tear thee *p*.' *Holy Grail* 825
Pied Then all the dry *p* things that be *The Mermaid* 48
Pier A thousand *p's* ran into the great Sea. *Holy Grail* 503
Dash back that ocean with a *p*, *Mechanophilus* 5
Pierce Yet could not all creation *p* *A Character* 5
watching still To *p* me thro' with pointed light; *Rosalind* 27
p The blackest files of clanging fight, *Kate* 25
Clear Love would *p* and cleave, *If I were loved* 6
Pointed itself to *p*, but sank down shamed *Lucretius* 63
p's the liver and blackens the blood; *The Islet* 35
P's the keen seraphic flame From orb to orb, *In Mem. xxx* 27
And one would *p* an outer ring, „ *lxxxvii* 27
With pointed lance as if to *p*, a shape, *Balin and Balan* 325
Ascending, *p* the glad and songful air, *Demeter and P.* 45
Pierced *p* thy heart, my love, my bride, *Oriana* 42
heart, *p* thro' with fierce delight, *Fatima* 34
Below were men and horses *p* with worms, *Vision of Sin* 209
wander from his wits *P* thro' with eyes, *Princess ii* 441
maybe *p* to death before mine eyes, *Marr. of Geraint* 104
same spear Wherewith the Roman *p* the side of Christ. *Balin and Balan* 114
and the head *P* thro' his side, *Lancelot and E.* 490
thro' those black walls of yew Their talk had *p*, „ 970
thro' the wind *P* ever a child's cry: *Last Tournament* 17
dying now *P* by a poison'd dart. *Death of Œnone* 34
Piercing the high dawn *p* the royal rose *Merlin and V.* 739
from the ground She raised her *p* orbs, *D. of F. Women* 171
Pierian fire from off a pure *P* altar, *Parnassus* 17
Pièro and he stabb'd my *P* with this. *Bandit's Death* 10
For he reek'd with the blood of *P*; „ 13
Pig great with *p*, wallowing in sun and mud. *Walk. to the Mail* 88

Pig (*continued*) An' p's didn't sell at fall, *Church-warden, etc.* 5
Pigeon quail and p, lark and leveret lay, *Audley Court* 24
p's, who in session on their roofs Approved him, *The Brook* 127
Like any p will I cram his crop, *Gareth and L.* 459
Pigg'd on the leads we kept her till she p. *Walk. to the Mail* 92
Pigmy That shriek and sweat in p wars *Lit. Squabbles* 2
and p spites of the village spire; *Vastness* 25
Pike (fish) but Charlie 'e cotch'd the p, *Village Wife* 43
Pike (hill) high field on the bushless P, *Ode to Memory* 96
Pike (weapon) when his bailiff brought A Chartist p. *Walk. to the Mail* 71
as prompt to spring against the p's, *Princess iii* 286
came with their p's and musqueteers, *The Revenge* 53
the p's were all broken or bent, „ 80
Pile (s) skins of wine, and p's of grapes. *Vision of Sin* 13
look'd the Lombard p's; *The Daisy* 54
When God hath made the p complete; *In Mem. liv* 8
Timour-Mammon grins on a p of children's bones, *Maud I i* 46
side of that long hall A stately p,— *Gareth and L.* 405
find What rotten p's uphold their mason-work, *Sir J. Oldcastle* 67
built their shepherd-prince a funeral p; *Death of Œnone* 63
she leapt upon the funeral p, „ 105
Pile (verb) Should p her barricades with dead. *In Mem. cxxvii* 8
Piled Life p on life Were all too little, *Ulysses* 24
Among p arms and rough accoutrements, *Princess v* 55
plunged him into a cell Of great p stones; *Holy Grail* 676
Pilgrimage '*P's?*' 'Drink, bagpipes, *Sir J. Oldcastle* 148
Piling P sheaves in uplands airy, *L. of Shalott i* 34
Pillar (*See also* **Porch-pillars**) A p of white light upon the wall *Ode to Memory* 53
Patient on this tall p I have borne *St. S. Stylites* 15
Three years I lived upon a p, „ 86
I, Simeon of the p, by surname Stylites, „ 161
slid From p unto p, until she reach'd The gateway; *Godiva* 50
glimmering shoulder under gloom Of cavern p's; *To E. L.* 18
The last remaining p of their house, *Aylmer's Field* 295
ample awnings gay Betwixt the p's, *Princess ii* 26
Her back against a p, her foot on one „ *iii* 180
As comes a p of electric cloud, „ *v* 524
azure p's of the hearth Arise to thee: „ *vii* 216
The p of a people's hope, *In Mem. lxiv* 15
shake The p's of domestic peace. „ *xc* 20
A p stedfast in the storm, „ *cxiii* 12
Who shall fix Her p's? „ *cxiv* 4
And sat by a p alone; *Maud I viii* 2
two p's which from earth uphold Our childhood, *Lover's Tale i* 220
Tether'd to these dead p's of the Church— *Sir J. Oldcastle* 121
a smoke who was once a p of fire, *Despair* 29
shook Those p's of a moulder'd faith, *Akbar's Dream* 81
Pillar'd Imbower'd vaults of p palm, *Arabian Nights* 39
star shot thro' the sky Above the p town. *Palace of Art* 124
pass'd thro' all The p dusk of sounding sycamores, *Audley Court* 16
And sleep beneath his p light! *The Voyage* 20
before us into rooms which gave Upon a p porch, *Princess i* 230
thy fresh and virgin soul Inform'd the p Parthenon, *Freedom* 3
Pillar-punishment For not alone this p-p, *St. S. Stylites* 60
Pillory P Wisdom in your markets, *Locksley H., Sixty* 134
Pillow (*See also* **Marriage-pillow**) Dripping with Sabæan spice On thy p, *Adeline* 54
Fancy came and at her p sat, *Caress'd or chidden* 5
Turn thee, turn thee on thy p: *Locksley Hall* 86
The gold-fringed p lightly prest: *Day-Dm., Sleep. B.* 22
or laid his feverous p smooth! *Aylmer's Field* 701
smooth my p, mix the foaming draught *Princess ii* 251
Or if lip were laid to lip on the p's of the wave. *The Flight* 48
Pillow'd one soft lap P us both: *Lover's Tale i* 236
Pilot (adj.) 'Enid, the p star of my lone life, *Geraint and E.* 306
Pilot (s) The summer p of an empty heart *Gardener's D.* 16
The p of the darkness and the dream. *Audley Court* 72
P's of the purple twilight, *Locksley Hall* 122
May wreck itself without the p's guilt, *Aylmer's Field* 716
But, your example p, told her all. *Princess iii* 137
I hope to see my P face to face *Crossing the Bar* 15
Pilot-star (*See also* **Pilot (adj.)**) eyes grown dim with gazing on the p-s's. *Lotos-Eaters, C. S.* 87
'In happy time behold our p-s! *Pelleas and E.* 63
Pimpernel As the p dozed on the lea; *Maud I xxii* 48
Pin Where children cast their p's and nails, *Merlin and V.* 430
Pinch And p their brethren in the throng, *Lit. Squabbles* 7
Or p a murderous dust into her drink, *Merlin and V.* 610
making with a kindly p Each poor pale cheek *The Ring* 314
Pindar Ghost of P in you Roll'd an Olympian; *To Prof. Jebb* 3
Pine (a tree) black-stemm'd p's only the far river shines. *Leonine Eleg.* 2
Twin peaks shadow'd with p slope to the dark hyaline. „ 10
A gleaming crag with belts of p's. *Two Voices* 189
creeps from p to p, And loiters, *Œnone* 4
And dewy dark aloft the mountain p: „ 49
within the cave Behind yon whispering tuft of oldest p, „ 88
away my tallest p's, My tall dark p's, „ 208
Up-clomb the shadowy p above the woven copse. *Lotos-Eaters* 18
sweet, stretch'd out beneath the p. „ *C. S.* 99
sweating rosin, plump'd the p *Amphion* 47
Fantastic plume or sable p; *The Voyage* 44
The petty marestail forest, fairy p's, *Aylmer's Field* 92
A perilous meeting under the tall p's „ 414
and above them roar'd the p. „ 431
Kept to the garden now, and grove of p's, „ 550
Whom all the p's of Ida shook to see *Lucretius* 86
No larger feast than under plane or p „ 213
standing like a stately P Set in a cataract *Princess v* 346
cease To glide a sunbeam by the blasted P, „ *vii* 196
her eagles flew Beyond the Pyrenean p's, *Ode on Well.* 113
And loyal p's of Canada murmur thee, *W. to Marie Alex.* 19
In lands of palm and southern p; *The Daisy* 2
Garrulous under a roof of p: *To F. D. Maurice* 20
For groves of p on either hand, „ 21
Above the valleys of palm and p.' *The Islet* 23
king of the wrens, from out of the p! *Window, Ay* 8
There amid perky larches and p, *Maud I x* 20
slender-shafted P Lost footing, fell, *Gareth and L.* 3
thro' tops of many thousand p's „ 796
so down among the p's He plunged; „ 808
but three Fled thro' the p's; „ 814
p's that fledged The hills that watch'd thee, *Lover's Tale i* 11
open'd on the p's with doors of glass, „ 41
till the morning light Sloped thro' the p's, „ 264
When first we came from out the p's at noon, „ 310
great p shook with lonely sounds of joy „ 325
Back to his mother's house among the p's. „ *iv* 15
the p shot aloft from the crag *V. of Maeldune* 16
Or watch the waving p which here *To Ulysses* 25
On their perpetual p, nor round the beech; *Prog. of Spring* 32
day long labour'd, hewing the p's, *Death of Œnone* 62
topmost p Spired into bluest heaven, „ 68
shriek of some lost life among the p's, „ 90
under the bridge By the great dead p— *Bandit's Death* 23
Pine (fruit) A raiser of huge melons and of p, *Princess, Con.* 87
Pine (verb) You p among your halls and towers: *L. C. V. de Vere* 58
p's in sad experience worse than death, *Princess vii* 315
To p in that reverse of doom, *In Mem. lxxii* 6
her too hast thou left To p and waste *Last Tournament* 598
Pined thro' her love her life Wasted and p, *Pelleas and E.* 496
Pinewood o'er a bridge of p crossing, *Princess iii* 335
the lake whiten'd and the p roar'd, *Merlin and V.* 637
Thy breath is of the p; *Lover's Tale i* 23
Piney lost his way between the p sides *Œnone* 93
Pining brake his very heart in p for it, *Gareth and L.* 57
And p life be fancy-fed. *In Mem. lxxxv* 96
P for the stronger heart *Locksley H., Sixty* 58
Pink P was the shell within, *Minnie and Winnie* 5
The tender p five-beaded baby-soles, *Aylmer's Field* 186
ye said I wur pretty i' p's, *Spinster's S's.* 17
its wreaths of dripping green—Its pale p shells— *Lover's Tale i* 40
Pinnace And a p, like a flutter'd bird, *The Revenge* 2
Pinnacle Three silent p's of aged snow, *Lotos-Eaters* 16
heroes tall Dislodging p and parapet *D. of F. Women* 26
And statued p's, mute as they. *The Daisy* 64
tipt with lessening peak And p, *Gareth and L.* 309
spires Prick'd with incredible p's into heaven. *Holy Grail* 423
summit and the p's Of a gray steeple— *Lover's Tale ii* 81
ablaze With creepers crimsoning to the p's, *The Ring* 82

Place (s) (*continued*) The battle deepen'd in its *p*, *Oriana* 51
in its *p* My heart a charmed slumber *Eleänore* 127
tho' I knew not in what time or *p*, *Sonnet To* —— 12
He pray'd, and from a happy *p* *Two Voices* 224
The *p* he knew forgetteth him.' „ 264
In her still *p* the morning wept: „ 275
'But, if I lapsed from nobler *p*, „ 358
Passing the *p* where each must rest, „ 410
I will grow round him in his *p*, *Fatima* 40
who have attain'd Rest in a happy *p* *Œnone* 131
'What! is not this my *p* of strength,' *Palace of Art* 233
Lost to her *p* and name; „ 264
The flower ripens in its *p*, *Lotos-Eaters, C. S.* 36
Spoke slowly in her *p*. *D. of F. Women* 92
'I was cut off from hope in that sad *p*, „ 105
The *p* of him that sleeps in peace. *To J. S.* 68
But lives and loves in every *p*; *On a Mourner* 5
There in her *p* she did rejoice, *Of old sat Freedom* 5
Nor toil for title, *p*, or touch Of pension, *Love thou thy land* 25
in the moon athwart the *p* of tombs, *M. d'Arthur* 46
rising bore him thro' the *p* of tombs. „ 175
old order changeth, yielding *p* to new, „ 240
In that still *p* she, hoarded in herself, *Gardener's D.* 49
Then, in that time and *p*, I spoke to her, „ 226
in that time and *p* she answer'd me, „ 231
he's abroad: the *p* is to be sold. *Walk. to the Mail* 16
purple beech among the greens Looks out of *p*: *Edwin Morris* 85
So left the *p*, left Edwin, „ 137
'Tis the *p*, and all around it, *Locksley Hall* 3
The rhymes are dazzled from their *p* *Day-Dm., Pro.* 19
The fountain to his *p* returns „ *Sleep P.* 11
Here all things in their *p* remain, „ 53
And alleys, faded *p's*, *Amphion* 86
Is there some magic in the *p*? *Will Water.* 79
How out of *p* she makes The violet „ 146
Then they started from their *p's*, *Vision of Sin* 33
And he sat him down in a lonely *p*, *Poet's Song* 5
Would Enoch have the *p*? *Enoch Arden* 125
Moved haunting people, things and *p's*, „ 604
Flared on him, and he came upon the *p*. „ 681
And him, that other, reigning in his *p*, „ 763
served, Long since, a bygone Rector of the *p*, *Aylmer's Field* 11
rustling once at night about the *p*, „ 547
all neglected *p's* of the field Broke „ 693
who beside your hearths Can take her *p*— „ 736
Trembled in perilous *p's* o'er a deep: *Sea Dreams* 11
something it should be to suit the *p*, *Princess, Pro.* 211
something made to suit with Time and *p*, „ 231
Found a still *p*, and pluck'd her likeness out; „ *i* 92
They fed her theories, in and out of *p* „ *i* 129
last not least, she who had left her *p*, „ *ii* 165
I find you here but in the second *p*, „ *iii* 157
A tree Was half-disrootod from his *p* „ *iv* 186
To push my rival out of *p* and power. „ 335
you stoop'd to me From all high *p's*, „ 430
Stole a maiden from her *p*, „ *vi* 9
work no more alone! Our *p* is much: „ *vii* 267
Who look'd all native to her *p*, „ 323
Jenny, my cousin, had come to the *p*, *Grandmother* 25
Fair is her cottage in its *p*, *Requiescat* 1
I see the *p* where thou wilt lie. *Sailor Boy* 8
From out waste *p's* comes a cry, *In Mem. iii* 7
And all the *p* is dark, „ *viii* 7
and feels Her *p* is empty, fall like these; „ *xiii* 4
rest And in the *p's* of his youth. „ *xviii* 8
It was but unity of *p* „ *xlii* 3
And so may *P* retain us still, „ 5
will speak out In that high *p*, „ *xliv* 16
I know that in thy *p* of rest „ *lxvii* 2
Again our ancient games had *p*, *In Mem lxxviii* 10
Thy sweetness from its proper *p*? „ *lxxxiii* 6
That beats within a lonely *p*, „ *lxxxv* 110
I find no *p* that does not breathe „ *c* 3
We leave the well-beloved *p* „ *cii* 1
For change of *p*, like growth of time, „ *cv* 11

Place (s) (*continued*) Ring out false pride in *p* and blood, *In Mem. cvi* 21
What find I in the highest *p*, „ *cviii* 9
Let her know her *p*; „ *cxiv* 15
To hold me from my proper *p*, „ *cxvii* 2
And of himself in higher *p*, „ *cxviii* 15
Thy *p* is changed; thou art the same. „ *cxxi* 20
Who moves about from *p* to *p*, „ *cxxvi* 10
maidens of the *p*, That pelt us in the porch „ *Con.* 67
if I fled from the *p* and the pit and the fear? *Maud I i* 64
The dark old *p* will be gilt by the touch „ 66
That old man never comes to his *p*: „ *xiii* 24
In the silent woody *p's* By the home „ *II iv* 6
Not making his high *p* the lawless perch *Ded. of Idylls* 22
old order changeth, yielding *p* to new; *Com. of Arthur* 509
To find, at some *p* I shall come at, arms *Marr. of Geraint* 219
roam the goodly *p's* that she knew; „ 646
swamps and pools, waste *p's* of the hern, *Geraint and E.* 31
And down a rocky pathway from the *p* „ 200
Enter'd, the wild lord of the *p*, Limours. „ 277
heap'd The pieces of his armour in one *p*, „ 374
Clear'd the dark *p's* and let in the law, „ 943
the *p* which now Is this world's hugest, *Lancelot and E.* 75
The sound not wonted in a *p* so still „ 818
all the *p* whereon she stood was green; „ 1200
my knights, Your *p's* being vacant at my side, *Holy Grail* 317
And mirthful sayings, children of the *p*, „ 555
Sir Lancelot, sitting in my *p* Enchair'd *Last Tournament* 103
Than thou reseated in thy *p* of light, *Guinevere* 525
glory cling To all high *p's* like a golden cloud *Pass. of Arthur* 54
in the moon athwart the *p* of tombs, „ 214
rising bore him thro' the *p* of tombs. „ 343
old order changeth, yielding *p* to new, „ 408
nor in the present time, Nor in the present *p*. *Lover's Tale i* 117
Thrust forward on to-day and out of *p*; „ 123
The beautiful in Past of act or *p*, „ 135
a *p* of burial Far lovelier than its cradle; „ 529
But taken with the sweetness of the *p*, „ 531
To centre in this *p* and time. „ 552
It was so happy an hour, so sweet a *p*, „ 558
I was the High Priest in her holiest *p*, „ 686
every bone seem'd out of its *p*— *In the Child. Hosp.* 13
Have I mislearnt our *p* of meeting?) *Sir J. Oldcastle* 153
perils of battle On *p's* of slaughter— *Batt. of Brunanburh* 86
taking the *p* of the pitying God *Despair* 42
but set no meek ones in their *p*; *Locksley H., Sixty* 133
and the Rome of freemen holds her *p*, *To Virgil* 34
mob's million feet Will kick you from your *p*, *The Fleet* 19
and give *p* to the beauty that endures, *Happy* 36
glimmer of relief In change of *p*. *To Mary Boyle* 48
from out our bourne of Time and *P* *Crossing the Bar* 13

Place (verb) foremost in thy various gallery *P* it, *Ode to Memory* 85
murmur'd Arthur, '*P* me in the barge,' *M. d'Arthur* 204
p their pride in Lancelot and the Queen. *Merlin and V.* 25
murmur'd Arthur, '*P* me in the barge.' *Pass. of Arthur* 372
And *p* them by themselves; *Lover's Tale i* 173
p a hand in his Like an honest woman's, *Forlorn* 19
Few at first will *p* thee well; *Poets and Critics* 10

Placed in the towers I *p* great bells *Palace of Art* 129
often *p* upon the sick man's brow Cool'd it, *Aylmer's Field* 700
they *p* a peacock in his pride Before the damsel, *Gareth and L.* 850
And over these is *p* a silver wand, *Marr. of Geraint* 483
And over these they *p* the silver wand, „ 549
And *p* them in this ruin; „ 643
p where morning's earliest ray Might strike it, *Lancelot and E.* 5
p My ring upon the finger of my bride. *Sisters (E. and E.)* 213

Placid In summer heats, with *p* lows Unfearing, *Supp. Confessions* 154
Crown'd Isabel, thro' all her *p* life, *Isabel* 27
Ere the *p* lips be cold? *Adeline* 20
high above them stood The *p* marble Muses, *Princess iv* 489
Sailest the *p* ocean-plains With my lost Arthur's loved remains, *In Mem. ix* 2
To feel once more, in *p* awe, „ *cxxii* 5
while the Queen, who sat With lips severely *p*, *Lancelot and E.* 740
their malice on the *p* lip Froz'n by sweet sleep, *Pelleas and E.* 432
Beside the *p* breathings of the King, *Guinevere* 69

Placid (*continued*) Crown'd with her highest act the *p* face — *Lover's Tale i* 216
The *p* gleam of sunset after storm ! — *Ancient Sage* 133
With your own shadow in the *p* lake, — *Romney's R.* 76
Placing *p* his true hand upon her heart, — *Lover's Tale iv* 75
Plagiarised Until he *p* a heart, — *Talking Oak* 19
Plagiarist calls her *p* ; I know not what : — *Princess iii* 94
Plague (s) (*See also* **Egypt-plague**) Blight and famine, *p* and earthquake, — *Lotos-Eaters, C. S.* 115
Remember what a *p* of rain ; — *The Daisy* 50
A *P* upon the people fell, — *The Victim* 1
Help us from famine And *p* and strife ! — „ 10
when I spake of famine, *p*, — *Tiresias* 60
an' a trouble an' *p* wi' indoor. — *Spinster's S's.* 50
to stay, Not spread the *p*, the famine ; — *Demeter and P.* 134
leper *p* may scale my skin but never taint my heart ; — *Happy* 27
Your *p* but passes by the touch. — „ 104
Plague (verb) began To vex and *p* her. — *Guinevere* 68
thou their tool, set on to *p* And play upon, — „ 359
Plagued *P* her with sore despair. — *Palace of Art* 224
worldly-wise begetters, *p* themselves — *Aylmer's Field* 482
P with a flitting to and fro, — *Maud II ii* 33
We that are *p* with dreams of something sweet — *Holy Grail* 625
to whom Tristram, half *p* by Lancelot's — *Last Tournament* 194
Plain (adj.) 'Will thirty seasons render *p* — *Two Voices* 82
Should that *p* fact, as taught by these, — „ 281
'I cannot make this matter *p*, — „ 343
Sleeps in the *p* eggs of the nightingale. — *Aylmer's Field* 103
That has but one *p* passage of few notes, — *Lancelot and E.* 895
who himself Besought me to be *p* and blunt, — „ 1301
Which lives with blindness, or *p* innocence — *Sisters (E. and E.)* 249
Fair garments, *p* or rich, and fitting close — *Akbar's Dream* 131
Plain (adv.) but, Emmie, you tell it him *p*, — *In the Child. Hosp.* 57
Plain (s) (*See also* **Battle-plain**, **Ocean-plain**) THE *p* was grassy, wild and bare, — *Dying Swan* 1
To stoop the cowslip to the *p's*, — *Rosalind* 16
By herds upon an endless *p*, — *Palace of Art* 74
Groves of swine That range on yonder *p*. — „ 200
with dead lips smiled at the twilight *p*, — *D. of F. Women* 62
The wild wind rang from park and *p*, — *The Goose* 45
She glanced across the *p* ; — *Talking Oak* 166
on the ringing *p's* of windy Troy. — *Ulysses* 17
Clothes and reclothes the happy *p's*, — *Day-Dm., Sleep. P.* 2
I leave the *p*, I climb the height ; — *Sir Galahad* 57
The maiden Spring upon the *p* — *Sir L. and Q. G.* 3
And fleeter now she skimm'd the *p's* — „ 32
lord of the ringing lists, And all the *p*,— — *Princess v* 503
And had a cousin tumbled on the *p*, — „ *vi* 319
But when we crost the Lombard *p* — *The Daisy* 49
the stars, the seas, the hills and the *p's*— — *High. Pantheism* 1
winds from off the *p* Roll'd the rich vapour — *Spec. of Iliad* 7
A thousand on the *p* ; — „ 19
brightens and darkens down on the *p*. — *Window, On the Hill* 2
Calm and still light on yon great *p* — *In Mem. xi* 9
Imperial halls, or open *p* ; — „ *xcviii* 29
The brook shall babble down the *p*, — „ *ci* 10
when their feet were planted on the *p* — *Gareth and L.* 187
Turn'd to the right, and past along the *p* ; — „ 295
gazing over *p* and wood ; — „ 668
'O trefoil, sparkling on the rainy *p*, — „ 1159
kindled all the *p* and all the wold. — *Balin and Balan* 441
while they rode together down the *p*, — *Merlin and V.* 123
sunlight on the *p* behind a shower : — „ 403
they would pare the mountain to the *p*, — „ 829
Returning o'er the *p* that then began — *Holy Grail* 217
hill, or *p*, at sea, or flooding ford. — „ 728
On some vast *p* before a setting sun, — *Guinevere* 77
You see yon Lombard poplar on the *p*. — *Sisters (E. and E.)* 79
bloom from every vale and *p* — *To Mary Boyle* 9
summer basking in the sultry *p's* — *Prog. of Spring* 77
hear their words On pathway'd *p's* ; — „ 83
Nor always on the *p*, — *Politics* 2
the black ox of the distant *p*. — *On one who ran down Eng.* 4
ere the mountain rolls into the *p*, — *Death of Œnone* 51
Plain *See also* **Plaäin**

Plain-faced gray tower, or *p-f* tabernacle, — *Aylmer's Field* 618
Plainness Nay, the *p* of her dresses? — *Maud I xx* 14
Plaintive Then from the *p* mother's teat he took — *The Brook* 129
The *p* cry jarr'd on her ire ; — *Princess iv* 393
'Yet blame not thou thy *p* song,' — *In Mem. lii* 5
Vext her with *p* memories of the child : — *Last Tournament* 29
Plaited (adj.) With *p* alleys of the trailing rose, — *Ode to Memory* 106
Falsehood shall bare her *p* brow : — *Clear-headed friend* 11
Until the *p* ivy-tress had wound — *Lover's Tale i* 618
Plaited (verb) she *p* broad and long A strong sword-belt, — *Holy Grail* 152
Plan (s) (*See also* **Ground-plan**) Old wishes, ghosts of broken *p's*, — *Will Water.* 29
Enoch lay long-pondering on his *p's* ; — *Enoch Arden* 133
comes the feebler heiress of your *p*, — *Princess iii* 237
Dismiss me, and I prophesy your *p*, — „ *iv* 354
'The *p* was mine. I built the nest.' — „ 365
she lightens scorn At him that mars her *p*, — „ *v* 132
build some *p* Foursquare to opposition.' — „ 230
I scarce am fit for your great *p's* : — „ *vi* 218
The world-compelling *p* was thine,— — *Ode Inter. Exhib.* 10
And mingles all without a *p*? — *In Mem. xvi* 20
the boundless *p* That makes you tyrants — *Maud I xviii* 36
a shadow of the planner or the *p* ? — *Locksley H., Sixty* 196
Nature's male and female *p*, — *On one who affec. E. M.* 3
Plan (verb) while I *p* and *p*, my hair Is gray — *Will Water.* 167
Plane (level surface) Athwart a *p* of molten glass, — *In Mem. xv* 11
Plane (tree) under *p* or pine With neighbours — *Lucretius* 213
beneath an emerald *p* Sits Diotima, — *Princess iii* 301
had our wine and chess beneath the *p's*, — „ *vi* 246
Planed you *p* her path To Lady Psyche, — „ *iv* 315
Planet I breathed In some new *p* : — *Edwin Morris* 115
O, happy *p*, eastward go ; — *Move eastward* 4
inhabitant Of some clear *p* close upon the Sun, — *Princess ii* 36
eddied into suns, that wheeling cast The *p's* : — „ 119
all the fair young *p* in her hands— — „ *vii* 264
That one fair *p* can produce, — *Ode Inter. Exhib.* 24
songs, that woke The darkness of our *p*, — *In Mem. lxxvi* 10
Whereof the man, that with me trod This *p*, — „ *Con.* 138
Our *p* is one, the suns are many, — *Maud I iv* 45
And the *p* of Love is on high, — „ *xxii* 8
A *p* equal to the sun Which cast it, — *To E. Fitzgerald* 35
homeless *p* at length will be wheel'd — *Despair* 83
earthquakes of the *p's* dawning years. — *Locksley H., Sixty* 40
All their *p's* whirling round them, — „ 204
touch'd on the whole sad *p* of man, — *Dead Prophet* 39
Like some conjectured *p* in mid heaven — *To Prin. Beatrice* 20
Many a *p* by many a sun may roll — *Vastness* 2
Plank blind with rage she miss'd the *p*, — *Princess iv* 177
shape it *p* and beam for roof and floor, — „ *vi* 46
Come stepping lightly down the *p*, — *In Mem. xiv* 7
Plann'd Below was all mosaic choicely *p* — *Palace of Art* 145
Planner a shadow of the *p* or the plan? — *Locksley H., Sixty* 196
Plant (s) Like to the mother *p* in semblance, — *The Poet* 23
frost in your breath Which would blight the *p's*. — *Poet's Mind* 18
'The sap dries up : the *p* declines. — *Two Voices* 268
'Single I grew, like some green *p*, — *D. of F. Women* 205
All creeping *p's*, a wall of green — *Day-Dm., Sleep. P.* 45
to watch the thirsty *p's* Imbibing ! — *Princess ii* 422
Wan-sallow as the *p* that feels itself Root-bitten — *Gareth and L.* 453
They will but sicken the sick *p* the more. — *Lover's Tale i* 766
quick as a sensitive *p* to the touch ; — *In the Child. Hosp.* 30
From each fair *p* the blossom choicest-grown — *Akbar's Dream* 22
Plant (verb) *P* thou no dusky cypress-tree, — *My life is full* 13
We *p* a solid foot into the Time, — *Princess v* 415
I go to *p* it on his tomb, — *In Mem viii* 22
make all clean, and *p* himself afresh. — *Geraint and E.* 905
That men *p* over graves. — *Lover's Tale i* 538
And *p* on shoulder, hand and knee, — *To E. Fitzgerald* 8
Plantagenet The lion-heart, *P*, — *Margaret* 34
Plantain hedgehog underneath the *p* bores, — *Aylmer's Field* 850
Plantation Is yon *p* where this byway joins — *Walk. to the Mail* 4
He left a small *p* ; — *Amphion* 20
To grow my own *p*. — „ 100
Planted (*See also* **Palm-planted**) But when we *p* level feet, — *Princess iv* 30
when their feet were *p* on the plain — *Gareth and L.* 187

Planted (*continued*) I was *p* now in a tomb; *The Wreck* 37
O rosetree *p* in my grief, *Ancient Sage* 163
off the tree We *p* both together, *Happy* 14
Plash *p* of rains, and refuse patch'd with moss. *Vision of Sin* 212
many a glancing *p* and sallowy isle, *Last Tournament* 422
Plash'd the tide *P*, sapping its worn ribs; *Lover's Tale i* 56
Plaster alum and *p* are sold to the poor *Maud I i* 39
Plaster'd almost *p* like a martin's nest *Holy Grail* 548
Plat I keep smooth *p's* of fruitful ground, *The Blackbird* 3
Platan clear-stemm'd *p's* guard The outlet, *Arabian Nights* 23
the thick-leaved *p's* of the vale. *Princess iii* 175
Plate (*See also* **Plaäte**) Came out clear *p's* of sapphire mail. *Two Voices* 12
Squadrons and squares of men in brazen *p's*, *D. of F. Women* 33
Lay your *P* for one minute down, *To Master of B.* 4
Platform (*See also* **Crag-platform**) reach'd The grassy *p* on some hill, *Lover's Tale i* 341
Plato *P* the wise, and large-brow'd Verulam, *Palace of Art* 163
Or lend an ear to *P* where he says, *Lucretius* 147
But Homer, *P*, Verulam; *Princess ii* 160
man's ideal Is high in Heaven, and lodged with *P's* God, *Sisters* (*E. and E.*) 131
Plaudit Omar drew Full-handed *p's* *To E. Fitzgerald* 38
Play (s) (*See also* **Hand-play**) At last, tired out with *p*, *Talking Oak* 206
That he shouts with his sister at *p*! *Break, break, etc.* 6
But now to leaven *p* with profit, *Princess iv* 149
Go in and out as if at merry *p*, *Maud I xviii* 31
That he left his wine and horses and *p*, „ *xix* 74
She is weary of dance and *p*.' „ *xxii* 22
all was joust and *p*, Leaven'd his hall. *Merlin and V.* 145
Would watch her at her petulance, and *p*, „ 175
I loved him better than *p*; *First Quarrel* 12
one, Whose life has been no *p* with him *Columbus* 224
but that was a perilous *p*, *V. of Maeldune* 95
p that they play'd with The children *Batt. of Brunanburh* 91
off the crag we clamber'd up in *p*, *The Flight* 22
He said it . . . in the *p*. *Romney's R.* 150
Play (verb) fingers *p* About his mother's neck, *Supp. Confessions* 42
Hither, come hither and frolic and *p*; *Sea-Fairies* 18
at night I would roam abroad and *p* *The Merman* 11
lightly vault from the throne and *p* *The Mermaid* 33
You needs must *p* such pranks as these. *L. C. V. de Vere* 64
'ill merrily glance and *p*, *May Queen* 39
Would *p* with flying forms and images, *Gardener's D.* 60
'*P* me no tricks,' said Lord Ronald, (repeat) *Lady Clare* 73, 75
To *p* their go-between as heretofore *Aylmer's Field* 523
why should I not *p* The Spartan Mother with emotion, *Princess ii* 282
And *p* the slave to gain the tyranny. „ *iv* 132
with your long locks *p* the Lion's mane! „ *vi* 164
And in thy heart the scrawl shall *p*.' *Sailor Boy* 12
dart again, and *p* About the prow, *In Mem. xii* 17
The tender-pencil'd shadow *p*. „ *xlix* 12
I'll have leave at times to *p* „ *lix* 11
You wonder when my fancies *p* „ *lxvi* 2
He *p's* with threads, he beats his chair „ 13
Or so shall grief with symbols *p* „ *lxxxv* 95
For him she *p's*, to him she sings „ *xcvii* 29
It circles round, and fancy *p's*, „ *Con.* 81
And *p* the game of the despot kings, *Maud I x* 39
died to live, long as my pulses *p*; „ *xviii* 66
With whom he used to *p* at tourney once, *Gareth and L.* 532
or the viler devil who *p's* his part, *Balin and Balan* 300
you might *p* me falsely, having power, *Merlin and V* 515
there he set himself to *p* upon her *Lancelot and E.* 646
Abbess and her nuns, To *p* upon me,' *Guinevere* 310
set on to plague And *p* upon, and harry me, „ 360
O golden hair, with which I used to *p* „ 547
begins to *p* That air which pleased her *Lover's Tale i* 20
How she would smile at 'em, *p* with 'em, *In the Child. Hosp.* 34
p the Saul that never will be Paul. *Sir J. Oldcastle* 103
tell King Ferdinand who *p's* with me, *Columbus* 223
I would *p* my part with the young *The Wreck* 39
realist, rhymester, *p* your part, *Locksley H., Sixty* 139
and felt An icy breath *p* on me, *The Ring* 131
For I used to *p* with the knife, *Charity* 15
Play'd 'That men with knowledge merely *p*, *Two Voices* 172
Play'd (*continued*) when thy father *p* In his free field, *Two Voices* 319
For scarce my life with fancy *p* *Miller's D.* 45
Here *p*, a tiger, rolling to and fro *Palace of Art* 151
with the time we *p*, We spoke of other things; *Gardener's D.* 221
here she came, and round me *p*, *Talking Oak* 133
The happy winds upon her *p*, *Sir L. and Q. G.* 38
p Among the waste and lumber of the shore, *Enoch Arden* 15
the children *p* at keeping house. „ 24
p with him And call'd him Father Philip. „ 353
hand that *p* the patron with her curls. *Princess, Pro.* 138
p Charades and riddles as at Christmas here, „ 188
as the beam Of the East, that *p* upon them, „ *v* 259
He *p* at counsellors and kings, *In Mem. lxiv* 23
p A chequer-work of beam and shade Along the hills, „ *lxxii* 14
Love but *p* with gracious lies, „ *cxxv* 7
I *p* with the girl when a child; *Maud I i* 68
I have *p* with her when a child; „ *vi* 87
And lightnings *p* about it in the storm, *Gareth and L.* 68
And only wondering wherefore *p* upon: „ 1252
and took the word and *p* upon it, *Geraint and E.* 291
the lovely blue *P* into green, „ 689
She *p* about with slight and sprightly talk, *Merlin and V.* 171
Surely I but *p* on Torre: *Lancelot and E.* 209
crisping white *P* ever back upon the sloping wave, *Holy Grail* 382
ye *p* at ducks and drakes With Arthur's vows *Last Tournament* 344
when we *p* together, I loved him *First Quarrel* 12
p with The children of Edward. *Batt. of Brunanburh* 91
Playest thou *p* that air with Queen Isolt, *Last Tournament* 263
Playful with *p* tail Crouch'd fawning in the weed. *Œnone* 200
Playing *P* mad pranks along the heathy leas; *Circumstance* 2
p with the blade he prick'd his hand, *Aylmer's Field* 239
p, now A twisted snake, and now a rain of pearls, *Princess, Pro.* 61
Then that old Seer made answer *p* on him *Gareth and L.* 252
And we took to *p* at ball, *V. of Maeldune* 94
And we took to *p* at battle, „ 95
foam in the dusk came *p* about our feet. *Despair* 50
Playmate Paris, once her *p* on the hills. *Œnone* 17
Doubled her own, for want of *p's*, *Aylmer's Field* 81
remembering the gay *p* rear'd Among them, *Death of Œnone* 59
Playwright Our *P* may show In some fifth Act *The Play* 3
Plea King Mused for a little on his *p*, *Marr. of Geraint* 42
Be not gull'd by a despot's *p*! *Riflemen form!* 9
Pleached *See* **Self-pleached**
Plead let her *p* in vain; *Enoch Arden* 166
twice I sought to *p* my cause, *Princess iv* 552
when I return, will *p* for thee. (repeat) *Gareth and L.* 987, 1052
Not all in vain may *p* *Epilogue* 80
Her sad eyes *p* for my own fame with me *Romney's R.* 55
Pleaded Although I *p* tenderly, *Miller's D.* 135
on a day When Cyril *p*, Ida came behind *Princess vii* 78
And yet hast often *p* for my love— *Balin and Balan* 571
Pleader jests, that flash'd about the *p's* room, *Aylmer's Field* 440
Pleadest What if Thou *p* still, *Supp. Confessions* 94
Pleading a sound Like sleepy counsel *p*; *Amphion* 74
before them paused Hortensia *p*: *Princess vii* 132
Pleasance my passion seeks *P* in love-sighs, *Lilian* 9
A realm of *p*, many a mound, *Arabian Nights* 101
Pleasant And all at once a *p* truth I learn'd, *The Bridesmaid* 9
Before I dream'd that *p* dream— *Miller's D.* 46
With your feet above my head in the long and *p* grass. *May Queen, N. Y's. E.* 32
'Beat quicker, for the time Is *p*, and the woods and ways Are *p*, *On a Mourner* 13
O ME, my *p* rambles by the lake, (repeat) *Edwin Morris* 1, 13
Well—were it not a *p* thing *Day-Dm., L'Envoi* 3
A *p* hour has passed away „ *Pro.* 2
By many *p* ways, *Will Water.* 34
But for my *p* hour, 'tis gone; „ 179
Love will make our cottage *p*, *L. of Burleigh* 15
made *p* by the baits Of gold and beauty, *Aylmer's Field* 486
A *p* game, she thought: *Princess, Pro.* 194
tell me *p* tales, and read My sickness „ *ii* 252
And many a *p* hour with her that's gone, „ *vi* 247
Often they come to the door in a *p* kind of a dream. *Grandmother* 82
So find I every *p* spot In which we two *In Mem. viii* 9

Pleasant (*continued*) They laid him by the *p* shore, *In Mem. xix* 3
To leave the *p* fields and farms; „ *cii* 22
Yet, for the field was *p* in our eyes, *Gareth and L.* 337
The field was *p* in my husband's eye.' „ 342
'Have thy *p* field again, „ 343
Thou hast a *p* presence. „ 1065
My twelvemonth and a day were *p* to me.' *Holy Grail* 750
The sins that made the past so *p* to us: *Guinevere* 375
Oh! *p* breast of waters, quiet bay, *Lover's Tale i* 6
A portion of the *p* yesterday, „ 122
for the sound Of the loud stream was *p*, „ *ii* 35
Those were the *p* times, *First Quarrel* 41
in the *p* times that had past, „ 55
I had past into perfect quiet at length out of *p* dreams, *Despair* 66
but ye knaw'd it wur *p* to 'ear, *Spinster's S's.* 21
So in this *p* vale we stand again, *Demeter and P.* 34
Pleasantry From talk of war to traits of *p*— *Lancelot and E.* 321
Please (*See also* **Pleäse**) Too fearful that you should not *p*. *Miller's D.* 148
O shapes and hues that *p* me well! *Palace of Art* 194
She could not *p* herself. *Talking Oak* 120
My gifts, when gifts of mine could *p*; *The Letters* 22
Edith whom his pleasure was to *p*, *Aylmer's Field* 232
sea-furbelow flap, Good man, to *p* the child. *Sea Dreams* 267
betwixt them both, to *p* them both, *Princess, Con.* 25
At that last hour to *p* him well; *In Mem. vi* 18
thinking 'this will *p* him best,' „ 31
here is truth, but an it *p* thee not, *Gareth and L.* 256
Enid, but to *p* her husband's eye, *Marr. of Geraint* 11
the King himself should *p* To cleanse „ 38
To *p* her, dwelling on his boundless love, „ 63
put off to *p* me this poor gown, *Geraint and E.* 679
I find that it always can *p* Our children, *In the Child. Hosp.* 51
I fail'd to *p* him, however I strove to *p*— *The Wreck* 28
Does it *p* you? *The Ring* 26
Still would you—if it *p* you—sit to me? *Romney's R.* 73
Pleäse but they wasn't that eäsy to *p*, *Village Wife* 117
Pleased (*See also* **Half-pleased, Well-pleased**) newness of thine art so *p* thee, *Ode to Memory* 88
It *p me* well enough.' *The Epic* 34
might have *p* the eyes of many men. *M. d'Arthur* 91
him We *p* not—he was seldom *p*: *The Voyage* 74
A song that *p* us from its worth; *You might have won* 22
saying that which *p* him, for he smiled. *Enoch Arden* 757
'but it *p* us not: in truth We shudder *Princess iii* 308
And maybe neither *p* myself nor them. „ *Con.* 28
But Lilia *p* me, for she took no part In our dispute: „ 29
Nor knew we well what *p* us most, *The Daisy* 25
But since it *p* a vanish'd eye, *In Mem. viii* 21
Which led by tracts that *p* us well, „ *xxii* 2
Like one with any trifle *p*. „ *lxvi* 4
They *p* him, fresh from brawling courts „ *lxxxix* 11
Nor less it *p* in livelier moods, „ 29
But each has *p* a kindred eye, „ *c* 17
pick'd the lance That *p* him best, *Geraint and E.* 180
wholly *p* To find him yet unwounded after fight, „ 370
Was in a manner *p*, and turning, stood. „ 456
(For thus it *p* the King to range me close *Holy Grail* 307
Who *p* her with a babbling heedlessness *Guinevere* 151
might have *p* the eyes of many men. *Pass. of Arthur* 259
begins to play That air which *p* her first. *Lover's Tale i* 21
And all the people were *p*; *Dead Prophet* 74
Shakespeare's bland and universal eye Dwells *p*, *To W. C. Macready* 14
knew not that which *p* it most, *The Ring* 165
Pleasing To make him *p* in her uncle's eye. *Dora* 84
Pleasurable Ev'n such a wave, but not so *p*, *Merlin and V.* 294
Pleasure (s) With *p* and love and jubilee: *Sea-Fairies* 36
Pain rises up, old *p's* pall. *Two Voices* 164
What *p* can we have To war with evil? *Lotos-Eaters, C. S.* 48
own anguish deep More than much *p*. *To J. S.* 43
Valuing the giddy *p* of the eyes. *M. d'Arthur* 128
Yet for the *p* that I took to hear, *Gardener's D.* 228
into my inmost ring A *p* I discern'd, *Talking Oak* 174
woman's *p*, woman's pain— *Locksley Hall* 149
Like a beast with lower *p's*, „ 176
Come, Care and *P*, Hope and Pain, *Day-Dm., Sleep. P.* 55

Pleasure (s) (*continued*) I will take my *p* there: *Day-Dm., L'Envoi* 32
You moved her at your *p*. *Amphion* 60
Built for *p* and for state. *L. of Burleigh* 32
not to see the world—For *p*?— *Enoch Arden* 298
Worried his passive ear with petty wrongs Or *p's* „ 353
Edith whom his *p* was to please, *Aylmer's Field* 232
Then made his *p* echo, hand to hand, „ 257
since the nobler *p* seems to fade, *Lucretius* 230
Without one *p* and without one pain, „ 269
What *p* lives in height (the shepherd sang) *Princess vii* 193
Some *p* from thine early years. *In Mem. iv* 10
That so my *p* may be whole; „ *lxxi* 8
And fulsome *P* clog him, and drown *Maud I xvi* 4
nor a vantage-ground For *p*; *Ded. of Idylls* 24
Merlin, who, they say, can walk Unseen at *p*— *Com. of Arthur* 348
thy charge Is an abounding *p* to me. *Gareth and L.* 982
desire To close with her lord's *p*; *Geraint and E.* 214
Came purer *p* unto mortal kind Than lived thro' her, „ 765
Should have some rest and *p* in himself, *Merlin and V.* 485
Should have small rest or *p* in herself, „ 490
she had her *p* in it, „ 604
Because of that high *p* which I had „ 877
For *p* all about a field of flowers: *Lancelot and E.* 793
P to have it, none; to lose it, pain; „ 1415
Nor slept that night for *p* in his blood, *Pelleas and E.* 138
on love And sport and tilts and *p*, *Guinevere* 387
It would have been my *p* had I seen. „ 659
Valuing the giddy *p* of the eyes. *Pass. of Arthur* 296
Some sudden vivid *p* hit him there. *Lover's Tale iv* 178
And I more *p* in your praise. *To E. Fitzgerald* 56
short, or long, as *P* leads, or Pain; *Ancient Sage* 101
her tears Are half of *p*, half of pain— *To Prin. Beatrice* 11
P who flaunts on her wide downway *Vastness* 16
Pain, that has crawl'd from the corpse of *P*, „ 17
Pleasure (verb) roll'd His hoop to *p* Edith, *Aylmer's Field* 85
Pleasure-boat A mountain nest—the *p-b* that rock'd, *Lover's Tale i* 42
Pleasure-house I BUILT my soul a lordly *p-h*, *Palace of Art* 1
Pledge (s) giving safe *p* of fruits, *Ode to Memory* 18
tell Of difference, reconcilement, *p's* given, *Gardener's D.* 257
P of a love not to be mine, *Princess vi* 197
arms On loan, or else for *p*; *Marr. of Geraint* 220
Pledge (verb) But *p* me in the flowing grape. *My life is full* 15
I *p* her not in any cheerful cup, *Wan Sculptor* 9
I *p* her, and she comes and dips *Will Water.* 17
I *p* her silent at her board; „ 25
We did but talk you over, *p* you all In wassail; *Princess, Pro.* 185
To *p* them with a kindly tear, *In Mem. xc* 10
here I *p* my troth, *Pelleas and E.* 341
Love *p* Hatred in her bitter draughts, *Lover's Tale i* 776
FIRST *p* our Queen this solemn night, *Hands all Round* 1
Pledged *p* To fight in tourney for my bride, *Princess v* 352
our knights at feast Have *p* us in this union, *Lancelot and E.* 115
and she hated all who *p*. „ 744
Queen, Who fain had *p* her jewels *Columbus* 229
Pledgest Who *p* now thy gallant son; *In Mem. vi* 10
Pledging *p* Lancelot and the lily maid *Lancelot and E.* 738
Pleiads Many a night I saw the *P's*, *Locksley Hall* 9
Plenteousness Set in this Eden of all *p*, *Enoch Arden* 561
Plenty Yet is there *p* of the kind.' *Two Voices* 33
P corrupts the melody That made thee famous once, *The Blackbird* 15
hand in hand with *P* in the maize, *Princess vii* 201
Their myriad horns of *p* at our feet. *Ode Inter. Exhib.* 6
boy Will have *p*: so let it be.' (repeat) *Maud I vii* 8, 16
Pliable No *p* idiot I to break my vow; *The Ring* 402
Pliant like the *p* bough That moving moves the nest *Sea Dreams* 290
He moving up with *p* courtliness, *Geraint and E.* 278
Plied round the lake A little clock-work steamer paddling *p* *Princess, Pro.* 71
p him with his richest wines, „ *i* 174
Plight (s) nor by *p* or broken ring Bound, *Aylmer's Field* 135
But in perilous *p* were we, *The Revenge* 75
Plight (verb) I to thee my troth did *p*, *Oriana* 26
Will I to Olive *p* my troth, *Talking Oak* 283
Plighted (adj.) Of early faith and *p* vows; *In Mem. xcvii* 30
Plighted (verb) *p* troth, and were at peace. *Princess vii* 83

Plighted (verb) (*continued*) The heart that never *p* troth *In Mem. xxvii* 10
Plot (conspiracy) A *p*, a *p*, a *p*, to ruin all!' 'No *p*, no *p*,' *Princess ii* 192
man of *p's*, Craft, poisonous counsels, *Gareth and L.* 431
for fine *p's* may fail, *Merlin and V.* 820
Plot (of ground) (*See also* **Diamond-plot**) Or opening upon level *p's* Of crowned lilies, *Ode to Memory* 108
Love paced the thymy *p's* of Paradise, *Love and Death* 2
I steal by lawns and grassy *p's*, *The Brook* 170
That all the turf was rich in *p's* *Marr. of Geraint* 660
Why grew we then together in one *p*? *Lover's Tale ii* 23
pools of salt, and *p's* of land— *Locksley H., Sixty* 207
Plot (verb) That he *p's* against me still. *Maud I xix* 81
Plotted He has *p* against me in this, „ 80
Plough-Plow (s) and morning driv'n her *plow* of pearl *Love and Duty* 99
He praised his *ploughs*, his cows, his hogs, *The Brook* 125
stood Eight daughters of the *plough*, *Princess iv* 278
Then those eight mighty daughters of the *plough* „ 550
and those eight daughters of the *plough* „ *v* 339
an' runn'd *plow* thruff it an' all, *N. Farmer, O. S.* 42
We could sing a good song at the *Plow*, (repeat) *North. Cobbler* 18
The steer fell down at the *plow* *V. of Maeldune* 30
take the suffrage of the *plow*. *Locksley H., Sixty* 118
an raäved slick thruf by the *plow*— *Owd Roä* 28
Plough-Plow (verb) an' Thurnaby hoälms to *plow*! *N. Farmer, O. S.* 52
Who *ploughs* with pain his native lea *In Mem. lxiv* 25
To whom a space of land is given to *plow*. *Holy Grail* 907
And *plow* the Present like a field, *Mechanophilus* 31
Ploughing and Charlie *p* the hill. *Grandmother* 80
Ploughman in the furrow broke the *p's* head, *Princess v* 221
Plover tufted *p* pipe along the fallow lea, *May Queen, N. Y's. E.* 18
There let the wind sweep and the *p* cry; *Come not, when, etc.* 5
great *p's* human whistle amazed Her heart, *Geraint and E.* 49
WHY wail you, pretty *p*? *Happy* 1
Plow *See* **Plough**
Plow'd (*See also* **Red-plow'd**) To mix with what he *p*; *Ancient Sage* 145
Plowing The plowman left his *p*, and fell down *Holy Grail* 404
Plowland Silvery willow, Pasture and *p*, *Merlin and the G.* 54
Plowman The *p* left his plowing, and fell down *Holy Grail* 404
The *p* passes, bent with pain, *Ancient Sage* 144
Plowmen, Shepherds, have I found, *Locksley H., Sixty* 121
Plowshare it smote the *p* in the field, *Holy Grail* 403
Pluck 'Hard task, to *p* resolve,' I cried, *Two Voices* 118
I will *p* it from my bosom, *Locksley Hall* 66
p's The mortal soul from out immortal hell, *Lucretius* 262
that men may *p* them from our hearts, *Princess iii* 257
this night should *p* your palace down; „ *iv* 414
theer's a craw to *p* wi' tha, Sam: *N. Farmer, N. S.* 5
I *p* you out of the crannies, *Flower in cran. wall* 2
whose splendour *p's* The slavish hat *Maud I x* 3
'to *p* the flower in season;' So says *Merlin and V.* 722
So, brother, *p* and spare not.' *Lover's Tale i* 351
p from this true breast the locket that I wear, *The Flight* 33
P the mighty from their seat, *Locksley H., Sixty* 133
Pluck'd-Pluckt Devils *pluck'd* my sleeve, *St. S. Stylites* 171
in a pet she started up, And *pluck'd* it out, *Talking Oak* 230
Each *pluck'd* his one foot from the grave *Amphion* 43
he thrice had *pluck'd* a life From the dread sweep *Enoch Arden* 54
when the children *pluck'd* at him to go, „ 369
left alone he *pluck'd* her dagger forth *Aylmer's Field* 470
hand from which Livid he *pluck'd* it forth, „ 627
Found a still place, and *pluck'd* her likeness out; *Princess i* 92
And *pluck'd* the ripen'd ears, „ *ii* 2
she *pluck'd* the grass, She flung it from her, „ *Con.* 31
I *pluck'd* a daisy, I gave it you. *The Daisy* 88
as the cur *Pluckt* from the cur he fights with, *Gareth and L.* 702
pluck'd the grass There growing longest *Geraint and E.* 256
bone Seems to be *pluck'd* at by the village boys „ 560
he had the gems *Pluck'd* from the crown, *Lancelot and E.* 57
each as each, Not to be *pluck'd* asunder; *Holy Grail* 777
touch or see the Holy Grail They might be *pluck'd* asunder. „ 780
That save they could be *pluck'd* asunder, „ 782
pluck'd one way by hate and one by love, *Last Tournament* 539
Lancelot *pluck'd* him by the heel, *Guinevere* 34
Prince Who scarce had *pluck'd* his flickering life *To the Queen ii* 5

Plucking *P* the harmless wild-flower on the hill?— *Maud II i* 3
Pluckt *See* **Pluck'd**
Pluksh *P*! ! ! the hens i' the peäs! *Village Wife* 124
Plum (*See also* **Sugar-plum**) Glowing with all-colour'd *p's* *V. of Maeldune* 60
Plumage Conjecture of the *p* and the form; *Marr. of Geraint* 333
Plume A funeral, with *p's* and lights *L. of Shalott ii* 31
She saw the helmet and the *p*, „ *iii* 40
From spur to *p* a star of tournament, *M. d'Arthur* 223
Ruffles her pure cold *p*, „ 268
Fantastic *p* or sable pine; *The Voyage* 44
A light-green tuft of *p's* she bore *Sir L. and Q. G.* 26
The slender coco's drooping crown of *p's*, *Enoch Arden* 574
till, each, in maiden *p's* We rustled: *Princess i* 202
all about were birds Of sunny *p* in gilded trellis-work; *Marr. of Geraint* 659
brandish'd *p* Brushing his instep, *Geraint and E.* 359
underneath a *p* of lady-fern, Sang, *Balin and Balan* 26
p fall'n from the wing Of that foul bird *Merlin and V.* 727
from spur to *p* Red as the rising sun *Lancelot and E.* 307
Their *p's* driv'n backward by the wind „ 480
shower and shorn *p* Went down it. *Last Tournament* 155
fell thick rain, *p* droopt and mantle clung, „ 213
storm and cloud Of shriek and *p*, „ 441
but with *p's* that mock'd the may, *Guinevere* 22
From spur to *p* a star of tournament, *Pass. of Arthur* 391
Ruffles her pure cold *p*, „ 436
Plumed pines, that *p* the craggy ledge *Œnone* 209
Empanoplied and *p* We enter'd in, *Princess v* 483
a shatter'd archway *p* with fern; *Marr. of Geraint* 316
green and gold, and *p* with green *Merlin and V.* 89
Plumelet When rosy *p's* tuft the larch, *In Mem. xci* 1
Plummet Two *p's* dropt for one to sound *Princess ii* 176
Plump Grew *p* and able-bodied; *The Goose* 18
O *P* head-waiter at The Cock, *Will Water.* 1
One shade more *p* than common; „ 150
blue wood-louse, and the *p* dormouse, *Window, Winter* 9
As well as the *p* cheek— *Sisters (E. and E.)* 184
Plump-arm'd A *p-a* Ostleress and a stable wench *Princess i* 226
Plump'd sweating rosin, *p* the pine *Amphion* 47
Plumper And cramm'd a *p* crop; *Will Water.* 124
Plunder (s) is a world of *p* and prey. *Maud I iv* 24
He found the sack and *p* of our house *Marr. of Geraint* 694
Earl Doorm with *p* to the hall. *Geraint and E.* 592
Plunder (verb) I cannot steal or *p*, no nor beg: „ 487
Plunder'd bark had *p* twenty nameless isles; *Merlin and V.* 559
Plunge (s) thro' the whitening hazels made a *p* *Enoch Arden* 379
waterfalls Pour'd in a thunderless *p* *V. of Maeldune* 14
'one *p*—then quiet for evermore.' *Charity* 16
Plunge (verb) should not *p* His hand into the bag: *Golden Year* 71
nor rather *p* at once, Being troubled, *Lucretius* 151
river sloped To *p* in cataract, *Princess iii* 291
To *p* old Merlin in the Arabian sea; *Gareth and L.* 211
and the sword That made it *p's* thro' the wound *Pelleas and E.* 530
she cried, '*P* and be lost—ill-fated as they were, *Last Tournament* 40
Not *p* headforemost from the mountain there, *Lover's Tale iv* 41
P's and heaves at a bank that is daily devour'd *Def. of Lucknow* 39
fearing not to *p* Thy torch of life *Tiresias* 158
Plunged *p* Among the bulrush-beds, *M. d'Arthur* 134
but woman-vested as I was *P*; *Princess iv* 182
P in the battery-smoke Right thro' the line *Light Brigade* 32
slowly rose and *p* Roaring, *Com. of Arthur* 381
so down among the pines He *p*; *Gareth and L.* 809
And down the shingly scaur he *p*, *Lancelot and E.* 53
Seized him, and bound and *p* him into a cell *Holy Grail* 675
p Among the bulrush beds, *Pass. of Arthur* 302
sea *p* and fell on the shot-shatter'd navy of Spain, *The Revenge* 117
P in the last fierce charge at Waterloo, *Sisters (E. and E.)* 64
P head down in the sea, *V. of Maeldune* 82
crest of the tides *P* on the vessel *The Wreck* 90
P up and down, to and fro, *Heavy Brigade* 31
woods *P* gulf on gulf thro' all their vales *Prog. of Spring* 73
wild horse, anger, *p* To fling me, *Akbar's Dream* 118
Plunging (*See also* **Heavy-plunging, Lazy-plunging**) peoples *p* thro' the thunder-storm; *Locksley Hall* 126

Plunging (*continued*) *p* seas draw backward from the land *Palace of Art* 251
all ablaze too *p* in the lake Head-foremost— *The Ring* 251
p down Thro' that disastrous glory, *St. Telemachus* 28
Ply joint of state, that *plies* Its office, *Love thou thy land* 47
plies His function of the woodland: *Lucretius* 45
Poach'd As the *p* filth that floods the middle street, *Merlin and V.* 798
Pocket I fun thy *p's* as full o' my pippins *Church-warden, etc.* 34
Pock-pitten That great *p-p* fellow *Aylmer's Field* 256
Poem (*See also* **Love-poem**) Look, I come to the test, a tiny *p* *Hendecasyllabics* 3
Poesy And this poor flower of *p* *In Mem. viii* 19
The *p* of childhood; *Lover's Tale ii* 184
all the sciences, *p*, varying voices of prayer? *Vastness* 31
Poet The *p* in a golden clime was born, *The Poet* 1
But one poor *p's* scroll, „ 55
Vex not thou the *p's* mind (repeat) *Poet's Mind* 1, 3
The parson Holmes, the *p* Everard Hall, *The Epic* 4
and the *p* little urged, „ 48
sing Like *p's*, from the vanity of song? *Gardener's D.* 100
days were brief Whereof the *p's* talk, *Talking Oak* 186
A tongue-tied *P* in the feverous days, *Golden Year* 10
Are but as *p's'* seasons when they flower, „ 28
this is truth the *p* sings, *Locksley Hall* 75
To prove myself a *p*: *Will Water.* 166
Hours, when the *P's* words and looks „ 193
You might have won the *P's* name, *You might have won* 1
doom Of those that wear the *P's* crown: „ 10
For now the *P* cannot die, „ 13
The rain had fallen, the *P* arose, *Poet's Song* 1
fair As ever painter painted, *p* sang, *Aylmers' Field* 106
P's, whose thoughts enrich the blood *Princess ii* 181
held A volume of the *P's* of her land: „ *vii* 174
such as lurks In some wild *P*, *In Mem. xxxiv* 7
read The Tuscan *p's* on the lawn: „ *lxxxix* 24
passionate heart of the *p* is whirl'd *Maud I iv* 39
take withal Thy *p's* blessing, *To the Queen ii* 46
Glorious *p* who never hast written a line, *To A. Tennyson* 5
word of the *P* by whom the deeps *The Wreck* 23
The *p* whom his Age would quote *Ancient Sage* 146
Hesper, whom the *p* call'd the Bringer *Locksley H., Sixty* 185
P of the happy Tityrus piping underneath *To Virgil* 13
P of the poet-satyr whom the laughing shepherd „ 15
blackbirds have their wills, The *p's* too. *Early Spring* 48
True *p*, surely to be found When Truth *Pref. Poem, Broth. Son* 15
'Ave atque Vale' of the *P's* hopeless woe, Tenderest of Roman *p's* *Frater Ave, etc.* 5
Old *p's* foster'd under friendlier skies, *Poets and their B.* 1
Had swampt the sacred *p's* with themselves. „ 14
faults your *P* makes Or many or few, *To Mary Boyle* 61
P, that evergreen laurel is blasted *Parnassus* 12
Yes, my wild little *P*. *The Throstle* 4
But seldom comes the *p* here, *Poets and Critics* 15
Poetess The ancient *p* singeth, *Leonine Eleg.* 13
I wish I were Some mighty *p*, *Princess, Pro.* 132
Poet-forms The *P-f* of stronger hours, *Day-Dm., L'Envoi* 14
Poetic More strong than all *p* thought; *In Mem. xxxvi* 12
Poetically 'What, if you drest it up *p*!' *Princess, Con.* 6
Poet-like *P-l* he spoke. *Edwin Morris* 27
Rather, O ye Gods, *P-l*, *Lucretius* 93
Poet-princess *P-p* with her grand Imaginations *Princess iii* 273
Poetry poor old *P*, passing hence, *Locksley H., Sixty* 249
Poet-satyr Poet of the *p-s* *To Virgil* 15
Point (s) clotted into *p's* and hanging loose, *M. d'Arthur* 219
sail with Arthur under looming shores, *P* after *p*; „ *Ep.* 18
slowly, creeping on from *p* to *p*: *Locksley Hall* 134
And now, the bloodless *p* reversed, *The Voyage* 71
talking from the *p*, he drew him in, *The Brook* 154
To our *p*: not war: Lest I lose all.' *Princess v* 204
touch'd upon the *p* Where idle boys are cowards „ 308
In conflict with the crash of shivering *p's*, „ 491
oration flowing free From *p* to *p*, *In Mem. lxxxvii* 33
'Nay, not a *p*: nor art thou victor here. *Gareth and L.* 1055
and the *p's* of lances bicker in it. *Geraint and E.* 449
p Across the maiden shield of Balan *Balin and Balan* 558
and faintly-venom'd *p's* Of slander, *Merlin and V.* 172

Point (s) (*continued*) It buzzes fiercely round the *p*; *Merlin and V.* 432
Touch'd at all *p's*, except the poplar grove, *Lancelot and E.* 617
that *p* where first she saw the King *Guinevere* 403
clotted into *p's* and hanging loose, *Pass. of Arthur* 387
Descending from the *p* and standing both, *Lover's Tale i* 411
Confined on *p's* of faith, „ *ii* 150
Glanced at the *p* of law, to pass it by, „ *iv* 276
wait till the *p* of the pickaxe be thro'! *Def. of Lucknow* 27
Still—could we watch at all *p's*? „ 49
the *p's* of the foam in the dusk came *Despair* 50
in that *p* of peaceful light? *Locksley H., Sixty* 190
p's of the Russian lances arose in the sky; *Heavy Brigade* 5
All at all *p's* thou canst not meet, *Poets and Critics* 7
Point (verb) *p* thee forward to a distant light, *Love and Duty* 95
p you out the shadow from the truth! *Princess i* 84
p to it, and we say, The loyal warmth of Florian „ *ii* 243
To *p* the term of human strife, *In Mem. l* 14
A hand that *p's*, and palled shapes „ *lxx* 7
And then *p* out the flower or the star? *Lover's Tale i* 175
An' 'e *p's* to the bottle o' gin, *North. Cobbler* 90
lights the clock! the hand *p's* five— *The Flight* 94
p and jeer, And gibber at the worm, *Romney's R.* 136
Point (pint) I've 'ed my *p* o' äale ivry noight *N. Farmer, O. S.* 7
Pointed (adj.) (*See also* **Clear-pointed, Sharp-pointed**) To pierce me thro' with *p* light; *Rosalind* 27
By zig-zag paths, and juts of *p* rock, *M. d'Arthur* 50
And sketching with her tender *p* foot *The Brook* 102
with now a wandering hand And now a *p* finger, *Princess v* 270
A mountain islet [illegible] and peak'd; *The Islet* 15
With *p* lance as [illegible] to pierce, a shape, *Balin and Balan* 325
A score with *p* lances, making at him— „ 401
The shadow of some piece of *p* lace, *Lancelot and E.* 1174
By zigzag paths, and juts of *p* rock, *Pass. of Arthur* 218
Pointed (verb) 'Courage!' he said, and *p* toward the land, *Lotos-Eaters* 1
Thereto she *p* with a laugh, *D. of F. Women* 159
He *p* out a pasturing colt, *The Brook* 136
I follow'd; and at top She *p* seaward: *Sea Dreams* 122
P itself to pierce, but sank down shamed *Lucretius* 63
p on to where A double hill ran up *Princess iii* 173
For this lost lamb (she *p* to the child) „ *iv* 361
I tarry for thee,' and *p* to Mars *Maud III vi* 13
Stood one who *p* toward the voice, *Com. of Arthur* 438
held Her finger up, and *p* to the dust. *Geraint and E.* 453
Are scatter'd,' and he *p* to the field, „ 802
rose And *p* to the damsel, and the doors. *Lancelot and E.* 1263
peak'd wings *p* to the Northern Star. *Holy Grail* 240
she *p* downward, 'Look, He haunts me— *Pelleas and E.* 226
red mark ran All round one finger *p* straight, *The Ring* 453
and *p* to the West, *St. Telemachus* 25
Pointing *p* to his drunken sleep, *Locksley Hall* 81
one was *p* this way, and one that, *Pelleas and E.* 58
Point-painted eyes had ever seen, *P-p* red; *Balin and Balan* 412
Poise In crystal eddies glance and *p*, *Miller's D.* 52
Poised (*See also* **Equal-poised**) court-Galen *p* his guilt-head cane, *Princess i* 19
A doom that ever *p* itself to fall, *Merlin and V.* 191
Dagonet with one foot *p* in his hand, *Last Tournament* 285
Poising And the rainbow hangs on the *p* wave, *Sea-Fairies* 29
a *p* eagle, burns Above the unrisen morrow:' *Princess iv* 82
Poison (s) Drew forth the *p* with her balmy breath, *D. of F. Women* 271
Full of weak *p*, turnspits for the clown, *Princess iv* 516
To pestle a poison'd *p* behind his crimson lights. *Maud I i* 44
The flowers that run *p* in their veins. *Lover's Tale i* 347
naked *p's* of his heart In his old age.' „ 356
And batten on her *p's*? Love forbid! „ 777
Cast the *p* from your bosom, *Locksley H., Sixty* 241
or shedding *p* in the fountains of the Will. „ 274
balm May clear the blood from *p*, *Death of Œnone* 36
menacing *p* of intolerant priests, *Akbar's Dream* 165
Poison (verb) now we *p* our babes, poor souls! *Maud II v* 63
Think ye this fellow will *p* the King's dish? *Gareth and L.* 471
devil's leaps, and *p's* half the young. *Guinevere* 522
Poison'd (adj. and part) (*See also* **Jungle-poison'd**) To pestle a *p* poison behind his crimson lights. *Maud I i* 44

Power (*continued*) Round us, each with different *p's*, *Ode on Well.* 263
And ruling by obeying Nature's *p's*, *Ode Inter. Exhib.* 40
Son of him with whom we strove for *p*— *W. to Marie Alex.* 1
is He not all but that which has *p* to feel *High. Pantheism* 8
all we have *p* to see is a straight staff „ 16
'The deep has *p* on the height, And the height has *p* on the deep; *Voice and the P.* 21
To Sleep I give my *p's* away; *In Mem. iv* 1
And stunn'd me from my *p* to think „ *xvi* 15
The chairs and thrones of civil *p*? „ *xxi* 16
p to see Within the green the moulder'd tree, „ *xxvi* 6
With gather'd *p*, yet the same, „ *xxx* 26
For Wisdom dealt with mortal *p's*, „ *xxxvi* 5
When all his active *p's* are still, „ *lxiv* 18
That Nature's ancient *p* was lost: „ *lxix* 2
Hath *p* to give thee as thou wert? „ *lxxv* 8
Conduct by paths of growing *p's*, „ *lxxxiv* 31
First love, first friendship, equal *p's*, „ *lxxxv* 107
with *p* and grace And music in the bounds of law, „ *lxxxvii* 33
P was with him in the night, „ *xcvi* 18
some novel *p* Sprang up for ever at a touch, „ *cxii* 9
burst All barriers in her onward race For *p*. „ *cxiv* 15
Who grewest not alone in *p* „ 26
The *P* in darkness whom we guess; „ *cxxiv* 4
To shift an arbitrary *p*, „ *cxxviii* 17
To feel thee some diffusive *p*, „ *cxxx* 7
And thou art worthy; full of *p*; „ *Con.* 37
Strong in the *p* that all men adore, *Maud I x* 14
Cold fires, yet with *p* to burn and brand „ *xviii* 39
P's of the height, *P's* of the deep, „ *II ii* 82
Have *p* on this dark land to lighten it, And *p* on this dead world to make it live.' *Com. of Arthur* 93
P's who walk the world Made lightnings „ 107
So, compass'd by the *p* of the King, „ 203
Hath *p* to walk the waters like our Lord. „ 294
Am much too gentle, have not used my *p*: *Marr. of Geraint* 467
dearer by the *p* Of intermitted usage; „ 810
Ye are in my *p* at last, are in my *p*. *Geraint and E.* 310
I will make use of all the *p* I have. „ 345
out of her there came a *p* upon him; „ 613
Than hardest tyrants in their day of *p*, „ 695
Disband himself, and scatter all his *p's*, „ 798
'and lo, the *p's* of Doorm Are scatter'd,' „ 801
wealth of beauty, thine the crown of *p*, *Merlin and V.* 79
The meanest having *p* upon the highest, „ 195
grant me some slight *p* upon your fate, „ 333
I will not yield to give you *p* Upon my life „ 373
Faith and unfaith can ne'er be equal *p's*: „ 388
Giving you *p* upon me thro' this charm, That you might play me falsely, having *p*, „ 514
Have turn'd to tyrants when they came to *p*) „ 518
learnt their elemental secrets, *p's* And forces; „ 632
like a ghost without the *p* to speak. *Lancelot and E.* 919
the owls Wailing had *p* upon her, „ 1001
p To lay the sudden heads of violence flat, *Holy Grail* 309
Drew me, with *p* upon me, till I grew „ 486
My God, the *p* Was once in vows when men believed *Last Tournament* 648
the *P's* that tend the soul, *Guinevere* 65
her beauty, grace and *p*, Wrought as a charm upon them, „ 143
And for the *p* of ministration in her, „ 694
And have not *p* to see it as it is: *Pass. of Arthur* 20
Laid widow'd of the *p* in his eye „ 290
Because it lack'd the *p* of perfect Hope; *Lover's Tale i* 453
P from whose right hand the light Of Life issueth, „ 497
tho' mine image, The subject of thy *p*, „ 782
an' the *p* ov 'is Graäce, *North. Cobbler* 73
But she wur a *p* o' coomfut, „ 79
had holden the *p* and glory of Spain so cheap *The Revenge* 106
misshaping vision of the *P's* Behind the world, *Sisters (E. and E.)* 230
scarce as great as Edith's *p* of love, „ 261
Dead Princess, living *P*, if that, *Ded. Poem Prin. Alice* 1
Lord give thou *p* to thy two witnesses! *Sir J. Oldcastle* 81
'Authority of the Church, *P* of the keys!'— „ 162
By quiet fields, a slowly-dying *p*, *De Prof., Two G.* 24

Power (*continued*) With *p* on thine own act and on the world. *De Prof., Two G.* 56
and grown In *p*, and ever growest, *To Dante* 2
upon me flash'd The *p* of prophesying—but to me No *p*— *Tiresias* 57
no *p* on Fate, Theirs, or mine own! „ 63
This *p* hath work'd no good to aught that lives, „ 77
Pity for all that aches in the grasp of an idiot *p*, *Despair* 43
His Love would have *p* over Hell „ 102
What *p* but the bird's could make This music *Ancient Sage* 21
The nameless *P*, or *P's*, that rule „ 29
'What *P*? aught akin to Mind, „ 78
Or *P* as of the Gods gone blind „ 80
'What *P* but the Years that make „ 91
P's of Good, the *P's* of Ill, *Locksley H., Sixty* 273
Heavenly *P* Makes all things new, (repeat) *Early Spring* 1, 43
thy will, a *p* to make This ever-changing world *To Duke of Argyll* 9
Men loud against all forms of *p*— *Freedom* 37
thunders often have confessed Thy *p*, *To W. C. Macready* 3
serpent-wanded *p* Draw downward into Hades *Demeter and P.* 25
P That lifts her buried life from gloom „ 97
Thro' manifold effect of simple *p's*— *Prog. of Spring* 86
banners blazoning a *P* That is not seen *Akbar's Dream* 137
but for *p* to fuse My myriads into union „ 156
Call'd on the *P* adored by the Christian, *Kapiolani* 32
On whom a happy home has *p* *The Wanderer* 10
purpose of that *P* which alone is great, *God and the Univ.* 5

Praäy'd (prayed) howsiver they *p* an' *p*, *Village Wife* 93

Practice run My faith beyond my *p* into his: *Edwin Morris* 54
I had not stinted *p*, O my God. *St. S. Stylites* 59
workman and his work, That *p* betters?' *Princess iii* 299
What *p* howsoe'er expert In fitting aptest words *In Mem. lxxv* 5
The sin that *p* burns into the blood, *Merlin and V.* 762
Nor yet forgot her *p* in her fright, „ 947

Practise And do not *p* on me, *Geraint and E.* 356

Practised (*See also* **Well-practised**) inasmuch as you have *p* on her, *Aylmer's Field* 302
I find Your face is *p* when I spell the lines, *Merlin and V.* 367
Strike down the lusty and long *p* knight, *Lancelot and E.* 1360
Truthful, trustful, looking upward to the *p* hustings-liar; *Locksley H., Sixty* 123

Praise (s) Blew his own *p's* in his eyes, *A Character* 22
Nor golden largess of thy *p*. *My life is full* 5
She still would take the *p*, and care no more. *The form, the form* 14
'That won his *p's* night and morn?' *Mariana in the S.* 34
While still I yearn'd for human *p*. *Two Voices* 123
But he is chill to *p* or blame. „ 258
neither count on *p*: *Love thou thy land* 26
express delight, in *p* of her Grew oratory. *Gardener's D.* 56
That only love were cause enough for *p*.' „ 105
She broke out in *p* To God, *Dora* 112
But yield not me the *p*: *St. S. Stylites* 185
And others, passing *p*, *Talking Oak* 58
But tho' the port surpasses *p*, *Will Water* 77
In *p* and in dispraise the same, *Ode on Well.* 73
after *p* and scorn, As one who feels the immeasurable world, *A Dedication* 6
The *p* that comes to constancy.' *In Mem. xxi* 12
Had surely added *p* to *p*. „ *xxxi* 8
I leave thy *p's* unexpress'd „ *lxxv* 1
To stir a little dust of *p*. „ 12
fills The lips of men with honest *p*, „ *lxxxiv* 26
whole wood-world is one full peal of *p*. *Balin and Balan* 450
have ye no one word of loyal *p* For Arthur, *Merlin and V.* 778
Dearer to true young hearts than their own *p*, *Lancelot and E.* 419
silent life of prayer, *P*, fast and alms; *Holy Grail* 5
to prayer and *p* She gave herself, „ 76
From prime to vespers will I chant thy *p* *Pelleas and E.* 349
He chill'd the popular *p's* of the King *Guinevere* 13
he was loud in weeping and in *p* Of her, *Lover's Tale ii* 87
Should earn from both the *p* of heroism, *Sisters (E. and E.)* 251
murmur of the people's *p* From thine own State, *Ded. Poem Prin. Alice* 7
P to our Indian brothers, *Def. of Lucknow* 69
In *p* to God who led me thro' the waste. *Columbus* 17
And I more pleasure in your *p*. *To E. Fitzgerald* 56

Praise (s) (*continued*) win all *p* from all Who past it, *Tiresias* 83
to slight *p* but suffer scorn ; *To Duke of Argyll* 4
the *p* And prayer of men, *Demeter and P.* 119
in *p* of Whom The Christian bell, *Akbar's Dream* 148
' All *p* to Alla by whatever hands „ 198
Praise (verb) *p* the heavens for what they have ? ' *Gardener's D.* 102
nothing else For which to *p* the heavens „ 104
And *p* thee more in both *Talking Oak* 290
' No, I cannot *p* the fire In your eye— *Vision of Sin* 183
And *p* the invisible universal Lord, *Ode Inter. Exhib.* 3
one would *p* the love that linkt the King *Gareth and L.* 492
child hath often heard me *p* Your feats of arms, *Marr. of Geraint* 434
crying, ' *P* the patient saints, *Last Tournament* 217
You *p* when you should blame *Epilogue* 4
in every language I hear spoken, people *p* thee. *Akbar's D., Inscrip.* 1
Praised One *p* her ancles, one her eyes, *Beggar Maid* 11
He *p* his land, his horses, his machines ; He *p* his ploughs, his cows, his hogs, his dogs ; He *p* his hens, his geese, his guinea-hens ; *The Brook* 124
p the waning red, and told The vintage— *Aylmer's Field* 406
And much I *p* her nobleness, *Princess, Pro.* 124
Then they *p* him, soft and low, „ *vi* 5
But if I *p* the busy town, *In Mem. lxxxix* 37
p him to his face with their courtly *The Revenge* 99
Praising Sipt wine from silver, *p* God, *Will Water.* 127
Pranced lightly *p* Three captains out ; *Princess v* 254
a hundred gamboll'd and *p* on the wrecks *V. of Maeldune* 102
Prancer she whose elfin *p* springs By night *Sir L. and Q. G.* 33
Prank Playing mad *p's* along the heathy leas ; *Circumstance* 2
must play such *p's* as these. *L. C. V. de Vere* 64
Sweet love on *p's* of saucy boyhood : *Princess vii* 344
Prasútagus Me the wife of rich *P*, *Boädicea* 48
Prate (s) child kill me with her foolish *p* ? ' *Guinevere* 225
Prate (verb) of the moral instinct would she *p* *Palace of Art* 205
p Of penances I cannot have gone thro', *St. S. Stylites* 100
we, that *p* Of rights and wrongs, *Godiva* 7
Boy, when I hear you *p* I almost think *Princess v* 152
Why do they *p* of the blessings of Peace ? *Maud I i* 21
Fools *p*, and perish traitors. *Balin and Balan* 530
Prated I that *p* peace, when first I heard *Princess v* 265
Pratest ' Thou *p* here where thou art least ; *In Mem. xxxvii* 2
Prattle full heart of yours Whereof ye *p*, *Merlin and V.* 549
Hers was the prettiest *p*, *In the Child. Hosp.* 31
I used To *p* to her picture— *The Ring* 116
Prattling *P* the primrose fancies of the boy, *The Brook* 19
Then said the little novice *p* to her, *Guinevere* 183
Unmannerly, with *p* and the tales „ 316
And once my *p* Edith ask'd him ' why ? ' *Sisters (E. and E.)* 58
Pratty (pretty) sa *p* an' neät an' sweeät, *North Cobbler* 43
smile o' the sun as danced in 'er *p* blue eye ; „ 50
sa *p*, an' feät, an' neät, an' sweeät ? „ 108
Pray While I do *p* to Thee alone, *Supp. Confessions* 12
Why *p* To one who heeds not, „ 89
I would *p*—that God would move And strike „ 115
P, Alice, *p*, my darling wife, *Miller's D.* 23
I *p* thee, pass before my light of life, *Œnone* 241
' Where I may mourn and *p*. *Palace of Art* 292
P Heaven for a human heart, *L. C. V. de Vere* 71
P for my soul. More things are wrought *M. d'Arthur* 247
fast Whole Lents, and *p*. *St. S. Stylites* 182
p them not to quarrel for her sake, *Enoch Arden* 35
O rather *p* for those and pity them, *Aylmer's Field* 775
p Your Highness would enroll them with your own, *Princess i* 238
' Yet I *p* Take comfort : live, dear lady, „ *v* 79
So I *p* you tell the truth to me. *The Victim* 48
take this and *p* that he Who wrote it, *A Dedication* 4
Leave thou thy sister when she *p's*, *In Mem. xxxiii* 5
p That we may meet the horsemen of Earl Doorm, *Geraint and E.* 491
' I *p* you of your courtesy, He being as he is, „ 641
P you be gentle, *p* you let me be : „ 708
Yea, God, I *p* you of your gentleness, „ 710
I *p* the King To let me bear some token *Balin and Balan* 187
I *p* you lend me one, if such you have, *Lancelot and E.* 193
let me hence I *p* you.' „ 770
P for my soul, and yield me burial. „ 1280

Pray (*continued*) *P* for my soul thou too, Sir Lancelot, *Lancelot and E.* 1281
P for thy soul ? Ay, that will I. „ 1395
I *p* him, send a sudden Angel down To seize me „ 1424
brother, fast thou too and *p*, And tell thy brother knights to fast and *p*, *Holy Grail* 125
P for him that he scape the doom of fire, *Guinevere* 347
said the little novice, ' I *p* for both ; „ 349
P and be pray'd for ; „ 681
P for my soul. More things are wrought *Pass. of Arthur* 415
O—to *p* with me—yes— *Rizpah* 15
P come and see my mother. *Sisters (E. and E.)* 191
' *P* come and see my mother, and farewell.' „ 196
to *p* Before *that* altar—so I think ; „ 238
and I *p* for them all as my own : ' *In the Child. Hosp.* 19
I *p* you tell King Ferdinand who plays with me, *Columbus* 222
and we pray'd as we heard him *p*, *V. of Maeldune* 125
I pray'd—' my child '—for I still could *p*— *The Wreck* 138
P God our greatness may not fail *Hands all Round* 31
To *p*, to do—To *p*, to do according to the prayer, *Akbar's Dream* 7
Make but one music, harmonising ' *P*.' „ 151
wines of heresy in the cup Of counsel—so—I *p* thee— „ 175
Let blow the trumpet strongly while I *p*, *Doubt and Prayer* 10
Pray'd (*See also* **Praäy'd**) He *p*, and from a happy place God's glory smote *Two Voices* 224
With all my strength I *p* for both, *May Queen, Con.* 31
p him, ' If they pay this tax, they starve.' *Godiva* 20
then he *p* ' Save them from this, whatever comes to me.' *Enoch Arden* 117
And while he *p*, the master of that ship „ 119
P for a blessing on his wife and babes „ 188
P for a sign ' my Enoch is he gone ? ' „ 491
dug His fingers into the wet earth, and *p*. „ 780
yet maiden-meek I *p* Concealment : *Princess iii* 134
She *p* me not to judge their cause „ *vii* 235
So *p* the men, the women : „ *Con.* 7
So *p* him well to accept this cloth of gold, *Gareth and L.* 398
p the King would grant me Lancelot To fight „ 856
had you cried, or knelt, or *p* to me, *Geraint and E.* 844
when of late ye *p* me for my leave „ 888
A hermit, who had *p*, labour'd and *p* *Lancelot and E.* 403
and she *p* and fasted all the more. *Holy Grail* 82
she *p* and fasted, till the sun Shone, „ 98
and myself fasted and *p* Always, „ 130
Fasted and *p* even to the uttermost, „ 132
Who scarce had *p* or ask'd it for myself— „ 691
Pray and be *p* for ; *Guinevere* 681
He waked for both : he *p* for both *Lover's Tale i* 227
By Edith *p* me not to whisper of it. *Sisters (E. and E.)* 207
I *p* them being so calumniated *Columbus* 123
and we *p* as we heard him pray, *V. of Maeldune* 125
I *p*—' my child '—for I still could pray— *The Wreck* 138
all night I *p* with tears, *The Flight* 17
Fasted and *p*, Telemachus the Saint. *St. Telemachus* 11
I *p* against the dream. *Akbar's Dream* 7
And we *p* together for *him*, *Charity* 39
Prayer For me outpour'd in holiest *p*— *Supp. Confessions* 72
Prevail'd not thy pure *p's* ? „ 89
In deep and daily *p's* would'st strive „ 101
If *p's* will not hush thee, *Lilian* 27
More things are wrought by *p* Than this worl dreams of. *M. d'Arthur* 247
knowing God, they lift not hands of *p* „ 252
Battering the gates of heaven with storms of *p*, *St. S. Stylites* 7
with hoggish whine They burst my *p*. „ 178
So keep I fair thro' faith and *p* A virgin heart *Sir Galahad* 23
Rejoicing at that answer to his *p*. *Enoch Arden* 127
evermore *P* from a living source within the will, „ 801
Give me your *p's*, for he is past your *p's*, *Aylmer's Field* 751
My mother pitying made a thousand *p's* ; *Princess i* 21
A liquid look on Ida, full of *p*, „ *iv* 369
one port of sense not flint to *p*, „ *vi* 182
grant my *p*. Help, father, brother, help ; „ 304
Blazon your mottoes of blessing and *p* ! *W. to Alexandra* 12
my *p* Was as the whisper of an air *In Mem. xvii* 2
Her eyes are homes of silent *p*, „ *xxxii* 1

Prayer (*continued*) Thrice blest whose lives are faithful *p's*, *In Mem. xxxii* 13
Who built him fanes of fruitless *p*, „ *lvi* 12
breathing a *p* To be friends, to be reconciled! *Maud I xix* 55
Not a bell was rung, not a *p* was read; „ *II v* 24
weary her ears with one continuous *p*, *Gareth and L.* 19
only breathe Short fits of *p*, *Geraint and E.* 155
silent life of *p*, Praise, fast, and alms; *Holy Grail* 4
to *p* and praise She gave herself, „ 76
'might it come To me by *p* and fasting?' „ 96
and enter'd, and we knelt in *p*. „ 460
And so wear out in almsdeed and in *p* *Guinevere* 687
More things are wrought by *p* Than this world dreams of. *Pass. of Arthur* 415
knowing God, they lift not hands of *p* „ 420
p of many a race and creed, and clime— *To the Queen, ii* 11
That strike across the soul in *p*, *Lover's Tale i* 364
'to seek the Lord Jesus in *p*; *In the Child. Hosp.* 18
good woman, can *p* set a broken bone?' „ 20
if our Princes harken'd to my *p*, *Columbus* 100
I send my *p* by night and day— „ 233
sheet Let down to Peter at his *p's*; *To E. Fitzgerald* 12
Gods, despite of human *p*, Are slower to forgive *Tiresias* 9
I would make my life one *p* *The Wreck* 10
where of old we knelt in *p*, *Locksley H., Sixty* 33
Thy *p* was 'Light—more Light— *Epit. on Caxton* 1
the praise And *p* of men, *Demeter and P.* 120
all the sciences, poesy, varying voices of *p*? *Vastness* 31
I that heard, and changed the *p* *Happy* 55
on stony hearts a fruitless *p* For pity. *Death of Œnone* 41
If it be a mosque people murmur the holy *p*, *Akbar's D., Inscrip.* 4
To pray, to do according to the *p*, *Akbar's Dream* 8
but the *p's*, That have no successor in deed, „ 9
Prayerful patient, and *p*, meek, Pale-blooded, *Last Tournament* 607
who am not meek, Pale-blooded, *p*. „ 611
Prayer-prelude labour'd thro' His brief *p-p*, *Aylmer's Field* 628
Praying *P* all I can, If prayers will not hush thee, *Lilian* 26
and sinking ships, and *p* hands. *Lotos-Eaters, C. S.* 116
tell her that I died Blessing her, *p* for her, *Enoch Arden* 879
my latest breath Was spent in blessing her and *p* for her. „ 884
p him To speak before the people of her child, *Aylmer's Field* 607
p God will save Thy sailor,— *In Mem. vi* 13
another, a lord of all things, *p* *Maud II v* 32
she was ever *p* the sweet heavens To save *Geraint and E.* 44
p him By that great love they both had borne the dead, *Lover's Tale iv* 180
p that, when I from hence Shall fade *Tiresias* 214
When I was *p* in a storm— *Happy* 80
Preach (*See also* **Preäch**) I will not even *p* to you, *To J. S.* 39
Whose foresight *p'es* peace, *Love and Duty* 34
Our own experience *p'es*. *Will Water.* 176
he heard his priest *P* an inverted scripture, *Aylmer's Field* 44
Yet who would *p* it as a truth *In Mem. liii* 11
To *p* our poor little army down, *Maud I x* 38
Good, this forward, you that *p* it, *Locksley H., Sixty* 216
Preäch I'd like tha to *p* 'em down, *Church-Warden, etc.* 52
Preach'd *p* An universal culture for the crowd, *Princess, Pro.* 108
Is it you, that *p* in the chapel *Despair* 1
p a Gospel, all men's good; *Locksley H., Sixty* 89
Preäch'd An' Muggins 'e *p* o' Hell-fire *North. Cobbler* 55
Preacher (*See also* **Wiclif-preacher**) when the *p's* cadence flow'd Softening *Aylmer's Field* 729
p says, our sins should make us sad: *Grandmother* 93
a harm no *p* can heal; *Maud I iv* 22
Why there? they came to hear their *p*. *Sir J. Oldcastle* 42
Burnt too, my faithful *p*, Beverley! „ 80
Dooms our unlicensed *p* to the flame, „ 105
p's linger'd o'er his dying words, *St. Telemachus* 75
Preaching (*See also* **A-preächin'**) *p* down a daughter's heart. *Locksley Hall* 94
Not *p* simple Christ to simple men, *Sea Dreams* 21
Preamble prolong Her low *p* all alone, *Palace of Art* 174
tricks and fooleries, O Vivien, the *p*? *Merlin and V.* 266
Precaution Creeps, no *p* used, among the crowd, *Guinevere* 519
Precedent slowly broadens down From *p* to *p*: *You ask me, why, etc.* 12
That codeless myriad of *p*, *Aylmer's Field* 436
Precedent (*continued*) Swallowing its *p* in victory. [*Lover's Tale i* 763
Precinct did I break Your *p*; *Princess iv* 422
What, in the *p's* of the chapel-yard, *Merlin and V.* 751
Precious pure quintessences of *p* oils In hollow'd moons of gems, *Palace of Art* 187
Surely a *p* thing, one worthy note, *M. d'Arthur* 89
Thou wouldst betray me for the *p* hilt; „ 126
All *p* things, discover'd late, *Day-Dm., Arrival* 1
To find the *p* morning hours were lost. *Enoch Arden* 302
They knew the *p* things they had to guard: *Third of Feb.* 41
Lo their *p* Roman bantling, *Boädicea* 31
Such *p* relics brought by thee; *In Mem. xvii* 18
With 'Love's too *p* to be lost, „ *lxv* 3
(Which Maud, like a *p* stone *Maud I xiv* 10
To dissolve the *p* seal on a bond, „ *xix* 45
Surely a *p* thing, one worthy note, *Pass. of Arthur* 257
Thou wouldst betray me for the *p* hilt; „ 294
The clear brow, bulwark of the *p* brain, *Lover's Tale i* 130
The *p* crystal into which I braided Edwin's hair! *The Flight* 34
Precipice Among the palms and ferns and *p's*; *Enoch Arden* 593
Down from the lean and wrinkled *p's*, *Princess iv* 22
breakers boom and blanch on the *p's*, *Boädicea* 76
Went slipping down horrible *p's*, *Geraint and E.* 379
Precipitancy Bearing all down in thy *p*— *Gareth and L.* 8
Precipitate Wheeling with *p* paces To the melody, *Vision of Sin* 37
such a *p* heel, Fledged as it were *Lucretius* 200
Precipitous sweep Of some *p* rivulet to the wave, *Enoch Arden* 587
Precontract 'Our king expects—was there no *p*? *Princess iii* 207
as to *p's*, we move, my friend, At no man's beck, „ 226
I wed with thee! *I* bound by *p* Your bride, „ *iv* 541
lagg'd in answer loth to render up My *p*, „ *v* 300
Predoom'd most *P* her as unworthy. *Lancelot and E.* 729
Preëminence To assail this gray *p* of man! *Princess iii* 234
Prefer each *p's* his separate claim, *In Mem. cii* 18
Preference But if there lie a *p* eitherway, *Sisters (E. and E.)* 290
Prefigured ah, you seem All he *p*, *Princess iii* 209
Prejudice Cut *P* against the grain: *Love thou thy land* 22
To leap the rotten pales of *p*, *Princess ii* 142
old-recurring waves of *p* Resmooth to nothing: „ *iii* 240
Prelude (s) (*See also* **Prayer-prelude**) With mellow *p's*, 'We are free.' *The winds, etc.* 4
But with some *p* of disparagement, Read, *The Epic* 49
This *p* has prepared thee. *Gardener's D.* 272
The *p* to some brighter world. *Day-Dm., L'Envoi* 40
Are but the needful *p's* of the truth: *Princess, Con.* 74
Green *p*, April promise, glad new-year *Lover's Tale i* 281
Oftentimes The vision had fair *p*, „ *ii* 124
by their clash, And *p* on the keys, *Sisters (E. and E.)* 2
Was *p* to the tyranny of all? *Tiresias* 74
Prelude (verb) And I—my harp would *p* woe— *In Mem. lxxxviii* 9
Preluded sweet breath *P* those melodious *D. of F. Women* 6
Premier city-roar that hails *P* or king! *Princess, Con.* 102
Prepare but *p*: I speak; it falls.' „ *ii* 224
Prepared This prelude has *p* thee. *Gardener's D.* 272
The rites *p*, the victim bared, *The Victim* 65
day *p* The daily burden for the back. *In Mem. xxv* 3
let there be *p* a chariot-bier To take me *Lancelot and E.* 1121
Presage after seen The dwarfs of *p*: *Princess iv* 447
No *p*, but the same mistrustful mood *Merlin and V.* 321
Presageful Dark in the glass of some *p* mood, „ 295
That three-days-long *p* gloom of yours „ 320
Prescient at length Prophetical and *p* *Lover's Tale ii* 132
Presence (adj.) That morning in the *p* room I stood *Princess i* 51
Presence (s) The light of thy great *p*; *Ode to Memory* 32
all the full-faced *p* of the Gods *Œnone* 80
I hate Her *p*, hated both of Gods and men. „ 229
To dwell in *p* of immortal youth, *Tithonus* 21
crimson'd all Thy *p* and thy portals, „ 57
Philip sitting at her side forgot Her *p*, *Enoch Arden* 385
A splendid *p* flattering the poor roofs *Aylmer's Field* 175
Your *p* will be sun in winter, *To F. D. Maurice* 3
gather'd strength and grace And *p*, *In Mem. ciii* 28
in his *p* I attend To hear the tidings „ *cxxvi* 2
As in the *p* of a gracious king. *Gareth and L.* 316
splendour of the *p* of the King Throned, „ 320

Pretty (*continued*) Niver wur p, not I, *Spinster's S's* 21
Thaw it warn't not me es wur p, „ 22
P anew when ya dresses 'em oop, „ 85
Prevail Let her work p. *In Mem. cxiv* 4
Let not thy moods p, when I am gone *Balin and Balan* 140
Prevail'd But why P not thy pure prayers? *Supp. Confessions* 89
has won His path upward, and p, *Ode on Well.* 214
And now the Barons and the kings p, *Com. of Arthur* 105
'Thou hast half p against me,' *Gareth and L.* 30
p So far that no caress could win *Sisters (E. and E.)* 257
Prevailing P in weakness, the coronach stole *Dying Swan* 26
not worthy ev'n to speak Of thy p mysteries; *In Mem. xxxvii* 12
And her words stole with most p sweetness *Lover's Tale i* 553
The King p made his realm:— *Last Tournament* 651
Prey (s) And stared, with his foot on the p, *Poet's Song* 12
biting laws to scare the beasts of p *Princess v* 393
The seeming p of cyclic storms, *In Mem. cxviii* 11
little wood where I sit is a world of plunder and p. *Maud I iv* 24
Bound on a foray, rolling eyes of p, *Geraint and E.* 538
bird of rapine whose whole p Is man's good name: *Merlin and V.* 728
Beneath the shadow of some bird of p; *Pelleas and E.* 608
Round whose sick head all night, like birds of p, *Last Tournament* 138
Prey (verb) and p By each cold hearth, *In Mem. xcviii* 17
Price four-field system, and the p of grain; *Audley Court* 34
learn the p, and what the p he ask'd, *The Brook* 142
the colt would fetch its p; „ 149
to give at last The p of half a realm, *Lancelot and E.* 1164
a robe Of samite without p, *Merlin and V.* 222
Ev'n by the p that others set upon it, *Lover's Tale iv* 152
You have set a p on his head: *Bandit's Death* 7
Priceless Rich arks with p bones of martyrdom, *Balin and Balan* 110
Stared at the p cognizance, and thought „ 430
A p goblet with a p wine Arising, *Lover's Tale iv* 227
Prick insects p Each leaf into a gall) *Talking Oak* 69
To p us on to combat 'Like to like! *Princess v* 304
the blood creeps, and the nerves p *In Mem. l* 2
plunges thro' the wound again, And p's it deeper: *Pelleas and E.* 531
they p's cleän thruf to the skin— *Spinster's S's.* 36
Prick'd p with goads and stings; *Palace of Art* 150
like a horse That hears the corn-bin open, p my ears; *The Epic* 45
peace which each had p to death. *Aylmer's Field* 52
playing with the blade he p his hand, „ 239
while each ear was p to attend A tempest, *Princess vi* 280
P by the Papal spur, we rear'd, *Third of Feb.* 27
half-way down P thro' the mist; *Gareth and L.* 194
And Gareth crying p against the cry; „ 1221
p their light ears, and felt Her low firm voice *Geraint and E.* 193
Geraint, who being p In combat with the follower of Limours, „ 500
I was p with some reproof, „ 890
p The hauberk to the flesh; *Balin and Balan* 559
couch'd their spears and p their steeds, *Lancelot and E.* 479
and a spear P sharply his own cuirass, „ 489
All ears were p at once, „ 724
P with incredible pinnacles into heaven. *Holy Grail* 423
Pricking (Look at it) p a cockney ear. *Maud I x* 22
Prickle (s) The furzy p fire the dells, *Two Voices* 71
Prickle (verb) P my skin and catch my breath, *Maud I xiv* 36
Prickled Gareth's head p beneath his helm; *Gareth and L.* 1397
Prickly His charger trampling many a p star *Marr. of Geraint* 313
Pride Is not my human p brought low? *Supp. Confessions* 14
And chastisement of human p; That p, the sin of devils, „ 108
I think that p hath now no place Nor sojourn in me. „ 120
all the outworks of suspicious p; *Isabel* 24
With merriment of kingly p, *Arabian Nights* 151
'Self-blinded are you by your p: *Two Voices* 23
waste wide Of that abyss, or scornful p! „ 120
Wilt thou find passion, pain or p? „ 243
on herself her serpent p had curl'd. *Palace of Art* 257
Your p is yet no mate for mine, *L. C. V. de Vere* 11
my brand Excalibur, Which was my p: *M. d'Arthur* 28
old Sir Robert's p, His books— *Audley Court* 58
shame and p, New things and old, *Walk. to the Mail* 60
our p Looks only for a moment whole *Aylmer's Field* 1
Pride (*continued*) his p Lay deeper than to wear it as his ring— *Aylmer's Field* 121
taking p in her, She look'd so sweet, „ 554
a time for these to flaunt their p? „ 770
your Princess cramm'd with erring p, *Princess iii* 102
welcome Russian flower, a people's p, *W. to Marie Alex.* 6
Ring out false p in place and blood, *In Mem. cvi* 21
The proud was half disarm'd of p, „ *cx* 6
The fire of a foolish p flash'd *Maud I iv* 16
We are puppets, Man in his p, „ 25
often a man's own angry p Is cap and bells „ *vi* 61
thought, is it p, and mused and sigh'd „ *viii* 12
'No surely, now it cannot be p.' „ 13
Down with ambition, avarice, p, „ *x* 47
I to cry out on p Who have won her favour! „ *xii* 17
Fool that I am to be vext with his p! „ *xiii* 5
For the keeper was one, so full of p, „ *II v* 79
shame, p, wrath Slew the May-white: *Gareth and L.* 656
placed a peacock in his p Before the damsel, „ 850
The damsel by the peacock in his p, „ 870
And doubling all his master's vice of p, *Marr. of Geraint* 195
Then will I fight him, and will break his p, „ 221
fight and break his p, and have it of him. „ 416
That I will break his p and learn his name, „ 424
Refused her to him, then his p awoke; „ 448
But that his p too much despises me: „ 464
In next day's tourney I may break his p.' „ 476
My p is broken: men have seen my fall.' „ 578
my p Is broken down, for Enid sees my fall!' „ 589
For once, when I was up so high in p *Geraint and E.* 790
They place their p in Lancelot and the Queen. *Merlin and V.* 25
dead love's harsh heir, jealous p? *Lancelot and E.* 1398
the heat Of p and glory fired her face; *Pelleas and E.* 172
My p in happier summers, at my feet. *Guinevere* 536
To whom my false voluptuous p, „ 641
my brand Excalibur, Which was my p: *Pass. of Arthur* 196
my house an' my man were my p, *First Quarrel* 41
Sir Richard cried in his English p, *The Revenge* 82
hesn't the call, nor the mooney, but hes the p, *Village Wife* 91
I have only wounded his p— *The Wreck* 14
he sail'd the sea to crush the Moslem in his p; *Locksley H., Sixty* 29
Prideful My nature's p sparkle in the blood *Geraint and E.* [illegible]
Priest (*See also* **Soldier-priest**) Speak, if there be a p, a man of God, *St. S. Stylites* 214
As the p, above his book Leering *Vision of Sin* 117
his p Preach an inverted scripture, *Aylmer's Field* 43
'Gash thyself, p, and honour thy brute Baäl, „ 644
one The silken p of peace, one this, one that, *Princess v* 184
with music, with soldier and with p, *Ode on Well.* 81
The P in horror about his altar *The Victim* 7
The P went out by heath and hill; „ 29
He seem'd a victim due to the p. The P beheld him, „ 36
For now the P has judged for me.' „ 56
the P was happy, (repeat) „ 61, 73
This faith has many a purer p, *In Mem. xxxvii* 3
Delicate-handed p intone; *Maud I viii* 11
p, who mumble worship in your quire— *Balin and Balan* 444
he had a difference with their p's, *Holy Grail* 674
Shone like the countenance of a p of old *Pelleas and E.* 144
I was the High P in her holiest place, *Lover's Tale i* 686
for your P Labels—to take the king along with him— *Sir J. Oldcastle* 48
P's Who fear the king's hard common-sense „ 65
Runs in the rut, a coward to the P. „ 78
The Gospel, the P's pearl, flung down to swine— „ 116
What profits an ill P Between me and my God? „ 144
that proud P, That mock-meek mouth of utter Antichrist, „ 169
I am damn'd already by the P „ 200
Bantering bridesman, reddening p, *Forlorn* 33
when The P pronounced you dead, *Happy* 50
P, who join'd you to the dead, „ 93
he buried you, the P; the P is not to blame, „ 105
The menacing poison of intolerant p's, *Akbar's Dream* 165
I will find the P and confess. *Bandit's Death* 18

Priest (*continued*) *P's* in the name of the Lord passing souls — *The Dawn* 4
Priestess O *P* in the vaults of Death, — *In Mem. iii* 2
Priesthood ever and aye the *P* moan'd, — *The Victim* 23
What said her *P*? — *Kapiolani* 19
Baffled her *p*, Broke the Taboo, — " 29
Primal grown at last beyond the passions of the *p* clan? — *Locksley H., Sixty* 93
Mount and mine, and *p* wood; — *Open I. and C. Exhib.* 6
Prime (adj.) On the *p* labour of thine early days: — *Ode to Memory* 94
P, which I knew; and so we sat and eat — *Audley Court* 28
While the *p* swallow dips his wing, — *Edwin Morris* 145
Better to clear *p* forests, heave and thump — *Princess iii* 127
And my *p* passion in the grave: — *In Mem. lxxxv* 76
from *p* youth Well-known well-loved. — *Lover's Tale ii* 175
Butter I warrants be *p*, — *Village Wife* 3
Prime (s) golden *p* Of good Haroun Alraschid. — *Arabian Nights* 10, 21, 32, 43, 54, 65, 76, 87, 98, 109, 120, 131, 142, 153
gray *p* Make thy grass hoar with early rime. — *Two Voices* 65
could she climb Beyond her own material *p*? — " 378
Raw from the *p*, and crushing down his mate; — *Princess ii* 121
about my barren breast In the dead *p*: — " *vi* 203
we fought for Freedom from our *p*, — *Third of Feb.* 23
And at the spiritual *p* Rewaken — *In Mem. xliii* 15
Dragons of the *p*, That tare each other — " *lvi* 22
The colours of the crescent *p*? — " *cxvi* 4
shook his wits they wander in his *p*— — *Gareth and L.* 715
From *p* to vespers will I chant thy praise — *Pelleas and E.* 349
Primrose (adj.) Prattling the *p* fancies of the boy, — *The Brook* 19
Primrose (s) *p* yet is dear, The *p* of the later year, — *In Mem. lxxxv* 118
Prince (*See also* **Lord-prince, Shepherd-prince**) else the island *p's* over-bold — *Lotos-Eaters, C. S.* 75
to greet Troy's wandering *p*, — *On a Mourner* 33
Among the powers and *p's* of this world, — *St. S. Stylites* 187
And bring the fated fairy *P*. — *Day-Dm., Sleep. P.* 56
A fairy *P*, with joyful eyes, — " *Arrival* 7
P of peace, the Mighty God, — *Aylmer's Field* 669
heads of chiefs and *p's* fall so fast, — " 763
and be you The *P* to win her! — *Princess, Pro.* 226
'Then follow me, the *P*,' I answer'd, — " 227
A *p* I was, blue-eyed, and fair in face, — " *i* 1
'You do us, *P*,' he said, — " 120
would you had her, *P*, with all my heart, — " 126
She answer'd, 'then ye know the *P*?' — " *ii* 49
in me behold the *P* Your countryman, — " 214
'O Sir, O *P*, I have no country none; — " 218
be swerved from right to save A *p*, a brother? — " 291
help my *p* to gain His rightful bride, — " *iii* 160
I know the *P*, I prize his truth: — " 232
tho' your *P's* love were like a God's, — " 248
'Fair daughter, when we sent the *P* your way — " *iv* 398
and like a gentleman. And like a *p*: — " 528
Arranged the favour, and assumed the *P*. — " 602
you could not slay Me, nor your *p*: — " *v* 66
He seems a gracious and a gallant *P*, — " 213
We would do much to gratify your *P*— — " 217
But let your *P* (our royal word upon it, — " 224
embattled squares, And squadrons of the *P*, — " 247
P, she can be sweet to those she loves, — " 289
and bore down a *P*, And Cyril, one. — " 518
Cyril seeing it, push'd against the *P*, — " 533
there went up a great cry, The *P* is slain. — " *vi* 26
on to the tents: take up the *P*.' — " 279
That you may tend upon him with the *p*.' — " 315
but the *P* Her brother came; — " 344
Never, *P*; You cannot love me.' — " *vii* 337
Has given our *P* his own imperial Flower, — *W. to Marie Alex.* 4
A princely people's awful *p's*, — *The Daisy* 39
in his coffin the *P* of courtesy lay. — *G. of Swainston* 10
a *P* indeed, Beyond all titles, — *Ded. of Idylls* 41
his wife Nursed the young *p*, and rear'd him — *Com. of Arthur* 224
thou art closer to this noble *p*, — " 314
p his heir, when tall and marriageable, — *Gareth and L.* 102
'*P*, thou shalt go disguised to Arthur's hall, — " 152
Lancelot answer'd, '*P*, O Gareth— — " 1236
Knight, knave, *p* and fool, I hate thee and for ever.' — " 1255
Prince (*continued*) *P*, Knight, Hail, Knight and *P*, — *Gareth and L.* 1270
'Nay, *P*,' she cried, 'God wot, — " 1332
O *P*, I went for Lancelot first, — " 1343
the *P* Three times had blown— — " 1377
A tributary *p* of Devon, — *Marr. of Geraint* 2
Allowing it, the *P* and Enid rode, — " 43
As of a *p* whose manhood was all gone, — " 59
Low bow'd the tributary *P*, and she, — " 174
'Late, late, Sir *P*,' she said, — " 177
P Had put his horse in motion toward the knight, — " 205
The *P's* blood spirted upon the scarf, — " 208
'Farewell, fair *P*,' answer'd the stately Queen. — " 224
P, as Enid past him, fain To follow, — " 375
and while the *P* and Earl Yet spoke together, — " 384
and prove her heart toward the *P*.' — " 513
Loudly spake the *P*, 'Forbear: — " 555
'This noble *p* who won our earldom back, — " 619
But being so beholden to the *P*, — " 623
P had found her in her ancient home; — " 644
While ye were talking sweetly with your *P*, — " 698
Our mended fortunes and a *P's* bride: — " 718
the *P* Hath pick'd a ragged-robin from the hedge, — " 723
might shame the *P* To whom we are beholden; — " 726
we beat him back, As this great *P* invaded us, — " 747
And did her honour as the *P's* bride, — " 835
pair Of comrades making slowlier at the *P*, — *Geraint and E.* 167
'Ye will be all the wealthier,' cried the *P*. — " 221
P had brought his errant eyes Home from the rock, — " 245
thus he moved the *P* To laughter and his comrades — " 295
when the *P* was merry, ask'd Limours, — " 297
the stout *P* bad him a loud good-night. — " 361
P, without a word, from his horse fell. — " 508
love you, *P*, with something of the love — " 788
'Follow me, *P*, to the camp, — " 808
till he saw her Pass into it, turn'd to the *P*, — " 887
'*P*, when of late ye pray'd me for — " 888
So spake the King: low bow'd the *P*, — " 920
call'd him the great *P* and man of men. — " 961
'*P*, Art thou so little loyal to thy Queen, — *Balin and Balan* 250
P, we have ridd'n before among the flowers — " 272
thou, Sir *P*, Wilt surely guide me to the warrior King, — " 477
nor *P* Nor knight am I, — " 483
a *P* In the mid might and flourish of his May, — *Lancelot and E.* 553
to whom the *P* Reported who he was, — " 627
ride no more at random, noble *P*! — " 633
P Accorded with his wonted courtesy, — " 637
'*P*, O loyal nephew of our noble King, — " 651
yon proud *P* who left the quest to me. — " 762
told him all the tale Of King and *P*, — " 824
P and Lord am I In mine own land, — " 916
And there the heathen *P*, Arviragus, — *Holy Grail* 61
he knew the *P* tho' marr'd with dust, — *Guinevere* 36
Sir Lancelot holp To raise the *P*, — " 46
the *P* Who scarce had pluck'd his flickering life — *To the Queen ii* 4
full city peal'd Thee and thy *P*! — " 27
Like to the wild youth of an evil *p*, — *Lover's Tale i* 354
if our *P's* harken'd to my prayer, — *Columbus* 100
brought your *P's* gold enough If left alone! — " 105
native *p's* slain or slaved, — " 174
A princelier looking man never stept thro' a *P's* hall. — *The Wreck* 16
now Your fairy *P* has found you, — *The Ring* 69
One raised the *P*, one sleek'd the squalid hair, — *Death of Œnone* 57
Princedom Drew all their petty *p's* under him, — *Com. of Arthur* 18
the King Drew in the petty *p's* under him, — " 517
In his own blood, his *p*, youth and hopes, — *Gareth and L.* 210
his *p* lay Close on the borders of a territory, — *Marr. of Geraint* 33
Forgetful of his *p* and its cares. — " 54
Princelier A *p* looking man never stept thro' a Prince's hall. — *The Wreck* 16
Princelike thro' these *P* his bearing shone; — *Marr. of Geraint* 545
Princely And *p* halls, and farms, and flowing lawns, — *Aylmer's Field* 654
A *p* people's awful princes, — *The Daisy* 39
Yniol's rusted arms Were on his *p* person, — *Marr. of Geraint* 544
she gazed upon the man Of *p* bearing, — *Pelleas and E.* 306
So *p*, tender, truthful, reverent, pure— — *D. of the Duke of C.* 4

Princely-proud too *p-p* To pass thereby; *Gareth and L.* 162
Princess (*See also* **Maiden-Princess, Poet-princess**) The happy *p* follow'd him. *Day-Dm., Depart.* 8
I wish That I were some great *p*, *Princess, Pro.* 134
'And make her some great *P*, six feet high, „ 224
Heroic seems our *P* as required— „ 230
betroth'd To one, a neighbouring *P*: „ *i* 33
Who moves about the *P*; „ 76
beauty compass'd in a female form, The *P*; „ *ii* 35
edge unturnable, our Head, The *P*.' „ 204
'Let the *P* judge Of that' she said: „ 234
the *P* should have been the Head, „ *iii* 34
early risen she goes to inform The *P*: „ 63
Not like your *P* cramm'd with erring pride, „ 102
My *p*, O my *p*! true she errs, „ 107
'That afternoon the *P* rode to take The dip „ 169
but with some disdain Answer'd the *P*, „ *iv* 62
'The Head, the Head, the *P*, O the Head!' „ 176
They haled us to the *P* where she sat High in the hall: „ 271
It was not thus, O *P*, in old days: „ 292
She ceased: the *P* answer'd coldly, 'Good: „ 359
The *P* with her monstrous woman-guard, „ 562
She was a *p* too: and so I swore. „ *v* 295
A gallant fight, a noble *p*— „ *Con.* 19
Like our wild *P* with as wise a dream „ 69
Or at thy coming, *P*, everywhere, *W. to Marie Alex.* 42
I full oft shall dream I see my *p* *Marr. of Geraint* 752
In such apparel as might well beseem His *p*, „ 759
hundred miles of coast, A palace and a *p*, *Merlin and V.* 589
hundred miles of coast, The palace and the *p*, „ 648
The *P* of that castle was the one, *Holy Grail* 578
And tame thy jailing *p* to thine hand. *Pelleas and E.* 344
And marriage with a *p* of that realm, *Last Tournament* 176
Dear *P*, living Power, if that, *Ded. Poem Prin. Alice* 1
Principle 'Some hidden *p* to move, *Two Voices* 133
P's are rain'd in blood; *Love thou thy land* 80
Print (s) (*See also* **Hoof-print, Jewel-print**) take the *p* Of the golden age— *Maud I i* 29
(Meaning the *p* that you gave us, *In the Child. Hosp.* 51
Print (verb) hill and wood and field did *p* *In Mem. lxxix* 7
Prior Archbishop, Bishop, *P's*, Canons, *Sir J. Oldcastle* 160
Priory sought A *p* not far off, there lodged, *Pelleas and E.* 214
Prism Make *p's* in every carven glass, *Day-Dm., Sleep. P.* 35
Prison (adj.) Sang looking thro' his *p* bars? *Margaret* 35
Prison (s) (*See also* **Shadow-prison**) I kiss'd my boy in the *p*, *Rizpah* 23
Flowers to these 'spirits in *p*' *In the Child. Hosp.* 37
My *p*, not my fortress, fall away! *Doubt and Prayer* 12
Prison'd *P*, and kept and coax'd and whistled to— *Gareth and L.* 14
Prisoner and himself The *p* at the bar, *Sea Dreams* 176
A *p*, and the vassal of thy will; *Pelleas and E.* 241
Being guiltless, as an innocent *p*, *Lover's Tale i* 787
As a vision Unto a haggard *p*, „ *ii* 148
I read no more the *p's* mute wail *Sir J. Oldcastle* 4
Private A *p* life was all his joy, *Will Water.* 129
'Is this an hour For *p* sorrow's barren song, *In Mem. xxi* 14
For I never whisper'd a *p* affair *Maud II v* 47
But the red life spilt for a *p* blow— „ 93
Privet (adj.) To one green wicket in a *p* hedge; *Gardener's D.* 110
Privet (s) white as *p* when it flowers. *Walk. to the Mail* 56
Privilege manlike end myself?—our *p*— *Lucretius* 232
It was our ancient *p*, my Lords, *Third of Feb.* 5
Prize (s) (*See also* **Tourney-prize**) Ride on! the *p* is near.' *Sir Galahad* 80
read and earn our *p*, A golden brooch: *Princess iii* 300
The *p* of beauty for the fairest there. *Marr. of Geraint* 485
He felt, were she the *p* of bodily force, „ 541
two years past have won for thee, The *p* of beauty.' „ 555
tho' ye won the *p* of fairest fair, „ 719
shook her pulses, crying 'Look, a *p*! *Geraint and E.* 123
since a diamond was the *p*. *Lancelot and E.* 33
Proclaiming his the *p*, who wore the sleeve Of scarlet, „ 501
'Advance and take thy *p* The diamond;' „ 503
Prize me no *p's*, for my *p* is death! „ 506
left his *p* Untaken, crying that his *p* is death.' „ 530
Will deem this *p* of ours is rashly given: „ 541
Came not to us, of us to claim the *p*, „ 544

Prize (s) (*continued*) with you? won he not your *p*?' *Lancelot and E.* 573
bore the *p* and could not find The victor, „ 629
'Your *p* the diamond sent you by the King:' „ 821
the *p* A golden circlet and a knightly sword, *Pelleas and E.* 11
Saving the goodly sword, his *p*, „ 359
p Of Tristram in the jousts of yesterday, *Last Tournament* 7
Innocence the King Gave for a *p*— „ 295
Of one—his name is out of me—the *p*, If *p* she were— „ 546
I mused nor yet endured to take So rich a *p*, *Lover's Tale iii* 50
Prize (verb) should I *p* thee, couldst thou last, *Will Water.* 203
I know the Prince, I *p* his truth: *Princess iii* 233
What dares not Ida do that she should *p* The soldier? „ *v* 174
sole men we shall *p* in the aftertime, „ 412
p the authentic mother of her mind. „ 433
what the King So *p's*—overprizes—gentleness. *Balin and Balan* 184
'I better *p* The living dog than the dead lion: „ 584
prized him more Than who should *p* him *Merlin and V.* 160
P me no prizes, for my prize is death! *Lancelot and E.* 506
To Canada whom we love and *p*, *Hands all Round* 19
my friend, To *p* your various book, *To Ulysses* 47
I *p* that soul where man and woman *On one who effec. E. M.* 2
Prized Or else we loved the man, and *p* his work; *M. d'Arthur, Ep.* 8
You *p* my counsel, lived upon my lips: *Princess iv* 293
p him more Than who should prize him *Merlin and V.* 159
No sisters ever *p* each other more. *Sisters (E. and E.)* 43
He would open the books that I *p*, *The Wreck* 21
is *p* for it smells of the beast, *The Dawn* 14
Prize-oxen A lord of fat *p-o* and of sheep, *Princess, Con.* 86
Process widen'd with the *p* of the suns. *Locksley Hall* 138
Eternal *p* moving on, *In Mem. lxxxii* 5
Who reads thy gradual *p*, Holy Spring. *Prog. of Spring* 106
Procession Let the long long *p* go, *Ode on Well.* 15
I came upon The rear of a *p*, *Lover's Tale ii* 75
Proclaim From my high nest of penance here *p* *St. S. Stylites* 167
'*P* the faults he would not show *You might have won* 17
For many and many an age *p* *Ode on Well.* 226
let *p* a joust At Camelot, *Lancelot and E.* 76
the King Had let *p* a tournament— *Pelleas and E.* 11
Proclaim'd Spake to the lady with him and *p*, *Marr. of Geraint* 552
Arthur's host *P* him Victor, and the day was won. *Balin and Balan* 90
p His Master as 'the Sun of Righteousness,' *Akbar's Dream* 82
Proclaiming *P* Enoch Arden and his woes; *Enoch Arden* 868
P social truth shall spread, *In Mem. cxxvii* 5
set him in the hall, *P*, 'Here is Uther's heir, *Com. of Arthur* 230
P his the prize, who wore the sleeve Of scarlet, *Lancelot and E.* 501
Proclamation sent His horns of *p* out *Merlin and V.* 581
Proctor he had breathed the *P's* dogs; *Princess, Pro.* 113
prudes for *p's*, dowagers for deans, „ 141
Two *P's* leapt upon us, crying, 'Names:' „ *iv* 259
Procuress *P* to the Lords of Hell. *In Mem. liii* 16
Prodigal Behind Were realms of upland, *p* in oil, *Palace of Art* 79
And *p* of all brain-labour he, *Aylmer's Field* 447
Prodigies These *p* of myriad nakednesses, *Lucretius* 156
Prodigious a match as this! Impossible, *p*!' *Aylmer's Field* 315
Or Gareth telling some *p* tale Of knights, *Gareth and L.* 508
Produce (s) *P* of your field and flood, *Open. I. and C. Exhib.* 5
Produce (verb) That one fair planet can *p*, *Ode Inter. Exhib.* 24
Profess seeing they *p* To be none other (repeat) *Last Tournament* 82, 85
Professor we heard The grave *P*. *Princess ii* 371
Sat compass'd with *p's*: „ 444
Proffer (s) She to Paris made *P* of royal power, *Œnone* 111
nor did mine own Refuse her *p*, *Princess vi* 347
Made *p* of the league of golden mines, *Merlin and V.* 646
Proffer (verb) *p* these The brethren of our blood *Princess vi* 70
Proffer'd At one dear knee we *p* vows, *In Mem. lxxix* 13
For howsoe'er at first he *p* gold, *Gareth and L.* 336
Profile Less *p*! turn to me—three-quarter face. *Romney's R.* 98
Profit (s) (*See also* **Self-profit**) With fuller *p's* lead an easier life, *Enoch Arden* 145
With daily-dwindling *p's* held the house; „ 696
But now to leaven play with *p*, *Princess iv* 149
The Lady Blanche: much *p*! „ *vi* 239
Will bloom to *p*, otherwhere. *In Mem. lxxxii* 12
What *p* lies in barren faith, „ *cviii* 5
It surely was my *p* had I known: *Guinevere* 658

Profit (verb) It little *p's* that an idle king, *Ulysses* 1
what *p's* it to put An idle case? *In Mem. xxxv* 17
what *p's* me my name Of greatest knight? *Lancelot and E.* 1413
What *p's* an ill Priest Between me and my God? *Sir J. Oldcastle* 144
Profound Passionless, pale, cold face, star-sweet on a gloom *p*; *Maud I iii* 4
Profulgent An image with *p* brows, *Supp. Confessions* 145
Progress Our *p* falter to the woman's goal.' *Princess vi* 127
With statelier *p* to and fro *In Mem. xcviii* 22
P halts on palsied feet, *Locksley H., Sixty* 219
Project *p* after *p* rose, and all of them were vain; *The Flight* 14
Prolong *p* Her low preamble all alone, *Palace of Art* 173
Promenaded With cypress *p*, *Amphion* 38
Promise (s) (*See also* **Hand-promise**) Leaving the *p* of my bridal bower, *D. of F. Women* 218
for the *p* that it closed: *Locksley Hall* 14
the crescent *p* of my spirit „ 187
With words of *p* in his walk, *Day-Dm., Arrival* 23
'I am bound: you have my *p*—in a year: *Enoch Arden* 437
stood once more before her face, Claiming her *p*. „ 458
falling in a land Of *p*; *Princess ii* 140
hold Your *p*: all, I trust, may yet be well.' „ 361
other distance and the hues Of *p*; „ *iv* 87
With *p* of a morn as fair; *In Mem. lxxxiv* 29
The *p* of the golden hours? „ *lxxxv* 106
Knowing your *p* to me; *Maud I xxii* 50
Thy *p*, King,' and Arthur glancing at him, *Gareth and L.* 652
Forgetful of his *p* to the King, *Marr. of Geraint* 50
Bribed with large *p's* the men who served „ 453
Woke and bethought her of her *p* given „ 602
He would not leave her, till her *p* given— „ 605
Made *p*, that whatever bride I brought, „ 783
Pelleas might obtain his lady's love, According to her *p*, *Pelleas and E.* 162
And thou hast given thy *p*, „ 245
With *p* of large light on woods and ways. „ 394
Green prelude, April *p*, glad new-year *Lover's Tale i* 281
A land of *p*, a land of memory, „ 333
A land of *p* flowing with the milk And honey „ 334
mother broke her *p* to the dead, *Sisters (E. and E.)* 252
p of blossom, but never a fruit! *V. of Maeldune* 51
but the *p* had faded away; *Despair* 27
Be truer to your *p*. *To Mary Boyle* 5
The still-fulfilling *p* of a light *Prog. of Spring* 90
Promise (verb) *p* thee The fairest and most loving wife in Greece,' *Œnone* 186
p (otherwise You perish) as you came, *Princess ii* 295
who might have shamed us: *p*, all.' „ 299
I *p* you Some palace in our land, „ *iii* 161
King, for hardihood I can *p* thee. *Gareth and L.* 557
'Now all be dumb, and *p* all of you *Lover's Tale iv* 351
Didn't you kiss me an' *p*? *First Quarrel* 53
We will make the Spaniard *p*, *The Revenge* 94
P me, Miriam not Muriel—she shall have the ring.' *The Ring* 293
Promise-bounden awed and *p-b* she forbore, *Enoch Arden* 869
Promised (adj.) (*See also* **Long-promised**) Full to the banks, close on the *p* good. *Maud I xviii* 6
Promised (verb) And Dora *p*, being meek. *Dora* 46
and once again She *p*. *Enoch Arden* 906
she *p* that no force, Persuasion, no, *Aylmer's Field* 417
What could we else, we *p* each; *Princess ii* 300
who *p* help, and oozed All o'er with honey'd answer „ *v* 241
she *p* then to be fair. *Maud I i* 68
He *p* more than ever king has given, *Merlin and V.* 586
She ceased: her father *p*; *Lancelot and E.* 1130
those who knew him near the King, And *p* for him: *Pelleas and E.* 16
Lancelot ever *p*, but remain'd, *Guinevere* 93
'You *p* to find me work near you, *First Quarrel* 52
an' 'e *p* a son to she, *Owd Roä* 95
fur I *p* ya'd niver not do it ageän. *Church-warden, etc.* 32
when he *p* to make me his bride, *Charity* 11
Promising like a household god *P* empire; *On a Mourner* 31
Miriam Lane Made such a voluble answer *p* all, *Enoch Arden* 903
Promontory Lingering about the thymy *promontories*, *Sea Dreams* 38
Who seems a *p* of rock, *Will* 6
winds of winter tear an oak on a *p*. *Boädicea* 77
Saw once a great piece of a *p*, *Geraint and E.* 162

Prompt as *p* to spring against the pikes, *Princess iii* 286
Prone Just where the *p* edge of the wood began (repeat) *Enoch Arden* 67, 373
falling *p* he dug His fingers into the wet earth, „ 779
Against the rush of the air in the *p* swing, *Aylmer's Field* 86
She veil'd her brows, and *p* she sank, *Princess v* 107
Thy climbing life, and cherish my *p* year, *Gareth and L.* 95
p from off her seat she fell, *Guinevere* 414
in *p* flight By thousands down the crags *Montenegro* 7
Pronest that most impute a crime Are *p* to it, *Merlin and V.* 826
Pronounce Nor can *p* upon it If one should ask *Maud I xx* 16
Pronounced the King *P* a dismal sentence, *Merlin and V.* 591
All that look'd on her had *p* her dead. *Lover's Tale iv* 35
himself *p* That my rich gift is wholly mine „ 349
and when The Priest *p* you dead, *Happy* 50
Prooemion my rich *p* makes Thy glory fly *Lucretius* 70
Proof To arm in *p*, and guard about *Supp. Confessions* 65
wall about thy cause With iron-worded *p*, *To J. M. K.* 9
lest thy heart be put to *p*, *Locksley Hall* 77
train Of flowery clauses onward to the *p* *Lucretius* 120
'Come, listen! here is *p* that you were miss'd: *Princess, Pro.* 177
If we could give them surer, quicker *p*— „ *iii* 282
The *p* and echo of all human fame, *Ode on Well.* 145
go then, an ye must: only one *p*, *Gareth and L.* 144
the *p* to prove me to the quick!' „ 150
Tho' yet there lived no *p*, *Marr. of Geraint* 26
Might well have served for *p* that I was loved, „ 796
As *p* of trust. O Merlin, teach it me. *Merlin and V.* 331
The great *p* of your love: „ 354
prurient for a *p* against the grain „ 487
p of trust—so often ask'd in vain! „ 920
by nine years' *p* we needs must learn *Lancelot and E.* 62
a *p* That I—even I—at times *Romney's R.* 92
Proofless Spleen-born, I think, and *p*. *Merlin and V.* 702
Prop falls A creeper when the *p* is broken, *Aylmer's Field* 810
Proper Upon my *p* patch of soil To grow my own plantation. *Amphion* 99
His *p* chop to each. *Will Water.* 116
this is *p* to the clown, Tho' smock'd, or furr'd *Princess iv* 246
Till happier times each to her *p* hearth: „ *vi* 303
To shroud me from my *p* scorn. *In Mem. xxvi* 16
He mixing with his *p* sphere, „ *lx* 5
Thy sweetness from its *p* place? „ *lxxxiii* 6
your work is this To hold me from my *p* place, „ *cxvii* 2
Property *See* **Proputty**
Prophecy If aught of *p* be mine, *Clear-headed friend* 8
At last She rose upon a wind of *p* *Princess ii* 171
They might not seem thy *prophecies*, *In Mem. xcii* 13
For the *p* given of old And then not understood, *Maud II v* 42
A prophet certain of my *p*, *Marr. of Geraint* 814
Or was there sooth in Arthur's *p*, *Holy Grail* 709
if ancient *prophecies* Have err'd not, *Guinevere* 449
Prophesied Approvingly, and *p* his rise: *Aylmer's Field* 474
I have *p*—Strike, thou art worthy *Gareth and L.* 1137
As holy John had *p* of me, *Columbus* 21
Prophesy I *p* that I shall die to-night, *St. S. Stylites* 220
Dismiss me, and I *p* your plan, *Princess iv* 354
all is lost In what they *p*, *Epilogue* 65
Prophesying *p* change Beyond all reason: *Princess i* 142
upon me flash'd The power of *p*— *Tiresias* 57
Prophet (*See also* **World-prophet**) My heart was like a *p* to my heart, *Gardener's D.* 63
Is there no *p* but the voice that calls *Aylmer's Field* 741
Cries 'Come up hither,' as a *p* to us? „ 745
fire on a masthead, *P* of storm: *Princess iv* 275
The *p's* blazon'd on the panes; *In Mem. lxxxvii* 8
P, curse me the blabbing lip, *Maud II v* 57
A naked babe, of whom the *P* spake, *Gareth and L.* 501
A *p* certain of my prophecy, *Marr. of Geraint* 814
The people call you *p*: let it be: *Merlin and V.* 317
think I show myself Too dark a *p*: *Holy Grail* 322
For every fiery *p* in old times, „ 876
Was I too dark a *p* when I said „ 889
to some old *p* might have seem'd A vision *Pelleas and E.* 51
ill *p's* were they all, Spirits and men: *Guinevere* 272
The *p* and the chariot and the steeds, *Lover's Tale i* 307
Or *p's* of them in his fantasy, „ *iv* 12

Prophet (*continued*) and *p* of the perfect man; — *De Prof., Two G.* 12
The *p's* beacon burn'd in vain, — *Ancient Sage* 142
And 'The Curse of the *P*' in Heaven. — *Dead Prophet* 28
Tho' a *p* should have his due, — „ 50
since he would sit on a *P's* seat, — „ 53
She tore the *P* after death, — „ 77
The *p* of his own, my Hubert— — *The Ring* 23
P of the gay time, *P* of the May time, *P* of the roses, — *The Snowdrop* 6
Never a *p* so crazy! — *The Throstle* 10
Issa Ben Mariam, his own *p*, — *Akbar's Dream* 75
he, That other, *p* of their fall, — „ 82
art *thou* the *P*? canst *thou* work Miracles?' — „ 117
had some *p* spoken true Of all we shall achieve, — *Mechanophilus* 25
Prophetess have dash'd The passion of the *p*; — *Princess iv* 140
sang the terrible *p'es*, — *Boädicea* 37
Prophet-eye *P-e's* may catch a glory — *Making of Man* 6
Prophetic Mothers,—that, all *p* pity, — *Princess v* 381
Prophetical at length *P* and prescient — *Lover's Tale ii* 132
Prophet-mind Self-gather'd in her *p-m*, — *Of old sat Freedom* 6
Propitiated Taranis be *p*. — *Boädicea* 16
Proportion gave him mind, the lordliest *P*, — *Two Voices* 20
Propose I *p* to-night To show you — *Lover's Tale iv* 251
Proposed Grave doubts and answers here *p*, — *In Mem. xlviii* 3
Propping in the naked hall, *p* his head, — *Geraint and E.* 581
And found his own dear bride *p* his head, — „ 584
Proprietress Is she The sweet *p* a shadow? — *Princess ii* 415
Propt my mother, when with brows *P* on thy knees, — *Supp. Confessions* 70
p on beds of amaranth and moly, — *Lotos-Eaters, C. S.* 88
So *p*, worm-eaten, ruinously old, — *Enoch Arden* 693
A broken statue *p* against the wall, — *Princess, Pro.* 99
she, half on her mother *p*, Half-drooping from her, — „ *iv* 367
Proputty (Property) *P*, *p*, *p*—that's what I 'ears 'em saäy. — *N. Farmer, N. S.* 2
P, *p*, *p*—Sam, thou's an ass for thy paaïns: — „ 3
P, *p*—woä then woä— — „ 8
But *p*, *p* sticks, an' *p*, *p* graws. — „ 16
Woä then, *p*, wiltha?— — „ 39
P, *p's* ivrything 'ere, — „ 43
Coom oop, *p*, *p*—that's what I 'ears 'im saäy— — „ 59
P, *p*, *p*—canter an' canter awaäy. — „ 60
Prose (s) I will work in *p* and rhyme, — *Talking Oak* 289
Let raffs be rife in *p* and rhyme, — *Will Water.* 61
Prose (verb) they *p* O'er books of travell'd seamen, — *Amphion* 81
Proserpine Like *P* in Enna, gathering flowers: — *Edwin Morris* 112
Prospect Large range of *p* had the mother sow, — *Walk. to the Mail* 93
My *p* and horizon gone. — *In Mem. xxxviii* 4
Arise in open *p*—heath and hill, — *Lover's Tale i* 397
Prosper While yon sun *p's* in the blue, — *The Blackbird* 22
And the third time may *p*, — *M. d'Arthur* 130
and thought He scarce would *p*. — *Princess iii* 76
May she mix With men and *p*! — *In Mem. cxiv* 3
I *p*, circled with thy voice; — „ *cxxx* 15
And the third time may *p*, — *Pass. of Arthur* 298
Prosper'd throve and *p*: so three years She *p*: — *Palace of Art* 217
so *p* that at last A luckier or a bolder fisherman, — *Enoch Arden* 48
And *p*; till a rout of saucy boys Brake on us — *Princess v* 394
Hath *p* in the name of Christ, — *Balin and Balan* 99
rich man, That, having always *p* in the world, — *Lover's Tale i* 716
Prosperity return In such a sunlight of *p* — *Aylmer's Field* 421
Prosperous lead Thro' *p* floods his holy urn. — *In Mem. ix* 8
While now thy *p* labour fills — „ *lxxxiv* 25
'Be *p* in this journey, as in all; — *Marr. of Geraint* 225
Now with *p* auguries Comes at last — *On Jub. Q. Victoria* 9
Prostrate Sprang from the midriff of a *p* king— — *Aylmer's Field* 16
Protector call'd him dear *p* in her fright, — *Merlin and V.* 946
Protestant found her beating the hard *P* doors. — *Sisters (E. and E.)* 240
Protesting some Vowing, and some *p*), 'what is this?' — *Holy Grail* 270
Protomartyr falling, *p* of our cause, Die: — *Princess iv* 505
Proud (adj.) (*See also* **Princely-proud**) I know you *p* to bear your name, — *L. C. V. de Vere* 10
Too *p* to care from whence I came. — „ 12
languid light of your *p* eyes Is wearied — „ 59
Be *p* of those strong sons of thine — *England and Amer.* 4
Thought her *p*, and fled over the sea; — *Edward Gray* 14
Their ancient name! they *might* be *p*; — *Aylmer's Field* 378

Proud (adj.) (*continued*) and mean Vileness, we are grown so *p*— — *Aylmer's Field* 756
P look'd the lips: — *Princess i* 96
and this *p* watchword rest Of equal; — „ *vii* 300
'O boy, tho' thou art young and *p*, — *Sailor Boy* 7
you wrong your beauty, believe it, in being so *p*; — *Maud I iv* 17
P on 'im, like, my lad, — *North. Cobbler* 97
Of saner worship sanely *p*; — *Freedom* 30
My nature was too *p*. — *Happy* 78
three of these *P* in their fantasy call themselves the Day, — *Gareth and L.* 633
And since the *p* man often is the mean, — *Marr. of Geraint* 449
overthrow My *p* self, and my purpose three years old, — *Geraint and E.* 849
There to his *p* horse Lancelot turn'd, — *Lancelot and E.* 347
And moved about her palace, *p* and pale. — „ 614
As yon *p* Prince who left the quest to me. — „ 762
wherefore would ye look On this *p* fellow again, — „ 1065
Against the *p* archbishop Arundel— — *Sir J. Oldcastle* 16
that *p* Priest, That mock-meek mouth of utter Antichrist, — „ 169
Slender warrant had *He* to be *p* of The welcome — *Batt. of Brunanburh* 67
Proud (s) Which rolling o'er the palaces of the *p*, — *Aylmer's Field* 636
The *p* was half disarm'd of pride, — *In Mem. cx* 6
'Turn, Fortune, turn thy wheel and lower the *p*; — *Marr. of Geraint* 347
Prouder She felt her heart grow *p*: — *The Goose* 22
Prove To put together, part and *p*, — *Two Voices* 134
To feel, altho' no tongue can *p*, — „ 445
You sought to *p* how I could love, — *L. C. V. de Vere* 21
p me what it is I would not do.' — *Godiva* 27
To *p* myself a poet: — *Will Water.* 166
Pale again as death did *p*: — *L. of Burleigh* 66
I fain would *p* A father to your children: — *Enoch Arden* 410
She must *p* true: for, brother, — *Aylmer's Field* 364
call him, love, Before you *p* him, rogue, — *Sea Dreams* 171
Your language *p's* you still the child. — *Princess ii* 58
or *p* The Danaïd of a leaky vase, — „ 339
I *p* Your knight, and fight your battle, — „ *iv* 594
may thy mother *p* As true to thee as false, — „ *vi* 203
no truer Time himself Can *p* you, — *A Dedication* 2
Believing where we cannot *p*; — *In Mem., Pro.* 4
I long to *p* No lapse of moons — „ *xxvi* 2
Her care is not to part and *p*; — „ *xlviii* 5
and I shall *p* A meeting somewhere, — „ *lxxxv* 98
Should *p* the phantom-warning true. — „ *xcii* 12
Let Science *p* we are, and then — „ *cxx* 6
Or thou wilt *p* their tool. — *Maud I vi* 59
'Well, if it *p* a girl, the boy — „ *vii* 7
'Well, if it *p* a girl, my boy — „ 15
the proof to *p* me to the quick!' — *Gareth and L.* 150
and *p* her heart toward the Prince.' — *Marr. of Geraint* 513
I someway *p* such force in her Link'd with such love — „ 805
That he might *p* her to the uttermost, — *Geraint and E.* 589
Shall I not rather *p* the worse for these? — *Balin and Balan* 228
We go to *p* it. Bide ye here the while.' — *Merlin and V.* 97
make me yearn still more to *p* you mine, — „ 328
That I should *p* it on you unawares, — „ 340
What other? for men sought to *p* me vile, — „ 495
For tho' you should not *p* it upon me, — „ 687
All—all—the wish to *p* him wholly hers.' — „ 865
They *p* to him his work: — *Lancelot and E.* 158
p No surer than our falcon yesterday, — „ 655
Yea, let her *p* me to the uttermost, — *Pelleas and E.* 211
look'd, as he is like to *p*, When Julian goes, — *Lover's Tale iv* 314
Terrible pity, if one so beautiful *P*, — „ 339
May *p* as peaceful as his own. — *Tiresias* 217
Thou canst not *p* the Nameless, O my son, Nor canst thou *p* the world thou movest in, Thou canst not *p* that thou art body alone, Nor canst thou *p* that thou art spirit alone, — *Ancient Sage* 57
Nor canst thou *p* that thou art both in one: — „ 61
Thou canst not *p* thou art immortal, — „ 62
Thou canst not *p* that I, who speak with thee, — „ 64
Proved Hadst thou less unworthy *p*— — *Locksley Hall* 63
Before you prove him, rogue, and *p*, forgive. — *Sea Dreams* 171
but him I *p* impossible; — *Lucretius* 193

Proved (*continued*) By which our lives are chiefly *p*, *In Mem. cv* 14
The truths that never can be *p* „ *cxxxi* 10
nor *p* Since that dark day a day like this; „ *Con.* 7
We have *p* we have hearts in a cause, *Maud III vi* 55
p him everyway One of our noblest, *Geraint and E.* 909
that also have we *p*; *Balin and Balan* 34
Nor is he the wisest man who never *p* himself a fool. *Locksley H., Sixty* 244
Proven *See* **Prov'n**
Provence hair Studded with one rich *P* rose— *Lover's Tale iii* 45
Provender For lust or lusty blood or *p*: *Lucretius* 198
Proverb This *p* flashes thro' his head, *Day-Dm., Arrival* 15
till their love Shall ripen to a *p*, *Lover's Tale i* 758
Providence sermonizing On *p* and trust in Heaven, *Enoch Arden* 205
Province they press in from all the *p's*, *Princess ii* 97
O Love, thy *p* were not large, *In Mem. xlvi* 13
tho' they sought Thro' all the *p's* *Marr. of Geraint* 730
p with a hundred miles of coast, (repeat) *Merlin and V.* 588, 647
leaves Some colder *p* in the North *The Ring* 481
and rule thy *P* of the brute. *By an Evolution.* 16
Proving converse in the hall, *P* her heart: *Marr. of Geraint* 521
this cursed charm, Were *p* it on me, *Merlin and V.* 436
nothing worthy *p* can be proven, *Ancient Sage* 66
Prov'n 'Not *p*' Averill said, or laughingly 'Some other race of Averills'—*p* or no, What cared he? *Aylmer's Field* 53
and a laugh Ringing like *p* golden coinage true, „ 182
who hath *p* him King Uther's son? *Com. of Arthur* 69
Ask'd me to tilt with him, the *p* knight. *Gareth and L.* 27
Not *p*, who swept the dust of ruin'd Rome „ 135
But justice, so thy say be *p* true. „ 346
the first quest: he is not *p*. „ 582
O star, my morning dream hath *p* true, „ 1000
And horrors only *p* a blooming boy. „ 1425
But rather *p* in his Paynim wars Than famous jousts; but see, or *p* or not, *Balin and Balan* 38
or a traitor *p*, or hound Beaten, *Pelleas and E.* 439
only *p* themselves Prisoners, murderers. *Sir J. Oldcastle* 167
nothing worthy proving can be *p*, *Ancient Sage* 66
Re-volution has *p* but E-volution *Beautiful City* 3
Prow shake The sparkling flints beneath the *p*. *Arabian Nights* 52
round about the *p* she wrote *The Lady of Shalott.* *L. of Shalott iv* 8
round the *p* they read her name, *The Lady of Shalott* „ 44
Lady's-head upon the *p* Caught the shrill salt, *The Voyage* 11
Now nearer to the *p* she seem'd „ 67
Sleep, gentle heavens, before the *p*; *In Mem. ix* 14
dart again, and play About the *p*, „ *xii* 18
vessel in mid-ocean, her heaved *p* Clambering, *Lover's Tale ii* 169
chains for him Who push'd his *p's* *Columbus* 24
their nail'd *p's* Parted the Norsemen, *Batt. of Brunanburh* 93
Prowess whereas I know Your *p*, Arac, *Princess v* 404
great deeds Of Lancelot, and his *p* in the lists, *Lancelot and E.* 82
His *p* was too wondrous. „ 542
learn If his old *p* were in aught decay'd; „ 584
acts of *p* done In tournament or tilt, *Holy Grail* 1
thought Of all my late-shown *p* in the lists, „ 362
Thou thoughtest of thy *p* and thy sins? „ 455
here and there a deed Of *p* done *Guinevere* 459
In height and *p* more than human, *Tiresias* 179
Prowest I chant thy praise As *p* knight and truest lover, *Pelleas and E.* 350
Prowling While the Fiend is *p*. *Forlorn* 66
Proxy-wedded *p-w* with a bootless calf *Princess i* 34
Prude *p's* for proctors, dowagers for deans, „ *Pro.* 141
Prudence a *p* to withhold; *Isabel* 15
by slow *p* to make mild A rugged people, *Ulysses* 36
Let not your *p*, dearest, drowse, *Princess ii* 339
Prudent The *p* partner of his blood *Two Voices* 415
these outbuzz'd me so That even our *p* king, *Columbus* 122
Pruned Thro' crowded lilac-ambush trimly *p*; *Gardener's D.* 112
Prurient *p* for a proof against the grain *Merlin and V.* 487
'In filthy sloughs they roll a *p* skin, *Palace of Art* 201
Prussian Last, the *P* trumpet blew; *Ode on Well.* 127
Pry not to *p* and peer on your reserve, *Princess iv* 419
Psalm with sound Of pious hymns and *p's*, *St. S. Stylites* 34
sound Of solemn *p's*, and silver litanies, *Princess ii* 477
Who roll'd the *p* to wintry skies, *In Mem. lvi* 11

Psalm (*continued*) As a *p* by a mighty master *The Wreck* 53
'Libera me, Domine!' you sang the *P*, *Happy* 49
Psyche Two widows, Lady *P*, Lady Blanche; *Princess i* 128
'Lady Blanche' she said, 'And Lady *P*.' „ 233
Which was prettiest, Best-natured? 'Lady *P*.' „ 234
with your own, As Lady *P's* pupils.' „ 240
Lady *P* will harangue The fresh arrivals „ *ii* 95
back again we crost the court To Lady *P's*: „ 101
'Well then, *P*, take my life, „ 204
'having seen And heard the Lady *P*.' „ 211
'Are you that Lady *P*,' I rejoin'd, „ 237
'Are you that *P*,' Florian added; „ 246
are you That *P*, wont to bind my throbbing brow, „ 250
are you That brother-sister *P*, both in one? „ 254
You were that *P*, but what are you now?' (repeat) „ 255, 277
'You are that *P*,' Cyril said, „ 256
'Are you that Lady *P*,' I began, „ 261
'Are you that *P*,' Florian ask'd, „ 269
Then Lady *P*, 'Ah—Melissa—you! „ 330
While *P* watch'd them, smiling, „ 365
you learnt No more from *P's* lecture, „ 393
The long-limb'd lad that had a *P* too; „ 406
And dear is sister *P* to my heart, „ 418
To rail at Lady *P* and her side. „ *iii* 33
Herself and Lady *P* the two arms; „ 35
Lady *P* was the right hand now, „ 37
Lady *P* will be crush'd; „ 63
Affirms your *P* thieved her theories, „ 92
Nor like poor *P* whom she drags in tow.' „ 103
then, climbing, Cyril kept With *P*, „ 355
P flush'd and wann'd and shook; „ *iv* 160
demanded if her mother knew, Or *P*, „ 234
She sent For *P*, but she was not there; „ 237
she call'd For *P's* child to cast it from the doors; „ 238
And where are *P*, Cyril? both are fled: „ 241
you planed her path To Lady *P*, „ 316
'We thank you, we shall hear of it From Lady *P*:' „ 329
later in the night Had come on *P* weeping: „ *v* 50
With *P's* babe, was Ida watching us, „ 512
With *P's* colour round his helmet, „ 534
after him Came *P*, sorrowing for Aglaïa. „ *vi* 29
high upon the palace Ida stood With *P's* babe in arm: „ 31
while *P* ever stole A little nearer, „ 132
Who turn'd half-round to *P* as she sprang „ 209
'Come hither. O *P*,' she cried out, „ 285
But *P* tended Florian: with her oft, Melissa came; „ *vii* 55
second suit obtain'd At first with *P*. „ 72
Ida came behind Seen but of *P*: „ 79
Ptarmigan know The *p* that whitens ere his hour *Last Tournment* 697
Public I raged against the *p* liar; *The Letters* 26
No *p* life was his on earth, *You might have won* 23
Drink we, last, the *p* fool, *Vision of Sin* 149
A lidless watcher of the *p* weal, *Princess iv* 325
But *p* use required she should be known; And since my oath was ta'en for *p* use, „ 336
Till *p* wrong be crumbled into dust, *Ode on Well.* 167
They call'd me in the *p* squares *In Mem. lxix* 11
Not let any man think for the *p* good, *Maud II v* 45
Friend, to be struck by the *p* foe, „ 89
That were a *p* merit, far, „ 91
And left him lying in the *p* way; *Geraint and E.* 478
not the King's—For *p* use: *Lancelot and E.* 60
I hold that man the worst of *p* foes *Guinevere* 512
And leave him in the *p* way to die. *Lover's Tale iv* 261
or flamed at a *p* wrong, *The Wreck* 68
Thy power, well-used to move the *p* breast. *To W.C. Macready* 3
That wanders from the *p* good, *Freedom* 26
Pucker'd And shoals of *p* faces drive; *In Mem. lxx* 10
Puddin' beslings *p* an' Adam's wine; *North. Cobbler* 112
Puddled 'So *p* as it is with favouritism.' *Princess iii* 146
Puff (s) Upon the level in little *p's* of wind, „ *iv* 256
Puff (verb) A wind to *p* your idol-fires, *Love thou thy land* 69
the vessel *p's* her sail: *Ulysses* 44
Puff'd (adj.) Where with *p* cheek the belted hunter *Palace of Art* 63
behind I heard the *p* pursuer; *Princess iv* 265

Puff'd (verb) angry gust of wind P out his torch — Merlin and V. 731
breaths of anger p Her fairy nostril out; — „ 848
morn That p the swaying branches into smoke — Holy Grail 15
Pug a score of p's And poodles yell'd — Edwin Morris 119
Puissance of her brethren, youths of p; — Princess i 37
Puissant (See also **All-puissant**) round The warrior's p shoulders Pallas flung — Achilles over the T. 3
Pull 'Yet p not down my palace towers, — Palace of Art 293
P off, p off, the brooch of gold, — Lady Clare 39
tears that make the rose P sideways, — In Mem. lxxii 11
Pulpit-drone humming of the drowsy p-d — To J. M. K. 10
Pulpiteer To chapel; where a heated p, — Sea Dreams 20
Pulsation Hung tranced from all p, — Gardener's D. 260
Make me feel the wild p — Locksley Hall 109
The wild p of her wings; — In Mem. xii 4
The deep p's of the world, — „ xcv 40
Pulse lent The p of hope to discontent. — Two Voices 450
Shall strike within thy p's, like a God's, — Œnone 162
stirr'd with languid p's of the oar, — Gardener's D. 41
And her whisper throng'd my p's — Locksley Hall 36
her palfrey's footfall shot Light horrors thro' her p's: — Godiva 59
lent my desire to kneel, and shook My p's, — Princess iii 194
you keep One p that beats true woman, — „ vi 180
p's at the clamouring of her enemy — Boädicea 82
My p's therefore beat again For other friends — In Mem. lxxxv 57
And every p of wind and wave Recalls, — „ 73
measured p of racing oars Among the willows; — „ lxxxvii 10
The p's of a Titan's heart; — „ ciii 32
force, that keeps A thousand p's dancing, — „ cxxv 16
my p's closed their gates with a shock — Maud I i 15
Lord of the p that is lord of her breast, — „ xvi 13
died to live, long as my p's play; — „ xviii 66
Is it gone? my p's beat— — „ II i 36
shook her p's, crying, 'Look, a prize! — Geraint and E. 123
and stirs the p With devil's leaps, — Guinevere 521
With its true-touched p's in the flow — Lover's Tale i 205
And faints, and hath no p, no breath— — „ 268
Unfrequent, low, as tho' it told its p's; — „ ii 55
had lain three days without a p: — „ iv 34
strike Thy youthful p's into rest — Tiresias 157
tho' every p would freeze, — The Flight 53
Look how the living p of Alla beats — Akbar's Dream 41
Pulse (vegetable) eating hoary grain and p the steeds, — Spec. of Iliad 21
Pulse (verb) began To p with such a vehemence — Lover's Tale iv 82
fountain p's high in sunnier jets, — Prog. of Spring 54
Pulsing (See also **Red-pulsing**) heather-scented air, P full man; — Last Tournament 692
Pummel dash'd the p at the foremost face, — Balin and Balan 402
Pun the p, the scurrilous tale,— — Aylmer's Field 441
Punched See **Poonch'd**
Punishment See **Pillar-punishment**
Puny This pretty, p, weakly little one,— — Enoch Arden 195
Pup See **Poop**
Pupil Some meeker p you must find, — L. C. V. de Vere 18
with your own, As Lady Psyche's p's.' — Princess i 240
A patient range of p's; — „ ii 104
angled with them for her p's love: — „ iii 93
Pupilage sons of kings loving in p — Merlin and V. 517
Puppet P to a father's threat, — Locksley Hall 42
We are p's, Man in his pride, — Maud I iv 25
Puppy blind and shuddering puppies, — The Brook 130
Purblind O P race of miserable men, — Geraint and E. 1
Purchase Yet he hoped to p glory, — The Captain 17
To p his own boat, and make a home For Annie: — Enoch Arden 47
We sent mine host to p female gear; — Princess i 199
Purchased p his own boat, and made a home For Annie, — Enoch Arden 58
Pure (See also **Perfect-pure**) 'Her court was p; her life serene; — To the Queen 25
But why Prevail'd not thy p prayers? — Supp. Confessions 89
P vestal thoughts in the translucent fane — Isabel 4
Of perfect wifehood and p lowlihead. — „ 12
P silver, underpropt a rich Throne — Arabian Nights 145
As p and true as blades of steel. — Kate 16
Pacing with downward eyelids p. — Two Voices 420
Disclosed a fruit of p Hesperian gold, — Œnone 66
Pure (continued) p law, Commeasure perfect freedom.' — Œnone 166
And p quintessences of precious oils — Palace of Art 187
daughter of the warrior Gileadite, A maiden p; — D. of F. Women 198
A man more p and bold and just — To J. S. 31
May He within Himself make p! — M. d'Arthur 245
Ruffles her p cold plume, and takes the flood — „ 268
all else of heaven was p Up to the Sun, — Gardener's D. 79
Gown'd in p white, that fitted to the shape— — „ 126
but what lot is p? — Walk. to the Mail 97
mysterious glimmer steals From thy p brows, and from thy shoulders p, — Tithonus 35
Make Thou my spirit p and clear — St. Agnes' Eve 9
To make me p of sin. — „ 32
Because my heart is p. — Sir Galahad 4
P spaces clothed in living beams, P lilies of eternal peace, — „ 66
otherwhere P sport: — Princess, Pro. 81
'An open-hearted maiden, true and p. — „ iii 98
But p as lines of green that streak the white — „ v 196
Is not our cause p? — „ 403
The single p and perfect animal, — „ vii 306
Which he has worn so p of blame, — Ode on Well. 72
And p as he from taint of craven guile, — „ 135
And keep the soldier firm, the statesman p: — „ 222
till Phosphor, bright As our p love, — In Mem. ix 11
Come then, p hands, and bear the head — „ xviii 9
As p and perfect as I say? — „ xxiv 2
What souls possess themselves so p, — „ xxxii 15
Her faith thro' form is p as thine, — „ xxxiii 9
And love will last as p and whole — „ xliii 13
How p at heart and sound in head, — „ xciv 1
Perplext in faith, but p in deeds, — „ xcvi 9
To one p image of regret. — „ cii 24
And passion p in snowy bloom — „ cix 11
Flow thro' our deeds and make them p, — „ cxxxi 4
Small and p as a pearl, — Maud II ii 2
'Tis a morning p and sweet, (repeat) — „ iv 31, 35
(For I cleaved to a cause that I felt to be p and true), — „ III vi 31
shyly glanced Eyes of p women, — Gareth and L. 314
with p Affection, and the light of victory, — „ 330
And p nobility of temperament, — Marr. of Geraint 212
Arthur the blameless, p as any maid, — Balin and Balan 479
P as our own true Mother is our Queen.' — „ 617
and the mask of p Worn by this court, — Merlin and V. 35
'This Arthur p! — „ 49
There is no being p, My cherub; — „ 51
And as it chanced they are happy, being p.' — „ 745
'A sober man is Percivale and p; — „ 755
Have all men true and leal, all women p; — „ 794
and down he sank For the p pain, — Lancelot and E. 518
Full many a holy vow and p resolve. — „ 879
And p Sir Galahad to uplift the maid; — „ 1265
Delicately p and marvellously fair, — „ 1369
P, as you ever wish your knights to be. — „ 1375
if not so p a love Clothes in so p a loveliness? — „ 1383
Whom Arthur and his knighthood call'd The P, — Holy Grail 3
'I know not, for thy heart is p as snow.' — „ 97
of such a kind, that all of p Noble, — „ 773
Some root of knighthood and p nobleness; — „ 886
For fair thou art and p as Guinevere, — Pelleas and E. 44
P on the virgin forehead of the dawn! — „ 505
'False! and I held thee p as Guinevere.' — „ 522
'Am I but false as Guinevere is p? — „ 524
can Arthur make me p As any maiden child? — Last Tournament 692
could speak Of the p heart, — Guinevere 502
Her station, taken everywhere for p, — „ 517
Hereafter in that world where all are p — „ 562
That p severity of perfect light— — „ 646
Then she, for her good deeds and her p life, — „ 693
May He within himself make p! — Pass. of Arthur 413
Ruffles her p cold plume, and takes the flood — „ 436
Into a clearer zenith, p of cloud. — Lover's Tale i 514
And why was I to darken their p love, — „ 727
Fill'd all with p clear fire, — „ ii 146
That makes the sequel p; — „ iv 157
Back to the p and universal church, — Sir J. Oldcastle 71

Pure (*continued*) To mould it into action *p* as theirs. *Tiresias* 129
The Good, the True, the *P*, the Just— *Locksley H., Sixty* 71
lest the stream should issue *p*. „ 144
Could make *p* light live on the canvas? *Romney's R.* 10
lips were touch'd with fire from off a *p* Pierian altar, *Parnassus* 17
So princely, tender, truthful, reverent, *p*— *D. of the Duke of C.* 4
Purelier on him breathed Far *p* in his rushings to and fro, *Aylmer's Field* 458
Pureness kiss'd her with all *p*, brother-like, *Geraint and E.* 884
To doubt her *p* were to want a heart— *Lancelot and E.* 1377
Sworn to be veriest ice of *p*, *Sir J. Oldcastle* 108
Purer With swifter movement and in *p* light *Isabel* 32
And fill'd the breast with *p* breath. *Miller's D.* 92
'Tis a *p* life than thine; *Locksley Hall* 88
Eight that were left to make a *p* world— *Aylmer's Field* 638
Mayst seem to have reach'd a *p* air, *In Mem. xxxiii* 2
This faith has many a *p* priest, „ *xxxvii* 3
With sweeter manners, *p* laws. „ *cvi* 16
A *p* sapphire melts into the sea. *Maud I xviii* 52
Came *p* pleasure unto mortal kind *Geraint and E.* 765
He boasts his life as *p* than thine own; *Balin and Balan* 104
as for gain Of *p* glory.' *Lancelot and E.* 587
Myself must tell him in that *p* life, *Guinevere* 653
with flame Milder and *p*. *Lover's Tale i* 323
Who made a nation *p* through their art. *To W. C. Macready* 8
The cloud was rifted by a *p* gleam *Akbar's Dream* 78
Purest Six hundred maidens clad in *p* white, *Princess ii* 472
There swung an apple of the *p* gold, *Marr. of Geraint* 170
To lead sweet lives in *p* chastity, *Guinevere* 474
I, and all, As fairest, best and *p*, *Balin and Balan* 350
I have seen; but best, Best, *p*? „ 357
From homage to the best and *p*, „ 376
Thou mightiest and thou *p* among men!' *Holy Grail* 426
the *p* of thy knights May win them for the *p* of my maids.' *Last Tournament* 49
Art thou the *p*, brother? „ 192
Purgatory seest the souls in Hell And *p*, *Columbus* 217
Purged When I have *p* my guilt.' *Palace of Art* 296
whom The wholesome realm is *p* of otherwhere, *Last Tournament* 96
Purify Perchance, and so thou *p* thy soul, *Guinevere* 561
Puritanic but all-too-full in bud For *p* stays: *Talking Oak* 60
Purity such a finish'd chasten'd *p*. *Isabel* 41
Who wove coarse webs to snare her *p*, *Aylmer's Field* 780
That out of naked knightlike *p* *Merlin and V.* 11
So passionate for an utter *p* „ 26
Purl loves To *p* o'er matted cress *Ode to Memory* 59
Purlieu And dusty *p's* of the law. *In Mem. lxxxix* 12
Purple (adj.) (*See also* **Dark-purple, Sullen-purple**) A pillar of white light upon the wall Of *p* cliffs, *Ode to Memory* 54
From the brain of the *p* mountain *Poet's Mind* 29
Rare broidry of the *p* clover. *A Dirge* 38
In the *p* twilights under the sea; *The Mermaid* 44
And the hearts of *p* hills, *Eleänore* 17
As often thro' the *p* night, *L. of Shalott iii* 24
The *p* flower droops: the golden bee Is lily-cradled: *Œnone* 29
river drawing slowly His waters from the *p* hill— *Lotos-Eaters, C. S.* 93
And makes the *p* lilac ripe, *On a Mourner* 7
And languish for the *p* seas. *You ask me, why, etc.* 4
That like a *p* beech among the greens *Edwin Morris* 84
Pilots of the *p* twilight, dropping down with costly bales; *Locksley Hall* 122
Across the *p* coverlet, *Day-Dm., Sleep. B.* 3
far away Beyond their utmost *p* rim, (repeat) „ *Depart.* 6, 30
P gauzes, golden hazes, liquid mazes, *Vision of Sin* 31
Flung ball, flew kite, and raced the *p* fly, *Princess ii* 248
Blow, let us hear the *p* glens replying: „ *iv* 11
And tumbled on the *p* footcloth, „ 286
and she Far-fleeted by the *p* island-sides, „ *vii* 166
And steering, now, from a *p* cove, *The Daisy* 20
Rolling on their *p* couches in their tender effeminacy. *Boädicea* 62
A solemn gladness even crown'd The *p* brows of Olivet. *In Mem. xxxi* 12
Save that the dome was *p*, and above, Crimson, *Gareth and L.* 912
A *p* scarf, at either end whereof *Marr. of Geraint* 169
And seeing one so gay in *p* silks, „ 284
Purple (adj.) (*continued*) but Yniol caught His *p* scarf, and held, *Marr. of Geraint* 377
And all the *p* slopes of mountain flowers *Last Tournament* 229
Filling with *p* gloom the vacancies *Lover's Tale i* 2
A *p* range of mountain-cones, „ 407
dragonfly Shot by me like a flash of *p* fire. „ *ii* 17
P or amber, dangled a hundred fathom of grapes, *V. of Maeldune* 56
fallen every *p* Cæsar's dome— *To Virgil* 30
When he spoke of his tropical home in the canes by the *p* tide, *The Wreck* 71
There beneath the Roman ruin where the *p* flowers grow, *Frater Ave, etc.* 4
Purple (s) Shot over with *p*, and green, and yellow. *Dying Swan* 20
And long *p's* of the dale. *A Dirge* 31
palfrey trapt In *p* blazon'd with armorial gold. *Godiva* 52
made No *p* in the distance, mystery, *Princess vi* 196
Or red with spirited *p* of the vats, „ *vii* 202
thistle bursting Into glossy *p's*, *Ode on Well.* 207
The *p* from the distance dies, *In Mem. xxxviii* 3
And blossom in *p* and red. *Maud I xxii* 74
In crimsons and in *p's* and in gems. *Marr. of Geraint* 10
An' my oän fine Jackman i' *p* *Spinster's S's.* 106
Purpled furr'd and *p*, still the clown, *Princess iv* 247
Purple-frosty Behind a *p-f* bank *In Mem. cvii* 3
Purple-skirted the *p-s* robe Of twilight *The Voyage* 21
Purple-spiked standing near *P-s* lavender: *Ode to Memory* 110
Purport with such a chain Of knitted *p*, *Two Voices* 168
surely, if your Highness keep Your *p*, *Princess iii* 212
delays his *p* till thou send To do the battle *Gareth and L.* 618
When all the *p* of my throne hath fail'd, *Pass. of Arthur* 160
Purpose I dimly see My far-off doubtful *p*, *Œnone* 251
lest the gems Should blind my *p*, *M. d'Arthur* 153
my *p* holds To sail beyond the sunset, *Ulysses* 59
He will answer to the *p*, *Locksley Hall* 55
one increasing *p* runs, „ 137
Enoch set A *p* evermore before his eyes, *Enoch Arden* 45
But had no heart to break his *p's* To Annie; „ 155
But let me hold my *p* till I die. „ 875
Faded with morning, but his *p* held. *Aylmer's Field* 412
A taunt that clench'd his *p* like a blow! *Princess v* 306
Unshaken, clinging to her *p*, „ 344
That like a broken *p* waste in air: „ *vii* 214
P in *p*, will in will, they grow, „ 305
Such splendid *p* in his eyes, *In Mem. lvi* 10
I embrace the *p* of God, *Maud III vi* 59
Fulfil the boundless *p* of their King!' *Com. of Arthur* 475
Preplext his outward *p*, till an hour, *Gareth and L.* 175
(With one main *p* ever at my heart) *Geraint and E.* 831
And, but for my main *p* in these jousts, „ 837
and my *p* three years old, „ 849
And the high *p* broken by the worm. *Merlin and V.* 196
With *p* to present them to the Queen, *Lancelot and E.* 69
For thou hast spoilt the *p* of my life. *Guinevere* 453
'lo mine helpmate, one to feel My *p* and rejoicing „ 486
The vast design and *p* of the King. „ 670
lest the gems Should blind my *p*, *Pass. of Arthur* 321
Maeldune, let be this *p* of thine! *V. of Maeldune* 119
everywhere they meet And kindle generous *p*, *Tiresias* 128
Stately *p's*, valour in battle, *Vastness* 7
Her firm will, her fix'd *p*. *The Ring* 293
Fear not thou the hidden *p* *God and the Univ.* 5
Purposed *p* with ourself Never to wed. *Princess ii* 60
Purr an soa *p* awaäy, my dear, *Spinster's S's.* 57
blackcap warbles, and the turtle *p's*, *Prog. of Spring* 55
Purr'd Thou 'ed wellnigh *p* ma awaäy *Spinster's S's.* 58
Purse loosed a mighty *p*, Hung at his belt, *Geraint and E.* 22
he took no life, but he took one *p*, *Rizpah* 31
With a *p* to pay for the show. *Dead Prophet* 8
felt a vacant hand Fill with *his p*. *To Mary Boyle* 32
Purse-mouth Maud with her sweet *p-m* *Maud I i* 71
Pursue *P* thy loves among the bowers *Talking Oak* 199
'Mine enemies *P* me, but, O peaceful Sisterhood, *Guinevere* 140
There the pursuer could *p* no more, *Pass. of Arthur* 88
Pursued my eyes *P* him down the street, *Sea Dreams* 165
who is dead?' 'The man your eye *p*. „ 272

Pursued (*continued*) on a sudden rush'd Among us, out of breath, as one *p*, *Princess iv* 375
For that small charm of feature mine, *p*— *Merlin and V.* 76
he *p* her, calling, 'Stay a little! *Lancelot and E.* 683
Pursuer behind I heard the puff'd *p*; *Princess iv* 265
There the *p* could pursue no more, *Pass. of Arthur* 88
Pursuit body half flung forward in *p*, *Aylmer's Field* 587
Pursuivant burst A spangled *p*, *Balin and Balan* 47
Push (*See also* **Shuvv**) *p* thee forward thro' a life of shocks, *Œnone* 163
P off, and sitting well in order smite *Ulysses* 58
To *p* my rival out of place and power. *Princess iv* 335
Here, *p* them out at gates.' „ 548
No will *p* me down to the worm, *Window, No Answer* 10
Should *p* beyond her mark, *In Mem. liii* 15
That *p'es* us off from the board, *Maud I iv* 27
Did he *p*, when he was uncurl'd, „ *II ii* 18
The new leaf ever *p'es* off the old. *Balin and Balan* 442
as a hand that *p'es* thro' the leaf *Pelleas and E.* 436
p me even In fancy from thy side, *Last Tournament* 638
drew back His hand to *p* me from him; *Lover's Tale ii* 93
Push'd behold thy bride, 'She *p* me from thee. *Love and Duty* 50
Old writers *p* the happy season back,— *Golden Year* 66
And *p* at Philip's garden-gate. *The Brook* 83
some were *p* with lances from the rock, *Princess, Pro.* 46
child *P* her flat hand against his face „ *ii* 366
but *p* alone on foot (For since her horse was lost „ *iv* 196
so from her face They *p* us, down the steps, „ 555
And *p* by rude hands from its pedestal, „ *v* 58
Cyril seeing it, *p* against the Prince, „ 533
So *p* them all unwilling toward the gate. *Gareth and L.* 212
P horse across the foamings of the ford, „ 1040
door, *P* from without, drave backward *Geraint and E.* 273
Hath *p* aside his faithful wife, *Balin and Balan* 106
P thro' an open casement down, lean'd on it, „ 413
Sir Bors, on entering, *p* Athwart the throng *Holy Grail* 752
thought, Why have I *p* him from me? *Pelleas and E.* 307
ever *p* Sir Modred, league by league, *Pass. of Arthur* 80
p me back again On these deserted sands *Lover's Tale i* 92
P from his chair of regal heritage, „ 118
deal-box that was *p* in a corner away, *First Quarrel* 48
chains for him Who *p* his prows into the setting sun, *Columbus* 24
a wing *p* out to the left and a wing to the right, *Heavy Brigade* 15
But she—she *p* them aside. *Dead Prophet* 58
Has *p* toward our faintest sun *To Ulysses* 23
Pushing *p* could move The chair of Idris. *Marr. of Geraint* 542
p his black craft among them all, *Merlin and V.* 563
Puss 'petty Ogress,' and 'ungrateful *P*,' *Princess, Pro.* 157
Put To *p* together, part and prove, *Two Voices* 134
P's forth an arm, and creeps from pine to pine, *Œnone* 4
and *p* your hand in mine, *May Queen, Con.* 23
P forth and feel a gladder clime.' *On a Mourner* 15
'Bring the dress and *p* it on her, *L. of Burleigh* 95
Now let me *p* the boy and girl to school: *Enoch Arden* 312
Philip *p* the boy and girl to school, „ 331
But she—she *p* him off— „ 460
Suddenly *p* her finger on the text, „ 497
How Philip *p* her little ones to school, „ 706
after that *P* on more calm and added suppliantly: *Princess vi* 215
He *p* our lives so far apart *In Mem. lxxxii* 15
This huckster *p* down war! *Maud I x* 44
p force To weary her ears with one continuous prayer. *Gareth and L.* 18
'Thou hast made us lords, and canst not *p* us down!' „ 1132
p on thy worst and meanest dress *Marr. of Geraint* 130
when she *p* her horse toward the knight, „ 200
Prince Had *p* his horse in motion toward the knight, „ 206
P on your worst and meanest dress,' „ 848
At least *p* off to please me this poor gown, *Geraint and E.* 679
'Thou shalt *p* the crown to use. *Balin and Balan* 202
in one moment, she *p* forth the charm *Merlin and V.* 967
P's his own baseness in him by default *Pelleas and E.* 81
strike him! *p* my hate into your strokes, „ 228
Loathing to *p* it from herself for ever, *Lover's Tale i* 214
He softly *p* his arm about her neck „ *iv* 71
better ha' *p* my naked hand in a hornets' nest. *First Quarrel* 50
To be hang'd for a thief—and then *p* away— *Rizpah* 36

Put (*continued*) never *p* on the black cap except for the worst *Rizpah* 65
But I *p's* it inter 'er 'ands *North. Cobbler* 72
an' *p's* 'im back i' the light. „ 98
Fur we *p's* the muck o' the land *Village Wife* 32
'Emmie, you *p* out your arms, *In the Child. Hosp.* 56
but she *p* thim all to the door. *Tomorrow* 44
when Molly 'd *p* out the light, *Spinster's S's.* 97
Her that shrank, and *p* me from her, *Locksley H., Sixty* 264
Thy gay lent-lilies wave and *p* them by, *Prog. of Spring* 37
They *p* him aside for ever, *Charity* 25
may there be no moaning of the bar, When I *p* out to sea, *Crossing the Bar* 4
Putting And made a Gardener *p* in a graff, *Merlin and V.* 479
Puzzle keep it like a *p* chest in chest, „ 654
That was a *p* for Annie. *In the Child. Hosp.* 55
P. W. Remains the lean *P. W.* on his tomb: *The Brook* 192
Pyebald three *p's* and a roan. *Walk. to the Mail* 114
Pyramid The Rhodope, that built the *p*, *Princess ii* 82
Pyramidal Whose eyes from under a *p* head *Aylmer's Field* 20
Pyre wars, and filial faith, and Dido's *p*; *To Virgil* 4
The *p* he burnt in.'— *The Ring* 340
The woman, gliding toward the *p*, *To Master of B.* 18
kindled the *p*, and all Stood round it, *Death of Œnone* 65
ask'd Falteringly, 'Who lies on yonder *p*?' „ 95
'Who burns upon the *p*?' „ 99
Pyrenean Beyond the *P* pines, *Ode on Well.* 113
Pythagoras weeks I tried Your table of *P*, *To E. Fitzgerald* 15

Q

Quaäker (Quaker) I knaw'd a *Q* feller as often 'as towd ma this: *N. Farmer, N. S.* 19
Quagmire follow wandering fires Lost in the *q*! (repeat) *Holy Grail* 320, 892
Quail (s) *q* and pigeon, lark and leveret lay, *Audley Court* 24
Quail (verb) *Q* not at the fiery mountain, *Faith* 3
Quail'd an eye so fierce She *q*; *Pelleas and E.* 602
Quaint bought *Q* monsters for the market of those times, *Enoch Arden* 539
as *q* a four-in-hand As you shall see— *Walk. to the Mail* 113
A crimson to the *q* Macaw, *Day-Dm., Pro.* 16
Quaker (*See also* **Quaäker**) Whatever the *Q* holds, from sin; *Maud II v* 92
Quality *See* **Quoloty**
Quantity All in *q*, careful of my motion, *Hendecasyllabics* 5
Quarrel (s) Why? What cause of *q*? *The Brook* 97
I remember a *q* I had with your father, *Grandmother* 21
For, call it lovers' *q's*, yet I know *Geraint and E.* 324
In all your *q's* will I be your knight. *Lancelot and E.* 961
my q—the first an' the last. *First Quarrel* 56
I am sorry for all the *q* „ 87
Quarrel (verb) With time I will not *q*: *Will Water.* 206
Would *q* with our lot; „ 226
And pray them not to *q* for her sake, *Enoch Arden* 35
I never could *q* with Harry— *First Quarrel* 16
Quarrell'd She and James had *q*. *The Brook* 96
if they *q*, Enoch stronger-made Was master: *Enoch Arden* 30
Before I *q* with Harry— *First Quarrel* 56
Had *q*, till the man repenting sent This ring *The Ring* 209
Quarried From scarped cliff and *q* stone *In Mem. lvi* 2
Among the *q* downs of Wight, *To Ulysses* 32
Quarry (*See also* **Chalk-quarry**) but as a block Left in the *q*; *Princess vii* 231
Nor *q* trench'd along the hill *In Mem. c* 11
the bird Who pounced her *q* and slew it. *Merlin and V.* 135
Quart I've 'ed my *q* ivry market-noight *N. Farmer, O. S.* 8
Wouldn't a pint a' sarved as well as a *q*? *North. Cobbler* 99
Quarter What is it now? A *q* to. *Walk. to the Mail* 10
men brought in whole hogs and *q* beeves, *Geraint and E.* 602
Quartering *q* your own royal arms of Spain, *Columbus* 115
Quarter-sessions A *q-s* chairman, abler none; *Princess, Con.* 90
Quay Humm'd like a hive all round the narrow *q*, *Audley Court* 5
From rock to rock upon the glooming *q*, „ 84
And I went down unto the *q*, *In Mem. xiv* 3
I walked with him down to the *q*, *First Quarrel* 20

Queeän (**Queen**) wi' a bran-new 'eäd o' the *Q*, *Spinster's S's.* 76
a roäbin' the 'ouse like a *Q*. „ 106

Queen (**adj.**) *Q* rose of the rosebud garden of girls, *Maud I xxii* 53
Q lily and rose in one; „ 56

Queen (**s**) (*See also* **Queeän**) *In her as Mother, Wife and* Q; *To the Queen* 28
q of marriage, a most perfect wife. *Isabel* 28
bind with bands That island *q* who sways *Buonaparte* 3
From me, Heaven's *Q*, Paris, to thee king-born, *Œnone* 127
And watch'd by weeping *q's*. *Palace of Art* 108
For were you *q* of all that is, *L. C. V. de Vere* 19
I'm to be *Q* o' the May, mother, I'm to be *Q* o' the May. *May Queen* 4, 8, 12, 16, 20, 24, 28, 32, 36, 40, 44
you'll be there, too, mother, to see me made the *Q*; *May Queen* 26
on the green they made me *Q* of May; *May Queen, N. Y's. E.* 10
A *q*, with swarthy cheeks and bold black eyes, *D. of F. Women* 127
'I died a *Q*. The Roman soldier found Me lying dead, „ 161
Three *Q's* with crowns of gold— *M. d'Arthur* 198
those three *Q's* Put forth their hands, „ 205
each man murmur'd, 'O my *Q*, *The Voyage* 63
'This beggar maid shall be my *q*!' *Beggar Maid* 16
Insipid as the *Q* upon a card; *Aylmer's Field* 28
thoughts would swarm as bees about their *q*. *Princess i* 40
from the *Q's* decease she brought her up. „ *iii* 86
good *Q*, her mother, shore the tress With kisses, „ *vi* 113
'Ah fool, and made myself a *Q* of farce! „ *vii* 243
You my *q* of the wrens! You the *q* of the wrens— *Window, Spring* 12
I'll be King of the *Q* of the wrens, „ 15
Lot's wife, the *Q* of Orkney, Bellicent, (repeat) *Com. of Arthur* 190, 245
One falling upon each of those fair *q's*, „ 276
the *Q* made answer, 'What know I? „ 326
Lancelot, to ride forth And bring the *Q*;— „ 449
They gazed on all earth's beauty in their *Q*, „ 463
the *Q* replied with drooping eyes, „ 469
and may thy *Q* be one with thee, „ 473
Q, who long had sought in vain To break him *Gareth and L.* 139
so the *Q* believed that when her son „ 158
High on the top were those three *Q's*, „ 229
built By magic, and by fairy Kings and *Q's*; „ 248
King And Fairy *Q's* have built the city, „ 259
good *Q*, Repentant of the word she made him swear, „ 526
Q herself, Grateful to Prince Geraint *Marr. of Geraint* 14
And Enid loved the *Q*, and with true heart „ 19
But when a rumour rose about the *Q*, „ 24
Q petition'd for his leave To see the hunt, „ 154
'Yea, noble *Q*,' he answer'd, „ 178
and she return'd Indignant to the *Q*; (repeat) „ 202, 414
'I will avenge this insult, noble *Q*, „ 215
'Farewell, fair Prince,' answer'd the stately *Q*. „ 224
Q Sent her own maiden to demand the name, „ 410
Avenging this great insult done the *Q*.' „ 425
'Remember that great insult done the *Q*,' „ 571
Crave pardon for that insult done the *Q*, „ 583
And there the *Q* forgave him easily. „ 592
there be made known to the stately *Q*, „ 607
came A stately *Q* whose name was Guinevere, „ 667
His princess, or indeed the stately *Q*, „ 759
our great *Q*, In words whose echo lasts, „ 781
our fair *Q*, No hand but hers, „ 787
Look'd the fair *Q*, but up the vale of Usk, „ 831
there the *Q* array'd me like the sun: *Geraint and E.* 701
all the penance the *Q* laid upon me „ 854
And you were often there about the *Q*, „ 869
great *Q* once more embraced her friend, „ 947
Q's fair name was breathed upon, „ 951
But this worship of the *Q*, *Balin and Balan* 179
pray the King To let me bear some token of his *Q* „ 188
if the *Q* disdain'd to grant it! „ 191
'No shadow' said Sir Balin 'O my *Q*, „ 206
the *Q*, and all the world Made music, „ 210
break Into some madness ev'n before the *Q*?' „ 230
the great *Q* Came with slow steps, „ 244
Follow'd the *Q*; Sir Balin heard her 'Prince, Art thou so little loyal to thy *Q*, As pass without good morrow to thy *Q*?' „ 250

Queen (**s**) (*continued*) 'Fain would I still be loyal to the *Q*.' *Balin and Balan* 254
'*Q*? subject? but I see not what I see. „ 281
'The *Q* we worship, Lancelot, I, and all, „ 349
by the great *Q's* name, arise and hence.' „ 482
Stoop at thy will on Lancelot and the *Q*.' „ 536
His loathing of our Order and the *Q*. „ 551
This fellow hath wrought some foulness with his *Q*: „ 565
Pure as our own true Mother is our *Q*.' „ 617
no unmarried girl But the great *Q* herself, *Merlin and V.* 13
They place their pride in Lancelot and the *Q*. „ 25
Cast herself down, knelt to the *Q*, „ 66
Q who stood All glittering like May sunshine „ 87
Beheld the *Q* and Lancelot get to horse. „ 102
our wise *Q*, if knowing that I know, „ 121
when the *Q* demanded as by chance „ 128
But Vivien half-forgotten of the *Q* „ 137
like the fair pearl-necklace of the *Q*, „ 451
made her *Q*: but those isle-nutured eyes „ 570
Some charm, which being wrought upon the *Q* „ 584
I mean, as noble, as their *Q* was fair! „ 608
then he taught the King to charm the *Q* „ 641
that commerce with the *Q*, I ask you, „ 770
With purpose to present them to the *Q*, *Lancelot and E.* 69
'Are you so sick, my *Q*, you cannot move „ 79
And the *Q* Lifted her eyes, „ 83
Love-loyal to the least wish of the *Q* „ 89
ye were not once so wise, My *Q*, „ 104
Shall I appear, O *Q*, at Camelot, „ 142
said the *Q*, 'A moral child without the craft „ 145
'Such be for *q's*, and not for simple maids.' „ 231
And only *q's* are to be counted so, „ 238
great and guilty love he bare the *Q*, „ 245
Then when he saw the *Q*, embracing ask'd, „ 570
the *Q* amazed, 'Was he not with you? „ 572
Ill news, my *Q*, for all who love him, „ 598
Some read the King's face, some the *Q's*, „ 727
old dame Came suddenly on the *Q* with the sharp news. „ 730
Forgot to drink to Lancelot and the *Q*, „ 737
Q, who sat With lips severely placid, „ 739
For any mouth to gape for save a *q's*— „ 775
And there the *Q* herself will pity me, „ 1059
He loves the *Q*, and in an open shame: „ 1082
'For Lancelot and the *Q* and all the world, „ 1107
deck it like the *Q's* For richness, and me also like the *Q* „ 1118
I go in state to court, to meet the *Q*. „ 1124
sent him to the *Q* Bearing his wish, whereto the *Q* agreed „ 1168
piece of pointed lace, In the *Q's* shadow, „ 1175
Lancelot kneeling utter'd, '*Q*, Lady, „ 1179
but, my *Q*, I hear of rumours flying thro' your court. „ 1189
half turn'd away, the *Q* Brake from the vast oriel-embowering vine „ 1197
In which as Arthur's *Q* I move and rule: „ 1221
An armlet for an arm to which the *Q's* Is haggard, „ 1226
the wild *Q*, who saw not, burst away To weep „ 1244
Look how she sleeps—the Fairy *Q*, so fair! „ 1255
And last the *Q* herself, and pitied her: „ 1269
said the *Q*, (Sea was her wrath, yet working after storm) „ 1308
'*Q*, she would not be content Save that I wedded her, „ 1314
And mass, and rolling music, like a *q*. „ 1336
the *Q*, Who mark'd Sir Lancelot when he moved apart, „ 1348
'This is love's curse; pass on, my *Q*, forgiven.' „ 1353
with a love Far tenderer than my *Q's*. „ 1395
Q, if I grant the jealousy as of love, „ 1399
in middle street the *Q*, Who rode by Lancelot, *Holy Grail* 355
So to the Gate of the three *Q's* we came, „ 358
O my *Q*, my Guinevere, *Pelleas and E.* 46
her name And title, '*Q* of Beauty,' „ 116
My *Q*, he had not won.' Whereat the *Q*, As one whose foot is bitten by an ant, „ 183
Pelleas had heard sung before the *Q*, „ 397
and wail'd, 'Is the *Q* false?' „ 532
Warm with a gracious parting from the *Q*, „ 558
blaze the crime of Lancelot and the *Q*.' „ 570

Raised (verb) (*continued*) Then r her head with lips compress, *The Letters* 19
When Annie would have r him Enoch said *Enoch Arden* 232
'You r your arm, you tumbled down and broke *Sea Dreams* 141
r the blinding bandage from his eyes: *Princess i* 244
At the word, they r A tent of satin, „ *iii* 347
And r the cloak from brows as pale „ *v* 73
They are r for ever and ever, *Voice and the P.* 23
Not r for ever and ever, „ 25
Behold a man r up by Christ! *In Mem. xxxi* 13
R my own town against me in the night *Marr. of Geraint* 457
arose, and r Her mother too, „ 535
Yet r and laid him on a litter-bier, *Geraint and E.* 566
He r his eyes and saw The tree that shone *Merlin and V.* 938
He r his head, their eyes met and hers fell, *Lancelot and E.* 1312
And r a bugle hanging from his neck, *Pelleas and E.* 364
The silk pavilions of King Arthur r *Guinevere* 394
And many more when Modred r revolt, „ 441
And r us hand in hand.' *Lover's Tale iv* 66
He r her softly from the sepulchre, „ 85
she r an eye that ask'd 'Where?' „ 94
a wave like the wave that is r by an earthquake grew, *The Revenge* 115
but ever we r thee anew, *Def. of Lucknow* 5
nor voice Nor finger r against him— *Sir J. Oldcastle* 45
r the school, and drain'd the fen. *Locksley H., Sixty* 268
I r her, call'd her 'Muriel,' *The Ring* 449
the mighty Muses have r to the heights *Parnassus* 2
One r the Prince, one sleek'd the squalid hair, *Death of Œnone* 57
had left His aged eyes, he r them, *St. Telemachus* 51
Still I r my heart to heaven, *Akbar's Dream* 6
Raiser A r of huge melons and of pine, *Princess, Con.* 87
Raising Annie seem'd to hear Her own death-scaffold r, *Enoch Arden* 175
r her Still higher, past all peril, *Lover's Tale i* 393
Rake (s) brag to his fellow r's of his conquest *Charity* 18
Rake (verb) (*See also* **Raäke**) Nor will she r: there is no baseness in her.' *Merlin and V.* 127
Raked And r in golden barley. *Will Water.* 128
Rake-ruin'd r-r bodies and souls go down in a common wreck, *The Dawn* 13
Raking R in that millennial touchwood-dust *Aylmer's Field* 514
Ralph And that was old Sir R's at Ascalon: *Princess, Pro.* 26
there was R himself, A broken statue propt „ 98
I read Of Old Sir R a page or two „ 121
or R Who shines so in the corner; „ 144
For which the good Sir R had burnt them all— „ 236
'Sir R has got your colours: „ *iv* 594
Disrobed the glimmering statue of Sir R „ *Con.* 117
R would fight in Edith's sight, For R was Edith's lover, *The Tourney* 1
R went down like a fire to the fight „ 3
'Gallant Sir R,' said the king. „ 6
'Take her Sir R,' said the king. „ 18
Ram (sheep) r's and geese Troop'd round a Paynim harper *Last Tournament* 321
Ram (battering-ram) shuddering War-thunder of iron r's; *Tiresias* 100
Ramble O ME, my pleasant r's by the lake, (repeat) *Edwin Morris* 1, 13
Rambling And oft in r's on the wold, *Miller's D.* 105
Ramp A lion r's at the top, *Maud I xiv* 7
'R ye lance-splintering lions, *Gareth and L.* 1305
Yea, r and roar at leaving of your lord!— „ 1307
lions, crown'd with gold, R in the field, *Lancelot and E.* 664
Rampaged An' they r about wi' their grooms, *Village Wife* 36
Rampant A r heresy, such as if it spread *Princess iv* 411
Rampart ranged r's bright From level meadow-bases *Palace of Art* 6
few, but more than wall And r, *Tiresias* 126
Rampart-lines designs Of his labour'd r-l, *Ode on Well.* 105
Ran (*See also* **Roon'd, Runn'd**) marble stairs R up with golden balustrade, *Arabian Nights* 118
words did gather thunder as they r, *The Poet* 49
With an inner voice the river r, *Dying Swan* 5
Young Nature thro' five cycles r, *Two Voices* 17
r Their course, till thou wert also man: „ 326
in many a wild festoon R riot, *Œnone* 101
round the cool green courts there r a row Of cloisters, *Palace of Art* 25
I r by him without speaking, *May Queen* 18
And r to tell her neighbours; *The Goose* 14

Ran (*continued*) R Gaffer, stumbled Gammer. *The Goose* 34
Then quickly rose Sir Bedivere, and r, *M. d'Arthur* 133
I boated over, r My craft aground, *Edwin Morris* 108
sting of shrewdest pain R shrivelling thro' me, *St. S. Stylites* 199
'Then r she, gamesome as the colt, *Talking Oak* 121
r itself in golden sands. *Locksley Hall* 32
And feet that r, and doors that clapt, *Day-Dm., Revival* 3
R forward to his rhyming, *Amphion* 30
Far r the naked moon across *The Voyage* 29
In curves the yellowing river r, *Sir L. and Q. G.* 15
R into its giddiest whirl of sound, *Vision of Sin* 29
A narrow cave r in beneath the cliff: *Enoch Arden* 23
And merrily r the years, seven happy years, „ 81
they r To greet his hearty welcome heartily; „ 349
and r Ev'n to the limit of the land, „ 577
where the rivulets of sweet water r; „ 642
and all round it r a walk Of shingle, „ 736
'Run, Katie!' Katie never r: *The Brook* 87
And r thro' all the coltish chronicle, „ 159
when they r To loose him at the stables, *Aylmer's Field* 125
r By sallowy rims, arose the labourers' homes, „ 146
Wife-hunting, as the rumour r, „ 212
thro' the bright lawns to his brother's r, „ 341
he r Beside the river-bank: „ 450
R a Malayan amuck against the times, „ 463
R in and out the long sea-framing caves, *Sea Dreams* 33
ever as their shrieks R highest up the gamut, „ 233
and r To greet him with a kiss, *Lucretius* 6
r in, Beat breast, tore hair, cried out „ 276
A petty railway r: a fire-balloon Rose gem-like *Princess, Pro.* 74
For so, my mother said, the story r. „ *i* 11
And some inscription r along the front, „ 212
R down the Persian, Grecian, Roman lines „ *ii* 130
A double hill r up its furrowy forks „ *iii* 174
a murmur r Thro' all the camp and inward raced „ *v* 110
on this side the palace r the field „ 361
My father heard and r In on the lists, „ *vi* 26
languor and self-pity r Mine down my face, „ *vii* 139
R the land with Roman slaughter, *Boädicea* 84
crying, 'How changed from where it r *In Mem. xxiii* 9
We talk'd: the stream beneath us r, „ *lxxxix* 43
his high sun flame, and his river billowing r, *Maud I iv* 32
And never yet so warmly r my blood „ *xviii* 3
her brother r in his rage to the gate, „ *II i* 12
months r on and rumour of battle grew, „ *III vi* 29
but the scholar r Before the master, *Com. of Arthur* 154
R like a colt, and leapt at all he saw: „ 322
out I r And flung myself down on a bank of heath, „ 342
There r a treble range of stony shields,— *Gareth and L.* 407
children in their cloth of gold R to her, *Marr. of Geraint* 669
A walk of roses r from door to door; *Balin and Balan* 242
Shot from behind him, r along the ground. „ 323
r the counter path, and found His charger, „ 417
sister pearls R down the silken thread *Merlin and V.* 455
R to the Castle of Astolat, *Lancelot and E.* 167
So r the tale like fire about the court, „ 734
For when the blood r lustier in him again, „ 881
all three in hurry and fear R to her, „ 1025
like a serpent, r a scroll Of letters *Holy Grail* 170
A thousand piers r into the great Sea. „ 503
And with exceeding swiftness r the boat, „ 514
Up r a score of damsels to the tower; *Pelleas and E.* 368
And down they r, Her damsels, „ 375
Pelleas, leaping up, R thro' the doors „ 539
With trumpet-blowings r on all the ways From Camelot *Last Tournament* 52
Then r across her memory the strange rhyme „ 131
straddling on the butts While the wine r: *Guinevere* 269
A murmuring whisper thro' the nunnery r, „ 410
Then quickly rose Sir Bedivere, and r, *Pass. of Arthur* 301
As mountain streams Our bloods r free: *Lover's Tale i* 327
R amber toward the west, and nigh the sea „ 432
I r down The steepy sea-bank, „ *ii* 73
upblown billow r Shoreward beneath red clouds, „ 178
r over The rippling levels of the lake, „ *iii* 3

Ran (*continued*) Where nymph and god r ever round in gold— *Lover's Tale iv* 197
and so The little Revenge r on *The Revenge* 33
Revenge r on thro' the long sea-lane between. „ 36
'are you ill?' (so r The letter) *Sisters (E. and E.)* 185
r Surging and swaying all round us, *Def. of Lucknow* 37
r into the hearts of my crew, *V. of Maeldune* 33
fig r up from the beach and rioted over the land, „ 58
By all my ways where'er they r, *Ancient Sage* 157
my life in golden sequence r, *Locksley H., Sixty* 47
sound r Thro' palace and cottage door, *Dead Prophet* 37
red mark r All round one finger pointed straight, *The Ring* 452
dead cords that r Dark thro' the mist, *Death of Œnone* 10
Slipt, and r on, and flung himself between *St. Telemachus* 61
In that vast Oval r a shudder of shame. „ 73
Rancorous A wounded thing with a r cry, *Maud I x* 34
Rancour hate the r of their castes and creeds, *Akbar's Dream* 65
Random (adj.) (*See also* **Seeming-random**) But we must hood your r eyes, *Rosalind* 37
A r arrow from the brain. *Two Voices* 345
A r string Your finer female sense offends. *Day-Dm., L'Envoi* 1
As dash'd about the drunken leaves The r sunshine lighten'd! *Amphion* 56
To make me write my r rhymes, *Will Water.* 13
He flash'd his r speeches, „ 198
Whistling a r bar of Bonny Doon, *The Brook* 82
Balmier and nobler from her bath of storm, At r ravage? *Lucretius* 176
As if to close with Cyril's r wish: *Princess iii* 101
I give you all The r scheme as wildly as it rose: „ *Con.* 2
For him nor moves the loud world's r mock, *Will* 4
And answering now my r stroke *In Mem. xxxix* 2
Let r influences glance, „ *xlix* 2
With all his rout of r followers, *Geraint and E.* 382
but had ridd'n a r round To seek him, *Lancelot and E.* 630
Or lulling r squabbles when they rise, *Holy Grail* 557
deed Of prowess done redress'd a r wrong. *Guinevere* 459
Along the years of haste and r youth Unshatter'd: *De Prof. Two G.* 21
Nor lend an ear to r cries, *Politics* 7
Random (s) as he lay At r looking over the brown earth *Pelleas and E.* 32
Random-blown sank Down on a drift of foliage r-b; *Last Tournament* 389
Rang The bridle bells r merrily *L. of Shalott iii* 13
The wild wind r from park and plain, *The Goose* 45
based His feet on juts of slippery crag that r *M. d'Arthur* 189
So these were wed, and merrily r the bells,(repeat) *Enoch Arden* 80, 511
shrill'd and r, Till this was ended, „ 175
Merrily r the bells and they were wed „ 512
That all the houses in the haven r. „ 911
a page or two that r With tilt and tourney; *Princess, Pro.* 121
with this our banquets r; „ *i* 132
for still my voice R false: „ *iv* 121
With Ida, Ida, Ida, r the woods; „ 433
R ruin, answer'd full of grief and scorn. „ *vi* 333
and r Beyond the bourn of sunset; „ *Con.* 99
And the ringers r with a will, *Grandmother* 58
And round us all the thicket r *In Mem. xxiii* 23
Then echo-like our voices r; „ *xxx* 13
The hall with harp and carol r. „ *ciii* 9
there r on a sudden a passionate cry, *Maud II i* 33
r Clear thro' the open casement of the hall, *Marr. of Geraint* 327
things that r Against the pavement, *Geraint and E.* 594
R by the white mouth of the violent Glem; *Lancelot and E.* 288
Then r the shout his lady loved: *Pelleas and E.* 171
Down r the grate of iron thro' the groove, „ 207
old echoes hidden in the wall R out „ 367
Till all the rafters r with woman-yells, *Last Tournament* 476
based His feet on juts of slippery crag that r *Pass. of Arthur* 357
There r her voice, when the full city *To the Queen ii* 26
r into the heart and the brain, *V. of Maeldune* 110
So r the clear voice of Æakidês; *Achilles over the T.* 21
a voice r out in the thunders of Ocean and Heaven *The Wreck* 88
'Forward' r the voices then, *Locksley H., Sixty* 77
cry that r thro' Hades, Earth, and Heaven! *Demeter and P.* 33
Weird whispers, bells that r without a hand, *The Ring* 411
r out all down thro' the dell, *Bandit's Death* 36
was a Scripture that r thro' his head, *The Dreamer* 2

Rang (*continued*) R the stroke, and sprang the blood, *The Tourney* 9
Range (s) (*See also* **Mountain-range**) storm Of running fires and fluid r *Supp. Confessions* 147
And r of evil between death and birth, *If I were loved* 3
Below the r of stepping-stones, *Miller's D.* 54
R's of glimmering vaults with iron grates, *D. of F. Women* 35
a lyre of widest r Struck by all passion, „ 165
the r of lawn and park: *The Blackbird* 6
over many a r Of waning lime the gray cathedral towers, *Gardener's D.* 217
Large r of prospect had the mother sow, *Walk. to the Mail* 93
On a r of lower feelings *Locksley Hall* 44
Soft lustre bathes the r of urns *Day-Dm., Sleep. P.* 9
o'er them many a flowing r Of vapour „ *Depart.* 21
Somewhere beneath his own low r of roofs, *Aylmer's Field* 47
A patient r of pupils; *Princess ii* 104
the day fled on thro' all Its r of duties *iii* 177
Rhymes and rhymes in the r of the times! *Spiteful Letter* 9
Our voices took a higher r; *In Mem. xxx* 21
O, therefore from thy sightless r „ *xciii* 9
There ran a treble r of stony shields,— *Gareth and L.* 407
that gave upon a r Of level pavement „ 666
down that r of roses the great Queen Came *Balin and Balan* 244
Merlin, who knew the r of all their arts, *Merlin and V.* 167
impute themselves, Wanting the mental r; „ 827
A purple r of mountain-cones, *Lover's Tale i* 407
past Over the r and the change of the world *The Wreck* 70
past the r of Night and Shadow— *Ancient Sage* 283
after his brief r of blameless days, *D. of the Duke of C.* 9
Range (verb) So let the wind r; *Nothing will Die* 32
So let the warm winds r, *All Things will Die* 42
Thro' light and shadow thou dost r, *Madeline* 4
'Not less the bee would r her cells, *Two Voices* 70
droves of swine That r on yonder plain. *Palace of Art* 200
Forward, forward let us r, *Locksley Hall* 181
That r above the region of the wind, *Princess, Con.* 112
'My love shall now no further r; *In Mem. lxxxi* 2
That r above our mortal state, „ *lxxxv* 22
To r the woods, to roam the park, „ *Con.* 96
it pleased the King to r me close After Sir Galahad); *Holy Grail* 307
To course and r thro' all the world, *Sir J. Oldcastle* 120
Is it well that while we r with Science, *Locksley H., Sixty* 217
The fairy fancies r, *Early Spring* 39
Ranged (adj.) r ramparts bright From level meadow-bases *Palace of Art* 6
Than all the r reasons of the world. *Pelleas and E.* 156
Ranged (verb) the solemn palms were r Above, *Arabian Nights* 79
presence of the Gods R in the halls of Peleus; *Œnone* 81
I r too high: what draws me down *Will Water.* 153
As down the shore he r, *Enoch Arden* 588
gain'd The terrace r along the Northern front, *Princess iii* 118
For now her little ones have r; *In Mem. xxi* 26
tall knights, that r about the throne, *Gareth and L.* 328
R with the Table Round that held the lists, *Lancelot and E.* 467
And a hundred r on the rock *V. of Maeldune* 101
Small pity for those that have r *Despair* 38
R like a storm or stood like a rock *Heavy Brigade* 56
He fain had r her thro' and thro', *To Marq. of Dufferin* 23
your eyes Have many a time r over when a babe. *The Ring* 151
so high they r about the globe? *St. Telemachus* 2
Ranging My fancy, r thro' and thro', *Day-Dm., L'Envoi* 34
some low fever r round to spy The weakness *Aylmer's Field* 569
That sittest r golden hair; *In Mem. vi* 26
Surprise thee r with thy peers. „ *xliv* 12
We r down this lower track, „ *xlvi* 1
R and ringing thro' the minds of men, *Com. of Arthur* 416
Rank (adj.) long, r, dark wood-walks drench'd in dew, *D. of F. Women* 75
Rank (line) When the r's are roll'd in vapour, *Locksley Hall* 104
The linden broke her r's *Amphion* 33
And clad in iron burst the r's of war, *Princess iv* 504
Should see thy passengers in r *In Mem. xiv* 6
glided winding under r's Of iris, „ *ciii* 23
The front r made a sudden halt; *Lover's Tale iii* 29
Rank (social station) To all duties of her r: *L. of Burleigh* 72
Whatever eldest-born of r or wealth Might lie *Aylmer's Field* 484

Rank (social station) (*continued*) heart is set On one whose *r* exceeds her own. *In Mem. lx* 4
up or down Along the scale of *r's*, „ *cxi* 2
likewise for the high *r* she had borne, *Guinevere* 695
Rank (verb) *r* you nobly, mingled up with me. *Princess ii* 46
She might not *r* with those detestable „ *v* 457
r with the best, Garrick and statelier Kemble, *To W. C. Macready* 6
Rank'd made me dream I *r* with him. *In Mem. xlii* 4
Rankled *R* in him and ruffled all his heart, *Guinevere* 49
Ransack'd *See* **Often-ransack'd**
Ransom'd (adj.) Thy *r* reason change replies *In Mem. lxi* 2
Ransom'd (verb) richer in His eyes Who *r* us, *Guinevere* 685
Raphaël I am not *R*, Titan—no *Romney's R.* 46
Rapid (adj.) Whose free delight, from any height of *r* flight, *Rosalind* 3
Her *r* laughters wild and shrill, *Kate* 3
Clash the darts and on the buckler beat with *r* unanimous hand, *Boädicea* 79
gyres *R* and vast, of hissing spray wind-driven *Lover's Tale ii* 198
A long loud clash of *r* marriage-bells. „ *iii* 23
Rapid (s) as the *r* of life Shoots to the fall— *A Dedication* 3
then a brook, With one sharp *r*, *Holy Grail* 381
Rapine For nature is one with *r*, *Maud I iv* 22
the wing Of that foul bird of *r* *Merlin and V.* 728
and the ways Were fill'd with *r*, *Guinevere* 458
Rapt So tranced, so *r* in ecstasies, *Eleänore* 78
R after heaven's starry flight, *Two Voices* 68
grunted 'Good!' but we Sat *r*: *M. d'Arthur, Ep.* 5
So *r*, we near'd the house; *Gardener's D.* 142
seedsman, *r* Upon the teeming harvest, *Golden Year* 70
And, *r* thro' many a rosy change, *Day-Dm., Depart.* 23
I all *r* in this, 'Come out,' he said, *Princess, Pro.* 50
peal'd the nightingale, *R* in her song, „ *i* 221
They stood, so *r*, we gazing, came a voice, „ *ii* 318
Intent on her, who *r* in glorious dreams, „ 442
She *r* upon her subject, he on her: „ *iii* 304
R to the horrible fall: „ *iv* 180
Came in long breezes *r* from inmost south „ 431
Ida spoke not, *r* upon the child. „ *vi* 220
we sat But spoke not, *r* in nameless reverie, „ *Con.* 108
'*R* from the fickle and the frail *In Mem. xxx* 25
r below Thro' all the dewy-tassell'd wood, „ *lxxxvi* 5
Who, but hung to hear The *r* oration flowing free „ *lxxxvii* 32
Tho' *r* in matters dark and deep „ *xcvii* 19
So *r* I was, they could not win An answer „ *ciii* 49
R in the fear and in the wonder of it; *Marr. of Geraint* 529
R in this fancy of his Table Round, *Lancelot and E.* 129
r By all the sweet and sudden passion of youth „ 281
R on his face as it if were a God's. „ 356
R in sweet talk or lively, *Guinevere* 386
Like odour *r* into the winged wind *Lover's Tale i* 801
car Of dark Aïdoneus rising *r* thee hence. *Demeter and P.* 39
Raptured Large dowries doth the *r* eye *Ode to Memory* 72
Rare wintertide shall star The black earth with brilliance *r*. „ 20
wreaths of floating dark upcurl'd, *R* sunrise flow'd. *The Poet* 36
R broidry of the purple clover. *A Dirge* 38
O *r* pale Margaret, (repeat) *Margaret* 2, 55
I had hope, by something *r* To prove myself a poet: *Will Water.* 165
Should bear a double growth of those *r* souls, *Princess ii* 180
stern and sad (so *r* the smiles Of sunlight) *The Daisy* 53
As some *r* little rose, a piece of inmost *Hendecasyllabics* 19
half-way down *r* sails, White as white clouds, *Lover's Tale i* 4
to reassume The semblance of those *r* realities „ *ii* 162
r or fair Was brought before the guest: „ *iv* 203
R in Fable or History, *On Jub. Q. Victoria* 5
Rarer Your loss is *r*; for this star *To J. S.* 25
Chose the green path that show'd the *r* foot, *Lancelot and E.* 162
And the Critic's *r* still. *Poets and Critics* 16
Rascal Tumbled the tawny *r* at his feet, *Aylmer's Field* 230
Read *r* in the motions of his back, *Sea Dreams* 167
Rash Stern he was and *r*; *The Captain* 10
With a crew that is neither rude nor *r*, *The Islet* 10
the hunter rued His *r* intrusion, manlike, *Princess iv* 204
R were my judgment then, *Lancelot and E.* 239
At times her steps are swift and *r*; *To Marq. of Dufferin* 2
Rash (*continued*) Not swift or *r*, when late she lent The sceptres *To Marq. of Dufferin* 5
Rashness if I should do This *r*, *Two Voices* 392
Rason (reason) there's *r* in all things, yer Honour, *Tomorrow* 6
Rat tapt at doors, And rummaged like a *r*: *Walk. to the Mail* 38
And curse me the British vermin, the *r*; *Maud II v* 58
Ah little *r* that borest in the dyke *Merlin and V.* 112
Lancelot will be gracious to the *r*, „ 120
'Black nest of *r's*,' he groan'd, *Pelleas and E.* 555
Ghoäst moästlins was nobbut a *r* or a mouse. *Owd Roä* 38
Rate (*See also* **Raäte, Third-rate**) Whom all men *r* as kind and hospitable: *Princess i* 71
I *r* your chance Almost at naked nothing.' „ 160
Till all men grew to *r* us at our worth, „ *iv* 145
we did not *r* him then This red-hot iron „ *v* 208
Whom all men *r* the king of courtesy. *Balin and Balan* 257
Rated (*See also* **Raäted**) must have *r* her Beyond all tolerance *Aylmer's Field* 380
such a one As all day long hath *r* at her child, *Gareth and L.* 1285
Rathe (early) The men of *r* and riper years: *In Mem. cx* 2
Till *r* she rose, half-cheated in the thought *Lancelot and E.* 340
Ratify every voice she talk'd with *r* it, *Princess v* 133
Rating (*See also* **Raätin**) like her none the less for *r* at her! „ 461
Rattled Siver the mou'ds *r* down upo' poor owd Squire *Village Wife* 95
Ravage from her bath of storm, At random *r*? *Lucretius* 176
noise of *r* wrought by beast and man, *Gareth and L.* 437
Ravaged left the *r* woodland yet once more To peace; *Merlin and V.* 963
Rave Let them *r*. (repeat) *A Dirge* 4, 7, 11, 14, 18, 21, 25, 28, 32, 35, 39, 42, 49
But let them *r*. *A Dirge* 46
'He will not hear the north-wind *r*, *Two Voices* 259
did seem to mourn and *r* On alien shores; *Lotos-Eaters* 32
For blasts would rise and *r* and cease, *The Voyage* 85
'Drink, and let the parties *r*: *Vision of Sin* 123
My father *r's* of death and wreck, *Sailor Boy* 19
I heard the voice *R* over the rocky bar, *Voice and the P.* 6
I roar and *r* for I fall. „ 12
And *r* at the lie and the liar, ah God, as he used to *r*. *Maud I i* 60
about the shuddering wreck the death-white sea should *r*, *The Flight* 47
Raved (*See also* **Raäved**) nor *r* And thus foam'd over at a rival name: *Balin and Balan* 566
Raven (adj.) Let darkness keep her *r* gloss: *In Mem. i* 10
knew not that which pleased it most, The *r* ringlet or the gold; *The Ring* 166
Raven (s) Bark an answer, Britain's *r*! *Boädicea* 13
For a *r* ever croaks, at my side, *Maud I vi* 57
A blot in heaven, the *R*, flying high, Croak'd, *Guinevere* 133
God 'ill pardon the hell-black *r* *Rizpah* 39
Left for the horny-nibb'd *r* to rend it, *Batt. of Brunanburh* 108
at the croak of a *R* who crost it, *Merlin and the G.* 24
Ravening Again their *r* eagle rose In anger, *Ode on Well.* 119
Ravine (mountain-gorge) brook falling thro' the clov'n *r* In cataract *Œnone* 8
wilt thou snare him in the white *r*, *Princess vii* 205
Or rosy blossom in hot *r*, *The Daisy* 32
Beyond a bridge that spann'd a dry *r*: *Marr. of Geraint* 246
Across the bridge that spann'd the dry *r*. „ 294
Every grim *r* a garden, *Locksley H., Sixty* 168
from out the long *r* below She heard a wailing cry, *Death of Œnone* 19
in front of that *r* Which drowsed in gloom, „ 75
Ravine (rapine) red in tooth and claw With *r*, *In Mem. lvi* 16
Raving (*See also* **Raävin'**) The wind is *r* in turret and tree. *The Sisters* 27
Now with dug spur and *r* at himself, *Balin and Balan* 310
R of dead men's dust and beating hearts. *Lover's Tale iv* 140
tears kill'd the flower, my *r's* hush'd The bird, *Demeter and P.* 108
Roaring London, *r* Paris, *Locksley H., Sixty* 190
R politics, never at rest— *Vastness* 3
Raving-wild I was mad, I was *r-w*, *Charity* 27
Raw nor wed *R* Haste, half-sister to Delay. *Love thou thy land* 96
Should see the *r* mechanic's bloody thumbs *Walk. to the Mail* 75
That we should mimic this *r* fool the world, „ 106
one they knew—*R* from the nursery— *Aylmer's Field* 264
R from the prime, and crushing down his mate; *Princess ii* 121
And drill the *r* world for the march of mind, *Ode on Well.* 168
shatter'd talbots, which had left the stones *R*, *Holy Grail* 720
'I have lighted on a fool, *R*, yet, so stale!' *Pelleas and E.* 114

Ray (Philip) *See* **Philip, Philip Ray**
Ray (s) lashes like to *r's* Of darkness, *Arabian Nights* 136
Make a carcanet of *r's*, *Adeline* 59
Thro' lips and eyes in subtle *r's*. *Rosalind* 24
neither hide the *r* From those, not blind, *Love thou thy land* 14
Heaven flash'd a sudden jubilant *r*, *Ode on Well.* 129
Flame-colour, vert and azure, in three *r's*, *Com. of Arthur* 275
gay with gold In streaks and *r's*, *Gareth and L.* 911
where morning's earliest *r* Might strike it, *Lancelot and E.* 5
emerald center'd in a sun Of silver *r's*, „ 296
shower'd down *R's* of a mighty circle, *Lover's Tale i* 418
May send one *r* to thee! *Ded. Poem Prin. Alice* 14
a *r* red as blood Glanced on the strangled face— *Bandit's Death* 31
Ray (verb) *R* round with flames her disk of seed, *In Mem. ci* 6
Ray'd His hair, a sun that *r* from off a brow *Last Tournament* 666
Ray-fringed *R-f* eyelids of the morn Roof *Clear-headed friend* 6
Raze and *r* The blessed tomb of Christ; *Columbus* 98
Reach (s) (*See also* **Eye-reach**) Beside the river's wooded *r*, *In Mem. lxxi* 13
not learnable, divine, Beyond *my r*. *Balin and Balan* 176
Reach (verb) And *r* the law within the law: *Two Voices* 141
example to mankind, Which few can *r* to. *St. S. Stylites* 189
r To each his perfect pint of stout, *Will Water.* 114
r its fatling innocent arms And lazy lingering fingers. *Princess vi* 138
Deeper than those weird doubts could *r* me, „ *vii* 51
Or *r* a hand thro' time to catch *In Mem. i* 7
And *r* the glow of southern skies, „ *xii* 10
When Science *r'es* forth her arms „ *xxi* 18
R out dead hands to comfort me. „ *lxxx* 16
Would *r* us out the shining hand, „ *lxxxiv* 43
Thy spirit up to mine can *r*; „ *lxxxv* 82
Or ev'n for intellect to *r* „ *xcv* 47
came the hands That *r* thro' nature, „ *cxxiv* 24
until we pass and *r* That other, *Geraint and E.* 6
Climb first and *r* me down thy hand. *Sir J. Oldcastle* 204
examples *r* a hand Far thro' all years, *Tiresias* 126
Earth may *r* her earthly-worst, *Locksley H., Sixty* 233
In summer if I *r* my day— *To Ulysses* 9
but echo'd on to *r* Honorius, *St. Telemachus* 76
Reach'd music *r* them on the middle sea. *Sea-Fairies* 6
For ere she *r* upon the tide *L. of Shalott iv* 33
We *r* a meadow slanting to the North; *Gardener's D.* 108
till I *r* The wicket-gate, „ 212
and set out, and *r* the farm. *Dora* 129
we *r* The griffin-guarded gates, *Audley Court* 14
till we *r* The limit of the hills; „ 82
until she *r* The gateway; *Godiva* 50
he *r* the home Where Annie lived and loved him, *Enoch Arden* 684
we *r* A mountain, like a wall of burs and thorns; *Sea Dreams* 118
when the note Had *r* a thunderous fulness, „ 214
and with long arms and hands *R* out, *Princess i* 29
we dropt, And flying *r* the frontier: „ 109
I would have *r* you, had you been Sphered „ *iv* 437
he *r* White hands of farewell to my sire, „ *v* 232
ere we *r* the highest summit I pluck'd a daisy, *The Daisy* 87
And *r* the ship and caught the rope, *Sailor Boy* 3
Mayst seem to have *r* a purer air, *In Mem. xxxiii* 2
He *r* the glory of a hand, „ *lxix* 17
When Arthur *r* a field-of-battle *Com. of Arthur* 96
But ever when he *r* a hand to climb, *Gareth and L.* 52
went her way across the bridge, And *r* the town, *Marr. of Geraint* 384
Thereafter, when I *r* this ruin'd hall, „ 785
r a hand, and on his foot She set her own *Geraint and E.* 759
when they *r* the camp the King himself „ 878
Then they *r* a glade, *Balin and Balan* 460
when they *r* the lists By Camelot in the meadow, *Lancelot and E.* 428
But when ye *r* The city, *Holy Grail* 707
O, when we *r* The city, „ 715
at the last I *r* a door, A light was in the crannies, „ 837
And when they *r* Caerleon, ere they past to lodging, *Pelleas and E.* 124
r The grassy platform on some hill, *Lover's Tale i* 340
One hand she *r* to those that came behind, „ *iii* 48
Reaching *r* thro' the night Her other, *Sea Dreams* 287
One *r* forward drew My burthen from mine arms; *Princess iv* 191
Read (*See also* **Reäd**) giving light To *r* those laws; *Isabel* 19
And round the prow they *r* her name, *L. of Shalott iv* 44

Read (*continued*) That *r* his spirit blindly wise, *Two Voices* 287
A love-song I had somewhere *r*, *Miller's D.* 65
Oh! teach the orphan-boy to *r*, *L. C. V. de Vere* 69
I *R*, before my eyelids dropt their shade, *D. of F. Women* 1
R, mouthing out his hollow oes and aes, *The Epic* 50
it was the tone with which he *r*— *M. d'Arthur, Ep.* 5
laugh'd, as one that *r* my thought, *Gardener's D.* 106
Who *r* me rhymes elaborately good, *Edwin Morris* 20
I *r*, and fled by night, and flying turn'd: „ 134
They flapp'd my light out as I *r*: *St. S. Stylites* 175
But tell me, did she *r* the name *Talking Oak* 153
They *r* Botanic Treatises, *Amphion* 77
They *r* in arbours clipt and cut, „ 85
'Your riddle is hard to *r*.' *Lady Clare* 76
I *r* and felt that I was there: *To E. L.* 8
And in their eyes and faces *r* his doom; *Enoch Arden* 73
In those two deaths he *r* God's warning 'wait.' „ 571
and *r* Writhing a letter from his child, *Aylmer's Field* 516
r; and tore, As if the living passion „ 534
R rascal in the motions of his back, *Sea Dreams* 167
I *r* Of old Sir Ralph a page or two *Princess, Pro.* 120
We seven stay'd at Christmas up to *r*; „ 178
And there we took one tutor as to *r*: „ 179
an officer Rose up, and *r* the statutes, „ *ii* 69
r My sickness down to happy dreams? „ 252
In this hand held a volume as to *r*, „ 455
'can he not *r*—no books? „ *iii* 214
r and earn our prize, A golden brooch: „ 300
Regarding, while she *r*, „ *iv* 382
on to me, as who should say '*R*,' and I *r*—two letters— „ 397
So far I *r*; And then stood up and spoke „ 417
I kiss'd it and I *r*. „ *v* 373
the maidens came, they talk'd, They sang, they *r*: „ *vii* 23
to herself, all in low tones, she *r*. „ 175
once more, as low, she *r*: „ 191
R my little fable: He that runs may *r*. *The Flower* 17
Which he may *r* that binds the sheaf, *In Mem. xxxvi* 13
as he lay and *r* The Tuscan poets on the lawn: „ *lxxxix* 23
I *r* Of that glad year which once had been, „ *xcv* 21
He *r's* the secret of the star, „ *xcvii* 22
Now sign your names, which shall be *r*, „ *Con.* 57
echo of something *R* with a boy's delight, *Maud I vii* 10
Sat with her, *r* to her, night and day, „ *xix* 75
(If I *r* her sweet will right) „ *xxi* 10
Not a bell was rung, not a prayer was *r*; „ *II v* 24
Gareth lookt and *r*—In letters *Gareth and L.* 1201
R but one book, and ever reading grew *Merlin and V.* 622
To dig, pick, open, find and *r* the charm: „ 660
Thou *r* the book, (repeat) „ 667, 676
And none can *r* the text, not even I; And none can *r* the comment but myself; „ 681
Stript off the case, and *r* the naked shield, *Lancelot and E.* 16
He thinking that he *r* her meaning there, „ 86
Lifted her eyes, and *r* his lineaments. „ 244
Some *r* the King's face, some the Queen's, „ 727
Stoopt, took, brake seal, and *r* it; „ 1271
Thus he *r*; And ever in the reading, „ 1283
looking often from his face who *r* To hers „ 1285
Mute of this miracle, so far as I have *r*. *Holy Grail* 66
ran a scroll Of letters in a tongue no man could *r*. „ 171
which oftentime I *r*, Who *r* but on my breviary with ease, „ 544
There is a custom in the Orient, friends—I *r* of it in Persia— *Lover's Tale iv* 231
this was the letter I *r*— *First Quarrel* 51
And *r* me a Bible verse of the Lord's good will *Rizpah* 61
I *r* no more the prisoner's mute wail *Sir J. Oldcastle* 4
Who *r's* of begging saints in Scripture?' „ 151
in your raised brows I *r* Some wonder *Columbus* 1
Who *r's* your golden Eastern lay, *To E. Fitzgerald* 32
We had *r* their know-nothing books *Despair* 55
banquet relish? let me *r*. *Ancient Sage* 18
R the wide world's annals, you, *Locksley H., Sixty* 104
that only those who cannot *r* can rule. „ 132
Because you heard the lines I *r* *Pro. to Gen. Hamley* 17
A storm-worn signpost not to be *r*, *Dead Prophet* 17

Read (*continued*) Take, *r* ! and be the faults your Poet makes *To Mary Boyle* 61
Who *r's* thy gradual process, Holy Spring. *Prog. of Spring* 106
And *r* a Grecian tale re-told, *To Master of B.* 5
Reäd a *r's* wonn sarmin a weeäk, *N. Farmer, O. S.* 28
'E *r's* of a sewèr an' sartan 'oäp *Village Wife* 92
like fur to hev soom soort of a sarvice *r.* *Owd Roä* 12
Reader make them wealthier in his *r's'* eyes ; *Poet's and their B.* 4
Readier And *r*, if the King would hear, *Columbus* 238
Readin' Fur atween 'is *r* an' writin' *Village Wife* 40
Reading (*See also* **Readin'**) *R* her perfect features in the gloom, *Gardener's D.* 175
The modern Muses *r.* *Amphion* 76
Yet bitterer from his *r's* : *Aylmer's Field* 553
Read but one book, and ever *r* grew *Merlin and V.* 622
And ever in the *r*, lords and dames *Lancelot and E.* 1284
heir That scarce can wait the *r* of the will *Lover's Tale i* 676
Ready Make thine heart *r* with thine eyes : *Gardener's D.* 273
I waited long ; My brows are *r.* *St. S. Stylites* 206
The lists were *r.* Empanoplied *Princess v* 483
And *r*, thou, to die with him, *In Mem. cxxi* 2
ever *r* to slander and steal ; *Maud I iv* 19
R in heart and *r* in hand, ,, *v* 9
R to burst in a colour'd flame ; ,, *vi* 19
I for three days seen, *r* to fall. *Merlin and V.* 296
And while she made her *r* for her ride, *Lancelot and E.* 779
and a barge Be *r* on the river, ,, 1123
R to spring, waiting a chance : *Guinevere* 12
Stands in a wind, *r* to break and fly, ,, 365
There were our horses *r* at the doors— *Lover's Tale iv* 385
R ! take aim at their leaders— *Def. of Lucknow* 42
R, be *r* against the storm ! (repeat) *Riflemen form !* 6, 20
R, be *r* to meet the storm ! (repeat) ,, 13, 27
Form, be *r* to do or die ! ,, 22
Real Keeps *r* sorrow far away. *Margaret* 44
' Thou hast not gain'd a *r* height, *Two Voices* 91
At half thy *r* worth ? *Will Water.* 204
men will say We did not know the *r* light, *Princess iv* 357
They hated banter, wish'd for something *r*, ,, *Con.* 18
some there be that hold The King a shadow, and the city *r* : *Gareth and L.* 266
Ideal manhood closed in *r* man, *To the Queen ii* 38
Thy frailty counts most *r*, *Ancient Sage* 51
Realist Betwixt the mockers and the *r's* : *Princess, Con.* 24
novelist, *r*, rhymester, play your part, *Locksley H., Sixty* 139
Reality Thy pain is a *r*.' *Two Voices* 387
The semblance of those rare *realities* *Lover's Tale ii* 162
Immeasurable *R* ! Infinite Personality ! *De Prof., Human C.* 3
Realm A *r* of pleasance, many a mound, *Arabian Nights* 101
Behind Were *r's* of upland, prodigal in oil, *Palace of Art* 79
shall hold a fretful *r* in awe, *Locksley Hall* 129
Were no false passport to that easy *r*, *Aylmer's Field* 183
Guarding *r's* and kings from shame ; *Ode on Well.* 68
She enters other *r's* of love ; *In Mem. xl* 12
From the *r's* of light and song, *Maud II iv* 82
over all whose *r's* to their last isle, *Ded. of Idylls* 12
and made a *r*, and reign'd. (repeat) *Com. of Arthur* 19, 519
Lords and Barons of his *r* Flash'd forth ,, 65
make myself in my own *r* Victor and lord. ,, 89
lest the *r* should go to wrack. ,, 208
So that the *r* has gone to wrack : ,, 227
Shall Rome or Heathen rule in Arthur's *r* ? ,, 485
swept the dust of ruin'd Rome From off the threshold of the *r*, *Gareth and L.* 136
' We sit King, to help the wrong'd Thro' all our *r.* ,, 372
wastest moorland of our *r* shall be Safe, ,, 603
this Order lives to crush All wrongers of the *R.* ,, 626
cleanse this common sewer of all his *r*, *Marr. of Geraint* 39
For in that *r* of lawless turbulence, *Geraint and E.* 521
cleanse this common sewer of all my *r*, ,, 895
Should make an onslaught single on a *r* ,, 917
his *r* restored But render'd tributary, *Balin and Balan* 2
seeing that thy *r* Hath prosper'd in the name of Christ, ,, 98
Roving the trackless *r's* of Lyonnesse, *Lancelot and E.* 35
snare her royal fancy with a boon Worth half her *r*, ,, 72

Realm (*continued*) Even to the half my *r* beyond the seas, *Lancelot and E.* 958
to give at last The price of half a *r*, ,, 1164
In mine own *r* beyond the narrow seas, ,, 1323
shrine which then in all the *r* Was richest, ,, 1330
wild bees That made such honey in his *r.* *Holy Grail* 215
for ye know the cries of all my *r* ,, 315
past thro' Pagan *r's*, and made them mine, ,, 478
Rode to the lonest tract of all the *r*, ,, 661
wholesome *r* is purged of otherwhere, *Last Tournament* 96
Or whence the fear lest this my *r*, ,, 122
And marriage with a princess of that *r*, ,, 176
The King prevailing made his *r* :— ,, 651
so the *r* was made ; but then their vows— ,, 681
Sir Modred had usurp'd the *r*, *Guinevere* 154
King's grief For his own self, and his own Queen, and *r*, ,, 197
Grieve with the common grief of all the *r* ? ' ,, 217
what has fall'n upon the *r* ? ' ,, 275
kings who drew The knighthood-errant of this *r* and all The *r's* together under me, ,, 461
all my *r* Reels back into the beast, *Pass of Arthur* 25
And wastes the narrow *r* whereon we move, ,, 140
From sunset and sunrise of all thy *r*, *To the Queen ii* 13
There in my *r* and even on my throne, *Lover's Tale i* 593
Like sounds without the twilight *r* of dreams, ,, *ii* 120
and all our breadth of *r*, *Ded. Poem Prin. Alice* 8
mightiest, wealthiest *r* on earth, *Columbus* 205
Nay—tho' that *r* were in the wrong *Epilogue* 34
kings and *r's* that pass to rise no more ; *To Virgil* 28
To those dark millions of her *r* ! *Hands all Round* 18
recks not to ruin a *r* in her name. *Vastness* 10
all her *r* Of sound and smoke, *To Mary Boyle* 65
in the heart of this most ancient *r* *Prog. of Spring* 102
Realm-ruining Rivals of *r-r* party, *Locksley H., Sixty* 120
Reap Sow the seed, and *r* the harvest *Lotos-Eaters, C. S.* 121
To-morrow yet would *r* to-day, *Love thou thy land* 93
God *r's* a harvest in me. *St. S. Stylites* 148
God *r's* a harvest in thee. ,, 149
r's not harvest of his youthful joys, *Locksley Hall* 139
r The flower and quintessence of change. *Day-Dm., L'Envoi* 23
perhaps might *r* the applause of Great, *Princess iii* 262
r's A truth from one that loves and knows ? *In Mem. xlii* 11
And *r's* the labour of his hands, ,, *lxiv* 26
Might sow and *r* in peace, *Epilogue* 13
r with me, Earth-mother, in the harvest *Demeter and P.* 147
I *r* No revenue from the field of unbelief. *Akbar's Dream* 66
Reap'd the reapers *r* And the sun fell, (repeat) *Dora* 78, 108
Reaper Only *r's*, reaping early *L. of Shalott i* 28
And by the moon the *r* weary, ,, 33
one, the *r's* at their sultry toil. *Palace of Art* 77
the *r's* reap'd And the sun fell, (repeat) *Dora* 78, 108
Once more the *r* in the gleam of dawn *Demeter and P.* 123
Homestead and harvest, *R* and gleaner, *Merlin and the G.* 58
Reaping Only reapers, *r* early *L. of Shalott i* 28
men the workers, ever *r* something new : *Locksley Hall* 117
Rear (s) Far-blazing from the *r* of Philip's house, *Enoch Arden* 727
I came upon The *r* of a procession, *Lover's Tale ii* 75
those who led the van, and those in *r*, ,, *iii* 24
Rear (verb) she shall *r* my dusky race. *Locksley Hall* 168
Her office there to *r*, to teach, *In Mem. xl* 13
Then gave it to his Queen to *r* : *Last Tournament* 22
Thou—when the nations *r* on high *Freedom* 27
Rear'd heart to scathe Flowers thou hadst *r*— *Supp. Confessions* 84
Freedom *r* in that august sunrise *The Poet* 37
Who took a wife, who *r* his race, *Two Voices* 328
ring To tempt the babe, who *r* his creasy arms, *Enoch Arden* 751
One *r* a font of stone And drew, *Princess, Pro.* 59
and your statues *R*, sung to, when, ,, *v* 414
Prick'd by the Papal spur, we *r*, *Third of Feb.* 27
r him with her own ; And no man knew. *Com. of Arthur* 224
three pavilions *r* Above the bushes, gilden-peakt : *Pelleas and E.* 428
than when we had *r* thee on high *Def. of Lucknow* 3
a statue, *r* To some great citizen, *Tiresias* 82
And dying rose, and *r* her arms, *The Ring* 222
remembering the gay playmate *r* Among them, *Death of Œnone* 59
sunset glared against a cross *R* on the tumbled ruins *St. Telemachus* 6

Rear'd (*continued*) stone by stone I *r* a sacred fane, *Akbar's Dream* 177
Reason (s) (*See also* **Rason**) Nor any train of *r* keep : *Two Voices* 50
' The end and the beginning vex His *r* : „ 299
' And men, whose *r* long was blind, „ 370
He utter'd rhyme and *r*, *The Goose* 6
God knows : he has a mint of *r's* : *The Epic* 33
We lack not rhymes and *r's*, *Will Water.* 62
' There is no *r* why we should not wed.' *Enoch Arden* 508
For save when shutting *r's* up in rhythm, *Lucretius* 223
prophesying change Beyond all *r* : *Princess i* 143
' worthy *r's* why she should Bide by this issue : „ *v* 325
With *r's* drawn from age and state, „ 357
Dark is the world to thee : thyself art the *r* why ; *High. Pantheism* 7
See thou, that countest *r* ripe *In Mem. xxxiii* 13
Thy ransom'd *r* change replies „ *lxi* 2
art *r* why I seem to cast a careless eye On souls, „ *cxii* 6
The freezing *r's* colder part, „ *cxxiv* 14
And *r* in the chase : *Com. of Arthur* 168
Albeit I give no *r* but my wish, *Marr. of Geraint* 761
(No *r* given her) she could cast aside „ 807
Than all the ranged *r's* of the world. *Pelleas and E.* 156
A crueller *r* than a crazy ear, *Lover's Tale iv* 32
with goodly rhyme and *r* for it— *Sisters (E. and E.)* 92
And not without good *r*, my good son— „ 287
Slender *r* had *He* to be glad of The clash *Batt. of Brunanburh* 76
This worn-out *R* dying in her house *Romney's R.* 145
I can but lift the torch Of *R* *Akbar's Dream* 121
And let not *R* fail me, *Doubt and Prayer* 5
Must my day be dark by *r*, *God and the Univ.* 2
Reason (verb Their's not to *r* why, *Light Brigade* 14
I am but a fool to *r* with a fool— *Last Tournament* 271
Reave like are we to *r* him of his crown *Gareth and L.* 419
Rebel (adj.) if the *r* subject seek to drag me from the throne, *By an Evolution.* 15
Rebel (s) Fire from ten thousand at once of the *r's* *Def. of Lucknow* 22
hang'd, poor friends, as *r's* And burn'd alive *Sir J. Oldcastle* 47
loosed My captives, feed the *r's* of the crown, *Columbus* 131
Rebell'd till the maid *R* against it, *Lancelot and E.* 651
Rebellion thirty-nine—Call'd it *r*— *Sir J. Oldcastle* 47
Rebloom'd Gather'd the blossom that *r*, *Aylmer's Field* 142
Reboant the echoing dance Of *r* whirlwinds, *Supp. Confessions* 97
Rebuke eighty winters freeze with one *r* *Ode on Well.* 186
Rebuked I so *r*, reviled, Missaid thee ; *Gareth and L.* 1164
Who being still *r*, would answer still „ 1249
Recall Gods themselves cannot *r* their gifts.' *Tithonus* 49
R's, in change of light or gloom, *In Mem. lxxxv* 74
Recall'd half a night's appliances, *r* Her fluttering life : *Lover's Tale iv* 93
but our Queen *R* me, *Columbus* 59
Receive And then one Heaven *r* us all. *Supp. Confessions* 32
but whoso did *r* of them, And taste, *Lotos-Eaters* 30
Make broad thy shoulders to *r* my weight, *M. d'Arthur* 164
I love the truth ; *R* it ; *Princess ii* 214
God accept him, Christ *r* him. *Ode on Well.* 281
R, and yield me sanctuary, *Guinevere* 141
Make broad thy shoulders to *r* my weight, *Pass. of Arthur* 332
Thou didst *r* the growth of pines *Lover's Tale i* 11
Received I stood like one that had *r* a blow : *Sea Dreams* 161
R and gave him welcome there ; *In Mem. lxxxv* 24
And many a costly cate, *r* the three. *Gareth and L.* 849
R at once and laid aside the gems *Lancelot and E.* 1202
in her white arms *R*, and after loved it tenderly, *Last Tournament* 24
was *r*, Shorn of its strength, *Lover's Tale i* 433
Is presently *r* in a sweet grave Of eglantines, „ 528
R unto himself a part of blame, „ 786
Reciting One walk'd *r* by herself, *Princess ii* 454
Reck And if ye slay him I *r* not : *Pelleas and E.* 269
r's not to ruin a realm in her name. *Vastness* 10
Reckless A *r* and irreverent knight was he, *Holy Grail* 856
Reckling there lay the *r*, one But one hour old ! *Merlin and V.* 709
Reckon I *r's* I 'annot sa mooch to larn. *N. Farmer, O. S.* 13
summun I *r's* 'ull 'a to wroite, „ 57
gross heart Would *r* worth the taking ? *Merlin and V.* 917
I *r's* tha'll light of a livin' *Church-warden, etc.* 47
Reckoning ' Thy *r*, friend ? ' and ere he learnt it, *Geraint and E.* 408
Reclined On silken cushions half *r* ; *Eleänore* 126
Reclined (*continued*) In the hollow Lotos-land to live and lie *r* On the hills *Lotos-Eaters, C. S.* 109
As by the lattice you *r*, *Day-Dm., Pro.* 5
Reclining Slowly, with pain, *r* on his arm, *M. d'Arthur* 168
Slowly, with pain, *r* on his arm, *Pass. of Arthur* 336
Reclothes Clothes and *r* the happy plains, *Day-Dm., Sleep. P.* 2
Recognise scarce can *r* the fields I know ; *St. S. Stylites* 40
Recollect We do but *r* the dreams that come *Lucretius* 35
Unruffling waters *r-c* the shape Of one *Last Tournament* 369
Recommenced A little ceased, but *r*. *Two Voices* 318
Poor fellow, could he help it ? *r*, *The Brook* 158
I *r* ; ' Decide not ere you pause. *Princess iii* 156
r, and let her tongue Rage like a fire *Merlin and V.* 801
Reconcile The Gods are hard to *r* : *Lotos-Eaters, C. S.* 81
Reconciled Nor did mine own, now *r* ; *Princess vii* 88
To be friends for her sake, to be *r* ; *Maud I xix* 50
breathing a prayer To be friends, to be *r* ! „ 56
but I—to be *r* ?—No, *Bandit's Death* 16
Reconcilement difference, *r*, pledges given, *Gardener's D.* 257
Quick while I melt ; make *r* sure *Princess vi* 286
Record Whereof this world holds *r*. *M. d'Arthur* 16
What *r*, or what relic of my lord „ 98
shaping faithful *r* of the glance That graced *Gardener's D.* 177
Sponged and made blank of crimeful *r* *St. S. Stylites* 158
in division of the *r's* of the mind ? *Locksley Hall* 69
Were caught within the *r* of her wrongs, *Princess v* 143
Whatever *r* leap to light He never shall be shamed. *Ode on Well.* 190
might be left some *r* of the things we said. *Third of Feb.* 18
There lives no *r* of reply, *In Mem. xxxi* 6
What *r* ? not the sinless years That breathed „ *lii* 11
Whereof this world holds *r*. *Pass. of Arthur* 184
What *r*, or what relic of my lord „ 266
Recorded each at other's ear What shall not be *r*— *Geraint and E.* 635
Recover'd *See* **Now-recover'd**
Recovering And while he lay *r* there, *Enoch Arden* 108
Recrost my feet *r* the deathful ridge *Holy Grail* 534
Rector Long since, a bygone *R* of the place, *Aylmer's Field* 11
Rectory And Averill Averill at the *R* Thrice over ; so that *R* and Hall, Bound in an immemorial intimacy, „ 37
Recurring (*See also* **Old-recurring, Still-recurring**) *R* and suggesting still ! *Will* 14
And be found of angel eyes In earth's *r* Paradise. *Helen's Tower* 12
Red (adj.) (*See also* **Blood-red, Rose-red**) The *r* cheek paling, The strong limbs failing ; *All Things will Die* 31
Some *r* heath-flower in the dew, *Rosalind* 41
And the *r* cloaks of market girls, *L. of Shalott ii* 17
One seem'd all dark and *r*—a tract of sand, *Palace of Art* 65
Before the *r* cock crows from the farm upon the hill, *May Queen, N. Y's. E.* 23
charmed sunset linger'd low adown In the *r* West : *Lotos-Eaters* 20
The dim *r* morn had died, her journey done, *D. of F. Women* 61
at the root thro' lush green grasses burn'd The *r* anemone. „ 72
We left the dying ebb that faintly lipp'd The flat *r* granite ; *Audley Court* 13
And grapes with bunches *r* as blood ; *Day-Dm., Sleep. P.* 44
Pale he turn'd and *r*, *The Captain* 62
r roofs about a narrow wharf In cluster ; *Enoch Arden* 3
When the *r* rose was redder than itself, And York's white rose as *r* as Lancaster's, *Aylmer's Field* 50
O there The *r* fruit of an old idolatry— „ 762
Fluctuated, as flowers in storm, some *r*, some pale, *Princess iv* 482
perforce He yielded, wroth and *r*, with fierce demur : „ *v* 358
They mark'd it with the *r* cross to the fall, „ *vi* 41
R grief and mother's hunger in her eye, „ 146
Or *r* with spirted purple of the vats, „ *vii* 202
A *r* sail, or a white ; and far beyond, „ *Con.* 47
The last *r* leaf is whirl'd away, *In Mem. xv* 3
Tho' Nature, *r* in tooth and claw With ravine, „ *lvi* 15
The *r* fool-fury of the Seine Should pile her barricades „ *cxxvii* 7
here on the landward side, by a *r* rock, glimmers the Hall ; *Maud I iv* 10
Has a broad-blown comeliness, *r* and white, „ *xiii* 9
Till the *r* man dance By his *r* cedar-tree, And the *r* man's babe Leap, „ *xvii* 17
The *r* rose cries, ' She is near, she is near ; ' „ *xxii* 63

Red (adj.) (*continued*) The day comes, a dull *r* ball Wrapt in drifts *Maud II iv* 65
But the *r* life spilt for a private blow— „ *v* 93
r berries charm the bird, And thee, mine innocent, *Gareth and L.* 85
who sliced a *r* life-bubbling way Thro' twenty folds „ 509
Round as the *r* eye of an Eagle-owl, „ 799
Huge on a huge *r* horse, and all in mail Burnish'd to blinding, „ 1026
Where bread and baken meats and good *r* wine Of Southland, „ 1190
than *r* and pale Across the face of Enid hearing her; *Marr. of Geraint* 523
Which was the *r* cock shouting to the light, *Geraint and E.* 384
At this he turn'd all *r* and paced his hall, „ 668
longest lance his eyes had ever seen, Point-painted *r*; *Balin and Balan* 412
Reputed to be *r* with sinless blood, „ 557
Turn *r* or pale, would often when they met Sigh fully, *Merlin and V.* 181
from spur to plume *R* as the rising sun with heathen blood, *Lancelot and E.* 308
A *r* sleeve Broider'd with pearls,' „ 372
And shot *r* fire and shadows thro' the cave, „ 414
who sat Robed in *r* samite, easily to be known, „ 433
What of the knight with the *r* sleeve? „ 621
up a slope of garden, all Of roses white and *r*, *Pelleas and E.* 422
in one, *R* after revel, droned her lurdane knights „ 430
R Knight Brake in upon me and drave them to his tower; *Last Tournament* 71
See, the hand Wherewith thou takest this, is *r*!' „ 193
till his Queen Graspt it so hard, that all her hand was *r*. „ 411
Then cried the Breton, 'Look, her hand is *r*! „ 412
the *R* Knight heard, and all, „ 441
r dream Fled with a shout, and that low lodge return'd, „ 487
tide within *R* with free chase and heather-scented air, „ 691
'but the *r* fruit Grown on a magic oak-tree in mid-heaven, „ 744
R ruin, and the breaking up of laws, *Guinevere* 426
blight Lives in the dewy touch of pity had made The *r* rose there a pale one— *Lover's Tale i* 696
One morning when the upblown billow ran Shoreward beneath *r* clouds, „ *ii* 179
Married among the *r* berries, an' all as merry as May— *First Quarrel* 40
Harsh *r* hair, big voice, big chest, big merciless hands! *In the Child. Hosp.* 4
for he look'd so coarse and so *r*, „ 7
R in thy birth, redder with household war, *Sir J. Oldcastle* 53
Redder to be, *r* rose of Lancaster— „ 55
And the *r* passion-flower to the cliffs, *V. of Maeldune* 39
And *r* with blood the Crescent reels from fight *Montenegro* 6
strike Thy youthful pulses into rest and quench The *r* God's anger, *Tiresias* 158
wi' a niced *r* faäce, an' es cleän Es a shillin' *Spinster's S's.* 75
The *r* 'Blood-eagle' of liver and heart; *Dead Prophet* 71
Fell—and flash'd into the *R* Sea, *To Marq. of Dufferin* 44
lighted from below By the *r* race of fiery Phlegethon; *Demeter and P.* 28
Then I seed at 'is faäce wur as *r* as the Yule-block *Owd Roä* 56
A *r* mark ran All round one finger pointed straight, *The Ring* 452
I well remember that *r* night When thirty ricks, All flaming, *To Mary Boyle* 35
but close to me to-day As this *r* rose, *Roses on the T.* 7
his kisses were *r* with his crime, *Bandit's Death* 13
and a ray *r* as blood Glanced on the strangled face— „ 31
An' 'e torn'd as *r* as a stag-tuckey's wattles, *Church-warden, etc.* 31
flush'd as *r* As poppies when she crown'd it. *The Tourney* 16

Red (s) (*See also* **Rose-red**) As I have seen the rosy *r* flushing in the northern night. *Locksley Hall* 26
No pint of white or *r* Had ever half the power to turn *Will Water.* 82
Blues and *r's* They talk'd of: *Aylmer's Field* 251
praised the waning *r*, and told The vintage— „ 406
And bickers into *r* and emerald, *Princess v* 263
Who tremblest thro' thy darkling *r* *In Mem. xcix* 5
And blossom in purple and *r*. *Maud I xxii* 74
Breaks from a coppice gemm'd with green and *r*, *Marr. of Geraint* 339
'Come to us, O come, come' in the stormy *r* of a sky *V. of Maeldune* 98
Molly Magee, wid the *r* o' the rose an' the white o' the May, *Tomorrow* 31

Red (s) (*continued*) *R* of the Dawn! (repeat) *The Dawn* 1, 6, 21
Is it turning a fainter *r*? *The Dawn* 22

Redan Out yonder. Guard the *R*! *Def. of Lucknow* 36

Redcap The *r* whistled; and the nightingale *Gardener's D.* 95

Redcoat our own good *r's* sank from sight, *Heavy Brigade* 42

Red-cross A *r-c* knight for ever kneel'd *L. of Shalott iii* 6

Redden cheek begins to *r* thro' the gloom, *Tithonus* 37
Sad as the last which *r's* over one *Princess iv* 46
and his anger *r's* in the heavens; „ 386
He *r's* what he kisses: „ *v* 165
These leaves that *r* to the fall; *In Mem. xi* 14
he *r's*, cannot speak, So bashful, he! *Balin and Balan* 519

Redden'd *r* with no bandit's blood: *Aylmer's Field* 597
And this was what had *r* her cheek *Maud I xix* 65
R at once with sinful, *Balin and Balan* 558
Miriam *r*, Muriel clench'd The hand that wore it, *The Ring* 261
The ring of faces *r* by the flames *Death of Œnone* 92
r by that cloud of shame when I . . . *Akbar's Dream* 64

Reddening Sir Aylmer *r* from the storm within, *Aylmer's Field* 322
And *r* in the furrows of his chin, *Princess vi* 228
heathen horde, *R* the sun with smoke and earth *Com. of Arthur* 37
She *r*, 'Insolent scullion: I of thee? *Gareth and L.* 976
He, *r* in extremity of delight, *Geraint and E.* 219
And where it dash'd the *r* meadow, *Lucretius* 49
Bantering bridesman, *r* priest, *Forlorn* 33

Redder When the red rose was *r* than itself, *Aylmer's Field* 50
The whole hill-side was *r* than a fox. *Walk. to the Mail* 3
Fair-hair'd and *r* than a windy morn; *Princess, Con.* 91
Shame never made girl *r* than Gareth joy. *Gareth and L.* 536
R than any rose, a joy to me, *Holy Grail* 521
r with household war, Now reddest with the blood of holy men, *R* to be, red rose of Lancaster— *Sir J. Oldcastle* 53
r than rosiest health or than utterest shame, *V. of Maeldune* 65

Reddest Now *r* with the blood of holy men, *Sir J. Oldcastle* 54

Redeem that From which I would *r* you: *Princess iv* 508

Redeem'd *R* it from the charge of nothingness— *M. d'Arthur, Ep.* 7

Red-faced But *r-f* war has rods of steel and fire; *Princess v* 118
A *r-f* bride who knew herself so vile, *Gareth and L.* 110

Red-hot This *r-h* iron to be shaped with blows. *Princess v* 209
Screams of a babe in the *r-h* palms of a Moloch of Tyre, *The Dawn* 2

Redolent brow of pearl Tressed with *r* ebony, *Arabian Nights* 138

Redound not without *r* Of use and glory to yourselves *Princess ii* 42

Red-plow'd domes the *r-p* hills With loving blue; *Early Spring* 3

Red-pulsing *R-p* up thro' Alioth and Alcor, *Last Tournament* 480

Red-rent arm *R-r* with hooks of bramble, *Holy Grail* 211

Redress What hope of answer, or *r*? *In Mem. lvi* 27
Ring in *r* to all mankind. „ *cvi* 12

Redress'd prowess done *r* a random wrong. *Guinevere* 459

Redressing Whose glory was, *r* human wrong; *Ded. of Idylls* 9
Than ride abroad *r* women's wrong, *Gareth and L.* 866
They ride abroad *r* human wrongs! *Merlin and V.* 693
To ride abroad *r* human wrongs, *Guinevere* 471

Red-ribb'd *r-r* ledges drip with a silent horror of blood, *Maud I i* 3
From the *r-r* hollow behind the wood, „ *II i* 25

Red Sea and flash'd into the *R S*, *To Marq. of Dufferin* 44

Redundant floods with *r* life Her narrow portals. *Lover's Tale i* 84

Reed Like Indian *r's* blown from his silver tongue, *The Poet* 13
the wavy swell of the soughing *r's*, *Dying Swan* 38
That sets at twilight in a land of *r's*. *Caress'd or chidden* 14
'I heard the ripple washing in the *r's*, *M. d'Arthur* 70
And the long ripple washing in the *r's*.' „ 117
What *r* was that on which I leant? *In Mem. lxxxiv* 45
Or low morass and whispering *r*, „ *c* 6
ranks Of iris, and the golden *r*; „ *ciii* 24
And mid-thigh-deep in bulrushes and *r*, *Gareth and L.* 810
strange knee rustle thro' her secret *r's*, *Balin and Balan* 354
and watch'd The high *r* wave, *Lancelot and E.* 1390
Rode far, till o'er the illimitable *r*, *Last Tournament* 421
'I heard the ripple washing in the *r's*, *Pass. of Arthur* 238
And the long ripple washing in the *r's*.' „ 285
A flat malarian world of *r* and rush! *Lover's Tale iv* 142

Reed-tops And took the *r-t* as it went. *Dying Swan* 10

Reedy Came up from *r* Simois all alone. *Œnone* 52

Reef league-long roller thundering on the *r*, *Enoch Arden* 584

Reef (*continued*) Down in the water, a long *r* of gold, *Sea Dreams* 127
Wreck'd on a *r* of visionary gold.' „ 139
In roarings round the coral *r*. *In Mem. xxxvi* 16
Reek'd For he *r* with the blood of Piero; *Bandit's Death* 13
Reel The horse and rider *r*: They *r*, they roll in clanging lists, *Sir Galahad* 8
We felt the good ship shake and *r*, *The Voyage* 15
Earth *R's*, and the herdsmen cry; *Princess v* 529
R's, as the golden Autumn woodland *r's* „ *vii* 357
When all my spirit *r's* At the shouts, *Maud II iv* 20
the spear spring, and good horse *r*, *Gareth and L.* 523
R back into the beast, and be no more?' *Last Tournament* 125
all my realm *R's* back into the beast, *Pass. of Arthur* 26
made the ground *R* under us, and all at once, *Lover's Tale ii* 194
My brain had begun to *r*— *In the Child. Hosp.* 60
Backward they *r* like the wave, *Def. of Lucknow* 43
red with blood the Crescent *r's* from fight *Montenegro* 6
song-built towers and gates *R*, *Tiresias* 99
r's not in the storm of warring words, *Ancient Sage* 70
Reel'd but in the middle aisle *R*, *Aylmer's Field* 819
part *r* but kept their seats: *Princess v* 496
R from the sabre-stroke Shatter'd and sunder'd. *Light Brigade* 35
and *r* Almost to falling from his horse; *Pelleas and E.* 23
and the morning star *R* in the smoke, „ 519
And pale he turn'd, and *r*, *Guinevere* 304
backward *r* the Trojans and allies; *Achilles over the T.* 31
foeman surged, and waver'd, and *r* *Heavy Brigade* 62
Reeling Garlon, *r* slowly backward, fell, *Balin and Balan* 397
Arise and fly The *r* Faun, *In Mem. cxviii* 26
crooked, *r*, livid, thro' the mist Rose, *Death of Œnone* 27
Re-father'd stoop'd, *r-f* o'er my wounds. *Princess vi* 129
Refectory Told us of this in our *r*, *Holy Grail* 41
Reflect For love *r's* the thing beloved; *In Mem. lii* 2
And each *r's* a kindlier day; „ *c* 18
makes Her heart a mirror that *r's* but you.' *The Ring* 366
Reflected *R*, sends a light on the forgiven. *Romney's R.* 161
Reflecting Opposed mirrors each *r* each— *Sonnet To* —— 11
Reflex The mellow'd *r* of a winter moon; *Isabel* 29
The *r* of a beauteous form, *Miller's D.* 77
The *r* of a legend past, *Day-Dm., Pro.* 11
swims The *r* of a human face. *In Mem. cviii* 12
depth of an unfathom'd woe *R* of action. *Lover's Tale i* 747
Refluent a phantom colony smoulder'd on the *r* estuary; *Boädicea* 28
Reform *R*, White Rose, Bellerophon, *The Brook* 161
Let your *r's* for a moment go! *Riflemen form!* 15
Refraction And such *r* of events *In Mem. xcii* 15
Refrain we *r* From talk of battles loud and vain, *Ode on Well.* 246
Refrain'd *r* From ev'n a word, *Marr. of Geraint* 213
Refresh'd leave thee frëer, till thou wake *r* *Love and Duty* 97
Reft *r* From my dead lord a field with violence: *Gareth and L.* 334
he *r* us of it Perforce, and left us neither gold nor field.' „ 338
heathen caught and *r* him of his tongue. *Lancelot and E.* 273
that was *r* of his Folk and his friends *Batt. of Brunanburh* 69
Refulgent Where some *r* sunset of India *Milton* 13
Refuse (s) and *r* patch'd with moss. *Vision of Sin* 212
Refuse (verb) nor did mine own *R* her proffer, *Princess vi* 347
Refused Nor yet *r* the rose, but granted it, *Gardener's D.* 160
R her to him, then his pride awoke; *Marr. of Geraint* 448
I *r* the hand he gave. *Locksley H., Sixty* 256
Refusing and thou *r* this Unvenerable *Tiresias* 131
Regal and a hope The child of *r* compact, *Princess iv* 421
Of freedom in her *r* seat Of England; *In Mem. cix* 14
Push'd from his chair of *r* heritage, *Lover's Tale i* 118
Regale Call your poor to *r* with you, *On Jub. Q. Victoria* 30
Regally Make it *r* gorgeous, „ 45
Regard *R* the weakness of thy peers: *Love thou thy land* 24
R gradation, lest the soul Of Discord „ 67
O blatant Magazines, *r* me rather— *Hendecasyllabics* 17
Regarded Bedivere Remorsefully *r* thro' his tears, *M. d'Arthur* 171
daughters in the pool; for none *R*; *Princess v* 330
And many past, but none *r* her, *Geraint and E.* 520
woman's love, Save one, he not *r*, *Lancelot and E.* 842
Bedivere Remorsefully *r* thro' his tears, *Pass. of Arthur* 339
Regarding Droops both his wings, *r* thee, *Eleänore* 119
any one, *R*, well had deem'd he felt the tale *Enoch Arden* 711
Regarding (*continued*) silent we with blind surmise *R*, *Princess iv* 382
Regather co-mates *r* round the mast; *Pref. Son. 19th Cent.* 5
Reggio Of rain at *R*, rain at Parma; *The Daisy* 51
Region How long this icy-hearted Muscovite Oppress the *r*?' *Poland* 11
Within this *r* I subsist, *You ask me, why, etc.* 2
girt the *r* with high cliff and lawn: *Vision of Sin* 47
That range above the *r* of the wind, *Princess, Con.* 112
No wing of wind the *r* swept, *In Mem. lxxviii* 6
To the *r's* of thy rest'? *Maud II iv* 88
Gawain the while thro' all the *r* round *Lancelot and E.* 615
fail'd to find him, tho' I rode all round The *r*: „ 710
saw Beneath her feet the *r* far away, *Lover's Tale i* 395
Register'd Are *r* and calendar'd for saints. *St. S. Stylites* 132
Regret (s) Love is made a vague *r*. *Miller's D.* 210
Deep as first love and wild with all *r*; *Princess iv* 57
debt Of boundless love and reverence and *r* *Ode on Well.* 157
So seems it in my deep *r*, *In Mem. viii* 17
And chains *r* to his decease, „ *xxix* 3
hopes and light *r's* that come Make April „ *xl* 7
O last *r*, *r* can die! „ *lxxviii* 17
To one pure image of *r*. „ *cii* 24
and my *r* Becomes an April violet, „ *cxv* 18
Is it, then, *r* for buried time That keenlier „ *cxvi* 1
Not all *r*: the face will shine Upon me, „ 9
embalm In dying songs a dead *r*, „ *Con.* 14
R is dead, but love is more „ 17
no *r's* for aught that has been, *Vastness* 23
Regret (verb) and *r* Her parting step, *Lancelot and E.* 866
Regular Faultily faultless, icily *r*, *Maud I ii* 6
Them as 'as coäts to their backs an' taäkes their *r* meäls. *N. Farmer, N. S.* 46
Rehearse 'This truth within thy mind *r*, *Two Voices* 25
Reign (verb) lips whereon perpetually did *r* The summer calm *Isabel* 7
I shall *r* for ever over all.' *Love and Death* 15
'*R* thou apart, a quiet king, *Palace of Art* 14
you shall *r* The head and heart of all our fair she-world, *Princess iii* 162
Then *r* the world's great bridals, „ *vii* 294
the wise who think, the wise who *r*, *Ode Inter. Exhib.* 32
O Soul, the Vision of Him who *r's*? *High. Pantheism* 2
What happiness to *r* a lonely king, *Com. of Arthur* 82
same child,' he said, 'Is he who *r's*; „ 393
'*R* ye, and live and love, „ 472
'Let the King *r*.' (repeat) *Com. of Arthur* 484, 487, 490, 493, 496, 499, 502
the worst were that man he that *r's*! *Guinevere* 523
where I hoped myself to *r* as king, *Lover's Tale i* 591
When only Day should *r*.' *Ancient Sage* 244
Reign (s) morning of my *r* Was redden'd by that cloud *Akbar's Dream* 63
The *R* of the Meek upon earth, *The Dreamer* 25
Reign'd A kindlier influence *r*; *Princess vii* 20
and made a realm, and *r*. (repeat) *Com. of Arthur* 19, 519
KING, that hast *r* six hundred years, *To Dante* 1
when Athens *r* and Rome, *Freedom* 9
Reigning him, that other, *r* in his place, *Enoch Arden* 763
And *r* with one will in everything *Com. of Arthur* 92
Rein (*See also* **Bridle-rein**) sway'd The *r* with dainty finger-tips, *Sir L. and Q. G.* 41
with slack *r* and careless of himself, *Balin and Balan* 309
he twitch'd the *r's*, And made his beast *Pelleas and E.* 550
Will firmly hold the *r*, *Politics* 6
Rein'd Edyrn *r* his charger at her side, *Geraint and E.* 820
Re-inspired With youthful fancy *r-i*, *Ode to Memory* 114
Reissuing whence *r*, robed and crown'd, *Godiva* 77
Rejected He should not be *r*. *Aylmer's Field* 422
return'd Leolin's *r* rivals from their suit So often, „ 493
Rejection with hands of wild *r* 'Go!'— *Edwin Morris* 124
Rejoice As when a mighty people *r* *Dying Swan* 31
Than him that said '*R*! *r*!' *Two Voices* 462
There in her place she did *r*, *Of old sat Freedom* 5
But Thou *r* with liberal joy, *England and Amer.* 11
Thus her heart *r's* greatly, *L. of Burleigh* 41
A people's voice, when they *r* At civic revel *Ode on Well.* 146
Roll and *r*, jubilant voice, *W. to Alexandra* 22
O Soul, and let us *r*, *High. Pantheism* 13

Rejoice (*continued*) I have thee still, and I *r*; *In Mem. cxxx* 14
With a joy in which I cannot *r*, *Maud I v* 21
R, small man, in this small world of mine, *Holy Grail* 559
young green leaf *r* in the frost *The Wreck* 20
In your welfare we *r*, *Open. I. and C. Exhib.* 2
Let the maim'd in his heart *r* *On Jub. Q. Victoria* 36
Rejoiced Thereat Leodogran *r*, *Com. of Arthur* 310
She spake and King Leodogran *r*, „ 425
Long in their common love *r* Geraint. *Marr. of Geraint* 23
Then suddenly she knew it and *r*, „ 687
while the women thus *r*, Geraint Woke „ 754
Never man *r* More than Geraint to greet her „ 771
Rejoicing *R* at that answer to his prayer. *Enoch Arden* 127
Stood round him, and *r* in his joy. *Com. of Arthur* 459
R in that Order which he made.' *Holy Grail* 327
R in ourselves and in our King— „ 687
one to feel My purpose and *r* in my joy.' *Guinevere* 486
not grieving at your joys, But not *r*; „ 680
thou *R* that the sun, the moon, *Tiresias* 160
R in the harvest and the grange. *Demeter and P.* 127
And send her home to you *r*. *The Ring* 320
And can no longer, But die *r*, *Merlin and the G.* 112
I, the finer brute *r* in my hounds, *By an Evolution.* 7
But while we stood *r*, I and thou, *Akbar's Dream* 182
Relate As old mythologies *r*, *Two Voices* 349
Relation That bears *r* to the mind. „ 177
Her deep *r's* are the same, *In Mem. lxxviii* 19
' Confusion, and illusion, and *r*, *Gareth and L.* 287
Relax'd memory of that token on the shield *R* his hold: *Balin and Balan* 370
and their law *R* its hold upon us, *Guinevere* 457
Release (s) can't be long before I find *r*; *May Queen, Con.* 11
Release (verb) *R* me, and restore me to the ground; *Tithonus* 72
And let who will *r* him from his bonds. *Pelleas and E.* 294
Released I arose, and I *r* The casement, *Two Voices* 403
Relent learning this, the bridegroom will *r*. *Guinevere* 172
Reliance Those, in whom he had *r* *The Captain* 57
Relic What record, or what *r* of my lord *M. d'Arthur* 98
I will leave my *r's* in your land, *St. S. Stylites* 194
Such precious *r's* brought by thee; *In Mem. xvii* 18
Some lost, some stolen, some as *r's* kept. *Merlin and V.* 453
What record, or what *r* of my lord *Pass. of Arthur* 266
Gray *r's* of the nurseries of the world, *Lover's Tale i* 290
Blood-redden'd *r* of Javelins *Batt. of Brunanburh* 95
guardian of her *r's*, of *her* ring. *The Ring* 441
sacred *r's* tost about the floor— „ 447
Relief on thy bosom, (deep-desired *r*!) *Love and Duty* 42
That sets the past in this *r*? *In Mem. xxiv* 12
In verse that brings myself *r*, „ *lxxv* 2
Demanding, so to bring *r* „ *lxxxv* 6
faltering hopes of *r*, Havelock baffled, *Def. of Lucknow* 90
glimmer of *r* In change of place. *To Mary Boyle* 47
Religion Each *r* says, ' Thou art one, without equal.' *Akbar's D., Inscrip.* 3
and *r* to the orthodox, „ 8
Relish Had *r* fiery-new, *Will Water.* 98
Re-listen seems, as I *r-l* to it, Prattling *The Brook* 18
Relive Can I but *r* in sadness? *Locksley Hall* 107
Reluctant bent or broke The lithe *r* boughs *Enoch Arden* 381
Remade *R* the blood and changed the frame, *In Mem., Con.* 11
Remain there like a sun *r* Fix'd— *Eleänore* 92
Those lonely lights that still *r*, *Two Voices* 83
Let what is broken so *r*. *Lotos-Eaters, C. S.* 80
And what *r's* to tell. *Talking Oak* 204
and of one to me Little *r's*: *Ulysses* 26
R's the lean P. W. on his tomb: *The Brook* 192
we must *r* Sacred to one another.' *Aylmer's Field* 425
I *r* on whom to wreak your rage, *Princess iv* 350
But then this question of your troth *r's*: „ *v* 279
r Orb'd in your isolation: „ *vi* 168
As long as we *r*, we must speak free, *Third of Feb.* 13
One writes, that ' Other friends *r*,' *In Mem. vi* 1
And what to me *r's* of good? „ 42
And what are they when these *r* „ *lxxvi* 15
My shame is greater who *r*, „ *cix* 23

Remain (*continued*) her name will yet *r* Untarnish'd as before; *Marr. of Geraint* 500
now *r's* But little cause for laughter: *Lancelot and E.* 596
and *r* Lord of the tourney. *Pelleas and E.* 162
others who *r*, And of the two first-famed for courtesy— *Guinevere* 322
I shared with her in whom myself *r's*. *Lover's Tale i* 248
But still the clouds *r*;' *Ancient Sage* 241
except The man himself *r*; *Epilogue* 70
The man *r's*, and whatsoe'er He wrought „ 75
every Faith and Creed, *r's* The Mystery. *To Mary Boyle* 52
But, while the hills *r*, *Politics* 10
Remain'd *r* among us In our young nursery still unknown, *Princess iv* 331
I *r*, whose hopes were dim, *In Mem. lxxxv* 29
the two *r* Apart by all the chamber's width, *Geraint and E.* 264
Balan warn'd, and went; Balin *r*: *Balin and Balan* 153
Pierced thro' his side, and there snapt, and *r*. *Lancelot and E.* 490
there that day *r*, and toward even „ 977
there I woke, but still the wish *r*. „ 1048
' Then there *r* but Lancelot, *Holy Grail* 760
Lancelot ever promised, but *r*, *Guinevere* 93
Remaineth The rest *r* unreveal'd; *In Mem. xxxi* 14
Remaining You love, *r* peacefully, *Margaret* 22
R betwixt dark and bright: „ 28
Than cry for strength, *r* weak, *Two Voices* 95
R utterly confused with fears, *Palace of Art* 269
The two *r* found a fallen stem; *Enoch Arden* 567
The last *r* pillar of their house, *Aylmer's Field* 295
r there Fixt like a beacon-tower *Princess iv* 492
And thou *r* here wilt learn the event; *Guinevere* 577
eyes *R* fixt on mine, *Tiresias* 47
None but the terrible Peelè *r* *Kapiolani* 28
Remains With my lost Arthur's loved *r*, *In Mem. ix* 3
Re-make gathering at the base *R's* itself, *Guinevere* 610
Remand *r* it thou For calmer hours *Love and Duty* 89
Remark her least *r* was worth The experience *Edwin Morris* 65
Remark'd *r* The lusty mowers labouring *Geraint and E.* 250
Remble (remove) a niver *r's* the stoäns. *N. Farmer, O. S.* 60
Rembled (removed) an' raäved an' *r* 'um out. „ 32
Remedy There is one *r* for all. (repeat) *Two Voices* 165, 201
Remember (*See also* **Remimber**) As one before, *r* much, „ 356
For you *r*, you had set, *Miller's D.* 81
How sadly, I *r*, rose the morning of the year! *May Queen, Con.* 3
The times when I *r* to have been Joyful *D. of F. Women* 79
Oh yet but I *r*, ten years back— *Walk. to the Mail* 50
I *r* one that perish'd: *Locksley Hall* 71
Such a one do I *r*, „ 72
I *r*, when I think, That my youth was half divine. *Vision of Sin* 77
how should the child *R* this?' *Enoch Arden* 234
We *r* love ourselves In our sweet youth: *Princess i* 122
' We *r* love ourself In our sweet youth; „ *v* 207
R him who led your hosts; *Ode on Well.* 171
yet *r* all He spoke among you, „ 177
I *r* a quarrel I had with your father, *Grandmother* 21
R what a plague of rain; *The Daisy* 50
R how we came at last To Como; „ 69
' Does my old friend *r* me?' *In Mem. lxiv* 28
That yet *r's* his embrace, „ *lxxxv* 111
I *r* the time, for the roots of my hair *Maud I i* 13
She *r's* it now we meet. „ *vi* 88
I *r*, I, When he lay dying there, „ *II ii* 66
but *r's* all, and growls Remembering, *Gareth and L.* 704
' *R* that great insult done the Queen,' *Marr. of Geraint* 571
Dost thou *r* at Caerleon once— *Balin and Balan* 503
' And I *r* now That pelican on the casque: *Holy Grail* 699
neither Love, Warm in the heart, his cradle, can *r* Love in the womb, *Lover's Tale i* 158
Once or twice she told me (For I *r* all things) „ 346
She *r's* you. Farewell. *Sisters (E. and E.)* 190
Nay you *r* our Emmie; *In the Child. Hosp.* 33
I bad them *r* my father's death, *V. of Maeldune* 70
I *r* I thought, as we past, *Despair* 11
I *r* how you kiss'd the miniature *Locksley H., Sixty* 12
r how the course of Time will swerve, „ 235
In this Hostel—I *r*— „ 255

Replied (*continued*) Percivale stood near him and r, — Pelleas and E. 523
his friend R, in half a whisper, — Lover's Tale iv 336
Replieth The hollow grot r — Claribel 20
Reply (s) To which the voice did urge r; — Two Voices 7
Kept watch, waiting decision, made r. — Œnone 143
There comes no murmur of r. — Palace of Art 286
And my disdain is my r. — L. C. V. de Vere 22
Oh your sweet eyes, your low replies: — „ 29
But since I heard him make r — Talking Oak 25
In courteous words return'd r: — Day-Dm., Revival 30
He spoke; the passion in her moan'd r — Enoch Arden 286
Their's not to make r, — Light Brigade 13
There lives no record of r, — In Mem. xxxi 6
Thy ransom'd reason change replies — „ lxi 2
The delight of low replies. — Maud II iv 30
And hung his head, and halted in r, — Geraint and E. 811
having no r, Gazed at the heaving shoulder, — Merlin and V. 895
Stammer'd, and could not make her a r. — Pelleas and E. 85
gunner said ' Ay, ay,' but the seamen made r: — The Revenge 91
in the thick of question and r — Sisters (E. and E.) 157
Reply (verb) She replies, in accents fainter, — L. of Burleigh 5
and the brook, why not? replies. — The Brook 22
And my Melpomene replies, — In Mem. xxxvii 9
Care not thou to r: — Maud II iii 7
Arthur all at once gone mad replies, — Gareth and L. 863
Replying Blow, let us hear the purple glens r: — Princess iv 11
Report (s) In this r, this answer of a king, — „ i 70
If one should bring me this r, — In Mem. xiv 1
when Yniol made r Of that good mother — Marr. of Geraint 756
' Sir King ' they brought r ' we hardly found, — Balin and Balan 94
And brought r of azure lands and fair, — „ 168
angels of our Lord's r. — Merlin and V. 16
Report (verb) Victor his men R him! — Com. of Arthur 250
Reported still r him As closing in himself — Gareth and L. 1338
a woodman there R of some demon in the woods — Balin and Balan 124
R who he was, and on what quest Sent, — Lancelot and E. 628
Reporting R of his vessel China-bound, — Enoch Arden 122
Repose sick man's room when he taketh r — A spirit haunts 14
Her manners had not that r — L. C. V. de Vere 39
For brief repast or afternoon r — Guinevere 395
Reposed God gave her peace; her land r; — To the Queen 26
centuries behind me like a fruitful land r; — Locksley Hall 13
A void where heart on heart r; — In Mem. xiii 6
Reposing His state the king r keeps. — Day-Dm., Sleep. P. 39
Repression what sublime r of himself, — Ded. of Idylls 19
Reproach (s) you may worship me without r; — St. S. Stylites 193
all these things fell on her Sharp as r. — Enoch Arden 488
Thro' light r'es, half exprest — In Mem. lxxxv 15
He never spake word of r to me, — Lancelot and E. 124
Mine own name shames me, seeming a r, — „ 1403
Seem'd my r? He is not of my kind. — Pelleas and E. 311
found my letter upon him, my wail of r and scorn; — Charity 23
Reproach (verb) the poor cause that men R you, — Marr. of Geraint 88
Reproachful Had floated in with sad r eyes, — The Ring 469
Reprobation Election, Election and R— — Rizpah 73
Reproof I have not lack'd thy mild r, — My life is full 4
Presses his without r: — L. of Burleigh 10
I was prick'd with some r, — Geraint and E. 890
her own r At some precipitance in her burial. — Lover's Tale iv 106
Reprove Was it gentle to r her For stealing — Maud I xx 8
' A welfare in thine eye r's Our fear — Holy Grail 726
Republic The vast R's that may grow, — Day-Dm., L'Envoi 15
Aroused the black r on his elms, — Aylmer's Field 529
Revolts, r's, revolutions, — Princess, Con. 65
And crown'd R's crowning common-sense, — To the Queen ii 61
Kingdoms and R's fall, — Locksley H., Sixty 159
Repulse cloaks the scar of some r with lies; — Merlin and V. 818
Repulsed being r By Yniol and yourself, — Geraint and E. 828
Repute bore a knight of old r to the earth, — Lancelot and E. 492
Reputed R to be red with sinless blood, — Balin and Balan 557
R the best knight and goodliest man, — Guinevere 382
Request then at my r He brought it; — The Epic 47
' To what r for what strange boon,' — Merlin and V. 264
Require I should r A sign! — Supp. Confessions 9
For this brief idyll would r A less diffuse — Tiresias 188
Required Heroic seems our Princess as r— — Princess, Pro. 230
But public use r she should be known; — „ iv 336
The men r that I should give throughout — Princess Con. 10
whom He trusted all things, and of him r His counsel: — Com. of Arthur 146
Requiring R, tho' I knew it was mine own, — Gardener's D. 227
R at her hand the greatest gift, — „ 229
Re-reiterated And grant my r-r wish, — Merlin and V. 353
Re-risen content R-r in Katie's eyes, — The Brook 169
Rescue Flights, terrors, sudden r's, — Aylmer's Field 99
Rescued diamonds that I r from the tarn, — Last Tournament 37
You r me—yet—was it well That you came — Despair 4
Reseated thou r in thy place of light, — Guinevere 525
Resembles And so my wealth r thine, — In Mem. lxxix 17
Reserve not to pry and peer on your r, — Princess iv 419
Such fine r and noble reticence, — Geraint and E. 860
Reserved from a binn r For banquets, — Aylmer's Field 405
And in my grief a strength r. — In Mem. lxxxv 52
Resettable gems Moveable and r at will, — Lover's Tale iv 199
Resign'd Asks what thou lackest, thought r, — Two Voices 98
I pray'd for both, and so I felt r, — May Queen, Con. 31
Resistance to know The limits of r, — To Duke of Argyll 2
Resmooth waves of prejudice R to nothing: — Princess iii 241
Resolder'd r peace, whereon Follow'd his tale. — „ v 47
Resolute The statesman-warrior, moderate, r, — Ode on Well. 25
Resolution Dispersed his r like a cloud. — Lancelot and E. 884
Resolve (s) ' Hard task, to pluck r,' I cried, — Two Voices 118
Assurance only breeds r.' — „ 315
His r Upbore him, and firm faith, — Enoch Arden 799
His gazing in on Annie, his r, — „ 863
Full many a holy vow and pure r. — Lancelot and E. 879
my fresh but fixt r To pass away into the quiet life, — Holy Grail 737
Resolve (verb) turn thee round, r the doubt; — In Mem. xliv 14
Nor can my dream r the doubt: — „ lxviii 12
Resolved (adj.) But he was all the more r to go, — Lover's Tale iv 179
and that r self-exile from a land He never would revisit, — „ 209
Resolved (verb) start in pain, R on noble things, — D. of F. Women 42
Here she woke, R, sent for him and said — Enoch Arden 507
Resort To which I most r, (repeat) — Will Water. 2, 210
Resound And solemn chaunts r between. — Sir Galahad 36
Milton, a name to r for ages; — Milton 4
Respeck (respect) but I r's tha fur that;' — North. Cobbler 90
fur I r's tha,' says 'e; — „ 92
Respect (*See also* **Respeck**) some r, however slight, was paid To woman, — Princess ii 136
Response Then did my r clearer fall: — Two Voices 34
Responsive Queenly r when the loyal hand — Aylmer's Field 169
Rest (remainder) Proportion, and, above the r, — Two Voices 20
' These words,' I said, ' are like the r; — „ 334
And there the Ionian father of the r; — Palace of Art 137
while the r were loud in merry-making, — Enoch Arden 77
But oft he work'd among the r and shook — „ 651
Arbaces, and Phenomenon, and the r, — The Brook 162
o'er the r Arising, did his holy oily best, — Sea Dreams 194
who this way runs Before the r— — Lucretius 192
And sister Lilia with the r.' — Princess, Pro. 52
Lilia with the r, and lady friends — „ 97
' He began, The r would follow, each in turn; — „ 201
So I began, And the r follow'd: — „ 244
and beckon'd us: the r Parted; — „ ii 182
Speak little; mix not with the r; — „ 360
Electric, chemic laws, and all the r, — „ 384
Arriving all confused among the r — „ iv 224
half-crush'd among the r A dwarf-like Cato cower'd — „ vii 125
nor can I weep for the r; — Grandmother 19
Perchance, perchance, among the r, — In Mem., Con. 87
the r Slew on and burnt, crying, — Com. of Arthur 438
among the r Fierce was the hearth, — Gareth and L. 1009
Speak, if ye be not like the r, hawk-mad, — Marr. of Geraint 280
a name that branches o'er the r, — Balin and Balan 182
eats And uses, careless of the r; — Merlin and V. 463
And being lustily holpen by the r, — Lancelot and E. 496
one, a fellow-monk among the r, Ambrosius, loved him much beyond the r, — Holy Grail 8
Gawain sware, and louder than the r.' — „ 202

Rest (remainder) (*continued*) My sister's vision, and the *r*, *Holy Grail* 272
to Bors Beyond the *r* : „ 653
the *r* Spake but of sundry perils in the storm ; „ 760
Thy brotherhood in me and all the *r*, *Pelleas and E.* 322
But newly-enter'd, taller than the *r*, *Last Tournament* 169
And trebling all the *r* in value— *Lover's Tale iv* 200
an' a letter along wi' the *r*, *First Quarrel* 49
thou'rt like the *r* o' the men, *North. Cobbler* 63
And the *r* they came aboard us, *The Revenge* 52
half of the *r* of us maim'd for life „ 77
brain that could think for the *r* ; *Def. of Lucknow* 20
Old friends outvaluing all the *r*, *To E. Fitzgerald* 40
An' Shamus along wid the *r*, *Tomorrow* 44
fur I stuck to tha moor na the *r*, *Spinster's S's*, 51
r Who made a nation purer through their art. *To W. C. Macready* 7
the *r* Were crumpled inwards. *The Ring* 453
London and Paris and all the *r* *The Dawn* 10

Rest (repose) happiness And perfect *r* so perfect is ; *Supp. Confessions* 51
In sweet dreams softer than unbroken *r* *Ode to Memmory* 29
Fold thine arms, turn to thy *r*. *A Dirge* 3
There is no *r* for me below, *Oriana* 3
Nor unhappy, nor at *r*, *Adeline* 4
A nobler yearning never broke her *r* *The form, the form* 2
But long disquiet merged in *r*. *Two Voices* 249
heart would beat against me, In sorrow and in *r* : *Miller's D.* 178
Floated her hair or seem'd to float in *r*. *Œnone* 19
who have attain'd *R* in a happy place „ 131
I kiss'd his eyelids into *r* : *The Sisters* 19
and the weary are at *r*. *May Queen, Con.* 60
all things else have *r* from weariness ? *Lotos-Eaters, C. S.* 14
All things have *r* : (repeat) „ 15, 51
Give us long *r* or death, „ 53
Sleep full of *r* from head to feet ; *To J. S.* 75
Had *r* by stony hills of Crete. *On a Mourner* 35
Thou wouldst have caught me up into thy *r*, *St. S. Stylites* 18
And shadow'd all her *r*— *Talking Oak* 226
yonder ivied casement, ere I went to *r*, *Locksley Hall* 7
turn thee on thy pillow : get thee to thy *r* again. „ 86
my latest rival brings thee *r*. „ 89
moving toward the stillness of his *r*. „ 144
A perfect form in perfect *r*. *Day-Dm., Sleep. B.* 24
That her spirit might have *r*. *L. of Burleigh* 100
With a nation weeping, and breaking on my *r* ? *Ode on Well.* 82
tired a little, that's all, and long for *r* ; *Grandmother* 99
And moan and sink to their *r*. *Voice and the P.* 16
And waves that sway themselves in *r*, *In Mem. xi* 18
Nor any want-begotten *r*. „ *xxvii* 12
surely *r* is meet : ' They rest,' we said, „ *xxx* 18
I know that in thy place of *r* „ *lxvii* 2
That wakens at this hour of *r* „ *civ* 6
To the regions of thy *r* ' ? *Maud II iv* 88
in that hope, dear soul, let trouble have *r*, „ *III vi* 12
Half disarray'd as to her *r*, *Marr. of Geraint* 516
moving without answer to her *r* She found no *r*, „ 530
scorn of Garlon, poisoning all his *r*, *Balin and Balan* 383
royal knight, we break on thy sweet *r*, „ 470
I brake upon thy *r*, And now full loth am I „ 499
Arriving at a time of golden *r*, *Merlin and V.* 142
charm so taught will charm us both to *r*. „ 332
and Love Should have some *r* and pleasure „ 485
Should have small *r* or pleasure in herself, „ 490
R must you have.' ' No *r* for me,' *Lancelot and E.* 832
' Nay, for near you, fair lord, I am at *r*.' „ 833
And found no ease in turning or in *r* ; „ 901
vext his heart, And marr'd his *r*— *Pelleas and E.* 399
Hath lain for years at *r*— *Last Tournament* 94
Farewell ! there is an isle of *r* for thee. *Pass. of Arthur* 35
But I had been at *r* for evermore. *Lover's Tale i* 625
and we thought her at *r*, *In the Child. Hosp.* 40
as he rose from his *r*, *V. of Maeldune* 85
strike Thy youthful pulses into *r* *Tiresias* 157
I would that I were gather'd to my *r*, „ 170
let me weep my fill once more, and cry myself to *r* ! To
r ? to rest and wake no more were better *r* for me, *The Flight* 6
human offspring this ideal man at *r* ? *Locksley H., Sixty* 234

Rest (repose) (*continued*) To that which looks like *r*, *Pref. Poem Broth. Son* 6
Raving politics, never at *r*— *Vastness* 3
Is memory with your Marian gone to *r*, *To Mary Boyle* 13
and the murderous father at *r*, . . . *Bandit's Death* 33
blight thy hope or break thy *r*, *Faith* 2

Rest (s) Go thou to *r*, but ere thou go to *r* *Marr. of Geraint* 512
Now both are gone to *r*. *To W. H. Brookfield* 8

Rest (verb) ' The doubt would *r*, I dare not solve. *Two Voices* 313
Passing the place where each must *r*, „ 410
his shadow on the stone, *R's* like a shadow, *Œnone* 28
r thee sure That I shall love thee well „ 159
Oh *r* ye, brother mariners, *Lotos-Eaters, C. S.* 128
came To *r* beneath thy boughs. (repeat) *Talking Oak* 36, 156
Where fairer fruit of Love may *r* „ 251
wealth no more shall *r* in mounded heaps, *Golden Year* 32
I cannot *r* from travel : *Ulysses* 6
Here *r's* the sap within the leaf, *Day-Dm., Sleep. P.* 3
And I desire to *r*. *Come not, when, etc.* 10
Who will not let his ashes *r* ! *You might have won* 28
and sighing ' Let me *r* ' she said : *Enoch Arden* 375
Fall back upon a name ! *r*, rot in that ! *Aylmer's Field* 385
Birdie, *r* a little longer, *Sea Dreams* 297
So she *r's* a little longer, „ 299
Sleep and *r*, sleep and *r*, *Princess iii* 9
R, *r*, on mother's breast, „ 11
Said Ida ; ' let us down and *r* ; ' „ *iv* 21
and this proud watchword *r* Of equal ; „ *vii* 300
There he shall *r* for ever *Ode on Well.* 51
To *r* in a golden grove, *Wages* 9
To *r* beneath the clover sod, *In Mem. x* 13
Among familiar names to *r* „ *xviii* 7
I sing to him that *r's* below, „ *xxi* 1
' They *r*,' we said, ' their sleep is sweet,' „ *xxx* 19
And *r's* upon the Life indeed. „ *xxxii* 8
In endless age ? It *r's* with God. „ *lxxiii* 12
My heart, tho' widow'd, may not *r* „ *lxxxv* 113
Who *r* to-night beside the sea. „ *Con.* 76
spangle all the happy shores By which they *r*, „ 121
so should he *r* with her, Closed in her castle *Gareth and L.* 162
R would I not, Sir King, an I were king, „ 597
' I nor mine *R* : so my knighthood keep the vows „ 602
R ! the good house, tho' ruin'd, *Marr. of Geraint* 378
eye rove in following, or *r* On Enid „ 399
I felt That I could *r*, a rock in ebbs and flows, „ 812
therefore, I do *r*, A prophet certain of my prophecy, „ 813
but to *r* awhile within her court ; *Geraint and E.* 855
Should *r* and let you *r*, knowing you mine. *Merlin and V.* 335
r : and Love Should have some rest and pleasure „ 484
after my long voyage I shall *r* ! ' *Lancelot and E.* 1061
' I will *r* here,' I said, *Holy Grail* 385
as who should say, ' *R* here ; ' „ 396
So shook him that he could not *r*, *Pelleas and E.* 412
but here, Here let me *r* and die,' „ 515
could not *r* for musing how to smoothe *Last Tournament* 390
' to pass, to sleep, To *r*, to be with her— *Lover's Tale iv* 64
striding fast, and now Sitting awhile to *r*, „ 88
Travelling that land, and meant to *r* an hour ; „ 133
Come, come, little wife, let it *r* ! *First Quarrel* 62
couldn't be idle—my Willy—he never could *r*. *Rizpah* 27
At times our Britain cannot *r*, *To Marq. of Dufferin* 1
To rest ? to *r* and wake no more, *The Flight* 6
He *r's* content, if his young music *To Mary Boyle* 63
whether, since our nature cannot *r*, *Prog. of Spring* 96
And here no longer can I *r* ; *The Wanderer* 2

Rested where man Hath moor'd and *r* ? *Supp. Confessions* 125
And *r* from her labours. *The Goose* 16
So Philip *r* with her well-content ; *Enoch Arden* 376
There Enoch *r* silent many days. „ 699
and gain'd the hall, and there *R* : *Princess vi* 353
But *r* with her sweet face satisfied ; *Marr. of Geraint* 776
She *r*, and her desolation came Upon her, *Geraint and E.* 518
He *r* well content that all was well. „ 952
But *r* in her fealty, till he crown'd „ 967
Nor *r* thus content, but day by day, *Lancelot and E.* 13

Rested (continued) Wander'd, the while we r: Lover's Tale i 235
Arthur the blameless R The Gleam. Merlin and the G. 74
Resteth but r satisfied, Looking on her Lover's Tale i 159
Resting R weary limbs at last on beds of asphodel. Lotos-Eaters, C. S. 125
Porch-pillars on the lion r, The Daisy 55
Resting-place come again, mother, from out my r-p; May Queen, N. Y's. E. 37
Restless But passionately r came and went, Aylmer's Field 546
and r forefoot plies His function of the woodland: Lucretius 45
swaying upon a r elm Drew the vague glance of Vivien, Balin and Balan 463
To which it made a r heart, he took, Lancelot and E. 550
And men have hopes, which race the r blood, Prog. of Spring 115
Restore ghost of passion that no smiles r— The form, the form 11
Release me, and r me to the ground; Tithonus 72
Restored tho' he built upon the babe r; Princess vii 75
had his realm r But render'd tributary, Balin and Balan 2
Restrain'd Restrain'd him with all manner of device, Pelleas and E. 204
Restrain'd himself quite to the close— Lover's Tale iv 10
Restraining Fierier and stormier from r, Balin and Balan 229
Restraint I spoke without restraint, Talking Oak 14
Result (s) The slow r of winter showers: Two Voices 452
Deep-chested music, and to this r. The Epic 51
from age to age With much the same r. Walk. to the Mail 80
and the long r of Time; Locksley Hall 12
But for some true r of good All parties Will Water. 55
victor Hours should scorn The long r of love, In Mem. i 14
self-infolds the large r's Of force " lxxiii 15
And that serene r of all.' " lxxxv 92
With old r's that look like new; " cxxviii 11
O, the r's are simple; Merlin and V. 684
work old laws of Love to fresh r's, Prog. of Spring 85
Result (verb) R in man, be born and think, In Mem., Con. 126
Resume r their life, They would but find " xc 6
Retain And so may Place r us still, " xlii 5
Which yet r's a memory of its youth, Sisters (E. and E.) 66
Retake stands Vacant, but thou r it, Balin and Balan 79
Retaught R the lesson thou hadst taught, England and Amer. 8
Reticence Such fine reserve and noble r, Geraint and E. 860
Not muffled round with selfish r. Merlin and V. 337
Down with R, down with Reverence— Locksley H., Sixty 142
Retinue The dark r reverencing death Aylmer's Field 842
and so Went forth in long r following up Princess iii 195
and far ahead Of his and her r moving, Guinevere 385
Retire How oft we saw the Sun r, The Voyage 17
And last the dance;—till I r: In Mem., Con. 105
Retired in after life r From brawling storms, Ode to Memory 111
I saw the snare, and I r: L. C. V. de Vere 6
Retiring Ever r thou dost gaze On the prime labour Ode to Memory 93
knights Clash like the coming and r wave, Gareth and L. 522
Re-told And read a Grecian tale r-t, To Master of B. 5
Retreat Ah, for some r Deep in yonder Locksley Hall 153
O joy to him in this r, In Mem. lxxxix 13
Retreated Leolin still R half-aghast, Aylmer's Field 330
The light r, The landskip darken'd, Merlin and the G. 30
Retreating up and down Advancing nor r. Sisters (E. and E.) 179
Retrospect 'Not such as moans about the r, Princess iv 85
yet in r That less than momentary thunder-sketch Sisters (E. and E.) 98
Return (s) (See also **Home-return**) Then she went back some paces of r, Geraint and E. 70
with how sweet grace She greeted my r! Balin and Balan 194
tho' my love had no r: Lancelot and E. 1094
I loved you, and my love had no r, " 1276
Return (verb) I may r with others there Palace of Art 295
some one said, 'We will r no more;' Lotos-Eaters 43
'I go, but I r: I would I were The pilot Audley Court 71
The fountain to his place r's Day-Dm., Sleep. P. 11
to r When others had been tested) Aylmer's Field 218
and r In such a sunlight of prosperity " 420
Returning, as the bird r's, at night, Sea Dreams 43
heard his foot R from pacings in the field, Lucretius 6
back r To where the body sits, In Mem. xii 18
How often she herself r, " xl 24
But Death r's an answer sweet: " lxxxi 9
Return (verb) (continued) r's the dark With no more hope of light. Maud I ix 15
humour of the kings of old R upon me! Gareth and L. 378
R, and meet, and hold him from our eyes, " 429
take his horse And arms, and so r him to the King. " 956
Myself, when I r, will plead for thee. (repeat) " 987, 1052
r, and fetch Fresh victual for these mowers Geraint and E. 224
and r With victual for these men, " 239
For the man's love once gone never r's. " 333
'Fly, they will r And slay you; " 748
And as the cageling newly flown r's, Merlin and V. 901
They prove to him his work: win and r.' Lancelot and E. 158
Rise and take This diamond, and deliver it, and r, " 546
And she r's his love in open shame; " 1083
Many of you, yea most, R no more: Holy Grail 321
He will r no more.' Pelleas and E. 259
Kick'd, he r's: do ye not hate him, ye? " 264
the warm hour r's With veer of wind, Last Tournament 230
weep not thou, lest, if thy mate r, " 499
And so r's belike within an hour. " 531
She is his no more—The dead r's to me, Lover's Tale iv 49
And you shall give me back when he r's.' " 112
When he r's, and then will I r, " 117
If we should never more r, The Flight 99
Australian dying hopes he shall r, Locksley H., Sixty 70
Return'd prest thy hand, and knew the press r, The Bridesmaid 12
One went, who never hath r. To J. S. 20
And so r unfarrow'd to her sty. Walk. to the Mail 100
Could hope itself r; Talking Oak 12
'Pardy,' r the King, 'but still My joints Day-Dm., Revival 25
In courteous words r reply: " 30
when the beauteous hateful isle R upon him, Enoch Arden 618
round again to meet the day When Enoch had r, " 823
r Leolin's rejected rivals from their suit Aylmer's Field 492
by a keeper shot at, slightly hurt, Raging r: " 549
To whom none spake, half-sick at heart, r. Princess iv 223
The King r from out the wild, The Victim 41
And home to Mary's house r, In Mem. xxxi 2
divine amends For a courtesy not r. Maud I vi 14
pathways for the hunter and the knight And so r. Com. of Arthur 62
r Among the flowers, in May, with Guinevere. " 451
she r Indignant to the Queen; (repeat) Marr. of Geraint 201, 413
the boy r And told them of a chamber, Geraint and E. 260
till she woke the sleepers, and r: " 404
r The huge Earl Doorm with plunder to the hall. " 591
In converse for a little, and r, " 882
spirit of his youth r On Arthur's heart; Balin and Balan 21
And lightly so r, and no man knew. " 42
till their embassage r. " 93
Full courtly, yet not falsely, thus r: Lancelot and E. 236
after two days' tarriance there, r. " 569
r To whence I came, the gate of Arthur's wars.' Holy Grail 538
talk And scandal of our table, had r; " 650
reach'd The city, found ye all your knights r, " 708
scarce r a tithe— " 894
these r, But still he kept his watch Pelleas and E. 222
Then turn'd, and so r, and groaning " 451
she gazed on Lancelot So soon r, " 590
Tristram—late From overseas in Brittany r, Last Tournament 175
one that in them sees himself, r; " 370
But left her all as easily, and r. " 403
and that low lodge r, Mid-forest, " 488
Had been, their wont, a-maying and r, Guinevere 23
'Perchance,' she said, 'r.' Lover's Tale i 581
Then, when her own true spirit had r, " iv 108
Then I r to the ward; In the Child. Hosp. 44
wept with me when I r in chains, Columbus 231
She in wrath R it on her birthday, The Ring 212
We r to his cave—the link was broken— Bandit's Death 29
Returning from the secret shrine R with hot cheek Alexander 14
human things r on themselves Move onward, Golden Year 25
And thee r on thy silver wheels. Tithonus 76
R like the pewit, Will Water. 230
As oft as needed—last, r rich, Enoch Arden 143
His fancy fled before the lazy wind R, " 658
Seem'd hope's r rose: Aylmer's Field 559

Returning (*continued*) That mock'd him with *r* calm, *Lucretius* 25
still to that *R*, as the bird returns, *Sea Dreams* 43
that great wave *R*, while none mark'd it, „ 234
And last, *r* from afar, *In Mem. lxxxix* 46
and on *r* found Not two but three? *Merlin and V.* 708
R brought the yet-unblazon'd shield, *Lancelot and E.* 379
To Astolat *r* rode the three. „ 905
Your limit, oft *r* with the tide. „ 1041
R o'er the plain that then began To darken *Holy Grail* 217
Around a king *r* from his wars. *Pass. of Arthur* 461
Reveal gorges, opening wide apart, *r* Troas *Œnone* 12
For all the past of Time *r's* *Love thou thy land* 50
Nor to *r* it, till you see me dead.' *Enoch Arden* 839
words, like Nature, half *r* And half conceal *In Mem. v* 3
A late-lost form that sleep *r's*, „ *xiii* 2
If any vision should *r* Thy likeness, „ *xcii* 1
Who shall now *r* it? *Forlorn* 8
Reveal'd first *r* themselves to English air, *Eleänore* 2
part by part to men *r* The fullness of her face— *Of old sat Freedom* 11
R their shining windows: *Gardener's D.* 220
A whisper half *r* her to herself. *Aylmer's Field* 144
Of comfort clasp'd in truth *r*; *In Mem. xxxvii* 22
A lifelong tract of time *r*; „ *xlvi* 9
doubtful dusk *r* The knolls once more where, „ *xcv* 49
where the works of the Lord are *r* *In the Child. Hosp.* 35
Revealing *R's* deep and clear are thine *Madeline* 10
Reveillée blew *R* to the breaking morn. *In Mem. lxviii* 8
Revel given to starts and bursts Of *r*; *Princess i* 55
At civic *r* and pomp and game, (repeat) *Ode on Well.* 147, 227
night goes In babble and *r* and wine. *Maud I xxii* 28
with dance And *r* and song, made merry over Death, *Gareth and L.* 1423
Red after *r*, droned her lurdane knights Slumbering, *Pelleas and E.* 430
kingcup, poppy, glanced About the *r's*, *Last Tournament* 235
To come and *r* for one hour with him *Lover's Tale iv* 182
wallow in fiery riot and *r* On Kilauēā, *Kapiolani* 8
Revelling bagpipes, *r*, devil's-dances, *Sir J. Oldcastle* 149
Revenge Therefore *r* became me well. *The Sisters* 5
Womanlike, taking *r* too deep for a transient wrong *Maud I iii* 5
whether the mind, With some *r*— *Lover's Tale ii* 127
Revenge (ship) so The little *R* ran on sheer *The Revenge* 33
R ran on thro' the long sea-lane between. „ 36
mann'd the *R* with a swarthier alien crew, „ 110
R herself went down by the island crags „ 118
Revenge (verb) He hiss'd, 'Let us *r* ourselves, *Happy* 63
Revenue overflowing *r* Wherewith to embellish *Œnone* 112
I reap No *r* from the field of unbelief. *Akbar's Dream* 67
Revere Whom we see not we *r*; We *r*, *Ode on Well.* 245
We *r*, and while we hear The tides of Music's „ 251
Revered R, *beloved,—O you that hold* *To the Queen* 1
R Isabel, the crown and head, *Isabel* 10
flattering the poor roofs *R* as theirs, *Aylmer's Field* 176
Reverence (s) (*See also* **Self-reverence**) *A thousand claims to* r *closed* *To the Queen* 27
with one mind the Gods Rise up for *r*. *Œnone* 110
But let her herald, *R*, fly Before her *Love thou thy land* 18
To all the people, winning *r*. *M. d'Arthur* 108
Meet for the *r* of the hearth, *Aylmer's Field* 333
Have not our love and *r* left them bare? „ 785
With some cold *r* worse than were she dead. *Princess v* 92
That mask'd thee from men's *r* up, „ *vii* 343
Some *r* for the laws ourselves have made, „ *Con.* 55
to pay the debt Of boundless love and *r* *Ode on Well.* 157
But more of *r* in us dwell; *In Mem., Pro.* 26
I had such *r* for his blame, „ *li* 6
To *r* and the silver hair; „ *lxxxiv* 32
In *r* and in charity. „ *cxiv* 28
As if in deepest *r* and in love. *Merlin and V.* 220
With no more sign of *r* than a beard. „ 279
Abash'd Lavaine, whose instant *r*, *Lancelot and E.* 418
A manner somewhat fall'n from *r*— *Last Tournament* 119
To all the people, winning *r*. *Pass. of Arthur* 276
Down with Reticence, down with *R*— *Locksley H., Sixty* 142
But every man was mute for *r*. *Death of Œnone* 96
Reverence (verb) swear To *r* the King, as if he were Their conscience, *Guinevere* 468
Reverenced he, he *r* his liege-lady there; *Princess i* 188
'Who *r* his conscience as his king; *Ded. of Idylls* 8
first they mock'd, but, after, *r* him. *Gareth and L.* 507
Then tho' he loved and *r* her too much *Marr. of Geraint* 119
He *r* his dear lady even in death; *Lover's Tale iv* 74
Reverencing The dark retinue *r* death *Aylmer's Field* 842
Self-reverent each and *r* each, *Princess vii* 290
And *r* the custom of the house Geraint, *Marr. of Geraint* 380
He, *r* king's blood in a bad man, *Guinevere* 37
Reverend Than hammer at this *r* gentlewoman. *Princess iii* 129
when she saw The haggard father's face and *r* beard „ *vi* 103
I past beside the *r* walls In which of old *In Mem. lxxxvii* 1
Reverent (*See also* **Self-reverent**) mighty *r* at our grace was he: *Holy Grail* 702
With *r* eyes mock-loyal, shaken voice, *Merlin and V.* 157
So princely, tender, truthful, *r*, pure— *D. of the Duke of C.* 4
a *r* people behold The towering car, *Ode on Well.* 54
Reverie rapt in nameless *r*, *Princess, Con.* 108
Reverse To pine in that *r* of doom, *In Mem. lxxii* 6
Reversed I sit, my empty glass *r*, *Will Water.* 159
And now, the bloodless point *r*, *The Voyage* 71
Reversion *R* ever dragging Evolution in the mud. *Locksley H., Sixty* 200
Revert Perforce will still *r* to you; *Day-Dm., L'Envoi* 36
Reverting 'Change, *r* to the years, *Vision of Sin* 159
Reviewer O YOU chorus of indolent *r's*, Irresponsible, indolent *r's*, *Hendecasyllabics* 1
Waking laughter in indolent *r's*. „ 8
All that chorus of indolent *r's*. „ 12
Too presumptuous, indolent *r's*. „ 16
Revile hear thee so missay me and *r*. *Gareth and L.* 945
Reviled Rode on the two, reviler and *r*; „ 794
Shamed am I that I so rebuked, *r*, Missaid thee; „ 1164
And when *r*, hast answer'd graciously, „ 1269
tongue that all thro' yesterday *R* thee, „ 1323
Reviler Rode on the two, *r* and reviled; „ 794
Reviling 'He heeded not *r* tones, *Two Voices* 220
Revisit from a land He never would *r*, *Lover's Tale iv* 210
Revolt arose The women up in wild *r*, *Princess vii* 123
R's, republics, revolutions, „ *Con.* 65
And many more when Modred raised *r*, *Guinevere* 441
Revolution Revolts, republics, *r's*, *Princess, Con.* 65
and all these old *r's* of earth; All new-old *r's* of Empire— *Vastness* 29
R-v has proven but E-volution *Beautiful City* 3
Revolve In the same circle we *r*. *Two Voices* 314
Revolver Keep the *r* in hand! *Def. of Lucknow* 26
if dynamite and *r* leave you courage *Locksley H., Sixty* 107
Revolving stood Sir Bedivere *R* many memories, *M. d'Arthur* 270
to rise again *R* toward fulfilment, *Edwin Morris* 39
(for still My mother went *r* on the word) *Princess iii* 54
common hate with the *r* wheel Should drag you down, „ *vi* 173
And tho' the months, *r* near, *In Mem. xcii* 11
stood Sir Bedivere *R* many memories, *Pass. of Arthur* 438
r in myself The word that is the symbol *Ancient Sage* 230
Rewaken *R* with the dawning soul. *In Mem. xliii* 16
Reward God bless you for it, God *r* you *Enoch Arden* 424
fain would I *r* thee worshipfully. *Gareth and L.* 829
Rex 'Death is king, and Vivat *R*! *Vision of Sin* 179
Rheumatis (rheumatism) I wur down wi' the *r* then— *Church-warden, etc.* 14
Rheumy Glimmer in thy *r* eyes. *Vision of Sin* 154
Rhine You leave us: you will see the *R*, *In Mem. xcviii* 1
Rhodope The *R*, that built the pyramid, *Princess ii* 82
Rhyme (s) *To make demand of modern* r *To the Queen* 11
With weary sameness in the *r's*, *Miller's D.* 70
He utter'd *r* and reason, *The Goose* 6
Who read me *r's* elaborately good, *Edwin Morris* 20
I will work in prose and *r*, *Talking Oak* 289
The *r's* are dazzled from their place *Day-Dm., Pro.* 19
To make me write my random *r's*, *Will Water.* 13
Let raffs be rife in prose and *r*, „ 61
We lack not *r's* and reasons, „ 62
lucky *r's* to him were scrip and share, *The Brook* 4
'O babbling brook, says Edmund in his *r*, „ 21
rolling in his mind Old waifs of *r*, „ 199
and *r's* And dismal lyrics, *Princess i* 141
***R's* and *r's* in the range of the times!** *Spiteful Letter* 9

Rhyme (s) (*continued*) Ah God! the petty fools of *r* *Lit. Squabbles* 1
For it's easy to find a *r*. (repeat) *Window, Ay* 6, 12
What hope is here for modern *r* *In Mem. lxxvii* 1
Ring out, ring out my mournful *r's*, „ *cvi* 19
As half but idle brawling *r's*, „ *Con.* 23
I think ye hardly know the tender *r* *Merlin and V.* 383
Master, do ye love my tender *r*?' „ 399
Vivien, when you sang me that sweet *r*, „ 434
this *r* Is like the fair pearl-necklace of the Queen, „ 450
so is it with this *r*: „ 456
The legend as in guerdon for your *r*? „ 554
This tender *r*, and evermore the doubt, *Pelleas and E.* 410
ran across her memory the strange *r* Of bygone Merlin, *Last Tournament* 131
therewithal came on him the weird *r*, *Pass. of Arthur* 444
The faded *r's* and scraps of ancient crones, *Lover's Tale i* 289
with goodly *r* and reason for it— *Sister's (E. and E.)* 92
who loved so well to mouth my *r's*, *To W. H. Brookfield* 2
You found some merit in my *r's*, *To E. Fitzgerald* 55
With present grief, and made the *r's*, *Tiresias* 196
louder than thy *r* the silent Word *Ancient Sage* 212
the name A golden portal to my *r*: *To Marq. of Dufferin* 16
forgotten mine own *r* By mine old self, *To Mary Boyle* 21
A *r* that flower'd betwixt the whitening sloe „ 25
hail thee monarch in their woodland *r*. *Akbar's D., Hymn* 6
Rhyme (verb) force to make me *r* in youth, *Miller's D.* 193
a happier lot Than ours, who *r* to-day. *Epilogue* 51
Rhymester novelist, realist, *r*, play your part, *Locksley H., Sixty* 139
Rhyming *R* forward to his *r*, *Amphion* 30
leave to head These *r's* with your name, *Pro. to Gen. Hamley* 20
Rhythm For save when shutting reasons up in *r*, *Lucretius* 223
into *r* have dash'd The passion of the prophetess; *Princess iv* 139
Tho' thine ocean-roll of *r* sound for ever *To Virgil* 31
Rib (s) sawn In twain beneath the *r's*; *St. S. Stylites* 53
Stuff his *r's* with mouldy hay. *Vision of Sin* 66
Rotting on some wild shore with *r's* of wreck, *Princess v* 147
And so belabour'd him on *r* and cheek „ 341
And on thy *r's* the limpet sticks, *Sailor Boy* 11
clangs Its leafless *r's* and iron horns *In Mem. cvii* 12
white breast-bone, and barren *r's* of Death, *Gareth and L.* 1382
Clung but to crate and basket, *r's* and spine. *Merlin and V.* 625
tide Plash'd, sapping its worn *r's*; *Lover's Tale i* 56
sitting on the *r's* of wreck. *Locksley H., Sixty* 14
Rib (verb) *r* and fret The broad-imbased beach, *Supp. Confessions* 127
Ribald Me the sport of *r* Veterans, *Boädicea* 50
Then with a *r* twinkle in his bleak eyes— *The Ring* 199
Riband She takes a *r* or a rose; *In Mem. vi* 32
Ribb'd long dun wolds are *r* with snow, *Oriana* 5
his visage *r* From ear to ear with dogwhip-weals, *Last Tournament* 57
was *r* And barr'd with bloom on bloom. *Lover's Tale i* 415
Ribbed (*See also* **Red-ribb'd**) To purl o'er matted cress and *r* sand, *Ode to Memory* 59
her echo'd song Throb thro' the *r* stone; *Palace of Art* 176
Ribbon Dangled a length of *r* and a ring *Enoch Arden* 750
blots of it about them, *r*, glove Or kerchief; *Aylmer's Field* 620
wasn't sa plaäin i' pink *r's*, *Spinster's S's.* 17
Rib-grated *r-g* dungeon of the holy human ghost, *Happy* 31
Rice many a tract of palm and *r*, *Palace of Art* 114
Rich (*See also* **Influence-rich, Royal-rich, Summer-rich**)
A spring *r* and strange, *Nothing will Die* 22
flower-bells and ambrosial orbs Of *r* fruit-bunches *Isabel* 37
Flush'd all the leaves with *r* gold-green, *Arabian Nights* 82
underpropt a *r* Throne of the massive ore, „ 145
At the moist *r* smell of the rotting leaves, *A spirit haunts* 17
and meadow-ledges midway down Hang *r* in flowers, *Œnone* 7
And three *r* sennights more, my love for her. *Edwin Morris* 30
The slumbrous light is *r* and warm, *Day-Dm., Sleep. B.* 7
This earth is *r* in man and maid; *Will Water.* 65
And many a slope was *r* in bloom *To E. L.* 20
returning *r*, Become the master of a larger craft, *Enoch Arden* 143
Annie—for I am *r* and well-to-do. „ 311
stranding on an isle at morn *R*, „ 553
A dagger, in *r* sheath with jewels on it *Aylmer's Field* 220
Forgetful how my *r* procemion makes *Lucretius* 70
But move as *r* as Emperor-moths, *Princess, Pro.* 144
Rich (*continued*) swell On some dark shore just seen that it was *r*. *Princess i* 249
And we as *r* as moths from dusk cocoons, „ *ii* 19
A classic lecture, *r* in sentiment, „ 374
I stored it full of *r* memorial: „ *v* 391
Immersed in *r* foreshadowings of the world, „ *vii* 312
Disrobed the glimmering statue of Sir Ralph From those *r* silks, „ *Con.* 118
R in saving common-sense, *Ode on Well.* 32
R in model and design; *Ode Inter. Exhib.* 13
r Virgilian rustic measure Of Lari Maxume, *The Daisy* 75
Me the wife of *r* Prasútagus, *Boädicea* 48
Streams o'er a *r* ambrosial ocean isle, *Milton* 14
Roll'd the *r* vapour far into the heaven. *Spec. of Iliad* 8
But he was *r* where I was poor, *In Mem. lxxix* 18
and lead The closing cycle *r* in good. „ *cv* 28
Ring out the feud of *r* and poor, „ *cvi* 11
R in the grace all women desire, *Maud I x* 13
a morning shine So *r* in atonement as this „ *xix* 6
Voice in the *r* dawn of an ampler day— *Ded. of Idylls* 36
r With jewels, elfin Urim, on the hilt, *Com. of Arthur* 298
r in emblem and the work Of ancient kings *Gareth and L.* 304
The shield of Gawain blazon'd *r* and bright, „ 416
All in a full-fair manor and a *r*, „ 846
house Once *r*, now poor, but ever open-door'd.' *Marr. of Geraint* 302
That all the turf was *r* in plots that look'd „ 660
With store of *r* apparel, sumptuous fare, „ 709
R arks with priceless bones of martyrdom, *Balin and Balan* 110
so *r* a fellowship Would make me wholly blest: „ 147
Past up the still *r* city to his kin, *Lancelot and E.* 802
Far up the dim *r* city to her kin; „ 845
across the fields Far into the *r* city, „ 891
and me also like the Queen In all I have of *r*, „ 1120
And all the dim *r* city, roof by roof, *Holy Grail* 228
So strange, and *r*, and dim; „ 342
R galleries, lady-laden, weigh'd the necks „ 346
The knights and ladies wept, and *r* and poor Wept, „ 353
Beyond all sweetness in a life so *r*,— „ 626
sight Of her *r* beauty made him at one glance *Pelleas and E.* 238
but rosier luck will go With these *r* jewels, *Last Tournament* 46
Far on into the *r* heart of the west: *Guinevere* 244
infuse *R* atar in the bosom of the rose, *Lover's Tale i* 270
like a vain *r* man, That, having always prosper'd „ 715
her hair Studded with one *r* Provence rose— „ *iii* 45
while I mused nor yet endured to take So *r* a prize, „ 50
such a feast So *r*, so strange, and stranger ev'n than *r*, But *r* as for the nuptials of a king. „ *iv* 211
He brings and sets before him in *r* guise „ 247
That my *r* gift is wholly mine to give. „ 350
And in the *r* vocabulary of Love *Sisters (E. and E.)* 291
Having lands at home and abroad in a *r* West-Indian isle; *The Wreck* 46
R was the rose of sunset there, „ 136
Strong in will and *r* in wisdom, Edith, *Locksley H., Sixty* 49
The kings and the *r* and the poor; *Dead Prophet* 40
R in symbol, in ornament, *On Jub. Q. Victoria* 47
Their *r* ambrosia tasted aconite. *Demeter and P.* 105
stood between The tower and that *r* phantom of the tower? *The Ring* 253
full thanks to you For your *r* gift, *To Ulysses* 34
Fair garments, plain or *r*, and fitting close *Akbar's Dream* 131
Richard (*See also* **Richard Grenville**) Sir *R* bore in hand all his sick men *The Revenge* 15
Good Sir *R*, tell us now, „ 26
And Sir *R* said again: 'We be all good English men. „ 29
Sir *R* spoke and he laugh'd, „ 32
Sir *R* cried in his English pride, „ 82
old Sir *R* caught at last, „ 98
Richard Grenville (*See also* **Richard**) At Flores in the Azores Sir *R G* lay, *The Revenge* 1
Then spake Sir *R G*: „ 8
With a joyful spirit I Sir *R G* die!' „ 103
Richard (king) That traitor to King *R* and the truth, *Sir J. Oldcastle* 171
Richer Love, then, had hope of *r* store: *In Mem. lxxxi* 5
And many of these in *r* arms than he, *Com. of Arthur* 52

Richer (*continued*) as a faith once fair Was *r* than these diamonds— *Lancelot and E.* 1229
she set A banquet *r* than the day before By me; *Holy Grail* 589
r in His eyes Who ransom'd us, *Guinevere* 684
Richest and a sweep Of *r* pauses, *Eleänore* 66
fetch'd His *r* beeswing from a binn reserved *Aylmer's Field* 405
call'd mine host To council, plied him with his *r* wines, *Princess i* 174
And those five years its *r* field. *In Mem. xlvi* 12
that shrine which then in all the realm Was *r*, *Lancelot and E.* 1331
Richest-toned voice the *r-t* that sings, *In Mem. lxxv* 7
Richness deck it like the Queen's For *r*, *Lancelot and E.* 1119
Rick A jackass heehaws from the *r*, *Amphion* 71
the *r* Flames, and his anger reddens *Princess iv* 385
The moon like a *r* on fire was rising *Grandmother* 39
and all the land from roof and *r*, *Com. of Arthur* 433
When thirty *r's*, All flaming, *To Mary Boyle* 36
Rick-fire years ago, In *r-f* days, „ 28
Rid If both be slain, I am *r* of thee; *Gareth and L.* 790
Ridden (*See also* **Hard-ridden**) How long, O God, shall men be *r* down, *Poland* 1
found that you had gone, *R* to the hills, *Princess iv* 343
Half *r* off with by the thing he rode, *Geraint and E.* 460
we have *r* before among the flowers In those fair days— *Balin and Balan* 272
added wound to wound, And *r* away to die?' *Lancelot and E.* 568
had *r* a random round To seek him, „ 630
'Then Sir Bors had *r* on Softly, *Holy Grail* 647
Riddle Dissolved the *r* of the earth. *Two Voices* 170
in seeking to undo One *r*, and to find the true, „ 233
oft the *r* of the painful earth Flash'd *Palace of Art* 213
'Your *r* is hard to read.' *Lady Clare* 76
Charades and *r's* as at Christmas here, *Princess, Pro.* 189
God unknits the *r* of the one, *Lover's Tale i* 181
Riddling So Merlin *r* anger'd me; *Com. of Arthur* 412
'Know ye not then the *R* of the Bards? *Gareth and L.* 286
Ride (s) while she made her ready for her *r*, *Lancelot and E.* 779
'Alas,' he said, 'your *r* hath wearied you. „ 831
Ride (verb) His son and heir doth *r* post-haste, *D. of the O. Year* 31
'*R* you naked thro' the town, *Godiva* 29
Then by some secret shrine I *r*; *Sir Galahad* 29
R on! the prize is near.' „ 80
All-arm'd I *r*, whate'er betide, „ 83
They love us for it, and we *r* them down. *Princess v* 157
r with us to our lines, And speak with Arac: „ 225
Down by the hill I saw them *r*, *Maud I ix* 11
Lancelot, to *r* forth And bring the Queen;— *Com. of Arthur* 448
And evermore a knight would *r* away. *Gareth and L.* 438
helm could *r* Therethro' nor graze: „ 673
Than *r* abroad redressing women's wrong, „ 866
beseemeth not a knave To *r* with such a lady.' „ 959
The buoy that *r's* at sea, „ 1146
'I lead no longer; *r* thou at my side; „ 1157
There *r's* no knight, not Lancelot, „ 1182
loving the battle as well As he that *r's* him.' „ 1302
Seeing he never *r's* abroad by day; „ 1334
And *r* with him to battle and stand by, *Marr. of Geraint* 94
'I will *r* forth into the wilderness; „ 127
put on thy worst and meanest dress And *r* with me.' „ 131
tho' I *r* unarm'd, I do not doubt To find, „ 218
knight whom late I saw *R* into that new fortress „ 407
Shalt *r* to Arthur's court, and coming there, „ 582
To *r* with him this morning to the court, „ 606
I can scarcely *r* with you to court, „ 749
That she *r* with me in her faded silk.' „ 762
I charge thee *r* before, *Geraint and E.* 14
when she saw him *r* More near by many a rood „ 441
'Then, Enid, shall you *r* Behind me.' „ 750
Hath learn'd black magic, and to *r* unseen. *Balin and Balan* 305
Up then, *r* with me! Talk not of shame! „ 522
We *r* a-hawking with Sir Lancelot. *Merlin and V.* 95
they *r* away—to hawk For waterfowl. „ 107
r, and dream The mortal dream „ 116
R, *r* and dream until ye wake— „ 118
They r abroad redressing human wrongs! „ 693
he will *r*, Joust for it, and win, *Lancelot and E.* 203

Ride (verb) (*continued*) To *r* to Camelot with this noble knight: *Lancelot and E.* 220
you *r* with Lancelot of the Lake,' „ 417
rise, O Gawain, and *r* forth and find the knight. „ 537
And *r* no more at random, noble Prince! „ 633
r A twelvemonth and a day in quest of it, *Holy Grail* 196
I have been the sluggard, and I *r* apace, „ 644
we are damsels-errant, and we *r*, Arm'd as ye see, *Pelleas and E.* 64
grizzlier than a bear, to *r* And jest with: „ 193
saw the King *R* toward her from the city, *Guinevere* 404
To *r* abroad redressing human wrongs, „ 471
r highly Above the perilous seas of change *Lover's Tale i* 805
war *R's* on those ringing axles! *Tiresias* 93
Rider The horse and *r* reel: *Sir Galahad* 8
But that his heavy *r* kept him down. *Vision of Sin* 4
r's front to front, until they closed *Princess v* 490
there a horse! the *r*? where is he? *Balin and Balan* 467
steed of Pelleas floundering flung His *r*, *Pelleas and E.* 575
Ridest '*R* thou then so hotly on a quest *Holy Grail* 642
That *r* here so blindly and so hard?' *Pelleas and E.* 564
Rideth who always *r* arm'd in black, *Gareth and L.* 636
Ridge (*See also* **Ocean-ridge**) his *r's* are not curls And ripples of an inland mere? *Supp. Confessions* 130
sand-built *r* Of heaped hills that mound the sea, *Ode to Memory* 97
A faint-blue *r* upon the right, *Mariana in the S.* 5
Across the *r*, and paced beside the mere, *M. d'Arthur* 83
And, leaping down the *r's* lightly, „ 134
But the other swiftly strode from *r* to *r*, „ 181
Or slip between the *r's*, *The Brook* 28
a *r* Of breaker issued from the belt, *Sea Dreams* 211
and then the great *r* drew, „ 220
storm Of galloping hoofs bare on the *r* of spears *Princess v* 489
Close to the *r* of a noble down. *To F. D. Maurice* 16
The fortress, and the mountain *r*, *In Mem. lxxi* 14
There lies a *r* of slate across the ford; *Gareth and L.* 1056
Southwesterns, rolling *r* on *r*, „ 1145
And climb'd upon a fair and even *r*, *Marr. of Geraint* 239
my feet recrost the deathful *r* No memory *Holy Grail* 534
heapt in mounds and *r's* all the sea Drove „ 798
Across the *r*, and paced beside the mere, *Pass. of Arthur* 251
And, leaping down the *r's* lightly, „ 302
But the other swiftly strode from *r* to *r*, „ 349
On that sharp *r* of utmost doom ride highly *Lover's Tale i* 805
that brave soldier, down the terrible *r* *Sisters (E. and E.)* 63
r's drew the cloud and brake the storm *Montenegro* 13
lie Subjected to the Heliconian *r* *Tiresias* 26
Watch'd again the hollow *r's* *Locksley H., Sixty* 2
we saw your soldiers crossing the *r*, *Bandit's Death* 21
Ridged (adj.) Leaning upon the *r* sea, *The Winds, etc.* 2
bleat Of the thick-fleeced sheep from wattled folds, Upon the *r* wolds, *Ode to Memory* 67
sharp clear twang of the golden chords Runs up the *r* sea. *Sea-Fairies* 39
Ridged (verb) *R* the smooth level, *Arabian Nights* 35
Ridging (*See also* **Slowly-ridging**) The Biscay, roughly *r* eastward, *Enoch Arden* 529
Ridin-erse (riding-horse) ivry darter o' Squire's hed her awn *r-e* *Village Wife* 35
Riding Stopt, and then with a *r* whip *Maud I xiii* 18
The knights come *r* two and two: *L. of Shalott ii* 25
A youth came *r* toward a palace-gate. *Vision of Sin* 2
He found the bailiff *r* by the farm, *The Brook* 153
r in, we call'd; A plump-arm'd Ostleress *Princess i* 225
r at set of day Over the dark moor land, Rapidly *r* far away, She waved to me *Maud I ix* 5
And down the long street *r* wearily, *Marr. of Geraint* 254
Then *r* close behind an ancient churl, „ 261
Then *r* further past an armourer's, „ 266
but *r* first, I hear the violent threats *Geraint and E.* 419
Came *r* with a hundred lances up; „ 539
R at noon, a day or twain before, *Pelleas and E.* 20
from the city gates Issued Sir Lancelot *r* airily, „ 557
For Arthur and Sir Lancelot *r* once *Last Tournament* 10
Scarlett and Scarlett's three hundred were *r* by *Heavy Brigade* 4
Riding-horse *See* **Ridin-erse**

Rife With dinning sound my ears are *r*, *Eleänore* 135
Let raffs be *r* in prose and rhyme, *Will Water.* 61
language *r* With rugged maxims hewn from life; *Ode on Well.* 183
Rifle-bullet Death from their *r-b's*, *Def. of Lucknow* 14
Rifleman *R*, true is your heart, „ 56
R, high on the roof, hidden there „ 63
Storm, Storm, *Riflemen* form! (repeat) *Riflemen form!* 5, 19
Riflemen, Riflemen, Riflemen form! (repeat) „ 7, 14, 21, 28
Form, Form, *Riflemen* Form! (repeat) „ 12, 26
Rift (s) 'It is the little *r* within the lute, *Merlin and V.* 390
'The little *r* within the lover's lute „ 393
gray heads beneath a gleaming *r*. *Demeter and P.* 83
Flattery gilding the *r* in a throne; *Vastness* 20
Rift (verb) *R* the hills, and roll the waters, *Locksley Hall* 186
Rifted (*See also* **Sallow-rifted**) methought The cloud was *r* by a purer gleam *Akbar's Dream* 78
Rigging masts and the *r* were lying over the side; *The Revenge* 81
storm grew with a howl and a hoot of the blast In the *r*, *The Wreck* 92
Right (adj. and adv.) (*See also* **Half-right**) whose strong *r* arm debased The throne of Persia, *Alexander* 1
The *r* ear, that is fill'd with dust, *Two Voices* 116
And I should know if it beat *r*, *Miller's D.* 179
Time will set me *r*.' *Edwin Morris* 88
My *r* leg chain'd into the crag, *St. S. Stylites* 73
For, am I *r*, or am I wrong, (repeat) *Day-Dm., L'Envoi* 29, 33
And on the *r* hand of the hearth he saw Philip, *Enoch Arden* 744
But Lady Psyche was the *r* hand now, *Princess iii* 37
is not Ida *r*? They worth it? „ 188
And so I often told her, *r* or wrong, „ 288
And, *r* or wrong, I care not: „ 290
she may sit Upon a king's *r* hand in thunderstorms, „ 439
he That loved me closer than his own *r* eye, „ 531
And *r* ascension, Heaven knows what; „ *vi* 257
she turns Once more to set a ringlet *r*; *In Mem. vi* 36
I cannot see the features *r*, „ *lxx* 1
And this wise world of ours is mainly *r*. *Geraint and E.* 901
'*R* was the King! our Lancelot! that true man!'
'And *r* was I,' *Lancelot and E.* 665
In her *r* hand the lily, in her left The letter— „ 1155
Power from whose *r* hand the light Of Life issueth, *Lover's Tale i* 497
'you are sure it 'll all come *r*,' *First Quarrel* 1
'Wait a little, my lass, I am sure it 'll all come *r*.' (repeat) „ 74, 91
Steevie be *r* good manners bang thruf *Spinster's S's.* 66
It still were *r* to crown with song *Epilogue* 36
Death for the *r* cause, death for the wrong cause, *Vastness* 8
I worship that *r* hand Which fell'd the foes *Happy* 41
Right (s) who stand now, when we should aid the *r*— *Poland* 13
because *r* is *r*, to follow *r* Were wisdom *Œnone* 149
hers by *r* of full-accomplish'd Fate; *Palace of Art* 207
Who wrench'd their *r's* from thee! *England and Amer.* 5
since I knew the *r* And did it; *Love and Duty* 29
we, that prate Of *r's* and wrongs, *Godiva* 8
And in the *r's* that name may give, *Day-Dm., L'Envoi* 54
'The man will cleave unto his *r*.' *Lady Clare* 46
reigning in his place, Lord of his *r's* *Enoch Arden* 764
A talk of college and of ladies' *r's*, *Princess, Pro.* 233
be swerved from *r* to save A prince, „ *ii* 290
Toward that great year of equal mights and *r's*, „ *iv* 74
To unfurl the maiden banner of our *r's*, „ 503
What have you done but *r*? „ *v* 65
As truthful, much that Ida claims as *r* „ 202
throat's would bawl for civil *r's*, No woman named: „ 387
With claim on claim from *r* to *r*, „ 417
r's or wrongs like potherbs in the street. „ 459
We will be liberal, since our *r's* are won. „ *vi* 68
wholly scorn'd to help their equal *r's* „ *vii* 233
All great self-seekers trampling on the *r*: *Ode on Well.* 187
only thirsting For the *r*, „ 204
Maakin' 'em goä togither as they've good *r* to do. *N. Farmer, N. S.* 34
At you, so careful of the *r*, *To F. D. Maurice* 10
Ring in the love of truth and *r*, *In Mem. cvi* 23
mine by a *r*, from birth till death. *Maud I xix* 42
a war would arise in defence of the *r*, „ *III vi* 19
in the space to left of her, and *r*, *Gareth and L.* 224
Right (s) (*continued*) mocker ending here Turn'd to the *r*, *Gareth and L.* 295
Would shape himself a *r*!' „ 348
bring him here, that I may judge the *r*, „ 380
mark'd not on his *r* a cavern-chasm *Balin and Balan* 312
on his *r* Stood, all of massiest bronze: „ 363
Made with her *r* a comb of pearl to part The lists *Merlin and V.* 244
lightnings here and there to left and *r* Struck, *Holy Grail* 494
To *r*? to left? straight forward? *Pelleas and E.* 67
as one That doest *r* by gentle and by churl, *Last Tournament* 74
King by courtesy, Or King by *r*— „ 342
What *r's* are his that dare not strike „ 527
Had Arthur *r* to bind them to himself? „ 684
For half of their feet to the *r*. *The Revenge* 35
but sane, if she were in the *r*. *The Flight* 58
Follow Light, and do the *R*— *Locksley H., Sixty* 277
The ring by *r*, she said, was hers again. *The Ring* 394
for the *r's* of an equal humanity, *Beautiful City* 2
I still would do the *r* Thro' all the vast dominion *Akbar's Dream* 13
Right (verb) When the wild peasant *r's* himself, *Princess iv* 385
to fight, to struggle, to *r* the wrong— *Wages* 3
'Bound am I to *r* the wrong'd, *Gareth and L.* 804
strength and will to *r* the wrong'd, *Holy Grail* 309
And leaving human wrongs to *r* themselves, „ 898
Righteous Not void of *r* self-applause, *Two Voices* 146
That even our prudent king, our *r* queen— *Columbus* 122
Righteousness yonder shines The Sun of *R*, *Enoch Arden* 504
proclaimed His Master as 'the Sun of *R*,' *Akbar's Dream* 83
Rightful help my prince to gain His *r* bride, *Princess iii* 161
Right-honest 'All of one mind and all *r-h* friends! *Geraint and E.* 484
Righting So I set to *r* the house, *First Quarrel* 47
Rigid a rough piece Of early *r* colour, *Aylmer's Field* 281
Rigtree (beam) when the *r* was tummlin' in— *Owd Roä* 115
Riled Eh but the moor she *r* me, *North. Cobbler* 30
Fur if iver thy feyther 'ed *r* me *Church-warden, etc.* 41
Rill Like sunshine on a dancing *r*, *Rosalind* 29
From old well-heads of haunted *r's*, *Eleänore* 16
Not any song of bird or sound of *r*; *D. of F. Women* 66
'Go down beside thy native *r*, *In Mem. xxxvii* 5
From hidden summits fed with *r's* „ *ciii* 7
The white-faced halls, the glancing *r's*, „ *Con.* 113
round with ragged *r's* and burning folds,— *Lover's Tale ii* 63
Rillet fall Of diamond *r's* musical, *Arabian Nights* 48
Rim ragged *r's* of thunder brooding low, *Palace of Art* 75
Beyond their utmost purple *r*, (repeat) *Day-Dm., Depart.* 6, 30
the *r* Changed every moment as we flew. *The Voyage* 27
ran By sallowy *r's*, arose the labourers' homes, *Aylmer's Field* 147
Now pacing mute by ocean's *r*; *The Daisy* 21
Roll'd into light, and turning on its *r's* *Lancelot and E.* 51
Rime Make thy grass hoar with early *r*. *Two Voices* 66
brows in silent hours become Unnaturally hoar with *r*, *St. S. Stylites* 166
the lawn as yet Is hoar with *r*, *To F. D. Maurice* 42
the hills are white with *r*. *The Flight* 4
Rimm'd length of bright horizon *r* the dark. *Gardener's D.* 181
Rind gleaming *r* ingrav'n 'For the most fair,' *Œnone* 72
Hard wood I am, and wrinkled *r*, *Talking Oak* 171
Is jutting thro' the *r*; *Ancient Sage* 122
Rinded *See* **Golden-rinded**
Ring (encompass) my followers *r* him round: *Geraint and E.* 336
Ring (s) (*See also* **Marriage-ring**) locks a-drooping twined Round thy neck in subtle *r* *Adeline* 58
his stedfast shade Sleeps on his luminous *r*.' *Palace of Art* 16
they drew into two burning *r's* All beams of Love, *D. of F. Women* 174
Five hundred *r's* of years— *Talking Oak* 84
'And even into my inmost *r* A pleasure I discern'd, „ 173
The dim curls kindle into sunny *r's*; *Tithonus* 54
Grave faces gather'd in a *r*. *Day-Dm., Sleep. P.* 38
Closed in a golden *r*. *Sir L. and Q. G.* 27
And gave the trinkets and the *r's*, *The Letters* 21
Enoch's golden *r* had girt Her finger, *Enoch Arden* 157
Dangled a length of ribbon and a *r* „ 750
fragile bindweed-bells and briony *r's*; *The Brook* 203
Lay deeper than to wear it as his *r*— *Aylmer's Field* 122
nor by plight or broken *r* Bound, „ 135
I'll stake my ruby *r* upon it you did.' *Princess, Pro.* 170
a thousand *r's* of Spring In every bole, „ *v* 237

Ring (s) *(continued)* And one would pierce an outer *r*, *In Mem. lxxxvii* 27
The *r* is on, The 'wilt thou' answer'd, „ *Con.* 53
sapphire-spangled marriage *r* of the land? *Maud I iv* 6
I noticed one of his many *r's* „ *II ii* 68
Now over, now beneath her marriage *r*, *Geraint and E.* 259
Spanish fleet with broken sides lay round us all in a *r*; *The Revenge* 71
placed My *r* upon the finger of my bride. *Sisters (E. and E.)* 214
he learnt that I hated the *r* I wore, *The Wreck* 57
diamond necklace dearer than the golden *r*, *Locksley H., Sixty* 21
Prince has found you, take this *r*. *The Ring* 69
This *r* bequeath'd you by your mother, „ 75
The *r* is doubly yours. „ 79
A *r* too which you kiss'd, „ 114
Like a seal'd book, all mention of the *r*, „ 123
while I stoopt To take and kiss the *r*. „ 132
This very *r* Io t'amo? „ 133
sold This *r* to me, then laugh'd 'the *r* is weird.' „ 195
souls Of two repentant Lovers guard the *r*;' „ 198
'And if you give the *r* to any maid, „ 200
And bind the maid to love you by the *r*; And if the *r* were stolen from the maid, „ 202
sent This *r* 'Io t'amo' to his best beloved, „ 210
half-frenzied by the *r*, He wildly fought „ 213
drew the *r* From his dead finger, „ 217
as the bygone lover thro' this *r* Had sent his cry „ 232
bad the man engrave 'From Walter' on the *r*, „ 236
Some younger hand must have engraven the *r*— „ 238
took the *r*, and flaunted it Before that other „ 243
But coming nearer—Muriel had the *r*—'O Miriam! have you given your *r* to her? „ 259
'O Miriam, if you love me take the *r*!' „ 263
Unclosed the hand, and from it drew the *r*, „ 269
Miriam loved me from the first, Not thro' the *r*; but on her marriage-morn, This birthday, death-day, and betrothal *r*, „ 275
My *r* too when she comes of age, „ 289
Miriam not Muriel—she shall have the *r*.' „ 294
But kept their watch upon the *r* and you. „ 300
'Ever since You sent the fatal *r*'— „ 362
Nor ever ceased to clamour for the *r*; Why had I sent the *r* at first to her? Why had I made her love me thro' the *r*, „ 389
The *r* by right, she said, was hers again. „ 394
But still she made her outcry for the *r*; „ 403
when the bridegroom murmur'd, 'With this *r*,' „ 439
The guardian of her relics, of *her r*, „ 441
The fatal *r* lay near her; „ 450
had stolen, worn the *r*—Then torn it from her finger, „ 455
from her own hand she had torn the *r* In fright, „ 470
You have the *r* she guarded; „ 475
saw The *r* of faces redden'd by the flames *Death of Œnone* 92
and never a *r* for the bride. *Charity* 6

Ring (to resound, etc.) How the merry bluebell *r's* *Adeline* 34
R sudden scritches of the jay, *My life is full* 20
a sound *R's* ever in her ears of armed men. *Œnone* 265
church-bells *r* in the Christmas-morn. *M. d'Arthur, Ep.* 31
R's in mine ears. The steer forgot to graze, *Gardener's D.* 85
did we hear the copses *r*, *Locksley Hall* 35
The shrill bell *r's*, the censer swings, *Sir Galahad* 35
When all the glimmering moorland *r's* *Sir L. and Q. G.* 35
world should *r* of him To shame these mouldy Aylmers *Aylmer's Field* 395
R's to the roar of an angel onset— *Milton* 8
'lights and *r's* the gateway bell, *In Mem. viii* 3
Shall *r* with music all the same; „ *lxxvii* 14
R out, wild bells, to the wild sky, „ *cvi* 1
R out, wild bells, and let him die. „ 4
R out the old, *r* in the new, *R*, happy bells, across the snow: „ 5
R out the false, *r* in the true. „ 8
R out the grief that saps the mind, „ 9
R out the feud of rich and poor, *R* in redress to all mankind. „ 11
R out a slowly dying cause, „ 13
R in the nobler modes of life, „ 15

Ring (to resound, etc.) *(continued)* *R* out the want, the care, the sin, *In Mem. cvi* 17
R out, *r* out my mournful rhymes, „ 19
But *r* the fuller minstrel in. „ 20
R out false pride in place and blood, „ 21
R in the love of truth and right, *R* in the common love of good. „ 23
R out old shapes of foul disease; *R* out the narrowing lust of gold; *R* out the thousand wars of old, *R* in the thousand years of peace. „ 25
R in the valiant man and free, „ 29
R out the darkness of the land, *R* in the Christ that is to be. „ 31
Now *r's* the woodland loud and long, „ *cxv* 5
r's to the yell of the trampled wife, *Maud I i* 38
r's Even in dreams to the chink of his pence, „ *x* 42
It will *r* in my heart and my ears, „ *II i* 35
And the woodland echo *r's*; „ *iv* 38
But there *r's* on a sudden a passionate cry, „ 47
And heard it *r* as true as tested gold.' *Last Tournament* 284
Four bells instead of one began to *r*, *Lover's Tale iii* 20
in this pavement but shall *r* thy name *Tiresias* 137
R little bells of change From word to word. *Early Spring* 41
if it be a Christian Church, people *r* the bell from love to Thee, *Akbar's D., Inscrip.* 4

Ringdove In which the swarthy *r* sat, *Talking Oak* 293

Ring'd white hand whose *r* caress Had wander'd *Balin and Balan* 512

Ringed *R* with the azure world, he stands. *The Eagle* 3

Ringer the *r's* rang with a will, and he gave the *r's* a crown. *Grandmother* 58

Ringing (*See also* **A-ringing, Hollow-ringing**) When midnight bells cease *r* suddenly, *D. of F. Women* 247
when the bells were *r*, Allan call'd *Dora* 41
in the *r* of thine ears; *Locksley Hall* 84
Let the great world spin for ever down the *r* grooves of change. „ 182
And, *r*, springs from brand and mail; *Sir Galahad* 54
With blissful treble *r* clear. *Sir L. and Q. G.* 22
Once likewise, in the *r* of his ears, *Enoch Arden* 613
R like proven golden coinage true, *Aylmer's Field* 182
but he must—the land was *r* of it— „ 262
with His message *r* in thine ears, „ 666
—Saäint's-daäy—they was *r* the bells. *N. Farmer, N. S.* 13
Maud the delight of the village, the *r* joy of the Hall, *Maud I i* 70
R thro' the valleys, „ *xii* 10
Clamour and rumble, and *r* and clatter, „ *II v* 13
Ranging and *r* thro' the minds of men, *Com. of Arthur* 416
r with their serpent hands, *Merlin and V.* 578
R within the fancy had updrawn A fashion *Lover's Tale i* 645
Surely the pibroch of Europe is *r* *Def. of Lucknow* 97
Far on the *r* plains of windy Troy. *Ulysses* 17
He rode the mellay, lord of the *r* lists, *Princess v* 502
those six maids With shrieks and *r* laughter on the sand Threw down the bier; *Lover's Tale iii* 32
what a weight of war Rides on those *r* axles! *Tiresias* 93

Ringlet comb my hair till my *r's* would fall *The Mermaid* 14
Tie up the *r's* on your cheek: *Margaret* 57
For hid in *r's* day and night, *Miller's D.* 173
'Thrice-happy he that may caress The *r's* waving balm— *Talking Oak* 178
shower'd the rippled *r's* to her knee; *Godiva* 47
Her full black *r's* downward roll'd, *Day-Dm., Sleep. B.* 12
Blowing the *r* from the braid: *Sir L. and Q. G.* 39
With lengths of yellow *r*, like a girl, *Princess i* 3
turns Once more to set a *r* right; *In Mem. vi* 36
Ere childhood's flaxen *r* turn'd „ *lxxix* 15
flaxen *r's* of our infancies Wander'd, *Lover's Tale i* 234
Fell on my face, and her long *r's* moved, „ 699
The raven *r* or the gold; *The Ring* 166

Ringleted *See* **Yellow-ringleted**

Ringlet-snake And numbs the Fury's *r-s*, *Lucretius* 262

Riot in many a wild festoon Ran *r*, *Œnone* 101
a noiseless *r* underneath Strikes through the wood, *Lucretius* 185
whereout was roll'd A roar of *r*, *Last Tournament* 426
wallow in fiery *r* and revel On Kilaueä, *Kapiolani* 8

Rioted *r* his life out, and made an end. *Aylmer's Field* 391

Rioted (*continued*) *r* in the city if Cúnobeline! — *Boädicea* 60
There they dwelt and there they *r*; — „ 63
and *r* over the land, — *V. of Maeldune* 58
Rioting over all the great wood *r* And climbing, — *Lover's Tale i* 403
Riotous show'd A *r* confluence of watercourses — *Lucretius* 30
She braved a *r* heart in asking for it. — *Lancelot and E.* 359
fling Thy royalty back into the *r* fits — *Sir J. Oldcastle* 100
Rip *R* your brothers' vices open, — *Locksley H., Sixty* 141
Ripe Your *r* lips moved not, but your cheek Flush'd — *Miller's D.* 131
when time was *r*, The still affection — „ 224
I was *r* for death. — *D. of F. Women* 208
And makes the purple lilac *r*, — *On a Mourner* 7
Made *r* in Sumner-chace: — *Talking Oak* 40
Till all be *r* and rotten. — *Will Water.* 16
Half-mused, or reeling *r*, — „ 74
'Yes, if the nuts' he said 'be *r* again: — *Enoch Arden* 459
Too *r*, too late! they come too late — *Sea Dreams* 67
See thou, that countest reason *r* — *In Mem. xxxiii* 13
Appearing ere the times were *r*, — „ *Con.* 139
you may call it a little too *r*, — *Maud I ii* 9
shaping an infant *r* for his birth, — „ *iv* 34
Ripen flower *r's* in its place, *R's* and fades, — *Lotos-Eaters, C. S.* 36
and *r* toward the grave In silence; *r*, fall, and cease: — „ 51
The unnetted black-hearts *r* dark, — *The Blackbird* 7
watch her harvest *r*, her herd increase, — *Maud III vi* 25
till their love Shall *r* to a proverb, — *Lover's Tale i* 758
Ripen'd And pluck'd the *r* ears, — *Princess ii* 2
But woman *r* earlier, and her life — „ 154
Ripeness but, when love is grown To *r*, — *To J. S.* 15
And gave all *r* to the grain, — *In Mem. lxxxi* 11
Riper *r* life may magnetise The baby-oak within. — *Talking Oak* 255
Not first, and third, which are a *r* first? — *Sea Dreams* 66
train To *r* growth the mind and will: — *In Mem. xlii* 8
The men of rathe and *r* years: — „ *cx* 2
Ripple (s) his ridges are not curls And *r's* — *Supp. Confessions* 131
watch the crisping *r's* on the beach, — *Lotos-Eaters, C. S.* 61
'I heard the *r* washing in the reeds, — *M. d'Arthur* 70
And the long *r* washing in the reeds.' — „ 117
Stared o'er the *r* feathering from her bows: — *Enoch Arden* 544
The seeming-wanton *r* break, — *In Mem. xlix* 11
shadowing down the horned flood In *r's*, — „ *lxxxvi* 8
'I heard the *r* washing in the reeds, — *Pass. of Arthur* 238
And the long *r* washing in the reeds.' — „ 285
so quiet the *r* would hardly blanch into spray — *The Wreck* 137
Slight *r* on the boundless deep — *Ancient Sage* 189
that one *r* on the boundless deep — „ 191
Ripple (verb) That *r* round the lonely grange; — *In Mem. xci* 12
rivulet at her feet *R's* on in light and shadow — *Maud II iv* 42
Rippled the *r* ringlets to her knee; — *Godiva* 47
which was lined And *r* like an ever-fleeting wave, — *Gareth and L.* 215
Rippling ran over The *r* levels of the lake, — *Lover's Tale iii* 4
Ripply and ran By *r* shallows of the lisping lake, — *Edwin Morris* 98
Rise (s) (*See also* **Moon-rise**) I turning saw, throned on a flowery *r*, — *D. of F. Women* 125
Approvingly, and prophesied his *r*: — *Aylmer's Field* 474
upon the *r* And long roll of the Hexameter— — *Lucretius* 10
Rise (verb) In roaring he shall *r* and on the surface die. — *The Kraken* 15
How could I *r* and come away, — *Oriana* 57
R from the feast of sorrow, lady, — *Margaret* 62
Pain *r's* up, old pleasures pall. — *Two Voices* 164
all day long to fall and *r* Upon her balmy bosom, — *Miller's D.* 182
with one mind the Gods *R* up for reverence. — *Œnone* 110
I will *r* and go Down into Troy, — „ 261
And that sweet incense *r*?' — *Palace of Art* 44
I would see the sun *r* (repeat) — *May Queen, N. Y's. E.* 2, 51
sweeter is the young lamb's voice to me that cannot *r*, — „ *Con.* 6
O look! the sun begins to *r*, — „ 49
threshold of the sun, Never to *r* again. — *D. of F. Women* 64
We saw the large white stars *r* one by one, — „ 223
And if some dreadful need should *r* — *Love thou thy land* 91
let thy voice *R* like a fountain for me — *M. d'Arthur* 249
to *r* again Revolving toward fulfilment, — *Edwin Morris* 38
and the shadows *r* and fall. — *Locksley Hall* 80

Rise (verb) (*continued*) And every hundred years to *r* — *Day-Dm., L'Envoi* 7
For blasts would *r* and rave and cease, — *The Voyage* 85
and *r* To glass herself in dewy eyes — *Move eastward* 6
Are but dust that *r's* up, (repeat) — *Vision of Sin* 133, 169
Till thy drooping courage *r*, — „ 152
Let me *r* and fly away. — *Sea Dreams* 304
The Samian Herè *r's* and she speaks — *Princess iii* 115
R in the heart, and gather to the eyes, — „ *iv* 41
R!' and stoop'd to updrag Melissa: — „ 366
they *r* or sink Together, dwarf'd or godlike, — „ *vii* 259
A devil *r's* in my heart, — *Sailor Boy* 23
That men may *r* on stepping-stones — *In Mem. i* 3
And see the sails at distance *r*, — „ *xii* 11
To-night the winds begin to *r* — „ *xv* 1
cloud That *r's* upward always higher, — „ 17
R, happy morn, *r*, holy morn, — „ *xxx* 29
When crown'd with blessing she doth *r* — „ *xl* 5
Did ever *r* from high to higher; — „ *xli* 2
If any vague desire should *r*, — „ *lxxx* 1
An iron welcome when they *r*: — „ *xc* 8
of events As often *r's* ere they *r*. — „ *xcii* 16
But served the seasons that may *r*; — „ *cxiii* 4
R in the spiritual rock, — „ *cxxxi* 3
They *r*, but linger; it is late; — „ *Con.* 91
And *r*, O moon, from yonder down, — „ 109
and thought he would *r* and speak And rave — *Maud I i* 59
And there *r's* ever a passionate cry — „ *II i* 5
Then I *r*, the eavedrops fall, — „ *iv* 62
but at night let go the stone, And *r*, — *Gareth and L.* 826
if he *r* no more, I will not look at wine — *Geraint and E.* 666
R therefore; robe yourself in this: — „ 685
Rose when they saw the dead man *r*, — „ 732
and crying, 'Sirs, *R*, follow! — *Balin and Balan* 48
R, my true knight. — „ 75
This old sun-worship, boy, will *r* again, — „ 457
'*R*, my sweet King, and kiss me on the lips, — „ 516
R!' and the damsel bidden *r* arose — *Merlin and V.* 68
r, O Gawain, and ride forth and find the knight. — *Lancelot and E.* 536
R and take This diamond, and deliver it, — „ 545
To *r* hereafter in a stiller flame — „ 1319
lulling random squabbles when they *r*. — *Holy Grail* 557
'*R*, weakling; I am Lancelot; — *Pelleas and E.* 582
but *r*, And fly to my strong castle overseas: — *Guinevere* 112
yet *r* now, and let us fly, — „ 120
r—I hear the steps of Modred in the west, — *Pass. of Arthur* 58
let thy voice *R* like a fountain for me — „ 417
from the woods That belt it *r* three dark, tall cypresses,— — *Lover's Tale i* 536
and dimly knows His head shall *r* no more: — „ 639
laid it in a sepulchre of rock Never to *r* again. — „ 684
that strove to *r* From my full heart. — „ 711
then I seem'd To *r*, and through the forest-shadow — „ *ii* 72
I could not *r* Albeit I strove to follow. — „ 97
An' the wind began to *r*, — *First Quarrel* 89
My Willy 'ill *r* up whole — *Rizpah* 57
wish yon moaning sea would *r* and burst the shore, — *The Flight* 11
my mother's ghost would *r*— — „ 51
kings and realms that pass to *r* no more; — *To Virgil* 28
heron *r's* from his watch beside the mere, — *Happy* 3
in their turn thy warblers *r* on wing. — *Prog. of Spring* 108
once again we see thee *r*. — *Akbar's D., Hymn* 1
Risen (*See also* **New-risen, Re-risen**) Nilus would have *r* before his time — *D. of F. Women* 143
Dora would have *r* and gone to him, — *Dora* 77
thus early *r* she goes to inform The Princess: — *Princess iii* 62
Has *r* and cleft the soil, — „ *vi* 35
those twin brothers, *r* again and whole; — „ *vii* 89
She might have *r* and floated when I saw her. — *Holy Grail* 100
sun is rising,' tho' the sun had *r*. — „ 408
they have *r* against me in their blood — *Pelleas and E.* 461
Lionel, who fain had *r*, but fell again, — *Lover's Tale iv* 361
nay but thirty-nine have *r* and stand, — *Sir J. Oldcastle* 83
Have we *r* from out the beast, — *Locksley H., Sixty* 148
This later light of Love have *r* in vain, — *To Prin. Beatrice* 16
Henceforth, as having *r* from out the dead, — *Demeter and P.* 144

Risen (*continued*) Not r to, she was bolder. *The Ring* 361
Look, the sun has r To flame along *Romney's R.* 57
vines Which on the touch of heavenly feet had r, *Death of Œnone* 5
Risest R thou thus, dim dawn, again, *In Mem. lxxii* 1
R thou thus, dim dawn, again, „ *xcix* 1
Rising (*See also* **Ever-rising, Later-rising**) r, from her bosom drew Old letters, *Mariana in the S.* 61
angels r and descending met With interchange *Palace of Art* 143
And of the r from the dead, „ 206
lest the soul Of Discord race the r wind; *Love thou thy land* 68
r bore him thro' the place of tombs. *M. d'Arthur* 175
made his forehead like the r sun High „ 217
r thro' the mellow shade, *Locksley Hall* 9
R to no fancy-flies. *Vision of Sin* 102
R, falling, like a wave, „ 125
I saw my father's face Grow long and troubled like a r moon, *Princess i* 59
r up Robed in the long night of her deep hair, „ *iv* 490
Look'd up, and r slowly from me, „ *vi* 151
Last little Lilia, r quietly, „ *Con.* 116
The moon like a rick on fire was r *Grandmother* 39
And r up, he rode to Arthur's court, *Marr. of Geraint* 591
And r on the sudden he said, 'Eat! *Geraint and E.* 614
Azure, an Eagle r or, the Sun In dexter chief; *Merlin and V.* 475
raise the Prince, who r twice or thrice *Guinevere* 46
Will draw me to the r of the sun, *Lover's Tale i* 27
for that day Love, r, shook his wings, „ 317
roll R and falling— *The Wreck* 54
the car Of dark Aïdoneus r rapt thee hence. *Demeter and P.* 39
fiery phœnix r from the smoke, *The Ring* 339
O r worlds by yonder wood. *In Mem. cv* 25
Thou standest in the r sun, „ *cxxx* 3
And on the downs a r fire: „ *Con.* 108
And half to the r day; *Maud I xxii* 24
The fires of Hell brake out of thy r sun, „ *II i* 9
but thought 'The sun is r,' tho' the sun had risen. *Holy Grail* 408
All in the middle of the r moon: „ 636
And r bore him thro' the place of tombs. *Pass. of Arthur* 343
made his forehead like a r sun High „ 385
to lower the r race of men; *Locksley H., Sixty* 147
Yet I would the r race were half as eager for the light. „ 228
Risk and r thine all, Life, limbs, *Gareth and L.* 128
Risk'd (for the man Had r his little) *Sea Dreams* 10
Take not his life: he r it for my own; *Princess v* 407
sweet son, had r himself and climb'd, *Gareth and L.* 60
Risking some knight of mine, r his life, *Geraint and E.* 915
Rite r's and forms before his burning eyes *The Poet* 39
and with solemn r's by candle-light— *Princess v* 292
Worthy of our gorgeous r's, *Ode on Well.* 93
The r's prepared, the victim bared, *The Victim* 65
mingle with your r's; Pray and be pray'd for; *Guinevere* 680
And those lone r's I have not seen, *To Marq. of Dufferin* 39
Ritual And hear the r of the dead. *In Mem. xviii* 12
all else Form, R, varying with the tribes of men. *Akbar's Dream* 125
Rivage From the green r many a fall *Arabian Nights* 47
Rival (adj.) Which fann'd the gardens of that r rose *Aylmer's Field* 455
the King Took, as in r heat, to holy things; *Balin and Balan* 100
nor raved And thus foam'd over at a r name: „ 567
He wildly fought a r suitor, *The Ring* 214
Rival (s) my latest r brings thee rest. *Locksley Hall* 89
Leolin's rejected r's from their suit *Aylmer's Field* 493
Leolin's one strong r upon earth; „ 557
wrathful, petulant, Dreaming some r, *Lucretius* 15
To push my r out of place and power. *Princess iv* 335
Poor r's in a losing game, *In Mem. cii* 19
far away the maid in Astolat, Her guiltless r, *Lancelot and E.* 746
R's of realm-ruining party, *Locksley H., Sixty* 120
Rivalries fruitful strifes and r of peace— *Ded. of Idylls* 38
Drove me from all vainglories, r, *Holy Grail* 32
Riven within my inmost frame Was r in twain: *Lover's Tale i* 596
Knights were thwack'd and r, *The Tourney* 10
River Clearly the blue r chimes in its flowing *All Things will Die* 1
Thoro' the crack-stemm'd pines only the far r shines. *Leonine Eleg.* 2
down a broad canal From the main r sluiced, *Arabian Nights* 26
River (*continued*) A motion from the r won Ridged the smooth level, *Arabian Nights* 34
Flowing like a crystal r; *Poet's Mind* 6
With an inner voice the r ran, *Dying Swan* 5
One willow over the r wept, „ 14
Like some broad r rushing down alone, *Mine be the strength* 2
On either side the r lie Long fields *L. of Shalott i* 1
By the island in the r Flowing down to Camelot. „ 13
From the r winding clearly, „ 31
There the r eddy whirls, „ *ii* 15
From the bank and from the r He flash'd „ *iii* 33
'Tirra lirra,' by the r Sang Sir Lancelot. „ 35
And down the r's dim expanse „ *iv* 10
full-flowing r of speech Came down upon my heart. *Œnone* 68
one, a full-fed r winding slow By herds *Palace of Art* 73
drew R's of melodies. „ 172
They saw the gleaming r seaward flow *Lotos-Eaters* 14
long bright r drawing slowly His waters „ *C. S.* 92
How fresh the meadows look Above the r, *Walk. to the Mail* 2
willows two and two By r's gallopaded. *Amphion* 40
In curves the yellowing r ran, *Sir L. and Q. G.* 15
A rivulet then a r: *A Farewell* 6
To join the brimming r, (repeat) *The Brook* 32, 48, 64, 183
there the r: and there Stands Philip's farm where brook and r meet. „ 37
Runs in a r of blood to the sick sea. *Aylmer's Field* 768
Set in a gleaming r's crescent-curve, *Princess i* 171
We follow'd up the r as we rode, „ 206
and the r made a fall Out yonder;' „ *iii* 172
The r as it narrow'd to the hills. „ 196
we came to where the r sloped To plunge „ 290
They faint on hill or field or r: „ *iv* 14
miss'd the plank, and roll'd In the r. „ 178
combing out her long black hair Damp from the r; „ 277
As waits a r level with the dam Ready to burst „ 473
Let the great r take me to the main: „ *vii* 13
That shines over city and r, *Ode on Well.* 50
Flash, ye cities, in r's of fire! *W. to Alexandra* 19
Beside the r's wooded reach, *In Mem. lxxi* 13
A r sliding by the wall. „ *ciii* 8
his high sun flame, and his r billowing ran, *Maud I iv* 32
a r Runs in three loops about her living-place; *Gareth and L.* 611
Wherethro' the serpent r coil'd, they came. „ 906
Down to the r, sink or swim, „ 1154
O'er the four r's the first roses blew, *Geraint and E.* 764
holding then his court Hard on the r *Lancelot and E.* 75
By the great r in a boatman's hut. „ 278
Up the great r in the boatman's boat. „ 1038
prepared a chariot-bier To take me to the r, and a barge Be ready on the r, „ 1122
Sat by the r in a cove, and watch'd „ 1389
and all the sand Swept like a r, *Holy Grail* 800
when I was leaning out Above the r— *Last Tournament* 44
saw the r's roll from Paradise! *Columbus* 27
streaming and shining on Silent r, *Merlin and the G.* 52
River-bank he ran Beside the r-b: *Aylmer's Field* 451
River-bed An empty r-b before, *Mariana in the S.* 6
The r-b was dusty-white; „ 54
River-breeze the soft r-b, Which fann'd the gardens *Aylmer's Field* 454
River-God I am the daughter of a R-G, *Œnone* 38
River-loop So when they touch'd the second r-l, *Gareth and L.* 1025
Lancelot, having swum the r-l's— „ 1216
River-rain Snapt in the rushing of the r-r *Merlin and V.* 958
River-shore Spread the light haze along the r-s's, *Gardener's D.* 264
creep down to the r-s, *Charity* 15
River-sunder'd r-s champaign clothed with corn, *Œnone* 114
River-tide On the misty r-t. *Maud II iv* 67
Riveted the eye Was r and charm-bound, *Lover's Tale ii* 188
Riveting Sat r a helmet on his knee, *Marr. of Geraint* 268
Riving r the spirit of man, *The Poet* 51
A cracking and a r of the roofs, *Holy Grail* 183
Rivulet Down by the poplar tall r's babble and fall. *Leonine Eleg.* 4
r in the flowery dale 'ill merrily glance and play, *May Queen* 39
Now by some tinkling r, *Sir L. and Q. G.* 29
Flow down, cold r, to the sea, *A Farewell* 1

Robby (name of man and cat) (*continued*) But if I 'ed married tha, *R*, *Spinster's S's.* 54
R, git down wi'tha, wilt tha? „ 67
Theere! Set it down! Now *R*! „ 119
Till *R* an' Steevie 'es 'ed their lap „ 121
Robe (s) no blood upon her maiden *r's* *The Poet* 41
She threw her royal *r's* away. *Palace of Art* 290
(With that she tore her *r* apart, *D. of F. Women* 157
the white *r* and the palm. *St. S. Stylites* 20
As these white *r's* are soil'd and dark, *St. Agnes' Eve* 13
How oft the purple-skirted *r* *The Voyage* 21
In *r* and crown the king stept down, *Beggar Maid* 5
wove A close-set *r* of jasmine sown with stars: *Aylmer's Field* 158
whirl'd her white *r* like a blossom'd branch *Princess iv* 179
rainbow *r's*, and gems and gemlike eyes, „ 480
he drew Her *r* to meet his lips, „ *vi* 156
Her falser self slipt from her like a *r*, „ *vii* 161
Till slowly worn her earthly *r*, *In Mem. lxxxiv* 33
In a cold white *r* before me, *Maud II iv* 19
a *r* Of samite without price, *Merlin and V.* 221
down his *r* the dragon writhed in gold, *Lancelot and E.* 435
'If I be loved, these are my festal *r's*, „ 909
'Take thou my *r*,' she said, *Holy Grail* 449
In hanging *r* or vacant ornament, *Guinevere* 506
A mystic light flash'd ev'n from her white *r* *Lover's Tale i* 370
Robed in those *r's* of light I must not wear, „ 671
throwing down his *r's*, And claspt her hand in his: „ *iii* 51
with her flying *r* and her poison'd rose; *Vastness* 16
Robe (verb) Rise therefore; *r* yourself in this: *Geraint and E.* 685
The music that *r's* it in language *The Wreck* 24
Robed (*See also* **White-robed**) but *r* in soften'd light Of orient state. *Ode to Memory* 10
Lying, *r* in snowy white That loosely flew *L. of Shalott iv* 19
lying *r* and crown'd, Worthy a Roman spouse.' *D. of F. Women* 163
reissuing, *r* and crown'd, To meet her lord, *Godiva* 77
hand that *r* your cottage-walls with flowers *Aylmer's Field* 698
And *r* the shoulders in a rosy silk, *Princess, Pro.* 103
R in the long night of her deep hair, „ *iv* 491
Loosely *r* in flying raiment, *Boädicea* 37
r herself, Help'd by the mother's careful hand *Marr. of Geraint* 737
And *r* them in her ancient suit again, „ 770
R in red samite, easily to be known, *Lancelot and E.* 433
R in those robes of light I must not wear, *Lover's Tale i* 671
cliffs all *r* in lianas that dropt *The Wreck* 73
R in universal harvest up to either pole *Locksley H., Sixty* 169
Ilion's lofty temples *r* in fire, *To Virgil* 2
r thee in his day from head to feet— *Demeter and P.* 21
Robert old Sir *R's* pride, His books— *Audley Court* 58
slight Sir *R* with his watery smile *Edwin Morris* 128
Robin (bird) In the spring a fuller crimson comes upon the *r's* breast; *Locksley Hall* 17
On the nigh-naked tree the *r* piped *Enoch Arden* 676
careful *r's* eye the delver's toil, *Marr. of Geraint* 774
careful *r's* eye the delver's toil; *Geraint and E.* 431
Robin (Christian name) But *R* leaning on the bridge *May Queen* 14
And say to *R* a kind word, „ *Con.* 45
Robin *See* **Ragged-robin**
Robing *See* **Roäbin'**
Robins (surname) Or a mowt 'a taäen young *R*— *N. Farmer, O. S.* 50
Naw, nor a moänt to *R*— „ 60
Rock (s) And strike the hard, hard *r*, *Supp. Confessions* 116
the mermaids in and out of the *r's*, *The Merman* 12
the mermen in and out of the *r's*; *The Mermaid* 34
Of ledge or shelf The *r* rose clear, *Palace of Art* 10
or a sound Of *r's* thrown down, „ 282
zig-zag paths, and juts of pointed *r*, *M. d'Arthur* 50
and leveret lay, Like fossils of the *r*, *Audley Court* 25
as we sank From *r* to *r* upon the glooming quay, „ 84
upon a *r* With turrets lichen-gilded like a *r*: *Edwin Morris* 7
forged a thousand theories of the *r's*, „ 18
he struck his staff against the *r's* *Golden Year* 59
lights begin to twinkle from the *r's*: *Ulysses* 54
His mantle glitters on the *r's*— *Day-Dm., Arrival* 6
The nutmeg *r's* and isles of clove. *The Voyage* 40
To him who sat upon the *r's*, *To E. L.* 23

Rock (s) (*continued*) Is there no stoning save with flint and *r*? *Aylmer's Field* 746
on the foremost *r's* Touching, *Sea Dreams* 51
some were push'd with lances from the *r*, *Princess, Pro.* 46
The morals, something of the frame, the *r*, „ *ii* 382
No *r* so hard but that a little wave „ *iii* 154
Glanced like a touch of sunshine on the *r's*, „ 357
Each was like a Druid *r*; „ *iv* 280
Part sat like *r's*: part reel'd but kept their seats: „ *v* 496
Pharos from his base Had left us *r*. „ *vi* 340
for Willy stood like a *r*. *Grandmother* 10
Who seems a promontory of *r*, *Will* 6
along the valley, by *r* and cave and tree, *V. of Cauteretz* 9
My love has talk'd with *r's* and trees; *In Mem. xcvii* 1
Nor runlet tinkling from the *r*; „ *c* 13
Rise in the spiritual *r*, „ *cxxxi* 3
There yet lies the *r* that fell with him *Maud I i* 8
by a red *r*, glimmers the Hall; „ *iv* 10
Athwart the ledges of *r*, „ *II ii* 28
smallest *r* far on the faintest hill, *Com. of Arthur* 99
As being all bone-shatter'd on the *r*, Yielded; *Gareth and L.* 1050
narrow comb wherein Were slabs of *r* with figures, „ 1194
Whose holy hand hath fashion'd on the *r* „ 1197
a *r* in ebbs and flows, Fixt on her faith. *Marr. of Geraint* 812
knights On horseback, wholly arm'd, behind a *r* In shadow, *Geraint and E.* 57
I saw three bandits by the *r* „ 72
A little town with towers, upon a *r*, „ 197
Prince had brought his errant eyes Home from the *r*, „ 246
gleam'd on *r's* Roof-pendent, sharp; *Balin and Balan* 314
In the white *r* a chapel and a hall *Lancelot and E.* 405
Shape to their fancy's eye from broken *r's* „ 1252
A castle like a *r* upon a *r*, *Holy Grail* 814
Far down beneath a winding wall of *r* *Last Tournament* 11
zigzag paths, and juts of pointed *r*, *Pass. of Arthur* 218
Thro' the *r's* we wound: *Lover's Tale i* 324
walls of battlemented *r* Gilded with broom, „ 399
Shut in the secret chambers of the *r* „ 521
laid it in a sepulchre of *r* Never to rise again. „ 683
And all the fragments of the living *r* „ *ii* 44
I find hard *r's*, hard life, hard cheer, *Sir J. Oldcastle* 6
And we left but a naked *r*, *V. of Maeldune* 54
And a hundred ranged on the *r* „ 101
that smooth *r* Before it, altar-fashion'd, *Tiresias* 146
as if she had struck and crash'd on a *r*; *The Wreck* 108
neck Of land running out into *r*— *Despair* 10
skull that is left in the *r's* „ 86
How slowly down the *r's* he went, *The Flight* 38
Ranged like a storm or stood like a *r* *Heavy Brigade* 56
When seated on a *r*, and foot to foot *Romney's R.* 75
Rock (verb) O *r* upon thy towery-top *Talking Oak* 265
r the snowy cradle till I died. *Princess iv* 104
The blind wall *r's*, and on the trees *In Mem., Con.* 63
Rock'd *R* the full-foliaged elms, „ *xcv* 58
A mountain nest—the pleasure-boat that *r*, *Lover's Tale i* 42
Rocket Rush to the roof, sudden *r*, *W. to Alexandra* 20
The *r* molten into flakes *In Mem. xcviii* 31
Rocking (*See also* **Scarce-rocking**) *R* with shatter'd spars, *Buonaparte* 11
Then lightly *r* baby's cradle *Enoch Arden* 194
Rock-throne rough *r-t* Of Freedom! *Montenegro* 9
Rock-thwarted *r-t* under bellowing caves, *Palace of Art* 71
Rocky Lift up thy *r* face, *England and Amer.* 12
Dash'd on every *r* square Their surging charges *Ode on Well.* 125
How richly down the *r* dell *The Daisy* 9
For all along the valley, down thy *r* bed, *V. of Cauteretz* 7
I heard the voice Rave over the *r* bar, *Voice and the P.* 6
And down a *r* pathway from the place *Geraint and E.* 200
And up the *r* pathway disappear'd, „ 243
Rod I must brook the *r* And chastisement *Supp. Confessions* 107
red-faced war has *r's* of steel and fire; *Princess v* 118
war's avenging *r* Shall lash all Europe *To F. D. Maurice* 33
be ruled with *r* or with knout? *Maud I iv* 47
THO' Sin too oft, when smitten by Thy *r*, *Doubt and Prayer* 1
Rode Ere I *r* into the fight, *Oriana* 21
He *r* between the barley-sheaves, *L. of Shalott iii* 2

Rode (*continued*) As he r down to Camelot: (repeat) *L. of Shalott* 14, 23, 32
And as he r his armour rung, „ 17
The man, my lover, with whom I r sublime *D. of F. Women* 141
And r his hunter down. *Talking Oak* 104
And far below the Roundhead r, „ 299
Then she r forth, clothed on with chastity: *Godiva* 53
The deep air listen'd round her as she r, „ 54
she r back, clothed on with chastity: „ 65
R thro' the coverts of the deer, *Sir L. and Q. G.* 21
He r a horse with wings, that would have flown, *Vision of Sin* 3
Who slowly r across a wither'd heath, „ 61
They r; they betted; made a hundred friends, *Princess, Pro.* 163
We r Many a long league back to the North. „ *i* 167
follow'd up the river as we r, And r till midnight „ 206
'That afternoon the Princess r to take „ *iii* 169
I r beside her and to me she said: „ 197
we r a league beyond, And, o'er a bridge of pinewood „ 334
Then r we with the old king across the lawns „ *v* 236
All o'er with honey'd answer as we r „ 242
Back r we to my father's camp, „ 331
as here and everywhere He r the mellay, „ 502
but Arac r him down: And Cyril seeing it, „ 532
R the six hundred. (repeat) *Light Brigade* 4, 8, 17, 26
Boldly they r and well, „ 23
Then they r back, but not Not the six hundred. „ 37
I bow'd to his lady-sister as she r by on the moor; *Maud I iv* 15
one of the two that r at her side Bound for the Hall, „ *x* 24
r a simple knight among his knights, *Com. of Arthur* 51
Smite on the sudden, yet r on, „ 57
thinking as he r, 'Her father said „ 78
A naked babe, and r to Merlin's feet, „ 384
Gareth r Down the slope street, *Gareth and L.* 699
thro' silent faces r Down the slope city, „ 734
R on the two, reviler and reviled; „ 794
Suddenly she that r upon his left „ 1319
r In converse till she made her palfrey halt, „ 1359
Prince and Enid r, And fifty knights r with them, *Marr. of Geraint* 43
there r Full slowly by a knight, lady, „ 186
r, By ups and downs, thro' many a grassy glade „ 235
And onward to the fortress r the three, „ 251
Then r Geraint, a little spleenful yet, „ 293
Then r Geraint into the castle court, „ 312
all unarm'd I r, and thought to find Arms „ 417
And rising up, he r to Arthur's court, „ 591
claspt and kiss'd her, and they r away. „ 825
forth they r, but scarce three paces on, *Geraint and E.* 19
And wildernesses, perilous paths, they r: „ 32
They r so slowly and they look'd so pale, „ 35
for he r As if he heard not, „ 451
Half ridden off with by the thing he r, „ 460
And so r on, nor told his gentle wife „ 503
R on a mission to the bandit Earl; „ 527
In this poor gown I r with him to court, „ 700
now we r upon this fatal quest Of honour, „ 703
cast her arms About him, and at once they r away. „ 762
Tho' thence I r all-shamed, hating the life „ 852
for a space they r, And fifty knights r with them „ 953
So claim'd the quest and r away, *Balin and Balan* 138
and r The skyless woods, but under open blue „ 292
with droopt brow down the long glades he r; „ 311
damsel-errant, warbling, as she r The woodland alleys, „ 438
the knight, with whom I r, Hath suffer'd misadventure, „ 475
Yet while they r together down the plain, *Merlin and V.* 123
of old—among the flowers—they r. „ 136
and all day long we r Thro' the dim land „ 424
He left it with her, when he r to tilt *Lancelot and E.* 30
They rose, heard mass, broke fast, and r away: „ 415
all the region round R with his diamond, „ 616
A true-love ballad, lightly r away. „ 705
fail'd to find him, tho' I r all round The region: „ 709
R o'er the long backs of the bushless downs „ 789
To Astolat returning r the three. „ 905
Nor bad farewell, but sadly r away. „ 987
to this hall full quickly r the King, *Holy Grail* 258
And in he r, and up I glanced, „ 262

Rode (*continued*) Queen, Who r by Lancelot, wail'd and shriek'd *Holy Grail* 356
'And on I r, and when I thought my thirst „ 379
on I r, and greater was my thirst. „ 401
I r on and found a mighty hill, „ 421
And in the strength of this I r, „ 476
And maddening what he r: „ 641
Sir Bors R to the lonest tract of all the realm, „ 661
while they r, the meaning in his eyes, *Pelleas and E.* 109
straight on thro' open door R Gawain, „ 383
but r Ere midnight to her walls, „ 412
R till the star above the wakening sun, „ 500
Lancelot slowly r his warhorse back To Camelot, „ 583
Down the slope city r, and sharply turn'd *Last Tournament* 127
R Tristram toward Lyonnesse and the west. „ 362
Thro' many a league-long bower he r. „ 374
Arthur with a hundred spears R far, „ 421
Arthur waved them back. Alone he r. „ 437
And r beneath an ever-showering leaf, „ 492
when first I r from our rough Lyonnesse, „ 664
and then they r to the divided way, *Guinevere* 124
And r thereto from Lyonnesse, and he said That as he r, an hour or maybe twain „ 236
R under groves that look'd a paradise „ 389
There r an armed warrior to the doors. „ 409
And then he r away; but after this, *Lover's Tale iv* 126
And thus our lonely lover r away, „ 130
and he r on ahead, as he waved his blade *Heavy Brigade* 9
R flashing blow upon blow, „ 32
they r like Victors and Lords „ 48
They r, or they stood at bay— „ 51
Thou's r of 'is back when a babby, *Owd Roä* 5
you my girl R on my shoulder home— *The Ring* 322

Roger Acton Burnt—good Sir R A, my dear friend! *Sir J. Oldcastle* 79

Rogue unctuous mouth which lured him, r, *Sea Dreams* 14
do not call him, love, Before you prove him, r, „ 171
And one the Master, as a r in grain *Princess, Pro.* 116
A r of canzonents and serenades. „ *iv* 135
snubnosed r would leap from his counter and till, *Maud I i* 51
listening r hath caught the manner of it. *Gareth and L.* 778
these caitiff r's Had wreak'd themselves on me; „ 819
Some meddling r has tamper'd with him— *Lancelot and E.* 128

Roisterer midmost of a rout of r's, *Geraint and E.* 274

Roky Last in a r hollow, belling, *Last Tournament* 502

Roll (s) (*See also* **Ocean-roll**) upon the rise And long r of the Hexameter— *Lucretius* 11
Nor ever lowest r of thunder moans, „ 108
Now, to the r of muffled drums, *Ode on Well.* 87
R of cannon and clash of arms, „ 116
I hear the r of the ages. *Spiteful Letter* 8
then one low r Of Autumn thunder, *Last Tournament* 152
Rush of Suns, and r of systems, *God. and the Univ.* 3
no discordance in the r And march *D. of the Duke of C.* 14

Roll (verb) (*See also* **Over-roll**) 'In filthy sloughs they r a prurient skin, *Palace of Art* 201
trees began to whisper, and the wind began to r, *May Queen, Con.* 27
'This mounting wave will r us shoreward soon.' *Lotos-Eaters* 2
And the great ages onward r. *To J. S.* 72
R onward, leading up the golden year. *Golden Year* 41
r the waters, flash the lightnings, *Locksley Hall* 186
the gates R back, and far within *St. Agnes' Eve* 30
They reel, they r in clanging lists, *Sir Galahad* 9
There did a thousand memories r upon him, *Enoch Arden* 724
r thy tender arms Round him, *Lucretius* 82
Our echoes r from soul to soul, *Princess iv* 15
r The torrents, dash'd to the vale: „ *v* 349
r the torrent out of dusky doors: „ *vii* 208
down r's the world In mock heroics „ *Con.* 63
world on world in myriad myriads r *Ode on Well.* 262
R and rejoice, jubilant voice, *W. to Alexandra* 22
R as a ground-swell dash'd on the strand, „ 23
And howsoever this wild world may r, *W. to Marie Alex.* 48
two and thirty years were a mist that r's away; *V. of Cauteretz* 6
You r up away from the light *Window, Winter* 8
I hear a wizard music r, *In Mem. lxx* 14

Roll (verb) *(continued)* And *r* it in another course, *In Mem. cxiii* 16
The strong imagination *r* A sphere „ *cxxii* 6
There *r's* the deep where grew the tree. „ *cxxiii* 1
To have her lion *r* in a silken net *Maud I vi* 29
swell Of the long waves that *r* in yonder bay ? „ *xviii* 63
and the war *r* down like a wind, „ *III vi* 54
and when the surface *r's*, *Com. of Arthur* 293
sea *r's*, and all the world is warm'd ? ' *Holy Grail* 672
because they *r* Thro' such a round in heaven, „ 685
The years will *r* into the centuries, *Guinevere* 626
more than man Which *r's* the heavens, *Tiresias* 22
r Rising and falling— *The Wreck* 53
Nor *r* thy viands on a luscious tongue *Ancient Sage* 267
and *r* their ruins down the slope. *Locksley H., Sixty* 138
While the silent Heavens *r*, „ 203
And when they *r* their idol down— *Freedom* 29
may *r* with the dust of a vanish'd race. *Vastness* 2
To *r* her North below thy deepening dome, *Prog. of Spring* 49
delight To *r* himself in meadow grass *Romney's R.* 14
may *r* The rainbow hues of heaven about it— „ 50
and *r* my voice from the summit, *Parnassus* 6
ere the mountain *r's* into the plain, *Death of Œnone* 51
Well if it do not *r* our way. *Riflemen form!* 4
Roll'd the tumult of their acclaim is *r* *Dying Swan* 33
And all about him *r* his lustrous eyes ; *Love and Death* 3
And all the war is *r* in smoke.' *Two Voices* 156
I *r* among the tender flowers : *Fatima* 11
R round by one fix'd law. *Palace of Art* 256
R to starboard, *r* to larboard, *Lotos-Eaters, C. S.* 106
R on each other, rounded, smooth'd, *D. of F. Women* 51
Whirl'd by the wind, had *r* me deep below, „ 119
' When the next moon was *r* into the sky, „ 229
So all day long the noise of battle *r* *M. d'Arthur* 1
R in one another's arms, *Locksley Hall* 58
When the ranks are *r* in vapour, „ 104
Her full black ringlets downward *r*, *Day-Dm., Sleep. B.* 12
R a sea-haze and whelm'd the world *Enoch Arden* 672
as the year *R* itself round again „ 822
once again he *r* his eyes upon her „ 904
and *r* His hoop to pleasure Edith, *Aylmer's Field* 84
babies *r* about Like tumbled fruit in grass ; *Princess, Pro.* 82
Kittenlike he *r* And paw'd about her sandal. „ *iii* 181
miss'd the plank, and *r* In the river. „ *iv* 177
slain with laughter *r* the gilded Squire. „ *v* 22
giant, Arac, *r* himself Thrice in the saddle, „ 274
Part *r* on the earth and rose again and drew : „ 497
r With music in the growing breeze of Time, „ *vi* 55
her eye with slow dilation *r* Dry flame, „ 189
the sound of the sorrowing anthem *r* *Ode on Well.* 60
Better the waste Atlantic *r* On her and us *Third of Feb.* 21
R the rich vapour far into the heaven. *Spec. of Iliad* 8
Who *r* the psalm to wintry skies, *In Mem. lvi* 11
And *r* the floods in grander space, „ *ciii* 26
And a sullen thunder is *r* ; *Maud II iv* 49
R incense, and there past along the hymns *Com. of Arthur* 464
the long night hath *r* away ! „ 483
down his enemy *r*, And there lay still ; *Geraint and E.* 160
He *r* his eyes about the hall, „ 610
The russet-bearded head *r* on the floor. „ 729
a forethought *r* about his brain, *Merlin and V.* 230
and *r* his enemy down, And saved him : *Lancelot and E.* 26
from the skull the crown *R* into light, „ 51
he *r* his eyes Yet blank from sleep, „ 819
roofs Of our great hall are *r* in thunder-smoke ! *Holy Grail* 220
whereout was *r* A roar of riot, *Last Tournament* 425
So all day long the noise of battle *r* *Pass. of Arthur* 170
And London *r* one tide of joy *To the Queen ii* 8
threshold clashing, *r* Her heaviest thunder— *Lover's Tale i* 605
And we *r* upon capes of crocus *V. of Maeldune* 47
r To meet me long-arm'd vines with grapes *To E. Fitzgerald* 26
whence he *r* himself At dead of night— *Tiresias* 145
And *r* them around like a cloud,— *Heavy Brigade* 40
And *r* his nakedness everyway *Dead Prophet* 15
once had *r* you round and round the Sun, *Poets and their B.* 10
Ghost of Pindar in you *R* an Olympian ; *To Prof. Jebb* 4
Roll'd *(continued)* Till earth has *r* her latest year— *To Ulysses* 28
R again back on itself in the tides *Beautiful City* 4
R them over and over. *The Tourney* 5
Roller league-long *r* thundering on the reef, *Enoch Arden* 584
slowly-ridging *r's* on the cliffs Clash'd, *Lover's Tale i* 57
Rollest *r* from the gorgeous gloom *In Mem. lxxxvi* 2
Rolling *(See also* **Crimson-rolling, Far-rolling, Myriad-rolling***)*
waves that up a quiet cove *R* slide, *Eleänore* 109
r to and fro The heads and crowns *Palace of Art* 151
R a slumbrous sheet of foam below. *Lotos-Eaters* 13
holy organ *r* waves Of sound on roof and floor *D. of F. Women* 191
her mighty voice Came *r* on the wind. *Of old sat Freedom* 8
r as in sleep, Low thunders bring the mellow rain, *Talking Oak* 278
Enoch *r* his gray eyes upon her, *Enoch Arden* 844
and *r* in his mind Old waifs of rhyme, *The Brook* 198
Breathed low around the *r* earth *The winds, etc.* 3
Is wearied of the *r* hours. *L. C. V. de Vere* 60
A *r* stone of here and everywhere, *Audley Court* 78
A *r* organ-harmony Swells up, *Sir Galahad* 75
Beneath a manelike mass of *r* gold, *Aylmer's Field* 68
And *r* as it were the substance of it „ 258
Which *r* o'er the palaces of the proud, „ 636
Who still'd the *r* wave of Galilee ! „ 709
And there was *r* thunder ; *Sea Dreams* 118
That stays the *r* Ixionian wheel, *Lucretius* 261
r thro' the court A long melodious thunder *Princess ii* 475
Over the *r* waters go, „ *iii* 5
Thy voice is heard thro' *r* drums, „ *iv* 577
and *r* words Oration-like. „ *v* 372
in the centre stood The common men with *r* eyes ; „ *vi* 360
fishes turn'd And whiten'd all the *r* flood ; *The Victim* 20
Ye watch, like God, the *r* hours *In Mem. li* 14
And thunder-music, *r*, shake The prophet „ *lxxxvii* 7
Let her great Danube *r* fair Enwind her isles, „ *xcviii* 9
To darken on the *r* brine That breaks the coast. „ *cvii* 14
Thy voice is on the *r* air ; „ *cxxx* 1
And, star and system *r* past, „ *Con.* 122
In drifts of smoke before a *r* wind, *Com. of Arthur* 434
And mass, and *r* music, like a queen. *Lancelot and E.* 1336
wrapt In unremorseful folds of *r* fire. *Holy Grail* 261
Thro' the tall oriel on the *r* sea. „ 831
light of heaven Burn'd at his lowest in the *r* year. *Pass of Arthur* 91
And *r* far along the gloomy shores „ 134
When the *r* eyes of the lighthouse there *Despair* 9
or the *r* Thunder, or the rending earthquake, *Faith* 3
sullen Lethe *r* doom On them and theirs *Lit. Squabbles* 11
R on their purple couches *Boädicea* 62
R her smoke about the Royal mount, *Gareth and L.* 190
Southwesterns, *r* ridge on ridge, „ 1145
Bound on a foray, *r* eyes of prey, *Geraint and E.* 538
when they clash'd, *R* back upon Balin, *Balin and Balan* 562
R his eyes, a moment stood, *Pelleas and E.* 581
The moony vapour *r* round the King, *Guinevere* 601
Funeral hearses *r* ! *Forlorn* 68
r of dragons By warble of water, *Merlin and the G.* 44
R her anger Thro' blasted valley *Kapiolani* 11
Roman (adj.) My Hercules, my *R* Antony, *D. of F. Women* 150
The *R* soldier found Me lying dead, „ 161
lying robed and crown'd, Worthy a *R* spouse.' „ 164
and the *R* brows Of Agrippina. *Princess ii* 84
the Persian, Grecian, *R* lines Of empire, „ 130
their foreheads drawn in *R* scowls, „ *vii* 129
What *R* strength Turbìa show'd In ruin, *The Daisy* 5
Blacken round the *R* carrion, *Boädicea* 14
horde of *R* robbers mock at a barbarous adversary. „ 18
hive of *R* liars worship an emperor-idiot. „ 19
Lo their precious *R* bantling, „ 31
Shall we teach it a *R* lesson ? „ 32
Tho' the *R* eagle shadow thee, „ 39
Take the hoary *R* head and shatter it, „ 65
Cut the *R* boy to pieces in his lust „ 66
Ran the land with *R* slaughter, „ 84
King Leodogran Groan'd for the *R* legions *Com. of Arthur* 34
To drive the heathen from your *R* wall, „ 512
for whose love the *R* Cæsar first Invaded Britai , *Marr. of Geraint* 745

Roman (adj.) (*continued*) Or thrust the heathen from the *R* wall, *Pass. of Arthur* 69
R Virgil, thou that singest *To Virgil* 1
There beneath the *R* ruin where the purple flowers grow, *Frater ave, etc.* 4
Tenderest of *R* poets nineteen-hundred years ago, „ 6
Roman (s) What *R* would be dragg'd in triumph thus? *Lucretius* 234
Wherewith the *R* pierced the side of Christ. *Balin and Balan* 114
For when the *R* left us, and their law *Guinevere* 456
Hard *R's* brawling of their monstrous games; *St. Telemachus* 40
Romance Victor in Drama, Victor in *R*, *To Victor Hugo* 1
he the knight for an amorous girl's *r*! *The Wreck* 44
Rome a steaming slaughter-house of *R*. *Lucretius* 84
The fading politics of mortal *R*, *Princess ii* 286
Such is *R*, and this her deity: *Boädicea* 20
Abroad, at Florence, at *R*, *Maud I xix* 58
Great Lords from *R* before the portal stood, *Com. of Arthur* 477
Shall *R* or Heathen rule in Arthur's realm? „ 485
at the banquet those great Lords from *R*, „ 504
and Arthur strove with *R*. „ 514
who swept the dust of ruin'd *R* From off the threshold *Gareth and L.* 135
brake the petty kings, and fought with *R*, *Pass. of Arthur* 68
brands that once had fought with *R*, „ 133
And own the holy governance of *R*.' *Columbus* 190
R's Vicar in our Indies? „ 195
R of Cæsar, *R* of Peter, *Locksley H., Sixty* 88
Ilion falling, *R* arising, *To Virgil* 3
sound for ever of Imperial *R*— „ 32
Now the *R* of slaves hath perish'd, and the *R* of freemen holds her place, „ 33
when Athens reign'd and *R*, *Freedom* 9
kinsman, dying, summon'd me to *R*— *The Ring* 178
Of ancient Art in Paris, or in *R*. *Romney's R.* 87
at his ear he heard a whisper '*R*' *St. Telemachus* 26
struck from his own shadow on to *R*. „ 33
decreed That *R* no more should wallow „ 78
and *R* was a babe in arms, *The Dawn* 9
Ronald Lord *R* brought a lily-white doe *Lady Clare* 3
Lord *R* is heir of all your lands, „ 19
And all you have will be Lord *R's*, „ 35
lily-white doe Lord *R* had brought Leapt up „ 61
Down stept Lord *R* from his tower: „ 65
'Play me no tricks,' said Lord *R*, (repeat) „ 73, 75
She look'd into Lord *R's* eyes, „ 79
Roob (rub) Loovs 'im, an' *r's* 'im, an' doosts 'im, *North. Cobbler* 98
Ay, *r* thy whiskers ageän ma, *Spinster's S's.* 81
Rood 'By holy *r*, a royal beard! *Day-Dm., Revival* 20
'Here by God's *r* is the one maid for me.' *Marr. of Geraint* 368
More near by many a *r* than yestermorn, *Geraint and E.* 442
by God's *r*, I trusted you too much.' *Merlin and V.* 376
Roof (s) (*See also* **Convent-roof, Under-roof**) The sparrow's chirrup on the *r*, *Mariana* 73
Hundreds of crescents on the *r* *Arabian Nights* 129
Living together under the same *r*, *To ——, With Pal. of Art* 12
And round the *r's* a gilded gallery *Palace of Art* 29
the *r* and crown of things? *Lotos-Eaters, C. S.* 24
and on *r's* Of marble palaces; *D. of F. Women* 23
organ rolling waves Of sound on *r* and floor „ 192
House in the shade of comfortable *r's*, *St. S. Stylites* 107
The *r's* of Sumner-place! (repeat) *Talking Oak* 32, 96, 152
And on the *r* she went, „ 114
and when the rain is on the *r*. *Locksley Hall* 78
Flew over *r* and casement: *Will Water.* 134
And they leave her father's *r*. *L. of Burleigh* 12
When beneath his *r* they come. „ 40
red *r's* about a narrow wharf In cluster; *Enoch Arden* 3
in session on their *r's* Approved him, *The Brook* 127
Somewhere beneath his own low range of *r's*, *Aylmer's Field* 47
presence flattering the poor *r's* Revered as theirs, „ 175
but every *r* Sent out a listener: „ 613
The *r* so lowly but that beam of Heaven „ 684
Flaying the *r's* and sucking up the drains, *Princess v* 525
there on the *r's* Like that great dame „ *vi* 31
shape it plank and beam for *r* and floor, „ 46
Clomb to the *r's*, and gazed alone „ *vii* 32
Rush to the *r*, sudden rocket, *W. to Alexandra* 20
Roof (s) (*continued*) I climb'd the *r's* at break of day; *The Daisy* 61
Garrulous under a *r* of pine: *To F. D. Maurice* 20
The *r's*, that heard our earliest cry, *In Mem. cii* 3
With tender gloom the *r*, the wall; „ *Con.* 118
and all the land from *r* and rick, *Com. of Arthur* 433
Struck up and lived along the milky *r's*; *Lancelot and E.* 409
A cracking and a riving of the *r's*, *Holy Grail* 183
r's Of our great hall are roll'd in thunder-smoke! „ 219
And all the dim rich city, *r* by *r*, „ 228
r's Totter'd toward each other in the sky, „ 342
Hell burst up your harlot *r's* Bellowing, *Pelleas and E.* 466
hath but dwelt beneath one *r* with me. *Pass. of Arthur* 156
Hate is strange beneath the *r* of Love. *Lover's Tale i* 779
Flying at top of the *r's* *Def. of Lucknow* 4
topmost *r* our banner of England blew. (repeat) „ 6, 30, 45, 60, 94
Rifleman, high on the *r*, „ 63
topmost *r* our banner in India blew. „ 72
And ever aloft on the palace *r* „ 106
Without a *r* that I can call mine own, *Columbus* 168
And the *r* sank in on the hearth, *V. of Maeldune* 32
Ruddy thro' both the *r's* of sight, *Tiresias* 3
Heard from the *r's* by night, „ 140
r's of slated hideousness! *Locksley H., Sixty* 246
rummle down when the *r's* gev waäy, *Owd Roä* 109
Was all ablaze with crimson to the *r*, *The Ring* 250
women shrieking 'Atheist' flung Filth from the *r*, *Akbar's Dream* 92
Roof (verb) *R* not a glance so keen as thine: *Clear-headed friend* 7
cloud that *r's* our noon with night, *Sisters (E. and E.)* 17
Roof'd (*See also* **Rooft**) *R* the world with doubt and fear, *Eleänore* 99
Roof-haunting *R-h* martins warm their eggs: *Day-Dm., Sleep. P.* 17
Roofless I lay Pent in a *r* close of ragged stones; *St. S. Stylites* 74
The fire that left a *r* Ilion, *Lucretius* 65
Roof-pendent gleam'd on rocks *R-p*, sharp; *Balin and Balan* 315
Rooft *See* **Bracken-rooft**
Roof-tree now for me the *r-t* fall. *Locksley Hall* 190
Rook building *r* 'ill caw from the windy tall elm-tree, *May Queen, N. Y's. E.* 17
The *r's* are blown about the skies; *In Mem. xv* 4
And Autumn, with a noise of *r's*, „ *lxxxv* 71
a clamour of the *r's* At distance, *Marr. of Geraint* 249
I heard the sober *r* And carrion crow *The Ring* 173
Rookery leads the clanging *r* home. *Locksley Hall* 68
long line of the approaching *r* swerve *Princess, Con.* 97
Room (apartment) (*See also* **Oak-room, Sitting-room**) close, As a sick man's *r* *A spirit haunts* 14
She made three paces thro' the *r*, *L. of Shalott iii* 38
pass, Well-pleased, from *r* to *r*. *Palace of Art* 56
Full of great *r's* and small the palace stood, „ 57
moss or musk, To grace my city *r's*; *Gardener's D.* 194
There was silence in the *r*; *Dora* 157
and not a *r* For love or money. *Audley Court* 1
Past thro' the solitary *r* in front, *Enoch Arden* 277
jests, that flash'd about the pleader's *r*, *Aylmer's Field* 440
That morning in the presence *r* I stood *Princess i* 51
r's which gave Upon a pillar'd porch, „ 229
And shuddering fled from *r* to *r*, „ *vi* 370
from this *r* into the next; *Grandmother* 103
To see the *r's* in which he dwelt. *In Mem. lxxxvii* 16
thro' the blindless casement of the *r*, *Marr. of Geraint* 71
'Your leave, my lord, to cross the *r*, *Geraint and E.* 298
And glimmer'd on his armour in the *r*. „ 386
shadow still would glide from *r* to *r*, *Guinevere* 504
It was a *r* Within the summer-house *Lover's Tale ii* 166
I hear in one dark *r* a wailing, *Locksley H., Sixty* 262
Room (space) seem'd no *r* for sense of wrong; *Two Voices* 456
What *r* is left for a hater? *Spiteful Letter* 14
strain to make an inch of *r* For their sweet selves, *Lit. Squabbles* 9
fillest all the *r* Of all my love, *In Mem. cxii* 5
no *r* was there For lance or tourney-skill: *Gareth and L.* 1041
Room'd *See* **Myriad-room'd**
Roomlin' (rumbling) I heard 'im a *r* by, *Village Wife* 122
Roon'd (ran) An' keeäper 'e seed ya an *r*, *Churchwarden, etc.* 28
Root grow awry From *r's* which strike so deep? *Supp. Confessions* 78
Cleaving, took *r*, and springing forth *The Poet* 21
at the *r* thro' lush green grasses burn'd *D. of F. Women* 71

Root (*continued*) whose *r* Creeps to the garden water-pipes beneath, *D. of F. Women* 205
The fat earth feed thy branchy *r*, *Talking Oak* 273
tho' my heart be at the *r*. *Locksley Hall* 66
And scirrhous *r's* and tendons. *Amphion* 64
Soft fruitage, mighty nuts, and nourishing *r's*; *Enoch Arden* 555
fixt As are the *r's* of earth and base of all; *Princess v* 446
hold you here, *r* and all, in my hand, *Flow. in cran. wall.* 3
What you are, *r* and all, „ 5
Thy *r's* are wrapt about the bones. *In Mem. ii* 4
By ashen *r's* the violets blow. „ *cxv* 4
for the *r's* of my hair were stirr'd *Maud I i* 13
Some *r* of knighthood and pure nobleness; *Holy Grail* 886
r's like some black coil of carven snakes, *Last Tournament* 13
Adown a natural stair of tangled *r's*, *Lover's Tale i* 527
His winter chills him to the *r*, *Ancient Sage* 119
Root-bitten *R-b* by white lichen, *Gareth and L.* 454
Rooted (*See also* **Fast-rooted, Serpent-rooted**) When *r* in the garden of the mind, *Ode to Memory* 26
'I, *r* here among the groves *Talking Oak* 181
night and day, and *r* in the fields, *Com. of Arthur* 24
He *r* out the slothful officer Or guilty, *Geraint and E.* 938
His honour *r* in dishonour stood, *Lancelot and E.* 876
jungle *r* in his shatter'd hearth, *Demeter and P.* 76
Rootless evermore Seem'd catching at a *r* thorn, *Geraint and E.* 378
Rope With hand and *r* we haled the groaning sow, *Walk. to the Mail* 91
I wore The *r* that haled the buckets *St. S. Stylites* 64
And reach'd the ship and caught the *r*, *Sailor Boy* 3
Torn as a sail that leaves the *r* is torn In tempest: *Holy Grail* 212
Rosa (Monte) how phantom-fair, Was Monte *R*, *The Daisy* 66
Rosalind bring me my love, *R*. *Leonine Eleg.* 14
where is my sweet *R*? „ 16
My *R*, my *R*, (repeat) *Rosalind* 1, 5
bold and free As you, my falcon *R*. „ 18
Come down, come home, my *R*, My gay young hawk, my *R*: „ 33
bind And keep you fast, my *R*, Fast, fast, my wild-eyed *R*, „ 43
face again, My *R* in this Arden— *Sisters (E. and E.)* 119
Rosamond I am that *R*, whom men call fair, *D. of F. Women* 251
Rosary (rose-garden) Thick *rosaries* of scented thorn, *Arabian Nights* 106
Rosary (string of beads) amber, ancient *rosaries*, *Princess, Pro.* 19
Rose (adj.) the lights, *r*, amber, emerald, blue, *Palace of Art* 169
Rose (Christian name) Who had not heard Of *R*, the Gardener's daughter? *Gardener's D.* 52
but she, a *R* In roses, „ 142
R, on this terrace fifty years ago, *Roses on the T.* 1
Two words '*My R*' set all your face aglow, „ 3
Rose (flower, colour) (*See also* **Baby-rose, Garden-rose**) With plaited alleys of the trailing *r*, *Ode to Memory* 106
And the year's last *r*. *A spirit haunts* 20
Bramble *r's*, faint and pale, *A Dirge* 30
Some spirit of a crimson *r* In love with thee *Adeline* 41
Wearing the *r* of womanhood. *Two Voices* 417
Her cheek had lost the *r*, *Œnone* 18
her hair Wound with white *r's*, slept St. Cecily; *Palace of Art* 99
petals from blown *r's* on the grass, *Lotos-Eaters, C. S.* 2
up the porch there grew an Eastern *r*, *Gardener's D.* 123
but she, a Rose In *r's*, „ 143
'Ah, one *r*, One *r*, but one, „ 149
Nor yet refused the *r*, but granted it, „ 160
Kissing the *r* she gave me o'er and o'er, „ 176
then for *r's*, moss or musk, To grace my city rooms; „ 193
shut Within the bosom of the *r*? *Day-Dm., Moral* 8
With a single *r* in her hair. *Lady Clare* 60
God made Himself an awful *r* of dawn, (repeat) *Vision of Sin* 50, 224
The late and early *r's* from his wall, *Enoch Arden* 339
the red *r* was redder than itself, *Aylmer's Field* 50
York's white *r* as red as Lancaster's, „ 51
Which fann'd the gardens of that rival *r* „ 455
Seem'd hope's returning *r*: „ 559
The wilderness shall blossom as the *r*. „ 649
Not ev'n a *r*, were offer'd to thee? *Lucretius* 69
In meshes of the jasmine and the *r*: *Princess i* 219
as tho' there were One *r* in all the world, „ *ii* 51

Rose (flower, colour) (*continued*) And sated with the innumerable *r*, *Princess iii* 122
any *r* of Gulistan Shall burst her veil: „ *iv* 122
Before me shower'd the *r* in flakes; „ 264
there's no *r* that's half so dear to them „ *v* 159
R's and lilies and Canterbury-bells.' *City Child* 5
some rare little *r*, a piece of inmost Horticultural art, *Hendecasyllabics* 19
R, *r* and clematis, (repeat) *Window, At the Window* 3, 10
She takes a riband or a *r*; *In Mem. vi* 32
quick tears that make the *r* Pull sideways, „ *lxxii* 10
May breathe, with many *r's* sweet, „ *xci* 10
and swung The heavy-folded *r*, and flung The lilies „ *xcv* 59
And every thought breaks out a *r*. „ *cxxii* 20
He too foretold the perfect *r*. „ *Con.* 34
an hour's defect of the *r*, *Maud I ii* 8
You have but fed on the *r's* „ *iv* 60
Maud has a garden of *r's* „ *xiv* 1
R's are her cheeks, And a *r* her mouth (repeat) „ *xvii* 7, 27
'Ah, be Among the *r's* to-night.' „ *xxi* 13
And the musk of the *r* is blown. „ *xxii* 6
All night have the *r's* heard The flute, „ 13
I said to the *r*, 'The brief night goes In babble „ 27
But mine, but mine,' so I sware to the *r*, „ 31
the soul of the *r* went into my blood, „ 33
the *r* was awake all night for your sake, „ 49
The lilies and *r's* were all awake, „ 51
Queen *r* of the rosebud garden of girls, „ 53
Queen lily and *r* in one; „ 56
The red *r* cries 'She is near, she is near;' „ 63
the white *r* weeps, 'She is late;' „ 64
All made up of the lily and *r* „ *II v* 74
I almost fear they are not *r's*, but blood; „ 78
O'er the four rivers the first *r's* blew, *Geraint and E.* 764
A walk of *r's* ran from door to door; *Balin and Balan* 242
down that range of *r's* the great Queen Came „ 244
'Sweeter to me' she said 'this garden *r* „ 269
make her paler with a poison'd *r*? *Merlin and V.* 611
To crop his own sweet *r* before the hour?' „ 725
Till the high dawn piercing the royal *r* „ 739
Redder than any *r*, a joy to me, *Holy Grail* 521
'A worm within the *r*.' *Pelleas and E.* 399
'A *r*, but one, none other *r* had I, A *r*, one *r*, and this was wondrous fair, One *r*, a *r* that gladden'd earth and sky, One *r*, my *r*, that sweeten'd all mine air— „ 400
'One *r*, a *r* to gather by and by, One *r*, a *r*, to gather and to wear, No *r* but one—what other *r* had I? One *r*, my *r*; a *r* that will not die,— „ 405
slope of garden, all Of *r's* white and red, „ 422
and so spilt itself Among the *r's*, „ 427
colour and the sweetness from the *r*, *Lover's Tale i* 172
infuse Rich atar in the bosom of the *r*, „ 270
Leaning its *r's* on my faded eyes. „ 621
made The red *r* there a pale one— „ 696
hair Studded with one rich Provence *r*— „ *iii* 45
who himself was crown'd With *r's*, „ *iv* 297
my *r*, there my allegiance due. *Sir J. Oldcastle* 59
the blush Of millions of *r's* *V. of Maeldune* 44
Rich was the *r* of sunset there, *The Wreck* 136
Youth began Had set the lily and *r* *Ancient Sage* 156
My *r* of love for ever gone, „ 159
They made her lily and *r* in one, „ 161
Molly Magee, wid the red o' the *r* *Tomorrow* 31
Feed the budding *r* of boyhood *Locksley H., Sixty* 143
Fifty times the *r* has flower'd and faded, *On Jub. Q. Victoria* 1
with her flying robe and her poison'd *r*; *Vastness* 16
Each poor pale cheek a momentary *r*— *The Ring* 315
My *r's*—will he take them *now*— *Happy* 13
The *r's* that you cast aside— „ 22
I brought you, you remember, these *r's*, „ 73
you wave me off—poor *r's*—must I go— „ 101
gather the *r's* whenever they blow, *Romney's R.* 107
close to me to-day As this red *r*, *Roses on the R.* 7
Prophet of the *r's*, *The Snowdrop* 8

Rose (flower, colour) (*continued*) Shall the *r* Cry to the lotus ' No flower thou ' ? *Akbar's Dream* 36

Rose (verb) Some blue peaks in the distance *r*, *Dying Swan* 11
Heaven over Heaven *r* the night. *Mariana in the S.* 92
At last you *r* and moved the light, *Miller's D.* 125
And *r*, and, with a silent grace Approaching, „ 159
R slowly to a music slowly breathed, *Œnone* 41
R feud, with question unto whom 'twere due : „ 82
I *r* up in the silent night : *The Sisters* 25
Of ledge or shelf The rock *r* clear, *Palace of Art* 10
that sweet incense *r* and never fail'd, „ 45
Here *r*, an athlete, strong to break or bind „ 153
How sadly, I remember, *r* the morning of the year ! *May Queen, Con.* 3
this star *R* with you thro' a little arc *To J. S.* 26
so that he *r* With sacrifice, *On a Mourner* 33
arm *R* up from out the bosom of the lake, *M. d'Arthur* 30
Then quickly *r* Sir Bedivere, and ran, „ 133
r an arm Clothed in white samite, mystic, „ 143
from the pavement he half *r*, Slowly, „ 167
from them *r* A cry that shiver'd to the tingling stars, „ 198
she, that *r* the tallest of them all And fairest, „ 207
And up we *r*, and on the spur we went. *Gardener's D.* 32
but I *r* up Full of his bliss, „ 210
passion *r* thro' circumstantial grades „ 240
she *r* and took The child once more, *Dora* 80
ere the night we *r* And saunter'd home *Audley Court* 79
To some full music *r* and sank the sun, *Edwin Morris* 34
I crouch'd on one that *r* Twenty by measure ; *St. S. Stylites* 88
When his man-minded offset *r* To chase the deer *Talking Oak* 51
flower, she touch'd on, dipt and *r*, „ 131
we two *r*, There—closing like an individual life— *Love and Duty* 78
While Ilion like a mist *r* into towers. *Tithonus* 63
There *r* a noise of striking clocks, *Day-Dm., Revival* 2
R a ship of France. *The Captain* 28
So fresh they *r* in shadow'd swells *The Letters* 46
R again from where it seem'd to fail, *Vision of Sin* 24
r and past Bearing a lifelong hunger *Enoch Arden* 78
Enoch *r*, Cast his strong arms „ 227
She *r*, and fixt her swimming eyes upon him, „ 325
r And sent his voice beneath him thro' the wood. „ 443
r And paced Back toward his solitary home again, „ 793
He woke, he *r*, he spread his arms abroad „ 912
full willingly he *r* : *The Brook* 121
R from the clay it work'd in as she past, *Aylmer's Field* 170
Darkly that day *r* : „ 609
a full tide *R* with ground-swell, *Sea Dreams* 51
a fire-balloon *R* gem-like up before *Princess, Pro.* 75
I *r* and past Thro' the wild woods „ *i* 90
Whereon a woman-statue *r* with wings „ 210
She *r* her height, and said : „ *ii* 41
an officer *R* up, and read the statutes, „ 69
She *r* upon a wind of prophecy Dilating on the future ; „ 171
We *r*, and each by other drest with care „ *iii* 19
Stirring a sudden transport *r* and fell. „ *iv* 29
on a tripod in the midst A fragrant flame *r*, „ 34
There *r* a shriek as of a city sack'd ; „ 165
there *r* A hubbub in the court of half the maids „ 475
I beheld her, when she *r* The yesternight, „ *v* 175
among them *r* a cry As if to greet the king ; „ 248
On his haunches *r* the steed, „ 493
Part roll'd on the earth and *r* again and drew : „ 497
R a nurse of ninety years, „ *vi* 13
and a day *R* from the distance on her memory, „ 112
He *r*, and while each ear was prick'd „ *vi* 280
nor seem'd it strange that soon He *r* up whole, „ *vii* 65
from mine arms she *r* Glowing all over noble shame ; „ 159
I give you all The random scheme as wildly as it *r* : „ *Con.* 2
Then *r* a little feud betwixt the two, „ 23
And yet to give the story as it *r*, „ 26
But that there *r* a shout : „ 36
a shout *r* again, and made The long line „ 96
Again their ravening eagle *r* *Ode on Well.* 119
He *r* at dawn and, fired with hope, *Sailor Boy* 1
While I *r* up against my doom, *In Mem. cxxii* 2

Rose (verb) (*continued*) The love that *r* on stronger wings, *In Mem. cxxviii* 1
when they *r*, knighted from kneeling, *Com. of Arthur* 263
voices, slowly *r* and plunged Roaring, „ 381
And all at once all round him *r* in fire, „ 389
He *r*, and out of slumber calling two *Gareth and L.* 178
That *r* between the forest and the field. „ 191
Lot and many another *r* and fought Against thee, „ 354
R, and high-arching overbrow'd the hearth. „ 408
He *r* and past ; then Kay, a man of mien „ 452
Sir Gareth call'd him from where he *r*, „ 645
r High that the highest-crested helm „ 672
Baron set Gareth beside her, but at once she *r*. „ 852
Fell, as if dead ; but quickly *r* and drew, „ 967
Death was cast to ground, and slowly *r*. „ 1403
But when a rumour *r* about the Queen, *Marr. of Geraint* 24
But *r* at last, a single maiden with her, „ 160
from the mason's hand, a fortress *r* ; „ 244
r a cry That Edyrn's men were on them, „ 638
the maiden *r*, And left her maiden couch, „ 736
Then *r* Limours, and looking at his feet, *Geraint and E.* 302
Anon she *r*, and stepping lightly, „ 373
And once again she *r* to look at it, „ 387
R when they saw the dead man rise, „ 732
Then Balin *r*, and Balan, *Balin and Balan* 43
His arm half *r* to strike again, but fell : „ 223
Dishorsed himself, and *r* again, and fled Far, „ 330
He *r*, descended, met The scorner in the castle court, „ 386
And Balin *r*, ' Thither no more ! „ 483
he *r* To leave the hall, and, Vivien following *Merlin and V.* 31
r Fixt on her hearer's, „ 86
then I *r* and fled from Arthur's court „ 297
It was the time when first the question *r* „ 410
He *r* without a word and parted from her : „ 742
she dislink'd herself at once and *r*, „ 909
some light jest among them *r* With laughter *Lancelot and E.* 178
r And drove him into wastes and solitudes „ 251
rathe she *r*, half-cheated in the thought „ 340
They *r*, heard mass, broke fast, and rode away : „ 415
Then flash'd into wild tears, and *r* again, „ 613
Then *r* Elaine and glided thro' the fields, „ 843
full meekly *r* the maid, Stript off the case, „ 978
Then *r* the dumb old servitor, „ 1153
and *r* And pointed to the damsel, „ 1262
and she *r* Opening her arms to meet me, *Holy Grail* 394
' There *r* a hill that none but man could climb, „ 489
so that I *r* and fled, But wail'd and wept, „ 608
when he saw me, *r*, and bad me hail, „ 725
two great beasts *r* upright like a man, „ 821
nor that One Who *r* again : „ 919
Pelleas *r*, And loosed his horse, *Pelleas and E.* 60
but *r* With morning every day, „ 214
they *r* up, and bound, and brought him in. „ 288
Arthur *r* and Lancelot follow'd him, *Last Tournament* 112
She *r*, and set before him all he will'd ; „ 723
Behind him *r* a shadow and a shriek— „ 753
aghast the maiden *r*, White as her veil, *Guinevere* 362
Then *r* the King and moved his host by night, *Pass. of Arthur* 79
and with that wind the tide *R*, „ 126
an arm *R* up from out the bosom of the lake, „ 198
Then quickly *r* Sir Bedivere, and ran, „ 301
r an arm Clothed in white samite, mystic, „ 311
from the pavement he half *r*, Slowly, „ 335
from them *r* A cry that shiver'd to the tingling stars, „ 366
she, that *r* the tallest of them all And fairest, „ 375
the new sun *r* bringing the new year. „ 469
Whence *r* as it were breath and steam of gold, *Lover's Tale i* 402
The fancy stirr'd him so He *r* and went, „ *iv* 52
While all the guests in mute amazement *r*— „ 305
then *r* up, and with him all his guests „ 359
he *r* upon their decks, and he cried : *The Revenge* 100
she *r* and fled Beneath a pitiless rush *Sisters (E. and E.)* 236
Then *r* the howl of all the cassock'd wolves, *Sir J. Oldcastle* 158
Who *r* and doom'd me to the fire. „ 172
Whom once he *r* from off his throne to greet *Columbus* 5
then the great ' Laudamus ' *r* to heaven. „ 18

Rose (verb) (*continued*) each man, as he *r* from his rest, *V. of Maeldune* 85
THEY *r* to where their sovran eagle sails, *Montenegro* 1
Then *r* Achilles dear to Zeus; *Achilles over the T.* 2
I *r* Following a torrent till its myriad falls *Tiresias* 36
he *r* as it were on the wings of an eagle *The Wreck* 69
project after project *r*, and all of them were vain; *The Flight* 14
Celtic Demos *r* a Demon, *Locksley H., Sixty* 90
Step by step we *r* to greatness,— „ 130
truckled and cower'd When he *r* in his wrath, *Dead Prophet* 63
And dying *r*, and rear'd her arms, *The Ring* 222
then she *r*, She clung to me with such a hard embrace, „ 434
From under *r* a muffled moan of floods; *Prog. of Spring* 70
crooked, reeling, livid, thro' the mist *R*, *Death of Œnone* 28
She *r* and slowly down, „ 84
Rose-blowing Creeping thro' blossomy rushes and bowers of *r-b* bushes, *Leonine Eleg.* 3
Rosebud (adj.) Queen rose of the *r* garden of girls, *Maud I xxii* 53
Rosebud (s) Where on the double *r* droops *Day-Dm., L'Envoi* 47
A *r* set with little wilful thorns, *Princess, Pro.* 154
Rose-bush And a *r-b* leans upon, *Adeline* 14
to train the *r* that I set About the parlour-window *May Queen, N. Y's. E.* 47
Rose-campion *R-c*, bluebell, kingcup, *Last Tournament* 234
Rose-carnation And many a *r-c* feed *In Mem. ci* 7
Rosed darken'd in the west, And *r* in the east: *Sea Dreams* 40
her white neck Was *r* with indignation: *Princess vi* 344
Rose-garden For I know her own *r-g*, *Maud I xx* 41
Rose-hued Flowing beneath her *r-h* zone; *Arabian Nights* 140
Rose-leaf Letting the *rose-leaves* fall: *Claribel* 3
Like a *r-l* I will crush thee, *Lilian* 29
Rose-lips Thy *r-l* and full blue eyes *Adeline* 7
Rosemary the boar hath *rosemaries* and bay. *Gareth and L.* 1074
Rose of Lancaster (*See also* **Lancaster, Roses**) *R o L*, Red in thy birth, *Sir J. Oldcastle* 52
Redder to be, red *r o L*— „ 55
Rose-petal dust of the *r-p* belongs to the heart *Akbar's D., Inscrip.* 9
Rose-red (adj.) soon From thy *r-r* lips MY name Floweth; *Eleänore* 133
down the long beam stole the Holy Grail, *R-r* with beatings in it, *Holy Grail* 118
from the star there shot A *r-r* sparkle to the city, „ 530
Rose-red (s) beyond a bridge of treble bow, All in a *r-r* from the west, *Gareth and L.* 1087
Roses (Wars of the Roses) civil wars and earlier too Among the *R*, *Sisters (E. and E.)* 76
Rosetree One look'd all *r*, and another wore *Aylmer's Field* 157
O *r* planted in my grief, *Ancient Sage* 163
Rosewood 'She left the novel half-uncut Upon the *r* shelf; *Talking Oak* 118
Rosier but *r* luck will go With these rich jewels, *Last Tournament* 45
taller indeed, *R* and comelier, thou— „ 710
Rosiest And all of them redder than *r* health *V. of Maeldune* 65
Rosin And, sweating *r*, plump'd the pine *Amphion* 47
Rosy Who lets his *r* fingers play About his mother's neck, *Supp. Confessions* 42
kiss away the bitter words From off your *r* mouth. *Rosalind* 51
When Sleep had bound her in his *r* band, *Caress'd or chidden* 6
Thro' *r* taper fingers drew Her streaming curls *Mariana in the S.* 15
Winds all the vale in *r* folds, *Miller's D.* 242
With *r* slender fingers backward drew *Œnone* 176
Ganymede, his *r* thigh Half-buried in the Eagle's down, *Palace of Art* 121
Dark faces pale against that *r* flame, *Lotos-Eaters* 26
'Then flush'd her cheek with *r* light, *Talking Oak* 165
Coldly thy *r* shadows bathe me, *Tithonus* 66
As I have seen the *r* red flushing in the northern night. *Locksley Hall* 26
And, rapt thro' many a *r* change, *Day-Dm., Depart.* 23
But when the dawn of *r* childhood past, *Enoch Arden* 37
came a boy to be The *r* idol of her solitudes, „ 90
Philip's *r* face contracting grew Careworn and wan; „ 486
Stout, *r*, with his babe across his knees; „ 746
This had a *r* sea of gillyflowers About it; *Aylmer's Field* 159
And *r* knees and supple roundedness, *Lucretius* 190
And robed the shoulders in a *r* silk, *Princess, Pro.* 103
A *r* blonde, and in a college gown, „ *ii* 323

Rosy (*continued*) all The *r* heights came out above the lawns. *Princess iii* 365
Or *r* blossom in hot ravine, *The Daisy* 32
Green-rushing from the *r* thrones of dawn! (repeat) *Voice and the P.* 4, 40
A *r* warmth from marge to marge. *In Mem. xlvi* 16
When *r* plumelets tuft the larch, „ *xci* 1
And left the daisies *r*. *Maud I xii* 24
R is the West, *R* is the South, (repeat) „ *xvii* 5, 25
three fair girls In gilt and *r* raiment came: *Gareth and L.* 927
His arms, the *r* raiment, and the star. „ 938
How from the *r* lips of life and love, *Merlin and V.* 846
With *r* colours leaping on the wall; *Holy Grail* 120
The *r* quiverings died into the night. „ 123
her bloom A *r* dawn kindled in stainless heavens, *Pelleas and E.* 72
Glanced from the *r* forehead of the dawn „ 502
himself was crown'd With roses, none so *r* as himself— *Lover's Tale iv* 297
Or on your head their *r* feet, *To E. Fitzgerald* 9
the moon was falling greenish thro' a *r* glow, *Locksley H., Sixty* 178
made The *r* twilight of a perfect day. *The Ring* 187
From off the *r* cheek of waking Day. *Akbar's Dream* 202
Rosy-bright There all in spaces *r-b* *Mariana in the S.* 89
Rosy-kindled *r-k* with her brother's kiss— *Lancelot and E.* 393
Rosy-tinted In tufts of *r-t* snow; *Two Voices* 60
Rosy-white her light foot Shone *r-w*, *Œnone* 180
Rot 'Why, if man *r* in dreamless ease, *Two Voices* 280
Fall back upon a name! rest, *r* in that! *Aylmer's Field* 385
Rotatory And *r* thumbs on silken knees, „ 200
Rotted my thighs are *r* with the dew; *St. S. Stylites* 41
There the smouldering fire of fever creeps across the *r* floor, *Locksley H., Sixty* 223
Rotten (*See also* **Rain-rotten**) Till all be ripe and *r*. *Will Water.* 16
When the *r* woodland drips, *Vision of Sin* 81
To leap the *r* pales of prejudice, *Princess ii* 142
when the *r* hustings shake In another month *Maud I vi* 54
on whom all spears Are *r* sticks! *Gareth and L.* 1306
r branch Snapt in the rushing of the river-rain *Merlin and V.* 957
Yea, *r* with a hundred years of death, *Holy Grail* 496
seeing too much wit Makes the world *r*, *Last Tournament* 247
What *r* piles uphold their mason-work, *Sir J. Oldcastle* 67
Better a *r* borough or so Than a *r* fleet *Riflemen form!* 17
Rotting At the moist rich smell of the *r* leaves, *A spirit haunts* 17
'At least, not *r* like a weed, *Two Voices* 142
R on some wild shore with ribs of wreck, *Princess v* 147
That *r* inward slowly moulders all. *Merlin and V.* 395
Rough The filter'd tribute of the *r* woodland, *Ode to Memory* 63
And from a heart as *r* as Esau's hand, *Godiva* 28
Buss me, thou *r* sketch of man, *Vision of Sin* 189
And Enoch Arden, a *r* sailor's lad *Enoch Arden* 14
How many a *r* sea had he weather'd in her! „ 135
a *r* piece Of early rigid colour, *Aylmer's Field* 280
befool'd and idioted By the *r* amity of the other, „ 591
Dropping the too *r* H in Hell and Heaven, *Sea Dreams* 196
But your *r* voice (You spoke so loud) „ 280
That ever butted his *r* brother-brute *Lucretius* 197
Discuss'd his tutor, *r* to common men, *Princess, Pro.* 114
but 'No!' Roar'd the *r* king, 'you shall not; „ *i* 87
tho' the *r* kex break The starr'd mosaic, „ *iv* 77
At length my Sire, his *r* cheek wet with tears, „ *v* 23
Among piled arms and *r* accoutrements, „ 55
These were the *r* ways of the world till now. „ *vii* 257
Not once or twice in our *r* island story, *Ode on Well.* 201
Fabric *r*, or fairy-fine, *Ode Inter. Exhib.* 18
And says he is *r* but kind, *Maud I xix* 70
R but kind? yet I know He has plotted against me „ 79
Well, *r* but kind; why let it be so: „ 83
Is it kind to have made me a grave so *r*, „ *II v* 97
To guard thee on the *r* ways of the world.' *Com. of Arthur* 336
Lest that *r* humour of the kings of old *Gareth and L.* 377
'*R*, sudden, And pardonable, worthy to be knight— „ 653
nor *r* face, or voice, Brute bulk of limb, „ 1329
For old am I, and *r* the ways and wild; *Marr. of Geraint* 750
Then tending her *r* lord, tho' all unask'd, *Geraint and E.* 405
In lieu of this *r* beast upon my shield, *Balin and Balan* 196

Rough (*continued*) And one was *r* with wattling, *Balin and Balan* 366
Meeker than any child to a *r* nurse, *Lancelot and E.* 857
she knew right well What the *r* sickness meant, „ 888
I pray you, use some *r* discourtesy „ 973
Then the *r* Torre began to heave and move, „ 1066
I might have put my wits to some *r* use, „ 1306
r crowd, Hearing he had a difference with their priests, *Holy Grail* 673
R wives, that laugh'd and scream'd against the gulls, *Pelleas and E.* 89
Some *r* old knight who knew the worldly way, „ 192
Her light feet fell on our *r* Lyonnesse, *Last Tournament* 554
when first I rode from our *r* Lyonnesse, „ 664
The *r* brier tore my bleeding palms; *Lover's Tale ii* 18
In a tone so *r* that I broke into passionate tears, *The Wreck* 122
r rock-throne Of Freedom! *Montenegro* 9
Rougher Here is a story which in *r* shape *Aylmer's Field* 7
women sang Between the *r* voices of the men, *Princess, Pro.* 245
the *r* hand Is safer: „ *vi* 278
whenever a *r* gust might tumble a stormier wave, *The Wreck* 131
Roughest A cloth of *r* web, and cast it down, *Gareth and L.* 683
Rough-redden'd *R-r* with a thousand winter gales, *Enoch Arden* 95
Rough-ruddy And *r-r* faces Of lowly labour, *Merlin and the G.* 59
Rough-thicketed *R-t* were the banks and steep; *Gareth and L.* 907
Round (adj.) And o'er it many, *r* and small, *Mariana* 39
We knew the merry world was *r*, *The Voyage* 7
We know the merry world is *r*, „ 95
For so the whole *r* earth is every way *M. d'Arthur* 254
A body slight and *r*, and like a pear *Walk. to the Mail* 53
Her *r* white shoulder shaken with her sobs, *Princess iv* 289
For so the whole *r* earth is every way *Pass. of Arthur* 422
R was their pace at first, but slacken'd soon: *Geraint and E.* 33
Round (adv.) Shall make the winds blow *R* and *r*, *Nothing will Die* 24
flashing *r* and *r*, and whirl'd in an arch, *M. d'Arthur* 138
I'd clasp it *r* so close and tight. *Miller's D.* 180
And 'while the world runs *r* and *r*,' *Palace of Art* 13
r and *r* A whirlwind caught and bore us; *Lover's Tale ii* 196
Hands all *r*! (repeat) *Hands all Round* 9, 21, 33
great name of England, *r* and *r*. (repeat) „ 12, 36
And all her glorious empire, *r* and *r*. „ 24
An' the dogs was a-yowlin' all *r*, *Owd Roä* 107
flashing *r* and *r*, and whirl'd in an arch, *Pass. of Arthur* 306
Round (prep.) once had roll'd you *r* and *r* the Sun, *Poets and their B.* 10
Round (s) runs the *r* of life from hour to hour. *Circumstance* 9
Like the tender amber *r*, *Margaret* 19
The dark *r* of the dripping wheel, *Miller's D.* 102
in the *r* of Time Still father Truth? *Love and Duty* 4
To yonder argent *r*; *St. Agnes' Eve* 16
Comes out a perfect *r*. *Will Water.* 68
This *r* of green, this orb of flame, *In Mem. xxxiv* 5
Should move his *r's*, and fusing all „ *xlvii* 2
slowly breathing bare The *r* of space, „ *lxxxvi* 5
they roll Thro' such a *r* in heaven, *Holy Grail* 686
Round (verb) Should slowly *r* his orb, *Eleänore* 91
So *r's* he to a separate mind *In Mem. xlv* 9
r A higher height, a deeper deep. „ *lxiii* 11
Rounded (adj. and part.) clear canal Is *r* to as clear a lake. *Arabian Nights* 46
Devolved his *r* periods. *A Character* 18
Roll'd on each other, *r*, smooth'd, *D. of F. Women* 51
Sweet faces, *r* arms, and bosoms prest To little harps of gold; *Sea-Fairies* 3
o'er her *r* form Between the shadows of the vine-bunches *Œnone* 180
r, smooth'd, and brought Into the gulfs of sleep. *D. of F. Women* 51
And moves not on the *r* curl. *Day-Dm., Sleep. B.* 8
O'er ocean-mirrors *r* large, *In Mem. xii* 9
vizoring up a red And cipher face of *r* foolishness, *Gareth and L.* 1039
only the *r* moon Thro' the tall oriel on the rolling sea. *Holy Grail* 830
Rounded (verb) slowly *r* to the east The one black shadow *Mariana in the S.* 79
And *r* by the stillness of the beach *Audley Court* 10
The men who met him *r* on their heels *Pelleas and E.* 142
Roundedness rosy knees and supple *r*, *Lucretius* 190
Roundel glorious *r* echoing in our ears, *Merlin and V.* 426
Roundelay Twice or thrice his *r*, (repeat) *The Owl i* 11, 12
Or carol some old *r*, *Gareth and L.* 506
U

Roundelay (*continued*) To dance without a catch, a *r* To dance to.' *Last Tournament* 250
Rounder softer all her shape And *r* seem'd: *Princess vii* 137
The *r* cheek had brighten'd into bloom. *The Ring* 351
Roundest making them An armlet for the *r* arm on earth, *Lancelot and E.* 1183
Roundhead And far below the *R* rode, *Talking Oak* 299
Rounding The level waste, the *r* gray. *Mariana* 44
Round Table (*See also* **Table, Table Round**) But now the whole *R T* is dissolved *M. d'Arthur* 234
'Have any of our *R T* held their vows?' *Pelleas and E.* 533
Have founded my *R T* in the North, *Last Tournament* 78
The glory of our *R T* is no more.' (repeat) „ 189, 212
But now the whole *R T* is dissolved *Pass. of Arthur* 402
Rouse (s) Have a *r* before the morn: (repeat) *Vision of Sin* 96, 120
Rouse (verb) From deep thought himself he *r's*, *L. of Burleigh* 21
Roused has *r* the child again. *Sea Dreams* 281
I am *r* by the wail of a child, *The Wreck* 7
r a snake that hissing writhed away; *Death of Œnone* 88
Rout (s) a *r* of saucy boys Brake on us at our books, *Princess v* 394
Down on a *r* of craven foresters. *Gareth and L.* 841
And midmost of a *r* of roisterers, *Geraint and E.* 274
With all his *r* of random followers, „ 382
And blindly rush'd on all the *r* behind. „ 466
whirling *r* Led by those two rush'd into dance, *Lover's Tale iii* 54
Rout (verb) O sound to *r* the brood of cares, *In Mem. lxxxix* 17
Rove How young Columbus seem'd to *r*, *The Daisy* 17
R's from the living brother's face, *In Mem. xxxii* 7
Let his eye *r* in following, *Marr. of Geraint* 399
Their lot with ours to *r* the world about; *Pref. Son. 19th Cent.* 11
Wild woods in which we *r* no more, *The Flight* 84
Roved While I *r* about the forest, *Boädicea* 35
I *r* at random thro' the town, *In Mem. lxxxvii* 3
Wild woods in which we *r* with him, *The Flight* 83
Rover and thou hast been a *r* too, *Last Tournament* 543
Roving When after *r* in the woods *Miller's D.* 58
R the trackless realms of Lyonnesse, *Lancelot and E.* 35
Row (s) The streams through many a lilied *r* *The Winds, etc.* 5
round the cool green courts there ran a *r* Of cloisters, *Palace of Art* 25
like white sea-birds in a *r*, *V. of Maeldune* 101
Row (verb) taught me how to skate, to *r*, *Edwin Morris* 19
he can steer and *r*, and he Will guide me *Lancelot and E.* 1128
R us out from Desenzano, to your Sirmione *r*! *Frater ave, etc.* 1
Row'd and how I *r* across And took it, *M. d'Arthur* 32
Arthur *r* across and took it— *Com. of Arthur* 298
and how I *r* across And took it, *Pass. of Arthur* 200
So they *r*, and there we landed— *Frater ave, etc.* 2
Rowel He dash'd the *r* into his horse, *Pelleas and E.* 486
Rowing 'Who, *r* hard against the stream, *Two Voices* 211
Royal (adj.) (*See also* **Crown-royal**) *Victoria,—since your R grace* *To the Queen* 5
With *r* frame-work of wrought gold; *Ode to Memory* 82
Died the sound of *r* cheer; *L. of Shalott iv* 48
She to Paris made Proffer of *r* power, *Œnone* 111
paintings of wise men I hung The *r* dais round. *Palace of Art* 132
She threw her *r* robes away. „ 290
'By holy rood, a *r* beard! *Day-Dm., Revival* 20
Cophetua sware a *r* oath: *Beggar Maid* 15
From whence the *R* mind, familiar with her, *Princess iv* 235
(our *r* word upon it, He comes back safe) „ *v* 224
Last, Ida's answer, in a *r* hand, „ 371
Till her people all around the *r* chariot agitated, *Boädicea* 73
He set his *r* signet there; *In Mem. cxxv* 12
Break not, for thou art *R*, but endure, *Ded. of Idylls* 45
For this an Eagle, a *r* Eagle, laid *Gareth and L.* 44
Rolling her smoke about the *R* mount, „ 190
r crown Sparkled, and swaying upon a restless elm *Balin and Balan* 462
Hail, *r* knight, we break on thy sweet rest, „ 470
Drove his mail'd heel athwart the *r* crown, „ 540
Boldness and *r* knighthood of the bird *Merlin and V.* 134
Till the high dawn piercing the *r* rose „ 739
but meaning all at once To snare her *r* fancy *Lancelot and E.* 71
Tho' quartering your own *r* arms of Spain, *Columbus* 115
Shall the *r* voice be mute? *By an Evolution.* 14
Royal (s) O LOYAL to the *r* in thyself, *To the Queen ii* 1

Royal-born a cotter's babe is *r-b* by right divine; *Locksley H., Sixty* 125
Royaller *R* game is mine. *Merlin and V.* 108
Royal-rich So *r-r* and wide.' *Palace of Art* 20
this great house so *r-r*, and wide, „ 191
Royalty fling Thy *r* back into the riotous fits *Sir J. Oldcastle* 100
Roystering her brother lingers late With a *r* company) *Maud I xiv* 15
Rub (*See also* **Roob**) We *r* each other's angles down, *In Mem. lxxxix* 40
Rubbed And yawn'd, and *r* his face, *Day-Dm., Revival* 19
Rubbish Or cast as *r* to the void, *In Mem. liv* 7
Ev'n in the jumbled *r* of a dream, *Merlin and V.* 347
Rubric set your thoughts in *r* thus *Princess iii* 50
Ruby (adj.) I'll stake my *r* ring upon it you did.' „ *Pro.* 170
With a satin sail of a *r* glow, *The Islet* 13
This *r* necklace thrice around her neck, *Last Tournament* 19
in the light's last glimmer Tristram show'd And swung the *r* carcanet. „ 740
Ruby (s) a carcanet Of *r* swaying to and fro, „ 7
an ye fling those *rubies* round my neck „ 312
These be no *rubies*, this is frozen blood, „ 413
Yet glowing in a heart of *r*— *Lover's Tale iv* 196
Ruby-budded break from the *r-b* lime *Maud I iv* 1
Ruby-chain show'd them both the *r-c*, *Last Tournament* 409
Ruby-circled Queen Isolt With *r-c* neck, „ 364
Ruddy (*See also* **Rough-ruddy**) His *r* cheek upon my breast. *The Sisters* 20
By and by The *r* square of comfortable light, *Enoch Arden* 726
R and white, and strong on his legs, *Grandmother* 2
His face was *r*, his hair was gold, *The Victim* 35
As he glow'd like a *r* shield on the Lion's breast. *Maud III vi* 14
R thro' both the roofs of sight, *Tiresias* 3
Ruddy-hearted Our elmtree's *r-h* blossom-flake *To Mary Boyle* 3
Rude sketches *r* and faint. *Aylmer's Field* 100
'As these *r* bones to us, are we to her *Princess iii* 296
And push'd by *r* hands from its pedestal, „ *v* 58
With a crew that is neither *r* nor rash, *The Islet* 10
into that *r* hall Stept with all grace, *Lancelot and E.* 262
Who will not *hear* denial, vain and *r* *Lover's Tale i* 628
He fought the boys that were *r*, *First Quarrel* 14
Ruder All night no *r* air perplex Thy sliding keel, *In Mem. ix* 9
Rudest (Those peerless flowers which in the *r* wind *Ode to Memory* 24
Rue Old year, we'll dearly *r* for you: *D. of the O. Year* 43
He could not ever *r* his marrying me— *Dora* 146
May *r* the bargain made.' *Princess i* 74
Rued the hunter *r* His rash intrusion, „ *iv* 203
But I *r* it arter a bit, *Spinster's S's.* 51
Ruffian (adj.) mine of *r* violators! *Boädicea* 50
Ruffian (s) vitriol madness flushes up in the *r's* head, *Maud I i* 37
so the *r's* growl'd, Fearing to lose, *Geraint and E.* 563
r's at their ease Among their harlot-brides, *Last Tournament* 427
Ruffle *R's* her pure cold plume, and takes the flood *M. d'Arthur* 268
R thy mirror'd mast, *In Mem. ix* 7
I swear it would not *r* me so much *Geraint and E.* 150
As the sharp wind that *r's* all day long *Guinevere* 50
R's her pure cold plume, and takes the flood *Pass. of Arthur* 436
Ruffled (adj.) To sleek her *r* peace of mind, *Merlin and V.* 899
Blurr'd like a landskip in a *r* pool,— *Romney's R.* 114
Ruffled (verb) not a hair *R* upon the scarfskin, *Aylmer's Field* 660
Rankled in him and *r* all his heart, *Guinevere* 49
Rugged And *r* barks begin to bud, *My life is full* 18
by slow prudence to make mild A *r* people, *Ulysses* 37
With *r* maxims hewn from life; *Ode on Well.* 184
Ruin (s) (*See also* **Abbey-ruin**) Boat, island, *r's* of a castle, *Edwin Morris* 6
Sit brooding in the *r's* of a life, *Love and Duty* 12
crash of *r*, and the loss of all But Enoch *Enoch Arden* 549
Hurt in that night of sudden *r* and wreck, „ 564
By that old bridge which, half in *r's* then, *The Brook* 79
Sat shuddering at the *r* of a world; *Sea Dreams* 30
but a gulf of *r*, swallowing gold, „ 79
the sea roars *R*: a fearful night!' „ 81
from the gaps and chasms of *r* left „ 225
but satiated at length Came to the *r's*, *Princess, Pro.* 91
echo like a ghostly woodpecker, Hid in the *r's*; „ 218
A Gothic *r* and a Grecian house, „ 232
when the crimson-rolling eye Glares *r*, „ *iv* 495
Rang *r*, answer'd full of grief and scorn. „ *vi* 333

Ruin (s) (*continued*) Roman strength Turbìa show'd In *r*, *The Daisy* 6
And placed them in this *r*; *Marr. of Geraint* 643
men may fear Fresh fire and *r*. *Geraint and E.* 823
And ending in a *r*—nothing left, *Merlin and V.* 883
our horses stumbling as they trode On heaps of *r*, *Holy Grail* 717
Red *r*, and the breaking up of laws, *Guinevere* 426
Which wrought the *r* of my lord the King.' „ 689
Great hills of *r's*, and collapsed masses *Lover's Tale ii* 65
R's, the *r* of all my life and me! „ 68
and roll their *r's* down the slope. *Locksley H., Sixty* 138
beneath the Roman *r* where the purple flowers grow, *Frater ave, etc.* 4
He that wrought my *r*— *Forlorn* 2
This Satan-haunted *r*, this little city of sewers, *Happy* 34
Rear'd on the tumbled *r's* of an old fane *St. Telemachus* 6
and there Gaze at the *r*, „ 14
from the *r* arose The shriek and curse *Akbar's Dream* 189
Ruin (verb) A plot, a plot, a plot, to *r* all!' *Princess ii* 192
for fear This whole foundation *r*, „ 341
heiress of your plan, And takes and *r's* all; „ *iii* 238
recks not to *r* a realm in her name. *Vastness* 10
Ruin'd (adj. and part.) (*See also* **Rake-ruin'd**) Tho' watching from a *r* tower *Two Voices* 77
I wish that somewhere in the *r* folds, *Œnone* 221
So saying, from the *r* shrine he stept *M. d'Arthur* 45
And lighted at a *r* inn, and said: *Vision of Sin* 62
R trunks on wither'd forks, „ 93
'We are men of *r* blood; „ 99
R! *r*! the sea roars Ruin: a fearful night!' *Sea Dreams* 80
The *r* shells of hollow towers? *In Mem. lxxvi* 16
Or *r* chrysalis of one. „ *lxxxii* 8
flying gold of the *r* woodlands drove thro' the air. *Maud I i* 12
Rest! the good house, tho' *r*, O my son, *Marr. of Geraint* 378
who swept the dust of *r* Rome From off the threshold *Gareth and L.* 135
But she, remembering her old *r* hall, *Geraint and E.* 254
So saying, from the *r* shrine he stept, *Pass. of Arthur* 213
And *r* by *him*, by *him*, *Despair* 77
Over all this *r* world of ours, *Sisters (E. and E.)* 22
I saw the tiger in the *r* fane Spring from his fallen God, *Demeter and P.* 79
Then home, and past the *r* mill. *The Ring* 156
Ruin'd (verb) And stirr'd this vice in you which *r* man Thro' woman the first hour: *Merlin and V.* 362
For a woman *r* the world, as God's own scriptures tell, And a man *r* mine, *Charity* 3
Ruining (*See also* **Realm-ruining**) *R* along the illimitable inane, *Lucretius* 40
In twelve great battles *r* overthrown. *Guinevere* 432
Ruinous He look'd and saw that all was *r*. *Marr. of Geraint* 315
And keeps me in this *r* castle here, „ 462
The *r* donjon as a knoll of moss, *Balin and Balan* 334
And thence I past Far thro' a *r* city, *Holy Grail* 429
Rule (s) royal power, ample *r* Unquestion'd, *Œnone* 111
Phantoms of other forms of *r*, *Love thou thy land* 59
Seeing obedience is the bond of *r*. *M. d'Arthur* 94
when shall all men's good Be each man's *r*, *Golden Year* 48
err from honest Nature's *r*! *Locksley Hall* 61
Averring it was clear against all *r's* *Princess i* 178
'They seek us: out so late is out of *r's*. „ *iv* 219
I beänt a-gawin' to breäk my *r*. *N. Farmer, O. S.* 4
I weänt breäk *r's* fur Doctor, „ 67
Seeing obedience is the bond of *r*. *Pass. of Arthur* 262
Your *r* has made the people love Their ruler. *To Marq. of Dufferin* 9
Rule (verb) *May you* r *us long*, *To the Queen* 20
sendest out the man To *r* by land and sea, *England and Amer.* 2
I should come again To *r* once more— *M. d'Arthur* 24
HE that only *r's* by terror *The Captain* 1
she That taught the Sabine how to *r*, *Princess ii* 79
wish'd to marry: they could *r* a house; „ 465
But they my troubled spirit *r*, *In Mem. xxviii* 17
O Sorrow, wilt thou *r* my blood, „ *lix* 5
Who can *r* and dare not lie. *Maud I x* 66
'Who is he That he should *r* us? *Com. of Arthur* 69
Moaning and wailing for an heir to *r* After him, „ 207
sought to *r* for his own self and hand, „ 219
'Shall Rome or Heathen *r* in Arthur's realm? „ 485
Then Gareth, 'Here he *r's*. *Gareth and L.* 1354
heathen, who, some say, shall *r* the land *Lancelot and E.* 65

Rule (verb) (*continued*) 'A moral child without the craft to *r*, Lancelot and E. 146
as Arthur's Queen I move and *r*: " 1221
Wed thou our Lady, and *r* over us, Holy Grail 605
King must guard That which he *r's*, " 906
he knows false, abide and *r* the house: Guinevere 515
I should come again To *r* once more; Pass. of Arthur 192
The nameless Power, or Powers, that *r* Ancient Sage 29
Night and Shadow *r* below " 243
only those who cannot read can *r*. Locksley H., Sixty 132
Or Might would *r* alone; Epilogue 29
thro' the Will of One who knows and *r's*— The Ring 42
and *r* thy Providence of the brute. By an Evolution. 16
For all they *r*—by equal law for all? Akbar's Dream 110
only let the hand that *r's*, With politic care, " 127
Power That is not seen and *r's* from far away— " 138
Ruled captain of my dreams *R* in the eastern sky. D. of F. Women 264
grim Earl, who *r* In Coventry: Godiva 12
Fairer his talk, a tongue that *r* the hour, Aylmer's Field 194
A nation yet, the rulers and the *r*— Princess, Con. 53
There they *r*, and thence they wasted Boädicea 54
infant civilisation be *r* with rod or with knout? Maud I iv 47
many a petty king ere Arthur came *R* in this isle, Com. of Arthur 6
listen to me, and by me be *r*, Geraint and E. 624
He saw the laws that *r* the tournament Last Tournament 160
if this earth be *r* by Perfect Love, D. of the Duke of C. 8
Ruler *And leave us* r's *of your blood* To the Queen 21
The deathless *r* of thy dying house Aylmer's Field 661
A nation yet, the *r's* and the ruled— Princess, Con. 53
The name was *r* of the dark—Isolt? Last Tournament 606
here the faith That made us *r's*? To the Queen ii 19
What *r's* but the Days and Hours Ancient Sage 95
Unprophetic *r's* they— Open. I. and C. Exhib. 26
Your rule has made the people love Their *r*. To Marq. of Dufferin 10
Ruling And *r* by obeying Nature's powers, Ode Inter. Exhib. 40
Dreams *r* when wit sleeps! Balin and Balan 143
r that which knows To its own harm: To the Queen ii 58
To one, that *r* has increased Her greatness To Marq. of Dufferin 7
Rumble (*See also* **Rummle**) Clamour and *r*, and ringing and clatter, Maud II v 13
Rumbled And round the attics *r*, The Goose 46
Rumbling *See* **Roomlin'**
Rummage from what side The blindfold *r* Balin and Balan 416
Rummaged tapt at doors, And *r* like a rat: Walk. to the Mail 38
Rummle (rumble) I eärd the bricks an' the baulks *r* down Owd Roä 109
Rumour empty breath And *r's* of a doubt? M. d'Arthur 100
Wife-hunting, as the *r* ran, was he: Aylmer's Field 212
down the wind With *r*, " 496
With *r* of Prince Arac hard at hand. Princess v 112
let the turbid streams of *r* flow Ode on Well. 181
months ran on and *r* of battle grew, Maud III vi 29
Sir, there be many *r's* on this head: Com. of Arthur 178
But when a *r* rose about the Queen, Marr. of Geraint 24
Vext at a *r* issued from herself Merlin and V. 153
A *r* runs, she took him for the King, " 776
Hid from the wide world's *r* by the grove Lancelot and E. 522
I hear of *r's* flying thro' your court. " 1190
let *r's* be: When did not *r's* fly? " 1193
This night, a *r* wildly blown about Came, Guinevere 153
Less noble, being, as all *r* runs, " 339
but empty breath And *r's* of a doubt? Pass. of Arthur 268
somewhere in the North, as *R* sang Sir J. Oldcastle 56
Run (s) so quick the *r*, We felt the good ship The Voyage 14
Lies the hawk's cast, the mole has made his *r*, Aylmer's Field 849
Run (verb) *r* short pains Thro' his warm heart; Supp. Confessions 161
When cats *r* home and light is come, The Owl i 1
trenched waters *r* from sky to sky; Ode to Memory 104
R's up the ridged sea. Sea-Fairies 39
And then the tears *r* down my cheek, Oriana 69
So *r's* the round of life from hour to hour. Circumstance 9
would *r* to and fro, and hide and seek, The Mermaid 35
r thro' every change of sharp and flat; Caress'd or chidden 4
And thro' the field the road *r's* by L. of Shalott i 4
Thro' the wave that *r's* for ever By the island " 12
'while the world *r's* round and round,' Palace of Art 13
r before the fluttering tongues of fire; D. of F. Women 30
Run (verb) (*continued*) where the bay *r's* up its latest horn. Audley Court 11
can *r* My faith beyond my practice into his: Edwin Morris 53
The Sun will *r* his orbit, Love and Duty 22
one increasing purpose *r's*, Locksley Hall 137
they shall dive, and they shall *r*, " 169
The vilest herb that *r's* to seed Amphion 95
Against its fountain upward *r's* Will Water. 35
To make my blood *r* quicker, " 110
Where the bloody conduit *r's*, Vision of Sin 144
he clamour'd from a casement, '*R*' The Brook 85
'*R*, Katie!' Katie never ran: " 87
R's in a river of blood to the sick sea. Aylmer's Field 768
enter'd one Of those dark caves that *r* beneath the cliffs. Sea Dreams 90
who this way *r's* Before the rest— Lucretius 191
Feyther *r* oop to the farm, an' I *r's* oop to the mill; N. Farmer, N. S. 54
An' I'll *r* oop to the brig, " 55
He that *r's* may read. The Flower 18
Cataract brooks to the ocean *r*, The Islet 17
'The stars,' she whispers, 'blindly *r*; In Mem. iii 5
Till all my widow'd race be *r*; " ix 18
Till all my widow'd race be *r*. " xvii 20
So *r's* my dream: but what am I? " liv 17
R out your measured arcs, " cv 27
For every grain of sand that *r's*, " cxvii 9
I hear thee where the waters *r*; " cxxx 2
And letting a dangerous thought *r* wild Maud I xix 52
long-lanced battle let their horses *r*. Com. of Arthur 104
a river *R's* in three loops about her living-place; Gareth and L. 612
these be for the snare (So *r's* thy fancy) " 1082
Shot from behind me, *r* along the ground; Balin and Balan 374
rumour *r's*, she took him for the King, Merlin and V. 776
let his eyes *R* thro' the peopled gallery Lancelot and E. 430
being snapt—We *r* more counter to the soul Last Tournament 659
being, as all rumour *r's*, The most disloyal friend Guinevere 339
flowers that *r* poison in their veins. Lover's Tale i 347
the sight *r* over Upon his steely gyves; " ii 156
r's out when ya breäks the shell. Village Wife 4
It is charged and we fire, and they *r*. Def. of Lucknow 68
R's in the rut, a coward to the Priest. Sir J. Oldcastle 78
make one people ere man's race be *r*: To Victor Hugo 11
as I saw the white sail *r*, And darken, The Flight 39
May we find, as ages *r*, Open I. and C. Exhib. 11
but I knaws they *r's* upo' four,— Owd Roä 17
'Ya mun *r* fur the lether. " 77
Sa I *r's* to the yard fur a lether, " 82
as this poor earth's pale history *r's*,— Vastness 3
She comes! The loosen'd rivulets *r*; Prog. of Spring 9
And I would that my race were *r*, The Dreamer 8
Or ever your race be *r*! " 30
Helter-skelter *r's* the age; Poets and Critics 2
Rung Loud, loud *r* out the bugle's brays, Oriana 48
And as he rode his armour *r*, L. of Shalott iii 17
The distant battle flash'd and *r*. Two Voices 126
Not a bell was *r*, not a prayer was read; Maud II v 24
Runlet And *r's* babbling down the glen. Mariana in the S. 44
Nor *r* tinkling from the rock; In Mem. c 13
Runn'd (ran) an' *r* plow thruff it an' all, N. Farmer, O. S. 42
An' 'e niver *r* arter the fox, Village Wife 41
An' sarvints *r* in an' out, " 56
the poodle *r* at tha once, an' thou *r* Spinster's S's. 38
an' the Freeä Traäde *r* 'i my 'ead, Owd Roä 54
Haäfe o' the parish *r* oop " 115
Runnel The babbling *r* crispeth, Claribel 19
dashing *r* in the spring Had liveried Lover's Tale ii 49
fallen Prone by the dashing *r* on the grass. " 101
Runnin' sthrames *r* down at the back o' the glin Tomorrow 24
Running (*See also* **Runnin'**) Him *r* on thus hopefully she heard, Enoch Arden 201
know his babes were *r* wild Like colts " 304
While you were *r* down the sands, Sea Dreams 265
Of *r* fires and fluid range Of lawless airs, Supp. Confessions 147
Betwixt the green brink and the *r* foam, Sea-Fairies 2
a stable wench Came *r* at the call, Princess i 227
The second was my father's *r* thus: " iv 406

Running (*continued*) fling Their pretty maids in the *r* flood, *Princess v* 382
All *r* on one way to the home of my love, *Window, On the Hill* 8
You are all *r* on, and I stand on the slope " 9
R down to my own dark wood; *Maud I xiv* 30
for *r* sharply with thy spit Down on a rout *Gareth and L.* 840
And *r* down the Soul, a Shape that fled " 1207
R too vehemently to break upon it. *Marr. of Geraint* 78
and by fountains *r* wine, *Last Tournament* 141
perchance of streams *R* far on within its inmost halls, *Lover's Tale i* 523
the mad little craft *R* on and on, *The Revenge* 39
highway *r* by it leaves a breadth Of sward *Sisters (E. and E.)* 80
r out below Thro' the fire *V. of Maeldune* 42
neck Of land *r* out into rock— *Despair* 10
dark little worlds *r* round them were worlds " 18
r after a shadow of good; " 92
Runnymede Is this the manly strain of *R*? *Third of Feb.* 34
Rush (s) thro' blossomy *r'es* and bowers *Leonine Eleg.* 3
the *r* of the air in the prone swing, *Aylmer's Field* 86
the shrieking *r* of the wainscot mouse, *Maud I vi* 71
Follow'd a *r* of eagle's wings, *Last Tournament* 417
A flat malarian world of reed and *r*! *Lover's Tale iv* 142
Beneath a pitiless *r* of Autumn rain *Sisters (E. and E.)* 237
The *r* of the javelins, *Batt. of Brunanburh* 88
R of Suns, and roll of systems, *God and the Univ.* 3
Rush (verb) those, who clench their nerves to *r* *Love and Duty* 77
To *r* abroad all round the little haven, *Enoch Arden* 867
A thousand arms and *r'es* to the Sun. *Princess vi* 37
R to the roof, sudden rocket, *W. to Alexandra* 20
would *r* on a thousand lances and die— *V. of Maeldune* 24
Rush'd And out spirits *r* together *Locksley Hall* 38
We *r* into each other's arms. *The Letters* 40
A wind arose and *r* upon the South, *Princess i* 97
on a sudden *r* Among us, out of breath, " *iv* 374
I am his dearest!' *r* on the knife. *The Victim* 72
And blindly *r* on all the rout behind. *Geraint and E.* 466
thro' the tree *R* ever a rainy wind, *Last Tournament* 16
R into dance, and like wild Bacchanals *Lover's Tale iii* 25
whirling rout Led by those two *r* into dance, " 55
Poor Julian—how he *r* away; " *iv* 2
R each at each with a cry, " 373
Rushing (*See also* **Green-rushing, Upward-rushing**) The shadow *r* up the sea, *Rosalind* 11
Like some broad river *r* down alone, *Mine be the strength* 2
The milldam *r* down with noise, *Miller's D.* 50
whisper of the south-wind *r* warm, *Locksley Hall* 125
Far purelier in his *r's* to and fro, *Aylmer's Field* 458
My lady's Indian kinsman *r* in, " 593
A *r* tempest of the wrath of God " 757
for thrice I heard the rain *R*; *Lucretius* 27
r battle-bolt sang from the three-decker *Maud I i* 50
we rode Thro' the dim land against a *r* wind, *Merlin and V.* 425
rotten branch Snapt in the *r* of the river-rain " 957
Lancelot, who *r* outward lionlike Leapt on him, *Guinevere* 107
Blaze by the *r* brook or silent well. " 400
the storm *r* over the down, *Rizpah* 6
I am flung from the *r* tide of the world *The Wreck* 6
hellish heat of a wretched life *r* back thro' the veins? *Despair* 68
Rushy Or dimple in the dark of *r* coves, *Ode to Memory* 60
Russet She clad herself in a *r* gown, *Lady Clare* 57
An old storm-beaten, *r*, many-stain'd Pavilion, *Gareth and L.* 1113
Broad-faced with under-fringe of *r* beard, *Geraint and E.* 537
And took his *r* beard between his teeth; " 713
Russet-bearded The *r-b* head roll'd on the floor. " 729
Russia *R* bursts our Indian barrier, *Locksley H., Sixty* 115
Russian (adj.) And welcome *R* flower, a people's pride, *W. to Marie Alex.* 6
the points of the *R* lances arose in the sky; *Heavy Brigade* 5
In the heart of the *R* hordes, " 50
Russian (s) Cossack and *R* Reel'd *Light Brigade* 34
thousands of *R's*, Thousands of horsemen, *Heavy Brigade* 2
Rust (s) fearing *r* or soilure fashion'd for it *Lancelot and E.* 7
That keeps the *r* of murder on the walls— *Guinevere* 74
Rust (verb) lest we *r* in ease. *Love thou thy land* 42
To *r* unburnish'd, not to shine in use! *Ulysses* 23
the cannon-bullet *r* on a slothful shore, *Maud III vi* 26
Rusted (adj.) The *r* nails fell from the knots *Mariana* 3

Rusted (adj.) (*continued*) Yniol's *r* arms Were on his princely person, *Marr. of Geraint* 543
Rusted (verb) when the bracken *r* on their crags, *Edwin Morris* 100
Rustic Not by the well-known stream and *r* spire, *The Brook* 188
that in the garden snared Picus and Faunus, *r* Gods? *Lucretius* 182
We dropt with evening on a *r* town *Princess i* 170
a *r* tower Half-lost in belts of hop and breadths of wheat; " *Con.* 44
The rich Virgilian *r* measure Of Lari Maxume, *The Daisy* 75
Ye think the *r* cackle of your bourg *Marr. of Geraint* 276
They take the *r* murmur of their bourg " 419
sound and honest, *r* Squire, *Locksley H., Sixty* 239
Rustiest drew The *r* iron of old fighters' hearts; *Merlin and V.* 574
Rusting Forgotten, *r* on his iron hills, *Princess v* 146
Rustle (verb) Sweet-Gale *r* round the shelving keel; *Edwin Morris* 110
heard In the dead hush the papers that she held *R*: *Princess iv* 391
A strange knee *r* thro' her secret reeds, *Balin and Balan* 354
Rustle (s) Past, as a *r* or twitter in the wood *Last Tournament* 365
Rustled each, in maiden plumes We *r*: *Princess i* 203
Rustling *r* thro' The low and bloomed foliage, *Arabian Nights* 12
And *r* once at night about the place, *Aylmer's Field* 547
Rusty Anchors of *r* fluke, and boats updrawn; *Enoch Arden* 18
Ah, let the *r* theme alone! *Will Water.* 177
I think they should not wear our *r* gowns, *Princess, Pro.* 143
I grate on *r* hinges here: " *i* 86
but old And *r*, old and *r*, Prince Geraint, *Marr. of Geraint* 478
Cries of the partridge like a *r* key *Lover's Tale ii* 115
Rut same old *r* would deepen year by year; *Aylmer's Field* 34
Runs in the *r*, a coward to the Priest. *Sir J. Oldcastle* 78
Ruth (proper name) Fairer than *R* among the fields of corn, *Aylmer's Field* 680
Ruth methinks Some *r* is mine for thee. *Gareth and L.* 895
r began to work Against his anger in him, *Geraint and E.* 101
Geraint Had *r* again on Enid looking pale: " 203
Then with another humorous *r* remark'd " 250
Ruthless As *r* as a baby with a worm, *Walk. to the Mail* 108
And gathering *r* gold— *Columbus* 135
r Mussulman Who flings his bowstrung Harem in the sea, *Romney's R.* 134
Rye Long fields of barley and of *r*, *L. of Shalott i* 2

S

Saäilor (sailor) what *s's* a' seëan an' a' doon; *North. Cobbler* 4
Saäint's-daäy (Saints-day) *S-d*—they was ringing the bells. *N. Farmer, N. S.* 13
Saäle (sale) fetch'd nigh to nowt at the *s*, *Village Wife* 73
Saäme (lard) An' I niver puts *s* i' *my* butter, " 119
Saätan (Satan) like *S* as fell Down out o' heaven *North. Cobbler* 57
Saäve (save) wur it nobbut to *s* my life; " 84
I may *s* mysen yit.' *Village Wife* 66
she beäld 'Ya mun *s* little Dick, *Owd Roä* 81
Saävin' (saving) in *s* a son fur me. " 96
Saäy (say) use to *s* the things that a do. *N. Farmer, O. S.* 6
I thowt a 'ad summut to *s*, " 19
I weänt *s* men be loiars, " 27
—that's what I 'ears 'em *s*. " *N. S.* 2
—that's what I 'ears 'im *s*— " 59
Feyther 'ud *s* I wur ugly es sin, *Spinster's S's.* 15
when they 'evn't a word to *s*. " 102
Saäyin' (saying) an' wur niver sa nigh *s* Yis. " 32
an' *s* ondecent things, " 90
Sabæan Dripping with *S* spice *Adeline* 53
Sabbath (adj.) 'Behold, it is the *S* morn.' *Two Voices* 402
Sabbath (s) Half God's good *s*, *To J. M. K.* 11
The *s's* of Eternity, One *s* deep and wide— *St Agnes' Eve* 33
fixt the *S*. Darkly that day rose: *Aylmer's Field* 609
woke, and went the next, The *S*, *Sea Dreams* 19
On that loud *s* shook the spoiler *Ode on Well.* 123
Sabbath-drawler art no *s-d* of old saws, *To J. M. K.* 5
Sabine she That taught the *S* how to rule, *Princess ii* 79
Sable Fantastic plume or *s* pine; *The Voyage* 44
The towering car, the *s* steeds: *Ode on Well.* 55

Sabre Flash'd all their *s's* bare, *Light Brigade* 27
Sway'd his *s*, and held his own *Heavy Brigade* 18
Whirling their *s's* in circles of light! „ 34
Sabre-stroke Reel'd from the *s-s* *Light Brigade* 35
Sabring *S* the gunners there, „ 29
Sack (bag) (*See also* **Meal-sacks**) With bag and *s* and basket, *Enoch Arden* 63
cling together in the ghastly *s*— *Aylmer's Field* 764
sweating underneath a *s* of corn, *Marr. of Geraint* 263
Sack (pillage) found the *s* and plunder of our house „ 694
Sack'd rose a shriek as of a city *s*; *Princess iv* 165
night Before my Enid's birthday, *s* my house; *Marr. of Geraint* 458
night of fire, when Edyrn *s* their house, „ 634
As of some lonely city *s* by night, *Pass. of Arthur* 43
who *s* My dwelling, seized upon my papers, *Columbus* 129
Sacrament Deliver me the blessed *s*; *St. S. Stylites* 218
Sacred a *s* name And when she spake, *The Poet* 47
tho' her *s* blood doth drown The fields, *Poland* 4
'Still sees the *s* morning spread *Two Voices* 80
girls all kiss'd Beneath the *s* bush and past away— *The Epic* 3
And either *s* unto you. *Day-Dm., Ep.* 12
betray the trust: Keep nothing *s*: *You might have won* 19
face All-kindled by a still and *s* fire, *Enoch Arden* 71
And pace the *s* old familiar fields, „ 625
we must remain *S* to one another.' *Aylmer's Field* 426
to mar Their *s* everlasting calm! *Lucretius* 110
s from the blight Of ancient influence and scorn. *Princess ii* 168
and half The *s* mother's bosom, „ *vi* 148
Love in the *s* halls Held carnival at will, „ *vii* 84
He bad you guard the *s* coasts. *Ode on Well.* 172
Mid-ocean, spare thee, *s* bark; *In Mem. xvii* 14
Ye never knew the *s* dust: „ *xxi* 22
Oh, *s* be the flesh and blood „ *xxxiii* 11
(And dear to me as *s* wine To dying lips „ *xxxvii* 19
O *s* essence, other form, „ *lxxxv* 35
Come sliding out of her *s* glove, *Maud I vi* 85
The *s* altar blossom'd white with May, *Com. of Arthur* 461
And o'er her breast floated the *s* fish; *Gareth and L.* 223
They came from out a *s* mountain-cleft „ 260
south-west that blowing Bala lake Fills all the *s* Dee. *Geraint and E.* 930
Guarded the *s* shield of Lancelot; *Lancelot and E.* 4
Then came on him a sort of *s* fear, „ 354
For all the *s* mount of Camelot, *Holy Grail* 227
Go, since your vows are *s*, „ 314
And all the *s* madness of the bard, „ 877
whom I made it o'er his grave *S*, *To the Queen ii* 36
A *s*, secret, unapproached woe, Unspeakable? *Lover's Tale i* 679
Or clutch'd the *s* crown of Prester John, *Columbus* 110
descending from the *s* peak Of hoar high-templed Faith, *Pref. Poem 19th Cent.* 9
Felt within themselves the *s* passion of the second life. *Locksley H., Sixty* 68
What are men that He should heed us? cried the king of *s* song; „ 201
Had swampt the *s* poets with themselves. *Poets and their B.* 14
And *s* is the latest word; *To Marq. of Dufferin* 37
So *s* those Ghost Lovers hold the gift.' *The Ring* 205
I kept it as a *s* amulet About me,— „ 442
The *s* relics tost about the floor— „ 447
WHAT be those crown'd forms high over the *s* fountain? *Parnassus* 1
What be those two shapes high over the *s* fountain, „ 9
an old fane No longer *s* to the Sun, *St. Telemachus* 7
Yet 'Alla,' says their *s* book, 'is Love,' *Akbar's Dream* 73
That stone by stone I rear'd a *s* fane, „ 177
Sacrifice (s) (*See also* **Self-sacrifice**) so that he rose With *s*, *On a Mourner* 34
To blow these *s's* thro' the world— *Aylmer's Field* 758
Have we not made ourself the *s*? *Princess iii* 249
Against the flame about a *s* *Pelleas and E.* 145
let mute Into her temple like a *s*; *Lover's Tale i* 685
As for a solemn *s* of love— „ *iv* 301
Dark with the smoke of human *s*, *Sir J. Oldcastle* 84
flight of birds, the flame of *s*, *Tiresias* 6
Is war, and human *s*— „ 112
miss'd The wonted steam of *s*, *Demeter and P.* 119
Sacrifice (verb) to thy worst self *s* thyself, *Aylmer's Field* 645

Sacring And at the *s* of the mass I saw *Holy Grail* 462
Sad Looks thro' in his *s* decline, *Adeline* 13
The broken sheds look'd *s* and strange: *Mariana* 5
'Madonna, *s* is night and morn,' *Mariana in the S.* 22
His memory scarce can make me *s*. *Miller's D.* 16
'I was cut off from hope in that *s* place, *D. of F. Women* 105
But while I mused came Memory with *s* eyes, *Gardener's D.* 243
The slow *s* hours that bring us all things ill, *Love and Duty* 58
Full of *s* experience, moving toward the stillness of his rest. *Locksley Hall* 144
Many a *s* kiss by day by night renew'd *Enoch Arden* 161
Set her *s* will no less to chime with his, „ 248
'Favour from one so *s* and so forlorn As I am!' „ 287
That after all these *s* uncertain years, „ 415
Too fresh and fair in our *s* world's best bloom, *The Brook* 218
Yet the *s* mother, for the second death *Aylmer's Field* 604
'Not *s*, but sweet.' *Sea Dreams* 106
I am *s* and glad To see you, Florian. *Princess ii* 306
talk'd The trash that made me sick, and almost *s*?' „ 394
S as the last which reddens over one That sinks „ *iv* 46
So *s*, so fresh, the days that are no more. „ 48
s and strange as in dark summer dawns „ 49
So *s*, so strange, the days that are no more „ 53
shone Thro' glittering drops on her *s* friend. „ *vi* 283
Or pines in *s* experience worse than death, „ *vii* 315
Lead out the pageant: *s* and slow, *Ode on Well.* 13
says, our sins should make us *s*: *Grandmother* 93
stern and *s* (so rare the smiles Of sunlight) *The Daisy* 53
The *s* mechanic exercise, *In Mem. v* 7
And one is *s*; her note is changed, „ *xxi* 27
In those *s* words I took farewell: „ *lviii* 1
Which makes me *s* I know not why „ *lxviii* 11
S Hesper o'er the buried sun And ready, „ *cxxi* 1
And my own *s* name in corners cried, *Maud I vi* 72
To a life that has been so *s*, „ *xi* 13
Than nursed at ease and brought to understand A *s* astrology, „ *xviii* 36
To have no peace in the grave, is that not *s*? „ *II v* 16
And *s* was Arthur's face Taking it, *Com. of Arthur* 305
and *s* At times he seem'd, and *s* with him was I, „ 352
Shamed had I been, and *s*—O Lancelot—thou!' *Gareth and L.* 1245
Before her birthday, three *s* years ago, *Marr. of Geraint* 633
And knew her sitting *s* and solitary. *Geraint and E.* 282
Art thou *s*? or sick? *Balin and Balan* 274
The *s* sea-sounding wastes of Lyonnesse— *Merlin and V.* 74
when she lifted up A face of *s* appeal, „ 234
Because I saw you *s*, to comfort you. „ 441
Till all her heart's *s* secret blazed itself *Lancelot and E.* 836
s chariot-bier Past like a shadow thro' the field, „ 1139
And Lancelot *s* beyond his wont, „ 1333
which our Lord Drank at the last *s* supper with his own. *Holy Grail* 47
and there, with slow *s* steps Ascending, *Last Tournament* 143
Come—let us gladden their *s* eyes, „ 222
remembering Her thought when first she came, wept the *s* Queen. *Guinevere* 182
Then to her own *s* heart mutter'd the Queen, „ 213
To vex an ear too *s* to listen to me, „ 315
rather think How *s* it were for Arthur, „ 496
And near him the *s* nuns with each a light Stood, „ 590
it melteth in the source Of these *s* tears, *Lover's Tale i* 784
S, sweet, and strange together— „ *iv* 304
With *s* eyes fixt on the lost sea-home, *The Wreck* 126
For he touch'd on the whole *s* planet of man, *Dead Prophet* 39
Had floated in with *s* reproachful eyes, *The Ring* 469
Her *s* eyes plead for my own fame with me *Romney's R.* 55
Sadden The gloom that *s's* Heaven and Earth, *The Daisy* 102
He *s's*, all the magic light *In Mem. viii* 5
While he that watch'd her *s*, *Marr. of Geraint* 67
And seen her *s* listening— *Pelleas and E.* 398
Let not all that *s's* Nature *Faith* 2
Sadden'd She fail'd and *s* knowing it; *Enoch Arden* 257
Told Enid, and they *s* her the more: *Marr. of Geraint* 64
s all her heart again. *Geraint and E.* 445
Saddening And *s* in her childless castle, *Gareth and L.* 528
And, *s* on the sudden, spake Isolt, *Last Tournament* 581

Sadder She, as her carol *s* grew, *Mariana in the S.* 13
Poor Fancy *s* than a single star, *Caress'd or chidden* 13
s age begins To war against ill uses of a life, *Gareth and L.* 1129
Saddle Arac, roll'd himself Thrice in the *s*, *Princess v* 275
I so shook him in the *s*, he said, *Gareth and L.* 29
And lets me from the *s*;' *Lancelot and E.* 94
Then crush'd the *s* with his thighs, *Pelleas and E.* 459
drew The foe from the *s* and threw *Heavy Brigade* 54
Saddle-bow A cavalier from off his *s-b*, *D. of F. Women* 46
But when it glitter'd o'er the *s-b*, *Gareth and L.* 1119
Saddle-leather Thick-jewell'd shone the *s-l*, *L. of Shalott iii* 20
Sadness Can I but relive in *s*? *Locksley Hall* 107
memories roll upon him, Unspeakable for *s*. *Enoch Arden* 725
But *s* on the soul of Ida fell, *Princess vii* 29
Or *s* in the summer moons? *In Mem. lxxxiii* 8
s flings Her shadow on the blaze of kings: „ *xcviii* 18
spake with such a *s* and so low We heard not *Holy Grail* 42
Thou majestic in thy *s* at the doubtful doom *To Virgil* 23
All her tale of *s*, *Forlorn* 80
may there be no *s* of farewell, *Crossing the Bar* 11
Saesneg Vailing a sudden eyelid with his hard 'Dim *S*' passes, *Sir J. Oldcastle* 21
Safe giving *s* pledge of fruits, *Ode to Memory* 18
S, damsel, as the centre of this hall. *Gareth and L.* 604
The loneliest ways are *s* from shore to shore. *Last Tournament* 102
So all the ways were *s* from shore to shore, „ 485
(our royal word upon it, He comes back *s*) *Princess v* 225
might be *s* our censures to withdraw; *Third of Feb.* 11
Safer the rougher hand Is *s*: *Princess vi* 279
Sagest some were left of those Held *s*, „ 382
Sagramore What say ye then to sweet Sir *S*, *Merlin and V.* 721
Sahib At once the costly *S* yielded to her. *Aylmer's Field* 233
Said I *s* that 'all the years invent; *Two Voices* 73
when I have *s* goodnight for evermore, *May Queen, N. Y's. E.* 41
I know not what was *s*; „ *Con.* 34
He thought that nothing new was *s*, or else Something so *s* 'twas nothing— *The Epic* 30
Eustace painted her, And *s* to me, *Gardener's D.* 21
And if I *s* that Fancy, led by Love, „ 59
he *s* That he was wrong to cross his father *Dora* 147
'Tis *s* he had a tuneful tongue, *Amphion* 17
'Cruel, cruel the words I *s*! *Edward Gray* 17
She told me all her friends had *s*; *The Letters* 25
I have ever *s* You chose the best among us— *Enoch Arden* 292
'This miller's wife' He *s* to Miriam „ 805
life in him Could scarce be *s* to flourish, *The Brook* 12
so like her? so they *s* on board. „ 223
and he meant, he *s* he meant, *Sea Dreams* 178
For so, my mother *s*, the story ran. *Princess i* 11
He *s* there was a compact; that was true: „ 47
I *s* no, Yet being an easy man, „ 148
some *s* their heads were less: „ *ii* 147
it shall be *s*, These women were too barbarous, „ 297
much I might have *s*, but that my zone „ 420
(For so they *s* themselves) inosculated; „ *iii* 89
I thought on all the wrathful king had *s*, „ *v* 473
so it seem'd, or so they *s* to me, „ *vi* 22
She *s* you had a heart— „ 234
All people *s* she had authority— „ 238
all, they *s*, as earnest as the close? „ *Con.* 21
left some record of the things we *s*. *Third of Feb.* 18
for he seldom *s* me nay: *Grandmother* 69
I thowt a *s* whot a owt to 'a *s* *N. Farmer, O. S.* 20
thaw summun *s* it in 'äaste: „ 27
The people *s*, a weed. *The Flower* 4
Somebody *s* that she'd say no; (repeat) *Window, Letter* 7, 14
The lesser griefs that may be *s*, *In Mem. xx* 1
And all he *s* of things divine, „ *xxxvii* 18
To dying lips is all he *s*), „ 20
Could I have *s* while he was here, „ *lxxxi* 1
s The dawn, the dawn,' and died away; „ *xcv* 60
Whatever I have *s* or sung, „ *cxxv* 1
And how she look'd, and what he *s*, „ *Con.* 99
How strange was what she *s*, *Maud I xix* 34
whether there were truth in anything *S* by these three, *Com. of Arthur* 243
Said (*continued*) For pastime; yea, he *s* it: joust can I. *Gareth and L.* 543
You *s* your say; Mine answer was my deed. „ 1174
She told him all that Earl Limours had *s*, *Geraint and E.* 391
I have *s*. Not so—not all. *Balin and Balan* 69
s a light came from her when she moved: *Merlin and V.* 567
What *s* the happy sire? „ 710
we hear it *s* That men go down before your spear *Lancelot and E.* 148
I *s* That *if* I went and *if* I fought and won it „ 215
one *s* to the other, 'Lo! What is he? „ 470
being weak in body *s* no more; „ 839
We heard not half of what he *s*. *Holy Grail* 43
asking him, 'What *s* the King? „ 204
what *s* each, and what the King? „ 710
one most holy saint, who wept and *s*, „ 781
Was I too dark a prophet when I *s* „ 889
There she that seem'd the chief among them *s*, *Pelleas and E.* 62
I know not what I would'—but *s* to her, *Last Tournament* 498
went To-day for three days' hunting—as he *s*— „ 530
But openly she spake and *s* to her, *Guinevere* 226
So *s* my father, and himself was knight „ 234
and he *s* That as he rode, „ 236
So *s* my father—yea, and furthermore, „ 250
S the good nuns would check her gadding tongue „ 313
as he *s*, that once was loving hearts, *Lover's Tale iv* 68
An' once I *s* to the Missis, *North. Cobbler* 103
Miss Annie she *s* it wur draäins, *Village Wife* 11
This tongue that wagg'd They *s* *Sir J. Oldcastle* 15
and I heard a voice that *s* *Tiresias* 48
'He *s* he would meet me tomorra!' *Tomorrow* 80
ye *s* I wur pretty i' pinks, *Spinster's S's.* 17
She *s*, that you and I Had been abroad *The Ring* 100
He *s* it . . . in the play. *Romney's R.* 150
Sa I warrants 'e niver *s* haafe wot 'e thowt, *Church-warden, etc.* 18
She *s* with a sudden glow On her patient face *Charity* 35
What *s* her Priesthood? *Kapiolani* 19
Saïd (Abû) *See* **Abû Saïd**
Sail (s) And the whirring *s* goes round, (repeat) *The Owl i* 4
In the silken *s* of infancy, *Arabian Nights* 2
come hither and furl your *s's*, *Sea-Fairies* 16
Mariner, mariner, furl your *s's*, „ 21
surf wind-scatter'd over *s's* and masts, *D. of F. Women* 31
barge with oar and *s* Moved from the brink, *M. d'Arthur* 265
'Fly, happy happy *s's*, and bear the Press; *Golden Year* 42
the vessel puffs her *s*: *Ulysses* 44
argosies of magic *s's*, *Locksley Hall* 121
Dry sang the tackle, sang the *s*: *The Voyage* 10
And never *s* of ours was furl'd, „ 81
whence were those that drove the *s* „ 86
to the last dip of the vanishing *s* *Enoch Arden* 245
waiting for a *s*: No *s* from day to day, „ 590
scarlet shafts of sunrise—but no *s*. „ 599
Crying with a loud voice 'A *s*! a *s*! „ 913
all the *s's* were darken'd in the west, *Sea Dreams* 39
boat Tacks, and the slacken'd *s* flaps, *Princess ii* 186
Silver *s's* all out of the west „ *iii* 14
'Fresh as the first beam glittering on a *s*, „ *iv* 44
trim our *s's*, and let old bygones be, „ 69
the seas; A red *s*, or a white; „ *Con.* 47
With a satin *s* of a ruby glow, *The Islet* 13
And see the *s's* at distance rise, *In Mem. xii* 11
glance about the approaching *s's*, „ *xiii* 18
And milkier every milky *s* „ *cxv* 11
far-off *s* is blown by the breeze *Maud I iv* 4
And white *s's* flying on the yellow sea; *Marr. of Geraint* 829
one side had sea And ship and *s* and angels *Balin and Balan* 365
She took the helm and he the *s*; *Merlin and V.* 200
Torn as a *s* that leaves the rope *Holy Grail* 212
had he set the *s*, or had the boat Become „ 518
the barge with oar and *s* Moved from the brink, *Pass. of Arthur* 433
and half-way down rare *s's*, *Lover's Tale i* 4
the *s* Will draw me to the rising of the sun, „ 26
the ravin wind In her *s* roaring. „ *ii* 171
Took the breath from our *s's*, and we stay'd. *The Revenge* 42
Till it smote on their hulls and their *s's* „ 116
look yonder,' he cried, 'a *s*' *The Wreck* 121

Sail (s) (*continued*) as I saw the white *s* run, And darken, *The Flight* 39
And sunshine on that *s* at last „ 92
Sail (verb) *s* with Arthur under looming shores, *M. d'Arthur, Ep.* 17
purpose holds To *s* beyond the sunset, *Ulysses* 60
On sleeping wings they *s*. *Sir Galahad* 44
And we might *s* for evermore. *The Voyage* 8
We seem'd to *s* into the Sun! „ 16
And we may *s* for evermore. „ 96
Annie, the ship I *s* in passes here *Enoch Arden* 214
Abiding with me till I *s* *In Mem. cxxv* 13
All night the shining vapour *s* „ *Con.* 111
I have seen the good ship *s* Keel upward, *Gareth and L.* 253
ready to *s* forth on one last voyage. *Columbus* 237
THEY rose to where their sovran eagle *s's*, *Montenegro* 1
and *s* to help them in the war; *Achilles over the T.* 13
We sail'd wherever ship could *s*, *Hands all Round* 29
Sail'd (*See also* **Full-sail'd, Silken-sail'd**) SLOW *s* the weary mariners and saw, *Sea-Fairies* 1
throne of Indian Cama slowly *s* *Palace of Art* 115
weeks before she *s*, *S* from this port. *Enoch Arden* 124
prosperously *s* The ship 'Good Fortune,' „ 527
in that harbour whence he *s* before. „ 666
s, Full-blown, before us into rooms *Princess i* 228
And those fair hills I *s* below, *In Mem. xcviii* 2
And he *s* away from Flores *The Revenge* 23
away she *s* with her loss and long'd for her own; „ 111
made West East, and *s* the Dragon's mouth, *Columbus* 25
I *s* On my first voyage, harass'd by the frights „ 66
—we *s* on a Friday morn— *V. of Maeldune* 7
we *s* away. (repeat) „ 26, 70, 114
and we *s* with our wounded away. „ 36
and in anger we *s* away. „ 54
and away we *s*, and we past Over that undersea isle, „ 76
we slew and we *s* away. „ 96
and hastily *s* away. „ 104
Saint who had *s* with St. Brendan of yore, „ 115
and sadly we *s* away. „ 126
he *s* the sea to crush the Moslem in his pride; *Locksley H., Sixty* 29
We *s* wherever ship could sail, *Hands all Round* 29
Sailest *S* the placid ocean-plains *In Mem. ix* 2
Sailing (*See also* **A-sailing**) *S* under palmy highlands Far within the South. *The Captain* 23
With here a blossom *s*, *The Brook* 56
S along before a gloomy cloud *Sea Dreams* 124
The *s* moon in creek and cove; *In Mem. ci* 16
S from Ireland. *Last Tournament* 555
Sailor (adj.) O well for the *s* lad, *Break, break, etc.* 7
In *s* fashion roughly sermonizing On providence *Enoch Arden* 204
Gone our *s* son thy father, Leonard early lost at sea; *Locksley H., Sixty* 55
Sailor (s) (*See also* **Saäilor**) *S's* bold and true. *The Captain* 8
And Enoch Arden, a rough *s's* lad *Enoch Arden* 14
and made himself Full *s*; „ 54
A shipwreck'd *s*, waiting for a sail: „ 590
The greatest *s* since our world began. *Ode on Well.* 86
praying God will save Thy *s*,— *In Mem. vi* 14
I see the *s* at the wheel. „ *x* 4
Thou bring'st the *s* to his wife, „ 5
passive *s* wrecks at last In ever-silent seas; *Ancient Sage* 136
Desolate as that *s*, whom the storm Had parted *The Ring* 307
Sailorless Desolate offing, *s* harbours, *Vastness* 14
Sailor-soul and thou, Heroic *s-s*, *Sir J. Franklin* 2
Saint (s) (*See also* **Francis of Assisi**) meed of *s's*, the white robe and the palm. *St. S. Stylites* 20
Who may be made a *s*, if I fail here? „ 48
thou and all the *s's* Enjoy themselves „ 105
To Christ, the Virgin Mother, and the *s's*; „ 112
The silly people take me for a *s*, „ 127
Are register'd and calendar'd for *s's*. „ 132
It may be, no one, even among the *s's*, „ 138
This is not told of any. They were *s's*. „ 151
Yea, crown'd a *s*. They shout, 'Behold a *s*!' „ 153
I am gather'd to the glorious *s's*. „ 197
Ah! let me not be fool'd, sweet *s's*: „ 212
Than Papist unto *S*. *Talking Oak* 16
Saint (s) (*continued*) statues, king or *s*, or founder fell; *Sea Dreams* 224
My mother was as mild as any *s*, *Princess i* 22
Swear by *S* something— „ *v* 293
Like a *S's* glory up in heaven: but she No *s*— inexorable—no tenderness— „ 514
your mother, now a *s* with *s's*. „ *vi* 233
arrived, by Dubric the high *s*, *Com. of Arthur* 453
For by the hands of Dubric, the high *s*, *Marr. of Geraint* 838
oft I talk'd with Dubric, the high *s*, *Geraint and E.* 865
descended from the *S* Arimathæan Joseph; *Balin and Balan* 101
I saw That maiden *S* who stands with lily „ 261
scarce could spy the Christ for *S's*, „ 409
but all the maiden *S's*, „ 520
the good *s* Arimathæan Joseph, journeying *Holy Grail* 50
larger, tho' the goal of all the *s's*— „ 528
I spake To one most holy *s*, „ 781
crying, 'Praise the patient *s's*, *Last Tournament* 217
I thank the *s's*, I am not great. *Guinevere* 199
Who wast, as is the conscience of a *s* „ 639
Who reads of begging *s's* in Scripture?' *Sir J. Oldcastle* 151
And we came to the Isle of a *S* *V. of Maeldune* 115
Wid his blessed Marthyrs an' *S's*;' *Tomorrow* 58
an' *S's* an' Marthyrs galore, „ 95
I cried to the *S's* to avenge me. *Bandit's Death* 14
But thanks to the Blessed *S's* „ 40
Saint (verb) lower voices *s* me from above. *St. S. Stylites* 154
St. Brendan *See* **Brendan**
St. Cecily *See* **Cecily**
St. Francis of Assisi *See* **Francis of Assisi**
St. Paul *See* **Paul**
Saintdom grasp the hope I hold Of *s*, *St. S. Stylites* 6
Saint-like women smile with *s-l* glances *Supp. Confessions* 22
Saintly The *s* youth, the spotless lamb of Christ, *Merlin and V.* 749
Therefore I communed with a *s* man, *Holy Grail* 742
Saint's-day *See* **Saäint's-daäy**
Saith *s* not Holy Writ the same?'— *Merlin and V.* 52
He, that *s* it, hath o'erstept *Lover's Tale i* 101
Sake 'Yet must I love her for your *s*; *Miller's D.* 142
Nor would I break for your sweet *s* *L. C. V. de Vere* 13
for his *s* I bred His daughter Dora: *Dora* 19
for the *s* of him that's gone, (repeat) *Dora* 62, 70, 94
for your *s*, the woman that he chose, „ 63
may be, for her own dear *s* but this, *Edwin Morris* 141
pray them not to quarrel for her *s*, *Enoch Arden* 35
for Annie's *s*, Fearing the lazy gossip „ 334
for God's *s*,' he answer'd, 'both our *s's*, „ 509
Katie, what I suffer'd for your *s*! *The Brook* 119
How prettily for his own sweet *s* *Maud I vi* 51
To be friends for her *s*, to be reconciled; „ *xix* 50
And for your sweet *s* to yours; „ 91
the rose was awake all night for your *s*, „ *xxii* 49
rather for the *s* of me, their King, *Gareth and L.* 571
the deed's *s* my knighthood do the deed, „ 572
for the deed's *s* have I done the deed, „ 832
Balan answer'd 'For the *s* Of glory; *Balin and Balan* 32
And were it only for the giver's *s*, *Lover's Tale iv* 364
freedom, or the *s* of those they loved, *Sir J. Oldcastle* 186
I know Less for its own than for the *s* *To E. Fitzgerald* 52
sorrow that I bear is sorrow for *his s*. *The Flight* 64
will you sicken for her *s*? *Locksley H., Sixty* 17
God stay me there, if only for your *s*, *Romney's R.* 34
for my *s*, According to my word?' „ 129
Sal (*See also* **Sally**) black *S*, es 'ed been disgraäced? *Spinster's S's.* 25
Salamanca Were *you* at *S*? No. *Columbus* 40
Sale *See* **Saäle**
Saleem heart is for my son, *S*, my heir,— *Akbar's Dream* 171
on the sudden, and with a cry '*S*' „ 184
Salient beneath Its *s* springs, and far apart, *Supp. Confessions* 56
Do beating hearts of *s* springs Keep measure *Adeline* 26
Salique fulmined out her scorn of laws *S* *Princess ii* 133
Sallow (adj.) (*See also* **Wan-sallow**) With *s* scraps of manuscript, *To E. Fitzgerald* 48
Sallow (s) satin-shining palm On *s's* *Merlin and V.* 225
Sallow-rifted the *s-r* glooms Of evening, *Lancelot and E.* 1002
Sallow-skin Many a livid one, many a *s-s*— *Batt. of Brunanburh* 106

Sallowy ran By *s* rims, arose the labourers' homes, Aylmer's Field 147
And many a glancing plash and *s* isle, Last Tournament 422
Sally (proper name) (*See also* **Sal**) to 's chooch afoor
moy *S* wur deäd, N. Farmer, O. S. 17
Waait till our *S* cooms in, North. Cobbler 1
That *S* she turn'd a tongue-banger, „ 23
S she wesh'd foälks' cloäths to keep the wolf fro' the door, „ 29
wheer *S's* owd stockin' wur 'id, „ 31
an' I gied our *S* a kick, „ 36
I seeäd that our *S* went laämed Cos' o' the kick as I gied 'er, „ 39
An' *S* wur sloomy an' draggle „ 41
then I minded our *S* sa pratty an' neät an' sweeät, „ 43
'I mun gie tha a kiss,' an' *S* says 'Noä, thou moänt,' „ 51
gied 'er a kiss, an' then anoother, an' *S* says 'doänt!' „ 52
upo' coomin' awaäy *S* gied me a kiss ov 'ersen. „ 56
fur to kick our *S* as kep the wolf fro' the door, „ 59
an' *S* looökt up an' she said, 'I'll upowd it tha weänt „ 62
'That caps owt,' says *S*, an' saw she begins to cry, „ 71
'*S*,' says I, 'Stan' 'im theer i' the naäme o' the Lord „ 72
An' *S* she tell'd it about, an' foälk „ 81
an' if *S* be left aloän, „ 105
'Ere be our *S* an' Tommy, an' we be a-goin to dine, „ 111
weänt shed a drop on 'is blood, noä, not fur *S's* oän kin. „ 114
Sally (a rush) I make a sudden *s*, The Brook 24
our *sallies*, their lying alarms, Def. of Lucknow 75
Sally (verb) the cave From which he *sallies*, Balin and Balan 132
all at once should *s* out upon me, Geraint and E. 149
Wroth that the King's command to *s* forth Lancelot and E. 560
Sallying *s* thro' the gate, Had beat her foes Princess, Pro. 33
s thro' the gates, and caught his hair, „ v 340
In blood-red armour *s*, howl'd to the King, Last Tournament 443
Saloon Or, in a shadowy *s*, Eleänore 125
Salt (adj.) And in the middle of the green *s* sea Mine be the strength 7
A still *s* pool, lock'd in with bars of sand, Palace of Art 249
The *s* sea-water passes by, In Mem. xix 6
old dwarf-elm That turns its back on the *s* blast, Pelleas and E. 544
Salt (s) stony drought and steaming *s*; Mariana in the S. 40
Caught the shrill *s*, and sheer'd the gale. The Voyage 12
By shards and scurf of *s*, Vision of Sin 211
The city sparkles like a grain of *s*. Will 20
she has neither savour nor *s*, Maud I ii 2
pools of *s*, and plots of land— Locksley H., Sixty 207
Salute (s) Take my *s*,' unknightly with flat hand, Geraint and E. 717
Salute (verb) Many a merry face *S's* them— In Mem., Con. 67
I *s* thee, Mantovano, To Virgil 37
Salvation and lost *S* for a sketch. Romney's R. 139
Salve Our Britain cannot *s* a tyrant o'er. Third of Feb. 20
Salver fruitage golden-rinded On golden *s's*, Eleänore 34
Chalice and *s*, wines that, Heaven knows when, Lover's Tale iv 193
Sam (*See also* **Sammy**) *S*, thou's an ass for thy
paaïns: N. Farmer, N. S. 3
theer's a craw to pluck wi' tha, *S*: „ 5
Same (*See also* **Self-same**) In the *s* circle we revolve. Two Voices 314
Living together under the *s* roof, To ——, With Pal. of Art 12
and still The *s* old sore breaks out from age to age
With much the *s* result. Walk. to the Mail 79
and that *s* song of his He told me; Golden Year 7
This *s* grand year is ever at the doors.' „ 74
A sleepy land, where under the *s* wheel The *s* old rut Aylmer's Field 33
thunders of the house Had fallen first, was Edith
that *s* night; „ 279
Then she told it, having dream'd Of that *s* coast. Sea Dreams 207
So stood that *s* fair creature at the door. Princess ii 329
Would this *s* mock-love, and this Mock-Hymen „ iv 143
Than when two dewdrops on the petal shake To the *s*
sweet air, „ vii 69
The *s* sweet forms in either mind. In Mem. lxxix 8
For us the *s* cold streamlet curl'd „ 9
and all about The *s* gray flats again, „ lxxxvii 13
and that *s* night, the night of the new year, Com. of Arthur 209
'And this *s* child,' he said, 'Is he who reigns; „ 392
Then that *s* day there past into the hall Gareth and L. 587
But that *s* strength which threw the Morning Star „ 1108
that *s* spear Wherewith the Roman pierced the
side of Christ. Balin and Balan 113
Same (*continued*) 'What, wear ye still that *s*
crown-scandalous?' Balin and Balan 390
for early that *s* day, Scaped thro' a cavern from a
bandit hold, Holy Grail 206
stood beside thee even now, the *s*. Balin and Balan 613
and felt The *s*, but not the *s*; In Mem. lxxxvii 14
saith not Holy Writ the *s*?'— Merlin and V. 52
Sameness With weary *s* in the rhymes, Miller's D. 70
Samian whene'er she moves The *S* Herè rises Princess iii 115
Samite Clothed in white *s*, mystic, wonderful, (repeat) M. d'Arthur 31, 144, 159
Clothed in white *s*, mystic, wonderful. Com. of Arthur 285
a robe Of *s* without price, Merlin and V. 222
King, who sat Robed in red *s*, Lancelot and E. 433
Pall'd all its length in blackest *s*, „ 1142
Clothed in white *s* or a luminous cloud. Holy Grail 513
All pall'd in crimson *s*, „ 847
hung with folds of pure White *s*, Last Tournament 141
Clothed in white *s*, mystic, wonderful, (repeat) Pass. of Arthur 199, 312, 327
Sammy (*See also* **Sam**) Me an' thy muther, *S*, 'as
beän a-talkin N. Farmer, N. S. 9
fur, *S*, 'e married fur luvv. „ 32
an', *S*, I'm blest If it isn't the saäme oop yonder, „ 43
Taäke my word for it, *S*, „ 48
Thim's my noätions, *S*, wheerby I means to stick; „ 57
Sanctimonious as a rogue in grain Veneer'd with *s* theory. Princess, Pro. 117
Sanction dare not ev'n by silence *s* lies. Third of Feb. 10
Sanction'd *See* **Mitre-sanction'd**
Sanctities And darken'd *s* with song.' In Mem. xxxvii 24
Sanctuary crowds in column'd *sanctuaries*; D. of F. Women 22
behold our *s* Is violate, our laws broken: Princess vi 59
So was their *s* violated, „ vii 16
For I will draw me into *s*, Guinevere 121
yield me *s*, nor ask Her name to whom ye yield it, „ 141
S granted To bandit, thief, assassin— Sir J. Oldcastle 112
Sand purl o'er matted cress and ribbed *s*, Ode to Memory 59
rainbow lives in the curve of the *s*; Sea-Fairies 27
the brine against the Coptic *s's*. Buonaparte 8
In glaring *s* and inlets bright. Mariana in the S. 8
to where the sky Dipt down to sea and *s's*. Palace of Art 32
seem'd all dark and red—a tract of *s*, „ 65
salt pool, lock'd in with bars of *s*, „ 249
sat them down upon the yellow *s*, Lotos-Eaters 37
roaring deeps and fiery *s's*, „ C. S. 115
foam-flakes scud along the level *s*, D. of F. Women 39
Should fill and choke with golden *s*— You ask me, why, etc. 24
I might as well have traced it in the *s's*; Audley Court 50
ran itself in golden *s's*. Locksley Hall 32
By *s's* and steaming flats, and floods The Voyage 45
in the chasm are foam and yellow *s's*; Enoch Arden 2
built their castles of dissolving *s* „ 19
All *s* and cliff and deep-inrunning cave, Sea Dreams 17
now on *s* they walk'd, and now on cliff, „ 37
While you were running down the *s's*, „ 265
May only make that footprint upon *s* Princess iii 239
Tall as a figure lengthen'd on the *s* „ vi 161
suck the blinding splendour from the *s*, „ vii 39
Tumbles a billow on chalk and *s*; To F. D. Maurice 24
Toiling in immeasureable *s*, Will 16
'The *s's* and yeasty surges mix In caves Sailor Boy 9
For every grain of *s* that runs, In Mem. cxvii 9
Low on the *s* and loud on the stone Maud I xxii 25
a tap Of my finger-nail on the *s*, „ II ii 22
scratch a ragged oval on the *s*, Gareth and L. 534
Come slipping o'er their shadows on the *s*, Geraint and E. 471
the *s* danced at the bottom of it. Balin and Balan 27
touching Breton *s's*, they disembark'd. Merlin and V 202
Glass'd in the slippery *s* before it breaks? „ 293
in a land of *s* and thorns, (repeat) Holy Grail 376, 390
wearying in a land of *s* and thorns. „ 420
and all the *s* Swept like a river, „ 799
Far over *s's* marbled with moon and cloud, Last Tournament 466
They found a naked child upon the *s's* Guinevere 293
mountains ended in a coast Of ever-shifting *s*, Pass. of Arthur 86

Sand (*continued*) On the waste *s* by the waste sea they closed. *Pass of Arthur* 92
A deathwhite mist slept over *s* and sea: „ 95
these deserted *s's* of barren life. *Lover's Tale i* 93
heats of the blinding noons Beat from the concave *s*; „ 140
leaves Low banks of yellow *s*; „ 535
upon the *s's* Insensibly I drew her name, „ *ii* 6
shrieks and ringing laughter on the *s* „ *iii* 32
melon lay like a little sun on the tawny *s*, *V. of Maeldune* 57
and pranced on the wrecks in the *s* below, „ 102
that bay with the colour'd *s*— *The Wreck* 135
in the chapel there looking over the *s*? *Despair* 1
'Lightly step over the *s's*! „ 47
his boat was on the *s*; *The Flight* 37
chains of mountains, grains of *s* *Locksley H., Sixty* 208
airs from where the deep, All down the *s*, *Early Spring* 22
dash'd half dead on barren *s's*, *The Ring* 309
I know not, your Arabian *s's*; *To Ulysses* 35
Are blinding desert *s*; *Akbar's Dream* 30
Sandal (shoe) he roll'd And paw'd about her *s*. *Princess iii* 182
Sandal (wood) toys in lava, fans Of *s*, „ *Pro.* 19
Sandal'd *See* **Silken-sandal'd**
Sandbank some dismal *s* far at sea, *Lover's Tale i* 809
Sand-built a *s-b* ridge Of heaped hills *Ode to Memory* 97
Sand-erased disgraced For ever—thee (thy pathway *s-e*) *Alexander* 5
Sandhill In this gap between the *s's*, *Locksley H., Sixty* 176
Sand-shore the waste *s-s's* of Trath Treroit, *Lancelot and E.* 301
Sandy Locksley Hall, that in the distance overlooks the *s* tracts, *Locksley Hall* 5
I make the netted sunbeam dance Against my *s* shallows. *The Brook* 177
and watch The *s* footprint harden into stone.' *Princess iii* 270
on *s* beaches A milky-bell'd amaryllis blew. *The Daisy* 15
Unloved, by many a *s* bar, *In Mem. ci* 9
half the morning have I paced these *s* tracts, *Locksley H., Sixty* 1
Sane I woke *s*, but well-nigh close to death *Princess vii* 119
O great and *s* and simple race of brutes *Pelleas and E.* 480
Till crowds at length be *s* *Ode on Well.* 169
but *s*, if she were in the right. *The Flight* 58
Saner Of *s* worship sanely proud; *Freedom* 30
A simpler, *s* lesson might he learn *Prog. of Spring* 105
Sanest valorous, *S* and most obedient: *Geraint and E.* 911
Sang (*See also* **Sing'd**) *S* looking thro' his prison bars? *Margaret* 35
'Tirra lirra,' by the river *S* Sir Lancelot. *L. of Shalott iii* 36
'Ah,' she *s*, 'to be all alone, (repeat) *Mariana in the S.* 11, 23
S to the stillness, till the mountain-shade *Œnone* 21
they *s*, 'Our island home Is far beyond the wave; *Lotos-Eaters* 44
'Glory to God,' she *s*, and past afar, *D. of F. Women* 242
and over them the sea-wind *s* Shrill, *M. d'Arthur* 48
nightingale *S* loud, as tho' he were the bird of day. *Gardener's D.* 96
clapt his hand in mine and *s*— *Audley Court* 39
He *s* his song, and I replied with mine: „ 56
So *s* we each to either, Francis Hale, „ 74
An angel stand and watch me, as I *s*. *St. S. Stylites* 35
s to me the whole Of those three stanzas *Talking Oak* 134
Dry *s* the tackle, *s* the sail: *The Voyage* 10
a couple, fair As ever painter painted, poet *s*, *Aylmer's Field* 106
sway'd The cradle, while she *s* this baby song. *Sea Dreams* 292
So *s* the gallant glorious chronicle; *Princess, Pro.* 49
the women *s* Between the rougher voices of the men, „ 244
Beyond all reason: these the women *s*; „ *i* 143
thro' the porch that *s* All round with laurel, „ *ii* 22
With whom I *s* about the morning hills, „ 247
maid, Of those beside her, smote her harp, and *s*. „ *iv* 38
the tear, She *s* of, shook and fell, „ 60
part made long since, and part Now while I *s*, „ 91
So Lilia *s*: we thought her half-possess'd, „ 585
Like that great dame of Lapidoth she *s*. „ *vi* 32
Violet, she that *s* the mournful song, „ 318
maidens came, they talk'd, They *s*, they read: „ *vii* 23
What pleasure lives in height (the shepherd *s*) „ 193
something in the ballads which they *s*, „ *Con.* 14
Nightingales *s* in his woods: *G. of Swainston* 6
Nightingales warbled and *s* Of a passion „ 8
in flying raiment, *s* the terrible prophetesses, *Boädicea* 37
many an old philosophy On Argive heights divinely *s*, *In Mem. xxiii* 22

Sang (*continued*) A merry song we *s* with him Last year: impetuously we *s*: *In Mem. xxx* 15
we *s*: 'They do not die Nor lose their mortal sympathy, „ 22
While now we *s* old songs that peal'd „ *xcv* 13
They *s* of what is wise and good And graceful. „ *ciii* 10
In the centre stood A statue veil'd, to which they *s*; „ 12
s from the three-decker out of the foam, *Maud I i* 50
Birds in our wood *s* Ringing thro' the valleys, „ *xii* 9
Arthur's knighthood *s* before the King:— *Com. of Arthur* 481
s the knighthood, moving to their hall. „ 503
And then she *s*, 'O morning star' *Gareth and L.* 995
the song that Enid *s* was one Of Fortune *Marr. of Geraint* 345
From underneath a plume of lady-fern, *S*, *Balin and Balan* 27
they drank and some one *s*, Sweet-voiced, „ 85
But, Vivien, when you *s* me that sweet rhyme, I felt *Merlin and V.* 434
And *s* it: sweetly could she make and sing. *Lancelot and E.* 1006
Then Tristram laughing caught the harp, and *s*: *Last Tournament* 730
Whereat full willingly *s* the little maid. *Guinevere* 167
So *s* the novice, while full passionately, „ 180
S Arthur's glorious wars, and *s* the King „ 286
then, he *s*, The twain together well might change „ 300
and over them the sea-wind *s* Shrill, *Pass. of Arthur* 216
And *s* aloud the matin-song of life. *Lover's Tale i* 232
If somewhere in the North, as Rumour *s* *Sir J. Oldcastle* 56
And we *s* of the triumphs of Finn, *V. of Maeldune* 88
more than he that *s* the Works and Days, *To Virgil* 6
I *s* the song, 'are bride And bridegroom.' *The Ring* 25
'Libera me, Domine!' you *s* the Psalm, *Happy* 49
And *s* the married 'nos' for the solitary 'me.' „ 56
Wed to the melody, *S* thro' the world; *Merlin and the G.* 98
Last year you *s* it as gladly. *The Throstle* 6
Sanguine *S* he was: a but less vivid hue *Aylmer's Field* 64
s Lazarus felt a vacant hand Fill with *his* purse. *To Mary Boyle* 31
Sank I *s* In cool soft turf upon the bank, *Arabian Nights* 95
And, while day *s* or mounted higher, *Palace of Art* 46
Her slow full words *s* thro' the silence drear, *D. of F. Women* 121
as we *s* From rock to rock upon the glooming quay, *Audley Court* 83
To some full music rose and *s* the sun, *Edwin Morris* 34
She *s* her head upon her arm *Talking Oak* 207
Tho' at times her spirit *s*: *L. of Burleigh* 70
s As into sleep again. *Aylmer's Field* 591
but *s* down shamed At all that beauty; *Lucretius* 63
leaning deep in broider'd down we *s* Our elbows: *Princess iv* 32
but again She veil'd her brows, and prone she *s*, „ *v* 107
And down dead-heavy *s* her curls, „ *vi* 147
after *s* and *s* And, into mournful twilight mellowing, „ 190
I *s* and slept, Fill'd thro' and thro' with Love, „ *vii* 171
voice Choked, and her forehead *s* upon her hands, „ 247
A bitter day that early *s* *In Mem. cvii* 2
show'd themselves against the sky, and *s*. *Marr. of Geraint* 240
S her sweet head upon her gentle breast; „ 527
half his blood burst forth, and down he *s* For the pure pain, *Lancelot and E.* 517
s Down on a drift of foliage random-blown; *Last Tournament* 388
s his head in mire, and slimed themselves: „ 471
breakers of the outer sea *S* powerless, *Lover's Tale i* 9
s his body with honour down into the deep, *The Revenge* 109
king, the queen, *S* from their thrones, *Columbus* 15
when drowning hope *S* all but out of sight, „ 157
And the roof *s* in on the hearth, *V. of Maeldune* 32
And his white hair *s* to his heels „ 118
till the glorious creature *S* to his setting. *Batt. of Brunanburh* 30
when our good redcoats *s* from sight, *Heavy Brigade* 42
Where I *s* with the body at times *By an Evolution.* 18
Became a shadow, *s* and disappear'd, *Death of Œnone* 50
Then her head *s*, she slept, „ 78
San Philip delay'd By their mountain-like *S P* *The Revenge* 40
the great *S P* hung above us like a cloud „ 43
But anon the great *S P*, she bethought „ 50
San Salvador I changed the name; *S S* I call'd it; *Columbus* 76
Sap (s) 'The *s* dries up: the plant declines. *Two Voices* 268
But yet my *s* was stirr'd: *Talking Oak* 172
Here rests the *s* within the leaf, *Day-Dm., Sleep. P.* 3
say rather, was my growth, My inward *s*, *Lover's Tale i* 166
Sap (verb) Ring out the grief that *s's* the mind, *In Mem. cvi* 9

Sat (*continued*) once when I *S* all alone, revolving — *Ancient Sage* 230
I *s* beside her dying, and she gaspt: — *The Ring* 287
I *s* beneath a solitude of snow; — *Prog. of Spring* 71
ŒNONE *s* within the cave from out — *Death of Œnone* 1
Œnone *s* Not moving, — „ 74
He stumbled in, and *s* Blinded; — *St. Telemachus* 48
she *s* day and night by my bed, — *Charity* 33
Satan (*See also* **Säätan**) '*S* take The old women and their shadows! — *Princess v* 33
I leap from *S's* foot to Peter's knee— — *Gareth and L.* 538
Or some black wether of St. *S's* fold. — *Merlin and V.* 750
Where one of *S's* shepherdesses caught — „ 758
Make their last head like *S* in the North. — *Last Tournament* 98
But Michaël trampling *S*; — „ 673
A stranger as welcome as *S*— — *Charity* 26
Satan-haunted This *S-h* ruin, this little city of sewers, — *Happy* 34
Sate (sat) Round the hall where I *s*, — *The Mermaid* 26
Sate (to gratify) things fair to *s* my various eyes! — *Palace of Art* 193
Sated And *s* with the innumerable rose, — *Princess iii* 122
Satiate Nor Arac, *s* with his victory. — „ *vii* 90
Satiated but *s* at length Came to the ruins. — „ *Pro.* 90
an anger, not by blood to be *s*. — *Boädicea* 52
With meats and wines, and *s* their hearts— — *Last Tournament* 725
Satin (adj.) dipt Beneath the *s* dome and enter'd in, — *Princess iv* 31
With a *s* sail of a ruby glow, — *The Islet* 13
Satin (s) A tent of *s*, elaborately wrought — *Princess iii* 348
In gloss of *s* and glimmer of pearls, — *Maud I xxii* 55
Satin-shining In colour like the *s-s* palm — *Merlin and V.* 224
Satin-wood Erect behind a desk of *s-w*, — *Princess ii* 105
Satire How like you this old *s*?' — *Sea Dreams* 198
Who first wrote *s*, with no pity in it. — „ 202
shafts Of gentle *s*, kin to charity, — *Princess ii* 469
Satisfied Look to thy wants, and send thee *s*— — *Gareth and L.* 434
But rested with her sweet face *s*; — *Marr. of Geraint* 776
And Geraint look'd and was not *s*. — *Geraint and E.* 435
s With what himself had done so graciously, — „ 644
But when at last his doubts were *s*, — *Lover's Tale iv* 84
Satisfy And *s* my soul with kissing her: — *Princess v* 103
Satrap when her *S* bled At Issus by the Syrian gates, — *Alexander* 2
Sattle (settle) An' *s* their ends upo stools — *Owd Roä* 24
Sattled (settled) an' *s* 'ersen o' my knee, — *North. Cobbler* 79
I gied tha a raätin that *s* thy coortin o' me. — *Spinster's S's.* 48
Saturate Tho' soak'd and *s*, out and out, — *Will Water.* 87
foul adulteries That *s* soul with body. — *Aylmer's Field* 377
Saturn while *S* whirls, his stedfast shade — *Palace of Art* 15
Satyr A *s*, a *s*, see—Follows; — *Lucretius* 192
Glorifying clown and *s*; — *Princess v* 187
Satyr-shape Or in his coarsest *S-s* — *In Mem. xxxv* 22
Saucy With a heaved shoulder and a *s* smile, — *Aylmer's Field* 466
They flash'd a *s* message to and fro — *Princess, Pro.* 78
till a rout of *s* boys Brake on us at our books, — „ *v* 394
forced Sweet love on pranks of *s* boyhood: — „ *vii* 344
Saul play the *S* that never will be Paul. — *Sir J. Oldcastle* 103
Saunter to those that *s* in the broad — *Aylmer's Field* 744
Saunter'd we rose And *s* home beneath a moon, — *Audley Court* 80
Savage (adj.) I mete and dole Unequal laws unto a *s* race, — *Ulysses* 4
I will take some *s* woman, she shall rear my dusky race. — *Locksley Hall* 168
For I was near him when the *s* yells Of Uther's peerage died, — *Com. of Arthur* 256
Balin, 'the *S*'—that addition thine— — *Balin and Balan* 53
here I dwell *S* among the *s* woods, here die— — „ 486
Chaste, frugal, *s*, arm'd by day and night — *Montenegro* 3
Savage (s) Mated with a squalid *s*— — *Locksley Hall* 177
'Peace, you young *s* of the Northern wild! — *Princess iii* 247
Savagery A huge man-beast of boundless *s*. — *Gareth and L.* 637
Brute bulk of limb, or boundless *s* — „ 1330
and tooth'd with grinning *s*.' — *Balin and Balan* 197
Save (*See also* **Saäve**) who can *s* But will not? — *Supp. Confessions* 90
And *s* me lest I die?' — *Palace of Art* 288
died To *s* her father's vow; — *D. of F. Women* 196
Dora stored what little she could *s*, — *Dora* 52
To *s* her little finger from a scratch — *Edwin Morris* 63
Jesus, if thou wilt not *s* my soul, — *St. S. Stylites* 46

Save (*continued*) To *s* from shame and thrall: — *Sir Galahad* 16
And vex the unhappy dust thou wouldst not *s*. — *Come not, when, etc.* 4
wish To *s* all earnings to the uttermost, — *Enoch Arden* 86
be pray'd '*S* them from this, whatever comes to me.' — „ 118
To *s* the offence of charitable, — „ 342
hope of life approach To *s* the life despair'd of, — „ 831
(I thought I could have died to *s* it) — *Sea Dreams* 134
be swerved from right to *s* A prince, a brother? — *Princess ii* 290
And *s* the one true seed of freedom — *Ode on Well.* 162
For, saving that, ye help to *s* mankind — „ 166
But as he *s's* or serves the state. — „ 200
her father was not the man to *s*, — *Grandmother* 5
O mother, praying God will *s* Thy sailor,— — *In Mem. vi* 13
And, influence-rich to sooth and *s*, — „ *lxxx* 14
If lowliness could *s* her. — *Maud I xii* 20
I know it the one bright thing to *s* My yet young life — „ *xvi* 20
To *s* from some slight shame one simple girl. — „ *xviii* 45
a monster unsubduable Of any *s* of him whom I call'd— — *Gareth and L.* 859
S that the dome was purple, and above, Crimson, — „ 912
To *s* her dear lord whole from any wound. — *Geraint and E.* 45
I *s* a life dearer to me than mine.' — „ 138
Truly *s* for fears, My fears for thee, — *Balin and Balan* 146
I that fain had died To *s* thy life, — „ 600
I fly to thee. *S*, *s* me thou— — *Merlin and V.* 78
Merlin, tho' you do not love me, *s*, Yet *s* me!' — „ 944
'*S* your great self, fair lord;' — *Lancelot and E.* 320
'If I lose myself, I *s* myself!' — *Holy Grail* 178
Thou hast not lost thyself to *s* thyself As Galahad.' — „ 456
And *s* it even in extremes, — *Guinevere* 67
To *s* his blood from scandal, — „ 514
S for some whisper of the seething seas, — *Pass. of Arthur* 121
And all the senses weaken'd, *s* in that, — *Lover's Tale i* 127
s in that Where to have been one had been — „ *ii* 26
but to *s* *my* soul, that is all your desire: — *Rizpah* 77
happier using the knife than in trying to *s* the limb, — *In the Child. Hosp.* 6
for it never could *s* us a life. — *Def. of Lucknow* 86
before their Gods, And wailing '*S* us.' — *Tiresias* 106
to the Faith that *s's*, — *The Wreck* 3
would you *s* A madman to vex you with wretched words, — *Despair* 107
Pierced by a poison'd dart. *S* me. — *Death of Œnone* 34
Take it, and *s* me from it! — *Bandit's Death* 38
darken'd with doubts of a Faith that *s's*, — *The Dreamer* 11
Saved Who may be *s*? who is it may be *s*? — *St. S. Stylites* 47
Can I work miracles and not be *s*? — „ 150
It cannot be but that I shall be *s*; — „ 152
every hour is *s* From that eternal silence, — *Ulysses* 26
'Thou shalt not be *s* by works: — *Vision of Sin* 91
'A sail! a sail! I am *s*;' — *Enoch Arden* 914
you may yet be *s*, and therefore fly: — *Princess iii* 64
You *s* our life: we owe you bitter thanks: — „ *iv* 531
'He *s* my life: my brother slew him for it.' — „ *vi* 108
let the land whose hearths he *s* from shame — *Ode on Well.* 225
how the King had *s* his life In battle twice,— — *Gareth and L.* 493
Good now, ye have *s* a life Worth somewhat — „ 827
the lord whose life he *s* Had, some brief space, — „ 888
There was I broken down: there was I *s*: — *Geraint and E.* 851
and roll'd his enemy down, And *s* him: — *Lancelot and E.* 27
Told him that her fine care had *s* his life. — „ 863
That *s* her many times, not fail— — *To the Queen ii* 62
fed, and cherish'd him, and *s* his life. — *Lover's Tale iv* 264
Who thrust him out, or him who *s* his life?' — „ 267
service of the one so *s* was due All to the saver— — „ 279
Dance to the pibroch!—*s*! we are *s*!— — *Def. of Lucknow* 103
S by the valour of Havelock, *s* — „ 104
'Heresy—Not shriven, not *s*?' — *Sir J. Oldcastle* 144
they had *s* many hundreds from wreck— — *Despair* 10
Does it matter how many they *s*? — „ 12
and you *s* me, a valueless life — „ 61
S when your life was wreck'd! — *The Ring* 305
Saver And *s* of my life; — *Gareth and L.* 879
The *s* of my life.' — „ 884
service of the one so saved was due All to the *s*— — *Lover's Tale iv* 280

Saving (*See also* **Saävin'**) For, *s* that, ye help to save mankind *Ode on Well.* 166
for *s* I be join'd To her that is the fairest *Com. of Arthur* 85
S that you mistrusted our good King *Gareth and L.* 1172
wrought some fury on myself, *S* for Balan: *Balin and Balan* 63
O brother, *s* this Sir Galahad, *Holy Grail* 561
Where *s* his own sisters he had known *Pelleas and E.* 87
S his life on the fallow flood. *Batt. of Brunanburh* 61
in thy virtue lies The *s* of our Thebes; *Tiresias* 110
S women and their babes, *Locksley H., Sixty* 64
Savings To hoard all *s* to the uttermost, *Enoch Arden* 46
Saviour O God Almighty, blessed *S*, „ 782
O *s* of the silver-coasted isle, *Ode on Well.* 136
She bows, she bathes the *S's* feet *In Mem. xxxii* 11
the *S* lives but to bless. *Rizpah* 64
Who finds the *S* in his mother tongue. *Sir J. Oldcastle* 115
Savour (s) she has neither *s* nor salt, *Maud I ii* 2
A name of evil *s* in the land, *Gareth and L.* 385
The *s* of thy kitchen came upon me „ 993
Savour (verb) *S's* well to thee and me. *Vision of Sin* 158
I *s* of thy—virtues? fear them? no. *Merlin and V.* 39
Saw (maxim) Thou art no sabbath-drawler of old *s's*, *To J. M. K.* 5
Not clinging to some ancient *s*; *Love thou thy land* 29
and cast thee back Thine own small *s*, *Last Tournament* 712
Saw (sow) *s's* 'ere a beän an' yonder a peä; *N. Farmer, O. S.* 46
Saw (tool) May never *s* dismember thee, *Talking Oak* 261
Shaping their pretty cabin, hammer and axe, Auger and *s*, *Enoch Arden* 174
Saw (verb) (*See also* **Seeäd, Seea'd, Seed, See'd**) She *s* the gusty shadow sway. *Mariana* 52
I *s* him—in his golden prime, *Arabian Nights* 153
that the dull *S* no divinity in grass, *A Character* 8
He *s* thro' life and death, thro' good and ill, He *s* thro' his own soul. *The Poet* 5
SLOW sail'd the weary mariners and *s*, *Sea-Fairies* 1
She *s* me fight, she heard me call, *Oriana* 32
they *s* thee from the secret shrine *Alexander* 13
She *s* the water-lily bloom, *L. of Shalott iii* 39
She *s* the helmet and the plume, „ 40
'To-day I *s* the dragon-fly Come from the wells *Two Voices* 8
'To search thro' all I felt or *s*, „ 139
S distant gates of Eden gleam, „ 212
But ere I *s* your eyes, my love, *Miller's D.* 43
I *s* the village lights below; „ 108
Sometimes I *s* you sit and spin; „ 121
To list a foot-fall, ere he *s* The wood-nymph, *Palace of Art* 110
standing *s* The hollow orb of moving Circumstance „ 254
nothing *s*, for her despair, But dreadful time, „ 266
I *s* the snare, and I retired: *L. C. V. de Vere* 6
To-night I *s* the sun set: *May Queen, N. Y's. E.* 5
I *s* you sitting in the house, „ *Con.* 30
They *s* the gleaming river seaward flow *Lotos-Eaters* 14
I *s*, wherever light illumineth, *D. of F. Women* 14
I *s* crowds in column'd sanctuaries; „ 22
At length I *s* a lady within call, „ 85
I turning *s*, throned on a flowery rise, „ 125
We *s* the large white stars rise one by one, „ 223
'*S* God divide the night with flying flame, „ 225
Ere I *s* her, who clasp'd in her last trance „ 266
But when he *s* the wonder of the hilt, *M. d'Arthur* 85
I never *s*, Nor shall see, here or elsewhere, „ 153
Born out of everything I heard and *s*, *Gardener's D.* 66
I, that whole day, *S* her no more, „ 164
Mary *s* the boy Was not with Dora. *Dora* 111
You *s* the man—on Monday, *Walk. to the Mail* 30
in these latter springs I *s* Your own Olivia blow, *Talking Oak* 75
s The dim curls kindle into sunny rings; *Tithonus* 53
Many a night I *s* the Pleiads, *Locksley Hall* 9
S the Vision of the world, (repeat) „ 16, 120
S the heavens fill with commerce, „ 121
she *s* The white-flower'd elder-thicket *Godiva* 62
And see the vision that I *s*, *Day-Dm., Pro.* 14
in a court he *s* A something-pottle-bodied boy *Will Water.* 130
Than all those she *s* before: *L. of Burleigh* 46
How oft we *s* the Sun retire, *The Voyage* 17
He *s* not far: his eyes were dim: „ 75

Saw (verb) (*continued*) And *s* the altar cold and bare. *The Letters* 4
I *s* with half-unconscious eye She wore the colours „ 15
I *s* that every morning, far withdrawn *Vision of Sin* 48
I *s* within my head A gray and gap-tooth'd man „ 59
s the pair, Enoch and Annie, sitting hand-in-hand, *Enoch Arden* 68
She *s* him not: and while he stood on deck „ 243
All these he *s*: but what he fain had seen „ 580
if griefs Like his have worse or better, Enoch *s*. „ 741
he *s* Philip, the slighted suitor of old times, „ 744
s The mother glancing often toward her babe, „ 753
and *s* the babe Hers, yet not his, „ 759
he *s* Death dawning on him, and the close of all. „ 831
And tell my daughter Annie, whom I *s* „ 882
I *s* where James Made toward us, *The Brook* 116
grizzled cripple, whom I *s* Sunning himself *Aylmer's Field* 8
S from his windows nothing save his own— „ 21
thro' every labyrinth till he *s* An end, „ 479
Broke into nature's music when they *s* her. „ 694
s No pale sheet-lightnings from afar, „ 725
that they *s*, the sea. *Sea Dreams* 36
Hyprocrisy, I *s* it in him at once. „ 64
then I *s* one lovely star Larger and larger. „ 93
Methought I never *s* so fierce a fork— *Lucretius* 28
I *s* the flaring atom-streams And torrents „ 38
Half-suffocated, and sprang up, and *s*— „ 58
I *s* The feudal warrior lady-clad; *Princess, Pro.* 118
they *s* the king; he took the gifts; „ *i* 46
I *s* my father's face Grow long and troubled „ 58
life! he never *s* the like; „ 186
How *s* you not the inscription on the gate, „ *ii* 194
turning round we *s* The Lady Blanche's daughter „ 320
Melissa hitting all we *s* with shafts Of gentle satire, „ 468
'Who ever *s* such wild barbarians? „ *iii* 42
s The soft white vapour streak the crowned towers „ 343
began to change—I *s* it and grieved— „ *iv* 299
S that they kept apart, no mischief done; „ 340
we *s* the lights and heard The voices murmuring. „ 558
when we *s* the embattled squares, „ *v* 246
and I *s* That equal baseness lived in sleeker times „ 384
and *s* the palace-front Alive with fluttering scarfs „ 508
Seeing I *s* not, hearing not I heard: Tho', if I *s* not, yet they told me all „ *vi* 19
when she *s* me lying stark, Dishelm'd and mute, „ 100
when she *s* The haggard father's face „ 102
she *s* them, and a day Rose from the distance „ 111
I *s* the forms: I knew not where I was: „ *vii* 133
s Thee woman thro' the crust of iron moods „ 341
turning *s* The happy valleys, half in light, „ *Con.* 40
And there we *s* Sir Walter where he stood, „ 81
he turn'd, and I *s* his eyes all wet, *Grandmother* 49
crossing, oft we *s* the glisten Of ice, *The Daisy* 35
For I in spirit *s* thee move *In Mem. xvii* 5
We *s* not, when we moved therein? „ *xxiv* 16
And *s* the tumult of the halls; „ *lxxxvii* 4
He brought an eye for all he *s*; „ *lxxxix* 9
That *s* thro' all the Muses' walk; „ *cix* 4
Wrapt in a cloak, as I *s* him, *Maud I i* 59
I *s* the treasured splendour, her hand, „ *vi* 84
Down by the hill I *s* them ride, „ *ix* 11
Yet I thought I *s* her stand, „ *II i* 38
Till I *s* the dreary phantom arise and fly „ *III vi* 36
She *s* him not, or mark'd not, if she *s*, *Com. of Arthur* 53
he *s* The smallest rock far on the faintest hill, „ 98
'And there I *s* mage Merlin, „ 280
Ran like a colt, and leapt at all he *s*: „ 322
nodded and slept, and *s*, Dreaming, a slope of land „ 427
s The splendour sparkling from aloft, *Gareth and L.* 48
they *s* the silver-misty morn Rolling her smoke „ 189
s nor one Nor other, but in all the listening eyes „ 326
Gareth *s* The shield of Gawain blazon'd rich „ 415
s the knights Clash like the coming and retiring wave, „ 521
s without the door King Arthur's gift, „ 676
s, Bowl-shaped, thro' tops of many thousand pines „ 795
horse thereon stumbled—ay, for I *s* it. „ 1057
and when he *s* the star Gleam, „ 1218

Saw (verb) (*continued*) *s* That Death was cast to ground, *Gareth and L.* 1402
He look'd and *s* that all was ruinous. *Marr. of Geraint* 315
For if he be the knight whom late I *s* „ 406
I *s* you moving by me on the bridge, „ 429
For this dear child, because I never *s*, „ 497
And looking round he *s* not Enid there, „ 506
Men *s* the goodly hills of Somerset, „ 828
By the flat meadow, till she *s* them come ; „ 832
I *s* three bandits by the rock Waiting to fall on you, *Geraint and E.* 72
S once a great piece of a promontory, „ 162
When now they *s* their bulwark fallen, „ 168
In former days you *s* me favourably. „ 315
when she *s* him ride More near by many a rood „ 441
turning round she *s* Dust, and the points of lances „ 448
Who *s* the chargers of the two that fell „ 481
Rose when they *s* the dead man rise, „ 732
But *s* me not, or mark'd not if you *s* ; „ 870
for a minute, till he *s* her Pass into it, „ 886
he *s* not whence, Strikes from behind. *Balin and Balan* 130
We *s* the hoof-print of a horse, no more.' „ 133
once he *s* the thrall His passion half had gauntleted „ 219
As if he *s* not, glanced aside, „ 248
Last night methought I *s* That maiden Saint „ 260
s The fountain where they sat together, „ 290
I *s* the flash of him but yestereven. „ 303
s, With pointed lance as if to pierce, a shape, „ 324
That *s* to-day the shadow of a spear, „ 373
in simple nakedness, *S* them embrace : „ 519
' I *s* the little elf-god eyeless once *Merlin and V.* 249
I look'd, and *s* you following still, „ 299
gloom'd Your fancy when ye *s* me following you, „ 326
Because I *s* you sad, to comfort you. „ 441
He *s* two cities in a thousand boats „ 561
men Became a crystal, and he *s* them thro' it, „ 630
Nor *s* she save the King, who wrought the charm, „ 643
s The knights, the court, the King, „ 874
since he *s* The slow tear creep from her closed eyelid „ 905
raised his eyes and *s* The tree that shone white-listed „ 938
s Fired from the west, far on a hill, *Lancelot and E.* 167
I *s* him, after, stand High on a heap of slain, „ 306
I never *s* his like : there lives No greater leader.' „ 316
s The maiden standing in the dewy light. „ 351
till he *s* Which were the weaker ; „ 461
when he *s* the Queen, embracing ask'd, „ 570
Gawain *s* Sir Lancelot's azure lions, „ 662
Whom when she *s*, ' Lavaine,' she cried, „ 794
there first she *s* the casque Of Lancelot on the wall : „ 805
Then she that *s* him lying unsleek, unshorn, „ 815
Lancelot *s* that she withheld her wish, „ 920
s One of her house, and sent him to the Queen „ 1167
s with a sidelong eye The shadow of some piece „ 1173
wild Queen, who *s* not, burst away To weep „ 1244
s the barge that brought her moving down, „ 1391
But who first *s* the holy thing to-day ? ' *Holy Grail* 67
She might have risen and floated when I *s* her. „ 100
s the bright boy-knight, and bound it on him, „ 156
found and *s* it, as the nun My sister *s* it ; „ 198
Some little of this marvel he too *s*, „ 216
s The golden dragon sparkling over all : „ 262
I heard the sound, I *s* the light, „ 280
I sware a vow to follow it till I *s*.' „ 282
s the Holy Grail, I *s* the Holy Grail „ 290
s deep lawns, and then a brook, „ 380
I *s* That man had once dwelt there ; „ 429
I *s* The holy elements alone ; „ 462
but he, ' *S* ye no more ? I, Galahad, *s* the Grail, The Holy Grail, „ 464
I *s* the fiery face as of a child That smote itself „ 466
At once I *s* him far on the great Sea, „ 510
If boat it were—I *s* not whence it came. „ 515
again Roaring, I *s* him like a silver star— „ 517
I *s* the least of little stars Down on the waste, „ 524
I *s* the spiritual city and all her spires „ 526
S ye none beside, None of your knights ? ' „ 631
I *s* The pelican on the casque of our Sir Bors „ 634

Saw (verb) (*continued*) Who, when he *s* me, rose, and bad me hail, *Holy Grail* 725
turn'd to whom at first He *s* not, „ 752
I may not speak of it : I *s* it ; ' „ 759
But nothing in the sounding hall I *s*, „ 828
yet methought I *s* the Holy Grail, „ 846
I had sworn I *s* That which I *s* ; but what I *s* was veil'd And cover'd ; „ 850
And as ye *s* it ye have spoken truth. „ 880
My greatest hardly will believe he *s* ; „ 896
but *s* Near him a mound of even-sloping side, *Pelleas and E.* 24
glancing thro' the hoary boles, he *s*, „ 50
She that *s* him cried, ' Damsels— „ 188
But *s* the postern portal also wide Yawning ; „ 420
hiss, snake—I *s* him there— „ 471
he *s* High up in heaven the hall that Merlin built, „ 552
He glanced and *s* the stately galleries, *Last Tournament* 145
He *s* the laws that ruled the tournament „ 160
as the water Moab *s* Come round by the East, „ 482
look'd and *s* The great Queen's bower was dark,— „ 757
s the Queen who sat betwixt her best Enid, *Guinevere* 27
and more than this He *s* not, „ 30
He *s* them—headland after headland flame „ 243
the golden days In which she *s* him first, „ 381
Came to that point where first she *s* the King „ 403
she *s*, Wet with the mists and smitten by the lights, „ 596
she look'd and *s* The novice, weeping, „ 663
I *s* One lying in the dust at Almesbury, *Pass. of Arthur* 76
since he *s* not whom he fought. „ 99
Look'd up for heaven, and only *s* the mist ; „ 112
But when he *s* the wonder of the hilt, „ 253
I never *s*, Nor shall see, here or elsewhere, „ 321
s, Straining his eyes beneath an arch of hand, „ 463
thought he *s*, the speck that bare the King, „ 465
Before he *s* my day my father died, And he was happy that he *s* it not ; *Lover's Tale i* 191
looking back, we *s* The clefts and openings „ 329
she *s* Beneath her feet the region far away, „ 394
And *s* the motion of all other things ; „ 574
I *s* There, where I hoped myself to reign „ 590
I *s* the moonlight glitter on their tears— „ 697
But cast a parting glance at me, you *s*, „ *iv* 4
he *s* His lady with the moonlight on her face ; „ 56
when I *s* her (and I thought him crazed, „ 163
Julian goes, the lord of all he *s*. „ 315
I, by Lionel sitting, *s* his face Fire, „ 322
s The bridesmaid pale, statuelike, *Sisters (E. and E.)* 211
when I *s* him come in at the door, *In the Child. Hosp.* 2
we *s* the rivers roll from Paradise ! *Columbus* 27
and I *s* The glory of the Lord flash up, „ 81
I *s* that we could not stay, *V. of Maeldune* 35
I *s* him and let him be. „ 128
He *s* not his daughter—he blest her : *To Prin. F. of H.* 3
meanings ambush'd under all they *s*, *Tiresias* 5
There in a secret olive-glade I *s* Pallas Athene „ 39
mask that I *s* so amazed me, *The Wreck* 117
I *s* that a boat was nearing us— „ 123
as I *s* the white sail run, And darken, *The Flight* 39
who *s* the death, but kept the deck, *Locksley H., Sixty* 63
You *s* the league-long rampart-fire *Pro. to Gen. Hamley* 27
A sudden nightingale *S* thee, *Demeter and P.* 12
crocus-purple hour That *s* thee vanish. „ 51
I *s* the tiger in the ruin'd fane „ 79
but trace of thee I *s* not ; „ 81
I never *s* it yet so all ablaze *The Ring* 81
stretch'd my hands As if I *s* her ; „ 117
We *s* far off an old forsaken house, „ 155
And *s* the world fly by me like a dream, „ 180
one day came And *s* you, shook her head, „ 313
and once we only *s* Your gilded vane, „ 330
the matron *s* That hinted love was only wasted bait, „ 359
Who *s* you kneel beside your bier, *Happy* 54
And him I *s* but once again, „ 79
I *s* beyond their silent tops The steaming marshes *Prog. of Spring* 74
I *s*, whenever In passing it glanced upon *Merlin and the G.* 102

Sayest 'Tis Kate—She *s* what she will: *Kate* 6
as thou *s*, a Fairy King And Fairy Queens *Gareth and L.* 258
as thou *s*, it is enchanted, son, „ 263
Saying (part.) (*See also* **Saäyin'**) *s* that which pleased him, for he smiled. *Enoch Arden* 757
S this, The woman half turn'd round *Sea Dreams* 285
and I (Pardon me *s* it) were much loth *Princess i* 156
So *s* from the court we paced, „ *iii* 117
Shame might befall Melissa, knowing, *s* not she knew: „ 148
S in odour and colour, 'Ah, be Among the roses *Maud I xxi* 12
King Made feast for, *s*, as they sat at meat, *Com. of Arthur* 247
s this the seer Went thro' the strait „ 394
s thou wert basely born. *Gareth and L.* 355
Reproach you, *s* all your force is gone? *Marr. of Geraint* 88
s all his force Is melted into mere effeminacy? „ 106
So *s*, from the carven flower above, *Lancelot and E.* 549
hopes are mine,' and *s* that, she choked, „ 607
S which she seized, And, thro' the casement „ 1233
s to me That Guinevere had sinn'd against the highest, *Last Tournament* 569
ev'n in *s* this, Her memory from old habit *Guinevere* 378
And well for thee, *s* in my dark hour, *Pass. of Arthur* 159
What am I *s*? and what are *you*? *Rizpah* 11
So *s*, light-foot Iris pass'd away. *Achilles over the T.* 1
What art thou *s*? 'And was not Alla *Akbar's Dream* 86
Saying (s) A *s*, hard to shape in act; *Love thou thy land* 49
a *s* learnt, In days far-off, *Tithonus* 47
What is their pretty *s*? jilted, is it? *Aylmer's Field* 353
dark *s's* from of old Ranging and ringing *Com. of Arthur* 415
thy foul *s's* fought for me: *Gareth and L.* 1180
And mirthful *s's*, children of the place, *Holy Grail* 555
a *s* that anger'd her. *Last Tournament* 628
Scabbard when she show'd the wealthy *s*, *Aylmer's Field* 236
Scaffold (*See also* **Death-scaffold**) *S's*, still sheets of water, *D. of F. Women* 34
Scald That let the bantling *s* at home, *Princess v* 458
Scale (for weighing) fortunes, justlier balanced, *s* with *s*,' „ *ii* 66
takes it up, And topples down the *s's*; „ *v* 445
While slowly falling as a *s* that falls, *Marr. of Geraint* 525
Scale (graduated series) Along the *s* of ranks, thro' all, *In Mem. cxi* 2
Scale (of armour) splendours and the golden *s* Of harness, *Princess v* 41
Scale (proportion) Because the *s* is infinite. *Two Voices* 93
Scale (verb) she that out of Lethe *s's* with man *Princess vii* 261
To *s* the heaven's highest height, *In Mem. cviii* 7
to *s* the highest of the heights With some strange hope *Tiresias* 28
The leper plague may *s* my skin *Happy* 27
Scaled Suddenly *s* the light. *Palace of Art* 8
And *s* in sheets of wasteful foam, *Sea Dreams* 53
Shall find the toppling crags of Duty *s* *Ode on Well.* 215
s with help a hundred feet Up from the base: *Balin and Balan* 170
High with the last line *s* her voice, *Lancelot and E.* 1019
The spiring stone that *s* about her tower, *Last Tournament* 511
I *s* the buoyant highway of the birds, *Prog. of Spring* 80
Scaling Tho' *s* slow from grade to grade; *Two Voices* 174
But after *s* half the weary down, *Enoch Arden* 372
crag and tree *S*, Sir Lancelot from the perilous nest, *Last Tournament* 18
Scalp From *s* to sole one slough and crust *St. S. Stylites* 2
Beat into my *s* and my brain, *Maud II v* 10
Scan I *s* him now Beastlier than any phantom *Lucretius* 195
We needs must *s* him from head to feet *Dead Prophet* 55
Scandal Begins the *s* and the cry: *You might have won* 16
Old *s's* buried now seven decads deep In other *s's* that have lived and died, And left the living *s* that shall die— *Aylmer's Field* 442
You'll have no *s* while you dine, *To F. D. Maurice* 17
like a city, with gossip, *s*, and spite; *Maud I iv* 8
Nun as she was, the *s* of the Court, *Holy Grail* 78
once the talk And *s* of our table, had return'd; „ 650
To spy some secret *s* if he might, *Guinevere* 26
make the smouldering *s* break and blaze Before the people, „ 91
To save his blood from *s*, „ 514
him The causer of that *s*, fought and fell; *The Ring* 215
While *s* is mouthing a bloodless name *The Dawn* 12
Scandalous (*See also* **Crown-scandalous**) To smoke the *s* hive of those wild bees *Holy Grail* 214
Scandalous (*continued*) I have scared you pale with my *s* talk, *Despair* 111
Scant 'Tis life, whereof our nerves are *s*, *Two Voices* 397
But work was *s* in the Isle, *First Quarrel* 43
Scanty Gain'd for her own a *s* sustenance, *Enoch Arden* 259
Thus earn'd a *s* living for himself: „ 818
Scape who may slay or *s* the three, *Gareth and L.* 641
Pray for him that he *s* the doom of fire, *Guinevere* 347
Scaped *S* thro' a cavern from a bandit hold, *Holy Grail* 207
'Scaped (escaped) by this way I *'s* them. *St. S. Stylites* 179
Scapegoat On that huge *s* of the race, *Maud I xiii* 42
Scar O sweet and far from cliff and *s* *Princess iv* 9
cloaks the *s* of some repulse with lies; *Merlin and V.* 818
Scarce upon the game, how *s* it was This season; *Audley Court* 32
I *s* can ask it thee for hate, *Gareth and L.* 361
He *s* is knight, yea but half-man, „ 1176
But *s* could see, as now we see, *Epilogue* 48
But *s* of such majestic mien *Freedom* 6
I *s* have learnt the title of your book, *The Ring* 126
saw you kneel beside your bier, and weeping *s* could see; *Happy* 54
Altho' the months have *s* begun, *To Ulysses* 22
we *s* can spell The Alif of Thine alphabet *Akbar's Dream* 30
Scarce-believable many a *s-b* excuse, *Enoch Arden* 469
Scarce-credited *S-c* at first but more and more, „ 648
Scarce-rocking *S-r*, her full-busted figure-head „ 543
Scare *s* church-harpies from the master's feast; *To J. M. K.* 3
Why wilt thou ever *s* me with thy tears, *Tithonus* 46
To *s* the fowl from fruit: *Princess ii* 228
biting laws to *s* the beasts of prey „ *v* 393
You cannot *s* me; nor rough face, *Gareth and L.* 1329
shadow of my spear had been enow To *s* them from me once; *Holy Grail* 792
Scarecrow Empty *s's*, I and you! *Vision of Sin* 94
Scared (*See also* **Skeärd**) 'O' she cried, *S* as it were, *Enoch Arden* 430
But *s* with threats of jail and halter *Aylmer's Field* 520
he heard her speak; She *s* him; *Princess i* 186
To lag behind, *s* by the cry they made, „ *v* 94
The king is *s*, the soldier will not fight, „ *Con.* 60
and this music now Hath *s* them both, *Gareth and L.* 251
foemen *s*, like that false pair who turn'd *Geraint and E.* 176
Nor need ye look so *s* at what I say: „ 339
So, *s* but at the motion of the man, „ 476
beauteous beast *S* by the noise upstarted *Merlin and V.* 422
some are *s*, who mark, Or wisely or unwisely, *To the Queen ii* 48
Do you think I was *s* by the bones? *Rizpah* 55
I have *s* you pale with my scandalous talk, *Despair* 111
that the foälk be sa *s* at, *Spinster's S's.* 24
My people too were *s* with eerie sounds, *The Ring* 408
Scarf One sitting on a crimson *s* unroll'd; *D. of F. Women* 126
Dark as a funeral *s* from stem to stern, *M. d'Arthur* 194
A *s* of orange round the stony helm, *Princess, Pro.* 102
palace-front Alive with fluttering *s's* and ladies' eyes, „ *v* 509
A purple *s*, at either end whereof *Marr. of Geraint* 169
Prince's blood spirted upon the *s*, „ 208
Yniol caught His purple *s*, and held, „ 377
Dark as a funeral *s* from stem to stern, *Pass. of Arthur* 362
Scarfskin not a hair Ruffled upon the *s*, *Aylmer's Field* 660
Scarlet (adj.) The sunrise broken into *s* shafts *Enoch Arden* 592
and again The *s* shafts of sunrise—but no sail. „ 599
and fulminated Against the *s* woman and her creed; *Sea Dreams* 23
her *s* sleeve, Tho' carved and cut, *Lancelot and E.* 806
The steaming marshes of the *s* cranes, *Prog. of Spring* 75
Scarlet (s) who wore the sleeve Of *s*, and the pearls; *Lancelot and E.* 502
upon his helm A sleeve of *s*, broider'd „ 604
Hued with the *s* of a fierce sunrise, *Lover's Tale i* 353
crimson and *s* of berries that flamed *V. of Maeldune* 61
Scarlet-mingled And hills and *s-m* woods *The Voyage* 47
Scarlett *S* and *S's* three hundred were riding by *Heavy Brigade* 4
Scarlett's Brigade three hundred of *S B*!' „ 45
Scarped From *s* cliff and quarried stone *In Mem. lvi* 2
Scarr'd *S* with a hundred wintry watercourses— *Holy Grail* 490
Scathe What Devil had the heart to *s* *Supp. Confessions* 83
as God's high gift from *s* and wrong, *Guinevere* 494
given my life To help his own from *s*, *Sir J. Oldcastle* 63
Scathed down in a furrow *s* with flame: *The Victim* 22
Scatter we will *s* all our maids Till happier times *Princess vi* 302

Scruple brakest thro' the *s* of my bond, *Last Tournament* 568
Scud foam-flakes *s* along the level sand, *D of F. Women* 39
thro' the gap Glimmer'd the streaming *s*: *Holy Grail* 682
Scudded Of mighty mouth, we *s* fast, *The Voyage* 46
Scudding Thro' *s* drifts the rainy Hyades Vext the dim sea: *Ulysses* 10
Scullery whinny shrills From tile to *s*, *Princess v* 453
Scullion (adj.) the King hath past his time—My *s* knave! *Gareth and L.* 710
Scullion (s) Among the *s's* and the kitchen-knaves, „ 154
To serve with *s's* and with kitchen-knaves; „ 170
What doest thou, *s*, in my fellowship? „ 765
Sir *S*, canst thou use that spit of thine? „ 791
I accept thee aught the more, *S*, „ 840
She reddening, 'Insolent *s*: I of thee? „ 976
'Be not so hardy, *s*, as to slay One nobler „ 980
Sculptor WAN *S*, weepest thou to take the cast *Wan Sculptor* 1
Musician, painter, *s*, critic, more: *Princess ii* 178
Sculpture some sweet *s* draped from head to foot, *Princess v* 57
And four great zones of *s*, set betwixt *Holy Grail* 232
Sculptured (*See also* **Weirdly-sculptured**) knights on horse *S*, and deckt in slowly-waning hues. *Gareth and L.* 1195
And darkling felt the *s* ornament *Merlin and V.* 734
Scum scurf of salt, and *s* of dross, *Vision of Sin* 211
a door for scoundrel *s* I open'd to the West, *Columbus* 170
Scurf *s* of salt, and scum of dross, *Vision of Sin* 211
Scurrilous Lightning of the hour, the pun, the *s* tale,— *Aylmer's Field* 441
Two lovers parted by a *s* tale Had quarrell'd, *The Ring* 208
Two lovers parted by no *s* tale— „ 427
Scurvy Cholera, *s*, and fever, *Def. of Lucknow* 84
Scymetar bright and sharp As edges of the *s*. *Kate* 12
Scythe The sweep of *s* in morning dew, *In Mem. lxxxix* 18
And watch'd the sun blaze on the turning *s*, *Geraint and E.* 252
Sdeath 'Our land invaded, '*s*! and he himself Your captive, yet my father wills not war: And, '*s*! myself, what care I, war or no? *Princess v* 276
I say she flies too high, '*s*! what of that? „ 286
'*S*—and with solemn rites by candle-light— „ 292
at once Decides it, '*s*! against my father's will.' „ 298
'*S*! but we will send to her,' „ 324
'Ida—'*s*! you blame the man; „ *vi* 221
'*S*! I would sooner fight thrice o'er than see it.' „ 226
Sea (*See also* **North-sea, Ocean-sea, Red Sea**) *And compass'd by the inviolate* s.' *To the Queen* 36
Ask the *s* At midnight, *Supp. Confessions* 125
Far, far beneath in the abysmal *s*, *The Kraken* 2
Leaning upon the ridged *s*, *The winds, etc.* 2
Down-carolling to the crisped *s*, „ 6
ridge Of heaped hills that mound the *s*, *Ode to Memory* 98
Shrill music reach'd them on the middle *s*. *Sea-Fairies* 6
clover-hill swells High over the full-toned *s*: „ 15
twang of the golden chords Runs up the ridged *s*. „ 39
When Norland winds pipe down the *s*, *Oriana* 91
I hear the roaring of the *s*, „ 98
Singing alone Under the *s*, *The Merman* 5
I would kiss them often under the *s*, (repeat) „ 15, 34
Soft are the moss-beds under the *s*; „ 39
Combing her hair Under the *s*, *The Mermaid* 5
Till that great sea-snake under the *s* „ 23
all the mermen under the *s* Would feel their immortality „ 28
Whose silvery spikes are nighest the *s*. „ 37
Of the bold merry mermen under the *s*; „ 42
In the purple twilights under the *s*; „ 44
In the branching jaspers under the *s*; „ 47
In the hueless mosses under the *s* „ 49
Would lean out from the hollow sphere of the *s*, „ 54
Your spirit is the calmed *s*, *Margaret* 25
The shadow rushing up the *s*, *Rosalind* 11
With motions of the outer *s*: *Eleänore* 113
And in the middle of the green salt *s* *Mine be the strength* 7
Floats far away into the Northern *s's* „ 13
Elsinore Heard the war moan along the distant *s*, *Buonaparte* 10
and past Into deep orange o'er the *s*, *Mariana in the S.* 26
There came a sound as of the *s*; „ 86
isled in sudden *s's* of light, My heart, *Fatima* 33
In cataract after cataract to the *s*. *Œnone* 9
Sea (*continued*) to where the sky Dipt down to *s* and sands. *Palace of Art* 32
Or in a clear-wall'd city on the *s*, „ 97
plunging *s's* draw backward from the land „ 251
hears the low Moan of an unknown *s*; „ 280
but evermore Most weary seem'd the *s*, *Lotos-Eaters* 41
Vaulted o'er the dark-blue *s*. „ *C. S.* 40
wallowing monster spouted his foam-fountains in the *s*. „ 107
As thunder-drops fall on a sleeping *s*: *D. of F. Women* 122
And languish for the purple *s's*. *You ask me, why, etc.* 4
And round them *s* and air are dark *Love thou thy land* 63
thou sendest out the man To rule by land and *s*, *England and Amer.* 2
The *s's* that shock thy base! „ 15
battle roll'd Among the mountains by the winter *s*; *M. d'Arthur* 2
isles of winter shock By night, with noises of the northern *s*. „ 141
And bowery hollows crown'd with summer *s*, „ 263
alighted from the boat, And breathing of the *s*. *Audley Court* 8
The *s* wastes all: but let me live my life. „ 51
my heart turn'd from her, as a thorn Turns from the *s*; „ 55
Beyond the fair green field and eastern *s*. *Love and Duty* 101
like a lane of beams athwart the *s*, *Golden Year* 50
the rainy Hyades Vext the dim *s*: *Ulysses* 11
There gloom the dark broad *s's*. „ 45
lying in dark-purple spheres of *s*. *Locksley Hall* 164
A light upon the shining *s*— *St. Agnes' Eve* 35
Thought her proud, and fled over the *s*; *Edward Gray* 14
The broad *s's* swell'd to meet the keel, *The Voyage* 13
At times the whole *s* burn'd, „ 51
Like Heavenly Hope she crown'd the *s*, „ 70
FLOW down, cold rivulet, to the *s*, *A Farewell* 1
The wrinkled *s* beneath him crawls; *The Eagle* 4
And fluted to the morning *s*. *To E. L.* 24
On thy cold gray stones, *O S*! *Break, break, etc.* 2
At the foot of thy crags, O *S*! „ 14
From the dread sweep of the down-streaming *s's*: *Enoch Arden* 55
Enoch was abroad on wrathful *s's*, „ 91
Enoch at times to go by land or *s*; „ 104
many a rough *s* had he weather'd in her! „ 135
the *s* is His, The *s* is His: He made it.' „ 225
but the loneliest in a lonely *s*. „ 553
And the low moan of leaden-colour'd *s's*. „ 612
Like fountains of sweet water in the *s*, „ 803
There came so loud a calling of the *s*, „ 910
By the long wash of Australasian *s's* *The Brook* 194
This had a rosy *s* of gillyflowers *Aylmer's Field* 159
Never since our bad earth became one *s*, „ 635
Runs in a river of blood to the sick *s*. „ 768
with a month's leave given them, to the *s*: *Sea Dreams* 6
Shall Babylon be cast into the *s*; „ 28
that they saw, the *s*. „ 36
the *s* roars Ruin: a fearful night!' „ 80
A full *s* glazed with muffled moonlight, *Princess i* 248
crystal currents of clear morning *s's*. „ *ii* 328
Wind of the western *s*, (repeat) „ *iii* 2, 4
Ask me no more: the moon may draw the *s*; „ *vii* 1
Blot out the slope of *s* from verge to shore, „ 38
the *s's*; A red sail, or a white; „ *Con.* 46
God bless the narrow *s* which keeps her off, „ 51
God bless the narrow *s's*! „ 70
Was great by land as thou by *s*. (repeat) *Ode on Well.* 84, 90
roughly set His Briton in blown *s's* „ 155
while we hear The tides of Music's golden *s* „ 252
broke them on the land, we drove them on the *s's*. *Third of Feb.* 30
SEA-KING's daughter from over the *s*, *W. to Alexandra* 1
Roar as the *s* when he welcomes the land, „ 24
Bride of the heir of the kings of the *s*— „ 28
voices of our universal *s* On capes *W. to Marie Alex.* 16
To lands of summer across the *s*; *The Daisy* 92
I take my part Of danger on the roaring *s*, *Sailor Boy* 22
Singing, 'And shall it be over the *s's* *The Islet* 9
a storm never wakes on the lonely *s*, „ 33
Sounds of the great *s* Wander'd about. *Minnie and Winnie* 7
flying by to be lost on an endless *s*— *Wages* 2
Calm on the *s's*, and silver sleep, *In Mem. xi* 17
To breathe thee over lonely *s's*. „ *xvii* 4

Sea (*continued*) Breaks hither over Indian *s's*, *In Mem. xxvi* 14
The moanings of the homeless *s*, „ *xxxv* 9
From belt to belt of crimson *s's* „ *lxxxvi* 13
The conscience as a *s* at rest: „ *xciv* 12
flew in a dove And brought a summons from the *s*: „ *ciii* 16
On winding stream or distant *s*; „ *cxv* 12
The stillness of the central *s*. „ *cxxiii* 4
Who rest to-night beside the *s*. „ *Con.* 76
better, war! loud war by land and by *s*, *Maud I i* 47
liquid azure bloom of a crescent of *s*, „ *iv* 5
Over blowing *s's*, Over *s's* at rest, „ *xvii* 13
the red man's babe Leap, beyond the *s*. „ 20
A purer sapphire melts into the *s*. „ *xviii* 52
And trying to pass to the *s*; „ *xxi* 7
shock Of cataract *s's* that snap „ *II ii* 26
While I am over the *s*! „ 76
Far into the North, and battle, and *s's* of death. „ *III vi* 37
held Tintagil castle by the Cornish *s*, *Com. of Arthur* 187
' A doubtful throne is ice on summer *s's*. „ 248
two Dropt to the cove, and watch'd the great *s* fall, „ 378
Descending in the glory of the *s's*— „ 400
To plunge old Merlin in the Arabian *s*; *Gareth and L.* 211
Far over the blue tarns and hazy *s's*, „ 499
The buoy that rides at *s*, and dips and springs „ 1146
And white sails flying on the yellow *s*; *Marr. of Geraint* 829
But not to goodly hill or yellow *s* „ 830
like a shoaling *s* the lovely blue Play'd into green, *Geraint and E.* 688
fell Against the heathen of the Northern *S* „ 969
Brought the great faith to Britain over *s's*; *Balin and Balan* 103
one side had *s* And ship and sail and angels „ 364
All fighting for a woman on the *s*. *Merlin and V.* 562
Even to the half my realm beyond the *s's*, *Lancelot and E.* 958
(*S* was her wrath, yet working after storm) „ 1309
In mine own realm beyond the narrow *s's*, „ 1323
A thousand piers ran into the great *S*. *Holy Grail* 503
At once I saw him far on the great *S*, „ 510
Strike from the *s*; and from the star there shot „ 529
And the *s* rolls, and all the world is warm'd?' „ 672
On hill, or plain, at *s*, or flooding ford. „ 728
So loud a blast along the shore and *s*, „ 796
heapt in mounds and ridges all the *s* Drove like a cataract, „ 798
And in the great *s* wash away my sin.' „ 806
With chasm-like portals open to the *s*, „ 815
moon Thro' the tall oriel on the rolling *s*. „ 831
A vision hovering on a *s* of fire, *Pelleas and E.* 52
Makers of nets, and living from the *s*. „ 90
served with choice from air, land, stream, and *s*, „ 149
flush'd The long low dune, and lazy-plunging *s*. *Last Tournament* 484
gain'd Tintagil, half in *s*, and high on land, „ 505
westward-smiling *s's* Watch'd from this tower. „ 587
For now the Heathen of the Northern *S*, *Guinevere* 135
strong man-breasted things stood from the *s*, „ 246
Of dark Tintagil by the Cornish *s*; „ 294
Godless hosts Of heathen swarming o'er the Northern *S*; „ 428
The phantom circle of a moaning *s*. *Pass. of Arthur* 87
On the waste sand by the waste *s* they closed. „ 92
deathwhite mist slept over sand and *s*: „ 95
Save for some whisper of the seething *s's*, „ 121
battle roll'd Among the mountains by the winter *s*; „ 171
isles of winter shock By night, with noises of the Northern *S*. „ 309
And bowery hollows crown'd with summer *s*, „ 431
Thunderless lightnings striking under *s* *To the Queen ii* 12
Some third-rate isle half-lost among her *s's*? „ 25
the sloping *s's* Hung in mid-heaven, *Lover's Tale i* 3
breakers of the outer *s* Sank powerless, „ 8
down to *s*, and far as eye could ken, „ 336
The incorporate blaze of sun and *s*. „ 409
nigh the *s* Parting my own loved mountains „ 432
the effect weigh'd *s's* upon my head To come my way! „ 660
Above the perilous *s's* of Change and Chance; „ 806
Knit to some dismal sandbank far at *s*, „ 809
Sometimes upon the hills beside the *s* „ *ii* 4
Hung round with paintings of the *s*, „ 168
Forthgazing on the waste and open *s*, „ 177

Sea (*continued*) Began to heave upon that painted *s*; *Lover's Tale i* 192
a little silver cloud Over the sounding *s's*: „ *iii* 37
an' I thought of him out at *s*, *First Quarrel* 89
wailing, wailing, the wind over land and *s*— *Rizpah* 1
the *s* that 'ill moan like a man? „ 72
' Spanish ships of war at *s*! *The Revenge* 3
stars came out far over the summer *s*, „ 56
sun smiled out far over the summer *s*, „ 70
And a day less or more At *s* or ashore, „ 87
s plunged and fell on the shot-shatter'd navy of Spain, „ 117
the wind Still westward, and the weedy *s's*— *Columbus* 72
The *s's* of our discovering over-roll Him „ 139
same chains Bound these same bones back thro' the Atlantic *s*, „ 214
blast blew us out and away thro' a boundless *s*. *V. of Maeldune* 10
their breath met us out on the *s's*, „ 37
from the sky to the blue of the *s*; „ 46
Plunged head down in the *s*, „ 82
sends the hidden sun Down yon dark *s*, *De Prof., Two G.* 34
In *s's* of Death and sunless gulfs of Doubt. *Pref. Son. 19th Cent.* 14
Fleeted his vessel to *s* with the king in it, *Batt. of Brunanburh* 60
With stormy light as on a mast at *s*, *Tiresias* 114
a huge *s* smote every soul from the decks of The Falcon *The Wreck* 109
a balmier breeze curl'd over a peacefuller *s*, „ 133
she is all alone in the *s*; *Despair* 63
blue of sky and *s*, the green of earth, *Ancient Sage* 41
sailor wrecks at last In ever-silent *s's*; „ 137
wish yon moaning *s* would rise and burst the shore, *The Flight* 11
about the shuddering wreck the death-white *s* should rave, „ 47
he sail'd the *s* to crush the Moslem in his pride; *Locksley H., Sixty* 29
Leonard early lost at *s*; „ 55
backward, forward, in the immeasureable *s*, „ 193
With one gray glimpse of *s*; *Pro. to Gen. Hamley* 8
Like drops of blood in a dark-gray *s*, *Heavy Brigade* 43
unlaborious earth and oarless *s*; *To Virgil* 20
Dominant over *s* and land. *Helen's Tower* 2
Our own fair isle, the lord of every *s*— *The Fleet* 7
Glorying between *s* and sky, *Open. I. and C. Exhib.* 18
And drew him over *s* to you— *To Marq. of Dufferin* 22
I climb'd on all the cliffs of all the *s's*, *Demeter and P.* 63
Trade flying over a thousand *s's* *Vastness* 13
Spring slides hither o'er the Southern *s*, *Prog. of Spring* 2
slant *s's* leaning on the mangrove copse, „ 76
Mussulman Who flings his bowstrung Harem in the *s*, *Romney's R.* 135
Like some old wreck on some indrawing *s*, *St. Telemachus* 44
Then one deep roar as of a breaking *s*, „ 67
clash of tides that meet in narrow *s's*.— *Akbar's Dream* 58
in blood-red cataracts down to the *s*! *Kapiolani* 12
When I put out to *s*, *Crossing the Bar* 4
Sea-bank I ran down The steepy *s-b*, *Lover's Tale ii* 74
Seabird And the lonely *s* crosses *The Captain* 71
ranged on the rock like white *s-b's* in a row, *V. of Maeldune* 101
Sea-blue Flits by the *s-b* bird of March; *In Mem. xci* 4
Sea-bud under my starry *s-b* crown *The Mermaid* 16
Sea-castle huge *s-c's* heaving upon the weather bow. *The Revenge* 24
Sea-cataract and fell In vast *s-c's*— *Sea Dreams* 54
Sea-circle first indeed Thro' many a fair *s-c*, *Enoch Arden* 542
Sea-cliff the *s-c* pathway broken short, *Merlin and V.* 882
You from the haven Under the *s-s*, *Merlin and the G.* 3
Sea-current *s-c* would sweep us out to the main. *Despair* 51
Sea-dune Some lodge within the waste *s-d's*, *The Flight* 90
Sea-flower Dressing their hair with the white *s-f*; *The Merman* 13
Sea-foam in the *s-f* sway'd a boat, Half-swallow'd in it, *Holy Grail* 802
Sea-framing Ran in and out the long *s-f* caves, *Sea Dreams* 33
Sea-friend Enoch parted with his old *s-f*, *Enoch Arden* 168
Sea-furbelow dimpled flounce of the *s-f* flap, *Sea Dreams* 266
Sea-grove the pale-green *s-g's* straight and high, *The Merman* 19
Sea-hall fill the *s-h's* with a voice of power; „ 10
blind wave feeling round his long *s-h* In silence: *Merlin and V.* 232
Sea-haze Roll'd a *s-h* and whelm'd the world *Enoch Arden* 672
Sea-home eyes fixt on the lost *s-h*, *The Wreck* 126
Sea-king *S-k's* daughter from over the sea, *W. to Alexandra* 1
The *S-k's'* daughter as happy as fair, „ 26
Seal *s*, that hung From Allan's watch, *Dora* 135
She sent a note, the *s* an *Elle vous suit*, *Edwin Morris* 105
Break lock and *s*: betray the trust: *You might have won* 18

Seal (*continued*) Burst his own wyvern on the *s*, *Aylmer's Field* 516
The *s* was Cupid bent above a scroll, *Princess i* 242
Claspt on her *s*, my sweet! *Window, The Answer* 2
To dissolve the precious *s* on a bond, *Maud I xix* 45
Stoopt, took, brake *s*, and read it; *Lancelot and E.* 1271
it was a bond and *s* Of friendship, *Lover's Tale ii* 181
Seal (an animal) follow you, as they say The *s* does music; *Princess iv* 456
Sea-lane Revenge ran on thro' a long *s-l* between. *The Revenge* 36
Seal'd Thro' the *s* ear to which a louder one Was all but silence— *Aylmer's Field* 696
S it with kisses? water'd it with tears? *Œnone* 234
This I *s*: The seal was Cupid bent above a scroll, *Princess i* 241
Knowledge is now no more a fountain *s*: „ *ii* 90
Delivering *s* dispatches which the Head Took half-amazed, „ *iv* 379
since my will *S* not the bond— „ *v* 399
Ask me no more: thy fate and mine are *s*: „ *vii* 11
or something *s* The lips of that Evangelist. *In Mem. xxxi* 15
Or *s* within the iron hills? „ *lvi* 20
S her mine from her first sweet breath. *Maud I xix* 41
I bad her keep, Like a *s* book, all mention of the grin, *The Ring* 123
Sea-light with a wild *s-l* about his feet, *Guinevere* 242
Sea-line And fixt upon the far *s-l*; *The Voyage* 62
Back to the dark *s-l* Looking, *Maud II ii* 45
Seaman prose O'er books of travell'd *seamen*, *Amphion* 82
the *seamen* Made a gallant crew, *The Captain* 5
set Annie forth in trade With all that *seamen* needed *Enoch Arden* 139
get you a *s's* glass, Spy out my face, „ 215
A haunt of brawling *seamen* once, „ 697
Mighty *S*, this is he Was great by land *Ode on Well.* 83
Mighty *S*, tender and true, „ 134
seem'd to hear Its murmur, as the drowning *s* hears, *Lover's Tale i* 635
only a hundred *seamen* to work the ship *The Revenge* 22
seamen made mock at the mad little craft „ 38
the gunner said 'Ay, ay,' but the *seamen* made reply: „ 91
Seam'd *S* with the shallow cares of fifty years: *Aylmer's Field* 814
S with an ancient swordcut on the cheek, *Lancelot and E.* 258
Chink'd as you see, and *s*— *Lover's Tale i* 131
Seamew Where now the *s* pipes, *In Mem. cxv* 13
Sear (adj.) (*See also* **Sere**) And woods are *s*, And fires burn clear, *Window, Winter* 3
Sear (verb) And let my lady *s* the stump for him, *Pelleas and E.* 339
leaf rejoice in the frost that *s's* it at night; *The Wreck* 20
Search (s) burst away In *s* of stream or fount, *Enoch Arden* 635
To seek him, and had wearied of the *s*. *Lancelot and E.* 631
went in *s* of thee Thro' many a palace, *Demeter and P.* 54
after hours of *s* and doubt and threats, *The Ring* 278
Search (verb) 'To *s* thro' all I felt or saw, *Two Voices* 139
To *s* a meaning for the song, *Day Dm., L'Envoi* 35
But it is thou whom I *s* from temple to temple. *Akbar's D., Inscrip.* 6
Searching *See* **Spirit-searching**
Sear'd *S* by the close ecliptic, *Aylmer's Field* 193
foreheads grimed with smoke, and *s*, *Holy Grail* 265
Searer The woods are all the *s*, *Window, Winter* 14
Sea-smoke upjetted in spirts of wild *s-s*, *Sea Dreams* 52
Sea-snake Till that great *s-s* under the sea *The Mermaid* 23
Season *knew the* s's *when to take Occasion* *To the Queen* 30
'Will thirty *s's* render plain *Two Voices* 82
Power fitted to the *s*; *Œnone* 123
And in its *s* bring the law; *Love thou thy land* 32
It is a stormy *s*.' *The Goose* 8
I heard the watchman peal The sliding *s*: *Gardener's D.* 183
Then touch'd upon the game, how scarce it was This *s*; *Audley Court* 33
Are but as poets' *s's* when they flower, *Golden Year* 28
Thro' all the *s* of the golden year. „ 36
Old writers push'd the happy *s* back,— „ 66
In divers *s's*, divers climes; *Day-Dm., L'Envoi* 18
We circle with the *s's*. *Will Water.* 64
The sunny and the rainy *s's* came and went *Enoch Arden* 623
But subject to the *s* or the mood, *Aylmer's Field* 71
The meteor of a splendid *s*, „ 205
yet out of *s*, thus I woo thee roughly, *Lucretius* 271
the cube and square Were out of *s*: *Princess, Pro.* 181
And mix the *s's* and the golden hours; *Ode Inter. Exhib.* 36
The *s's* bring the flower again, *In Mem. ii* 5
And, crown'd with all the *s* lent. „ *xxii* 6

Season (*continued*) No joy the blowing *s* gives, *In Mem. xxxviii* 5
break At *s's* thro' the gilded pale: „ *cxi* 8
But served the *s's* that may rise; „ *cxiii* 4
Like things of the *s* gay, like the bountiful *s* bland, *Maud I iv* 3
That blow by night, when the *s* is good, „ *II v* 75
Fixt in her will, and so the *s's* went. *Merlin and V.* 188
'to pluck the flower in *s*,' „ 722
all men's hearts became Clean for a *s*, *Holy Grail* 91
with living waters in the change Of *s's*: *Pelleas and E.* 512
birds that change Their *s* in the night *Pass. of Arthur* 39
such a one As dawns but once a *s*. *Lover's Tale i* 300
Banner of England, not for a *s*, *Def. of Lucknow* 1
leaves possess the *s* in their turn, *Prog. of Spring* 107
O yes! I hired you for a *s* there, *Romney's R.* 20
Season'd Which bears a *s* brain about, *Will Water.* 85
Season-earlier cool as these, Tho' *s-e*. *Balin and Balan* 274
Sea-sounding sad *s-s* wastes of Lyonesse— *Merlin and V.* 74
Sea-sunset *s-s* glorying round her hair *Last Tournament* 508
Seat (s) downward to her *s* from the upper cliff. *Œnone* 22
Rest in a happy place and quiet *s's* „ 131
had cast the curtains of their *s* aside— *Aylmer's Field* 803
and lady friends From neighbour *s's*: *Princess, Pro.* 98
part reel'd but kept their *s's*: „ *v* 496
no quiet *s's* of the just, *Wages* 8
freedom in her regal *s* Of England; *In Mem. cix* 14
mine is the firmer *s*, The truer lance: *Lancelot and E.* 446
prone from off her *s* she fell, *Guinevere* 414
Pluck the mighty from their *s*, *Locksley H., Sixty* 133
since he would sit on a Prophet's *s*, *Dead Prophet* 53
I sprang from my *s*, I wept, *Charity* 37
Seat (verb) we will *s* you highest: *Princess iii* 159
To *s* you sole upon my pedestal Of worship— *Merlin and V.* 878
Then waving as a sign to *s* ourselves, *Lover's Tale iv* 320
Seated (*See also* **Deep-seated**) but Annie, *s* with her grief, *Enoch Arden* 280
Then, *s* on a serpent-rooted beech, *The Brook* 135
Laurence Aylmer, *s* on a stile In the long hedge, „ 197
the king, the queen Bad me be *s*, *Columbus* 11
he was *s*—speaking aloud To women, *The Wreck* 48
Angel *s* in the vacant tomb. *Locksley H., Sixty* 278
Blessing his field, or *s* in the dusk Of even, *Demeter and P.* 125
When *s* on a rock, and foot to foot *Romney's R.* 75
Seating And, *s* Gareth at another board, *Gareth and L.* 871
Sea-village Yonder lies our young *s-v*— *Locksley H., Sixty* 245
Sea-voice sent a deep *s-v* thro' all the land, *Guinevere* 247
Seaward Your cannons moulder on the *s* wall; *Ode on Well.* 173
Seaward-bound *s-b* for health they gain'd a coast, *Sea Dreams* 16
Seaward-gazing in a *s-g* mountain-gorge They built, *Enoch Arden* 558
all day long Sat often in the *s-g* gorge, „ 589
Sea-water The salt *s-w* passes by, *In Mem. xix* 6
Sea-wave voice of the long *s-w* as it swell'd *Maud I xiv* 31
Sea-wind and over them the *s-w* sang Shrill, *M. d'Arthur* 48
and over them the *s-w* sang Shrill, *Pass. of Arthur* 216
sounds of joy That came on the *s-w*. *Lover's Tale i* 326
Sea-wold On the broad *s-w's* in the crimson shells, *The Mermaid* 36
Seaworm lie Battening upon huge *s's* *The Kraken* 12
Sea-worthy The vessel scarce *s-w*; *Enoch Arden* 656
Of others their old craft *s* still, *Pref. Son. 19th Cent.* 3
Second (adj.) A *s* voice was at mine ear, *Two Voices* 427
Is bodied forth the *s* whole. *Love thou thy land* 66
And hid Excalibur the *s* time, *M. d'Arthur* 111
'Tis like the *s* world to us that live; *Golden Year* 56
And o'er her *s* father stoopt a girl, *Enoch Arden* 747
Yet the sad mother, for the *s* death *Aylmer's Field* 604
But when the *s* Christmas came, escaped His keepers, „ 838
Is it so true that *s* thoughts are best? *Sea Dreams* 65
I find you here but in the *s* place, *Princess iii* 157
and you me Your *s* mother: „ *iv* 297
'The *s* two: they wait,' he said, 'pass on; „ *v* 4
Less prosperously the *s* suit obtain'd At first with Psyche. „ *vii* 71
We flung the burthen of the *s* James. *Third of Feb.* 28
And unto me no *s* friend. *In Mem. vi* 44
Beyond the *s* birth of Death. „ *xlv* 16
If, in thy *s* state sublime, „ *lxi* 1
She is the *s*, not the first „ *cxiv* 16
When he comes to the *s* corpse in the pit? *Maud II v* 88

See (*continued*) *S* what I *s*, be thou where I have been, *Balin and Balan* 572
I scarce can *s* thee now. Goodnight! „ 621
I *s* thee now no more. „ 624
Nor could he *s* but him who wrought the charm *Merlin and V.* 212
s you not, dear love, That such a mood as that, „ 324
that no man could *s* her more, „ 642
S's what his fair bride is and does, „ 782
s Her godlike head crown'd with spiritual fire, „ 836
ask you not to *s* the shield he left, *Lancelot and E.* 653
an ye will it let me *s* the shield.' „ 661
'Going? and we shall never *s* you more. „ 926
to *s* your face, To serve you, „ 938
'Not to be with you, not to *s* your face— „ 946
To *s* that she be buried worshipfully.' „ 1329
to *s* The maiden buried, not as one unknown, „ 1333
if a man Could touch or *s* it, he was heal'd *Holy Grail* 55
for thou shalt *s* what I have seen, „ 160
none might *s* who bare it, and it past. „ 190
But since I did not *s* the Holy Thing, „ 281
What go ye into the wilderness to *s*?' „ 287
one hath seen, and all the blind will *s*. „ 313
what thy sister taught me first to *s*, „ 469
thou shalt *s* the vision when I go.' „ 484
On either hand, as far as eye could *s*, „ 498
Which never eyes on earth again shall *s*. „ 532
if ever loyal man and true Could *s* it, „ 757
cannot *s* for slime, Slime of the ditch: „ 771
could I touch or *s* the Holy Grail „ 779
Being too blind to have desire to *s*. „ 872
'*S*! look at mine! but wilt thou fight *Pelleas and E.* 127
Content am I so that I *s* thy face But once a day: „ 243
from the vermin that he *s's* Before him, „ 285
Vex not yourself: ye will not *s* me more.' „ 304
Thus to be bounden, so to *s* her face, „ 326
Let me be bounden, I shall *s* her face; „ 331
S, the hand Wherewith thou takest this, *Last Tournament* 192
Tuwhoo! do ye *s* it? do ye *s* the star?' „ 346
'Nay, nor will: I *s* it and hear. „ 348
shape Of one that in them *s's* himself, „ 370
forgotten all in my strong joy To *s* thee— „ 583
Who *s* your tender grace and stateliness. *Guinevere* 190
sworn never to *s* him more, To *s* him more.' „ 376
pity almost makes me die To *s* thee, „ 535
Never lie by thy side; *s* thee no more— „ 579
I might *s* his face, and not be seen.' „ 588
so she did not *s* the face, „ 595
now I *s* thee what thou art, „ 648
We needs must love the highest when we *s* it, „ 660
And have not power to *s* it as it is: *Pass. of Arthur* 20
because we *s* not to the close;— „ 21
one last act of knighthood shalt thou *s* „ 163
Watch what I *s*, and lightly bring thee word.' „ 212
I *s* thee what thou art, „ 291
'Now *s* I by thine eyes that this is done. „ 317
Nor shall *s*, here or elsewhere, till I die, „ 322
now I *s* the true old times are dead, „ 397
thou should'st never *s* my face again, „ 414
S, sirs, Even now the Goddess of the Past, *Lover's Tale i* 15
Chink'd as you *s*, and seam'd— „ 131
Waiting to *s* some blessed shape in heaven, „ 312
FROM that time forth I would not *s* her more; „ *ii* 1
in her you *s* That faithful servant „ *iv* 341
to *s* if work could be found; *First Quarrel* 44
When I cannot *s* my own hand, *Rizpah* 7
Couldn't *s* 'im, we 'eärd 'im *North. Cobbler* 47
'Doesn't tha *s* 'im, she axes, 'fur I can *s* 'im?' „ 49
For *s*—this wine—the grape from whence *Sisters (E. and E.)* 61
That time I did not *s*. „ 90
when she thought I did not *s*— „ 166
The Lord has so *much* to *s* to! *In the Child Hosp.* 57
and we went to *s* to the child. „ 68
perchance the neighbours round May *s*, *Achilles over the T.* 13
Whom yet I *s* as there you sit *To E. Fitzgerald* 5
strange hope to *s* the nearer God. *Tiresias* 29
eyes, that cannot *s* thine own, *S* this, „ 108

See (*continued*) *S*, we were nursed in the drear night-fold *Despair* 21
s's and stirs the surface-shadow *Ancient Sage* 38
s's the Best that glimmers thro' the Worst, „ 72
Who *s* not what they do?' „ 81
s The high-heaven dawn of more than mortal day „ 283
waken every morning to that face I loathe to *s*: *The Flight* 8
And *s* the ships from out the West „ 91
I seem to *s* a new-dug grave up yonder by the yew! „ 98
people 'ud *s* it that wint in to mass— *Tomorrow* 74
Thou *s's* that i' spite o' the men *Spinster's S's.* 11
guide us thro' the days I shall not *s*? *Locksley H., Sixty* 158
whence you *s* the Locksley tower, „ 176
and even where you *s* her now— „ 179
We should *s* the Globe we groan in, „ 188
Man or Mind that *s's* a shadow „ 196
those about us whom we neither *s* nor name, „ 272
s the highest Human Nature is divine. „ 276
But scarce could *s*, as now we *s*, *Epilogue* 48
all in vain As far as man can *s*, „ 69
Shall we *s* to it, I and you? *Dead Prophet* 52
'*S*, what a little heart,' she said, „ 75
both our Houses, may they *s* Beyond the borough *Hands all Round* 27
those gilt gauds men-children swarm to *s*. *To W. C. Macready* 11
For, *s*, thy foot has touch'd it; *Demeter and P.* 48
Will *s* me by the landmark far away, „ 124
s no more The Stone, the Wheel, „ 149
I couldn't *s* fur the smoäke *Owd Roä* 87
not shown To dazzle all that *s* them? *The Ring* 144
that *s's* A thousand squares of corn and meadow, „ 148
and cried 'I *s* him, Io t'amo, Io t'amo.' „ 223
'*S*!—Found in a chink of that old moulder'd floor!' „ 279
and *s* beneath our feet The mist of autumn „ 328
In all the world my dear one *s's* but you— „ 364
as a man Who *s's* his face in water, „ 370
till she *s's* Her maiden coming like a Queen, „ 479
He *s's* me, waves me from him. *Happy* 19
and weeping scarce could *s*; „ 54
S, I sinn'd but for a moment. „ 85
And *s* my cedar green, and there My giant ilex *To Ulysses* 17
gladly *s* I thro' the wavering flakes *Prog. of Spring* 29
Beyond the darker hour to *s* the bright, „ 88
The best in me that *s's* the worst in me, And groans to *s* it, finds no comfort there. *Romney's R.* 44
S, there is hardly a daisy. *The Throstle* 12
O GOD in every temple I *s* people that *s* thee, *Akbar's D., Inscrip.* 1
once again we *s* thee rise. „ *Hymn* 1
SIR, do you *s* this dagger? *Bandit's Death* 5
He *s's* not her like anywhere in this pitiless world *Charity* 43
And *s* and shape and do. *Mechanophilus* 4
I hope to *s* my Pilot face to face *Crossing the Bar* 15

Seeä (see) when they *s's* ma a passin' boy, *N. Farmer, O. S.* 53
if tha *s's* 'im an' smells 'im *North. Cobbler* 66
I browt what tha *s's* stannin' theer, „ 70

Seeä'd (saw) *S* her todaäy goä by— *N. Farmer, N. S.* 13

Seeäd I *s* that our Sally went laämed *North. Cobbler* 39
S nobbut the smile o' the sun „ 50

Seeäd (seed) an' some on it down i' *s*. *N. Farmer, O. S.* 40

Seeädin' (seeding) wool of a thistle a-flyin' an' *s* tha häated to see; *Spinster's S's.* 79

Seeäm (seem) 'E *s's* naw moor nor watter, *North. Cobbler* 76

Seeäm'd (seemed) an' *s* as blind as a poop, *Owd Roä* 101

Seed (*See also* **Arrow-seed, Seeäd**) having sown some generous *s*, *Two Voices* 143
Sow the *s*, and reap the harvest *Lotos-Eaters, C. S.* 121
Bear *s* of men and growth of minds. *Love thou thy land* 20
That sought to sow themselves like winged *s's*, *Gardener's D.* 65
Not only we, the latest *s* of Time, *Godiva* 5
Nor cared for *s* or scion! *Amphion* 12
The vilest herb that runs to *s* „ 95
But in my words were *s's* of fire. *The Letters* 28
and thus a noble scheme Grew up from *s* *Princess iv* 310
the *s*, The little *s* they laugh'd at in the dark, „ *vi* 33
save the one true *s* of freedom sown *Ode on Well.* 162
Once in a golden hour I cast to earth a *s*. *The Flower* 2
thieves from o'er the wall Stole the *s* by night. „ 12

Seed (*continued*) For all have got the *s*. *The Flower* 20
And finding that of fifty *s's* *In Mem. lv* 11
This bitter *s* among mankind; „ *xc* 4
Ray round with flames her disk of *s*, „ *ci* 6
Long sleeps the summer in the *s*; „ *cv* 26
is but *s* Of what in them is flower „ *Con.* 135
three gray linnets wrangle for the *s*: *Guinevere* 255
winds, Laden with thistledown and *s's* *Lover's Tale ii* 13
Eastern gauze With *s's* of gold— „ *iv* 292
for I loathe The *s* of Cadmus— *Tiresias* 117
Daughter of the *s* of Cain, *Forlorn* 39
Accomplish that blind model in the *s*, *Prog. of Spring* 114
Seed (saw) nor 'e niver not *s* to owt, *Village Wife* 51
but Robby I *s* thruf ya theere. *Spinster's S's.* 14
Fur I *s* that Steevie wur coomin', „ 40
fur I *s* that it couldn't be, „ 47
Fur I *s* the beck coomin' down *Owd Roä* 40
I *s* at 'is faäce wur as red as the Yule-block „ 56
then I *s* 'er a-cryin', I did. „ 80
'at summun *s* i' the flaäme, „ 94
Ay, an' ya *s* the Bishop. *Church-warden, etc.* 17
An' keeäper 'e *s* ya an roon'd, „ 28
Seed (seen) I niver ha *s* it sa white wi' the Maäy *Village Wife* 80
An' they niver 'ed *s* sich ivin' *Owd Roä* 26
See'd (saw) white wi' the Maäy es I *s* it to-year— *Village Wife* 80
See'd (seen) boooks, I ha' *s* 'em, belong'd to the Squire, „ 71
Seeded Across the silent *s* meadow-grass Borne, *Pelleas and E.* 561
Seeding *See* **Seeädin'**
Seedling as Nature packs Her blossom or her *s*, *Enoch Arden* 179
Seedsman *s*, rapt Upon the teeming harvest, *Golden Year* 70
Seeing (*See also* **All-seeing**) *S* all his own mischance— *L. of Shalott iv* 12
s men, in power Only, are likest gods, *Œnone* 129
s not That Beauty, Good, and Knowledge, *To ——, With Pal. of Art* 9
Averill *s* How low his brother's mood had fallen, *Aylmer's Field* 403
we should find the land Worth *s*; *Princess iii* 172
S I saw not, hearing not I heard: „ *vi* 19
s either sex alone Is half itself, „ *vii* 301
And our *s* is not sight. *Voice and the P.* 36
S his gewgaw castle shine, *Maud I x* 18
her men, *S* the mighty swarm about their walls, *Com. of Arthur* 200
S that ye be grown too weak and old „ 511
s the city is built To music, *Gareth and L.* 276
s he hath sent us cloth of gold, „ 428
s who had work'd Lustier than any, „ 695
And *s* now thy words are fair, „ 1181
S he never rides abroad by day; „ 1334
And all the three were silent *s*, „ 1362
And *s* them so tender and so close, *Marr. of Geraint* 22
And *s* one so gay in purple silks, „ 284
And *s* her so sweet and serviceable, „ 393
s I have sworn That I will break his pride „ 423
Danced in his bosom, *s* better days. „ 505
Then *s* cloud upon the mother's brow, „ 777
Arthur *s* ask'd 'Tell me your names; *Balin and Balan* 49
s that thy realm Hath prosper'd in the name of Christ, „ 98
Balin first woke, and *s* that true face, „ 590
And *s* me, with a great voice he cried, *Lancelot and E.* 309
s that ye forget Obedience is the courtesy „ 717
S it is no more Sir Lancelot's fault „ 1075
Yet, *s* you desire your child to live, „ 1095
S I never stray'd beyond the cell, *Holy Grail* 628
s that the King must guard That which he rules, „ 905
and *s* Pelleas droop, Said Guinevere, *Pelleas and E.* 178
so went back, and *s* them yet in sleep „ 445
s they profess To be none other (repeat) *Last Tournament* 82, 85
s too much wit Makes the world rotten, „ 246
Let be thy Mark, *s* he is not thine.' „ 522
Flatter me rather, *s* me so weak, „ 642
S it is not bounded save by love.' „ 703
S forty of our poor hundred were slain, *The Revenge* 76
s what a door for scoundrel scum I open'd *Columbus* 170
Seek When my passion *s's* Pleasance *Lilian* 8
What wantest thou? whom dost thou *s*, *Oriana* 71
We would run to and fro, and hide and *s*, *The Mermaid* 35
And seem to find, but still to *s*. *Two Voices* 96
Seek (*continued*) I *s* a warmer sky, *You ask me, why, etc.* 26
'Tis not too late to *s* a newer world. *Ulysses* 57
to *s*, to find, and not to yield. „ 70
To those that *s* them issue forth; *Day-Dm., Arrival* 2
He comes, scarce knowing what he *s's*: „ 17
'O *s* my father's court with me, „ *Depart.* 27
childless mother went to *s* her child; *Aylmer's Field* 829
'Hist O Hist,' he said, 'They *s* us: *Princess iv* 219
where you *s* the common love of these, „ *vi* 172
He *s's* at least Upon the last *In Mem. xlvii* 12
s A friendship for the years to come. „ *lxxxv* 79
But *s's* to beat in time with one „ 115
To *s* thee on the mystic deeps, „ *cxxv* 14
And so that he find what he went to *s*, *Maud I xvi* 3
I will *s* thee out Some comfortable bride *Gareth and L.* 93
twelvemonth and a day, nor *s* my name. „ 446
S, till we find.' „ 1279
I *s* a harbourage for the night.' *Marr. of Geraint* 299
To *s* a second favour at his hands. „ 626
had ridd'n a random round To *s* him, *Lancelot and E.* 631
my craven *s's* To wreck thee villainously: *Last Tournament* 548
'to *s* the Lord Jesus in prayer; *In the Child. Hosp.* 18
made by me, may *s* to unbury me, *Columbus* 206
sworn to *s* If any golden harbour *Pref. Son. 19th Cent.* 12
then so keen to *s* The meanings ambush'd *Tiresias* 4
the rebel subject *s* to drag me from the throne, *By an Evolution.* 15
Seeker *See* **Self-seeker**
Seeking in *s* to undo One riddle, *Two Voices* 232
S a tavern which of old he knew, *Enoch Arden* 691
For love or fear, or *s* favour of us, *Marr. of Geraint* 700
weak beast *s* to help herself By striking *Merlin and V.* 498
Seeling Diet and *s*, jesses, leash „ 125
Seem (*See also* **Seeäm**) And children all *s* full of Thee! *Supp. Confessions* 21
things that *s*, And things that be, „ 173
I *s* to see Thought folded over thought, *Eleänore* 83
or *s* To lapse far back in some confused dream *Sonnet To ——* 2
'He *s's* to hear a Heavenly Friend, *Two Voices* 295
'Moreover, something is or *s's*, „ 379
So sweet it *s's* with thee to walk, *Miller's D.* 29
It *s's* in after-dinner talk „ 31
I may *s*, As in the nights of old, „ 165
would *s* to award it thine, *Œnone* 73
Howe'er it be, it *s's* to me, *L. C. V. de Vere* 53
And now it *s's* as hard to stay, *May Queen, Con.* 10
O sweet and strange it *s's* to me, „ 53
s to mourn and rave On alien shores; *Lotos-Eaters* 32
It *s's* I broke a close with force and arms: *Edwin Morris* 131
She *s's* a part of those fresh days to me; „ 142
So *s's* she to the boy. *Talking Oak* 108
'So strange it *s's* to me. *Lady Clare* 52
Evermore she *s's* to gaze On that cottage *L. of Burleigh* 34
I *s* so foolish and so broken down. *Enoch Arden* 316
s's, as I re-listen to it, *The Brook* 18
My mother, as it *s's* you did, „ 225
I *s* to be ungraciousness itself.' *Aylmer's Field* 245
King of the East altho' he *s*, *Lucretius* 133
s's some unseen monster lays His vast and filthy hands „ 219
since the nobler pleasure *s's* to fade. „ 230
I would be that for ever which I *s*, *Princess ii* 257
Methinks he *s's* no better than a girl; „ *iii* 218
I s no more: *I* want forgiveness too: „ *vi* 290
That *s* to keep her up but drag her down— „ *vii* 270
I *s* A mockery to my own self. „ 336
Mourn, for to us he *s's* the last, *Ode on Well.* 19
Who *s's* a promontory of rock, *Will* 6
tho' He be not that which He *s's*? *High. Pantheism* 3
So *s's* it in my deep regret, *In Mem. viii* 17
I *s* to meet their least desire, „ *lxxxiv* 17
I *s* to love thee more and more. „ *cxxx* 12
It *s's* that I am happy, *Maud I xviii* 50
undercurrent woe That *s's* to draw— „ 84
indeed He *s's* to me Scarce other *Ded. of Idylls* 6
I *s* as nothing in the mighty world, *Com. of Arthur* 87
there is nothing in it as it *s's* Saving the King; *Gareth and L.* 264

Seem (*continued*) *s's* Wellnigh as long as thou art statured tall! — *Gareth and L.* 281
see ye not how weak and hungerworn I *s*— „ 444
S I not as tender to him As any mother? „ 1283
ye *s* agape to roar! „ 1306
For tho' it *s's* my spurs are yet to win, *Marr. of Geraint* 128
Who *s's* no bolder than a beaten hound; *Geraint and E.* 61
who sits apart, And *s's* so lonely?' „ 300
It *s's* another voice in other groves; *Balin and Balan* 215
s's a flame That rages in the woodland far below, „ 233
For thanks it *s* till now neglected, *Merlin and V.* 308
makes you *s* less noble than yourself, „ 322
since ye *s* the Master of all Art, „ 468
That *s* a sword beneath a belt of three, „ 510
wreathen round it made it *s* his own; „ 735
My father, howsoe'er I *s* to you, *Lancelot and E.* 1092
but *s* Mute of this miracle, *Holy Grail* 65
Until this earth he walks on *s's* not earth, „ 912
mine the blame that oft I *s* as he *Last Tournament* 115
the glance That only *s's* half-loyal to command,— „ 118
Behold, I *s* but King among the dead.' *Pass. of Arthur* 146
(For they *s* many and my most of life, *Lover's Tale i* 185
All this *S's* to the quiet daylight of your minds „ 296
S's but a cobweb filament to link „ 376
tho' she *s* so like the one you lost, „ *iv* 365
eyes frown: the lips *S* but a gash. *Sisters (E. and E.)* 107
s Like would-be guests an hour too late, *Tiresias* 197
brain was drunk with the water, it *s's*; *Despair* 65
s to flicker past thro' sun and shade, *Ancient Sage* 100
I *s* to see a new-dug grave up yonder *The Flight* 98
s's to me now like a bit of yisther-day *Tomorrow* 8
The days that *s* to-day, *Pref. Poem Broth. S.* 24
A 'Miriam' that might *s* a 'Muriel'; *The Ring* 241
May *s* the black ox of the distant plain. *To one who ran down Eng.* 4
I *s* no longer like a lonely man *Akbar's Dream* 20
But such a tide as moving *s's* asleep, *Crossing the Bar* 5

Seem'd (*See also* **Seeäm'd**) In sleep she *s* to walk forlorn, *Mariana* 30
s to shake The sparkling flints *Arabian Nights* 51
there *s* Hundreds of crescents on the roof „ 128
And *s* knee-deep in mountain grass, *Mariana in the S.* 42
Such *s* the whisper at my side: *Two Voices* 439
There *s* no room for sense of wrong; „ 456
S half-within and half-without, *Miller's D.* 7
Floated her hair or *s* to float in rest. *Œnone* 19
on every peak a statue *s* To hang on tiptoe, *Palace of Art* 37
One *s* all dark and red—a tract of sand, „ 65
You *s* to hear them climb and fall „ 70
without light Or power of movement, *s* my soul, „ 246
It *s* so hard at first, mother, *May Queen, Con.* 9
s to go right up to Heaven and die „ 40
In which it *s* always afternoon. *Lotos-Eaters* 4
A land where all things *s* the same! „ 24
And deep-asleep he *s*, yet all awake, „ 35
Most weary *s* the sea, weary the oar, „ 41
I started once, or *s* to start in pain, *D. of F. Women* 41
in her throat Her voice *s* distant, *To J. S* 55
there *s* A touch of something false, *Edwin Morris* 73
'Yet *s* the pressure thrice as sweet *Talking Oak* 145
how hard it *s* to me, When eyes, *Love and Duty* 35
he *s* To his great heart none other than a God! *Tithonus* 13
We *s* to sail into the Sun! *The Voyage* 16
Now nearer to the prow she *s* „ 67
She *s* a part of joyous Spring: *Sir L. and Q. G.* 23
Rose again from where it *s* to fail, *Vision of Sin* 24
the girl *S* kinder unto Philip than to him; *Enoch Arden* 42
He *s*, as in a nightmare of the night, „ 114
while Annie *s* to hear Her own death-scaffold raising, „ 174
for Enoch *s* to them Uncertain as a vision „ 355
A footstep *s* to fall beside her path, „ 514
There often as he watch'd or *s* to watch, „ 600
idiotlike it *s*, With inarticulate rage, „ 639
it *s* he saw No pale sheet-lightnings from afar, *Aylmer's Field* 725
Fought with what *s* my own uncharity; *Sea Dreams* 73
That *s* a fleet of jewels under me, „ 123
for it *s* A void was made in Nature; *Lucretius* 36

Seem'd (*continued*) I *s* to move among a world of ghosts, *Princess i* 17
the snake, My secret, *s* to stir within my breast; „ *iii* 44
I *s* to move among a world of ghosts; „ *iv* 561
neither *s* there more to say: „ *v* 330
and *s* to charm from thence The wrath „ 436
I *s* to move in old memorial tilts, „ 479
Yet it *s* a dream, I dream'd Of fighting. „ 492
For so it *s*, or so they said to me, „ *vi* 22
pitying as it *s*, Or self-involved; „ 157
nor *s* it strange that soon He rose up whole, „ *vii* 64
meek *S* the full lips, and mild the luminous eyes, „ 226
Had ever *s* to wrestle with burlesque, „ *Con.* 16
He is gone who *s* so great.— *Ode on Well.* 271
That *s* to touch it into leaf: *In Mem. lxix* 18
The gentleness he *s* to be, „ *cxi* 12
Best *s* the thing he was, and join'd „ 13
tho' there often *s* to live A contradiction „ *cxxv* 3
If Maud were all that she *s*, (repeat) *Maud I vi* 36, 92
S her light foot along the garden walk, „ *xviii* 9
Ever and ever afresh they *s* to grow. „ *II i* 28
sad At times he *s*, and sad with him was I, *Com. of Arthur* 353
high upon the dreary deeps It *s* in heaven, „ 374
it *s* The dragon-boughts and elvish emblemings *Gareth and L.* 232
that ev'n to him they *s* to move. „ 237
all Naked it *s*, and glowing in the broad „ 1088
for he *s* as one That all in later, „ 1128
so Gareth *s* to strike Vainly, „ 1133
s The dress that now she look'd on *Marr. of Geraint* 612
But evermore it *s* an easier thing *Geraint and E.* 108
Whereof one *s* far larger than her lord, „ 122
and *s* So justified by that necessity, „ 395
How far beyond him Lancelot *s* to move, *Balin and Balan* 172
The music in him *s* to change, „ 217
fought Hard with himself, and *s* at length in peace. „ 239
Ev'n when they *s* unloveable, *Merlin and V.* 176
The man so wrought on ever *s* to lie „ 208
s a lovely baleful star Veil'd in gray vapour; „ 262
You *s* that wave about to break upon me „ 302
course of life that *s* so flowery to me „ 880
he *s* the goodliest man That ever among ladies *Lancelot and E.* 254
He *s* to me another Lancelot— „ 534
When some brave deed *s* to be done in vain, *Holy Grail* 274
s to me the Lord of all the world, „ 414
s Shoutings of all the sons of God: „ 508
in a dream I *s* to climb For ever: „ 836
It *s* to Pelleas that the fern without *Pelleas and E.* 34
have *s* A vision hovering on a sea of fire, „ 51
she that *s* the chief among them said, „ 62
She might have *s* a toy to trifle with, „ 76
S my reproach? He is not of my kind. „ 311
hard his eyes; harder his heart *S*; „ 513
S those far-rolling, westward-smiling seas, *Last Tournament* 587
he *s* to me no man, But Michaël trampling Satan; „ 672
from the dawn it *s* there came, *Pass. of Arthur* 457
It *s* to keep its sweetness to itself, Yet was not the less sweet for that it *s*? *Lover's Tale i* 154
the sunshine *s* to brood More warmly „ 327
s a gossamer filament up in air, „ 413
I died then, I had not *s* to die, „ 494
I *s* the only part of Time stood still, „ 573
then it *s* as tho' a link Of some tight chain „ 594
and then I *s* to hear Its murmur, „ 634
The spirit *s* to flag from thought to thought, „ *ii* 51
motions of my heart *s* far within me, „ 54
then I *s* To rise, and through the forest-shadow „ 71
at his feet I *s* to faint and fall, „ 96
it *s* By that which follow'd— „ *iv* 21
Found, as it *s*, a skeleton alone, „ 139
such a feast, ill-suited as it *s* To such a time, „ 207
S stepping out of darkness with a smile. „ 220
veil, that *s* no more than gilded air, „ 290
cry, that rather *s* For some new death „ 373
Often I *s* unhappy, and often as happy too, *First Quarrel* 31
We *s* like ships i' the Channel „ 42
to be found Long after, as it *s*, *Sisters (E. and E.)* 111

Seem'd (*continued*) I spent What *s* my crowning hour, *Sisters (E. and E.)* 124
every bone *s* out of its place— *In the Child. Hosp.* 13
it *s* she stood by me and smiled, „ 67
s at first ' a thing enskied ' *To E. Fitzgerald* 16
I *s* in Paradise then With the first great love *The Wreck* 75
For He spoke, or it *s* that He spoke, *Despair* 26
S nobler than their hard Eternities. *Demeter and P.* 107
voice Came on the wind, and *s* to say ' Again.' *The Ring* 154
s my lodestar in the Heaven of Art, *Romney's R.* 39
cry, that *s* at first Thin as the batlike *Death of Œnone* 20
Seemest thou art not who Thou *s*, *Gareth and L.* 291
Seeming (*See also* **Hard-seeming**) My needful *s* harshness, pardon it. *Princess ii* 309
Till taken with her *s* openness „ *iv* 300
The *s* prey of cyclic storms, *In Mem. cxviii* 11
Which *s* for the moment due to death, *Lover's Tale i* 508
He falling sick, and *s* close on death, „ *iv* 258
This double *s* of the single world !— *Ancient Sage* 105
s stared upon By ghastlier than the Gorgon head, *Death of Œnone* 70
Seeming-bitter words are *s-b*, Sharp and few, but *s-b* *Rosalind* 30
Seemimg-deathless Here we stood and claspt each other, swore the *s-d* vow. . . . *Locksley H., Sixty* 180
Seeming-genial Or *s-g* venial fault, *Will* 13
Seeming-injured The *s-i* simple-hearted thing *Merlin and V.* 902
Seeming-leafless pass His autumn into *s-l* days— *A Dedication* 10
Seeming-random grew to *s-r* forms, *In Mem. cxviii* 10
Seeming-wanton make The *s-w* ripple break, „ *xlix* 11
Seen (*See also* **Far-seen, One-day-seen, Seed, See'd**) Then once by man and angels to be *s*, *The Kraken* 14
And faint, rainy lights are *s*, *Margaret* 60
But who hath *s* her wave her hand ? Or at the casement *s* her stand ? *L. of Shalott i* 24
(Beauty *s* In all varieties of mould and mind) *To ——, With Pal. of Art* 6
thro' mountain clefts the dale Was *s* far inland, *Lotos-Eaters* 21
'Tis long since I have *s* a man. *D. of F. Women* 131
Such joy as you have *s* with us, *D. of the O. Year* 17
Two years his chair is *s* Empty before us. *To J. S.* 22
What is it thou hast *s* ? (repeat) *M. d'Arthur* 68, 114
what is it thou hast heard, or *s* ? ' „ 150
from his youth in grief, That, having *s*, forgot ? *Gardener's D.* 55
You should have *s* him wince *Walk. to the Mail* 71
nor have *s* Him since, nor heard of her, *Edwin Morris* 137
I have *s* some score of those Fresh faces, *Talking Oak* 49
Much have I *s* and known ; *Ulysses* 13
As I have *s* the rosy red flushing *Locksley Hall* 26
glimpsing over these, just *s*, High up, *Day-Dm., Sleep. P.* 47
High towns on hills were dimly *s*, *The Voyage* 34
She in her poor attire was *s* : *Beggar Maid* 10
Faint as a figure *s* in early dawn *Enoch Arden* 357
what he fain had *s* He could not see, „ 580
For since the mate had *s* at early dawn „ 631
Because things *s* are mightier than things heard, „ 766
If you could tell her you had *s* him dead, „ 808
little port Had seldom *s* a costlier funeral. „ 917
Squire had *s* the colt at grass, *The Brook* 139
He must have *s*, himself had *s* it long ; *Aylmer's Field* 345
she herself Had *s* to that : „ 805
Or, maybe, I myself, my bride once *s*, *Princess i* 72
some dark shore just *s* that it was rich. „ 249
' having *s* And heard the Lady Psyche.' „ *ii* 210
As bottom agates *s* to wave and float „ 327
after *s* The dwarfs of presage : „ *iv* 446
nor ever had I *s* Such thews of men : „ *v* 255
So often that I speak as having *s*. „ *vi* 21
Ida came behind *S* but of Psyche : „ *vii* 79
Ere *s* I loved, and loved thee *s*, „ 341
Imagined more than *s*, the skirts of France. „ *Con.* 48
World-victor's victor will be *s* no more. *Ode on Well.* 42
Colossal, *s* of every land, „ 221
s A light amid its olives green ; *The Daisy* 29
Whom we, that have not *s* thy face, *In Mem., Pro.* 2
If Death were *s* At first as Death, „ *xxxv* 18
How many a father have I *s*, „ *liii* 1
A likeness, hardly *s* before, „ *lxxiv* 3

Seen (*continued*) I have not *s*, I will not see Vienna ; *In Mem. xcviii* 11
O earth, what changes hast thou *s* ! „ *cxxiii* 2
(for her eyes were downcast, not to be *s*) *Maud I ii* 5
Shall I believe him ashamed to be *s* ? „ *xiii* 25
' I have *s* the cuckoo chased by lesser fowl, *Com. of Arthur* 167
And gone as soon as *s*. „ 377
' Son, I have *s* the good ship sail Keel upward, *Gareth and L.* 253
Accursed, who strikes nor lets the hand be *s* ! ' „ 435
have I watch'd thee victor in the joust, And *s* thy way.' „ 1357
milky-white, First *s* that day : *Marr. of Geraint* 151
Tho' having *s* all beauties of our time, „ 498
My pride is broken : men have *s* my fall.' „ 578
She never yet had *s* her half so fair ; „ 741
That other, where we see as we are *s* ! *Geraint and E.* 7
have ye *s* how nobly changed ? „ 897
Far *s* to left and right ; *Balin and Balan* 169
' Fairest I grant her : I have *s* ; „ 356
The longest lance his eyes had ever *s*, „ 411
I for three days *s*, ready to fall. *Merlin and V.* 296
You should have *s* him blush ; „ 481
Him have I *s* : the rest, his Table Round, *Lancelot and E.* 185
' One, One have I *s*—that other, „ 423
I might say that I had *s*.' „ 427
So great a knight as we have *s* to-day— „ 533
peradventure had he *s* her first She might have made „ 872
' O brother, I have *s* this yew-tree smoke, *Holy Grail* 18
' Sweet brother, I have *s* the Holy Grail : „ 107
the vision may be *s* By thee and those, „ 127
for thou shalt see what I have *s*, „ 160
Because I had not *s* the Grail, „ 196
as I have *s* it more than once, „ 273
' Art thou so bold and hast not *s* the Grail ? ' „ 279
knight by knight, if any Had *s* it, „ 284
' Lo now,' said Arthur, ' have ye *s* a cloud ? „ 286
never yet Had Camelot *s* the like, since Arthur came ; „ 332
' Where is he ? hast thou *s* him—Lancelot ?— „ 639
well had been content Not to have *s*, so Lancelot might have *s*, The Holy Cup „ 654
—hast thou *s* the Holy Cup, „ 734
thou hast *s* the Grail ; ' „ 757
For these have *s* according to their sight. „ 875
if the King Had *s* the sight he would have sworn „ 904
ye have *s* what ye have *s*.' „ 919
thou hast *s* me strain'd And sifted to the utmost, *Pelleas and E.* 247
And *s* her sadden listening—vext his heart, „ 398
for I have *s* him wan enow To make one doubt *Last Tournament* 563
I might see his face, and not be *s*.' *Guinevere* 588
It would have been my pleasure had I *s*. „ 659
What is it thou hast *s* ? (repeat) *Pass. of Arthur* 236, 282
what is it thou hast heard, or *s* ? ' „ 318
Here far away, *s* from the topmost cliff, *Lover's Tale i* 1
These have not *s* thee, these can never know thee, „ 285
(As I have *s* them many a hundred times) „ *ii* 145
Would you had *s* him in that hour of his ! „ *iv* 8
O love, I have not *s* you for so long. „ 45
He, but for you, had never *s* it once. „ 173
We should be *s*, my dear ; *Rizpah* 5
and half to the left were *s*, *The Revenge* 35
passion, *s* And lost and found again, *Sisters (E. and E.)* 146
an which was a shaame to be *s* ; *Village Wife* 50
I never had *s* him before, *In the Child. Hosp.* 1
he had *s* it and made up his mind, „ 16
apples, the hugest that ever were *s*, *V. of Maeldune* 63
be blind, for thou hast *s* too much, *Tiresias* 49
This wealth of waters might but *s* to draw *Ancient Sage* 9
that rule Were never heard or *s*.' „ 30
Here where yer Honour *s* her— *Tomorrow* 9
I tould yer Honour whativer I hard an' *s*, „ 97
I have *s* her far away— *Locksley H., Sixty* 166
in the wars your own Crimean eyes had *s* ; *Pro. to Gen. Hamley* 12
eyes Have *s* the loneliness of earthly thrones, *To Prin. Beatrice* 14
And those lone rights I have not *s*, *To Marq. of Dufferin* 39
eyes That oft had *s* the serpent-wanded power *Demeter and P.* 25
Stranger than earth has ever *s* ; *The Ring* 38
I had *s* the man but once ; „ 190

Seen (*continued*) one betwixt the dark and light had *s* Her, *The Ring* 414
never had I *s* her show remorse— „ 457
But *s* upon the silent brow *Happy* 52
—a sun but dimly *s* Here, *Akbar's Dream* 95
That is not *s* and rules from far away— „ 138
were *s* or heard Fires of Sûttee, „ 195
To have *s* thee, and heard thee, and known. *Bandit's Death* 4
Seër Like some bold *s* in a trance, *L. of Shalott iv* 11
Seer Then that old *S* made answer playing on him *Gareth and L.* 252
S replied, 'Know ye not then the Riddling of the Bards? „ 285
the *S* Would watch her at her petulance, *Merlin and V.* 174
Her *s*, her bard, her silver star of eve, „ 954
From out his ancient city came a *S* *Ancient Sage* 2
Seest Thou pleadest still, and *s* me drive *Supp. Confessions* 94
Thou *s* the Nameless of the hundred names. *Ancient Sage* 49
Seëst Watch what thou *s*, and lightly bring me word.' *M. d'Arthur* 38
I am going a long way With these thou *s*— „ 257
s all things, thou wilt see my grave: *Tithonus* 73
Watch what thou *s*, and lightly bring me word.' *Pass. of Arthur* 206
I am going a long way With these thou *s*— „ 425
s Universal Nature moved by Universal Mind; *To Virgil* 21
See'st And *s* the moving of the team. *In Mem. cxxi* 16
Seethe Began to move, *s*, twine and curl: *Gareth and L.* 234
Seethed *S* like the kid in its own mother's milk! *Merlin and V.* 869
Seething when the surge was *s* free, *Lotos-Eaters, C. S.* 106
Shot o'er the *s* harbour-bar, *Sailor Boy* 2
Save for some whisper of the *s* seas, *Pass. of Arthur* 121
Seine The red fool-fury of the *S* *In Mem. cxxvii* 7
Seize '*s* the strangers' is the cry. *Princess iv* 220
To *s* and throw the doubts of man; *In Mem. cix* 6
But sorrow *s* me if ever that light *Maud I iv* 12
To *s* me by the hair and bear me far, *Lancelot and E.* 1425
Seized till at last a fever *s* On William, *Dora* 54
Then desperately *s* the holy Book, *Enoch Arden* 495
S it, took home, and to my lady,— *Aylmer's Field* 532
Me they *s* and me they tortured, *Boädicea* 49
A hunger *s* my heart; I read *In Mem. xcv* 21
And standeth *s* of that inheritance *Gareth and L.* 359
therewithal one came and *s* on her, *Marr. of Geraint* 673
suddenly *s* on her, And bare her by main violence *Geraint and E.* 653
I should have slain your father, *s* yourself. „ 838
a fury *s* them all, A fiery family passion *Lancelot and E.* 476
Saying which she *s*, And, thro' the casement „ 1233
There fever *s* upon him: *Lover's Tale iv* 132
S him, and bound and plunged him *Holy Grail* 675
They *s* me and shut me up: *Rizpah* 46
who sack'd My dwelling, *s* upon my papers, *Columbus* 130
and *s* one another and slew; *V. of Maeldune* 34
Seizing *s* thereupon Push'd thro' an open casement *Balin and Balan* 412
Seizure Myself too had weird *s's*, *Princess i* 14
'what, if these weird *s's* come Upon you „ 82
On a sudden my strange *s* came Upon me, „ *iii* 183
came On a sudden the weird *s* and the doubt: „ *iv* 560
Seldom-frowning The *s-f* King frown'd, *Lancelot and E.* 715
Self (*See also* **Half-self, Sen, World-self**) Smote the chord of *S*, *Locksley Hall* 43
Half fearful that, with *s* at strife, *Will Water.* 161
He not for his own *s* caring but her, *Enoch Arden* 165
chafing at his own great *s* defied, *Aylmer's Field* 537
And to thy worst *s* sacrifice thyself, „ 645
with thy worst *s* hast thou clothed thy God. „ 646
We touch on our dead *s*, *Princess iii* 221
Her falser *s* slipt from her like a robe, „ *vii* 161
lives A drowning life, besotted in sweet *s*, „ 314
I seem A mockery to my own *s*. „ 337
learns to deaden Love of *s*, *Ode on Well.* 205
strain to make an inch of room For their sweet *selves*, *Lit. Squabbles* 10
stepping-stones Of their dead *selves* *In Mem. i* 4
transient form In her deep *s*, „ *xvi* 8
fusing all The skirts of *s* again, „ *xlvii* 3
praying To his own great *s*, as I guess; *Maud II v* 33
Bound them by so strait vows to his own *s*, *Com. of Arthur* 262
There rides no knight, not Lancelot, his great *s*, *Gareth and L.* 1182
fool'd Of others, is to fool one's *s*. „ 1275
after her own *s*, in all the court. *Marr. of Geraint* 18
that and these to her own faded *s* „ 652
Self (*continued*) whether some false sense in her own *s* *Marr. of Geraint* 800
overthrow My proud *s*, and my purpose *Geraint and E.* 849
crown'd With my slain *s* the heaps of whom I slew— *Balin and Balan* 178
To keep me all to your own *s*,— *Merlin and V.* 523
imputing her whole *s*, Defaming and defacing, „ 803
'Save your great *s*, fair lord;' *Lancelot and E.* 320
There morn by morn, arraying her sweet *s* „ 906
There surely I shall speak for mine own *s*, „ 1125
wail'd and wept, and hated mine own *s*, *Holy Grail* 609
for nothing moved but his own *s*, *Pelleas and E.* 417
the King's grief For his own *s*, *Guinevere* 197
judge between my slander'd *s* and me— *Columbus* 125
dive into the Temple-cave of thine own *s*, *Ancient Sage* 32
mortal limit of the *S* was loosed, „ 232
thro' loss of *S* The gain of such large life „ 236
memories once again On thy lost *s*. *Demeter and P.* 11
while I communed with my truest *s*, *The Ring* 181
she loves her own hard *s*, „ 292
forgotten mine own rhyme By mine old *s*, *To Mary Boyle* 22
Into the common day, the sounder *s*. *Romney's R.* 33
Rose, like the wraith of his dead *s*, *Death of Œnone* 28
Self-applause Not void of righteous *s-a*, *Two Voices* 146
Self-balanced *S-b* on a lightsome wing: *In Mem. lxv* 8
Self-blinded '*S-b* are you by your pride: *Two Voices* 23
Self-conceit some *s-c*, Or over-smoothness: *Edwin Morris* 74
Self-contain'd High, *s-c*, and passionless, *Guinevere* 406
Self-contempt Perish in thy *s-c*! *Locksley Hall* 96
Self-content increased Her greatness and her *s-c*. *To Marq. of Dufferin* 8
Self-control 'Self-reverence, self-knowledge, *s-c*, *Œnone* 144
With faith that comes of *s-c*, *In Mem. cxxxi* 9
Self-darken'd *S-d* in the sky, descending slow! *Prog. of Spring* 28
Which drowsed in gloom, *s-d* from the west, *Death of Œnone* 76
Self-distrust It is my shyness, or my *s-d*, *Edwin Morris* 86
Self-exile that resolved *s-e* from a land *Lover's Tale iv* 209
Self-gather'd *S-g* in her prophet-mind, *Of old sat Freedom* 6
Self-infold *s-i's* the large results Of force *In Mem. lxxiii* 15
Self-involved Which all too dearly *s-i*, *Day-Dm., L'Envoi* 49
dull and *s-i*, Tall and erect, *Aylmer's Field* 118
pitying as it seem'd, Or *s-i*; *Princess vi* 158
Selfish Nor in a merely *s* cause— *Two Voices* 147
I was left a trampled orphan, and a *s* uncle's ward. *Locksley Hall* 156
Which made a *s* war begin; *To F. D. Maurice* 30
Perhaps from a *s* grave. *Maud I xvi* 23
Not muffled round with *s* reticence. *Merlin and V.* 337
S, strange! What dwarfs are men! *Sisters (E. and E.)* 198
Self-knowledge Self-reverence, *s-k*, self-control, *Œnone* 144
Selfless As high as woman in her *s* mood. *Merlin and V.* 443
O *s* man and stainless gentleman, „ 792
lazying out a life Of self-suppression, not of *s* love.' *St. Telemachus* 22
Self-perplext look'd so *s-p*, That Katie laugh'd, *The Brook* 213
Self-pity for languor and *s-p* ran Mine down my face, *Princess vii* 139
And sweet *s-p*, or the fancy of it, *Geraint and E.* 349
Self-pleached Round thee blow, *s-p* deep, *A Dirge* 29
Self-possess'd neither *s-p* Nor startled, *Gardener's D.* 154
Self-profit judge of fair, Unbias'd by *s-p*, *Œnone* 159
Self-renew'd and freshness ever *s-r*. *Lover's Tale i* 106
Self-reverence *S-r*, self-knowledge, self-control, *Œnone* 144
Self-reverent *S-r* each and reverencing each, *Princess vii* 290
Self-sacrifice The long *s-s* of life is o'er. *Ode on Well.* 41
And all her sweet *s-s* and death. *Sisters (E. and E.)* 255
Self-same *s-s* influence Controlleth all the soul *Eleänore* 114
With the *s* impulse wherewith he was thrown *Mine be the strength* 3
That we may die the *s-s* day. *Miller's D.* 24
when to land Bustler the winds and tides the *s-s* way, *D. of F. Women* 38
He put the *s-s* query, but the man *Marr. of Geraint* 269
He took the *s* track as Balan, *Balin and Balan* 290
Under the *s* aspect of the stars, *Lover's Tale i* 199
And mine made garlands of the *s* flower, „ 343
Self-scorn Laughter at her *s-s*. *Palace of Art* 232
Self-seeker All great *s-s's* trampling on the right: *Ode on Well.* 187
Self-starved *S-s*, they say—nay, murder'd, *Sir J. Oldcastle* 60
Self-styled those *s-s* our lords ally Your fortunes, *Princess ii* 65
Self-suppression lazying out a life Of *s-s*, *St. Telemachus* 22
Sell To *s* the boat—and yet he loved her *Enoch Arden* 134

Sell (*continued*) And yet to *s* her—then with what she brought *Enoch Arden* 137
s her, those good parents, for her good. *Aylmer's Field* 483
An' pigs didn't *s* at fall, *Church-warden, etc.* 5
Seller (*See also* **Absolution-seller**) belongs to the heart of the perfume *s*. *Akbar's D., Inscrip.* 9
Semblance Like to the mother plant in *s*, *The Poet* 23
edict of the will to reassume The *s* *Lover's Tale ii* 162
Semicircle Leapt in a *s*, and lit on earth ; *Balin and Balan* 414
the *s* Of dark-blue waters and the narrow fringe *Lover's Tale i* 37
Semi-jealousy A flash of *s-j* clear'd it to her. *Aylmer's Field* 189
Semi-smile *s-s* As at a strong conclusion— *Lover's Tale iv* 281
Sempstress Master scrimps his haggard *s* of her daily bread, *Locksley H., Sixty* 221
Sen (**self**) 'E seeäms naw moor nor watter, an' 'e's the Divil's oän *s*.' *North. Cobbler* 76
An' Squire, his oän very *s*, walks down fro' the 'All to see, „ 91
An' 'e'd wrote an owd book, his awn *s*, *Village Wife* 46
An' I'd voät fur 'im, my oän *s*, if 'e could but stan fur the Shere. *Owd Roä* 14
Send—I *s* you here a sort of allegory, *To ——, With Pal. of Art* 1
fear'd To *s* abroad a shrill and terrible cry, *Enoch Arden* 768
he would *s* a hundred thousand men, *Princess i* 64
unless you *s* us back Our son, „ *iv* 415
'Sdeath ! but we will *s* to her,' „ *v* 324
You *s* a flash to the sun. *Window, Marr. Morn.* 2
But *s* it slackly from the string ; *In Mem. lxxxvii* 26
and *s* thee satisfied— *Gareth and L.* 434
delays his purport till thou *s* To do the battle with him, „ 618
they *s* That strength of anger thro' mine arms, „ 947
render'd tributary, fail'd of late To *s* his tribute ; *Balin and Balan* 4
I undertake them as we pass, And *s* them to thee ?' „ 15
King will *s* thee his own leech— „ 275
s One flash, that, missing all things else, *Merlin and V.* 931
of us to claim the prize, Ourselves will *s* it after. *Lancelot and E.* 545
This will he *s* or come for : „ 635
I pray him, *s* a sudden Angel down „ 1424
If God would *s* the vision, well : *Holy Grail* 658
she *s* her delegate to thrall These fighting hands *Pelleas and E.* 336
S ! bid him come ; ' but Lionel was away— *Lover's Tale iv* 101
but *s* me notice of him When he returns, „ 116
you used to *s* her the flowers ; *In the Child. Hosp.* 33
May *s* one ray to thee ! *Ded. Poem Prin. Alice* 14
I *s* my prayer by night and day— *Columbus* 233
ninth moon, that *s's* the hidden sun *De Prof., Two G.* 33
I *s* a birthday line Of greeting ; *To E. Fitzgerald* 45
S no such light upon the ways of men *Tiresias* 161
s the day into the darken'd heart ; *Ancient Sage* 261
S the drain into the fountain, *Locksley H., Sixty* 144
' *S* them no more, for evermore. *Dead Prophet* 3
I fail'd To *s* my life thro' olive-yard *Demeter and P.* 110
To *s* the moon into the night and break „ 135
Shalt ever *s* thy life along with mine „ 145
bad the man engrave ' From Walter ' on the ring, and *s* it— *The Ring* 236
And *s* her home to you rejoicing. „ 320
and *s* A gift of slenderer value, *To Ulysses* 47
Take then this spring-flower I *s*, *To Mary Boyle* 19
Reflected, *s's* a light on the forgiven. *Romney's R.* 161
dust *s* up a steam of human blood, *St. Telemachus* 53
Sendest O THOU, that *s* out the man To rule *England and Amer.* 1
when thou *s* thy free soul thro' heaven, *Ancient Sage* 47
Seneschal Then came Sir Kay, the *s*, and cried, *Gareth and L.* 367
let Kay the *s* Look to thy wants, „ 433
' Sir *S*, Sleuth-hound thou knowest, and gray, „ 461
But Kay the *s*, who loved him not, „ 483
Sir Kay, the *s*, would come Blustering upon them, „ 513
S, No mellow master of the meats and drinks ! „ 559
page, and maid, and squire, and *s*, *Marr. of Geraint* 710
Arthur turn'd to Kay the *s*, *Last Tournament* 89
Sennight three rich *s's* more, my love for her. *Edwin Morris* 30
Sense (*See also* **Common-sense**) did all confound Her *s* ; *Mariana* 77
feedeth The *s's* with a still delight *Margaret* 17
Controlleth all the soul and *s* *Eleänore* 115
Is cancell'd in the world of *s* ?' *Two Voices* 42
Unmanacled from bonds of *s*, „ 236
' The simple *s's* crown'd his head : „ 277

Sense (*continued*) By which he doubts against the *s* ? *Two Voices* 285
There seem'd no room for *s* of wrong ; „ 456
Lord of the *s's* five ; *Palace of Art* 180
Slowly my *s* undazzled. *D. of F. Women* 177
Flutter'd about my *s's* and my soul ; *Gardener's D.* 67
Or have they any *s* of why they sing ? „ 101
He lost the *s* that handles daily life— *Walk. to the Mail* 22
weigh'd Upon my brain, my *s's* and my soul ! *Love and Duty* 44
If the *s* is hard To alien ears, „ 51
the common *s* of most shall hold *Locksley Hall* 129
cancell'd a *s* misused : *Godiva* 72
Your finer female *s* offends. *Day-Dm., L'Envoi* 2
I grow in worth, and wit, and *s*, *Will Water.* 41
it was a crime Of *s* avenged by *s* *Vision of Sin* 214
crime of *s* became The crime of malice, „ 215
less of sentiment than *s* Had Katie ; *The Brook* 91
a *s* Of meanness in her unresisting life. *Aylmer's Field* 800
And such a *s*, when first I fronted him, *Sea Dreams* 70
s of wrong had touch'd her face With colour) *Princess, Pro.* 219
Or master'd by the *s* of sport, „ *iv* 156
I broke the letter of it to keep the *s*. „ 338
I grant in her some *s* of shame, „ 349
' Nay, nay, you spake but *s* ' Said Gama. „ *v* 206
Love to sloughs That swallow common *s*, „ 442
Or own one port of *s* not flint to prayer, „ *vi* 182
My haunting *s* of hollow shows : „ *vii* 349
Some *s* of duty, something of a faith, „ *Con.* 54
Joänes, as 'ant not a 'äapoth o' *s*, *N. Farmer, O. S.* 49
moor *s* i' one o' 'is legs nor in all thy braaïns. „ *N. S.* 4
Unfetter'd by the *s* of crime, *In Mem. xxvii* 7
an awful *s* Of one mute Shadow watching all. „ *xxx* 7
the hoarding *s* Gives out at times „ *xliv* 6
Drug down the blindfold *s* of wrong „ *lxxi* 7
The quiet *s* of something lost. „ *lxxviii* 8
The *s* of human will demands „ *lxxxv* 39
O tell me where the *s's* mix, „ *lxxxviii* 3
Where all the nerve of *s* is numb ; „ *xciii* 7
Cry thro' the *s* to hearten trust „ *cxvi* 7
Who wants the finer politic *s* *Maud I vi* 47
Suddenly strike on a sharper *s* „ *II ii* 63
sent him from his *s's* : let me go.' *Gareth and L.* 71
whether some false *s* in her own self *Marr. of Geraint* 800
such a *s* might make her long for court „ 803
with every *s* as false and foul *Merlin and V.* 797
conscience of a saint Among his warring *s's*, *Guinevere* 640
and shadowing *S* at war with Soul, *To the Queen ii* 37
all the *s's* weaken'd, save in that, *Lover's Tale i* 127
scarce can tune his high majestic *s* „ 475
No longer in the dearest *s* of mine— „ 587
Entering all the avenues of *s* „ 630
And now first heard with any *s* of pain, „ 709
Falling in whispers on the *s*, „ 720
A shameful *s* as of a cleaving crime— „ 794
face was flash'd thro' *s* and soul *Sisters (E. and E.)* 109
Scarce feels the *s's* break away *Ancient Sage* 152
Await the last and largest *s* „ 180
soul and *s* in city slime ? *Locksley H., Sixty* 218
moor good *s* na the Parliament man *Owd Roä* 13
His crime was of the *s's* ; *Romney's R.* 151
Why not bask amid the *s's* *By an Evolution.* 6
wi' a hoonderd haäcre o' *s*— *Church-warden, etc.* 22
Senseless O *s* cataract, Bearing all down in thy precipitancy— *Gareth and L.* 7
The little *s*, worthless, wordless babe, *The Ring* 304
Sensible worth the life That made it *s*. *Lover's Tale i* 800
Sensitive Or the least little delicate aquiline curve in a *s* nose, *Maud I ii* 10
Patient of pain tho' as quick as a *s* plant to the touch ; *In the Child. Hosp.* 30
Sensual Bursts of great heart and slips in *s* mire, *Princess v* 199
Arise and fly The reeling Faun, the *s* feast ; *In Mem. cxviii* 26
For such a supersensual *s* bond *Merlin and V.* 109
Nor own'd a *s* wish, „ 628
Sensuous Makes noble thro' the *s* organism *Princess ii* 87
Be near me when the *s* frame Is rack'd *In Mem. l* 5

Sent *s* it them by stealth, nor did they know Who *s* it; *Dora* 53
She *s* a note, the seal an *Elle vous suit,* *Edwin Morris* 105
She *s* her voice thro' all the holt *Talking Oak* 123
She *s* a herald forth, And bade him cry, *Godiva* 35
With peals of genial clamour *s* *Will Water.* 187
yet he *s* Gifts by the children, *Enoch Arden* 337
s his voice beneath him thro' the wood. „ 444
s for him and said wildly to him „ 507
And *s* her sweetly by the golden isles, „ 536
They *s* a crew that landing burst away „ 634
he *s* the bailiff to the farm To learn *The Brook* 141
S to the harrow'd brother, praying him *Aylmer's Field* 607
but every roof *S* out a listener: „ 614
S like the twelve-divided concubine „ 759
s out a cry Which mixt with little Margaret's, *Sea Dreams* 245
My father *s* ambassadors with furs *Princess i* 42
We *s* mine host to purchase female gear; „ 199
I gave the letter to be *s* with dawn; „ 245
s For Psyche, but she was not there; „ *iv* 236
s for Blanche to accuse her face to face; „ 239
S out a bitter bleating for its dam; „ 392
when we *s* the Prince your way We knew not „ 398
some one *s* beneath his vaulted palm „ *v* 31
found He thrice had *s* a herald to the gates, „ 332
S from a dewy breast a cry for light: „ *vii* 253
A soul on highest mission *s*, *In Mem. cxiii* 10
My Maud has *s* it by thee *Maud I xxi* 9
the King *S* to him, saying, 'Arise, *Com. of Arthur* 44
he *s* Ulfius, and Brastias, and Bedivere, „ 135
Died but of late, and *s* his cry to me, „ 361
while the phantom king *S* out at times a voice; „ 437
Leodogran awoke, and *s* Ulfius, and Brastias and Bedivere, „ 444
That *s* him from his senses: let me go. *Gareth and L.* 71
seeing he hath *s* us cloth of gold, „ 428
s, Between the in-crescent and de-crescent moon, „ 528
s her wish that I would yield thee thine. „ 551
thy much folly hath *s* thee here His kitchen-knave: „ 919
'A kitchen-knave, and *s* in scorn of me: „ 952
and say His kitchen-knave hath *s* thee. „ 985
and Gareth *s* him to the King. „ 1051
Had *s* her coming champion, waited him. „ 1192
Had *s* thee down before a lesser spear, „ 1244
S all his heart and breath thro' all the horn. „ 1369
s Her maiden to demand it of the dwarf; *Marr. of Geraint* 192
S her own maiden to demand the name, „ 411
S forth a sudden sharp and bitter cry, *Geraint and E.* 722
s a thousand men To till the wastes, „ 941
ye be *s* for by the King,' They follow'd; *Balin and Balan* 48
wrath *S* me a three-years' exile from thine eyes. „ 59
the hall Of him to whom ye *s* us, Pellam, „ 96
being jealous, that he *s* His horns of proclamation out *Merlin and V.* 580
Reported who he was, and on what quest *S*, *Lancelot and E.* 629
And lose the quest he *s* you on, „ 655
'Your prize the diamond *s* you by the King:' „ 821
the tale Of King and Prince, the diamond *s*, „ 824
and toward even *S* for his shield: „ 978
he saw One of her house, and *s* him to the Queen „ 1168
'For on a day she *s* to speak with me. *Holy Grail* 101
She *s* the deathless passion in her eyes „ 163
S hands upon him, as to tear him, *Pelleas and E.* 521
golden grove Appearing, *s* his fancy back *Last Tournament* 380
then what folly had *s* him overseas „ 394
That *s* the face of all the marsh aloft „ 439
the voice about his feet *S* up an answer, „ 761
s a deep sea-voice thro' all the land, *Guinevere* 247
S notes of preparation manifold, *Lover's Tale i* 207
and *s* his soul Into the songs of birds, „ 320
s my cry Thro' the blank night to Him „ 751
S such a flame into his face, „ *iv* 177
s at once to Lionel, praying him By that great love „ 180
he *s*, an' the father agreed; *First Quarrel* 18
And then he *s* me a letter, „ 85
Better have *s* Our Edith thro' the glories *Sisters (E. and E.)* 224
'OUSE-KEEPER *s* tha my lass, *Village Wife* 1

Sent (*continued*) But he *s* a chill to my heart *In the Child. Hosp.* 2
The Lord had *s* this bright, *Columbus* 91
They *s* me out *his* tool, Bovadilla, „ 127
we have *s* them very fiends from Hell; „ 184
Thrice from the dyke he *s* his mighty shout, *Achilles over the T.* 30
S the shadow of Himself, *Locksley H., Sixty* 211
Sons and brothers that have *s*, *Open. I. and C. Exhib.* 3
the man repenting *s* This ring "Io t'amo" to his best beloved, And *s* it on her birthday. *The Ring* 209
Had *s* his cry for her forgiveness, „ 233
Muriel's mother *s*, And sure am I, „ 311
'Ever since You *s* the fatal ring'—I told her '*s* To Miriam,' „ 362
Why had I *s* the ring at first to her? „ 390
s him charr'd and blasted to the deathless fire *Happy* 84
I *s* him a desolate wail and a curse, *Charity* 14
I *s* him back what he gave,— „ 19

Sentence And mystic *s* spoke; *Talking Oak* 294
I hear the *s* that he speaks; *In Mem. lxxx* 10
there he broke the *s* in his heart Abruptly, *Geraint and E.* 41
the King Pronounced a dismal *s*, *Merlin and V.* 591
when the woful *s* hath been past, *Lover's Tale i* 788

Sentiment less of *s* than sense Had Katie; *The Brook* 91
A classic lecture, rich in *s*, *Princess ii* 374

Sentinel And hear at times a *s* *In Mem. cxxvi* 9
to be soldier all day and be *s* all thro' the night— *Def. of Lucknow* 74

Separate So rounds he to a *s* mind *In Mem. xlv* 9
That each, who seems a *s* whole, „ *xlvii* 1
and is Eternal, *s* from fears: „ *lxxxv* 66
And each prefers his *s* claim, „ *cii* 18
And all the *s* Edens of this earth, *Lover's Tale i* 551

September on your third *S* birthday *The Ring* 130
Your fifth *S* birthday. „ 423

Sepulchral Like echoes in *s* halls, *In Mem. lviii* 2

Sepulchre (*See also* **Bosom-sepulchre**) Gross darkness of the inner *s* *D. of F. Women* 67
While thou, a meteor of the *s*, *Lover's Tale i* 99
laid it in a *s* of rock Never to rise again. „ 683
He raised her softly from the *s*, „ *iv* 85
There came two voices from the *S*, *Columbus* 95
And free the Holy *S* from thrall. „ 104
And save the Holy *S* from thrall. „ 240
icy breath, As from the grating of a *s*, *The Ring* 400

Sequel *S* of guerdon could not alter me To fairer. *Œnone* 153
'The *s* of to-day unsolders all *M. d'Arthur* 14
OF love that never found his earthly close, What *s*? *Love and Duty* 2
For love in *s* works with fate, *Day-Dm., Arrival* 3
I shudder at the *s*, but I go.' *Princess ii* 236
the *s* of the tale Had touch'd her; „ *Con.* 30
'The *s* of to-day unsolders all *Pass. of Arthur* 182
the soul: *That* makes the *s* pure; *Lover's Tale iv* 157
Beginning at the *s* know no more. „ 158

Sequence And in the fatal *s* of this world *Ancient Sage* 274
for forty years my life in golden *s* ran, *Locksley H., Sixty* 47

Seraglio iron grates, And hush'd *s's*. *D. of F. Women* 36

Seraph there was Milton like a *s* strong, *Palace of Art* 133
Pontius and Iscariot by my side Show'd like fair *s's*. *St. S. Stylites* 169

Seraphic Pierces the keen *s* flame From orb to orb, *In Mem. xxx* 27
S intellect and force To seize and throw the doubts „ *cix* 5

Sere (*See also* **Sear**) in the rudest wind Never grow *s*, *Ode to Memory* 25
Shrank one sick willow *s* and small. *Mariana in the S.* 53
And, tho' thy violet sicken into *s*, *Prog. of Spring* 25

Serenade A rogue of canzonets and *s's*. *Princess iv* 135

Serene '*Her court was pure; her life s;* *To the Queen* 25
S with argent-lidded eyes Amorous, *Arabian Nights* 135
S, imperial Eleänore. (repeat) *Eleänore* 81, 121
My mother, looks as whole as some *s* *Princess v* 193
And that *s* result of all.' *In Mem. lxxxv* 92
O heart, look down and up *S*, secure, *Early Spring* 28

Serenest Now towering o'er him in *s* air, *Lucretius* 178

Serf Who made the *s* a man, and burst his chain— *W. to Marie Alex.* 3

Serious Her bright hair blown about the *s* face *Lancelot and E.* 392

Sermon *See* **Sarmin**

Sermonizing In sailor fashion roughly *s* *Enoch Arden* 204

Serpent (adj.) Back on herself her *s* pride had curl'd. *Palace of Art* 257
in whom all evil fancies clung Like *s* eggs together, *Enoch Arden* 480

Set (verb) (*continued*) He never yet had *s* his daughter forth *Aylmer's Field* 347
and one was *s* to watch The watcher, „ 551
'*S* them up! they shall not fall!' *Sea Dreams* 227
I had *s* my heart on your forgiving him „ 269
s's all the tops quivering— *Lucretius* 186
show'd the house, Greek, *s* with busts: *Princess, Pro.* 11
rosebud *s* with little wilful thorns, „ 154
S in a gleaming river's crescent-curve, „ *i* 171
when we *s* our hand To this great work, „ *ii* 59
Till toward the centre *s* the starry tides, „ 117
You need not *s* your thoughts in rubric „ *iii* 50
but we *S* forth to climb; „ 354
foot shone like a jewel *s* In the dark crag: „ 358
Blow, bugle, blow, *s* the wild echoes flying, (repeat) „ *iv* 5, 17
Norway sun *S* into sunrise; „ 576
S in a cataract on an island-crag, „ *v* 347
I *s* my face Against all men, „ 388
S his child upon her knee— „ *vi* 14
Till at the last she *s* herself to man, „ *vii* 285
and roughly *s* His Briton in blown seas *Ode on Well.* 154
Sun *s's*, moon *s's*, *Window, When* 3
Once more to *s* a ringlet right; *In Mem. vi* 36
Since our first Sun arose and *s*. „ *xxiv* 8
That *s's* the past in this relief? „ 12
On thy Parnassus *s* thy feet, „ *xxxvii* 6
And *s* thee forth, for thou art mine, „ *lix* 13
Like some poor girl whose heart is *s* „ *lx* 3
I would *s* their pains at ease. „ *lxiii* 8
Whate'er thy hands are *s* to do „ *lxxv* 19
And in a moment *s* thy face „ *lxxvi* 2
His credit thus shall *s* me free; „ *lxxx* 13
my feet are *s* To leave the pleasant fields „ *cii* 21
S light by narrower perfectness. „ *cxii* 4
She *s's* her forward countenance And leaps „ *cxiv* 6
He *s* his royal signet there; „ *cxxv* 12
But now *s* out: the noon is near, „ *Con.* 41
make my heart as a millstone, *s* my face as a flint, *Maud I i* 31
S in the heart of the carven gloom, „ *xiv* 11
He *s's* the jewel-print of your feet „ *xxii* 41
Till God's love *s* Thee at his side again! *Ded. of Idylls* 55
So when the King had *s* his banner broad, *Com. of Arthur* 101
Brought Arthur forth, and *s* him in the hall, Proclaiming, „ 229
thereupon the King *S* two before him. *Gareth and L.* 104
Southward they *s* their faces. „ 182
s To turn the broach, draw water, or hew wood, „ 485
Arthur's men are *s* along the wood; „ 788
Gareth loosed his bonds and on free feet *S* him, „ 818
and the Baron *s* Gareth beside her, „ 851
further wrong Than *s* him on his feet, „ 955
Which *s* the horror higher: „ 1394
and *s* foot upon his breast, *Marr. of Geraint* 574
When my dear child is *s* forth at her best, „ 728
in charge of whom? a girl: *s* on.' *Geraint and E.* 125
then *s* down His basket, „ 209
on his foot She *s* her own and climb'd; „ 760
s his foot upon me, and give me life. „ 850
in their chairs *s* up a stronger race „ 940
Lest we should *s* one truer on his throne. *Balin and Balan* 7
beside The carolling water *s* themselves again, „ 44
s himself To learn what Arthur meant by courtesy, „ 157
See now, I *s* thee high on vantage ground, „ 534
after that, she *s* herself to gain Him, *Merlin and V.* 165
If ye know, *S* up the charge ye know, „ 703
and caught, And *s* it on his head, *Lancelot and E.* 54
And *s* it in this damsel's golden hair, „ 205
S every gilded parapet shuddering; „ 299
more amazed Than if seven men had *s* upon him, „ 351
in the costly canopy o'er him *s*, „ 443
kith and kin, not knowing, *s* upon him; „ 599
he *s* himself to play upon her With sallying wit, „ 646
S in her hand a lily, o'er her hung The silken case „ 1148
s betwixt With many a mystic symbol, *Holy Grail* 232
s the sail, or had the boat Become a living creature „ 518

Set (verb) (*continued*) while I tarried, every day she *s* A banquet *Holy Grail* 588
s his name High on all hills, *Last Tournament* 336
ye *s* yourself To babble about him, „ 339
and *s* me far In the gray distance, „ 639
She rose, and *s* before him all he will'd; „ 723
Lancelot got her horse, *S* her thereon, *Guinevere* 123
thought the Queen 'Lo! they have *s* her on, „ 308
thou their tool, *s* on to plague And play upon, „ 359
Which are as gems *s* in my memory, *Lover's Tale i* 291
Ev'n by the price that others *s* upon it, „ *iv* 152
He brings and *s's* before him in rich guise „ 247
So I *s* to righting the house, *First Quarrel* 47
they *s* him so high That all the ships *Rizpah* 37
little of us left by the time this sun be *s*.' *The Revenge* 28
Had *s* the blossom of her health again, *Sisters (E. and E.)* 151
will she never *s* her sister free?' „ 218
good woman, can prayer *s* a broken bone?' *In the Child. Hosp.* 20
hour and the wine Had *s* the wits aflame. *Sir J. Oldcastle* 95
A thousand marks are *s* upon my head. „ 195
S thee in light till time shall be no more? *Columbus* 150
s me climbing icy capes And glaciers, *To E. Fitzgerald* 25
Had *s* the lily and rose By all my ways *Ancient Sage* 156
s The lamps alight, and call For golden music, „ 195
some that never *s*, but pass From sight and night „ 202
ye *s* me heart batin' to music wid ivery word! *Tomorrow* 34
ye'll niver *s* eyes an the face „ 50
stick oop thy back, an' *s* oop thy taäil, *Spinster's S's.* 31
as if they was *s* upo' springs, „ 89
Theere! *S* it down! Now Robby! „ 118
but *s* no meek ones in their place; *Locksley H., Sixty* 133
S the feet above the brain „ 136
S the maiden fancies wallowing „ 145
S the sphere of all the boundless Heavens „ 210
NOT this way will you *s* your name *Epilogue* 1
S the mountain aflame to-night, *On Jub. Q. Victoria* 16
And *s* the mother waking in amaze *Demeter and P.* 57
an' *s's* 'im ageän the wall, *Owd Roä* 82
Nor ever cared to *s* you on her knee, *The Ring* 386
And *s* a crueller mark than Cain's on him, *Happy* 18
—from the bush we both had *s*— „ 102
pine which here The warrior of Caprera *s*, *To Ulysses* 26
'*My* Rose' *s* all your faces aglow, *Roses on the T.* 3
s his face By waste and field and town *St. Telemachus* 29
You have *s* a price on his head: *Bandit's Death* 7
calls to them '*S* yourselves free!' *Kapiolani* 3

Set *See also* **Close-set, Deep-set, Hard-set, High-set, Silver-set, Solid-set, Stately-set, Stiff-set, Thick-set**

Setting *s* round thy first experiment *Ode to Memory* 81
It was when the moon was *s*; *May Queen, Con.* 26
s wide the doors that bar The secret bridal chambers *Gardener's D.* 248
s the *how much* before the *how*, *Golden Year* 11
at *s* forth The Biscay, roughly ridging eastward, *Enoch Arden* 528
Music's golden sea *S* toward eternity, *Ode on Well.* 253
And in the *s* thou art fair. *In Mem. cxxx* 4
S this knave, Lord Baron, at my side. *Gareth and L.* 854
Who push'd his prows into the *s* sun, *Columbus* 24
And a hush with the *s* moon. *Maud I xxii* 18
Now half to the *s* moon are gone, „ 23
On some vast plain before a *s* sun, *Guinevere* 77
Down those loud waters, like a *s* star, *Lover's Tale i* 59
s, when Even descended, the very sunset aflame; *V. of Maeldune* 66
glorious creature Sank to his *s*. *Batt. of Brunanburh* 30
up that lane of light into the *s* sun. *The Flight* 40
Charity *s* the martyr aflame; *Vastness* 9
his The words, and mine the *s*. *The Ring* 24
And while the moon was *s*. *Forlorn* 84
Those cobras ever *s* up their hoods— *Akbar's Dream* 166

Settle (s) Down on an oaken *s* in the hall, *Geraint and E.* 573

Settle (verb) (*See also* **Sattle**) 'Tis hard to *s* order once again. *Lotos-Eaters, C. S.* 82
the cloud that *s's* round his birth Hath lifted *Gareth and L.* 130
ere they *s* for the night. *Marr. of Geraint* 250
s's, beaten back, and beaten back *S's*, *Merlin and V.* 371
Nor *s's* into hueless gray, *To Marq. of Dufferin* 50

Settled (*See also* **Sattled**) A land of *s* government, *You ask me, why, etc.* 9
Until I woke, and found him *s* down *The Epic* 17
seem but to be Weak symbols of the *s* bliss, *Miller's D.* 233
wheeling round The central wish, until we *s* there. *Gardener's D.* 225
And loosely *s* into form. *Day-Dm., Pro.* 12
Nothing to mar the sober majesties Of *s*, sweet, Epicurean life. *Lucretius* 218
s in her eyes, The green malignant light *Princess iii* 131
on my spirits *S* a gentle cloud of melancholy; „ *iv* 570
by overthrow Of these or those, the question *s* die.' „ *v* 317
Now looking to some *s* end, *In Mem. lxxxv* 97
to her old perch back, and *s* there. *Merlin and V.* 903
Waiting to see the *s* countenance Of her I loved, *Lover's Tale iii* 39
Settling *s* circled all the lists. *Marr. of Geraint* 547
Seven (adj.) The *s* elms, the poplars four *Ode to Memory* 56
s happy years, *S* happy years of health and competence, *Enoch Arden* 82
In those far-off *s* happy years were born; „ 686
till the Bear had wheel'd Thro' a great arc his *s* slow suns. *Princess iv* 213
and more amazed Than if *s* men had set upon him, *Lancelot and E.* 351
thro' the gap The *s* clear stars of Arthur's Table Round— *Holy Grail* 684
Across the *s* clear stars—O grace to me— „ 692
S days I drove along the dreary deep, „ 808
S strong Earls of the army of Anlaf *Batt. of Brunanburh* 53
I can hear Too plainly what full tides of onset sap Our *s* high gates, *Tiresias* 92
His fingers were so stiffen'd by the frost Of *s* and ninety winters, *The Ring* 240
Seven (s) It should 'a been 'ere by *s*, *Spinster's S's.* 114
Sevenfold Would slowly trail himself *s* *The Mermaid* 25
and so We forged a *s* story. *Princess, Pro.* 202
Seven-headed *S-h* monsters only made to kill Time „ 204
Seven-months' A *s-m* babe had been a truer gift. *Merlin and V.* 711
Seventeen petitionary grace Of sweet *s* *The Brook* 113
Maud is not *s*, *Maud I xii* 15
Seventh Like a beam of the *s* Heaven, down to my side, „ *xiv* 21
on the *s* night I heard the shingle grinding *Holy Grail* 810
Seventimes-heated a heat As from a *s-h* furnace, „ 843
Seventy *S* years ago, my darling, *s* years ago. (repeat) *Grandmother* 24, 56
Hallus aloän wi' 'is booöks, thaw nigh upo' *s* year. *Village Wife* 27
Seventy-five While you have touch'd at *s-f*, *To E. Fitzgerald* 44
Seventy-four And I am nearing *s-f*, „ 43
Seventy-seven To you that are *s-s*, *June Bracken, etc.* 6
Several I bump'd the ice into three *s* stars, *The Epic* 12
Sever'd Her lips are *s* as to speak: *Day-Dm., Sleep. P.* 30
Severe The grave, *s* Genovese of old. *The Daisy* 40
across him came a cloud Of melancholy *s*, *Lancelot and E.* 325
Severer *S* in the logic of a life? *Princess v* 190
Severity That pure *s* of perfect light— *Guinevere* 646
Severn The Danube to the *S* gave *In Mem. xix* 1
There twice a day the *S* fills; „ 5
fifty knights rode with them, to the shores Of *S*, and they past to their own land; *Marr. of Geraint* 45
fifty knights rode with them to the shores Of *S*, and they past to their own land. *Geraint and E.* 955
Seville Let us bang these dogs of *S*, *The Revenge* 30
Sew Or teach the orphan girl to *s*, *L. C. V. de Vere* 70
Sewer cleanse this common *s* of all his realm, *Marr. of Geraint* 39
cleanse this common *s* of all my realm, *Geraint and E.* 895
with the drainage of your *s*; *Locksley H., Sixty* 143
Or the foulest *s* of the town— *Dead Prophet* 48
this little city of *s's*, *Happy* 34
Sewer (sure) But I beänt that *s* es the Lord, *Village Wife* 93
Naäy to be *s* it be past 'er time. *Spinster's S's.* 5
I wur *s* that it couldn't be true; „ 20
Robby wur fust to be *s*, „ 69
Sex 'No more of love; your *s* is known: *The Letters* 29
Madam—if I know your *s*, *Vision of Sin* 181
If our old halls could change their *s*, *Princess, Pro.* 140
not a scorner of your *s* But venerator, „ *iv* 422
She wrongs herself, her *s*, and me, „ *v* 117
either *s* alone Is half itself, „ *vii* 301
hustled together, each *s*, like swine, *Maud I i* 34
Shaäky (shaky) Nasty an' snaggy an' *s*, *North. Cobbler* 78
Shaame (shame) an which was a *s* to be seen; *Village Wife* 50
Shaämed (ashamed) I be hafe *s* on it now, *North. Cobbler* 17
we was *s* to cross Gigglesby Greeän, *Spinster's S's.* 33
niver done nowt to be *s* on, *Owd Roä* 10
Shackle The *s's* of an old love straiten'd him, *Lancelot and E.* 875
Shadda (shadow) Shamus O'Shea was yer *s*, *Tomorrow* 38
Shade (*See also* **Mountain-shade**) From the long alley's latticed *s* *Arabian Nights* 112
Life eminent creates the *s* of death; *Love and Death* 13
Your sorrow, only sorrow's *s*, *Margaret* 43
lavish lights, and floating *s's*: *Eleänore* 12
There in a silent *s* of laurel brown *Alexander* 9
'Let me not cast in endless *s* *Two Voices* 5
A merry boy in sun and *s*? „ 321
when in the chestnut *s* I found the blue Forget-me-not. *Miller's D.* 201
Untouch'd with any *s* of years, „ 219
stedfast *s* Sleeps on his luminous ring.' *Palace of Art* 15
And hollow *s's* enclosing hearts of flame, „ 241
You'll bury me, my mother, just beneath the hawthorn *s*, *May Queen, N. Y's. E.* 29
I READ, before my eyelids dropt their *s*, *D. of F. Women* 1
A cedar spread his dark-green layers of *s*. *Gardener's D.* 116
trembled on her waist—Ah, happy *s*— „ 132
Half light, half *s*, She stood, „ 140
Danced into light, and died into the *s*; „ 203
House in the *s* of comfortable roofs, *St. S. Stylites* 107
What's here? a shape, a *s*, „ 202
'Yet, since I first could cast a *s*, *Talking Oak* 85
rising thro' the mellow *s*, *Locksley Hall* 9
Breadths of tropic *s* and palms in cluster, „ 160
This whole wide earth of light and *s* *Will Water.* 67
One *s* more plump than common; „ 150
By peaks that flamed, or, all in *s*, *The Voyage* 41
As fast she fled thro' sun and *s*, *Sir L. and Q. G.* 37
Slided, they moving under *s*: *Princess vi* 82
Thine are these orbs of light and *s*; *In Mem., Pro.* 5
there no *s* can last In that deep dawn „ *xlvi* 5
What slender *s* of doubt may flit, „ *xlviii* 7
The *s* by which my life was crost, „ *lxvi* 5
play'd A chequer-work of beam and *s* „ *lxxii* 15
No visual *s* of some one lost, „ *xcii* 5
And every span of *s* that steals, „ *cxvii* 10
The sport of random sun and *s*. „ *Con.* 24
A *s* falls on us like the dark „ 93
The *s* of passing thought, „ 102
And touch with *s* the bridal doors, „ 117
never light and *s* Coursed one another *Marr. of Geraint* 521
our fortune swerved from sun to *s*, „ 714
behold In the first shallow *s* of a deep wood, *Geraint and E.* 119
There is no *s* or fold of mystery *Lover's Tale i* 182
Boughs on each side, laden with wholesome *s*, „ 230
All day I watch'd the floating isles of *s*, „ *ii* 5
seem to flicker past thro' sun and *s*, *Ancient Sage* 100
and yet no *s* of doubt, „ 235
mantle, every *s* of glancing green, *Prog. of Spring* 63
And light, with more or less of *s*, *Akbar's Dream* 46
a glory slowly gaining on the *s*, *Making of Man* 6
Shaded (*See also* **Sun-shaded**) To light her *s* eye; *Talking Oak* 218
Shading that other gazed, *S* his eyes *Lover's Tale i* 306
Shadow (s) (*See also* **Citron-shadow, Forest-shadow, Half-shadow, Shadda, Surface-shadow**) on his light there falls A *s*; *Supp. Confessions* 164
Were fixed *s's* of thy fixed mood, *Isabel* 9
She saw the gusty *s* sway. *Mariana* 52
The *s* of the poplar fell Upon her bed, „ 55
Thro' light and *s* thou dost range, *Madeline* 4
S's of the silver birk Sweep the green *A Dirge* 5
Light and *s* ever wander O'er the green „ 12
Thou art the *s* of life, *Love and Death* 10
The *s* passeth when the tree shall fall, „ 14
The *s* rushing up the sea, *Rosalind* 11
S's of the world appear. *L. of Shalott ii* 12
'I am half-sick of *s's*,' „ 35
WITH one black *s* at its feet, *Mariana in the S.* 1
The one black *s* from the wall. „ 80

Shadow (s) (*continued*) S's thou dost strike, Embracing cloud, *Two Voices* 194
A s on the graves I knew, „ 272
'From grave to grave the s crept: „ 274
Sometimes your s cross'd the blind. *Miller's D.* 124
s of the chair Flitted across into the night, „ 126
with his s on the stone, Rests like a s, *Œnone* 27
Between the s's of the vine-bunches „ 181
thro' wavering lights and s's broke, *Lotos-Eaters* 12
The s's flicker to and fro: *D. of the O. Year* 39
Fall into s, soonest lost: *To J. S.* 11
s of the flowers Stole all the golden gloss, *Gardener's D.* 129
mix'd with s's of the common ground! „ 135
Should my S cross thy thoughts Too sadly *Love and Duty* 88
white-hair'd s roaming like a dream *Tithonus* 8
Alas! for this gray s, once a man— „ 11
Coldly thy rosy s's bathe me, „ 66
and the s's rise and fall. *Locksley Hall* 80
Thro' the s of the globe we sweep „ 183
Faint s's, vapours lightly curl'd, *Day-Dm., Sleep. P.* 5
s's of the convent-towers Slant down *St. Agnes' Eve* 5
And waves of s went over the wheat, *Poet's Song* 4
So now that s of mischance appear'd *Enoch Arden* 128
like a wounded life He crept into the s: „ 387
o'er his countenance No s past, nor motion: „ 710
following our own s's thrice as long *The Brook* 166
Than his own s in a sickly sun. *Aylmer's Field* 30
Shot up their s's to the Heaven of Heavens, „ 642
That knit themselves for summer s, „ 724
dance, and flew thro' light And s, *Princess, Pro.* 85
Seven and yet one, like s's in a dream.— „ 229
burnt Because he cast no s, „ *i* 7
should know The s from the substance, and that one Should come to fight with s's and to fall. „ 9
And feel myself the s of a dream. „ 18
To point you out the s from the truth! „ 84
inscription ran along the front, But deep in s: „ 213
do I chase The substance or the s? „ *ii* 409
Well, Are castles s's? „ 414
Is she The sweet proprietress a s? „ 415
Descended to the court that lay three parts In s, „ *iii* 21
As flies the s of a bird, she fled. „ 96
'O hard task,' he cried; 'No fighting s's here! „ 125
And I myself the s of a dream, „ 188
Our weakness somehow shapes the s, Time; „ 330
But in the s will we work, „ 331
cataract and the tumult and the kings Were s's; „ *iv* 565
He has been among his s's.' „ *v* 33
Satan take The old women and their s's! „ 34
all about his motion clung The s of his sister, „ 258
one should fight with s's and should fall; „ 476
To dream myself the s of a dream: „ 481
o'er her forehead past A s, and her hue changed, „ *vi* 107
S and shine is life, little Annie, *Grandmother* 60
And on thro' zones of light and s *To F. D. Maurice* 27
S's of three dead men (repeat) *G. of Swainston* 3, 5
light and s illimitable, *Boädicea* 42
The lights and s's fly! *Window, On the Hill* 1
winds and lights and s's that cannot be still, „ 7
and left me in s here! „ *Gone* 3
s of a lark Hung in the s of a heaven? *In Mem. xvi* 9
There sat the S fear'd of man; „ *xxii* 12
The S sits and waits for me. „ 20
The S cloak'd from head to foot, „ *xxiii* 4
That S waiting with the keys, „ *xxvi* 15
Of one mute S watching all. „ *xxx* 8
The tender-pencil'd s play. „ *xlix* 12
My Arthur found your s's fair, „ *lxxxix* 6
His own vast s glory-crown'd; „ *xcvii* 3
Her s on the blaze of kings: „ *xcviii* 19
Let cares that petty s's cast, „ *cv* 13
hills are s's, and they flow From form to form, „ *cxxiii* 5
I saw her stand, A s there at my feet, *Maud II i* 39
A s flits before me, Not thou, but like to thee: „ *iv* 11
And the light and s fleet; „ 36
rivulet at her feet Ripples on in light and s „ 42

Shadow (s) (*continued*) The s still the same, *Maud II iv* 72
the s flits and fleets And will not let me be; „ 90
The s of His loss drew like eclipse, *Ded. of Idylls* 14
hold The King a s, and the city real: *Gareth and L.* 266
Who cannot brook the s of any lie.' „ 293
Even the s of Lancelot under shield. „ 1311
And muffled voices heard, and s's past; „ 1373
Then, like a s, past the people's talk *Marr. of Geraint* 82
Thy wheel and thou are s's in the cloud; „ 357
Among the dancing s's of the birds, „ 601
That never s of mistrust can cross Between us. „ 815
wholly arm'd, behind a rock In s, *Geraint and E.* 58
That s of mistrust should never cross „ 248
Come slipping o'er their s's on the sand, „ 471
And spake no word until the s turn'd; *Balin and Balan* 45
The crown is but the s of the King, And this a s's s, let him have it, „ 203
'No s' said Sir Balin. 'O my Queen, But light to me! no s, O my King, „ 206
all in s from the counter door Sir Lancelot „ 246
then the s of a spear, Shot from behind him, „ 322
'Eyes have I That saw to-day the s of a spear, „ 373
So thou be s, here I make thee ghost,' „ 394
And like a silver s slipt away *Merlin and V.* 423
And the cairn'd mountain was a s, „ 638
shot red fire and s's thro' the cave, *Lancelot and E.* 414
Past like a s thro' the field, „ 1140
s of some piece of pointed lace, In the Queen's s, „ 1174
s of my spear had been enow To scare them *Holy Grail* 791
once the s of a bird Flying, and then a fawn; *Pelleas and E.* 38
beneath the s of those towers A villainy, „ 276
nothing moved but his own self, And his own s. „ 418
Creep with his s thro' the court again, „ 441
Beneath the s of some bird of prey; „ 608
the world Is flesh and s— *Last Tournament* 316
Behind him rose a s and a shriek— „ 753
A ghastly something, and its s flew *Guinevere* 79
the world, and all its lights And s's, „ 344
Thy s still would glide from room to room, „ 504
The s of another cleaves to me, „ 618
friend and foe were s's in the mist, *Pass. of Arthur* 100
From halfway down the s of the grave, *To the Queen ii* 6
their fears Are morning s's huger than the shapes „ 63
Light-green with its own s, keel to keel, *Lover's Tale i* 43
from whose left hand floweth The S of Death, „ 499
We trod the s of the downward hill; „ 515
To stand a s by their shining doors, „ 731
Beneath the s of the curse of man, „ 790
look you here—the s's are too deep, *Sisters (E. and E.)* 103
from out This s into Substance— *Ded. Poem Prin. Alice* 6
Dashing the fires and the s's of dawn *V. of Maeldune* 99
sun and moons And all the s's. *De Prof., Two G.* 39
Spirit half-lost In thine own s „ 40
Σκιᾶς ὄναρ—dream of a s, go—God bless you. *To W. H. Brookfield* 13
sick For s—not one bush was near— *Tiresias* 36
And oldest age in s from the night, „ 104
The daisy will shut to the s, *The Wreck* 38
worm in the dust and the s of its desire— *Despair* 30
running after a s of good; „ 92
all thy world Might vanish like thy s in the dark. *Ancient Sage* 52
But make the passing s serve thy will. „ 110
Her s crown'd with stars— „ 201
Themselves but s's of a shadow-world. „ 239
Night and S rule below When only Day should reign.' „ 243
past the range of Night and S— „ 283
I was left within the s sitting *Locksley H., Sixty* 16
Near us Edith's holy s, „ 54
Man or Mind that sees a s „ 196
Set the s of Himself, the boundless, „ 211
But since, our mortal s, *Epilogue* 22
Golden branch amid the s's, *To Virgil* 27
shifting ladders of s and light, *Dead Prophet* 21
But not the s's which that light would cast, Till s's vanish in the Light of Light. *Epit. on Caxton* 3
Henry's fifty years are all in s, *On Jub. Q. Victoria* 39

Shadow (s) (*continued*) That *s* of a likeness to the king
Of *s's*, *Demeter and P.* 16
and thy *s* past Before me, crying " 93
So the *S* wail'd. " 101
Three dark ones in the *s* with thy King. " 122
And all the *S* die into the Light, " 138
Slander, her *s*, sowing the nettle *Vastness* 22
Strike upward thro' the *s*; *The Ring* 372
s leave the Substance in the brooding light of noon? *Happy* 99
Phra-Chai, the *S* of the Best, *To Ulysses* 41
O'er his uncertain *s* droops the day. *Prog. of Spring* 8
the valley Named of the *s*, *Merlin and the G.* 87
Fell on the *s*, No longer a *s*, " 92
With your own *s* in the placid lake, *Romney's R.* 76
double *s* the crown'd ones all disappearing! *Parnassus* 13
Became a *s*, sank and disappear'd, *Death of Œnone* 50
dawn Struck from him his own *s* *St. Telemachus* 33
s of a dream—an idle one It may be. *Akbar's Dream* 5
your *s* falls on the grave. *Charity* 20
All about him *s* still, but, *Making of Man* 5
Who was a *s* in the brain, *Mechanophilus* 15
Nor the myriad world, His *s*, *God and the Univ.* 6
s of a crown, that o'er him hung, Has vanish'd
in the *s* cast by Death. *D. of the Duke of C.* 2
His *s* darkens earth: " 13
Shadow (verb) Let Thy dove *S* me over, *Supp. Confessions* 181
S forth thee:—the world hath not another *Isabel* 38
tree Stands in the sun and *s's* all beneath, *Love and Death* 11
S forth the banks at will: *Eleänore* 110
And *s* all my soul, that I may die. *Œnone* 242
And *s* Sumner-chace! *Talking Oak* 150
You *s* forth to distant men, *To E. L.* 7
s forth The all-generating powers *Lucretius* 96
Tho' the Roman eagle *s* thee, *Boädicea* 39
Shadow-casting sunders ghosts and *s-c* men *Merlin and V.* 629
Shadow-chequer'd And many a *s-c* lawn *Arabian Nights* 102
Shadow'd (*See also* **Faintly-shadow'd, Softly-shadow'd**)
Twin peaks *s* with pine slope *Leonine Eleg.* 10
I have *s* many a group Of beauties, *Talking Oak* 61
And *s* all her rest— " 226
Hung, *s* from the heat: *Princess ii* 459
warmth of Arthur's hall *S* an angry distance: *Balin and Balan* 237
whom waitest thou With thy soften'd, *s* brow, *Adeline* 46
And *s* coves on a sunny shore, *Eleänore* 18
So fresh they rose in *s* swells *The Letters* 46
Nor thou with *s* hint confuse A life that leads
melodious days. *In Mem. xxxiii* 7
Is *s* by the growing hour, " *xlvi* 3
Shadowing (adj. and part.) (*See also* **Cavern-shadowing, Europe-shadowing, Far-shadowing**) All along the
s shore, *Eleänore* 41
Mast-throng'd beneath her *s* citadel *Œnone* 118
s down the champaign till it strikes On a wood, *Princess v* 526
s down the horned flood In ripples, *In Mem. lxxxvi* 7
And *s* bluff that made the banks, *In Mem. ciii* 22
S the snow-limb'd Eve from whom she came. *Maud I xviii* 28
pour'd Into the *s* pencil's naked forms *Lover's Tale ii* 180
Far from out the west in *s* showers, *Sisters (E. and E.)* 7
Shadowing (s) for spite of doubts And sudden
ghostly *s's* *Princess iv* 572
Shadow-like Vanish'd *s-l* Gods and Goddesses, *Kapiolani* 26
Shadow-maker *S-m*, shadow-slayer, *Akbar's D., Hymn* 5
Shadow-prison Her breast as in a *s-p*, *Lover's Tale iv* 58
Shadow-slayer Shadow-maker, *s-s*, *Akbar's D., Hymn* 5
Shadow-streak With *s-s's* of rain. *Palace of Art* 76
Shadow-world Themselves but shadows of a *s-w*. *Ancient Sage* 239
Shadowy faintest sunlights flee About his *s* sides: *The Kraken* 5
S, dreaming Adeline? (repeat) *Adeline* 10, 39
Or, in a *s* saloon, *Eleänore* 125
Up-clomb the *s* pine above the woven copse. *Lotos-Eaters* 18
walls Of *s* granite, in a gleaming pass; *Lotos-Eaters, C. S.* 4
palled shapes In *s* thoroughfares of thought; *In Mem. lxx* 8
High over the *s* land. *Maud II i* 40
Camelot, a city of *s* palaces And stately, *Gareth and L.* 303
There with her milkwhite arms and *s* hair *Guinevere* 416

Shadowy (*continued*) and hunters race The *s* lion, *Tiresias* 178
s warrior glide Along the silent field of Asphodel. *Demeter and P.* 152
once a flight of *s* fighters crost The disk, *St. Telemachus* 23
Shadowy-pencill'd A thousand *s-p* valleys And snowy dells *The Daisy* 67
Shady arching limes are tall and *s*, *Margaret* 59
Parks with oak and chestnut *s*, *L. of Burleigh* 29
Shaft (*See also* **Spear-shaft**) With shrilling *s's* of
subtle wit. *Clear-headed friend* 13
to fling The winged *s's* of truth, *The Poet* 26
A thousand little *s's* of flame *Fatima* 17
Betwixt the slender *s's* were blazon'd *Palace of Art* 167
lean a ladder on the *s*, And climbing up *St. S. Stylites* 216
And shrill'd his tinsel *s*. *Talking Oak* 68
universal Peace Lie like a *s* of light across the land, *Golden Year* 49
sunrise broken into scarlet *s's* *Enoch Arden* 592
again The scarlet *s's* of sunrise—but no sail. " 599
s's Of gentle satire, kin to charity, *Princess ii* 468
the beard-blown goat Hang on the *s*, " *iv* 79
brand, mace, and *s*, and shield— " *v* 503
To silver all the valleys with her *s's*— *Tiresias* 32
serpent coil'd about his broken *s*, *Demeter and P.* 77
Shafted *See* **Golden-shafted, Slender-shafted, Stubborn-shafted**
Shaggy drew The vast and *s* mantle of his beard
Across her neck *Merlin and V.* 256
Shake *The sun-lit almond-blossom s's*— *To the Queen* 16
seemed to *s* The sparkling flints *Arabian Nights* 51
name to *s* All evil dreams of power— *The Poet* 46
And now *s* hands across the brink *My life is full* 6
S hands once more: I cannot sink So far— " 8
A wither'd palsy cease to *s*?' *Two Voices* 57
S hands, before you die. *D. of the O. Year* 42
s the darkness from their loosen'd manes, *Tithonus* 41
in the thoughts that *s* mankind. *Locksley Hall* 166
You *s* your head. A random string *Day-Dm., L'Envoi* 1
Twang out, my fiddle! *s* the twigs! *Amphion* 61
Swells up, and *s's* and falls. *Sir Galahad* 76
We felt the good ship *s* and reel, *The Voyage* 15
from some bay-window *s* the night; *Princess i* 106
a sight to *s* The midriff of despair with laughter, " 200
To break my chain, to *s* my mane: " *ii* 424
The long light *s's* across the lakes, " *iv* 3
The drowsy folds of our great ensign *s* " *v* 8
two dewdrops on the petal *s* To the same sweet air, " *vii* 68
A cypress in the moonlight *s*, *The Daisy* 82
s The prophet blazon'd on the panes; *In Mem. lxxxvii* 7
and *s* The pillars of domestic peace. " *xc* 19
That so, when the rotten hustings *s* *Maud I vi* 54
The slender acacia would not *s* " *xxii* 45
For a tumult *s's* the city, " *II iv* 50
Shall *s* its threaded tears in the wind no more. " *III vi* 28
whatsoever storms May *s* the world, *Com. of Arthur* 293
s them aside, Dreams ruling when wit sleeps! *Balin and Balan* 142
hard earth *s*, and a low thunder of arms. *Lancelot and E.* 460
As we *s* off the bee that buzzes at us; " 785
now yearn'd to *s* The burthen off his heart *Last Tournament* 179
shook beneath them, as the thistle *s's* *Guinevere* 254
this great voice that *s's* the world, *Pass. of Arthur* 139
shook 'em off as a dog that *s's* his ears *The Revenge* 54
Then a peal that *s's* the portal— *Locksley H., Sixty* 263
Your hand *s's*. I am ashamed. *Romney's R.* 24
or *s* with her thunders and shatter her island, *Kapiolani* 10
Shaken I am too forlorn, Too *s*: *Supp. Confessions* 136
s with a sudden storm of sighs— *Locksley Hall* 27
Every moment, lightly *s*, ran itself " 32
Her round white shoulder *s* with her sobs, *Princess iv* 289
in a royal hand, But *s* here and there, " *v* 372
The King was *s* with holy fear; *The Victim* 57
That grief hath *s* into frost! *In Mem. iv* 12
But thou and I have *s* hands, " *xl* 29
And my bones are *s* with pain, *Maud II v* 5
With reverent eyes mock-loyal, *s* voice, *Merlin and V.* 157
clouded heavens Were *s* with the motion *Holy Grail* 801
so lay, Till *s* by a dream, that Gawain fired *Pelleas and E.* 517
Shaker O *s* of the Baltic and the Nile, *Ode on Well.* 137
Shakespeare Beside him *S* bland and mild; *Palace of Art* 134

Shakespeare (*continued*) My *S's* curse on clown and knave — *You might have won* 27
The soul of *S* love thee more. — *In Mem. lxi* 12
'a thing enskied' (As *S* has it) — *To E. Fitzgerald* 17
Our *S's* bland and universal eye Dwells pleased, — *To W. C. Macready* 13
Shakest *s* in thy fear: there yet is time: — *Gareth and L.* 940
Shaking *S* their pretty cabin, hammer and axe, — *Enoch Arden* 173
S a little like a drunkard's hand, — „ 465
He, *s* his gray head pathetically, — „ 714
the singer *s* his curly head Turn'd as he sat, — *The Islet* 6
thousand battles, and *s* a hundred thrones — *Maud I i* 48
S her head at her son and sighing — „ *xix* 24
S his hands, as from a lazar's rag, — *Pelleas and E.* 317
it is coming—*s* the walls— — *Rizpah* 85
How your hand is *s*! — *Forlorn* 38
Shaky *See* **Shaäky**
Shale stony names Of *s* and hornblende, — *Princess iii* 362
Shallop Anight my *s*, rustling thro' — *Arabian Nights* 12
My *s* thro' the star-strown calm, — „ 36
s flitteth silken-sail'd Skimming down to Camelot: — *L. of Shalott i* 22
Some to a low song oar'd a *s* by, — *Princess ii* 457
In a *s* of crystal ivory-beak'd, — *The Islet* 12
To where a little *s* lay — *In Mem. ciii* 19
Shallow (adj.) Vex not thou the poet's mind With thy *s* wit: *Poet's Mind* 2
Seam'd with the *s* cares of fifty years: — *Aylmer's Field* 814
For into a *s* grave they are thrust, — *Maud ii v* 6
Came quickly flashing thro' the *s* ford Behind them, — *Marr. of Geraint* 167
In the first *s* shade of a deep wood, — *Geraint and E.* 119
S skin of green and azure— — *Locksley H., Sixty* 208
Shallow (s) And *s's* on a distant shore, — *Mariana in the S.* 7
ran By ripply *s's* of the lisping lake, — *Edwin Morris* 98
sunbeam dance Against my sandy *s's*. — *The Brook* 177
shone the Noonday Sun Beyond a raging *s*. — *Gareth and L.* 1028
He from beyond the roaring *s* roar'd, — „ 1033
And she athwart the *s* shrill'd again, — „ 1035
Shallower Nature made them blinder motions bounded in a *s* brain: — *Locksley Hall* 150
The mother flow'd in *s* acrimonies: — *Aylmer's Field* 563
Shallow-hearted O my cousin, *s-h*! O my Amy, — *Locksley Hall* 39
Shalott The island of *S*. — *L. of Shalott i* 9
The Lady of *S*. (repeat) — *L. of Shalott i* 18, 27; *ii* 9, 27, 36; *iii* 45; *iv* 9, 18, 27, 36, 45, 54
'Tis the fairy Lady of *S*.' — *L. of Shalott i* 36
red cloaks of market girls, Pass onward from *S*. — „ *ii* 18
Beside remote *S*. (repeat) — „ *iii* 9, 18
bearded meteor, trailing light, Moves over still *S*. — „ 27
Shambles The land all *s*—naked marriages — *Aylmer's Field* 765
Shambling For, ere I mated with my *s* king, — *Last Tournament* 544
Shame (s) (*See also* **Shaame**) The flush of anger'd *s* — *Madeline* 32
Some grow to honour, some to *s*,— — *Two Voices* 257
She mix'd her ancient blood with *s*. — *The Sisters* 8
Inwrapt tenfold in slothful *s*, — *Palace of Art* 262
I heard sounds of insult, *s*, and wrong, — *D. of F. Women* 19
Her loveliness with *s* and with surprise — „ 89
To hold his hope thro' *s* and guilt, — *Love thou thy land* 82
What betwixt *s* and pride, New things and old, — *Walk. to the Mail* 60
To save from *s* and thrall: — *Sir Galahad* 16
Sold him unto *s*. — *The Captain* 60
S and wrath his heart confounded, — „ 61
As it were with *s* she blushes, — *L. of Burleigh* 63
'Sit thee down, and have no *s*, — *Vision of Sin* 83
bearing in myself the *s* The woman should have borne, — *Aylmer's Field* 355
The poor child of *s* The common care — „ 687
Whose *s* is that, if he went hence with *s*? — „ 718
S might befall Melissa, knowing, — *Princess iii* 147
So much a kind of *s* within me wrought, — „ *iv* 194
And full of cowardice and guilty *s*, — „ 348
I grant in her some sense of *s*, she flies; — „ 349
dismiss'd in *s* to live No wiser than their mothers, — „ 513
The horror of the *s* among them all: — „ *v* 95
Where idle boys are cowards to their *s*, — „ 309
And hatred of her weakness, blent with *s*. — „ *vii* 30
Glowing all over noble *s*; — *Princess vii* 160

Shame (s) (*continued*) Guarding realms and kings from *s*; *Ode on Well.* 68
land whose hearths he saved from *s* — „ 225
A touch of *s* upon her cheek: — *In Mem. xxxvii* 10
holds it sin and *s* to draw The deepest measure — „ *xlviii* 11
See with clear eye some hidden *s* — „ *li* 7
And hide thy *s* beneath the ground. — „ *lxxii* 28
My *s* is greater who remain, — „ *cix* 23
chuckle, and grin at a brother's *s*; — *Maud I iv* 29
save from some slight *s* one simple girl. — „ *xviii* 45
My anguish hangs like *s*. — „ *II iv* 74
peace that was full of wrongs and *s's*, — „ *III vi* 40
How can ye keep me tether'd to you—*S*. — *Gareth and L.* 115
as is a *s* A man should not be bound by, — „ 270
S never made girl redder than Gareth joy. — „ 536
s, pride, wrath Slew the May-white: — „ 656
Who will cry *s*? — „ 942
For this were *s* to do him further wrong — „ 954
Care not for *s*: — „ 1006
Than that my lord thro' me should suffer *s*. — *Marr. of Geraint* 101
Than that my lord should suffer loss or *s*.' — *Geraint and E.* 69
That causer of his banishment and *s*, — *Balin and Balan* 221
This fair wife-worship cloaks a secret *s*? — „ 360
I fly from *s*, A lustful King, — „ 473
My violence, and my villainy, come to *s*.' — „ 492
Up then, ride with me! Talk not of *s*! — „ 523
Do these more *s* than these have done themselves.' — „ 524
And *s*, could *s* be thine, that *s* were mine. — *Merlin and V.* 448
The *s* that cannot be explained for *s*. — „ 698
For what *s* in love, So love be true, — „ 861
Face Hand-hidden, as for utmost grief or *s*; — „ 897
He loves the Queen, and in an open *s*: And she returns his love in open *s*; — *Lancelot and E.* 1082
did Pelleas in an utter *s* Creep — *Pelleas and E.* 440
For why should I have loved her to my *s*? — „ 482
I loathe her, as I loved her to my *s*. — „ 483
'I am wrath and *s* and hate and evil fame, — „ 568
while he mutter'd, 'Craven crests! O *s*! — *Last Tournament* 187
dreading worse than *s* Her warrior Tristram, — „ 384
'Mine be the *s*; mine was the sin: — *Guinevere* 112
Mine is the *s*, for I was wife, — „ 119
S on her own garrulity garrulously, — „ 312
happy, dead before thy *s*? — „ 423
must I leave thee, woman, to thy *s*. — „ 511
nor can I kill my *s*; — „ 622
Meek maidens, from the voices crying '*s*.' — „ 672
left her alone with her sin an' her *s*, — *First Quarrel* 25
an' *she*—in her *s* an' her sin— — „ 69
The blast and the burning *s* — *Rizpah* 18
then put away—isn't that enough *s*? — „ 36
drew back with her dead and her *s*. — *The Revenge* 60
—thy *s*, and mine, Thy comrade— — *Sir J. Oldcastle* 101
s to speak of them—Among the heathen— — „ 110
redder than rosiest health or than utterest *s*, — *V. of Maeldune* 65
flung from the rushing tide of the world as a waif of *s*, *The Wreck* 6
mother's *s* will enfold her and darken her life.' — „ 100
glory and *s* dying out for ever in endless time, — *Despair* 75
Paint the mortal *s* of nature — *Locksley H., Sixty* 140
S and marriage, *S* and marriage, — *Forlorn* 31
In that vast Oval ran a shudder of *s*. — *St. Telemachus* 73
Was redden'd by that cloud of *s* when I . . . . — *Akbar's Dream* 64
I need no wages of *s*. — *Charity* 40
Is it *S*, so few should have climb'd — *The Dawn* 17
Shame (verb) look'd to *s* The hollow-vaulted dark, — *Arabian Nights* 125
To *s* the boast so often made, — *Love thou thy land* 71
'O Lady Clare, you *s* your worth! — *Lady Clare* 66
To *s* these mouldy Aylmers in their graves: — *Aylmer's Field* 396
'Or surely I shall *s* myself and him.' — „ 734
Some mighty poetess, I would *s* you then, — *Princess, Pro.* 132
to *s* That which he says he loves: — „ *iv* 248
You *s* your mother's judgment too. — „ *vi* 261
Lest he should come to *s* thy judging of him.' — *Gareth and L.* 469
s the King for only yielding me My champion — „ 898
S me not, *s* me not. — „ 1137
one that will not *s* Ever the shadow of Lancelot — „ 1310
were ye shamed, and, worse, might *s* the Prince — *Marr. of Geraint* 726

Shame (verb) (*continued*) 'Nay father, nay good father, s me not | *Lancelot and E.* 207
Mine own name s's me, | " 1403
my brother, Why wilt thou s me to confess | *Holy Grail* 567
Nor let me s my father's memory, | *Guinevere* 318
whereof we lately heard A strain to s us | *To the Queen ii* 15
Our sons will s our own; | *Mechanophilus* 22
Shamed (*See also* **All-shamed**) I am s thro' all my nature | *Locksley Hall* 148
Far too naked to be s! | *Vision of Sin* 190
but sank down s At all that beauty; | *Lucretius* 63
Pardon, I am s That I must needs repeat | *Princess iii* 51
He never shall be s. | *Ode on Well.* 191
Nor s to bawl himself a kitchen-knave. | *Gareth and L.* 717
the new knight Had fear he might be s; | " 1044
S am I that I so rebuked, | " 1164
S! care not! thy foul sayings fought for me: | " 1180
she ask'd him, 'S and overthrown, | " 1227
S had I been, and sad—O Lancelot—thou!' | " 1245
O damsel, be you wise To call him s, | " 1260
Then were ye s, and, worse, | *Marr. of Geraint* 726
'I have s thee so that now thou shamest me, | *Balin and Balan* 431
and yet I should be s to say it— | *Pelleas and E.* 189
'The end is come, And I am s for ever;' | *Guinevere* 111
S in their souls. | *Batt. of Brunanburh* 99
a child Had s me at it— | *Romney's R.* 112
Shameful This is a s thing for men to lie. | *M. d'Arthur* 78
Dabbling a shameless hand with s jest, | *Princess iii* 314
And with a s swiftness: | *Com. of Arthur* 205
Or seeming s—for what shame in love, | *Merlin and V.* 861
Then came thy s sin with Lancelot; | *Guinevere* 487
in his agony conceives A s sense as of a cleaving crime— | *Lover's Tale i* 794
Shamefulness Arthur were the child of s, | *Com. of Arthur* 239
Shameless Ah s! for he did but sing A song | *You might have won* 21
s noon Was clash'd and hammer'd from a hundred towers, | *Godiva* 74
will she fling herself, S upon me? | *Lucretius* 203
Dabbling a s hand with shameful jest, | *Princess iii* 314
'Lo the s ones, who take Their pastime | *Lancelot and E.* 100
Anon there past a crowd With s laughter, | *St. Telemachus* 39
Shamest shamed thee so that now thou s me, | *Balin and Balan* 431
Shamus (*See also* **Shamus O'Shea**) An' S along wid the rest, | *Tomorrow* 44
Shamus O'Shea (*See also* **Shamus**) Dhrinkin' yer health wid S O'S | " 12
An' S O'S was yer shadda, | " 38
S O'S that has now ten childer, | " 85
Shape (s) A gleaming s she floated by, | *L. of Shalott iv* 39
A cloud that gather'd s: | *Œnone* 42
tears Of angels to the perfect s of man. | *To ——, With Pal. of Art* 19
O s's and hues that please me well! | *Palace of Art* 194
in dark corners of her palace stood Uncertain s's; | " 238
So s chased s as swift as, | *D. of F. Women* 37
Gown'd in pure white, that fitted to the s— | *Gardener's D.* 126
What's here? a s, a shade, | *St. S. Stylites* 202
Ten thousand broken lights and s's, | *Will Water.* 59
The peaky islet shifted s's, | *The Voyage* 33
Suffused them, sitting, lying, languid s's, | *Vision of Sin* 12
Here is a story which in rougher s | *Aylmer's Field* 7
In such a s dost thou behold thy God. | " 657
And twisted s's of lust, unspeakable, | *Lucretius* 157
cloud may stoop from heaven and take the s | *Princess vii* 2
Titanic s's, they cramm'd The forum, | " 124
softer all her s And rounder seem'd: | " 136
And s's and hues of Art divine! | *Ode Inter. Exhib.* 22
Those niched s's of noble mould, | *The Daisy* 38
palled s's In shadowy thoroughfares | *In Mem. lxx* 7
And wheel'd or lit the filmy s's | " *xcv* 10
The s of him I loved, and love | " *ciii* 14
Ring out old s's of foul disease; | " *cvi* 25
with the shocks of doom To s and use. | " *cxviii* 25
To a lord, a captain, a padded s, | *Maud I x* 29
a ship, the s thereof A dragon wing'd, | *Com. of Arthur* 374
S that fled With broken wings, | *Gareth and L* 1207
With pointed lance as if to pierce, a s, | *Balin and Balan* 325
Shape (s) (*continued*) The s and colour of a mind and life, | *Lancelot and E.* 335
her s From forehead down to foot, perfect— | " 641
around Great angels, awful s's, and wings and eyes. | *Holy Grail* 848
slender was her hand and small her s; | *Pelleas and E.* 74
Unruffling waters re-collect the s | *Last Tournament* 369
morning shadows huger than the s's That cast them, | *To the Queen ii* 63
Waiting to see some blessed s in heaven, | *Lover's Tale i* 312
shadows of dawn on the beautiful s's, | *V. of Maeldune* 99
two s's high over the sacred fountain, | *Parnassus* 9
s with wings Came sweeping by him, | *St. Telemachus* 24
The s with wings. | " 38
æon pass and touch him into s? | *Making of Man* 4
Shape (verb) thoughts Do s themselves within me, | *Œnone* 247
A saying, hard to s in act; | *Love thou thy land* 49
that which s's it to some perfect end. | *Love and Duty* 26
To s the song for your delight | *Day-Dm., Ep.* 6
and check'd His power to s: | *Lucretius* 23
Our weakness somehow s's the shadow, Time; | *Princess iii* 330
s it plank and beam for roof and floor, | " *vi* 46
And s the whisper of the throne; | *In Mem. lxiv* 12
Then fancy s's, as fancy can, | " *lxxx* 5
s His action like the greater ape, | " *cxx* 10
Like clouds they s themselves and go. | " *cxxiii* 8
Would s himself a right!' | *Gareth and L.* 348
face that men S to their fancy's eye | *Lancelot and E.* 1252
But had not force to s it as he would, | *Pass. of Arthur* 15
Ye cannot s Fancy so fair as is this | *Lover's Tale i* 547
Was my sight drunk that it did s to me | " 642
Virtue must s itself in deed, | *Tiresias* 86
and s it at the last According to the Highest | *Ancient Sage* 89
S your heart to front the hour, | *Locksley H., Sixty* 106
You that s for Eternity, | *On Jub. Q. Victoria* 43
And see and s and do. | *Mechanophilus* 4
Shaped (*See also* **Bow-shaped, Man-shaped**) s *The city's ancient legend into this*:— | *Godiva* 3
S her heart with woman's meekness | *L. of Burleigh* 71
This red-hot iron to be s with blows. | *Princess v* 209
s, it seems, By God for thee alone, | *Lancelot and E.* 1366
foot was on a stool S as a dragon; | *Last Tournament* 672
S by the audible and visible, | *Lover's Tale ii* 104
motion lives Be prosperously s, | *De Prof., Two G.* 20
Who s the forms, obey them, | *Akbar's Dream* 143
Shaping '*By* s *some august decree*, | *To the Queen* 33
'Here sits he s wings to fly: | *Two Voices* 289
s faithful record of the glance That graced | *Gardener's D.* 177
And one the s of a star; | *In Mem. ciii* 36
s an infant ripe for its birth, | *Maud I iv* 34
S their way toward Dyflen again, | *Batt. of Brunanburh* 98
Shard By s's and scurf of salt, | *Vision of Sin* 211
dash'd Your cities into s's with catapults, | *Princess v* 138
Share (s) rhymes to him were scrip and s, | *The Brook* 4
To buy strange s's in some Peruvian mine. | *Sea Dreams* 15
O then to ask her of my s's, | " 115
Then beast and man had had their s of me: | *Com. of Arthur* 163
Who leaving s in furrow come to see | *Gareth and L.* 243
dividend, consol, and s— | *The Wreck* 30
Share (verb) Now could you s your thought; | *Princess vi* 252
s's with man His nights, his days, | " *vii* 262
Who stay to s the morning feast, | *In Mem., Con.* 75
him who had ceased to s her heart, | *Maud I xix* 30
For ye shall s my earldom with me, girl, | *Geraint and E.* 626
and to s Their marriage-banquet. | *The Ring* 430
To s his living death with him, | *Happy* 8
Shared one sorrow and she s it not? | *Aylmer's Field* 702
I s with her in whom myself remains. | *Lover's Tale i* 248
all my griefs were s with thee, | *Pref. Poem Broth. S.* 25
Sharer S's of our glorious past, | *Open. I. and C. Exhib.* 31
Sharp (adj.) Edged with s laughter, cuts atwain | *Clear-headed friend* 2
When the s clear twang of the golden chords | *Sea-Fairies* 38
S and few, but seeming-bitter From excess | *Rosalind* 31
bright and s As edges of the scymetar. | *Kate* 11
And utterly consumed with s distress, | *Lotos-Eaters, C. S* 13
I made my dagger s and bright. | *The Sisters* 26
He thought of that s look, Mother, I gave him yesterday, | *May Queen* 15

Sharp (adj.) (*continued*) All those *s* fancies, by down-lapsing thought *D. of F. Women* 49
With that *s* sound the white dawn's creeping beams, „ 261
His face is growing *s* and thin. *D. of the O. Year* 46
all these things fell on her *S* as reproach. *Enoch Arden* 488
dying, gleam'd on rocks Roof-pendent, *s*; *Balin and Balan* 315
s breaths of anger puff'd Her fairy nostril out; *Merlin and V.* 848
Thro' her own side she felt the *s* lance go; *Lancelot and E.* 624
dame Came suddenly on the Queen with the *s* news. „ 730
With one *s* rapid, where the crisping white *Holy Grail* 381
close upon it peal'd A *s* quick thunder.' „ 696
As the *s* wind that ruffles all day long *Guinevere* 50
On that *s* ridge of utmost doom ride highly *Lover's Tale i* 805
S is the fire of assault, *Def. of Lucknow* 57
'Ya mun saäve little Dick, an' be *s* about it an' all,' *Owd Roä* 81
Sharp (s) thro' every change of *s* and flat; *Caress'd or chidden* 4
In little *s's* and trebles, *The Brook* 40
Sharpen'd Are *s* to a needle's end; *In Mem. lxxvi* 4
and ice Makes daggers at the *s* eaves, „ *cvii* 8
his aims Were *s* by strong hate for Lancelot. *Guinevere* 20
Sharper she was *s* than an eastern wind, *Audley Court* 53
Suddenly strike on a *s* sense For a shell, *Maud II ii* 63
Sharpest Upon the last and *s* height, *In Mem. xlvii* 13
Shall *s* pathos blight us, knowing all *Love and Duty* 85
Sharp-headed busy fret Of that *s-h* worm begins *Supp. Confessions* 186
Sharpness *s* of that pain about her heart: *Geraint and E.* 190
Sharp-pointed He! where is some *s-p* thing? *The Flight* 72
Sharp-smitten *S-s* with the dint of armed heels— *M. d'Arthur* 190
S-s with the dint of armed heels— *Pass. of Arthur* 358
Shatter And *s*, when the storms are black, *England and Amer.* 13
Would *s* all the happiness of the hearth. *Enoch Arden* 770
Take the hoary Roman head and *s* it, *Boädicea* 65
ere the onward whirlwind *s* it, *Lover's Tale i* 451
shake with her thunders and *s* her island, *Kapiolani* 10
Shatter'd (*See also* **Still-shatter'd**) Spars were splinter'd, decks were *s*, *The Captain* 45
S into one earthquake in one day *Lucretius* 251
arms were *s* to the shoulder blade. *Princess vi* 52
from the sabre-stroke *S* and sunder'd. *Light Brigade* 36
some were sunk and many were *s*, *The Revenge* 61
Rocking with *s* spars, with sudden fires Flamed over: *Buonaparte* 11
And loosed the *s* casque, and chafed his hands, *M. d'Arthur* 209
So like a *s* column lay the King; „ 221
And these are but the *s* stalks, *In Mem. lxxxii* 7
On a horror of *s* limbs and a wretched swindler's lie? *Maud I i* 56
Here stood a *s* archway plumed with fern; *Marr. of Geraint* 316
And one with *s* fingers dangling lame, *Last Tournament* 60
the crash Of battleaxes on *s* helms, *Pass. of Arthur* 110
And loosed the *s* casque, and chafed his hands, „ 377
So like a *s* column lay the King; „ 389
a stream Flies with a *s* foam along the chasm. *Lover's Tale i* 383
Gilded with broom, or *s* into spires, „ 400
but *s* nerve, Yet haunting Julian, „ *iv* 105
And *s* phantom of that infinite One, *De Prof., Two G.* 47
Wreck'd—your train: or all but wreck'd? a *s* wheel? a vicious boy *Locksley H., Sixty* 215
The jungle rooted in his *s* hearth, *Demeter and P.* 76
Spurning a *s* fragment of the God, *St. Telemachus* 16
Shattering (*See also* **Shrine-shattering**) plunge in cataract, *s* on black blocks *Princess iii* 291
The *s* trumpet shrilleth high, *Sir Galahad* 5
I rode, *S* all evil customs everywhere, *Holy Grail* 477
Shaw (show) an' 'e *s's* it to me, *North. Cobbler* 85
Shawm With *s's*, and with cymbals, *Dying Swan* 32
Sheaf (*See also* **Autumn-sheaf, Barley-sheaves**) Piling *sheaves* in uplands airy, *L. of Shalott i* 34
In front they bound the *sheaves.* *Palace of Art* 78
The varying year with blade and *s* *Day-Dm., Sleep. P.* 1
bind the scatter'd scheme of seven Together in one *s*? *Princess, Con.* 9
Which he may read that binds the *s*, *In Mem. xxxvi* 13
And whirl the ungarner'd *s* afar, „ *lxxii* 23
Where stood the *s* of Peace: *The Ring* 247
Shear I did but *s* a feather, *Princess v* 541
Sheath (*See also* **Flower-sheath**) New from its silken *s.* *D. of F. Women* 60
A dagger, in rich *s* with jewels on it *Aylmer's Field* 220

Sheath (*continued*) More crumpled than a poppy from the *s*, *Princess v* 29
tearing out of *s* The brand, Sir Balin with a fiery 'Ha! *Balin and Balan* 392
when, prest together In its green *s*, *Lover's Tale i* 153
Sheathe To draw, to *s* a useless sword, *In Mem. cxxviii* 13
Sheathing To *s* splendours and the golden scale *Princess v* 41
Sheba That *S* came to ask of Solomon.' „ *ii* 346
For Solomon may come to *S* yet.' „ 349
Shebeen (grog-shop) wid Shamus O'Shea at Katty's *s*; *Tomorrow* 12
he says to me wanst, at Katty's *s*, „ 63
Shed (s) broken *s's* look'd sad and strange: *Mariana* 5
Became no better than a broken *s*, *Holy Grail* 398
boäth slinkt 'oäm by the brokken *s* *Spinster's S's.* 37
An' tha squeedg'd my 'and i' the *s*, „ 39
Shed (verb) They have not *s* a many tears, *Miller's D.* 221
Yet tears they *s*: they had their part „ 223
I thought that all the blood by Sylla *s* *Lucretius* 47
dry up these tears *S* for the love of Love; *Lover's Tale i* 781
I weänt *s* a drop on 'is blood, *North. Cobbler* 114
since Sylvester *s* the venom of world-wealth *Sir J. Oldcastle* 166
Shedding *s* poison in the fountains of the Will. *Locksley H., Sixty* 274
Sheeny And many a *s* summer-morn, *Arabian Nights* 5
Hues of the silken *s* woof *Madeline* 22
Love wept and spread his *s* vans for flight; *Love and Death* 8
Sheep livelong bleat Of the thick-fleeced *s* *Ode to Memory* 66
are men better than *s* or goats *M. d'Arthur* 250
A lord of fat prize-oxen and of *s*, *Princess, Con.* 86
oxen from the city, and goodly *s* In haste they drove, *Spec. of Iliad* 4
As well as ever shepherd knew his *s*, *Holy Grail* 551
Old milky fables of the wolf and *s*, *Pelleas and E.* 196
are men better than *s* or goats *Pass. of Arthur* 418
Sheepcot or from *s* or king's hall, *Gareth and L.* 467
Sheepwalk Or *s* up the windy wold; *In Mem. c* 8
Sheer Revenge ran on *s* into the heart of the foe, *The Revenge* 33
Stock-still for *s* amazement. *Will Water.* 136
Sheer-astounded And *s-a* were the charioteers *Achilles over the T.* 26
Sheer'd Caught the shrill salt, and *s* the gale. *The Voyage* 12
Sheet (adj.) In the middle leaps a fountain Like *s* lightning, *Poet's Mind* 25
Sheet (s) I wrapt his body in the *s*, *The Sisters* 34
Rolling a slumbrous *s* of foam below. *Lotos-Eaters* 13
Scaffolds, still *s's* of water, *D. of F. Women* 34
See that *s's* are on my bed; *Vision of Sin* 68
falls Of water, *s's* of summer glass, *To E. L.* 2
And scaled in *s's* of wasteful foam, *Sea Dreams* 53
A music out of *s* and shroud, *In Mem. ciii* 54
s's of hyacinth That seem'd the heavens *Guinevere* 390
Whatever moved in that full *s* *To E Fitzgerald* 11
Sheeted *See* **Silver-sheeted**
Sheet-lightnings saw No pale *s-l* from afar, *Aylmer's Field* 726
Sheik but I know it—*his*, the hoary *S*, *Akbar's Dream* 90
Shelf Of ledge or *s* The rock rose clear, *Palace of Art* 9
Upon the rosewood *s*; *Talking Oak* 118
With *s* and corner for the goods and stores. *Enoch Arden* 171
That strikes by night a craggy *s*, *In Mem. xvi* 13
see your Art still shrined in human *shelves*, *Poets and their B.* 11
Laid on the *s*— *To Mary Boyle* 24
Shell (*See also* **Egg-shell**) A walk with vary-colour'd *s's* *Arabian Nights* 57
They freshen the silvery-crimson *s's*, *Sea-Fairies* 13
pelt me with starry spangles and *s's*, *The Merman* 28
broad sea-wolds in the crimson *s's*, *The Mermaid* 36
Jewel or *s*, or starry ore, *Eleänore* 20
when the *s* Divides threefold to show the fruit (repeat) *The Brook* 72, 207
the bird, the fish, the *s*, the flower, *Princess ii* 383
Storm'd at with shot and *s* (repeat) *Light Brigade* 22, 43
Minnie and Winnie Slept in a *s*. *Minnie and Winnie* 2
Pink was the *s* within, Silver without; „ 5
stars Peep'd into the *s*. „ 14
Should toss with tangle and with *s's*. *In Mem. x* 20
Time hath sunder'd *s* from pearl.' „ *lii* 16
The ruin'd *s's* of hollow towers? „ *lxxvi* 16
See what a lovely *s*, *Maud II ii* 1
For a *s*, or a flower, little things „ 64
How fast they hold like colours of a *s* *Marr. of Geraint* 681
hast broken *s*, Art yet half-yolk, *Balin and Balan* 568

Shell (*continued*) life had flown, we sware but by the *s*— *Last Tournament* 270
its wreaths of dripping green—Its pale pink *s's*— *Lover's Tale i* 40
runs out when ya breäks the *s*. *Village Wife* 4
crashing thro' it, their shot and their *s*, *Def. of Lucknow* 18
Be yet but yolk, and forming in the *s*? *Ancient Sage* 130
s must break before the bird can fly. „ 154
Shelley My *S* would fall from my hands *The Wreck* 25
Shelter (s) Nor, moaning, household *s* crave *Two Voices* 260
No branchy thicket *s* yields; *Sir Galahad* 58
wings of brooding *s* o'er her peace, *Aylmer's Field* 139
For help and *s* to the hermit's cave. *Gareth and L.* 1209
To get me *s* for my maidenhood. *Balin and Balan* 480
by strong storm Blown into *s* at Tintagil, *Merlin and V.* 10
O yield me *s* for mine innocency „ 83
Shelter (verb) Will *s* one of stranger race. *In Mem. cii* 4
Call'd her to *s* in the hollow oak, *Merlin and V.* 894
Shelter'd Oracle divine *S* his unapproached mysteries: *Alexander* 11
'O Walter, I have *s* here *Talking Oak* 37
While I *s* in this archway from a day *Locksley H., Sixty* 259
Sheltering you sit Beneath your *s* garden-tree, *To E. Fitzgerald* 6
Shelving The Sweet-Gale rustle round the *s* keel: *Edwin Morris* 110
Shepherd the *s* who watcheth the evening star. *Dying Swan* 35
A *s* all thy life but yet king-born, *Œnone* 128
Ah me, my mountain *s*, „ 202
And *s's* from the mountain-eaves *Amphion* 53
pleasure lives in height (the *s* sang) *Princess vii* 193
the children call, and I Thy *s* pipe, „ 218
stars Shine, and the *S* gladdens in his heart: *Spec. of Iliad* 16
As well as ever *s* knew his sheep, *Holy Grail* 551
The *S*, when I speak, Vailing a sudden eyelid *Sir J. Oldcastle* 19
Plowmen, *S's*, have I found, *Locksley H., Sixty* 121
the laughing *s* bound with flowers; *To Virgil* 16
to thee The *s* brings his adder-bitten lamb, *Death of Œnone* 38
and of the *s's* one Their oldest, „ 52
shouted, and the *s's* heard and came. „ 56
Shepherd-dog Barketh the *s-d* cheerly; *Leonine Eleg.* 5
Shepherdess one of Satan's *s'es* caught *Merlin and V.* 758
Shepherd-lad Sometimes a curly *s-l*, *L. of Shalott ii* 21
Shepherd-prince built their *s-p* a funeral pile; *Death of Œnone* 63
Shere (shire) afoor 'e coom'd to the *s*. *N. Farmer, N. S.* 28
but 'e dosn' not coom fro' the *s*; *Village Wife* 23
call'd me es pretty es ony lass i' the *S*; *Spinster's S's.* 13
if 'e could but stan fur the *S*. *Owd Roä* 14
Sheriff token from the king To greet the *s*, *Edwin Morris* 133
Sherris-warm'd But, all his vast heart *s-w*, *Will Water.* 197
She-slip 'The slight *s-s's* of loyal blood, *Talking Oak* 57
She-society long'd, All else was well, for *s-s*. *Princess, Pro.* 159
She-world head and heart of all our fair *s-w*, „ *iii* 163
Shiah warms the blood of *S* and Sunnee, *Akbar's Dream* 107
Shield A fairy *s* your Genius made *Margaret* 41
red-cross knight for ever kneel'd To a lady in his *s*, *L. of Shalott iii* 7
Of her own halo's dusky *s*; *The Voyage* 32
in whose capacious hall, Hung with a hundred *s's*, *Aylmer's Field* 15
silver sickle of that month Became her golden *s*, *Princess i* 102
brand, mace, and shaft, and *s*— „ *v* 503
Close by her, like supporters on a *s*, „ *vi* 358
like a ruddy *s* on the Lion's breast. *Maud III vi* 14
since he neither wore on helm or *s* *Com. of Arthur* 49
shall the *s* of Mark stand among these?' *Gareth and L.* 403
There ran a treble range of stony *s's*,— „ 407
And under every *s* a knight was named: „ 409
The *s* was blank and bare without a sign „ 414
s of Gawain blazon'd rich and bright, „ 416
Cover the lions on thy *s*, „ 585
This bare a maiden *s*, a casque; „ 680
took the *s* And mounted horse and graspt a spear, „ 690
These arm'd him in blue arms, and gave a *s* Blue also, „ 931
Till Gareth's *s* was cloven; „ 971
Thy *s* is mine—farewell; „ 988
flash'd the fierce *s*, All sun; „ 1030
And gave a *s* whereon the Star of Even „ 1117
'Peradventure he, you name, May know my *s*. „ 1299
Gareth, wakening, fiercely clutch'd the *s*; „ 1304
Even the shadow of Lancelot under *s*. „ 1311

Shield (*continued*) Clung to the *s* that Lancelot lent him, *Gareth and L.* 1320
wrought on Lancelot now To lend thee horse and *s*: „ 1324
give him back the *s*.' „ 1344
How best to manage horse, lance, sword and *s*, „ 1351
Or two wild men supporters of a *s*, *Geraint and E.* 267
nor glance The one at other, parted by the *s*. „ 269
All in the hollow of his *s*, „ 569
(It lay beside him in the hollow *s*), „ 726
In lieu of this rough beast upon my *s*, *Balin and Balan* 196
To bear her own crown-royal upon *s*, „ 200
memory of that cognizance on *s* Weighted it down, „ 224
he sharply caught his lance and *s*, „ 287
Why wear ye this crown-royal upon *s*?' „ 338
Thro' memory of that token on the *s* „ 369
Balin drew the *s* from off his neck, „ 429
I charge thee by that crown upon thy *s*, „ 481
and cast on earth, the *s*, „ 539
And tramples on the goodly *s* to show „ 550
s of Balan prick'd The hauberk to the flesh; „ 559
Why had ye not the *s* I knew? „ 601
carved himself a knightly *s* of wood, *Merlin and V.* 473
Guarded the sacred *s* of Lancelot; *Lancelot and E.* 4
devices blazon'd on the *s* In their own tinct, „ 9
Stript off the case, and read the naked *s*, „ 16
How came the lily maid by that good *s* „ 28
I by mere mischance have brought, my *s*. „ 189
—and the *s*—I pray you lend me one, „ 192
And so, God wot, his *s* is blank enough. „ 197
'This *s*, my friend, where is it?' „ 345
Returning brought the yet-unblazon'd *s*, „ 379
to have my *s* In keeping till I come.' „ 382
standing near the *s* In silence, „ 394
Then to her tower she climb'd, and took the *s*, „ 397
Here was the knight, and here he left a *s*; „ 634
Why ask you not to see the *s* he left, „ 653
But an ye will it let me see the *s*.' „ 661
when the *s* was brought, and Gawain saw „ 662
and toward even Sent for his *s*: full meekly rose the maid, Stript off the case, and gave the naked *s*; „ 978
His very *s* was gone; only the case, „ 990
let the *s* of Lancelot at her feet Be carven, „ 1341
painting on the wall Or *s* of knight; *Holy Grail* 830
and on *s* A spear, a harp, a bugle— *Last Tournament* 173
and on the boughs a *s* Showing a shower of blood „ 432
Till each would clash the *s*, and blow the horn. „ 436
Men of the Northland Shot over *s*. *Batt. of Brunanburh* 34
with the *s* of Locksley—there, *Locksley H., Sixty* 34
one old Hostel left us where they swing the Locksley *s*, „ 247
Shield-breaking *S-b's*, and the clash of brands, *Pass. of Arthur* 109
Shielded (*See also* **Many-shielded**) That *s* all her life from harm *In Mem., Con.* 47
Shielding The gentle wizard cast a *s* arm. *Merlin and V.* 908
Shield-lion His blue *s-l's* cover'd— *Gareth and L.* 1217
Shield-wall Brake the *s-w*, *Batt. of Brunanburh* 11
Shift As winds from all the compass *s* *Godiva* 33
We fret, we fume, would *s* our skins, *Will Water.* 225
glance and *s* about her slippery sides, *Lucretius* 189
To *s* an arbitrary power, *In Mem. cxxviii* 17
craven *s's*, and long crane legs of Mark— *Last Tournament* 729
Shifted She *s* in her elbow-chair, *The Goose* 27
The peaky islet *s* shapes, *The Voyage* 33
Shifting (*See also* **Ever-shifting**) With *s* ladders of shadow and light, *Dead Prophet* 21
You all but sicken at the *s* scenes. *The Play* 2
Shillin' is it *shillins* an' pence? *N. Farmer, N. S.* 42
cleän Es a *shillin'* fresh fro' the mint *Spinster's S's.* 76
Shimmering The *s* glimpses of a stream; the seas; *Princess, Con.* 46
Shine (s) (*See also* **Star-shine**) With spires of silver *s*.' *D of F. Women* 188
Shadow and *s* is life, little Annie, *Grandmother* 60
Shine (verb) Thoro' the black-stemm'd pines only the far river *s's*. *Leonine Eleg.* 2
waterfall Which ever sounds and *s's* *Ode to Memory* 52
The house thro' all the level *s's*, *Mariana in the S.* 2
'Sometimes a little corner *s's*, *Two Voices* 187
the wild marsh-marigold *s's* like fire *May Queen* 31

Shine (verb) (*continued*) the summer sun 'ill *s*, *May Queen, N. Y's. E.* 22
He *s's* upon a hundred fields, „ *Con.* 50
and there his light may *s*— „ 51
That her fair form may stand and *s*, *Of old sat Freedom* 21
To make the necklace *s*; *Talking Oak* 222
To rust unburnish'd, not to *s* in use! *Ulysses* 23
S's in those tremulous eyes that fill with tears *Tithonus* 26
The beams, that thro' the Oriel *s*, *Day-Dm., Sleep. P.* 34
As *s's* the moon in clouded skies, *Beggar Maid* 9
yonder *s's* The Sun of Righteousness, *Enoch Arden* 503
he would only *s* among the dead Hereafter; *Lucretius* 129
or Ralph Who *s's* so in the corner; *Princess, Pro.* 145
That *s's* over city and river, *Ode on Well.* 50
Fairily-delicate palaces *s* *The Islet* 18
the stars *S*, and the Shepherd gladdens *Spec. of Iliad* 16
I see their unborn faces *s* *In Mem. lxxxiv* 19
Not all regret: the face will *s* „ *cxvi* 9
Seeing his gewgaw castle *s*, *Maud I x* 18
But now *s* on, and what care I, „ *xviii* 41
O when did a morning *s* So rich in atonement „ *xix* 5
S out, little head, sunning over with curls, „ *xxii* 57
s in the sudden making of splendid names, „ *III vi* 47
as *s's* A field of charlock in the sudden sun *Gareth and L.* 387
And sleeker shall he *s* than any hog.' „ 460
that layest all to sleep again, *S* sweetly: „ 1062
brother-star, why *s* ye here so low? „ 1097
three colours after rain, *S* sweetly: „ 1161
tell her, she *s's* me down: *Lancelot and E.* 1225
And one will ever *s* and one will pass. *Last Tournament* 737
And *s* the level lands, *Early Spring* 15
once more in varnish'd glory *s* Thy stars of celandine. *Prog. of Spring* 38
while the sun of morning *s's*, *By an Evolution.* 6
Some too low would have thee *s*, *Poets and Critics* 11

Shined an' 'e *s* like a sparkle o' fire. *North. Cobbler* 48

Shingle and all round it ran a walk Of *s*, *Enoch Arden* 737
Lest the harsh *s* should grate underfoot, „ 772
Waves on a diamond *s* dash, *The Islet* 16
After sod and *s* ceased to fly Behind her, *Gareth and L.* 761
I heard the *s* grinding in the surge, *Holy Grail* 811
again the stormy surf Crash'd in the *s*: *Lover's Tale iii* 54

Shingly I linger by my *s* bars; *The Brook* 180
As of a broad brook o'er a *s* bed Brawling, *Marr. of Geraint* 248
And down the *s* scaur he plunged, *Lancelot and E.* 53

Shining (*See also* **Far-shining, Lily-shining, Satin-shining, Silver-shining**) And the clear spirit *s* thro'. *Supp. Confessions* 76
Droops blinded with his *s* eye: *Fatima* 38
She sat betwixt the *s* Oriels, *Palace of Art* 159
Came on the *s* levels of the lake. *M. d'Arthur* 51
Reveal'd their *s* windows: *Gardener's D.* 220
This dull chrysalis Cracks into *s* wings, *St. S. Stylites* 156
Ah, for some retreat Deep in yonder *s* Orient, *Locksley Hall* 154
A summer crisp with *s* woods. *Day-Dm., Pro.* 8
To yonder *s* ground; *St. Agnes' Eve* 14
A light upon the *s* sea— „ 35
In *s* draperies, headed like a star, *Princess ii* 109
turn'd her sumptuous head with eyes Of *s* expectation fixt on mine. „ *iv* 153
The sleek and *s* creatures of the chase, „ *v* 155
tender face Peep'd, *s* in upon the wounded man „ *vii* 61
leaves A *s* furrow, as thy thoughts in me. „ 185
she that out of Lethe scales with man The *s* steps of Nature, „ 262
Are close upon the *s* table-lands *Ode on Well.* 216
Would reach us out the *s* hand, *In Mem. lxxxiv* 43
Unloved, the sun-flower, *s* fair, „ *ci* 5
to where we saw A great ship lift her *s* sides. „ *ciii* 40
All night the *s* vapour sail And pass the silent-lighted town, „ *Con.* 111
The *s* daffodil dead, and Orion low in his grave. *Maud I iii* 14
crest Of a peacock, sits on her *s* head, „ *xvi* 17
Go not, happy day, From the *s* fields, „ *xvii* 2
My bird with the *s* head, „ *II iv* 45
s daffodil dies, and the Charioteer And starry Gemini „ *III vi* 6
Bright with a *s* people on the decks, *Com. of Arthur* 376
The *s* dragon and the naked child „ 399

Shining (*continued*) Clear honour *s* like the dewy star Of dawn, *Gareth and L.* 329
S in arms, 'Damsel, the quest is mine. „ 745
But lift a *s* hand against the sun, *Geraint and E.* 473
far up the *s* flood Until we found the palace *Lancelot and E.* 1043
for all her *s* hair Was smear'd with earth, *Holy Grail* 209
'I found Him in the *s* of the stars, *Pass. of Arthur* 9
Came on the *s* levels of the lake. „ 219
To stand a shadow by their *s* doors, *Lover's Tale i* 731
And streaming and *s* on Silent river, *Merlin and the G.* 51

Ship and sinking *s's*, and praying hands. *Lotos-Eaters, C. S.* 116
did we watch the stately *s's*, *Locksley Hall* 37
Rose a *s* of France. *The Captain* 28
'Chase,' he said; the *s* flew forward, „ 33
We felt the good *s* shake and reel, *The Voyage* 15
'A *s* of fools,' he shriek'd in spite, „ 77
'A *s* of fools,' he sneer'd and wept. „ 78
stately *s's* go on To their haven under the hill; *Break, break, etc.* 9
master of that *s* Enoch had served in, *Enoch Arden* 119
Annie, the *s* I sail in passes here „ 214
s was lost,' he said, 'the *s* was lost! „ 393
prosperously sail'd The *s* 'Good Fortune,' „ 528
Another *s* (She wanted water) blown by baffling winds, „ 627
Some *s* of battle slowly creep, *To F. D. Maurice* 26
reach'd the *s* and caught the rope, *Sailor Boy* 3
many a fire between the *s's* and stream *Spec. of Iliad* 17
Fair *s*, that from the Italian shore *In Mem. ix* 1
A great *s* lift her shining sides. „ *ciii* 40
blush the news Over glowing *s's*; *Maud I xvii* 12
whether he came in the Hanover *s*, „ *II v* 59
a *s*, the shape thereof A dragon wing'd, *Com. of Arthur* 374
I have seen the good *s* sail Keel upward, *Gareth and L.* 253
ere he came, like one that hails a *s*, *Geraint and E.* 540
one side had sea And *s* and sail and angels *Balin and Balan* 365
Had built the King his havens, *s's*, *Merlin and V.* 168
As the tall *s*, that many a dreary year *Lover's Tale i* 808
We seem'd like *s's* i' the Channel *First Quarrel* 42
s's of the world could stare at him, *Rizpah* 38
'Spanish *s's* of war at sea! *The Revenge* 3
for my *s's* are out of gear, „ 5
We are six *s's* of the line; „ 7
past away with five *s's* of war that day, „ 13
only a hundred seamen to work the *s* and to fight, „ 22
S after *s*, the whole night long, (repeat) „ 58, 59, 60
Sink me the *s*, Master Gunner—sink her, „ 89
dared her with one little *s* and his English few; „ 107
s stagger'd under a thunderous shock, *The Wreck* 107
and the *s* stood still, „ 115
on Edwin's *s*, with Edwin, ev'n in death, *The Flight* 46
And see the *s's* from out the West „ 91
We sail'd wherever *s* could sail, *Hands all Round* 29

Shipcrew Fell the *s's* Doom'd to the death. *Batt. of Brunanburh* 22

Shipman numbers, *Shipmen* and Scotsmen. „ 55

Shipshape Keep everything *s*, for I must go. *Enoch Arden* 220

Shipwreck Made orphan by a winter *s*, „ 15
s's, famines, fevers, fights, Mutinies, *Columbus* 225
Quail not at the fiery mountain, at the *s*, *Faith* 3

Shipwreck'd A *s* sailor, waiting for a sail: *Enoch Arden* 590
Like a *s* man on a coast Of ancient fable *Maud II ii* 31

Shipwrecking Listening now to the tide in its broad-flung *s* roar, „ *I iii* 11

Shire (*See also* **Shere**) A sign to many a staring *s* *Will Water.* 139
Master of half a servile *s*, *Maud I x* 10
an orphan with half a *s* of estate,— *Charity* 13
see Beyond the borough and the *s*! *Hands all Round* 28

Shiver Little breezes dusk and *s* *L. of Shalott i* 11
The hard brands *s* on the steel, *Sir Galahad* 6
And here thine aspen *s*; *A Farewell* 10
Consonant chords that *s* to one note; *Princess iii* 90
woodlands, when they *s* in January, *Boädicea* 75
the *s* of dancing leaves is thrown *Maud I vi* 73
Thorns of the crown and *s's* of the cross, *Balin and Balan* 111
s's, ere he springs and kills. *Pelleas and E.* 286
why, you *s* tho' the wind is west *The Ring* 29

Shiver'd Were *s* in my narrow frame. *Fatima* 18

Shiver'd (continued) A cry that s to the tingling stars, M. d'Arthur 199
Like light in many a s lance In Mem. xlix 3
And s brands that once had fought with Rome, Pass. of Arthur 133
A cry that s to the tingling stars, „ 367
Shivering crack of earthquake s to your base Pelleas and E. 465
In conflict with the crash of s points, Princess v 491
Shoal And s's of pucker'd faces drive; In Mem. lxx 10
panic-stricken, like a s Of darting fish, Geraint and E. 468
Shoaling Where like a s sea the lovely blue Play'd into green, „ 688
Shock (s) push thee forward thro' a life of s's, Œnone 163
With twelve great s's of sound, Godiva 74
whom the electric s Dislink'd with shrieks Princess, Pro. 69
In middle ocean meets the surging s, Will 8
Or has the s, so harshly given, In Mem. xvi 11
Diffused the s thro' all my life, „ lxxxv 55
The steps of Time—the s's of Chance— „ xcv 42
With thousand s's that come and go, „ cxiii 17
And batter'd with the s's of doom „ cxviii 24
When all that seems shall suffer s, „ cxxxi 2
my pulses closed their gates with a s Maud I i 15
the s Of cataract seas that snap „ II ii 25
In those brain-stunning s's, and tourney-falls, Gareth and L. 89
burthen off his heart in one full s Last Tournament 180
ever and anon with host to host S's, Pass. of Arthur 108
What s has fool'd her since, that she should speak To the Queen ii 22
that s of gloom had fall'n Unfelt, Lover's Tale i 505
Above, below, S after s, Tiresias 98
ship stagger'd under a thunderous s, The Wreck 107
suddenly s upon s Stagger'd the mass Heavy Brigade 58
great s may wake a palsied limb, St. Telemachus 57
Shock (verb) Must ever s, like armed foes, Love thou thy land 78
The seas that s thy base! England and Amer. 15
where the moving isles of winter s By night, M. d'Arthur 140
you will s him ev'n to death, Princess iii 212
Meet in the midst, and there so furiously S, Lancelot and E. 458
And felt the boat s earth, and looking up, Holy Grail 812
where the moving isles of winter s By night, Pass. of Arthur 308
Shock'd (See also **Earth-shock'd**) S, like an iron-clanging anvil Princess v 504
they s, and Kay Fell shoulder-slipt, Gareth and L. 758
at fiery speed the two S on the central bridge, „ 963
when strength is s With torment, Lover's Tale ii 150
And they s on each other and butted each other V. of Maeldune 108
Shock-head The s-h willows two and two Amphion 39
Shod See **Slip-shod, Wet-shod**
Shoe Shall fling her old s after. Will Water. 216
and s's wi' the best on 'em all, North. Cobbler 13
Why 'edn't tha wiped thy s's? Spinster's S's. 46
Shone S out their crowning snows. Dying Swan 13
Thick-jewell'd s the saddle-leather, L. of Shalott iii 20
from the violets her light foot S rosy-white, Œnone 180
s, the silver boss Of her own halo's dusky shield; The Voyage 31
on the burnish'd board Sparkled and s; Enoch Arden 743
S like a mystic star Aylmer's Field 72
near his tomb a feast S, silver-set; Princess, Pro. 106
For on my cradle s the Northern star. „ i 4
a light foot s like a jewel set In the dark crag: „ iii 358
No bigger than a glow-worm s the tent „ iv 25
s Their morions, wash'd with morning, „ v 263
A column'd entry s and marble stairs, „ 364
and s Thro' glittering drops on her sad friend. „ vi 282
light that s when Hope was born. In Mem. xxx 32
star Which s so close beside Thee Ded. of Idylls 47
Far s the fields of May thro' open door, Com. of Arthur 460
at times the great gate s Only, Gareth and L. 194
and s far-off as shines A field of charlock „ 387
in the stream beneath him s Inmingled with Heaven's azure „ 935
s the Noonday Sun Beyond a raging shallow. „ 1027
Half-tarnish'd and half-bright, his emblem s, „ 1118
thro' these Princelike his bearing s; Marr. of Geraint 545
so thickly s the gems. Geraint and E. 693
Past like a shadow thro' the field, that s Full-summer, Lancelot and E. 1140
Shone (continued) sun S, and the wind blew, thro' her, Holy Grail 99
all her form s forth with sudden light „ 450
In silver armour suddenly Galahad s Before us, „ 458
like bright eyes of familiar friends, In on him s: „ 689
his face S like the countenance of a priest Pelleas and E. 144
with the gorgeous west the lighthouse s, Lover's Tale i 60
so those fair eyes S on my darkness, „ ii 158
suns of the limitless Universe sparkled and s in the sky, Despair 15
but, however they sparkled and s, „ 17
Shook Hard by a poplar s alway, Mariana 41
and with his word She s the world. The Poet 56
And s the wave as the wind did sigh; Dying Swan 15
splendours of the morning star S in the stedfast blue. D. of F. Women 56
Above her s the starry lights: Of old sat Freedom 3
But s his song together as he near'd Gardener's D. 91
a jolly ghost, that s The curtains, Walk. to the Mail 36
'I s him down because he was The finest on the tree. Talking Oak 237
she s her head, And shower'd the rippled ringlets Godiva 46
A sudden hubbub s the hall, Day-Dm., Revival 7
I s her breast with vague alarms— The Letters 38
s And almost overwhelm'd her, Enoch Arden 529
work'd among the rest and s His isolation from him. „ 651
Stagger'd and s, holding the branch, „ 767
s the heart of Edith hearing him. Aylmer's Field 63
like a storm he came, And s the house, „ 216
but not a word; she s her head. Sea Dreams 116
Like her, he s his head. „ 148
Whom all the pines of Ida s to see Lucretius 86
clock-work steamer paddling plied And s the lilies: Princess, Pro. 72
s aside The hand that play'd the patron „ 137
And s the songs, the whispers, „ i 98
Melissa s her doubtful curls, and thought „ iii 75
my knee desire to kneel, and s My pulses, „ 193
O'er it s the woods, And danced the colour, „ 292
the tear, She sang of, s and fell, „ iv 60
Psyche flush'd and wann'd and s; „ 160
Palpitated, her hand s, and we heard In the dead hush „ 389
Not long; I s it off; for spite of doubts „ 571
s the branches of the deer From slope to slope „ Con. 98
On that loud sabbath s the spoiler Ode on Well. 123
And s to all the liberal air In Mem. lxxxix 7
brighten like the star that s Betwixt the palms „ Con. 31
s my heart to think she comes once more; Maud I xviii 10
Then I so s him in the saddle, Gareth and L. 29
So s his wits they wander in his prime— „ 715
And s his drowsy squire awake and cried, Marr. of Geraint 125
And s her pulses, crying, 'Look, a prize! Geraint and E. 123
She s from fear, and for her fault she wept Merlin and V. 952
Then s his hair, strode off, Lancelot and E. 722
But she was happy enough and s it off, „ 784
While he spoke She neither blush'd nor s, „ 965
wild with wind That s her tower, „ 1021
s this newer, stronger hall of ours, Holy Grail 731
So s him that he could not rest, Pelleas and E. 412
So s to such a roar of all the sky, Last Tournament 621
That s beneath them, as the thistle shakes Guinevere 254
And s him thro' the north. Pass. of Arthur 70
for that day Love, rising, s his wings, Lover's Tale i 317
great pine s with lonely sounds of joy „ 325
yet it s me, that my frame would shudder, „ ii 56
a strong sympathy S all my soul: „ 89
s and throbb'd From temple unto temple. „ iii 7
She s, and cast her eyes down, „ iv 329
And a dozen times we s 'em off The Revenge 54
in many a merry tale That s our sides— Sir J. Oldcastle 92
For the whole isle shudder'd and s V. of Maeldune 74
and a boundless panic s the foe. Achilles over the T. 18
She s her head, And the Motherless Mother kiss'd it, The Wreck 61
ship stagger'd under a thunderous shock, That s us asunder, „ 108
I s as I open'd the letter— „ 145
Fires that s me once, Locksley H., Sixty 41
s her head, and patted yours, And smiled, The Ring 313
what a fury s Those pillars of a moulder'd faith, Akbar's Dream 8

Shoot (s) and earliest s's Of orient green, *Ode to Memory* 17
Shoot (verb) Life s's and glances thro' your veins, *Rosalind* 22
s into the dark Arrows of lightnings. *To J. M. K.* 13
I would s, howe'er in vain, *Two Voices* 344
While all the neighbours s thee round, *The Blackbird* 2
The northern morning o'er thee s, *Talking Oak* 275
At times a carven craft would s *The Voyage* 53
The little boys begin to s and stab, *Princess, Con.* 61
as the rapid of life S's to the fall— *A Dedication* 4
S your stars to the firmament, *On Jub. Q. Victoria* 17
Shore (s) (*See also* **River-shore, Sand-shore, Table-shore**) And the blue wave beat the s; *All Things will Die* 43
and the happy blossoming s? *Sea-Fairies* 8
Who can light on as happy a s All the world o'er, " 40
And shadow'd coves on a sunny s, *Eleänore* 18
All along the shadowing s, " 41
And shallows on a distant s, *Mariana in the S.* 7
lock'd in with bars of sand, Left on the s; *Palace of Art* 250
mourn and rave On alien s's; *Lotos-Eaters* 33
Between the sun and moon upon the s; " 38
the s Than labour in the deep mid-ocean, " *C. S.* 126
The crowds, the temples, waver'd, and the s; *D. of F. Women* 114
To sail with Arthur under looming s's, *M. d'Arthur, Ep.* 17
pilot of an empty heart Unto the s's of nothing! *Gardener's D.* 17
on s, and when Thro' scudding drifts *Ulysses* 9
O the barren, barren s! *Locksley Hall* 40
wisdom lingers, and I linger on the s, " 141
On open main or winding s! *The Voyage* 6
O hundred s's of happy climes, " 49
Among the waste and lumber of the s, *Enoch Arden* 16
As down the s he ranged, or all day long " 588
and fill'd the s's With clamour. " 635
By s's that darken with the gathering wolf, *Aylmer's Field* 767
forth they came and paced the s, *Sea Dreams* 32
Swept with it to the s, and enter'd one Of those dark caves " 89
Here than ourselves, spoke with me on the s; " 264
swell On some dark s just seen that it was rich. *Princess i* 249
grasping down the boughs I gain'd the s. " *iv* 189
Rotting on some wild s with ribs of wreck, " *v* 147
Blot out the slope of sea from verge to s, " *vii* 38
heave the hill And break the s, *Ode on Well.* 260
WHILE about the s of Mona *Boädicea* 1
Fair ship, that from the Italian s *In Mem. ix* 1
They laid him by the pleasant s, " *xix* 3
'The sound of that forgetful s " *xxxv* 14
Yet turn thee to the doubtful s, " *lxi* 9
And lazy lengths on boundless s's; " *lxx* 12
Dip down upon the northern s, " *lxxxiii* 1
To the other s, involved in thee, " *lxxxiv* 40
'I watch thee from the quiet s; " *lxxxv* 81
paced the s's And many a bridge, " *lxxxvii* 11
And still as vaster grew the s " *ciii* 25
The boat is drawn upon the s; " *cxxi* 6
And heard an ever-breaking s " *cxxiv* 11
To spangle all the happy s's " *Con.* 120
More than a mile from the s, *Maud I ix* 2
That made it stir on the s. " *II ii* 15
Nor the canon-bullet rust on a slothful s, " *III vi* 26
Then to the s of one of those long loops *Gareth and L.* 905
fifty knights rode with them, to the s's Of Severn, *Marr. of Geraint* 44
fifty knights rode with them to the s's Of Severn, *Geraint and E.* 954
O did ye never lie upon the s, *Merlin and V.* 291
in the four loud battles by the s Of Duglas; *Lancelot and E.* 289
I came All in my folly to the naked s, *Holy Grail* 793
So loud a blast along the s and sea, " 769
in the flat field by the s of Usk Holden: *Pelleas and E.* 164
The loneliest ways are safe from s to s. *Last Tournament* 102
all the ways were safe from s to s, " 485
the thundering s's of Bude and Bos, *Guinevere* 291
death Or deathlike swoon, thus over all that s, *Pass. of Arthur* 120
And rolling far along the gloomy s's " 134
we found The dead man cast upon the s? *Lover's Tale i* 295
sometimes on the s, upon the sands " *ii* 6
the breakers on the s Sloped into louder surf: " *iii* 14

Shore (s) (*continued*) About the soft Mediterranean s's, *Sir J. Oldcastle* 30
came happily to the s. *Columbus* 141
and there on the s was he. (repeat) *V. of Maeldune* 9, 127
ocean always broke on a silent s, " 12
our world is but the bounding s— *De Prof., Two G.* 31
Drew to this s lit by the suns " 38
fleeted far and fast To touch all s's, *Pref. Son. 19th Cent.* 2
alone on that lonely s— *Despair* 33
No phantoms, watching from a phantom s *Ancient Sage* 179
wish yon moaning sea would rise and burst the s, *The Flight* 11
we shall light upon some lonely s, " 89
star that gildest yet this phantom s; *To Virgil* 26
The breakers lash the s's: *Pref. Son. Broth. S.* 2
But ere he left your fatal s, *To Marq. of Dufferin* 33
Shore (verb) good Queen, her mother, s the tress *Princess vi* 113
with a sweep of it S thro' the swarthy neck, *Geraint and E.* 728
Shore-cliff From the long s-c's windy walls " 164
a hall On massive columns, like a s cave, *Lancelot and E.* 406
Shoreward wave will roll us s soon.' *Lotos-Eaters* 2
upblown billow ran S beneath red clouds, *Lover's Tale ii* 179
Shorn And, issuing s and sleek, *Talking Oak* 42
and shower and s plume Went down it. *Last Tournament* 155
S of its strength, into the sympathy *Lover's Tale i* 434
Short (*See also* **Fiery-short**) run s pains Thro' his warm heart; *Supp. Confessions* 161
He led me thro' the s sweet-smelling lanes *The Brook* 122
But rather loosens from the lip S swallow-flights of song, *In Mem. xlviii* 15
For one s hour to see The souls we loved, *Maud II iv* 14
only breathe S fits of prayer, *Geraint and E.* 155
when half of the s summer night was gone, *The Revenge* 65
Up, get up, the time is s, *Forlorn* 73
Why should I so disrelish that s word? *Romney's R.* 11
Shot (s) (*See also* **Bow-shot, Cannon-shot, Musket-shot, Stone-shot**) Storm'd at with s and shell (repeat) *Light Brigade* 22, 43
A s, ere half thy draught be done, *In Mem. vi* 11
an' I started awaäy like a s, *North. Cobbler* 69
crashing thro' it, their s and their shell, *Def. of Lucknow* 18
Shot (verb) S thro' and thro' with cunning words. *Clear-headed friend* 17
Momently s into each other. *Madeline* 23
S over with purple, and green, and yellow. *Dying Swan* 20
flying star s thro' the sky Above the pillar'd town. *Palace of Art* 123
S on the sudden into dark. *To J. S.* 28
S like a streamer of the northern morn, *M. d'Arthur* 139
S thro' the lists at Camelot, " 224
Be s for sixpence in a battle-field, *Audley Court* 41
her palfrey's footfall s Light horrors *Godiva* 58
The fire s up, the martin flew, *Day-Dm. Revival* 11
climbing up the valley; at whom he s: *Aylmer's Field* 228
There by a keeper s at, slightly hurt, " 548
S up their shadows to the Heaven of Heavens, " 642
S out of them, and scorch'd me that I woke. *Lucretius* 66
S sidelong daggers at us, *Princess ii* 450
And s from crooked lips a haggard smile. " *iv* 364
and s A flying splendour out of brass and steel, " *vi* 364
S up and shrill'd in flickering gyres, " *vii* 46
toäner 'ed s 'um as deäd as a naäil. *N. Farmer, O. S.* 35
S o'er the seething harbour-bar, *Sailor Boy* 2
but s from Arthur's heaven With all disaster *Gareth and L.* 1100
star s: 'Lo,' said Gareth, 'the foe falls!' " 1317
shadow of a spear, S from behind him, *Balin and Balan* 323
S from behind me, run along the ground; " 374
s red fire and shadows thro' the cave, *Lancelot and E.* 414
glanced and s Only to holy things; *Holy Grail* 75
from the star there s A rose-red sparkle to the city, " 529
thy vanity so s up It frighted all free fool *Last Tournament* 306
S like a streamer of the northern morn, *Pass. of Arthur* 307
S thro' the lists at Camelot, " 392
and s forth Boughs on each side, *Lover's Tale i* 229
And s itself into the singing winds; " 369
that s the sunset In lightnings round me; " 442
The meaning of the letters s into My brain; " *ii* 8
dragonfly S by me like a flash of purple fire. " 17
An' 'e niver not s one 'are, *Village Wife* 42
S thro' the staff or the halyard, *Def. of Lucknow* 5

Shot (verb) *(continued)*) pine *s* aloft from the crag — *V. of Maeldune* 16
Men of the Northland *S* over shield. — *Batt. of Brunanburh* 34
'Ud 'a *s* his own sowl dead — *Tomorrow* 40
A light *s* upward on them from the lake. — *The Ring* 256

Shotted *See* **Heavy-shotted**

Shoulder over his left *s* laugh'd at thee, — *The Bridesmaid* 7
a leopard skin Droop'd from his *s*, — *Œnone* 59
Upon her pearly *s* leaning cold, — „ 140
golden round her lucid throat And *s*: — „ 179
From off her *s* backward borne: — *Palace of Art* 118
clapt his hand On Everard's *s*, — *The Epic* 22
Make broad thy *s's* to receive my weight, — *M. d'Arthur* 161
O'er both his *s's* drew the languid hands, — „ 174
From thy pure brows, and from thy *s's* pure, — *Tithonus* 35
Till over thy dark *s* glow Thy silver sister-world, — *Move eastward* 5
Naiads oar'd A glimmering *s* — *To E. L.* 17
With a heaved *s* and a saucy smile, — *Aylmer's Field* 466
Among the honest *s's* of the crowd, — *Sea Dreams* 166
And robed the *s's* in a rosy silk, — *Princess, Pro.* 103
Her round white *s* shaken with her sobs, — „ *iv* 289
lanes of splendour slanted o'er a press Of snowy *s's*, — „ 479
But on my *s* hung their heavy hands, — „ 553
Leapt from the dewy *s's* of the Earth, — „ *v* 43
Down on the *s's* of the twain, his men, — *Gareth and L.* 440
On either shining *s* laid a hand, — *Marr. of Geraint* 518
and the squire Chafing his *s*: — *Geraint and E.* 27
letting her left hand Droop from his mighty *s*, — *Merlin and V.* 243
Gazed at the heaving *s*, and the face Hand-hidden, — „ 896
Lancelot turn'd, and smooth'd The glossy *s*, — *Lancelot and E.* 348
Each gript a *s*, and I stood between; — *Holy Grail* 822
Make broad thy *s's* to receive my weight, — *Pass. of Arthur* 332
O'er both his *s's* drew the languid hands, — „ 342
warrior's puissant *s's* Pallas flung — *Achilles over the T.* 3
And plant on *s*, hand and knee, — *To E. Fitzgerald* 8
lay thine uphill *s* to the wheel, — *Ancient Sage* 279
fur the merk's o' thy *s* yit; — *Owd Roä* 90
you my girl Rode on my *s* home— — *The Ring* 322

Shoulder Blade (*See also* **Blade**) arms were shatter'd to the *s b*, — *Princess vi* 52

Shoulder'd (*See also* **Broad-shoulder'd**) Then we *s* thro' the swarm, — *Audley Court* 9
in the cellars merry bloated things *S* the spigot, — *Guinevere* 268

Shoulder-slipt they shock'd, and Kay Fell *s-s*, — *Gareth and L.* 759

Shout (s) Herod, when the *s* was in his ears, — *Palace of Art* 219
shall the braggart *s* For some blind glimpse — *Love and Duty* 5
But that there rose a *s*: — *Princess, Con.* 36
a *s* rose again, and made The long line — „ 96
a *s* More joyful than the city-roar — „ 100
And caught once more the distant *s*, — *In Mem. lxxxvii* 9
At the *s's*, the leagues of lights, — *Maud II iv* 21
And *s's*, and clarions shrilling unto blood, — *Com. of Arthur* 103
voice As dreadful as the *s* of one who sees — „ 117
s's Ascended, and there brake a servingman — *Gareth and L.* 800
whereupon Their common *s* in chorus, — *Balin and Balan* 87
Then rang the *s* his lady loved: — *Pelleas and E.* 171
the red dream Fled with a *s*, — *Last Tournament* 488
s's of heathen and the traitor knights, — *Pass. of Arthur* 113
on a sudden the garrison utter a jubilant *s*, — *Def. of Lucknow* 98
from the dyke he sent his mighty *s*, — *Achilles over the T.* 30
jingle of bits, *S's*, arrows, — *Tiresias* 94
an' maäkin' ma deaf wi' their *s's*, — *Spinster's S's.* 88
gallopt up with a cheer and a *s*, — *Heavy Brigade* 61
the *s* Of His descending peals from Heaven, — *Romney's R.* 126

Shout (verb) hark! they *s* 'St. Simeon Stylites.' — *St. S. Stylites* 146
They *s*, 'Behold a saint!' — „ 153
That he *s's* with his sister at play! — *Break, break, etc.* 6
S Icenian, Catieuchlanian, *s* Coritanian, — *Boädicea* 57
dying while they *s* her name. — *Locksley H., Sixty* 128

Shouted Till I struck out and *s*; — *Princess v* 540
But I heard it *s* at once from the top — *Maud II v* 50
Then the third brother *s* o'er the bridge, — *Gareth and L.* 1096
Lancelot *s*, 'Stay me not! — *Holy Grail* 643
'No name, no name,' he *s*, 'a scourge am I — *Pelleas and E.* 565
roar'd And *s* and leapt down upon the fall'n; — *Last Tournament* 469
Till they *s* along with the shouting — *V. of Maeldune* 34

Shouted *(continued)* standing, *s*, and Pallas far away — *Achilles over the T.* 17
lighted on him there, And *s*, — *Death of Œnone* 56

Shouting Heard the heavens fill with *s*, — *Locksley Hall* 123
With a loyal people *s* a battle cry, — *Maud III vi* 35
thro' lanes of *s* Gareth rode Down the slope street, — *Gareth and L.* 699
Which was the red cock *s* to the light, — *Geraint and E.* 384
S, 'Sir Galahad and Sir Percivale!' — *Holy Grail* 337
seem'd *S's* of all the sons of God: — „ 509
and *s's* and soundings to arms, — *Def. of Lucknow* 76
And we came to the Isle of *S*, — *V. of Maeldune* 27
And the *s* of these wild birds — „ 33
Till they shouted along with the *s* — „ 34

Shove *See* **Shuvv**

Shovell'd *s* up into some bloody trench — *Audley Court* 42

Show (s) Thou comest not with *s's* of flaunting vines — *Ode to Memory* 48
Had made him talk for *s*; — *Will Water.* 196
Princess Ida seem'd a hollow *s*, — *Princess iii* 185
camp and college turn'd to hollow *s's*; — „ *v* 478
They did but look like hollow *s's*; — „ *vii* 134
My haunting sense of hollow *s's*: — „ 349
hang'd him in chains for a *s*— — *Rizpah* 35
With a purse to pay for the *s*. — *Dead Prophet* 8

Show (verb) (*See also* **Shaw**) Nor canst thou *s* the dead are dead. — *Two Voices* 267
Some one might *s* it at a joust of arms, — *M. d'Arthur* 102
S me the man hath suffer'd more than I. — *St. S. Stylites* 49
That *s* the year is turn'd. — *Talking Oak* 176
and *s's* At distance like a little wood; — *Day-Dm., Sleep. P.* 41
And all that else the years will *s*, — „ *L'Envoi* 13
s you slips of all that grows — *Amphion* 83
So *s's* my soul before the Lamb, — *St. Agnes' Eve* 17
Shall *s* thee past to Heaven: — *Will Water.* 246
All he *s's* her makes him dearer: — *L. of Burleigh* 33
'Proclaim the faults he would not *s*: — *You might have won* 17
Divides threefold to *s* the fruit within. (Repeat) — *The Brook* 73, 208
call'd old Philip out To *s* the farm: — „ 121
into Darnley chase To *s* Sir Arthur's deer. — „ 133
'*S* me the books!' — *Sea Dreams* 148
these I thought my dream would *s* to me, — *Lucretius* 51
and *s* That life is not as idle ore, — *In Mem. cxviii* 19
That *will s* itself without. — *Maud II iv* 61
To *s* that who may slay or scape the three, — *Gareth and L.* 641
to *s* His loathing of our Order and the Queen. — *Balin and Balan* 550
think I *s* myself Too dark a prophet: — *Holy Grail* 321
babble about him, all to *s* your wit— — *Last Tournament* 340
Bear with me for the last time while I *s*, — *Guinevere* 454
Some one might *s* it at a joust of arms, — *Pass. of Arthur* 270
and *s* us That we are surely heard. — *Lover's Tale i* 364
he brings And *s's* them whatsoever he accounts — „ *iv* 233
'O my heart's lord, would I could *s* you,' he says, — „ 250
I propose to-night To *s* you what is dearest to my heart, — „ 252
while I *s* you all my heart.' — „ 353
s us that the world is wholly fair. — *Ancient Sage* 182
Let the trampled serpent *s* you — *Locksley H., Sixty* 242
never had I seen her *s* remorse— — *The Ring* 457
Our Playwright may *s* In some fifth Act — *The Play* 3
I will *s* it you by-and-by. — *Bandit's Death* 8

Show'd the world Like one great garden *s*, — *The Poet* 34
One *s* an iron coast and angry waves. — *Palace of Art* 69
for he *s* me all the sin. — *May Queen, Con.* 17
Pontius and Iscariot by my side *S* like fair seraphs. — *St. S. Stylites* 169
S her the fairy footings on the grass, — *Aylmer's Field* 90
And when she *s* the wealthy scabbard, — „ 236
s their eyes Glaring, and passionate looks, — *Sea Dreams* 235
and *s* A riotous confluence of watercourses — *Lucretius* 29
s the house, Greek, set with busts: — *Princess, Pro.* 10
s the late-writ letters of the king. — „ *i* 175
He *s* a tent A stone-shot off: — „ *v* 53
What Roman strength Turbia *s* — *The Daisy* 5
Who *s* a token of distress? — *In Mem. lxxviii* 13
And *s* him in the fountain fresh — „ *lxxxv* 26
knight Had visor up, and *s* a youthful face, — *Marr. of Geraint* 189
s themselves against the sky, and sank. — „ 240
For while the mother *s* it, — „ 636
And *s* an empty tent allotted her, — *Geraint and E.* 885
This gray King *S* us a shrine — *Balin and Balan* 109

Show'd (*continued*) This woodman *s* the cave From which he sallies, *Balin and Balan* 131
gems Pluck'd from the crown, and *s* them to his knights, *Lancelot and E.* 57
Chose the green path that *s* the rarer foot, „ 162
And *s* him, like a vermin in its hole, *Last Tournament* 165
And *s* them both the ruby-chain, „ 409
in the light's last glimmer Tristram *s* „ 739
s he drank beyond his use; *Lover's Tale iv* 228
s Turning my way, the loveliest face *Sisters (E. and E.)* 86

Shower (s) (*See also* **Thunder-shower**) sweet *s's* Of festal flowers, *Ode to Memory* 77
These in every *s* creep Thro' the green *A Dirge* 33
Like moonlight on a falling *s*? *Margaret* 4
like the rainbow from the *s*, *Two Voices* 444
The slow result of winter *s's*: „ 452
I thirsted for the brooks, the *s's*: *Fatima* 10
I'll take the *s's* as they fall, *Amphion* 101
Perfume and flowers fall in *s's*, *Sir Galahad* 11
The gentle *s*, the smell of dying leaves, *Enoch Arden* 611
s's of random sweet on maid and man. *Princess vii* 86
Briton in blown seas and storming *s's*, *Ode on Well.* 155
s and storm and blast Had blown the lake *The Daisy* 70
daisy close Her crimson fringes to the *s*; *In Mem. lxxii* 12
Sweet after *s's*, ambrosial air, *lxxxvi* 1
in the sudden sun Between two *s's*, *Gareth and L.* 389
Was cared as much for as a summer *s*; *Geraint and E.* 523
Like sunlight on the plain behind a *s*: *Merlin and V.* 403
poplars made a noise of falling *s's*. *Lancelot and E.* 411
poplars with their noise of falling *s's*, „ 523
s's of flowers Fell as we past; *Holy Grail* 348
and *s* and shorn plume Went down it. *Last Tournament* 155
with Queen Isolt Against a *s*, „ 379
Showing a *s* of blood in a field noir, „ 433
the wind and the *s* and the snow. *Rizpah* 68
from out the west in shadowing *s's*, *Sisters (E. and E.)* 7
Thro' the blotting mist, the blinding *s's*, „ 18
Stony *s's* Of that ear-stunning hail of Arês *Tiresias* 95
from a day of driving *s's*— *Locksley H., Sixty* 259
Before them fleets the *s*, *Early Spring* 13
a s of stones that stoned him dead, *St. Telemachus* 68

Shower (verb) Down *s* the gambolling waterfalls *Sea-Fairies* 10
s the fiery grain Of freedom broadcast *Princess v* 421
S's slanting light upon the dolorous wave. *Lover's Tale i* 811

Shower'd (adj.) To enrich the threshold of the night With *s* largess of delight *In Mem. xxix* 7

Shower'd (verb) *s* the rippled ringlets to her knee; *Godiva* 47
s His oriental gifts on everyone And most on Edith: *Aylmer's Field* 213
Before me *s* the rose in flakes; *Princess iv* 264
Lavish Honour *s* all her stars, *Ode on Well.* 196
s down Rays of a mighty circle, *Lover's Tale i* 417

Showerful in a *s* spring Stared at the spate. *Gareth and L.* 2

Showering (*See also* **Ever-showering**) *S* thy gleaned wealth into my open breast *Ode to Memory* 23
s wide Sleet of diamond-drift and pearly hail; *Vision of Sin* 21
fountains spouted up and *s* down In meshes *Princess i* 218

Showery Grow green beneath the *s* gray, *My life is full* 17
dew'd with *s* drops, Up-clomb the shadowy pine *Lotos-Eaters* 17
last, she fixt A *s* glance upon her aunt, *Princess, Con.* 33

Showing (*See also* **A-Shawin'**) *S* a gaudy summer-morn, *Palace of Art* 62
she pointed with a laugh, *S* the aspick's bite.) *D. of F. Women* 160
S a shower of blood in a field noir, *Last Tournament* 433
Not only *s*? and he himself pronounced *Lover's Tale iv* 349
And *s* them, souls have wings! *Dead Prophet* 12

Shown (*See also* **Late-shown**) Half *s*, are broken and withdrawn. *Two Voices* 306
and *s* the truth betimes, That old true filth, *Merlin and V.* 46
after he hath *s* him gems or gold, *Lover's Tale iv* 246
France had *s* a light to all men, *Locksley H., Sixty* 89
not *s* To dazzle all that see them? *The Ring* 143

Shrank *S* one sick willow sere and small. *Mariana in the S.* 53
Enid *s* far back into herself, *Geraint and E.* 607
his charger at her side, She *s* a little. „ 821
and he *s* and wail'd, 'Is the Queen false?' *Pelleas and E.* 531
He *s* and howl'd, and from his brow drew back *Lover's Tale ii* 92

Shrank (*continued*) her weight *S* in my grasp, *Lover's Tale ii* 203
I turn'd: my heart *S* in me, „ *iii* 38
Her that *s*, and put me from her, *Locksley H., Sixty* 264

Shrew woodland thing, Or *s*, or weasel, *Gareth and L.* 749

Shrewdest a sting of *s* pain Ran shrivelling thro' me, *St. S. Stylites* 198

Shrewdness nor compensating the want By *s*, *Enoch Arden* 251

Shrewish Puppet to a father's threat, and servile to a *s* tongue! *Locksley Hall* 42

Shriek (s) (*See also* **Flittermouse-shriek**) myriad *s* of wheeling ocean-fowl, *Enoch Arden* 583
the keen *s* 'Yes love, yes, Edith, yes,' *Aylmer's Field* 582
their *s's* Ran highest up the gamut, *Sea Dreams* 232
One *s* of hate would jar all the hymns of heaven: „ 259
Dislink'd with *s's* and laughter: *Princess, Pro.* 70
yonder, *s's* and strange experiments „ 235
the whispers, and the *s's* Of the wild woods together; „ *i* 98
There rose a *s* as of a city sack'd: „ *iv* 165
another *s*, 'The Head, the Head, the Princess, „ 175
A kingdom topples over with a *s* „ *Con.* 62
The shrill-edged *s* of a mother *Maud I i* 16
there was *love* in the passionate *s*, „ 57
And all in passion uttering a dry *s*, *Geraint and E.* 461
Unearthlier than all *s* of bird or beast, *Balin and Balan* 545
clapt her hands Together with a wailing *s*, *Merlin and V.* 867
Lancelot gave A marvellous great *s* *Lancelot and E.* 516
upward-rushing storm and cloud Of *s* and plume, *Last Tournament* 441
Behind him rose a shadow and a *s*— „ 753
s's and ringing laughter on the sand *Lover's Tale iii* 32
wail came borne in the *s* of a growing wind, *The Wreck* 87
s for the rights of an equal humanity, *Beautiful City* 2
she heard The *s* of some lost life *Death of Œnone* 90
arose The *s* and curse of trampled millions, *Akbar's Dream* 190

Shriek (verb) if any came near I would call, and *s*, *The Mermaid* 38
S out 'I hate you, Enoch,' *Enoch Arden* 33
and *s* 'You are not Ida;' *Princess vii* 94
That *s* and sweat in pigmy wars *Lit. Squabbles* 2
shall I *s* if a Hungary fail? *Maud I iv* 46
That ever *s's* before a death,' *Lancelot and E.* 1023
and *s's* After the Christ, *Pass. of Arthur* 110
glance the tits, and *s* the jays, *Prog. of Spring* 15
If every single star Should *s* its claim *Akbar's Dream* 43

Shriek'd (*See also* **Screeäd**) mouse Behind the mouldering wainscot *s*, *Mariana* 64
'No voice,' she *s* in that lone hall, *Palace of Art* 258
Again they *s* the burthen—'Him!' *Edwin Morris* 123
'A ship of fools,' he *s* in spite, *The Voyage* 77
For sideways up he swung his arms, and *s* *Sea Dreams* 24
s That she but meant to win him back, *Lucretius* 278
Daintily she *s* And wrung it. *Princess, Pro.* 175
'Boys!' *s* the old king, „ *v* 328
s The virgin marble under iron heels: „ *vi* 350
Yell'd and *s* between her daughters (repeat) *Boädicea* 6, 72
s against his creed— *In Mem. lvi* 16
His helmet as to slay him, but she *s*, *Gareth and L.* 979
S to the stranger, 'Slay not a dead man!' *Geraint and E.* 779
moved so much the more, and *s* again, „ 782
s out 'Traitor' to the unhearing wall, *Lancelot and E.* 612
Who rode by Lancelot, wail'd and *s* aloud, *Holy Grail* 356
The words of Arthur flying *s*, arose, *Last Tournament* 139
Who *s* and wail'd, the three whereat we gazed *Pass. of Arthur* 453
Aloud she *s*: My heart was cloven with pain; *Lover's Tale ii* 199
s and slaked the light with blood. *Locksley H., Sixty* 90
s, and started from my side— „ 264
One *s* 'The fires of Hell!' *Dead Prophet* 80
when I learnt it at last, I *s*, *Charity* 37

Shrieking fell The woman *s* at his feet, *Aylmer's Field* 811
And *s* '*I* am his dearest, I— *The Victim* 71
And the *s* rush of the wainscot mouse, *Maud I vi* 71
s out 'O fool!' the harlot leapt Adown the forest, *Merlin and V.* 972
On whom the women *s* "Atheist" flung Filth *Akbar's Dream* 91

Shrift And number'd bead, and *s*, *Talking Oak* 46
Wrapt in her grief, for housel or for *s*, *Guinevere* 149

Shrike the sparrow spear'd by the *s*, *Maud I iv* 23

Shrill (adj.) And the *s* winds were up and away, *Mariana* 50

Shrill (adj.) (*continued*) S music reach'd them on the middle sea. — Sea-Fairies 6
Springing alone With a s inner sound, — The Mermaid 20
Her rapid laughters wild and s, — Kate 3
Lest their s happy laughter come to me — Œnone 258
over them the sea-wind sang S, chill, — M. d'Arthur 49
The s bell rings, the censer swings, — Sir Galahad 35
The Lady's-head upon the prow Caught the s salt, — The Voyage 12
and fear'd To send abroad a s and terrible cry, — Enoch Arden 768
S, till the comrade of his chambers woke, — Aylmer's Field 583
she lifted up a voice Of s command, — Death of Œnone 99
Shrill (adv.) Thereat she suddenly laugh'd and s, — Balin and Balan 493
over them the sea-wind sang S, chill, — Pass. of Arthur 217
Shrill (verb) wind, that s's All night in a waste land, — M. d'Arthur 201
her whinny s's From tile to scullery, — Princess v 452
wind that s's All night in a waste land, — Pass. of Arthur 369
like the clear voice when a trumpet s's, — Achilles over the T. 19
Shrill-edged The s-e shriek of a mother — Maud I i 16
Shrill'd (s the cotton-spinning chorus); — Edwin Morris 122
And s his tinsel shaft. — Talking Oak 68
s and rang, Till this was ended, — Enoch Arden 175
merrily-blowing s the martial fife; — Princess v 251
Shot up and s in flickering gyres, — „ vii 46
And she athwart the shallow s again, — Gareth and L. 1035
she tower'd her bells, Tone under tone, s; — Merlin and V. 132
Dagonet clapt his hands and s, — Last Tournament 353
down the long wind the dream S; — Pass. of Arthur 41
all the night an answer s, — Demeter and P. 61
Shrilleth The shattering trumpet s high, — Sir Galahad 5
Shrilling (*See also* **Sudden-shrilling**) nipt her slender nose With petulant thumb and finger, s, 'Hence! — Gareth and L. 750
she s 'Let me die!' — Lancelot and E. 1026
in a voice S along the hall to Arthur, — Holy Grail 289
and past his ear Went s, 'Hollow, — Pass. of Arthur 33
With s shafts of subtle wit. — Clear-headed friend 13
At times too s in her angrier moods, — The Ring 395
Thin as the batlike s's of the Dead — Death of Œnone 21
wind of the Night s out Desolation and wrong — The Dreamer 15
Shrilly The s whinnyings of the team of Hell, — Demeter and P. 44
Shrine (*See also* **Altar-shrine**) By Bagdat's s's of fretted gold, — Arabian Nights 7
From one censer in one s, — Eleänore 59
they saw thee from the secret s — Alexander 13
Still-lighted in a secret s, — Mariana in the S. 18
Going before to some far s, — On a Mourner 17
from the ruin'd s he stept And in the moon — M. d'Arthur 45
And you may carve a s about my dust, — St. S. Stylites 195
My knees are bow'd in crypt and s: — Sir Galahad 18
Then by some secret s I ride; — „ 29
The desecrated s, the trampled year, — Princess v 127
two Sware at the s of Christ a deathless love: — Com. of Arthur 466
when they left the s Great Lords from Rome — „ 476
Show'd us a s wherein were wonders— — Balin and Balan 109
Saint who stands with lily in hand In yonder s. — „ 262
but while he stared about the s, — „ 408
that s which then in all the realm Was richest, — Lancelot and E. 1330
The Holy Grail, descend upon the s: — Holy Grail 465
lie before your s's; Do each low office — Guinevere 681
from the ruin'd s he stept, And in the moon — Pass. of Arthur 213
So that they pass not to the s of sound. — Lover's Tale i 470
lay me in some s of this old Spain, — Columbus 207
Falling about their s's before their Gods, — Tiresias 105
Shrined Methinks my friend is richly s; — In Mem. lvii 7
see your Art still s in human shelves, — Poets and their B. 11
S him within the temple of her heart, — The Ring 219
Shrine-doors s-d burst thro' with heated blasts — D. of F. Women 29
Shrine-shattering S-s earthquake, fire, flood, thunderbolt, — Tiresias 61
Shrink It would s to the earth if you came in. — Poet's Mind 37
Smite, s not, spare not. — St. S. Stylites 181
nor s For fear our solid aim be dissipated — Princess iii 265
her small goodman S's in his arm-chair — „ v 454
Nor make a snail's horn s for wantonness; — Ancient Sage 272
Shrive let me s me clean, and die.' — Lancelot and E. 1100
s myself No, not to an Apostle.' — Sir J. Oldcastle 146
Shrivel Lightning may s the laurel of Cæsar, — Parnassus 4
Shrivell'd Were s into darkness in his head, — Godiva 70
Wine is good for s lips, — Vision of Sin 79
Is s in a fruitless fire, — In Mem. liv 11
kernel of the s fruit Is jutting thro' the rind; — Ancient Sage 121
Shrivelling sting of shrewdest pain Ran s thro' me, — St. S. Stylites 199
Shriven 'Heresy—Not s, not saved?' — Sir J. Oldcastle 144
Shroud (s) (*See also* **Hammock-shroud**) Nor was the night thy s. — Ode to Memory 28
A music out of sheet and s, — In Mem. ciii 54
bird with a warble plaintively sweet Perch'd on the s's, — The Wreck 82
Shroud (verb) s this great sin from all! — Aylmer's Field 773
To s me from my proper scorn. — In Mem. xxvi 16
mist of autumn gather from your lake, And s the tower; — The Ring 330
Shrouded *See* **Half-shrouded**
Shrub (*See also* **Laurel-shrubs**) Tall orient s's, and obelisks — Arabian Nights 107
Shrunk S like a fairy changeling lay the mage; — Com. of Arthur 363
s by usage into commonest commonplace! — Locksley H., Sixty 76
Shtreet (street) whiniver ye walkt in the s, — Tomorrow 37
Shudder (s) her child!—a s comes Across me: — Œnone 253
In that vast Oval ran a s of shame. — St. Telemachus 73
Shudder (verb) I s at the sequel, but I go.' — Princess ii 236
We s but to dream our maids should ape — „ iii 309
Nor s's at the gulfs beneath, — In Mem. xli 15
O ye stars that s over me, — Com. of Arthur 83
'I s, some one steps across my grave;' — Guinevere 57
So let me, if you do not s at me, — „ 675
yet it shook me, that my frame would s, — Lover's Tale ii 56
heart of motherhood Within me s, — Demeter and P. 42
I s at the Christian and the stake; — Akbar's Dream 72
Shudder'd s, lest a cry Should break his sleep — Walk. to the Mail 73
'Why—these—*are*—men:' I s: — Princess iii 58
all dabbled with the blood Of his own son, s, — „ vi 105
Yet I s and thought like a fool — Maud I xiv 38
Then s, as the village wife who cries — Guinevere 56
For the whole isle s and shook — V. of Maeldune 74
Shudderest S when I strain my sight, — Fatima 3
Shuddering delight and s took hold of all my mind, — May Queen, Con. 35
he knew not wherefore, started up S, — Enoch Arden 617
from the plaintive mother's teat he took Her blind and s puppies, — The Brook 130
Sat s at the ruin of a world; — Sea Dreams 30
And s fled from room to room, — Princess vi 370
Set every gilded parapet s; — Lancelot and E. 299
and thought With s, 'Hark the Phantom — „ 1022
There in the s moonlight brought its face — Lover's Tale i 650
till one of them Said, s, 'Her spectre!' — „ iv 335
shrill-edged shriek of a mother divide the s night. — Maud I i 16
In the s dawn, behold, — „ II iv 52
bruised and butted with the s War-thunder of iron rams; — Tiresias 99
about the s wreck the death-white sea should rave, — The Flight 47
Shuffled for the roots of my hair were stirr'd By a s step, — Maud I i 14
Shun on our dead self, nor s to do it, — Princess iii 221
My drooping memory will not s The foaming grape — In Mem., Con. 79
s the wild ways of the lawless tribe. — Geraint and E. 608
do not s To speak the wish most near to your true heart; — Lancelot and E. 913
Would s to break those bounds of courtesy — „ 1220
did not s to smite me in worse way, — Guinevere 435
Nor s to call me sister, — „ 676
She used to s the wailing babe, — The Ring 358
Shunn'd But Enoch s the middle walk — Enoch Arden 738
thence That which he better might have s, — „ 740
nor broke, nor s a soldier's death, — Princess, Pro. 38
had not s the death, No, not the soldier's: — „ v 178
Shushan brawl at S underneath the palms.' — „ iii 230
Shut (*See also* **Half-shut**) I s my life from happier chance. — Two Voices 54
I s my sight for fear: — Œnone 188
And he that s's Love out, in turn shall be S out from Love, — To ——, With Pal. of Art 14
S up as in a crumbling tomb, — Palace of Art 273
Two handfuls of white dust, s in an urn of brass! — Lotos-Eaters, C. S. 68
She left the new piano s: — Talking Oak 119
said he lived s up within himself, — Golden Year 9
all Should keep within, door s, and window barr'd. — Godiva 41

Shut (*continued*) is there any moral *s* Within the bosom of the rose? *Day-Dm., Moral* 7
By squares of tropic summer *s* *Amphion* 87
gentle creature *s* from all Her charitable use, *Aylmer's Field* 565
To one deep chamber *s* from sound, *Princess vi* 376
an' 'e 'ant got *s* on 'em yet. *N. Farmer, N. S.* 30
Now, sometimes in my sorrow *s*, *In Mem. xxiii* 1
Were *s* between me and the sound: „ *xxviii* 8
Or been in narrowest working *s*, „ *xxxv* 20
God *s* the doorways of his head. „ *xliv* 4
A gulf that ever *s's* and gapes, „ *lxx* 6
I will not *s* me from my kind, „ *cviii* 1
'O little maid, *s* in by nunnery walls. *Guinevere* 227
s me round with narrowing nunnery-walls, „ 671
little hour was bound *S* in from Time, *Lover's Tale i* 438
S in the secret chambers of the rock. „ 521
I was *s* up with Grief; „ 680
They seized me and *s* me up: *Rizpah* 46
The daisy will *s* to the shadow, *The Wreck* 38
Shutter Close the door, the *s's* close, *Deserted House* 9
Shutting when *s* reasons up in rhythm, *Lucretius* 223
Shuvv (Shove) wi' noän to lend 'im a *s*, *N. Farmer, N. S.* 31
Shy (*See also* **Half-shy**) '*S* she was, and I thought her cold; *Edward Gray* 13
A little *s* at first, but by and by We twain, *Princess v* 45
Fine of the fine, and *s* of the *s*? *Window, Letter* 2
Ay or no, from *s* of the *s*? „ 10
but he look'd at me sidelong and *s*, *First Quarrel* 35
Shyness It is my *s*, or my self-distrust, *Edwin Morris* 86
Sibilation He with a long low *s*, stared *Princess i* 176
Sicilian as the great *S* called Calliope *Lucretius* 93
Sick (adj.) (*See also* **Half-sick**) thought, 'My life is *s* of single sleep: *The Bridesmaid* 13
'I am half *s* of shadows,' *L. of Shalott ii* 35
'*S* art thou—a divided will Still heaping *Two Voices* 106
King is *s*, and knows not what he does. *M. d'Arthur* 97
s of home went overseas for change. *Walk. to the Mail* 24
This girl, for whom your heart is *s*, *Talking Oak* 71
half the crew are *s* or dead, *The Voyage* 92
blind or lame or *s* or sound, „ 93
but I am *s* of Time, And I desire to rest. *Come not, when, etc.* 9
(His father lying *s* and needing him) *Enoch Arden* 65
As lightly as a *s* man's chamber-door, „ 776
—it makes me *s* to quote him— *Sea Dreams* 159
S for the hollies and the yews of home— *Princess, Pro.* 187
you that talk'd The trash that made me *s*, „ *ii* 394
Were you *s*, ourself Would tend upon you. „ *iii* 320
The land is *s*, the people diseased, *The Victim* 45
S for thy stubborn hardihood, *In Mem. ii* 14
heart is *s*, And all the wheels of Being slow. „ *l* 3
I am *s* of the Hall and the hill, I am *s* of the moor *Maud I i* 61
S, am I *s* of a jealous dread? „ *x* 1
S, *s* to the heart of life, am I. „ 36
his essences turn'd the live air *s*, „ *xiii* 11
S once, with a fear of worse, „ *xix* 73
S of a nameless fear, „ *II ii* 44
Art thou sad? or *s*? *Balin and Balan* 274
S? or for any matter anger'd at me?' „ 276
we maidens often laugh When *s* at heart, „ 498
Spake (for she had been *s*) to Guinevere, 'Are you so *s*, my Queen, you cannot move *Lancelot and E.* 78
'Stay with me, I am *s*; „ 87
'Love, are you yet so *s*?' „ 571
sound not wonted in a place so still Woke the *s* knight, „ 819
Milder than any mother to a *s* child, „ 858
And the *s* man forgot her simple blush, „ 864
that other world Another world for the *s* man; „ 874
for what force is yours to go So far, being *s*? „ 1064
all too faint and *s* am I For anger: „ 1086
King is *s*, and knows not what he does. *Pass. of Arthur* 265
Floats from his *s* and filmed eyes, *Supp. Confessions* 166
As a *s* man's room when he taketh repose *A spirit haunts* 14
steady glare Shrank one *s* willow sere and small. *Mariana in the S.* 53

Sick (adj.) (*continued*) And here once more like some *s* man declined, *Palace of Art* 155
But she, with *s* and scornful looks averse, *D. of F. Women* 101
Teach that *s* heart the stronger choice, *On a Mourner* 18
How often placed upon the *s* man's brow *Aylmer's Field* 700
Runs in a river of blood to the *s* sea. „ 768
The *s* weak beast seeking to help herself *Merlin and V.* 498
Round whose *s* head all night, like birds of prey, *Last Tournament* 138
and distribute dole To poor *s* people, *Guinevere* 684
A body journeying onward, *s* with toil, *Lover's Tale i* 124
lisp'd To kisses of the wind, that, *s* with love, „ 545
They will but sicken the *s* plant the more. „ 766
He falling *s*, and seeming close on death, „ *iv* 258
And the half my men are *s*. *The Revenge* 6
But I've ninety men and more that are lying *s* ashore. „ 10
But Sir Richard bore in hand all his *s* men „ 15
s men down in the hold were most of them stark and cold, „ 79
Some birds are *s* and sullen when they moult. *Sisters (E. and E.)* 73
and *s* For shadow—not one bush *Tiresias* 35
in amaze To find her *s* one whole; *Demeter and P.* 58
Doänt maäke thysen *s* wi' the caäke. *Owd Roä* 34
Is he *s* your mate like mine? *Happy* 2
Sick (s) Low voices with the ministering hand Hung round the *s*: *Princess vii* 22
And found fair peace once more among the *s*. „ 44
cheating the *s* of a few last gasps, *Maud I i* 43
With her hundred fighters on deck, and her ninety *s* below; *The Revenge* 34
S from the hospital echo them, *Def. of Lucknow* 100
Sicken Here at least, where nature *s's*, *Locksley Hall* 153
I hate, abhor, spit, *s* at him; *Lucretius* 199
Or *s* with ill-usage, *Princess v* 86
'A time to *s* and to swoon, *In Mem. xxi* 17
loss So pains him that he *s's* nigh to death; *Geraint and E.* 499
They will but *s* the sick plant the more. *Lover's Tale i* 766
will you *s* for her sake? *Locksley H., Sixty* 17
that *s* at your lawless din, „ 149
tho' thy violet *s* into sere, *Prog. of Spring* 25
all but *s* at the shifting scenes. *The Play* 2
Sicken'd Which *s* every living bloom, *In Mem. lxxii* 7
successful war On all the youth, they *s*; *Merlin and V.* 572
by and by she *s* of the farce, *The Ring* 383
Sickening (*See also* **Half-sickening**) But *s* of a vague disease, *L. C. V. de Vere* 62
once again the *s* game; *Locksley H., Sixty* 127
Sickle ere the silver *s* of that month *Princess i* 101
Sicklier sickly-born and grew Yet *s*, *Enoch Arden* 262
Like echoes from beyond a hollow, came Her *s* iteration. *Aylmer's Field* 299
Sickly And far away into the *s* light, *The Kraken* 7
Cursed be the *s* forms that err from honest Nature's rule! *Locksley Hall* 61
Bore him another son, a *s* one: *Enoch Arden* 109
Nursing the *s* babe, her latest-born. „ 150
But for the third, the *s* one, who slept „ 230
bearing hardly more Than his own shadow in a *s* sun. *Aylmer's Field* 30
Sickly-born Now the third child was *s-b* *Enoch Arden* 261
Sickness (*See also* **Mid-sickness**) 'Some turn this *s* yet might take, *Two Voices* 55
a languor came Upon him, gentle *s*, *Enoch Arden* 824
and read My *s* down to happy dreams? *Princess ii* 253
and due To languid limbs and *s*; „ *vi* 377
serviceable To noble knights in *s*, *Lancelot and E.* 768
as but born of *s*, could not live: „ 880
she knew right well What the rough *s* meant, „ 888
Side (*See also* **Cliff-side, Fountain-side, Hill-side, Island-sides, Mountain-side, Water-side**) faintest sunlights flee About his shadowy *s's*: *The Kraken* 5
Madonna-wise on either *s* her head; *Isabel* 6
Six columns, three on either *s*, *Arabian Nights* 144
and Thought have gone away *S* by *s*, *Deserted House* 2
Wander from the *s* of the morn, *Adeline* 52
the couple standing *s* by *s*, *The Bridesmaid* 5
On either *s* the river lie Long fields *L. of Shalott i* 1
The mirror crack'd from *s* to *s*; „ *iii* 43

Side (*continued*) Such seem'd the whisper at my *s*: *Two Voices* 439
the piney *s's* Of this long glen. *Œnone* 93
And Effie on the other *s*, *May Queen, Con.* 24
and thrust The dagger thro' her *s*.' *D. of F. Women* 260
I lived up there on yonder mountain *s*. *St. S. Stylites* 72
On one *s* lay the Ocean, and on one Lay a great water, *M. d'Arthur* 11
That only by thy *s* Will I to Olive plight *Talking Oak* 282
clamber'd half way up The counter *s*; *Golden Year* 7
Had cast upon its crusty *s* *Will Water.* 103
S by *s* beneath the water Crew and Captain lie; *The Captain* 67
Fading slowly from his *s*: *L. of Burleigh* 86
Philip sitting at her *s* forgot Her presence, *Enoch Arden* 384
On either *s* the hearth, indignant; *Aylmer's Field* 288
To glance and shift about her slippery *s's*, *Lucretius* 189
The very *s's* of the grave itself shall pass, „ 257
With that he drove the knife into his *s*: „ 275
lovelier than their names, Grew *s* by *s*; *Princess, Pro.* 13
Whichever *s* be Victor, „ *ii* 231
To rail at Lady Psyche and her *s*. „ *iii* 33
That when our *s* was vanquish'd and my cause „ *vi* 24
and fain had slept at his *s*. *Grandmother* 74
Should still be near us at our *s*? *In Mem. li* 2
' Thou canst not move me from thy *s*, „ *lii* 7
A great ship left her shining *s's*. „ *ciii* 40
Up the *s* I went, And fell in silence „ 43
moving *s* by *s* With wisdom, „ *cxiv* 19
grave That has to-day its sunny *s*. „ *Con.* 72
And here on the landward *s*, *Maud I iv* 10
For a raven ever croaks, at my *s*, „ *vi* 57
There were two at her *s*, „ *ix* 9
Was not one of the two at her *s* „ *x* 2
For one of the two that rode at her *s* „ 24
To the sweeter blood by the other *s*; „ *xiii* 34
of the seventh Heaven, down to my *s*, „ *xiv* 21
Would he have that hole in his *s*? „ *II v* 82
Up to my throne, and *s* by *s* with me? *Com. of Arthur* 81
At once from either *s*, with trumpet-blast, „ 102
Not ever to be question'd any more Save on the further *s*; „ 397
Wept from her *s's* as water flowing away; *Gareth and L.* 217
midway down the *s* of that long hall A stately pile,— „ 404
Setting this knave, Lord Baron, at my *s*. „ 854
on the further *s* Arose a silk pavilion, „ 909
lead no longer; ride thou at my *s*; „ 1157
' Not at my *s*. I charge thee ride before, *Geraint and E.* 14
Bow'd at her *s* and utter'd whisperingly: „ 305
so turning *s* by *s* They past, *Balin and Balan* 279
one *s* had sea And ship and sail and angels „ 364
harkening from what *s* The blindfold rummage „ 415
Like its own mists to all the mountain *s*: *Lancelot and E.* 38
and the head Pierced thro' his *s*, „ 490
He up the *s*, sweating with agony, „ 494
parted from the jousts Hurt in the *s*,' „ 623
Thro' her own *s* she felt the sharp lance go; „ 624
All in an oriel on the summer *s*, „ 1177
thou hast been in battle by my *s*, „ 1358
after heaven, on our dull *s* of death, „ 1382
Your places being vacant at my *s*, *Holy Grail* 317
fail'd from my *s*, nor come Cover'd, „ 470
Stood near it but a lion on each *s* „ 817
Near him a mound of even-sloping *s*, *Pelleas and E.* 25
from her *s* Restrain'd him with all manner of device, „ 203
and he call'd, ' I strike upon thy *s*— „ 279
on the hither *s* of that loud morn *Last Tournament* 56
push me even In fancy from thy *s*, „ 639
Never lie by thy *s*; see thee no more— *Guinevere* 579
On one *s* lay the Ocean, and on one Lay a great water, *Pass. of Arthur* 179
dimplings of the wave, That blanch'd upon its *s*. *Lover's Tale i* 45
and shot forth Boughs on each *s*, „ 230
On the other *s*, the moon, Half-melted „ 420
Love wraps his wings on either *s* the heart, „ 467
On the other *s* Is scoop'd a cavern „ 516
they are mine—not theirs—they had moved in my *s*. *Rizpah* 54

Side (*continued*) was wounded again in the *s* and the head, *The Revenge* 68
Spanish fleet with broken *s's* „ 71
masts and the rigging were lying over the *s*; „ 81
sewer an' sartan 'oäp o' the tother *s*; *Village Wife* 92
as ocean on every *s* Plunges *Def. of Lucknow* 38
a merry tale That shook our *s's*— *Sir J. Oldcastle* 92
all took *s's* with the Towers, *V. of Maeldune* 111
swept in a cataract off from her *s's*, *The Wreck* 90
They lower'd me down the *s*, „ 125
you bawl'd the dark *s* of your faith *Despair* 39
and we lean'd to the darker *s*— „ 55
Cleave ever to the sunnier *s* of doubt, *Ancient Sage* 68
When he will tear me from your *s*, *The Flight* 19
Wild flowers blowing *s* by *s* „ 81
shriek'd, and started from my *s*— *Locksley H., Sixty* 264
Lies upon this *s*, lies upon that *s*, *Vastness* 5
die with him *s* by *s*? *Happy* 8
my faithful counsellor, Sit by my *s*. *Akbar's Dream* 19
tho' sitting close at his *s*. *Charity* 22

Sided *See* **Many-sided**

Sidelong And *s* glances at my father's grief, *Princess vii* 107
saw with a *s* eye The shadow of some piece of pointed lace, *Lancelot and E.* 1173
but he look'd at me *s* and shy, *First Quarrel* 35
But often in the *s* eyes a gleam of all things ill— *The Flight* 31

Side-path By one *s-p*, from simple truth; *To Marq. of Dufferin* 28

Sideway *s's* he let them glance At Enid, *Geraint and E.* 246

Siding Wheedling and *s* with them! *Princess v* 158

Sidled I *s* awaäy an' awaäy *Spinster's S's.* 28

Siege in the ghastly *s* of Lucknow— *Def. of Lucknow* 4
Merlin call'd it ' The *S* perilous,' *Holy Grail* 172

Sift *s* his doubtings to the last, *Com. of Arthur* 311

Sifted (And heedfully I *s* all my thought) *St. S. Stylites* 56
Every heart, when *s* well, *Vision of Sin* 112
Thro' her this matter might be *s* clean.' *Princess i* 80
thou hast seen me strain'd And *s* to the utmost, *Pelleas and E.* 248

Sigh (s) (*See also* **Love-sighs**) wasting odorous *s's* All night long *Adeline* 43
Kate will not hear of lovers' *s's*. *Kate* 20
With her laughter or her *s's*, *Miller's D.* 184
my voice was thick with *s's* *D. of F. Women* 109
in *s's* Which perfect Joy, perplex'd *Gardener's D.* 254
A welcome mix'd with *s's*. *Talking Oak* 212
shaken with a sudden storm of *s's*— *Locksley Hall* 27
With half a *s* she turn'd the key, *The Letters* 18
from my breast the involuntary *s* Brake, *Princess iii* 191
The bosom with long *s's* labour'd; „ *vii* 225
Love would answer with a *s*, *In Mem. xxxv* 13
Nor feed with *s's* a passing wind: „ *cviii* 4
And in my thoughts with scarce a *s* „ *cxix* 11
young lord-lover, what *s's* are those, *Maud I xxii* 29
Half the night I waste in *s's*, „ *II iv* 23
songs, *S's*, and slow smiles, and golden eloquence *Lancelot and E.* 649

Sigh (verb) you may hear him sob and *s* *A spirit haunts* 5
shook the wave as the wind did *s*; *Dying Swan* 15
' To breathe and loathe, to live and *s*, *Two Voices* 104
But here will *s* thine alder tree, *A Farewell* 9
She *s's* amid her narrow days, *In Mem. lx* 10
and *s* The full new life that feeds thy breath „ *lxxxvi* 9
That whenever a March-wind *s's* *Maud I xxii* 40
s's to see the peak Sun-flush'd, *Balin and Balan* 165
would often when they met *S* fully, *Merlin and V.* 182
to *s*, and to stretch and yawn, *V. of Maeldune* 91
s's after many a vanish'd face, *Vastness* 1
silver year should cease to mourn and *s*— *To Mary Boyle* 57

Sigh'd when I heard my name *S* forth with life *D. of F. Women* 154
So *s* the King, Muttering and murmuring at his ear, *M. d'Arthur* 178
they that heard it *s*, *Vision of Sin* 18
Cold ev'n to her, she *s*; *Princess vi* 102
I *s*: a touch Came round my wrist, „ *vii* 137
Long have I *s* for a calm: *Maud I ii* 1
thought, is it pride, and mused and *s* „ *viii* 12

Silence (s) (*continued*) To s from the paths of men; *Day-Dm., L'Envoi* 6
But Philip loved in s; *Enoch Arden* 41
let my query pass Unclaim'd, in flushing s, *The Brook* 105
Vocal, with here and there a s, *Aylmer's Field* 146
face to face With twenty months of s, „ 567
a louder one Was all but s— „ 697
he felt the s of his house About him, „ 830
escaped His keepers, and the s which he felt, „ 839
And silenced by that s lay the wife, *Sea Dreams* 46
him we gave a costly bribe To guerdon s, *Princess i* 204
We dare not ev'n by s sanction lies. *Third of Feb.* 10
We feel, at least, that s here were sin, „ 37
S, till I be silent too. *In Mem. xiii* 8
And makes a s in the hills. „ *xix* 8
And s follow'd, and we wept. „ *xxx* 20
So here shall s guard thy fame; „ *lxxv* 17
They haunt the s of the breast, „ *xciv* 9
And strangely on the s broke „ *xcv* 25
And fell in s on his neck: „ *ciii* 44
And, tho' in s, wishing joy. „ *Con.* 88
Till a s fell with the waking bird, *Maud I xxii* 17
I wish Your warning or your s? *Geraint and E.* 77
Debating his command of s given, „ 366
Then breaking his command of s given, „ 390
In s, did him service as a squire; „ 406
blind wave feeling round his long sea-hall In s: *Merlin and V.* 233
let me think S is wisdom: „ 253
such a s is more wise than kind.' „ 289
grew darker toward the storm In s, „ 891
Dark-splendid, speaking in the s, *Lancelot and E.* 338
standing near the shield In s, „ 395
Now bolden'd by the s of his King,— *Holy Grail* 857
Then a long s came upon the hall, *Pelleas and E.* 609
little maid, who brook'd No s, brake it, *Guinevere* 160
I cry my cry in s, „ 201
howsoever much they may desire S, „ 207
then came s, then a voice, „ 419
after wail Of suffering, s follows, *Pass. of Arthur* 119
They stood before his throne in s, „ 455
till helpless death And s made him bold— *Lover's Tale iv* 73
Evelyn clung In utter s for so long, *Sisters (E. and E.)* 217
Found s in the hollows underneath. *Tiresias* 38
only heard in s from the s of a tomb. *Locksley H., Sixty* 74
Death and S hold their own. „ 237
Swallow'd in Vastness, lost in S, *Vastness* 34
And found a corpse and s, *The Ring* 217
That icy winter s—how it froze you *Happy* 71
In s wept upon the flowerless earth. *Death of Œnone* 9
A s follow'd as of death, *St. Telemachus* 65
then once more a s as of death. „ 69

Silence (verb) ever widening slowly s all. *Merlin and V.* 392
Them surely can I s with all ease. *Lancelot and E.* 109

Silenced s by that silence lay the wife, *Sea Dreams* 46
S for ever—craven—a man of plots, *Gareth and L.* 431

Silent (*See also* **All-silent, Ever-silent**) Losing his fire and active might In a s meditation, *Eleänore* 105
There in a s shade of laurel brown *Alexander* 9
And the s isle imbowers The Lady of Shalott. *L. of Shalott i* 17
For often thro' the s nights A funeral, „ *ii* 30
S into Camelot. „ *iv* 41
And s in its dusty vines: *Mariana in the S.* 4
And deepening thro' the s spheres „ 91
Thereto the s voice replied; *Two Voices* 22
'Still sees the sacred morning spread The s summit overhead. „ 81
The phantom of a s song, *Miller's D.* 71
And rose, and, with a s grace Approaching, „ 159
The grasshopper is s in the grass: *Œnone* 26
O s faces of the Great and Wise! *Palace of Art* 195
Three s pinnacles of aged snow, *Lotos-Eaters* 16
Drops in a s autumn night. „ *C. S.* 34
Lower'd softly with a threefold cord of love Down to a s grave. *D. of F. Women* 212
I rose up in the s night: *The Sisters* 25
a s cousin stole Upon us and departed: *Edwin Morris* 115

Silent (*continued*) I, whose bald brows in s hours become Unnaturally hoar with rime, *St. S. Stylites* 165
Roll'd in one another's arms, and s in a last embrace. *Locksley Hall* 58
He gazes on the s dead: *Day-Dm., Arrival* 13
I pledge her s at the board; *Will Water.* 25
And watch'd by s gentlemen, „ 231
'Dark porch,' I said, 'and s aisle, *The Letters* 47
A deedful life, a s voice: *You might have won* 8
And lived a life of s melancholy. *Enoch Arden* 260
Her own son Was s, tho' he often look'd his wish; „ 482
Till s in her oriental haven. „ 537
The s water slipping from the hills, „ 633
There Enoch rested s many days. „ 699
and ever bears about A s court of justice in his breast, *Sea Dreams* 174
Too often, in that s court of yours— „ 183
Why were you s when I spoke to-night? „ 268
question'd if she knew us men, at first Was s; *Princess iv* 232
s we with blind surmise Regarding, „ 381
glaring with his whelpless eye, S; „ *vi* 100
stood Erect and s, striking with her glance „ 152
all s, save When armour clash'd or jingled, „ 362
Lay s in the muffled cage of life: „ *vii* 47
s light Slept on the painted walls, „ 120
Now slides the s meteor on, and leaves „ 184
Or in their s influence as they sat, „ *Con.* 15
Thro' all the s spaces of the worlds, „ 114
His voice is s in your council-hall *Ode on Well.* 174
and whatever tempests lour For ever s; even if they broke In thunder, s; „ 176
O s father of our Kings to be *Ode Inter. Exhib.* 7
Where oleanders flush'd the bed Of s torrents, *The Daisy* 34
I stood among the s statues, „ 63
And look'd at by the s stars: *Lit. Squabbles* 4
But thou wert s in heaven, *Voice and the P.* 7
So the s colony hearing her tumultuous adversaries *Boädicea* 78
Silence, till I be s too. *In Mem. xiii* 8
Sat s, looking each at each. „ *xxx* 12
Her eyes are homes of s prayer, „ *xxxii* 1
And s traces of the past Be all the colour of the flower: „ *xliii* 7
The s snow possess'd the earth, „ *lxxviii* 3
And s under other snows: „ *cv* 6
The red-ribb'd ledges drip with a s horror of blood, *Maud I i* 3
Love for the s thing that had made false haste to the grave— „ 58
The s sapphire-spangled marriage ring of the land? „ *iv* 6
When I was wont to meet her In the s woody places „ *II iv* 6
But is ever the one thing s here. „ *v* 68
That like a s lightning under the stars „ *III vi* 9
he is gone: We know him now: all narrow jealousies Are s; *Ded. of Idylls* 17
on thro' s faces rode Down the slope city, *Gareth and L.* 734
And Gareth s gazed upon the knight, „ 933
S the s field They traversed. „ 1313
And all the three were s seeing, „ 1362
Worn by the feet that now were s, *Marr. of Geraint* 321
Her mother s too, nor helping her, „ 768
I am s then, And ask no kiss;' *Merlin and V.* 253
We could not keep him s, „ 416
For s, tho' he greeted her, she stood Rapt on his face *Lancelot and E.* 355
from his face who read To hers which lay so s, „ 1286
Had pass'd into the s life of prayer, *Holy Grail* 4
Lancelot left The hall long s, „ 854
Cares but to pass into the s life. „ 899
Hot was the night and s; *Pelleas and E.* 395
Across the s seeded meadow-grass Borne, „ 561
Speak, Lancelot, thou art s: *Last Tournament* 107
It makes a s music up in heaven, „ 349
With s smiles of slow disparagement; *Guinevere* 14
bow'd down upon her hands S, until the little maid, „ 159
Blaze by the rushing brook or s well. „ 400
witness, too, the s cry, The prayer of many a race and creed, *To the Queen ii* 10
one string That quivers, and is s, *Lover's Tale i* 18
till the things familiar to her youth Had made a s answer: „ *iv* 96

Silent (*continued*) Till he melted like a cloud in the *s* summer heaven; *The Revenge* 14
we came to the *S* Isle that we never had touch'd at before, Where a *s* ocean always broke on a *s* shore, *V. of Maeldune* 11
low down in a rainbow deep *S* palaces, „ 80
Remembering all the golden hours Now *s*, *Tiresias* 211
But louder than thy rhyme the *s* Word *Ancient Sage* 212
Sorra the *s* throat but we hard it cryin' 'Ochone!' *Tomorrow* 84
Fires that shook me once, but now to *s* ashes fall'n away. *Locksley H., Sixty* 41
Clinging to the *s* mother! Are we devils? „ 99
While the *s* Heavens roll, and Suns along their fiery way, „ 203
S echoes! You, my Leonard, use and not abuse your day, „ 265
But thou art *s* underground, *Pref. Poem Broth. S.* 13
Here *s* in our Minster of the West *Epit. on Stratford* 3
Along the *s* field of Asphodel. *Demeter and P.* 153
But seen upon the *s* brow when life has ceased to beat. *Happy* 52
I saw beyond their *s* tops The steaming marshes *Prog. of Spring* 74
And streaming and shining on *S* river, *Merlin and the G.* 52
For out of the darkness *S* and slowly The Gleam, „ 82
The *s* Alphabet-of-heaven-in-man Made vocal— *Akbar's Dream* 136
S Voices of the dead, *Silent Voices* 4
Call me rather, *s* voices, „ 7
Nor the myriad world, His shadow, nor the *s* Opener of the Gate.' *God. and the Univ.* 6
Silent-creeping *s-c* winds Laid the long night *Lover's Tale ii* 111
Silent-lighted And pass the *s-l* town, *In Mem., Con.* 112
Silently But *s*, in all obedience, *Marr. of Geraint* 767
Silent-speaking on the silence broke The *s-s* words, *In Mem. xcv* 26
Silk (adj.) *s* star-broider'd coverlid Unto her limbs *Day-Dm., Sleep. B.* 9
and on the further side Arose a *s* pavilion, *Gareth and L.* 910
But found a *s* pavilion in a field, *Holy Grail* 745
s pavilions of King Arthur raised For brief repast *Guinevere* 394
Silk (s) And trod on *s*, as if the winds *A Character* 21
s's, and fruits, and spices, clear of toll, *Golden Year* 45
A gown of grass-green *s* she wore, *Sir L. and Q. G.* 24
And robed the shoulders in a rosy *s*, *Princess, Pro.* 103
She brought us Academic *s's*, „ *ii* 16
thro' the parted *s's* the tender face Peep'd, „ *vii* 60
statue of Sir Ralph From those rich *s's*, „ *Con.* 118
Then she bethought her of a faded *s*, *Marr. of Geraint* 134
In summer suit and *s's* of holiday. „ 173
And seeing one so gay in purple *s's*, „ 284
Moved the fair Enid, all in faded *s*, „ 366
All staring at her in her faded *s*: „ 617
That she ride with me in her faded *s*.' „ 762
But Enid ever kept the faded *s*, „ 841
And tearing off her veil of faded *s* *Geraint and E.* 514
Display'd a splendid *s* of foreign loom, „ 687
fearing rust or soilure fashion'd for it A case of *s*, *Lancelot and E.* 8
Figs out of thistles, *s* from bristles, *Last Tournament* 356
fold Thy presence in the *s* of sumptuous looms: *Ancient Sage* 266
till I maäkes tha es smooth es *s*, *Spinster's S's.* 53
spice and her vintage, her *s* and her corn; *Vastness* 13
Silken Hues of the *s* sheeny woof *Madeline* 22
breeze of a joyful dawn blew free In the *s* sail of infancy, *Arabian Nights* 2
We'll bind you fast in *s* cords, *Rosalind* 49
On *s* cushions half reclined; *Eleänore* 126
New from its *s* sheath. *D. of F. Women* 60
'Her eyelids dropp'd their *s* eaves. *Talking Oak* 209
And rotatory thumbs on *s* knees, *Aylmer's Field* 200
A feudal knight in *s* masquerade, *Princess, Pro.* 234
in hue The lilac, with a *s* hood to each, „ *ii* 17
one The *s* priest of peace, one this, „ *v* 184
In *s* fluctuation and the swarm Of female whisperers: „ *vi* 355
To have her lion roll in a *s* net *Maud I vi* 29
from out the *s* curtain-folds Bare-footed *Gareth and L.* 925
This *s* rag, this beggar-woman's weed: *Geraint and E.* 680
Ran down the *s* thread to kiss each other *Merlin and V.* 455
o'er her hung The *s* case with braided blazonings, *Lancelot and E.* 1149
Which made a *s* mat-work for her feet; *Holy Grail* 151

Silken (*continued*) In its green sheath, close-lapt in *s* folds, *Lover's Tale i* 153
A *s* cord let down from Paradise, *Akbar's Dream* 139
Silken-folded fancies hatch'd In *s-f* idleness; *Princess iv* 67
Silken-sail'd The shallop flitteth *s-s* *L. of Shalott i* 22
Silken-sandal'd She tapt her tiny *s-s* foot: *Princess, Pro.* 150
Silk-soft In *s-s* folds, upon yielding down, *Eleänore* 28
Silky All grass of *s* feather grow— *Talking Oak* 269
Silver (adj.) but a most *s* flow Of subtle-paced counsel *Isabel* 20
With *s* anchor left afloat, *Arabian Nights* 93
Like Indian reeds blown from his *s* tongue, *The Poet* 13
Shadows of the *s* birk Sweep the green *A Dirge* 5
Would curl round my *s* feet silently, *Mermaid* 50
the violet woos To his heart the *s* dews? *Adeline* 32
from his blazon'd baldric slung A mighty *s* bugle hung, *L. of Shalott iii* 16
Three fingers round the old *s* cup— *Miller's D.* 10
The wind sounds like a *s* wire, *Fatima* 29
With narrow moon-lit slips of *s* cloud, *Œnone* 218
Moved of themselves, with *s* sound; *Palace of Art* 130
O blessings on his kindly voice and on his *s* hair! *May Queen, Con.* 13
O blessings on his kindly heart and on his *s* head! 15
A golden bill! the *s* tongue, *The Blackbird* 13
momently The twinkling laurel scatter'd *s* lights. *Gardener's D.* 118
The *s* fragments of a broken voice, „ 234
High up, in *s* spikes! *Talking Oak* 276
Close over us, the *s* star, thy guide, *Tithonus* 25
And thee returning on thy *s* wheels. „ 76
Glitter like a swarm of fire-flies tangled in a *s* braid. *Locksley Hall* 10
The *s* vessels sparkle clean, *Sir Galahad* 34
s boss Of her own halo's dusky shield; *The Voyage* 31
Till over thy dark shoulder glow Thy *s* sister-world, *Move eastward* 6
on the swell The *s* lily heaved and fell; *To E. L.* 19
s sickle of that month Became her golden shield, *Princess i* 101
like *s* hammers falling On *s* anvils, „ 216
sound Of solemn psalms, and *s* litanies, „ *ii* 477
S sails all out of the west Under the *s* moon: „ *iii* 14
call'd On flying Time from all their *s* tongues— „ *vii* 105
nor cares to walk With Death and Morning on the *s* horns, „ 204
Pink was the shell within, *S* without; *Minnie and Winnie* 6
Calm on the seas, and *s* sleep, *In Mem. xi* 17
As slowly steals a *s* flame „ *lxvii* 6
To reverence and the *s* hair; „ *lxxxiv* 32
Or into *s* arrows break The sailing moon in creek and cove; „ *ci* 15
s knell Of twelve sweet hours that past *Maud I xviii* 64
And over these is placed a *s* wand, *Marr. of Geraint* 483
And over these they placed the *s* wand, „ 549
went In *s* tissue talking things of state; „ 663
And all the light upon her *s* face Flow'd *Balin and Balan* 263
And like a *s* shadow slipt away Thro' the dim land; *Merlin and V.* 423
Her seer, her bard, her *s* star of eve, „ 954
one emerald center'd in a sun Of *s* rays, *Lancelot and E.* 296
I heard a sound As of a *s* horn from o'er the hills *Holy Grail* 109
Stream'd thro' my cell a cold and *s* beam, „ 116
wove with *s* thread And crimson in the belt a strange device, A crimson grail within a *s* beam; „ 154
In *s* armour suddenly Galahad shone Before us, „ 458
for every moment glanced His *s* arms and gloom'd: „ 493
I saw him like a *s* star— „ 517
There tript a hundred tiny *s* deer, *Last Tournament* 171
Laid the long night in *s* streaks and bars, *Lover's Tale ii* 112
blew it far Until it hung, a little *s* cloud Over the sounding seas: „ *iii* 36
Smoothing their locks, as golden as his own Were *s*, *Sisters (E. and E.)* 57
By firth and loch thy *s* sister grow, *Sir J. Oldcastle* 58
S crescent-curve, Coming soon, *The Ring* 13
The *s* year should cease to mourn and sigh— *To Mary Boyle* 57
Silver (s) million tapers flaring bright From twisted *s's* *Arabian Nights* 125
Six columns, three on either side, Pure *s*, „ 145
Twilights of airy *s*, *Audley Court* 82
Sipt wine from *s*, praising God, *Will Water.* 127
cups and *s* on the burnish'd board Sparkled and shone; *Enoch Arden* 742
spread Their sleeping *s* thro' the hills; *In Mem., Con.* 116
bars Of black and bands of *s*, *Lover's Tale iv* 59

Sin (s) (*continued*) And all is past, the *s* is sinn'd, *Guinevere* 543
Gone thro' my *s* to slay and to be slain! „ 613
I cannot kill my *s*, If soul be soul; „ 621
in mine own heart I can live down *s* „ 636
alone with her *s* an' her shame, *First Quarrel* 25
an' *she*—in her shame an' her *s*— „ 69
S? O yes—we are sinners, I know— *Rizpah* 60
they have told you he never repented his *s*. „ 69
trouble, the strife and the *s*, *V. of Maeldune* 129
driven by storm and *s* and death to the ancient fold, *The Wreck* 2
prayer for a soul that died in his *s*, „ 10
Ten long days of summer and *s*— „ 77
But if *s* be *s*, not inherited fate, „ 85
My *s* to my desolate little one found me „ 86
'The wages of *s* is death,' „ 93
I cried, 'for the *s* of the wife, „ 99
be never gloom'd by the curse Of a *s*, „ 140
death alive, is a mortial *s*.' *Tomorrow* 51
Feyther 'ud saäy I wur ugly es *s*, *Spinster's S's*. 15
Shall we sin our fathers' *s*, *Open I. and C. Exhib.* 24
Murder will not veil your *s*, *Forlorn* 49
For bolder *s's* than mine, *Romney's R.* 133
Fur they wesh'd their *s's* i' *my* pond, *Church-warden, etc.* 16
Tha mun tackle the *s's* o' the Wo'ld, „ 46
leäved their nasty *s's* i' *my* pond, „ 54
THO' *S* too oft, when smitten by Thy rod, *Doubt and Prayer* 1
From *s* thro' sorrow into Thee we pass „ 3
Sin (verb) *s* against the strength of youth! *Locksley Hall* 59
Leolin, I almost *s* in envying you: *Aylmer's Field* 360
of one who sees To one who *s's*, *Com. of Arthur* 118
is your beauty, and I *s* In speaking, *Lancelot and E.* 1186
I could hardly *s* against the lowest.' *Last Tournament* 572
If this be sweet, to *s* in leading-strings, „ 574
Shall we *s* our fathers' sin, *Open I. and C. Exhib.* 24
Sinaï As over *S's* peaks of old, *In Mem. xcvi* 22
Sine Of *s* and arc, spheroïd and azimuth, *Princess vi* 256
Sinecure So moulder'd in a *s* as he: „ *Pro.* 182
Sinew home is in the *s's* of a man, „ *v* 267
Burst vein, snap *s*, and crack heart, *Sir J. Oldcastle* 123
Sinew-corded supple, *s-c*, apt at arms; *Princess v* 535
Sinew'd (*See also* **Supple-sinew'd**) until endurance grow *S* with action, *Œnone* 165
Sinful A *s* soul possess'd of many gifts, *To ——, With Pal. of Art* 3
A *s* man, conceived and born in sin: *St. S. Stylites* 122
Redden'd at once with *s*, for the point *Balin and Balan* 558
so glad were spirits and men Before the coming of the *s* Queen.' *Guinevere* 270
Such as they are, were you the *s* Queen.' „ 353
Sing it *s's* a song of undying love; *Poet's Mind* 33
We will *s* to you all the day: *Sea-Fairies* 20
I would sit and *s* the whole of the day; *The Merman* 9
I would *s* to myself the whole of the day; *The Mermaid* 10
still as I comb'd I would *s* and say, „ 12
Than but to dance and *s*, be gaily drest, *The form, the form* 3
Nor bird would *s*, nor lamb would bleat, *Mariana in the S.* 37
Sometimes I heard you *s* within; *Miller's D.* 123
Ah, well—but *s* the foolish song I gave you, „ 161
So *s* that other song I made, „ 199
To *s* her songs alone. *Palace of Art* 160
Nor harken what the inner spirit *s's*, *Lotos-Eaters, C. S.* 22
the minstrel *s's* Before them of the ten years' war „ 76
O BLACKBIRD! *s* me something well: *The Blackbird* 1
Take warning! he that will not *s* „ 21
Shall *s* for want, ere leaves are new, „ 23
Think you they *s* Like poets, *Gardener's D.* 99
have they any sense of why they *s*? „ 101
pits of fire, that still *S* in mine ears. *St. S. Stylites* 185
Like that strange song I heard Apollo *s*, *Tithonus* 62
this is truth the poet *s's*, *Locksley Hall* 75
Not even of a gnat that *s's*. *Day-Dm., Sleep. P.* 21
Ah shameless! for he did but *s* A song *You might have won* 21
That he *s's* in his boat on the bay! *Break, break, etc.* 8
For he *s's* of what the world will be *Poet's Song* 15
and every bird that *s's*: *Sea Dreams* 102
well then, sleep, And I will *s* you 'birdie.' „ 284

Sing (*continued*) let the ladies *s* us, if they will, *Princess, Pro.* 240
'Let some one *s* to us: lightlier move „ *iv* 36
as far As I could ape their treble, did I *s*. „ 92
I hear them too—they *s* to their team: *Grandmother* 81
O skill'd to *s* of Time or Eternity, *Milton* 2
I HELD it truth, with him who *s's* *In Mem. i* 1
I *s* to him that rests below, „ *xxi* 1
I do but *s* because I must, „ 23
And pipe but as the linnets *s*: „ 24
But in the songs I love to *s* „ *xxxviii* 7
Then are these songs I *s* of thee „ 11
That lay their eggs, and sting and *s* „ *l* 11
we do him wrong To *s* so wildly: „ *lvii* 4
And in that solace can I *s*, „ *lxv* 5
Or voice the richest-toned that *s's*, „ *lxxv* 7
For him she plays, to him she *s's* „ *xcvii* 29
As one would *s* the death of war, „ *ciii* 33
And *s* the songs he loved to hear. „ *cvii* 24
To the ballad that she *s's*. *Maud II iv* 43
Do I hear her *s* as of old, „ 44
so great bards of him will *s* Hereafter; *Com. of Arthur* 414
O birds that warble as the day goes by, *S* sweetly: *Gareth and L.* 1077
That *s's* so delicately clear, *Marr. of Geraint* 332
I heard the great Sir Lancelot *s* it once, *Merlin and V.* 385
And every minstrel *s's* it differently; „ 458
Will *s* the simple passage o'er and o'er *Lancelot and E.* 896
sweetly could she make and *s*. „ 1006
one hath sung and all the dumb will *s*. *Holy Grail* 301
Murmuring a light song I had heard thee *s*, *Last Tournament* 614
'O maiden, if indeed ye list to *s*, *S*, *Guinevere* 165
We could *s* a good song at the Plow, (repeat) *North. Cobbler* 18
Bullets would *s* by our foreheads, *Def. of Lucknow* 21
They love their mates, to whom they *s*; *The Flight* 65
To *s* thee to thy grave, *Freedom* 36
My birds would *s*, You heard not. *To Mary Boyle* 18
S like a bird and be happy, *Parnassus* 14
S the new year in under the blue. *The Throstle* 5
Our hymn to the sun. They *s* it. *Akbar's Dream* 203
S thou low or loud or sweet, *Poet and Critics* 6
Singe The moth will *s* her wings, *Sir J. Oldcastle* 189
Sing'd (sang) But, arter, we *s* the 'ymn togither *North. Cobbler* 54
Singed singe her wings, and *s* return, *Sir J. Oldcastle* 189
Singeing *See* **A-singein'**
Singer The sweet little wife of the *s* said, *The Islet* 3
the *s* shaking his curly head Turn'd as he sat, „ 6
A crown the *S* hopes may last, *Epilogue* 38
here the *S* for his Art Not all in vain may plead „ 79
their music here be mortal need the *s* greatly care? *Parnassus* 18
Singest ROMAN VIRGIL, thou that *s* *To Virgil* 1
Thou that *s* wheat and woodland, „ 9
Singeth The ancient poetess *s*, *Leonine Eleg.* 13
Singin' (singing) An' *s* yer 'Aves' an' 'Pathers' *Tomorrow* 96
Singing (*See also* **A-singin', Singin'**) *S* alone Under the sea, *The Merman* 4
A mermaid fair, *S* alone, *The Mermaid* 3
And *s* airy trifles this or that, *Caress'd or chidden* 2
They heard her *s* her last song, *L. of Shalott iv* 26
S in her song she died, „ 35
S and murmuring in her feastful mirth, *Palace of Art* 177
And *s* clearer than the crested bird *D. of F Women* 179
he is *s* Hosanna in the highest: *Enoch Arden* 502
S, 'And shall it be over the seas *The Islet* 9
And we with *s* cheer'd the way, *In Mem. xxii* 5
She is *s* an air that is known to me, *Maud I v* 3
S alone in the morning of life, „ 6
S of men that in battle array, „ 8
S of Death, and of Honour that cannot die, „ 16
She is *s* in the meadow And the rivulet at her feet „ *II iv* 40
thro' the open casement of the hall, *S*; *Marr. of Geraint* 329
Half whistling and half *s* a coarse song, *Geraint and E.* 528
voice *s* in the topmost tower To the eastward: *Holy Grail* 834
And shot itself into the *s* winds; *Lover's Tale i* 369
S 'Hail to the glorious Golden year *On Jub. Q. Victoria* 64
Single For in thee Is nothing sudden, nothing *s*; *Eleänore* 57
Poor Fancy sadder than a *s* star, *Caress'd or chidden* 13

Single (*continued*) And thought, 'My life is sick of *s* sleep : The Bridesmaid 13
'*S* I grew, like some green plant, D. of F. Women 205
induce a time When *s* thought is civil crime, You ask me, why, etc. 19
s note From that deep chord which Hampden smote England and Amer. 18
A *s* stream of all her soft brown hair Gardener's D. 128
And spake not of it to a *s* soul, St. S. Stylites 66
With a *s* rose in her hair. Lady Clare 60
That wilderness of *s* instances, Aylmer's Field 437
a cave Of touchwood, with a *s* flourishing spray. „ 512
than by *s* act Of immolation, Princess iii 284
made the *s* jewel on her brow Burn like the mystic fire „ iv 273
A *s* band of gold about her hair, „ v 513
The *s* pure and perfect animal, „ vii 306
And his compass is but of a *s* note, The Islet 28
Be tenants of a *s* breast, In Mem. xvi 3
Love would cleave in twain The lading of a *s* pain, „ xxv 11
So careless of the *s* life ; „ lv 8
No *s* tear, no mark of pain : „ lxxviii 14
And take us as a *s* soul. „ lxxxiv 44
A *s* church below the hill Is pealing, „ civ 3
A *s* peal of bells below, „ 5
A *s* murmur in the breast, „ 7
this a bridge of *s* arc Took at a leap ; Gareth and L. 908
But rose at last, a *s* maiden with her, Marr. of Geraint 160
Made but a *s* bound, and with a sweep of it Geraint and E. 727
Should make an onslaught *s* on a realm „ 917
a *s* misty star, Which is the second in a line of stars Merlin and V. 508
a *s* glance of them Will govern a whole life Lover's Tale i 75
'What can it matter, my lass, what I did wi' my *s* life ? First Quarrel 59
a *s* piece Weigh'd nigh four thousand Castillanos Columbus 135
His fathers have slain thy fathers in war or in *s* strife, V. of Maeldune 121
This double seeming of the *s* world !— Ancient Sage 105
Earth at last a warless world, a *s* race, a *s* tongue— Locksley H., Sixty 165
There a *s* sordid attic holds the living and the dead. „ 222
Mother weeps At that white funeral of the *s* life, Prin. Beatrice 9
If every *s* star Should shriek its claim Akbar's Dream 42

Singleness Arthur bound them not to *s* Merlin and V. 28

Singular I have heard, I know not whence, of the *s* beauty of Maud ; Maud I i 67

Sink I cannot *s* So far—far down, My life is full 8
And while he *s*'s or swells Talking Oak 270
wholly out of sight, and *s* Past earthquake— Lucretius 152
'There *s*'s the nebulous star we call the Sun, Princess iv 19
That *s*'s with all we love below the verge ; „ 47
they rise or *s* Together, dwarf'd or godlike, „ vii 259
And moan and *s* to their rest. Voice and the P. 16
And *s* again into sleep.' „ 24
And staggers blindly ere she *s* ? In Mem. xvi 14
So much the vital spirits *s* „ xx 18
'Twere best at once to *s* to peace, „ xxxiv 13
When in the down I *s* my head, „ lxviii 1
And the great Æon *s*'s in blood, „ cxxvii 16
A gloomy-gladed hollow slowly *s* To westward— Gareth and L. 797
Down to the river, *s* or swim, „ 1154
we scarce can *s* as low : Merlin and V. 813
By fire, to *s* into the abyss again ; Pass. of Arthur 83
S me the ship, Master Gunner—*s* her, split her in twain ! The Revenge 89
s Thy fleurs-de-lys in slime again, Sir J. Oldcastle 98

Sinking and *s* ships, and praying hands. Lotos-Eaters, C. S. 116
To follow knowledge like a *s* star, Ulysses 31
The voice of Britain, or a *s* land, To the Queen ii 24
I kiss'd him, I clung to the *s* form, The Wreck 105
'We are *s*, and yet there's hope : „ 121
slowly *s* now into the ground, Locksley H., Sixty 27
and *s* with the *s* wreck, „ 64

Sinless their *s* faith, A maiden moon that sparkles on a sty, Princess v 185
not the *s* years That breathed beneath the Syrian blue : In Mem. lii 11
Reputed to be red with *s* blood, Balin and Balan 557

Sinn'd I have *s*, for it was all thro' me Dora 60
Alas, my child, I *s* for thee.' Lady Clare 50
s in grosser lips Beyond all pardon— Princess iv 251
And that he *s* is not believable ; Merlin and V. 760
but if he *s*, The sin that practice burns „ 761
Guinevere had *s* against the highest, Last Tournament 570
Ev'n for thy sake, the sin which thou hast *s*. Guinevere 455
drawing foul ensample from fair names, *S* also, „ 491
And all is past, the sin is *s*, „ 543
And in the flesh thou hast *s* ; „ 554
S thro' an animal vileness, The Wreck 42
thunders of Ocean and Heaven 'Thou hast *s*.' „ 88
See, I *s* but for a moment. Happy 85
And—well, if I *s* last night, Bandit's Death 18

Sinner I am a *s* viler than you all. St. S. Stylites 135
In haunts of hungry *s*'s, Will Water. 222
Thou hast been a *s* too : Vision of Sin 92
Or sin seem less, the *s* seeming great ? Lancelot and E. 1418
Sin ? O yes—we are *s*'s, I know— Rizpah 60

Sinning Another *s* on such heights with one, Lancelot and E. 248

Sipt *S* wine from silver, praising God, Will Water. 127

Sir these great *S*'s Give up their parks Princess, Con. 102

Sire to die For God and for my *s* ! D. of F. Women 232
That we are wiser than our *s*'s. Love thou thy land 72
I read—two letters—one her *s*'s. Princess iv 397
At length my *S*, his rough cheek wet with tears, „ v 23
reach'd White hands of farewell to my *s*, „ 233
'O *S*,' she said, 'he lives : „ vi 122
then brake out my *s*, Lifting his grim head „ 271
Were those your *s*'s who fought at Lewes ? Third of Feb. 33
yet-loved *s* would make Confusion worse In Mem. xc 18
thou that slewest the *s* hast left the son. Gareth and L. 360
What said the happy *s* ? Merlin and V. 710

Siren O sister, *S*'s tho' they be, were such Princess ii 198

Sirius as the fiery *S* alters hue, „ v 262

Sirmio 'O venusta *S* !' Frater Ave, etc. 2
all-but-island, olive-silvery *S* ! „ 9

Sirmione Row us from Desenzano, to your *S* row ! „ 1

Sister (adj.) same two *s* pearls Ran down the silken thread Merlin and V. 454

Sister (s) (*See also* **Brother-sister, Foster-sister, Half-sister, Lady-sister, Mock-sister, Star-sisters, Twin-sister**) Thy *s* smiled and said, 'No tears for me ! The Bridesmaid 3
three *s*'s That doat upon each other, To ——, With Pal. of Art 10
To greet their fairer *s*'s of the East. Gardener's D. 188
Stole from her *s* Sorrow. „ 256
Sleep, Ellen, folded in thy *s*'s arm, Audley Court 63
he shouts with his *s* at play ! Break, break, etc. 6
'I have a *s* at the foreign court, Princess i 75
'My *s*.' 'Comely, too, by all that's fair,' „ ii 114
she cried, 'My brother !' 'Well, my *s*.' „ 188
O *s*, Sirens tho' they be, were such As chanted „ 198
Here lies a brother by a s *slain*, „ 208
when your *s* came she won the heart Of Ida : „ iii 87
To compass our dear *s*'s' liberties.' „ 288
Shall croak thee *s*, or the meadow-crake „ iv 124
'Lift up your head, sweet *s* : „ v 64
all about his motion clung The shadow of his *s*, „ 258
and in our noble *s*'s cause ? „ 312
My *s*'s crying, 'Stay for shame ;' Sailor Boy 18
Old *s*'s of a day gone by, In Mem. xxix 13
Leave thou thy *s* when she prays, „ xxxiii 5
A guest, or happy *s*, sung, „ lxxxix 26
Has not his *s* smiled on me ? Maud I xiii 45
Hath ever like a loyal *s* cleaved To Arthur,— Com. of Arthur 191
closer to this noble prince, Being his own dear *s* ;' „ 315
'And therefore Arthur's *s* ?' ask'd the King. „ 317
a knight To combat for my *s*, Lyonors, Gareth and L. 608
as any knight Toward thy *s*'s freeing.' „ 1018
Among her burnish'd *s*'s of the pool ; Marr. of Geraint 655
Would call her friend and *s*, sweet Elaine, Lancelot and E. 865
'Ah *s*,' answer'd Lancelot, 'what is this ?' „ 931
came her brethren saying, 'Peace to thee, Sweet *s*,' „ 997
To whom the gentle *s* made reply, „ 1073
'*S*, farewell for ever,' and again 'Farewell, sweet *s*,' „ 1151

Sister (s) (continued) no further off in blood from me Than s ; Holy Grail 70
My s's vision, fill'd me with amaze ; „ 140
'S or brother none had he ; „ 143
I found and saw it, as the nun My s saw it ; „ 199
Hath what thy s taught me first to see, „ 469
Where saving his own s's he had known Pelleas and E. 87
I must strike against the man they call My s's son— Guinevere 573
Nor shun to call me s, dwell with you ; „ 676
The s of my mother—she that bore Camilla Lover's Tale i 202
My mother's s, mother of my love, „ 209
I replied, 'O s, My will is one with thine ; „ 462
So shalt thou love me still as s's do ; „ 768
It was ill-done to part you, S's fair ; „ 814
My s, and my cousin, and my love, „ iii 43
She never had a s. I knew none. „ iv 326
Meä an' thy s was married, North. Cobbler 11
No s's ever prized each other more. Sisters (E. and E.) 43
mother and her s loved More passionately still. „ 44
The younger s, Evelyn, enter'd— „ 152
The s's closed in one another's arms, „ 155
Yet so my path was clear To win the s. „ 203
'What, will she never set her s free ?' „ 218
The s's glide about me hand in hand, „ 275
By firth and loch thy silver s grow, Sir J. Oldcastle 58
One naked peak—the s of the sun Tiresias 30
do not sleep, my s dear ! The Flight 1
Ah, clasp me in your arms, s, „ 5
Speak to me, s ; counsel me ; „ 75
Arise, my own true s, come forth ! „ 96
S's, brothers—and the beasts— Locksley H., Sixty 102
Sister-eyelids The dewy s-e lay. Day-Dm., Pro. 4
Sisterhood O peaceful S, Receive, Guinevere 140
Sister-world glow Thy silver s-w, Move eastward 6
Sit Low-cowering shall the Sophist s ; Clear-headed friend 10
The white owl in the belfry s's. (repeat) The Owl i 7, 14
I would s and sing the whole of the day ; The Merman 9
all day long you s between Joy and woe, Margaret 63
Nor care to s beside her where she s's— Wan Sculptor 10
'Here s's he shaping wings to fly : Two Voices 289
In yonder chair I see him s, Miller's D. 9
'by that lamp,' I thought, 'she s's !' „ 114
Sometimes I saw you s and spin ; „ 121
I s as God holding no form of creed, Palace of Art 211
But s beside my bed, mother, May Queen, Con. 23
to s, to sleep, to wake, to breathe.' Edwin Morris 40
S with their wives by fires, St. S. Stylites 108
S brooding in the ruins of a life, Love and Duty 12
Here s's the Butler with a flask Day-Dm., Sleep. P. 25
I s, my empty glass reversed, Will Water. 159
'S thee down, and have no shame, Vision of Sin 83
God bless him, he shall s upon my knees Enoch Arden 197
S, listen.' Then he told her of his voyage, „ 861
S down again ; mark me and understand, „ 876
Where s the best and stateliest of the land ? Lucretius 172
if I might s beside your feet, And glean Princess ii 258
beneath an emerald plane S's Diotima, „ iii 302
I will go and s beside the doors, „ v 96
she may s Upon a king's right hand in thunderstorms, „ 438
To s a star upon the sparkling spire ; „ vii 197
upon the skirts of Time, S side by side, „ 288
They come and s by my chair, Grandmother 83
To s with empty hands at home. Sailor Boy 16
See they s, they hide their faces, Boädicea 51
I s within a helmless bark, In Mem. iv 3
back return To where the body s's, „ xii 19
For by the hearth the children s „ xx 13
The Shadow s's and waits for me. „ xxii 20
Alone, alone, to where he s's, „ xxiii 3
But, he was dead, and there he s's, „ xxxii 3
And we shall s at endless feast, „ xlvii 9
Her life is lone, he s's apart, „ xcvii 17
But on her forehead s's a fire : „ cxiv 5
In the little grove where I s— Maud I iv 2
And the whole little wood where I s „ 24
Why s's he here in his father's chair ? „ xiii 23

Sit (continued) when alone She s's by her music and books Maud I xiv 13
s's on her shining head, And she knows it not : „ xvi 17
Our one white lie s's like a little ghost Gareth and L. 297
Arthur, 'We s King, to help the wrong'd „ 371
and they s within our hall. „ 425
Why s ye there ? Rest would I not, „ 596
O s beside a noble gentlewoman.' „ 867
and speak To your good damsel there who s's apart, Geraint and E. 299
I see with joy, Ye s apart, „ 321
He s's unarm'd ; I hold a finger up ; „ 337
strange knights Who s near Camelot at a fountain-side, Balin and Balan 11
let them s, Until they find a lustier 18
'Fair Sirs,' said Arthur, 'wherefore s ye here ?' „ 31
song that once I heard By this huge oak, sung nearly where we s : Merlin and V. 406
I s and gather honey ; yet, methinks, „ 601
They s with knife in meat and wine in horn ! „ 694
'No man could s but he should lose himself :' Holy Grail 174
Galahad would s down in Merlin's chair. „ 181
Must be content to s by little fires. „ 614
But s within the house. „ 715
Who s's and gazes on a faded fire, Last Tournament 157
To s once more within his lonely hall, Guinevere 497
But thou didst s alone in the inner house, Lover's Tale i 112
Why did you s so quiet ? Rizpah 14
kind of you, Madam, to s by an old dying wife. „ 21
S thysen down fur a bit : Village Wife 5
Naay s down—naw 'urry—sa cowd !— „ 20
While 'e s like a greät glimmer-gowk „ 38
Who s's beside the blessed Virgin Columbus 232
Whom yet I see as there you s To E. Fitzgerald 5
I will s at your feet, I will hide my face, The Wreck 12
So I s's i' my oän armchair Spinster's S's. 9
Or s's wi' their 'ands afoor 'em, „ 86
I s's i' my oän little parlour, „ 103
since he would s on a Prophet's seat, Dead Prophet 53
and with Grief S face to face, To Mary Boyle 46
in her open palm a halcyon s's Patient— Prog. of Spring 20
To s once more ? Cassandra, Romney's R. 4
would you—if it please you—s to me ? „ 73
Your song—S, listen ! „ 92
my faithful counsellor, S by my side. Akbar's Dream 19
an' s's o' the Bishop's throän. Church-warden, etc. 20
Sit (set) an' the tongue's s afire o' Hell, „ 24
Site Storm-strengthen'd on a windy s, Gareth and L. 692
Sittest That s ranging golden hair ; In Mem. vi 26
Sittin' an' a s 'ere o' my bed. N. Farmer, O. S. 9
one night I wur s aloän, Owd Roä 29
Sitting (See also Sittin') wish to charm Pallas and Juno s by : A Character 15
A merman bold, S alone, The Merman 3
s, burnish'd without fear The brand, Two Voices 128
on this hand, and s on this stone ? Œnone 233
I saw you s in the house, May Queen, Con. 30
One s on a crimson scarf unroll'd ; D. of F. Women 126
Tho' s girt with doubtful light. Love thou thy land 16
So s, served by man and maid, The Goose 21
s in the deeps Upon the hidden bases of the hills.' M. d'Arthur 105
but we s, as I said, The cock crew loud ; „ Ep. 9
And said to me, she s with us then, Gardener's D. 21
And, s muffled in dark leaves, „ 37
s straight Within the low-wheel'd chaise, Talking Oak 109
Push off, and s well in order smite Ulysses 58
Suffused them, s, lying, languid shapes, Vision of Sin 12
Enoch and Annie, s hand-in-hand, Enoch Arden 69
Philip s at her side forgot Her presence, „ 384
When lo ! her Enoch s on a height, „ 500
s all alone, his face Would darken, Sea Dreams 12
As night to him that s on a hill Princess iv 574
I am oftener s at home in my father's farm Grandmother 90
They found the mother s still ; The Victim 31
I see thee s crown'd with good, In Mem. lxxxiv 5
Peace s under her olive, Maud I i 33

Sitting (*continued*) am I *s* here so stunn'd and still, *Maud II i* 2
his good mates Lying or *s* round him, *Gareth and L.* 512
There on a day, he *s* high in hall, *Marr. of Geraint* 147
And knew her *s* sad and solitary. *Geraint and E.* 282
Balin and Balan *s* statuelike, *Balin and Balan* 24
as makes The white swan-mother, *s*, „ 353
s in thine own hall, canst endure To mouth „ 378
Sir Lancelot, *s* in my place Enchair'd to-morrow, *Last Tournament* 103
s in the deeps Upon the hidden bases of the hills.' *Pass. of Arthur* 273
And *s* down upon the golden moss, *Lover's Tale i* 540
now striding fast, and now *S* awhile to rest, „ *iv* 88
And *s* down to such a base repast, „ 134
'There is more than one Here *s* who desires it „ 242
I, by Lionel *s*, saw his face Fire, „ 322
But Julian, *s* by her, answer'd all: „ 340
The face of one there *s* opposite, *Sisters* (*E. and E.*) 88
summer days upon deck, *s* hand in hand— *The Wreck* 64
children in a sunbeam *s* on the ribs of wreck. *Locksley H., Sixty* 14
left within the shadow *s* on the wreck alone. „ 16
Who '*s* on green sofas contemplate The torment *Akbar's Dream* 48
wife was unharm'd, tho' *s* close to his side. *Charity* 22
Sitting-room To fit their little streetward *s-r* *Enoch Arden* 170
Six *S* columns, three on either side, *Arabian Nights* 144
high *S* cubits, and three years on one of twelve; *St. S. Stylites* 87
'And make her some great Princess, *s* feet high, *Princess, Pro.* 224
S hundred maidens clad in purest white, „ *ii* 472
S thousand years of fear have made you „ *iv* 507
Among *s* boys, head under head, and look'd „ *Con.* 83
And *s* feet two, as I think, he stands; *Maud I xiii* 10
Saw *s* tall men haling a seventh along, *Gareth and L.* 811
S stately virgins, all in white, upbare *Lover's Tale ii* 77
Save those *s* virgins which upheld the bier, „ 84
those *s* maids With shrieks and ringing laughter „ *iii* 31
An' he wrote 'I ha' *s* weeks' work, little wife, *First Quarrel* 45
I ha' *s* weeks' work in Jersey an' go to-night „ 88
We are *s* ships of the line; *The Revenge* 7
KING, that hast reign'd *s* hundred years, *To Dante* 1
S foot deep of burial mould Will dull their comments! *Romney's R.* 125
Six hundred Rode the *s h.* (repeat) *Light Brigade* 4, 8, 17, 26
rode back, but not Not the *s h.* „ 38
All that was left of them, Left of *s h.* „ 49
Honour the Light Brigade, Noble *s h*! „ 55
Sixpence Be shot for *s* in a battle-field, *Audley Court* 41
Sixty in one month They wedded her to *s* thousand pounds, *Edwin Morris* 126
when every hour Must sweat her *s* minutes to the death, *Golden Year* 69
And *s* feet the fountain leapt. *Day-Dm., Revival* 8
Here we met, our latest meeting—Amy—*s* years ago— *Locksley H., Sixty* 177
Strove for *s* widow'd years to help his homelier brother men, „ 267
thro' this midnight breaks the sun Of *s* years away, *Pref. Poem Broth. Son.* 22
Size His double chin, his portly *s*, *Miller's D.* 2
This weight and *s*, this heart and eyes, *Sir Galahad* 71
For often fineness compensated *s*; *Princess ii* 149
Skate taught me how to *s*, to row, to swim, *Edwin Morris* 19
Skater Like the *s* on ice that hardly bears him, *Hendecasyllabics* 6
Skeärd (scared) an' tellin' me not to be *s*, *Owd Roä* 85
Skeleton make the carcase a *s*, *Boädicea* 14
And bears a *s* figured on his arms, *Gareth and L.* 640
Flash'd the bare-grinning *s* of death! *Merlin and V.* 847
unawares Had trodden that crown'd *s*, *Lancelot and E.* 49
Gaunt as it were the *s* of himself, (repeat) „ 764, 816
Not from the *s* of a brother-slayer, *Last Tournament* 47
Found, as it seem'd, a *s* alone, *Lover's Tale iv* 139
But that half *s*, like a barren ghost *The Ring* 227
Skelpt (overturned) she *s* ma haäfe ower i' the chair, *Owd Roä* 76
Sketch (*See also* **Thunder-sketch**) No matter what the *s* might be; *Ode to Memory* 95
Buss me, thou rough *s* of man, *Vision of Sin* 189
s'es rude and faint. *Aylmer's Field* 100
and lost Salvation for a *s*. *Romney's R.* 139
Sketch'd Miriam *s* and Muriel threw the fly; *The Ring* 159
Sketcher I was a *s* then: See here, *Edwin Morris* 4
Sketching *s* with her slender pointed foot *The Brook* 102
Skiff drive Thro' utter dark a full-sail'd *s*, *Supp. Confessions* 95
Skill (*See also* **Tourney-skill**) Nor mine the sweetness or the *s*, *In Mem. cx* 17
with force and *s* To strive, to fashion, „ *cxiii* 6
fill up the gap where force might fail With *s* and fineness. *Gareth and L.* 1353
And might of limb, but mainly use and *s*, *Last Tournament* 198
now leaving to the *s* Of others their old craft *Pref. Son. 19th Cent.* 2
As we surpass our fathers' *s*, *Mechanophilus* 21
Skill'd O *s* to sing of Time or Eternity, *Milton* 2
in a moment—at one touch Of that *s* spear, *Gareth and L.* 1223
the hermit, *s* in all The simples and the science *Lancelot and E.* 861
to keep So *s* a nurse about you always— *The Ring* 374
Skim dip Their wings in tears, and *s* away. *In Mem. xlviii* 16
Before her *s's* the jubilant woodpecker, *Prog. of Spring* 16
Skimm'd fleeter now she *s* the plains *Sir L. and Q. G.* 32
Skimming *S* down to Camelot: *L. of Shalott i* 23
Among my *s* swallows; *The Brook* 175
Skin (s) (*See also* **Sallow-skin**) a leopard *s* Droop'd from his shoulder, *Œnone* 58
A million wrinkles carved his *s*; *Palace of Art* 138
'In filthy sloughs they roll a prurient *s*, „ 201
a *s* As clean and white as privet when it flowers. *Walk. to the Mail* 55
a scratch No deeper than the *s*: *Edwin Morris* 64
Until the ulcer, eating thro' my *s*, *St. S. Stylites* 67
We fret, we fume, would shift our *s's*, *Will Water.* 225
s's of wine, and piles of grapes. *Vision of Sin* 13
Tattoo'd or woaded, winter-clad in *s's*, *Princess ii* 120
hunt them for the beauty of their *s's*; „ *v* 156
Prickle my *s* and catch my breath, *Maud I xiv* 36
wrapt in harden'd *s's* That fit him like his own; *Gareth and L.* 1093
His arms are old, he trusts the harden'd *s*— „ 1139
But lash'd in vain against the harden'd *s*, „ 1143
the *s* Clung but to crate and basket, *Merlin and V.* 624
he was all wet thro' to the *s*, *First Quarrel* 76
they pricks cleän thruf to the *s*— *Spinster's S's.* 36
Shallow *s* of green and azure— *Locksley H., Sixty* 208
'Small blemish upon the *s*! *Dead Prophet* 66
The leper plague may scale my *s* *Happy* 27
Skin (verb) like a man That *s's* the wild beast after slaying him, *Geraint and E.* 93
Skip 'Why *s* ye so, Sir Fool?' (repeat) *Last Tournament* 9, 243
belike I *s* To know myself the wisest knight „ 247
S to the broken music of my brains „ 258
Arthur and the angels hear, And then we *s*.' „ 351
Skipping Dagonet, *s*, 'Arthur, the King's; „ 262
Skipt But when the twangling ended, *s* again; And being ask'd, 'Why *s* ye not, Sir Fool?' „ 255
Skirt (s) Brightening the *s's* of a long cloud, *M. d'Arthur* 54
thro' the gray *s's* of a lifting squall *Enoch Arden* 829
thro' warp and woof From *s* to *s*; *Princess i* 63
your ingress here Upon the *s* and fringe of our fair land, „ *v* 219
upon the *s's* of Time, Sit side by side, „ *vii* 287
Imagined more than seen, the *s's* of France. „ *Con.* 48
fusing all The *s's* of self again, *In Mem. xlvii* 3
And grasps the *s's* of happy chance, „ *lxiv* 6
s's are loosen'd by the breaking storm, *Geraint and E.* 459
the gloomy *s's* Of Celidon the forest; *Lancelot and E.* 291
Tho' somewhat draggled at the *s*. *Last Tournament* 219
Brightening the *s's* of a long cloud, *Pass. of Arthur* 222
Skirt (verb) oft when sundown *s's* the moor *In Mem. xli* 17
Skirted *See* **Purple-skirted**
Skull Is but modell'd on a *s*. *Vision of Sin* 178
thy foot Is on the *s* which thou hast made. *In Mem., Pro.* 8
And wears a helmet mounted with a *s*, *Gareth and L.* 639
with one stroke Sir Gareth split the *s*. „ 1404
clove the helm As throughly as the *s*; „ 1407
I smote upon the naked *s* A thrall of thine in open hall, *Balin and Balan* 55
and the *s* Brake from the nape, and from the *s* the crown Roll'd into light, *Lancelot and E.* 49
Black as the harlot's heart—hollow as a *s*! *Pelleas and E.* 468
fossil *s* that is left in the rocks *Despair* 86

Sliding (*continued*) Unconscious of the *s* hour, *In Mem. xliii* 5
A river *s* by the wall. „ *ciii* 8
Come *s* out of her sacred glove, *Maud I vi* 85
Went *s* down so easily, and fell, *Gareth and L.* 1224
On to the palace-doorway *s*, paused. *Lancelot and E.* 1246
and *s* down the blacken'd marsh Blood-red, *Holy Grail* 473
Slieäve (sleeve) Roäver a-tuggin' an' teärin' my *s*. *Owd Roä* 60
Slight (adj.) 'You're too *s* and fickle,' I said, *Edward Gray* 19
S was his answer 'Well—I care not for it:' *Aylmer's Field* 238
When some respect, however *s*, was paid To woman, *Princess ii* 136
for such, my friend, We hold them *s*: „ *iv* 127
No doubt, for *s* delay, remain'd among us „ 331
We are fools and *s*; *In Mem., Pro.* 29
How dimly character'd and *s*, „ *lxi* 6
To save from some *s* shame one simple girl. *Maud I xviii* 45
S, to be crush'd with a tap Of my finger-nail „ *II ii* 21
For ah! the *s* coquette, she cannot love, *The form, the form* 12
'The *s* she-slips of loyal blood, *Talking Oak* 57
A body *s* and round, and like a pear In growing, *Walk. to the Mail* 53
And *s* Sir Robert with his watery smile *Edwin Morris* 128
She play'd about with *s* and sprightly talk, *Merlin and V.* 171
For, grant me some *s* power upon your fate, „ 333
Flush'd slightly at the *s* disparagement *Lancelot and E.* 234
I am not made of so *s* elements. *Guinevere* 510
and death at our *s* barricade, *Def. of Lucknow* 15
S ripple on the boundless deep That moves, *Ancient Sage* 189
Future glimpse and fade Thro' some *s* spell, *Early Spring* 32
Slight (s) To look at her with *s*, and say *Mariana in the S.* 66
bare in bitter grudge The *s's* of Arthur and his Table, *Merlin and V.* 7
Slight (verb) and yet you dared To *s* it. *Dora* 99
he will teach him hardness, and to *s* His mother; „ 120
he will learn to *s* His father's memory; „ 153
Wherefore *s* me not wholly, *Hendecasyllabics* 15
He seems to *s* her simple heart. *In Mem. xcvii* 20
A song that *s's* the coming care, „ *xcix* 10
Why *s* your King, And lose the quest *Lancelot and E.* 654
I, would *s* our marriage oath: *Happy* 89
Slighted saw Philip, the *s* suitor of old times, *Enoch Arden* 745
Going? I am old and *s*: *Columbus* 241
Slighter Yours has been a *s* ailment, *Locksley H., Sixty* 17
Near us Edith's holy shadow, smiling at the *s* ghost. „ 54
Slightest The *s* air of song shall breathe *In Mem. xlix* 7
Slightly Flush'd *s* at the slight disparagement *Lancelot and E.* 234
Slight-natured If she be small, *s-n*, miserable, *Princess vii* 265
Slime That tare each other in their *s*, *In Mem. lvi* 23
that cannot see for *s*, *S* of the ditch: *Holy Grail* 771
sink Thy fleurs-de-lys in *s* again, *Sir J. Oldcastle* 99
soul and sense in city *s*? *Locksley H., Sixty* 218
labour'd in lifting them out of *s*, *Dead Prophet* 11
Slimed snake-like *s* his victim ere he gorged; *Sea Dreams* 193
And sank his head in mire, and *s* themselves *Last Tournament* 471
Slink As boys that *s* From ferule *Princess v* 37
a coward *s's* from what he fears To cope with, *Pelleas and E.* 438
Slip (s) (*See also* **She-slip**) narrow moon-lit *s's* of silver cloud, *Œnone* 218
And show you *s's* of all that grows *Amphion* 83
Bursts of great heart and *s's* in sensual mire, *Princess v* 199
those white *s's* Handed her cup and piped, *Last Tournament* 295
there was but a *s* of a moon, *Tomorrow* 9
Slip (verb) Could *s* its bark and walk. *Talking Oak* 188
'Sometimes I let a sunbeam *s*, „ 217
Or *s* between the ridges, *The Brook* 28
I *s*, I slide, I gloom, I glance, „ 174
to *s* away To-day, to-morrow, soon: *Princess ii* 296
And *s* at once all-fragrant into one. „ *vii* 70
And *s's* into the bosom of the lake: „ 187
and *s* Into my bosom and be lost in me.' „ 188
Sun comes, moon comes, Time *s's* away. *Window, When* 2
I *s* the thoughts of life and death; *In Mem. cxxii* 16
I will not let his name *S* from my lips *Marr. of Geraint* 446
and by and by *S's* into golden cloud, „ 736
Slipper fit to wear your *s* for a glove. *Geraint and E.* 623
Slippery (*See also* **Slaäpe**) as he based His feet on juts of *s* crag *M. d'Arthur* 189
To glance and shift about her *s* sides, *Lucretius* 189
Glass'd in the *s* sand before it breaks? *Merlin and V.* 293

Slippery (*continued*) And that it was too *s* to be held, *Lancelot and E.* 213
as he based His feet on juts of *s* crag *Pass. of Arthur* 357
hath o'erstept The *s* footing of his narrow wit, *Lover's Tale i* 102
Slipping The *s* thro' from state to state. *Two Voices* 351
three times *s* from the outer edge, *The Epic* 11
The silent water *s* from the hills, *Enoch Arden* 633
and then Went *s* down horrible precipices, *Geraint and E.* 379
Come *s* o'er their shadows on the sand, „ 471
Went *s* back upon the golden days *Guinevere* 380
Slip-shod '*S-s* waiter, lank and sour, *Vision of Sin* 71
Slipt (*See also* **Shoulder-slipt**) 'Tis gone: a thousand such have *s* *Will Water.* 181
The snake *s* under a spray, *Poet's Song* 10
And *s* aside, and like a wounded life *Enoch Arden* 75
by mischance he *s* and fell: „ 106
Till half-another year had *s* away. „ 471
She *s* across the summer of the world, „ 531
S into ashes, and was found no more. *Aylmer's Field* 6
S o'er those lazy limits down the wind „ 495
out I *s* Into a land all sun and blossom, *Sea Dreams* 100
And I *s* out: but whither will you now? *Princess iv* 240
S round and in the dark invested you, „ 404
And blossom-fragrant *s* the heavy dews „ *v* 243
Her falser self *s* from her like a robe, „ *vii* 161
The hoof of his horse *s* in the stream, *Gareth and L.* 1046
like a silver shadow *s* away Thro' the dim land; *Merlin and V.* 423
the braid *S* and uncoil'd itself, „ 889
And *s* and fell into some pool or stream, *Lancelot and E.* 214
Who lost the hern we *s* her at, „ 657
Lightly, her suit allow'd, she *s* away, „ 778
At once she *s* like water to the floor. „ 830
Heavy as it was, a great stone *s* and fell, *Holy Grail* 680
S, and ran on, and flung himself between *St. Telemachus* 61
Slit And Uther *s* thy tongue: *Gareth and L.* 376
Slither'd I *s* an' hurted my huck, *North. Cobbler* 19
Sloe blackthorn-blossom fades and falls and leaves the bitter *s*, *The Flight* 15
betwixt the whitening *s* And kingcup blaze, *To Mary Boyle* 25
Sloe-tree Poussetting with a *s-t*: *Amphion* 44
Sloomy (sluggish) An' Sally wur *s* an' draggle *North. Cobbler* 41
Slope (adj.) when the crisp *s* waves After a tempest, *Supp. Confessions* 126
Took horse, descended the *s* street, *Gareth and L.* 662
thro' lanes of shouting Gareth rode Down the *s* street, „ 700
on thro' silent faces rode Down the *s* city, „ 735
Down the *s* city rode, and sharply turn'd *Last Tournament* 127
Slope (s) (*See also* **Hill-slope**) his native *s*, Where he was wont to leap *Supp. Confessions* 164
And on the *s*, an absent fool, *Miller's D.* 62
Upon the freshly-flower'd *s*. „ 112
The downward *s* to death. *D. of F. Women* 16
There, on a *s* of orchard, Francis laid *Audley Court* 20
At last I heard a voice upon the *s* *Vision of Sin* 219
And many a *s* was rich in bloom *To E. L.* 20
drew, from butts of water on the *s*, *Princess, Pro.* 60
Blot out the *s* of sea from verge to shore, „ *vii* 38
we climb'd The *s* to Vivian-place, „ *Con.* 40
From *s* to *s* thro' distant ferns, „ 99
and I stand on the *s* of the hill, *Window, On the Hill* 9
Follow them down the *s*! „ 16
To slant the fifth autumnal *s*, *In Mem. xxii* 10
Becomes on Fortune's crowning *s* „ *lxiv* 14
Upon a pastoral *s* as fair, *Maud I xviii* 19
on the *s* The sword rose, the hind fell, *Com. of Arthur* 431
after one long *s* was mounted, saw, Bowl-shaped, *Gareth and L.* 795
I was halfway down the *s* to Hell, *Geraint and E.* 791
up a *s* of garden, all Of roses white and red, *Pelleas and E.* 421
purple *s's* of mountain flowers Pass *Last Tournament* 229
Was blackening on the *s's* of Portugal, *Sisters (E. and E.)* 62
and roll their ruins down the *s*. *Locksley H., Sixty* 138
Thro' the great gray *s* of men, *Heavy Brigade* 17
and flamed On one huge *s* beyond, *St. Telemachus* 8
Slope (verb) peaks shadow'd with pine *s* to the dark hyaline. *Leonine Eleg.* 10
the summits *s* Beyond the furthest flights *Two Voices* 184
swimming vapour *s's* athwart the glen, *Œnone* 3
leave The monstrous ledges there to *s*, *Princess vii* 212

Slope (verb) (*continued*) That *s* thro' darkness up to God, *In Mem. lv* 16
As *s's* a wild brook o'er a little stone, *Marr. of Geraint* 77
Sloped the mountain-shade *S* downward to her seat *Œnone* 22
we came to where the river *s* To plunge *Princess iii* 290
down from this a lordly stairway *s* *Gareth and L.* 669
arms on which the standing muscle *s*, *Marr. of Geraint* 76
till the morning light *S* thro' the pines, *Lover's Tale i* 264
breakers on the shore *S* into louder surf: „ *iii* 15
Sloping (*See also* **Even-sloping, Onward-sloping**) Was *s* toward his western bower. *Mariana* 80
s of the moon-lit sward Was damask-work, *Arabian Nights* 27
great Orion *s* slowly to the West. *Locksley Hall* 8
s down to make Arms for his chair, *Lancelot and E.* 437
In some fair space of *s* greens *Palace of Art* 106
For all the *s* pasture murmur'd, sown *Princess, Pro.* 55
Who, smitten by the dusty *s* beam, *Marr. of Geraint* 262
crisping white Play'd ever back upon the *s* wave, *Holy Grail* 382
the *s* seas Hung in mid-heaven, *Lover's Tale i* 3
Slot But at the *s* or fewmets of a deer, *Last Tournament* 371
Sloth But stagnates in the weeds of *s*; *In Mem. xxvii* 11
Slothful Inwrapt tenfold in *s* shame, *Palace of Art* 262
But wink no more in *s* overtrust. *Ode on Well.* 170
Nor the cannon-bullet rust on a *s* shore, *Maud III vi* 26
He rooted out the *s* officer Or guilty, *Geraint and E.* 938
Slough (*See also* **Woman-slough**) 'In filthy *s's* they roll a prurient skin, *Palace of Art* 201
From scalp to sole one *s* and crust of sin, *St. S. Stylites* 2
mountain there has cast his cloudy *s*, *Lucretius* 177
dazzled by the wildfire Love to *s's* That swallow common sense, *Princess v* 441
times in the *s's* of a low desire, *By an Evolution.* 18
Slow (*See also* **Too-slow**) The *s* clock ticking, and the sound *Mariana* 74
So full, so deep, so *s*, *Eleänore* 95
The *s* result of winter showers: *Two Voices* 452
The *s* wise smile that, round about *Miller's D.* 5
Her *s* full words sank thro' the silence drear, *D. of F. Women* 121
Nor swift nor *s* to change, but firm: *Love thou thy land* 31
A league of grass, wash'd by a *s* broad stream, *Gardener's D.* 40
If I may measure time by yon *s* light, *St. S. Stylites* 94
I hardly, with *s* steps, With *s*, faint steps, „ 182
my heart so *s* To feel it! *Love and Duty* 34
The *s* sweet hours that bring us all things good, The *s* sad hours that bring us all things ill, „ 57
by *s* prudence to make mild A rugged people, *Ulysses* 36
The long day wanes: the *s* moon climbs: „ 55
his long wooing her, Her *s* consent, and marriage, *Enoch Arden* 708
By *s* approaches, than by single act *Princess iii* 284
till the Bear had wheel'd Thro' a great arc his seven *s* suns. „ *iv* 213
At first her eye with *s* dilation roll'd „ *vi* 189
Lead out the pageant: sad and *s*, *Ode on Well.* 13
The sound of streams that swift or *s* *In Mem. xxxv* 10
And all the wheels of Being *s*. „ *l* 4
One set *s* bell will seem to toll „ *lvii* 10
With *s* steps from out An old storm-beaten, *Gareth and L.* 1112
the great Queen Came with *s* steps, *Balin and Balan* 245
Here her *s* sweet eyes Fear-tremulous, *Merlin and V.* 85
The *s* tear creep from her closed eyelid yet, „ 906
Sighs, and *s* smiles, and golden eloquence *Lancelot and E.* 649
But ten *s* mornings past, and on the eleventh „ 1133
Then with a *s* smile turn'd the lady round *Pelleas and E.* 91
Spread the *s* smile thro' all her company. „ 95
and there, with *s* sad steps Ascending, *Last Tournament* 143
With silent smiles of *s* disparagement; *Guinevere* 14
Methought by *s* degrees the sullen bell Toll'd quicker, *Lover's Tale iii* 13
Some thro' age and *s* diseases, *Locksley H., Sixty* 46
Æonian Evolution, swift or *s*, Thro' all the Spheres— *The Ring* 44
But after ten *s* weeks her fix'd intent, „ 345
Slow-arching crest of some *s-a* wave, *Last Tournament* 462
Slow-develop'd A *s-d* strength awaits Completion *Love thou thy land* 57
Slow-dropping *S-d* veils of thinnest lawn, *Lotos-Eaters* 11
Slower Are *s* to forgive than human kings. *Tiresias* 10
And *s* and fainter, Old and weary, *Merlin and the G.* 99
Slow-falling westward—under yon *s-f* star, *Akbar's Dream* 152
Slow-flaming Would seem *s-f* crimson fires *Palace of Art* 50

Slowly Ring out a *s* dying cause, *In Mem. cvi* 13
out of the darkness Silent and *s* *Merlin and the G.* 82
Slowly-dying (*See also* **Slowly**) and winks behind a *s-d* fire. *Locksley Hall* 136
By quiet fields, a *s-d* power, *De Prof., Two G.* 24
Slowly-fading The *s-f* mistress of the world, *Com. of Arthur* 505
Slowly-grown if our *s-g* And crown'd Republic's crowning common-sense, *To the Queen ii* 60
Slowly-mellowing thro' the *s-m* avenues *Last Tournament* 360
Slowly-painful More *s-p* to subdue this home Of sin, *St. S. Stylites* 57
Slowly-ridging The *s-r* rollers on the cliffs Clash'd, *Lover's Tale i* 57
Slowly-thickening I see the *s-t* chestnut towers *Prog. of Spring* 42
Slowly-waning and deckt in *s-w* hues. *Gareth and L.* 1195
Slow-measure have moved *s-m* to my tune, *Last Tournament* 282
Slow-moving *S-m* as a wave against the wind, *Lover's Tale iv* 293
Slow-worm *s-w* creeps, and the thin weasel *Aylmer's Field* 852
Sludge tends her bristled grunters in the *s*:' *Princess v* 27
Sluggard I have been the *s*, and I ride apace, *Holy Grail* 644
Sluggish (*See also* **Sloomy**) Mere fellowship of *s* moods, *In Mem. xxxv* 21
Sluice A *s* with blacken'd waters slept, *Mariana* 38
Sluiced canal From the main river *s*, *Arabian Nights* 26
Slumber (s) hum of swarming bees Into dreamful *s* lull'd. *Eleänore* 30
in its place My heart a charmed *s* keeps, „ 128
Nor steep our brows in *s's* holy balm; *Lotos-Eaters, C. S.* 21
surely, *s* is more sweet than toil, „ 126
As thro' the *s* of the globe *The Voyage* 23
Betwixt the *s* of the poles, *In Mem. xcix* 18
Breaking a *s* in which all spleenful folly *Maud I iii* 2
I envied your sweet *s*, *The Flight* 9
Slumber (verb) *S's* not like a mountain tarn? *Supp. Confessions* 129
And the kindly earth shall *s*, *Locksley Hall* 130
In some long trance should *s* on; *In Mem. xliii* 4
Slumber'd the garden-bowers and grots *S*: *Arabian Nights* 79
While Enoch *s* motionless and pale, *Enoch Arden* 908
Slumbering Winnow with giant arms the *s* green. *The Kraken* 10
Red after revel, droned her lurdane knights *S*, *Pelleas and E.* 431
Who slowly paced among the *s* host, *Pass. of Arthur* 7
Slumbrous The *s* wave outwelleth, *Claribel* 18
if a bolt of fire Would rive the *s* summer noon *Supp. Confessions* 11
Rolling a *s* sheet of foam below. *Lotos-Eaters* 13
The *s* light is rich and warm, *Day-Dm., Sleep. B.* 7
Slung from his blazon'd baldric *s* *L. of Shalott iii* 15
Slur seem'd to *s* With garrulous ease *Princess i* 163
how men *s* him, saying all his force Is melted *Marr. of Geraint* 106
Slurring and *s* the days gone by, *Maud I i* 33
Slushin' *s* down fro' the bank to the beck, *Owd Roä* 41
Slut *See* **Trollope**
Sly *See* **Half-sly**
Smack'd Their nectar *s* of hemlock on the lips, *Demeter and P.* 104
Smacking the sight and *s* of the time; *Princess, Pro.* 89
Small o'er it many, round and *s*, *Mariana* 39
Nothing but the *s* cold worm Fretteth *A Dirge* 9
A STILL *s* voice spake unto me, *Two Voices* 1
Then to the still *s* voice I said; „ 4
He left a *s* plantation; *Amphion* 20
great and *s*, Went nutting to the hazels. *Enoch Arden* 63
With one *s* gate that open'd on the waste, „ 733
For which his gains were dock'd, however *s*: *S* were his gains, *Sea Dreams* 7
the master took *S* notice, or austerely, *Lucretius* 8
His name was Gama; crack'd and *s* his voice, *Princess i* 114
heads were less: Some men's were *s*; „ *ii* 148
her *s* goodman Shrinks in his arm-chair „ *v* 453
So said the *s* king moved beyond his wont. „ *vi* 265
here and there the *s* bright head, „ *vii* 58
she found a *s* Sweet Idyl, „ 190
If she be *s*, slight-natured, „ 265
When one *s* touch of Charity Could lift *Lit. Squabbles* 13
the village, and looks how quiet and *s*! *Maud I iv* 7
S and pure as a pearl, „ *II ii* 2
S, but a work divine, „ 23
by Mark the King For that *s* charm of feature mine, *Merlin and V.* 76
grieving that their greatest are so *s*, „ 833
Rejoice, *s* man, in this *s* world of mine, *Holy Grail* 559
S heart was his after the Holy Quest: „ 657

Small (*continued*) ' And then, with *s* adventure met, Sir Bors *Holy Grail* 660
And slender was her hand and *s* her shape ; *Pelleas and E.* 74
and if he fly us, *S* matter ! let him.' „ 200
And mindful of her *s* and cruel hand, „ 201
s pity upon his horse had he, „ 540
The twelve *s* damosels white as Innocence, *Last Tournament* 291
and cast thee back Thine own *s* saw, „ 712
s violence done Rankled in him and ruffled *Guinevere* 48
But let my words, the words of one so *s*, „ 185
Of that *s* bay, which out to open main *Lover's Tale i* 435
The *s* sweet face was flush'd, *The Wreck* 60
With all the peoples, great and *s*, *Epilogue* 20
' *S* blemish upon the skin ! *Dead Prophet* 66
Her dauntless army scatter'd, and so *s*, *The Fleet* 11
At times the *s* black fly upon the pane *To One who ran down Eng.* 3
Smaller O God, that I had loved a *s* man ! *Merlin and V.* 872
Hid under grace, as in a *s* time, *Lancelot and E.* 264
I am thine husband—not a *s* soul, *Guinevere* 566
When I was *s* than the statuette *The Ring* 109
Smallest he saw The *s* rock far on the faintest hill, *Com. of Arthur* 99
O *s* among peoples ! *Montenegro* 9
Smash (*See also* **Mash**) *S* the bottle to smithers, *North. Cobbler* 104
Smashed *See* **Mash'd**
Smashing *See* **Mashin'**
Smear'd shining hair Was *s* with earth, *Holy Grail* 210
Their idol *s* with blood, *Freedom* 28
Smell (s) moist rich *s* of the rotting leaves, *A spirit haunts* 17
The *s* of violets, hidden in the green, *D. of F. Women* 77
The gentle shower, the *s* of dying leaves, *Enoch Arden* 611
A great black swamp and of an evil *s*, *Holy Grail* 499
and the sweet *s* of the fields Past, *Pelleas and E.* 5
wind Came wooingly with woodbine *s's*. *Lover's Tale ii* 36
blew Coolness and moisture and all *s's* of bud And foliage „ *iii* 5
and the loathsome *s's* of disease *In the Child. Hosp.* 25
On *them* the *s* of burning had not past. *Sir J. Oldcastle* 177
sympathies, how frail, In sound and *s* ! *Early Spring* 36
Smell (verb) rarely *s's* the new-mown hay, *The Owl i* 9
I *s* the meadow in the street ; *In Mem. cxix* 4
as one That *s's* a foul-flesh'd agaric in the holt, *Gareth and L.* 747
how sweetly *s's* the honeysuckle In the hush'd night, „ 1287
if tha seeäs 'im an' *s's* 'im *North. Cobbler* 66
is prized for it *s's* of the beast, *The Dawn* 14
Smell'd Fur 'e *s* like a herse a-singein', *Owd Roä* 101
Smellest thou *s* all of kitchen-grease. *Gareth and L.* 751
Thou *s* all of kitchen as before.' „ 771
Nay—for thou *s* of the kitchen still. „ 843
Smelling (*See also* **Ocean-smelling, Sweet-smelling**) *S* of musk and of insolence, *Maud I vi* 45
over-full Of sweetness, and in *s* of itself, *Lover's Tale i* 272
Smelt Hesperian gold, That *s* ambrosially, *Œnone* 67
S of the coming summer, as one large cloud *Gardener's D.* 78
Brought out a dusky loaf that *s* of home, *Audley Court* 22
Smile (s) deep and clear are thine Of wealthy *s's* : but who may know Whether *s* or frown be fleeter ? Whether *s* or frown be sweeter, *Madeline* 11
Thy *s* and frown are not aloof From one another, „ 19
heart entanglest In a golden-netted *s* ; „ 41
Hollow *s* and frozen sneer Come not here. *Poet's Mind* 10
Wherefore those faint *s's* of thine, *Adeline* 21
Wherefore that faint *s* of thine, „ 38
Hence that look and *s* of thine, „ 63
The very *s* before you speak, *Margaret* 14
Comes out thy deep ambrosial *s*. *Eleänore* 74
ghost of passion that no *s's* restore— *The form, the form* 11
The slow wise *s* that, round about *Miller's D.* 5
She with a subtle *s* in her mild eyes, *Œnone* 184
She, flashing forth a haughty *s*, *D. of F. Women* 129
slight Sir Robert with his watery *s* *Edwin Morris* 128
thou grant mine asking with a *s*, *Tithonus* 16
With one *s* of still defiance *The Captain* 59
With tears and *s's* from heaven again *Sir L. and Q. G.* 2
With half-allowing *s's* for all the world, *Aylmer's Field* 120
Sir Aylmer half forgot his lazy *s* Of patron „ 197
With a heaved shoulder and a saucy *s*, „ 466
Smile (s) (*continued*) Never one kindly *s*, one kindly word : *Aylmer's Field* 564
with the fat affectionate *s* That makes the widow lean. *Sea Dreams* 155
s that like a wrinkling wind On glassy water *Princess i* 115
She paused, and added with a haughtier *s* „ *iii* 225
shot from crooked lips a haggard *s*. „ *iv* 364
s, that look'd A stroke of cruel sunshine „ 523
common light of *s's* at our disguise „ *v* 271
doubtful *s* dwelt like a clouded moon „ *vi* 270
' Ay so,' said Ida with a bitter *s*, „ 316
blush and *s*, a medicine in themselves „ *vii* 62
(so rare the *s's* Of sunlight) *The Daisy* 53
Is matter for a flying *s*. *In Mem. lxii* 12
In glance and *s*, and clasp and kiss, „ *lxxxiv* 7
I know it, and smile a hard-set *s*, *Maud I iv* 20
touch'd my hand with a *s* so sweet, „ *vi* 12
And *s* as sunny as cold, „ 24
And her *s* were all that I dream'd, „ 37
And her *s* had all that I dream'd, „ 93
But a *s* could make it sweet. (repeat) „ *I vi* 39, 95
With a glassy *s* his brutal scorn— „ 49
Perhaps the *s* and tender tone „ 63
The sun look'd out with a *s* „ *ix* 3
' I shall assay,' said Gareth with a *s* That madden'd her, *Gareth and L.* 783
' Turn, Fortune, turn thy wheel with *s* or frown ; *Marr. of Geraint* 350
With frequent *s* and nod departing found, „ 515
when he mark'd his high sweet *s* In passing, *Balin and Balan* 160
slight and sprightly talk, And vivid *s's*, *Merlin and V.* 172
when the living *s* Died from his lips, *Lancelot and E.* 323
he bound Her token on his helmet, with a *s* „ 374
Sighs, and slow *s's*, and golden eloquence „ 649
Smiled with his lips—a *s* beneath a cloud, *Holy Grail* 705
with a slow *s* turn'd the lady round *Pelleas and E.* 91
With silent *s's* of slow disparagement ; *Guinevere* 14
Heart-hiding *s*, and gray persistent eye : „ 64
Flicker'd like doubtful *s's* about her lips, *Lover's Tale i* 68
when I wept, Her *s* lit up the rainbow on my tears, „ 254
her love did clothe itself in *s's* About his lips ! „ 658
her lips were sunder'd With *s's* of tranquil bliss, „ *ii* 143
bond and seal Of friendship, spoken of with tearful *s's* ; „ 182
stepping out of darkness with a *s*. „ *iv* 220
—adding, with a *s*, The first for many weeks— „ 280
Seeäd nobbut the *s* o' the sun *North. Cobbler* 50
The bright quick *s* of Evelyn, *Sisters (E. and E.)* 243
and the *s*, and the comforting eye— *In the Child. Hosp.* 12
And greet it with a kindly *s* ; *To E. Fitzgerald* 4
bask'd in the light of a dowerless *s*, *The Wreck* 45
But wakes a dotard *s*.' *Ancient Sage* 132
The cruel *s*, the courtly phrase that masks *The Flight* 30
If greeted by your classic *s*, *To Prof. Jebb.* 10
Miriam nodded with a pitying *s*, *The Ring* 281
Nor ever cheer'd you with a kindly *s*, „ 388
in the tearful splendour of her *s's* *Prog. of Spring* 41
Smile (verb) (*See also* **Smoile**) women *s* with saint-like glances *Supp. Confessions* 22
S at the claims of long descent. *L. C. V. de Vere* 52
Where they *s* in secret, looking over wasted lands, *Lotos-Eaters, C. S.* 114
But they *s*, they find a music centred „ 117
' No fair Hebrew boy Shall *s* away my maiden blame *D. of F. Women* 214
He will not *s*—not speak to me Once more. *To J. S.* 21
Did they *s* on him. *The Captain* 56
The very graves appear'd to *s*, *The Letters* 45
Seeing with how great ease Nature can *s*, *Lucretius* 174
empire upon empire *s's* to-day, *W. to Marie Alex.* 33
I know it, and *s* a hard-set smile, *Maud I iv* 20
S sweetly, thou ! my love hath smiled on me.' *Gareth and L.* 1001
S and we *s*, the lords of many lands ; *Marr. of Geraint* 353
Frown and we *s*, the lords of our own hands ; „ 354
S at him, as he deem'd, presumptuously : *Balin and Balan* 222
To make her *s*, her golden ankle-bells. *Merlin and V.* 579
smiling as a master *s's* at one That is not of his school, „ 662
you yourself will *s* at your own self *Lancelot and E.* 951

Smile (verb) (*continued*) I shall never make thee *s* again.' *Last Tournament* 762
They *s* upon me, till, remembering all *Sisters (E. and E.)* 279
How she would *s* at 'em, play with 'em, *In the Child. Hosp.* 34
thine Imperial mother *s* again, *Ded. Poem Prin. Alice* 13
ghost of our great Catholic Queen *S's* on me, *Columbus* 188
s's at her sleepin' child— *Tomorrow* 26
up to either pole she *s's*, *Locksley H., Sixty* 169
Where man, nor only Nature *s's*; *To Ulysses* 39
Smiled who *s* when she was torn in three; *Poland* 12
Thy sister *s* and said, 'No tears for me! *The Bridesmaid* 3
And now and then he gravely *s*. *Two Voices* 414
He *s*, and opening out his milk-white palm *Œnone* 65
And somewhat grimly *s*. *Palace of Art* 136
At me you *s*, but unbeguiled I saw the snare, *L. C. V. de Vere* 5
with dead lips *s* at the twilight plain, *D. of F. Women* 62
She faintly *s*, she hardly moved; *The Letters* 14
that which pleased him, for he *s*. *Enoch Arden* 757
He look'd upon my crown and *s*: *In Mem. lxix* 16
Has not his sister *s* on me? *Maud I xiii* 45
with a kindly hand on Gareth's arm *S* the great King, *Gareth and L.* 579
Smile sweetly, thou! my love hath *s* on me.' „ 1001
twice my love hath *s* on me.' (repeat) „ 1062, 1077
thrice my love hath *s* on me.' „ 1161
Then sigh'd and *s* the hoary-headed Earl, *Marr. of Geraint* 307
He spoke: the mother *s*, but half in tears, „ 823
Then like a stormy sunlight *s* Geraint, *Geraint and E.* 480
From being *s* at happier in themselves— *Balin and Balan* 163
Whereat she *s* and turn'd her to the King, „ 201
Garlon, hissing; then he sourly *s*. „ 355
Sunnily she *s* 'And even in this lone wood, „ 528
till he sadly *s*: 'To what request for what strange boon,' *Merlin and V.* 263
S at each other, while the Queen, *Lancelot and E.* 739
But fast asleep, and lay as tho' she *s*. „ 1161
S with his lips—a smile beneath a cloud, *Holy Grail* 705
and they too *s*, Scorning him; *Pelleas and E.* 96
Full sharply smote his knees, and *s*, *Guinevere* 47
An' he *s* at me, 'Ain't you, my love? *First Quarrel* 62
the sun *s* out far over the summer sea, *The Revenge* 70
An' Squire 'e *s* an' 'e *s* (repeat) *Village Wife* 61, 88
an' 'e *s*, fur 'e hedn't naw friend, „ 89
it seem'd she stood by me and *s*, *In the Child. Hosp.* 67
it coo'd to the Mother and *s*. *The Wreck* 60
an' Hiven in its glory *s*, *Tomorrow* 25
looking still as if she *s*, *Locksley H., Sixty* 35
shook her head, and patted yours, And *s*, *The Ring* 314
Smiler Thou faint *s*, Adeline? *Adeline* 48
Smilest Thou *s*, but thou dost not speak, *Oriana* 68
Thou that faintly *s* still, *Adeline* 15
And *s*, knowing all is well. *In Mem. cxxvii* 20
'O morning star that *s* in the blue, *Gareth and L.* 999
Smiling (*See also* **A-smilin', Silver-smiling, Westward-smiling**)
S, never speaks: *Lilian* 12
S, frowning, evermore, (repeat) *Madeline* 8, 25
Faintly *s* Adeline, *Adeline* 2
Thought folded over thought, *s* asleep, *Eleänore* 84
Sat *s*, babe in arm. *Palace of Art* 96
Eustace turn'd, and *s* said to me, *Gardener's D.* 97
And, *s*, put the question by. *Day-Dm., Revival* 32
And one said *s* 'Pretty were the sight *Princess, Pro.* 139
Took both his hands, and *s* faintly said: „ *ii* 304
While Psyche watch'd them, *s*, „ 365
but *s* 'Not for thee,' she said, „ *iv* 121
Then turn'd the noble damsel *s* at him, *Gareth and L.* 1188
And, gravely *s*, lifted her from horse, *Geraint and E.* 883
And Vivien answer'd, *s* scornfully, *Merlin and V.* 37
And Vivien answer'd *s* saucily, (repeat) „ 268, 651
And Vivien answer'd *s* mournfully: (repeat) „ 311, 438
And Vivien answer'd *s* as in wrath: „ 526
And *s* as a master smiles at one That is not of his school, „ 662
while the king Would listen *s*. *Lancelot and E.* 116
'So ye will grace me,' answer'd Lancelot, *S* a moment, „ 224
with *s* face arose, With *s* face and frowning heart, „ 552
past the barge Whereon the lily maid of Astolat Lay *s*, „ 1243

Smiling (*continued*) To whom Sir Tristram *s*, 'I am here. *Last Tournament* 521
made garlands of the selfsame flower, Which she took *s*, *Lover's Tale i* 344
a light Of *s* welcome round her lips— „ *iii* 46
s at the slighter ghost. *Locksley H., Sixty* 54
s downward at this earthlier earth of ours, „ 183
as the low dark hull dipt under the *s* main, *The Wreck* 127
Smirk'd The parson *s* and nodded. *The Goose* 20
Smit *s* with freër light shall slowly melt *Golden Year* 33
S with exceeding sorrow unto Death. *Lover's Tale i* 601
Smite Tho' one should *s* him on the cheek, *Two Voices* 251
S, shrink not, spare not. *St. S. Stylites* 181
his footsteps *s* the threshold stairs Of life— „ 191
sitting well in order *s* The sounding furrows; *Ulysses* 58
S on the sudden, yet rode on, *Com. of Arthur* 57
Utterly *s* the heathen underfoot, „ 423
This air that *s's* his forehead is not air But vision— *Holy Grail* 914
That did not shun to *s* me in worse way, *Guinevere* 435
Smither (piece) Smash the bottle to *s's*, *North. Cobbler* 104
Smitten (*See also* **Sharp-smitten, Sun-smitten**) I am so deeply *s* thro' the helm *M. d'Arthur* 25
Aidless, alone, and *s* thro' the helm. „ 41
A Memnon *s* with the morning Sun.' *Princess iii* 116
Who, *s* by the dusty sloping beam, *Marr. of Geraint* 262
Then from the *s* surface flash'd, as it were, *Lancelot and E.* 1236
Pray Heaven, they be not *s* by the bolt.' *Holy Grail* 221
And, when I would have *s* them, „ 823
young life Being *s* in mid heaven with mortal cold *Last Tournament* 27
Wet with the mists and *s* by the lights, *Guinevere* 597
I am so deeply *s* thro' the helm *Pass. of Arthur* 193
Aidless, alone, and *s* thro' the helm— „ 209
Tho' Sin too oft, when *s* by Thy rod, *Doubt and Prayer* 1
Smoäke (smoke) I couldn't see fur the *s* *Owd Roä* 87
Smoäkin' (smoking) Guzzlin' an' soäkin' an' *s* *North. Cobbler* 24
An' *s* an' thinkin' o' things— *Owd Roä* 34
Smock'd Tho' *s*, or furr'd and purpled, *Princess iv* 247
Smoile (smile) Looök 'ow quoloty *s's* *N. Farmer, O. S.* 53
Smoke (s) (*See also* **Sea-smoke, Smoäke, Thunder-smoke, Water-smoke**) With thunders, and with lightnings, and with *s*,— *Buonaparte* 6
And all the war is roll'd in *s*.' *Two Voices* 156
And like a downward *s*, the slender stream *Lotos-Eaters* 8
A land of streams! some, like a downward *s*, „ 10
Beneath its drift of *s*; *Talking Oak* 6
thro' the *s* The blight of low desires— *Aylmer's Field* 672
A *s* go up thro' which I loom to her *Princess v* 130
Athwart the *s* of burning weeds. „ *vii* 358
Where, far from noise and *s* of town, *To F. D. Maurice* 13
like the *s* in a hurricane whirl'd. *Boädicea* 59
With fruitful cloud and living *s*, *In Mem. xxxix* 3
streets were black with *s* and frost, „ *lxix* 3
Wrapt in drifts of lurid *s* *Maud II iv* 66
Reddening the sun with *s* and earth with blood, *Com. of Arthur* 37
In drifts of *s* before a rolling wind, „ 434
walks thro' fire will hardly heed the *s*. *Gareth and L.* 143
Rolling her *s* about the Royal mount, „ 190
'Out of the *s*, at once I leap from Satan's foot „ 537
Out of the *s* he came, and so my lance Hold, „ 722
if the King awaken from his craze, Into the *s* again.' „ 725
puff'd the swaying branches into *s* *Holy Grail* 15
their foreheads grimed with *s*, and sear'd, „ 265
the morning star Reel'd in the *s*, *Pelleas and E.* 519
daylight of your minds But cloud and *s*, *Lover's Tale i* 297
Dark thro' the *s* and the sulphur *Def. of Lucknow* 33
Dark with the *s* of human sacrifice, *Sir J. Oldcastle* 84
when a *s* from a city goes to heaven *Achilles over the T.* 7
He is only a cloud and a *s* *Despair* 29
'A fiery phœnix rising from the *s*, *The Ring* 339
all her realm Of sound and *s*, *To Mary Boyle* 66
s of war's volcano burst again From hoary deeps *Prog. of Spring* 97
Smoke (verb) The long way *s* beneath him in his fear; *Geraint and E.* 532
stormy crests that *s* against the skies, *Lancelot and E.* 484
I have seen this yew-tree *s*, Spring after spring, *Holy Grail* 18
went To *s* the scandalous hive of those wild bees „ 214

Snivel I that heard her whine And *s*, *Last Tournament* 450
Snorin' 'What arta *s* theere fur? *Owd Roä* 68
Snow (*See also* **Snaw**) rites and form before his burning eyes Melted like *s*. *The Poet* 40
Shone out their crowning *s's*. *Dying Swan* 13
When the long dun wolds are ribb'd with *s*, *Oriana* 5
thorn will blow In tufts of rosy-tinted *s*; *Two Voices* 60
solitary morning smote The streaks of virgin *s*. *Œnone* 56
And highest, *s* and fire. *Palace of Art* 84
I wish the *s* would melt and the sun come out *May Queen, N. Y's. E.* 15
Three silent pinnacles of aged *s*, *Lotos-Eaters* 16
Full knee-deep lies the winter *s*, *D. of the O. Year* 1
over the *s* I heard just now the crowing cock. „ 37
Where falls not hail, or rain, or any *s*, *M. d'Arthur* 260
wind, frost, heat, hail, damp, and sleet, and *s*; *St. S. Stylites* 16
with rain or hail, or fire or *s*; *Locksley Hall* 193
Deep on the convent-roof the *s's* *St. Agnes' Eve* 1
The streets are dumb with *s*. *Sir Galahad* 52
Nor ever falls the least white star of *s*, *Lucretius* 107
like the flakes In a fall of *s*, „ 167
From flower to flower, from *s* to *s*: *In Mem. xxii* 4
The silent *s* possess'd the earth, „ *lxxviii* 3
And silent under other *s's*: „ *cv* 6
Ring, happy bells, across the *s*: „ *cvi* 6
Now fades the last long streak of *s*, „ *cxv* 1
yet thou art but swollen with cold *s's* *Gareth and L.* 9
glittering star of morn Parts from a bank of *s*, *Marr. of Geraint* 735
'I know not, for thy heart is pure as *s*.' *Holy Grail* 97
like a bank Of maiden *s* mingled with sparks *Last Tournament* 149
cold Falls on the mountain in midsummer *s's*, „ 228
Where falls not hail, or rain, or any *s*, *Pass. of Arthur* 428
like cold *s*, it melteth in the source *Lover's Tale i* 783
and the full moon stares at the *s*. *Rizpah* 4
the wind and the shower and the *s*. „ 68
The *s* and the sky so bright— „ 83
mountain was lilies in lieu of *s*, *V. of Maeldune* 41
kiss fell chill as a flake of *s* on the cheek: *The Wreck* 32
And cap our age with *s*?' *Ancient Sage* 98
was as light as *s* an the lan', *Tomorrow* 36
hair was as white as the *s* an a grave. „ 60
high hill-passes of stainless *s*, *Dead Prophet* 47
blanching apricot like *s* in *s*. *Prog. of Spring* 30
I sat beneath a solitude of *s*; „ 71
Where am I? *s* on all the hills! *Romney's R.* 12
I have climb'd to the *s's* of Age, *By an Evolution.* 17
Snow-cold Over her *s-c* breast and angry cheek *Œnone* 142
Snowdon we that day had been Up *S*; *Golden Year* 4
Snowdrop to live till the *s's* come again: *May Queen, N. Y's. E.* 14
To die before the *s* came, „ *Con.* 4
Or this first *s* of the year *St. Agnes' Eve* 11
the white Of the first *s's* inner leaves; *Princess v* 197
The *s* only, flowering thro' the year, *Last Tournament* 220
Like *s's*, pure! *Early Spring* 30
Wavers on her thin stem the *s* cold *Prog. of Spring* 3
Snow'd A hundred winters *s* upon his breast, *Palace of Art* 139
Tore the king's letter, *s* it down, *Princess i* 61
Snowflake like a *s* in the hand, *Lover's Tale iii* 38
Snowlike Down to the *s* sparkle of a cloth *Sisters (E. and E.)* 117
Snow-limb'd the *s-l* Eve from whom she came. *Maud I xviii* 28
Snowshoe Claymore and *s*, toys in lava, *Princess, Pro.* 18
Snow-white The snowy peak and *s-w* cataract *Œnone* 211
Snowy Lying, robed in *s* white *L. of Shalott iv* 19
between The *s* peak and snow-white cataract *Œnone* 211
Slant down the *s* sward, *St. Agnes' Eve* 6
Fair gleams the *s* altar-cloth, *Sir Galahad* 33
Airing a *s* hand and signet gem, *Princess i* 121
And *s* summits old in story: „ *iv* 2
Would rock the *s* cradle till I died. „ 104
as flies A troop of *s* doves athwart the dusk, „ 168
Long lanes of splendour slanted o'er a press Of *s* shoulders, „ 479
And *s* dells in a golden air, *The Daisy* 68
And up the *s* Splugen drew, „ 86
And passion pure in *s* bloom *In Mem. cix* 11
made A *s* penthouse for his hollow eyes, *Merlin and V.* 808

Snowy (*continued*) one *s* knee was prest Against the margin flowers; *Tiresias* 42
Snowy-banded The *s-b*, dilettante, *Maud I viii* 10
Snubnosed smooth-faced *s* rogue would leap from his counter „ *i* 51
Snuff An' 'is noäse sa grufted wi' *s* *Village Wife* 39
Soäber (sober) Thaw thou was es *s* es daäy, *Spinster's S's.* 75
Soak City children *s* and blacken *Locksley H., Sixty* 218
Soak'd Tho' *s* and saturate, out and out, *Will Water.* 87
Soäk'd Moother 'ed beän sa *s* wi' the thaw *Owd Roä* 113
Soäkin' Guzzlin' an' *s* an' smoäkin' *North. Cobbler* 24
Soaking (*See also* **Soäkin'**) I *s* here in winter wet— *To Ulysses* 6
Soar she answered, 'Ay, And men to *s*:' *Lover's Tale i* 305
my wings That I may *s* the sky, *Mechanophilus* 10
Soaring from my vapour-girdle *s* forth *Prog. of Spring* 79
Sob (s) all at once the old man burst in *s's*:— *Dora* 158
shaken with her *s's*, Melissa knelt; *Princess iv* 289
dark crowd moves, and there are *s's* *Ode on Well.* 268
her false voice made way, broken with *s's*: *Merlin and V.* 857
And bluster into stormy *s's* and say, *Lancelot and E.* 1067
Sob (verb) hear him *s* and sigh In the walks; *A spirit haunts* 5
and to clamour, mourn and *s*, *St. S. Stylites* 6
Sobb'd for three hours he *s* o'er William's child *Dora* 167
And *s*, and you *s* with it, *Princess ii* 273
he *s* and he wept, And cursed himself; *Bandit's Death* 29
Sobbing See, there is one of us *s*, *Maud II v* 30
A voice clung *s* till he question'd it, *Last Tournament* 759
Set up an answer, *s*, 'I am thy fool, „ 761
Sober (*See also* **Soäber**) Nothing to mar the *s* majesties Of settled, *Lucretius* 217
That *s* freedom out of which there springs *Ode on Well.* 164
A *s* man, among his boys, *In Mem. liii* 2
'A *s* man is Percivale and pure; *Merlin and V.* 755
Envy wears the mask of Love, and, laughing *s* fact to scorn, *Locksley H., Sixty* 109
I heard the *s* rook And carrion crow cry *The Ring* 173
Soberer-hued Autumn-changed, *S-h* Gold again. *The Oak* 9
Sober-suited That *s-s* Freedom chose, *You ask me, why, etc.* 6
Social Cursed be the *s* wants that sin against the strength of youth! *Locksley Hall* 59
Cursed be the *s* lies that warp us from the living truth! „ 60
To pass with all our *s* ties *Day-Dm., L'Envoi* 5
'Have patience,' I replied, 'ourselves are full Of *s* wrong; *Princess, Con.* 73
For 'ground in yonder *s* mill We rub each other's angles down, *In Mem. lxxxix* 39
and join'd Each office of the *s* hour „ *cxi* 14
Proclaiming *s* truth shall spread, „ *cxxvii* 5
Society *See* **She-society**
Socratic Or threaded some *S* dream; *In Mem. lxxxix* 36
Sod The blackness round the tombing *s*, *On a Mourner* 27
mouldering with the dull earth's mouldering *s*, *Palace of Art* 261
To rest beneath the clover *s*, *In Mem. x* 13
after *s* and shingle ceased to fly Behind her, *Gareth and L.* 761
And over hard and soft, striking the *s* *Pelleas and E.* 498
nor the *s* Draw from my death Thy living flower *Doubt and Prayer* 5
Sodden Men, women, on their *s* faces, *Last Tournament* 474
Sofa And broider'd *s's* on each side: *Arabian Nights* 19
Who 'sitting on green *s's* contemplate *Akbar's Dream* 48
Soft (*See also* **Silk-soft**) as in sleep I sank In cool *s* turf upon the bank, *Arabian Nights* 96
S are the moss-beds under the sea; *The Merman* 39
things that are forked, and horned, and *s*, *The Mermaid* 53
A single stream of all her *s* brown hair Pour'd on one side: *Gardener's D.* 128
The *s* wind blowing over meadowy holms *Edwin Morris* 95
thro' *s* degrees Subdue them to the useful and the good. *Ulysses* 37
A *s* air fans the cloud apart; *Tithonus* 32
S lustre bathes the range of urns On every slanting terrace-lawn. *Day-Dm., Sleep. P.* 9
S fruitage, mighty nuts, and nourishing roots; *Enoch Arden* 555
half-embraced the basket cradle-head With one *s* arm, *Sea Dreams* 290
saw The *s* white vapour streak the crowned towers *Princess iii* 344
and so Laid the *s* babe in his hard-mailed hands. „ *vi* 208

Soft (*continued*) Say one *s* word and let me part forgiven.' *Princess vi* 219
The *s* and milky rabble of womankind, .. 309
glow Of your *s* splendours that you look so bright? *Maud I xviii* 79
massacring Man, woman, lad and girl—yea, the *s* babe! *Gareth and L.* 1341
And over hard and *s*, striking the sod From out the *s*, the spark from off the hard, *Pelleas and E.* 498
And thine is more to me—*s*, gracious, kind— *Last Tournament* 560
one *s* lap Pillow'd us both: *Lover's Tale i* 235
As rain of the midsummer midnight *s*, .. 722
s winds, Laden with thistledown and seeds of flowers, .. *ii* 12
Ah—you, that have lived so *s*, *Rizpah* 17
Hallus a *s* un Squire! an' 'e smiled, *Village Wife* 89
About the *s* Mediterranean shores, *Sir J. Oldcastle* 30
Tha thowt tha would marry ma, did tha? but that wur a bit ower *s*, *Spinster's S's.* 74
She turn'd, and in her *s* imperial way *The Ring* 267
Soften And *s* as if to a girl, *Maud I x* 16
Steel me with patience! *s* me with grief! *Doubt and Prayer* 9
Soften'd but robed in *s* light Of orient state. *Ode to Memory* 10
whom waitest thou With thy *s*, shadow'd brow, *Adeline* 46
Like *s* airs that blowing steal, *Two Voices* 406
and the brazen fool Was *s*, *In Mem. cx* 12
Softening *S* thro' all the gentle attributes *Aylmer's Field* 730
Softer *S* than sleep—all things in order *Palace of Art* 87
' who could think The *s* Adams of your Academe, *Princess ii* 197
and *s* all her shape And rounder seem'd: „ *vii* 136
When the far-off sail is blown by the breeze of a *s* clime, *Maud I iv* 4
Softly-shadow'd Glows forth each *s-s* arm *Day-Dm., Sleep. B.* 13
Softness *S* breeding scorn of simple life, *To the Queen ii* 53
Soil (s) Fast-rooted in the fruitful *s*. *Lotos-Eaters, C. S.* 38
ill-used race of men that cleave the *s*, „ 120
That numbers forty cubits from the *s*. *St. S. Stylites* 91
Upon my proper patch of *s* *Amphion* 99
Know you no song, the true growth of your *s*, *Princess iv* 150
Has risen and cleft the *s*, .. *vi* 35
The *s*, left barren, scarce had grown *In Mem. liii* 7
three were clad like tillers of the *s*. *Gareth and L.* 181
Gareth, ' We be tillers of the *s*, „ 242
Soil (verb) evil thought may *s* thy children's blood; *Ancient Sage* 275
Soil'd When, *s* with noble dust, he hears *Two Voices* 152
As these white robes are *s* and dark, *St. Agnes' Eve* 13
And *s* with all ignoble use. *In Mem. cxi* 24
Soiling *s* another, Annie, will never make *Grandmother* 36
Soilure fearing rust or *s* fashion'd for it *Lancelot and E.* 7
'Soize (assize) Noäks wur 'ang'd for it oop at '*s*— *N. Farmer, O. S.* 36
Solace (s) Vain *s*! Memory standing near *To J. S.* 53
Nay, but Nature brings thee *s*; *Locksley Hall* 87
A doubtful gleam of *s* lives. *In Mem. xxxviii* 8
And in that *s* can I sing, „ *lxv* 5
From his great hoard of happiness distill'd Some drops of *s*; *Lover's Tale i* 715
S at least—before he left his home. „ *iv* 7
In his own well, draw *s* as he may. *Tiresias* 89
Nay, you were my one *s*; *The Ring* 310
Were tender *s*. Yet be comforted; *D. of the Duke of C.* 7
Solace (verb) A little hint to *s* woe, *Two Voices* 433
Solaced Whom Averill *s* as he might, *Aylmer's Field* 343
Sold (*See also* **Sowd**) Himself unto himself he *s*: *A Character* 26
Nor *s* his heart to idle moans, *Two Voices* 221
he's abroad: the place is to be *s*. *Walk. to the Mail* 16
S him unto shame. *The Captain* 60
s her wares for less Than what she gave in buying what she *s*: *Enoch Arden* 255
The horse he drove, the boat he *s*, „ 609
' That was the four-year-old I *s* the Squire.' *The Brook* 137
Where our Caucasians let themselves be *s*. *Aylmer's Field* 349
never *s* the truth to serve the hour, *Ode on Well.* 179
chalk and alum and plaster are *s* to the poor for bread, *Maud I i* 39
being *s* and *s* had bought them bread: *Marr. of Geraint* 641
S the crown-farms for all but nothing, *Columbus* 132
nearing his own hundred, *s* This ring to me, *The Ring* 194
Soldan he, the fierce *S* of Egypt, *Columbus* 98
Soldier (adj.) No more in *s* fashion will he greet *Ode on Well.* 21

Soldier (s) (*See also* **Patriot-soldier, Woman-soldier**)
The Roman *s* found Me lying dead, *D. of F. Women* 161
men like *s's* may not quit the post *Lucretius* 148
nor broke, nor shunn'd a *s's* death, *Princess, Pro.* 38
Pitiful sight, wrapp'd in a *s's* cloak, .. *v* 56
The *s*? No: What dares not Ida do that she should prize The *s*? .. 173
not shunn'd the death, No, not the *s's*: .. 179
one loves the *s*, one The silken priest .. 183
The king is scared, the *s* will not fight, .. *Con.* 60
banner and with music, with *s* and with priest, *Ode on Well.* 81
To thee the greatest *s* comes; .. 88
So great a *s* taught us there, .. 131
And keep the *s* firm, the statesman pure: „ 222
the *s* knew Some one had blunder'd: *Light Brigade* 11
were the *s's* wont to hear His voice in battle, *Geraint and E.* 174
The King should have made him a *s*, *Rizpah* 28
Thousands of their *s's* look'd down *The Revenge* 37
that brave *s*, down the terrible ridge *Sisters (E. and E.)* 63
they shall know we are *s's* and men! *Def. of Lucknow* 41
to be *s* all day and be sentinel all thro' the night— „ 74
Were *s's* to her heart's desire, *Pro. to Gen. Hamley* 25
My *s* of the Cross? it is he and he indeed! *Happy* 12
we saw your *s's* crossing the ridge, *Bandit's Death* 21
Soldier-brother *S-b's* bridal orange-bloom *Ded. Poem Prin. Alice* 11
Soldier-city led Threading the *s-c*, *Princess v* 7
Soldier-laddie violin Struck up with *S-l*, „ *Pro.* 86
Soldierlike anger-charm'd from sorrow, *s*, *Aylmer's Field* 728
Soldierly His own, tho' keen and bold and *s* „ 192
Soldier-priest A latter Luther, and a *s-p* *To J. M. K.* 2
Soldiership mind, So quick, so capable in *s*, *Sir J. Oldcastle* 75
Sole (adj.) *S* star of all that place and time, *Arabian Nights* 152
Thy *s* delight is, sitting still, *The Blackbird* 10
S star of phosphorescence in the calm, *Audley Court* 87
The *s* succeeder to their wealth, their lands, *Aylmer's Field* 294
you The *s* men to be mingled with our cause, *Princess v* 411
The *s* men we shall prize in the aftertime, „ 412
S comfort of my dark hour, when a world „ *vi* 194
Nor Britain's one *s* God be the millionaire: *Maud III vi* 22
And since he kept his mind on one *s* aim, *Merlin and V.* 626
To seat you *s* upon my pedestal Of worship— „ 878
S Queen of Beauty and of love, *Last Tournament* 208
his one true knight—*S* follower of the vows'— „ 303
And I stood *s* beside the vacant bier. *Lover's Tale iii* 58
My *s* memorial Of Edith—no, the other,— *Sisters (E. and E.)* 107
Sole (s) (*See also* **Baby-sole**) From scalp to *s* one slough and crust *St. S. Stylites* 2
Solecism Chimeras, crotchets, Christmas *s's*, *Princess, Pro.* 203
Solemn (*See also* **Mock-solemn**) But the *s* oak-tree sigheth, *Claribel* 4
the *s* palms were ranged Above, *Arabian Nights* 79
Yet not the less held she her *s* mirth, *Palace of Art* 215
and grief became A *s* scorn of ills. *D. of F. Women* 228
With *s* gibe did Eustace banter me *Gardener's D.* 168
And hear me swear a *s* oath, *Talking Oak* 281
And *s* chaunts resound between. *Sir Galahad* 36
Heroic, for a hero lies beneath, Grave, *s*!' *Princess, Pro.* 213
At last a *s* grace Concluded, „ *ii* 452
Of *s* psalms, and silver litanies, .. 477
'Sdeath—and with *s* rites by candle-light— .. *v* 292
And drove us, last, to quite a *s* close— .. *Con.* 17
Too comic for the *s* things they are, Too *s* for the comic touches in them, „ 67
For such a wise humility As befits a *s* fane: *Ode on Well.* 250
A *s* gladness even crown'd The purple brows of Olivet. *In Mem. xxxi* 11
O *s* ghost, O crowned soul! „ *lxxxv* 36
And hold it *s* to the past. „ *cv* 16
And I will make a *s* offering of you *Lover's Tale iv* 118
And Julian made a *s* feast: „ 187
Well then—our *s* feast—we ate and drank, „ 221
decked them out As for a *s* sacrifice of love— „ 301
First pledge our Queen this *s* night, *Hands all Round* 1
Solemnity watching here At this, our great *s*. *Ode on Well.* 244
And Lancelot's, at this night's *s* *Last Tournament* 223
Solemnly And *s* as when ye sware to him, „ 647
Solent Harry went over the *S* to see if work *First Quarrel* 44

Solid This excellence and *s* form Of constant beauty. *Supp. Confessions* 149
girt round With blackness as a *s* wall, *Palace of Art* 274
Man is made of *s* stuff. *Edwin Morris* 49
I forced a way Thro' *s* opposition crabb'd and gnarl'd. *Princess iii* 126
For fear our *s* aim be dissipated „ 266
He has a *s* base of temperament: „ *iv* 254
We plant a *s* foot into the Time, „ *v* 415
Earth, these *s* stars, this weight of body and limb, *High. Pantheism* 5
To make a *s* core of heat; *In Mem. cvii* 18
They say, The *s* earth whereon we tread „ *cxviii* 8
They melt like mist, the *s* lands, „ *cxxiii* 7
O let the *s* ground Not fail beneath my feet *Maud I xi* 1
and the *s* earth became As nothing, *Com. of Arthur* 442
And *s* turrets topsy-turvy in air: *Gareth and L.* 255
carves A portion from the *s* present, *Merlin and V.* 462
O towers so strong, Huge, *s*, *Pelleas and E.* 464
your flower Waits to be *s* fruit of golden deeds, *Last Tournament* 100
stood A *s* glory on her bright black hair; *Lover's Tale i* 367
came a broad And *s* beam of isolated light, „ *ii* 173
This wall of *s* flesh that comes between *Happy* 35
Solid-set But like a statue *s-s*, *In Mem., Con.* 15
Solitary (adj.) Far up the *s* morning smote The streaks of virgin snow. *Œnone* 55
Past thro' the *s* room in front, *Enoch Arden* 277
Their voices make me feel so *s*.' „ 397
paced Back toward his *s* home again, „ 794
And knew her sitting sad and *s*. *Geraint and E.* 282
And there among the *s* downs, *Lancelot and E.* 163
Bound upon *s* adventure, saw Low down *Pelleas and E.* 275
And *s* passes of the wood Rode Tristram *Last Tournament* 361
Far off a *s* trumpet blew. *Guinevere* 529
So bore her thro' the *s* land *Lover's Tale iv* 90
And all the land was waste and *s*: „ 125
Is that the leper's hut on the *s* moor, *Happy* 9
And sang the married 'nos' for the *s* 'me.' „ 56
Ever as of old time, *S* firstling, *Snowdrop* 4
Solitary (s) Stept the long-hair'd long-bearded *s*, *Enoch Arden* 637
Solitude You move not in such *s's*, *Margaret* 45
Deep dread and loathing of her *s* *Palace of Art* 229
The rosy idol of her *s's*, *Enoch Arden* 90
Surely the man had died of *s*. „ 621
My grief and *s* have broken me; „ 857
And drove him into wastes and *s's* *Lancelot and E.* 252
Broken with Mark and hate and *s*, *Last Tournament* 643
Solomon That Sheba came to ask of *S*.' *Princess ii* 346
For *S* may come to Sheba yet.' „ 349
had I brought From *S's* now-recover'd Ophir all The gold that *S's* navies carried home, *Columbus* 112
Solstice league of street in summer *s* down, *Princess iii* 128
Soluble More *s* is this knot, By gentleness „ *v* 135
Solve 'The doubt would rest, I dare not *s*. *Two Voices* 313
'But *s* me first a doubt. I knew a man, *Lover's Tale iv* 254
Solved *S* in the tender blushes of the peach; *Prog. of Spring* 34
Sombre Thridding the *s* boskage of the wood, *D. of F. Women* 243
And *s*, old, colonnaded aisles. *The Daisy* 56
The *s* close of that voluptuous day, *Guinevere* 688
Some When *s* respect, however slight, was paid To woman, *Princess ii* 136
Like *s* wild creature newly-caged, „ 301
Than *s* strong bond which is to be. *In Mem. cxvi* 16
Grant me *s* knight to do the battle for me, *Gareth and L.* 362
woodman there Reported of *s* demon in the woods *Balin and Balan* 124
Somebody *S* said that she'd say no; (repeat) *Window, Letter* 7, 14
S knows that she'll say ay! (repeat) „ 8, 15
s, surely, some kind heart will come *Maud II v* 102
Somerset Men saw the goodly hills of *S*, *Marr. of Geraint* 828
Something (*See also* **Summat**) And *s* in the darkness draws *Supp. Confessions* 167
s which possess'd The darkness of the world, *Arabian Nights* 71
At such strange war with *s* good, *Two Voices* 302
'Moreover, *s* is or seems, „ 379
'Of *s* felt, like *s* here; Of *s* done, I know not where; „ 382
And then did *s* speak to me— *May Queen, Con.* 34
O BLACKBIRD! sing me *s* well: *The Blackbird* 1
S to love He lends us; *To J. S.* 13
Something (*continued*) Yet *s* I did wish to say: *To J. S.* 60
or else *S* so said 'twas nothing— *The Epic* 31
Or this or *s* like to this he spoke. *Edwin Morris* 41
s jarr'd; Whether he spoke too largely; that there seem'd A touch of *s* false, „ 72
s more, A bringer of new things; *Ulysses* 27
s ere the end, Some work of noble note, „ 51
men the workers, ever reaping *s* *Locksley Hall* 117
He trusts to light on *s* fair; *Day-Dm., Arrival* 20
I had hope, by *s* rare *Will Water.* 165
Philip, with *s* happier than myself. *Enoch Arden* 425
S divine to warn them of their foes: *Sea Dreams* 69
The phantom husks of *s* foully done, *Lucretius* 160
Shall seem no more a *s* to himself, „ 254
Ah, were I *s* great! *Princess, Pro.* 131
And chiefly you were born for *s* great, „ *iv* 307
And there is *s* in it as you say: „ *v* 211
s may be done—I know not what— „ 227
Swear by St. *s*—I forget her name— „ 293
to think I might be *s* to thee, „ *vi* 201
s wild within her breast, „ *vii* 237
we believe him *S* far advanced in State, *Ode on Well.* 275
S it is which thou hast lost, *In Mem. iv* 9
And *s* written, *s* thought; „ *vi* 20
'Tis well; 'tis *s*; we may stand „ *xviii* 1
But thou art turn'd to *s* strange, „ *xli* 5
have grown To *s* greater than before; „ *Con.* 20
Is it an echo of *s* Read with a boy's delight, *Maud I vii* 9
none of us thought of a *s* beyond, „ *xix* 47
sun there swiftly made at her A ghastly *s*, *Guinevere* 79
That seeming *s*, yet was nothing, *Lover's Tale iv* 104
And *s* weird and wild about it all: „ 224
he had *s* further to say, *Rizpah* 43
We feel we are *s*— *De Prof., Human C.* 7
teach us there is *s* in descent. *Locksley H., Sixty* 26
S kindlier, higher, holier— „ 160
S other than the wildest modern guess „ 232
Something-pottle-bodied in a court he saw A *s-p-b* boy *Will Water.* 131
Somewhat Oh teach me yet *S* before the heavy clod *Supp. Confessions* 184
Touch'd with a *s* darker hue, *Margaret* 50
There's *s* in this world amiss *Miller's D.* 19
There's *s* flows to us in life, „ 21
Ha! ha! They think that I am *s*. *St. S. Stylites* 126
Felt ye were *s*, yea, and by your state *Marr. of Geraint* 430
Or this, or *s* like to this, I spake, *Lover's Tale i* 772
one is *s* deeper than the other, As one is *s* graver than the other— *Sisters (E. and E.)* 25
you have dared *S* perhaps in coming? *Columbus* 242
tho' *s* finer than their own, *By an Evolution.* 13
Somewhere Have I not met you *s* long ago? *Romney's R.* 18
Son 'His *s's* grow up that bear his name, *Two Voices* 256
Or mythic Uther's deeply-wounded *s* *Palace of Art* 105
Our *s's* inherit us: our looks are strange: *Lotos-Eaters, C. S.* 73
His *s* and heir doth ride post-haste, *D. of the O. Year* 31
Be proud of those strong *s's* of thine *England and Amer.* 4
William was his *s*, And she is niece. *Dora* 2
Allan call'd his *s*, and said, 'My *s*: I married late, „ 10
if you speak with him that was my *s*, „ 43
I have kill'd my *s*. I have kill'd him—but I loved him—my dear *s*. „ 159
Francis Hale, The farmer's *s*, *Audley Court* 75
O my *s's*, my *s's*, I, Simeon of the pillar, *St. S. Stylites* 160
This is my *s*, mine own Telemachus, *Ulysses* 33
Gallant *s's* of English freemen, *The Captain* 7
Every mother's *s*—Down they dropt— „ 50
As looks a father on the things Of his dead *s*, *The Letters* 24
On the first-born of her *s's*. *Vision of Sin* 146
Philip Ray the miller's only *s*, *Enoch Arden* 13
Bore him another *s*, a sickly one: „ 109
Her own *s* Was silent, tho' he often look'd his wish; „ 481
Her *s*, who stood beside her tall and strong, „ 756
So like her mother, and the boy, my *s*.' „ 791
tell my *s* that I died blessing him. „ 885
One whom the strong *s's* of the world despise; *The Brook* 3
s's of men Daughters of God; *Aylmer's Field* 44

Son (*continued*) for I have loved you more as *s* Than brother, *Aylmer's Field* 351
Born of a village girl, carpenter's *s*, " 668
but some, *S's* of the glebe, with other frowns " 723
visiting the *s*,—the *s* A Walter too,— *Princess, Pro.* 7
Slew both his *s's*: and I, shall I, " *ii* 288
she that has a *s* And sees him err: " *iii* 260
And here he keeps me hostage for his *s*.' " *iv* 405
'You have our *s*: touch not a hair of his head: " 407
unless you send us back Our *s*, on the instant, " 416
We did but keep you surety for our *s*, " *v* 25
then took the king His three broad *s's*; " 269
dabbled with the blood Of his own *s*, " *vi* 105
were half fool'd to let you tend our *s*, " 274
O sire, Grant me your *s*, to nurse, " 298
Against the *s's* of men, and barbarous laws. " *vii* 234
'nor blame Too much the *s's* of men and barbarous laws; " 256
The Tory member's elder *s*, " *Con.* 50
thanks to the Giver, England, for thy *s*. *Ode on Well.* 45
For this is England's greatest *s*, " 95
What England was, shall her true *s's* forget? *Third of Feb.* 44
S of him with whom we strove for power— *W. to Marie Alex.* 1
Gone for a minute, my *s*, *Grandmother* 103
They have taken our *s*, *The Victim* 49
We have his dearest, His only *s*!' " 64
STRONG *S* of God, immortal Love, *In Mem., Pro.* 1
Who pledgest now thy gallant *s*; " *vi* 10
Dear as the mother to the *s*, " *ix* 19
All knowledge that the *s's* of flesh " *lxxxv* 27
Yea, tho' their *s's* were none of these, " *xc* 17
Shaking her head at her *s* and sighing *Maud I xix* 24
Who dares foreshadow for an only *s* *Ded. of Idylls* 29
Or how should England dreaming of *his s's* " 31
The love of all Thy *s's* encompass Thee, " 52
Who cried, 'He is not Uther's *s*'— *Com. of Arthur* 43
who hath proven him King Uther's *s*? " 70
This is the *s* of Gorloïs, not the King; " 73
This is the *s* of Anton, not the King.' " 74
daughter saving to a king, And a king's *s*?'— " 144
Hold ye this Arthur for King Uther's *s*?' " 172
—but a *s* she had not borne. " 192
s of Gorloïs he, Or else the child of Anton, " 232
Or born the *s* of Gorloïs, after death, Or Uther's *s*, and born before his time, " 240
Gawain and young Modred, her two *s's*, " 244
and sign'd To those two *s's* to pass, " 319
No *s* of Uther, and no king of ours;' " 440
THE last tall *s* of Lot and Bellicent, *Gareth and L.* 1
'True love, sweet *s*, had risk'd himself " 60
Stay, my best *s*! ye are yet more boy than man.' " 98
'Sweet *s*, for there be many who deem him not, " 121
lifted but a little. Stay, sweet *s*.' " 131
Found her *s's* will unwaveringly one, " 141
when her *s* Beheld his only way to glory " 158
Thy *s* am I, And since thou art my mother, " 166
saying, 'Who be ye, my *s's*?' " 241
'*S*, I have seen the good ship sail Keel upward, " 253
And Fairy Queens have built the city, *s*; " 259
as thou sayest, it is enchanted, *s*, " 263
my husband's brother had my *s* Thrall'd in his castle, " 357
thou that slewest the sire hast left the *s*. " 360
Kill the foul thief, and wreak me for my *s*.' " 363
Arms for her *s*, and loosed him from his vow. " 530
'*S*, the good mother let me know thee here, " 550
lay Among the ashes and wedded the King's *s*.' " 904
s Of old King Lot and good Queen Bellicent, " 1230
'Whither, fair *s*?' to whom Geraint replied, *Marr. of Geraint* 298
Rest! the good house, tho' ruin'd, O my *s*, " 378
be not wroth or grieved At thy new *s*, " 780
Know well that Envy calls you Devil's *s*, *Merlin and V.* 467
And then did Envy call me Devil's *s*: " 497
(As *s's* of kings loving in pupilage " 517
With two strong *s's*, Sir Torre and Sir Lavaine, *Lancelot and E.* 174
Hurt in his first tilt with my *s*, " 196
But I, my *s's* and little daughter fled " 276

Son (*continued*) furthermore Our *s* is with him; *Lancelot and E.* 636
s's Born to the glory of thy name and fame, " 1371
'Thou art fair, my child, As a king's *s*,' " 1410
but some Call'd him a *s* of Lancelot, *Holy Grail* 144
'O *s*, thou hast not true humility, " 445
seem'd Shoutings of all the *s's* of God: " 509
Who call'd him the false *s* of Gorloïs: *Guinevere* 288
strike against the man they call My sister's *s*— " 573
Are loyal to their own far *s's*, *To the Queen ii* 28
And grovel and grope for my *s* *Rizpah* 8
I'll none of it, said my *s*. " 32
know you worthy everyway To be my *s*, *Sisters (E. and E.)* 49
my good *s*—Is yet untouch'd: " 287
but 'e leäved it to Charlie 'is *s*, *Village Wife* 42
An' 'e calls fur 'is *s*, " 62
But Squire wur afear'd o' 'is *s*, " 63
Sa feyther an' *s* was buried togither, " 90
the fourth Was like the *S* of God! *Sir J. Oldcastle* 176
we, We and our *s's* for ever. *Columbus* 29
was it otherwise With thine own *S*?' " 154
Stay, my *s* Is here anon: my *s* " 218
To younger England in the boy my *s*. *To Victor Hugo* 14
S's of Edward with hammer'd brands. *Batt. of Brunanburh* 14
Leaving his *s* too Lost in the carnage, " 72
my *s*, who dipt In some forgotten book *To E. Fitzgerald* 46
My *s*, the Gods, despite of human prayer, *Tiresias* 9
fathers call'd The Gods own *s*. " 17
S, in the hidden world of sight, " 51
My *s*, No sound is breathed so potent to coerce, " 119
Thither, my *s*, and there Thou, " 163
the *s's* of a winterless day. *The Wreck* 74
one *s* had forged on his father and fled, *Despair* 69
but, *s*, the source is higher, *Ancient Sage* 10
I am wearied of our city, *s*, " 15
To me, my *s*, more mystic than myself, " 45
Thou canst not prove the Nameless, O my *s*, " 57
nay my *s*, Thou canst not prove that I, " 63
But some in yonder city hold, my *s*, " 82
The wife, the *s's*, who love him best " 125
My *s*, the world is dark with griefs and graves, " 171
If utter darkness closed the day, my *s*— " 199
more, my *s*! for more than once when I Sat all alone, " 229
such counter-terms, my *s*, Are border-races, " 250
Gone our sailor *s* thy father, *Locksley H., Sixty* 55
S's of God, and kings of men " 122
To all our noble *s's*, the strong New England *Hands all Round* 15
S's and brothers that have sent, *Open I. and C. Exhib.* 3
The mother featured in the *s*; " 12
Britain fought her *s's* of yore— " 21
'*S's*, be welded each and all, " 36
why The *s's* before the fathers die, *To Marq. of Dufferin* 47
summun 'ed hax'd fur a *s*, an' 'e promised a *s* i' säävin' a *s* fur me. *Owd Roä* 95
" 96
Tell my *s*—O let me lean my head upon your breast. *Romney's R.* 153
Dying in childbirth of dead *s's*. *Akbar's Dream* 12
heart is for my *s*, Saleem, mine heir,— " 171
watch'd my *s*, And those that follow'd, " 187
In a while I bore him a *s*, *Bandit's Death* 15
Glared on at the murder'd *s*, " 33
Our *s's* will shame our own; *Mechanophilus* 22

Song (*Se ealso* **Battle-song, Death-song, Drinking-song, Love-song, Matin-song, War-song**) *Take, Madam, this poor book of* s; *To the Queen* 17
Her *s* the lintwhite swelleth, *Claribel* 15
And it sings a *s* of undying love; *Poet's Mind* 33
Were flooded over with eddying *s*. *Dying Swan* 42
What *s's* below the waning stars *Margaret* 33
Hear a *s* that echoes cheerly *L. of Shalott i* 30
They heard her singing her last *s*, " *iv* 26
Singing in her *s* she died, " 35
The woods were fill'd so full with *s*, *Two Voices* 455
sleep was broken thro' By some wild skylark's matin *s*. *Miller's D.* 40
The phantom of a silent *s*, " 71
Ah, well—but sing the foolish *s* I gave you, " 161
So sing that other *s* I made, " 199

Song (*continued*) and build up all My sorrow with my *s*, *Œnone* 40
there the world-worn Dante grasp'd his *s*, *Palace of Art* 135
To sing her *s's* alone. „ 160
More than my soul to hear her echo'd *s* „ 175
they find a music centred in a doleful *s* *Lotos-Eaters, C. S.* 117
Sung by the morning star of *s*, *D. of F. Women* 3
far-renowned brides of ancient *s* Peopled the hollow dark, „ 17
Not any *s* of bird or sound of rill; „ 66
With timbrel and with *s*. „ 200
Leaving the dance and *s*, „ 216
shook his *s* together as he near'd His happy home, *Gardener's D.* 91
Like poets, from the vanity of *s*? „ 100
He sang his *s*, and I replied with mine: *Audley Court* 56
I found it in a volume, all of *s's*, „ 57
in the Latin *s* I learnt at school, *Edwin Morris* 79
you shall have that *s* which Leonard wrote: *Golden Year* 1
and that same *s* of his He told me; „ 7
Like that strange *s* I heard Apollo sing, *Tithonus* 62
falser than all *s's* have sung, *Locksley Hall* 41
And a *s* from out the distance „ 84
You'd have *my* moral from the *s*, *Day-Dm., L'Envoi* 31
To search a meaning for the *s*, „ 35
To shape the *s* for your delight „ *Ep.* 6
had I lived when *s* was great (repeat) *Amphion* 9, 13
When, ere his *s* was ended, „ 50
Let him hear my *s*. *The Captain* 4
Sometimes the linnet piped his *s*: *Sir L. and Q. G.* 10
I turn'd and humm'd a bitter *s* *The Letters* 9
Storm'd in orbs of *s*, a growing gale; *Vision of Sin* 25
A *s* that pleased us from its worth; *You might have won* 22
nightingale thought, 'I have sung many *s's*, *Poet's Song* 13
As tho' it were the burthen of a *s*, *Enoch Arden* 797
sway'd The cradle, while she sang this baby *s*. *Sea Dreams* 292
girt With *s* and flame and fragrance, *Lucretius* 134
time to time, some ballad or a *s* *Princess, Pro.* 241
And here I give the story and the *s's*. „ 247
And shook the *s's*, the whispers, „ *i* 98
about us peal'd the nightingale, Rapt in her *s*, „ 221
Some to a low *s* oar'd a shallop by, „ *ii* 457
'Know you no *s* of your own land,' „ *iv* 84
But great is *s* Used to great ends: „ 137
for *s* Is duer unto freedom, „ 140
Know you no *s*, the true growth of your soil, „ 150
I dragg'd my brains for such a *s*, „ 154
the *s* Might have been worse and sinn'd „ 250
pardon ask'd and given For stroke and *s*, „ *v* 47
a *s* on every spray Of birds that piped „ 238
noise of *s's* they would not understand: „ *vi* 40
Remembering his ill-omen'd *s*, „ 159
Then Violet, she that sang the mournful *s*, „ 318
And ever-echoing avenues of *s*. *Ode on Well.* 79
My name in *s* has done him much wrong, *Spiteful Letter* 3
Who hate each other for a *s*, *Lit. Squabbles* 5
Glory of warrior, glory of orator, glory of *s*, *Wages* 1
Birds' love and birds' *s* *Window, Spring* 1
Birds' *s* and birds' love, (repeat) „ 3, 5
Men's *s* and men's love, „ 7
Ay is the *s* of the wedded spheres, „ *No Answer* 7
I brim with sorrow drowning *s*. *In Mem. xix* 12
For private sorrow's barren *s*, „ *xxi* 14
Or breaking into *s* by fits, „ *xxiii* 2
In dance and *s* and game and jest? „ *xxix* 8
A merry *s* we sang with him Last year: „ *xxx* 15
To lull with *s* an aching heart, „ *xxxvii* 15
And darken'd sanctities with *s*.' „ 24
But in the *s's* I love to sing „ *xxxviii* 7
Then are these *s's* I sing of thee „ 11
Short swallow-flights of *s*, „ *xlviii* 15
The slightest air of *s* shall breathe „ *xlix* 7
'Yet blame not thou thy plaintive *s*,' „ *lii* 5
the *s* of woe Is after all an earthly *s*: „ *lvii* 1
And round thee with the breeze of *s* „ *lxxv* 11
if the matin *s's*, that woke The darkness „ *lxxvi* 9
With fifty Mays, thy *s's* are vain; „ 14
who turns a musing eye On *s's*, and deeds. „ *lxxvii* 3

Song (*continued*) And dance and *s* and hoodman-blind. *In Mem. lxxviii* 12
And flood a fresher throat with *s*. „ *lxxxiii* 16
all within was noise Of *s's*, and clapping hands, „ *lxxxvii* 19
we sang old *s's* that peal'd From knoll to knoll, „ *xcv* 13
With sport and *s*, in booth and tent, „ *xcviii* 28
A *s* that slights the coming care, „ *xcix* 10
'Here thy boyhood sung Long since its matin *s*, „ *cii* 10
Be neither *s*, nor game, nor feast; „ *cv* 21
And sing the *s's* he loved to hear. „ *cvii* 24
The lark becomes a sightless *s*. „ *cxv* 8
the *s's*, the stirring air, The life re-orient „ *cxvi* 5
And if the *s* were full of care, „ *cxxv* 9
He breathed the spirit of the *s*; „ 10
Is music more than any *s*. „ *Con.* 4
In dying *s's* a dead regret, „ 14
Which makes appear the *s's* I made „ 21
A martial *s* like a trumpet's call! *Maud I v* 5
An old *s* vexes my ear; „ *II ii* 47
descend, From the realms of light and *s*, „ *iv* 82
Gawain went, and breaking into *s* Sprang out, *Com. of Arthur* 320
with dance And revel and *s*, made merry over Death, *Gareth and L.* 1423
It chanced the *s* that Enid sang was one Of Fortune *Marr. of Geraint* 345
by the bird's *s* ye may learn the nest,' „ 359
Half whistling and half singing a coarse *s*, *Geraint and E.* 528
Sweet-voiced, a *s* of welcome, *Balin and Balan* 86
other was the *s* that once I heard By this huge oak, *Merlin and V.* 405
And into such a *s*, such fire for fame, „ 417
there We lost him: such a noble *s* was that. „ 433
howe'er ye scorn my *s*, Take one verse more— „ 444
So says the *s*, 'I trow it is no treason.' „ 723
Or sung in *s*! O vainly lavish'd love! „ 859
graces of the court, and *s's*, Sighs, *Lancelot and E.* 648
in those days she made a little *s*, „ 1004
call'd her *s* 'The *S* of Love and Death,' „ 1005
'Taliessin is our fullest throat of *s*, *Holy Grail* 300
And all talk died, as in a grove all *s* *Pelleas and E.* 607
a wire as musically as thou Some such fine *s*— *Last Tournament* 324
Among their harlot-brides, an evil *s*. „ 428
Murmuring a light *s* I had heard thee sing, „ 614
But even in the middle of his *s* He falter'd, *Guinevere* 302
and sent his soul Into the *s's* of birds, *Lover's Tale i* 321
the morning *s* of the lark, *First Quarrel* 33
We could sing a good *s* at the Plow, (repeat) *North. Cobbler* 18
I know the *s*, Their favourite— *Sisters (E. and E.)* 2
One bright May morning in a world of *s*, „ 82
brave in the fight as the bravest hero of *s*, *V. of Maeldune* 5
And we chanted the *s's* of the Bards „ 90
are a *s* Heard in the future; *Tiresias* 124
touching on all things great, Science, philosophy, *s*— *The Wreck* 51
some treasure of classical *s*, „ 67
With *s's* in praise of death, *Ancient Sage* 209
their *s's*, that meet The morning with such music, *The Flight* 65
wid his *s* to the Sun an' the Moon, *Tomorrow* 91
cried the king of sacred *s*; *Locksley H., Sixty* 201
to crown with *s* The warrior's noble deed— *Epilogue* 36
But *S* will vanish in the Vast; „ 40
And deed and *s* alike are swept Away, „ 67
'The *s* that nerves a nation's heart, „ 81
flash'd into a frolic of *s* And welcome; *Demeter and P.* 12
sung their *s's* an' 'ed 'ed their beer, *Owd Roä* 35
I sang the *s*, 'are bride And bridegroom.' *The Ring* 25
spring-flower I send, This *s* of spring, *To Mary Boyle* 20
I hear a charm of *s* thro' all the land. *Prog. of Spring* 47
with a *s* Which often echo'd in me, *Romney's R.* 84
Your *s*—Sit, listen! I remember it, „ 91
Other *s's* for other worlds! *Parnassus* 19
'Love again, *s* again, nest again, *The Throstle* 9
I was lilting a *s* to the babe, — *Bandit's Death* 20
he answer'd her wail with a *s*— *The Dreamer* 16

Song-built Shock after shock, the *s-b* towers and gates Reel, *Tiresias* 98
Songful Ascending, pierce the glad and *s* air, *Demeter and P.* 45
Songless high in the heaven above it there flicker'd a *s* lark, *V. of Maeldune* 17

Songless (*continued*) She hears the lark within the *s* egg, *Ancient Sage* 76
Songster Catullus, whose dead *s* never dies ; *Poets and their B.* 8
Sonorous Echoing all night to that *s* flow *Palace of Art* 27
Soon There will come a witness *s* *Forlorn* 25
Will it ever ? late or *s* ? *Locksley H., Sixty* 173
Soon (sun) ' Cast awaäy on a disolut land wi' a vartical *s* ! ' *North. Cobbler* 3
Soonday (Sunday) I gits the plaäte fuller o' *S's* *Church-warden, etc.* 40
Sooner I'd *s* fold an icy corpse dead *The Flight* 54
Soort (sort) Naw *s* o' koind o' use to saäy the things *N. Farmer, O. S.* 6
like fur to hev soom *s* of a sarvice reäd. *Owd Roä* 12
Sootflake (The *s* of so many a summer still *Sea Dreams* 35
Sooth Good *s* ! I hold He scarce is knight, *Gareth and L.* 1175
' for in *s* These ancient books— *Holy Grail* 540
Or was there *s* in Arthur's prophecy, „ 709
Soothe How *should* I *s* you anyway, *To J. S.* 58
S him with thy finer fancies, *Locksley Hall* 54
One spiritual doubt she did not *s* ? *Aylmer's Field* 704
O for thy voice to *s* and bless ! *In Mem. lvi* 26
And, influence-rich to *s* and save, „ *lxxx* 14
hurt Whom she would *s*, *Guinevere* 355
Soothed This fiat somewhat *s* himself *Aylmer's Field* 26
Sooty underwent The *s* yoke of kitchen-vassalage ; *Gareth and L.* 479
Sophist Low-cowering shall the *S* sit ; *Clear-headed friend* 10
Dark-brow'd *s*, come not anear ; *Poet's Mind* 8
Sophister That every *s* can lime. *Love thou thy land* 12
Sorcerer Some *s*, whom a far-off grandsire burnt *Princess i* 6
I have no *s's* malison on me, „ *ii* 410
I remember'd that burnt *s's* curse „ *v* 475
Sorcery drave the heathen hence by *s* And Merlin's glamour.' *Gareth and L.* 204
Whom thou by *s* or unhappiness Or some device, „ 997
Device and *s* and unhappiness— „ 1235
Sordid Love, that endures not *s* ends, *Love thou thy land* 6
Till I well could weep for a time so *s* and mean, *Maud I v* 17
There a single *s* attic holds the living and the dead. *Locksley H., Sixty* 222
Sore (adj.) (*See also* **Foot-sore**) Plagued her with *s* despair. *Palace of Art* 224
S task to hearts worn out by many wars *Lotos-Eaters, C. S.* 86
Sore (s) old *s* breaks out from age to age *Walk. to the Mail* 79
Sorrow (s) waste place with joy Hidden in *s* : *Dying Swan* 23
delight Of dainty *s* without sound, *Margaret* 18
Your *s*, only *s's* shade, Keeps real *s* far away. .. 43
Rise from the feast of *s*, lady, .. 62
' Whatever crazy *s* saith, *Two Voices* 394
her heart would beat against me, In *s* and in rest : *Miller's D.* 178
they had their part Of *s* : .. 224
build up all My *s* with my song, *Œnone* 40
Still from one *s* to another thrown : *Lotos-Eaters, C. S.* 18
The star-like *s's* of immortal eyes, *D. of F. Women* 91
Stole from her sister *S*. *Gardener's D.* 256
this high dial, which my *s* crowns— *St. S. Stylites* 95
a *s's* crown of *s* is remembering *Locksley Hall* 76
When you came in my *s* broke me down ; *Enoch Arden* 317
Had you one *s* and she shared it not ? *Aylmer's Field* 702
Sat anger-charm'd from *s*, soldier-like, .. 728
Their own gray hairs with *s* to the grave— .. 777
Her crampt-up *s* pain'd her, „ 800
Nor sound of human *s* mounts to mar *Lucretius* 109
And *s* darkens hamlet and hall. *Ode on Well.* 7
And makes it a *s* to be.' *The Islet* 36
O *S*, cruel fellowship, *In Mem. iii* 1
Or *s* such a changeling be ? .. *xvi* 4
I brim with *s* drowning song. .. *xix* 12
For private *s's* barren song, .. *xxi* 14
Now, sometimes in my *s* shut, .. *xxiii* 1
They bring me *s* touch'd with joy, .. *xxviii* 19
But *S*—fixt upon the dead, .. *xxxix* 8
If these brief lays, of *S* born, .. *xlviii* 1
Ay me, the *s* deepens down, .. *xlix* 14
O *S*, wilt thou live with me No casual mistress, .. *lix* 1
O *S*, wilt thou rule my blood, .. 5
O *s*, then can *s* wane ? „ *lxxviii* 15
Delayest the *s* in my blood, „ *lxxxiii* 14

Sorrow (s) (*continued*) trust in things above Be dimm'd of *s*, *In Mem. lxxxv* 10
take what fruit may be Of *s* under human skies : .. *cviii* 14
'Tis held that *s* makes us wise, .. 15
'Tis held that *s* makes us wise ; .. *cxiii* 1
Yet less of *s* lives in me .. *cxvi* 13
Would there be *s* for *me* ? *Maud I i* 57
But *s* seize me if ever that light .. *iv* 12
and the *s* dimm'd her sight, *Lancelot and E.* 889
Comfort your *s's* ; for they do not flow *Guinevere* 188
weigh your *s's* with our lord the King's, .. 191
Stay'd on the cloud of *s* ; *Lover's Tale i* 255
Smit with exceeding *s* unto Death. .. 601
s of my spirit Was of so wide a compass .. *ii* 134
chiefly to my *s* by the Church, *Columbus* 56
he heal'd me with *s* for evermore. *The Wreck* 58
the *s* that I bear is *s* for *his* sake. *The Flight* 64
Sorrowing with the *s's* of the lowest ! *On Jub. Q. Victoria* 27
From sin thro' *s* into Thee we pass *Doubt and Prayer* 3
Sorrow (verb) who most have cause to *s* for her— *Aylmer's Field* 678
And he should *s* o'er my state *In Mem. xiv* 15
I feel it, when I *s* most ; „ *xxvii* 14
I *s* after The delight of early skies ; *Maud II iv* 24
In a wakeful doze I *s* For the hand, „ 26
Sorrow'd those who *s* o'er a vanish'd race, *Aylmer's Field* 844
I felt it, when I *s* most, *In Mem. lxxxv* 2
Love mourn'd long, and *s* after Hope ; *Lover's Tale i* 819
Sorrowest O *s* thou, pale Painter, for the past, *Wan Sculptor* 3
Sorrowing after him Came Psyche, *s* for Aglaïa. *Princess vi* 29
Went *s* in a pause I dared not break ; .. *vii* 249
s Lancelot should have stoop'd so low, *Lancelot and E.* 732
and *s* for our Lancelot, *Holy Grail* 648
And let the *s* crowd about it grow, *Ode on Well.* 16
And the sound of the *s* anthem roll'd .. 60
S with the sorrows of the lowest ! *On Jub. Q. Victoria* 27
Sorry an' *s* when he was away, *First Quarrel* 11
I am *s* for all the quarrel an' *s* .. 87
Sort (*See also* **Soort**) older *s*, and murmur'd that their May *Princess ii* 463
fused with female grace In such a *s*, *In Mem. cix* 18
' Ay, truly of a truth, And in a *s*, *Gareth and L.* 838
Sottin' ' *S* thy braäins Guzzlin' an' soäkin' *North. Cobbler* 23
Soudan Now somewhere dead far in the waste *S*, *Epit. on Gordon* 2
Soughing And the wavy swell of the *s* reeds, *Dying Swan* 38
Sought Still moving after truth long *s*, *Two Voices* 62
You *s* to prove how I could love, *L. C. V. de Vere* 21
I *s* to strike Into that wondrous track *D. of F. Women* 278
That *s* to sow themselves like winged seeds, *Gardener's D.* 65
She *s* her lord, and found him, *Godiva* 16
s and found a witch Who brew'd the philtre *Lucretius* 15
I *s* but peace ; No critic I— *Princess i* 144
grace Concluded, and we *s* the gardens : .. *ii* 453
some hid and *s* In the orange thickets : .. 459
twice I *s* to plead my cause, .. *iv* 552
and I—I *s* for one—All people said she had authority— .. *vi* 237
s far less for truth than power In knowledge : .. *vii* 236
one that *s* but Duty's iron crown *Ode on Well.* 122
whereon he *s* The King alone, and found, *Gareth and L.* 540
when they *s* and found, Sir Gareth drank and ate, „ 1279
though they *s* Thro' all the provinces *Marr. of Geraint* 729
after, when we *s* The tribute, answer'd *Balin and Balan* 115
And Arthur, when Sir Balin *s* him, said .. 198
King, who *s* to win my love Thro' evil ways : .. 474
a wanton damsel came, And *s* for Garlon at the castle-gates, .. 610
And Vivien ever *s* to work the charm *Merlin and V.* 215
What other ? for men *s* to prove me vile, .. 495
darkness falling, *s* A priory not far off, *Pelleas and E.* 213
s To make disruption in the Table Round *Guinevere* 16
nor *s*, Wrapt in her grief, for housel .. 148
At last she *s* out Memory, and they trod *Lover's Tale i* 820
Chiefly I *s* the cavern and the hill .. *ii* 33
Hath *s* the tribute of a verse from me, *To Dante* 5
at home if I *s* for a kindly caress, *The Wreck* 31
The Count who *s* to snap the bond *Happy* 61

Soul (*continued*) That strike across the *s* in prayer, *Lover's Tale i* 364
my life, love, *s*, spirit, and heart and strength. ,, 460
And *s* and heart and body are all at ease : ,, 556
Come like an angel to a damned *s*, ,, 673
Memory fed the *s* of Love with tears. .. 822
a strong sympathy Shook all my *s* : .. *ii* 89
all at once, *s*, life And breath and motion, ,, 194
This love is of the brain, the mind, the *s* : .. *iv* 156
' body and *s* And life and limbs, ,, 282
but to save *my s*, that is all your desire : Do you think I care for *my s* *Rizpah* 77
face was flash'd thro' sense and *s* *Sisters (E. and E.)* 109
—wrought us harm, Poor *s*, not knowing) ,, 185
a thousand lives To save his *s*. *Sir J. Oldcastle* 64
How now, my *s*, we do not heed the fire ? .. 191
' O *s* of little faith, slow to believe ! *Columbus* 147
who seest the *s's* in Hell And purgatory, ,, 216
Shamed in their *s's*. *Batt. of Brunanburh* 99
make my life one prayer for a *s* that died in his sin, *The Wreck* 10
for Mother, the voice was the voice of the *s* ; .. 54
the sun of the *s* made day in the dark .. 55
a huge sea smote every *s* from the decks .. 109
No *s* in the heaven above, no *s* on the earth below, *Despair* 19
Come from the brute, poor *s's*—no *s's*— .. 36
if the *s's* of men were immortal, .. 99
thou sendest thy free *s* thro' heaven, *Ancient Sage* 47
daughter yield her life, heart, *s* to one— *The Flight* 28
She bad us love, like *s's* in Heaven, ,, 88
shadow of Himself, the boundless, thro' the human *s* ; *Locksley H., Sixty* 211
s and sense in city slime ? .. 218
Worthier *s* was he than I am, ,, 239
count them all My friends and brother *s's*, *Epilogue* 19
And showing them, *s's* have wings ! *Dead Prophet* 12
As a lord of the Human *s*, ,, 54
While yet thy fresh and virgin *s* *Freedom* 2
Till every *S* be free ; ,, 20
One with Britain, heart and *s* ! *Open. I. and C. Exhib.* 38
A *s* that, watch'd from earliest youth, *To Marq. of Dufferin* 25
And *s's* of men, who grew beyond their race, *Demeter and P.* 140
cotch'd 'er death o' cowd that night, poor *s*, i' the straw. *Owd Roä* 114
and you the *s* of Truth In Hubert ? *The Ring* 62
' The *s's* Of two repentant Lovers guard the ring ; ' ,, 197
wall of solid flesh that comes between your *s* and mine, *Happy* 35
s in *s* and light in light, ,, 39
So wed thee with my *s*, that I may mark *Prog. of Spring* 92
Lord let the house of a brute to the *s* of a man, *By an Evolution.* 1
my *s* uncertain, or a fable, ,, 5
Hold the sceptre, Human *S*, ,, 16
prize that *s* where man and woman meet, *On One who Eff. E. M.* 2
thoughts that lift the *s* of men, *To Master of B.* 14
And bravest *s* for counsellor and friend. *Akbar's Dream* 69
guess at the love of a *s* for a *s* ? *Charity* 30
passing *s's* thro' fire to the fire, *The Dawn* 4
bodies and *s's* go down in a common wreck, .. 13
Men, with a heart and a *s*, .. 18

Soul-stricken *S-s* at their kindness to him, *Aylmer's Field* 525

Sound (adj.) So healthy, *s*, and clear and whole, *Miller's D.* 15
What ails us, who are *s*, *Walk. to the Mail* 105
But, blind or lame or sick or *s*, *The Voyage* 93
Looks only for a moment whole and *s* ; *Aylmer's Field* 2
let your sleep for this one night be *s* : *Sea Dreams* 315
If that hypothesis of theirs be *s* ' *Princess iv* 20
felt it *s* and whole from head to foot, .. *vi* 211
Or, if we held the doctrine *s* *In Mem. liii* 9
How pure at heart and *s* in head, .. *xciv* 1
' *S* sleep be thine ! *s* cause to sleep hast thou. *Gareth and L.* 1282
Worthier soul was he than I am, *s* and honest, *Locksley H., Sixty* 239

Sound (s) the *s* Which to the wooing wind aloof *Mariana* 74
Full of the city's stilly *s*, *Arabian Nights* 103
no more of mirth Is here or merry-making *s*. *Deserted House* 14
Springing alone With a shrill inner *s*, *The Mermaid* 20
Of dainty sorrow without *s*, *Margaret* 18
With dinning *s* my ears are rife, *Eleänore* 135
Died the *s* of royal cheer ; *L. of Shalott iv* 48

Sound (s) (*continued*) There came a *s* as of the sea ; *Mariana in the S.* 8
I hear Dead *s's* at night come from the inmost hills, *Œnone* 246
a *s* Rings ever in her ears of armed men. ,, 264
Moved of themselves, with silver *s* ; *Palace of Art* 130
seem'd to hear the dully *s* Of human footsteps fall. ,, 275
or a *s* Of rocks thrown down, ,, 281
With *s's* that echo still. *D. of F. Women* 8
I heard *s's* of insult, shame, and wrong, ,, 19
Not any song or bird or *s* of rill ; ,, 66
and fill'd with light The interval of *s*. .. 172
Hearing the holy organ rolling waves Of *s* .. 192
With that sharp *s* the white dawn's creeping beams, .. 261
and tell o'er Each little *s* and sight. ,, 277
Parson, sent to sleep with *s*, And waked with silence, *M. d'Arthur, Ep.* 3
That with the *s* I woke, and heard ,, 30
In *s* of funeral or of marriage bells ; *Gardener's D.* 36
hour just flown, that morn with all its *s*, ,, 83
Delighted with the freshness and the *s*. *Edwin Morris* 99
with *s* Of pious hymns and psalms, *St. S. Stylites* 33
' I took the swarming *s* of life— *Talking Oak* 213
south-breeze around thee blow The *s* of minster bells. ,, 272
and the winds are laid with *s*. *Locksley Hall* 104
And bade him cry, with *s* of trumpet, *Godiva* 36
With twelve great shocks of *s*, ,, 74
no *s* is made, Not even of a gnat that sings. *Day-Dm., Sleep. P.* 20
a *s* Like sleepy counsel pleading ; *Amphion* 73
A gentle *s*, an awful light ! *Sir Galahad* 41
How fresh was every sight and *s* *The Voyage* 5
By grassy capes with fuller *s* *Sir L. and Q. G.* 14
There comes a *s* of marriage bells. *The Letters* 48
Then methought I heard a mellow *s*, *Vision of Sin* 14
Ran into its giddiest whirl of *s*, ,, 29
And the *s* of a voice that is still ! *Break, break, etc.* 12
and find A sort of absolution in the *s* *Sea Dreams* 61
Nor *s* of human sorrow mounts to mar *Lucretius* 109
melodious thunder to the *s* Of solemn psalms, *Princess ii* 476
hundred doors To one deep chamber shut from *s*, .. *vi* 376
That afternoon a *s* arose of hoof And chariot, .. 379
and sweet is every *s*, Sweeter thy voice, but every *s* is sweet ; ,, *vii* 218
Let the *s* of those he wrought for, *Ode on Well.* 10
the *s* of the sorrowing anthem roll'd .. 60
In that dread *s* to the great name, ,, 71
compass'd round with turbulent *s*, *Will* 7
S's of the great sea Wander'd about. *Minnie and Winnie* 7
Phantom *s* of blows descending, *Boädicea* 25
When was a harsher *s* ever heard, *Trans. of Homer* 3
Calm is the morn without a *s*, *In Mem. xi* 1
door Were shut between me and the *s* : .. *xxviii* 8
The streets were fill'd with joyful *s*, .. *xxxi* 10
The *s* of streams that swift or slow .. *xxxv* 10
' The *s* of that forgetful shore .. 14
And up thy vault with roaring *s* .. *lxxii* 25
O *s* to rout the brood of cares, .. *lxxxix* 17
and growing upon me without a *s*, *Maud I iii* 7
I heard no *s* where I stood But the rivulet ,, *xiv* 28
To the *s* of dancing music and flutes : ,, *II v* 76
and the *s* was good to Gareth's ear. *Gareth and L.* 312
but heard instead A sudden *s* of hoofs, *Marr. of Geraint* 164
the tender *s* of his own voice And sweet self-pity, *Geraint and E.* 348
s of many a heavily-galloping hoof Smote on her ear, ,, 447
Such a *s* (for Arthur's knights Were hated strangers *Balin and Balan* 351
s not wonted in a place so still Woke the sick knight, *Lancelot and E.* 818
Lancelot knew the little clinking *s* ; ,, 983
And the strange *s* of an adulterous race, *Holy Grail* 80
I heard a *s* As of a silver horn from o'er the hills ,, 108
slender *s* As from a distance beyond distance grew ,, 111
I heard the *s*, I saw the light, ,, 280
heavens Were shaken with the motion and the *s*. ,, 801
Suddenly waken'd with a *s* of talk *Pelleas and E.* 48
but a *s* Of Gawain ever coming, and this lay— ,, 395
' A *s* is in his ears ' ? *Last Tournament* 116
S's, as if some fair city were one voice *Pass. of Arthur* 460
we loved The *s* of one-another's voices *Lover's Tale i* 256

Sound (s) (*continued*) great pine shook with lonely *s's* of joy — *Lover's Tale i* 325
So that they pass not to the shrine of *s*. — „ 470
I too have heard a *s*— — „ 522
Her words did of their meaning borrow *s*, — „ 568
With such a *s* as when an iceberg splits — „ 603
for the *s* Of that dear voice so musically low, — „ 707
for the *s* Of the loud stream was pleasant, — „ *ii* 34
All crisped *s's* of wave and leaf and wind, — „ 106
Like *s's* without the twilight realm of dreams, — „ 120
No *s* is breathed so potent to coerce, — *Tiresias* 120
sweet *s* ran Thro' palace and cottage door, — *Dead Prophet* 37
sympathies, how frail, In *s* and smell! — *Early Spring* 36
one drear *s* I have not heard, — *To Marq. of Dufferin* 40
A *s* of anger like a distant storm. — *The Ring* 119
My people too were scared with eerie *s's*, — „ 408
all her realm Of *s* and smoke, — *To Mary Boyle* 66
A *s* from far away, No louder than a bee — *Romney's R.* 81
What *s* was dearest in his native dells? — *Far—far—away* 4
THERE is a *s* of thunder afar, — *Riflemen form!* 1
Be not deaf to the *s* that warns, — „ 8
Too full for *s* and foam, — *Crossing the Bar* 6
Sound (verb) the waterfall Which ever *s's* and shines — *Ode to Memory* 52
how thy name may *s* Will vex thee lying underground? — *Two Voices* 110
The wind *s's* like a silver wire, — *Fatima* 29
S all night long, in falling thro' the dell, — *D. of F. Women* 183
when you want me, *s* upon the bugle-horn. — *Locksley Hall* 2
Like strangers' voices here they *s*, — *In Mem. civ* 9
S on a dreadful trumpet, summoning her; — *Geraint and E.* 383
rhythm *s* for ever of Imperial Rome— — *To Virgil* 32
that would *s* so mean That all the dead, — *Romney's R.* 131
S's happier than the merriest marriage-bell. — *D. of the Duke of C.* 11
Sound (fathom) Two plummets dropt for one to *s* the abyss Of science. — *Princess ii* 176
Sounded (*See also* **Far-sounded**) Then the voice Of Ida *s*, issuing ordinance: — „ *vi* 373
from the castle a cry *S* across the court, — *Balin and Balan* 400
The sudden trumpet *s* as in a dream — *Last Tournament* 151
bound Not by the *s* letter of the word, — *Sisters (E. and E.)* 162
thunder of the brook *S* 'Œnone'; — *Death of Œnone* 24
Sounder Of *s* leaf than I can claim; — *You might have won* 4
I have stumbled back again Into the common day, the *s* self. — *Romney's R.* 33
Sounding (*See also* **Long-sounding, Ocean-sounding, Sea-sounding**) my merry comrades call me, *s* on the bugle-horn, — *Locksley Hall* 145
Breathing and *s* beauteous battle, — *Princess v* 161
The great city *s* wide; — *Maud II iv* 64
Made answer, *s* like a distant horn. — *Guinevere* 249
and shoutings and *s's* to arms, — *Def. of Lucknow* 76
The pillar'd dusk of *s* sycamores, — *Audley Court* 16
and sitting well in order smite The *s* furrows; — *Ulysses* 59
into the *s* hall I past; But nothing in the *s* hall I saw, — *Holy Grail* 827
a little silver cloud Over the *s* seas: — *Lover's Tale iii* 37
ear-stunning hail of Arês crash Along the *s* walls. — *Tiresias* 97
while the golden lyre Is ever *s* in heroic ears — „ 181
Well be grateful for the *s* watchword 'Evolution' here, — *Locksley H., Sixty* 198
and alarms *S* 'To arms! to arms!' — *Prog. of Spring* 104
S for ever and ever thro' Earth — *Parnassus* 7
'*S* for ever and ever?' pass on! — „ 15
Sour 'Slip-shod waiter, lank and *s*, — *Vision of Sin* 71
A little grain of conscience made him *s*.' — „ 218
Come, thou art crabb'd and *s*: — *Last Tournament* 272
All out like a long life to a *s* end— — „ 288
Source A teardrop trembled from its *s*, — *Talking Oak* 161
Like torrents from a mountain *s* — *The Letters* 39
Prayer from a living *s* within the will, — *Enoch Arden* 801
The very *s* and fount of Day — *In Mem. xxiv* 3
it melteth in the *s* Of these sad tears, — *Lover's Tale i* 783
but, son, the *s* is higher, — *Ancient Sage* 10
Soured she *s* To what she is: — *Walk. to the Mail* 61
South by day or night, From North to *S*, — *Rosalind* 48
Warmly and broadly the *s* winds are blowing — *All Things will Die* 3
For look, the sunset, *s* and north, — *Miller's D.* 241
Of that long desert to the *s*. — *Fatima* 14

South (*continued*) Four courts I made, East, West and *S* and North, — *Palace of Art* 21
The palms and temples of the *S*. — *You ask me, why* 28
I was at school—a college in the *S*: — *Walk. to the Mail* 83
Sailing under palmy highlands Far within the *S*. — *The Captain* 24
As fast we fleeted to the *S*: — *The Voyage* 4
Came murmurs of her beauty from the *S*, — *Princess i* 36
That bright and fierce and fickle is the *S*, — „ *iv* 97
Say to her, I do but wanton in the *S*, — „ 109
And brief the moon of beauty in the *S*. — „ 113
long breezes rapt from inmost *s* — „ 431
My fancy fled to the *S* again. — *The Daisy* 108
To North, *S*, East, and West; — *Voice and the P.* 14
Thine the North and thine the *S* — *Boädicea* 44
Down in the *s* is a flash and a groan: — *Window, Gone.* 8
Rosy is the West, Rosy is the *S*, (repeat) — *Maud I xvii* 6, 26
And looking to the *S*, and fed With honey'd rain — „ *xviii* 20
All the west And ev'n unto the middle *s* — *Lover's Tale i* 415
Who whilome spakest to the *S* in Greek — *Sir J. Oldcastle* 29
'From the *S* I bring you balm, — *Prog. of Spring* 66
Storm in the *S* that darkens the day! — *Riflemen form!* 2
South-breeze The full *s-b* around thee blow — *Talking Oak* 271
Southern The lavish growths of *s* Mexico. — *Mine be the strength* 14
Would still be dear beyond the *s* hills: — *Princess ii* 265
Between the Northern and the *S* morn.' — „ *v* 423
In lands of palm and *s* pine; — *The Daisy* 2
And reach the glow of *s* skies, — *In Mem. xii* 10
New England of the *S* Pole! — *Hands all Round* 16
So fair in *s* sunshine bathed, — *Freedom* 5
Fair Spring slides hither o'er the *S* sea, — *Prog. of Spring* 2
Southland meats and good red wine Of *S*, — *Gareth and L.* 1191
South-sea-isle under worse than *S-s-i* taboo, — *Princess iii* 278
Southward *S* they set their faces. — *Gareth and L.* 182
South-west the *s-w* that blowing Bala lake — *Geraint and E.* 929
South-western loud *S's*, rolling ridge on ridge, — *Gareth and L.* 1145
South-wind whisper of the *s-w* rushing warm, — *Locksley Hall* 125
Sovereign These three alone lead life to *s* power. — *Œnone* 145
Creation minted in the golden moods Of *s* artists; — *Princess v* 195
Sovran THEY rose to where their *s* eagle sails, — *Montenegro* 1
Sow (s) He had a *s*, sir. — *Walk. to the Mail* 86
With hand and rope we haled the groaning *s*, — „ 91
Large range of prospect had the mother *s*, — „ 93
As never *s* was higher in this world— — „ 96
all the swine were *s's*, And all the dogs'— — *Princess i* 192
Sow (verb) (*See also* **Saw**) He *s's* himself on every wind. — *Two Voices* 294
S the seed, and reap the harvest — *Lotos-Eaters, C. S.* 121
sought to *s* themselves like winged seeds, — *Gardener's D.* 65
and *s* The dust of continents to be; — *In Mem. xxxv* 11
And *s* the sky with flying boughs, — „ *lxxii* 24
Might *s* and reap in peace, — *Epilogue* 13
Sowd (sold) why shouldn't thy boooks be *s*? — *Village Wife* 69
Sow'd *S* all their mystic gulfs with fleeting stars; — *Gardener's D.* 262
s her name and kept it green In living letters, — *Aylmer's Field* 88
S it far and wide By every town and tower, — *The Flower* 13
He *s* a slander in the common ear, — *Marr. of Geraint* 450
Sow-droonk (very drunk) Soä *s-d* that tha doesn not touch thy 'at to the Squire;' — *North. Cobbler* 25
Sowing *s* hedgerow texts and passing by, — *Aylmer's Field* 171
Dispensing harvest, *s* the To-be, — *Princess vii* 289
And *s* one ill hint from ear to ear, — *Merlin and V.* 143
s the nettle on all the laurel'd graves of the Great; — *Vastness* 22
Sowl (soul) 'Ud 'a shot his own *s* dead — *Tomorrow* 40
Sown But, having *s* some generous seed, — *Two Voices* 143
another wore A close-set robe of jasmine *s* with stars: — *Aylmer's Field* 158
murmur'd, *s* With happy faces and with holiday. — *Princess, Pro.* 55
Grew up from seed we two long since had *s*; — „ *iv* 310
save the one true seed of freedom *s* — *Ode on Well.* 162
S in a wrinkle of the monstrous hill, — *Will* 19
That had the wild oat not been *s*, — *In Mem. liii* 6
Among the dead and *s* upon the wind— — *Merlin and V.* 45
Space (*See also* **Breathing-space**) Oh! narrow, narrow was the *s*, — *Oriana* 46
Overlook a *s* of flowers, — *L. of Shalott i* 16
But Lancelot mused a little *s*; — „ *iv* 51

Space (*continued*) all in *s's* rosy-bright Large Hesper glitter'd — *Mariana in the S.* 89
Free *s* for every human doubt, — *Two Voices* 137
In some fair *s* of sloping greens Lay, — *Palace of Art* 106
Hath time and *s* to work and spread. — *You ask me, why, etc.* 16
The ever-silent *s's* of the East, — *Tithonus* 9
shall have scope and breathing *s* — *Locksley Hall* 167
Pure *s's* clothed in living beams, — *Sir Galahad* 66
The *s* was narrow,—having order'd all — *Enoch Arden* 177
little *s* was left between the horns, — *Princess iv* 207
ask'd but *s* and fairplay for her scheme; — „ *v* 282
leave her *s* to burgeon out of all Within her— — „ *vii* 271
Thro' all the silent *s's* of the worlds, — „ *Con.* 114
The height, the *s*, the gloom, — *The Daisy* 59
starry heavens of *s* Are sharpen'd to a needle's end; — *In Mem. lxxvi* 3
slowly breathing bare The round of *s*, — „ *lxxxvi* 5
And roll'd the floods in grander *s*, — „ *ciii* 26
And whispers to the worlds of *s*, — „ *cxxvi* 11
countercharm of *s* and hollow sky, — *Maud I xviii* 43
It is but for a little *s* I go: — „ 75
And after these King Arthur for a *s*, — *Com. of Arthur* 16
Arthur and his knighthood for a *s* Were all one will, — „ 515
And in the *s* to left of her, and right, — *Gareth and L.* 224
Gareth for so long a *s* Stared at the figures, — „ 231
some brief *s*, convey'd them on their way — „ 889
Then for a *s*, and under cloud that grew — „ 1358
Painted, who stare at open *s*, — *Geraint and E.* 268
Thence after tarrying for a *s* they rode, — „ 953
bode among them yet a little *s* — *Lancelot and E.* 921
the hind To whom a *s* of land is given to plow. — *Holy Grail* 907
But for a mile all round was open *s*, — *Pelleas and E.* 28
Then at Caerleon for a *s*— — „ 176
and either knight Drew back a *s*, — „ 573
Held for a *s* 'twixt cloud and wave, — *Lover's Tale i* 417
finite-infinite *s* In finite-infinite Time— — *De Prof., Two G.* 45
will be wheel'd thro' the silence of *s*, — *Despair* 83
triumphs over time and *s*, — *Locksley H., Sixty* 75
The man in *S* and Time, — *Epilogue* 49
s Of blank earth-baldness clothes itself afresh, — *Demeter and P.* 48
Fill out the *s's* by the barren tiles. — *Prog. of Spring* 43

Spacious A *s* garden full of flowering weeds, — *To ——, With Pal. of Art* 4
'My *s* mansion built for me, — *Palace of Art* 234
The *s* times of great Elizabeth — *D. of F. Women* 7
And flowing odour of the *s* air, — *Lover's Tale i* 478

Spade death while we stoopt to the *s*, — *Def. of Lucknow* 16

Spain To these Inquisition dogs and the devildoms of *S*.' — *The Revenge* 12
that they were not left to *S*, — „ 20
not into the hands of *S*!' — „ 90
had holden the power and glory of *S* so cheap — „ 106
sea plunged and fell on the shot-shatter'd navy of *S*, — „ 117
more empire to the kings Of *S* than all battles! — *Columbus* 23
Eighteen long years of waste, seven in your *S*, — „ 36
We fronted there the learning of all *S*, — „ 41
thought to turn my face from *S*, — „ 57
When *S* was waging war against the Moor— — „ 93
I strove myself with *S* against the Moor. — „ 94
if *S* should oust The Moslem from her limit, — „ 96
Blue blood of *S*, Tho' quartering your own royal arms of *S*, — „ 114
blue blood and black blood of *S*, — „ 116
S Pour'd in on all those happy naked isles— — „ 172
Their babies at the breast for hate of *S*— — „ 180
hard memorials of our truth to *S* — „ 196
S once the most chivalric race on earth, *S* — „ 204
To lay me in some shrine of this old *S*, Or in that vaster *S* I leave to *S*. — „ 207
I sorrow for that kindly child of *S* — „ 212
S in his blood and the Jew— — *The Wreck* 15
No! father, *S*, but Hubert brings me home — *The Ring* 59

Spake When angels *s* to men aloud, — *Supp. Confessions* 25
He *s* of beauty: that the dull Saw no divinity in grass, — *A Character* 7
He *s* of virtue: not the gods More purely, — „ 13
when she *s*, Her words did gather thunder — *The Poet* 48
A STILL small voice *s* unto me, — *Two Voices* 1
It *s*, moreover, in my mind: — „ 31
Again the voice *s* unto me: — „ 46

Spake (*continued*) Her eyelid quiver'd as she *s*. — *Miller's D.* 144
Still she *s* on and still she *s* of power, — *Œnone* 121
She *s* some certain truths of you. — *L. C. V. de Vere* 36
and if his fellow *s*, His voice was thin, — *Lotos-Eaters* 33
I heard Him, for He *s*, — *D. of F. Women* 227
So *s* he, clouded with his own conceit, — *M. d'Arthur* 110
And *s*, 'Be wise: not easily forgiven Are those, — *Gardener's D.* 247
And *s* not of it to a single soul, — *St. S. Stylites* 66
While I *s* then, a sting of shrewdest pain — „ 198
some one *s*: 'Behold! it was a crime — *Vision of Sin* 213
while they *s*, I saw my father's face — *Princess i* 58
And on the fourth I *s* of why we came, — „ 119
companion yestermorn; Unwillingly we *s*.' — „ *iii* 200
'but to one of whom we *s* Your Highness — „ 201
She *s* With kindled eyes: — „ 333
To whom none *s*, half-sick at heart, — „ *iv* 223
Stood up and *s*, an affluent orator. — „ 291
roughly *s* My father, 'Tut, you know them not, — „ *v* 150
To such as her! if Cyril *s* her true, — „ 168
'Nay, nay, you *s* but sense' — „ 206
So Hector *s*; the Trojans roar'd applause; — *Spec. of Iliad* 1
Yea, tho' it *s* and made appeal — *In Mem. xcii* 4
Yea, tho' it *s* and bared to view — „ 9
Dumb is that tower which *s* so loud, — „ *Con.* 106
s no slander, no, nor listen'd to it; — *Ded. of Idylls* 10
Then *s* the hoary chamberlain and said, — *Com. of Arthur* 148
when he *s* and cheer'd his Table Round — „ 267
s sweet words, and comforted my heart, — „ 349
Lash'd at the wizard as he *s* the word, — „ 388
She *s* and King Leodogran rejoiced, — „ 425
holy Dubric spread his hands and *s*, — „ 471
had the thing I *s* of been Mere gold— — *Gareth and L.* 65
But slowly *s* the mother looking at him, — „ 151
Gareth *s* Anger'd, 'Old Master, — „ 279
With all good cheer, He *s* and laugh'd, — „ 302
Nay, for he *s* too fool-like: — „ 472
Lancelot ever *s* him pleasantly, — „ 482
A naked babe, of whom the Prophet *s*, — „ 501
when the damsel *s* contemptuously, — „ 806
Gareth sharply *s*, 'None! for the deed's sake — „ 831
So she *s*. A league beyond the wood, — „ 845
Sir Gareth *s*, 'Lead, and I follow.' — „ 890
He *s*; and all at fiery speed the two Shock'd — „ 962
s 'Methought, Knave, when I watch'd thee striking — „ 991
advanced The monster, and then paused, and *s* no word. — „ 1385
But Gareth *s* and all indignantly, — „ 1386
he *s* no word; Which set the horror higher: — „ 1393
But none *s* word except the hoary Earl: — *Marr. of Geraint* 369
So *s* the kindly-hearted Earl, — „ 514
S to the lady with him and proclaim'd, — „ 552
Loudly *s* the Prince, 'Forbear: — „ 555
He *s*, and past away, But left two brawny spearmen, — *Geraint and E.* 557
none *s* word, but all sat down at once, — „ 604
She *s* so low he hardly heard her speak, — „ 643
s, 'Go thou with him and him and bring it to us, — *Balin and Balan* 5
And *s* no word until the shadow turn'd; — „ 45
Then *s* the men of Pellam crying 'Lord, — „ 337
Sir Balin *s* not word, But snatch'd — „ 553
he kiss'd it, moan'd and *s*; — „ 598
S (for she had been sick) to Guinevere, — *Lancelot and E.* 78
He never *s* word of reproach to me, — „ 124
hath come Despite the wound he *s* of, — „ 566
He *s* and parted. Wroth, but all in awe, — „ 719
Then *s* the lily maid of Astolat: — „ 1085
Arthur *s* among them, 'Let her tomb Be costly, — „ 1339
S thro' the limbs and in the voice— — *Holy Grail* 23
But *s* with such a sadness and so low — „ 42
S often with her of the Holy Grail, — „ 86
leaving the pale nun, I *s* of this To all men; — „ 129
as she *s* She sent the deathless passion in her eyes — „ 162
Then *s* the monk Ambrosius, — „ 203
King *S* to me, being nearest, 'Percivale,' — „ 268
'While thus he *s*, his eye, dwelling on mine, — „ 485
Sir Bors it was Who *s* so low and sadly — „ 701
the rest *S* but of sundry perils in the storm; — „ 761

Spake (*continued*) Then I *s* To one most holy saint, who wept *Holy Grail* 780
'And *s* I not too truly, O my knights? „ 888
s the King: I knew not all he meant.' „ 920
and when she *s* to him, Stammer'd, *Pelleas and E.* 84
Yet with good cheer he *s*, 'Behold me, Lady, „ 240
She *s*; and at her will they couch'd their spears, „ 273
While thus he *s*, she gazed upon the man „ 305
then *s*: 'Rise, weakling; I am Lancelot; „ 581
saw the laws that ruled the tournament Broken, but *s* not; *Last Tournament* 161
Tristram, *s* not any word, But bode his hour, „ 385
and *s* To Tristram, as he knelt before her, „ 540
And, saddening on the sudden, *s* Isolt, „ 581
once or twice I *s* thy name aloud. „ 615
while she *s*, Mindful of what he brought „ 714
when she came to Almesbury she *s* There to the nuns, *Guinevere* 138
But openly she *s* and said to her, „ 226
To play upon me,' and bowed her head nor *s*. „ 310
As at a friend's voice, and he *s* again: „ 531
while he *s* to these his helm was lower'd, „ 593
Except he mock'd me when he *s* of hope; „ 631
Arthur woke and call'd, 'Who *s*? *Pass. of Arthur* 46
This heard the bold Sir Bedivere and *s*: „ 50
Then *s* King Arthur to Sir Bedivere: (repeat) „ 65, 136
Then *s* the bold Sir Bedivere: „ 147
Then *s* the King: 'My house hath been my doom. „ 154
So *s* he, clouded with his own conceit, „ 278
she *s* on, for I did name no wish, (repeat) *Lover's Tale i* 578, 583
ask'd, Unanswer'd, since I *s* not; „ 707
Or this, or somewhat like to this, I *s*, „ 772
Within the summer-house of which I *s*, „ *ii* 167
Then *s* Sir Richard Grenville: *The Revenge* 8
he *s* to me, 'O Maeldune, let be this purpose *V. of Maeldune* 119
when I *s* of famine, plague, *Tiresias* 60
never *s* with man, And never named the Name'— *Ancient Sage* 55
Well *s* thy brother in his hymn to heaven *Akbar's Dream* 27
A Voice *s* out of the skies *Voice spake, etc.* 1
Spake (speak) She began to *s* to herself, *Tomorrow* 54
Spakest he were the swine thou *s* of, *Holy Grail* 885
Who whilome *s* to the South in Greek *Sir J. Oldcastle* 29
Spakin' (speaking) Her, that yer Honour was *s'* to? *Tomorrow* 1
Span (s) every *s* of shade that steals, *In Mem. cxvii* 10
Span (verb) She strove to *s* my waist: *Talking Oak* 138
Span (*See also* **Spick-span-new**)
Spangle (s) the *s* dances in bight and bay, *Sea-Fairies* 24
They would pelt me with starry *s's* and shells, *The Merman* 28
Spangle (verb) To *s* all the happy shores *In Mem., Con.* 120
Spangled (*See also* **Sapphire-spangled**) Flung inward over *s* floors, *Arabian Nights* 116
from a fringe of coppice round them burst A *s* pursuivant, *Balin and Balan* 47
Spaniard till the *S* came in sight, *The Revenge* 23
We will make the *S* promise, „ 94
Spanish '*S* ships of war at sea! „ 3
Four galleons drew away From the *S* fleet that day, „ 47
S fleet with broken sides lay round us „ 71
stately *S* men to their flagship bore him then, „ 97
wives and children *S* concubines, *Columbus* 175
Spank (strike) An' 'e *s's* 'is 'and into mine, *North. Cobbler* 92
Spanless and grown a bulk Of *s* girth, *Princess vi* 36
Spann'd Beyond a bridge that *s* a dry ravine: *Marr. of Geraint* 246
Across the bridge that *s* the dry ravine. „ 294
Spar Rocking with shatter'd *s's*, *Buonaparte* 11
S's were splinter'd, (repeat) *The Captain* 45, 49
Buoy'd upon floating tackle and broken *s's*, *Enoch Arden* 551
Spare (adj.) But far too *s* of flesh.' *Talking Oak* 92
Except the *s* chance-gift of those that came *St. S. Stylites* 78
Spare (verb) But, if thou *s* to fling Excalibur, *M. d'Arthur* 131
Smite, shrink not, *s* not. *St. S. Stylites* 181
one little kindly word, Not one to *s* her: *Princess vi* 259
we will not *s* the tyrant one hard word. *Third of Feb.* 42
whatever tempest mars Mid-ocean, *s* thee, sacred bark; *In Mem. xvii* 14
And yet I *s* them sympathy, „ *lxiii* 7
A little *s* the night I loved, „ *cv* 15
If the wolf *s* me, weep my life away, *Merlin and V.* 885

Spare (verb) (*continued*) But, if thou *s* to fling Excalibur, *Pass. of Arthur* 299
So, brother, pluck and *s* not.' *Lover's Tale i* 351
As if they knew your diet *s's* *To E. Fitzgerald* 10
hallus to hax of a man how much to *s* or to spend; *Spinster's S's.* 111
S not now to be bountiful, *On Jub. Q. Victoria* 29
Spared Yet, tho' I *s* thee all the spring, *The Blackbird* 9
and they *s* To ask it. *Guinevere* 144
He *s* to lift his hand against the King „ 437
And the Lord hath *s* our lives. *The Revenge* 93
Hast *s* the flesh of thousands, *Happy* 17
Sparhawk (*See also* **Sparrow-hawk**) Sometimes the *s*, wheel'd along, *Sir L. and Q. G.* 12
Sparing *S* not any of Those that with Anlaf, *Batt. of Brunanburh* 45
Spark the haft twinkled with diamond *s's*, *M. d'Arthur* 56
As this pale taper's earthly *s*, *St. Agnes' Eve* 15
She lit the *s* within my throat, *Will Water.* 109
Mix'd with cunning *s's* of hell. *Vision of Sin* 114
a delicate *s* Of glowing and growing light *Maud I vi* 15
Like a sudden *s* Struck vainly in the night, „ *ix* 13
a *s* of will Not to be trampled out. „ *II ii* 56
the soft, the *s* from off the hard, *Pelleas and E.* 499
snow mingled with *s's* of fire. *Last Tournament* 149
the haft twinkled with diamond *s's*, *Pass. of Arthur* 224
match'd with ours Were Sun to *s*— *Ancient Sage* 238
scatters on her throat the *s's* of dew, *Prog. of Spring* 58
new developments, whatever *s* „ 94
Will my tiny *s* of being wholly vanish *God and the Univ.* 1
Sparkle (s) That sent a blast of *s's* up the flue: *M. d'Arthur, Ep.* 15
With one green *s* ever and anon *Audley Court* 88
Caught the *s's*, and in circles, *Vision of Sin* 30
Like *s's* in the stone Avanturine. *Gareth and L.* 930
make My nature's prideful *s* in the blood *Geraint and E.* 827
from the star there shot A rose-red *s* to the city, *Holy Grail* 530
an' 'e shined like a *s* o' fire. *North. Cobbler* 48
to the snowlike *s* of a cloth *Sisters (E. and E.)* 117
Sparkle (verb) I wake: the chill stars *s*; *St. S. Stylites* 114
The silver vessels *s* clean, *Sir Galahad* 34
And *s* out among the fern, *The Brook* 25
stretch'd forefinger of all Time *S* for ever: *Princess ii* 379
A maiden moon that *s's* on a sty, „ *v* 186
The city *s's* like a grain of salt. *Will* 20
wont to glance and *s* like a gem Of fifty facets; *Geraint and E.* 294
while she watch'd their arms far-off *S*, *Lancelot and E.* 396
heats that spring and *s* out Among us *Holy Grail* 33
Sparkled shield, That *s* on the yellow field, *L. of Shalott iii* 8
And *s* keen with frost against the hilt: *M. d'Arthur* 55
From Allan's watch, and *s* by the fire. *Dora* 136
cups and silver on the burnish'd board *S* and shone; *Enoch Arden* 743
when some heat of difference *s* out, *Aylmer's Field* 705
The yule-log *s* keen with frost, *In Mem. lxxviii* 5
royal crown *S*, and swaying upon a restless elm *Balin and Balan* 463
pride and glory fired her face; her eye *S*; *Pelleas and E.* 173
And *s* keen with frost against the hilt: *Pass. of Arthur* 223
jewels Of many generations of his house *S* and flash'd, *Lover's Tale iv* 300
s and shone in the sky, *Despair* 15
but, however they *s* and shone, „ 17
What *s* there? whose hand was that? *The Ring* 257
Sparkling the snows Are *s* to the moon: *St Agnes' Eve* 2
The *s* flints beneath the prow. *Arabian Nights* 52
who often saw The splendour *s* from aloft, *Gareth and L.* 49
Only to hear and see the far-off *s* brine, *Lotos-Eaters, C. S.* 98
'O trefoil, *s* on the rainy plain, *Gareth and L.* 1159
and saw The golden dragon *s* over all: *Holy Grail* 263
To sit a star upon the *s* spire; *Princess vii* 197
Sparkling-fresh hue Is so *s-f* to view, *Rosalind* 40
Sparrow The *s's* chirrup on the roof, *Mariana* 73
very *s's* in the hedge Scarce answer *Amphion* 67
And swallow and *s* and throstle, *Window, Ay* 14
the *s* spear'd by the shrike, *Maud I iv* 23
O wretched set of *s's*, one and all, *Marr. of Geraint* 278
Sparrow-grass an' my oän bed o' *s-g*, *Spinster's S's.* 104
Sparrow-hawk (*See also* **Sparhawk**) Who told him, scouring still, 'The *s-h*!' *Marr. of Geraint* 260
Who answer'd gruffly, 'Ugh! the *s-h*.' „ 265
'Friend, he that labours for the *s-h* „ 271

Sparrow-hawk (*continued*) 'A thousand pips eat up your *s-h*! *Marr. of Geraint* 274
Who pipe of nothing but of *s-h's*! „ 279
'So that ye do not serve me *s-h's* „ 304
To curse this hedgerow thief, the *s-h*: „ 309
'This *s-h*, what is he? tell me of him. „ 404
The second was your foe, the *s-h*, „ 444
if the *s-h*, this nephew, fight In next day's tourney „ 475
And over that a golden *s-h*, „ 484
Has earn'd himself the name of *s-h*. „ 492
And over that the golden *s-h*. „ 550

Spartan play The Mother with emotion, *Princess ii* 283

Spasm in these *s's* that grind Bone against bone. *Columbus* 220
The tiger *s's* tear his chest, *Ancient Sage* 123

Spat *S*—pish—the cup was gold, *Last Tournament* 298

Spate in a showerful spring Stared at the *s*. *Gareth and L.* 3

Spawn 'Thro' slander, meanest *s* of Hell— *The Letters* 33

Speak (*See also* **Spake, Speäk**) Hark! death is calling While I *s* to ye, *All Things will Die* 29
Smiling, never *s's*: *Lilian* 12
kiss sweet kisses, and *s* sweet words: *Sea-Fairies* 34
Thou smilest, but thou dost not *s*, *Oriana* 68
The very smile before you *s*, *Margaret* 14
Come down, come down, and hear me *s*: „ 56
If one but *s's* or hems or stirs his chair, *Sonnet to* —— 5
'Twere better not to breathe or *s*, *Two Voices* 94
And on the mouth, he will not *s*. „ 252
'I may not *s* of what I know.' „ 435
But when at last I dared to *s*, *Miller's D.* 129
Hear me, for I will *s*, and build up all *Œnone* 39
for it may be That, while I *s* of it, „ 43
that I might *s* my mind, And tell her to her face „ 227
Tho' I cannot *s* a word, *May Queen, N. Y's. E.* 39
And then did something *s* to me— „ *Con.* 34
Resolved on noble things, and strove to *s*, *D. of F. Women* 42
'Still strove to *s*: my voice was thick „ 109
And tread softly and *s* low, *D. of the O. Year* 4
And tho' his foes *s* ill of him, „ 22
S out before you die. „ 45
He will not smile—not *s* to me Once more. *To J. S.* 21
A man may *s* the thing he will; *You ask me, why, etc.* 8
some old man *s* in the aftertime To all the people, *M. d'Arthur* 107
S out: what is it thou hast heard, „ 150
if you *s* with him that was my son, *Dora* 43
S! is there any of you halt or maim'd? *St. S. Stylites* 142
let him *s* his wish. „ 144
S, if there be a priest, a man of God, „ 214
To alien ears, I did not *s* to these— *Love and Duty* 52
was it not well to *s*, To have spoken once? „ 55
s, and *s* the truth to me, *Locksley Hall* 23
sweetly did she *s* and move: „ 71
O Lady Flora, let me *s*: *Day-Dm., Pro.* 1
Her lips are sever'd as to *s*: „ *Sleep. P.* 30
S a little, Ellen Adair!' *Edward Gray* 24
Said Lady Clare 'that ye *s* so wild?' *Lady Clare* 22
'I *s* the truth: you are my child. „ 24
I *s* the truth, as I live by bread! „ 26
'I will *s* out, for I dare not lie. „ 38
And they *s* in gentle murmur, *L. of Burleigh* 49
I came to *s* to you of what he wish'd, *Enoch Arden* 291
'Tired, Annie?' for she did not *s* a word. „ 390
Should still be living; well then—let me *s*: „ 405
Lets none, who *s's* with Him, seem all alone, „ 620
But turning now and then to *s* with him, „ 755
My children too! must I not *s* to these? „ 788
mark me and understand, While I have power to *s*. „ 877
To *s* before the people of her child, *Aylmer's Field* 608
Friends, I was bid to *s* of such a one „ 677
—of him I was not bid to *s*— „ 710
'Love, forgive him:' but he did not *s*; *Sea Dreams* 45
My tongue Trips, or I *s* profanely. *Lucretius* 74
yet, to *s* the truth, I rate your chance *Princess i* 160
Had given us letters, was he bound to *s*? „ 181
he heard her *s*; She scared him; life! „ 185
scarce could hear each other *s* for noise „ 215

Speak (*continued*) Not for three years to *s* with any men; *Princess ii* 72
my vow Binds me to *s*, and O that iron will, „ 202
but prepare: I *s*; it falls.' „ 224
S little; mix not with the rest; „ 360
Abate the stride, which *s's* of man, „ 429
some classic Angel *s* In scorn of us, „ *iii* 70
she *s's* A Memnon smitten with the morning Sun.' „ 115
And she replied, her duty was to *s*, „ 151
s, and let the topic die.' „ 205
That surely she will *s*; if not, then I: „ *iv* 344
made a sudden turn As if to *s*, „ 395
there she lies, But will not *s*, nor stir.' „ *v* 52
and she of whom you *s*, My mother, „ 192
ride with us to our lines, And *s* with Arac: „ 226
So often that I *s* as having seen. „ *vi* 21
Or *s* to her, your dearest, „ 185
yet *s* to me, Say one soft word and let us part forgiven.' „ 218
Is it kind? *S* to her I say: „ 249
Help, father, brother, help; *s* to the king: „ 305
cannot *s*, nor move, nor make one sign, „ *vii* 153
S no more of his renown, *Ode on Well.* 278
My Lords, we heard you *s*: *Third of Feb.* 1
As long as we remain, we must *s* free, „ 13
But the one voice in Europe: we *must s*; „ 16
let her *s* of you well or ill; *Grandmother* 51
'but I needs must *s* my mind, „ 53
S to Him thou for He hears, *High. Pantheism* 11
They should *s* to me not without a welcome, *Hendecasyllabics* 11
And I can *s* a little then. *In Mem. xix* 16
Who *s* their feeling as it is, „ *xx* 5
And sometimes harshly will he *s*: „ *xxi* 6
Behold, ye *s* an idle thing: „ 21
Urania *s's* with darken'd brow: „ *xxxvii* 1
'I am not worthy ev'n to *s* „ 11
My guardian angel will *s* out In that high place, „ *xliv* 15
Nor *s* it, knowing Death has made „ *lxxiv* 11
I hear the sentence that he *s's*; „ *lxxx* 10
We cannot hear each other *s*. „ *lxxxii* 16
A part of stillness, yearns to *s*: „ *lxxxv* 78
Still *s* to me of me and mine: „ *cxvi* 12
thought he would rise and *s* And rave at the lie *Maud I i* 59
But this is the day when I must *s*, „ *xvi* 7
I am sure I did but *s* Of my mother's faded cheek „ *xix* 18
To *s* of the mother she loved As one scarce less forlorn, „ 27
Chid her, and forbid her to *s* To me, „ 63
But *s* to her all things holy and high, „ *II ii* 78
for she never *s's* her mind, „ *v* 67
as he *s's* who tells the tale— *Com. of Arthur* 95
speech ye *s* yourself, 'Cast me away!' „ 304
hear him *s* before he left his life. „ 362
S of the King; „ 419
nor sees, nor hears, nor *s's*, nor knows. *Gareth and L.* 81
Live pure, *s* true, right wrong, „ 118
And heard him Kingly *s*, and doubted him „ 125
King will doom me when I *s*.' „ 324
My deeds will *s*: it is but for a day.' „ 577
I but *s* for thine avail, The saver of my life.' „ 883
I *am* the cause, because I dare not *s* *Marr. of Geraint* 89
Thou art not worthy ev'n to *s* of him;' „ 199
S, if ye be not like the rest, hawk-mad, „ 280
S!' Whereat the armourer turning all amazed „ 282
They would not hear me *s*: „ 421
Nor *s* I now from foolish flattery; „ 433
Nor did she lift an eye nor *s* a word, „ 528
Whatever happens, not to *s* to me, *Geraint and E.* 17
If he would only *s* and tell me of it.' „ 54
I laid upon you, not to *s* to me, „ 78
That she *could s* whom his own ear had heard „ 113
Needs must I *s*, and tho' he kill me for it, „ 137
'Have I leave to *s*?' He said, „ 140
and *s* To your good damsel there who sits apart, „ 298
'Get her to *s*: she doth not *s* to me.' „ 301
Ye sit apart, you do not *s* to him, „ 321
dumbly *s's* Your story, that this man loves you „ 328
Good, *s* the word: my followers ring him round: „ 336

Speak (continued) s but the word: Or s it not; Geraint and E. 342
that ye s not but obey.' „ 417
spake so low he hardly heard her s, „ 643
in the King's own ear S what has chanced; „ 809
(I s as one S's of a service done him) „ 847
Nor did I care or dare to s with you, „ 871
Bound are they To s no evil. Balin and Balan 146
I will s. Hail, royal knight, „ 469
he reddens, cannot s, So bashful, he! „ 519
And we will s at first exceeding low. „ 532
Take one verse more—the lady s's it— Merlin and V. 445
let her eyes S for her, glowing on him, „ 616
Urged him to s against the truth, Lancelot and E. 92
for to s him true, Ye know right well, „ 154
little need to s Of Lancelot in his glory! „ 463
S therefore: shall I waste myself in vain?' „ 670
To s the wish most near to your true heart; „ 914
But like a ghost without the power to s. „ 919
' Delay no longer, s your wish, „ 924
' S: that I live to hear,' he said, „ 928
There surely I shall s for mine own self, And none of you can s for me so well. „ 1125
So cannot s my mind. An end to this! „ 1222
' He is enchanted, cannot s—and she, „ 1254
S, as it waxes, of a love that wanes? „ 1401
For on a day she sent to s with me. Holy Grail 101
And when she came to s, behold her eyes „ 102
and the King himself could hardly s „ 354
Ah, blessed Lord, I s too earthlywise, „ 627
Bors, ' Ask me not, for I may not s of it: „ 758
could but s His music by the framework and the chord; „ 878
S, Lancelot, thou art silent: Last Tournament 107
To s no slander, no, nor listen to it, Guinevere 472
could s Of the pure heart, nor seem „ 501
And he forgave me, and I could not s. „ 614
some old man s in the aftertime To all the people, Pass. of Arthur 275
S out: what is it thou hast heard, „ 318
that she should s So feebly? To the Queen ii 22
—I will not s of thee, Lover's Tale i 284
I did not s: I could not s my love. „ 465
I wish'd, yet wish'd her not to s; „ 577
It makes me angry yet to s of it— „ iv 135
question'd if she came From foreign lands, and still she did not s. „ 331
The spectre that will s if spoken to. „ 337
An' he didn't s for a while First Quarrel 66
I learnt it first. I had to s. Sisters (E. and E.) 242
Now let it s, and you fire, Def. of Lucknow 29
The Shepherd, when I s, Sir J. Oldcastle 19
a shame to s of them—Among the heathen— „ 110
s, and tell them all The story of my voyage, Columbus 11
And when I ceased to s, the king, „ 14
my son will s for me Ablier than I can „ 219
whenever we strove to s Our voices were thinner V. of Maeldune 21
s the truth that no man may believe.' Tiresias 50
I s the truth Believe I s it, „ 155
canst not prove that I, who s with thee, Ancient Sage 64
I know not and I s of what has been. „ 228
Come, s a little comfort! The Flight 17
S to me, sister; counsel me; „ 75
when you s were wholly true. Locksley H., Sixty 120
Which may s to the centuries, On Jub. Q. Victoria 48
You s so low, what is it? The Ring 49
' She too might s to-day,' she mumbled. „ 125
You will not s, my friends, The Wanderer 3

Speäk woä then woä—let ma 'ear mysén s. N. Farmer, N. S. 8
But Parson 'e will s out, Church-warden, etc. 43
But niver not s plaain out, „ 49
tha mun s hout to the Baptises here i' the town, „ 51

Speaker hurl his cup Straight at the s, Merlin and V. 31

Speaking (See also **Spakin', Silent-speaking, Truth-speaking**)
And I ran by him without s, May Queen 18
The voice, that now is s, „ Con. 54
make a man feel strong in s truth; Love and Duty 70
He said, ' Ye take it, s,' Geraint and E. 141

Speaking (continued) And s not, but leaning over him, Merlin and V. 477
Suddenly s of the wordless man, Lancelot and E. 271
Dark-splendid, s in the silence, „ 338
S a still good-morrow with her eyes. „ 1033
Your beauty is your beauty, and I sin In s, „ 1187
' So s, and here ceasing, Holy Grail 853
Not s other word than ' Hast thou won? Last Tournament 191
And s clearly in thy native tongue— Sir J. Oldcastle 133
s aloud To women, the flower of the time, The Wreck 48

Spear (See also **Barley-spear**) The brand, the buckler, and the s— Two Voices 129
O'erthwarted with the brazen-headed s Œnone 139
Into that phalanx of the summer s's Aylmer's Field 111
hoofs bare on the ridge of s's And riders Princess v 489
And the s spring, the good horse reel, Gareth and L. 523
that held The horse, the s; „ 681
And mounted horse and graspt a s, „ 691
and either s Bent but not brake, „ 963
in a moment—at one touch Of that skill'd s, „ 1223
Had sent thee down before a lesser s, „ 1244
on whom all s's Are rotten sticks! „ 1305
and thrice they break their s's. Marr. of Geraint 562
Drave the long s a cubit thro' his breast Geraint and E. 86
call'd for flesh and wine to feed his s's. „ 601
s Wherewith the Roman pierced the side of Christ. Balin and Balan 113
and then the shadow of a s, Shot „ 322
' Eyes have I That saw to-day the shadow of a s, „ 373
King Pellam's holy s, Reputed to be red „ 556
That men go down before your s at a touch, Lancelot and E. 149
couch'd their s's and prick'd their steeds, „ 479
and a s Down-glancing lamed the charger, and a s Prick'd sharply his own cuirass, „ 487
That men went down before his s at a touch, „ 578
shadow of my s had been enow To scare Holy Grail 791
I will make thee with my s and sword Pelleas and E. 45
and at her will they couch'd their s's, „ 273
and on shield A s, a harp, a bugle— Last Tournament 174
Arthur with a hundred s's Rode far, „ 420
the splintering s, the hard mail hewn, Pass. of Arthur 108
died Among their s's and chariots. Achilles over the T. 33
s and helmet tipt With stormy light Tiresias 113
The s of ice has wept itself away, Prog. of Spring 6

Spear'd the sparrow s by the shrike, Maud I iv 23

Spearman But left two brawny spearmen, Geraint and E. 558
His lusty spearmen follow'd him with noise: „ 593
And mingled with the spearmen: „ 599
the brawny s let his cheek Bulge „ 630

Spear-shaft The splinter'd s-s's crack and fly, Sir Galahad 7

Spear-stricken A knight of thine s-s Balin and Balan 121

Special (adj.) Oh! sure it is a s care Of God, Supp. Confessions 63

Special (s) loved all maidens, but no maid In s, Pelleas and E. 41

Speck little pitted s in garner'd fruit, Merlin and V. 394
thought he saw, the s that bare the King, Pass. of Arthur 465

Spectral A s doubt which makes me cold, In Mem. xli 19
He linkt a dead man there to a s bride; Maud II v 80

Spectre There stands a s in your hall: L. C. V. de Vere 42
Nightmare of youth, the s of himself? Love and Duty 13
He faced the s's of the mind In Mem. xcvi 15
and fled Yelling as from a s, Geraint and E. 733
one of them Said, shuddering, ' Her s!' Lover's Tale iv 335
The s that will speak if spoken to. „ 337
Are there s's moving in the darkness? On Jub. Q. Victoria 67
thunders pass, the s's vanish, „ 69
with his drift Of flickering s's, Demeter and P. 27

Speculation for a vast s had fail'd, Maud I i 9

Speech God's great gift of s abused A Dirge 44
either lived in either's heart and s. Sonnet to —— 14
full-flowing river of s Came down upon my heart. Œnone 68
To hear each other's whisper'd s; Lotos-Eaters, C. S. 59
and with surprise Froze my swift s: D. of F. Women 90
He flash'd his random s'es, Will Water. 198
Joyful came his s: The Captain 30
There s and thought and nature fail'd Enoch Arden 792
address'd to s—Who spoke few words Princess, Con. 93
Ere Thought could wed itself with S; In Mem. xxiii 16

Speech (*continued*) But in dear words of human *s* — *In Mem. lxxxv* 83
In matter-moulded forms of *s*, — „ *xcv* 46
Against the feast, the *s*, the glee, — „ *Con.* 101
And written in the *s* ye speak yourself, — *Com. of Arthur* 304
Knowest thou not the fashion of our *s*? — *Pelleas and E.* 100
So that he could not come to *s* with her. — „ 205
But in the onward current of her *s*, — *Lover's Tale i* 565
Fair *s* was his and delicate of phrase, — „ 719
Fair *s* was his, and delicate of phrase. — „ *iv* 273
I would I knew their *s*; — *Sir J. Oldcastle* 11
Speed (*See also* **God-speed**) Those writhed limbs of lightning *s*; — *Clear-headed friend* 23
a favourable *s* Ruffle thy mirror'd mast, — *In Mem. ix* 6
and all at fiery *s* the two Shock'd — *Gareth and L.* 962
named us each by name, Calling 'God *s*!' — *Holy Grail* 352
Speedwell The little *s's* darling blue, — *In Mem. lxxxiii* 10
Spell (s) I feel with thee the drowsy *s*. — *Maud I xviii* 72
glimpse and fade Thro' some slight *s*, — *Early Spring* 32
Spell (verb) A trifle, sweet! which true love *s's*— — *Miller's D.* 187
face is practised when I *s* the lines, — *Merlin and V.* 367
we scarce can *s* The Alif of Thine alphabet — *Akbar's Dream* 30
Spence Bluff Harry broke into the *s* — *Talking Oak* 47
Spend Where they twain will *s* their days — *L. of Burleigh* 36
To *s* my one last year among the hills. — *Ancient Sage* 16
how much to spare or to *s*; — *Spinster's S's.* 111
Spent passion shall have *s* its novel force, — *Locksley Hall* 49
my latest breath Was *s* in blessing her — *Enoch Arden* 884
'We fear, indeed, you *s* a stormy time — *Princess v* 121
I scarce have *s* the worth of one!' — *Geraint and E.* 411
the storm, its burst of passion *s*, — *Merlin and V.* 961
and the powder was all of it *s*; — *The Revenge* 80
I *s* What seem'd my crowning hour, — *Sisters (E. and E.)* 123
Sphere (adj.) By two *s* lamps blazon'd like Heaven and Earth — *Princess i* 223
Sphere (s) Dark-blue the deep *s* overhead, — *Arabian Nights* 89
Sure she was nigher to heaven's *s's*, — *Ode to Memory* 40
lean out from the hollow *s* of the sea, — *The Mermaid* 54
What is there in the great *s* of the earth, — *If I were loved* 2
And deepening thro' the silent *s's* — *Mariana in the S.* 91
In yonder hundred million *s's*?' — *Two Voices* 30
'And men, thro' novel *s's* of thought — „ 61
daughter of a cottager, Out of her *s*. — *Walk. to the Mail* 60
centred in the *s* Of common duties, — *Ulysses* 39
in dark-purple *s's* of sea. — *Locksley Hall* 164
The *s* thy fate allots: — *Will Water.* 218
Laborious orient ivory *s* in *s*, — *Princess, Pro.* 20
An eagle clang an eagle to the *s*. — „ *iii* 106
seem'd to touch upon a *s* Too gross to tread, — „ *vii* 324
Ay is the song of the wedded *s's*, — *Window, No Answer* 7
He mixing with his proper *s*, — *In Mem. lx* 5
A *s* of stars about my soul, — „ *cxxii* 7
Unto the thundersong that wheels the *s's*, — *Lover's Tale i* 476
hereafter—earth A *s*. — *Columbus* 39
half-assured this earth might be a *s*. — „ 60
or pain in every peopled *s*? — *Locksley H., Sixty* 197
Set the *s* of all the boundless Heavens — „ 210
For dare we dally with the *s* As he did half in jest, — *Epilogue* 44
draws the child To move in other *s's*. — *To Prin. Beatrice* 8
glancing downward on the kindly *s* — *Poets and their B.* 9
Thro' all the *S's*—an ever opening height, — *The Ring* 45
She lean'd to from her Spiritual *s*, — „ 484
the *s* Of westward-wheeling stars; — *St. Telemachus* 31
Sphere (verb) *S* all your lights around, above; — *In Mem. ix* 13
Sphered and *s* Whole in ourselves and owed to none. — *Princess iv* 147
had you been *S* up with Cassiopëia, — „ 438
Sphere-music *S-m* such as that you dream'd about, — *Sea Dreams* 256
S-m of stars and of constellations. — *Parnassus* 8
that were such *s-m* as the Greek — *Akbar's Dream* 44
For moans will have grown *s-m* — *The Dreamer* 29
Spheroïd Of sine and arc, *s* and azimuth, — *Princess vi* 256
Sphinx woman-breasted *S*, with wings — *Tiresias* 148
Spice (s) Dripping with Sabæan *s* On thy pillow, — *Adeline* 53
A summer fann'd with *s*. — *Palace of Art* 116
silks, and fruits, and *s's*, clear of toll, — *Golden Year* 45
Bring me *s's*, bring me wine; — *Vision of Sin* 76

Spice (s) (*continued*) With summer *s* the humming air; — *In Mem. ci* 8
like the sultan of old in a garden of *s*. — *Maud I iv* 42
And the woodbine *s's* are wafted abroad, — „ *xxii* 5
with her *s* and her vintage, her silk — *Vastness* 13
Spice (verb) *S* his fair banquet with the dust of death? — *Maud I xviii* 56
Spiced charged the winds With *s* May-sweets — *Lover's Tale i* 318
Spick-span-new thebbe ammost *s-s-n*, — *North. Cobbler* 109
Spicy Holy water will I pour Into every *s* flower — *Poet's Mind* 13
Round and round the *s* downs the yellow Lotos-dust is blown. — *Lotos-Eaters, C. S.* 104
They fuse themselves to little *s* baths, — *Prog. of Spring* 33
Spider the bastion'd walls Like threaded *s's*, — *Princess i* 108
Caught in a great old tyrant *s's* web, — *Merlin and V.* 259
Spied came into the field And *s* her not; — *Dora* 75
He *s* her, and he left his men at work, — „ 86
Uncared for, *s* its mother and began — *Princess vi* 136
But Arthur *s* the letter in her hand, — *Lancelot and E.* 1270
methought I *s* A dying fire of madness — *Holy Grail* 767
And *s* not any light in hall or bower, — *Pelleas and E.* 419
Sir Lancelot passing by *S* where he couch'd, — *Guinevere* 31
That I niver not *s* sa much es a poppy — *Spinster's S's.* 78
Spigot merry bloated things Shoulder'd the *s*, — *Guinevere* 268
Spike Whose silvery *s's* are nighest the sea. — *The Mermaid* 37
High up, in silver *s's*! — *Talking Oak* 276
he had climb'd across the *s's*, — *Princess, Pro.* 111
s that split the mother's heart Spitting the child, — *Com. of Arthur* 38
darted *s's* and splinters of the wood — *Merlin and V.* 937
A *s* of half-accomplish'd bells— — *To Ulysses* 24
Spiked (*See also* **Purple-spiked**) and grimly *s* the gates. — *Princess iv* 206
Spikenard Sweet! sweet! *s*, and balm, — *St. S. Stylites* 211
With costly *s* and with tears. — *In Mem. xxxii* 12
Spill slope, and *s* Their thousand wreaths — *Princess vii* 212
To *s* his blood and heal the land: — *The Victim* 44
From that best blood it is a sin to *s*.' — *Gareth and L.* 600
you *s* The drops upon my forehead. — *Romney's R.* 23
Spilt have died and *s* our bones in the flood— — *Princess iv* 532
A little grain shall not be *s*.' — *In Mem. lxv* 4
the true blood *s* had in it a heat — *Maud I xix* 44
the red life *s* for a private blow— — „ *II v* 93
burst in dancing, and the pearls were *s*; — *Merlin and V.* 452
and so *s* itself Among the roses, — *Pelleas and E.* 426
Spin *S's*, toiling out his own cocoon. — *Two Voices* 180
Sometimes I saw you sit and *s*; — *Miller's D.* 121
Let the great world *s* for ever — *Locksley Hall* 182
for we *s* the lives of men, And not of Gods, and know not why we *s*! — *Demeter and P.* 85
Spindling (adj.) *s* king, This Gama swamp'd in lazy tolerance. — *Princess v* 442
Spindling (s) The *s's* look unhappy. — *Amphion* 92
Spine my stiff *s* can hold my weary head, — *St. S. Stylites* 43
The three-decker's oaken *s* — *Maud II ii* 27
skin Clung but to crate and basket, ribs and *s*. — *Merlin and V.* 625
Spinning behold a woman at a door *S*; — *Holy Grail* 392
Or *s* at your wheel beside the vine— — *Romney's R.* 5
Spinster An' a *s* I be an' I will be, — *Spinster's S's.* 112
Spire Looks down upon the village *s*: — *Miller's D.* 36
And tipt with frost-like *s's*. — *Palace of Art* 52
With *s's* of silver shine.' — *D. of F. Women* 188
To watch the three tall *s's*; — *Godiva* 3
High up, the topmost palace *s*. — *Day-Dm., Sleep. P.* 48
But he, by farmstead, thorpe and *s*, — *Will Water.* 137
Not by the well-known stream and rustic *s*, — *The Brook* 188
Whose blazing wyvern weathercock'd the *s*, — *Aylmer's Field* 17
Or like a *s* of land that stands apart — *Princess iv* 281
To sit a star upon the sparkling *s*; — „ *vii* 197
Utter your jubilee, steeple and *s*! — *W. to Alexandra* 17
A mount of marble, a hundred *s's*! — *The Daisy* 60
Bring orchis, bring the foxglove *s*, — *In Mem. lxxxiii* 9
The *s's* of ice are toppled down, — „ *cxxvii* 12
With delicate *s* and whorl, — *Maud II ii* 6
the *s's* and turrets half-way down Prick'd thro' the mist; — *Gareth and L.* 193
and had made it *s* to heaven. — „ 309
Tower after tower, *s* beyond *s*, — *Holy Grail* 229
s's Prick'd with incredible pinnacles into heaven. — „ 422

Spire (*continued*) I saw the spiritual city and all her *s's* And gateways — *Holy Grail* 526
Gilded with broom, or shatter'd into *s's*, — *Lover's Tale i* 400
overhead The aërial poplar wave, an amber *s*. — *Sisters (E. and E.)* 84
topmost *s* of the mountain was lilies in lieu of snow, — *V. of Maeldune* 41
and pigmy spites of the village *s*; — *Vastness* 25
Spired cypress-cones That *s* above the wood; — *Lover's Tale ii* 39
every topmost pine *S* into bluest heaven, — *Death of Œnone* 69
Spiring *s* stone that scaled about her tower, — *Last Tournament* 511
Spirit The boastings of my *s* still? — *Supp. Confessions* 15
S of happiness And perfect rest so inward is; — ,, 50
And the clear *s* shining thro'. — ,, 76
My judgment, and my *s* whirls, — ,, 137
O *s* and heart made desolate! — ,, 189
thoughts in the translucent fane Of her still *s*; — *Isabel* 5
To the young *s* present — *Ode to Memory* 73
A *S* haunts the year's last hours — *A spirit haunts* 1
Life in dead stones, or *s* in air; — *A Character* 9
riving the *s* of man, — *The Poet* 51
Some *s* of a crimson rose In love — *Adeline* 41
Your *s* is the calmed sea, — *Margaret* 25
Touch'd by thy *s's* mellowness, — *Eleänore* 103
Kate hath a *s* ever strung Like a new bow, — *Kate* 10
MINE be the strength of *s*, full and free, — *Mine be the strength* 1
by degrees May into uncongenial *s's* flow; — ,, 11
She thought, 'My *s* is here alone, — *Mariana in the S.* 47
'Go, vexed *S*, sleep in trust; — *Two Voices* 115
That read his *s* blindly wise, — ,, 287
For all the *s* is his own. — *Miller's D.* 190
who wrought Two *s's* to one equal mind— — ,, 236
In my dry brain my *s* soon, — *Fatima* 26
the thought of power Flatter'd his *s*; — *Œnone* 137
Music that gentlier on the *s* lies, — *Lotos-Eaters, C. S.* 5
Nor harken what the inner *s* sings, — ,, 22
lend our hearts and *s's* wholly To the influence — ,, 63
Sweetens the *s* still. — *D. of F. Women* 236
Drawn from the *s* thro' the brain, — *To J. S.* 38
Sleep, holy *s*, blessed soul, — ,, 70
Whose *s's* falter in the mist, — *You ask me, why, etc.* 3
The *S* of the years to come Yearning to mix — *Love thou thy land* 55
And in thy *s* with thee fought— — *England and Amer.* 9
Juliet, she So light of foot, so light of *s*— — *Gardener's D.* 14
that crush'd My *s* flat before thee. — *St. S. Stylites* 26
And this gray *s* yearning in desire — *Ulysses* 30
All the *s* deeply dawning in the dark — *Locksley Hall* 28
And our *s's* rush'd together — ,, 38
And his *s* leaps within him to be gone — ,, 115
crescent promise of my *s* hath not set. — ,, 187
To *s's* folded in the womb. — *Day-Dm., Sleep. P.* 8
His *s* flutters like a lark, — ,, *Arrival* 29
Make Thou my *s* pure and clear — *St. Agnes' Eve* 9
My *s* before Thee; — ,, 18
My *s* beats her mortal bars, — *Sir Galahad* 46
And her *s* changed within. — *L. of Burleigh* 64
Tho' at times her *s* sank: — ,, 70
That her *s* might have rest. — ,, 100
I found My *s's* in the golden age. — *To E. L.* 12
So lifted up in *s* he moved away. — *Enoch Arden* 330
Call'd all her vital *s's* into each ear — *Aylmer's Field* 201
But they that cast her *s* into flesh. — ,, 481
meek, Exceeding 'poor in *s*'— — ,, 754
with shameful jest, Encarnalize their *s's*: — *Princess iii* 315
force and growth Of *s* than to junketing — ,, *iv* 142
on my *s's* Settled a gentle cloud of melancholy; — ,, 569
My *s* closed with Ida's at the lips; — ,, *vii* 158
Touch a *s* among things divine, — *Ode on Well.* 139
and *S* with *S* can meet— — *High. Pantheism* 11
hear it, *S* of Cássivëlaún! — *Boädicea* 20
A *S*, not a breathing voice. — *In Mem. xiii* 12
For I in *s* saw thee move — ,, *xvii* 5
So much the vital *s's* sink — ,, *xx* 18
But they my troubled *s* rule, — ,, *xxviii* 17
Survive in *s's* render'd free, — ,, *xxxviii* 10
And look on *S's* breathed away, — ,, *xl* 2

Spirit (*continued*) Thy *s* ere our fatal loss — *In Mem. xli* 1
That stir the *s's* inner deeps, — ,, *xlii* 10
And every *s's* folded bloom — ,, *xliii* 2
Before the *s's* fade away, — ,, *xlvii* 14
The *S* of true love replied; — ,, *lii* 6
'What keeps a *s* wholly true — ,, 9
The *s* does but mean the breath — ,, *lvi* 7
My *s* loved and loves him yet, — ,, *lx* 2
I loved thee, *S*, and love, — ,, *lxi* 11
From state to state the *s* walks; — ,, *lxxxii* 6
Thy *s* should fail from off the globe; — ,, *lxxxiv* 36
Thy *s* up to mine can reach; — ,, *lxxxv* 82
A hundred *s's* whisper 'Peace.' — ,, *lxxxvi* 16
fierce extremes employ Thy *s's* — ,, *lxxxviii* 6
I know Thy *s* in time among thy peers; — ,, *xci* 6
No *s* ever brake the band — ,, *xciii* 2
But he, the *S* himself, may come — ,, 6
S to *S*, Ghost to Ghost. — ,, 8
call The *s's* from their golden day, — ,, *xciv* 6
My *s* is at peace with all. — ,, 8
And of my *s* as of a wife. — ,, *xcvii* 8
Two *s's* of a diverse love — ,, *cii* 7
Thro' which the *s* breathes no more? — ,, *cv* 20
The churl in *s*, up or down — ,, *cxi* 1
The churl in *s*, howe'er he veil — ,, 5
But in my *s* will I dwell, — ,, *cxxiii* 9
He breathed the *s* of the song; — ,, *cxxv* 10
While thou, dear *s*, happy star, — ,, *cxxvii* 18
Let all my genial *s's* advance — ,, *Con.* 77
And lust of gain, in the *s* of Cain, — *Maud I i* 23
And the *s* of murder works — ,, 40
eye well-practised in nature, a *s* bounded and poor; — ,, *iv* 38
Peace, angry *s*, and let him be! — ,, *xiii* 44
When all my *s* reels At the shouts, — ,, *II iv* 20
Would the happy *s* descend, — ,, 81
like a household *S* at the walls Beat, — *Geraint and E.* 403
light-wing'd *s* of his youth return'd — *Balin and Balan* 21
his evil *s* upon him leapt, — ,, 537
whimpering of the *s* of the child, — *Last Tournament* 418
heard the *S's* of the waste and weald — *Guinevere* 129
Himself beheld three *s's* mad with joy — ,, 252
so glad were *s's* and men — ,, 269
ill prophets were they all, *S's* and men: — ,, 273
When round him bent the *s's* of the hills — ,, 283
Thou art light, To which my *s* leaneth — *Lover's Tale i* 104
and his *s* From bitterness of death. — ,, 142
Which to the imprison'd *s* of the child, — ,, 204
while I gazed My *s* leap'd as with those thrills — ,, 363
S of Love! that little hour was bound — ,, 437
life, love, soul, *s*, and heart and strength. — ,, 460
O innocent of *s*—let my heart Break rather— — ,, 737
s seem'd to flag from thought to thought, — ,, *ii* 51
clear-eyed *S*, Being blunted in the Present, — ,, 130
sorrow of my *s* Was of so wide a compass — ,, 134
Moved with one *s* round about the bay, — ,, *iii* 17
when her own true *s* had return'd, — ,, *iv* 108
With a joyful *s* I Sir Richard Grenville die!' — *The Revenge* 103
Flowers to these '*s's* in prison' — *In the Child. Hosp.* 37
Whereon the *S* of God moves as he will— — *De Prof., Two G.* 28
Out of the deep, *S*, out of the deep, — ,, 32
S half-lost In thine own shadow — ,, 39
Nor canst thou prove that thou art *s* alone, — *Ancient Sage* 60
And some new *S* o'erbear the old, — *Epilogue* 14
out the fleshless world of *s's*, — *The Ring* 228
Her *s* hovering by the church, — ,, 478
fashion'd and worship a *S* of Evil, — *Kapiolani* 1
'*S*, nearing yon dark portal — *God and the Univ.* 4
Spirited *See* **Tender-spirited**
Spirit-searching thro' mine down rain'd Their *s-s* splendours. — *Lover's Tale ii* 147
Spirit-thrilling Those *s-t* eyes so keen and beautiful: — *Ode to Memory* 39
Spiritual (adj.) (*See also* **Half-spiritual**) *S* Adeline? (repeat) — *Adeline* 22, 64
One *s* doubt she did not soothe? — *Aylmer's Field* 704
And at the *s* prime Rewaken with the dawning soul. — *In Mem. xliii* 15

Spiritual (adj.) (*continued*) That loved to handle *s* strife, *In Mem. lxxxv* 54
But *s* presentiments, „ *xcii* 14
Rise in the *s* rock, „ *cxxxi* 3
Flow'd from the *s* lily that she held. *Balin and Balan* 264
see Her godlike head crown'd with *s* fire, *Merlin and V.* 837
and waste the *s* strength Within us, *Holy Grail* 35
one will crown thee king Far in the *s* city: ' „ 162
one will crown me king Far in the *s* city; „ 483
I saw the *s* city and all her spires „ 526
grim faces came and went Before her, or a vague *s* fear— *Guinevere* 71
the babe She lean'd to from her *S* sphere, *The Ring* 484
The beauty that endures on the *S* height, *Happy* 37
The Christians own a *S* Head; *Akbar's Dream* 153
Spiritual (s) *S* in Nature's market-place— „ 135
Spirt upjetted in *s's* of wild sea-smoke, *Sea Dreams* 52
Spirted (adj.) Or red with *s* purple of the vats, *Princess vii* 202
Spirted (verb) Prince's blood *s* upon the scarf, *Marr. of Geraint* 208
Spit (s) bits of roasting ox Moan round the *s*— *Lucretius* 132
Sir Scullion, canst thou use that *s* of thine? *Gareth and L.* 791
Scullion, for running sharply with thy *s* „ 840
these be for the *s*, Larding and basting. „ 1082
Spit (verb) I hate, abhor, *s*, sicken at him; *Lucretius* 199
Spite (*See also* **Monkey-spite**) Delicious *s's* and darling angers, *Madeline* 6
half in love, half *s*, he woo'd and wed *Dora* 39
Fill'd I was with folly and *s*, *Edward Gray* 15
' A ship of fools,' he shriek'd in *s*, *The Voyage* 77
envy, hate and pity, and *s* and scorn, *Lucretius* 77
sins of emptiness, gossip and *s* And slander, *Princess ii* 92
Should all our churchmen foam in *s* *To F. D. Maurice* 9
How I hate the *s's* and the follies! *Spiteful Letter* 24
And scratch the very dead for *s*: *Lit. Squabbles* 8
The civic slander and the *s*; *In Mem. cvi* 22
Nor ever narrowness or *s*, „ *cxi* 17
a city, with gossip, scandal and *s*; *Maud I iv* 8
His face, as I grant, in *s* of *s*, „ *xiii* 8
to see your beauty marr'd Thro' evil *s*: *Pelleas and E.* 299
Marr'd tho' it be with *s* and mockery „ 327
tho' she hath me bounden but in *s*, „ 329
when I were so crazy wi' *s*, *First Quarrel* 73
craft and madness, lust and *s*, *Locksley H., Sixty* 189
pigmy *s's* of the village spire; *Vastness* 25
Spiteful And with it a *s* letter. *Spiteful Letter* 2
all hearts Applauded, and the *s* whisper died: *Geraint and E.* 958
Spitting split the mother's heart *S* the child, *Com. of Arthur* 39
s at their vows and thee. *Pass. of Arthur* 62
Splash and the *s* and stir Of fountains *Princess i* 217
Splash'd *s* and dyed The strong White Horse *Holy Grail* 311
And a hundred *s* from the ledges, *V. of Maeldune* 103
Spleen They are fill'd with idle *s*; *Vision of Sin* 124
cook'd his *s*, Communing with his captains *Princess i* 66
with the least little touch of *s*. *Maud I ii* 11
Geraint flash'd into sudden *s*: *Marr. of Geraint* 273
is your *s* froth'd out, or have ye more?' *Merlin and V.* 767
Spleen-born *S-b*, I think, and proofless. „ 702
Spleenful Breaking a slumber in which all *s* folly was drown'd, *Maud I iii* 2
rode Geraint, a little *s* yet, *Marr. of Geraint* 293
Splendid (*See also* **Dark-splendid**) Sees whatever fair and *s* Lay betwixt his home *L. of Burleigh* 27
A *s* presence flattering the poor roofs *Aylmer's Field* 175
The meteor of a *s* season, she, „ 205
Till all the people cried, ' *S* is the flower.' *The Flower* 16
Such *s* purpose in his eyes, *In Mem. lvi* 10
There has fallen a *s* tear From the passion-flower *Maud I xxii* 59
And shine in the sudden making of *s* names, „ *III vi* 47
So *s* in his acts and his attire, *Marr. of Geraint* 620
Display'd a *s* silk of foreign loom, *Geraint and E.* 687
Splendour A sudden *s* from behind Flush'd *Arabian Nights* 81
The maiden's *s's* of the morning star *D. of F. Women* 55
Made lightnings in the *s* of the moon, *M. d'Arthur* 137
The *s* falls on castle walls *Princess iv* 1
Long lanes of *s* slanted o'er a press „ 478
sheathing *s's* and the golden scale Of harness, „ *v* 41
A flying *s* out of brass and steel, „ *vi* 365
suck the blinding *s* from the sand, „ *vii* 39
Splendour (*continued*) height and cold, the *s* of the hills? *Princess vii* 194
and a stifled *s* and gloom. *High. Pantheism* 10
And blurr'd the *s* of the sun; *In Mem. lxxii* 8
All her *s* seems No livelier „ *xcviii* 6
And breaking let the *s* fall „ *Con.* 119
I saw the treasured *s*, her hand, *Maud I vi* 84
new-made lord, whose *s* plucks The slavish hat „ *x* 3
nearer to the glow Of your soft *s's* „ *xviii* 79
Queen Maud in all her *s*. „ *xx* 50
And a dewy *s* falls On the little flower „ *II iv* 32
past and leaves The Crown a lonely *s*. *Ded. of Idylls* 49
often saw The *s* sparkling from aloft, *Gareth and L.* 49
s of the presence of the King Throned, „ 320
daily fronted him In some fresh *s*; *Marr. of Geraint* 14
Made a low *s* in the world, „ 598
she could cast aside A *s* dear to women, „ 808
And on the *s* came, flashing me blind; *Holy Grail* 413
Made lightnings in the *s* of the moon, *Pass. of Arthur* 305
We paused amid the *s*. *Lover's Tale i* 414
mine down rain'd Their spirit-searching *s's*. „ *ii* 147
glory in all The *s's* and the voices of the world! *Ancient Sage* 177
native to that *s* or in Mars, *Locksley H., Sixty* 187
And *s's* of the morning land, *Open. I and C. Exhib.* 8
the secret *s* of the brooks. *Prog. of Spring* 21
But in the tearful *s* of her smiles „ 41
All her *s* fail'd To lure those eyes *St. Telemachus* 35
Splenetic And therefore *s*, personal, base, *Maud I x* 33
Splinter (s) into fiery *s's* leapt the lance, *Princess v* 494
With darted spikes and *s's* of the wood *Merlin and V.* 937
Splinter (verb) gay navy there should *s* on it, *Sea Dreams* 131
and to *s* it into feuds Serving his traitorous end; *Guinevere* 18
Splinter'd All night the *s* crags that wall the dell *D. of F. Women* 187
The *s* spear-shafts crack and fly, *Sir Galahad* 7
Spars were *s*, (repeat) *The Captain* 45, 49
A lance that *s* like an icicle, *Geraint and E.* 89
Crack'd basilisks, and *s* cockatrices, *Holy Grail* 718
Then, sputtering thro' the hedge of *s* teeth, *Last Tournament* 65
For every *s* fraction of a sect Will clamour *Akbar's Dream* 33
Splintering (*See also* **Lance-splintering**) the blade flew *S* in six, *Balin and Balan* 396
and the *s* spear, the hard mail hewn, *Pass. of Arthur* 108
Split upon the corn-laws, where we *s*, *Audley Court* 35
the wild figtree *s* Their monstrous idols, *Princess iv* 79
takes, and breaks, and cracks, and *s's*, „ *v* 527
spike that *s* the mother's heart Spitting the child, *Com. of Arthur* 38
with one stroke Sir Gareth *s* the skull. *Gareth and L.* 1404
earthquake shivering to your base *S* you, *Pelleas and E.* 466
an iceberg *s's* From cope to base— *Lover's Tale i* 603
sink her, *s* her in twain! *The Revenge* 89
Splugen And up the snowy *S* drew, *The Daisy* 86
Spoil (s) (*See also* **Ocean-spoil**) the children laden with their *s*; *Enoch Arden* 445
Spoil (verb) and *s's* My bliss in being; *Lucretius* 221
Begin to slay the folk, and *s* the land.' *Guinevere* 137
Spoil'd still the foeman *s* and burn'd, *The Victim* 17
Because the twain had *s* her carcanet. *Last Tournament* 419
Spoiler loud sabbath shook the *s* down; *Ode on Well.* 123
Bow'd the *s*, Bent the Scotsman, *Batt. of Brunanburh* 20
Spoilt You have *s* this child; *Princess v* 116
thou hast *s* the purpose of my life. *Guinevere* 453
Spoke I *s*, but answer came there none: *Two Voices* 425
She *s* at large of many things, And at the last she *s* of me; *Miller's D.* 155
Last night, when some one *s* his name, *Fatima* 15
She *s* and laugh'd: I shut my sight *Œnone* 188
S slowly in her place. *D. of F. Women* 92
We *s* of other things; we coursed about *Gardener's D.* 222
in that time and place, I *s* to her, „ 226
I *s*, while Audley feast Humm'd like a hive *Audley Court* 4
Poet-like he *s*. *Edwin Morris* 27
Or this or something like to this he *s*. „ 41
I *s* her name alone. „ 68
Whether he *s* too largely; „ 73
So *s* I knowing not the things that were. „ 89

Spoke (*continued*) I *s* without restraint, *Talking Oak* 14
And mystic sentence *s*; „ 294
He *s*; and high above, I heard them blast *Golden Year* 75
yawn'd, and rubb'd his face, and *s*, *Day-Dm., Revival* 19
Sweet Emma Moreland *s* to me: *Edward Gray* 5
I *s* with heart, and heat and force, *The Letters* 37
and Enoch *s* his love, But Philip loved in silence; *Enoch Arden* 40
till the morrow, when he *s*. „ 156
Philip coming somewhat closer *s*. „ 398
Then answer'd Annie; tenderly she *s*: „ 422
Saying gently 'Annie, when I *s* to you, „ 448
There Enoch *s* no word to any one, „ 667
He said to Miriam 'that you *s* about, „ 805
and so fell back and *s* no more. „ 914
Of sweet seventeen subdued me ere she *s*) *The Brook* 113
while she *s*, I saw where James Made toward us, „ 116
I know not, for he *s* not, *Aylmer's Field* 213
While thus he *s*, his hearers wept; „ 722
s with me on the shore; *Sea Dreams* 264
Why were you silent when I *s* to-night? „ 268
your rough voice (You *s* so loud) „ 281
Petulant she *s*, and at herself she laugh'd; *Princess, Pro.* 153
Thus he *s*, Part banter, part affection. „ 166
At last I *s*. 'My father, let me go. „ *i* 68
She *s*, and bowing waved Dismissal: „ *ii* 99
s of those That lay at wine with Lar and Lucumo; „ 128
it was duty *s*, not I. „ 308
I *s* of war to come and many deaths, „ *iii* 150
She *s* and turn'd her sumptuous head „ *iv* 152
I *s* not then at first, but watch'd „ 339
And then stood up and *s* impetuously. „ 418
being caught feign death, *S* not, nor stirr'd. „ *v* 109
Yet she neither *s* nor moved. „ *vi* 8
Ida *s* not, rapt upon the child. „ 220
Ida *s* not, gazing on the ground, „ 227
But Ida stood nor *s*, drain'd of her force „ *vi* 266
Old studies fail'd; seldom she *s*: „ *vii* 31
Hortensia *s* against the tax; „ 127
Who *s* few words and pithy, „ *Con.* 94
But *s* not, rapt in nameless reverie, „ 108
He *s* among you, and the Man who *s*; *Ode on Well.* 178
Who never *s* against a foe; „ 185
I started, and *s* I scarce knew how; *Grandmother* 43
Till I with as fierce an anger *s*, *Maud II i* 17
s of a hope for the world in the coming wars— „ *III vi* 11
Perforce she stay'd, and overtaken *s*. *Gareth and L.* 764
Half inwardly, half audibly she *s*, *Marr. of Geraint* 109
He *s* and fell to work again. „ 292
Prince and Earl Yet *s* together, „ 385
if he *s* at all, would break perforce *Geraint and E.* 12
He *s*, and one among his gentlewomen „ 686
He *s*, and Enid easily believed, „ 874
he *s* Closed his death-drowsing eyes, *Balin and Balan* 630
He *s* in words part heard, *Merlin and V.* 839
Lancelot *s* And answer'd him at full, *Lancelot and E.* 285
He *s*, and vanish'd suddenly from the field „ 508
s, he answer'd not, Or short and coldly, „ 886
passionately she *s*: 'I have gone mad. „ 930
While he *s* She neither blush'd nor shook, „ 964
thus he *s*, half turn'd away, the Queen „ 1197
Then freely *s* Sir Lancelot to them all: „ 1289
and even as he *s* Fell into dust, *Holy Grail* 435
s, and taking all his younger knights, *Last Tournament* 126
He *s*, he turn'd, then, flinging round her neck, „ 749
S loudly even into my inmost heart *Lover's Tale i* 428
she *s* 'Here! and how came I here?' „ *iv* 96
What was it? for our lover seldom *s*, „ 225
That faithful servant whom we *s* about, „ 342
Sir Richard *s* and he laugh'd, *The Revenge* 32
I *s* it—told her of my passion, *Sisters (E. and E.)* 146
when we parted, Edith *s* no word, „ 215
while I *s* The crowd's roar fell *Columbus* 12
When he *s* of his tropical home *The Wreck* 71
And he *s* not—only the storm; „ 103

Spoke (*continued*) For He *s*, or it seem'd that He *s*, *Despair* 26
'Ah God' tho' I felt as I *s* „ 52
From darkness into daylight, turn'd and *s*. *Ancient Sage* 8
We *s* of what has been Most marvellous *Pro. to Gen. Hamley* 10
for he *s* and the people heard, *Dead Prophet* 33
No voice for either *s* within my heart *The Ring* 162
And *s* no more, but turn'd and pass'd away. „ 342
Spoken (*See also* **Fairest-spoken, Fair-spoken, Free-spoken, Low-spoken**) High things were *s* there, *Alexander* 12
would have *s*, but be found not words, *M. d'Arthur* 172
was it not well to speak, To have *s* once? *Love and Duty* 56
Down they dropt—no word was *s*— *The Captain* 51
I would have *s*, And warn'd that madman *Vision of Sin* 55
had not his poor heart *S* with That, *Enoch Arden* 619
you shall say that having *s* with me, *Aylmer's Field* 311
so she would have *s*, but there rose A hubbub *Princess iv* 475
And every *s* tongue should lord you. „ 544
And out of hauntings of my *s* love, „ *vii* 109
sweet soul, had hardly *s* a word, *Maud II i* 11
Hath *s* also, not in jest, *Com. of Arthur* 420
he fain had *s* to her, And loosed in words *Geraint and E.* 105
I heard He had *s* evil of me; *Balin and Balan* 58
Said Arthur 'Thou hast ever *s* truth; „ 73
half her realm, had never *s* word. *Lancelot and E.* 72
is there more? Has Arthur *s* aught? „ 117
Then every evil word I had *s* once, *Holy Grail* 371
as ye saw it ye have *s* truth. „ 880
would have *s*, but he found not words; *Pass. of Arthur* 340
s of with tearful smiles; *Lover's Tale ii* 182
To one who had not *s*, Lionel. „ *iv* 272
The spectre that will speak if *s* to. „ 337
Than ha' *s* as kind as you did, *First Quarrel* 73
you never have *s* a word. *Rizpah* 14
When was age so cramm'd with menace? madness? written, *s* lies? *Locksley H., Sixty* 108
in every language I hear *s*, people praise thee, *Akbar's D., Inscrip.* 1
And had some prophet *s* true *Mechanophilus* 25
Sponge Huge *s*'s of millennial growth *The Kraken* 6
Sponged *S* and made blank of crimeful record *St. S. Stylites* 158
Spongy-wet Is hoar with rime, or *s-w*; *To F. D. Maurice* 42
Sport (s) But take it—earnest wed with *s*, *Day-Dm., Ep.* 11
so that *s* Went hand in hand with Science; otherwhere Pure *s*: *Princess, Pro.* 79
Lilia, wild with *s*, Half child half woman „ 100
Or master'd by the sense of *s*, „ *iv* 156
—the striplings!—for their *s*!— „ *v* 399
The *s* half-science, fill me with a faith, „ *Con.* 76
Me the *s* of ribald Veterans, *Boädicea* 50
He mixt in all our simple *s*'s; *In Mem. lxxxix* 10
and loud With *s* and song, in booth and tent, „ *xcviii* 28
The *s* of random sun and shade. „ *Con.* 24
Or when the thralls had *s* among themselves, *Gareth and L.* 516
Began to break her *s*'s with graver fits, *Merlin and V.* 180
Your pretty *s*'s have brighten'd all again. „ 305
Brake up their *s*'s, then slowly to her bower Parted, *Last Tournament* 238
on love And *s* and tilts and pleasure, *Guinevere* 387
Sport (verb) came To *s* beneath thy boughs. *Talking Oak* 100
And hence, indeed, she *s*'s with words, *In Mem. xlviii* 9
Spot A *s* of dull stagnation, without light *Palace of Art* 245
So find I every pleasant *s* *In Mem. viii* 9
Spotless The saintly youth, the *s* lamb of Christ, *Merlin and V.* 749
Spousal and one The later-rising Sun of *s* Love, *Prin. Beatrice* 6
Spouse Worthy a Roman *s*.' *D. of F. Women* 164
Came Hope and Memory, *s* and bride, *On a Mourner* 23
If ever maid or *s*, As fair as my Olivia, *Talking Oak* 34
With only Fame for *s* and your great deeds *Princess iii* 242
Spout (s) little wide-mouth'd heads upon the *s* *Godiva* 56
s whereon the gilded ball Danced like a wisp: *Princess, Pro.* 63
Spout (verb) *S* from the maiden fountain in her heart. *Lucretius* 240
Spouted that sonorous flow Of *s* fountain-floods. *Palace of Art* 28
golden gorge of dragons *s* forth „ 23
monster *s* his foam-fountains in the sea. *Lotos-Eaters, C. S.* 107
Till the fountain *s*, showering wide *Vision of Sin* 21
fountains *s* up and showering down *Princess i* 218

Spouting as a stream that *s* from a cliff — *Guinevere* 608
Sprang Who *s* from English blood ! — *England and Amer.* 10
S from the midriff of a prostrate king— — *Aylmer's Field* 16
s No dragon warriors from Cadmean teeth, — *Lucretius* 49
yell'd again Half-suffocated, and *s* up, — „ 58
And from it *s* the Commonwealth, — „ 241
Out I *s* from glow to gloom : — *Princess iv* 178
And out of stricken helmets *s* the fire. — „ *v* 495
turn'd half-round to Psyche as she *s* To meet it, — „ *vi* 209
To the altar-stone she *s* alone, — *The Victim* 67
S up for ever at a touch, — *In Mem. cxii* 10
Gawain went, and breaking into song *S* out, — *Com. of Arthur* 321
He laugh'd ; he *s*. — *Gareth and L.* 537
but forth that other *s*, And, all unknightlike, — „ 1149
s the happier day from underground ; — „ 1421
ground his teeth together, *s* with a yell, — *Balin and Balan* 538
the blood *S* to her face and fill'd her with delight ; — *Lancelot and E.* 377
An outraged maiden *s* into the hall — *Holy Grail* 208
rotten with a hundred years of death, *S* into fire : — „ 497
S into fire and vanish'd, — „ 506
I burst the chain, I *s* into the boat. — „ 807
Forth *s* Gawain, and loosed him from his bonds, — *Pelleas and E.* 315
S from the door into the dark. — „ 603
but *s* Thro' open doors, and swording right — *Last Tournament* 472
current to the fountain whence it *s*,— — *Lover's Tale i* 503
S up a friendship that may help us yet. — „ *iv* 144
he *s* from the oldest race upon earth. — *V. of Maeldune* 4
s without leaf or a thorn from the bush ; — „ 44
A panther *s* across her path, — *Death of Œnone* 89
Turn'd him again to boy, for up he *s*, — *St. Telemachus* 58
I *s* from my seat, I wept, — *Charity* 37
Rang the stroke, and *s* the blood, — *The Tourney* 9
Spray (foam) tender curving lines of creamy *s* ; — *Lotos-Eaters, C. S.* 62
Torn from the fringe of *s*. — *D. of F. Women* 40
of hissing *s* wind-driven Far thro' the dizzy dark. — *Lover's Tale ii* 198
and bosom'd the burst of the *s*, — *V. of Maeldune* 103
the ripple would hardly blanch into *s* — *The Wreck* 137
Spray (twig) (*See also* **Holly-spray**) From *s*, and branch, and stem, — *Talking Oak* 190
The snake slipt under a *s*, — *Poet's Song* 10
touchwood, with a single flourishing *s*. — *Aylmer's Field* 512
a song on every *s* Of birds that piped — *Princess v* 238
faces flat against the panes, *S's* grated, — *Balin and Balan* 345
Blinkt the white morn, *s's* grated, — „ 385
Spread (*See also* **Gravel-spread**) *s* his sheeny vans for flight ; — *Love and Death* 8
'Still sees the sacred morning *s* — *Two Voices* 80
That every cloud, that *s's* above And veileth love, — „ 446
Hath time and space to work and *s*. — *You ask me, why, etc.* 16
So muscular he *s*, so broad of breast. — *Gardener's D.* 8
A cedar *s* his dark-green layers of shade. — „ 116
S the light haze along the river-shores, — „ 264
hope ere death *S's* more and more — *St. S. Stylites* 157
The life that *s's* in them, — *Talking Oak* 192
'Then close and dark my arms I *s*, — „ 225
S upward till thy boughs discern — „ 247
light shall *s*, and man be liker man — *Golden Year* 35
But o'er the dark a glory *s's*, — *Sir Galahad* 55
To *s* into the perfect fan, — *Sir L. and Q. G.* 17
The chap-fallen circle *s's* : — *Vision of Sin* 172
He woke, he rose, he *s* his arms abroad — *Enoch Arden* 912
To *s* the Word by which himself had thriven.' — *Sea Dreams* 197
and the branches thereupon *S* out at top, — *Princess iv* 206
A rampant heresy, such as if it *s* — „ 411
S thy full wings, and waft him o'er. — *In Mem. ix* 4
s his mantle dark and cold, — „ *xxii* 14
Proclaiming social truth shall *s*, — „ *cxxvii* 5
And o'er the friths that branch and *s* — „ *Con.* 115
over whom thy darkness must have *s* — *Maud I xviii* 25
Dubric *s* his hands and spake, — *Com. of Arthur* 471
boil'd the flesh, and *s* the board, — *Marr. of Geraint* 391
S the slow smile thro' all her company. — *Pelleas and E.* 95
Lower down *S's* out a little lake, — *Lover's Tale i* 534
I *s* mine arms, God's work, I said, — *Sir J. Oldcastle* 136

Spread (*continued*) call'd the heavens a hide, a tent *S* over earth, — *Columbus* 48
hope was mine to *s* the Catholic faith, — „ 230
to stay, Not *s* the plague, the famine ; — *Demeter and P.* 134
and to *s* the Divine Faith Like calming oil — *Akbar's Dream* 159
Spreadeth Which the moon about her *s*, — *Margaret* 20
Spreading *s* made Fantastic plume or sable pine ; — *The Voyage* 43
peaks they stand ever *s* and heightening ; — *Parnassus* 11
Sprig Blow, flute, and stir the stiff-set *s's*, — *Amphion* 63
s's of summer laid between the folds, — *Marr. of Geraint* 138
Sprightly at first She play'd about with slight and *s* talk, — *Merlin and V.* 171
Spring (elastic contrivance) a-joompin' about ma as if they was set upo' *s's*, — *Spinster's S's.* 89
Spring (fountain) Life of the fountain there, beneath Its salient *s's*, — *Supp. Confessions* 56
Do beating hearts of salient *s's* — *Adeline* 26
Fresh-water *s's* come up through bitter brine. — *If I were loved* 8
The *s's* of life, the depths of awe, — *Two Voices* 140
Who sets her pitcher underneath the *s*, — *Enoch Arden* 207
(If Death so taste Lethean *s's*), — *In Mem. xliv* 10
While yet beside its vocal *s's* — „ *lxiv* 22
Nor ever drank the inviolate *s* — „ *xc* 2
The bitter *s's* of anger and fear ; — *Maud I x* 49
Brethren, to right and left the *s*, — *Balin and Balan* 25
In mine own lady palms I cull'd the *s* — *Merlin and V.* 273
Flow back again unto my slender *s* — *Lover's Tale i* 147
runnel in the *s* Had liveried them all over. — „ *ii* 49
as we sat by the gurgle of *s's*, — *V. of Maeldune* 89
who found Beside the *s's* of Dircê, — *Tiresias* 14
the *s's* Of Dircê laving yonder battle-plain, — „ 138
Spring (rise) 'tween the *s* and downfall of the light, — *St. S. Stylites* 110
Spring (season) But *s*, a new comer, A *s* rich and strange, — *Nothing will Die* 21
S will come never more. — *All Things will Die* 15
the breathing *s* Of Hope and Youth. — *The Poet* 27
S Letters cowslips on the hill ? — *Adeline* 61
Sweet as new buds in *S*. — *D. of F. Women* 272
Yet, tho' I spared thee all the *s*, — *The Blackbird* 9
Caught in the frozen palms of *S*. — „ 24
But in these latter *s's* I saw — *Talking Oak* 75
Like those blind motions of the *S*, — „ 175
In the *S* a fuller crimson comes upon the robin's breast ; — *Locksley Hall* 17
In the *S* the wanton lapwing gets himself another crest ; — „ 18
In the *S* a livelier iris changes on the burnish'd dove ; — „ 19
In the *S* a young man's fancy lightly turns to thoughts of love. — „ 20
throng'd my pulses with the fullness of the *S*. — „ 36
The maiden *S* upon the plain — *Sir L. and Q. G.* 3
She seem'd a part of joyous *S* ; — „ 23
a thousand rings of *S* In every bole, — *Princess v* 237
Shall strip a hundred hollows bare of *S*, — „ *vi* 65
My *s* is all the nearer, — *Window, Winter* 17
S is here with leaf and grass : — „ *No Answer* 23
And all the secret of the *S* — *In Mem. xxiii* 19
The herald melodies of *s*, — „ *xxxviii* 6
And men the flies of latter *s*, — „ *l* 10
And every winter change to *s*. — „ *liv* 16
I dream'd there would be *S* no more, — „ *lxix* 1
S that swells the narrow brooks, — „ *lxxxv* 70
As not unlike to that of *S*. — „ 120
and in my breast *S* wakens too ; — „ *cxv* 18
in a showerful *s* Stared at the spate. — *Gareth and L.* 2
Hath earnest in it of far *s's* to be. — *Merlin and V.* 557
I have seen this yew-tree smoke, *S* after *s*, — *Holy Grail* 19
the *s* Pour with such sudden deluges of light — *Lover's Tale i* 314
recalling fragrance and the green Of the dead *s* : — „ 724
are all they can know of the *s*, — *In the Child. Hosp.* 37
For the *S* and the middle Summer sat — *V. of Maeldune* 38
winter sunset fairer than a morn of *S*. — *Locksley H., Sixty* 22
S and Summer and Autumn and Winter, — *Vastness* 29
spring-flower I send, This song of *s*, — *To Mary Boyle* 20
S slides hither o'er the Southern sea, — *Prog. of Spring* 2
Come, *S*, for now from all the dripping eaves — „ 5
Come, *S* ! She comes on waste and wood, — „ 22

Squire (*continued*) and their three *s's* across their feet: *Pelleas and E.* 431
doesn not touch thy 'at to the *S*;' *North. Cobbler* 25
An' *S*, his oän very sen, walks down fro' the 'All „ 91
fur New *S* coom'd last night. *Village Wife* 1
I liked the owd *S* an' 'is gells „ 6
the *S* an' 'is darters an' me, „ 7
new *S's* coom'd wi' 'is taäil in 'is 'and, an' owd *S's* gone. (repeat) „ 14, 121
We'd anew o' that wi' the *S*, „ 24
Fur *S* wur a Varsity scholard, „ 25
An' *S* wur hallus a-smilin', „ 33
ivry darter o' *S's* hed her awn ridin-erse „ 35
An' *S* 'e smiled an' 'e smiled (repeat) „ 61, 88
But *S* wur afear'd o' 'is son, „ 63
booöks, I ha' see'd 'em, belong'd to the *S*, „ 71
And *S* were at Charlie ageän „ 74
Hallus a soft un *S*! „ 89
rattled down upo' poor owd *S* i' the wood, „ 95
Fur I'd ha done owt for the *S* „ 112
sound and honest, rustic *S*, *Locksley H., Sixty* 239
Till I dreäm'd 'at *S* walkt in, an' I says to him '*S*, ya're laäte,' *Owd Roä* 55
an' not the faults o' the *S*. *Church-warden, etc.* 46
Squireling political dinner To half the *s's* near; *Maud I xx* 26
Squirrel And snared the *s* of the glen? *Princess ii* 249
merry linnet knew me, The *s* knew me, *Lover's Tale ii* 16
While *s's* from our fiery beech *Pro. to Gen. Hamley* 3
Squoire (Squire) Thaw a knaws I hallus voäted wi' *S* *N. Farmer, O. S.* 15
wi' haäte hoonderd haäcre o' *S's*, „ 44
An' *S* 'ull be sa mad an' all— „ 47
I 'a managed for *S* coom Michaelmas thutty year. „ 48
Fur they knaws what I beän to *S* „ 55
I done moy duty by *S* „ 56
S's i' Lunnon, an' summun I reckons „ 57
Staäin'd (stained) An' the taäble *s* wi' 'is aäle, *Spinster's S's.* 99
Staäte (state) voäted wi' Squoire an' choorch an' *s*, *N. Farmer, O. S.* 15
I thowt shall I chaänge my *s*? *Spinster's S's.* 44
I thowt if the *S* was a gawin' *Owd Roä* 45
'Staäte (estate) Fur 's be i' taäil, my lass: *Village Wife* 15
I've gotten the 's by the taäil „ 68
Stab (s) deathful *s's* were dealt apace, *Oriana* 50
Stab (verb) little boys begin to shoot and *s*, *Princess, Con.* 61
I was not going to *s* you, *Bandit's Death* 6
Stabb'd They should have *s* me where I lay, (repeat) *Oriana* 55, 60
Three times I *s* him thro' and thro'. *The Sisters* 29
She would have *s* him; *Merlin and V.* 853
'*S* thro' the heart's affections to the heart! „ 868
bride who *s* her bridegroom on her bridal night— *The Flight* 57
and he *s* my Piero with this. *Bandit's Death* 10
Stable a *s* wench Came running at the call, *Princess i* 226
they ran To loose him at the *s's*, *Aylmer's Field* 126
brute rejoicing in my hounds, and in my *s*, *By an Evolution.* 7
Staff (*See also* **Sceptre-staff**) he struck his *s* against the rocks *Golden Year* 59
is a straight *s* bent in a pool; *High. Pantheism* 16
Shot thro' the *s* or the halyard, *Def. of Lucknow* 5
the carven *s*—and last the light, *Columbus* 74
Stage actor mouth his last upon the *s*. *Locksley H., Sixty* 152
this Earth, a *s* so gloom'd with woe *The Play* 1
Stagger 'I *s* in the stream: *Princess vi* 321
And *s's* blindly ere she sink? *In Mem. xvi* 14
I *s* at the Korân and the sword. *Akbar's Dream* 71
Stagger'd *S* and shook, holding the branch, *Enoch Arden* 767
s thy strong Gawain in a tilt For pastime; *Gareth and L.* 542
Into the hall *s*, his visage ribb'd *Last Tournament* 57
the ship *s* under a thunderous shock, *The Wreck* 107
shock upon shock *S* the mass from without, *Heavy Brigade* 59
Staggering and *s* back With stroke on stroke *Princess v* 522
Staghorn-moss brought you down A length of *s-m*, *Romney's R.* 79
Stagnant A black yew gloom'd the *s* air, *The Letters* 2
Stagnate But *s's* in the weeds of sloth: *In Mem. xxvii* 11
As one that let foul wrong *s* and be, *Geraint and E.* 891
Stagnation A spot of dull *s*, without light *Palace of Art* 245
Stag-tuckey (turkey-cock) An' 'e torn'd as red as a *s-t's* wattles, *Churchwarden, etc,* 31

Staid (*See also* **Stay'd**) I had not *s* so long to tell you all, *Gardener's D.* 242
Staid (adj.) Altho' a grave and *s* God-fearing man, *Enoch Arden* 112
Stain (s) Some *s* or blemish in a name of note, *Merlin and V.* 832
to have loved One peerless, without *s*: *Lancelot and E.* 1091
Stain (verb) And I, 'Can clouds of nature *s* *In Mem. lxxxv* 85
Stain'd (*See also* **Staäin'd, Many-stain'd**) deep-set windows, *s* and traced, *Palace of Art* 49
Stainless But she, a *s* wife to Gorloïs, *Com. of Arthur* 194
King That morn was married, while in *s* white, „ 456
Would mar their charm of *s* maidenhood.' *Balin and Balan* 268
Thy blessing, *s* King! *Merlin and V.* 54
O Heaven's own white Earth-angel, *s* bride of *s* King— „ 81
A *s* man beside a *s* maid; „ 737
Arthur, blameless King and *s* man?' „ 779
O selfless man and *s* gentleman, „ 792
her bloom A rosy dawn kindled in *s* heavens, *Pelleas and E.* 72
White-robed in honour of the *s* child, *Last Tournament* 147
Thro' her high hill-passes of *s* snow, *Dead Prophet* 47
Stair (*See also* **Altar-stairs, Tower-stairs**) Broad-based flights of marble *s's* *Arabian Nights* 117
The rock rose clear, or winding *s*. *Palace of Art* 10
up the corkscrew *s* With hand and rope *Walk. to the Mail* 90
his footsteps smite the threshold *s's* *St. S. Stylites* 191
adown the *s* Stole on; *Godiva* 48
His golden feet on those empurpled *s's* *Lucretius* 135
And up a flight of *s's* into the hall. *Princess ii* 31
A column'd entry shone and marble *s's*, „ *v* 364
And me they bore up the broad *s's*, „ *vi* 374
And high above a piece of turret *s*, *Marr. of Geraint* 320
All up the marble *s*, tier over tier, *Lancelot and E.* 1248
Then from the boat I leapt, and up the *s's*. *Holy Grail* 819
Or ghostly footfall echoing on the *s*. *Guinevere* 507
Adown a natural *s* of tangled roots, *Lover's Tale i* 527
and climb'd The moulder'd *s's* „ *iv* 137
I stood upon the *s's* of Paradise. *Sisters (E. and E.)* 144
as far as the head of the *s*, *In the Child. Hosp.* 43
A stealthy foot upon the *s*! *The Flight* 70
an' the mud o' 'is boots o' the *s's*, *Spinster's S's.* 99
tummled up *s's*, fur I 'eärd 'im, *Owd Roä* 63
'But the *s's* is afire,' she said; „ 80
And glided lightly down the *s's*, *St. Telemachus* 59
Stairway down from this a lordly *s* sloped *Gareth and L.* 669
The *s* to the hall; and look'd and saw *Last Tournament* 757
Stake (verb) I'll *s* my ruby ring upon it you did.' *Princess, Pro.* 170
Stake (s) To the thumbscrew and the *s*, *The Revenge* 21
And the *s* and the cross-road, fool, *Despair* 116
I shudder at the Christian and the *s*; *Akbar's Dream* 72
Stale a fool, Raw, yet so *s*!' *Pelleas and E.* 114
Him, glaring, by his own *s* devil spurr'd, *Aylmer's Field* 290
Staled *S* by frequence, shrunk by usage *Locksley H., Sixty* 76
Stalk Earthward he boweth the heavy *s's* *A spirit haunts* 7
And these are but the shatter'd *s's*, *In Mem. lxxxii* 7
Stall and even beasts have *s's*, *St. S. Stylites* 109
The *s's* are void, the doors are wide, *Sir Galahad* 31
A man upon a *s* may find, *In Mem. lxxvii* 9
Take him to *s*, and give him corn, *Marr. of Geraint* 371
Enid took his charger to the *s*; „ 382
Stall'd *s* his horse, and strode across the court, *Balin and Balan* 341
Stalling chamber for the night, And *s* for the horses, *Geraint and E.* 239
Stalwart on free feet Set him, a *s* Baron, Arthur's friend. *Gareth and L.* 818
but afterwards He made a *s* knight. *Merlin and V.* 482
Stamford-town Burleigh-house by *S-t*. *L. of Burleigh* 92
Stammer That made my tongue so *s* and trip *Maud I vi* 83
left him leave to *s*, 'Is it indeed?' *Lancelot and E.* 420
Stammer'd I *s* that I knew him—could have wish'd— *Princess iii* 206
and when she spake to him, *S*, *Pelleas and E.* 85
Stammering *s* 'scoundrel' out of teeth that ground *Aylmer's Field* 328
deafen'd with the *s* cracks and claps That follow'd, *Merlin and V.* 942
on the border of her couch they sat *S* and staring. *Guinevere* 102
Stamp Which *s's* the caste of Vere de Vere. *L. C. V. de Vere* 40
meant to *s* him with her master's mark; *Merlin and V.* 759
I could *s* my image on her heart! *Sisters (E. and E.)* 195
Stamp'd-Stampt And the leaf is *stamp'd* in clay. *Vision of Sin* 82
Stampt all into defacement, *Balin and Balan* 541
Stamp'd with the image of the King; *Holy Grail* 27

Stamp'd-Stampt (*continued*) *Stampt* into dust—tremulous, all awry, *Romney's R.* 113
Stan' *S* 'im theer i' the naäme o' the Lord *North. Cobbler* 73
S 'im theer, fur I'll looök my hennemy „ 74
S 'im theer i' the winder, „ 75
theer 'e *s's* an' theer 'e shall *s* „ 95
'e can naither *s* nor goä. *Owd Roä* 2
moor good sense na the Parliament man 'at *s's* fur us 'ere, „ 13
if 'e could but *s* fur the Shere. „ 14
British farmers to *s* ageän o' their feeät. „ 46
Stanch'd bare him in, There *s* his wound; *Lancelot and E.* 520
Stand (*See also* **Stan'**) Truth may *s* forth unmoved of change, *Supp. Confessions* 144
That *s* beside my father's door, *Ode to Memory* 57
Where you *s* you cannot hear From the groves *Poet's Mind* 19
Which *s's* in the distance yonder: „ 30
S's in the sun and shadows all beneath, *Love and Death* 11
I *s* before thee, Eleänore; *Eleänore* 69
To *s* apart, and to adore, „ 79
I will *s* and mark. *To J. M. K.* 14
Us, who *s* now, when we should aid the right— *Poland* 13
Hope at Beauty's call would perch and *s*, *Caress'd or chidden* 3
Or at the casement seen her *s*? *L. of Shalott i* 25
Gargarus *S's* up and takes the morning: *Œnone* 11
There *s's* a spectre in your hall: *L. C. V. de Vere* 42
charm'd and tied To where he *s's*,— *D. of F. Women* 194
That her fair form may *s* and shine, *Of old sat Freedom* 21
half *s's* up And bristles; *Walk. to the Mail* 31
saw An angel *s* and watch me, as I sang. *St. S. Stylites* 35
That *s* within the chace. *Talking Oak* 4
young beech That here beside me *s's*, „ 142
Than that earth should *s* at gaze *Locksley Hall* 180
And when the tide of combat *s's*, *Sir Galahad* 10
See the lordly castles *s*: *L. of Burleigh* 18
Ring'd with the azure world, he *s's*. *The Eagle* 3
When all the wood *s's* in a mist of green, *The Brook* 14
there *S's* Philip's farm where brook and river meet. „ 38
S's at thy gate for thee to grovel to— *Aylmer's Field* 652
Shall *s*: ay surely: then it fails at last *Lucretius* 264
Or like a spire of land that *s's* apart *Princess iv* 281
That beat to battle where he *s's*; „ 578
'*S*, who goes?' 'Two from the palace' I. „ *v* 3
this is all, I *s* upon her side: „ 291
see how you *s* Stiff as Lot's wife, „ *vi* 240
Let his great example *s* Colossal, *Ode on Well.* 220
these in our Thermopylæ shall *s*, *Third of Feb.* 47
To break the blast of winter, *s*; *To F. D. Maurice* 22
and I *s* on the slope of the hill, *Window, On the Hill* 9
'And all the phantom, Nature, *s's*— *In Mem. iii* 9
Dark house, by which once more I *s* „ *vii* 1
we may *s* Where he in English earth is laid, „ *xviii* 1
Or in the furrow musing *s's*; „ *lxiv* 27
leave This laurel, let this holly *s*: „ *cv* 2
From form to form, and nothing *s's*; „ *cxxiii* 6
And six feet two, as I think, he *s's*; *Maud I xiii* 10
Yet I thought I saw her *s*, „ *II i* 38
Did he *s* at the diamond door Of his house „ *ii* 16
glory of manhood *s* on his ancient height, „ *III vi* 21
shall the shield of Mark *s* among these?' *Gareth and L.* 403
There *s's* the third fool of their allegory.' „ 1085
And ride with him to battle and *s* by, *Marr. of Geraint* 94
Am I so bold, and could I so *s* by, „ 102
good knight's horse *s's* in the court; „ 370
S aside, And if I fall, cleave to the better man.' *Geraint and E.* 151
But if a man who *s's* upon the brink „ 472
s's Vacant, but thou retake it, *Balin and Balan* 78
Let be: ye *s*, fair lord, as in a dream.' „ 258
I saw That maiden Saint who *s's* with lily in hand „ 261
Set up the charge ye know, to *s* or fall!' *Merlin and V.* 703
saw him, after, *s* High on a heap of slain, *Lancelot and E.* 306
she seem'd to *s* On some vast plain *Guinevere* 76
S's in a wind, ready to break and fly, „ 365
yonder *s's*, Modred, unharm'd, *Pass. of Arthur* 152
To *s* a shadow by their shining doors, *Lover's Tale i* 731
nay but thirty-nine have risen and *s*, *Sir J. Oldcastle* 83
Stand (*continued*) but scarcely could *s* upright, *V. of Maeldune* 73
Could *that s* forth, and like a statue, *Tiresias* 82
Thebes thro' thee shall *s* Firm-based „ 141
HELEN'S TOWER, here I *s*, *Helen's Tower* 1
Canning, *s* among our best And noblest, *Epit. on Stratford* 1
in this pleasant vale we *s* again, *Demeter and P.* 34
then here I *s* apart, *Happy* 25
When we shall *s* transfigured, „ 38
the height I *s* upon Even from myself? *s*? *Romney's R.* 65
And *s* with my head in the zenith, *Parnassus* 6
peaks they *s* ever spreading and heightening; „ 11
As he *s's* on the heights of his life *By an Evolution.* 20
Look, he *s's*, Trunk and bough, *The Oak* 13
neither of them *s's* behind the screen of thy truth. *Akbar's D., Inscrip.* 7
Now first we *s* and understand, *Mechanophilus* 1
Standard (ensign) With the *s's* of the peoples *Locksley Hall* 126
The struggle of *s's*, The rust of the javelins, *Batt. of Brunanburh* 87
Standard (tree) espaliers and the *s's* all Are thine; *The Blackbird* 5
Standest That *s* high above all? *Voice and the P.* 10
Thou *s* in the rising sun, *In Mem. cxxx* 3
Standeth let him in That *s* there alone, *D. of the O. Year* 50
And *s* seized of that inheritance *Gareth and L.* 359
Standin' *S* here be the bridge, *Tomorrow* 2
Standing (*See also* **A-stanning, Standin', Stannin'**)
lilies, *s* near Purple-spiked lavender: *Ode to Memory* 109
the couple *s* side by side, *The Bridesmaid* 5
Join'd not, but stood, and *s* saw *Palace of Art* 254
Stiller than chisell'd marble, *s* there; *D. of F. Women* 86
Memory *s* near Cast down her eyes, *To J. S.* 53
I reach'd The wicket-gate, and found her *s* there. *Gardener's D.* 213
Then Philip *s* up said falteringly *Enoch Arden* 284
The Virgin Mother *s* with her child *Sea Dreams* 242
He, *s* still, was clutch'd; *Princess iv* 260
and *s* like a stately Pine Set in a cataract „ *v* 346
Boädicéa, *s* loftily charioted, (repeat) *Boädicea* 3, 70
And *s*, muffled round with woe, *In Mem. xiv* 5
she is *s* here at my head; *Maud II v* 65
And arms on which the *s* muscle sloped, *Marr. of Geraint* 76
Then Lancelot *s* near, 'Sir Seneschal, *Gareth and L.* 461
The maiden *s* in the dewy light. *Lancelot and E.* 352
s near the shield In silence, „ 394
thro' the casement *s* wide for heat, „ 1234
Descending from the point and *s* both, There *Lover's Tale i* 411
Then some one *s* by my grave will say, *Columbus* 209
There *s*, shouted, and Pallas far away Call'd; *Achilles over the T.* 17
And were only *s* at gaze, *Heavy Brigade* 37
Muriel *s* ever statue-like— *The Ring* 266
He! is he *s* at the door, *Happy* 11
Stannin' (standing) What atta *s* theer fur, *N. Farmer, O. S.* 65
I browt what tha seeäs *s* theer, *North. Cobbler* 70
s theere o' the brokken stick; *Owd Roä* 25
Stanza those three *s's* that you made *Talking Oak* 135
Star (s) (*See also* **Beacon-star, Brother-star, Evening-star, Morning-star, Pilot-star, Sun-star**) Distinct with vivid *s's* inlaid, *Arabian Nights* 90
Sole *s* of all that place and time, „ 152
Was cloven with the million *s's* *Ode to Memory* 35
With golden *s's* above; *The Poet* 2
the shepherd who watcheth the evening *s*. *Dying Swan* 35
There would be neither moon nor *s*; *The Merman* 21
Neither moon nor *s*. „ 24
You are the evening *s*, alway Remaining *Margaret* 27
What songs below the waning *s's* The lion-heart, „ 33
As thou a *s*, in inmost heaven set, *Eleänore* 89
Her heart is like a throbbing *s*. *Kate* 9
Fancy sadder than a single *s*, *Caress'd or chidden* 13
Like to some branch of *s's* we see *L. of Shalott iii* 11
white-breasted like a *s* Fronting the dawn *Œnone* 57
wanton pard, Eyed like the evening *s*, „ 200
Between the loud stream and the trembling *s's*. „ 219
and ere the *s's* come forth Talk with the wild Cassandra, „ 262
Sole as a flying *s* shot thro' the sky *Palace of Art* 123
Crown'd dying day with *s's*, „ 184
A *s* that with the choral starry dance „ 253

Star (s) (*continued*) happy *s's* above them seem to brighten — *May Queen* 34
up to Heaven and die among the *s's*. — „ *Con.* 40
Sung by the morning *s* of song, — *D. of F. Women* 3
Peopled the hollow dark, like burning *s's*, — „ 18
maiden splendours of the morning *s* Shook — „ 55
We saw the large white *s's* rise one by one, — „ 223
this *s* Rose with you thro' a little arc — *To J. S.* 25
While the *s's* burn, the moons increase, — „ 71
Thro' silence and the trembling *s's* — *On a Mourner* 28
if Nature's evil *s* Drive men in manhood, — *Love thou thy land* 73
I bump'd the ice into three several *s's*, — *The Epic* 12
cry that shiver'd to the tingling *s's*, — *M. d'Arthur* 199
From spur to plume a *s* of tournament, — „ 223
ere a *s* can wink, beheld her there. — *Gardener's D.* 122
Love's white *s* Beam'd thro' the thicken'd cedar — „ 165
Sow'd all their mystic gulfs with fleeting *s's*; — „ 262
Sole *s* of phosphorescence in the calm, — *Audley Court* 87
I wake: the still *s's* sparkle; — *St. S. Stylites* 114
paused Among her *s's* to hear us; *s's* that hung Love-charm'd — *Love and Duty* 74
To follow knowledge like a sinking *s*, — *Ulysses* 31
and the baths Of all the western *s's*, — „ 61
Close over us, the silver *s*, — *Tithonus* 25
Ere yet they blind the *s's*, — „ 39
And o'er them many a sliding *s*, — *Day-Dm., Depart.* 13
On secrets of the brain, the *s's*, — „ *L'Envoi* 11
Draw me, thy bride, a glittering *s*, — *St. Agnes' Eve* 23
And star-like mingles with the *s's*. — *Sir Galahad* 48
New *s's* all night above the brim — *The Voyage* 25
We parted: sweetly gleam'd the *s's*, — *The Letters* 41
the great *s's* that globed themselves — *Enoch Arden* 597
I murmur under moon and *s's* In brambly wildernesses; — *The Brook* 178
and holds her head to other *s's*, — „ 195
Shone like a mystic *s* between the less — *Aylmer's Field* 72
A close-set robe of jasmine sown with *s's*: — „ 158
S to *s* vibrates light: may soul to soul — „ 578
such a *s* of morning in their blue, — „ 692
'if every *s* in heaven Can make it fair: — *Sea Dreams* 83
then I saw one lovely *s* Larger and larger. — „ 93
crown'd with *s's* and high among the *s's*,— — „ 241
Nor ever falls the least white *s* of snow, — *Lucretius* 107
For on my cradle shone the Northern *s*. — *Princess i* 4
dry old man, without a *s*, Not like a king: — „ 117
four wing'd horses dark against the *s's*; — „ 211
In shining draperies, headed like a *s*, — „ *ii* 109
glorious names Were fewer, scatter'd *s's*, — „ 156
The *s*, the bird, the fish, the shell, — „ 383
Morn in the white wake of the morning *s* — „ *iii* 17
'There sinks the nebulous *s* we call the Sun, — „ *iv* 19
Now poring on the glowworm, now the *s*, — „ 211
leader wildswan in among the *s's* Would clang it, — „ 434
those three *s's* of the airy Giant's zone, — „ *v* 260
The tops shall strike from *s* to *s*, — „ *vi* 57
S after *s*, arose and fell; but I, — „ *vii* 50
Now lies the Earth all Danaë to the *s's*, — „ 182
To sit a *s* upon the sparkling spire; — „ 197
Lavish Honour shower'd all her *s's*, — *Ode on Well.* 196
Brought from under every *s*, — *Ode Inter. Exhib.* 25
Melt into *s's* for the land's desire! — *W. to Alexandra* 21
And whistled to the morning *s*. — *Sailor Boy* 4
Two bright *s's* Peep'd into the shell. — *Minnie and Winnie* 13
And look'd at by the silent *s's*: — *Lit. Squabbles* 4
THE sun, the moon, the *s's*, the seas, — *High. Pantheism* 1
Earth, these solid *s's*, this weight of body — „ 5
Above thee glided the *s*. — *Voice and the P.* 8
The valley, the voice, the peak, the *s* Pass, — „ 27
Peak is high, and the *s's* are high, — „ 31
the *s's* about the moon Look beautiful, — *Spec. of Iliad* 11
the *s's* Shine, and the Shepherd gladdens in his heart: — „ 15
Taken the *s's* from the night — *Window, Gone* 5
And you are his morning *s*. — *Marr. Morn.* 12
'The *s's*,' she whispers, 'blindly run; — *In Mem. iii* 5
Slide from the bosom of the *s's*. — „ *xvii* 16
And orb into the perfect *s* — „ *xxiv* 15
Look also, Love, a brooding *s*, — „ *xlvi* 15

Star (s) (*continued*) And grapples with his evil *s*; — *In Mem. lxiv* 8
Thro' clouds that drench the morning *s*, — „ *lxxii* 22
To where in yonder orient *s* — „ *lxxxvi* 15
Before the crimson-circled *s* — „ *lxxxix* 47
He reads the secret of the *s*, — „ *xcvii* 22
Is twisting round the polar *s*; — „ *ci* 12
And one the shaping of a *s*; — „ *ciii* 36
A sphere of *s's* about my soul, — „ *cxxii* 7
While thou, dear spirit, happy *s*, — „ *cxxvii* 18
But tho' I seem in *s* and flower — „ *cxxx* 6
And brighten like the *s* that shook — „ *Con.* 31
And, *s* and system rolling past, — „ 122
sorrow seize me if ever that light be my leading *s*! — *Maud I iv* 12
you fair *s's* that crown a happy day — „ *xviii* 30
Beat, happy *s's*, timing with things below, — „ 81
like a silent lightning under the *s's* — „ *III vi* 9
Remembering all the beauty of that *s* — *Ded. of Idylls* 46
O ye *s's* that shudder over me, — *Com. of Arthur* 83
And even in high day the morning *s*. — „ 100
thereafter follow'd calm, Free sky and *s's*: — „ 392
wholesome *s's* of love; — *Gareth and L.* 314
honour shining like the dewy *s* Of dawn, — „ 329
and thereon the morning *s*. — „ 932
His arms, the rosy raiment, and the *s*. — „ 938
And he that bore The *s*, when mounted, — „ 951
And then she sang, 'O morning *s*' — „ 996
'O morning *s* that smilest in the blue, O *s*, my morning dream hath proven true, — „ 999
That named himself the *S* of Evening, — „ 1090
'No *s* of thine, but shot from Arthur's heaven — „ 1100
so wilt thou, Sir *S*; Art thou not old?' — „ 1103
that same strength which threw the Morning *S* — „ 1108
a shield whereon the *S* of Even Half-tarnish'd — „ 1117
and when he saw the *s* Gleam, — „ 1218
s shot: 'Lo,' said Gareth, 'the foe falls!' — „ 1317
cloud that grew To thunder-gloom palling all *s's*, — „ 1359
now by night With moon and trembling *s's*, — *Marr. of Geraint* 8
His charger trampling many a prickly *s* — „ 313
as the white and glittering *s* of morn — „ 734
'Enid, the pilot *s* of my lone life, — *Geraint and E.* 306
Kiss'd the white *s* upon his noble front, — „ 757
or touch at night the northern *s*; — *Balin and Balan* 166
rather seem'd a lovely baleful *s* — *Merlin and V.* 262
misty *s*, Which is the second in a line of *s's* — „ 508
Of some vast charm concluded in that *s* — „ 512
Her seer, her bard, her silver *s* of eve, — „ 954
like a *s* in blackest night. — *Lancelot and E.* 1243
And peak'd wings pointed to the Northern *S*. — *Holy Grail* 240
like a flying *s* Led on the gray-hair'd wisdom — „ 452
I saw him like a silver *s*— — „ 517
I saw the least of little *s's* Down on the waste, and straight beyond the *s* I saw the spiritual city — „ 524
from the *s* there shot A rose-red sparkle — „ 529
which can trace The wandering of the *s's*, — „ 667
The seven clear *s's* of Arthur's Table Round— — „ 684
a round in heaven, we named the *s's*, — „ 686
Across the seven clear *s's*—O grace to me— — „ 692
Rode till the *s* above the wakening sun, — *Pelleas and E.* 500
'O sweet *s*, Pure on the virgin forehead — „ 504
and the morning *s* Reel'd in the smoke, — „ 518
Peace at his heart, and gazing at a *s* — „ 559
Dost thou know the *s* We call the harp — *Last Tournament* 332
do ye see it? do ye see the *s*?' — „ 346
The night was dark; the true *s* set. Isolt! — „ 605
s in heaven, a *s* within the mere! Ay, ay, O ay,—a *s* — „ 732
And one was water, and one *s* was fire, — „ 736
'I found Him in the shining of the *s's*, — *Pass. of Arthur* 9
cry that shiver'd to the tingling *s's*, — „ 367
From spur to plume a *s* of tournament, — „ 391
lucid chambers of the morning *s*, — *Lover's Tale i* 28
Down those loud waters, like a setting *s*, — „ 59
Their Notions and their brightness from the *s's*, And then point out the flower or the *s*? — „ 174
Under the selfsame aspect of the *s's*, — „ 199
Suck'd into oneness like a little *s* — „ 308

Star (s) (*continued*) Even then the *s's* Did tremble in their stations — *Lover's Tale i* 581
cross between their happy *s* and them? — „ 730
s's came out far over the summer sea, — *The Revenge* 56
peak sent up one league of fire to the Northern *S*; — *V. of Maeldune* 72
Rejoicing that the sun, the moon, the *s's* — *Tiresias* 160
Her shadow crown'd with *s's*— — *Ancient Sage* 201
the *s's* went down across the gleaming pane, — *The Flight* 13
fairest of their evening *s's*. — *Locksley H., Sixty* 188
glancing heavenward on a *s* so silver-fair, — „ 191
the *S* that lights a desert pathway, — „ 275
the *s's* in heaven Paled, and the glory grew. — *Pro. to Gen. Hamley* 31
A *s* among the *s's*. (repeat) — *Epilogue* 2, 42
'The *s's* with head sublime,' — „ 47
s that gildest yet this phantom shore; — *To Virgil* 26
s's are from their hands Flung thro' the woods, — *Early Spring* 17
This order of Her Human *S*, — *Freedom* 23
hard Arabian moon And alien *s's*. — *To Marq. of Dufferin* 46
Shoot your *s's* to the firmament, — *On Jub. Q. Victoria* 17
S of the morning, Hope in the sunrise; — *Vastness* 15
in varnish'd glory shine Thy *s's* of celandine. — *Prog. of Spring* 39
Sphere-music of *s's* and of constellations. — *Parnassus* 8
ladder-of-heaven that hangs on a *s*. — *By an Evolution*. 12
many a pendent bell and fragrant *s*, — *Death of Œnone* 13
s of eve was drawing light From the dead sun, — „ 64
when she woke beneath the *s's*. — „ 82
What *s* could burn so low? not Ilion yet. — „ 83
sphere Of westward-wheeling *s's*; — *St. Telemachus* 32
after one quick glance upon the *s's*, — *Akbar's Dream* 3
If every single *s* Should shriek its claim — „ 42
westward—under yon slow-falling *s*, — „ 152
—not a *s* in the sky— — *Bandit's Death* 25
SUNSET and evening *s*, — *Crossing the Bar* 1
Star (verb) *s* The black earth with brilliance rare. — *Ode to Memory* 19
Starboard Roll'd to *s*, roll'd to larboard, — *Lotos-Eaters, C. S.* 106
two upon the larboard and two upon the *s* lay, — *The Revenge* 48
Star-broider'd The silk *s-b* coverlid — *Day-Dm., Sleep. B.* 9
Starcraft (Oh falsehood of all *s*!) — *Lover's Tale i* 200
Star-crown the high *s-c's* of his palms — *The Wreck* 72
Stare (s) And, last, you fix'd a vacant *s*, — *L. C. V. de Vere* 47
With a stony British *s*. — *Maud I xiii* 22
that *s* of a beast of prey. — *Charity* 10
Stare (verb) 'Wherefore *s* ye so? — *Gareth and L.* 939
Painted, who *s* at open space, — *Geraint and E.* 268
and the full moon *s's* at the snow. — *Rizpah* 4
That all the ships of the world could *s* at him, — „ 38
forward—naked—let them *s*. — *Locksley H., Sixty* 142
That all the crowd might *s*. — *Dead Prophet* 16
Stared Whereat he *s*, replying, half-amazed, — *Godiva* 21
Fantastic gables, crowding, *s*: — „ 61
And *s*, with his foot on the prey, — *Poet's Song* 12
full-busted figure-head *S* o'er the ripple — *Enoch Arden* 544
In much amaze he *s* On eyes a bashful azure, — *The Brook* 205
as I *s*, a fire, The fire that left a roofless Ilion, — *Lucretius* 64
s As blank as death in marble; — *Princess i* 176
S with great eyes, and laugh'd with alien lips, — „ *iv* 119
Fear *S* in her eyes, and chalk'd her face, — „ 377
aghast The women *s* at these, all silent, — „ *vi* 362
in a showerful spring *S* at the spate. — *Gareth and L.* 3
for so long a space *S* at the figures, — „ 232
and he started up and *s* at her. — *Geraint and E.* 389
the unswallow'd piece, and turning *s*; — „ 631
but while he *s* about the shrine, — *Balin and Balan* 408
S at the priceless cognizance, — „ 430
mounting on his horse *S* at her towers that, — *Pelleas and E.* 457
they *s* at the dead that had been so valiant and true, — *The Revenge* 105
how they *s*, That was their main test-question— — *Sir J. Oldcastle* 154
and I *s* from every eagle-peak, — *Demeter and P.* 68
And while she *s* at those dead cords — *Death of Œnone* 10
and ever seeming *s* upon By ghastlier — „ 70
rabble in half-amaze *S* at him dead, — *St. Telemachus* 72
Staring (*See also* **A-gawinin'**) and thou art *s* at the wall, — *Locksley Hall* 79
The *s* eye glazed o'er with sapless days, — *Love and Duty* 16
A sign to many a *s* shire Came crowing over Thames. — *Will Water.* 139
S for ever from their gilded walls — *Aylmer's Field* 833
Staring (*continued*) Turn, turn thy wheel above the *s* crowd; — *Marr. of Geraint* 356
All *s* at her in her faded silk: — „ 617
Were men and women *s* and aghast, — *Geraint and E.* 804
all at once they found the world, *S* wild-wide; — *Balin and Balan* 596
Linger'd that other, *s* after him; — *Lancelot and E.* 721
And *s* each at other like dumb men Stood, — *Holy Grail* 193
on the border of her couch they sat Stammering and *s*. — *Guinevere* 102
and *s* wide And hungering for the gilt — *Lover's Tale iv* 312
Stark but when she saw me lying *s*, — *Princess vi* 100
men down in the hold were most of them *s* and cold, — *The Revenge* 79
S and dark in his funeral fire. — *To Master of B.* 20
Stark-naked wherever she go *S-n*, and up or down, — *Dead Prophet* 46
Starless Walking the cold and *s* road of Death Uncomforted, — *Œnone* 259
Starlight Thro' all yon *s* keen, — *St. Agnes' Eve* 22
Not of the moonlight, Not of the *s*! — *Merlin and the G.* 122
from the lava-lake Dazing the *s*, — *Kapiolani* 15
Star-like The *s-l* sorrows of immortal eyes, — *D. of F. Women* 91
And *s-l* mingles with the stars. — *Sir Galahad* 48
Starling *s* claps his tiny castanets. — *Prog. of Spring* 56
Starr'd (*See also* **Evil-starr'd**) *S* from Jehovah's gorgeous armouries, — *Milton* 6
tho' the rough kex break The *s* mosaic, — *Princess iv* 78
streak'd or *s* at intervals With falling brook — *Lover's Tale i* 404
And *s* with a myriad blossom — *V. of Maeldune* 40
Starry They would pelt me with *s* spangles and shells, — *The Merman* 28
From under my *s* sea-bud crown — *The Mermaid* 16
Jewel or shell, or *s* ore, — *Eleänore* 20
Below the *s* clusters bright, — *L. of Shalott iii* 25
Rapt after heaven's *s* flight, — *Two Voices* 68
A star that with the choral *s* dance Join'd not, — *Palace of Art* 253
The night is *s* and cold, my friend, — *D. of the O. Year* 34
Above her shook the *s* lights: — *Of old sat Freedom* 3
All *s* culmination drop Balm-dews to bathe thy feet! — *Talking Oak* 267
All heaven bursts her *s* floors, — *St. Agnes' Eve* 27
Dip forward under *s* light, — *Move eastward* 10
Till toward the centre set the *s* tides, — *Princess ii* 118
Where all the *s* heavens of space Are sharpen'd — *In Mem. lxxvi* 3
'Can clouds of nature stain The *s* clearness of the free? — „ *lxxxv* 86
haunted by the *s* head Of her whose gentle will — *Maud I xviii* 22
Charioteer And *s* Gemini hang like glorious crowns — „ *III vi* 7
Was also Bard, and knew the *s* heavens; — *Merlin and V.* 169
Forward to the *s* track Glimmering up the heights — *Silent Voices* 8
Starry-clear silver-shining armour *s-c*; — *Holy Grail* 511
Starry-fair a face Most *s-f*, but kindled — *Lover's Tale i* 73
Star-shine By *s-s* and by moonlight, — *Oriana* 24
Star-sisters *S-s* answering under crescent brows; — *Princess ii* 428
Star-strown My shallop thro' the *s-s* calm, — *Arabian Nights* 36
Star-sweet *s-s* on a gloom profound; — *Maud I iii* 4
Start (s) given to *s's* and bursts Of revel; — *Princess i* 54
Start (verb) I started once, or seem'd to *s* in pain, — *D. of F. Women* 41
But as the waterlily *s's* and slides — *Princess iv* 255
Would *s* and tremble under her feet, — *Maud I xxii* 73
S from their fallen lords, and wildly fly, — *Geraint and E.* 482
ye would *s* back agin into life, — *Tomorrow* 81
nay, why do you *s* aside? — *Bandit's Death* 5
Started I *s* once, or seem'd to start in pain, — *D. of F. Women* 41
'But in a pet she *s* up, — *Talking Oak* 229
Then they *s* from their places, — *Vision of Sin* 33
Forward she *s* with a happy cry, — *Enoch Arden* 151
S from bed, and struck herself a light, — „ 494
he knew not wherefore, *s* up Shuddering, — „ 616
Then of the latest fox—where *s*— — *Aylmer's Field* 253
s on his feet, Tore the king's letter, — *Princess i* 60
Back *s* she, and turning round we saw — „ *ii* 320
I smote him on the breast; he *s* up; — „ *iv* 164
And many a bold knight *s* up in heat, — „ *v* 359
Up *s* from my side The old lion, — „ *vi* 98
And now and then an echo *s* up, — „ 369
Out into the road I *s*, and spoke — *The Grandmother* 43
S a green linnet Out of the croft; — *Minnie and Winnie* 17
Back from the gate *s* the three, — *Gareth and L.* 239
But up like fire he *s*: — „ 1123
seized on her, And Enid *s* waking, — *Marr. of Geraint* 674
either *s* while the door, Push'd from without, — *Geraint and E.* 272
and he *s* up and stared at her. — „ 389

Started (*continued*) and Balin *s* from his bower. *Balin and Balan* 280
Sideways he *s* from the path, and saw, „ 324
Yet blank from sleep, she *s* to him, *Lancelot and E.* 820
s thro' mid air Bearing an eagle's nest: *Last Tournament* 14
Flush'd, *s*, met him at the doors, „ 512
an' I *s* awaäy like a shot, *North. Cobbler* 69
shriek'd, and *s* from my side— *Locksley H., Sixty* 264
Starting *S* up at once, As from a dismal dream *Lover's Tale i* 747
then *s*, thought His dreams had come again. „ *iv* 77
Startled neither self-possess'd Nor *s*, *Gardener's D.* 155
Life was *s* from the tender love *Lover's Tale i* 616
Starve clamouring, 'If we pay, we *s*!' *Godiva* 15
'If they pay this tax, they *s*.' „ 20
s not thou this fire within thy blood, *Balin and Balan* 453
The first discoverer *s's*—his followers, *Columbus* 166
When all men *s*, the wild mob's million feet *The Fleet* 18
Starved (*See also* **Self-starved**) my husband's brother had my son Thrall'd in his castle, and hath *s* him dead; *Gareth and L.* 358
s the wild beast that was linkt with thee eighty years back. *By an Evolution.* 11
State (adj.) That crown'd the *s* pavilion of the King, *Guinevere* 399
State (body politic) (*See also* **Staäte**) Tho' every channel of the *S* *You ask me, why, etc.* 23
And work, a joint of *s*, that plies Its office, *Love thou thy land* 47
New Majesties of mighty *S's*— „ 60
'Who'd serve the *s*? for if I carved my name *Audley Court* 48
Visions of a perfect *S*: *Vision of Sin* 148
the *s*, The total chronicles of man, *Princess ii* 380
But as he saves or serves the *s*. *Ode on Well.* 200
No little German *s* are we, *Third of Feb.* 15
To mould a mighty *s's* decrees, *In Mem. lxiv* 11
Or touch'd the changes of the *s*, „ *lxxxix* 35
the *s* has done it and thrice as well: *Maud I x* 40
In silver tissue talking things of *s*; *Marr. of Geraint* 663
people's praise From thine own *S*, *Ded. Poem Prin. Alice* 8
bring on both the yoke Of stronger *s's*, *Tiresias* 70
Break the *S*, the Church, the Throne, *Locksley H., Sixty* 138
We founded many a mighty *s*; *Hands all Round* 30
Were she . . . a fallen *s*? *The Fleet* 10
In our ancient island *S*, *Open. I. and C. Exhib.* 16
To serve her myriads and the *S*,— *To Marq. of Dufferin* 24
and men at the helm of *s*— *The Wreck* 49
State (condition) Thrice happy *s* again to be The trustful infant on the knee! *Supp. Confessions* 40
O damned vacillating *s*! „ 190
in some confused dream To *s's* of mystical similitude; *Sonnet to ——* 4
The slipping thro' from *s* to *s*. *Two Voices* 351
'So might we, if our *s* were such As one before, „ 355
Such doubts and fears were common to her *s*, *Enoch Arden* 521
Roman lines Of empire, and the woman's *s* in each, *Princess ii* 131
still she rail'd against the *s* of things. „ *iii* 84
As in some mystic middle *s* I lay; „ *vi* 18
Charity Could lift them nearer God-like *s* *Lit. Squabbles* 14
And he should sorrow o'er my *s* *In Mem. xiv* 15
The lowness of the present *s*, „ *xxiv* 11
If, in thy second *s* sublime, „ *lxi* 1
From *s* to *s* the spirit walks; „ *lxxxii* 6
That range above our mortal *s*, „ *lxxxv* 22
Who first had found and loved her in a *s* Of broken fortunes, *Marr. of Geraint* 12
dazed and dumb With passing thro' at once from *s* to *s*, *Demeter and P.* 7
nearing yon dark portal at the limit of thy human *s*, *God and the Univ.* 4
State (chair of state) His *s* the king reposing keeps. *Day-Dm., Sleep. P.* 39
Summon'd out She kept her *s*, *Princess iii* 229
State (dignity) overflowing revenue Wherewith to embellish *s*, *Œnone* 113
Built for pleasure and for *s*. *L. of Burleigh* 32
Here he lives in *s* and bounty, „ 57
There she walks in her *s* And tends upon bed and bower, *Maud I xiv* 3
all his land and wealth and *s* were hers. *Holy Grail* 587
State (mien) and by your *s* And presence might have guess'd you one *Marr. of Geraint* 430
for by thy *s* And presence I might guess thee chief of those, *Lancelot and E.* 182
State (pomp) Where we withdrew from summer heats and *s*, *Princess vi* 245
I go in *s* to court, to meet the Queen. *Lancelot and E.* 1124
Led his dear lady to a chair of *s*. *Lover's Tale iv* 321
State (rank) And bow'd her *s* to them, that they might grow *Princess ii* 166
With reasons drawn from age and *s*, „ *v* 357
we believe him Something far advanced in *S*, *Ode on Well.* 275
And, for himself was of the greater *s*, *Gareth and L.* 395
As Mark would sully the low *s* of churl: „ 427
State (splendour) but robed in soften'd light Of orient *s*. *Ode to Memory* 11
Statelier (adj.) Then comes the *s* Eden back to men: *Princess vii* 293
With *s* progress to and fro The double tides of chariots flow *In Mem. xcviii* 22
Garrick and *s* Kemble, and the rest *To W. C. Macready* 7
Then, with a melody Stronger and *s*, *Merlin and the G.* 63
Statelier (s) Could find no *s* than his peers *Two Voices* 29
Stateliest sit the best and *s* of the land? *Lucretius* 172
King Arthur, like a modern gentleman Of *s* port; *M. d'Arthur, Ep.* 23
nor end of mine, *S*, for thee! *Princess vii* 170
Adored her, as the *s* and the best *Marr. of Geraint* 20
and as the *s* under heaven. *Holy Grail* 224
Wielder of the *s* measure ever moulded by the lips of man. *To Virgil* 39
Stateliness harmony Of thy swan-like *s*, *Eleänore* 47
Who see your tender grace and *s*. *Guinevere* 190
Stately The *s* flower of female fortitude, *Isabel* 11
deep myrrh-thickets blowing round The *s* cedar, *Arabian Nights* 105
maid, whose *s* brow The dew-impearled winds of dawn *Ode to Memory* 13
To throng with *s* blooms the breathing spring *The Poet* 27
To her full height her *s* stature draws; *D. of F. Women* 102
all the decks were dense with *s* forms Black-stoled, *M. d'Arthur* 196
Many an evening by the waters did we watch the *s* ships, *Locksley Hall* 37
s ships go on To their haven under the hill; *Break, break, etc.* 9
long convolvuluses That coil'd around the *s* stems, *Enoch Arden* 577
Stept thro' the *s* minuet of those days: *Aylmer's Field* 207
we stroll'd For half the day thro' *s* theatres *Princess ii* 369
standing like a *s* Pine Set in a cataract on an island-crag, „ *v* 346
leader of the herd That holds a *s* fretwork to the Sun, „ *vi* 86
crimson-hued the *s* palm-woods Whisper in odorous heights *Milton* 15
But she is tall and *s*. *Maud I xii* 16
From mother unto mother, *s* bride, *W. to Marie Alex.* 9
Camelot, a city of shadowy palaces And *s*, *Gareth and L.* 304
midway down the side of that long hall A *s* pile,— „ 405
'Farewell, fair Prince,' answer'd the *s* Queen. *Marr. of Geraint* 224
And there be made known to the *s* Queen, „ 607
came A *s* queen whose name was Guinevere, „ 667
His princess, or indeed the *s* Queen, „ 759
And moving out they found the *s* horse, *Geraint and E.* 752
Manners so kind, yet *s*, such a grace Of tenderest courtesy, „ 861
Being mirthful he, but in a *s* kind— *Lancelot and E.* 322
Whereon a hundred *s* beeches grew, *Pelleas and E.* 26
He glanced and saw the *s* galleries, *Last Tournament* 145
So the *s* Queen abode For many a week, unknown, *Guinevere* 146
all the decks were dense with *s* forms, Black-stoled, *Pass. of Arthur* 364
A *s* mountain nymph she look'd! *Lover's Tale i* 359
in front of which Six *s* virgins, all in white, „ *ii* 77
s vestibules To caves and shows of Death: „ 125
the *s* Spanish men to their flagship bore him then, *The Revenge* 97
s and tall—A princelier looking man never stept thro' a Prince's hall. *The Wreck* 15
Raise a *s* memorial, Make it regally gorgeous, *On Jub. Q. Victoria* 44
S purposes, valour in battle, *Vastness* 7
Edith bow'd her *s* head, *The Tourney* 13
Stately-gentle nay Being so *s-g*, *Balin and Balan* 192
Stately-set the fair hall-ceiling *s-s* *Palace of Art* 141
State-oracle O friends, our chief *s-o* is mute: *Ode on Well.* 23
States (United) He's gone to the *S's*, aroon, *Tomorrow* 49
Statesman (*See also* **Statesman-warrior**) '*And* statesmen *at her council met* *To the Queen* 29
No blazon'd *s* he, nor king. *You might have won* 24
O *Statesmen*, guard us, guard the eye, *Ode on Well.* 160
keep the soldier firm, the *s* pure: „ 222

Statesman (*continued*) a *s* there, betraying His party-secret, *Maud II v* 34
When he flouted a *s's* error, *The Wreck* 68
O PATRIOT *S*, be thou wise to know *To Duke of Argyll* 1
Whatever *s* hold the helm. *Hands all Round* 20
To all our *statesmen* so they be True leaders „ 25
as honouring your fair fame Of *S*, *To Marq. of Dufferin* 15
Statesman-warrior The *s-w*, moderate, resolute, *Ode on Well.* 25
Station all the wheels of Time Spun round in *s*, *Love and Duty* 76
message to and fro Between the mimic *s's*; *Princess, Pro.* 79
thro' his cowardice allow'd Her *s*, *Guinevere* 517
Did tremble in their *s's* as I gazed; *Lover's Tale i* 582
Stationary We stumbled on a *s* voice, *Princess v* 2
Station'd Ida *s* there Unshaken, „ 343
Statuary break the works of the *s*, *Boädicea* 64
Statue (*See also* **Statute, Woman-statue**) high on every peak a *s* seem'd To hang on tiptoe, *Palace of Art* 37
The *s's*, king or saint, or founder fell; *Sea Dreams* 224
A broken *s* propt against the wall, *Princess, Pro.* 99
Look, our hall! Our *s's*!— „ *ii* 76
Two great *s's*, Art And Science, „ *iv* 200
Half turning to the broken *s*, said, „ 593
and your *s's* Rear'd, sung to, „ *v* 413
And highest, among the *s's*, statue-like, „ 510
April of ovation round Their *s's*, „ *vi* 67
o'er the *s's* leapt from head to head, „ 366
Disrobed the glimmering *s* of Sir Ralph „ *Con.* 117
I stood among the silent *s's*, *The Daisy* 63
down their *s* of Victory fell. *Boädicea* 30
In the centre stood A *s* veil'd, *In Mem. ciii* 12
But like a *s* solid-set, „ *Con.* 15
She might have seem'd her *s*, but that he, *Lancelot and E.* 1171
one *s* in the mould Of Arthur, made by Merlin, *Holy Grail* 238
And eastward fronts the *s*, „ 241
And from the *s* Merlin moulded for us „ 732
like a *s*, rear'd To some great citizen, *Tiresias* 82
Statued And *s* pinnacles, mute as they. *The Daisy* 64
Statue-like *s-l*, In act to render thanks. *Gardener's D.* 161
And highest, among the statues, *s-l*, *Princess v* 510
Muriel standing ever *s-l*— *The Ring* 266
Statuelike Balin and Balan sitting *s*, *Balin and Balan* 24
The bridesmaid pale, *s*, passionless— *Sisters (E. and E.)* 212
Statuette When I was smaller than the *s* *The Ring* 109
Stature To her full height her stately *s* draws; *D. of F. Women* 102
Her *s* more than mortal in the burst Of sunrise, *Princess, Pro.* 40
Statured as long as thou art *s* tall! *Gareth and L.* 282
Statute an officer Rose up, and read the *s's*, *Princess ii* 69
Statute (statue) An' 'e bowt little *s's* all-naäkt *Village Wife* 50
Statute-book According to your bitter *s-b*, *Princess iv* 454
Stave (s) 'Chant me now some wicked *s*, *Vision of Sin* 151
Stave (verb) *s* off a chance That breaks upon them *Geraint and E.* 353
Stay Thou, willing me to *s*, *Madeline* 37
S's on her floating locks the lovely freight *Ode to Memory* 16
Whither away? listen and *s*: *Sea-Fairies* 42
That will not *s*, upon his way, *Rosalind* 15
steady sunset glow, That *s's* upon thee? *Eleänore* 56
A curse is on her if she *s* *L. of Shalott ii* 4
And now it seems as hard to *s*, *May Queen, Con.* 10
Here *s's* the blood along the veins. *Day-Dm., Sleep. P.* 4
'Pray *s* a little: pardon me; *The Brook* 210
And here he *s's* upon a freezing orb *Lucretius* 139
That *s's* the rolling Ixionian wheel, „ 261
S's all the fair young planet in her hands— *Princess vii* 264
I have not long to *s*; *Grandmother* 15
But *s* with the old woman now: you cannot have long to *s*. „ 108
To those that *s* and those that roam, *Sailor Boy* 14
My sisters crying, '*S* for shame;' „ 18
Like her I go; I cannot *s*; *In Mem. xii* 5
What *s's* thee from the clouded noons, „ *lxxxiii* 5
That *s's* him from the native land „ *xciii* 3
At least to me? I would not *s*. „ *cxx* 8
Who *s* to share the morning feast, „ *Con.* 75
Why should I *s*? can a sweeter chance *Maud I i* 62
may *s* for a year who has gone for a week: „ *xvi* 6
Let it go or *s*, so I wake to the higher aims „ *III vi* 38

Stay (*continued*) *S* therefore thou; red berries charm the bird, *Gareth and L.* 85
but *s*: follow the deer By these tall firs „ 90
S, my best son! ye are yet more boy than man.' „ 98
S, till the cloud that settles round his birth Hath lifted but a little. *S*, sweet son.' „ 130
ere a man in hall could *s* her, turn'd „ 660
'*S*, felon knight, I avenge me for my friend.' „ 1220
And *s* the world from Lady Lyonors. „ 1412
and Pellam's feeble cry '*S*, *s* him! *Balin and Balan* 421
could make me *s*—That proof of trust— *Merlin and V.* 919
'*S* with me, I am sick; *Lancelot and E.* 87
But he pursued her, calling, '*S* a little! „ 683
Lancelot shouted, '*S* me not! *Holy Grail* 643
clave To Modred, and a remnant *s's* with me. *Guinevere* 443
To *s* his feet from falling, *Lover's Tale i* 142
'*S* then a little,' answer'd Julian, „ *iv* 113
I may not *s*, No, not an hour; „ 115
S, my son Is here anon: *Columbus* 218
I saw that we could not *s*, *V. of Maeldune* 35
he grasp't at my arm—'*s* there'— *The Wreck* 120
Hence! she is gone! can I *s*? *Despair* 113
to *s*, Not spread the plague, the famine; *Demeter and P.* 133
God *s* me there, if only for your sake, *Romney's R.* 34
Stay'd (*See also* **Iron-stay'd, Staid**) Hesper is *s* between the two peaks; *Leonine Eleg.* 11
s beneath the dome Of hollow boughs.— *Arabian Nights* 41
Would they could have *s* with us! *Deserted House* 22
s the Ausonian king to hear Of wisdom *Palace of Art* 111
rummaged like a rat: no servant *s*: *Walk. to the Mail* 38
'But as for her, she *s* at home, *Talking Oak* 113
In these, in those the life is *s*. *Day-Dm., Sleep. P.* 18
Philip *s* (His father lying sick and needing him) *Enoch Arden* 64
S by this isle, not knowing where she lay: „ 630
We seven *s* at Christmas up to read; *Princess, Pro.* 178
there *s*; Knelt on one knee,— „ *vi* 90
I *s* the wheels at Cogoletto, *The Daisy* 23
He *s* his arms upon his knee: *The Victim* 54
Stiles where we *s* to be kind, *Window, Marr. Morn.* 7
But *s* in peace with God and man. *In Mem. lxxx* 8
caught And *s* him, 'Climb not lest thou *Gareth and L.* 54
ye know we *s* their hands From war among themselves, „ 421
holds her *s* In her own castle, „ 615
Perforce she *s*, and overtaken spoke. „ 764
on a little knoll beside it, *s* *Marr. of Geraint* 162
Nor *s* to crave permission of the King, *Balin and Balan* 288
And *s*; and cast his eyes on fair Elaine: *Lancelot and E.* 640
S in the wandering warble of a brook; *Last Tournament* 254
woman, weeping near a cross, *S* him. „ 494
have fall'n, But that they *s* him up; *Guinevere* 305
S on the cloud of sorrow; *Lover's Tale i* 255
And thus he *s* and would not look at her— „ *iv* 26
'This, I *s* for this; O love, „ 44
Took the breath from our sails, and we *s*. *The Revenge* 42
we *s* three days, and we gorged and we madden'd, *V. of Maeldune* 67
'Had I *s* with *him*, I had now— *The Wreck* 128
horsemen, drew to the valley—and *s*; *Heavy Brigade* 3
A mountain *s* me here, a minster there, *The Ring* 245
Stays all-too-full in bud For puritanic *s*: *Talking Oak* 60
Stead But in their *s* thy name and glory cling *Pass. of Arthur* 53
Steadfast (*See also* **Stedfast**) A pillar *s* in the storm, *In Mem. cxiii* 12
Steady And the *s* sunset glow, That stays upon thee? *Eleänore* 55
s glare Shrank one sick willow sere and small. *Mariana in the S.* 52
Steak Among the chops and *s's*! *Will Water.* 148
Steal (*See also* **Steäl**) Like soften'd airs that blowing *s*, *Two Voices* 406
old mysterious glimmer *s's* From thy pure brows, *Tithonus* 34
Her gradual fingers *s* And touch *Will Water.* 26
I *s* by lawns and grassy plots, *The Brook* 170
And *s* you from each other! *Aylmer's Field* 707
As slowly *s's* a silver flame *In Mem. lxvii* 6
And every span of shade that *s's*, „ *cxvii* 10
ever ready to slander and *s*; *Maud I iv* 19
It lightly winds and *s's* In a cold white robe „ *II iv* 18
I *s*, a wasted frame, „ 69
wolf would *s* The children and devour, *Com. of Arthur* 26
I cannot *s* or plunder, no nor beg: *Geraint and E.* 487

Stephen (the speaker's lover) we fondled it, *S* and I, But it died, *The Wreck* 83
'O *S*, I love you, I love you, and yet '— „ 101
'O *S*,' I moan'd, 'I am coming to thee „ 132
Stepmother you hear Far-off, is Muriel—your *s's* voice. *The Ring* 139
Your Mother and *s-m*— „ 146
Steppe golden news along the *s's* is blown, *W. to Marie Alex.* 11
Steppeth *S* from Heaven to Heaven, from light to light, *Lover's Tale i* 512
Stepping (*See also* **A-steppin'**) He, *s* down By zig-zag paths, *M. d'Arthur* 49
Come *s* lightly down the plank, *In Mem. xiv* 7
she rose, and *s* lightly, heap'd The pieces *Geraint and E.* 373
He, *s* down By zigzag paths, *Pass. of Arthur* 217
Seem'd *s* out of darkness with a smile. *Lover's Tale iv* 220
Stepping-stones Below the range of *s-s*, *Miller's D.* 54
That men may rise on *s-s* *In Mem. i* 3
Stept When forth there *s* a foeman tall, *Oriana* 33
Then *s* she down thro' town and field *Of old sat Freedom* 9
from the ruin'd shrine he *s* *M. d'Arthur* 45
And out I *s*, and up I crept: *Edwin Morris* 111
S forward on a firmer leg, *Will Water.* 123
Down *s* Lord Ronald from his tower: *Lady Clare* 65
In robe and crown the king *s* down, *Beggar Maid* 5
S the long-hair'd long-bearded solitary, *Enoch Arden* 637
S thro' the stately minuet of those days: *Aylmer's Field* 207
Then *s* a buxom hostess forth, *Princess i* 228
Lightly to the warrior *s*, „ *vi* 10
a healthful people *s* As in the presence *Gareth and L.* 315
And inward to the wall; he *s* behind; *Balin and Balan* 406
found a little boat, and *s* into it; *Merlin and V.* 198
close behind them *s* the lily maid Elaine, *Lancelot and E.* 176
into that rude hall *S* with all grace, „ 263
from the ruin'd shrine he *s*, *Pass. of Arthur* 213
the man who stood with me *S* gaily forward, *Lover's Tale iii* 51
From wall to dyke he *s*, *Achilles over the T.* 15
princelier looking man never *s* thro' a Prince's hall. *The Wreck* 16
she *s* an the chapel-green, *Tomorrow* 27
Christ-like creature that ever *s* on the ground. *Charity* 32
Sterling most, of *s* worth, is what Our own experience preaches. *Will Water.* 175
Stern (adj.) Or gay, or grave, or sweet, or *s*, *Palace of Art* 91
The *s* black-bearded kings with wolfish eyes, *D. of F. Women* 111
S he was and rash; *The Captain* 10
Grave, florid, *s*, as far as eye could see, *Sea Dreams* 219
s and sad (so rare the smiles Of sunlight) *The Daisy* 53
The *s* were mild when thou wert by, *In Mem. cx* 9
S too at times, and then I loved him not, *Com. of Arthur* 354
To such a *s* and iron-clashing close, *Merlin and V.* 419
Stern (s) Dark as a funeral scarf from stem to *s*, *M. d'Arthur* 194
from stem to *s* Bright with a shining people *Com. of Arthur* 375
Dark as a funeral scarf from stem to *s*, *Pass. of Arthur* 362
Steward The wrinkled *s* at his task, *Day-Dm., Sleep. P.* 27
The butler drank, the *s* scrawl'd, „ *Revival* 10
'Tis but a *s* of the can, *Will Water.* 149
Sthrame (stream) comin' down be the *s*, *Tomorrow* 7
s's runnin' down at the back o' the glin „ 24
Stick (s) on whom all spears Are rotten *s's*! *Gareth and L.* 1306
an' sweär'd as I'd breäk ivry *s* *North. Cobbler* 35
Molly kem limpin' up wid her *s*, *Tomorrow* 77
stannin' theere o' the brokken *s*; *Owd Roä* 25
Stick (verb) And on thy ribs the limpet *s's* *Sailor Boy* 11
But proputty, proputty *s's*, *N. Farmer, N. S.* 16
a villain fitter to *s* swine Than ride abroad *Gareth and L.* 865
Thim's my noätions, Sammy, wheerby I means to *s*; *N. Farmer, N. S.* 57
what *s* ye round The pasty? *Gareth and L.* 1072
s oop thy back, an' set oop thy taäil, *Spinster's S's.* 31
if t'ōne *s* alongside t'uther *Church-warden, etc.* 10
Sa I *s's* like the ivin as long as I lives „ 15
Stiff While my *s* spine can hold my weary head, *St. S. Stylites* 43
wet With drenching dews, or *s* with cracking frost. „ 115
'but still My joints are somewhat *s* or so. *Day-Dm., Revival* 26
That stood from out a *s* brocade in which, *Aylmer's Field* 204
see how you stand *S* as Lot's wife, *Princess vi* 241

Stiff (*continued*) and stood *S* as a viper frozen; *Merlin and V.* 845
That whistled *s* and dry about the marge. *Pass. of Arthur* 232
That whistled *s* and dry about the marge. *M. d'Arthur* 64
Stiffen And, lest I *s* into stone, *In Mem. cviii* 2
Stiffen'd His fingers were so *s* by the frost *The Ring* 239
Stiffening Sir Aylmer Aylmer slowly *s* spoke: *Aylmer's Field* 273
Stiffer My nerves have dealt with *s*. *Will Water.* 78
Stiff-set Blow, flute, and stir the *s-s* sprigs, *Amphion* 63
Stiff-stricken She sat *S-s*, listening; *Guinevere* 412
Stifled She whisper'd, with a *s* moan *Mariana in the S.* 57
Making Him broken gleams, and a *s* splendour and gloom. *High. Pantheism* 10
breathless burthen of low-folded heavens *S* and chill'd at once; *Aylmer's Field* 613
my strangled vanity Utter'd a *s* cry— *Sisters (E. and E.)* 200
Stile So Lawrence Aylmer, seated on a *s* *The Brook* 197
S's where we stay'd to be kind, *Window, Marr. Morn.* 7
By meadow and *s* and wood, „ 14
Over the meadows and *s's*, „ 22
Or simple *s* from mead to mead, *In Mem. c* 7
That ever bided tryst at village *s*, *Merlin and V.* 378
Still Pure vestal thoughts in the translucent fane Of her *s* spirit; *Isabel* 5
Wash'd with *s* rains and daisy blossomed; *Circumstance* 7
senses with a *s* delight Of dainty sorrow *Margaret* 17
Falling into a *s* delight, *Eleänore* 106
Come only, when the days are *s*, *My life is full* 23
A *S* small voice spake unto me, *Two Voices* 1
Then to the *s* small voice I said; „ 4
In her *s* place the morning wept: „ 275
The *s* voice laugh'd. 'I talk,' said he, „ 385
The pool beneath it never *s*, *Miller's D.* 100
s affection of the heart Became an outward breathing type, „ 225
fit for every mood And change of my *s* soul. *Palace of Art* 60
'I marvel if my *s* delight In this great house „ 190
A *s* salt pool, lock'd in with bars of sand, „ 249
All the valley, mother, 'ill be fresh and green and *s*, *May Queen* 37
When you are warm-asleep, mother, and all the world is *s*. *May Queen, N. Y's. E.* 24
Or night-dews on *s* waters between walls *Lotos-Eaters, C. S.* 3
Scaffolds, *s* sheets of water, divers woes, *D. of F. Women* 34
not so deadly *s* As that wide forest. „ 68
Thy sole delight is, sitting *s*, *The Blackbird* 10
One after one, thro' that *s* garden pass'd; *Gardener's D.* 201
By this *s* hearth, among these barren crags, *Ulysses* 2
With one smile of *s* defiance Sold him *The Captain* 59
detaching, fold by fold, From those *s* heights, *Vision of Sin* 52
And the sound of a voice that is *s*! *Break, break, etc.* 12
face All-kindled by a *s* and sacred fire, *Enoch Arden* 71
Found a *s* place, and pluck'd her likeness out; *Princess i* 92
doubtful smile dwelt like a clouded moon In a *s* water „ *vi* 271
strong on his legs, but *s* of his tongue! *Grandmother* 13
I look'd at the *s* little body— „ 66
Calm and *s* light on yon great plain *In Mem. xi* 9
The moon is hid; the night is *s*; „ *xxviii* 2
So that *s* garden of the souls In many a figured leaf „ *xliii* 10
The fruitful hours of *s* increase; „ *xlvi* 10
When all his active powers are *s*, „ *lxiv* 18
Looks thy fair face and makes it *s*. „ *lxx* 16
And fluctuate all the *s* perfume, „ *xcv* 56
The moon is hid, the night is *s*; „ *civ* 2
One *s* strong man in a blatant land, *Maud I x* 63
Why am I sitting here so stunn'd and *s*, „ *II i* 2
Always I long to creep Into some *s* cavern deep, „ *iv* 96
the two Left the *s* King, and passing forth *Com. of Arthur* 369
A STORM was coming, but the winds were *s*, *Merlin and V.* 1
Past up the *s* rich city to his kin, *Lancelot and E.* 802
Speaking a *s* good-morrow with her eyes. „ 1033
As hard and *s* as is the face that men „ 1251
then came a night *S* as the day was loud; *Holy Grail* 683
Who yells Here in the *s* sweet summer night, *Pelleas and E.* 473
Clung to the dead earth, and the land was *s*. *Guinevere* 8
took and bare him off, And all was *s*: „ 110
There came a day as *s* as heaven, „ 292

Still (*continued*) A man in some *s* garden should infuse Rich atar — *Lover's Tale i* 269
at the last they found I had grown so stupid and *s* — *Rizpah* 49
that last deep where we and thou are *s*. — *De Prof., Two G.* 25

Still'd Who *s* the rolling wave of Galilee! — *Aylmer's Field* 709
bees are *s*, and the flies are kill'd, — *Window, Winter* 10
Hath *s* the life that beat from thee. — *In Mem. vi* 12
smote, and *s* Thro' all its folds — *Tiresias* 14
Hath *s* the blast and strown the wave, — *Freedom* 34
You *s* it for the moment with a song — *Romney's R.* 84

Stiller *S* than chisell'd marble, — *D. of F. Women* 86
haunt of brawling seamen once, but now *S*, — *Enoch Arden* 698
Nor count me all to blame if I Conjecture of a *s* guest, — *In Mem., Con.* 86
She comes from another *s* world of the dead, *S*, — *Maud II v* 70
would darken down To rise hereafter in a *s* flame — *Lancelot and E.* 1319

Stillest Or in *s* evenings With what voice — *Adeline* 30

Still-eyed gazing like The Indian on a *s-e* snake, — *Lover's Tale ii* 189

Still-fulfilling The *s-f* promise of a light — *Prog. of Spring* 90

Still-lighted *S-l* in a secret shrine, — *Mariana in the S.* 18

Stillness That into *s* past again, — *Miller's D.* 227
Sang to the *s*, till the mountain-shade — *Œnone* 21
'No voice breaks thro' the *s* of this world: — *Palace of Art* 259
This murmur broke the *s* of that air — *Gardener's D.* 147
rounded by the *s* of the beach — *Audley Court* 10
moving toward the *s* of his rest. — *Locksley Hall* 144
Her constant beauty doth inform *S* with love, — *Day-Dm., Sleep. B.* 16
Assumed from thence a half-consent involved In *s*, — *Princess vii* 83
Is perfect *s* when they brawl. — *Lit. Squabbles* 20
A part of *s*, yearns to speak: — *In Mem. lxxxv* 78
The *s* of the central sea. — " *cxxiii* 4
In scornful *s* gazing as they past; — *Com. of Arthur* 478
Balin the *s* of a minute broke Saying — *Balin and Balan* 51
s of the dead world's winter dawn — *Pass. of Arthur* 442
Why in the utter *s* of the soul — *Lover's Tale i* 276
the bells Lapsed into frightful *s*; — " *iii* 30
From either by the *s* of the grave— — *Sisters (E. and E.)* 282

Still-recurring chased away the *s-r* gnat, — *Caress'd or chidden* 7

Still-shatter'd coming down on the *s-s* walls Millions of musket-bullets, — *Def. of Lucknow* 92

Still-working From this my vantage ground To those *s-w* energies — *Mechanophilus* 19

Stilly many a shadow-chequer'd lawn Full of the city's *s* sound, — *Arabian Nights* 103

Sting (s) Toil'd onward, prick'd with goads and *s's*; — *Palace of Art* 150
a *s* of shrewdest pain Ran shrivelling thro' me, — *St. S. Stylites* 198
and draw The *s* from pain; — *Princess vii* 64
lose thy life by usage of thy *s*; — *Ancient Sage* 270

Sting (verb) Not *s* the fiery Frenchman into war. — *Third of Feb.* 4
That lay their eggs, and *s* and sing — *In Mem. l* 11
That *s* each other here in the dust; — *Maud II i* 47
can stir them till they *s*.' — *Merlin and V.* 36
—we scorn them, but they *s*.' — *Lancelot and E.* 139
And *s's* itself to everlasting death, — *Last Tournament* 452
they fear'd that we still could *s*, — *The Revenge* 72
s's him back to the curse of the light; — *Vastness* 18

Stink An' the *s* o' 'is pipe i' the 'ouse, — *Spinster's S's.* 100

Stinted I had not *s* practice, O my God. — *St. S. Stylites* 59
That brought the *s* commerce of those days; — *Enoch Arden* 817
When have I *s* stroke in foughten field? — *Holy Grail* 860

Stir (s) Begin to feel the truth and *s* of day, — *M. d'Arthur, Ep.* 19
the splash and *s* Of fountains spouted up — *Princess i* 217
came a little *s* About the doors, — " *iv* 373
I scarce could brook the strain and *s* — *In Mem. xv* 12
no need to make such a *s*.' — *First Quarrel* 63

Stir (verb) speaks or hems or *s's* his chair, — *Sonnet to ——* 5
So fleetly did she *s*, — *Talking Oak* 130
Blow, flute, and *s* the stiff-set sprigs, — *Amphion* 63
Let Whig and Tory *s* their blood; — *Will Water.* 53
Yet dared not *s* to do it, — *Aylmer's Field* 806
secret, seem'd to *s* within my breast; — *Princess iii* 44
but for those That *s* this hubbub— — " *iv* 509
there she lies, But will not speak, nor *s*.' — " *v* 52
S in me as to strike: — " 268
That *s* the spirit's inner deeps, — *In Mem. xlii* 10

Stir (verb) (*continued*) To *s* a little dust of praise. — *In Mem. lxxv* 12
That made it *s* on the shore. — *Maud II ii* 15
Do these your lords *s* up the heat of war, — *Com. of Arthur* 169
S, as they stirr'd of old, — *Balin and Balan* 89
Not dead; he *s's*!—but sleeping. — " 469
can *s* them till they sting.' — *Merlin and V.* 36
and *s's* the pulse With devil's leaps, — *Guinevere* 521
That sees and *s's* the surface-shadow there — *Ancient Sage* 38
And *s* the sleeping earth, and wake The bloom — " 93
at night *S's* up again in the heart of the sleeper, — *Vastness* 18
Across my garden! and the thicket *s's*, — *Prog. of Spring* 53

Stirr'd (*See also* **Laughter-stirr'd**) It *s* the old wife's mettle: — *The Goose* 26
s with languid pulses of the oar, — *Gardener's D.* 41
and *s* her lips For some sweet answer, — " 158
But yet my sap was *s*: — *Talking Oak* 172
The fragrant tresses are not *s* — *Day-Dm., Sleep. B.* 19
The mountain *s* its bushy crown, — *Amphion* 25
feign death, Spoke not, nor *s*. — *Princess v* 109
And at thy name the Tartar tents are *s*; — *W. to Marie Alex.* 12
the roots of my hair were *s* By a shuffled step, — *Maud I i* 13
All night has the casement jessamine *s* — " *xxii* 15
lets His heart be *s* with any foolish heat — *Gareth and L.* 1178
Stir, as they *s* of old, when Arthur's host — *Balin and Balan* 89
s this vice in you which ruin'd man — *Merlin and V.* 362
And by the gateway *s* a crowd; — *Holy Grail* 424
The fancy *s* him so He rose and went, — *Lover's Tale iv* 51
but mine that *s* Among our civil wars — *Sisters (E. and E.)* 74
the deeps of the world are *s*, — *The Wreck* 23
And, lightly *s*, Ring little bells of change — *Early Spring* 40

Stirring It was the *s* of the blood. — *Two Voices* 159
Little about it *s* save a brook! — *Aylmer's Field* 32
Not all: the songs, the *s* air, — *In Mem. cxvi* 5
S a sudden transport rose and fell. — *Princess iv* 29

Stitches In coughs, aches, *s*, ulcerous throes — *St. S. Stylites* 13

Sto one Pou *S* whence afterwards May move — *Princess iii* 263

Stoän (stone) a niver rembles the *s's*. — *N. Farmer, O. S.* 60
fear'd fur to tell tha 'ow much—fur an owd scratted *s*, — *Village Wife* 47
an' sleeäpin still as a *s*, — *Owd Roä* 30

Stoän-deäf (stone-deaf) Fur the dog's *s-d*, an' e's blind, — " 2

Stoat Lion and *s* have isled together, — *Gareth and L.* 893

Stock like an oaken *s* in winter woods, — *Golden Year* 62

Stockin' wheer Sally's owd *s* wur 'id, — *North. Cobbler* 31

Stock-still stood *S-s* for sheer amazement. — *Will Water.* 136
moved slow-measure to my tune, Not stood *s*. — *Last Tournament* 283

Stoic like a *s*, or like A wiser epicurean, — *Maud I iv* 20

Stole (s) With folded feet, in *s's* of white, — *Sir Galahad* 43

Stole (verb) Then *s* I up, and trancedly Gazed — *Arabian Nights* 133
Prevailing in weakness, the coronach *s* — *Dying Swan* 26
shadow of the flowers *S* all the golden gloss, — *Gardener's D.* 130
O'er the mute city *s* with folded wings, — " 186
S from her sister Sorrow. — " 256
we *s* his fruit, His hens, his eggs; — *Walk. to the Mail* 84
a silent cousin *s* Upon us and departed: — *Edwin Morris* 115
adown the stair *S* on; — *Godiva* 49
s Up by the wall, behind the yew; — *Enoch Arden* 738
I *s* from court With Cyril and with Florian, — *Princess i* 102
Away we *s*, and transient in a trice — " *v* 39
S a maiden from her place, — " *vi* 9
while Psyche ever *s* A little nearer, — " 132
thieves from o'er the wall *S* the seed by night. — *The Flower* 12
As the gray dawn *s* o'er the dewy world, — *Geraint and E.* 385
The wily Vivien *s* from Arthur's court. — *Merlin and V.* 149
First as in fear, step after step, she *s* — *Lancelot and E.* 342
And down the long beam *s* the Holy Grail, — *Holy Grail* 117, 188
underneath Her castle-walls, she *s* upon my walk, And calling me — " 594
words *s* with most prevailing sweetness — *Lover's Tale i* 553
I *s* them all from the lawyers— — *Rizpah* 52
earth's green *s* into heaven's own hue, — *Far—far—away* 2
slept Ay, till dawn *s* into the cave, — *Bandit's Death* 31

Stoled (*See also* **Black-stoled**) Were *s* from head to foot in flowing black; — *Lover's Tale ii* 85

Stol'n dawn's creeping beams, *S* to my brain, — *D. of F. Women* 262
Then down the long street having slowly *s*, — *Enoch Arden* 682
Because her brood is *s* away. — *In Mem. xxi* 28

Stol'n (*continued*) and *s* away To dreamful wastes — *Maud I xviii* 68
(Who hearing her own name had *s* away) — *Marr. of Geraint* 507
Some lost, some *s*, some as relics kept. — *Merlin and V.* 453
Art with poisonous honey *s* from France, — *To the Queen ii* 56
And if the ring were *s* from the maid, — *The Ring* 203
had *s*, worn the ring—Then torn it from her finger, — „ 455
Stomach Less having *s* for it than desire — *Geraint and E.* 213
Stomach'd *See* **Faint-stomach'd**
Stomacher He cleft me thro' the *s*; — *Princess ii* 407
Stone (*See also* **Altar-stone, Foundation-stone, Stepping-stones, Stoän**) Life in dead *s's*, or spirit in air; — *A Character* 9
cursed and scorn'd, and bruised with *s's*: — *Two Voices* 222
The lizard, with his shadow on the *s*, — *Œnone* 27
Ev'n on this hand, and sitting on this *s*? — „ 233
one a foreground black with *s's* and slags, — *Palace of Art* 81
song Throb thro' the ribbed *s*; — „ 176
A rolling *s* of here and everywhere, — *Audley Court* 78
Till all my limbs drop piecemeal from the *s*, — *St. S. Stylites* 44
I lay Pent in a roofless close of ragged *s's*; — „ 74
On the mossy *s*, as I lay, — *Edward Gray* 26
'Bitterly wept I over the *s*: — „ 33
Tread a measure on the *s's*, — *Vision of Sin* 180
On thy cold gray *s's*, O Sea! — *Break, break, etc.* 2
His eyes upon the *s's*, he reach'd the home — *Enoch Arden* 684
or one *s* Left on another, — *Aylmer's Field* 788
men of flesh and blood, and men of *s*, — *Sea Dreams* 237
on the pavement lay Carved *s's* of the Abbey-ruin — *Princess, Pro.* 14
One rear'd a font of *s* And drew, — „ 59
and watch The sandy footprint harden into *s*.' — „ *iii* 271
Old Yew, which graspest at the *s's* — *In Mem. ii* 1
Dark yew, that graspest at the *s's* — „ *xxxix* 4
From scarped cliff and quarried *s* — „ *lvi* 2
And, lest I stiffen into *s*, — „ *cviii* 2
On a heart half-turn'd to *s*. — *Maud I vi* 78
O heart of *s*, are you flesh, — „ 79
Wept over her, carved in *s*; — „ *viii* 4
(Which Maud, like a precious *s* Set in the heart — „ *xiv* 10
Low on the sand and loud on the *s* — „ *xxii* 25
Courage, poor heart of *s*! — „ *II iii* 1
Courage, poor stupid heart of *s*.— — „ 5
Of ancient kings who did their days in *s*; — *Gareth and L.* 305
by two yards in casting bar or *s* Was counted best; — „ 518
A *s* about his neck to drown him in it. — „ 812
Gareth loosed the *s* From off his neck, — „ 814
and with a *s* about his neck; — „ 823
but at night let go the *s*, And rise, — „ 825
Like sparkles in the *s* Avanturine. — „ 930
Hurl'd as a *s* from out of a catapult — „ 965
slopes a wild brook o'er a little *s*, — *Marr. of Geraint* 77
star Of sprouted thistle on the broken *s's*. — „ 314
suck'd the joining of the *s's*, and look'd A knot, — „ 324
Right o'er a mount of newly-fallen *s's* — „ 361
blade flew Splintering in six, and clinkt upon the *s's*. — *Balin and Balan* 396
when she heard his horse upon the *s's*, — *Lancelot and E.* 980
With knees of adoration wore the *s*, — *Holy Grail* 71
and the *s's* They pitch up straight to heaven: — „ 664
bound and plunged him into a cell Of great piled *s's*; — „ 676
Heavy as it was, a great *s* slipt and fell, — „ 680
shatter'd talbots, which had left the *s's* Raw, — „ 719
s is flung into some sleeping tarn, — *Pelleas and E.* 93
spiring *s* that scaled about her tower, — *Last Tournament* 511
A little bitter pool about a *s* — *Guinevere* 51
I CAME one day and sat among the *s's* — *Lover's Tale iii* 1
you are just as hard as a *s*. — *Rizpah* 80
Scribbled or carved upon the pitiless *s*; — *Sir J. Oldcastle* 5
and we took to throwing the *s*, — *V. of Maeldune* 94
One was of smooth-cut *s*, — „ 106
There were some for the clean-cut *s*, — „ 112
Beyond all work of those who carve the *s*, — *Tiresias* 53
No *s* is fitted in yon marble girth — „ 135
and mute below the chancel *s's*, — *Locksley H., Sixty* 43
Tho' carved in harder *s*— — *Epilogue* 59
I am mortal *s* and lime. — *Helen's Tower* 6
and see no more The *S*, the Wheel, — *Demeter and P.* 150

Stone (*continued*) a *s*, That glances from the bottom of the pool, — *The Ring* 370
a shower of *s's* that stoned him dead, — *St. Telemachus* 68
I dream'd That *s* by *s* I rear'd a sacred fane, — *Akbar's Dream* 177
loosen, *s* from *s*, All my fair work; — „ 188
Who fitted *s* to *s* again, and Truth, Peace, — „ 193
Stone (disease) Past earthquake—ay, and gout and *s*, — *Lucretius* 153
Stone-cast About a *s-c* from the wall — *Mariana* 37
Stoned either they were *s*, or crucified, — *St. S. Stylites* 51
a shower of stones that *s* him dead, — *St. Telemachus* 68
Stone-deaf *See* **Stoän-deäf**
Stone-shot He show'd a tent A *s-s* off: — *Princess v* 54
Stonest O thou that *s*, hadst thou understood — *Aylmer's Field* 739
Stoning no *s* save with flint and rock? — „ 746
Stony On *s* drought and steaming salt; — *Mariana in the S.* 40
lion on your old *s* gates Is not more cold to you than I. — *L. C. V. de Vere* 23
while all the fleet Had rest by *s* hills of Crete. — *On a Mourner* 35
Better the narrow brain, the *s* heart, — *Love and Duty* 15
I chatter over *s* ways, — *The Brook* 39
Before the *s* face of Time, — *Lit. Squabbles* 3
had wound A scarf of orange round the *s* helm, — *Princess, Pro.* 102
chattering *s* names Of shale and hornblende, — „ *iii* 361
the fangs Shall move the *s* bases of the world. — „ *vi* 58
Gorgonised me from head to foot With a *s* British stare. — *Maud I xiii* 22
There ran a treble range of *s* shields,— — *Gareth and L.* 407
S showers Of that ear-stunning hail of Arês — *Tiresias* 95
Gods Avenge on *s* hearts a fruitless prayer — *Death of Œnone* 41
Stood *s* Betwixt me and the light of God! — *Supp. Confessions* 109
at last *s* out This excellence and solid form — „ 148
heaven's mazed signs *s* still In the — *Clear-headed friend* 28
And *s* aloof from other minds — *A Character* 23
She *s* upon the castle wall, — *Oriana* 28
you *s* Between the rainbow and the sun. — *Margaret* 12
Pallas where she *s* Somewhat apart, — *Œnone* 137
Full of great rooms and small the palace *s*, — *Palace of Art* 57
in dark corners of her palace *s* Uncertain shapes; — „ 237
That *s* against the wall. — „ 244
Join'd not, but *s*, and standing saw — „ 254
Full-faced above the valley *s* the moon; — *Lotos-Eaters* 7
silent pinnacles of aged snow, *S* sunset flush'd: — „ 17
I appeal'd To one that *s* beside. — *D. of F. Women* 100
so *s* I, when that flow Of music left the lips — „ 194
She lock'd her lips: she left me where I *s*: — „ 241
Losing her carol I *s* pensively, — „ 245
That *s* on a dark strait of barren land. — *M. d'Arthur* 10
both his eyes were dazzled, as he *s*, — „ 59
Long *s* Sir Bedivere Revolving many memories, — „ 269
those that *s* upon the hills behind Repeated— — „ *Ep.* 25
s, Leaning his horns into the neighbour field, — *Gardener's D.* 86
Holding the bush, to fix it back, she *s*, — „ 127
Half light, half shade, She *s*, — „ 141
to Mary's house, and *s* Upon the threshold. — *Dora* 110
and while we *s* like fools Embracing, — *Edwin Morris* 118
brothers of the weather *s* Stock-still — *Will Water.* 135
O and proudly *s* she up! — *Lady Clare* 77
He turn'd and kiss'd her where she *s*: — „ 82
STILL on the tower *s* the vane, — *The Letters* 1
wild hawk *s* with the down on his beak, — *Poet's Song* 11
and while he *s* on deck Waving, — *Enoch Arden* 243
there he *s* once more before her face, — „ 457
Her son, who *s* beside her tall and strong, — „ 756
There *s* a maiden near, Waiting to pass. — *The Brook* 204
S from his walls and wing'd his entry-gates — *Aylmer's Field* 18
That *s* from out a stiff brocade in which, — „ 204
under his own lintel *s* Storming with lifted hands, — „ 331
to the lychgate, where his chariot *s*, — „ 824
I *s* like one that had received a blow: — *Sea Dreams* 161
s out the breasts, The breasts of Helen, — *Lucretius* 60
in the presence room I *s* With Cyril — *Princess i* 51
There *s* a bust of Pallas for a sign, — „ 222
while They *s*, so rapt, we gazing, came a voice, — „ *ii* 318
saw The Lady Blanche's daughter where she *s*, — „ 321
So *s* that same fair creature at the door. — „ 329
There while we *s* beside the fount, — „ *iii* 23

Stood (*continued*) She *s* Among her maidens, higher by the head, *Princess iii* 178
s, Engirt with many a florid maiden-cheek, .. 349
Alone I *s* With Florian, cursing Cyril, .. *iv* 170
There *s* her maidens glimmeringly group'd .. 190
Lady Blanche erect *S* up and spake, .. 291
You *s* in your light and darken'd mine. .. 314
And then *s* up and spoke impetuously. .. 418
high above them *s* The placid marble Muses, .. 488
I *s* and seem'd to hear, As in a poplar grove .. *v* 12
storming in extremes, *S* for her cause, .. 177
high upon the palace Ida *s* With Psyche's babe .. *vi* 30
So *s* the unhappy mother open-mouth'd, .. 143
rising slowly from me, *s* Erect and silent, .. 151
But Ida *s* nor spoke, drain'd of her force .. 266
had you *s* by us, The roar that breaks the Pharos .. 338
in the centre *s* The common men with rolling eyes; .. 359
And there we saw Sir Walter where he *s*, .. *Con.* 81
now him, of those That *s* the nearest— ,, 93
Which *s* four-square to all the winds that blew! *Ode on Well.* 39
Where he greatly *s* at bay, .. 106
for Willy *s* like a rock. *Grandmother* 10
and *s* by the road at the gate. ,, 38
Willy *s* up like a man, ,, 45
I *s* among the silent statues, *The Daisy* 63
In the centre *s* A statue veil'd, *In Mem. ciii* 11
S up and answer'd 'I have felt.' ,, *cxxiv* 16
He *s* on the path a little aside; *Maud I xiii* 7
And *s* by her garden-gate; .. *xiv* 6
I thought as I *s*, if a hand, as white .. 17
And long by the garden lake I *s*, .. *xxii* 35
For front to front in an hour we *s*, ,, *II i* 23
And I *s* on a giant deck and mix'd my breath ,, *III vi* 34
Guinevere *S* by the castle walls to watch him pass; *Com. of Arthur* 48
Who *s* in silence near his throne, .. 277
'And near him *s* the Lady of the Lake, .. 283
S one who pointed toward the voice, .. 438
but the King *s* out in heaven, Crown'd. .. 443
his knights *S* round him, and rejoicing in his joy. .. 459
The Lady of the Lake *s*: all her dress Wept *Gareth and L.* 216
near it *s* The two that out of north .. 678
Hear me—this morn I *s* in Arthur's hall, .. 855
Who *s* a moment, ere his horse was brought, .. 934
The Lady Lyonors at a window *s*, ,, 1375
And *s* behind, and waited on the three. *Marr. of Geraint* 392
And Enid *s* aside to wait the event, *Geraint and E.* 153
When now they saw their bulwark fallen, *s*; .. 168
Was in a manner pleased, and turning, *s*. .. 456
While the great charger *s*, grieved like a man. .. 535
on his right *S*, all of massiest bronze: *Balin and Balan* 364
the one Who *s* beside thee even now, ,, 613
arose And *s* with folded hands and downward eyes *Merlin and V.* 69
Queen who *s* All glittering like May sunshine .. 87
and *s* Stiff as a viper frozen; .. 844
and *s*, A virtuous gentlewoman deeply wrong'd, .. 910
Lancelot, where he *s* beside the King. *Lancelot and E.* 85
she drew Nearer and *s*. .. 350
For silent, tho' he greeted her, she *s* .. 355
His honour rooted in dishonour *s*, .. 876
but deadly-pale *S* grasping what was nearest, .. 966
all the place whereon she *s* was green; .. 1200
There two *s* arm'd, and kept the door; ,, 1247
In our great hall there *s* a vacant chair, *Holy Grail* 167
And staring each at other like dumb men *S*, .. 194
And those that had not, *s* before the King, .. 724
and there, half-hidden by him, *s*, .. 754
there was none *S* near it but a lion on each side .. 817
Breast-high in that bright line of bracken *s*: *Pelleas and E.* 56
he *s* There on the castle-bridge once more, .. 442
here he *s*, and might have slain Me and thyself.' .. 491
But Percivale *s* near him and replied, .. 523
Rolling his eyes, a moment *s*, then spake: .. 581
And while they *s* without the doors, *Last Tournament* 113
there with gibes and flickering mockeries *S*, ,, 187
while he twangled little Dagonet *s* Quiet ,, 252

Stood (*continued*) moved slow-measure to my tune, Not *s* stockstill. *Last Tournament* 283
machicolated tower That *s* with open doors, .. 425
near me *s*, In fuming sulphur blue and green, .. 616
strong man-breasted things *s* from the sea, *Guinevere* 246
s before the Queen As tremulously as foam .. 363
near him the sad nuns with each a light *S*, .. 591
That *s* on a dark strait of barren land: *Pass. of Arthur* 178
That both his eyes were dazzled as he *s*, .. 227
Long *s* Sir Bedivere Revolving many memories, .. 437
They *s* before his throne in silence, .. 455
Were drunk into the inmost blue, we *s*, *Lover's Tale i* 309
near'd the bay, For there the Temple *s*. .. 339
and *s* A solid glory on her bright black hair; .. 366
Half-melted into thin blue air, *s* still .. 421
For bliss *s* round me like the light of Heaven,— .. 495
I seem'd the only part of Time *s* still, .. 573
forms which ever *s* Within the magic cirque .. *ii* 158
the man who *s* with me Stept gaily forward, .. *iii* 50
And I *s* stole beside the vacant bier. .. 58
Before the board, there paused and *s*, .. *iv* 307
I *s* upon the stairs of Paradise. *Sisters (E. and E.)* 144
Death while we *s* with the musket, *Def. of Lucknow* 16
s on each of the loftiest capes, *V. of Maeldune* 100
he *s*, nor join'd The Achæans— *Achilles over the T.* 15
S out before a darkness, crying 'Thebes, *Tiresias* 115
and the ship *s* still, and the skies were blue, *The Wreck* 115
ruin'd by *him*, by *him*, I *s* there, naked, amazed *Despair* 77
An' Dan *s* there for a minute, *Tomorrow* 22
s up strait as the Queen of the world— ,, 79
an' *s* By the claäy'd-oop pond, *Spinster's S's.* 23
I feel'd thy arm es I *s* wur a-creeäpin ,, 26
often I and Amy in the mouldering aisle have *s*, *Locksley H., Sixty* 31
There again I *s* to-day, .. 33
Here we *s* and claspt each other, .. 180
They rode, or they *s* at bay— *Heavy Brigade* 51
Ranged like a storm or *s* like a rock ,, 56
s stark by the dead; And behind him, *Dead Prophet* 19
wife and his child *s* by him in tears, ,, 57
An' then as I *s* i' the doorwaäy, *Owd Roä* 42
Where *s* the sheaf of Peace: *The Ring* 247
who were those that *s* between The tower .. 252
whose hand was that? they *s* So close together. ,, 257
Even from myself? stand? *s* . . . no more. *Romney's R.* 66
s Before the great Madonna-masterpieces ,, 85
kindled the pyre, and all *S* round it, *Death of Œnone* 66
But while we *s* rejoicing, I and thou, *Akbar's Dream* 182
An' ya *s* oop naäkt i' the beck, *Church-warden, etc.* 29

Stook (stuck) *S* to his taäil they did, *N. Farmer, N. S.* 30

Stool Perch'd like a crow upon a three-legg'd *s*, *Audley Court* 45
his foot was on a *s* Shaped as a dragon; *Last Tournament* 671
An' sattle their ends upo *s's* *Owd Roä* 24

Stoop *S's* at all game that wing the skies, *Rosalind* 4
To *s* the cowslip to the plains, ,, 16
The skies *s* down in their desire; *Fatima* 32
I could not *s* to such a mind. *L. C. V. de Vere* 20
Enormous elm-tree-boles did *s* and lean *D. of F. Women* 57
He *s's*—to kiss her—on his knee. *Day-Dm., Arrival* 30
The cloud may *s* from heaven and take the shape *Princess vii* 2
S down and seem to kiss me ere I die.' ,, 150
To *s* and kiss the tender little thumb, *Marr. of Geraint* 395
watch the time, and eagle-like *S* at thy will *Balin and Balan* 536
I said to her, 'A day for Gods to *s*,' *Lover's Tale i* 304
A clamorous cuckoo *s's* to meet her hand; *Prog. of Spring* 45

Stoop'd-Stoopt He *stoop'd* and clutch'd him, fair and good, *Will Water.* 133
And o'er her second father *stoopt* a girl, *Enoch Arden* 747
stoop'd To drench his dark locks in the gurgling wave *Princess iv* 186
Rise!' and *stoop'd* to updrag Melissa: .. 366
when a boy, you *stoop'd* to me From all high places, .. 429
My father *stoop'd*, re-father'd o'er my wounds. .. *vi* 129
She turn'd; she paused; She *stoop'd*; ,, *vii* 155
rode to Merlin's feet, Who *stoopt* and caught the babe, *Com. of Arthur* 385

Stoop'd-Stoopt (*continued*) and *stoop'd* With a low whinny toward the pair: *Geraint and E.* 755
sorrowing Lancelot should have *stoop'd* so low, *Lancelot and E.* 732
Stoopt, took, break seal, and read it; „ 1271
I *stoop'd*, I gather'd the wild herbs, *Lover's Tale i* 341
and death while we *stoopt* to the spade, *Def. of Lucknow* 16
dreamer *stoopt* and kiss'd her marble brow. *Locksley H., Sixty* 38
while I *stoopt* To take and kiss the ring. *The Ring* 131

Stopt The swallow *s* as he hunted the fly, *Poet's Song* 9
All of a sudden he *s*: *Grandmother* 41
S, and then with a riding whip *Maud I xiii* 18
when he *s* we long'd to hurl together, *Merlin and V.* 420

Store (s) then with what she brought Buy goods and *s's*— *Enoch Arden* 138
Bought Annie goods and *s's*, and set his hand „ 169
With shelf and corner for the goods and *s's*. „ 171
How best to help the slender *s*, *To F. D. Maurice* 37
Love, then, had hope of richer *s*: *In Mem. lxxxi* 5
We wish them *s* of happy days. „ *Con.* 84
With *s* of rich apparel, sumptuous fare, *Marr. of Geraint* 709
of whate'er The Future had in *s*: *Lover's Tale ii* 133

Store (verb) For some three suns to *s* and hoard myself, *Ulysses* 29

Stored all things in order *s*, *Palace of Art* 87
S in some treasure-house of mighty kings, *M. d'Arthur* 101
Dora *s* what little she could save, *Dora* 52
honeycomb of eloquence *S* from all flowers? *Edwin Morris* 27
I *s* it full of rich memorial: *Princess v* 391
In this wide hall with earth's invention *s*, *Ode Inter. Exhib.* 2
S in some treasure-house of mighty kings, *Pass. of Arthur* 269
summers are *s* in the sunlight still, *The Dawn* 19

Storied where sweetest sunlight falls Upon the *s* walls; *Ode to Memory* 86
with love far-brought From out the *s* Past, *Love thou thy land* 2

Storing *S* yearly little dues of wheat, *Lotos-Eaters, C. S.* 122

Stork Went by me, like a *s*: *Talking Oak* 56

Storm (*See also* **Thunder-storm**) as from the *s* Of running fires and fluid range *Supp. Confessions* 146
Whither in after life retired From brawling *s's*, *Ode to Memory* 112
And shatter, when the *s's* are black, *England and Amer.* 13
Henceforward squall nor *s* Could keep me *Gardener's D.* 190
I turn'd once more, close-button'd to the *s*; *Edwin Morris* 136
Battering the gates of heaven with *s's* of prayer, *St. S. Stylites* 7
shaken with a sudden *s* of sighs— *Locksley Hall* 27
But blessed forms in whistling *s's* *Sir Galahad* 59
S, such as drove her under moonless heavens *Enoch Arden* 547
like a *s* he came, And shook the house, and like a *s* he went. *Aylmer's Field* 215
Caught in a burst of unexpected *s*, „ 285
Sir Aylmer reddening from the *s* within, „ 322
but presently Wept like a *s*: „ 403
sheet-lightnings from afar, but fork'd Of the near *s*, „ 727
but when the wordy *s* Had ended, *Sea Dreams* 31
'*S* in the night! for thrice I heard the rain *Lucretius* 26
'*S*, and what dreams, ye holy Gods, „ 33
Balmier and nobler from her bath of *s*, „ 175
The green malignant light of coming *s*. *Princess iii* 132
mystic fire on a mast-head, Prophet of *s*: „ *iv* 275
Fluctuated, as flowers in *s*, some red, „ 482
On me, me, me, the *s* first breaks: „ 499
When *s* is on the heights, „ *v* 348
at which the *s* Of galloping hoofs bare on the ridge „ 488
Let our girls flit, Till the *s* die! „ *vi* 338
Tho' all the *s* of Europe on us break; *Third of Feb.* 14
s and blast Had blown the lake beyond his limit, *The Daisy* 70
And a *s* never wakes on the lonely sea, *The Islet* 33
a cloud in my heart, and a *s* in the air! *Window, Gone* 6
No is trouble and cloud and *s*, „ *No Answer* 8
The touch of change in calm or *s*; *In Mem. xvi* 6
O thou that after toil and *s* „ *xxxiii* 1
And lash with *s* the streaming pane? „ *lxxii* 4
The *s* their high-built organs make, „ *lxxxvii* 6
A pillar stedfast in the *s*, „ *cxiii* 12
The seeming prey of cyclic *s's*, „ *cxviii* 11
Well roars the *s* to those that hear A deeper voice across the *s*, „ *cxxvii* 3
should burst and drown with deluging *s's* *Maud II i* 42

Storm (*continued*) whatsoever *s's* May shake the world, *Com. of Arthur* 292
And lightnings play'd about it in the *s*, *Gareth and L.* 68
A censer, either worn with wind and *s*; „ 222
world's loud whisper breaking into *s*, *Marr. of Geraint* 27
Turn thy wild wheel thro' sunshine, *s*, and cloud; „ 348
Whose skirts are loosen'd by the breaking *s*, *Geraint and E.* 459
A *S* was coming, but the winds were still, *Merlin and V.* 1
A minstrel of Caerleon by strong *s* „ 9
s Brake on the mountain and I cared not for it. „ 502
And lash'd it at the base with slanting *s*; „ 635
dark wood grew darker toward the *s* In silence, „ 890
'Come from the *s*,' and having no reply, „ 895
(For now the *s* was close above them) „ 935
Till now the *s*, its burst of passion spent, „ 961
(Sea was her wrath, yet working after *s*) *Lancelot and E.* 1309
S at the top, and when we gain'd it, *s* Round us and death; *Holy Grail* 491
Spake but of sundry perils in the *s*; „ 761
upward-rushing *s* and cloud Of shriek and plume, *Last Tournament* 440
When that *s* of anger brake From Guinevere, *Guinevere* 361
Or wisely or unwisely, signs of *s*, *To the Queen ii* 49
mind Lies folded, often sweeps athwart in *s*— *Lover's Tale i* 50
S, sunset, glows and glories of the moon „ *ii* 110
my lost love Symbol'd in *s*. „ 185
sway and whirl Of the *s* dropt to windless calm, „ 207
and the *s* rushing over the down, *Rizpah* 6
when the *s* on the downs began, „ 71
A moonless night with *s*— *Sisters (E. and E.)* 96
bleat of a lamb in the *s* and the darkness without; *In the Child. Hosp.* 64
S at the Water-gate! *s* at the Bailey-gate! *s*, and it ran *Def. of Lucknow* 37
in days Of doubt and cloud and *s*, *Columbus* 156
the poplar and cypress unshaken by *s* *V. of Maeldune* 15
ridges drew the cloud and brake the *s* *Montenegro* 13
driven by *s* and sin and death to the ancient fold, *The Wreck* 2
I would hide from the *s* without, I would flee from the *s* within, „ 9
great *s* grew with a howl and a hoot „ 91
And he spoke not—only the *s*; till after a little, „ 103
the *s* went roaring above us, and he—was out of the *s*. „ 106
the *s* and the days went by, but I knew no more— „ 111
And gone—that day of the *s*— „ 148
She reels not in the *s* of warring words, *Ancient Sage* 70
The placid gleam of sunset after *s*! „ 133
But wirrah! the *s* that night— *Tomorrow* 23
Ranged like a *s* or stood like a rock *Heavy Brigade* 56
And glared at a coming *s*. *Dead Prophet* 24
s's Of Autumn swept across the city, *Demeter and P.* 70
A sound of anger like a distant *s*. *The Ring* 119
The *s*, you hear Far-off, is Muriel— „ 138
One year without a *s*, or even a cloud; „ 284
whom the *s* Had parted from his comrade „ 307
When the *s's* are blowing. *Forlorn* 6
When I was praying in a *s*— *Happy* 80
And bring or chase the *s*, *Mechanophilus* 14
S in the South that darkens the day! *Riflemen form!* 2
S of battle and thunder of war! „ 3
S, *S*, Riflemen form! (repeat) „ 5, 19
Ready, be ready against the *s*! (repeat) „ 6, 20
Ready, be ready to meet the *s*! (repeat) „ 13, 27

Storm-beaten With slow steps from out An old *s-b*, russet, *Gareth and L.* 1113

Storm'd *S* in orbs of song, a growing gale; *Vision of Sin* 25
and *s* At the Oppian law. *Princess vii* 123
S at with shot and shell (repeat) *Light Brigade* 22, 43

Stormier Fierier and *s* from restraining, *Balin and Balan* 229
For whenever a rougher gust might tumble a *s* wave, *The Wreck* 131

Storming *s* a hill-fort of thieves He got it; *Aylmer's Field* 225
under his own lintel stood *S* with lifted hands, „ 332
and *s* in extremes, Stood for her cause, *Princess v* 176
roughly set His Briton in blown seas and *s* showers, *Ode on Well.* 155

Stormless pass With all fair theories only made to gild A *s* summer.' *Princess ii* 234

Storm-strengthen'd of grain *S-s* on a windy site, *Gareth and L.* 692

Storm-worn A s-w signpost not to be read, Dead Prophet 17
Stormy In the s east-wind straining, L. of Shalott iv 1
It is a s season.' The Goose 8
It is a s morning.' „ 44
When down the s crescent goes, Sir Galahad 25
There must be s weather; Will Water. 54
overboard one s night He cast his body, The Voyage 79
As of some fire against a s cloud, Princess iv 384
'We fear, indeed, you spent a s time „ v 121
Morning arises s and pale, Maud I vi 1
Who in this s gulf have found a pearl „ xviii 42
To catch a friend of mine one s day; „ II v 85
Then like a s sunlight smiled Geraint, Geraint and E. 480
with all Its s crests that smoke against the skies, Lancelot and E. 484
And bluster into s sobs and say, „ 1067
thro' a s glare, a heat As from a seventimes-heated furnace, Holy Grail 842
years Have hollow'd out a deep and s strait Lover's Tale i 24
again the s surf Crash'd in the shingle: „ iii 53
'Come to us, O come, come' in the s red of a sky V. of Maeldune 98
S voice of France! Who dost not love our England— To Victor Hugo 8
spear and helmet tipt With s light as on a mast at sea, Tiresias 114
After all the s changes shall we find a changeless May? Locksley H., Sixty 156
Forward, let the s moment fly and mingle with the Past. „ 279
stood like a rock In the wave of a s day; Heavy Brigade 57
Muses cried with a s cry 'Send them no more, Dead Prophet 2
Like calming oil on all their s creeds, Akbar's Dream 160
Story (See also **Island-story**) make the name Of his vessel great in s, The Captain 19
—all the s of his house. Enoch Arden 704
Here is a s which in rougher shape Aylmer's Field 7
but as he told The s, storming a hill-fort „ 225
and so We forged a sevenfold s. Princess, Pro. 202
And here I give the s and the songs. „ 247
For so, my mother said, the s ran. „ i 11
And snowy summits old in s: „ iv 2
And yet to give the s as it rose, „ Con. 26
Till in all lands and thro' all human s Ode on Well. 223
All for a slanderous s, Grandmother 22
Hear the child's s.' Gareth and L. 39
Hear yet once more the s of the child. „ 100
dumbly speaks Your s, that this man loves you no more. Geraint and E. 329
And let the s of her dolorous voyage Lancelot and E. 1343
That s which the bold Sir Bedivere, Pass. of Arthur 1
A woful man (for so the s went) Lover's Tale i 379
I learnt the drearier s of his life; „ iv 147
then began the s of his love As here to-day, „ 354
I told your wayside s to my mother Sisters (E. and E.) 189
tell them all The s of my voyage, Columbus 12
Story (floor) And set in Heaven's third s, Will Water. 70
Stout (adj.) S, rosy, with his babe across his knees; Enoch Arden 746
'ye are overfine To mar s knaves with foolish courtesies:' Gareth and L. 733
And the s Prince bad him a loud good-night. Geraint and E. 361
that had need Of a good s lad at his farm; First Quarrel 18
Stout (s) To each his perfect pint of s, Will Water. 115
Stow'd Or s, when classic Canning died, „ 101
Straänge (strange) S an' cowd fur the time! Village Wife 21
S an' unheppen Miss Lucy! „ 100
S an' owd-farran'd the 'ouse, Owd Roä 21
Straät (straight) S as a pole an' cleän as a flower North. Cobbler 44
Straddling s on the butts While the wine ran: Guinevere 268
Straight (See also **Straät, Strait, Straït**) 'If s thy track, or if oblique, Two Voices 193
To the pale-green sea-groves s and high, The Merman 19
S, but as lissome as a hazel wand; The Brook 70
Should, as by miracle, grow s and fair— Aylmer's Field 676
For all we have power to see is a s staff bent in a pool; High. Pantheism 16
All round one finger pointed s, The Ring 453
Strain (s) quick lark's closest-caroll'd s's, Rosalind 10
An echo from a measured s, Miller's D. 66
Strain (s) (continued) Is this the manly s of Runnymede? Third of Feb. 34
I scarce could brook the s and stir In Mem. xv 12
A s to shame us 'keep you to yourselves; To the Queen ii 15
Strain (verb) cords that bind and s The heart Clear-headed Friend 4
Shudderest when I s my sight, Fatima 3
s to make an inch of room For their sweet selves, Lit. Squabbles 9
Strain'd A little in the late encounter s, Geraint and E. 158
thou hast seen me s And sifted to the utmost, Pelleas and E. 247
Straining In the stormy east-wind s, L. of Shalott iv 1
but s ev'n his uttermost Cast, Gareth and L. 1152
S his eyes beneath an arch of hand, Pass. of Arthur 464
Strait (adj.) Bound them by so s vows to his own self, Com. of Arthur 262
Went thro' the s and dreadful pass of death, „ 395
Strait (s) That stood on a dark s of barren land. M. d'Arthur 10
I'll serve you better in a s; Princess i 85
hovering o'er the dolorous s To the other shore, In Mem. lxxxiv 39
That stood on a dark s of barren land: Pass. of Arthur 178
years Have hollow'd out a deep and stormy s Lover's Tale i 24
wreaths of all that would advance, Beyond our s, To Victor Hugo 6
Strait (straight) stood up s as the Queen of the world— Tomorrow 79
Straït fur I'll looök my hennemy s i' the faäce, North. Cobbler 74
Strait-besieged being s-b By this wild king Princess, Pro. 36
Straiten'd (adj.) Cursed be the gold that gilds the s forehead of the fool! Locksley Hall 62
Straiten'd (verb) shackles of an old love s him, Lancelot and E. 875
Strait-laced S-l, but all-too-full in bud Talking Oak 59
Straitlier But s bound am I to bide with thee.' Gareth and L. 805
Strand (shore) as a ground-swell dash'd on the s, W. to Alexandra 23
Here on the Breton s! Maud II ii 29
fringe Of that great breaker, sweeping up the s, Com. of Arthur 387
He seem'd to pace the s of Brittany Last Tournament 407
Before Isolt of Brittany on the s, „ 589
Strand (thread) 'The dusky s of Death inwoven here Maud I xviii 60
Stranded For sure no gladlier does the s wreck Enoch Arden 828
Stranding s on an isle at morn Rich, „ 552
Strange (See also **Straänge**) A spring rich and s, Nothing will Die 22
The broken sheds look'd sad and s: Mariana 5
Like that s angel which of old, Clear-headed friend 24
Sudden glances, sweet and s, Madeline 5
With a music s and manifold, Dying Swan 29
At such s war with something good, Two Voices 302
shafts were blazon'd fair In diverse raiment s: Palace of Art 168
As in s lands a traveller walking slow, „ 277
You put s memories in my head. L. C. V. de Vere 26
O sweet and s it seems to me, May Queen, Con. 53
Our sons inherit us: our looks are s: Lotos-Eaters, C. S. 73
'Tis s that those we lean on most, To J. S. 9
Nothing comes to thee new or s. „ 74
Among new men, s faces, other minds.' M. d'Arthur 238
Like that s song I heard Apollo sing, Tithonus 62
Thro' sunny decads new and s, Day-Dm., L'Envoi 22
'So s it seems to me. Lady Clare 52
'That were s. What surname?' The Brook 211
she grieved In her s dream, she knew not why, Sea Dreams 230
She brought s news. „ 267
s was the sight to me; Princess, Pro. 54
S was the sight and smacking of the time; „ 89
And, yonder, shrieks and s experiments „ 235
An old and s affection of the house. „ i 13
On a sudden my s seizure came Upon me, „ iii 183
we give you, being s, A license: speak, „ 204
If that s Poet-princess with her grand Imaginations „ 273
'Ah, sad and s as in dark summer dawns „ iv 49
So sad, so s, the days that are no more. „ 53
and s experiences Unmeet for ladies. „ 158
you spent a stormy time With our s girl: „ v 122
And how the s betrothment was to end: „ 474
That all things grew more tragic and more s; „ vi 23
nor seem'd it s that soon He rose up whole, „ vii 64
I have heard Of your s doubts: „ 336
I moved as in a s diagonal, „ Con. 27
For now so s do these things seem, In Mem. xiii 15
I should not feel it to be s. „ xiv 20
But thou art turn'd to something s, „ xli 5
The days that grow to something s, „ lxxi 11

Strange (*continued*) and *s* Was love's dumb cry defying change — *In Mem. xcv* 26
S friend, past, present, and to be; — „ *cxxix* 9
S, that I hear two men, — *Maud I vii* 13
How *s* was what she said, — „ *xix* 34
S, that I felt so gay, *S*, that *I* tried to-day — „ *xx* 1
S, that the mind, when fraught With a passion — „ *II ii* 58
terror grew Of that *s* bright and dreadful thing, — *Marr. of Geraint* 616
And for my *s* petition I will make Amends — „ 817
ye surely have endured *S* chances here alone;' — *Geraint and E.* 810
there be two *s* knights Who sit near Camelot — *Balin and Balan* 10
A *s* knee rustle thro' her secret reeds, — „ 354
'To what request for what *s* boon,' — *Merlin and V.* 264
Boon, ay, there was a boon, one not so *s*— — „ 287
And take this boon so *s* and not so *s*.' — „ 310
'O not so *s* as my long asking it, Not yet so *s* as you yourself are *s*, Nor half so *s* as that dark mood of yours. — „ 312
nothing wild or *s*, Or seeming shameful— — „ 860
—this, however *s*, My latest: — *Lancelot and E.* 1112
An end to this! A *s* one! — „ 1223
And the *s* sound of an adulterous race, — *Holy Grail* 80
And crimson in the belt a *s* device, — „ 154
And carven with *s* figures; — „ 169
So *s*, and rich, and dim; — „ 342
Among the *s* devices of our kings; — „ 730
but in me lived a sin So *s*, — „ 773
S as to some old prophet might have seem'd — *Pelleas and E.* 51
and *s* knights From the four winds came in: — „ 147
Then ran across her memory the *s* rhyme — *Last Tournament* 131
he heard *S* music, and he paused, and turning— — *Guinevere* 239
Among new men, *s* faces, other minds.' — *Pass. of Arthur* 406
All—all but one; and *s* to me, and sweet, Sweet thro' *s* years to know that — *Lover's Tale i* 243
And Hate is *s* beneath the roof of Love. — „ 779
Made *s* division of its suffering With her, — „ *ii* 128
Wonder'd at some *s* light in Julian's eyes — „ *iv* 205
such a feast So rich, so *s*, and stranger ev'n than rich, — „ 211
I never yet beheld a thing so *s*, Sad, sweet, and *s* together— — „ 303
thence Down to this last *s* hour in his own hall; — „ 358
S fur to goä fur to think what saäilors — *North. Cobbler* 4
On whom I brought a *s* unhappiness, — *Sisters (E. and E.)* 89
and for a face Gone in a moment—*s*. — „ 94
Selfish, *s*! What dwarfs are men! — „ 198
The Lord had sent this bright, *s* dream to me — *Columbus* 91
With some *s* hope to see the nearer God. — *Tiresias* 29
The *s* misfeaturing mask that I saw so amazed me, — *The Wreck* 117
I touch'd my limbs, the limbs Were *s* not mine— — *Ancient Sage* 235
S! She used to shun the wailing babe, — *The Ring* 357
Strangeness feels a glimmering *s* in his dream. — *The Brook* 216
Stranger (adj. and s) Two *s's* meeting at a festival: — *Circumstance* 3
There strode a *s* to the door, (repeat) — *The Goose* 3, 39
And God forget the *s*!' — „ 56
s's at my hearth Not welcome, — *Lucretius* 158
The first-fruits of the *s*: — *Princess ii* 44
Moreover 'seize the *s's*' is the cry. — „ *iv* 220
And Love has led thee to the *s* land, — *W. to Marie Alex.* 31
Will shelter one of *s* race. — *In Mem. cii* 4
And answer'd, 'Pardon me, O *s* knight; — *Marr. of Geraint* 286
Queen demanded as by chance 'Know ye the *s* woman?' — *Merlin and V.* 129
Flush'd slightly at the slight disparagement Before the *s* knight, — *Lancelot and E.* 235
landscape grow Familiar to the *s's* child; — *In Mem. ci* 20
Like *s's'* voices here they sound, — „ *civ* 9
We live within the *s's* land, — „ *cv* 3
Why mockest thou the *s* that hath been — *Gareth and L.* 283
A *s* meeting them had surely thought — *Geraint and E.* 34
Shriek'd to the *s* 'Slay not a dead man!' — „ 779
(for Arthur's knights Were hated *s's* in the hall) — *Balin and Balan* 352
I bid the *s* welcome. — *Merlin and V.* 270
Yet *s's* to the tongue, and with blunt stump — *Last Tournament* 66
A *s* as welcome as Satan— — *Charity* 26
Stranger (compar.) nor *s* seem'd that hearts So gentle, — *Princess vii* 66

Stranger (compar.) (*continued*) such a feast So rich, so strange, and *s* ev'n than rich, — *Lover's Tale iv* 211
And *s* yet, at one end of the hall — „ 213
S than earth has ever seen; — *The Ring* 38
Strange-statued under the *s-s* gate, Where Arthur's wars — *Lancelot and E.* 800
Strangled felt, despite his mail, *S*, — *Gareth and L.* 1152
and then A *s* titter, — *Princess v* 16
my *s* vanity Utter'd a stifled cry— — *Sisters (E. and E.)* 199
and a ray red as Blood Glanced on the *s* face— — *Bandit's Death* 32
Strata dip of certain *s* to the North. — *Princess iii* 170
Straw lance Broken, and his Excalibur a *s*.' — *Last Tournament* 88
cotch'd 'er death o' cowd that night, poor soul, i' the *s*. — *Owd Roä* 114
Stray Beyond the bounding hill to *s*, — *In Mem. lxxxix* 30
In lands where not a memory *s's*, — „ *civ* 10
Stray'd Thy feet have *s* in after hours — „ *cii* 14
Nor ever *s* beyond the pale: — *Holy Grail* 21
Seeing I never *s* beyond the cell, — „ 628
Streak (s) (*See also* **Shadow-streak**) solitary morning smote The *s's* of virgin snow. — *Œnone* 56
Now fades the last long *s* of snow, — *In Mem. cxv* 1
gay with gold In *s's* and rays, — *Gareth and L.* 911
winds Laid the long night in silver *s's* and bars, — *Lover's Tale ii* 112
The first gray *s* of earliest summer-dawn, — *Ancient Sage* 220
Streak (verb) white vapour *s* the crowned towers — *Princess vii* 344
But pure as lines of green that *s* the white — „ *v* 196
Streak'd (*See also* **Silvery-streak'd**) *s* or starr'd at intervals With falling brook — *Lover's Tale i* 404
Stream (s) (*See also* **Atom-stream, Gulf-stream, Sthrame**)
WHEN will the *s* be aweary of flowing — *Nothing will Die* 1
The *s* flows, The wind blows, — „ 9
The *s* will cease to flow; — *All Things will Die* 9
The *s's* through many a lilied row — *The winds, etc.* 5
A clear *s* flowing with a muddy one, — *Isabel* 30
And the far-off *s* is dumb, — *The Owl i* 3
The leaping *s*, the very wind, — *Rosalind* 14
Like two *s's* of incense free From one censer — *Eleänore* 58
The broad *s* in his banks complaining, — *L. of Shalott iv* 3
The broad *s* bore her far away, — „ 17
the babble of the *s* Fell, and, without, — *Mariana in the S.* 51
'Who, rowing hard against the *s*, — *Two Voices* 211
Like those long mosses in the *s*. — *Miller's D.* 48
Beside the mill-wheel in the *s*, — „ 167
Between the loud *s* and the trembling stars. — *Œnone* 219
like a downward smoke, the slender *s* — *Lotos-Eaters* 8
A land of *s's*! some, like a downward smoke, — „ 10
in the *s* the long-leaved flowers weep, — „ *C. S.* 10
How sweet it were, hearing the downward *s*, — „ 54
A league of grass, wash'd by a slow broad *s*, — *Gardener's D.* 40
A single *s* of all her soft brown hair — „ 128
Night slid down one long *s* of sighing wind, — „ 267
In many *s's* to fatten lower lands, — *Golden Year* 34
And all the long-pent *s* of life — *Day-Dm., Revival* 15
burst away In search of *s* or fount, — *Enoch Arden* 635
Not by the well-known *s* and rustic spire, — *The Brook* 188
Bright with the sun upon the *s* beyond: — *Sea Dreams* 97
drifting up the *s* In fancy, till I slept again, — „ 108
Before two *s's* of light from wall to wall, — *Princess ii* 473
s's that float us each and all To the issue, — „ *iv* 70
'I stagger in the *s*: — „ *vi* 321
I strove against the *s* and all in vain: — „ *vii* 12
The shimmering glimpses of a *s*; — „ *Con.* 46
Who let the turbid *s's* of rumour flow — *Ode on Well.* 181
ALL along the valley, *s* that flashest white, — *V. of Cauteretz* 1
many a fire between the ships and *s* — *Spec. of Iliad* 17
The sound of *s's* that swift or slow — *In Mem. xxxv* 10
A secret sweetness in the *s*, — „ *lxiv* 20
We talk'd: the *s* beneath us ran, — „ *lxxxix* 43
On winding *s* or distant sea; — „ *cxv* 12
The market boat is on the *s*, — „ *cxxi* 13
With never an end to the *s* of passing feet, — *Maud II v* 11
the *s* Full, narrow; this a bridge of single arc — *Gareth and L.* 907
and in the *s* beneath him, shone Immingled — „ 935
hoof of his horse slipt in the *s*, the *s* Descended, — „ 1046

Stream (s) (*continued*) Well hast thou done; for all the s is freed, *Gareth and L.* 1267
They hoped to slay him somewhere on the s, „ 1419
And slipt and fell into some pool or s, *Lancelot and E.* 214
to that s whereon the barge, Pall'd all its length .. 1141
of Arthur's palace toward the s, They met, .. 1178
and down they flash'd, and smote the s. .. 1235
barge that brought her moving down, Far-off, a blot upon the s, „ 1392
I walking to and fro beside a s *Holy Grail* 592
served with choice from air, land, s, and sea, *Pelleas and E.* 149
as a s that spouting from a cliff Fails in mid air, *Guinevere* 608
The s of life, one s, one life, one blood, *Lover's Tale i* 239
As mountain s's Our bloods ran free: .. 326
a s Flies with a shatter'd foam along the chasm. „ 382
s. Forth issuing from his portals in the crag „ 429
perchance of s's Running far on within „ 522
the sound Of the loud s was pleasant, „ *ii* 35
lest the s should issue pure. *Locksley H., Sixty* 144
And borne along by that full s of men, *St. Telemachus* 43
Stream (verb) A thousand suns will s on thee, *A Farewell* 13
S's o'er a rich ambrosial ocean isle, *Milton* 14
And crowds that s from yawning doors, *In Mem. lxx* 9
In the long breeze that s's to thy delicious East, *Maud I xviii* 16
S's thro' the twelve great battles of our King. *Holy Grail* 250
S's like a cloud, man-shaped, *To the Queen ii* 40
And o'er thee s's the rain, *Pref. Poem Broth. Son.* 14
Stream'd s Upon the mooned domes aloof In inmost Bagdat, *Arabian Nights* 126
Across the mountain s below In misty folds, *Palace of Art* 34
S onward, lost their edges, *D. of F. Women* 50
And, s thro' many a golden bar, *Day-Dm., Depart.* 15
The vine s out to follow, *Amphion* 46
How swiftly s ye by the bark! *The Voyage* 50
And in we s Among the columns, *Princess ii* 434
I likewise, and in groups they s away. „ *Con.* 105
S to the peak, and mingled with the haze *Com. of Arthur* 435
half the pearls away, S from it still; *Lancelot and E.* 808
S thro' my cell a cold and silver beam, *Holy Grail* 116
And all the pavement s with massacre: *Last Tournament* 477
Streamer Shot like a s of the northern morn, *M. d'Arthur* 139
Shot like a s of the northern morn, *Pass. of Arthur* 307
Streaming (*See also* **Down-streaming**) Forth s from a braid of pearl: *Day-Dm., Sleep. B.* 6
The torrent vineyard s fell To meet the sun *The Daisy* 10
And lash with storm the s pane? *In Mem. lxxii* 4
On leagues of odour s far, „ *lxxxvi* 14
And high in heaven the s cloud, „ *Con.* 107
—all her bright hair s down— *Lancelot and E.* 1156
people, from the high door s, brake Disorderly, „ 1347
hill and wood Went ever s by him till the gloom, *Pelleas and E.* 548
Up or down the s wind? *Rosalind* 9
In many a s torrent back, *England and Amer.* 14
What sequel? S eyes and breaking hearts? *Love and Duty* 2
Struck out the s mountain-side, *Lucretius* 29
And down the s crystal dropt; *Princess vii* 165
Here, in s London's central roar. *Ode on Well.* 9
Hath left crag-carven o'er the s Gelt— *Gareth and L.* 1203
grayly draped With s grass, appear'd, *Balin and Balan* 333
and thro' the gap Glimmer'd the s scud: *Holy Grail* 682
Crook and turn upon itself in many a backward s curve. *Locksley H., Sixty* 236
and aloft the glare Flies s, *Achilles over the T.* 12
And s and shining on Silent river, *Merlin and the G.* 51
Streamlet For us the same cold s curl'd *In Mem. lxxix* 9
Streeät (street) yon laädy a-steppin' along the s, *North. Cobbler* 107
Street (*See also* **Shtreet, Streeät**) till noon no foot should pace the s, *Godiva* 39
The s's are dumb with snow. *Sir Galahad* 52
Till, where the s grows straiter, *Will Water.* 142
He pass'd by the town and out of the s, *Poet's Song* 2
long s climbs to one tall-tower'd mill; *Enoch Arden* 5
narrow s that clamber'd toward the mill. .. 60
From distant corners of the s they ran .. 349
The climbing s, the mill, the leafy lanes, .. 607

Z

Street (*continued*) Then down the long s having slowly stolen, *Enoch Arden* 682
For Philip's dwelling fronted on the s, .. 731
All down the long and narrow s he went .. 795
I mind him coming down the s; „ 847
'yesterday I met him suddenly in the s, *Sea Dreams* 146
then my eyes Pursued him down the s, „ 165
A little s half garden and half house; *Princess i* 214
heave and thump A league of s in summer solstice down, .. *iii* 128
We cross'd the s and gain'd a petty mound .. *iv* 557
brawl Their rights or wrongs like potherbs in the s. .. *v* 459
With lifted hand the gazer in the s. *Ode on Well.* 22
Welcome her, thundering cheer of the s! *W. to Alexandra* 7
Till, in a narrow s and dim, *The Daisy* 22
Here in the long unlovely s, *In Mem. vii* 2
On the bald s breaks the blank day. .. 12
The field, the chamber and the s, .. *viii* 11
The s's were fill'd with joyful sound, .. *xxxi* 10
The s's were black with smoke and frost, .. *lxix* 3
I smell the meadow in the s; .. *cxix* 4
There where the long s roars, „ *cxxiii* 3
At the head of the village s, *Maud I vi* 10
For only once, in the village s, .. *xiii* 26
In the chamber or the s, .. *II iv* 83
I loathe the squares and s's, .. 92
Only a yard beneath the s, „ *v* 7
Took horse, descended the slope s, and past *Gareth and L.* 662
Gareth rode Down the slope s, „ 700
Beheld the long s of a little town *Marr. of Geraint* 242
And down the long s riding wearily, „ 254
On a sudden, many a voice along the s, *Geraint and E.* 270
That glance of theirs, but for the s, *Merlin and V.* 105
As the poach'd filth that floods the middle s, „ 798
Met foreheads all along the s *Holy Grail* 344
in middle s the Queen, Who rode by Lancelot, „ 355
from over the breadth of a s, *Def. of Lucknow* 23
and, yelling with the yelling s, *Locksley H., Sixty* 135
maidens by the thousand on the s. „ 220
would it matter so much if I came on the s? *Charity* 8
Streetward To fit their little s sitting-room *Enoch Arden* 170
Streetway a s hung with folds of pure White samite, *Last Tournament* 140
Strength The unsunn'd freshness of my s, *Supp. Confessions* 140
MINE be the s of spirit, *Mine be the strength* 1
Than cry for s, remaining weak, *Two Voices* 95
'What, is not this my place of s,' *Palace of Art* 233
With all my s I pray'd for both, *May Queen, Con.* 31
S came to me that equall'd my desire. *D. of F. Women* 230
s of some diffusive thought Hath time *You ask me, why, etc.* 15
A slow-develop'd s awaits Completion *Love thou thy land* 57
We are not now that s which in old days *Ulysses* 66
that sin against the s of youth! *Locksley Hall* 59
My s is as the s of ten, *Sir Galahad* 3
aid me, give me s Not to tell her, *Enoch Arden* 785
and truth and love are s, *Aylmer's Field* 365
I wonder'd at her s, and ask'd her of it: *Sea Dreams* 113
He took advantage of his s to be First in the field: *Princess ii* 152
O fall'n at length that tower of s *Ode on Well.* 38
What Roman s Turbìa show'd In ruin, *The Daisy* 5
Corrupts the s of heaven-descended Will, *Will* 11
And in my grief a s reserved. *In Mem. lxxxv* 52
He fought his doubts and gather'd s, .. *xcvi* 13
The maidens gather'd s and grace „ *ciii* 27
Blow trumpet! live the s and die the lust! *Com. of Arthur* 492
thro' that s the King Drew in the petty princedoms .. 516
Have s and wit, in my good mother's hall *Gareth and L.* 12
That s of anger thro' mine arms, „ 948
same s which threw the Morning Star „ 1108
As closing in himself the s of ten, „ 1339
'Fool, for thou hast, men say, the s of ten, „ 1387
And s against all odds, and what the King *Balin and Balan* 183
they lifted up Their eager faces, wondering at the s, *Merlin and V.* 133
and waste the spiritual s Within us, *Holy Grail* 35
said he, 'but men With s and will to right the wrong'd, „ 309
may count The yet-unbroken s of all his knights, „ 326
for a s Was in us from the vision, „ 333
And in the s of this I rode, „ 476

Strength (*continued*) and in the *s* of this Come victor. *Holy Grail* 480
S of heart And might of limb, *Last Tournament* 197
chance and craft and *s* in single fights, *Pass. of Arthur* 106
image, like a charm of light and *s* Upon the waters, *Lover's Tale i* 91
Fierce in the *s* of far descent, a stream „ 382
Shorn of its *s*, into the sympathy Of that small bay, „ 434
With my life, love, soul, spirit, and heart and *s*. „ 460
In confidence of unabated *s*, „ 511
when *s* is shock'd With torment, „ *ii* 150
Strong with the *s* of the race to command, *Def. of Lucknow* 47
and the *s* To mould it into action pure as theirs. *Tiresias* 128
That old *s* and constancy Which has made your fathers great *Open. I. and C. Exhib.* 14
Trunk and bough, Naked *s*. *The Oak* 15
A sudden *s* from heaven, *St. Telemachus* 56

Strengthen *S* me, enlighten me! (repeat) *Ode to Memory* 5, 43, 122

Strengthen'd *See* **Storm-strengthen'd**

Stretch The garden *s'es* southward. *Gardener's D.* 115
I felt my veins *S* with fierce heat; *Princess v* 538
I *s* lame hands of faith, and grope, *In Mem. lv* 17
But free to *s* his limbs in lawful fight, *Geraint and E.* 754
at length we began to be weary, to sigh, and to *s* and yawn, *V. of Maeldune* 91

Stretch'd *S* wide and wild the waste enormous marsh *Ode to Memory* 101
s out beneath the pine. *Lotos-Eaters, C. S.* 99
lad *s* out And babbled for the golden seal, *Dora* 134
his long arms *s* as to grasp a flyer: *Aylmer's Field* 588
jewels five-words long That on the *s* forefinger of all Time Sparkle *Princess ii* 378
Thereat the Lady *s* a vulture throat, „ *iv* 363
She *s* her arms and call'd Across the tumult „ 496
arms *S* under all the cornice and upheld: *Gareth and L.* 219
drunkard, as he *s* from horse To strike him, *Last Tournament* 459
she *s* out her arms and cried aloud 'Oh Arthur!' *Guinevere* 606
—*s* my hands As if I saw her; *The Ring* 116

Stretching A bounded field, nor *s* far; *In Mem. xlvi* 14
Lets down his other leg, and *s*, *Gareth and L.* 1186

Strew *See* **Strow**

Strewn *S* in the entry of the moaning cave; *Lover's Tale iii* 2

Stricken (*See also* **Awe-stricken, Horror-stricken, Panic-stricken, Spear-stricken, Sun-stricken, Well-stricken, Wonder-stricken**) And, *s* by an angel's hand, *Sir Galahad* 69
And out of *s* helmets sprang the fire. *Princess v* 495
Was cancell'd, *s* thro' with doubt. *In Mem. xcv* 44
knave-knight, well *s*, O good knight-knave— *Gareth and L.* 1135
then were I *s* blind That minute, *Lancelot and E.* 426
With all her damsels, he was *s* mute; *Pelleas and E.* 251
And have but *s* with the sword in vain; *Pass. of Arthur* 23
I might have *s* a lusty stroke for him, *Sir J. Oldcastle* 69
I WAS the chief of the race—he had *s* my father dead— *V. of Maeldune* 1

Stride (s) He parted, with great *s's* among his dogs. *Godiva* 31
Abate the *s*, which speaks of man, *Princess ii* 429
the Prince, as Enid past him, fain To follow, strode a *s*, *Marr. of Geraint* 376

Stride (verb) hard heir *s's* about their lands, *In Mem. xc* 15

Stridest warrior-wise thou *s* thro' his halls *Last Tournament* 517

Striding now *s* fast, and now Sitting awhile *Lover's Tale iv* 87

Strife To hear the murmur of the *s*, *Margaret* 23
'Waiting to strive a happy *s*, *Two Voices* 130
The flattery and the *s*, *D. of F. Women* 148
Ev'n now we hear with inward *s* *Love thou thy land* 53
pulsation that I felt before the *s*, *Locksley Hall* 109
The maid and page renew'd their *s*, *Day-Dm., Revival* 13
Half fearful that, with self at *s*, *Will Water.* 161
'Help us from famine And plague and *s*! *The Victim* 10
To point the term of human *s*, *In Mem. l* 14
Are God and Nature then at *s*, „ *lv* 5
That loved to handle spiritual *s*, „ *lxxxv* 54
And ancient forms of party *s*; „ *cvi* 14
To fruitful *s's* and rivalries of peace— *Ded. of Idylls* 38
And see my dear lord wounded in the *s*, *Marr. of Geraint* 103
In the crash of the cannonades and the desperate *s*; *The Revenge* 78
slain thy fathers in war or in single *s*, *V. of Maeldune* 121
weary was I of the travel, the trouble, the *s* and the sin, „ 129

Strife (*continued*) Theirs that so often in *S* with their enemies *Batt. of Brunanburh* 18

Strike (*See also* **Spank**) grow awry From roots which *s* so deep? *Supp. Confessions* 78
God would move And *s* the hard, hard rock, „ 116
And strongly *s* to left and right, *Kate* 27
Shadows thou dost *s*, Embracing cloud, *Two Voices* 194
Shall *s* within thy pulses, like a God's, *Œnone* 162
As when a great thought *s's* along the brain, *D. of F. Women* 43
I sought to *s* Into that wondrous track of dreams „ 278
Would *s*, and firmly, and one stroke: *Love thou thy land* 92
earth feed thy branchy root, That under deeply *s's*! *Talking Oak* 274
till he madly *s's* Against it, and beats out his weary life. *Enoch Arden* 729
S thro' a finer element of her own? *Aylmer's Field* 579
when she *s's* thro' the thick blood Of cattle, *Lucretius* 98
a noiseless riot underneath *S's* thro' the wood, „ 186
And *s's* him dead for thine and thee. *Princess iv* 584
Stir in me as to *s*: „ *v* 268
Fight and fight well: *s* and *s* home. „ 409
shadowing down the champaign till it *s's* „ 526
The tops shall *s* from star to star, „ *vi* 57
Look up, and let thy nature *s* on mine, „ *vii* 351
Should *s* a sudden hand in mine, *In Mem. xiv* 11
The sunbeam *s's* along the world: „ *xv* 8
That *s's* by night a craggy shelf, „ *xvi* 13
And *s* his being into bounds, „ *Con.* 124
And *s*, if he could, were it but with his *Maud I i* 52
Arise, my God, and *s*, for we hold Thee just, „ *II i* 45
S dead the whole weak race of venomous worms, „ 46
Suddenly *s* on a sharper sense For a shell, „ *ii* 63
Then to *s* him and lay him low, „ *v* 90
'Take thou and *s*! *Com. of Arthur* 307
'*S* for the King and live! „ 488
'*S* for the King and die! „ 494
Accursed, who *s's* nor lets the hand be seen! *Gareth and L.* 435
Sun Heaved up a ponderous arm to *s* the fifth, „ 1045
so Gareth seem'd to *s* Vainly, „ 1133
I have prophesied—*S*, thou art worthy of the Table Round— „ 1138
S—*s*—the wind will never change again.' „ 1140
Lancelot thro' his warm blood felt Ice *s*, „ 1399
At once without remorse to *s* her dead, *Geraint and E.* 109
dawn ascending lets the day *S* where it clung: „ 693
tongues he saw not whence, *S's* from behind. *Balin and Balan* 131
His arm half rose to *s* again, but fell: „ 223
I yet should *s* upon a sudden means To dig, *Merlin and V.* 659
placed where morning's earliest ray Might *s* it, *Lancelot and E.* 6
Set lance in rest, *s* spur, suddenly move, „ 456
I fear me, that will *s* my blossom dead. „ 971
Then will I *s* at him and *s* him down, „ 1070
Give me good fortune, I will *s* him dead, „ 1071
S down the lusty and long practised knight, „ 1360
S from the sea; and from the star there shot *Holy Grail* 529
This light that *s's* his eyeball is not light, „ 913
Down! *s* him! put my hate into your strokes, *Pelleas and E.* 228
No men to *s*? Fall on him all at once, „ 268
and he call'd, 'I *s* upon thy side— „ 279
drunkard, as he stretch'd from horse To *s* him, *Last Tournament* 460
What rights are his that dare not *s* for them? „ 527
Where I must *s* against the man they call *Guinevere* 572
and *s* him dead, and meet myself Death, „ 575
stroke That *s's* them dead is as my death to me. *Pass. of Arthur* 74
thrills of bliss That *s* across the soul in prayer, *Lover's Tale i* 364
hemlock, Brow-high, did *s* my forehead as I past; „ *ii* 19
live to fight again and to *s* another blow.' *The Revenge* 95
I swore I would *s* off his head. *V. of Maeldune* 2
let thine own hand *s* Thy youthful pulses *Tiresias* 156
hand points five—O me—it *s's* the hour— *The Flight* 94
'I will *s*' said he 'The stars with head sublime,' *Epilogue* 46
aiming at an all but hopeless mark To *s* it, struck; *The Ring* 347
S upward thro' the shadow; „ 372
Thou wilt *s* Thy glory thro' the day. *Doubt and Prayer* 14

Strikest but thou *s* a strong stroke, *Gareth and L.* 877
Ay, knave, because thou *s* as a knight, „ 1020

Strikin' an' theere—it be s height— Spinster's S's. 114
waäit till tha 'ëars it be s the hour. Owd Roä 18
Striking (See also **Strikin'**) blow Before him, s on my brow. Fatima 25
There rose a noise of s clocks, Day-Dm., Revival 2
Now s on huge stumbling-blocks of scorn Aylmer's Field 538
s with her glance, The mother, me, the child; Princess vi 152
Struck for the throne, and s found his doom. Com. of Arthur 325
when I watch'd thee s on the bridge Gareth and L. 992
watch his mightful hand s great blows At caitiffs Marr. of Geraint 95
And strongly s out her limbs awoke; Geraint and E. 380
beast seeking to help herself By s at her better, Merlin and V. 499
And over hard and soft, s the sod Pelleas and E. 498
S the last stroke with Excalibur, Pass. of Arthur 168
Thunderless lightnings s under sea To the Queen ii 12
S the hospital wall, crashing thro' it, Def. of Lucknow 18
String (See also **Bow-string, Leading-strings**) Shall it not be scorn to me to harp on such a moulder'd s? Locksley Hall 147
But send it slackly from the s; In Mem. lxxxvii 26
I cannot all command the s's; " lxxxviii 10
and sometimes touches but one s That quivers, Lover's Tale i 17
coostom flitted awaäy like a kite wi' a brokken s. North. Cobbler 28
Strip Shall s a hundred hollows bare of Spring, Princess vi 65
shall we s him there Your lover? Geraint and E. 488
blacksmith 'e s's me the thick ov 'is airm, North. Cobbler 85
s your own foul passions bare; Locksley H., Sixty 141
Stripe Blackening against the dead-green s's Pelleas and E. 554
The last long s of waning crimson gloom, Ancient Sage 221
Striped dropping bitter tears against his brow S with dark blood: M. d'Arthur 212
dropping bitter tears against a brow S with dark blood: Pass. of Arthur 380
Stripling the s's!—for their sport!—I tamed my leopards: Princess v 399
'The years that made the s wise Ancient Sage 111
Stript our long walks were s as bare as brooms, Princess, Pro. 184
S from the three dead wolves of woman born Geraint and E. 94
entering barr'd her door, S off the case, Lancelot and E. 16
meekly rose the maid, S off the case, " 979
His friends had s him bare, Dead Prophet 14
Strive s To reconcile me with thy God. Supp. Confessions 101
'Waiting to s a happy strife, Two Voices 130
And s and wrestle with thee till I die: St. S. Stylites 119
strong in will To s, to seek, to find, Ulysses 70
But for one hour, O Love, I s To keep In Mem. xxxv 6
When on the gloom I s to paint The face I know; " lxx 2
To s, to fashion, to fulfil— " cxiii 7
s Again for glory, while the golden lyre Tiresias 179
Striven 'I cannot hide that some have s, Two Voices 208
These two have s half the day, In Mem. cii 17
With sword we have not s; Gareth and L. 1264
lily maid had s to make him cheer, Lancelot and E. 327
Stroäk (stroke) Naäy—let ma s tha down Spinster's S's. 53
Stroäkin (stroking) Ye was s ma down wi' the 'air, " 19
Strode There s a stranger to the door, (repeat) The Goose 3, 39
So s he back slow to the wounded King. M. d'Arthur 65
And so s back slow to the wounded King. " 112
But the other swiftly s from ridge to ridge, " 181
where he s About the hall, among his dogs, Godiva 16
S from the porch, tall and erect again. Aylmer's Field 825
S in, and claim'd their tribute as of yore. Com. of Arthur 506
Then s a good knight forward, Gareth and L. 364
Sir Gareth s, and saw without the door " 676
Prince, as Enid past him, fain To follow, s a stride, Marr. of Geraint 376
s the brute Earl up and down his hall, Geraint and E. 712
stall'd his horse, and s across the court, Balin and Balan 341
shook his hair, s off, and buzz'd abroad Lancelot and E. 722
So s he back slow to the wounded King. Pass. of Arthur 233
And so s back slow to the wounded King. " 280
But the other swiftly s from ridge to ridge, " 349
Stroke (See also **Sabre-stroke, Stroäk, Sword-stroke**)
'Then dying of a mortal s, Two Voices 154
Would strike, and firmly, and one s: Love thou thy land 92
A s of cruel sunshine on the cliff, Princess iv 524
mutual pardon ask'd and given For s and song, " v 47
With s on s the horse and horseman, came " 523
two-cell'd heart beating, with one full s, Life.' " vii 307
Stroke (continued) answering now my random s With fruitful cloud In Mem. xxxix 2
Struck for himself an evil s; Maud II i 21
but thou strikest a strong s, For strong thou art Gareth and L. 877
one s Laid him that clove it grovelling on the ground. " 971
four s's they struck With sword, and these were mighty; " 1042
But with one s Sir Gareth split the skull. " 1404
Short fits of prayer, at every s a breath. Geraint and E. 155
God's mercy, what a s was there! Lancelot and E. 24
For twenty s's of the blood, " 720
When have I stinted s in foughten field? Holy Grail 860
strike him! put my hate into your s's, Pelleas and E. 228
the s That strikes them dead is as my death to me. Pass. of Arthur 73
Striking the last s with Excalibur, " 168
I might have stricken a lusty s for him, Sir J. Oldcastle 69
Not one s firm. Romney's R. 115
Rang the s, and sprang the blood, The Tourney 9
Stroked Sat on his knee, s his gray face Lancelot and E. 749
Stroking See **A-stroäkin, Stroäkin**
Stroll all that from the town would s, Talking Oak 53
Stroll'd then we s For half the day thro' stately theatres Princess ii 368
Strong The s limbs failing; All Things will Die 32
Great in faith, and s Against the grief of circumstance Supp. Confessions 91
whose s right arm debased The throne of Persia, Alexander 1
For there was Milton like a seraph s, Palace of Art 133
s to break or bind All force in bonds " 153
Whereof the s foundation-stones were laid " 235
tale of little meaning tho' the words are s; Lotos-Eaters, C. S. 119
as s gales Hold swollen clouds from raining, D. of F. Women 10
Thro' many agents making s, Love thou thy land 39
S mother of a Lion-line, Be proud of those s sons of thine England and Amer. 3
I was s and hale of body then; St. S. Stylites 29
words That make a man feel s in speaking truth; Love and Duty 70
s in will To strive, to seek, to find, Ulysses 69
But thy s Hours indignant work'd their wills, Tithonus 18
The s tempestuous treble throbb'd and palpitated; Vision of Sin 28
Cast his s arms about his drooping wife, Enoch Arden 228
You chose the best among us—a s man: " 293
Her son, who stood beside her tall and s, " 756
So past the s heroic soul away. " 915
One whom the s sons of the world despise; The Brook 3
To make disproof of scorn, and s in hopes, Aylmer's Field 446
that one kiss Was Leolin's one s rival upon earth: " 557
But she with her s feet up the steep hill Sea Dreams 120
And mould a generation s to move Princess v 416
S, supple, sinew-corded, apt at arms; " 535
'O fair and s and terrible! " vi 163
Ruddy and white, and s on his legs, Grandmother 2
S of his hands, and s on his legs, " 13
Well for him whose will is s! Will 1
S Son of God, immortal Love, In Mem., Pro. 1
More s than all poetic thought; " xxxvi 12
Then bring an opiate trebly s, " lxxi 6
For thou wert s as thou wert true? " lxxiii 4
The wish too s for words to name; " xciii 14
Than some s bond which is to be. " cxvi 16
The s imagination roll A sphere of stars " cxxii 6
And if the words were sweet and s " cxxv 11
But, I fear, the new s wine of love, Maud I vi 82
S in the power that all men adore, " x 14
One still s man in a blatant land, " 63
So many those that hate him, and so s, Com. of Arthur 251
One was fair, s, arm'd—But to be won by force— Gareth and L. 104
'I have stagger'd thy s Gawain in a tilt For pastime; " 542
Morning-Star, and Noon-Sun, and Evening-Star, Being s fools; " 635
but thou strikest a s stroke, For s thou art and goodly therewithal, " 877
'O Sun' (not this s fool whom thou, Sir Knave, " 1058
And heated the s warrior in his dreams; Marr. of Geraint 72
And the s passion in her made her weep " 110
and the blood Of their s bodies, flowing, " 569
With streaming grass, appear'd, low-built but s; Balin and Balan 333

Strong (*continued*) A minstrel of Caerleon by *s* storm Blown into shelter *Merlin and V.* 9
but God Broke the *s* lance, and roll'd his enemy down, *Lancelot and E.* 26
found the Lord of Astolat With two *s* sons, .. 174
When the *s* neighings of the wild white Horse .. 298
S men, and wrathful that a stranger knight .. 468
Gawain, surnamed The Courteous, fair and *s*, „ 555
out of this she plaited broad and long A *s* sword-belt, *Holy Grail* 153
dyed The *s* White Horse in his own heathen blood— .. 312
How my *s* lance had beaten down the knights, .. 363
their wise men Were *s* in that old magic „ 666
had felt the sun Beat like a *s* knight on his helm, *Pelleas and E.* 23
beholding him so *s*, she thought That peradventure he will fight .. 117
'O the *s* hand,' she said, 'See! look at mine! .. 126
so by that *s* hand of his The sword and golden circlet .. 169
Then let the *s* hand, which had overthrown .. 234
O towers so *s*, Huge, solid, „ 463
his *s* hands gript And dinted the gilt dragons *Last Tournament* 181
'I had forgotten all in my *s* joy To see thee— „ 582
all his aims Were sharpen'd by *s* hate for Lancelot *Guinevere* 20
And fly to my *s* castle overseas: „ 112
Round that *s* castle where he holds the Queen; .. 194
And *s* man-breasted things stood from the sea, „ 246
a *s* sympathy Shook all my soul: *Lover's Tale ii* 88
a semi-smile As at a *s* conclusion— „ *iv* 282
S with the strength of the race to command, *Def. of Lucknow* 47
Seven *s* Earls of the army of Anlaf *Batt. of Brunanburh* 53
There was a *s* sea-current would sweep us *Despair* 51
S in will and rich in wisdom, *Locksley H., Sixty* 49
Would my granite girth were *s* As either love, *Helen's Tower* 7
The century's three *s* eights have met *To Ulysses* 7

Stronger Teach that sick heart the *s* choice, *On a Mourner* 18
Then wax'd her anger *s*. *The Goose* 30
The Poet-forms of *s* hours, *Day-Dm., L'Envoi* 14
Till the little wings are *s*. *Sea Dreams* 298
Till the little limbs are *s*. „ 306
Eight daughters of the plough, *s* than men, *Princess iv* 278
But tougher, heavier, *s*, he that smote .. *v* 536
Love and Nature, there are two more terrible And *s*. „ *vi* 166
Are mine for the moment *s*? *Spiteful Letter* 10
he came at length To find a *s* faith his own; *In Mem. xcvi* 17
The love that rose on *s* wings, „ *cxxviii* 1
suddenly, sweeter, my heart beat *s* And thicker, *Maud I viii* 8
Then with a *s* buffet he clove the helm *Gareth and L.* 1405
My malice is no deeper than a moat, No *s* than a wall: *Geraint and E.* 341
in their chairs set up a *s* race With hearts „ 940
Yea, shook this newer, *s* hall of ours, *Holy Grail* 731
then he hurl'd into it Against the *s*; *Lancelot and E.* 463
The vast occasion of our *s* life— *Columbus* 35
and bring on both the yoke Of *s* states, *Tiresias* 70
Pining for the *s* heart that once had beat beside her own. *Locksley H., Sixty* 58
With *s* life from day to day; *Hands all Round* 6
Tho' you'll ne'er be *s*; *Forlorn* 62
Then, with a melody *S* and statelier, *Merlin and the G.* 63

Stronger-made Enoch *s-m* Was master: *Enoch Arden* 30

Strongest Is this enough to say That my desire, like all *s* hopes, *Gardener's D.* 237
where two fight The *s* wins, *Aylmer's Field* 365
Cries to Weakest as to *S*, *Locksley H., Sixty* 110
my *s* wish Falls flat before your least unwillingness. *Romney's R.* 71

Stronglier And Gareth hearing ever *s* smote, *Gareth and L.* 1141

Strong-wing'd THESE lame hexameters the *s-w* music of Homer! *Trans. of Homer* 1

Strove Resolved on noble things, and *s* to speak, *D. of F. Women* 42
blinded with my tears, Still *s* to speak: „ 109
She *s* to span my waist: *Talking Oak* 138
Not unbecoming men that *s* with Gods. *Ulysses* 53
That *s* in other days to pass, *Day-Dm., Arrival* 10
So she *s* against her weakness, *L. of Burleigh* 69
And still they *s* and wrangled: *Sea Dreams* 229
S to buffet to land in vain. *Princess iv* 185

Strove (*continued*) I *s* against the stream and all in vain: *Princess vii* 12
Son of him with whom we *s* for power— *W. to Marie Alex.* 1
Shall be for whose applause I *s*, *In Mem. li* 5
But ever *s* to make it true: „ *xcvi* 8
And while she wept, and I *s* to be cool, *Maud II i* 15
lords Drew back in wrath, and Arthur *s* with Rome. *Com. of Arthur* 514
yet he *s* To learn the graces of their Table, *Balin and Balan* 237
I yearn'd and *s* To tear the twain asunder *Holy Grail* 785
when we *s* in youth, And brake the petty kings, *Pass. of Arthur* 67
I *s* to disengage myself, but fail'd, *Lover's Tale i* 692
thou *s* to rise From my full heart. .. 711
I could not rise Albeit I *s* to follow. „ *ii* 98
I *s* myself with Spain against the Moor. *Columbus* 94
for whenever we *s* to speak Our voices *V. of Maeldune* 21
But ever I fail'd to please him, however I *s* to please— *The Wreck* 28
S for sixty widow'd years to help *Locksley H., Sixty* 267
S yonder mountain flat, *Mechanophilus* 6

Strow And *s*'s her lights below, *St. Agnes' Eve* 28

Strowing the happy people *s* cried 'Hosanna *Enoch Arden* 505
S balm, or shedding poison in the fountains *Locksley H., Sixty* 274

Strown (*See also* **Strewn, Star-strown**) And would have *s* it, and are fall'n themselves. *Princess vi* 42
s With gold and scatter'd coinage, *Geraint and E.* 25
loosely *s* with crags: We mounted slowly; *Lover's Tale i* 384
Hath still'd the blast and *s* the wave, *Freedom* 34

Struck light *S* up against the blinding wall. *Mariana in the S.* 56
S thro' with pangs of hell. *Palace of Art* 220
a lyre of widest range *S* by all passion, *D. of F. Women* 166
And *s* upon the corn-laws, where we split, *Audley Court* 35
he *s* his staff against the rocks And broke it,— *Golden Year* 59
Then *s* it thrice, and, no one opening, *Enoch Arden* 279
Started from bed, and *s* herself a light, „ 494
S out the streaming mountain-side, *Lucretius* 29
Whose death-blow *s* the dateless doom of kings, „ 236
twangling violin *S* up with Soldier-laddie, *Princess, Pro.* 86
I *s* in: 'Albeit so mask'd, Madam, .. *ii* 212
'you wrong him more than I That *s* him: .. *iv* 246
She *s* such warbling fury thro' the words; .. 586
Till I *s* out and shouted; .. *v* 540
our enemies have fall'n, have fall'n: they *s*; .. *vi* 48
while the day, Descending, *s* athwart the hall, .. 364
and flying *s* With showers of random sweet „ *vii* 85
That if to-night our greatness were *s* dead, *Third of Feb.* 17
s the keys There at his right with a sudden crash, *The Islet* 7
I hear the bell *s* in the night: *In Mem. x* 2
When the dark hand *s* down thro' time, „ *lxxii* 19
Like a sudden spark *S* vainly in the night, *Maud I ix* 14
And he *s* me, madman, over the face, *S* me before the languid fool, .. *II i* 18
S for himself an evil stroke; „ 21
Friend, to be *s* by the public foe, „ *v* 89
afterward *S* for the throne, and striking found his doom. *Com. of Arthur* 325
four strokes they *s* With sword, and these were mighty: *Gareth and L.* 1042
S at her with his whip, (repeat) *Marr. of Geraint* 201, 413
S at him with his whip, and cut his cheek. „ 207
S thro' the bulky bandit's corselet home, *Geraint and E.* 159
Earl Doorm *S* with a knife's haft „ 600
In those fierce wars, *s* hard— *Balin and Balan* 177
Dragg'd him, and *s*, but from the castle a cry „ 399
s Furrowing a giant oak, and javelining *Merlin and V.* 935
S up and lived along the milky roofs; *Lancelot and E.* 409
lightnings here and there to left and right *S*, *Holy Grail* 495
moon *S* from an open grating overhead *Lover's Tale iv* 60
bullet *s* him that was dressing it suddenly dead, *The Revenge* 67
and ever they *s* and they slew; *V. of Maeldune* 68
S for their hoards and their hearths *Batt. of Brunanburh* 19
as if she had *s* and crash'd on a rock; *The Wreck* 108
S hard at the tender heart of the mother, *Despair* 74
S with the sword-hand and slew, *Heavy Brigade* 52
aiming at an all but hopeless mark To strike it, *s*; *The Ring* 347
Be *s* from out the clash of warring wills; *Prog. of Spring* 95
S by a poison'd arrow in the fight, *Death of Œnone* 26

Struck (continued) every dawn S from him his own shadow on to Rome. St. Telemachus 33
S to the left and s to the right The Tourney 4
Struggle (s) The s of standards, Batt. of Brunanburh 87
Struggle (verb) Glory of Virtue, to fight, to s, Wages 3
ruby-chain, and both Began to s for it, Last Tournament 410
Struggled boy that cried aloud And s hard. Dora 102
Strumming With s and with scraping, Amphion 70
Strung Kate hath a spirit ever s Kate 10
Stubb'd (hoed) an' I 'a s Thurnaby waäste. N. Farmer, O. S. 28
But I s 'um oop wi' the lot, „ 32
an' I meän'd to 'a s it at fall, „ 41
Stubble Fire in a dry s a nine-days' wonder Lancelot and E. 735
Stubborn He thought to quell the s hearts of oak, Buonaparte 1
'S, but she may sit Upon a king's right hand Princess v 438
He shall find the s thistle bursting Ode on Well. 206
Sick for thy s hardihood, In Mem. ii 14
Stubborn-shafted Before a gloom of s-s oaks, Geraint and E. 120
Stuck (See also **Stook**) S; and he clamour'd from a casement, The Brook 85
s out The bones of some vast bulk that lived Princess iii 293
Hoänly Miss Annie were saw s oop, Village Wife 59
fur I s to tha moor na the rest, Spinster's S's. 51
I couldn't a' s by my word. „ 96
Studded others s wide With disks and tiars, Arabian Nights 63
her hair S with one rich Provence rose— Lover's Tale iii 45
Student Drove in upon the s once or twice, Aylmer's Field 462
Hers more than half the s's, all the love. Princess iii 39
What s came but that you planed her path „ iv 315
To cramp the s at his desk, In Mem. cxxviii 18
Study Back would he to his studies, Aylmer's Field 394
Old studies fail'd; seldom she spoke: Princess vii 31
Stuff (s) and chairs, And all his household s; Walk. to the Mail 40
Man is made of solid s. Edwin Morris 49
'What s is this! Old writers push'd the happy season Golden Year 65
household s, Live chattels, mincers Princess iv 514
Stuff (verb) S his ribs with mouldy hay. Vision of Sin 66
Stumble my mind S's, and all my faculties are lamed Lucretius 123
Stumbled Ran Gaffer, s Gammer. The Goose 34
We s on a stationary voice, Princess v 2
Part s mixt with floundering horses. „ 498
lies a ridge of slate across the ford; His horse thereon s— Gareth and L. 1057
horse, Arising wearily at a fallen oak, S headlong, Balin and Balan 426
I S on deck, half mad. The Wreck 118
I have s back again Into the common day, Romney's R. 32
He s in, and sat Blinded; St. Telemachus 48
Stumbling S across the market to his death, Aylmer's Field 820
our horses s as they trode On heaps of ruin, Holy Grail 716
Stumbling-block striking on huge s-b's of scorn Aylmer's Field 538
Stump And let my lady sear the s for him, Pelleas and E. 339
A s of oak half-dead, From roots like some black coil Last Tournament 12
with blunt s Pitch-blacken'd sawing the air, „ 66
Stump'd with clamour bowl'd And s the wicket; Princess, Pro. 82
Stung poisoning all his rest, S him in dreams. Balin and Balan 384
S by his loss had vanish'd, none knew where. Lover's Tale iv 102
'The shaft of scorn that once had s Ancient Sage 131
Dead!—and maybe s With some remorse, The Ring 454
Stunn'd And s me from my power to think In Mem. xvi 15
I sitting here so s and still, Maud II i 2
and s the twain Or slew them, Geraint and E. 91
and so left him s or dead, „ 464
hurl'd him headlong, and he fell S, Guinevere 109
Stunning See **Ear-stunning**
Stunt (obstinate) Do'ant be s: taäke time: N. Farmer, N. S. 17
Stunted I lived for years a s sunless life; Aylmer's Field 357
Nor s squaws of West or East; Princess ii 78
Stupid Courage, poor s heart of stone.— Maud II iii 5
She felt so blunt and s at the heart: Geraint and E. 747
O s child! Yet you are wise who say it; Merlin and V. 251
with such a s heart To interpret ear and eye, Lancelot and E. 941
then at the last they found I had grown so s and still Rizpah 49
Sty so return'd unfarrow'd to her s. Walk. to the Mail 100
A maiden moon that sparkles on a s, Princess v 186
Style take the s of those heroic times? The Epic 35
What s could suit? Princess, Con. 9
Styled See **Self-styled**
Stylites (See also **Simeon, Simeon Stylites**) Simeon of the pillar, by surname, S, among men; St. S. Stylites 162
Subdue to s this home Of sin, my flesh, „ 57
S them to the useful and the good. Ulysses 38
foil'd at the last by the handful they could not s; Def. of Lucknow 44
he thought he could s me to his will. Happy 64
Subdued I s me to my father's will; D. of F. Women 234
grace Of sweet seventeen s me ere she spoke) The Brook 113
S me somewhat to that gentleness, Geraint and E. 867
Subject (adj.) s to the season or the mood, Aylmer's Field 71
Subject (s) knowledge of his art Held me above the s, D. of F. Women 10
we coursed about The s most at heart, Gardener's D. 223
She rapt upon her s, he on her: Princess iii 304
My s with my s's under him, Geraint and E. 916
'Queen? s? but I see not what I see. Balin and Balan 281
mine image, The s of thy power, be cold in her, Lover's Tale i 782
Artificer and s, lord and slave, „ ii 103
if the rebel s seek to drag me from the throne, By an Evolution. 15
Sublime my lover, with whom I rode s On Fortune's neck: D. of F. Women 141
'Name and fame! to fly s Thro' the courts, Vision of Sin 103
raillery, or grotesque, or false s— Princess iv 588
In his simplicity s. Ode on Well. 34
nourishing a youth s With the fairy tales of science, Locksley Hall 11
If, in thy second state s, In Mem. lxi 1
With what s repression of himself, Ded. of Idylls 19
Farewell, Macready; moral, grave, s; To W. C. Macready 12
'The stars with head s,' Epilogue 47
Submit S, and hear the judgment of the King.' Geraint and E. 799
Submitting S all things to desire. In Mem. cxiv 8
Subscribed which hastily s, We enter'd on the boards: Princess ii 73
Subserve Or but s's another's gain. In Mem. liv 12
Subsist Within this region I s, You ask me, why, etc. 2
Substance island princes over-bold Have eat our s, Lotos-Eaters, C. S. 76
And rolling as it were the s of it Aylmer's Field 258
none of all our blood should know The shadow from the s, Princess i 9
do I chase The s or the shadow? „ ii 409
everywhere I know the s when I see it. „ 413
spirit flash not all at once from out This shadow into S— Ded. Poem Prin. Alice 6
shadow leave the S in the brooding light Happy 99
Subtil Her s, warm, and golden breath, Supp. Confessions 60
Subtilising See **All-subtilising**
Subtle A s, sudden flame, Madeline 28
With shrilling shafts of s wit. Clear-headed friend 13
Round thy neck in s ring Adeline 58
Thro' lips and eyes in s rays. Rosalind 24
She with a s smile in her mild eyes, Œnone 184
All s thought, all curious fears, In Mem. xxxii 9
one indeed I knew In many a s question versed, „ xcvi 6
he that like a s beast Lay couchant with his eyes Guinevere 10
the s beast, Would track her guilt until he found, „ 59
I knew Of no more s master under heaven „ 478
Works of s brain and hand, Open. I. and C. Exhib. 7
How s at tierce and quart of mind In Mem., W. G. Ward 5
Subtle-paced silver flow Of s-p counsel Isabel 21
Subtler Who knows a s magic than his own— Com. of Arthur 284
Subtlest Myriads of topaz-lights, and jacinth-work Of s jewellery. M. d'Arthur 58
Myriads of topaz-lights, and jacinth-work Of s jewellery. Pass. of Arthur 226
Subtle-thoughted S-t, myriad-minded. Ode to Memory 118
Suburb (See also **Wheat-suburb**) By park and s under brown Of lustier leaves; In Mem. xcviii 24
mitre-sanction'd harlot draws his clerks Into the s— Sir J. Oldcastle 107
Old Fitz, who from your s grange, To E. Fitzgerald 1
Succeed 'I know that age to age s's, Two Voices 205
'The many fail: the one s's.' Day-Dm., Arrival 16
pushes us off from the board, and others ever s? Maud I iv 27
That after many changes may s Life, Prog. of Spring 116
Succeeder The sole s to their wealth, Aylmer's Field 294

Summer (adj.) (*continued*) Who yells Here in the still sweet *s* night, *Pelleas and E.* 473
Built for a *s* day with Queen Isolt Against a shower, *Last Tournament* 378
one *s* noon, an arm Rose up from out the bosom of the lake, *Pass. of Arthur* 197
And bowery hollows crown'd with *s* sea, „ 431
as thronging fancies come To boys and girls when *s* days are new, *Lover's Tale i* 555
Till he melted like a cloud in the silent *s* heaven; *The Revenge* 14
the stars came out far over the *s* sea, „ 56
when half of the short *s* night was gone, „ 65
and the sun smiled out far over the *s* sea, „ 70
Ten long sweet *s* days upon deck, *The Wreck* 64
'Ten long sweet *s* days' of fever, „ 147
who, on that *s* day When I had fall'n off the crag *The Flight* 21
now to these unsummer'd skies The *s* bird is still, *Pref. Poem Broth. Son.* 18
The two that love thee, lead a *s* life, *Prin. Beatrice* 18
Are cheeping to each other of their flight To *s* lands! *The Ring* 87
I dream'd last night of that clear *s* noon, *Romney's R.* 74
'wasting the sweet *s* hours'? *Charity* 1

Summer (s) (*See also* **Full-summer, Mid-summer**)
Autumn and *s* Are gone long ago; *Nothing will Die* 18
S herself should minister To thee, *Eleänore* 32
A *s* fann'd with spice. *Palace of Art* 116
come back again with *s* o'er the wave, *May Queen, N. Y's. E.* 19
Smelt of the coming *s*, *Gardener's D.* 78
The good old *S's*, year by year *Talking Oak* 39
'Old *S's*, when the monk was fat, „ 41
Thro' all the *s* of my leaves „ 211
It was last *s* on a tour in Wales: *Golden Year* 2
And after many a *s* dies the swan. *Tithonus* 4
s's to such length of years should come *Locksley Hall* 67
The woman of a thousand *s's* back, *Godiva* 11
A *s* crisp with shining woods. *Day-Dm., Pro.* 8
Till all the hundred *s's* pass, „ *Sleep. P.* 33
When will the hundred *s's* die, „ 49
'A hundred *s's*! can it be? „ *Depart.* 25
By squares of tropic *s* shut And warm'd *Amphion* 87
whose father-grape grew fat On Lusitanian *s's*. *Will Water.* 8
She slipt across the *s* of the world, *Enoch Arden* 531
Dwelt with eternal *s*, ill-content. „ 562
in branding *s's* of Bengal, *The Brook* 16
(The sootflake of so many a *s* still *Sea Dreams* 35
A Martin's *s* of his faded love, *Aylmer's Field* 560
all a *s's* day Gave his broad lawns *Princess, Pro.* 1
'Kill him now, The tyrant! kill him in the *s* too,' „ 207
'Why not a *s's* as a winter's tale? A tale for *s* as befits the time, „ 209
there did a compact pass Long *s's* back, „ *i* 124
The *s* of the vine in all his veins— „ 183
hither side, or so she look'd, Of twenty *s's*. „ *ii* 108
all fair theories only made to gild A stormless *s*.' „ 234
And brief the sun of *s* in the North, „ *iv* 112
this shall grow A night of *S* from the heat, „ *vi* 54
Far on in *s's* that we shall not see: *Ode on Well.* 234
To lands of *s* across the sea; *The Daisy* 92
The bitter east, the misty *s* And gray metropolis „ 103
For a score of sweet little *s's* or so?' *The Islet* 2
The child was only eight *s's* old, *The Victim* 33
Thine the lands of lasting *s*, *Boädicea* 43
But *S* on the steaming floods, *In Mem. lxxxv* 69
When *s's* hourly-mellowing change „ *xci* 9
o'er the sky The silvery haze of *s* drawn; „ *xcv* 4
Long sleeps the *s* in the seed; „ *cv* 26
Than in the *s's* that are flown, „ *Con.* 18
So many a *s* since she died, *Maud I vi* 66
Nor will be when our *s's* have deceased. „ *xviii* 14
With sprigs of *s* laid between the folds, *Marr. of Geraint* 138
For now the wine made *s* in his veins, „ 398
Like flaws in *s* laying lusty corn: „ 764
My Queen, that *s*, when ye loved me first. *Lancelot and E.* 104
ere the *s* when he died, The monk Ambrosius *Holy Grail* 16
felt his eyes Harder and drier than a fountain bed In *s*: *Pelleas and E.* 508

Summer (s) (*continued*) Kill'd in a tilt, come next, five *s's* back, *Guinevere* 321
My pride in happier *s's*, at my feet. „ 536
sudden deluges of light Into the middle *s*; *Lover's Tale i* 316
the Spring and the middle *S* sat each *V. of Maeldune* 38
Ten long days of *s* and sin— *The Wreck* 77
A THOUSAND *s's* ere the time of Christ *Ancient Sage* 1
She spies the *s* thro' the winter bud, „ 74
where *s* never dies, with Love, the Sun of life! *The Flight* 44
all the *s* long we roam'd in these wild woods „ 79
S's of the snakeless meadow, *To Virgil* 19
O THOU so fair in *s's* gone, *Freedom* 1
Gray with distance Edward's fifty *s's*, *On Jub. Q. Victoria* 40
Sunn'd with a *s* of milder heat. *To Prof. Jebb* 8
Spring and *S* and Autumn and Winter, *Vastness* 29
wind is west With all the warmth of *s*. *The Ring* 30
Who meant to sleep her hundred *s's* out „ 66
In the winter of the Present for the *s* of the Past; *Happy* 70
In *s* if I reach my day— *To Ulysses* 9
And *s* basking in the sultry plains *Prog. of Spring* 77
When over the valley, In early *s's*, *Merlin and the G.* 18
'*S* is coming, *s* is coming. *The Throstle* 1
S is coming, is coming, my dear, „ 15
In that four-hundredth *s* after Christ, *St. Telemachus* 4
I had one brief *s* of bliss. *Bandit's Death* 9
But if twenty million of *s's* are stored *The Dawn* 19
men of a hundred thousand, a million *s's* away? „ 25

Summer-blanch'd here was one that, *s-b*, *Aylmer's Field* 152
Summer-bright How *s-b* are yonder skies, *Ancient Sage* 23
Summer-dawn gray streak of earliest *s-d*, „ 220
Summerhouse the *s* aloft That open'd on the pines *Lover's Tale i* 40
It was a room Within the *s-h* of which I spake, „ *ii* 167
Summer-morn And many a sheeny *s-m*, *Arabian Nights* 5
Showing a gaudy *s-m*, *Palace of Art* 62
Summer-new fancy as *s-n* As the green of the bracken *June Bracken, etc.* 8
Summer-palace a boon, A certain *s-p* *Princess i* 147
Summer-rich *S-r* Then; and then Autumn-changed, *The Oak* 6
Summertime came With Modred hither in the *s*, *Gareth and L.* 26
Summer-wan Arthur's harp tho' *s-w*, „ 1314
Summer-winter who breathe the balm Of *s-w's* *To Ulysses* 11
Summit sacred morning spread The silent *s* overhead. *Two Voices* 81
'Cry, faint not, climb: the *s's* slope „ 184
Cry to the *s*, 'Is there any hope?' *Vision of Sin* 220
splendour falls on castle walls And snowy *s's* old in story: *Princess iv* 2
But ere we reach'd the highest *s* I pluck'd a daisy, *The Daisy* 87
voice and the Peak Far over *s* and lawn, *Voice and the P.* 2
From hidden *s's* fed with rills *In Mem. ciii* 7
At times the *s* of the high city flash'd; *Gareth and L.* 192
Green-glimmering toward the *s*, bears, *Lancelot and E.* 483
great tower fill'd with eyes Up to the *s*, *Pelleas and E.* 167
s and the pinnacles Of a gray steeple— *Lover's Tale ii* 81
Cried from the topmost *s* with human voices *V. of Maeldune* 28
Yon *s* half-a-league in air— *Ancient Sage* 11
and roll my voice from the *s*, *Parnassus* 6
Summon But *s* here before me yet once more *Com. of Arthur* 164
They *s* me their King to lead mine hosts *Guinevere* 570
Summon'd Then *s* to the porch we went. *Princess iii* 178
S out She kept her state, „ 228
A kinsman, dying, *s* me to Rome— *The Ring* 178
Summoner Far-sighted *s* of War and Waste *Ded. of Idylls* 37
at Pardoners, *S's*, Friars, absolution-sellers, *Sir J. Oldcastle* 92
Summoning Then, after *s* Lancelot privily, *Gareth and L.* 581
Sound on a dreadful trumpet, *s* her; *Geraint and E.* 383
Summons And brought a *s* from the sea: *In Mem. ciii* 16
Waiting for your *s* . . . *Forlorn* 22
Sumner-chace Broad oak of *S-c*, *Talking Oak* 30
good old Sumners, year by year Made ripe in *S-c*: „ 40
And shadow *S-c*! „ 150
Sumner-place The roofs of *S-p*! (repeat) „ 32, 96, 152
till thy boughs discern The front of *S-p*. „ 248
Sumptuous turn'd her *s* head with eyes Of shining expectation *Princess iv* 152
With store of rich apparel, *s* fare, *Marr. of Geraint* 709

Sumptuous (*continued*) Thy presence in the silk of *s* looms ; *Ancient Sage* 266
Sumptuously and *s* According to his fashion, *Geraint and E.* 284
Sun (s) (*See also* **Noon-Sun, Soon**) as the tree Stands in the *s* and shadows all beneath, *Love and Death* 11
Like a lily which the *s* Looks thro' *Adeline* 12
tho' you stood Between the rainbow and the *s*. *Margaret* 13
The *s* is just about to set, „ 58
grow To a full face, there like a *s* remain Fix'd— *Eleänore* 92
The *s* came dazzling thro' the leaves, *L. of Shalott iii* 3
A merry boy in *s* and shade ? *Two Voices* 321
Many *s's* arise and set. *Miller's D.* 205
O *s*, that from thy noonday height *Fatima* 2
While this great bow will waver in the *s*, *Palace of Art* 43
I would see the *s* rise upon the glad New-year. (repeat) *May Queen, N. Y's. E.* 2, 51
To-night I saw the *s* set : „ 5
I wish the snow would melt and the *s* come out on high : „ 15
In the early early morning the summer *s* 'ill shine, „ 22
It seem'd so hard at first, mother, to leave the blessed *s*, „ *Con.* 9
O look ! the *s* begins to rise, „ 49
voice, that now is speaking, may be beyond the *s*— „ 54
Between the *s* and moon upon the shore ; *Lotos-Eaters* 38
Half-fall'n across the threshold of the *s*, *D. of F. Women* 63
We drank the Libyan *S* to sleep, „ 145
While yon *s* prospers in the blue, *The Blackbird* 22
That broods above the fallen *s*, *To J. S.* 51
That made his forehead like a rising *s* *M. d'Arthur* 217
but all else of heaven was pure Up to the *S*, *Gardener's D.* 80
the *s* fell, and all the land was dark. (repeat)— *Dora* 79, 109
Lay great with pig, wallowing in *s* and mud. *Walk. to the Mail* 88
To some full music rose and sank the *s*, *Edwin Morris* 34
The cloudy porch oft opening on the *S* ? *Love and Duty* 9
The *S* will run his orbit, and the Moon Her circle. „ 22
The *S* flies forward to his brother *S* ; *Golden Year* 23
For some three *s's* to store and hoard *Ulysses* 29
widen'd with the process of the *s's*. *Locksley Hall* 138
hurl their lances in the *s* ; „ 170
what to me were *s* or clime ? „ 177
flash the lightnings, weigh the *S*— „ 186
Thro' many an hour of summer *s's*, *Will Water.* 33
To keep the best man under the *s* *Lady Clare* 31
We seem'd to sail into the *S* ! *The Voyage* 16
How oft we saw the *S* retire, „ 17
As fast she fled thro' *s* and shade, *Sir L. and Q. G.* 37
A thousand *s's* will stream on thee, *A Farewell* 13
Close to the *s* in lonely lands, *The Eagle* 2
As when the *s*, a crescent of eclipse, *Vision of Sin* 10
A light wind blew from the gates of the *s*, *Poet's Song* 3
new warmth of life's ascending *s* Was felt by either, *Enoch Arden* 38
Cuts off the fiery highway of the *s*, „ 130
Under a palm-tree, over him the *S* : „ 501
yonder shines The *S* of Righteousness, „ 504
We turn'd our foreheads from the falling *s*, *The Brook* 165
found the *s* of sweet content Re-risen in Katie's eyes, „ 168
bearing hardly more Than his own shadow in a sickly *s*. *Aylmer's Field* 30
' Let not the *s* go down upon your wrath,' *Sea Dreams* 44
Bright with the *s* upon the stream beyond : „ 97
out I slipt Into a land all *s* and blossom, „ 101
another of our Gods, the *S*, Apollo, Delius, *Lucretius* 124
how the *s* delights To glance and shift about „ 188
until the set of *s* Up to the people : *Princess, Pro.* 2
inhabitant Of some clear planet close upon the *S*, „ *ii* 36
set the starry tides, And eddied into *s's*, „ 118
A Memnon smitten with the morning *S*.' „ *iii* 116
They with the *s* and moon renew their light „ 255
white vapour streak the crowned towers Built to the *S* : „ 345
till the *S* Grew broader toward his death and fell, „ 363
' There sinks the nebulous star we call the *S*, „ *iv* 19
And brief the *s* of summer in the North, „ 112
till the Bear had wheel'd Thro' a great arc his seven slow *s's*. „ 213

Sun (s) (*continued*) Up in one night and due to sudden *s* : *Princess iv* 312
Sees the midsummer, midnight, Norway *s* Set into sunrise ; „ 575
issued in the *s*, that now Leapt from the dewy shoulders „ *v* 42
lays on every side A thousand arms and rushes to the *S*. „ *vi* 37
leader of the herd That holds a stately fretwork to the *S*, „ 86
So drench'd it is with tempest, to the *s*, „ *vii* 142
Till the *S* drop, dead, from the signs.' „ 245
underneath another *s*, Warring on a later day, *Ode on Well.* 101
To which our God Himself is moon and *s*. „ 217
To meet the *s* and sunny waters, *The Daisy* 11
Your presence will be *s* in winter, *To F. D. Maurice* 3
With many a rivulet high against the *S* *The Islet* 21
Wake, little ladies, The *s* is aloft ! *Minnie and Winnie* 20
THE *s*, the moon, the stars, the seas, *High. Pantheism* 1
stars from the night and the *s* from the day ! *Window, Gone* 5
S comes, moon comes, „ *When* 1
S sets, moon sets, „ 3
Blaze upon her window, *s*, „ 15
You send a flash to the *s*. *Window, Marr. Morn* 2
Nor branding summer *s's* avail *In Mem. ii* 11
And murmurs from the dying *s* : „ *iii* 8
Since our first *S* arose and set. „ *xxiv* 8
And blurr'd the splendour of the *s* ; „ *lxxii* 8
And, while we breathe beneath the *s*, „ *lxxv* 14
s by *s* the happy days Descend below „ *lxxxiv* 27
And all the courses of the *s's*. „ *cxvii* 12
Sad Hesper o'er the buried *s* And ready, „ *cxxi* 1
I found Him not in world or *s*, „ *cxxiv* 5
Thou standest in the rising *s*, „ *cxxx* 3
The sport of random *s* and shade. „ *Con.* 24
To meet and greet a whiter *s* ; „ 78
For him did his high *s* flame, *Maud I iv* 32
Our planet is one, the *s's* are many, „ 45
No *s*, but a wannish glare In fold upon fold „ *vi* 2
s look'd out with a smile Betwixt the cloud „ *ix* 3
Something flash'd in the *s*, „ 10
To faint in the light of the *s* that she loves, „ *xxii* 11
To the flowers, and be their *s*. „ 58
fires of Hell brake out of thy rising *s*, „ *II i* 9
And noble thought be freër under the *s*, „ *III vi* 48
heathen horde, Reddening the *s* with smoke and earth with blood, *Com. of Arthur* 37
and fell'd The forest, letting in the *s*, „ 60
' Rain, rain, and *s* ! a rainbow in the sky ! „ 403
Rain, rain, and *s* ! a rainbow on the lea ! „ 406
Rain, *s*, and rain ! and the free blossom blows : „ 409
S, rain, and *s* ! and where is he who knows ? „ 410
The *S* of May descended on their King, „ 462
paced a city all on fire With *s* and cloth of gold, „ 480
' Blow, for our *S* is mighty in his May ! „ 497
Blow, for our *S* is mightier day by day ! „ 498
ever-highering eagle-circles up To the great *S* of Glory, *Gareth and L.* 22
field of charlock in the sudden *s* Between two showers, „ 389
shone the Noonday *S* Beyond a raging shallow. „ 1027
flash'd the fierce shield, All *s* ; „ 1031
' Ugh ! ' cried the *S*, and vizoring up a red „ 1038
the *S* Heaved up a ponderous arm to strike the fifth, „ 1044
the stream Descended, and the *S* was wash'd away. „ 1047
' O *S* ' (not this strong fool whom thou, Sir Knave, „ 1058
S, that wakenest all to bliss or pain, „ 1060
' O dewy flowers that open to the *s*, „ 1066
new *s* Beat thro' the blindless casement *Marr. of Geraint* 70
Will clothe her for her bridals like the *s*.' „ 231
wound Bare to the *s*, and monstrous ivy-stems „ 322
pale and bloodless east began To quicken to the *s*, arose, „ 535
But since our fortune swerved from *s* to shade, „ 714
Herself would clothe her like the *s* in Heaven. „ 784
And clothed her for her bridals like the *s* ; „ 836
watch'd the *s* blaze on the turning scythe, *Geraint and E.* 252
But while the *s* yet beat a dewy blade, „ 446
But lift a shining hand against the *s*, „ 473
Had bared her forehead to the blistering *s*, „ 515
And bear him hence out of this cruel *s* ? „ 544
there the Queen array'd me like the *s* : *Geraint and E.* 701

Sun (s) (*continued*) Past eastward from the falling *s*. *Balin and Balan* 320
an Eagle rising or, the *S* In dexter chief; *Merlin and V.* 475
often o'er the *s's* bright eye Drew the vast eyelid .. 633
But who can gaze upon the *S* in heaven? *Lancelot and E.* 123
The low *s* makes the colour: .. 134
emerald center'd in a *s* Of silver rays, .. 295
Red as the rising *s* with heathen blood, .. 308
when the next *s* brake from underground, ,, 1137
till the *s* Shone, and the wind blew, thro' her, *Holy Grail* 98
' So when the *s* broke next from under ground, .. 328
' The *s* is rising, tho' the *s* had risen. .. 408
had felt the *s* Beat like a strong knight *Pelleas and E.* 22
Rode till the star above the wakening *s*, ,, 500
His hair, a *s* that ray'd from off a brow *Last Tournament* 666
On some vast plain before a setting *s*, *Guinevere* 77
And from the *s* there swiftly made at her ,, 78
That made his forehead like a rising *s* *Pass. of Arthur* 385
And the new *s* rose bringing the new year ,, 469
sail Will draw me to the rising of the *s*, *Lover's Tale i* 27
and blew Fresh fire into the *s*, .. 319
light flash'd ev'n from her white robe As from a glass in the *s*, .. 371
The incorporate blaze of *s* and sea. .. 409
s below, Held for a space 'twixt cloud .. 416
Glow'd intermingling close beneath the *s*. .. 436
other, like the *s* I gazed upon, .. 507
Why fed we from one fountain? drew one *s*? .. *ii* 24
Had suck'd the fire of some forgotten *s*, .. *iv* 194
That flings a mist behind it in the *s*— .. 294
All over glowing with the *s* of life, ,, 381
An' then 'e turn'd to the *s*, *North. Cobbler* 48
Seeäd nobbut the smile o' the *s* ,, 50
little of us left by the time this *s* be set.' *The Revenge* 28
the *s* went down, and the stars came out ,, 56
and the *s* smiled out far over the summer sea, ,, 70
S himself has limn'd the face for me. *Sisters (E. and E.)* 101
hidden there from the light of the *s*— *Def. of Lucknow* 63
Who push'd his prows into the setting *s*, *Columbus* 24
melon lay like a little *s* on the tawny sand, *V. of Maeldune* 57
sends the hidden *s* Down yon dark sea, *De Prof., Two G.* 33
Drew to this shore lit by the *s's* and moons ,, 38
the numerable-innumerable *S*, *s*, and *s*, ,, 45
with set of *s* Their fires flame thickly, *Achilles over the T.* 10
A planet equal to the *s* Which cast it, *To E. Fitzgerald* 35
One naked peak—the sister of the *s* *Tiresias* 30
Rejoicing that the *s*, the moon, the stars ,, 160
And the *s* of the soul made day *The Wreck* 55
Of a life without *s*, without health, *Despair* 7
s's of the limitless Universe sparkled ,, 15
When the light of a *S* that was coming .. 23
and crows to the *s* and the moon, .. 90
Till the *S* and the Moon of our science .. 91
She feels the *S* is hid but for a night, *Ancient Sage* 73
seem to flicker past thro' *s* and shade, .. 100
such large life as match'd with ours Were *S* to spark— .. 238
clouds themselves are children of the *S*. .. 242
Day and Night are children of the *S*, .. 245
up that lane of light into the setting *s*. *The Flight* 40
we watch'd the *s* fade from us thro' the West, ,, 41
An' the *s* kem out of a cloud *Tomorrow* 37
wid his song to the *S* an' the Moon, ,, 91
over darkness—from the still unrisen *s*. *Locksley H., Sixty* 92
and the *s* himself will pass. .. 182
earthlier earth of ours, Closer on the *S*, .. 184
All the *s's*—are these but symbols of innumerable man, .. 195
and *S's* along their fiery way, .. 203
And that bright hair the modern *s*, *Epilogue* 8
The *s* hung over the gates of Night, *Dead Prophet* 23
And he sung not alone of an old *s* set, But a *s* coming up in his youth! ,, 41
thro' this midnight breaks the *s* Of sixty years away, *Pref. Poem Broth. S.* 21
Two *S's* of Love make day of human life, *To Prin. Beatrice* 1
one, the *S* of dawn That brightens ,, 3
—and one The later-rising *S* of spousal Love, ,, 6

Sun (s) (*continued*) conjectured planet in mid heaven Between two *S's*, *To Prin. Beatrice* 21
had roll'd you round and round the *S*, *Poets and their B.* 10
S Burst from a swimming fleece of winter gray, *Demeter and P.* 19
And lighted from above him by the *S*? .. 31
s, Pale at my grief, drew down before his time .. 113
Till thy dark lord accept and love the *S*, .. 137
Many a planet by many a *s* may roll *Vastness* 2
in the gleam of a million million of *s's*? ,, 4
We often walk In open *s*, *The Ring* 328
sword that lighten'd back the *s* of Holy land, *Happy* 43
Has push'd toward our faintest *s* *To Ulysses* 23
Her mantle, slowly greening in the *S*, *Prog. of Spring* 11
May float awhile beneath the *s*, *Romney's R.* 50
s has risen To flame along another dreary day. ,, 57
bask amid the senses while the *s* of morning shines, *By an Evolution.* 6
star of eve was drawing light From the dead *s*, *Death of Œnone* 65
an old fane No longer sacred to the *S*, *St. Telemachus* 7
That glances from the *s* of our Islâm. *Akbar's Dream* 79
proclaimed His Master as the '*S* of Righteousness,' .. 83
Alla call'd In old Irân the *S* of Love? .. 87
—a *s* but dimly seen Here, till the mortal morning mists .. 95
The *s*, the *s*, they rail At me the Zoroastrian. .. 103
Let the *S*, Who heats our earth to yield us grain .. 104
Our hymn to the *s*. They sing it. ,, 203
I whirl, and I follow the *S*.' *The Dreamer* 14
Whirl, and follow the *S*! (repeat) ,, 20, 24, 28, 32
Rush of *S's*, and roll of systems, *God and the Univ.* 3
The face of Death is toward the *S* of Life, *D. of the Duke of C.* 12

Sun (verb) doves That *s* their milky bosoms on the thatch, *Princess ii* 103

Sunbeam thick-moted *s* lay Athwart the chambers, *Mariana* 78
As when a *s* wavers warm Within the dark *Miller's D.* 79
' Sometimes I let a *s* slip, *Talking Oak* 217
like a creeping *s*, slid From pillar unto pillar, *Godiva* 49
I make the netted *s* dance *The Brook* 176
old warrior from his ivied nook Glow like a *s*: *Princess, Pro.* 105
To glide a *s* by the blasted Pine, ,, *vii* 196
The *s* strikes along the world: *In Mem. xv* 8
But where the *s* broodeth warm, ,, *xci* 14
Happy children in a *s* sitting *Locksley H., Sixty* 14

Sunbright glitter'd o'er us a *s* hand, *V. of Maeldune* 84
and the *s* hand of the dawn, ,, 92

Sun-cluster vast *s-c's'* gather'd blaze, *Epilogue* 54

Sunday (*See also* **Soonday**) 'is best of a *S* at murn, *North. Cobbler* 46
An' Doctor 'e calls o' *S* ,, 87

Sunder *s's* ghosts and shadow-casting men Became a crystal, *Merlin and V.* 629
S the glooming crimson on the marge, *Gareth and L.* 1365
And *s* false from true, *Mechanophilus* 2

Sunder'd (*See also* **River-sunder'd**) And never can be *s* without tears. *To ——, With Pal. of Art* 13
Quite *s* from the moving Universe, *Princess vii* 52
from the sabre-stroke Shatter'd and *s*. *Light Brigade* 36
Time hath *s* shell from pearl.' *In Mem. lii* 16
Be *s* in the night of fear; ,, *cxxvii* 2
Some cause had kept him *s* from his wife: *Merlin and V.* 715
high doors Were softly *s*, and thro' these a youth, *Pelleas and E.* 4
her lips were *s* With smiles of tranquil bliss, *Lover's Tale ii* 142
and fought till I *s* the fray, *V. of Maeldune* 69
s once from all the human race, *To Virgil* 36
Gods had marr'd our peace, And *s* each from each. *Death of Œnone* 33

Sundown Yet oft when *s* skirts the moor *In Mem. xli* 17

Sundry for the rest Spake but of *s* perils in the storm; *Holy Grail* 761

Sun-flame *S-f* or sunless frost, *Epilogue* 66

Sunflower Heavily hangs the broad *s* (repeat) *A spirit haunts* 9, 21
Unloved, the *s-f*, shining fair, *In Mem. ci* 5

Sun-fringed Like little clouds *s-f*, are thine, *Madeline* 17

Sun-flushed sighs to see the peak *S-f*, *Balin and Balan* 166

Sung The cock *s* out an hour ere light: *Mariana* 27
The blue fly *s* in the pane; ,, 63
And the cock hath *s* beneath the thatch *The Owl i* 10
Died round the bulbul as he *s*; *Arabian Nights* 70
From Calpe into Caucasus they *s*, *The Poet* 15
At eve a dry cicala *s*, *Mariana in the S.* 85

Sung (*continued*) Among the tents I paused and *s*, — Two Voices 125
'I *s* the joyful Pæan clear, — „ 127
S by the morning star of song, — D. of F. Women 3
anthem *s*, is charm'd and tied To where he stands,— — „ 193
And, wheresoever I am *s* or told In aftertime, — M. d'Arthur 34
falser than all songs have *s*, — Locksley Hall 41
Wherever he sat down and *s* — Amphion 19
nightingale thought, 'I have *s* many songs, — Poet's Song 13
s to, when, this gad-fly brush'd aside, — Princess v 414
Peace, his triumph will be *s* By some — Ode on Well. 232
We *s*, tho' every eye was dim, — In Mem. xxx 14
S by a long-forgotten mind. — „ lxxvii 12
A guest, or happy sister, *s*, — „ lxxxix 26
One whispers, 'Here thy boyhood *s* — „ cii 9
Whatever I have said or *s*, — „ cxxv 1
song that once I heard By this huge oak, *s* nearly where we sit: — Merlin and V. 406
'O crueller than was ever told in tale, Or *s* in song! — „ 859
And one hath *s* and all the dumb will sing. — Holy Grail 301
more Than any have *s* thee living, — Pelleas and E. 351
Pelleas had heard *s* before the Queen, — „ 397
many a noble war-song had he *s*, — Guinevere 278
And, wheresoever I am *s* or told In aftertime, — Pass. of Arthur 202
we whirl'd giddily; the wind *S*; — Lover's Tale ii 202
Noble! he *s*, and the sweet sound ran — Dead Prophet 37
And he *s* not alone of an old sun set, — „ 41
men ater supper 'ed *s* their songs an' 'ed 'ed their beer, — Owd Roä 35
Sunk some were *s* and many were shatter'd, — The Revenge 61
Have we *s* below them? — Locksley H., Sixty 95
Sunless I lived for years a stunted *s* life; — Aylmer's Field 357
S and moonless, utter light—but no! — Columbus 90
Sun-flame or *s* frost, — Epilogue 66
The *s* halls of Hades into Heaven? — Demeter and P. 136
In seas of Death and *s* gulfs of Doubt. — Pref. Son. 19th Cent. 14
And thro' the *s* winter morning-mist — Death of Œnone 8
Sunlight faintest *s*'s flee About his shadowy sides: — The Kraken 4
Place it, where sweetest *s* falls — Ode to Memory 85
The *s* driving down the lea, — Rosalind 13
His broad clear brow in *s* glow'd; — L. of Shalott iii 28
as *s* drinketh dew. — Fatima 21
Floated the glowing *s*'s, as she moved. — Œnone 182
Are as moonlight unto *s*, — Locksley Hall 152
and return In such a *s* of prosperity — Aylmer's Field 421
(so rare the smiles Of *s*) — The Daisy 54
And the *s* broke from her lip? — Maud I vi 86
Then like a stormy *s* smiled Geraint, — Geraint and E. 480
Like *s* on the plain behind a shower: — Merlin and V. 403
Crown'd with *s*—over darkness— — Locksley H., Sixty 92
Yet the moonlight is the *s*, — „ 182
Not of the *s*, Not of the moonlight, — Merlin and the G. 120
million of summers are stored in the *s* still, — The Dawn 19
And the *s* that is gone! — Silent Voices 6
Sunlike make your Enid burst *S* from cloud— — Marr. of Geraint 789
Sun-lit *The s-l almond-blossom shakes*— — To the Queen 16
maiden Spring upon the plain Came in a *s-l* fall of rain. — Sir L. and Q. G. 4
There the *s* ocean tosses O'er them mouldering, — The Captain 69
Sunn'd *S* by those orient skies; — The Poet 42
day dwelt on her brows, and *s* Her violet eyes, — Gardener's D. 136
S itself on his breast and his hands. — Maud I xiii 13
cairn'd mountain was a shadow, *s* The world to peace again: — Merlin and V. 638
had *s* The morning of our marriage, — Sisters (E. and E.) 243
S with a summer of milder heat. — To Prof. Jebb 8
Sunnee warms the blood of Shiah and *S*, — Akbar's Dream 107
Sunnier Cleave ever to the *s* side of doubt, — Ancient Sage 68
The fountain pulses high in *s* jets, — Prog. of Spring 54
Sunning *S* himself in a waste field alone— — Aylmer's Field 9
Shine out, little head, *s* over with curls, — Maud I xxii 57
Sunny And shadow'd coves on a *s* shore, — Eleänore 18
but his *s* hair Cluster'd about his temples — Œnone 59
Another slid, a *s* fleck, — Talking Oak 223
saw The dim curls kindle into *s* rings; — Tithonus 54
Thro' *s* decads new and strange, — Day-Dm., L'Envoi 22
The *s* and rainy seasons came and went — Enoch Arden 623

Sunny (*continued*) Bright was that afternoon, *S* but chill; — Enoch Arden 670
S tokens of the Line, — Ode Inter. Exhib. 19
To meet the sun and *s* waters, — The Daisy 11
they pass the grave That has to-day its *s* side. — In Mem., Con. 72
And wild voice pealing up to the *s* sky, — Maud I v 13
And feet like *s* gems on an English green, — „ 14
What if with her *s* hair, And smile as *s* as cold, — „ vi 23
birds Of *s* plume in gilded trellis-work; — Marr. of Geraint 659
But heaven had meant it for a *s* one: — Holy Grail 706
To make it wholly thine on *s* days. — Lover's Tale i 14
Sunny-sweet Of tower or duomo, *s-s*, — The Daisy 46
Sunny-warm In tracts of pasture *s-w*, — Palace of Art 94
Sunrise (adj.) At his highest with *s* fire; — Voice and the P. 30
Sunrise (s) Rare *s* flow'd. — The Poet 36
And Freedom rear'd in that august *s* — „ 37
look'd upon the breath Of the lilies at *s*? — Adeline 37
heath-flower in the dew, Touch'd with *s*. — Rosalind 42
lights of sunset and of *s* mix'd In that brief night; — Love and Duty 72
every day The *s* broken into scarlet shafts — Enoch Arden 592
The scarlet shafts of *s*—but no sail. — „ 599
Her stature more than mortal in the burst Of *s*, — Princess, Pro. 41
Norway sun Set into *s*; — „ iv 576
came from out a mountain-cleft Toward the *s*, — Gareth and L. 261
level pavement where the King would pace At *s*, — „ 668
light of Heaven varies, now At *s*, now at sunset, — Marr. of Geraint 7
flame At *s* till the people in far fields, — Holy Grail 243
Damsels in divers colours like the cloud Of sunset and *s*, — Pelleas and E. 54
From sunset and *s* of all thy realm, — To the Queen ii 13
Hued with the scarlet of a fierce *s*, — Lover's Tale i 353
Star of the morning, Hope in the *s*; — Vastness 15
Who found me at *s* Sleeping, — Merlin and the G. 12
One from the *S* Dawn'd on His people, — Kapiolani 24
Sunset (adj.) Back to the *s* bound of Lyonnesse— — Pass. of Arthur 81
Sunset (s) (*See also* **Sea-sunset**) Breathes low between the *s* and the moon; — Eleänore 124
the *s*, south and north, Winds all the vale — Miller's D. 241
charmed *s* linger'd low adown In the red West: — Lotos-Eaters 19
lights of *s* and of sunrise mix'd In that brief night; — Love and Duty 72
for my purpose holds To sail beyond the *s*, — Ulysses 60
and leave Yon orange *s* waning slow: — Move eastward 2
the gates were closed At *s*, — Princess, Con. 37
and rang Beyond the bourn of *s*; — „ 100
Where some refulgent *s* of India — Milton 13
when the *s* burn'd On the blossom'd gable-ends — Maud I vi 8
Under the half-dead *s* glared; — Gareth and L. 800
light of Heaven varies, now At sunrise, now at *s*, — Marr. of Geraint 7
Damsels in divers colours like the cloud Of *s* and sunrise, — Pelleas and E. 54
The wide-wing'd *s* of the misty marsh — Last Tournament 423
an hour or maybe twain After the *s*, — Guinevere 238
From *s* and sunrise of all thy realm, — To the Queen ii 13
that shot the *s* In lightnings round me; — Lover's Tale i 442
Storm, *s*, glows and glories of the moon — „ ii 110
setting, when Even descended, the very *s* aflame; — V. of Maeldune 66
Rich was the rose of *s* there, — The Wreck 136
The placid gleam of *s* after storm! — Ancient Sage 133
She that finds a winter *s* — Locksley H., Sixty 22
As if perpetual *s* linger'd there, — The Ring 83
The *s* blazed along the wall of Troy. — Death of Œnone 77
The wrathful *s* glared against a cross — St. Telemachus 5
Following a hundred *s*'s, and the sphere — „ 31
From out the *s* pour'd an alien race, — Akbar's Dream 192
S and evening star, — Crossing the Bar 1
Sunset-flush'd pinnacles of aged snow, Stood *s-f* — Lotos-Eaters 17
Sun-shaded *S-s* in the heat of dusty fights) — Princess ii 241
Sunshine Like *s* on a dancing rill, — Rosalind 29
where broad *s* laves The lawn by some cathedral, — D. of F. Women 189
Simeon, whose brain the *s* bakes; — St. S. Stylites 164
frolic welcome took The thunder and the *s*, — Ulysses 48
The random *s* lighten'd! — Amphion 56
Autumn's mock *s* of the faded woods — Aylmer's Field 610
past In *s*: right across its track there lay, — Sea Dreams 126
Many a little hand Glanced like a touch of *s* on the rocks, — Princess iii 357

Sunshine (*continued*) A stroke of cruel *s* on the cliff, *Princess iv* 524
When the tide ebbs in *s*, „ *vi* 162
clover sod, That takes the *s* and the rains, *In Mem. x* 14
Turn thy wild wheel thro' *s*, storm and cloud; *Marr. of Geraint* 348
This was the *s* that hath given the man *Balin and Balan* 181
glittering like May *s* on May leaves *Merlin and V.* 88
and the *s* came along with him. *Pelleas and E.* 6
s seem'd to brood More warmly on the heart *Lover's Tale i* 327
s on that sail at last which brings our Edwin home. *The Flight* 92
So fair in southern *s* bathed, *Freedom* 5
The gleam of household *s* ends, *The Wanderer* 1
Sun-smitten *S-s* Alps before me lay. *The Daisy* 62
Sun-star great *S-s* of morningtide, *Batt. of Brunanburh* 26
Sun-steep'd *S-s* at noon, and in the moon *Lotos-Eaters, C. S.* 29
Sun-stricken fell *S-s*, and that other lived alone. *Enoch Arden* 570
Sun-worship Their sweet *s-w*? *Gareth and L.* 1081
This old *s-w*, boy, will rise again, *Balin and Balan* 457
Superhuman Thrice multiplied by *s* pangs, *St. S. Stylites* 11
Superlative 'Most dearest' be a true *s*— *Sisters (E. and E.)* 292
Supersede one deep love doth *s* All other, *In Mem. xxxii* 5
Supersensual For such a *s* sensual bond *Merlin and V.* 109
Superstition was paid To woman, *s* all awry: *Princess ii* 137
Supper And after *s*, on a bed, *The Sisters* 16
dreams Of goodly *s* in the distant pool, *Gareth and L.* 1187
'So that ye do not serve me sparrow-hawks For *s*, *Marr. of Geraint* 305
cup itself, from which our Lord Drank at the last sad *s* *Holy Grail* 47
How oft the Cantab *s*, host and guest, *To W. H. Brookfield* 4
Fur the men ater *s* 'ed sung their songs *Owd Roä* 35
Supple *s*, sinew-corded, apt at arms; *Princess v* 535
And rosy knees and *s* roundedness, *Lucretius* 190
Supple-sinew'd Iron jointed, *s-s*, they shall dive, *Locksley Hall* 169
Supple-sliding scoundrel in the *s-s* knee.' *Sea Dreams* 168
Supplest and Death will freeze the *s* limbs— *Happy* 46
Suppliant many another *s* crying came *Gareth and L.* 436
look'd and saw The novice, weeping, *s*, *Guinevere* 664
Supplicated shall I brook to be *s*? *Boädicea* 9
Supplicating Besought him, *s*, if he cared *Enoch Arden* 163
would they listen, did they pity me *s*? *Boädicea* 8
Supplication With *s* both of knees and tongue: *Holy Grail* 602
Supplied And he *s* my want the more *In Mem. lxxix* 19
Supporter like *s's* on a shield, Bow-back'd *Princess vi* 358
Or two wild men *s's* of a shield, *Geraint and E.* 267
Suppose 'Good soul! *s* I grant it thee, *Two Voices* 38
Suppression *See* **Self-suppression**
Supremacy In knowledge of their own *s*.' *Œnone* 133
Supreme every legend fair Which the *s* Caucasian mind *Palace of Art* 126
Supt The kitchen brewis that was ever *s* *Gareth and L.* 781
Sure (*See also* **Sewer**) Not make him *s* that he shall cease? *Two Voices* 282
'Ah! *s* within him and without, „ 307
'Mid onward-sloping motions infinite Making for one *s* goal. *Palace of Art* 248
rest thee *s* That I shall love thee well *Œnone* 159
To be *s* the preacher says, *Grandmother* 93
'Fool,' he answer'd, 'death is *s* *Sailor Boy* 13
Bound for the Hall, I am *s* was he: *Maud I x* 25
I am quite quite *s* That there is one to love me; „ *xi* 10
O Maud were *s* of Heaven If lowliness could save her. „ *xii* 19
Most *s* am I, quite *s*, he is not dead.' *Geraint and E.* 545
they do not flow From evil done; right *s* am I of that, *Guinevere* 189
'you are *s* it 'll all come right,' *First Quarrel* 1
I am *s* it 'ill all come right.' (repeat) „ 74, 91
lit by *s* hands,—With thunders, and with lightnings, *Buonaparte* 5
He means me I'm *s* to be happy *Rizpah* 76
well, I am not *s*—But if there lie a preference *Sisters (E. and E.)* 289
let come what will; at last the end is *s*, *The Flight* 103
And *s* am I, by Muriel, one day came And saw you, *The Ring* 312
I am all but *s* I have—in Kendal church— *Romney's R.* 19
For you forgive me, you are *s* of that— „ 160
Surely I am not *s* one of those Caught by the flower *The Ring* 343
How *s* glidest thou from March to May, *Prog. of Spring* 109
Surer For *s* sign had follow'd, either hand, *M. d'Arthur* 76
Surer (*continued*) If we could give them *s*, quicker proof— *Princess iii* 282
For *s* sign had follow'd, either hand, *Pass. of Arthur* 244
Surety We did but keep you *s* for our son, *Princess v* 25
Surf White *s* wind-scatter'd over sails and masts, *D. of F. Women* 31
like a wader in the *s*, Beyond the brook, *The Brook* 117
the breakers on the shore Sloped into louder *s*: *Lover's Tale iii* 15
again the stormy *s* Crash'd in the shingle: „ 53
Surface (adj.) Then, for the *s* eye, that only doats *The Ring* 163
Surface (s) In roaring he shall rise and on the *s* die. *The Kraken* 15
But ere he dipt the *s*, rose an arm *M. d'Arthur* 143
And down my *s* crept. *Talking Oak* 162
These flashes on the *s* are not he. *Princess iv* 253
To make the sullen *s* crisp. *In Mem. xlix* 8
when the *s* rolls, Hath power to walk the waters *Com. of Arthur* 293
Then from the smitten *s* flash'd, *Lancelot and E.* 1236
But ere he dipt the *s*, rose an arm *Pass. of Arthur* 311
Who with his head below the *s* dropt *Lover's Tale i* 636
You, what the cultured *s* grows, *Mechanophilus* 33
Surface-shadow sees and stirs the *s-s* *Ancient Sage* 38
Surge tho' the *s* Of some new deluge *If I were loved* 11
when the *s* was seething free, *Lotos-Eaters, C. S.* 106
sands and yeasty *s's* mix In caves *Sailor Boy* 9
I heard the shingle grinding in the *s*, *Holy Grail* 811
the *s* fell From thunder into whispers; *Lover's Tale iii* 30
Surged foeman *s*, and waver'd, and reel'd *Heavy Brigade* 62
Surgery-school Fresh from the *s-s's* of France *In the Child. Hosp.* 3
Surging In middle ocean meets the *s* shock, *Will* 8
Their *s* charges foam'd themselves away; *Ode on Well.* 126
and it ran *S* and swaying all round us, *Def. of Lucknow* 38
Surly And there the *s* village-churls, *L. of Shalott ii* 16
And humm'd a *s* hymn. *Talking Oak* 300
Surmise silent, we with blind *s* Regarding, *Princess iv* 381
Surname Simeon of the pillar, by *s* Stylites, *St. S. Stylites* 161
'Katie.' 'That were strange. What *s*?' *The Brook* 212
wrote Name, *s*, all as clear as noon, *The Ring* 237
Surpass But tho' the port *s'es* praise, *Will Water.* 77
As we *s* our fathers' skill, *Mechanophilus* 21
Surprise (s) with *s* Froze my swift speech: *D. of F. Women* 89
With some *s* and thrice as much disdain Turn'd, *Marr. of Geraint* 557
But kept it for a sweet *s* at morn. Yea, truly is it not a sweet *s*? „ 703
Surprise (verb) *S* thee ranging with thy peers. *In Mem. xliv* 12
Surrender 'Never *s*, I charge you, *Def. of Lucknow* 10
Survive *S* in spirits render'd free, *In Mem. xxxviii* 10
Suspend And he *s's* his converse with a friend, *Marr. of Geraint* 340
Suspicion A vague *s* of the breast: *Two Voices* 336
There gleam'd a vague *s* in his eyes: *Lancelot and E.* 127
Suspicious *S* that her nature had a taint. *Marr. of Geraint* 68
Thro' all the outworks of *s* pride; *Isabel* 24
Sussex Green *S* fading into blue *Pro. to Gen. Hamley* 7
Sustain bad him with good heart *s* himself— *Aylmer's Field* 544
Sustain'd Be dimm'd of sorrow, or *s*; *In Mem. lxxxv* 10
Sustaining They tremble, the *s* crags: „ *cxxvii* 11
Sustenance Gain'd for her own a scanty *s*, *Enoch Arden* 259
No want was there of human *s*, „ 554
One *s*, which, still as thought grew large, *Lover's Tale i* 240
Sùttee were seen or heard Fires of *S*, *Akbar's Dream* 196
Swallies (swallow) whin they *s* the man intire! *Tomorrow* 66
Swallow (s) Above in the wind was the *s*, *Dying Swan* 16
the *s* 'ill come back again with summer *May Queen. N. Y's. E.* 19
While the prime *s* dips his wing, *Edwin Morris* 145
The *s* stopt as he hunted the fly, *Poet's Song* 9
I glance, Among my skimming *s's*; *The Brook* 175
Where they like *s's* coming out of time *Princess ii* 431
I watch'd the *s* winging south From mine own land, „ *iv* 89
'O *S*, *S*, flying, flying South, „ 93
O tell her, *S*, thou that knowest each, „ 96
'O *S*, *S*, if I could follow, and light „ 99
'O tell her, *S*, that thy brood is flown: „ 108
'O *S*, flying from the golden woods, „ 114
And *s* and sparrow and throstle, *Window, Ay* 14
The Mayfly is torn by the *s*, *Maud I iv* 23
'The *s* and the swift are near akin, *Com. of Arthur* 313
For Knowledge is the *s* on the lake *Ancient Sage* 37
Hubert brings me home With April and the *s*. *The Ring* 60

Swear (*continued*) 'I s (and else may insects prick Each leaf *Talking Oak* 69
'I s, by leaf, and wind, and rain, „ 81
And hear me s a solemn oath, „ 281
I have a secret—only s, Before I tell you—s upon the book Not to reveal it, *Enoch Arden* 837
'S' added Enoch sternly 'on the book.' „ 842
I s you shall not make them out of mine. *Aylmer's Field* 301
she made me s it—'Sdeath— *Princess v* 291
S by St. something—I forget her name— „ 293
I s to you, lawful and lawless war *Maud II v* 94
but, so thou dread to s, Pass not beneath this gateway, *Gareth and L.* 272
Repentant of the word she made him s, „ 527
I s thou canst not fling the fourth.' „ 1327
I s it would not ruffle me so much *Geraint and E.* 150
I s I will not ask your meaning in it: „ 743
But ere I leave thee let me s once more *Merlin and V.* 929
I s by truth and knighthood that I gave *Lancelot and E.* 1297
But by mine eyes and by mine ears I s, *Holy Grail* 864
Will ye not lie? not s, as there ye kneel, *Last Tournament* 646
I say, S to me thou wilt love me ev'n when old, „ 652
Than had we never sworn. I s no more. „ 660
lay their hands in mine and s To reverence the King, *Guinevere* 467
where is he can s But that some broken gleam *Ded. Poem Prin. Alice* 17
O my lord, I s to you I heard his voice *Columbus* 145
I s and s forsworn To love him most, *The Flight* 49
and s the brain is in the feet. *Locksley H., Sixty* 136
who shall s it cannot be? „ 269

Sweär an' 'e s's, an' 'e says to 'im 'Noa. *Village Wife* 67
Ye niver 'eärd Steevie s 'cep' it wur at a dog *Spinster's S's.* 60

Sweär'd (swore) an' s as I'd breäk ivry stick *North. Cobbler* 35

Sweärin S agean, you Toms, *Spinster's S's.* 59

Swearing (*See also* **Sweärin**) s he had glamour enow In his own blood, *Gareth and L.* 209
And s men to vows impossible, *Lancelot and E.* 130

Sweat bloody thumbs S on his blazon'd chairs; *Walk. to the Mail* 76
every hour Must s her sixty minutes to the death, *Golden Year* 69
That shriek and s in pigmy wars *Lit. Squabbles* 2
S, writhings, anguish, labouring of the lungs *Pass. of Arthur* 115

Sweating And, s rosin, plump'd the pine *Amphion* 47
With a weird bright eye, s and trembling, *Aylmer's Field* 585
Then loosed their s horses from the yoke, *Spec. of Iliad* 2
Went s underneath a sack of corn, *Marr. of Geraint* 263
He up the side, s with agony, got, *Lancelot and E.* 494

Sweeät (sweet) sa pratty an' neät an' s, *North. Cobbler* 43
sa pratty, an' feät, an' neät, an' s? „ 108

Sweep (s) and a s Of richest pauses, *Eleänore* 65
The parson taking wide and wider s's, *The Epic* 14
by many a s Of meadow smooth from aftermath *Audley Court* 13
From the dread s of the down-streaming seas: *Enoch Arden* 55
or the s Of some precipitous rivulet „ 586
The s of scythe in morning dew, *In Mem. lxxxix* 18
Made but a single bound, and with a s of it *Geraint and E.* 727

Sweep (verb) S the green that folds thy grave. *A Dirge* 6
Would s the tracts of day and night. *Two Voices* 69
never more Shall lone Œnone see the morning mist S thro' them; *Œnone* 217
we s into the younger day: *Locksley Hall* 183
Who s the crossings, wet or dry, *Will Water.* 47
those long swells of breaker s The nutmeg rocks *The Voyage* 39
There let the wind s and the plover cry; *Come not, when, etc.* 5
That s's with all its autumn bowers, *In Mem. xi* 10
We heard them s the winter land; „ *xxx* 10
while the wind began to s A music „ *ciii* 53
But s's away as out we pass To range the woods, „ *Con.* 95
to s In ever-highering eagle-circles *Gareth and L.* 20
And s me from my hold upon the world, *Merlin and V.* 303
heard the hollow-ringing heavens s Over him till by miracle— *Holy Grail* 678
S's suddenly all its half-moulder'd chords *Lover's Tale i* 19
often s's athwart in storm— „ 50
sea-current would s us out to the main. *Despair* 51

Sweeping (*See also* **Earth-sweeping, Long-sweeping**) And with a s of the arm, *A Character* 16
passion s thro' me left me dry, *Locksley Hall* 131
Sweeping (*continued*) S the frothfly from the fescue brush'd *Aylmer's Field* 530
Of that great breaker, s up the strand, *Com. of Arthur* 387
sudden gust that s down Took the edges of the pall, *Lover's Tale iii* 34
shape with wings Came s by him, *St. Telemachus* 25

Sweet (*See also* **Heaven-sweet, Lowly-sweet, May-sweet, Perfect-sweet, Star-sweet, Sunny-sweet, Sweeät**)
False-eyed Hesper, unkind, where is my s Rosalind? *Leonine Eleg.* 16
How s to have a common faith! *Supp. Confessions* 33
S in their utmost bitterness, „ 117
S lips whereon perpetually did reign The summer calm *Isabel* 7
She could not look on the s heaven, *Mariana* 15
Sudden glances, s and strange, *Madeline* 5
vaults of pillar'd palm, Imprisoning s's, *Arabian Nights* 40
In s dreams softer than unbroken rest *Ode to Memory* 29
With music and s showers Of festal flowers, „ 77
S faces, rounded arms, and bosoms prest *Sea-Fairies* 3
And s is the colour of cove and cave, And s shall your welcome be: „ 30
We will kiss s kisses, and speak s words: „ 34
O pale, pale face so s and meek, *Oriana* 66
O S pale Margaret, (repeat) *Margaret* 1, 54
Your melancholy s and frail „ 7
'His little daughter, whose s face He kiss'd, *Two Voices* 253
The s church bells began to peal. „ 408
These three made unity so s, „ 421
'What is it thou knowest, s voice?' „ 440
My own s Alice, we must die. *Miller's D.* 18
So s it seems with thee to walk, „ 29
S Alice, if I told her all?' „ 120
A trifle, s! which true love spells— „ 187
S gales, as from deep gardens, blow *Fatima* 24
And that s incense rise?' *Palace of Art* 44
For that s incense rose and never fail'd, „ 45
Or gay, or grave, or s, or stern, „ 91
Or s Europa's mantle blew unclasp'd, „ 117
Making s close of his delicious toils— „ 185
Nor would I break for your s sake *L. C. V. de Vere* 13
Oh your s eyes, your low replies: „ 29
by the meadow-trenches blow the faint s cuckoo-flowers; *May Queen* 30
O s is the new violet, *May Queen, Con.* 5
And s is all the land about, „ 7
O s and strange it seems to me, „ 53
THERE is s music here that softer falls *Lotos-Eaters, C. S.* 1
Music that brings s sleep down from the blissful skies. „ 7
How s it were, hearing the downward stream, „ 54
How s (while warm airs lull us, blowing lowly) „ 89
Only to hear were s, „ 99
Surely, surely, slumber is more s than toil, „ 126
And s it was to dream of Fatherland, *Lotos-Eaters* 39
whose s breath Preluded those melodious bursts *D. of F. Women* 5
S as new buds in Spring. „ 272
Failing to give the bitter of the s, „ 286
Sleep till the end, true soul and s. *To J. S.* 73
and stirr'd her lips For some s answer, *Gardener's D.* 159
Of that which came between, more s than each, „ 252
My s, wild, fresh three quarters of a year, *Edwin Morris* 2
made it s To walk, to sit, to sleep, to wake, „ 39
Then low and s I whistled thrice; „ 113
S! s! spikenard, and balm, and frankincense. *St. S. Stylites* 211
Ah! let me not be fool'd, s saints: „ 212
'Yet seem'd the pressure thrice as s *Talking Oak* 145
The slow s hours that bring us all things good, *Love and Duty* 57
Thy s eyes brighten slowly close to mine, *Tithonus* 38
Whispering I knew not what of wild and s, „ 61
How s are looks that ladies bend *Sir Galahad* 13
S Emma Moreland of yonder town *Edward Gray* 1
S Emma Moreland spoke to me: „ 5
'S Emma Moreland, love no more „ 7
I buried her like my own s child, *Lady Clare* 27
colour flushes Her s face from brow to chin: *L. of Burleigh* 62
So s a face, such angel grace, *Beggar Maid* 13
Who make it seem more s to be *You might have won* 29
And chanted a melody loud and s, *Poet's Song* 6
To where the rivulets of s water ran; *Enoch Arden* 642
'If I might look on her s face again „ 718

Sweet (*continued*) Like fountains of *s* water in the sea, *Enoch Arden* 803
Or ev'n the *s* half-English Neilgherry air *The Brook* 17
'*S* Katie, once I did her a good turn, „ 74
Of *s* seventeen subdued me ere she spoke) „ 113
Arrived and found the sun of *s* content Re-risen .. 168
I move the *s* forget-me-nots „ 172
her *s* face and faith Held him from that: *Aylmer's Field* 392
She look'd so *s*, he kiss'd her tenderly „ 555
'That was then your dream,' she said, 'Not sad, but *s*.' *Sea Dreams* 106
'So *s*, I lay,' said he, 'And mused upon it, „ 107
Their wildest wailings never out of tune With that *s* note; „ 232
Nothing to mar the sober majesties Of settled, *s*, Epicurean life. *Lucretius* 218
And *s* girl-graduates in their golden hair. *Princess, Pro.* 142
And *s* as English air could make her, „ 155
S thoughts would swarm as bees about their queen. „ *i* 40
We remember love ourselves In our *s* youth: „ 123
S household talk, and phrases of the hearth, „ *ii* 315
Is she The *s* proprietress a shadow? „ 415
S and low, *s* and low, „ *iii* 1
'What pardon, *s* Melissa, for a blush?' „ 66
'O how *s*' I said (For I was half-oblivious of my mask) „ 337
O *s* and far from cliff and scar „ *iv* 9
And *s* as those by hopeless fancy feign'd „ 55
So *s* a voice and vague, fatal to men, „ 64
Like some *s* sculpture draped from head to foot, „ *v* 57
'Lift up your head, *s* sister: lie not thus. .. 64
S is it to have done the thing one ought, .. 67
My one *s* child, whom I shall see no more! „ 83
My babe, my *s* Aglaïa, my one child: .. 101
Twice as magnetic to *s* influences Of earth and heaven? „ 191
'We remember love ourself In our *s* youth; „ 208
Prince, she can be *s* to those she loves, „ 289
'*S* my child, I live for thee.' „ *vi* 16
by and by *S* order lived again with other laws: .. *vii* 19
two dewdrops on the petal shake To the same *s* air, „ 69
showers of random *s* on maid and man. „ 86
And call her *s*, as if in irony, „ 97
nor more *S* Ida: palm to palm she sat: „ 135
'If you be, what I think you, some *s* dream, „ 145
only, if a dream, *S* dream, be perfect. „ 149
she found a small *S* Idyl, and once more, as low, she read: „ 191
and *s* is every sound, Sweeter thy voice, but every sound is *s*; .. 218
she had fail'd In *s* humility; had fail'd in all; „ 229
could we make her as the man, *S* Love were slain: „ 277
lives A drowning life, besotted in *s* self, .. 314
forced *S* love on pranks of saucy boyhood: .. 344
Lay thy *s* hands in mine and trust to me.' „ 366
Uplift a thousand voices full and *s*, *Ode Inter. Exhib.* 1
Welcome her, all things youthful and *s*, *W. to Alexandra* 8
he turn'd, and I saw his eyes all wet, in the *s* moonshine: *Grandmother* 49
There lay the *s* little body that never had drawn a breath. „ 62
Sin' I mun doy I mun doy, thaw loife they says is *s*, *N. Farmer, O. S.* 63
thou's *s* upo' parson's lass— „ *N. S.* 11
For a score of *s* little summers or so?' *The Islet* 2
The *s* little wife of the singer said, „ 3
To a *s* little Eden on earth that I know, „ 14
And strain to make an inch of room For their *s* selves, *Lit. Squabbles* 10
honouring your *s* faith in him, May trust himself; *A Dedication* 5
O lights, are you flying over her *s* little face? *Window, On the Hill* 13
Where is another *s* as my *s*, „ *Letter* 1
Claspt on her seal, my *s*! „ *Answer* 2
O *s* and bitter in a breath, *In Mem. iii* 3
Thro' four *s* years arose and fell, „ *xxii* 3
'They rest,' we said, 'their sleep is *s*,' „ *xxx* 19
I strive To keep so *s* a thing alive:' „ *xxxv* 7
hear thy laurel whisper *s* About the ledges of the hill.' .. *xxxvii* 7
S soul, do with me as thou wilt; „ *lxv* 1
To utter love more *s* than praise. .. *lxxvii* 16
The same *s* forms in either mind. „ *lxxix* 8

Sweet (*continued*) But Death returns an answer *s*: *In Mem. lxxxi* 9
O *s* new-year delaying long; „ *lxxxiii* 2
S after showers, ambrosial air, „ *lxxxvi* 1
Wild bird, whose warble, liquid *s*, „ *lxxxviii* 1
regret for buried time That keenlier in *s* April wakes, „ *cxvi* 2
Desire of nearness doubly *s*; „ *cxvii* 6
S Hesper-Phosphor, double name „ *cxxi* 17
And if the words were *s* and strong „ *cxxv* 11
S human hand and lips and eye; „ *cxxix* 6
Maud with her *s* purse-mouth when my father dangled the grapes, *Maud I i* 71
And she touch'd my hand with a smile so *s*, „ *vi* 12
But a smile could make it *s*. (repeat) .. 39, 95
How prettily for his own *s* sake .. 51
What some have found so *s*; .. *xi* 4
Let the *s* heavens endure, .. 8
Maud is as true as Maud is *s*: .. *xiii* 32
Think I may hold dominion *s*, .. *xvi* 12
In our low world, where yet 'tis *s* to live. .. *xviii* 48
silver knell Of twelve *s* hours that past in bridal white, .. 65
Seal'd her mine from her first *s* breath. „ *xix* 41
That, if left uncancell'd, had been so *s*: .. 46
And for your *s* sake to yours; „ 91
(If I read her *s* will right) .. *xxi* 10
From the meadow your walks have left so *s* .. *xxii* 39
She is coming, my own, my *s*; „ 67
For she, *s* soul, had hardly spoken a word, „ *II i* 11
'Tis a morning pure and *s*, (repeat) .. *iv* 31, 35
'Take me, *s*, To the regions of thy rest'? „ 87
S nature gilded by the gracious gleam Of letters, *Ded. of Idylls* 39
Call him baseborn, and since his ways are *s*, *Com. of Arthur* 180
friends Of Arthur, gazing on him, tall, with bright *S* faces, „ 279
And spake *s* words, and comforted my heart, „ 349
But *s* again, and then I loved him well. „ 355
S mother, do ye love the child?' *Gareth and L.* 35
so the boy, *S* mother, neither clomb, „ 56
'True love, *s* son, had risk'd himself and climb'd, „ 60
S is the chase: „ 93
'*S* son, for there be many who deem him not, „ 121
Stay, *s* son.' „ 131
Rather than—O *s* heaven! „ 741
S lord, how like a noble knight he talks! „ 777
Their *s* sun-worship? these be for the snare „ 1081
He compass'd her with *s* observances And worship, *Marr. of Geraint* 48
in the *s* face of her Whom he loves most, „ 122
Lost in *s* dreams, and dreaming of her love For Lancelot, „ 158
Singing; and as the *s* voice of a bird, „ 329
So the *s* voice of Enid moved Geraint; „ 334
And Enid brought *s* cakes to make them cheer, „ 388
And seeing her so *s* and serviceable, „ 393
Sank her *s* head upon her gentle breast; „ 527
And softly to her own *s* heart she said: .. 618
S heaven, how much I shall discredit him! „ 621
But kept it for a *s* surprise at morn. Yea, truly is it not a *s* surprise? .. 703
But rested with her *s* face satisfied; .. 776
In words whose echo lasts, they were so *s*, „ 782
To compass her with *s* observances, *Geraint and E.* 39
And she was ever praying the *s* heavens To save her dear lord „ 44
But keep a touch of *s* civility Here in the heart „ 312
tender sound of his own voice And *s* self-pity, „ 349
But ended with apology so *s*, „ 394
'Your *s* faces make good fellows fools And traitors. „ 399
S lady, never since I first drew breath Have I beheld „ 619
breath Of her *s* tendance hovering over him, „ 926
but when he mark'd his high *s* smile In passing, *Balin and Balan* 160
and with how *s* grace She greeted my return! „ 193
Hail, royal knight, we break on thy *s* rest, „ 470
Again she sigh'd 'Pardon, *s* lord! „ 497
'Rise, my *s* King, and kiss me on the lips, „ 516
S lord, ye do right well to whisper this. „ 529
Here her slow *s* eyes Fear-tremulous, *Merlin and V.* 85

Sweet (*continued*) With dark *s* hints of some who prized him more *Merlin and V.* 159
But, Vivien, when you sang me that *s* rhyme, .. 434
S were the days when I was all unknown, .. 501
Those twelve *s* moons confused his fatherhood.' .. 712
What say ye then to *s* Sir Sagramore, .. 721
To crop his own *s* rose before the hour?' .. 725
And they, *s* soul, that most impute a crime Are pronest to it, " 825
rapt By all the *s* and sudden passion of youth *Lancelot and E.* 282
She needs must bid farewell to *s* Lavaine. .. 341
'Ah my *s* lord Sir Lancelot,' said Lavaine, .. 512
For if you love, it will be *s* to give it; And if he love, it will be *s* to have it .. 692
S father, will you let me lose my wits?' .. 752
S father, I behold him in my dreams .. 763
to be *s* and serviceable To noble knights in sickness, .. 767
Would call her friend and sister, *s* Elaine, .. 865
arraying her *s* self In that wherein she deem'd she look'd her best, .. 906
I had been wedded earlier, *s* Elaine: .. 935
for true you are and *s* Beyond mine old belief in womanhood, .. 954
'Peace to thee, *S* sister,' .. 997
'*S* is true love tho' given in vain, in vain; And *s* is death who puts an end to pain: .. 1007
'Love, art thou *s*? then bitter death must be: Love, thou art bitter; *s* is death to me. .. 1010
'*S* love, that seems not made to fade away, *S* death, that seems to make us loveless clay, .. 1013
'*S* brothers, yesternight I seem'd a curious little maid again, .. 1034
S father, all too faint and sick am I For anger: .. 1086
'*S* father, and bid call the ghostly man Hither, .. 1099
'O *s* father, tender and true, Deny me not,' she said— .. 1110
'Farewell, *s* sister,' parted all in tears. .. 1152
Ah simple heart and *s*, Ye loved me, damsel, " 1393
But the *s* vision of the Holy Grail *Holy Grail* 31
'*S* brother, I have seen the Holy Grail: .. 107
'But she, the wan *s* maiden, shore away .. 149
We that are plagued with dreams of something *s* .. 625
the *s* Grail Glided and past, and close upon it peal'd .. 694
A *s* voice singing in the topmost tower To the eastward: " 834
and the *s* smell of the fields Past, *Pelleas and E.* 5
their malice on the placid lip Froz'n by *s* sleep, .. 433
Who yells Here in the still *s* summer night, but I— .. 473
'O *s* star, Pure on the virgin forehead of the dawn!' .. 504
Till the *s* heavens have fill'd it from the heights .. 510
But the *s* body of a maiden babe. *Last Tournament* 48
New loves are *s* as those that went before: .. 280
that desert lodge to Tristram lookt So *s*, .. 388
the *s* name Allured him first, and then the maid herself, .. 398
If this be *s*, to sin in leading-strings, .. 574
thy *s* memories Of Tristram in that year he was away.' .. 579
To pine and waste in those *s* memories. .. 598
'May God be with thee, *s*, when old and gray, .. 627
'May God be with thee, *s*, when thou art old, And *s* no more to me!' .. 629
that I should suck Lies like *s* wines: .. 645
'Press this a little closer, *s*, " 718
'Have we not heard the bridegroom is so *s*? *Guinevere* 177
Ah *s* lady, the King's grief For his own self, .. 196
'and, *s* lady, if I seem To vex an ear too sad to listen to me, " 314
As I could think, *s* lady, yours would be Such as they are, " 352
Rapt in *s* talk or lively, all on love And sport " 386
Thou hast not made my life so *s* to me, " 451
To lead *s* lives in purest chastity, " 474
yet in him keeps A draught of that *s* fountain that he loves, *Lover's Tale i* 141
Yet was not the less *s* for that it seem'd? " 155
All—all but one; and strange to me, and *s*, *S* thro' strange years to know " 243
Still to believe it—'tis so *s* a thought, .. 275
Absorbing all the incense of *s* thoughts " 469

Sweet (*continued*) Is presently received in a *s* grave Of eglantines, *Lover's Tale i* 528
Held converse *s* and low—low converse *s*, .. 541
It was so happy an hour, so *s* a place, .. 558
At first her voice was very *s* and low, .. 563
A morning air, *s* after rain, ran over The rippling levels .. *iii* 3
That will not hear my call, however *s*, .. *iv* 160
So the *s* figure folded round with night .. 219
Sad, *s*, and strange together—floated in— " 304
A *s* voice that—you scarce could better that. *Sisters (E. and E.)* 14
the *s* eyes frown: the lips Seem but a gash. .. 106
And all her *s* self-sacrifice and death. .. 255
his voice was low as from other worlds, and his eyes were *s*, *V. of Maeldune* 117
For that *s* mother land which gave them birth *Tiresias* 122
The small *s* face was flush'd, *The Wreck* 60
Ten long *s* summer days upon deck, .. 64
one morning a bird with a warble plaintively *s* .. 81
'Ten long *s* summer days' of fever, " 147
she was always loyal and *s*— *Despair* 49
The morning with such music, would never be so *s*! *The Flight* 66
O *s*, they tell me that the world is hard, " 101
Achora, yer laste little whishper was *s* as the lilt of a bird! *Tomorrow* 33
I calls 'em arter the fellers es once was *s* upo' me? *Spinster's S's.* 4
I remember how you kiss'd the miniature with those *s* eyes. *Locksley H., Sixty* 12
S St. Francis of Assisi, would that he were here again, " 100
the *s* sound ran Thro' palace and cottage door, *Dead Prophet* 37
S Catullus's all-but-island, olive-silvery Sirmio! *Frater Ave, etc.* 9
torpid mummy wheat Of Egypt bore a grain as *s* *To Prof. Jebb* 6
In your *s* babe she finds but you— *The Ring* 365
Beat upon mine! you are mine, my *s*! All mine from your pretty blue eyes to your feet, My *s*.' *Romney's R.* 95
And find the white heather wherever you go, My *s*.' " 109
'wasting the *s* summer hours'? *Charity* 1
All very well just now to be calling me darling and *s*, " 7
Sing thou low or loud or *s*, *Poets and Critics* 6

Sweet-'arts (sweet-hearts) Lucy wur läame o' one leg, *s-a* she niver 'ed none— *Village Wife* 99
Milk for my *s-a*, Bess! *Spinster's S's.* 1
S-a! Molly belike may 'a lighted to-night upo' one. .. 7
S-a! thanks to the Lord that I niver not listen'd to noän! .. 8
An' noän of my four *s-a* 'ud 'a let me 'a hed my oän waäy, .. 101

Sweeten *S*'s the spirit still. *D. of F. Women* 236
They freshen and *s* the wards *In the Child. Hosp.* 38

Sweeten'd Lo! *s* with the summer light, *Lotos-Eaters, C. S.* 32
One rose, my rose, that *s* all mine air— *Pelleas and E.* 403

Sweeter Whether smile or frown be *s*, *Madeline* 13
And *s* is the young lamb's voice *May Queen, Con.* 6
And *s* far is death than life to me " 8
There came a *s* token when the night and morning meet: " 22
s than the dream Dream'd by a happy man, *Gardener's D.* 71
'Your own will be the *s*,' *Sea Dreams* 318
S thy voice, but every sound is sweet; *Princess vii* 219
'*S* to me' she said 'this garden rose *Balin and Balan* 269
s still The wild-wood hyacinth and the bloom of May. " 270
I know not which is *s*, no, not I. (repeat) *Lancelot and E.* 1009, 1015
O Love, if death be *s*, let me die. " 1012
O *s* than all memories of thee, *Last Tournament* 585
Then—while a s music wakes, *To the Queen* 13
Chaunteth not the brooding bee *S* tones than calumny? *A Dirge* 17
Drip *s* dews than traitor's tear. " 24
You could not light upon a *s* thing: *Walk. to the Mail* 52
Ah, *s* to be drunk with loss, *In Mem. i* 11
s seems To rest beneath the clover sod, .. *x* 12
With *s* manners, purer laws. " *cvi* 16
can a *s* chance ever come to me here? *Maud I i* 62
To the *s* blood by the other side; .. *xiii* 34
For nothing can be *s* Than maiden Maud in either. .. *xx* 21
Mixt with kisses *s s* Than anything on earth. .. *II iv* 9

Sweeter (*continued*) And *s* than the bride of Cassivelaun, *Marr. of Geraint* 744
And you, that wear a wreath of *s* bay, *Poets and their B.* 7
Sweetest The *s* lady of the time, *Arabian Nights* 141
where *s* sunlight falls Upon the storied walls; *Ode to Memory* 85
Then her *s* meal she makes On the first-born of her sons. *Vision of Sin* 145
' The mother of the *s* little maid, *Princess ii* 279
The passing of the *s* soul That ever look'd with human eyes. *In Mem. lvii* 11
tiny-trumpeting gnat can break our dream When *s*; *Lancelot and E.* 138
love Of man and woman when they love their best, Closest and *s*, „ 870
Sweet-Gale *S-G* rustle round the shelving keel; *Edwin Morris* 110
Sweetheart (*See also* **Sweet-'arts**) ' *S*, I love you so well *Grandmother* 50
' *S* '—this was the letter— *First Quarrel* 51
Sweet-hearted *S-h*, you, whose light-blue eyes *In Mem. xcvi* 2
Sweetness Now folds the lily all her *s* up, *Princess vii* 186
He gain in *s* and in moral height, „ 281
Will change my *s* more and more, *In Mem. xxxv* 15
A secret *s* in the stream, „ *lxiv* 20
Thy *s* from its proper place? „ *lxxxiii* 6
Nor mine the *s* or the skill, „ *cx* 17
For your *s* hardly leaves me a choice *Maud I v* 24
Tho' I fancy her *s* only due „ *xiii* 33
Foregoing all her *s*, like a weed. *Holy Grail* 623
dreams of something sweet Beyond all *s* „ 626
It seem'd to keep its *s* to itself, *Lover's Tale i* 154
Can ye take off the *s* from the flower, The colour and the *s* from the rose, „ 171
and over-full Of *s*, and in smelling of itself, „ 272
wild youth of an evil prince, Is without *s*, „ 355
But taken with the *s* of the place, „ 531
her words stole with most prevailing *s* Into my heart, „ 553
And with the excess of *s* and of awe, „ *ii* 155
Desolate *s*—far and far away— *Ancient Sage* 226
Sweet-smelling led me thro' the short *s-s* lanes *The Brook* 122
Sweet-voiced *S-v*, a song of welcome, *Balin and Balan* 86
Swell (s) (*See also* **Ground-swell**) And the wavy *s* of the soughing reeds, *Dying Swan* 38
From those four jets four currents in one *s* *Palace of Art* 33
up the valley came a *s* of music on the wind. *May Queen, Con.* 32
those long *s's* of breaker sweep The nutmeg rocks *The Voyage* 39
So fresh they rose in shadow'd *s's* *The Letters* 46
on the *s* The silver lily heaved and fell; *To E. L.* 18
That only heaved with a summer *s*. *The Daisy* 12
only the *s* Of the long waves that roll *Maud I xviii* 62
Swell (verb) above him *s* Huge sponges of millennial growth *The Kraken* 5
thick with white bells the clover-hill *s's* *Sea-Fairies* 14
Or sometimes they *s* and move, *Eleänore* 111
And while he sinks or *s's* *Talking Oak* 270
S's up, and shakes and falls. *Sir Galahad* 76
s On some dark shore just seen that it was rich. *Princess i* 248
S out and fail, as if a door Were shut *In Mem. xxviii* 7
Spring that *s's* the narrow brooks, „ *lxxxv* 70
Swell'd The broad seas *s* to meet the keel, *The Voyage* 13
low musical note *S* up and died; and, as it *s*, a ridge Of breaker issued from the belt, *Sea Dreams* 211
past into the belt and *s* again Slowly to music: „ 222
But still her lists were *s* and mine were lean; *Princess iv* 319
voice of the long sea-wave as it *s* *Maud I xiv* 31
Swelleth Her song the lintwhite *s*, *Claribel* 15
Swelling Of such a tide *s* toward the land, *Sea Dreams* 87
Swept And with a flying finger *s* my lips, *Gardener's D.* 246
A breeze thro' all the garden *s*, *Day-Dm., Revival* 6
swell'd to meet the keel, And *s* behind; *The Voyage* 14
He cast his body, and on we *s*. „ 80
S with it to the shore, and enter'd one *Sea Dreams* 89
and *s* away The men of flesh and blood, „ 236
down we *s* and charged and overthrew. *Ode on Well.* 130
No wing of wind the region *s*, *In Mem. lxxviii* 6
s the dust of ruin'd Rome From off the threshold *Gareth and L.* 135
voice *S* bellowing thro' the darkness on to dawn, „ 177
and all the sand *S* like a river, *Holy Grail* 800
S like a torrent of gems from the sky *V. of Maeldune* 46

Swept (*continued*) and *s* in a cataract off from her sides, *The Wreck* 90
And deed and song alike are *s* Away, *Epilogue* 67
she *s* The dust of earth from her knee. *Dead Prophet* 31
in the storms Of Autumn *s* across the city, *Demeter and P.* 71
Swerve *S* from her duty to herself and us— *Aylmer's Field* 304
line of the approaching rookery *s* From the elms, *Princess, Con.* 97
Nor pastoral rivulet that *s's* *In Mem. c* 14
made his beast that better knew it, *s* *Pelleas and E.* 551
remember how the course of Time will *s*, *Locksley H., Sixty* 235
Swerved be *s* from right to save A prince, *Princess ii* 290
And so my passion hath not *s* *In Mem. lxxxv* 49
they *s* and brake Flying, and Arthur call'd *Com. of Arthur* 119
But since our fortune *s* from sun to shade, *Marr. of Geraint* 714
And Holy Church, from whom I never *s* *Columbus* 63
Had never *s* for craft or fear, *To Marq. of Dufferin* 27
Swerving And at a sudden *s* of the road, *Geraint and E.* 506
' One night my pathway *s* east, *Holy Grail* 634
Swift (a bird) The swallow and the *s* are near akin, *Com. of Arthur* 313
Swift (adj.) but seeming-bitter From excess of *s* delight. *Rosalind* 32
' Not less *s* souls that yearn for light, *Two Voices* 67
From my *s* blood that went and came *Fatima* 16
Her loveliness with shame and with surprise Froze my *s* speech: *D. of F. Women* 90
Not *s* nor slow to change, but firm: *Love thou thy land* 31
This way and that dividing the *s* mind, *M. d'Arthur* 60
The sound of streams that *s* or slow *In Mem. xxxv* 10
This way and that dividing the *s* mind, *Pass. of Arthur* 228
At times her steps are *s* and rash; *To Marq. of Dufferin* 2
Not *s* or rash, when late she lent „ 5
Æonian Evolution, *s* or slow, Thro' all the Spheres— *The Ring* 44
Swifter With *s* movement and in purer light *Isabel* 32
Moved with one spirit round about the bay, Trod *s* steps; *Lover's Tale iii* 18
Swiftness And with a shameful *s*: *Com. of Arthur* 205
And with exceeding *s* ran the boat, *Holy Grail* 514
borne With more than mortal *s*, *Lover's Tale ii* 73
Swim ' High up the vapours fold and *s*: *Two Voices* 262
taught me how to skate, to row, to *s*, *Edwin Morris* 19
A light before me *s's*, *Sir Galahad* 26
The mystic glory *s's* away; *In Mem. lxvii* 9
And on the depths of death there *s's* „ *cviii* 11
Down to the river, sink or *s*, *Gareth and L.* 1154
read but on my breviary with ease, Till my head *s's*; *Holy Grail* 546
Swimming The *s* vapour slopes athwart the glen, *Œnone* 3
She rose, and fixt her *s* eyes upon him, *Enoch Arden* 325
Sun Burst from a *s* fleece of winter gray, *Demeter and P.* 20
Swindler and a wretched *s's* lie? *Maud I i* 56
Swine I watch the darkening droves of *s* *Palace of Art* 199
Upon her tower, the Niobe of *s*, *Walk. to the Mail* 99
all the *s* were sows, And all the dogs'— *Princess i* 192
poor are hovell'd and hustled together, each sex, like *s*. *Maud I i* 34
a villain fitter to stick *s* Than ride abroad *Gareth and L.* 865
one of all the drove should touch me: *s*!' *Merlin and V.* 699
S in the mud, that cannot see for slime, *Holy Grail* 771
Save that he were the *s* thou spakest of, „ 885
Lord, I was tending *s*, and the Red Knight *Last Tournament* 71
Who knew thee *s* enow before I came, „ 304
less than *s*, A naked aught—yet *s* I hold thee still, „ 308
For I have flung thee pearls and find thee *s*.' „ 310
S? I have wallow'd, I have wash'd— „ 315
S, say ye? *s*, goats, asses, rams and geese „ 321
' Then were *s*, goats, asses, geese The wiser fools, „ 325
Priest's pearl, flung down to *s*—The *s*, *Sir J. Oldcastle* 116
my lord is lower than his oxen or his *s*. *Locksley H., Sixty* 126
Swine-flesh men may taste *S-f*, drink wine; *Akbar's Dream* 54
Swineherd the *s's* malkin in the mast? *Last Tournament* 632
Swing (s) the rush of the air in the prone *s*, *Aylmer's Field* 86
Swing (verb) *s's* the trailer from the crag; *Locksley Hall* 162
The shrill bell rings, the censer *s's*, *Sir Galahad* 35
thrones and peoples are as waifs that *s*, *W. to Marie Alex.* 26
where they *s* the Locksley shield, *Locksley H., Sixty* 247
Swollen thou art but *s* with cold snows *Gareth and L.* 9
as strong gales Hold *s* clouds from raining, *D. of F. Women* 11
And blew the *s* cheek of a trumpeter, *Princess ii* 364
On yon *s* brook that bubbles fast By meadows *In Mem. xcix* 6

Swoon (s) as in a *s*, With dinning sound *Eleänore* 134
Down-deepening from *s* to *s*, *Fatima* 27
Till at the last he waken'd from his *s*, *Geraint and E.* 583
or thro' death Or deathlike *s*, *Pass. of Arthur* 120
First falls asleep in *s*, wherefrom awaked, *Lover's Tale i* 791
Swoon (verb) All round the coast the languid air did *s*, *Lotos-Eaters* 5
Lest he should *s* and tumble and be found, *Enoch Arden* 774
' A time to sicken and to *s*, *In Mem. xxi* 17
Swoon'd fell The woman shrieking at his feet, and *s*. *Aylmer's Field* 811
She nor *s*, nor utter'd cry : *Princess vi* 2
Which set the horror higher : a maiden *s* ; *Gareth and L.* 1394
and either fell, and *s* away. *Balin and Balan* 563
sank For the pure pain, and wholly *s* away. *Lancelot and E.* 518
Thereon she smote her hand : wellnigh she *s* : „ 625
With such a fierceness that I *s* away— *Holy Grail* 845
That here in utter dark I *s* away, *Last Tournament* 622
Swooning Lash the maiden into *s*, *Boädicea* 67
And I was faint to *s*, and you lay *Merlin and V.* 281
thus they bore her *s* to her tower. *Lancelot and E.* 968
for all my madness and my sin, And then my *s*, *Holy Grail* 850
Swoop and *s's* The vulture, beak and talon, *Princess v* 382
and thence *s* Down upon all things base, *Gareth and L.* 22
Swop *See* **Swap**
Sword Nor martyr-flames, nor trenchant *s's* *Clear-headed friend* 14
No *s* Of wrath her right arm whirl'd, *The Poet* 53
Many drew *s's* and died. *D. of F. Women* 95
Certain, if knowledge bring the *s*, That knowledge takes the *s* away. *Love thou thy land* 87
Clothed in white samite, mystic, wonderful, Holding the *s*— *M. d'Arthur* 32
Saying, ' King Arthur's *s*, Excalibur, „ 103
clutch'd the *s*, And strongly wheel'd and threw it. „ 135
No desolation but by *s* and fire ! *Aylmer's Field* 748
hoveringly a *s* Now over and now under, *Lucretius* 61
Man for the *s* and for the needle she : *Princess v* 448
And *s* to *s*, and horse to horse we hung, „ 539
Yet Harold's England fell to Norman *s's* ; *W. to Marie Alex.* 22
To draw, to sheathe a useless *s*, *In Mem. cxxviii* 13
The viler, as underhand, not openly bearing the *s*. *Maud I i* 28
She gave the King his huge cross-hilted *s*, *Com. of Arthur* 286
s That rose from out the bosom of the lake, „ 296
s rose, the hind fell, the herd was driven, „ 432
And down from one a *s* was hung, *Gareth and L.* 221
and knowing both of lance and *s*.' „ 731
four strokes they struck With *s*, and these were mighty ; „ 1043
Out, *s* ; we are thrown ! ' „ 1236
With *s* we have not striven ; „ 1264
How best to manage horse, lance, *s* and shield, „ 1351
This heard Geraint, and grasping at his *s*, *Geraint and E.* 725
touch it with a *s*, It buzzes fiercely *Merlin and V.* 431
That seem a *s* beneath a belt of three, „ 510
Of every dint a *s* had beaten in it, *Lancelot and E.* 19
knights, to whom the moving of my *s* *Holy Grail* 790
from the boat I leapt, and up the stairs. There drew my *s*. „ 820
with violence The *s* was dash'd from out my hand, „ 826
the prize A golden circlet and a knightly *s*, *Pelleas and E.* 12
for his lady won The golden circlet, for himself the *s* : „ 14
I will make thee with thy spear and *s* As famous— „ 45
The *s* and golden circlet were achieved. „ 170
Saving the goodly *s*, his prize, „ 359
and drew the *s*, and thought, ' What ! „ 447
groaning laid The naked *s* athwart their naked throats, „ 452
And the *s* of the tourney across her throat. „ 455
Awaking knew the *s*, and turn'd herself To Gawain : „ 489
the *s* That made it plunges thro' the wound „ 529
' Thou art false as Hell : slay me : I have no *s*.' „ 576
and he, hissing ' I have no *s*,' „ 602
Arthur deign'd not use of word or *s*, *Last Tournament* 458
children born of thee are *s* and fire, *Guinevere* 425
And have but stricken with the *s* in vain ; *Pass. of Arthur* 23
that helm which many a heathen *s* Had beaten thin ; „ 166
Clothed in white samite, mystic, wonderful, Holding the *s*— „ 200
Saying, ' King Arthur's *s*, Excalibur, „ 271
clutch'd the *s*, And strongly wheel'd and threw it. „ 303
Sword (*continued*) thou bringest Not peace, a *s*, a fire. *Sir J. Oldcastle* 36
Him, who should bear the *s* Of Justice— „ 87
drew His *s* on his fellow to slay him, *V. of Maeldune* 68
with *s's* that were sharp from the grindstone, *Batt. of Brunanburh* 41
Thro' the forest of lances and *s's* *Heavy Brigade* 49
warrior of the Holy Cross and of the conquering *s*, *Happy* 21
sway'd the *s* that lighten'd back the sun „ 43
flung himself between The gladiatorial *s's*, *St. Telemachus* 62
Thro' all the vast dominion which a *s*, *Akbar's Dream* 14
I stagger at the Korân and the *s*. „ 71
Sword-belt broad and long A strong *s-b*, *Holy Grail* 153
Swordcut Seam'd with an ancient *s* on the cheek, *Lancelot and E.* 258
Sword-edge Slew with the *s-e* There by Brunanburh, *Batt. of Brunanburh* 9
Slaughter of heroes Slain by the *s-e*— „ 113
Sword-grass On the oat-grass and the *s-g*, *May Queen, N. Y's. E.* 28
Sword-hand Struck with the *s-h* and slew, *Heavy Brigade* 52
Sword-handle Fingering at his *s-h* until he stood *Pelleas and E.* 442
Swording and *s* right and left Men, women, *Last Tournament* 473
Sword-stroke Five young kings put asleep by the *s-s*, *Batt. of Brunanburh* 52
Swore (*See also* **Sware, Sweär'd**) She turn'd, we closed, we kiss'd, *s* faith, *Edwin Morris* 114
and *s* They said he lived shut up within himself, *Golden Year* 8
laugh'd, and *s* by Peter and by Paul : *Godiva* 24
The barons *s*, with many words, *Day-Dm., Revival* 23
But ours he *s* were all diseased. *The Voyage* 76
And on the book, half-frighted, Miriam *s*. *Enoch Arden* 843
And how the bailiff *s* that he was mad, *The Brook* 143
s besides To play their go-between as heretofore *Aylmer's Field* 522
to those that *s* Not by the temple but the gold, „ 793
And *s* he long'd at college, only long'd, *Princess, Pro.* 158
She was a princess too ; and so I *s*. „ *v* 295
caught By that you *s* to withstand ? *Maud I vi* 80
so my knighthood keep the vows they *s*, *Gareth and L.* 602
I *s* That I would track this caitiff to his hold, *Marr. of Geraint* 414
I *s* to the great King, and am forsworn. *Last Tournament* 661
s that he dare not rob the mail, and he *s* that he would ; *Rizpah* 30
I *s* I would strike off his head. *V. of Maeldune* 2
s the seeming-deathless vow . . . *Locksley H., Sixty* 180
I *s* the vow, then with my latest kiss *The Ring* 298
Sworn True Mussulman was I and *s*, *Arabian Nights* 9
Hath he not *s* his love a thousand times, *Œnone* 231
Not tho' Blanche had *s* That after that dark night *Princess vii* 72
Mine, mine—our fathers have *s*. *Maud I xix* 43
So now I have *s* to bury All this dead body „ 96
s Tho' men may wound him that he will not die, *Com. of Arthur* 420
for these have *s* To wage my wars, „ 507
my knights are *s* to vows Of utter hardihood, *Gareth and L.* 552
See now, *s* have I, Else yon black felon „ 1292
then have I *s* From his own lips to have it— *Marr. of Geraint* 408
I have *s* That I will break his pride and learn his name, „ 423
' Have I not *s* ? I am not trusted. *Merlin and V.* 527
' Had I been here, ye had not *s* the vow.' *Holy Grail* 276
My King, thou wouldst have *s*.' „ 278
and therefore have we *s* our vows.' „ 285
I had *s* I saw That which I saw ; „ 850
if the King Had seen the sight he would have *s* the vow : „ 904
for I have *s* my vows, *Pelleas and E.* 244
the King hath bound And *s* me to this brotherhood ; ' „ 449
And whatsoever his own knights have *s* My knights have *s* the counter to it— *Last Tournament* 79
Than had we never *s*. I swear no more. „ 660
And I have *s* never to see him more, *Guinevere* 376
S to be veriest ice of pureness, *Sir J. Oldcastle* 108
s to seek If any golden harbour *Pref. Son. 19th Cent.* 12
Bright and Dark have *s* that I, *Demeter and P.* 96
Swum with an eye that *s* in thanks ; *Princess vi* 210
Lancelot, having *s* the riser-loops— *Gareth and L.* 1216
and *s* with balanced wings To some tall mountain : *Lover's Tale i* 302
Swung bells that *s*, Moved of themselves, *Palace of Art* 129
S themselves, and in low tones replied ; *Vision of Sin* 20
For sideways up he *s* his arms, *Sea Dreams* 24
and *s* The heavy-folded rose, *In Mem. xcv* 58
There *s* an apple of the purest gold, *Marr. of Geraint* 170
S from his brand a windy buffet *Geraint and E.* 90

T

Table Round (*continued*) I, therefore, made him of our *T R*, *Geraint and E.* 908
question rose About the founding of a *T R*, *Merlin and V.* 411
Assay it on some one of the *T R*, .. 689
And blinds himself and all the *T R* .. 784
I know the *T R*, my friends of old; .. 816
else Rapt in this fancy of his *T R*, *Lancelot and E.* 129
the rest, his *T R*, Known as they are, .. 185
And much they ask'd of court and *T R*, .. 268
beheld the King Charge at the head of all his *T R*, .. 304
Ranged with the *T R* that held the lists, .. 467
And all the *T R* that held the lists, .. 499
any knight, And mine, as head of all our *T R*, .. 1328
The marshall'd Order of their *T R*, .. 1332
Tell me, what drove thee from the *T R*, *Holy Grail* 28
Sin against Arthur and the *T R*, .. 79
And when King Arthur made His *T R*, .. 90
The seven clear stars of Arthur's *T R*— „ 684
Yea, by the honour of the *T R*, *Pelleas and E.* 342
a scourge am I To lash the treasons of the *T R*.' „ 566
Had made mock-knight of Arthur's *T R*, *Last Tournament* 2
A goodly brother of the *T R* „ 431
sought To make disruption in the *T R* Of Arthur, *Guinevere* 17
whose disloyal life Hath wrought confusion in the *T R* .. 220
What canst thou know of Kings and *T's R*, .. 228
In that fair order of my *T R*, .. 463
Table-shore Heard in dead night along that *t-s*, *Last Tournament* 463
Tablet Upon the blanched *t's* of her heart; *Isabel* 17
Thy *t* glimmers to the dawn. *In Mem. lxvii* 16
Their pensive *t's* round her head, .. *Con.* 51
Table-talk genial *t-t*, Or deep dispute, „ *lxxxiv* 23
Taboo worse than South-sea-isle *t*, *Princess iii* 278
Broke the *T*, Dipt to the crater, *Kapiolani* 30
Tack till as when a boat *T's*, and the slacken'd sail flaps, *Princess ii* 186
Tackle (s) Dry sang the *t*, sang the sail: *The Voyage* 10
Buoy'd upon floating *t* and broken spars, *Enoch Arden* 551
Tackle (verb) Tha mun *t* the sins o' the Wo'ld, *Church-warden, etc.* 46
Tact So gracious was her *t* and tenderness: *Princess i* 24
The graceful *t*, the Christian art; *In Mem. cx* 16
And she by *t* of love was well aware *Lancelot and E.* 984
Ta'en (taken) clay *t* from the common earth *To ——, With Pal. of Art* 17
And *t* my fiddle to the gate, (repeat) *Amphion* 11, 15
And since my oath was *t* for public use, *Princess iv* 337
he be nor *t* nor slain.' *Gareth and L.* 586
Tagg'd my beard Was *t* with icy fringes in the moon, *St. S. Stylites* 32
Tail (*See also* **Taäil**) from head to *t* Came out clear plates of sapphire mail. *Two Voices* 11
with playful *t* Crouch'd fawning in the weed. *Œnone* 200
Twinkled the innumerable ear and *t*. *The Brook* 134
Tail'd *See* **Long-tail'd, White-tail'd**
Tailor *See* **Taäilor**
Taint pure as he from *t* of craven guile, *Ode on Well.* 135
Defects of doubt, and *t's* of blood; *In Mem. liv* 4
Had suffer'd, or should suffer any *t* In nature: *Marr. of Geraint* 31
Suspicious that her nature had a *t*. „ 68
leper plague may scale my skin but never *t* my heart; *Happy* 27
Take (*See also* **Taäke**) T, *Madam, this poor book of song*; *To the Queen* 17
knew the seasons when to t *Occasion by the hand*, „ 30
T the heart from out my breast. *Adeline* 8
Whence shall she *t* a fitting mate? *Kate* 13
She still would *t* the praise, and care no more. *The form, the form*, 14
weepest thou to *t* the cast Of those dead lineaments *Wan Sculptor* 1
'Some turn this sickness yet might *t*, *Two Voices* 55
Gargarus Stands up and *t's* the morning: *Œnone* 11
'I *t* possession of man's mind and deed. *Palace of Art* 209
What is it that will *t* away my sin, „ 287
Let her *t* 'em: they are hers: *May Queen, N. Y's. E.* 46
I thought, I *t* it for a sign. „ *Con.* 38
there Grows green and broad, and *t's* no care, *Lotos-Eaters, C. S.* 28
T warning! he that will not sing *The Blackbird* 21
And the New-year will *t* 'em away. *D. of the O. Year* 14
Comes up to *t* his own. „ 36
That *t's* away a noble mind. *To J. S.* 48
t The place of him that sleeps in peace. „ 67
That knowledge *t's* the sword away— *Love thou thy land* 88

Take (*continued*) Here, *t* the goose, and keep you warm, *The Goose* 7
'Go, *t* the goose, and wring her throat, „ 31
Quoth she, 'The Devil *t* the goose, „ 55
'Why *t* the style of those heroic times? *The Epic* 35
Thou therefore *t* my brand Excalibur, *M. d'Arthur* 27
t Excalibur, And fling him far into the middle mere: „ 36
and *t's* the flood With swarthy webs. „ 268
The lusty bird *t's* every hour for dawn: .. *Ep.* 11
I bred His daughter Dora: *t* her for your wife; *Dora* 20
Consider, William: *t* a month to think, „ 29
let me *t* the boy, And I will set him in my uncle's eye .. 66
but *t* the child, And bless him for the sake of him .. 93
Well—for I will *t* the boy; „ 99
That thou shouldst *t* my trouble on thyself: .. 118
And I will beg of him to *t* thee back: .. 123
But if he will not *t* thee back again, .. 124
I come For Dora: *t* her back; she loves you well. .. 143
t Dora back, And let all this be as it was before.' .. 154
I a beast To *t* them as I did? *Edwin Morris* 72
Have mercy, Lord, and *t* away my sin. *St. S. Stylites* 8
O *t* the meaning, Lord: I do not breathe, „ 21
Have mercy, mercy: *t* away my sin. „ 45
The silly people *t* me for a saint, „ 127
let them *t* Example, pattern: „ 223
Let me go: *t* back thy gift: *Tithonus* 27
kiss him: *t* his hand in thine. *Locksley Hall* 52
I will *t* some savage woman, „ 168
Then *t* the broidery-frame, and add A crimson *Day-Dm., Pro.* 15
So, Lady Flora, *t* my lay, .. *Moral* 1
So much your eyes my fancy *t*— .. *L'Envoi* 26
And I will *t* my pleasure there: „ 32
So, Lady Flora, *t* my lay, „ *Ep.* 1
But *t* it—earnest wed with sport, „ 11
I'll *t* the showers as they fall, *Amphion* 101
nor *t* Half-views of men and things. *Will Water.* 51
I *t* myself to task; „ 162
T my brute, and lead him in, *Vision of Sin* 65
'*T* your own time, Annie, *t* your own time.' *Enoch Arden* 466
was it hard to *t* The helpless life so wild „ 556
'Too hard to bear! why did they *t* me thence? „ 781
T, give her this, for it may comfort her: „ 899
'O would I *t* her father for one hour, *The Brook* 114
'*T* it,' she added sweetly, 'tho' his gift; *Aylmer's Field* 246
who beside your hearths Can *t* her place— „ 736
Will not another *t* their heritage? „ 786
did I *t* That popular name of thine to shadow forth *Lucretius* 95
to *t* Only such cups as left us friendly-warm, „ 214
Great Nature, *t*, and forcing far apart „ 245
And *t's* a lady's finger with all care, *Princess, Pro.* 173
'*T* Lilia, then, for heroine,' clamour'd he, .. 223
Cyril whisper'd: '*T* me with you too.' .. *i* 81
T me: I'll serve you better in a strait; .. 85
'Well then, Psyche, *t* my life, .. *ii* 204
limed ourselves With open eyes, and we must *t* the chance. .. *iii* 143
Princess rode to *t* The dip of certain strata .. 169
And *t's* and ruins all; .. 238
'O were I thou that she might *t* me in, .. *iv* 102
Our mind is changed: we *t* it to ourself.' „ 362
What hinders me To *t* such bloody vengeance on you both?— „ 534
'Satan *t* The old women and their shadows! .. *v* 33
'Yet I pray *T* comfort: live, dear lady, .. 80
Or they will *t* her, they will make her hard, „ 90
And I will *t* her up and go my way, .. 102
t them all-in-all, Were we ourselves but half as good, .. 200
I *t* her for the flower of womankind, „ 287
Still *T* not his life: he risk'd it for my own; „ 407
When the man wants weight, the woman *t's* it up, .. 444
but you—she's yet a colt—*T*, break her: „ 456
And on the little clause '*t* not his life:' „ 470
t's, and breaks, and cracks, and splits, „ 527
'All good go with thee! *t* it Sir,' „ *vi* 207
kiss her; *t* her hand, she weeps: 'Sdeath! „ 225
on to the tents: *t* up the Prince.' „ 279

Take (*continued*) cloud may stoop from heaven and *t* the shape *Princess vii* 2
Let the great river *t* me to the main: „ 13
the crowd were swarming now, To *t* their leave, „ *Con.* 38
he wouldn't *t* my advice. *Grandmother* 4
(*T* it and come) to the Isle of Wight; *To F. D. Maurice* 12
'God help me! save I *t* my part Of danger *Sailor Boy* 21
T you his dearest, Give us a life.' *The Victim* 27
t this and pray that he Who wrote it, *A Dedication* 4
T the hoary Roman head and shatter it, *Boädicea* 65
T my love, for love will come, *Window, No Answer* 20
T my love and be my wife. „ 24
Must I *t* you and break you, „ *The Answer* 3
I must *t* you, and break you, „ 5
T, *t*,—break, break—Break— „ 7
And shall I *t* a thing so blind, *In Mem. iii* 13
She *t's* a riband or a rose; „ *vi* 32
That *t's* the sunshine and the rains, „ *x* 14
seem to *t* The touch of change in calm or storm; „ *xvi* 5
I *t* the grasses of the grave, „ *xxi* 3
envy not the beast that *t's* His license in the field of time, „ *xxvii* 5
To *t* her latest leave of home, „ *xl* 6
She *t's*, when harsher moods remit, „ *xlviii* 6
And thou shalt *t* a nobler leave.' „ *lviii* 12
Who *t's* the children on his knee, „ *lxvi* 11
T wings of fancy, and ascend, „ *lxxvi* 1
T wings of foresight; lighten thro' The secular abyss „ 5
And *t* us as a single soul. „ *lxxxiv* 44
Can *t* no part away from this: „ *lxxxv* 68
Ah, *t* the imperfect gift I bring, „ 117
I'll rather *t* what fruit may be „ *cviii* 13
The distance *t's* a lovelier hue, „ *cxv* 6
t's The colours of the crescent prime? „ *cxvi* 3
I *t* the pressure of thine hand. „ *cxix* 12
t the print Of the golden age—why not? *Maud I i* 29
To *t* a wanton dissolute boy For a man „ *x* 58
Shall I not *t* care of all that I think, „ *xv* 7
Or to ask her, '*T* me, sweet, „ *II iv* 87
He may *t* her now; for she never speaks her mind, „ *v* 67
'*T* me,' but turn the blade and ye shall see, *Com. of Arthur* 303
'*T* thou and strike! the time to cast away „ 307
T thou the truth as thou hast told it me. *Gareth and L.* 257
Yet *t* thou heed of him, for, so thou pass „ 267
Abide: *t* counsel; for this lad is great And lusty, „ 730
t his horse And arms, and so return him to the King. „ 955
'*T* not my life: I yield.' „ 973
'But thou begone, *t* counsel, and away, „ 1002
and *t* my charger, fresh, „ 1300
T him to stall, and give him corn, *Marr. of Geraint* 371
They *t* the rustic murmur of their bourg „ 419
'Advance and *t*, as fairest of the fair, „ 553
He said, 'You *t* it, speaking,' and she spoke. *Geraint and E.* 141
but *t* A horse and arms for guerdon; „ 217
'I *t* it as free gift, then,' said the boy, „ 222
'*T* Five horses and their armours;' „ 409
'Would some of your kind people *t* him up, „ 543
Here, *t* him up, and bear him to our hall: „ 552
See ye *t* the charger too, A noble one.' „ 555
T warning: yonder man is surely dead; „ 672
T my salute,' unknightly with flat hand, „ 717
tho' Geraint could never *t* again That comfort „ 949
thou would'st *t* me gladlier back, *Balin and Balan* 67
Help, for he follows! *t* me to thyself! *Merlin and V.* 82
Courteous—amends for gauntness—*t's* her hand— „ 104
And *t* this boon so strange and not so strange.' „ 310
T Vivien for expounder; she will call „ 319
T one verse more—the lady speaks it— „ 445
And being found *t* heed of Vivien. „ 529
Good: *t* my counsel: let me know it at once: „ 653
He brought, not found it therefore: *t* the truth.' „ 719
shameless ones, who *t* Their pastime *Lancelot and E.* 100
'Advance and *t* thy prize The diamond;' „ 503
Rise and *t* This diamond, and deliver it, „ 545
ye used to *t* me with the flood Up the great river „ 1037
Then *t* the little bed on which I died „ 1117

Take (*continued*) a chariot-bier To *t* me to the river, *Lancelot and E.* 1122
T, what I had not won except for you, „ 1181
A strange one! yet I *t* it with Amen. „ 1223
Or come to *t* the King to Fairyland? „ 1257
Hither, to *t* my last farewell of you. „ 1275
'What said the King? Did Arthur *t* the vow?' *Holy Grail* 204
'*T* thou my robe,' she said, 'for all is thine,' „ 449
t him to you, keep him off, *Pelleas and E.* 194
'Yet, *t* him, ye that scarce are fit to touch, „ 292
'*T* thou the jewels of this dead innocence, *Last Tournament* 31
'*T* thou my churl, and tend him curiously „ 90
But how to *t* last leave of all I loved? *Guinevere* 546
I cannot *t* thy hand; that too is flesh, „ 553
Thou therefore *t* my brand Excalibur, *Pass. of Arthur* 195
t Excalibur, And fling him far into the middle mere: „ 204
and *t's* the flood With swarthy webs. „ 436
t withal Thy poet's blessing, *To the Queen ii* 45
that *t's* The heart, and sometimes touches *Lover's Tale i* 16
But *t's* it all for granted: „ 157
Can ye *t* off the sweetness from the flower, „ 171
reading of the will Before he *t's* possession? „ 677
while I mused nor yet endured to *t* So rich a prize, „ *iii* 49
'*T* my free gift, my cousin, for your wife; „ *iv* 363
I didn't *t* heed o' *them*, *First Quarrel* 29
Which voice most *t's* you? *Sisters (E. and E.)* 30
an' 'e didn't *t* kind to it like; *Village Wife* 44
To *t* me to that hiding in the hills. *Sir J. Oldcastle* 2
to *t* the king along with him— „ 49
which you will *t* My Fitz, and welcome, *To E. Fitzgerald* 50
Nor *t* thy dial for thy deity, *Ancient Sage* 109
Shall I *t him*? I kneel with *him*? *The Flight* 49
'The Divil *t* all the black lan', *Tomorrow* 64
T the charm 'For ever' from them, *Locksley H., Sixty* 72
and *t* their wisdom for your friend. „ 104
eyes may *t* the growing glimmer for the gleam withdrawn. „ 230
like old-world inns that *t* Some warrior for a sign *Pro. to Gen. Hamley* 13
let the patriot-soldier *t* His meed of fame *Epilogue* 32
Prince has found you, *t* this ring. *The Ring* 69
I stoopt To *t* and kiss the ring. „ 132
'I *t* thee Muriel for my wedded wife'— „ 377
My roses—will he *t* them *now*— *Happy* 13
Not *t* them? Still you wave me off— „ 101
you still delay to *t* Your leave of Town, *To Mary Boyle* 1
T then this spring-flower I send, „ 19
T, read! and be the faults your Poet makes „ 61
'*T* comfort you have won the Painter's fame,' *Romney's R.* 43
T it, and save me from it! *Bandit's Death* 38
Look to your butts, and *t* good aims! *Riflemen form!* 16
'*T* her Sir Ralph,' said the king. *The Tourney* 18

Taken (*See also* **Taäen, Ta'en**) But more is *t* quite away. *Miller's D.* 22
All things are *t* from us, *Lotos-Eaters, C. S.* 46
Those we love first are *t* first. *To J. S.* 12
yet I fear My wound hath *t* cold, and I shall die.' *M. d'Arthur* 166
Are *t* by the forelock. *Golden Year* 19
Tho' much is *t*, much abides; *Ulysses* 65
Till *t* with her seeming openness *Princess iv* 300
'They have *t* the child To spill his blood *The Victim* 43
They have *t* our son, „ 49
T the stars from the night and the sun from the day! *Window, Gone* 5
Were *t* to be such as closed Grave doubts *In Mem. xlviii* 2
and *t* but the form. *Gareth and L.* 1200
As of a wild thing *t* in the trap, *Geraint and E.* 723
Nay, friend, for we have *t* our farewells. *Guinevere* 117
t everywhere for pure, She like a new disease, „ 517
I fear My wound hath *t* cold, and I shall die.' *Pass. of Arthur* 334
But *t* with the sweetness of the place, *Lover's Tale i* 531
As it had *t* life away before, „ 710
a picture of his lady, *t* Some years before, „ *iv* 216
I have *t* them home, I have number'd the bones, *Rizpah* 10
you are *t* With one or other: *Sisters (E. and E.)* 31
each *t* a life for a life, *V. of Maeldune* 122
Lest she be *t* captive— *Tiresias* 102

Takest See, the hand Wherewith thou *t* this, is red!' *Last Tournament* 193

Taketh sick man's room when he *t* repose *A spirit haunts* 14

Takin' been t' a dhrop o' the crathur' — Tomorrow 11
Taking (See also **A-taäkin', Leave-taking, Takin'**) He kiss'd, t his last embrace, — Two Voices 254
The parson t wide and wider sweeps, — The Epic 14
Titanic forces t birth In divers seasons, — Day-Dm., L'Envoi 17
hand crept too across his trade T her bread and theirs: — Enoch Arden 111
Nor asking overmuch and t less, — „ 252
So often, that the folly t wings — Aylmer's Field 494
or t pride in her, She look'd so sweet, — „ 554
Womanlike, t revenge too deep for a transient wrong — Maud I iii 5
sad was Arthur's face T it, but old Merlin — Com. of Arthur 306
By t true for false, or false for true; — Geraint and E. 4
gross heart Would reckon worth the t? — Merlin and V. 917
Come, for you left me t no farewell, — Lancelot and E. 1274
T my war-horse from the holy man, — Holy Grail 537
T his hand, 'O the strong hand,' — Pelleas and E. 126
He spoke, and t all his younger knights, — Last Tournament 126
Then t his dear lady by one hand, — Lover's Tale iv 369
t the place of the pitying God — Despair 42
felt as I spoke I was t the name in vain- — „ 52
What is this you're t? . . . — Forlorn 40
Talbot shatter'd t's, which had left the stones Raw, — Holy Grail 719
Tale (See also **Fairy-tale, Taäle**) A deeper t my heart divines — Two Voices 269
With cycles of the human t Of this wide world, — Palace of Art 146
an ancient t of wrong, Like a t of little meaning — Lotos-Eaters, C. S. 118
Brimful of those wild t's, — D. of F. Women 12
With the fairy t's of science, — Locksley Hall 12
And told him all her nurse's t. — Lady Clare 80
'Tell me t's of thy first love— — Vision of Sin 163
And I will tell him t's of foreign parts, — Enoch Arden 198
And there the t he utter'd brokenly, — „ 647
he felt the t Less than the teller: — „ 711
her father came across With some long-winded t, — The Brook 109
And there he told a long long-winded t — „ 138
Lightning of the hour, the pun, the scurrilous t,— — Aylmer's Field 441
t's! for never yet on earth Could dead flesh creep, — Lucretius 130
rustic Gods! a t To laugh at—more to laugh at — „ 182
Dived in a hoard of t's that dealt with knights, — Princess, Pro. 29
the t of her That drove her foes with slaughter — „ 122
often told a t from mouth to mouth As here at Christmas.' — „ 191
what kind of t's did men tell men, — „ 196
'Why not a summer's as a winter's t? A t for summer as befits the time, — „ 209
we should have him back Who told the 'Winter's t' — „ 238
tell me pleasant t's, and read My sickness — „ ii 252
he that next inherited the t Half turning — „ iv 592
whereon Follow'd his t. — „ v 48
infuse my t of love In the old king's ears, — „ 240
So closed our t, of which I give you all — „ Con. 1
the sequel of the t Had touch'd her; — „ 30
And I fear you'll listen to t's, — Grandmother 54
To bear thro' Heaven a t of woe, — In Mem. xii 2
When truth embodied in a t Shall enter — „ xxxvi 7
Then be my love an idle t, — „ lxii 3
Thereafter—as he speaks who tells the t— — Com. of Arthur 95
'But let me tell thee now another t: — „ 359
Or Gareth telling some prodigious t Of knights, — Gareth and L. 508
turning to Lynette he told The t of Gareth, — „ 1273
And he that told the t in older times — „ 1427
And call'd her like that maiden in the t, — Marr. of Geraint 742
And there lay still; as he that tells the t — Geraint and E. 161
Earl Limours Drank till he jested with all ease, and told Free t's, — „ 291
and cursed the t, The told-of, and the teller. — Balin and Balan 542
Were I not woman, I could tell a t. — Merlin and V. 696
Then answer'd Merlin 'Nay, I know the t. — „ 713
'O ay,' said Vivien, 'overtrue a t. — „ 720
he never wrong'd his bride. I know the t. — „ 730
'O crueller than was ever told in t, — „ 858
She blamed herself for telling hearsay t's: — „ 951
So ran the t like fire about the court, — Lancelot and E. 734
when the maid had told him all her t, — „ 798
when the maid had told him all the t Of King and Prince, — „ 823
Tale (continued) he that tells the t Says that her ever-veering fancy — Pelleas and E. 492
for he that tells the t Liken'd them, — Last Tournament 226
And fault and doubt—no word of that fond t— — „ 578
prattling and the t's Which my good father told me, — Guinevere 316
accept this old imperfect t, New-old, — To the Queen ii 36
and drank her whisper'd t's. — Lover's Tale i 817
I'll tell you the t o' my life. — First Quarrel 9
I told them my t, God's own truth— — Rizpah 33
in many a merry t That shook our sides— — Sir J. Oldcastle 91
A t, that told to me, When but thine age, — Tiresias 18
Two lovers parted by a scurrilous t — The Ring 208
Two lovers parted by no scurrilous t— — „ 427
All her t of sadness, — Forlorn 80
your t of lands I know not, your Arabian sands; — To Ulysses 34
And read a Grecian t re-told, — To Master of B. 5
I have told you my t. Get you gone. — Charity 44
Tale (number) The t of diamonds for his destined boon) — Lancelot and E. 91
Talent health, wealth, and time, And t, — Princess iv 353
Taliessin 'T is our fullest throat of song, — Holy Grail 300
Talk (s) (See also **Table-talk**) It seems in after-dinner t — Miller's D. 31
we held a t, How all the old honour — The Epic 6
Delight our souls with t of knightly deeds, — M. d'Arthur 19
he turn'd The current of his t to graver things — Enoch Arden 203
Fairer his t, a tongue that ruled the hour, — Aylmer's Field 194
remembering His former t's with Edith, — „ 457
Made more and more allowance for his t; — Sea Dreams 75
Whose pious t, when most his heart was dry, — „ 186
A t of college and of ladies' rights, — Princess, Pro. 233
Our dances broke and buzz'd in knots of t; — „ i 133
Sweet household t, and phrases of the hearth, — „ ii 315
From t of battles loud and vain, — Ode on Well. 247
But honest t and wholesome wine, — To F. D. Maurice 18
Heart-affluence in discursive t — In Mem. cix 1
Just now the dry-tongued laurels' pattering t — Maud I xviii 8
vext her and perplext her With his wordly t — „ xx 7
And when the thralls had t among themselves, — Gareth and L. 491
But if their t were foul, — „ 504
Then, like a shadow, past the people's t — Marr. of Geraint 82
I will tell him all their caitiff t; — Geraint and E. 66
his t, When wine and free companions kindled him, — „ 292
Here the huge Earl cried out upon her t, — „ 651
Felon t! Let be! no more!' — Balin and Balan 380
Their t was all of training, terms of art, — Merlin and V. 124
She play'd about with slight and sprightly t, — „ 171
Tho' harlots paint their t as well as face — „ 821
And t and minstrel melody entertain'd. — Lancelot and E. 267
From t of war to traits of pleasantry— — „ 321
Than Lancelot told me of a common t — „ 577
those black walls of yew Their t had pierced, — „ 970
Was noble man but made ignoble t. — „ 1088
once the t And scandal of our table, — Holy Grail 649
Suddenly waken'd with a sound of t — Pelleas and E. 48
And all t died, as in a grove all song — „ 607
'Will the child kill me with her innocent t?' — Guinevere 214
Rapt in sweet t or lively, all on love — „ 386
And miss to hear high t of noble deeds — „ 499
Delight our souls with t of knightly deeds, — Pass. of Arthur 187
from that necessity for t Which lives with blindness, — Sisters (E. and E.) 248
I have scared you pale with my scandalous t, — Despair 111
an' doesn't not 'inder the t! — Spinster's S's. 86
Is girlish t at best; — Epilogue 43
And all her t was of the babe she loved; — The Ring 353
Talk (verb) To himself he t's; — A spirit haunts 3
And ye t together still, — Adeline 60
'I t,' said he, 'Not with thy dreams. — Two Voices 385
And makes me t too much in age. — Miller's D. 194
ere the stars come forth T with the wild Cassandra, — Œnone 263
But you can t: yours is a kindly vein: — Edwin Morris 81
the days were brief Whereof the poets t, — Talking Oak 186
'O ay, ay, ay, you t!' — Godiva 26
all his life the charm did t About his path, — Day-Dm., Arrival 21
Had made him t for show; — Will Water. 196
clamour'd the good woman, 'hear him t! — Enoch Arden 840

Tamesa (Thames) Bloodily flow'd the T rolling phantom bodies Boädicea 27
Tamper embassies of love, To t with the feelings, Gardener's D. 19
Tamper'd Some meddling rogue has t with him— Lancelot and E. 128
And t with the Lords of the White Horse, Guinevere 15
Tangle (s) Should toss with t and with shells. In Mem. x 20
Tangle (verb) cuts atwain The knots that t human creeds, Clear-headed friend 3
Tangled (adj. and part.) The t water-courses slept, Dying Swan 19
Glitter like a swarm of fire-flies t in a silver braid. Locksley Hall 10
Two in the t business of the world, Princess ii 174
passing lightly Adown a natural stair of t roots, Lover's Tale i 527
Tantivy Black Bess, T, Tallyho, The Brook 160
Tap (a touch) crush'd with a t Of my finger-na Maud II ii 21
Tap (tap-room) Thou'll goä sniffin' about the t North. Cobbler 64
I weänt goä sniffin' about the t.' „ 67
Taper (adj.) If my lips should dare to kiss Thy t fingers amorously, Madeline 44
Thro' rosy t fingers drew Her streaming curls Mariana in the S. 15
Taper (s) A million t's flaring bright Arabian Nights 124
I knew your t far away, Miller's D. 109
Her t glimmer'd in the lake below: Edwin Morris 135
As this pale t's earthly spark, St. Agnes' Eve 15
The t's burning fair. Sir Galahad 32
And calm that let the t's burn Unwavering: In Mem. xcv 5
fingers of a hand Before a burning t, Holy Grail 694
Tapestry Working a t, lifted up her head, Last Tournament 129
Tapping Leisurely t a glossy boot, Maud I xiii 19
Tapt whined in lobbies, t at doors, Walk. to the Mail 37
She t her tiny silken-sandal'd foot: Princess, Pro. 150
Taranis T be propitiated. Boädicea 16
Tare That t each other in their slime, In Mem. lvi 23
And when his anger t him, Gareth and L. 1340
Target passion were a t for their scorn: Locksley Hall 146
Or from the tiny pitted t blew Aylmer's Field 93
Tarn Slumbers not like a mountain t? Supp. Confessions 129
And quenching lake by lake and t by t Princess vii 40
Far over the blue t's and hazy seas, Gareth and L. 499
Had found a glen, gray boulder and black t. Lancelot and E. 36
A horror lived about the t, and clave „ 37
Fled like a glittering rivulet to the t: „ 52
A stone is flung into some sleeping t, Pelleas and E. 93
Those diamonds that I rescued from the t, Last Tournament 37
Tarnish'd (See also **Half-tarnish'd**) Mark hath t the great name of king, Gareth and L. 426
Tarquin brooking not the T in her veins, Lucretius 237
Tarriance after two days' t there, return'd. Lancelot and E. 569
Tarried And while I t, every day she set Holy Grail 588
Where once I t for a while, To E. Fitzgerald 2
Tarry 'He dared not t,' men will say, Two Voices 101
I must go: I dare not t,' Princess iii 95
Knowing I t for thee,' Maud III vi 13
Would he could t with us here awhile, Marr. of Geraint 622
Yet if he could but t a day or two, „ 627
For if thou t we shall meet again, Guinevere 89
Tarrying after t for a space they rode, Geraint and E. 953
Tartar at thy name the T tents are stirr'd; W. to Marie Alex. 12
thine own land had bow'd to T hordes „ 23
Task (s) 'Hard t, to pluck resolve,' I cried, Two Voices 118
Sore t to hearts worn out by many wars Lotos-Eaters, C. S. 86
Deliver not the t's of might To weakness, Love thou thy land 13
The wrinkled steward at his t, Day-Dm., Sleep. P. 27
I take myself to t; Will Water. 162
came Cyril, and yawning 'O hard t,' he cried; Princess iii 124
or hew wood, Or grosser t's; Gareth and L. 487
kiss the child That does the t assign'd, Lancelot and E. 829
Task (verb) as we t ourselves To learn a language Aylmer's Field 432
Tassel-hung In native hazels t-h.' In Mem. cii 12
Tassell'd See **Dewy-tassell'd**
Taste (s) Made all our t's and fancies like, Lover's Tale i 242
Taste (verb) (See also **Taäste**) but whoso did receive of them, And t, Lotos-Eaters 31
(If Death so t Lethean springs), In Mem. xliv 10
She t's the fruit before the blossom falls, Ancient Sage 75
that men may t Swine-flesh, drink wine; Akbar's Dream 53
Tasted He t love with half his mind, In Mem. xc 1
Tasted (continued) Nor ever touch'd fierce wine, nor t flesh, Merlin and V. 627
till I t flesh again One night To E. Fitzgerald 20
Tattoo'd then the man; T or woaded, Princess ii 120
Taught (See also **Larn'd**) We t him lowlier moods, Buonaparte 9
at Trafalgar yet once more We t him: „ 13
Should that plain fact, as t by these, Two Voices 281
He t me all the mercy, May Queen, Con. 17
Retaught the lesson thou hadst t, England and Amer. 8
I must be t my duty, and by you! Dora 97
Who t me how to skate, to row, to swim, Edwin Morris 19
leaders of their Institute T them with facts. Princess, Pro. 59
And I would teach them all that men are t; „ 136
but she That t the Sabine how to rule, „ ii 79
Here might they learn whatever men were t: „ 146
And whatsoever can be t and known; „ 385
what woman t you this?' „ vii 310
With those deep voices our dead captain t The tyrant, Ode on Well. 69
So great a soldier t us there, „ 131
Bleys, Who t him magic; Com. of Arthur 154
The charm so t will charm us both to rest. Merlin and V. 332
then he t the King to charm the Queen „ 641
never yet Hath what thy sister t me first to see, Holy Grail 469
My knighthood t me this— Last Tournament 658
began to hum An air the nuns had t her; Guinevere 163
should he not be t, Ev'n by the price Lover's Tale iv 151
I t myself as I could To make a good wife First Quarrel 29
Who t me in childhood, Merlin and the G. 115
Thou knowest, T by some God, Death of Œnone 35
Taunt (s) A t that clench'd his purpose like a blow! Princess v 306
Taunt (verb) I know it; T me no more: „ vi 301
Tavern Seeking a t which of old he knew, Enoch Arden 691
Tavern-catch To troll a careless, careless t-c Princess iv 157
Tavern-door sent From many a t-d, Will Water. 188
Tavern-fellow My boon companion, t-f— Sir J. Oldcastle 90
Tavern-hour The t-h's of mighty wits— Will Water. 191
Taw boy That knuckled at the t: „ 132
Tawnier the swan's Is t than her cygnet's: Lancelot and E. 1185
Tawny to tear away Their t clusters, Enoch Arden 382
Tumbled the t rascal at his feet, Aylmer's Field 230
warm melon lay like a little sun on the t sand, V. of Maeldune 57
Tax Honour,' she said, 'and homage, t and toll, Œnone 116
for when he laid a t Upon his town, Godiva 13
'If they pay this t, they starve.' „ 20
she took the t away And built herself „ 78
Levied a kindly t upon themselves, Enoch Arden 663
Hortensia spoke against the t; Princess vii 127
Ta-year (this year, to-year) (See also **To-year**) Done it t-y I meän'd, N. Farmer, O. S. 42
fur a lot on 'em coom'd t-y— Church-warden, etc. 13
Tea an' offens we hed 'em to t. Village Wife 56
Teach Oh t me yet Somewhat before the heavy clod Supp. Confessions 183
T me the nothingness of things. A Character 4
Oh! t the orphan boy to read, Or t the orphan-girl to sew, L. C. V. de Vere 69
T that sick heart the stronger choice, On a Mourner 18
For he will t him hardness, Dora 120
And, as tradition t'es, Amphion 26
And others' follies t us not, Will Water. 173
Nor much their wisdom t'es; „ 174
And I would t them all that men are taught; Princess, Pro. 136
Shall we t it a Roman lesson? Boädicea 32
Come Time, and t me, many years, In Mem. xiii 13
My own dim life should t me this, „ xxxiv 1
Her office there to rear, to t, „ xl 13
And t true life to fight with mortal wrongs. Maud I xviii 54
As proof of trust. O Merlin, t it me. Merlin and V. 331
To find a wizard who might t the King „ 583
But t high thought, and amiable words Guinevere 481
Ev'n the homely farm can t us Locksley H., Sixty 26
T your flatter'd kings that only those who cannot read „ 132
I too would t the man Beyond the darker hour Prog. of Spring 87
Teacher Left by the T, whom he held divine. Lucretius 13
Blest be the Voice of the T Kapiolani 2

Teaching *t* him that died Of hemlock ; *Princess iii* 302
Teacup-times In *t-t* of hood and hoop, *Talking Oak* 63
Team (*See also* **Teäm**) and the wild *t* Which love thee, *Tithonus* 39
I hear them too—they sing to their *t* : *Grandmother* 81
The *t* is loosen'd from the wain, *In Mem. cxxi* 5
And see'st the moving of the *t*. „ 16
The shrilly whinnyings of the *t* of Hell, *Demeter and P.* 44
Teäm blessed feälds wi' the Divil's oän *t*. *N. Farmer, O. S.* 62
Tear (s) Would issue *t's* of penitence *Supp. Confessions* 118
Her *t's* fell with the dews at even ; *Mariana* 13
Her *t's* fell ere the dews were dried ; „ 14
Crocodiles wept *t's* for thee ; *A Dirge* 22
woodbine and eglatere Drip sweeter dews than traitor's *t*. „ 24
While blissful *t's* blinded my sight *Oriana* 23
And then the *t's* run down my cheek, „ 69
I feel the *t's* of blood arise „ 77
A matter to be wept with *t's* of blood ! *Poland* 14
A moment came the tenderness of *t's*, *The form, the form* 9
My *t's*, no *t's* of Love, are flowing fast, *Wan Sculptor* 7
No *t's* of love, but *t's* that Love can die. „ 8
Thy sister smiled and said, ' No *t's* for me ! *The Bridesmaid* 3
I loved thee for the *t* thou couldst not hide, „ 11
The home of woe without a *t*. *Mariana in the S.* 20
Larger Hesper glitter'd on her *t's*, „ 90
' Whose eyes are dim with glorious *t's*, *Two Voices* 151
And dews, that would have fall'n in *t's*, *Miller's D.* 151
Eyes with idle *t's* are wet. „ 211
They have not shed a many *t's*, „ 221
Yet *t's* they shed : they had their part Of sorrow : „ 223
My eyes are full of *t's*, my heart of love, *Œnone* 31
water'd it with *t's* ? O happy *t's*, „ 234
And never can be sunder'd without *t's*. *To ——, With Pal. of Art* 13
and temper'd with the *t's* Of angels „ 18
white-eyed phantasms weeping *t's* of blood, *Palace of Art* 239
And ever unrelieved by dismal *t's*, „ 271
embraces of our wives And their warm *t's* : *Lotos-Eaters, C. S.* 71
Charged both mine eyes with *t's*. *D. of F. Women* 13
I, blinded with my *t's*, ' Still strove to speak : „ 108
She ceased in *t's*, fallen from hope and trust : „ 257
By sighs or groans or *t's* ; „ 284
and a *t* Dropt on the letters as I wrote. *To J. S.* 55
May perpetual youth Keep dry their light from *t's* ; *Of old sat Freedom* 20
Him Sir Bedivere Remorsefully regarded thro' his *t's*, *M. d'Arthur* 171
dropping bitter *t's* against his brow „ 211
Mary sat And look'd with *t's* upon her boy, *Dora* 57
When eyes, love-languid thro' half *t's* *Love and Duty* 36
Rain out the heavy mist of *t's*, „ 43
burn'd upon its object thro' such *t's* As flow but once a life. „ 63
those tremulous eyes that fill with *t's* *Tithonus* 26
and thy *t's* are on my cheek. „ 45
Why wilt thou ever scare me with thy *t's*, „ 46
to the *t's* that thou wilt weep. *Locksley Hall* 82
She told him of their *t's*, And pray'd him, *Godiva* 19
With *t's* and smiles from heaven again *Sir L. and Q. G.* 2
To drop thy foolish *t's* upon my grave, *Come not, when, etc.* 2
What there is in loving *t's*, *Vision of Sin* 161
eyes All flooded with the helpless wrath of *t's*, *Enoch Arden* 32
But manifold entreaties, many a *t*, „ 160
Fast flow'd the current of her easy *t's*, „ 865
Who dabbling in the fount of fictive *t's*, *The Brook* 93
their own bitter *t's*, *T's*, and the careless rain *Aylmer's Field* 428
Deity false in human-amorous *t's* ; *Lucretius* 90
And kiss'd again with *t's*. *Princess ii* 5
And kiss again with *t's* ! „ 9
We kiss'd again with *t's*. „ 14
round her dewy eyes The circled Iris of a night of *t's* ; „ *iii* 27
She bow'd as if to veil a noble *t* ; „ 289
' *T's*, idle *t's*, I know not what they mean, „ *iv* 39
T's from the depth of some divine despair „ 40
the *t*, She sang of, shook and fell, „ 59
At length my Sire, his rough cheek wet with *t's*, „ *v* 23
Like summer tempest came her *t's*— „ *vi* 15

Tear (s) (*continued*) The leaves were wet with women's *t's* : *Princess vi* 39
Passionate *t's* Follow'd : the king replied not : „ 311
Love, like an Alpine harebell hung with *t's* „ *vii* 115
a touch Came round my wrist, and *t's* upon my hand „ 138
dark crowd moves, and there are sobs and *t's* : *Ode on Well.* 268
All for a slanderous story, that cost me many a *t*. *Grandmother* 22
time to catch The far-off interest of *t's* ? *In Mem. i* 8
Break, thou deep vase of chilling *t's*, „ *iv* 11
T's of the widower, when he sees „ *xiii* 1
Mine eyes have leisure for their *t's* ; „ 16
When fill'd with *t's* that cannot fall, „ *xix* 11
And *t's* that at their fountain freeze ; „ *xx* 12
With costly spikenard and with *t's*. „ *xxxii* 12
And *t's* are on the mother's face, „ *xl* 10
dip Their wings in *t's*, and skim away. „ *xlviii* 16
motions blindly drown The bases of my life in *t's*. „ *xlix* 16
grieve Thy brethren with a fruitless *t* ? „ *lviii* 10
With thy quick *t's* that make the rose Pull sideways, „ *lxxii* 10
No single *t*, no mark of pain : „ *lxxviii* 14
But with long use her *t's* are dry. „ 20
To pledge them with a kindly *t*, „ *xc* 10
And dipt in baths of hissing *t's*, „ *cxviii* 23
There has fallen a splendid *t* *Maud I xxii* 59
Shall shake its threaded *t's* in the wind no more. „ *III vi* 28
I consecrate with *t's*—These Idylls. *Ded. of Idylls* 4
Enforced she was to wed him in her *t's*, *Com. of Arthur* 204
comforted my heart, And dried my *t's*, „ 350
True *t's* upon his broad and naked breast, *Marr. of Geraint* 111
the mother smiled, but half in *t's*, „ 823
Ye mar a comely face with idiot *t's*. *Geraint and E.* 550
And felt the warm *t's* falling on his face ; „ 586
Made answer, either eyelid wet with *t's* : *Merlin and V.* 379
So sweetly gleam'd her eyes behind her *t's* „ 402
The slow *t* creep from her closed eyelid yet, „ 906
Then flash'd into wild *t's*, and rose again, *Lancelot and E.* 613
' Farewell, sweet sister,' parted all in *t's*. „ 1152
grant my worship of it Words, as we grant grief *t's*. „ 1188
and the *t's* were in his eyes. *Holy Grail* 759
and my *t's* have brought me good : *Guinevere* 202
Made my *t's* burn—is also past—part. „ 542
Him Sir Bedivere Remorsefully regarded thro' his *t's*, *Pass. of Arthur* 339
And dropping bitter *t's* against a brow „ 379
Her smile lit up the rainbow on my *t's*, *Lover's Tale i* 254
and mine Were dim with floating *t's*, „ 442
I saw the moonlight glitter on their *t's*— „ 697
The dew of *t's* in an unwholesome dew, „ 765
if thou be'st Love, dry up these *t's* „ 780
it melteth in the source Of these sad *t's*, „ 784
And Memory fed the soul of Love with *t's*. „ 822
I flung myself upon him In *t's* and cries : „ *ii* 90
poor lad, an' we parted in *t's*. *First Quarrel* 20
Edith spoke no word, She wept no *t*, *Sisters (E. and E.)* 216
it often moved me to *t's*, *In the Child. Hosp.* 31
hand of the Highlander wet with their *t's* ! *Def. of Lucknow* 102
Sank from their thrones, and melted into *t's*, *Columbus* 15
Lord of human *t's* ; Child-lover ; *To Victor Hugo* 3
I felt one warm *t* fall upon it. *Tiresias* 167
a tone so rough that I broke into passionate *t's*, *The Wreck* 122
But vain the *t's* for darken'd years As laughter over wine, And vain the laughter as the *t's*, *Ancient Sage* 183
all night I pray'd with *t's*, *The Flight* 17
I watch'd her at mass lettin' down the *t*, *Tomorrow* 29
the follies, furies, curses, passionate *t's*, *Locksley H., Sixty* 39
wife and his child stood by him in *t's* *Dead Prophet* 57
her *t's* Are half of pleasure, half of pain— *To Prin. Beatrice* 10
My quick *t's* kill'd the flower, *Demeter and P.* 108
So glad ? no *t* for him, who left you wealth, *The Ring* 188
And then the *t* fell, the voice broke. „ 367
Blister'd every word with *t's*, *Forlorn* 81
Are they *t's* ? For me— *Romney's R.* 26
Tear (verb) To *t* his heart before the crowd ! *You might have won* 36
to *t* away Their tawny clusters, *Enoch Arden* 381
T the noble heart of Britain, *Boädicea* 12
the winds of winter *t* an oak on a promontory. „ 77

Tear (verb) (*continued*) fiends, Who leap at thee to *t* thee; *Balin and Balan* 142
and strove To *t* the twain asunder in my heart, *Holy Grail* 786
the beasts Will *t* thee piecemeal.' „ 825
Sent hands upon him, as to *t* him, *Pelleas and E.* 521
Left for the white-tail'd eagle to *t* it, *Batt. of Brunanburh* 107
The tiger spasms *t* his chest, *Ancient Sage* 123
When he will *t* me from your side, *The Flight* 19
Teär'd (torn) lasses 'ed *t* out leaves i' the middle *Village Wife* 72
Teardrop 'A *t* trembled from its source, *Talking Oak* 161
Tearful What lit your eyes with *t* power, *Margaret* 3
From all things outward you have won A *t* grace, „ 12
I knew The *t* glimmer of the languid dawn *D. of F. Women* 74
And could I look upon her *t* eyes? *Lover's Tale i* 735
And looking round upon his *t* friends, „ 792
spoken of with *t* smiles; „ *ii* 182
But in the *t* splendour of her smiles *Prog. of Spring* 41
Teärin' an' cryin' and *t* 'er 'aäir, *North. Cobbler* 34
mayhap to my faäce, or a *t* my gown— *Spinster's S's.* 91
Roäver a-tuggin' an' *t* my slieäve. *Owd Roa* 60
a-tuggin' an' *t* me wuss nor afoor, „ 66
Tearing (*See also* **Teärin'**) And *t* off her veil of faded silk *Geraint and E.* 514
and *t* out of sheath The brand, *Balin and Balan* 392
with mad hand *T* the bright leaves *Lover's Tale ii* 40
Tearless And dropt the dust on *t* eyes; *In Mem. lxxx* 4
Tease *t* her till the day draws by: „ *lx* 14
Teat from the plaintive mother's *t* he took *The Brook* 129
lent her fierce *t* To human sucklings; *Com. of Arthur* 28
Teem and they would win thee—*t*, *Holy Grail* 541
Teeming rapt Upon the *t* harvest, *Golden Year* 71
Above the *t* ground. *Sir L. and Q. G.* 18
For *t* with liars, and madmen, *The Dreamer* 9
Teens The maiden blossoms of her *t* *Talking Oak* 79
Teething And ills and aches, and *t's*, *Holy Grail* 554
Teetotaler *See* **Toättler**
Telegraph there thro' twenty posts of *t* *Princess, Pro.* 77
Tel-el-Kebir Flare from *T-e-K* Thro' darkness, *Pro. to Gen. Hamley* 28
Telemachus This is my son, mine own *T*, *Ulysses* 33
Fasted and pray'd, *T* the Saint. *St. Telemachus* 11
Telescope here were *t's* For azure views; *Princess, Pro.* 67
Tell Would'st *t* me I must brook the rod *Supp. Confessions* 107
She'll not *t* me if she love me, *Lilian* 6
Exquisite Margaret, who can *t* *Margaret* 36
Yet *t* my name again to me, *Eleänore* 142
And *t* me if the woodbines blow. *My life is full* 25
t her to her face how much I hate Her presence, *Œnone* 228
t her, when I'm gone, to train the rosebush *May Queen, N. Y's. E.* 47
Effie on the other side, and I will *t* the sign. „ *Con.* 24
say to Robin a kind word, and *t* him not to fret; „ 45
If I had lived—I cannot *t*— „ 47
and *t* o'er Each little sound and sight. *D. of F. Women* 276
I will not *t* you not to weep. *To J. S.* 36
And ran to *t* her neighbours; *The Goose* 14
I had not staid so long to *t* you all, *Gardener's D.* 242
Yet might I *t* of meetings, of farewells— „ 251
Might I not *t* Of difference, reconcilement, „ 256
Dare *t* him Dora waited with the child; *Dora* 76
But *t* me, did she read the name I carved *Talking Oak* 153
thanks for what I learn And what remains to *t*. „ 204
And I will *t* it. Turn your face, *Day-Dm., Pro.* 17
And whither goest thou, *t* me where?' „ *Depart.* 26
'If my heart by signs can *t*, *L. of Burleigh* 2
'*T* me tales of thy first love— *Vision of Sin* 163
I will *t* him tales of foreign parts, *Enoch Arden* 198
who best could *t* What most it needed— „ 266
Not to *t* her, never to let her know. (repeat) „ 786, 798
If you could *t* her you had seen him dead, „ 808
I have a secret—only swear, Before I *t* you— „ 838
When you shall see her, *t* her that I died Blessing her, „ 878
And *t* my daughter Annie, whom I saw „ 882
And *t* my son that I died blessing him. „ 885
have loved you more as son Than brother, let me ***t* you**: *Aylmer's Field* 352
nor at all can *t* Whether I mean this day *Lucretius* 145

Tell (*continued*) *t* me pleasant tales, and read My sickness *Princess ii* 252
'no—I would not *t*, No, not for all Aspasia's cleverness, „ 343
'*T* us,' Florian ask'd, 'How grew this feud „ *iii* 76
But children die; and let me *t* you, girl, „ 253
And *t* her, *t* her, what I *t* to thee. „ *iv* 95
'O *t* her, Swallow, thou that knowest each, „ 96
'O *t* her, Swallow, that thy brood is flown: „ 108
'O *t* her, brief is life but love is long, „ 111
And *t* her, *t* her, that I follow thee.' „ 116
To *t* her what they were, and she to hear: „ 323
I came to *t* you; found that you had gone, „ 342
my nurse would *t* me of you; „ 427
'You—*t* us what we are' who might have told, „ *Con.* 34
I knew, but I would not *t*. *Grandmother* 26
Git ma my aäle I *t* tha, *N. Farmer, O. S.* 68
And now it *t's* of Italy. *The Daisy* 90
'What are they dreaming of? Who can *t*?' *Minnie and Winnie* 16
I pray you *t* the truth to me. *The Victim* 48
And which the dearest I cannot *t*!' „ 60
T my wish to her dewy blue eye: *Window, Letter* 13
Who mused on all I had to *t*, *In Mem. vi* 19
And I should *t* him all my pain, „ *xiv* 13
And *t* them all they would have told, „ *xl* 25
In that high place, and *t* thee all. „ *xliv* 16
Could hardly *t* what name were thine. „ *lix* 16
passing, turn the page that *t's* A grief, „ *lxxvii* 10
O *t* me where the senses mix, „ *lxxxviii* 3
O *t* me where the passions meet, „ 4
You *t* me, doubt is Devil-born. „ *xcvi* 4
the clash and clang that *t's* The joy „ *Con.* 61
can he *t* Whether war be a cause or a consequence? *Maud I x* 44
I must *t* her before we part, I must *t* her, or die. „ *xvi* 33
Beat with my heart more blest than heart can *t*, „ *xviii* 82
And *t's* me, when she lay Sick once, „ *xix* 72
that they might *t* us What and where they be. „ *II iv* 15
T him now: she is standing here at my head; „ *v* 65
as he speaks who *t's* the tale— *Com. of Arthur* 95
T me, ye yourselves, Hold ye this Arthur „ 171
'O King,' she cried, 'and I will *t* thee: „ 254
comfortable words, Beyond my tongue to *t* thee— „ 269
'O King!' she cried, 'and I will *t* thee true: „ 339
'But let me *t* thee now another tale: „ 359
Nor shalt thou *t* thy name to anyone. *Gareth and L.* 156
Nor *t* my name to any—no, not the King.' „ 171
but *t* thou these the truth.' „ 251
'Tut, *t* not me,' said Kay, 'ye are overfine „ 732
'And wherefore, damsel? *t* me all ye know. „ 1328
And day by day she thought to *t* Geraint, *Marr. of Geraint* 65
And *t* him what I think and what they say. „ 90
And yet not dare to *t* him what I think, „ 105
sparrow-hawk, what is he? *t* me of him. „ 404
t me, seeing I have sworn That I will break „ 423
T her, and prove her heart toward the Prince.' „ 513
Ashamed am I that I should *t* it thee. „ 577
Look on it, child, and *t* me if ye know it. „ 684
And yester-eve I would not *t* you of it, „ 702
If he would only speak and *t* me of it.' *Geraint and E.* 54
And I will *t* him all their caitiff talk; „ 66
And I will *t* him all their villany. „ 132
And there lay still; as he that *t's* the tale „ 161
I will *t* him How great a man thou art: „ 227
Arthur seeing ask'd '*T* me your names; *Balin and Balan* 50
for shall I *t* you truth? *Merlin and V.* 301
Heaven that hears I *t* you the clean truth, „ 343
if ye talk of trust I *t* you this, „ 360
T me, was he like to thee?' „ 613
Were I not woman, I could *t* a tale. „ 696
And mutter'd in himself, '*T her* the charm! „ 809
O *t* us—for we live apart— *Lancelot and E.* 284
Deck her with these; *t* her, she shines me down: „ 1225
T me, what drove thee from the Table Round, *Holy Grail* 28
T me, and what said each, and what the King?' „ 710
I need not *t* thee foolish words,— „ 855
Well, I will *t* thee: 'O King, „ 858

Tell (*continued*) straight forward? back again? Which?
t us quickly.' *Pelleas and E.* 68
Such as the wholesome mothers *t* their boys. .. 197
he that *t's* the tale Says that her ever-veering .. 492
'*T* thou the King and all his liars, *Last Tournament* 77
T's of a manhood ever less and lower? .. 121
for he that *t's* the tale Liken'd them, .. 226
Let me *t* thee now. .. 611
till her time To *t* you:' *Guinevere* 143
nor would he *t* His vision; .. 305
Is there none Will *t* the King I love him tho' so late? .. 651
Myself must *t* him in that purer life, .. 653
When I began to love. How should I *t* you? *Lover's Tale i* 145
How should the broad and open flower *t* What sort of bud it was, .. 151
life and love, And *t* me where I am? .. 177
As was our childhood, so our infancy, They *t* me, .. 250
They *t* me we would not be alone,— .. 252
nor *t* Of this our earliest, our closest-drawn, .. 277
If I should *t* you how I hoard in thought .. 288
To *t* him of the bliss he had with God— .. 674
And none but you yourself shall *t* him of it, .. *iv* 111
Ah heavens! Why need I *t* you all?— .. 201
I'll *t* you the tale o' my life. *First Quarrel* 9
fur thou mun a' sights to *t*. *North. Cobbler* 1
an' I'll *t* tha why. " 10
Good Sir Richard, *t* us now, *The Revenge* 26
(I did not *t* you—A widow with less guile *Sisters (E. and E.)* 181
Did I not *t* you they were twins?— .. 257
nor can I *t* One from the other, .. 276
nor care to *t* One from the other, .. 277
can tha *t* ony harm on 'im lass?— *Village Wife* 19
I be fear'd fur to *t* tha 'ow much— " 47
but, Emmie, you *t* it him plain, *In the Child. Hosp.* 57
who can *t*—Thou—England's England-loving daughter— *Ded. Poem Prin. Alice* 14
who can *t* but the traitors had won? *Def. of Lucknow* 66
They *t* me—weigh'd him down into the abysm— *Columbus* 137
I pray you *t* King Ferdinand who plays with me, .. 222
—but you will *t* the King, that I, .. 234
Half hid, they *t* me, now in flowing vines— *Tiresias* 144
will hide my face, I will *t* you all. *The Wreck* 12
You are curious. How should I *t*? *Despair* 3
In vain you *t* me 'Earth is fair' *Ancient Sage* 169
they *t* me that the world is hard, and harsh of mind, *The Flight* 101
An' *t* thim in Hiven about Molly Magee *Tomorrow* 92
for owt I can *t*—Robby wur fust *Spinster's S's.* 41
who can *t* how all will end? *Locksley H., Sixty* 103
t them 'old experience is a fool,' .. 131
Fur I wants to *t* tha o' Roä when we lived *Owd Roä* 19
I myself would *t* you all to-day. *The Ring* 124
Up, get up, and *t* him all, *T* him you were lying! *Forlorn* 55
T him now or never! *T* him all before you die, " 74
do you scorn me when you *t* me, O my lord, *Happy* 23
Bid him farewell for me, and *t* him—Hope! *Romney's R.* 147
T my son—O let me lean my head upon your breast. " 153
woman ruin'd the world, as God's own scriptures *t*, *Charity* 3
My dear, I will *t* you before I go.' " 36
only the Devil can *t* what he means. *Riflemen form!* 25
But what may follow who can *t*? *The Wanderer* 14
What is true at last will *t*: *Poets and Critics* 9
Tell'd (told) An Sally she *t* it about, *North. Cobbler* 81
I *t* ya, na moor o' that! *Spinster's S's.* 93
Moother 'ed *t* ma to bring tha down, *Owd Roä* 50
as I offens 'ev *t* 'er mysen, " 73
I *t* 'er 'Yeäs I mun goä.' " 98
ya *t* 'im to knaw his awn plaäce *Church-warden, etc.* 29
Teller (*See also* **Truth-teller**) he felt the tale Less than the *t*: *Enoch Arden* 712
The told-of, and the *t*. *Balin and Balan* 543
Tellin' an' she beän a *t* it me. *N. Farmer, N. S.* 10
an' *t* me not to be skeärd, *Owd Roä* 85
Telling (*See also* **Tellin'**) Which *t* what it is to die *In Mem. xxxi* 7
She blamed herself for *t* hearsay tales: *Merlin and V.* 951
Or Gareth *t* some prodigious tale Of knights, *Gareth and L.* 508
So she came in:—I am long in *t* it, *Lover's Tale iv* 302

Temper One equal *t* of heroic hearts, *Ulysses* 68
Of *t* amorous, as the first of May, *Princess i* 2
We, conscious of what *t* you are built, .. *iv* 400
Whence drew you this steel *t*? .. *vi* 232
Temperament But yet your mother's jealous *t*— .. *ii* 338
He has a solid base of *t*: .. *iv* 254
manfulness And pure nobility of *t*, *Marr. of Geraint* 212
Temperate That I, who gaze with *t* eyes *In Mem. cxii* 2
but keep a *t* brain; *Maud I iv* 40
Our loyal passion for our *t* kings; *Ode on Well* 165
Temper'd and *t* with the tears Of angels *To ——, With Pal. of Art* 18
Tempest when the crisp slope waves After a *t*, *Supp. Confessions* 127
The *t* crackles on the leads, *Sir Galahad* 53
A rushing *t* of the wrath of God *Aylmer's Field* 757
After a *t* woke upon a morn *Lucretius* 24
Fixt like a beacon-tower above the waves Of *t*, *Princess iv* 494
Like summer *t* came her tears— .. *vi* 15
while each ear was prick'd to attend A *t*, .. 281
So drench'd it is with *t*, to the sun, .. *vii* 142
whatever *t's* lour For ever silent; *Ode on Well.* 175
So may whatever *t* mars Mid-ocean, *In Mem. xvii* 13
And tracts of calm from *t* made, " *cxii* 14
And felt that *t* brooding round his heart, *Geraint and E.* 11
and ever overhead Bellow'd the *t*, *Merlin and V.* 957
Torn as a sail that leaves the rope is torn In *t*: *Holy Grail* 213
But after *t*, when the long wave broke *Guinevere* 290
his trust that Heaven Will blow the *t* *To the Queen ii* 47
Tempest-buffeted *T-b*, citadel-crown'd. *Will* 9
Tempestuous The strong *t* treble throbb'd and palpitated; *Vision of Sin* 28
Unfurnish'd brows, *t* tongues— *Freedom* 38
Temple (building) Her *t* and her place of birth, *Supp. Confessions* 53
The crowds, the *t's*, waver'd, and the shore; *D. of F. Women* 114
The palms and *t's* of the South. *You ask me, why, etc.* 28
swore Not by the *t* but the gold, *Aylmer's Field* 794
Lo the palaces and the *t*, *Boädicea* 53
For there the *T* stood. *Lover's Tale i* 339
I was led mute Into her *t* like a sacrifice; " 685
Ilion's lofty *t's* robed in fire, *To Virgil* 2
and heard The murmur of their *t's* chanting me, *Demeter and P.* 72
Shrined him within the *t* of her heart, *The Ring* 219
O God in every *t* I see people that see thee, *Akbar's D., Inscrip.* 1
But it is thou whom I search from *t* to *t*. " 6
A *t*, neither Pagod, Mosque, nor Church, *Akbar's Dream* 178
Temple (part of head) Cluster'd about his *t's* like a God's. *Œnone* 60
Flush'd in her *t's* and her eyes, *Palace of Art* 170
brows that shook and throbb'd From *t* unto *t*. *Lover's Tale iii* 8
but how my *t's* burn! *The Flight* 73
Temple-bar High over roaring *T-b*, *Will Water.* 69
Temple-cave *T-c* of thine own self, *Ancient Sage* 32
Temple-eaten college-times Or *T-e* terms, *Aylmer's Field* 105
Temple-gates And drops at Glory's *t-g*, *You might have won* 34
Tempt length of ribbon and a ring To *t* the babe, *Enoch Arden* 751
t The Trojan, while his neat-herds were abroad; *Lucretius* 87
Temptation Who feel no touch of my *t*, *Romney's R.* 121
Tempted I well believe she *t* them and fail'd, *Merlin and V.* 819
Tempter I was the *t*, Mother, *The Wreck* 11
Ten (adj.) minstrel sings Before them of the *t* years' war in Troy, *Lotos-Eaters, C. S.* 77
that thrice *t* years, Thrice multiplied by superhuman pangs, *St. S. Stylites* 10
I grew Twice *t* long weary weary years to this, " 90
T thousand broken lights and shapes, *Will Water.* 59
Had cast upon its crusty side The gloom of *t* Decembers. " 104
so *t* years Since Enoch left his hearth *Enoch Arden* 359
That he who left you *t* long years ago " 404
And that was *t* years back, or more, if I don't forget *Grandmother* 75
T thousand-fold had grown, flash'd the fierce shield, *Gareth and L.* 1030
this cut is fresh; That *t* years back; *Lancelot and E.* 22
t years before, The heathen caught and reft him of his tongue, .. 272
'*t* times nay! This is not love: .. 948
But *t* slow mornings past, and on the eleventh .. 1133
T year sin', and wa 'greed as well as a fiddle i' tune: *North. Cobbler* 12
Fire from *t* thousand at once of the rebels *Def. of Lucknow* 22

Ten (adj.) (*continued*) And once for *t* long weeks I tried Your table of Pythagoras, *To E. Fitzgerald* 14
T long sweet summer days upon deck, *The Wreck* 64
T long days of summer and sin— „ 77
' *T* long sweet summer days' of fever, „ 147
An' Shamus O'Shea that has now *t* childer, *Tomorrow* 85
Let us hush this cry of ' Forward ' till *t* thousand years have gone. *Locksley H., Sixty* 78
Old Virgil who would write *t* lines, *Poets and their B.* 2
Ull be fun' upo' four short legs *t* times fur one upo' two. *Owd Roä* 16
T year sin—Naäy—naäy ! „ 20
Too laäte—but it's all ower now—hall hower—an' *t* year sin ; „ 116
For *t* thousand years Old and new ? *The Ring* 19
But after *t* slow weeks her fix'd intent, „ 345
Ten (s) Warless ? when her *t's* are thousands, *Locksley H., Sixty* 171
Tenant Careless *t's* they ! *Deserted House* 4
As well as with his *t*, Jocky Dawes. *Walk. to the Mail* 28
thither flock'd at noon His *t's*, wife and child, *Princess, Pro.* 4
Be *t's* of a single breast, *In Mem. xvi* 3
Tenanted We bought the farm we *t* before. *The Brook* 222
Tend Live happy : *t* thy flowers ; *Love and Duty* 87
Were you sick, ourself Would *t* upon you. *Princess iii* 321
That *t's* her bristled grunters in the sludge : ' „ *v* 27
we will *t* on him Like one of these ; „ *vi* 124
And were half fool'd to let you *t* our son, „ 274
That you may *t* upon him with the prince.' „ 315
And *t's* upon bed and bower, *Maud I xiv* 4
' O I that wasted time to *t* upon her, *Geraint and E.* 38
and *t* him curiously Like a king's heir, *Last Tournament* 90
Henceforward too, the Powers that *t* the soul, *Guinevere* 65
Tendance nor from her *t* turn'd Into the world without ; *Gardener's D.* 144
And pensive *t* in the all-weary noons, *Princess vii* 102
breath Of her sweet *t* hovering over him, *Geraint and E.* 926
Tended *t* by Pure vestal thoughts in the translucent fane *Isabel* 3
tend thy flowers ; be *t* by My blessing ! *Love and Duty* 87
But Psyche *t* Florian : with her oft, Melissa came ; *Princess vii* 55
And *t* her like a nurse. *Maud I xix* 76
That still had *t* on him from his birth, *Gareth and L.* 179
And Enid *t* on him there ; *Geraint and E.* 924
and every day she *t* him, *Lancelot and E.* 850
women who *t* the hospital bed, *Def. of Lucknow* 87
Tender Like the *t* amber round, *Margaret* 19
For while the *t* service made thee weep, *The Bridesmaid* 10
And oft I heard the *t* dove *Miller's D.* 41
I roll'd among the *t* flowers : *Fatima* 11
And *t* curving lines of creamy spray ; *Lotos-Eaters, C. S.* 62
Sleep sweetly, *t* heart, in peace : *To J. S.* 69
cushions of whose touch may press The maiden's *t* palm. *Talking Oak* 180
for a *t* voice will cry. *Locksley Hall* 87
But the *t* grace of a day that is dead *Break, break, etc.* 15
On a sudden a low breath Of *t* air made tremble *The Brook* 202
The *t* pink five-beaded baby-soles, *Aylmer's Field* 186
nor from *t* hearts, And those who sorrow'd o'er a vanish'd race, „ 843
Where she, who kept a *t* Christian hope, *Sea Dreams* 41
Made havock among those *t* cells, *Lucretius* 22
roll thy *t* arms Round him, „ 82
And dark and true and *t* is the North. *Princess iv* 98
Delaying as the *t* ash delays To clothe herself, „ 106
Like *t* things that being caught feign death, „ *v* 108
there the *t* orphan hands Felt at my heart, „ 435
t ministries Of female hands and hospitality. „ *vi* 72
Steps with a *t* foot, light as on air, „ 88
Or thro' the parted silks the *t* face Peep'd, „ *vii* 60
Not perfect, nay, but full of *t* wants, „ 319
Mighty Seaman, *t* and true, *Ode on Well.* 134
Rolling on their purple couches in their *t* effeminacy. *Boädicea* 62
That breathe a thousand *t* vows, *In Mem. xx* 2
hopes and light regrets that come Make April of her *t* eyes ; „ *xl* 8
What time his *t* palm is prest „ *xlv* 2
whose light-blue eyes Are *t* over drowning flies, „ *xcvi* 3
The *t* blossom flutter down, Unloved, „ *ci* 3
With *t* gloom the roof, the wall ; „ *Con.* 118
Tender (*continued*) Perhaps the smile and *t* tone Came out of her pitying womanhood, *Maud I vi* 63
And dream of her beauty with *t* dread, „ *xvi* 14
For, Maud, so *t* and true, „ *xix* 85
My own dove with the *t* eye ? „ *II iv* 46
Seem I not as *t* to him As any mother ? *Gareth and L.* 1283
And seeing them so *t* and so close, *Marr. of Geraint* 22
To stoop and kiss the *t* little thumb, „ 395
' Mother, a maiden is a *t* thing, „ 510
and felt Her low firm voice and *t* government. *Geraint and E.* 194
At this the *t* sound of his own voice „ 348
And Enid could not say one *t* word, „ 746
I think ye hardly know the *t* rhyme *Merlin and V.* 383
O Master, do ye love my *t* rhyme ? ' „ 399
So *t* was her voice, so fair her face, „ 401
Then Merlin to his own heart, loathing, said : ' O true and *t* ! „ 791
Yet with all ease, so *t* was the work : *Lancelot and E.* 442
Utter'd a little *t* dolorous cry. „ 817
' O sweet father, *t* and true, Deny me not,' „ 1110
This *t* rhyme, and evermore the doubt, *Pelleas and E.* 410
Who see your *t* grace and stateliness. *Guinevere* 190
and all The careful burthen of our *t* years *Lover's Tale i* 222
Frail Life was startled from the *t* love „ 616
' Never the heart among women,' he said, ' more *t* and true.' *The Wreck* 96
Struck hard at the *t* heart of the mother, *Despair* 74
Sun of dawn That brightens thro' the Mother's *t* eyes, *Prin. Beatrice* 4
Woman to her inmost heart, and woman to her *t* feet, *Locksley H., Sixty* 50
Legend or true ? so *t* should be true ! *The Ring* 224
Solved in the *t* blushes of the peach ; *Prog. of Spring* 34
slowly moving again to a melody Yearningly *t*, *Merlin and the G.* 91
So princely, *t*, truthful, reverent, pure— *D. of the Duke of C.* 4
Tenderer surely with a love Far *t* than my Queen's. *Lancelot and E.* 1395
Tenderest The fancy's *t* eddy wreathe, *In Mem. xlix* 6
such a grace Of *t* courtesy, *Geraint and E.* 862
T of Roman poets nineteen-hundred years ago, *Frater Ave, etc.* 6
in wife and woman I found The *t* Christ-like creature *Charity* 32
Tenderest-hearted Vivien, like the *t-h* maid *Merlin and V.* 377
Tenderest-touching by *t-t* terms, To sleek her ruffled peace „ 898
Tenderly in what limits, and how *t* ; *Ded. of Idylls* 20
Tender-natured Gone thy *t-n* mother, wearying to be left alone, *Locksley H., Sixty* 57
Tenderness A moment came the *t* of tears, *The form, the form* 9
decent not to fail In offices of *t*, *Ulysses* 41
His bashfulness and *t* at war, *Enoch Arden* 289
So gracious was her tact and *t* : *Princess i* 24
That lute and flute fantastic *t*, „ *iv* 129
No saint—inexorable—no *t*— „ *v* 515
The *t*, not yours, that could not kill, „ *vi* 186
T touch by touch, and last, „ *vii* 114
that might express All-comprehensive *t*, *In Mem. lxxxv* 47
A face of *t* might be feign'd, *Maud I vi* 52
Thro' that great *t* for Guinevere, *Marr. of Geraint* 30
There brake a sudden-beaming *t* Of manners *Lancelot and E.* 328
His *t* of manner, and chaste awe, *Pelleas and E.* 110
offices Of watchful care and trembling *t*. *Lover's Tale i* 226
Tender-pencil'd The *t-p* shadow play. *In Mem. xlix* 12
Tender-spirited The low-voiced, *t-s* Lionel, *Lover's Tale i* 655
Tending *t* her rough lord, tho' all unask'd, *Geraint and E.* 405
Tendon And scirrhous roots and *t's*. *Amphion* 64
Teneriffe great flame-banner borne by *T*, *Columbus* 69
Tenfold-complicated abyss Of *t-c* change, *In Mem. xciii* 12
Ten-hundred-fold Pain heap'd *t-h-f* to this, were still Less burthen, by *t-h-f*, *St. S. Stylites* 23
Tennis Quoit, *t*, ball—no games ? *Princess iii* 215
Tenor My blood an even *t* kept, *In Mem. lxxxv* 17
Tent Among the *t's* I paused and sung, *Two Voices* 125
they raised A *t* of satin, elaborately wrought *Princess iii* 348
No bigger than a glow-worm shone the *t* „ *iv* 25
They bore her back into the *t* : „ 193
blazon'd lions o'er the imperial *t* „ *v* 9
He show'd a *t* A stone-shot off : „ 53

Tent (*continued*) lie in the t's with coarse mankind, Princess vi 69
You shall not lie in the t's but here, „ 94
on to the t's: take up the Prince.' „ 279
And at thy name the Tartar t's are stirr'd; W. to Marie Alex. 12
and loud With sport and song, in booth and t, In Mem. xcviii 28
and pitch'd His t's beside the forest. Com. of Arthur 58
And show'd an empty t allotted her, Geraint and E. 885
And past to Enid's t; and thither came „ 922
Heard in his t the moanings of the King: Pass. of Arthur 8
the heavens a hide, a t Spread over earth, Columbus 47
Tented The t winter-field was broken up Aylmer's Field 110
Ten-thousand The bearded Victor of t-t hymns, Princess iii 352
Ten-times And make, as t-t worthier to be thine Balin and Balan 68
Tenting-pin Tore my pavilion from the t-p, Holy Grail 747
Term (academic) save for college-times Or Temple-eaten t's, Aylmer's Field 105
caught the blossom of the flying t's, Princess, Pro. 164
Term (of time) To sleep thro' t's of mighty wars, Day-Dm., L'Envoi 9
days Were clipt by horror from his t of life. Aylmer's Field 603
To point the t of human strife, In Mem. l 14
Pass we then A t of eighteen years. Lover's Tale i 287
Clung closer to us for a longer t Columbus 197
five-fold thy t Of years, I lay; Tiresias 33
I spy nor t nor bound. Mechanophilus 20
Term (word, etc.) (*See also* **Counter-term**) Not master'd by some modern t; Love thou thy land 30
mixt with inmost t's Of art and science: Princess ii 446
Heap'd on her t's of disgrace, Maud II i 14
may merit well Your t of overstrain'd. Merlin and V. 535
Then thrice essay'd, by tenderest-touching t's, „ 898
after that vile t of yours, I find with grief! „ 921
Terrace The t ranged along the Northern front, Princess iii 118
I paced the t, till the Bear had wheel'd „ iv 212
The moonlight touching o'er a t The Daisy 83
I used to walk This T—morbid, The Ring 168
Rose, on this t fifty years ago, Roses on the T. 1
which on our t here Glows in the blue „ 7
Terrace-lawn On every slanting t-l. Day-Dm., Sleep. P. 10
Terrible fear'd To send abroad a shrill and t cry, Enoch Arden 768
recollect the dreams that come Just ere the waking: t! Lucretius 36
'O fair and strong and t! Princess vi 163
Love and Nature, these are two more t And stronger. „ 165
sang the t prophetesses, Boädicea 37
Spurr'd with their t war-cry; Geraint and E. 170
T pity, if one so beautiful Prove, Lover's Tale iv 338
down the t ridge Plunged in the last fierce charge Sisters (E. and E.) 63
These are Astronomy and Geology, t Muses! Parnassus 16
None but the t Peelè remaining Kapiolani 28
Territorial *See* **Lord-territorial**
Territory You lying close upon his t, Princess iv 403
they wasted all the flourishing t, Boädicea 54
And Arthur gave him back his t, Gareth and L. 78
his princedom lay Close on the borders of a t, Marr. of Geraint 34
loves to know When men of mark are in his t: Geraint and E. 229
Led from the t of false Limours „ 437
Endow you with broad land and t Lancelot and E. 957
Estate them with large land and t „ 1322
Terror He that only rules by t The Captain 1
Brook'd not the expectant t of her heart, Enoch Arden 493
wreck, Flights, t's, sudden rescues, Aylmer's Field 99
But must, to make the t of thee more, Gareth and L. 1389
Then those that did not blink the t, „ 1402
still she look'd, and still the t grew Marr. of Geraint 615
leech forsake the dying bed for t of his life? Happy 98
When from the t's of Nature a people Kapiolani 1
Test (s) I come to the t, a tiny poem Hendecasyllabics 3
Test (verb) defying change To t his worth; In Mem. xcv 28
Well, we shall t thee farther; Merlin and V. 94
Tested to return When others had been t) Aylmer's Field 219
And heard it ring as true as t gold.' Last Tournament 284
Testify Yes, as the dead we weep for t— Aylmer's Field 747
For I must live to t by fire. Sir J. Oldcastle 206
Testimony To this I call my friends in t, Lancelot and E. 1299
to the basement of the tower For t; Guinevere 105
Test-question That was their main t-q— Sir J. Oldcastle 155
Tether'd How can ye keep me t to you— Gareth and L. 115
should be T to these dead pillars of the Church— Sir J. Oldcastle 121
Teuton T or Celt, or whatever we be, W. to Alexandra 32
Slav, T, Kelt, I count them all My friends Epilogue 18
Tew (a worry) (*See also* **Tued**) at fust she wur all in a t, North. Cobbler 53
Text Suddenly put her finger on the t, Enoch Arden 497
Not sowing hedgerow t's and passing by, Aylmer's Field 171
And being used to find her pastor t's, „ 606
Christian hope, Haunting a holy t, Sea Dreams 42
the maiden Aunt Took this fair day for t, Princess, Pro. 108
And the parson made it his t that week, Grandmother 29
A square of t that looks a little blot, The t no larger than the limbs of fleas; And every square of t an awful charm, Merlin and V. 671
And none can read the t, not even I; „ 681
Thack (thatch) an' thou runn'd oop o' the t; Spinster's S's. 38
Thames (*See also* **Tamesa**) Came crowing over T. Will Water. 140
Thank Light on a broken word to t him with. Enoch Arden 347
I fear'd To meet a cold 'We t you, Princess iv 328
T Him who isled us here, and roughly set Ode on Well. 154
t God that I keep my eyes. Grandmother 106
And t the Lord I am King Arthur's fool. Last Tournament 320
I t the saints, I am not great. Guinevere 199
I would t him, the other is dead, Despair 70
't God that I hevn't naw cauf o' my oän.' Spinster's S's. 116
We t thee with our voice, To W. C. Macready 4
I t him. I am happy, happy. Happy 107
Raise me. I t you. Romney's R. 60
Thanked God be t!' said Alice the nurse, Lady Clare 17
Assumed that she had t him, adding, Geraint and E. 646
Thankful Not t that his troubles are no more. Lucretius 143
Thanks statue-like, In act to render t. Gardener's D. 162
A thousand t for what I learn Talking Oak 203
I do forgive him!' 'T, my love,' Sea Dreams 317
Their debt of t to her who first had dared Princess ii 141
But 'T,' she answer'd 'Go: „ 357
you have our t for all: „ iv 528
You saved our life: we owe you bitter t: „ 531
To lighten this great clog of t, „ vi 126
with an eye that swum in t; „ 210
Render t to the Giver, (repeat) Ode on Well. 44, 47
For this, for all, we weep our t to thee! Open. Inter. Exhib. 9
T, for the fiend best knows whether Maud I i 75
'T, venerable friend,' replied Geraint; Marr. of Geraint 303
maybe, shall have learn'd to lisp you t.' „ 822
to which She answer'd, 'T, my lord;' Geraint and E. 264
my t, For these have broken up my melancholy.' Merlin and V. 266
I bid the stranger welcome. T at last! „ 270
O no more t than might a goat have given „ 278
your feet before her own? And yet no t: „ 285
next For t it seems till now neglected, „ 308
T, but you work against your own desire; Lancelot and E. 1096
And love, and boundless t— Lover's Tale iv 382
an' arn'd naw t fur 'er paäins. Village Wife 12
my poor t! I am but an alien and a Genovese. Columbus 242
Yield thee full t for thy full courtesy To Victor Hugo 13
t to the Lord that I never not listen'd to noän! Spinster's S's. 8
would yield full t to you For your rich gift, To Ulysses 33
But t to the Blessed Saints that I came Bandit's Death 40
Thatch (*See also* **Thack**) Weeded and worn the ancient t Mariana 7
And the cock hath sung beneath the t The Owl i 10
doves That sun their milky bosoms on the t, Princess ii 103
It sees itself from t to base Requiescat 3
and drive Innocent cattle under t, Locksley H., Sixty 96
Thatch'd They built, and t with leaves of palm, Enoch Arden 559
Thaw (verb) T this male nature to some touch Princess vi 306
And t's the cold, and fills The flower Early Spring 45
Thaw (s) an' the däale was all of a t, Owd Roä 39
Moother 'ed beän sa soäk'd wi' the t „ 113
Theatre stately t's Bench'd crescent-wise. Princess ii 369
Thebes in thy virtue lies The saving of our T; Tiresias 110
crying 'T, Thy T shall fall and perish, „ 115
will murmur thee To thine own T, while T thro' thee shall stand „ 141

Thebes (*continued*) Folded her lion paws, and look'd to *T*. *Tiresias* 149
Theft and you, will you call it a *t* ?— *Rizpah* 52
The *t* were death or madness to the thief, *The Ring* 204
Theme Seem but the *t* of writers, *Edwin Morris* 48
Ah, let the rusty *t* alone ! *Will Water.* 177
warming with her *t* She fulmined out her scorn *Princess ii* 132
Whereat we glanced from *t* to *t*, *In Mem. lxxxix* 33
Then (*See also* **Thin**) Break into '*T's*' and 'Whens' *Ancient Sage* 104
Theodolind castle Of Queen *T*, where we slept ; *The Daisy* 80
Theory forged a thousand *theories* of the rocks, *Edwin Morris* 18
as a rogue in grain Veneer'd with sanctimonious *t*. *Princess, Pro.* 117
They fed her *theories*, in and out of place " *i* 129
pass With all fair *theories* only made to gild " *ii* 233
my mother still Affirms your Psyche thieved her *theories*, " *iii* 92
For she was cramm'd with *theories* out of books, " *Con.* 35
Thermopylæ these in our *T* shall stand, *Third of Feb.* 47
Thesis The *t* which thy words intend— *Two Voices* 338
Thessalian Or that *T* growth, *Talking Oak* 292
Thew nor ever had I seen Such *t's* of men : *Princess v* 256
Nor lose the wrestling *t's* that throw the world ; " *vii* 282
I felt the *t's* of Anakim, *In Mem. ciii* 31
Thick (*See also* **Jewel-thick**) *faults were* t *as dust In vacant chambers,* *To the Queen* 18
t with white bells the clover-hill swells *Sea-Fairies* 14
chestnuts near, that hung In masses *t* with milky cones. *Miller's D.* 56
t as Autumn rains Flash in the pools *Œnone* 205
my voice was *t* with sighs As in a dream. *D. of F. Women* 109
with a grosser film made *t* These heavy, horny eyes. *St. S. Stylites* 200
We gain'd the mother-city *t* with towers, *Princess i* 112
snowy shoulders, *t* as herded ewes, " *iv* 479
T rosaries of scented thorn, *Arabian Nights* 106
And thro' *t* veils to apprehend *Two Voices* 296
from beneath Whose *t* mysterious boughs in the dark morn *Œnone* 213
when she strikes thro' the *t* blood Of cattle, *Lucretius* 98
Climb thy *t* noon, disastrous day ; *In Mem. lxxii* 26
So *t* with lowings of the herds, " *xcix* 3
t By ashen roots the violets blow. " *cxv* 3
Then fell *t* rain, plume droopt and mantle clung, *Last Tournament* 213
Thro' the *t* night I hear the trumpet blow : *Guinevere* 569
T with wet woods, and many a beast therein, *Com. of Arthur* 21
so quick and *t* The lightnings here and there *Holy Grail* 493
Thicken'd (adj.) (*See also* **Grape-thicken'd**) Love's white star Beam'd thro' the *t* cedar in the dusk. *Gardener's D.* 166
Thicken'd (verb) A clamour *t*, mixt with inmost terms *Princess ii* 446
Thickening *See* **Slowly-thickening**
Thicker *T* the drizzle grew, deeper the gloom ; *Enoch Arden* 679
Now thinner, and now *t*, like the flakes *Lucretius* 166
and mingled with the haze And made it *t* ; *Com. of Arthur* 436
t down the front With jewels than the sward *Geraint and E.* 689
T than drops from thunder, *Holy Grail* 348
Then spoke King Arthur, drawing *t* breath : *M. d'Arthur* 148
my heart beat stronger And *t*, *Maud I viii* 9
Then spoke King Arthur, drawing *t* breath : *Pass. of Arthur* 316
Thickest When *t* dark did trance the sky, *Mariana* 18
Among the *t* and bore down a Prince, *Princess v* 518
Thicket (*See also* **Elder-thicket, Myrrh-thicket**) Athwart the *t* lone : *Claribel* 10
Or the dry *t's*, I could meet with her *Œnone* 223
No branchy *t* shelter yields ; *Sir Galahad* 58
some hid and sought In the orange *t's* : *Princess ii* 460
round us all the *t* rang To many a flute *In Mem. xxiii* 23
and the *t* closed Behind her, *Merlin and V.* 973
Across my garden ! and the *t* stirs, *Prog. of Spring* 53
Thicketed *See* **Rough-thicketed**
Thick-fleeced livelong bleat Of the *t-f* sheep *Ode to Memory* 66
Thick-jewell'd *T-j* shone the saddle-leather, *L. of Shalott iii* 20
Thick-leaved oak-tree sigheth, *T-l*, ambrosial, *Claribel* 5
Beyond the *t-l* platans of the vale. *Princess iii* 175
Thick-moted When the *t-m* sunbeam lay *Mariana* 78
Thick-set from thy topmost head The *t-s* hazel dies ; *Will Water.* 234
Thick-twined cave to cave thro' the *t-t* vine— *Lotos-Eaters, C. S.* 95
Thief therefore turning softly like a *t*, *Enoch Arden* 771
storming a hill-fort of *thieves* He got it ; *Aylmer's Field* 225

Thief (*continued*) But *thieves* from o'er the wall Stole the seed *The Flower* 11
Kill the foul *t*, and wreak me for my son.' *Gareth and L.* 363
wood is nigh as full of *thieves* as leaves : " 789
for my wont hath ever been To catch my *t*, " 822
To curse this hedgerow *t*, the sparrow-hawk : *Marr. of Geraint* 309
Who now no more a vassal to the *t*, *Geraint and E.* 753
Thieves, bandits, leavings of confusion, *Last Tournament* 95
To be hang'd for a *t*—and then put away— *Rizpah* 36
Sanctuary granted To bandit, *t*, assassin— *Sir J. Oldcastle* 113
theft were death or madness to the *t*, *The Ring* 204
Thieved my mother still Affirms your Psyche *t* her theories, *Princess iii* 92
Thigh (*See also* **Mid-thigh-deep**) flush'd Ganymede, his rosy *t* Half-buried *Palace of Art* 121
it is written that my race Hew'd Ammon, hip and *t*, *D. of F. Women* 238
And both my *t's* are rotted with the dew ; *St. S. Stylites* 41
Ramp in the field, he smote his *t*, and mock'd : *Lancelot and E.* 664
Then crush'd the saddle with his *t's*, *Pelleas and E.* 459
Thimbleby Noäks or *T*—toäner 'ed shot 'um *N. Farmer, O. S.* 35
Thin (adj.) if his fellow spake, His voice was *t*, *Lotos-Eaters* 34
His face is growing sharp and *t*. *D. of the O. Year* 46
O hark, O hear ! how *t* and clear, *Princess iv* 7
When it slowly grew so *t*, *Maud I xix* 20
Tho' Modred biting his *t* lips was mute, *Gareth and L.* 31
the moon, Half-melted into *t* blue air, *Lover's Tale i* 421
and her *t* hands crost on her breast— *In the Child. Hosp.* 39
Wavers on her *t* stem the snowdrop cold *Prog. of Spring* 3
Hath ever and anon a note so *t* *Balin and Balan* 214
T as the batlike shrillings of the Dead *Death of Œnone* 21
Thin (verb) or would seem to *t* her in a day, *Aylmer's Field* 76
waters break Whitening for half a league, and *t* themselves, *Last Tournament* 465
Thin (then) An' where 'ud the poor man, *t*, cut his bit o' turf for the fire ? *Tomorrow* 65
Thing All *t's* will change (repeat) *Nothing will Die* 15, 38
Yet all *t's* must die. *All Things will Die* 8
For all *t's* must die. (repeat) " 13, 49
All *t's* must die. " 14
All *t's* were born. " 47
that Hesperus all *t's* bringeth, *Leonine Eleg.* 13
And trust and hope till *t's* should cease, *Supp. Confessions* 31
and *t's* that seem, And *t's* that be, " 173
Teach me the nothingness of *t's*. *A Character* 4
all the dry pied *t's* that be In the hueless mosses *The Mermaid* 48
All *t's* that are forked, and horned, " 53
From all *t's* outward you have won A tearful grace, *Margaret* 11
But good *t's* have not kept aloof, *My life is full, etc.* 2
High *t's* were spoken there, *Alexander* 12
'Lord, how long shall these *t's* be ? *Poland* 9
Will learn new *t's* when I am not.' *Two Voices* 63
There is no other *t* express'd But long disquiet " 248
'These *t's* are wrapt in doubt and dread, " 266
Not simple as a *t* that dies. " 288
many *t's* perplex, With motions, checks, " 299
He may not do the *t* he would. " 303
She spoke at large of many *t's*, *Miller's D.* 155
all *t's* in order stored, A haunt of ancient Peace. *Palace of Art* 87
'O all *t's* fair to sate my various eyes ! " 193
But all these *t's* have ceased to be, *May Queen, Con.* 48
A land where all *t's* always seem'd the same ! *Lotos-Eaters* 24
While all *t's* else have rest from weariness ? " *C. S.* 14
All *t's* have rest : why should we toil alone, " 15
We only toil, who are the first of *t's*, " 16
the roof and crown of *t's* ? " 24
All *t's* are taken from us, " 46
All *t's* have rest, and ripen toward the grave " 51
And our great deeds, as half-forgotten *t's*. " 78
to start in pain, Resolved on noble *t's*, *D. of F. Women* 42
How beautiful a *t* it was to die For God " 231
A man may speak the *t* he will ; *You ask me, why, etc.* 8
keep a *t*, its use will come. *The Epic* 42
A little *t* may harm a wounded man. *M. d'Arthur* 42
This is a shameful *t* for men to lie. " 78
and do the *t* I bad thee, watch, " 80
Such a precious *t*, one worthy note, " 89
More *t's* are wrought by prayer Than this world dreams of. " 247

Thing (*continued*) 'Come With all good *t's*, and war shall be no more.' *M. d'Arthur, Ep.* 28
We spoke of other *t's*; we coursed about *Gardener's D.* 222
and thought Hard *t's* of Dora. *Dora* 58
And all the *t's* that had been. „ 107
(For they had pack'd the *t* among the beds,) *Walk. to the Mail* 44
You could not light upon a sweeter *t*: „ 52
betwixt shame and pride, New *t's* and old, „ 61
should have seen him wince As from a venomous *t*: „ 72
spoke I knowing not the *t's* that were. *Edwin Morris* 89
slow sweet hours that bring us all *t's* good, The slow sad hours that bring us all *t's* ill, And all good *t's* from evil, *Love and Duty* 57
'We sleep and wake and sleep, but all *t's* move; *Golden Year* 22
human *t's* returning on themselves Move onward, „ 25
something more, A bringer of new *t's*; *Ulysses* 28
Thou seëst all *t's*, thou wilt see my grave: *Tithonus* 73
easy *t's* to understand— *Locksley Hall* 55
sorrow's crown of sorrow is remembering happier *t's*. „ 76
but earnest of the *t's* that they shall do: „ 118
all *t's* here are out of joint: „ 133
to have loved so slight a *t*. „ 148
Howsoever these *t's* be, a long farewell „ 189
Here all *t's* in their place remain, *Day-Dm., Sleep. P.* 53
All precious *t's*, discover'd late, „ *Arrival* 1
Well—were it not a pleasant *t* To fall asleep „ *L'Envoi* 3
nor take Half-views of men and *t's*. *Will Water.* 52
If old *t's*, there are new; „ 58
I look at all *t's* as they are, „ 71
Like all good *t's* on earth! „ 202
I hold it good, good *t's* should pass: „ 205
thou shalt from all *t's* suck Marrow „ 213
She will order all *t's* duly, *L. of Burleigh* 39
As looks a father on the *t's* Of his dead son, *The Letters* 23
Callest thou that *t* a leg? *Vision of Sin* 89
Tomohrit, Athos, all *t's* fair, *To E. L.* 5
came a change, as all *t's* human change. *Enoch Arden* 101
turn'd The current of his talk to graver *t's* „ 203
he set his hand To do the *t* he will'd, „ 295
Annie, there is a *t* upon my mind, „ 399
and all these *t's* fell on her Sharp as reproach. „ 487
he himself Moved haunting people, *t's* and places, „ 604
Because *t's* seen are mightier than *t's* heard, „ 766
Almost to all *t's* could he turn his hand. „ 813
Nor could he understand how money breeds, Thought it a dead *t*; yet himself could make The *t* that is not as the *t* that is. *The Brook* 7
And how it was the *t* his daughter wish'd, „ 140
Re-risen in Katie's eyes, and all *t's* well. „ 169
Took joyful note of all *t's* joyful, *Aylmer's Field* 67
And neither loved nor liked the *t* he heard. „ 250
T's in an Aylmer deem'd impossible, „ 305
The *t's* belonging to thy peace and ours! „ 740
is it a light *t* That I, their guest, their host, „ 789
all *t's* work together for the good Of those '— *Sea Dreams* 158
Another and another frame of *t's* For ever: *Lucretius* 42
Which *t's* appear the work of mighty Gods. „ 102
universal culture for the crowd, And all *t's* *Princess, Pro.* 110
made it death For any male *t* but to peep at us.' „ 152
And they that know such *t's*— „ *i* 144
not to answer, Madam, all those hard *t's* „ *ii* 345
And two dear *t's* are one of double worth, „ 419
And still she rail'd against the state of *t's*. „ *iii* 84
One mind in all *t's*: „ 91
For all *t's* were and were not. „ 189
Your Highness might have seem'd the *t* you say.' „ 202
for all *t's* serve their time Toward that great year „ *iv* 73
To harm the *t* that trusts him, „ 248
And all *t's* were and were not. „ 567
Sweet is it to have done the *t* one ought, „ *v* 67
Like tender *t's* that being caught feign death, „ 108
As he that does the *t* they dare not do, „ 160
I myself, What know I of these *t's*? „ 284
That all *t's* grew more tragic and more strange; „ *vi* 23

Thing (*continued*) May these *t's* be!' Sighing she spoke 'I fear They will not.' *Princess vii* 296
trust in all *t's* high Comes easy to him, „ 329
Too comic for the solemn *t's* they are, „ *Con.* 67
If aught of *t's* that here befall Touch a spirit among *t's* divine, *Ode on Well.* 138
let all good *t's* await Him who cares not to be great, „ 198
There might be left some record of the *t's* we said. *Third of Feb.* 18
They knew the precious *t's* they had to guard: „ 41
Welcome her, all *t's* youthful and sweet, *W. to Alexandra* 8
And all *t's* look'd half-dead, *Grandmother* 34
and look'd the *t* that he meant; „ 45
laughing at *t's* that have long gone by. „ 92
o' use to saäy the *t's* that a do. *N. Farmer, O. S.* 6
On them and theirs and all *t's* here: *Lit. Squabbles* 12
Of their dead selves to higher *t's*. *In Mem. i* 4
And shall I take a *t* so blind, „ *iii* 13
like a guilty *t* I creep At earliest morning „ *vii* 7
For now so strange do these *t's* seem, „ *xiii* 15
And ask a thousand *t's* of home; „ *xiv* 12
Behold, ye speak an idle *t*: „ *xxi* 21
hardly worth my while to choose Of *t's* all mortal, „ *xxxiv* 11
To keep so sweet a *t* alive:' „ *xxxv* 7
And all he said of *t's* divine, „ *xxxvii* 18
Shall count new *t's* as dear as old: „ *xl* 28
May some dim touch of earthly *t's* „ *xliv* 11
And other than the *t's* I touch.' „ *xlv* 8
For love reflects the *t* beloved: „ *lii* 2
How should he love a *t* so low?' „ *lx* 16
So little done, such *t's* to be, „ *lxxiii* 2
In fitting aptest words to *t's*, „ *lxxv* 6
But over all *t's* brooding slept „ *lxxviii* 7
whether trust in *t's* above Be dimm'd of sorrow, „ *lxxxv* 9
Where all *t's* round me breathed of him. „ 32
these *t's* pass, and I shall prove A meeting somewhere, „ 98
The glory of the sum of *t's* „ *lxxxviii* 11
And he, he knows a thousand *t's*. „ *xcvii* 32
talk and treat Of all *t's* ev'n as he were by; „ *cvii* 20
Best seem'd the *t* he was, and join'd „ *cxi* 13
Submitting all *t's* to desire. „ *cxiv* 8
But I was *born* to other *t's*. „ *cxx* 12
Thou watchest all *t's* ever dim And dimmer, „ *cxxi* 3
I cannot think the *t* farewell. „ *cxxiii* 12
That sees the course of human *t's*. „ *cxxviii* 4
Love for the silent *t* that had made false haste *Maud I i* 58
cannot I be Like *t's* of the season gay, „ *iv* 3
A wounded *t* with a rancorous cry, „ *x* 34
This broad-brimm'd hawker of holy *t's*, „ 41
Her mother has been a *t* complete, „ *xiii* 35
I know it the one bright *t* to save „ *xvi* 20
Had given her word to a *t* so low? „ 27
Beat, happy stars, timing with *t's* below, „ *xviii* 81
I have cursed him even to lifeless *t's*) „ *xix* 15
For a shell, or a flower, little *t's* „ *II ii* 64
Comfort her, comfort her, all *t's* good, „ 75
But speak to her all *t's* holy and high, „ 78
another, a lord of all *t's*, praying „ *v* 32
But is ever the one *t* silent here. „ 68
I come to be grateful at last for a little *t*: „ *III vi* 3
in a weary world my one *t* bright; „ 17
his chamberlain, to whom He trusted all *t's*, *Com. of Arthur* 146
wrote All *t's* and whatsoever Merlin did „ 157
She answer'd, 'These be secret *t's*,' „ 318
and ask'd him if these *t's* were truth— „ 398
King In whom high God hath breathed a secret *t*. „ 501
and thence swoop Down upon all *t's* base, *Gareth and L.* 23
had the *t* I spake of been Mere gold— „ 65
New *t's* and old co-twisted, as if Time Were nothing, „ 226
and flash'd as those Dull-coated *t's*, „ 686
And deems it carrion of some woodland *t*, „ 748
these *t's* he told the King. *Marr. of Geraint* 151
And may you light on all *t's* that you love, „ 226
His dwarf, a vicious under-shapen *t*, „ 412
'Mother, a maiden is a tender *t*, „ 510

Thing (*continued*) ' These two *t's* shalt thou do, or else thou diest. *Marr. of Geraint* 580
These two *t's* shalt thou do, or thou shalt die.' And Edyrn answer'd, ' These *t's* will I do, „ 586
In silver tissue talking *t's* of state ; „ 663
But evermore it seem'd an easier *t* *Geraint and E.* 108
Tho' men may bicker with the *t's* they love, „ 325
What *t* soever ye may hear, or see, „ 415
Half ridden off with by the *t* he rode, „ 460
Each hurling down a heap of *t's* that rang „ 594
I never yet beheld a *t* so pale. „ 615
I will do the *t* I have not done, „ 625
or what had been those gracious *t's*, „ 636
As of a wild *t* taken in the trap, „ 723
Took, as in rival heat, to holy *t's* ; *Balin and Balan* 100
I suffer from the *t's* before me, „ 284
he defileth heavenly *t's* With earthly uses '— „ 421
' The fire of Heaven is lord of all *t's* good, „ 452
My mind involved yourself the nearest *t* *Merlin and V.* 300
unashamed, On all *t's* all day long, „ 666
But when the *t* was blazed about the court, „ 743
To *t's* with every sense as false and foul „ 797
The seeming-injured simple-hearted *t* „ 902
In truth, but one *t* now—better have died „ 918
One flash, that, missing all *t's* else, „ 932
speaking in the silence, full Of noble *t's*, *Lancelot and E.* 339
Lavaine gaped upon him As on a *t* miraculous, „ 453
For if I could believe the *t's* you say „ 1097
in half disdain At love, life, all *t's*, „ 1239
We moulder—as to *t's* without I mean— *Holy Grail* 39
But who first saw the holy *t* to-day ? ' „ 67
glanced and shot Only to holy *t's* ; „ 76
So now the Holy *T* is here again Among us. „ 124
But since I did not see the Holy *T*, „ 281
all these *t's* at once Fell into dust, „ 388
the Lord of all *t's* made Himself Naked of glory „ 447
thy sister taught me first to see, This Holy *T*, „ 470
And this high Quest as at a simple *t* : „ 668
' Gawain, and blinder unto holy *t's* „ 870
strong man-breasted *t's* stood from the sea, *Guinevere* 246
in the cellars merry bloated *t's* Shoulder'd the spigot, „ 267
A little *t* may harm a wounded man : *Pass. of Arthur* 210
This is a shameful *t* for men to lie. „ 246
and do the *t* I bade thee, watch, „ 248
Surely a precious *t*, one worthy note, „ 257
More *t's* are wrought by prayer Than this world dreams of. „ 415
Moved from the cloud of unforgotten *t's*, *Lover's Tale i* 48
Once or twice she told me (For I remember all *t's*) „ 346
And saw the motion of all other *t's* ; „ 574
Why were we one in all *t's*, „ *ii* 26
till the *t's* familiar to her youth Had made „ *iv* 95
I never yet beheld a *t* so strange, „ 303
Of all *t's* upon earth the dearest to me.' „ 319
That which of all *t's* is the dearest to me, „ 348
I that hold them both Dearest of all *t's*— *Sisters (E. and E.)* 289
that ever such *t's* should be ! *In the Child. Hosp.* 10
God's free air, and hope of better *t's*. *Sir J. Oldcastle* 10
wroth at *t's* of old—No fault of mine. „ 21
greatness and touching on all *t's* great, *The Wreck* 50
some have gleams or so they say Of more than mortal *t's*.' *Ancient Sage* 215
in the sidelong eyes a gleam of all *t's* ill— *The Flight* 31
He ! where is some sharp-pointed *t* ? „ 72
there's rason in all *t's*, yer Honour, *Tomorrow* 6
That a man be a durty *t* an' a trouble *Spinster's S's.* 50
an' saäyin' ondecent *t's*, „ 90
Bringer home of all good *t's*. *Locksley H., Sixty* 185
All good *t's* may move in Hesper, „ 186
the Heavenly Power Makes all *t's* new, (repeat) *Early Spring* 2, 44
Expecting all *t's* in an hour— *Freedom* 39
FAIR *t's* are slow to fade away, *To Prof. Jebb* 1
An' smoäkin' an' thinkin' o' *t's*— *Owd Roä* 34
A thousand *t's* are hidden still *Mechanophilus* 23
THIS *t*, that *t* is the rage, *Poets and Critics* 1

Think *T* my belief would stronger grow ! *Supp. Confessions* 13
I *t* that pride hath now no place Nor sojourn in me. „ 120
I walk, I dare not *t* of thee, *Oriana* 93
' *T* you this mould of hopes and fears *Two Voices* 28
Thou canst not *t*, but thou wilt weep. „ 51
When she would *t*, where'er she turn'd *Palace of Art* 225
As I came up the valley whom *t* ye should I see, *May Queen* 13
low i' the mould and *t* no more of me. *May Queen, N. Y's. E.* 4
often with you when you *t* I'm far away. „ 40
I *t* it can't be long before I find release ; „ *Con.* 11
So now I *t* my time is near. I trust it is. „ 41
I *t* that we Shall never more, *M. d'Arthur* 17
T you they sing Like poets, *Gardener's D.* 99
Consider, William : take a month to *t*, *Dora* 29
And, now I *t*, he shall not have the boy, „ 119
Edwin, do not *t* yourself alone Of all men happy. *Edwin Morris* 77
I have, I *t*,—Heaven knows—as much within ; „ 82
I *t* that I have borne as much as this— *St. S. Stylites* 92
Ha ! ha ! They *t* that I am somewhat. „ 126
let me *t* 'tis well for thee and me— *Love and Duty* 32
t not they are glazed with wine. *Locksley Hall* 51
Can I *t* of her as dead, „ 73
' What wonder, if he *t's* me fair ? ' *Day-Dm., Ep.* 4
I *t* he came like Ganymede, *Will Water* 119
And I *t* thou lov'st me well.' *L. of Burleigh* 4
I remember, when I *t*, *Vision of Sin* 77
I *t* we know the hue Of that cap upon her brows. „ 141
I *t* your kindness breaks me down ; *Enoch Arden* 318
I do *t* They love me as a father : „ 411
T upon it : For I am well-to-do— „ 417
I *t* I have not three days more to live ; „ 851
t—For people talk'd—that it was wholly wise *Aylmer's Field* 267
To *t* that in our often-ransack'd world *Sea Dreams* 129
I *t* they should not wear our rusty gowns, *Princess, Pro.* 143
I *t* the year in which our olives fail'd. „ *i* 125
I confess with right) you *t* me bound In some sort, „ 158
' who could *t* The softer Adams of your Academe, „ *ii* 196
I *t* no more of deadly lurks therein, „ 226
Nor *t* I bear that heart within my breast, „ 334
What *t* you of it, Florian ? „ 408
You grant me license : might I use it ? *t* ; „ *iii* 235
I almost *t* That idiot legend credible. „ *v* 152
for since you *t* me touch'd In honour— „ 401
indeed I *t* Our chiefest comfort is the little child „ 429
to *t* I might be something to thee, „ *vi* 200
And *t* that you might mix his draught with death, „ 277
—verily I *t* to win.' „ 329
' If you be, what I *t* you, some sweet dream, „ *vii* 145
O ye, the wise who *t*, the wise who reign, *Ode Inter. Exhib.* 32
you *t* I am hard and cold ; *Grandmother* 17
Time to *t* on it then ; for thou'll *N. Farmer, N. S.* 7
an' we boäth on us *t's* tha an ass. (repeat) „ 12, 38
She's a beauty thou *t's*— „ 14
I *t* not much of yours or of mine, *Spiteful Letter* 7
He *t's* he was not made to die ; *In Mem., Pro.* 11
And stunn'd me from my power to *t* „ *xvi* 15
To see the vacant chair, and *t* ' How good ! how kind ! „ *xx* 19
And *t*, that somewhere in the waste „ *xxii* 19
He looks so cold : she *t's* him kind. „ *xcvii* 24
I *t* once more he seems to die. „ *c* 20
And *t* of early days and thee, „ *cxix* 8
I *t* we are not wholly brain, „ *cxx* 2
I cannot *t* the thing farewell. „ *cxxiii* 12
Result in man, be born and *t*, „ *Con.* 126
Bound for the Hall, and I *t* for a bride. *Maud I x* 26
And six feet two, as I *t*, he stands ; „ *xiii* 10
Shall I not take care of all that I *t*, „ *xv* 7
T I may hold dominion sweet, „ *xvi* 12
shook my heart to *t* she comes once more ; „ *xviii* 10
t that it well Might drown all life in the eye,— „ *II ii* 60
Not let any man *t* for the public good, „ *v* 45
I could even weep to *t* of it ; „ 86
Yea, but ye—*t* ye this king— *Com. of Arthur* 250
T ye this fellow will poison the King's dish ? *Gareth and L.* 471
And tell him what I *t* and what they say. *Marr. of Geraint* 90

Think (*continued*) And yet not dare to tell him what I *t*, *Marr. of Geraint* 105
Ye *t* the rustic cackle of your bourg „ 276
Moves him to *t* what kind of bird it is That sings „ 331
To *t* or say, ‘ There is the nightingale ; ’ „ 342
Let never maiden *t*, however fair, „ 721
let me *t* Silence is wisdom : *Merlin and V.* 252
O, if you *t* this wickedness in me, „ 339
but *t* or not, By Heaven that hears I tell you „ 342
because I *t*, However wise, ye hardly know me yet.’ „ 354
I *t* ye hardly know the tender rhyme „ 383
O Vivien, For you, methinks you *t* you love me well ; „ 483
However well ye *t* ye love me now „ 516
Spleen-born, I *t*, and proofless. „ 702
Farewell ; *t* gently of me, for I fear „ 926
there, I *t*, So ye will learn the courtesies of the court, *Lancelot and E.* 698
sure I *t* this fruit is hung too high „ 774
ye *t* I show myself Too dark a prophet : *Holy Grail* 321
to *t* of Modred's dusty fall, *Guinevere* 55
As I could *t*, sweet lady, yours would be „ 352
Not ev'n in inmost thought to *t* again „ 374
but rather *t* How sad it were for Arthur, „ 495
t not, tho' thou wouldst not love thy lord, „ 508
Yet *t* not that I come to urge thy crimes, „ 532
what hope ? I *t* there was a hope, „ 630
I *t* that we Shall never more, *Pass. of Arthur* 185
(They told her somewhat rashly as I *t*) *Lover's Tale iv* 98
Do you *t* I was scared by the bones ? *Rizpah* 55
Do you *t* that I care for *my* soul „ 78
I *t* that you mean to be kind, „ 81
t what saäilors a' seëan an' a' doon ; *North. Cobbler* 4
as 'appy as 'art could *t*, „ 15
yet she *t's* She sees you when she hears. *Sisters (E. and E.)* 192
I *t* this gross hard-seeming world „ 229
I *t* *I* likewise love your Edith most. „ 293
t he was one of those who would break *In the Child. Hosp.* 8
bullet broke thro' the brain that could *t* for the rest ; *Def. of Lucknow* 20
I beänt sich a fool as ye *t's* ; *Spinster's S's.* 18
I *t's* as I'd like fur to hev *Owd Roä* 12
I *t's* leästwaäys as I wasn't afeärd ; „ 86
thaw I didn't haäfe *t* as 'e'd 'ear, „ 91
tho' I *t* I hated him less, *Bandit's Death* 17
Thinketh then *t*, ‘ I have found A new land, *Palace of Art* 283
Thinkin' An' smoäkin' an' *t'* o' things— *Owd Roä* 34
Thinking (*See also* **Half-thinking, Thinkin'**) for three hours he sobb'd o'er William's child *T* of William. *Dora* 168
Still downward *t* ‘ dead or dead to me ! ’ *Enoch Arden* 689
Enoch *t* ‘ after I am gone, „ 834
t that her clear germander eye Droopt *Sea Dreams* 4
And *t* of the days that are no more. *Princess iv* 43
She flung it from her, *t* : „ *Con.* 32
t, ‘ here to-day,’ Or ‘ here to-morrow *In Mem. vi* 23
And *t* ‘ this will please him best,’ „ 31
Looking, *t* of all I have lost ; *Maud II ii* 46
t as he rode, ‘ Her father said That there between *Com. of Arthur* 78
t, that if ever yet was wife True to her lord, *Marr. of Geraint* 46
Geraint, now *t* that he heard The noble hart at bay, „ 232
He *t* that he read her meaning there, *Lancelot and E.* 86
t ‘ Is it Lancelot who has come Despite the wound „ 565
Thinn'd *T*, or would seem to thin her in a day, *Aylmer's Field* 76
councils *t*, And armies waned, for magnet-like she drew *Merlin and V.* 572
Thinner Then her cheek was pale and *t* *Locksley Hall* 21
they fly Now *t*, and now thicker, like the flakes *Lucretius* 166
And *t*, clearer, farther going ! *Princess iv* 8
Our voices were *t* and fainter *V. of Maeldune* 22
Thinnest Slow-dropping veils of *t* lawn, did go ; *Lotos-Eaters* 11
Which is *t* ? thine or mine ? *Vision of Sin* 90
Third And set in Heaven's *t* story, *Will Water.* 70
t child was sickly-born and grew Yet sicklier, *Enoch Arden* 261
Then the *t* night after this, „ 907
There stands the *t* fool of their allegory.' *Gareth and L.* 1085
Then the *t* brother shouted o'er the bridge, „ 1096
And on the *t* day will again be here, *Marr. of Geraint* 222

Third (*continued*) But when the *t* day from the hunting-morn *Marr. of Geraint* 597
So bent he seem'd on going the *t* day, „ 604
Bent as he seem'd on going this *t* day, „ 625
hope The *t* night hence will bring thee news of gold.' *Pelleas and E.* 357
t night brought a moon With promise of large light „ 393
THOU *t* great Canning, stand among our best *Epit. on Stratford* 1
I brought you to that chamber on your *t* September birthday *The Ring* 129
Third-rate Some *t-r* isle half-lost among her seas ? *To the Queen ii* 25
Thirst In hungers and in *t's*, fevers and cold, *St. S. Stylites* 12
her *t* she slakes Where the bloody conduit runs, *Vision of Sin* 143
and when I thought my *t* Would slay me, *Holy Grail* 379
‘ And on I rode, and greater was my *t*. „ 401
there the hermit slaked my burning *t*, „ 461
with *t* in the middle-day heat. *V. of Maeldune* 50
Thirsted I *t* for the brooks, the showers : *Fatima* 10
Thirsteth He that *t*, come and drink ! *Sir J. Oldcastle* 134
Thirsting only *t* For the right, *Ode on Well.* 203
and I was left alone, And *t*, *Holy Grail* 390
Thirsty O to watch the *t* plants Imbibing ! *Princess ii* 422
And I was *t* even unto death ; *Holy Grail* 377
Thirty (*See also* **Thutty**) ‘ Will *t* seasons render plain *Two Voices* 82
But *t* moons, one honeymoon to that, *Edwin Morris* 29
larded with the steam Of *t* thousand dinners. *Will Water.* 224
By *t* hills I hurry down, *The Brook* 27
I walk'd with one I loved two and *t* years ago. *V. of Cauteretz* 4
The two and *t* years were a mist that rolls away ; „ 6
I well remember that red night When *t* ricks, All flaming, *To Mary Boyle* 36
Thistle I could not move a *t* ; *Amphion* 66
Let there be *t's*, there are grapes ; *Will Water.* 57
stubborn *t* bursting Into glossy purples, *Ode on Well.* 206
many a prickly star Of sprouted *t* *Marr. of Geraint* 314
Figs out of *t's*, silk from bristles, *Last Tournament* 356
flower, That shook beneath them, as the *t* shakes *Guinevere* 254
the wool of a *t* a-flyin' an' seeädin' *Spinster's S's.* 79
Are figs of *t's* ? or grapes of thorns ? *Riflemen form !* 10
Thistledown soft winds, Laden with *t* *Lover's Tale ii* 13
Thomas Howard (*See also* **Howard**) Then sware Lord *T H* : *The Revenge* 4
Thor To *T* and Odin lifted a hand : *The Victim* 8
Thorn (*See also* **Thurn**) my sin was as a *t* Among the *t's* *Supp. Confessions* 5
Thick rosaries of scented *t*, *Arabian Nights* 106
I know That all about the *t* will blow *Two Voices* 59
as a *t* Turns from the sea ; *Audley Court* 54
like me, with scourges and with *t's* ; *St. S. Stylites* 180
T's, ivies, woodbine, mistletoes, *Day-Dm., Sleep. P.* 43
we reach'd A mountain, like a wall of burs and *t's* ; *Sea Dreams* 119
A rosebud set with little wilful *t's*, *Princess, Pro.* 154
Shadow and shine is life, little Annie, flower and *t*. *Grandmother* 60
I have heard of *t's* and briers. *Window, Marr. Morn.* 20
Over the *t's* and briers, „ 21
The path we came by, *t* and flower, *In Mem. xlvi* 2
I took the *t's* to bind my brows, „ *lxix* 7
The fool that wears a crown of *t's* : „ 12
bristles all the brakes and *t's* „ *cvii* 9
evermore Seem'd catching at a rootless *t*, *Geraint and E.* 378
T's of the crown and shivers of the cross, *Balin and Balan* 111
where the winter *t* Blossoms at Christmas, *Holy Grail* 52
in a land of sand and *t's*, (repeat) „ 376, 390
And wearying in a land of sand and *t's*. „ 420
I cared not for the *t's* ; the *t's* were there. *Pelleas and E.* 404
fall on its own *t's*—if this be true— *Lover's Tale i* 273
Its knotted *t's* thro' my unpaining brows, „ 620
roses that sprang without leaf or a *t* from the bush ; *V. of Maeldune* 44
Are figs of thistles ? or grapes of *t's* ? *Riflemen form !* 10
Thornless thy great Forefathers of the *t* garden, *Maud I xviii* 27
Thorny Are wither'd in the *t* close, *Day-Dm., Arrival* 11
I found a wood with *t* boughs : *In Mem. lxix* 6
Thorough-edged *t-e* intellect to part Error from crime ; *Isabel* 14
Thoroughfare In shadowy *t's* of thought ; *In Mem. lxx* 8
He left the barren-beaten *t*, *Lancelot and E.* 161
Thorpe But he, by farmstead, *t* and spire, *Will Water.* 137

Thorpe (*continued*) By twenty *thorps*, a little town, *The Brook* 29
Then *t* and byre arose in fire, *The Victim* 3
Down to the little *t* that lies so close, *Holy Grail* 547

Thought (s) (*See also* **Thowt**) He hath no *t* of coming woes ; *Supp. Confessions* 47
tended by Pure vestal *t's* in the translucent fane *Isabel* 4
Small *t* was there of life's distress ; *Ode to Memory* 37
The viewless arrows of his *t's* were headed *The Poet* 11
LIFE and *T* have gone away Side by side, *Deserted House* 1
for Life and *T* Here no longer dwell ; „ 17
mortal dower Of pensive *t* and aspect pale, *Margaret* 6
who can tell The last wild *t* of Chatelet, „ 37
Moulded thy baby *t*. *Eleänore* 5
And flattering thy childish *t* „ 13
T and motion mingle, Mingle ever. „ 60
I seem to see *T* folded over *t*, smiling asleep, „ 84
T seems to come and go In thy large eyes, „ 96
Our *t* gave answer each to each, *Sonnet to ——* 10
' And men, thro' novel spheres of *t* *Two Voices* 61
Asks what thou lackest, *t* resign'd, „ 98
Fruitful of further *t* and deed, „ 144
but overtakes Far *t* with music that it makes : „ 438
mind was brought To anchor by one gloomy *t* ; „ 459
I least should breathe a *t* of pain. *Miller's D.* 26
With blessings beyond hope or *t*, „ 237
so much the *t* of power Flatter'd his spirit ; *Œnone* 136
for fiery *t's* Do shape themselves within me, „ 246
and divided quite The kingdom of her *t*. *Palace of Art* 228
As when a great *t* strikes along the brain, *D. of F. Women* 43
by down-lapsing *t* Stream'd onward, „ 49
' It comforts me in this one *t* to dwell, „ 233
deep Gold-mines of *t* to lift the hidden ore „ 274
strength of some diffusive *t* Hath time and space *You ask me, why, etc.* 15
When single *t* is civil crime, „ 19
Thro' future time by power of *t*. *Love thou thy land* 4
Wherever *T* hath wedded Fact. „ 52
Counting the dewy pebbles, fix'd in *t* ; *M. d'Arthur* 84
His own *t* drove him, like a goad. „ 185
all kinds of *t*, That verged upon them, *Gardener's D.* 70
These birds have joyful *t's*. „ 99
Lightly he laugh'd, as one that read my *t*, „ 106
A *t* would fill my eyes with happy dew ; „ 197
or should have, but for a *t* or two, *Edwin Morris* 83
(And heedfully I sifted all my *t*) *St. S. Stylites* 56
Should my Shadow cross thy *t's* *Love and Duty* 88
tho' the times, when some new *t* can bud, *Golden Year* 27
Beyond the utmost bound of human *t*. *Ulysses* 32
Spring a young man's fancy lightly turns to *t's* of love. *Locksley Hall* 20
touch him with thy lighter *t*. „ 54
t's of men are widen'd with the process of the suns. „ 138
in the railway, in the *t's* that shake mankind. „ 166
And would you have the *t* I had, *Day-Dm., Pro.* 13
And *t* and time be born again, „ *Sleep. P.* 50
From deep *t* himself he rouses, *L. of Burleigh* 21
Whited *t* and cleanly life As the priest, *Vision of Sin* 116
utter The *t's* that arise in me. *Break, break, etc.* 4
So the *t* Haunted and harass'd him, *Enoch Arden* 719
There speech and *t* and nature fail'd a little, „ 792
Her all of *t* and bearing hardly more *Aylmer's Field* 29
worst *t* she has Is whiter even than her pretty hand : „ 362
Is it so true that second *t's* are best ? *Sea Dreams* 65
Sweet *t's* would swarm as bees about their queen. *Princess i* 40
A *t* flash'd thro' me which I clothed in act, „ 195
whose *t's* enrich the blood of the world.' „ *ii* 181
And all her *t's* as fair within her eyes, „ 326
You need not set your *t's* in rubric thus „ *iii* 50
And she broke out interpreting my *t's* : „ 275
And live, perforce, from *t* to *t*, „ 328
tost on *t's* that changed from hue to hue, „ *iv* 210
to those *t's* that wait On you, their centre : „ 443
not a *t*, a touch, But pure as lines of green „ *v* 195
but other *t's* than Peace Burnt in us, „ 245
Now could you share your *t* ; „ *vi* 252
A shining furrow, as thy *t's* in me. „ *vii* 185

Thought (s) (*continued*) and always *t* in *t*, Purpose in purpose, *Princess vii* 304
Beyond all *t* into the Heaven of Heavens. „ *Con.* 115
And the *t* of a man is higher. *Voice and the P.* 32
And my *t's* are as quick and as quick, *Window, On the Hill* 12
And with the *t* her colour burns ; *In Mem. vi* 34
An awful *t*, a life removed, „ *xiii* 10
And *T* leapt out to wed with *T* Ere *T* could wed itself with Speech ; „ *xxiii* 15
Nor other *t* her mind admits „ *xxxii* 2
All subtle *t*, all curious fears, „ 9
More strong than all poetic *t* ; „ *xxxvi* 12
The lightest wave of *t* shall lisp, „ *xlix* 5
and moved Upon the topmost froth of *t*. „ *lii* 4
There flutters up a happy *t*, „ *lxv* 7
In shadowy thoroughfares of *t* ; „ *lxx* 8
A grief as deep as life or *t*, „ *lxxx* 7
And fix my *t's* on all the glow „ *lxxxiv* 3
Leaving great legacies of *t*, „ 35
Whose life, whose *t's* were little worth, „ *lxxxv* 30
I find not yet one lonely *t* „ *xc* 23
Should be the man whose *t* would hold „ *xciv* 3
About empyreal heights of *t*, „ *xcv* 38
sway'd In vassal tides that follow'd *t*. „ *cxii* 16
And in my *t's* with scarce a sigh „ *cxix* 11
I slip the *t's* of life and death ; „ *cxxii* 16
And every *t* breaks out a rose. „ 20
shade of passing *t*, the wealth Of words and wit, „ *Con.* 102
wrong Done but in *t* to your beauty, *Maud I iii* 6
And letting a dangerous *t* run wild „ *xix* 52
And noble *t* be freër under the sun, „ *III vi* 48
Another *t* was mine ; *Marr. of Geraint* 793
Grant me pardon for my *t's* : „ 816
They hated her, who took no *t* of them, *Geraint and E.* 639
and heard in *t* Their lavish comment *Merlin and V.* 150
So grated down and filed away with *t*, „ 623
rathe she rose, half-cheated in the *t* *Lancelot and E.* 340
And every evil *t* I had thought of old, *Holy Grail* 372
remembering Her *t* when first she came, *Guinevere* 182
what is true repentance but in *t*—Not ev'n in inmost *t* to think „ 373
grew half-guilty in her *t's* again, „ 408
But teach high *t*, and amiable words „ 481
wrath which forced my *t's* on that fierce law, „ 537
Counting the dewy pebbles, fixed in *t* ; *Pass. of Arthur* 252
His own *t* drove him like a goad. „ 353
Leapt like a passing *t* across her eyes ; *Lover's Tale i* 70
And length of days, and immortality Of *t*, „ 106
One sustenance, which, still as *t* grew large, Still larger moulding all the house of *t*, „ 240
At *t* of which my whole soul languishes „ 267
Still to believe it—'tis so sweet a *t*, „ 275
tell you how I hoard in *t* The faded rhymes „ 288
A graceful *t* of hers Grav'n on my fancy ! „ 357
Absorbing all the incense of sweet *t's* „ 469
Oh friend, *t's* deep and heavy as these „ 688
The brightness of a burning *t*, „ 743
The spirit seem'd to flag from *t* to *t*, „ *ii* 51
Alway the inaudible invisible *t*, „ 102
burst through the cloud of *t* Keen, irrepressible. „ 164
T's of the breezes of May blowing *Def. of Lucknow* 83
That Lenten fare makes Lenten *t*, *To E. Fitzgerald* 31
thin minds, who creep from *t* to *t*, *Ancient Sage* 103
Do-well will follow *t*, „ 273
An evil *t* may soil thy children's blood ; „ 275
I am old, and think gray *t's*, *Locksley H., Sixty* 155
To *t's* that lift the soul of men, *To Master of B.* 14
For *t* into the outward springs, *Mechanophilus* 11

Thought (verb) (*See also* **Thowt**) HE *t* to quell the stubborn hearts *Buonaparte* 1
And *t*, ' My life is sick of single sleep : *The Bridesmaid* 13
She *t*, ' My spirit is here alone, *Mariana in the S.* 47
I cast me down, nor *t* of you, *Miller's D.* 63
My mother *t*, What ails the boy ? „ 93
And ' by that lamp,' I *t*, ' she sits ! ' „ 114
she *t* I might have look'd a little higher ; „ 139

Thought (verb) (*continued*) she *t*, ' And who shall gaze upon My palace *Palace of Art* 41
You *t* to break a country heart For pastime, *L. C. V. de Vere* 3
He *t* of that sharp look, mother, *May Queen* 15
He *t* I was a ghost, mother, „ 17
I *T* to pass away before, and yet alive I am ; „ *Con.* 1
lying broad awake I *t* of you and Effie dear ; „ 29
I *t* that it was fancy, and I listen'd in my bed, „ 33
I *t*, I take it for a sign. „ 38
He *t* that nothing new was said, *The Epic* 30
And often *t* ' I'll make them man and wife.' *Dora* 4
had been always with her in the house, *T* not of Dora. „ 8
She *t*, ' It cannot be : my uncle's mind will change ! ' „ 46
and *t* Hard things of Dora. „ 57
he *t* himself A mark for all, *Walk. to the Mail* 72
God only thro' his bounty hath *t* fit, *St. S. Stylites* 186
toil'd, and wrought, and *t* with me— *Ulysses* 46
' Shy she was, and I *t* her cold ; *T* her proud, and fled over the sea ; *Edward Gray* 13
and I *t* I would have spoken, *Vision of Sin* 55
nightingale *t*, ' I have sung many songs, *Poet's Song* 13
' I *t* not of it : but—I know not why— *Enoch Arden* 396
Some *t* that Philip did but trifle with her ; „ 475
' He is gone,' she *t* ' he is happy, „ 502
Philip *t* he knew : „ 520
He *t* it must have gone ; „ 694
he *t* ' After the Lord has call'd me she shall know, „ 809
And *t* to bear it with me to my grave ; „ 896
how money breeds, *T* it a dead thing ; *The Brook* 7
blues were sure of it, he *t* : *Aylmer's Field* 252
Some one, he *t*, had slander'd Leolin to him. „ 350
' O pray God that he hold up ' she *t* „ 733
But I that *t* myself long-suffering, meek, „ 753
I *t* the motion of the boundless deep *Sea Dreams* 91
' What a world,' I *t*, ' To live in ! ' „ 94
O then to ask her of my shares, I *t* ; „ 115
(I *t* I could have died to save it) „ 134
I *t* that all the blood by Sylla shed *Lucretius* 47
For these I *t* my dream would show to me, „ 51
I *t* I lived securely as yourselves— „ 210
A pleasant game, she *t* : *Princess, Pro.* 194
But my good father *t* a king a king ; „ *i* 25
they had but been, she *t*, As children ; „ 136
' We scarcely *t* in our own hall to hear „ *ii* 53
once or twice I *t* to roar, „ 423
and *t* He scarce would prosper. „ *iii* 75
One anatomic.' ' Nay, we *t* of that,' „ 307
and my foot Was to you : but I *t* again : „ *iv* 327
I *t*, That surely she will speak ; „ 343
we *t* her half-possess'd, She struck such warbling fury „ 585
I *t* her half-right talking of her wrongs ; „ *v* 285
I *t* on all the wrathful king had said, „ 473
I *t*, can this be he From Gama's dwarfish lions ? „ 505
Woman, whom we *t* woman even now, „ *vi* 273
first time, too, that ever I *t* of death. *Grandmother* 61
T on all her evil tyrannies, *Boädicea* 80
And something written, something *t* ; *In Mem. vi* 20
Has never *t* that ' this is I : ' „ *xlv* 4
You *t* my heart too far diseased ; „ *lxvi* 1
I look'd on these and *t* of thee „ *xcvii* 6
For all we *t* and loved and did, „ *Con.* 134
and *t* he would rise and speak And rave *Maud I i* 59
t, is it pride, and mused and sigh'd „ *viii* 12
I *t* as I stood, if a hand, as white „ *xiv* 17
Now I *t* that she cared for me, Now I *t* she was kind „ 25
and *t* like a fool of the sleep of death. „ 38
And none of us *t* of a something beyond, „ *xix* 47
Yet I *t* I saw her stand, „ *II i* 38
and *t* It is his mother's hair. „ *ii* 69
For I *t* the dead had peace, „ *v* 15
When I *t* that a war would arise in defence „ *III vi* 19
but *t* To sift his doubtings to the last, *Com. of Arthur* 310
For then I surely *t* he would be king. „ 358
And *t*, ' For this half-shadow of a lie *Gareth and L.* 323
and *t* the King Scorn'd me and mine ; „ 1165

Thought (verb) (*continued*) And day by day she *t* to tell Geraint, *Marr. of Geraint* 65
t within herself, Was ever man so grandly made „ 80
And then he *t*, ' In spite of all my care, „ 115
So fared it with Geraint, who *t* and said, „ 343
In a moment *t* Geraint, ' Here by God's rood „ 367
and *t* to find Arms in your town, „ 417
And *t* it never yet had look'd so mean. „ 610
while she *t* ' They will not see me,' „ 666
likewise *t* perhaps, That service done so graciously „ 789
I *t*, That could I someway prove such force „ 804
A stranger meeting them had surely *t* *Geraint and E.* 34
Then *t* again, ' If there be such in me, „ 52
Held his head high, and *t* himself a knight, „ 242
I *t*, but that your father came between, „ 314
Then *t* she heard the wild Earl at the door, „ 381
he *t* ' was it for him she wept In Devon ? ' „ 397
And since she *t*, ' He had not dared to do it, „ 720
You *t* me sleeping, but I heard you say, „ 741
' I will be gentle ' he *t* ' And passing gentle ' *Balin and Balan* 370
and *t* ' I have shamed thee so that now thou shamest me, „ 430
I *t* the great tower would crash down on both— „ 515
heard and *t* ' The scream of that Wood-devil „ 547
I *t* that he was gentle, being great : *Merlin and V.* 871
and she *t* That all was nature, *Lancelot and E.* 329
But *t* to do while he might yet endure, „ 495
Yea, twenty times I *t* him Lancelot— „ 535
for she *t* ' If I be loved, these are my festal robes, „ 908
the brothers heard, and *t* With shuddering, „ 1021
dwelt the father on her face, and *t* ' Is this Elaine ? ' „ 1030
t That now the Holy Grail would come again ; *Holy Grail* 91
I *t* She might have risen and floated „ 99
t ' It is not Arthur's use To hunt by moonlight ; ' „ 110
and *t* Of all my late-shown prowess in the lists, „ 361
And every evil thought I had *t* of old, „ 372
and when I *t* my thirst Would slay me, „ 379
but *t* ' The sun is rising,' „ 407
But when I *t* he meant To crush me, „ 415
Pelleas gazing *t*, ' Is Guinevere herself so beautiful ? ' *Pelleas and E.* 69
she *t* That peradventure he will fight for me, „ 117
' O happy world,' *t* Pelleas, ' all, meseems, „ 136
' These be the ways of ladies,' Pelleas *t*, „ 209
t, Why have I push'd him from me ? „ 306
' Ay,' *t* Gawain, ' and you be fair enow : „ 388
and *t*, ' I will go back, and slay them „ 443
and drew the sword, and *t*, ' What ! „ 447
Modred *t*, ' The time is hard at hand.' „ 610
until himself had *t* He loved her also, *Last Tournament* 401
whereon he *t*—' What, if she hate me now ? „ 495
t she heard them moan : And in herself she moan'd *Guinevere* 130
she *t* ' He spies a field of death ; „ 134
then she *t*, ' With what a hate the people and the King „ 156
Then *t* the Queen within herself again, „ 224
t the Queen, ' Lo ! they have set her on, „ 308
glanced at him, *t* him cold, High, self-contain'd, „ 405
I *t* I could not breathe in that fine air „ 645
I, being simple, *t* to work His will, *Pass. of Arthur* 22
Or *t* he saw, the speck that bare the King, „ 465
I *t* it was an adder's fold, *Lover's Tale i* 691
Sometimes I *t* Camilla was no more, „ *ii* 69
I *t* Four bells instead of one began to ring, „ *iii* 19
knew the meaning of the whisper now, *T* that he knew it. „ *iv* 44
then starting, *t* His dreams had come again. „ 77
when I saw her (and I *t* him crazed, „ 163
For he *t*—there were other lads— *First Quarrel* 38
an' I *t* of him out at sea, „ 89
for now and then I *t* Laziness, vague love-longings, *Sisters (E. and E.)* 127
eyes Upon me when she *t* I did not see— „ 166
I *t* ' What, will she never set her sister free ? „ 217
and we *t* her at rest, Quietly sleeping— *In the Child. Hosp.* 40
but I *t* that it never would pass. „ 61
Some *t* it heresy, but that would not hold. *Columbus* 46

Thought (verb) *(continued)* And *t* to turn my face from Spain, *Columbus* 57
I woke, and *t*—death—I shall die— „ 87
and I *t* of the child for a moment, *The Wreck* 84
then All on a sudden I *t*, „ 124
I remember I *t*, as we past, *Despair* 11
God of Love and of Hell together—they cannot be *t*, „ 105
Och, Molly, we *t*, machree, *Tomorrow* 81
Vext, that you *t* my Mother came to me ? *The Ring* 140
A lie by which he *t* he could subdue *Happy* 64
I *t* to myself I would offer this book *June Bracken, etc.* 4
once, he *t*, a shape with wings Came sweeping *St. Telemachus* 24
Yet he *t* he answer'd her wail with a song— *The Dreamer* 16
Thoughted *See* **Subtle-thoughted**
Thoughtest *t* of thy prowess and thy sins ? *Holy Grail* 455
Thousand (adj.) *(See also* **Eighty-Thousand, Ten-thousand)**
A t *claims to reverence closed* *To the Queen* 27
And flashes off a *t* ways, *Rosalind* 23
And if you kiss'd her feet a *t* years, *The form, the form* 13
deluge from a *t* hills Flung leagues of roaring foam *If I were loved* 12
That went and came a *t* times. *Miller's D.* 72
A *t* little shafts of flame Were shiver'd *Fatima* 17
My love hath told me so a *t* times. *Œnone* 197
Hath he not sworn his love a *t* times, „ 231
A *t* times I blest him, as he knelt beside my bed. *May Queen, Con.* 16
a *t* times I would be born and die. *D. of F. Women* 203
The wisdom of a *t* years Is in them. *Of old sat Freedom* 18
Who forged a *t* theories of the rocks, *Edwin Morris* 18
in one month They wedded her to sixty *t* pounds, „ 126
Bow down one *t* and two hundred times, *St. S. Stylites* 111
A *t* thanks for what I learn *Talking Oak* 203
The woman of a *t* summers back, *Godiva* 11
Ten *t* broken lights and shapes, *Will Water.* 59
larded with the steam Of thirty *t* dinners. „ 224
A *t* suns will stream on thee, A *t* moons will quiver ; *A Farewell* 13
face, Rough-redden'd with a *t* winter gales, *Enoch Arden* 95
There did a *t* memories roll upon him, „ 724
These partridge-breeders of a *t* years, *Aylmer's Field* 382
many *t* days Were clipt by horror „ 602
There moved the multitude, a *t* heads : *Princess, Pro.* 57
My mother pitying made a *t* prayers ; „ *i* 21
he sware That he would send a hundred *t* men, „ 64
A *t* hearts lie fallow in these halls, And round these halls a *t* baby loves „ *ii* 400
May beat admission in a *t* years, „ *iii* 155
a race Of giants living, each, a *t* years, „ 269
With many *t* matters left to do, „ *iv* 458
Six *t* years of fear have made you that „ 507
a *t* rings of Spring In every bole, „ *v* 237
A *t* arms and rushes to the Sun. „ *vi* 37
spill Their *t* wreaths of dangling water-smoke, „ *vii* 213
UPLIFT a *t* voices full and sweet, *Ode Inter. Exhib.* 1
A *t* shadowy-pencill'd valleys And snowy dells *The Daisy* 67
' A *t* voices go To North, South, East, and West ; *Voice and the P.* 13
To touch thy *t* years of gloom : *In Mem. ii* 12
And ask a *t* things of home ; „ *xiv* 12
That breathe a *t* tender vows, „ *xx* 2
She cries, ' A *t* types are gone : „ *lvi* 3
Or when a *t* moons shall wane „ *lxxvii* 8
Upon the *t* waves of wheat, „ *xci* 11
And he, he knows a *t* things. „ *xcvii* 32
a *t* wants Gnarr at the heels of men, „ *xcviii* 16
Ring out the *t* wars of old, Ring in the *t* years of peace. „ *cvi* 27
To whom a *t* memories call, „ *cxi* 10
With *t* shocks that come and go, „ *cxiii* 17
electric force, that keeps A *t* pulses dancing, „ *cxxv* 16
Before a *t* peering littlenesses, *Ded. of Idylls* 26
War with a *t* battles, and shaking a hundred thrones. *Maud I i* 48
thro' tops of many *t* pines A gloomy-gladed *Gareth and L.* 796
' A *t* pips eat up your sparrow-hawk ! *Marr. of Geraint* 274
and sent a *t* men To till the wastes, *Geraint and E.* 941
He saw two cities in a *t* boats *Merlin and V.* 561
Fare you well A *t* times !—a *t* times farewell ! *Lancelot and E.* 696
Gawain, who bad a *t* farewells to me, „ 1056
A *t* piers ran into the great Sea. *Holy Grail* 503
up I climb'd a *t* steps With pain : „ 835

Thousand (adj.) *(continued)* Had drawn herself From many *t* years, *Lover's Tale i* 550
a *t* lives To save his soul. *Sir J. Oldcastle* 63
A *t* marks are set upon my head. „ 195
a single piece Weigh'd nigh four *t* Castillanos *Columbus* 136
hundred who heard it would rush on a *t* lances and die— *V. of Maeldune* 24
A *T* summers ere the time of Christ *Ancient Sage* 1
Let us hush this cry of ' Forward ' till ten *t* years have gone. *Locksley H., Sixty* 78
Timur built his ghastly tower of eighty *t* human skulls, „ 82
' Tho' a name may last for a *t* years, *Dead Prophet* 59
Trade flying over a *t* seas with her spice *Vastness* 13
For ten *t* years Old and new ? *The Ring* 19
They made a *t* honey moons of one ? „ 22
that sees A *t* squares of corn and meadow, „ 149
And from the *t* squares, one silent voice „ 153
And eighty *t* Christian faces watch Man murder man. *St. Telemachus* 55
press of a *t* cities is prized for it smells of the beast, *The Dawn* 14
In a hundred, a *t* winters ? „ 24
A *t* things are hidden still *Mechanophilus* 23
Thousand (s) Who had mildew'd in their *t's*, *Aylmer's Field* 383
' There are *t's* now Such women, *Princess, Pro.* 127
many *t's* that if they be bold enough, *Def. of Lucknow* 40
when her tens are *t's*, and her *t's* millions, *Locksley H. Sixty* 171
Thousand-fold Ten *t-f* had grown, flash'd the fierce shield, *Gareth and L.* 1030
seems to me A *t-f* more great and wonderful *Geraint and E.* 914
Then Lancelot's needs must be a *t-f* Less noble, *Guinevere* 338
Thowt (thought) (s) —I niver giv it a *t*— *N. Farmer, N. S.* 23
Thowt (thought) (verb) I *t* a 'ad summut to saäy, *N. Farmer, O. S.* 19
An' I *t* a said whot a owt to 'a said „ 20
an' mysen I *t* i' mysen ' mayhap.' *North. Cobbler* 68
An' I *t* 'twur the will o' the Lord, *Village Wife* 11
I *t* it wur Charlie's ghoäst i' the derk, „ 82
thaw soom 'ud 'a *t* ma plaäin, *Spinster's S's.* 16
But Robby, I *t* o' tha all the while „ 43
An' I *t* shall I chaänge my staäte ? „ 44
Tha *t* tha would marry ma, did tha ? „ 74
I *t* to mysen ' thank God that I hevn't naw cauf „ 116
I *t* o' the good owd times 'at was goan, *Owd Roä* 43
t if the Staäte was a gawin' to let in furriners' wheät, „ 45
An' I *t* as 'e'd goän cleän-wud, „ 61
I *t* it was Roäver a-tuggin' „ 66
An' I *t* 'at I kick'd 'im ageän, „ 67
t she was nobbut a-rilin' ma then. „ 74
Sa I warrants 'e niver said haafe wot 'e *t*, *Church-warden, etc.* 18
Thraithur (traitor) niver set eyes an the face of the *t* agin *Tomorrow* 50
Thraldom *T* who walks with the banner of Freedom, *Vastness* 10
Thrall (thraldom) To save from shame and *t* : *Sir Galahad* 16
Loosed from their simple *t* they had flow'd abroad, *Lover's Tale i* 703
And free the Holy Sepulchre from *t*. *Columbus* 104
And save the Holy Sepulchre from *t*. „ 240
Thrall (s) Let not my tongue be a *t* to my eye, *Maud I xvi* 32
' The *t* in person may be free in soul, *Gareth and L.* 165
then wilt thou become A *t* to his enchantments, „ 269
And when the *t's* had talk among themselves, „ 491
Or when the *t's* had sport among themselves, „ 516
So for a month he wrought among the *t's* ; „ 525
from out of kitchen came The *t's* in throng, „ 695
T's to your work again, „ 710
' smote upon the naked skull A *t* of mine in open hall, *Balin and Balan* 56
For I that did that violence to thy *t*, „ 61
being knighted till he smote the *t*, „ 155
once he saw the *t* His passion half had gauntleted „ 219
Thrall (verb) she send her delegate to *t* These fightings *Pelleas and E.* 336
Thrall'd my husband's brother had my son *T* in his castle, *Gareth and L.* 358
Thraw'd (threw) an' ya *t* the fish i' 'is faäce,— *Churchwarden, etc.* 30
Thread Draws different *t's*, and late and soon *Two Voices* 179
He plays with *t's*, he beats his chair *In Mem. lxvi* 13
Ran down the silken *t* to kiss each other *Merlin and V.* 455
wove with silver *t* And crimson in the belt *Holy Grail* 153
Threadbare theme of writers, and indeed Worn *t*. *Edwin Morris* 49

Threaded (adj.) (*See also* **Crimson-threaded**) from the bastion'd walls Like *t* spiders, one by one, we dropt, *Princess i* 108
Shall shake its *t* tears in the wind no more. *Maud III vi* 28
Threaded (verb) he *t* The secretest walks of fame : *The Poet* 9
Or *t* some Socratic dream ; *In Mem. lxxxix* 36
Threading led *T* the soldier-city, *Princess v* 7
Threat Puppet to a father's *t*, *Locksley Hall* 42
But scared with *t's* of jail and halter *Aylmer's Field* 520
Our Boanerges with his *t's* of doom, *Sea Dreams* 251
I hear the violent *t's* you do not hear, *Geraint and E.* 420
after hours of search and doubt and *t's*, And hubbub, *The Ring* 278
Threaten'd Had wink'd and *t* darkness, *M. d'Arthur, Ep.* 2
Three (adj.) (*See also* **Fifty-three, Three Hundred**) She made *t* paces thro' the room, *L. of Shalott iii* 38
T fingers round the old silver cup— *Miller's D.* 10
Or those *t* chestnuts near, that hung „ 55
T times I stabb'd him thro' and thro'. *The Sisters* 29
brandish'd him *T* times, and drew him under in the mere.' (repeat) *M. d'Arthur* 146, 161
Not tho' I live *t* lives of mortal men, „ 155
by these *T* Queens with crowns of gold— „ 198
There those *t* Queens Put forth their hands, „ 205
to *t* arches of a bridge Crown'd with the minster-towers. *Gardener's D.* 43
And in the compass of *t* little words, „ 232
And for *t* hours he sobb'd o'er William's child *Dora* 167
T winters, that my soul might grow to thee, *St. S. Stylites* 71
and *t* years on one of twelve ; And twice *t* years I crouch'd on one that rose „ 87
Is *t* times worth them all ; *Talking Oak* 72
those *t* stanzas that you made About my " giant bole ; " „ 135
For some *t* suns to store and hoard myself, *Ulysses* 29
To watch the t *tall spires ;* *Godiva* 3
T fair children first she bore him, *L. of Burleigh* 87
I think I have not *t* days more to live ; *Enoch Arden* 851
he past To turn and ponder those *t* hundred scrolls *Lucretius* 12
One babe was theirs, a Margaret, *t* years old : *Sea Dreams* 3
The lady of *t* castles in that land : *Princess i* 79
' *T* ladies of the Northern empire pray „ 238
Not for *t* years to correspond with home ; Not for *t* years to cross the liberties ; Not for *t* years to speak with any men ; „ *ii* 70
To give *t* gallant gentlemen to death.' „ 335
Till like *t* horses that have broken fence, „ 386
For dear are those *t* castles to my wants, „ 417
Descended to the court that lay *t* parts In shadow, „ *iii* 20
being herself *T* times more noble than *t* score of men, „ 109
And our *t* lives. „ 142
Now, scarce *t* paces measured from the mound, „ *v* 1
A smoke go up thro' which I loom to her *T* times a monster : „ 131
anon to meet us lightly pranced *T* captains out ; „ 255
made them glance Like those *t* stars of the airy Giant's zone, „ 260
then took the king His *t* broad sons ; „ 269
t times he went : The first, be blew and blew, „ 335
Shadows of *t* dead men (repeat) *G. of Swainston* 3, 5
T dead men have I loved and thou art last of the three. „ 15
Tho' I since then have number'd o'er Some thrice *t* years : *In Mem., Con.* 10
cataract seas that snap The *t* decker's oaken spine *Maud II ii* 27
Flame-colour, vert and azure, in *t* rays, One falling upon each of *t* fair queens, *Com. of Arthur* 275
over all High on the top were those *t* Queens, *Gareth and L.* 229
a river Runs in *t* loops about her living-place ; And o'er it are *t* passings, and *t* knights „ 612
t fair girls In gilt and rosy raiment came : „ 926
O rainbow with *t* colours after rain, „ 1160
but when the Prince *T* times had blown— „ 1378
Slay me not : my *t* brethren bad me do it, „ 1410
night Before her birthday, *t* sad years ago, *Marr. of Geraint* 633
And forth they rode, but scarce *t* paces on, *Geraint and E.* 19
Then Enid was aware of *t* tall knights On horseback, „ 56
I saw *t* bandits by the rock Waiting to fall on you, „ 72
Stript from the *t* dead wolves of woman born The *t* gay suits of armour „ 94

Three (adj.) (*continued*) *T* other horsemen waiting, wholly arm'd, *Geraint and E.* 121
' There lurk *t* villains yonder in the wood, „ 142
Their *t* gay suits of armour, each from each, „ 181
and my purpose *t* years old, „ 849
those *t* kingless years Have past— *Balin and Balan* 63
for but *t* brief moons had glanced away „ 154
Had I for *t* days seen, ready to fall. *Merlin and V.* 296
So to the Gate of the *t* Queens we came, *Holy Grail* 358
T knights were thereamong ; and they too smiled, *Pelleas and E.* 96
Then glanced askew at those *t* knights of hers, „ 134
And those *t* knights all set their faces home, „ 187
Then calling her *t* knights, she charged them, „ 219
while walking on the walls With her *t* knights, „ 226
Give me *t* days to melt her fancy, „ 356
So those *t* days, aimless about the land, „ 391
Then was he ware of *t* pavilions rear'd „ 428
and their *t* squires across their feet : „ 431
hence he went To-day for *t* days' hunting— *Last Tournament* 530
Himself beheld *t* spirits mad with joy *Guinevere* 252
When *t* gray linnets wrangle for the seed : „ 255
lived For *t* brief years, and there, „ 697
brandish'd him *T* times, and drew him under in the mere. (repeat) *Pass. of Arthur* 314, 329
Not tho' I live *t* lives of mortal men, „ 323
by these *T* Queens with crowns of gold : „ 366
There those *t* Queens Put forth their hands, „ 373
from the woods That belt it rise *t* dark, tall cypresses,—*T* cypresses, *Lover's Tale i* 536
Fixing my eyes on those *t* cypress-cones „ *ii* 38
The mountain, the *t* cypresses, the cave, „ 109
Dead—and had lain *t* days without a pulse : „ *iv* 34
An' he took *t* turns in the rain, *First Quarrel* 75
which our house has held *T* hundred years— *Sisters (E. and E.)* 53
I had sat *t* nights by the child— *In the Child. Hosp.* 59
And we stay'd *t* days, and we gorged *V. of Maeldune* 67
T days since, *t* more dark days of the Godless gloom *Despair* 6
Those *t* hundred millions under one Imperial sceptre now, *Locksley H., Sixty* 117
came On *t* gray heads beneath a gleaming rift. *Demeter and P.* 83
T dark ones in the shadow with thy King. „ 122
those *t* sweet Italian words, *The Ring* 406
The century's *t* strong eights have met *To Ulysses* 7
T slaves were trailing a dead lion away, *St. Telemachus* 47
Thro' those *t* words would haunt him when a boy, *Far—far—away* 8
Three (s) Three dead men have I loved and thou art last of the *t*. *G. of Swainston* 15
Three-days-long That *t-d-l* presageful gloom of yours *Merlin and V.* 320
Three-decker rushing battle-bolt sang from the *t-d* *Maud I i* 50
cataract seas that snap The *t d's* oaken spine „ *II ii* 27
Threefold Lower'd softly with a *t* cord of love *D. of F. Women* 211
Three hundred The charge of the gallant *t h*, *Heavy Brigade* 1
Scarlett and Scarlett's *t h* were riding by „ 4
gallant *t h* whose glory will never die— „ 10
Gallopt the gallant *t h*, the Heavy Brigade. „ 25
'Lost are the gallant *t h* of Scarlett's Brigade ! ' „ 45
Glory to all the *t h*, and all the Brigade ! „ 66
Three-months-old On corpses *t-m-o* at noon she came, *Palace of Art* 243
Three-parts-sick *t-p-s* With strumming and with scraping, *Amphion* 69
Three-times-three The crowning cup, the *t-t-t*, *In Mem., Con.* 104
Three-years' Sent me a *t-y* exile from thine eyes. *Balin and Balan* 59
Thresher *t* with his flail had scatter'd them. *Gareth and L.* 842
Threshing-floor by the lonely *t-f*, *Demeter and P.* 126
Threshold (adj.) footsteps smite the *t* stairs Of life— *St. S. Stylites* 191
Threshold (s) and on her *t* lie Howling in outer darkness. *To ——, With Pal. of Art* 15
see me carried out from the *t* of the door ; *May Queen, N. Y's. E.* 42
Corpses across the *t* ; *D. of F. Women* 25
Half-fall'n across the *t* of the sun, „ 63
Dora went to Mary's house, and stood Upon the *t*. *Dora* 111
That float about the *t* of an age, *Golden Year* 16
wrinkled feet Upon thy glimmering *t's*, *Tithonus* 68
And burn the *t* of the night, *The Voyage* 18
And seldom crost her *t*, *Enoch Arden* 337
dark retinue reverencing death At golden *t's* ; *Aylmer's Field* 843

Threshold (s) (*continued*) come thou down And find him ; by the happy *t*, he, — *Princess vii* 200
Upon the *t* of the mind ? — *In Mem. iii* 16
guest To enrich the *t* of the night — „ *xxix* 6
From off the *t* of the realm, — *Gareth and L.* 136
Here on the *t* of our enterprise. — „ 298
Was all the marble *t* flashing, — *Geraint and E.* 25
With all her golden *t's* clashing, — *Lover's Tale i* 605
Love passeth not the *t* of cold Hate, — „ 778
Falls on the *t* of her native land, — *Demeter and P.* 3
Threw (*See also* **Thraw'd**) She *t* her royal robes away. — *Palace of Art* 290
clutch'd the sword, And strongly wheel'd and *t* it. — *M. d'Arthur* 136
heavier, stronger, he that smote And *t* him : — *Princess v* 537
t the kings Carádos, Urien, Cradlemont of Wales, — *Com. of Arthur* 111
Mounted in arms, *t* up their caps — *Gareth and L.* 697
same strength which *t* the Morning Star Can throw the Evening.' — „ 1108
Lancelot !—thine the hand That *t* me ? — „ 1242
By overthrowing me you *t* me higher. — *Geraint and E.* 792
clutch'd the sword, And strongly wheel'd and *t* it. — *Pass. of Arthur* 304
on the sand *T* down the bier ; — *Lover's Tale iii* 33
I *t* myself all abroad— — *The Wreck* 39
and *t* Underfoot there in the fray— — *Heavy Brigade* 54
Miriam sketch'd and Muriel *t* the fly ; — *The Ring* 159
She *t* the fly for me ; — „ 355
how long—till you *t* me aside ! — *Charity* 5
Thrice *T* happy state again to be — *Supp. Confessions* 40
Thrice-beaten weakling, and *t-b* hound : — *Pelleas and E.* 291
Thrice-happy *T-h* days ! The flower of each, — *Edwin Morris* 68
' *T-h* he that may caress The ringlet's — *Talking Oak* 177
Thrice-turn'd chew'd The *t-t* cud of wrath, — *Princess i* 66
Thrid To *t* the musky-circled mazes, — „ *iv* 261
He *t's* the labyrinth of the mind, — *In Mem. xcvii* 21
Thridded I *t* the black heart of all the woods, — *Demeter and P.* 69
Thridding *T* the sombre boskage of the wood, — *D. of F. Women* 243
Thried (tried) I *t* her meself av the bird 'ud come — *Tomorrow* 45
Thrift like the little *t*, Trembled in perilous places — *Sea Dreams* 10
Thrifty *t* too beyond her age. — *Dora* 16
Earn well the *t* months, nor wed Raw Haste, — *Love thou thy land* 95
Thrill His country's war-song *t* his ears : — *Two Voices* 153
Me mightier transports move and *t* ; — *Sir Galahad* 22
My spirit leap'd as with those *t's* of bliss — *Lover's Tale i* 363
with some electric *t* A cold air pass'd between us, — *The Ring* 379
Thrill'd a clear under-tone *T* thro' mine ears — *D. of F. Women* 82
T thro' the woods ; and Balan lurking there — *Balin and Balan* 546
Thrilleth Thro' my very heart it *t* — *Lilian* 22
Thrilling *See* **Spirit-thrilling**
Thrive those Fresh faces, that would *t* — *Talking Oak* 50
Thriven Word by which himself had *t*.' — *Sea Dreams* 197
That on dumb death had *t* ; — *Dead Prophet* 26
Throän (throne) an' täake 'im afoor the *T*. — *North. Cobbler* 106
an' sits o' the Bishop's *t*. — *Church-warden, etc.* 20
Throat golden round her lucid *t* And shoulder : — *Œnone* 178
From cheek and *t* and chin. — *Palace of Art* 140
But there was that across his *t* — *L. C. V. de Vere* 31
bright death quiver'd at the victim's *t* ; — *D. of F. Women* 115
and in her *t* Her voice seem'd distant, — *To J. S.* 54
' Go, take the goose, and wring her *t*, — *The Goose* 31
All *t's* that gurgle sweet ! — *Talking Oak* 266
She lit the spark within my *t*, — *Will Water.* 109
Faltering and fluttering in her *t*, — *Princess ii* 187
Make liquid treble of that bassoon, my *t* ; — „ 426
Thereat the Lady stretch'd a vulture *t*, — „ *iv* 363
Millions of *t's* would bawl for civil rights, — „ *v* 387
Tho' niggard *t's* of Manchester may bawl, — *Third of Feb.* 43
There is but one bird with a musical *t*, — *The Islet* 27
And flood a fresher *t* with song. — *In Mem. lxxxiii* 16
cobweb woven across the cannon's *t* — *Maud III vi* 27
bared the knotted column of his *t*, — *Marr. of Geraint* 74
many-winter'd fleece of *t* and chin. — *Merlin and V.* 841
felt the knot Climb in her *t*, — *Lancelot and E.* 741
' Taliessin is our fullest *t* of song, — *Holy Grail* 300
The naked sword athwart their naked *t's*, — *Pelleas and E.* 452
the sword of the tourney across her *t*. — „ 455
that felt the cold touch on her *t*, — „ 488
Throat (*continued*) The warm white apple of her *t*, — *Last Tournament* 717
he bow'd to kiss the jewell'd *t*, — „ 751
yea to him Who hacks his mother's *t*— — *Sir J. Oldcastle* 114
Sorra the silent *t* but we hard it — *Tomorrow* 84
scatters on her *t* the sparks of dew, — *Prog. of Spring* 58
you will not deny my sultry *t* One draught — *Romney's R.* 22
He gript it so hard by the *t* — *Bandit's Death* 28
Throated *See* **Glossy-throated, Hundred-throated, Serpent-throated, Yellow-throated**)
Throb (s) Perchance, to lull the *t's* of pain, — *The Daisy* 105
Throb (verb) and *t's* Thro' earth, and all her graves, — *Romney's R.* 127
T thro' the ribbed stone ; — *Palace of Art* 176
The sight that *t's* and aches beneath my touch, — *Lover's Tale i* 33
Throbb'd Till the war-drum *t* no longer, — *Locksley Hall* 127
tempestuous treble *t* and palpitated ; — *Vision of Sin* 28
T thunder thro' the palace floors, — *Princess vii* 104
brows that shook and *t* From temple unto temple. — *Lover's Tale iii* 7
Throbbing *T* thro' all thy heat and light, — *Fatima* 4
Her heart is like a *t* star. — *Kate* 9
When last with *t* heart I came To rest — *Talking Oak* 155
A footstep, a low *t* in the walls, — *The Ring* 409
Throe coughs, aches, stitches, ulcerous *t's* — *St. S. Stylites* 13
Travail, and *t's* and agonies of the life, — *Com. of Arthur* 76
Throne (*See also* **Bosom-throne, Daïs-throne, Rock-throne, Throän**) *Which kept her* t *unshaken still,* — *To the Queen* 34
underpropt a rich *T* of the massive ore, — *Arabian Nights* 146
to own A crown, a sceptre, and a *t* ! — *Ode to Memory* 121
With a crown of gold, On a *t* ? — *The Merman* 7
With a comb of pearl, On a *t* ? — *The Mermaid* 8
Over the *t* In the midst of the hall ; — „ 21
lightly vault from the *t* and play With the mermen — „ 33
Thou from a *t* Mounted in heaven — *To J. M. K.* 12
whose strong right arm debased The *t* of Persia, — *Alexander* 2
The *t* of Indian Cama slowly sail'd — *Palace of Art* 115
bells Began to chime. She took her *t* : — „ 158
held she her solemn mirth, And intellectual *t*. — „ 216
two tame leopards couch'd beside her *t*, — *Princess ii* 33
glittering bergs of ice, *T* after *t*, — „ *iv* 72
the crowd dividing clove An advent to the *t* : — „ 284
and winged Her transit to the *t*, — „ 378
at the further end Was Ida by the *t*, — „ *vi* 357
And barking for the *t's* of kings ; — *Ode on Well.* 121
Betwixt a people and their ancient *t*, — „ 163
joy to the people and joy to the *t*, — *W. to Alexandra* 29
English Harold gave its *t* a wife, — *W. to Marie Alex.* 24
t's and peoples are as waifs that swing, — „ 26
Green-rushing from the rosy *t's* of dawn ! (repeat) — *Voice and the P.* 4, 40
The chairs and *t's* of civil power ? — *In Mem. xxi* 16
And shape the whisper of the *t* ; — „ *lxiv* 12
thousand battles, and shaking a hundred *t's*. — *Maud I i* 48
In that fierce light which beats upon a *t*, — *Ded. of Idylls* 27
from this land of beasts Up to my *t*, — *Com. of Arthur* 81
' A doubtful *t* is ice on summer seas. — „ 248
Who stood in silence near his *t*, — „ 277
same that afterward Struck for the *t*, — „ 325
those tall knights, that ranged about the *t*, — *Gareth and L.* 328
Which down he laid before the *t*, and knelt, — „ 390
Lest we should set one truer on his *t*. — *Balin and Balan* 7
a knight cast down Before his *t* — *Last Tournament* 162
Lay couchant with his eyes upon the *t*, — *Guinevere* 11
When all the purport of my *t* hath fail'd, — *Pass. of Arthur* 160
They stood before his *t* in silence, — „ 455
and her *t* In our vast Orient, — *To the Queen ii* 30
There in my realm and even on my *t*, — *Lover's Tale i* 593
Whom once he rose from off his *t* to greet — *Columbus* 5
the king, the queen, Sank from their *t's*, — „ 15
the mountain arose like a jewell'd *t* — *V. of Maeldune* 59
as a slave to his intellectual *t*, — *The Wreck* 66
Break the State, the Church, the *T*, — *Locksley H., Sixty* 138
seen the loneliness of earthly *t's*, — *To Prin. Beatrice* 14
One life, one flag, one fleet, one *T* ! ' — *Open. I. and C. Exhib.* 39
Flattery gilding the rift in a *t* ; — *Vastness* 20
rebel subject seek to drag me from the *t*, — *By an Evolution.* 15
all the *T's* are clouded by your loss, — *D. of the Duke of C.* 6

Throned (*See also* **Low-throned**) wisdom-bred And *t* of wisdom— *Œnone* 124
I turning saw, *t* on a flowery rise, *D. of F. Women* 125
And *t* races may degrade ; *In Mem. cxxviii* 7
splendour of the presence of the King *T*, *Gareth and L.* 321
That victor of the Pagan *t* in hall— *Last Tournament* 665
Throng (s) in among the *t's* of men : *Locksley Hall* 116
And pinch their brethren in the *t*, *Lit. Squabbles* 7
A head with kindling eyes above the *t*, *Gareth and L.* 646
from out of kitchen came The thralls in *t*, „ 695
push'd Athwart the *t* to Lancelot, *Holy Grail* 753
Throng (verb) To *t* with stately blooms *The Poet* 27
marish-flowers that *t* The desolate creeks *Dying Swan* 40
and *t*, their rags and they The basest, *Lucretius* 170
the people *t* The chairs and thrones *In Mem. xxi* 15
Throng'd (*See also* **Mast-throng'd**) And her whisper *t* my pulses *Locksley Hall* 36
Every gate is *t* with suitors, „ 101
In their own darkness, *t* into the moon. *Pelleas and E.* 458
Their people *t* about them from the hall, *Sisters (E. and E.)* 156
a crowd *T* the waste field about the city gates : *Sir J. Oldcastle* 40
Thronging Or *t* all one porch of Paradise *Palace of Art* 101
Till *t* in and in, to where they waited, *Vision of Sin* 26
as *t* fancies come To boys and girls *Lover's Tale i* 554
Throstle *And thro' wild March the* t *calls*, *To the Queen* 14
The callow *t* lispeth, *Claribel* 17
Sometimes the *t* whistled strong : *Sir L. and Q. G.* 11
And swallow and sparrow and *t*, *Window, Ay* 14
blackbirds have their wills, The *t's* too. *Early Spring* 6
Throve And so she *t* and prosper'd : *Palace of Art* 217
that on which it *t* Falls off, *To J. S.* 15
But *t* not in her trade, not being bred To barter, *Enoch Arden* 249
And in it *t* an ancient evergreen, „ 735
Who *t* and branch'd from clime to clime, *In Mem. cxviii* 13
And all this *t* until I wedded thee, *Guinevere* 484
Throw I would *t* to them back in mine *The Merman* 31
dividing the swift mind, In act to *t*: *M. d'Arthur* 61
Nor lose the wrestling thews that *t* the world ; *Princess vii* 282
To seize and *t* the doubts of man ; *In Mem. cix* 6
being but knave, I *t* thine enemies.' *Gareth and L.* 1023
Morning Star Can *t* the Evening.' „ 1109
dividing the swift mind, In act to *t*: *Pass. of Arthur* 229
Throwing *t* down his robes, And claspt her hand *Lover's Tale iii* 51
and we took to *t* the stone, *V. of Maeldune* 94
Thrown selfsame impulse wherewith he was *t* *Mine be the strength* 3
thunder, or a sound Of rocks *t* down, *Palace of Art* 282
Still from one sorrow to another *t*: *Lotos-Eaters, C. S.* 18
broad-limb'd Gods at random *t* By fountain-urns ;— *To E. L.* 15
the shiver of dancing leaves is *t* *Maud I vi* 73
knight of Arthur, here lie *t* by whom I know not, *Gareth and L.* 1233
Out, sword ; we are *t*!' „ 1236
T have I been, nor once, but many a time. „ 1261
Thrue (true) yer Honour's the *t* ould blood *Tomorrow* 5
Thrum to flaunt, to dress, to dance, to *t*, *Princess iv* 519
Thrumm'd who *t* On such a wire as musically *Last Tournament* 322
Thrumming And *t* on the table : *Will Water.* 160
Thrush (*See also* **Mavis**) rarely pipes the mounted *t*; *In Mem. xci* 2
Thrust (s) here a *t* that might have kill'd, *Lancelot and E.* 25
Thrust (verb) and *t* The dagger thro' her side.' *D. of F. Women* 259
Who *t* him in the hollows of his arm, *Dora* 132
And with grim laughter *t* us out at gates. *Princess iv* 556
T in between ; but Arac rode him down : „ *v* 532
For into a shallow grave they are *t*, *Maud II v* 6
And *t* the dish before her, crying, 'Eat.' *Geraint and E.* 655
Unbind him now, And *t* him out of doors ; *Pelleas and E.* 257
and unbound, and *t* him from the gate. „ 260
Far less to bind, your victor, and *t* him out, „ 293
but *t* him bounden out of door. „ 314
Or *t* the heathen from the Roman wall, *Pass. of Arthur* 69
portion of the pleasant yesterday, *T* forward on to-day *Lover's Tale i* 123
Had *t* his wife and child and dash'd „ 380
him Who *t* him out, or him who saved his life ?' „ *iv* 267
Thrusteth My tough lance *t* sure, *Sir Galahad* 2
Thud the hollow-beaten mosses *t* *Balin and Balan* 321
Thumb his nice eyes Should see the raw mechanic's bloody *t's* *Walk. to the Mail* 75
And rotatory *t's* on silken knees, *Aylmer's Field* 200
nipt her slender nose With petulant *t* and finger, *Gareth and L.* 750
stoop and kiss the tender little *t*, *Marr. of Geraint* 395
Thumbscrew To the *t* and the stake, *The Revenge* 21
Thump heave and *t* A league of street *Princess iii* 127
Thunder (s) (*See also* **Battle-thunder, Tundher, War-thunder**) BELOW the *t's* of the upper deep ; *The Kraken* 1
Her words did gather *t* as they ran, *The Poet* 49
And as the lightning to the *t* Which follows it, „ 50
Ever brightening With a low melodious *t*; *Poet's Mind* 27
Low *t* and light in the magic night— *The Merman* 23
With *t's*, and with lightnings, *Buonaparte* 6
Rest in a happy place and quiet seats Above the *t*, *Œnone* 132
The ragged rims Of *t* brooding low, *Palace of Art* 75
t, or a sound of rocks thrown down, „ 281
And *t* on the everlasting hills. *D. of F. Women* 226
The *t's* breaking at her feet : *Of old sat Freedom* 2
Black'd with thy branding *t*, *St. S. Stylites* 76
Low *t's* bring the mellow rain, *Talking Oak* 279
frolic welcome took The *t* and the sunshine, *Ulysses* 48
But they heard the foeman's *t* *The Captain* 41
for on her the *t's* of the house Had fallen *Aylmer's Field* 278
flood, fire, earthquake, *t*, wrought Such waste „ 639
Dead claps of *t* from within the cliffs *Sea Dreams* 55
And there was rolling *t*; „ 118
Nor ever lowest roll of *t* moans, *Lucretius* 108
A long melodious *t* to the sound Of solemn psalms, *Princess ii* 476
shattering on black blocks A breadth of *t*. „ *iii* 292
with the crash of shivering points, And *t*. „ *v* 492
Throbb'd *t* thro' the palace floors, „ *vii* 104
even if they broke In *t*, silent ; *Ode on Well.* 177
Welcome her, *t's* of fort and of fleet ! *W. to Alexandra* 6
if he thunder by law the *t* is yet His voice. *High. Pantheism* 14
T, a flying fire in heaven, *Boädicea* 24
And a sullen *t* is roll'd ; *Maud II iv* 49
Made lightnings and great *t's* over him, *Com. of Arthur* 108
break perforce Upon a head so dear in *t*, said : *Geraint and E.* 13
crash of the near cataract hears The drumming *t* „ 173
The hard earth shake, and a low *t* of arms. *Lancelot and E.* 460
and overhead *T*, and in the *t* was a cry. *Holy Grail* 185
Thicker than drops from *t*, „ 348
the heavens Open'd and blazed with *t* „ 508
and close upon it peal'd A sharp quick *t*.' „ 696
then one low roll Of Autumn *t*, *Last Tournament* 153
thresholds clashing, roll'd Her heaviest *t*— *Lover's Tale i* 606
the surge fell From *t* into whispers ; „ *iii* 31
I heard his voice between The *t's* *Columbus* 146
t of God peal'd over us all the day, *V. of Maeldune* 113
a voice rang out in the *t's* of Ocean and Heaven *The Wreck* 88
Full-handed *t's* often have confessed Thy power, *To W. C. Macready* 2
Are there *t's* moaning in the distance ? *On Jub. Q. Victoria* 66
Till the *t's* pass, the spectres vanish, „ 69
Downward *t* in hollow and glen, *To Master of B.* 16
Across the downward *t* of the brook *Death of Œnone* 23
or shake with her *t's* and shatter her island, *Kapiolani* 10
THERE is a sound of *t* afar, *Riflemen form!* 1
Storm of battle and *t* of war ! „ 3
and hew'd Like broad oaks with *t*. *The Tourney* 11
at the shipwreck, or the rolling *T*, *Faith* 4
Thunder (verb) That not one moment ceased to *t*, *Sea Dreams* 125
And the volleying cannon *t* his loss ; *Ode on Well.* 62
T 'Anathema,' friend, at you ; *To F. D. Maurice* 8
if He *t* by law the thunder is yet His voice. *High. Pantheism* 14
Thunderbolt in its breast a *t*. *Locksley Hall* 192
And like a *t* he falls. *The Eagle* 6
and once the flash of a *t*— *Lucretius* 27
And, falling on them like a *t*, *Princess, Pro.* 43
the *t* Hangs silent ; but prepare : I speak ; „ *ii* 223
I dare All these male *t's*: „ *iv* 500
Whence the *t* will fall Long and loud, *The Revenge* 44
Shrine-shattering earthquake, fire, flood, *t*, *Tiresias* 61
Burst like a *t*, Crash'd like a hurricane, *Heavy Brigade* 27

Thunderbolt (*continued*) Gods, To quench, not hurl the t, to stay, *Demeter and P.* 133
Thunderclap There was a t once, *In the Child. Hosp.* 62
blast of that underground t echo'd away, *Def. of Lucknow* 32
Thunder-cloud As t-c's that, hung on high, *Eleänore* 98
like a t-c Whose skirts are loosen'd *Geraint and E.* 458
Thunder-drops As t-d fall on a sleeping sea : *D. of F. Women* 122
Thunder'd Volleyed and t; (repeat) *Light Brigade* 21, 42
t up into Heaven the Christless code, *Maud II i* 26
war That t in and out the gloomy skirts *Lancelot and E.* 291
Thunder-gloom cloud that grew To t-g *Gareth and L.* 1359
Thundering The league-long roller t on the reef, *Enoch Arden* 584
Welcome her, t cheer of the street! *W. to Alexandra* 7
All down the t shores of Bude and Bos, *Guinevere* 291
Thunderless T lightnings striking under sea *To the Queen ii* 12
waterfalls Pour'd in a t plunge to the base *V. of Maeldune* 14
Thunder-music t-m, rolling, shake The prophet *In Mem. lxxxvii* 7
Thunderous when the note Had reach'd a t fulness, *Sea Dreams* 214
the ship stagger'd under a t shock, *The Wreck* 107
Thunder-peals A bridal dawn of t-p, *Love thou thy land* 51
Thundershaken collapsed masses Of t columns indistinct, *Lover's Tale ii* 66
Thunder-shower are drown'd in azure gloom Of t-s, *Princess iv* 526
Thunder-sketch t-s Of lake and mountain *Sisters (E. and E.)* 99
Thunder-smoke roofs Of our great hall are roll'd in t-s! *Holy Grail* 220
Thundersong the t that wheels the spheres, *Lover's Tale i* 476
Thunder-storm the peoples plunging thro' the t-s; *Locksley Hall* 126
Upon a king's right hand in t-s's, *Princess v* 439
Thundrous With scraps of t Epic lilted out „ *ii* 375
Thurn (thorn) and a t be a-grawin' theer, *Village Wife* 79
As fer as fro' Thursby t *North. Cobbler* 14
fust kiss I gied 'er by Thursby t; „ 45
Thurnaby an' I 'a stubb'd T waäste. *N. Farmer, O. S.* 28
an' T hoälms to plow! „ 52
Thursby As fer as fro' T thurn *North. Cobbler* 14
fust kiss I gied 'er by T thurn; „ 45
Thutty (thirty) I eärs es 'e'd gie fur a howry owd book t pound an' moor, *Village Wife* 45
I 'a managed for Squoire coom Michaelmas t year. *N. Farmer, O. S.* 48
Thwack'd Knights were t and riven, *The Tourney* 10
Thwarted T by one of these old father-fools, *Aylmer's Field* 390
wrong'd and lied and t us— *Princess iv* 540
Thwarting t their traditions of Himself, *Sir J. Oldcastle* 181
Thymy Love paced the t plots of Paradise, *Love and Death* 2
Lingering about the t promontories, *Sea Dreams* 38
Tiar studded wide With disks and t's, *Arabian Nights* 64
Ticking The slow clock t, and the sound *Mariana* 74
Tickle t the maggot born in an empty head, *Maud II v* 38
Tickled And secret laughter t all my soul. *Princess iv* 267
Ticklin' ya was t' o' trout, *Church-warden, etc.* 27
Tickling (*See also* **Ticklin'**) caught the younker t trout— *Walk. to the Mail* 33
t the brute brain within the man's *Lucretius* 21
Tide (*See also* **Autumn-tide, High-tide, Hunting-tide, River-tide**) The t of time flow'd back with me, *Arabian Nights* 3
The forward-flowing t of time; „ 4
For ere she reach'd upon the t *L. of Shalott iv* 33
Bluster the winds and t's the self-same way *D. of F. Women* 38
And when the t of combat stands, *Sir Galahad* 10
As down dark t's the glory slides, „ 47
On whose dull sameness his full t of youth Broke *Aylmer's Field* 115
a full t Rose with ground-swell, *Sea Dreams* 50
you do but hear the t. „ 84
Of such a t swelling toward the land, „ 87
No!' said he, 'but this t's roar, „ 250
at high t of feast, In masque or pageant *Princess i* 197
Till toward the centre set the starry t's, „ *ii* 117
a t of fierce Invective seem'd to wait „ *iv* 471
When the t ebbs in sunshine, „ *vi* 162
we hear The t's of Music's golden sea *Ode on Well.* 252
Dream in the sliding t's. *Requiescat* 4
The t flows down, the wave again *In Mem. xix* 13
The double t's of chariots flow „ *xcviii* 23
forward-creeping t's Began to foam, „ *ciii* 37
In vassal t's that follow'd thought. „ *cxii* 16
t in its broad-flung ship-wrecking roar, *Maud I iii* 11

Tide (*continued*) Your limit, oft returning with the t. *Lancelot and E.* 1041
t within Red with free chase and heather-scented air, *Last Tournament* 690
and with that wind the t Rose, *Pass. of Arthur* 125
And London roll'd one t of joy *To the Queen ii* 8
where the t Plash'd, sapping its worn ribs; *Lover's Tale i* 55
a-sailing with wind an' t. *First Quarrel* 42
bank that is daily devour'd by the t— *Def. of Lucknow* 39
t's of onset sap Our seven high gates, *Tiresias* 91
flung from the rushing t of the world *The Wreck* 6
home in the canes by the purple t, „ 71
towering crest of the t's Plunged on the vessel „ 89
change of the t—what is all of it worth? *Vastness* 30
in the t's of a civic insanity! *Beautiful City* 4
clash of t's that meet in narrow seas.— *Akbar's Dream* 58
But such a t as moving seems asleep, *Crossing the Bar* 5
Tided *See* **Full-tided**
Tidings Be cheer'd with t of the bride, *In Mem. xl* 23
To hear the t of my friend, „ *cxxvi* 3
Tie (s) To pass with all our social t's *Day-Dm., L'Envoi* 5
ancient t's Would still be dear beyond *Princess ii* 264
strand of Death inwoven here With dear Love's t, *Maud I xviii* 61
Tie (verb) T up the ringlets on your cheek: *Margaret* 57
Close up his eyes: t up his chin: *D. of the O. Year* 48
Tied BRIDESMAID, ere the happy knot was t, *The Bridesmaid* 1
is charm'd and t To where he stands,— *D. of F. Women* 193
t it round his hat To make him pleasing *Dora* 83
t the bridal-reins of all the three (repeat) *Geraint and E.* 98, 183
That 'is taäil were soä t up *Village Wife* 30
Tier All up the marble stair, t over t, *Lancelot and E.* 1248
high above us with her yawning t's of guns, *The Revenge* 41
Tierce subtle at t and quart of mind *In Mem., W. G. Ward* 5
Tiger (adj.) The t spasms tear his chest, *Ancient Sage* 123
Every t madness muzzled, every serpent passion kill'd, *Locksley H., Sixty* 167
Tiger (s) Here play'd, a t, rolling to and fro *Palace of Art* 151
And let the ape and t die. *In Mem. cxviii* 28
if the t's leap into the fold unawares— *Def. of Lucknow* 51
I saw the t in the ruin'd fane Spring *Demeter and P.* 79
hunt the t of oppression out From office; *Akbar's Dream* 158
From the lower world within him, moods of t, or of ape? *Making of Man* 2
Tiger-cat a t-c In act to spring, *Princess ii* 450
Tiger-lily Heavily hangs the t-l. (repeat) *A spirit haunts* 12, 24
Tight I'd clasp it round so close and t. *Miller's D.* 180
that trims us up, And keeps us t; *Edwin Morris* 47
Would twist his girdle t, *Talking Oak* 43
link Of some t chain within my inmost frame Was riven in twain: *Lover's Tale i* 595
Tighten made her lithe arm round his neck T, *Merlin and V.* 615
Tigress To trip a t with a gossamer, *Princess v* 170
Tigris Adown the T I was borne, *Arabian Nights* 6
Tile her whinny shrills From t to scullery, *Princess v* 453
Fill out the spaces by the barren t's. *Prog. of Spring* 43
Till (s) rogue would leap from his counter and t, *Maud I i* 51
Till (verb) It is the land that freemen t, *You ask me, why, etc.* 5
Man comes and t's the field and lies beneath, *Tithonus* 3
year by year the labourer t's His wonted glebe, *In Mem. ci* 21
sent a thousand men To t the wastes, *Geraint and E.* 942
Till'd for miles about Was t by women; *Princess i* 192
Every grim ravine a garden, every blazing desert t, *Locksley H., Sixty* 168
Tiller three were clad like t's of the soil. *Gareth and L.* 181
Gareth, 'We be t's of the soil, „ 242
Tilt (cart-cover) his wife upon the t, *Walk. to the Mail* 41
Tilt (knightly exercise) that rang With t and tourney; *Princess, Pro.* 122
I seem'd to move in old memorial t's, „ *v* 479
stagger'd thy strong Gawain in a t For pastime; *Gareth and L.* 542
Forgetful of the t and tournament, *Marr. of Geraint* 52
And victor at the t and tournament, *Geraint and E.* 960
Hurt in his first t was my son, *Lancelot and E.* 196
That he should wear her favour at the t. „ 358
many a time have watch'd thee at the t „ 1359
acts of prowess done In tournament or t, Sir Percivale, *Holy Grail* 2
Killed in a t, come next, five summers back, *Guinevere* 321

Tilt (knightly exercise) (*continued*) on love And sport and *t's* and pleasure, *Guinevere* 387
Tilt (verb) Himself would *t* it out among the lads: *Princess v* 355
Ask'd me to *t* with him, the proven knight. *Gareth and L.* 27
Who *t* for lady's love and glory here, „ 740
But in this tournament can no man *t*, *Marr. of Geraint* 480
And *t's* with my good nephew thereupon, „ 488
He left it with her, when he rode to *t* *Lancelot and E.* 30
to *t* against the knights There at Caerleon, *Pelleas and E.* 65
t with a lance Becomes thee well— *Last Tournament* 636
Tilted *See* **Tip-tilted**
Tilth wither'd holt or *t* or pasturage. *Enoch Arden* 675
and so by *t* and grange, And vines, *Princess i* 110
t and vineyard, hive and horse and herd; *To Virgil* 10
Tilting-field In open battle or the *t-f* (repeat) *Guinevere* 330, 332
Timber And fiddled in the *t*! *Amphion* 16
Timber-crost A front of *t-c* antiquity, *Enoch Arden* 692
Timbrel With *t* and with song. *D. of F. Women* 200
Time (s) (*See also* **Bridal-time, College-time, Cradle-time, Ten-times, Toime**) *yield you* t *To make demand of modern rhyme* *To the Queen* 10
Nine *t's* goes the passing bell: *All Things will Die* 35
In a *t*, Of which he wots not, *Supp. Confessions* 160
The tide of *t* flow'd back with me, The forward-flowing tide of *t*; *Arabian Nights* 3
In sooth it was a goodly *t*, „ 20
A goodly place, a goodly *t*, (repeat) „ 31, 53
A goodly *t*, For it was in the golden prime „ 42
fed the *t* With odour in the golden prime „ 64
Apart from place, withholding *t*, „ 75
A lovely *t*, For it was in the golden prime „ 86
Entranced with that place and *t*, „ 97
Graven with emblems of the *t*, „ 108
After the fashion of the *t*, „ 119
night new-risen, that marvellous *t* „ 130
The sweetest lady of the *t*, „ 141
Sole star of all that place and *t*, „ 152
What *t* the amber morn Forth gushes *Ode to Memory* 70
WHAT *t* the mighty moon was gathering light *Love and Death* 1
That tho' I knew not in what *t* or place, *Sonnet to* —— 12
said the secret voice, 'some *t*, Sooner or later, *Two Voices* 64
'Forerun thy peers, thy *t*, and let Thy feet, „ 88
memory of the wither'd leaf In endless *t* „ 113
What *t* the foeman's line is broke, „ 155
'For memory dealing but with *t*, „ 376
Beat *t* to nothing in my head *Miller's D.* 67
That went and came a thousand *t's*. „ 72
when *t* was ripe, The still affection of the heart „ 224
from that *t* to this I am alone, *Œnone* 193
My love hath told me so a thousand *t's*. „ 197
Hath he not sworn his love a thousand *t's*, „ 231
Three *t's* I stabb'd him thro' and thro'. *The Sisters* 29
the *t's* of every land So wrought, *Palace of Art* 147
What *t* I watch the darkening droves of swine „ 199
But dreadful *t*, dreadful eternity, „ 267
And ever worse with growing *t*, „ 270
You know so ill to deal with *t*, *L. C. V. de Vere* 63
If *t* be heavy on your hands, „ 66
To-morrow 'ill be the happiest *t* of all the glad New-year; (repeat) *May Queen* 2, 42
The good old year, the dear old *t*, „ *N. Y's. E.* 6
A thousand *t's* I blest him, „ *Con.* 16
And if it comes three *t's*, I thought, „ 38
So now I think my *t* is near. „ 41
T driveth onward fast, *Lotos-Eaters, C. S.* 43
The spacious *t's* of great Elizabeth *D. of F. Women* 7
The *t's* when I remember to have been „ 79
wood is all thine own, Until the end of *t*.' „ 84
The Nilus would have risen before his *t* „ 143
This is the curse of *t*. Alas! *To J. S.* 17
'Beat quicker, for the *t* Is pleasant, *On a Mourner* 12
Hath *t* and space to work and spread. *You ask me, why, etc.* 16
induce a *t* When single thought is civil crime, „ 18
transfused Thro' future *t* by power of thought. *Love thou thy land* 4
But pamper not a hasty *t*, „ 9

Time (s) (*continued*) For all the past of *T* reveals A bridal dawn *Love thou thy land* 50
And this be true, till *T* shall close, „ 79
'Why take the style of those heroic *t's*? *The Epic* 35
For nature brings not back the Mastodon, Nor we those *t's*; „ 37
Shall never more, at any future *t*, *M. d'Arthur* 18
And hid Excalibur the second *t*, „ 111
brandish'd him Three *t's*, and drew him under in the mere. (repeat) „ 146, 161
'tis *t* that I were gone. „ 163
I see the true old *t's* are dead, „ 229
Such *t's* have been not since the light „ 232
cock crew loud; as at that *t* of year The lusty bird „ *Ep.* 10
we listen'd; with the *t* we play'd, *Gardener's D.* 221
Then, in that *t* and place, I spoke to her, „ 226
And in that *t* and place she answer'd me, „ 231
the *t* Is come to raise the veil. „ 273
But in my *t* a father's word was law, *Dora* 27
and in harvest *t* he died. „ 55
T will set me right.' *Edwin Morris* 88
for so long a *t*, If I may measure *t* *St. S. Stylites* 93
Heaven, and Earth, and *T* are choked. „ 104
Bow down one thousand and two hundred *t's*, To Christ, „ 111
I do not say But that a *t* may come— „ 190
Yet I do not say, that *t* is at the doors „ 192
'But could I, as in *t's* foregone, *Talking Oak* 189
Shall Error in the round of *t* Still father Truth? *Love and Duty* 4
O three *t's* less unworthy! „ 20
Wait; my faith is large in *T*, „ 25
when a hundred *t's* In that last kiss, „ 66
all the wheels of *T* Spun round in station, „ 75
'Ah tho' the *t's*, when some new thought can bud, *Golden Year* 27
Not in our *t*, nor in our children's *t*, „ 55
all *t's* I have enjoy'd Greatly, *Ulysses* 7
Made weak by *t* and fate, but strong in will „ 69
fairy tales of science, and the long result of *T*; *Locksley Hall* 12
Love took up the glass of *T*, „ 31
in the foremost files of *t*— „ 178
Not only we, the latest seed of *T*, *Godiva* 5
And thought and *t* be born again, *Day-Dm., Sleep. P.* 50
And in the morning of the *t's*. „ *L'Envoi* 20
For since the *t* when Adam first Embraced his Eve „ 41
How goes the *t*? 'Tis five o'clock. *Will Water.* 3
Nor add and alter, many *t's*, „ 15
on this whirligig of *T* We circle „ 63
With *t* I will not quarrel: „ 206
IT was the *t* when lilies blow, *Lady Clare* 1
Tho' at *t's* her spirit sank: *L. of Burleigh* 70
Then before her *t* she died. „ 88
At *t's* the whole sea burn'd, at *t's* *The Voyage* 51
At *t's* a carven craft would shoot „ 53
Wed whom thou wilt, but I am sick of *T*, *Come not, when, etc.* 9
Is to be the ball of *T*, *Vision of Sin* 105
crime Of sense avenged by sense that wore with *t*.' „ 214
at *t's* Enoch would hold possession for a week: *Enoch Arden* 26
Enoch at *t's* to go by land or sea; „ 104
'Take your own *t*, Annie, take your own *t*.' „ 466
bought Quaint monsters for the market of those *t's*, „ 539
saw Philip, the slighted suitor of old *t's*, „ 745
Lord has call'd me she shall know, I wait His *t*, „ 811
touch'd On such a *t* as goes before the leaf, *The Brook* 13
and then indeed Harder the *t's* were, *Aylmer's Field* 452
Ran a Malayan amuck against the *t's*, „ 463
Beholding how the years which are not *T's* Had blasted him— „ 601
Is this a *t* to madden madness then? „ 769
Was this a *t* for these to flaunt their pride? „ 770
Which else had link'd their race with *t's* to come— „ 779
this, at *t's*, she mingled with his drink, *Lucretius* 18
Huge Ammonites, and the first bones of *T*; *Princess, Pro.* 15
Strange was the sight and smacking of the *t*; „ 89
one wide chasm of *t* and frost they gave The park, „ 93
monsters only made to kill *T* by the fire in winter.' „ 205
A tale for summer as befits the *t*, „ 210

Time (s) (*continued*) something made to suit with *T* and
place, *Princess Pro.* 231
From *t* to *t*, some ballad or a song ,, 241
still from *t* to *t* Came murmurs of her beauty ,, *i* 35
Some future *t*, if so indeed you will, ,, *ii* 64
on the stretch'd forefinger of all *T* Sparkle for ever: ,, 378
like swallows coming out of *t* ,, 431
your great name flow on with broadening *t* ,, *iii* 164
Our weakness somehow shapes the shadow, *T*; ,, 330
all things serve their *t* Toward that great year ,, *iv* 73
What *t* I watch'd the swallow winging south ,, 89
Like the Ithacensian suitors in old *t*, ,, 118
they mind us of the *t* When we made bricks in Egypt. ,, 127
those were gracious *t's*. ,, 297
fellow-worker be, When *t* should serve; ,, 309
I that have wasted here health, wealth, and *t*, ,, 352
drunkard's football, laughing-stocks of *T*, ,, 517
you spent a stormy *t* With our strange girl: ,, *v* 121
three *t's* he went: The first, he blew and blew, ,, 335
equal baseness lived in sleeker *t's* ,, 385
We plant a solid foot into the *T*, ,, 415
roll'd With music in the growing breeze of *T*, ,, *vi* 56
we will scatter all our maids Till happier *t's* ,, 303
many a maiden passing home Till happier *t's*; ,, 381
call'd On flying *T* from all their silver tongues— ,, *vii* 105
Much had she learnt in little *t*. ,, 240
these twain, upon the skirts of *T*, Sit side by side, ,, 287
Give it *t* To learn its limbs: ,, *Con.* 78
Give up their parks some dozen *t's* a year ,, 103
Foremost captain of his *t*, *Ode on Well.* 31
For many a *t* in many a clime His captain's-ear ,, 64
That Jenny had tript in her *t*: *Grandmother* 26
was the first *t*, too, that ever I thought of death. ,, 61
I could not weep—my own *t* seem'd so near. ,, 72
mine is a *t* of peace, (repeat) ,, 89, 94
And age is a *t* of peace, ,, 97
What *t* have I to be vext? ,, 104
T to think on it then; *N. Farmer, N. S.* 7
Do'ant be stunt: taäke *t*: ,, 17
But ill for him who, bettering not with *t*, *Will* 10
Rhymes and rhymes in the range of the *t's*! *Spiteful Letter* 9
But this is the *t* of hollies. ,, 22
Before the stony face of *T*, *Lit. Squabbles* 3
no truer *T* himself Can prove you, *A Dedication* 1
O skill'd to sing of *T* or Eternity, *Milton* 2
Sun comes, moon comes, *T* slips away. *Window, When* 2
Or reach a hand thro' *t* to catch *In Mem. i* 7
Come *T*, and teach me, many years, ,, *xiii* 13
My fancies *t* to rise on wing, ,, 17
'A *t* to sicken and to swoon, ,, *xxi* 17
And all was good that *T* could bring, ,, *xxiii* 18
envy not the beast that takes His license in the field of *t*, ,, *xxvii* 6
The *t* draws near the birth of Christ: ,, *xxviii* 1
Why should they miss their yearly due Before their *t*? ,, *xxix* 16
As when he loved me here in *T*, ,, *xliii* 14
What *t* his tender palm is prest ,, *xlv* 2
A lifelong tract of *t* reveal'd; ,, *xlvi* 9
And *T*, a maniac scattering dust, ,, *l* 7
When *T* hath sunder'd shell from pearl.' ,, *lii* 16
The perfect flower of human *t*; ,, *lxi* 4
When the dark hand struck down thro' *t*, ,, *lxxii* 19
Foreshorten'd in the tract of *t*? ,, *lxxvii* 4
What *t* mine own might also flee, ,, *lxxxiv* 37
Shall gather in the cycled *t's*. ,, *lxxxv* 28
such A friendship as had master'd *T*; ,, 64
Which masters *T* indeed, and is Eternal, ,, 65
Thy spirit in *t* among thy peers; ,, *xci* 6
Æonian music measuring out The steps of *T*— ,, *xcv* 42
The *t* draws near the birth of Christ; ,, *civ* 1
There in due *t* the woodbine blows, ,, *cv* 7
For change of place, like growth of *t*, ,, 11
The faithless coldness of the *t's*; ,, *cvi* 18
The *t* admits not flowers or leaves ,, *cvii* 5
Becoming, when the *t* has birth, ,, *cxiii* 14
Is it, then, regret for buried *t* ,, *cxvi* 1

Time (s) (*continued*) Contemplate all this work of *T*, *In Mem. cxviii* 1
If so he type this work of *t* ,, 16
vast eddies in the flood Of onward *t* ,, *cxxviii* 6
As echoes out of weaker *t's*, ,, *Con.* 22
But they must go, the *t* draws on, ,, 89
Appearing ere the *t's* were ripe, ,, 139
I remember the *t*, for the roots of my hair *Maud I i* 13
I well could weep for a *t* so sordid and mean, ,, *v* 17
My yet young life in the wilds of *T*, ,, *xvi* 21
She is but dead, and the *t* is at hand ,, *II iii* 8
Wretchedest age, since *T* began, ,, *v* 21
My mood is changed, for it fell at a *t* of year ,, *III vi* 4
'It is *t*, it is *t*, O passionate heart,' ,, 30
'It is *t*, O passionate heart and morbid eye, ,, 32
Hereafter, thro' all *t's*, Albert the Good. *Ded. of Idylls* 43
from *t* to *t* the heathen host Swarm'd overseas, *Com. of Arthur* 8
ye know that in King Uther's *t* The prince ,, 185
all before his *t* Was Arthur born, ,, 211
Of Uther's son, and born before his *t*, ,, 241
the *t* to cast away Is yet far-off.' ,, 307
And many a *t* he came, and evermore ,, 351
and sad At *t's* he seem'd, and sad with him was I,
Stern too at *t's*, and then I loved him not, ,, 353
answer'd me In riddling triplets of old *t*, ,, 402
and Merlin in our *t* Hath spoken also, ,, 419
while the phantom king Sent out at *t's* a voice; ,, 437
The fair beginners of a nobler *t*, ,, 457
For it was past the *t* of Easterday. *Gareth and L.* 186
At *t's* the summit of the high city flash'd; At *t's* the
spires and turrets half-way down Prick'd thro' the
mist; at *t's* the great gate shone Only, ,, 192
New things and old co-twisted, as if *T* Were nothing, ,, 226
the King hath past his *t*— ,, 709
Lion and stoat have isled together, knave, In *t* of flood. ,, 894
Thou shakest in thy fear: there yet is *t*: ,, 940
Far liefer had I fight a score of *t's* ,, 944
So many a *t* he vaulted up again; ,, 1125
The war of *T* against the soul of man. ,, 1198
Thrown have I been, nor once, but many a *t*. ,, 1261
but when the Prince Three *t's* had blown— ,, 1378
And he that told the tale in older *t's* ,, 1427
Has little *t* for idle questioners.' *Marr. of Geraint* 272
And there is scantly *t* for half the work. ,, 288
Tho' having seen all beauties of our *t*, ,, 498
Constrain'd us, but a better *t* has come; ,, 716
'O I that wasted *t* to tend upon her, *Geraint and E.* 38
in scarce longer *t* Than at Caerleon ,, 115
cursing their lost *t*, and the dead man, ,, 576
cry of children, Enids and Geraints Of *t's* to be; ,, 966
Groan'd, and at *t's* would mutter, *Balin and Balan* 173
From whence to watch the *t*, ,, 535
Many a *t* As once—of old—among the flowers— *Merlin and V.* 135
Arriving at a *t* of golden rest, ,, 142
the most famous man of all those *t's*, ,, 166
at *t's* Would flatter his own wish in age for love, ,, 184
for thus at *t's* He waver'd; ,, 186
Upon the great Enchanter of the *T*, ,, 216
It was the *t* when first the question rose ,, 410
nine tithes of *t's* Face-flatterer and backbiter ,, 823
when the *t* drew nigh Spake (for she had been sick) *Lancelot and E.* 77
Had marr'd his face, and mark'd it ere his *t*. ,, 247
with half disdain Hid under grace, as in a smaller *t*, ,, 264
Yea, twenty *t's* I thought him Lancelot— ,, 535
Fare you well A thousand *t's*—a thousand *t's* farewell! ,, 696
at *t's* Brain-feverous in his heat and agony, ,, 853
The simples and the science of that *t*, ,, 862
drave her ere her *t* across the fields ,, 890
he answer'd 'ten *t's* nay! This is not love: ,, 948
and at *t's*, So touch'd were they, ,, 1286
many a *t* have watch'd thee at the tilt ,, 1359
then the *t's* Grew to such evil that the holy cup *Holy Grail* 56
each of these a hundred winters old, From our Lord's *t*. ,, 89
beam of light seven *t's* more clear than day: ,, 187
But my *t* is hard at hand, And hence I go; ,, 481
Embraced me, and so kiss'd me the first *t*, ,, 596

Time (s) (*continued*) For every fiery prophet in old *t's*, *Holy Grail* 876
Come, as they will, and many a *t* they come, „ 911
'In happy *t* behold our pilot-star! *Pelleas and E.* 63
So for the last *t* she was gracious to him. „ 175
Modred thought, 'The *t* is hard at hand.' „ 610
in *t* the carcanet Vext her with plaintive memories *Last Tournament* 28
They served their use, their *t*; „ 676
Many a *t* for hours, Beside the placid breathings *Guinevere* 68
till her *t* To tell you:' „ 142
(for the *t* Was maytime, and as yet no sin „ 387
Bear with me for the last *t* while I show, „ 454
And be the fair beginning of a *t*. „ 466
Dwelt with them, till in *t* their Abbess died. „ 692
Shall never more, at any future *t*, *Pass. of Arthur* 186
And hid Excalibur the second *t*, „ 279
caught him by the hilt, and brandish'd him Three *t's*, (repeat) „ 314, 329
'tis *t* that I were gone. „ 331
For now I see the true old *t's* are dead, „ 397
Such *t's* have been not since the light „ 400
Touch'd by the adulterous finger of a *t* *To the Queen ii* 43
That saved her many *t's*, not fail— „ 62
For *T* and Grief abode too long with Life, *Lover's Tale i* 107
So *T* and Grief did beckon unto Death, „ 110
Yet is my life nor in the present *t*, „ 116
Heart beating *t* to heart, lip pressing lip, „ 260
that little hour was bound Shut in from *T*, „ 438
strait girth of *T* Inswathe the fulness of Eternity, „ 482
To centre in this place and *t*. „ 552
And heralded the distance of this *t*! „ 562
I seem'd the only part of *T* stood still, „ 573
Long *t* entrancement held me. „ 626
From that *t* forth I would not see her more; „ *ii* 1
(As I have seen them many a hundred *t's*) „ 145
ill-suited as it seem'd To such a *t*, „ *iv* 208
Laud me not Before my *t*, but hear me to the close. „ 243
Those were the pleasant *t's*, *First Quarrel* 41
in the pleasant *t's* that had past, „ 55
I was near my *t* wi' the boy, „ 82
little of us left by the *t* this sun be set.' *The Revenge* 28
For a dozen *t's* they came with their pikes and musqueteers, And a dozen *t's* we shook 'em off „ 53
That *t* I did not see. *Sisters (E. and E.)* 90
Straänge an' cowd fur the *t*! *Village Wife* 21
but the foe sprung his mine many *t's*, *Def. of Lucknow* 31
(My good friend By this *t* should be with me.) *Sir J. Oldcastle* 139
Set thee in light till *t* shall be no more? *Columbus* 150
Towers of a happier *t*, low down in a rainbow deep *V. of Maeldune* 79
O never was *t* so good! „ 87
And we came in an evil *t* to the Isle „ 105
finite-infinite space In finite-infinite *T*— *De Prof., Two G.* 46
the lost light of those dawn-golden *t's*, *To W. H. Brookfield* 7
for the sake Of one recalling gracious *t's*, *To E. Fitzgerald* 53
And mixt the dream of classic *t's* *Tiresias* 194
To women, the flower of the *t*, *The Wreck* 49
glory and shame dying out for ever in endless *t*, *Despair* 75
I have had some glimmer, at *t's*, „ 103
A Thousand summers ere the *t* of Christ *Ancient Sage* 1
cock has crow'd already once, he crows before his *t*; *The Flight* 3
Not he, not yet! and *t* to act— „ 73
many's the *t* that I watch'd her at mass *Tomorrow* 29
fur it mun be the *t* about now When Molly *Spinster's S's.* 1
Naäy to be sewer it be past 'er *t*. „ 5
triumphs over *t* and space, *Locksley H., Sixty* 75
Then, and here in Edward's *t*, „ 83
we range with Science, glorying in the *T*, „ 217
Lame and old, and past his *t*, „ 227
remember how the course of *T* will swerve, „ 235
The man in Space and *T*, *Epilogue* 49
Dead, who had served his *t*, *Dead Prophet* 9
Love is in and out of *t*, *Helen's Tower* 5
'Light—more Light—while *T* shall last!' *Epit. on Caxton* 1
At *t's* our Britain cannot rest, At *t's* her steps are swift and rash; *To Marq. of Dufferin* 1
But since your name will grow with *T*, „ 13

Time (s) (*continued*) Fifty *t's* the rose has flower'd and faded, Fifty *t's* the golden harvest fallen, *On Jub. Q. Victoria* 1
drew down before his *t* Sickening, *Demeter and P.* 114
fun' upo' four short legs ten *t's* fur one upo' two. *Owd Roä* 16
I thowt o' the good owd *t's* 'at was goan, „ 43
an' the *t's* 'at was coomin' on; „ 44
a jubilant challenge to *T* and to Fate; *Vastness* 21
Twelve *t's* in the year Bring me bliss, *The Ring* 5
Moon, you fade at *t's* From the night. „ 9
landscape which your eyes Have many a *t* ranged over „ 151
At *t's* too shrilling in her angrier moods, „ 395
Up, get up, the *t* is short, *Forlorn* 73
I tolerant of the colder *t*, *To Ulysses* 13
As I shall be forgotten by old *T*, *To Mary Boyle* 23
When Dives loathed the *t's*, „ 29
in their *t* thy warblers rise on wing. *Prog. of Spring* 108
The true Alcestis of the *t*. *Romney's R.* 91
a proof That I—even I—at *t's* remember'd *you*. „ 93
I sank with the body at *t's* in the sloughs *By an Evolution.* 18
At *t's* the small black fly upon the pane *To one who ran down Eng.* 3
Ever as of old *t*, Solitary firstling, *The Snowdrop* 3
Coming in the cold *t*, Prophet of the gay *t*, Prophet of the May *t*, „ 5
But in due *t* for every Mussulmân, *Akbar's Dream* 24
Still—at *t's* A doubt, a fear,— „ 168
even As in the *t* before; „ 191
in the flame that measures *T*! „ *Hymn* 8
They heard, they bided their *t*. *Bandit's Death* 14
there is *t* for the race to grow. *The Dawn* 20
that Eternal Harmony Whereto the worlds beat *t*, *D. of the Duke of C.* 16
For tho' from out our bourne of *T* and Place *Crossing the Bar* 13
Time (verb) Death's twin-brother, *t's* my breath; *In Mem. lxviii* 2
Timeless Kneel adoring Him the *T* *Akbar's D., Hymn* 8
Timid and said to him With *t* firmness, *Geraint and E.* 140
Amy loved me, Amy fail'd me, Amy was a *t* child; *Locksley H., Sixty* 19
Timing happy stars, *t* with things below, *Maud I xviii* 81
Timour-Mammon *T-M* grins on a pile of children's bones, „ *i* 46
Timur *T* built his ghastly tower of eighty *Locksley H., Sixty* 82
Tin polish'd *t's*, To serve the hot-and-hot; *Will Water.* 227
Tinct blazon'd on the shield In their own *t*, *Lancelot and E.* 10
Tinged *t* with wan from lack of sleep, *Princess iii* 25
Tingle and the nerves prick And *t*: *In Mem. l* 3
Tingling A cry that shiver'd to the *t* stars, *M. d'Arthur* 199
A cry that shiver'd to the *t* stars, *Pass. of Arthur* 367
Tinkled *See* **Low-tinkled**
Tinkling Now by some *t* rivulet, *Sir L. and Q. G.* 29
Nor rivulet *t* from the rock; *In Mem. c* 13
Here at the head of a *t* fall, *Maud I xxi* 6
Tinsel And shrill'd his *t* shaft. *Talking Oak* 68
Light coin, the *t* clink of compliment. *Princess ii* 55
Tint (s) days have vanish'd, tone and *t*, *In Mem. xliv* 5
Tint (verb) As light a flush As hardly *t's* the blossom *Balin and Balan* 267
Tintagil held *T* castle by the Cornish sea, *Com. of Arthur* 187
Uther in his wrath and heat besieged Ygerne within *T*, „ 199
on the night When Uther in *T* past away „ 367
by strong storm Blown into shelter at *T*, *Merlin and V.* 10
Perchance in lone *T* far from all The tonguesters *Last Tournament* 392
turning, past and gain'd *T*, half in sea, „ 505
sands Of dark *T* by the Cornish sea; *Guinevere* 294
Tinted *See* **Rosy-tinted**
Tiny Claps her *t* hands above me, *Lilian* 4
Annie from her baby's forehead clipt A *t* curl, and gave it: *Enoch Arden* 236
Or from the *t* pitted target blew *Aylmer's Field* 93
She tapt her *t* silken-sandal'd foot: *Princess, Pro.* 150
a *t* poem All composed in a metre of Catullus, *Hendecasyllabics* 3
The *t* cell is forlorn, *Maud II ii* 13
Save that one rivulet from a *t* cave *Pelleas and E.* 425
whereon There tript a hundred *t* silver deer, *Last Tournament* 171
t fist Had graspt a daisy from your Mother's grave— *The Ring* 322
The starling claps his *t* castanets. *Prog. of Spring* 56
Will my *t* spark of being wholly vanish *God and the Univ.* 1
Tiny-trumpeting The *t-t* gnat can break our dream *Lancelot and E.* 137

Tip (*See also* **Finger-tips**) thro' her to the *t's* of her long hands, — *Princess ii* 40
Thy gloom is kindled at the *t's*, — *In Mem. xxxix* 11
Tipmost to *t* lance and topmost helm, — *Last Tournament* 442
Tipt And *t* with frost-like spires. — *Palace of Art* 52
with their fires Love *t* his keenest darts; — *D. of F. Women* 173
t with lessening peak And pinnacle, — *Gareth and L.* 308
and *t* With trenchant steel, — „ 692
spear and helmet *t* With stormy light — *Tiresias* 113
Tip-tilted *T-t* like the petal of a flower; — *Gareth and L.* 591
Tiptoe on every peak a statue seem'd To hang on *t*, — *Palace of Art* 38
On *t* seem'd to touch upon a sphere — *Princess vii* 324
Tire Bore and forebore, and did not *t*, — *Two Voices* 218
For a love that never *t's*? — *Window, Marr. Morn.* 18
But mine the love that will not *t*, — *In Mem. cx* 18
Tired *t* out With cutting eights that day — *The Epic* 9
Than *t* eyelids upon *t* eyes; — *Lotos-Eaters, C. S.* 6
At last, *t* out with play, — *Talking Oak* 206
Ascending *t*, heavily slept till morn. — *Enoch Arden* 181
'*T*, Annie?' for she did not speak a word. — „ 390
'*T*?' but her face had fall'n upon her hands; — „ 391
T of so much within our little life, — *Lucretius* 226
I began to be *t* a little, — *Grandmother* 74
I seem to be *t* a little, — „ 99
Tirra lirra '*T l*,' by the river Sang Sir Lancelot. — *L. of Shalott iii* 35
Tissue In silver *t* talking things of state; — *Marr. of Geraint* 663
Tit tumble the blossom, the mad little *t's*! — *Window, Ay* 9
T's, wrens, and all wing'd nothings peck — *Marr. of Geraint* 275
glance the *t's*, and shriek the jays, — *Prog. of Spring* 15
Titan (adj.) Whose *T* angels, Gabriel, Abdiel, — *Milton* 5
Titan (s) The pulses of a *T's* heart; — *In Mem. ciii* 32
Weird *T* by thy winter weight of years — *To Victor Hugo* 7
Titanic *T* forces taking birth In divers seasons, — *Day Dm., L'Envoi* 17
T shapes, they cramm'd The forum, — *Princess vii* 124
Tithe (church rate) (*See also* **Toithe**) paid our *t's* in the days that are gone, — *Maud II v* 23
Fur moäst on 'em talks ageän *t*, — *Church-warden, etc.* 52
Tithe (tenth part) nine *t's* of times Face-flatterer and backbiter — *Merlin and V.* 823
Wasted and worn, and but a *t* of them, — *Holy Grail* 723
And a lean Order—scarce return'd a *t*— — „ 894
When I landed again, with a *t* of my men, — *V. of Maeldune* 130
Titian I am not Raphaël, *T*—no — *Romney's R.* 46
Titianic in hues to dim The *T* Flora. — *Gardener's D.* 171
Title Nor toil for *t*, place, or touch Of pension, — *Love thou thy land* 25
New as his *t*, built last year, — *Maud I x* 19
a Prince indeed, Beyond all *t's*, — *Ded. of Idylls* 42
her name And *t*, 'Queen of Beauty,' — *Pelleas and E.* 116
heirless flaw In his throne's *t* — *Sir J. Oldcastle* 73
Our *t*, which we never mean to yield, — *Columbus* 32
scarce have learnt the *t* of your book, — *The Ring* 126
Title-scroll *t-s's* and gorgeous heraldries. — *Aylmer's Field* 656
Titmouse *t* hope to win her With his chirrup — *Maud I xx* 29
Titter and then A strangled *t*, — *Princess v* 16
Tityrus Poet of the happy *T* piping underneath — *To Virgil* 13
To-and-fro commenced A *t-a-f*, so pacing — *Princess ii* 302
'Toättler (teetotaler) Doctor's a '*t*, lass, — *N. Farmer, O. S.* 66
To-be Dispensing harvest, sowing the *T-b*, — *Princess vii* 289
Thro' all the secular *t-b*, — *In Mem. xli* 23
To-come and all the rich *t-c* Reels, — *Princess vii* 356
To-daay (to-day) As I says to my missis *t-d*, — *Church-warden, etc.* 25
Todaäy (to-day) Seeäd her *t* goä by— — *N. Farmer, N. S.* 13
To-day (*See also* **To-daay, Todaäy**) To-morrow yet would reap *t-d*, — *Love thou thy land* 93
'*T-d* I saw the dragon-fly — *Two Voices* 8
Herè comes *t-d*, Pallas and Aphroditè, — *Œnone* 85
I care not if I go *t-d*. — *May Queen, Con.* 43
'The sequel of *t-d* unsolders all — *M. d'Arthur* 14
I die here *T-d*, and whole years long, — *St. S. Stylites* 54
T-d I sat for an hour and wept, — *Edward Gray* 11
Cruelly came they back *t-d*: — „ 18
T-d the Lady Psyche will harangue — *Princess ii* 95
to slip away *T-d*, to-morrow, soon: — „ 297
And told me she would answer us *t-d*, — „ *iii* 166
Let us dream our dream *t-d*. — *Ode Inter. Exhib.* 31

To-day (*continued*) See, empire upon empire smiles *t-d*, — *W. to Marie Alex.* 33
All along the valley, while I walk'd *t-d*, — *V. of Cauteretz* 5
Be merry, all birds, *t-d*, — *Window, Ay* 1
thinking 'here *t-d*,' Or 'here to-morrow — *In Mem. vi* 23
That thou hadst touch'd the land *t-d*, — „ *xiv* 2
Nor will it lessen from *t-d*; — „ *lix* 10
T-d they count as kindred souls; — „ *xcix* 19
That has *t-d* its sunny side. — „ *Con.* 72
T-d the grave is bright for me, — „ 73
Strange, that *I* tried *t-d* To beguile her — *Maud I xx* 2
So well thine arm hath wrought for me *t-d*.' — *Com. of Arthur* 127
By this King Arthur as by thee *t-d*, — „ 162
'Forward! and *t-d* I charge you, — *Geraint and E.* 413
A man of thine *t-d* Abash'd us both, — *Balin and Balan* 70
'Eyes have I That saw *t-d* the shadow of a spear, — „ 373
He cares not for me: only here *t-d* — *Lancelot and E.* 126
grace to me,' She answer'd, 'twice *t-d*. — „ 384
So great a knight as we have seen *t-d*— — „ 533
speak your wish, Seeing I go *t-d*:' — „ 925
But who first saw the holy thing *t-d*?' — *Holy Grail* 67
hence he went *T-d* for three days' hunting— — *Last Tournament* 530
'The sequel of *t-d* unsolders all — *Pass. of Arthur* 182
Thrust froward on *t-d* and out of place; — *Lover's Tale i* 123
As here *t-d*, but not so wordily— — „ *iv* 355
'O worms and maggots of *t-d* — *Ancient Sage* 210
T-d? but what of yesterday? — „ 216
There again I stood *t-d*, — *Locksley H., Sixty* 33
Here *t-d* was Amy with me, — „ 53
Those eyes the blue *t-d*, — *Epilogue* 9
happier lot Than ours, who rhyme *t-d*. — „ 51
The days that seem *t-d*, — *Pref. Poem Broth. Son.* 24
Miriam, breaks her latest earthy link With me *t-d*. — *The Ring* 48
For I myself would tell you all *t-d*. — „ 124
'She too might speak *t-d*,' — „ 125
Ay, *t-d*! I brought you to that chamber — „ 128
but close to me *t-d* As this red rose, — *Roses on the T.* 6
T-d, before you turn again To thoughts — *To Master of B.* 13
and wield The forces of *t-d*, — *Mechanophilus* 30
Toddle Poor little life that *t's* half an hour — *Lucretius* 228
Toil (s) But enter not the *t* of life. — *Margaret* 24
And one, the reapers at their sultry *t*. — *Palace of Art* 77
Making sweet close of his delicious *t's*— — „ 185
Ripens and fades, and falls, and hath no *t*, — *Lotos-Eaters, C. S.* 37
and reap the harvest with enduring *t*, — „ 121
surely, slumber is more sweet than *t*, — „ 126
a Rose In roses, mingled with her fragrant *t*, — *Gardener's D.* 143
Old age hath yet his honour and his *t*; — *Ulysses* 50
I must work thro' months of *t*, — *Amphion* 97
And mutual love and honourable *t*; — *Enoch Arden* 83
On with *t* of heart and knees and hands, — *Ode on Well.* 212
O thou that after *t* and storm — *In Mem. xxxiii* 1
Is *t* cöoperant to an end. — „ *cxxviii* 24
As careful robins eye the delver's *t*, — *Marr. of Geraint* 774
As careful robins eye the delver's *t*; — *Geraint and E.* 431
body journeying onward, sick with *t*. — *Lover's Tale i* 124
T and ineffable weariness, — *Def. of Lucknow* 90
If night, what barren *t* to be! — *Tiresias* 207
Toil (verb) I said, 'I *t* beneath the curse, — *Two Voices* 229
why should we *t* alone, We only *t*, — *Lotos-Eaters, C. S.* 15
Why should we only *t*, — „ 24
Nor *t* for title, place, or touch Of pension, — *Love thou thy land* 25
Who *t's* across the middle moonlit nights, — *Lover's Tale i* 138
Toil'd *T* onward, prick'd with goads and stings; — *Palace of Art* 150
Souls that have *t*, and wrought, — *Ulysses* 46
t Mastering the lawless science of our law, — *Aylmer's Field* 434
Has often *t* to clothe your little ones; — „ 699
Toiling late and soon Spins, *t* out his own cocoon. — *Two Voices* 180
A motion *t* in the gloom— — *Love thou thy land* 54
T in immeasurable sand, — *Will* 16
Of loyal vassals *t* for their liege. — *Com. of Arthur* 282
Toime (time) i' the woost o' *t's* I wur niver — *N. Farmer, O. S.* 16
Toithe (tithe) an's *t* were due, an' I gied it in hond; — „ 11
an' ageän the *t* an' the raäte, — *Church-warden, etc.* 11
Token There came a sweeter *t* when the night — *May Queen, Con.* 22

Token (*continued*) There came a mystic *t* from the king *Edwin Morris* 132
It will moreover be a *t* to her, That I am he.' *Enoch Arden* 900
Sunny *t's* of the Line, *Ode Inter. Exhib.* 19
Who show'd a *t* of distress? *In Mem. lxxviii* 13
In *t* of true heart and fealty. *Gareth and L.* 399
pray the King To let me bear some *t* of his Queen *Balin and Balan* 188
Thro' memory of that *t* on the shield „ 369
then he bound Her *t* on h s helmet, *Lancelot and E.* 374
know When these have worn their *t's*: „ 769

Told (*See also* **Re-told, Tell'd, Tould, Towd**) I *t* thee—hardly nigher made, *Two Voices* 173
Sweet Alice, if I *t* her all?' *Miller's D.* 120
My love hath *t* me so a thousand times. *Œnone* 197
the clergyman, has *t* me words of peace. *May Queen, Con.* 12
wheresoever I am sung or *t* In aftertime, *M. d'Arthur* 34
And *t* me I should love. *Gardener's D.* 64
The cuckoo *t* his name to all the hills; „ 93
This is not *t* of any. They were saints. *St. S. Stylites* 151
And *t* him of my choice, *Talking Oak* 18
and that same song of his He *t* me; *Golden Year* 8
She *t* him of their tears, And pray'd him, *Godiva* 19
And *t* him all her nurse's tale. *Lady Clare* 80
She *t* me all her friends had said; *The Letters* 25
T him, with other annals of the port, *Enoch Arden* 702
tho' Miriam Lane had *t* him all, „ 765
Then he *t* her of his voyage, His wreck, „ 861
'She *t* me. She and James had quarrell'd. *The Brook* 96
he *t* a long long-winded tale Of how the Squire „ 138
And been himself a part of what he *t*. *Aylmer's Field* 12
t her fairy-tales, Show'd her the fairy footings „ 89
as he *t* The story, storming a hill-fort „ 224
praised the waning red, and *t* The vintage— „ 406
Then she *t* it, having dream'd Of that same coast. *Sea Dreams* 206
My golden work in which I *t* a truth *Lucretius* 260
but we, unworthier, *t* Of college: *Princess, Pro.* 110
And often *t* a tale from mouth to mouth „ 191
have him back Who *t* the 'Winter's tale' „ 238
But your example pilot, *t* her all. „ *iii* 137
But such extremes, I *t* her, well might harm „ 144
And *t* me she would answer us to-day, „ 166
How came you here?' I *t* him: „ *iv* 221
And me none *t*: not less to an eye like mine „ 324
you had gone to her, She *t*, perforce; „ 330
Go: Cyril *t* us all.' „ *v* 36
now a pointed finger, *t* them all: „ 270
And so I often *t* her, right or wrong, „ 288
I *t* the king that I was pledged To fight „ 352
if I saw not, yet they *t* me all „ *vi* 20
who might have *t*, For she was cramm'd „ *Con.* 34
you *t* us all That England's honest censure *Third of Feb.* 1
It *t* of England then to me, *The Daisy* 89
These have *t* us all their anger *Boädicea* 23
There was one who watch'd and *t* me— „ 30
He *t* it not; or something seal'd *In Mem. xxxi* 15
And tell them all they would have *t*, „ *xl* 25
He *t* me, lives in any crowd, „ *xcviii* 26
Since first he *t* me that he loved „ *Con.* 6
What if he had *t* her yestermorn *Maud I vi* 50
Who *t* *him* we were there? „ *II v* 52
Horrible, hateful, monstrous, not to be *t*; „ *III vi* 41
when I enter'd *t* me that himself And Merlin *Com. of Arthur* 364
nor could I part in peace Till this were *t*.' „ 394
That God hath *t* the King a secret word. „ 489
Take thou the truth as thou hast *t* it me. *Gareth and L.* 257
t, How once the wandering forester at dawn, „ 497
he sought The King alone, and found, and *t* him all. „ 541
And *t* him of a cavern hard at hand, „ 1189
turning to Lynette he *t* The tale of Gareth, „ 1272
And he that *t* the tale in older times „ 1427
But he, that *t* it later, says Lynette. „ 1429
T Enid, and they sadden'd her the more: *Marr. of Geraint* 64
journey to her, as himself Had *t* her, „ 144
these things he *t* the King. „ 151
Who *t* him, scouring still, 'The sparrow-hawk!' „ 260

Told (*continued*) And *t* her all their converse in the hall, *Marr. of Geraint* 520
journey toward her, as himself Had *t* her, „ 846
the boy return'd And *t* them of a chamber, *Geraint and E.* 261
t Free tales, and took the word and play'd „ 290
She *t* him all that Earl Limours had said, „ 391
nor *t* his gentle wife What ail'd him, „ 503
then he plainlier *t* How the huge Earl lay slain „ 805
therewithal (for thus he *t* us) brought *Balin and Balan* 112
Then Balan *t* him brokenly, and in gasps, „ 603
this good knight *T* me, that twice a wanton damsel „ 609
For Merlin once had *t* her of a charm, *Merlin and V.* 205
Than when I *t* you first of such a charm. „ 359
Too much I trusted when I *t* you that, „ 361
'O crueller than was ever *t* in tale, „ 858
t her all the charm, and slept. „ 966
What is it? and she *t* him 'A red sleeve Broider'd with pearls,' *Lancelot and E.* 372
Than Lancelot *t* me of a common talk „ 577
there *t* the King What the King knew, „ 706
But when the maid had *t* him all her tale, „ 798
And when the maid had *t* him all the tale „ 823
T him that her fine care had saved his life. „ 863
I *t* her that her love Was but the flash of youth, „ 1317
T us of this in our refectory, *Holy Grail* 41
And he to whom she *t* her sins, or what „ 83
'O brother, when I *t* him what had chanced, „ 271
To whom I *t* my phantoms, and he said: „ 444
T him he follow'd—almost Arthur's words— „ 669
So when I *t* him all thyself hast heard, „ 736
'Lo! Pelleas is dead—he *t* us— *Pelleas and E.* 377
Sir Lancelot *t* This matter to the Queen, *Guinevere* 53
Vivien, lurking, heard. She *t* Sir Modred. „ 99
Nor with them mix'd, nor *t* her name, „ 148
and the tales Which my good father *t* me, „ 317
T, when the man was no more than a voice *Pass. of Arthur* 3
wheresoever I am sung or *t* In aftertime, „ 202
Once or twice she *t* me (For I remember all things) *Lover's Tale i* 345
The wind *T* a lovetale beside us, „ 543
What marvel my Camilla *t* me all? (repeat) „ 557, 579
She *t* me all her love: she shall not weep. „ 742
Unfrequent, low, as tho' it *t* its pulses; „ *ii* 55
Some one had *t* me she was dead, „ 70
I *t* him all my love, How I had loved her „ 90
but of this I deem As of the visions that he *t*— „ *iv* 23
(They *t* her somewhat rashly as I think) „ 98
(I *t* you that he had his golden hour), „ 206
till he *t* me that so many years had gone by, *First Quarrel* 36
An' he *t* it me all at once, as simple as any child, „ 58
and he never has *t* me a lie. *Rizpah* 24
I *t* them my tale, God's own truth— „ 33
they have *t* you he never repented his sin. „ 69
Then *t* them of his wars, and of his wound. *Sisters (E. and E.)* 60
I *t* your wayside story to my mother And Evelyn. „ 189
And *t* the living daughter with what love „ 253
'All the more need,' I *t* him, *In the Child. Hosp.* 18
their marksmen were *t* of our best, *Def. of Lucknow* 19
is it true what was *t* by the scout, „ 95
tale, that *t* to me, When but thine age, *Tiresias* 18
souls of men were immortal, as men have been *t*, *Despair* 99
And then he *t* their legend: *The Ring* 206
I *t* her 'sent To Miriam,' „ 362
I *t* her of my vow, „ 401
I have *t* you my tale. Get you gone. *Charity* 44

Told-of and cursed the tale, The *t-o*, *Balin and Balan* 543

Tolerance must have rated her Beyond all *t*. *Aylmer's Field* 381
This Gama swamp'd in lazy *t*. *Princess v* 443

Tolerant *T* of what he half disdain'd, *Merlin and V.* 178
I *t* of the colder time, *To Ulysses* 13

Toll (s) 'Honour,' she said, 'and homage, tax and *t*, *Œnone* 116
With silks, and fruits, and spices, clear of *t*, *Golden Year* 45
The *t* of funeral in an Angel ear *D. of the Duke of C.* 10

Toll (verb) *T* ye the church-bell sad and slow, *D. of the O. Year* 3
One set slow bell will seem to *t* *In Mem. lvii* 10
Would you could *t* me out of life, *Lover's Tale iv* 30

Toll (verb) (*continued*) when they *t* the Chapel bell! *Locksley H., Sixty* 261
Toll'd like a bell *T* by an earthquake in a trembling tower, *Princess vi* 332
Let the bell be *t*. (repeat) *Ode on Well.* 46, 53, 58
by slow degrees the sullen bell *T* quicker, *Lover's Tale iii* 14
Tolling thence at intervals A low bell *t*. „ *ii* 83
Then came on me The hollow *t* of the bell, „ *iii* 10
Heard yet once more the *t* bell, „ *iv* 29
For that low knell *t* his lady dead— „ 33
t of his funeral bell Broke on my Pagan Paradise, *Tiresias* 192
Bridal bells with *t*! . . . *Forlorn* 70
Tom (name of men and cats) (*See also* **Tommy**) *T*, lig theere o' the cushion, an' tother *T* 'ere o' the mat. *Spinster's S's.* 94
Sweäring agean, you *T's*, „ 59
Tomb Shut up as in a crumbling *t*, *Palace of Art* 273
And in the moon athwart the place of *t's*, *M. d'Arthur* 46
rising bore him thro' the place of *t's*. „ 175
Shall hold their orgies at your *t*. *You might have won* 12
Remains the lean P. W. on his *t*: *The Brook* 192
her, that is the womb and *t* of all, *Lucretius* 244
near his *t* a feast Shone, silver-set; *Princess, Pro.* 105
her empty glove upon the *t* Lay by her „ *iv* 596
I go to plant it on his *t*, *In Mem. viii* 22
In that deep dawn behind the *t*, „ *xlvi* 6
My old affection of the *t*, (repeat) „ *lxxxv* 75,77
As it were a duty done to the *t*, *Maud I xix* 49
' Let her *t* Be costly, and her image thereupon, *Lancelot and E.* 1339
all true hearts be blazon'd on her *t* In letters gold and azure!' „ 1344
And in the moon athwart the place of *t's*, *Pass. of Arthur* 214
rising bore him thro' the place of *t's*. „ 343
break down and raze The blessed *t* of Christ; *Columbus* 99
I was planted now in a *t*; *The Wreck* 37
And growing, on her *t*, *Ancient Sage* 164
heard in silence from the silence of a *t*. *Locksley H., Sixty* 74
Angel seated in the vacant *t*. „ 278
I peer'd thro' *t* and cave, *Demeter and P.* 70
' Among the *t's* in this damp vale of yours! *The Ring* 325
Tombing The blackness round the *t* sod, *On a Mourner* 27
Tome at a board by *t* and paper sat, *Princess ii* 32
Tommy (lovers and cats) (*See also* **Tom**) *T* the fust, an' *T* the second, *Spinster's S's.* 10
and one o' the *Tommies* beside. „ 40
I mun part them *Tommies*— „ 92
Hed I married the *Tommies*—O Lord, „ 95
To loove an' obaäy the *Tommies*! „ 96
You *Tommies* shall waäit to-night „ 120
Tommy (name of boy) *T's* faäce be as fresh as a codlin *North. Cobbler* 110
'Ere be our Sally an' *T*, „ 111
Tomohrit *T*, Athos, all things fair, *To E. L.* 5
Tomorra (to-morrow) ye gev her the top of the mornin', ' *T* ' says she. *Tomorrow* 3
I'll meet you agin *t*,' says he, „ 16
ye'll meet me *t*?' ' *T*, *t*, Machree!' „ 18
an' whishper, an' say ' *T*, *T*!' „ 55
' *T*, *T*,' she says, an' she didn't intind „ 59
' He said he would meet me *t*!' „ 80
To-morrow (*See also* **Morrow, Tomorra**) I come *t-m* morn. ' I go, but I return: *Audley Court* 70
We two will wed *t-m* morn, *Lady Clare* 87
We hold a tourney here *t-m* morn, *Marr. of Geraint* 287
T-m 'ill be the happiest time of all the glad New-year; (repeat) *May Queen* 2, 42
Effie shall go with me *t-m* to the green, „ 25
T-m 'ill be of all the year the maddest merriest day, „ 43
T-m yet would reap to-day, *Love thou thy land* 93
' *T-m* he weds with me.' *Lady Clare* 16
to slip away To-day, *t-m*, soon: *Princess ii* 297
' *T-m*, love, *t-m*, And that's an age away.' *Window, When* 13
thinking, ' here to-day,' Or ' here *t-m* *In Mem. vi* 24
But *t-m*, if we live, *Maud I xx* 23
Lancelot, sitting in my place Enchair'd *t-m*, *Last Tournament* 104
Hail, King! *T-m* thou shalt pass away. *Pass. of Arthur* 34
I'll come for an hour *t-m*, *First Quarrel* 46
Nurse, I must do it *t-m*; *In the Child. Hosp.* 42

To-morrow (*continued*) Not to-night in Locksley Hall—*t-m*— *Locksley H., Sixty* 214
Here to-night, the Hall *t-m*, „ 261
Tomyris bronze valves, emboss'd with *T* *Princess v* 365
Ton Than were those lead-like *t's* of sin, *St. S. Stylites* 25
San Philip that, of fifteen hundred *t's*, *The Revenge* 40
Tone (*See also* **Under-tone**) Wears all day a fainter *t*. *The Owl ii* 7
Sweeter *t's* than calumny? *A Dirge* 17
Ah pity—hint it not in human *t's*, *Wan Sculptor* 11
' O cruel heart,' she changed her *t*, *Mariana in the S.* 69
' He heeded not reviling *t's*, *Two Voices* 220
All day the wind breathes low with mellower *t*: *Lotos-Eaters, C. S.* 102
fall down and glance From *t* to *t*, *D. of F. Women* 167
it was the *t* with which he read— *M. d'Arthur, Ep.* 5
Swung themselves, and in low *t's* replied; *Vision of Sin* 20
There to herself, all in low *t's*, she read. *Princess vii* 175
To one clear harp in divers *t's*, *In Mem. i* 2
With all the music in her *t*, „ *iii* 10
The days have vanish'd, *t* and tint, „ *xliv* 5
He past; a soul of nobler *t*: „ *lx* 1
Perhaps the smile and tender *t* *Maud I vi* 63
Then the King in low deep *t's*, *Com. of Arthur* 260
she tower'd her bells, *T* under *t*, shrill'd; *Merlin and V.* 132
Then came her father, saying in low *t's*, *Lancelot and E.* 994
Is this the *t* of empire? *To the Queen ii* 18
in the utterance Of silver-chorded *t's*: *Lover's Tale ii* 142
a *t* so rough that I broke into passionate tears, *The Wreck* 122
Toned *See* **Full-toned, Heavenly-toned, Low-toned, Richest-toned**
Tongue (s) Thou of the many *t's*, the myriad eyes! *Ode to Memory* 47
Like Indian reeds blown from his silver *t*, *The Poet* 13
My tremulous *t* faltereth, *Eleänore* 136
For Kate hath an unbridled *t*, *Kate* 7
' When, wide in soul and bold of *t*, *Two Voices* 124
Blowing a noise of *t's* and deeds, „ 206
To feel, altho' no *t* can prove, „ 445
That run before the fluttering *t's* of fire; *D. of F. Women* 30
A golden bill! the silver *t*, *The Blackbird* 13
and servile to a shrewish *t*! *Locksley Hall* 42
'Tis said he had a tuneful *t*, *Amphion* 17
Let me loose thy *t* with wine: *Vision of Sin* 88
' Fear not thou to loose thy *t*; „ 155
But in a *t* no man can understand; „ 222
I would that my *t* could utter The thoughts *Break, break, etc.* 3
his long-bounden *t* Was loosen'd, *Enoch Arden* 644
Fairer his talk, a *t* that ruled the hour, *Aylmer's Field* 194
My *t* Trips, or I speak profanely. *Lucretius* 73
Not in this frequence can I lend full *t*, *Princess iv* 442
And every spoken *t* should lord you. „ 544
On flying Time from all their silver *t's*— „ *vii* 105
his triumph will be sung By some yet unmoulded *t* *Ode on Well.* 233
Far, how far no *t* can say, *Ode Inter. Exhib.* 30
strong on his legs, but still of his *t*! *Grandmother* 13
t is a fire as you know, my dear, the *t* „ 28
Whatever fickle *t's* may say. *In Mem. xxvi* 4
To flicker with his double *t*. „ *cx* 8
seem'd to live A contradiction on the *t*, „ *cxxv* 4
That made my *t* so stammer and trip *Maud I vi* 83
With the evil *t* and the evil ear, „ *x* 51
Let not my *t* be a thrall to my eye, „ *xvi* 32
words, Beyond my *t* to tell thee— *Com. of Arthur* 269
Graven in the oldest *t* of all this world, „ 302
And Uther slit thy *t*: *Gareth and L.* 376
I curse the *t* that all thro' yesterday Reviled thee, „ 1322
as a man upon his *t* May break it, *Geraint and E.* 42
man, who driven by evil *t's* From all his fellows, *Balin and Balan* 125
as the man in life Was wounded by blind *t's* he saw not „ 130
Woods have *t's*, As walls have ears: „ 530
neither eyes nor *t*—O stupid child! *Merlin and V.* 251
yet, methinks Thy *t* has tript a little: „ 602
and let her *t* Rage like a fire „ 801
heathen caught and reft him of his *t*. *Lancelot and E.* 273
prick'd at once, all *t's* were loosed: „ 724
such a *t* To blare its own interpretation— „ 942
rain a scroll Of letters in a *t* no man could read. *Holy Grail* 171

Tongue (s) *(continued)* With supplication both of knees and *t*: *Holy Grail* 602
given thee a fair face, Lacking a *t*? ' *Pelleas and E.* 102
Queen, May help them, loose thy *t*, and let me know.' „ 600
Yet strangers to the *t*, and with blunt stamp *Last Tournament* 66
lock up my *t* From uttering freely „ 693
good nuns would check her gadding *t* *Guinevere* 313
This *t* that wagg'd They said with such heretical arrogance *Sir J. Oldcastle* 14
Must learn to use the *t's* of all the world. „ 34
Who finds the Saviour in his mother *t*. „ 115
speaking clearly in thy native *t*—No Latin— „ 133
the men that were mighty of *t* *V. of Maeldune* 23
Of diverse *t*, but with a common will *Pref. Son. 19th Cent.* 6
their *t's* may have babbled of me— *The Wreck* 41
Nor roll thy viands on a luscious *t* *Ancient Sage* 267
a single race, a single *t*— *Locksley H., Sixty* 165
Unfurnish'd brows, tempestuous *t's*— *Freedom* 38
But Moother was free of 'er *t*, *Owd Roä* 73
waste and field and town of alien *t*, *St. Telemachus* 30
Tha'd niver not hopple thy *t*, an' the *t's* sit afire o' Hell, *Church-warden, etc.* 24
Tongue (verb) Whose echo shall not *t* thy glorious doom, *Tiresias* 136
Tongue-banger Sally she turn'd a *t-b*, *North. Cobbler* 23
Tongued *See* **Dry-tongued, Low-tongued**
Tongueless then turn'd the *t* man From the half-face to the full eye, *Lancelot and E.* 1261
Tonguester (adj.) madden'd to the height By *t* tricks, *To Mary Boyle* 34
Tonguester (s) far from all The *t's* of the court *Last Tournament* 393
thro' the *t's* we may fall. *Locksley H., Sixty* 130
Tongue-tied A *t-t* Poet in the feverous days, *Golden Year* 10
And thus *t-t*, it made him wroth the more *Geraint and E.* 112
To-night *T-n* I saw the sun set: *May Queen, N. Y's. E.* 5
I go *t-n*: I come to-morrow morn, *Audley Court* 70
I prophesy that I shall die *t-n*, *St. S. Stylites* 220
'Tho' I should die *t-n*.' *Lady Clare* 48
how pale she had look'd Darling, *t-n*! *Aylmer's Field* 380
Why were you silent when I spoke *t-n*? *Sea Dreams* 268
t-n—the song Might have been worse *Princess iv* 250
Sweet dream, be perfect. I shall die *t-n*. „ *vii* 149
if *t-n* our greatness were struck dead, *Third of Feb.* 17
Yet here *t-n* in this dark city, *The Daisy* 95
For he will see them on *t-n*; *In Mem. vi* 33
T-n the winds begin to rise „ *xv* 1
T-n ungather'd let us leave „ *cv* 1
Who rest *t-n* beside the sea. „ *Con.* 76
Her brother is coming back *t-n* *Maud I xix* 1
On my fresh hope, to the Hall *t-n*. „ 103
'Ah, be Among the roses *t-n*.' „ *xxi* 13
Leave me *t-n*: I am weary to the death.' *Geraint and E.* 358
And yet *t-n*, *t-n*—when all my wealth *Lover's Tale i* 668
I propose *t-n* To show you what is dearest „ *iv* 251
I have here *t-n* a guest So bound to me „ 344
an' go *t-n* by the boat.' *First Quarrel* 88
Why should he call me *t-n*, *Rizpah* 3
But I go *t-n* to my boy, „ 74
Molly belike may 'a lighted *t-n* upo' one. *Spinster's S's.* 7
You Tommies shall waäit *t-n* „ 120
Not *t-n* in Locksley Hall— *Locksley H., Sixty* 214
Not the Hall *t-n*, my grandson! „ 237
Here *t-n*! the Hall to-morrow, „ 261
FAREWELL, Macready, since *t-n* we part; *To W. C. Macready* 1
Set the mountain aflame *t-n*, *On Jub. Q. Victoria* 16
'can ya paäy me the rent *t-n*?' *Owd Roä* 57
'Then hout *t-n* tha shall goä.' „ 58
'what has darken'd thee *t-n*?' *Akbar's Dream* 2
Tonsured A *t* head in middle age forlorn, *The Brook* 200
Tonup (turnip) Whoäts or *t's* or taätes— *Village Wife* 26
Goan into mangles an' *t's*, *Owd Roä* 28
t's was haäfe on 'em fingers an' toäs, *Church-warden, etc.* 4
Too-earnest Nor look with that *t-e* eye— *Day-Dm., Pro.* 18
Too-fearful *t-f* guilt, Simpler than any child, *Guinevere* 370
Took *(See also* **Taäked, Tuk**) So *t* echo with delight, (repeat) *The Owl ii* 4
Cleaving, *t* root, and springing forth anew *The Poet* 21
And *t* the reed-tops as it went. *Dying Swan* 10

Took *(continued)* *t* the soul Of that waste place with joy *Dying Swan* 21
'Who *t* a wife, who rear'd his race, *Two Voices* 328
those great Bells Began to chime. She *t* her throne: *Palace of Art* 158
great delight and shuddering *t* hold of all my mind, *May Queen, Con.* 35
He *t* the goose upon his arm, *The Goose* 41
I row'd across And *t* it, and have worn it, *M. d'Arthur* 33
Then *t* with care, and kneeling on one knee, „ 173
Put forth their hands, and *t* the King, „ 206
Yet for the pleasure that I *t* to hear, *Gardener's D.* 228
Dora *t* the child, and went her way *Dora* 71
she rose and *t* The child once more, „ 80
he *t* the boy that cried aloud And struggled hard. „ 101
Dora said, 'My uncle *t* the boy; „ 114
as years Went forward, Mary *t* another mate; „ 171
As one by one we *t* them— *Walk. to the Mail* 95
We *t* them all, till she was left alone „ 98
'I *t* the swarming sound of life— *Talking Oak* 213
Why *t* ye not your pastime? *Love and Duty* 28
Love himself *t* part against himself „ 45
with a frolic welcome *t* The thunder and the sunshine, *Ulysses* 47
Love *t* up the glass of Time, *Locksley Hall* 31
Love *t* up the harp of Life, „ 33
she *t* the tax away And built herself an everlasting name. *Godiva* 78
'Then I *t* a pencil, and wrote On the mossy stone, *Edward Gray* 25
She *t* the little ivory chest, *The Letters* 17
And *t* him by the curls, and led him in, *Vision of Sin* 6
Enoch *t*, and handled all his limbs, *Enoch Arden* 153
when their casks were fill'd they *t* aboard: „ 646
he *t* Her blind and shuddering puppies, *The Brook* 129
still *T* joyful note of all things joyful, *Aylmer's Field* 67
innocent hare Falter before he *t* it. „ 491
Seized it, *t* home, and to my lady,— „ 532
So false, he partly *t* himself for true; *Sea Dreams* 185
So never *t* that useful name in vain, „ 189
the master *t* Small notice, or austerely, *Lucretius* 7
the maiden Aunt *T* this fair day for text, *Princess, Pro.* 108
And there we *t* one tutor as to read: „ 179
they saw the King; he *t* the gifts; „ *i* 46
she *t* A bird's-eye-view of all ungracious past; „ *ii* 124
He *t* advantage of his strength to be „ 152
T both his hands, and smiling faintly said: „ 304
We turn'd to go, but Cyril *t* the child, „ 362
We *t* this palace; but even from the first „ *iv* 313
dispatches which the Head *T* half-amazed, „ 380
She *t* it and she flung it. „ 598
then *t* the king His three broad sons; „ *v* 268
I *t* it for an hour in mine own bed This morning: „ 434
I *t* my leave, for it was nearly noon: „ 468
T the face-cloth from the face; „ *vi* 11
she *t* it: Pretty bud! Lily of the vale! „ 192
for she *t* no part In our dispute: „ *Con.* 29
What more? We *t* our last adieu, *The Daisy* 85
Our voices *t* a higher range; *In Mem. xxx* 21
In those sad words I *t* farewell: „ *lviii* 1
I *t* the thorns to bind my brows, „ *lxix* 7
She *t* the kiss sedately; *Maud I xii* 14
Wherefore Merlin *t* the child, *Com. of Arthur* 221
And Arthur row'd across and *t* it— „ 298
So this great brand the king *T*, „ 309
T horse, descended the slope street, *Gareth and L.* 662
t the shield And mounted horse and graspt a spear, „ 690
this a bridge of single arc *T* at a leap; „ 909
She *t* them, and array'd herself therein, *Marr. of Geraint* 139
T horse, and forded Usk, and gain'd the wood; „ 161
So Enid *t* his charger to the stall; „ 382
Ah, dear, he *t* me from a goodly house, „ 708
she found And *t* it, and array'd herself therein. „ 849
And Enid *t* a little delicately, *Geraint and E.* 212
and *t* the word and play'd upon it, „ 291
One *t* him for a victim of Earl Doorm, „ 524
They hated her, who *t* no thought of them, „ 639
And *t* his russet beard between his teeth; „ 713
I *t* you for a bandit knight of Doorm; „ 786
and *t* a paramour; Did her mock-honour „ 832
converse which he *t* Before the Queen's fair name „ 950

Tore (*continued*) She crouch'd, she *t* him part from part, *Dead Prophet* 69
She *t* the Prophet after death, „ 77
Torment when strength is shock'd With *t*, *Lover's Tale ii* 151
and infinite *t* of flies, *Def. of Lucknow* 82
all the hateful fires Of *t*, *Demeter and P.* 152
contemplate The *t* of the damn'd' *Akbar's Dream* 49
Tormented *See* **Long-tormented**
Torn (*See also* **Raäved, Teär'd, Turn**) who smiled when she was *t* in three; *Poland* 12
T from the fringe of spray. *D. of F. Women* 40
All the air was *t* in sunder, *The Captain* 43
I was drench'd with ooze, and *t* with briers, *Princess v* 28
and the household flower *T* from the lintel— „ 129
her blooming mantle *t*, „ *vi* 145
The Mayfly is *t* by the swallow, *Maud I iv* 23
By which our houses are *t*: „ *xix* 33
a Shape that fled With broken wings, *t* raiment *Gareth and L.* 1208
would have *t* the child Piecemeal among them, *Com. of Arthur* 217
T as a sail that leaves the rope is *t* In tempest: *Holy Grail* 212
Then *t* it from her finger, *The Ring* 456
from her own hand she had *t* the ring In fright, „ 470
Torn'd (turned) An' 'e *t* as red as a stag-tuckey's wattles, *Church-warden, etc.* 31
Torpid That here the *t* mummy wheat Of Egypt *To Prof. Jebb.* 5
Torre two strong sons, Sir *T* and Sir Lavaine, *Lancelot and E.* 174
'Here is *T's*: Hurt in his first tilt was my son Sir *T*. „ 195
added plain Sir *T*, 'Yea, since I cannot use it, „ 198
Surely I but play'd on *T*: „ 209
Then far away with good Sir *T* for guide „ 788
He amazed, '*T* and Elaine! why here? „ 796
Then turn'd Sir *T*, and being in his moods „ 799
Then the rough *T* began to heave and move, „ 1066
Torrent (adj.) 'The *t* brooks of hallow'd Israel *D. of F. Women* 181
Flung the *t* rainbow round: *Vision of Sin* 32
The *t* vineyard streaming fell *The Daisy* 10
That listens near a *t* mountain-brook, *Geraint and E.* 171
Torrent (s) Far-off the *t* call'd me from the cleft: *Œnone* 54
She heard the *t's* meet. *Of old sat Freedom* 4
In many a streaming *t* back, *England and Amer.* 14
Like *t's* from a mountain source *The Letters* 39
For me the *t* ever pour'd And glisten'd— *To E. L.* 13
And *t's* of her myriad universe, *Lucretius* 39
roll The *t's*, dash'd to the vale: *Princess v* 350
To roll the *t* out of dusky doors: „ *vii* 208
let the *t* dance thee down To find him in the valley; „ 209
oleanders flush'd the bed Of silent *t's*, *The Daisy* 34
must fain have *t's*, lakes, Hills, *Sisters (E. and E.)* 221
Swept like a *t* of gems from the sky *V. of Maeldune* 46
Following a *t* till its myriad falls *Tiresias* 37
in a popular *t* of lies upon lies; *Vastness* 6
Of cataract music Of falling *t's*, *Merlin and the G.* 47
By the long *t's* ever-deepen'd roar, *Death of Œnone* 85
Torrent-bow floating as they fell Lit up a *t-b*. *Palace of Art* 36
Tortoise Upon the *t* creeping to the wall; *D. of F. Women* 27
Torture *T* and trouble in vain,— *Def. of Lucknow* 86
Why should we bear with an hour of *t*, *Despair* 81
Tortured a twitch of pain *T* her mouth, *Princess vi* 106
Me they seized and me they *t*, *Boädicea* 49
Tory (adj.) The *T* member's elder son, *Princess, Con.* 50
Tory (s) I myself, A *T* to the quick, *Walk. to the Mail* 81
Let Whig and *T* stir their blood; *Will Water.* 53
A gathering of the *T*, *Maud I xx* 33
Toss There the sunlit ocean *t'es* *The Captain* 69
That *t'es* at the harbour-mouth; *The Voyage* 2
Should *t* with tangle and with shells. *In Mem. x* 20
but wherefore *t* me this Like a dry bone *Last Tournament* 195
and *t* them away with a yawn, *The Wreck* 21
Tossing *t* up A cloud of incense of all odour *Palace of Art* 38
Tost (*See also* **Trouble-tost**) Had *t* his ball and flown his kite, *Aylmer's Field* 84
T over all her presents petulantly: „ 235
Discuss'd a doubt and *t* it to and fro: *Princess ii* 445
others *t* a ball Above the fountain-jets, „ 460
t on thoughts that changed from hue to hue, „ *iv* 210
Elaine, and heard her name so *t* about, *Lancelot and E.* 233
Tost (*continued*) was a phantom cry that I heard as I *t* about, *In the Child. Hosp.* 63
The sacred relics *t* about the floor— *The Ring* 447
Total The *t* chronicles of man, the mind, *Princess ii* 381
The *t* world since life began; *In Mem. xliii* 12
Tother (other) 'E reäds of a sewer an' sartan 'oäp o' the *t* side; *Village Wife* 92
Or like *t* Hangel i' Scriptur *Owd Roä* 94
Totter Till she began to *t*, *Sea Dreams* 244
what is it? there? yon arbutus *T's*; *Lucretius* 185
Totter'd roofs *T* toward each other in the sky, *Holy Grail* 343
Tottering yester-even, suddenly giddily *t*— *Boädicea* 29
Touch (s) And weary with a finger's *t* *Clear-headed friend* 22
Nor toil for title, place, or *t* Of pension, *Love thou thy land* 25
Perhaps some modern *t'es* here and there *M. d'Arthur, Ep.* 6
Such *t'es* are but embassies of love, *Gardener's D.* 18
But I have sudden *t'es*, and can run My faith *Edwin Morris* 53
there seem'd A *t* of something false, „ 74
My sense of *t* is something coarse, *Talking Oak* 163
The cushions of whose *t* may press „ 179
Baby fingers, waxen *t'es*, *Locksley Hall* 90
A *T*, a kiss! the charm was snapt *Day-Dm., Revival* 1
O for the *t* of a vanish'd hand, *Break, break, etc.* 11
Which at a *t* of light, an air of heaven, *Aylmer's Field* 5
so finely, that a troublous *t* Thinn'd, „ 75
hand Glanced like a *t* of sunshine on the rocks, *Princess iii* 357
To whom the *t* of all mischance but came „ *iv* 573
not a thought, a *t*, But pure as lines of green „ *v* 195
some *t* of that Which kills me with myself, „ *vi* 306
No more, dear love, for at a *t* I yield; „ *vii* 14
Tenderness *t* by *t*, and last, to these, „ 114
a *t* Came round my wrist, and tears upon my hand „ 137
Too solemn for the comic *t'es* in them, „ *Con.* 68
When one small *t* of Charity *Lit. Squabbles* 13
And I too, talk, and lose the *t* I talk of. „ 17
And I perceived no *t* of change, *In Mem. xiv* 17
The *t* of change in calm or storm; „ *xvi* 6
A *t* of shame upon her cheek: „ *xxxvii* 10
May some dim *t* of earthly things „ *xliv* 11
If such a dreamy *t* should fall, „ 13
You say, but with no *t* of scorn, „ *xcvi* 1
Sprang up for ever at a *t*, „ *cxii* 10
old place will be gilt by the *t* of a millionaire: *Maud I i* 66
heart-free, with the least little *t* of spleen. „ *ii* 11
A *t* of their office might have sufficed, „ *II v* 27
in a moment—at one *t* Of that skill'd spear, *Gareth and L.* 1222
But keep a *t* of sweet civility *Geraint and E.* 312
The pale blood of the wizard at her *t* *Merlin and V.* 949
For who loves me must have a *t* of earth; *Lancelot and E.* 133
That men go down before your spear at a *t*, „ 149
save it be some far-off *t* Of greatness „ 450
That men went down before his spear at a *t*, „ 578
Courtesy with a *t* of traitor in it, „ 639
she, that felt the cold *t* on her throat, *Pelleas and E.* 488
I'll hold thou hast some *t* Of music, *Last Tournament* 313
The sight that throbs and aches beneath my *t*, *Lover's Tale i* 33
quick as a sensitive plant to the *t*; *In the Child. Hosp.* 30
Your plague but passes by the *t*. *Happy* 104
Who feel no *t* of my temptation, *Romney's R.* 121
vines Which on the *t* of heavenly feet *Death of Œnone* 5
Would the man have a *t* of remorse *Charity* 17
Touch (verb) For those two likes might meet and *t*. *Two Voices* 357
That *t'es* me with mystic gleams, „ 380
I'd *t* her neck so warm and white. *Miller's D.* 174
touch'd with some new grace Or seem'd to *t* her, *Gardener's D.* 205
came To *t* my body and be heal'd, and live: *St. S. Stylites* 79
It may be we shall *t* the Happy Isles, *Ulysses* 63
t him with thy lighter thought. *Locksley Hall* 54
love no more Can *t* the heart of Edward Gray. *Edward Gray* 8
And *t* upon the master-chord *Will Water.* 27
So,—from afar,—*t* as at once? *Aylmer's Field* 580
O Goddess, like ourselves *T*, and be touch'd, *Lucretius* 81
We *t* on our dead self, nor shun to do it, *Princess iii* 221
Which *t'es* on the workman and his work. „ 322
'You have our son: *t* not a hair of his head: „ *iv* 407

Touch (verb) (*continued*) seem'd to *t* upon a sphere Too gross to tread, — *Princess vii* 324
T a spirit among things divine, — *Ode on Well.* 139
To *t* thy thousand years of gloom: — *In Mem. ii* 12
O Father, *t* the east, and light — „ *xxx* 31
And other than the things I *t*.' — „ *xlv* 8
That seem'd to *t* it into leaf: — „ *lxix* 18
T thy dull goal of joyless gray, — „ *lxxii* 27
Descend, and *t*, and enter; — „ *xciii* 13
And *t* with shade the bridal doors, — „ *Con.* 117
Not *t* on her father's sin: — *Maud I xix* 17
We will not *t* upon him ev'n in jest.' — *Marr. of Geraint* 311
or *t* at night the northern star; — *Balin and Balan* 166
T flax with flame—a glance will serve— — *Merlin and V.* 111
but *t* it with a sword, It buzzes fiercely — „ 431
Not one of all the drove should *t* me: — „ 699
if a man Could *t* or see it, he was heal'd at once, — *Holy Grail* 55
Nor aught we blow with breath, or *t* with hand, — „ 114
if I find the Holy Grail itself And *t* it, — „ 439
That could I *t* or see the Holy Grail — „ 779
'Yet, take him, ye that scarce are fit to *t*, — *Pelleas and E.* 292
Save that to *t* a harp, tilt with a lance — *Last Tournament* 636
had let one finger lightly *t* The warm white apple — „ 716
I cannot *t* thy lips, they are not mine, — *Guinevere* 551
sometimes *t'es* but one string That quivers, — *Lover's Tale i* 17
doesn not *t* thy 'at to the Squire;' — *North. Cobbler* 25
But they dared not *t* us again, — *The Revenge* 72
gleam from our poor earth May *t* thee, — *Ded. Poem Prin. Alice* 19
fleeted far and fast To *t* all shores, — *Pref. Son. 19th Cent.* 2
I *t* thy world again— — *Ancient Sage* 249
Earth would never *t* her worst, — *Locksley H., Sixty* 270
Did he *t* me on the lips? — *Happy* 66
Human forgiveness *t'es* heaven, and thence— — *Romney's R.* 159
æon after æon pass and *t* him into shape? — *Making of Man* 4

Touch'd (*See also* **True-touched**) *T* with a somewhat darker hue, — *Margaret* 50
heath-flower in the dew, *T* with sunrise. — *Rosalind* 42
T by thy spirit's mellowness, — *Eleänore* 103
T by his feet the daisy slept. — *Two Voices* 276
T; and I knew no more.' — *D. of F. Women* 116
ere it *t* a foot, that might have danced — *Gardener's D.* 133
each in passing *t* with some new grace — „ 204
Then *t* upon the game, how scarce it was — *Audley Court* 32
The flower, she *t* on, dipt and rose, — *Talking Oak* 131
Are *t*, are turn'd to finest air. — *Sir Galahad* 72
Then the music *t* the gates and died; — *Vision of Sin* 23
When that cold vapour *t* the palace gate, — „ 58
And ere he *t* his one-and-twentieth May — *Enoch Arden* 57
t On such a time as goes before the leaf, — *The Brook* 12
for the second death Scarce *t* her — *Aylmer's Field* 605
And oaken finials till he *t* the door; — „ 823
T, clink'd, and clash'd, and vanish'd, — *Sea Dreams* 135
O Goddess, like ourselves Touch, and be *t*, — *Lucretius* 81
(A little sense of wrong had *t* her face With colour) — *Princess, Pro.* 219
t on Mahomet With much contempt, — „ *ii* 134
the Muses' heads were *t* Above the darkness — „ *iii* 21
t upon the point Where idle boys are cowards — „ *v* 308
for since you think me *t* In honour— — „ 401
the sequel of the tale Had *t* her; — „ *Con.* 31
That thou hadst *t* the land to-day, — *In Mem. xiv* 2
God's finger *t* him, and he slept. — „ *lxxxv* 20
Or *t* the changes of the state, — „ *lxxxix* 35
The dead man *t* me from the past, — „ *xcv* 34
Who *t* a jarring lyre at first, — „ *xcvi* 7
Nor harp be *t*, nor flute be blown; — „ *cv* 22
But *t* with no ascetic gloom; — „ *cix* 10
she *t* my hand with a smile so sweet, — *Maud I vi* 12
For her feet have *t* the meadows — „ *xii* 23
I find whenever she *t* on me — „ *xix* 59
Mage at Arthur's Court, Knowing all arts, had *t*, — *Gareth and L.* 307
So when they *t* the second river-loop, — „ 1025
rose to look at it, But *t* it unawares: — *Geraint and E.* 388
Nor ever *t* fierce wine, nor tasted flesh, — *Merlin and V.* 627
T at all points, except the poplar grove, — *Lancelot and E.* 617
at times, So *t* were they, half-thinking — „ 1287

Touch'd (*continued*) but when I *t* her, lo! she, too, Fell into dust — *Holy Grail* 396
up I went and *t* him, and he, too, Fell into dust, — „ 418
I *t* The chapel-doors at dawn I know; — „ 535
Out of the dark, just as the lips had *t*, — *Last Tournament* 752
its shadow flew Before it, till it *t* her, — *Guinevere* 80
T by the adulterous finger of a time — *To the Queen ii* 43
and *t* far-off His mountain-altars, — *Lover's Tale i* 321
Thy fires from heaven had *t* it, — „ 439
But all from these to where she *t* on earth, — „ *iv* 167
our lover seldom spoke, Scarce *t* the meats; — „ 226
we came to the Silent Isle that we never had *t* at before, — *V. of Maeldune* 11
dark orb *T* with earth's light— — *De Prof., Two G.* 10
you have *t* at seventy-five, — *To E. Fitzgerald* 44
I *t* my limbs, the limbs Were strange — *Ancient Sage* 234
t on the whole sad planet of man, — *Dead Prophet* 39
For, see, thy foot has *t* it; — *Demeter and P.* 48
T at the golden Cross — *Merlin and the G.* 67
If the lips were *t* with fire — *Parnassus* 17
he *t* his goal, The Christian city. — *St. Telemachus* 34

Touching (*See also* **Tenderest-touching**) *T* the sullen pool below: — *Miller's D.* 244
our spirits rush'd together at the *t* of the lips. — *Locksley Hall* 38
Answer'd all queries *t* those at home — *Aylmer's Field* 465
which, on the foremost rocks *T*, upjetted — *Sea Dreams* 52
moonlight *t* o'er a terrace One tall Agavè — *The Daisy* 83
T her guilty love for Lancelot, — *Marr. of Geraint* 25
And *t* Breton sands, they disembark'd. — *Merlin and V.* 202
And *t* fame, howe'er ye scorn my song, — „ 444
crown'd with spiritual fire, And *t* other worlds. — „ 838
and *t* on all things great, — *The Wreck* 50

Touchwood a cave Of *t*, with a single flourishing spray. — *Aylmer's Field* 512
the stem Less grain than *t*, — *Princess iv* 333

Touchwood-dust Raking in that millennial *t-d* — *Aylmer's Field* 514

Tough My *t* lance thrusteth sure, — *Sir Galahad* 2
t, Strong, supple, sinew-corded, — *Princess v* 534

Tougher *t*, heavier, stronger, he that smote — „ 536

Tould (told) Call'd from her cabin an' *t* her — *Tomorrow* 20
I *t* yer Honour whativer I hard an' seen, — „ 97

Tour last summer on a *t* in Wales: — *Golden Year* 2

Tournament From spur to plume a star of *t*, — *M. d'Arthur* 223
For Lancelot was the first in *T*, — *Gareth and L.* 495
Forgetful of the tilt and *t*, — *Marr. of Geraint* 52
But in this *t* can no man tilt, — „ 480
And victor at the tilt and *t*, — *Geraint and E.* 960
and acts of prowess done In *t* or tilt, — *Holy Grail* 2
heard the King Had let proclaim a *t*— — *Pelleas and E.* 11
And this was call'd 'The *T* of Youth:' — „ 158
But when the morning of a *t*, — *Last Tournament* 134
in mockery call'd The *T* of the Dead Innocence, — „ 136
He saw the laws that ruled the *t* Broken, — „ 160
From spur to plume a star of *t*, — *Pass. of Arthur* 391
Flash'd on the *T*, — *Merlin and the G.* 69

Tourney (s) a page or two that rang With tilt and *t*; — *Princess, Pro.* 122
pledged To fight in *t* for my bride, — „ *v* 353
With whom he used to play at *t* once, — *Gareth and L.* 532
beside The field of *t*, murmuring 'kitchen-knave.' — „ 664
But by the field of *t* lingering yet — „ 736
We hold a *t* here to-morrow morn, — *Marr. of Geraint* 287
this nephew, fight In next day's *t* — „ 476
—will you wear My favour at this *t*?' — *Lancelot and E.* 362
closed And clash'd in such a *t* and so full, — *Holy Grail* 330
and remain Lord of the *t*. — *Pelleas and E.* 163
The circlet of the *t* round her brows, And the sword of the *t* across her throat. — „ 454

Tourney (verb) But meant once more perchance to *t* in it. — *Lancelot and E.* 810

Tourney-fall In those brain-stunning shocks, and *t-f's*, — *Gareth and L.* 89

Tourney-prize And make them, an thou wilt a *t-p*.' — *Last Tournament* 32
And won by Tristram as a *t-p*, — „ 746

Tourney-skill no room was there For lance or *t-s*: — *Gareth and L.* 1042

Tow Nor like poor Psyche whom she drags in *t*.' — *Princess iii* 103

Towd (told) An' a *t* ma my sins, — *N. Farmer, O. S.* 11
knawed a Quaäker fellow as often 'as *t* ma this: — „ *N. S.* 19
I knaws the law, I does, for the lawyer ha *t* it me. — *Village Wife* 16

Traitor (s) (*continued*) Fools prate, and perish *t's*. — *Balin and Balan* 530
shriek'd out '*T*' to the unhearing wall, — *Lancelot and E.* 612
Courtesy with a touch of *t* in it, — „ 639
a coward slinks from what he fears To cope with, or a *t* proven, — *Pelleas and E.* 439
'*T*, come out, ye are trapt at last,' — *Guinevere* 106
Modred whom he left in charge of all, The *t*— — „ 196
If this false *t* have displaced his lord, — „ 216
heathen, and knights, *T's*— — „ 575
I lean'd in wife and friend Is *t* to my peace, — *Pass. of Arthur* 25
Modred, unharm'd, the *t* of thine house.' — „ 153
But call not thou this *t* of my house — „ 155
her own true eyes Are *t's* to her; — *Sisters (E. and E.)* 285
who can tell but the *t's* had won? — *Def. of Lucknow* 66
but to call men *t's* May make men *t's*. — *Sir J. Oldcastle* 50
That *t* to King Richard and the truth, — „ 171
T and trickster And spurner of treaties— — *Batt. of Brunanburh* 79
God the *t's* hope confound! (repeat) — *Hands all Round* 10, 22, 34
Traitor-hearted unkind, untrue, Unknightly, *t-h*! — *M. d'Arthur* 120
unkind, untrue, Unknightly, *t-h*! — *Pass. of Arthur* 288
Traitorous when a world Of *t* friend and broken system — *Princess vi* 195
to splinter it into feuds Serving his *t* end; — *Guinevere* 19
Ever the day with its *t* death from the loopholes around, — *Def. of Lucknow* 79
Traitress nip me flat, If I be such a *t*. — *Merlin and V.* 351
and harry me, petty spy And *t*.' — *Guinevere* 361
Tram laying his *t's* in a poison'd gloom — *Maud I x* 8
Tramp (a vagrant) an' gied to the *t's* goin' by— — *Village Wife* 33
Tramp (sound) *t* of the hornfooted horse That grind — *Tiresias* 94
Tramp (verb) To *t*, to scream, to burnish, — *Princess iv* 520
Trample To *t* round my fallen head, — *Come not, when, etc.* 3
I *t* on your offers and on you: — *Princess iv* 546
on my chargers, *t* them under us.' — *Boädicea* 69
Behold me overturn and *t* on him. — *Geraint and E.* 843
And *t's* on the goodly shield to show — *Balin and Balan* 550
'*T* me, Dear feet, that I have follow'd — *Merlin and V.* 226
and burns the feet would *t* it to dust. — *The Flight* 68
Trampled (adj.) I was left a *t* orphan, — *Locksley Hall* 156
The desecrated shrine, the *t* year, — *Princess v* 127
Till the filthy by-lane rings to the yell of the *t* wife, — *Maud I i* 38
Let the *t* serpent show you that you have not lived in vain. — *Locksley H., Sixty* 242
arose The shriek and curse of *t* millions, — *Akbar's Dream* 190
Trampled (verb) And *t* under by the last and least — *Poland* 2
She *t* some beneath her horses' heels, — *Princess, Pro.* 44
a spark of will Not to be *t* out. — *Maud II ii* 57
and why *T* ye thus on that which bare the Crown?' — *Balin and Balan* 602
There *t* out his face from being known, — *Last Tournament* 470
man's word, Here *t* by the populace underfoot, — *Tiresias* 174
Trampling *t* the flowers With clamour: — *Princess v* 247
All great self-seekers *t* on the right: — *Ode on Well.* 187
hollow *t's* up and down And muffled voices heard, — *Gareth and L.* 1372
His charger *t* many a prickly star — *Marr. of Geraint* 313
But Michaël *t* Satan; — *Last Tournament* 673
Trance (s) I muse, as in a *t*, (repeat) — *Eleänore* 72, 75
Like some bold seër in a *t*, — *L. of Shalott iv* 11
'As here we find in *t's*, men Forget the dream that happens then, Until they fall in *t* again. — *Two Voices* 352
who clasp'd in her last *t* Her murder'd father's head, — *D. of F. Women* 266
The *t* gave way To those caresses, — *Love and Duty* 65
I could no more, but lay like one in *t*, — *Princess vii* 151
In some long *t* should slumber on; — *In Mem. xliii* 4
Sleep, kinsman thou to death and *t* And madness, — „ *lxxi* 1
At length my *t* Was cancell'd, — „ *xcv* 43
But when the Queen immersed in such a *t*, — *Guinevere* 401
led on with light In *t's* and in visions: — *Lover's Tale i* 78
Thro' dreams by night and *t's* of the day, — *Sisters (E. and E.)* 274
Till I woke from the *t*, — *The Wreck* 115
following, as in *t*, the silent cry. — *Death of Œnone* 86
Trance (verb) When thickest dark did *t* the sky, — *Mariana* 18
Tranced (*See also* **Deep-tranced**) So *t*, so rapt in ecstasies, — *Eleänore* 78
No *t* summer calm is thine, — *Madeline* 2
Hung *t* from all pulsation, — *Gardener's D.* 260
Tranced (*continued*) On either side her *t* form Forth streaming — *Day-Dm., Sleep. B.* 5
nature fail'd a little, And he lay *t*; — *Enoch Arden* 793
We stood *t* in long embraces Mixt with kisses — *Maud II iv* 8
Tranquil her lips were sunder'd With smiles of *t* bliss, — *Lover's Tale ii* 143
Tranquillity O Thou, Passionless bride, divine *T*, — *Lucretius* 266
Marr'd her friend's aim with pale *t*. — *Lancelot and E.* 733
Transfer That foolish sleep *t's* to thee. — *In Mem. lxviii* 16
t The whole I felt for him to you. — „ *lxxxv* 103
Transferr'd my dull agony, Ideally to her *t*, — *Lover's Tale ii* 137
Transfigured When we shall stand *t*, — *Happy* 38
Transfixt So lay the man *t*. — *Geraint and E.* 166
Transfused but *t* Thro' future time by power — *Love thou thy land* 3
Transgress *T* his ample bound to some new crown:— — *Poland* 8
Transgression So for every light *t* — *The Captain* 11
Transient Away we stole, and *t* in a trice — *Princess v* 39
But knows no more of *t* form In her deep self, — *In Mem. xvi* 7
Womanlike, taking revenge too deep for a *t* wrong — *Maud I iii* 5
And wordy trucklings to the *t* hour, — *To the Queen ii* 51
And the *t* trouble of drowning— — *Despair* 67
Transit and wing'd Her *t* to the throne, — *Princess iv* 378
Transitory and a *t* word Made knight or churl or child — *Balin and Balan* 161
Translucent Pure vestal thoughts in the *t* fane — *Isabel* 4
Transmitter The one *t* of their ancient name, — *Aylmer's Field* 296
Transparent That dimples your *t* cheek, — *Margaret* 15
Transplanted I know *t* human worth Will bloom to profit, — *In Mem. lxxxii* 11
Transplanting And Methods of *t* trees — *Amphion* 79
Transport 'But heard, by secret *t* led, — *Two Voices* 214
Me mightier *t's* move and thrill; — *Sir Galahad* 22
Stirring a sudden *t* rose and fell. — *Princess iv* 29
Trap (rock) hornblende, rag and *t* and tuff, — „ *iii* 362
Trap (snare) As of a wild thing taken in the *t*, — *Geraint and E.* 723
Trap (verb) Christ the bait to *t* his dupe — *Sea Dreams* 191
Trapesed *See* **Traäpes'd**
Trapper Which sees the *t* coming thro' the wood. — *Geraint and E.* 724
Trapt (adorned) there she found her palfrey *t* — *Godiva* 51
On horses, and the horses richly *t* — *Pelleas and E.* 55
Trapt (caught) 'Traitor, come out, ye are *t* at last,' — *Guinevere* 106
Trash you that talk'd The *t* that made me sick, — *Princess ii* 394
'O *t*' he said, 'but with a kernel in it. — „ 395
Trath Treroit down the waste sand-shores of *T T*, — *Lancelot and E.* 301
Travail *T*, and throes and agonies of the life, — *Com. of Arthur* 76
Camilla's *t* came Upon her, — *Lover's Tale iv* 127
Travel (s) I cannot rest from *t*: — *Ulysses* 6
if it had not been For a chance of *t*, — *Maud I ii* 8
overtoil'd By that day's grief and *t*, — *Geraint and E.* 377
O weary was I of the *t*, — *V. of Maeldune* 129
Travel (verb) blasts of balm To one that *t's* quickly, — *Gardener's D.* 69
He *t's* far from other skies— — *Day-Dm., Arrival* 5
here and there a foamy flake Upon me, as I *t* — *The Brook* 60
Travell'd how they prose O'er books of *t* seamen, — *Amphion* 82
And *t* men from foreign lands; — *In Mem. x* 6
Traveller in strange lands a *t* walking slow, — *Palace of Art* 277
The *t* hears me now and then, — *In Mem. xxi* 5
Traveller's-joy Was parcel-bearded with the *t-j* — *Aylmer's Field* 153
Travelling quite worn out, *T* to Naples. — *The Brook* 36
His kinsman *t* on his own affair — *Merlin and V.* 717
myself was then *T* that land, — *Lover's Tale iv* 133
Traversed Silent the silent field They *t*. — *Gareth and L.* 1314
blossom-dust of those Deep meadows we had *t*, — *Merlin and V.* 283
Treacherous Making a *t* quiet in his heart, — *Lancelot and E.* 883
Treachery tript on such conjectural *t*— — *Merlin and V.* 348
fevers, fights, Mutinies, *treacheries*— — *Columbus* 226
Tread (s) Were it ever so airy a *t*, — *Maud I xxii* 68
Tread (verb) And *t* softly and speak low, — *D. of the O. Year* 4
ere the hateful crow shall *t* The corners — *Will Water.* 235
While he *t's* with footstep firmer, — *L. of Burleigh* 51
Freedom, gaily doth she *t*; — *Vision of Sin* 136
T a measure on the stones, — „ 180
The wisp that flickers where no foot can *t*.' — *Princess iv* 358
And *t* you out for ever: — „ *vi* 176
seem'd to touch upon a sphere Too gross to *t*, — „ *vii* 325
The solid earth whereon we *t* — *In Mem. cxviii* 8
t me down And I will kiss you for it;' — *Merlin and V.* 228
You that would not *t* on a worm — *Forlorn* 45

Treading Then her people, softly *t*, *L. of Burleigh* 97
Treason says the song, I ' trow it is no *t*.' *Merlin and V.* 723
To lash the *t's* of the Table Round.' *Pelleas and E.* 566
fool,' he said, ' ye talk Fool's *t* : *Last Tournament* 352
The doom of *t* and the flaming death, *Guinevere* 538
king along with him—All heresy, *t* : *Sir J. Oldcastle* 50
Treasure handed down the golden *t* to him.' *Gareth and L.* 61
a peculiar *t*, brooking not Exchange *Lover's Tale i* 447
accounts Of all his *t's* the most beautiful, „ *iv* 234
in her behold Of all my *t's* the most beautiful, „ 318
coin'd into English gold some *t* of classical song, *The Wreck* 67
Treasured When I saw the *t* splendour, her hand, *Maud I vi* 84
Treasure-house Stored in some *t-h* of mighty kings, *M. d'Arthur* 101
Stored in some *t-h* of mighty kings, *Pass. of Arthur* 269
Treasurer wherefore Arthur call'd His *t*, *Balin and Balan* 5
Treasure-trove Found for himself a bitter *t-t* ; *Aylmer's Field* 515
Thro' the dim meadow toward his *t-t*, „ 531
Treasuring *T* the look it cannot find, *In Mem. xviii* 19
Treat then we dipt in all That *t's* of whatsoever is, *Princess ii* 380
talk and *t* Of all things ev'n as he were by ; *In Mem. cvii* 19
T him with all grace, *Gareth and L.* 468
t their loathsome hurts and heal mine own ; *Guinevere* 686
Treated Too awful, sure, for what they *t* of, *Princess i* 139
And waiting to be *t* like a wolf, *Geraint and E.* 857
Treatise They read Botanic *T's*, *Amphion* 77
Treaty trickster And spurner of *treaties*— *Batt. of Brunanburh* 80
Treble (adj.) (*See also* **Silver-treble**) The *t* works, the vast designs *Ode on Well.* 104
A *t* darkness, Evil haunts The birth, *In Mem. xcviii* 13
There ran a *t* range of stony shields,— *Gareth and L.* 407
For there beyond a bridge of *t* bow, „ 1086
Treble (s) With blissful *t* ringing clear. *Sir L. and Q. G.* 22
tempestuous *t* throbb'd and palpitated ; *Vision of Sin* 28
In little sharps and *t's*, *The Brook* 40
Make liquid *t* of that bassoon, my throat ; *Princess ii* 426
maidenlike as far As I could ape their *t*, „ *iv* 92
Trebled (adj.) London roll'd one tide of joy thro' all Her *t* millions, *To the Queen ii* 9
Trebled (verb) Love *t* life within me, *Gardener's D.* 198
hath not our great Queen My dole of beauty *t* ? ' *Last Tournament* 558
Trebling And *t* all the rest in value— *Lover's Tale iv* 200
Tree (*See also* **Apple-tree, Aspen-tree, Boor-tree, Cedar-tree, Elm-tree, Figtree, Garden-tree, Hazel-tree, Oak-tree, Palm-tree, Poplartree, Roof-tree, Rosetree, Sloe-tree, Wayfaring-tree, Yew-tree**) no other *t* did mark The level waste, *Mariana* 43
Rain makes music in the *t* *A Dirge* 26
as the *t* Stands in the sun and shadows *Love and Death* 10
The shadow passeth when the *t* shall fall, „ 14
Thou liest beneath the greenwood *t*, *Oriana* 95
The wind is blowing in turret and *t*. (repeat) *The Sisters* 3, 33
The wind is howling in turret and *t*. „ 9
The wind is roaring in turret and *t*. „ 15
The wind is raging in turret and *t*. „ 21
The wind is raving in turret and *t*. „ 27
twilight pour'd On dewy pastures, dewy *t's*, *Palace of Art* 86
the leaf upon the *t*. *May Queen, N. Y's. E.* 8
The *t's* began to whisper, „ *Con.* 27
Their humid arms festooning *t* to *t*, *D. of F. Women* 70
I shook him down because he was The finest on the *t*. *Talking Oak* 238
Thou art the fairest-spoken *t* „ 263
hangs the heavy-fruited *t*— *Locksley Hall* 163
A garden too with scarce a *t*, *Amphion* 3
And legs of *t's* were limber, „ 14
Like some great landslip, *t* by *t*, „ 51
And Methods of transplanting *t's* „ 79
Then move the *t's*, the copses nod, *Sir Galahad* 77
And fly, like a bird, from *t* to *t* ; *Edward Gray* 30
But here will sigh thine alder *t*, *A Farewell* 9
And dies unheard within his *t*, *You might have won* 32
The moving whisper of huge *t's* *Enoch Arden* 585
On the nigh-naked *t* the robin piped Disconsolate, „ 676
the family *t* Sprang from the midriff *Aylmer's Field* 15
Have also set his many-shielded *t* ? „ 48
Once grovelike, each huge arm a *t*, „ 510
Tree (*continued*) *t's* As high as heaven, and every bird that sings : *Sea Dreams* 101
bathed In the green gleam of dewy-tassell'd *t's* : *Princess i* 94
A *t* Was half-disrooted from his place „ *iv* 185
across the lawns Beneath huge *t's*, „ *v* 237
lo the *t* ! But we will make it faggots for the hearth, „ *vi* 44
From the high *t* the blossom wavering fell, „ 80
all along the valley, by rock and cave and *t*, *V. of Cauteretz* 9
For the bud ever breaks into bloom on the *t*, *The Islet* 32
And gazing on thee, sullen *t*, *In Mem. ii* 13
And wildly dash'd on tower and *t* „ *xv* 7
Within the green the moulder'd *t*, „ *xxvi* 7
the *t's* Laid their dark arms about the field. (repeat) „ *xcv* 15, 51
My love has talk'd with rocks and *t's* ; „ *xcvii* 1
There rolls the deep where grew the *t*. „ *cxxiii* 1
on the *t's* The dead leaf trembles to the bells. „ *Con.* 63
A voice by the cedar *t* In the meadow *Maud I v* 1
One long milk-bloom on the *t* ; „ *xxii* 46
stairway sloped Till lost in blowing *t's* and tops of towers ; *Gareth and L.* 670
saw The *t* that shone white-listed thro' the gloom. *Merlin and V.* 939
then binding his good horse To a *t*, *Pelleas and E.* 31
thro' the *t* Rush'd ever a rainy wind, *Last Tournament* 15
and crag and *t* Scaling, Sir Lancelot „ 17
High on a grim dead *t* before the tower, „ 430
As the *t* falls so must it lie. *Rizpah* 12
they would hang him again on the cursed *t*. „ 59
es he couldn't cut down a *t* ! ' Drat the *t's*,' says I, *Village Wife* 30
could it be That *t's* grew downward, *Columbus* 50
isle-side flashing down from the peak without ever a *t* *V. of Maeldune* 45
And *t's* like the towers of a minster, *The Wreck* 74
birds Begin to warble in the budding orchard *t's* ! *The Flight* 61
And a *t* with a moulder'd nest *Dead Prophet* 18
from off the *t* We planted both together, *Happy* 13
Her tribes of men, and *t's*, and flowers, *To Ulysses* 3
cords that ran Dark thro' the mist, and linking *t* to *t*, *Death of Œnone* 11
an' coom'd to the top o' the *t*, *Church-warden, etc.* 38
Tree-bower beneath the tall *T-b's*, *Sisters (E. and E.)* 112
Tree-fern Your cane, your palm, *t-f*, bamboo, *To Ulysses* 36
Tree-top On the *t-t's* a crested peacock lit, *Œnone* 104
Trefoil *t*, sparkling on the rainy plain, *Gareth and L.* 1159
Trellis-work birds Of sunny plume in gilded *t-w* ; *Marr. of Geraint* 659
Tremble stars which *t* O'er the deep mind *Ode to Memory* 35
the jewel That *t's* in her ear : *Miller's D.* 172
whispers of the leaves That *t* round a nightingale— *Gardener's D.* 254
And make me *t* lest a saying learnt, *Tithonus* 47
Begins to move and *t*. *Will Water.* 32
breath Of tender air made *t* in the hedge *The Brook* 202
and *t* deeper down, And slip at once all-fragrant *Princess vii* 69
In that fine air I *t*, all the past Melts „ 354
A breeze began to *t* o'er The large leaves *In Mem. xcv* 54
They *t*, the sustaining crags ; „ *cxxvii* 11
The dead leaf *t's* to the bells. „ *Con.* 64
Would start and *t* under her feet, *Maud I xxii* 73
He felt the hollow-beaten mosses thud And *t*, *Balin and Balan* 322
stars Did *t* in their stations as I gazed ; *Lover's Tale i* 582
excess of sweetness and of awe, Makes the heart *t*, „ *ii* 156
felt him *t* too, And heard him muttering, „ *iv* 324
That *t's* not to kisses of the bee : *Prog. of Spring* 4
Trembled Lovingly lower, *t* on her waist— *Gardener's D.* 131
' A teardrop *t* from its source, *Talking Oak* 161
Low voluptuous music winding *t*, *Vision of Sin* 17
T in perilous places o'er a deep : *Sea Dreams* 11
And the voice *t* and the hand. *Princess vii* 227
but in his heat and eagerness *T* and quiver'd, *Pelleas and E.* 284
burthen of our tender years *T* upon the other. *Lover's Tale i* 223
I heard and *t*, yet I could but hear ; „ 570
and the Paradise *t* away. *V. of Maeldune* 82
Tremblest Who *t* thro' thy darkling red *In Mem. xcix* 5
Trembling But ever *t* thro' the dew *Margaret* 52
And full at heart of *t* hope, *Miller's D.* 110
Between the loud stream and the *t* stars. *Œnone* 219
Thro' silence and the *t* stars *On a Mourner* 28

Trembling (*continued*) Smote the chord of Self, that, *t*, pass'd in music out of sight. *Locksley Hall* 34
With a weird bright eye, sweating and *t*, *Aylmer's Field* 585
Toll'd by an earthquake in a *t* tower, *Princess vi* 332
And letters unto *t* hands ; *In Mem. x* 7
With *t* fingers did we weave The holly „ *xxx* 1
now by night With moon and *t* stars, *Marr. of Geraint* 8
all offices Of watchful care and *t* tenderness. *Lover's Tale i* 226
(Huge blocks, which some old *t* of the world „ *ii* 45
dragon, which our *t* fathers call'd The God's own son. *Tiresias* 16
Tower and altar *t* . . . *Forlorn* 34
Tremulous (*See also* **Ever-tremulous, Fear-tremulous**) My *t* tongue faltereth, *Eleänore* 136
Perhaps her eye was dim, hand *t* ; *Enoch Arden* 242
Shines in those *t* eyes that fill with tears *Tithonus* 26
over them the *t* isles of light Slided, *Princess vi* 81
And in the meadows *t* aspen-trees *Lancelot and E.* 410
There on the *t* bridge, that from beneath *Lover's Tale i* 412
When first she peers along the *t* deep, *Demeter and P.* 14
Stampt into dust—*t*, all awry, *Romney's R.* 113
Trench (*See also* **Meadow-trenches**) shovell'd up into some bloody *t* *Audley Court* 42
Trenchant nor *t* swords Can do away that ancient lie ; *Clear-headed friend* 14
tipt With *t* steel, around him slowly prest *Gareth and L.* 693
Trenched The *t* waters run from sky to sky ; *Ode to Memory* 104
Nor quarry *t* along the hill *In Mem. c* 11
Trencher tender little thumb, That crost the *t* *Marr. of Geraint* 396
Treroit And down the waste sand-shores of Trath *T*, *Lancelot and E.* 302
Trespass-chiding slink From ferule and the *t-c* eye, *Princess v* 38
Tress (*See also* **Ivy-tress**) I see thee roam, with *t'es* unconfined, *Eleänore* 122
The fragrant *t'es* are not stirr'd *Day-Dm., Sleep. B.* 19
'Love, if thy *t'es* be so dark, „ *Arrival* 31
I wore her picture by my heart, And one dark *t* ; *Princess i* 39
With all her autumn *t'es* falsely brown, „ *ii* 449
Drew from my neck the painting and the *t*, „ *vi* 110
good Queen, her mother, shore the *t* With kisses, „ 113
Tressed *T* with redolent ebony, *Arabian Nights* 138
Trial and true love Crown'd after *t* ; *Aylmer's Field* 100
Girl after girl was call'd to *t* : *Princess iv* 228
So there were any *t* of mastery, *Gareth and L.* 517
'To those who love them, *t's* of our faith. *Pelleas and E.* 210
I know That all these pains are *t's* of my faith, „ 246
Dishonour'd all for *t* of true love— „ 477
Tribe twelve-divided concubine To inflame the *t's* : *Aylmer's Field* 760
Girt by half the *t's* of Britain, *Boädicea* 5
'They that scorn the *t's* and call us „ 7
A *t* of women, dress'd in many hues, *Geraint and E.* 598
shun the wild ways of the lawless *t*. „ 608
Her *t's* of men, and trees, and flowers, *To Ulysses* 3
Form, Ritual, varying with the *t's* of men. *Akbar's Dream* 125
Tributary A *t* prince of Devon, *Marr. of Geraint* 2
Low bow'd the *t* Prince, and she, „ 174
and had his realm restored But render'd *t*, *Balin and Balan* 3
Tribute (adj.) Thy *t* wave deliver : *A Farewell* 2
Tribute (s) The filter'd *t* of the rough woodland, *Ode to Memory* 63
Strode in, and claim'd their *t* as of yore. *Com. of Arthur* 506
No *t* will we pay : ' „ 513
fail'd of late To send his *t* ; *Balin and Balan* 4
after, when we sought The *t*, answer'd „ 116
a liar is he, And hates thee for the *t* ! ' „ 608
Hath sought the *t* of a verse from me, *To Dante* 5
Trice Away we stole, and transient in a *t* *Princess v* 39
Trick (s) 'I see it is a *t* Got up betwixt you *Dora* 95
'Play me no *t's*,' said Lord Ronald, (repeat) *Lady Clare* 73, 75
The *t's*, which make us toys of men, *Princess ii* 63
What was it ? a lying *t* of the brain ? *Maud II i* 37
'Are these your pretty *t's* and fooleries, *Merlin and V.* 265
madden'd to the height By tonguester *t's*, *To Mary Boyle* 34
Trick (verb) *T* thyself out in ghastly imageries *Gareth and L.* 1390
Trick'd and leaves me fool'd and *t*, „ 1251
Trickling That gather'd *t* dropwise from the cleft, *Merlin and V.* 274
Trickster Traitor and *t* And spurner of treaties— *Batt. of Brunanburh* 79
Tried (*See also* **Thried**) This dress and that by turns you *t*, *Miller's D.* 147
Tried (*continued*) this frail bark of ours, when sorely *t*, *Aylmer's Field* 715
I *t* the mother's heart. *Princess iii* 147
ourself have often *t* Valkyrian hymns, „ *iv* 138
I your old friend and *t*, she new in all ? „ 318
O true in word, and *t* in deed, *In Mem. lxxxv* 5
O true and *t*, so well and long, „ *Con.* 1
Strange, that *I t* to-day To beguile her *Maud I xx* 2
But on all those who *t* and fail'd, *Merlin and V.* 590
And many *t* and fail'd, because the charm „ 595
Then, if I *t* it, who should blame me then ? ' „ 661
tho' he *t* the villages round, *First Quarrel* 43
I couldn't get back tho' I *t*, *Rizpah* 43
weeks I *t* Your table of Pythagoras, *To E. Fitzgerald* 14
Trifle (s) And singing airy *t's* this or that, *Caress'd or chidden* 2
A *t*, sweet ! which true love spells— *Miller's D.* 187
A *t* makes a dream, a *t* breaks.' *Sea Dreams* 144
'No *t*,' groan'd the husband ; „ 145
Like one with any *t* pleased. *In Mem. lxvi* 4
They chatter'd *t's* at the door : „ *lxix* 4
There is but a *t* left you, *Grandmother* 107
Trifle (verb) gentlemen, That *t* with the cruet. *Will Water.* 232
Some thought that Philip did but *t* with her ; *Enoch Arden* 475
She might have seem'd a toy to *t* with, *Pelleas and E.* 76
Trifled Or like a king, not to be *t* with— *Merlin and V.* 593
Trifling As many little *t* Lilias— *Princess, Pro.* 188
Trill Upon her lattice, I would pipe and *t*, *Princess iv* 100
That hears the latest linnet *t*, *In Mem. c* 10
Trilleth Silver-treble laughter *t* : *Lilian* 24
Trim (adj.) sward was *t* as any garden lawn : *Princess, Pro.* 95
T hamlets ; here and there a rustic tower „ *Con.* 44
Trim (verb) have a dame indoors, that *t's* us up, *Edwin Morris* 46
t our sails, and let old bygones be, *Princess iv* 69
Trinacrian Tho' dead in its *T* Enna, *To Prof. Jebb* 11
Trinity All glory to the all-blessed *T*, *Columbus* 61
Trinket And gave the *t's* and the rings, *The Letters* 21
Trinobant hear Coritanian, *T* ! (repeat) *Boädicea* 10, 34, 47
Gods have answer'd, Catieuchlanian, *T*. „ 22
Shout Icenian, Catieuchlanian, shout Coritanian, *T*, „ 57
Trip My tongue *T's*, or I speak profanely. *Lucretius* 74
To *t* a tigress with a gossamer, *Princess v* 170
tho' he *t* and fall He shall not blind his soul „ *vii* 331
That made my tongue so stammer and *t* *Maud I vi* 83
Triple Who, God-like, grasps the *t* forks, *Of old sat Freedom* 15
Triple-mailèd and guard about With *t-m* trust, *Supp. Confessions* 66
Triplet In riddling *t's* of old time, *Com. of Arthur* 402
Tripod on a *t* in the midst A fragrant flame *Princess iv* 33
Tript That Jenny had *t* in her time : *Grandmother* 26
Have *t* on such conjectural treachery— *Merlin and V.* 348
yet, methinks Thy tongue has *t* a little : „ 602
There *t* a hundred tiny silver deer, *Last Tournament* 171
Tristram (a Knight of the Round Table) Had made his goodly cousin, *T*, knight, *Gareth and L.* 394
after Lancelot, *T*, and Geraint And Gareth, *Lancelot and E.* 556
the prize Of *T* in the jousts of yesterday, *Last Tournament* 8
T, saying, 'Why skip ye so, Sir Fool ?' (repeat) „ 9, 243
T—late From overseas in Brittany return'd, „ 174
Sir *T* of the Woods—Whom Lancelot knew, „ 177
in one full shock With *T* ev'n to death : „ 181
Drew from before Sir *T* to the bounds, „ 185
So *T* won, and Lancelot gave, the gems, „ 190
T, half-plagued by Lancelot's languorous mood, „ 194
T round the gallery made his horse Caracole ; „ 205
And wroth at *T* and the lawless jousts, „ 237
'Ay, fool,' said *T*, 'but 'tis eating dry To dance „ 249
Then *T*, waiting for the quip to come, „ 260
Sir fool,' said *T*, 'I would break thy head. „ 268
And *T*, 'Was it muddier than thy gibes ? „ 299
And *T*, 'Then were swine, goats, asses, „ 325
And *T*, 'Ay, Sir Fool, for when our King „ 334
'Nay, fool,' said *T*, 'not in open day.' „ 347
Rode *T* toward Lyonnesse and the west. „ 362
when *T* was away, And snatch'd her hence; „ 383
yet dreading worse than shame Her warrior *T*, „ 385
now that desert lodge to *T* lookt So sweet, „ 387
out of *T* waking, the red dream Fled with a shout, „ 487

True (adj.) (*continued*) 'I have fought for Queen and Faith like a valiant man and *t*; *The Revenge* 101
they stared at the dead that had been so valiant and *t*, „ 105
if *t* Love Were not his own imperial all-in-all. *Sisters* (*E. and E.*) 226
she That loved me—our *t* Edith— „ 235
and her own *t* eyes Are traitors to her; „ 284
'Most dearest' be a *t* superlative— „ 293
which lived *T* life, live on—and if the fatal kiss, Born of *t* life and love, *Prin. Alice* 2
t is your heart, but be sure that your hand be as *t*! *Def. of Lucknow* 56
is it *t* what was told by the scout, „ 95
From that *t* world within the world we see, *De Prof., Two G.* 30
Our *t* co-mates regather round the mast; *Pref. Son. 19th Cent.* 5
'Never the heart among women,' he said, 'more tender and *t*.' *The Wreck* 96
that would pluck from this *t* breast the locket *The Flight* 33
Arise, my own *t* sister, come forth! „ 96
I wur sewer that it couldn't be *t*; *Spinster's S's.* 20
so es all that I 'ears be *t*; „ 56
being *t* as he was brave; *Locksley H., Sixty* 59
when you speak were wholly *t*. „ 120
a guest may make *T* cheer with honest wine— *Pro. to Gen. Hamley* 16
he needs must fight To make *t* peace his own, *Epilogue* 27
T brother, only to be known By those who love thee best. *Pref. Poem Broth. Son.* 7
T poet, surely to be found When Truth „ 15
That man's the *t* Conservative *Hands all Round* 7
T leaders of the land's desire! „ 26
but Thou, *T* daughter, whose all-faithful, *Prin. Beatrice* 13
Queen, as *t* to womanhood as Queenhood, *On Jub. Q. Victoria* 25
'Faäithful an' *T*'—them words be i' Scriptur—an' Faäithful an' *T* *Owd Roä* 15
Legend or *t*? so tender should be *t*! *The Ring* 224
Make all *t* hearts thy home. *Prog. of Spring* 52
The *t* Alcestis of the time. *Romney's R* 91
Not the Great Voice not the *t* Deep. *Akbar's Dream* 59
And following thy *t* counsel, by thine aid, „ 154
T gentleman, heart, blood and bone, *Bandit's Death* 2
And had some prophet spoken *t* *Mechanophilus* 25
T we have got—*such* a faithful ally *Riflemen form!* 24
I count you kind, I hold you *t*; *The Wanderer* 13
What is *t* at last will tell: *Poets and the Critics* 9
By that same path our *t* forefathers trod; *Doubt and Prayer* 4
True (s) undo One riddle, and to find the *t*, *Two Voices* 233
Yet glimpses of the *t*. *Will Water.* 60
Who battled for the *T*, the Just, *In Mem. lvi* 18
Ring out the false, ring in the *t*. „ *cvi* 8
taking *t* for false, or false for *t*; *Geraint and E.* 4
Could all of *t* and noble in knight and man *Holy Grail* 882
The Good, the *T*, the Pure, the Just— *Locksley H., Sixty* 71
And sunder false from *t*, *Mechanophilus* 2
True-heroic why Not make her *t-h*— *Princess, Con.* 20
True-love (adj.) and carolling as he went A *t-l* ballad, *Lancelot and E.* 705
True-love (s) He gave me a friend, and a true *t-l*, *D. of the O. Year* 13
Truer A heart that doats on *t* charms, *L. C. V. de Vere* 14
t to the law within? *Princess v* 189
And that he wears a *t* crown *Ode on Well.* 276
no *t* Time himself Can prove you, *A Dedication* 1
Lest we should set one *t* on his throne. *Balin and Balan* 7
A seven-months' babe had been a *t* gift. *Merlin and V.* 711
Henceforth be *t* to your faultless lord? *Lancelot and E.* 119
mine is the firmer seat, The *t* lance: „ 447
But mine are *t*, seeing they profess *Last Tournament* 85
'Bury them as God's *t* images Are daily buried.' *Sir J. Oldcastle* 140
Be *t* to your promise. There! *To Mary Boyle* 5
his *t* name Is 'Onward,' no discordance *D. of the Duke of C.* 13
Truer-hearted There is no *t-h*—ah, you seem *Princess iii* 208
Truest *T* friend and noblest foe; „ *vi* 7
Not die; but live a life of *t* breath, *Maud I xviii* 53
Our noblest brother, and our *t* man, *Gareth and L.* 565
Thy noblest and thy *t*!' „ 568
The *t* eyes that ever answer'd Heaven, *Geraint and E.* 842
Truest (*continued*) Deeming our courtesy is the *t* law, *Lancelot and E.* 712
As prowest knight and *t* lover, *Pelleas and E.* 350
'No frost there,' so he said, 'as in *t* Love no Death.' *The Wreck* 80
And while I communed with my *t* self, *The Ring* 181
The *t*, kindliest, noblest-hearted wife *Romney's R.* 35
True-sublime Why not make her true-heroic—*t-s*? *Princess, Con.* 20
True-touched With its *t-t* pulses in the flow *Lover's Tale i* 205
Truly For *t* as thou sayest, a Fairy King *Gareth and L.* 258
'Ay, *t* of a truth, And in a sort, „ 837
Trumpet And *t's* blown for wars; *D. of F. Women* 20
And bade him cry, with sound of *t*, *Godiva* 36
The shattering *t* shrilleth high, *Sir Galahad* 5
Brake with a blast of *t's* from the gate, *Princess, Pro.* 42
in the halloo Will topple to the *t* down, „ *ii* 232
we hear A *t* in the distance pealing news „ *iv* 81
A moment, while the *t's* blow, „ 581
With the air of the *t* round him, „ *v* 162
till the *t* blared At the barrier like a wild horn „ 485
and once more The *t*, and again: „ 488
Last, the Prussian *t* blew; *Ode on Well.* 127
Warble, O bugle, and *t*, blare! *W. to Alexandra* 14
Altho' the *t* blew so loud. *In Mem. xcvi* 24
A martial song like a *t's* call! *Maud I v* 5
the *t's* blew, And Arthur's knighthood *Com. of Arthur* 480
'Blow *t*, for the world is white with May; Blow *t*, the long night hath roll'd away! „ 482
'Blow *t*! he will lift us from the dust. Blow *t*! live the strength and die the lust! „ 491
Then Yniol's nephew, after *t* blown, *Marr. of Geraint* 551
Sound on a dreadful *t*, summoning her; *Geraint and E.* 383
and anon The *t's* blew; *Lancelot and E.* 454
then the *t's* blew Proclaiming his the prize, „ 500
after *t* blown, her name And title, *Pelleas and E.* 115
Up to the summit, and the *t's* blew. „ 167
The sudden *t* sounded as in a dream *Last Tournament* 151
Far off a solitary *t* blew. *Guinevere* 529
Thro' the thick night I hear the *t* blow: „ 569
when the *t* of judgment 'ill sound, *Rizpah* 57
like the clear voice when a *t* shrills, *Achilles over the T.* 19
Pause! before you sound the *t*, *Locksley H., Sixty* 116
The *t*, the gallop, the charge, *Heavy Brigade* 13
t's of victory, groans of defeat; *Vastness* 8
Fame blowing out from her golden *t* „ 21
All at once the *t* blew, *Happy* 75
Let blow the *t* strongly while I pray, *Doubt and Prayer* 10
Trumpet-blast either side, with *t-b*, *Com. of Arthur* 102
Trumpet-blowings such fire for fame, Such *t-b* in it, *Merlin and V.* 418
cry of a great jousts With *t-b* ran on *Last Tournament* 52
Trumpeter blew the swoll'n cheek of a *t*, *Princess ii* 364
he bad his *t* sound To the charge, *Heavy Brigade* 8
Trumpeting *See* **Tiny-trumpeting**
Trundled Her mother *t* to the gate *Talking Oak* 111
Trunk Ruin'd *t's* on wither'd forks, *Vision of Sin* 93
till the dry old *t's* about us, dead, *Holy Grail* 495
Look, he stands, *T* and bough, *The Oak* 14
Trust (s) And *t* and hope till things should cease, *Supp. Confessions* 31
and guard about With triple-mailèd *t*, „ 66
'Go, vexed Spirit, sleep in *t*; *Two Voices* 115
She ceased in tears, fallen from hope and *t*: *D. of F. Women* 257
breathing love and *t* against her lip: *Audley Court* 69
Break lock and seal: betray the *t*: *You might have won* 18
On providence and *t* in Heaven, *Enoch Arden* 205
and *t* in all things high Comes easy to him, *Princess vii* 329
On God and Godlike men we build our *t*. *Ode on Well.* 266
sensuous frame Is rack'd with pangs that conquer *t*; *In Mem. l* 6
whether *t* in things above Be dimm'd of sorrow, „ *lxxxv* 9
Cry thro' the sense to hearten *t* „ *cxvi* 7
why not? I have neither hope nor *t*; *Maud I i* 30
charm Of woven paces and of waving hands, As proof of *t*. *Merlin and V.* 331
I, feeling that you felt me worthy *t*, „ 334
Too curious Vivien, tho' you talk of *t*, „ 358
Yea, if ye talk of *t* I tell you this, „ 360
Poor Vivien had not done to win his *t* „ 863
That proof of *t*—so often ask'd in vain! „ 920

Trust (s) (*continued*) Should have in it an absoluter t To make — *Lancelot and E.* 1192
and his *t* that Heaven Will blow the tempest — *To the Queen ii* 46
My lily of truth and *t*— — *Ancient Sage* 160

Trust (verb) *I could* t *Your kindness.* — *To the Queen* 19
' *T* me, in bliss I shall abide — *Palace of Art* 18
To make him *t* his modest worth, — *L. C. V. de Vere* 46
T me, Clara Vere de Vere, — „ 49
I think my time is near. I *t* it is. — *May Queen, Con.* 41
I *t* That I am whole, and clean, — *St. S. Stylites* 212
t me on my word, Hard wood I am, — *Talking Oak* 170
T me, cousin, all the current of my being — *Locksley Hall* 24
He *t's* to light on something fair; — *Day-Dm., Arrival* 20
Henceforth I *t* the man alone, — *The Letters* 31
And *t* me while I turn'd the page, — *To E. L.* 9
Raw from the nursery—who could *t* a child? — *Aylmer's Field* 264
first I fronted him, Said, ' *T* him not; ' — *Sea Dreams* 71
' I *t* you,' said that other ' for we two all, I *t*, may yet be well.' — *Princess ii* 336
„ 361
' O friend, we *t* that you esteem'd us not Too harsh — „ *iii* 198
To harm the thing that *t's* him, — „ *iv* 248
nest of traitors—none to *t* Since our arms fail'd— — „ *v* 426
I *t* that there is no one hurt to death, — „ *vi* 242
And *t*, not love, you less. — „ 296
Lay thy sweet hands in mine and *t* to me.' — „ *vii* 366
May *t* himself; and after praise and scorn, — *A Dedication* 6
And yet we *t* it comes from thee, — *In Mem., Pro.* 23
I *t* he lives in thee, — „ 39
Yet if some voice that man could *t* — „ *xxxv* 1
Nor dare she *t* a larger lay, — „ *xlviii* 13
Oh yet we *t* that somehow good — „ *liv* 1
I can but *t* that good shall fall At last— — „ 14
And faintly *t* the larger hope. — „ *lv* 20
But *t* that those we call the dead — „ *cxviii* 5
I *t* I have not wasted breath: — „ *cxx* 1
To one that with us works, and *t*, — „ *cxxxi* 8
For I *t* if an enemy's fleet came yonder — *Maud I i* 49
I *t* that it is not so. — „ *xvi* 30
I *t* that I did not talk (repeat) — „ *xix* 12, 16
Let chance what will, I *t* thee to the death.' — *Com. of Arthur* 134
thy chief man Sir Lancelot whom he *t's* to overthrow, — *Gareth and L.* 620
His arms are old, he *t's* the harden'd skin— — „ 1139
Canst thou not *t* the limbs thy God hath given, — „ 1388
' *t* me not at all or all in all.' (repeat) — *Merlin and V.* 384, 398, 449
I *t* That you *t* me in your own nobleness, — *Lancelot and E.* 1194
I *t* We are green in Heaven's eyes; — *Holy Grail* 37
T me, long ago I should have died, — *Lover's Tale i* 86
says The common voice, if one may *t* it: — *Sisters (E. and E.)* 37
T the Hand of Light will lead her people, — *On Jub. Q. Victoria* 68
To make him *t* his life, and give His fealty — *The Wanderer* 11

Trusted some sick man declined, And *t* any cure. — *Palace of Art* 156
t as he was with her, The sole succeeder — *Aylmer's Field* 293
fool! and *t* him with all, All my poor scrapings — *Sea Dreams* 76
Who *t* God was love indeed — *In Mem. lvi* 13
his chamberlain, to whom He *t* all things, — *Com. of Arthur* 146
t his liege-lord Would yield him this large honour — *Gareth and L.* 396
Too much I *t* when I told you that, — *Merlin and V.* 361
Yea, by God's rood, I *t* you too much.' — „ 376
Have I not sworn? I am not *t*. — „ 527
A woman and not *t*, — „ 530
To have *t* me as he hath *t* thee. — *Lancelot and E.* 591

Trustee came *T's* and Aunts and Uncles. — *Edwin Morris* 121

Trustful The *t* infant on the knee! — *Supp. Confessions* 41
the child would twine A *t* hand, — *In Mem. cix* 19
who take Their pastime now the *t* King is gone!' — *Lancelot and E.* 101
And *t* courtesies of household life, — *Guinevere* 86
Truthful, *t*, looking upward to the practised hustings-liar; — *Locksley H., Sixty* 123
Our kindlier, *t* Jaques, past away! — *To W. H. Brookfield* 11

Trusting *T* no longer that earthly flower — *Despair* 35

Truth When I went forth in quest of *t*, — *Supp. Confessions* 141
T may stand forth unmoved of change, — „ 144
Fair-fronted *T* shall droop not now — *Clear-headed friend* 12

Truth (*continued*) Weak *T* a-leaning on her crutch, Wan, wasted *T* in her utmost need. — *Clear-headed friend* 18
to fling The winged shafts of *t*, — *The Poet* 26
Thus *t* was multiplied on *t*, — „ 33
And all at once a pleasant *t* I learn'd, — *The Bridesmaid* 9
' This *t* within thy mind rehearse, — *Two Voices* 25
Still moving after *t* long sought, — „ 62
Named man, may hope some *t* to find, — „ 176
' Cry, faint not: either *T* is born — „ 181
was there Not less than *t* design'd. — *Palace of Art* 92
She spake some certain *t's* of you. — *L. C. V. de Vere* 36
In *t*, How *should* I soothe you anyway, — *To J. S.* 57
Her open eyes desire the *t*. — *Of old sat Freedom* 17
To follow flying steps of *T* — *Love thou thy land* 75
a *t* Looks freshest in the fashion of the day: — *The Epic.* 31
Begin to feel the *t* and stir of day, — *M. d'Arthur, Ep.* 19
Shall Error in the round of time Still father *T*? — *Love and Duty* 5
That make a man feel strong in speaking *t*; — „ 70
With quiet eyes unfaithful to the *t*, — „ 94
Like *t's* of Science waiting to be caught— — *Golden Year* 17
Amy, speak, and speak the *t* to me, — *Locksley Hall* 23
Cursed be the social lies that warp us from the living *t*! — „ 60
this is *t* the poet sings, — „ 75
Bring *t* that sways the soul of men? — *Day-Dm., Sleep. P.* 52
Nor finds a closer *t* than this All-graceful head, — „ *L'Envoi* 37
The *t*, that flies the flowing can, — *Will Water.* 171
' I speak the *t*: you are my child. — *Lady Clare* 24
I speak the *t*, as I live by bread! — „ 26
Trying his *t* and his long-sufferance, — *Enoch Arden* 470
and *t* and love are strength, And you are happy: — *Aylmer's Field* 365
To make a *t* less harsh, I often grew Tired — *Lucretius* 225
My golden work in which I told a *t* — „ 260
point you out the shadow from the *t*! — *Princess i* 84
yet, to speak the *t*, I rate your chance — „ 160
' Albeit so mask'd, Madam, I love the *t*; — „ *ii* 213
So my mother clutch'd The *t* at once, — „ *iii* 61
wears her error like a crown To blind the *t* and me: — „ 112
I know the Prince, I prize his *t*: — „ 233
and dream and *t* Flow'd from me; — „ *v* 541
call her hard and cold which seem'd a *t*: — „ *vii* 98
sought far less for *t* than power In knowledge: — „ 236
dreams Are but the needful preludes of the *t*: — „ *Con.* 74
never sold the *t* to serve the hour, — *Ode on Well.* 179
Between your peoples *t* and manful peace, — *W. to Marie Alex.* 49
That a lie which is half a *t* — *Grandmother* 30
But a lie which is part a *t* — „ 32
I know for a *t*, there's none of them — „ 85
So I pray you tell the *t* to me. — *The Victim* 48
Forgive them where they fail in *t*, — *In Mem., Pro.* 43
I HELD it *t*, with him who sings — „ *i* 1
To which she links a *t* divine! — „ *xxxiii* 12
Tho' *t's* in manhood darkly join, — „ *xxxvi* 1
Where *t* in closest words shall fail, — „ 6
When *t* embodied in a tale Shall enter — „ 7
Of comfort clasp'd in *t* reveal'd; — „ *xxxvii* 22
reaps A *t* from one that loves and knows? — „ *xlii* 12
Yet who would preach it as a *t* — „ *liii* 11
I wake, and I discern the *t*; — „ *lxviii* 14
This *t* came borne with bier and pall, — „ *lxxxv* 1
Ring in the love of *t* and right, — „ *cvi* 23
Nor dream of human love and *t*, — „ *cxviii* 3
Because he felt so fix'd in *t*: — „ *cxxv* 8
Proclaiming social *t* shall spread, — „ *cxxvii* 5
The *t's* that never can be proved — „ *cxxxi* 10
I have walk'd awake with *T*. — *Maud I xix* 4
whether there were *t* in anything Said by these three, — *Com. of Arthur* 242
and ask'd him if these things were *t*— — „ 398
And *t* is this to me, and that to thee; — „ 407
And *t* or clothed or naked let it be. — „ 408
but tell thou these the *t*.' — *Gareth and L.* 251
' And here is *t*; but an it please thee not, Take thou the *t* as thou hast told it me. — „ 256
beard That looks as white as utter *t*, — „ 281
' Ay, truly of a *t*, And in a sort, — „ 837

Truth (*continued*) Where should be t if not in Arthur's hall, — Gareth and L. 1254
Arms? t! I know not: all are wanted here. — Marr. of Geraint 289
t, good t, I know not, save, — „ 290
Said Arthur 'Thou hast ever spoken t; — Balin and Balan 73
'Nay' said the churl, 'our devil is a t, — „ 302
But thou art man, and canst abide a t, — „ 501
lightest word Is mere white t in simple nakedness, — „ 518
Breathed in a dismal whisper 'Is it t.' — „ 527
and shown the t betimes, That old true filth, and bottom of the well, Where T is hidden. — Merlin and V. 46
for shall I tell you t? You seem'd that wave — „ 301
By Heaven that hears I tell you the clean t, — „ 343
He brought, not found it therefore: take the t.' — „ 719
In t, but one thing now— — „ 918
Urged him to speak against the t, — Lancelot and E. 92
In lieu of idly dallying with the t, — „ 590
I swear by t and knighthood that I gave No cause, — „ 1297
And as ye saw it ye have spoken t. — Holy Grail 880
And love of t, and all that makes a man. — Guinevere 483
yet, in t, Fair speech was his and delicate of phrase, — Lover's Tale i 718
told them my tale, God's own t— — Rizpah 34
That traitor to King Richard and the t, — Sir J. Oldcastle 171
showing courts and kings a t — Columbus 37
morning-star to the full round of t. — „ 44
and murmur down T in the distance— — „ 121
These hard memorials of our t to Spain — „ 196
And speak the t that no man may believe.' — Tiresias 50
I speak the t Believe I speak it, — „ 155
My lily of t and trust— — Ancient Sage 160
every heart that loves with t is equal to endure. — The Flight 104
T, for T is T, he worshipt, — Locksley H., Sixty 59
T for t, and good for good! — „ 71
these would feel and follow T — „ 119
led by Justice, Love, and T; — „ 161
For man is a lover of T, — Dead Prophet 44
Yet a t is a t,' she cried. — „ 60
surely to be found When T is found again. — Pref. Poem Broth. Son. 16
By one side-path, from simple t; — To Marq. of Dufferin 28
and you the soul of T In Hubert? — The Ring 62
Grafted on half a t; — Romney's R. 42
One t will damn me with the mindless mob, — „ 120
neither of them stands behind the screen of thy t. — Akbar's D., Inscrip. 7
held His people by the bridle-rein of T. — Akbar's Dream 85
and Love The net of t?' — „ 88
Thro' after ages in the love of T, The t of Love. — „ 101
nurse my children on the milk of T, — „ 162
T and Peace And Love and Justice came and dwelt therein; — „ 180
T, Peace, Love and Justice came and dwelt therein, — „ 193
violates virgin T for a coin or a cheque. — The Dawn 15
And I clash with an iron T, — The Dreamer 6
Truthful half as good, as kind, As t, — Princess v 202
This t change in thee has kill'd it. — „ vii 350
The t King will doom me when I speak.' — Gareth and L. 324
T, trustful, looking upward to the practised hustings-liar; — Locksley H., Sixty 123
So princely, tender, t, reverent, pure— — D. of the Duke of C. 4
Truthless t violence mourn'd by the Wise, — Vastness 5
Truth-lover T-l was our English Duke; — Ode on Well. 189
Truth-speaking T-s, brave, good livers, — Gareth and L. 424
Truth-teller T-t was our England's Alfred named; — Ode on Well. 188
Try 'Twere well to question him, and t — Talking Oak 27
Nor thro' the questions men may t, — In Mem. cxxiv 7
Like him who *tries* the bridge he fears may fail, — Geraint and E. 303
Should t this charm on whom ye say ye love.' — Merlin and V. 525
should ye t him with a merry one — Pelleas and E. 198
Trying T his truth and his long-sufferance, — Enoch Arden 470
And t to pass to the sea; — Maud I xxi 7
happier using the knife than in t to save the limb, — In the Child. Hosp. 6
Tryst That ever bided t at village stile, — Merlin and V. 378
Tsernogora Great T! never since thine own — Montenegro 12
Tudor-chimnied a T-c bulk Of mellow brickwork — Edwin Morris 11
Tued (worried) (*See also* **Tew**) But 'e t and moil'd issén deäd, — N. Farmer, N. S. 52
Tuff hornblende, rag and trap and t, — Princess iii 362
Tuft (s) In t's of rosy-tinted snow; — Two Voices 60
Behind yon whispering t of oldest pine, — Œnone 88
A light-green t of plumes she bore — Sir L. and Q. G. 26
Tuft (verb) When rosy plumelets t the larch, — In Mem. xci 1
And t with grass a feudal tower; — „ cxxviii 20
Tufted And the t plover pipe along the fallow lea, — May Queen, N. Y's. E. 18
Filling with purple gloom the vacancies Between the t hills, — Lover's Tale i 3
Tugging *See* **A-tuggin**
Tuk (took) Father Molowny he t her in han', — Tomorrow 55
Tulip sometimes a Dutch love For t's; — Gardener's D. 193
Deep t's dash'd with fiery dew, — In Mem. lxxxiii 11
Thro' the fire of the t and poppy, — V. of Maeldune 43
Tumble (s) after a long t about the Cape — Enoch Arden 532
Should I flounder awhile without a t — Hendacasyllabics 9
Maud with her venturous climbings and t's — Maud I i 69
Tumble (verb) Lest he should swoon and t — Enoch Arden 774
'They mounted, Ganymedes, To t, Vulcans, — Princess iii 72
T's a billow on chalk and sand; — To F. D. Maurice 24
Hard, hard, hard is it, only not to t, — Hendecasyllabics 13
Look how they t the blossom, the mad little tits! — Window, Ay 9
Dark bulks that t half alive, — In Mem. lxx 11
like a crag that t's from the cliff, — Marr. of Geraint 318
a rougher gust might t a stormier wave, — The Wreck 131
Tumbled (adj. and part.) Among the fragments t from the glens, — Œnone 222
babies roll'd about Like t fruit in grass; — Princess, Pro. 83
And had a cousin t on the plain, — „ vi 319
Among the t fragments of the hills.' — Lancelot and E. 1427
Rear'd on the t ruins of an old fane — St. Telemachus 6
Tumbled (verb) (*See also* **Tummled**) And half the chimneys t. — The Goose 48
T the tawny rascal at his feet, — Aylmer's Field 230
you t down and broke The glass — Sea Dreams 141
And every Muse t a science in. — Princess ii 399
And t on the purple footcloth, — „ iv 286
And t half the mellowing pears! — In Mem. lxxxix 20
That t in the Godless deep; — „ cxxiv 12
then in the mere beside T it; — Gareth and L. 816
And t back into the kitchen-knave, — „ 1228
To hang whatever knight of thine I fought And t. — Last Tournament 454
She t his helpless corpse about. — Dead Prophet 65
Tumbling (*See also* **Tummlin'**) T the hollow helmets of the fallen, — Pass. of Arthur 132
Tummled (tumbled) An' I t athurt the craädle — North. Cobbler 35
t up stairs, fur I 'eärd 'im, — Owd Roä 63
Tummlin' (tumbling) when the rigtree was t' in— — „ 115
Tumult the t of their acclaim is roll'd — Dying Swan 33
Laid by the t of the fight. — Margaret 26
and the t of my life; — Locksley Hall 110
in an hour Of civic t jam the doors, — Lucretius 169
call'd Across the t and the t fell. — Princess iv 497
The cataract and the t and the kings — „ 564
Is wrought with t of acclaim. — In Mem. lxxv 20
And saw the t of the halls; — „ lxxxvii 4
O'erlook'st the t from afar, — „ cxxvii 19
For a t shakes the city, — Maud II iv 50
'What means the t in the town?' — Marr. of Geraint 259
And ate with t in the naked hall, — Geraint and E. 605
(Because the hall was all in t— — Holy Grail 269
Tumultuous So the silent colony hearing her t adversaries — Boädicea 78
Tumultuously t Down thro' the whitening hazels — Enoch Arden 378
Tundher (thunder) the t, an' rain that fell, — Tomorrow 23
Tune (s) wildest wailings never out of t — Sea Dreams 231
howl in t With nothing but the Devil!' — „ 260
Their hearts of old have beat in t, — In Mem. xcvii 10
To the dancers dancing in t; — Maud I xxii 16
'Ye might have moved slow-measure to my t, — Last Tournament 282
and learn'd To lisp in t together; — Lover's Tale i 258
MIDNIGHT—in no midsummer t — Pref. Poem Broth. Son. 1
Tune (verb) Who scarce can t his high majestic sense — Lover's Tale i 475
Tuned *See* **Full-tuned**

Tuneful 'Tis said he had a *t* tongue, — *Amphion* 17
Tunic display A *t* white as May ! — *Prog. of Spring* 65
Tunnel A railway there, a *t* here, — *Mechanophilus* 7
Turbia What Roman strength *T* show'd — *The Daisy* 5
Turbid Who let the *t* streams of rumour flow — *Ode on Well.* 181
Turbulence For in that realm of lawless *t*, — *Geraint and E.* 521
Turbulent I that knew him fierce and *t* — *Marr. of Geraint* 447
That, compass'd round with *t* sound, — *Will* 7
Turf (s) In cool soft *t* upon the bank, — *Arabian Nights* 96
all the *t* was rich in plots — *Marr. of Geraint* 660
cut his bit o' *t* for the fire ? — *Tomorrow* 65
no one came, the *t* was fresh, — *Prog. of Spring* 72
Turf (verb) after furious battle *t's* the slain — *Merlin and V.* 657
Turk arm'd by day and night Against the *T* ; — *Montenegro* 4
Turkey-cock *See* **Stag-tuckey**
Turkis *T* and agate and almondine : — *The Merman* 32
Each like a garnet or a *t* in it ; — *Marr. of Geraint* 661
Turkish beating back the swarm Of *T* Islam — *Montenegro* 11
Turn (s) thro' many a bowery *t* A walk — *Arabian Nights* 56
In every elbow and *t*, — *Ode to Memory* 62
Every *t* and glance of thine, — *Eleänore* 52
'Some *t* this sickness yet might take, — *Two Voices* 55
he that shuts Love out, in *t* shall be Shut out from Love, — *To ——, With Pal. of Art* 14
Katie, once I did her a good *t*, — *The Brook* 74
with every *t* Lived thro' her to the tips — *Princess ii* 39
made a sudden *t* As if to speak, — „ *iv* 394
When each by *t's* was guide to each, — *In Mem. xxiii* 13
As some wild *t* of anger, or a mood — *Merlin and V.* 521
Might feel some sudden *t* of anger — „ 531
every *t* and depth Between is clearer in my life — *Lover's Tale i* 148
An' he took three *t's* in the rain, — *First Quarrel* 75
Thy leaves possess the season in their *t*, — *Prog. of Spring* 107
Turn (verb) But when I *t* away, — *Madeline* 36
did I *t* away The boat-head down a broad canal — *Arabian Nights* 24
Fold thine arms, *t* to thy rest. — *A Dirge* 3
Thou wilt not *t* upon thy bed ; — „ 15
'*T* and look on me : I am that Rosamond, — *D. of F. Women* 250
Imitates God, and *t's* her face To every land — *On a Mourner* 2
as a thorn *T's* from the sea ; — *Audley Court* 55
Jack, *t* the horses' heads and home again.' — *Walk. to the Mail* 46
with what delighted eyes I *t* to yonder oak. — *Talking Oak* 8
In the Spring a young man's fancy lightly *t's* to thoughts of love. — *Locksley Hall* 20
T thee, *t* thee on thy pillow : — „ 86
What is that which I should *t* to, — „ 99
I will *t* that earlier page. — „ 107
I will tell it. *T* your face, — *Day-Dm., Pro.* 17
Had ever half the power to *t* This wheel — *Will Water.* 83
And beneath the gate she *t's* ; — *L. of Burleigh* 44
Proudly *t's* he round and kindly, — „ 55
'Mine too' said Philip '*t* and *t* about :' — *Enoch Arden* 29
to all things could he *t* his hand. — „ 813
he past To *t* and ponder those three hundred scrolls — *Lucretius* 12
as a parrot *t's* Up thro' gilt wires — *Princess, Pro.* 171
secular emancipation *t's* Of half this world, — „ *ii* 289
but brooding *t* The book of scorn, — „ *v* 141
Yet, as it may, *t's* toward him, — „ *vii* 143
I heard her *t* the page ; — „ 190
Till you should *t* to dearer matters, — *To F. D. Maurice* 35
t's Once more to set a ringlet right ; — *In Mem. vi* 35
I should *t* mine ears and hear — „ *xxxv* 8
O *t* thee round, resolve the doubt ; — „ *xliv* 14
Yet *t* thee to the doubtful shore, — „ *lxi* 9
I *t* about, I find a trouble — „ *lxviii* 9
who *t's* a musing eye On songs, and deeds, — „ *lxxvii* 2
passing, *t* the page that tells A grief, — „ 10
But *t's* his burthen into gain. — „ *lxxx* 12
I *t* to go : my feet are set — „ *cii* 21
knew not whither he should *t* for aid. — *Com. of Arthur* 40
but *t* the blade and ye shall see, — „ 303
To *t* the broach, draw water, or hew wood, — *Gareth and L.* 486
Larded thy last, except thou *t* and fly. — „ 1084
ye cleave His armour off him, these will *t* the blade.' — „ 1095
T, Fortune, *t* thy wheel and lower the proud ; — *Marr. of Geraint* 347
'*T*, Fortune, *t* thy wheel with smile or frown ; — „ 350
Turn (verb) (*continued*) *T* thy wild wheel thro' sunshine, storm, — *Marr. of Geraint* 348
'*T*, *t* thy wheel above the staring crowd ; — „ 356
Before he *t* to fall seaward again, — *Geraint and E.* 117
break her sports with graver fits, *T* red or pale, — *Merlin and V.* 181
in a wink the false love *t's* to hate) — „ 852
That *t's* its back on the salt blast, — *Pelleas and E.* 544
What miracle could *t* ? — *Sir J. Oldcastle* 180
And thought to *t* my face from Spain, — *Columbus* 57
I know not where to *t* ; — *The Flight* 74
Crook and *t* upon itself — *Locksley H., Sixty* 236
an' the wind wasn't like to *t*. — *Owd Roä* 104
But you will *t* the pages. — *The Ring* 127
Less profile ! *t* to me—three-quarter face. — *Romney's R.* 98
Would *t*, and glare at me, and point and jeer, — „ 136
To-day, before you *t* again To thoughts — *To Master of B.* 13
drew from out the boundless deep *T's* again home. — *Crossing the Bar* 8
Turn (torn) Sally wur sloomy an' draggle taäil'd in an owd *t* gown, — *North. Cobbler* 41
Turn'd (*See also* **Half-turn'd, Thrice-turn'd, Torn'd**)
eyes were darken'd wholly, *T* to tower'd Camelot. — *L. of Shalott iv* 32
think, where'er she *t* her sight The airy hand — *Palace of Art* 225
Growths of jasmine *t* Their humid arms — *D. of F. Women* 69
True love *t* round on fixed poles, — *Love thou thy land* 5
Eustace *t*, and smiling said to me, — *Gardener's D.* 97
'Look ! look !' Before he ceased I *t*, — „ 121
nor from her tendance *t* Into the world without ; — „ 144
Then he *t* His face and pass'd— — *Dora* 150
And all my heart *t* from her, — *Audley Court* 54
She *t*, we closed, we kiss'd, — *Edwin Morris* 114
I read, and fled by night, and flying *t* : — „ 134
I *t* once more, close-button'd to the storm ; — „ 136
And *t* the cowls adrift : — *Talking Oak* 48
dipt and rose, And *t* to look at her. — „ 132
That show the year is *t*. — „ 176
And she *t*—her bosom shaken — *Locksley Hall* 27
and *t* it in his glowing hands ; — „ 31
Are touch'd, are *t* to finest air. — *Sir Galahad* 72
Bitterly weeping I *t* away : (repeat) — *Edward Gray* 6, 34
He *t* and kiss'd her where she stood : — *Lady Clare* 82
Pale he *t* and red, — *The Captain* 62
I *t* and humm'd a bitter song — *The Letters* 9
With half a sigh she *t* the key, — „ 18
And trust me while I *t* the page, — *To E. L.* 9
when he *t* The current of his talk to graver things — *Enoch Arden* 202
But *t* her own toward the wall and wept. — „ 283
There she *t*, She rose, and fixt her swimming eyes — „ 324
t our foreheads from the falling sun, — *The Brook* 165
crippled lad, and coming *t* to fly, — *Aylmer's Field* 519
then *t*, and groaning said, 'Forgive ! — *Sea Dreams* 59
The woman half *t* round from him she loved, — „ 286
t to me with 'As you will ; Heroic if you will, — *Princess, Pro.* 220
We *t* to go, but Cyril took the child, — „ *ii* 362
then we *t*, we wound About the cliffs, — „ *iii* 359
She spoke, and *t* her sumptuous head — „ *iv* 152
You *t* your warmer currents all to her, — „ 301
Half-drooping from her, *t* her face, — „ 368
Gama *t* to me : 'We fear, indeed, — „ *v* 120
King, camp and college *t* to hollow shows ; — „ 478
And *t* each face her way : — „ *vi* 144
Who *t* half-round to Psyche as she sprang — „ 209
So she, and *t* askance a wintry eye : — „ 330
She *t* ; the very nape of her white neck — „ 343
So their fair college *t* to hospital ; — „ *vii* 17
She *t* ; she paused ; She stoop'd ; — „ 154
Flash'd as they *t* in air — *Light Brigade* 28
And he *t*, and I saw his eyes all wet, — *Grandmother* 49
But he *t* and claspt me in his arms, — „ 55
T as he sat, and struck the keys — *The Islet* 7
And bird in air, and fishes *t* — *The Victim* 19
even when she *t*, the curse Had fall'n, — *In Mem. vi* 37
But thou art *t* to something strange, — „ *xli* 5
Ere childhood's flaxen ringlet *t* — „ *lxxix* 15
And left his coal all *t* into gold — *Maud I x* 11
But his essences *t* the live air sick, — „ *xiii* 11
turning toward him wheresoe'er he *t*, — *Gareth and L.* 174

Turn'd (*continued*) mocker ending here *T* to the right, *Gareth and L.* 295
t Fled down the lane of access to the King, „ 660
Before them when he *t* from watching him. „ 1032
Then *t* the noble damsel smiling at him, „ 1188
Who, with back *t*, and bow'd above his work, *Marr. of Geraint* 267
T, and beheld the four, and all his face „ 558
Who, after, *t* her daughter round, „ 740
like that false pair who *t* Flying, *Geraint and E.* 176
Enid, the loss of whom hath *t* me wild— „ 308
With that he *t* and look'd as keenly at her „ 430
At this he *t* all red and paced his hall, „ 668
he *t* his face And kiss'd her climbing, „ 760
saw her Pass into it, *t* to the Prince, „ 887
And spake no word until the shadow *t*; *Balin and Balan* 45
Whereat she smiled and *t* her to the King, „ 201
and *t* aside into the woods, „ 433
and, Vivien following him, *T* to her: *Merlin and V.* 33
Have *t* to tyrants when they came to power) „ 518
She paused, she *t* away, she hung her head, „ 887
There to his proud horse Lancelot *t*, *Lancelot and E.* 347
he *t* Her counsel up and down within his mind, „ 368
And sharply *t* about to hide her face, „ 608
From foot to forehead exquisitely *t*: „ 643
Then *t* Sir Torre, and being in his moods „ 799
so *t* Sighing, and feign'd a sleep until he slept. „ 841
And now to right she *t*, and now to left, „ 900
While thus he spoke, half *t* away, the Queen Brake „ 1197
then *t* the tongueless man From the half-face „ 1261
' He ceased; and Arthur *t* to whom at first *Holy Grail* 751
with a slow smile *t* the lady round *Pelleas and E.* 91
Glanced down upon her, *t* and went her way. „ 185
And this persistence *t* her scorn to wrath. „ 218
Then *t*, and so return'd, and groaning „ 451
Awaking knew the sword, and *t* herself „ 489
her ever-veering fancy *t* To Pelleas, „ 493
Then Arthur *t* to Kay the seneschal, *Last Tournament* 89
the King *T* to him saying, ' Is it then so well? „ 114
and sharply *t* North by the gate. „ 127
' Good: an I *t* away my love for thee „ 705
He spoke, he *t*, then, flinging round her neck, „ 749
till it touch'd her, and she *t*— *Guinevere* 80
And pale he *t*, and reel'd, „ 304
And even then he *t*; and more and more „ 600
he slowly *t* and slowly clomb The last hard foot-step *Pass. of Arthur* 446
We *t*: our eyes met: hers were bright, *Lover's Tale i* 441
Cries of the partridge like a rusty key *T* in a lock, „ *ii* 116
I *t*: my heart Shrank in me, „ *iii* 37
At once they *t*, and caught and brought him in „ *iv* 376
But I *t* my face from *him*, an' he *t* *his* face an' he went. *First Quarrel* 84
Sally she *t* a tongue-banger, *North. Cobbler* 23
I fun', when 'er back wur *t*, „ 31
An' then 'e *t* to the sun, „ 48
I never *t* my back upon Don or devil yet.' *The Revenge* 31
Their favourite—which I call ' The Tables *T*.' *Sisters (E. and E.)* 3
' No harm, no harm ' I *t* again, „ 213
he *t* to me, ' Ay, good woman, *In the Child. Hosp.* 20
Who ever *t* upon his heel to hear *Tiresias* 72
and *t* in her haste and fled. *The Wreck* 62
as I *t*—' The heart, the heart! ' „ 104
And we *t* to the growing dawn, *Despair* 22
and we *t* to each other, we kiss'd, „ 53
are both of them *t* into blood, „ 91
From darkness into daylight, *t* and spoke. *Ancient Sage* 8
hope I catch at vanishes and youth is *t* to woe. *The Flight* 16
she *t* herself roun' Wid a diamond dhrop *Tomorrow* 27
t half round, and he bad his trumpeter sound *Heavy Brigade* 8
we *t* to each other, whispering, all dismay'd, „ 44
—and *t*, And fled by many a waste, *Demeter and P.* 73
I *t* in ageän, an' I thowt o' the good owd times *Owd Roä* 43
An' all along o' the feller as *t* 'is back „ 48
She *t*, and in her soft imperial way *The Ring* 267
spoke no more, but *t* and pass'd away. „ 342
Door-handles *t* when none was at the door, „ 412
He groan'd, he *t*, and in the mist at once *Death of Œnone* 49

Turn'd (*continued*) *T* him again to boy, for up he sprang, *St. Telemachus* 58
I *t* away And the hard blue eyes have it still, *Charity* 9
So I *t* my face to the wall, „ 27
Turner *See* **Broach-turner**
'Turney (Attorney) fur the '*t's* letters they foller'd sa fast; *Village Wife* 62
Turning (*See also* **A-turnin'**) *t* round a cassia, full in view, *Love and Death* 4
And *t* look'd upon your face, *Miller's D.* 157
t yellow Falls, and floats adown the air. *Lotos-Eaters, C. S.* 30
she *t* on my face The star-like sorrows *D. of F. Women* 90
and *t* I appeal'd To one that stood beside. „ 99
I *t* saw, throned on a flowery rise, „ 125
T to scorn with lips divine *Of old sat Freedom* 23
And dropt the branch she held, and *t*, *Gardener's D.* 157
But *t* now and then to speak with him, *Enoch Arden* 755
He therefore *t* softly like a thief, „ 771
and *t* to the warmth The tender pink *Aylmer's Field* 185
T beheld the Powers of the House „ 287
t round we saw The Lady Blanche's daughter *Princess ii* 320
t to her maids, ' Pitch our pavilion here „ *iii* 345
Half *t* to the broken statue, said, „ *iv* 593
and *t* saw The happy valleys, half in light, „ *Con.* 40
And *t* toward him wheresoe'er he turn'd, *Gareth and L.* 174
on Sir Gareth's *t* to him, cried, ' Stay, felon knight, „ 1219
when *t* to Lynette he told The tale of Gareth, „ 1272
the man Not *t* round, nor looking at him, *Marr. of Geraint* 270
Whereat the armourer *t* all amazed „ 283
and the two Were *t* and admiring it, „ 637
And watch'd the sun blaze on the *t* scythe, *Geraint and E.* 252
t round she saw Dust, and the points of lances „ 448
Was in a manner pleased, and *t*, stood. „ 456
cheek Bulge with the unswallow'd piece, and *t* stared; „ 631
so *t* side by side They past, and Balin started *Balin and Balan* 279
t to her Squire ' This fire of Heaven, „ 456
Roll'd into light, and *t* on its rims *Lancelot and E.* 51
And found no ease in *t* or in rest; „ 901
answer'd not, but, sharply *t*, ask'd Of Gawain, *Holy Grail* 739
the gloom, That follows on the *t* of the world, *Pelleas and E.* 549
Then she, *t* to Pelleas, ' O young knight, „ 595
Dagonet, *t* on the ball of his foot, *Last Tournament* 329
t, past and gain'd Tintagil, half in sea, „ 504
Strange music, and he paused, and *t*— *Guinevere* 239
ever *t* round To gaze upon thee till their eyes *Lover's Tale i* 490
that *t* to me And saying ' It is over: let us go '— „ *iv* 383
T my way, the loveliest face on earth. *Sisters (E. and E.)* 87
And *t* slowly toward him, Akbar said *Akbar's Dream* 4
Is it *t* a fainter red? *The Dawn* 22
Turnip *See* **Tonup**
Turnpike where this byway joins The *t*? *Walk. to the Mail* 5
Turnspit *t's* for the clown, *Princess iv* 516
Turquoise *See* **Turkis**
Turret (adj.) And high above a piece of *t* stair, *Marr. of Geraint* 320
Turret (s) The wind is blowing in *t* and tree. (repeat) *The Sisters* 3, 33
The wind is howling in *t* and tree. „ 9
The wind is roaring in *t* and tree. „ 15
The wind is raging in *t* and tree. „ 21
The wind is raving in *t* and tree. „ 27
upon a rock With *t's* lichen-gilded like a rock: *Edwin Morris* 8
Flags, flutter out upon *t's* and towers! *W. to Alexandra* 15
flower that clings To the *t's* and the walls; *Maud II iv* 34
In the garden by the *t's* Of the old manorial hall. „ 79
spires and *t's* half-way down Prick'd thro' the mist; *Gareth and L.* 193
And solid *t's* topsy-turvy in air: „ 255
clamour of the daws About her hollow *t*, *Geraint and E.* 256
Turtle blackcap warbles, and the *t* purrs, *Prog. of Spring* 55
Tuscan read The *T* poets on the lawn: *In Mem. lxxxix* 24
Tusklike from the floor *T*, arising, *Balin and Balan* 316
Tussle foe perhaps—a *t* for it then! *Sir J. Oldcastle* 196
Tutor (s) one Discuss'd his *t*, rough to common men, *Princess, Pro.* 114
And there we took one *t* as to read: „ 179
her we ask'd of that and this, And who were *t's*. „ *i* 232
Tutor (verb) nor tame and *t* with mine eye *D. of F. Women* 138
Tuwhit Thy *t's* are lull'd, I wot, *The Owl ii* 1
Thee to woo to thy *t*, (repeat) „ 11
Tuwhoo, *t*, *t*, tuwhoo-o-o. „ 14
Tuwhoo Thy *t's* of yesternight, „ 2
Not a whit of thy *t*, „ 10

Tuwhoo (*continued*) *T*, tuwhit, tuwhit, *t-o-o*. *The Owl ii* 14
T ! do you see it ? do ye see the star ? ' *Last Tournament* 346
Twain yearn'd and strove To tear the *t* asunder *Holy Grail* 786
when I knew the *t* Would each waste each, *Tiresias* 68
Twang (s) sharp clear *t* of the golden chords *Sea-Fairies* 38
Twang (verb) *T* out, my fiddle ! shake the twigs ! *Amphion* 61
Twanging Clear as the *t* of a harp. *Kate* 8
Fly *t* headless arrows at the hearts, *Princess ii* 402
Twangled Then he *t* on his harp, And while he *t* *Last Tournament* 251
Twangling while the *t* violin Struck up with Soldier-laddie, *Princess, Pro.* 85
But when the *t* ended, skipt again ; *Last Tournament* 255
Twelve ' he burnt His epic, his King Arthur, some *t* books '— *The Epic* 28
these *t* books of mine Were faint Homeric echoes, „ 38
With *t* great shocks of sound, *Godiva* 74
silver knell Of *t* sweet hours that past *Maud I xviii* 65
in *t* great battles overcame The heathen hordes, *Com. of Arthur* 518
With all the passion of a *t* hours' fast.' *Marr. of Geraint* 306
made Those banners of *t* battles overhead *Balin and Balan* 88
Those *t* sweet moons confused his fatherhood.' *Merlin and V.* 712
Where *t* great windows blazon Arthur's wars, *Holy Grail* 248
Streams thro' the *t* great battles of our King. „ 250
Knights that in *t* great battles splash'd and dyed „ 311
The *t* small damosels white as Innocence, *Last Tournament* 291
In *t* great battles ruining overthrown. *Guinevere* 432
ten or *t* good paces or more. *Def. of Lucknow* 62
—and those *t* gates, Pearl—and I woke, *Columbus* 86
as ye used to do *t* year sin' ! *Spinster's S's.* 59
T times in the year Bring me bliss, *The Ring* 5
Twelve-divided Sent like the *t-d* concubine *Aylmer's Field* 759
Twelvemonth thou shalt serve a *t* and a day.' *Gareth and L.* 157
meat and drink among thy kitchen-knaves A *t* and a day, „ 446
would ride A *t* and a day in quest of it, *Holy Grail* 196
My *t* and a day were pleasant to me.' „ 750
Twenty By *t* thorps, a little town, *The Brook* 29
For here I came, *t* years back— „ 77
About these meadows, *t* years ago.' „ 220
wealth enough for theirs For *t* matches. *Aylmer's Field* 370
Why *t* boys and girls should marry on it, „ 371
So old, that *t* years before, a part Falling „ 508
face to face With *t* months of silence, „ 567
And there thro' *t* posts of telegraph *Princess, Pro.* 77
or so she look'd, Of *t* summers. „ *ii* 108
And cheep and twitter *t* million loves. „ *iv* 101
There was not his like that year in *t* parishes round. *Grandmother* 12
Time to think on it then ; for thou'll be *t* to weeäk. *N. Farmer, N. S.* 7
Thro' *t* folds of twisted dragon, *Gareth and L.* 510
Old, with the might and breath of *t* boys.' „ 1106
ten-times worthier to be thine Than *t* Balins, *Balin and Balan* 69
Whose bark had plunder'd *t* nameless isles ; *Merlin and V.* 559
O ay, it is but *t* pages long, „ 668
Yea, *t* times I thought him Lancelot— *Lancelot and E.* 535
For *t* strokes of the blood, without a word, „ 720
' I had liefer *t* years Skip to the broken music *Last Tournament* 257
I sarved 'em wi' butter an' heggs fur huppuds o' *t* year. *Village Wife* 114
still for *t* years Bound by the golden cord *The Ring* 428
But if *t* million of summers are stored in the sunlight still, *The Dawn* 19
Twenty-five so bitter When I am but *t-f* ? *Maud I vi* 34
Twenty-fold I scent it *t-f*.' *Gareth and L.* 995
Twice And *t* three years I crouch'd on one *St. S. Stylites* 88
Twig Twang out, my fiddle ! shake the *t's* ! *Amphion* 61
low bushes dip their *t's* in foam, *Prog. of Spring* 51
Twilight (adj.) Long alleys falling down to *t* grots, *Ode to Memory* 107
Than our poor *t* dawn on earth— *Tiresias* 206
Twilight (s) In the purple *t's* under the sea ; *The Mermaid* 44
That sets at *t* in a land of reeds. *Caress'd or chidden* 14
About him broods the *t* dim : *Two Voices* 263
gray *t* pour'd On dewy pastures, dewy trees, *Palace of Art* 85
rain'd about the leaf *T's* of airy silver, *Audley Court* 82
And either *t* and the day between ; *Edwin Morris* 37
And beat the *t* into flakes of fire. *Tithonus* 42
Pilots of the purple *t*, *Locksley Hall* 122
The *t* melted into morn. *Day-Dm., Depart.* 16
The *t* died into the dark. „ 24
purple-skirted robe Of *t* slowly downward drawn, *The Voyage* 22
November day Was growing duller *t*, *Enoch Arden* 722
And, into mournful *t* mellowing, *Princess vi* 191
Twilight (s) (*continued*) And *t* dawn'd ; and morn by morn the lark *Princess vii* 45
And *t* gloom'd ; and broader-grown the bowers „ *vii* 48
Deepening the courts of *t* broke them up „ *Con.* 113
I watch the *t* falling brown *To F. D. Maurice* 14
The *t* of eternal day. *In Mem. l* 16
All winds that roam the *t* came *In Mem. lxxix* 11
When *t* was falling, *Maud I xii* 2
thro' the feeble *t* of this world Groping, *Geraint and E.* 5
when the gloom Of *t* deepens round it, *Balin and Balan* 233
day by day she past In either *t* ghost-like to and fro *Lancelot and E.* 849
Thro' that green-glooming *t* of the grove, *Pelleas and E.* 33
day Grew drearier toward *t* falling, *Pass. of Arthur* 123
The rosy *t* of a perfect day. *The Ring* 187
T and evening bell, *Crossing the Bar* 9
Twin (adj.) *T* peaks shadow'd with pine slope to the dark hyaline. *Leonine Eleg.* 10
nor yet Did those *t* brothers, risen again and whole ; *Princess vii* 89
Twin (s) nor the *t's* Her brethren, tho' they love her, „ *i* 153
two crowned *t's*, Commerce and conquest, „ *v* 420
A lusty brace Of *t's* may weed her of her folly. „ 464
Henceforth that mystic bond betwixt the *t's*—
Did I not tell you they were *t's* ?— *Sisters* (*E. and E.*) 256
Twin-brother Sleep, Death's *t-b*, (repeat) *In Mem. lxviii* 2, 3
Twine (s) reverend beard Of grisly *t*, *Princess vi* 104
Twine (verb) Clasp her window, trail and *t* ! *Window, At the Window* 2
Trail and *t* and clasp and kiss, „ 4
the child would *t* A trustful hand, *In Mem. cix* 18
Began to move, seethe, *t* and curl : *Gareth and L.* 234
T round one sin, whatever it might be, *Holy Grail* 883
soul *t's* and mingles with the growths *Lover's Tale i* 132
Twined (*See also* **Thick-twined**) locks a-drooping *t* Round thy neck *Adeline* 57
leaning on a fragrant *t* with vine, *Œnone* 20
Behind his ankle *t* her hollow feet *Merlin and V.* 240
knightly in me *t* and clung Round that one sin, *Holy Grail* 774
an' *t* like a band o' haäy. *Owd Roä* 22
and this you *t* About her cap. *Romney's R.* 79
Twinkle (s) There is not left a *t* of a fin *Geraint and E.* 474
Then with a ribald *t* in his bleak eyes— *The Ring* 199
Twinkle (verb) I see his gray eyes *t* yet *Miller's D.* 11
The lights begin to *t* from the rocks : *Ulysses* 54
That *t* into green and gold : *In Mem xi* 8
A livelier emerald *t's* in the grass, *Maud I xviii* 51
Twinkled For all the haft *t* with diamond sparks, *M. d'Arthur* 56
T the innumerable ear and tail. *The Brook* 134
Echo'd the walls ; a light *t* ; *Gareth and L.* 1370
For all the haft *t* with diamond sparks, *Pass. of Arthur* 224
Twinkling momently The *t* laurel scatter'd silver lights. *Gardener's D.* 118
Till at thy chuckled note, Thou *t* bird, *Early Spring* 38
Twinn'd *t* as horse's ear and eye. *Princess i* 57
Twin-sister Than your *t-s*, Adeline. *Margaret* 48
like *t-s's* grew, *T-s's* differently beautiful. *Edwin Morris* 32
Twist (s) A *t* of gold was round her hair ; *Merlin and V.* 221
Twist (verb) Would *t* his girdle tight, and pat *Talking Oak* 43
And *t's* the grain with such a roar *Princess v* 528
Sware by the scorpion-worm that *t's* in hell, *Last Tournament* 451
Twisted (*See also* **A-twizzen'd, Co-twisted**) A million tapers flaring bright From *t* silvers *Arabian Nights* 125
T as tight as I could knot the noose ; *St. S. Stylites* 65
With *t* quirks and happy hits, *Will Water.* 189
Now on some *t* ivy-net, *Sir L. and Q. G.* 28
how the words Have *t* back upon themselves, *Aylmer's Field* 755
And *t* shapes of lust, unspeakable, *Lucretius* 157
now A *t* snake, and now a rain of pearls, *Princess, Pro.* 62
Thro' twenty folds of *t* dragon, *Gareth and L.* 510
T hard in fierce embraces, *Vision of Sin* 40
Winking his eyes, and *t* all his face. *Lancelot and E.* 1145
T hard in mortal agony *Locksley H., Sixty* 98
Twisting Is *t* round the polar star ; *In Mem. ci* 12
Twit to *t* me with the cause ! *Lover's Tale i* 661
Twitch Paled at a sudden *t* of his iron mouth ; *Aylmer's Field* 732
a *t* of pain Tortured her mouth, *Princess vi* 105
Twitch'd *t* the reins, And made his beast *Pelleas and E.* 550
Then his pale face *t* ; *The Wreck* 101
Twitter (verb) cheep and *t* twenty million loves. *Princess iv* 101

Twitter (s) as a rustle or *t* in the wood Made dull his inner, *Last Tournament* 365
Two Low-throned Hesper is stayed between the *t* peaks; *Leonine Eleg.* 11
With Cyril and with Florian, my *t* friends: *Princess i* 52
T widows, Lady Psyche, Lady Blanche; „ 128
With *t* tame leopards couch'd beside her throne, „ *ii* 33
'everywhere *T* heads in council, *t* beside the hearth, *T* in the tangled business of the world, *T* in the liberal offices of life, *T* plummets dropt for one to sound the abyss „ 173
And *t* dear things are one of double worth, „ 419
Before *t* streams of light from wall to wall, „ 473
Herself and Lady Psyche the *t* arms; „ *iii* 35
'Read,' and I read—*t* letters—one her sire's. „ *iv* 397
Till one of those *t* brothers, half aside „ *v* 302
Down From those *t* bulks at Arac's side, „ 499
So those *t* foes above my fallen life, „ *vi* 130
T women faster welded in one love „ 253
the *t* great cats Close by her, „ 357
From those *t* hosts that lay beside the walls, „ 383
Than when *t* dewdrops on the petal shake „ *vii* 68
wherein were wrought *T* grand designs; „ 122
I walk'd with one I loved *t* and thirty years ago. *V. of Cauteretz* 4
t and thirty years were a mist that rolls away; „ 6
T dead men have I known *G. of Swainston* 11
T dead men have I loved „ 13
T bright stars Peep'd into the shell. *Minnie and Winnie* 13
T little hands that meet, (repeat) *Window, Answer* 1, 4
With Gawain and young Modred, her *t* sons, *Com. of Arthur* 244
sign'd To those *t* sons to pass, and let them be. „ 319
field of charlock in the sudden sun Between *t* showers, *Gareth and L.* 389
by *t* yards in casting bar or stone Was counted best; „ 518
Now *t* great entries open'd from the hall, „ 665
T forks are fixt into the meadow ground, *Marr. of Geraint* 482
What I these *t* years past have won for thee, „ 554
'These *t* things shalt thou do, (repeat) „ 580, 586
And made it of *t* colours; *Geraint and E.* 292
And we will live like *t* birds in one nest, „ 627
But Enid in their going had *t* fears, „ 817
But nevermore the same *t* sister pearls *Merlin and V.* 454
He saw *t* cities in a thousand boats „ 561
And *t* fair babes, and went to distant lands; „ 707
For here *t* brothers, one a king, had met *Lancelot and E.* 39
With *t* strong sons, Sir Torre and Sir Lavaine, „ 174
from the carven-work behind him crept *T* dragons gilded, „ 437
after *t* days' tarriance there, return'd. „ 569
those *t* brethren slowly with bent brows Accompanying, „ 1138
So those *t* brethren from the chariot took „ 1146
Those *t* great beasts rose upright like a man, *Holy Grail* 821
So from each Of those *t* pillars which from earth *Lover's Tale i* 220
at one end of the hall *T* great funereal curtains, „ *iv* 214
On a sudden after *t* Italian years *Sisters (E. and E.)* 150
then *t* weeks—no more—she joined, „ 271
Roar upon roar in a moment *t* mines by the enemy *Def. of Lucknow* 54
Lord give thou power to thy *t* witnesses! *Sir J. Oldcastle* 81
I So mock'd, so spurn'd, so baited *t* whole days— „ 163
so might there be *T* Adams, *t* mankinds, *Columbus* 54
There came *t* voices from the Sepulchre, *T* friars crying that if Spain should oust „ 95
T voices heard on earth no more; *To E. Fitzgerald* 41
'His *t* wild woodland flowers.' *The Flight* 80
I' a kep' thruf thick an' thin my *t* 'oonderd a-year to mysen; *Spinster's S's.* 12
Thou 'ed wellnigh purr'd ma awaäy fro' my oän *t* 'oonderd a-year. „ 58
Like some conjectured planet in mid heaven Between *t* Suns, *Prin. Beatrice* 21
An' the Heagle 'as hed *t* heäds stannin' theere *Owd Roä* 25
'The souls Of *t* repentant Lovers guard the ring;' *The Ring* 198
T lovers parted by a scurrilous tale Had quarrell'd, „ 208
T lovers parted by no scurrilous tale— „ 427
—those *t* Ghost lovers— *Father.* Lovers yet— „ 459
What be those *t* shapes high over the sacred fountain, *Parnassus* 9
t known peaks they stand ever spreading „ 11
T words, '*My* Rose' set all your face aglow, *Roses on the T.* 3
T trains clash'd: then and there he was crush'd *Charity* 21

Two-cell'd The *t-c* heart beating, with one full stroke, *Princess vii* 307
Twofold One *t* mightier than the other was, *Lover's Tale i* 211
Twofooted *T* at the limit of his chain, *Aylmer's Field* 127
Twy-natured *T-n* is no nature: *Lucretius* 194
Type (s) Tho' all her fairest forms are *t's* of thee, *Isabel* 39
'That *t* of Perfect in his mind *Two Voices* 292
Became an outward breathing *t*, *Miller's D.* 226
carved cross-bones, the *t's* of Death, *Will Water.* 245
And ev'n for want of such a *t*. *In Mem. xxxiii* 16
So careful of the *t* she seems, „ *lv* 7
'So careful of the *t*?' but no. „ *lvi* 1
She cries, 'A thousand *t's* are gone: „ 3
man, that with me trod This planet, was a noble *t* „ *Con.* 138
Pass, thou deathlike *t* of pain, *Maud II iv* 58
Type (verb) 'Dear, but let us *t* them now *Princess vii* 299
If so he *t* this work of time *In Mem. cxviii* 16
Which *t's* all Nature's male and female *On One who aff. E. M.* 3
Tyrannous And fused together in the *t* light— *Lover's Tale ii* 67
Tyranny And play the slave to gain the *t*. *Princess iv* 132
Thought on all her evil *tyrannies*, *Boädicea* 80
Out of evil evil flourishes, out of *t t* buds. „ 83
iron *t* now should bend or cease, *Maud III vi* 20
My warning that the *t* of one Was prelude to the *t* of all? My counsel that the *t* of all Led backward to the *t* of one? *Tiresias* 73
Tyrant (adj.) Caught in a great old *t* spider's web, *Merlin and V.* 259
No father now, the *t* vassal of a *t* vice! *The Flight* 25
Tyrant (s) Faster binds a *t's* power; And the *t's* cruel glee Forces on the freer hour, *Vision of Sin* 128
Pity, the violet on the *t's* grave. *Aylmer's Field* 845
'Kill him now, The *t*! *Princess, Pro.* 207
our dead captain taught The *t*, *Ode on Well.* 70
Our Britain cannot salve a *t* o'er. *Third of Feb.* 20
we will not spare the *t* one hard word. „ 42
makes you *t's* in your iron skies, *Maud I xviii* 37
Than hardest *t's* in their day of power, *Geraint and E.* 695
Have turn'd to *t's* when they came to power) *Merlin and V.* 518
Gone the *t* of my youth, *Locksley H., Sixty* 43
WARRIOR of God, man's friend, and *t's* foe, *Epit. on Gordon* 1
Tyre Against the guiltless heirs of him from *T*, *Tiresias* 12
red-hot palms of a Moloch of *T*, *The Dawn* 2
Tyrol A cap of *T* borrow'd from the hall, *Princess iv* 601

U

Udder Nosing the mother's *u*, *Lucretius* 100
Udder'd *See* **Deep-udder'd**
Ugly (*See also* **Hugly**) Feyther 'ud saäy I wur *u* es sin, *Spinster's S's.* 15
Ulama our *U*, Who "sitting on green sofas *Akbar's Dream* 47
Ulcer the *u*, eating thro' my skin, *St. S. Stylites* 67
Ulcerous aches, stitches, *u* throes and cramps, „ 13
Ulfius (a Knight of the Round Table) *U*, and Brastias, and Bedivere, (repeat) *Com. of Arthur* 136, 165
And *U* and Brastias answer'd, 'Ay.' „ 173
Ulric Where noble *U* dwells forlorn, *Happy* 10
Who whisper'd me 'your *U* loves'— „ 62
'Let us revenge ourselves, your *U* woos my wife'— „ 63
Ultramontane Most generous of all *U's*, Ward, *In Mem., W. G. Ward* 4
Ulysses *U*, much-experienced man, *To Ulysses* 1
Umpire by common voice, Elected *u*, *Œnone* 85
Sat their great *u*, looking o'er the lists. *Last Tournament* 159
Unabated In confidence of *u* strength, *Lover's Tale i* 511
Unaccomplish'd The hope of *u* years *In Mem. xci* 7
and Balan lurking there (His quest was *u*) *Balin and Balan* 547
Unanimous Clash the darts and on the buckler beat with rapid *u* hand, *Boädicea* 79
Unannounced My lady's Indian kinsman *u* *Aylmer's Field* 190
Unanswer'd *U*, since I spake not; *Lover's Tale i* 707
Unapproached Shelter'd his *u* mysteries: *Alexander* 11
not rather A sacred, secret, *u* woe, *Lover's Tale i* 679
Unarm'd the lawless warrior paced *U*, *Gareth and L.* 915
See that he fall not on thee suddenly, And slay thee *u*: „ 922
For tho' I ride *u*, I do not doubt To find, *Marr. of Geraint* 218

Unarm'd (*continued*) all *u* I rode, and thought to find Arms *Marr. of Geraint* 417
He sits *u* ; I hold a finger up ; *Geraint and E.* 337
Unashamed Delivers brawling judgments, *u*, *Merlin and V.* 665
Unask'd half abash'd him ; yet *u*, *Enoch Arden* 288
A trustful hand, *u*, in thine, *In Mem. cix* 19
Then tending her rough lord, tho' all *u*, *Geraint and E.* 405
You follow'd me *u* ; And when I look'd, *Merlin and V.* 298
And clear myself *u*—not I. *Happy* 78
Unauthorized Yet that I came not all *u* *Princess iv* 467
Unavenged With life-long injuries burning *u*, *Geraint and E.* 696
Unaware rose to look at it, But touch'd it *u's* : „ 388
so blind in rage that *u's* He burst his lance *Balin and Balan* 328
All *u's* before his half-shut eyes, *Lover's Tale ii* 153
Unbeautiful ' Nothing in nature is *u* ; „ *i* 350
Unbecoming Not *u* men that strove with Gods. *Ulysses* 53
Unbeguiled At me you smiled, but *u* *L. C. V. de Vere* 5
Unbeheld Mayst well behold them *u*, *Œnone* 89
Unbelief curse Of blindness and their *u*, *Tiresias* 59
I reap No revenue from the field of *u*. *Akbar's Dream* 67
Till this embattled wall of *u* My prison, *Doubt and Prayer* 11
Unbelievable pine shot aloft from the crag to an *u* height, *V. of Maeldune* 16
Unbias'd *U* by self-profit, oh ! *Œnone* 159
Unbidden camels knelt *U*, *Merlin and V.* 576
O warble, unchidden, *u* ! *The Throstle* 14
Unbind *U* him now, And thrust him out of doors ; *Pelleas and E.* 256
Sing, and *u* my heart that I may weep.' *Guinevere* 166
Unblazon'd *See* **Yet-unblazon'd**
Unblest never child be born of me *U*, *Œnone* 255
I care no longer, being all *u* : *Come not, when, etc.* 8
Unblinded who shall gaze upon My palace with *u* eyes, *Palace of Art* 42
Unblissful Thrill'd thro' mine ears in that *u* clime, *D. of F. Women* 82
Unboding *U* critic-pen, *Will Water.* 42
Unborn (*See also* **Born-unborn**) But where a passion yet *u* perhaps Lay hidden *Aylmer's Field* 101
I see their *u* faces shine *In Mem. lxxxiv* 19
By village eyes as yet *u* ; „ *Con.* 59
The cackle of the *u* about the grave, *Merlin and V.* 507
Unbound being, as I think, *U* as yet, and gentle, *Lancelot and E.* 1386
Laugh'd, and *u*, and thrust him from the gate. *Pelleas and E.* 260
Unbridled For Kate hath an *u* tongue, *Kate* 7
Unbroken (*See also* **Yet-unbroken**) In sweet dreams softer than *u* rest *Ode to Memory* 29
Caught his *u* limbs from the dark field, *Pelleas and E.* 585
Weird Titan by thy winter weight of years As yet *u*, *To Victor Hugo* 8
Unburiable yet-warm corpse, and yet *u*, *Gareth and L.* 80
Unburnish'd To rust *u*, not to shine in use ! *Ulysses* 23
Unbury made by me, may seek to *u* me, *Columbus* 206
Uncall'd That you came unwish'd for, *u*, *Despair* 5
Uncall'd for (power of herself Would come *u f*) *Œnone* 147
Uncancell'd if left *u*, had been so sweet : *Maud I xix* 46
Uncared for *U f*, spied its mother and began *Princess vi* 136
U f, gird the windy grove, *In Mem. ci* 13
He must not pass *u f*. *Lancelot and E.* 536
Uncertain in dark corners of her palace stood *U* shapes ; *Palace of Art* 238
U as a vision or a dream, *Enoch Arden* 356
That after all these sad *u* years, „ 415
moving thro' the *u* gloom, *Princess iv* 216
O'er his *u* shadow droops the day. *Prog. of Spring* 8
If my body come from brutes, my soul *u*, *By an Evolution.* 5
Unchain'd Which he *u* for all the world to come.' *Columbus* 215
Unchallenged deeds will come and go *U*, *Holy Grail* 319
Uncharity Fought with what seem'd my own *u* ; *Sea Dreams* 73
Uncharm'd may now assure you mine ; So live *u*. *Merlin and V.* 550
Unchidden O warble *u*, unbidden ! *The Throstle* 14
Unclad *U* herself in haste ; adown the stair *Godiva* 48
Unclaim'd query pass *U*, in flushing silence, *The Brook* 105
Unclasp'd I scarce should be *u* at night. *Miller's D.* 186
Or sweet Europa's mantle blew *u*, *Palace of Art* 117
U the wedded eagles of her belt, *Godiva* 43
Unclasping *U* flung the casement back, *Lancelot and E.* 981
Uncle Now Dora felt her *u's* will in all, *Dora* 5
' It cannot be : my *u's* mind will change ! ' „ 47
' I have obey'd my *u* until now, „ 59

Uncle (*continued*) I will set him in my *u's* eye Among the wheat ; *Dora* 67
tied it round his hat To make him pleasing in her *u's* eye. „ 84
And Dora said, ' My *u* took the boy ; „ 114
and out they came Trustees and Aunts and *U's*. *Edwin Morris* 121
I was left a trampled orphan, and a selfish *u's* ward. *Locksley Hall* 156
Had babbled ' *U* ' on my knee ; *In Mem. lxxxiv* 13
Your good *U*, whom You count the father of your fortune, *Sisters* (*E. and E.*) 27
my best And oldest friend, your *U*, wishes it, „ 47
Unclosed *U* the hand, and from it drew the ring, *The Ring* 269
Unclouded All in the blue *u* weather *L. of Shalott iii* 19
Uncoil'd the braid Slipt and *u* itself, *Merlin and V.* 889
Uncomforted *U*, leaving my ancient love *Œnone* 260
Unconfined From cells of madness *u*, *Two Voices* 371
But when I see thee roam, with tresses *u*, *Eleänore* 122
Uncongeal When meres begin to *u*, *Two Voices* 407
Uncongenial by degrees May into *u* spirits flow ; *Mine be the strength* 11
Unconjectured With gods in *u* bliss, *In Mem. xciii* 10
Unconquerable I believed myself *U*, *Geraint and E.* 836
Unconscious (*See also* **Half-unconscious**) frail at first And feeble, all *u* of itself, *Princess vii* 117
O somewhere, meek, *u* dove, *In Mem. vi* 25
U of the sliding hour, „ *xliii* 5
Uncourteous in his heat and agony, seem *U*, *Lancelot and E.* 855
Unctuous laying down an *u* lease Of life, *Will Water.* 243
And that one *u* mouth which lured him, *Sea Dreams* 14
Uncurl'd Did he push, when he was *u*, *Maud II ii* 18
Uncut *See* **Half-uncut**
Undazzled Slowly my sense *u*. *D. of F. Women* 177
Under Now gnaw'd his *u*, now his upper lip, *Geraint and E.* 669
Undercurrent some dark *u* woe That seems to draw— *Maud I xviii* 83
Under-flame Grew darker from that *u-f* : *Arabian Nights* 91
Underfoot Lest the harsh shingle should grate *u*, *Enoch Arden* 772
For *u* the herb was dry ; *In Mem. xcv* 2
then or now Utterly smite the heathen *u*, *Com. of Arthur* 423
and threw *U* there in the fray— *Heavy Brigade* 55
Under-fringe Broad-faced with *u-f* of russet beard, *Geraint and E.* 537
Undergone both have *u* That trouble which has left me „ 736
Underground (**adj.**) as the blast of that *u* thunderclap echo'd away, *Def. of Lucknow* 32
Underground (**adv. and s**) Will vex thee lying *u* ? *Two Voices* 111
Averill was a decad and a half His elder, and their parents *u*) *Aylmer's Field* 83
Then sprang the happier day from *u* ; *Gareth and L.* 1421
But when the next day broke from *u*, *Lancelot and E.* 413
But when the next sun brake from *u*, „ 1137
So when the sun broke next from *under ground*, *Holy Grail* 328
But when the next day brake from *under ground*— „ 338
iron-stay'd In damp and dismal dungeons *u*, *Lover's Tale ii* 149
But thou art silent *u*, *Pref. Poem Broth. Son.* 13
Underhand that of a kind The viler, as *u*, *Maud I i* 28
Under-kingdom hundred *u-k's* that he sway'd *Merlin and V.* 582
Underlip *u*, you may call it a little too ripe, *Maud I ii* 9
Under-lying That name the *u-l* dead, *In Mem. ii* 2
Underneath from end to end Of all the landscape *u*, „ *c* 2
Underpropt *u* a rich Throne of the massive ore, *Arabian Nights* 145
Under-roof An *u-r* of doleful gray. *Dying Swan* 4
Undersea and we past Over that *u* isle, *V. of Maeldune* 77
Underscored only yours ; ' and this Thrice *u*. *Edwin Morris* 107
Under-shapen His dwarf, a vicious *u-s* thing, *Marr. of Geraint* 412
Under-sky And floating about the *u-s*, *Dying Swan* 25
Understand (*See also* **Understond, Undherstan'**) He answers not, nor *u's*. *Two Voices* 246
a sort of allegory, (For you will *u* it) *To ——, With Pal. of Art.* 2
what he whisper'd under Heaven None else could *u* ; *Talking Oak* 22
He will answer to the purpose, easy things to *u*— *Locksley Hall* 55
When thy nerves could *u* *Vision of Sin* 160
But in a tongue no man could *u* ; „ 222
tongue Was loosen'd, till he made them *u* ; *Enoch Arden* 645
mark me and *u*, While I have power to speak. „ 876
Nor could he *u* how money breeds, *The Brook* 6
A noise of songs they would not *u* : *Princess vi* 40
but *if* I could *u* What you are, *Flow. in cran. wall* 4

Understand (*continued*) The words were hard to *u*. *In Mem. lxix* 20
'I cannot *u*: I love.' „ *xcvii* 36
What is, and no man *u's*; „ *cxxiv* 22
nursed at ease and brought to *u* A sad astrology, *Maud I xviii* 35
Thou canst not *u* That thou art left for ever alone: „ *II iii* 3
I hold a finger up; They *u*: *Geraint and E.* 338
But you are man, you well can *u* *Merlin and V.* 697
these can never know thee, They cannot *u* me. *Lover's Tale i* 286
if you shall fail to *u* What England is, *The Fleet* 1
Now first we stand and *u*, *Mechanophilus* 1
Understandest Nor *u* bound nor boundlessness, *Ancient Sage* 48
Understanding *u* all the foolish work Of Fancy, *Princess vi* 116
Understond (understand) I kep 'um, my lass, tha mun *u*; *N. Farmer, O. S.* 23
Understood A notice faintly *u*, *Two Voices* 431
O thou that stonest, hadst thou *u* *Aylmer's Field* 739
The land, he *u*, for miles about Was till'd by women; *Princess i* 191
Loved deeplier, darklier *u*; *In Mem. cxxix* 10
the prophecy given of old And then not *u*, *Maud II v* 43
And best by her that bore her *u*. *Marr. of Geraint* 511
Undertake Wilt thou I *u* them as we pass, *Balin and Balan* 14
Under-tone And from within me a clear *u-t* *D. of F. Women* 81
Underwent Did more, and *u*, and overcame, *Godiva* 10
Gareth all for glory *u* The sooty yoke of kitchen-vassalage; *Gareth and L.* 478
Underworld That brings our friends up from the *u*, *Princess iv* 45
Undescried tho' *u*, Winning its way with extreme gentleness *Isabel* 22
Undevelopt For woman is not *u* man, *Princess vii* 275
Undherstan' (understand) 'me dear, av I *u*,' *Tomorrow* 56
Undimmed And holdeth his *u* forehead far *Lover's Tale i* 513
Undiscover'd And thine in *u* lands. *In Mem. xl* 32
Undissolved A sleep by kisses *u*, *Day-Dm., L'Envoi* 51
Undo Thoroughly to *u* me, *Lilian* 11
in seeking to *u* One riddle, and to find the true, *Two Voices* 232
To know her beauty might half *u* it. *Maud I xvi* 19
fineness, Lancelot, some fine day *U* thee not— *Gareth and L.* 477
And never could *u* it: ask no more: *Merlin and V.* 686
Undoing flattery and the craft Which were my *u* . . . *Forlorn* 4
Undone What harm, *u*? deep harm to disobey, *M. d'Arthur* 93
What harm, *u*? Deep harm to disobey, *Pass. of Arthur* 261
Undrainable labour'd mine *u* of ore. *Œnone* 115
Undress'd wear an *u* goatskin on my back; *St. S. Stylites* 116
Undulated *u* The banner: anon to meet us *Princess v* 253
Undulation cries, And *u's* to and fro. *In Mem. cxiii* 20
Undying Clear, without heat, *u*, *Isabel* 3
And it sings a song of *u* love; *Poet's Mind* 33
with *u* bliss In knowledge of their own supremacy.' *Œnone* 132
Unearn'd doubtless, all *u* by noble deeds. *Balin and Balan* 471
Unearthlier *U* than all shriek of bird or beast, „ 545
Unequal in true marriage lies Nor equal, nor *u*: *Princess vii* 303
I mete and dole *U* laws unto a savage race, *Ulysses* 4
Unexhausted bloodily fall the battle-axe, *u*, *Boädicea* 56
Unexpected as one Caught in a burst of *u* storm, *Aylmer's Field* 285
Unexpress'd I leave thy praises *u* *In Mem. lxxv* 1
Unfair Who shall call me ungentle, *u*, *Maud I xiii* 14
Unfaith Faith and *u* can ne'er be equal powers: *Merlin and V.* 388
U in aught is want of faith in all. „ 389
Unfaithful With quiet eyes *u* to the truth, *Love and Duty* 94
And faith *u* kept him falsely true. *Lancelot and E.* 877
Unfamiliar But *u* Arno, and the dome Of Brunelleschi; *The Brook* 189
Unfarrow'd And so return'd *u* to her sty. *Walk. to the Mail* 100
Unfathom'd There on the depth of an *u* woe *Lover's Tale i* 746
Unfelt shock of gloom had fall'n *U*, „ 506
Unfetter'd *U* by the sense of crime, *In Mem. xxvii* 7
Unfinish'd work is left *U*—*if* I go. *Lucretius* 104
Unfit *U* for earth, *u* for heaven, *St. S. Stylites* 3
Unfold I see thy beauty gradually *u*, *Eleänore* 70
And like a flower that cannot all *u*, *Princess vii* 141
Unfolding hour by hour *u* woodbine leaves *Prog. of Spring* 7
Unforgotten Moved from the cloud of *u* things, *Lover's Tale i* 48
Unfrequent *U*, low, as tho' it told its pulses; „ *ii* 55
Unfriendly *U* of your parted guest. *The Wanderer* 4
Unfrowardly thou canst not bide, *u*, *Pelleas and E.* 597
Unfulfill'd O therefore that the *u* desire, *Tiresias* 79
Unfurl *u* the maiden banner of our rights, *Princess iv* 503
Unfurnish'd *U* brows, tempestuous tongues— *Freedom* 38
Ungainliness mocking at the much *u*, *Last Tournament* 728
Ungainly *See* **Unheppen**
Ungarner'd And whirl the *u* sheaf afar, *In Mem. lxxii* 23
Ungather'd To-night *u* let us leave „ *cv* 1
Ungenerous '*U*, dishonourable, base, *Aylmer's Field* 292
Ungentle Who shall call me *u*, unfair, *Maud I xiii* 14
to be gentle than *u* with you; *Geraint and E.* 716
The most *u* knight in Arthur's hall.' *Gareth and L.* 757
Ungracious I am more *u* ev'n than you, *Aylmer's Field* 247
A bird's-eye-view of all the *u* past; *Princess ii* 125
'*U*!' answer'd Florian; 'have you learnt „ 392
We knew not your *u* laws, „ *iv* 399
Ungraciousness I seem to be *u* itself.' *Aylmer's Field* 245
Ungrateful Not all *u* to thine ear. *In Mem. xxxviii* 12
And 'petty Ogress,' and '*u* Puss,' *Princess, Pro.* 157
Unguent heal'd Thy hurt and heart with *u* and caress— *Last Tournament* 595
Unhail'd *u* The shallop flitteth silken-sail'd *L. of Shallott i* 21
Unhallow'd But all is new *u* ground. *In Mem. civ* 12
Unhanded High things were spoken there, *u* down; *Alexander* 12
Unhappiness by some device Full cowardly, or by mere *u*, *Gareth and L.* 768
by sorcery or *u* Or some device, hast foully overthrown), „ 997
Hast overthrown thro' mere *u*), „ 1059
all thro' mere *u*— „ 1234
Device and sorcery and *u*— „ 1235
thro' the mere *u* Of one who came to help thee, „ 1237
Else must I die thro' mine *u*.' *Pelleas and E.* 332
On whom I brought a strange *u*, *Sisters (E. and E.)* 89
Unhappy Nor *u*, nor at rest, *Adeline* 4
There are enough *u* on this earth, *Œnone* 239
he turn'd His face and pass'd—*u* that I am! *Dora* 151
The spindlings look *u*. *Amphion* 92
He was not all *u*. His resolve Upbore him, *Enoch Arden* 799
Not all *u*, having loved God's best And greatest, *Lancelot and E.* 1093
made The happy and the *u* love, *Lover's Tale i* 753
Often I seem'd *u*, and often as happy too, *First Quarrel* 31
In the dead *u* night, and when the rain is on the roof. *Locksley Hall* 78
And vex the *u* dust thou wouldst not save. *Come not, when, etc.* 4
So stood the *u* mother open-mouth'd, *Princess vi* 143
Confused me like the *u* bark *In Mem. xvi* 12
So sadly lost on that *u* night; *Marr. of Geraint* 689
that *u* child Past in her barge: *Last Tournament* 44
wail For ever woke the *u* Past again, *Sisters (E. and E.)* 263
has it come to this, O *u* creature? *Forlorn* 44
Unharm'd yonder stands, Modred, *u*, *Pass. of Arthur* 153
But the new-wedded wife was *u*, *Charity* 22
Unheard grief of circumstance Wert thou, and yet *u*. *Supp. Confessions* 93
behold them unbeheld, *u* Hear all, *Œnone* 89
They were modulated so To an *u* melody, *Eleänore* 64
And dies *u* within his tree, *You might have won* 32
Unhearing shriek'd out 'Traitor' to the *u* wall, *Lancelot and E.* 612
Unheeded *U*: and detaching, fold by fold, *Vision of Sin* 51
U: and I thought I would have spoken, „ 55
Unheedful or as once we met *U*, *Gardener's D.* 266
Unheppen (ungainly) Straänge an' *u* Miss Lucy! *Village Wife* 100
Unhooded and *u* casting off The goodly falcon *Merlin and V.* 130
Unicorn hornless *u's*, Crack'd basilisks, *Holy Grail* 717
Unimpassion'd Beneath a pale and *u* moon, *Aylmer's Field* 334
Uninvaded *u* sleep The Kraken sleepeth: *The Kraken* 3
Uninvited The Abominable, that *u* came *Œnone* 224
Union Should banded *u's* persecute Opinion, *You ask me, why, etc.* 17
our knights at feast Have pledged us in this *u*, *Lancelot and E.* 115
Here's to your happy *u* with my child! *Sisters (E. and E.)* 68
power to fuse My myriads into *u* under one; *Akbar's Dream* 157
Unison All your voices in *u*, *On Jub. Q. Victoria* 63
Unity These three made *u* so sweet, *Two Voices* 421
It was but *u* of place *In Mem. xlii* 3
Universal and *u* Peace Lie like a shaft of light *Golden Year* 48
the kindly earth shall slumber, lapt in *u* law. *Locksley Hall* 130
from it preach'd An *u* culture for the crowd, *Princess, Pro.* 109
sad and slow, As fits an *u* woe, *Ode on Well.* 14

Universal (*continued*) And praise the invisible *u* Lord, *Ode Inter. Exhib.* 3
The voices of our *u* sea *W. to Marie Alex.* 16
led my friend Back to the pure and *u* church, *Sir J. Oldcastle* 71
Robed in *u* harvest up to either pole she smiles,
U ocean softly washing all her warless Isles, *Locksley H., Sixty* 169
Thou that seëst *U* Nature moved by *U* Mind; *To Virgil* 21
Our Shakespeare's bland and *u* eye Dwells *To W. C. Macready* 13
Universe wanderings Of this most intricate *U* *A Character* 3
That in a boundless *u* Is boundless better, *Two Voices* 26
knowing not the *u*, I fear to slide from bad to worse. „ 230
atom-streams And torrents of her myriad *u*, *Lucretius* 39
And fleeting thro' the boundless *u*, „ 161
Quite sunder'd from the moving *U*, *Princess vii* 52
suns of the limitless *U* sparkled and shone *Despair* 15
University (*See also* **Varsity**) All wild to found an *U* For maidens, *Princess i* 150
Unjust and yet Pardon—too harsh, *u*. *Columbus* 199
Unkept vintage, yet *u*, Had relish fiery-new, *Will Water.* 97
Unkind False-eyed Hesper, *u*, *Leonine Eleg.* 16
Ah, miserable and *u*, untrue, *M. d'Arthur* 119
be jealous and hard and *u*.' *Grandmother* 54
' Ah, miserable and *u*, untrue, *Pass. of Arthur* 287
Unkindliness Kill'd with unutterable *u*.' *Merlin and V.* 886
Unkinglike wall them up perforce in mine—unwise, *U*;— *Akbar's Dream* 63
Unknightlike all *u*, writhed his wiry arms Around him, *Gareth and L.* 1150
Unknightly *U*, traitor-hearted! Woe is me! *M. d'Arthur* 120
u with flat hand, However lightly, *Geraint and E.* 717
U, traitor-hearted! Woe is me! *Pass. of Arthur* 288
Unknit God *u's* the riddle of the one, *Lover's Tale i* 181
Unknown And left a want *u* before; *Miller's D.* 228
hears the low Moan of an *u* sea; *Palace of Art* 280
His wife, an *u* artist's orphan child— *Sea Dreams* 2
remain'd among us In our young nursery still *u*, *Princess iv* 332
Known and *u*; human, divine; *In Mem. cxxix* 5
Sweet were the days when I was all *u*, *Merlin and V.* 501
your great name, This conquers: hide it therefore; go *u*: Win! *Lancelot and E.* 151
Known as they are, to me they are *u*.' .. 186
But since I go to joust as one *u* At Camelot .. 190
That he might joust *u* of all, .. 583
The maiden buried, not as one *u*, .. 1334
Queen abode For many a week, *u*, among the nuns; *Guinevere* 147
With some revenge—even to itself *u*,— *Lover's Tale ii* 127
Shall fade with him into the *u*, *Tiresias* 215
Unlaborious *u* earth and oarless sea; *To Virgil* 20
Unlaced *u* my casque And grovell'd on my body, *Princess vi* 27
Gareth there *u* His helmet as to slay him, *Gareth and L.* 978
Unlading At lading and *u* the tall barks, *Enoch Arden* 816
Unlamed to find his charger yet *u*, *Balin and Balan* 428
Unlawful *U* and disloyal brotherhood— *Sisters (E. and E.)* 174
Unlearn'd In grief I am not all *u*; *To J. S.* 18
Unled (His gentle charger following him *u*) *Geraint and E.* 571
Unlicensed Dooms our *u* preacher to the flame, *Sir J. Oldcastle* 105
Unlifted *U* was the clinking latch; *Mariana* 6
Unlike O happy tears, and how *u* to these! *Œnone* 235
Said Ida, tremulously, ' so all *u*— *Princess vii* 333
As not *u* to that of Spring. *In Mem. lxxxv* 120
With miracles and marvels like to these, Not all *u*; *Holy Grail* 544
Unlikeness As his *u* fitted mine. *In Mem. lxxix* 20
Unlimited The Heavenly-unmeasured or *u* Love, *Lover's Tale i* 474
Unloveable Ev'n when they seem'd *u*, *Merlin and V.* 176
Unloved *U*, that beech will gather brown, *In Mem. ci* 3
U, the sun-flower, shining fair, .. 5
U, by many a sandy bar, .. 9
Unlovely I stand Here in the long *u* street, „ *vii* 2
Unloverlike most *u*, Since in his absence *Lover's Tale i* 424
Unmanacled *U* from bonds of sense, *Two Voices* 236
Unmann'd but that my zone *U* me: *Princess ii* 421
Unmannerly *U*, with prattling and the tales *Guinevere* 316
Unmark'd Enwind her isles, *u* of me: *In Mem. xcviii* 10
Unmarried But Dora lived *u* till her death. *Dora* 172
Sir Lancelot worshipt no *u* girl *Merlin and V.* 12
Unmeasured (*See also* **Heavenly-unmeasured**) clamouring etiquette to death, *U* mirth; *Princess v* 18
Unmeet and strange experiences *U* for ladies. „ *iv* 159
Maud, you milkwhite fawn, you are all *u* for a wife. *Maud I iv* 57
Unmelodious Saying ' An *u* name to thee, *Balin and Balan* 52
Unmockingly *U* the mocker ending here *Gareth and L.* 294
Unmortised The feet *u* from their ankle-bones *Merlin and V.* 552
Unmoulded By some yet *u* tongue *Ode on Well.* 233
Unmoved With such and so *u* a majesty *Lancelot and E.* 1170
Unmown deep inlay Of braided blooms *u*, *Arabian Nights* 29
Unnetted The *u* black-hearts ripen dark, *The Blackbird* 7
Unnoticed For that *u* failing in herself, *Geraint and E.* 47
Unnumber'd *U* and enormous polypi *The Kraken* 9
Unopen'd and dash'd *U* at her feet: *Princess iv* 471
Unpaining driven Its knotted thorns thro' my *u* brows, *Lover's Tale i* 620
Unpalsied *U* when he met with Death, *In Mem. cxxviii* 2
Unparallel'd That various wilderness a tissue of light *U*. *Lover's Tale i* 420
Unpeopled Whose crime had half *u* Ilion, *Death of Œnone* 61
Unperceived Love, *u*, A more ideal Artist *Gardener's D.* 24
stole from court With Cyril and with Florian, *u*, *Princess i* 103
Unpiloted *U* i' the echoing dance Of reboant whirlwinds, *Supp. Confessions* 96
Unpitied *U*: for he groped as blind, *Aylmer's Field* 821
Unprofitable if a king demand An act *u*, *M. d'Arthur* 96
if a king demand An act *u*, *Pass. of Arthur* 264
Unprogressive Cries of *u* dotage ere the dotard fall asleep, *Locksley H., Sixty* 153
Unprophetic *U* rulers they— *Open. I. and C. Exhib.* 26
Unproportion'd So *u* to the dwelling-place,) *Lover's Tale i* 187
Unproven and every younger knight, *U*, *Holy Grail* 304
Unquenched Like Stephen, an *u* fire. *Two Voices* 219
Unquestion'd ample rule *U*, *Œnone* 112
Unquiet But, for the *u* heart and brain, *In Mem. v* 5
Unreal but these *u* ways Seem but the theme *Edwin Morris* 47
past and flow'd away To those *u* billows: *Lover's Tale ii* 196
Unrecorded a wife as you Should vanish *u*. *Romney's R.* 69
Unrecording Thro' troops of *u* friends, *You might have won* 7
Unrelieved and ever *u* by dismal tears, *Palace of Art* 271
Unremember'd and my sins Be *u*, *Supp. Confessions* 182
Unremorseful wrapt In *u* folds of rolling fire. *Holy Grail* 261
Unrepress'd Ceasing not, mingled, *u*, *Arabian Nights* 74
Unresisting and a sense Of meanness in her *u* life. *Aylmer's Field* 801
Unrest but the Naiad Throbbing in mild *u* *Leonine Eleg.* 12
The wild *u* that lives in woe *In Mem. xv* 15
Can calm despair and wild *u* „ *xvi* 2
Unreveal'd The rest remaineth *u*; „ *xxxi* 14
Unriddled Shall be *u* by and by. *Miller's D.* 20
Unrisen a poising eagle, burns Above the *u* morrow:' *Princess iv* 83
—over darkness—from the still *u* sun. *Locksley H., Sixty* 92
Unroll'd One sitting on a crimson scarf *u*; *D. of F. Women* 126
hail once more to the banner of battle *u*! *Maud III vi* 42
Unruffling *U* waters re-collect the shape *Last Tournament* 369
Unsaid And what I see I leave *u*, *In Mem. lxxiv* 10
Unsay *U* it, unswear! *Last Tournament* 641
Unscarr'd And all *u* from beak or talon, „ 20
Unscathed Render him up *u*: *Princess iv* 408
Unseal'd Falling, *u* our eyelids, and we woke *Lover's Tale i* 265
Unseen Then leaping out upon them *u* *The Merman* 33
the dark East, *U*, is brightening to his bridal morn. *Gardener's D.* 73
Her face was evermore *u*, *The Voyage* 61
And far, in forest-deeps *u*, *Sir L. and Q. G.* 7
Had his dark hour *u*, and rose and past *Enoch Arden* 78
But now it seems some *u* monster lays *Lucretius* 219
Into the *u* for ever,—till that hour, „ 259
or are moved by an *u* hand at a game *Maud I iv* 26
His love, *u* but felt, o'ershadow Thee, *Ded. of Idylls* 51
Merlin, who, they say, can walk *U* at pleasure— *Com. of Arthur* 348
with her feet *u* Crush'd the wild passion *Lancelot and E.* 741
for *u*, But taken with the sweetness of the place, *Lover's Tale i* 530
Unshadowable *u* in words, Themselves but shadows *Ancient Sage* 238
Unshaken *Which kept her throne* u *still*, *To the Queen* 34
Thro' open doors of Ida stationed there *U*, *Princess v* 344
Unshatter'd haste and random youth *U*; *De Prof., Two G.* 22
Unshorn she that saw him lying unsleek, *u*, *Lancelot and E.* 815

Unskill'd And let the younger and *u* go by — *Lancelot and E.* 1361
Unsleek she that saw him lying *u*, unshorn, — „ 815
Unsolder sequel of to-day *u's* all The goodliest fellowship — *M. d'Arthur* 14
sequel of to-day *u's* all The goodliest fellowship — *Pass. of Arthur* 182
Unsown sat upon a mound That was *u*, — *Dora* 73
Unspeakable memories roll upon him, *U* for sadness. — *Enoch Arden* 725
And twisted shapes of lust, *u*, — *Lucretius* 157
A sacred, secret, unapproached woe, *U* ? — *Lover's Tale i* 680
Dying, ' *U* ' he wrote ' Their kindness,' — *To Marq. of Dufferin* 35
Unstain'd A lovelier life, a more *u*, than his ! — *Ded. of Idylls* 30
Unsubduable The last a monster *u* — *Gareth and L.* 858
Unsubject *U* to confusion, — *Will Water.* 86
Unsummer'd And, now to these *u* skies — *Pref. Poem Broth. Son.* 17
Unsunn'd The *u* freshness of my strength, — *Supp. Confessions* 140
Unsunny O damsel, wearing this *u* face — *Pelleas and E.* 180
Unswallow'd brawny spearman let his cheek Bulge with the *u* piece, — *Geraint and E.* 631
Unswear Unsay it, *u* ! — *Last Tournament* 641
Unsweet Is faith as vague as all *u* : — *In Mem. xlvii* 5
Untaken and hath left his prize *U*, — *Lancelot and E.* 531
Untarnish'd name will yet remain *U* as before ; — *Marr. of Geraint* 501
Untidy *See* **Hugger-mugger**
'Untin' (hunting) an' was *'u'* arter the men, — *Village Wife* 36
Untold Nor left *u* the craft herself had used ; — *Geraint and E.* 393
Untouch'd *U* with any shade of years, — *Miller's D.* 219
my good son—Is yet *u* : — *Sisters (E. and E.)* 288
Untravell'd experience is an arch wherethro' Gleams that *u* world, — *Ulysses* 20
Untrue Ah, miserable and unkind, *u*, — *M. d'Arthur* 119
I wrong the grave with fears *u* : — *In Mem. li* 9
She might by a true descent be *u* ; — *Maud I xiii* 31
' Ah, miserable and unkind, *u*, — *Pass. of Arthur* 287
Untruth never had a glimpse of mine *u*, — *Lancelot and E.* 125
Too wholly true to dream *u* in thee, — *Guinevere* 541
Untuneful That her voice *u* grown, — *The Owl ii* 6
Unused *U* example from the grave — *In Mem. lxxx* 15
Unvenerable *U* will thy memory be — *Tiresias* 132
Unvext *u* She slipt across the summer — *Enoch Arden* 530
Unwatch'd *U*, the garden bough shall sway, — *In Mem. ci* 1
Unwavering calm that let the tapers burn *U* : — „ *xcv* 6
Unwedded I was wife, and thou *U* : — *Guinevere* 120
Unwilling Waged such *u* tho' successful war — *Merlin and V.* 571
The lady never made *u* war With those fine eyes : — „ 603
Unwillingly *See* **Half-unwillingly**
Unwillingness wish Falls flat before your least *u*. — *Romney's R.* 72
Unwise What wonder I was all *u*, — *Day-Dm., Ep.* 5
wall them up perforce in mine—*u*, Unkinglike ;— — *Akbar's Dream* 62
Unwisely wisely or *u*, signs of storm, — *To the Queen ii* 49
Unwish'd That you came *u* for, uncall'd, — *Despair* 5
Unwish'd-for With proffer of *u-f* services) — *Lover's Tale i* 629
Unwitty If these *u* wandering wits of mine, — *Merlin and V.* 346
Unwonted Should kiss with an *u* gentleness. — *Lover's Tale i* 739
Unwoo'd palms were ranged Above, *u* of summer wind : — *Arabian Nights* 80
Unworldly My friend, the most *u* of mankind, — *In Mem. W. G. Ward* 3
Unworthier but we, *u*, told Of college : — *Princess, Pro.* 110
Unworthily some *u* ; their sinless faith, — „ *v* 185
Unworthiness lay Contemplating her own *u* ; — *Marr. of Geraint* 533
Unworthy O three times less *u* ! — *Love and Duty* 20
Hadst thou less *u* proved— — *Locksley Hall* 63
Vext with *u* madness, and deform'd. — *Aylmer's Field* 335
chiefest comfort is the little child Of one *u* mother; — *Princess v* 431
On some *u* heart with joy, — *In Mem. lxii* 7
but most Predoom'd her as *u*. — *Lancelot and E.* 729
Unwounded To find him yet *u* after fight, — *Geraint and E.* 371
Unwove Wove and *u* it, till the boy return'd — „ 260
Up *See* **Steep-up**
Upbare *u* A broad earth-sweeping pall of whitest lawn, — *Lover's Tale ii* 77
Upbearing A leaning and *u* parasite, — *Isabel* 34
Upblown *u* billow ran Shoreward beneath red clouds, — *Lover's Tale ii* 178
Upbore His resolve *U* him, and firm faith, — *Enoch Arden* 800
but her deep love *U* her ; — *Lancelot and E.* 861
Upbreaking the heavens *u* thro' the earth, — *Guinevere* 391
Up-clomb *U-c* the shadowy pine above the woven copse. — *Lotos-Eaters* 18
Upcurl'd wreaths of floating dark *u*, — *The Poet* 35
Updrag Rise ! ' and stoop'd to *u* Melissa : — *Princess iv* 366
Updrawn Anchors of rusty fluke, and boats *u* ; — *Enoch Arden* 18
Upheaven land of old *u* from the abyss By fire, — *Pass. of Arthur* 82
Upheld under all the cornice and *u* : — *Gareth and L.* 219
Uphill lay thine *u* shoulder to the wheel, — *Ancient Sage* 279
Uphold (*See also* **Upowd**) didst *u* me on my lonely isle, *U* me, — *Enoch Arden* 783
To break the heathen and *u* the Christ, — *Guinevere* 470
Which yet *u's* my life, and evermore — *Lover's Tale i* 168
two pillars which from earth *u* Our childhood, — „ 220
Genius of that hour which dost *u* Thy coronal of glory — „ 487
Upjetted *u* in spirts of wild sea-smoke, — *Sea Dreams* 52
Upland Piling sheaves in *u's* airy, — *L. of Shalott i* 34
Behind Were realms of *u*, prodigal in oil, — *Palace of Art* 79
Uplift *U* a thousand voices full and sweet, — *Ode Inter. Exhib.* 1
A lever to *u* the earth — *In Mem. cxiii* 15
And pure Sir Galahad to *u* the maid ; — *Lancelot and E.* 1265
Uplifted *U* was the clinking latch ; — *Mariana* 6
The bold Sir Bedivere *u* him, — *M. d'Arthur* 6
U high in heart and hope are we, — *Ode on Well.* 254
And been thereby *u*, should thro' me, — *Balin and Balan* 491
The bold Sir Bedivere *u* him, — *Pass. of Arthur* 175
Uplooking *u* and almost Waiting to see some blessed shape — *Lover's Tale i* 311
Up-on-end *See* **Hup-on-end**
Upowd (uphold) ' I'll *u* it tha weänt ; — *North. Cobbler* 63
Upper BELOW the thunders of the *u* deep ; — *The Kraken* 1
Old footsteps trod the *u* floors, — *Mariana* 67
Too long you keep the *u* skies ; — *Rosalind* 35
Now gnaw'd his under, now his *u* lip, — *Geraint and E.* 669
Uprear'd And in his chair himself *u*, — *Day-Dm., Revival* 18
Or whence the fear fest this my realm, *u*, — *Last Tournament* 122
Upright *U* and flush'd before him : — *Merlin and V.* 912
but scarcely could stand *u*, — *V. of Maeldune* 73
Uprising The knife *u* toward the blow — *The Victim* 66
Uproar not without an *u* made by those Who cried, — *Com. of Arthur* 42
Uprose *u* the mystic mountain-range : — *Vision of Sin* 208
Upshoot All round a hedge *u's*, and shows — *Day-Dm., Sleep. P.* 41
Upside *See* **Hupside**
Upsprang gain'd her castle, *u* the bridge, — *Pelleas and E.* 206
Upsprung In closest coverture *u*, — *Arabian Nights* 68
Upstarted Scared by the noise *u* at our feet, — *Merlin and V.* 422
Upstay'd Bent o'er me, and my neck his arm *u*. — *Lover's Tale i* 690
Upswell *u's* The gold-fringed pillow lightly prest : — *Day-Dm., Sleep. B.* 21
Upward Strike *u* thro' the shadow ; — *The Ring* 372
Tho' following with an *u* mind — *In Mem. xli* 21
Upward-rushing ever *u-r* storm and cloud Of shriek and plume, — *Last Tournament* 440
Urania *U* speaks with darken'd brow : — *In Mem. xxxvii* 1
Uranian o'er his head *U* Venus hung, — *Princess i* 243
Urge To which the voice did *u* reply ; — *Two Voices* 7
' Yet think not that I come to *u* thy crimes, — *Guinevere* 532
U him to foreign war. — *Sir J. Oldcastle* 68
Urged brought it ; and the poet little *u*, — *The Epic* 48
I *u* the fierce inscription on the gate, — *Princess iii* 141
Lancelot on him *u* All the devisings — *Gareth and L.* 1348
U him to speak against the truth, — *Lancelot and E.* 92
Urien then his brother king, *U*, assail'd him : — *Com. of Arthur* 36
Carádos, *U*, Cradlemont of Wales, — „ 112
Urim rich With jewels, elfin *U*, on the hilt, — „ 298
Urn (*See also* **Fountain-urns**) From fluted vase, and brazen *u* — *Arabian Nights* 60
Drawing into his narrow earthen *u*, — *Ode to Memory* 61
white dust, shut in an *u* of brass ! — *Lotos-Eaters, C. S.* 68
Soft lustre bathes the range of *u's* — *Day-Dm., Sleep. P.* 9
Found lying with his *u's* and ornaments, — *Aylmer's Field* 4
and with great *u's* of flowers. — *Princess ii* 26
Thro' prosperous floods his holy *u*. — *In Mem. ix* 8
And on the board the fluttering *u* : — „ *xcv* 8
An angel watching an *u* Wept — *Maud I viii* 3
swathe thyself all round Hope's quiet *u* For ever ? — *Lover's Tale i* 100
immerging, each, his *u* In his own well, — *Tiresias* 88

'Urry (hurry) Naay sit down—naw *'u*—sa cowd !— *Village Wife* 20
Usage (*See also* **Ill-usage**) tenfold dearer by the power Of intermitted *u* ; *Marr. of Geraint* 811
And lose thy life by *u* of thy sting ; *Ancient Sage* 270
shrunk by *u* into commonest commonplace ! *Locksley H., Sixty* 76
Use (s) keep a thing, its *u* will come. *The Epic* 42
' God made the woman for the *u* of man, *Edwin Morris* 91
To rust unburnish'd, not to shine in *u* ! *Ulysses* 23
to what *u's* shall we put The wildweed-flower *Day-Dm., Moral* 5
So 'twere to cramp its *u*, if I Should hook „ 15
gentle creature shut from all Her charitable *u*, *Aylmer's Field* 566
too late ! they come too late for *u*. *Sea Dreams* 67
or of older *u* All-seeing Hyperion— *Lucretius* 125
From childly wont and ancient *u* I call— „ 209
redound Of *u* and glory to yourselves ye come, *Princess ii* 43
might grow To *u* and power on this Oasis, „ 167
public *u* required she should be known ; „ *iv* 336
since my oath was ta'en for public *u*, „ 337
And boats and bridges for the *u* of men. „ *vi* 47
What *u* to keep them here—now ? „ 304
void was her *u*, And she as one that climbs a peak „ *vii* 34
All of beauty, all of *u*, *Ode Inter. Exhib.* 23
Naw soort o' koind o' *u* to saäy *N. Farmer, O. S.* 6
' O wife, what *u* to answer now ? *The Victim* 55
A *u* in measured language lies ; *In Mem. v* 6
Make one wreath more for *U* and Wont, „ *xxix* 11
And learns the *u* of ' I,' and ' me,' „ *xlv* 6
This *u* may lie in blood and breath, „ 13
But with long *u* her tears are dry. „ *lxxviii* 20
because he bare The *u* of virtue out of earth : „ *lxxxii* 10
Has broke the bond of dying *u*. „ *cv* 12
And soil'd with all ignoble *u*. „ *cxi* 24
batter'd with the shocks of doom To shape and *u*. „ *cxviii* 25
And thrice the gold for Uther's *u* thereof, *Gareth and L.* 344
To war against ill *u's* of a life, „ 1130
I will make *u* of all the power I have. *Geraint and E.* 345
(tho' I count it of small *u* To charge you) „ 416
' Thou shalt put the crown to *u*. *Balin and Balan* 202
he defileth heavenly things With earthly *u's* '— „ 422
lost to life and *u* and name and fame. (repeat) *Merlin and V.* 214, 970
My *u* and name and fame. „ 304
Upon my life and *u* and name and fame, „ 374
With this for motto, ' Rather *u* than fame.' „ 480
U gave me Fame at first, and Fame again Increasing gave me *u*. „ 493
I rather dread the loss of *u* than fame ; „ 519
and she lay as dead, And lost all *u* of life : „ 645
kingdom's, not the King's—For public *u* : *Lancelot and E.* 60
ourselves shall grow In *u* of arms and manhood, „ 64
I might have put my wits to some rough *u*, „ 1306
Now grown a part of me : but what *u* in it ? „ 1416
' It is not Arthur's *u* To hunt by moonlight ; ' *Holy Grail* 110
heart And might of limb, but mainly *u* and skill, *Last Tournament* 198
and with mirth so loud Beyond all *u*, „ 236
Arthur deign'd not *u* of word or sword, „ 458
They served their *u*, their time ; „ 676
or what *u* To know her father left us *Lover's Tale i* 292
for henceforth what *u* were words to me ! „ 609
show'd he drank beyond his *u* ; „ *iv* 228
What *u* to brood ? this life of mingled pains *To Mary Boyle* 49
Use (verb) and *u* Her influence on the mind, *Will Water.* 11
You grant me license ; might I *u* it ? *Princess iii* 235
to *u* A little patience ere I die ; *In Mem. xxxiv* 11
before my lance if lance Were mine to *u*— *Gareth and L.* 7
And answer'd with such craft as women *u*, *Geraint and E.* 352
u Both grace and will to pick the vicious quitch „ 902
eats And *u's*, careless of the rest ; *Merlin and V.* 463
Might *u* it to the harm of anyone, „ 685
since I cannot *u* it, ye may have it.' *Lancelot and E.* 199
I pray you, *u* some rough discourtesy „ 973
Besought me to be plain and blunt, and *u*, „ 1301
who cared Only to *u* his own, *Lover's Tale iv* 312
my Leonard, *u* and not abuse your day, *Locksley H., Sixty* 265
Used (*See also* **Ill-used**) out the storied Past, and *u* Within the Present, *Love thou thy land* 2
Used (*continued*) *U* all her fiery will, and smote Her life *Will Water.* 111
And she the left, or not, or seldom *u* ; *Princess iii* 38
But great is song *U* to great ends : „ *iv* 138
Fatherly fears—you *u* us courteously— „ *v* 216
It is all *u* up for that. *Maud II v* 64
Am much too gentle, have not *u* my power : *Marr. of Geraint* 467
Nor left untold the craft herself had *u* ; *Geraint and E.* 393
' Enid, I have *u* you worse than that dead man ; „ 735
wrought too long with delegated hands, Not *u* mine own : „ 894
So *u* as I, My daily wonder is, *Merlin and V.* 535
This was the one discourtesy that he *u*. *Lancelot and E.* 988
Used (accustomed) We are *u* to that : *Princess iii* 277
Used (was or were accustomed) Musing on him that *u* to fill it for her, *Enoch Arden* 208
ah God, as he *u* to rave. *Maud I i* 60
full of wolves, where he *u* to lie ; „ *II v* 54
With whom he *u* to play at tourney once, *Gareth and L.* 532
whom he *u* To harry and hustle. „ 706
when I am gone Who *u* to lay them ! *Balin and Balan* 141
golden hair, with which I *u* to play Not knowing ! *Guinevere* 547
as ye *u* to do twelve year sin' ! *Spinster's S's.* 59
you *u* to call me once The lonely maiden-Princess *The Ring* 64
as I *u* To prattle to her picture— „ 115
I *u* to walk This Terrace—morbid, „ 167
She *u* to shun the wailing babe, „ 358
she *u* to gaze Down at the Troad ; *Death of Œnone* 2
For I *u* to play with the knife, *Charity* 15
Useful Should hook it to some *u* end. *Day-Dm., Moral* 16
So never took that *u* name in vain, *Sea Dreams* 189
Before the *u* trouble of the rain : *Geraint and E.* 771
Subdue them to the *u* and the good. *Ulysses* 38
Useless To draw, to sheathe a *u* sword, *In Mem. cxxviii* 13
these blind hands were *u* in their wars. *Tiresias* 78
This *u* hand ! I felt one warm tear fall upon it. „ 166
Usherest Who *u* in the dolorous hour *In Mem. lxxii* 9
Using like the hand, and grew With *u* ; *Princess ii* 151
Usk Held court at old Caerleon upon *U*. *Marr. of Geraint* 146
Took horse, and forded *U*, and gain'd the wood ; „ 161
but up the vale of *U*, By the flat meadow, „ 831
the full-tided *U*, Before he turn to fall seaward *Geraint and E.* 116
they past With Arthur to Caerleon upon *U*. „ 946
By the great tower—Caerleon upon *U*— *Balin and Balan* 506
Who never sawest Caerleon upon *U*— „ 570
the flat field by the shore of *U* Holden : *Pelleas and E.* 164
Usurp'd Sir Modred had *u* the realm, *Guinevere* 154
Usury kiss for kiss, With *u* thereto.' *Talking Oak* 196
Uther Or mythic *U's* deeply-wounded son *Palace of Art* 105
And after him King *U* fought and died, *Com. of Arthur* 14
Who cried, ' He is not *U's* son '— „ 43
who hath proven him King *U's* son ? „ 70
Are like to those of *U* whom we knew. „ 72
wise man that served King *U* thro' his magic art ; „ 152
Hold ye this Arthur for King *U's* son ? ' „ 172
for ye know that in King *U's* time „ 185
And *U* cast upon her eyes of love : „ 193
That Gorloïs and King *U* went to war : „ 196
Then *U* in his wrath and heat besieged Ygerne „ 198
Left her and fled, and U enter'd in, „ 201
King *U* died himself, Moaning and wailing for an heir „ 206
And many hated *U* for the sake Of Gorloïs. „ 220
an old knight And ancient friend of *U* ; „ 223
' Here is *U's* heir, your king,' „ 230
Or *U's* son, and born before his time, „ 241
near him when the savage yells Of *U's* peerage died, „ 257
and dark was *U* too, Wellnigh to blackness ; „ 329
Merlin ever served about the King, *U*, before he died ; and on the night When *U* in Tintagil past away „ 366
' The King ! Here is an heir for *U* ! ' „ 386
No son of *U*, and no king of ours ; ' „ 440
Thy father, *U*, reft From my dead lord a field *Gareth and L.* 334
And thrice the gold for *U's* use thereof, „ 344
A knight of *U* in the Barons' war, „ 353
And *U* slit thy tongue : „ 376
whom *U* left in charge Long since, *Geraint and E.* 933

Utmost Sweet in their *u* bitterness, *Supp. Confessions* 117
Wan, wasted Truth in her *u* need. *Clear-headed friend* 19
Beyond the *u* bound of human thought. *Ulysses* 32
Beyond their *u* purple rim, (repeat) *Day-Dm., Depart.* 6, 30
as for *u* grief or shame ; *Merlin and V.* 897
His party, knights of *u* North and West, *Lancelot and E.* 526
when thou hast seen me strain'd And sifted to the *u*, *Pelleas and E.* 248
On that sharp ridge of *u* doom ride highly *Lover's Tale i* 805
Utter (adj.) seest me drive Thro' *u* dark a full-sail'd skiff, *Supp. Confessions* 95
silence seems to flow Beside me in my *u* woe, *Oriana* 87
' Then, then, from *u* gloom stood out the breasts, *Lucretius* 60
reverence thine own beard That looks as white as *u* truth, *Gareth and L.* 281
my knights are sworn to vows Of *u* hardihood, *u* gentleness, And, loving, *u* faithfulness in love, „ 553
The King in *u* scorn Of thee and thy much folly „ 918
as if the world were one Of *u* peace, and love, and gentleness ! „ 1289
Geraint, from *u* courtesy, forbore. *Marr. of Geraint* 381
Then Enid, in her *u* helplessness, *Geraint and E.* 719
So passionate for an *u* purity *Merlin and V.* 26
or what Her all but *u* whiteness held for sin, *Holy Grail* 84
did Pelleas in an *u* shame Creep with his shadow thro' the court again, *Pelleas and E.* 440
That here in *u* dark I swoon'd away, *Last Tournament* 622
You lose yourself in *u* ignorance ; *Lover's Tale i* 79
Why in the *u* stillness of the soul „ 276
All thro' the livelong hours of *u* dark, „ 810
but round my Evelyn clung In *u* silence for so long, *Sisters (E. and E.)* 217
That mock-meek mouth of *u* Antichrist, *Sir J. Oldcastle* 170
Sunless and moonless, *u* light—but no ! *Columbus* 90
If *u* darkness closed the day, my son— *Ancient Sage* 199
Sons of God, and kings of men in *u* nobleness of mind, *Locksley H., Sixty* 122
Were *u* darkness—one, the Sun of dawn *Prin. Beatrice* 3
lost in *u* grief I fail'd To send my life *Demeter and P.* 109
And *u* knowledge is but *u* love— *The Ring* 43
colour'd bubble bursts above the abyss Of Darkness, *u* Lethe. *Romney's R.* 53
With politic care, with *u* gentleness, *Akbar's Dream* 128
Utter (verb) I would that my tongue could *u* *Break, Break, etc.* 3
U your jubilee, steeple and spire ! *W. to Alexandra* 17
To *u* love more sweet than praise. *In Mem. lxxvii* 16
what dream ye when they *u* forth May-music *Gareth and L.* 1079
on a sudden the garrison *u* a jubilant shout, *Def. of Lucknow* 98
Utterance glided thro' all change Of liveliest *u*. *D. of F. Women* 168
in sighs Which perfect Joy, perplex'd for *u*, *Gardener's D.* 255
Gave *u* by the yearning of an eye, *Love and Duty* 62
As if to speak, but, *u* failing her, *Princess iv* 395
told us all their anger in miraculous *u's*, *Boädicea* 23
His broken *u's* and bashfulness, *Pelleas and E.* 111
Went on in passionate *u* : *Guinevere* 611
her gracious lips Did lend such gentle *u*, *Lover's Tale i* 457
As if she were afraid of *u* ; „ 564
breath floated in the *u* Of silver-chorded tones : „ *ii* 141
Utter'd *brows Of him that* u *nothing base ;* *To the Queen* 8
He *u* rhyme and reason, *The Goose* 6
He *u* words of scorning ; „ 42
Caught up the whole of love and *u* it, *Love and Duty* 82
And there the tale he *u* brokenly, *Enoch Arden* 647
She nor swoon'd, nor *u* cry : *Princess vi* 2
on her Fixt my faint eyes, and *u* whisperingly : „ *vii* 144
Bow'd at her side and *u* whisperingly : *Geraint and E.* 305
To whom the woodman *u* wonderingly *Balin and Balan* 297
But when Sir Garlon *u* mocking-wise ; „ 389
While he *u* this, Low to her own heart *Lancelot and E.* 318
U a little tender dolorous cry. „ 817
Lancelot kneeling *u*, ' Queen, Lady, my liege, „ 1179
For when had Lancelot *u* aught so gross *Last Tournament* 631
my strangled vanity *U* a stifled cry— *Sisters (E. and E.)* 200
Before the first ' I will ' was *u*, „ 211
you heard the lines I read Nor *u* word of blame, *Pro. to Gen. Hamley* 18

Utter'd (*continued*) heart of this most ancient realm A hateful voice be *u*, *Prog. of Spring* 103
till the little one *u* a cry. *Bandit's Death* 26
Utterest all of them redder than rosiest health or than *u* shame, *V. of Maeldune* 65
Uttering all in passion *u* a dry shriek, *Geraint and E.* 461
lock up my tongue From *u* freely what I freely hear ? *Last Tournament* 694
brook'd No silence, brake it, *u* ' Late ! so late ! What hour, *Guinevere* 160
And *u* this the King Made at the man : *Pass. of Arthur* 164
Utterly and brake it *u* to the hilt. *Gareth and L.* 1148
Uttermost (adj.) Is He not yonder in those *u* Parts of the morning ? *Enoch Arden* 223
And *u* obedience to the King.' *Gareth and L.* 555
For *u* obedience make demand „ 558
In *u* obedience to the King. „ 833
Uttermost (s) To hoard all savings to the *u*, *Enoch Arden* 46
wish To save all earnings to the *u*, „ 86
So aid me Heaven when at mine *u*, *Marr. of Geraint* 502
That he might prove her to the *u*, *Geraint and E.* 589
Fasted and pray'd even to the *u*, *Holy Grail* 132
Yea, let her prove me to the *u*, For loyal to the *u* am I.' *Pelleas and E.* 211
when the guest Is loved and honour'd to the *u*. *Lover's Tale iv* 245
you are honour'd now Ev'n to the *u* : „ 317
Uxoriousness And molten down in mere *u*. *Marr. of Geraint* 60
past the people's talk And accusation of *u* „ 83

V

Vaäin (vain) an' I beänt not *v*, *Spinster's S's.* 15
An' I beänt not *v*, but I knaws „ 71
Vacancy we shall see The nakedness and *v* *Deserted House* 11
gloom the *vacancies* Between the tufted hills, *Lover's Tale i* 2
Vacant *In* v *chambers, I could trust Your kindness.* *To the Queen* 19
And, last, you fix'd a *v* stare, *L. C. V. de Vere* 47
v of our glorious gains, *Locksley Hall* 175
Will haunt the *v* cup : *Will Water.* 172
I cry to *v* chairs and widow'd walls, *Aylmer's Field* 720
Whence follows many a *v* pang ; *Princess ii* 403
Perchance, to charm a *v* brain, *The Daisy* 106
And *v* chaff well meant for grain. *In Mem. vi* 4
vital spirits sink To see the *v* chair, „ *xx* 19
Of *v* darkness and to cease. „ *xxxiv* 16
And *v* yearning, tho' with might „ *cviii* 6
stands *V*, but thou retake it, mine again ! ' *Balin and Balan* 79
In our great hall there stood a *v* chair, *Holy Grail* 167
Your places being *v* at my side, „ 317
In hanging robe or *v* ornament, *Guinevere* 506
And I stood sole beside the *v* bier. *Lover's Tale iii* 58
Till you find the deathless Angel seated in the *v* tomb. *Locksley H., Sixty* 278
And sanguine Lazarus felt a *v* hand *To Mary Boyle* 31
Vacillating O damned *v* state ! *Supp. Confessions* 190
in my good mother's hall Linger with *v* obedience, *Gareth and L.* 13
Vagrant And *v* melodies the winds which bore *The Poet* 17
' If all be dark, *v* voice,' I said, *Two Voices* 265
A *v* suspicion of the breast : „ 336
' Some *v* emotion of delight „ 361
Love is made a *v* regret. *Miller's D.* 210
But sickening of a *v* disease, *L. C. V. de Vere* 62
But *v* in vapour, hard to mark ; *Love thou thy land* 62
And *v* desires, like fitful blasts of balm *Gardener's D.* 68
I shook her breast with *v* alarms— *The Letters* 38
And therewithal an answer *v* as wind : *Princess i* 45
moulder'd lodges of the Past So sweet a voice and *v*, „ *iv* 64
as babies for the moon, *V* brightness ; „ 429
To that *v* fear implied in death ; *In Mem. xli* 14
Is faith as *v* as all unsweet : „ *xlvii* 5
If any *v* desire should rise, „ *lxxx* 1
V words ! but ah, how hard to frame „ *xcv* 45

Vagrant (*continued*) *v* desire That spurs an imitative will. *In Mem. cx* 19
swaying upon a restless elm Drew the *v* glance of Vivien, *Balin and Balan* 464
To one at least, who hath not children, *v*, *Merlin and V.* 506
'You breathe but accusation vast and *v*, „ 701
There gleam'd a *v* suspicion in his eyes: *Lancelot and E.* 127
came and went Before her, or a *v* spiritual fear— *Guinevere* 71
Laziness, *v* love-longings, the bright May, *Sisters (E. and E.)* 128
What *v* world-whisper, mystic pain or joy, *Far—far—away* 7
Till, led by dream and *v* desire, *To Master of B.* 17

Vaguer *v* voices of Polytheism Make but one music, *Akbar's Dream* 150

Vail her hand Grasp'd, made her *v* her eyes: *Guinevere* 663

Vail'd He look'd but once, and *v* his eyes again. *Last Tournament* 150

Vain (adj.) (*See also* **Vaäin**) Of knitted purport, all were *v*. *Two Voices* 168
The chancellor, sedate and *v*, *Day-Dm., Revival* 29
blank And waste it seem'd and *v*; *Princess vii* 43
From talk of battles loud and *v*, *Ode on Well.* 247
V solace! Memory standing near *To J. S.* 53
No *v* libation to the Muse, *Will Water.* 9
Who will not *hear* denial, *v* and rude *Lover's Tale i* 628
like a *v* rich man, That, having always prosper'd „ 715
'But *v* the tears for darken'd years *Ancient Sage* 183
And *v* the laughter as the tears, „ 185
Rail at 'Blind Fate' with many a *v* 'Alas!' *Doubt and Prayer* 2
Help thy *v* worlds to bear thy light. *In Mem., Pro.* 32
making *v* pretence Of gladness, „ *xxx* 6
That not a moth with *v* desire „ *liv* 10
At night she weeps, 'How *v* am I! „ *lx* 15
With fifty Mays, thy songs are *v*; „ *lxxvi* 14
Thy likeness, I might count it *v* „ *xcii* 2
Half-grown as yet, a child, and *v*— „ *cxiv* 9
man of science himself is fonder of glory, and *v*, *Maud I iv* 37
She murmur'd, '*V*, in vain: it cannot be. *Lancelot and E.* 892
project after project rose, and all of them were *v*; *The Flight* 14
I was jealous, anger'd, *v*, *Happy* 66
May your fears be *v*! *To One who ran down Eng.* 2

Vain (s) I would shoot, howe'er in *v*, *Two Voices* 344
Her and her children, let her plead in *v*; *Enoch Arden* 166
Borrow'd a glass, but all in *v*: „ 240
If all be not in *v*; *In Mem. cxiv* 18
the Queen, who long had sought in *v* To break him *Gareth and L.* 139
Foredooming all his trouble was in *v*, „ 1127
that ye blew your boast in *v*?' „ 1229
To sleek her ruffled peace of mind, in *v*. *Merlin and V.* 899
That proof of trust—so often ask'd in *v*! „ 920
She murmur'd, 'Vain, in *v*: it cannot be. *Lancelot and E.* 892
When some brave deed seem'd to be done in *v*, *Holy Grail* 274
all My quest were but in *v*; „ 783
And now his chair desires him here in *v*, „ 901
her life Wasted and pined, desiring him in *v*. *Pelleas and E.* 496
have but stricken with the sword in *v*; *Pass. of Arthur* 23
And we had not fought them in *v*, *The Revenge* 74
Torture and trouble in *v*,— *Def. of Lucknow* 86
Or you may drive in *v*, *Politics* 8
But the Bandit had woo'd me in *v*, *Bandit's Death* 10

Vainglorious Nothing of the vulgar, or *v*, *On Jub. Q. Victoria* 13

Vainglory Drove me from all *vainglories*, *Holy Grail* 32

Vainlier *v* than a hen To her false daughters *Princess v* 328

Vale Winds all the *v* in rosy folds, *Miller's D.* 242
THERE lies a *v* in Ida, *Œnone* 1
many a *v* And river-sunder'd champaign „ 113
Lay, dozing in the *v* of Avalon, *Palace of Art* 107
'Make me a cottage in the *v*,' „ 291
and many a winding *v* And meadow, *Lotos-Eaters* 22
Beyond the thick-leaved platans of the *v*. *Princess iii* 175
roll The torrents, dash'd to the *v*: „ *v* 350
'Pretty bud! Lily of the *v*! „ *vi* 193
come; for all the *v's* Await thee; „ *vii* 215
Light, so low in the *v* You flash and lighten afar, *Window, Marr. Morn.* 9
The flocks are whiter down the *v*, *In Mem. cxv* 10
up the *v* of Usk, By the flat meadow, *Marr. of Geraint* 831
'And thence I dropt into a lowly *v*, *Holy Grail* 440
and where the *v* Was lowest, found a chapel, „ 441

Vale (*continued*) Re-makes itself, and flashes down the *v*— *Guinevere* 610
By thousands down the crags and thro' the *v's*. *Montenegro* 8
and every way the *v's* Wind, *Tiresias* 182
A gleam from yonder *v*, *Early Spring* 33
in this pleasant *v* we stand again, *Demeter and P.* 34
'Among the tombs in this damp *v* of yours! *The Ring* 325
Our vernal bloom from every *v* and plain *To Mary Boyle* 9
gulf on gulf thro' all their *v's* below. *Prog. of Spring* 73
But when she gain'd the broader *v*, *Death of Œnone* 91
Came that 'Ave atque *V*' of the Poet's *Frater Ave, etc.* 5
'Frater Ave atque *V*'—as we wander'd to and fro „ 7

Valence 'O ay, what say ye to Sir *V*, *Merlin and V.* 705
Sir *V* wedded with an outland dame: „ 714
Was charged by *V* to bring home the child. „ 718

Valentine birds that piped their *V's*, *Princess v* 239

Valiant Ring in the *v* man and free, *In Mem. cvi* 29
'I have fought for Queen and Faith like a *v* man and true; *The Revenge* 101
they stared at the dead that had been so *v* and true, „ 105

Valkyrian ourself have often tried *V* hymns, *Princess iv* 139

Valley (*See also* **Island-valley**) the broad *v* dimm'd in the gloaming: *Leonine Eleg.* 1
or fills The horned *v's* all about, *Supp. Confessions* 152
lovelier Than all the *v's* of Ionian hills. *Œnone* 2
Behind the *v* topmost Gargarus Stands up „ 10
panther's roar came muffled, while I sat Low in the *v*. „ 215
In this green *v*, under this green hill, „ 232
As I came up the *v* whom think ye should I see, *May Queen* 13
All the *v*, mother, 'ill be fresh and green „ 37
up the *v* came a swell of music on the wind. „ *Con.* 32
And up the *v* came again the music on the wind. „ 36
Wild flowers in the *v* for other hands than mine. „ 52
Full-faced above the *v* stood the moon; *Lotos-Eaters* 7
bolts are hurl'd Far below them in the *v's*, „ *C.S.* 112
others in Elysian *v's* dwell, „ 124
The *v's* of grape-loaded vines that glow *D. of F. Women* 219
Where yon dark *v's* wind forlorn, *On a Mourner* 22
I lived In the white convent down the *v* there, *St. S. Stylites* 62
from the *v's* underneath Came little copses *Amphion* 31
From some delightful *v*. *Will Water.* 120
To bicker down a *v*. *The Brook* 26
fought their last below, Was climbing up the *v*; *Aylmer's Field* 228
come, for Love is of the *v*, come, For Love is of the *v*, come thou down *Princess vii* 198
let the torrent dance thee down To find him in the *v*; „ 210
turning saw The happy *v's*, half in light, „ *Con.* 41
Follow'd up in *v* and glen With blare of bugle, *Ode on Well.* 114
All in the *v* of Death Rode the six hundred. *Light Brigade* 3
Into the *v* of Death Rode the six hundred. (repeat) „ 7, 16
A thousand shadowy-pencill'd *v's* *The Daisy* 67
ALL along the *v*, stream that flashest white, *V. of Cauteretz* 1
All along the *v*, where thy waters flow, „ 3
All along the *v*, while I walk'd to-day, „ 5
For all along the *v*, down thy rocky bed, „ 7
And all along the *v*, by rock and cave and tree, „ 9
Above the *v's* of palm and pine.' *The Islet* 23
The *v*, the voice, the peak, *Voice and the P.* 27
and jutting peak And *v*, *Spec. of Iliad* 14
Fly to the light in the *v* below— *Window, Letter* 12
Ringing thro' the *v's*, *Maud I xii* 10
And the *v's* of Paradise. „ *xxii* 44
Flee down the *v* before he get to horse. *Gareth and L.* 941
thro' many a grassy glade And *v*, *Marr. of Geraint* 237
long street of a little town In a long *v*, „ 243
And out of town and *v* came a noise „ 247
That glooms his *v*, sighs to see the peak Sun-flush'd, *Balin and Balan* 165
fill'd With the blue *v* and the glistening brooks, *Lover's Tale i* 331
men dropt dead in the *v's* *V. of Maeldune* 31
To silver all the *v's* with her shafts— *Tiresias* 32
horsemen, drew to the *v*—and stay'd; *Heavy Brigade* 3
When over the *v*, In early summers, *Merlin and the G.* 17
Drew to the *v* Named of the Shadow, „ 86
while we dwelt Together in this *v*— *Death of Œnone* 30
Thro' blasted *v* and flaring forest *Kapiolani* 12

Valorous many a *v* legionary, *Boädicea* 85
our most *v*, Sanest and most obedient: *Geraint and E.* 910
a *v* weapon in olden England! *Kapiolani* 4
Valour *V* and charity more and more. *To F. D. Maurice* 40
courtesy wins woman all as well As *v* may, *Last Tournament* 708
Stately purposes, *v* in battle, *Vastness* 7
Value To loyal hearts the *v* of all gifts *Lancelot and E.* 1214
The *v* of that jewel he had to guard? *Lover's Tale iv* 153
And trebling all the rest in *v*— „ 200
A gift of slenderer *v*, mine. *To Ulysses* 48
Valued he knew the man and *v* him. *Enoch Arden* 121
Valueless and you saved me, a *v* life, *Despair* 61
Valuing *V* the giddy pleasure of the eyes. *M. d'Arthur* 128
V the giddy pleasure of the eyes. *Pass. of Arthur* 296
Valve and betwixt were *v's* Of open-work *Princess iv* 202
marble stairs, And great bronze *v's*, „ *v* 365
Descending, burst the great bronze *v's*, „ *vi* 75
Van Love wept and spread his sheeny *v's* for flight; *Love and Death* 8
Then those who led the *v*, and those in rear, *Lover's Tale iii* 24
Van Diemen grows From England to *V D.* *Amphion* 84
Vane not the County Member's with the *v*: *Walk. to the Mail* 12
Still on the tower stood the *v*, *The Letters* 1
Waverings of every *v* with every wind, *To the Queen ii* 50
and once we only saw Your gilded *v*, *The Ring* 331
Vanish So *v* friendships only made in wine. *Geraint and E.* 479
and pass And *v* in the woods; *Balin and Balan* 327
Dreamlike, should on the sudden *v*, *Holy Grail* 260
From less to less and *v* into light. *Pass. of Arthur* 468
madden'd the peoples would *v* at last, *Despair* 24
And ever vanishing, never *v'es*, *Ancient Sage* 44
thy world Might *v* like thy shadow in the dark. „ 52
The hope I catch at *v'es* and youth *The Flight* 16
But Song will *v* in the Vast; *Epilogue* 40
Till shadows *v* in the Light of Light. *Epit. on Caxton* 4
Will *v* and give place to the beauty *Happy* 36
ere it *v'es* Over the margin, *Merlin and the G.* 128
if such a wife as you Should *v* unrecorded. *Romney's R.* 69
Let the golden Iliad *v*, *Parnassus* 20
v in your deeps and heights? *God and the Univ.* 1
Vanish'd (adj. and part.) But O for the touch of a *v* hand, *Break, break, etc.* 11
And those who sorrow'd o'er a *v* race, *Aylmer's Field* 844
But since it pleased a *v* eye, *In Mem. viii* 21
And, thy dark freight, a *v* life. „ *x* 8
The days have *v*, tone and tint, „ *xliv* 5
And thou hast *v* from thine own *Pref. Poem Broth. Son.* 5
Far among the *v* races, old Assyrian kings would flay *Locksley H., Sixty* 79
All I loved are *v* voices, all my steps are on the dead. „ 252
When, in the *v* year, You saw the league-long rampart-fire *Pro. to Gen. Hamley* 26
Light among the *v* ages; *To Virgil* 25
Stung by his loss had *v*, none knew where. *Lover's Tale iv* 102
Many a hearth upon our dark globe sighs after many a *v* face, *Vastness* 1
Many a planet by many a sun may roll with the dust of a *v* race. „ 2
Arthur had *v* I knew not whither, *Merlin and the G.* 77
Has *v* in the shadow cast by Death. *D. of the Duke of C.* 3
Vanish'd (verb) she cast back upon him A piteous glance, and *v*. *Aylmer's Field* 284
clink'd, and clash'd, and *v*, and I woke, *Sea Dreams* 135
v panic-stricken, like a shoal Of darting fish, *Geraint and E.* 468
Until they *v* by the fairy well *Merlin and V.* 428
And *v*, and his book came down to me.' „ 650
v suddenly from the field With young Lavaine *Lancelot and E.* 508
every bridge as quickly as he crost Sprang into fire and *v*, *Holy Grail* 506
now there is a lion in the way.' So *v*." „ 646
bounded forth and *v* thro' the night. *Pelleas and E.* 487
Or ev'n a fall'n feather, *v* again. *Last Tournament* 372
watch'd them till they *v* from my sight *Lover's Tale ii* 42
flash'd thro' sense and soul And by the poplar *v*— *Sisters (E. and E.)* 110
power over Hell till it utterly *v* away. *Despair* 102
when the white fog *v* like a ghost Before the day, *Death of Œnone* 67

Vanish'd (verb) *(continued)* before him *V* shadow-like Gods and Goddesses, *Kapiolani* 26
Vanishing *(See also* **Ever-vanishing***)* grave itself shall pass, *V*, atom and void, *Lucretius* 258
to the last dip of the *v* sail She watch'd it, *Enoch Arden* 245
And ever *v*, never vanishes, *Ancient Sage* 44
Vanity Oh! *v*! Death waits at the door. *All Things will Die* 16
they sing Like poets, from the *v* of song? *Gardener's D.* 100
thy *v* so shot up It frighted all free fool *Last Tournament* 306
my strangled *v* Utter'd a stifled cry— *Sisters (E. and E.)* 199
Vanquish knew that Love can *v* Death, *D. of F. Women* 269
Vanquish'd when our side was *v* and my cause For ever lost, *Princess vi* 24
We *v*, you the Victor of your will. „ 167
Victor from *v* issues at the last, *Gareth and L.* 1262
Vantage I set thee high on *v* ground, *Balin and Balan* 534
Vantage-ground With such a *v-g* for nobleness! *Aylmer's Field* 387
nor a *v-g* For pleasure; *Ded. of Idylls* 23
Vapid But languidly adjust My *v* vegetable loves *Talking Oak* 183
Vapour 'High up the *v's* fold and swim: *Two Voices* 262
swimming *v* slopes athwart the glen, *Œnone* 3
But vague in *v*, hard to mark; *Love thou thy land* 62
The *v's* weep their burthen to the ground, *Tithonus* 2
When the ranks are roll'd in *v*, *Locksley Hall* 104
Comes a *v* from the margin, „ 191
Faint shadows, *v's* lightly curl'd, *Day-Dm., Sleep. P.* 5
flowing range Of *v* buoy'd the crescent-bark, „ *Depart.* 22
My breath to heaven like *v* goes: *St. Agnes' Eve* 3
In crystal *v* everywhere *Sir L. and Q. G.* 5
A *v* heavy, hueless, formless, cold, *Vision of Sin* 53
When that cold *v* touch'd the palace gate, „ 58
A belt, it seem'd, of luminous *v*, lay, *Sea Dreams* 209
saw The soft white *v* streak the crowned towers *Princess iii* 344
Roll'd the rich *v* far into the heaven. *Spec. of Iliad* 8
Behind a purple-frosty bank Of *v*, *In Mem. cvii* 4
All night the shining *v* sail „ *Con.* 111
yellow *v's* choke The great city sounding wide; *Maud II iv* 63
a lovely baleful star Veil'd in gray *v*; *Merlin and V.* 263
The moony *v* rolling round the King, *Guinevere* 601
silvery *v* in daylight Over the mountain Floats, *Kapiolani* 16
Vapour-braided And sweet the *v-b* blue, *The Letters* 42
Vapour-girdle from my *v-g* soaring forth *Prog. of Spring* 79
Vapour-swathed forehead *v-s* In meadows ever green; *Freedom* 7
Variable Then follow'd calms, and then winds *v*, *Enoch Arden* 545
Varied With all the *v* changes of the dark, *Edwin Morris* 36
The coming year's great good and *v* ills, *Prog. of Spring* 93
Varier pious *v's* from the church, To chapel; *Sea Dreams* 19
Varieties (Beauty seen In all *v* of mould and mind) *To ——, With Pal. of Art* 7
Various Each month is *v* to present The world *Two Voices* 74
All *v*, each a perfect whole From living Nature, *Palace of Art* 58
'O all things fair to sate my *v* eyes! „ 193
So beautiful, vast, *v*, *Ancient Sage* 84
foremost in thy *v* gallery Place it, *Ode to Memory* 84
That *v* wilderness a tissue of light *Lover's Tale i* 419
To prize your *v* book, and send A gift *To Ulysses* 47
Varmint (vermin) 'Gaw up ageän fur the *v*?' *Owd Roä* 98
Varnish'd once more in *v* glory shine Thy stars *Prog. of Spring* 38
Varsity (university) 'e coom'd to the parish wi' lots o' *V* debt, *N. Farmer, N. S.* 29
Fur Squire wur a *V* scholard, *Village Wife* 25
Vartical (vertical) 'Cast awaäy on a disolut land wi' a *v* soon!' *North. Cobbler* 3
Vary To *v* from the kindly race of men, *Tithonus* 29
violet *varies* from the lily as far As oak from elm: *Princess v* 182
And as the light of Heaven *varies*, *Marr. of Geraint* 6
so loved Geraint To make her beauty *v* day by day, „ 9
value of all gifts Must *v* as the giver's. *Lancelot and E.* 1215
V like the leaves and flowers, *Poets and Critics* 4
Vary-colour'd A walk with *v-c* shells *Arabian Nights* 57
Varying *v* to and fro, We know not wherefore; *Aylmer's Field* 73
Form, Ritual, *v* with the tribes of men. *Akbar's Dream* 125
Ever *v* Madeline. (repeat) *Madeline* 3, 18, 27
The *v* year with blade and sheaf *Day-Dm., Sleep. P.* 1
By many a *v* influence and so long. *Princess vi* 267

Varying (*continued*) poesy, *v* voices of prayer ? — *Vastness* 31
Vase From fluted *v*, and brazen urn In order, — *Arabian Nights* 60
from *v's* in the hall Flowers of all heavens, — *Princess, Pro.* 11
or prove The Danaïd of a leaky *v*, — „ *ii* 340
Break, thou deep *v* of chilling tears, — *In Mem. iv* 11
Years that make And break the *v* of clay, — *Ancient Sage* 92
Vashti O *V*, noble *V* ! Summon'd out She kept her state, — *Princess iii* 228
Vassal (adj.) In *v* tides that follow'd thought. — *In Mem. cxii* 16
Delivering, that his lord, the *v* king, — *Gareth and L.* 391
follow'd up by her *v* legion of fools ; — *Vastness* 12
Vassal (s) Not *v's* to be beat, nor pretty babes — *Princess iv* 146
And makes it *v* unto love : — *In Mem. xlviii* 8
feeble *v's* of wine and anger and lust, — *Maud II i* 43
loyal *v's* toiling for their liege. — *Com. of Arthur* 282
Doorm, whom his shaking *v's* call'd the Bull, — *Geraint and E.* 439
Who now no more a *v* to the thief, — „ 753
But work as *v* to the larger love, — *Merlin and V.* 491
A prisoner, and the *v* of thy will ; — *Pelleas and E.* 241
The Present is the *v* of the Past : — *Lover's Tale i* 119
And make thy gold thy *v* not thy king, — *Ancient Sage* 259
the tyrant *v* of a tyrant vice ! — *The Flight* 25
Vassalage *See* **Kitchen-vassalage**
Vast (adj.) *V* images in glimmering dawn, — *Two Voices* 305
The *v* Republics that may grow, — *Day-Dm., L'Envoi* 15
But, all his *v* heart sherris-warm'd, — *Will Water.* 197
The *v* Akrokeraunian walls, — *To E. L.* 4
and fell In *v* sea-cataracts— — *Sea Dreams* 54
lays His *v* and filthy hands upon my will, — *Lucretius* 220
then how *v* a work To assail this gray — *Princess iii* 233
The bones of some *v* bulk that lived — „ 294
the *v* designs Of his labour'd rampart-lines, — *Ode on Well.* 104
And in the *v* cathedral leave him, — „ 280
fur I luvv'd 'er a *v* sight moor fur it : — *N. Farmer, N. S.* 36
Drops in his *v* and wandering grave. — *In Mem. vi* 16
His own *v* shadow glory-crown'd ; — „ *xcvii* 3
No doubt *v* eddies in the flood — „ *cxxviii* 5
for a *v* speculation had fail'd — *Maud I i* 9
whose *v* wit And hundred winters — *Com. of Arthur* 280
drew The *v* and shaggy mantle of his beard — *Merlin and V.* 256
but I dreamt Of some *v* charm concluded — „ 512
Drew the *v* eyelid of an inky cloud, — „ 634
And whelm all this beneath as *v* a mound — „ 656
' You breathe but accusation *v* and vague, — „ 701
The *v* necessity of heart and life. — „ 925
Brake from the *v* oriel-embowering vine — *Lancelot and E.* 1198
Then Arthur made *v* banquets, and strange knights — *Pelleas and E.* 147
On some *v* plain before a setting sun, — *Guinevere* 77
I, whose *v* pity almost makes me die — „ 534
who broke The *v* design and purpose of the King. — „ 670
and her throne In our *v* Orient, and one isle, — *To the Queen ii* 31
mighty gyres Rapid and *v*, — *Lover's Tale ii* 198
The *v* occasion of our stronger life— — *Columbus* 35
So beautiful, *v*, various, so beyond — *Ancient Sage* 84
The *v* sun-clusters' gather'd blaze, — *Epilogue* 54
In that *v* Oval ran a shudder of shame. — *St. Telemachus* 73
Thro' all the *v* dominion which a sword, — *Akbar's Dream* 14
Vast (s) Thine own shall wither in the *v*, — *In Mem. lxxvi* 11
A soul shall draw from out the *v* — „ *Con.* 123
But Song will vanish in the *V* ; — *Epilogue* 40
Vaster May make one music as before, But *v*. — *In Mem., Pro.* 29
What *v* dream can hit the mood Of Love — „ *xlvii* 11
As, unto *v* motions bound, — „ *lxiii* 10
And still as *v* grew the shore — „ *ciii* 25
My love is *v* passion now ; — „ *cxxx* 10
Or in that *v* Spain I leave to Spain. — *Columbus* 208
Sway'd by *v* ebbs and flows than can be known — *Locksley H., Sixty* 194
Vastness In *v* and in mystery, — *In Mem. xcvii* 7
Swallow'd in *V*, lost in Silence, — *Vastness* 34
Vat flask of cider from his father's *v's*, — *Audley Court* 27
red with spirted purple of the *v's*, — *Princess vii* 202
Vault (s) Imbower'd *v's* of pillar'd palm, — *Arabian Nights* 39
Nor any cloud would cross the *v*, — *Mariana in the S.* 38
Ranges of glimmering *v's* with iron grates, — *D. of F. Women* 35
O Priestess in the *v's* of Death, — *In Mem. iii* 2
In *v's* and catacombs, they fell ; — „ *lviii* 4

Vault (s) (*continued*) up thy *v* with roaring sound Climb thy thick noon, — *In Mem. lxxii* 25
Far beneath a blazing *v*, — *Will* 18
from the deep *v* where the heart of Hope Fell into dust, — *Lover's Tale i* 94
And laid her in the *v* of her own kin. — „ *iv* 39
entering the dim *v*, And, making there a sudden light, — „ 52
Then at the far end of the *v* he saw His lady — „ 56
Drown'd in the gloom and horror of the *v*. — „ 62
Vault (verb) lightly *v* from the throne and play — *The Mermaid* 33
Far as the Future *v's* her skies, — *Mechanophilus* 17
Vaulted (*See also* **Hollow-vaulted, Long-vaulted, Over-vaulted**) *V* o'er the dark-blue sea. — *Lotos-Eaters, C. S.* 40
Then some one sent beneath his *v* palm — *Princess v* 31
So many a time he *v* up again ; — *Gareth and L.* 1125
And *v* on his horse, and so they crash'd In onset, — *Balin and Balan* 555
Ran thro' the doors and *v* on his horse And fled : — *Pelleas and E.* 539
v upon him, And rode beneath an ever-showering leaf, — *Last Tournament* 491
Vauntcourier that *one V* to this *double?* — *Lover's Tale ii* 30
Vaunted and *v* our kith and our kin, — *V. of Maeldune* 47
Veer the warm hour returns With *v* of wind, — *Last Tournament* 231
Veering (*See also* **Ever-veering**) bird that still is *v* there Above his four gold letters) — *The Ring* 332
By *v* passion fann'd, — *Madeline* 29
Vegetable But languidly adjust My vapid *v* loves — *Talking Oak* 183
Veil (s) inner impulse rent the *v* Of his old husk : — *Two Voices* 10
thro' thick *v's* to apprehend A labour — „ 296
Slow-dropping *v's* of thinnest lawn, — *Lotos-Eaters* 11
the time Is come to raise the *v*. — *Gardener's D.* 274
And draws the *v* from hidden worth. — *Day-Dm., Arrival* 4
rose of Gulistan Shall burst her *v* : — *Princess iv* 123
From orb to orb, from *v* to *v*.' — *In Mem. xxx* 28
Behind the *v*, behind the *v*. — „ *lvi* 28
A lucid *v* from coast to coast, — „ *lxvii* 14
We heard behind the woodbine *v* — „ *lxxxix* 50
an Isis hid by the *v*. — *Maud I iv* 43
A faded mantle and a faded *v*, — *Marr. of Geraint* 135
And in her *v* enfolded, manchet bread. — „ 389
And tearing off her *v* of faded silk — *Geraint and E.* 514
I knew the *v* had been withdrawn. — *Holy Grail* 522
aghast the maiden arose, White as her *v*, — *Guinevere* 363
from under this A *v*, that seemed no more than gilded air, — *Lover's Tale iv* 290
our mortal *v* And shatter'd phantom — *De Prof., Two G.* 46
the *v* Is rending, and the Voices of the day — *The Ring* 38
She comes to dress me in my bridal *v*. — „ 98
But the bridal *v*—Your nurse is waiting. — „ 488
Veil (verb) I cannot *v*, or droop my sight, — *Eleänore* 87
gleams of good that broke From either side, nor *v* his eyes : — *Love thou thy land* 90
She bow'd as if to *v* a noble tear ; — *Princess iii* 289
v His want in forms for fashion's sake, — *In Mem. cxi* 5
Well might I wish to *v* her wickedness, — *Guinevere* 211
and now He *v's* His flesh in bread, — *Sir J. Oldcastle* 156
Murder would not *v* your sin, — *Forlorn* 49
Veil'd (*See also* **Willow-veil'd**) eyes have been intent On that *v* picture—*v*, for what it holds — *Gardener's D.* 270
That *v* the world with jaundice, — *Walk. to the Mail* 20
he *v* His face with the other, and at once, — *Aylmer's Field* 808
again She *v* her brows, and prone she sank, — *Princess v* 107
In the centre stood A statue *v*, to which they sang ; And which, tho' *v*, was known to me, — *In Mem. ciii* 12
seem'd a lovely baleful star *V* in gray vapour ; — *Merlin and V.* 263
but what I saw was *v* And cover'd ; — *Holy Grail* 851
walk'd abreast with me, and *v* his brow, — *Lover's Tale ii* 86
I walk'd behind with one who *v* his brow. — „ *iii* 12
' He *v* Himself in flesh, — *Sir J. Oldcastle* 156
Veileth every cloud, that spreads above And *v* love, — *Two Voices* 447
Veilless He drove the dust against her *v* eyes : — *Geraint and E.* 529
Vein (s) Life shoots and glances thro' your *v's*, — *Rosalind* 22
a languid fire creeps Thro' my *v's* — *Eleänore* 131
you can talk : yours is a kindly *v* : — *Edwin Morris* 81
Here stays the blood along the *v's*. — *Day-Dm., Sleep P.* 4

Vein (s) (*continued*) brooking not the Tarquin in her *v's*, *Lucretius* 237
The summer of the vine in all his *v's*— *Princess i* 183
But branches current yet in kindred *v's*.' „ *ii* 245
From out a common *v* of memory Sweet household talk, „ 314
I felt my *v's* Stretch with fierce heat ; „ *v* 537
half the wolf's-milk curdled in their *v's*, „ *vii* 130
now the wine made summer in his *v's*, *Marr. of Geraint* 398
his forehead *v's* Bloated, and branch'd ; *Balin and Balan* 391
The flowers that run poison in their *v's*. *Lover's Tale i* 347
Burst *v*, snap sinew, and crack heart, *Sir J. Oldcastle* 123
heat of a wretched life rushing back thro' the *v's* ? *Despair* 68
Vein (verb) all the gold That *v's* the world *Princess iv* 543
Velvet (adj.) added fulness to the phrase Of 'Gauntlet in the *v* glove.' *To Marq. of Dufferin* 12
Velvet (s) dusted *v's* have much need of thee : *To J. M. K.* 4
Black *v* of the costliest— *Aylmer's Field* 804
Veneer'd *V* with sanctimonious theory. *Princess, Pro.* 117
Venerable 'Thanks, *v* friend,' replied Geraint ; *Marr. of Geraint* 303
Among the Roses, the more *v*. *Sisters (E. and E.)* 76
Venerator not a scorner of your sex But *v*, *Princess iv* 423
Vengeance 'Is this thy *v*, holy Venus, *Lucretius* 67
What hinders me To take such bloody *v* on you both ?— *Princess iv* 534
when he told us '*V* is mine !' *V. of Maeldune* 120
Venial Or seeming-genial *v* fault, *Will* 13
Venice then I pass'd Home, and thro' *V*, *The Ring* 192
Venom Not one to flirt a *v* at her eyes, *Merlin and V.* 609
Venom'd *See* **Faintly-venom'd**
Venomous You should have seen him wince As from a *v* thing : *Walk. to the Mail* 72
Strike dead the whole weak race of *v* worms, *Maud II i* 46
Venture my poor *v* but a fleet of glass *Sea Dreams* 138
would *v* to give him the nay ? *The Wreck* 17
Ventured Alone at home, nor *v* out alone. *Enoch Arden* 517
And boldly *v* on the liberties. *Princess i* 205
or half the world Had *v*— *Gareth and L.* 65
Venturous Maud with her *v* climbings *Maud I i* 69
Venus 'Is this thy vengeance, holy *V*, *Lucretius* 67
And o'er his head Uranian *V* hung, *Princess i* 243
And silver-smiling *V* ere she fell *Lover's Tale i* 61
V near her ! smiling downward *Locksley H., Sixty* 183
Hesper—*V*—were we native to that splendour „ 187
Veragua thunders in the black *V* nights, *Columbus* 146
Verbiage This barren *v*, current among men, *Princess ii* 54
Vere de Vere (*See also* **Clara Vere de Vere**) repose Which stamps the caste of *V d V*. *L. C. V. de Vere* 40
Verge Float by you on the *v* of night. *Margaret* 31
That lent broad *v* to distant lands, *Palace of Art* 30
hull Look'd one black dot against the *v* of dawn, *M. d'Arthur* 271
May from *v* to *v*, And May with me from head to heel. *Gardener's D.* 80
That sinks with all we love below the *v* ; *Princess iv* 47
Blot out the slope of sea from *v* to shore, „ *vii* 38
And on the low dark *v* of life *In Mem. l* 15
hull Look'd one black dot against the *v* of dawn, *Pass. of Arthur* 439
Each way from *v* to *v* a Holy Land, *Lover's Tale i* 337
dipping his head low beneath the *v*, „ 509
Verged kinds of thought, That *v* upon them, *Gardener's D.* 71
Veriest The *v* beauties of the work appear *Sisters (E. and E.)* 105
Sworn to be *v* ice of pureness, *Sir J. Oldcastle* 108
Vermeil-white near her, like a blossom *v-w*, *Marr. of Geraint* 364
Vermin (adj.) and the *v* voices here May buzz so loud— *Lancelot and E.* 138
Vermin (s) (*See also* **Varmint**) As fancies like the *v* in a nut *Princess vi* 263
curse me the British *v*, the rat ; *Maud II v* 58
and then like *v* here Drown him, *Gareth and L.* 822
I will track this *v* to their earths : *Marr. of Geraint* 217
from the *v* that he sees Before him, *Pelleas and E.* 285
show'd him, like a *v* in its hole, *Last Tournament* 165
Vernal till all Our *v* bloom from every vale *To Mary Boyle* 9
Broaden the glowing isles of *v* blue. *Prog. of Spring* 60
Versatility The grace and *v* of the man ! *Lancelot and E.* 472
Verse How may full-sail'd *v* express, *Eleänore* 44
invade Even with a *v* your holy woe. *To J. S.* 8
another which you had, I mean of *v* *The Epic* 26
Verse (*continued*) gave the *v* 'Behold, Your house is left unto you desolate !' *Aylmer's Field* 628
great Sicilian called Calliope to grace his golden *v*— *Lucretius* 94
In *v* that brings myself relief, *In Mem. lxxv* 2
Take one *v* more—the lady speaks *Merlin and V.* 445
the name at the head of my *v* is thine. *To A. Tennyson* 6
read me a Bible *v* of the Lord's good will *Rizpah* 61
sought the tribute of a *v* from me, *To Dante* 5
in his hand A scroll of *v*— *Ancient Sage* 6
patriot-soldier take His meed of fame in *v* ; *Epilogue* 33
Versed In many a subtle question *v*, *In Mem. xcvi* 6
Version which I know no *v* done In English *To E. Fitzgerald* 33
Vert Flame-colour, *v* and azure, in three rays, *Com. of Arthur* 275
Vertical *See* **Vartical**
Verulam (Lord, Francis Bacon) Plato the wise, and large-brow'd *V*, *Palace of Art* 163
But Homer, Plato, *V* ; *Princess ii* 160
Verulam (Roman Colony) London, *V*, Cámulodúne *Boädicea* 86
Very The *v* graves appear'd to smile, *The Letters* 45
And some that men were in the *v* walls, *Princess iv* 485
The *v* source and fount of Day *In Mem. xxiv* 3
But brake his *v* heart in pining for it, *Gareth and L.* 57
I fear'd The *v* fountains of her life were chill'd ; *Sisters (E. and E.)* 266
when Even descended, the *v* sunset aflame ; *V. of Maeldune* 66
This *v* ring Io t'amo ? *The Ring* 133
Vesper From prime to *v's* will I chant *Pelleas and E.* 349
Vessel On the coals I lay, A *v* full of sin : *St. S. Stylites* 170
There lies the port ; the *v* puffs her sail: *Ulysses* 44
The silver *v's* sparkle clean, *Sir Galahad* 34
to make the name Of his *v* great in story, *The Captain* 19
Reporting of his *v* China-bound, *Enoch Arden* 122
Waving, the moment and the *v* past. „ 244
The *v* scarce sea-worthy ; „ 656
And o'er his head the Holy *V* hung (repeat) *Holy Grail* 512, 520
And to the Holy *V* of the Grail.' „ 840
one A *v* in mid-ocean, her heaved prow Clambering, *Lover's Tale ii* 169
when all at once That painted *v*, „ 191
Tho' his *v* was all but a wreck ; *The Revenge* 64
Fleeted his *v* to sea with the king in it, *Batt. of Brunanburh* 60
crest of the tides Plunged on the *v* *The Wreck* 90
Launch your *v*, And crowd your canvas, *Merlin and the G.* 126
Vestal tended by Pure *v* thoughts in the translucent fane *Isabel* 4
love-whispers may not breathe Within this *v* limit, *Princess ii* 222
in the *V* entry shriek'd The virgin marble „ *vi* 350
The flower of all their *v* knighthood, *Balin and Balan* 508
Vested *See* **Woman-vested**
Vestibule *v's* To caves and shows of Death : *Lover's Tale ii* 125
Veteran Me the sport of ribald *V's*, *Boädicea* 50
Vex *V* not thou the poet's mind (repeat) *Poet's Mind* 1, 3
Will *v* thee lying underground ? *Two Voices* 111
'The end and the beginning *v* His reason : „ 298
to *v* me with his father's eyes ! *Œnone* 255
And an eye shall *v* thee, *Locksley Hall* 85
I will not *v* my bosom : *Amphion* 102
want of pence, Which *v'es* public men, *Will Water.* 44
v the unhappy dust thou wouldst not save. *Come not, when, etc.* 4
And it would *v* him even in his grave, *Enoch Arden* 303
For my dead face would *v* her after-life. „ 891
Ere you were born to *v* us ? *Princess vi* 248
ill counsel had misled the girl To *v* true hearts : „ *vii* 242
As daily *v'es* household peace, *In Mem. xxix* 2
I *v* my heart with fancies dim : „ *xlii* 1
Let this not *v* thee, noble heart ! „ *lxxix* 2
An old song *v'es* my ear ; *Maud II ii* 47
boys Who love to *v* him eating, *Geraint and E.* 561
V not yourself : ye will not see me more.' *Pelleas and E.* 304
began To *v* and plague her. *Guinevere* 68
I seem To *v* an ear too sad to listen to me, „ 315
And *v* them with my darkness ? *Lover's Tale i* 732
A madman to *v* you with wretched words, *Despair* 108
To *v* the noon with fiery gems, *Ancient Sage* 265
Vexed-Vext *Vex'd* with a morbid devil in his blood *Walk. to the Mail* 19
The farmer *vext* packs up his beds and chairs, „ 39
Draw down into his *vexed* pools *Supp. Confessions* 133
The *vexed* eddies of its wayward brother : *Isabel* 33

Vexed-Vext *(continued)* ' Go, *vexed* Spirit, sleep in trust ; *Two Voices* 115
scudding drifts the rainy Hyades *Vext* the dim sea : *Ulysses* 11
if he come again, *vext* will he be To find *Enoch Arden* 301
And James departed *vext* with him and her.' *The Brook* 110
Vext with unworthy madness, and deform'd. *Aylmer's Field* 335
Then their eyes *vext* her ; „ 802
they *vext* the souls of deans ; *Princess, Pro.* 162
I stood With Florian, cursing Cyril, *vext* at heart, „ *iv* 171
What time have I to be *vext* ? *Grandmother* 104
Fool that I am to be *vext* with his pride ! *Maud I xiii* 5
Vext with lawyers and harass'd with debt : „ *xix* 22
But he *vext* her and perplext her „ *xx* 6
Vext with waste dreams ? *Com. of Arthur* 85
bitterness and grief That *vext* his mother, „ 211
And *vext* his day, but blesses him asleep— *Gareth and L.* 1286
A little *vext* at losing of the hunt, *Marr. of Geraint* 234
' No, no,' said Enid, *vext*, ' I will not eat *Geraint and E.* 656
Vext at a rumour issued from herself *Merlin and V.* 153
Then Lancelot *vext* at having lied in vain : *Lancelot and E.* 102
He seem'd so sullen, *vext* he could not go : „ 210
Glad that no phantom *vext* me more, *Holy Grail* 538
vext his heart, And marr'd his rest— *Pelleas and E.* 398
carcanet *Vext* her with plaintive memories of the child: *Last Tournament* 29
I should evermore be *vext* with thee *Guinevere* 505
Vext me a bit, till he told me *First Quarrel* 36
to have *vext* myself And all in vain for her— *Sisters (E. and E.)* 200
Never since I was nurse, had I been so grieved and so *vext* ! *In the Child. Hosp.* 45
Vext, that you thought my Mother came to me ? *The Ring* 140
A demon *vext* me, The light retreated, *Merlin and the G.* 29
Vexillary In letters like to those the *v* *Gareth and L.* 1202
Vexing O Mary, Mary ! *V* you with words ! *Romney's R.* 29
Vext *See* **Vexed**
Vial A man with knobs and wires and *v's* *Princess, Pro.* 65
Viand Lay out the *v's*.' „ *iii* 347
before us glow'd Fruit, blossom, *v*, amber wine, „ *iv* 35
many a *v* left, And many a costly cate, *Gareth and L.* 848
Nor roll thy *v's* on a luscious tongue, *Ancient Sage* 267
Vibrate chord which Hampden smote Will *v* to the doom. *England and Amer.* 20
Star to star *v's* light : *Aylmer's Field* 578
In the Queen's shadow, *v* on the walls, *Lancelot and E.* 1175
Vicar Rome's *V* in our Indies ? *Columbus* 195
Vice Or crush her, like a *v* of blood, *In Mem. iii* 15
heart of the poet is whirl'd into folly and *v*. *Maud I iv* 39
And doubling all his master's *v* of pride, *Marr. of Geraint* 195
stirr'd this *v* in you which ruin'd man *Merlin and V.* 362
I call it,—well, I will not call it *v* : „ 368
They fain would make you Master of all *v*.' „ 469
bagpipes, revelling, devil's-dances, *v*. *Sir J. Oldcastle* 149
But pity—the Pagan held it a *v*— *Despair* 41
the tyrant vassal of a tyrant *v* ! *The Flight* 25
Rip your brothers' *v's* open, *Locksley H., Sixty* 141
Viceregal Your *v* days Have added fulness *To Marq. of Dufferin* 10
Vicious Who being *v*, old and irritable, *Marr. of Geraint* 194
His dwarf, a *v* under-shapen thing, „ 412
Both grace and will to pick the *v* quitch *Geraint and E.* 903
a shatter'd wheel ? a *v* boy *Locksley H., Sixty* 215
Vicisti Galilæe often mutter low ' *V G* ' ; louder again,
Spurning a shatter'd fragment of the God, ' *V G* ! ' *St. Telemachus* 15
Victim (*See also* **Fellow-victim**) death quiver'd at the *v's* throat ; *D. of F. Women* 115
snake-like slimed his *v* ere he gorged ; *Sea Dreams* 193
And dress the *v* to the offering up. *Princess iv* 130
He seem'd a *v* due to the priest. *The Victim* 36
Priest was happy, His *v* won : „ 62
The rites prepared, the *v* bared, „ 65
Till the *v* hear within and yearn *Boädicea* 58
One took him for a *v* of Earl Doorm, *Geraint and E.* 524
If not, the *v's* flowers before he fall.' *Lancelot and E.* 910
lurks, listens, fears his *v* may have fled— *The Flight* 71
A virgin *v* to his memory, *The Ring* 221
O you that can flatter your *v's*, *Charity* 29
Victor (adj.) Than that the *v* Hours should scorn *In Mem. i* 13
Victor (s) (*See also* **World-victor**) Whichever side be *V*, in the halloo *Princess ii* 231
The bearded *V* of ten-thousand hymns, „ *iii* 352
We vanquish'd, you the *V* of your will. „ *vi* 167
great World-victor's *v* will be seen no more. *Ode on Well.* 42
And *V* he must ever be. „ 258
And fawn at a *v's* feet. *Maud I vi* 30
nor make myself in my own realm *V* and lord. *Com. of Arthur* 90
V his men Report him ! „ 249
' Nay, not a point : nor art thou *v* here. *Gareth and L.* 1055
And *v* of the bridges and the ford, „ 1232
V from vanquish'd issues at the last, „ 1262
Who doubts thee *v* ? „ 1296
' Hark the *v* pealing there ! ' „ 1318
I watch'd thee *v* in the joust, „ 1356
On whom the *v*, to confound them more, *Geraint and E.* 169
And *v* at the tilt and tournament, „ 960
Arthur's host Proclaim'd him *V*, *Balin and Balan* 90
bore the prize and could not find The *v*, *Lancelot and E.* 630
and in the strength of this Come *v*. *Holy Grail* 481
Far less to bind, your *v*, and thrust him out, *Pelleas and E.* 293
for when our King Was *v* wellnigh day by day, *Last Tournament* 335
beheld That *v* of the Pagan throned in hall— „ 665
V in Drama, *V* in Romance, *To Victor Hugo* 1
iron-hearted *v's* they. *Locksley H., Sixty* 80
But they rode like *V's* and Lords *Heavy Brigade* 48
the Light is *V*, and the darkness Dawns *On Jub. Q. Victoria* 70
Victoria V,—*since your Royal grace* *To the Queen* 5
Victory Not Arac, satiate with his *v*. *Princess vii* 90
Bellowing *v*, bellowing doom : *Ode on Well.* 66
down their statue of *V* fell. *Boädicea* 30
and there cometh a *v* now. „ 46
with pure Affection, and the light of *v*, *Gareth and L.* 331
Whether ye wish me *v* or defeat, *Geraint and E.* 80
in steepness overcome, And *victories* of ascent, *Lover's Tale i* 387
Swallowing its precedent in *v*. „ 763
trumpets of *v*, groans of defeat ; *Vastness* 8
Victual in his hand Bare *v* for the mowers : *Geraint and E.* 202
Geraint Ate all the mowers' *v* unawares, „ 215
fetch Fresh *v* for these mowers of our Earl ; „ 225
and return With *v* for these men, „ 240
Vied Sappho and others *v* with any man : *Princess ii* 164
Vienna That in *V's* fatal walls *In Mem. lxxxv* 19
I have not seen, I will not see *V* ; „ *xcviii* 12
View (*See also* **Half-views**) full in *v*, Death, walking all alone *Love and Death* 4
whose brilliant hue Is so sparkling-fresh to *v*, *Rosalind* 40
When thus he met his mother's *v*, *L. C. V. de Vere* 34
Half-invisible to the *v*, *Vision of Sin* 36
here were telescopes For azure *v's* ; *Princess, Pro.* 68
Her early Heaven, her happy *v's* ; *In Mem. xxxiii* 6
But somewhere, out of human *v*, „ *lxxv* 18
Yea, tho' it spake and bared to *v* „ *xcii* 9
to reprove her For stealing out of *v* *Maud I xx* 9
lands in your *v* From this bay window— *Sisters (E. and E.)* 51
loved the *v* Long-known and loved by me, *Pro. to Gen. Hamley* 5
She held them up to the *v* ; *Dead Prophet* 72
but the goodly *v* Was now one blank, *Death of Œnone* 3
View'd suffering *v* had been Extremest pain ; *Lover's Tale ii* 129
Viewless The *v* arrows of his thoughts were headed *The Poet* 11
Vignette In bright *v's*, and each complete, *The Daisy* 45
Vigorous with the growths Of *v* early days, *Lover's Tale i* 133
Vigorously So *v* yet mildly, that all hearts *Geraint and E.* 957
Vigour So that my *v*, wedded to thy blood, *Œnone* 161
The faith, the *v*, bold to dwell *In Mem. xcv* 29
Yourself shall see my *v* is not lost.' *Geraint and E.* 82
Vile And yonder a *v* physician, *Maud II v* 36
A little at the *v* occasion, rode, *Marr. of Geraint* 235
' This is more *v*,' he made reply, *Two Voices* 103
v it were For some three suns to store *Ulysses* 28
Hired animalisms, *v* as those that made *Lucretius* 53
A red-faced bride who knew herself so *v*, *Gareth and L.* 110
for men sought to prove me *v*, *Merlin and V.* 495
How justly, after that *v* term of yours, „ 921
climb'd The moulder'd stairs (for everything was *v*) *Lover's Tale iv* 137

Vile (*continued*) *V*, so near the ghost Himself, *The Ring* 230
Vileness mean *V*, we are grown so proud— *Aylmer's Field* 756
No inner *v* that we dread? *In Mem. li* 4
Sinn'd thro' an animal *v*, *The Wreck* 42
Viler I am a sinner *v* than you all. *St. S. Stylites* 135
or the *v* devil who plays his part, *Balin and Balan* 300
of a kind The *v*, as underhand, *Maud I i* 28
Vilest The *v* herb that runs to seed *Amphion* 95
Village (adj.) Looks down upon the *v* spire: *Miller's D.* 36
I saw the *v* lights below; „ 108
Why come you drest like a *v* maid, *Lady Clare* 67
'If I come drest like a *v* maid, „ 69
At the head of the *v* street, *Maud I vi* 10
She came to the *v* church, „ *viii* 1
For only once, in the *v* street, „ *xiii* 26
maid That ever bided tryst at *v* stile, *Merlin and V.* 378
came the *v* girls And linger'd talking, *Pelleas and E.* 508
'A hignorant *v* wife as 'ud hev to be larn'd *Village Wife* 106
and pigmy spites of the *v* spire; *Vastness* 25
And darkness in the *v* yew. *Two Voices* 273
And a *v* maiden she. *L. of Burleigh* 8
Leads her to the *v* altar, „ 11
as the *v* girl Who sets her pitcher underneath *Enoch Arden* 206
Born of a *v* girl, carpenter's son, *Aylmer's Field* 668
And on a simple *v* green; *In Mem. lxiv* 4
Thou hear'st the *v* hammer clink, „ *cxxi* 15
By *v* eyes as yet unborn; „ *Con.* 59
Seems to be pluck'd at by the *v* boys *Geraint and E.* 560
as the *v* wife who cries 'I shudder, *Guinevere* 56
having climb'd one step beyond Our *v* miseries, *Ancient Sage* 207
Village (s) (*See also* **Sea-village**) Two children in two neighbour *v's* *Circumstance* 1
Where almost all the *v* had one name; *Aylmer's Field* 35
The little *v* looks forlorn; *In Mem. lx* 9
Maud the delight of the *v*, *Maud I i* 70
Below me, there, is the *v*, „ *iv* 7
For one from out his *v* lately climb'd *Balin and Balan* 167
tho' he tried the *v's* round, *First Quarrel* 43
Village-churls And there the surly *v-c*, *L. of Shalott ii* 16
Villager slavish hat from the *v's* head? *Maud I x* 4
Villain (adj.) Low down thro' *v* kitchen-vassalage, *Gareth and L.* 160
Villain (s) One says, we are *v's* all. *Maud I i* 17
How the *v* lifted up his voice, *Gareth and L.* 716
a *v* fitter to stick swine Than ride abroad „ 865
'There lurk three *v's* yonder in the wood, *Geraint and E.* 142
Villainous the *v* centre-bits Grind on the wakeful ear *Maud I i* 41
Villainously foully slain And *v*! *Balin and Balan* 136
Villainy *V* somewhere! whose? One says, *Maud I i* 17
And I will tell him all their *v*. *Geraint and E.* 132
My violence, and my *v*, come to shame.' *Balin and Balan* 492
beneath the shadow of those towers A *v*, three to one: *Pelleas and E.* 277
So Gawain, looking at the *v* done, Forbore, „ 282
lust, *V*, violence, avarice, of your Spain *Columbus* 172
Vine (*See also* **Briony-vine**) comest not with shows of flaunting *v's* *Ode to Memory* 48
And silent in its dusty *v's*: *Mariana in the S.* 4
leaning on a fragment twined with *v*, *Œnone* 20
And overhead the wandering ivy and *v*, „ 99
From cave to cave thro' the thick-twined *v*— *Lotos-Eaters, C. S.* 95
valleys of grape-loaded *v's* that glow *D. of F. Women* 219
And chimneys muffled in the leafy *v*. *Audley Court* 19
Old elms came breaking from the *v*, *Amphion* 45
The *v* stream'd out to follow, „ 46
from a bower of *v* and honeysuckle: *Aylmer's Field* 156
and so by tilth and grange, And *v's*, *Princess i* 111
The summer of the *v* in all his veins— „ 183
we two Were always friends, none closer, elm and *v*: „ *ii* 337
At last I hook'd my ankle in a *v*, „ *iv* 268
Or foxlike in the *v*; „ *vii* 203
Beating from the wasted *v's* *Ode on Well.* 109
Of olive, aloe, and maize and *v*. *The Daisy* 4
Mixt with myrtle and clad with *v*, *The Islet* 19
V, *v*, and eglantine, (repeat) *Window, At the Window* 1, 8
and go By summer belts of wheat and *v* *In Mem. xcviii* 4

Vine (*continued*) Queen Brake from the vast oriel-embowering *v* *Lancelot and E.* 1198
berries that flamed upon bine and *v*, *V. of Maeldune* 61
v's with grapes Of Eshcol hugeness; *To E. Fitzgerald* 27
they tell me, now in flowing *v's*— *Tiresias* 144
send my life thro' olive-yard and *v* And golden grain, *Demeter and P.* 110
spinning at your wheel beside the *v*— *Romney's R.* 5
serpent *v's* Which on the touch of heavenly feet *Death of Œnone* 4
Vine-bunches Between the shadows of the *v-b* *Œnone* 181
Vine-clad an oriel on the summer side, *V-c*, *Lancelot and E.* 1178
Vineyard Peace in her *v*—yes!— *Maud I i* 36
torrent *v* streaming fell To meet the sun *The Daisy* 10
tilth and *v*, hive and horse and herd; *To Virgil* 10
Vinous And softly, thro' a *v* mist, *Will Water.* 39
Vintage Whether the *v*, yet unkept, „ 97
praised the waning red, and told The *v*— *Aylmer's Field* 407
Whom they with meats and *v* of their best *Lancelot and E.* 266
with her spice and her *v*, her silk and her corn; *Vastness* 13
Violate behold our sanctuary Is *v*, our laws broken: *Princess vi* 60
And that she now perforce must *v* it, *Geraint and E.* 367
Which flesh and blood perforce would *v*: *Last Tournament* 689
v's virgin Truth for a coin or a cheque. *The Dawn* 15
Violated So was their sanctuary *v*, *Princess vii* 16
Violating Not *v* the bond of like to like.' *Lancelot and E.* 241
Violator mine of ruffian *v's*! *Boädicea* 50
Violence Moved with *v*, changed in hue, *Vision of Sin* 34
and shriek'd 'Thus, thus with *v*, *Sea Dreams* 25
'Thus with *v* Shall Babylon be cast into the sea; „ 27
Uther, reft From my dead lord a field with *v*: *Gareth and L.* 335
Was nigh to burst with *v* of the beat, „ 763
And snatch me from him as by *v*; *Geraint and E.* 357
And bare her by main *v* to the board, „ 654
Edyrn wrought upon himself After a life of *v*, „ 913
For I that did that *v* to thy thrall, *Balin and Balan* 61
forget My heats and *v's*? „ 190
So this will help him of his *v's*!' „ 205
Moaning 'My *v's*, my *v's*!' „ 435
My *v*, and my villainy, come to shame.' „ 492
power To lay the sudden heads of *v* flat, *Holy Grail* 310
with *v* The sword was dash'd from out my hand, „ 825
From flat confusion and brute *v's*, *Last Tournament* 124
small *v* done Rankled in him and ruffled *Guinevere* 48
Villainy, *v*, avarice, of your Spain *Columbus* 172
truthless *v* mourn'd by the Wise, *Vastness* 5
Violent I hear the *v* threats you do not hear, *Geraint and E.* 420
Rang by the white mouth of the *v* Glem; *Lancelot and E.* 288
Violet (adj.) and sunn'd Her *v* eyes, *Gardener's D.* 137
For large her *v* eyes look'd, *Pelleas and E.* 71
Violet (Christian Name) *V*, she that sang the mournful song, *Princess vi* 318
Violet (flower, colour) With what voice the *v* woos *Adeline* 31
V, amaracus, and asphodel, Lotos and lilies: *Œnone* 97
from the *v's* her light foot Shone rosy-white, „ 179
To die before the snowdrop came, and now the *v's* here. *May Queen, Con.* 4
O sweet is the new *v*, that comes beneath the skies, „ 5
The smell of *v's*, hidden in the green, *D. of F. Women* 77
The *v* of a legend blow Among the chops *Will Water.* 147
In mosses mixt with *v* Her cream-white mule *Sir L. and Q. G.* 30
Pity, the *v* on the tyrant's grave. *Aylmer's Field* 845
The *v* varies from the lily as far As oak from elm: *Princess v* 182
Crocus, anemone, *v*, *To F. D. Maurice* 44
The *v* of his native land. *In Mem. xviii* 4
A wither'd *v* is her bliss: „ *xcvii* 26
The *v* comes, but we are gone. „ *cv* 8
By ashen roots the *v's* blow. „ *cxv* 4
and my regret Becomes an April *v*, „ 19
jewel-print of your feet In *v's* blue as your eyes, *Maud I xxii* 42
with earliest *v's* And lavish carol *Lover's Tale i* 282
And, tho' thy *v* sicken into sere, *Prog. of Spring* 25
Violet-hooded Epic lilted out By *v-h* Doctors, *Princess ii* 376
Violin twangling *v* Struck up with Soldier-laddie, „ *Pro.* 85
All night have the roses heard The flute, *v*, bassoon; *Maud I xxii* 14
Viper fling it like a *v* off, and shriek *Princess vii* 94

Voice (*continued*) Thy living *v* to me was as the *v* of the dead, *V. of Cauteretz* 8
The *v* of the dead was a living *v* to me. „ 10
Paid with a *v* flying by to be lost on an endless sea— *Wages* 2
if He thunder by law the thunder is yet His *v*. *High. Pantheism* 14
The *v* and the Peak (repeat) *Voice and the P.* 1, 37
All night have I heard the *v* .. 5
Hast thou no *v*, O Peak, .. 9
'I am the *v* of the Peak, .. 11
A thousand *v's* go To North, South, East, and West; .. 13
The valley, the *v*, the peak, the star Pass, .. 27
A Spirit, not a breathing *v*. *In Mem. xiii* 12
Four *v's* of four hamlets round, .. *xxviii* 5
Each *v* four changes on the wind, .. 9
Then echo-like our *v's* rang; .. *xxx* 13
Our *v's* took a higher range; „ 21
Yet if some *v* that man could trust .. *xxxv* 1
And many an abler *v* than thou. .. *xxxvii* 4
O for thy *v* to soothe and bless! .. *lvi* 26
The *v* was low, the look was bright; .. *lxix* 15
The *v* was not the *v* of grief, .. 19
Or *v* the richest-toned that sings, .. *lxxv* 7
So loud with *v's* of the birds, .. *xcix* 2
Like strangers' *v's* here they sound, .. *civ* 9
A potent *v* of Parliament, .. *cxiii* 11
And that dear *v*, I once have known, .. *cxvi* 11
And *v's* hail it from the brink; .. *cxxi* 14
I heard a *v* 'believe no more' „ *cxxiv* 10
A deeper *v* across the storm, „ *cxxvii* 4
Thy *v* is on the rolling air; .. *cxxx* 1
I prosper, circled with thy *v*; „ 15
A *v* as unto him that hears, .. *cxxxi* 6
A *v* by the cedar tree In the meadow *Maud I v* 1
And wild *v* pealing up to the sunny sky, „ 13
Silence, beautiful *v*! Be still, .. 19
Not her, not her, but a *v*. „ 28
And simper and set their *v's* lower, „ *x* 15
Or the *v* of the long sea-wave as it swell'd „ *xiv* 31
V in the rich dawn of an ampler day— *Ded. of Idylls* 36
And find nor face nor bearing, limbs nor *v*, *Com. of Arthur* 71
before a *v* As dreadful as the shout of one .. 116
lifted his *v*, and call'd A hoary man, .. 144
A hundred *v's* cried, 'Away with him! .. 231
heard among the holy hymns A *v* as of the waters, .. 291
gathering half the deep And full of *v's*, .. 381
while the phantom king Sent out at times a *v*; and here or there Stood one who pointed toward the *v*, .. 437
past along the hymns A *v* as of the waters, .. 465
full *v* Swept bellowing thro' the darkness *Gareth and L.* 176
heard A *v*, the *v* of Arthur, .. 318
'A boon, Sir King (his *v* was all ashamed), .. 442
How the villain lifted up his *v*, .. 716
nor rough face, or *v*, Brute bulk of limb, .. 1329
nor have I heard the *v*. .. 1336
And muffled *v's* heard, and shadows past; .. 1373
Not hearing any more his noble *v*, *Marr. of Geraint* 98
'The *v* of Enid, Yniol's daughter, rang „ 327
and as the sweet *v* of a bird, „ 329
So the sweet *v* of Enid moved Geraint; .. 334
'Here, by God's grace, is the one *v* for me.' „ 344
the soldiers wont to hear His *v* in battle, *Geraint and E.* 175
and felt Her low firm *v* and tender government. „ 194
On a sudden, many a *v* along the street, „ 270
the tender sound of his own *v* And sweet self-pity, „ 348
Cried out with a big *v*, 'What, is he dead?' „ 541
answer'd in low *v*, her meek head yet Drooping, „ 640
'The *v* of Enid,' said the knight; .. 780
It seems another *v* in other groves; *Balin and Balan* 215
Mark The Cornish King, had heard a wandering *v*, *Merlin and V.* 8
With reverent eyes mock-loyal, shaken *v*, .. 157
O my Master, have ye found your *v*? „ 269
So tender was her *v*, so fair her face, „ 401
And heard their *v's* talk behind the wall, .. 631
Then her false *v* made way, broken with sobs: „ 857
When its own *v* clings to each blade of grass, And every *v* is nothing. *Lancelot and E.* 107

Voice (*continued*) and the vermin *v's* here May buzz so loud— *Lancelot and E.* 138
Won by the mellow *v* before she look'd, .. 243
And seeing me, with a great *v* he cried, .. 309
like a friend's *v* from a distant field .. 999
High with the last line scaled her *v*, .. 1019
a courtesy Spake thro' the limbs and in the *v*—I knew *Holy Grail* 23
till I found a *v* and sware a vow. .. 194
in a *v* Shrilling along the hall to Arthur, „ 288
but found at top No man, nor any *v*. .. 428
and he had Scarce any *v* to answer, .. 434
heard a *v*, 'Doubt not, go forward; .. 823
v singing in the topmost tower To the eastward: .. 834
He heard her *v*; Then let the strong hand, *Pelleas and E.* 233
'I never heard his *v* But long'd to break away. .. 255
he heard The *v* that billow'd round the barriers *Last Tournament* 167
He ended: Arthur knew the *v*; .. 455
about his feet A *v* clung sobbing till he question'd it, .. 759
and the *v* about his feet Sent up an answer, .. 760
crying with full *v* 'Traitor, come out, *Guinevere* 105
then came silence, then a *v*, Monotonous and hollow .. 419
the warhorse neigh'd As at a friend's *v*, .. 531
there her *v* brake suddenly, .. 607
Meek maidens, from the *v's* crying 'shame.' .. 672
To where beyond these *v's* there is peace. .. 698
when the man was no more than a *v* *Pass. of Arthur* 3
Thine, Gawain, was the *v*— .. 47
Moans of the dying, and *v's* of the dead. .. 117
The *v* of days of old and days to be. .. 135
'Hearest thou this great *v* that shakes the world, .. 139
Or *v*, or else a motion of the mere. .. 245
as it were one *v*, an agony Of lamentation, „ 368
let thy *v* Rise like a fountain for me night and day. „ 416
as if some fair city were one *v* Around a king .. 460
this, indeed, her *v* And meaning, *To the Queen ii* 19
The *v* of Britain, or a sinking land, .. 24
There rang her *v*, when the full city peal'd .. 26
Or Labour, with a groan and not a *v*, .. 55
loved The sound of one-another's *v's* *Lover's Tale i* 256
low converse sweet, In which our *v's* bore least part. .. 542
At first her *v* was very sweet and low, „ 563
for the sound Of that dear *v* so musically low, .. 708
for my *v* Was all of thee: .. *ii* 14
And *v's* in the distance calling to me „ 118
Willy's *v* in the wind, 'O mother, come out to me.' *Rizpah* 2
for my Willy's *v* in the wind— „ 82
A sweet *v* that—you scarce could better that. *Sisters (E. and E.)* 14
Marvellously like, their *v's*—and themselves! .. 24
let me ask you then, Which *v* most takes you? .. 30
says The common *v*, if one may trust it: .. 37
Harsh red hair, big *v*, big chest, *In the Child. Hosp.* 4
our children would die But for the *v* of Love, .. 12
but his *v* and his face were not kind, .. 15
V of the dead whom we loved, *Def. of Lucknow* 11
nor *v* Nor finger raised against him— *Sir J. Oldcastle* 44
lifted hand and heart and *v* In praise to God *Columbus* 16
There came two *v's* from the Sepulchre, .. 95
I heard his *v* between The thunders .. 145
I heard his *v*, 'Be not cast down. .. 157
And I shall hear his *v* again— .. 159
His *v* again. .. 162
God's Own *v* to justify the dead— .. 203
Our *v's* were thinner and fainter *V. of Maeldune* 22
with human *v's* and words; „ 28
whenever their *v's* peal'd The steer fell down „ 29
his *v* was low as from other worlds, „ 117
Stormy *v* of France? *To Victor Hugo* 8
For like the clear *v* when a trumpet shrills, *Achilles over the T.* 19
So rang the clear *v* of Æakidês; „ 21
Two *v's* heard on earth no more; *To E. Fitzgerald* 41
I heard a *v* that said 'Henceforth be blind, *Tiresias* 48
was mine the *v* to curb The madness of our cities „ 70
I knew not what, when I heard that *v*,— *The Wreck* 52
Mother, the *v* was the *v* of the soul; „ 54
a *v* rang out in the thunders of Ocean and Heaven „ 88

Voice (continued) In the rigging, v's of hell— The Wreck 92
I yearn'd For his v again, „ 104
May'st haply learn the Nameless hath a v, Ancient Sage 34
The splendours and the v's of the world ! „ 177
Nor list for guerdon in the v of men, „ 262
'Forward' rang the v's then, Locksley H., Sixty 77
hear the v's from the field. „ 116
You that woo the V's—tell them „ 131
Poor old v of eighty crying after v's that have fled !
All I loved are vanish'd v's, „ 251
Hears he now the V that wrong'd him ? „ 269
Too many a v may cry That man can have Epilogue 72
Who wert the v of England in the East. Epit. on Stratford 4
thy v, a music heard Thro' all the yells To Duke of Argyll 7
WELCOME, welcome, with one v ! Open. I. and C. Exhib. 1
Britain's myriad v's call, „ 35
We thank thee with our v, and from the heart. To W. C. Macready 4
One full v of allegiance, On Jub. Q. Victoria 22
All your v's in unison, „ 63
from all the world the v's came 'We know not, Demeter and P. 66
I heard one v from all the three 'We know not, „ 84
Thousands of v's drowning his own Vastness 6
all the sciences, poesy, varying v's of prayer ? „ 31
I hear your Mother's v in yours. The Ring 28
V's of the day Are heard across the V's of the dark. „ 39
is Muriel—your stepmother's v. „ 139
one silent v Came on the wind, „ 153
No v for either spoke within my heart „ 162
And then the tear fell, the v broke. „ 367
All the world will hear a v Scream Forlorn 27
A hateful v be utter'd, Prog. of Spring 103
and roll my v from the summit, Parnassus 6
Shall the royal v be mute ? By an Evolution. 14
she lifted up a v Of shrill command, Death of Œnone 98
Not the Great V not the true Deep. Akbar's Dream 59
A v from old Irân ! Nay, but I know it— „ 89
vaguer v's of Polytheism Make but one music, „ 150
clatter of arms, and v's, and men passing Bandit's Death 24
Blest be the v of the Teacher Kapiolani 2
their v's blend in choric Hallelujah Making of Man 7
dream'd that a V of the Earth went wailingly The Dreamer 3
A V spake out of the skies Voice spake, etc. 1
Silent V's of the dead, Silent Voices 4
Call me rather, silent v's, „ 7
Voiced See **Clear-voiced, Low-voiced, Sweet-voiced**
Voiceless creatures v thro' the fault of birth, Geraint and E. 266
Void I am v, Dark, formless, Supp. Confessions 121
Kate saith 'the world is v of might.' Kate 17
Not v of righteous self-applause, Two Voices 146
Naked I go, and v of cheer : „ 239
The stalls are v, the doors are wide, Sir Galahad 31
for it seem'd A v was made in Nature ; Lucretius 37
Vanishing, atom and v, atom and v, „ 258
v was her use, And she as one that climbs Princess vii 34
A v where heart on heart reposed ; In Mem. xiii 6
The captive v of noble rage, „ xxvii 2
Or cast as rubbish to the v, „ liv 7
V of the little living will Maud II ii 14
from within The city comes a murmur v of joy, Tiresias 101
Volcano Cold upon the dead v sleeps the gleam Locksley H., Sixty 42
The smoke of war's v burst again Prog. of Spring 97
Volley v on v, and yell upon yell— Def. of Lucknow 34
Volley'd V and thunder'd ; (repeat) Light Brigade 21, 42
Volleying And the v cannon thunder his loss ; Ode on Well. 62
Volubility all that heard her in her fierce v, Boädicea 4
Yell'd and shriek'd between her daughters in her fierce v. „ 72
Voluble Miriam Lane Made such a v answer Enoch Arden 903
Volume I found it in a v, all of songs, Audley Court 57
In this hand held a v as to read, Princess ii 455
held A v of the Poets of her land : „ vii 174
She moved, and at her feet the v fell. „ 254
Voluptuous Low v music winding trembled, Vision of Sin 17
which outredden All v garden-roses. Ode on Well. 208
To whom my false v pride, Guinevere 641
The sombre close of that v day, „ 688
Voluptuousness in his lust and v, Boädicea 66
And leave the hot swamp of v Ancient Sage 277
Vote (See also **Voät**) A wretched v may be gain'd. Maud I vi 56
Voted See **Voäted**
Vow (s) I listen'd to thy v's, Supp. Confessions 71
Kate snaps her fingers at my v's ; Kate 19
O would she give me v for v, Miller's D. 119
that died To save her father's v ; D. of F. Women 196
v's, where there was never need of v's, Gardener's D. 258
That oft hast heard my v's, Talking Oak 98
did she read the name I carved with many v's „ 154
Before you hear my marriage v.' The Letters 8
Kissing his v's upon it like a knight. Aylmer's Field 472
my v Binds me to speak, and O that iron will, Princess ii 201
That breathe a thousand tender v's, In Mem. xx 2
At one dear knee we proffer'd v's, „ lxxix 13
Of early faith and plighted v's ; „ xcvii 30
Bound them by so strait v's to his own self, Com. of Arthur 262
And glorying in their v's and him, „ 458
for the King Will bind thee by such v's, Gareth and L. 270
Arms for her son, and loosed him from his v. „ 530
my knights are sworn to v's Of utter hardihood, „ 552
so my knighthood keep the v's they swore, „ 602
v's like theirs, that high in heaven Merlin and V. 14
They bound to holy v's of chastity ! „ 695
And swearing men to v's impossible, Lancelot and E. 130
Full many a holy v and pure resolve. „ 879
till I found a voice and sware a v. Holy Grail 194
I sware a v before them all, „ 195
and Galahad sware the v, And good Sir Bors, „ 199
Did Arthur take the v ?' „ 204
'Had I been here, ye had not sworn the v.' „ 276
I sware a v to follow it till I saw.' „ 282
'Nay, lord, therefore have we sworn our v's.' „ 285
Go, since your v's are sacred, being made : „ 314
All men, to one so bound by such a v, „ 565
How far I falter'd from my quest and v ? „ 568
Had never kiss'd a kiss, or vow'd a v. „ 584
but one night my v Burnt me within, „ 607
Hope not to make thyself by idle v's, „ 871
if the King Had seen the sight he would have sworn the v : „ 904
for I have sworn my v's, Pelleas and E. 244
But when she mock'd his v's and the great King, „ 252
O noble v's ! O great and sane and simple race „ 479
'Have any of our Round Table held their v's ?' „ 533
By noble deeds at one with noble v's, Last Tournament 123
his one true knight—Sole follower of the v's'— „ 303
With Arthur's v's on the great lake of fire. „ 345
My God, the power Was once in v's „ 649
thro' their v's The King prevailing made his realm :— „ 650
'V's ! did you keep the v you made to Mark „ 655
The v that binds too strictly snaps itself— „ 657
The v's ! O ay—the wholesome madness of an hour— „ 674
but then their v's—First mainly thro' „ 681
a doubtful lord To bind them by inviolable v's, „ 688
v's—I am woodman of the woods, „ 699
spitting at their v's and thee. Pass. of Arthur 62
My house are rather they who sware my v's, „ 157
strange dream to me To mind me of the secret v I made Columbus 92
and heard his passionate v, The Flight 83
swore the seeming-deathless v . . . Locksley H., Sixty 180
V's that will last to the last deathruckle, and v's that are snapt in a moment of fire ; Vastness 26
I swore the v, then with my latest kiss The Ring 298
I told her of my v, No pliable idiot I to break my v ; „ 401
Vow (verb) Godless Jephtha v's his child . . . The Flight 26
While she v's 'till death shall part us,' Locksley H., Sixty 24
Vow'd I v that could I gain her, our fair Queen, Marr. of Geraint 787
Had never kiss'd a kiss, or v a vow. Holy Grail 584
I v That I would work according as he will'd. „ 783
I v That, if our Princes harken'd to my prayer, Columbus 99
I v Whate'er my dreams, Akbar's Dream 12
Vowing some V, and some protesting), Holy Grail 270
Voyage (See also **Home-voyage**) go This v more than once ? yea twice or thrice— Enoch Arden 142

Voyage (*continued*) this *v* by the grace of God Will bring fair weather — *Enoch Arden* 190
And dull the *v* was with long delays, „ 655
Then he told her of his *v*, His wreck, „ 861
And after my long *v* I shall rest!' *Lancelot and E.* 1061
And let the story of her dolorous *v* „ 1343
and tell them all The story of my *v*, *Columbus* 12
I sail'd On my first *v*, harrass'd by the frights „ 67
Who fain had pledged her jewels on my first *v*, „ 229
yet Am ready to sail forth on one last *v*. „ 237
Art passing on thine happier *v* now *Sir J. Franklin* 3
Vulcan mounted, Ganymedes, To tumble, *V's*, *Princess iii* 72
Vulgar Nothing of the *v*, or vainglorious, *On Jub. Q. Victoria* 13
Vulture (adj.) Thereat the Lady stretch'd a *v* throat, *Princess iv* 363
Vulture (s) For whom the carrion *v* waits *You might have won* 35
swoops The *v*, beak and talon, at the heart *Princess v* 383
Vulturous Then glided a *v* Beldam forth, *Dead Prophet* 25

W

Waäist (waist) wur a-creeäpin' about my *w*; *Spinster's S's.* 26
Waäit (wait) *W* till our Sally cooms in, *North. Cobbler* 1
You Tommies shall *w* to-night *Spinster's S's.* 120
but *w* till tha 'eärs it be strikin' the hour. *Owd Roä* 18
Waäked (waked) An' when I *w* i' the murnin' *North. Cobbler* 39
To be horder'd about, an' *w*, *Spinster's S's.* 97
Then I *w* an' I fun it was Roäver *Owd Roä* 60
Waäste (waste) D'ya moind the *w*, my lass? *N. Farmer, O. S.* 29
Dubbut looök at the *w*: „ 37
an' I 'a stubb'd Thurnaby *w*. „ 28
Waäy (way) in anoother kind of a *w*, *North. Cobbler* 96
lasses 'ud talk o' their Missis's *w's*, *Village Wife* 57
'ud 'a let me 'a hed my oän *w* *Spinster's S's.* 101
An' 'ed goän their *w's*; *Owd Roä* 36
I wur gawin' that *w* to the bad, „ 71
wind blawin' hard tother *w*, „ 104
rummle down when the roof gev *w*, „ 109
I fun that it warn't not the gaäinist *w* to the narra Gaäte. *Church-warden, etc.* 12
Wader James Made toward us, like a *w* in the surf, *The Brook* 117
Waft (s) crosses With one *w* of the wing. *The Captain* 72
like the *w* of an Angel's wing; *In the Child. Hosp.* 38
Waft (verb) Yet *w* me from the harbour-mouth, *You ask me, why, etc.* 25
Spread thy full wings, and *w* him o'er. *In Mem. ix* 4
Wafted the woodbine spices are *w* abroad, *Maud I xxii* 5
Wag kings Began to *w* their baldness up and down, *Princess v* 19
The palsy *w's* his head; *Ancient Sage* 124
Wage I *w* not any feud with Death *In Mem. lxxxii* 1
'Behold, for these have sworn To *w* my wars, *Com. of Arthur* 508
To *w* grim war against Sir Lancelot there, *Guinevere* 193
I *w* His wars, and now I pass and die. *Pass. of Arthur* 12
Waged *W* such unwilling tho' successful war *Merlin and V.* 571
Wages The *w* of sin is death: if the *w* of Virtue be dust, *Wages* 6
Give her the *w* of going on, „ 10
Will pay thee all thy *w*, and to boot. *Gareth and L.* 1005
'The *w* of sin is death,' *The Wreck* 93
I need no *w* of shame. *Charity* 40
Wage-work comfort after their *w-w* is done, *Com. of Arthur* 418
Wagg'd Till his eye darken'd and his helmet *w*; *Geraint and E.* 505
This tongue that *w* They said with such *Sir J. Oldcastle* 14
Waggled till 'e *w* 'is taäil fur a bit, *Owd Roä* 105
Waging and ever *w* war Each upon other, *Com. of Arthur* 6
while the King Was *w* war on Lancelot: *Guinevere* 156
From *w* bitter war with him: „ 434
Waif rolling in his mind Old *w's* of rhyme, *The Brook* 199
thrones and peoples are as *w's* that swing, *W. to Marie Alex.* 26
flung from the rushing tide of the world as a *w* of shame, *The Wreck* 6
Wail (s) gets for greeting but a *w* of pain; *Lucretius* 138
Phantom *w* of women and children, *Boädicea* 26
whose dying eyes Were closed with *w*, *In Mem. xc* 6
then with a childlike *w*, And drawing down *Balin and Balan* 596
wife and child with *w* Pass to new lords; *Pass. of Arthur* 44
as by some deathbed after *w* Of suffering, „ 118

Wail (s) (*continued*) a *w* That seeming something, yet was nothing, *Lover's Tale iv* 103
the sudden *w* his lady made Dwelt in his fancy: „ 149
the mother's garrulous *w* For ever woke *Sisters (E. and E.)* 262
I read no more the prisoner's mute *w* *Sir J. Oldcastle* 4
I am roused by the *w* of a child, *The Wreck* 7
w came borne in the shriek of a growing wind, „ 87
and the *w* Of a beaten babe, „ 122
Let be thy *w* and help thy fellow men, *Ancient Sage* 258
Among the *w* of midnight winds, *Demeter and P.* 59
As we forget our *w* at being born. *The Ring* 465
nor *w* of baby-wife, Or Indian widow; *Akbar's Dream* 196
I sent him a desolate *w* and a curse, *Charity* 14
my *w* of reproach and scorn; „ 23
To the *w* of my winds, *The Dreamer* 13
thought that he answer'd her *w* with a song— „ 16
Wail (verb) Here it is only the mew that *w's*; *Sea-Fairies* 19
Cease to *w* and brawl! *Two Voices* 199
the Dead March *w's* in the people's ears: *Ode on Well.* 267
if he be not dead, Why *w* ye for him thus? *Geraint and E.* 547
wherefore *w* for one, Who put your beauty „ 674
burst away To weep and *w* in secret; *Lancelot and E.* 1245
beneath a winding wall of rock Heard a child *w*. *Last Tournament* 12
and *w* their way From cloud to cloud, *Pass. of Arthur* 39
At once began to wander and to *w*, *Lover's Tale iv* 99
Whereat the very babe began to *w*?' „ 375
The wind that 'ill *w* like a child *Rizpah* 72
And they *w* to thee! *Tiresias* 107
Wherefore do ye *w*?' *Demeter and P.* 60
'We know not, and we know not why we *w*.' „ 62
Why *w* you, pretty plover? *Happy* 1
Wail'd *w* and woke The mother, and the father suddenly cried, *Sea Dreams* 57
fell on him, Clasp'd, kiss'd him, *w*: *Lucretius* 280
and *w* about with mews. *Princess iv* 282
They wept and *w*, but led the way *In Mem. ciii* 18
the wind like a broken worldling *w*, *Maud I i* 11
Cast herself down, knelt to the Queen, and *w*. *Merlin and V.* 66
Queen, Who rode by Lancelot, *w* and shriek'd *Holy Grail* 356
But *w* and wept, and hated mine own self, „ 609
and he shrank and *w*, 'Is the Queen false?' *Pelleas and E.* 531
Queens in yon black boat, Who shriek'd and *w*, *Pass. of Arthur* 453
finds the fountain where they *w* 'Mirage'! *Ancient Sage* 77
So the Shadow *w*. Then I, Earth-Goddess, *Demeter and P.* 101
and the dream *W* in her, when she woke *Death of Œnone* 82
Wailest who *w* being born And banish'd *De Prof., Two G.* 41
Wailing (*See also* **Keenin'**) And on the mere the *w* died away. *M. d'Arthur* 272
To ailing wife or *w* infancy Or old bedridden palsy,— *Aylmer's Field* 177
After much *w*, hush'd itself at last „ 542
Their wildest *w's* never out of tune *Sea Dreams* 231
they hate to hear me like a wind *W* for ever, *Princess v* 99
Moaning and *w* for an heir (repeat) *Com. of Arthur* 207, 368
Your *w* will not quicken him: *Geraint and E.* 549
clapt her hands Together with a *w* shriek, *Merlin and V.* 867
the owls *W* had power upon her, *Lancelot and E.* 1001
And on the mere the *w* died away. *Pass. of Arthur* 440
W, *w*, *w*, the wind over land and sea— *Rizpah* 1
before their Gods, And *w* 'Save us.' *Tiresias* 106
hear in one dark room a *w*, *Locksley H., Sixty* 262
She used to shun the *w* babe, *The Ring* 358
O the night, When the owls are *w*! *Forlorn* 30
She heard a *w* cry, that seem'd at first *Death of Œnone* 20
Wailingly Voice of the Earth went *w* past him *The Dreamer* 3
Wain or when the lesser *w* Is twisting *In Mem. ci* 11
The team is loosen'd from the *w*, „ cxxi 5
Wainscot (adj.) And the shrieking rush of the *w* mouse, *Maud I vi* 71
Wainscot (s) Behind the mouldering *w* shriek'd, *Mariana* 64
Waist (*See also* **Waäist**) the girdle About her dainty dainty *w*, *Miller's D.* 176
You should have clung to Fulvia's *w*, *D. of F. Women* 259
Lovingly lower, trembled on her *w*— *Gardener's D.* 131
She strove to span my *w*: *Talking Oak* 138
And round her *w* she felt it fold, *Day-Dm., Depart.* 2
And held her round the knees against his *w*, *Princess ii* 363

Wake (verb) (*continued*) But *w's* a dotard smile.' — Ancient Sage 132
to rest and *w* no more were better rest for me, — The Flight 7
how early would I *w*! — „ 63
Before a kiss should *w* her. — The Ring 67
I rais'd her, call'd her 'Muriel, Muriel *w*!' — „ 449
his young music *w's* A wish in you — To Mary Boyle 63
an answer '*W* Thou deedless dreamer, — St. Telemachus 20
great shock may *w* a palsied limb, — „ 57
Waked (*See also* **Waäked**) to sleep with sound, And *w* with silence, — M. d'Arthur, Ep. 4
w at dead of night, I heard a sound — Holy Grail 108
He *w* for both: he pray'd for both: — Lover's Tale i 227
I remember once that being *w* By noises in the house— — The Ring 416
She *w* a bird of prey that scream'd and past; — Death of Œnone 87
Wakeful Beginning, and the *w* bird; — In Mem. cxxi 11
Grind on the *w* ear in the hush of the moonless nights, — Maud I i 42
Before the *w* mother heard him, went. — Gareth and L. 180
A *w* portress, and didst parle with Death,— — Lover's Tale i 113
Wakefulness After a night of feverous *w*, — Enoch Arden 231
Waken (*See also* **Wakken**) The fire-fly *w's*: *w* thou with me. — Princess vii 179
That *w's* at this hour of rest — In Mem. civ 6
and in my breast Spring *w's* too; — „ cxv 18
Than to *w* every morning to that face I loathe — The Flight 8
Waken'd the first matin-song hath *w* loud — Ode to Memory 68
What eyes, like thine, have *w* hopes, — Day-Dm., L'Envoi 45
For thrice I *w* after dreams. — Lucretius 34
Till at the last he *w* from his swoon, — Geraint and E. 583
A way by love that *w* love within, — Holy Grail 11
Suddenly *w* with a sound of talk — Pelleas and E. 48
Wakenest Who *w* with thy balmy breath — In Mem. xcix 13
Sun, that *w* all to bliss or pain, — Gareth and L. 1060
Wakening Gareth, *w*, fiercely clutch'd the shield; — „ 1304
Rode till the star above the *w* sun, — Pelleas and E. 500
Waking *W* she heard the night-fowl crow: — Mariana 26
If you're *w* call me early, — May Queen, N. Y's. E. 1
if you're *w*, call me, call me early, — „ 52
the dreams that come Just ere the *w*: — Lucretius 36
And, truly, *w* dreams were, more or less, — Princess i 12
W laughter in indolent reviewers. — Hendecasyllabics 8
Till a silence fell with the *w* bird, — Maud I xxii 17
But come to her *w*, find her asleep, — „ II ii 81
And Enid started *w*, with her heart — Marr. of Geraint 674
Tristram *w*, the red dream Fled with a shout, — Last Tournament 487
set the mother *w* in amaze To find her sick — Demeter and P. 57
From off the rosy cheek of *w* Day. — Akbar's Dream 202
Wakken (waken) I couldn't *w* 'im oop, — Owd Roä 102
Wales It was last summer on a tour in *W*: — Golden Year 2
Urien, Cradlemont of *W*, Claudias, — Com. of Arthur 112
ears for Christ in this wild field of *W*— — Sir J. Oldcastle 13
Walk (s) (*See also* **Garden-walks, Wood-walk**) A *w* with vary-colour'd shells — Arabian Nights 57
you may hear him sob and sigh In the *w's*; — A spirit haunts 6
with echoing feet he threaded The secretest *w's* of fame: — The Poet 10
said Death, 'these *w's* are mine.' — Love and Death 7
yielding, gave into a grassy *w* — Gardener's D. 111
last night's gale had caught, And blown across the *w*. — „ 125
With words of promise in his *w*, — Day-Dm., Arrival 23
and all round it ran a *w* Of shingle, and a *w* divided it: — Enoch Arden 736
Enoch shunn'd the middle *w* and stole — „ 738
Katie somewhere in the *w's* below, — The Brook 86
Would often, in his *w's* with Edith, claim — Aylmer's Field 61
our long *w's* were stript as bare as brooms, — Princess, Pro. 184
the chapel bells Call'd us: we left the *w's*; — „ ii 471
Dropt on the sward, and up the linden *w's*, — „ iv 209
Nor waves the cypress in the palace *w*; — „ vii 177
Or *w's* in Boboli's ducal bowers. — The Daisy 44
Shadows of three dead men Walk'd in the *w's* with me, — G. of Swainston 4
In those deserted *w's*, may find — In Mem. viii 14
partner in the flowery *w* Of letters, — „ lxxxiv 22
Up that long *w* of limes I past — „ lxxxvii 15
That saw thro' all the Muses' *w*, — „ cix 4
her light foot along the garden *w*, — Maud I xviii 9
I did not talk To gentle Maud in our *w* — „ xix 13
From the meadow your *w's* have left so sweet — „ xxii 39

Walk (s) (*continued*) Glanced at the doors or gambol'd down the *w's*; — Marr. of Geraint 665
A *w* of roses ran from door to door; A *w* of lilies crost it to the bower: — Balin and Balan 242
paced The long white *w* of lilies toward the bower. — „ 249
she stole upon my *w*, And calling me the greatest — Holy Grail 594
How oft with him we paced that *w* of limes, — To W. H. Brookfield 6
an' they goäs fur a *w*, — Spinster's S's. 85
He dreams of that long *w* thro' desert life — To Mary Boyle 55
Walk (verb) In sleep she seem'd to *w* forlorn, — Mariana 30
I *w*, I dare not think of thee, — Oriana 93
W's forgotten, and is forlorn.' — Mariana in the S. 48
So sweet it seems with thee to *w*, — Miller's D. 29
made it sweet To *w*, to sit, to sleep, to wake, — Edwin Morris 40
Could slip its bark and *w*. — Talking Oak 188
But any man that *w's* the mead, — Day-Dm., Moral 9
Katie *w's* By the long wash of Australasian seas — The Brook 193
Averill *w* So freely with his daughter? — Aylmer's Field 269
nor cares to *w* With Death and Morning — Princess vii 203
O we will *w* this world, Yoked in all exercise — „ 360
He that *w's* it, only thirsting For the right, — Ode on Well. 203
Nor follow, tho' I *w* in haste, — In Mem. xxii 18
That nothing *w's* with aimless feet; — „ liv 5
I *w* as ere I walk'd forlorn, — „ lxviii 5
From state to state the spirit *w's*; — „ lxxxii 6
to *w* all day like the sultan of old — Maud I iv 42
each man *w's* with his head in a cloud of poisonous flies — „ 54
There she *w's* in her state — „ xiv 3
the Powers who *w* the world Made lightnings — Com. of Arthur 107
Hath power to *w* the waters like our Lord. — „ 294
Merlin, who, they say, can *w* Unseen at pleasure— — „ 347
I will *w* thro' fire, Mother, to gain it— — Gareth and L. 133
'Will ye *w* thro' fire? Who *w's* thro' fire will hardly heed the smoke. — „ 142
w with me, and move To music with thine Order — Balin and Balan 76
Until this earth he *w's* on seems not earth, — Holy Grail 912
W your dim cloister, and distribute dole — Guinevere 683
Who *w* before thee, ever turning round — Lover's Tale i 490
his wont to *w* Between the going light — „ 663
Where Love could *w* with banish'd Hope — „ 813
w's down fro' the' All to see, — North. Cobbler 91
To *w* within the glory of the Lord — Columbus 89
lies all in the way that you *w*. — Despair 112
An' maäybe they'll *w* upo' two — Owd Roä 17
Thraldom who *w's* with the banner of Freedom, — Vastness 10
I used to *w* This Terrace— — The Ring 167
We often *w* In open sun, and see beneath our feet — „ 327
Walk'd-Walkt One *walk'd* between his wife and child, — Two Voices 412
The little maiden *walk'd* demure, — „ 419
But, as he *walk'd*, King Arthur panted hard, — M. d'Arthur 176
and looking, as he *walk'd*, Larger than human — „ 182
I'm glad I *walk'd*. How fresh the meadows look — Walk. to the Mail 1
what home? had he a home? His home, he *walk'd*. — Enoch Arden 669
for she *walk'd* Wearing the light yoke — Aylmer's Field 707
So now on sand they *walk'd*, and now on cliff, — Sea Dreams 37
And that the woman *walk'd* upon the brink: — „ 11?
And while I *walk'd* and talk'd as heretofore, — Princess i 16
there One *walk'd* reciting by herself, — „ ii 454
she you *walk'd* with, she You talk'd with, — „ vi 254
Walk'd at their will, and everything was changed. — „ 384
I *walk'd* with one I loved two and thirty years ago. — V. of Cauteretz 4
while I *walk'd* to-day, The two and thirty years — „ 5
Shadows of three dead men *Walk'd* in the walks — G. of Swainston 4
where the path we *walk'd* began To slant — In Mem. xxii 9
I walk as ere I *walk'd* forlorn, — „ lxviii 5
In walking as of old we *walk'd* — „ lxxi 12
Where first he *walk'd* when claspt in clay? — „ xciii 4
out he *walk'd* when the wind like a broken — Maud I i 11
Walk'd in a wintry wind by a ghastly glimmer, — „ iii 13
I have *walk'd* awake with Truth. — „ xix 4
He *walk'd* with dreams and darkness, — Merlin and V. 190
For all that *walk'd*, or crept, or perch'd, or flew. — Last Tournament 367
But, as he *walk'd*, King Arthur panted hard, — Pass. of Arthur 344
and looking, as he *walk'd*, Larger than human — „ 350
same old paths where Love had *walk'd* with Hope, — Lover's Tale i 821

Walk'd-Walkt (*continued*) One *walk'd* abreast with me, and veil'd his brow, — *Lover's Tale ii* 86
I *walk'd* behind with one who veil'd his brow. — „ *iii* 12
and while I *walk'd* with these In marvel — „ 18
I *walked* with him down to the quay, — *First Quarrel* 20
Fur Molly the long un she *walkt* awaäy — *Village Wife* 97
I *walk'd* with our kindly old doctor — *In the Child. Hosp.* 43
men *Walk'd* like the fly on ceilings? — *Columbus* 51
whiniver ye *walkt* in the shtreet, — *Tomorrow* 37
Fur I *walk'd* wi' tha all the way hoam — *Spinster's S's.* 32
Till I dreäm'd 'at Squire *walkt* in, — *Owd Roä* 55

Walking (*See also* **A-walkin'**) Death, *w* all alone beneath a yew, — *Love and Death* 5
W the cold and starless road of Death — *Œnone* 259
As in strange lands a traveller *w* slow, — *Palace of Art* 277
Beauty and anguish *w* hand in hand — *D. of F. Women* 15
W about the gardens and the halls Of Camelot, — *M. d'Arthur* 20
Met me *w* on yonder way, — *Edward Gray* 2
W up and pacing down, — *L. of Burleigh* 90
Would care no more for Leolin's *w* with her — *Aylmer's Field* 124
In *w* as of old we walk'd — *In Mem. lxxi* 12
I was *w* a mile, More than a mile — *Maud I ix* 1
She is *w* in the meadow, — „ *II iv* 37
For once, when Arthur *w* all alone, — *Merlin and V.* 152
one fair morn, I *w* to and fro beside a stream — *Holy Grail* 592
once, A week beyond, while *w* on the walls — *Pelleas and E.* 225
W about the gardens and the halls Of Camelot, — *Pass. of Arthur* 188
Brute that is *w* and haunting us yet, — *The Dawn* 23

Walkt *See* **Walk'd-Walkt**

Wall (s) (*See also* **Abbey-wall, Castle-wall, Cottage-walls, Gable-wall, Garden-wall, Mountain-wall, Nunnery-walls, Palace-walls, Shield-wall**) About a stone-cast from the *w* — *Mariana* 37
A pillar of white light upon the *w* — *Ode to Memory* 53
sunlight falls Upon the storied *w's*; — „ 86
She stood upon the castle *w*, — *Oriana* 28
Atween me and the castle *w*, — „ 35
Two lovers whispering by an orchard *w*; — *Circumstance* 4
When from her wooden *w's*,— — *Buonaparte* 5
Four gray *w's*, and four gray towers, — *L. of Shalott i* 15
Struck up against the blinding *w*. — *Mariana in the S.* 56
The one black shadow from the *w*. — „ 80
as yonder *w's* Rose slowly to a music — *Œnone* 40
bellowing caves, Beneath the windy *w*. — *Palace of Art* 72
That stood against the *w*. — „ 244
girt round With blackness as a solid *w*, — „ 274
between *w's* Of shadowy granite, — *Lotos-Eaters, C. S.* 3
Upon the tortoise creeping to the *w*; — *D. of F. Women* 27
All thine, against the garden *w*. — *The Blackbird* 8
its *w's* And chimneys muffled in the leafy vine. — *Audley Court* 18
and thou art staring at the *w*, — *Locksley Hall* 79
the blind *w's* Were full of chinks and holes; — *Godiva* 59
Gleam thro' the Gothic archway in the *w*. — „ 64
That watch the sleepers from the *w*. — *Day-Dm., Sleep. P.* 24
All creeping plants, a *w* of green Close-matted, — „ 45
He watches from his mountain *w's*, — *The Eagle* 5
The vast Akrokeraunian *w's*, — *To E. L.* 4
But turn'd her own toward the *w* and wept. — *Enoch Arden* 283
Then Annie with her brows against the *w* — „ 314
The late and early roses from his *w*, — „ 339
compass'd round by the blind *w* of night — „ 492
blown across her ghostly *w*: — „ 661
and stole Up by the *w*, behind the yew; — „ 739
Stood from his *w's* and wing'd his entry-gates — *Aylmer's Field* 18
I cry to vacant chairs and widow'd *w's*, — „ 720
Staring for ever from their gilded *w's* — „ 833
A mountain, like a *w* of burs and thorns; — *Sea Dreams* 119
higher on the *w's*, Betwixt the monstrous horns — *Princess, Pro.* 22
Had beat her foes with slaughter from her *w's*. — „ 34
some were whelm'd with missiles of the *w*, — „ 45
A broken statue propt against the *w*, — „ 99
That drove her foes with slaughter from her *w's*, — „ 123
from the bastion'd *w's* Like threaded spiders, — „ *i* 107
The foundress of the Babylonian *w*, — „ *ii* 80
Before two streams of light from *w* to *w*, — „ 473
The splendour falls on castle *w's* — „ *iv* 1

Wall (s) (*continued*) And some that men were in the very *w's*, — *Princess iv* 485
By glimmering lanes and *w's* of canvas — „ *v* 6
From those two hosts that lay beside the *w's*, — „ *vi* 383
cloud Drag inward from the deeps, a *w* of night, — „ *vii* 37
silent light Slept on the painted *w's*, — „ 121
the *w's* Blacken'd about us, bats wheel'd, — „ *Con.* 109
Your cannons moulder on the seaward *w*; — *Ode on Well.* 173
But thieves from o'er the *w* Stole the seed by night. — *The Flower* 11
FLOWER in the crannied *w*, — *Flow. in cran. wall* 1
Is vocal in its wooded *w's*; — *In Mem. xix* 14
There comes a glory on the *w's*: — „ *lxvii* 4
That in Vienna's fatal *w's* — „ *lxxxv* 19
I past beside the reverend *w's* — „ *lxxxvii* 1
A river sliding by the *w*. — „ *ciii* 8
The blind *w* rocks, and on the trees — „ *Con.* 63
With tender gloom the roof, the *w*; — „ 118
little flower that clings To the turrets and the *w's*; — *Maud II iv* 34
and Guinevere Stood by the castle *w's* — *Com. of Arthur* 48
Seeing the mighty swarm about their *w's*, — „ 200
To drive the heathen from your Roman *w*, — „ 512
fools have suck'd their allegory From these damp *w's*, — *Gareth and L.* 1200
Echo'd the *w's*; a light twinkled; — „ 1370
And enter'd, and were lost behind the *w's*. — *Marr. of Geraint* 252
ivy-stems Claspt the gray *w's* with hairy-fibred arms, — „ 323
now and then from distant *w's* There came a clapping — „ 565
slide From the long shore-cliff's windy *w's* — *Geraint and E.* 164
Push'd from without, drave backward to the *w*, — „ 273
No stronger than a *w*: there is the keep; — „ 341
like a household Spirit at the *w's* Beat, — „ 403
Along the *w's* and down the board; — *Balin and Balan* 84
the *w's* Of that low church he built at Glastonbury. — „ 366
portal of King Pellam's chapel wide And inward to the *w*; — „ 406
rummage buried in the *w's* Might echo, — „ 416
Woods have tongues, As *w's* have ears: — „ 531
Closed in the four *w's* of a hollow tower, (repeat) — *Merlin and V.* 209, 543
And many a wizard brow bleach'd on the *w's*: — „ 597
to him the *w* That sunders ghosts and shadow-casting men — „ 628
And heard their voices talk behind the *w*, — „ 631
and she watch'd him from her *w's*. — „ 775
'Traitor' to the unhearing *w*, — *Lancelot and E.* 612
first she saw the casque Of Lancelot on the *w*: — „ 806
to whom thro' those black *w's* of yew — „ 969
And grew between her and the pictured *w*. — „ 993
In the Queen's shadow, vibrate on the *w's*, — „ 1175
Till all the white *w's* of my cell were dyed With rosy colours leaping on the *w*; — *Holy Grail* 119
from the *w's* The rosy quiverings died into the night. — „ 122
necks Of dragons clinging to the crazy *w's*, — „ 347
plaster'd like a martin's nest To these old *w's*— — „ 549
painting on the *w* Or shield of knight; — „ 829
upon his charger all day long Sat by the *w's*, — *Pelleas and E.* 217
'Out! And drive him from the *w's*.' — „ 220
still he kept his watch beneath the *w*. — „ 223
while walking on the *w's* With her three knights, — „ 225
And drive him from my *w's*.' — „ 229
loosed him from his bonds, And flung them o'er the *w's*; — „ 316
Then bounded forward to the castle *w's*, — „ 363
That all the echoes hidden in the *w* Rang out — „ 366
there he waits below the *w*, Blowing his bugle — „ 380
but rode Ere midnight to her *w's*, — „ 413
Far down beneath a winding *w* of rock — *Last Tournament* 11
So from the high *w* and the flowering grove — *Guinevere* 33
That keeps the rust of murder on the *w's*— — „ 74
Or thrust the heathen from the Roman *w*, — *Pass. of Arthur* 69
Or build a *w* betwixt my life and love, — *Lover's Tale i* 176
And steep-down *w's* of battlemented rock — „ 399
thro' the ragged *w's*, All unawares — „ *ii* 152
from an open grating overhead High in the *w*, — „ *iv* 61
—in the night by the churchyard *w*. — *Rizpah* 56
it is coming—shaking the *w's*— — „ 85
fell, Striking the hospital *w*, crashing — *Def. of Lucknow* 18
into perilous chasms our *w's* and our poor palisades. — „ 55

Wall (s) (*continued*) coming down on the still-shatter'd *w's* — *Def. of Lucknow* 92
And breach'd the belting *w* of Cambalu, — *Columbus* 108
to the base of the mountain *w's*, — *V. of Maeldune* 14
From *w* to dyke he stept, — *Achilles over the T.* 15
hail of Arês crash Along the sounding *w's*. — *Tiresias* 97
more than *w* And rampart, their examples reach — " 125
phantom *w's* of this illusion fade, — *Ancient Sage* 181
A dying echo from a falling *w*; — " 263
an' sets 'im ageän the *w*, — *Owd Roä* 82
A footstep, a low throbbing in the *w's*, — *The Ring* 409
This *w* of solid flesh that comes between — *Happy* 35
The sunset blazed along the *w* of Troy. — *Death of Œnone* 77
So I turn'd my face to the *w*, — *Charity* 27
Till this embattled *w* of unbelief My prison, — *Doubt and Prayer* 11
Wall (verb) To embattail and to *w* about thy cause — *To J. M. K.* 8
splinter'd crags that *w* the dell With spires — *D. of F. Women* 187
And *w* them up perforce in mine— — *Akbar's Dream* 62
Wall'd (*See also* **Clear-wall'd**) Flourish'd a little garden square and *w*: — *Enoch Arden* 734
And on the top, a city *w*: — *Holy Grail* 422
Wallow They graze and *w*, breed and sleep; — *Palace of Art* 202
wolf and wolfkin, from the wilderness, *w* in it, — *Boädicea* 15
To *w* in that winter of the hills. — *Romney's R.* 15
decreed That Rome no more should *w* in this old lust — *St. Telemachus* 78
Peelè the Goddess would *w* in fiery riot — *Kapiolani* 8
Wallow'd And *w* in the gardens of the King. — *Com. of Arthur* 25
I have *w*, I have wash'd— — *Last Tournament* 315
an I *w*, then I wash'd— — " 318
And we *w* in beds of lilies, — *V. of Maeldune* 48
Wallowing great with pig, *w* in sun and mud. — *Walk. to the Mail* 88
When the *w* monster spouted his foam-fountains in the sea. — *Lotos-Eaters, C. S.* 107
w in the troughs of Zolaism,— — *Locksley H., Sixty* 145
draw The crowd from *w* in the mire of earth, — *Akbar's Dream* 141
Walnut Across the *w's* and the wine— — *Miller's D.* 32
Walter (*See also* **Walter Vivian**) 'O *W*, I have shelter'd here Whatever maiden grace — *Talking Oak* 37
visiting the son,—the son A *W* too,— — *Princess, Pro.* 8
me that morning *W* show'd the house, — " 10
Ask'd *W*, patting Lilia's head (she lay Beside him) — " 125
But *W* hail'd a score of names upon her, — " 156
W nodded at me; *He* began, The rest would follow, — " 200
W warp'd his mouth at this To something — " 214
and *W* said, 'I wish she had not yielded!' — " *Con.* 4
And there we saw Sir *W* where he stood, — " 81
'From *W*,' and for me from you then? — *The Ring* 71
bad the man engrave 'From *W*' on the ring, — " 236
Walter Vivian (*See also* **Walter**) Sir *W V* all a summer's day — *Princess, Pro.* 1
Wan (*See also* **Wan-sallow**) Philip's rosy face contracting grew Careworn and *w*; — *Enoch Arden* 487
tinged with *w* from lack of sleep, — *Princess iii* 25
w was her cheek With hollow watch, — " *vi* 144
As *w*, as chill, as wild as now; — *In Mem. lxxii* 17
'But she, the *w* sweet maiden, shore away — *Holy Grail* 149
I was changed to *w* And meagre, — " 571
W was her cheek; for whatso'er of blight — *Lover's Tale i* 694
an' looks so *w* an' so white: — *First Quarrel* 2
W, but as pretty as heart can desire, — *In the Child. Hosp.* 40
W, wasted Truth in her utmost need. — *Clear-headed friend* 19
W Sculptor, weepest thou to take the cast — *Wan Sculptor* 1
under this *w* water many of them Lie rotting, — *Gareth and L.* 824
'He hears the judgment of the King of kings,' Cried the *w* Prince; — *Geraint and E.* 801
Familiar up from cradle-time, so *w*, — *Balin and Balan* 591
w day Went glooming down in wet and weariness: — *Last Tournament* 214
for I have seen him *w* enow To make one doubt — " 563
only the *w* wave Brake in among dead faces, — *Pass. of Arthur* 129
Wan (one) an' meself remimbers *w* night comin' down — *Tomorrow* 7
afther her päärints had inter'd glory, an' both in *w* day, — " 53
his Riverence buried thim both in *w* grave — " 87
Wand Straight, but as lissome as a hazel *w*; — *The Brook* 70
He held his sceptre like a pedant's *w* — *Princess i* 27
And over these is placed a silver *w*, — *Marr. of Geraint* 483
And over these they placed the silver *w*, — " 549

Wanded *See* **Serpent-wanded**
Wander Hating to *w* out on earth, — *Supp. Confessions* 57
Light and shadow ever *w* O'er the green — *A Dirge* 12
Wild words *w* here and there: — " 43
Alone I *w* to and fro, — *Oriana* 8
And then we would *w* away, — *The Merman* 18
But at night I would *w* away, away, — *The Mermaid* 31
W from the side of the morn, — *Adeline* 52
Hope is other Hope and *w's* far, — *Caress'd or chidden* 10
Arise, and let us *w* forth, — *Miller's D.* 239
My heart may *w* from its deeper woe. — *Œnone* 44
brother mariners, we will not *w* more. — *Lotos-Eaters, C. S.* 128
there to *w* far away, — *Locksley Hall* 157
might a man not *w* from his wits — *Princess ii* 440
Dainty little maiden, whither would you *w*? (repeat) — *City Child* 1, 6
I *w*, often falling lame, — *In Mem. xxiii* 6
To *w* on a darken'd earth, — " *lxxxv* 31
you *w* about at your will; — *Maud I iv* 59
An old man's wit may *w* ere he die. — *Com. of Arthur* 405
So shook his wits they *w* in his prime— — *Gareth and L.* 715
Who may not *w* from the allotted field — *Holy Grail* 908
She felt the King's breath *w* o'er her neck, — *Guinevere* 582
Which *w* round the bases of the hills, — *Lover's Tale ii* 121
At once began to *w* and to wail, — " *iv* 99
They that can *w* at will where the works of the Lord — *In the Child. Hosp.* 35
I will *w* till I die about the barren moors. — *The Flight* 56
You will not leave me thus in grief to *w* forth forlorn; — " 85
but *w* hand in hand With breaking hearts, — " 99
That *w's* from the public good, — *Freedom* 26
And *w's* on from home to home! — *The Wanderer* 8
Wander'd A walk with vary-coloured shells *W* — *Arabian Nights* 58
Nor *w* into other ways: — *My life is full* 3
I blest them, and they *w* on: — *Two Voices* 424
I had *w* far In an old wood: — *D. of F. Women* 53
nor having *w* far Shot on the sudden into dark. — *To J. S.* 27
'O yes, she *w* round and round These knotted knees — *Talking Oak* 157
Here about the beach I *w*, — *Locksley Hall* 11
Years have *w* by, — *The Captain* 66
W at will, but oft accompanied By Averill: — *Aylmer's Field* 137
Who knows? but so they *w*, hour by hour — " 141
Sounds of the great sea *W* about. — *Minnie and Winnie* 8
I *w* from the noisy town, — *In Mem. lxix* 5
whose ring'd caress Had *w* from her own King's golden head, — *Balin and Balan* 513
The flaxen ringlets of our infancies *W*, — *Lover's Tale i* 235
And we *w* about it and thro' it. — *V. of Maeldune* 87
W back to living boyhood — *Locksley H., Sixty* 3
while I *w* down the coast, — " 53
as we *w* to and fro Gazing at the Lydian laughter — *Frater Ave, etc.* 7
perhaps indeed She *w*, having *w* now so far — *The Ring* 107
Wanderer Charm, as a *w* out in ocean, — *Milton* 12
Wandering (adj. and part.) (*See also* **Often-wandering**)
Wrestled with *w* Israel, — *Clear-headed friend* 26
Mournful Œnone, *w* forlorn Of Paris, — *Œnone* 16
And overhead the *w* ivy and vine, — " 99
Weary the *w* fields of barren foam. — *Lotos-Eaters* 42
Once heard at dead of night to greet Troy's *w* prince, — *On a Mourner* 33
Inswathed sometimes in *w* mist, — *St. S. Stylites* 75
with yet a bed for *w* men. — *Enoch Arden* 698
with now a *w* hand And now a pointed finger, — *Princess v* 269
Forgive these wild and *w* cries, — *In Mem., Pro.* 41
Drops in his vast and *w* grave. — " *vi* 16
Yet as that other, *w* there In those deserted walks, — " *viii* 13
Is dash'd with *w* isles of night. — " *xxiv* 4
How often, hither *w* down, — " *lxxxix* 5
The joy to every *w* breeze; — " *Con.* 62
How once the *w* forester at dawn, — *Gareth and L.* 498
Mark The Cornish King, had heard a *w* voice, — *Merlin and V.* 8
when the dead Went *w* o'er Moriah— — *Holy Grail* 50
Wealthy with *w* lines of mount and mere, — " 252
while ye follow *w* fires Lost in the quagmire! — " 319
That most of us would follow *w* fires, (repeat) — " 369, 599
That most of them would follow *w* fires, — " 891
Lost in a doubt, Pelleas *w* Waited, — *Pelleas and E.* 392

Wandering (adj. and part.) (*continued*) Stay'd in the *w* warble of a brook; *Last Tournament* 254
name Went *w* somewhere darkling in his mind. „ 457
ghost of Gawain blown Along a *w* wind, *Pass. of Arthur* 32
And I am blown along a *w* wind, „ 36
As moonlight *w* thro' a mist: *Lover's Tale ii* 52
we gazed at the *w* wave as we sat *V. of Maeldune* 89

Wandering (s) 'The *w's* Of this most intricate Universe *A Character* 2
fold our wings, And cease from *w's*, *Lotos-Eaters, C. S.* 20
Down shower the gambolling waterfalls From *w* over the lea: *Sea-Fairies* 11
(For often in lonely *w's* I have cursed him *Maud I xix* 14
magic which can trace The *w* of the stars, *Holy Grail* 667
Then, in my *w's* all the lands that lie *Tiresias* 25

Wane The long day *w's*: the slow moon climbs: *Ulysses* 55
Or when a thousand moons shall *w* *In Mem. lxxvii* 8
O sorrow, then can sorrow *w*? „ *lxxviii* 15
Speak, as it waxes, of a love that *w's*? *Lancelot and E.* 1401
when the day began to *w*, we went. *Holy Grail* 488

Waned councils thinn'd, And armies *w*, *Merlin and V.* 573
to this present My full-orb'd love has *w* not. *Lover's Tale i* 734
The day *w*; Alone I sat with her: „ *ii* 139
Gleam, that had *w* to a wintry glimmer *Merlin and the G.* 83

Waning (*See also* **Slowly-waning**) The pale yellow woods were *w*, *L. of Shalott iv* 2
Yon orange sunset *w* slow: *Move eastward* 2
'Bitter barmaid, *w* fast! *Vision of Sin* 67
What songs below the *w* stars *Margaret* 33
When the flowers come again, mother, beneath the *w* light *May Queen, N. Y's. E.* 25
over many a range Of *w* lime the gray cathedral towers, *Gardener's D.* 218
praised the *w* red, and told The vintage— *Aylmer's Field* 406
rooks, That gather in the *w* woods, *In Mem. lxxxv* 72
The last long stripe of *w* crimson gloom, *Ancient Sage* 221

Wann'd Psyche flush'd and *w* and shook; *Princess iv* 160
and ever *w* with despair, *Maud I i* 10

Wannish No sun, but a *w* glare In fold upon fold „ *vi* 2

Wan-sallow a man of mien *W-s* as the plant *Gareth and L.* 453

Want (s) And left a *w* unknown before; *Miller's D.* 228
Shall sing for *w*, ere leaves are new, *The Blackbird* 23
'tis from no *w* in her: It is my shyness, *Edwin Morris* 85
And to the *w*, that hollow'd all the heart, *Love and Duty* 61
Cursed be the social *w's* that sin *Locksley Hall* 59
Or that eternal *w* of pence, *Will Water.* 43
nor compensating the *w* By shrewdness, *Enoch Arden* 250
Or thro' the *w* of what it needed most, „ 265
No *w* was there of human sustenance, „ 554
Doubled her own, for *w* of playmates, *Aylmer's Field* 81
any of our people there In *w* or peril, *Princess ii* 267
For dear are those three castles to my *w's*, „ 417
And either she will die from *w* of care, „ *v* 85
Not perfect, nay, but full of tender *w's*, „ *vii* 319
And ev'n for *w* of such a type. *In Mem. xxxiii* 16
Shall love be blamed for *w* of faith? „ *li* 10
And he supplied my *w* the more „ *lxxix* 19
a thousand *w's* Gnarr at the heels of men, „ *xcviii* 16
Ring out the *w*, the care, the sin, „ *cvi* 17
veil His *w* in forms for fashion's sake, „ *cxi* 6
let Kay the seneschal Look to thy *w's*, *Gareth and L.* 434
Unfaith in aught is *w* of faith in all. *Merlin and V.* 389
And I must die for *w* of one bold word.' *Lancelot and E.* 927
I—misyoked with such a *w* of man— *Last Tournament* 571
the daily *w* Of Edith in the house, the garden, *Sisters (E. and E.)* 245
days' of fever, and *w* of care! *The Wreck* 147
Mere *w* of gold—and still for twenty years *The Ring* 428

Want (verb) More life, and fuller, that I *w*.' *Two Voices* 399
Of those that *w*, and those that have: *Walk. to the Mail* 78
when you *w* me, sound upon the bugle-horn. *Locksley Hall* 2
I *w* her love. *Princess v* 136
When the man *w's* weight, the woman takes it up, „ 444
I w forgiveness too: „ *vi* 290
thy muther says thou *w's* to marry the lass, *M. Farmer, N. S.* 37
Who *w's* the finer politic sense To mask, *Maud I vi* 47
And if he *w* me, let him come to me. *Geraint and E.* 237

Want (verb) (*continued*) To doubt her fairness were to *w* an eye, *Lancelot and E.* 1376
To doubt her pureness were to *w* a heart— „ 1377
For we that *w* the warmth of double life, *Holy Grail* 624
But if thou *w's* thy grog, *North. Cobbler* 8
But if tha *w's* ony grog „ 113
Fur I *w's* to tell tha o' Roä *Owd Roä* 19
if tha *w's* to git forrards a bit, *Church-warden, etc.* 49

Want-begotten Nor any *w-b* rest. *In Mem. xxvii* 12

Wanted Another ship (She *w* water) *Enoch Arden* 628
nor *w* at his end The dark retinue *Aylmer's Field* 841
truth! I know not: all are *w* here. *Marr. of Geraint* 289

Wantest What *w* thou? whom dost thou seek, *Oriana* 71

Wanting And *w* yet a boatswain. Would he go? *Enoch Arden* 123
I grieve to see you poor and *w* help: „ 406
He look'd and found them *w*; *Geraint and E.* 935
impute themselves, *W* the mental range; *Merlin and V.* 827

Wanton (adj.) (*See also* **Seeming-wanton**) When I past by, a wild and *w* pard, *Œnone* 199
And *w* without measure; *Amphion* 58
In the Spring the *w* lapwing gets himself another crest; *Locksley Hall* 18
To take a *w* dissolute boy For a man *Maud I x* 58
And that within her, which a *w* fool, *Geraint and E.* 432
Told me, that twice a *w* damsel came, *Balin and Balan* 609
Half overtrailed with a *w* weed, *Lover's Tale i* 525
(like a *w* too-officious friend, „ 627
anon the *w* billow wash'd Them over, „ *ii* 9

Wanton (s) What did the *w* say? *Merlin and V.* 812

Wanton (verb) Say to her, I do but *w* in the South, *Princess iv* 109

Wantonness That hover'd between war and *w*, *To the Queen ii* 44

War (s) (*See also* **World-war**) Elsinore Heard the *w* moan along the distant sea, *Buonaparte* 10
And all the *w* is roll'd in smoke.' *Two Voices* 156
At such strange *w* with something good, „ 302
And let the world have peace or *w's*, *Palace of Art* 182
minstrel sings Before them of the ten years' *w* in Troy, *Lotos-Eaters, C. S.* 77
Sore task to hearts worn out by many *w's* „ 86
And trumpets blown for *w's*; *D. of F. Women* 20
when fresh from *w's* alarms, My Hercules, „ 149
Across the brazen bridge of *w*— *Love thou thy land* 76
'Come With all good things, and *w* shall be no more.' *M. d'Arthur, Ep.* 28
Made *w* upon each other for an hour, *Godiva* 34
To sleep thro' terms of mighty *w's*, *Day-Dm., L'Envoi* 9
His bashfulness and tenderness at *w*, *Enoch Arden* 289
They hate me: there is *w* between us, *Aylmer's Field* 424
Communing with his captains of the *w*. *Princess i* 67
The Carian Artemisia strong in *w*, „ *ii* 81
arts of *w* The peasant Joan and others; „ 162
If more and acted on, what follows? *w*; „ 229
I spoke of *w* to come and many deaths, „ *iii* 150
And clad in iron burst the ranks of *w*, „ *iv* 504
clapt her hands and cried for *w*, „ 590
o'er the imperial tent Whispers of *w*. „ *v* 10
red-faced *w* has rods of steel and fire; She yields, or *w*.' „ 118
say you, *w* or not?' 'Not *w*, if possible, „ *v* 124
I said, 'lest from the abuse of *w*, „ 126
More soluble is this knot By gentleness than *w*. „ 136
I would the old God of *w* himself were dead, „ 145
To our point: not *w*: Lest I lose all.' „ 204
yet my father wills not *w*: And, 'sdeath! myself, what care I, *w* or no? „ 277
loth by brainless *w* To cleave the rift „ 300
Great in council and great in *w*, *Ode on Well.* 30
Such a *w* had such a close. „ 118
the leader in these glorious *w's* „ 192
Not sting the fiery Frenchman into *w*. *Third of Feb.* 4
Wild *W*, who breaks the converse of the wise; „ 8
The works of peace with works of *w*. *Ode Inter. Exhib.* 28
discuss the Northern sin Which made a selfish *w* begin; *To F. D. Maurice* 30
w's avenging rod Shall lash all Europe into blood; „ 33
That shriek and sweat in pigmy *w's* *Lit. Squabbles* 2
these all night upon the bridge of *w* Sat glorying; *Spec. of Iliad* 9

War (s) (*continued*) As one would sing the death of *w*, *In Mem. ciii* 33
Ring out the thousand *w's* of old, „ *cvi* 27
heart of the citizen hissing in *w* *Maud I i* 24
Is it peace or *w*? Civil *w*, as I think, „ 27
Is it peace or *w*? better *w*! loud *w* by land and by sea, *W* with a thousand battles, „ 47
At *w* with myself and a wretched race, „ *x* 35
This huckster put down *w*! can he tell Whether *w* be a cause or a consequence? „ 44
For each is at *w* with mankind. „ 52
I swear to you, lawful and lawless *w* „ *II v* 94
spoke of a hope for the world in the coming *w's*— „ *III vi* 11
I thought that a *w* would arise in defence of the right, „ 19
flames The blood-red blossom of *w* „ 53
and the *w* roll down like a wind, „ 54
Commingled with the gloom of imminent *w*, *Ded. of Idylls* 13
Far-sighted summoner of *W* and Waste „ 37
and ever waging *w* Each upon other, *Com. of Arthur* 6
Lords and Barons of his realm Flash'd forth and into *w*: „ 66
as here and there that *w* Went swaying; „ 106
So like a painted battle the *w* stood Silenced, „ 122
Do these your lords stir up the heat of *w*, „ 169
That Gorloïs and King Uther went to *w*: „ 196
lords Banded, and so brake out in open *w*.' „ 237
for these have sworn To wage my *w's*, „ 508
mine innocent, the jousts, the *w's*, *Gareth and L.* 86
Were Arthur's *w's* in weird devices done, „ 225
A knight of Uther in the Barons' *w*, „ 353
ye know we stay'd their hands From *w* „ 422
w of Time against the soul of man. „ 1198
who held and lost with Lot In that first *w*, *Balin and Balan* 2
But rather proven in his Paynim *w's* „ 38
In those fierce *w's*, struck hard— „ 177
Waged such unwilling tho' successful *w* *Merlin and V.* 571
The lady never made *unwilling w* „ 603
you know Of Arthur's glorious *w's*.' *Lancelot and E.* 285
then the *w* That thunder'd in and out „ 290
nor cares For triumph in our mimic *w's*, „ 312
Yet in this heathen *w* the fire of God Fills him: „ 315
From talk of *w* to traits of pleasantry— „ 321
Where Arthur's *w's* were render'd mystically, „ 801
Where twelve great windows blazon Arthur's *w's*, *Holy Grail* 248
perchance, when all our *w's* are done, „ 256
Where Arthur's *w's* are rendered mystically, „ 359
To whence I came, the gate of Arthur's *w's*.' „ 539
I came late, the heathen *w's* were o'er, *Last Tournament* 269
while the King Was waging *w* on Lancelot: *Guinevere* 156
To wage grim *w* against Sir Lancelot there, „ 193
that night the bard Sang Arthur's glorious *w's*, „ 286
From waging bitter *w* with him: „ 434
I waged His *w's*, and now I pass and die. *Pass. of Arthur* 12
Gawain kill'd In Lancelot's *w*, „ 31
Around a king returning from his *w's*. „ 461
and shadowing Sense at *w* with Soul, *To the Queen ii* 37
That hover'd between *w* and wantonness, „ 44
'Spanish ships of *w* at sea! *The Revenge* 3
past away with five ships of *w* that day, „ 13
Then told them of his *w's*, and of his wound. *Sisters (E. and E.)* 60
mine that stirr'd Among our civil *w's* „ 75
Red in thy birth, redder with household *w*, *Sir J. Oldcastle* 53
Urge him to foreign *w*. „ 68
Spain was waging *w* against the Moor— *Columbus* 93
slain thy fathers in *w* or in single strife, *V. of Maeldune* 121
There was the Scotsman Weary of *w*. *Batt. of Brunanburh* 36
Mangled to morsels, A youngster in *w*! „ 74
own in his own West-Saxon-land, Glad of the *w*. „ 104
men contend in grievous *w* From their own city, *Achilles over the T.* 9
and sail to help them in the *w*; „ 13
the crowd would roar For blood, for *w*, *Tiresias* 65
these blind hands were useless in their *w's*. „ 78
a weight of *w* Rides on those ringing axles! „ 92
whose one bliss Is *w*, and human sacrifice— „ 112
holding, each its own By endless *w*: *Ancient Sage* 252
w will die out late then. *Locksley H., Sixty* 173

War (s) (*continued*) Could we dream of *w's* and carnage, *Locksley H., Sixty* 189
Most marvellous in the *w's* your own *Pro. to Gen. Hamley* 11
You praise when you should blame The barbarian of *w's*. *Epilogue* 5
I would that *w's* would cease, „ 11
Or Trade re-frain the Powers From *w* „ 16
who loves *W* for *W's* own sake Is fool, „ 30
w's, and filial faith, and Dido's pyre; *To Virgil* 4
An' the munney they maäde by the *w*, *Owd Roä* 44
'A warrior's crest above the cloud of *w*'— *The Ring* 338
You were parting for the *w*, *Happy* 74
You parted for the Holy *W* without a word to me, „ 77
The smoke of *w's* volcano burst again *Prog. of Spring* 97
bolt of *w* dashing down upon cities *The Dawn* 8
Storm of battle and thunder of *w*! *Riflemen form!* 3
War (verb) To *w* with falsehood to the knife, *Two Voices* 131
What pleasure can we have To *w* with evil? *Lotos-Eaters, C. S.* 49
To *w* against ill uses of a life, *Gareth and L.* 1130
To *w* against my people and my knights. *Pass. of Arthur* 71
War (was) An' I went wheer munny *w*: *N. Farmer, N. S.* 21
Warble (s) at first to the ear The *w* was low, *Dying Swan* 24
Wild bird, whose *w*, liquid sweet, *In Mem. lxxxviii* 1
a bird with a *w* plaintively sweet Perch'd *The Wreck* 81
And rolling of dragons By *w* of water, *Merlin and the G.* 45
Warble (verb) thou may'st *w*, eat and dwell. *The Blackbird* 4
Than he that *w's* long and loud *You might have won* 33
W, O bugle, and trumpet, blare! *W. to Alexandra* 14
'O birds, that *w* to the morning sky, O birds that *w* as the day goes by, *Gareth and L.* 1075
birds Begin to *w* yonder in the budding *The Flight* 61
The blackcap *w's*, and the turtle purrs, *Prog. of Spring* 55
O *w* unchidden, unbidden! *The Throstle* 14
Warbled NIGHTINGALES *w* without, *G. of Swainston* 1
Nightingales *w* and sang Of a passion „ 8
That she *w* alone in her joy! *Maud I x* 55
Warbler Dan Chaucer, the first *w*, *D. of F. Women* 5
in their time thy *w's* rise on wing. *Prog. of Spring* 108
Warbling springs By night to eery *w's*, *Sir L. and Q. G.* 34
She struck such *w* fury thro' the words; *Princess iv* 586
Her *w* voice, a lyre of widest range *D. of F. Women* 165
damsel-errant, *w*, as she rode The woodland alleys, *Balin and Balan* 438
War-cry Spurr'd with his terrible *w-c*; *Geraint and E.* 170
Ward (surname) generous of all Untramontanes, *W*, *In Mem., W. G. Ward* 4
Ward (minor) and a selfish uncle's *w*. *Locksley Hall* 156
Ward (of a hospital) Here was a boy in the *w*, *In the Child. Hosp.* 13
O how could I serve in the *w's* „ 24
past to this *w* where the younger children are laid: „ 27
They freshen and sweeten the *w's* „ 38
Then I return'd to the *w*; „ 44
such a lot of beds in the *w*!' „ 54
caught when a nurse in a hospital *w*. *Charity* 41
Ward (guard) Keep watch and *w*, (repeat) *Maud I vi* 58
why shine ye here so low? Thy *w* is higher up: *Gareth and L.* 1098
Warded For each had *w* either in the fight, *Com. of Arthur* 131
Warder The *w's* of the growing hour, *Love thou thy land* 61
Old *w* of these buried bones, *In Mem. xxxix* 1
War-drum Till the *w-d* throbb'd no longer, *Locksley Hall* 127
Ware (adj.) they were *w* That all the decks were dense *M. d'Arthur* 195
Then was I *w* of one that on me moved *Holy Grail* 409
He woke, and being *w* of some one nigh, *Pelleas and E.* 520
they were *w* That all the decks were dense *Pass. of Arthur* 363
Ware (s) As when a hawker hawks his *w's*. *The Blackbird* 20
sold her *w's* for less Than what she gave *Enoch Arden* 255
faith in a tradesman's *w* or his word? *Maud I i* 26
Ware (verb) *w* their ladies' colours on the casque, *Last Tournament* 184
War-field Earls of the army of Anlaf Fell on the *w-f*, *Batt. of Brunanburh* 54
War-glaive The clash of the *w-g*— „ 78
War-harden'd Kissing the *w-h* hand of the Highlander *Def. of Lucknow* 102
War-hawk Gave to the garbaging *w-h* to gorge it, *Batt. of Brunanburh* 109
War-horse On burnish'd hooves his *w-h* trode; *L. of Shalott iii* 29
A *w* of the best, and near it stood *Gareth and L.* 678
Death's dark *w-h* bounded forward with him. „ 1401
and thence Taking my *w-h* from the holy man, *Holy Grail* 537

Waste (verb) (*continued*) The sea w's all: but let me live my life. *Audley Court* 51
To w his whole heart in one kiss *Sir L. and Q. G.* 44
That like a broken purpose w in air: So w not thou; but come; *Princess vii* 214
Forgive me, I w my heart in signs: let be. „ 359
Half the night I w in sighs, *Maud II iv* 23
Nor dared to w a perilous pity on him: *Geraint and E.* 525
Speak therefore: shall I w myself in vain?' *Lancelot and E.* 670
and w the spiritual strength Within us, *Holy Grail* 35
her too hast thou left To pine and w *Last Tournament* 598
when I knew the twain Would each w each, *Tiresias* 69
Ill To w this earth began— *Epilogue* 23
Wasted (adj. and part.) My heart is w with my woe, *Oriana* 1
Wan, w Truth in her utmost need. *Clear-headed friend* 19
Where they smile in secret, looking over w lands, *Lotos-Eaters, C. S.* 114
I that have w here health, wealth, and time, *Princess iv* 352
And wordless broodings on the w cheek— „ *vii* 112
Beating from the w vines Back to France *Ode on Well.* 109
Confusions of a w youth; *In Mem., Pro.* 42
I trust I have not w breath: „ *cxx* 1
Thro' the hubbub of the market I steal, a w frame, *Maud II iv* 69
W so often by the heathen hordes, *Holy Grail* 244
W and worn, and but a tithe of them, „ 723
But when the matron saw That hinted love was only w bait, *The Ring* 360
You that lie with w lungs Waiting for your summons . . . *Forlorn* 21
Wasted (verb) Last night I w hateful hours *Fatima* 8
And beat me down and marr'd and w me, *Tithonus* 19
He w hours with Averill; *Aylmer's Field* 109
There they ruled, and thence they w *Boädicea* 54
waging war Each upon other, w all the land; *Com. of Arthur* 7
'O I that w time to tend upon her, *Geraint and E.* 38
and thro' her love her life W and pined, *Pelleas and E.* 496
Wasteful And scaled in sheets of w foam, *Sea Dreams* 53
disciple, richly garb'd, but worn From w living, follow'd— *Ancient Sage* 5
Waster And w than a warren: *Amphion* 4
Wastest The w moorland of our realm shall be Safe, *Gareth and L.* 603
Wasting w odorous sighs All night long *Adeline* 43
leapt To greet her, w his forgotten heart, *Aylmer's Field* 689
'w the sweet summer hours'? *Charity* 1
Watch (s) (*See also* **Death-watch**) Kept w, waiting decision, *Œnone* 143
wan was her cheek With hollow w, *Princess vi* 145
And w'es in the dead, the dark, „ *vii* 103
Come: not in w'es of the night, *In Mem. xci* 13
Keep w and ward, keep w and ward, *Maud I vi* 58
did Enid, keeping w, behold In the first shallow shade *Geraint and E.* 118
still he kept his w beneath the wall. *Pelleas and E.* 223
Wide open were the gates, And no w kept; „ 415
But kept their w upon the ring and you. *The Ring* 300
heron rises from his w beside the mere, *Happy* 3
Watch (time-piece) seal, that hung From Allan's w, *Dora* 136
Watch (verb) I w thy grace; and in its place *Eleänore* 127
Fancy w'es in the wilderness, *Caress'd or chidden* 12
I w the darkening droves of swine *Palace of Art* 199
To w the crisping ripples on the beach, *Lotos-Eaters, C. S.* 61
To w the long bright river drawing slowly „ 92
To w the emerald-colour'd water falling „ 96
W what main-currents draw the years: *Love thou thy land* 21
W what thou seëst, and lightly bring me word.' *M. d'Arthur* 38
W what I see, and lightly bring thee word.' „ 44
I bad thee, w, and lightly bring me word.' „ 81
saw An angel stand and w me, as I sang. *St. S. Stylites* 35
I used to w—if I be he that watch'd— *Tithonus* 52
did we w the stately ships, *Locksley Hall* 37
To w *the three tall spires;* *Godiva* 3
That w the sleepers from the wall. *Day-Dm., Sleep. P.* 24
He w'es from his mountain walls, *The Eagle* 5
dewy eyes That w me from the glen below. *Move Eastward* 8
built their castles of dissolving sand To w them overflow'd, *Enoch Arden* 20
There often as he watch'd or seem'd to w, „ 600
Watch (verb) (*continued*) 'Good,' said his friend, 'but w!' *Aylmer's Field* 275
and one was set to w The watcher, „ 551
and w A full sea glazed with muffled moonlight, *Princess i* 247
O to w the thirsty plants Imbibing! „ *ii* 422
Or seem'd to w the dancing bubble, „ *iii* 24
and w The sandy footprint harden into stone.' „ 270
I w the twilight falling brown *To F. D. Maurice* 14
if that eye which w'es guilt And goodness, *In Mem. xxvi* 5
And those wild eyes that w the wave „ *xxxvi* 15
Ye w, like God, the rolling hours „ *li* 14
So may'st thou w me where I weep, „ *lxiii* 9
To those that w it more and more, „ *lxxiv* 2
'I w thee from the quiet shore; „ *lxxxv* 81
For who was left to w her but I? *Maud I xix* 10
And w her harvest ripen, her herd increase, „ *III vi* 25
Guinevere Stood by the castle walls to w him pass; *Com. of Arthur* 48
w his mightful hand striking great blows *Marr. of Geraint* 95
last bethought her how she used to w, „ 647
Not dare to w the combat, *Geraint and E.* 154
Geraint Waving an angry hand as who should say 'Ye w me,' „ 445
From whence to w the time, and eagle-like *Balin and Balan* 535
the Seer Would w her at her petulance, *Merlin and V.* 175
and laugh As those that w a kitten; „ 177
And w the curl'd white of the coming wave „ 292
while women w Who wins, who falls; *Holy Grail* 34
'There he w'es yet, There like a dog *Pelleas and E.* 262
W what thou seëst, and lightly bring me word.' *Pass. of Arthur* 206
W what I see, and lightly bring thee word.' „ 212
I bad thee, w, and lightly bring me word.' „ 249
I could not w her for four— *In the Child. Hosp.* 59
Still—could we w at all points? *Def. of Lucknow* 49
w the chariot whirl About the goal again, *Tiresias* 176
Or w the waving pine which here *To Ulysses* 25
'Father and Mother will w you grow'— (repeat) *Romney's R.* 104, 106
Christian faces w Man murder man. *St. Telemachus* 55
Watch'd She w my crest among them all, *Oriana* 30
In lazy mood I w the little circles die; *Miller's D.* 74
I w the little flutterings, „ 153
And w by weeping queens. *Palace of Art* 108
I used to watch—if I be he that w— *Tithonus* 52
And w by silent gentlemen, *Will Water.* 231
Maiden, I have w thee daily, *L. of Burleigh* 3
to the last dip of the vanishing sail She w it, *Enoch Arden* 246
There often as he w or seem'd to watch, „ 600
Miriam w and dozed at intervals, „ 909
They parted, and Sir Alymer Aylmer w. *Aylmer's Field* 277
conscious of the rageful eye That w him, „ 337
Or made occasion, being strictly w, „ 478
and groves of pines, W even there; „ 551
and Sir Aylmer w them all, „ 552
the wife, who w his face, Paled at a sudden twitch „ 731
and w it lying bathed In the green gleam *Princess i* 93
While Psyche w them, smiling, „ *ii* 365
and w Or seem'd to watch the dancing bubble, „ *iii* 23
I w the swallow winging south „ *iv* 89
but w them well, Saw that they kept apart, „ 339
but w awake A cypress in the moonlight shake, *The Daisy* 81
There was one who w and told me— *Boädicea* 30
And I myself, who sat apart And w them, *In Mem. ciii* 30
That w her on her nurse's arm, „ *Con.* 46
and w the great sea fall, Wave after wave, *Com. of Arthur* 378
and w him from the gates: „ 449
Then she that w him, 'Wherefore stare ye so? *Gareth and L.* 939
Knave, when I w thee striking on the bridge „ 992
But w him have I like a phantom pass „ 1335
Yet have I w thee victor in the joust, „ 1356
While he that w her sadden, *Marr. of Geraint* 67
he w The being he loved best in all the world, *Geraint and E.* 102
And w the sun blaze on the turning scythe, „ 252
Eyes too that long have w how Lancelot draws *Balin and Balan* 375
Queen Among her damsels broidering sat, heard, w And whisper'd: *Merlin and V.* 138
one had w, and had not held his peace: „ 162

Watch'd (*continued*) and she *w* him from her walls. *Merlin and V.* 775
while she *w* their arms far-off Sparkle, *Lancelot and E.* 395
many a time have *w* thee at the tilt „ 1359
Sat by the river in a cove, and *w* The high reed wave, „ 1389
all along the street of those Who *w* us pass ; *Holy Grail* 345
W her lord pass, and knew not that she sigh'd. *Last Tournament* 130
the knights, who *w* him, roar'd And shouted „ 468
westward-smiling seas, *W* from this tower. „ 588
fledged The hills that *w* thee, as Love *Lover's Tale i* 12
All day I *w* the floating isles of shade, „ *ii* 5
And *w* them till they vanish'd from my sight „ 42
an' I *w* him, an' when he came in *First Quarrel* 75
So they *w* what the end would be. *The Revenge* 73
How often have we *w* the sun fade *The Flight* 41
many's the time that I *w* her at mass *Tomorrow* 29
W again the hollow ridges *Locksley H., Sixty* 2
A soul that, *w* from earliest youth, *To Marq. of Dufferin* 25
W my far meadow zoned with airy morn ; *Prog. of Spring* 69
You *w* not I, she did not grow, *Romney's R.* 105
I *w* my son, And those that follow'd, *Akbar's Dream* 187
She *w* me, she nursed me, she fed me, *Charity* 33
Watcher The *w* on the column till the end ; *St. S. Stylites* 163
and one was set to watch The *w*, *Aylmer's Field* 552
A lidless *w* of the public weal, *Princess iv* 325
Sat watching like a *w* by the dead. „ *v* 62
kinsman left him *w* o'er his wife And two fair babes, *Merlin and V.* 706
Heard by the *w* in a haunted house, *Guinevere* 73
Watchest Thou *w* all things ever dim *In Mem. cxxi* 3
Watcheth shepherd who *w* the evening star. *Dying Swan* 35
Watchful Leolin ever *w* of her eye, *Aylmer's Field* 210
all offices Of *w* care and trembling tenderness. *Lover's Tale i* 226
for I do not doubt Being a *w* parent, *Sisters (E. and E.)* 31
Watching with triumph, *w* still To pierce me thro' *Rosalind* 26
Tho' *w* from a ruin'd tower How grows the day *Two Voices* 77
W your growth, I seem'd again to grow. *Aylmer's Field* 359
Sat *w* like a watcher by the dead. *Princess v* 62
With Psyche's babe, was Ida *w* us, „ 512
All her maidens, *w*, said, „ *vi* 3
w here At this, our great solemnity. *Ode on Well.* 243
Now *w* high on mountain cornice, *The Daisy* 19
awful sense Of one mute Shadow *w* all. *In Mem. xxx* 8
In *w* thee from hour to hour, „ *cxii* 12
An angel *w* an urn Wept over her, *Maud I viii* 3
Darken'd *w* a mother decline And that dead man „ *xix* 8
when he turn'd from *w* him. *Gareth and L.* 1032
w overhead The aërial poplar wave, *Sisters (E. and E.)* 83
No phantoms, *w* from a phantom shore *Ancient Sage* 179
w till the day begun— *Locksley H., Sixty* 91
W her large light eyes and gracious looks, *Prog. of Spring* 19
You that are *w* The gray Magician *Merlin and the G.* 4
Watchman the *w* peal The sliding season : *Gardener's D.* 182
Watch-word Nor deal in *w-w's* overmuch : *Love thou thy land* 28
and this proud *w* rest Of equal ; *Princess vii* 300
be grateful for the sounding *w* ' Evolution '
here. *Locksley H., Sixty* 198
Water (*See also* **Bog-wather, Fresh-water, Sea-water, Watter**) the glimmering *w* outfloweth : *Leonine Eleg.* 9
A sluice with blacken'd *w's* slept, *Mariana* 38
which crept Adown to where the *w* slept. *Arabian Nights* 30
The trenched *w's* run from sky to sky ; *Ode to Memory* 104
Holy *w* will I pour Into every spicy flower *Poet's Mind* 12
Winds were blowing, *w's* flowing, *Oriana* 14
Keeps his blue *w's* fresh for many a mile. *Mine be the strength* 8
Their moon-led *w's* white. *Palace of Art* 252
night-dews on still *w's* between walls *Lotos-Eaters, C. S.* 3
river drawing slowly His *w's* from the purple hill— „ 93
To watch the emerald colour'd *w* falling „ 96
Scaffolds, still sheets of *w*, divers woes, *D. of F. Women* 34
On one side lay the Ocean, and on one Lay a
great *w*, *M. d'Arthur* 12
And the wild *w* lapping on the crag.' „ 71
' I heard the *w* lapping on the crag, „ 116
Many an evening by the *w's* did we watch *Locksley Hall* 37
as moonlight unto sunlight, and as *w* unto wine— „ 152
Rift the hills, and roll the *w's*, „ 186

Water (*continued*) Side by side beneath the *w* Crew and
Captain lie ; *The Captain* 67
stars all night above the brim Of *w's* *The Voyage* 26
Down the waste *w's* day and night, „ 58
ILLYRIAN woodlands, echoing falls Of *w*, *To E. L.* 2
The blaze upon the *w's* to the east ; *Enoch Arden* 594
The blaze upon the *w's* to the west ; „ 596
Another ship (She wanted *w*) „ 628
The silent *w* slipping from the hills, „ 633
To where the rivulets of sweet *w* ran ; „ 642
Like fountains of sweet *w* in the sea, „ 803
Beyond it, where the *w's* marry— *The Brook* 81
Down in the *w*, a long reef of gold, *Sea Dreams* 127
And drew, from butts of *w* on the slope, *Princess, Pro.* 60
smile that like a wrinkling wind On glassy *w* „ *i* 116
Over the rolling *w's* go, „ *iii* 5
smile dwelt like a clouded moon In a still *w* : „ *vi* 271
To meet the sun and sunny *w's*, *The Daisy* 11
All along the valley, where thy *w's* flow, *V. of Cauteretz* 3
Where yon broad *w* sweetly slowly glides. *Requiescat* 2
The forest crack'd, the *w's* curl'd, *In Mem. xv* 5
Is on the *w's* day and night, „ *xvii* 11
As drop by drop the *w* falls „ *lviii* 3
By that broad *w* of the west, „ *lxvii* 3
I hear thee where the *w's* run ; „ *cxxx* 2
was heard among the holy hymns A voice as of
the *w's*, *Com. of Arthur* 291
Hath power to walk the *w's* like our Lord. „ 294
there past along the hymns A voice as of the *w's*, „ 464
all her dress Wept from her sides as *w* flowing
away ; *Gareth and L.* 217
And drops of *w* fell from either hand ; „ 220
To turn the broach, draw *w*, or hew wood, „ 486
under this wan *w* many of them Lie rotting, „ 824
and beside The carolling *w* set themselves *Balin and Balan* 44
as an enemy that has left Death in the living *w's*, *Merlin and V.* 148
At once she slipt like *w* to the floor. *Lancelot and E.* 830
Heard on the winding *w's*, eve and morn „ 1408
Ye could not hear the *w's* for the blast, *Holy Grail* 797
with living *w's* in the change Of seasons : *Pelleas and E.* 511
Unruffling *w's* re-collect the shape *Last Tournament* 369
after the great *w's* break Whitening for half a league, „ 464
as the *w* Moab saw Come round by the East, „ 482
And one was *w* and one star was fire, „ 736
On one side lay the Ocean, and on one Lay a
great *w*, *Pass. of Arthur* 180
And the wild *w* lapping on the crag.' „ 239
' I heard the *w* lapping on the crag, „ 284
Down that long *w* opening on the deep „ 466
pleasant breast of *w's*, quiet bay, *Lover's Tale i* 6
semicircle Of dark-blue *w's* and the narrow fringe „ 38
and thro' the arch Down those loud *w's*, „ 59
charm of light and strength Upon the *w's*, „ 92
And glory of broad *w's* interfused, „ 401
how he woo'd The *w's*, and the *w's* answering lisp'd „ 544
Like *w*, drop by drop, upon my ear Fell ; „ 576
When he leaps from the *w* to the land. *The Revenge* 55
And the *w* began to heave and the weather „ 113
Rather to thee, thou living *w*, *Sir J. Oldcastle* 131
where the *w* is clearer than air : *V. of Maeldune* 77
Warriors over the Weltering *w's* *Batt. of Brunanburh* 48
the *w's*—you hear them call ! *Despair* 47
for my brain was drunk with the *w*, „ 65
This wealth of *w's* might but seem to draw *Ancient Sage* 9
and hear the *w's* roar, *The Flight* 90
as a man Who sees his face in *w*, *The Ring* 370
rolling of dragons By warble of *w*, *Merlin and the G.* 45
you will not deny my sultry throat One draught
of icy *w*. *Romney's R.* 23
A fall of *w* lull'd the noon asleep. „ 83
Waterbreak With many a silvery *w* *The Brook* 61
Water-circle Gleams of the *w-c's* as they broke, *Lover's Tale i* 67
Water-course The tangled *w-c's* slept, *Dying Swan* 19
and show'd A riotous confluence of *w-c's* *Lucretius* 30
Scarr'd with a hundred wintry *w-c's*— *Holy Grail* 490

Wavering (*continued*) Woo her and gain her then : no *w*, boy ! — *Sisters* (*E. and E.*) 39
The flame of life went *w* down ; — *To Marq. of Dufferin* 32
Fled *w* o'er thy face, and chased away — *Demeter and P.* 15
see I thro' the *w* flakes Yon blanching apricot — *Prog. of Spring* 29
some thro' *w* lights and shadows broke, — *Lotos-Eaters* 12
In every *w* brake an ambuscade. — *Geraint and E.* 51
Waveringly Immingled with Heaven's azure *w*, — *Gareth and L.* 936
Wave-worn the *w-w* horns of the echoing bank, — *Dying Swan* 39
Waving and while he stood on deck *W*, — *Enoch Arden* 244
w to him White hands, and courtesy ; — *Gareth and L.* 1376
Geraint *W* an angry hand as who should say — *Geraint and E.* 444
Perceived the *w* of his hands that blest. — *Guinevere* 584
Then *w* us a sign to seat ourselves, — *Lover's Tale iv* 320
But one—he was *w* a flag— — *The Wreck* 119
O slender lily *w* there, — *Ancient Sage* 167
'Thrice-happy he that may caress The ringlet's *w* balm — *Talking Oak* 178
With woven paces and with *w* arms, — *Merlin and V.* 207
Of woven paces and of *w* hands, (repeat) — „ 330, 968
Or watch the *w* pine which here — *To Ulysses* 25
Wavy And the *w* swell of the soughing reeds, — *Dying Swan* 38
honeysuckle round the porch has wov'n its *w* bowers, — *May Queen* 29
Wax (s) I will melt this marble into *w* — *Princess iii* 73
Wax (verb) Thou shalt *w* and he shall dwindle, — *Boädicea* 40
Speak, as it *w'es*, of a love that wanes ? — *Lancelot and E.* 1401
Wax'd Then *w* her anger stronger. — *The Goose* 30
And watch'd them, *w* in every limb ; — *In Mem. ciii* 30
So *w* in pride, that I believed myself Unconquerable, — *Geraint and E.* 835
Waxen Baby fingers, *w* touches, press me from my mother's breast. — *Locksley Hall* 90
And melt the *w* hearts of men.' — *In Mem. xxi* 8
A bought commission, a *w* face, — *Maud I x* 30
Waxeth Ever the wonder *w* more and more, — *Sonnet to* —— 6
Waxing The full-juiced apple, *w* over-mellow, — *Lotos-Eaters, C. S.* 33
But tho' his eyes are *w* dim, — *D. of the O. Year* 21
Way (*See also* **Half-way, Milky-way, Waäy, Wood-way**)
Winning its *w* with extreme gentleness — *Isabel* 23
A weary, weary *w* I go, — *Oriana* 89
That will not stay, upon his *w*, — *Rosalind* 15
And flashes off a thousand *w's*, — „ 23
Nor wander'd into other *w's* : — *My life is full* 3
one silvery cloud Had lost his *w* — *Œnone* 93
This *w* and that, in many a wild festoon Ran riot, — „ 100
The blessed music went that *w* my soul — *May Queen, Con.* 42
Bluster the winds and tides the self-same *w*, — *D. of F. Women* 38
and the woods and *w's* Are pleasant, — *On a Mourner* 13
Till all thy life one *w* incline — „ 19
The goose flew this *w* and flew that, — *The Goose* 35
And God fulfils himself in many *w's*, — *M. d'Arthur* 241
I am going a long *w* With these thou seëst— — „ 256
all the livelong *w* With solemn gibe — *Gardener's D.* 167
his *w's* were harsh ; But Dora bore them meekly. — *Dora* 35
and went her *w* Across the wheat, — „ 71
these unreal *w's* Seem but the theme of writers, — *Edwin Morris* 47
Bear witness, if I could have found a *w* — *St. S. Stylites* 55
Yet this *w* was left, And by this *w* I 'scaped them. — „ 178
And down the *w* you use to come, — *Talking Oak* 115
The trance gave *w* To those caresses, — *Love and Duty* 65
Met me walking on yonder *w*, — *Edward Gray* 2
summer suns, By many pleasant *w's*, — *Will Water.* 34
And follow'd her all the *w*. — *Lady Clare* 64
To meet and greet her on her *w* ; — *Beggar Maid* 6
All the windy *w's* of men (repeat) — *Vision of Sin* 132, 168
caught His bundle, waved his hand, and went his *w*. — *Enoch Arden* 238
And wherefore did he go this weary *w*, — „ 296
While yet she went about her household *w's*, — „ 453
winding glades high up like *w's* to Heaven, — „ 573
led the *w* To where the rivulets of sweet water ran ; — „ 641
I chatter over stony *w's*, — *The Brook* 39
A childly *w* with children, — *Aylmer's Field* 181
won mysterious *w* Thro' the seal'd ear — „ 695
Is not our own child on the narrow *w*, — „ 743
as a footsore ox in crowded *w's* — „ 819
'That's your light *w* ; — *Princess, Pro.* 151

Way (*continued*) She once had past that *w* ; — *Princess Pro. i* 185
And thus (what other *w* was left) I came.' — „ *ii* 217
true she errs, But in her own grand *w* : — „ *iii* 107
I forced a *w* Thro' solid opposition — „ 125
when we sent the Prince your *w* — „ *iv* 398
done the thing one ought, When fall'n in darker *w's*.' — „ *v* 68
And I will take her up and go my *w*, — „ 102
for everything Gave *w* before him : — „ 530
or was it chance, She past my *w*. — „ *vi* 98
And turn'd each face her *w* : — „ 144
to them the doors gave *w* Groaning, — „ *vi* 349
These were the rough *w's* of the world till now. — „ *vii* 257
one Not learned, save in gracious household *w's*, — „ 318
The path of duty was the *w* to glory : (repeat) — *Ode on Well.* 202, 210
The path of duty be the *w* to glory : — „ 224
like a man, too, would have his *w* : — *Grandmother* 70
Of Lari Maxume, all the *w*, — *The Daisy* 76
And dead men lay all over the *w*, — *The Victim* 21
All running on one *w* to the home of my love, — *Window, On the Hill* 8
And ever met him on his *w* — *In Mem. vi* 22
And we with singing cheer'd the *w*, — „ *xxii* 5
Still onward winds the dreary *w* ; — „ *xxvi* 1
And look thy look, and go thy *w*, — „ *xlix* 9
Moving about the household *w's*, — „ *lx* 11
My darken'd *w's* Shall ring with music — „ *lxxvii* 13
Whatever *w* my days decline, — „ *lxxxv* 41
That will not yield each other *w*. — „ *cii* 20
They wept and wail'd, but led the *w* — „ *ciii* 18
and let the world have its *w* : — *Maud I iv* 21
Who knows the *w's* of the world, — „ 44
Be mine a philosopher's life in the quiet woodland *w's*, — „ 49
I know the *w* she went Home — „ *xii* 21
what am I That I dare to look her *w* ; — „ *xvi* 11
his *w's* are sweet, And their's are bestial, — *Com. of Arthur* 180
To guard thee on the rough *w's* of the world.' — „ 336
son Beheld his only *w* to glory lead — *Gareth and L.* 159
the vassal king, Was ev'n upon his *w* to Camelot ; — „ 392
who sliced a red life-bubbling *w* — „ 509
I have miss'd the only *w* (repeat) — „ 787, 792
convey'd them on their *w* And left them — „ 889
I watch'd thee victor in the joust, And seen thy *w*.' — „ 1357
And after went her *w* across the bridge, — *Marr. of Geraint* 383
I have let men be, and have their *w* ; — „ 466
For old am I, and rough the *w's* and wild ; — „ 750
I charge thee ride before, Ever a good *w* on before ; — *Geraint and E.* 15
I will not fight my *w* with gilded arms, — „ 21
pain she had To keep them in the wild *w's* of the wood, — „ 187
Them forward by a *w* which, beaten broad, — „ 436
And left him lying in the public *w* ; — „ 478
answering not one word, she led the *w*. — „ 495
and she wept beside the *w*. — „ 519
The long *w* smoke beneath him in his fear ; — „ 532
To shun the wild *w's* of the lawless tribe. — „ 608
'The fire of Heaven is on the dusty *w's*. — *Balin and Balan* 448
who sought to win my love Thro' evil *w's* : — „ 475
And then she follow'd Merlin all the *w*, — *Merlin and V.* 203
Then her false voice made *w*, broken with sobs : — „ 857
Glanced first at him, then her, and went his *w*. — *Lancelot and E.* 95
Full often lost in fancy, lost his *w* ; — „ 164
in the *w's* below The knights and ladies wept, — *Holy Grail* 352
And thence departed every one his *w*. — „ 360
some ancient king Had built a *w*, — „ 502
For now there is a lion in the *w*.' — „ 645
one was pointing this *w*, and one that, Because the *w* was lost. — *Pelleas and E.* 58
tilt against the knights There at Caerleon, but have lost our *w* ; — „ 66
Glanced down upon her, turn'd and went her *w*. — „ 185
Some rough old knight who knew the worldly *w*, — „ 192
These be the *w's* of ladies,' Pelleas thought, — „ 209
With promise of large light on woods and *w's*. — „ 394
But he by wild and *w*, for half the night, — „ 497
With trumpet-blowings ran on all the *w's* From Camelot — *Last Tournament* 52
loneliest *w's* are safe from shore to shore. — „ 102

Way (*continued*) So all the *w's* were safe from shore to shore, *Last Tournament* 485
Mark's *w*, my soul !—but eat not thou with Mark, „ 532
So, pluck'd one *w* by hate and one by love, „ 539
Mark's *w's* to steal behind one in the dark— „ 618
And cast him as a worm upon the *w* ; *Guinevere* 35
And then they rode to the divided *w*, „ 124
That did not shun to smite me in worse *w*, „ 435
and the *w's* Were filled with rapine, „ 457
But in His *w's* with men I find Him not. *Pass. of Arthur* 11
and wail their *w* From cloud to cloud, „ 39
find or feel a *w* Thro' this blind haze, „ 75
And God fulfils himself in many *w's*, „ 409
I am going a long *w* With these thou seëst— „ 424
that *w* my wish leads me evermore Still to believe it— *Lover's Tale i* 274
Each *w* from verge to verge a Holy Land, „ 337
effect weigh'd seas upon my head To come my *w* ! „ 661
Was not the land as free thro' all her *w's* „ 662
Could that be more because he came my *w* ? „ 666
Why should he not come my *w* if he would ? „ 667
why *should* he come my *w* Robed in those robes „ 670
what gleam on those black *w's* Where Love „ 812
Had died almost to serve them any *w*, „ *iv* 124
And leave him in the public *w* to die. „ 261
And balanced either *w* by each, „ 269
he patted my hand in his gentle *w*, *First Quarrel* 67
and now you may go your *w*. *Rizpah* 20
Turning my *w*, the loveliest face on earth. *Sisters* (*E. and E.*) 87
Flower into fortune—our world's *w*— *Columbus* 167
sometimes wish I had never led the *w*. „ 186
Shaping their *w* toward Dyflen again, *Batt. of Brunanburh* 98
moves unseen among the *w's* of men. *Tiresias* 24
Send no such light upon the *w's* of men „ 161
and every *w* the vales Wind, „ 182
By all my *w's* where'er they ran, *Ancient Sage* 157
he—some one—this *w* creeps— *The Flight* 70
and Suns along their fiery *w*, *Locksley H., Sixty* 203
know them, follow him who led the *w*, „ 266
Not this *w* will you set your name *Epilogue* 1
Yon myriad-worlded *w*— „ 53
Well, One *w* for Miriam. *The Ring* 73
She turn'd, and in her soft imperial *w* „ 267
I am on the Perfect *W*, All else is to perdition.' *Akbar's Dream* 34
Here on this bank in *some w* live the life „ 144
Will you move a little that *w* ? *Charity* 20
Well if it do not roll our *w*. *Riflemen form !* 4
Toward the lowland *w's* behind me, *Silent Voices* 5
Wayfaring-tree Black holly, and white-flower'd *w-t* ! *Sir J. Oldcastle* 130
Wayside Craft, poisonous counsels, *w* ambushings— *Gareth and L.* 432
The *w* blossoms open to the blaze. *Balin and Balan* 449
Come dashing down on a tall *w* flower, *Guinevere* 253
I told your *w* story to my mother *Sisters* (*E. and E.*) 189
Wayward—The vexed eddies of its *w* brother : *Isabel* 33
I have been wild and *w*, but you'll forgive me now ; *May Queen, N. Y's. E.* 33
Or something of a *w* modern mind *Edwin Morris* 87
I went thro' many *w* moods *Day-Dm., Pro.* 6
No more shall *w* grief abuse The genial hour *In Mem. cv* 9
And yet so wild and *w* that my dream— *Akbar's Dream* 172
Waywardness At any gentle damsel's *w*. *Gareth and L.* 1179
Way-worn Foot-sore, *w-w*, at length *St. Telemachus* 34
Weak (adj.) *W* Truth a-leaning on her crutch, *Clear-headed friend* 18
Than cry for strength, remaining *w*, *Two Voices* 95
' For I go, *w* from suffering here : „ 238
W symbols of the settled bliss, *Miller's D.* 233
And in my *w*, lean arms I lift the cross, *St. S. Stylites* 118
Made *w* by time and fate, but strong in will *Ulysses* 69
Pass on, *w* heart, and leave me where I lie : *Come not, when, etc.* 11
Half-parted from a *w* and scolding hinge, *The Brook* 84
Full of *w* poison, turnspits for the clown, *Princess iv* 516
' This fellow would make weakness *w*, *In Mem. xxi* 7
Strike dead the whole *w* race of venomous worms, *Maud II i* 46
Seeing that ye be grown too *w* and old *Com. of Arthur* 511
For see ye not how *w* and hungerworn I seem— *Gareth and L.* 443

Weak (adj.) (*continued*) The sick *w* beast seeking to help herself *Merlin and V.* 498
And being *w* in body said no more ; *Lancelot and E.* 839
Flatter me rather, seeing me so *w*, *Last Tournament* 642
Of eyes too *w* to look upon the light ; *Lover's Tale i* 614
An' Hetty wur *w* i' the hattics, *Village Wife* 101
being woman and *w*, His formal kiss fell *The Wreck* 31
' That *w* and watery nature love you ? No ! *The Ring* 396
Weak (s) if from Arthur's hall, To help the *w*. *Balin and Balan* 473
Weaken'd And all the senses *w*, save in that, *Lover's Tale i* 127
' Muriel's health Had *w*, nursing little Miriam. *The Ring* 357
Weakening gentle sickness, gradually *W* the man, *Enoch Arden* 825
Weaker Words *w* than your grief would make *To J. S.* 65
And ever *w* grows thro' acted crime, *Will* 12
' I might forget my *w* lot ; *Two Voices* 367
songs I made As echoes out of *w* times, *In Mem., Con.* 22
till he saw Which were the *w* ; *Lancelot and E.* 462
Weakest Cries to *W* as to Strongest, *Locksley H., Sixty* 110
Weakling Poor *w* ev'n as they are.' *Princess vi* 310
Of craven, *w*, and thrice-beaten hound : *Pelleas and E.* 291
' Rise, *w* ; I am Lancelot ; say thy say.' „ 582
Weakly This pretty, puny, *w* little one,— *Enoch Arden* 195
Weakness my own *w* fools My judgment, *Supp. Confessions* 136
Prevailing in *w*, the coronach stole *Dying Swan* 26
Deliver not the tasks of might To *w*, *Love thou thy land* 14
Regard the *w* of thy peers : „ 24
W to be wroth with *w* ! *Locksley Hall* 149
So she strove against her *w*, *L. of Burleigh* 69
That was your hour of *w*. *Enoch Arden* 449
And Enoch bore his *w* cheerfully. „ 827
to spy The *w* of a people or a house, *Aylmer's Field* 570
Our *w* somehow shapes the shadow, *Princess iii* 330
And hatred of her *w*, blent with shame. „ *vii* 30
but well-nigh close to death For *w* : „ 120
' This fellow would make *w* weak, *In Mem. xxi* 7
my passion hath not swerved To works of *w*, „ *lxxxv* 50
Forgot his *w* in thy sight. „ *cx* 4
those Whom *w* or necessity have cramp'd *Tiresias* 87
Weal (*See also* **Dogwhip-weals**) he for the common *w*, The fading politics *Princess ii* 285
A lidless watcher of the public *w*, „ *iv* 325
So far, so near in woe and *w* ; *In Mem. cxxix* 2
Be moulded by your wishes for her *w* ; *Marr. of Geraint* 799
Hours That cancel *w* with woe, *Ancient Sage* 96
Weald Fled all night long by glimmering waste and *w*, And heard the Spirits of the waste and *w* *Guinevere* 128
That gray beast, the wolf of the *w*. *Batt. of Brunanburh* 110
Wealth (*See also* **World-wealth**) Showering thy gleaned *w* into my open breast *Ode to Memory* 23
The choicest *w* of all the earth, *Eleänore* 19
In glowing health, with boundless *w*, *L. C. V. de Vere* 61
' When *w* no more shall rest in mounded heaps, *Golden Year* 32
The sole succeeder to their *w*, their lands, *Aylmer's Field* 294
heiress, *w*, Their *w*, their heiress ! *w* enough was theirs For twenty matches. „ 368
May beat a pathway out to *w* and fame. „ 439
Whatever eldest-born of rank or *w* „ 484
I that have wasted here health, *w*, and time, *Princess iv* 352
O more than poor men *w*, Than sick men health— „ 459
Abide : thy *w* is gather'd in, *In Mem. lii* 15
And so my *w* resembles thine, „ *lxxix* 17
the *w* Of words and wit, the double health, „ *Con.* 102
Your father has *w* well-gotten, *Maud I iv* 18
joy that blazed itself in woodland *w* Of leaf, *Balin and Balan* 82
all his land and *w* and state were hers. *Holy Grail* 587
And gave herself and all her *w* to me. „ 597
all the *w* and all the woe ? *Guinevere* 344
And so much *w* as God had charged her with— *Lover's Tale i* 213
when all my *w* Flash'd from me in a moment „ 668
Whatever *w* I brought from that new world *Columbus* 101
with the wisdom and *w* of his own, *The Wreck* 65
W with his wines and his wedded harlots ; *Vastness* 19
kinsman, dying, summon'd me to Rome—He left me *w*— *The Ring* 179
no tear for him, who left you *w*, „ 188
The *w* of tropic bower and brake ; *To Ulysses* 37

Wealth (*continued*) Youth and Health, and birth and *w*, *By an Evolution.* 8
Wealthier and himself Be wealthy still, ay *w*. *Aylmer's Field* 373
Then closed her access to the *w* farms, „ 503
Then were I *w* than a leash of kings.' *Gareth and L.* 51
' Ye will be all the *w*,' (repeat) *Geraint and E.* 221, 412
A *w* life than heretofore with these And Balin, *Balin and Balan* 92
w—*w*—hour by hour ! *To the Queen ii* 23
Jilted for a *w* ! *w* ? *Locksley H., Sixty* 11
To make them *w* in his readers' eyes ; *Poets and their B.* 4
Wealthiest Spain then the mightiest, *w* realm on earth, *Columbus* 205
Wealthy Revealings deep and clear are thine Of *w* smiles : *Madeline* 11
I SEE the *w* miller yet, *Miller's D.* 1
Like *w* men who care not how they give. *Tithonus* 17
Where the *w* nobles dwell.' *L. of Burleigh* 24
And when she show'd the *w* scabbard, *Aylmer's Field* 236
and himself Be *w* still, ay wealthier. „ 373
Days order'd in a *w* peace, *In Mem. xlvi* 11
W with wandering lines of mount and mere, *Holy Grail* 252
Hold her a *w* bride within thine arms, „ 621
Tho' *w* enough to have bask'd in the light *The Wreck* 45
Weapon With thine own *w* art thou slain, *Two Voices* 311
wearing neither hunting-dress Nor *w*, *Marr. of Geraint* 166
The wielding of *w's*— *Batt. of Brunanburh* 90
a valorous *w* in olden England ! *Kapiolani* 4
Wear (s) keeps the *w* and polish of the wave. *Marr. of Geraint* 682
Wear (verb) *W's* all day a fainter tone. *The Owl ii* 7
And King-like, *w's* the crown : *Of old sat Freedom* 16
eat wholesome food, And *w* warm clothes, *St. S. Stylites* 109
w an undress'd goatskin on my back ; „ 116
shall *w* Alternate leaf and acorn-ball *Talking Oak* 286
This mortal armour that I *w*, *Sir Galahad* 70
Of those that *w* the Poet's crown : *You might have won* 10
spears That soon should *w* the garland ; *Aylmer's Field* 112
his pride Lay deeper than to *w* it as his ring— „ 122
I think they should not *w* our rusty gowns, *Princess, Pro.* 143
than *w* Those lilies, better blush „ *iii* 67
And so she *w's* her error like a crown „ 111
he *w's* a truer crown Than any wreath *Ode on Well.* 276
bear the head That sleeps or *w's* the mask of sleep, *In Mem. xviii* 10
When first she *w's* her orange-flower ! „ *xl* 4
Who *w's* his manhood hale and green : „ *liii* 4
The fool that *w's* a crown of thorns : „ *lxix* 12
Come, *w* the forms by which I know „ *xci* 5
But ill for him that *w's* a crown, „ *cxxvii* 9
And Maud will *w* her jewels, *Maud I xx* 27
And *w's* a helmet mounted with a skull, *Gareth and L.* 639
your fair child shall *w* your costly gift *Marr. of Geraint* 819
Were fit to *w* your slipper for a glove. *Geraint and E.* 623
Why *w* ye this crown-royal upon shield ? ' *Balin and Balan* 338
' Why *w* ye that crown-royal ? ' „ 348
' What, *w* ye still that same crown-scandalous ? ' „ 390
this maid Might *w* as fair a jewel as is on earth, *Lancelot and E.* 240
That he should *w* her favour at the tilt. „ 358
will you *w* My favour at this tourney ? ' „ 361
Well, I will *w* it : fetch it out to me : „ 371
One rose, a rose, to gather and to *w*, *Pelleas and E.* 406
Why ye not *w* on arm, or neck, or zone *Last Tournament* 36
Lancelot won, methought, for thee to *w*.' „ 38
W black and white, and be a nun like you, *Guinevere* 677
And so *w* out in almsdeed and in prayer „ 687
Robed in those robes of light I must not *w*, *Lover's Tale i* 671
pluck from this true breast the locket that I *w*, *The Flight* 33
Envy *w's* the mask of Love, *Locksley H., Sixty* 109
I should *w* my crown entire *Helen's Tower* 9
you, that *w* a wreath of sweeter bay, *Poets and their B.* 7
I myself Am half afraid to *w* it. *The Ring* 472
and *w's* the leper's weed ? *Happy* 10
Weär'd (spent) I *w* it o' liquor, I did. *North. Cobbler* 32
Wearied Is *w* of the rolling hours. *L. C. V. de Vere* 60
Smoothing the *w* mind : *Leonine Eleg.* 14
And closing eaves of *w* eyes I sleep till dusk *In Mem. lxvii* 11
I felt Thy manhood thro' that *w* lance of thine. *Gareth and L.* 1266
and Balin's horse Was *w* to the death, *Balin and Balan* 561
And *w* out made for the couch and slept, *Merlin and V.* 736

Wearied (*continued*) Wounded and *w* needs must he be near. *Lancelot and E.* 538
Rode with his diamond, *w* of the quest, „ 616
To seek him, and had *w* of the search. „ 631
all *w* of the quest Leapt on his horse, „ 703
' Alas,' he said, ' your ride hath *w* you. „ 831
I am *w* of our city, son, *Ancient Sage* 15
And *w* of Autocrats, Anarchs, and Slaves, *The Dreamer* 10
Wearier Thro' weary and yet ever *w* hours, *Aylmer's Field* 828
Wearieth Gaiety without eclipse, *W* me, *Lilian* 21
Weariness all things else have rest from *w* ? *Lotos-Eaters, C. S.* 14
As all but empty heart and *w* *Geraint and E.* 652
Settles, till one could yield for *w* : *Merlin and V.* 372
wan day Went glooming down in wet and *w* : *Last Tournament* 215
Toil and ineffable *w*, faltering hopes of relief, *Def. of Lucknow* 90
those three sweet Italian words, became a *w*. *The Ring* 407
He, all but deaf thro' age and *w*, *St. Telemachus* 41
Wearing And *w* on my swarthy brows The garland *Kate* 23
W the rose of womanhood. *Two Voices* 417
W the light yoke of that Lord of love, *Aylmer's Field* 708
W his wisdom lightly, like the fruit *A Dedication* 12
w all that weight Of learning lightly *In Mem., Con.* 39
W the white flower of a blameless life, *Ded. of Idylls* 25
w neither hunting-dress Nor weapon, *Marr. of Geraint* 165
in *w* mine Needs must be lesser likelihood, *Lancelot and E.* 366
damsel, *w* this unsunny face To him who won *Pelleas and E.* 180
And *w* but a holly-spray for crest, *Last Tournament* 172
I, *w* but the garland of a day, *To Dante* 6
Weary (adj.) (*See also* **Heart-weary**) O *w* life ! O *w* death ! *Supp. Confessions* 188
w with a finger's touch Those writhed limbs *Clear-headed friend* 22
From brawling storms, From *w* wind, *Ode to Memory* 113
SLOW sail'd the *w* mariners and saw, *Sea-Fairies* 1
Ever the *w* wind went on, *Dying Swan* 9
A *w*, *w* way I go, Oriana. *Oriana* 89
MY life is full of *w* days, *My life is full* 1
Which some green Christmas crams with *w* bones. *Wan Sculptor* 14
And by the moon the reaper *w*, *L. of Shalott i* 33
give me grace To help me of my *w* load.' *Mariana in the S.* 30
With *w* sameness in the rhymes, *Miller's D.* 70
Breathing like one that hath a *w* dream. *Lotos-Eaters* 6
but evermore Most *w* seem'd the sea, *w* the oar, *W* the wandering fields of barren foam. „ 41
Resting *w* limbs at last on beds of asphodel. „ *C. S.* 125
While my stiff spine can hold my *w* head, *St. S. Stylites* 43
Twice ten long *w* *w* years to this, „ 90
since I heard him make reply Is many a *w* hour ; *Talking Oak* 26
It may be my lord is *w*, *Locksley Hall* 53
And wherefore did he go this *w* way, *Enoch Arden* 296
But after scaling half the *w* down, „ 372
and beats out his *w* life. „ 730
Beating it in upon his *w* brain, „ 796
all about the fields you caught His *w* daylong chirping, *The Brook* 53
Thro' *w* and yet ever wearier hours, *Aylmer's Field* 828
For many *w* moons before we came, *Princess iii* 319
Panted from *w* sides ' King, you are free ! „ *v* 24
When ill and *w*, alone and cold, *The Daisy* 96
And o'er a *w* sultry land, *Will* 17
That it makes one *w* to hear.' *The Islet* 29
With *w* steps I loiter on, *In Mem. xxxviii* 1
She is *w* of dance and play.' *Maud I xxii* 22
However *w*, a spark of will Not to be trampled out. „ *II ii* 56
That has been in a *w* world my one thing bright ; „ *III vi* 17
and thy good horse And thou are *w* ; *Gareth and L.* 1265
My lord is *w* with the fight before, *Geraint and E.* 133
Leave me to-night : I am *w* to the death.' „ 358
I am *w* of her.' *Merlin and V.* 838
Now *w* of my service and devoir, *Lancelot and E.* 118
but so *w* were his limbs, that he, *Pelleas and E.* 513
at once The *w* steed of Pelleas floundering „ 574
The white light of the *w* moon above, *Lover's Tale i* 640
But many *w* moons I lived alone— „ *ii* 2
Over all this *w* world of ours, *Sisters (E. and E.)* 12
But at length we began to be *w*, *V. of Maeldune* 91
O *w* was I of the travel, „ 129

Weary (adj.) (*continued*) There was the Scotsman *W* of war. *Batt. of Brunanburh* 36
Old and *w*, But eager to follow, *Merlin and the G.* 100
Good, I am never *w* painting you. *Romney's R.* 3
O *w* one, has it begun? *The Dreamer* 26
Weary (s) And the wicked cease from troubling, and the *w* are at rest. *May Queen, Con.* 60
Let the *w* be comforted, *On Jub. Q. Victoria* 34
Weary (verb) Nor could I *w*, heart or limb, *In Mem. xxv* 9
till the ear *Wearies* to hear it, *Lancelot and E.* 898
Wearying And *w* in a land of sand and thorns. *Holy Grail* 420
Gone thy tender-natured mother, *w* to be left alone, *Locksley H., Sixty* 57
Weasel the thin *w* there Follows the mouse, *Aylmer's Field* 852
nail me like a *w* on a grange For warning: *Princess ii* 205
deems it carrion of some woodland thing, Or shrew, or *w*, *Gareth and L.* 749
Weather (adj.) huge sea-castles heaving upon the *w* bow. *The Revenge* 24
Weather (s) Careless both of wind and *w*, *Rosalind* 7
All in the blue unclouded *w* *L. of Shalott iii* 19
And it was windy *w*. (repeat) *The Goose* 4, 40
There must be stormy *w*; *Will Water.* 54
His brothers of the *w* stood Stock-still „ 135
Will bring fair *w* yet to all of us. *Enoch Arden* 191
Passing with the *w*, *Window, Spring* 6
water began to heave and the *w* to moan, *The Revenge* 113
Nasty, casselty *w*! *Church-warden, etc.* 2
Weather-beaten Denying not these *w-b* limbs *St. S. Stylites* 19
His large gray eyes and *w-b* face *Enoch Arden* 70
Weathercock'd Whose blazing wyvern *w* the spire, *Aylmer's Field* 17
Weather'd many a rough sea had he *w* in her! *Enoch Arden* 135
Weave There she *w's* by night and day *L. of Shalott ii* 1
To *w* the mirror's magic sights, „ 29
Than any wreath that man can *w* him. *Ode on Well.* 277
With trembling fingers did we *w* *In Mem. xxx* 1
And *w* their petty cells and die. „ *l* 12
Again at Christmas did we *w* „ *lxxviii* 1
She meant to *w* me a snare *Maud I vi* 25
Weaver *See* **Cloud-weaver**
Weaveth And so she *w* steadily, *L. of Shalott ii* 7
Weaving *w* over That various wilderness *Lover's Tale i* 418
Web A magic *w* with colours gay. *L. of Shalott ii* 2
in her *w* she still delights To weave „ 28
She left the *w*, she left the loom, „ *iii* 37
Out flew the *w* and floated wide; „ 42
and takes the flood With swarthy *w's*. *M. d'Arthur* 269
Who wove coarse *w's* to snare her purity, *Aylmer's Field* 780
A *w* is wov'n across the sky; *In Mem. iii* 6
A cloth of roughest *w*, and cast it down, *Gareth and L.* 683
Caught in a great old tyrant spider's *w*, *Merlin and V.* 259
and takes the flood With swarthy *w's*. *Pass. of Arthur* 437
Wed young spirit present When first she is *w*; *Ode to Memory* 74
Came two young lovers lately *w*; *L. of Shalott ii* 34
And I was young—too young to *w*: *Miller's D.* 141
nor *w* Raw Haste, half-sister to Delay. *Love thou thy land* 95
he woo'd and *w* A labourer's daughter, *Dora* 39
But take it—earnest *w* with sport, *Day-Dm., Ep.* 11
They two will *w* the morrow morn: *Lady Clare* 7
'To-morrow he *w's* with me.' „ 16
We two will *w* to-morrow morn, „ 87
That she wore when she was *w*.' *L. of Burleigh* 96
In the dress that she was *w* in, „ 99
W whom thou wilt, but I am sick of Time, *Come not, when, etc.* 9
It is long before you *w*. *Vision of Sin* 70
So these were *w*, and merrily rang the bells, (repeat) *Enoch Arden* 80, 511
To *w* the man so dear to all of them „ 484
'There is no reason why we should not *w*.' „ 508
So you will *w* me, let it be at once.' „ 510
Merrily rang the bells and they were *w* „ 512
when the days drew nigh that I should *w*, *Princess i* 41
certain, would not *w*. „ 50
we purposed with ourself Never to *w*. „ *ii* 61
I w with thee! *I* bound by precontract „ *iv* 541
Besides, the woman *w* is not as we, „ *v* 462
Wed (*continued*) She needs must *w* him for her own good name; *Princess vii* 74
On the day that follow'd the day she was *w*, *The Islet* 4
Thought leapt out to *w* with Thought Ere Thought could *w* itself with Speech; *In Mem. xxiii* 15
But lives to *w* an equal mind; „ *lxii* 8
And talk of others that are *w*, „ *Con.* 98
Enforced she was to *w* him in her tears, *Com. of Arthur* 204
he needs Must *w* that other, whom no man desired, *Gareth and L.* 109
break her will, and make her *w* with him: „ 617
whom he trusts to overthrow, Then *w*, with glory: but she will not *w* Save whom she loveth, „ 621
And live to *w* with her whom first you love: But ere you *w* with any, bring your bride, *Marr. of Geraint* 227
when it *w's* with manhood, makes a man. *Geraint and E.* 868
'Had I chosen to *w*, I had been wedded earlier, *Lancelot and E.* 934
W thou our Lady, and rule over us, *Holy Grail* 605
but could I *w* her Loving the other? *Sisters (E. and E.)* 167
and *w's* me to my grave. *The Flight* 20
not Love but Hate that *w's* a bride against her will; „ 32
W him! I will not *w* him, „ 55
when Hubert *w's* in you The heart of Love, *The Ring* 61
So *w* thee with my soul, *Prog. of Spring* 92
W to the melody, Sang thro' the world; *Merlin and the G.* 97
Wedded (adj. and part.) (*See also* **New-wedded, Proxy-wedded**)
So that my vigour, *w* to thy blood, *Œnone* 161
Dear is the memory of our *w* lives, *Lotos-Eaters, C. S.* 96
Wherever Thought hath *w* Fact. *Love thou thy land* 52
there Unclasp'd the *w* eagles of her belt, *Godiva* 43
Lucilia, *w* to Lucretius, found Her master cold; *Lucretius* 1
but she says (God help her) she was *w* to a fool; *Princess iii* 83
I had been *w* wife, I knew mankind, „ *vi* 327
So Willy and I were *w*: I wore a lilac gown; *Grandmother* 57
Ay is the song of the *w* spheres, *Window, No Answer* 7
Was *w* with a winsome wife, Ygerne: *Com. of Arthur* 188
And there be *w* with all ceremony. *Marr. of Geraint* 608
They twain were *w* with all ceremony. „ 839
Seeing that ye are *w* to a man, *Geraint and E.* 425
I had been *w* earlier, sweet Elaine: *Lancelot and E.* 935
And one had *w* her, and he was dead, *Holy Grail* 586
until himself had thought He loved her also, *w* easily, *Last Tournament* 402
'He has *w* her,' she said, Not said, but hiss'd it: „ 619
but Lionel and the girl Were *w*, *Lover's Tale iv* 14
'get them *w*' would he say. *Sisters (E. and E.)* 57
Wealth with his wines and his *w* harlots; *Vastness* 19
'I take thee Muriel for my *w* wife'— *The Ring* 377
Wedded (verb) and in one month They *w* her to sixty thousand pounds, *Edwin Morris* 126
Who *w* with a nobleman from thence: *Princess i* 77
who lay Among the ashes and *w* the King's son.' *Gareth and L.* 904
Says that Sir Gareth *w* Lyonors, „ 1428
Sir Valence *w* with an outland dame: *Merlin and V.* 714
'Queen, she would not be content Save that I *w* her, *Lancelot and E.* 1315
More specially were he, she *w*, poor, „ 1321
W her? Fought in her father's battles? *Last Tournament* 591
And all this throve before I *w* thee, *Guinevere* 484
Wedged *W* themselves in between horse and horse, *Heavy Brigade* 22
Wedlock welded in one love Than pairs of *w*; *Princess vi* 254
The boy was born in *w*, *First Quarrel* 6
Weeäk (week) But 'e reäds wonn sarmin a *w*, *N. Farmer, O. S.* 28
for thou'll be twenty to *w*. „ *N. S.* 7
Weed (dress) In words, like *w's*, I'll wrap me o'er, *In Mem. v* 9
But stagnates in the *w's* of sloth: „ *xxvii* 11
This silken rag, this beggar woman's *w*; *Geraint and E.* 680
And wears the leper's *w*? *Happy* 10
Weed (plant) (*See also* **Willow-weed**) creeping mosses and clambering *w's*, *Dying Swan* 36
At least, not rotting like a *w*, *Two Voices* 142
Crouch'd fawning in the *w*. *Œnone* 201
A spacious garden full of flowering *w's*, *To ——, With Pal. of Art* 4
Better to me the meanest *w* That blows *Amphion* 93
Athwart the smoke of burning *w's*. *Princess vii* 358
The people said, a *w*. *The Flower* 4

Weed (plant) (*continued*) again the people Call it but a w. — *The Flower* 24
Is dim, or will be dim, with w's: — *In Mem. lxxiii* 10
hurl'd it from him Among the forest w's, — *Balin and Balan* 542
'I once was looking for a magic w, — *Merlin and V.* 471
Foregoing all her sweetness, like a w. — *Holy Grail* 623
Half overtrailed with a wanton w, — *Lover's Tale i* 525
Weed (verb) brace Of twins may w her of her folly. — *Princess v* 464
As I will w this land before I go. — *Geraint and E.* 907
as now Men w the white horse on the Berkshire hills — „ 936
Weeded W and worn the ancient thatch — *Mariana* 7
Weeding Edyrn has done it, w all his heart — *Geraint and E.* 906
Weedy the wind Still westward, and the w seas— — *Columbus* 72
Week (*See also* **Weeäk**) whole w's and months, and early and late, — *The Sisters* 10
For many w's about my loins I wore — *St. S. Stylites* 63
Enoch would hold possession for a w: — *Enoch Arden* 27
There yet were many w's before she sail'd, — „ 124
In that same w when Annie buried it, — „ 271
the w Before I parted with poor Edmund; — *The Brook* 77
They lost their w's; — *Princess, Pro.* 162
harangue The fresh arrivals of the w before; — „ *ii* 96
she had nursed me there from w to w: — „ *vii* 239
'Here's a leg for a babe of a w!' — *Grandmother* 11
And the parson made it his text that w, — „ 29
Willy had not been down to the farm for a w and a day; — „ 33
'A w hence, a w hence.' — *Window, When* 9
W after w: the days go by: — *In Mem. xvii* 7
He bears the burthen of the w's — „ *lxxx* 11
Last w came one to the county town, — *Maud I x* 37
He may stay for a year who has gone for a w: — „ *xvi* 6
But in the w's that follow'd, — *Gareth and L.* 526
And all that w was old Caerleon gay, — *Marr. of Geraint* 837
many w's a troop of carrion crows Hung — *Merlin and V.* 598
for many a w Hid from the wide world's rumour — *Lancelot and E.* 521
many among us many a w Fasted and pray'd — *Holy Grail* 131
once, A w beyond, while walking on the walls — *Pelleas and E.* 225
after this, a w beyond, again She call'd them, — „ 261
Queen abode For many a w, unknown, — *Guinevere* 147
days will grow to w's, the w's to months, — „ 624
adding, with a smile, The first for many w's— — *Lover's Tale iv* 281
'I ha' six w's' work, little wife, — *First Quarrel* 45
I ha' six w's' work in Jersey — „ 88
then two w's—no more—she join'd, — *Sisters (E. and E.)* 271
for ten long w's I tried Your table of Pythagoras, — *To E. Fitzgerald* 14
all but yours—A w betwixt— — *The Ring* 249
But after ten slow w's her fix'd intent, — „ 345
after a w—no more—A stranger as welcome — *Charity* 25
Weep (*See also* **Blubber'd**) Prythee w, May Lilian! (repeat) — *Lilian* 19, 25
W on: beyond his object Love can last: His object lives: more cause to w have I: — *Wan Sculptor* 5
For while the tender service made thee w, — *The Bridesmaid* 10
Who'll w for thy deficiency? — *Two Voices* 39
Thou canst not think, but thou wilt w. — „ 51
Nay, nay, you must not w, — *May Queen, N. Y's. E.* 35
in the stream the long-leaved flowers w, — *Lotos-Eaters, C. S.* 10
I will not tell you not to w. — *To J. S.* 36
'W, weeping dulls the inward pain.' — „ 40
Let her will Be done—to w or not to w. — „ 44
The vapours w their burthen to the ground, — *Tithonus* 2
to the tears that thou wilt w. — *Locksley Hall* 82
at this The little wife would w for company, — *Enoch Arden* 34
Yes, as the dead we w for testify— — *Aylmer's Field* 747
Wiser to w a true occasion lost, — *Princess iv* 68
'She must w or she will die.' — „ *vi* 4
kiss her; take her hand, she w's: — „ 225
For this, for all, we w our thanks to thee! — *Ode Inter. Exhib.* 9
I cannot w for Willy, nor can I w for the rest; — *Grandmother* 19
For Willy I cannot w, — „ 67
I could not w—my own time seem'd so near. — „ 72
But how can I w for Willy, — „ 102
Which w a loss for ever new, — *In Mem. xiii* 5
Which w the comrade of my choice, — „ 9
And come, whatever loves to w, — „ *xviii* 11
And w the fulness from the mind: — „ *xx* 6

Weep (*continued*) At night she w's, 'How vain am I! — *In Mem. lx* 15
So mayst thou watch me where I w, — „ *lxiii* 9
He loves her yet, she will not w, — „ *xcvii* 18
not as one that w's I come once more; — „ *cxix* 2
Shall I w if a Poland fall? — *Maud I iv* 46
Till I well could w for a time so sordid and mean, — „ *v* 17
And the white rose w's, 'She is late;' — „ *xxii* 64
There to w, and w, and w My whole soul out — „ *II iv* 97
Yet now I could even w to think of it; — „ *v* 86
a light shall darken, and many shall w — „ *III vi* 43
strong passion in her made her w — *Marr. of Geraint* 110
said to his own heart, 'She w's for me': (repeat) — *Geraint and E.* 587, 590
God's curse, it makes me mad to see you w. — „ 616
were I dead who is it would w for me? — „ 618
she did not w, But o'er her meek eyes — „ 768
When sick at heart, when rather we should w. — *Balan and Balan* 498
If the wolf spare me, w my life away, — *Merlin and V.* 885
burst away To w and wail in secret; — *Lancelot and E.* 1245
'Why w ye?' 'Lord,' she said, — *Last Tournament* 494
'Yet w not thou, lest, if thy mate return, — „ 499
Sing, and unbind my heart that I may w.' — *Guinevere* 166
'O pray you, noble lady, w no more; — „ 184
they cannot w behind a cloud: — „ 207
And w for her who drew him to his doom.' — „ 348
What had *she* done to w? Why should *she* w? — *Lover's Tale i* 736
She told me all her love: she shall not w. — „ 742
When I beheld her w so ruefully; — „ 773
I felt myself ready to w For I knew not what, — *The Wreck* 51
and there I began to w, — „ 93
For all that laugh, and all that w — *Ancient Sage* 187
let me w my fill once more, and cry myself to rest! — *The Flight* 6
Mother w's At that white funeral of the single life, — *To Prin. Beatrice* 8
Weepest Wan sculptor, w thou to take the cast — *Wan Sculptor* 1
Weeping And w then she made her moan, — *Mariana in the S.* 93
And watch'd by w queens. — *Palace of Art* 108
white-eyed phantasms w tears of blood, — „ 239
'Weep, w dulls the inward pain.' — *To J. S.* 40
or fruits and cream Served in the w elm; — *Gardener's D.* 195
w, 'I have loved thee long.' — *Locksley Hall* 30
Bitterly w I turn'd away: (repeat) — *Edward Gray* 6, 34
W, w late and early, — *L. of Burleigh* 89
and departed w for him; — *Enoch Arden* 246
Then Annie w answer'd 'I am bound.' — „ 451
later in the night Had come on Psyche w: — *Princess v* 50
With a nation w, and breaking on my rest? — *Ode on Well.* 82
Within was w for thee: — *G. of Swainston* 2
And linger w on the marge, — *In Mem. xii* 12
To hear her w by his grave? — „ *xxxi* 4
A mother w, and I hear her say, — *Com. of Arthur* 334
woman w, 'Nay, my lord, The field was pleasant — *Gareth and L.* 341
W for some gay knight in Arthur's hall.' — *Marr. of Geraint* 118
A woman w for her murder'd mate — *Geraint and E.* 522
suddenly she took To bitter w like a beaten child, A long, long w, not consolable. — *Merlin and V.* 855
one lone woman, w near a cross, Stay'd him. — *Last Tournament* 493
sat There in the holy house at Almesbury W, — *Guinevere* 3
There kiss'd, and parted w: — „ 125
she look'd and saw The novice, w, — „ 664
beheld the holy nuns All round her, w; — „ 667
he was loud in w and in praise Of her, — *Lover's Tale ii* 87
He left us w in the woods; — *The Flight* 37
and w scarce could see; — *Happy* 54
Weigh before the heavy clod W's on me, — *Supp. Confessions* 185
lightly w's With thee unto the love — *Ode to Memory* 90
W heavy on my eyelids: let me die. — *Œnone* 244
flash the lightnings, w the Sun. — *Locksley Hall* 186
w Whether thou wilt not with thy damsel — *Gareth and L.* 880
w your sorrows with our lord the King's, — *Guinevere* 191
Weigh'd Why are we w upon with heaviness, — *Lotos-Eaters, C. S.* 12
heavy mist of tears, that w Upon my brain, — *Love and Duty* 43
But a trouble w upon her, — *L. of Burleigh* 77
why, the causes w, Fatherly fears— — *Princess v* 215
w the necks Of dragons clinging to the crazy walls, — *Holy Grail* 346
while I w thy heart with one Too wholly true — *Guinevere* 540
the effect w seas upon my head — *Lover's Tale i* 660

Weigh'd (*continued*) The whole land *w* him down as Ætna does — *Lover's Tale iv* 17
—his loss *W* on him yet— „ 275
single piece *W* nigh four thousand Castillanos—so They tell me—*w* him down into the abysm— *Columbus* 136
Weighest Thou *w* heavy on the heart within, *Œnone* 243
Weighing And *w* find them less ; *Guinevere* 192
Weight O happy earth, how canst thou bear my *w* ? *Œnone* 237
Make broad thy shoulders to receive my *w*, *M. d'Arthur* 164
will have *w* to drag thee down. *Locksley Hall* 48
This *w* and size, this heart and eyes, *Sir Galahad* 71
Is it the *w* of that half-crown, *Will Water.* 155
Appraised his *w* and fondled father-like, *Enoch Arden* 154
dead *w* of the dead leaf bore it down : „ 678
The *w* of all the hopes of half the world, *Princess iv* 184
Caryatids, lifted up A *w* of emblem, „ 202
their heavy hands, The *w* of destiny : „ 554
When the man wants *w*, the woman takes it up, „ *v* 444
This nightmare *w* of gratitude, „ *vi* 300
Then us they lifted up, dead *w's*, „ 348
Once the *w* and fate of Europe hung. *Ode on Well.* 240
these solid stars, this *w* of body and limb, *High. Pantheism* 5
A *w* of nerves without a mind, *In Mem. xii* 7
I loved the *w* I had to bear, „ *xxv* 7
And falling with my *w* of cares „ *lv* 14
Can hang no *w* upon my heart „ *lxiii* 3
wearing all that *w* Of learning lightly „ *Con.* 39
By a shuffled step, by a dead *w* trail'd, *Maud I i* 14
The lighter by the loss of his *w* ; „ *xvi* 2
By the loss of that dead *w*, „ *xix* 99
When *w* is added only grain by grain, *Marr. of Geraint* 526
Make broad thy shoulders to receive my *w*, *Pass. of Arthur* 332
The *w* as if of age upon my limbs, *Lover's Tale i* 125
her *w* Shrank in my grasp, „ *ii* 202
commission one of *w* and worth To judge *Columbus* 124
w of war Rides on those ringing axles ! *Tiresias* 92
noise of falling *w's* that never fell, *The Ring* 410
Less *w* now for the ladder-of-heaven *By an Evolution.* 12
and the *w* that dragg'd at my hand ; *Bandit's Death* 39
Weighted cognizance on shield *W* it down, *Balin and Balan* 225
Weightier his mind Half buried in some *w* argument, *Lucretius* 9
Weird With a *w* bright eye, sweating and trembling, *Aylmer's Field* 585
Myself too had *w* seizures, Heaven knows what : *Princess i* 14
' what, if these *w* seizures come Upon you „ 82
strange seizure came Upon me, the *w* vision of our house : „ *iii* 184
came On a sudden the *w* seizure and the doubt : „ *iv* 560
And like a flash the *w* affection came : „ *v* 477
Deeper than those *w* doubts could reach me, „ *vii* 51
Were Arthur's wars in *w* devices done, *Gareth and L.* 225
past The *w* white gate, and paused without, „ 663
That *w* yell, Unearthlier than all shriek of bird *Balin and Balan* 544
Moreover, that *w* legend of his birth, *Last Tournament* 669
Then, ere that last *w* battle in the west, *Pass. of Arthur* 29
Like this last, dim, *w* battle of the west. „ 94
And therewithal came on him the *w* rhyme, „ 444
And something *w* and wild about it all : *Lover's Tale iv* 224
W Titan by thy winter weight of years *To Victor Hugo* 7
since The key to that *w* casket, which for thee *Ancient Sage* 254
then laugh'd ' the ring is *w*.' And *w* and worn and wizard-like was he. ' Why *w* ? ' I ask'd him ; *The Ring* 195
W whispers, bells that rang without a hand, „ 411
Weirdly-sculptured And past beneath the *w-s* gates *Lancelot and E.* 844
Welcome (inter. and adj.) Should come most *w*, seeing men, *Œnone* 129
Each enter'd like a *w* guest. *Two Voices* 411
W, fellow-citizens, *Vision of Sin* 173
From Mizpeh's tower'd gate with *w* light, *D. of F. Women* 199
But she—you will be *w*—O, come in ! ' *The Brook* 228
lastly there At Christmas ; ever *w* at the Hall, *Aylmer's Field* 114
strangers at my hearth Not *w*, *Lucretius* 159
Which brings no more a *w* guest *In Mem. xxix* 5
And *w* Russian flower, a people's pride, *W. to Marie Alex.* 6
Cried to me climbing, ' *W*, Percivale ! *Holy Grail* 425
Cold, but as *w* as free airs of heaven *Sisters (E. and E.)* 197
W, *w* with one voice ! *Open. I. and C. Exhib.* 1
says to tha ' keeap 'em, an' *w* ' *Church-warden, etc.* 36

Welcome (inter. and adj.) (*continued*) A stranger as *w* as Satan— *Charity* 26
Welcome (s) And sweet shall your *w* be : *Sea-Fairies* 31
A *w* mix'd with sighs. *Talking Oak* 212
Farewell, like endless *w*, lived and died. *Love and Duty* 68
with a frolic *w* took The thunder and the sunshine, *Ulysses* 47
To greet his hearty *w* heartily ; *Enoch Arden* 350
' We give you *w* : not without redound *Princess ii* 42
glowing full-faced *w*, she Began to address us, „ 183
Less *w* find among us, if you came Among us, „ *ii* 354
W, farewell, and *w* for the year To follow : „ *Con.* 95
O give him *w*, this is he Worthy *Ode on Well.* 92
all of us Danes in our *w* of thee, *W. to Alexandra* 4
We are each all Dane in our *w* of thee, „ 33
Yet one lay-hearth would give you *w* *To F. D. Maurice* 11
They should speak to me not without a *w*, *Hendecasyllabics* 11
Received and gave him *w* there ; *In Mem. lxxxv* 24
An iron *w* when they rise : „ *xc* 8
means of goodly *w*, flesh and wine. *Marr. of Geraint* 387
Embraced her with all *w* as a friend, „ 834
In the mid-warmth of *w* and graspt hand, *Geraint and E.* 280
Sweet-voiced, a song of *w*, *Balin and Balan* 86
Witness their flowery *w*. „ 145
I bid the stranger *w*. *Merlin and V.* 270
roar An ocean-sounding *w* to one knight, *Last Tournament* 168
and loud leagues of man And *w* ! *To the Queen ii* 10
a light Of smiling *w* round her lips— *Lover's Tale iii* 46
and a noise of *w* at the doors— *Sisters (E. and E.)* 149
made the rhymes, That miss'd his living *w*, *Tiresias* 197
and flash'd into frolic of song And *w* ; *Demeter and P.* 13
where the loyal bells Clash *w*— *The Ring* 483
Many, many *w's*, February fair-maid, (repeat) *Snowdrop* 1, 9
Welcome (verb) *W* her, thunders of fort and of fleet ! *W* her, thundering cheer of the street ! *W* her, all things youthful and sweet, *W. to Alexandra* 6
W her, *w* her, all that is ours ! „ 13
Roar as the sea when he *w's* the land, And *w* her, *w* the land's desire, „ 24
And all the gentle court will *w* me, *Lancelot and E.* 1060
Up leaps the lark, gone wild to *w* her, *Prog. of Spring* 14
Welcomed Not beat him back, but *w* him *Marr. of Geraint* 748
Welded Two women faster *w* in one love *Princess vi* 253
' Sons, be *w* each and all, *Open. I. and C. Exhib.* 36
Welfare How much their *w* is a passion to us. *Princess iii* 281
' A *w* in thine eye reproves Our fear *Holy Grail* 726
In your *w* we rejoice, *Open. I. and C. Exhib.* 2
Well (adj. and adv.) Nor would I now be *w*, mother, *May Queen, Con.* 19
A pretty face is *w*, and this is *w*, *Edwin Morris* 45
'Tis *w* ; 'tis something ; we may stand *In Mem. xviii* 1
O true and tried, so *w* and long, „ *Con.* 1
O father ! O God ! was it *w* ?— *Maud I i* 6
Let all be *w*, be *w*. „ *xviii* 85
He rested *w* content that all was *w*. *Geraint and E.* 952
Speak, Lancelot, thou art silent : is it *w* ? ' *Last Tournament* 107
Sir Lancelot answer'd, ' It is *w* : „ 108
Else, for the King has will'd it, it is *w*.' „ 111
King Turn'd to him saying, ' Is it then so *w* ? „ 114
Election, Election and Reprobation—it's all very *w*. *Rizpah* 73
but I be maäin glad to seeä tha sa 'arty an' *w*. *North. Cobbler* 2
an' I knaws, as knaws tha sa *w*, „ 65
And, Robby, I niver 'a liked tha sa *w*, *Spinster's S's.* 29
or I mowt 'a liked tha sa *w*. „ 42
is it *w* to wish you joy ? Is it *w* that while we range with Science, *Locksley H., Sixty* 216
all's *w* that ends *w*, (repeat) *The Dreamer* 19, 23, 27, 32
Well (s) (*See also* **Castle-well, Dropping-wells**) As a Naiad in a *w*, Looking at the set of day. *Adeline* 16
Come from the *w's* where he did lie. *Two Voices* 9
Fresh as the foam, new-bathed in Paphian *w's*, *Œnone* 175
rope that haled the buckets from the *w*, *St. S. Stylites* 64
Fairer than Rachel by the palmy *w*, *Aylmer's Field* 679
fawn Came flying while you sat beside the *w* ? *Princess ii* 271
Or by denial flush her babbling *w's* „ *v* 334
Than if with thee the roaring *w's* *In Mem. x* 17
Or dive below the *w's* of Death ? „ *cviii* 8

Went (*continued*) as here and there that war *W* swaying ; *Com. of Arthur* 107
Gawain *w*, and breaking into song Sprang out, „ 320
'How he *w* down,' said Gareth, 'as a false knight *Gareth and L.* 5
Gareth *w*, and hovering round her chair „ 33
Before the wakeful mother heard him, *w*. „ 180
Then those who *w* with Gareth were amazed, „ 197
W sliding down so easily, and fell, „ 1224
a page Who came and *w*, and still reported „ 1338
O Prince, I *w* for Lancelot first, „ 1343
W sweating underneath a sack of corn, *Marr. of Geraint* 263
And after *w* her way across the bridge, „ 383
lords and ladies of the high court *w* „ 662
W Yniol thro' the town, „ 693
Yniol with that hard message *w* ; „ 763
Then she *w* back some paces of return, *Geraint and E.* 70
'Yea, my kind lord,' said the glad youth, and *w*, „ 241
And told them of a chamber, and they *w* ; „ 261
and then *W* slipping down horrible precipices, „ 379
W Enid with her sullen follower on. „ 440
'Enough,' he said, 'I follow,' and they *w*. „ 816
But *w* apart with Edyrn, whom he held „ 881
blameless King *w* forth and cast his eyes „ 932
he arm'd himself and *w*, *Balin and Balan* 22
So Balan warn'd, and *w* ; Balin remain'd : „ 153
Fixt in her will, and so the seasons *w*. *Merlin and V.* 188
that old man *W* back to his old wild, „ 649
two fair babes, and *w* to distant lands ; „ 707
Sir Lancelot *w* ambassador, at first, „ 774
her hand half-clench'd *W* faltering sideways downward „ 850
Her eyes and neck glittering *w* and came ; „ 960
King Glanced first at him, then her, and *w* his way. *Lancelot and E.* 95
That *if* I *w* and *if* I fought and won it „ 216
So all in wrath he got to horse and *w* ; „ 563
men *w* down before his spear at a touch, „ 578
So that he *w* sore wounded from the field : „ 600
and *w* To all the winds ?' „ 657
and carolling as he *w* A true-love ballad, „ 704
the simple maid *W* half the night repeating, „ 899
Lancelot, who coldly *w*, nor bad me one : „ 1057
Oar'd by the dumb, *w* upward with the flood— „ 1154
slowly *w* The marshall'd Order of their Table Round, „ 1331
he *w*, And at the inrunning of a little brook „ 1387
when the dead *W* wandering o'er Moriah— *Holy Grail* 50
King arose and *w* To smoke the scandalous hive „ 213
And up I *w* and touch'd him, and he, too, „ 418
That smote itself into the bread, and *w* ; „ 467
Then, when the day began to wane, we *w*. „ 488
all my heart *W* after her with longing : „ 583
And forth I *w*, and while I yearn'd and strove „ 785
To those who *w* upon the Holy Quest, „ 890
'Lead then,' she said ; and thro' the woods they *w*. *Pelleas and E.* 108
Glanced down upon her, turn'd and *w* her way. „ 185
they *w*, And Pelleas overthrew them one by one ; „ 229
w on, and found, Here too, all hush'd below „ 423
so *w* back, and seeing them yet in sleep „ 445
hill and wood *W* ever streaming by him „ 548
and shower and shorn plume *W* down it. *Last Tournament* 156
New loves are sweet as those that *w* before : „ 280
name *W* wandering somewhere darkling in his mind. „ 457
hence he *w* To-day for three days' hunting— „ 529
I sware, Being amazed : but this *w* by— „ 674
sharply smote his knees, and smiled, and *w* : *Guinevere* 47
grim faces came and *w* Before her, „ 70
W slipping back upon the golden days „ 380
W on in passionate utterance : „ 611
and past his ear *W* shrilling, 'Hollow, hollow *Pass. of Arthur* 33
w Sir Bedevere the second time Across the ridge, „ 250
And lightly *w* the other to the King. „ 315
A woful man (for so the story *w*) *Lover's Tale i* 379
those that *w* with me, And those that held „ *iii* 15
The fancy stirr'd him so He rose and *w*, „ *iv* 52
The light was but a flash, and *w* again. „ 55
but warming as he *w*, Glanced at the point of law, „ 275
And years *w* over till I that was little *First Quarrel* 27

Went (*continued*) Harry *w* over the Solent to see if work *First Quarrel* 44
an' he turn'd *his* face an' he *w*. „ 84
the boat *w* down that night— (repeat) „ 92
I kiss'd my boy in the prison, before he *w* out to die. *Rizpah* 23
she bethought herself and *w* *The Revenge* 50
the sun *w* down, and the stars came out „ 56
the night *w* down, and the sun smiled „ 70
Revenge herself *w* down by the island crags „ 118
Far off we *w*. My God, I would not live *Sisters (E. and E.)* 228
Not thaw ya *w* fur to raäke out Hell *Village Wife* 76
es soon es they *w* awaäy, Fur, lawks ! 'ow I cried when they *w*, „ 110
So he *w*. And we past to this ward *In the Child. Hosp.* 27
and we *w* to see to the child. „ 68
And round it we *w*, and thro' it, *V. of Maeldune* 19
W to his own in his own West-Saxon-land, *Batt. of Brunanburh* 103
And the storm *w* roaring above us, *The Wreck* 106
the storm and the days *w* by, but I knew no more— „ 111
stars *w* down across the gleaming pane, *The Flight* 13
How slowly down the rocks he *w*, „ 38
w in search of thee Thro' many a palace, *Demeter and P.* 54
I fetcht 'im a kick an' 'e *w*. *Owd Roä* 62
I came, I *w*, was happier day by day ; *The Ring* 348
I parted from her, and I *w* alone. „ 437
Voice of the Earth *w* wailingly past *The Dreamer* 3
Ralph *w* down like a fire to the fight *The Tourney* 3

Wept She *w*, 'I am aweary, aweary, *Mariana* 83
One willow over the river *w*, *Dying Swan* 14
Crocodiles *w* tears for thee ; *A Dirge* 22
Love *w* and spread his sheeny vans for flight ; *Love and Death* 8
A matter to be *w* with tears of blood ! *Poland* 14
Thine eyes so *w* that they could hardly see ; *The Bridesmaid* 2
I *w* 'Tho' I should die, I know *Two Voices* 58
To perish, *w* for, honour'd, known, „ 149
In her still place the morning *w* : „ 275
and took the King, and *w*. *M. d'Arthur* 206
She bow'd down And *w* in secret ; *Dora* 108
But I believe she *w*. *Talking Oak* 164
To-day I sat for an hour and *w*, *Edward Gray* 11
'Bitterly *w* I over the stone : „ 33
'A ship of fools,' he sneer'd and *w*. *The Voyage* 78
But turn'd her own toward the wall and *w*. *Enoch Arden* 283
Annie could have *w* for pity of him ; „ 467
but presently *W* like a storm : *Aylmer's Field* 403
While thus he spoke, his hearers *w* ; „ 722
her that o'er her wounded hunter *w* *Lucretius* 89
blood Was sprinkled on your kirtle, and you *w*. *Princess ii* 274
That was fawn's blood, not brother's, yet you *w*. „ 275
'My fault' she *w* 'my fault ! „ *iii* 30
She *w* her true eyes blind for such a one, „ *iv* 134
Yet she neither moved nor *w*. „ *vi* 12
Down thro' her limbs a drooping languor *w* : „ 268
I could have *w* with the best. (repeat) *Grandmother* 20, 100
I had not *w*, little Annie, not since I had been a wife ; But I *w* like a child that day, „ 63
But I *w* like a child for the child that was dead „ 68
Thou comest, much *w* for : *In Mem. xvii* 1
And silence follow'd, and we *w*. „ *xxx* 20
They *w* and wail'd, but led the way „ *ciii* 18
W over her, carved in stone ; *Maud I viii* 4
And while she *w*, and I strove to be cool, „ *II i* 15
And *w*, and wish'd that I were dead ; *Com. of Arthur* 345
all her dress *W* from her sides as water *Gareth and L.* 217
Lady Lyonors wrung her hands and *w*, „ 1395
'was it for him she *w* In Devon ?' *Geraint and E.* 397
and she *w* beside the way. „ 519
Then he remember'd her, and how she *w* ; „ 612
braid Slipt and uncoil'd itself, she *w* afresh, *Merlin and V.* 889
and for her fault she *w* Of petulancy ; „ 952
W, looking often from his face who read *Lancelot and E.* 1285
The knights and ladies *w*, and rich and poor *W*, *Holy Grail* 353
But wail'd and *w*, and hated mine own self, „ 609
To one most holy saint, who *w* and said, „ 781
he would have *w*, but felt his eyes Harder *Pelleas and E.* 506
when first she came, *w* the sad Queen. *Guinevere* 182

Wept (*continued*) her heart was loosed Within her, and she *w* *Guinevere* 668
and took the King, and *w*. *Pass. of Arthur* 374
when I *w*, Her smile lit up the rainbow on my tears, *Lover's Tale i* 253
' He casts me out,' she *w*, ' and goes ' „ *iv* 103
Edith spoke no word, She *w* no tear, *Sisters (E. and E.)* 216
Who *w* with me when I return'd in chains, *Columbus* 231
She knelt—' We worship him '—all but *w*— *Dead Prophet* 29
but I *w* alone, and sigh'd In the winter *Happy* 69
The spear of ice has *w* itself away, *Prog. of Spring* 6
In silence *w* upon the flowerless earth. *Death of Œnone* 9
he sobb'd and he *w*, And cursed himself; *Bandit's Death* 29
I *w*, and I kiss'd her hands, *Charity* 38
Wesh (wash) to *my* pond to *w* thessens theere— *Churchwarden, etc.* 14
Wesh'd (washed) Sally she *w* foälks' cloäths *North. Cobbler* 29
An' the babby's faäce wurn't *w* „ 42
Tommy's faäce be as fresh as a codlin *w* i' the dew. „ 110
Fur they *w* their sins i' *my* pond, *Church-warden, etc.* 16
West (adj.) Four courts I made, East, *W* and South and North, *Palace of Art* 21
wet *w* wind and the world will go on. (repeat) *Window, No Answer* 6, 12
Wet *w* wind how you blow, you blow! „ 14
wet *w* wind and the world may go on. „ 18
why, you shiver tho' the wind is *w* *The Ring* 29
West (s) (*See also* **South-west**) sunset linger'd low adown In the red *W*: *Lotos-Eaters* 20
Across a hazy glimmer of the *w*, *Gardener's D.* 219
Orion sloping slowly to the *W*. *Locksley Hall* 8
The blaze upon the waters to the *w*; *Enoch Arden* 596
Here in the woman-markets of the *w*, *Aylmer's Field* 348
Till all the sails were darken'd in the *w*, *Sea Dreams* 39
Nor stunted squaws of *W* or East; *Princess ii* 78
Silver sails all out of the *w* „ *iii* 14
and half Far-shadowing from the *w*, „ *Con.* 42
and a feast Of wonder, out of *W* and East, *Ode Inter. Exhib.* 21
So now thy fuller life is in the *w*, *W. to Marie Alex.* 36
voices go To North, South, East, and *W*; *Voice and the P.* 14
Flown to the east or the *w*, *Window, Gone* 7
And topples round the dreary *w*, *In Mem. xv* 19
By that broad water of the *w*, „ *lxvii* 3
And East and *W*, without a breath, „ *xcv* 62
Rosy is the *W*, Rosy is the South, (repeat) *Maud I xvii* 5, 25
Blush it thro' the *W*; (repeat) „ 16, 24
Blush from *W* to East, Blush from East to *W*, Till the *W* is East, „ 21
Orion's grave low down in the *w*, „ *III vi* 8
Will there be dawn in *W* and eve in East? *Gareth and L.* 712
All in a rose-red from the *w*, „ 1087
he saw Fired from the *w*, far on a hill, *Lancelot and E.* 168
The flower of all the *w* and all the world, „ 249
knights of utmost North and *W*, „ 526
And also one to the *w*, and counter to it, And blank: *Holy Grail* 254
Rode Tristram toward Lyonnesse and the *w*. *Last Tournament* 362
Far on into the rich heart of the *w*: *Guinevere* 244
Far down to that great battle in the *w*, „ 571
ere that last weird battle in the *w*, *Pass. of Arthur* 29
I hear the steps of Modred in the *w*, „ 59
' Far other is this battle in the *w* Whereto we move, „ 66
this last, dim, weird battle of the *w*. „ 94
forego The darkness of that battle in the *W*, *To the Queen ii* 65
Mixt with the gorgeous *w* the lighthouse shone, *Lover's Tale i* 60
Framing the mighty landscape to the *w*, „ 406
All the *w* And ev'n unto the middle south „ 414
Ran amber toward the *w*, and nigh the sea „ 432
Far from out the *w* in shadowing showers, *Sisters (E. and E.)* 7
made *W* East, and sail'd the Dragon's mouth, *Columbus* 25
a door for scoundrel scum I open'd to the *W*, „ 171
till the labourless day dipt under the *W*; *V. of Maeldune* 86
we watch'd the sun fade from us thro' the *W*. *The Flight* 41
And see the ships from out the *W* „ 91
And behind him, low in the *W*, *Dead Prophet* 20
Here silent in our Minster of the *W* *Epit. on Stratford* 3
That young eagle of the *W* *Open. I. and C. Exhib.* 28
The golden keys of East and *W*. *To Marq. of Dufferin* 4
she lent The sceptres of her *W*, her East, „ 6
hoary deeps that belt the changeful *W*, *Prog. of Spring* 98

West (s) (*continued*) drowsed in gloom, self-darken'd from the *w*, *Death of Œnone* 76
' Is earth On fire to the *W*? *St. Telemachus* 19
shape with wings Came sweeping by him, and pointed to the *W*, „ 25
Western day Was sloping toward his *w* bower. *Mariana* 80
baths Of all the *w* stars, until I die. *Ulysses* 61
Wind of the *w* sea, (repeat) *Princess iii* 2, 4
West-Indian lands at home and abroad in a rich *W-I* isle; *The Wreck* 46
West Indies *See* **Indies**
West-Saxon-land Went to his own in his own *W-S-l*, *Batt. of Brunanburh* 103
West-Saxons We the *W-S*, „ 37
Westward gloomy-gladed hollow slowly sink To *w*— *Gareth and L.* 798
For on their march to *w*, Bedivere, *Pass. of Arthur* 6
and the wind Still *w*, and the weedy seas— *Columbus* 72
There *w*—under yon slow-falling star, *Akbar's Dream* 152
Westward-smiling far-rolling, *w-s* seas, *Last Tournament* 587
Westward-wheeling sphere Of *w-w* stars; *St. Telemachus* 32
Westward-winding From the *w-w* flood, *Margaret* 9
Wet (adj.) (*See also* **Spongy-wet**) Thro' crofts and pastures *w* with dew *Two Voices* 14
Eyes with idle tears are *w*. *Miller's D.* 211
I am *w* With drenching dews, *St. S. Stylites* 114
Who sweep the crossings, *w* or dry, *Will Water.* 47
so that falling prone he dug His fingers into the *w* earth, *Enoch Arden* 780
Made *w* the crafty crowsfoot round his eye; *Sea Dreams* 187
my Sire, his rough cheek *w* with tears, *Princess v* 23
The leaves were *w* with women's tears: „ *vi* 39
I saw his eyes all *w*, in the sweet moonshine: *Grandmother* 49
w west wind and the world will go on. (repeat) *Window, No Answer* 6, 12
W west wind how you blow, you blow! „ 14
w west wind and the world may go on. „ 18
often I caught her with eyes all *w*, *Maud I xix* 23
Thick with *w* woods, and many a beast therein, *Com. of Arthur* 21
came a forester of Dean, *W* from the woods, *Marr. of Geraint* 149
Made answer, either eyelid *w* with tears: *Merlin and V.* 379
Brake with a *w* wind blowing, Lancelot, *Last Tournament* 137
W with the mists and smitten by the lights, *Guinevere* 597
he was all *w* thro' to the skin, *First Quarrel* 76
hand of the Highlander *w* with their tears! *Def. of Lucknow* 102
These *w* black passes and foam-churning chasms— *Sir J. Oldcastle* 9
dhry eye thin but was *w* for the frinds that was gone! *Tomorrow* 83
Wet (s) The wind and the *w*, the wind and the *w*! *Window, No Answer* 13
Woods where we hid from the *w*, „ *Marr. Morn.* 6
day Went glooming down in *w* and weariness: *Last Tournament* 215
An' I never said ' off wi' the *w*,' *First Quarrel* 77
I soaking here in winter *w*— *To Ulysses* 6
Wether Or some black *w* of St. Satan's fold. *Merlin and V.* 750
Wet-shod Came *w-s* alder from the wave, *Amphion* 41
Wharf Out upon the *w's* they came, *L. of Shalott iv* 42
red roofs about a narrow *w* In cluster; *Enoch Arden* 3
Down to the pool and narrow *w* he went, „ 690
famishing populace, *wharves* forlorn; *Vastness* 14
Whate (wheat) ' Goin' to cut the Sassenach *w* ' *Tomorrow* 14
' niver crasst over say to the Sassenach *w*; „ 48
betther nor cuttin' the Sassenach *w* „ 94
What's my thought *w m t* and *when* and *where* and *how*, *Princess, Pro.* 190
Whatsoever For *w* knight against us came *Balin and Balan* 35
Wheat (*See also* **Whate, Wheät**) Storing yearly little dues of *w*, and wine and oil; *Lotos-Eaters, C. S.* 122
I will set him in my uncle's eye Among the *w*; *Dora* 68
and went her way Across the *w*, „ 72
And waves of shadow went over the *w*, *Poet's Song* 4
Half-lost in belts of hop and breadths of *w*; *Princess, Con.* 45
Upon the thousand waves of *w*, *In Mem. xci* 11
and go By summer belts of *w* and vine „ *xcviii* 4
Thou that singest *w* and woodland, *To Virgil* 9
torpid mummy *w* Of Egypt bore a grain as sweet *To Prof. Jebb* 5
Rain-rotten died the *w*, the barley-spears *Demeter and P.* 112
Wheät sa much es a poppy along wi' the *w*, *Spinster's S's.* 78
if the Staäte was a gawin' to let in furriners' *w*, *Owd Roä* 45

Wheat-suburb sweet-smelling lanes Of his *w-s*, *The Brook* 123
Wheedle And *w* a world that loves him not, *Maud II v* 39
Wheedling *W* and siding with them! *Princess v* 158
Wheel (s) (*See also* **Mill-wheel**) The dark round of the dripping *w*, *Miller's D.* 102
all the *w's* of Time Spun round in station, *Love and Duty* 75
And thee returning on thy silver *w's*. *Tithonus* 76
men, that in the flying of a *w* Cry down the past, *Godiva* 6
power to turn This *w* within my head, *Will Water.* 84
land, where under the same *w* The same old rut *Aylmer's Field* 33
That stays the rolling Ixionian *w*, *Lucretius* 261
The common hate with the revolving *w* *Princess vi* 173
And he call'd 'Left *w* into line!' *Heavy Brigade* 6
Loom and *w* and enginery, *Ode Inter. Exhib.* 15
I stay'd the *w's* at Cogoletto, *The Daisy* 23
I see the sailor at the *w*. *In Mem. x* 4
And all the *w's* of Being slow. „ *l* 4
And every kiss of toothed *w's*, „ *cxvii* 11
The last *w* echoes away. *Maud I xxii* 26
And the roaring of the *w's*. „ *II iv* 22
And the *w's* go over my head, „ *v* 4
song that Enid sang was one Of Fortune and her *w*, *Marr. of Geraint* 346
'Turn, Fortune, turn thy *w* and lower the proud; „ 347
Turn thy wild *w* thro' sunshine, storm, and cloud; „ 348
Thy *w* and thee we neither love nor hate. (repeat) „ 349, 358
'Turn, Fortune, turn thy *w* with smile or frown; „ 350
With that wild *w* we go not up or down; „ 351
'Turn, turn thy *w* above the staring crowd; „ 356
Thy *w* and thou are shadows in the cloud; „ 357
I heard *W's*, and a noise of welcome at the doors— *Sisters (E. and E.)* 149
And lay thine uphill shoulder to the *w*, *Ancient Sage* 279
a shatter'd *w*? a vicious boy! *Locksley H., Sixty* 215
and see no more The Stone, the *W*, *Demeter and P.* 150
Or spinning at your *w* beside the vine— *Romney's R.* 5
WE move, the *w* must always move, *Politics* 1
Wheel (verb) Too long you roam and *w* at will; *Rosalind* 36
And *w's* the circled dance, *In Mem. xcviii* 30
Unto the thundersong that *w's* the spheres, *Lover's Tale i* 476
That *w* between the poles. *Epilogue* 21
round her forehead *w's* the woodland dove, *Prog. of Spring* 57
Wheel'd (*See also* **Low-wheel'd**) clutch'd the sword, And strongly *w* and threw it. *M. d'Arthur* 136
Earth follows *w* in her ellipse; *Golden Year* 24
Sometimes the sparhawk, *w* along, *Sir L. and Q. G.* 12
Bear had *w* Thro' a great arc his seven slow suns. *Princess iv* 212
bats *w*, and owls whoop'd, „ *Con.* 110
w on Europe-shadowing wings, *Ode on Well.* 120
w or lit the filmy shapes That haunt the dusk, *In Mem. xcv* 10
W round on either heel, Dagonet replied, *Last Tournament* 244
w and broke Flying, and link'd again, and *w* and broke Flying, *Guinevere* 257
clutch'd the sword, And strongly *w* and threw it. *Pass. of Arthur* 304
planet at length will be *w* thro' the silence of space, *Despair* 83
and they *w* and obey'd. *Heavy Brigade* 6
Wheeling (*See also* **Westward-wheeling**) with both hands I flung him, *w* him; *M. d'Arthur* 157
w round The central wish, *Gardener's D.* 224
The myriad shriek of *w* ocean-fowl, *Enoch Arden* 583
W with precipitate paces To the melody, *Vision of Sin* 37
eddied into suns, that *w* cast The planets: *Princess ii* 118
with both hands I flung him, *w* him; *Pass. of Arthur* 325
Glance at the *w* Orb of change, *To E. Fitzgerald* 3
Whelm or to *w* All of them in one massacre? *Lucretius* 206
And *w* all this beneath as vast a mound *Merlin and V.* 656
Whelm'd Roll'd a sea-haze and *w* the world in gray; *Enoch Arden* 672
some were *w* with missiles of the wall, *Princess, Pro.* 45
Whelp (*See also* **Lion-whelp**) bones for his o'ergrown *w* to crack; *Maud II v* 55
Whelpless glaring with his *w* eye, Silent; *Princess vi* 99
When and where and how *what's my thought* and *when* and *where* and *how*, „ *Pro.* 190
Whens Break into 'Thens' and '*W*' *Ancient Sage* 104
Wherewithal having *w*, And in the fallow leisure of my life *Audley Court* 76
Wherewithal (*continued*) for the *w* To give his babes a better bringing-up *Enoch Arden* 298
Whiff yonder, *w*! there comes a sudden heat, *Princess, Con.* 58
Whig Let *W* and Tory stir their blood; *Will Water.* 53
While we might make it worth his *w*. *Princess i* 184
'Twere hardly worth my *w* to choose *In Mem. xxxiv* 10
Bide ye here the *w*.' *Merlin and V.* 97
Pelleas in brief *w* Caught his unbroken limbs *Pelleas and E.* 584
Whim hurt to death, For your wild *w*: *Princess vi* 243
Whimper Who love her still, and *w*, *Romney's R.* 117
Whimpering then A *w* of the spirit of the child, *Last Tournament* 418
Whine (s) colt-like whinny and with hoggish *w* *St. S. Stylites* 177
Whine (verb) I that heard her *w* And snivel, *Last Tournament* 449
Whined ghost, that shook The curtains, *w* in lobbies, *Walk. to the Mail* 37
canker'd boughs without *W* in the wood; *Balin and Balan* 346
and old boughs, *W* in the wood. „ 386
Whinny colt-like *w* and with hoggish whine *St. S. Stylites* 177
her *w* shrills From tile to scullery, *Princess v* 452
and stoop'd With a low *w* toward the pair: *Geraint and E.* 756
Whinnying At which her palfrey *w* lifted heel, „ 533
thence The shrilly *w's* of the team of Hell, *Demeter and P.* 44
Whip Stopt, and then with a riding *w* *Maud I xiii* 18
Struck at her with his *w*, (repeat) *Marr. of Geraint* 201, 413
Struck at him with his *w*, and cut his cheek. „ 207
Up hill 'Too-slow' will need the *w*, *Politics* 11
Whipt And *w* me into the waste fields far away; *Holy Grail* 788
I *w* him for robbing an orchard once *Rizpah* 25
Whirl (s) Ran into its giddiest *w* of sound, *Vision of Sin* 29
sway and *w* Of the storm dropt to windless calm, *Lover's Tale ii* 206
Whirl (verb) My judgment, and my spirit *w's*, *Supp. Confessions* 137
There the river eddy *w's*, *L. of Shalott ii* 15
I *w* like leaves in roaring wind. *Fatima* 7
while Saturn *w's*, his stedfast shade *Palace of Art* 15
W's her to me: but will she fling herself, *Lucretius* 202
And *w* the ungarner'd sheaf afar, *In Mem lxxii* 23
w the dust of harlots round and round *Pelleas and E.* 470
watch the chariot *w* About the goal again, *Tiresias* 176
I *w*, and I follow the Sun.' *The Dreamer* 14
W, and follow the Sun! (repeat) „ 20, 24, 28, 32
Whirl'd No sword Of wrath her right arm *w*, *The Poet* 54
heavy-plunging foam, *W* by the wind, *D. of F. Women* 119
flashing round and round, and *w* in an arch, *M. d'Arthur* 138
w her white robe like a blossom'd branch *Princess iv* 179
She *w* them on to me, as who should say „ 396
like the smoke in a hurricane *w* *Boädicea* 59
The last red leaf is *w* away, *In Mem. xv* 3
and *w* About empyreal heights of thought, „ *xcv* 37
heart of the poet is *w* into folly and vice. *Maud I iv* 39
Pine Lost footing, fell, and so was *w* away. *Gareth and L.* 4
flashing round and round, and *w* in an arch, *Pass. of Arthur* 306
we *w* giddily; the wind Sung; *Lover's Tale ii* 201
An open landaulet *W* by, which, *Sisters (E. and E.)* 86
W for a million æons thro' the vast Waste dawn *De Prof., Two G.* 3
full-maned horses *w* The chariots backward, *Achilles over the T.* 24
Whirligig As on this *w* of Time We circle *Will Water.* 63
Whirling All their planets *w* round them, *Locksley H., Sixty* 204
Yet in the *w* dances as we went, *The form, the form* 5
Flash in the pools of *w* Simois. *Œnone* 206
part were drown'd within the *w* brook: *Princess, Pro.* 47
w rout Led by those two rush'd into dance, *Lover's Tale iii* 54
phantom of the *w* landaulet For ever past me by: *Sisters (E. and E.)* 114
W their sabres in circles of light! *Heavy Brigade* 34
Whirlwind the echoing dance Of reboant *w's*, *Supp. Confessions* 97
And loud the Norland *w's* blow, *Oriana* 6
And a *w* clear'd the larder: *The Goose* 52
Across the *w's* heart of peace, *The Voyage* 87
And bring her in a *w*: *Princess i* 65
Like the leaf in a roaring *w*, *Boädicea* 59
A moment, ere the onward *w* shatter it, *Lover's Tale i* 451
round and round A *w* caught and bore us; „ *ii* 197
a *w* blow these woods, as never blew before. *The Flight* 12
Whirr *See* **Dorhawk-whirr**
Whirring And the *w* sail goes round, (repeat) *The Owl i* 4, 5
Whishper (whisper) (s) laste little *w* was sweet as the lilt of a bird! *Tomorrow* 33

Whishper (verb) the crathur, an' *w*, an' say *Tomorrow* 54
Whisker his watery smile And educated *w*. *Edwin Morris* 129
Ay, roob thy *w's* ageän ma, *Spinster's S's.* 81
Whisky *See* **Crathur'**
Whisper (s) (*See also* **Love-whispers, Whishper, World-whisper**) She has heard a *w* say, *L. of Shalott ii* 3
A little *w* silver-clear, *Two Voices* 428
A hint, a *w* breathing low, „ 434
Such seem'd the *w* at my side : „ 439
In *w's*, like the *w's* of the leaves *Gardener's D.* 253
And her *w* throng'd my pulses *Locksley Hall* 36
w of the south-wind rushing warm, „ 125
a *w* on her ear, She knew not what ; *Enoch Arden* 515
w of huge trees that branch'd And blossom'd „ 585
Again in deeper inward *w's* ' lost ! ' „ 716
A *w* half reveal'd her to herself. *Aylmer's Field* 144
But honeying at the *w* of a lord ; *Princess, Pro.* 115
shook the songs, the *w's*, and the shrieks „ *i* 98
o'er the imperial tent *W's* of war. „ *v* 10
Would lisp in honey'd *w's* of this monstrous fraud ! *Third of Feb.* 36
and my prayer Was as the *w* of an air *In Mem. xvii* 3
And shape the *w* of the throne ; „ *lxiv* 12
In *w's* of the beauteous world. „ *lxxix* 12
This haunting *w* makes me faint, „ *lxxxi* 7
And lightly does the *w* fall ; „ *lxxxv* 89
world's loud *w* breaking into storm, *Marr. of Geraint* 27
all hearts Applauded, and the spiteful *w* died : *Geraint and E.* 958
Breathed in a dismal *w* ' It is truth.' *Balin and Balan* 527
He spoke in words part heard, in *w's* part, *Merlin and V.* 839
whose lightest *w* moved him more *Pelleas and E.* 155
A murmuring *w* thro' the nunnery ran, *Guinevere* 410
Save for some *w* of the seething seas, *Pass. of Arthur* 121
Falling in *w's* on the sense, *Lover's Tale i* 720
the surge fell From thunder into *w's* ; „ *iii* 31
Surely, but for a *w*, ' Go not yet,' „ *iv* 20
He knew the meaning of the *w* now, „ 43
But his friend Replied, in half a *w*, „ 336
Not to break in on what I say by word Or *w*, „ 353
There was a *w* among us, but only a *w* *Def. of Lucknow* 50
thro' the roar of the breaker a *w*, *Despair* 13
A breath, a *w*—some divine farewell— *Ancient Sage* 225
Weird *w's*, bells that rang without a hand, *The Ring* 411
A *w* from his dawn of life ? *Far—far—away* 10
And at his ear he heard a *w* ' Rome ' *St. Telemachus* 26
Whisper (verb) (*See also* **Whishper**) all day long you sit between Joy and woe, and *w* each. *Margaret* 64
And at my headstone *w* low, *My life is full* 24
Listening, *w's* ' 'Tis the fairy Lady of Shalott.' *L. of Shalott i* 35
While those full chestnuts *w* by. *Miller's D.* 168
The trees began to *w*, and the wind began to roll, *May Queen, Con.* 27
Not *w*, any murmur of complaint. *St. S. Stylites* 22
O *w* to your glass, and say, *Day-Dm., Ep.* 3
And *w* lovely words, and use Her influence *Will Water.* 11
In her ear he *w's* gaily, *L. of Burleigh* 1
Heard the good mother softly *w* *Aylmer's Field* 187
W in odorous heights of even. *Milton* 16
What *w's* from thy lying lip ? *In Mem. iii* 4
' The stars,' she *w's*, ' blindly run ; „ 5
And hear thy laurel *w* sweet „ *xxxvii* 7
A hundred spirits *w* ' Peace.' „ *lxxxvi* 16
One *w's*, ' Here thy boyhood sung „ *cii* 9
And *w's* to the worlds of space, „ *cxxvi* 11
We *w*, and hint, and chuckle, *Maud I iv* 29
And the lily *w's*, ' I wait.' „ *xxii* 66
Sweet lord, ye do right well to *w* this. *Balin and Balan* 529
Edith pray'd me not to *w* of it. *Sisters (E. and E.)* 207
She *w's*, ' From the South I bring you balm, *Prog. of Spring* 66
I hear a death-bed Angel *w* ' Hope.' *Romney's R.* 148
Whisper'd (adj. and part.) (*See also* **Half-whisper'd**)
To hear each other's *w* speech ; *Lotos-Eaters, C. S.* 59
and they suffer—some, 'tis *w*—down in hell „ 123
Thou shalt hear the ' Never, never,' *w* by the phantom years, *Locksley Hall* 83
And *w* voices at his ear. *Day-Dm., Arrival* 24
A *w* jest to some one near him, ' Look, *Princess v* 32
Whisper'd (adj. and part.) (*continued*) By a shuffled step, by a dead weight trail'd, by a *w* fright, *Maud I i* 14
Love drew in her breath In that close kiss, and drunk her *w* tales. *Lover's Tale i* 817
Whisper'd (verb) She *w*, with a stifled moan *Mariana in the S.* 57
what he *w* under Heaven None else could understand ; *Talking Oak* 21
W, ' Listen to my despair : *Edward Gray* 22
Cyril *w* ; ' Take me with you too.' *Princess i* 81
no livelier than the dame That *w* ' Asses' ears,' „ *ii* 113
' Come,' he *w* to her ' Lift up your head, „ *v* 63
What *w* from her lying lips ? *In Mem. xxxix* 10
' The fault was mine,' he *w*, ' fly ! ' *Maud II i* 30
For I never *w* a private affair „ *v* 47
Lifted an arm, and softly *w*, ' There.' *Gareth and L.* 1361
sat, heard, watch'd And *w* : thro' the peaceful court she crept And *w* : *Merlin and V* . 139
Or *w* in the corner ? do ye know it ? ' „ 772
half-awake he *w*, ' Where ? O where ? *Pelleas and E.* 41
For all that ample woodland *w* ' debt,' *The Ring* 170
Who *w* me ' your Ulric loves '— *Happy* 62
Master *w* ' Follow the Gleam.' *Merlin and the G.* 33
I *w* ' give it to me,' but he would not *Bandit's Death* 27
Whisperer and the swarm Of female *w's* : *Princess vi* 356
Whispering within the cave Behind yon *w* tuft of oldest pine, *Œnone* 88
beneath a *w* rain Night slid down one long stream *Gardener's D.* 266
Or low morass and *w* reed, *In Mem. c* 6
these few lanes of elm And *w* oak. *To Mary Boyle* 68
W to each other half in fear, *Sea-Fairies* 5
Two lovers *w* by an orchard wall ; *Circumstance* 4
W I knew not what of wild and sweet, *Tithonus* 61
or, *w*, play'd A chequer-work of beam *In Mem. lxxii* 14
turn'd to each other, *w*, all dismay'd, *Heavy Brigade* 44
Whistle (s) Scarce answer to my *w* ; *Amphion* 68
And bustling *w* of the youth *Marr. of Geraint* 257
great plover's human *w* amazed Her heart, *Geraint and E.* 49
Whistle (verb) *W* back the parrot's call, *Locksley Hall* 171
Then would he *w* rapid as any lark, *Gareth and L.* 505
But if my neighbour *w* answers him— *Lover's Tale iv* 161
Whistled waterflags, That *w* stiff and dry about the marge. *M. d'Arthur* 64
redcap *w* ; and the nightingale Sang loud, *Gardener's D.* 95
Then low and sweet I *w* thrice ; *Edwin Morris* 113
Sometimes the throstle *w* strong : *Sir L. and Q. G.* 11
flour From his tall mill that *w* on the waste. *Enoch Arden* 343
And *w* to the morning star. *Sailor Boy* 4
And while he *w* long and loud „ 5
Prison'd, and kept and coax'd and *w* to— *Gareth and L.* 14
He *w* his good warhorse left to graze *Last Tournament* 490
waterflags, That *w* stiff and dry about the marge. *Pass. of Arthur* 232
Whistling *W* a random bar of Bonny Doon, *The Brook* 82
But blessed forms in *w* storms *Sir Galahad* 59
Half *w* and half singing a coarse song, *Geraint and E.* 528
Whit Not a *w* of thy tuwhoo, *The Owl ii* 10
And *w*, *w*, *w*, in the bush beside me *Grandmother* 40
and never a *w* more wise The fourth, *Gareth and L.* 635
White (adj.) *See also* **Cold-white, Death-white, Dusty-white, Lily-white, May-white, Milk-white, Milky-white, Rosy-white, Snow-white, Vermeil-white, Winter-white**)
And *w* against the cold-white sky, *Dying Swan* 12
One after another the *w* clouds are fleeting ; *All Things will Die* 5
In the *w* curtain, to and fro, *Mariana* 51
The *w* owl in the belfry sits. (repeat) *The Owl i* 7, 14
Flinging the gloom of yesternight On the *w* day ; *Ode to Memory* 10
A pillar of *w* light upon the wall Of purple cliffs, „ 53
thick with *w* bells the clover-hill swells *Sea-Fairies* 14
The *w* chalk-quarry from the hill *Miller's D.* 115
The lanes, you know, were *w* with may, „ 130
I'd touch her neck so warm and *w*. „ 174
All barr'd with long *w* cloud the scornful crags, *Palace of Art* 83
her hair Wound with *w* roses, slept St. Cecily ; „ 99
seas draw backward from the land Their moon-led waters *w*. „ 252
Till Charles's Wain came out above the tall *w* chimney-tops. *May Queen, N. Y's. E.* 12

White (adj.) (*continued*) Two handfuls of *w* dust, shut in an urn of brass ! — *Lotos-Eaters, C. S.* 68
W surf wind-scatter'd over sails and masts, — *D. of F. Women* 31
'I would the *w* cold heavy-plunging foam, — „ 118
'The light *w* cloud swam over us. — „ 221
We saw the large *w* stars rise one by one, — „ 223
With that sharp sound the *w* dawn's creeping beams, — „ 261
She caught the *w* goose by the leg, — *The Goose* 9
more the *w* goose laid It clack'd and cackled louder. — „ 23
Clothed in *w* samite, mystic, wonderful, (repeat) — *M. d'Arthur* 31, 144, 159
for all his face was *w* And colourless, — „ 212
Love's *w* star Beam'd thro' the thicken'd cedar — *Gardener's D.* 165
As clean and *w* as privet when it flowers. — *Walk. to the Mail* 56
The meed of saints, the *w* robe and the palm. — *St. S. Stylites* 20
I lived In the *w* convent down the valley there, — „ 62
As these *w* robes are soil'd and dark, — *St. Agnes' Eve* 13
In raiment *w* and clean. — „ 24
or following up And flying the *w* breaker, — *Enoch Arden* 21
Enoch's *w* horse, and Enoch's ocean-spoil — „ 93
And York's *w* rose as red as Lancaster's, — *Aylmer's Field* 51
Nor ever falls the least *w* star of snow, — *Lucretius* 107
Morn in the *w* wake of the morning star — *Princess iii* 17
saw The soft *w* vapour streak the crowned towers — „ 344
There whirl'd her *w* robe like a blossom'd branch — „ *iv* 179
Her round *w* shoulder shaken with her sobs, — „ 289
Here he reach'd *W* hands of farewell to my sire, — „ *v* 233
very nape of her *w* neck Was rosed with indignation : — „ *vi* 343
'Now sleeps the crimson petal, now the *w* ; — „ *vii* 176
Nor wilt thou snare him in the *w* ravine, — „ 205
A red sail, or a *w* ; and far beyond, — „ *Con.* 47
Ruddy and *w*, and strong on his legs, he looks like a man. — *Grandmother* 2
We loved that hall, tho' *w* and cold, — *The Daisy* 37
All along the valley, stream that flashest *w*, — *V. of Cauteretz* 1
With blasts that blow the poplar *w*, — *In Mem. lxxii* 3
The *w* kine glimmer'd, and the trees (repeat) — „ *xcv* 15, 51
Has a broad-blown comeliness, red and *w*, — *Maud I xiii* 9
if a hand, as *w* As ocean-foam in the moon, — „ *xiv* 17
The *w* lake-blossom fell into the lake — „ *xxii* 47
And the *w* rose weeps, 'She is late ;' — „ 64
It lightly winds and steals In a cold *w* robe before me, — „ *II iv* 19
Wearing the *w* flower of a blameless life, — *Ded. of Idylls* 25
Clothed in *w* samite, mystic, wonderful. — *Com. of Arthur* 285
'Blow trumpet, for the world is *w* with May ; — „ 482
reverence thine own beard That looks as *w* as utter truth, — *Gareth and L.* 281
Our one *w* lie sits like a little ghost — „ 297
plant that feels itself Root-bitten by *w* lichen, — „ 454
past The weird *w* gate, and paused without, — „ 663
With *w* breast-bone, and barren ribs of Death, — „ 1382
often with her own *w* hands Array'd and deck'd her, — *Marr. of Geraint* 16
W from the mason's hand, (repeat) — „ 244, 408
Then, as the *w* and glittering star of morn — „ 734
And *w* sails flying on the yellow sea ; — „ 829
Betwixt the cressy islets *w* in flower ; — *Geraint and E.* 475
she Kiss'd the *w* star upon his noble front, — „ 757
Men weed the *w* horse on the Berkshire hills — „ 936
and paced The long *w* walk of lilies toward the bower. — *Balin and Balan* 249
as makes The *w* swan-mother, sitting, — „ 353
and dim thro' leaves Blinkt the *w* morn, — „ 385
And mumbled that *w* hand whose ring'd caress — „ 512
whose lightest word Is mere *w* truth in simple nakedness, — „ 518
O Heaven's own *w* Earth-angel, — *Merlin and V.* 80
As clean as blood of babes, as *w* as milk : — „ 344
Ran down the silken thread to kiss each other On her *w* neck— — „ 456
A maid so smooth, so *w*, so wonderful, — „ 566
Is thy *w* blamelessness accounted blame !' — „ 799
bare-grinning skeleton of death ! *W* was her cheek ; — „ 848
Rang by the *w* mouth of the violent Glem ; — *Lancelot and E.* 288
When the strong neighings of the wild *w* Horse — „ 298

White (adj.) (*continued*) In the *w* rock a chapel and a hall On massive columns, — *Lancelot and E.* 405
And innocently extending her *w* arms, — „ 932
Till all the *w* walls of my cell were dyed — *Holy Grail* 119
ever moved Among us in *w* armour, Galahad. — „ 135
dyed The strong *W* Horse in his own heathen blood— — „ 312
Not to be bound, save by *w* bonds and warm, — *Pelleas and E.* 353
up a slope of garden, all Of roses *w* and red, — „ 422
in her *w* arms Received, and after loved it tenderly, — *Last Tournament* 23
down a streetway hung with folds of pure *W* samite, — „ 141
Isolt the *w*—Sir Tristram of the Woods— — „ 177
Our one *w* day of Innocence hath past, — „ 218
The twelve small damosels *w* as Innocence, — „ 291
one of those *w* slips Handed her cup and piped, — „ 295
'Isolt Of the *w* hands' they call'd her : — „ 398
Who served him well with those *w* hands of hers, — „ 400
Is all as cool and *w* as any flower.' — „ 416
there Belted his body with her *w* embrace, — „ 513
Calling me thy *w* hind, and saying to me — „ 569
The warm *w* apple of her throat, — „ 717
The *w* mist, like a face-cloth to the face, — *Guinevere* 7
And in the light the *w* mermaiden swam, — „ 245
aghast the maiden rose, *W* as her veil, — „ 363
who leagues With Lords of the *W* Horse, heathen, — „ 574
when the man was no more than a voice In the *w* winter of his age, — *Pass. of Arthur* 4
Clothed in *w* samite, mystic, wonderful, (repeat) — „ 199, 312, 327
for all his face was *w* And colourless, — „ 380
W as *w* clouds, floated from sky to sky. — *Lover's Tale i* 5
Or when the *w* heats of the blinding noons — „ 139
A mystic light flash'd ev'n from her *w* robe — „ 370
then came in The *w* light of the weary moon above, — „ 640
But the boy was born i' trouble, an' looks so wan an' so *w* : — *First Quarrel* 2
I niver ha seed it sa *w* wi' the Maäy es I see'd it to-year— — *Village Wife* 80
Fur I thowt it wur Charlie's ghoäst i' the derk, fur it looökt sa *w*. — „ 82
Blessing the wholesome *w* faces of Havelock's good fusileers, — *Def. of Lucknow* 101
And a hundred ranged on the rock like *w* sea-birds — *V. of Maeldune* 101
And his *w* hair sank to his heels and his *w* beard fell to his feet, — „ 118
Not here ! the *w* North has thy bones ; — *Sir J. Franklin* 1
The broad *w* brow of the Isle— — *The Wreck* 135
the hills are *w* with rime. — *The Flight* 4
all my life was darken'd, as I saw the *w* sail run, — „ 39
an' her hair was as *w* as the snow an a grave. — *Tomorrow* 60
All in *w* Italian marble, looking still as if she smiled, — *Locksley H., Sixty* 35
Mother weeps At that *w* funeral of the single life, — *Prin. Beatrice* 9
dwell For nine *w* moons of each whole year with me, — *Demeter and P.* 121
Of a Christmas Eäve, an' as cowd as this, an' the midders as *w*, — *Owd Roä* 31
Flies back in fragrant breezes to display A tunic *w* as May ! — *Prog. of Spring* 65
And find the *w* heather wherever you go, — *Romney's R.* 108
my *w* heather only blooms in heaven — „ 110
And on this *w* midwinter day— — *To Master of B.* 9
But when the *w* fog vanish'd like a ghost — *Death of Œnone* 67
And now that I am *w*, and you are gray, — *Roses on the T.* 4

White (s) (*See also* **May-white**) Lying, robed in snowy *w* — *L. of Shalott iv* 19
He thought I was a ghost, mother, for I was all in *w*, — *May Queen* 17
Gown'd in pure *w*, that fitted to the shape— — *Gardener's D.* 126
Which charts us all in its coarse blacks or *w's*, — *Walk. to the Mail* 107
With folded feet, in stoles of *w*, — *Sir Galahad* 43
No pint of *w* or red Had ever half the power — *Will Water.* 82
Six hundred maidens clad in purest *w*, — *Princess ii* 472
But pure as lines of green that streak the *w* — „ *v* 196
Of twelve sweet hours that past in bridal *w*, — *Maud I xviii* 65
King That morn was married, while in stainless *w*, — *Com. of Arthur* 456
Muriel and Miriam, each in *w*, and like May-blossoms — *The Ring* 254

White (s) *(continued)* And watch the curl'd *w* of the coming wave *Merlin and V.* 292
and she herself in *w* All but her face, *Lancelot and E.* 1158
where the crisping *w* Play'd ever back upon the sloping wave, *Holy Grail* 381
Where children sat in *w* with cups of gold, *Last Tournament* 142
all the purple slopes of mountain flowers Pass under *w*, " 230
So dame and damsel cast the simple *w*, " 232
Wear black and *w*, and be a nun like you, *Guinevere* 677
in front of which Six stately virgins, all in *w*, *Lover's Tale ii* 77
Leapt lightly clad in bridal *w*— " *iii* 44
might be borne in *w* To burial or to burning, *Ancient Sage* 207
Molly Magee, wid the red o' the rose an' the *w* o' the May, *Tomorrow* 31
All his virtues—I forgive them—black in *w* above his bones. *Locksley H., Sixty* 44
White-breasted *w-b* like a star Fronting the dawn *Œnone* 57
Whited *W* thought and cleanly life As the priest, *Vision of Sin* 116
White-eyed *w-e* phantasms weeping tears of blood, *Palace of Art* 239
White-faced The *w-f* halls, the glancing rills, *In Mem., Con.* 113
White-favour'd And those *w-f* horses wait; " 90
White-flower'd saw The *w-f* elder-thicket from the field *Godiva* 63
Black holly, and *w-f* wayfaring-tree! *Sir J. Oldcastle* 130
White-hair'd A *w-h* shadow roaming like a dream *Tithonus* 8
White-headed I this old *w-h* dreamer stoopt *Locksley H., Sixty* 38
White-hooved Leading a jet-black goat white-horn'd, *w-h*, *Œnone* 51
White-horn'd Leading a jet-black goat *w-h*, white-hooved, " 51
White-listed tree that shone *w-l* thro' the gloom. *Merlin and V.* 939
Whiten Willows *w*, aspens quiver, *L. of Shalott i* 10
The ptarmigan that *w's* ere his hour *Last Tournament* 697
Whiten'd (adj. and part.) Part black, part *w* with the bones of men, *Holy Grail* 500
The meal-sacks on the *w* floor, *Miller's D.* 101
Whiten'd (verb) And *w* all the rolling flood; *The Victim* 20
When the lake *w* and the pinewood roar'd, *Merlin and V.* 637
Whiteness all but utter *w* held for sin, *Holy Grail* 84
Whitening Down thro' the *w* hazels made a plunge *Enoch Arden* 379
after the great waters break *W* for half a league, *Last Tournament* 465
A rhyme that flower'd betwixt the *w* sloe *To Mary Boyle* 25
Whiter Is *w* even than her pretty hand: *Aylmer's Field* 363
The flocks are *w* down the vale, *In Mem. cxv* 10
To meet and greet a *w* sun; " *Con.* 78
And *w* than the mist that all day long *Pass. of Arthur* 137
White-robed *W-r* in honour of the stainless child, *Last Tournament* 147
White Rose *W R*, Bellerophon, the Jilt, *The Brook* 161
Whitest With *w* honey in fairy gardens cull'd— *Eleänore* 26
The very *w* lamb in all my fold Loves you: *Aylmer's Field* 361
A broad earth-sweeping pall of *w* lawn, *Lover's Tale ii* 78
White-tail'd Left for the *w-t* eagle to tear it, *Batt. of Brunanburh* 107
White-wing'd let the fair *w-w* peacemaker fly *Ode Inter. Exhib.* 34
Whither Arthur had vanish'd I knew not *w*, *Merlin and the G.* 78
Whitsuntide Arthur on the *W* before Held court *Marr. of Geraint* 145
And this was on the last year's *W*. " 840
Whizz'd An arrow *w* to the right, one to the left, *Balin and Balan* 419
Whoäts (oats) *W* or tonups or taätes— *Village Wife* 26
Whole (adj.) *(See also* **'Ole***)* Oft lose *w* years of darker mind. *Two Voices* 372
So healthy, sound, and clear and *w*, *Miller's D.* 15
With one long kiss my *w* soul thro' My lips, *Fatima* 20
My *w* soul waiting silently, " 36
W weeks and months, and early and late, *The Sisters* 10
And blessings on his *w* life long, *May Queen, Con.* 14
But now the *w* ROUND TABLE is dissolved *M. d'Arthur* 234
I, that *w* day, Saw her no more, *Gardener's D.* 163
But this *w* hour your eyes have been intent " 269
but I die here To-day, and *w* years long, a life of death. *St. S. Stylites* 54
If it may be, fast *W* Lents, and pray. " 182
I trust That I am *w*, and clean, and meet for Heaven. " 213
This *w* wide earth of light and shade *Will Water.* 67
At times the *w* sea burn'd, at times *The Voyage* 51
To waste his *w* heart in one kiss Upon her perfect lips. *Sir L. and Q. G.* 44
our pride Looks only for a moment *w* and sound; *Aylmer's Field* 2

Whole (adj.) *(continued)* for fear This *w* foundation ruin, *Princess ii* 341
sphered *W* in ourselves and owed to none. " *iv* 148
unless you send us back Our son, on the instant, *w*.' " 416
but half Without you; with you, *w*; " 461
My mother, looks as *w* as some serene " *v* 193
and slips in sensual mire, But *w* and one: " *v* 200
Then felt it sound and *w* from head to foot, " *vi* 211
she You talk'd with, *w* nights long, up in the tower, " 255
nor seem'd it strange that soon He rose up *w*, " *vii* 65
nor yet Did those twin brothers, risen again and *w*; " 89
And keeps our Britain, *w* within herself, " *Con.* 52
I wish they were a *w* Atlantic broad.' " 71
W in himself, a common good, *Ode on Well.* 26
keep our noble England *w*, " 161
And love will last as pure and *w* *In Mem. xliii* 13
That so my pleasure may be *w*; " *lxxi* 8
To which the *w* creation moves. " *Con.* 144
Has our *w* earth gone nearer to the glow *Maud I xviii* 78
Strike dead the *w* weak race of venomous worms, " *II i* 46
and weep My *w* soul out to thee. " *iv* 98
W, like a crag that tumbles from the cliff, *Marr. of Geraint* 318
To save her dear lord *w* from any wound. *Geraint and E.* 45
And men brought in *w* hogs and quarter beeves, " 602
Then, when Geraint was *w* again, " 945
The *w* wood-world is one full peal of praise. *Balin and Balan* 450
Polluting, and imputing her *w* self, *Merlin and V.* 803
the one passionate love Of her *w* life; " 956
'Sir King, mine ancient wound is hardly *w*, *Lancelot and E.* 93
Right fain were I to learn this knight were *w*, " 772
Whereof he should be quickly *w*, " 853
But when Sir Lancelot's deadly hurt was *w*, " 904
Yet still thy life is *w*, and still I live Who love thee; *Pass. of Arthur* 150
But now the *w* Round Table is dissolved " 402
For so the *w* round earth is every way " 422
single glance of them Will govern a *w* life from birth to death, *Lover's Tale i* 76
At thought of which my *w* soul languishes " 267
The *w* land weigh'd him down as Ætna does The Giant of Mythology: " *iv* 17
Ship after ship, the *w* night long, (repeat) *The Revenge* 58, 59, 60
And the *w* sea plunged and fell on the shot-shatter'd navy of Spain, " 117
So mock'd, so spurn'd, so baited two *w* days— *Sir J. Oldcastle* 163
And the *w* isle-side flashing down from the peak *V. of Maeldune* 45
For the *w* isle shudder'd and shook like a man " 74
Out of His *w* World-self and all in all— *De Prof., Two G.* 49
For he touch'd on the *w* sad planet of man, *Dead Prophet* 39
dwell For nine white moons of each *w* year with me, *Demeter and P.* 121
When thou shalt dwell the *w* bright year with me, " 139
National hatreds of *w* generations, *Vastness* 25
Whole (s) All various, each a perfect *w* From living Nature, *Palace of Art* 58
Is bodied forth the second *w*. *Love thou thy land* 66
That each, who seems a separate *w*, *In Mem. xlvii* 1
The wish, that of the living *w* " *lv* 1
Boundless inward, in the atom, boundless outward, in the *W*. *Locksley H., Sixty* 212
be welded each and all, Into one imperial *w*, *Open. I. and C. Exhib.* 37
Wholeness He that in his Catholic *w* *Locksley H., Sixty* 101
Wholesale You need not set your thoughts in rubric thus For *w* comment.' *Princess iii* 51
Wholesome You changed a *w* heart to gall. *L. C. V. de Vere* 44
eat *w* food, And wear warm clothes, *St. S. Stylites* 108
That mock'd the *w* human heart, *The Letters* 10
But honest talk and *w* wine, *To F. D. Maurice* 18
But better serves a *w* law, *In Mem. xlviii* 10
glanced Eyes of pure women, *w* stars of love; *Gareth and L.* 314
None; or the *w* boon of gyve and gag.' " 370
But now the *w* music of the wood *Balin and Balan* 436
until the *w* flower And poisonous grew together, *Holy Grail* 775
Such as the *w* mothers tell their boys. *Pelleas and E.* 197
whom The *w* realm is purged of otherwhere, *Last Tournament* 96
O ay—the *w* madness of an hour— " 675
Boughs on each side, laden with *w* shade, *Lover's Tale i* 230

Wholesome (*continued*) Whereof to all that draw the *w* air, *Lover's Tale i* 500
Blessing the *w* white faces of Havelock's good fusileers, *Def. of Lucknow* 101
came back That *w* heat the blood had lost, *To E. Fitzgerald* 24
Dust in *w* old-world dust before the newer world begin. *Locksley H., Sixty* 150
Wholly Then I cannot be *w* dumb; *Maud II v* 100
Whoop (*See also* **Owl-whoop**) Call to each other and *w* and cry *The Merman* 26
Whoop'd-Whoopt bats wheel'd, and owls *whoop'd*, *Princess, Con.* 110
An owl *whoopt*: 'Hark the victor pealing there!' *Gareth and L.* 1318
Whooping I drown'd the *w's* of the owl with sound *St. S. Stylites* 33
Whoopt *See* **Whoop'd**
Whorl With delicate spire and *w*, *Maud II ii* 6
Wicked (adj.) 'Chant me now some *w* stave, *Vision of Sin* 151
for the *w* broth Confused the chemic labour of the blood, *Lucretius* 19
About the good King and his *w* Queen, *Guinevere* 209
Makes *w* lightnings of her eyes, „ 520
'Ye know me then, that *w* one, „ 669
And so she was *w* with Harry; *First Quarrel* 26
Wicked (s) And the *w* cease from troubling, *May Queen, Con.* 60
Wickedness if you think this *w* in me, *Merlin and V.* 339
If you—and not so much from *w*, „ 520
And heal the world of all their *w*! *Holy Grail* 94
Well might I wish to veil her *w*, *Guinevere* 211
who hath forgiven My *w* to him, „ 635
Wicket (*See also* **Wicket-gate**) one green *w* in a privet hedge; *Gardener's D.* 110
Wicket (in cricket) clamour bowl'd And stump'd the *w*; *Princess, Pro.* 82
Wicket-gate I reach'd The *w-g*, and found her standing there. *Gardener's D.* 213
Wiclif He might have come to learn Our *W's* learning: *Sir J. Oldcastle* 65
By this good *W* mountain down from heaven, „ 132
Wiclif-preacher My frighted *W-p* whom I crost „ 38
Wide (*See also* **Wild-wide, World-wide**) *W*, wild, and open to the air, *Dying Swan* 2
Look up thro' night: the world is *w*. *Two Voices* 24
and the waste *w* Of that abyss, or scornful pride! „ 119
'When, *w* in soul and bold of tongue, „ 124
mansion, that is built for me, So royal-rich and *w*.' *Palace of Art* 20
With cycles of the human tale Of this *w* world, „ 147
In this great house so royal-rich, and *w*, „ 191
The stalls are void, the doors are *w*, *Sir Galahad* 31
Suddenly set it *w* to find a sign, *Enoch Arden* 496
the suns are many, the world is *w*. *Maud I iv* 45
shiver of dancing leaves is thrown About its echoing chambers *w*, „ *vi* 74
portal of King Pellam's chapel *w* And inward to the wall; *Balin and Balan* 405
my spirit Was of so *w* a compass *Lover's Tale ii* 135
coostom ageän draw'd in like a wind fro' far an' *w*, *North. Cobbler* 93
Stretch'd *w* and wild the waste enormous marsh, *Ode to Memory* 101
Is not so deadly still As that *w* forest. *D. of F. Women* 69
The parson taking *w* and wider sweeps, *The Epic* 14
looking wistfully with *w* blue eyes As in a picture. *M. d'Arthur* 169
One sabbath deep and *w*— *St. Agnes' Eve* 34
This whole *w* earth of light and shade *Will Water.* 67
Till the fountain spouted, showering *w* *Vision of Sin* 21
Thro' one *w* chasm of time and frost they gave *Princess, Pro.* 93
'Fling our doors *w*! all, all, not one, but all, „ *vi* 334
In this *w* hall with earth's invention stored, *Open. Inter. Exhib.* 2
Calm and deep peace in this *w* air, *In Mem. xi* 13
Hid from the *w* world's rumour by the grove *Lancelot and E.* 522
W flats, where nothing but coarse grasses grew; *Holy Grail* 794
W open were the gates, And no watch kept; *Pelleas and E.* 414
The *w* world laughs at it. *Last Tournament* 695
Arise, my own true sister, come forth! the world is *w*. *The Flight* 96
Read the *w* world's annals, you, *Locksley H., Sixty* 104
Wide-dispread locks not *w-d*, *Isabel* 5
Wide-mouth'd The little *w-m* heads upon the spout *Godiva* 56
Widen The circle *w's* till it lip the marge, *Pelleas and E.* 94
Widen'd And the thoughts of men are *w* *Locksley Hall* 138
Widening (*See also* **Ever-widening**) And ever *w* slowly silence all. *Merlin and V.* 392
Wider *and make The bounds of freedom* w *yet* *To the Queen* 32
a lyre of *w* range Struck by all passion, *D. of F. Women* 165
The parson taking wide and *w* sweeps, *The Epic* 14
Wide-wing'd *w-w* sunset of the misty marsh *Last Tournament* 423
Widow (*See also* **Would-be-widow**) his *w* Miriam Lane, With daily-dwindling profits *Enoch Arden* 695
affectionate smile That makes the *w* lean. *Sea Dreams* 156
but there were *w's* here, Two *w's*, *Princess i* 127
Then came a *w* crying to the King, *Gareth and L.* 333
Came yet another *w* crying to him, „ 350
w with less guile than many a child. *Sisters (E. and E.)* 182
nor wail of baby-wife, Or Indian *w*; *Akbar's Dream* 197
a *w* came to my door: *Charity* 26
Widow-bride made The wife of wives a *w-b*, *Romney's R.* 138
Widow'd Laid *w* of the power in his eye *M. d'Arthur* 122
To thy *w* marriage-pillows, to the tears that thou wilt weep. *Locksley Hall* 82
I cry to vacant chairs and *w* walls, *Aylmer's Field* 720
Till all my *w* race be run; *In Mem. ix* 18
Till all my *w* race be run. „ *xvii* 20
Could we forget the *w* hour „ *xl* 1
My heart, tho' *w*, may not rest „ *lxxxv* 113
Laid *w* of the power in his eye *Pass. of Arthur* 290
Wilt neither quit the *w* Crown nor let *Prin. Beatrice* 15
Widower (adj.) there the *w* husband and dead wife *Lover's Tale iv* 372
Widower (s) Tears of the *w*, when he sees *In Mem. xiii* 1
Widowhood praise To God, that help'd her in her *w*. *Dora* 113
Thro' all the clouded years of *w*, *Death of Œnone* 103
Width two remain'd Apart by all the chamber's *w*, *Geraint and E.* 265
Wield So the Higher *w's* the Lower, *Locksley H., Sixty* 124
my brothers, work, and *w* The forces of to-day, *Mechanophilus* 29
Wielded Nor *w* axe disjoint, *Talking Oak* 262
Wielder *W* of the stateliest measure *To Virgil* 39
Wielding The *w* of weapons— *Batt. of Brunanburh* 90
Wife (*See also* **Baby-wife, Missis**) *In her as Mother*, W, *and Queen;* *To the Queen* 28
The queen of marriage, a most perfect *w*. *Isabel* 28
'Who took a *w*, who rear'd his race, *Two Voices* 328
One walk'd between his *w* and child, „ 412
Pray, Alice, pray, my darling *w*, *Miller's D.* 23
True *w*, Round my true heart thine arms entwine „ 215
fairest and most loving *w* in Greece,' *Œnone* 187
Fairest—why fairest *w*? am I not fair? „ 196
The gardener Adam and his *w* *L. C. V. de Vere* 51
cannot tell—I might have been his *w*; *May Queen, Con.* 47
dream of Fatherland, Of child, and *w*, *Lotos-Eaters* 40
dear the last embraces of our *wives* „ *C. S.* 70
I KNEW an old *w* lean and poor, *The Goose* 1
It stirr'd the old *w's* mettle: „ 26
often thought, 'I'll make them man and *w*.' *Dora* 4
take her for your *w*; „ 20
Or change a word with her he calls his *w*, „ 44
I had been a patient *w*: „ 147
his *w* upon the tilt, *Walk. to the Mail* 41
He left *his* w behind; for so I heard. „ 47
Sit with their *wives* by fires, *St. S. Stylites* 108
Match'd with an aged *w*, I mete and dole *Ulysses* 3
As the husband is, the *w* is: *Locksley Hall* 47
loved thee more than ever *w* was loved. „ 64
Godiva, *w* to that grim Earl, *Godiva* 12
But break it. In the name of *w*, *Day-Dm., L'Envoi* 53
Lord Ronald's, When you are man and *w*.' *Lady Clare* 36
Little can I give my *w*. *L. of Burleigh* 14
above his book Leering at his neighbour's *w*. *Vision of Sin* 118
'This is my house and this my little *w*.' *Enoch Arden* 28
The little *w* would weep for company, „ 34
And say she would be little *w* to both. „ 36
his *w* Bore him another son, a sickly one: „ 108
yet the *w*—When he was gone— „ 131

Wild (adj.) (*continued*) *w* marsh-marigold shines like fire in swamps *May Queen* 31
I have been *w* and wayward, *May Queen N. Y's. E.* 33
you must not weep, nor let your grief be *w*, „ 35
All in the *w* March-morning I heard the angels call; „ *Con.* 25
in the *w* March-morning I heard them call my soul. „ 28
W flowers in the valley for other hands than mine. „ 52
Brimful of those *w* tales, *D. of F. Women* 12
And the *w* kiss, when fresh from war's alarms, „ 149
'Heaven heads the count of crimes With that *w* oath.' „ 202
Yet waft me from the harbour-mouth, *W* wind! *You ask me, why, etc.* 26
w hearts and feeble wings That every sophister *Love thou thy land* 11
The *w* wind rang from park and plain, *The Goose* 45
And the *w* water lapping on the crag.' *M. d'Arthur* 71
swan That, fluting a *w* carol ere her death, „ 267
where the heart on one *w* leap Hung tranced *Gardener's D.* 259
My sweet, *w*, fresh three quarters of a year, *Edwin Morris* 2
Again with hands of *w* rejection 'Go!— „ 124
Till that *w* wind made work *Talking Oak* 54
And in the chase grew *w*, „ 126
and the *w* team Which love thee, *Tithonus* 39
Whispering I knew not what of *w* and sweet, „ 61
Make me feel the *w* pulsation that I felt *Locksley Hall* 109
Where in *w* Mahratta-battle fell my father evil-starr'd;— „ 155
Catch the *w* goat by the hair, „ 170
but I *know* my words are *w*, „ 173
As *w* as aught of fairy lore; *Day Dm., L'Envoi* 12
But it is *w* and barren, *Amphion* 2
Caught each other with *w* grimaces, *Vision of Sin* 35
w hawk stood with the down on his beak, *Poet's Song* 11
If he could know his babes were running *w* *Enoch Arden* 304
The helpless life so *w* that it was tame. „ 557
upjetted in spirts of *w* sea-smoke, *Sea Dreams* 52
but if there were A music harmonizing our *w* cries, „ 255
By this *w* king to force her to his wish, *Princess, Pro.* 37
Lilia, *w* with sport, Half child half woman „ 100
Thro' the *w* woods that hung about the town; „ *i* 91
and the shrieks Of the *w* woods together; „ 99
All *w* to found an University For maidens, „ 150
Like some *w* creature newly-caged, „ *ii* 301
'Who ever saw such *w* barbarians? „ *iii* 42
And the *w* cataract leaps in glory. „ *iv* 4
Blow, bugle, blow, set the *w* echoes flying, (repeat) „ 5, 17
Deep as first love, and *w* with all regret; „ 57
and the *w* figtree split Their monstrous idols, „ 79
When the *w* peasant rights himself, „ 385
w birds on the light Dash themselves dead. „ 495
And make a *w* petition night and day, „ *v* 97
Rotting on some *w* shore with ribs of wreck, „ 147
'*W* natures need wise curbs. „ 173
'for this *w* wreath of air, „ 318
so belabour'd him on rib and cheek They made him *w*: „ 342
I mused on that *w* morning in the woods, „ 471
At the barrier like a *w* horn in a land Of echoes, „ 486
I trust that there is no one hurt to death, For your *w* whim: „ *vi* 243
catch Her hand in *w* delirium, gripe it hard, „ *vii* 93
for on one side arose The women up in *w* revolt, „ 123
let the *w* Lean-headed Eagles yelp alone, „ 210
something *w* within her breast, „ 237
Like our *w* Princess with as wise a dream „ *Con.* 69
W War, who breaks the converse of the wise; *Third of Feb.* 8
O the *w* charge they made! *Light Brigade* 51
And howsoever this *w* world may roll, *W. to Marie Alex.* 48
Yell'd and shriek'd between her daughters o'er a *w* confederacy. *Boädicea* 6
Forgive these *w* and wandering cries, *In Mem., Pro.* 41
The *w* pulsation of her wings; „ *xii* 4
The *w* unrest that lives in woe „ *xv* 15
Can calm despair and *w* unrest „ *xvi* 2
such as lurks In some *w* Poet, „ *xxxiv* 7
And those *w* eyes that watch the wave „ *xxxvi* 15
That had the *w* oat not been sown, „ *liii* 6
As wan, as chill, as *w* as now; „ *lxxii* 17

Wild (adj.) (*continued*) Ring out, *w* bells, to the *w* sky, *In Mem. cvi* 1
Ring out, *w* bells, and let him die. „ 4
But some *w* Pallas from the brain Of Demons? „ *cxiv* 12
W Hours that fly with Hope and Fear, „ *cxxviii* 9
And *w* voice pealing up to the sunny sky, *Maud I v* 13
So that *w* dog, and wolf and boar and bear *Com. of Arthur* 23
W beasts, and surely would have torn the child „ 217
lords Have foughten like *w* beasts among themselves, „ 226
'Being a goose and rather tame than *w*, *Gareth and L.* 38
As slopes a *w* brook o'er a little stone, *Marr. of Geraint* 77
Turn thy *w* wheel thro' sunshine, „ 348
With that *w* wheel we go not up or down; „ 351
I know not, but he past to the *w* land. „ 443
For old am I, and rough the ways and *w*; „ 750
That skins the *w* beast after slaying him, *Geraint and E.* 93
To keep them in the *w* ways of the wood, „ 187
Or two *w* men supporters of a shield, „ 267
Enter'd, the *w* lord of the place, Limours. „ 277
Enid, the loss of whom hath turn'd me *w*— „ 308
I call mine own self *w*, „ 311
Then thought she heard the *w* Earl at the door, „ 381
And in the moment after, *w* Limours, „ 457
To shun the *w* ways of the lawless tribe. „ 608
As of a *w* thing taken in the trap, „ 723
And in the *w* woods of Broceliande, *Merlin and V.* 2
Ev'n to the *w* woods of Broceliande. „ 204
Who meant to eat her up in that *w* wood „ 260
all thro' this *w* wood And all this morning „ 285
To chase a creature that was current then In these *w* woods, „ 409
And all thro' following you to this *w* wood, „ 440
As some *w* turn of anger, or a mood „ 521
On some *w* down above the windy deep, „ 658
O cruel, there was nothing *w* or strange, „ 860
When the strong neighings of the *w* white Horse *Lancelot and E.* 298
Suddenly flash'd on her a *w* desire, „ 357
Bare, as a *w* wave in the wide North-sea, „ 482
Then flash'd into *w* tears, and rose again, „ 613
'Well—if I bide, lo! this *w* flower for me!' „ 644
Crush'd the *w* passion out against the floor „ 742
All in a fiery dawning *w* with wind „ 1020
But the *w* Queen, who saw not, burst away „ 1244
To smoke the scandalous hive of those *w* bees *Holy Grail* 214
'O *w* and of the woods, *Pelleas and E.* 99
But thou, thro' ever harrying thy *w* beasts— *Last Tournament* 635
Becomes thee well—art grown *w* beast thyself. „ 637
And with a *w* sea-light about his feet, *Guinevere* 242
To guard thee in the *w* hour coming on, „ 446
like *w* birds that change Their season in the night *Pass. of Arthur* 38
And the *w* water lapping on the crag.' „ 239
swan That, fluting a *w* carol ere her death, „ 435
I stoop'd, I gather'd the *w* herbs, *Lover's Tale i* 342
Like to the *w* youth of an evil prince, „ 354
w brier had driven Its knotted thorns „ 619
Embathing all with *w* and woful hues, „ *ii* 64
like *w* Bacchanals Fled onward to the steeple „ *iii* 25
And something weird and *w* about it all: „ *iv* 224
an' I flung him the letter that drove me *w*, *First Quarrel* 57
he was always so *w*— *Rizpah* 26
But he lived with a lot of *w* mates, „ 29
w earthquake out-tore Clean from our lines of defence *Def. of Lucknow* 61
Some ears for Christ in this *w* field of Wales— *Sir J. Oldcastle* 13
when the *w* hour and the wine Had set the wits aflame. „ 94
a score of *w* birds Cried from the topmost summit *V. of Maeldune* 27
shouting of these *w* birds ran into the hearts „ 33
For a *w* witch naked as heaven stood on each „ 100
all the summer long we roam'd in these *w* woods *The Flight* 79
'His two *w* woodland flowers.' „ 80
W flowers blowing side by side in God's free light „ 81
W flowers of the secret woods, „ 82
W woods in which we roved with him, „ 83
W woods in which we rove no more, „ 84
she had never driven me *w*. *Locksley H., Sixty* 20
Ages after, while in Asia, he that led the *w* Moguls, „ 81

Will (s) (*continued*) that I make My *w* of yours, *Lancelot and E.* 916
then I said, 'Now shall I have my *w*:' „ 1047
mine now to work my *w*— „ 1231
men With strength and *w* to right the wrong'd, *Holy Grail* 309
her longing and her *w* Was toward me as of old; „ 590
baseness in him by default Of *w* and nature, *Pelleas and E.* 82
A prisoner, and the vassal of thy *w*; „ 241
and at her *w* they couch'd their spears, „ 273
He needs no aid who doth his lady's *w*.' „ 281
As let these caitiffs on thee work their *w*?' „ 323
Pelleas answer'd, 'O, their *w's* are hers „ 324
'Slay then,' he shrieked, 'my *w* is to be slain,' „ 579
this honour after death, Following thy *w*! *Last Tournament* 35
I, being simple, thought to work His *w*, *Pass. of Arthur* 22
power in his eye That bow'd the *w*. „ 291
My *w* is one with thine; *Lover's Tale i* 463
heir That scarce can wait the reading of the *w* „ 676
In battle with the glooms of my dark *w*, „ 744
edict of the *w* to reassume The semblance „ *ii* 161
And I will do your *w*. I may not stay, „ *iv* 115
And I will do *your w*, and none shall know.' „ 120
some with gems Moveable and resettable at *w*, „ 199
all his to work his *w*.' „ 283
but the creatures had worked their *w*. *Rizpah* 50
An' I thowt 'twur the *w* o' the Lord, *Village Wife* 11
not yet too old to work his *w*— *Columbus* 161
not Love but Hate that weds a bride against her *w*; *The Flight* 32
Strong in *w* and rich in wisdom, *Locksley H., Sixty* 49
shedding poison in the fountains of the *W*. „ 274
Perchance from some abuse of *W* In worlds *Epilogue* 24
and had yielded her *w* To the master, *Dead Prophet* 63
The blackbirds have their *w's*, (repeat) *Early Spring* 5, 47
thy *w*, a power to make This ever-changing world *To Duke of Argyll* 9
Howe'er blind force and brainless *w* *Freedom* 15
But thro' the *W* of One who knows and rules— *The Ring* 42
Her firm *w*, her fix'd purpose. „ 293
thought he could subdue me to his *w*. *Happy* 64
Diffuse thyself at *w* thro' all my blood, *Prog. of Spring* 24
Be struck from out the clash of warring *w's*; „ 95
were you hired? or came of your own *w* *Romney's R.* 16
no slaves of a four-footed *w*? *The Dawn* 18
we will work thy *w* Who love thee.' *Com. of Arthur* 259
Hold thine own, and work thy *w*! *Poets and Critics* 13

Will (verb) A man may speak the thing he *w*; *You ask me, why, etc.* 8
when Enoch comes again Why then he shall repay me—if you *w*, *Enoch Arden* 310
yet my father *w's* not war: *Princess v* 277
cannot *w* my will, nor work my work Wholly, *Com. of Arthur* 88
knight-errantry Who ride abroad, and do but what they *w*; *Gareth and L.* 630
Lord am I In mine own land, and what I *w* I can.' *Lancelot and E.* 917
'That were against me: what I can I *w*;' „ 976
not without She *w's* it: would I, „ 1422
Let visions of the night or of the day Come, as they *w*; *Holy Grail* 911
'Why, let my lady bind me if she *w*, And let my lady beat me if she *w*: *Pelleas and E.* 334
and does what he *w* with his own; *Despair* 97

Will be was, and is, and *w b*, are but is; *Princess iii* 324
Who am, and was, and *w b* his, his own and only own, *Happy* 7

Will'd set his hand To do the thing he w, *Enoch Arden* 295
might not Averill, had he *w* it so, *Aylmer's Field* 46
Her words had issue other than she *w*. *Merlin and V.* 806
would I, if she *w* it? nay, Who knows? *Lancelot and E.* 1422
I would work according as he *w*. *Holy Grail* 784
Else, for the King has *w* it, it is well.' *Last Tournament* 111
She rose, and set before him all he *w*; „ 723
had he *w* I might have stricken a lusty stroke *Sir J. Oldcastle* 68

Willest if Thou *w*, let my day be brief, *Doubt and Prayer* 13

William (*See also* **Willy**) at the farm abode *W* and Dora. *W* was his son, *Dora* 2
And yearn'd toward *W*; but the youth, „ 6
But *W* answer'd short; 'I cannot marry Dora; „ 22
Consider, *W*: take a month to think, „ 29
But *W* answer'd madly; bit his lips, „ 33
days went on, and there was born a boy To *W*; „ 49

William (*continued*) till at last a fever seized On *W*, *Dora* 55
all thro' me This evil came on *W* at the first. „ 61
And answer'd softly, 'This is *W's* child!' „ 90
work for *W's* child, until he grows Of age „ 126
never came a-begging for myself, Or *W*, or this child; „ 142
when *W* died, he died at peace With all men; „ 144
for three hours he sobb'd o'er *W's* child Thinking of *W*. „ 167

Willing Thou, *w* me to stay, *Madeline* 37
Nor *w* men should come among us, *Princess iii* 318
w she should keep Court-favour: „ *vii* 57
A *w* ear We lent him. *In Mem. lxxxvii* 30
Wroth at himself. Not *w* to be known, *Lancelot and E.* 160

Willingly 'Yea, *w*,' replied the youth; *Geraint and E.* 207
You say that you can do it as *w* *Sisters (E. and E)* 70

Willis I niver puts saäme i' *my* butter, they does it at *W's* farm, *Village Wife* 119

Willow One *w* over the river wept, *Dying Swan* 14
W's whiten, aspens quiver, *L. of Shalott i* 10
found a boat Beneath a *w* left afloat, „ *iv* 7
Shrank one sick *w* sere and small. *Mariana in the S.* 53
There by the humpback'd *w*; *Walk. to the Mail* 31
shock-head *w's* two and two By rivers gallopaded. *Amphion* 39
measured pulse of racing oars Among the *w's*; *In Mem. lxxxvii* 11
Silvery *w*, Pasture and plowland, *Merlin and the G.* 53

Willow-branches And the *w-b* hoar and dank, *Dying Swan* 37

Willows (*See also* **James, James Willows, Katie, Katie Willows**) What surname?' '*W*.' 'No!' *The Brook* 212

Willow-veil'd By the margin, *w-v*, *L. of Shalott i* 19

Willow-weed fairy foreland set With *w-w* and mallow. *The Brook* 46

Willowy boat-head wound along The *w* hills and fields among, *L. of Shalott iv* 25

Willy (*See also* **William**) And *W*, my eldest-born, is gone, you say, *Grandmother* 1
And *W's* wife has written: (repeat) „ 3, 105
Never the wife for *W*: „ 4
and *W*, you say, is gone. „ 8
W, my beauty, my eldest-born, the flower of the flock; Never a man could fling him: for *W* stood like a rock. „ 9
I cannot weep for *W*, nor can I weep for the rest; „ 19
W had not been down to the farm for a week and a day; „ 33
W,—he didn't see me,—and Jenny hung on his arm. „ 42
W stood up like a man, and look'd the thing „ 45
'Marry you, *W*!' said I, „ 53
So *W* and I were wedded: I wore a lilac gown; „ 57
For *W* I cannot weep, I shall see him another morn: „ 67
W, my eldest-born, at nigh threescore and ten; „ 87
So *W* has gone, my beauty, my eldest-born, my flower; But how can I weep for *W*, „ 101
And *W's* wife has written, she never was over-wise. „ 105
W's voice in the wind, 'O mother, *Rizpah* 2
couldn't be idle—my *W*—he never could rest. „ 27
My *W* 'ill rise up whole when the trumpet „ 57
I'm sure to be happy with *W*, I know not where. „ 76
for my *W's* voice in the wind— „ 82
W—the moon's in a cloud—Good-night. „ 86

Wilt thou The '*w t*' answer'd, and again The '*w t*' ask'd, *In Mem., Con.* 54

Wily At Merlin's feet the *w* Vivien lay. *Merlin and V.* 5
The *w* Vivien stole from Arthur's court. „ 149

Wimple From beneath her gather'd *w* *Lilian* 14

Win Woo me, and *w* me, and marry me, *The Mermaid* 46
power which ever to its sway Will *w* the wise at once, *Mine be the strength* 10
And *w* all eyes with all accomplishment: *The form, the form* 4
To *w* his love I lay in wait: *The Sisters* 11
Of me you shall not *w* renown: *L. C. V. de Vere* 2
The warmth it thence shall *w* *Talking Oak* 254
Which did *w* my heart from me!' *L. of Burleigh* 84
where two fight The strongest *w's*, *Aylmer's Field* 365
How roughly men may woo thee so they *w*— *Lucretius* 273
That she but meant to *w* him back, „ 279
and be you The Prince to *w* her! *Princess, Pro.* 226
'Follow, follow, thou shalt *w*.' „ *i* 100
And partly that I hoped to *w* you back, „ *iv* 304

Win (*continued*) *w's*, tho' dash'd with death He reddens — *Princess v* 164
if we fail, we fail, And if we *w*, we fail: — „ 323
And on the 'Follow, follow, thou shalt *w*:' — „ 472
W you the hearts of women; — „ *vi* 171
—verily I think to *w*.' — „ 329
Emperor, Ottoman, which shall *w*: — *To F. D. Maurice* 32
That out of words a comfort *w*; — *In Mem. xx* 10
the past will always *w* A glory from its being far; — „ *xxiv* 13
they could not *w* An answer from my lips, — „ *ciii* 49
And the titmouse hope to *w* her — *Maud I xx* 29
Belike he *w's* it as the better man: — *Gareth and L.* 1346
To dash against mine enemy and to *w*. — „ 1355
For tho' it seems my spurs are yet to *w*, — *Marr. of Geraint* 128
I know men: nor will ye *w* him back, — *Geraint and E.* 332
who sought to *w* my love Thro' evil ways: — *Balin and Balan* 474
Vivien had not done to *w* his trust — *Merlin and V.* 863
W! by this kiss you will: — *Lancelot and E.* 152
They prove to him his work: *w* and return.' — „ 158
Joust for it, and *w*, and bring it in an hour, — „ 204
W shall I not, but do my best to *w*: — „ 221
And you shall *w* this diamond,— — „ 227
To *w* his honour and to make his name, — „ 1362
while women watch Who *w's*, who falls; — *Holy Grail* 35
and they would *w* thee—teem, — „ 541
he will fight for me, And *w* the circlet: — *Pelleas and E.* 119
And *w* me this fine circlet, Pelleas, — „ 128
he cried, 'Ay! wilt thou if I *w*?' 'Ay, that will I,' — „ 131
purest of thy knights May *w* them — *Last Tournament* 50
For courtesy *w's* woman all as well As valour may, — „ 707
Yet so my path was clear To *w* the sister. — *Sisters (E. and E.)* 203
no caress could *w* my wife Back to that passionate answer — „ 258
w all praise from all Who past it, — *Tiresias* 83
To *w* her back before I die— — *Romney's R.* 118

Wince You should have seen him *w* — *Walk. to the Mail* 71

Wind (s) (*See also* **East-wind, March-wind, Night-wind, North-wind, Sea-wind, South-wind**)
When will the *w* be aweary of blowing — *Nothing will Die* 3
The stream flows, The *w* blows, — „ 10
Shall make the *w's* blow Round and round, — „ 23
So let the *w* range; — „ 32
south *w's* are blowing Over the sky. — *All Things will Die* 3
The *w* will cease to blow; — „ 10
Nor the *w* on the hill. — „ 26
So let the warm *w's* range, — „ 42
W's creep; dews fall chilly: — *Leonine Eleg.* 7
THE *w's*, as at their hour of birth, — *The winds, etc.* 1
Till cold *w's* woke the gray-eyed morn — *Mariana* 31
the shrill *w's* were up and away, — „ 50
wild *w's* bound within their cell, — „ 54
sound Which to the wooing *w* aloof The poplar made, — „ 75
palms were ranged Above, unwoo'd of summer *w*: — *Arabian Nights* 80
The dew-impearled *w's* of dawn have kiss'd, — *Ode to Memory* 14
flowers which in the rudest *w* Never grow sere, — „ 24
From brawling storms, From weary *w*, — „ 113
w's Blew his own praises in his eyes, — *A Character* 21
the *w's* which bore Them earthward — *The Poet* 17
Bright as light, and clear as *w*. — *Poet's Mind* 7
Ever the weary *w* went on, — *Dying Swan* 9
shook the wave as the *w* did sigh; — „ 15
Above in the *w* was the swallow, — „ 16
W's were blowing, waters flowing, — *Oriana* 14
When Norland *w's* pipe down the sea, — „ 91
Lovest thou the doleful *w* — *Adeline* 49
Careless both of *w* and weather, — *Rosalind* 7
Up or down the streaming *w*? — „ 9
The leaping stream, the very *w*, — „ 14
the amorous, odorous *w* Breathes low — *Eleänore* 123
'Tho' thou wert scatter'd to the *w*, — *Two Voices* 32
He sows himself on every *w*. — „ 294
And, in the pauses of the *w*, — *Miller's D.* 122
I whirl like leaves in roaring *w*. — *Fatima* 7
The *w* sounds like a silver wire, — „ 29
Rests like a shadow, and the *w's* are dead. — *Œnone* 28
the foam-bow brightens When the *w* blows the foam, — „ 62

Wind (s) (*continued*) a *w* arose, And overhead the wandering ivy — *Œnone* 98
The *w* is blowing in turret and tree. (repeat) — *The Sisters* 3, 33
The *w* is howling in turret and tree. — „ 9
The *w* is roaring in turret and tree. — „ 15
The *w* is raging in turret and tree. — „ 21
The w is raving in turret and tree. — „ 27
And hoary to the *w*. — *Palace of Art* 80
trees began to whisper, and the *w* began to roll, — *May Queen, Con.* 27
up the valley came a swell of music on the *w*. — „ 32
up the valley came again the music on the *w*. — „ 36
With *w's* upon the branch, — *Lotos-Eaters, C. S.* 27
All day the *w* breathes low with mellower tone: — „ 102
w and wave and oar; — „ 127
Bluster the *w's* and tides the self-same way, — *D. of F. Women* 38
Whirl'd by the *w*, had roll'd me deep below, — „ 119
And the winter *w's* are wearily sighing: — *D. of the O. Year* 2
THE *w*, that beats the mountain, blows — *To J. S.* 1
God's ordinance Of Death is blown in every *w*;' — „ 46
waft me from the harbour mouth, Wild *w*! — *You ask me, why, etc.* 26
voice Came rolling on the *w*. — *Of old sat Freedom* 8
Make knowledge circle with the *w's*; — *Love thou thy land* 17
lest the soul Of Discord race the rising *w*; — „ 68
A *w* to puff your idol-fires, — „ 69
The wild *w* rang from park and plain, — *The Goose* 45
like a *w*, that shrills All night in a waste land, — *M. d'Arthur* 201
Nor ever *w* blows loudly; — „ 261
Beneath a broad and equal-blowing *w*, — *Gardener's D.* 77
Night slid down one long stream of sighing *w*, — „ 267
But she was sharper than an eastern *w*, — *Audley Court* 53
soft *w* blowing over meadowy holms And alders, — *Edwin Morris* 95
Rain, *w*, frost, heat, hail, — *St. S. Stylites* 16
Till that wild *w* made work — *Talking Oak* 54
'I swear, by leaf, and *w*, and rain, — „ 81
'A light *w* chased her on the wing, — „ 125
light as any *w* that blows So fleetly — „ 129
and the *w's* are laid with sound. — *Locksley Hall* 104
For the mighty *w* arises, roaring seaward, — „ 194
As *w's* from all the compass shift and blow, — *Godiva* 33
And all the low *w* hardly breathed for fear. — „ 55
And many a merry *w* was borne, — *Day-Dm., Depart.* 14
And the *w* did blow; — *The Captain* 34
The happy *w's* upon her play'd, — *Sir L. and Q. G.* 38
There let the *w* sweep and the plover cry; — *Come not, when, etc.* 5
A light *w* blew from the gates of the sun, — *Poet's Song* 3
Then follow'd calms, and then *w's* variable, — *Enoch Arden* 545
blown by baffling *w's*, Like the Good Fortune, — „ 628
His fancy fled before the lazy *w* — „ 657
the *w* blew; The rain of heaven, — *Aylmer's Field* 427
o'er those lazy limits down the *w* With rumour, — „ 495
Where never creeps a cloud, or moves a *w*, — *Lucretius* 106
Like linnets in the pauses of the *w*: — *Princess, Pro.* 246
And therewithal an answer vague as *w*: — „ *i* 45
A *w* arose and rush'd upon the South, — „ 97
smile that like a wrinkling *w* On glassy water — „ 115
She rose upon a *w* of prophecy — „ *ii* 171
W of the western sea, (repeat) — „ *iii* 2, 4
often fretful as the *w* Pent in a crevice: — „ 80
Upon the level in little puffs of *w*, — „ *iv* 256
Huge women blowzed with health, and *w*, and rain, — „ 279
light *w* wakes A lisping of the innumerous leaf — „ *v* 13
Until they hate to hear me like a *w* — „ 98
That range above the region of the *w*, — „ *Con.* 112
four-square to all the *w's* that blew! — *Ode on Well.* 39
Yell'd as when the *w's* of winter tear an oak — *Boädicea* 77
w's from off the plain Roll'd the rich vapour — *Spec. of Iliad* 7
moon Look beautiful, when all the *w's* are laid, — „ 12
the *w's* are up in the morning? (repeat) — *Window, On the Hill* 5, 10, 15, 20
w's and lights and shadows that cannot be still, — „ 7
wet west *w* and the world will go on. (repeat) — „ *No Answer* 6, 12
The *w* and the wet, the *w* and the wet! — „ 13
Wet west *w* how you blow, you blow! — „ 14
wet west *w* and the world may go on. — „ 18
W's are loud and you are dumb, — „ 19
W's are loud and *w's* will pass! — „ 22

Window (s) (*continued*) Or thro' the *w's* we shall see The nakedness *Deserted House* 10
the deep-set *w's*, stain'd and traced, *Palace of Art* 49
forms that pass'd at *w's* and on roofs *D. of F. Women* 23
Reveal'd their shining *w's*: *Gardener's D.* 220
all Should keep within, door shut, and *w* barr'd. *Godiva* 41
Saw from his *w's* nothing save his own— *Aylmer's Field* 21
so To the open *w* moved, remaining there *Princess iv* 492
The giant *w's'* blazon'd fires, *The Daisy* 58
Clasp her *w*, trail and twine! *Window, At the Window* 2
Blaze upon her *w*, sun, „ *When* 15
were laid On the hasp of the *w*, *Maud I xiv* 19
The Lady Lyonors at a *w* stood, *Gareth and L.* 1375
glancing on the *w*, when the gloom Of twilight *Balin and Balan* 232
Where twelve great *w's* blazon Arthur's wars, *Holy Grail* 248
lands in your view From this bay *w*— *Sisters (E. and E.)* 52
May leave the *w's* blinded, *Romney's R.* 146
Window-bars it came, and close beside the *w-b*, *May Queen, Con.* 39
Window-pane Oh is it the brook, or a pool, or her *w p*, *Window, On the Hill* 4
I follow them down to the *w-p* of my dear, „ 17
And never a glimpse of her *w p*! „ *No Answer* 3
Wind-scatter'd surf *w-s* over sails and masts, *D. of F. Women* 31
Windy Beneath the *w* wall. *Palace of Art* 72
building rook 'll caw from the *w* tall elm-tree, *May Queen, N. Y's. E.* 17
And it was *w* weather. (repeat) *The Goose* 4, 40
you hear The *w* clanging of the minster clock; *Gardener's D.* 38
Far on the ringing plains of *w* Troy. *Ulysses* 17
Fly o'er waste fens and *w* fields. *Sir Galahad* 60
By Ellen's grave, on the *w* hill. *Edward Gray* 12
All the *w* ways of men Are but dust that rises up, (repeat) *Vision of Sin* 132, 168
And swang besides on many a *w* sign— *Aylmer's Field* 19
That climb into the *w* halls of heaven: *Lucretius* 136
ere the *w* jest Had labour'd down within *Princess v* 272
Fair-hair'd and redder than a *w* morn; „ *Con.* 91
Flames, on the *w* headland flare! *W. to Alexandra* 16
Or sheepwalk up the *w* wold; *In Mem. c* 8
Uncared for, gird the *w* grove, „ *ci* 13
of grain Storm-strengthen'd on a *w* site, *Gareth and L.* 692
Comes flying over many a *w* wave To Britain, *Marr. of Geraint* 337
Swung from his brand a *w* buffet out Once, *Geraint and E.* 90
slide From the long shore-cliff's *w* walls „ 164
And all the *w* clamour of the daws „ 255
On sallows in the *w* gleams of March: *Merlin and V.* 225
On some wild down above the *w* deep, „ 658
Wine (*See also* **Adam's wine, Cowslip wine**) our friends are all forsaking The *w* and the merry-making. *All Things will Die* 19
Across the walnuts and the *w*— *Miller's D.* 32
little dues of wheat, and *w* and oil; *Lotos-Eaters, C. S.* 122
think not they are glazed with *w*. *Locksley Hall* 51
as moonlight unto sunlight, and as water unto *w*— „ 152
And beaker brimm'd with noble *w*. *Day-Dm., Sleep. P.* 36
she comes and dips Her laurel in the *w*, *Will Water.* 18
Sipt *w* from silver, praising God, „ 127
By heaps of gourds, and skins of *w*, *Vision of Sin* 13
Bring me spices, bring me *w*; „ 76
W is good for shrivell'd lips, „ 79
Let me loose thy tongue with *w*: „ 88
Charier of sleep, and *w*, and exercise, *Aylmer's Field* 448
Warm'd with his *w's*, or taking pride in her, „ 554
Sat at his table; drank his costly *w's*; *Sea Dreams* 74
they talk'd At *w*, in clubs, of art, of politics; *Princess, Pro.* 161
call'd mine host To council, plied him with his richest *w's*, „ *i* 174
those That lay at *w* with Lar and Lucumo; „ *ii* 129
Fruit, blossom, viand, amber *w*, „ *iv* 35
not a death's-head at the *w*.' „ 87
And had our *w* and chess beneath the planes, „ *vi* 246
Steel and gold, and corn and *w*, *Ode Inter. Exhib.* 17
But honest talk and wholesome *w*, *To F. D. Maurice* 18
honey-hearted *w* And bread from out the houses *Spec. of Iliad* 5
(And dear to me as sacred *w* To dying lips *In Mem. xxxvii* 19
'Twas well, indeed, when warm with *w*, „ *xc* 9
Wine (*continued*) fetch the *w*, Arrange the board and brim the glass; *In Mem. cvii* 15
yes!—but a company forges the *w*. *Maud I i* 36
I fear, the new strong *w* of love, „ *vi* 82
Betrothed us over their *w*, „ *xix* 39
That he left his *w* and horses and play, „ 74
brief night goes In babble and revel and *w*. „ *xxii* 28
feeble vassals of *w* and anger and lust, „ *II i* 43
baken meats and good red *w* Of Southland, *Gareth and L.* 1190
Go to the town and buy us flesh and *w*; *Marr. of Geraint* 372
means of goodly welcome, flesh and *w*. „ 387
For now the *w* made summer in his veins, „ 398
A creature wholly given to brawls and *w*, „ 441
cried Geraint for *w* and goodly cheer *Geraint and E.* 283
And *w* and food were brought, „ 289
When *w* and free companions kindled him, „ 293
So vanish friendships only made in *w*. „ 479
call'd for flesh and *w* to feed his spears. „ 601
(And fill'd a horn with *w* and held it to her,) „ 659
Drink therefore and the *w* will change your will.' „ 663
I will not look at *w* until I die.' „ 667
Nor ever touch'd fierce *w*, nor tasted flesh, *Merlin and V.* 627
They sit with knife in meat and *w* in horn! „ 694
But once in life was fluster'd with new *w*, „ 756
and by fountains running *w*, *Last Tournament* 141
did ye mark that fountain yesterday Made to run *w*?— „ 287
To hand the *w* to whosoever came— „ 290
hurl'd The tables over and the *w's*, „ 475
that I should suck Lies like sweet *w's*: „ 645
meat, *W*, *w*—and I will love thee to the death, „ 720
these had comforted the blood With meats and *w's*, „ 725
straddling on the butts While the *w* ran: *Guinevere* 269
Till, drunk with its own *w*, *Lover's Tale i* 271
w's that, Heaven knows when, Had suck'd the fire „ *iv* 193
the *w's* being of such nobleness— „ 222
priceless goblet with a priceless *w* Arising, „ 227
Crazy with laughter and babble and earth's new *w*, *To A. Tennyson* 2
For see—this *w*—the grape from whence *Sisters (E. and E.)* 61
hev a glass o' cowslip *w*! *Village Wife* 5
Droonk wi' the Quoloty's *w*, „ 77
Taäste another drop o' the *w*— „ 120
the wild hour and the *w* Had set the wits aflame. *Sir J. Oldcastle* 94
riotous fits Of *w* and harlotry— „ 101
was the poisonous pleasure of *w*; *V. of Maeldune* 62
of a hand giving bread and *w*, *The Wreck* 114
As laughter over *w*, *Ancient Sage* 184
'Yet *w* and laughter friends! „ 195
Nor drown thyself with flies in honied *w*; „ 268
guest may make True cheer with honest *w*— *Pro. to Gen. Hamley* 16
Wealth with his *w's* and his wedded harlots; *Vastness* 19
and choice of women and of *w's*? *By an Evolution.* 8
men may taste Swine-flesh, drink *w*; *Akbar's Dream* 54
one of those Who mix the *w's* of heresy „ 174
brag to his fellow rakes of his conquest over the *w*? *Charity* 18
Wine-flask The *w-f* lying couch'd in moss, *In Mem. lxxxix* 44
Wine-heated Moist as they were, *w-h* from the feast; *Geraint and E.* 351
Wing (s) (*See also* **Ankle-wing**) What they say betwixt their *w's*? *Adeline* 29
And clip your *w's*, and make you love: *Rosalind* 45
Droops both his *w's*, regarding thee, *Eleänore* 119
'He dried his *w's*: like gauze they grew; *Two Voices* 13
'Here sits he shaping *w's* to fly: „ 289
fold our *w's*, And cease from wanderings, *Lotos-Eaters, C. S.* 19
crested bird That claps his *w's* at dawn. *D. of F. Women* 180
hearts and feeble *w's* That every sophister *Love thou thy land* 11
lime a summer home of murmurous *w's*. *Gardener's D.* 48
O'er the mute city stole with folded *w's*, Distilling odours „ 186
While the prime swallow dips his *w*, *Edwin Morris* 145
This dull chrysalis Cracks into shining *w's*, *St. S. Stylites* 156
'A light wind chased her on the *w*, *Talking Oak* 125
On sleeping *w's* they sail. *Sir Galahad* 44
W's flutter, voices hover clear: „ 78
Tho' fortune clip my *w's*, *Will Water.* 50

Wing (s) (*continued*) seabird crosses With one waft of the *w*. *The Captain* 72
He rode a horse with *w's*, *Vision of Sin* 3
hung With *w's* of brooding shelter o'er her peace, *Aylmer's Field* 139
So often, that the folly taking *w's* „ 494
Till the little *w's* are stronger. *Sea Dreams* 298
Whereon a woman-statue rose with *w's* *Princess i* 210
wheel'd on Europe-shadowing *w's*, *Ode on Well.* 120
you have gotten the *w's* of love, *Window, Ay* 15
Spread thy full *w's*, and waft him o'er *In Mem. ix* 4
The wild pulsation of her *w's*; „ *xii* 4
My fancies time to rise on *w*, „ *xiii* 17
that dip Their *w's* in tears, and skim away. „ *xlviii* 16
Self-balanced on a lightsome *w*: „ *lxv* 8
Take *w's* of fancy, and ascend, „ *lxxvi* 1
Take *w's* of foresight; lighten thro' „ 5
No *w* of wind the region swept, „ *lxxxviii* 6
Or eagle's *w*, or insect's eye; „ *cxxiv* 6
The love that rose on stronger *w's*, „ *cxxviii* 1
My life has crept so long on a broken *w* *Maud III vi* 1
a Shape that fled With broken *w's*, *Gareth and L.* 1208
and *w's* Moved in her ivy, *Marr. of Geraint* 598
made his feet *W's* thro' a glimmering gallery, *Balin and Balan* 404
To catch a loathly plume fall'n from the *w* *Merlin and V.* 727
And on the fourth are men with growing *w's*, *Holy Grail* 237
And peak'd *w's* pointed to the Northern Star. „ 240
And both the *w's* are made of gold, „ 242
Became a living creature clad with *w's*? „ 519
Half-wrench'd a golden *w*; „ 733
Great angels, awful shapes, and *w's* and eyes. „ 848
Follow'd a rush of eagle's *w's*, *Last Tournament* 417
swum with balanced *w's* To some tall mountain: *Lover's Tale i* 302
Love, rising, shook his *w's*, and charged the winds „ 317
Love wraps his *w's* on either side the heart, „ 467
like the waft of an Angel's *w*; *In the Child. Hosp.* 38
The moth will singe her *w's*, *Sir J. Oldcastle* 189
Sphinx, with *w's* drawn back, *Tiresias* 148
rose as it were on the *w's* of an eagle *The Wreck* 69
Without their hope of *w's*!' *Ancient Sage* 211
w push'd out to the left and a *w* to the right, *Heavy Brigade* 15
Russian crowd Folded its *w's* „ 39
And showing them, souls have *w's*! *Dead Prophet* 12
in their turn thy warblers rise on *w*. *Prog. of Spring* 108
a shape with *w's* Came sweeping by him, *St. Telemachus* 24
The shape with *w's*. „ 38
Bring me my horse—my horse? my *w's* *Mechanophilus* 9

Wing (verb) Stoops at all game that *w* the skies, *Rosalind* 4
Far as the wild swan *w's*, to where the sky *Palace of Art* 31
That I could *w* my will with might *In Mem. xli* 10

Wing-case slide apart Their dusk *w-c's*, *Gareth and L.* 687

Wing'd (*See also* **Black-wing'd, Light-wing'd, Strong-wing'd, White-wing'd, Wide-wing'd**) arrows of his thoughts were headed And *w* with flame, *The Poet* 12
bravely furnish'd all abroad to fling The *w* shafts of truth, „ 26
That sought to sow themselves like *w* seeds, *Gardener's D.* 65
Stood from his walls and *w* his entry-gates *Aylmer's Field* 18
From four *w* horses dark against the stars; *Princess i* 211
and *w* Her transit to the throne, „ *iv* 377
Or keeps his *w* affections clipt with crime: „ *vii* 316
Not making his high place the lawless perch Of *w* ambitions, *Ded. of Idylls* 23
Tits, wrens, and all *w* nothings peck him dead! *Marr. of Geraint* 275
Like odour rapt into the *w* wind *Lover's Tale i* 801

Winging What time I watch'd the swallow *w* *Princess iv* 89

Wink (s) Till with a *w* his dream was changed, *Com. of Arthur* 441
(For in a *w* the false love turns to hate) *Merlin and V.* 852

Wink (verb) ere a star can *w*, beheld her there. *Gardener's D.* 122
one that nods and *w's* behind a slowly dying fire. *Locksley Hall* 136
W at our advent: help my prince to gain *Princess iii* 160
Nor *w's* the gold fin in the porphyry font: „ *vii* 178
But *w* no more in slothful overtrust. *Ode on Well.* 170
'Man! is he man at all, who knows and *w's*? Sees what his fair bride is and does, and *w's*? *Merlin and V.* 781

Wink'd last light, that long Had *w* and threaten'd darkness, *M. d'Arthur, Ep.* 2
Wink'd (*continued*) which for bribe had *w* at wrong, *Geraint and E.* 939
Mutinies, treacheries—*w* at, and condoned— *Columbus* 226

Winking The landscape *w* thro' the heat: *In Mem. lxxxix* 16
W his eyes, and twisted all his face. *Lancelot and E.* 1145

Winner Are *w's* in this pastime of our King. *Last Tournament* 199

Winnie Minnie and *W* Slept in a shell. *Minnie and Winnie* 1

Winning *W* its way with extreme gentleness *Isabel* 23
To all the people, *w* reverence. *M. d'Arthur* 108
If such be worth the *w* now, *You might have won* 2
w easy grace, No doubt, for slight delay, *Princess iv* 330
a good mother, a good wife, Worth *w*; „ *v* 167
To all the people, *w* reverence. *Pass. of Arthur* 276

Winnow enormous polypi *W* with giant arms *The Kraken* 10

Winsome Was wedded with a *w* wife, Ygerne: *Com. of Arthur* 188
Peept the *w* face of Edith like a flower *Locksley H., Sixty* 260

Wint (went) an' thin *w* into the dark. *Tomorrow* 22
people 'ud see it that *w* in to mass— „ 74

Winter (adj.) (*See also* **Midwinter**) The mellow'd reflex of a *w* moon; *Isabel* 29
From *w* rains that beat his grave. *Two Voices* 261
The slow result of *w* showers: „ 452
Full knee-deep lies the *w* snow, And the *w* winds are wearily sighing: *D. of the O. Year* 1
Among the mountains by the *w* sea; *M. d'Arthur* 2
w moon, Brightening the skirts of a long cloud, „ 53
And the long glories of the *w* moon. „ 192
And like an oaken stock in *w* woods, *Golden Year* 62
Made orphan by a *w* shipwreck, *Enoch Arden* 15
face, Rough-redden'd with a thousand *w* gales, „ 95
Mock-Hymen were laid up like *w* bats, *Princess iv* 144
Which in our *w* woodland looks a flower. *A Dedication* 13
We heard them sweep the *w* land; *In Mem. xxx* 10
Glastonbury, where the *w* thorn Blossoms at Christmas, *Holy Grail* 52
Among the mountains by the *w* sea; *Pass. of Arthur* 171
w moon, Brightening the skirts of a long cloud, „ 221
And the long glories of the *w* moon. „ 360
The stillness of the dead world's *w* dawn „ 442
Weird Titan by thy *w* weight of years *To Victor Hugo* 7
She spies the summer thro' the *w* bud, *Ancient Sage* 74
She that finds a *w* sunset fairer than a morn of Spring. *Locksley H., Sixty* 22
Dumb on the *w* heath he lay. *Dead Prophet* 13
Sun Burst from a swimming fleece of *w* gray, *Demeter and P.* 20
and Ætna kept her *w* snow. „ 115
That icy *w* silence—how it froze you *Happy* 71
I soaking here in *w* wet— *To Ulysses* 6
Who love the *w* woods, to trace On paler heavens „ 14
thro' the sunless *w* morning-mist In silence wept *Death of Œnone* 8

Winter (s) (*See also* **Midwinter, Summer-winter**) 'Tis the world's *w*; *Nothing will Die* 17
A hundred *w's* snow'd upon his breast, *Palace of Art* 139
where the moving isles of *w* shock By night, *M. d'Arthur* 140
Three *w's*, that my soul might grow to thee, *St. S. Stylites* 71
monsters only made to kill Time by the fire in *w*.' *Princess, Pro.* 205
'Why not a summer's as a *w's* tale? „ 209
we should have him back Who told the '*W's* tale' „ 238
Those *w's* of abeyance all worn out, „ *iv* 440
Whose eighty *w's* freeze with one rebuke *Ode on Well.* 186
Your presence will be sun in *w*, *To F. D. Maurice* 3
To break the blast of *w*, stand; „ 22
Yell'd as when the winds of *w* *Boädicea* 77
Till growing *w's* lay me low; *In Mem. xl* 30
And every *w* change to spring. „ *liv* 16
As in the *w's* left behind, „ *lxxviii* 9
Merlin, whose vast wit And hundred *w's* *Com. of Arthur* 281
A man wellnigh a hundred *w's* old, *Holy Grail* 85
And each of these a hundred *w's* old, „ 88
man was no more than a voice In the white *w* of his age, *Pass. of Arthur* 4
seen where the moving isles of *w* shock By night, „ 308
and his *w's* were fifteen score, *V. of Maeldune* 116
His *w* chills him to the root, *Ancient Sage* 119
Eighty *w's* leave the dog too lame to follow *Locksley H., Sixty* 226
Spring and Summer and Autumn and *W*, *Vastness* 29

Winter (s) (*continued*) a breath that past With all the cold of *w*. *The Ring* 33
fingers were so stiffen'd by the frost Of seven and ninety *w's*, „ 240
sigh'd In the *w* of the Present for the summer of the Past; *Happy* 70
My yucca, which no *w* quells, *To Ulysses* 21
To wallow in that *w* of the hills. *Romney's R.* 15
And all the *w's* are hidden. *The Throstle* 16
In a hundred, a thousand *w's*? *The Dawn* 24
Winter-black One night when earth was *w-b*, *To E. Fitzgerald* 21
Winter-clad Tattoo'd or woaded, *w-c* in skins, *Princess ii* 120
Winter'd *See* **Many-winter'd**
Winter-field The tented *w-f* was broken up *Aylmer's Field* 110
Winterless the sons of a *w* day. *The Wreck* 74
Wintertide in *w* shall star The black earth *Ode to Memory* 19
Would make the world as blank as *W-t*. *Last Tournament* 221
Winter-white by age as *w-w* As mine is now, *Tiresias* 19
Wintry So she, and turn'd askance a *w* eye: *Princess vi* 329
Who roll'd the psalm to *w* skies, *In Mem. lvi* 11
Walk'd in a *w* wind by a ghastly glimmer, *Maud I iii* 13
Scarr'd with a hundred *w* water-courses— *Holy Grail* 490
Gleam, that had waned to a *w* glimmer On icy fallow *Merlin and the G.* 83
Wiped Why 'edn't tha *w* thy shoes? *Spinster's S's.* 46
Wire The wind sounds like a silver *w*, *Fatima* 29
The parrot in his gilded *w's*. *Day-Dm., Sleep. P.* 16
A man with knobs and *w's* and vials fired A cannon: *Princess, Pro.* 65
Up thro' gilt *w's* a crafty loving eye, „ 172
who thrumm'd On such a *w* as musically *Last Tournament* 323
Wirer The nightly *w* of their innocent hare *Aylmer's Field* 490
Wiry writhed his *w* arms Around him, *Gareth and L.* 1150
Wisdom her raiment's hem was traced in flame *W*, *The Poet* 46
Could his dark *w* find it out, *Two Voices* 308
wisdom-bred And throned of *w*— *Œnone* 124
Were *w* in the scorn of consequence.' „ 150
stay'd the Ausonian king to hear Of *w* *Palace of Art* 112
The *w* of a thousand years Is in them. *Of old sat Freedom* 18
flower of knowledge changed to fruit Of *w*. *Love and Duty* 25
Knowledge comes, but *w* lingers, (repeat) *Locksley Hall* 141, 143
Not much their *w* teaches; *Will Water.* 174
yet for all your *w* well know I That I shall look *Enoch Arden* 211
a tigress with a gossamer, Were *w* to it.' *Princess v* 171
bearing and the training of a child Is woman's *w*.' „ 466
Wearing his *w* lightly, like the fruit *A Dedication* 12
And in thy *w* make me wise. *In Mem. Pro.* 44
For *W* dealt with mortal powers, „ *xxxvi* 5
There must be *w* with great Death: „ *li* 11
Whatever *w* sleep with thee. „ *cviii* 16
Nor let thy *w* make me wise. „ *cix* 24
High *w* holds my *w* less, „ *cxii* 1
Yet how much *w* sleeps with thee „ *cxiii* 2
moving side by side With *w*, „ *cxiv* 20
But *W* heavenly of the soul. „ 22
let me think Silence is *w*: *Merlin and V.* 253
'And lo, I clothe myself with *w*, „ 255
till he let his *w* go For ease of heart, „ 892
Led on the gray-hair'd *w* of the east; *Holy Grail* 453
with the *w* and wealth of his own, *The Wreck* 65
Strong in will and rich in *w*, *Locksley H., Sixty* 49
and take their *w* for your friend. „ 104
Pillory *W* in your markets, „ 134
move to such a goal As *W* hopes to gain, *Politics* 4
'Thy glory baffles *w*. *Akbar's Dream* 28
Wisdom-bred *w-b* And throned of wisdom— *Œnone* 123
Wise (adj.) That read his spirit blindly *w*, *Two Voices* 287
The slow *w* smile that, round about *Miller's D.* 5
No one can be more *w* than destiny. *D. of F. Women* 94
with choice paintings of *w* men I hung The royal dais round. *Palace of Art* 131
Great Nature is more *w* than I: *To J. S.* 35
'Be *w*: not easily forgiven Are those, *Gardener's D.* 247
Therefore comes it we are *w*. *Vision of Sin* 100
'O Enoch, you are *w*; And yet for all your wisdom *Enoch Arden* 210

Wise (adj.) (*continued*) wholly *w* To let that handsome fellow *Aylmer's Field* 268
Should I not call her *w*, who made me *w*? *Princess ii* 396
Lady Psyche, younger, not so *w*, „ *iv* 316
Like our wild Princess with as *w* a dream „ *Con.* 69
Attain the *w* indifference of the wise; *A Dedication* 8
For such a *w* humility As befits a solemn fane: *Ode on Well.* 249
And in thy wisdom make me *w*. *In Mem., Pro.* 44
If thou wilt have me *w* and good. „ *lix* 8
She darkly feels him great and *w*, „ *xcvii* 34
They sang of what is *w* and good „ *ciii* 10
'Tis held that sorrow makes us *w*, „ *cviii* 15
Nor let thy wisdom make me *w*. „ *cix* 24
'Tis held that sorrow makes us *w*; „ *cxiii* 1
But that blind clamour made me *w*; „ *cxxiv* 18
Were it not *w* if I fled from the place *Maud I i* 64
How modest, kindly, all-accomplish'd, *w*, *Ded. of Idylls* 18
we have heard from our *w* man at home To Northward, *Gareth and L.* 201
and never a whit more *w* The fourth, „ 635
O damsel, be you *w* To call him shamed, „ 1259
whether very *w* Or very foolish; *Marr. of Geraint* 469
'Yea so,' said he, 'do it: be not too *w*; *Geraint and E.* 424
And this *w* world of ours is mainly right. „ 901
And our *w* Queen, if knowing that I know, *Merlin and V.* 121
'Who are *w* in love Love most, say least,' „ 247
Yet you are *w* who say it; „ 252
surely ye are *w*, But such a silence is more *w* than kind.' „ 288
However *w*, ye hardly know me yet.' „ 355
'I never was less *w*, however *w*, „ 357
'Are ye so *w*? ye were not once so *w*, *Lancelot and E.* 103
their *w* men Were strong in that old magic *Holy Grail* 665
the heart that was *w*! *The Wreck* 56
By which thou wilt abide, if thou be *w*, *Ancient Sage* 35
wherefore thou be *w*, Cleave ever to the sunnier side „ 67
But thou be *w* in this dream-world of ours, „ 108
years that made the stripling *w* Undo their work again, „ 111
yet perhaps she was not *w*; *Locksley H., Sixty* 11
if dynamite and revolver leave you courage to be *w*: „ 107
PATRIOT Statesman, be thou *w* to know *To Duke of Argyll* 1
Then let *w* Nature work her will, *My life is full* 21
Merlin, the *w* man that ever served King Uther *Com. of Arthur* 151
Not even thy *w* father with his signs *Guinevere* 274
'If I,' said the *w* little Annie, 'was you, *In the Child. Hosp.* 48
Achæans—honouring his *w* mother's word— *Achilles over the T.* 16
To cast *w* words among the multitude *Tiresias* 66
but thou art *w* enough, Tho' young to love thy wiser, „ 153
w man's word, Here trampled by the populace „ 173
In what they prophesy, our *w* men, *Epilogue* 65
Horace, you the *w* Adviser of the nine-years-ponder'd lay, *Poets and their B.* 5
VOICE spake out of the skies To a just man and a *w*— *Voice spake, etc.* 2
Wise (s) to its sway Will win the *w* at once, *Mine be the strength* 10
O silent faces of the Great and *W*, *Palace of Art* 195
Not yet the *w* of heart would cease *Love thou thy land* 81
her least remark was worth The experience of the *w*. *Edwin Morris* 66
Thro' madness, hated by the *w*, *Love and Duty* 7
Yearn'd after by the wisest of the *w*, *Lucretius* 267
Among the *w* and the bold. *Ode on Well.* 52
War, who breaks the converse of the *w*; *Third of Feb.* 8
the *w* who think, the *w* who reign, *Ode Inter. Exhib.* 32
God is law, say the *w*; *High. Pantheism* 13
Attain the wise indifference of the *w*; *A Dedication* 8
With all the circle of the *w*, *In Mem. lxi* 3
Thy likeness to the *w* below, „ *lxxiv* 7
truthless violence mourn'd by the *W*, *Vastness* 5
Wise *See* **Broken-wise, Crescent-wise, Dropwise, Earthly-wise, Elsewise, Heavenly-wise, Madonna-wise, Mocking-wise, Over-wise, Warrior-wise, Worldly-wise**
Wisely Or *w* or unwisely, signs of storm, *To the Queen ii* 49
Wiser That we are *w* than our sires. *Love thou thy land* 72
Surely I shall be *w* in a year: *Enoch Arden* 433
nor is it *W* to weep a true occasion lost, *Princess iv* 68

Wiser (*continued*) dismiss'd in shame to live No *w* than their mothers, *Princess iv* 514
A young man will be *w* by and by ; *Com. of Arthur* 404
As children learn, be thou *W* for falling ! *Balin and Balan* 76
fierce beast found A *w* than herself, *Tiresias* 152
thou art wise enough, Tho' young, to love thy *w*, „ 154
W there than you, that crowning barren Death *Locksley H., Sixty* 61
But you have made the *w* choice, *You might have won* 5
Let him, the *w* man who springs Hereafter, *In Mem. cxx* 9
like a stoic, or like A *w* epicurean, *Maud I iv* 21
' Belike for lack of *w* company ; *Last Tournament* 245
' Then were swine, goats, asses, geese The *w* fools, „ 326

Wisest Yearn'd after by the *w* of the wise, *Lucretius* 267
' Madam, he the *w* man Feasted the woman *w* then, *Princess ii* 350
Her that talk'd down the fifty *w* men ; „ *v* 294
To know myself the *w* knight of all.' *Last Tournament* 248
Nor is he the *w* man who never proved himself a fool. *Locksley H., Sixty* 244
DOUBT no longer that the Highest is the *w* and the best, *Faith* 1

Wish (s) phantom of a *w* that once could move, *The form, the form* 10
wheeling round The central *w*, *Gardener's D.* 225
And let me have an answer to my *w* ; *Dora* 30
let him speak his *w*. *St. S. Stylites* 144
Old *w'es*, ghosts of broken plans, *Will Water.* 29
the noble *w* To save all earnings to the uttermost, *Enoch Arden* 85
a *w* renew'd, When two years after came a boy „ 88
his had been, or yours : that was his *w*. „ 300
He oft denied his heart his dearest *w*, „ 336
He laugh'd, and yielded readily to their *w*, „ 370
son Was silent, tho' he often look'd his *w* ; „ 482
this wild king to force her to his *w*, *Princess, Pro.* 37
As if to close with Cyril's random *w* : „ *iii* 101
But led by golden *w'es*, and a hope „ *iv* 420
Tell my *w* to her dewy blue eye : *Window, Letter* 13
And ever met him on his way With *w'es*, *In Mem. vi* 22
The *w*, that of the living whole „ *lv* 1
That cries against my *w* for thee. „ *xc* 24
The *w* too strong for words to name ; „ *xciii* 14
sent her *w* that I would yield thee thine. *Gareth and L.* 551
knight art thou To the King's best *w*. „ 1259
Albeit I give no reason but my *w*, *Marr. of Geraint* 761
Be moulded by your *w'es* for her weal ; „ 799
I know Your *w*, and would obey ; *Geraint and E.* 419
Beholding how ye butt against my *w*, „ 677
at times Would flatter his own *w* in age for love, *Merlin and V.* 185
And grant my re-reiterated *w*, „ 353
Nor own'd a sensual *w*, „ 628
the *w* to prove him wholly hers.' „ 865
Love-loyal to the least *w* of the Queen *Lancelot and E.* 89
To speak the *w* most near to your true heart ; „ 914
And Lancelot saw that she withheld her *w*, „ 920
' Delay no longer, speak your *w*, „ 924
And there I woke, but still the *w* remain'd. „ 1048
and sent him to the Queen Bearing his *w*, „ 1169
that he wellnigh deem'd His *w* by hers was echo'd ; *Pelleas and E.* 121
Love-loyal to the least *w* of the Queen, *Guinevere* 126
way my *w* leads me evermore Still to believe it— *Lover's Tale i* 274
But she spake on, for I did name no *w*, „ 578
But she spake on, for I did name no *w*, No *w*—no hope. „ 583
' It was my *w*,' he said, ' to pass, to sleep, „ *iv* 63
such her dying *w*—Given on the morning *The Ring* 76
if his young music wakes A *w* in you *To Mary Boyle* 64
my strongest *w* Falls flat before your least unwillingness. *Romney's R.* 71

Wish (verb) Where she would ever *w* to dwell, *Supp. Confessions* 54
they *w* to charm Pallas and Juno sitting by : *A Character* 14
I *w* that somewhere in the ruin'd folds, *Œnone* 221
only *w* to live till the snowdrops come again : *May Queen, N. Y's. E.* 14
I *w* the snow would melt and the sun come out „ 15
Yet something I did *w* to say : *To J. S.* 60
I would *w* to see My grandchild on my knees *Dora* 12
Is it well to *w* thee happy ?— *Locksley Hall* 43
I cannot help you as I *w* to do Unless— *Enoch Arden* 407
I *w* you for my wife. „ 410

Wish (verb) (*continued*) do I *w*—What ?—that the bush were leafless ? *Lucretius* 205
I *w* I were Some mighty poetess, *Princess, Pro.* 131
O I *w* That I were some great princess, „ 133
I could not help it, did not *w* : „ *ii* 332
that *w'es* at a dance to change The music— „ *iv* 589
I *w* it Gentle as freedom '— „ *vi* 205
I *w* she had not yielded ! ' „ *Con.* 5
I *w* they were a whole Atlantic broad.' „ 71
To talk them o'er, to *w* them here, *In Mem. xc* 11
We *w* them store of happy days „ *Con.* 84
I *w* I could hear again The chivalrous battle-song *Maud I x* 53
And *w'es* me to approve him, „ *xix* 71
She did not *w* to blame him— „ *xx* 5
I have not fall'n so low as some would *w*. *Marr. of Geraint* 129
' Did I *w* Your warning or your silence ? *Geraint and E.* 76
Whether ye *w* me victory or defeat, „ 80
Then said Geraint, ' I *w* no better fare : „ 232
make me *w* still more to learn this charm *Merlin and V.* 329
I well could *w* a cobweb for the gnat, „ 370
Pure, as you ever *w* your knights to be. *Lancelot and E.* 1375
Well—can I *w* her any huger wrong *Last Tournament* 596
Well might I *w* to veil her wickedness, *Guinevere* 211
an' I *w* I was dead— *First Quarrel* 52
died o' your going away, an' I *w* that I had.' „ 54
I too *w* that I had—in the pleasant times „ 55
best And oldest friend, your Uncle, *w'es* it, *Sisters (E. and E.)* 47
Could sometimes *w* I had never led the way. *Columbus* 186
I *W* I were in the years of old, *Tiresias* 1
And *w* the dead, as happier than ourselves *Ancient Sage* 205
I could *w* yon moaning sea would rise *The Flight* 11
is it well to *w* you joy ? *Locksley H., Sixty* 216
W me joy ! *Father.* What need to *w* when Hubert weds in you The heart of Love, *The Ring* 60
' HE is fled—I *w* him dead— *Forlorn* 1

Wish'd She *w* me happy, but she thought *Miller's D.* 139
I have *w* this marriage, night and day, *Dora* 21
' I *w* myself the fair young beech *Talking Oak* 141
and I *w* for Leonard there, *Golden Year* 4
' I came to speak to you of what he *w*, *Enoch Arden* 291
roll'd his eyes upon her Repeating all he *w*, „ 905
And how it was the thing his daughter *w*, *The Brook* 140
I *w* my voice A rushing tempest *Aylmer's Field* 756
They *w* to marry ; they could rule a house ; *Princess ii* 465
I stammer'd that I knew him—could have *w*— „ *iii* 206
Because he might have *w* it— „ *vi* 275
They hated banter, *w* for something real, „ *Con.* 18
But I *w* it had been God's will that I, *Grandmother* 73
I almost *w* no more to wake, *In Mem. xxviii* 14
And wept, and *w* that I were dead ; *Com. of Arthur* 345
w The Prince had found her in her ancient home ; *Marr. of Geraint* 643
W it had been my mother, *Lancelot and E.* 674
and I *w*, yet *w* her not to speak ; *Lover's Tale i* 577
But I niver not *w* fur childer, *Spinster's S's.* 84

Wishing And, tho' in silence, *w* joy. *In Mem., Con.* 88

Wisp the gilded ball Danced like a *w* : *Princess, Pro.* 64
w that flickers where no foot can tread.' „ *iv* 358
the *w* that gleams On Lethe in the eyes of Death. *In Mem. xcviii* 7

Wistful ' Then I fixt My *w* eyes on two fair images, *Sea Dreams* 240
mother's eye Full of the *w* fear that he would go, *Gareth and L.* 173

Wit With shrilling shafts of subtle *w*. *Clear-headed friend* 13
Alone and warming his five *w's*, (repeat) *The Owl i* 6, 13
The fruitful *w* Cleaving, took root, *The Poet* 20
With thy shallow *w* : *Poet's Mind* 2
O the dalliance and the *w*, *D. of F. Women* 147
I grow in worth, and *w*, and sense, *Will Water.* 41
The tavern-hours of mighty *w's*— „ 191
Thro' which a few, by *w* or fortune led, *Aylmer's Field* 438
gave To him that fluster'd his poor parish *w's* „ 521
How might a man not wander from his *w's* *Princess ii* 440
the wealth Of words and *w*, *In Mem., Con.* 103
Merlin, whose vast *w* And hundred winters *Com. of Arthur* 280
An old man's *w* may wander ere he die. „ 405
Have strength and *w*, in my good mother's hall *Gareth and L.* 12
shook his *w's* they wander in his prime— „ 715

Wit (*continued*) but, being knave, Hast mazed my *w*: *Gareth and L.* 1170
Dreams ruling when *w* sleeps! *Balin and Balan* 143
I loved thee first, That warps the *w*.' *Merlin and V.* 61
If these unwitty wandering *w's* of mine, „ 346
I fain had given them greater *w's*: „ 496
added, of her *w*, A border fantasy of branch and flower, *Lancelot and E.* 10
but listen to me, If I must find you *w*: „ 148
set himself to play upon her With sallying *w*, „ 647
Sweet father, will you let me lose my *w's*?' „ 752
'Ye will not lose your *w's* for dear Lavaine: „ 755
I might have put my *w's* to some rough use, „ 1306
Beast too, as lacking human *w*— *Pelleas and E.* 476
seeing too much *w* Makes the world rotten, *Last Tournament* 246
To babble about him, all to show your *w*— „ 340
The slippery footing of his narrow *w*, *Lover's Tale i* 102
wild hour and the wine Had set the *w's* aflame. *Sir J. Oldcastle* 95
But her *w's* wor dead, an' her hair was as white *Tomorrow* 60
Witch sought and found a *w* Who brew'd the philtre *Lucretius* 15
And we past to the Isle of *W'es* *V. of Maeldune* 97
For a wild *w* naked as heaven stood „ 100
Witch-elm *W-e's* that counterchange the floor *In Mem. lxxxix* 1
Withdraw 'To pass, when Life her light *w's*, *Two Voices* 145
Else I *w* favour and countenance *Aylmer's Field* 307
It might be safe our censures to *w*; *Third of Feb.* 11
still *w* themselves Quite into the deep soul, *Lover's Tale i* 81
if the Nameless should *w* from all *Ancient Sage* 50
Withdrawing *W* by the counter door to that *Aylmer's Field* 282
Withdrawn (*See also* **Long-withdrawn**) Half shown, are broken and *w*. *Two Voices* 306
Deep in the garden lake *w*. *Day-Dm., Sleep. P.* 12
every morning, far *w* Beyond the darkness *Vision of Sin* 48
on the glimmering limit far *w* „ 223
Far into heaven *w*, *Voice and the P.* 38
Death in the living waters, and *w*, *Merlin and V.* 148
I knew the veil had been *w*. *Holy Grail* 522
Withdrew As she *w* into the golden cloud, *Œnone* 191
Where we *w* from summer heats and state, *Princess vi* 245
W themselves from me and night, *In Mem. xcv* 18
Wither *W* beneath the palate, and the heart Faints, *D. of F. Women* 287
I *w* slowly in thine arms, *Tithonus* 6
lest I *w* by despair. *Locksley Hall* 98
And the individual *w's*, „ 142
Now for me the woods may *w*, „ 190
Thine own shall *w* in the vast, *In Mem. lxxvi* 11
as anger falls aside And *w's* on the breast *Lover's Tale i* 10
He *w's* marrow and mind; *Ancient Sage* 120
laurel of Cæsar, but mind would not *w*. *Parnassus* 4
Wither'd parch'd and *w*, deaf and blind, *Fatima* 6
My suit had *w*, nipt to death by him *Edwin Morris* 101
Are *w* in the thorny close, *Day-Dm., Arrival* 11
The naked Three, were *w* long ago, *Death of Œnone* 7
'What drug can make A *w* palsy cease to shake?' *Two Voices* 57
'The memory of the *w* leaf In endless time „ 112
like the *w* moon Smote by the fresh beam of the springing east; *M. d'Arthur* 213
The *w* Misses! how they prose O'er books *Amphion* 81
Who slowly rode across a *w* heath, *Vision of Sin* 61
Ruin'd trunks on w forks, „ 93
to left and right Of *w* holt or tilth or pasturage. *Enoch Arden* 675
A *w* violet is her bliss: *In Mem. xcvii* 26
as the worm draws in the *w* leaf And makes it earth, *Geraint and E.* 633
Danced like a *w* leaf before the hall. (repeat) *Last Tournament* 4, 242
like the *w* moon Smote by the fresh beam of the springing east; *Pass. of Arthur* 381
And pale and fibrous as a *w* leaf, *Lover's Tale i* 422
Withering O Love, Love, Love! O *w* might! *Fatima* 1
Withheld Lancelot saw that she *w* her wish, *Lancelot and E.* 920
w His older and his mightier from the lists; *Pelleas and E.* 159
Withhold a prudence to *w*; *Isabel* 15
Withholding Apart from place, *w* time, *Arabian Nights* 75
Within *See* **Half-within**
Without *See* **Half-without**
Withstand caught By that you swore to *w*? *Maud I vi* 80
Frail, but of force to *w*, „ *II ii* 24

Witness (s) (*See also* **Eye-witness**) Bear *w*, if I could have found a way *St. S. Stylites* 55
in truth (thou wilt bear *w* here) „ 129
thine own *w* that thou bringest Not peace, *Sir J. Oldcastle* 35
Lord give thou power to thy two *w'es*! „ 81
Bear *w* you, that yesterday *To Prof. Jebb.* 2
'Who was *w* of the crime? *Forlorn* 7
There will come a *w* soon Hard to be confuted, „ 25
when creed and race Shall bear false *w*, *Akbar's Dream* 98
Witness (verb) Yes, as your moanings *w*, *Aylmer's Field* 749
W their flowery welcome. *Balin and Balan* 145
Wittier Evelyn is gayer, *w*, prettier, *Sisters (E. and E.)* 36
our quick Evelyn—The merrier, prettier, *w*, „ 286
Witty grew So *w* that ye play'd at ducks and drakes *Last Tournament* 344
Wizard (adj.) Some figure like a *w* pentagram *The Brook* 103
I hear a *w* music roll, *In Mem. lxx* 14
The *w* lightnings deeply glow, „ *cxxii* 19
Wizard (s) Lash'd at the *w* as he spake the word, *Com. of Arthur* 388
The people call'd him *W*; *Merlin and V.* 170
To find a *w* who might teach the King „ 583
but did they find A *w*? Tell me, was he like to thee?' „ 613
The gentle *w* cast a shielding arm. „ 908
pale blood of the *w* at her touch Took gayer colours, „ 949
Mighty the *W* Who found me at sunrise *Merlin and the G.* 11
Wizard-like And weird and worn and *w-l* was he. *The Ring* 196
Woä (stop) *W*—theer's a craw to pluck wi' tha, Sam: *N. Farmer, N. S.* 5
—*w* then *w*—let ma 'ear mysén speäk. „ 8
W then, proputty, wiltha?— „ 39
W then, wiltha? dangtha!— „ 40
Woaded Tattoo'd or *w*, winter-clad in skins, *Princess ii* 120
Woe He hath no thought of coming *w's*; *Supp. Confessions* 47
My heart is wasted with my *w*, *Oriana* 1
silence seems to flow Beside me in my utter *w*, „ 87
all day long you sit between Joy and *w*, *Margaret* 64
The home of *w* without a tear. *Mariana in the S.* 20
A little hint to solace *w*, *Two Voices* 433
My heart may wander from its deeper *w*. *Œnone* 44
Or hearing would not hear me, *w* is me! „ 171
still sheets of water, divers *w's*, *D. of F. Women* 34
That makes my only *w*. „ 136
Even with a verse your holy *w*. *To J. S.* 8
Proclaiming Enoch Arden and his *w's*; *Enoch Arden* 868
As fits an universal *w*, *Ode on Well.* 14
it cost me a world of *w*, *Grandmother* 23
To bear thro' Heaven a tale of *w*, *In Mem. xii* 2
And standing, muffled round with *w*, „ *xiv* 5
The wild unrest that lives in *w* „ *xv* 15
Peace; come away: the song of *w* „ *lvii* 1
Likewise the imaginative *w*, „ *lxxxv* 53
And I—my harp would prelude *w*— „ *lxxxviii* 9
Or, crown'd with attributes of *w* „ *cxviii* 18
So far, so near in *w* and weal; „ *cxxix* 2
for some dark undercurrent *w* That seems to draw— *Maud I xviii* 83
Wrought for his house an irredeemable *w*; „ *II i* 22
'O brother' answer'd Balin '*w* is me! *Balin and Balan* 618
'*W* is me, my knights,' he cried, *Holy Grail* 275
all the wealth and all the *w*? *Guinevere* 344
we came To what our people call 'The Hill of *W*.' *Lover's Tale i* 374
Three cypresses, symbols of mortal *w*, „ 537
A sacred, secret, unapproached *w*, „ 679
on the depth of an unfathom'd *w* Reflex of action. „ 746
were worlds of *w* like our own— *Despair* 18
scroll written over with lamentation and *w*. „ 20
had some glimmer, at times, in my gloomiest *w*, „ 103
Days and Hours That cancel weal with *w*, *Ancient Sage* 96
and youth is turn'd to *w*. *The Flight* 16
this Earth, a stage so gloom'd with *w* *The Play* 1
'*W* to this island if ever a woman (repeat) *Kapiolani* 20, 22
Woful (*See also* **Dainty-woeful**) A *w* man (for so the story went) *Lover's Tale i* 379
when the *w* sentence hath been past, „ 788
Embathing all with wild and *w* hues, „ *ii* 64
Woild (wild) Down i' the *w* 'enemies afoor I coom'd to the plaäce. *N. Farmer, O. S.* 34
Woke Till cold winds *w* the gray-eyed morn *Mariana* 31

Woke (*continued*) Ind to Ind, but in far daylight *w*, *Buonaparte* 4
And *w* her with a lay from fairy land. *Caress'd or chidden* 8
She *w*: the babble of the stream Fell, *Mariana in the S.* 51
Until I *w*, and found him settled down *The Epic* 17
That with the sound I *w*, and heard *M. d'Arthur, Ep.* 30
'O happy kiss, that *w* thy sleep!' *Day-Dm., Depart.* 19
In him *w*, With his first babe's first cry, *Enoch Arden* 84
Here she *w*, Resolved, sent for him „ 506
He *w*, he rose, he spread his arms abroad „ 912
out a despot dream The father panting *w*, *Aylmer's Field* 528
till the comrade of his chambers *w*, „ 583
slept, *w*, and went the next, The Sabbath, *Sea Dreams* 18
wail'd and *w* The mother, „ 57
I *w*, I heard the clash so clearly. „ 135
mixt with little Margaret's, and I *w*, „ 246
After a tempest *w* upon a morn *Lucretius* 24
Shot out of them, and scorch'd me that I *w*. „ 66
Lilia *w* with sudden-shrilling mirth *Princess, Pro.* 216
w Desire in me to infuse my tale of love „ *v* 239
And ere I *w* it was the point of noon, „ 482
Last I *w* sane, but well-nigh close to death „ *vii* 119
Deep in the night I *w*: she, near me, „ 173
That early *w* to feed her little ones, „ 252
This year I slept and *w* with pain, *In Mem. xxviii* 13
songs, that *w* The darkness of our planet, „ *lxxvi* 9
Enid *w* and sat beside the couch, *Marr. of Geraint* 79
W and bethought her of her promise given „ 602
Geraint *W* where he slept in the high hall, „ 755
Beat, till she *w* the sleepers, *Geraint and E.* 404
Balin first *w*, and seeing that true face, *Balin and Balan* 590
W the sick knight, and while he roll'd his eyes *Lancelot and E.* 819
There bode the night: but *w* with dawn, „ 846
there I *w*, but still the wish remain'd. „ 1048
damsel,' answer'd he, 'I *w* from dreams; *Pelleas and E.* 104
He *w*, and being ware of some one nigh, „ 520
And *w* again in utter dark, and cried, *Last Tournament* 623
Far cities burnt, and with a cry she *w*. *Guinevere* 83
Arthur *w* and call'd, 'Who spake? *Pass. of Arthur* 45
and we *w* To gaze upon each other. *Lover's Tale i* 265
when I *w*, Something she ask'd, I know not what, „ 705
I dozed; I *w*. An open landaulet Whirl'd by, *Sisters (E. and E.)* 85
wail For ever *w* the unhappy Past again, „ 263
I *w*, and thought—death—I shall die— *Columbus* 87
and *w* These eyes, now dull, but then so keen *Tiresias* 3
Till I *w* from the trance, *The Wreck* 115
I *w* to all of truest in myself, *The Ring* 182
w me And learn'd me Magic! *Merlin and the G.* 13
dream Wail'd in her, when she *w* beneath the stars. *Death of Œnone* 82
His dream became a deed that *w* the world, *St. Telemachus* 70

Wold (*See also* **Sea-wold, Wowd**) sheep from wattled folds, Upon the ridged *w's*, *Ode to Memory* 67
the long dun *w's* are ribb'd with snow, *Oriana* 5
That clothe the *w* and meet the sky; *L. of Shalott i* 3
And oft in ramblings on the *w*, *Miller's D.* 105
From off the *w* I came, and lay „ 111
To yon old mill across the *w's*; „ 240
from the dry dark *w* the summer airs blow cool *May Queen, N. Y's. E.* 27
blows More softly round the open *w*, *To J. S.* 2
Calm and deep peace on this high *w*, *In Mem. xi* 5
Or sheepwalk up the windy *w*; „ *c* 8
And kindled all the plain and all the *w*. *Balin and Balan* 441

Wolf By shores that darken with the gathering *w*, *Aylmer's Field* 767
a *w* within the fold! A pack of *wolves*! *Princess ii* 190
Then came these *wolves*: *they* knew her: „ *iv* 321
Kite and kestrel, *w* and wolfkin, *Boädicea* 15
A gray old *w* and a lean. *Maud I xiii* 28
Not that gray old *w*, for he came not back From the wilderness, full of *wolves*, „ *II v* 53
dog, and *w* and boar and bear Came night and day, *Com. of Arthur* 23
the *w* would steal The children and devour, „ 26
grew up to wolflike men, Worse than the *wolves*. „ 33
Stript from the three dead *wolves* of woman born *Geraint and E.* 94
drew from those dead *wolves* Their three gay suits „ 180
And waiting to be treated like a *w*, „ 857
And find that it had been the *w's* indeed: „ 864

Wolf (*continued*) heard them pass like *wolves* Howling; *Balin and Balan* 407
let the *wolves'* black maws ensepulchre „ 487
'Leave them to the *wolves*.' „ 588
If the *w* spare me, weep my life away, *Merlin and V.* 885
Old milky fables of the *w* and sheep, *Pelleas and E.* 196
Let the fox bark, let the *w* yell. „ 472
'Why then let men couple at once with *wolves*. „ 536
Sally she wesh'd foälks' cloäths to keep the *w* fro' the door, *North. Cobbler* 29
Meä fur to kick our Sally as kep the *w* fro' the door, „ 59
the howl of all the cassock'd *wolves*, *Sir J. Oldcastle* 158
That gray beast, the *w* of the weald. *Batt. of Brunanburh* 110
When the *wolves* are howling. *Forlorn* 72

Wolfish stern black-bearded kings with *w* eyes, *D. of F. Women* 111
Wolfkin Kite and kestrel, wolf and *w*, *Boädicea* 15
Wolf-like they grew up to *w-l* men, Worse than the wolves. *Com. of Arthur* 32
Wolfskin mighty hands Lay naked on the *w*, *Lancelot and E.* 813
Wolf's-milk half the *w-m* curdled in their veins, *Princess vii* 130
Wolseley foe was driven, And *W* overthrew Arâbi, *Pro. to Gen. Hamley* 30

Woman (*See also* **Beggar-woman, Countrywoman, Gentlewoman, Lay-women, Man-woman**) And *women* smile with saint-like glances *Supp. Confessions* 22
my ancient love With the Greek *w*. *Œnone* 261
'*The Legend of Good Women*' long ago Sung *D. of F. Women* 2
This *w* was the cause. „ 104
the greatest gift, A *w's* heart, *Gardener's D.* 230
for your sake, the *w* that he chose, *Dora* 63
Got up betwixt you and the *w* there. „ 96
So the *women* kiss'd Each other, and set out, „ 128
I woo'd a *w* once, But she was sharper *Audley Court* 52
A *w* like a butt, and harsh as crabs. *Walk. to the Mail* 49
God made the *w* for the man, (repeat) *Edwin Morris* 43, 50
'God made the *w* for the use of man, „ 91
w's pleasure, *w's* pain— *Locksley Hall* 149
W is the lesser man, „ 151
I will take some savage *w*, „ 168
The *w* of a thousand summers back, *Godiva* 11
As just and mere a serving-man As any born of *w*. *Will Water.* 152
Shaped her heart with *w's* meekness *L. of Burleigh* 71
The *w* cannot be believed. *The Letters* 32
And *women's* slander is the worst, „ 34
Scarce could the *w* when he came upon her, *Enoch Arden* 345
they say that *women* are so quick— „ 408
'*W*, I have a secret—only swear, „ 837
'Dead,' clamour'd the good *w*, „ 840
At which the *w* gave A half-incredulous, „ 852
As the *w* heard, Fast flow'd the current „ 864
'*W*, disturb me not now at the last, „ 874
the shame The *w* should have borne, *Aylmer's Field* 356
fell The *w* shrieking at his feet, „ 811
fulminated Against the scarlet *w* and her creed; *Sea Dreams* 23
And near the light a giant *w* sat, „ 98
that the *w* walked upon the brink: „ 112
the *w* honest Work; „ 137
That which I ask'd the *w* in my dream. „ 147
Came men and *women* in dark clusters round, „ 226
The *w* half turn'd round from him she loved, „ 286
when the *w* heard his foot Return from pacings *Lucretius* 5
'O miracle of *women*,' said the book, *Princess, Pro.* 35
Half child half *w* as she was, „ 101
'lives there such a *w* now?' „ 126
'There are thousands now Such *women*, „ 128
the rest follow'd: and the *women* sang „ 244
loved to live alone Among her *women*; „ *i* 50
The *w* were an equal to the man. „ 131
they must lose the child, assume The *w*: „ 138
these the *women* sang; „ 143
for miles about Was till'd by *women*; „ 192
and the *w's* state in each, How far from just; „ *ii* 131
respect, however slight was paid To *w*, „ 137
but that which made *W* and man. „ 145
But *w* ripen'd earlier, and her life Was longer; „ 154
Plato, Verulam; even so With *w*: „ 161

Woman (*continued*) be that for ever which I seem, *W*, *Princess ii* 258
These *women* were too barbarous, would not learn; „ 298
wisest man Feasted the *w* wisest then, „ 351
But when did *w* ever yet invent?' „ 391
Men hated learned *women*: „ 466
And with that *w* closeted for hours!' „ *iii* 56
She sees herself in every *w* else, „ 110
extremes, I told her, well might harm The *w's* cause. „ 145
To lift the *w's* fall'n divinity „ 223
what every *w* counts her due, Love, children, „ 244
for *women*, up till this Cramp'd under worse „ 277
and mould The *w* to the fuller day.' „ 332
Disorderly the *women*. „ *iv* 170
Huge *women* blowzed with health, „ 279
You hold the *w* is the better man; „ 410
all *women* kick against their Lords „ 412
That many a famous man and *w*, „ 445
And you look well too in your *w's* dress: „ 529
'Satan take The old *women* and their shadows! „ *v* 34
We left her by the *w*, „ 113
Man is the hunter; *w* is his game: „ 154
and leaps in Among the *women*, „ 163
yet I hold her, king, True *w*: „ 180
The *w's* garment hid the *w's* heart.' „ 305
those that iron-cramp'd their *women's* feet; „ 376
throats would bawl for civil rights, No *w* named: „ 388
the *w's* Angel guards you, „ 410
When the man wants weight, the *w* takes it up, „ 444
Man for the field, and *w* for the hearth: „ 447
Man with the head and *w* with the heart: „ 449
Man to command and *w* to obey; „ 450
Besides, the *w* wed is not as we, „ 462
bearing and the training of a child Is *w's* wisdom: „ 466
The leaves were wet with *women's* tears: „ *vi* 39
make Our progress falter to the *w's* goal.' „ 127
Win you the hearts of *women*; „ 171
you keep One pulse that beats true *w*, „ 180
the *w* is so hard Upon the *w*. „ 222
men see Two *women* faster welded in one love „ 253
W, whom we thought *w* even now, „ 273
amazed They glared upon the *women*, and aghast The *women* stared at these, „ 361
for on one side arose The *women* up in wild revolt, „ *vii* 123
And left her *w*, lovelier in her mood „ 162
that know The *w's* cause is man's: „ 259
For *w* is not undevelopt man, „ 275
The man be more of *w*, she of man; „ 280
what *w* taught you this?' „ 310
I loved the *w*: he, that doth not, lives A drowning life, „ 313
Thee *w* thro' the crust of iron moods „ 342
So pray'd the men, the *women*: „ *Con.* 7
The *women*—and perhaps they felt their power, „ 13
kingdom topples over with a shriek Like an old *w*, „ 63
But stay with the old *w* now: *Grandmother* 108
Phantom wail of *women* and children, *Boädicea* 26
And *women's* love and men's! *Window, Spring* 10
fiend best knows whether *w* or man be the worse. *Maud I i* 75
Rich in the grace all *women* desire, „ *x* 13
Nor fronted man or *w*, eye to eye— *Gareth and L.* 112
shyly glanced Eyes of pure *women*, „ 314
To whom the *w* weeping, 'Nay, my lord, „ 341
The *w* loves her lord. Peace to thee, *w*, with thy loves and hates! „ 372
Than ride abroad redressing *women's* wrong, „ 866
massacring Man, *w*, lad and girl— „ 1341
And loveliest of all *women* upon earth. *Marr. of Geraint* 21
This too the *women* who attired her head, „ 62
O never yet had *w* such a pair Of suitors „ 439
But while the *women* thus rejoiced, „ 754
she cast aside A splendour dear to *women*, „ 808
Stript from the three dead wolves of *w* born *Geraint and E.* 94
Call for the *w* of the house,' „ 263
And answer'd with such craft as *women* use, „ 352
A *w* weeping for her murder'd mate „ 522
A tribe of *women*, dress'd in many hues, „ 598

Woman (*continued*) *women* they, *Women*, or what had been those gracious things, *Geraint and E.* 635
all the men and *women* in the hall Rose „ 731
Were men and *women* staring and aghast, „ 804
To worship *w* as true wife beyond *Merlin and V.* 23
Save, save me thou—*W* of *women*— „ 78
'Know ye the stranger *w*?' „ 129
vice in you which ruin'd man Thro' *w* the first hour; „ 363
they never mount As high as *w* in her selfless mood. „ 443
'Man dreams of Fame while *w* wakes to love.' „ 460
or else A sudden spurt of *w's* jealousy,— „ 524
A *w* and not trusted, „ 530
And as to *w's* jealousy, O why not? „ 537
All fighting for a *w* on the sea. „ 562
Were I not *w*, I could tell a tale. „ 696
Have all men true and leal, all *women* pure; „ 794
But *women*, worst and best, as Heaven and Hell. „ 815
w's love, Save one, he not regarded, *Lancelot and E.* 840
And never *w* yet, since man's first fall, „ 859
love Of man and *w* when they love their best, „ 869
loved me with a love beyond all love In *women*, „ 1294
while *women* watch Who wins, who falls; *Holy Grail* 34
'A *w*,' answer'd Percivale, 'a nun, „ 68
behold a *w* at a door Spinning; „ 391
And kind the *w's* eyes and innocent, „ 393
none but phantoms in your quest, No man, no *w*?' „ 563
And *women* were as phantoms. „ 566
known Scarce any but the *women* of his isles, *Pelleas and E.* 88
'Ay,' said Gawain, 'for *women* be so light.' „ 362
Men, *women*, on their sodden faces, *Last Tournament* 474
one lone *w*, weeping near a cross, Stay'd him. „ 493
For courtesy wins *w* all as well As valour may, „ 707
'this is all *w's* grief, That *she* is *w*, *Guinevere* 218
could he find A *w* in her womanhood as great „ 299
Yet must I leave thee, *w*, to thy shame. „ 511
And beauty such as never *w* wore, „ 549
The moaning of the *w* and the child, *Lover's Tale i* 520
The man isn't like the *w*, *First Quarrel* 63
good *w*, can prayer set a broken bone?' *In the Child. Hosp.* 20
Women and children among us, *Def. of Lucknow* 8
Valour of delicate *women* who tended „ 87
Horror of *women* in travail among the dying „ 88
women and children come out, „ 100
What omens may foreshadow fate to man And *w*, *Tiresias* 8
is a man to be loved by the *women* they say. *The Wreck* 18
I sought for a kindly caress, being *w* and weak, „ 31
speaking aloud To *women*, the flower of the time, „ 49
'Never the heart among *women*,' he said, „ 96
'*W*'—he graspt at my arm—'stay there'— „ 120
Danny O'Roon wid his ould *w*, Molly Magee. *Tomorrow* 88
She with all the charm of *w*, *Locksley H., Sixty* 48
W to her inmost heart, and *w* to her tender feet, „ 50
Very *w* of very *w*, nurse of ailing body and mind, „ 51
Saving *women* and their babes, „ 64
a *w* came And caught me from my nurse. *The Ring* 117
place a hand in his Like an honest *w's*, *Forlorn* 20
and choice of *women* and of wines? *By an Evolution.* 8
WHILE man and *w* are still incomplete, I prize that soul where man and *w* meet, *On One who eff. E. M.* 1
The *w*, gliding toward the pyre, *To Master of B.* 18
the *women* shrieking "Atheist" flung Filth *Akbar's Dream* 91
I am dressing the grave of a *w* with flowers. *Charity* 2
For a *w* ruin'd the world, „ 3
but a *w*, God bless her, kept me from Hell. „ 4
I had cursed the *w* he married, „ 24
I had cursed her as *w* and wife, and in wife and *w* I found „ 31
Great and greater, and greatest of *women*, *Kapiolani* 5
if ever a *w* should handle or gather the berries „ 20
if ever a *w* should climb to the dwelling of Peelè „ 22
WHERE is one that, born of *w*, *Making of Man* 1

Woman-breasted *w-b* Sphinx, with wings drawn back, *Tiresias* 148
Woman-built As of a new-world Babel, *w-b*, *Princess iv* 487
Woman-conquer'd *w-c* there The bearded Victor „ *iii* 351
Woman-conqueror many a florid maiden-cheek, The *w-c*; „ 351
Woman-grown more and more, the maiden *w-g*, *Aylmer's Field* 108

Woman-guard Princess with her monstrous *w-g*, *Princess iv* 562
Womanhood Wearing the rose of *w*. *Two Voices* 417
O miracle of noble *w*!' *Princess, Pro.* 48
A charr'd and wrinkled piece of *w*, „ *v* 61
All that not harms distinctive *w*. „ *vii* 274
Came out of her pitying *w*, *Maud I vi* 64
and with all grace Of *w* and queenhood, *Marr. of Geraint* 176
Could call him (were it not for *w*) *Merlin and V.* 786
Beyond mine old belief in *w*, *Lancelot and E.* 955
And round her limbs, mature in *w*; *Pelleas and E.* 73
A woman in her *w* as great As he was in his manhood, *Guinevere* 299
Beyond all dreams of Godlike *w*, *Tiresias* 54
Queen, as true to *w* as Queenhood, *On Jub. Q. Victoria* 25
Womankind *All for the common good of* w.' *Princess ii* 209
I take her for the flower of *w*, „ *v* 287
The soft and milky rabble of *w*, „ *vi* 309
faith in *w* Beats with his blood, „ *vii* 328
Womanlike *W*, taking revenge too deep *Maud I iii* 5
Woman-man man-woman is not *w-m*. *On One who eff. E. M.* 4
Woman-markets Here in the *w-m* of the west, *Aylmer's Field* 348
Woman-post A *w-p* in flying raiment. *Princess iv* 376
Woman's-heart Break not, O *w-h*, but still endure; *Ded. of Idylls* 44
Woman-slough what was left of faded *w-s* *Princess v* 40
Woman-soldier My *w-s*, gallant Kate, *Kate* 15
Woman-statue Whereon a *w-s* rose with wings *Princess i* 210
Woman-vested but *w-v* as I was Plunged; „ *iv* 181
Woman-world *w-w* Of wives and mothers. *The Ring* 486
Woman-worshipper The *w-w*? Yea, God's curse, *Last Tournament* 447
Woman-yell slew Till all the rafters rang with *w-y's*, „ 476
Womb To spirits folded in the *w*. *Day-Dm., Sleep. P.* 8
Let her, that is the *w* and tomb of all, *Lucretius* 244
can remember Love in the *w*, *Lover's Tale i* 159
within her *w* that had left her ill content; *The Revenge* 51
Won (*See also* **Hard-won, Well-won**) A motion from the river *w* Ridged the smooth level, *Arabian Nights* 34
things outward you have *w* A tearful grace, *Margaret* 11
'That *w* his praises night and morn?' *Mariana in the S.* 34
I *w* his love, I brought him home. *The Sisters* 14
You might have *w* the Poet's name, *You might have won* 1
but *w* mysterious way Thro' the seal'd ear *Aylmer's Field* 695
when your sister came she *w* the heart Of Ida: *Princess iii* 87
Imaginations might at all be *w*. „ 274
thus I *w* Your mother, a good mother, „ *v* 165
w it with a day Blanch'd in our annals, „ *vi* 62
We will be liberal, since our rights are *w*. „ 68
Clash'd with his fiery few and *w*; *Ode on Well.* 100
has *w* His path upward, and prevail'd, „ 213
Priest was happy, His victim *w*: *The Victim* 62
Faint heart never *w*— *Window, The Answer* 9
Who have *w* her favour! *Maud I xii* 18
fair, strong, arm'd—But to be *w* by force— *Gareth and L.* 105
That save he *w* the first by force, „ 108
So large mirth lived and Gareth *w* the quest. „ 1426
Has ever *w* it for the lady with him, *Marr. of Geraint* 490
What I these two years past have *w* for thee, „ 554
'This noble prince who *w* our earldom back, „ 619
For tho' ye *w* the prize of fairest fair, „ 719
Proclaim'd him Victor, and the day was *w*. *Balin and Balan* 90
Had Lancelot *w* the diamond of the year, With purpose to present them to the Queen, When all were *w*; *Lancelot and E.* 68
That *if* I went and *if* I fought and *w* it „ 216
W by the mellow voice before she look'd, „ 243
'Lo, Sire, our knight, thro' whom we *w* the day, „ 529
'Was he not with you? *w* he not your prize?' „ 573
What of the knight with the red sleeve?, 'He *w*.' „ 621
Hard-won and hardly *w* with bruise and blow, „ 1165
Take, what I had not *w* except for you, „ 1181
Pelleas for his lady *w* The golden circlet, *Pelleas and E.* 13
wearing this unsunny face To him who *w* thee glory!' „ 181
My Queen, he had not *w*.' „ 183
yea and he that *w* The circlet? „ 320
their wills are hers For whom I *w* the circlet; „ 325
Lancelot *w* methought, for thee to wear.' *Last Tournament* 38
Won (*continued*) So Tristram *w*, and Lancelot gave, the gems, Not speaking other word than 'Hast thou *w*? *Last Tournament* 190
And *w* by Tristram as a tourney-prize, „ 746
years of noble deeds, Until they *w* her; *Guinevere* 477
attracted, *w*, Married, made one with, *Lover's Tale i* 133
We have *w* great glory, my men! *The Revenge* 85
Whom I woo'd and *w*. *Sisters (E. and E.)* 204
who can tell but the traitors had *w*? *Def. of Lucknow* 66
till his Word Had *w* him a noble name. *Dead Prophet* 36
'Take comfort you have *w* the Painter's fame,' *Romney's R.* 43
sword, That only conquers men to conquer peace, Has *w* me. *Akbar's Dream* 16
And less will be lost than *w*, *The Dreamer* 22
Won (one) (*See also* **Wonn**) I minds when i' Howlaby beck *w* daäy *Church-warden, etc.* 27
Wonder (s) Ever the *w* waxeth more and more, *Sonnet to ——* 6
What *w*, if in noble heat Those men thine arms *England and Amer.* 6
But when he saw the *w* of the hilt, *M. d'Arthur* 85
'this *w* keeps the house.' *Gardener's D.* 119
this *w*, dead, become Mere highway dust? *Love and Duty* 10
The *w* of the eagle were the less, *Golden Year* 39
and all the *w* that would be.—(repeat) *Locksley Hall* 16, 120
For there are greater *w's* there.' *Day-Dm., Depart.* 28
'What *w*, if he thinks me fair?' What *w* I was all unwise, „ *Ep.* 4
'It is no *w*,' said the lords, *Beggar Maid* 7
and rent The *w* of the loom thro' warp and woof *Princess i* 62
a feast Of *w*, out of West and East, *Ode Inter. Exhib.* 21
The *w's* that have come to thee, *In Mem. xli* 22
skill'd spear, the *w* of the world— *Gareth and L.* 1223
w's ye have done; Miracles ye cannot: „ 1324
Rapt in the fear and in the *w* of it; *Marr. of Geraint* 529
Show'd us a shrine wherein were *w's*— *Balin and Balan* 109
My daily *w* is, I love at all. *Merlin and V.* 536
What *w*, being jealous, that he sent „ 580
Fire in dry stubble a nine-days' *w* flared: *Lancelot and E.* 735
Becomes a *w*, and we know not why, „ 1029
Expectant of the *w* that would be. *Holy Grail* 133
With signs and miracles and *w's*, *Guinevere* 222
Or what of signs and *w's*, „ 229
the land was full of signs And *w's* „ 233
thy wise father with his signs And *w's*, „ 275
But when he saw the *w* of the hilt, *Pass. of Arthur* 253
Your *w* of the boiling lake; *To Ulysses* 40
What *w*! I decreed That even the dog was clean, *Akbar's Dream* 52
The *w's* were so wildly new, *Mechanophilus* 27
Wonder (verb) riving the spirit of man, Making earth *w*, *The Poet* 52
And, while now she *w's* blindly, *L. of Burleigh* 53
swallows coming out of time Will *w* why they came: *Princess ii* 432
I *w* he went so young. *Grandmother* 14
You *w* when my fancies play *In Mem. lxvi* 2
'But wherefore would ye men should *w* at you? *Gareth and L.* 570
But there the fine Gawain will *w* at me, *Lancelot and E.* 1054
Heated am I? you—you *w*— *Locksley H., Sixty* 151
Wonder'd I *w* at the bounteous hours, *Two Voices* 451
I *w*, while I paced along: „ 454
I *w* at her strength, and ask'd her of it: *Sea Dreams* 113
what kind of tales did men tell men, She *w*, *Princess, Pro.* 197
All the world *w*: (repeat) *Light Brigade* 31, 52
with such blows, that all the crowd *W*, *Marr. of Geraint* 565
Then came the fine Gawain and *w* at her, *Lancelot and E.* 1267
men who met him rounded on their heels And *w* *Pelleas and E.* 143
W at some strange light in Julian's eyes *Lover's Tale iv* 205
Wonderful Clothed in white samite, mystic, *w*, (repeat) *M. d'Arthur* 31, 144, 159
W, Prince of peace, the Mighty God, *Aylmer's Field* 669
Clothed in white samite, mystic, *w*. *Com. of Arthur* 285
This work of his is great and *w*. *Geraint and E.* 898
A thousand-fold more great and *w* „ 914
felt His work was neither great nor *w*, „ 921
A maid so smooth, so white, so *w*, *Merlin and V.* 566
Beyond all knowing of them, *w*, *Holy Grail* 104
Clothed in white samite, mystic, *w*, (repeat) *Pass. of Arthur* 199, 312, 327
W cures he had done, O yes, *In the Child. Hosp.* 5

Wonderful (*continued*) sun of the soul made day in the dark of his *w* eyes. *The Wreck* 55
Wondering *w*, ask'd her 'Are you from the farm?' *The Brook* 209
And only *w* wherefore play'd upon: *Gareth and L.* 1252
lifted up Their eager faces, *w* at the strength, *Merlin and V.* 133
I sat, Lonely, but musing on thee, *w* where, *Last Tournament* 613
Wonderingly *w* she gazed on Lancelot So soon return'd, *Pelleas and E.* 589
Wonder-stricken kiss'd his *w-s* little ones; *Enoch Arden* 229
Wondrous From many a *w* grot and secret cell *The Kraken* 8
strike Into that *w* track of dreams again, *D. of F. Women* 279
O thou *w* Mother-Age! *Locksley Hall* 108
yet her cheek Kept colour: *w*! *Aylmer's Field* 506
His prowess was too *w*. *Lancelot and E.* 542
w one Who passes thro' the vision of the night— „ 1405
Wonn (one) (*See also* **Won**) But 'e reäds *w* sarmin a weeäk, *N. Farmer, O. S.* 28
Wont (s) From childly *w* and ancient use I call— *Lucretius* 209
'tis her *w* from night to night To rail *Princess iii* 32
So said the small king moved beyond his *w*. „ *vi* 265
Make one wreath more for Use and *W*, *In Mem. xxix* 11
He laugh'd as is his *w*, and answer'd *Com. of Arthur* 401
my *w* hath ever been To catch my thief, *Gareth and L.* 821
Such is my *w*, as those, who know me, know.' *Lancelot and E.* 365
such his *w*, as we, that know him, know.' „ 475
He wore, against his *w*, upon his helm „ 603
Lancelot sad beyond his *w*, to see The maiden buried, „ 1333
Had been, their *w*, a-maying and return'd, *Guinevere* 23
Wont (adj.) Where he was *w* to leap and climb, *Supp. Confessions* 165
Psyche, *w* to bind my throbbing brow, *Princess ii* 250
In which we two were *w* to meet, *In Mem. viii* 10
When I was *w* to meet her In the silent woody places *Maud II iv* 5
soldiers *w* to hear His voice in battle, *Geraint and E.* 174
w to glance and sparkle like a gem Of fifty facets; „ 294
Wonted As year by year the labourer tills His *w* glebe, *In Mem. ci* 22
To this the courteous Prince Accorded with his *w* courtesy, *Lancelot and E.* 638
The sound not *w* in a place so still „ 818
And miss the *w* number of my knights, *Guinevere* 498
when he miss'd The *w* steam of sacrifice, *Demeter and P.* 119
Woo Thee to *w* to thy tuwhit, (repeat) *The Owl ii* 11
They would sue me, and *w* me, and flatter me, *The Mermaid* 43
W me, and win me, and marry me, „ 46
With what voice the violet *w's* *Adeline* 31
And once again to *w* thee mine— *Miller's D.* 30
I *w* thee not with gifts. *Œnone* 152
There's many a bolder lad 'll *w* me *May Queen* 23
gold and beauty, wooing him to *w*. *Aylmer's Field* 487
thus I *w* thee roughly, for thou carest not How roughly men may *w* thee so they win— *Lucretius* 272
Fly to her, and pipe and *w* her, *Princess iv* 115
these men came to *w* Your Highness— „ *vi* 328
I *w* your love; I count it crime *In Mem. lxxxv* 61
One is come to *w* her. *Maud I xii* 28
whitens ere this hour *W's* his own end; *Last Tournament* 698
W her and gain her then: *Sisters (E. and E.)* 39
'Let us revenge ourselves, your Ulric *w's* my wife'— *Happy* 63
Wood (trees) (*See also* **Cedar-wood, Palmwood, Pine-wood, Yew-wood**) the *w's* that belt the gray hill-side, *Ode to Memory* 55
From the evening-lighted *w*, *Margaret* 10
field and *w* Grow green beneath the showery gray, *My life is full* 16
The pale yellow *w's* were waning, *L. of Shalott iv* 2
The *w's* were fill'd so full with song, *Two Voices* 455
When after roving in the *w's* *Miller's D.* 58
cloisters, branch'd like mighty *w's*, *Palace of Art* 26
Lo! in the middle of the *w*, *Lotos-Eaters, C. S.* 25
I had wander'd far In an old *w*: *D. of F. Women* 54
'Pass freely thro': the *w* is all thine own, „ 83
I have no men to govern in this *w*: „ 135
Thridding the sombre boskage of the *w*, „ 243
and the *w's* and ways Are pleasant, *On a Mourner* 13
From the *w's* Came voices of the well-contented doves. *Gardener's D.* 88
And like an oaken stock in winter *w's*, *Golden Year* 62
THE *w's* decay, the *w's* decay and fall, *Tithonus* 1
Now for me the *w's* may wither, *Locksley Hall* 190
A summer crisp with shining *w's*. *Day-Dm., Pro.* 8

Wood (trees) (*continued*) and shows At distance like a little *w*; *Day-Dm., Sleep. P.* 42
Summer *w's*, about them blowing, *L. of Burleigh* 19
And hills and scarlet-mingled *w's* *The Voyage* 47
where the prone edge of the *w* began (repeat) *Enoch Arden* 67, 373
Crept down into the hollows of the *w*; „ 76
To go with others, nutting to the *w*, „ 363
calling, here and there, about the *w*. „ 383
remember'd one dark hour Here in this *w*, „ 386
How merry they are down yonder in the *w*. „ 389
sent his voice beneath him thro' the *w*. „ 444
all the *w* stands in a mist of green, *The Brook* 14
Autumn's mock sunshine of the faded *w's* *Aylmer's Field* 610
I rose and past Thro' the wild *w's* *Princess i* 91
and the shrieks Of the wild *w's* together; „ 99
O'er it shook the *w's*, And danced the colour, „ *iii* 292
when all the *w's* are green? „ *iv* 107
'O Swallow, flying from the golden *w's*, „ 114
Across the *w's*, and less from Indian craft „ 198
With Ida, Ida, Ida, rang the *w's*; „ 433
mused on that wild morning in the *w's*, „ *v* 471
strikes On a *w*, and takes, and breaks, „ 527
half-open'd bell of the *w's*! „ *vi* 193
Nightingales sang in his *w's*: *G. of Swainston* 6
And a worm is there in the lonely *w*, *The Islet* 34
And cattle died, and deer in *w*, *The Victim* 18
And *w's* are sear, And fires burn clear, *Window, Winter* 3
The *w's* are all the searer, „ 14
Oh, the *w's* and the meadows, *W's* where we hid from the wet, „ *Marr. Morn.* 5
By meadow and stile and *w*, „ 14
That never knew the summer *w's*: *In Mem. xxvii* 4
And bask'd and batten'd in the *w's*. „ *xxxv* 24
I found a *w* with thorny boughs: „ *lxix* 6
hill and *w* and field did print The same sweet forms „ *lxxix* 7
noise of rooks, That gather in the waning *w's*, „ *lxxxv* 72
Thro' all the dewy-tassell'd *w*, „ *lxxxvi* 6
With banquet in the distant *w's*; „ *lxxxix* 32
Of rising worlds by yonder *w*. „ *cv* 25
Above the *w* which grides and clangs „ *cvii* 11
To range the *w's*, to roam the park, „ *Con.* 96
I HATE the dreadful hollow behind the little *w*, *Maud I i* 1
little *w* where I sit is a world of plunder „ *iv* 24
the budded peaks of the *w* are bow'd „ *vi* 4
Here half-hid in the gleaming *w*, „ 69
Where was Maud? in our *w*; „ *xii* 5
Birds in our *w* sang „ 9
Running down to my own dark *w*; „ *xiv* 30
From the lake to the meadow and on to the *w*, „ *xxii* 37
Our *w*, that is dearer than all; „ 38
From the red-ribb'd hollow behind the *w*, „ *II i* 25
Then glided out of the joyous *w* „ 31
Thick with wet *w's*, and many a beast therein, *Com. of Arthur* 21
gazing over plain and *w*; *Gareth and L.* 668
Down the long avenues of a boundless *w*, „ 785
Where Arthur's men are set along the *w*; The *w* is nigh as full of thieves as leaves: „ 788
Flying from out of the black *w*, „ 802
somewhat as the cleanser of this *w*. „ 828
So she spake. A league beyond the *w*, „ 845
damsel's headlong error thro' the *w*— „ 1215
a forester of Dean, Wet from the *w's*, *Marr. of Geraint* 149
Took horse, and forded Usk, and gain'd the *w*; „ 161
At last they issued from the world of *w*, „ 238
In the first shallow shade of a deep *w*, *Geraint and E.* 119
'There lurk three villains yonder in the *w*, „ 142
'And if there were an hundred in the *w*, „ 147
and she drove them thro' the *w*. „ 185
keep them in the wild ways of the *w*, „ 187
thro' the green gloom of the *w* they past, „ 195
Which sees the trapper coming thro' the *w*. „ 724
in those deep *w's* we found A knight *Balin and Balan* 120
Reported of some demon in the *w's* Was once a man, „ 124
who will hunt for me This demon of the *w's*?' „ 137
and rode The skyless *w's*, but under open blue „ 293

Wood (trees) (*continued*) thou couldst lay the Devil of these *w's* — *Balin and Balan* 298
and pass And vanish in the *w's*; .. 327
the canker'd boughs without Whined in the *w*; .. 346
and old boughs Whined in the *w*. .. 386
and turn'd aside into the *w's*, .. 433
the wholesome music of the *w* Was dumb'd .. 436
Before another *w*, the royal crown Sparkled, .. 462
yonder lies one dead within the *w*. .. 468
I dwell Savage among the savage *w's*, .. 486
she smiled 'And even in this lone *w*, Sweet lord, .. 528
W's have tongues, As walls have ears: .. 530
shriek of bird or beast, Thrill'd thro' the *w's*; .. 546
'She dwells among the *w's*' he said „ 614
the wild *w's* of Broceliande, (repeat) *Merlin and V.* 2, 204
Who meant to eat her up in that wild *w* .. 260
and all thro' this wild *w* And all this morning .. 285
chase a creature that was current then In these wild *w's*, „ 409
And all thro' following you to this wild *w*, „ 440
the dark *w* grew darker toward the storm „ 890
dwelt among the *w's* By the great river *Lancelot and E.* 277
As happy as when we dwelt among the *w's*, „ 1036
And laughter at the limit of the *w*, *Pelleas and E.* 49
Again she said, 'O wild and of the *w's*, „ 99
'Lead then,' she said; and thro' the *w's* they went. .. 108
Other than when I found her in the *w's*; „ 328
Rang out like hollow *w's* at hunting-tide. „ 367
With promise of large light on *w's* and ways. „ 394
hill and *w* Went ever streaming by him „ 547
At Camelot, high above the yellowing *w's*, *Last Tournament* 3
Sir Tristram of the *W's*—Whom Lancelot knew, „ 177
The *w's* are hush'd, their music is no more: „ 276
I made it in the *w's*. And heard it ring „ 283
avenues And solitary passes of the *w* .. 361
as a rustle or twitter in the *w* Made dull his inner, „ 365
and when thou passest any *w* Close vizor, „ 534
vows—I am a woodman of the *w's*, „ 699
Next morning, while he past the dim-lit *w's*, *Guinevere* 251
over all the great *w* rioting And climbing, *Lover's Tale i* 403
and from the *w's* That belt it rise three dark, „ 535
three cypress-cones That spired above the *w*; „ *ii* 39
From out the yellow *w's* upon the hill „ 80
The cloud-pavilion'd element, the *w*, „ 108
foliage from the dark and dripping *w's* .. *iii* 6
Fled onward to the steeple in the *w's*: „ 26
the *w's* upon the hill Waved with a sudden gust „ 33
fled Wind-footed to the steeple in the *w's*, „ 56
What matter? there are others in the *w*. „ *iv* 162
From column on to column, as in a *w*, „ 189
rattled down upo' poor owd Squire i' the *w*, *Village Wife* 95
a whirlwind blow these *w's*, as never blew *The Flight* 12
These ancient *w's*, this Hall at last will go— „ 27
He left us weeping in the *w's*; „ 37
all the summer long we roam'd in these wild *w's* .. 79
Wild flowers of the secret *w's*, „ 82
Wild *w's* in which we roved with him, „ 83
Wild *w's* in which we rove no more, „ 84
foälk be sa scared at, i' Gigglesby *w*, *Spinsters S's.* 24
stars are from their hands Flung thro' the *w's*, *Early Spring* 18
The *w's* with living airs How softly fann'd, „ 19
Mount and mine, and primal *w*; *Open. I. and C. Exhib.* 6
thridded the black heart of all the *w's*, *Demeter and P.* 69
you used to call me once The lonely maiden-Princess of the *w*, *The Ring* 65
Who love the winter *w's*, to trace *To Ulysses* 14
She comes on waste and *w*, On farm and field: *Prog. of Spring* 22
w's Plunged gulf on gulf thro' all their vales below. „ 72
found Paris, a naked babe, among the *w's* Of Ida, *Death of Œnone* 54
on man in the tropical *w*, *The Dawn* 3

Wood (substance) (*See also*, **Pinewood**, **Satin-wood**)
Hard *w* I am, and wrinkled rind, *Talking Oak* 171
a noiseless riot underneath Strikes thro' the *w*, *Lucretius* 186
'Ye are green *w*, see ye warp not. *Princess ii* 75
draw water, or hew *w*, Or grosser tasks; *Gareth and L.* 486

Wood (substance) (*continued*) Had carved himself a knightly shield of *w*, *Merlin and V.* 473
javelining With darted spikes and splinters of the *w* „ 937
To thee, dead *w*, I bow not head nor knees. *Sir J. Oldcastle* 128
fell'd the foes before you as the woodman fells the *w*, *Happy* 42

Woodbine (adj.) rent The *w* wreaths that bind her, *Amphion* 34
And the *w* spices are wafted abroad, *Maud I xxii* 5
wind Came wooingly with *w* smells, *Lover's Tale ii* 36
And hour by hour unfolding *w* leaves *Prog. of Spring* 7

Woodbine (s) *w* and eglatere Drip sweeter dews *A Dirge* 23
And tell me if the *w's* blow. *My life is full* 25
as sweet As *w's* fragile hold, *Talking Oak* 146
Thorns, ivies, *w*, mistletoes, *Day-Dm., Sleep. P.* 43
There in due time the *w* blows, *In Mem. cv* 7
my oän door-poorch wi' the *w* an' jessmine *Spinster's S's.* 105

Woodcraft Look to thy *w*,' and so leaving him, *Balin and Balan* 308

Wood-devil scream of that *W-d* I came to quell!' „ 548

Wood-dove Deeply the *w-d* coos; *Leonine Eleg.* 6

Wooded (*See also* **Deep-wooded**) The mountain *w* to the peak, *Enoch Arden* 572
And hollow lined and *w* to the lips, *Lover's Tale i* 398
the wave again Is vocal in its *w* walls; *In Mem. xix* 14
Beside the river's *w* reach, „ *lxxi* 13

Wooden When from her *w* walls,—lit by sure hands,— *Buonaparte* 5

Woodland (adj.) Be mine a philosopher's life in the quiet *w* ways, *Maud I iv* 49
Gathering *w* lilies, Myriads blow together. .. *xii* 7
And the *w* echo rings; „ *II iv* 38
And deem it carrion of some *w* thing, *Gareth and L.* 748
With joy that blazed itself in *w* wealth *Balin and Balan* 82
A damsel-errant, warbling, as she rode The *w* alleys, „ 439
Now talking of their *w* paradise, *Last Tournament* 726
My Edwin loved to call us then 'His two wild *w* flowers.' *The Flight* 80
While round her brows a *w* culver flits, *Prog. of Spring* 18
Still round her forehead wheels the *w* dove, „ 57
Hear thy myriad laureates hail thee monarch in their *w* rhyme. *Akbar's D., Hymn* 6

Woodland (s) filter'd tribute of the rough *w*, *Ode to Memory* 63
In firry *w's* making moan; *Miller's D.* 42
Slides the bird o'er lustrous *w*, *Locksley Hall* 162
That grows within the *w*. *Amphion* 8
When the rotten *w* drips, *Vision of Sin* 81
ILLYRIAN *w's*, echoing falls Of water, *To E. L.* 1
the broad *w* parcell'd into farms; *Aylmer's Field* 847
forefoot plies His function of the *w*: *Lucretius* 46
as the golden Autumn *w* reels Athwart the smoke *Princess vii* 357
Which in our winter *w* looks a flower. *A Dedication* 13
'Fear not, isle of blowing *w*, *Boädicea* 38
Made the noise of frosty *w's*, „ 75
And *w's* holy to the dead; *In Mem. xcix* 8
Now rings the *w* loud and long, „ *cxv* 5
flying gold of the ruin'd *w's* drove thro' the air. *Maud I i* 12
a flame That rages in the *w* far below, *Balin and Balan* 234
left the ravaged *w* yet once more To peace; *Merlin and V.* 963
Over all the *w's* flooded bowers, *Sisters (E. and E.)* 20
Thou that singest wheat and *w*, *To Virgil* 9
For all that ample *w* whisper'd 'debt,' *The Ring* 170
and glancing at Elf of the *w*, *Merlin and the G.* 38

Wood-louse blue *w-l*, and the plump dormouse, *Window, Winter* 9

Woodman see the *w* lift His axe to slay my kin. *Talking Oak* 235
they came, The *woodmen* with their axes: *Princess vi* 44
a *w* there Reported of some demon in the woods *Balin and Balan* 123
This *w* show'd the cave From which he sallies, .. 131
Came on the hoarhead *w* at a bough „ 294
To whom the *w* utter'd wonderingly „ 297
vows—I am *w* of the woods, *Last Tournament* 699
fell'd the foes before you as the *w* fells the wood, *Happy* 42

Wood-nymph a foot-fall, ere he saw The *w-n*, *Palace of Art* 111

Woodpecker As laughters of the *w* *Kate* 4
An echo like a ghostly *w*, *Princess, Pro.* 217
Before her skims the jubilant *w*, *Prog. of Spring* 16

Wood-walk dark *w-w's* drench'd in dew, *D. of F. Women* 75

Wood-way green *w-w's*, and eyes among the leaves; *Pelleas and E.* 139

Woodwork Fled ever thro' the *w*, till they found *Lancelot and E.* 440

Wood-world *w-w* is one full peal of praise. *Balin and Balan* 450

Woody To the *w* hollows in which we meet *Maud I xxii* 43
In the silent *w* places By the home that gave me birth, „ *II iv* 6
Woo'd folded leaf is *w* from out the bud *Lotos-Eaters, C. S.* 26
he *w* and wed A labourer's daughter, *Dora* 39
who would love? I *w* a woman once, *Audley Court* 52
Drunk even when he *w*; *Marr. of Geraint* 442
how he *w* The waters, and the waters answering *Lover's Tale i* 543
I *w* her then, nor unsuccessfully, *Sisters (E. and E.)* 125
Whom I *w* and won. „ 204
But the Bandit had *w* me in vain, *Bandit's Death* 10
Wooest *W* not, nor vainly wranglest; *Madeline* 38
Woof Hues of the silken sheeny *w* „ 22
thro' warp and *w* From skirt to skirt; *Princess i* 62
Wooing his long *w* her, Her slow consent, *Enoch Arden* 707
baits Of gold and beauty, *w* him to woo. *Aylmer's Field* 487
All my *w* is done. *Window, Marr. Morn.* 4
Edith had welcomed my brief *w* of her, *Sisters (E. and E.)* 254
sound Which to the *w* wind aloof The poplar made, *Mariana* 75
Wool Like footsteps upon *w*. *Œnone* 250
needs it we should cram our ears with *w* *Princess iv* 65
w of a thistle a-flyin' an' seeädin' *Spinster's S's.* 79
but *w's* looking oop ony how. *Church-warden, etc.* 6
Woolly And *w* breasts and beaded eyes; *In Mem. xcv* 12
Woorse (worse) *W* nor a far-welter'd yowe: *N. Farmer, N. S.* 32
Woost (worst) And i' the *w* o' toimes „ *O. S.* 16
Word (*See also* **Watch-word**) Shot thro' and thro' with cunning *w's*. *Clear-headed friend* 17
Her *w's* did gather thunder as they ran, *The Poet* 49
So was their meaning to her *w's*. „ 53
and with *his w* She shook the world. „ 55
kiss sweet kisses, and speak sweet *w's*: *Sea-Fairies* 34
Wild *w's* wander here and there: *A Dirge* 43
And your *w's* are seeming-bitter *Rosalind* 30
And kiss away the bitter *w's* „ 50
How may measur'd *w's* adore The full-flowing harmony *Eleänore* 45
'These *w's*,' I said, 'are like the rest; *Two Voices* 334
The thesis which thy *w's* intend— „ 338
if I waste *w's* now, in truth You must blame Love. *Miller's D.* 191
With blessings which no *w's* can find. „ 238
Indeed I heard one bitter *w* *L. C. V. de Vere* 37
Tho' I cannot speak a *w*, I shall harken *May Queen, N. Y's. E.* 39
the clergyman, has told me *w's* of peace. „ *Con.* 12
say to Robin a kind *w*, and tell him not to fret; „ 45
little meaning tho' the *w's* are strong; *Lotos-Eaters, C. S.* 119
Her slow full *w's* sank thro' the silence drear, *D. of F. Women* 121
My *w's* leapt forth: 'Heaven heads the count of crimes „ 201
Because all *w's*, tho' cull'd with choicest art, „ 285
I had not dared to flow In these *w's* toward you, *To J. S.* 7
W's weaker than your grief would make „ 65
But gentle *w's* are always gain: *Love thou thy land* 23
Would serve his kind in deed and *w*, „ 86
He utter'd *w's* of scorning; *The Goose* 42
Watch what thou seëst, and lightly bring me *w*.' *M. d'Arthur* 38
Watch what I see, and lightly bring thee *w*.' „ 44
I bad thee, watch, and lightly bring me *w*.' „ 81
would have spoken, but he found not *w's*, „ 172
(My *w's* were half in earnest, half in jest,) *Gardener's D.* 23
A *w* could bring the colour to my cheek; „ 196
And in the compass of three little *w's*, „ 232
Here, then, my *w's* have end. „ 250
he and I Had once hard *w's*, and parted, *Dora* 18
But in my time a father's *w* was law, „ 27
Or change a *w* with her he calls his wife, „ 44
You knew my *w* was law, and yet you dared „ 98
I set the *w's*, and added names I knew. *Audley Court* 61
Caught *in flagrante*—what's the Latin *w*?— *Walk. to the Mail* 34
And well his *w's* became him: *Edwin Morris* 25
Were not his *w's* delicious, „ 71
That, trust me on my *w*, *Talking Oak* 170
w's That make a man feel strong in speaking truth; *Love and Duty* 69
These measured *w's*, my work of yestermorn. *Golden Year* 21
but I *know* my *w's* are wild, *Locksley Hall* 173
And order'd *w's* asunder fly. *Day-Dm., Pro.* 20
With *w's* of promise in his walk, „ *Arrival* 23

Word (*continued*) The barons swore, with many *w's*, *Day-Dm., Revival* 23
In courteous *w's* return'd reply: „ 30
'Cruel, cruel the *w's* I said! *Edward Gray* 17
And whisper lovely *w's*, and use *Will Water.* 11
Hours, when the Poet's *w's* and looks „ 193
For I am yours in *w* and in deed. *Lady Clare* 74
Down they dropt—no *w* was spoken— *The Captain* 51
She was more fair than *w's* can say: *Beggar Maid* 2
But in my *w's* were seeds of fire. *The Letters* 28
Light on a broken *w* to thank him with. *Enoch Arden* 347
for she did not speak a *w*. „ 390
Ev'n as she dwelt upon his latest *w's*, „ 454
Enoch spoke no *w* to any one, „ 667
for Enoch hung A moment on her *w's*, „ 873
Poor Philip, of all his lavish waste of *w's* *The Brook* 191
were *w's*, As meted by his measure of himself, *Aylmer's Field* 315
Never one kindly smile, one kindly *w*: „ 564
how the *w's* Have twisted back upon themselves, „ 754
his one *w* was 'desolate;' „ 836
but not a *w*; she shook her head. *Sea Dreams* 116
To spread the *W* by which himself had thriven.' „ 197
Of Heliconian honey in living *w's*, *Lucretius* 224
'Doubt my *w* again!' he said. *Princess, Pro.* 176
At those high *w's*, we conscious of ourselves, „ *ii* 67
at these *w's* the snake, My secret, „ *iii* 43
(for still My mother went revolving on the *w*) „ 54
Then came these dreadful *w's* out one by one, „ 57
The truth at once, but with no *w* from me; „ 61
She struck such warbling fury thro' the *w's*; „ *iv* 586
(our royal *w* upon it, He comes back safe) „ *v* 224
Arac's *w* is thrice As ours with Ida: „ 226
roll'd himself Thrice in the saddle, then burst out in *w's*. „ 275
And you shall have her answer by the *w*.' „ 327
and rolling *w's* Oration-like. „ 372
at the happy *w* 'he lives' My father stoop'd, „ *vi* 128
Say one soft *w* and let me part forgiven.' „ 219
Not one *w*? not one? „ 231
Not one *w*; No! tho' your father sues: „ 239
A *w*, but one, one little kindly *w*, „ 258
king her father charm'd Her wounded soul with *w's*: „ 346
Like perfect music unto noble *w's*; „ *vii* 286
It seems you love to cheat yourself with *w's*: „ 334
The *w's* are mostly mine: „ *Con.* 3
Who spoke few *w's* and pithy, such as closed Welcome, „ 94
To fling whate'er we felt, not fearing, into *w's*. *Third of Feb.* 6
we will not spare the tyrant one hard *w*. „ 42
Täake my *w* for it, Sammy, *N. Farmer, N. S.* 48
To put in *w's* the grief I feel; For *w's*, like Nature, half reveal *In Mem. v* 2
In *w's*, like weeds, I'll wrap me o'er, „ 9
What *w's* are these have fall'n from me? „ *xvi* 1
The *w's* that are not heard again. „ *xviii* 20
That out of *w's* a comfort win; „ *xx* 10
Where truth in closest *w's* shall fail, „ *xxxvi* 6
And so the *W* had breath, and wrought „ 9
And hence, indeed, she sports with *w's*, „ *xlviii* 9
My *w's* are only *w's*, and moved „ *lii* 3
In those sad *w's* I took farewell: „ *lviii* 1
The *w's* were hard to understand. „ *lxix* 20
In fitting aptest *w's* to things, „ *lxxv* 6
O true in *w*, and tried in deed, „ *lxxxv* 5
Your *w's* have virtue such as draws „ 13
But in dear *w's* of human speech „ 83
The wish too strong for *w's* to name; „ *xciii* 14
strangely on the silence broke The silent-speaking *w's*, „ *xcv* 26
So *w* by *w*, and line by line, „ 33
Vague *w's*! but ah, how hard to frame „ 45
And if the *w's* were sweet and strong „ *cxxv* 11
To change the bearing of a *w*, „ *cxxviii* 16
living *w's* of life Breathed in her ear. „ *Con.* 52
the wealth Of *w's* and wit, the double health, „ 103
faith in a tradesman's ware or his *w*? *Maud I i* 26
Dare I bid her abide by her *w*? „ *xvi* 25
Had given her *w* to a thing so low? „ 27
Can break her *w* were it even for me? „ 29

Word (*continued*) For she, sweet soul, had hardly spoken a *w*, *Maud II i* 11
'Man's *w* is God in man: *Com. of Arthur* 133
For bold in heart and act and *w* was he, „ 176
And simple *w's* of great authority, „ 261
With large, divine, and comfortable *w's*, „ 268
spake sweet *w's*, and comforted my heart, „ 349
Lash'd at the wizard as he spake the *w*, „ 388
God hath told the King a secret *w*. „ 489
Repentant of the *w* she made him swear, *Gareth and L.* 527
Fair *w's* were best for him who fights for thee; „ 946
And seeing now thy *w's* are fair, „ 1181
Instant were his *w's*. „ 1353
and then paused, and spake no *w*. „ 1385
he spake no *w*; Which set the horror higher: „ 1393
He heard but fragments of her later *w's*, *Marr. of Geraint* 113
refrain'd From ev'n a *w*, and so returning said: „ 214
But none spake *w* except the hoary Earl: „ 369
Nor did she lift an eye nor speak a *w*, „ 528
In *w's* whose echo lasts, they were so sweet, „ 782
that at a *w* (No reason given her) „ 806
not to speak to me, No, not a *w*!' *Geraint and E.* 18
And loosed in *w's* of sudden fire the wrath „ 106
took the *w* and play'd upon it, „ 291
speak the *w*: my followers ring him round: „ 336
speak but the *w*: Or speak it not; „ 342
Low-spoken, and of so few *w's*, „ 395
Because she kept the letter of his *w*, „ 455
answering not one *w*, she led the way. „ 495
Prince, without a *w*, from his horse fell. „ 508
none spake *w*, but all sat down at once, „ 604
And Enid could not say one tender *w*, „ 746
Tho' pale, yet happy, ask'd her not a *w*, „ 880
Man's *w* is God in man.' *Balin and Balan* 8
And spake no *w* until the shadow turn'd; „ 45
transitory *w* Make knight or churl or child „ 161
lad, whose lightest *w* Is mere white truth „ 517
Sir Balin spake not *w*, But snatch'd „ 553
eat her up in that wild wood Without one *w*. *Merlin and V.* 261
knew no more, nor gave me one poor *w*; „ 277
Then answer'd Merlin careless of her *w's*: „ 700
He rose without a *w* and parted from her: „ 742
But have ye no one *w* of loyal praise For Arthur, „ 778
Her *w's* had issue other than she will'd. „ 806
He spoke in *w's* part heard, in whispers part, „ 839
Kill'd with a *w* worse than a life of blows! „ 870
half her realm, had never spoken *w*. *Lancelot and E.* 72
He never spake *w* of reproach to me, „ 124
therefore hear my *w's*: go to the jousts: „ 136
Before a King who honours his own *w*, „ 143
Nor often loyal to his *w*, and now Wroth „ 559
without a *w*, Linger'd that other, „ 720
Her father's latest *w* humm'd in her ear, „ 780
And I must die for want of one bold *w*.' „ 927
As when we dwell upon a *w* we know, Repeating, till the *w* we know so well Becomes a wonder, „ 1027
as she devised A letter, *w* for *w*; „ 1104
these are *w's*: Your beauty is your beauty, „ 1185
O grant my worship of it *W's*, „ 1188
Such sin in *w's*, Perchance, we both can pardon: „ 1188
Then every evil *w* I had spoken once, *Holy Grail* 371
I remember'd Arthur's warning *w*, „ 598
Told him he follow'd—almost Arthur's *w's*— „ 669
since the living *w's* Of so great men „ 712
I need not tell thee foolish *w's*,— „ 855
and the great King, Lighted on *w's*: *Pelleas and E.* 253
For so the *w's* were flash'd into his heart „ 503
And Percivale made answer not a *w*. „ 534
The *w's* of Arthur flying shriek'd, arose, *Last Tournament* 139
Not speaking other *w* than 'Hast thou won? „ 191
Tristram, spake not any *w*, But bode his hour, „ 385
Arthur deign'd not use of *w* or sword, „ 458
fault and doubt—no *w* of that fond tale— „ 578
But let my *w's*, the *w's* of one so small, *Guinevere* 185
To honour his own *w* as if his God's, „ 473

Word (*continued*) teach high thought, and amiable *w's* *Guinevere* 481
Watch what thou seëst, and lightly bring me *w*.' *Pass. of Arthur* 206
Watch what I see, and lightly bring thee *w*,' „ 212
I bad thee, watch, and lightly bring me *w*.' „ 249
would have spoken, but he found not *w's*; „ 340
Be cabin'd up in *w's* and syllables, *Lover's Tale i* 480
her *w's* stole with most prevailing sweetness „ 553
Her *w's* did of their meaning borrow sound, Her cheek did catch the colour of her *w's*. „ 568
While her *w's*, syllable by syllable, „ 575
for henceforth what use were *w's* to me! „ 609
deals comfortable *w's* To hearts wounded „ 717
To all their queries answer'd not a *w*, „ *iv* 333
Not to break in on what I say by *w* Or whisper, „ 352
you never have spoken a *w*. *Rizpah* 14
As yet I had not bound myself by *w's*, *Sister's (E. and E.)* 137
The golden gates would open at a *w*. „ 145
Not by the sounded letter of the *w*, „ 162
Cold *w's* from one I had hoped to warm so far „ 194
when we parted, Edith spoke no *w*, „ 215
Had he God's *w* in Welsh He might be kindlier: *Sir J. Oldcastle* 22
for in thee the *w* was born again. „ 27
Heaven-sweet Evangel, ever-living *w*, „ 28
and that was clean Against God's *w*: *Columbus* 55
You will not. One last *w*. „ 221
with human voices and *w's*; *V. of Maeldune* 28
Remember the *w's* of the Lord „ 120
The Achæans—honouring his wise mother's *w*— *Achilles over the T.* 16
To cast wise *w's* among the multitude *Tiresias* 66
—the wise man's *w*, Here trampled by the populace „ 173
The *w* of the Poet by whom the deeps *The Wreck* 23
language beneath and beyond the *w*! „ 24
A madman to vex you with wretched *w's*, *Despair* 108
The reels not in the storm of warring *w's*, *Ancient Sage* 70
My *w's* are like the babblings in a dream „ 106
But louder than thy rhyme the silent *W* „ 212
revolving in myself The *w* that is the symbol „ 231
unshadowable in *w's*, Themselves but shadows „ 238
but *w's* are only *w's*! *The Flight* 59
We never changed a bitter *w*, „ 86
heart batin' to music wid ivery *w*! *Tomorrow* 34
I couldn't a' stuck by my *w*. *Spinster's S's.* 96
when they 'evn't a *w* to saäy. „ 102
lines I read Nor utter'd *w* of blame, *Pro. to Gen. Hamley* 18
were the *w's* Mutter'd in our dismay; *Heavy Brigade* 46
Muses often flowering in a lonely *w*; *To Virgil* 12
till his *W* Had won him a noble name. *Dead Prophet* 35
Ring little bells of change From *w* to *w*. *Early Spring* 42
And sacred is the latest *w*; *To Marq. of Dufferin* 37
them *w's* be i' Scriptur— *Owd Roä* 15
his The *w's*, and mine the setting. 'Air and *W's*,' Said Hubert, *The Ring* 24
you—you loved me, kept your *w*. „ 290
those three sweet Italian *w's*, became a weariness. „ 407
Blister'd every *w* with tears, *Forlorn* 81
Foul! foul! the *w* was yours not mine, *Happy* 41
parted for the Holy War without a *w* to me, „ 77
Be needle to the magnet of your *w*, *To Mary Boyle* 7
hear their *w's* On pathway'd plains; *Prog. of Spring* 82
Why should I so disrelish that short *w*? *Romney's R.* 11
Vexing you with *w's*! *W's* only, „ 29
—*w's*, Wild babble. „ 31
for my sake, According to my *w*?' „ 130
those three *w's* would haunt him when a boy, *Far—far—away* 8
What charm in *w's*, a charm no *w's* could give? „ 16
O dying *w's*, can Music make you live „ 17
Two *w's*, '*My* rose' set all your face aglow, *Roses on the T.* 3
A man who never changed a *w* with men, *St. Telemachus* 10
his dying *w's*, Which would not die, „ 75

Worded *See* **Iron-worded**

Wordily As here to-day, but not so *w*— *Lover's Tale iv* 355

Wordless And Lancelot marvell'd at the *w* man; *Lancelot and E.* 172
Suddenly speaking of the *w* man, „ 271
The little senseless, worthless, *w* babe, *The Ring* 304

Wordless (*continued*) And *w* broodings on the wasted cheek— *Princess vii* 112
Wordy but when the *w* storm Had ended, *Sea Dreams* 31
And keen thro' *w* snares to track Suggestion *In Mem. xcv* 31
And *w* trucklings to the transient hour, *To the Queen ii* 51
Wore (*See also* **Ware, Weär'd**) For many weeks about my loins I *w* *St. S. Stylites* 63
That she *w* when she was wed.' *L. of Burleigh* 96
A gown of grass-green silk she *w*, *Sir L. and Q. G.* 24
She *w* the colours I approved. *The Letters* 16
crime Of sense avenged by sense that *w* with time.' *Vision of Sin* 214
another *w* A close-set robe of jasmine *Aylmer's Field* 157
And still I *w* her picture by my heart, *Princess i* 38
I *w* a lilac gown; *Grandmother* 57
it grew so tall It *w* a crown of light, *The Flower* 10
Never morning *w* To evening, *In Mem. vi* 7
I *w* them like a civic crown: „ *lxix* 8
In which of old I *w* the gown; „ *lxxxvii* 2
since he neither *w* on helm or shield *Com. of Arthur* 49
three gay suits of armour which they *w*, *Geraint and E.* 95
his the prize, who *w* the sleeve Of scarlet, *Lancelot and E.* 501
He *w*, against his wont, upon his helm „ 603
he *w* your sleeve: Would he break faith „ 684
but I lighted on the maid Whose sleeve he *w*; „ 711
With knees of adoration *w* the stone, *Holy Grail* 71
all she *w* Torn as a sail that leaves the rope „ 211
And beauty such as never woman *w*, *Guinevere* 549
She deem'd I *w* a brother's mind: *Lover's Tale i* 741
he learnt that I hated the ring I *w*, *The Wreck* 57
w it till her death, Shrined him within the temple *The Ring* 218
Muriel clench'd The hand that *w* it, „ 262
That ever *w* a Christian marriage-ring. *Romney's R.* 36
Work (s) (*See also* **Branch-work, Chequer-work, Damask-work, Frame-work, Handmaid-work, Jacinth-work, Mat-work, Trellis-work, Works and Days**) At his *w* you may hear him sob and sigh *A spirit haunts* 5
Now is done thy long day's *w*; *A Dirge* 1
Grave mother of majestic *w's*, *Of old sat Freedom* 13
Thy *w* is thine—The single note *England and Amer.* 18
we loved the man, and prized his *w*; *M. d'Arthur, Ep.* 8
'Tis not your *w*, but Love's. *Gardener's D.* 24
and he left his men at *w*, And came and said: *Dora* 86
Till that wild wind made *w* *Talking Oak* 54
To that man My *w* shall answer, *Love and Duty* 29
These measured words, my *w* of yestermorn. *Golden Year* 21
He works his *w*, I mine. *Ulysses* 43
Some *w* of noble note, may yet be done, „ 52
A virgin heart in *w* and will. *Sir Galahad* 24
'Thou shalt not be saved by *w's*: *Vision of Sin* 91
Nor of what race, the *w*; *Aylmer's Field* 224
Small were his gains, and hard his *w*; *Sea Dreams* 8
the woman honest *W*; „ 137
Which things appear the *w* of mighty Gods. *Lucretius* 102
and if I go *my w* is left Unfinish'd—*if* I go. „ 103
when we set our hand To this great *w*, *Princess ii* 60
Your own *w* marr'd: „ 230
and silver litanies, The *w* of Ida, „ 478
how vast a *w* To assail this gray preëminence „ *iii* 233
That we might see our own *w* out, „ 270
as the workman and his *w*, That practice betters?' „ 298
Which touches on the workman and his *w*. „ 322
and known at last (my *w*) „ *iv* 347
understanding all the foolish *w* Of Fancy, „ *vi* 116
The treble *w's*, the vast designs *Ode on Well.* 104
Whose life was *w*, whose language rife „ 183
Such was he: his *w* is done. „ 218
There must be other nobler *w* to do „ 256
The *w's* of peace with *w's* of war. *Ode Inter. Exhib.* 28
Fur *w* mun 'a gone to the gittin' *N. Farmer, N. S.* 50
burn the palaces, break the *w's* of the statuary, *Boädicea* 64
Man, her last *w*, who seem'd so fair, *In Mem. lvi* 9
I shall pass; my *w* will fail. „ *lvii* 8
my passion hath not swerved To *w's* of weakness, „ *lxxxv* 50
Let her *w* prevail. „ *cxiv* 4
O days and hours, your *w* is this „ *cxvii* 1

Work (s) (*continued*) Contemplate all this *w* of Time, *In Mem. cxviii* 1
If so he type this *w* of time Within himself, „ 16
By thee the world's great *w* is heard Beginning, „ *cxxi* 10
the *w's* of the men of mind, *Maud I i* 25
Awe-stricken breaths at a *w* divine, „ *x* 17
Frail, but a *w* divine, „ *II ii* 4
Small, but a *w* divine, „ 23
There is none that does his *w*, not one; „ *v* 26
cannot will my will, nor work my *w* Wholly, *Com. of Arthur* 88
Man am I grown, a man's *w* must I do. *Gareth and L.* 116
rich in emblem and the *w* Of ancient kings „ 304
Thralls to your *w* again, „ 710
with back turn'd, and bow'd above his *w*, *Marr. of Geraint* 267
And there is scantly time for half the *w*. „ 288
He spoke and fell to *w* again. „ 292
the *w* To both appear'd so costly, „ 637
This *w* of his is great and wonderful. *Geraint and E.* 898
This *w* of Edyrn wrought upon himself „ 912
felt His *w* was neither great nor wonderful, „ 921
Yet needs must work my *w*. *Merlin and V.* 505
They prove to him his *w*: *Lancelot and E.* 158
Yet with all ease, so tender was the *w*: „ 442
Her own poor *w*, her empty labour, left. „ 991
Before his *w* be done; *Holy Grail* 909
I will be leal to thee and work thy *w*, *Pelleas and E.* 343
This evil *w* of Lancelot and the Queen? *Guinevere* 307
and with my *w* thus Crown'd her clear forehead. *Lover's Tale i* 344
But *w* was scant in the Isle, *First Quarrel* 43
to see if *w* could be found; „ 44
'I ha' six weeks' *w*, little wife, „ 45
'You promised to find me *w* near you, „ 52
'I've gotten my *w* to do; „ 85
I ha' six weeks' *w* in Jersey „ 88
couldn't do naw *w* an' all, *North. Cobbler* 77
where the *w's* of the Lord are reveal'd *In the Child. Hosp.* 35
Frail were the *w's* that defended the hold *Def. of Lucknow* 7
Beyond all *w* of those who carve the stone, *Tiresias* 53
beyond All *w* of man, yet, like all *w* of man, *Ancient Sage* 85
Undo their *w* again, And leave him, „ 112
aisier *w* av they lived be an Irish bog. *Tomorrow* 72
but 'a left me the *w* to do, *Spinster's S's.* 55
of the chasm between *W* and Ideal? *Romney's R.* 64
now thy long day's *w* hath ceased, *Epit. on Stratford* 2
W's of subtle brain and hand, *Open I. and C. Exhib.* 7
Whose Faith and *W's* were bells of full accord, *In Mem., W. G. Ward* 2
loosen, stone from stone, All my fair *w*; *Akbar's Dream* 189
Work (literary production) Botanic Treatises, And *W's* on Gardening *Amphion* 78
My golden *w* in which I told a truth *Lucretius* 260
Work (verb) Then let wise Nature *w* her will, *My life is full* 21
Hath time and space to *w* and spread. *You ask me, why, etc.* 16
And *w*, a joint of state, that plies Its office, *Love thou thy land* 47
but *w* in hues to dim The Titianic Flora. *Gardener's D.* 170
And hired himself to *w* within the fields; *Dora* 38
Mary, let me live and *w* with you: „ 115
w for William's child, until he grows Of age, „ 126
Can I *w* miracles and not be saved? *St. S. Stylites* 150
I will *w* in prose and rhyme, *Talking Oak* 289
w itself Thro' madness, hated by the wise, *Love and Duty* 6
That unto him who *w's*, and feels he *w's*, *Golden Year* 73
He *w's* his work, I mine. *Ulysses* 43
For love in sequel *w's* with fate, *Day-Dm., Arrival* 3
I must *w* thro' months of toil, *Amphion* 97
All parties *w* together. *Will Water.* 56
Who needs would *w* for Annie to the last, *Enoch Arden* 180
Scorning an alms, to *w* whereby to live. „ 812
but labour for himself, *W* without hope, „ 820
all things *w* together for the good Of those'— *Sea Dreams* 158
Embrace our aims: *w* out your freedom. *Princess ii* 89
nor would we *w* for fame; „ *iii* 261
But in the shadow will we *w*, „ 331
but *w* no more alone! Our place is much: „ *vii* 266
Make and break, and *w* their will; *Ode on Well.* 261
And all men *w* in noble brotherhood, *Ode Inter. Exhib.* 38
w's Without a conscience or an aim. *In Mem. xxxiv* 7

Work (verb) (*continued*) To one that with us *w's*, and trust, *In Mem. cxxxi* 8
spirit of murder *w's* in the very means of life, *Maud I i* 40
cannot will my will, nor *w* my work Wholly, *Com. of Arthur* 88
and we will *w* thy will Who love thee.' „ 259
but an he *w*, Like any pigeon will I cram *Gareth and L.* 458
Myself would *w* eye dim, and finger lame, *Marr. of Geraint* 628
ruth began to *w* Against his anger in him, *Geraint and E.* 101
Vivien ever sought to *w* the charm *Merlin and V.* 215
But *w* as vassal to the larger love, „ 491
You needs must *w* my work. „ 505
To all the foulness that they *w*. „ 785
Thanks, but you *w* against your own desire; *Lancelot and E.* 1096
Or hers or mine, mine now to *w* my will— „ 1231
to whom I vow'd That I would *w* *Holy Grail* 784
As let these caitiffs on thee *w* their will?' *Pelleas and E.* 323
I will be leal to thee and *w* thy work, „ 343
I, being simple, thought to *w* His will, *Pass. of Arthur* 22
And life and limbs, all his to *w* his will.' *Lover's Tale iv* 283
an' I *w* an' I wait to the end. *First Quarrel* 7
gave All but free leave for all to *w* the mines, *Columbus* 133
I am not yet too old to *w* his will— „ 161
hourly *w* their brother insect wrong, *Locksley H., Sixty* 202
To *w* old laws of Love to fresh results, *Prog. of Spring* 85
art *thou* the Prophet? canst *thou w* Miracles?' *Akbar's Dream* 117
Meanwhile, my brothers, *w*, and wield *Mechanophilus* 29
Hold thine own, and *w* thy will! *Poets and Critics* 13

Work'd-Workt But my full heart, that *work'd* below, *Two Voices* 44
And they say then that I *work'd* miracles, *St. S. Stylites* 80
thy strong Hours indignant *work'd* their wills, *Tithonus* 18
But oft he *work'd* among the rest and shook *Enoch Arden* 651
Rose from the clay it *work'd* in as she past, *Aylmer's Field* 170
seeing who had *work'd* Lustier than any, *Gareth and L.* 695
I ha' *work'd* for him fifteen years, *First Quarrel* 7
He *workt* me the daisy chain— „ 13
a girl, a hussy, that *workt* with him up at the farm, „ 24
but the creatures had *worked* their will. *Rizpah* 50
Because the simple mother *work'd* upon By Edith *Sisters (E. and E.)* 206
This power hath *work'd* no good to aught that lives, *Tiresias* 77

Worker (*See also* **Fellow-worker, War-worker**) Men, my brothers, men the *w's*, *Locksley Hall* 117

Working (*See also* **Still-working**) A labour *w* to an end. *Two Voices* 297
Life, that, *w* strongly, binds— *Love thou thy land* 34
Him, like the *w* bee in blossom-dust, *Enoch Arden* 366
'It came,' she said, 'by *w* in the mines:' *Sea Dreams* 114
The jest and earnest *w* side by side, *Princess iv* 563
Or been in narrowest *w* shut, *In Mem. xxxv* 20
His being *w* in mine own, „ *lxxxv* 43
Move upward, *w* out the beast, „ *cxviii* 27
A knight of Arthur, *w* out his will, *Gareth and L.* 24
(Sea was her wrath, yet *w* after storm) *Lancelot and E.* 1309
Queen, *W* a tapestry, lifted up her head, *Last Tournament* 129
Demos end in *w* its own doom. *Locksley H., Sixty* 114

Workman Which wrought us, as the *w* and his work, *Princess iii* 298
Which touches on the *w* and his work. „ 322
Workmen up at the Hall!— *Maud I i* 65

Workmanship I admire Joints of cunning *w*. *Vision of Sin* 186
'Look what a lovely piece of *w*!' *Aylmer's Field* 237

Works and Days more than he that sang the *W a D*, *To Virgil* 6

Workt *See* **Work'd**

Wo'ld (world) Tha mun tackle the sins o' the *W*, *Church-warden, etc.* 46

World (*See also* **Dream-world, Half-world, New-world, Old-world, Shadow-world, She-world, Sister-world, Water-world, Wo'ld, Woman-world, Wood-world**) 'Tis the *w's* winter; *Nothing will Die* 17
The *w* was never made; „ 30
a *w* of peace And confidence, day after day; *Supp. Confessions* 29
w hath not another (Tho' all her fairest forms *Isabel* 38
which possess'd The darkness of the *w*, *Arabian Nights* 72
the *w* Like one great garden show'd, *The Poet* 33
and with *his* word She shook the *w*. „ 56
All the *w* o'er, (repeat) *Sea-Fairies* 41
Roof'd the *w* with doubt and fear, *Eleänore* 99
Kate saith 'the *w* is void of might.' *Kate* 17

World (*continued*) All the inner, all the outer *w* of pain *If I were loved* 5
Shadows of the *w* appear. *L. of Shalott ii* 12
I said 'When first the *w* began, *Two Voices* 16
Look up thro' night: the *w* is wide. „ 24
Is cancell'd in the *w* of sense?' „ 42
to present The *w* with some development. „ 75
And full of dealings with the *w*? *Miller's D.* 8
There's somewhat in this *w* amiss „ 19
'while the *w* runs round and round,' *Palace of Art* 13
cycles of the human tale Of this wide *w*, „ 147
And let the *w* have peace or wars, „ 182
'No voice breaks thro' the stillness of this *w*: „ 259
and all the *w* is still. *May Queen, N. Y's. E.* 24
girdled with the gleaming *w*: *Lotos-Eaters, C. S.* 113
gently comes the *w* to those That are cast *To J. S.* 3
harmonies of law The growing *w* assume, *England and Amer.* 17
general decay of faith Right thro' the *w*, *The Epic* 19
famous knights Whereof this *w* holds record. *M. d'Arthur* 16
Or hath come, since the making of the *w*. „ 203
Which was an image of the mighty *w*; „ 235
Lest one good custom should corrupt the *w*. „ 242
More things are wrought by prayer Than this *w* dreams of. „ 248
Not wholly in the busy *w*, nor quite Beyond it, *Gardener's D.* 33
And Beauty such a mistress of the *w*. „ 58
nor from her tendance turn'd Into the *w* without; „ 145
to hold From thence thro' all the *w's*: „ 210
That veil'd the *w* with jaundice, *Walk. to the Mail* 20
That these two parties still divide the *w*— „ 77
As never sow was higher in this *w*— „ 96
we should mimic this raw fool the *w*, „ 106
for the good and increase of the *w*.' (repeat) *Edwin Morris* 51, 92
Among the powers and princes of this *w*, *St. S. Stylites* 187
O this *w's* curse,—beloved but hated— *Love and Duty* 47
If all the *w* were falcons, what of that? *Golden Year* 38
like the second *w* to us that live; „ 56
arch wherethro' Gleams that untravell'd *w*, *Ulysses* 20
'Tis not too late to seek a newer *w*. „ 57
Here at the quiet limit of the *w*, *Tithonus* 7
comes A glimpse of that dark *w* where I was born. „ 33
Saw the Vision of the *w*, (repeat) *Locksley Hall* 16, 120
the Federation of the *w*. „ 128
and the *w* is more and more. „ 142
Let the great *w* spin for ever „ 182
Like hints and echoes of the *w* *Day-Dm., Sleep. P.* 7
In that new *w* which is the old: „ *Depart.* 4
Thro' all the *w* she follow'd him. „ 32
And learn the *w*, and sleep again; „ *L'Envoi* 8
The prelude to some brighter *w*. „ 40
And all the *w* go by them. *Will Water.* 48
Ah yet, tho' all the *w* forsake, „ 49
We knew the merry *w* was round, *The Voyage* 7
We lov'd the glories of the *w*, „ 83
We know the merry *w* is round, „ 95
Ring'd with the azure *w*, he stands. *The Eagle* 3
And my mockeries of the *w*. *Vision of Sin* 202
he sings of what the *w* will be When the years *Poet's Song* 15
not to see the *w*—For pleasure?— *Enoch Arden* 297
She slipt across the summer of the *w*, „ 531
She passing thro' the summer *w* again, „ 534
And glories of the broad belt of the *w*, „ 579
Roll'd a sea-haze and whelm'd the *w* in gray; „ 672
And beating up thro' all the bitter *w*, „ 802
One whom the strong sons of the *w* despise; *The Brook* 3
Too fresh and fair in our sad *w's* best bloom, „ 218
With half-allowing smiles for all the *w*, *Aylmer's Field* 120
the *w* should ring of him To shame these „ 395
And fain had haled him out into the *w*, „ 467
Against the desolations of the *w*. „ 634
Eight that were left to make a purer *w*— „ 638
To blow these sacrifices thro' the *w*— „ 758
Doubtless our narrow *w* must canvass it: „ 774
And left their memories a *w's* curse— „ 796
wife Sat shuddering at the ruin of a *w*; *Sea Dreams* 30
'What a *w*,' I thought, 'To live in!' „ 94
think that in our often-ransack'd *w* „ 129

World *(continued)* The lucid interspace of *w* and *w*, *Lucretius* 105
I seem'd to move among a *w* of ghosts, *Princess i* 17
One rose in all the *w*, your Highness that, „ *ii* 51
'This *w* was once a fluid haze of light, „ 116
Two in the tangled business of the *w*, „ 174
Poets, whose thoughts enrich the blood of the *w*.' „ 181
secular emancipation turns Of half this *w*, „ 290
A blessing on her labours for the *w*. „ 479
whence after-hands May move the *w*, „ *iii* 264
weight of all the hopes of half the *w*, „ *iv* 184
women kick against their Lords Thro' all the *w*, „ 413
dam Ready to burst and flood the *w* with foam: „ 474
tho' all the gold That veins the *w* were pack'd „ 543
I seem'd to move among a *w* of ghosts; „ 561
The wrath I nursed against the *w*: „ *v* 437
Shall move the stony bases of the *w*. „ *vi* 58
when a *w* Of traitorous friend and broken systen „ 194
and tarn by tarn Expunge the *w*: „ *vii* 41
So blacken'd all her *w* in secret, „ 42
I believed that in the living *w* My spirit closed „ 157
notice of a change in the dark *w* Was lispt „ 250
These were the rough ways of the *w* till now. „ 257
Nor lose the wrestling thews that throw the *w*; „ 282
Then reign the *w's* great bridals, „ 294
Immersed in rich foreshadowings of the *w*, „ 312
O we will walk this *w*, Yoked in all exercise „ 360
and down rolls the *w* In mock heroics „ *Con.* 63
This fine old *w* of ours is but a child „ 77
Thro' all the silent spaces of the *w's*, „ 114
The greatest sailor since our *w* began. *Ode on Well.* 86
And drill the raw *w* for the march of mind, „ 168
Thro' either babbling *w* of high and low; „ 182
Tho' *w* on *w* in myriad myriads roll Round us, „ 262
hold against the *w* this honour of the land. *Third of Feb.* 48
All the *w* wonder'd: (repeat) *Light Brigade* 31, 52
diviner air Breathe thro' the *w* and change *W. to Marie Alex.* 44
And howsoever this wild *w* may roll, „ 48
it cost me a *w* of woe, *Grandmother* 23
For him nor moves thel oud *w's* random mock, *Will* 4
Dark is the *w* to thee: *High. Pantheism* 7
As one who feels the immeasurable *w*, *A Dedication* 7
wet west wind and the *w* will go on. (repeat) *Window, No Answer* 6, 12
wet west wind and the *w* may go on. „ 18
Over the *w* to the end of it „ *Marr. Morn.* 23
Help thy vain *w's* to bear thy light. *In Mem., Pro.* 32
The sunbeam strikes along the *w*: „ *xv* 8
Science reaches forth her arms To feel from *w* to *w*, „ *xxi* 19
Thou fail not in a *w* of sin, „ *xxxiii* 15
The total *w* since life began; „ *xliii* 12
Upon the great *w's* altar-stairs „ *lv* 15
breathes a novel *w*, the while His other passion „ *lxii* 9
The centre of a *w's* desire; „ *lxiv* 16
So many *w's*, so much to do, „ *lxxiii* 1
The *w* which credits what is done Is cold to all „ *lxxv* 15
In whispers of the beauteous *w*. „ *lxxix* 12
The deep pulsations of the *w*, „ *xcv* 40
Of rising *w's* by yonder wood. „ *cv* 25
I would the great *w* grew like thee, „ *cxiv* 25
In that which made the *w* so fair. „ *cxvi* 8
the *w's* great work is heard Beginning, „ *cxxi* 10
I found Him not in *w* or sun, „ *cxxiv* 5
And whispers to the *w's* of space, „ *cxxvi* 11
And mingle all the *w* with thee. „ *cxxix* 12
and let the *w* have its way: *Maud I iv* 21
wood where I sit is a *w* of plunder and prey. „ 24
Who knows the ways of the *w*, „ 44
the suns are many, the *w* is wide. „ 45
I have not made the *w*, „ 48
From the long-neck'd geese of the *w* „ 52
If I find the *w* so bitter „ *vi* 33
Then the *w* were not so bitter (repeat) „ 38, 94
a *w* in which I have hardly mixt, „ 76
More life to Love than is or ever was In our low *w*, „ *xviii* 48
A *w* of trouble within! „ *xix* 25
makes us loud in the *w* of the dead; „ *II v* 25

World *(continued)* a *w* that loves him not, For it is but a *w* of the dead. *Maud II v* 39
She comes from another stiller *w* of the dead, „ 70
Fairer than aught in the *w* beside, „ 73
spoke of a hope for the *w* in the coming wars— „ *III vi* 11
in a weary *w* my one thing bright; „ 17
His loss drew like eclipse, Darkening the *w*. *Ded. of Idylls* 15
I seem as nothing in the mighty *w*, *Com. of Arthur* 87
And power on this dead *w* to make it live.' „ 94
the *w* Was all so clear about him, „ 97
the Powers who walk the *w* Made lightnings „ 107
deems himself alone And all the *w* asleep, „ 119
whatsoever storms May shake the *w*, „ 293
Graven in the oldest tongue of all this *w*, „ 302
To guard thee on the rough ways of the *w*.' „ 336
And hated this fair *w* and all therein, „ 344
live and love, and make the *w* Other, „ 472
'Blow trumpet, for the *w* is white with May; „ 482
Blow thro' the living *w*— „ 484
The slowly-fading mistress of the *w*, „ 505
working out his will, To cleanse the *w*. *Gareth and L.* 25
or half the *w* Had ventured— „ 64
that skill'd spear, the wonder of the *w*— „ 1223
if the *w* were one Of utter peace, and love, „ 1288
And stay the *w* from Lady Lyonors. „ 1412
The *w's* loud whisper breaking into storm, *Marr. of Geraint* 27
At caitiffs and at wrongers of the *w*. „ 96
At last they issued from the *w* of wood, „ 238
cackle of your bourg The murmur of the *w*! „ 277
the great wave that echoes round the *w*; „ 420
Made a low splendour in the *w*, „ 598
thro' the feeble twilight of this *w* Groping, *Geraint and E.* 5
The being he loved best in all the *w*, „ 103
As the gray dawn stole o'er the dewy *w*, „ 385
Henceforth in all the *w* at anything, „ 649
The *w* will not believe a man repents: And this wise *w* of ours is mainly right. „ 900
I have quite foregone All matters of this *w*: *Balin and Balan* 117
the Queen, and all the *w* Made music, „ 210
Old monk and nun, ye scorn the *w's* desire, „ 445
all at once they found the *w*, Staring wild-wide; „ 595
as Arthur in the highest Leaven'd the *w*, *Merlin and V.* 141
Dear feet, that I have follow'd thro' the *w*, „ 227
And sweep me from my hold upon the *w*, „ 303
Who have to learn themselves and all the *w*, „ 365
noble deeds, the flower of all the *w*. „ 413
I well believe that all about this *w* „ 541
sunn'd The *w* to peace again: „ 639
The brute *w* howling forced them into bonds, „ 744
And touching other *w's*. „ 838
the place which now Is this *w's* hugest, *Lancelot and E.* 76
flower of all the west and all the *w*, „ 249
Hid from the wide *w's* rumour by the grove Of poplars „ 522
this and that other *w* Another *w* for the sick man; „ 873
To serve you, and to follow you thro' the *w*.' „ 939
'Nay, the *w*, the *w*, All ear and eye, „ 940
'For Lancelot and the Queen and all the *w*, „ 1107
Then might she follow me thro' the *w*, „ 1316
For never have I known the *w* without, *Holy Grail* 20
And heal the *w* of all their wickedness! „ 94
and all the *w* be heal'd.' „ 128
Then flash'd a yellow gleam across the *w*, „ 402
And seem'd to me the Lord of all the *w*, „ 414
Rejoice, small man, in this small *w* of mine, „ 559
the sea rolls, and all the *w* is warm'd?' „ 672
'O happy *w*,' thought Pelleas, 'all, meseems, *Pelleas and E.* 136
Than all the ranged reasons of the *w*. „ 156
That follows on the turning of the *w*, „ 549
brother, thou nor I have made the *w*; *Last Tournament* 203
Would make the *w* as blank as Winter-tide. „ 221
seeing too much wit Makes the *w* rotten, „ 247
the *w* Is flesh and shadow— „ 315
Who fain had clipt free manhood from the *w*— „ 446
The wide *w* laughs at it. And worldling of the *w* am I, and know The ptarmigan „ 695

World (*continued*) There hold thee with my life against the *w*.' *Guinevere* 115
twain together well might change the *w*. „ 301
The most disloyal friend in all the *w*.' „ 340
What knowest thou of the *w*, „ 343
To serve as model for the mighty *w*, „ 465
in that *w* where all are pure We two may meet „ 563
Let the *w* be; that is but of the *w* What else? „ 629
What might I not have made of thy fair *w*, „ 655
As if some lesser god had made the *w*, *Pass. of Arthur* 14
Or else as if the *w* were wholly fair, „ 18
Hath folded in the passes of the *w*.' „ 78
'Hearest thou this great voice that shakes the *w*, „ 139
famous knights Whereof this *w* holds record. „ 184
Or hath come, since the making of the *w*. „ 371
Which was an image of the mighty *w*, „ 403
More things are wrought by prayer Than this *w* dreams of. „ 416
stillness of the dead *w's* winter dawn Amazed him, „ 442
As from beyond the limit of the *w*, „ 458
goal of this great *w* Lies beyond sight: *To the Queen ii* 59
Like to a quiet mind in a loud *w*, *Lover's Tale i* 7
And, like all other friends i' the *w*, „ 108
And mellow'd echoes of the outer *w*— „ 208
In giving so much beauty to the *w*, „ 212
Gray relics of the nurseries of the *w*, „ 290
She said, 'The evil flourish in the *w*.' „ 348
having always prosper'd in the *w*, „ 716
(Huge blocks, which some old trembling of the *w* „ *ii* 45
A flat malarian *w* of reed and rush! „ *iv* 142
hungering for the gilt and jewell'd *w* About him, „ 313
I am all alone in the *w*, *First Quarrel* 8
all the ships of the *w* could stare at him, *Rizpah* 38
ever a battle like this in the *w* before? *The Revenge* 62
Over all this weary *w* of ours, *Sister's (E. and E.)* 12
Over all this ruin'd *w* of ours, „ 22
One bright May morning in a *w* of song, „ 82
I think this gross hard-seeming *w* Is our mis-shaping vision of the Powers Behind the *w*, „ 229
if the hope of the *w* were a lie? *In the Child. Hosp.* 24
Must learn to use the tongues of all the *w*. *Sir J. Oldcastle* 34
More worth than all the kingdoms of this *w*, „ 77
Who took the *w* so easily heretofore, „ 89
To course and range thro' all the *w*, „ 120
God pardon all—Me, them, and all the *w*— „ 169
And came upon the Mountain of the *W*, *Columbus* 26
Whatever wealth I brought from that new *w* „ 101
I who have deceived thee or the *w* ? „ 151
Flower into fortune—our *w's* way— „ 167
Which he unchain'd for all the *w* to come.' „ 215
his voice was low as from other *w's*, *V. of Maeldune* 117
Thro' all this changing *w* of changeless law, *De Prof., Two G.* 6
From that great deep, before our *w* begins, „ 27
From that true *w* within the *w* we see, Whereof our *w* is but the bounding shore— „ 30
For in the *w*, which is not ours, „ 35
pain Of this divisible-indivisible *w* „ 43
With power on thine own act and on the *w*. „ 56
Son, in the hidden *w* of sight, *Tiresias* 51
I am flung from the rushing tide of the *w* *The Wreck* 6
word of the Poet by whom the deeps of the *w* are stirr'd, „ 23
By the low foot-lights of the *w*— „ 40
Over the range and change of the *w* „ 70
dark little *w's* running round them were *w's* of woe like our own— *Despair* 18
Of a worm as it writhes in a *w* „ 31
Of a dying worm in a *w*, „ 32
Never a cry so desolate, not since the *w* began, „ 59
In a *w* of arrogant opulence, „ 78
thy *w* Might vanish like thy shadow in the dark. *Ancient Sage* 51
Nor canst thou prove the *w* thou movest in, „ 58
This double seeming of the single *w*!— „ 105
the *w* is dark with griefs and graves, „ 171
splendours and the voices of the *w*! „ 177
show us that the *w* is wholly fair. „ 182

World (*continued*) I touch thy *w* again—No ill no good! *Ancient Sage* 249
in the fatal sequence of this *w* An evil thought „ 274
know the love that makes the *w* a *w* to me! *The Flight* 76
my own true sister, come forth! the *w* is wide. „ 96
they tell me that the *w* is hard, and harsh of mind, „ 101
stood up strait as the Queen of the *w*— *Tomorrow* 79
old-world dust before the newer *w* begin. *Locksley H., Sixty* 150
Earth at last a warless *w*, „ 165
outworn earth be dead as yon dead *w* the moon? „ 174
perhaps a *w* of never fading flowers. „ 184
All the *w* is ghost to me, „ 253
In *w's* before the man Involving ours— *Epilogue* 25
like a flame From zone to zone of the *w*, *Dead Prophet* 35
This ever-changing *w* of circumstance, *To Duke of Argyll* 10
And warms the child's awakening *w*— *To Prin. Beatrice* 5
ask'd the waves that moan about the *w* *Demeter and P.* 64
from all the *w* the voices came 'We know not, „ 66
And saw the *w* fly by me like a dream, *The Ring* 180
From out the fleshless *w* of spirits, „ 228
In all the *w* my dear one sees but you— „ 364
All the *w* will hear a voice Scream *Forlorn* 27
Wed to the melody, Sang thro' the *w*; *Merlin and the G.* 98
And yet The *w* would lose, *Romney's R.* 68
in the loud *w's* bastard judgment-day, „ 119
Other songs for other *w's*! *Parnassus* 19
His dream became a deed that woke the *w*, *St. Telemachus* 70
Thro' all the warring *w* of Hindustan *Akbar's Dream* 26
the living pulse of Alla beats Thro' all His *w*. „ 42
gaze on this great miracle, the *W*, „ 122
For a woman ruin'd the *w*, *Charity* 3
see not her like anywhere in this pitiless *w* of ours! „ 43
can escape From the lower *w* within him, *Making of Man* 2
And loves the *w* from end to end, *The Wanderer* 7
'The *w* and all within it (repeat) *Voice spake, etc.* 3, 9
Nor the myriad *w*, His shadow, *God and the Univ.* 6
Eternal Harmony Whereto the *w's* beat time, *D. of the Duke of C.* 16

World-compelling The *w-c* plan was thine,— *Ode Inter. Exhib.* 10
World-domain Whose will is lord thro' all his *w-d*— *W. to Marie Alex.* 2
World-earthquake In that *w-e*, Waterloo! *Ode on Well.* 133
Worlded *See* **Myriad-worlded**
World-isle *W-i's* in lonely skies, *Epilogue* 55
Worldless From where his *w* heart had kept it warm, *Aylmer's Field* 471
Worldling the wind like a broken *w* wail'd, *Maud I i* 11
And *w* of the world am I, *Last Tournament* 696
But your Judith—but your *w*— *Locksley H., Sixty* 20
She the *w* born of *w's*— „ 25
Worldly And all his *w* worth for this, *Sir L. and Q. G.* 43
he vext her and perplext her With his *w* talk and folly: *Maud I xx* 7
Some rough old knight who knew the *w* way, *Pelleas and E.* 192
w Priests Who fear the king's hard common-sense *Sir J. Oldcastle* 65
Like *w* beauties in the Cell, not shown *The Ring* 143
Worldly-wise *w-w* begetters, plagued themselves *Aylmer's Field* 482
World-old as, they sat Beneath a *w-o* yew-tree, *Holy Grail* 13
World-prophet that *w-p* in the heart of man. *Ancient Sage* 213
World-self His whole *W-s* and all in all— *De Prof., Two G.* 49
World-to-be Who will embrace me in the *w-t-b* *Enoch Arden* 893
World-victor great *W-v's* victor will be seen no more. *Ode on Well.* 42
World-war *W-w* of dying flesh against the life, *Merlin and V.* 193
World-wealth venom of *w-w* Into the church, *Sir J. Oldcastle* 166
World-whisper vague *w-w*, mystic pain or joy, *Far—far—away* 7
World-wide *w-w* whisper of the south-wind rushing warm, *Locksley Hall* 125
w-w fluctuation sway'd In vassal tides *In Mem. cxii* 15
Mourn! That a *w-w* Empire mourns with you, *D. of the Duke of C.* 5
World-worn the *w-w* Dante grasp'd his song, *Palace of Art* 135
Worm (*See also* **Brother-worm, Glow-worm, Scorpion-worm, Slow-worm**) fret Of that sharp-headed *w* begins *Supp. Confessions* 186
Nothing but the small cold *w* *A Dirge* 9
every *w* beneath the moon Draws different threads, *Two Voices* 178
with a *w* I balk'd his fame. *D. of F. Women* 155
As ruthless as a baby with a *w*, *Walk. to the Mail* 108
Below were men and horses pierced with *w's*, *Vision of Sin* 209
Crown thyself, *w*, and worship thine own lusts!— *Aylmer's Field* 650
And a *w* is there in the lonely wood, *The Islet* 34

Worm (*continued*) for the life of the *w* and the fly? *Wages* 7
No will push me down to the *w*, *Window, No Answer* 10
That not a *w* is cloven in vain; *In Mem. liv* 9
Strike dead the whole weak race of venomous *w's*, *Maud II i* 46
many rings (For he had many, poor *w*) „ *ii* 69
Wroth to be wroth at such a *w*, *Marr. of Geraint* 213
as the *w* draws in the wither'd leaf *Geraint and E.* 633
And the high purpose broken by the *w*. *Merlin and V.* 196
'A *w* within the rose.' *Pelleas and E.* 399
He dies who loves it,—if the *w* be there.' „ 409
And cast him as a *w* upon the way; *Guinevere* 35
The guess of a *w* in the dust *Despair* 30
Of a *w* as it writhes in a world „ 31
Of a dying *w* in a world, „ 32
When the *w* shall have writhed its last, „ 85
'O *w's* and maggots of to-day *Ancient Sage* 210
a *w* which writhes all day, and at night Stirs up *Vastness* 17
You that would not tread on a *w* *Forlorn* 45
flesh at last is filth on which the *w* will feast; *Happy* 30
point and jeer, And gibber at the *w*, *Romney's R.* 137
Worm-canker'd Distill'd from some *w-c* homily; *To J. M. K.* 6
Worm-eaten So propt, *w-e*, ruinously old, *Enoch Arden* 693
Wormwood banquet, where the meats became As *w*, *Lancelot and E.* 744
Wormwood-bitter were *w-b* to me. *Balin and Balan* 64
Worn (*See also* **Fever-worn, Storm-worn, Wave-worn, Way-worn, Well-worn, World-worn**) Weeded and *w* the ancient thatch *Mariana* 7
both Brake into hall together, *w* and pale. *Pelleas and E.* 587
where the tide Plash'd, sapping its *w* ribs; *Lover's Tale i* 56
plaited ivy-tress had wound Round my *w* limbs, „ 619
And weird and *w* and wizard-like was he. *The Ring* 196
hearts *w* out by many wars And eyes grown dim *Lotos-Eater's, C. S.* 86
took it, and have *w* it, like a king: *M. d'Arthur* 33
theme of writers, and indeed W threadbare. *Edwin Morris* 49
Or while the patch was *w*; *Talking Oak* 64
Till now the dark was *w*, *Love and Duty* 71
he died at Florence, quite *w* out, *The Brook* 35
Those winters of abeyance all *w* out, *Princess iv* 440
Which he has *w* so pure of blame, *Ode on Well.* 72
Till slowly *w* her earthly robe, *In Mem. lxxxiv* 33
A censer, either *w* with wind and storm; *Gareth and L.* 222
W by the feet that now were silent, *Marr. of Geraint* 321
It never yet was *w*, I trow: „ 683
I myself unwillingly have *w* My faded suit, „ 705
and the mask of pure *W* by this court, *Merlin and V.* 36
King Had on his cuirass *w* our Lady's Head, *Lancelot and E.* 294
w Favour of any lady in the lists. (repeat) „ 363, 473
When these have *w* their tokens: „ 769
Wasted and *w*, and but a tithe of them, *Holy Grail* 723
took it, and have *w* it, like a king; *Pass. of Arthur* 201
richly garb'd, but *w* From wasteful living, *Ancient Sage* 4
Never *w* by a worthier, *On Jub. Q. Victoria* 8
had stolen, *w* the ring—Then torn it from her finger, *The Ring* 455
I have *w* them year by year— *Happy* 102
Worn-out while the *w-o* clerk Brow-beats his desk *To J. M. K.* 11
This *w-o* Reason dying in her house *Romney's R.* 145
Worried *W* his passive ear with petty wrongs *Enoch Arden* 352
Worry (*See also* **Tew, Tued**) a dog am I, To *w*, and not to flee— *Gareth and L.* 1015
Worse (*See also* **Woorse, Wuss**) Is boundless better, boundless *w*. *Two Voices* 27
I fear to slide from bad to *w*. „ 231
And ever *w* with growing time, *Palace of Art* 270
There *is* confusion *w* than death, *Lotos-Eaters, C. S.* 83
laughingly Would hint at *w* in either. *Enoch Arden* 481
if griefs Like his have *w* or better, „ 741
the song Might have been *w* and sinn'd *Princess iv* 251
some cold reverence *w* than were she dead. „ *v* 92
Or pines in sad experience *w* than death, „ *vii* 315
Far *w* than any death to me.' *Sailor Boy* 24
Hexameters no *w* than daring Germany gave us, *Trans. of Homer* 5
would make Confusion *w* than death, *In Mem. xc* 19
better or *w* Than the heart of the citizen *Maud I i* 23
fiend best knows whether woman or man be the *w*. „ 75

Worse (*continued*) Sick once, with a fear of *w*, *Maud I xix* 73
grew up to wolflike men, *W* than the wolves. *Com. of Arthur* 33
A *w* were better; yet no *w* would I. *Gareth and L.* 17
for *w* than being fool'd Of others, „ 1274
Shall I not rather prove the *w* for these? *Balin and Balan* 228
Kill'd with a word *w* than a life of blows! *Merlin and V.* 870
To make men *w* by making my sin known? *Lancelot and E.* 1417
That did not shun to smite me in *w* way, *Guinevere* 435
and expectancy of *w* Upon the morrow, *Lover's Tale ii* 151
The *w* for her, for me! was I content? *Sisters (E. and E.)* 126
I am handled *w* than had I been a Moor, *Columbus* 107
which was crueller? which was *w*? *Locksley H., Sixty* 88
War for War's own sake Is fool, or crazed, or *w*; *Epilogue* 31
cuckoo of a *w* July Is calling thro' the dark: *Pref. Poem Broth. Son.* 11
and paced his land In fear of *w*, *To Mary Boyle* 30
of the mind Mine; *w*, cold, calculated. *Romney's R.* 152
Worse-confounded Babel, woman-built, And *w-c*: *Princess iv* 488
Worship (s) (*See also* **Sun-worship, Wife-worship**) deck'd her out For *w* without end; „ *vii* 169
compass'd her with sweet observances And *w*, *Marr. of Geraint* 49
But this *w* of the Queen, *Balin and Balan* 179
'Old priest, who mumble *w* in your quire— „ 444
And I will pay you *w*; *Merlin and V.* 228
To seat you sole upon my pedestal Of *w*— „ 879
now my loyal *w* is allow'd Of all men: *Lancelot and E.* 110
yet O grant my *w* of it Words, „ 1187
It will be to thy *w*, as my knight, „ 1327
Dame, damsel, each thro' *w* of their Queen *Last Tournament* 146
There crown'd with *w*— *Tiresias* 175
Of saner *w* sanely proud; *Freedom* 30
that *w* which is Fear, Henceforth, *Demeter and P.* 143
harvest hymns of Earth The *w* which is Love, „ 149
in all Man-modes of *w*; *Akbar's Dream* 47
Worship (verb) That here come those that *w* me? *St. S. Stylites* 125
When you may *w* me without reproach; „ 193
Crown thyself, worm, and *w* thine own lusts!— *Aylmer's Field* 650
He *w's* your ideal:' she replied: *Princess ii* 52
hive of Roman liars *w* an emperor-idiot. *Boädicea* 19
To wage my wars, and *w* me their King; *Com. of Arthur* 508
'Fair damsel, you should *w* me the more, *Gareth and L.* 1022
Her likewise would I *w* an I might. *Balin and Balan* 185
The Queen we *w*, Lancelot, I, and all, „ 349
To *w* woman as true wife beyond *Merlin and V.* 23
And beasts themselves would *w*; „ 575
For Lancelot's kith and kin so *w* him *Holy Grail* 651
'Fair damsels, each to him who *w's* each *Last Tournament* 207
And *w* her by years of noble deeds, *Guinevere* 476
There also will I *w* thee as King. *Pass. of Arthur* 149
I anger'd Arundel asking me To *w* Holy Cross! *Sir J. Oldcastle* 136
She knelt—'We *w* him'— *Dead Prophet* 29
I *w* that right hand Which fell'd the foes *Happy* 41
both, to *w* Alla, but the prayers, *Akbar's Dream* 9
I let men *w* as they will, „ 66
a people have fashion'd and *w* a Spirit *Kapiolani* 1
Worshipfully Sir Lavaine did well and *w*; *Lancelot and E.* 491
would I reward thee *w*. *Gareth and L.* 829
Worshipp'd-Worshipt And *worshipt* their own darkness in the Highest? *Aylmer's Field* 643
Sir Lancelot *worshipt* no unmarried girl *Merlin and V.* 12
and him his new-made knight *Worshipt*, *Pelleas and E.* 155
Thy name is ever *worshipp'd* among hours! *Lover's Tale i* 493
Truth, for Truth is Truth, he *worshipt*, *Locksley H., Sixty* 59
once I *worshipt* all too well this creature *Happy* 45
Worshipper (*See also* **Woman-worshipper**) outlast thy Deity? Deity? nay, thy *w's*. *Lucretius* 73
Worst (*See also* **Earthly-worst, Woost**) 'Never, dearest, never: here I brave the *w*:' *Edwin Morris* 118
And women's slander is the *w*, *The Letters* 34
His *w* he kept, his best he gave. *You might have won* 26
'His deeds yet live, the *w* is yet to come. *Sea Dreams* 314
of her court The wiliest and the *w*; *Guinevere* 29
I hold that man the *w* of public foes „ 512
W of the *w* were that man he that reigns! „ 523
An' *she* wasn't one o' the *w*.' *First Quarrel* 61
never put on the black cap except for the *w* of the *w*, *Rizpah* 65

Worst (*continued*) She sees the Best that glimmers thro' the *W*, *Ancient Sage* 72
Do your best to charm the *w*, *Locksley H., Sixty* 147
Earth would never touch her *w*, „ 270
The best in me that sees the *w* in me, *Romney's R.* 44
For with thy *w* self sacrifice thyself, *Aylmer's Field* 646
And wretched age—and *w* disease of all, *Lucretius* 155
put on thy *w* and meanest dress And ride with me.' *Marr. of Geraint* 130
Put on your *w* and meanest dress,' „ 848
But women, *w* and best, as Heaven and Hell. *Merlin and V.* 815

Worth (adj.) (*See also* **Little-worth, Nothing-worth**) Is *w* a hundred coats-of-arms. *L. C. V. de Vere* 16
her least remark was *w* The experience of the wise. *Edwin Morris* 65
Is three times *w* them all; *Talking Oak* 72
'No doubt that we might make it *w* his while. *Princess i* 184
we should find the land *W* seeing; „ *iii* 172
beauty in detail Made them *w* knowing; „ *iv* 449
a good mother, a good wife, *W* winning; „ *v* 167
is not Ida right? They *w* it? „ 189
Warnt *w* nowt a haäcre, *N. Farmer, O. S.* 39
hardly *w* my while to choose Of things all mortal, *In Mem. xxxiv* 10
Whose life, whose thoughts were little *w*, „ *lxxxv* 30
A goodly youth and *w* a goodlier boon! *Gareth and L.* 449
'It is not *w* the keeping: let it go: *Merlin and V.* 396
gross heart Would reckon *w* the taking? „ 917
snare her royal fancy with a boon *W* half her realm, *Lancelot and E.* 72
mebbe *w* their weight i' gowd.' *Village Wife* 70
What life, so maim'd by night, were *w* Our living out? *Tiresias* 208
Were never *w* the while'— *Ancient Sage* 128
thou'd not 'a been *w* thy milk, *Spinster's S's.* 54
fuller franchise—what would that be *w*— *The Fleet* 8
change of the tide—what is all of it *w*? *Vastness* 30
Is it *w* his while to eat, *Voice spake, etc.* 7

Worth (s) *If aught of ancient* w *be there;* *To the Queen* 12
Old letters, breathing of her *w*, *Mariana in the S.* 62
To make him trust his modest *w*, *L. C. V. de Vere* 46
his mute dust I honour and his living *w*: *To J. S.* 30
And draws the veil from hidden *w*. *Day-Dm., Arrival* 4
I grow in *w*, and wit, and sense, *Will Water.* 41
most, of sterling *w*, is what Our own experience „ 175
couldst thou last, At half thy real *w*? „ 204
He loves me for my own true *w*, *Lady Clare* 11
'O Lady Clare, you shame your *w*! „ 66
And all his worldly *w* for this, *Sir L. and Q. G.* 43
A song that pleased us from its *w*; *You might have won* 22
they *might* be proud; its *w* Was being Edith's. *Aylmer's Field* 378
two dear things are one of double *w*, *Princess ii* 419
Till all men grew to rate us at our *w*, „ *iv* 145
What seem'd my *w* since I began; *In Mem., Pro.* 34
I know transplanted human *w* „ *lxxxii* 11
defying change To test his *w*; „ *xcv* 28
the *w* of half a town, A warhorse of the best, *Gareth and L.* 677
I scarce have spent the *w* of one!' *Geraint and E.* 411
they had been thrice their *w* Being your gift, *Lancelot and E.* 1212
did he know her *w*, Her beauty even? *Lover's Tale iv* 150
commission one of weight and *w* To judge *Columbus* 124
and was noble in birth as in *w*, *V. of Maeldune* 3

Worthier many a *w* than I, would make him happy yet. *May Queen, Con.* 46
I find him *w* to be loved. *In Mem., Pro.* 40
Modred for want of *w* was the judge. *Gareth and L.* 28
'Forbear: there is a *w*,' *Marr. of Geraint* 556
ten-times *w* to be thine Than twenty Balins, *Balin and Balan* 68
But thine are *w*, seeing they profess *Last Tournament* 82
Never worn by a *w*, *On Jub. Q. Victoria* 8
W soul was he than I am, sound and honest, rustic Squire, *Locksley H., Sixty* 239

Worthiest and of those halves You *w*; *Princess iv* 462
To follow up the *w* till he die: „ 466

Worthless The little senseless, *w*, wordless babe, *The Ring* 304

Worthy *w* of the golden prime (repeat) *Arabian Nights* 98, 142
W a Roman spouse.' *D. of F. Women* 164
Surely a precious thing, one *w* note, *M. d'Arthur* 89
it will be *w* of the two. *Locksley Hall* 92
Him too you loved, for he was *w* love. *Aylmer's Field* 712

Worthy (*continued*) '*w* reasons why she should Bide by this issue: *Princess v* 325
Call'd him *w* to be loved, „ *vi* 6
this is he *W* of our gorgeous rites, And *w* to be laid by thee; *Ode on Well.* 93
'I am not *w* ev'n to speak *In Mem. xxxvii* 11
And thou art *w*; full of power; „ *Con.* 37
We are not *w* to live, *Maud II i* 48
loved with that full love I feel for thee, nor *w* such a love: *Gareth and L.* 84
And pardonable, *w* to be knight— „ 654
Strike, thou art *w* of the Table Round— „ 1138
'Thou art not *w* ev'n to speak of him;' *Marr. of Geraint* 199
not *w* to be knight; A churl, a clown!' *Balin and Balan* 285
I, feeling that you felt me *w* trust, *Merlin and V.* 334
the quest Assign'd to her not *w* of it, *Lancelot and E.* 825
Toward one more *w* of her— „ 1320
if what is *w* love Could bind him, „ 1378
'I am not *w* of the Quest;' *Holy Grail* 386
I had liefer ye were *w* of my love, *Pelleas and E.* 301
Surely a precious thing, one *w* note, *Pass. of Arthur* 257
that I know you *w* everyway To be my son, *Sisters (E. and E.)* 48
An old and *w* name! „ 74

Would-be You *w-b* quenchers of the light to be, *Princess iv* 536

Would-be-widow While she vows 'till death shall part us,' she the *w-b-w* wife. *Locksley H., Sixty* 24

Wound (s) then, because his *w* was deep, *M. d'Arthur* 5
I fear My *w* hath taken cold, „ 166
Where I will heal me of my grievous *w*.' „ 264
Like flies that haunt a *w*, or deer, or men, *Aylmer's Field* 571
My father stoop'd, re-father'd o'er my *w's*. *Princess vi* 129
Lifting his grim head from my *w's*. „ 272
To save her dear lord whole from any *w*. *Geraint and E.* 45
till she had lighted on his *w*, „ 513
'Sir King, mine ancient *w* is hardly whole, *Lancelot and E.* 93
and bare him in, There stanch'd his *w*; „ 520
Lancelot who hath come Despite the *w* he spake of, „ 566
added *w* to *w* And ridd'n away to die?' „ 567
Had made the pretext of a hindering *w*, „ 582
tho' he call'd his *w* a little hurt „ 852
Then fared it with Sir Pelleas as with one Who gets a *w* in battle, and the sword that made it plunges thro' the *w* again, *Pelleas and E.* 529
Then, because his *w* was deep, *Pass. of Arthur* 174
I fear My *w* hath taken cold, „ 334
Where I will heal me of my grievous *w*.' „ 432
after healing of his grievous *w* He comes again; „ 450
With a grisly *w* to be drest he had left the deck, *The Revenge* 66
told them of his wars, and of his *w*. *Sisters (E. and E.)* 60
Death to the dying, and *w's* to the wounded, *Def. of Lucknow* 17
the *w* that *would* not be heal'd, „ 84

Wound (to wind) as the boat-head *w* along The willowy hills *L. of Shalott iv* 24
Where Past and Present, *w* in one, *Miller's D.* 197
that my arms Were *w* about thee, *Œnone* 203
her hair *W* with white roses, slept St. Cecily; *Palace of Art* 99
and turning, *w* Her looser hair in braid, *Gardener's D.* 157
w A scarf of orange round the stony helm, *Princess, Pro.* 101
we *w* About the cliffs, the copses, out and in, „ *iii* 359
Thro' open field into the lists they *w* Timorously; „ *vi* 84
And mine in this was *w*, *In Mem. xcv* 37
w Bare to the sun, and monstrous ivy-stems *Marr. of Geraint* 321
Thro' the rocks we *w*: *Lover's Tale i* 324
plaited ivy-tress had *w* Round my worn limbs, „ 618
I *w* my arms About her: „ *ii* 200

Wound (to wound) creaking cords which *w* and eat *Supp. Confessions* 36
Tho' men may *w* him that he will not die, *Com. of Arthur* 421

Wounded (adj. and part.) (*See also* **Arrow-wounded, Deeply-wounded**) Till himself was deadly *w* *The Captain* 63
With *w* peace which each had prick'd to death. *Aylmer's Field* 52
Is *w* to the death that cannot die; „ 662
And see my dear lord *w* in the strife, *Marr. of Geraint* 103
For those that might be *w*; *Geraint and E.* 568
And were himself nigh *w* to the death.' „ 919
man in life Was *w* by blind tongues he saw not *Balin and Balan* 130

Wreath (*continued*) thine The *w* of beauty, thine the crown of power, *Merlin and V.* 79
A *w* of airy dancers hand-in-hand *Guinevere* 261
—its *w's* of dripping green— *Lover's Tale i* 39
Darkening the *w's* of all that would advance, *To Victor Hugo* 5
This *w*, above his honour'd head, *Tiresias* 213
I caught the *w* that was flung. *The Wreck* 40
Or Love with *w's* of flowers. *Epilogue* 17
And you, that wear a *w* of sweeter bay, *Poets and their B.* 7
Wreath'd (*See also* **New-wreathed**) Love's arms were *w* about the neck of Hope, *Lover's Tale i* 815
Beneath the bower of *w* eglantines: „ *ii* 43
W round the bier with garlands: „ 79
the belted hunter blew His *w* bugle-horn. *Palace of Art* 64
around his head The glorious goddess *w* a golden cloud, *Achilles over the T.* 5
Wreathe Now *w* thy cap with doleful crape, *My life is full* 14
The fancy's tenderest eddy *w*, *In Mem. xlix* 6
To *w* a crown not only for the king *Akbar's Dream* 23
Wreathen (*See also* **Mist-wreathen**) the sculptured ornament That *w* round it *Merlin and V.* 735
Wreck (s) Hurt in that night of sudden ruin and *w*, *Enoch Arden* 564
sure no gladlier does the stranded *w* „ 828
his voyage, His *w*, his lonely life, „ 862
battle, bold adventure, dungeon, *w*, *Aylmer's Field* 98
the father suddenly cried, 'A *w*, a *w*!' *Sea Dreams* 59
Rotting on some wild shore with ribs of *w*, *Princess v* 147
My father raves of death and *w*, *Sailor Boy* 19
Tho' his vessel was all but a *w*; *The Revenge* 64
pranced on the *w's* in the sand below, *V. of Maeldune* 102
My brain is full of the crash of *w's*, *The Wreck* 4
My life itself is a *w*, „ 5
the one man left on the *w*— „ 119
they had saved many hundreds from *w*— *Despair* 10
about the shuddering *w* the death-white sea *The Flight* 47
children in a sunbeam sitting on the ribs of *w*. *Locksley H., Sixty* 14
I was left within the shadow sitting on the *w* alone. „ 16
and sinking with the sinking *w*, „ 64
Like some old *w* on some indrawing sea, *St. Telemachus* 44
bodies and souls go down in a common *w*, *The Dawn* 13
Wreck (verb) sought'st to *w* my mortal ark, *Two Voices* 389
May *w* itself without the pilot's guilt, *Aylmer's Field* 716
my craven seeks To *w* thee villainously: *Last Tournament* 549
love is wreck'd—if Love can *w*— *Lover's Tale i* 804
passive sailor *w's* at last In ever-silent seas; *Ancient Sage* 136
Wreck'd *W* on a reef of visionary gold.' *Sea Dreams* 139
when their love is *w*—if Love can wreck— *Lover's Tale i* 804
we are all of us *w* at last— *Despair* 12
W—your train—or all but *w*? *Locksley H., Sixty* 215
Saved when your life was *w*! *The Ring* 305
Wren 'Shall eagles not be eagles? *w's* be *w's*? *Golden Year* 37
And you my *w* with a crown of gold, You my queen of the *w's*! You the queen of the *w's*— *Window, Spring* 11
I'll be the King of the Queen of the *w's*, „ 15
The fire-crown'd king of the *w's*, „ *Ay* 8
flit like the king of the *w's* with a crown of fire. „ 16
Tits, *w's*, and all wing'd nothings *Marr. of Geraint* 275
Wrench'd (*See also* **Half-wrench'd**) Who *w* their rights from thee! *England and Amer.* 5
and *w* with pains Gain'd in the service *Columbus* 235
dearer ghost had— *Father*. —*w* it away. *The Ring* 468
Wrenching *W* it backward into his; *Lucretius* 221
Wrestle strive and *w* with thee till I die: *St. S. Stylites* 119
Had ever seem'd to *w* with burlesque, *Princess, Con.* 16
Wrestled *W* with wandering Israel, *Clear-headed friend* 26
Wrestling Nor lose the *w* thews that throw the world; *Princess vii* 282
Wretch Poor *w*—no friend!— *Merlin and V.* 75
W you must abide it . . . *Forlorn* 52
then he yawn'd, for the *w could* sleep,— *Bandit's Death* 30
Wretched Except his wrath were wreak'd on *w* man, *Lucretius* 128
And *w* age—and worst disease of all, „ 155
'*W* boy, How saw you not the inscription on the gate, *Princess ii* 193
On a horror of shatter'd limbs and a *w* swindler's lie? *Maud I i* 56
A *w* vote may be gain'd. „ *vi* 56
At war with myself and a *w* race, „ *x* 35

Wretched (*continued*) Yea ev'n of *w* meat and drink, *Maud I xv* 8
May God make me more *w* Than ever I have been yet! „ *xix* 94
O *w* set of sparrows, one and all, *Marr. of Geraint* 278
and your *w* dress, A *w* insult on you, *Geraint and E.* 327
pains Of the hellish heat of a *w* life *Despair* 68
A madman to vex you with *w* words, „ 108
Wretchedest *W* age, since Time began, *Maud II v* 21
Wretchedness But bode his hour, devising *w*. *Last Tournament* 386
Wrigglesby beck Loook thou theer wheer *W b* cooms out by the 'll! *N. Farmer, N. S.* 53
Wring take the goose, and *w* her throat, *The Goose* 31
Wrinkle Whose *w's* gather'd on his face, *Two Voices* 329
The busy *w's* round his eyes? *Miller's D.* 4
A million *w's* carved his skin; *Palace of Art* 138
Sown in a *w* of the monstrous hill, *Will* 19
Wrinkled (*See also* **Myriad-wrinkled**) Hard wood I am, and *w* rind, *Talking Oak* 171
cold my *w* feet Upon thy glimmering thresholds, *Tithonus* 67
and there The *w* steward at his task, *Day-Dm., Sleep. P.* 27
The *w* sea beneath him crawls; *The Eagle* 4
'*W* ostler, grim and thin! *Vision of Sin* 63
w benchers often talk'd of him Approvingly, *Aylmer's Field* 473
Down from the lean and *w* precipices, *Princess iv* 22
A charr'd and *w* piece of womanhood, „ *v* 61
When have I bow'd to her father, the *w* head of the race? *Maud I iv* 13
God help the *w* children that are Christ's *Sisters (E. and E.)* 183
Wrinkling But bland the smile that like a *w* wind *Princess i* 115
Wrist I sigh'd: a touch Came round my *w*, „ *vii* 138
The *w* is parted from the hand that waved, *Merlin and V.* 551
But I will slice him handless by the *w*, *Pelleas and E.* 338
Writ (s) saith not Holy *W* the same?'— *Merlin and V.* 52
Perhaps, like him of Cana in Holy *W*, *Holy Grail* 762
Writ (verb) *W* in a language that has long gone by. *Merlin and V.* 674
wrote The letter she devised; which being *w* And folded, *Lancelot and E.* 1109
old writers Have *w* of in histories— *Batt. of Brunanburh* 115
Write (*See also* **Wroite**) To make me *w* my random rhymes, *Will Water.* 13
you shall *w*, and not to her, but me: *Aylmer's Field* 310
'*W* to me! They loved me, „ 422
Shall I *w* to her? shall I go? *Window, Letter* 5
One *w's*, that 'Other friends remain,' *In Mem. vi* 1
Besought Lavaine to *w* as she devised A letter, *Lancelot and E.* 1103
Old Virgil who would *w* ten lines, *Poets and their B.* 2
Writer Seem but the theme of *w's*, *Edwin Morris* 48
Old *w's* push'd the happy season back,— *Golden Year* 66
old *w's* Have writ of in histories— *Batt. of Brunanburh* 114
Writhe a worm which *w's* all day, *Vastness* 17
Writhed (adj. and part.) Those *w* limbs of lightning speed; *Clear-headed friend* 23
When the worm shall have *w* its last, *Despair* 85
Writhed (verb) *w* his wiry arms Around him, till he felt, *Gareth and L.* 1150
W toward him, slided up his knee and sat, *Merlin and V.* 239
down his robe the dragon *w* in gold, *Lancelot and E.* 435
Down on the great King's couch, and *w* upon it, „ 610
She roused a snake that hissing *w* away; *Death of Œnone* 88
Writhen *See* **Battle-writhen**
Writhing read *W* a letter from his child, *Aylmer's Field* 517
w barbarous lineäments, *Boädicea* 74
Sweat, *w's*, anguish, labouring of the lungs *Pass. of Arthur* 115
Writin' atween 'is reädin' an' *w* 'e snifft *Village Wife* 40
Writing (*See also* **Writin'**) crazed myself over their horrible infidel *w's*? *Despair* 87
Written (*See also* **Wrote**) it is *w* that my race Hew'd Ammon, *D. of F. Women* 237
w as she found Or made occasion, *Aylmer's Field* 477
And Willy's wife has *w*: (repeat) *Grandmother* 3, 105
And something *w*, something thought; *In Mem. vi* 20
And *w* in the speech ye speak yourself, *Com. of Arthur* 304
'Ye have the book: the charm is *w* in it; *Merlin and V.* 652
oft I seem as he Of whom was *w*, *Last Tournament* 116
Glorious poet who never hast *w* a line, *To A. Tennyson* 5
I am *w* in the Lamb's own Book of Life *Columbus* 88
scroll *w* over with lamentation and woe. *Despair* 20
Wroite (write) summun I reckons 'ull 'a to *w*, *N. Farmer, O. S.* 57
Wrong (adj.) he was *w* to cross his father thus: *Dora* 148

Wrong (adj.) (*continued*) His nerves were *w*. *Walk. to the Mail* 105
am I right, or am I *w*, (repeat) *Day-Dm., L'Envoi* 29, 33
What! I am not all as *w* As a bitter jest *Vision of Sin* 197
I was *w*, I am always bound to you, *Enoch Arden* 449
'Would I—was it *w*?' *The Brook* 111
And so I often told her, right or *w*, *Princess v* 288
And, right or *w*, I care not: this is all, " 290
Death for the right cause, death for the *w* cause, *Vastness* 8
She offens 'ud spy summut *w* *Owd Roä* 70
W there! The painter's fame? *Romney's R.* 48
Wrong (s) There seem'd no room for sense of *w*; *Two Voices* 456
lamentation and an ancient tale of *w*, *Lotos-Eaters, C. S.* 118
I heard sounds of insult, shame, and *w*, *D. of F. Women* 19
'I have hid my feelings, fearing they should do me *w*;' *Locksley Hall* 29
we, that prate Of rights and *w's*, *Godiva* 8
He that only rules by terror Doeth grievous *w*. *The Captain* 2
Hush'd all the groves from fear of *w*: *Sir L. and Q. G.* 13
And then we met in wrath and *w*, *The Letters* 11
Worried his passive ear with petty *w's* Or pleasures, *Enoch Arden* 352
Began to chafe as at a personal *w*. " 474
if he did that *w* you charge him with, *Sea Dreams* 279
He can do no more *w*: forgive him, " 311
(A little sense of *w* had touch'd her face *Princess, Pro.* 219
Bow'd on her palms and folded up from *w*, " *iv* 288
Came all in haste to hinder *w*, " 401
Tho' man, yet human, whatsoe'er your *w's*, " 425
Torn from the lintel—all the common *w*— " *v* 129
chance Were caught within the record of her *w's*, " 143
I thought her half-right talking of her *w's*; " 285
brawl Their rights or *w's* like potherbs in the street. " 459
'ourselves are full Of social *w*; " *Con.* 73
Till public *w* be crumbled into dust, *Ode on Well.* 167
He suffers, but he cannot suffer *w*: *Will* 3
My name in song has done him much *w*, *Spiteful Letter* 3
to fight, to struggle, to right the *w*— *Wages* 3
Nor human frailty do me *w*. *In Mem. lii* 8
we do him *w* To sing so wildly: " *lvii* 3
Drug down the blindfold sense of *w* " *lxxi* 7
Thou doest expectant nature *w*; " *lxxxiii* 3
Bewail'd their lot; I did them *w*: " *ciii* 46
taking revenge too deep for a transient *w* *Maud I iii* 5
She would not do herself this great *w*, " *x* 57
teach true life to fight with mortal *w's*. " *xviii* 54
Or to say 'Forgive the *w*,' " *II iv* 86
peace that was full of *w's* and shames, " *III vi* 40
Whose glory was, redressing human *w*; *Ded. of Idylls* 9
speak true, right *w*, follow the King— *Gareth and L.* 118
from the *w's* his father did Would shape himself " 347
Give me to right her *w*, and slay the man.' " 366
Than ride abroad redressing women's *w*, " 866
For this were shame to do him further *w* " 954
To noble hearts who see but acts of *w*: *Marr. of Geraint* 438
That each had suffer'd some exceeding *w*. *Geraint and E.* 36
smoulder'd *w* that burnt him all within; " 107
worse than that dead man; Done you more *w*: " 736
As one that let foul *w* stagnate and be, " 891
which for bribe had wink'd at *w*, " 939
Once for *w* done you by confusion, *Merlin and V.* 307
And see, yourself have own'd ye did me *w*. " 316
They ride abroad redressing human *w's*! " 693
many a year have done despite and *w* *Lancelot and E.* 1209
leaving human *w's* to right themselves, *Holy Grail* 898
Well—can I wish her any huger *w* *Last Tournament* 596
deed Of prowess done redress'd a random *w*. *Guinevere* 459
To ride abroad redressing human *w's*, " 471
Yet who had done, or who had suffer'd *w*? *Lover's Tale i* 726
No, no, you are doing me *w*! *First Quarrel* 4
Loving the other? do her that great *w*? *Sisters (E. and E.)* 168
than have done one another a *w*. *V. of Maeldune* 6
or flamed at a public *w*, *The Wreck* 68
that hourly work their brother insect *w*, *Locksley H., Sixty* 202
tho' that realm were in the *w* *Epilogue* 34
I wrought thee bitter *w*, but thou forgive, *Death of Œnone* 43
wind of the Night shrilling out Desolation and *w* *The Dreamer* 15

Wrong (verb) he that *w's* his friend *W's* himself *Sea Dreams* 172
'you *w* him more than I That struck him: *Princess iv* 245
She *w's* herself, her sex, and me, " *v* 117
You *w* yourselves—the woman is so hard " *vi* 222
I *w* the grave with fears untrue: *In Mem. li* 9
O child, you *w* your beauty, believe it, *Maud I iv* 17
dream That any of these would *w* thee, *w's* thyself. *Balin and Balan* 144
—nay, but I *w* him, *Lover's Tale iv* 73
You *w* me, passionate little friend. *Epilogue* 10
I can *w* thee now no more, Œnone, *Death of Œnone* 80
Wrong'd (part.) I knew thee *w*. I brake upon thy rest, *Balin and Balan* 499
How had I *w* you? surely ye are wise, *Merlin and V.* 288
A virtuous gentlewoman deeply *w*, " 911
'Can he be *w* who is not ev'n his own, *Last Tournament* 524
May'st thou never be *w* by the name *To A. Tennyson* 7
I never have *w* his heart, *The Wreck* 14
Wrong'd (s) to help the *w* Thro' all our realm. *Gareth and L.* 371
Then Gareth, 'Bound am I to right the *w*, " 804
With strength and will to right the *w*, *Holy Grail* 309
Wrong'd (verb) *w* and lied and thwarted us— *Princess iv* 540
judge their cause from her That *w* it, " *vii* 236
he never *w* his bride. I know the tale. *Merlin and V.* 729
Hears he now the Voice that *w* him? *Locksley H., Sixty* 269
Wronger this Order lives to crush All *w's* of the Realm. *Gareth and L.* 626
At caitiffs and at *w's* of the world. *Marr. of Geraint* 96
Brutes, the brutes are not your *w's*— *Locksley H., Sixty* 97
Wrote round about the prow she *w* *L. of Shalott iv* 8
W, 'Mene, mene,' and divided quite *Palace of Art* 227
and a tear Dropt on the letters as I *w*. *To J. S.* 56
I *w* I know not what. In truth, " 57
you shall have that song which Leonard *w*: *Golden Year* 1
'Then I took a pencil, and *w* On the mossy stone, *Edward Gray* 25
tho' Averill *w* And bad him with good heart *Aylmer's Field* 543
Who first *w* satire, with no pity in it. *Sea Dreams* 202
then, Sir, awful odes she *w*, Too awful, *Princess i* 138
and I sat down and *w*, In such a hand " 235
take this and pray that he Who *w* it, *A Dedication* 5
and sat him down, and *w* All things *Com. of Arthur* 156
Then he *w* The letter she devised; *Lancelot and E.* 1108
An' he *w* 'I ha' six weeks' work, *First Quarrel* 45
an' sorry for what she *w*, " 87
Edith *w*: 'My mother bids me ask' *Sisters (E. and E.)* 180
and besides, The great Augustine *w* *Columbus* 52
I *w* to the nurse Who had borne my flower *The Wreck* 142
He knows not ev'n the book he *w*, *Ancient Sage* 148
he *w* 'Their kindness,' and he *w* no more; *To Marq. of Dufferin* 35
w Name, surname, all as clear as noon, *The Ring* 236
Up she got, and *w* him all, *Forlorn* 79
Wrote (written) An' 'e'd *w* an owd book, his awn sen, *Village Wife* 46
Wroth (*See also* **Half-wroth**) Then the old man Was *w*, *Dora* 25
Weakness to be *w* with weakness! *Locksley Hall* 149
Sullen, defiant, pitying, *w*, *Aylmer's Field* 492
perforce He yielded, *w* and red, with fierce demur: *Princess v* 358
A third is *w*: 'Is this an hour For private sorrow's *In Mem. xxi* 13
W to be *w* at such a worm, *Marr. of Geraint* 213
my new mother, be not *w* or grieved At thy new son, " 779
For, be he *w* even to slaying me, *Geraint and E.* 67
it made him *w* the more That she *could* speak " 112
neither dame nor damsel then *W* at a lover's loss? *Merlin and V.* 607
W at himself. Not willing to be known, *Lancelot and E.* 160
W that the King's command to sally forth " 560
W, but all in awe, For twenty strokes " 719
Fret not yourself, dear brother, nor be *w*, " 1074
And *w* at Tristram and the lawless jousts, *Last Tournament* 237
is the Demon-god *W* at his fall?' *St. Telemachus* 20
Wrought '*She w her people lasting good;* *To the Queen* 24
And all so variously *w*, *Two Voices* 457
With royal frame-work of *w* gold; *Ode to Memory* 82
who *w* Two spirits to one equal mind— *Miller's D.* 235
times of every land So *w*, they will not fail. *Palace of Art* 148
she turn'd her sight The airy hand confusion *w*, " 226
But by degrees to fulness *w* *You ask me, why, etc.* 14
W by the lonely maiden of the Lake. *M. d'Arthur* 104
Nine years she *w* it, sitting in the deeps " 105

Wrought (*continued*) More things are *w* by prayer Than this world dreams of. *M. d'Arthur* 247
damask napkin *w* with horse and hound, *Audley Court* 21
It may be I have *w* some miracles, *St. S. Stylites* 136
Souls that have toil'd, and *w*, and thought with me— *Ulysses* 46
and *w* To make the boatmen fishing-nets, *Enoch Arden* 814
her counsel all had *w* About them: *Aylmer's Field* 151
w Such waste and havock as the idolatries, „ 639
'Dare we dream of that,' I ask'd, 'Which *w* us *Princess iii* 298
our device; *w* to the life; „ 303
raised A tent of satin, elaborately *w* „ 348
with whom the bell-mouth'd glass had *w*, „ *iv* 155
So much a kind of shame within me *w*, „ 194
wherein were *w* Two grand designs; „ *vii* 121
Let the sound of those he *w* for, *Ode on Well.* 10
When he with those deep voices *w*, „ 67
Ye know no more than I who *w* *In Mem. vi* 17
and *w* With human hands the creed of creeds „ *xxxvi* 9
Till out of painful phases *w* There flutters „ *lxv* 6
Cloud-towers by ghostly masons *w*, „ *lxx* 5
Is *w* with tumult of acclaim. „ *lxxv* 20
The grief my loss in him had *w*, „ *lxxx* 6
For changes *w* on form and face; „ *lxxxii* 2
Her lavish mission richly *w*, „ *lxxxiv* 34
Whatever change the years have *w*, „ *xc* 22
For what was it else within me *w* *Maud I vi* 81
W, till he crept from a gutted mine „ *x* 9
W for his house an irredeemable woe; „ *II i* 22
and *w* All kind of service with a noble ease *Gareth and L.* 488
So for a month he *w* among the thralls; „ 525
hath *w* on Lancelot now To lend thee horse and shield: „ 1323
Themselves had *w* on many an innocent. *Geraint and E.* 178
I schemed and *w* Until I overturn'd him; „ 829
And *w* too long with delegated hands, „ 893
work of Edyrn *w* upon himself After a life of violence, „ 912
Had often *w* some fury on myself, *Balin and Balan* 62
This fellow hath *w* some foulness with his Queen: „ 565
What evil have ye *w*? Rise!' *Merlin and V.* 67
'None *w*, but suffer'd much, an orphan maid! „ 71
Would fain have *w* upon his cloudy mood „ 156
which if any *w* on anyone With woven paces „ 206
man so *w* on ever seem'd to lie „ 208
could he see but him who *w* the charm Coming and going, „ 212
those who *w* it first, The wrist is parted „ 550
Some charm, which being *w* upon the Queen „ 584
Nor saw she save the King, who *w* the charm, „ 643
And of the horrid foulness that he *w*, „ 748
w upon his mood and hugg'd him close. „ 948
In letters gold and azure!' which was *w* Thereafter; *Lancelot and E.* 1345
w into his heart A way by love that waken'd love *Holy Grail* 10
In horror lest the work by Merlin *w*, „ 259
grace and power, *W* as a charm upon them, *Guinevere* 144
Hath *w* confusion in the Table Round „ 220
My love thro' flesh hath *w* into my life So far, „ 558
Which *w* the ruin of my lord the King.' „ 689
W by the lonely maiden of the Lake. Nine years she *w* it, sitting in the deeps *Pass. of Arthur* 272
More things are *w* by prayer Than this world dreams of. „ 415
Were *w* into the tissue of my dream: *Lover's Tale ii* 113
she *w* us harm, Poor soul, not knowing) *Sisters (E. and E.)* 184
who *w* Not Matter, nor the finite-infinite, *De Prof., Two G.* 53
w To mould the dream; *To E. Fitzgerald* 29
and whatsoe'er He *w* of good or brave *Epilogue* 76
He that *w* my ruin— *Forlorn* 2
I *w* thee bitter wrong, but thou forgive, *Death of Œnone* 43
Wrung Caught at his hand, and *w* it passionately, *Enoch Arden* 328
Daintily she shriek'd And *w* it. *Princess, Pro.* 176
From our first Charles by force we *w* our claims. *Third of Feb.* 26
Lady Lyonors *w* her hands and wept, *Gareth and L.* 1395
The griefs by which he once was *w* *Ancient Sage* 127
Wud (mad) an' screeäd like a Howl gone *w*— *Owd Roä* 76
Wuss (worse) Ye be *w* nor the men-tommies, you. *Spinster's S's.* 93
a-tuggin' an' teärin' me *w* nor afoor, *Owd Roä* 66
Wye And hushes half the babbling *W*, *In Mem. xix* 7
Wye (*continued*) The *W* is hush'd nor moved along, *In Mem. xix* 9
Wyvern Whose blazing *w* weathercock'd the spire, *Aylmer's Field* 17
Burst his own *w* on the seal, „ 516
men and boys astride On *w*, lion, dragon, *Holy Grail* 350

X

Xanthus between the ships and stream Of *X* *Spec. of Iliad* 18

Y

Yabbok brook Past *Y b* the livelong night, *Clear-headed friend* 27
Yaffingale hear the garnet-headed *y* Mock them: *Last Tournament* 700
Yard (*See also* **Chapel-yard, Olive-yard**) and his hair A *y* behind. *Godiva* 19
Only a *y* beneath the street, *Maud II v* 7
by two *y's* in casting bar or stone Was counted best; *Gareth and L.* 518
Sa I runs to the *y* fur a lether, *Owd Roä* 82
Yardwand but with his cheating *y*, home.— *Maud I i* 52
Yaupin' (yelping) a-yowlin' an' *y'* like mad; *Owd Roä* 88
Yawl'd Then yelp'd the cur, and *y* the cat; *The Goose* 33
Yawn (s) and toss them away with a *y*, *The Wreck* 21
Yawn (verb) 'Heaven opens inward, chasms *y*, *Two Voices* 304
black earth *y's*: the mortal disappears; *Ode on Well.* 269
on his right a cavern-chasm *Y* over darkness, *Balin and Balan* 313
to sigh, and to stretch and *y*, *V. of Maeldune* 91
Fiend would yell, the grave would *y*, *The Flight* 51
naked glebe Should *y* once more into the gulf, *Demeter and P.* 43
Yawn'd *y*, and rubb'd his face, and spoke, *Day-Dm., Revival* 19
then he *y*, for the wretch *could* sleep, *Bandit's Death* 30
Yawning (adj. and part.) Hither came Cyril, and *y* *Princess iii* 124
And crowds that stream from *y* doors, *In Mem. lxx* 9
Not all mismated with a *y* clown, *Geraint and E.* 426
But saw the postern portal also wide *Y*; *Pelleas and E.* 421
earth beneath me *y* cloven With such a sound *Lover's Tale i* 602
up-shadowing high above us with her *y* tiers of guns, *The Revenge* 41
While the grave is *y*. *Forlorn* 60
Yawning (s) The *y* of an earthquake-cloven chasm. *Lover's Tale i* 377
Year (*See also* **After-years, A-year, Cycle-year, New-year, Nine-years-fought-for, Nine-years-ponder'd, Old-year, Ta-year, Three-years', To-year**) and clear Delight, the infant's dawning *y*. *Supp. Confessions* 67
The lamb rejoiceth in the *y*, „ 157
Because they are the earliest of the *y*). *Ode to Memory* 27
music flowing from The illimitable *y's*. „ 42
A SPIRIT haunts the *y's* last hours *A Spirit haunts* 1
And the *y's* last rose. „ 20
And if you kiss'd her feet a thousand *y's*, *The form, the form* 13
mirror clear That hangs before her all the *y*, *L. of Shalott ii* 11
I said, 'The *y's* with change advance: *Two Voices* 52
I said that 'all the *y's* invent; „ 73
'I found him when my *y's* were few; „ 271
For is not our first *y* forgot? „ 368
Oft lose whole *y's* of darker mind. „ 372
Many a chance the *y's* beget. *Miller's D.* 206
Untouch'd with any shade of *y's*, „ 219
so three *y's* She prosper'd: *Palace of Art* 217
So when four *y's* were wholly finished, „ 289
To-morrow 'ill be of all the *y* the maddest merriest day, *May Queen* 43
The good old *y*, the dear old time, *May Queen, N. Y's. E.* 6
How sadly, I remember, rose the morning of the *y*! „ *Con.* 3
Which men call'd Aulis in those iron *y's*: *D. of F. Women* 106
And the old *y* is dead. „ 248
Desiring what is mingled with past *y's*, „ 282
For the old *y* lies a-dying. *D. of the O. Year* 5
Old *y*, you must not die; „ 6
Old *y*, you shall not die. (repeat) „ 9, 24
Old *y*, you must not go; „ 15
Old *y*, you shall not go. „ 18

Year (*continued*) New as his title, built last *y*, *Maud I x* 19
Last *y*, I caught a glimpse of his face, „ *xiii* 27
He may stay for a *y* who has gone for a week: „ *xvi* 6
To me, her friend of the *y's* before; „ *xix* 64
but of force to withstand, *Y* upon *y*, „ *II ii* 25
For *y's*, a measureless ill, For *y's*, for ever, „ 49
My mood is changed, for it fell at a time of *y* „ *III vi* 4
thro' all this tract of *y's* Wearing *Ded. of Idylls* 24
that same night, the night of the new *y*, *Com. of Arthur* 209
This *y*, when Merlin (for his hour had come) „ 228
grace Thy climbing life, and cherish my prone *y*, *Gareth and L.* 95
gold for Uther's use thereof, According to the *y's*. „ 345
What I these two *y's* past have won *Marr. of Geraint* 554
three sad *y's* ago, That night of fire, „ 633
Her suitor in old *y's* before Geraint, *Geraint and E.* 276
' Earl, if you love me as in former *y's*, „ 355
and my purpose three *y's* old, „ 849
Arthur call'd His treasurer, one of many *y's*, *Balin and Balan* 5
those three kingless *y's* Have past— „ 63
from the presence into *y's* Of exile— „ 156
A *y* ago—nay, then I love thee not— „ 504
Was one *y* gone, and on returning found *Merlin and V.* 708
this cut is fresh; That ten *y's* back; *Lancelot and E.* 22
Once every *y*, a joust for one of these: „ 61
by nine *y's'* proof we needs must learn „ 62
eight *y's* past, eight jousts had been, and still Had Lancelot won the diamond of the *y*, „ 67
However marr'd, of more than twice her *y's*, „ 257
Heard from the Baron that, ten *y's* before, „ 272
now for forty *y's* A hermit, who had pray'd, „ 402
This many a *y* have done despite and wrong „ 1209
not to love again; Not at my *y's*, „ 1296
Spring after spring, for half a hundred *y's*: *Holy Grail* 19
' Then came a *y* of miracle: „ 166
Yea, rotten with a hundred *y's* of death, „ 496
Hath lain for *y's* at rest— *Last Tournament* 94
The snowdrop only, flowering thro' the *y*, „ 220
Made answer, ' I had liefer twenty *y's* „ 257
memories Of Tristram in that *y* he was away.' „ 580
Table Round Which good King Arthur founded, *y's* ago, *Guinevere* 221
And worship her by *y's* of noble deeds, „ 476
months will add themselves and make the *y's*, The *y's* will roll into the centuries, „ 625
there, an Abbess, lived For three brief *y's*, „ 697
Burn'd at his lowest in the rolling *y*. *Pass. of Arthur* 91
Nine *y's* she wrought it, sitting in the deeps „ 273
days darken round me, and the *y's*, „ 405
And the new sun rose bringing the new *y*. „ 469
y's Have hollow'd out a deep and stormy strait *Lover's Tale i* 23
many *y's*, (For they seem many and my most of life, „ 184
As Love and I do number equal *y's*, „ 195
careful burthen of our tender *y's* Trembled „ 222
Sweet thro' strange *y's* to know „ 244
Pass we then A term of eighteen *y's*. „ 287
Thou art blessed in the *y's*, divinest day! „ 486
Had drawn herself from many thousand *y's*, „ 550
As the tall ship, that many a dreary *y* „ 808
And kept it thro' a hundred *y's* of gloom, „ *iv* 195
picture of his lady, taken Some *y's* before, „ 217
I knew a man, nor many *y's* ago; „ 255
Now that the flower of a *y* and a half is thine, *To A. Tennyson* 3
I ha' work'd for him fifteen *y's*, *First Quarrel* 7
Harry was bound to the Dorsetshire farm for *y's* an' for *y's*; „ 19
y's went over till I that was little „ 27
till he told me that so many *y's* had gone by, „ 36
he call'd in the dark to me *y* after *y*— *Rizpah* 47
Y after *y* in the mist and the wind „ 68
back-end o' June, Ten *y* sin', *North. Cobbler* 12
our house has held Three hundred *y's*— *Sisters* (*E. and E.*) 53
On a sudden after two Italian *y's* „ 150
and in the second *y* was born A second— „ 269
thaw nigh upo' seventy *y*. *Village Wife* 27
sarved 'em wi' butter an' heggs fur huppuds o' twenty *y*. „ 114
gratefullest heart I have found in a child of her *y's*— *In the Child. Hosp.* 32

Year (*continued*) Eighteen long *y's* of waste, *Columbus* 36
Along the *y's* of haste and random youth *De Prof., Two G.* 21
Of Turkish Islam for five hundred *y's*, *Montenegro* 11
Titan by thy winter weight of *y's* As yet unbroken, *To Victor Hugo* 7
KING, that hast reign'd six hundred *y's*, *To Dante* 1
And dating many a *y* ago, Has hit on this, *To E. Fitzgerald* 49
I WISH I were in the *y's* of old, *Tiresias* 1
five-fold thy term Of *y's*, I lay; „ 34
their examples reach a hand Far thro' all *y's*, „ 127
To spend my one last *y* among the hills. *Ancient Sage* 16
' What Power but the *Y's* that make „ 91
The *y's* that made the stripling wise „ 111
The *y's* that when my Youth began „ 155
But vain the tears for darken'd *y's* „ 183
Whin, yer Honour? last *y*— *Tomorrow* 1
Danny was there, yer Honour, for forty *y*. „ 30
as ye used to do twelve *y* sin'! *Spinster's S's.* 59
Dead—and sixty *y's* ago, *Locksley H., Sixty* 37
floods and earthquakes of the planet's dawning *y's*. „ 40
Gone with whom for forty *y's* my life „ 47
till ten thousand *y's* have gone. „ 78
Here we met, our latest meeting—Amy—sixty *y's* ago— „ 177
far and far from here is all the hope of eighty *y's*. „ 254
Strove for sixty widow'd *y's* to help „ 267
in the vanish'd *y*, You saw the league-long rampart-fire *Pro. to Gen. Hamley* 26
glorying in the blissful *y's* again to be, *To Virgil* 18
a name may last for a thousand *y's*, *Dead Prophet* 59
midnight breaks the sun Of sixty *y's* away, *Pref. Poem Broth. Son.* 22
Tenderest of Roman poets nineteen-hundred *y's* ago, *Frater Ave, etc.* 6
and the *y* Against the day; *To Duke of Argyll* 6
through twice a hundred *y's*, on thee. *To W. C. Macready* 14
And on thro' many a brightening *y*, *To Marq. of Dufferin* 26
Crowning *y* of her Jubilee. *On Jub. Q. Victoria* 11
Ceremonial Of this *y* of her Jubilee. „ 24
And this *y* of her Jubilee. (repeat) „ 38, 51
Henry's fifty *y's* are all in shadow, „ 39
Fifty *y's* of ever-broadening Commerce! Fifty *y's* of ever-brightening Science! Fifty *y's* of ever-widening Empire! „ 52
' Hail to the glorious Golden *y* of her Jubilee!' „ 65
nine white moons of each whole *y* with me, *Demeter and P.* 121
When thou shalt dwell the whole bright *y* with me, „ 139
Ten *y* sin—Naäy—naäy! *Owd Roä* 20
'ud coom at the fall o' the *y*, „ 23
hall hower—an' ten *y* sin; „ 116
Twelve times in the *y* Bring me bliss, *The Ring* 5
For ten thousand *y's* Old and new? „ 19
Then I and she were married for a *y*, One *y* without a storm, „ 283
And you my Miriam born within the *y*; And she my Miriam dead within the *y*. „ 285
for twenty *y's* Bound by the golden cord „ 428
I have worn them *y* by *y*— *Happy* 102
Till earth has roll'd her latest *y*— *To Ulysses* 28
And more than half a hundred *y's* ago, *To Mary Boyle* 27
silver *y* should cease to mourn and sigh— „ 57
Lodge with me all the *y*! *Prog. of Spring* 26
mark The coming *y's* great good and varied ills, „ 93
wild beast that was linkt with thee eighty *y's* back. *By an Evolution.* 11
ROSE, on this terrace fifty *y's* ago, *Roses on the T.* 1
That blush of fifty *y's* ago, my dear, „ 5
Sing the new *y* in under the blue. Last *y* you sang it as gladly. *The Throstle* 5
' Here again, here, here, here, happy *y*'! „ 13
Thro' all the clouded *y's* of widowhood, *Death of Œnone* 103
I beän chuch-warden mysen i' the parish fur fifteen *y*. *Church-warden, etc.* 8
Y will graze the heel of *y*, *Poets and Critics* 14

Yearlong ' From *y* poring on thy pictured eyes, *Princess vii* 340

Yearly Why should they miss their *y* due *In Mem. xxix* 15

Yearn ' Not less swift souls that *y* for light, *Two Voices* 67
I *y* to breathe the airs of heaven *Sir Galahad* 63
and *y* to hurry precipitously *Boädicea* 58

Yearn (*continued*) A part of stillness, *y's* to speak : *In Mem. lxxxv* 78
but made me *y* For larger glimpses *Tiresias* 20
and the miser would *y* for his gold, *Despair* 100
Y, and clasp the hands and murmur, *Locksley H., Sixty* 192
y to lay my loving head upon your leprous breast. *Happy* 26
Yearn'd While still I *y* for human praise. *Two Voices* 123
And *y* toward William ; but the youth, *Dora* 6
But Enoch *y* to see her face again ; *Enoch Arden* 717
While in her heart she *y* incessantly „ 866
Y after by the wisest of the wise, *Lucretius* 267
y To hear her weeping by his grave ? *In Mem. xxxi* 3
And *y* to burst the folded gloom, „ *cxxii* 3
he *y* to make complete The tale of diamonds *Lancelot and E.* 90
Sprang into fire and vanish'd, tho' I *y* To follow ; *Holy Grail* 506
I *y* and strove To tear the twain asunder „ 785
now *y* to shake The burthen off his heart *Last Tournament* 179
I *y* for warmth and colour which I found In Lancelot *Guinevere* 647
I *y* For his voice again, *The Wreck* 103
To lure those eyes that only *y* to see, *St. Telemachus* 36
Yearning (*See also* **Heart-yearning**) A nobler *y* never broke her rest *The form, the form* 2
Some *y* toward the lamps of night ; *Two Voices* 363
In *y's* that can never be exprest By signs *D. of F. Women* 283
Y to mix himself with Life. *Love thou thy land* 56
Gave utterance by the *y* of an eye, *Love and Duty* 62
gray spirit *y* in desire To follow knowledge *Ulysses* 30
team Which love thee, *y* for thy yoke, *Tithonus* 40
Y for the large excitement *Locksley Hall* 111
profit lies in barren faith, And vacant *y*, *In Mem. cviii* 6
Less *y* for the friendship fled, „ *cxvi* 15
The leaf is dead, the *y* past away : *Last Tournament* 277
y's ?—ay ! for, hour by hour, „ 583
Deeper than any *y's* after thee „ 586
The boundless *y* of the Prophet's heart— *Tiresias* 81
Yearningly moving again to a melody *Y* tender, *Merlin and the G.* 91
Yeasty ' The sands and *y* surges mix *Sailor Boy* 9
Yell (s) (*See also* **Counter-yell, Woman-yell**) rings to the *y* of the trampled wife, *Maud I i* 38
I was near him when the savage *y's* *Com. of Arthur* 256
He ground his teeth together, sprang with a *y*, *Balin and Balan* 538
weird *y*, Unearthlier than all shriek of bird „ 544
echoing *y* with *y*, they fired the tower, *Last Tournament* 478
volley on volley, and *y* upon *y*— *Def. of Lucknow* 34
Thro' all the *y's* and counter-yells *To Duke of Argyll* 8
dog : it was chain'd, but its horrible *y* *Bandit's Death* 35
Yell (verb) Let the fox bark, let the wolf *y*. *Pelleas and E.* 472
Who *y's* Here in the still sweet summer night, „ 472
Fiend would *y*, the grave would yawn, *The Flight* 51
Yell'd score of pugs And poodles *y* within, *Edwin Morris* 120
y and round me drove In narrowing circles till I *y* again *Lucretius* 56
they made a halt ; The horses *y* ; *Princess v* 250
Y and shriek'd between her daughters (repeat) *Boädicea* 6, 72
Y as when the winds of winter tear an oak „ 77
' Fight therefore,' *y* the youth, *Pelleas and E.* 572
caged beast *Y*, as he *y* of yore for Christian blood. *St. Telemachus* 46
Y ' hast *thou* brought us down a new Korân *Akbar's Dream* 116
Yelling and fled *Y* as from a spectre, *Geraint and E.* 733
and, *y* with the *y* street, *Locksley H., Sixty* 135
Yellow (adj.) (*See also* **Dim-yellow**) That sparkled on the *y* field, *L. of Shalott iii* 8
The pale *y* woods were waning, „ *iv* 2
and the *y* down Border'd with palm, *Lotos-Eaters* 21
They sat them down upon the *y* sand, „ 37
turning *y* Falls, and floats adown the air. „ *C. S.* 30
Round and round the spicy downs the *y* Lotos-dust is blown. „ 104
And in the chasm are foam and *y* sands ; *Enoch Arden* 2
And here upon a *y* eyelid fall'n *Lucretius* 141
With lengths of *y* ringlet, like a girl, *Princess i* 3
Yet the *y* leaf hates the greener leaf, *Spiteful Letter* 15
y vapours choke The great city sounding wide ; *Maud II iv* 63
And white sails flying on the *y* sea ; But not to goodly hill or *y* sea *Marr. of Geraint* 829
Then flash'd a *y* gleam across the world, *Holy Grail* 402
little lake, that, flooding, leaves Low banks of *y* sand ; *Lover's Tale i* 535

Yellow (adj.) (*continued*) From out the *y* woods upon the hill *Lover's Tale ii* 80
Yellow (s) Shot over with purple, and green, and *y*. *Dying Swan* 20
Yellow-banded Or the *y-b* bees, *Eleänore* 22
Yellowing Dwelling amid these *y* bowers : *A spirit haunts* 2
In curves the *y* river ran, *Sir L. and Q. G.* 15
At Camelot, high above the *y* woods, *Last Tournament* 3
and *y* leaf And gloom and gleam, „ 154
High over all the *y* Autumn-tide, „ 241
Our birches *y* and from each The light leaf falling fast, *Pro. to Gen. Hamley* 1
Yellow-ringleted Thither at their will they haled the *y-r* Britoness— *Boädicea* 55
Yellow-throated And *y-t* nestling in the nest. *Lancelot and E.* 12
Yelp (s) With inward *y* and restless forefoot *Lucretius* 45
But I hear no *y* of the beast, *By an Evolution.* 19
Yelp (verb) Lean-headed Eagles *y* alone, *Princess vii* 211
felt the goodly hounds *Y* at his heart, *Last Tournament* 504
Yelp'd-Yelpt Then *yelp'd* the cur, and yawl'd the cat ; *The Goose* 33
that chain'd rage, which ever *yelpt* within, *Balin and Balan* 319
Yelping *See* **Yaupin'**
Yeoman And let the foolish *y* go. *L. C. V. de Vere* 72
A mockery to the *yoemen* over ale, *Aylmer's Field* 497
Yerl (earl) Then 'e married a greät *Y's* darter, *Church-warden, etc.* 20
Yes (*See also* **Yis**) keen shriek ' *Y* love, *y*, Edith, *y*,' *Aylmer's Field* 582
When the happy *Y* Falters from her lips, *Maud I xvii* 9
brightens at the clash of ' *Y* ' and ' No,' *Ancient Sage* 71
Yester —and *y* afternoon I dream'd,— *Akbar's Dream* 169
Yesterday (*See also* **Yisther-day**) for *y*, When I past by, a wild and wanton pard, *Œnone* 198
sharp look, mother, I gave him *y*, *May Queen* 15
And now, As tho' 'twere *y*, *Gardener's D.* 82
' Where were you *y* ? Whose child is that ? *Dora* 87
' O *y*, you know, the fair Was holden at the town ; *Talking Oak* 101
' *y* I met him suddenly in the street, *Sea Dreams* 145
I curse the tongue that all thro' *y* Reviled thee, *Gareth and L.* 1322
But *y* you never open'd lip, *Merlin and V.* 271
the prize Of Tristram in the jousts of *y*, *Last Tournament* 8
' Friend, did ye mark that fountain *y* „ 286
A portion of the pleasant *y*, *Lover's Tale i* 122
To-day ? but what of *y* ? *Ancient Sage* 216
that *y* From out the Ghost of Pindar *To Prof. Jebb* 2
I climb'd the hill with Hubert *y*, *The Ring* 152
O the grief when *y* They bore the Cross *Happy* 47
Found *y*—forgotten mine own rhyme *To Mary Boyle* 21
Yester-eve But light-foot Iris brought it *y-e*, *Œnone* 83
Where all but *y-e* was dusty-dry. *Lucretius* 32
and *y-e*, While ye were talking sweetly *Marr. of Geraint* 697
And *y-e* I would not tell you of it, „ 702
Yester-even Lastly yonder *y-e*, *Boädicea* 29
I saw the flash of him but *y*. *Balin and Balan* 303
Yestermorn These measured words, my work of *y*. *Golden Year* 21
Too harsh to your companion *y* ; *Princess iii* 199
Long-closeted with her the *y*, „ *iv* 322
What if he had told her *y* *Maud I vi* 50
saw him ride More near by many a rood than *y*, *Geraint and E.* 442
tho' mine own ears heard you *y*— „ 740
Had I not dream'd I loved her *y* ? *Sisters (E. and E.)* 169
Who breaking in upon us *y*, *Akbar's Dream* 114
Yesternight Thy tuwhoos of *y*, *The Owl ii* 2
Flinging the gloom of *y* On the white day ; *Ode to Memory* 9
I beheld her, when she rose The *y*, *Princess v* 176
' Sweet brothers, *y* I seem'd a curious little maid *Lancelot and E.* 1034
for, *y*, To me, the great God Arês, *Tiresias* 110
Yet-loved the *y-l* sire would make Confusion *In Mem. xc* 18
Yet-unblazon'd Returning brought the *y-u* shield, *Lancelot and E.* 379
Yet-unbroken count The *y-u* strength of all his knights, *Holy Grail* 326
Yet-warm and now lies there A *y-w* corpse, *Gareth and L.* 80
Yew Death, walking all alone beneath a *y*, *Love and Death* 5
And darkness in the village *y*. *Two Voices* 273
Came *y's*, a dismal coterie ; *Amphion* 42
A black *y* gloom'd the stagnant air, *The Letters* 2
and stole Up by the wall, behind the *y* ; *Enoch Arden* 739
Sick for the hollies and the *y's* of home— *Princess, Pro.* 187
Old *Y*, which graspest at the stones *In Mem. ii* 1
Dark *y*, that graspest at the stones „ *xxxix* 4

Yew (*continued*) Before the mouldering of a *y*; *In Mem. lxxvi* 8
And oft they met among the garden *y's*, *Lancelot and E.* 645
He found her in among the garden *y's*, „ 923
to whom thro' those black walls of *y* „ 969
Break thro' the *y's* and cypress of thy grave, *Ded. Poem Prin. Alice* 12
I seem to see a new-dug grave up yonder by the *y*! *The Flight* 98

Yew-tree (*See also* **Peacock-yewtree**) Up higher with the *y-t* by it, *Walk. to the Mail* 13
in it throve an ancient evergreen, A *y*, *Enoch Arden* 736
and as they sat Beneath a world-old *y-t*, *Holy Grail* 13
'O brother, I have seen this *y-t* smoke, „ 18

Yew-wood In the *y-w* black as night, *Oriana* 19

Ygerne Was wedded with a winsome wife, *Y*: *Com. of Arthur* 188
Uther in his wrath and heat besieged *Y* within Tintagil, „ 199
'Daughter of Gorloïs and *Y* am I;' „ 316

Yield *y you time To make demand of modern rhyme* *To the Queen* 10
To *y* consent to my desire: *Miller's D.* 138
But *y* not me the praise: *St. S. Stylites* 185
To strive, to seek, to find, and not to *y*. *Ulysses* 70
excitement that the coming years would *y*, *Locksley Hall* 111
No branchy thicket shelter *y's*; *Sir Galahad* 58
a little will I *y*. *Princess ii* 291
To *y* us farther furlough:' and he went. „ *iii* 74
rods of steel and fire; She *y's*, or war.' „ *v* 119
No more, dear love, for at a touch I *y*; „ *vii* 14
She still were loth to *y* herself to one „ 232
I love thee: come, *Y* thyself up: „ 364
We *y* all blessing to the name *In Mem. xxxvi* 3
nature rarely *y's* To that vague fear „ *xli* 13
And will not *y* them for a day. „ *xc* 16
That will not *y* each other way. „ *cii* 20
Go not, happy day, Till the maiden *y's*. *Maud I xvii* 4
brands That hack'd among the flyers, 'Ho! they *y*!' *Com. of Arthur* 121
Heaven *y* her for it, but in me put force *Gareth and L.* 18
'Not an hour, So that ye *y* me— „ 133
I therefore *y* me freely to thy will; „ 168
Would *y* him this large honour all the more; „ 397
sent her wish that I would *y* thee thine. „ 551
But wilt thou *y* this damsel harbourage?' „ 834
But an this lord will *y* us harbourage, „ 844
'Take not my life: I *y*.' „ 973
Would handle scorn, or *y* you, asking, „ 1173
crying, '*Y*, *y* him this again: 'tis he must fight: „ 1321
O *y* me shelter for mine innocency *Merlin and V.* 83
Y my boon, Till which I scarce can *y* you all I am; „ 351
till one could *y* for weariness: „ 372
But since I will not *y* to give you power „ 373
And since the pirate would not *y* her up, „ 568
And *y* it to this maiden, if ye will.' *Lancelot and E.* 229
when you *y* your flower of life To one „ 952
Pray for my soul, and *y* me burial. „ 1280
wilt at length *Y* me thy love and know me for thy knight.' *Pelleas and E.* 249
Only to *y* my Queen her own again? *Last Tournament* 106
Pale-blooded, she will *y* herself to God.' „ 608
to *y* thee grace beyond thy peers.' „ 743
y me sanctuary, nor ask Her name to whom ye *y* it, *Guinevere* 141
promise, if we *y*, to let us go; *The Revenge* 94
Our title, which we never mean to *y*, *Columbus* 32
daughter *y* her life, heart, soul to one— *The Flight* 28
shall we fight her? shall we *y*? *Locksley H., Sixty* 115
Not less would *y* full thanks to you *To Ulysses* 33
Who heats our earth to *y* us grain and fruit, *Akbar's Dream* 105

Yielded He laugh'd, and *y* readily to their wish, *Enoch Arden* 370
At once the costly Sahib *y* to her. *Aylmer's Field* 233
perforce He *y*, wroth and red, with fierce demur: *Princess v* 358
Nor tho' she liked him, *y* she, „ *vii* 76
'I wish she had not *y*!' „ *Con.* 5
was but a dream, yet it *y* a dear delight *Maud III vi* 15
the field was pleasant in our eyes, We *y* not; *Gareth and L.* 338
Loving his lusty youthhood *y* to him. „ 580
He might have *y* to me one of those „ 739
being all bone-batter'd on the rock, *Y*; „ 1051

Yielded (*continued*) at last—The huge pavilion slowly *y* up, *Gareth and L.* 1379
Had *y*, told her all the charm, *Merlin and V.* 966
y; and a heart Love-loyal to the least wish *Lancelot and E.* 88
the great Queen Have *y* him her love.' *Last Tournament* 565
But counterpressures of the *y* hand *Sisters (E. and E.)* 163
and they *y* to the foe. *The Revenge* 96
and had *y* her will To the master, *Dead Prophet* 63

Yielding old order changeth, *y* place to new, *M. d'Arthur* 240
In silk-soft folds, upon *y* down, *Eleänore* 28
This, *y*, gave into a grassy walk *Gardener's D.* 111
old order changeth, *y* place to new; *Com. of Arthur* 509
shame the King for only *y* me My champion *Gareth and L.* 898
And *y* to his kindlier moods, *Merlin and V.* 174

Yis (yes) an' wur niver sa nigh saäyin' *Y*. *Spinster's S's.* 32

Yisther-day (yesterday) like a bit of *y-d* in a dhrame— *Tomorrow* 8

'Ymn (hymn) arter, we sing'd the '*y* togither *North. Cobbler* 54

Yniol Had married Enid, *Y's* only child, *Marr. of Geraint* 4
save, It may be, at Earl *Y's*, o'er the bridge „ 291
voice of Enid, *Y's* daughter, rang Clear „ 327
by the bird's song ye may learn the nest,' Said *Y*; „ 360
Y caught His purple scarf, and held, „ 376
cried Earl *Y*, 'Art thou he indeed, Geraint, „ 426
Y's heart Danced in his bosom, „ 504
And waited there for *Y* and Geraint. „ 538
Y's rusted arms Were on his princely person, „ 543
Then *Y's* nephew, after trumpet blown, „ 551
But either's force was match'd till *Y's* cry, „ 570
Went *Y* thro' the town, and everywhere „ 693
And howsoever patient, *Y* his. „ 707
But *Y* goes, and I full oft shall dream „ 751
Y made report Of that good mother making Enid gay „ 756
Y with that hard message went; „ 763
being repulsed By *Y* and yourself, *Geraint and E.* 829

Yoke (s) Which love thee, yearning for thy *y*, *Tithonus* 40
she walk'd Wearing the light *y* of that Lord of love, *Aylmer's Field* 708
And, if thou needs must bear the *y*, *Princess vi* 205
loosed their sweating horses from the *y*, *Spec. of Iliad* 2
The sooty *y* of kitchen-vassalage; *Gareth and L.* 479
bring on both the *y* Of stronger states, *Tiresias* 69

Yoke (verb) *the care That* y's *with empire,* *To the Queen* 10

Yoked Whose name is *y* with children's, *Princess v* 418
Y in all exercise of noble end, „ *vii* 361

Yolk (*See also* **Half-yolk**) with golden *y's* Imbedded and injellied: *Audley Court* 25
this earth-narrow life Be yet but *y*, *Ancient Sage* 130

Yon To *y* old mill across the wolds; *Miller's D.* 240
Behind *y* whispering tuft of oldest pine, *Œnone* 88
While *y* sun prospers in the blue, *The Blackbird* 22
Where *y* dark valleys wind forlorn, *On a Mourner* 22
Is *y* plantation where this byway joins *Walk. to the Mail* 4
Thro' all *y* starlight keen, *St. Agnes' Eve* 22
Y orange sunset waning slow: *Move eastward* 2
what is it? there? *y* arbutus Totters; *Lucretius* 184
O love, they die in *y* rich sky, *Princess iv* 13
Where *y* broad water sweetly slowly glides. *Requiescat* 2
Calm and still light on *y* great plain *In Mem. xi* 9
On *y* swoll'n brook that bubbles fast „ *xcix* 6
To *y* hard crescent, as she hangs „ *cvii* 10
And *y* four fools have suck'd their allegory *Gareth and L.* 1199
Else *y* black felon had not let me pass, „ 1293
May *y* just heaven, that darkens o'er me, *Merlin and V.* 931
As *y* proud Prince who left the quest to me. *Lancelot and E.* 762
O me, be *y* dark Queens in *y* black boat, *Pass. of Arthur* 452
y big black bottle o' gin. *North. Cobbler* 70
y laädy a-steppin' along the streeät, „ 107
You see *y* Lombard poplar on the plain. *Sisters (E. and E.)* 79
Down *y* dark sea, thou comest, darling boy. *De Prof., Two G.* 34
No stone is fitted in *y* marble girth *Tiresias* 135
but seem to draw From *y* dark cave, *Ancient Sage* 10
but night enough is there In *y* dark city: „ 253
But I could wish *y* moaning sea would rise *The Flight* 11
till this outworn earth be dead as *y* dead world the moon? *Locksley H., Sixty* 174

Yon (*continued*) *Y* myriad-worlded way— *Epilogue* 53
Young and old, Like *y* oak, *The Oak* 3
There westward—under *y* slow-falling star, *Akbar's Dream* 152
'Spirit, nearing *y* dark portal *God and the Univ.* 4
Yonder In *y* hundred million spheres?' *Two Voices* 30
In *y* chair I see him sit, *Miller's D.* 9
as *y* walls Rose slowly to a music *Œnone* 40
droves of swine That range on *y* plain. *Palace of Art* 200
To dream and dream, like *y* amber light, *Lotos-Eaters, C. S.* 57
So great a miracle as *y* hilt. *M. d'Arthur* 156
I lived up there on *y* mountain side. *St. S. Stylites* 72
with what delighted eyes I turn to *y* oak. *Talking Oak* 8
To *y* oak within the field „ 13
Many a night from *y* ivied casement, *Locksley Hall* 7
Deep in *y* shining Orient, „ 154
To *y* shining ground; *St. Agnes' Eve* 14
To *y* argent round; „ 16
Met me walking on *y* way, *Edward Gray* 2
It is but *y* empty glass *Will Water.* 207
'Come down, O maid, from *y* mountain height: *Princess vii* 192
Like *y* morning on the blind half-world; „ 352
Lastly *y* yester-even, *Boädicea* 29
And roar from *y* dropping day: *In Mem. xv* 2
Would dote and pore on *y* cloud „ 16
To where in *y* orient star „ *lxxxvi* 15
For 'ground in *y* social mill „ *lxxxix* 39
And drown'd in *y* living blue „ *cxv* 7
or dives In *y* greening gleam, „ 14
And rise, O moon, from *y* down, „ *Con.* 109
Of the long waves that roll in *y* bay? *Maud I xviii* 63
'I will not eat Till *y* man upon the bier arise, *Geraint and E.* 657
Take warning: *y* man is surely dead; „ 672
Saint who stands with lily in hand In *y* shrine. *Balin and Balan* 262
So great a miracle as *y* hilt. *Pass. of Arthur* 324
springs Of Dircê laving *y* battle-plain, *Tiresias* 139
How summer-bright are *y* skies, *Ancient Sage* 23
But some in *y* city hold, my son, „ 82
O yes, if *y* hill be level with the flat. *Locksley H., Sixty* 111
A gleam from *y* vale, *Early Spring* 33
Falteringly, 'Who lies on *y* pyre?' *Death of Œnone* 95
Strow *y* mountain flat, *Mechanophilus* 6
Yore Strode in, and claim'd their tribute as of *y*. *Com. of Arthur* 506
York lands in Kent and messuages in *Y*, *Edwin Morris* 127
Y's white rose as red as Lancaster's. *Aylmer's Field* 51
Young And I was *y*—too *y* to wed: *Miller's D.* 141
made thee famous once, when *y*: *The Blackbird* 16
She stood, a sight to make an old man *y*. *Gardener's D.* 141
What is loathsome to the *y* Savours well *Vision of Sin* 157
Have all his pretty *y* ones educated, *Enoch Arden* 146
I wonder he went so *y*. *Grandmother* 14
'O boy, tho' thou art *y* and proud, *Sailor Boy* 7
'Old friend, too old to be so *y*, depart, *Balin and Balan* 17
devil's leaps, and poisons half the *y*. *Guinevere* 522
'Love again, song again, nest again, *y* again,' *The Throstle* 9
Y and old, Like yon oak, *The Oak* 2
As a *y* lamb, who cannot dream, *Supp. Confessions* 170
To the *y* spirit present *Ode to Memory* 73
My gay *y* hawk, my Rosalind: *Rosalind* 34
Came two *y* lovers lately wed; *L. of Shalott ii* 34
Y Nature thro' five cycles ran, *Two Voices* 17
Since I beheld *y* Laurence dead. *L. C. V. de Vere* 28
sweeter is the *y* lamb's voice to me *May Queen, Con.* 6
I wish'd myself the fair *y* beech *Talking Oak* 141
In the Spring a *y* man's fancy *Locksley Hall* 20
her cheek was pale and thinner than should be for one so *y*, „ 21
Y ashes pirouetted down Coquetting with *y* beeches; *Amphion* 27
So these *y* hearts not knowing that they loved, *Aylmer's Field* 133
'Peace, you *y* savage of the Northern wild! *Princess iii* 247
remain'd among us In our *y* nursery still unknown, „ *iv* 332
fresh *y* captains flash'd their glittering teeth, „ *v* 20
Stays all the fair *y* planet in her hands— „ *vii* 264
As thou with thy *y* lover hand in hand *W. to Marie Alex.* 34
How *y* Columbus seem'd to rove, *The Daisy* 17
Or a mowt 'a taäen *y* Robins— *N. Farmer, O. S.* 50

Young (*continued*) My yet *y* life in the wilds of Time, *Maud I xvi* 21
O *y* lord-lover, what sighs are those, „ *xxii* 29
and his wife Nursed the *y* prince, *Com. of Arthur* 224
With Gawain and *y* Modred, her two sons, „ 244
A *y* man will be wiser by and by; „ 404
But felt his *y* heart hammering in his ears, *Gareth and L.* 322
Some *y* lad's mystery— „ 466
Ate with *y* lads his portion by the door, „ 480
being *y*, he changed and came to loathe *Marr. of Geraint* 593
all thro' that *y* traitor, cruel need „ 715
and yet—God guide them—*y*.' *Merlin and V.* 29
And found a fair *y* squire who sat alone, „ 472
said *y* Lavaine, 'For nothing. *Lancelot and E.* 208
Y as I am, yet would I do my best.' „ 222
Dearer to true *y* hearts than their own praise, „ 419
Then Lancelot answer'd *y* Lavaine and said, „ 445
With *y* Lavaine into the poplar grove. „ 509
In so *y* youth, was ever made a knight *Holy Grail* 138
All the *y* beauty of his own soul to hers, *Pelleas and E.* 83
For Arthur, loving his *y* knight, „ 159
'O *y* knight, Hath the great heart of knighthood „ 595
till that *y* life Being smitten in mid heaven *Last Tournament* 26
For *y* Life knows not when *y* Life was born, *Lover's Tale i* 156
To greet us, her *y* hero in her arms! „ *iv* 171
O *y* life Breaking with laughter from the dark; *De Prof., Two G.* 17
Five *y* kings put asleep by the sword-stroke, *Batt. of Brunanburh* 52
Or the *y* green leaf rejoice in the frost *The Wreck* 20
y man Danny O'Roon wid his ould woman, *Tomorrow* 88
for is not Earth as yet so *y*?— *Locksley H., Sixty* 166
Yonder lies our *y* sea-village— „ 245
o'er the mountain-walls *Y* angels pass. *Early Spring* 12
That *y* eagle of the West *Open. I. and C. Exhib.* 28
I loved you first when *y* and fair, *Happy* 29
To you, yet *y*, who breathe the balm *To Ulysses* 10
if his *y* music wakes A wish in you *To Mary Boyle* 63
O *Y* Mariner, You from the haven *Merlin and the G.* 1
O *y* Mariner, Down to the haven, „ 123
Younger Wherein the *y* Charles abode *Talking Oak* 297
Thro' the shadow of the globe we sweep into the *y* day: *Locksley Hall* 183
The *y* people making holiday, *Enoch Arden* 62
While all the *y* ones with jubilant cries „ 377
To Lady Psyche, *y*, not so wise, *Princess iv* 316
With wisdom, like the *y* child: *In Mem. cxiv* 20
For both thy *y* brethren have gone down *Gareth and L.* 1102
Not many a moon his *y*, 'My fair child, „ 1415
Allow him! but Lavaine, my *y* here, *Lancelot and E.* 202
And let the *y* and unskill'd go by „ 1361
Five knights at once, and every *y* knight, *Holy Grail* 303
My *y* knights, new-made, in whom your flower *Last Tournament* 99
The leading of his *y* knights to me. „ 110
He spoke, and taking all his *y* knights, „ 126
The *y* Julian, who himself was crown'd *Lover's Tale iv* 296
The *y* sister, Evelyn, enter'd—there, *Sisters (E. and E.)* 152
we past to this ward where the *y* children are laid: *In the Child. Hosp.* 27
To *y* England in the boy my son. *To Victor Hugo* 14
When, in our *y* London days, *To E. Fitzgerald* 54
But *y* kindlier Gods to bear us down, *Demeter and P.* 131
Some *y* hand must have engraven the ring— *The Ring* 238
You, loved by all the *y* gown There at Balliol, *To Master of B.* 2
Youngest *Y* Autumn, in a bower Grape-thicken'd *Eleänore* 35
For one, the *y*, hardly more than boy, *Enoch Arden* 563
And while we waited, one, the *y* of us, *Merlin and V.* 415
Youngster Mangled to morsels, A *y* in war! *Batt. of Brunanburh* 75
Younker there he caught the *y* tickling trout— *Walk. to the Mail* 33
Youth (adolescence) 'Yet,' said I, in my morn of *y*, *Supp. Confessions* 139
the breathing spring Of Hope and *Y*. *The Poet* 28
His early rage Had force to make me rhyme in *y*, *Miller's D.* 193
'My *y*,' she said, 'was blasted with a curse: *D. of F. Women* 103
Who miss the brother of your *y*? *To J. S.* 59
May perpetual *y* Keep dry their light from tears; *Of old sat Freedom* 19
Drive men in manhood, as in *y*, *Love thou thy land* 74
At such a distance from his *y* in grief, *Gardener's D.* 54

Z

A CONCORDANCE TO THE DRAMATIC WORKS

OF

ALFRED, LORD TENNYSON.

A

A that all the louts to whom Their *A* B C is darkness, *Queen Mary* III iv 35
Aäle (ale) They ha' broached a barrel of *a* i' the long barn, *Prom. of May* I 426
Abbacy From all the vacant sees and *abbacies*, *Becket* I iii 652
Abbess I think our *A* knew it and allow'd it. „ V ii 95
Abbey The kingliest *A* in all Christian lands, *Harold* III i 204
He shelter'd in the *A* of Pontigny. *Becket* II i 84
Hard as the stones of his *a*. *Foresters* I ii 270
Abbeyland new Lords Are quieted with their sop of *A's*, *Queen Mary* III i 142
Abbot there were *A's*—but they did not bring their women; *Becket* III iii 135
sits and eats his heart for want of money to pay the *A*. *Foresters* I i 5
he borrowed the monies from the *A* of York, the Sheriff's brother. And if they be not paid back at the end of the year, the land goes to the *A*. „ I i 68
Those two thousand marks lent me by the *A* „ I i 264
I believed this *A* of the party of King Richard, „ I i 266
Or I forfeit my land to the *A*. „ I ii 152
You shall wait for mine till Sir Richard has paid the *A*. „ I ii 232
I fear this *A* is a heart of flint, „ I ii 268
I ran into my debt to the *A*, Two thousand marks in gold. „ II i 463
We spoil'd the prior, friar, *a*, monk, „ III 167
Then that bond he hath Of the *A*— „ IV 85
I have sent to the *A* and justiciary „ IV 87
The *A* of York and his justiciary. „ IV 334
it was agreed when you borrowed these monies from the *A* „ IV 467
these monies should be paid in to the *A* at York, „ IV 507
Save for this maiden and thy brother *A*, „ IV 633
You, my lord *A*, you Justiciary, I made you *A*, you Justiciary: „ IV 841
Our rebel *A* then shall join your hands, „ IV 933
Here *A*, Sheriff—no—no, Robin Hood. „ IV 989
Abeär (bear) I can't *a* to think on 'er now, *Prom. of May* II 32
I can't *a* to see her. „ III 758
Abel light darkness, *A* Cain, The soul the body, *Becket* I iii 715
Abetting They say, his wife was knowing and *a*. *Harold* II ii 307
Abhor all of us *a* The venomous, bestial, devilish revolt *Queen Mary* II ii 286
and refuse, Reject him, and *a* him. „ IV iii 279
—the whole world *A* you; *Becket* V iii 184
Abide You must *a* my judgment, and my father's, *Queen Mary* V i 145
and on thee, Edith, if thou *a* it,— *Harold* III i 317
King will not *a* thee with thy cross. *Becket* I iii 488
then he called me a rude naäme, and I can't *a* 'im. *Prom. of May* II 159
but he wur so rough wi' ma, I couldn't *a* 'im. „ III 104
as the good Sally says, 'I can't *a* him'— „ III 174
If it be her ghoäst, we mun *a* it. „ III 460
but *a* with me who love thee. *Foresters* II i 602
Ability Hath he the large *a* of the Emperor? *Queen Mary* I v 323
Hath he the large *a* of his father? „ I v 438
Able The man is *a* enough—no lack of wit, *Foresters* I ii 103
Abler while in Normanland God speaks thro' *a* voices, *Harold* I i 167
Abolish to cancel and *a* all bonds of human allegiance, *Queen Mary* V iv 49
Abroach Not set myself *a* And run my mind out *The Cup* I ii 106
Abrogation Towards the *a* and repeal Of all such laws *Queen Mary* III iii 141
Absalom Deal gently with the young man *A*. *Becket* I iii 757
Absence Which in his *a* had been all my wealth. *Queen Mary* I v 361
But since mine *a* will not be for long, „ III vi 216
Thine *a* well may seem a want of care. *Harold* I i 322
and you look thin and pale. Is it for his *a*? *Prom. of May* I 782
this world Is brighter for his *a* as that other Is darker for his presence. „ II 458
but can he trace me Thro' five years' *a*, „ II 615
Absolution Pole, to give us all that holy *a* which—— *First Citizen*. Old Bourne to the life! *Second Citizen*. Holy *a*! *Queen Mary* I iii 28
Legate's coming To bring us *a* from the Pope. „ III i 432
To take this *a* from your lips, „ III ii 116
Thro' this most reverend Father, *a*, „ III iii 148
Stigand shall give me *a* for it— *Harold* II ii 798
Hast thou had *a* for thine oath? „ III i 212
Stigand hath given me *a* for it. „ III i 213
Not I, the Pope. Ask *him* for *a*. *Becket* V ii 379
Absolve commission from the Pope To *a* thee *Queen Mary* III ii 53
He by His mercy *a* you! „ III iii 209
Do here *a* you and deliver you And every one of you, „ III iii 214
Cannot the Pope *a* thee if thou sign? *Becket* I iii 230
A the left-hand thief and damn the right? „ II ii 392
Forgive me and *a* me, holy father. „ II ii 441
Son, I *a* thee in the name of God. „ II ii 442
He shall *a* you . . . you shall have redress. „ V i 86
Our Becket, who will not *a* the Bishops. „ V i 223
he shall *a* The bishops—they but did my will— „ V i 253
Oh, if you have, *a* him! „ V ii 131
to *a* the bishops Whom you have excommunicated. „ V ii 376
Save that you will *a* the bishops. „ V iii 120
Absolved Tut, tut, I have *a* thee: *Harold* III i 104
A-burnin' Queen Mary gwoes on *a-b* and *a-b*, *Queen Mary* IV iii 523
A-b, and *a-b*, and a-makin' „ IV iii 531
Abused Her name is much *a* among these traitors. „ II ii 110
Modest maiden lily *a*, *Foresters* II ii 158
A-bussin' (kissing) thou and me *a-b* o' one another t'other side o' the haäycock, *Prom. of May* II 231
Abysm Steam'd upward from the undescendible *A*. *Harold* I i 16
Abyss rough road That breaks off short into the *a'es*— *Prom. of May* I 230
A-callin' they ha' ta'en the body up inter your chaumber, and they be all *a-c* for ye. „ II 571
Accept France would not *a* her for a bride *Queen Mary* I ii 67
beseech Your Highness to *a* our lowliest thanks „ II ii 131
tell him That I *a* the diadem of Galatia— *The Cup* II 158
So I would, Robin, if any man would *a* her. *Foresters* III 74
A this horn! if e'er thou be assail'd „ IV 423
Acceptable more the love, the more *a* The sacrifice *Harold* III i 348
nobler The victim was, the more *a* Might be the sacrifice. *The Falcon* 880
Accepting For that would seem *a* of your love. „ 739

Accepting (*continued*) Have I done wisely, then, in *a* him? *Prom. of May* III 184

Access A stranger monk desires *a* to you. *Becket* V ii 65
Mine enemies barr'd all *a* to the boy. „ V ii 451

Accomplish'd to see my solemn vow *A*. *Harold* III i 308
The purpose of my being is *a*, *The Falcon* 926
To-day he hath *a* his thirtieth birthday, *Foresters* I i 298

Account There's half an angel wrong'd in your *a*; *Queen Mary* V iii 2
King Demands a strict *a* of all those revenues *Becket* I iii 650
dead; gone to his *a*—dead and buried. *Prom. of May* III 145
Then by thine own *a* thou shouldst be mine. *Foresters* IV 1038

Accruing Judgment, and pain *a* thereupon; *Queen Mary* III iii 219

Accursed my men Hold that the shipwreckt are *a* of God;— *Harold* II i 100
for the two were fellow-prisoners So many years in yon *a* Tower— *Queen Mary* I iv 200
With that vile Cranmer in the *a* lie Of good Queen Catharine's divorce— „ III iv 231
'We pray continually for the death Of our *a* Queen and Cardinal Pole.' „ V ii 181
Nay, ev'n the *a* heathen Saladeen—— Strike! *Becket* IV ii 251

Accuse Lest men *a* you of indifference To all faiths, *Queen Mary* III iv 223
Shall these *a* him to a foreign prince? „ IV i 24
must *A* himself, excuse himself; *The Cup* II 115

Accused 'If any cleric be *a* of felony, the Church shall not protect him; *Becket* I iii 87

Accuser appear before the Pope, And answer thine *a's* . . . „ I iii 603

Achage his *a*, and his breakage, if that were all: *Queen Mary* I i 128

Ache full of *a's* and broken before his day. „ I i 124
Against the moral excess No physical *a*, *Becket* I i 382

Acies *A*, *A* Prona sternatur! *Harold* V i 581

Acknowledge and *a* The primacy of the Pope? *Queen Mary* III iii 107

Acknowledged Mary hath *a* you her heir. „ V iii 30
She knew me, and *a* me her heir, „ V v 255

A-coomin' (**coming**) I seed that one cow o' thine i' the pinfold ageän as I wur *a-c* 'ere. *Prom. of May* I 191

Acorn On nuts and *a's*, ha! Or the King's deer? *Foresters* IV 882

Acre (**seaport**) like the woman at *A* when the Turk shot her „ II i 307

Acre (**land**) (*See also* **Haäcre, Ten-aäcre**) her advowsons, granges, farms, And goodly *a's*— *Becket* I i 163
I took it For some three thousand *a's*. *Prom. of May* III 614

Acrid Ah, what an *a* wine has Luther brew'd! *Queen Mary* IV iii 545

Acrisius Danaë has escaped again Her tower, and her *A*— *Becket* I i 396

A-crying and they was all *a-c* out at the bad times, *Prom. of May* I 138

Act (**s**) he begs you to forget it As scarce his *a*:— *The Cup* II 53

Act (**verb**) (*See also* **Re-act**) that these may *a* On Harold when they meet. *Harold* II ii 91
King would *a* servitor and hand a dish to his son; *Becket* III iii 139
Veiling one sin to *a* another. *Prom. of May* III 773

Actable Is naked truth *a* in true life? *Harold* III i 109

Acted why should not the parable of our blessed Lord be *a* again? *Becket* I iv 77
Who made the second mitre play the first, And *a* me? „ III iii 213
Well *a*, was it? A comedy meant to seem a tragedy— „ IV ii 321
and *a* on would yield A nobler breed *The Falcon* 753

Acting tear it all to pieces, never dream'd Of *a* on it. *The Cup* I ii 248
No! *a*, playing on me, both of them. *Prom. of May* III 693

Action (*See also* **Re-action**) *A* and re-action, The miserable see-saw of our child-world, *Queen Mary* IV iii 384

Act of Parliament they be both bastards by *A o P* and Council. „ I i 24
Corroborate by your *a's o P*: „ II ii 173

Actor Should play the second *a* in this pageant „ III iii 13

A-cum (**come**) there wur an owld lord *a-c* to dine wi' un, „ IV iii 504

Adage there's An old world English *a* to the point. „ IV i 175

Adam-clay Cleaving to your original *A-c*, „ IV iii 418

Add Leave it with him and *a* a gold mark thereto. *Foresters* III 210

Added the clauses *a* To that same treaty *Queen Mary* III iii 68

Adder To the deaf *a* thee, that wilt not dance *Harold* I i 385
the Norman *a* Hath bitten us; we are poison'd: „ III i 38
he that lookt a fangless one, Issues a venomous *a*. *Becket* I iii 453

Addled Eggs? *Filippo*. One, but *a*. *The Falcon* 129

Address (**s**) All hangs on her *a*, And upon you, Lord Mayor. *Queen Mary* II ii 55
he gave me no *a*, and there was no word of marriage; *Prom. of May* III 332

Address (**verb**) She will *a* your guilds and companies. *Queen Mary* II ii 15

Adieu Both be happy, and *a* for ever and for evermore —*a*. *Foresters* II ii 196

Adit Here His turtle builds; his exit is our *a*: *Becket* III ii 7

Adjudge at this time *A* him to the death. *Queen Mary* IV iii 38

Admiral Her freaks and frolics with the late Lord *A*? „ I iv 20

Admiration begets An *a* and an indignation, „ III iv 170

Admired But having now *a* it long enough, *Becket* IV ii 262
'To the *a* Camma, wife of Sinnatus, the Tetrarch, *The Cup* I i 36
'To the *a* Camma,—beheld you afar off— „ I ii 70

Admit Ay, gentle friend, *a* them. I will go. *Queen Mary* I ii 110

A-doing What be he *a-d* here ten mile an' moor fro' a raäil? *Prom. of May* I 209

Adore and *a* This Vicar of their Vicar. *Queen Mary* III iii 243

Adorer an *a* of our great goddess, Artemis, *The Cup* I i 38

Adulterous *A* to the very heart of Hell. *Queen Mary* V v 163
A dog! (repeat) *The Cup* I iii 108, 122

Adultery She seethed with such *adulteries*, *Queen Mary* III iv 189

Advance *A* our Standard of the Warrior, *Harold* IV i 248
told me he would *a* me to the service of a great lady, *Becket* III i 123
He has a friend there will *a* the monies, *Foresters* II i 628
There was no room to *a* or to retire. „ IV 534
A, *a*! (repeat) „ IV 735, 761

Advanced *A* thee at his instance by the Jews, *Becket* I iii 643

Advantage To be of rich *a* to our realm, *Queen Mary* II ii 235
I, that taking The Fiend's *a* of a throne, *Becket* II i 152
We have him at last; we have him at *a*. *Foresters* II i 415
O no, we took *A* of the letter— „ IV 621

Advent To celebrate this *a* of our King! „ IV 1048

Advice With our *a* and in our company, *Queen Mary* I iii 150
and your Grace, So you will take *a* of mine, „ V i 301
and by the *a* of his Government.' *Becket* I iii 112

Advise I would *a* That we should thoroughly *Queen Mary* III iv 194
A him: speak him sweetly, he will hear thee. *Harold* I i 116
could do No other than this way *a* the king „ V i 281

Advised The Queen is ill *a*: *Queen Mary* I iv 5
He cannot dream that *I a* the war; „ V ii 57
But you *a* the Pope. *Becket* V ii 380

Advising On any man's *a* but your own. „ V ii 551

Advowson have graspt Her livings, her *a's*, „ I i 161
'All causes of *a's* and presentations, „ I iii 79

A-dying I ha' three sisters *a-d* at home o' the sweating sickness. „ I iv 246

Æsop Inverted *Æ*—mountain out of mouse. *Queen Mary* II i 67

Afear'd (**afraid**) I was *a* it was the ghost, your worship. *Foresters* II i 225
I am mortally *a* o' thee, thou big man, „ IV 316

Affable you were bland And *a* to men of all estates, *Queen Mary* III vi 81

Affair His Highness is so vex'd with strange *a's*— *Mary*. That his own wife is no *a* of his. „ V ii 560
Has let his farm, all his *a's*, I fear, *Prom. of May* II 420
for I must hence upon The King's *a*. *Foresters* IV 342

Affect Her Majesty Hears you *a* the Prince— *Queen Mary* I iv 82
what shall I call it, *a* her thine own self. *Becket, Pro.* 513
Your lordship *a's* the unwavering perpendicular; „ II ii 325

Affection old *a* master'd you, You falter'd into tears. „ V ii 143
from you except Return of his *a*— *The Falcon* 717
and her *a's* Will flower toward the light *Prom. of May* I 484

Affinity the man, the woman, Following their best *affinities*, „ I 523

Affirm and *a's* The Queen has forfeited her right *Queen Mary* V i 289

Affright yet the word *A's* me somewhat: „ I iv 9
Doth this *a* thee? *Harold* I i 23

Affrighted scurrying of a rat *A* me, *Queen Mary* III v 144

A-fobbing (**to put of**) hallus *a-f* ma off, tho' ye knaws I love ye. *Prom. of May* I 108

A-follering (**following**) then back ageän, *a-f* my oän shadder— „ I 371

Afraid (*See also* **Afear'd, Half-afraid**) I was *a* of her, and I hid myself. „ I 551
I am half *a* to pass. „ II 328
Be not *a* of me, For these are no conventional flourishes. „ II 561

After *A*[illegible] that this noble realm thro' *a* years May in this unity *Queen Mary* III iii 156
and all thy flock should catch An *a* ague-fit of trembling. *Becket* III iii 33

After-dinner Not now, not now—with *a-d* grace. *Foresters* IV 937

After-life man perceives that The lost gleam of an *a-l* *Prom. of May* I 503
greater nearness to the birthday Of the *a-l*, *Foresters* II i 45
After-marriage link rusts with the breath of the first *a-m* kiss, *Becket, Pro.* 362
Afternoon (*See also* **Arternoon**) The clamour'd darling of their *a* ! *The Cup* II 125
You had better attend to your hayfield. Good *a*. *Prom. of May* II 123
Good *a*, my friends. „ III 20
Agatha ask his forgiveness before he dies.—SISTER *A*.' Sister *A* is right. „ III 402
A-gawin' (going) Be thou *a-g* to the long barn? „ I 1
Age (*See also* **Lisping-age**) tho' by your *a*, And by your looks you are not worth the having, *Queen Mary* I iv 12
Song flies you know For *a's*. „ II i 82
it is an *a* Of brief life, and brief purpose, „ III iv 412
'what am I, Cranmer, against whole *a's*?' „ IV ii 104
gray dawn Of an old *a* that never will be mine „ V ii 235
From child to child, from Pope to Pope, from *a* to *a*, *Harold* V i 330
he would be mine *a* Had he lived now; *Becket* I iii 249
A, orphans, and babe-breasting mothers— „ II i 72
Will enter on the larger golden *a*; *Prom. of May* I 590
may not those, who march Before their *a*, „ II 633
I could make his *a* A comfort to him— „ II 661
your Father must be now in extreme old *a*. „ III 400
poor Steer looks The very type of *A* in a picture, „ III 514
Some hollow-hearted from exceeding *a*— *Foresters* III 97
Aged How doubly *a* this Queen of ours hath grown *Queen Mary* V i 227
A-getting he makes moan that all be *a-g* cold. *Becket* I iv 61
when I was *a-g* o' bluebells for your ladyship's nose to smell on— „ III i 161
A-gittin' and my missus *a-g* ower 'er lyin'-in. *Prom. of May* III 74
A-glorifying our master been *a-g* and a-velveting and a-silking himself, *The Falcon* 98
A-going We be *a-g* home after our supper in all humbleness, *Becket* I iv 206
Agony Fire—inch by inch to die in *a* ! *Queen Mary* IV ii 223
in her *a* The mother came upon her— „ V iv 19
star That dances in it as mad with *a* ! *Harold* I i 9
all promises Made in our *a* for help from heaven? „ III i 288
Only this morning in his *a* *Foresters* IV 453
Agree (*See also* **'Grees**) *A* with him quickly again, even for the sake of the Church. *Becket* II ii 376
Agreed are well *a* That those old statutes touching Lollardism *Queen Mary* III iv 6
it was *a* when you borrowed these monies from the Abbot *Foresters* IV 465
A-groänin' He's been a-moänin' and *a-g* in 'is sleep, *Prom. of May* III 411
Ague Harvestless autumns, horrible *a's*, plague *Queen Mary* V i 98
Wet, famine, *a*, fever, storm, wreck, wrath,— „ V v 108
Ague-fit thy flock should catch An after *a-f* of trembling. *Becket* III iii 33
A-harrowin' Hodge 'ud ha' been *a-h* o' white peasen i' the outfield *Queen Mary* IV iii 492
A-hawking *A-h, a-h* ! If I sit, I grow fat. *Becket, Pro.* 413
ride *a-h* with the help of the men. *Foresters* I i 213
A-hell-fire and sets the church-tower over there all *a-h-f* as it were? *Becket* III iii 51
A-hunting King's verdurer caught him *a-h* in the forest, „ I iv 95
Aid (s) But with Cecil's *a* And others, *Queen Mary* V v 279
Aid (verb) as I love The people! whom God *a* ! „ V iii 36
Believing I should ever *a* the Church— *Becket, Pro.* 417
Ail What *a's* you? *Harold*. Speak. *Prom. of May* III 661
Ailmer (John, Bishop of London) *A* and Bullingham, and hundreds more; *Queen Mary* I ii 11
Aim stateliest deer in all the herd—Beyond his *a*— „ V ii 427
I am *not* Beyond his *a*, or was not. „ V ii 450
man that hath to foil a murderous *a* May, surely, play with words. *Harold* II ii 417
Their *a* is ever at that which flies highest— *Foresters* I i 261
Mine eye most true to one hair's-breadth of *a*. „ IV 695
Aim'd spoil and sackage *a* at by these rebels, *Queen Mary* II ii 248
but failure it may be Of all we *a* at. *Becket* I i 383
The point you *a* at, and pray God she prove „ II ii 77
Aiming in *a* at your love, It may be sometimes „ V i 35
Air (atmosphere) Like universal *a* and sunshine! *Queen Mary* III ii 182
A and sunshine. I would we had you, „ V ii 605
Free *a* ! free field! *Harold* II ii 230
Air (atmosphere) (*continued*) he flings His brand in *a* and catches it again, *Harold* V i 494
and fling them out to the free *a*. *Becket* I i 288
Blurt thy free mind to the *a*? „ I iii 239
when I flee from this For a gasp of freer *a*, „ II i 29
Let all the *a* reel into a mist of odour, *The Cup* II 185
give him limbs, then *a*, and send him forth „ II 261
come as freely as heaven's *a* and mother's milk? *Foresters* I i 210
We should be free as *a* in the wild wood— „ I iii 124
I breathe Heaven's *a*, and Heaven looks down on me, „ IV 725
if ye cannot breathe but woodland *a*, „ IV 953
'Air (hair) I ha' heärd 'im a-gawin' on 'ud make your '*a*—God bless it!—stan' on end. *Prom. of May* I 135
Air (strain of music) Play the *a*, Little John. *Foresters* III 418
A and word, my lady, are maid and man. „ III 419
Aisle (*See also* **Minster-aisle**) The nave and *a's* all empty as a fool's jest! *Queen Mary* IV iii 286
Did not a man's voice ring along the *a*, *Becket* V ii 151
Alarm my master hears with much *a*, *Queen Mary* I v 250
Have you had any *a*? no stranger? *Becket* III i 28
Alarum clang and clash *a* as we pass, *Queen Mary* II i 230
A-laughin' I'd like to leather 'im black and blue, and she to be *a-l* at it. *Prom. of May* II 596
Alberighi (Federigo degli) *See* **Federigo degli Alberighi**
Alchemic and jealousy Hath in it an *a* force to fuse *Queen Mary* III vi 181
Alchemy backward-working *a* Should change this gold to silver, *Foresters* IV 39
Alder We parted like the brook yonder about the *a* island, *Prom. of May* I 773
Alder-island Close by that *a-i* in your brook, „ II 535
Aldred (Archbishop of York) take, sign it, Stigand, *A* ! Sign it, *Harold* III i 198
Ask it of *A*. „ III i 226
Come, *A*, join our hands before the hosts, „ IV i 241
Aldwyth (daughter of Alfgar and widow of Griffyth, King of Wales) The Lady *A* Was here to-day, „ I ii 34
not like *A* . . . For which I strangely love him. Should not England Love *A*, „ I ii 175
Courage, noble *A* ! „ I ii 183
They say thou art to wed the Lady *A*. „ III ii 108
A ! *A* ! (repeat) „ IV i 19, 25
A, Harold, *A* ! „ IV i 132
His conqueror conquer'd *A*. „ IV i 218
A, *A*, Canst thou love me, „ IV i 225
Harold, Harold and *A* ! „ IV i 244
Hail! Harold! *A* ! hail, bridegroom and bride „ IV iii 1
Hail, Harold, *A* ! Bridegroom and bride! „ IV iii 42
Leave them! and thee too, *A*, „ IV iii 227
Ale (*See also* **Äale**) Brain-dizzied with a draught of morning *a*. *Queen Mary* II i 72
and she brew'd the best *a* in all Glo'ster, *Becket* III i 197
I am misty with my thimbleful of *a*. *Foresters* IV 278
The king's good health in *a* and Malvoisie. „ IV 968
Ale-house spent all your last Saturday's wages at the *a-h*; *Prom. of May* III 79
Alençon hast thou never heard His savagery at *A*,— *Harold* II ii 382
Alfgar (Earl of Mercia) (*See also* **Half-Alfgar**) light enough for *A's* house To strike thee down „ I i 307
It means the lifting of the house of *A*. „ I i 473
feuds that part The sons of Godwin from the sons of *A* „ I ii 181
Godwin still at feud with *A*, And *A* hates King Harold. „ IV i 124
Alfred (the Great, King of the West Saxons) They blinded my young kinsman, *A*— „ II ii 511
And that my wife descends from *A*? „ II ii 594
tell me tales Of *A* and of Athelstan the Great „ IV i 74
Less than a star among the goldenest hours Of *A*, „ IV iii 52
A Was England. Ethelred was nothing. „ V i 373
Alfwig Abbot *A*, Leofric, and all the monks „ V i 445
sure this body Is *A*, the king's uncle. „ V ii 68
Alice (a Lady in Waiting to Queen Mary) Shall *A* sing you One of her pleasant songs? *A*, my child, Bring us your lute. *Queen Mary* V ii 354
Alien Philip's no sudden *a*—the Queen's husband, „ III iii 42
forfeited her right to reign By marriage with an a— „ V i 291
So strange among them—such an *a* there, ***The Cup*** II 143

Alight (lighted) Last night, I dream'd the faggots were *a*, *Queen Mary* IV ii 2
Alighted *See* **Lighted**
A-limpin' I seed tha *a-l* up just now wi' the roomatics i' the knee. *Prom. of May* I 384
Alington Ah, gray old castle of *A*, *Queen Mary* II i 243
Alive (*See also* **Half-alive**) become Hideously *a* again from head to heel, „ IV iii 447
while famished rats Eat them *a*. „ V ii 198
Dead or *a* you cannot make him happy. „ V v 71
And flay me all *a*. *Harold* IV i 191
All (*See also* **All-but-nothing, All-in-all, Hall**) Long live Queen Mary! down with *a* traitors! *Queen Mary* I i 66
but *a* things here At court are known; „ I iv 56
but God hath sent me here To take such order with *a* heretics „ I v 34
now that *a* traitors Against our royal state have lost the heads „ III iv 2
The devil take *a* boots were ever made Since man went barefoot. „ III v 197
But held from you *a* papers sent by Rome, „ V ii 45
That *a* day long hath wrought his father's work, „ V ii 118
Methinks I am *a* angel, that I bear it Without more ruffling. „ V iii 3
But by *a* Saints— *Leofwin.* Barring the Norman! *Harold* V i 224
and *a* left-handedness and under-handedness. *Becket, Pro.* 340
Father, I am so tender to *a* hardness! „ I i 316
Mine enemies barr'd *a* access to the boy. „ V ii 451
Lady, I say it with *a* gentleness, *The Cup* I iii 99
And fill *a* hearts with fatness and the lust Of plenty— „ II 272
Richer than *a* the wide world-wealth of May, *The Falcon* 466
A Quietist taking *a* things easily—why— *Prom. of May* I 290
I've hed the long barn cleared out of *a* the machines, „ I 451
Who leaves me *a* his land at Littlechester, „ I 511
drest like a gentleman, too. Damn *a* gentlemen, says I! „ II 579
and they both love me—I am *a* in *a* to both; „ III 213
a in *a* to one another from the time when we first peeped „ III 273
Push'd from *a* doors as if we bore the plague, „ III 804
but go about to come at their love with *a* manner of homages, *Foresters* I i 102
Sleep, happy soul! *a* life will sleep at last. „ I iii 48
in the name of *a* our woodmen, present her with this oaken chaplet as Queen of the wood, „ III 57
Out upon *a* hard-hearted maidenhood! „ IV 50
And *a* I love, Robin, and *a* his men, „ IV 722
Are *a* our guests here? „ IV 993
All-but-nothing if *a-b-n* be anything, and one plate of dried prunes be *a-b-n*, *The Falcon* 134
Allegiance promise full *A* and obedience to the death. *Queen Mary* II ii 169
to cancel and abolish all bonds of human *a*, „ V iv 50
Lay hands of full *a* in thy Lord's And crave his mercy, *Harold* V i 11
thou hast sworn a voluntary *a* to him? *Becket Pro.* 439
Allen (a farm labourer) so, *A*, I may as well begin with you. *Prom. of May* III 29
I spoke of your names, *A*, „ III 35
But, *A*, tho' you can't read, „ III 42
What is all this, *A*? „ III 123
Allen (Sally) *See* **Sally Allen**
Allendale The warrior Earl of *A*, *Foresters* I i 6
Alley so many *a's*, crossings, Paths, avenues— *Becket* IV ii 6
Alliance Have you *a's*? Bithynia, Pontus, Paphlagonia? *The Cup* I ii 99
Break thine *a* with this faithless John, *Foresters* IV 323
Allied Art thou for Richard, or *a* to John? *Richard.* I am *a* to John. „ IV 135
for how canst thou be thus *a* With John, „ IV 350
All-in-all (*See also* **All**) Their Flemish go-between And *a-i-a*. *Queen Mary* III vi 5
Allow your Highness will *a* Some spice of wisdom „ II iv 133
His Highness and myself (so you *a* us) „ III iv 324
rage of one who hates a truth He cannot but *a*. „ III vi 145
A me the same answer as before— „ V i 237
world *a's* I fall no inch Behind this Becket, *Becket* V i 39
A me, sir, to pass you. *Prom. of May* II 354
A me to go with you to the farm. „ II 574
Allowance I can make *a* for thee, *Queen Mary* I v 326
Make no *a* for the naked truth. „ I v 328
To make *a* for their rougher fashions, *Harold* II ii 8
easier then for you to make *A* for a mother— *The Falcon* 826
ready To make *a's*, and mighty slow To feel offences. *Prom. of May* III 629
Allow'd tho' a stranger fain would be *a* To join the hunt. *The Cup* I i 196
I think our Abbess knew it and *a* it. *Becket* V ii 95
All-prepared The best of all not *a-p* to die. „ V ii 564
All-royal Look rather thou *a-r* as when first I met thee. „ II i 46
Almighty floated downward from the throne Of God *A*. *Harold* I i 19
Harold and God *A*! „ V i 526
Almoner This *A* hath tasted Henry's gold. *Becket* I iii 294
Almost *See* **Ommost**
Alms his wealth A fountain of perennial *a*— *Queen Mary* II ii 385
she holds it in Free and perpetual *a*, *Becket* I iii 680
boldness of this hand hath won it Love's *a*, „ II i 184
pale beggar-woman seeking *a* For her sick son, *The Falcon* 853
sweet saints bless your worship for your *a* to the old woman! *Foresters* II i 364
O your honour, I pray you too to give me an *a*. „ II i 390
Almshouses Part shall go to the *a* at Nottingham, „ III 206
Aloän (alone) Let ma *a* afoor foälk, wilt tha? *Prom. of May* II 213
I tell'd tha to let ma *a*! „ II 229
I can't let tha *a* if I would, Sally. „ II 233
A-lodgin' What dost a knaw o' this Mr Hedgar as be *a-l'* wi' ye? „ I 200
A-lolluping (hanging down) tongue on un cum *a-l* out o' 'is mouth as black as a rat. *Queen Mary* IV iii 519
Alone (*See also* **Aloän**) And think not we shall be *a*— „ II i 191
and not *a* from this, Likewise from any other, „ II ii 236
Harold Hear the king's music, all *a* with him, *Harold* I ii 194
I leave thee to thy talk with him *a*; „ II ii 324
And Wulfnoth is *a* in Normandy. „ III i 81
The Church *a* hath eyes—and now I see That I was blind— *Becket* II ii 436
So many happy hours *a* together, „ III iii 39
That I would speak with you once more *a*. „ III iii 41
Can I speak with you *A*, my father? „ V ii 70
will you have it *a*, Or with these listeners near you? „ V ii 304
We are all *a* with him. „ V ii 312
A I do it. „ V ii 459
Too early to be here *a* with thee; *The Cup* I iii 82
Can I not speak with you once more *a*? *The Falcon* 689
Ay, the dear nurse will leave you *a*; „ 703
Let him *a*! A worthy messenger! *Foresters* I iii 84
Thou art *a* in the silence of the forest „ IV 630
Let him *a* a while. He loves the chivalry of his single arm. „ IV 784
A-lookin' then a-scrattin upon a bit o' paäper, then *a-l* ageän; *Prom. of May* I 203
I'd like to drag 'im thruff the herse-pond, and she to be *a-l* at it. „ II 594
Alphabetical (*See also* **Halfabitical**) but he sent me an *a* list of those that remain, „ III 28
Alphege (Archbishop of Canterbury) St. Denis of France and St. *A* of England, *Becket* V iii 165
Altar (*See also* **Haltar**) Our *a* is a mound of dead men's clay, *Queen Mary* V ii 161
a dead man Rose from behind the *a*, *Harold* I ii 79
let our high *a* Stand where their standard fell . . . „ V ii 139
look how the table steams, like a heathen *a*; nay, like the *a* at Jerusalem. *Becket* I iv 69
he hath made his bed between the *a's*, „ I iv 264
You on this side the *a*. You on that. *The Cup* I 254
Altar-flame Rouse the dead *a-f*, fling in the spices, „ II 182
Alter every tongue *A's* it passing, *Queen Mary* III v 36
Altered He is much *a*; but I trust that your return— *Prom. of May* III 420
Alva (Duke) The Duke Of *A*, an iron soldier. *Queen Mary* III i 194
for their heresies, *A*, they will fight; „ III ii 204
Duke *A* will but touch him on the horns, „ V i 155
For *A* is true son of the true church— „ V i 159
Always *See* **Hallus**
A-makin' and *a-m'* o' volk madder and madder; „ IV iii 532
Amaze one step in the dark beyond Our expectation, that *a's* us. *The Cup* I i 213

Amazed (*See also* **Maäzed**) Madam, I am *a*: *Queen Mary* I v 308
brake into woman-tears, Ev'n Gardiner, all *a*, „ I v 566
were much *a* To find as fair a sun „ III ii 21
Why lookest thou so *a*? *Foresters* I i 130
Ambassador King of France, Noailles the *A*, *Queen Mary* I iv 110
The *A* from France, your Grace. „ I v 239
Who waits? *Usher*. The *A* of Spain, „ I v 342
Ambition The proud *a's* of Elizabeth, „ III ii 169
For hath not thine *a* set the Church This day *Becket* I iii 584
that *a* Is like the sea wave, *The Cup* I iii 137
a, pride So bloat and redden his face— „ II 169
Ambush Where have you lain in *a* all the morning? *Prom. of May* I 544
Amen Serve God and both your Majesties.
Voices. *A*. *Queen Mary* III iii 160
They groan *a*; they swarm into the fire „ V ii 110
A. Come on. „ V iv 9
A to all Your wish, and further. „ V iv 28
Deserts! *A* to what? Whose deserts? „ V iv 30
Amenable Like other lords *a* to law. *Becket, Pro.* 25
Amends They make *a* for the tails. *Queen Mary* III i 227
I make thee full *a*. *Becket* III iii 219
To make *a* I come this day to break my fast *The Falcon* 275
I cannot find the word—forgive it—*A*. *Prom. of May* III 791
Amiss I know I have done *a*, have been a fool. *Foresters* II ii 51
Amity Are now once more at perfect *a*. *Becket* III iii 229
Amnesty more of olive-branch and *a* For foes at home— „ V ii 15
A-moänin' He's been *a-m* and a-groänin' in 'is sleep, *Prom. of May* III 411
Amomum Nard, Cinnamon, *a*, benzoin. *The Cup* II 184
Amorous If I tried her and la—she's *a*. *Queen Mary* I iv 17
nor yet so *a* That I must needs be husbanded; „ II ii 215
a Of good old red sound liberal Gascon wine: *Becket, Pro.* 99
Amount How much might that *a* to, my lord Leicester? „ I iii 655
Amour Thomas, lord Not only of your vassals but *a's*, „ V i 205
Amourist he, your rustic *a*, The polish'd Damon *Prom. of May* III 561
Amphisbæna Two vipers of one breed—an *a*, Each
end a sting: *Queen Mary* III iv 39
Ampler Farewell, Madam, God grant you *a* mercy
at your call „ IV i 189
Amplier *A* than any field on our poor earth „ III iii 197
Amulet that are *a's* against all The kisses of all kind *Harold* I ii 112
Mine *a* . . . This last . . . „ I ii 124
Anabaptist world-hating beast, A haggard *A*. *Queen Mary* II ii 92
Anathema He is pronounced *a*. „ IV i 187
The Pope's *A*—the Holy Rood That bow'd to me *Harold* V i 382
and let them be *a*, And all that speak for them *a*. *Becket* I i 170
I charge thee, upon pain of mine *a*, „ I iii 719
Go, lest I blast thee with *a*, „ IV ii 287
gone to the King And taken our *a* with him. „ V ii 8
Anathematise (*See also* **De-Anathematise**) I would *a* him.
I will not seal. „ I iii 314
Anathematised Cursed and *a* us right and left, „ V i 4
Anatomized *a* The flowers for her— *Prom. of May* II 302
Ancestor bowl my *a* Fetch'd from the farthest east— *The Falcon* 484
Ancestral lest the crown should be Shorn of *a* splendour. *Becket* I iii 157
Anchor such a one Was without rudder, *a*, compass— *Prom. of May* III 534
Ancient Who now recalls her to His *a* fold. *Queen Mary* III iii 167
Which frights you back into the *a* faith; „ IV ii 143
he stood More like an *a* father of the Church, „ IV iii 598
And for these Royal customs, These *a* Royal customs—
they *are* Royal, *Becket* I i 167
These *a* laws and customs of the realm. (repeat) „ I iii 7, 18
For I was musing on an *a* saw, „ V ii 538
It is our *a* custom in Galatia *The Cup* II 358
Andrew, St. *See* **St. Andrew**
Andrew's Laughs at the last red leaf, and *A* Day. *Queen Mary* III iii 87
Anew Why, tha looks häale *a* to last to a hoonderd. *Prom. of May* I 354
Angel Let the great *a* of the church come with him; *Queen Mary* I v 377
As an *a* among *a's*. „ I v 449
His friends—as *A's* I received 'em, „ I v 625
flocks of swans, As fair and white as *a's*; „ III ii 16
True, and I am the *A* of the Pope. „ III ii 144
how the blessed *a's* who rejoice Over one saved „ III iii 180
There's half an *a* wrong'd in your account; Methinks
I am all *a*, „ V iii 1
May the great *a's* join their wings, „ V iv 6
Angel (*continued*) Then a great *A* past along the highest *Harold* III i 134
great *A* rose And past again along „ III i 153
Are those the blessed *a's* quiring, father? „ V i 472
Whisper! God's *a's* only know it. Ha! „ V ii 31
will be reflected in the spiritual body among the *a's*. *Becket, Pro.* 398
So now he bears the standard of the *a's*. „ I iii 497
till it break Into young *a's*. „ V ii 257
face of an *a* and the heart of a—that's too positive! *The Falcon* 86
Seem my good *a* who may help me from it. *Prom. of May* II 388
God's good *A* Help him back hither, *Foresters* I ii 10
Thou comest a very *a* out of heaven. „ II i 105
I am but an *a* by reflected light. „ II i 108
Your heaven is vacant of your *a*. „ II i 109
Anger (s) no more rein upon thine *a* Than any child! *Queen Mary* III iv 303
The King is quick to *a*; if thou anger him, *Becket* I iii 165
betwixt thine Appeal, and Henry's *a*, yield. „ I iii 623
Our brother's *a* puts him, Poor man, „ II ii 234
When I was in mine *a* with King Louis, „ III iii 257
A noble *a*! but Antonius To-morrow *The Cup* I ii 95
My five-years' *a* cannot die at once, *Prom. of May* II 462
Anger (verb) The King is quick to anger; if thou *a* him, *Becket* I iii 165
Nay—go. What! will you *a* me? „ III i 209
King plucks out their eyes Who *a* him, „ IV ii 407
talk not of cows. You *a* the spirit. *Foresters* II i 330
A the scritch-owl. „ II i 331
A brave old fellow but he *a's* me. „ II i 471
Away, away, wife, wilt thou *a* him? „ III 255
Anger'd And if her people, *a* thereupon, *Queen Mary* I iii 90
That had *a* me Had I been William. *Harold* II ii 386
How he flamed When Tostig's *a* earldom flung him, „ III i 54
Tostig, poor brother, Art *thou* so *a*? V i 274
I deny not That I was somewhat *a*. *Becket* IV ii 351
and yet You know me easily *a*. „ V i 84
But *a* at their flaunting of our flag, *The Falcon* 628
I have *a* your good nurse; „ 706
he kneels! he has *a* the foul witch, *Foresters* II i 670
Angerest Thou *a* me, man: I do not jest. *Becket, Pro.* 299
Angle *A*, Jute, Dane, Saxon, Norman, *Harold* II ii 762
yet he held that Dane, Jute, *A*, Saxon, „ IV i 77
As once he bore the standard of the *A's*, *Becket* I iii 495
Angler's Home Close by that alder-island in your
brook 'The *A H*.' *Prom. of May* II 536
Anglia Pereant, pereant, *A* precatur. *Harold* V i 534
Angliae Hostis per *A* Plagas bacchatur; „ V i 510
Angliam Hostis in *A* Ruit prædator, „ V i 506
Angry Thro' all her *a* chronicles hereafter By loss of
Calais. *Queen Mary* V ii 304
Animal What, is not man a hunting *a*? *Foresters* IV 224
Anjou (French province) When I am out in Normandy
or *A*. *Becket, Pro.* 144
We take her from her secret bower in *A* „ *Pro.* 182
A hundred, too, from Normandy and *A*: „ II ii 174
My *A* bower was scarce as beautiful. „ III i 52
Glancing at the days when his father was only
Earl of *A*, „ III iii 150
Anne (Christian name) He loved the Lady *A*; *Foresters* I i 7
Anne (Queen) Queen *A* loved him. All the women
loved him. *Queen Mary* II i 33
Anne (Wharton) (*See also* **Anne Wharton**) and the
Lady *A* Bow'd to the Pyx; „ I v 41
wherefore bow ye not, says Lady *A*, „ I v 46
Anne Wharton (*See also* **Anne**) with her Lady *A W*,
and the Lady Anne „ I v 41
Annex'd and the legateship *A* to Canterbury— „ V ii 37
Another —*a* recantation Of Cranmer at the stake. „ IV iii 299
There! there! *a* paper! „ V ii 329
revolt? A new Northumberland, *a* Wyatt? „ V v 188
for what right had he to get himself wrecked on *a*
man's land? *Harold* II i 60
a hill Or fort, or city, took it, „ IV i 49
With whom I fought *a* fight than this Of Stamford-bridge. „ IV iii 23
And then *a* wood, and in the midst A garden and
my Rosamund. *Becket, Pro.* 168
You bad me take revenge *a* way— „ IV ii 153
There is yet *a* old woman. *Foresters* II i 244

Another (*continued*) Your worship may find *a* rhyme if you care to drag your brains for such a minnow. *Foresters* II i 322
Doubtless, like judges of *a* bench, „ III 153
Anselm (Archbishop of Canterbury) And I'll have no more *A's*. *Becket, Pro.* 276
Thou art the man—be thou A mightier *A*. „ I i 134
But *A* crown'd this Henry o'er again. „ III iii 203
Answer (s) Is it England, or a party? Now, your *a*. *Queen Mary* I v 143
My *a* is, I wear beneath my dress A shirt of mail: „ I v 144
I would your *a* had been other, Madam, „ I v 274
It craves an instant *a*, Ay or No. „ I v 589
And by their *a's* to the question ask'd, „ II ii 153
Is that your *a*? „ V i 68
Allow me the same *a* as before— „ V i 237
And my *a* to it—See here— *Harold* I ii 56
Be careful of thine *a*, my good friend. „ II ii 605
How ran that *a* which King Harold gave „ IV iii 108
Take thou mine *a* in bare commonplace— *Becket, Pro.* 282
My heart is full of tears—I have no *a*. „ *Pro.* 407
cannot yield thee an *a* altogether to thy satisfaction. „ I iv 21
That is not altogether an *a*, my lord. „ I iv 27
With Cain's *a* my lord. Am I his keeper? „ I iv 186
Your *a*, beauty! „ IV ii 52
Vouchsafe a gracious *a* to your Queen? „ IV ii 359
had she but given Plain *a* to plain query? „ IV ii 386
You had my *a* to that cry before. „ V iii 124
Answer not; but strike. *De Tracy.* There is my *a* then. „ V iii 187
He waits your *a*. *The Cup* II 138
Weänt ye gi'e me a kind *a* at last? *Prom. of May* II 64
her *a*—I think I have it about me—yes, there it is! „ III 394
Answer (verb) *A* thou for him, then! *Queen Mary* I i 40
We *a* him with ours, and there are messengers „ I iii 136
And *a* them in song. „ II i 53
And cannot *a* sanely . . . What it means? *Harold* I i 88
but thou must not this way *a him*. „ II ii 372
To which the lover *a's* lovingly 'I am beside thee.' „ III ii 13
Full hope have I that love will *a* love. „ IV i 238
A them thou! Is this our marriage-banquet? „ IV iii 3
A then! „ IV iii 44
Our javelins *A* their arrows. „ V i 522
let me go. *Henry.* *A* me first. *Becket, Pro.* 280
he shall *a* to the summons of the King's court „ I iii 88
appear before the Pope, And *a* thine accusers . . . „ I iii 603
lustiest and lousiest of this Cain's brotherhood, *a*. „ I iv 185
Thou wast too shamed to *a*. „ II i 66
I cannot *a* it Till better times, „ III i 2
I challenge thee to meet me before God. *A* me there. „ IV ii 255
Madam, I will not *a* you one word. „ IV ii 363
calls you oversea To *a* for it in his Norman courts. „ V ii 355
A not, but strike. *De Tracy.* There is my answer then. „ V iii 186
Come once more to me Before the crowning,—I will *a* you. *The Cup* II 79
No chord in me that would not *a* you In music. *The Falcon* 456
And ask'd me what I could not *a*. *Prom. of May* I 555
I cannot Well *a* for my father; „ II 519
he would *a* nothing, I could make nothing of him; „ III 495
and it *a's*, I am thine to the very heart of the earth— *Foresters* I i 336
and if her beauties *a* their report. „ I ii 28
Yes, my lord, fear not. I will *a* for you. „ I ii 33
My Lady, will you *a* me a question? „ I ii 136
I will not *a* it, my lord, „ I ii 140
I cannot *a* thee till Richard come. „ I ii 220
And *a* it in flowers. „ III 353
Answer'd Or *a* them in smiling negatives; *Queen Mary* IV iii 603
And the Lord *a* me, 'Thou art the man, (repeat) *Becket* I i 82, 98
he *a* me, As if he wore the crown already— „ II ii 5
I *a* for myself that I never spoke more „ III i 121
Rosamund hath not *a* you one word; „ IV ii 361
Methought I *a* moderately enough. „ V ii 546
Thou hast *a* for me, but I know not *Foresters* I i 310
Ant Tut, your sonnet's a flying *a*, *Queen Mary* II i 84
Anthem Their *a's* of no church, how sweet they are! *Harold* III ii 91
Antichrist terms Of Satan, liars, blasphemy, *A*, *Queen Mary* I ii 95
Antichrist As for the Pope I count him *A*, *Queen Mary* IV iii 277
Anti-marrying black, bell-silencing, *a-m*, burial-hindering interdict *Becket* III iii 55
Antioch And felt the sun of *A* scald our mail, „ II ii 93
Arab soldan, who, When I was there in *A*, „ IV ii 301
central diamond, worth, I think, Half of the *A* „ V i 166
Anti-papal so much of the *a-p* leaven Works in him yet, *Queen Mary* IV i 15
Antipope Who had my pallium from an *A*! *Harold* I i 82
prest upon By the fierce Emperor and his *A*. *Becket* I iii 203
And then thy King might join the *A*, „ I iii 211
between The Pope and *A*— „ II ii 70
Anti-Roman Our *a-R* faction? *The Cup* I ii 196
I have enough—their *a-R* faction. „ I ii 200
Antonius (a Roman General) '*A* leader of the Roman Legion.' „ I i 167
shrine Of our great Goddess, in some city where *A* past. „ I ii 58
Most like the city rose against *A*, „ I ii 63
A To-morrow will demand your tribute— „ I ii 95
Returns with this *A*. „ I ii 179
paper sign'd *A*—will you take it, read it? „ I ii 226
All that Lies with *A*. „ I ii 293
A, So gracious toward women, „ I ii 298
wrong'd Without there, knew thee with *A*. „ I ii 320
Where is *A*? (repeat) *The Cup* I iii 48, 79, 87, 97
To find *A* here. *The Cup* I iii 55
walk with me we needs must meet *A* coming, „ I iii 93
A would not suffer me to break Into the sanctuary. „ I iii 120
Our *A*, Our faithful friend of Rome, „ II 243
Welcome, my lord *A*, to our Temple. „ II 252
A, Much graced are we that our Queen „ II 333
A, Where wast thou on that morning „ II 389
A—'Camma!' who spake? „ II 400
A, If you had found him plotting against Rome, „ II 405
A, tell the Senate I have been most true to Rome— „ II 481
A, is *he* there? „ II 496
Antony (an adherent of Wyatt) (*See also* **Antony Knyvett, Knyvett**) Come, you bluster, *A*! *Queen Mary* II i 119
Antony Knyvett Here's *A K*. „ II i 73
Antwerp To Strasburg, *A*, Frankfort, Zurich, „ I ii 1
There is *A* and the Jews. „ V i 182
Anvil *A* on hammer bang— *Harold* IV iii 161
Hammer on *a*, hammer on *a*. „ IV iii 162
set the Church This day between the hammer and the *a*— *Becket* I iii 586
Any (*See also* **Ony**) Nay, if by chance you hear of *a* such, *Queen Mary* I iv 175
Good Prince, art thou in need of *a* gold? *Foresters* I ii 163
Anyhow *See* **Onyhow**
Anything (*See also* **Onythink, Owt**) or whether They should believe in *a*; *Queen Mary* IV iii 407
A or nothing? *Filippo.* Well, my lord, if all-but-nothing be *a*, *The Falcon* 133
then there is *a* in your lordship's larder at your lordship's service, „ 137
tell me *a* of our sweet Eva When in her brighter girlhood, *Prom. of May* II 520
Apart Remain within the chamber, but *a*. *Queen Mary* V iii 12
A-parting saw your ladyship *a-p* wi' him even now i' the coppice, *Becket* III i 160
A-passing Who's *a-p*? King Edward or King Richard? *Queen Mary* I i 31
The blessed Mary's *a-p*! „ I i 36
Apathy And, lest we freeze in mortal *a*, *The Cup* I iii 130
numb'd me into *a* Against the unpleasant jolts *Prom. of May* I 227
Ape A Parliament of imitative *a's*! *Queen Mary* III iii 235
a feeder Of dogs and hawks, and *a's*, *Becket* I i 80
A-peacocking (showing off) *a-p* and a-spreading to catch her eye for a dozen year, *The Falcon* 99
Apicius that Lucullus or *A* might have sniffed it *Becket* III iii 117
A-plaäyin' (playing) *a-p* the saäme gaäme wi' my Dora— *Prom. of May* II 591
Apoplexy O would it were His third last *a*! *The Cup* II 172
Apostate The *a* monk that was with Randulf here. *Becket* V ii 574
Apostle His prophets, and *a's*, in the Testaments, *Queen Mary* IV iii 232
we be liker the blessed *A's*; *they* were fishers of men, *Harold* II i 34
spirit of the twelve *A's* enter'd Into thy making. *Becket* I i 50

Apostolic And from the *A* see of Rome ; *Queen Mary* III iii 127
by your intercession May from the *A* see obtain, „ III iii 147
And we by that authority *A* Given unto us, his Legate, „ III iii 210
Appall'd And yet I seem *a*—on such a sudden *Becket* I i 137
Appeal for their sake who stagger betwixt thine *A*, „ I iii 623
make *a* To all the archbishops, bishops, „ V ii 403
Appeal'd You were sent for, You were *a* to, *Queen Mary* III iv 256
I *a* to the Sister again, her answer— *Prom. of May* III 394
Appear doth *a* this marriage is the least Of all their quarrel. *Queen Mary* II ii 154
And cite thee to *a* before the Pope, *Becket* I iii 602
Appearance for *a* sake, stay with the Queen. *Queen Mary* II i 137
'Appen (happen) To be true to each other, let *'a* what maäy, (repeat) *Prom. of May* II 206, 236, 257
Appertaining myself Half beast and fool as *a* to it ; *Queen Mary* IV iii 415
Applaud I say Ye would *a* that Norman *Harold* II ii 539
Apple (adj.) No, not that way—here, under the *a* tree. *Prom. of May* I 83
Apple (s) cut out the rotten from your *a*, Your *a* eats *Queen Mary* II ii 6
That bears not its own *a's*. „ III i 23
if I had been Eve i' the garden I shouldn't ha' minded the *a*, for what's an *a*, *Becket* III i 140
you have robb'd poor father Of ten good *a's*. *Prom. of May* I 616
Appoint Or he the bridegroom may *a* ? *Becket* I iii 687
Appointed He, whom the Father had *a* Head Of all his church, *Queen Mary* III iii 206
the King, till another be *a*, shall receive the revenues thereof,' *Becket* I iii 101
Appreciation commend them to your ladyship's most peculiar *a*. *The Falcon* 568
Apprehend 'Whosoever will *a* the traitor Thomas Wyatt *Queen Mary* II iii 59
Approve I am happy you *a* it. „ V iii 63
Which you would scarce *a* of : *Prom. of May* III 624
Approved the Emperor *A* you, and when last he wrote, *Queen Mary* III vi 77
When I was made Archbishop, he *a* me. „ V ii 86
Appurtenance so descend again with some of her ladyship's own *a's* ? *The Falcon* 417
'Appy (happy) They can't be many, my dear, but I 'oäpes they'll be 'a. *Prom. of May* I 353
Apricot walnut, *a*, Vine, cypress, poplar, myrtle, *The Cup* I i 2
April (adj.) Like *A* sap to the topmost tree, *Foresters* I iii 24
April (s) I was but fourteen and an *A* then. *Becket* I i 279
Apt And *a* at arms and shrewd in policy. *Foresters* I ii 104
Aquitaine (a French province) but our sun in *A* lasts longer. I would I were in *A* again— *Becket, Pro.* 328
'Eleanor of *A*, Eleanor of England ! „ IV ii 241
To take my life might lose him *A*. „ IV ii 396
Of England ? Say of *A*. I am no Queen of England. „ V i 100
I will go live and die in *A*. (repeat) „ V i 109, 143
Ha, you of *A* ! O you of *A* ! You were but *A* to Louis—no wife ; You are only *A* to me— „ V i 114
I be wife to one That only wedded me for *A* ? „ V i 121
And what would my own *A* say to that ? „ V i 182
Arab I had it from an *A* soldan, who, „ IV ii 300
Araby free wing The world were all one *A*. *Queen Mary* III v 210
Aragon (a Spanish province) The voices of Castille and *A*, „ V i 43
O Saint of *A*, with that sweet worn smile „ V v 198
Arbour *See* **Harbour**
Archbishop (*See also* **Chancellor-Archbishop, Dis-Archbishop**) The false *a* fawning on him, „ I v 30
That when I was *a* held with me. „ IV ii 160
Chief prelate of our Church, *a*, „ IV iii 70
burnin' o' the owld *a* 'll burn the Pwoap „ IV iii 535
When I was made *A*, he approved me. „ V ii 85
Did ye not outlaw your *a* Robert, *Harold* I i 56
Ask *our A*. Stigand should know the purposes of Heaven. „ I i 63
A Robert ! Robert the *A* ! „ II ii 528
No, nor *a*, nor my confessor yet. *Becket, Pro.* 84
Why—look—is this a sleeve For an *a* ? „ *Pro.* 251
A more awful one. Make *me a* ! „ *Pro.* 289
Me A ! God's favour and king's favour „ *Pro.* 293

Archbishop (*continued*) My liege, the good *A* is no more. *Becket, Pro.* 392
And this plebeian like to be *A* ! .. *Pro.* 459
A ? I can see further into a man .. *Pro.* 462
but the Chancellor's and the *A's* Together .. I i 23
Make an *A* of a soldier ? .. I i 41
'My young *A*—thou wouldst make A stately *A* !' .. I i 65
And how been made *A* hadst thou told him, .. I i 121
The *A* ! *Becket*. Ay ! what wouldst thou, .. I i 185
Come, come, my lord *A* ; .. I i 201
can I be under him As Chancellor ? as *A* over him ? .. I i 349
my Lord *A*, 'Tis known you are midwinter to all women, .. I ii 26
first *a* fled, And York lay barren for a hundred years. .. I iii 53
Is it thy will, My lord *A*, .. I iii 272
Loyally and with good faith, my lord *A* ? .. I iii 279
My lord *A*, thou hast yet to seal. .. I iii 306
Say that a cleric murder'd an *a*, .. I iii 399
Hoped, were he chosen *a*, .. I iii 442
Now as *A* goest against the King ; .. I iii 530
and no forsworn *A* Shall helm the Church. .. I iii 597
To see the proud *A* mutilated. .. I iii 614
Know that when made *A* I was freed, .. I iii 707
That none should wrong or injure your *A*. .. I iii 755
My lord *A*, wilt thou permit us— .. I iv 5
My lord *A*, may I come in with my poor friend, my dog ? .. I iv 93
Is the *A* a thief who gives thee thy supper ? .. I iv 115
if the barons and bishops hadn't been a-sitting on the *A*. .. I iv 128
Where is my lord *A* ? .. I iv 184
for the *A* loves humbleness, my lord ; .. I iv 208
the *A* washed my feet o' Tuesday. .. I iv 234
for the *A* likes the smell on it, .. I iv 240
I bring the taint on it along wi' me, for the *A* likes it, .. I iv 253
for to-night ye have saved our *A* ! .. I iv 257
My friends, the *A* bids you good night. .. I iv 261
then to be made *A* and go against the King .. II i 237
nor our *A* Stagger on the slope decks .. II ii 105
Blessed be the Lord *A*, who hath withstood .. II ii 275
My dear Lord *A*, I learn but now .. II ii 426
God bless the great *A* ! .. II ii 452
you had safelier have slain an *a* than a she-goat : .. III iii 68
What more, my lord *A* ? What more, Thomas ? .. III iii 217
But kinglike fought the proud *a*,— .. IV ii 438
Down with King Henry ! up with the *A* ! .. V i 261
I told him I was bound to see the *A* ; .. V ii 100
she had seen the *A* once, So mild, so kind. .. V ii 119
No, daughter, you mistake our good *A* ; .. V ii 138
How the good *A* reddens ! .. V ii 298
To all the *a's*, bishops, prelates, barons, .. V ii 404
My vassals—and yet threaten your *A* In his own house. .. V ii 505
Here is the great *A* ! He lives ! he lives ! .. V iii 29
my lord *A*, A score of knights all arm'd .. V iii 70
Where is the *A*, Thomas Becket ? .. V iii 109
Strike our *A* in his own cathedral ! .. V iii 180
the great *A* ! Does he breathe ? No ? .. V iii 202
they plunder—yea, ev'n bishops, Yea, ev'n *a's*— *Foresters* IV 911
Archbishoprick as his successor in the *a*. *Becket, Pro.* 402
From out his grave to this *a*. „ *Pro.* 420
and chosen me For this thy great *a*, „ I i 91
Save from the throne of thine *a* ? „ I i 119
I care not for thy new *a*. „ I i 217
Shall I forget my new *a* „ I i 220
It well befits thy new *a* To take the vagabond woman „ I i 225
Found two *a's*, London and York ? .. I iii 50
King Would throne me in the great *A* : „ I iii 694
Archdeacon The Pope and that *A* Hildebrand His master, *Harold* III ii 144
Archiepiscopari but *Nolo A*, my good friend, *Becket, Pro.* 286
Archiepiscopally As magnificently and *a* as our Thomas would have done : „ III iii 87
A-reädin' arter she'd been *a-r* me the letter wi' 'er voice a-shaäkin', *Prom. of May* II 128
Argue and I can't *a* upon it ; *Queen Mary* I i 55

Argued While this same marriage question was being *a*, *Queen Mary* II ii 38
Argument And thousand-times recurring *a* „ IV ii 93
Arise *A* against her and dethrone the Queen— „ I iii 91
And over thee the suns *a* and set, *Harold* II ii 433
A, Scatter thy people home, descend the hill, „ V i 9
and *a* again Disjointed: „ V i 297
a, And dash thyself against me that I may slay thee! *Becket* IV ii 194
The traitor's dead, and will *a* no more. „ V iii 200
Ark over His gilded *a* of mummy-saints, *Harold* V i 304
Arm (s) her babe in *a's* Had felt the faltering *Queen Mary* II ii 81
Into the wide-spread *a's* of fealty, „ II ii 264
he was deliver'd To the secular *a* to burn; „ IV ii 214
and you know me strong of *a*; „ V ii 470
I felt his *a's* about me, and his lips— „ V v 99
I will see none except the priest. Your *a*. „ V v 197
Thou art *my* nun, thy cloister in mine *a's*. *Harold* I ii 63
I touch mine *a's*, My limbs— „ II ii 794
heads And *a's* are sliver'd off and splinter'd „ V i 540
Must I hack her *a's* off? How shall I part them? „ V ii 147
the *a* within Is Becket's, who hath beaten down *Becket*, *Pro.* 252
A soldier's, not a spiritual *a*. „ *Pro.* 256
To take the vagabond woman of the street Into thine *a's*! „ I i 229
He fast! is that an *a* of fast? „ I iii 520
I ha' carried him ever so many miles in my *a's*, „ I iv 99
To the fond *a's* of her first love, Fitzurse, „ IV ii 334
Mine *a* is sever'd. I can no more— „ V iii 188
and open *a's* To him who gave it; *The Cup* I i 84
Your *a*—a moment—It will pass. „ II 448
Give me your *a*. Lead me back again. *Prom. of May* III 473
What a shape! what lovely *a's*! *Foresters* I i 109
Take thou mine *a*. Who art thou, gallant knight? „ II i 439
with this skill of fence! let go mine *a*. „ II ii 39
Nor care to leap into each other's *a's*, „ III 7
and thine *a's*, and thy legs, and thy heart, and thy liver, „ IV 203
He loves the chivalry of his single *a*. „ IV 786
Arm (verb) And *a* and strike as with one hand, *Queen Mary* II ii 292
Good! let them *a*. *Becket* V ii 571
Arm'd a thousand of them—more—All *a*, *Queen Mary* II i 108
And see the citizens *a*. Good day; „ II ii 378
And *a* men Ever keep watch beside my chamber door, *Harold* II ii 244
There is an *a* man ever glides behind! „ II ii 247
tell him we stand *a* on Senlac Hill, „ V i 59
Herbert, take out a score of *a* men To guard this bird of passage to her cage; *Becket* I i 328
Why dost thou presume, *A* with thy cross, „ I iii 509
He rides abroad with *a* followers, „ V i 2
My lord, the city if full of *a* men. „ V ii 188
she told us of *a* men Here in the city. „ V ii 227
But these *a* men—will you not hide yourself? „ V ii 247
Ay—but these *a* men—will *you* drown *yourself?* „ V ii 276
These *a* men in the city, these fierce faces— „ V iii 3
Those *a* men in the cloister. „ V iii 49
score of knights all *a* with swords and axes— „ V iii 71
Armful for who could embrace such an *a* of joy? *Foresters* I ii 71
Arming the knights are *a* in the garden Beneath the sycamore. *Becket* V ii 569
Armour fair a likeness As your great King in *a* *Queen Mary* V v 29
Not heavier than thine *a* at Thoulouse? *Becket* I i 26
He had been hurt, And bled beneath his *a*. *Foresters* II ii 5
Beetle's jewel *a* crack'd, „ II ii 160
I left mine horse and *a* with a Squire, „ IV 414
Armour'd Haled thy shore-swallow'd, *a* Normans up *Harold* II ii 57
Arms Ay, all in *a*. *Queen Mary* II ii 3
And I would have my warrior all in *a*. „ V v 34
Thou art in *a* against us. *Harold* IV ii 8
Our Church in *a*—the lamb the lion— „ V i 440
To *a*! *Becket*. De Morville, I had thought so well of you; *Becket* V ii 518
And apt at *a* and shrewd in policy. *Foresters* I ii 104
by force and *a* hath trespassed against the king „ I iii 62
Army Hold office in the household, fleet, forts, *a*; *Queen Mary* III iii 73
I am foraging For Norway's *a*. *Harold* IV ii 6
in a city thro' which he past with the Roman *a*: *The Cup* I i 43
'Arold (Harold) '*A*! '*A*! '*A*! so they be. *Prom. of May* II 724
'*A*! The feller's cleän daäzed, „ II 728
Mr. *A*, Miss. *Dora*. Below? „ III 478
Pleäse, Mister '*A*. „ III 700
Arouse Thou didst *a* the fierce Northumbrians! *Harold* V i 347
Arraign Who dares *a* us, king, of such a plot? „ IV i 168
Arrange *A* my dress—the gorgeous Indian shawl *Queen Mary* V ii 538
Arranged they are *a* here according to their first letters. *Prom. of May* III 36
Arrant Convicted by their conscience, *a* cowards, *Queen Mary* II ii 9
I know them *a* knaves in Nottingham. *Foresters* III 301
Arrogance I always hated boundless *a*. *Becket* V i 13
our John By his Norman *a* and dissoluteness, *Foresters* II i 85
Arrogant What, daunted by a garrulous, *a* girl! „ IV 736
Arrow (*See also* **Vane-arrow**) see there the *a's* flying. *Queen Mary* II iv 51
Sanguelac! Sanguelac! the *a*! the *a*! *Harold* III i 402
It is the *a* of death in his own heart— „ III i 404
Sanguelac! Sanguelac! The *a*! the *a*! (repeat) „ V i 262, 672
The king's last word—'the *a*!' „ V i 266
What is that whirring sound? *Stigand*. The Norman *a*! „ V i 483
Our javelins Answer their *a's*. „ V i 522
The Norman sends his *a's* up to Heaven, „ V i 666
a which the Saints Sharpen'd and sent against him— „ V ii 167
Give him a bow and *a's*—follow—follow. *The Cup* I i 208
my good fellow, *My a* struck the stag. „ I ii 28
besides the wind Went with *my a*. „ I ii 32
Why so I said, *my a*. Well, to sleep. „ I ii 385
Whose *a* is the plague—whose quick flash „ II 291
A's whistle all about. *Foresters* II ii 165
Take thou my bow and *a* and compel them to pay toll. „ III 263
How much? how much? Speak, or the *a* flies. „ III 278
By *a* and gray goosewing, „ III 427
By *a* and by bowstring, „ III 442
like a deer that hath escaped thine *a*! „ IV 61
What deer when I have mark'd him ever yet Escaped mine *a*? „ IV 64
Give me my bow and *a's*. „ IV 603
Each of us has an *a* on the cord; „ IV 607
I am here, my *a* on the cord. „ IV 732
Will hear our *a's* whizzing overhead, „ IV 1090
Arrow-points Prick 'em in the calves with the *a-p*— „ IV 561
Art illogically, out of passion, without *a*— *Becket*, *Pro.* 337
with some sense of *a*, to live By brush and pencil. *Prom. of May* I 497
Follow my *a* among these quiet fields, „ I 743
Artemis (a goddess) himself an adorer of our great goddess, *A*, *The Cup* I i 39
take this holy cup To lodge it in the shrine of *A*. „ I ii 435
To lodge this cup Within the holy shrine of *A*, „ I iii 53
A, *A*, hear us, O Mother, hear us, and bless us! „ II 1
A, thou that art life to the wind, „ II 3
this oracle of great *A* Has no more power „ II 33
Great *A*! O Camma, can it be well, „ II 80
A, *A*, hear him, Ionian *A*! „ II 276
A, *A*, hear her, Ephesian *A*! „ II 310
A, *A*, hear me, Galatian *A*! „ II 312
A, *A*, hear her, Galatian *A*! „ II 316
These are strange words to speak to *A*. „ II 327
many-breasted mother *A* Emboss'd upon it. „ II 340
Our *A* Has vanquish'd their Diana. „ II 456
Arternoon (afternoon) holler laäne be hallus sa dark i' the *a*, *Prom. of May* III 93
Arthur (King) The veriest Galahad of old *A's* hall. *Becket*, *Pro.* 129
Article Philip by these *a's* is bound From stirring hand or foot *Queen Mary* III iii 59
In every *a* of the Catholic faith, „ IV iii 230
Artillery *See* **Real Hard Tillery**
Artist (*See also* **Hartist**) Eva told me that he was taking her likeness. He's an *a*. *Prom. of May* I 128
Asaph (the Levite, musician to King David) sing, *A*! clash The cymbal, Heman! *Harold* III i 187
Ascended He is not yet *a* to the Father. *Becket* V iii 150
A-scrattin (scratching) then *a-s* upon a bit o' paäper, then a-lookin' agean; *Prom. of May* I 202

Ash (cinder) (*See also* **Ashes**) fain had calcined all Northumbria To one black *a*, *Harold* III i 57
Ash (tree) (*See also* **Ashtree**) And wattled thick with *a* and willow-wands; „ V i 190
This is the hottest of it: hold, *a*! hold, willow! „ V i 628
I remember, Scarlet hacking down A hollow *a*, *Foresters* II ii 96
A-shaäkin' (shaking) arter she'd been a-reädin' me the letter wi' 'er voice *a-s*, *Prom. of May* II 129
Ashamed (*See also* **Shaämed**) I am *a* that I am Bagenhall, English. *Queen Mary* III iii 248
Thou mak'st me much *a* That I was for a moment wroth at thee. „ III iv 305
Till I myself was half *a* for him. „ IV ii 171
I am *a* to lift my eyes to heaven, „ IV iii 127
you yourself are *a* of me, and I do not wonder at it. *Prom. of May* III 269
I fall before thee, clasp Thy knees. I am *a*. *Foresters* II i 600
Ashes (*See also* **Ash**) those *a* Which all must be. *The Cup* I iii 134
to such a heat As burns a wrong to *a*, *Foresters* II i 700
Ashridge means to counsel your withdrawing to *A*, *Queen Mary* I iv 226
Permission of her Highness to retire To *A*, „ I IV 237
Ashtree (*See also* **Ash, Eshtree**) always told Father that the huge old *a* there would cause an accident some day; *Prom. of May* III 244
A-silking (dressing in silk) master been a-glorifying and a-velveting and *a-s* himself, *The Falcon* 99
A-sitting if the barons and bishops hadn't been *a-s* on the Archbishop. *Becket* I iv 128
Didn't I spy 'em *a-s* i' the woodbine harbour togither? *Prom. of May* I 124
Ask (*See also* **Ax**) Why do you *a*? you know it. *Queen Mary* I iv 34
A thou Lord Leofwin what he thinks of this! *Harold* I i 40
A it of King Edward! „ I i 78
a of *me* Who had my pallium from an Antipope! „ I i 81
A our broad Earl. „ I i 90
I *a* thee, wilt thou help me to the crown? „ II ii 627
A me for this at thy most need, son Harold, „ III i 14
A it of Aldred. „ III i 225
A me not, Lest I should yield it, „ III ii 46
I *a* again When had the Lateran and the Holy Father „ V i 16
I have a power—would Harold *a* me for it— „ V i 451
I *a* no more. Heaven bless thee! hence! *Becket* I i 320
That which you *a* me Till better times. „ III i 6
What did you *a* her? „ III i 79
Not I, the Pope. *A him* for absolution. „ V ii 379
I *a* no leave of king, or mortal man, „ V ii 458
You will not easily make me credit that. *Phœbe*. *A* her. *The Cup* II 26
His falcon, and I come to *a* for his falcon, *The Falcon* 220
How can I *a* for his falcon? „ 234
Yet if I *a*, He loves me, and he knows I know „ 244
How can I, dare I, *a* him for his falcon? „ 264
Yet I come To *a* a gift. „ 299
for the gift I *a* for, to *my* mind „ 778
love for my dying boy, Moves me to *a* it of you. „ 788
Will pardon me for asking what I *a*. „ 805
Might I *a* your name? *Harold*. Harold. *Prom. of May* II 393
Go back to him and *a* his forgiveness before he dies.— „ III 401
I *a* you all, did none of you love young Walter Lea? *Foresters* I i 54
will you answer me a question? *Marian*. Any that you may *a*. „ I ii 137
A question that every true man *a's* of a woman once in his life. „ I ii 139
we be beggars, we come to *a* o' you. We ha' nothing. „ III 190
bond he hath Of the Abbot—wilt thou *a* him for it? „ IV 85
I fear to *a* who left us even now. „ IV 808
Ask'd (*See also* **Axed, Haxed**) And by their answers to the question *a*, *Queen Mary* II ii 153
a him, childlike: 'Will you take it off „ III i 401
they clapt their hands Upon their swords when *a*; „ V i 174
when he *a* for England? *Harold* IV iii 110
Was there not someone *a* me for forgiveness? „ V ii 82
I *a* the way. *Rosamund*. I think so. *Becket* II i 62
I but *a* her One question, and she primm'd her mouth „ III i 73
a our mother if I could keep a quiet tongue i' my head, „ III i 118
I *a* A ribbon from her hair to bind it with; *The Falcon* 358
you *a* to eat with me. „ 868
Ask'd (*continued*) And *a* me what I could not answer. *Prom. of May* I 555
and I *a* her once more to help me, „ III 387
I would ha' given my whole body to the King had *he a* for it, *Foresters* II i 306
criedst 'I yield' almost before the thing was *a*, „ II i 567
Asking Have for thine *a* aught that I can give, *Queen Mary* II iii 7
Will pardon me for *a* what I ask. *The Falcon* 805
a his consent—you wish'd me— *Prom. of May* III 493
Asleep wholesome medicine here Puts that belief *a*. *Becket* IV ii 52
Shall I find you *a* when I come back? „ IV ii 64
with as little pain As it is to fall *a*. *Prom. of May* II 342
The sick lady here might have been *a*. „ III 344
Some hunter in day-dreams or half *a* *Foresters* IV 1088
A-spitting you'll set the Divil's Tower *a-s*, *Queen Mary* II iii 103
A-spreading and *a-s* to catch her eye for a dozen year, *The Falcon* 100
Ass with an *a's*, not a horse's head, *Queen Mary* I iii 169
Sir Thomas Stafford, a bull-headed *a*, „ V i 284
Assail And might *a* you passing through the street, „ IV ii 34
To *a* our Holy Mother lest she brood Too long *Becket* V ii 251
Assail'd if e'er thou be *a* In any of our forests, *Foresters* IV 423
woman's fealty when *A* by Craft and Love. *The Cup* I i 177
Assassin even now You seem the least *a* of the four. *Becket* V ii 522
Assaulted my house hath been *a*, *Queen Mary* I v 147
Assembled And Commons here in Parliament *a*, „ III iii 114
Assembly But there the great A choose their king, *Harold* II ii 126
Assent This marriage had the *a* of those *Queen Mary* II ii 206
Thine is a half voice and a lean *a*. „ III i 311
That were but as the shadow of an *a*. *Becket* I iii 195
Assertion *See* **Self-assertion**
Assessor But his *a* in the throne, *Queen Mary* I v 501
Assize *See* **'Size**
Assure I do *a* you, that it must be look'd to: „ V i 2
I do most earnestly *a* you that Your likeness— *Prom. of May* II 563
Assured Art thou *a* By this, that Harold loves but Edith? *Harold* I ii 209
A-steälin' cotched 'im once *a-s* coäls an' I sent fur 'im, *Prom. of May* I 412
Astride with the Holy Father *a* of it down upon his own head. *Becket* III iii 77
Asunder here I gash myself *a* from the King, „ I i 175
A-supping be we not *a-s* with the head of the family? „ I iv 178
They be dead while I be *a-s*. „ I iv 247
A-sweäring I be afeard I shall set him *a-s* like onythink. *Prom. of May* III 359
At (hat) we fun' 'im out a-walkin' i' West Field wi' a white '*a*, „ III 135
A-talkin' What feller wur it as 'a' been *a-t* fur haäfe an hour wi' my Dora? „ II 576
A-telling Robin the Earl, is always *a-t* us that every man, *Foresters* I i 95
Atheling (a Saxon prince) The *A* is nearest to the throne. *Harold* II ii 569
So that ye will not crown the *A*? „ II ii 598
Who inherits? Edgar the *A*? „ III i 240
Athelstan (King of the English) and tell me tales Of Alfred and of *A* the Great „ IV i 74
Or *A*, or English Ironside Who fought with Knut, „ IV iii 53
A-top and your worship *a-t* of it. *Queen Mary* II i 66
A-tryin' if she weänt listen to me when I be *a-t* to saäve 'er— *Prom. of May* II 694
Attainder Ye have reversed the *a* laid on us *Queen Mary* III iii 194
Attainted Thou hast disgraced me and *a* me, „ III ii 54
Thou, Robin Hood Earl of Huntingdon, art *a* *Foresters* I iii 57
Attend so you well *a* to the king's moves, *Queen Mary* I iii 152
I *a* the Queen To crave most humble pardon— „ III iv 431
You should *a* the office, give them heart. *Becket* V ii 598
He said, '*A* the office.' *Becket*. *A* the office? „ V ii 607
You had better *a* to your hayfield. *Prom. of May* II 122
I am sorry Mr. Steer still continues too unwell to *a* to you, „ III 22
'I am sorry that we could not *a* your Grace's party on the 10th!' „ III 313
Attendance must we dance *a* all the day? *Foresters* IV 551
Attending I've been *a* on his deathbed and his burial. *Prom. of May* II 4
Attraction fine *a's* and repulses, the delicacies, *Becket, Pro*. 499
Audience Your *a* is concluded, sir. *Queen Mary* I v 337
Aught (*See also* **Ought, Owt**) Have you *a* else to tell me? „ V iii 100
Augustine *See* **Austin**
Aureole Sees ever such an *a* round the Queen, „ V ii 413

Austin (Augustine, first Archbishop of Canterbury) Gregory bid St. *A* here Found two archbishopricks, *Becket* I iii 48
bravest in our roll of Primates down From *A*— „ v ii 59
Author This *a*, with his charm of simple style *Prom. of May* I 223
Authority Under and with your Majesties' *authorities*, *Queen Mary* III iii 138
we by that *a* Apostolic Given unto us, „ III iii 210
And under his *a*—I depart. *Becket* I iii 728
Not punish of your own *a*? „ v ii 450
I would stand Clothed with the full *a* of Rome, „ v ii 493
Automatic all but proving man An *a* series of sensations, *Prom. of May* I 226
Autumn (adj.) Sick as an *a* swallow for a voyage, *Harold* I i 101
Autumn (s) Harvestless *a's*, horrible agues, plague— *Queen Mary* v i 98
Avarice shakes at mortal kings—her vacillation, *A*, craft— *Becket* II ii 407
A-velveting (dressing in velvet) master been a-glorifying and *a-v* and a-silking himself, *The Falcon* 98
Avenge Who will *a* me of mine enemies— *Queen Mary* III ii 166
Avenged that blighted vow Which God *a* to-day. *Harold* v ii 157
Avenue —so many alleys, crossings, Paths, *a's*— *Becket* IV ii 7
A-vire (on fire) and a set un all *a-v*, so 'z the tongue *Queen Mary* IV iii 518
Avoid I may as well *a* him. *Prom. of May* II 619
Avouch I dare *a* you'd stand up for yourself, *Queen Mary* II ii 360
Await My lord! the Duke *a's* thee at the banquet. *Harold* II ii 805
Awaked (*See also* **Half-waked**) He hath *a*! he hath *a*! *Queen Mary* III ii 156
Awaken Love will hover round the flowers when they first *a*; „ v ii 371
Awaken'd It seems her Highness hath *a*. „ v ii 522
Awakening *See* **New-wakening**
A-walkin' we fun' 'im out *a-w* i' West Field wi' a white 'at, *Prom. of May* III 134
Award Thou shalt receive the penitent thief's *a*, *Queen Mary* IV iii 87
Awe —they cannot speak—for *a*; *Harold* I i 33
Awful A more *a* one. Make *me* archbishop! *Becket, Pro.* 288
Awry Nothing; but 'come, come, come,' and all *a*, *Queen Mary* v v 16
Ax (ask) Shall I foller 'er and *a* 'er to maäke it up? *Prom. of May* II 131
Axe (*See also* **Battle-axe, War-axe**) there is *a* and cord. *Queen Mary* III iv 47
How oft the falling *a*, that never fell, „ III v 134
I have a mind to brain thee with mine *a*. *Harold* II i 74
Our *a's* lighten with a single flash „ v i 537
Against the shifting blaze of Harold's *a*! „ v i 587
score of knights all arm'd with swords and *a's*— *Becket* v iii 72
Axed (asked) when I *a* 'im why, he telled me 'at sweet'arts *Prom. of May* II 155
an' *a* ma to be 'is little sweet'art, „ III 120
Axle rear and run And break both neck and *a*. *Harold* I i 374

B

Baaby (baby) to get her *b* born; *Queen Mary* IV iii 524
Baaed black sheep *b* to the miller's ewe-lamb, *Becket* I iv 162
Baäker (baker) and *B*, thaw I sticks to hoäm-maäde— *Prom. of May* I 448
Baal The priests of *B* tread her underfoot— *Becket* III iii 179
Babble (*See also* **Bird-babble**) *B* in bower Under the rose! „ III i 96
Thou art cold thyself To *b* of their coldness. *Queen Mary* v ii 292
And doth so bound and *b* all the way „ v v 86
convene This conference but to *b* of our wives? *Becket* II ii 90
Not while the rivulet *b's* by the door, *Foresters* I ii 321
Babbled I follow'd You and the child: he *b* all the way. *Becket* IV ii 140
Babe but your king stole her a *b* from Scotland *Queen Mary* I v 291
her *b* in arms Had felt the faltering „ II ii 80
The Queen hath felt the motion of her *b*! „ III ii 214
baptized in fire, the *b* Might be in fire for ever. „ v iv 23
The *b* enwomb'd and at the breast is cursed, *Harold* v i 65
B's, orphans, mothers! is that royal, Sire? *Becket* II i 80
Out of the mouths of *b's* and sucklings, praise! „ II ii 278
Will greet us as our *b's* in Paradise. „ v ii 225
I had once A boy who died a *b*; *The Cup* I ii 149
be curious About the welfare of their *b's*, „ I ii 362
O Thou that slayest the *b* within the womb „ II 279
Babe-breasting Age, orphans, and *b-b* mothers— *Becket* II i 72

Baby (adj.) some waxen doll Thy *b* eyes have rested on, belike; *Queen Mary* I v 9
whose *b* eye Saw them sufficient. *Harold* III ii 65
Baby (s) (*See also* **Baaby**) strike Their hearts, and hold their *babies* up to it. „ I i 35
That's all nonsense, you know, such a *b* as you are. *Prom. of May* I 785
King, thy god-father, gave it thee when a *b*. *Foresters* I i 286
Babyhood Was she not betroth'd in her *b* to the Great Emperor *Queen Mary* I i 118
Baby-king Stirring her *b-k* against me? ha! *Becket* v i 106
Bacchatur Hostis per Angliae Plagas *b*; *Harold* v i 511
Bachelor *See* **Batchelor**
Back bald o' the *b*, and bursten at the toes, *Queen Mary* I i 52
show'd his *b* Before I read his face. „ II i 132
scorn'd the man, Or lash'd his rascal *b*, *Harold* II ii 507
but the *b* methought was Rosamund— *Becket, Pro.* 470
be bound Behind the *b* like laymen-criminals? „ I iii 96
so dusted his *b* with the meal in his sack, „ I iv 174
wi' bare *b's*, but the *b's* 'ud ha' countenanced one another, „ III i 147
Can't you hear that you are saying behind his *b* *The Falcon* 107
nor behind your lordship's *b*, „ 113
When I vaulted on his *b*, *Foresters* II ii 150
which longs to break itself across their *b's*. „ IV 918
Backbone Stiff as the very *b* of heresy. *Queen Mary* I v 44
Back'd *B* by the power of France, and landing here, „ III i 447
Back'd *See* **Broken-back'd**
Backward courtesy which hath less loyalty in it than the *b* scrape of the clown's heel— *Becket* III iii 143
my child is so young, So *b* too; „ IV ii 85
Backwardness Hath rated for some *b* *Queen Mary* IV iii 307
Backward-working if his *b-w* alchemy Should change *Foresters* IV 38
Bad (adj.) I will take Such order with all *b*, heretical books *Queen Mary* IV i 95
Eh, my rheumatizy be that *b* howiver be I to win to the burnin'. „ IV iii 474
Eh, but I do know ez Pwoaps and vires be *b* things; „ IV iii 501
And love to hear *b* tales of Philip. „ v ii 429
for the people do say that his is *b* beyond all reckoning, *Becket* III i 175
There are good fairies and *b* fairies, and sometimes she cries, and can't sleep sound o' nights because of the *b* fairies. „ IV i 29
Very *b*. Somebody struck him. „ IV i 50
and they was all a-crying out at the *b* times, *Prom. of May* I 139
But I täakes 'im fur a *b* lot and a burn fool, „ I 153
Thruf slush an' squad When roäds was *b*, „ II 310
And what harm will that do you, so that you do not copy his *b* manners? „ III 361
It be one o' my *b* daäys. „ III 465
You heard him say it was one of his *b* days. „ III 469
It is almost the last of my *b* days, I think. „ III 471
We be fairies of the wood, We be neither *b* nor good. *Foresters* II ii 119
Robin, I do, but I have a *b* wife. „ III 70
they put it upon me because I have a *b* wife. „ III 437
Bad-bade (verb) *Bad* you so softly with your heretics here, *Queen Mary* I v 392
Bad me to tell you that she counts on you „ II ii 104
Cranmer. Fly would he not, when all men *bad* him fly. „ III i 171
I *bad* my chaplain, Castro, preach Against these burnings. „ III vi 73
And *bad* me have good courage; „ IV ii 8
bad the king Who doted on him, *Harold* IV i 101
Edward *bad* me spare thee. „ IV ii 11
And *bad* me seal against the rights of the Church, *Becket* I iii 312
I *bad* them clear A royal pleasaunce for thee, „ II i 127
Thy true King *bad* thee be A fisher of men; „ II ii 285
bad me whatever I saw not to speak one word, „ III i 132
You *bad* me take revenge another way— „ IV ii 152
life which Henry *bad* me Guard from the stroke „ IV ii 269
He *bad* me put her into a nunnery— „ v i 214
Bade me beware Of John: *Foresters* I ii 255
Badger highback'd polecat, the wild boar, The burrowing *b*— „ I iii 121
Baffle We'll *b* them, I warrant. *Becket* I i 299
Bag We'll dust him from a *b* of Spanish gold. *Queen Mary* I v 421
Bagenhall (*See also* **Ralph, Ralph Bagenhall**) *B*, I see The Tudor green and white. „ III i 179

Bagenhall (*continued*) Worth seeing, *B*! *Queen Mary* III iii 188
I am ashamed that I am *B*, English. " III i 248
For freeing my friend *B* from the Tower; " III vi 7
Baited summon'd hither But to be mock'd and *b*. " III iv 270
Bake To sing, love, marry, churn, brew, *b*, and die, " III v 111
I can *b* and I can brew, *Foresters* I i 214
Baker (*See also* **Baäker**) ah! she said, The *b* made him. *Queen Mary* I v 56
Balance But—if let be—*b* and compromise; " V v 223
Bald (*See also* **Egg-bald**) *b* o' the back, and bursten at the toes, " I i 52
And this *b* priest, and she that hates me, " I iv 282
it seems that we shall fly These *b*, blank fields, " III v 252
Baldness fierce old Gardiner—his big *b*, " I iv 264
Bale (Bishop of Ossory) Poinet, Barlow, *B*, Scory, Coverdale; " I ii 7
Baleful My star! a *b* one. " I v 412
Balk come to London Bridge; But how to cross it *b's* me. " II iii 10
power to *b* Thy puissance in this fight *Harold* V i 118
Take it not that way—*b* not the Pope's will. *Becket* I iii 242
Balk'd The jealous fool *b* of her will— " IV ii 423
Ball I have lost the boy who play'd at *b* with me, *Harold* IV iii 22
same head they would have play'd at *b* with *The Cup* II 127
Is but a *b* chuck'd between France and Spain, *Queen Mary* III i 110
Here is a *b*, my boy, thy world, *Becket* II i 244
Geoffrey have not tost His *b* into the brook! " II i 321
I saw the *b* you lost in the fork of the great willow over the brook. " IV ii 57
you bid me go, and I'll have my *b* anyhow. " IV ii 63
Ballad But there I am sure the *b* is at fault. *Foresters* I i 122
Balm and science now could drug and *b* us *Prom. of May* II 340
We know all *b's* and simples of the field *Foresters* II ii 11
Balmy Thou whose breath Is *b* wind to robe our hills with grass, *The Cup* II 265
Or in the *b* breathings of the night, *Foresters* IV 1068
Balsam Heart-comfort and a *b* to thy blood? *Becket* I i 14
Ban hurl the dread *b* of the Church on those " III iii 210
Band (*See also* **Swaddling-band**) who went with your train *b's* To fight with Wyatt, *Queen Mary* II ii 27
who be those three yonder with bows?—not of my *b*— *Foresters* II i 172
can I trust myself With your brave *b*? " II i 704
She is my queen and thine, The mistress of the *b*. " II ii 42
You caught a lonely woodman of our *b*, " III 360
To break our *b* and scatter us to the winds. " III 453
For those of thine own *b* who would betray thee? " IV 832
I never found one traitor in my *b*. " IV 836
Bandit Before these *b's* brake into your presence. *Becket* V ii 556
I thank you, noble sir, the very blossom Of *b's*. *Foresters* III 248
they that suffer by him call the blossom Of *b's*. " IV 373
Bandy *B* their own rude jests with them, *The Cup* I ii 360
Bang Anvil on hammer *b*— *Harold* IV iii 161
Banish'd *b* us to Woodstock, and the fields. *Queen Mary* III v 3
From lack of Tostig—thou hast *b* him. *Harold* III i 168
That brother whom I love beyond the rest, My *b* Tostig. " III i 296
For when your people *b* Tostig hence, " IV i 97
Robin Hood Earl of Huntingdon is outlawed and *b*. *Foresters* I iii 68
Art thou that *b* lord of Huntingdon, " IV 139
Banishment In quiet—home your *b* countryman. *Queen Mary* III ii 31
Thus, after twenty years of *b*, " III ii 46
After my twenty years of *b*, " V ii 69
Our sister hates us for his *b*; *Harold* III i 78
sanction your decree Of Tostig's *b*, " IV i 104
So thou be chasten'd by thy *b*, " IV ii 50
on a Tuesday pass'd From England into bitter *b*; *Becket* V ii 289
Bank parch'd *b's* rolling incense, as of old, *Queen Mary* I v 91
My *b* Of wild-flowers. At thy feet! *Becket* II i 125
Past the *b* Of foxglove, then to left by that one yew. *Foresters* IV 973
Bank'd-up like A *b-u* fire that flashes out again *The Cup* I ii 166
Banner *b*, Blaze like a night of fatal stars *Harold* IV i 250
The king of England stands between his *b's*. " V i 487
He stands between the *b's* with the dead " V i 656
And join'd my *b* in the Holy Land, *Foresters* IV 1000
Banns When shall your parish-parson bawl our *b* *Prom. of May* I 686

Banquet (*See also* **Marriage-banquet**) murmurs of their *b* clank The shackles *Harold* II ii 408
My lord! the Duke awaits thee at the *b*. " II ii 806
If there be those At *b* in this hall, " IV iii 93
Break the *b* up . . . Ye four! " IV iii 231
who never saw nor dreamed of such a *b*. *Becket* I iv 84
I must leave you to your *b*. " I iv 151
we came on to the *b*, from whence there puffed " III iii 114
prays your ladyship and your ladyship's father to be present at his *b* to-night. *Foresters* I i 300
let us be merry to-night at the *b*. " I i 344
Banquet-board To chain the free guest to the *b-b*; *Harold* II ii 193
Baptized being but *b* in fire, the babe Might be in fire *Queen Mary* V iv 23
that thus *b* in blood Grew ever high and higher, *Harold* III i 146
and on a Tuesday *B*; *Becket* V ii 286
Bar (s) when he springs And maims himself against the *b's*, *Queen Mary* V v 67
feud between our houses is the *b* I cannot cross; *The Falcon* 254
Bar (verb) leagued together To *b* me from my Philip. *Queen Mary* I iv 140
jail you from free life, *b* you from death. " III v 172
B the bird From following the fled summer— *Becket* I i 257
wouldst *b* me fro' the milk o' my cow, *Foresters* II i 355
Barabbas Still choose *B* rather than the Christ, *Becket* II ii 390
Barbarism Deigns to look in upon our *b's*. *The Cup* II 337
Barbarossa (Surname of Frederick I., Emperor) This *B* butts him from his chair, *Becket, Pro.* 217
Crow over *B*—at last tongue-free. " II ii 50
Barbarous *See* **Semi-barbarous**
Barber The common *b* clipt your hair, *Queen Mary* IV ii 131
Bare (adj.) Nay, for *b* shame of inconsistency, " I ii 39
and flying to our side Left his all *b*, " II iii 5
Take thou mine answer in *b* commonplace— *Becket, Pro.* 282
wi' *b* backs, but the backs 'ud ha' countenanced one another, " III i 146
how *b* and spare I be on the rib: *Foresters* I i 50
A thousand winters Will strip you *b* as death, " IV 1056
Bare (verb) he hath risen again—he *b's* his face— *Harold* V i 557
He bows, he *b's* his head, he is coming hither. *Becket* III iii 34
Barefoot all boots were ever made Since man went *b*. *Queen Mary* III v 198
crawl over knife-edge flint *B*, *Becket* II i 273
Barely Where there is *b* room to shift thy side, *Harold* II ii 441
Barer throat of mine, *B* than I should wish a man to see it,— *Queen Mary* V ii 462
Bargain mine hour! I *b* for mine hour. *Becket* II i 212
Bargainer Lady, I find you a shrewd *b*. *The Falcon* 757
But you will find me a shrewd *b* still. " 774
Barge all lost, all yielded! A *b*, a *b*! *Queen Mary* II iv 72
We had your royal *b*, and that same chair, " III ii 6
Bark (of a tree) What breadth, height, strength—torrents of eddying *b*! *Foresters* III 95
Bark (verb) And when to *b* and how. *The Cup* I ii 114
Bark (vessel) winds than that which crack'd Thy *b* at Ponthieu,— *Harold* II ii 200
Bark'd I have but *b* my hands. " II i 5
B out at me such monstrous charges, *Becket* IV ii 342
Barlow (Bishop) Poinet, *B*, Bale, Scory, Coverdale; *Queen Mary* I ii 6
Barn broken down our *b's*, Wasted our diocese, *Becket* V ii 430
To the bleak church doors, like kites upon a *b*. *Harold* IV iii 38
Be thou a-gawin' to the long *b*? *Prom. of May* I 2
and 'e telled all on us to be i' the long *b* by one o'clock, " I 8
Why coöm awaäy, then, to the long *b*. " I 36
the farming men 'ull hev their dinner i' the long *b*, " I 167
They ha' broached a barrel of äale i' the long *b*, " I 427
look for 'im, Eva, and bring 'im to the *b*. " I 438
I've hed the long *b* cleared out of all the machines, " I 451
and make them happy in the long *b*, " I 792
Baron But that my *b's* might believe thy word, *Harold* II ii 725
widow And orphan child, whom one of thy wild *b's*— *Becket, Pro.* 189
How should a *b* love a beggar on horseback, " *Pro.* 443
Laics and *b's*, thro' The random gifts of careless kings, " I i 157
And many a *b* holds along with me— " I ii 52
Where I shall meet the *B's* and my King. " I ii 84
Save the King's honour here before his *b's*. " I iii 188
B's and bishops of our realm of England, " I iii 336
When every *b* ground his blade in blood; " I iii 349

Baron (*continued*) Yea, heard the churl against the *b*— *Becket* I iii 365
Did not your *B's* draw their swords against me? „ I iii 501
The King and all his *b's*—— *Becket*. Judgment! *B's*! „ I iii 683
B's of England and of Normandy, „ I iii 741
Ay, my lord, and divers other earls and *b's*. „ I iv 59
these earls and *b's*, that clung to me, „ I iv 66
They shall henceforward be my earls and *b's*— „ I iv 87
if the *b's* and bishops hadn't been a-sitting on the Archbishop. „ I iv 127
Summon your *b's*; take their counsel: „ V i 74
for he did his best To break the *b's*, „ V i 235
To all the archbishops, bishops, prelates, *b's*, „ V ii 405
So that our *B's* bring his baseness under. *Foresters* I ii 117
horn, that scares The *B* at the torture of his churls, „ III 106
these proud priests, and these *B's*, Devils, „ III 126
Baronage confirm it now Before our gather'd Norman *b*, *Harold* II ii 695
A bulwark against Throne and *B*. *Becket* I i 17
Baron-brute These be those *b-b's* That havock'd all the land „ I i 240
Baronial Among my thralls in my *b* hall *Foresters* II i 61
Barony The Church should hold her *baronies* of me, *Becket Pro.* 24
In fee and *b* of the King, „ I iii 675
I hold Nothing in fee and *b* of the King. „ I iii 678
Barr'd Mine enemies *b* all access to the boy. „ V ii 451
Not if I *b* thee up in thy chamber, *Foresters* I i 314
Barrel They ha' broached a *b* of äale i' the long barn, *Prom. of May* 426
Barren 'The King hath wearied of his *b* bride.' *Queen Mary* III vi 140
Is God's best dew upon the *b* field. „ V i 102
Then for thy *b* jest Take thou mine answer in bare common-place— *Becket, Pro.* 281
And York lay *b* for a hundred years. „ I iii 54
like a *b* shore That grew salt weeds, *The Cup* II 231
Barricade Their horse are thronging to the *b's*; *Harold* V i 547
They thunder again upon the *b's*. „ V i 626
Barrin' and *b* the wet, Hodge 'ud ha' been a-harrowin' *Queen Mary* IV iii 491
b the wind, Dumble wur blow'd wi' the wind, „ IV iii 493
Barring (*See also* **Barrin'**) But by all Saints— *Leofwin*. *B* the Norman! *Harold* V i 225
Barton, Elizabeth *See* **Joan of Kent**
Base were all as *b* as—who shall I say—Fitzurse and his following— *Becket* III iii 307
His own true people cast him from their doors Like a *b* coin. *The Cup* I ii 353
Baseness and great *b* loathed as an exception: *Becket* III iii 304
Would bow to such a *b* as would make me „ IV ii 234
So that our Barons bring his *b* under. *Foresters* I ii 117
hands Of these same Moors thro' nature's *b*, „ II i 564
That *b* which for fear or monies, „ II i 706
Baser lower and *b* Than even I can well believe you. *Prom. of May* III 814
Bashful eyes So *b* that you look'd no higher? *Queen Mary* III i 65
Our *b* Legate, saw'st not how he flush'd? „ III iv 350
Was yet too *b* to return for it? *The Falcon* 540
Basket *See* **Lobster-basket**
Basle Zurich, Worms, Geneva, *B*— *Queen Mary* I ii 3
Bass This burst and *b* of loyal harmony, „ II ii 285
Bastard (adj.) then the *b* sprout, My sister, is far fairer than myself. *Queen Mary* I v 71
A *b* hate born of a former love. *Becket* II i 174
Bastard (s) It means a *b*. *Queen Mary* I i 13
Why, didn't the Parliament make her a *b*? „ I i 16
Then which is the *b*? „ I i 22
they be both *b's* by Act of Parliament and Council. „ I i 24
Parliament can make every true-born man of us a *b*. Old Nokes, can't it make thee a *b*? „ I i 28
and so they can't make me a *b*. „ I i 47
But if Parliament can make the Queen a *b*, „ I i 49
Juggler and *b*—*b*—he hates that most—William the tanner's *b*! *Harold* II ii 773
And given thy realm of England to the *b*. „ III ii 155
Then for the *b* Six feet and nothing more! „ IV iii 115
The tanner's *b*! „ IV iii 173
hath borne at times A *b* false as William. „ V i 176
Ay, my girl, no tricks in him—No *b* he! „ V i 403
We can't all of us be as pretty as thou art—little *b* *Becket* IV i 39
thereupon he call'd my children *b's*. „ IV ii 45
Bastard (s) (*continued*) Then is thy pretty boy a *b*? *Becket* IV ii 113
This in thy bosom, fool, And after in thy *b's*! „ IV ii 258
Bastardise And done your best to *b* our Queen, *Queen Mary* III iv 238
Bastard-making that was afore *b-m* began. „ I i 44
Bastardy What are you cackling of *b* under „ I i 59
Bat What's here? a dead *b* in the fairy ring— *Foresters* II ii 93
a *b* flew out at him In the clear noon, „ II ii 96
Crush'd my *b* whereon I flew! „ II ii 146
Batchelor And out upon all simple *b's*! „ IV 52
Bathe To *b* this sacred pavement with my blood. *Becket* V iii 131
Battel we should have better *b's* at home. *Foresters* I i 58
Batter Began to *b* at your English Church, *Queen Mary* III iv 186
Battering *B* the doors, and breaking thro' the walls? *Becket* V ii 626
Battle (*See also* **Mid-battle**) or wave And wind at their old *b*: *Queen Mary* I v 357
Hark, there is *b* at the palace gates, „ II iv 47
I myself Will down into the *b* and there bide „ II iv 85
and hurl'd our *b's* Into the heart of Spain; „ III i 108
many English in your ranks To help your *b*. „ V i 112
I had heard of him in *b* over seas, „ V v 33
For thou hast done the *b* in my cause; *Harold* II ii 555
To do the *b* for me here in England, „ IV ii 70
than his league With Norway, and this *b*. „ IV iii 89
and had my constant 'No' For all but instant *b*. „ V i 7
After the *b*—after the *b*. Go. „ V i 362
Whose life was all one *b*, incarnate war, „ V i 397
Waste not thy might before the *b*! „ V i 416
I will bear thy blessing into the *b* „ V i 435
until I find Which way the *b* balance. „ V i 461
O God of *b's*, make their wall of shields „ V i 478
Look out upon the *b*—is he safe? (repeat) „ V i 484, 654
O God of *b's*, make his battle-axe keen „ V i 562
O God of *b's*, they are three to one, „ V i 575
Look out upon the *b*! „ V i 624
build a church to God Here on the hill of *b*; „ V ii 138
Since I knew *b*, And that was from my boyhood, „ V ii 174
Lest there be *b* between Heaven and Earth, *Becket* I iii 226
The glory and grief of *b* won or lost *The Cup* I ii 161
a rumour then That you were kill'd in *b*. *The Falcon* 382
having his right hand Lamed in the *b*, „ 445
The story of your *b* and your wound. „ 594
in this same *b* We had been beaten— „ 602
I tear away The leaves were darken'd by the *b*— „ 913
if he had not gone to fight the king's *b's*, *Foresters* I i 57
I saved his life once in *b*. „ I i 273
Battle-axe they With their good *b's* will do you right *Queen Mary* II iv 66
And strike among them with thy *b-a*— *Harold* I ii 89
b-a Was out of place; it should have been the bow.— „ I ii 105
With nothing but my *b-a* and him To spatter his brains! „ II ii 779
were man's to have held The *b-a* by thee! „ IV iii 13
and our *b-a's* broken The Raven's wing, „ IV iii 64
we must use our *b-a* to-day. „ V i 205
My *b-a* against your voices. „ V i 265
And Loathing wield a Saxon *b-a*— „ V i 414
Cowl, helm; and crozier, *b-a*. „ V i 444
make his *b-a* keen As thine own sharp-dividing justice, „ V i 563
Battled I would have *b* for it to the death. *Foresters* II i 664
Battle-field and seen the red of the *b-f*, *The Falcon* 549
Battle-hymns ghostly horn Blowing continually, and faint *b-h*, *Harold* III i 373
Battlement flung them streaming over the *b's* „ II ii 391
Bawl When shall your parish-parson *b* our banns *Prom. of May* I 685
Bay (arm of the sea) *b's* And havens filling with a blissful sea. *The Cup* II 235
And over this Robin Hood's *b*! *Foresters* II ii 177
Bay (verb) Tho' all the world should *b* like winter wolves. *Queen Mary* II ii 361
how those Roman wolfdogs howl and *b* him! „ IV iii 355
Bayeux I saw him coming with his brother Odo The *B* bishop, *Harold* II ii 348
from Guy To mine own hearth at *B*, „ II ii 43
Beach drave and crack'd His boat on Ponthieu *b*; „ II ii 36
They stood on Dover *b* to murder me, *Becket* V ii 436
A child's sand-castle on the *b* *The Cup* I ii 254
And the great breaker beats upon the *b*! *Foresters* I ii 324

Bead Counts his old *b's*, and hath forgotten thee. *Harold* II ii 447
they are but blue *b's*—my Piero, *The Falcon* 48
Beak His buzzard *b* and deep-incavern'd eyes *Queen Mary* I iv 266
Beam (*See also* **Side-beam**) so the *b's* of both may shine upon us, „ III iv 20
My grayhounds fleeting like a *b* of light, *Harold* I ii 129
That *b* of dawn upon the opening flower, *Foresters* IV 3
Beaming his fine-cut face bowing and *b* with all that courtesy *Becket* III iii 141
Her bright face *b* starlike down upon me *Prom. of May* II 248
Bear (s) Like the rough *b* beneath the tree, *Harold* I i 327
No, my *b*, thou hast not. *Becket, Pro.* 497
O drunken ribaldry! Out, beast! out, *b*! „ I i 231
Dares the *b* slouch into the lion's den? „ IV ii 282
Bear (verb) (*See also* **Abeär**) You needs must *b* it hardly. *Queen Mary* I iv 36
B witness, Renard, that I live and die „ II iv 41
The tree that only *b's* dead fruit is gone. „ III i 19
That *b's* not its own apples. „ III i 23
How should he *b* a bridegroom out of Spain? „ III iii 25
How should he *b* the headship of the Pope? „ III iii 29
I think the Queen may never *b* a child; „ III v 231
Lose the sweet hope that I may *b* a prince. „ III vi 201
I could mould myself To *b* your going better; „ III vi 236
yet what hatred Christian men *B* to each other, „ IV iii 184
that I *b* it Without more ruffling. „ V iii 3
And Tostig is not stout enough to *b* it. *Harold* I i 402
And thy love? *Aldwyth.* As much as thou canst *b*. „ I i 484
I can *b* all, And not be giddy. „ I i 485
Let all men *b* witness of our bond! „ II ii 698
That mortal men should *b* their earthly heats „ V i 283
I will *b* thy blessing into the battle „ V i 434
B me true witness—only for this once— „ V ii 115
My punishment is more than I can *b*. „ V ii 202
Together more than mortal man can *b*. *Becket* I i 24
Permit me, my good lord, to *b* it for thee, „ I iii 490
So now he *b's* the standard of the angels. „ I iii 496
I am the Dean of the province: let me *b* it. „ I iii 499
Wherefore dost thou presume to *b* thy cross, „ I iii 504
Let York *b* his to mate with Canterbury. „ I iii 512
But *b* with Walter Map, „ II ii 307
—The Cross!—who *b's* my Cross before me? „ V ii 610
Would that I could *b* thy cross indeed! „ V ii 614
It *b's* an evil savour among women. *The Cup* I iii 86
body of that dead traitor Sinnatus. *B* him away. „ I iii 181
the love I *b* to thee Glow thro' thy veins? „ II 426
The love I *b* to thee Glows thro' my veins „ II 428
I *b* with him no longer. *The Falcon* 884
And he will have to *b* with it as he may. „ 887
But if it be so we must *b* with John. *Foresters* I ii 102
Risk not the love I *b* thee for a girl. „ IV 742
It is the King Who *b's* all down. „ IV 784
Beard (s) tell me, did you ever Sigh for a *b*? *Queen Mary* I v 609
Dare-devils, that would eat fire and spit it out At Philip's *b*: „ III i 158
but he hath a yellow *b*. „ III i 216
A fine *b*, Bonner, a very full fine *b*. „ III iv 338
His long white *b*, which he had never shaven „ IV iii 592
Your Philip hath gold hair and golden *b*; „ V iii 57
The rosy face, and long down-silvering *b*, *Harold* III i 47
The rosy face and long down-silvering *b*— „ IV i 262
The tan of southern summers and the *b*? *Prom. of May* II 618
thy father will not grace our feast With his white *b* to-day. *Foresters* IV 81
Beard (verb) A bold heart yours to *b* that raging mob! *Queen Mary* I iii 96
Bearer The King may rend the *b* limb from limb. *Becket* I i 378
He all but pluck'd the *b's* eyes away. „ I iii 11
Bearing (adj. and part.) I, *b* this great ensign, make it clear „ I iii 544
wherewithal he cleft the tree From off the *b* trunk, *Harold* III i 138
—the stream is *b* us all down, *Foresters* I i 239
Bearing (bringing forth) To go twelve months in *b* of a child? *Queen Mary* III vi 91
Her fierce desire of *b* him a child, „ IV iii 429
Since she lost hope of *b* us a child? „ V i 229
Bearing (mien) Philip shows Some of the *b* of your blue blood— *Queen Mary* I v 434
His *b* is so courtly-delicate; „ III iv 397
Beast (*See also* **Beast-body, Wild-beast**) pounce like a wild *b* out of his cage to worry Cranmer. „ I i 88
world-hating *b*, A haggard Anabaptist. „ II ii 91
but I thought he was a *b*. „ III i 221
Bonner cannot out-Bonner his own self—*B*!— „ III vi 28
Because these islanders are brutal *b's*? „ III vi 153
and in itself a *b*. „ IV i 33
creep down into some dark hole Like a hurt *b*, „ IV i 142
Stand watching a sick *b* before he dies? „ IV iii 7
the *b* might roar his claim To being in God's image, „ IV iii 367
I conclude the King a *b*; Verily a lion if you will—the world A most obedient *b* and fool—myself Half *b* and fool as appertaining to it; „ IV iii 412
Thou's thy way wi' man and *b*, Tib. „ IV iii 499
like a timorous *b* of prey Out of the bush *Harold* I ii 212
The wolf! the *b*! „ II ii 301
O drunken ribaldry! Out, *b*! out, bear! *Becket* I i 231
Poor *b*, poor *b*! set him down. „ I iv 105
Like the wild *b*—if you can call it love. „ IV ii 121
The world God made—even the *b*—the bird! „ V ii 243
Ay, still a lover of the *b* and bird? „ V ii 246
How should *you* guess What manner of *b* it is? *The Cup* I ii 371
leaves him A *b* of prey in the dark, *Prom. of May* I 505
Beast-body this *b-b* That God has plunged my soul in— *Becket* II i 149
Beastly These *b* swine make such a grunting here, *Queen Mary* I iii 12
Beat I can play well, and I shall *b* you there. „ I iii 129
Make all tongues praise and all hearts *b* for you. „ I v 118
which every now and then *B's* me half dead: „ I v 525
whether It *b's* hard at this marriage. „ III i 39
for to-day My heart *b's* twenty, „ III ii 59
Your father had a will that *b* men down; Your father had a brain that *b* men down— „ IV i 108
God will *b* down the fury of the flame, „ IV iii 98
I wonder at tha', it *b's* me! „ IV iii 499
You *b* upon the rock. „ V i 210
How Harold used to *b* him! *Harold* I i 432
Leofwin would often fight me, and I *b* him. „ I i 434
only pulsed for Griffyth, *b* For his pursuer. „ I ii 151
or the sword that *b's* them down. „ II ii 136
There somewhere *b's* an English pulse in thee! „ II ii 266
let him flap The wings that *b* down Wales! „ IV i 247
I should *b* Thy kingship as my bishop *Becket, Pro.* 90
Yet my fingers itch to *b* him into nothing. „ I iv 229
best heart that ever *B* for one woman. *The Falcon* 668
No other heart Of such magnificence in courtesy *B's*—out of heaven. „ 724
would you *b* a man for his brother's fault? *Prom. of May* III 154
broke the heart That only *b* for you; „ III 763
the great breaker *b's* upon the beach! *Foresters* I ii 323
That thou mightst *b* him down at quarterstaff! „ IV 517
Will chill the hearts that *b* for Robin Hood! „ IV 1064
Beaten You are *b*. *Becket, Pro.* 45
I loathe being *b*; had I fixt my fancy Upon the game I should have *b* thee, „ *Pro.* 49
beat Thy kingship as my bishop hath *b* it. „ *Pro.* 91
who hath *b* down my foes. „ *Pro.* 253
Becket hath *b* thee again— „ *Pro.* 314
in this same battle We had been *b*— *The Falcon* 603
Our Robin *b*, pleading for his life! *Foresters* II i 674
Lusty bracken *b* flat, „ II ii 154
Sit here by me, where the most *b* track Runs thro' the forest, „ III 89
Or else be bound and *b*. (repeat) „ III 370, 390
Beating the rain *b* in my face all the way, *Prom. of May* III 367
Beautiful I left her lying still and *b*, More *b* *Queen Mary* V V 261
O *b*! May I have it as mine, *Becket* II i 297
My Anjou bower was scarce as *b*. „ III i 52
The Lady Camma, Wise I am sure as she is *b*, *The Cup* I ii 139
She b: sleek as a miller's mouse! Meal enough, meat enough, well fed; but *b*—bah! *The Falcon* 164
you look as *b* this morning as the very Madonna „ 198
A lady that was *b* as day Sat by me „ 349

Beautiful (*continued*) And she was the most *b* of all; Then but fifteen, and still as *b*. *The Falcon* 353
Come, give me your hand and kiss me This *b* May-morning. *Prom. of May* I 565
The most *b* May we have had for many years! „ I 566
And here Is the most *b* morning of this May. „ I 569
You, the most *b* blossom of the May, „ I 574
all the world is *b* If we were happy, „ I 577
How *b* His manners are, and how unlike the farmer's! „ II 530
no maids like English maids So *b* as they be. *Foresters* II i 20
And love is joyful, innocent, *b*, „ II ii 64
Beauty a head So full of grace and *b*! *Queen Mary* I v 64
B passes like a breath and love is lost in loathing: „ V ii 365
She hath won upon our people thro' her *b*, *Harold* IV i 23
cowling and clouding up That fatal star, thy *B*, *Becket* I i 312
Your answer, *b*! „ IV ii 53
She calls you *b*, but I don't like her looks. „ IV ii 61
my sleeping-draught May bloat thy *b* out of shape, „ IV ii 170
By thy leave, *b*. Ay, the same! „ IV ii 203
marvell'd at Our unfamiliar *beauties* of the west; „ IV ii 303
You have *b*,—O great *b*,—and Antonius, *The Cup* I ii 297
for her *b*, stateliness, and power, Was chosen Priestess „ II 16
To-day, my *b*, thou must dash us down *The Falcon* 152
With other *beauties* on a mountain meadow, „ 351
I whisper'd, Let me crown you Queen of *B*, „ 361
crown you Again with the same crown my Queen of *B*. „ 916
like the Moslem *beauties* waiting To clasp their lovers *Prom. of May* I 246
—her main law Whereby she grows in *b*— „ I 283
prize The pearl of *B*, even if I found it „ III 601
and if her *beauties* answer their report. *Forsters* I ii 27
Becamest when thou *b* Man in the Flesh, *Queen Mary* IV iii 140
Beck (brook) leästwaäys they niver cooms 'ere but fur the trout i' our *b*, *Prom. of May* I 213
Becket (Chancellor of England, 1154-1162 Archbishop of Canterbury, 1162-1170) (*See also* **Dare - Becket, Godstow - Becket, Thomas, Thomas Becket, Thomas of Canterbury**)
As proud as *B*. *Queen Mary* III i 332
You would not have him murder'd as *B* was? „ III i 334
the arm within Is *B's*, who hath beaten down my foes. *Becket, Pro.* 253
The chart is not mine, but *B's*: take it, Thomas. „ *Pro.* 311
B! O—ay—and these chessmen on the floor— „ *Pro.* 312
B hath beaten thee again— „ *Pro.* 314
Ha, *B*! thou rememberest our talk! „ *Pro.* 404
this *B*, her father's friend, like enough staved us „ *Pro.* 517
B, I am the oldest of the Templars; „ I iii 247
Behold thy father kneeling to thee, *B*. „ I iii 253
And *B* had my bosom on all this; „ I iii 433
Our Lord *B's* our great sitting-hen cock, „ I iv 125
B, beware of the knife! „ I iv 133
B shall be king, and the Holy Father shall be king, „ I iv 269
With *B*? I have but one hour with thee— „ II i 23
Why thou, my bird, thou pipest *B*, *B*— „ II i 32
Must be the nightmare breaking on my peace with '*B*.' „ II i 38
We have but one bond, her hate of *B*. „ II i 166
Nay! nay! what art thou muttering? *I hate B*? „ II i 168
'Tis true what *B* told me, that the mother „ II ii 9
and *B*—*B* should crown him were he crown'd at all: „ II ii 16
Brother of France, what shall be done with *B*? „ II ii 65
Master *B*, you That owe to me your power over me— „ II ii 151
sure to wake As great a wrath in *B*—— *Rosamund*. Always *B*! „ III i 88
Henry—*B* tells him this—To take my life „ IV ii 394
But *B* ever moves against a king. „ V i 25
world allows I fall no inch Behind this *B*, „ V i 40
B hath trodden on us like worms, „ V i 60
scarcely dare to bless the good we eat Because of *B*. „ V i 72
I know—could swear—as long as *B* breathes, „ V i 76
The brideless *B* is thy king and mine: „ V i 107
B is like enough to make all his. „ V i 134
Methought I had recover'd of the *B*, „ V i 137
Why do you thrust this *B* on me again? „ V i 155
Lest *B* thrust you even from your throne. „ V i 159
Your *B* knew the secret of your bower. „ V i 177
Becket (*continued*) Our *B*, who will not absolve the Bishops. *Becket* V i 222
I think ye four have cause to love this *B*. „ V i 225
You are no King's men—you—you—you are *B's* men. „ V i 259
What say ye there of *B*? „ V ii 56
B, it *is* too late. „ V ii 526
Where is the traitor *B*? „ V iii 103
Becket (Gilbert) *See* **Gilbert Becket**
Beckon the right hand still *B's* me hence. *Queen Mary* V v 138
Becomes nay, it well *b* him. „ I v 436
Bed (*See also* **Down, Flower-bed**) As tho' the nightmare never left her *b*. „ I v 606
Spain in our ships, in our forts, in our houses, in our *b's*? „ II i 180
No Spain in our *b's*— „ II i 182
and the *b's* I know. I hate Spain. „ II i 184
on a soft *b*, in a closed room, with light, „ V iv 36
gather'd one From out a *b* of thick forget-me-nots, „ V v 94
It lies beside thee, king, upon thy *b*. *Harold* III i 196
get thee to thine own *b*. *Becket* I i 8
he hath made his *b* between the altars, „ I iv 264
My *b*, where ev'n the slave is private— „ V i 251
I measured his foot wi' the mark i' the *b*, but it wouldn't fit *Prom. of May* I 414
seen us that wild morning when we found Her *b* unslept in, „ II 471
Strike up a song, my friends, and then to *b*. *Foresters* I iii 31
Bedingfield (Sir Henry) *See* **Henry, Henry Bedingfield**
Bedroom We found a letter in your *b* torn into bits. *Prom. of May* III 323
Bee As the first flower no *b* has ever tried. *Queen Mary* I iv 63
Are you the *b* to try me? „ I iv 64
b's, If any creeping life invade their hive „ III iii 53
your wise *b's* had stung him first to death. „ III iii 64
The people are as thick as *b's* below, They hum like *b's*,— *Harold* I i 31
B mustn't buzz, Whoop—but he knows. (repeat) *Becket* III i 98, 239
So rare the household honeymaking *b*, „ V ii 218
As happy as the *b's* there at their honey *Prom. of May* I 606
Swarm to thy voice like *b's* to the brass pan. *Foresters* I iii 108
B's rather, flying to the flower for honey. „ IV 12
The *b* buzz'd up in the heat. „ IV 14
And the *b* buzz'd down from the heat. „ IV 20
And the *b* buzz'd up in the cold „ IV 21
And the *b* buzz'd off in the cold. „ IV 27
And yet in tune with Nature and the *b's*. „ IV 33
Thy *b* should buzz about the Court of John. „ IV 44
Beech Pine, *b* and plane, oak, walnut, *The Cup* I i 1
Beef and there is a piece of *b* like a house-side, *Prom. of May* I 793
Beelzebub By Mahound I could dine with *B*! *Foresters* IV 971
Beer Owd Steer gi'es nubbut cowd tea to 'is men, and owd Dobson gi'es *b*. *Prom. of May* II 225
But I'd like owd Steer's cowd tea better nor Dobson's *b*. „ II 227
That *b* be as good fur 'erses as men. „ II 315
The *b's* gotten oop into my 'eäd. „ II 320
worked at all the worse upon the cold tea than you would have done upon the *b*? „ III 57
but we'd ha' worked better upo' the *b*. „ III 60
Beeswax By bonds of *b*, like your creeping thing; *Queen Mary* III iii 62
Beetle *B's* jewel armour crack'd, *Foresters* II ii 160
Befall No ill *b* on him or thee when I Am gone. *Becket* II i 260
get you hence in haste Lest worse *b* you. „ IV ii 28
Befit It well *b's* thy new archbishoprick „ I i 225
Befitting But ill *b* such a festal day *Foresters* I iii 37
Beg You are to *b* the people to pray for you; *Queen Mary* IV iii 76
—there to *b*, starve, die— *Becket* II i 74
I will *b* my bread along the world „ IV ii 103
he *b's* you to forget it As scarce his act:— *The Cup* II 51
Dare *b* him to receive his diamonds back.— *The Falcon* 262
Beget sire *b's* Not half his likeness in the son. *Queen Mary* II i 54
b's An admiration and an indignation, „ III iv 169
Beggar (s) How should a baron love a *b* on horseback, *Becket, Pro.* 444
half-rag, half-sore,—*b's*, poor rogues „ I iv 82
If the King hold his purpose, I am myself a *b*. „ I iv 90
—like some loud *b* at thy gate— „ II i 180
mastiff, That all but kill'd the *b*, *Prom. of May* I 559

Beggar (s) (*continued*) but if he do not I and thou are but *b's*. — *Foresters* I i 200
Canst thou endure to be a *b* whose whole life „ I i 205
Here come three *b's*. „ III 187
we be *b's*, we come to ask o' you. We ha' nothing. „ III 189
B's, you are sturdy rogues that should be set to work. „ III 196
How much for a *b*? „ III 216
will you not hear one of these *b's*' catches? „ III 405
by St. Mary these *b's* and these friars shall join you. „ III 417
Beggar (verb) Down to the devil with this bond that *b's* me! „ I i 340
Beggared She has *b* him. — *The Falcon* 157
He hath become so *b*, that his falcon „ 229
We will be *b* then and be true to the King. — *Foresters* I i 201
Beggarly This *b* life, This poor, flat, hedged-in field— *Prom. of May* II 343
Beggar-woman rags Of some pale *b-w* seeking alms — *The Falcon* 852
Begin old Gospeller, sour as midwinter, *B* with him. — *Queen Mary* I iii 41
But he *b's* to flutter. — *Harold* II ii 3
He *b's* at top with me: — *Becket* I iii 617
so, Allen, I may as well *b* with you. — *Prom. of May* III 30
Beginning In your old place? and vespers are *b*. — *Becket* V ii 597
Begone Do, and *b*! „ I i 233
Begun hath *b* to re-edify the true temple— *Queen Mary* I iii 58
Your people have *b* to learn your worth. „ I v 109
she hath *b* Her life-long prayer for thee. — *Harold* III i 323
Behalf Stood out against the King in your *b*, — *Queen Mary* IV i 126
Behaviour I promise you that if you forget yourself in your *b* to this gentleman, — *Prom. of May* I 162
Behold *B* him— *People*. Oh, unhappy sight! — *Queen Mary* IV iii 1
B him, brethren: he hath cause to weep!— „ IV iii 13
Beholden Thanks, Sir Thomas, we be *b* to you, „ II iii 121
Thou art much *b* to this foot of mine, „ III ii 49
But I am much *b* to your King. „ V iii 99
I am much *b* to the King, your master. „ V iii 111
We should be all the more *b* to him. — *Foresters* IV 292
Being From the dim dawn of *B*— *Prom. of May* I 281
Belated I and my friend, this monk, were here *b*, — *Foresters* I ii 193
Belief wholesome medicine here Puts that *b* asleep. — *Becket* IV ii 52
Believe He *did* *b* the bond incestuous. — *Queen Mary* I ii 77
I do *b* she'd yield. „ I iv 22
I *b* you mine; And so you may continue mine, „ I iv 136
I myself *B* it will be better for your welfare. „ I iv 254
I do *b* he holp Northumberland Against me. „ I v 278
I do *b*, I have dusted some already, „ I v 423
some *b* that he will go beyond him. „ I v 440
his fault So thoroughly to *b* in his own self. „ II ii 386
Yet thoroughly to *b* in one's own self, „ II ii 387
I *b* Sir Thomas Stafford? „ III i 31
And I, by God, *b* myself a man. „ III i 168
I *b* so, cousin. „ III ii 72
who not *B's* the Pope, nor any of them *b*— „ III iii 238
I do *b* in God, Father of all; „ IV iii 228
men Have hardly known what to *b*, or whether They should *b* in anything; „ IV iii 405
I hear unhappy rumours—nay, I say not, I *b*. „ V i 36
And I *b*, Spite of your melancholy Sir Nicholas, „ V ii 326
I do *b* I lamed his Majesty's For a day or two, „ V ii 471
He had his gracious moment, Altho' you'll not *b* me. „ V v 39
Lord Leofwin, dost thou *b*, that these Three rods — *Harold* I i 43
an honest world Will not *b* them. „ I i 348
And makes *b* that he *b's* my word— „ II ii 668
For they will not *b* thee—as I *b*. „ II ii 696
But that my barons might *b* thy word, „ II ii 725
I do *b* My old crook'd spine would bud „ III i 23
b that lying And ruling men are fatal twins „ III i 126
prayers go up as fast as my tears fall, I well *b*, „ III i 167
Let not our great king *B* us sullen— „ IV i 7
b thee The veriest Galahad of old Arthur's hall. — *Becket, Pro.* 128
I do *b* thee, then. I am the man. „ I i 135
Do you *b* that you are married to him? (repeat) „ IV ii 46,54
I *should* *b* it. *Eleanor*. You must not *b* it, „ IV ii 48
Do you *b* it? I pray you then to take my sleeping-draught; „ IV ii 68
Do you hear me? *B* or no, I care not. „ IV ii 353
I *b* him The bravest in our roll of Primates „ V ii 57
But she would not *b* me, and she wish'd „ V ii 116

Believe (*continued*) You will *b* Now that he never struck the stag— *The Cup* I ii 429
he prays you to *b* him. *Camma*. I pray him to *b*—that I *b* him. „ II 55
I scarce *b* it! *Elisabetta*. Shame upon her then! — *The Falcon* 517
I doänt *b* he's iver a 'eart under his waistcoat. — *Prom. of May* I 130
they that love do not *b* that death Will part them. „ I 662
My father's death, Let her *b* it mine; „ II 454
I do *b* I lost my heart to him the very first time we met, „ III 283
I do *b* I could forgive—well, almost anything— „ III 630
lower and baser Than even I can well *b* you. „ III 815
but I *b* there lives No man who truly loves — *Foresters* II i 74
I *b* She came with me into the forest here. „ II i 484
I *b* thou fell'st into the hands Of these same Moors „ II i 562
b There came some evil fairy at my birth And cursed me, „ II ii 107
I *b* thee, thou art a good fellow, though a friar. „ III 341
O my good liege, we did *b* you dead. „ IV 846
Believed His friends would praise him, I *b* 'em, — *Queen Mary* I v 623
Stigand *b* he knew not what he spake. — *Harold* III ii 61
—some *b* she was his paramour. „ V ii 102
b that Rome Made war upon the peoples not the Gods. — *The Cup* I ii 58
I *b* thee to be too solemn and formal to be a ruffler. — *Foresters* I i 168
I *b* this Abbot of the party of King Richard, „ I i 266
Believer as I am a true *b* in true love myself, „ I i 162
Believing *B* I should ever aid the Church— *Becket, Pro.* 417
b That I should go against the Church with him, „ I i 91
b that our brother Had wrong'd you; „ II ii 237
Theer ye goäs ageän, Miss niver *b* owt I says to ye— *Prom. of May* I 107
Bell (*See also* **Minster-bell**) The *b's* are ringing at Maidstone. — *Queen Mary* II i 18
The *b's* must ring; Te Deums must be sung; „ III ii 211
Toll of a *b*, Stroke of a clock, „ III v 142
clash'd their *b's*, Shot off their lying cannon, „ III vi 96
A passing *b* toll'd in a dying ear— „ V ii 41
And hear my peregrine and her *b's* in heaven; And other *b's* on earth, — *Harold* I ii 131
Our scouts have heard the tinkle of their *b's*. „ V i 221
like the gravedigger's child I have heard of, trying to ring the *b*, — *Becket* III iii 74
—the *b's* rang out even to deafening, „ V ii 363
Bell-silencing black, *b-s*, anti-marrying, burial-hindering interdict „ III iii 54
Belly since the Sheriff left me naught but an empty *b*, — *Foresters* II i 279
Belonging His kin, all his *b's*, overseas; — *Becket* II i 71
Of and *b* to the King of England, „ IV ii 23
I am mine own self Of and *b* to the King. „ IV ii 30
King Hath divers ofs and ons, ofs and *b's*, „ IV ii 32
It is the cup *b* our own Temple. — *The Cup* II 345
B's, paramours, whom it pleases him — *Becket* IV ii 35
Beloved *See* **Well-beloved**
Bench There is a *b*. Come, wilt thou sit? — *Becket* II i 124
Help me to move this *b* for him into the sun. — *Prom. of May* I 81
Doubtless, like judges of another *b*, — *Foresters* III 153
Bend seeks To *b* the laws to his own will, — *Queen Mary* II ii 184
Bended and we'll pray for you all on our *b* knees. „ II iii 109
and we'll pray for you on our *b* knees till our lives' end. „ II iii 122
Benedict O blessed saint, O glorious *B*,— *Becket* V iii 2
Benedicta Ave Maria, gratia plena, *B* tu in mulieribus. — *Queen Mary* III ii 1
Benedictus Sit *b* fructus ventris tui!' „ III ii 83
Bent (*See also* **Bow-bent**) *b* to his saddle-bow, As if to win the man „ II ii 310
Benzoin Nard, Cinnamon, amomum, *b*. — *The Cup* II 184
Bequeath Edward might *b* the crown Of England, — *Queen Mary* I ii 26
Berkeley (Sir Maurice) *See* **Maurice Berkeley**
Berkhamstead Due from his castles of *B* and Eye — *Becket* I iii 628
Beset O Renard, I am much *b*, — *Queen Mary* I v 385
I should be hard *b* with thy fourscore. — *Foresters* IV 179
Beside lost and found together, None *b* them. — *Harold* III ii 8
'I am *b* thee.' „ III ii 14
Besotted One half *b* in religious rites. — *The Cup* I i 74

Best (adj.) Dumble's the *b* milcher in Islip. (repeat) *Queen Mary* IV iii 478, 497
The blood and sweat of heretics at the stake Is God's *b* dew upon the barren field. „ V i 102
You had *b* go home. What are you? „ V iv 43
Noble Gurth! *B* son of Godwin! *Harold* V i 135
Serve my *b* friend and make him my worst foe; *Becket* I iii 567
Only my *b* bower-maiden died of late, „ III i 67
Stain'd with the blood of the *b* heart that ever Beat for one woman. *The Falcon* 667
yet that might be The *b* way out of it, *Prom. of May* I 476
Then the man, the woman, Following their *b* affinities, „ I 523
this is a true woodman's bow of the *b* yew-wood to slay the deer. *Foresters* II i 393
Heaven looks down on me, And smiles at my *b* meanings, „ IV 727
Best (s) I do my most and *b*. *Queen Mary* II ii 24
it is a day to test your health Ev'n at the *b*: „ IV ii 118
You have done your *b*. *Pole.* Have done my *b*, „ V ii 115
But thou canst hear the *b* and wisest of us. *Harold* I i 300
I have done my *b*. I am not learn'd. *Becket* III i 24
it's all for the *b*, come when they will— *The Falcon* 201
I and Filippo here had done our *b*, „ 607
Bested *See* **Ill-bested**
Bestial all of us abhor The venomous, *b*, devilish revolt Of Thomas Wyatt. *Queen Mary* II ii 287
Did ye not cast with *b* violence Our holy Norman bishops down *Harold* I i 49
O *b*! O how unlike our goodly Sinnatus. *The Cup* II 172
Bethink And now, I do *b* me, thou wast by *Foresters* II i 540
Betray Before he would *b* it. *Becket* II i 268
And if you should *b* me to your husband— *The Cup* I ii 242
Will *you b* him by this order? „ I ii 244
And I will not *b* you. „ I ii 316
for fear or monies, might *B* me to the wild Prince. *Foresters* II i 708
For those of thine own band who would *b* thee? „ IV 833
Betray'd Cast off, *b*, defamed, *Queen Mary* I v 26
They have *b* the treason of their hearts: „ II ii 156
Thou hast *b* us on these rocks of thine! *Harold* II i 23
O Wulfnoth, Wulfnoth, brother, thou hast *b* me! „ II ii 802
Herbert, Herbert, have I *b* the Church? *Becket* I iii 284
But thou the shepherd hast *b* the sheep, „ I iii 524
hast *b* Thy father to the losing of his land. *Foresters* II i 569
Betroth In order to *b* her to your Dauphin. *Queen Mary* I v 293
Betrothal (adj.) it was her own *B* ring. *Foresters* I ii 295
Thou hast robb'd my girl of her *b* ring. „ II i 586
Betrothal (s) Of her *b* to the Emperor Charles, *Queen Mary* V v 233
Betroth'd Was she not *b* in her babyhood to the Great Emperor „ I i 118
and presently That I and Harold are *b*— *Harold* I ii 223
Betrothing Hapless doom of woman happy in *b*! *Queen Mary* V ii 364
Better and I myself Believe it will be *b* for your welfare. „ I iv 254
He must deserve his surname *b*. „ III ii 197
A *b* and a worse—the worse is here To persecute, „ III iv 114
I could mould myself To bear your going *b*; „ III vi 236
The *b* for him. He burns in Purgatory, not in Hell. „ IV i 55
There is no hope of *b* left for him, „ IV iii 79
Our Daisy's cheeses be *b*. „ IV iii 484
I thought you knew me *b*. „ V ii 186
I am not well, but it will *b* me, „ V ii 554
I wish her Highness *b*. „ V ii 615
Nay! *B* die than lie! *Harold* I i 158
Because I love the Norman *b*—no, „ I i 171
and left me time And peace for prayer to gain a *b* one. „ I i 220
B die than lie! „ II ii 281
Is it not *b* still to speak the truth? „ II ii 373
B methinks have slain the man at once! „ II ii 498
Who hath a *b* claim then to the crown „ II ii 596
b die Than credit this, for death is death, „ III ii 77
Hadst thou been braver, I had *b* braved All— „ III ii 178
the king like his own man, No *b*; „ IV iii 59
I could pity this poor world myself that it is no *b* ordered. *Becket, Pro.* 366
Friend, am I so much *b* than thyself „ I i 3
You have had the *b* of us In secular matters. „ II ii 80
B have been A fisherman at Bosham, my good Herbert, „ II ii 290
Better (*continued*) I cannot answer it Till *b* times, *Becket* III i 3
That which you ask me Till *b* times. „ III i 7
And I thought if it were the King's brother he had a *b* bride than the King, „ III i 173
b Than raised to take a life which Henry bad me „ IV ii 267
Why then *B* perhaps to speak with them apart. „ V ii 310
to submit at once Is *b* than a wholly-hopeless war, *The Cup* I ii 141
I meant thee to have follow'd—*b* thus. „ II 498
that's positive again—that's *b*! *The Falcon* 95
and *b* late than never—but come when they will— „ 199
'*B* a man without riches, than riches without a man.' „ 751
Hath served me *b* than her living— „ 901
Betting *b*, Mr. Dobson. *Prom. of May* I 69
B step out of his road, then, for he's walking to us, „ I 218
I'm sorry for it, for, tho' he never comes to church, I thought *b* of him. „ I 261
Niver man 'ed *b* friends, and I will saäy niver master 'ed *b* men: „ I 322
thaw I says it mysen, niver men 'ed a *b* master— „ I 327
So much the *b*, so much the *b*. „ I 435
B and higher than Nature, we might be As happy as the bees „ I 604
Noä; I knaws a deäl *b* now. „ II 26
You had *b* attend to your hayfield. „ II 122
knaw'd *b* nor to cast her sister's misfortin inter 'er teeth „ II 127
But I'd like owd Steer's cowd tea *b* nor Dobson's beer. „ II 227
b death With our first wail than life— „ II 289
Why, you look *b*. *Eva.* And I feel so much *b*, „ III 220
it might have been *b* for her, for him, and for you. „ III 251
B for me! That's good. How *b* for me? „ III 253
B not. Has he offered you marriage, this gentleman? „ III 289
but you seem somewhat *b* to-day. „ III 322
if you cram me crop-full I be little *b* than Famine in the picture, *Foresters* I i 47
we should have *b* battels at home. „ I i 58
Till *b* times. *Robin.* But if the *b* times should never come? „ I ii 286
Why then I will be *b* than the time. „ I ii 291
Would it be *b* for thee in the wood? „ I iii 140
Am I worse or *b*? I am outlaw'd. „ II i 49
and all the *b* For this free forest-life, „ II i 59
B than heart-sick, friar. „ IV 674
Bevell'd That all was planed and *b* smooth again, *Becket* V i 138
Beware *B*, Lord Legate, of a heavier crime Than heresy is itself; *b*, I say, Lest men accuse you of indifference *Queen Mary* III iv 221
Ay, ay, *b* of France. „ IV iii 434
Bewitch'd And thought thou wert *b*. *Foresters* II i 684
Bible I'll have their *b's* burnt. The *b* is the priest's. *Queen Mary* III i 284
Look to your *B*, Paget! we are fallen. „ III iv 80
And may not read your *B*, „ III iv 83
never merry world In England, since the *B* came among us. „ V v 241
Till all men have their *B*, rich and poor. „ V v 248
Bid the Lord Chancellor. *Mary.* *B* him come in. „ I v 97
B him come in. Good morning, Sir de Noailles. „ I v 241
Gregory *b* St. Austin here Found two archbishopricks, *Becket* I iii 48
And *b* him re-create me, Gilbert Foliot. „ I iii 126
My friends, the Archbishop *b's* you good night. „ I iv 261
he sends me to *b* you this night pray for him „ I iv 265
you *b* me go, and I'll have my ball anyhow. „ IV ii 63
B their old bond farewell with smiles, not tears; *Prom. of May* I 524
Do not till I *b* you. *Eva.* No, Philip, no. „ I 732
Will *b* you welcome, and will listen to you. „ II 522
I Titania *b* you flit, *Foresters* II ii 126
Bidd'n and *b* him Charge one against a thousand, *Queen Mary* IV iii 308
Was not my lord of Leicester *b* to our supper? *Becket* I iv 56
Bide and there *b* The upshot of my quarrel, *Queen Mary* II iv 85
and a wur so owld a couldn't *b* vor his dinner, but a had to *b* howsomiver, „ IV iii 505
But now I cannot *b*. „ V i 93
Ay, so your Grace would *b* a moment yet. „ V ii 547
And *b* the doom of God. *Harold* V i 61
tho' I can drink wine I cannot *b* water, *Becket* I iv 220

Bide (*continued*) in Nottingham they say There *b's* a foul witch — *Foresters* II i 203
But how then if I will not *b* to be search'd? — „ IV 168
Bided so they *b* on and on till vour o' the clock, — *Queen Mary* IV iii 509
Biding So sick am I with *b* for this child. — „ III vi 89
Big his *b* baldness, That irritable forelock which he rubs, — „ I iv 264
Is that it? That's a *b* lot of money. — „ II iii 62
Map, tho' you make your butt too *b*, you overshoot it. — *Becket* III iii 122
be i' the long barn by one o'clock, fur he'll gie us a *b* dinner, — *Prom. of May* I 9
and a plum-pudding as *b* as the round haystack. — „ I 794
and I wur ballus scaäred by a *b* word; — „ III 33
and wheere the *b* eshtree cuts athurt it, — „ III 94
I am mortally afear'd o' thee, thou *b* man, — *Foresters* IV 317
Bigger *B* in our small world than thou art. — *Becket* V i 128
Not yet, but here comes one of *b* mould. — *Foresters* IV 115
Bigot To be nor mad, nor *b*—have a mind— — *Queen Mary* V v 216
Bill (beak) gaping *b's* in the home-nest Piping for bread— — *Becket* II ii 300
No bird? *Filippo*. Half a tit and a hern's *b*. — *The Falcon* 131
Bill (document) In several *b's* and declarations, — *Queen Mary* IV i 48
ay; if Bonner have not forged the *b's*. — „ IV i 51
Billing nor priestly king to cross Their *b's* ere they nest. — *Harold* III ii 95
Bind To *b* me first by oaths I could not keep, — *Queen Mary* I v 557
And *b* him in from harming of their combs. — „ III iii 57
Which *b's* us friendship-fast for ever! — *Harold* II ii 162
The shackles that will *b* me to the wall. — „ II ii 410
And I would *b* thee more, — „ II ii 559
b a score All in one faggot, snap it over knee, — „ IV i 57
bound To that necessity which *b's* us down; — „ V i 108
Tho' she that *b's* the bond, herself should see — *Becket* I ii 76
I will *b* up his wounds with my napkin. — „ I iv 106
striving still to break or *b* The spiritual giant — „ IV ii 443
I ask'd A ribbon from her hair to *b* it with; — *The Falcon* 359
if you *will b* love to one for ever, — *Prom. of May* I 644
Thou hast risk'd thy life for mine: *b* these two men. — *Foresters* IV 894
Bird (*See also* **Sea-bird**) These *b's* of passage come before their time: — *Queen Mary* I iii 75
To kiss and cuff among the *b's* and flowers— — „ III v 258
I never breathed it to a *b* in the eaves, — „ V ii 454
I whistle to the *b* has broken cage, And all in vain. — „ V v 19
let fly the *b* within the hand, To catch the *b* again — *Harold* II ii 65
Poor *b* of passage! so I was; but, father, — *Becket* I i 253
Bar the *b* From following the fled summer— — „ I i 258
To guard this *b* of passage to her cage; — „ I i 329
b that moults sings the same song again, — „ I iii 447
I wrong the *b*; she leaves only the nest she built, — „ I iv 45
thou, my *b*, thou pipest Becket, Becket— — „ II i 32
B mustn't tell, Whoop—he can see. (repeat) — *Becket* III i 106, 254
I have lived, poor *b*, from cage to cage, — *Becket* III i 222
The world God made—even the beast—the *b*! — „ V ii 244
Ay, still a lover of the beast and *b*? — „ V ii 246
See, see, my white *b* stepping toward the snare. — *The Cup* I iii 35
Hear that, my *b*! Art thou not jealous of her? — *The Falcon* 5
Buss me, my *b*! — „ 29
No *b*? *Filippo*. Half a tit and a hern's bill. — „ 130
A noble *b*, each perfect of the breed. — „ 320
What do you rate her at? *Count*. My *b*? — „ 323
Nothing but my brave *b*, my noble falcon, — „ 873
dying of my noble *b* Hath served me better than her living— — „ 900
all in all to one another from the time when we first peeped into the *b's* nest, — *Prom. of May* III 274
barred thee up in thy chamber, like a *b* in a cage. — *Foresters* I i 315
tree-Cupids half-way up in heaven, The *b's*— — „ III 37
And all the *b's* that sing When all the leaves are green; — „ III 440
And live with us and the *b's* in the green wood. — „ IV 325
Let the *b's* sing, and do you dance to their song. — „ IV 556
All the *b's* in merry Sherwood sing and sing him home again. — „ IV 1109
Bird-babble *B-b* for my falcon! Let it pass. — *The Falcon* 38
Bird-echoing Their long *b-e* minster-aisles,— — *Becket* III i 44
Birdlime I think there may be *b* here for me; — *Queen Mary* III v 227
Bird-Robin If my man-Robin were but a *b-R*, — *Foresters* III 39
Birth every rebel *b* That passes out of embryo. — *Queen Mary* III vi 51
We have the man that rail'd against thy *b*. — *Harold* II ii 486

Birth (*continued*) The child, a thread within the house of *b*, — *The Cup* II 260
There came some evil fairy at my *b* — *Foresters* II ii 108
Birthdaäy (birthday) Why, o' coorse, fur it be the owd man's *b*. — *Prom. of May* I 6
Owd Steer wur afeärd she wouldn't be back i' time to keep his *b*, — „ I 18
I be coomed to keep his *b* an' all. — „ I 76
—to celebrate my *b* i' this fashion. — „ I 321
Birthday (adj.) A *b* welcome! happy days and many! — *Harold* V i 431
Birthday (s) (*See also* **Birthdaäy**) My father on a *b* gave it me, — *Queen Mary* I v 527
Plots and feuds! This is my ninetieth *b*. (repeat) — *Harold* IV i 121, 127
Thy death!—to-day! Is it not thy *b*? — „ V i 429
hath kinglike fought and fallen, His *b*, too. — „ V ii 126
I came back to keep his *b*. — *Prom. of May* I 74
but is not to-day his *b*? — *Foresters* I i 219
that thou keepest a record of his *b's*? — „ I i 222
To-day he hath accomplished his thirtieth *b*, — „ I i 298
last time When I shall hold my *b* in this hall: — „ I ii 89
Cloud not thy *b* with one fear for me. — „ I ii 125
I am only merry for an hour or two Upon a *b*: — „ I iii 12
It is my *b*. — „ II i 35
greater nearness to the *b* Of the after-life, — „ II i 44
Birthplace Bosham, my good Herbert, Thy *b*— — *Becket* II ii 293
Bishop (ecclesiastic) our *B's* from their sees Or fled, they say, or flying— — *Queen Mary* I ii 3
—and now that your good *b*, Bonner, — „ I iii 35
Why, my lord *B*? (repeat) — „ I iv 223, 227
Some six or seven *B's*, diamonds, pearls, — „ III i 52
I am but of the laity, my Lord *B*, — „ III iv 81
Thou Christian *B*, thou Lord Chancellor Of England! — „ III iv 300
Tut, Master *B*, Our bashful Legate, — „ III iv 349
B Thirlby, And my Lord Paget and Lord William Howard, — „ IV i 4
These are but natural graces, my good *B*, — „ IV i 177
'I wunt dine,' says my Lord *B*, — „ IV iii 507
'Now,' says the *B*, says he, 'we'll gwo to dinner;' — „ IV iii 513
Our holy Norman *b's* down from all Their thrones in England? — *Harold* I i 50
I saw him coming with his brother Odo The Bayeux *b*, — „ II ii 348
thou art but deacon, not yet *b*, — *Becket*, *Pro.* 83
beat Thy kingship as my *b* hath beaten it. — „ *Pro.* 91
Hell take thy *b* then, and my kingship too! — „ *Pro.* 93
Barons and *b's* of our realm of England, — „ I iii 336
B's—York, London, Chichester, Westminster— — „ I iii 385
where our *b's* And our great lords will sit in judgment — „ I iii 548
What say the *b's*? — „ I iii 589
—and these craven *b's*! — „ I iv 92
if the barons and *b's* hadn't been a-sitting on the Archbishop. — „ I iv 127
Knights, *b's*, earls, this London spawn— — „ II ii 143
Our Becket, who will not absolve the *B's*. — „ V i 223
he shall absolve The *b's*—they but did my will— — „ V i 254
to absolve the *b's* Whom you have excommunicated. — „ V ii 376
To all the archbishops, *b's*, prelates, barons, — „ V ii 404
Save that you will absolve the *b's*. — „ V iii 120
they plunder—yea, ev'n *b's*, Yea, ev'n archbishops— — *Foresters* IV 910
Bishop (chess) My liege, I move my *b*. — *Becket*, *Pro.* 28
you see my *b* Hath brought your king to a standstill. — „ *Pro.* 43
Why, there then—down go *b* and king together. — „ *Pro.* 47
Bishoprick fill'd All offices, all *b's* with English— — *Harold* II ii 535
Saving thro' Norman *b's*— — „ II ii 538
'When a *b* falls vacant, the King, — *Becket* I iii 99
And let another take his *b*! — „ II ii 260
Bit (s) smash all our *b's* o' things worse than Philip o' Spain. — *Queen Mary* II iii 104
Beänt Miss Eva gone off a *b* of 'er good looks o' laäte? *Man*. Noä, not a *b*. — *Prom. of May* I 33
fur owd Dobson 'll gi'e us a *b* o' supper. — „ II 217
Taäke one o' the young 'uns fust, Miss, fur I be a *b* deaf, — „ III 32
We found a letter in your bedroom torn into *b's*. — „ III 324
b by *b*—for she promised secrecy—I told her all. — „ III 379
Bit (verb) if a mad dog *b* your hand, my Lord, — *Queen Mary* III iv 204

Bit (verb) (*continued*) And *b* his shield, and dash'd it on the ground, *Harold* v i 405
And I was *b* by a mad dog o' Friday, *Becket* I iv 217
Bite (s) The mad *b* Must have the cautery— *Queen Mary* III iv 275
Bite (verb) to turn and *b* the hand Would help thee *Harold* I i 381
and I want to *b*, I want to *b*, *Becket* I iv 221
Well, well, well! I *b* my tongue. *The Falcon* 624
Bithynia Have you alliances? *B*, Pontus, Paphlagonia? *The Cup* I ii 100
Bitten Would you not chop the *b* finger off, *Queen Mary* III iv 206
the Norman adder Hath *b* us; we are poison'd: *Harold* III i 39
Bitter (adj.) Before these *b* statutes be requicken'd. *Queen Mary* III iv 197
And, whether it bring you *b* news or sweet, „ III v 201
Hath, like a brief and *b* winter's day, „ IV iii 430
And thrust his right into the *b* flame; „ IV iii 610
bound me too With *b* obligation to the Count— *Harold* II ii 221
To plunge into this *b* world again— *Becket* V ii 81
on a Tuesday pass'd From England into *b* banishment; „ V ii 289
Bitter (s) The *b* in the sweet. *Queen Mary* I v 235
Bitterer And mine a *b* illegitimate hate, *Becket* II i 173
Bitterness She hath wean'd me from it with such *b*. *Harold* IV ii 28
Bitters and I put the *b* on my breast to wean him, *The Falcon* 189
your ladyship has given him *b* enough in this world, „ 192
B before dinner, my lady, to give you a relish. *Foresters* III 434
Blaäme (blame) but summun else—*b't* if I beänt! *Prom. of May* II 140
Black I see but the *b* night, and hear the wolf. *Queen Mary* I v 413
It roll'd as *b* as death; „ II iii 20
four guns gaped at me, *B*, silent mouths: „ II iii 32
or you'll make the White Tower a *b* 'un for us this blessed day. „ II iii 100
These *b* dog-Dons Garb themselves bravely. „ III i 189
I thought this Philip had been one of those *b* devils of Spain, „ III i 215
Those damp, *b*, dead Nights in the Tower; „ III v 138
so 'z the tongue on un cum a-lolluping out o' 'is mouth as *b* as a rat. „ IV iii 519
A drinker of *b*, strong, volcanic wines, „ V ii 93
lash'd to death, or lie Famishing in *b* cells, „ V ii 196
For twenty miles, where the *b* crow flies five, „ V v 84
Ay, but thou liest as loud as the *b* herring-pond behind thee. *Harold* II i 26
He fain had calcined all Northumbria To one *b* ash, „ III i 57
Night, as *b* as a raven's feather; „ III ii 6
And thou, my carrier-pigeon of *b* news, „ IV iii 233
I have an inherited loathing of these *b* sheep of the Papacy. *Becket, Pro.* 461
Is *b* and white at once, and comes to nought. „ I iii 32
The *b* sheep baaed to the miller's ewe-lamb, „ I iv 162
B sheep, quoth she, too *b* a sin for me. And what said the *b* sheep, my masters? We can make a *b* sin white. „ I iv 165
That he made the *b* sheep white. „ I iv 176
Out from among us; thou art our *b* sheep. „ I iv 181
Then I saw Thy high *b* steed among the flaming furze, „ II i 55
How ghostly sounds that horn in the *b* wood! „ III ii 17
Do you see that great *b* cloud that hath come over the sun „ III iii 46
It is this *b*, bell-silencing, anti-marrying, „ III iii 54
Who else, with this *b* thunderbolt of Rome Above him, *The Cup* I ii 265
poor worm, crawl down thine own *b* hole To the lowest Hell. „ II 495
heat and fire Of life will bring them out, and *b* enough, *Prom. of May* II 287
I'd like to leather 'im *b* and blue, „ II 595
and the *b* river Flow'd thro' my dreams— „ II 649
It mun be true, fur it wur i' print as *b* as owt. „ II 731
the river, *b*, slimy, swirling under me in the lamplight, „ III 369
these lilies to lighten Sir Richard's *b* room, *Foresters* I i 3
Sour milk and *b* bread. „ II i 272
They might be harder upon thee, if met in a *b* lane at midnight: „ III 224
The *b* fiend grip her! „ III 380
B news, *b* news from Nottingham! „ III 446
Black-blooded You are too *b-b*. *Queen Mary* III i 126
Black-blooded (*continued*) Yea, you yourself, altho' you are *b-b*: *Queen Mary* III i 166
You call me too *b-b*— „ III i 347
He grovels to the Church when he's *b-b*, *Becket* IV ii 437
Blacken I will hide my face, *B* and gipsyfy it; „ IV ii 100
Whose lava-torrents blast and *b* a province *The Cup* II 302
Blackest Traced in the *b* text of Hell— *Queen Mary* III i 426
Black-faced Philip and the *b-f* swarms of Spain, „ II i 98
Blackness I see the *b* of my dungeon loom *Harold* II ii 405
thirty feet below the smiling day—In *b*— „ II ii 431
But what a blotch of *b* underneath! *The Cup* I ii 398
Blacksmith and *B*, thaw he niver shoes a herse to my likings; *Prom. of May* I 447
Blade take heed! The *b* is keen as death. *Queen Mary* V v 175
When every baron ground his *b* in blood; *Becket* I iii 349
Blaise (Bishop of Sebaste) To the chapel of St. *B* beneath the roof! „ V iii 82
Blame (*See also* **Blaäme**) His foes would *b* him, and I scorned 'em, *Queen Mary* I v 624
it is the Pope Will be to *b*—not thou. *Becket* I iii 222
I was to *b*—the love you said you bore me— *The Falcon* 857
Blamed Praised, where you should have *b* him, *Queen Mary* I v 600
Blameless condemn The *b* exile?— *Becket* II ii 396
Blanch And *b* the crowd with horror. *The Cup* II 154
Blanch'd A doll-face *b* and bloodless, *Becket* IV ii 175
Bland you were *b* And affable to men of all estates, *Queen Mary* III vi 80
Blank it seems that we shall fly These bald, *b* fields, „ III v 252
A poor philosopher who call'd the mind Of children a *b* page, *Prom. of May* II 282
Blanketed who dream'd us *b* In ever-closing fog, *Queen Mary* III ii 20
Blared *B* from the heights of all the thrones of her kings, *Becket* V ii 489
Blasphemous Monstrous! *b*! She ought to burn. *Queen Mary* I v 57
Blasphemy terms Of Satan, liars, *b*, Antichrist, „ I ii 95
Blast (s) (*See also* **Thunder-blast**) The *b* that came So suddenly hath fallen as suddenly— *Harold* II i 12
Put thou the comet and this *b* together— „ II i 15
Which hunted *him* when that un-Saxon *b*, „ II ii 31
showers of blood are blown Before a never ending *b*, „ III i 395
The sign in heaven—the sudden *b* at sea— „ V i 378
Blast (verb) Would'st thou not burn and *b* them *Queen Mary* III iv 282
if yon weird sign Not *b* us in our dreams.— *Harold* I i 122
b your infants, dash The torch of war among your standing corn, „ II ii 747
will *b* and blind you like a curse. *Becket* I iv 39
To *b* my realms with excommunication And interdict. „ II i 52
Go, lest I *b* thee with anathema, „ IV ii 287
—and *b* the king and me, *The Cup* II 152
Whose lava-torrents *b* and blacken a province „ II 302
That *b* our natural passions into pains! *Prom. af May* III 724
when they look at a maid they *b* her. *Foresters* I i 257
Blatant But lack of happiness in a *b* wife. „ I iii 132
Blaze (s) hiss Against the *b* they cannot quench— *Harold* III i 396
Against the shifting *b* of Harold's axe! „ V i 587
Blaze (verb) banner, *B* like a night of fatal stars „ IV i 251
But *b* not out before the Frenchmen here. *Becket* III iii 221
Blazed *B* false upon her heart. *Queen Mary* III i 70
Blazing A sacred cup saved from a *b* shrine *The Cup* I ii 54
Bleak and those *b* manners thaw, *Queen Mary* III ii 160
fierce forekings had clench'd their pirate hides To the *b* church doors, *Harold* IV iii 37
Bled He had been hurt, And *b* beneath his armour. *Foresters* II ii 5
Bless and I return As Peter, but to *b* thee: *Queen Mary* III ii 56
And may God *b* you, Thirlby! „ IV ii 197
God *b* him! „ IV iii 256
owld lord fell to 's meat wi' a will, God *b* un! „ IV iii 515
Let all thy people *b* thee! *Harold* I i 184
And *b* the Queen of England. „ I ii 207
And even as I should *b* thee saving mine, „ II ii 651
God *b* thee, wedded daughter. *Queen.* *B* thou too That brother whom I love beyond the rest, „ III i 293
All the sweet Saints *b* him! „ III i 298
I ask no more. Heaven *b* thee! hence! *Becket* I i 321
Wilt thou not say, 'God *b* you,' ere we go? *Becket.* God *b* you all! „ I iv 33
and see it mounting to Heaven, my God *b* you, „ I iv 38

Bless (*continued*) beggars, poor rogues (Heaven *b* 'em) *Becket* I iv 83
God *b* the great Archbishop ! „ II ii 451
all on us ha' had to go, *b* the Saints, wi' bare backs, „ III i 146
We scarcely dare to *b* the food we eat „ V i 70
To *b* thine enemies—— *Becket.* Ay, mine, not Heaven's. „ V ii 24
God *b* him for it. „ V ii 146
hear us, O Mother, hear us, and *b* us ! *The Cup* II 2
Why, *b* the saints ! *The Falcon* 171
and *b* your sweet face, you look as beautiful „ 197
I ha' heärd 'im a-gawin' on 'ud make your 'air— God *b* it !—stan' on end. *Prom. of May* I 135
The Lord *b* boath on 'em ! „ I 341
—the Lord *b* 'er—'er oän sen ; „ II 40
God *b* our well-beloved Robin, Earl of Huntingdon. *Foresters* I i 247
sweet saints *b* your worship for your alms to the old woman ! „ II i 363
those poor serfs whom we have served will *b* us, „ IV 1075

Blessed-Blest The *blessed* Mary's a-passing ! *Queen Mary* I i 36
Holy Virgin, Plead with thy *blessed* Son ; „ I v 85
or you'll make the White Tower a black 'un for us this *blessed* day. „ II iii 101
Oh how the *blessed* angels who rejoice „ III iii 180
And God hath *blest* or cursed me with a nose— „ III v 178
And Thy most *blessed* Son's, who died for man. „ IV iii 154
Have I not heard them mock the *blessed* Host In songs so lewd, „ IV iii 365
'O *blessed* relics !' 'O Holy Peter !' *Harold* I ii 169
Nay then, we be liker the *blessed* Apostles ; „ II i 33
Yet the curse is on him For swearing falsely by those *blessed* bones ; „ III i 246
have sent him back A holy gonfanon, and a *blessed* hair Of Peter, „ III ii 148
Thou swarest falsely by our *blessed* bones, „ V i 259
Are those the *blessed* angels quiring, father ? „ V i 472
Yea, by the *Blessed* Virgin ! *Becket, Pro.* 520
Blessed is he that cometh in the name of the Lord ! „ I iii 758
That is the parable of our *blessed* Lord. *Becket.* And why should not the parable of our *blessed* Lord be acted again ? „ I iv 75
Blessed be the Lord Archbishop, who hath withstood two Kings „ II ii 274
Thanks to the *blessed* Magdalen, whose day it is. „ III iii 171
Man's help ! but we, we have the *Blessed* Virgin For worship, „ V ii 219
O *blessed* saint, O glorious Benedict,— „ V iii 1
Row to the *blessed* Isles ! the *blessed* Isles !— *The Cup* II 525
in hope that the saints would send us this *blessed* morning ; *The Falcon* 186
they are made by the *blessed* saints—these marriages. „ 203
It served me for a *blessed* rosary. „ 632
more *blessed* were the rags Of some pale beggar-woman seeking alms For her sick son, „ 850
but I wur so ta'en up wi' leädin' the owd man about all the *blessed* murnin' *Prom. of May* III 3
For all the blessed souls in heaven Are both forgivers and forgiven.' „ III 10
O brook, that brawlest merrily by Thro' fields that once were *blest*, „ III 202
for the sake of the great *blessed* Mother in heaven, *Foresters* I i 96
I keep it For holy vows made to the *blessed* Saints Not pleasures, „ I ii 175
My mother, For whose sake, and the *blessed* Queen of Heaven, „ II i 38
Devils, that make this *blessed* England hell. „ III 127
That by the *blessed* Mother no man, „ III 239
Our Lady's *blessed* shrines throughout the land Be all the richer for us. „ IV 1079

Blessing (part.) pauper, who had died in his misery *b* God, *Prom. of May* III 378

Blessing (s) I will bear thy *b* into the battle *Harold* V i 434
Was not the people's *b* as we past Heart-comfort *Becket* I i 12
Nay, father, first thy *b*. „ I i 317
Our humblest thanks for your *b*. „ I iv 42
But that might bring a Roman *b* on us. *The Cup* II 372
This *b* is for Synorix and for me. „ II 376

Blessing (s) (*continued*) *B's* on your pretty voice, Miss Dora. *Prom. of May* I 63
and the old woman's *b* with them to the last fringe. *Foresters* II i 195
The silent *b* of one honest man Is heard in heaven— „ III 321
Thou shalt pronounce the *b* of the Church „ IV 927

Blest *See* **Blessed**

Blew Rose never *b* that equall'd such a bud. *Queen Mary* III i 373
Until the powder suddenly *b* him dead. „ IV iii 340
Of Provence *b* you to your English throne ; *Becket* V i 123

Blighted till that *b* vow Which God avenged to-day. *Harold* V ii 155

Blind (adj.) (*See also* **Stone-blind**) Are you *b* ? *Queen Mary* I iv 151
She, with her poor *b* hands feeling—'where is it ? „ III i 407
with offal thrown Into the *b* sea of forgetfulness. „ III iii 193
There is a movement there, A *b* one— *Harold* I i 355
now I see That I was *b*—suffer the phrase— *Becket* II ii 438
'What are we, says the *b* old man in Lear ? *Prom. of May* I 262
I would taäke the owd *b* man to my oän fireside. „ II 74
What was that ? my poor *b* father— „ II 566
Poor *b* Father's little guide, Milly, „ III 231
niver been surprised but once i' my life, and I went *b* upon it. „ III 440
That Love is *b*, but thou hast proven it true. *Foresters* II i 644

Blind (verb) It frights the traitor more to maim and *b*. *Harold* II ii 504
Say that he *b* thee and tear out thy tongue. *Becket* I iii 615
will blast and *b* you like a curse. „ I iv 40

Blinded into some more costly stone Than ever *b* eye. *Queen Mary* I v 371
No, no ; her innocent blood had *b* me. „ III i 346
They *b* my young kinsman, Alfred— *Harold* II ii 511
be sure they be, but he *b* 'em for all that, *Becket* III i 128
Not caught, maim'd, *b* him. *The Cup* I ii 271
and the hunters, if caught, are *b*, or worse than *b*. *Foresters* IV 226

Blindfold was a pity to *b* such eyes as mine, *Becket* III i 127

Blindness and my father's breaking down, and his *b*. *Prom. of May* II 70
My father stricken with his first paralysis, And then with *b*— „ II 482
And cheer his *b* with a traveller's tales ? „ II 515

Blissful bounteous bays And havens filling with a *b* sea. *The Cup* II 236

Bloat my sleeping-draught May *b* thy beauty out of shape, *Becket* IV ii 170
ambition, pride So *b* and redden his face— *The Cup* II 170

Block (s) The Tower ! the *b* ! *Queen Mary* I v 470
Like that poor heart, Northumberland, at the *b*. „ II ii 334
Who changed not colour when she saw the *b*, „ III i 400
To say 'I did not ?' and my rod's the *b*. „ III v 130
My heart is no such *b* as Bonner's is : „ IV ii 174
like the bloodless head Fall'n on the *b*, „ V ii 21

Block (verb) How can I come When you so *b* the entry ? *Becket* V iii 37

Block'd All passes *b*. *Harold* II ii 317

Blood of royal *b*, of splendid feature, *Queen Mary* I i 111
Why not ? I am king's *b*. „ I iii 105
I am the noblest *b* in Europe, Madam, „ I iv 84
I have sworn upon the body and *b* of Christ „ I v 215
Some of the bearing of your blue *b*— „ I v 434
Your houses fired—your gutters bubbling *b*— „ II ii 280
Scarlet, as if her feet were wash'd in *b*, „ III i 62
No, no ; her innocent *b* had blinded me. „ III i 346
Her dark dead *b* is in my heart with mine. „ III i 349
Her dark dead *b* that ever moves with mine „ III i 352
trusted God would save her thro' the *b* Of Jesus Christ „ III i 387
a little letting of the *b*. „ III ii 40
With His own *b*, and wash'd us from our sins, „ III iii 203
Nay, I know They hunt my *b*. „ III v 78
'Martyr's *b*—seed of the Church.' „ IV i 146
b and sweat of heretics at the stake Is God's best dew „ V i 100
And panting for my *b* as I go by. „ V ii 219
Some few of Gothic *b* have golden hair, „ V iii 60
sure she hates thee, Pants for thy *b*. *Harold* I ii 39
the *b* That should have only pulsed for Griffyth, „ I ii 149
She hath but *b* enough to live, not love.— „ I ii 161
shown And redden'd with his people's *b* „ I ii 243
'This Harold is not of the royal *b*, „ II i 354
Thou art of my *b*, and so methinks, my boy, „ II ii 449
helpless folk Are wash'd away, wailing, in their own *b*— „ II ii 472
Dabble your hearths with your own *b*. „ II ii 751
Where they eat dead men's flesh, and drink their *b*. „ II ii 808
he soak'd the trunk with human *b*, „ III i 143

Blood (*continued*) thus baptized in *b* Grew ever high and higher, — *Harold* III i 147
Senlac! Sanguelac, The Lake of *B*! — „ III i 386
showers of *b* are blown Before a never ending blast, — „ III i 393
A sea of *b*—we are drown'd in *b*— — „ III i 398
Mixing our *b's*, that thence a king may rise — „ IV i 142
Trampling thy mother's bosom into *b*? — „ IV ii 26
sight of Danish *b* Might serve an end not English— — „ IV iii 97
did the dead man call it—Sanguelac, The lake of *b*? — „ V i 185
Praise the Saints. It is over. No more *b*! — „ V ii 195
Ay! *b*, perchance, except thou see to her. — *Becket, Pro.* 175
Heart-comfort and a balsam to thy *b*? — „ I i 14
like Egypt's plague, had fill'd All things with *b*; — „ I iii 346
When every baron ground his blade in *b*; — „ I iii 350
household dough was kneaded up with *b*; — „ I iii 352
The millwheel turn'd in *b*; — „ I iii 353
God redden your pale *b*! But mine is human-red; — „ I iv 35
there be those about our King who would have thy *b*.' — „ I iv 55
Which it will quench in *b*! — „ IV ii 192
not life shot up in *b*, But death drawn in;— — „ IV ii 381
Save him, his *b* would darken Henry's name; — „ V iii 10
To bathe this sacred pavement with my *b*. — „ V iii 132
hand Red with the sacred *b* of Sinnatus? — *The Cup* II 84
Hot *b*, ambition, pride So bloat and redden — „ II 169
Wine Ran down the marble and lookt like *b*, like *b*. — „ II 205
frost That help'd to check the flowing of the *b*. — *The Falcon* 646
Stain'd with the *b* of the best heart that ever Beat — „ 666
servants Are all but flesh and *b* with those they serve. — „ 709
would not crush The fly that drew her *b*; — *Prom. of May* II 494
We Steers are of old *b*, tho' we be fallen. — „ III 604
thro' the *b* the wine leaps to the brain — *Foresters* I iii 22
Red with his own and enemy's *b*— — „ II i 32
soul of the woods hath stricken thro' my *b*, — „ II i 67
one of those mercenaries that suck the *b* of England. — „ II i 175
I wouldn't have thy *b* on my hearth. — „ II i 356
clothes itself In maiden flesh and *b*, — „ III 117
And thou wouldst run more wine than *b*. — „ III 338
Boldness is in the *b*, Truth in the bottle. — „ IV 240
Blooded *See* **Black-blooded, Blue-blooded, Hot-blooded, Norman-blooded, Red-blooded**
Bloodier Why, she's grown *b*! — *Queen Mary* III i 416
Bloodless And look'd as *b*. — „ II ii 84
What makes thy favour like the *b* head Fall'n on the block, — „ V ii 19
mortal men should bear their earthly heats Into yon *b* world, — *Harold* V i 285
A doll-face blanch'd and *b*, — *Becket* IV ii 175
Blood-red that these Three rods of *b-r* fire up yonder — *Harold* I i 44
This *b-r* line? *Henry*. Ay! blood, perchance, — *Becket, Pro.* 174
Bloody King's courts would use thee worse than thy dog —they are too *b*. — „ I iv 103
Bloom (s) To me, tho' all your *b* has died away, — *The Falcon* 468
Bloom (verb) You *b* again, dead mountain-meadow flowers.' — „ 470
Blossom (*See also* **Myrtle-blossom**) She to shut up my *b* in the dark! — *Harold* I ii 62
one fancy hath taken root, and borne *b* too, — *Becket, Pro.* 481
were more than I buzzing round the *b*— — „ *Pro.* 522
wither'd wreath is of more worth to me Than all the *b*, — *The Falcon* 339
never saw The land so rich in *b* as this year. — „ 342
tree that my lord himself planted here in the *b* of his boyhood— — „ 563
dead garland Will break once more into the living *b*. — „ 920
The *b* had open'd on every bough; — *Prom. of May* I 42
Look how full of rosy *b* it is. — „ I 84
Theer be redder *b's* nor them, Miss Dora. — „ I 85
they'll hev' a fine cider-crop to-year if the *b* 'owds. — „ I 316
You, the most beautiful *b* of the May. — „ I 574
happy as the bees there at their honey In these sweet *b's*. — „ I 607
But, look, how wasteful of the *b* you are! — „ I 612
upon me Thro' that rich cloud of *b*. — „ II 250
the *b* of his youth, Has faded, falling fruitless— — „ II 332
I that held the orange *b* Dark as the yew? — „ II 629
whose whole life hath been folded like a *b* in the sheath, — *Foresters* I i 206
I thank you, noble sir, the very *b* Of bandits. — „ III 247
they that suffer by him call the *b* Of bandits, — „ IV 372
Blossom'd sow'd therein The seed of Hate, it *b* Charity. — *Queen Mary* IV i 172
That ever *b* on this English isle. — *Foresters* I ii 124
Blossoming And a salt wind burnt the *b* trees; — *Prom. of May* I 57
Blot I'll have the paper back—*b* out my name. — *Becket* I iii 286
Blotch But what a *b* of blackness underneath! — *The Cup* I ii 398
Blotted (*See also* **Self-blotted**) And *b* by her tears. This cannot last. — *Queen Mary* V v 17
if a state submit At once, she may be *b* out — *The Cup* I ii 157
That desolate letter, *b* with her tears, — *Prom. of May* II 475
Blow (s) *b's*—Hark, there is battle at the palace gates, — *Queen Mary* II iv 46
To strike too soon is oft to miss the *b*. — „ III vi 72
The *b* that brains the horseman cleaves the horse, — *Harold* V i 593
Nor ever strike him *b* for *b*; — *Prom. of May* III 6
Blow (verb) *b* this Philip and all Your trouble to the dogstar — *Queen Mary* I iv 290
Daisies grow again, Kingcups *b* again, — „ III v 90
Which way does it *b*? — *Harold* II ii 151
b the trumpet, priest! — „ III i 188
we must fight. How *b's* the wind? — „ III ii 135
William's or his own As wind *b's*, or tide flows: — „ V i 163
As one that *b's* the coal to cool the fire. — *Becket* V ii 548
Where do they *b*, Mr. Dobson? — *Prom. of May* I 87
b upon it Three mots, this fashion—listen! — *Foresters* IV 424
Wait till he *b* the horn. — „ IV 787
I *b* the horn against this rascal rout! — „ IV 794
Blow'd but Dumble wur *b* wi' the wind, — *Queen Mary* IV iii 477
barrin' the wind, Dumble wur *b* wi' the wind, — „ IV iii 494
Blowest Thou *b* hot and cold. Where is she then? — *Foresters* II i 490
Why *b* thou not the horn? — „ IV 790
Blowing there are trumpets *b* now: what is it? — *Queen Mary* IV ii 13
Why are the trumpets *b*, Father Cole? — „ IV ii 23
B for England, ha? Not yet. — *Harold* II ii 152
The cold, white lily *b* in her cell: — „ III i 274
A ghostly horn *B* continually, — „ III i 373
Were the great trumpet *b* doomsday dawn, — „ V i 227
B the world against me, — *Becket* V ii 491
Not like the vintage *b* round your castle. — *The Falcon* 579
Blown fate hath *b* me hither, bound me too — *Harold* II ii 219
showers of blood are *b* Before a never ending blast, — „ III i 394
He hath *b* himself as red as fire with curses. — „ V i 86
B everyway with every gust and wreck On any rock; — *Prom. of May* III 536
Her face on flame, her red hair all *b* back, — *Queen Mary* II ii 70
for any rough sea *B* by the breath of kings. — *Becket* II ii 108
B like a true son of the woods. — *Foresters* IV 427
Blubber'd knelt And *b* like a lad, — *Queen Mary* III i 150
Blue Philip shows Some of the bearing of your *b* blood— — „ I v 434
This old thing here, they are but *b* beads—my Piero, — *The Falcon* 48
And your eyes be as *b* as— — *Prom. of May* I 91
Noä, Miss Dora; as *b* as— (repeat) — „ I 95, 99
The sky? or the sea on a *b* day? *Dobson*. Naäy then. I meän'd they be as *b* as violets. — „ I 101
An' the midders all mow'd, an' the sky sa *b*— (repeat) — *Prom. of May* II 177, 189, 201
I'd like to leather 'im black and *b*, — *Prom. of May* II 595
Bluebell *B*, harebell, speedwell, bluebottle, — „ I 97
when I was a-getting o' *b's* for your ladyship's nose to smell on— — *Becket* III i 162
Blue-blooded this fine *b-b* Courtenay seems Too princely for a pawn. — *Queen Mary* I iii 165
Bluebottle speedwell, *b*, succory, forget-me-not? — *Prom. of May* I 98
Bluff He comes, a rough, *b*, simple-looking fellow. — *The Cup* I i 173
Blunt Ever a rough, *b*, and uncourtly fellow— — *Queen Mary* V v 120
Blur would not *b* A moth's wing by the touching; — *Prom. of May* II 491
Blurt But if thou *b* thy curse among our folk, — *Harold* V i 89
B thy free mind to the air? — *Becket* I iii 239
Blush Make *b* the maiden-white of our tall cliffs, — *Harold* II ii 332
Blush'd That heaven wept and earth *b*. — *Queen Mary* III iv 193
every doorway *b*, Dash'd red with that unhallow'd passover; — *Becket* I iii 347
Bluster (verb) Come, you *b*, Antony! — *Queen Mary* II i 118
Bluster (s) One of much outdoor *b*. — „ II ii 381

Boar highback'd polecat, the wild *b*, The burrowing badger— *Foresters* i iii 120
Venison, and wild *b*, hare, geese, „ iv 191
Board (for a game) thou hast kicked down the *b*. I know thee of old. *Becket, Pro.* 315
Board (ship) thy leave to set my feet On *b*, *Harold* i i 229
Board (table) *See* **Banquet-board**
Boast (s) make your *b* that after all She means *Queen Mary* i iv 88
The pleasure of his eyes—*b* of his hand— *The Falcon* 221
Boast (verb) Let all that be. I *b* not: *Becket* v i 46
And *b* that he hath trampled it. *Foresters* i ii 112
Boat hardly, save by *b*, swimming, or wings. *Queen Mary* ii iii 12
There yet is time, take *b* and pass to Windsor. „ ii iv 27
b's that follow'd, were as glowing-gay As regal gardens; „ iii ii 12
in that last inhospitable plunge Our *b* hath burst her ribs; *Harold* ii i 3
drave and crack'd His *b* on Ponthieu beach; „ ii ii 36
Tho' all the world should go about in *b's*. *Foresters* iv 671
Boaz (a brass pillar, entrance to Solomon's Temple) lo! my two pillars, Jachin and *B*!— *Harold* iii i 192
Bodily You do not own The *b* presence in the Eucharist, *Queen Mary* i ii 44
Look on me as I were thy *b* son, *Becket* i iii 263
Body (*See also* **Beast-body**) quiet as a dead *b*. (repeat) *Queen Mary* i iv 182, 187
I have sworn upon the *b* and blood of Christ „ i v 214
and all rebellions lie Dead *bodies* without voice. „ ii i 80
Some fruit of mine own *b* after me, „ ii ii 223
Presenting the whole *b* of this realm Of England, „ iii iii 116
Lest your whole *b* should madden with the poison? „ iii iv 207
secular kingdom is but as the *b* Lacking a soul; „ iv i 32
soul descending out of heaven Into a *b* generate. „ iv i 36
before The flame had reach'd his *b*; „ iv iii 616
and soft raiment about your *b*; „ v iv 33
peril mine own soul By slaughter of the *b*? „ v v 169
Harold slain?—I cannot find his *b*. *Harold* v ii 20
They are stripping the dead *bodies* naked yonder, „ v ii 34
I am sure this *b* Is Alfwig, the king's uncle. „ v ii 67
And what *b* is this? *Edith.* Harold, thy better! „ v ii 87
Will not thy *b* rebel, man, if thou flatter it? *Becket, Pro.* 102
will be reflected in the spiritual *b* among the angels. „ *Pro.* 397
The soul the *b*, and the Church the Throne, „ i iii 717
and make Thy *b* loathsome even to thy child; „ iv ii 172
b of that dead traitor Sinnatus. Bear him away. *The Cup* i iii 179
they ha' ta'en the *b* up inter your chaumber, and they be all a-callin' for ye. *Prom. of May* ii 570
The *b*!—Heavens! I come! „ ii 572
given my whole *b* to the King had *he* asked for it, *Foresters* ii i 306
Who hunger for the *b*, not the soul— „ iv 700
Marriage is of the soul, not of the *b*. „ iv 720
Boil'd burn'd, *b*, buried alive, worried by dogs; *Queen Mary* ii i 210
Bold A *b* heart yours to beard that raging mob! „ i iii 96
You've a *b* heart; keep it so. „ i iv 269
Wherefore be *b*, and with your lawful Prince „ ii ii 240
he hath been so *b* to-day, „ ii ii 347
Magdalen, sin is *b* as well as dull. „ v ii 442
Stupid soldiers oft are *b*. „ v ii 446
I would not be *b*, Yet hoped ere this you might— *Becket* iii i 64
that I was *b* enough To take it down, *The Falcon* 427
Shall I be *b*? shall I touch her? *Foresters* i i 125
no men like Englishmen So tall and *b* as they be. „ ii i 8
Bolder why should I be *b* than the rest, *Queen Mary* iii i 438
At your trial Never stood up a *b* man than you; „ iv ii 122
Boldness I won by *b* once. „ i v 548
was it *b* Or weakness that won there? „ i v 559
No! *b*, which will give my followers *b*. „ ii iii 70
happy *b* of this hand hath won it Love's alms, *Becket* ii i 182
This friar is of much *b*, noble captain. *Foresters* iv 235
B out of the bottle! „ iv 238
B is in the blood, Truth in the bottle. „ iv 240
Bole Pillaring a leaf-sky on their monstrous *b's*, „ iii 101
Boleyn Who knows if *B's* daughter be my sister? *Queen Mary* v v 194
a *B*, too, Glancing across the Tudor— „ v v 227
Bolingbroke (Harry) *See* **Harry Bolingbroke**

Bolster'd Who so *b* up The gross King's headship *Queen Mary* iii iv 244
O *b* up with stubbornness and pride, *Becket* i iii 34
Bolt (s) One, whose *b's*, That jail you from free life, *Queen Mary* iii v 171
And *b's* of thunder moulded in high heaven *Harold* ii ii 32
heavy As thine own *b's* that fall on crimeful heads „ v i 565
That so the Papal *b* may pass by England, *Becket, Pro.* 226
to stay his hand Before he flash'd the *b*. „ ii i 275
Bolt (verb) And will you *b* them out, and have *them* slain? „ v iii 60
Bond (*See also* **Church-bond, Counter-bond**) He *did* believe the *b* incestuous. *Queen Mary* i ii 77
Bonner, who hath lain so long under *b's* for the faith— „ i iii 36
hatred of another to us Is no true *b* of friendship. „ i iv 46
Be the rough preface of some closer *b*? „ i iv 48
And thro' this common knot and *b* of love, „ ii ii 198
By *b's* of beeswax, like your creeping thing; „ iii iii 62
The *b* between the kingdoms be dissolved; „ iii iii 76
thou That layest so long in heretic *b's* with me; „ iii iv 280
And I: lead on; ye loose me from my *b's*. „ iv ii 241
to cancel and abolish all *b's* of human allegiance, „ v iv 50
For thou art truthful, and thy word thy *b*. *Harold* ii ii 646
He call'd my word my *b*! „ ii ii 666
Thy naked word thy *b*! „ ii ii 693
Let all men here bear witness of our *b*! „ ii ii 698
The worldly *b* between us is dissolved, *Becket* i i 347
Tho' she that binds the *b*, herself should see „ i ii 76
If ever man by *b's* of gratefulness— „ i iii 435
every *b* and debt and obligation Incurr'd as Chancellor. „ i iii 710
broken Your *b* of peace, your treaty with the King— „ v ii 350
Prate not of *b's*, for never, oh, never again „ v ii 356
Bid their old *b* farewell with smiles, not tears; *Prom. of May* i 524
Altho' at first he take his *b* for flowers, „ i 645
Down to the devil with this *b* that beggars me! *Foresters* i i 340
Then that *b* he hath Of the Abbot— „ iv 84
if they come I will not tear the *b*, „ iv 98
What wilt thou do with the *b* then? „ iv 105
I bring the *b*. „ iv 109
There is our *b*. *Robin.* I thank thee. „ iv 435
Here is my father's *b*. „ iv 463
but you see the *b* and the letter of the law. „ iv 505
Look o'er these *b's*, my liege. „ iv 839
for the moment strike the *b's* From these three men, „ iv 962
Bond-breaking Shall the waste voice of the *b-b* sea *Becket* v ii 358
Bone dog that snapt the shadow, dropt the *b*.— *Harold* i ii 189
our good King Kneels mumbling some old *b*— „ ii ii 469
The holy *b's* of all the Canonised „ ii ii 734
For swearing falsely by those blessed *b's*; „ iii i 247
Thou swarest falsely by our blessed *b's*, „ v i 259
Give him a *b*, give him a *b*! *Becket* i iv 108
Has left his *b's* upon the way to Rome Unwept, „ ii ii 409
once I wish'd to scourge them to the *b's*. *The Cup* i i 28
Bruised; but no *b's* broken. *Prom. of May* iii 242
we be dogs that have only the *b's*, till we be only *b's* our own selves. *Foresters* i i 25
Bonner (Bishop of London) (*See also* **Out-Bonner**) *B*, who hath lain so long under bonds for the faith— *Queen Mary* i iii 35
Speak, friend *B*, And tell this learned Legate he lacks zeal. „ iii iv 271
A fine beard, *B*, a very full fine beard. „ iii iv 338
B, it will be carried. „ iii iv 405
Pleasure as well as duty, worthy *B*,— „ iii iv 430
B cannot out-Bonner his own self— „ iii vi 27
Gardiner burns, And *B* burns; „ iii vi 60
ay; if *B* have not forged the bills. „ iv i 50
Writ by himself and *B*? „ iv i 93
O *B*, if I ever did you kindness— „ iv ii 152
My heart is no such block as *B's* is: „ iv ii 174
this *B* or another Will in some lying fashion misreport „ iv iii 325
'twas I and *B* did it, And Pole; „ v v 141
Book (*See also* **Booök**) I in my country hall Been reading some old *b*, „ iii i 44
Hath not your Highness ever read his *b*, „ iv i 91
take Such order with all bad, heretical *b's* „ iv i 95
and retract That Eucharistic doctrine in your *b*. „ iv ii 81
Without a friend, a *b*, my faith would seem Dead „ iv ii 96

Book (*continued*) same *b* You wrote against my Lord of Winchester; *Queen Mary* IV iii 264
I hold by all I wrote within that *b*. „ IV iii 275
thank'd her father sweetly for his *b* Against that godless German. „ V v 237
There is a pleasant fable in old *b's*, *Harold* IV i 56
fur him as be handy wi' a *b* bean't but haäfe a hand at a pitchfork. *Prom. of May* I 188
for he's walking to us, and with a *b* in his hand. „ I 220
I'll git the *b* ageän, and larn mysen the rest, „ III 12
Bookman A *b*, flying from the heat and tussle, *Queen Mary* III iv 251
Boon (adj.) My comrade, *b* companion, my co-reveller, *Becket* I iii 460
Boon (s) Wyatt, but now you promised me a *b*. *Queen Mary* II iii 82
My life is not so happy, no such *b*, „ IV i 130
And after those twelve years a *b*, my king, *Harold* I i 226
And afterwards a *b* to crave of you. *The Falcon* 712
to let me know the *b* By granting which, „ 766
First, king, a *b*! *Foresters* IV 945
Booök (book) An' I haätes *b's* an' all, fur they puts foälk off the owd waäys. *Prom. of May* I 221
Boot Your *b's* are from the horses. *Queen Mary* III v 180
O God, sir, do you look upon your *b's*, „ III v 191
I thought not on my *b's*; The devil take all *b's* „ III v 196
seeäms to me the mark wur maäde by a Lunnon *b*. *Prom. of May* I 416
and I think ye weärs a Lunnon *b*. „ I 461
Boot (in addition) A man of this world and the next to *b*. *Becket, Pro.* 259
and the weight of the church to *b* on my shoulders, *Foresters* I ii 58
Booth citizens Stood each before his shut-up *b*, *Queen Mary* II ii 63
Booty a troop, Laden with *b* and with a flag of ours *The Falcon* 612
Bore I never found he *b* me any spite. *Queen Mary* V ii 474
Of this dead King, who never *b* revenge. *Harold* V ii 85
My mother, ere she *b* me, Dream'd that twelve stars *Becket* I i 45
When Canterbury hardly *b* a name. „ I iii 60
As once he *b* the standard of the Angles, „ I iii 494
—the love you said you *b* me— *The Falcon* 858
Push'd from all doors as if we *b* the plague, *Prom. of May* III 804
Born (*See also* **Burn, English-born, Galatian-born, Half-born, True-born**) thou was *b* i' the tail end of old Harry the Seventh. *Queen Mary* I i 42
I was *b* true man at five in the forenoon „ I i 45
I was *b* of a true man and a ring'd wife, „ I i 54
True, Mary was *b*, But France would not accept her for a bride As being *b* from incest; „ I ii 66
Yea, were there issue *b* to her, „ I v 301
Would I had been *B* Spaniard! „ III iii 246
If such a prince were *b* and you not here! „ III vi 203
I should be here if such a prince were *b*. „ III vi 206
to get her baaby *b*; „ IV iii 524
in her agony The mother came upon her—a child was *b*— „ V iv 21
wise and holy men That shall be *b* hereafter. *Harold* III i 210
laughter in old Rome Before a Pope was *b*, „ III ii 165
Not made but *b*, like the great king of all, „ IV i 85
Wild was he, *b* so: but the plots against him „ IV i 110
for a spark Of self-disdain *b* in me „ V i 302
My day when I was *b*. „ V ii 122
I was *b* with it, and sulphur won't bring it out o' me. *Becket* I iv 232
Love that is *b* of the deep coming up with the sun from the sea. (repeat) „ II i 9, 19
A bastard hate *b* of a former love. „ II i 174
I had sooner have been *b* a Mussulman— „ II ii 145
And this no wife has *b* you four brave sons, „ V i 125
On a Tuesday was I *b*, „ V ii 284
Because thou wast *b* excommunicate. „ V ii 472
slayest the babe within the womb Or in the being *b*, *The Cup* II 280
wasn't my lady *b* with a golden spoon in her ladyship's mouth, *The Falcon* 401
left his heir, *B*, happily, with some sense of art, *Prom. of May* I 497
though fortune had *b you* into the estate of a gentleman, „ II 120
O this mortal house, Which we are *b* into, „ II 274
Yet I, *b* here, not only love the country, „ II 544
Wasn't Miss Vavasour, our schoolmistress at Littlechester, a lady *b*? „ III 299
shamed of her among The ladies, *b* his equals. „ III 582
—they were *b* and bred on it—it was their mother— *Foresters* I i 332

Born (*continued*) saints were so kind to both on us that he was dead before he was *b*. *Foresters* II i 374
Borne (*See also* **Shield-borne**) And their strong torment bravely *b*, *Queen Mary* III iv 168
they see not how they are *b*, Nor whither. „ IV iii 410
Good for good hath *b* at times *Harold* V i 174
one fancy hath taken root, and *b* blossom too, *Becket, Pro.* 481
You had not *b* it, no, not for a day. „ II ii 305
Borrowed he *b* the monies from the Abbot of York, the Sheriff's brother. *Foresters* I i 67
it was agreed when you *b* these monies from the Abbot „ IV 466
Bosham To-morrow—first to *B*, then to Flanders. *Harold* I ii 239
Better have been A fisherman at *B*, my good Herbert, *Becket* II ii 292
Bosom (adj.) Should fly like *b* friends when needed most. *The Falcon* 527
Bosom (s) come to cast herself On loyal hearts and *b's*, *Queen Mary* II ii 263
received into the *b* And unity of Universal Church; „ III iii 154
we restore you to the *b* And unity of Universal Church. „ III iii 220
And put it in my *b*, and all at once I felt his arms „ V v 98
Trampling thy mother's *b* into blood? *Harold* IV ii 26
twelve stars fell glittering out of heaven Into her *b*. *Becket* I i 48
And Becket had my *b* on all this; „ I iii 433
To rest upon thy *b* and forget him— „ II i 31
Beware of opening out thy *b* to it, „ III iii 30
that *b* never Heaved under the King's hand „ IV ii 188
This in thy *b*, fool, And after in thy bastard's! „ IV ii 257
Bottle like a *b* full up to the cork, or as hollow as a kex, *Foresters* IV 210
He hath got it from the *b*, noble knight. „ IV 237
Boldness out of the *b*! „ IV 239
Boldness is in the blood, Truth in the *b*. „ IV 241
so she glided up into the heart O' the *b*, „ IV 245
Bottom not even Hope Left at the *b*! *Prom. of May* II 349
We are almost at the *b* of the well: „ III 161
as they call it so truly, to the grave at the *b*, „ III 193
why did you write 'Seek me at the *b* of the river'? „ III 364
Hoäm? fro' the *b* o' the river? „ III 443
She lay so long at the *b* of her well *Foresters* IV 242
The deer fell dead to the *b*, „ IV 543
Bough shot out sidelong *b's* across the deep *Harold* III i 150
Were there no *b's* to hang on, Rivers to drown in? *The Cup* I ii 77
The blossom had open'd on every *b*; *Prom. of May* I 42
The tawny squirrel vaulting thro' the *b's*, *Foresters* I iii 118
Bought (*See also* **Bowt**) God rest his honest soul, he *b* 'em for me, *The Falcon* 49
She rich enough to have *b* it for herself! „ 62
But the King hath *b* half the College of Redhats. *Becket* II ii 373
Bound (limit) More like a school-boy that hath broken *b's*, *Queen Mary* I v 171
Put on your hood and see me to the *b's*. *Becket* III i 95
That your own people cast you from their *b's*, *The Cup* I i 138
Bound (part) if I save him, he and his Are *b* to me— *Queen Mary* II iv 125
and when her innocent eyes were *b*, „ III i 406
Philip by these articles is *b* From stirring hand or foot „ III iii 59
b me too With bitter obligation to the Count— *Harold* II ii 219
I am doubly *b* to thee . . . „ II ii 557
Ay! No!—he hath not *b* me by an oath— „ II ii 660
I mean to be a liar—I am not *b*— „ II ii 797
we be not *b* by the king's voice In making of a king, „ III i 236
Rood itself were *b* To that necessity which binds us down; „ V i 107
to whom thou art *b* By Holy Church. *Becket, Pro.* 67
be *b* Behind the back like laymen-criminals? „ I iii 95
For which the King was *b* security. „ I iii 645
I am *b* For that one hour to stay with good King Louis, „ III iii 246
Or else be *b* and beaten. (repeat) *Foresters* III 370, 390
Bound (past of bind) chain, Wherewith they *b* him to the stake, *Queen Mary* IV iii 596
And *b* me by his love to secrecy Till his own time. *Becket* III i 228
but I *b* the seller To silence, *The Falcon* 72
I *b* myself, and by a solemn vow, „ 679
Bound (verb) And doth so *b* and babble all the way *Queen Mary* V v 86
Wherever the horn sound, and the buck *b*, *Foresters* III 346
Wherever the buck *b*, and the horn sound, „ III 355
Bounden ruler of a land Is *b* by his power and place to see *Queen Mary* III iv 212
and would myself Be *b* to thee more. *Harold* II ii 561

Bounden (*continued*) The crime be on his head—not *b*—no. *Harold* II ii 670
Being *b* by my coronation oath To do men justice. *Becket* I iii 396
holy Palmer, *b* by a vow not to show his face, *Foresters* I ii 236
Boundless I always hated *b* arrogance. *Becket* V i 12
Here crawling in this *b* Nature. *Prom. of May* III 637
Bounteous the *b* bays And havens filling with a blissful sea. *The Cup* II 234
Bourne I cannot catch what Father *B* is saying. *Queen Mary* I iii 14
Old *B* to the life! „ I iii 30
Bout Come now, I fain would have a *b* with thee. *Foresters* II i 552
but thyself Shalt play a *b* with me, „ IV 252
I am overbreathed, Friar, by my two *b's* at quarter-staff. „ IV 267
Bow (s) (*See also* **Saddle-bow**) battle-axe Was out of place; it should have been the *b*.— *Harold* I ii 107
and Death has drawn the *b*— „ III i 401
Give him a *b* and arrows—follow—follow. *The Cup* I i 208
shoot almost as closely with the *b* as the great Earl himself. *Foresters* I i 216
but who be those three yonder with *b's*?— „ II i 172
who art more bow-bent than the very *b* thou carriest? „ II i 378
This is no *b* to hit nightingales; this is a true woodman's *b* of the best yew-wood to slay the deer. „ II i 391
Take thou my *b* and arrow and compel them to pay toll. „ III 263
Give me my *b* and arrows. „ IV 603
Bow (verb) wherefore *b* ye not, says Lady Anne, *Queen Mary* I v 45
Lords and Commons will *b* down before him— „ III i 433
He *b's*, he bares his head, he is coming hither. *Becket* III iii 34
or I Would *b* to such a baseness as would make me „ IV ii 234
But crowns must *b* when mitres sit so high. „ IV ii 297
Life yields to death and wisdom *b's* to Fate, *The Cup* II 89
Bow-bent who art more *b-b* than the very bow thou carriest? „ II i 378
Bow'd (part. and adj.) over his *b* shoulder Scowl'd that world-hated and world-hating beast, *Queen Mary* II ii 89
Men now are *b* and old, the doctors tell you, „ III iv 408
Now, even now, when *b* before my time, „ V ii 64
They told me that the Holy Rood had lean'd And *b* above me; *Harold* V i 104
b To the earth he came from, to the grave he goes to, *Prom. of May* III 514
B to the dust beneath the burthen of sin. „ III 521
Had she but *b* herself to meet the wave *Becket* IV ii 388
Bow'd (verb) and the Lady Anne *B* to the Pyx; *Queen Mary* I v 42
all the rest of England *b* theirs to the Norman, „ II i 160
Whether it *b* at all but in their fancy; Or if it *b*, *Harold* V i 109
the Holy Rood That *b* to me at Waltham— „ V i 383
Bowel bury her Even in the *b's* of the earth *Foresters* III 462
Bower (*See also* **Haveringatte-bower, Vine-bower**) I have built a secret *b* in England, Thomas, *Becket, Pro.* 153
take her from her secret *b* in Anjou And pass her to her secret *b* in England. „ *Pro.* 181
This chart with the red line! her *b*! whose *b*? „ *Pro.* 308
one rose will outblossom the rest, one rose in a *b*. „ *Pro.* 346
chart with the red line—thou sawest it—her *b*. *Fitzurse*. Rosamund's? „ *Pro.* 428
To pass thee to thy secret *b* to-morrow. „ I i 249
Must speed you to your *b* at once. „ I i 291
heard her cry 'Where is this *b* of mine?' „ I ii 42
With the red line—'her *b*.' „ I ii 62
thou my golden dream of Love's own *b*, „ II i 35
Thine enemy knows the secret of my *b*. „ II i 265
warder of the *b* hath given himself Of late to wine. „ III i 30
Springs from the loneliness of my poor *b*, „ III i 41
My Anjou *b* was scarce as beautiful. „ III i 52
Babble in *b* Under the rose! „ III i 96
Kiss in the *b*, Tit on the tree! „ III i 104
John of Salisbury committed The secret of the *b*, „ III iii 6
Know you not this *b* is secret, „ IV ii 22
Found out her secret *b* and murder'd her. „ V i 175
Your Becket knew the secret of your *b*. „ V i 178
The monk's disguise thou gavest me for my *b*: „ V ii 94
When first he meets his maiden in a *b*. *The Cup* I iii 42
I have lodged my pretty Katekin in her *b*. *Foresters* II i 418
Bowering-in myrtle, *b-i* The city where she dwells. *The Cup* I i 3
Bower-maiden Only my best *b-m* died of late, *Becket* III i 67
Bowing his fine-cut face *b* and beaming with all that courtesy „ III iii 141
Bowl *b* my ancestor Fetch'd from the farthest east— *The Falcon* 483
as she has broken My china *b*. „ 524
Bowl'd no man yet has ever *b* me down. *Foresters* IV 288
more of a man than to be *b* over like a ninepin. „ IV 304
Bowman Our *bowmen* are so true They strike the deer „ IV 524
Bowstring By arrow and by *b*, „ III 442
Bowt (bought) an' it belongs to the Steers ageän: I *b* it back ageän; *Prom. of May* III 452
Boxed if you *b* the Pope's ears with a purse, you might stagger him, *Becket* II ii 370
Boy (*See also* **School-boy**) After him *b's*! and pelt him from the city. *Queen Mary* I iii 85
while the *b* she held Mimick'd and piped her „ II ii 72
So wife-like humble to the trivial *b* „ III i 364
seven-years' friend was with me, my young *b*; „ III iii 48
the *b* Not out of him—but neither cold, „ V ii 480
I am eleven years older than he, Poor *b*! „ V v 47
That was a lusty *b* of twenty-seven; „ V v 48
Why—how they fought when *b's*— *Harold* I i 430
Why, *b's* will fight. Leofwin would often fight me, „ I i 433
The *b* would fist me hard, and when we fought „ I i 444
Thou art the Queen; ye are *b* and girl no more: „ I i 455
stuff'd the *b* with fears that these may act „ II ii 90
Father. *William*. Well, *b*. „ II ii 104
Why, *b*? *Rufus*. Because I broke The horse's leg— „ II ii 108
methinks, my *b*, Thy fears infect me beyond reason. „ II ii 450
B, thou hast forgotten That thou art English. „ II ii 473
I have lost the *b* who play'd at ball with me, „ IV iii 21
How the *b* grows! *Becket* II i 217
Dost thou know, my *b*, what it is to be Chancellor of England? „ II i 231
It is, my *b*, to side with the King when Chancellor, „ II i 235
Here is a ball, my *b*, thy world, „ II i 244
A pretty lusty *b*. *Rosamund*. So like to thee; „ II i 247
I spoke of late to the *b*, he answer'd me, „ II ii 5
I love thy mother, my pretty *b*. „ IV i 45
The *b* so late; pray God, he be not lost. „ IV ii 1
Geoffrey, my *b*, I saw the ball you lost „ IV ii 56
—let me go With my young *b*, „ IV ii 98
beg my bread along the world With my young *b*, „ IV ii 104
Then is thy pretty *b* a bastard? „ IV ii 112
I will fly with my sweet *b* to heaven, „ IV ii 237
Even when you both were *b's* at Theobald's. „ V i 10
How fares thy pretty *b*, the little Geoffrey? „ V ii 167
Mine enemies barr'd all access to the *b*. „ V ii 452
B, dost thou know the house of Sinnatus? *The Cup* I i 49
My *b*, Take thou this letter and this cup „ I i 60
Why, whither runs the *b*? „ I i 70
I had once A *b* who died a babe; „ I ii 149
As helplessly as some unbearded *b's* „ I iii 40
or after slayest him As *b* or man, „ II 281
O my sick *b*! My daily fading Florio, *The Falcon* 235
But my *b*—No, no! not yet— „ 303
That bright inheritor of your eyes—your *b*? „ 307
How charm'd he was! what wonder?—A gallant *b*, „ 319
love for my dying *b*, Moves me to ask it of you. „ 787
How often has my sick *b* yearn'd for this! „ 829
The *b* may die: more blessed were the rags „ 850
Our men and *b's* would hoot him, stone him, *Prom. of May* II 425
the *b* was taken prisoner by the Moors. *Foresters* I i 60
Come, *b*! 'tis but to see if thou canst fence. „ II i 571
I am like a *b* now going to be whipt; „ II ii 50
'This *b* will never wed the maid he loves, „ II ii 111
Boyhood knew battle, And that was from my *b*, *Harold* V ii 175
tree that my lord himself planted here in the blossom of his *b*— *The Falcon* 564
Boy-king *b-k*, with his fast-fading eyes Fixt hard *Queen Mary* I ii 30
Brace Out of the church, you *b* of cursed crones, „ IV iii 539
Braced Are *b* and brazen'd up with Christmas wines *Becket* V ii 423
Bracelet A man may hang gold *b's* on a bush, *Harold* II i 87
Bracken Lusty *b* beaten flat, *Foresters* II ii 154

Bragging is he *b* still that he will come *Harold* IV iii 124
Brain (s) what, have you eyes, ears, *b's*? *Queen Mary* II i 97
Your father had a *b* that beat men down— „ IV i 110
With nothing but my battle-axe and him To spatter his *b's*! *Harold* II ii 781
All my *b* is full of sleep. *The Cup* I ii 445
thro' the blood the wine leaps to the *b* *Foresters* I iii 23
if you care to drag your *b's* for such a minnow. „ II i 323
Brain (verb) I have a mind to *b* thee with mine axe. *Harold* II i 73
blow that *b's* the horseman cleaves the horse, „ V i 593
Brain-dazing After the long *b-d* colloquies, *Queen Mary* IV ii 92
Brain-dizzied *B-d* with a draught of morning ale. „ II i 71
Brain'd Methought they would have *b* me with it, John. *Becket* V ii 612
Brainless over this the *b* loons That cannot spell Esaïas from St. Paul, *Queen Mary* III i 280
Brake (*See also* **Broke**) those hard men *b* into woman-tears, Ev'n Gardiner, „ I v 564
some fool that once *B* bread with us, perhaps: „ III v 45
Who *b* into Lord Tostig's treasure-house *Harold* IV i 114
Before these bandits *b* into your presence. *Becket* V ii 556
Branch (*See also* **Olive-branch**) Would'st thou not burn and blast them root and *b*? *Queen Mary* III iv 283
Brand (a sword) flings His *b* in air and catches it again, *Harold* V i 494
Brand (verb) So *b's* me in the stare of Christendom A heretic! *Queen Mary* V ii 62
Brandish With hands too limp to *b* iron— *Harold* V i 449
Brandish'd *See* **Treble-brandish'd**
Brass Swarm to thy voice like bees to the *b* pan. *Foresters* I iii 108
Brat The washerwoman's *b*! *Harold* IV iii 172
Brave (adj.) For all that, Most honest, *b*, and skilful; *Queen Mary* II ii 383
No, girl; most *b* and loyal, *b* and loyal. „ II iv 11
b Lord William Thrust him from Ludgate, „ II iv 91
There's a *b* man, if any. „ III i 175
Might it not be the other side rejoicing In his *b* end? „ IV iii 358
that our *b* English Had sallied out from Calais „ V ii 255
B, wary, sane to the heart of her— „ V v 224
And being *b* he must be subtly cow'd, *Harold* II ii 75
thou, *b* banner, Blaze like a night of fatal stars „ IV i 250
No, no—*b* Gurth, one gash from brow to knee! „ V ii 70
Hate him? as *b* a soldier as Henry and a goodlier man: *Becket, Pro.* 436
And this no wife has born you four *b* sons, „ V i 125
Why said you not as much to my *b* Sinnatus? *The Cup* I ii 260
B—ay—too *b*, too over-confident, „ I ii 261
a *b* one Which you shall see to-morrow. „ I ii 431
That this *b* heart of mine should shake me so, „ I iii 38
I am sure that more than one *b* fellow owed His death *The Falcon* 633
Nothing but my *b* bird, my noble falcon, „ 873
She struck him, my *b* Marian, struck the Prince, *Foresters* II i 134
A *b* old fellow but he angers me. „ II i 471
he As gentle as he's *b*— „ II i 659
I know not, can I trust myself With your *b* band? „ II i 704
Honour to thee, *b* Marian, and thy Kate. „ III 299
For our *b* Robin is a man indeed. „ IV 1037
Brave (verb) Nay, nay, my lord, thou must not *b* the King. *Becket* I iii 515
I must hence to *b* The Pope, King Louis, and this turbulent priest. „ II i 311
To break the barons, and now *b's* the King. „ V i 235
I dare not *b* my brother, Break with my kin. *The Falcon* 255
I cannot *b* my brother—but be sure „ 741
Braved Hadst thou been braver, I had better *b* All— *Harold* III ii 179
Brave-hearted My *b-h* Rose! Hath he ever been to see thee? *Becket* II i 287
Braver Hadst thou been *b*, I had better braved All— *Harold* III ii 178
Bravest *b* in our roll of Primates down From Austin— *Becket* V ii 58
the *b* English heart Since Hereward the Wake *Foresters* II i 686
Brawl (s) witness the *b's*, the gibbets. *Queen Mary* V i 85
Peace, friends! what idle *b* is this? *Becket* I ii 3
Wakening such *b's* and loud disturbances In England, „ V ii 352
brazen'd up with Christmas wines For any murderous *b*. „ V ii 425
yet they prate Of mine, my *b's*, when those, „ V ii 427
This last to rid thee of a world of *b's*! „ V iii 199
His grandsire struck my grandsire in a *b* At Florence, *The Falcon* 251
Brawl (verb) You *b* beyond the question; speak, Lord Legate! *Queen Mary* III iv 97
Brawler torn Down the strong wave of *b's*. *Queen Mary* III i 186
Even this *b* of harsh truths— *Foresters* IV 948
Brawlest O brook, that *b* merrily by *Prom. of May* III 201
Brazen'd Are braced and *b* up with Christmas wines *Becket* V ii 423
Bread (*See also* **Manchet-bread**) when the traitor wife came out for *b* *Queen Mary* III i 12
fool that once Brake *b* with us, perhaps: „ III v 45
Fed with rank *b* that crawl'd upon the tongue, „ IV iii 442
had they remained true to me whose *b* they have partaken. *Becket* I iv 150
live by the King's venison and the *b* o' the Lord, „ I iv 272
gaping bills in the home-nest Piping for *b*— „ II ii 301
and to win my own *b*, „ III i 118
I will beg my *b* along the world With my young boy, „ IV ii 103
The slave that eat my *b* has kick'd his King! „ V i 242
How oft in coming hast thou broken *b*? *Harold* IV iii 200
No *b*? *Filippo.* Half a breakfast for a rat! *The Falcon* 122
Sour milk and black *b*. *Foresters* II i 272
and her *b* is beyond me: and the milk—faugh! „ II i 292
In the sweat of thy brow, says Holy Writ, shalt thou eat *b*, „ IV 202
Breadth What *b*, height, strength—torrents of eddying bark! „ III 94
Break draw back your heads and your horns before I *b* them, *Queen Mary* I i 5
Pray God he do not be the first to *b* them, „ I v 269
It *b's* my heart to hear her moan at night „ I v 603
These Kentish ploughmen cannot *b* the guards. „ II iv 17
The King of France will help to *b* it. „ III i 105
Beheld our rough forefathers *b* their Gods, „ III ii 120
You must *b* them or they *b* you. „ III ii 205
B's into feather'd merriments, „ III v 13
Whose colours in a moment *b* and fly, „ IV iii 169
Whose colours in a moment *b* and fly!' „ V ii 206
And *b* your paces in, and make you tame; „ V iii 121
to *b* down all kingship and queenship, „ V iv 47
for thy brother *b's* us With over-taxing— *Harold* I i 109
lest they rear and run And *b* both neck and axle. „ I i 374
close as our shield-wall, Who *b's* us then? „ I i 400
to swear Vows that he dare not *b*. „ II ii 77
—it was mine own to *b*; „ II ii 111
I like to have my toys, and *b* them too. „ II ii 112
And may I *b* his legs? „ II ii 115
Tho' scarce at ease; for, save our meshes *b*, „ II ii 141
Or is it the same sin to *b* my work As *b* mine oath? „ II ii 664
Enough! Thou wilt not *b* it! „ II ii 753
Ye take a stick, and *b* it; „ IV i 57
Who made this Britain England, *b* the North: „ IV iii 154
B the banquet up . . . Ye four! „ IV iii 231
our shield wall—Wall—*b* it not—*b* not—*b*— „ V i 233
made too good an use of Holy Church To *b* her close! „ V i 314
he holp the King to *b* down our castles, *Becket, Pro.* 447
it is the will of God To *b* me, „ I iii 292
Nay, if I cannot *b* him as the prelate, „ I iii 333
If pretty Geoffrey do not *b* his own, „ IV ii 177
striving still to *b* or bind The spiritual giant „ IV ii 442
And *b* the soul from earth. „ V i 44
for he did his best To *b* the barons, „ V i 235
till it *b* Into young angels. „ V i 256
Antonius would not suffer me to *b* Into the sanctuary. *The Cup* I iii 120
They will *b* in the earth—I am sinking— „ II 477
I dare not brave my brother, *B* with my kin. *The Falcon* 257
I come this day to *b* my fast with you. „ 276
I did *b* it, my lord: it is broken! „ 494
How shall I *b* it to him? how shall I tell him? „ 848
I *b* with him for ever! „ 889
dead garland Will *b* once more into the living blossom. „ 919
She *will* *b* fence. I can't keep her in order. *Prom. of May* I 194
rough road That *b's* off short into the abysses— „ I 230
There! let me *b* some off for you. „ I 609
B's thro' them, and so flies away for ever; „ I 650
If that should *b* before we meet again? „ I 755
B! nay, but call for Philip when you will, „ I 757
And as ready to *b* it again. „ III 86
I think That I should *b* my heart, „ III 556

Break (*continued*) I would *b* through them all, like the King of England. *Foresters* I i 325
I will *b* thy sconce with my quarterstaff. „ I ii 75
Who *b's* the stillness of the morning thus? „ I iii 50
Why *b* you thus upon my lonely hour? „ II i 93
b it all to pieces, as you *b* the poor, „ II i 285
he would *b*, Far as he might, the power of John— „ II i 695
To *b* our band and scatter us to the winds. „ III 453
The chief of these outlaws who *b* the law? „ IV 141
being out of the law how should we *b* the law? if we broke into it again we should *b* the law, „ IV 145
B thine alliance with this faithless John, „ IV 323
I cannot *b* it, Robin, if I wish'd. „ IV 327
Then on the instant I will *b* thy head. „ IV 680
That thou wilt *b* our forest laws again „ IV 888
They *b* thy forest laws—nay, by the rood „ IV 907
which longs to *b* itself across their backs. „ IV 918
And have thy fees, and *b* the law no more. „ IV 955
Breakage his achage and his *b*, if that were all: *Queen Mary* I i 128
we never use it For fear of *b*— *The Falcon* 487
Breaker the great *b* beats upon the beach! *Foresters* I ii 323
Breakfast No bread? *Filippo.* Half a *b* for a rat! *The Falcon* 123
Call him back and say I come to *b* with him. „ 213
Holy Mother! To *b*! „ 215
Breaking (part.) (*See also* **Bond-breaking**) Is guiltier keeping this, than *b* it. *Harold* III i 231
the nightmare *b* on my peace 'With Becket.' *Becket* II i 36
O God! some dreadful truth is *b* on me— „ III i 266
B already from thy noviciate To plunge „ V ii 79
Battering the doors, and *b* thro' the walls? „ V ii 626
Fairy realm is *b* down *Foresters* II ii 134
Breaking (s) His *b* with Northumberland broke Northumberland. *Queen Mary* II iv 13
A day may save a heart from *b* too. „ III vi 241
what with the fear of *b* it, I did break it, *The Falcon* 494
and my father's *b* down, and his blindness. *Prom. of May* II 69
Breast (s) natural brother Of the same roof, same *b*. *Queen Mary* IV iii 191
The babe enwomb'd and at the *b* is cursed, *Harold* V i 65
Parthian shaft of a forlorn Cupid at the King's left *b*, *Becket, Pro.* 340
On this left *b* before so hard a heart, „ *Pro.* 375
I put the bitters on my *b* to wean him, *The Falcon* 190
but in the sweat of thy brow, and thy *b*, *Foresters* IV 203
Breast (verb) there make strength to *b* Whatever chance, *Harold* V i 127
Breasted *See* **Many-breasted**
Breath Did not his last *b* Clear Courtenay *Queen Mary* III i 134
All her *b* should, incenselike, Rise to the heavens „ III iii 163
it takes my *b*: „ III v 190
All that is gracious in the *b* of heaven „ III vi 224
Pray with one *b*, one heart, one soul for me. „ IV iii 104
Beauty passes like a *b* and love is lost in loathing: „ V ii 365
He hath swoon'd! Death? . . . no, as yet a *b*. *Harold* III i 319
A *b* that fleets beyond this iron world, „ III ii 197
link rusts with the *b* of the first after-marriage kiss, *Becket, Pro.* 361
there stole into the city a *b* Full of the meadows, „ I i 262
—John, and out of *b*! „ I i 389
and they do say the very *b* catches. „ I iv 222
stay it But for a *b*. „ II i 178
any rough sea Blown by the *b* of kings. „ II ii 108
Thou whose *b* Is balmy wind to robe *The Cup* II 264
Breathe let them sit. I must have time to *b*. *Queen Mary* I v 546
that she *b's* in England Is life and lungs „ III vi 49
And every soul of man that *b's* therein. „ III vi 107
B the free wind from off our Saxon downs, *Harold* II ii 186
for the sake Of any king that *b's*. *Becket* II ii 221
I know—could swear—as long as Becket *b's*, „ V i 77
And *b* one prayer for my liege-lord the King, „ V ii 191
the great Archbishop! Does he *b*? No? „ V iii 203
That I might *b* for a moment free of shield *Foresters* IV 128
I *b* Heaven's air, and Heaven looks down on me, „ IV 725
Then, if ye cannot *b* but woodland air, „ IV 952
Breathed (*See also* **Over-breathed**) Girl never *b* to rival such a rose; *Queen Mary* III i 372
I never *b* it to a bird in the eaves, „ V ii 453
since I *b*, A houseless head beneath the sun *Foresters* II i 63
lips that never *b* Love's falsehood to true maid „ IV 72
Breathing (part.) *B* an easy gladness . . . not like Aldwyth . . . *Harold* I ii 174
Breathing (s) Like sun-gilt *b's* on a frosty dawn— *Queen Mary* V iii 50
Or in the balmy *b's* of the night, *Foresters* IV 1068
Breathing-time But in this narrow *b-t* of life *The Cup* I i 29
Breathing-while a *b-w* To rest upon thy bosom *Becket* II i 29
Breathless lying chain'd In *b* dungeons over steaming sewers, *Queen Mary* IV iii 440
Bred *That b* the doubt! but I am wiser now . . . *Harold* V ii 111
Tho' I *b* thee The full-train'd marvel *The Falcon* 24
—they were born and *b* on it—it was their mother— *Foresters* I i 332
Traitors are rarely *b* Save under traitor kings. „ II i 80
only they that be *b* in it can find their way a-nights in it. „ II i 264
Breed (s) Two vipers of one *b*—an amphisbæna, *Queen Mary* III iv 39
Thy *b* will die with thee, and mine with me: *The Falcon* 18
A noble bird, each perfect of the *b*. „ 320
A nobler *b* of men and women. „ 755
Breed (verb) And if I *b* confusion anyway— *Queen Mary* I iii 93
world would grow mouldy, would only *b* the past again. *Becket, Pro.* 410
And if my pleasure *b* another's pain, *Prom. of May* I 278
Breeding (*See also* **Fever-breeding**) In *b* godless vermin. *Queen Mary* III iv 329
b A fierce resolve and fixt heart-hate „ III vi 31
Breeze which a *b* of May Took ever and anon, *The Cup* I ii 406
Brethren (*See also* **Brother**) Behold him, *b*: he hath cause to weep!— *Queen Mary* IV iii 13
I pray you all to live together Like *b*; „ IV iii 182
seeming not as *b*, But mortal foes! „ IV iii 185
Hear him, my good *b*. „ IV iii 227
Join hands, let *b* dwell in unity; *Harold* I i 397
To help us from their *b* yonder? „ III i 221
Can ye not Be *b*? Godwin still at feud with Alfgar, „ IV i 123
Have thy two *b* sent their forces in? „ V i 342
have I fought men Like Harold and his *b*, „ V ii 179
Stay, Dine with my *b* here, *Foresters* IV 346
Brett (adherent of Wyatt) You know that after The Captain *B*, *Queen Mary* II ii 26
B, when the Duke of Norfolk moved against us „ II iii 1
for which I love thee, *B*. „ II iii 6
Last night I climb'd into the gate-house, *B*, „ II iii 15
Brevity Tit, for love and *b*, *Foresters* II ii 128
Brew To sing, love, marry, churn, *b*, bake, and die, *Queen Mary* III v 111
b from out This Godstow-Becket intermeddling *Becket* IV ii 455
I can bake and I can *b*, *Foresters* I i 215
Brew'd what an acrid wine has Luther *b*, *Queen Mary* IV iii 545
and she *b* the best ale in all Glo'ster, *Becket* III i 196
Briar Wi' the *b* sa green, an' the willer sa graäy, *Prom. of May* II 186
Bribe *b's* our nobles with her gold, *Queen Mary* II i 202
but they *b* Each other, and so often, *Harold* I i 346
—*b* all the Cardinals— *Becket* II ii 473
Bribed Except this old hag have been *b* to lie. *Robin.* We old hags should be *b* to speak truth, *Foresters* II i 235
Brickwork This labyrinthine *b* maze in maze, *Becket, Pro.* 166
Bridal tore away My marriage ring, and rent my *b* veil; *Harold* I ii 80
Like the Love-goddess, with no *b* veil, *Prom. of May* I 596
Bride France would not accept her for a *b* *Queen Mary* I ii 68
Were I in Devon with my wedded *b*, „ I iv 119
Had mark'd her for my brother Edward's *b*; „ I v 290
I live and die The true and faithful *b* of Philip— „ II iv 43
To purchase for Himself a stainless *b*; „ III iii 205
White as the light, the spotless *b* of Christ, „ III iv 199
King hath wearied of his barren *b*.' „ III vi 141
there is one Death stands behind the *B*— „ V ii 168
B of the mightiest sovereign upon earth? „ V ii 544
Hail! Harold! Aldwyth! hail, bridegroom and *b*! *Harold* IV iii 2
Hail, Harold, Aldwyth! Bridegroom and *b*! „ IV iii 43
Full thanks for your fair greeting of my *b*! „ IV iii 47
I could not: Thou art my *b*! „ V i 322
Who but the bridegroom dares to judge the *b*. *Becket* I iii 686
thought if it were the King's brother he had a better *b* than the King, „ III i 173
I had dream'd I was the *b* of England, and a queen. „ V i 103
while you dream'd you were the *b* of England,— „ V i 105
and our Mother Church for *b*; „ V ii 222

Bride (*continued*) And Camma for my *b*—The people love her— *The Cup* I iii 152
I am the *b* of Death, and only Marry the dead. „ II 28
The king should pace on purple to his *b*, „ II 190
She too—she too—the *b*! the Queen! and I— „ II 467
An outlaw's *b* may not be wife in law. *Foresters* II ii 90
This other, willy-nilly, for his *b*. „ IV 768
Bridegroom (*See also* **Groom**) How should he bear a *b* out of Spain? *Queen Mary* III iii 25
But softly as a *b* to his own. *Harold* II ii 758
Hail! Harold! Aldwyth! hail, *b* and bride! „ IV iii 2
Hail, Harold, Aldwyth! *B* and bride! „ IV iii 43
Who but the *b* dares to judge the bride. Or he the *b* may appoint? *Becket* I iii 685
Brideless The *b* Becket is thy king and mine: „ V i 107
Bridesmaid Our *b's* are not lovely—Disappointment, *Queen Mary* V ii 154
Bridge And broken *b*, or spavin'd horse, „ I v 355
thro' thine help we are come to London *B*; „ II iii 9
On over London *B* We cannot: stay we cannot; „ II iii 41
we must round By Kingston *B*. „ II iii 48
And then a brook, a *b*; *Becket, Pro.* 164
This *b* again! How often have I stood With Eva here! *Prom. of May* II 295
madman, is it, Gesticulating there upon the *b*? „ II 327
I dozed upon the *b*, and the black river „ II 649
dead midnight when I came upon the *b*; „ III 369
Bridged and brooks Were *b* and damm'd with dead, *Harold* III ii 130
Brief it is an age Of *b* life, and *b* purpose, and *b* patience, As I have shown to-day. *Queen Mary* III iv 413
Care more for our *b* life in their wet land, „ III vi 62
Latimer Had a *b* end—not Ridley. „ IV ii 225
in *b*, so miserable, „ IV iii 78
Hath, like a *b* and bitter winter's day, „ IV iii 430
Suffer not That my *b* reign in England be defamed „ V ii 302
Brief-sighted And warble those *b-s* eyes of hers? „ III vi 155
B-s tho' they be, I have seen them, „ III vi 157
Bright And dazzled men and deafen'd by some *b* Loud venture, „ III i 452
the *b* sky cleave To the very feet of God, *Harold* II ii 741
the *b* link rusts with the breath of the first after-marriage kiss, *Becket, Pro.* 361
Gleam upon gloom, *B* as my dream, „ III i 278
To-day they are fixt and *b*— *The Cup* II 20
Ay, how is he, That *b* inheritor of your eyes—your boy? *The Falcon* 306
And the day's *b* like a friend, *Prom. of May* I 79
I remember Her *b* face beaming starlike down upon me „ II 248
To sleep! to sleep! The long *b* day is done, *Foresters* I iii 41
So now the forest lawns are all as *b* As ways to heaven, „ II i 631
Brighten or it is but past That *b's* in retiring? *Prom. of May* II 645
Brighter Cousin Pole, You are fresh from *b* lands. *Queen Mary* III iv 322
this world Is *b* for his absence as that other Is darker for his presence. *Prom. of May* II 458
but if you Can tell me anything of our sweet Eva When in her *b* girlhood, „ II 521
Brightest In Britain's calendar the *b* day *Queen Mary* III ii 118
Brim Fill to the *b*. *Foresters* III 343
To the *b* and over till the green earth „ III 349
Brimming green field Beside the *b* Medway, *Queen Mary* II i 244
Bring I do but *b* the message, know no more. „ I iv 228
I'll have one mark it And *b* it me. „ I v 373
messenger Who *b's* that letter which we waited for— „ I v 586
This marriage should *b* loss or danger to you, „ II ii 227
Find out his name and *b* it to me „ III i 253
Legate's coming To *b* us absolution from the Pope. „ III i 432
second actor in this pageant That *b's* him in; „ III iii 15
To *b* the heretic to the stake, „ III iv 9
'I come not to *b* peace but a sword'? „ III iv 88
sends His careful dog to *b* them to the fold. „ III iv 105
And, whether it *b* you bitter news or sweet, „ III v 201
b it Home to the leisure wisdom of his Queen, „ III vi 22
lo! thou art reclaim'd; He *b's* thee home: „ IV iii 84
you *b* the smoke Of Cranmer's burning with you. „ IV iii 560
B's the new learning back. „ V i 202
My liege, I *b* you goodly tidings. „ V i 279

Bring (*continued*) Why do you *b* me these? *Queen Mary* V ii 185
Why do they *b* me these? „ V ii 198
he may *b* you news from Philip. „ V ii 229
I *b* your Majesty such grievous news I grieve to *b* it. „ V ii 239
Alice, my child, *B* us your lute. „ V ii 357
No, no, he *b's* a letter. „ V ii 548
to read the letter which you *b*. *Feria.* Madam, I *b* no letter. *Mary.* How! no letter? „ V ii 556
that I am in state to *b* forth death— „ V ii 592
I pray thee, let me hence and *b* him home. *Harold* I i 241
thunder may *b* down That which the flash „ I ii 234
I want thy voice with him to *b* him round; „ II ii 73
make A league with William, so to *b* him back? „ II ii 461
wilt thou *b* another, Edith, upon his head? „ III i 260
B not thy hollowness On our full feast. „ IV iii 203
b her to the level of the dust, so that the King— *Becket, Pro.* 530
And *b* us all to shame? „ I iii 38
If Canterbury *b* his cross to court, „ I iii 511
I was born with it, and sulphur won't *b* it out o' me. „ I iv 233
I *b* the taint on it along wi' me, for the Archbishop likes it, „ I iv 252
till the weight of Germany or the gold of England *b's* one of them down to the dust— „ II ii 364
there were Abbots—but they did not *b* their women; „ III iii 135
To *b* her to the dust . . . „ IV ii 154
we *b* a message from the King Beyond the water; „ V ii 301
Moon *b* him home, *b* him home Safe from the dark and the cold, Home, sweet moon, *b* him home, *The Cup* I ii 5
B me The costly wines we use in marriages. „ II 364
But that might *b* a Roman blessing on us. „ II 371
Lady, you *b* your light into my cottage *The Falcon* 283
look for 'im, Eva, and *b* 'im to the barn. *Prom. of May* I 438
but I thowt I'd *b* tha them roses fust. „ II 50
And *b* us to confusion. „ II 279
the heat and fire Of life will *b* them out, „ II 287
Let me *b* you in here where there is still full daylight. „ III 217
and the man must *b* it out of her. *Foresters* I i 118
So that our Barons *b* his baseness under. „ I ii 117
I trust he *b's* us news of the King's coming. „ I iii 53
To *b* their counter-bond into the forest. „ IV 89
I *b* the bond. „ IV 109
I can *b* down Fourscore tall fellows on thee. „ IV 175
Shall I not after him and *b* him back? „ IV 812
Bristle So that he *b* himself against my will. *Harold* II ii 19
Bristled monarch mane *B* about his quick ears— *The Cup* I ii 121
Britain In *B's* calendar the brightest day *Queen Mary* III ii 118
sons of those Who made this *B* England, *Harold* IV iii 154
Brito (**Richard de**) (**knight of King Henry II.'s household**) (*See also* **De Brito, Richard**) France! Ha! De Morville, Tracy, *B*—fled is he? *Becket* I iv 199
Brittany brought Thy war with *B* to a goodlier close *Harold* II ii 49
one that should be grateful to me overseas, a Count in *B*— *Foresters* I i 271
Broach *See* **Abroach**
Broached They ha' *b* a barrel of äale i' the long barn, *Prom. of May* I 426
Broad What it means? Ask our *b* Earl. *Harold* I i 90
he is *b* and honest, Breathing an easy gladness. . . . „ I ii 172
Brocade —O he Flamed in *b*— *Queen Mary* III i 76
Broider these poor hands but sew, Spin, *b*— *Harold* IV iii 11
maidens who can only *b* and mayhap ride a-hawking *Foresters* I i 213
Broke (*See also* **Brake**) When Henry *b* the carcase of your church *Queen Mary* I v 397
His breaking with Northumberland *b* Northumberland. „ II iv 13
Charing Cross; the rebels *b* us there, „ II iv 76
Because I *b* The horse's leg— *Harold* II ii 109
I trod upon him even now, my lord, in my hurry, and *b* him. *The Falcon* 410
Immanuel Goldsmiths was *b* into o' Monday night, *Prom. of May* I 392
b the heart That only beat for you; „ III 761
I have shelter'd some that *b* the forest laws. *Foresters* I iii 70
She *b* my head on Tuesday with a dish. „ I iii 133
if we *b* into it again we should break the law, „ IV 145
This young warrior *B* his prison „ IV 999
Broken (*See also* **Brokken, Neck-broken**) I hear that he too is full of aches and *b* before his day. *Queen Mary* I i 125
that *b*, out you flutter Thro' the new world, „ I iv 52
More like a school-boy that hath *b* bounds, „ I i 171

Broken (*continued*) And *b* bridge, or spavin'd horse, or wave And wind at their old battle: *Queen Mary* I v 355
And I have *b* with my father— „ I v 528
Wyatt, your Grace, hath *b* thro' the guards „ II iv 20
They are too crush'd, too *b*, „ IV iii 360
And I am *b* there. „ V i 211
I have *b* off the head. „ V ii 3
Saints, I have rebuilt Your shrines, set up your *b* images; „ V ii 300
thou Hast *b* all my foes, *Harold* I i 217
the teeth That shall be *b* by us— „ I ii 245
my son! Are all oaths to be *b* then, „ III i 286
and our battle-axes *b* The Raven's wing, „ IV iii 64
How oft in coming hast thou *b* bread? „ IV iii 200
Have we not *b* Wales and Norseland? „ V i 395
They have *b* the commandment of the king! „ V i 614
His oath was *b*—O holy Norman Saints, „ V i 616
chessmen on the floor—the king's crown *b*! *Becket, Pro.* 314
Thou hast *b* thro' the pales Of privilege, „ III iii 193
While this but leaves thee with a *b* heart, „ IV ii 173
It must be *b* for him. „ IV ii 178
Hath *b* all his promises to thyself, „ V i 3
Not one whose back his priest has *b*. „ V i 146
every thread of thought Is *b* ere it joins— „ V ii 207
You have *b* Your bond of peace, your treaty „ V ii 349
have *b* down our barns, Wasted our diocese, „ V ii 429
And the great deeps were *b* up again, „ V iii 43
I did break it, my lord: it is *b*! *The Falcon* 495
my nurse has *b* The thread of my dead flowers, as she has *b* „ 521
I have *b* My fast already. „ 574
poor father, utterly *b* down By losing her— *Prom. of May* II 417
Bruised; but no bones *b*. „ III 242
the poor young heart *B* at last—all still— „ III 681
Not having *b* fast the livelong day— *Foresters* IV 186
though he be the chief of rogues, he hath never *b* his word. „ IV 433
Hast *b* all our Norman forest laws, „ IV 886

Broken-back'd Reed I rock'd upon *b-b*, „ II ii 162

Brokken (broken) the walls sa thin, and the winders *b*, *Prom. of May* III 73

Brood lest she *b* Too long o'er this hard egg, *Becket* V ii 252
drew the light From heaven to *b* upon her, *The Cup* I iii 58
To-day? Too sudden. I will *b* upon it. „ II 73

Brooding I was *b* Upon a great unhappiness *Prom. of May* II 381

Brook (s) (*See also* **Beck**) There runs a shallow *b* across our field *Queen Mary* V v 83
both were silent, letting the wild *b* Speak for us— „ V v 91
dykes and *b's* Were bridged and damm'd with dead, *Harold* III ii 129
wolf Mudded the *b* and predetermined all. „ V i 3
And then a *b*, a bridge; *Becket, Pro.* 164
drop The mud I carried, like yon *b*, „ II i 159
Geoffrey have not tost His ball into the *b*! „ II i 321
the voice Of the perpetual *b*, „ III i 46
The *b's* voice is not yours, and no flower, „ III i 55
I saw the ball you lost in the fork of the great willow over the *b*. „ IV ii 58
We parted like the *b* yonder about the alder island, *Prom. of May* I 773
The *b* among its flowers! Forget-me-not, „ II 297
Close by that alder-island in your *b*, „ II 535
O *b*, that brawlest merrily by Thro' fields „ III 201
waded in the *b*, ran after the butterflies, „ III 275

Brook (verb) Will *b* nor Pope nor Spaniard here to play The tyrant, *Queen Mary* I v 189
ye will not *b* that anyone Should seize our person, „ II ii 177
B for an hour such brute malignity? „ IV iii 544
I cannot *b* the turmoil thou hast raised. *Becket* I iii 575
I will not *b* to see Three upon two. *Foresters* II i 423
maiden freedom which Would never *b* the tyrant. „ III 121

Brother (*See also* **Brethren, Foster-brother, Traitor-brother**) 'Thou shalt not wed thy *b's* wife.' *Queen Mary* I ii 63
as tho' My father and my *b* had not lived. „ I v 36
My *b* rather hated me than loved; „ I v 82
Had mark'd her for my *b* Edward's bride; „ I v 289
dallying over seas Even when his *b's*, „ III iv 294
Ay, one and all, dear *b's*, pray for me; „ IV iii 103
Hurt no man more Than you would harm your loving natural *b* „ IV iii 190

Brother (*continued*) What sort of *b's* then be those that lust *Queen Mary* IV iii 197
B! why so pale? *Harold* I i 28
for thy *b* breaks us With over-taxing— „ I i 109
mysteries of heaven Than thou, good *b*. „ I i 201
B, the king is wiser than he seems; „ I i 272
Well, *b*, When didst thou hear from thy Northumbria? „ I i 280
Leave me alone, *b*, with my Northumbria: „ I i 285
My most worthy *b*, Thou art the quietest man „ I i 311
Like the rough bear beneath the tree, good *b*, „ I i 328
O Tostig, O dear *b*—If they prance, „ I i 371
B, *b*! *Tostig.* Away! „ I i 416
I leave thee, *b*. „ I i 461
Against thy *b* Tostig's governance; „ II ii 290
Poor *b*! still a hostage! „ II ii 329
Why, *b*, so he will; But on conditions. „ II ii 342
And, *b*, we will find a way,' said he— „ II ii 367
for my sake, oh *b*! oh! for my sake! „ II ii 401
Not ev'n for thy sake, *b*, would I lie. „ II ii 420
Ay, *b*—for the sake of England—ay. „ II ii 638
Swear, dearest *b*, I beseech thee, swear! „ II ii 720
O Wulfnoth, Wulfnoth, *b*, thou hast betray'd me! „ II ii 801
Forgive me, *b*, I will live here and die. „ II ii 803
Good *b*, By all the truths that ever priest „ III i 96
Bless thou too That *b* whom I love beyond the rest, „ III i 295
There might be more than *b* in my kiss, „ III ii 83
Good even, my good *b*! „ III ii 117
Our hapless *b*, Tostig—He, „ III ii 121
Thou art Tostig's *b*, Who wastes the land. „ IV i 92
This *b* comes to save Your land from waste; „ IV i 94
I, who loved my *b*, bad the king Who doted on him, „ IV i 101
King! thy *b*, if one may dare to speak the truth, „ IV i 107
not *his* fault, if our two houses Be less than *b's*. „ IV i 131
O *b*, What art thou doing here? „ IV ii 3
O *b*, *b*, O Harold— „ IV ii 61
—*b*—*I* have not sworn— „ V i 121
Tell that again to all. *Gurth.* I will, good *b*. „ V i 199
O *b*, from my ghastly oubliette I send my voice „ V i 244
No more, no more, dear *b*, nevermore— „ V i 247
O *b*, most unbrotherlike to me, „ V i 250
Tostig, poor *b*, Art *thou* so anger'd? „ V i 273
Him who crown'd Stephen—King Stephen's *b*! *Becket, Pro.* 274
Henry the King hath been my friend, my *b*, „ I i 88
O *b*!—I may come to martyrdom. „ I i 361
my good lord Leicester, The King and I were *b's*. „ I iii 661
for he would murder his *b* the State. „ I iv 190
B of France, what shall be done with Becket? „ II ii 64
B, you have traffick'd Between the Emperor and the Pope, „ II ii 66
ay, good *b*, They call you the Monk-King. „ II ii 72
Come, confess, good *b*, „ II ii 82
and, *b*, Holy Church May rock, but will not wreck, „ II ii 102
B of France, you have taken, „ II ii 154
believing that our *b* Had wrong'd you; „ II ii 238
I wish you joy o' the King's *b*. „ III i 156
I thought if it were the King's *b* he had a better bride than the King, „ III i 173
whom you call—fancy—my husband's *b's* wife. „ III i 202
Spare this defence, dear *b*. „ V iii 168
Son, husband, *b* gash'd to death in vain, *The Cup* I ii 143
I dare not brave my *b*, Break with my kin. My *b* hates him, *The Falcon* 256
I cannot brave my *b*—but be sure „ 741
Is this your *b's* order? „ 745
not you! My *b*! my hard *b*! O Federigo, Federigo, I love you! Spite of ten thousand *b's*, Federigo. „ 895
I will make Your *b* love me. „ 912
What's become of your *b*? *Prom. of May* III 107
Then yon mun be his *b*, an' we'll leather *'im*. „ III 150
I never heard that he had a *b*. „ III 153
would you beat a man for his *b's* fault? „ III 155
he borrowed the monies from the Abbot of York, the Sheriff's *b*. *Foresters* I i 69
I would pay My *b* all his debt and save the land. „ I ii 218
Himself would pay this mortgage to his *b*, „ I ii 264
Sheriff Would pay this cursed mortgage to his *b* „ II i 145

Brother (*continued*) Thou art her *b*, and her voice is thine, *Foresters* II i 478
Thou art Her *b*—I forgive thee. Come be thou My *b* too. „ II i 516
O thou unworthy *b* of my dear Marian! „ II i 538
That such a *b*—*she* marry the Sheriff! „ II i 550
go not yet, stay with us, and when thy *b*— „ II i 641
to dream that he My *b*, my dear Walter— „ II i 652
See, thou hast wrong'd my *b* and myself. „ II i 665
Ha, *b*. Toll, my dear? the toll of love. „ III 270
For so this maid would wed our *b*, „ IV 483
When Richard comes he is soft enough to pardon His *b*; „ IV 748
What! go to slay his *b*, and make *me* The monkey „ IV 804
Thou art tann'd almost beyond my knowing, *b*. „ IV 1016
Brotherhood lustiest and lousiest of this Cain's *b*, answer. *Becket* I iv 185
find The common *b* of man has been Wrong'd *Prom. of May* III 543
Brother-like That is not *b-l*. *Foresters* II i 504
Brought (*See also* **Browt**) and he *b* his doubts And fears to me. *Queen Mary* I ii 74
And *b* us back the mass. „ I v 184
Hast thou *B* me the letter which thine Emperor promised „ I v 347
cause that hath *b* us together is not the cause „ II i 161
They have *b* it in large measure on themselves. „ IV iii 363
Indian shawl That Philip *b* me in our happy days!— „ V ii 540
Madam, I *b* My King's congratulations; „ V ii 569
b Thy war with Brittany to a goodlier close *Harold* II ii 48
And *b* the sunder'd tree again, „ III i 144
Alas! poor man, *His* promise *b* it on me. „ III i 338
being *b* before the courts of the Church, *Becket, Pro.* 12
my bishop Hath *b* your king to a standstill. „ *Pro.* 44
I *b* them In from the wood, and set them here. „ II i 130
My liege, what hast thou *b* me? „ II i 223
I *b* not ev'n my crucifix. *Henry.* Take this. „ II i 295
and so *b* me no-hows as I may say, „ III i 129
Your old child *b* me hither! „ IV ii 13
B me again to her own city?— *The Cup* I i 14
but this day has *b* A great occasion. *The Falcon* 488
I think I never can be *b* to love any man. *Prom. of May* II 78
Superstitious fool, What *b* me here? „ II 351
now that you have been *b* to us as it were from the grave, „ III 235
If marriage ever *b* a woman happiness „ III 639
Thro' that dishonour which you *b* upon us, „ III 765
could be *b* to love me As I loved you— „ III 779
new term *B* from the sacred East, his harem? *Foresters* IV 705
like the man In Holy Writ, who *b* his talent back; „ IV 981
Brow The *b's* unwrinkled as a summer mere.— *Harold* III i 48
—brave Gurth, one gash from *b* to knee! „ V ii 71
There's no jest on the *b's* of Herbert there. *Becket, Pro.* 390
Life on the face, the *b's*—clear innocence! „ II i 195
Ay, and his *b's* are thine; „ II i 218
bust of Juno and the *b's* and eyes Of Venus; *The Cup* I i 120
In the sweat of thy *b*, says Holy Writ, shalt thou eat bread, but in the sweat of thy *b* *Foresters* IV 201
Browt (**brought**) I ha' *b* these roses to ye—I forgits what they calls 'em, *Prom. of May* II 14
so I allus *b* soom on 'em to her; „ II 20
to saäy he's *b* some of Miss Eva's roses „ III 346
Bruised as having been so *b* By Harold, King of Norway; *Harold* IV i 9
B; but no bones broken. *Prom. of May* III 242
Honest daisy deadly *b*, *Foresters* II ii 156
And *b* him almost to the death, „ III 361
Brunanburg What's *B* To Stamford-bridge? *Harold* IV iii 142
And chanting that old song of *B* „ V i 215
Brush (**s**) with some sense of art, to live By *b* and pencil. *Prom. of May* I 499
Brush (**verb**) and *b* This Wyatt from our shoulders, *Queen Mary* II ii 293
Her cap would *b* his heels. „ III i 14
Brussels We meet at *B*. „ III vi 215
Brutal Because these islanders are *b* beasts? „ III vi 153
almost *b*, and matched with my Harold *Prom. of May* III 175
Curse on your *b* strength! „ III 732
Brute (**adj.**) Brook for an hour such *b* malignity? *Queen Mary* IV iii 544
Brute (**s**) (*See also* **Baron-brute**) Mutilated, poor *b*, my sumpter-mule, *Becket* V ii 440
Bubble Many so dote upon this *b* world, *Queen Mary* IV iii 168
'O *b* world, Whose colours in a moment break and fly!' „ V ii 204
Bubbled you so *b* over with hot terms Of Satan, „ I ii 94
Buck *B*; deer, as you call it. *Becket* I iv 139
Wherever the horn sound, and the *b* bound, *Foresters* III 345
Wherever the *b* bound, and the horn sound, „ III 355
Buckingham (**Duke of**) And I the race of murder'd *B*— *Queen Mary* III i 454
Bud (**s**) Rose never blew that equall'd such a *b*. „ III i 373
that shoots New *b's* to heaven, *Foresters* I iii 26
Bud (**verb**) court is always May, *b's* out in masques, *Queen Mary* III v 11
believe My old crook'd spine would *b* out two young wings *Harold* III i 24
Buffet (**s**) I will give thee a *b* on the face. *Foresters* I i 146
Then thou shalt play the game of *b's* with us. „ IV 259
I give thee A *b*, and thou me. „ IV 263
Buffet (**verb**) you stroke me on one cheek, *B* the other. *Queen Mary* II i 118
Build Too gross to be thrust out, will *b* him round, „ III iii 55
help to *b* a throne Out-towering hers of France . . . *Harold* II ii 763
I vow to *b* a church to God Here on the hill of battle; „ V ii 137
Here His turtle *b's*; his exit is our adit: *Becket* III ii 7
as she was helping to *b* the mound against the city. *Foresters* II i 309
would cower to any Of mortal *b*. „ II i 690
whose return *B's* up our house again? „ IV 1009
Builded (*See also* **Built**) I have *b* the great church of Holy Peter: *Harold* I i 179
Builder she leaves only the nest she built, they leave the *b*. *Becket* I iv 47
Built (*See also* **Builded**) They have *b* their castles here; *Harold* III i 36
I have *b* the Lord a house—(repeat) *Harold* III i 178, 180, 186
loftiest minster ever *b* To Holy Peter in our English isle! *Harold* III i 206
I have *b* a secret bower in England, Thomas, *Becket, Pro.* 153
I wrong the bird; she leaves only the nest she *b*, „ I iv 46
Bull-headed Sir Thomas Stafford, a *b-h* ass, *Queen Mary* V i 284
Bullingham (**Nicholas, afterwards Bishop of Worcester**) Ailmer and *B*, and hundreds more; „ I ii 11
Bullock I'd like to fell 'im as deäd as a *b*! *Prom. of May* II 597
Bully Keep silence, *b* friar, before the King. *Foresters* IV 919
Bulrush Had I a *b* now in this right hand For sceptre, „ III 76
Bulwark A *b* against Throne and Baronage. *Becket* I i 17
Burgher My *b's* son—Nay, if I cannot break „ I iii 331
Burgundy all France, all *B*, Poitou, all Christendom *Harold* III ii 149
Burial We will not give him A Christian *b*: „ V ii 154
I've been attending on his deathbed and his *b*. *Prom. of May* II 4
Burial-hindering bell-silencing, anti-marrying, *b-h* interdict *Becket* III iii 55
Buried (**part. and adj.**) boil'd, *b* alive, worried by dogs; *Queen Mary* II i 210
There lies a treasure *b* down in Ely: *Harold* III i 11
Let me be *b* there, and all our kings, „ III i 208
Buried (**verb**) traitor-brother, Tostig, him Reverently we *b*. „ IV iii 85
Burn but I and my old woman 'ud *b* upon it, *Queen Mary* I i 56
her hate Will *b* till you are burn'd. „ I ii 59
I wrote it, and God grant me power to *b*! „ I ii 99
Monstrous! blasphemous! She ought to *b*. „ I v 58
and *b* the throne Where you should sit with Philip: „ I v 509
Let the dead letter *b*! „ III iv 41
If we could *b* out heresy, my Lord Paget, „ III iv 53
yet I would not say *B*! and we cannot *b* whole towns; „ III iv 175
many of them Would *b*—have burnt each other; „ III iv 217
Would'st thou not *b* and blast them root and branch? „ III iv 282
He'll *b* a diocese to prove his orthodoxy. „ III iv 353
Smiles that *b* men. „ III iv 404
they play with fire as children do, And *b* the house. „ III vi 30
Gardiner *b's*, And Bonner *b's*; „ III vi 59
Did not More die, and Fisher? he must *b*. „ IV i 53
The better for him. He *b's* in Purgatory, not in Hell. „ IV i 56
The heretic must *b*. „ IV i 123
But if you *b* him,—well, your Highness knows „ IV i 144
It were more merciful to *b* him now. „ IV i 153
Philip's will, and mine, that he should *b*. „ IV i 186
It is against all precedent to *b* One who recants; „ IV ii 49
Well, *b* me or not *b* me I am fixt; „ IV ii 54
Will they *b* me, Thirlby? „ IV ii 181
And they will surely *b* me? „ IV ii 190

Burn (*continued*) he was deliver'd To the secular arm to *b*; *Queen Mary* IV ii 214
You shall *b* too, *B* first when I am burnt. „ IV ii 220
What sort of brothers then be those that lust To *b* each other? „ IV iii 198
And watch a good man *b*. „ IV iii 293
all her burnins' 'ill never *b* out the hypocrisy „ IV iii 525
There's nought but the vire of God's hell ez can *b* out that. „ IV iii 527
'll *b* the Pwoap out o' this 'ere land vor iver and iver. „ IV iii 535
B more! *Mary*. I will, I will; and you will stay? „ V i 103
They know nothing; They *b* for nothing. „ V ii 114
Thou hast burnt others, do thou *b* thyself, Or I will *b* thee;' „ V ii 176
Seize him and *b* him for a Lutheran. „ V ii 245
How her hand *b's*! (repeat) „ V ii 552, 616
Gardiner *b's* Already; but to pay them full in kind, „ V iv 13
sir, in Guernsey, I watch'd a woman *b*; „ V iv 18
And *b* the tares with unquenchable fire! *B*!— Fie, what a savour! „ V v 114
but take back thy ring. It *b's* my hand— *Harold* III ii 186
They *b* themselves *within*-door. *Becket* I i 289
grow to such a heat As *b's* a wrong to ashes, *Foresters* II i 700
Burn (born) But I taäkes 'im fur a bad lot and a *b* fool, *Prom. of May* I 153
but I taäkes 'im for a Lunnun swindler, and a *b* fool. „ I 309
b a plowman, and now, as far as money goäs, „ I 330
afoor ony o' ye wur *b*—ye all knaws the ten äacre— „ I 366
but I were *b* afoor schoolin-time. „ III 40
Burn'd (*See also* **Burnt**) her hate Will burn till you are *b*. *Queen Mary* I ii 59
b, boil'd, buried alive, worried by dogs; „ II i 210
Hooper *b* Three-quarters of an hour. „ IV ii 226
hand!' So held it till it all was *b*, „ IV iii 615
Burner are profitless to the *b's*, And help the other side. „ IV ii 219
My fancy takes the *b's* part, „ IV ii 231
Burnin' my rheumatizy be that bad howiver be I to win to the *b*. „ IV iii 474
wi' dree hard eggs for a good pleace at the *b*; „ IV iii 490
but all her *b's*' 'ill niver burn out the hypocrisy „ IV iii 524
the *b* o' the owld archbishop 'll burn „ IV iii 535
Burning (part.) (*See also* **A-burnin'**) Ridley was longer *b*; but he died As manfully „ IV iii 342
Burning (s) (*See also* **Burnin'**) bad my chaplain, Castro, preach Against these *b's*. „ III vi 75
His learning makes his *b* the more just. „ IV i 159
these *b's* will not help The purpose of the faith; „ IV ii 183
'twas you That sign'd the *b* of poor Joan of Kent; „ IV ii 206
these *b's*, As Thirlby says, are profitless to the burners, „ IV ii 217
You have not gone to see the *b*? „ IV iii 290
I warrant you they talk about the *b*. „ IV iii 463
you bring the smoke Of Cranmer's *b* with you. „ IV iii 562
this cup rescued from the *b* of one of her shrines *The Cup* I i 41
Burnish'd I'll have it *b* firelike; *Queen Mary* I v 373
I flash out at times Of festival like *b* summer-flies, *Foresters* I ii 276
Burnt (*See also* **Burn'd**) I'll have you flogg'd and *b* too, *Queen Mary* I i 60
she said that no one in her time should be *b* for heresy. „ I i 97
I'll have their bibles *b*. The bible is the priest's. „ III i 285
many of them Would burn—have *b* each other; „ III iv 217
It would have *b* both speakers. „ III vi 164
Burn first when I am *b*. „ IV ii 222
my hand shall first be *b*; So I may come to the fire. „ IV iii 250
When we had come where Ridley *b* with Latimer, „ IV iii 585
Thou hast *b* others, do thou burn thyself, „ V ii 176
hands that write them should be *b* clean off As Cranmer's, „ V ii 191
Gardiner, out of love for him, *B* it, „ V ii 503
We have but *b* The heretic priest, „ V v 105
Sir, you were *b* for heresy, not for treason, „ V v 139
sacred shrine By chance was *b* along with it. *The Cup* I ii 66
And a salt wind *b* the blossoming trees; *Prom. of May* I 57
Burrow far-off *b* where the King Would miss her and for ever. *Becket* IV ii 158
Burrowing the wild boar, The *b* badger— *Foresters* I iii 121
Burst (adj.) And like a river in flood thro' a *b* dam *Harold* II ii 466
Burst (s) This *b* and bass of loyal harmony, *Queen Mary* II ii 285

Burst (verb) (*See also* **Bust**) in that last inhospitable plunge Our boat hath *b* her ribs; *Harold* II i 3
Hot-headed fools—to *b* the wall of shields! „ V i 612
Fly, fly, my lord, before they *b* the doors! *Becket* V iii 56
Bursten *b* at the toes, and down at heels. *Queen Mary* I i 52
Burthen (load) the monk-king, Louis, our former *b*, *Becket* IV ii 306
One slow, fat, white, a *b* of the hearth; „ V ii 211
grave he goes to, Beneath the *b* of years. *Prom. of May* III 517
Bow'd to the dust beneath the *b* of sin. „ III 521
Burthen (refrain) That is the *b* of it—lost and found *Harold* III ii 9
Bury *B* him and his paramour together. „ V ii 150
b me in the mound, says the woman. *Foresters* II i 312
let him *b* her Even in the bowels of the earth „ III 461
Bush like a timorous beast of prey Out of the *b* by night? *Harold* I ii 214
A man may hang gold bracelets on a *b*, „ II i 88
To catch the bird again within the *b*! „ II ii 67
A nest in a *b*. *Becket*. And where, my liege? *Becket, Pro.* 155
stray'd From love's clear path into the common *b*, „ III i 248
Miss Eva, she set the *b* by my dairy winder *Prom. of May* II 18
Softly! softly! there may be a thief in every *b*. *Foresters* II i 368
Crouch all into the *b*! „ IV 596
Business (adj.) whether thou be Hedgar, or Hedgar's *b* man, *Prom. of May* II 735
Business (s) pray'd me to confess In Wyatt's *b*, *Queen Mary* III v 167
Your Grace's *b* will not suffer, sire, „ III vi 244
Sire, the *b* Of thy whole kingdom waits me: *Becket, Pro.* 277
Well, *b*. I must leave you, love, to-day. *Prom. of May* I 624
for as I used to transact all his *b* for him, „ II 719
whether thou be Hedgar, or Hedgar's business man, thou hesn't naw *b* 'ere wi' *my* Dora, „ II 735
I trust I may be able by-and-by to help you in the *b* of the farm; „ III 223
That *b* which we have in Nottingham— *Foresters* III 229
And may your *b* thrive in Nottingham! „ III 244
Buss *B* me, my bird! *The Falcon* 28
Bussing *See* **A-bussin'**
Bust *b* of Juno and the brows and eyes Of Venus; *The Cup* I i 120
Bust (burst) he be fit to *b* hissen wi' spites and jalousies. *Prom. of May* II 164
Let 'im *b* hissen, then, for owt *I* cares. „ II 166
Bustle gather your men—Myself must *b*. *Queen Mary* II ii 374
Butcher they call me now, The scourge and *b* „ V ii 106
What, Mr. Dobson? A *b's* frock? *Prom. of May* I 94
Butt This Barbarossa *b's* him from his chair, *Becket, Pro.* 217
Butter Our Daisy's *b's* as good 'z hern. *Queen Mary* IV iii 481
the making of your *b*, and the managing of your poultry? *Prom. of May* II 93
Butterfly like a *b* in a chrysalis, You spent your life; *Queen Mary* I iv 51
but now I called you *b*. „ I iv 66
I love not to be called a *b*: Why do you call me *b*? „ I iv 68
Wi' the *butterflies* out, and the swallers at plaäy, *Prom. of May* II 198
waded in the brook, ran after the *butterflies*, „ III 275
Buy Gardiner *b's* them With Philip's gold. *Queen Mary* III i 144
B you their cheeses, and they'll side with you; „ IV iii 548
if we *will* *b* diamond necklaces To please our lady, *The Falcon* 44
And sold thine own To *b* it for her. „ 77
but I couldn't *b* my darter back ageän when she lost hersen, *Prom. of May* III 453
How hadst thou then the means to *b* a cow? *Foresters* II i 304
Would *b* me for a thousand marks in gold— „ IV 652
Who thought to *b* your marrying me with gold. „ IV 718
Buzz (s) Little doubt This *b* will soon be silenced; *Queen Mary* V i 293
We make but one hour's *b*, *Foresters* I ii 277
Buzz (verb) Bee mustn't *b*, Whoop—but he knows. (repeat) *Becket* III i 98, 240
Thy bee should *b* about the Court of John. *Foresters* IV 44
Buzzard (adj.) His *b* beak and deep-incavern'd eyes *Queen Mary* I iv 266
Buzzard (s) Hawk, *b*, jay, the mavis and the merle, *Foresters* I iii 115
Buzzed Were freely *b* among them. *Queen Mary* II ii 98
The bee *b* up in the heat. *Foresters* IV 14
And the bee *b* down from the heat. „ IV 20
And the bee *b* up in the cold „ IV 21
And the bee *b* off in the cold. „ IV 27
Buzzing were more than I *b* round the blossom— *Becket, Pro.* 521
For ever *b* at your lady's face. *Foresters* IV 11

By-and-by I trust I shall forgive him—*b-a-b*—not now. *Prom. of May* II 466
She said herself She would forgive him, *b-a-b*, not now—For her own sake *then*, if not for mine—not now—But *b-a-b*. „ II 681
B-a-b—eh, lad, dosta knaw this paäper? „ II 686
Eh, lad, dosta knaw what tha meäns wi' *b-a-b*? „ II 691
then, *b-a-b*, if she weänt listen to me when I be a-tryin' to saäve 'er— „ II 693
I trust I may be able *b-a-b* to help you in the business of the farm; „ III 222
Let me rest. I'll call you *b a b*. *Becket* v i 90
Byblow The Falaise *b*! *Harold* IV iii 174
Bygone (adj.) and smile At *b* things till that eternal peace. *The Cup* I iii 172
Bygone (s) Let *b's* be *b's*. Go home! Good-night! *Prom. of May* III 156
By-thing These are *b-t's* In the great cause. *Becket* III iii 11
The *b-t's* of the Lord Are the wrong'd innocences „ III iii 13
Byway The leprous flutterings of the *b*, *Queen Mary* IV iii 76
From all the hidden *b-w's* of the world *Becket* III iii 15
Byword I am a *b*. Heretic and rebel Point at me *Queen Mary* v ii 316

C

Cabin Show me some cave or *c* where I may rest *Foresters* II i 130
Cackling What are you *c* of bastardy under *Queen Mary* I i 58
Cadaver Perinde ac *c*—as the priest says, „ I iv 180
Cade And he will prove an Iden to this *C*, „ II ii 369
Cæsar (*See also* **Scizzars**) kindly rendering Of 'Render unto *C*.' . . . *Harold* III ii 168
the first Christian *C* drew to the East „ v i 22
make the soil For *C's*, Cromwells, and Napoleons *Prom. of May* III 593
Cage (s) pounce like a wild beast out of his *c* *Queen Mary* I i 88
It is the heat and narrowness of the *c* „ III v 207
I whistle to the bird has broken *c*, And all in vain. „ v v 20
To guard this bird of passage to her *c*; *Becket* I i 329
I have lived, poor bird, from *c* to *c*, „ III i 222
fondest pair of doves will jar, Ev'n in a *c* of gold, „ IV ii 42
barred thee up in thy chamber, like a bird in a *c*. *Foresters* I i 315
Cage (verb) Catch the wild cat, *c* him, and when he springs *Queen Mary* v v 65
Cain And mark'd me ev'n as *C*, „ III ii 55
light darkness, Abel *C*, The soul the body, *Becket* I iii 716
Thou the lustiest and lousiest of this *C's* brotherhood, answer. „ I iv 185
With *C's* answer, my lord. Am I his keeper? Thou shouldst call him *C*, not me. „ I iv 186
With *C* belike, in the land of Nod, „ I iv 195
Caitiff From councillor to *c*—fallen so low, *Queen Mary* IV iii 75
Ay, go in peace, *c*, *c*! *Becket* I iii 735
Cake He speaks As if it were a *c* of gingerbread. „ II i 230
Caked And *c* and plaster'd with a hundred mires, *Harold* IV iii 177
Calais withdraw Part of our garrison at *C*. *Mary*. *C*! *Queen Mary* I v 123
take mine eyes, mine heart, But do not lose me *C*. „ I v 129
C is but ill-garrison'd, in Guisnes „ v i 4
Or you will lose your *C*. „ v i 11
And you must look to *C* when I go. „ v i 17
Is *C* taken? „ v ii 27
sharper harm to England and to Rome, Than *C* taken. „ v ii 30
Madam, *C* is taken. „ v ii 241
that our brave English Had sallied out from *C* „ v ii 256
Let every craft that carries sail and gun Steer toward *C*. „ v ii 276
Ah! much heresy Shelter'd in *C*. „ v ii 299
angry chronicles hereafter By loss of *C*. Grant me *C*. „ v ii 305
C gone—Guisnes gone, too—and Philip gone! „ v v 22
you will find written Two names, Philip and *C*; „ v v 155
Calcined fain had *c* all Northumbria To one black ash, *Harold* III i 56
Calculated —all seen,—all *c*, All known by Rome. *The Cup* I ii 255
Calender In Britain's *c* the brightest day *Queen Mary* III ii 118
Calf (of the leg) Prick 'em in the *calves* with the arrow-points—prick 'em in the *calves*. *Foresters* IV 560
Prick him in the *calves*! „ IV 567
Calf (young of the cow, etc.) By God's death, thou shalt stick him like a *c*! *Becket* I iii 184
but Salisbury was a *c* cowed by Mother Church, „ III iii 95
Calf (young of the cow, etc.) (*continued*) the fatting of your *calves*, the making of your butter, *Prom. of May* II 93
Calixtus (the first, Pope) The day of St. *C*, and the day, *Harold* v ii 121
Call (s) There's no *c* As yet for me; *Queen Mary* II i 24
and no *c* for sonnet-sorting now, „ II i 59
God grant you ampler mercy at your *c* „ IV i 189
Heaven curse him if he come not at your *c*! *Prom. of May* I 765
He did it so well there was no *c* for me. *Foresters* II i 548
Call (verb) let me *c* her our second Virgin Mary, *Queen Mary* I iii 57
C him a Knight, That, with an ass's, „ I iii 167
Why do you *c* me butterfly? „ I iv 69
They *c* him cold, Haughty, ay, worse. „ I v 431
I do not love your Grace should *c* me coward. „ II iv 89
Why do they *c* him so? „ III i 199
I cannot tell you why they *c* him so. „ III i 205
You *c* me too black-blooded— „ III i 347
William the Silent They *c* him— „ III ii 193
Or a high-dropsy, as the doctors *c* it. „ III ii 225
We come not to compel, but *c* again; „ III iii 187
c they not The one true faith, a loathsome idol-worship? „ III iv 218
And let him *c* me truckler. „ III iv 355
Nor shame to *c* it nature. „ III v 77
New learning as they *c* it; „ IV i 78
Ay—gentle as they *c* you—live or die! „ IV ii 161
Did I *c* him heretic? A huge heresiarch! „ IV iii 45
if thou *c* on God and all the saints, „ IV iii 96
so past martyr-like—Martyr I may not *c* him— „ IV iii 625
Ay, ay; but many voices *c* me hence. „ v i 32
What voices *c* you Dearer than mine „ v i 36
He *c's* us worse than Jews, Moors, Saracens. „ v i 150
they *c* me now, The scourge and butcher of their English church. „ v ii 104
They *c* him away: Ye do him wrong, *Harold* I ii 14
C it to temporize; and not to lie; „ II ii 415
They *c* me near, for I am close to thee „ III i 6
C me not King, but Harold. „ III ii 33
He *c's* us little! „ IV i 41
Somewhere hard at hand. *C* and she comes. „ IV i 186
What did the dead man *c* it—Sanguelac, „ v i 184
C when the Norman moves— „ v i 229
C not for help from me. I knew him not. „ v ii 54
what shall I *c* it, affect her thine own self. *Becket*, *Pro.* 513
As Canterbury *c's* them, wandering clouds, „ I iii 70
Or constitutions, or whate'er ye *c* them, „ I iii 138
C in the poor from the streets, and let them feast. „ I iv 72
C in the poor! „ I iv 78
C them in, I say. „ I iv 85
Buck; deer, as you *c* it. „ I iv 139
Thou shouldst *c* him Cain, not me. „ I iv 188
I'll *c* thee little Geoffrey. *Henry*. *C* him! „ II i 214
See if our pious—what shall I *c* him, John?— „ II ii 38
Ay, ay, good brother, They *c* you the Monk-King. „ II ii 73
Who *c's* me? she That was my wife, „ II ii 74
if the city be sick, and I cannot *c* the kennel sweet, „ II ii 348
They *c* thee John the Swearer. „ II ii 462
whom you *c*—fancy—my husband's brother's wife. „ III i 202
They *c* her—But she lives secret, you see. „ IV i 11
What does she *c* him? *Geoffrey*. My liege. „ IV i 18
whom it pleases him To *c* his wives; „ IV ii 37
She *c's* you beauty, but I don't like her looks. „ IV ii 61
Like the wild beast—if you can *c* it love. „ IV ii 121
Let me rest. I'll *c* you by and by. „ v i 90
Then you have done it, and I *c you* cruel. „ v ii 135
I know not why You *c* these old things back „ v ii 270
c's you oversea To answer for it in his Norman courts. „ v ii 354
Who is our guest? *Sinnatus*. Strato he *c's* himself. *The Cup* I ii 48
they *c* it so in Rome. *Sinnatus*. Province! „ I ii 93
C first upon the Goddess, Synorix. „ II 256
I *c* thee To make my marriage prosper to my wish! „ II 307
I *c* on our own Goddess in our own Temple. „ II 314
Speak freely, tho' to *c* a madman mad *The Falcon* 81
if your lordship care to *c* for it. „ 139
C him back and say I come to breakfast with him. „ 211
my nobleness Of nature, as you deign to *c* it, „ 811
he cooms up, and he *c's* out among our oän men, *Prom. of May* I 139

Call (verb) (*continued*) Would *c* this vice; but one time's vice — *Prom. of May* I 534
grant you what they *c* a license To marry. ,, I 695
but *c* for Philip when you will, And he returns. ,, I 757
I ha' browt these roses to ye—I forgits what they *c's* 'em. ,, II 15
Might I *c* Upon your father— ,, II 512
C if you will, and when you will. ,, II 517
—the crowd would *c* it conscience— ,, II 638
'I *c* you, Philip Edgar, Philip Edgar! ,, II 657
an' whether thou *c's* thysen Hedgar or Harold, ,, II 737
as they *c* it so truly, to the grave at the bottom, ,, III 193
Master Hedgar, Harold, or whativer They *c's* ye, ,, III 728
The fool-people *c* her a witch— *Foresters* II i 178
I have forgotten my horn that *c's* my men together. ,, II i 185
And you dare to *c* me Tit. ,, II ii 127
Wouldst thou *c* my Oberon Ob? ,, II ii 131
but *c* Kate when you will, for I am close at hand. ,, III 49
Sit there, knaves, till the captain *c* for you. ,, III 220
Do you *c* that in my honour? ,, III 432
did ye not *c* me king in your song? ,, IV 220
I could but sneak and smile and *c* it courtesy, ,, IV 366
they that suffer by him *c* the blossom Of bandits. ,, IV 371
shall I *c* it by that new term Brought ,, IV 703
men will *c* him An Eastern tyrant, ,, IV 902

Call'd took her hand, *c* her sweet sister, *Queen Mary* I i 80
but now I *c* you butterfly. ,, I iv 66
I love not to be *c* a butterfly: ,, I iv 68
c my friends together, Struck home and won. ,, I v 552
and ye have *c* me to be your leader. ,, II i 165
Lo! thou hast *c* them up! here they come— ,, III i 233
The islands *c* into the dawning church ,, III iii 172
You know I never come till I be *c*. ,, III v 215
He *c* my word my bond! *Harold* II ii 665
when that which reign'd *C* itself God— ,, III ii 167
Cram thy crop full, but come when thou art *c*. ,, IV iii 235
well train'd, and easily *c* Off from the game. *Becket, Pro.* 120
I sign'd them—being a fool, as Foliot *c* me. ,, I iii 562
father's eye was so tender it would have *c* a goose off the green, ,, III iii 102
And thereupon he *c* my children bastards. ,, IV ii 44
I am most sure that some one *c*. *The Cup* II 509
then I was *c* away; And presently all rose, *The Falcon* 365
then he *c* me a rude naäme, and I can't abide 'im. *Prom. of May* II 158
Her phantom *c* me by the name she loved. ,, II 242
who *c* the mind Of children a blank page, ,, II 281
not forgotten his promise to come when I *c* him. ,, III 330
I that have been *c* a Socialist, A Communist, a Nihilist— ,, III 584
a fine! he hath *c* plain Robin a lord. *Foresters* III 215
Sit there till you be *c* for. ,, III 296
fine him! he hath *c* plain Robin an earl. ,, IV 151
a fine! He hath *c* plain Robin a king. ,, IV 218

Calling (part.) (*See also* **A-callin'**) ten thousand men on Penenden Heath all *c* after *Queen Mary* II i 61

Calling (s) The dog followed his *c*, my lord. *Becket* I iv 97

Callous *c* with a constant stripe, Unwoundable. *Queen Mary* V v 171

Calm and less than I would in a *c*. *Harold* II i 68
lest ye should draw together like two ships in a *c*. *Becket* III iii 298

Calumny Twice did thy malice and thy *calumnies* Exile me ,, I iii 42

Calved *See* **Cawved**

Cambridge Thou art but yesterday from *C*, Grim; ,, V ii 55

Came (*See also* **Coomed, Cum**) my good mother *c* (God rest her soul) Of Spain, *Queen Mary* I v 11
Your royal mother *c* of Spain, ,, I v 16
and his right *c* down to me, ,, II ii 171
when the traitor wife *c* out for bread ,, III i 11
I *c* to feel the pulse of England, ,, III i 37
as the new-made couple *C* from the Minster, ,, III i 95
She *c* upon the scaffold, ,, III i 375
C with a sudden splendour, shout, and show, ,, III i 449
And how *c* you round again? ,, III ii 36
And you *c* and kiss'd me milking the cow. (repeat) ,, III v 91, 98
Robin *c* behind me, ,, III v 92
I *c* to thank her Majesty For freeing my friend Bagenhall ,, III vi 5
She *c* upon it, read it, and then rent it, ,, III vi 142

Came (*continued*) *c* to the fire on earth. *Queen Mary* IV i 60
So worshipt of all those that *c* across him; ,, IV i 162
hands *C* from the crowd and met his own; ,, IV iii 583
when I *c* to wed your majesty, Lord Howard, ,, V i 56
I *c* to sue Your Council and yourself (repeat) ,, V i 107, 114
what *you* said When last you *c* to England? ,, V ii 568
the child *c* not, and the husband *c* not; ,, V ii 581
and in her agony The mother *c* upon her— ,, V iv 20
never merry world In England, since the Bible *c* among us. ,, V v 241
These meteors *c* and went before our day, *Harold* I i 131
An evil dream that ever *c* and went— ,, I ii 70
blast that *c* So suddenly hath fallen as suddenly— ,, II i 13
We be fishermen; I *c* to see after my nets. ,, II i 27
He *c* not to see me, had past me by ,, II ii 27
whereby we *c* to know Thy valour and thy value, ,, II ii 201
Your comet *c* and went. ,, III i 359
The Lord was God and *c* as man— ,, III ii 172
Since Tostig *c* with Norway— ,, IV i 173
Last night King Edward *c* to me in dreams— (repeat) *Harold* IV i 259, 265
and woke and *c* Among us again, *Harold* IV iii 151
Our guardsmen have slept well, since we *c* in? ,, V i 208
who *c* before To tell thee thou shouldst win ,, V i 235
There is one Come as Goliath *c* of yore— ,, V i 493
then the King *c* honeying about her, *Becket, Pro.* 516
What *c* of that? The first archbishop fled, ,, I iii 52
When Henry *c* into his own again, ,, I iii 153
I *c*, your King! Nor dwelt alone, ,, I iii 356
I *c* on certain wholesome usages, ,, I iii 412
Which *c* into thy hands when Chancellor. ,, I iii 653
But the miller *c* home that night, ,, I iv 173
Besides, we *c* away in such a heat, ,, II i 293
I *c* to England suddenly, ,, III i 86
we *c* on to the banquet, from whence there puffed ,, III iii 113
Ha, you! How *c* you hither? ,, IV ii 12
No, for it *c* to nothing—only a feint. ,, IV ii 398
The fellow that on a lame jade *c* to court, ,, V i 246
we *c* upon A wild-fowl sitting on her nest, ,, V ii 232
at Pontigny *c* to me The ghostly warning ,, V ii 290
C to the front of the wood— *The Cup* I ii 119
I dare not tell him how I *c* to know it; ,, I ii 275
Why *c* ye not before? ,, I iii 175
c To plead to thee for Sinnatus's life, ,, II 391
c back last night with her son to the castle. *The Falcon* 3
when he *c* last year To see me hawking, ,, 312
I *c* In person to return them. ,, 726
c and dipt your sovereign head Thro' these low doors, ,, 866
The maid to her dairy *c* in from the cow, *Prom. of May* I 39
I *c* back to keep his birthday. ,, I 73
stateliness and sweetness! How *c* she by it?— ,, II 622
who *c* to us three years after you were gone, how should she know you? ,, III 232
dead midnight when I *c* upon the bridge; ,, III 368
bow'd To the earth he *c* from, ,, III 515
Only fifteen when first you *c* on her, ,, III 750
to her you *c* Veiling one sin to act another. ,, III 772
I *c* to give thee the first kiss, and thou hast given it me. *Foresters* I i 132
I *c* To eat him up and make an end of him. ,, II i 124
How *c* we to be parted from our men? ,, II i 254
I believe She *c* with me into the forest here. ,, II i 485
There *c* some evil fairy at my birth And cursed me, ,, II ii 108
no man, so His own true wife *c* with him, ,, III 240
first part—made before you *c* among us— ,, III 436
delicate-footed creature *C* stepping o'er him, ,, IV 537

Cameleon such a *c* he! *Queen Mary* III iii 15

Camest When *c* thou thither? *Gamel.* To-day, good Earl. *Harold* I i 105
How *c* thou hither? *Geoffrey.* On my legs. *Becket* IV i 4
Pretty one, how *c* thou? ,, IV i 20
Show me where thou *c* out of the wood. ,, IV i 45

Camma (wife of Sinnatus, afterwards Priestess in the Temple of Artemis) 'To the admired *C*, wife of Sinnatus, the Tetrarch, *The Cup* I i 36
Take thou this letter and this cup to *C*, ,, I i 62

Camma (*continued*) 'To the admired *C*,—beheld you afar off— *The Cup* I ii 71
C, Wise I am sure as she is beautiful, „ I ii 138
C, Rome has a glimpse of this conspiracy; „ I ii 232
C the stately, *C* the great-hearted, „ I iii 72
And *C* for my bride—Thy people love her— „ I iii 151
C—well, well, I never found the woman „ I iii 165
Since *C* fled from Synorix to our Temple, „ II 14
Great Artemis! O *C*, can it be well, „ II 80
shout of Synorix and *C* sitting Upon one throne, „ II 146
I thank thee, *C*,—I thank thee. (repeat) „ II 331, 355
There, *C*! I have almost drain'd the cup— „ II 384
Antonius—'*C*!' who spake? „ II 401
Synorix, first King, *C*, first Queen o' the Realm, „ II 440
Thou—coming my way too—*C*—good-night. „ II 492
and though a Roman I Forgive thee, *C*. „ II 506
'*C*!'—why there again I am most sure that some one call'd. „ II 507
'*C*, *C*!' Sinnatus, Sinnatus! „ II 536
Camp In the full face of all the Roman *c*? „ I ii 269
I hardly gain'd The *c* at midnight. „ I iii 19
I must lure my game into the *c*. „ I iii 64
The *c* is half a league without the city; „ I iii 89
or at least shall find him There in the *c*. „ I iii 95
Cancel to *c* and abolish all bonds of human allegiance, *Queen Mary* V iv 49
spites at Rome, Is like enough to *c* them, *The Cup* I i 92
Cancell'd (adj.) all Our *c* warrior-gods, our grim Walhalla, *Harold* III ii 73
Cancell'd (verb) Not know that Edward *c* his own promise? „ V i 51
Candle (*See also* **Corpse-candles**) a *c* in the sun Is all but smoke— *Queen Mary* V i 77
Canker'd for there are men Of *c* judgment everywhere— *Becket* V ii 61
Cannon clash'd their bells, Shot off their lying *c*, *Queen Mary* III vi 97
Canon (adj.) There wore his time studying the *c* law *Becket* II i 85
Canon (s) seem According to the *c's* pardon due *Queen Mary* IV iii 33
No, daughter, but the *c's* out of Waltham, *Harold* V i 474
since your *c* will not let you take Life for a life, *Becket* I iii 389
Canonical Stigand is not *c* enough *Harold* III i 215
was thine own election so *c*, Good father? *Becket* I iii 121
by that *c* obedience Thou still hast owed thy father, „ I iii 274
Canonised bones of all the *C* From all the holiest shrines *Harold* II ii 734
Canonists The *C* and Schoolmen were with me. *Queen Mary* I ii 61
Canopy moving side by side Beneath one *c*, „ III i 97
Canterbury (adj.) Methought I stood in *C* Minster, *Becket* I i 73
Because I had my *C* pallium, From one whom they dispoped? *Harold* III i 106
Canterbury (s) slander'd you For setting up a mass at *C* To please the Queen. *Queen Mary* I ii 88
and the legateship Annex'd to *C*— „ V ii 37
Who shall crown him? *C* is dying. *Becket*. The next *C*. *Becket, Pro.* 240
This *C* is only less than Rome, „ I i 147
I cast upon the side of *C*—Our holy mother *C*, „ I i 155
Now I am *C* and thou art York. „ I iii 44
And is not York the peer of *C*? „ I iii 47
When *C* hardly bore a name. „ I iii 60
Who made thee, London? Who, but *C*? „ I iii 67
As *C* calls them, wandering clouds, „ I iii 70
among you those that hold Lands reft from *C*. „ I iii 141
Shall I do less for *C* Than Henry for the crown? „ I iii 147
Shall I do less for mine own *C*? „ I iii 159
Because my lord of *C*! *De Tracy*. Ay, This lord of *C*— „ I iii 424
Claim'd some of our crown lands for *C*— „ I iii 459
If *C* bring his cross to court, Let York bear his to mate with *C*. „ I iii 511
I would, my lord Thomas of *C*, Thou wert plain Thomas and not *C*, Or that thou wouldst deliver *C* „ I iii 577
This *C*, like a wounded deer, Has fled our presence „ II ii 21
Reseat him on his throne of *C*, „ II ii 118
Our castle, my lord, belongs to *C*. „ II ii 262
that hath squeezed out this side-smile upon *C*, „ III iii 57
And send thee back again to *C*? „ III iii 184
crowning thy young son by York, London and Salisbury—not *C*. „ III iii 196
Canterbury (s) (*continued*) York crown'd the Conqueror—not *C*. *Becket*. There was no *C* in William's time. *Becket* III iii 198
My friend of *C* and myself Are now once more „ III iii 228
York against *C*, York against God! „ V ii 66
Divide me from the mother church of England, My *C*. „ V ii 362
And trampled on the rights of *C*. „ V ii 394
The holy follower founded *C*— „ V iii 5
Save that dear head which now is *C*, „ V iii 6
And all the tutelar Saints of *C*. „ V iii 167
Cantrip Save from some hateful *c* of thine own. „ V i 140
Canvas Madam, you have but cut the *c* out; *Queen Mary* V v 183
Canvass Would freely *c* certain Lutheranisms. „ V ii 76
Cap (s) Her *c* would brush his heels. „ III i 14
Knave, wilt thou wear thy *c* before the Queen? „ III i 237
Knock off his *c* there, some of you about him! „ III i 241
Cap (verb) You would not *c* the Pope's commissioner— „ IV ii 123
Capering And *c* hand in hand with Oberon. *Foresters* II i 498
What are you *c* for? „ IV 614
Caprice I am a man not prone to jealousies, *C's*, *Prom. of May* III 627
Captain Then followed the thunder of the *c's* and the shouting, *Becket* III iii 112
Ah dear Robin! ah noble *c*, friend of the poor! *Foresters* II i 182
It is the very *c* of the thieves! „ II i 412
C, we saw thee cowering to a knight „ II i 682
Sit there, knaves, till the *c* call for you. „ III 220
C, nay, it wasn't me. „ III 364
This friar is of much boldness, noble *c*. „ IV 235
Captive That makes the *c* testy; *Queen Mary* III v 208
First, free thy *c* from *her* hopeless prison. *Becket* V i 183
Captivity Translating his *c* from Guy *Harold* II ii 42
Caraffa But this new Pope *C*, Paul the Fourth, *Queen Mary* V ii 32
Carcase When Henry broke the *c* of your church „ I v 397
and make thine old *c* a target for us three. *Foresters* II i 404
Card Hath no more mortice than a tower of *c's*; *Queen Mary* III i 443
Cardinal again to her cousin Reginald Pole, now *C*; „ I i 123
Yet my Lord *C*— *Pole*. I am your Legate; „ III iv 178
—this *C's* fault—I have gulpt it down. „ III iv 376
Good morrow, my Lord *C*; „ IV i 42
'We pray continually for the death Of our accursed Queen and *C* Pole.' „ V ii 181
So is *C* Pole. „ V iv 5
thy King swore to our *c's* He meant no harm *Becket* I iii 215
The *c's* have finger'd Henry's gold. „ I iii 295
—bribe all the *C's*— „ II ii 473
Cardinalate Pope could dispense with his *C*, *Queen Mary* I i 127
Cardinal-Deacon You, Lord Legate And *C-D*, „ III iv 261
Care (s) (*See also* **Take care**) 'Tis the good Count's *c* for thee! *Harold* II ii 251
C dwell with me for ever, when I cease To care for thee *Becket* II i 120
Care (verb) You do right well. I do not *c* to know; *Queen Mary* I iv 189
But will he *c* for that? „ I v 69
Spit them like larks for aught I *c*. „ I v 395
And *c* but little for the life to be. „ III iv 60
And if he did I *c* not, my Lord Howard. „ IV i 129
will hardly *c* to overlook This same petition „ IV i 192
They *c* for nothing else. „ IV iii 171
I do much fear that England will not *c*. „ V ii 283
And cried I was not clean, what should I *c*? „ V ii 325
C not for me who love thee. *Harold* III ii 113
And what *c* I for that? *Becket* I i 200
I *c* not for thy new archbishoprick. „ I i 217
And I say, I *c* not for *thy* saying. (repeat) „ II i 112
who *c's* not for the word, Makes '*c* not'—*c*. „ II i 116
Care dwell with me for ever, when I cease To *c* for thee „ II i 120
Return to Sens, where we will *c* for you. „ II ii 445
But if you should not *c* to take it— „ IV ii 71
Let 'im bust hissen, then, for owt *I c's*. *Prom. of May* II 167
He is all for love, he *c's* not for the land. *Foresters* IV 489
Cared Thou hast but *c* to make thyself a king— *Harold* IV ii 74
if you *c* To live some time among them. *Prom. of May* II 549
Careful but sends His *c* dog to bring them to the fold. *Queen Mary* III iv 105
Be *c* of thine answer, my good friend. *Harold* II ii 604
Carefuller made him all the *c* To find a means „ III i 340
Careless thro' The random gifts of *c* kings, *Becket* I i 159

Careless (*continued*) like a *c* sleeper in the down; *Foresters* I i 207
Caress in some lewd *c* Has wheedled it off the King's neck *Becket* IV ii 200
Carew (*See also* **Peter Carew**) I do not hear from *C* or the Duke Of Suffolk, *Queen Mary* II i 2
C stirs In Devon: „ II i 4
I must not move Until I hear from *C* and the Duke. „ II i 122
C is there, and Thomas Stafford there. „ V i 125
Carle little help without our Saxon *c's* Against Hardrada. *Harold* IV i 35
Carlos But is Don *C* such a goodly match? *Queen Mary* V iii 86
Don *C*, Madam, is but twelve years old. „ V iii 87
Don *C*? Madam, if you marry Philip, „ V iii 117
Carnage So packt with *c* that the dykes and brooks *Harold* III ii 128
Carpet Lay down the Lydian *c's* for the king. *The Cup* II 187
Carried Bonner, it will be *c*. *Queen Mary* III iv 405
I ha' *c* him ever so many miles in my arms, *Becket* I iv 98
drop The mud I *c*, like yon brook, „ II i 159
c off the casks, Kill'd half the crew, „ V ii 442
one shock upon the field when all The harvest has been *c*. *The Falcon* 302
you kept your veil too close for that when they *c* you in; *Prom. of May* III 227
Carrier-pigeon And thou, my *c-p* of black news, *Harold* IV iii 233
Carriest who art more bow-bent than the very bow thou *c*? *Foresters* II i 379
Carrion (adj.) didst thou ever see a *c* crow Stand watching a sick beast *Queen Mary* IV iii 6
and dumb'd his *c* croak From the gray sea for ever. *Harold* IV iii 65
I'd think na moor o' maäkin' an end o' tha nor a *c* craw— *Prom. of May* II 697
Carrion (s) And rolls himself in *c* like a dog. *Queen Mary* I v 169
Carrion-nosing Made even the *c-n* mongrel vomit „ IV iii 448
Carrot Like a *c's*, as thou say'st, and English *c* 's better „ III i 218
Carry I trust that he will *c* you well to-day, „ I iv 145
For all that I can *c* it in my head. „ II i 88
If you can *c* your head upon your shoulders. „ II i 89
I fear you come to *c* it off my shoulders, „ II i 91
that every Spaniard *carries* a tail like a devil „ III i 223
Let every craft that *carries* sail and gun „ V ii 275
C her off among you; *Becket, Pro.* 524
We shall be overwhelm'd. Seize him and *c* him! „ V iii 142
C fresh rushes into the dining-hall, *Foresters* I i 80
C her off, and let the old man die. „ IV 677
Seize him and truss him up, and *c* her off. „ IV 690
Seize her and *c* her off into my castle. „ IV 738
Cart fur she tell'd ma to taäke the *c* to Littlechester. *Prom. of May* II 322
Dan Smith's *c* hes runned ower a laädy i' the holler laäne, „ II 568
Besides it was you that were driving the *c*— „ III 88
our horse and our little *c*— *Foresters* II i 192
Carter our *c's* and our shepherds Still find a comfort there. *Harold*. *C's* and shepherds! *Prom. of May* III 527
Cartwhip and doänt laäy my *c* athurt 'is shou'ders, „ II 138
Carve And *c* my coat upon the walls again! *Queen Mary* II iv 110
to *c* One lone hour from it, *Foresters* II i 42
Casa *C* crematur, Pastor fugatur *Harold* V i 512
Case And first I say it is a grievous *c*, *Queen Mary* IV iii 167
Is that my *c*? so if the city be sick, *Becket* II ii 347
as the *c* stood, you had safelier have slain an archbishop than a she-goat: „ III iii 67
Casement moonlight *c's* pattern'd on the wall, *Queen Mary* V v 9
Ay! yonder is her *c*. *Prom. of May* II 246
storm and shower lashing Her *c*, „ II 473
Then I would drop from the *c*, like a spider. *Foresters* I i 317
Cask carried off the *c's*, Kill'd have the crew, *Becket* V ii 443
c of wine whereof we plunder'd The Norman prelate? *Foresters* III 306
Casket Close as a miser's *c*. Listen: *Queen Mary* I iv 108
Hand me the *c* with my father's sonnets. „ II i 43
Cast *C* off, betray'd, defamed, divorced, forlorn! „ I v 26
C myself down upon my knees before them, „ I v 562
come to *c* herself On loyal hearts and bosoms, „ II ii 261
She *c* on him a vassal smile of love, „ III i 98
pine in Italy that *c* its shadow Athwart a cataract; „ III iv 136
to *c* myself Upon the good Queen's mercy; „ III v 167
and then *C* on the dunghill naked, „ IV iii 446
The Pope would *c* the Spaniard out of Naples: „ V i 148
Cast (*continued*) His early follies *c* into his teeth, *Queen Mary* V ii 124
C it o'er again. „ V iii 4
Did ye not *c* with bestial violence *Harold* I i 49
I *c* me down prone, praying; „ V i 100
I *c* upon the side of Canterbury— *Becket* I i 155
Let either *c* him away like a dead dog! „ II ii 257
black cloud that hath come over the sun and *c* us all into shadow? „ III iii 47
your own people *c* you from their bounds, *The Cup* I i 137
His own true people *c* him from their doors „ I ii 351
I cannot help the mould that I was *c* in. „ I iii 25
Might *c* my largess of it to the crowd! „ II 224
knaw'd better nor to *c* her sister's misfortin inter 'er teeth *Prom. of May* II 127
Be not so *c* down, my sweet Eva. „ III 468
Would you *c* An eye of favour on me, *Foresters* I ii 216
That if I *c* an eye of favour on him, „ I ii 261
to *c* All threadbare household habit, „ I iii 111
C them into our treasury, the beggars' mites, „ III 204
Castaly wells of *C* are not wasted upon the desert. *Becket, Pro.* 387
Castille voices of *C* and Aragon, Granada, *Queen Mary* V i 42
Castle (adj.) All in the *c* garden, *Foresters* I i 10
Castle (s) (*See also* **Sand-castle**) Ah, gray old *c* of Alington, *Queen Mary* II i 243
They have built their *c's* here; *Harold* III i 36
he holp the King to break down our *c's*, *Becket, Pro.* 447
De Tracy and De Brito, from our *c*. „ I i 278
Lord Fitzurse reported this In passing to the *C* even now. „ I ii 13
You are going to the *C*, „ I ii 45
My drift is to the *C*, Where I shall meet the Barons „ I ii 83
To the *C*? *De Broc.* Ay! „ I ii 86
thou, De Broc, that holdest Saltwood *C*— „ I iii 160
Due from his *c's* of Berkhamstead and Eye „ I iii 628
Here is a missive left at the gate by one from the *c*. „ I iv 50
Our *c*, my lord, belongs to Canterbury. „ II ii 261
cursed those De Brocs That hold our Saltwood *C* „ II ii 269
Perchance the fierce De Brocs from Saltwood *C*, „ V ii 249
dungeon'd the other half In Pevensey *C*— „ V ii 446
Undo the doors: the Church is not a *c*: „ V iii 63
came back last night with her son to the *c*. *The Falcon* 4
there is Monna Giovanna coming down the hill from the *c*. „ 161
mount with your lordship's leave to her ladyship's *c*, „ 414
Not like the vintage blowing round your *c*. „ 580
Shall I return to the *c* with you? „ 793
I would set my men-at-arms to oppose thee, like the Lord of the *C*. *Foresters* I i 324
and seeing the hospitable lights in your *c*, „ I ii 195
he hath seized On half the royal *c's*. „ I iii 83
whereon she struck him, And fled into the *c*. „ II i 118
Seize her and carry her off into my *c*. „ IV 738
Thy *c*? (repeat) *Foresters* IV 739, 743
Castro I bad my chaplain, *C*, preach Against these burnings. *Queen Mary* III vi 73
Cat Catch the wild *c*, cage him, and when he springs „ V v 65
He hath as much of *c* as tiger in him. *Harold* I i 154
Milk? *Filippo.* Three laps for a *c*! *The Falcon* 125
And a *c* to the cream, and a rat to the cheese; *Prom. of May* I 53
If a *c* may look at a king, may not a friar speak to one? *Foresters* IV 921
Cataract (*See also* **Winter-cataracts**) A pine in Italy that cast its shadow Athwart a *c*; firm stood the pine—The *c* shook the shadow. *Queen Mary* III iv 137
c typed the headlong plunge and fall Of heresy „ III iv 140
Catch I cannot *c* what Father Bourne is saying. „ I iii 14
We have our spies abroad to *c* her tripping, „ I v 468
there's no Renard here to '*c* her tripping.' *C* me who can; yet, sometime I have wish'd That I were caught, „ III v 159
C the wild cat, cage him, and when he springs „ V v 65
Fellow, dost thou *c* crabs? *Harold* II i 66
I have a mind that thou shalt *c* no more. „ II i 71
To *c* the bird again within the bush! „ II ii 67
flings His brand in air and *c'es* it again, „ V i 494
You *c* 'em, so, Softly, and fling them out to the free air. *Becket* I i 286

Catch (*continued*) and they do say the very breath *c'es.* *Becket* I iv 222
thy flock should *c* An after ague-fit of trembling. „ III iii 32
Take thy one chance ; *C* at the last straw. „ IV ii 221
and a-spreading to *c* her eye for a dozen year, *The Falcon* 100
c A glimpse of them and of their fairy Queen— *Foresters* II ii 102
And *c* the winding of a phantom horn. „ IV 1091
Catechize But who art thou to *c* me— „ III 14
Catharine (**first queen of Henry VIII.**) you divorced Queen *C* and her father ; *Queen Mary* I ii 57
accursed lie Of good Queen *C's* divorce— „ III iv 232
Cathedral nor any ground but English, Where his *c* stands. *Becket* III iii 262
Take refuge in your own *c*, (repeat) „ V ii 584, 590
Strike our Archbishop in his own *c* ! „ V iii 180
Catholic (adj.) But if this Philip, the proud *C* prince, *Queen Mary* I iv 280
where you gave your hand To this great *C* King. „ III ii 92
Can we not have the *C* church as well „ III iii 97
Which in the *C* garden are as flowers, „ IV i 178
Have you remain'd in the true *C* faith I left you in ? *Cranmer.* In the true *C* faith, „ IV ii 17
Yet wherefore should he die that hath return'd To the one *C* Universal Church, „ IV iii 21
In every article of the *C* faith, „ IV iii 230
Peters, you know me *C*, but English. „ IV iii 566
The Queen of Scots at least is *C*. *Philip.* Ay, Madam, *C* ; „ V i 195
But—he would have me *C* of Rome, „ V iii 93
Catholic (s) for we are many of us *C's*, but few Papists, „ I i 114
a pious *C*, Mumbling and mixing up in his scared prayers „ II ii 85
there be some disloyal *C's*, And many heretics loyal ; „ III iv 43
tho' a *C*, I would not, For the pure honour of our common nature, „ IV iii 296
I do hold The *C*, if he have the greater right, „ IV iii 382
Peters, my gentleman, an honest *C*, „ IV iii 553
It is a saying among the *C's*. „ V v 245
Cattle Hath harried mine own *c*—God confound him ! *Harold* IV iii 190
Caught (*See also* **Cotched**) And then if *c*, to the Tower. *Queen Mary* I v 469
sometime I have wish'd That I were *c*, „ III v 163
He *c* a chill in the lagoons of Venice, „ V ii 515
if I *c* them, they should hang Cliff-gibbeted *Harold* II i 95
I shame to quote 'em—*c*, my lord, *Becket* I ii 7
King's verdurer *c* him a-hunting in the forest, „ I iv 95
Not *c*, maim'd, blinded him. *The Cup* I ii 271
when you put it in green, and your stack *c* fire. *Prom. of May* II 56
I am outlaw'd, and if *c*, I die. *Foresters* I iii 163
He *c* her round the waist, „ II i 116
You *c* a lonely woodman of our band, „ III 359
and the hunters, if *c*, are blinded, or worse than blinded. „ IV 226
Cause (s) you had time and *c* enough To sicken *Queen Mary* I v 23
the *c* that hath brought us together is not the *c* „ II i 160
under colour Of such a *c* as hath no colour, „ II ii 183
This was the *c*, and hence the judgment on her. „ III iv 187
Crave, in the same *c*, hearing of your Grace. „ IV i 8
Behold him, brethren : he hath *c* to weep !— „ IV iii 14
thro' the fear of death Gave up his *c*, „ IV iii 28
there *c's* Wherefore our Queen and Council „ IV iii 35
Much less shall others in like *c* escape, „ IV iii 62
I come to the great *c* that weighs Upon my conscience „ IV iii 237
I will move then in your *c* again, „ V i 178
and mine own natural man (It was God's *c*) ; „ V ii 104
We fought like great states for grave *c* ; *Harold* I i 441
I have given her *c*—I fear no woman. „ I ii 41
For thou hast done the battle in my *c* ; „ II ii 555
Refer my *c*, my crown to Rome ! . . . „ V i 1
' All *c's* of advowsons and presentations, *Becket* I iii 78
For the King's pleasure rather than God's *c* „ I iii 698
My lord, We have claspt your *c*, „ II ii 237
That in thy *c* were stirr'd against King Henry, „ II ii 429
These are by-things In the great *c*. „ III iii 12
as one That mars a *c* with over-violence. „ IV ii 327
In mine own *c* I strove against him there, „ V i 14
Cause (s) (*continued*) And in thy *c* I strive against him now. *Becket* V i 16
I do commend my *c* to God, the Virgin, „ V iii 163
not so much for the *c* as for the Earl. *Foresters* I ii 38
I cannot sleep o' nights by *c* on 'em. „ II i 384
What rightful *c* could grow to such a heat „ II i 698
I can defend my *c* against the traitors „ IV 898
Cause (verb) always told Father that the huge old ashtree there would *c* an accident some day ; *Prom. of May* III 245
Causest Who *c* the safe earth to shudder and gape, *The Cup* II 298
Cautery mad bite Must have the *c*—tell him— *Queen Mary* III iv 276
Cavalier And Counts, and sixty Spanish *c's*, „ III i 51
Cave seven sleepers in the *c* at Ephesus Have turn'd *Harold* I i 192
As find a hare's form in a lion's *c*. *Becket* I iii 177
Show me some *c* or cabin where I may rest. *Foresters* II i 130
Cawved (calved) Hes the cow *c* ? *Dora.* No, Father. *Prom. of May* III 427
Cease When will ye *c* to plot against my house ? *Harold* IV i 161
when I *c* To care for thee as ever ! *Becket* II i 121
Well, well, until they *c* to go together, *Foresters* II ii 67
Ceased Until your throne had *c* to tremble. *Queen Mary* I v 393
Cecil (William, Baron Burghley, Queen Elizabeth's chief Minister) *C* . . . God guide me lest I lose the way. „ V v 209
But with *C's* aid And others, „ V v 279
Cedar now you are enclosed with boards of *c*, „ III ii 102
Cede now and then to *c* A point to her demand ? „ III vi 169
Ceded father *c* Naples, that the son Being a King, „ III i 74
Ceiling under no *c* but the cloud that wept on them, „ V iv 39
Celebrate —*c*—to *c* my birthdaäy i' this fashion. *Prom. of May* I 321
To *c* this advent of our King ! *Foresters* IV 1048
Celibate Dan John, how much we lose, we *c's*, *Becket* V ii 197
Cell lash'd to death, or lie Famishing in black *c's*, *Queen Mary* V ii 196
The cold, white lily blowing in her *c* : *Harold* III i 274
In cold, white *c's* beneath an icy moon— „ V i 325
Cellar Our *c* is hard by. Take him, good Little John, *Foresters* II i 468
Censure (*See also* **Church-censure**) release from danger of all *c's* Of Holy Church *Queen Mary* III iii 151
All schism, and from all and every *c*, „ III iii 217
I refuse to stand By the King's *c*, *Becket* I iii 723
pass the *c's* of the Church On those that crown'd „ V ii 390
Centaur That *C* of a monstrous Commonweal, *Queen Mary* III iv 163
Central Not ev'n the *c* diamond, worth, I think, *Becket* V i 164
Centre Henceforth a *c* of the living faith. *Queen Mary* III ii 155
And oubliette in the *c*—No ! *Becket* IV ii 150
weight of the very land itself, Down to the inmost *c*. *Foresters* IV 1027
Century fire that flashes out again From *c* to *c*, *The Cup* I ii 167
Ceremony Why do you palter with the *c* ? „ II 420
But wherefore slur the perfect *c* ? „ II 431
Certain I am not *c* but that Philibert Shall be the man ; *Queen Mary* V i 263
because I am not *c* : You understand, Feria. „ V i 268
Would freely canvass *c* Lutheranisms. „ V ii 76
I came on *c* wholesome usages, *Becket* I iii 412
No, no ! we have *c* news he died in prison. *Foresters* IV 778
Chafe Why *c* me then ? *Harold* I i 296
Chain (s) this golden *c*—My father on a birthday *Queen Mary* I v 526
c, Wherewith they bound him to the stake, „ IV iii 595
here is a golden *c* I will give thee *Becket* IV i 40
Thou art happier than thy king. Put him in *c's*. *Foresters* IV 838
Chain (verb) This *c's* me to your service, *Queen Mary* I v 537
To *c* the free guest to the banquet-board ; *Harold* II ii 193
if he be conspirator, Rome will *c*, Or slay him. *The Cup* I i 18
Chain'd lying *c* In breathless dungeons over steaming sewers, *Queen Mary* IV iii 439
Chair (*See also* **Cheer**) How deathly pale !—a *c*, your Highness. „ I v 636
same *c*, Or rather throne of purple, on the deck. „ III ii 7
The Eternal Peter of the changeless *c*, „ III iv 380
Out friends, the Normans, holp to shake his *c*. *Harold* I i 86
sat within the Norman *c* A ruler all for England— „ II ii 533
This Barbarossa butts him from his *c*, *Becket, Pro.* 217
let me place this *c* for your ladyship. *The Falcon* 178
Chair'd yea, and thou *C* in his place. *Harold* I ii 247

Challenge —a shift, a trick Whereby to *c*, *Becket* II ii 165
Strike! I *c* thee to meet me before God. „ IV ii 254
Chamber (adj.) arm'd men Ever keep watch beside my *c* door, *Harold* II ii 245
Chamber (s) (*See also* **Chaumber**) I hear them stirring in the Council *C*. *Queen Mary* I v 628
And in this very *c*, fuse the glass, „ III v 54
Remain within the *c*, but apart. „ V iii 12
Is not yon light in the Queen's *c*? „ V iv 2
To shake my throne, to push into my *c*— *Becket* V i 250
Peace, let him be: it is the *c* of Death! *Prom. of May* III 741
Not if I barred thee up in thy *c*, *Foresters* I i 315
Chamberlain As if the *c* were Death himself! *Queen Mary* V v 204
Chance (adj.) may but hang On the *c* mention of some fool „ III v 43
And save for that *c* arrow which the Saints Sharpen'd *Harold* V ii 167
Chance (s) if by *c* you hear of any such, *Queen Mary* I iv 175
Looms the least *c* of peril to our realm. „ II ii 238
was no wicked wilfulness, Only a natural *c*. „ III v 73
A *c*—perchance One of those wicked wilfuls „ III v 74
That lies within the shadow of the *c*. *Harold* II ii 464
So less *c* for false keepers. „ II ii 688
Remains beyond all *c's* and all churches, „ III ii 182
What *c* That he should ever spread into the man *Becket* III i 21
the *c* gone, She lives—but not for him; „ IV ii 414
drowning man, they say, remembers all The *c's* of his life, „ V ii 274
I fear some strange and evil *c* Coming upon me, *The Cup* I iii 75
would dare the *c* Of double, or losing all. „ I iii 147
Chance (verb) may *c* That I shall never look upon you more. *Queen Mary* II i 245
It may *c*, that England Will be Mistress of the Indies yet, „ V iii 75
we might *c*—perchance—To guess their meaning. *Harold* IV i 137
it *c's*, child, That I am his main paramour, *Becket* IV ii 37
Chanced Before I *c* upon the messenger *Queen Mary* I v 585
there hath *c* A sharper harm to England and to Rome, „ V ii 28
how it *c* That this young Earl was sent on foreign travel, „ V ii 488
Chancellor Gardiner for one, who is to be made Lord *C*, „ I i 87
The Lord *C* (I count it as a kind of virtue in him, „ I iv 191
Who waits, sir? *Usher*. Madam, the Lord *C*. „ I v 96
that were hard upon you, my Lord *C*. „ I v 159
The Lord *C* himself is on our side. „ II i 193
Renard and the *C* sharpen'd them. „ III i 5
No, my Lord Legate, the Lord *C* goes. „ III ii 152
Hush! hush! You wrong the *C*: „ III iii 67
Thou Christian Bishop, thou Lord *C* Of England! „ III iv 300
My Lord *C*, You have an old trick of offending us; „ III iv 313
I have gone beyond your late Lord *C*,— „ V ii 98
Sir Nicholas Heath, the *C*, Would see your Highness. „ V ii 225
Madam, your *C*, Sir Nicholas Heath. „ V ii 248
When Wyatt sack'd the *C's* house in Southwark. „ V ii 504
longed much to see your Grace and the *C* ere he past, *Becket*, *Pro.* 399
and the King gave it to his *C*. „ *Pro.* 432
but thou—dost thou love this *C*, „ *Pro.* 438
Is it so much heavier than thy *C's* robe? *Becket*. No; but the *C's* and the Archbishop's Together „ I i 21
I served King Henry well as *C*; „ I i 144
And all the wisdom of the *C*, „ I i 153
Make him thy prisoner. I am *C* yet. „ I i 332
can I be under him As *C*? as Archbishop over him? „ I i 349
For he, when having dofft the *C's* robe— „ I iii 454
As *C* thou wast against the Church, „ I iii 528
Which came into thy hands when *C*. „ I iii 653
every bond and debt and obligation Incurr'd as *C*, „ I iii 712
Dost thou know, my boy, what it is to be *C* of England? „ II i 232
It is, my boy, to side with the King when *C*, „ II i 236
when I was *C* to the King, I fear I was as cruel as the King. „ V ii 122
sworn Yourselves my men when I was *C*— „ V ii 502
Chancellor-Archbishop *C-A*, he might well have sway'd „ I iii 466
Chancellorship He did prefer me to the *c*, „ *Pro.* 416
Chancellorship (*continued*) in my *c* I more than once have gone against the Church. *Becket* I i 28
often in your *c* you served The follies of the King. „ I ii 29
What say'st thou to the *C* of England? „ II i 225
Change (s) in the whirl of *c* may come to be one. *Queen Mary* I iii 106
Beyond the seas—a *c*! *Harold* I i 104
They are but of spring, They fly the winter *c*— „ III ii 97
Beyond all *c* and in the eternal distance „ III ii 101
Sudden *c* is a house on sand; *Becket* III iii 59
can he trace me Thro' five years' absence, and my *c* of name, *Prom. of May* II 615
Change (verb) God *c* the pebble which his kingly foot *Queen Mary* I v 368
and may *c* a word again. „ III iv 16
He falters, ha? 'fore God, we *c* and *c*; „ III iv 406
if we *c* at all We needs must do it quickly; „ III iv 410
And I to *c* my manners, Simon Renard, „ III vi 151
offal of the city would not *c* Estates with him; „ IV iii 77
the currents So shift and *c*, „ IV iii 409
You do mistake. I am not one to *c*. „ V i 218
They are not so true, They *c* their mates. *Harold* III ii 105
I will never *c* word with you again. *Prom. of May* I 163
backward-working alchemy Should *c* this gold to silver, *Foresters* IV 40
Changed *c* not colour when she saw the block, *Queen Mary* III i 399
I have *c* a word with him In coming, „ III iv 14
Pray you, remembering how yourself have *c*, „ IV ii 156
Do not seem so *c*. Say go; „ V i 215
Much *c*, I hear, Had put off levity and put graveness on. „ V ii 509
William the Norman, for the wind had *c*— *Harold* IV iii 182
The sun himself, should he be *c* to one, *Becket* III i 57
To see if years have *c* her. *The Cup* I i 125
Changeless The Eternal Peter of the *c* chair, *Queen Mary* III iv 380
wherefore waste your heart In looking on a chill and *c* Past? *Prom. of May* II 504
Channel His Highness makes his moves across the *C*, *Queen Mary* I iii 135
Back thro' their widow'd *c* here, „ I v 89
Chant *c's* and hymns In all the churches, *Becket* V ii 365
Chanted they led Processions, *c* litanies, *Queen Mary* III vi 95
Chanting And *c* that old song of Brunanburg *Harold* V i 215
He is *c* some old warsong. „ V i 495
Chaos and all her loves and hates Sing again into *c*. *Foresters* I ii 330
Chapel she was passing Some *c* down in Essex, *Queen Mary* I v 40
To the *c* of St. Blaise beneath the roof! *Becket* V iii 82
the election shall be made in the *C* Royal, „ I iii 111
Chaplain I bad my *c*, Castro, preach Against these burnings. *Queen Mary* III vi 73
to bear it for thee, Being thy *c*. *Becket* I iii 492
Chaplet And softly placed the *c* on her head. *The Falcon* 362
Ah! she had thrown my *c* on the grass, „ 368
Had she not thrown my *c* on the grass, „ 378
I wore the lady's *c* round my neck; „ 631
And then this *c*—No more feuds, but peace, „ 909
present her with this oaken *c* as Queen of the wood, *Foresters* III 59
Chapman We spared the craftsman, *c*, „ III 163
Chapter the King shall summon the *c* of that Church to court, *Becket* I iii 109
sometimes been moved to tears by a *c* of fine writing in a novel; *Prom. of May* III 209
Char *c* us back again into the dust We spring from, *Queen Mary* III v 55
Charge (care) We gave thee to the *c* of John of Salisbury, *Becket* I i 247
thou wast not happy taking *c* Of this wild Rosamund „ I i 391
Nor am I happy having *c* of her— „ I i 394
Charge (imputation, etc.) from the *c* Of being his co-rebels? *Queen Mary* III i 136
I free From this foul *c*— *Harold* II ii 518
By oath and compurgation from the *c*. „ II ii 521
Bark'd out at me such monstrous *c's*, *Becket* IV ii 342
Charge (to enjoin) this I *c* you, Tell Courtenay nothing. *Queen Mary* I iv 189
I *c* thee, upon pain of mine anathema, *Becket* I iii 719
c you that ye keep This traitor from escaping. „ V ii 509

Charge (to enjoin) (*continued*) Back ! back ! I *c* thee, back ! *Foresters* II i 425
Charge (to accuse) dare you *c* the King with treachery ? *Becket* V ii 396
Charge (to rush) and bidd'n him *C* one against a thousand, *Queen Mary* IV iii 309
Charged (enjoined) no, nor if the Pope, *C* him to do it— „ IV iii 558
He *c* me not to question any of those About me. *Becket* III i 210
Charged (filled) Tho' *c* with all the wet of all the west. *Harold* II ii 188
C with the weight of heaven wherefrom they fall ! „ V i 567
one So *c* with tongue, that every thread of thought *Becket* V ii 205
Charing Cross From *C C* ; the rebels broke us there, *Queen Mary* II iv 75
Charity sow'd therein The seed of Hate, it blossom'd *C.* „ IV i 172
Let them flow forth in *c,* „ IV iii 208
To rival him in Christian *c.* *Becket* III iii 233
Your Christian's Christian *c* ! „ V ii 476
Perhaps you judge him With feeble *c* : *The Cup* I ii 186
Charles (V., King of Spain, Emperor) rumour that *C,* the master of the world, *Queen Mary* I i 104
He is every way a lesser man than *C* ; „ I v 330
My master, *C,* Bad you go softly with your heretics „ I v 391
And *C,* the lord of this low world, is gone ; „ V v 54
prattling to her mother Of her betrothal to the Emperor *C,* „ V v 233
Charm (s) To draw him nearer with a *c* Like thine to thine. *Harold* I ii 8
more than one brave fellow owed His death to the *c* in it. *The Falcon* 635
with his *c* of simple style And close dialectic, *Prom. of May* I 223
And *her c* Of voice is also yours ; „ II 380
and the country Has many *c's,* „ II 541
Might have more *c* for me than all the country. „ II 553
True soul of the Saxon churl for whom song has no *c.* *Foresters* II i 386
Charm (verb) In hope to *c* them from their hate of Spain. *Queen Mary* III vi 82
May serve to *c* the tiger out of him. *Harold* I i 153
kiss that *c's* thine eyelids into sleep, „ I ii 139
I do not then *c* this secret out of our loyal Thomas, *Becket, Pro.* 466
how to *c* and waste the hearts of men. *Foresters* II i 502
Charm'd that wilt not dance However wisely *c.* *Harold* I i 387
When you have *c* our general into mercy, *The Cup* I ii 311
How *c* he was ! what wonder ?—A gallant boy, *The Falcon* 318
ruddiest cheek That ever *c* the plowman of your wolds *Prom. of May* III 488
Charon Not be my *C* to the counter side ? *Queen Mary* III ii 149
Chart This *c* here mark'd '*Her Bower,*' *Becket, Pro.* 160
but this Draws thro' the *c* to her. „ *Pro.* 173
This *c* with the red line ! her bower ! „ *Pro.* 308
The *c* is not mine, but Becket's : take it, Thomas. „ *Pro.* 310
Fitzurse, that *c* with the red line—thou sawest it— „ *Pro.* 427
c which Henry gave you With the red line— „ I ii 60
Charter Your rights and *c's* hobnail'd into slush— *Queen Mary* II ii 278
Where is the *c* of our Westminster ? *Harold* III i 194
Chase (s) thyself wast wont To love the *c* : „ I i 228
More sacred than his forests for the *c* ? *Becket* IV ii 25
running down the *c* is kindlier sport Ev'n than the death. „ IV ii 213
climb The mountain opposite and watch the *c.* *The Cup* I i 118
I am a life-long lover of the *c,* „ I i 195
Roused by the clamour of the *c* he woke, „ I ii 117
Chased *C* deer-like up his mountains, *Harold* I ii 148
would have *c* the stag to-day In the full face *The Cup* I ii 267
I am *c* by my foes. *Foresters* II i 184
Chasm o'er the *c* I saw Lord William Howard *Queen Mary* II iii 28
and flatten in her closing *c* Domed cities, hear. *The Cup* II 300
Chaste *C* as your Grace ! *Queen Mary* I v 456
Your Grace hath a most *c* and loving wife. „ III vi 129
The Queen of Philip should be *c.* „ III vi 132
no wives like English wives So fair and *c* as they be. *Foresters* II i 16
Chasten'd So thou be *c* by thy banishment, *Harold* IV ii 50
Chastest Thro' *c* honour of the Decalogue *Becket* V i 206
Chattel thou art dispossessed of all thy lands, goods, and *c's* ; *Foresters* I iii 60
Chaumber (chamber) winder at the end o' the passage, that goäs by thy *c.* *Prom. of May* I 397
Did 'e git into thy *c* ? „ I 400
they ha' ta'en the body up inter your *c,* „ II 570
By haäfe a scoor o' naämes—out o' the *c.* „ III 730

Chaumber (chamber) (*continued*) Out o' the *c* ! I'll mash tha into nowt. *Prom. of May* III 734
Out o' the *c,* dang tha ! „ III 737
Check I never knew thee *c* thy will for ought *Harold* II ii 120
C—you move so wildly. *Becket, Pro.* 40
frost That help'd to *c* the flowing of the blood. *The Falcon* 645
Cheek you stroke me on one *c,* Buffet the other. *Queen Mary* II i 117
'Wyatt,' as red as she In hair and *c* ; „ II ii 76
gave me a great pat o' the *c* for a pretty wench, *Becket* III i 125
a *c* like a peach and a heart like the stone in it— *The Falcon* 93
ruddiest *c* That ever charm'd the plowman of your wolds *Prom. of May* III 487
Here—give me one sharp pinch upon the *c* *Foresters* IV 1012
Cheeked *See* **Red-cheek'd**
Cheer (s) good *c* ! thou art Harold, I am Edith ! *Harold* V i 391
You, Strato, make good *c* till I return. *The Cup* I ii 20
Yeas, yeas ! Three *c's* for Mr. Steer ! *Prom. of May* I 455
Cheer (verb) And *c* his blindness with a traveller's tales ? „ II 515
Cheer (chair) they wunt set i' the Lord's *c* o' that daay. *Queen Mary* IV iii 470
Cheerful He, with a *c* smile, as one whose mind Is all made up, „ IV iii 587
Cheerless Your people are as *c* as your clime ; „ V i 83
For me, whose *c* Houris after death Are Night and Silence, *Prom. of May* I 249
Cheese Our Daisy's *c's* be better. *Queen Mary* IV iii 484
Buy you their *c's,* and they'll side with you ; „ IV iii 548
C ! *Filippo.* A supper for twelve mites. *The Falcon* 126
And a cat to the cream, and a rat to the *c* ; *Prom. of May* I 54
Cherish'd *c* him Who thief-like fled from his own church *Becket* II ii 155
Cherubim golden *c* With twenty-cubit wings *Harold* III i 183
Chess The Game of *C.* (repeat) *Queen Mary* I iii 127
Strange game of *c* ! a King That with her own powers „ I iii 161
Chessmen and these *c* on the floor— *Becket, Pro.* 313
Chest Did the *c* move ! did it move ? *Harold* II ii 799
Chichester Bishops—York, London, *C,* Westminster— *Becket* I iii 385
Chief (adj.) *C* prelate of our Church, archbishop, first In Council, *Queen Mary* IV iii 70
Before the Prince and *c* Justiciary, *Becket* I iii 709
Did not some old Greek Say death was the *c* good ? *The Cup* II 515
Chief (s) The *c* of these outlaws who break the law ? *Foresters* IV 141
Child (*See also* **Childer, Children**) of the good Lady Jane as a poor innocent *c* *Queen Mary* I i 94
c by *c,* you know, Were momentary sparkles „ I ii 71
I think she entreats me like a *c.* „ I iii 112
she is but a *c.* We do not kill the *c* for doing that „ I v 61
the *c* obey'd her father. „ I v 493
perchance A *c* more innocent than Lady Jane. „ I v 502
nursery-cocker'd *c* will jeer at aught „ II ii 394
He is *c* and fool, and traitor to the State. „ II ii 403
That if the Queen should die without a *c,* „ III iii 75
no more rein upon thine anger Than any *c* ! „ III iv 304
Threaten the *c* ; 'I'll scourge you if you did it :' „ III v 126
What weapon hath the *c,* save his soft tongue, „ III v 128
I think the Queen may never bear a *c* ; „ III v 232
So sick am I with biding for this *c.* Is it the fashion in this clime for women To go twelve months in bearing of a *c* ? „ III vi 89
Her fierce desire of bearing him a *c,* „ IV iii 429
Since she lost hope of bearing us a *c* ? „ V i 230
Alice, my *c,* Bring us your lute. „ V ii 356
But the *c* came not, and the husband came not ; „ V ii 581
in her agony The mother came upon her—a *c* was born— „ V iv 20
Now the spoilt *c* sways both. *Harold* I i 453
my *c* ; Thou hast misread this merry dream of thine, „ I ii 97
tenfold, than this fearful *c* can do ; „ I ii 143
But sickly, slight, half-witted and a *c,* „ II ii 572
From *c* to *c,* from Pope to Pope, from age to age, „ V i 329
widow And orphan *c,* whom one of thy wild barons— *Becket, Pro.* 188
And when I was a *c,* The Virgin, „ I i 52
The *c* Is there already. *Rosamund.* Yes—the *c*—the *c*— „ I i 292
Who misuses a dog would misuse a *c*— „ I iv 109
Why, the *c* will drown himself. „ II i 322

Child (*continued*) And one fair *c* to fondle ! *Becket* III i 12
the *c* We waited for so long—heaven's gift at last— „ III i 13
But then the *c is* such a *c*. „ III i 20
what's an apple, you know, save to a *c*, and I'm no *c*, „ III i 141
like the gravedigger's *c* I have heard of, trying to ring the bell, „ III iii 73
Thou art the prettiest *c* I ever saw. „ IV i 7
Your own *c* brought me hither ! „ IV ii 13
C, I am mine own self Of and belonging to the King. „ IV ii 29
so it chances, *c*, That I am his main paramour, „ IV ii 38
—my *c* is so young, So backward too ; „ IV ii 84
But the *c* is so young. You have children—his ; And mine is the King's *c* ; „ IV ii 89
I follow'd You and the *c* : he babbled all the way. „ IV ii 140
and make Thy body loathsome even to thy *c* ; „ IV ii 172
The *c* . . . No . . . mercy ! No ! „ IV ii 185
His *c* and mine own soul, and so return. „ V ii 193
Lacking the love of woman and of *c*. „ V ii 199
Save him, he saved my life, he saved my *c*, „ V iii 9
A *c's* sand-castle on the beach For the next wave— *The Cup* I ii 253
that dost inspire the germ with life, The *c*, „ II 259
and she, A girl, a *c*, then but fifteen, *The Falcon* 537
My one *c* Florio lying still so sick, „ 678
best way out of it, if the *c* could keep Her counsel. *Prom. of May* I 476
when the man, The *c* of evolution, flings aside „ I 585
C, do you love me now ? „ I 640
For ever, you foolish *c* ! What's come over you ? „ I 771
Ay, *c* ; and you look thin and pale. „ I 781
Well, my *c*, let us join them. „ I 796
So the *c* grow to manhood : „ II 289
—she was his favourite *c*— „ II 419
Our old nurse crying as if for her own *c*, „ II 480
so that you do not copy his bad manners ? Go, *c*. „ III 362
' My dear C,—I can do no more for you. „ III 397
C, read a little history, you will find „ III 542
C, can't you see ? Tell them to fly for a doctor. „ III 711
A *c*, and all as trustful as a *c* ! „ III 759
C, thou shouldst marry one who will pay the mortgage. *Foresters* I i 279
by this Holy Cross Which good King Richard gave me when a *c*— „ I ii 311
Nor leave a *c* behind him ' „ II ii 113
Has never glanced upon me when a *c*. „ IV 5
C, thou shalt wed him, Or thine old father will go mad— „ IV 643
Childer (children) theer be a thousand i' the parish, taäkin' in the women and *c* ; *Prom. of May* I 146
Them be what they larns the *c'* at school, „ III 39
Childhood Away from Philip, Back in her *c*— *Queen Mary* V v 231
Childish No—the *c* fist That cannot strike again. *Harold* IV iii 30
Childless 'Tis written, ' They shall be *c*.' *Queen Mary* I ii 65
Evil for good, it seems, Is oft as *c* of the good *Harold* V i 172
Than all my *c* wealth, if mine must die. *The Falcon* 855
Childlike ask'd him, *c* : ' Will you take it off *Queen Mary* III i 401
great motion of laughter among us, part real, part *c*, *Becket* III iii 155
part *c* again—when we felt we had laughed too long „ III iii 159
Childlike-jealous And *c-j* of him again— *Queen Mary* V v 234
Children (*See also* **Child, Childer**) These princes are like *c*, must be physick'd, „ I v 234
Dumb *c* of my father, that will speak „ II i 77
cannot tell How mothers love their *c* ; „ II ii 190
naturally may love his people As these their *c* ; „ II ii 193
The man had *c*, and he whined for those. „ II ii 335
Away ! Women and *c* ! „ II iii 97
So that we may, as *c* penitent, „ III iii 153
Watch'd *c* playing at *their* life to be, „ III iv 63
They had not reach'd right reason ; little *c* ! „ III iv 73
wholesome scripture, ' Little *c*, Love one another.' „ III iv 85
but they play with fire as *c* do, And burn the house. „ III vi 28
His *c* and his concubine, belike. „ IV i 165
To the poor flock—to women and to *c*— „ IV ii 159
fire seem To those three *c* like a pleasant dew. „ IV iii 91
burnt The heretic priest, workmen, and women and *c*. „ V v 107
Old, miserable, diseased, Incapable of *c*. „ V v 179
That tread the kings their *c* under-heel— *Becket, Pro.* 213
and her *c*—canst thou not—that secret matter „ *Pro.* 486
Children (*continued*) my *c*, your prayers will do more for me *Becket* I iv 143
And thereupon he call'd my *c* bastards. „ IV ii 44
You have *c*—his ; And mine is the King's child ; „ IV ii 90
new-made *c* Of our imperial mother see the show. *The Cup* II 164
More specially sick *c*, have strange fancies, *The Falcon* 817
who call'd the mind Of *c* a blank page, *Prom. of May* II 282
they tell me that you—and you have six *c*— „ III 77
and when the *c* grew too old for me, „ III 386
love that *c* owe to both I give To him alone. *Foresters* IV 7
Child-world The miserable see-saw of our *c-w*, *Queen Mary* IV iii 385
Chill (adj.) Come, come, you are *c* here ; „ III v 275
wherefore waste your heart In looking on a *c* and changeless Past ? *Prom. of May* II 504
Chill (s) He caught a *c* in the lagoons of Venice, *Queen Mary* V ii 515
Chill (verb) —your north *c's* me. *Becket, Pro.* 330
Will *c* the hearts that beat for Robin Hood ! *Foresters* IV 1064
Chilled He warmed to you to-day, and you have *c* him again. *Becket* II ii 375
Chime fawn upon him ? *C* in with all ? *Harold* I ii 167
Low words best *c* with this solemnity. *The Cup* II 217
world is beautiful If we were happy, and could *c* in with it. *Prom. of May* I 578
Chin both her knees drawn upward to her *c*. *Queen Mary* V ii 392
Not in my *c*, I hope ! That threatens double. *Becket* II i 250
China as she has broken My *c* bowl. *The Falcon* 524
Chink (crevice) A twilight conscience lighted thro' a *c* ; *Harold* III i 66
—a *c*—he's out, Gone ! *Becket* I i 259
Chink (verb) wholesome use of these To *c* against the Norman, *Harold* III i 22
Chirp we will *c* among our vines, and smile *The Cup* I iii 170
Chivalry yet I hate him for his want of *c*. *Foresters* I ii 107
He loves the *c* of his single arm. „ IV 786
Choice The *c* of England is the voice of England. *William.* I will be king of England by the laws, The *c*, and voice of England. *Harold* II ii 128
Tostig's banishment, and *c* of Morcar, „ IV i 104
To do with England's *c* of her own king ? „ V i 19
weight down all free *c* beneath the throne. *Becket* I iii 118
The wiser *c*, because my sleeping-draught „ IV ii 168
Choir To the *c*, to the *c* ! *Becket.* Shall I too pass to the *c*, „ V iii 73
Choose not so set on wedlock as to *c* But where I list, *Queen Mary* II ii 214
dead I cannot *c* but love her. „ III i 340
Pray God the people *c* thee for their king ! *Harold* I i 314
there the great Assembly *c* their king, „ II ii 127
C therefore whether thou wilt have thy conscience „ II ii 282
c A hundred of the wisest heads from England, *Becket* II ii 170
Still *c* Barabbas rather than the Christ, „ II ii 390
Choosing old Northumbrian crown, And kings of our own *c*. *Harold* IV i 33
Chop Would you not *c* the bitten finger off, *Queen Mary* III iv 206
Chord touch No *c* in me that would not answer *The Falcon* 456
Chosen thought I might be *c* Pope, But then withdrew it. *Queen Mary* V ii 82
coming from the people, And *c* by the people— *Harold* V i 387
c by his people And fighting for his people ! „ V i 490
and *c* me For this thy great archbishoprick, *Becket* I i 90
Hoped, were he *c* archbishop, „ I iii 442
for her beauty, stateliness, and power, Was *c* Priestess *The Cup* II 17
Christ (*See also* **Christ Jesus, Jesus Christ**) And stand within the porch, and *C* with me : *Queen Mary* I ii 51
and kindled with the palms of *C* ! „ I v 94
sworn upon the body and blood of *C* I'll none but Philip. „ I v 215
And keep with *C* and conscience— „ I v 558
And clasp the faith in *C* ; „ III ii 122
what saith *C* ? ' Compel them to come in.' „ III iv 29
White as the light, the spotless bride of *C*, „ III iv 200
Like *C* himself on Tabor, „ III iv 201
And be with *C* the Lord in Paradise. „ IV iii 88
Either to live with *C* in Heaven with joy, „ IV iii 220
seen the true men of *C* lying famine-dead by scores, „ V iv 38
the one King, the *C*, and all things in common, „ V iv 53

Christ (*continued*) Or till the Pope be *C's*. *Harold* v i 332
for I be his lord and master i' *C*, my lord. *Becket* I iv 241
if they were defective as St. Peter Denying *C*, „ II ii 216
Still choose Barabbas rather than the *C*, „ II ii 391

Christchurch Deans Of *C*, Durham, Exeter, and Wells— *Queen Mary* I ii 9

Christendom your worship the first man in Kent and *C*, „ II i 64
So brands me in the stare of *C* A heretic ! „ v ii 62
Poitou, all *C* is raised against thee ; *Harold* III ii 150
make Our island-Church a schism from *C*, *Becket* I iii 116
you are known Thro' all the courts of *C* „ IV ii 325

Christian (adj.) Thou *C* Bishop, thou Lord Chancellor Of England ! *Queen Mary* III iv 300
yet what hatred *C* men Bear to each other, „ IV iii 182
The *C* manhood of the man who reigns ! *Harold* II i 104
The kingliest Abbey in all *C* lands, „ III i 204
We will not give him A *C* burial : „ v ii 154
To rival him in *C* charity. *Becket* III iii 233
Your Christian's *C* charity ! „ v ii 475

Christian (s) But for your *C*, look you, you shall have „ II ii 227
Your *C's* Christian charity ! „ v ii 475
More like the picture Of *C* in my ' Pilgrim's Progress ' *Prom. of May* III 519

Christian-charitiest human-heartedest, *C-c* of all crab-catchers. *Harold* II i 63

Christ Jesus (*See also* **Christ, Jesus Christ**) as in the day of the first church, when *C J* was King. *Queen Mary* v iv 55
our lords and masters in *C J*. *Becket* I iv 87

Christmas (adj.) Are braced and brazen'd up with *C* wines „ v ii 424

Christmas (s) for thou art as white as three *C'ses*. *Queen Mary* I i 30

Chronicle and my poor *c* Is but of glass. „ III v 46
be defamed Thro' all her angry *c's* hereafter „ v ii 304
And swallow'd in the conqueror's *c*. *The Cup* I ii 158

Chrysalis like a butterfly in a *c*, You spent your life ; *Queen Mary* I iv 51

Chuck'd England now Is but a ball *c* between France and Spain, „ III i 110

Church (adj.) clench'd their pirate hides To the bleak *c* doors, *Harold* IV iii 37
stir not yet This matter of the *C* lands. *Queen Mary* I v 409
Thou art the man to fill out the *C* robe ; *Becket, Pro.* 262
In the *c* rope ?—no. „ III iii 80

Church (s) (*See also* **Island-Church**) not to yield His *C* of England to the Papal wolf And Mary ; *Queen Mary* I ii 36
Have I climb'd back into the primal *c*, „ I ii 50
All the *c* is grateful. „ I v 178
to play The tyrant, or in commonwealth or *c*. „ I v 192
Let the great angel of the *c* come with him ; „ I v 377
Henry broke the carcase of your *c* To pieces, „ I v 398
Steadying the tremulous pillars of the *C*— „ I v 518
Ay, even in the *c* there is a man—Cranmer. „ III i 169
Can we not have the Catholic *c* as well „ III iii 97
of all censures Of Holy *C* that we be fall'n into, „ III iii 152
received into the bosom And unity of Universal *C* ; „ III iii 155
islands call'd into the dawning *c* Out of the dead, „ III iii 172
Father hath appointed Head Of all his *c*, „ III iii 208
to the bosom And unity of Universal *C*. „ III iii 221
but now, The unity of Universal *C*, Mary would have it ; „ III iii 229
Old Rome, that first made martyrs in the *C*, „ III iv 127
What, my Lord ! The *C* on Peter's rock ? never ! „ III iv 134
It was the shadow of the *C* that trembled ; „ III iv 144
Your *c* was but the shadow of a *c*, „ III iv 146
Began to batter at your English *C*, „ III iv 186
we should thoroughly cleanse the *C* within „ III iv 196
bolster'd up The gross King's headship of the *C*, „ III iv 246
The *C's* evil is not as the King's, „ III iv 273
Legate Is here as Pope and Master of the *C*, „ III iv 347
I kept my head for use of Holy *C* ; „ III iv 359
and plunge His foreign fist into our island *C* „ III iv 364
Then have my simple headstone by the *c*, „ III v 114
that His *c* May flourish. „ III vi 69
Yet to save Cranmer were to serve the *C*, „ IV i 136
' Martyr's blood—seed of the *C*.' *Mary*. Of the true *C* ; but his is none, „ IV i 147

Church (s) (*continued*) read your recantation Before the people in St. Mary's *C*. *Queen Mary* IV ii 29
farewell ; Until I see you in St. Mary's *C*. „ IV ii 47
Against the huge corruptions of the *C*, „ IV ii 101
O higher, holier, earlier, purer *c*, „ IV ii 108
in the *c* Repeat your recantation in the ears „ IV ii 192
that hath return'd To the one Catholic Universal *C*, „ IV iii 21
So poisoning the *C*, so long continuing, „ IV iii 48
Chief prelate of our *C*, archbishop, „ IV iii 70
misreport His ending to the glory of their *c*. „ IV iii 327
Crying ' Forward ! '—set our old *c* rocking, „ IV iii 403
Out of the *c*, you brace of cursed crones, „ IV iii 538
stood More like an ancient father of the *C*, „ IV iii 598
For Alva is true son of the true *c*— „ v i 160
When I should guide the *C* in peace at home, „ v ii 67
The scourge and butcher of their English *c*. „ v ii 107
as in the day of the first *c*, when Christ Jesus was King. „ v iv 55
And done such mighty things by Holy *C*, „ v v 74
and your *c'es* Uncouth, unhandsome, *Harold* I i 164
I have builded the great *c* of Holy Peter : „ I i 179
and saw the *c* all fill'd With dead men „ I ii 81
king Hath given his virgin lamb to Holy *C* „ III i 335
loved within the pale forbidden By Holy *C* : „ III ii 24
Scared by the *c*— „ III ii 87
Their anthems of no *c*, how sweet they are ! „ III ii 91
Remains beyond all chances and all *c'es*, „ III ii 183
Our Saints have moved the *C* that moves the world, „ v i 41
made too good an use of Holy *C* To break her close ! „ v i 313
Our *C* in arms—the lamb the lion— „ v i 440
I vow to build a *c* to God Here on the hill of battle ; „ v ii 137
being brought before the courts of the *C*, *Becket, Pro.* 13
The *C* in the pell-mell of Stephen's time „ *Pro.* 19
The *C* should hold her baronies of me, „ *Pro.* 24
to whom thou art bound By Holy *C*. „ *Pro.* 68
I, true son Of Holy *C*—no croucher to the Gregories „ *Pro.* 211
King, *C*, and State to him but foils wherein „ *Pro.* 268
Believing I should ever aid the *C*— „ *Pro.* 417
if there ever come feud between *C* and Crown, „ *Pro.* 465
The people know their *C* a tower of strength, „ I i 15
I more than once have gone against the *C*. „ I i 30
C should pay her scutage like the lords. „ I i 34
That I should go against the *C* with him, And I shall go against him with the *C*, „ I i 93
My truest and mine utmost for the *C* ? „ I i 114
For how have fought thine utmost for the *C*, „ I i 118
' I mean to fight mine utmost for the *C*, Against the King ' ? „ I i 124
I am his no more, and I must serve the *C*. „ I i 146
they *are* Royal, Not of the *C*— „ I i 169
these new railers at the *C* May plaister „ I i 307
Knowing how much you reverence Holy *C*, „ I ii 48
Are not so much at feud with Holy *C*, „ I ii 54
That *C* must scorn herself whose fearful Priest „ I ii 64
The *C* must play into the hands of kings ; „ I ii 68
And take the *C's* danger on myself. „ I ii 72
The customs of the *C* are Peter's rock. „ I iii 24
Wilt thou destroy the *C* in fighting for it, „ I iii 36
' If any cleric be accused of felony, the *C* shall not protect him ; „ I iii 87
Is not the *C* the visible Lord on earth ? „ I iii 92
A fit place for the monies of the *C*, „ I iii 105
the King shall summon the chapter of that *c* to court, „ I iii 109
He meant no harm nor damage to the *C*. „ I iii 217
He heads the *C* against the King with thee. „ I iii 245
Herbert, Herbert, have I betray'd the *C* ? „ I iii 285
bad me seal against the rights of the *C*, „ I iii 313
murders done By men, the scum and offal of the *C* ; „ I iii 409
C and Crown, Two sisters gliding in an equal dance, „ I iii 443
As Chancellor thou wast against the *C*, „ I iii 529
The spire of Holy *C* may prick the graves— „ I iii 553
The *C* will hate thee. „ I iii 565
Fight for the *C*, and set the *C* against me ! „ I iii 569
set the *C* This day between the hammer and the anvil— „ I iii 584
and no forsworn Archbishop Shall helm the *C*. „ I iii 598

Church (s) (*continued*) now the glory of the *C* Hath swallow'd up the glory of the King; *Becket* I iii 665
Whatever the *C* owns—she holds it in Free and perpetual alms, „ I iii 679
The soul the body, and the *C* the Throne, „ I iii 717
The King, these customs, all the *C*, „ I iii 726
The *C* is ever at variance with the kings, „ I iv 78
Were the *C* king, it would be otherwise. „ I iv 104
for the sake of the *C* itself, if not for my own, „ I iv 153
And I have been as royal with the *C*. „ II i 83
Shrink from me, like a daughter of the *C*. „ II i 278
Quarrel of Crown and *C*—to rend again. „ II ii 56
We never hounded on the State at home To spoil the *C*. „ II ii 97
Holy *C* May rock, but will not wreck, „ II ii 102
Who thief-like fled from his own *c* by night, „ II ii 156
all the *C* of France Decide on their decision, „ II ii 176
thanks of Holy *C* are due to those That went before us „ II ii 190
we grant the *C* King over this world's kings, „ II ii 242
—the green field—the gray *c*— „ II ii 296
Agree with him quickly again, even for the sake of the *C*. „ II ii 378
The *C* alone hath eyes—and now I see That I was blind— „ II ii 436
Perish she, I, all, before The *C* should suffer wrong! „ III iii 20
I have been more for the King than the *C* in this matter—yea, even for the sake of the *C*: „ III iii 65
so violated the immemorial usage of the *C*, „ III iii 73
half-hanged himself in the rope of the *C*, or rather pulled all the *C* „ III iii 76
but Salisbury was a calf cowed by Mother *C*, „ III iii 96
puffed out such an incense of unctuosity into the nostrils of our Gods of *C* and State, „ III iii 116
hurl the dread ban of the *C* on those „ III iii 210
The State will die, the *C* can never die. „ III iii 336
God's grace and Holy *C* deliver'd us. „ IV ii 309
He grovels to the *C* when he's black-blooded, „ IV ii 436
The *C* is all—the crime to be a king. „ V i 26
I have overshot My duties to our Holy Mother *C*, „ V i 38
Are push'd from out communion of the *C*. „ V i 59
Hath used the full authority of his *C* „ V i 207
The *C*! the *C*! God's eyes! I would the *C* were down in hell! „ V i 216
crying On Holy *C* to thunder out her rights „ V ii 31
she would not believe me, and she wish'd The *C* were king: „ V ii 118
and our Mother *C* for bride; „ V ii 221
Divide me from the mother *c* of England, My Canterbury. „ V ii 360
chants and hymns In all the *c'es*, „ V ii 367
pass the censures of the *C* On those that crown'd young Henry „ V ii 391
my dream foretold my martyrdom In mine own *c*. „ V ii 634
Undo the doors: the *c* is not a castle: „ V iii 62
Seen by the *C* in heaven, the *C* on earth— „ V iii 98
Except they make submission to the *C*. „ V iii 123
—for thy *C*, O Lord—Into thy hands, „ V iii 194
tho' he never comes to *c*, I thought better of him. *Prom. of May* I 261
Thrones, *c'es*, ranks, traditions, customs, „ I 519
Ring, trinket of the *C*, „ I 598
Not in our *c*—I think I scarce could hold my head up „ I 688
and the weight of the *c* to boot on my shoulders, *Foresters* I ii 58
weight of the flesh at odd times overbalance the weight of the *c*, „ I ii 62
which a pious son of the *C* gave me this morning „ III 281
Thou hast roll'd over the *C* militant „ IV 272
C and Law, halt and pay toll! „ IV 429
When the *C* and the law have forgotten God's music, „ IV 554
Beware, O King, the vengeance of the *C*. „ IV 914
let me execute the vengeance of the *C* upon them. „ IV 916
the vengeance of the *C*! Thou shalt pronounce the blessing of the *C* „ IV 926

Church-bond that stale *C-b* which link'd me with him *Becket* IV ii 447
Church-censure I fear *C-c's* like your King. „ IV ii 434
Church-land We have given the *c-l's* back: *Queen Mary* V i 171
Churchless Back from her *c* commerce with the King *Becket* IV ii 332
Churchman her needle perfect, and her learning Beyond the *churchmen*; *Queen Mary* III i 362
Churchman (*continued*) being English *c* How should he bear the headship of the Pope? *Queen Mary* III iii 28
And by the *c's* pitiless doom of fire, „ III iv 49
lives Of many among your *churchmen* were so foul „ III iv 191
Statesman not *C* he. *Becket, Pro.* 450
thou, that art *c* too In a fashion, *Foresters* IV 410
Church-policy State-policy and *c-p* are conjoint, *Queen Mary* III ii 73
Church-tower sets the *c-t* over there all a-hell-fire as it were? *Becket* III iii 51
Churchwarden *C* be a coomin, thaw me and 'im we niver 'grees about the tithe; *Prom. of May* I 443
Churl Thine, thine, or King or *c*! *Harold* III ii 37
he speaks to a noble as tho' he were a *c*, and to a *c* *Becket, Pro.* 455
C! I will have thee frighted into France, „ I ii 93
Yea, heard the *c* against the baron— „ I iii 365
Lout, *c*, clown! *Prom. of May* III 739
True soul of the Saxon *c* for whom song has no charm. *Foresters* II i 386
scares The Baron at the torture of his *c's*, „ III 106
Churn To sing, love, marry, *c*, brew, bake, and die, *Queen Mary* III v 111
Cider-crop they'll hev' a fine *c-c* to-year if the blossom 'owds. *Prom. of May* I 316
Cinder I wish some thunderbolt Would make this Cole a *c*, *Queen Mary* IV iii 11
lava-torrents blast and blacken a province To a *c*, hear. *The Cup* II 304
Cinnamon Nard, *C*, amomum, benzoin. „ II 184
Cipher Ha! Courtenay's *c*. *Queen Mary* II i 134
Circe Our woodland *C* that hath witch'd the King? *Becket* III ii 32
Circling See, first, a *c* wood, „ *Pro.* 161
Circumbendibuses all manner of homages, and observances, and *c*. *Foresters* I i 103
Circumstance The painful *c's* which I heard— *Prom. of May* II 402
Cistercian as I hate the dirty gap in the face of a *C* monk, *Becket* II ii 381
Cite And *c* thee to appear before the Pope, „ I iii 602
Cited He hath *c* me to Rome, for heresy, *Queen Mary* V ii 42
Citizen (*See also* **Fellow-citizen**) *c's* Stood each before his shut-up booth, „ II ii 62
With execrating execrable eyes, Glared at the *c*. „ II ii 68
we pray That we, you true and loyal *c's*, „ II ii 135
And see the *c's* arm'd. Good day; „ II ii 378
Ay, and for Gardiner! being English *c*, „ III iii 24
The *c's* heir hath conquer'd me For the moment. *Becket* II ii 60
Our gallant *c's* murder'd all in vain, *The Cup* I ii 142
Would clap his honest *c's* on the back, „ I ii 358
Here comes a *c*, and I think his wife. *Foresters* III 227
City After him, boys! and pelt him from the *c*. *Queen Mary* I iii 86
make Your *c* loyal, and be the mightiest man „ II ii 19
How look'd the *c* When now you past it? „ II ii 57
Like our Council, Your *c* is divided. „ II ii 60
So I say Your *c* is divided, „ II ii 99
on you, In your own *c*, as her right, my Lord, „ II ii 106
I leave Lord William Howard in your *c*, „ II ii 245
We thank your Lordship and your loyal *c*. „ II ii 301
I have notice from our partisans Within the *c* „ II iii 52
scum And offal of the *c* would not change Estates with him; „ IV iii 77
Saints to scatter sparks of plague Thro' all your *cities*, *Harold* II ii 747
A hill, a fort, a *c*—that reach'd a hand „ IV i 44
another hill Or fort, or *c*, took it, „ IV i 50
Would God she were—no, here within the *c*. *Becket, Pro.* 180
Last night I followed a woman in the *c* here. „ *Pro.* 469
there stole into the *c* a breath Full of the meadows, „ I i 261
where to seek? I have been about the *c*. „ I i 398
I made him porcelain from the clay of the *c*— „ I iii 439
if the *c* be sick, and I cannot call the kennel sweet, „ II ii 348
plagues That smite the *c* spare the solitudes. „ V ii 173
My lord, the *c* is full of armed men. „ V ii 187
she told us of arm'd men Here in the *c*. „ V ii 228
These arm'd men in the *c*, these fierce faces— „ V iii 3
myrtle, bowering-in The *c* where she dwells. *The Cup* I i 4
Brought me again to her own *c*?— „ I i 14
in a *c* thro' which he past with the Roman army: „ I i 42
in some *c* where Antonius past. „ I ii 56
Most like the *c* rose against Antonius, „ I ii 62

City (*continued*) The Roman is encampt without your *c*— The Cup I ii 84
The camp is half a league without the *c*; „ I iii 90
and flatten in her closing chasm Domed *cities*, hear. „ II 301
as she was helping to build the mound against the *c*. Foresters II i 309
Civil Would perish on the *c* slaughter-field, Queen Mary III i 118
The *c* wars are gone for evermore: „ III v 150
for that would drag The cleric before the *c* judgment-seat, Becket I iii 84
Civil-spoken He's a Somersetshire man, and a very *c-s* gentleman. Prom. of May I 207
'Good daäy then, Dobson!' *C-s* i'deed! „ I 301
Claim (s) beast might roar his *c* To being in God's image, Queen Mary IV iii 368
know'st my *c* on England Thro' Edward's promise: Harold II i 12
Who hath a better *c* then to the crown „ II ii 596
Wilt *thou* uphold my *c*? „ II ii 603
Claim (verb) the people *C* as their natural leader— Queen Mary I iv 210
Foliot may *c* the pall For London too. Becket I iii 55
Claim'd *C* some of our crown lands for Canterbury— „ I iii 458
Clamour Roused by the *c* of the chase he woke, The Cup I ii 117
with no fear Of the world's gossiping *c*, Prom. of May I 528
Clamour'd The *c* darling of their afternoon! The Cup II 125
Clan The weakness and the dissonance of our *c's*, „ I i 24
'I go to fight in Scotland With many a savage *c*;' Foresters I i 15
Clang every parish tower Shall *c* and clash Queen Mary II i 230
Iron on iron *c*, Harold IV iii 160
Clank *c* The shackles that will bind me to the wall. „ II ii 409
Clap Except I *c* thee into prison here, Becket V i 110
Would *c* his honest citizens on the back, The Cup I ii 358
Clapt (adj.) we shall hear him presently with *c* wing Crow over Barbarossa— Becket II ii 49
Clapt (verb) Which a young lust had *c* upon the back, Queen Mary IV iii 401
they *c* their hands Upon their swords when ask'd; „ V i 172
wicked sister *c* her hands and laugh'd; Harold V ii 48
i' the poorch as soon as he *c* eyes of 'er. Prom. of May I 23
Clarence (lady in waiting to Queen Mary) *C*, they hate me; even when I speak Queen Mary V ii 214
he may bring you news from Philip. *Mary.* So, *C.* „ V ii 230
C, *C*, what have I done? „ V ii 338
Our *C* there Sees ever such an aureole „ V ii 412
Clash (s) cries, and *c'es*, and the groans of men; Harold III i 375
Clash (verb) every parish tower Shall clang and *c* Queen Mary II i 230
Let all the steeples *c*, „ III ii 237
If ever, as heaven grant, we *c* with Spain, „ IV iii 346
Smooth thou my way, before he *c* with me; Harold II ii 69
sing, Asaph! *c* The cymbal, Heman! „ III i 187
and king's favour might so *c* That thou and I— Becket, Pro. 296
Clash'd *c* their bells, Shot off their lying cannon, Queen Mary III vi 95
Tho' earth's last earthquake *c* the minster-bells, Becket V iii 41
Clashing Ye make this *c* for no love o' the customs „ I iii 136
Sceptre and crozier *c*, and the mitre Grappling „ II i 25
Less *c* with their priests— „ II ii 147
C of swords—three upon one, and that one our Robin! Foresters II i 419
Clasp And *c* the faith in Christ; Queen Mary III ii 122
c a hand Red with the sacred blood of Sinnatus? The Cup II 82
waiting To *c* their lovers by the golden gates. Prom. of May I 248
I fall before thee, *c* Thy knees. Foresters II i 599
I thought I saw thee *c* and kiss a man „ II ii 72
Thou see me *c* and kiss a man indeed, „ II ii 76
Fancied he saw thee *c* and kiss a man. „ III 23
I have seen thee *c* and kiss a man indeed, „ IV 1035
Claspt Then *c* the cross, and pass'd away in peace. Queen Mary V v 259
My lord, We have *c* your cause, Becket II ii 237
Clause the *c's* added To that same treaty Queen Mary III iii 67
Claw Such hold-fast *c's* that you perforce Becket II ii 86
Clay (*See also* **Adam-clay**) Statesmen that are wise Shape a necessity, as a sculptor *c*, Queen Mary III iii 33
Our altar is a mound of dead men's *c*, „ V ii 162
I made him porcelain from the *c* of the city— Becket I iii 438
Clean (*See also* **Cleän**) And cried I was not *c*, what should I care? Queen Mary V ii 324
May plaister his *c* name with scurrilous rhymes! Becket I i 308
that Is *c* against God's honour— „ II ii 163
Only see your cloth be *c*. The Falcon 420
Cleän The feller's *c* daäzed, an' maäzed, an' maäted, Prom. of May II 728
Cleanse we should thoroughly *c* the Church within Queen Mary III iv 195
Clear (adj.) Stand back, keep a *c* lane! Queen Mary I i 2
In *c* and open day were congruent With that vile Cranmer „ III iv 230
So from a *c* sky falls the thunderbolt! „ V iii 115
I think that they would Molochize them too, To have the heavens *c*. Harold I i 38
Like on the face, the brows—*c* innocence! Becket II i 195
Hath he stray'd From love's *c* path into the common bush, „ III i 247
a bat flew out at him In the *c* noon, and hook'd him by the hair, Foresters II ii 97
Clear (verb) his last breath *C* Courtenay and the Princess Queen Mary III i 135
I bad them *c* A royal pleasaunce for thee, Becket II i 127
I say that those Who went before us did not wholly *c* The deadly growths of earth, „ II ii 202
Fasts, disciplines that *c* the spiritual eye, „ V i 42
Clear'd The king, the lords, the people *c* him of it. Harold II ii 522
I've hed the long barn *c* out of all the machines, Prom. of May I 451
Clearer gray dawn Of an old age that never will be mine Is all the *c* seen. Queen Mary V ii 236
Cleave (to adhere) and *c* unto each other As man and wife? „ V ii 137
in hope the crown Would *c* to me that but obey'd Becket V i 50
—if I win her love, They too will *c* to me, The Cup I iii 154
I'll *c* to you rich or poor. Foresters I i 155
C to him, father! he will come home at last. „ I i 197
Cleave (to divide) bright sky *c* To the very feet of God, Harold II ii 742
C heaven, and send thy saints that I may say „ II ii 785
blow that brains the horseman *c's* the horse, „ V i 593
Cleaved thro' all this quarrel I still have *c* to the crown, Becket V i 48
Cleaving Is like the *c* of a heart; Queen Mary III vi 196
C to your original Adam-clay, „ IV iii 418
Cleft *c* the tree From off the bearing trunk, Harold III i 137
And *c* the Moslem turban at my side. Foresters IV 1001
Clench'd fierce forekings had *c* their pirate hides Harold IV iii 35
Cleric A *c* lately poison'd his own mother, Becket, Pro. 10
whether between laymen or *c's*, shall be tried in the King's court.' „ I iii 80
would drag The *c* before the civil judgment-seat, „ I iii 84
'If any *c* be accused of felony, the Church shall not protect him; „ I iii 86
A *c* violated The daughter of his host, „ I iii 382
Say that a *c* murder'd an archbishop, „ I iii 399
the lady holds the *c* Lovelier than any soldier, „ V i 193
Your *c* hath your lady. „ V i 200
Lifted our produce, driven our *c's* out— „ V ii 432
Clever And speak for him after—you that are so *c*! Prom. of May I 620
Cliff Make blush the maiden-white of our tall *c's*, Harold II ii 333
make their wall of shields Firm as thy *c's*, „ V i 480
voice of the deep as it hollows the *c's* of the land. Becket II i 4
Cliff-gibbeted they should hang *C-g* for sea-marks; Harold II i 97
Clifford (*See also* **Rosamund, Rosamund de Clifford**) and it minded me Of the sweet woods of *C*, Becket I i 264
The mouth is only *C*, my dear father. „ II i 220
I am a *C*, My son a *C* and Plantagenet. „ IV ii 226
Climb we will *c* The mountain opposite and watch the chase. The Cup I i 116
He *c's* the throne. Hot blood, ambition, „ II 168
Climb'd Have I *c* back into the primal church, Queen Mary I ii 49
Last night I *c* into the gate-house, Brett, „ II iii 14
Hath *c* the throne and almost clutch'd the crown; Becket, Pro. 21
That hath *c* up to nobler company. „ I i 351
his politic Holiness Hath all but *c* the Roman perch „ II ii 46
Clime Is it the fashion in this *c* for women Queen Mary III vi 90
Your people are as cheerless as your *c*; „ V i 84
Cling now thy love to mine Will *c* more close, „ III ii 160
C to their love; for, now the sons of Godwin Harold I i 324
women *C* to the conquer'd, if they love, „ IV i 213
I *c* to you all the more. Foresters I i 160
Your names will *c* like ivy to the wood. „ IV 1085
Clinging *c* thus Felt the remorseless outdraught Harold II i 7
c to thee Closer than ever. Becket II i 285
Clip rather than so *c* The flowery robe of Hymen, The Cup II 435
Clipt The common barber *c* your hair, Queen Mary IV ii 131
Cloak like his *c*, his manners want the nap „ III v 69

Cloak (*continued*) Wrap them together in a purple *c* — *Harold* V ii 158
A ragged *c* for saddle—he, he, he, — *Becket* V i 248
Clock Toll of a bell, Stroke of a *c*, — *Queen Mary* III v 143
so they bided on and on till vour o' the *c*, — „ IV iii 510
Cloister Thou art *my* nun, thy *c* in mine arms. — *Harold* I ii 63
then would find Her nest within the *c*, — „ IV i 234
Get thou into thy *c* as the king Will'd it: — „ V i 309
Those arm'd men in the *c*. — *Becket* V iii 50
Cloister'd She must be *c* somehow, lest the king — *Harold* I ii 157
The silent, *c*, solitary life, — „ III i 277
Cloistral Retiring into *c* solitude — *Queen Mary* III vi 209
Close (adj. and adv.) Can you be *c*? *Elizabeth*. Can you, my Lord? *Courtenay*. *C* as a miser's casket. Listen: — „ I iv 106
They call me near, for I am *c* to thee And England— — *Harold* III i 6
with his charm of simple style And *c* dialectic, — *Prom. of May* I 225
From the farm Here, *c* at hand. — „ II 361
C by that alder-island in your brook, — „ II 535
you kept your veil too *c* for that when they carried you in; — „ III 227
but call Kate when you will, for I am *c* at hand. — *Foresters* III 50
Close (an end) Gone narrowing down and darkening to a *c*. — *Queen Mary* IV iii 432
war with Brittany to a goodlier *c* Than else had been, — *Harold* II ii 49
And never a flower at the *c*; (repeat) — *Becket, Pro.* 332, 342
Close (verb) all too much at odds to *c* at once — *Queen Mary* I v 632
Tell her to come and *c* my dying eyes, — „ V ii 599
tell the cooks to *c* The doors of all the offices below. — „ V v 116
To make all England one, to *c* all feuds, — *Harold* IV i 141
Over! the sweet summer *c's*, (repeat) — *Becket, Pro.* 302, 324, 331
that the rift he made May *c* between us, — „ II ii 132
C the great gate—ho, there—upon the town. — „ V ii 529
Will *c* with me that to submit at once — *The Cup* I ii 140
c not yet the door upon a night That looks half day. — „ I ii 387
She—*c* the Temple door. Let her not fly. — „ II 460
and warm hands *c* with warm hands, — *Foresters* I iii 20
Closed (adj. and part.) on a soft bed, in a *c* room, with light, fire, physic, tendance; — *Queen Mary* V iv 36
Thro' all *c* doors a dreadful whisper crept — *Becket* V ii 88
or *c* For ever in a Moorish tower, — *Foresters* II i 655
Closed (verb) King *c* with me last July That I should pass — *Becket* V ii 388
Closer Might it not Be the rough preface of some *c* bond? — *Queen Mary* I iv 48
So that your sister were but look'd to *c*. — „ I v 461
Hast thou not mark'd—come *c* to mine ear— — „ V i 225
clinging to thee *C* than ever. — *Becket* II i 286
Why, an old woman can shoot *c* than you two. — *Foresters* II i 400
Closet listening In some dark *c*, — *Queen Mary* V ii 217
Get thee into the *c* there, — *Foresters* II i 215
Closing gulf and flatten in her *c* chasm Domed cities, hear. — *The Cup* II 300
Cloth (*See also* **Cloth of gold, Dust-cloth**) Only see your *c* be clean. — *The Falcon* 420
see your *c* be white as snow! — „ 498
Clothe His faith shall *c* the world that will be his, — *Queen Mary* III i 180
And tropes are good to *c* a naked truth, — „ III iv 150
c's itself In maiden flesh and blood, — *Foresters* III 115
Clothed stand *C* with the full authority of Rome, — *Becket* V ii 493
C with the mystic silver of her moon. — *Foresters* II i 608
Cloth of gold That royal commonplace too, *c o g*, — *Queen Mary* III i 54
Cloud (s) (*See also* **Thunder-cloud**) then King Harry look'd from out a *c*, — „ IV ii 7
under no ceiling but the *c* that wept on them, — „ V iv 40
be as the shadow of a *c* Crossing your light. — *Harold* II ii 177
Come, Harold, shake the *c* off! — „ III i 74
Fall, *c*, and fill the house— — „ III i 190
Customs, traditions,—*c's* that come and go; — *Becket* I iii 22
As Canterbury calls them, wandering *c's*, — „ I iii 71
My sun, no *c*! Let there not be one frown in this one hour. — „ II i 42
Out of the *c*, my Sun—out of the eclipse — „ II i 202
black *c* that hath come over the sun and cast — „ III iii 46
King at last is fairly scared by this *c*—this interdict. — „ III iii 64
My princess of the *c*, my plumed purveyor — *The Falcon* 7
upon me Thro' that rich *c* of blossom. — *Prom. of May* II 250
And the white *c* is roll'd along the sky! — *Foresters* I ii 319
Flung by the golden mantle of the *c*, — „ II i 28
Cloud (verb) *C* not thy birthday with one fear for me. — *Foresters* I ii 125
Cloudless But *c* heavens which we have found together — *The Cup* I ii 415
Clown Their A B C is darkness, *c's* and grooms May read it! — *Queen Mary* III iv 35
one that pares his nails; to me? the *c*! — „ III v 66
Insolent *c*. Shall I smite him — *Becket* I iv 223
less loyalty in it than the backward scrape of the *c's* heel— — „ III iii 144
parish-parson bawl our banns Before your gaping *c's*? — *Prom. of May* I 687
How the *c* glared at me! that Dobbins, is it, — „ II 611
Lout, churl, *c*! — „ III 739
Club *See* **War-club**
Cluckt The hen *c* late by the white farm gate, — „ I 38
Clumsy O the *c* word! *Robin*. Take thou this light kiss for thy *c* word. — *Foresters* III 133
You lovers are such *c* summer-flies — „ IV 10
Clung these earls and barons, that *c* to me, — *Becket* I iv 66
Clutch Here is one would *c* Our pretty Marian for his paramour, — *Foresters* IV 766
Clutch'd and almost *c* the crown; — *Becket, Pro.* 22
Coal (*See also* **Coäl**) As one that blows the *c* to cool the fire. — „ V ii 549
my father and I forgave you stealing our *c's*. — *Prom. of May* III 69
Coäl cotched 'im once a-steälin' *c's* an' I sent fur 'im, — „ I 412
Coalscuttle fell ageän *c* and my kneeä gev waäy — „ I 403
Coarse This hard *c* man of old hath crouch'd to me — *Queen Mary* IV ii 169
but neither cold, *c*, cruel, And more than all— — „ V ii 481
Coarseness This *c* is a want of phantasy. — „ V ii 438
Coat And carve my *c* upon the walls again! — „ II iv 110
This Gardiner turn'd his *c* in Henry's time; — „ III iii 17
Down with him, tear his *c* from his back. — *Foresters* I iii 73
Cobbled for mine own father Was great, and *c*. — *Harold* IV i 91
Cobbler the psalm-singing weavers, *c's*, scum— — *Queen Mary* III iv 290
Cock Our Lord Becket's our great sitting-hen *c*, — *Becket* I iv 126
He was the *c* o' the walk; — *Foresters* II i 320
Cockboat he look'd the Great Harry, You but his *c*; — *Queen Mary* V ii 147
Cocker'd *See* **Nursery-cocker'd**
Cockerel thou'rt no such *c* thyself, — „ I i 41
Cockle-shell Scuttle his *c-s*? — *Harold* IV iii 142
Cocksbody It must be thus; and yet, *c*! — *Queen Mary* III iii 4
He's here, and king, or will be—yet *c*! — „ III iii 45
Codlin as sleek and as round-about as a mellow *c*. — *Foresters* I i 43
Coesnon from the liquid sands of *C* Haled — *Harold* II ii 56
Coffin like Mahound's *c* hung between heaven and earth— — *Becket* II ii 361
Cognisant told Sir Maurice there was one *C* of this, — *Queen Mary* II iv 100
Wyatt did confess the Princess *C* thereof, — „ II iv 113
Coif Disguise me—thy gown and thy *c*. — *Foresters* II i 187
Ay, ay, gown, *c*, and petticoat, — „ II i 194
Coil'd And *c* himself about her sacred waist. — „ II i 138
Coin He can but read the king's face on his *c's*. — *Harold* I i 71
Spare not thy tongue! be lavish with our *c's*, — *Becket* II ii 470
cast him from their doors Like a base *c*. — *The Cup* I ii 353
Then after we have eased them of their *c's* — *Foresters* III 173
Co-king *C-k's* we were, and made the laws together. — *Becket* II ii 123
Cold (adj.) (*See also* **Cowd, Ice-cold**) Madam, methinks a *c* face and a haughty. — *Queen Mary* I v 196
If *c*, his life is pure. — „ I v 333
They call him *c*, Haughty, ay, worse. — „ I v 431
know that whether A wind be warm or *c*, — „ I v 620
Ay, and then as *c* as ever. Is Calais taken? — „ V ii 26
Ah, Madam, but your people are so *c*; — „ V ii 281
Thou art *c* thyself To babble of their coldness. — „ V ii 290
but neither *c*, coarse, cruel, And more than all—, — „ V ii 481
The *c*, white lily blowing in her cell: — *Harold* III i 274
Vying a tear with our *c* dews, — „ V i 151
In *c*, white cells beneath an icy moon— — „ V i 325
John of Salisbury Hath often laid a *c* hand on my heats, — *Becket* I i 384
he makes moan that all be a-getting *c*. — „ I iv 62
C after warm, winter after summer, — „ I iv 64
frosted off me by the first *c* frown of the King. *C*, but look how the table steams, — „ I iv 68
You are too *c* to know the fashion of it. — „ II ii 126
And when the *c* corners of the King's mouth began To thaw, — „ III iii 153
To warm the *c* bounds of our dying life — *The Cup* I iii 128

Cold (adj.) (*continued*) It is but thin and *c*, Not like the vintage — *The Falcon* 578
Why, what a *c* grasp is thine— *Foresters* I ii 242
Thou blowest hot and *c*. Where is she then? „ II i 490
What makes you seem so *c* to Robin, lady? „ III 1
What makes thee think I seem so *c* to Robin? „ III 4
In the *c* water that she lost her voice, „ IV 243
Did you find that you worked at all the worse upon the *c* tea — *Prom. of May* III 56
Cold (s) bring him home Safe from the dark and the *c*, *The Cup* I ii 6
O heavens! the very letters seem to shake With *c*, *The Falcon* 449
And the bee buzz'd up in the *c*. *Foresters* IV 21
And the bee buzz'd off in the *c*. „ IV 27
Colder To-day I almost fear'd your kiss was *c*— *Becket* III i 18
Cold-manner'd *c-m* friend may strangely do us The truest service, *The Falcon* 642
Coldness Thou art cold thyself To babble of their *c*. *Queen Mary* V ii 292
God's revenge upon this realm For narrowness and *c*: *Harold* I i 174
Cole Why are the trumpets blowing, Father *C*? *Queen Mary* IV ii 24
I wish some thunderbolt Would make this *C* a cinder, „ IV iii 11
Collar on his neck a *c*, Gold, thick with diamonds; „ III i 79
Colleagued yet the Pope is now *c* with France; „ V i 140
Collect *c* the fleet; Let every craft that carries „ V ii 273
Morcar, *c* thy men; Edwin, my friend— *Harold* IV i 256
College But the King hath bought half the *C* of Redhats. *Becket* II ii 374
Colloquy After the long brain-dazing *colloquies*, *Queen Mary* IV ii 92
Her Highness is too ill for *c*. „ V ii 613
Colossal Your father was a man Of such *c* kinghood, „ IV i 101
Colour (s) under *c* Of such a cause as hath no *c*, „ II ii 182
The *c* freely play'd into her face, „ II ii 321
Who changed not *c* when she saw the block, „ III i 399
The *c's* of our Queen are green and white, „ III v 5
Whose *c's* in a moment break and fly, „ IV iii 169
declare to you my very faith Without all *c*. „ IV iii 226
Whose *c's* in a moment break and fly!' „ V ii 206
A *c*, which has colour'd all my life, *The Falcon* 364
C Flows thro' my life again, *Prom. of May* II 666
He wore thy *c's* once at a tourney. *Foresters* I i 250
Colour (verb) She *c's*! *Dora*. Sir! *Prom. of May* II 559
Colour'd A colour, which has *c* all my life, *The Falcon* 364
Colt *c* winced and whinnied and flung up her heels; *Becket, Pro.* 514
Be the *c* deäd? *Dora*. No, Father. *Prom. of May* III 429
deer from a dog, or a *c* from a gad-fly, *Foresters* II i 434
Column For smooth stone *c's* of the sanctuary, *Harold* I ii 101
hurls the victor's *c* down with him That crowns it, *The Cup* II 295
Co-mate *C-m's* we were, and had our sport together, *Becket* II ii 121
Comb And bind him in from harming of their *c's*. *Queen Mary* III iii 58
Combat My lords, is this a *c* or a council? *Becket* I iii 133
Come (*See also* **A-cum, Coom, Coomed**) They love thee, and thou canst not *c* to harm. *Queen Mary* I iii 67
These birds of passage *c* before their time: „ I iii 75
And in the whirl of change may *c* to be one. „ I iii 107
Prince of fluff and feather *c* To woo you, „ I iv 163
This *c's* of parleying with my Lord of Devon. „ I iv 251
Your time will *c*. *Elizabeth*. I think my time will *c*. „ I iv 255
C, *c*, I will go with you to the Queen. „ I iv 297
Madam, the Lord Chancellor. *Mary*. Bid him *c* in. „ I v 97
C you to tell me this, my Lord? „ I v 106
Bid him *c* in. Good morning, Sir de Noailles. „ I v 241
Let the great angel of the church *c* with him; „ I v 377
To save your crown that it must *c* to this. „ I v 479
No, Renard; it must never *c* to this. „ I v 482
he will not *c* Till she be gone. „ I v 512
For Philip *c's*, one hand in mine, „ I v 515
No, say I *c*. I won by boldness once. „ I v 547
Why *c's* that old fox-Fleming back again? „ I v 581
Her Highness *c's*. „ I v 635
No new news that Philip *c's* to wed Mary, „ II i 16
Ay, for the Saints are *c* to reign again. „ II i 21
I fear you *c* to carry it off my shoulders, „ II i 91
C locusting upon us, eat us up, „ II i 101
C, you bluster, Antony! „ II i 118
and if Philip *c* to be King, O, my God! „ II i 199
C, now, you're sonnetting again. „ II i 247

Come (*continued*) I trust the Queen *c's* hither with her guards. *Queen Mary* II ii 1
One word before she *c's*. „ II ii 109
Queen had written her word to *c* to court: „ II ii 117
Here *c's* her Royal Grace. „ II ii 126
In mine own person am I *c* to you, „ II ii 142
Your lawful Prince hath *c* to cast herself „ II ii 261
C, sirs, we prate; hence all— „ II ii 372
Wyatt *c's* to Southwark; „ II ii 374
thro' thine help we are *c* to London Bridge; „ II iii 8
make Those that we *c* to serve our sharpest foes? „ II iii 77
we know that ye be *c* to kill the Queen, „ II iii 108
I have not *c* to kill the Queen Or here or there: „ II iii 116
Whence *c* you, sir? „ II iv 74
Philip would not *c* Till Guildford Dudley „ II iv 136
An hour will *c* When they will sweep her from the seas. „ III i 161
here they *c*—a pale horse for Death „ III i 234
The Queen *c's* first, Mary and Philip. „ III i 299
C to me to-morrow.— „ III i 320
He *c's*, and my star rises. „ III ii 167
Oh, Philip, *c* with me; „ III ii 185
Nay *c* with me—one moment! „ III ii 189
We *c* not to condemn, but reconcile; We *c* not to compel, but call again; We *c* not to destroy, but edify; „ III iii 186
what saith Christ? 'Compel them to *c* in.' „ III iv 30
'I *c* not to bring peace but a sword'? „ III iv 88
The end's not *c*. *Pole*. No—nor this way will *c*, „ III iv 110
I *c* for counsel and ye give me feuds, „ III iv 307
pray Heaven That you may see according to our sight. *C*, cousin. „ III iv 332
C, *c*, the morsel stuck—this Cardinal's fault— „ III iv 375
Rogers and Ferrar, for their time is *c*, „ III iv 425
not like a word, That *c's* and goes in uttering. „ III v 30
Is like a word that *c's* from olden days, „ III v 34
But there hath some one *c*; „ III v 82
C, Robin, Robin, *C* and kiss me now; „ III v 99
C behind and kiss me milking the cow! „ III v 105
Rose hand in hand, and whisper'd, '*c* away! „ III v 148
Thou last of all the Tudors, *c* away! „ III v 151
When next there *c's* a missive from the Queen „ III v 182
For I will *c* no nearer to your Grace; „ III v 200
You know I never *c* till I be call'd. „ III v 215
C, *c*, the worst! „ III v 219
You are to *c* to Court on the instant; „ III v 223
C, *c*, you are chill here; „ III v 275
the fools, of this fair prince to *c*; „ III vi 100
As else we might be—here she *c's*. „ III vi 190
Here *c* the Cranmerites! „ IV i 40
Cranmer, I *c* to question you again; „ IV ii 15
refusing none That *c* to Thee for succour, unto Thee, Therefore, I *c*; „ IV iii 132
forasmuch as I have *c* To the last end of life, „ IV iii 217
I *c* to the great cause that weighs Upon my conscience „ IV iii 236
So I may *c* to the fire. „ IV iii 251
So that she *c* to rule us. „ IV iii 390
When we had *c* where Ridley burnt with Latimer, „ IV iii 585
C out, my Lord, it is a world of fools. „ IV iii 639
Knows where he nested—ever *c's* again. „ V i 26
I am faint with fear that you will *c* no more. „ V i 30
Sire, I obey you. *C* quickly. „ V i 221
Hast thou not mark'd—*c* closer to mine ear— „ V i 225
When back he *c's* at evening hath the door „ V ii 120
they *c* back upon my dreams. „ V ii 188
what good could *c* of that? „ V ii 309
And says, he will *c* quickly. „ V ii 565
you said more; You said he would *c* quickly. „ V ii 575
And yet he will *c* quickly . . . „ V ii 583
And tell him that I know he *c's* no more. „ V ii 589
Tell her to *c* and close my dying eyes, „ V ii 599
Amen. *C* on. „ V iv 9
'I am dying, Philip; *c* to me.' „ V v 3
Nothing; but '*c*, *c*, *c*,' and all awry, „ V v 15
I cannot doubt but that he *c's* again; „ V v 26
No, Philip *c's* and goes, but never goes. „ V v 150

Come (*continued*) *C* thou down. Lie there. *Queen Mary* v v 179
Madam, your royal sister *c's* to see you. „ v v 192
C, *c*! as yet thou art not gone so wild *Harold* I i 298
C, *c*, Join hands, let brethren dwell in unity; „ I i 395
Love is *c* with a song and a smile, „ I ii 10
I will demand his ward From Edward when I *c* again. „ I ii 60
C, thou shalt dream no more such dreams; „ I ii 108
tho' I would not That it should *c* to that. „ I ii 227
Not to *c* back till Tostig shall have shown „ I ii 241
Here *c's* the would-be what I will be . . . „ II ii 138
the lark sings, the sweet stars *c* and go, „ II ii 434
I will not hear thee—William *c's*. „ II ii 480
C hither, I have a power; „ III i 5
C, Harold, shake the cloud off! „ III i 73
Spare and forbear him, Harold, if he *c's*! „ III i 300
Pray God that *c* not suddenly! „ III i 364
not so with us—No wings to *c* and go. „ III ii 99
Ill news hath *c*! Our hapless brother, „ III ii 120
—the Pope Is man and *c's* as God.— „ III ii 174
This brother *c's* to save Your land from waste; „ IV i 94
Somewhere hard at hand. Call and she *c's*. „ IV i 186
Who is it *c's* this way? Tostig? „ IV ii 1
I *c* for mine own Earldom, my Northumbria; „ IV ii 29
C back with him. Know what thou dost; „ IV ii 47
C thou back, and be Once more a son of Godwin. „ IV ii 59
Nay then, *c* thou back to us! „ IV ii 64
bragging still that he will *c* To thrust our Harold's throne „ IV iii 125
Let him *c*! let him *c*. „ IV iii 132
Cram thy crop full, but *c* when thou art call'd. „ IV iii 234
C yet once more, from where I am at peace, „ V i 238
There is one *C* as Goliath came of yore— „ V i 493
And thou art *c* to rob them of their rings! „ V ii 36
C, *c*, thou art but deacon, not yet bishop, *Becket*, *Pro.* 82
C, *c*, I love thee and I know thee, I know thee, „ *Pro.* 95
C, I would give her to thy care in England „ *Pro.* 142
Whatever *c* between us? *Becket.* What should *c* Between us, Henry? „ *Pro.* 194
Well—whatever *c* between us. „ *Pro.* 199
C to me to-morrow. „ *Pro.* 410
C with me. Let me learn at full The manner of his death, „ *Pro.* 424
and if there ever *c* feud between Church and Crown, „ *Pro.* 464
C, *c*, my lord Archbishop; „ I i 201
O brother!—I may *c* to martyrdom. „ I i 361
Customs, traditions,—clouds that *c* and go; „ I iii 22
Is black and white at once, and *c's* to nought. „ I iii 32
but an he *c* to Saltwood, By God's death, „ I iii 182
should harm *c* of it, it is the Pope Will be to blame— „ I iii 220
snake that sloughs *c's* out a snake again. „ I iii 449
Arm'd with thy cross, to *c* before the King? „ I iii 509
The King's 'God's eyes!' *c* now so thick and fast, „ I iii 609
C on, *c* on! it is not fit for us To see the proud Archbishop mutilated. „ I iii 613
My lord, I *c* unwillingly. „ I iii 648
may I *c* in with my poor friend, my dog? „ I iv 93
C, *c*! thou hadst thy share on her. „ I iv 123
I must fly to France to-night. *C* with me. „ I iv 154
C, you filthy knaves, let us pass. „ I iv 203
There is a bench. *C*, wilt thou sit? „ II i 124
no hand to mate with *her*, If it should *c* to that. „ II i 191
C, *c*, mine hour! „ II i 212
The word should *c* from him. „ II ii 134
I pray you *c* and take it. „ II ii 263
For here he *c's* to comment on the time. „ II ii 308
No one *c's*, Nor foe nor friend; „ III i 37
Always Becket! He always *c's* between us. „ III i 90
for here *c's* my lady, and, my lady, „ III i 153
if it should *c* to that!—To that—to what? „ III i 259
when the horn sounds she *c's* out as a wolf. „ III ii 23
black cloud that hath *c* over the sun and cast us all into shadow? „ III iii 46
so that the smell of their own roast had not *c* across it— „ III iii 120
from those, as I said before, there may *c* a conflagration— „ III iii 164
ere Pope or King Had *c* between us! „ III iii 268
That perfect trust may *c* again between us, „ III iii 351

Come (*continued*) *C* to me, little one. How camest thou hither? *Becket* IV i 3
Ay, but some one *c's* to see her now and then. „ IV i 15
C, here is a golden chain I will give thee „ IV i 40
C along, then? we shall see the silk here and there, „ IV i 55
I sent this Margery, and she *c's* not back; I sent another, and she *c's* not back. „ IV ii 3
C with me, love, And I will love thee . . . „ IV ii 154
C hither, man; stand there. „ IV ii 219
C thou with me to Godstow nunnery, „ IV ii 366
What! Is the end *c*? „ V i 148
C you to confess? „ V ii 71
Hark! Is it they? *C*! „ V iii 15
C, then, with us to vespers. „ V iii 34
How can I *c* When you so block the entry? „ V iii 36
C in, my friends, *c* in! „ V iii 68
C with us—nay—thou art our prisoner—*c*! „ V iii 143
C; as he said, thou art our prisoner. „ V iii 155
You *c* here with your soldiers to enforce *The Cup* I i 75
Stand aside, Stand aside; here she *c's*! „ I i 105
He *c's*, a rough, bluff, simple-looking fellow. „ I i 172
c upon *her* Again, perhaps, to-day—*her*. „ I i 179
Nay, here he *c's*. „ I ii 25
C, *c*, we will not quarrel about the stag. „ I ii 38
Think,—torture,—death,—and *c*. „ I ii 314
C, *c*, could he deny it? What did he say? „ I ii 344
If I be not back in half an hour, *C* after me. „ I ii 439
Will she *c* to me Now that she knows me Synorix? „ I iii 19
Nay, she will not *c*. „ I iii 31
Why *c* we now? Whom shall we seize upon? „ I iii 177
C once more to me Before the crowning,— „ II 78
Let him *c*—a legion with him, if he will. „ II 250
Why *c's* he not to meet me? „ II 528
C, *c*, Filippo, what is there in the larder? *The Falcon* 117
I knew it would *c* to this. (repeat) „ 156, 174
I always knew it would *c* to this! (repeat) „ 158, 175
C in, Madonna, *c* in. „ 176
—but *c* when they will—then or now—it's all for the best, *c* when they will— „ 200
Call him back and say I *c* to breakfast with him. „ 213
His falcon, and I *c* to ask for his falcon, „ 220
I *c* this day to break my fast with you. „ 276
Yet I *c* To ask a gift. „ 298
That seem'd to *c* and go. „ 650
who *c's* To rob you of your one delight on earth. „ 827
tho' he never *c's* to church, I thought better of him. *Prom. of May* I 261
when Thought *C's* down among the crowd, „ I 501
Heaven curse him if he *c* not at your call! „ I 764
For ever, you foolish child! What's *c* over you? „ I 772
to *c* together again in a moment and to go on together again, „ I 774
C, then, and make them happy in the long barn, „ I 790
What are you? Where do you *c* from? „ II 359
The body!—Heavens! I *c*! „ II 572
C, you will set all right again, „ II 658
if the farming-men be *c* for their wages, to send them up to me. „ III 16
C, *c*, you worked well enough, „ III 61
that you did not *c* into the hayfield. „ III 82
C, *c*, keep a good heart! „ III 252
not forgotten his promise to *c* when I called him. „ III 330
Well, Milly, why do you *c* in so roughly? „ III 342
a Sister of Mercy, *c* from the death-bed of a pauper, „ III 376
She would have persuaded me to *c* back here, „ III 384
Must *c* to in our spring-and-winter world „ III 510
C, *c*, my girl, enough Of this strange talk. „ III 619
C, *c*, why do ye loiter here? *Foresters* I i 79
to *c* at their love with all manner of homages, „ I i 102
'You have *c* for you saw Wealth coming,' „ I i 152
Cleave to him, father! he will *c* home at last. „ I i 198
have *c* as freely as heaven's air and mother's milk? „ I i 209
Say, we will *c*. „ I i 302
I *c* here to see this daughter of Sir Richard of the Lea „ I ii 26
the Earl and Sir Richard *c* this way. „ I ii 148

Come (*continued*) I cannot answer thee till Richard *c*. *Sheriff.* And when he *c's*? *Marian.* Well, you must wait till then. *Foresters* I ii 221
C away, daughter. „ I ii 283
But if the better times should never *c*? „ I ii 288
And if the worst time *c*? „ I ii 290
Have they *c* for me? Here is the witch's hut. „ II i 177
C in, *c* in; I would give my life for thee, „ II i 188
C in, *c* in. *John.* Why did ye keep us at the door so long? „ II i 222
He will *c* to the gibbet at last. „ II i 328
And here *c's* another. „ II i 399
C now, I fain would have a bout with thee. „ II i 552
C to him. *Marian.* O my poor father! „ II ii 7
there *c's* a deputation From our finikin fairy nation. „ II ii 144
warm thy heart to Little John. Look where he *c's*! „ III 46
we be beggars, we *c* to ask o' you. We ha' nothing. „ III 190
Here *c's* a citizen, and I think his wife. „ III 227
and I pray you to *c* between us again, „ III 413
c between me and my Kate and make us one again. „ III 422
So *c*, *c*!' 'Hum!' „ IV 18
But *c*, *c*!' 'Hum!' „ IV 25
Till thou thyself shalt *c* to sing it—in time. „ IV 36
thou seest the land has *c* between us, And my sick father here has *c* between us And this rich Sheriff too has *c* between us; „ IV 53
But will they *c*? „ IV 91
if they *c* I will not tear the bond, „ IV 97
but here *c's* one of bigger mould. „ IV 114
Rogue, we *c* not alone. „ IV 573
save King Richard, when he *c's*, forbid me. „ IV 665
C, girl, thou shalt along with us on the instant. „ IV 678
You, Prince, our king to *c*— „ IV 696
When Richard *c's* he is soft enough to pardon His brother; „ IV 746
and she will not marry till Richard *c*. „ IV 773
But look, who *c's*? „ IV 977
C from out That oak-tree! „ IV 996
Comedy A *c* meant to seem a tragedy— *Becket* IV ii 322
players In such a *c* as our court of Provence „ V i 189
Comelier She looks *c* than ordinary to-day; *Queen Mary* I i 70
Comely (*See also* **Coomly**) Master Dobson, you are a *c* man to look at. *Prom. of May* I 156
Comest Why *c* thou like a death's head at my feast? *Foresters* I ii 210
Thou *c* a very angel out of heaven. „ II i 105
Comet and look upon my face, Not on the *c*. *Harold* I i 27
That were too small a matter for a *c*! „ I i 471
Too small! a *c* would not show for that! „ I i 474
Put thou the *c* and the blast together— „ II i 15
Your *c* came and went. „ III i 359
Cometh Blessed is he that *c* in the name of the Lord! *Becket* I iii 758
Comfort (*See also* **Heart-comfort**) And it would be your *c*, as I trust; *Queen Mary* II ii 225
when last he wrote, declared His *c* in your Grace „ III vi 79
I could make his age A *c* to him— *Prom. of May* II 662
our carters and our shepherds Still find a *c* there. „ III 529
Comfortable set up your broken images; Be *c* to me. *Queen Mary* V ii 301
Comforted Be *c*. Thou art the man— *Becket* I i 132
Coming (adj. and part.) (*See also* **A-coomin', Coomin**)
Prince of Spain *c* to wed our Queen! *Queen Mary* I iii 83
Gardiner, *c* with the Queen, And meeting Pembroke, „ II ii 309
same tide Which, *c* with our coming, seem'd to smile „ II iii 22
They are *c* now. „ III i 181
Legate's *c* To bring us absolution from the Pope. „ III i 431
there's the face *c* on here of one Who knows me. „ III i 470
I fain would hear him *c*! . . . *Harold* I ii 5
leave them for a year, and *c* back Find them again. „ II i 89
I saw him *c* with his brother Odo The Bayeux bishop, „ II ii 347
Not *c* fiercely like a conqueror, now, „ II ii 757
First of a line that *c* from the people, „ V i 386
why, then it is my will—Is he *c*? *Becket* I iii 474
voice *c* up with the voice of the deep from the strand, One *c* up with a song „ II i 5
Love that is born of the deep *c* up with the sun from the sea. (repeat) „ II i 9, 19
Some dreadful thing is *c* on me. „ III i 267
He bows, he bares his head, he is *c* hither. „ III iii 34

Coming (adj. and part.) (*continued*) Is he *c*? I thought I heard A footstep. *The Cup* I ii 10
I fear some strange and evil chance *C* upon me, „ I iii 76
walk with me we needs must meet Antonius *c*, „ I iii 93
Thou—*c* my way too—Camma—good-night. „ II 492
there is Monna Giovanna *c* down the hill from the castle. *The Falcon* 160
C to visit my lord, for the first time in her life too! „ 169
I'm *c* down, Mr. Dobson. *Prom. of May* I 45
But see they are *c* out for the dance already. „ I 795
Hark, Dora, some one is *c*. „ III 339
'You have come for you saw Wealth *c*,' *Foresters* I i 152
But they are *c* hither for the dance— „ I ii 52
but the twilight of the *c* day already glimmers in the east. „ I ii 247
Is *c* with a swarm of mercenaries To break our band „ III 452
mark'd if those two knaves from York be *c*? „ IV 113
Coming (s) At his *c* Your star will rise. *Queen Mary* I v 410
at once may know The wherefore of this *c*, „ II ii 138
same tide Which, coming with our *c*, seem'd to smile „ II iii 22
I have changed a word with him In *c*, „ III iv 16
and think of this in your *c*. 'MARY THE QUEEN.' „ III v 224
And wait my *c* back. „ III vi 219
How oft in *c* hast thou broken bread? *Harold* IV iii 199
with my lady's *c* that had so flurried me, *The Falcon* 492
I trust he brings us news of the King's *c*. *Foresters* I iii 54
To warn us of his *c*! „ III 458
We told the Prince and the Sheriff of our *c*. „ IV 576
Command (s) so my Lord of Pembroke in *c* Of all her force be safe; *Queen Mary* II ii 305
Lord Pembroke in *c* of all our force „ II iv 3
I have the Count's *c's* to follow thee. *Harold* II ii 235
I have the Count's *c's*. „ II ii 239
But by the King's *c* are written down, *Becket* I iii 72
by the King's *c* I, John of Oxford, „ I iii 74
Now, sirs, the King's *c's*! „ V ii 322
Command (verb) Her Grace the Queen *c's* you to the Tower. *Queen Mary* III iii 270
and *c* That kiss my due when subject *Harold* III ii 41
The king *c's* thee, woman! „ V i 340
Power now from Harold to *c* thee hence „ V i 456
King *c's* you upon pain of death, *Becket* I iii 752
C's you to be dutiful and leal To your young King „ V ii 325
King *c's* you to absolve the bishops „ V ii 375
King *c's* you. We are all King's men. „ V ii 383
How if the King *c* it? *Foresters* IV 868
Commandment Obey my first and last *c*. Go! *Harold* V i 359
They have broken the *c* of the king! „ V i 614
she kept the seventh *c* better than some I know on, *Becket* III i 194
Commend He *c's* me now From out his grave „ *Pro.* 418
when thou seest him next, *C* me to thy friend. „ I i 324
I do *c* my cause to God, the Virgin, „ V iii 163
c them to your ladyship's most peculiar appreciation. *The Falcon* 567
Commendation his last words were a *c* of Thomas Becket *Becket, Pro.* 401
Commended It has been much *c* as a medicine. *The Falcon* 587
Comment here he comes to *c* on the time. *Becket* II ii 308
Commerce Back from her churchless *c* with the King „ IV ii 332
Commission That hastes with full *c* from the Pope *Queen Mary* III ii 51
That our *c* is to heal, not harm; „ III iii 185
Our letters of *c* will declare this plainlier. „ III iii 222
Commission'd Thou art *c* to Elizabeth, And not to me! „ V ii 594
I have *c* thee to save the man: *Harold* II ii 98
Commissioner You would not cap the Pope's *c*— *Queen Mary* IV ii 123
Commit to whom The king, my father, did *c* his trust; „ II ii 208
Committed John of Salisbury *c* The secret of the bower, *Becket* III iii 4
Common (adj.) the tongue yet quiver'd with the jest When the head leapt—so *c*! *Queen Mary* I v 477
And thro' this *c* knot and bond of love, „ II ii 198
The *c* barber clipt your hair, „ IV ii 131
For the pure honour of our *c* nature, „ IV iii 297
Things that seem jerk'd out of the *c* rut Of Nature *Harold* I i 137
Now must I send thee as a *c* friend *Becket* I i 341
when murder *c* As nature's death, „ I iii 343
Hath he stray'd From love's clear path into the *c* bush, „ III i 247
Lost in the *c* good, the *c* wrong, „ V ii 40

Common (adj.) (*continued*) you will find The *c* brotherhood of man has been Wrong'd — *Prom. of May* III 543
Common (s) lanker than an old horse turned out to die on the *c*. — *Foresters* I i 52
Commoner Should we so doat on courage, were it *c*? — *Queen Mary* II ii 340
Commonplace That royal *c* too, cloth of gold, — „ III i 54
Take thou mine answer in bare *c*— — *Becket, Pro.* 282
Commons however the Council and the *C* may fence — *Queen Mary* II i 171
Lords and *C* will bow down before him— — „ III i 433
And *C* here in Parliament assembled, — „ III iii 114
Commonweal That Centaur of a monstrous *C*, — „ III iv 163
Commonwealth to play The tyrant, or in *c* or church. — „ I v 191
Communion It is but a *c*, not a mass: (repeat) — „ IV ii 56, 111
you have put so many of the King's household out of *c*, — *Becket* III iii 311
Are push'd from out *c* of the Church. — „ V i 58
Communist I that have been call'd a Socialist, A *C*, a Nihilist,— — *Prom. of May* III 585
Companion Leave me now, Will you, *c* to myself, sir? — *Queen Mary* III v 212
My comrade, boon *c*, my co-reveller, — *Becket* I iii 460
His one *c* here—nay, I have heard That, — *The Falcon* 225
Company With our advice and in our *c*, — *Queen Mary* I iii 151
She will address your guilds and *companies*. — „ II ii 15
and these our *companies* And guilds of London, — „ II ii 128
I, Lord Mayor Of London, and our guilds and *companies*. — „ II ii 141
Three voices from our guilds and *companies*! — „ II ii 256
With all your trades, and guilds, and *companies*. — „ II ii 297
That hath climb'd up to nobler *c*. — *Becket* I i 351
Oh, do not damn yourself for *c*! — „ V ii 523
Ay, prune our *c* of thine own and go! — *The Falcon* 695
Compass (s) such a one Was without rudder, anchor, *c*— — *Prom. of May* III 534
Compass (verb) To *c* which I wrote myself to Rome, — *Queen Mary* V ii 49
Not small for thee, if thou canst *c* it. — *Harold* I i 477
Compel We come not to *c*, but call again; — *Queen Mary* III iii 187
what saith Christ? '*C* them to come in.' — „ III iv 29
for the sake of Sinnatus your husband, I must *c* you. — *The Cup* I iii 102
Take thou my bow and arrow and *c* them to pay toll. — *Foresters* III 263
Complain If this be so, *c* to your young King, — *Becket* V ii 448
Complexion The peoples are unlike as their *c*; — *Queen Mary* V i 89
Compliment Mere *c's* and wishes. — „ V ii 596
Comport And how did Roger of York *c* himself? — *Becket* III iii 85
Compose to *c* the event In some such form as least — *Queen Mary* I v 223
Compromise But—if let be—balance and *c*; — „ V v 223
Compurgation freed himself By oath and *c* — *Harold* II ii 520
Comrade My *c*, boon companion, my co-reveller, — *Becket* I iii 460
My *c* of the house, and of the field. — *The Falcon* 875
C's, I thank you for your loyalty, — *Foresters* III 78
Conciliation No more feuds, but peace, Peace and *c*! — *The Falcon* 911
Conclude I *c* the King a beast; Verily a lion — *Queen Mary* IV iii 411
Concluded Your audience is *c*, sir. — „ I v 337
Concubine His children and his *c*, belike. — „ IV i 165
Condemn We come not to *c*, but reconcile; — „ III iii 186
c The blameless exile?— — *Becket* II ii 395
The King *c's* your excommunicating— — „ V ii 317
If the King *C* us without trial, — *Foresters* IV 902
Condemn'd said she was *c* to die for treason; — *Queen Mary* III i 377
Condition Nay—but there be *c's*, easy ones, — *Harold* II ii 206
C's? What *c's*? pay him back His ransom? — „ II ii 212
I must not hence Save on *c's*. — „ II ii 262
Obey the Count's *c's*, my good friend. — „ II ii 276
But on *c's*. Canst thou guess at them? — „ II ii 343
Conduct (*See also* **Safe-conduct**) They have given me a safe *c*: — *Queen Mary* I ii 101
Conduit The *c* painted—the nine worthies—ay! — „ III i 258
Confer and *c* with her ladyship's seneschal, — *The Falcon* 415
Conference We'll have no private *c*. Welcome to England! — *Queen Mary* V iii 13
convene This *c* but to babble of our wives? — *Becket* II ii 90
Confess Wyatt did *c* the Princess Cognisant thereof, — *Queen Mary* II iv 111
Went on his knees, and pray'd me to *c* In Wyatt's business, — „ III v 166
c Your faith before all hearers; — „ IV ii 79
Thou shalt *c* all thy sweet sins to me. — *Becket* II i 291

Confess (*continued*) Come, *c*, good brother, — *Becket* II ii 82
Come you to *c*? — „ V ii 71
I'll be bound to *c* her love to him at last. — *The Falcon* 172
Confessed Father Philip that has *c* our mother for twenty years, — *Becket* III i 111
Confession Shamed a too trustful widow whom you heard In her *c*; — *Foresters* III 387
Confessor Saving my *c* and my cousin Pole. — *Queen Mary* V ii 527
No, nor archbishop, nor my *c* yet. — *Becket, Pro.* 84
for I should find An easy father *c* in thee. — „ *Pro.* 88
And it is so lonely here—no *c*. — „ II i 290
Thou art the Earl's *c* and shouldst know. — *Foresters* I ii 55
Confident *See* **Over-confident**
Confirm Thy naked word thy bond! *c* it now Before — *Harold* II ii 693
Name him; the Holy Father will *c* him. — *Becket, Pro.* 245
Confirm'd By Heaven's grace, I am more and more *c*. — *Queen Mary* IV ii 22
Confiscate *C* lands, goods, money— — „ II i 102
Conflagration that hath squeezed out this side-smile upon Canterbury, whereof may come *c*. — *Becket* III iii 58
from those, as I said before, there may come a *c*— — „ III iii 165
Confound Their Graces, our disgraces! God *c* them! — *Queen Mary* III i 415
and weave the web That may *c* thee yet. — *Harold* I i 212
Hath harried mine own cattle—God *c* him! — „ IV iii 190
Confounded Lest you should be *c* with it. — *Queen Mary* I iv 178
I am *c* by thee. Go in peace. — *Becket* I iii 731
Confounder A shaker and *c* of the realm; — *Queen Mary* IV iii 40
Confuse *C* her not; she hath begun Her life-long prayer. — *Harold* III i 322
Confused Myself *c* with parting from the King. — *Becket* III i 237
Confusion And if I breed *c* anyway— — *Queen Mary* I iii 93
I have heard the Normans Count upon this *c*— — *Harold* II ii 459
see *c* fall On thee and on thine house. — „ II ii 489
that had found a King Who ranged *c's*, — *Becket* I iii 371
I see it—some *c*, Some strange mistake. — „ III i 234
And bring us to *c*. — *Prom. of May* II 279
C!—Ah well, well! — „ III 508
Congratulate Kiss and *c* me, my good Kate. — *Foresters* IV 1033
Congratulation Madam, I brought My King's *c's*; — *Queen Mary* V ii 570
Congruent In clear and open day were *c* With that vile Cranmer — „ III iv 230
Conjecture (s) My liege, to your *c*. — *Becket* I ii 50
Conjecture (verb) If Mary will not hear us—well—*c*— — *Queen Mary* I iv 117
Conjoint State-policy and church-policy are *c*, — „ III ii 73
Conjured *C* the mightier Harold from his North — *Harold* IV ii 68
Conquer He told me I should *c*:— — „ IV i 263
And told me we should *c*. — „ IV i 267
Conquer'd and when we fought I *c*, — „ I i 446
we are Danes, Who *c* what we walk on, — „ IV i 38
and women Cling to the *c*, if they love, — „ IV i 213
His conqueror *c* Aldwyth. — „ IV i 218
when at thy side He *c* with thee. — „ IV iii 29
chanting that old song of Brunanburg Where England *c*. — „ V i 216
citizen's heir hath *c* me For the moment. — *Becket* II ii 60
Conqueror Not coming fiercely like a *c*, now, — *Harold* II ii 757
If not, they cannot hate the *c*. — „ IV i 215
His *c* conquer'd Aldwyth. — „ IV i 218
York crown'd the *C*—not Canterbury. — *Becket* III iii 197
—fight out the good fight—die *C*. — „ V iii 191
And swallow'd in the *c's* chronicle. — *The Cup* I ii 158
Conscience And keep with Christ and *c*— — *Queen Mary* I v 558
Convicted by their *c*, arrant cowards, — „ II ii 9
This was against her *c*—would be murder! — „ III i 418
which God's hand Wrote on her *c*, — „ III i 422
cause that weighs Upon my *c* more than anything — „ IV iii 238
have thy *c* White as a maiden's hand, — *Harold* II ii 283
A *c* for his own soul, not his realm; — „ III i 63
A twilight *c* lighted thro' a chink; — „ III i 65
That scared the dying *c* of the king, — „ V i 211
Who like my *c* never lets me be. — *Becket* V ii 75
—the crowd would call it *c*— — *Prom. of May* II 638
What pricks thee save it be thy *c*, man? — *Foresters* IV 626
Consecrate sware To *c* my virgin here to heaven— — *Harold* III i 276
Consent (s) with the *c* of our lord the King, and by the advice — *Becket* I iii 111
Consent (verb) I would never *C* thereto, nor marry while I live; — *Queen Mary* II ii 231

Consent (verb) (*continued*) Ay . . . if the Witan will *c* to this. *Harold* II ii 616
Consider Pray—*c*— *Queen Mary* I iv 141
But as to Philip and your Grace—*c*,— „ V iii 65
Consistory In full *c*, When I was made Archbishop, „ V ii 84
Consonant As may be *c* with mortality. „ IV iii 419
Consort I dream'd I was the *c* of a king, *Becket* V i 144
Conspiracy With some *c* against the wolf. *The Cup* I ii 16
There will be more *conspiracies*, I fear. *Queen Mary* IV iii 433
This is the fifth *c* hatch'd in France; „ V i 297
Rome has a glimpse of this *c*; *The Cup* I ii 233
Conspirator But if he be *c*, Rome will chain, Or slay him. „ I i 18
Rome never yet hath spar'd *c*. „ I ii 234
Constancy draws From you, and from my *c* to you. *The Falcon* 812
Constant callous with a *c* stripe, Unwoundable. *Queen Mary* V v 171
and had my *c* 'No' For all but instant battle. *Harold* V i 6
Constitution for no love o' the customs, Or *c's*, *Becket* I iii 138
Content (adj.) Must be *c* with that; and so, farewell. *Queen Mary* I v 271
They smile as if *c* with one another. „ III i 210
So the wine run, and there be revelry, *C* am I. „ III ii 237
Is now *c* to grant you full forgiveness, „ III iv 389
I am *c*, For thou art truthful, *Harold* II ii 644
Decide on their decision, I am *c*. *Becket* II ii 178
Let him do the same to me—I am *c*. „ II ii 182
No woman but should be *c* with that— „ III i 11
Content (verb) *C* you, Madam; You must abide my judgment, *Queen Mary* V i 144
Let it *c* you now There is no woman that I love *Becket* III i 7
Continue And so you may *c* mine, farewell, *Queen Mary* I iv 137
I am sorry Mr. Steer still *c's* too unwell to attend to you, *Prom. of May* III 22
Continuing So poisoning the Church, so long *c*, *Queen Mary* IV iii 48
Control but I am Tudor, And shall *c* them. „ I v 176
Controversy I here deliver all this *c* Into your royal hands. *Becket* II ii 136
Convene did we *c* This conference but to babble of our wives? „ II ii 89
Convent praised The *c* and lone life—within the pale— *Harold* I ii 47
What monk of what *c* art thou? *Foresters* I ii 205
Conventional Then, if we needs must be *c*, *Prom. of May* I 684
For these are no *c* flourishes. „ II 562
Conventionalism *C*, Who shrieks by day at what she does by night, „ I 531
Conversion He is glorified In thy *c*: *Queen Mary* IV iii 83
doubt The man's *c* and remorse of heart, „ IV iii 108
Converted Ay, that am I, new *c*, „ I iii 47
Convicted *C* by their conscience, arrant cowards, „ II ii 9
Coo Ringdoves *c* again, All things woo again. „ III v 103
Coo'd The stock-dove *c* at the fall of night, *Prom. of May* I 41
And the stock-dove *c*, till a kite dropt down, „ I 55
Cook tell the *c's* to close The doors of all the offices below. *Queen Mary* V v 116
But the hour is past, and our brother, Master *C*, *Becket* I iv 60
Cookery I know your Norman *c* is so spiced, *Harold* II ii 810
Cool (adj.) *C* as the light in old decaying wood; *Queen Mary* IV ii 5
Cool (verb) As one that blows the coal to *c* the fire. *Becket* V ii 549
Noä, not yet. Let 'er *c* upon it; *Prom. of May* II 132
Cooler What power this *c* sun of England hath *Queen Mary* III iv 327
Coöm (come) Why *c* awaäy, then, to the long barn. *Prom. of May* I 35
he *c's* up, and he calls out among our oän men, „ I 139
and see that all be right and reg'lar fur 'em afoor he *c*. „ I 170
leästwaäys they niver *c's* 'ere but fur the trout i' our beck, „ I 212
but *c*, *c*! let's be gawin. „ I 425
C along then, all the rest o' ye! „ I 442
C, *c*, that's a good un. „ I 467
but if iver I *c's* upo' Gentleman Hedgar ageän, „ II 136
Why, *c* then, owd feller, I'll tell it to you; „ II 202
now she be fallen out wi' ma, and I can't *c* at 'er. „ II 601
How *c* thou to be sa like 'im, then? „ II 712
An' ow *c* thou by the letter to 'im? „ II 716
she moänt *c* here. What would her mother saäy? „ III 458
but he'll *c* up if ye lets 'im. „ III 481
Coomberland (Cumberland) An' how did ye leäve the owd uncle i' *C*? „ I 68
So the owd uncle i' *C* be deäd, Miss Dora, „ II 1
Coom'd (came) I *c* upon 'im t'other daäy lookin' at the coontry, „ I 201
Coom'd (came) (*continued*) afoor I *c* up he got thruff the winder ageän. *Prom. of May* I 405
He *c* up to me yisterdaäy i' the haäyfield, „ II 150
when owd Dobson *c* upo' us? „ II 232
Coomed (come) Miss Dora be *c* back, then? „ I 13
I be *c* to keep his birthdaäy an' all. „ I 75
I warrants ye'll think moor o' this young Squire Edgar as ha' *c* among us— „ I 110
you be *c*—what's the newspaäper word, Wilson? „ I 319
darters to marry gentlefoälk, and see what's *c* on it. „ II 117
The owd man's *c* ageän to 'issen, „ III 702
Coomin (coming) Churchwarden be a *c*, thaw me and 'im we niver 'grees about the tithe; „ I 443
'ow should I see to laäme the laädy, and meä *c* along pretty sharp an' all? „ III 96
Coomly (comely) *C*, says she. I niver thowt o' mysen i' that waäy; „ I 175
'*C* to look at,' says she—but she said it spiteful-like. To look at—yeas, '*c*'; „ I 179
Coontry (country) I coom'd upon 'im t'other daäy lookin' at the *c*, „ I 202
Cope How should we *c* with John? *Foresters* I iii 79
I cannot *c* with him: my wrist is strain'd. „ IV 312
Coppice saw your ladyship a-parting wi' him even now i' the *c*, *Becket* III i 161
Copse how he fells The mortal *c* of faces! *Harold* V i 589
Copy so that you do not *c* his bad manners? *Prom. of May* III 361
Cord there is axe and *c*. *Queen Mary* III iv 47
Each of us has an arrow on the *c*; *Foresters* IV 607
I am here, my arrow on the *c* „ IV 733
Core For thou and thine are Roman to the *c*. *Queen Mary* III ii 230
Sound at the *c* as we are. *Foresters* III 102
Co-rebels from the charge Of being his *c-r's*? *Queen Mary* III i 137
Co-reveller My comrade, boon companion, my *c-r*, *Becket* I iii 460
Cork like a bottle full up to the *c*, or as hollow as a kex, *Foresters* IV 210
Corn dash The torch of war among your standing *c*, *Harold* II ii 750
Much *c*, repeopled towns, a realm again. *Becket* I iii 377
Corner do not you Be seen in *c's* with my Lord of Devon. *Queen Mary* I iv 154
And whisking round a *c*, show'd his back „ II i 131
skulk into *c's* Like rabbits to their holes. „ II iv 55
The hog hath tumbled himself into some *c*, *Becket* I i 370
the cold *c's* of the King's mouth began to thaw, „ III iii 153
Cornhill Where dost thou live? *Man.* In *C*. *Queen Mary* III i 317
Cornwall *C's* hand or Leicester's: they write marvellously alike. *Becket* I iv 51
Cornwallis (Sir Thomas) Sent *C* and Hastings to the traitor, *Queen Mary* II ii 31
Coronation (adj.) Being bounden by my *c* oath To do men justice. *Becket* I iii 396
Coronation (s) would make his *c* void By cursing those „ V ii 329
Corpore *Gratior in pulchro* c *virtus.* „ V ii 542
Corpse *c* thou whelmest with thine earth is cursed, *Harold* V i 67
Corpse-candles *C-c* gliding over nameless graves— „ III i 381
Corridor My window look'd upon the *c*; *Queen Mary* V ii 459
I was in the *c*, I saw him coming with his brother *Harold* II ii 346
Corroborate *C* by your acts of Parliament: *Queen Mary* II ii 173
Corrupt Manners be so *c*, and these are the days of Prince John. *Foresters* I i 177
Corruption Against the huge *c's* of the Church, *Queen Mary* IV ii 100
sucking thro' fools' ears The flatteries of *c*— *Becket* I iii 362
Cost (s) be The one man, he shall be so to his *c*. *Queen Mary* III iii 276
Cost (verb) some secret that may *c* Philip his life. „ III i 201
'After his kind it *c's* him nothing,' „ IV i 173
Costly into some more *c* stone Than ever blinded eye. „ I v 370
Well—Well—too *c* to be left or lost. *Becket* IV ii 299
Bring me The *c* wines we use in marriages. *The Cup* II 365
And this last *c* gift to mine own self, *The Falcon* 228
Cotched (caught) my kneeä gev waäy or I'd ha' *c* 'im, *Prom. of May* I 404
c 'im once a-steälin' coäls an' I sent fur 'im, „ I 412
'A *c* ma about the waaist, Miss, „ III 118
Cottage (adj.) while the smoke floats from the *c* roof, *Foresters* I ii 318
Cottage (s) Stops and stares at our *c*. *The Falcon* 162
Welcome to this poor *c*, my dear lady. „ 270
And welcome turns a *c* to a palace. „ 273

Cottage (s) (*continued*) Lady, you bring your light into my *c* — *The Falcon* 284
My palace wanting you was but a *c*; My *c*, while you grace it, is a palace. „ 287
In *c* or in palace, being still Beyond your fortunes, „ 289
you could whitewash that *c* of yours — *Prom. of May* III 43
Make for the *c* then! — *Foresters* II i 210
Couch'd with mine old hound *C* at my hearth. — *Queen Mary* III i 46
Cough No fever, *c*, croup, sickness? — *Becket* V ii 169
Could How *c* you—Oh, how *c* you?—nay, how *c* I? — *Prom. of May* I 716
Council (adj.) I hear them stirring in the *C* Chamber. — *Queen Mary* I v 628
Council (s) both bastards by Act of Parliament and *C*. .. I i 25
the *c* and all her people wish her to marry. .. I i 112
Those that are now her Privy *C*, sign'd Before me: .. I ii 22
She cannot pass her traitor *c* by, .. I ii 40
The *C*, people, Parliament against him; .. I v 78
we will leave all this, sir, to our *c*. .. I v 318
Your *C* is in Session, please your Majesty. .. I v 543
And when the *C* would not crown me— .. I v 555
An instant Ay or No! the *C* sits. .. I v 591
The *C*! *Mary*. Ay! My Philip is all mine. .. I v 639
Gardiner knows, but the *C* are all at odds, .. II i 139
however the *C* and the Commons may fence round his power .. II i 171
The *C*, the Court itself, is on our side. .. II i 192
And four of her poor *C* too, my Lord, .. II ii 42
What do and say Your *C* at this hour? .. II ii 46
The *C*, The Parliament as well, are troubled waters; .. II ii 49
Like our *C*, Your city is divided. .. II ii 59
But we sent divers of our *C* to them, .. II ii 152
theretoward unadvised Of all our Privy *C*; .. II ii 205
heard One of your *C* fleer and jeer at him. .. II ii 393
Lord Paget Waits to present our *C* to the Legate. .. III ii 98
And she impress her wrongs upon her *C*, .. III vi 184
Cranmer, it is decided by the *C* That you to-day .. IV ii 26
Or seek to rescue me. I thank the *C*. .. IV ii 39
I must obey the Queen and *C*, man. .. IV ii 164
causes Wherefore our Queen and *C* at this time .. IV iii 36
which our Queen And *C* at this present .. IV iii 56
first In *C*, second person in the realm, .. IV iii 72
came to sue Your *C* and yourself to declare war. (repeat) .. V i 108, 114
Alas! the *C* will not hear of war. „ V i 163
the *C* (I have talked with some already) are for war. .. V i 294
Tell my mind to the *C*—to the Parliament: „ V ii 288
Then our great *C* wait to crown thee King— — *Harold* III i 3
Siding with our great *C* against Tostig, „ III i 59
Nay—but the *c*, and the king himself, „ III i 170
And our great *C* wait to crown thee King. „ III i 406
Thou gavest thy voice against me in the *C*— „ IV ii 78
I, John of Oxford, The President of this *C*, — *Becket* I iii 76
My lords, is this a combat or a *c*? „ I iii 134
whene'er your royal rights Are mooted in our *c's*— „ I iii 431
Let us go in to the *C*, where our bishops „ I iii 547
Councillor Place and displace our *c's*, — *Queen Mary* II ii 160
Your faithful friend and trusty *c*. „ IV i 89
From *c* to caitiff—fallen so low, „ IV iii 75
is it then with thy goodwill that I Proceed against thine evil *c's*, — *Becket* III iii 209
It may be they were evil *c's*. „ III iii 216
Counsel (advice) I follow your good *c*, gracious uncle. — *Queen Mary* I iv 186
She hath harken'd evil *c*— .. I v 54
So would your cousin, Cardinal Pole; ill *c*! .. I v 406
I come for *c* and ye give me feuds, .. III iv 307
Good *c* yours—No one in waiting? „ V v 202
Good *c* truly! I heard from my Northumbria yesterday. — *Harold* I i 330
Good *c* tho' scarce needed. „ I i 376
My one grain of good *c* which you will not swallow. — *Becket* II ii 379
second grain of good *c* I ever proffered thee, .. III iii 318
Summon your barons; take their *c*: .. V i 75
a man may take good *c* Ev'n from his foe. .. V ii 3
Counsel (deliberation) You should have taken *c* with your friends „ V ii 555
My *c* is already taken, John. „ V ii 560

Counsel (deliberation) (*continued*) Have shut you from our *c's*. — *Queen Mary* III iv 320
Counsel (secret) if the child could keep Her *c*. — *Prom. of May* I 478
Counsel (verb) means to *c* your withdrawing To Ashridge, — *Queen Mary* I iv 224
Till when, my Lords, I *c* tolerance. „ III iv 203
Harold, I do not *c* thee to lie. — *Harold* II ii 416
O good son Louis, do not *c* me, — *Becket* II ii 219
Counsell'd Emperor *c* me to fly to Flanders. — *Queen Mary* I v 549
I had *c* him To rest from vain resistance. — *The Cup* II 413
Counsellor who am your friend And ever faithful *c*, — *Queen Mary* I v 135
Count (s) and *C's*, and sixty Spanish cavaliers, .. III i 51
I might dare to tell her that the *C*— „ V ii 524
What *C*? *Magdalen*. The Count de Feria, .. V ii 530
Sir *C*, to read the letter which you bring. .. V ii 555
My Lord *C*? Her Highness is too ill for colloquy. .. V ii 612
I shine! What else, Sir *C*? „ V iii 17
Is not the Norman *C* thy friend and mine? — *Harold* I i 247
C of the Normans, thou hast ransom'd us, „ II ii 157
C, I thank thee, but had rather Breathe the free wind „ II ii 184
With bitter obligation to the *C*— .. II ii 221
I have the *C's* commands to follow thee. .. II ii 234
I have the *C's* commands. .. II ii 239
'Tis the good *C's* care for thee! .. II ii 251
Obey the *C's* conditions, my good friend. „ II ii 276
C! if there sat within the Norman chair .. II ii 532
Sir *C*, He had but one foot, .. II ii 674
I, the *C*—the King—Thy friend— „ II ii 753
perjury-mongering *C* Hath made too good an use „ V i 311
The Norman *C* is down. „ V i 553
Can I speak with the *C*? — *The Falcon* 180
Where is the *C*? *Elisabetta*. Just gone To fly his falcon, .. 208
'Get the *C* to give me his falcon, .. 241
'I should be well again If the good *C* would give me——' „ 838
There is one that should be grateful to me overseas, a *C* in Brittany— — *Foresters* I i 271
Count (verb) (I *c* it as a kind of virtue in him, — *Queen Mary* I iv 193
she *c's* on you And on myself as her two hands; „ II ii 104
As for the Pope I *c* him Antichrist, „ IV iii 277
C's his old beads, and hath forgotten thee. — *Harold* II ii 447
I have heard the Normans *C* upon this confusion— „ II ii 459
Take and slay me, I say, Or I shall *c* thee fool. „ IV ii 16
tho' I *c* Henry honest enough, yet when fear creeps — *Becket* III iii 60
Why now I *c* it all but miracle, — *The Cup* I iii 37
However, staying not to *c* how many, — *The Falcon* 627
C the money and see if it's all right. — *Prom. of May* III 64
Count-crab and our great *C-c* will make his nippers — *Harold* II i 76
Counted When all men *c* Harold would be king, „ V II 132
Countenanced but the backs 'ud ha' *c* one another, — *Becket* III i 147
Counter not Spear into pruning-hook—the—*c* way— — *Harold* V i 442
Counter-bond To bring their *c-b* into the forest. — *Foresters* IV 89
Counterpoint Veer to the *c*, and jealousy — *Queen Mary* III vi 180
Country (adj.) Far liefer had I in my *c* hall .. III i 43
She means to counsel your withdrawing To Ashridge, or some other *c* house. .. I IV 226
Country (s) (*See also* **Coontry**) there's no glory Like his who saves his *c*: „ II i 110
I swear you do your *c* wrong, Sir Ralph. „ III i 153
and the *c* Has many charms, — *Prom. of May* ii 540
not only love the *c*, But its inhabitants too; „ II 545
Might have more charm for me than all the *c*. „ II 554
to save his *c*, and the liberties of his people! — *Foresters* I i 246
You are those that tramp the *c*, „ III 198
Countryfolk Not leave these *c* at court. — *Becket* II i 129
Countryman —home your banish'd *c*. — *Queen Mary* III ii 31
Earls, Thanes, and all our *countrymen*! — *Harold* IV iii 48
Country-wives poor garrulous *c-w*. — *Queen Mary* IV iii 547
County is not the cause of a *c* or a shire, „ II i 162
and make Musters in all the *counties*; „ V ii 272
went abroad Thro' all my *counties*, — *Becket* I iii 363
Couple as the new-made *c* Came from the Minster, — *Queen Mary* III i 94
They hunt in *c's*, and when they look at a maid — *Foresters* I i 256
Courage *C*, sir, *That* makes or man or woman — *Queen Mary* II ii 328
Should we so doat on *c*, were it commoner? „ II ii 339

Courage (*continued*) All greed, no faith, no *c*! *Queen Mary* III i 146
And bad me have good *c*; „ IV ii 8
Have *c*, your reward is Heaven itself. „ V ii 108
C, noble Aldwyth! *Harold* I ii 182
C, *c*! and all will go well. *Prom. of May* III 215
Course So far my *c*, albeit not glassy-smooth, *Becket* I iii 379
sat Thro' every sensual *c* of that full feast *Prom. of May* II 254
Court (s) (*See also* **Hampton Court**) You've but a dull life in this maiden *c*, *Queen Mary* I iii 114
And certain of his *c*. „ I iii 133
out all things here At *c* are known; „ I iv 58
I freed him from the Tower, placed him at *C*; „ I v 164
You have sent her from the *c*, „ I v 462
heard Slanders against Prince Philip in our *C*? „ I v 571
a fine courtier of the old *C*, old Sir Thomas. *Wyatt*. Courtier of many *c's*, „ II i 46
The Council, the *C* itself, is on our side. „ II i 192
Queen had written her word to come to *c*: „ II ii 118
Before our own High *C* of Parliament, „ II ii 234
Your *c's* of justice will determine that. „ II iv 130
But *c* is always May, buds out in masques, „ III v 11
his manners want the nap And gloss of *c*; „ III v 71
You are to come to *C* on the instant; „ III v 223
you want the sun That shines at *c*; „ III v 277
trifling royally With some fair dame of *c*, „ III vi 160
The foreign *c's* report him in his manner „ V ii 511
scarce touch'd or tasted The splendours of our *C*. *Harold* II ii 175
Am I in danger in this *c*? „ II ii 237
being brought before the *c's* of the Church, *Becket*, *Pro.* 12
My *C's* of Love would have held thee guiltless of love— „ *Pro.* 498
whether between laymen or clerics, shall be tried in the King's *c*.' „ I iii 81
he shall answer to the summons of the King's *c* to be tried therein.' „ I iii 89
the King shall summon the chapter of that church to *c*, „ I iii 110
sat in mine own *c's* Judging my judges, „ I iii 368
Ye haled this tonsured devil into your *c's*; „ I iii 388
If Canterbury bring his cross to *c*, „ I iii 511
The King's *c's* would use thee worse than thy dog— „ I iv 102
Not leave these countryfolk at *c*. „ II i 129
you are known Thro' all the *c's* of Christendom „ IV ii 325
such a comedy as our *c* of Provence Had laugh'd at. „ V i 189
The fellow that on a lame jade came to *c*, „ V i 247
I said it was the King's *c's*, not the King; „ V ii 114
calls you oversea To answer for it in his Norman *c's*. „ V ii 355
The bee should buzz about the *C* of John. *Foresters* IV 44
ye shall with us to *c*. „ IV 951
And we must hence to the King's *c*. „ IV 1050
Court (verb) Why will you *c* it By self-exposure? *Becket* I i 281
Courtenay (Earl of Devon) (*See also* **Devon (Earl of)**)
C, to be made Earl of Devon, *Queen Mary* I i 110
Son *C*, wilt thou see the holy father Murdered „ I iii 63
A *C*! a *C*! „ I iii 74
this fine blue-blooded *C* seems Too princely for a pawn. „ I iii 165
A *C* of Devon, and her cousin. „ I iv 86
I charge you, Tell *C* nothing. „ I iv 192
Hath taken to this *C*. „ I iv 201
And when your Highness talks of *C*— „ I v 198
C, Save that he fears he might be crack'd in using, „ II i 6
Ha! *C's* cipher. „ II i 134
The names of Wyatt, Elizabeth, *C*, „ II ii 95
die with those That are no cowards and no *C's*. „ II iv 87
breath Clear *C* and the Princess from the charge „ III i 135
So they have sent poor *C* over sea. „ III v 2
C, belike— *Mary*. A fool and featherhead! „ V i 127
with full proof Of *C's* treason? „ V ii 499
Courteous a man Of such colossal kinghood, yet so *c*, „ IV i 101
C enough too when he wills; *Foresters* I ii 105
Courteousness They shall be handled with all *c*. „ IV 102
Courtesan He wrecks his health and wealth on *c's*, *Queen Mary* I v 168
There may be *c's* for aught I know *The Cup* I ii 192
Courtesy But lest we turn the scale of *c* *Harold* II ii 164
that *c* which hath less loyalty in it than *Becket* III iii 142
Might not your *c* stoop to hand it me? „ IV ii 295
yet of his *c* Entreats he may be present *The Cup* II 247
Courtesy (*continued*) you are still the king Of *c* and liberality. *The Falcon* 293
I trust I still maintain my *c*; „ 295
No other heart Of such magnificence in *c* „ 723
turn back at times, and make *C* to custom? *Prom. of May* II 635
thou didst repent thy *c* even in the doing it. *Foresters* I ii 243
Richard's the king of *c*, „ IV 363
I could but sneak and smile and call it *c*, „ IV 367
And that is only *c by c*—But Robin is a thief of *c* „ IV 369
There—to be a thief of *c*— „ IV 374
Courtier He was a fine *c*, he; Queen Anne loved him. *Queen Mary* II i 33
a fine *c* of the old Court, old Sir Thomas. *Wyatt*. *C* of many courts, „ II i 45
and a favourer Of players, and a *c*, *Becket* I i 79
Courtly He said it was not *c* to stand helmeted Before the Queen. *Queen Mary* V v 35
Courtly-delicate His bearing is so *c-d*; „ III iv 397
Cousin (*See also* **Dear-cousin, Legate-cousin, Side-cousin, Royal-cousin**) again to her *c* Reginald Pole, now Cardinal; „ I i 123
but you, *c*, are fresh and sweet As the first flower „ I iv 61
A Courtenay of Devon, and her *c*. „ I iv 86
Nay, pout not, *c*. „ I iv 134
So would your *c*, Cardinal Pole; „ I v 405
with what haste I might To save my royal *c*. „ II iv 78
Loyal and royal *c*, humblest thanks. „ III ii 3
We heard that you were sick in Flanders, *c*. „ III ii 34
c, as the heathen giant Had but to touch the ground, „ III ii 42
My heart beats twenty, when I see you *c*. Ah, gentle *c*, „ III ii 60
True, good *c* Pole; And there were also those „ III ii 68
I believe so, *c*. „ III ii 72
No, *c*, happy—Happy to see you; „ III ii 86
Sweet *c*, you forget That long low minster „ III ii 89
True, *c*, I am happy. „ III ii 113
Our good Queen's *c*—dallying over seas „ III iv 292
see according to our sight. Come, *c*. „ III iv 332
C, there hath chanced A sharper harm „ V ii 28
And so must you, good *c*;— „ V ii 39
I knew it, *c*, But held from you all papers sent by Rome, „ V ii 44
To sleep, to die—I shall die of it, *c*. „ V ii 128
Poor *c*! Have not I been the fast friend of your life „ V ii 132
Ah, *c*, I remember How I would dandle you upon my knee „ V ii 140
Peace, *c*, peace! I am sad at heart myself. „ V ii 159
Your pardon, Sweet *c*, and farewell! „ V ii 204
Thou knowest I am his *c*, *Harold* II ii 593
seem at most Sweet guests, or foreign *c's*, *Becket* II i 135
Cover (s) I saw the *c's* laying. *Philip*. Let us have it. *Queen Mary* III vi 258
'Will your Ladyship ride to *c* to-day? *Prom. of May* III 310
Cover (verb) That *c's* all. *Queen Mary* V ii 542
I saw the hand of Tostig *c* it. *Harold* IV iii 82
Coverdale (Bishop of Exeter) Poinet, Barlow, Bale, Scory, *C*; *Queen Mary* I ii 7
Coveted your hand Will be much *c*! What a delicate one! „ V iii 44
Covetousness 'Lust, Prodigality, *C*, Craft, *Prom. of May* II 284
Cow with my hands Milking the *c*? (repeat) *Queen Mary* III v 88, 95, 102
you came and kiss'd me milking the *c*. (repeat) *Queen Mary* III v 91, 98
Come behind and kiss me milking the *c*! „ III v 105
the *c* kick'd, and all her milk was spilt. „ III v 266
I had kept My Robins and my *c's* in sweeter order „ III v 270
The maid to her dairy came in from the *c*, *Prom. of May* I 40
I seed that one *c* o' thine i' the pinfold ageän „ I 190
An' if tha can't keep thy one *c* i' horder, „ I 197
take to the milking of your *c's*, the fatting of your calves, „ II 92
Hes the *c* cawved? *Dora*. No, Father. „ III 427
Thou hast a *c* then, hast thou? *Foresters* II i 298
How hadst thou then the means to buy a *c*? „ II i 304
but the *c*? *Robin*. She was given me. „ II i 314
That *c* was mine. I have lost a *c* from my meadow. „ II i 325
O sweet sir, talk not of *c's*. „ II i 330
wouldst bar me fro' the milk o' my *c*, „ II i 355
or the *c* that jumped over the moon. „ II i 435

Coward Convicted by their conscience, arrant *c's*, *Queen Mary* II ii 10
die with those That are no *c's* and no Courtenays. „ II iv 87
I do not love your Grace should call me *c*. „ II iv 89
The soft and tremulous *c* in the flesh? „ IV ii 107
We have so play'd the *c*; „ V v 110
True test of *c*, ye follow with a yell. *Becket* I iii 745
I cannot tell why monks should all be *c's*. „ V ii 582
Why should all monks be *c's*? „ V ii 588
what, a truckler! a word-eating *c*! *Foresters* IV 162
Cowardice Coveteousness, Craft, C, Murder'— *Prom. of May* II 285
Cowd (cold) Owd Steer gi'es nubbut *c* tea to *'is* men, and owd Dobson gi'es beer. *Sally*. But I'd like owd Steer's *c* tea better nor Dobson's beer. „ II 224
we worked naw wuss upo' the *c* tea; „ III 59
and the winders brokken, and the weather sa *c*, „ III 73
Cow'd The knaves are easily *c*. *Queen Mary* III i 330
And being brave he must be subtly *c*, *Harold* II ii 75
but Salisbury was a calf *c* by Mother Church, *Becket* III iii 95
Cower My sister *c's* and hates me. *Queen Mary* I v 83
would *c* to any Of mortal build *Foresters* II i 688
Cowering we saw thee *c* to a knight „ II i 682
Cow-herd only grandson To Wulfnoth, a poor *c-h*. *Harold* IV i 70
this *c-h*, like my father, Who shook the Norman scoundrels „ IV i 79
Cowl *C*, helm; and crozier, battle-axe. „ V i 444
I scatter all their *c's* to all the hells. *Becket* II i 93
so that you keep the *c* down and speak not? *Foresters* I ii 22
Why wearest thou thy *c* to hide thy face? „ I ii 206
Cowling *c* and clouding up That fatal star, thy Beauty, *Becket* I i 311
Crab (*See also* **Count-crab**) thou didst stand by her and give her thy *c's*, *Harold* II i 49
And I'll give her my *c's* again, „ II i 52
Fellow, dost thou catch *c's*? „ II i 66
I crawl'd like a sick *c* from my old shell, *Foresters* IV 126
Crabb'd by the patient Saints, she's as *c* as ever. *Harold* II i 51
Crab-catcher human-heartedest, Christian-charitiest of all *c-c's*. „ II i 63
Crabstick I have a stout *c* here, which longs to break itself *Foresters* IV 917
Crack'd he fears he might be *c* in using, *Queen Mary* II i 7
drave and *c* His boat on Ponthieu beach; *Harold* II ii 35
winds than that which *c* Thy bark at Ponthieu,— „ II ii 199
thou wouldst hug thy Cupid till his ribs *c*— *Becket, Pro.* 505
one piece of earthenware to serve the salad in to my lady, and that *c*! *The Falcon* 482
Beetle's jewel armour *c*, *Foresters* II ii 160
Crackled fire, Like that which lately *c* underfoot *Queen Mary* III v 53
Craft (art, etc.) —a sweet violence, And a sweet *c*. „ III v 109
violence and the *c* that do divide The world „ III v 120
shakes at mortal kings—her vacillation, Avarice, *c*— *Becket* II ii 407
woman's fealty when Assailed by *C* and Love. *The Cup* I i 177
' Lust, Prodigality, Covetousness, *C*, *Prom. of May* II 284
Craft (vessel) Let every *c* that carries sail and gun *Queen Mary* V ii 275
Craftier shall I play The *c* Tostig with him? *Harold* I ii 165
Men would but take him for the *c* liar. „ III i 114
Craftsman We spared the *c*, chapman, *Foresters* III 163
Crafty Robin was violent, And she was *c*— *Queen Mary* III v 108
Cram if the truth be gall, *C* me not thou with honey, *Harold* IV i 16
C thy crop full, but come when thou art call'd. „ IV iii 234
if you *c* me crop-full I be little better than Famine in the picture, *Foresters* I i 46
Cramm'd dog I *c* with dainties worried me! *Becket* V i 244
Cranmer (Archbishop of Canterbury) pounce like a wild beast out of his cage to worry *C*. *Queen Mary* I i 89
Fly, *C*! were there nothing else, your name „ I ii 15
even in the church there is a man—*C*. „ III i 170
Ay, Lambeth has ousted *C*. „ III ii 133
were congruent With that vile *C* in the accursed lie „ III iv 231
Our old friend *C*, Your more especial love, „ III iv 417
C and Hooper, Ridley and Latimer, „ III iv 424
To spare the life of *C*. „ IV i 4
That *C* may withdraw to foreign parts, „ IV i 45
never seen That any one recanting thus at full, As *C* hath, „ IV i 60
C is head and father of these heresies, „ IV i 76
You sit upon this fallen *C's* throne; „ IV i 114
Cranmer (Archbishop of Canterbury) (*continued*) To ours in plea for *C* than to stand *Queen Mary* IV i 119
Yet to save *C* were to serve the Church, „ IV i 135
Than you have shown to *C*. „ IV i 190
petition of the foreign exiles For *C's* life. „ IV i 194
C, I come to question you again; „ IV ii 15
C, it is decided by the Council That you to-day „ IV ii 25
Pray you write out this paper for me, *C*. „ IV ii 61
' what am I, *C*, against whole ages?' „ IV ii 104
And make you simple *C* once again. „ IV ii 129
Which was not pleasant for you, Master *C*. „ IV ii 137
How are the mighty fallen, Master *C*! „ IV ii 147
We are ready To take you to St. Mary's, Master *C*. „ IV ii 239
Yet, *C*, be thou glad. This is the work of God. „ IV iii 81
Speak, Master *C*, Fulfil your promise made me, „ IV iii 111
Be plainer, Master *C*. „ IV iii 235
another recantation Of *C* at the stake. „ IV iii 300
Think you then That *C* read all papers that he sign'd? „ IV iii 318
We talk and *C* suffers. „ IV iii 420
Who follow'd with the crowd to *C's* fire. „ IV iii 554
you bring the smoke Of *C's* burning with you. „ IV iii 562
smoke of *C's* burning wrapt me round. „ IV iii 564
But *C*, as the helmsman at the helm Steers, „ IV iii 578
but *C* only shook his head, „ IV iii 601
Then *C* lifted his left hand to heaven, „ IV iii 608
and needs must moan for him; O *C*! „ IV iii 637
hands that write them should be burnt clean off As *C's*, „ V ii 192
If *C's* spirit were a mocking one, „ V ii 210
Cranmerite Here come the *C's*! „ IV i 40
Crash (*See also* **War-crash**) may come a *c* and embroilment as in Stephen's time; *Becket, Pro.* 485
Crater One *c* opens when another shuts. *Queen Mary* III i 322
Crave meant to *c* Permission of her Highness „ I iv 235
It *c's* an instant answer, Ay or No. „ I v 589
So that you *c* full pardon of the Legate. „ III iv 391
I attend the Queen To *c* most humble pardon— „ III iv 432
C, in the same cause, hearing of your Grace. „ IV i 8
allegiance in thy Lord's And *c* his mercy, *Harold* V i 12
I *c* Thy pardon—I shall still thy leave *Becket* V ii 43
And afterwards a boon to *c* of you. *The Falcon* 712
I *c* your worship's pardon. *Foresters* II i 243
Robin—I *c* pardon—you always seem to me „ III 53
I *c* pardon, I always think of you as my lord, „ III 409
Craven Did the chest move! did it move! I am utter *c*! *Harold* II ii 800
The *c*! There is a faction risen again for Tostig, „ IV i 171
Forty thousand marks! forty thousand devils—and these *c* bishops? *Becket* I iv 91
than the swords of the *c* sycophants would have done „ I iv 148
if the followers Of him, who heads the movement, held him *c*? *Foresters* II i 702
Craw (crow) I'd think na moor o' maäkin' an end o' tha nor a carrion *c*— *Prom. of May* II 697
Crawl *c* over knife-edge flint Barefoot, *Becket* II i 271
c down thine own black hole To the lowest Hell. *The Cup* II 494
Crawl'd Fed with rank bread that *c* upon the tongue, *Queen Mary* IV iii 442
I *c* like a sick crab from my old shell, *Foresters* IV 126
Crawling Foul maggots *c* in a fester'd vice! *Queen Mary* V v 161
Here *c* in this boundless Nature. *Prom. of May* III 637
I see two figures *c* up the hill. *Foresters* IV 333
Crazed She is *c*! *Edith*. That doth not matter *Harold* V ii 61
Did you not tell me he was *c* with jealousy, *Prom. of May* III 565
I am *c* no longer, so I have the land. *Foresters* IV 855
I had despair'd of thee—that sent me *c*. „ IV 1022
Crazeling And this old *c* in the litter there. „ IV 634
Cream And a cat to the *c*, and a rat to the cheese; *Prom. of May* I 53
Create (*See also* **Re-create**) Shall hands that do *c* the Lord be bound *Becket* I iii 94
Creator Illorum lanceas Frange *C*! *Harold* V i 584
Creature By God's light a noble *c*, right royal! *Queen Mary* I i 69
the red man, that good helpless *c*, „ II i 209
—we are fallen *c's*; Look to your Bible, „ III iv 79

Creature (*continued*) says she will live And die true maid—a goodly *c* too. *Queen Mary* III vi 46
and yet We are self-uncertain *c's*, *Becket* V ii 48
strange starched stiff *c*, Little John, the Earl's man. *Foresters* I i 184
Man, lying here alone, Moody *c*, „ II ii 187
delicate-footed *c* Came stepping o'er him, „ IV 536
Credit (s) Tell, tell me ; save my *c* with myself. *Queen Mary* V ii 452
for heaven's *c* Makes it on earth : *Harold* I i 141
Credit (verb) better die Than *c* this, for death is death, „ III ii 79
You will not easily make me *c* that. *The Cup* II 25
Creed Your *c* will be your death. *Queen Mary* I ii 46
The heathen priesthood of a heathen *c* ! *Becket* I iii 64
Creek *See* **Sea-creek**
Creel Tell him what hath crept into our *c*, *Harold* II i 56
Creep and *c's*, *c's* snake-like about our legs *Queen Mary* II i 203
He can but *c* down into some dark hole „ IV i 140
I would *c*, crawl over knife-edge flint *Becket* II i 271
fear *c's* in at the front, honesty steals out at the back, „ III iii 61
Creep'st Why *c* thou like a timorous beast *Harold* I ii 212
Creeping By bonds of beeswax, like your *c* thing ; *Queen Mary* III iii 63
And all manner of *c* things too ? *Becket* III iii 132
Crematur Casa *c*, Pastor fugatur *Harold* V i 512
Crept I *c* along the gloom and saw They had hewn *Queen Mary* II iii 17
Out *c* a wasp, with half the swarm behind. „ III iii 49
Tell him what hath *c* into our creel, *Harold* II i 56
dreadful lights *c* up from out the marsh— „ III i 379
c Up even to the tonsure, and he groan'd, *Becket* I iii 326
Thro' all closed doors a dreadful whisper *c* „ V ii 89
Poverty *c* thro' the door. *Foresters* I i 157
The serpent that had *c* into the garden „ II i 136
Crescent I that have turn'd their Moslem *c* pale— „ IV 793
Crew Kill'd half the *c*, dungeon'd the other half *Becket* V ii 444
Cried *C* no God-bless-her to the Lady Jane, *Queen Mary* III iv 45
He *c* Enough ? enough ? before his death.— „ V ii 100
And *c* I was not clean, what should I care ? „ V ii 324
If the field *C* out ' I am mine own ; ' *Harold* IV i 49
she *c* out on him to put me forth in the world *Becket* III i 115
Rome ! Rome ! Twice I *c* Rome. *The Cup* I iii 175
So they *c* Sinnatus Not so long since— „ II 110
C out against the cruelty of the King. *Becket* V ii 112
Cried'st Thou *c* ' A Wyatt ! ' and flying to our side *Queen Mary* II iii 3
Crime of a heavier *c* Than heresy is itself ; „ III iv 221
The *c* be on his head—not bounden—no. *Harold* II ii 670
O crowning *c* ! Hast murder'd thine own guest, „ IV ii 36
The Church is all—the *c* to be a king. *Becket* V i 26
Crimeful heavy As thine own bolts that fall on *c* heads *Harold* V i 565
Criminal *See* **Laymen-criminals**
Crimson We might go softlier than with *c* rowel And streaming lash. *Queen Mary* III iv 182
Crippled man Fell with him, and was *c* ever after. *Foresters* IV 545
Critic You as poor a *c* As an honest friend : *Queen Mary* II i 115
Croak (*See also* **Raven-croak**) dumb'd his carrion *c* From the gray sea for ever. *Harold* IV iii 66
I grieve I am the Raven who *c's* it. *Foresters* III 448
Cromwell make the soil For Cæsars, *C's*, and Napoleons *Prom. of May* III 593
Crone Out of the church, you brace of cursed *c's*, *Queen Mary* IV iii 539
Crookback Speak straight out, *c*. *Foresters* II i 271
Crooked His eighty years Look'd somewhat *c* *Queen Mary* IV iii 332
I do believe My old *c* spine would bud out two young wings *Harold* III i 24
Crop (of a bird) Cram thy *c* full, but come when thou art call'd. „ IV iii 234
Crop (verb) If possible, here ! to *c* the flower and pass. *Prom. of May* I 253
Crop-full if you cram me *c-f* I be little better than Famine in the picture, *Foresters* I i 46
Cross (adj.) but look, there is a *c* line o' sudden death. „ II i 353
Cross (s) (*See also* **Charing Cross**) Our silver *c* sparkled before the prow, *Queen Mary* III ii 9
The triumph of St. Andrew on his *c*, „ IV iii 94
Then claspt the *c*, and pass'd away in peace. „ V v 259
Forward ! Forward ! Harold and Holy *C* ! *Harold* IV i 269
Harold and Holy *C* ! „ V i 439
Harold and Holy *C* ! Out ! out ! „ V i 519

Cross (s) (*continued*) swear nay to that by this *c* on thy neck. God's eyes ! what a lovely *c* ! *Becket, Pro.* 370
holds his *c* before him thro' the crowd, „ I iii 477
His *c* ! *Roger of York.* His *c* ! I'll front him, *c* to *c*. „ I iii 480
His *c* ! it is the traitor that imputes „ I iii 483
King will not abide thee with thy *c*. „ I iii 489
Wherefore dost thou presume to bear thy *c*, „ I iii 504
Why dost thou presume, Arm'd with thy *c*, „ I iii 509
If Canterbury bring his *c* to court, „ I iii 511
There may be *c'es* in my line of life. „ II i 188
By very God, the *c* I gave the King ! „ IV ii 199
sworn on this my *c* a hundred times Never to leave him —and that merits death, False oath on holy *c*— „ IV ii 205
Do you know this *c*, my liege ? „ V i 161
Why then—The *C* !—who bears my *C* before me ? „ V ii 610
Would that I could bear thy *c* indeed ! „ V ii 615
Father, you see this *c* ? *Foresters* I i 284
on this *c* I have sworn that till I myself pass away, „ I i 289
by this Holy *C* Which good King Richard gave me „ I ii 309
Cross (verb) come to London Bridge ; But how to *c* it balks me. *Queen Mary* II iii 10
her shadow *c's* one by one The moonlight casements „ V v 7
The winds so *c* and jostle among these towers. *Harold* II ii 155
but stark as death To those that *c* him.— „ II ii 322
nor priestly king to *c* Their billings ere they nest. „ III ii 94
C me not ! I am seeking one who wedded me „ V ii 28
No man without my leave shall *c* the seas *Becket, Pro.* 35
I mean to *c* the sea to France, „ I iii 124
Wilt not be suffer'd so to *c* the seas „ I iii 129
C swords all of you ! swear to follow him ! „ I iv 199
feud between our houses is the bar I cannot *c* ; *The Falcon* 255
Crossing (part.) be as the shadow of a cloud *C* your light. *Harold* II ii 178
Crossing (s) so many alleys, *c's*, Paths, avenues— *Becket* IV ii 6
Cross-staff Shall I not smite him with his own *c-s* ? „ V ii 313
Crost *C* and recrost, a venomous spider's web— „ II i 199
Thou hast *c* him in love, *Foresters* II i 343
You *c* him with a quibble of your law. „ IV 850
Crouch *C* even because thou hatest him ; *Becket* IV ii 223
C all into the bush ! *Foresters* IV 596
Crouch'd This hard coarse man of old hath *c* to me *Queen Mary* IV ii 170
Croucher no *c* to the Gregories That tread the kings *Becket, Pro.* 211
Croup No fever, cough, *c*, sickness ? „ V ii 169
Crow (s) (*See also* **Craw**) didst thou ever see a carrion *c* Stand watching *Queen Mary* IV iii 6
where the black *c* flies five, „ V v 84
You ought to dangle up there among the *c's*. *Foresters* III 367
Crow (verb) *C* over Barbarossa—at last tongue-free *Becket* II ii 50
Crowd Friend Roger, steal thou in among the *c*, *Queen Mary* I iii 38
Stave off the *c* upon the Spaniard there. „ I iii 77
here's a *c* as thick as herring-shoals. „ III i 182
I stand so squeezed among the *c* „ III i 239
Push'd by the *c* beside— „ IV iii 397
Who follow'd with the *c* to Cranmer's fire. „ IV iii 554
You saw him how he past among the *c* ; „ IV iii 575
hands Came from the *c* and met his own ; „ IV iii 583
With a *c* of worshippers, *Becket* I iii 475
holds his cross before him thro' the *c*, „ I iii 478
There is a movement yonder in the *c*— „ II ii 37
The *c* that hungers for a crown in Heaven „ II ii 282
for I have pleasure in the pleasure of *c's*, „ III iii 82
The *c* are scattering, let us move away ! „ III iii 357
not fear the *c* that hunted me Across the woods, *The Cup* I iii 16
And blanch the *c* with horror. „ II 154
Might cast my largess of it to the *c* ! „ II 224
when Thought Comes down among the *c*, *Prom. of May* I 501
the *c* May wreak my wrongs upon my wrongers. „ I 506
—the *c* would call it conscience— „ II 637
Crown (adj.) King Stephen gave Many of the *c* lands to those that helpt him ; *Becket* I iii 150
Claim'd some of our *c* lands for Canterbury— „ I iii 458
Crown (s) That gave her royal *c* to Lady Jane. *Queen Mary* I ii 19
Edward might bequeath the *c* Of England, „ I ii 27
Yet by your *c* you are. „ I iv 15

Crown (s) (*continued*) To make the *c* of Scotland one with ours, *Queen Mary* I v 287
Spain and we, One *c*, might rule the world. „ I v 303
To save your *c* that it must come to this. „ I v 479
that young girl who dared to wear your *c*? „ I v 492
and in that passion Gave me my *c*. „ I v 568
let Rebellion Roar till throne rock, and *c* fall. „ II i 145
in whose *c* our Kent is the fairest jewel. „ II i 163
I trust this day, thro' God, I have saved the *c*. „ II ii 303
I pass to Windsor and I lose my *c*. „ II iv 30
And leave the people naked to the *c*, And the *c* naked to the people; „ III i 119
And nothing of the titles to the *c*; „ III i 383
'You will give me my true *c* at last, „ III i 395
Were but a thankless policy in the *c*, „ III iv 51
We reck not tho' we lost this *c* of England— „ III iv 55
and you know The *c* is poor. „ V i 170
And wear my *c*, and dance upon my grave. „ V ii 601
God save the *C*! the Papacy is no more. „ V v 285
That thou wouldst have his promise for the *c*? *Harold* I i 204
lighten'd for me The weight of this poor *c*, „ I i 218
Their old *c* Is yet a force among them, „ I i 305
I want his voice in England for the *c*, „ II ii 72
Can have no right to the *c*,' „ II ii 355
Who hath a better claim then to the *c* „ II ii 597
Good, good, and thou wilt help me to the *c*? „ II ii 614
I ask thee, wilt thou help me to the *c*? „ II ii 628
Swear thou to help me to the *c* of England. „ II ii 705
I swear to help thee to the *c* of England (repeat) *Harold* II ii 713, 721
old Northumbrian *c*, And kings of our own choosing. „ IV i 32
Your old *c* Were little help without our Saxon carles „ IV i 34
Refer my cause, my *c* to Rome! . . . „ V i 1
Wash up that old *c* of Northumberland. „ V i 167
I have lost both *c* And husband. „ V ii 39
climb'd the throne and almost clutch'd the *c*; *Becket*, *Pro.* 22
Surely too young Even for this shadow of a *c*; „ *Pro.* 231
chessmen on the floor—the king's *c* broken! „ *Pro.* 313
if there ever come feud between Church and *C*, „ *Pro.* 465
he would grant thee The *c* itself. „ I iii 30
Sign, and obey the *c*! *Becket.* The *c*? Shall I do less for Canterbury Than Henry for the *c*? „ I iii 145
lest the *c* should be Shorn of ancestral splendour. „ I iii 155
Church and *C*, Two sisters gliding in an equal dance, „ I iii 443
and the mitre Grappling the *c*— „ II i 27
leave the royalty of my *c* Unlessen'd to mine heirs. „ II i 107
he answer'd me, As if he wore the *c* already— „ II ii 7
Quarrel of *C* and Church—to rend again. „ II ii 56
I thank you, sons; when kings but hold by *c's*, The crowd that hungers for a *c* in Heaven „ II ii 281
in her time when she had the '*C*.' *Rosamond.* The *c*! who? „ III i 198
But *c's* must bow when mitres sit so high. „ IV ii 297
lord of more land Than any *c* in Europe, „ V i 30
thro' all this quarrel I still have cleaved to the *c*, in hope the *c* Would cleave to me that but obey'd the *c*, „ V i 48
his poor tonsure A *c* of Empire. „ V i 196
Rather than dim the splendour of his *c* „ V ii 344
We must not force the *c* of martyrdom. „ V iii 28
I heard in Rome, This tributary *c* may fall to you. *The Cup* I i 97
The king, the *c*! their talk in Rome? „ I i 98
I here return like Tarquin—for a *c*. „ I i 142
play'd into their hands, Means me the *c*. „ I iii 151
She will be glad at last to wear my *c*. „ I iii 168
This all too happy day, *c*—queen at once. „ II 451
Have I the *c* on? I will go To meet him, „ II 518
It is the *c* Offends him— „ II 529
crown you Again with the same *c* my Queen of Beauty. *The Falcon* 915
When the fairy slights the *c*. *Foresters* II ii 135
all the *c's* Of all this world, „ IV 404
Crown (verb) Look to you as the one to *c* their ends. *Queen Mary* I iv 171
And when the Council would not *c* me— „ I v 555
your people will not *c* me— „ V i 81
So that ye will not *c* the Atheling? *Harold* II ii 598
Crown (verb) (*continued*) our great Council wait to *c* thee King— (repeat) *Harold* III i 3, 406
Should they not know free England *c's* herself? „ V i 48
Who shall *c* him? Canterbury is dying. *Becket*, *Pro.* 239
Becket should *c* him were he crown'd at all: „ II ii 17
For England, *c* young Henry there, „ II ii 456
to Westminster and *c* Young Henry there to-morrow. „ III ii 9
And thou shalt *c* my Henry o'er again. „ III iii 205
will you *c* my foe My victor in mid-battle? „ V i 148
The prelates whom he chose to *c* his son! „ V ii 399
This very day the Romans *c* him king *The Cup* II 64
When do they *c* him? *Messenger.* Even now. „ II 74
kick'd it featureless—they now would *c*. „ II 129
Yea, that ye saw me *c* myself withal. „ II 159
Ay, there they *c* him. „ II 181
hurls the victor's column down with him That *c's* it, hear. „ II 297
I whisper'd, Let me *c* you Queen of Beauty, *The Falcon* 360
—*c* you Again with the same crown my Queen of Beauty. „ 914
honour, worship thee, *C* thee with flowers; *Foresters* II ii 19
Crown'd never yet so happy Since I was *c*. *Queen Mary* III ii 88
C slaves of slaves, and mitred kings of kings, „ III iv 381
C, *c* and lost, *c* King—and lost to me! *Harold* III ii 1
Than ere they *c* me one, „ III ii 54
My young son Henry *c* the King of England, *Becket*, *Pro.* 224
Him who *c* Stephen—King Stephen's brother! „ *Pro.* 273
You have not *c* young Henry yet, „ II ii 1
C! by God's eyes, we will not have him *c*. „ II ii 3
We will not have him *c*. „ II ii 8
Not have him *c*? „ II ii 14
Becket should crown him were he *c* at all: „ II ii 17
England scarce would hold Young Henry king, if only *c* by York, „ II ii 32
I go to have young Henry *c* by York. „ II ii 478
Hereford, you know, *c* the first Henry. *Becket.* But Anselm *c* this Henry o'er again. „ III iii 202
coronation void By cursing those who *c* him. „ V ii 331
On those that *c* young Henry in this realm, „ V ii 392
As you would force a king from being *c*. „ V iii 26
Is he *c*? *Phœbe.* Ay, there they crown him. *The Cup* II 180
Across the hills when I was being *c*. „ II 321
I will go To meet him, *c*! *c* victor of my will— „ II 519
one sweet face *C* with the wreath. *The Falcon* 649
Crowning (adj. and part.) *c* thy young son by York, London and Salisbury—not Canterbury. *Becket* III iii 194
that but obey'd the crown, *C* your son; „ V i 52
O *c* crime! Hast murder'd thine own guest, the son of Orm, *Harold* IV ii 35
Crowning (s) He glitters on the *c* of the hill. „ V i 488
hath in this *c* of young Henry by York and London *Becket* III iii 70
I was at the *c*, for I have pleasure „ III iii 81
Come once more to me Before the *c*,— *The Cup* II 79
Crownling as to the young *c* himself, he look'd so malapert in the eyes, *Becket* III iii 108
Crozier Cowl, helm; and *c*, battle-axe. *Harold* V i 444
And smite thee with my *c* on the skull? *Becket* I i 221
and lay My *c* in the Holy Father's hands, „ I iii 125
Sceptre and *c* clashing, and the mitre Grappling „ II i 25
Crucified They *c* St. Peter downward. „ I iii 619
Crucifix I brought not ev'n my *c*. *Henry.* Take this. „ II i 295
Crucifying Horrible! flaying, scourging, *c*— *The Cup* I ii 235
Cruel And *c* at it, killing helpless flies; *Queen Mary* III iv 65
but neither cold, coarse, *c*, And more than all— „ V ii 482
lost and found Together in the *c* river Swale *Harold* III ii 10
I fear I was as *c* as the King. *Becket* V ii 124
C? Oh, no—it is the law, not he; „ V ii 125
Then you have done it, and I call *you c*. „ V ii 136
Crueller and makes The fire seem even *c* than it is. *Queen Mary* IV ii 233
if he have the greater right, Hath been the *c*. „ IV iii 383
Cruellest The hardest, *c* people in the world, „ II i 100
Cruelty haughtiness of their nobles; the *c* of their priests. „ II i 169
loathed the *cruelties* that Rome Wrought on her vassals. *The Cup* I ii 373
Wrong'd by the *cruelties* of his religions *Prom. of May* III 545
Cruor Illorum in lacrymas *C* fundatur! *Harold* V i 532

Crush In hope to *c* all heresy under Spain. *Queen Mary* III vi 84
C it at once With all the power I have !— *Harold* I i 356
I must—I will !—*C* it half-born ! „ I i 359
I'll *c* him as the subject. *Becket* I iii 334
And how to *c* them easily. *The Cup* I i 25
Rome Will *c* you if you wrestle with her ; „ I ii 131
would not *c* The fly that drew her blood ; *Prom. of May* II 493
Crush'd Over, your Grace, all *c* ; *Queen Mary* II iv 91
They are too *c*, too broken, „ IV iii 359
Being so *c* and so humiliated We scarcely dare *Becket* V i 68
C, hack'd at, trampled underfoot. *The Falcon* 640
C my bat whereon I flew ! *Foresters* II ii 146
Crust and to speak truth, nigh at the end of our last *c*, *Becket* III i 114
Crutch we daren't fight you with our *c'es*, „ I iv 210
C'es, and itches, and leprosies, and ulcers. „ I iv 254
Cry (s) (*See also* **War-cry**) Their *c* is, Philip never shall be king. *Queen Mary* II iv 1
Will front their *c* and shatter them into dust. „ II iv 5
Cries of the moment and the street— „ II iv 128
Will stir the living tongue and make the *c*. „ III i 355
Whereat Lord Williams gave a sudden *c* :— „ IV iii 605
Or you, for heretic *cries* ? „ V ii 326
A *c* ! What's that ? Elizabeth ? revolt ? „ V v 187
And *cries*, and clashes, and the groans of men : *Harold* III i 375
Thou hast sold me for a *c*.— „ IV ii 76
O God, the God of truth hath heard my *c*. „ V i 601
may at least have my *c* against him and her,— *Becket, Pro.* 510
hast thou heard this *c* of Gilbert Foliot „ I i 36
make my *c* to the Pope, By whom I will be judged ; „ I iii 723
I heard your savage *c*. „ IV ii 320
My savage *c* ? Why, she—she—when I strove „ IV ii 338
trumpets in the halls, Sobs, laughter, *cries* : „ V ii 368
You had my answer to that *c* before. „ V iii 124
And her *c* rang to me across the years, *Prom. of May* II 655
The phantom *c* ! *You*—did *you* hear a *c* ? „ III 651
he flutter'd his wings with a sweet little *c*, *Foresters* I i 154
Cry (verb) all men *c*, She is queenly, she is goodly. *Queen Mary* II ii 343
If ever I *c* out against the Pope „ III i 351
Swallows fly again, Cuckoos *c* again, „ III v 97
I heard An angel *c* ' There is more joy in Heaven,'— „ IV ii 10
One who *cries* continually with sweat and tears „ V iv 44
I likewise *c* ' no more.' *Harold* I i 389
Why *c* thy people on thy sister's name ? „ IV i 20
Is thy wrath Hell, that I should spare to *c*, „ V i 38
he licks my face and moans and *cries* out against the King. *Becket* I iv 100
innocences that will *c* From all the hidden by-ways „ III iii 14
sometimes she *cries*, and can't sleep sound o' nights „ IV i 29
She shall *c* no more ; she shall sleep sound enough „ IV i 32
c out for thee Who art too pure for earth. „ IV ii 132
one half, but half-alive, *Cries* to the King. „ V i 65
What made the King *c* out so furiously ? „ V i 220
When you *c* ' Rome, Rome,' to seize *The Cup* I iii 5
Dost thou *c* out upon the Gods of Rome ? „ II 454
throat might gape before the tongue could *c* who ? *Foresters* III 226
The Sheriff ! This ring *cries* out against thee. „ IV 69
Crying (part.) (*See also* **A-crying**) Thro' many voices *c* right and left, *Queen Mary* I ii 48
And Ignorance *c* in the streets, „ IV iii 377
C, ' Forward ! '—set our old church rocking, „ IV iii 403
c, in his deep voice, more than once, „ IV iii 611
What are you *c* for, when the sun shines ? *Becket* III i 269
when *c* On Holy Church to thunder out her rights „ V ii 30
Our old nurse *c* as if for her own child, *Prom. of May* II 479
She must be *c* out ' Edgar ' in her sleep. *Harold.* Who must be *c* out ' Edgar ' in her sleep ? „ III 653
Crying (s) ye did wrong in *c* ' Down with John ; ' *Foresters* I ii 96
Crypt Her *c* among the stars. *Becket* I iii 555
No, to the *c* ! Twenty steps down. „ V iii 77
To the *c* ? no—no, To the chapel of St. Blaise „ V iii 81
Cubit *See* **Twenty-cubit**
Cuckoo Swallows fly again, *C's* cry again, *Queen Mary* III v 97
Cuff I had to *c* the rogue For infant treason. „ III iii 51
C him could I ? with my hands Milking the cow ? „ III v 94
To kiss and *c* among the birds and flowers— „ III v 258
Cuirass And *c* in this forest where I dream'd *Foresters* IV 130
Cum (came) I *c* behind tha, gall, and couldn't make tha hear. *Queen Mary* IV iii 465
till his man *c* in post vro' here, „ IV iii 511
the tongue on un *c* a-lolluping out o' 'is mouth as black as a rat. „ IV iii 518
Cumberland (*See also* **Coomberland**) In *C*, Mr. Dobson. *Prom. of May* I 66
I met her first at a farm in *C*—Her uncle's. „ II 397
Cup wines Of wedding had been dash'd into the *c's* Of victory, *Harold* IV iii 7
Thy *c's* full ! „ IV iii 80
Hath stumbled on our *c's* ? „ IV iii 179
not at all ; the *c's* empty. *Becket, Pro.* 478
Ye have eaten of my fish and drunken of my *c* for a dozen years. „ I iv 30
and now this *c*—I never felt such passion *The Cup* I i 33
sends you this *c* rescued from the burning „ I i 41
it is the *c* we use in our marriages. „ I i 44
Take thou this letter and this *c* to Camma, „ I i 61
Take thou this *c* and leave it at her doors. „ I i 67
Is that the *c* you rescued from the fire ? „ I i 71
now this pious *c* Is passport to their house, „ I i 82
sacred *c* saved from a blazing shrine Of our great Goddess, „ I ii 54
Had you then No message with the *c* ? „ I ii 68
sends you this *c*—the *c* we use in our marriages— „ I ii 72
know myself am that Galatian Who sent the *c*. „ I ii 210
take this holy *c* To lodge it in the shrine of Artemis. „ I ii 434
To lodge this *c* Within the holy shrine of Artemis, „ I iii 52
the marriage *c* Wherefrom we make libation „ II 198
You see this *c*, my lord. „ II 338
It is the *c* belonging our own Temple. „ II 345
That Synorix should drink from his own *c*. „ II 354
They two should drink together from one *c*, „ II 362
I have almost drain'd the *c*—A few drops left. „ II 385
Have I not drunk of the same *c* with thee ? „ II 463
Here, here—a *c* of wine—drink and begone ! *Foresters* I iii 89
Cupid (*See also* **Tree-cupid**) Parthian shaft of a forlorn *C* at the King's left breast, *Becket, Pro.* 340
thou wouldst hug thy *C* till his ribs cracked— „ *Pro.* 504
St. *C*, that is too irreverent. „ V i 198
Cur as a mastiff dog May love a puppy *c* *Queen Mary* I iv 195
Why did you slink away like a *c* ? *Becket* IV ii 431
Curb their children under-heel—Must *c* her ; „ *Pro.* 215
Because we seek to *c* their viciousness. *Foresters* III 393
Curb'd Your lavish household *c*, *Queen Mary* I v 113
Cure I trust the kingly touch that *c's* the evil *Harold* I i 152
Curious be *c* About the welfare of their babes, *The Cup* I ii 361
You see this cup, my lord. *Antonius.* Most *c* ! „ II 339
Curiousness I have some time, for *c*, my Lord, *Queen Mary* III iv 61
Current (*See also* **Side-current**) the *c's* So shift and change, „ IV iii 408
that one time sway to the *c*, And to the wind another. *Becket* I iii 594
if man be only A willy-nilly *c* of sensations— *Prom of May* II 263
Curse (s) the *c* is on him For swearing falsely *Harold* III i 244
those heavenly ears have heard, Their *c* is on him ; „ III i 260
prayer against the *c* That lies on thee and England. „ III i 278
Then on thee remains the *c*, „ III i 315
lamb to Holy Church To save thee from the *c*. „ III i 336
To find a means whereby the *c* might glance „ III i 342
and the second *c* Descend upon thine head, „ III ii 48
Fool and wise, I fear This *c*, and scorn it. „ III ii 68
It burns my hand—a *c* to thee and me. „ III ii 186
The *c* of England ! these are drown'd in wassail, „ IV iii 222
He hath blown himself as red as fire with *c's*. „ V i 87
if thou blurt thy *c* among our folk, I know not— „ V i 89
will blast and blind you like a *c*. *Becket* I iv 40
God's full *c* Shatter you all to pieces „ V iii 134
My *c* on all This world of mud, *Prom. of May* III 721
C on your brutal strength ! I cannot pass that way. „ III 731
Curse (verb) God *c* her and her Legate ! *Queen Mary* V iv 12
you *c* so loud, The watch will hear you. „ V iv 62
The Pope, the King, will *c* you— *Becket* V iii 182
Heaven *c* him if he come not at your call ! *Prom. of May* I 764

Curse (verb) (*continued*) *C* him ! but thou art mocking me. — *Foresters* II i 514
Cursed God hath blest or *c* me with a nose— — *Queen Mary* III v 178
Out of the church, you brace of *c* crones, — „ IV iii 539
Why let earth rive, gulf in These *c* Normans— — *Harold* II ii 783
He hath *c* thee, and all those who fight for thee, — „ III ii 152
The King hath *c* him, if he marry me ; The Pope hath *c* him, marry me or no ! — „ III ii 189
The realm for which thou art forsworn is *c*, The babe enwomb'd and at the breast is *c* The corpse thou whelmest with thine earth is *c*, The soul who fighteth on thy side is *c*, The seed thou sowest in thy field is *c*, The steer wherewith thou plowest thy field is *c*, The fowl that fleeth o'er thy field is *c*, — „ V i 64
But since he *c* My friends at Veselay, — *Becket* II i 88
C be John of Oxford, Roger of York, And Gilbert Foliot ! *c* those De Brocs That hold our Saltwood Castle from our see ! *C* Fitzurse, and all the rest of them — „ II ii 265
C and anathematised us right and left, — „ V i 4
O the Sheriff Would pay this *c* mortgage to his brother — *Foresters* II i 144
came some evil fairy at my birth And *c* me, — „ II ii 109
Cursing Our Tostig parted *c* me and England ; — *Harold* III i 76
coronation void By *c* those who crown'd him. — *Becket* V ii 331
Curtsey *C* to him, wife, and thank him. — *Foresters* III 248
Cushion Throw *c's* on that seat, and make it throne-like. — *Queen Mary* V ii 536
Custom you that have kept your old *c's* upright, — „ II i 158
But by the royal *c's* of our realm — *Becket*, *Pro.* 23
And for these Royal *c's*, These ancient Royal *c's*— — „ I i 166
Will you subscribe the *c's* ? — „ I ii 46
we might take your side against the *c's*— — „ I ii 57
sign'd These ancient laws and *c's* of the realm. — „ I iii 7
to obey These ancient laws and *c's* of the realm ? — „ I iii 18
C's, traditions,—clouds that come and go ; The *c's* of the Church are Peter's rock. — „ I iii 22
these *c's* are no longer As Canterbury calls them, — „ I iii 69
another of these *c's* thou Wilt not be suffer'd — „ I iii 128
for no love o' the *c's* Or constitutions, — „ I iii 137
ye set these *c's* by my death Ringing their own death-knell — „ I iii 170
That thou wilt hear no more o' the *c's*. — „ I iii 256
And swear to obey the *c's*. — „ I iii 270
Good royal *c's*—had them written fair — „ I iii 415
I promised The King to obey these *c's*, — „ I iii 557
Are these your *c's* ? — „ I iii 659
The King, these *c's*, and the Church, — „ I iii 726
as you suspended yourself after sub-writing to the *c's*. — „ II ii 352
our recoverer and upholder of *c's* hath in this crowning — „ III iii 70
and I warrant the *c's*. Did the King Speak of the *c's* ? — „ III iii 331
spiritual giant with our island laws And *c's*, — „ IV ii 445
since we likewise swore to obey the *c's*, — „ V i 55
it is the law, not he ; The *c's* of the realm. *Becket.* The *c's* ! *c's* ! — „ V ii 127
It is our ancient *c* in Galatia That ere two souls — *The Cup* II 358
Thrones, churches, ranks, traditions, *c's*, — *Prom. of May* I 520
turn back at times, and make Courtesy to *c* ? — „ II 635
according to the law and *c* of the kingdom of England — *Foresters* I iii 66
It is our forest *c* they should revel Along with Robin. — „ III 174
Customary decide on what was *c* In olden days, — *Becket* II ii 175
Cut *c* out the rotten from your apple, — *Queen Mary* II ii 5
'I would they were *c* off That trouble you.' — „ III iv 32
C with a diamond; so to last like truth. — „ III v 25
Madam, you have but *c* the canvas out ; — „ V v 183
King's verdurer caught him a-hunting in the forest, and *c* off his paws. — *Becket* I iv 96
wheere the big eshtree *c's* athurt it, it gi'es a turn like, — *Prom. of May* III 94
he would never *c* it down, because one of the Steers — „ III 246
if we kill a stag, our dogs have their paws *c* off, — *Foresters* IV 225
Cut *See also* **Fine-cut, Stone-cut**
Cymbal sing, Asaph ! clash The *c*, Heman ! — *Harold* III i 188
Cypress apricot, Vine, *c*, poplar, myrtle, — *The Cup* I i 3
Cyprus Again this Richard is the lion of *C*, — *Foresters* IV 391

FF

D

Daay (day) (*See also* **Wedding-daäy**) What a day, what a day ! nigh upo' judgement *d* loike. — *Queen Mary* IV iii 468
they wunt set i' the Lord's cheer o' that *d*. — „ IV iii 470
He be heighty this very *d*, and 'e telled — *Prom. of May* I 7
When theer wur a meeting o' farmers at Littlechester to'ther *d*, — „ I 138
I coom'd upon 'im t'other *d* lookin' at the coontry, — „ I 201
'Good *d* then, Dobson !' Civil-spoken i'deed ! — „ I 300
fur thaw I be heighty this very *d*, — „ I 359
and the larks 'ud sing i' them *d's*, — „ I 374
plaäy the pianner, if ye liked, all *d* long, like a laädy, — „ II 101
At the end of the *d*, For the last loäd hoäm ? (repeat) — *Prom. of May* II 183, 194
Till the end of the *d* And the last loäd hoäm. — „ II 208
Till the end o' the *d* An' the last loäd hoäm.' (repeat) — „ II 238, 292
To the end o' the *d* An' the last loäd hoäm.' — „ II 259
Naäy, but 'Good *d*, Dobbins.' — „ II 732
'Good *d*, Dobbins.' Dang tha ! — „ II 741
Taäke me awaäy, little gell. It be one o' my bad *d's*. — „ III 466
Daäzed (dazed) feller's cleän *d*, an' maäzed, an' maäted, — „ II 729
Dabble *D* your hearths with your own blood. — *Harold* II ii 751
Daft Is he deaf, or dumb, or *d*, or drunk — *Foresters* I ii 208
Dagger With fingers pointed like so many *d's*, — *Queen Mary* I v 149
Or I will dig thee with my *d*. — „ II iii 96
even while I speak There lurks a silent *d*, — „ V ii 216
I have my *d* here to still their throats. — *Becket* III ii 49
stand beside thee One who might grapple with thy *d*, — „ IV ii 230
Take up your *d*; put it in the sheath. — „ IV ii 293
Madam, I saw your *d* at her throat; — „ IV ii 319
sure my *d* was a feint Till the worm turn'd— — „ IV ii 379
I go, but I will have my *d* with me, — *The Cup* I ii 457
mine own *d* driven by Synorix found All good — „ II 85
Daily Save for my *d* range Among the pleasant fields of Holy Writ — *Queen Mary* III v 78
and England's sake That suffers in the *d* want of thee, — *Harold* II ii 275
The more or less of *d* labour done—The pretty gaping bills in the home-nest Piping for bread—the *d* want supplied— — *Becket* II ii 299
Some *d* something-nothing. — „ III i 80
O my sick boy ! My *d* fading Florio, — *The Falcon* 236
Dainty dog I cramm'd with *dainties* worried me ! — *Becket* V i 244
Dairy (adj.) she set the bush by my *d* winder afoor she went to school — *Prom. of May* II 18
Dairy (s) The maid to her *d* came in from the cow, — „ I 39
Daisy (a plant) *Daisies* grow again, Kingcups blow again, — *Queen Mary* III v 89
O graves in *daisies* drest, — *Prom. of May* III 204
Honest *d* deadly bruised, — *Foresters* II ii 156
Daisy (name of a cow) Our *D's* as good 'z her. *Tib.* Noa, Joan. — *Queen Mary* IV iii 479
Our *D's* butter's as good 'z hern. — „ IV iii 481
Our *D's* cheeses be better. — „ IV iii 484
Dale Among these happy *d's*, run clearer, — *Becket* II i 157
Dallied But *d* with a single lettuce-leaf ; — *The Falcon* 673
Dally We *d* with our lazy moments here, — *Queen Mary* V iii 108
On those sweet lips that dare to *d* with it. — *Foresters* IV 75
Dallying *d* over seas Even when his brother's, — *Queen Mary* III iv 292
Dam (mother) 'Ewe lamb, ewe lamb, I am here by the *d*.' — *Becket* I iv 172
Dam (obstruction) like a river in flood thro' a burst *d* — *Harold* II ii 466
Damage He meant no harm nor *d* to the Church. — *Becket* I iii 216
Dame trifling royally With some fair *d* of court, — *Queen Mary* III vi 160
Damn (*See also* **Dang**) hear him ; let his own words *d* the Papist. — „ I iii 53
Absolve the left-hand thief and *d* the right ? — *Becket* II ii 392
Oh, do not *d* yourself for company ! — „ V ii 523
—drest like a gentleman, too. *D* all gentlemen, says I ! — *Prom. of May* II 579

Damn'd my Lord, He is *d* enough already. *Queen Mary* II ii 407
and brooks Were bridged and *d* with dead, *Harold* III ii 130
Damon The polish'd *D* of your pastoral here, *Prom. of May* III 562
Damp hand, *D* with the sweat of death, *Queen Mary* I ii 33
Those *d*, black, dead Nights in the Tower; dead— „ III v 137
Damsel I love him as a *d* of his day *Foresters* I i 227
if ever A Norman *d* fell into our hands, „ III 181
You hide this *d* in your forest here, „ IV 476
D, is this the truth? *Marian.* Ay, noble knight. „ IV 769
Danaë included *D* has escaped again Her tower, *Becket* I i 395
Dance (s) (*See also* **Diamond-dance**) Have you been looking at the '*D* of Death'? *Queen Mary* V ii 170
Two sisters gliding in an equal *d*, *Becket* I iii 444
She saw it at a *d*, upon a neck Less lovely *The Falcon* 54
and the lads and lasses 'ull hev a *d*. *Prom. of May* I 428
But see they were coming out for the *d* already. „ I 796
But they are coming hither for the *d*— *Foresters* I ii 53
Dance (verb) Till the sun *d*, as upon Easter Day. *Queen Mary* III ii 238
and *d* into the sun That shines on princes. „ III v 252
And wear my crown, and *d* upon my grave. „ V ii 601
star That *d's* in it as mad with agony! *Harold* I i 9
that wilt not *d* However wisely charm'd. „ I i 386
D! small heart have I to *d*. *Prom. of May* I 429
weight of the church to boot on my shoulders, I would *d* too. *Foresters* I ii 59
Go now and ask the maid to *d* with thee, „ I ii 185
Pretty mistress, will you *d*? „ I ii 204
What? must we *d* attendance all the day? „ IV 550
D! ay, by all the saints and all the devils ye shall *d*. „ IV 552
they shall *d* to the music of the wild wood. Let the birds sing, and do you *d* to their song. „ IV 555
Rouge, I am full of gout. I cannot *d*. „ IV 563
for by my life, you shall *d* till he can. „ IV 566
Prick him where thou wilt, so that he *d*. „ IV 572
Let us hang, so thou *d* meanwhile; „ IV 581
Take care, take care! I *d*—I will *d*—I *d*. „ IV 586
Dancing I watch'd you *d* once With your huge father; *Queen Mary* V ii 143
I should seem to be *d* upon a grave. *Prom. of May* I 431
Dandle I would *d* you upon my knee At lisping-age. *Queen Mary* V ii 141
Dane Angle, Jute, *D*, Saxon, Norman, *Harold* II ii 763
we are *D's*, Who conquer'd what we walk on, „ IV i 37
Thou art but a West Saxon: *we* are *D's*! *Harold.* My mother is a *D*, and I am English; „ IV i 53
Athelstan the Great Who drove you *D's*; and yet he held That *D*, Jute, Angle, Saxon, „ IV i 75
or Knut who coming *D* Died English. „ IV iii 55
Dang (damn) 'Good daäy, Dobbins.' *D* tha! *Prom. of May* II 742
Out o' the chaumber, *d* tha „ III 73
Danger But your own state is full of *d* here. *Queen Mary* I iv 169
This marriage should bring loss or *d* to you, „ II ii 227
release from *d* of all censures Of Holy Church „ III iii 150
How dense a fold of *d* nets him round, *Harold* II ii 17
Am I in *d* in this court? „ II ii 236
And take the Church's *d* on myself. *Becket* I ii 72
is there *d*? *Camma.* Nay, None that I know: *The Cup* I ii 440
Dangerous therefore is he *d*. *Queen Mary* I iv 161
he is *d* everyway. „ I iv 164
Not every *d* that way, my good uncle. „ I iv 166
Altho' we grant when kings are *d* *Becket* I ii 67
Dangle You ought to *d* up there among the crows. *Foresters* III 366
Dangled The traitor husband *d* at the door, *Queen Mary* III i 10
Daniel I am the messenger of God, His Norman *D*! *Harold* V i 35
Danish that sight of *D* blood Might serve an end not English— „ IV iii 96
Dan Smith (farm labourer) *D S*, fur I cotched 'im once a-steälin' coäls *Prom. of May* I 411
D S's cart hes runned ower a laädy i' the holler laäne, „ II 567
D S, my father and I forgave you stealing our coals. „ III 68
But, *D S*, they tell me that you— „ III 76
Dare I *d* not leave my post. *Queen Mary* I ii 55
for all that I *d* not stay. „ I ii 102
I cannot, and I *d* not, „ I v 49
Yet others are that *d* the stake and fire, „ III iv 167
Before I *d* to glance upon your Grace. „ III v 186
This last—I *d* not read it her. „ V ii 183
Dare (*continued*) How *d* you say it? *Queen Mary* V ii 379
I might *d* to tell her that the Count— „ V ii 523
The Queen is dying, or you *d* not say it. „ V v 251
I *d* not well be seen in talk with thee. *Harold* II ii 481
I *d* not. *Harold.* Scared by the church— „ III ii 86
I *d* not wear it. *Harold.* But I *d*. God with thee! „ III ii 187
If one may *d* to speak the truth, „ IV i 108
D's the bear slouch into the lion's den? *Becket* IV ii 282
I *d* not, sir! Throne him—and then the marriage— *The Cup* II 155
D beg him to receive his diamonds back—How can I, *d* I, *The Falcon* 262
I do not *d*, like an old friend, to shake it. *Prom. of May* II 526
That I *d* not tell how much I love him. „ III 287
Dare-Becket only there was a dare-devil in his eye—I should say a *d-B*. *Becket* III iii 89
Dared If they *d* To harm you, I would blow *Queen Mary* I iv 289
Ev'n that young girl who *d* to wear your crown? *Mary.* *D*? nay, not so; „ I v 491
How *d* he? *Magdalen.* Stupid soldiers oft are bold. „ V ii 444
Nobles we *d* not touch. „ V v 104
Which even Peter had not *d*? *Becket* II ii 395
How *d* you? Know you not this bower is secret, „ IV ii 21
He *d* not—liar! yet, yet I remember— „ V i 211
May they not say you *d* not show yourself „ V ii 594
but to-day I *d* not—so much weaker, *The Falcon* 832
Dare-devil *D-d's*, that would eat fire and spit it out *Queen Mary* III i 156
only there was a *d-d* in his eye—I should say a dare-Becket. *Becket* III iii 88
Daring ice-cold—no dash of *d* in him. *Queen Mary* I v 331
Dark (adj.) For I foresee *d* days. „ I v 275
true enough Her *d* dead blood is in my heart with mine. „ III i 349
Her *d* dead blood that ever moves with mine „ III i 352
He can but creep down into some *d* hole „ IV i 140
listening In some *d* closet, some long gallery, „ V ii 217
D among gems and gold; *Harold* IV i 249
My fatal oath—the dead Saints—the *d* dreams— „ V i 380
Gloom upon gleam, *D* as my doom— *Becket* III i 282
Have track'd the King to this *d* inland wood; „ III ii 3
And far on in the *d* heart of the wood „ III ii 47
D even from a side glance of the moon, „ IV ii 148
Growing *d* too—but light enough to row. *The Cup* II 523
What, I that held the orange blossom *D* as the yew? *Prom. of May* II 631
Ye sees the holler laäne be hallus sa *d* i' the arternoon, „ III 93
How *d* your room is! „ III 217
even if I found it *D* with the soot of slums. „ III 602
our King is gone, the light Of these *d* hours; *Foresters* I ii 85
O look! before the shadow of these *d* oaks „ II i 604
A maiden now Were ill-bested in these *d* days of John, „ II ii 45
In this *d* wood when all was in our power „ III 182
Dark (s) Your master works against me in the *d*. *Queen Mary* I v 277
She to shut up my blossom in the *d*! *Harold* I ii 62
I am in the *d*. *Becket* III i 221
one step in the *d* beyond Our expectation, *The Cup* I i 212
Safe from the *d* and the cold, „ I ii 6
I runned arter thief i' the *d*. *Prom. of May* I 403
leaves him A beast of prey in the *d*, „ I 505
Death As against Life! all, all, into the *d*— „ II 338
and saäy it to ye afoor *d*; „ III 14
Darken Save him, his blood would *d* Henry's name; *Becket* V iii 10
Darken'd I tear away The leaves were *d* by the battle— *The Falcon* 913
Darkening Gone narrowing down and *d* to a close. *Queen Mary* IV iii 431
Darker Thy Duke will seem the *d*. Hence, I follow. *Harold* II ii 817
They told me, from the farm—and *d* news. *Prom. of May* II 408
this world Is brighter for his absence as that other Is *d* for his presence. „ II 459
Darkness He stirs within the *d*! *Queen Mary* III ii 158
that all the louts to whom Their A B C is *d*, „ III iv 35
—the Lord hath dwelt In *d*. *Harold* III i 180
As gold Outvalues dross, light *d*, *Becket* I iii 715
Could shine away the *d* of that gap „ III i 59
Stumble not in the *d*, Lest they should seize thee. „ V iii 79
And fear not I should stumble in the *d*, Not tho' it be their hour, the power of *d*, But my hour too, the power of light in *d*! „ V iii 92

Darkness (*continued*) I am not in the *d*, but the light, *Becket* v iii 97
in the gulf Of never-dawning *d*? *Prom. of May* I 542
lie down there together in the *d* which would seem but for a moment, „ III 194
but this new moon, I fear, Is *d*. *Foresters* I ii 87
And *d* rises from the fallen sun. „ I iii 42
You see the *d* thro' the lighter leaf. „ IV 975
Darling His village *d* in some lewd caress *Becket* IV ii 200
The clamour'd *d* of their afternoon! *The Cup* II 125
She has disappear'd, poor *d*, from the world— *Prom. of May* II 410
Darn necklaces To please our lady, we must *d*, *The Falcon* 45
Darning What art thou doing there? *Elisabetta*. *D* your lordship. „ 41
Dart To hide the scar left by thy Parthian *d*. *Becket, Pro.* 377
Darter (daughter) I ha' nine *d's* i' the spital that be dead „ I iv 249
to turn out boäth my *d's* right down fine laädies. *Prom. of May* I 336
Thy feyther eddicated his *d's* to marry gentlefoälk, „ II 116
but I couldn't buy my *d* back ageän when she lost hersen, „ III 453
Dash (s) ice-cold—no *d* of daring in him. *Queen Mary* I v 331
Dash (verb) *d* The torch of war among your standing corn, *Harold* II ii 748
wields His war-club, *d'es* it on Gurth, „ v i 640
I *d* myself to pieces—I stay myself— *Becket* II ii 150
d thyself against me that I may slay thee! „ IV ii 195
thou must *d* us down Our dinner from the skies. *The Falcon* 152
Dash'd (rushed) We mounted, and we *d* into the heart of 'em. „ 629
Dash'd (sprinkled) then he *d* and drench'd, He dyed, *Harold* III i 140
D red with that unhallow'd passover; *Becket* I iii 348
Dash'd (threw) insolent shot that *d* the seas Upon us, *Queen Mary* v i 57
bit his shield, and *d* it on the ground, *Harold* v i 405
Dash'd (thrown) wines Of wedding had been *d* into the cups Of victory, „ IV iii 7
Daub This is a *d* to Philip. *Queen Mary* I v 447
Daughter (*See also* **Darter**) Mary, the lawful and legitimate *d* of Harry the Eighth! „ I i 8
(I have a *d* in her service who reported it) „ I i 76
my *d* said that when there rose a talk of the late rebellion, „ I i 91
I am Harry's *d*, Tudor, and not Fear. „ II iv 52
'Hail, *D* of God, and saver of the faith. „ III ii 82
I am Harry's *d*: „ III v 117
Who knows if Boleyn's *d* be my sister? „ v v 194
God bless thee, wedded *d*. *Harold* III i 293
so will I, *d*, until I find Which way the battle balance. „ v i 459
No, *d*, but the canons out of Waltham, „ v i 474
Look, *d*, look. *Edith*. Nay, father, look for *me*! „ v i 535
No, *d*, no—they fall behind the horse— „ v i 545
A cleric violated The *d* of his host, *Becket* I iii 383
Shrink from me, like a *d* of the Church. „ II i 277
like the Greek king when his *d* was sacrificed, „ III iii 105
The *d* of Zion lies beside the way— „ III iii 177
D, the world hath trick'd thee. Leave it, *d*; Come thou with me to Godstow nunnery, „ IV ii 364
I am grieved, my *d*. „ v ii 83
D, *d*, Deal not with things you know not. „ v ii 132
No, *d*, you mistake our good Archbishop; „ v ii 137
D, my time is short, I shall not do it. „ v ii 157
Liker the King. *Becket*. No, *d*. „ v ii 182
Tho' you are a gentleman, I but a farmer's *d*— *Prom. of May* I 668
—a *d* of the fields, This Dora! „ II 622
shamed of his poor farmer's *d* among the ladies in his drawing-room? „ III 294
if a gentleman Should wed a farmer's *d*, „ III 579
only there was left A second *d*, „ III 772
I come here to see this *d* of Sir Richard of the Lea *Foresters* I ii 26
Come away, *d*. „ I ii 283
then each man That owns a wife or *d*, „ III 460
dishonour The *d's* and the wives of your own faction— „ IV 698
Daunted What, *d* by a garrulous, arrogant girl! „ IV 736
Dauphin In order to betroth her to your *D*. *Queen Mary* I v 293
Mary of Scotland, married to your *D*, „ I v 296
your Scottish namesake marrying The *D*, „ v i 136
The Queen of Scots is married to the *D*, „ v v 53

David gloom of Saul Was lighten'd by young *D's* harp. *Queen Mary* v ii 359
And no *D* To meet him? *Harold* v i 496
Dawn (s) If Ludgate can be reach'd by *d* to-morrow. *Queen Mary* II iii 53
gray *d* Of an old age that never will be mine „ v ii 234
Like sun-gilt breathings on a frosty *d*— „ v iii 51
Shall see the dewy kiss of *d* no more *Harold* II ii 331
by dead Norway without dream or *d*! „ IV iii 122
Were the great trumpet blowing doomsday *d*, „ v i 228
wind of the *d* that I hear in the pine overhead? *Becket* II i 1
In the gray *d* before the Temple doors. *The Cup* I ii 295
I rise to-morrow In the gray *d*, „ I ii 434
Hang'd at mid-day, their traitor of the *d* „ II 124
From the dim *d* of Being— *Prom. of May* I 281
That beam of *d* upon the opening flower, *Foresters* IV 3
yet I think these oaks at *d* and even, „ IV 1067
Dawn (verb) day of peril that *d's* darkly and drearily *Becket* I iv 145
Dawning (*See also* **Never-dawning**) The islands call'd into the *d* church Out of the dead, *Queen Mary* III iii 172
Day (*See also* **Daay, Gala-day, Good-day, Mid-day, Saint's-day**) too full of aches and broken before his *d*. „ I i 125
I have seen enough for this *d*. „ I i 131
For I foresee dark *d's*. *Mary*. And so do I, sir; „ I v 275
and be the mightiest man This *d* in England. „ II ii 20
I trust this *d*, thro' God, I have saved the crown. „ II ii 302
And see the citizens arm'd. Good *d*; good *d*. „ II ii 378
a black 'un for us this blessed *d*. „ II iii 101
the brightest *d* Beheld our rough forefathers „ III ii 119
Might not St. Andrew's be her happiest *d*? *Mary*. Then these shall meet upon St. Andrew's *d*. „ III ii 124
Till the sun dance, as upon Easter *D*. „ III ii 238
St. Andrew's *d*; sit close, sit close, we are friends. „ III iii 1
Laughs at the last red leaf, and Andrew's *D*. „ III iii 87
Should not this *d* be held in after years „ III iii 89
This is the loveliest *d* that ever smiled On England. „ III iii 161
I found One *d*, a wholesome scripture, „ III iv 84
In clear and open *d* were congruent With that vile Cranmer „ III iv 230
Is like a word that comes from olden *d's*, „ III v 34
Queen hath been three *d's* in tears For Philip's going— „ III vi 12
Still Parleying with Renard, all the *d* with Renard, „ III vi 116
And scarce a greeting all the *d* for me— „ III vi 118
Methinks that would you tarry one *d* more „ III vi 233
Madam, a *d* may sink or save a realm. *Mary*. A *d* may save a heart from breaking too. *Philip*. Well, Simon Renard, shall we stop a *d*? *Renard*. Your Grace's business will not suffer, sire, For one *d* more, so far as I can tell. *Philip*. Then one *d* more to please her Majesty. „ III vi 238
Good *d*, old friend; what, you look somewhat worn; „ IV ii 115
yet it is a *d* to test your health „ IV ii 117
Win thro' this *d* with honour to yourself, „ IV ii 165
It is a *d* of rain. „ IV ii 229
Hath, like a brief and bitter winter's *d*, „ IV iii 430
Expectant of the rack from *d* to *d*, „ IV iii 437
What a *d*, what a *d*! nigh upo' judgement daay „ IV iii 467
What, not one *d*? „ v i 209
That all *d* long hath wrought his father's work, „ v ii 118
believe I lamed his Majesty's For a *d* or two, „ v ii 472
Indian shawl That Philip brought me in our happy *d's*!— „ v ii 541
On all the road from Dover, *d* and night; On all the road from Harwich, night and *d*; „ v ii 577
as in the *d* of the first church, when Christ Jesus was King. „ v iv 54
Ah, those *d's* Were happy. „ v v 239
These meteors came and went before our *d*, *Harold* I i 132
wilt thou fly my falcons this fair *d*? „ II ii 147
Down thirty feet below the smiling *d*— „ II ii 430
in thy father's *d* They blinded my young kinsman, „ II ii 510
O friends, I shall not overlive the *d*. „ III i 233
Lost, lost, the light of *d*, „ III ii 12
The *d* is won! „ IV i 270
the *d*, Our *d* beside the Derwent will not shine „ IV iii 49

Day (*continued*) guest, As haggard as a fast of forty *d's*, *Harold* IV iii 176
I have ridden night and *d* from Pevensey— „ IV iii 192
but leave this *d* to me. „ V i 128
Because I loved thee in my mortal *d*, „ V i 240
I am dead as Death this *d* to ought of earth's „ V i 425
that happy *d*! A birthday welcome! happy *d's* and many! „ V i 430
Stigand, O father, have we won the *d*? „ V i 544
and enough of death for this one *d*, The *d* of St. Calixtus, and the *d*, My *d* „ V ii 120
His *d*, with all his rooftree ringing 'Harold,' „ V ii 129
A sauce-deviser for thy *d's* of fish, *Becket, Pro.* 98
Follow me this Rosamund *d* and night, „ *Pro.* 506
Thou art wearied out With this *d's* work, „ I i 7
That havock'd all the land in Stephen's *d*. „ I i 243
O rare, a whole long *d* of open field. „ I i 296
made the twilight *d*, „ I iii 372
Lost in desuetude, of my grandsire's *d*, „ I iii 414
set the Church This *d* between the hammer and the anvil— „ I iii 585
Grant me one *d* To ponder these demands. „ I iii 668
d of peril that dawns darkly and drearily „ I iv 144
yea, and in the *d* of judgment also, „ I iv 147
that be dead ten times o'er i' one *d* wi' the putrid fever; „ I iv 251
Like sudden night in the main glare of *d*. „ II i 58
decide on what was customary In olden *d's*, „ II ii 176
but this *d* he proffer'd peace. „ II ii 239
You had not borne it, no, not for a *d*. „ II ii 305
In the great *d* against the wronger. „ III iii 17
Glancing at the *d's* when his father was only Earl of Anjou, „ III iii 149
Thanks to the blessed Magdalen, whose *d* it is. „ III iii 172
out with Henry in the *d's* When Henry loved me, „ V ii 231
What *d* of the week? Tuesday? „ V ii 281
to people heaven in the great *d* When God makes up his jewels. „ V ii 496
Do they not fight the Great Fiend *d* by *d*? „ V ii 586
Fair Sir, a happy *d* to you! *The Cup* I i 188
I have had a weary *d* in watching you. „ I ii 40
close not yet the door upon a night That looks half *d*. „ I ii 389
This very *d* the Romans crown him king „ II 63
He wills you then this *d* to marry him, „ II 66
And join your life this *d* with his, „ II 135
to make the *d* memorial, when Synorix, first King, „ II 439
This all too happy *d*, crown—queen at once. „ II 451
been on my knees every *d* for these half-dozen years *The Falcon* 184
I come this *d* to break my fast with you. „ 276
A lady that was beautiful as *d* Sat by me „ 349
but this *d* has brought A great occasion. „ 487
so much worse For last *d's* journey. „ 834
And the *d's* bright like a friend, but the wind east like an enemy. *Prom. of May* I 79
The sky? or the sea on a blue *d*? „ I 102
Good *d*! *Wilson.* Good *d*, sir. „ I 294
Good *d*, then, Dobson. „ I 299
Many happy returns of the *d*, father. „ I 351
Who shrieks by *d* at what she does by night, „ I 532
and it seems to me nobbut t'other *d*. „ II 7
My name is Harold! Good *d*, Dobbins! „ II 726
always told Father that the huge old ashtree there would cause an accident some *d*; „ III 245
may drop off any *d*, any hour. You must see at once. „ III 407
You heard him say it was one of his bad *d's*. „ III 469
It is almost the last of my bad *d's*, I think. „ III 472
Or ever the *d* began, *Foresters* I i 11
and these are the *d's* of Prince John. „ I i 177
I love him as a damsel of his *d* „ I i 227
Sufficient for the *d*, dear father! „ I i 343
twilight of the coming *d* already glimmers in the east. „ I ii 247
But ill befitting such a festal *d* „ I iii 37
To sleep! to sleep! The long bright *d* is done, „ I iii 41
Whate'er thy joys, they vanish with the *d*; „ I iii 44
There is no land like England Where'er the light of *d* be; (repeat) *Foresters* II i 2, 6, 14. 18
king of *d* hath stept from off his throne, *Foresters* II i 26

Day (*continued*) Perchance this *d* may sink so gloriously, *Foresters* II i 31
Whene'er this *d* should come about, „ II i 41
A maiden now Were ill-bested in these dark *d's* of John, „ II ii 45
In the night, in the *d*, „ II ii 182
Dear, in these *d's* of Norman license, „ III 177
having lived For twenty *d's* and nights in mail, „ IV 124
Not having broken fast the livelong *d*— „ IV 186
must we dance attendance all the *d*? „ IV 551
Daybreak Send the Great Seal by *d*. *Becket* I i 405
Day-dream Some hunter in *d-d's* or half asleep *Foresters* IV 1088
Daylight (adj.) Hath shock'd me back into the *d* truth *Queen Mary* III v 135
Daylight (s) Let me bring you in here where there is still full *d*. *Prom. of May* III 218
Dazed (*See also* **Daäzed**) Edward wakes!—*D*—he hath seen a vision. *Harold* III i 131
Dazing *See* **Brain-dazing**
Deacon (*See also* **Cardinal-deacon**) thou art but *d*, not yet bishop, *Becket, Pro.* 83
Dead (adj.) (*See also* **Deäd, Famine-dead**) You know your Latin—quiet as a *d* body. *Queen Mary* I iv 181
Quiet as a *d* body. „ I iv 187
which every now and then Beats me half *d*: „ I v 525
When I and thou and all rebellions lie *D* bodies „ II i 80
The tree that only bears *d* fruit is gone. „ III i 19
Sir, this *d* fruit was ripening overmuch, And had to be removed lest living Spain Should sicken at *d* England. *Stafford.* Not so *d*, But that a shock may rouse her. „ III i 25
d I cannot choose but love her. „ III i 339
true enough Her dark *d* blood is in my heart with mine. „ III i 349
Her dark *d* blood that ever moves with mine „ III i 352
And unto no *d* world; but Lambeth palace, „ III ii 153
The islands call'd into the dawning church Out of the *d*, deep night „ III iii 173
should be No longer a *d* letter, but requicken'd. „ III iv 10
Let the *d* letter live.' „ III iv 33
Let the *d* letter burn! „ III iv 40
d—with the fear of death Too *d* ev'n for a death-watch! „ III v 139
my faith would seem *D* or half-drown'd, „ IV ii 98
Until the power suddenly blew him *d*. „ IV iii 341
The parson from his own spire swung out *d*, „ IV iii 376
Our altar is a mound of *d* men's clay, „ V ii 161
A letter which the Count de Noailles wrote To that *d* traitor Wyatt, „ V ii 498
Let *d* things rest. „ V ii 506
Tell him at last I know his love is *d*, „ V ii 591
D or alive you cannot make him happy. „ V v 71
Women, when I am *d*, Open my heart, „ V v 152
The Queen is *d*. „ V v 252
For my *d* father's loyalty to thee? *Harold* I i 240
a *d* man Rose from behind the altar, „ I ii 78
saw the church all fill'd With *d* men upright from their graves, and all The *d* men made at thee to murder thee, „ I ii 83
The shadows of a hundred fat *d* deer For *d* men's ghosts. „ I ii 103
Where they eat *d* men's flesh, and drink their blood. „ II ii 807
Dry as an old wood-fungus on a *d* tree, „ III i 8
and sell not thou Our living passion for a *d* man's dream; „ III ii 60
Our dear, *d*, traitor-brother, Tostig, „ IV iii 83
How ran that answer which King Harold gave To his *d* namesake, „ IV iii 110
Sound sleep to the man Here by *d* Norway „ IV iii 122
By God, we thought him *d*— „ IV iii 148
What did the *d* man call it—Sanguelac, „ V i 184
My fatal oath—the *d* Saints—the dark dreams— „ V i 380
I am *d* as Death this day to ought of earth's „ V i 425
They are stripping the *d* bodies naked yonder, „ V ii 34
I tell thee, girl, I am seeking my *d* Harold, „ V ii 43
being the true wife Of this *d* King, who never bore revenge. „ V ii 85
And this *d* king's Who, king or not, „ V ii 123
Pluck the *d* woman off the *d* man, Malet! „ V ii 144
D is he, my Queen? *Becket, Pro.* 368
A *d* man's dying wish should be of weight. „ *Pro.* 422
We wait but the King's word to strike thee *d*. „ I iii 167
They be *d* while I be a-supping. „ I iv 247
that be *d* ten times o'er i' one day wi' the putrid fever; „ I iv 250

Dead (adj.) *(continued)* Let either cast him away like a *d* dog! *Becket* II ii 257
For tho' the drop may hollow out the *d* stone, „ III iii 315
Trodden one half *d*; one half, but half-alive, „ v i 63
Would he were *d*! (repeat) „ v i 91, 95
She sends it back, as being *d* to earth, So *d* henceforth to you. *Henry. D*! you have murder'd her, „ v i 170
Why, then you are a *d* man; flee! „ v iii 126
The traitor's *d*, and will arise no more. „ v iii 200
No, Reginald, he is *d*. „ v iii 204
The body of that *d* traitor Sinnatus. *The Cup* I iii 179
Rouse the *d* altar-flame, fling in the spices, „ II 182
My liberality perforce is *d* Thro' lack of means of giving. *The Falcon* 296
'*D* mountain.' Nay, for who could trace a hand „ 437
'*D* mountain flowers, *d* mountain-meadow flowers, „ 460
You bloom again, *d* mountain-meadow flowers.' „ 470
'*D* flowers! „ 476
'*D* mountain flowers'—Ah well, my nurse has broken The thread of my *d* flowers, as she has broken My china bowl. My memory is as *d*. „ 519
They left us there for *d*! „ 651
Ay, and I left two fingers there for *d*. „ 654
I left him there for *d* too! „ 659
I could almost think that the *d* garland Will break „ 918
is haunted by The ghosts of the *d* passions of *d* men; *Prom. of May* II 275
if the wretch were *d* I might forgive him; We know not whether he be *d* or living. „ II 433
One Philip Edgar of Toft Hall in Somerset Is lately *d*. *Dora. D*!— „ II 447
That one, is he then—*d*! „ II 452
D! and this world Is brighter for his absence „ II 457
for I am closely related to the *d* man's family. „ II 715
He's *d*, man—*d*; gone to his account—*d* and buried. „ III 144
Shall I tell her he is *d*? No; she is still too feeble. „ III 337
d midnight when I came upon the bridge; „ III 368
Living . . . *d* . . . She said 'all still. „ III 683
She hid this sister, told me she was *d*—I have wasted pity on her—not *d* now— „ III 690
—not *d* now—a swoon—a scene—Yet— „ III 696
Yes, deathlike! *D*? I dare not look: if *d*, „ III 716
For be he *d*, then John may be our King. *Foresters* I ii 98
being outlaw'd in a land Where law lies *d*, „ II i 91
and the son Is most like *d*— „ II i 147
I ha' served the King living, says she, and let me serve him *d*, „ II i 311
saints were so kind to both on us that he was *d* before he was born. „ II i 373
or wreckt And *d* beneath the midland ocean, „ II i 657
I am but a stone and a *d* stock to thee. „ II ii 69
What's here? a *d* bat in the fairy ring— „ II ii 93
Found him *d* and drench'd in dew, „ II ii 147
The deer fell *d* to the bottom, „ IV 543
O my good liege, we did believe you *d*. „ IV 846
Was justice *d* because the King was *d*? „ IV 847
Dead (s) And after that, the trumpet of the *d*. *Queen Mary* IV ii 12
and the *d* were found Sitting, and in this fashion; „ v ii 395
Peace is with the *d*. „ v v 268
Peace with the *d*, who never were at peace! „ v v 273
With looking on the *d*. And I so white? *Harold* II ii 815
dykes and brooks Were bridged and damm'd with *d*, „ III ii 130
Drink to the *d* who died for us, „ IV iii 69
Hail to the living who fought, the *d* who fell! „ IV iii 106
with the *d* So piled about him he can hardly move. „ v i 657
What art *thou* doing here among the *d*? „ v ii 33
Then all the *d* fell on him. „ v ii 50
Love that can lift up a life from the *d*. *Becket* II i 14
I am the bride of Death, and only Marry the *d*. *The Cup* II 30
Is not this To speak too pitilessly of the *d*? *Prom. of May* II 461
it is not So easy to forgive—even the *d*. „ II 486
—how she made her wail as for the *d*! „ III 699
sheeted *d* Are shaken from their stillness in the grave *Foresters* II i 45
Deäd (adj.) So the owd uncle i' Coomberland be *d*, *Prom. of May* II 2
I'd like to fell 'im as *d* as a bullock! „ II 597
D! It mun be true, fur it wur i' print as black as owt. „ II 730
Deäd (adj.) *(continued)* Be the colt *d*? *Dora.* No, Father. *Prom. of May* III 429
Be he *d*? *Dora.* Not that I know. „ III 433
Deadly Tho' I be ever *d* sick at sea. *Queen Mary* III vi 88
Who went before us did not wholly clear The *d* growths of earth, *Becket* II ii 203
Deaf To the *d* adder thee, that will not dance *Harold* I i 385
Art thou *d*? *Becket.* I hear you. *Becket* I iii 604
Are you *d*? What, have I lost authority among you? „ v iii 65
I be a bit *d*, and I wur hallus scäared by a big word; *Prom. of May* III 32
I am not *d*! you fright me. „ III 660
Is he *d*, or dumb, or daft, or drunk belike? *Foresters* I ii 208
Deafen'd and *d* by some bright Loud venture, *Queen Mary* III i 451
Edward's prayers Were *d* and he pray'd them dumb, *Harold* I ii 22
Deal (*See also* **Deäl**) To *d* with heresy gentlier. *Queen Mary* III vi 58
D gently with the young man Absalom. *Becket* I iii 756
D not with things you know not. „ v ii 133
So that they *d* with us like honest men, *Foresters* IV 101
And I might *d* with four. „ IV 171
Deäl Noä; I knaws a *d* better now. *Prom. of May* II 26
Dealt We *d* in the wild justice of the woods. *Foresters* IV 1072
Dean *D's* Of Christchurch, Durham, Exeter, and Wells— *Queen Mary* I ii 8
I am the *D* of the province: let me bear it. *Becket* I iii 498
De-anathematise Can the King *d-a* this York? „ v ii 10
Dear I fear, I fear, I see you, *D* friend, for the last time; *Queen Mary* I ii 103
Ay, one and all, *d* brothers, pray for me; „ IV iii 102
seeing now The poor so many, and all food so *d*. „ IV iii 209
Low, *d* lute, low! „ v ii 376
It is the Count de Feria, my *d* lady. „ v ii 529
D Madam, Philip is but at the wars; „ v v 24
Mightily, my *d* lady! *Harold* I i 24
My most *d* Master, What matters? „ I i 194
O Tostig, O *d* brother—If they prance, Rein in, „ I i 371
War, my *d* lady, War, waste, plague, famine, „ I i 465
he shall be my *d* friend As well as thine, „ II ii 79
we are poison'd: our *d* England Is demi-Norman. „ III i 40
and *d* son, swear When thou art king, to see my solemn vow Accomplish'd. „ III i 304
Nay, *d* lord, for I have sworn Not to swear falsely twice. „ III i 309
Our *d*, dead, traitor-brother, Tostig, „ IV iii 83
No more, no more, *d* brother, nevermore— „ v i 247
Given me by my *d* friend the King of England— *Becket* I i 337
O, my *d* friend, the King! O brother! „ I i 359
The mouth is only Clifford, my *d* father. „ II i 220
Then, my *d* liege, I here deliver all this controversy „ II ii 135
My *d* lord Archbishop, I learn but now that those poor Poitevins, „ II ii 426
Save that *d* head which now is Canterbury, „ v iii 6
Spare this defence, *d* brother. „ v iii 168
I fear my *d* lord mixt With some conspiracy against the wolf. *The Cup* I ii 14
Welcome to this poor cottage, my *d* lady. *The Falcon* 270
O my *d* son, be not unkind to me. „ 509
Giovanna, my *d* lady, in this same battle We had been beaten— „ 601
And thou too leave us, my *d* nurse, alone. „ 701
Ay, the *d* nurse will leave you alone; „ 702
Giovanna, *d* Giovanna, I that once The wildest of the random youth „ 806
D Philip, all the world is beautiful If we were happy, *Prom. of May* I 576
D Eva Was always thought the prettier. „ II 378
Wasn't *d* mother herself at least by one side a lady? „ III 300
But, O *d* friend, If thro' the want of any— „ III 549
Take it again, *d* father, *Foresters* I i 341
Sufficient for the day, *d* father! „ I i 343
And thou, *d* Little John, Who hast that worship for me „ I iii 159
thou art the very woman who waits On my *d* Marian. „ II i 103
Ah *d* Robin! ah noble captain, friend of the poor! „ II i 182
O thou unworthy brother of my *d* Marian! „ II i 538
O my *d* Marian, Is it thou? is it thou? „ II i 597
to dream that he My brother, my *d* Walter— „ II i 652
O *d* wife, we have fallen into the hands Of Robin Hood. „ III 232

Dear (*continued*) why, the silver Were *d* as gold, *Foresters* IV 42
You Much, you Scarlet, your *d* Little John, „ IV 1083
Dear-cousin Do so *d-c* and royal-cousin him, *Queen Mary* III iv 400
Dearer What voices call you *D* than mine that should be dearest to you? „ V i 38
D than when you made your mountain gay, *The Falcon* 463
Dearest not with gold, But *d* links of love. *Queen Mary* I v 539
What voices call you Dearer than mine that should be *d* to you? „ V i 38
Nay, *d* Lady, see your good physician. „ V v 58
Swear, *d* brother, I beseech thee, swear! *Harold* II ii 719
And all is safe again. O *d* lady, *The Cup* I ii 313
'*D* Dora,—I have lost myself, and am lost for ever *Prom. of May* II 83
But now that you have been brought to us as it were from the grave, *d* Eva, „ III 236
Death God save her grace; and *d* to Northumberland! *Queen Mary* I i 67
transparent hand, Damp with the sweat of *d*, „ I ii 33
Your creed will be your *d*. „ I ii 46
Fly and farewell, and let me die the *d*. „ I ii 106
when you put Northumberland to *d*, „ I v 486
another, mute as *d*, And white as her own milk; „ II ii 79
promise full Allegiance and obedience to the *d*. „ II ii 169
It roll'd as black as *d*; „ II iii 20
He'll be the *d* on us; „ II iii 102
D and the Devil—if he find I have one— „ III i 231
a pale horse for *D* and Gardiner for the Devil. „ III i 235
since your Herod's *d*, How oft hath Peter knock'd „ III ii 62
But your wise bees had stung him first to *d*. „ III iii 65
with the fear of *d* Too dead ev'n for a death-watch! „ III v 140
For there was life—And there was life in *d*— „ III v 146
bolts, That jail you from free life, bar you from *d*. „ III v 173
what think you, Is it life or *d*? „ III v 194
D would not grieve him more. „ IV i 25
thro' the fear of *d* Gave up his cause, „ IV iii 27
Queen and Council at this time Adjudge him to the *d*. „ IV iii 38
Didst thou yield up thy Son to human *d*; „ IV iii 145
some saying that may live After his *d* „ IV iii 160
For *d* gives life's last word a power to live, „ IV iii 161
Written for fear of *d*, to save my life, „ IV iii 242
I saw the *d's* of Latimer and Ridley. „ IV iii 295
—he is white as *d*. „ IV iii 559
Where he shall rest at night, moved to his *d*; „ IV iii 581
beard, which he had never shaven Since Henry's *d*, „ IV iii 594
He cried Enough! enough! before his *d*.— „ V ii 101
there is one *D* stands behind the Groom, And there is one *D* stands behind the Bride— „ V ii 165
Have you been looking at the 'Dance of *D*'? „ V ii 170
'We pray continually for the *d* Of our accursed Queen and Cardinal Pole.' „ V ii 180
lash'd to *d*, or lie Famishing in black cells, „ V ii 194
My people hate me and desire my *d*. „ V ii 345
My husband hates me, and desires my *d*. „ V ii 348
I hate myself, and I desire my *d*. „ V ii 352
that I am in state to bring forth *d*— „ V ii 593
God's *d*! and wherefore spake you not before? „ V iii 106
Then I and he will snaffle your 'God's *d*,' „ V iii 120
God's *d*, forsooth—you do not know King Philip. „ V iii 123
poor Pole pines of it, As I do, to the *d*. „ V v 130
take heed! The blade is keen as *d*. „ V v 175
As if the chamberlain were *D* himself! „ V v 204
a Tudor School'd by the shadow of *d*— „ V v 226
but stark as *d* To those that cross him.— *Harold* II ii 321
Delay is *d* to thee, ruin to England. „ II ii 717
My lord! thou art white as *d*. „ II ii 814
If this be *d*, Then our great Council wait „ III i 2
He hath swoon'd! *D*? . . . no, as yet a breath. „ III i 319
This lightning before *d* Plays on the word,— „ III i 387
fill'd the quiver, and *D* has drawn the bow— „ III i 400
It is the arrow of *d* in his own heart— „ III i 404
for *d* is *d*, or else Lifts us beyond the lie. „ III ii 79
and threaten us thence Unschool'd of *D*? „ V i 287
Two *d's* at every swing, ran in upon us „ V i 409
I am dead as *D* this day to ought of earth's Save William's *d* or mine. *Edith.* Thy *d*!— „ V i 425
our good Gurth hath smitten him to the *d*. „ V i 503

Death (*continued*) *D*!—and enough of *d* for this one day, *Harold* V ii 119
move as true with me To the door of *d*. „ V ii 186
Let me learn at full The manner of his *d*, *Becket, Pro.* 426
Strike, and I die the *d* of martyrdom; Strike, and ye set these customs by my *d* „ I iii 169
By God's *d*, thou shalt stick him like a calf! „ I iii 183
Degrade, imprison him—Not *d* for *d*. „ I iii 402
I, my liege, could swear, To *d* for *d*. „ I iii 405
King commands you, upon pain of *d*, „ I iii 753
O my life's life, not to smile Is all but *d* to me. „ II i 41
Thine—as I am—till *d*! *Rosamund.* *D*? no! „ II i 300
that merits *d*, False oath on holy cross— „ IV ii 207
running down the chase is kindlier sport Ev'n than the *d*. „ IV ii 215
dooms thee after *d* To wail in deathless flame. „ IV ii 271
not life shot up in blood, But *d* drawn in;— „ IV ii 382
'The King is sick and almost unto *d*.' „ V ii 153
Thrills to the topmost tile—no hope but *d*; „ V ii 210
They seek—you make—occasion for your *d*. „ V ii 559
Some would stand by you to the *d*. „ V ii 605
The power of life in *d* to make her free! „ V iii 100
whole world Abhor you; ye will die the *d* of dogs! „ V iii 184
Son, husband, brother gash'd to *d* in vain, *The Cup* I ii 143
keep it, or you sell me To torment and to *d*. „ I ii 216
I know they mean to torture him to *d*. „ I ii 274
Think,—torture,—*d*,—and come. „ I ii 314
Shall I go? Shall I go? *D*, torture— „ I ii 454
Stay!—too near is *d*. „ I iii 104
I am the bride of *D*, and only Marry the dead. „ II 29
Life yields to *d* and wisdom bows to Fate, „ II 89
ere two souls be knit for life and *d*, „ II 360
Would you have tortured Sinnatus to *d*? *Antonius.* No thought was mine of torture or of *d*, „ II 409
some old Greek Say *d* was the chief good? „ II 515
more than one brave fellow owed His *d* to the charm in it. *The Falcon* 635
whose cheerless Houris after *d* Are Night and Silence, *Prom. of May* I 250
'Till *d* us part'—those are the only words, „ I 658
they that love do not believe that *d* Will part them. „ I 663
better *d* With our first wail than life— „ II 290
not so much for *D* As against Life! „ II 337
My father's *d*, Let her believe it mine; „ II 453
Not all at once with *d* and him. „ II 464
the man himself, When hearing of that piteous *d*, „ II 500
but I mun git out on 'is waäy now, or I shall be the *d* on 'im. „ II 610
I have been telling her of the *d* of one Philip Edgar of Toft Hall, Somerset. „ II 706
Look there—under the *d's*. „ II 710
and that, I am sure, would be the *d* of him. „ III 167
Peace, let him be: it is the chamber of *D*! „ III 741
Laid famine-striken at the gates of *D*— „ III 808
but if you starve me I be Gaffer *D* himself. *Foresters* I i 48
I think I should have stricken him to the *d*. „ II i 141
the scritch-owl bodes *d*, my lord. „ II i 333
there is a cross line o' sudden *d*. „ II i 354
Not mortal! after *d*, if after *d*—— *Robin.* Life, life. I know not *d*. Why do you vex me With raven-croaks of *d* and after *d*? „ II i 619
I would have battled for it to the *d*. „ II i 664
And bruised him almost to the *d*, „ III 361
They strike the deer at once to *d*— „ IV 525
A thousand winters Will strip you bare as *d*, „ IV 1056
Deathbed I've been attending on his *d* and his burial. *Prom. of May* II 4
a Sister of Mercy, come from the *d-b* of a pauper, „ III 377
Death-knell Ringing their own *d-k* thro' all the realm. *Becket* I iii 172
Deathless ghosts of Luther and Zuinglius fade Into the *d* hell *Queen Mary* III ii 175
stroke that dooms thee after death To wail in *d* flame. *Becket* IV ii 272
Deathlike Yes, *d*! Dead? I dare not look: *Prom. of May* III 716
Deathly How *d* pale!—a chair, your Highness. *Queen Mary* I v 636
Death-watch Too dead ev'n for a *d-w*! „ III v 141
Debased downfallen and *d* From councillor to caitiff— „ IV iii 74
Debonair only *d* to those That follow where he leads, *Harold* II ii 319

De Brito (knight of King Henry II.'s household) (*See also* **Brito, Richard**) De Tracy—even that flint *D B.* *Becket, Pro.* 523
De Tracy and *D B*, from our castle. „ I i 278
De Broc thou, *D B*, that holdest Saltwood Castle— „ I iii 160
cursed those *D B's* That hold our Saltwood Castle „ II ii 267
Perchance the fierce *D B's* from Saltwood Castle, „ V ii 249
your friends, those ruffians, the *D B's*, „ V ii 435
And one of the *D B's* is with them, „ V ii 572
Debt Your pious wish to pay King Edward's *d's*, *Queen Mary* I v 112
Pray'd me to pay her *d's*, and keep the Faith; „ V v 257
—thou art drowned in *d*— *Becket, Pro.* 491
every bond and *d* and obligation Incurr'd as Chancellor. „ I iii 710
but the ill success of the farm, and the *d's*, *Prom. of May* II 69
I would pay My brother all his *d* *Foresters* I ii 218
For whom I ran into my *d* to the Abbot, „ II i 462
No, not an hour: the *d* is due to-day. „ IV 448
he Would pay us all the *d* at once, „ IV 485
The *d* hath not been paid. „ IV 612
Decalogue Thro' chastest honour of the *D* *Becket* V i 206
Decaying Cool as the light in old *d* wood; *Queen Mary* IV ii 5
Decent We be more like scarecrows in a field than *d* serving men; *Foresters* I i 35
Decide *d* on what was customary In olden days, *Becket* II ii 175
all the Church of France *D* on their decision, „ II ii 178
Decided Cranmer, it is *d* by the Council *Queen Mary* IV ii 25
Decision all the Church of France Decide on their *d*, *Becket* II ii 178
Deck Stand on the *d* and spread his wings for sail! *Queen Mary* I v 379
same chair, Or rather throne of purple, on the *d*. „ III ii 8
Stagger on the slope *d's* for any rough sea *Becket* II ii 106
Declaration In several bills and *d's*, *Queen Mary* IV i 48
Declare *d* our penitence and grief For our long schism „ III iii 128
Our letters of commission will *d* this plainlier. „ III iii 222
D the Queen's right to the throne; „ IV ii 78
I shall *d* to you my very faith Without all colour. „ IV iii 225
came to sue Your Council and yourself to *d* war. (repeat) „ V i 108, 116
Declared when last he wrote, *d* His comfort in your Grace „ III vi 78
As I have many a time *d* to you— *The Cup* II 48
Decline *d* The judgment of the King? *Becket* I iii 675
Decree sanction your *d* Of Tostig's banishment, *Harold* IV i 103
Deed With golden *d's* and iron strokes that brought „ II ii 47
Some said it was thy father's *d*. *Harold.* They lied. „ II ii 513
Nothing, so thy promise be thy *d*. *Becket* III iii 224
The *d's* done—Away! „ V iii 207
Deem needs must *d* This love by you return'd as heartily; *Queen Mary* II ii 196
Who *d's* it a most just and holy war. „ V i 147
Deeming *D* him one that thro' the fear of death „ IV iii 26
Deep (adj. and adv.) *D*—I shall fathom him. „ I iii 158
islands call'd into the dawning church Out of the dead, *d* night of heathendom, „ III iii 173
And crying, in his *d* voice, more than once, „ IV iii 611
strike hard and *d* into The prey they are rending from her— „ V ii 267
There thou prick'st me *d*. *Harold* II ii 424
Drink and drink *d*—our marriage will be fruitful. Drink and drink *d*, and thou wilt make me happy. *The Cup* II 380
We lie too *d* down in the shadow here. *The Falcon* 581
I only wish This pool were *d* enough, *Prom. of May* II 304
Lead us thou to some *d* glen, *Foresters* II ii 168
Deep (s) outdraught of the *d* Haul like a great strong fellow *Harold* II i 10
boughs across the *d* That dropt themselves, „ III i 151
voice of the *d* as it hollows the cliffs of the land. *Becket* II i 3
voice coming up with the voice of the *d* from the strand, „ II i 6
Love that is born of the *d* coming up with the sun from the sea. (repeat) „ II i 9, 19
And the great *d's* were broken up again, „ V iii 43
Deep-down And deeper still the *d-d* oubliette, *Harold* II ii 428
Deeper see *D* into the mysteries of heaven „ I i 200
D still. *Wulfnoth.* And *d* still the deep-down oubliette, „ II ii 427
that tempest which will set it trembling Only to base it *d*. *Becket, Pro.* 210
Deepest Sunk in the *d* pit of pauperism, *Prom. of May* III 803
Deep-incavern'd His buzzard-beak and *d-i* eyes Half fright me. *Queen Mary* I iv 266
Deer You are the stateliest *d* in all the herd— „ V ii 425
The shadows of a hundred fat red *d* *Harold* I ii 103
Buck; *d*, as you call it. *Becket* I iv 139
This Canterbury, like a wounded *d*, „ II ii 21
Huntsman, and hound, and *d* were all neck-broken! *The Cup* I ii 23
That hold by Richard, tho' they kill his *d*. *Foresters* I iii 101
The *d*, the highback'd polecat, the wild boar, „ I iii 119
true woodman's bow of the best yew-wood to slay the *d*. „ II i 393
Robin, like a *d* from a dog, „ II i 433
By all the *d* that spring Thro' wood and lawn „ III 424
Gone, like a *d* that hath escaped thine arrow! „ IV 60
What *d* when I have mark'd him ever yet Escaped „ IV 62
They strike the *d* at once to death— „ IV 525
He drove his knife into the heart of the *d*, The *d* fell dead to the bottom, „ IV 542
On nuts and acorns, ha! Or the King's *d*? „ IV 884
Deer-like Chased *d-l* up his mountains, *Harold* I ii 148
Defamed betray'd, *d*, divorced, forlorn! *Queen Mary* I v 26
Suffer not That my brief reign in England be *d* „ V ii 302
Defeat What! are thy people sullen from *d*? *Harold* IV i 2
and now but shuns The semblance of *d*; *Becket* I iii 191
Defect We hold by his defiance, not his *d*. „ II ii 218
Defective seeing they were men *D* or excessive, „ II ii 213
Nay, if they were *d* as St. Peter Denying Christ, „ II ii 215
Defence or any harm done to the people if my jest be in *d* of the Truth? „ II ii 340
And private hates with our *d* of Heaven. „ V ii 52
Spare this *d*, dear brother. „ V iii 168
Whereas in wars of freedom and *d* *The Cup* I ii 160
Defend I pray you, Do not *d* yourself. *Becket* II ii 112
Except she could *d* her innocence. *Foresters* II ii 47
I can *d* my cause against the traitors „ IV 898
Defender The great unborn *d* of the Faith, *Queen Mary* III ii 165
Till Truth herself be shamed of her *d*. *Becket* II ii 345
Defensoribus *Non* d *istis*, Walter Map. „ II ii 346
Defiance We hold by his *d*, not his defect. „ II ii 218
Defied who yet *d* the tyrant, „ II ii 216
—kinglike *D* the Pope, and, like his kingly sires, „ IV ii 440
Defy I hate thee, and despise thee, and *d* thee. *Harold* IV ii 79
Boldness out of the bottle! I *d* thee. *Foresters* IV 239
Nay, I *d* thee still. „ IV 276
Degradation scarce have spoken with you Since when?—your *d*. *Queen Mary* IV ii 120
papers by my hand Sign'd since my *d*— „ IV iii 244
What doth hard murder care For *d*? *Becket* I iii 394
Degrade and *d* the realm By seeking justice *Queen Mary* IV i 18
D, imprison him—Not death for death. *Becket* I iii 400
Degraded the courts of the Church, They but *d* him. „ *Pro.* 14
ye but *d* him Where I had hang'd him. „ I iii 391
Degree There stands a man, once of so high *d*, *Queen Mary* IV iii 69
Dei Ha—Verbum *D*—verbum—word of God! „ III i 262
Deign my nobleness Of nature, as you *d* to call it, *The Falcon* 811
Who *d* to honour this my thirtieth year, *Foresters* I ii 79
If you will *d* to tread a measure with me. „ I ii 132
Deign'd Who never *d* to shine into my palace. *The Falcon* 285
The diamonds that you never *d* to wear. „ 761
Dejiciatur Equus cum equite *D*! *Harold* V i 580
Delay *D* is death to thee, ruin to England. „ II ii 717
Delicacy repulses, the *delicacies*, the subtleties. *Becket, Pro.* 500
Delicate (*See also* **Courtly-delicate**) your hand Will be much coveted! What a *d* one! *Queen Mary* V iii 44
Be men less *d* than the Devil himself? *Harold* III i 116
I have been a lover of wines, and *d* meats, *Becket* I i 76
That's a *d* Latin lay Of Walter Map: „ V i 191
I am none of your *d* Norman maidens *Foresters* I i 212
Delicate-footed the *d-f* creature Came stepping o'er him, „ IV 535
Delight (s) comes To rob you of your one *d* on earth. *The Falcon* 828
but I Take some *d* in sketching, *Prom. of May* II 539
Delight (verb) *D* to wallow in the grossness of it, *Becket* II ii 343
Delighted Affrighted me, and then *d* me, *Queen Mary* III v 144
Deliver Do here absolve you and *d* you And every one of you, „ III iii 214
wouldst *d* Canterbury To our King's hands again, *Becket* I iii 580

Deliver (*continued*) I here *d* all this controversy Into your royal hands. *Becket* II ii 136
I might *d* all things to thy hand— „ III iii 270
Delivered 'The Queen of England is *d* of a dead dog!' *Queen Mary* III ii 219
he was *d* To the secular arm to burn; „ IV ii 213
God's grace and Holy Church *d* us. *Becket* IV ii 309
are *d* here in the wild wood an hour after noon. *Foresters* IV 509
Demand (s) then to cede A point to her *d*? *Queen Mary* III vi 170
Grant me one day To ponder these *d's*. *Becket* I iii 669
Demand (verb) I will *d* his ward From Edward *Harold* I ii 58
the King *d's* three hundred marks, *Becket* I iii 626
the King *d's* seven hundred marks, „ I iii 634
the King *d's* five hundred marks, „ I iii 641
King *D's* a strict account of all those revenues „ I iii 650
Antonius To-morrow will *d* your tribute— *The Cup* I ii 97
Demanded *d* Possession of her person and the Tower. *Queen Mary* II ii 40
Demi-Norman our dear England Is *d-N*. *Harold* III i 41
De-miracled fish, they *d-m* the miraculous draught, *Becket* III iii 124
Democracy when the tide Of full *d* has overwhelm'd This Old world, *Prom. of May* I 593
When the great *D* Makes a new world— „ I 670
De Morville (knight of the household of King Henry II.) (*See also* **Hugh**) France! Ha! *D M*, Tracy, Brito—fled is he? *Becket* I iv 198
D M, I had thought so well of you; „ V ii 519
This wanton here. *D M*, Hold her away. „ V iii 171
Den Who dragg'd the scatter'd limbs into their *d*. *Queen Mary* I v 402
hottest hold in all the devil's *d* „ V iv 15
Dares the bear slouch into the lion's *d*? *Becket* IV ii 282
Denial Treble *d* of the tongue of flesh, *Harold* III i 281
Denied Renard *d* her, Ev'n now to me. *Queen Mary* III vi 2
or more *D* the Holy Father! „ III iv 248
St. Peter in his time of fear *D* his Master, „ III iv 264
Albeit I have *d* him. „ IV ii 236
Nay, but, my Lord, he *d* purgatory. „ IV iii 629
Would not—if penitent—have *d* him *her* Forgiveness. *Prom. of May* II 496
Denis (Bishop of Paris and Patron Saint of France) St. *D*, that thou shouldst not. *Becket, Pro.* 89
By St. *D*—— *De Brito.* Ay, by St. *D*, now will he flame out, And lose his head as old St. *D* did. „ V ii 477
St. *D* of France and St. Alphege of England, „ V iii 165
Denmark the King of *D* is with us; *Queen Mary* II i 195
Dense How *d* a fold of danger nets him round, *Harold* II ii 17
Deny I *d* not to have been Your faithful friend *Queen Mary* IV i 88
against the Norseman, If thou *d* them this. *Harold* IV i 159
D not thou God's honour for a king. *Becket* II ii 424
Nay, I *d* not That I was somewhat anger'd. „ IV ii 350
Come, come, could he *d* it? What did he say? *The Cup* I ii 345
can *d* Nothing to you that you require of him. *The Falcon* 717
Denying if they were defective as St. Peter *D* Christ, *Becket* II ii 216
Depart And under his authority—I *d*. „ I iii 728
Departed And presently all rose, and so *d*. *The Falcon* 367
Depend all *d's* Upon the skill and swiftness *Queen Mary* I iii 142
All *d's* on me—Father, this poor girl, *Prom. of May* III 211
Deputation comes a *d* From our finikin fairy nation. *Foresters* II ii 144
Derwent Where lie the Norsemen? on the *D*? *Harold* IV i 253
Our day beside the *D* will not shine „ IV iii 50
Descend *D's* the ruthless Norman— „ II ii 467
And that my wife *d's* from Alfred? „ II ii 594
the second curse *D* upon thine head, „ III ii 49
Scatter thy people home, *d* the hill, „ V i 10
so *d* again with some of her ladyship's own appurtenances? *The Falcon* 416
Descending as the soul *d* out of heaven Into a body generate. *Queen Mary* IV i 35
Desert (merit) fierier than fire To yield them their *d's*. „ V iv 27
D's! Amen to what? Whose *d's*? „ V iv 30
Desert (waste) wells of Castaly are not wasted upon the *d*. *Becket, Pro.* 388
Deserve He must *d* his surname better. *Queen Mary* III ii 197
that worship for me which Heaven knows I ill *d*— *Foresters* I iii 162
Designer *See* **Dish-designer**
Desire (s) She had no *d* for that, and wrung her hands, *Queen Mary* III i 384
Desire (s) (*continued*) And hot *d* to imitate; *Queen Mary* III iv 171
Her fierce *d* of bearing him a child, „ IV iii 429
O yield them all their *d*! *The Cup* II 8
and no need Of veiling their *d's*. *Prom. of May* I 530
The love of freedom, the *d* of God, *Foresters* II i 68
Desire (verb) My people hate me and *d* my death, *Queen Mary* V ii 345
My husband hates me, and *d's* my death. „ V ii 348
I hate myself, and I *d* my death. „ V ii 351
A stranger monk *d's* access to you. *Becket* V ii 65
Desolate That *d* letter, blotted with her tears, *Prom. of May* II 475
Despair I am almost in *d*. *Queen Mary* I v 385
Shall I *d* then?—God forbid! „ IV iii 129
but O girl, girl, I am almost in *d*. *Foresters* I i 263
Despair'd I had *d* of thee—that sent me crazed. „ IV 1021
Despise Those of the wrong side will *d* the man, *Queen Mary* IV iii 25
Make us *d* it at odd hours, my Lord. „ IV iii 386
I hate thee, and *d* thee, and defy thee. *Harold* IV ii 79
Despite *d* his fearful heresies, I loved the man, *Queen Mary* IV iii 633
And *he* hath learnt, *d* the tiger in him, *Harold* I i 147
d his kingly promise given To our own self of pardon, *Becket* II ii 431
Despondency When left alone in my *d*, *Queen Mary* IV ii 95
Destiny Moved in the iron grooves of *D*? Remorse then is a part of *D*, *Prom. of May* II 267
Destroy We come not to *d*, but edify; *Queen Mary* III iii 188
Take heed, lest he *d* thee utterly. *Becket* I iii 13
Wilt thou *d* the Church in fighting for it, „ I iii 36
Desuetude wholesome usages, Lost in *d*, „ I iii 413
Determine Your courts of justice will *d* that. *Queen Mary* II iv 131
Dethrone Arise against her and *d* the Queen— „ I iii 91
De Tracy (Sir William, knight of the household of King Henry II.) (*See also* **Tracy**) *D T*—even that flint De Brito. *Becket, Pro.* 522
D T and De Brito, from our castle. „ I i 278
Deum bells must ring; Te *D's* must be sung; *Queen Mary* III ii 211
Deus Jacta tonitrua *D* bellator! *Harold* V i 570
Fulmina, fulmina *D* vastator! „ V i 574
Device put some fresh *d* in lieu of it— *Queen Mary* III i 268
but follow'd the *d* of those Her nearest kin: „ III i 379
Devil (*See also* **Dare-devil, Divil**) has offer'd her his son Philip, the Pope and the *D*. „ I i 106
all Your trouble to the dogstar and the *d*. „ I iv 292
His foes—the *D* had suborn'd 'em, „ I v 626
ordnance On the White Tower and on the *D's* Tower, „ II iii 44
Philip had been one of those black *d's* of Spain, „ III i 215
that every Spaniard carries a tale like a *d* „ III i 224
Death and the *D*—if he find I have one— „ III i 231
a pale horse for Death and Gardiner for the *D*. „ III i 235
Not for the seven *d's* to enter in? „ III ii 140
d take all boots were ever made Since man went barefoot. „ III v 197
Or to be still in pain with *d's* in hell; „ IV iii 222
With all his *d's* doctrines; „ IV iii 278
Pole Will tell you that the *d* helpt them thro' it. „ IV iii 352
give the *D* his due, I never found he bore me any spite „ V ii 472
I were whole *d* if I wrong'd you, Madam. „ V iii 6
hottest hold in all the *d's* den „ V iv 15
wrath of Heaven hath three tails, The *d* only one. *Harold* I i 62
Fishermen? *d's*! Who, while ye fish for men with your false fires, Let the great *D* fish for your own souls. „ II i 29
Like Jonah, than have known there were such *d's*. „ II i 39
would make the hard earth rive To the very *D's* horns, „ II ii 741
Be men less delicate than the *D* himself? I thought that naked Truth would shame the *D* The *D* is so modest. „ III i 117
A lying *d* Hath haunted me— „ V i 317
Ye haled this tonsured *d* into your courts; *Becket* I iii 387
Forty thousand marks! forty thousand *d's*— „ I iv 91
Saving the *D's* honour, his yes and no. „ II ii 142
if this *if* be like the *D's* '*if* Thou wilt fall down and worship me.' „ III iii 285
O *d*, can I free her from the grave? „ V i 185
Down to the *d* with this bond that beggars me! *Foresters* I i 340
By all the *d's* in and out of Hell! „ II ii 27
proud priests, and these Barons, *D's*, „ III 127
And wake the *D*, and I may sicken by 'em. „ III 325

Devil (*continued*) by all the saints and all the *d's* ye shall dance. *Foresters* IV 553
Or, like the *D's* they are, straight up from Hell. „ IV 594
Devilish all of us abhor The venomous, bestial, *d* revolt Of Thomas Wyatt. *Queen Mary* II ii 287
Devilry What game, what juggle, what *d* are you playing? *Becket* V i 153
Devilstow Into Godstow, into Hellstow, *D*! „ V i 215
Devon (County) Were I in *D* with my wedded bride, *Queen Mary* I iv 119
Carew stirs In *D*: „ II i 6
should be in *D* too. „ II i 11
Devon (Earl of) (*See also* **Courtenay**) Courtenay, to be made Earl of *D*, „ I i 111
Good-day, my Lord of *D*; „ I iii 95
What are you musing on, my Lord of *D*? „ I iv 27
This dress was made me as the Earl of *D* To take my seat in; „ I iv 73
A Courtenay of *D*, and her cousin. „ I iv 86
Was that my Lord of *D*? do not you Be seen in corners with my Lord of *D*. „ I iv 152
What was my Lord of *D* telling you? „ I iv 183
This comes of parleying with my Lord of *D*. „ I iv 252
But our young Earl of *D*— *Mary.* Earl of *D*? I freed him from the Tower, placed him at Court; I made him Earl of *D*, and—the fool— „ I v 161
My Lord of *D* is a pretty man. „ I v 614
and party thereunto, My Lord of *D*. „ II iv 101
not now and save the life Of *D*: „ II iv 124
could have wedded that poor youth, My Lord of *D*— „ V ii 477
Lord *D*, girls! what are you whispering here? „ V ii 485
Devour run in upon her and *d* her, one and all *Becket, Pro.* 525
Dew To those three children like a pleasant *d*. *Queen Mary* IV iii 92
Is God's best *d* upon the barren field. „ V i 102
Vying a tear with our cold *d's*, *Harold* V i 151
hath the fire in her face and the *d* in her eyes. *Foresters* I i 167
Found him dead and drench'd in *d*, „ II ii 147
Dewy I Shall see the *d* kiss of dawn no more *Harold* II ii 331
Diadem He sends you This *d* of the first Galatian Queen, *The Cup* II 132
tell him That I accept the *d* of Galatia— „ II 158
Diagonalise if he move at all, Heaven stay him, is fain to *d*. *Herbert.* *D*! thou art a word-monger. Our Thomas never will *d*. Thou art a jester and a verse-maker. *D*! *Becket* II ii 330
Dialectic with his charm of simple style And close *d*, *Prom. of May* I 225
Diamond (adj.) if we *will* buy *d* necklaces To please our lady, *The Falcon* 44
Diamond (s) set it round with gold, with pearl, with *d*. *Queen Mary* I v 376
Some six or seven Bishops, *d's*, pearls, „ III i 52
A *d*, And Philip's gift, as proof of Philip's love, „ III i 66
on his neck a collar, Gold, thick with *d's*; „ III i 80
Cut with a *d*; so to last like truth. „ III v 25
Not ev'n the central *d*, worth, I think, *Becket* V i 164
Dare beg him to receive his *d's* back— *The Falcon* 262
Then I require you to take back your *d's*— „ 720
But have you ever worn my *d's*? „ 737
The *d's* that you never deign'd to wear. „ 761
I cannot keep your *d's*, for the gift I ask for, „ 776
These *d's* are both yours and mine— „ 903
Diamond-dance ripples twinkled at their *d-d*, *Queen Mary* III ii 10
Dian Behold a pretty *D* of the wood, *Foresters* III 267
Diana Our Artemis Has vanquish'd their *D*. *The Cup* II 457
Dickon here's little *D*, and little Robin, and little Jenny— *Queen Mary* II iii 112
This paper, *D*. I found it fluttering at the palace gates:— „ III ii 217
Die Fly and farewell, and let me *d* the death. „ I ii 106
order with all heretics That it shall be, before I *d*, „ I v 35
D like the torn fox dumb, „ II ii 331
I live and *d* The true and faithful bride of Philip— „ II iv 42
or *d* with those That are no cowards and no Courtenays. „ II iv 86
And Lady Jane had left us. *Mary.* They shall *d*. *Renard.* And your so loving sister? *Mary.* She shall *d*. *Queen Mary* II iv 140
Did not Lord Suffolk *d* like a true man? „ III i 164
Did you see her *d*? „ III i 344
said she was condemn'd to *d* for treason; „ III i 377
light of this new learning wanes and *d's*: „ III ii 173
That if the Queen should *d* without a child, „ III iii 74

Die (*continued*) Thou knowest we had to dodge, or duck, or *d*; *Queen Mary* III iv 358
To sing, love, marry, churn, brew, bake, and *d*, „ III v 112
says she will live And *d* true maid— „ III vi 46
Did not More *d*, and Fisher? he must burn. „ IV i 52
and hide himself and *d*; „ IV i 143
—they give the poor who *d*. „ IV ii 53
Ay—gentle as they call you—live or *d*? „ IV ii 162
Fire—inch by inch to *d* in agony! „ IV ii 223
Stand watching a sick beast before he *d's*? „ IV iii 8
Yet—It is expedient for one man to *d*, Yea, for the people, lest the people *d*. Yet wherefore should he *d* that hath return'd „ IV iii 17
therefore he must *d*, For warning and example. „ IV iii 51
Hurls his soil'd life against the pikes and *d's*. „ IV iii 312
howsoever hero-like the man *D's* in the fire, „ IV iii 325
And you saw Latimer and Ridley *d*? „ IV iii 328
Did he *d* bravely? Tell me that, or leave All else untold. „ IV iii 568
To sleep, to *d*—I shall *d* of it, cousin. „ V ii 127
I may *d* Before I read it. Let me see him at once. „ V ii 549
Make me full fain to live and *d* a maid. „ V iii 98
Nay! Better *d* than lie! *Harold* I i 158
Better *d* than lie! „ II ii 281
Forgive me, brother, I will live here and *d*. „ II ii 804
better *d* Than credit this, for death is death, „ III ii 78
Blaze like a night of fatal stars on those Who read their doom and *d*. „ IV i 252
till *her* voice *D* with the world. „ IV iii 76
To tell thee thou shalt *d* on Senlac hill— „ V i 241
I shall *d*—I *d* for England then, who lived for England—What nobler? men must *d*. „ V i 267
live or *d*, I would I were among them! „ V i 463
honeymoon is the gall of love; he *d's* of his honeymoon. *Becket, Pro.* 365
old men must *d*, or the world would grow mouldy, „ *Pro.* 409
Lo! I must out or *d*. *Becket.* Or out *and d*. „ I i 268
For we would live and *d* for thee, my lord, „ I ii 16
Strike, and I *d* the death of martyrdom; „ I iii 168
—there to beg, starve, *d*— „ II i 75
you still move against him, you may have no less than to *d* for it; „ III iii 326
To *d* for it—I live to *d* for it, I *d* to live for it. The State will *d*, the Church can never *d*. The King's not like to *d* for that which *d's*; But I must *d* for that which never *d's*. „ III iii 334
I am not so happy I could not *d* myself, „ IV ii 87
I am to *d* then, tho' there stand beside thee „ IV ii 228
both of us will *d*, And I will fly with my sweet boy „ IV ii 236
I will go live and *d* in Aquitaine. (repeat) „ V i 109, 142
The chances of his life, just ere he *d's*. „ V ii 274
foremost of their files, who *d* For God, „ V ii 495
I am prepared to *d*. „ V ii 562
The best of all not all-prepared to *d*. „ V ii 564
D with him, and be glorified together. „ V iii 31
And *d* upon the Patriarchal throne Of all my predecessors? „ V iii 75
whole world Abhor you; ye will *d* the death of dogs! „ V iii 184
—fight out the good fight—*d* Conqueror. „ V iii 190
I'd sooner *d* than do it. *The Cup* I ii 224
A woman I could live and *d* for. What! *D* for a woman, what new faith is this? „ I iii 65
I will be faithful to thee till thou *d*. „ II 330
to live And *d* together. „ II 444
Thy breed will *d* with thee, and mine with me: *The Falcon* 18
The boy may *d*: more blessed were the rags „ 850
Than all my childless wealth, if mine must *d*. „ 856
She had to *d* for it—she died for you. „ 877
'Let us eat and drink, for to-morrow we *d*.' *Prom. of May* I 260
I shall go mad for utter shame and *d*. „ I 682
And poor old father not *d* miserable. „ I 722
My five-years' anger cannot *d* at once, „ II 463
and father Will not *d* miserable.' „ II 660
Go back to him and ask his forgiveness before he *d's*.— „ III 402
I would almost *d* to have it! *Dora.* And he may *d* before he gives it; „ III 405

Die (*continued*) *d*, and make the soil For Cæsars, Cromwells, *Prom. of May* III 591
lanker than an old horse turned out to *d* on the common. *Foresters* I i 52
O Lord, I will live and *d* for King Richard— .. I ii 37
I am outlaw'd, and if caught, I *d*. .. I iii 163
But if you follow me, you may *d* with me. .. I iii 166
We will live and *d* with thee, (repeat) .. I iii 168
That we would *d* for a Queen— .. III 444
and if thou prick me there I shall *d*. .. IV 570
Carry her off, and let the old man *d*. .. IV 677
He *d's* who dares to touch thee. .. IV 734
Died doubtless you can tell me how she *d*? *Queen Mary* III i 357
And Thy most blessed Son's, who *d* for man. .. IV iii 154
he *d* As manfully and boldly, and, 'fore God, .. IV iii 342
Until they *d* of rotted limbs; .. IV iii 445
My Lord, he *d* most bravely. .. IV iii 570
Ay, and with him who *d* Alone in Italy. .. V ii 507
caught a chill in the lagoons of Venice, And *d* in Padua. *Mary*. *D* in the true faith? .. V ii 516
That she would see your Grace before she—*d*. .. V iii 105
or Knut who coming Dane *D* English. *Harold* IV iii 56
Drink to the dead who *d* for us, the living Who fought and would have *d*, „ IV iii 69
ran in upon us And *d* so, „ V i 411
remembering One who *d* for thee, *Becket* II i 307
Only my best bower-maiden *d* of late, „ III i 68
She *d* of leprosy. „ V ii 268
I had once A boy who *d* a babe; *The Cup* I ii 149
To me, tho' all your bloom has *d* away, *The Falcon* 468
She had to die for it—she *d* for you, „ 877
Oh, yes, indeed, I would have *d* for you. *Prom. of May* I 714
pauper, who had *d* in his misery blessing God, .. III 378
when the mistress *d*, and I appealed to the Sister again, „ III 393
we have certain news he *d* in prison. *Foresters* IV 778
Dies Illa Their '*d I*,' which will test their sect. *Queen Mary* III iv 428
Dies Iræ Their hour is hard at hand, their '*d I*,' „ III iv 426
Differing where the man and the woman, only *d* as the stronger and the weaker, *Prom. of May* III 190
Dig Or I will *d* thee with my dagger. *Queen Mary* II iii 96
And *d* it from the root for ever. *Becket* IV ii 77
Dilated Seem'd thro' that dim *d* world of hers, *Queen Mary* II ii 324
Dim (adj.) Seem'd thro' that *d* dilated world of hers, .. II ii 324
You droop in your *d* London. .. V ii 609
Mine eyes are *d*: what hath she written? read. .. V v 1
Well—is not that the course of Nature too, From the *d* dawn of Being— *Prom. of May* I 281
Dim (verb) Rather than *d* the splendour of his crown *Becket* V ii 343
Dimple silver Were dear as gold, the wrinkle as the *d*. *Foresters* IV 43
Dine there wur an owld lord a-cum to *d* wi' un, *Queen Mary* IV iii 504
'I wunt *d*,' says my Lord Bishop, „ IV iii 507
He wishes you to *d* along with us, *Prom. of May* I 618
Stay, *D* with my brethren here, *Foresters* IV 346
bonds From these three men, and let them *d* with us, .. IV 963
By Mahound I could *d* with Beelzebub! .. IV 971
there's yet one other: I will not *d* without him. .. IV 996
Dined let that wait till we have *d*. .. IV 992
Dingle And loves and dotes on every *d* of it. .. IV 390
Dining-hall Carry fresh rushes into the *d-h*, .. I i 81
Dinner (*See also* **After-dinner**) and a wur so owld a couldn't bide vor his *d*, *Queen Mary* IV iii 506
'Now,' says the Bishop, says he, 'we'll gwo to *d*;' „ IV iii 513
thou must dash us down Our *d* from the skies. *The Falcon* 154
his falcon Ev'n wins his *d* for him in the field. „ 231
fur he'll gie us a big *d*, *Prom. of May* I 9
there wudn't be a *d* for nawbody, and I should ha' lost the pig. „ I 149
the farming men 'ull hev their *d* i' the long barn, „ I 166
Why if Steer han't haxed schoolmaster to *d*, „ I 185
and we'll git 'im to speechify for us arter *d*. „ I 440
his monies, his oxen, his *d's*, himself. *Foresters* I i 234
I love my *d*—but I can fast, I can fast; „ I ii 64
Bitters before *d*, my lady, to give you a relish. „ III 434
he that pays not for his *d* must fight for it. „ IV 200
thou fight at quarterstaff for thy *d* with our Robin, „ IV 208
So now which way to the *d*? „ IV 972
Diocese He'll burn a *d* to prove his orthodoxy. *Queen Mary* III iv 353
Wasted our *d*, outraged our tenants, *Becket* V ii 431
Dip A lake that *d's* in William As well as Harold. *Harold* V i 186
Dipping Have I been *d* into this again *Prom. of May* I 292
Dipt *d* your sovereign head Thro' these low doors, *The Falcon* 866
Directed Half a score of them, all *d* to me— *Prom. of May* II 722
Dirty as I hate the *d* gap in the face of a Cistercian monk, *Becket* II ii 381
Disaffected The *d*, heretics, reformers, Look to you *Queen Mary* I iv 170
Disappear my voice Is martyr'd mute, and this man *d's*, *Becket* III iii 350
Disappear'd She has *d*, They told me, from the farm— *Prom. of May* ii 406
She has *d*, poor darling, from the world— „ II 409
Disappointment *D*, Ingratitude, Injustice, Evil-tongue, *Queen Mary* V ii 154
Dis-archbishop after that, We had to *d-a* and unlord, „ IV ii 128
Disarm Is it not easy to *d* a woman? *The Cup* I iii 106
Disastrous And fared so ill in this *d* world. *Queen Mary* V ii 344
Discipline *d's* that clear the spiritual eye, *Becket* V i 42
Disconsolate I pray you be not so *d*; *Queen Mary* V ii 129
Discontent Hath made *me* king of all the *d* *Foresters* II i 87
Discourage to *d* and lay lame The plots of France, *Queen Mary* V i 187
Discourtesy I shall remember this *D*. *Becket* I i 239
Discrown Who did *d* thine husband, unqueen thee? *Harold* IV i 193
Disdain (*See also* **Self-disdain**) for I much *d* thee, but if ever Thou see me clasp *Foresters* II ii 74
Diseased Old, miserable, *d*, Incapable of children. *Queen Mary* V v 178
Disgrace Their Graces, our *d's*! God confound them! .. III i 414
Disgraced Thou hast *d* me and attainted me, .. III ii 54
Why do you so my-lord me, Who am *d*? „ IV ii 177
D, dishonour'd!—not by them, „ IV ii 200
Disguise (s) No! the *d* was perfect. Let's away. „ I iii 178
The monk's *d* thou gavest me for my bower: *Becket* V ii 93
Shall I be known? is my *d* perfect? *Foresters* I ii 18
Disguise (verb) *D* me—thy gown and thy coif. „ II i 186
Disguised I am ill *d*. *Queen Mary* III i 33
Ay, but you go *d*. *Becket* I i 297
Thou art no old woman—thou art *d*— *Foresters* II i 410
this is Maid Marian Flying from John—*d*. „ II i 680
Dish which cannot tell A good *d* from a bad, *Becket*, *Pro.* 106
Ye have eaten of my *d* and drunken of my cup for a dozen years. .. I iv 29
King would act servitor and hand a *d* to his son; .. III iii 139
She broke my head on Tuesday with a *d*. *Foresters* I iii 134
Dish-designer A *d-d*, and most amorous *Becket*, *Pro.* 99
Dishonour (s) —did *D* to our wives. *The Cup* I ii 184
willing wives enough To feel *d*, honour. „ I ii 189
courteous for aught I know Whose life is one *d*. „ I ii 194
Thro' that *d* which you brought upon us, *Prom. of May* III 765
Dishonour (verb) you that *d* The daughters and wives of your own faction— *Foresters* IV 697
Dishonour'd Disgraced, *d*!—not by them, *Queen Mary* IV ii 200
old man, Seven-fold *d* even in the sight Of thine own sectaries— „ V v 133
I have not *d* thee—I trust I have not; *Becket* I i 354
Dislocation And lamed and maim'd to *d*, „ IV ii 267
Disloyal Yet there be some *d* Catholics, *Queen Mary* III iv 42
Disobedience and grief For our long schism and *d*, „ III iii 129
Disobey and that you might not seem To *d* his Holiness. „ V ii 53
Dispense the Pope could *d* with his Cardinalate, „ I i 127
Displace Place and *d* our councillors, „ II ii 160
Displease sheathe your swords, ye will *d* the King. *Becket* I iii 179
For whatsoever may *d* him— „ II ii 162
Something that would *d* me. „ III i 245
If the phrase 'Return' *d* you, we will say— *The Falcon* 729
Dispoped From one whom they *d*? *Harold* III i 107
Dispossessed thou art *d* of all thy lands, goods, and chattels; *Foresters* I iii 59
Disruption shake the North With earthquake and *d*— *Harold* I ii 200
Dissemble *D* not; play the plain Christian man. *Queen Mary* IV iii 267
I *did d*, but the hour has come For utter truth and plainness; „ IV iii 272
Dissembler Liar! *d*! traitor! to the fire! „ IV iii 259
Dissoluteness our John By his Norman arrogance and *d*, *Foresters* II i 85
Dissolved The bond between the kingdoms be *d*; *Queen Mary* III iii 77
The worldly bond between us is *d*, *Becket* I i 347

Dissonance The weakness and the *d* of our clans. *The Cup* I i 23
Distance in the eternal *d* To settle on the Truth. *Harold* III ii 102
our prophet hopes Let in the happy *d*, *The Cup* I ii 414
This poor, flat, hedged-in field—no *d*— *Prom. of May* II 344
what full hands, may be Waiting you in the *d*? „ II 511
Distaste Philip with a glance of some *d*, *Queen Mary* III i 99
Distracted I could hate her for it But that she is *d*. *The Cup* II 179
Distress Queen in that *d* Sent Cornwallis and Hastings *Queen Mary* II ii 30
Distrust Philip and Mary! *Gardiner.* I *d* thee. „ III i 310
Disturb no more feuds *D* our peaceful vassalage to Rome. *The Cup* II 71
Disturbance such brawls and loud *d's* In England, *Becket* V ii 352
Loud *d's*! Oh, ay—the bells rang out „ V ii 362
Ditch hog hath tumbled himself into some corner, Some *d*, „ I i 371
Divers *D* honest fellows, The Duke of Suffolk lately freed from prison, *Queen Mary* I iii 119
hath trespassed against the king in *d* manners, *Foresters* I iii 64
Diverse But Janus-faces looking *d* ways. *Queen Mary* III ii 75
Divide that do *d* The world of nature; „ III v 120
God gave us to *d* us from the wolf! *Harold* IV iii 101
moon *D's* the whole long street with light and shade. *Becket* I i 365
D me from the mother church of England, My Canterbury. „ V ii 360
Divided (tho' some say they be much *d*) *Queen Mary* I i 79
so this unhappy land, long *d* in itself, „ I iii 21
Like our Council, Your city is *d*. „ II ii 60
So I say Your city is *d*, „ II ii 99
Dividing *See* **Sharp-dividing**
Divil (devil) niver 'a been talkin' haäfe an hour wi' the *d* 'at killed her oän sister, *Prom. of May* II 604
we'd as lief talk o' the *D* afoor ye as 'im, „ III 130
you'll set the *D's* Tower a-spitting, *Queen Mary* II iii 102
Division With earthquake and disruption—some *d*— *Harold* I ii 201
Divorce lie Of good Queen Catharine's *d*— *Queen Mary* III iv 232
when I forget Her foul *d*—my sainted mother—No!— „ IV i 81
when the King's *d* was sued at Rome, „ IV iii 41
Divorced (adj.) Cast off, betray'd, defamed, *d*, forlorn! „ I v 26
Divorced (verb) I, that thro' the Pope *d* King Louis, *Becket* IV ii 417
you *d* Queen Catharine and her father; *Queen Mary* I ii 56
Dizzied *See* **Brain-dizzied**
Dizziness you were sick in Flanders, cousin. *Pole.* A *d*. *Queen Mary* III ii 35
Dizzying I have a *d* headache. Let me rest. *Becket* V i 88
Doat Should we so *d* on courage, were it commoner? *Queen Mary* II ii 339
not old enough To *d* on one alone. *The Cup* I iii 70
Doated And how you *d* on him then! *Becket* III i 16
Dobbins (Edgar's mistake for Dobson) *D*, I think. *Dobson.* *D*, you thinks; *Prom. of May* I 459
that *D*, is it, With whom I used to jar? „ II 612
May not this *D*, or some other, spy Edgar in Harold? „ II 673
D, I think. *Dobson.* I beänt *D*. „ II 699
My name is Harold. Good day, *D*! „ II 727
Naäy, but 'Good daäy, *D*.' „ II 732
'Good daäy, *D*.' Dang tha! „ II 742
Dobson (a farmer) (*See also* **Dobbins**) I'm coming down, Mr. *D*. „ I 46
In Cumberland, Mr. *D*. „ I 66
Getting better, Mr. *D*. „ I 69
The owd man be heighty to-daäy, beänt he? *Dora.* Yes, Mr. *D*. „ I 78
Where do they blow, Mr. *D*? „ I 88
What, Mr. *D*? A butcher's frock? „ I 93
Perhaps, Master *D*. I can't tell, „ I 114
Master *D*, did you hear what I said? „ I 171
Very likely, Mr. *D*. She *will* break fence. „ I 193
Nor I either, Mr. *D*. „ I 237
But I have Mr. *D*. It's the old Scripture text, „ I 258
D. *Edgar.* Good day, then, *D*. „ I 298
'Good daäy then, *D*!' Civil-spoken i'deed! „ I 300
You never find one for me, Mr. *D*. „ I 306
Beänt there house-breäkers down in Littlechester, *D*— „ I 389
Yes, Mr. *D*, I've been attending on his deathbed „ II 3
Hesn't he left ye nowt? *Dora.* No, Mr. *D*. „ II 8
Cannot you understand plain words, Mr. *D*? „ II 113
That is enough, Farmer *D*. „ II 118
you would still have been Farmer *D*. „ II 122
Dobson (a farmer) (*continued*) 'Farmer *D*!' Well, I be Farmer *D*; but I thinks Farmer *D's* dog *Prom. of May* II 124
Farmer *D*! I be Farmer *D*, sewer anew; „ II 135
why then I beänt Farmer *D*, but summun else— „ II 139
an' owd *D* should be glad on it. „ II 146
fur owd *D* 'll gi'e us a bit o' supper. *Sally.* I weänt goä to owd *D*; „ II 216
Owd Steer gi'es nubbut cowd tea to '*is* men, and owd *D* gi'es beer. *Sally.* But I'd like owd Steer's cowd tea better nor *D's* beer. „ II 225
when owd *D* coom'd upo' us? „ II 232
Sally Allen, you worked for Mr. *D*, didn't you? „ III 102
Farmer *D*, were I to marry him, has promised „ III 168
Mr. *D* telled me to saäy he's browt some of Miss Eva's roses „ III 345
This *D* of your idyll? „ III 563
Doctor Or a high-dropsy, as the *d's* call it. *Queen Mary* III ii 225
the *d's* tell you, At three-score years; „ III iv 408
Ay, ay, but mighty *d's* doubted there. „ IV i 83
Tell them to fly for a *d*. *Prom. of May* III 712
Doctrine hatred of the *d's* Of those who rule, *Queen Mary* III iv 159
and retract That Eucharistic *d* in your book. „ IV ii 81
With all his devil's *d's*; „ IV iii 278
Dodge Thou knowest we had to *d*, or duck, or die; „ III iv 357
And see you, we shall have to *d* again, „ III iv 360
Doe I found this white *d* wandering thro' the wood, *Foresters* II i 95
Dofft For he, when having *d* the Chancellor's robe— *Becket* I iii 454
Dog (*See also* **House-dog**) as a mastiff *d* May love a puppy cur for no more reason *Queen Mary* I iv 194
And rolls himself in carrion like a *d*. „ I v 169
boil'd, buried alive, worried by *d's*; „ II i 211
'The Queen of England is delivered of a dead *d*!' „ III ii 220
sends His careful *d* to bring them to the fold. „ III iv 105
if a mad *d* bit your hand, my Lord, „ III iv 204
Like *d's* that set to watch their master's gate, „ III iv 309
The *d* that snapt the shadow, dropt the bone.— *Harold* I ii 188
play the note Whereat the *d* shall howl and run, „ I ii 192
d, with thy lying lights Thou hast betray'd us „ II i 21
—*d's'* food thrown upon thy head. „ II ii 431
Better to be a liar's *d*, and hold My master honest, „ III i 124
Old *d*, Thou art drunk, old *d*! „ IV iii 163
Good *d's*, my liege, well train'd, *Becket, Pro.* 119
a feeder Of *d's* and hawks, and apes, and lions, „ I i 80
may I come in with my poor friend, my *d*? „ I iv 94
The *d* followed his calling, my lord. „ I iv 97
Better thy *d* than thee. The King's courts would use thee worse than thy *d*— „ I iv 101
Who misuses a *d* would misuse a child— „ I iv 109
Away, *d*! *Beggar.* And I was bit by a mad *d* o' Friday, an' I be half *d* „ I iv 216
Shame fall on those who gave it a *d's* name— „ II i 141
Let either cast him away like a dead *d*! „ II ii 257
The *d* I cramm'd with dainties worried me! „ V i 244
whole world Abhor you; ye will die the death of *d's*! „ V iii 184
two-legg'd *d's* Among us who can smell a true occasion, *The Cup* I ii 112
Adulterous *d*! *Synorix.* What! will you have it? „ I iii 108
'Adulterous *d*!' that red-faced rage at me! „ I iii 122
Farmer Dobson's *d* 'ud ha' knaw'd better nor to cast *Prom. of May* II 126
and we be *d's* that have only the bones, *Foresters* I i 25
Robin, like a deer from a *d*, „ II i 433
if we kill a stag, our *d's* have their paws cut off, „ IV 225
Dog-Dons These black *d*-*D* Garb themselves bravely. *Queen Mary* III i 189
Dogma Whose *d's* I have reach'd: „ IV ii 212
they swarm into the fire Like flies—for what? no *d*. „ V ii 112
Dogstar and all Your trouble to the *d* and the devil. „ I iv 292
Doin' it be the Lord's *d*, noän o' mine; *Prom. of May* III 49
Doing (part.) (*See also* **A-doing**) for *d* that His father whipt him into *d*— *Queen Mary* I v 62
O brother, What art thou *d* here? *Harold* IV ii 4
The Norman, What is he *d*? „ V i 218
What art *thou d* here among the dead? „ V ii 32
Doing (s) (*See also* **Doin'**) Whose *d's* are a horror to the east, A hissing in the west!' *Becket* IV ii 244
Dolefully then what is it That makes you talk so *d*? *Prom. of May* III 572
Doll some waxen *d* Thy baby eyes have rested on, *Queen Mary* I v 8

Doll-face A *d-f* blanch'd and bloodless, *Becket* iv ii 175
Domed gulf and flatten in her closing chasm *D* cities, hear. *The Cup* ii 301
Domine Illorum, *D*, Scutum scindatur! *Harold* v i 508
Illos trucida, *D*. „ v i 515
Dominion realm Of England, and *d's* of the same, *Queen Mary* iii iii 117
all the realm And its *d's* from all heresy, „ iii iii 216
To leave the Pope *d* in the West. *Harold* v i 23
Don Carlos *See* **Carlos**
Doom (s) some great *d* when God's just hour Peals— *Queen Mary* i iv 261
Into the deathless hell which is their *d* „ iii iii 175
And by the churchman's pitiless *d* of fire, „ iii iv 49
Reversed his *d*, and that you might not seem „ v ii 51
Hapless *d* of woman happy in betrothing! „ v ii 364
mean The *d* of England and the wrath of Heaven? *Harold* i i 46
War there, my son? is that the *d* of England? „ i i 125
Why not the *d* of all the world as well? „ i i 127
Crying 'the *d* of England,' and at once He stood „ iii i 134
along the highest crying 'The *d* of England!'— „ iii i 157
Blaze like a night of fatal stars on those Who read their *d* and die. „ iv i 252
And bide the *d* of God. „ v i 61
If I fall, I fall—The *d* of God! „ v i 136
And not on thee—nor England—fall God's *d*! „ v i 371
And front the *d* of God. „ v i 436
the man shall seal, Or I will seal his *d*. *Becket* i iii 331
Dark as my *d*— „ iii i 282
To draw you and your husband to your *d*. *The Cup* i ii 223
thy *d* and mine—Thou—coming my way too— „ ii 490
Doom (verb) stroke that *d's* thee after death To wail *Becket* iv ii 270
Doomsday (adj.) Were the great trumpet blowing *d* dawn, *Harold* v i 227
Doomsday (s) Till *d* melt it. *Queen Mary* iii v 51
Door (*See also* **Hall-door, In-door, Within-door**) The traitor husband dangled at the *d*, „ iii i 10
hath the *d* Shut on him by the father whom he loved, „ v ii 121
tell the cooks to close The *d's* of all the offices below. „ v v 117
arm'd men Ever keep watch beside my chamber *d*, *Harold* ii ii 245
clench'd their pirate hides To the bleak church *d's*, „ iv iii 37
move as true with me To the *d* of death. „ v ii 186
I saw that *d* Close even now upon the woman. *Becket* i i 202
when he hears a *d* open in the house and thinks 'the master.' „ iii iii 98
Thro' all closed *d's* a dreadful whisper crept „ v ii 88
No, look! the *d* is open: let him be. „ v ii 315
Battering the *d's*, and breaking thro' the walls? „ v ii 626
Shut the *d's*! We will not have him slain „ v iii 53
Fly, fly, my lord, before they burst the *d's*! „ v iii 57
Undo the *d's*: the church is not a castle: „ v iii 62
Take thou this cup and leave it at her *d's*. *The Cup* i i 68
In the gray dawn before the Temple *d's*. „ i ii 295
this *d* Opens upon the forest! Out, begone! „ i ii 328
His own true people cast him from their *d's* „ i ii 352
close not yet the *d* upon a night That looks half day. „ i ii 387
Fling wide the *d's* and let the new-made children „ ii 163
She—close the Temple *d*. Let her not fly. „ ii 460
and dipt your sovereign head Thro' these low *d's*, *The Falcon* 868
Push'd from all *d's* as if we bore the plague, *Prom. of May* iii 804
As Wealth walk'd in at the *d*. *Foresters* i i 151
Poverty crept thro' the *d*. „ i i 157
Not while the rivulet babbles by the *d*, „ i ii 322
open, or I will drive the *d* from the door-post. „ ii i 220
Why did ye keep us at the *d* so long? „ ii i 224
Door-post open, or I will drive the door from the *d-p*. „ ii i 220
I will fasten thee to thine own *d-p* „ ii i 403
Doorway when every *d* blush'd, Dash'd red *Becket* i iii 346
Dora (daughter of Farmer Steer) (*See also* **Dora Steer**)
an' Miss *D*, an' Miss Eva, an' all! *Prom. of May* i 11
Miss *D* be coomed back, then? „ i 12
Blessings on your pretty voice, Miss *D*. „ i 64
Theer be redder blossoms nor them, Miss *D*. „ i 86
Under your eyes, Miss *D*. „ i 89
Noä, Miss *D*; as blue as— (repeat) „ i 95, 99
He'll be arter you now, Miss *D*. „ i 119
And I tells ye what, Miss *D*: he's no respect for the Queen, „ i 131
I thank you for that, Miss *D*, onyhow. „ i 158
Dora (daughter of Farmer Steer) (*continued*) They say your sister, *D*, has return'd, *Prom. of May* i 546
Oh, *D*, *D*, how long you have been away from home! „ i 767
So the owd uncle i' Coomberland be deäd, Miss *D*, .. ii 2
Not like me, Miss *D*; and I ha' browt these roses to ye— .. ii 13
and now she be gone, will ye täake 'em, Miss *D*? .. ii 21
an' weänt ye täake 'em now, Miss *D*, .. ii 41
I feel sewer, Miss *D*, that I ha' been noän too sudden wi' you, „ ii 60
'Dearest *D*,—I have lost myself, .. ii 83
Are you—you are—that *D*, The sister. .. ii 363
Miss *D*, Dan Smith's cart hes runned ower a läady .. ii 567
What feller wur it as 'a' been a-talkin' fur häafe an hour wi' my *D*? .. ii 576
a-pläayin' the säame gäame wi' my *D*— „ ii 591
—a daughter of the fields, This *D*! „ ii 624
if ye be goin' to sarve our *D* as ye sarved our Eva— .. ii 692
What hasta been säayin' to *my D*? .. ii 704
thou hesn't naw business 'ere with *my D*, as I knaws on, „ ii 736
Miss *D*, meä and my määtes, us three, we wants to hev three words wi' ye. „ iii 124
Has anyone found me out, *D*? .. iii 225
See *D*; you yourself are shamed of me, „ iii 268
and I love him so much— *Eva.* Poor *D*! „ iii 286
O *D*, he signed himself 'Yours gratefully'—fancy, *D*, „ iii 333
Hark! *D*, some one is coming. „ iii 339
Oh, *D*, *D*! .. iii 425
Miss *D*! Miss *D*! *Dora.* Quiet! quiet! .. iii 475
You are pale, my *D*! but the ruddiest cheek .. iii 486
D, If marriage ever brought a woman happiness .. iii 638
O *D*, *D*! .. iii 787
Dora Steer (*See also* **Dora**) doänt tha knaw he be sweet upo' *D S*, „ ii 161
kill'd her oän sister, or she beänt *D S*. .. ii 605
Dotage love her less For such a *d* upon such a man. *Queen Mary* v ii 421
Stigand, unriddle This vision, canst thou? *Stigand.* *D*! *Harold* iii i 176
Dote Many so *d* upon this bubble world, *Queen Mary* iv iii 168
The old man *d's*. *Foresters* ii ii 83
And loves and *d's* on every dingle of it. „ iv 390
Doted bad the king Who *d* on him, *Harold* iv i 103
Doter A *d* on white pheasant-flesh at feasts, *Becket, Pro.* 97
Double (adj.) this *d* thundercloud That lours on England— *Harold* iii ii 159
Double (s) Fight thou with thine own *d*, not with me, „ iv iii 168
would dare the chance Of *d*, or losing all. *The Cup* i iii 148
Doubly I am *d* bound to thee . . . *Harold* ii ii 557
Doubt (s) he brought his *d's* And fears to me. *Queen Mary* i ii 75
Which found me full of foolish *d's*, „ i v 530
but there are *d's*. „ ii ii 307
all my *d's* I fling from me like dust, *Becket* i i 148
Doubt (verb) I *d* it not, Madam, most loyal. *Queen Mary* i iv 248
D not they will be speedily overthrown. „ ii ii 200
I not *d* that God will give me strength, „ iv ii 234
lest anyone among you *d* The man's conversion „ iv iii 107
I cannot *d* but that he comes again; „ v v 26
Thanks, truthful Earl; I did not *d* thy word, *Harold* ii ii 724
what is it you *d*? Behold your peace at hand. *Becket* ii ii 199
Wherefore should you *d* it? *The Cup* i ii 340
I *d* not they are yours. *The Falcon* 721
I *d* not, I *d* not, and though I be down in the mouth, *Foresters* i ii 43
Doubted ay, but mighty doctors *d* there. *Queen Mary* iv i 84
Dough household *d* was kneaded up with blood; *Becket* i iii 351
Dove (*See also* **Stock-dove**) *d*, who flutters Between thee and the porch, *Harold* iv i 230
But since the fondest pair of *d's* will jar, *Becket* iv ii 40
Dovecote Our *d* flown! I cannot tell why monks „ v ii 580
Dover Your Majesty shall go to *D* with me, *Queen Mary* iii vi 218
To *D*? no, I am too feeble. „ iii vi 220
On all the road from *D*, day and night; „ v ii 577
We could not move from *D* to the Humber *Harold* ii ii 536
They stood on *D* beach to murder me, *Becket* v ii 436
Down (adj.) (*See also* **Deep-down**) and bursten at the toes, and *d* at heels. *Queen Mary* i i 53
ha! he is *d*! *Edith.* He *d*. Who *d*? *Stigand.* The Norman Count is *d*. *Harold* v i 551
Down (bed) like a careless sleeper in the *d*; *Foresters* i i 207
And make *D* for their heads to heaven! *Queen Mary* v iv 8
Down (hill) Breathe the free wind from off our Saxon *d's*, *Harold* ii ii 187

Downfall The *d* of so many simple souls, *Queen Mary* I ii 54
Downfallen *d* and debased From councillor to caitiff— „ IV iii 74
Down-silvering The rosy face, and long *d-s* beard, *Harold* III i 46
The rosy face, and long *d-s* beard— „ IV i 261
Down-sweeping *d-s* to the chain, Wherewith they bound *Queen Mary* IV iii 594
Downward One *d* plunge of his paw would rend away *Becket* IV ii 283
Doze He *d's.* I have left her watching him. *Foresters* II ii 80
Dozed I *d* upon the bridge, and the black river *Prom. of May* II 649
Dozen (*See also* **Half-dozen**) And drunken of my cup for a *d* years. *Becket* I iv 30
a-peacocking and a-spreading to catch her eye for a *d* year, *The Falcon* 101
Drag To *d* us with them. Fishermen? devils! *Harold* II i 28
would *d* The cleric before the civil judgment-seat, *Becket* I iii 83
Nay, *d* me not. We must not seem to fly. „ V ii 636
I will not only touch, but *d* thee hence. „ V iii 152
The women of the Temple *d* her in. *The Cup* I iii 118
I'd like to *d* 'im thruff the herse-pond, and she to be a-lookin' at it. *Prom. of May* II 593
They *d* the river for her! no, not they! „ III 694
if you care to *d* your brains for such a minnow. *Foresters* II i 323
Dragg'd Who *d* the scatter'd limbs into their den. *Queen Mary* I v 401
and we *d* The Littlechester river all in vain: *Prom. of May* II 413
Dragon Our Wessex *d* flies beyond the Humber, *Harold* IV i 3
Set forth our golden *D*, „ IV i 245
by the *d* of St. George, we shall Do some injustice, *Foresters* IV 939
Drain And *d's* the heart and marrow from a man. „ II i 672
Drain'd thou hast *d* them shallow by thy tolls, *Harold* I i 319
I have almost *d* the cup—A few drops left. *The Cup* II 385
Draught (*See also* **Sleeping-draught**) Brain-dizzied with a *d* of morning ale. *Queen Mary* II i 71
they de-miracled the miraculous *d*, *Becket* III iii 124
No not a *d* of milk, no not an egg, *The Falcon* 871
drink Her health along with us in this rich *d*, *Foresters* III 352
Drave (*See also* **Drove**) *d* and crack'd His boat on Ponthieu beach; *Harold* II ii 34
Draw *d* back your heads and your horns before I break them, *Queen Mary* I i 4
D with your sails from our poor land, „ III vi 226
where Edward *d's* A faint foot hither, *Harold* I i 143
To *d* him nearer with a charm Like thine to thine. „ I ii 7
D nearer,—I was in the corridor, „ II ii 345
D thou to London, there make strength „ V i 126
but this *D's* thro' the chart to her. *Becket, Pro.* 173
Did not your barons *d* their swords against me? „ I iii 501
we pray you, *d* yourself from under The wings of France. „ II ii 247
lest ye should *d* together like two ships in a calm. „ III iii 297
To *d* you and your husband to your doom. *The Cup* I ii 222
d's From you, and from my constancy to you. *The Falcon* 811
If thou *d* one inch nearer, *Foresters* I i 145
I will not harm thee. *D*! „ II i 556
'tis but to see if thou canst fence. *D*! „ II i 573
Drawbridge I'll have the *d* hewn into the Thames, *Queen Mary* II ii 376
They had hewn the *d* down into the river. „ II iii 18
I would hoist the *d*, like thy master. *Foresters* I i 319
Drawing-room shamed of his poor farmer's daughter among the ladies in his *d-r*? *Prom. of May* III 295
Shamed of me in a *d-r*! (repeat) „ III 296, 307
Drawl'd fat fool! He *d* and prated so, *Harold* IV ii 41
Drawn Will he be *d* to her? *Queen Mary* I v 73
fain have some fresh treaty *d* between you. „ I v 261
I say they have *d* the fire On their own heads: „ IV iii 379
In some dark closet, some long gallery, *d*, „ V i 218
With both her knees *d* upward to her chin. „ V ii 391
hath mainly *d* itself From lack of Tostig— *Harold* III i 167
fill'd the quiver, and Death has *d* the bow— „ III i 401
Hast not thou *d* the short straw? *Becket* I iv 3
not life shot up in blood, But death *d* in;— „ IV ii 382
We are almost at the bottom of the well; little more to be *d* from it— *Prom. of May* III 162
Dread (adj.) And hurl the *d* ban of the Church on those *Becket* III iii 210
Dread (s) not for *d* Of these alone, but from the fear of Him *Queen Mary* IV iii 178
Dread (verb) lied like a lad That *d's* the pendent scourge, *Harold* II ii 658
Dread (verb) (*continued*) They fear you slain: they *d* they know not what. *Becket* V ii 600
Dreadful And *d* shadows strove upon the hill, *Harold* III i 377
O God! some *d* truth is breaking on me—Some *d* thing is coming on me. *Becket* III i 265
Thro' all closed doors a *d* whisper crept „ V ii 88
Left but one *d* line to say, that we Should find her in the river; *Prom. of May* II 411
that *d* night! that lonely walk to Littlechester, „ III 366
Dreading But *d* God's revenge upon this realm *Harold* I i 172
Dream (s) (*See also* **Day-dream, Love-dream**) men-at-arms Guard my poor *d's* for England. *Queen Mary* I v 154
It was a *d*; I must not dream, not wink, „ III v 153
they come back upon my *d's*. „ V ii 189
Wide of the mark ev'n for a madman's *d*. „ V iii 82
Nor let Priests' talk, or *d* of worlds to be, „ V v 217
if yon weird sign Not blast us in our *d's*.— *Harold* I i 122
An evil *d* that ever came and went— „ I ii 70
what a *d*! *Harold.* Well, well,—a *d*—no more! „ I ii 91
Did not Heaven speak to men in *d's* of old? „ I ii 95
Thou hast misread this merry *d* of thine, „ I ii 98
Come, thou shalt dream no more such *d's*; „ I ii 108
upon thine eyelids, to shut in A happier *d*. „ I ii 127
Our living passion for a dead man's *d*; „ III ii 60
Last night King Edward came to me in *d's*—(repeat) *Harold* IV i 259, 266
I am no woman to put faith in *d's*. „ IV i 264
by dead Norway without *d* or dawn! „ IV iii 122
only *d's*—where mine own self Takes part „ V i 298
My fatal oath—the dead Saints—the dark *d's*— „ V i 381
D, Or prophecy, that? *Becket* I i 55
Well, *d* and prophecy both. „ I i 57
thou my golden *d* of Love's own bower, „ II i 34
Bright as my *d*, „ III i 278
my *d* foretold my martyrdom In mine own church. „ V ii 632
the black river Flow'd thro' my *d's*—if *d's* they were. *Prom. of May* II 651
which is my *d* of a true marriage. „ III 179
I have freed myself From all such *d's* „ III 595
Dream (verb) It was a dream; I must not *d*, not wink, *Queen Mary* III v 154
He cannot *d* that *I* advised the war; „ V ii 57
Come, thou shalt *d* no more such dreams; *Harold* I ii 108
Good-night, and *d* thyself Their chosen Earl. „ I ii 248
Who knows I may not *d* myself their king! „ I ii 251
He sees me not—and yet he *d's* of me, „ II ii 144
I did not *d* then I should be king.— „ III i 270
king can scarcely *d* that we, who know „ IV i 163
Tell him the Saints are nobler than he *d's*, „ V i 56
that none may *d* I go against God's honour— *Becket* III ii 167
D of it, then, all the way back, *Foresters* I i 140
to *d* that he My brother, my dear Walter— „ II i 651
You dared to *d* That our great Earl, „ II i 685
I fear I *d*. „ IV 1010
Dream'd who *d* us blanketed In ever-closing fog, *Queen Mary* III ii 19
Not *d* of by the rabidest gospeller. „ III vi 138
Last night, I *d* the faggots were alight, „ IV ii 1
and I *d* that I loved Louis of France: and I loved Henry of England, and Henry of England *d* that he loved me; *Becket, Pro.* 356
D that twelve stars fell glittering out of heaven, „ I i 46
who never saw nor *d* of such a banquet. „ I iv 84
I had *d* I was the bride of England, and a queen. „ V i 102
while you *d* you were the bride of England,— „ V i 104
I *d* I was the consort of a king, „ V i 144
This mountain shepherd never *d* of Rome. *The Cup* I ii 17
tear it all to pieces, never *d* Of acting on it. „ I ii 247
Who knows that he had ever *d* of flying? *Prom. of May* I 654
cuirass in this forest where I *d* That all was peace— *Foresters* IV 130
Dreaming old enough To scare me into *d*, *Queen Mary* IV ii 103
I am *d*; for the past Look'd thro' the present, *Prom. of May* II 639
I was *d* of it all the way hither. *Foresters* I i 139
Dree (three) and awaay betimes wi' *d* hard eggs for a good pleace at the burnin'; *Queen Mary* IV iii 489
Drench'd then he dash'd and *d*, He dyed, *Harold* III i 141

Drench'd (*continued*) Found him dead and *d* in dew, *Foresters* II ii 147
Dress This *d* was made me as the Earl of Devon *Queen Mary* I iv 72
I wear beneath my *d* A shirt of mail: „ I v 145
And what was Mary's *d*? „ III i 56
I was too sorry for the woman To mark the *d*. „ III i 59
Arrange my *d*—the gorgeous Indian shawl „ V ii 538
if I hadn't a sprig o' wickentree sewn into my *d*, *Foresters* II i 250
Drest —*d* like a gentleman, too. Damn all gentlemen, says I! *Prom. of May* II 578
O graves in daisies *d*, „ III 204
Drew He *d* this shaft against me to the head, *Queen Mary* V ii 80
Earl, the first Christian Cæsar *d* to the East *Harold* V i 22
thereupon, methought, He *d* toward me, *Becket* I i 102
loveliest life that ever *d* the light From heaven *The Cup* I iii 56
D here the richest lot from Fate, „ II 442
would not crush The fly that *d* her blood; *Prom. of May* II 494
Robin fancied me a man, And *d* his sword upon me, *Foresters* III 21
Drewest And never *d* sword to help the old man „ II i 541
Drift That is your *d*. *Queen Mary* I v 305
And queens also! What is your *d*? *Becket.* My *d* is to the Castle, *Becket* I ii 82
I see your *d* . . . it may be so . . . „ V i 82
Drill how should thy one tooth *d* thro' this? *Foresters* II i 276
Drill-sergeant yet are we now *d-s* to his lordship's lettuces, *The Falcon* 550
Drink thou could'st *d* in Spain if I remember. *Queen Mary* II i 38
eat dead men's flesh, and *d* their blood. *Harold* II ii 808
D to the dead who died for us, „ IV iii 69
tho' I can *d* wine I cannot bide water, *Becket* I iv 220
which the more you *d*, The more you thirst—yea—*d* too much, *The Cup* I iii 139
That Synorix should *d* from his own cup. „ II 353
They two should *d* together from one cup, „ II 361
See here, I fill it. Will you *d*, my lord? „ II 367
make libation to the Goddess, And now I *d*. „ II 378
D and *d* deep—our marriage will be fruitful. *D* and *d* deep, and thou wilt make me happy. „ II 380
'Let us eat and *d*, for to-morrow we die.' *Prom. of May* I 259
D to the Lion-heart Every one! *Foresters* I ii 5
Here, here—a cup of wine—*d* and begone! „ I iii 89
Shall *d* the health of our new woodland Queen. „ III 314
till the green earth *d* Her health along with us „ III 350
D to the health of our new Queen o' the woods, „ III 368
We *d* the health of thy new Queen o' the woods. „ III 372
D to the Queen o' the woods, „ III 388
And lie with us among the flowers, and *d*— „ IV 966
Drinker A *d* of black, strong, volcanic wines, *Queen Mary* V ii 93
Drive Do you mean to *d* me mad? „ V ii 200
applaud that Norman who should *d* The stranger *Harold* II ii 540
and yet I saw thee *d* him up his hills— „ IV i 211
he join'd with thee To *d* me outlaw'd. „ IV ii 14
Follow them, follow them, *d* them to the sea! „ V i 602
Louis Returning, ah! to *d* thee from his realm. *Becket* II ii 418
as men Have done on rafts of wreck—it *d's* you mad. *The Cup* I iii 142
and I'd *d* the plow straäit as a line *Prom. of May* I 369
open, or I will *d* the door from the door-post. *Foresters* II i 220
Driven The guards are all *d* in, *Queen Mary* II iv 54
and *d* back The Frenchmen from their trenches? „ V ii 256
eat it like the serpent, and be *d* out of her paradise. *Becket, Pro.* 533
Lifted our produce, *d* our clerics out— „ V ii 432
mine own dagger *d* by Synorix found *The Cup* II 86
Have our loud pastimes *d* them all away? *Foresters* II ii 105
Driving it was you that were *d* the cart— *Prom. of May* III 87
Droop faith that seem'd to *d* will feel your light, *Queen Mary* III iv 22
You *d* in your dim London. „ V ii 609
Drooping and maiden moon Our *d* Queen should know! „ V ii 457
Drop (s) And putrid water, every *d* a worm, „ IV iii 444
tho' the *d* may hollow out the dead stone, *Becket* III iii 314
I have almost drain'd the cup—A few *d's* left. *The Cup* II 386
niver touched a *d* of owt till my oän wedding-daäy, *Prom. of May* I 362
p'raps ye hears 'at I soomtimes taäkes a *d* too much; „ II 108
voice a-shaäkin', and the *d* in 'er eye. „ II 130
Drop (verb) His in whose hand she *d's*; *Queen Mary* III i 112
not *d* the mask before The masquerade is over— „ III vi 109
d The mud I carried, like yon brook, *Becket* II i 158

Drop (verb) (*continued*) may *d* off any day, any hour. You must see him at once. *Prom. of May* III 407
Then I would *d* from the casement, like a spider. *Foresters* I i 316
Dropsy (*See also* **High-dropsy**) but I hear she hath a *d*, lad, *Queen Mary* III ii 224
Fie on her *d*, so she have a *d*! „ III ii 226
Dropt Have I *d* it? I have but shown a loathing face „ III vi 112
dog that snapt the shadow, *d* the bone.— *Harold* I ii 188
boughs across the deep That *d* themselves, „ III i 152
He sat down there And *d* it in his hands, *Becket* I iii 324
royal promise might have *d* into thy mouth „ III iii 276
and *d* Their streamers earthward, *The Cup* I ii 404
And the stock-dove coo'd, till a kite *d* down, *Prom. of May* I 55
dosta knaw this paäper? Ye *d* it upo' the road. „ II 687
Wealth *d* out of the window, *Foresters* I i 156
Dross As gold Outvalues *d*, light darkness, *Becket* I iii 715
Drove (*See also* **Drave**) When he we speak of *d* the window back, *Queen Mary* V ii 464
my father *d* the Normans out Of England?— *Harold* I i 251
thou and he *d* our good Normans out From England, „ II ii 524
Athelstan the Great Who *d* you Danes; „ IV i 75
my father *d* him and his friends, De Tracy *Becket* I i 276
d me From out her memory. *Prom. of May* II 404
My lord John, In wrath because you *d* him from the forest, *Foresters* III 450
He *d* his knife into the heart of the deer, „ IV 541
Drown Why, the child will *d* himself. *Becket* II i 322
but these arm'd men—will *you d yourself*? „ V ii 276
even *d* you In the good regard of Rome. *The Cup* I i 150
Were there no boughs to hang on, Rivers to *d* in? „ I ii 79
Must all Galatia hang or *d* herself? „ I ii 87
d all poor self-passion in the sense Of public good? „ II 101
how often justice *d's* Between the law and the letter of the law! *Foresters* IV 512
Drown'd (*See also* **Half-drown'd**) A sea of blood—we are *d* in blood— *Harold* III i 398
The curse of England! these are *d* in wassail, „ IV iii 223
—thou art *d* in debt— *Becket, Pro.* 491
all *d* in love And glittering at full tide— *The Cup* II 233
Drowning The *d* man, they say, remembers all The chances of his life, *Becket* V ii 272
Drudge went into service—the *d* of a lodging-house— *Prom. of May* III 392
Drug (s) *D's*—but he knows they cannot help me— *Queen Mary* V v 60
Drug (verb) and science now could *d* and balm us *Prom. of May* II 339
Drunk has *d* and gambled out All that he had, *Queen Mary* II iii 87
Make themselves *d* and mad, „ III i 282
and our marriage and thy glory Been *d* together! *Harold* IV iii 9
Old dog, Thou art *d*, old dog! „ IV iii 164
Too *d* to fight with thee! „ IV iii 165
Thou hast *d* deep enough to make me happy. *The Cup* II 424
Have I not *d* of the same cup with thee? „ II 463
you were stupid *d* all Sunday, and so ill in consequence all Monday, *Prom. of May* III 80
Is he deaf, or dumb, or daft, or *d* belike? *Foresters* I ii 208
Drunken My Lord, the world is like a *d* man, *Queen Mary* IV iii 393
O *d* ribaldry! Out, beast! out, bear! *Becket* I i 230
Ye have eaten of my dish and *d* of my cup for a dozen years. „ I iv 30
Drunkenness to snore away his *d* Into the sober headache,— „ I i 371
Dry *D* as an old wood-fungus on a dead tree, *Harold* III i 8
if you follow Not the *d* light of Rome's straight-going policy, *The Cup* I i 145
Duchy You have her *D*, The point you aim'd at, *Becket* II ii 76
You did your best or worst to keep her *D*. „ II ii 84
Duck Thou knowest we had to dodge, or *d*, or die; *Queen Mary* III iv 357
Duck'd Or I will have you *d*! „ IV iii 540
Dudley (Guildford) *See* **Guildford Dudley**
Due (adj.) *D* from his castles of Berkhamstead and Eye *Becket* I iii 628
thanks of Holy Church are *d* to those That went „ II ii 190
According to the canon's pardon *d* To him that so repents, *Queen Mary* IV iii 33
No, not an hour: the debt is *d* to-day. *Foresters* IV 448
Due (s) command That kiss my *d* when subject, *Harold* III ii 42
Dug *D* from the grave that yawns for us beyond; *Queen Mary* V ii 163
I *d* mine into My old fast friend the shore, *Harold* II i 6
The trenches *d*, the palisades uprear'd „ V i 189

E

Ear (*continued*) For your *e* only—I love you— *The Cup* I ii 217
'Eär (hear) says the master goäs cleän off his 'eäd when he *'e's* the naäme on 'im; *Prom. of May* III 132
'Eärd (heard) Well, I never *'e* the likes o' that afoor. „ I 255
Why, Wilson, tha *'e* 'im thysen— „ I 302
Earl Ay, if Dukes, and *E's*, And Counts, *Queen Mary* III i 50
this young *E* was sent on foreign travel, „ V ii 489
Ask our broad *E*. *Harold* I i 90
Art thou sick, good *E*? „ I i 100
When camest thou hither? *Gamel.* To-day, good *E*. „ I i 106
The King hath made me *E*; make me not fool! Nor make the King a fool, who made me *E*! „ I i 288
Who made the King who made thee, make thee *E*. „ I i 295
Tostig, Edward hath made him *E*: „ I ii 186
Follow my lead, and I will make thee *e*. „ I ii 217
Good-night, and dream thyself Their chosen *E*. „ I ii 249
E first, and after that Who knows I may not dream myself their king! „ I ii 250
E, wilt thou fly my falcons this fair day? „ II ii 146
Thy valour and thy value, noble *e*. „ II ii 202
Look not amazed, fair *e*! „ II ii 494
And I will make thee my great *E* of *E's*, „ II ii 629
Thou must swear absolutely, noble *E*. „ II ii 716
Thanks, truthful *E*; I did not doubt thy word, „ II ii 723
Who make thy good their own—all England, *E*. „ III i 331
E's and Thanes! Full thanks for your fair greeting of my bride! *E's*, Thanes, and all our countrymen! „ IV iii 45
E, the first Christian Cæsar drew to the East „ V i 21
So!—did he?—*E*—I have a mind to play The William „ V i 25
E—ay—thou art but a messenger of William. „ V i 29
Ay, my lord, and divers other *e's* and barons. *Becket* I iv 59
golden leaves, these *e's* and barons, that clung to me, „ I iv 66
They shall henceforward be my *e's* and barons— „ I iv 86
Knights, bishops, *e's*, this London spawn— „ II ii 143
The lady gave a rose to the *E*, (repeat) *Foresters* I i 12, 105
The lady gave her hand to the *E*, (repeat) „ I i 16, 92
'Farewell, farewell, my warrior *E*!' „ I i 18
She gave a weeping kiss to the *E*, (repeat) „ I i 20, 119
never was an *E* so true a friend of the people „ I i 188
A gallant *E*. I love him as I hate John. „ I i 190
shoot almost as closely with the bow as the great *E* himself. „ I i 217
so flustered me that I forgot my message from the *E*. „ I i 297
I am a silent man myself, and all the more wonder at our *E*. „ I ii 36
not so much for the cause as for the *E*. O Lord, I am easily led by words, but I think the *E* hath right. Scarlet, hath not the *E* right? „ I ii 39
I will swear by the head of the *E*. „ I ii 45
Thou Much, miller's son, hath not the *E* right? „ I ii 47
but for all that I will swear the *E* hath right. „ I ii 51
Thou art the *E's* confessor and shouldst know. „ I ii 55
the *E* and Sir Richard come this way. „ I ii 147
And learn from her if she do love this *E*. „ I ii 188
Ay, noble *E*, and never part with it. „ I ii 303
Robin, *E*— *Robin.* Let be the *E*. „ I iii 93
You dared to dream That our great *E*, „ II i 686
E—— *Robin.* Nay, no *E* am I. I am English yeoman. „ III 129
But, *E*, if thou be he—— *Friar Tuck.* Fine him! fine him! he hath called plain Robin an *e*. „ IV 148
Robin, Earl of Huntingdon, For *E* thou art again, „ IV 830
Earldom yet hear! thine *e*, Tostig, *Harold* I i 303
I would it went as well as with mine *e*, „ I i 337
I have to make report of my good *e* To the good king „ I i 406
It means the fall of Tostig from his *e*. „ I i 469
In mine *e* A man may hang gold bracelets „ II i 86
Thou art a mighty man In thine own *e*! „ II i 93
We have few prisoners in mine *e* there, „ II ii 687
ever-jarring *E's* move To music and in order— „ II ii 760
he flamed When Tostig's anger'd *e* flung him, „ III i 54
I come for mine own *E*, my Northumbria; „ IV ii 29
be chasten'd by thy banishment, Some easier *e*. „ IV ii 51
Fain had I kept thine *e* in thy hands „ V i 275
Earlier O higher, holier, *e*, purer church, *Queen Mary* IV ii 108
Early Not here as yet. You are too *e* for him. *The Cup* I iii 50
Early (*continued*) As I said before, you are still too *e*. *Camma.* Too *e* to be here alone with thee; *The Cup* I iii 81
His *e* follies cast into his teeth, *Queen Mary* V ii 124
Earn'd Hast thou not fought for it, and *e* it? *Foresters* IV 345
Earshot Stand out of *e* then, *Harold* II ii 240
'Eart (heart) I doänt believe he's iver a *'e* under his waistcoat. *Prom. of May* I 130
Earth To him within there who made Heaven and *E*? *Queen Mary* I v 48
in his scared prayers Heaven and *e's* Maries; „ II ii 88
Between the two most high-set thrones on *e*, „ III ii 107
Amplier than any field on our poor *e* „ III iii 197
With heaven for *e*. „ III iii 201
Julius, God's Vicar and Viceregent upon *e*, „ III iii 213
That heaven wept and *e* blush'd. „ III iv 193
God upon *e*? what more? „ III iv 383
As Cranmer hath, came to the fire on *e*. „ IV i 61
On *e*; but saved in heaven By your recanting. „ IV ii 178
I have offended against heaven and *e* „ IV iii 124
And I can find no refuge upon *e*. „ IV iii 128
You are the mightiest monarch upon *e*, „ V i 52
Bride of the mightiest sovereign upon *e*? „ V ii 545
Should make the mightiest empire *e* has known. „ V iii 70
for heaven's credit Makes it on *e*: *Harold* I i 142
In heaven signs! Signs upon *e*! „ I i 160
Not stagger'd by this ominous *e* and heaven: But heaven and *e* are threads „ I i 207
And other bells on *e*, which yet are heavens; „ I ii 133
would make the hard *e* rive To the very Devil's horns, „ II ii 740
let *e* rive, gulf in These cursed Normans— „ II ii 781
And signs on *e*! Knowest thou Senlac hill? „ III i 360
'Seven feet of English *e*, or something more, „ IV iii 112
corpse thou whelmest with thine *e* is cursed, „ V i 68
dead as Death this day to ought of *e's* „ V i 426
Is not the Church the visible Lord on *e*? *Becket* I iii 93
Lest there be battle between Heaven and *E*, And *E* should get the better— „ I iii 227
and when ye shall hear it is poured out upon *e*, „ I iv 37
did not wholly clear The deadly growths of *e*, „ II ii 203
like Mahound's coffin hung between heaven and *e*— „ II ii 362
E's falses are heaven's truths. „ III iii 348
cry out for thee Who art too pure for *e*. „ IV ii 134
And break the soul from *e*. „ V i 44
She sends it back, as being dead to *e*, „ V i 171
Flash sometimes out of *e* against the heavens. „ V ii 37
Tho' all the loud-lung'd trumpets upon *e* „ V ii 488
Too late on *e* may be too soon in hell. „ V ii 528
Tho' *e's* last earthquake clash'd the minster-bells, „ V iii 41
Seen by the Church in Heaven, the Church on *e*— „ V iii 99
Will the *e* gape and swallow us? „ V iii 205
and enrich *E* with her shadow! *The Cup* I iii 60
Who causest the safe *e* to shudder and gape, „ II 298
They will break in the *e*—I am sinking— „ II 477
Thou art the last friend left me upon *e*— *The Falcon* 32
Outvalues all the jewels upon *e*. „ 779
comes To rob you of your one delight on *e*. „ 828
For all the souls on *e* that live To be forgiven *Prom. of May* III 7
bow'd To the *e* he came from, „ III 515
fiercest storm That ever made *e* tremble— „ III 798
for the love of his own little mother on *e*, *Foresters* I i 98
it answers, I am thine to the very heart of the *e*— „ I i 337
till the green *e* drink Her health along with us „ III 350
bury her Even in the bowels of the *e* „ III 462
Earthly Is it possible That mortal men should bear their *e* heats *Harold* V i 283
unsubject to Our *e* sceptre. *Becket* I iii 681
Earthquake and underfoot An *e*; *Queen Mary* IV iii 399
shake the North With *e* and disruption— *Harold* I ii 200
midriff-shaken even to tears, as springs gush out after *e's*— *Becket* III iii 163
Tho' earth's last *e* clash'd the minster-bells, „ V iii 41
Earthware one piece of *e* to serve the salad in to my lady, *The Falcon* 481
Earthworm What poor *e's* are all and each of us, *Prom. of May* III 635
Ease Tho' scarce at *e*; for, save our meshes break, *Harold* II ii 140
Eased Then after we have *e* them of their coins *Foresters* III 172

Easier Thy life at home Is *e* than mine here. *Harold* I i 97
So thou be chasten'd by thy banishment, Some *e* earldom. „ IV ii 51
which we Inheriting reap an *e* harvest. *Becket* II ii 194
It might be *e* then for you to make Allowance for a mother— *The Falcon* 825
East (adj.) but the wind *e* like an enemy. *Prom. of May* I 80
East (s) (*See also* **North-east**) And all the fair spice-islands of the *E*. *Queen Mary* V i 50
the first Christian Cæsar drew to the *E* *Harold* V i 22
dwelt alone, like a soft lord of the *E*, *Becket* I iii 359
We fought in the *E*, And felt the sun of Antioch „ II ii 92
Whose doings are a horror to the *e*, A hissing in the west!' „ IV ii 244
bowl my ancestor Fetch'd from the farthest *e*— *The Falcon* 485
twilight of the coming day already glimmers in the *e*. *Foresters* I ii 248
new term Brought from the sacred *E*, his harem? „ IV 705
Easter Till the sun dance, as upon *E* Day. *Queen Mary* III ii 238
Eastern We have had our leagues of old with *E* kings. *The Cup* I ii 102
men will call him An *E* tyrant, not an English king. *Foresters* IV 904
Easy (*See also* **Eäsy**) Breathing an *e* gladness . . . not like Aldwyth . . . *Harold* I ii 174
Nay—but there be conditions, *e* ones, „ II ii 206
'*e*'—that were *e*—nay—No money-lover he! „ II ii 214
for I should find An *e* father confessor in thee. *Becket, Pro.* 88
Rest you *e*, For I am *e* to keep. I shall not fly. „ V ii 512
Is it not *e* to disarm a woman? *The Cup* I iii 106
then you would know it is not So *e* to forgive— *Prom. of May* II 486
Eäsy Määke thysen *e*. I'll hev the winder naäiled up, „ I 419
I could put all that o' one side *e* anew. „ II 111
Eat I couldn't *e* in Spain, I couldn't sleep in Spain. *Queen Mary* II i 36
Come locusting upon us, *e* us up, „ II i 101
Your apple *e's* the better. Let them go. „ II ii 7
Dare-devils, that would *e* fire and spit it out „ III i 156
while famish'd rats *E* them alive. „ V ii 198
Where they *e* dead men's flesh, *Harold* II ii 807
Sit down, sit down, and *e*, „ IV iii 207
Let her *e* it like the serpent, *Becket, Pro.* 532
We scarcely dare to bless the food we *e* „ V i 71
slave that *e* my bread has kick'd his King! „ V i 242
I could not *e*, sleep, pray: „ V ii 92
Sit and *e*, And take a hunter's vengeance *The Cup* I ii 42
Will you not *e* a little? „ I ii 425
Will you not *e* with me, my lord? *The Falcon* 570
I can *e* no more! „ 670
you ask'd to *e* with me. „ 868
'Let us *e* and drink, for to-morrow we die.' *Prom. of May* I 259
sits and *e's* his heart for want of money to pay the Abbot. *Foresters* I i 4
I came To *e* him up and make an end of him. „ II i 125
Well, set them forth. I could *e* anything. „ II i 274
before you can *e* it you must hack it with a hatchet, „ III 284
Something to *e*. *Robin.* And thou shalt have it, man. „ IV 187
in the sweat of thy brow, says Holy Writ, shalt thou *e* bread, „ IV 202
in the fear of thy life shalt thou *e* the King's venison— „ IV 206
Eaten Ye have *e* of my dish and drunken of my cup for a dozen years. *Becket* I iv 29
—we have *e*—we are heated. Wine! *The Cup* I ii 45
Not *e* anything. *The Falcon* 674
she that has *e* the yolk is scarce like to swallow the shell. „ 704
Eating (*See also* **Word-eating**) so thou be Squeamish at *e* the King's venison. *Foresters* IV 194
'Eaven (heaven) Granny says marriages be määde i' '*e*. *Prom. of May* III 709
Eaves I never breathed it to a bird in the *e*, *Queen Mary* V ii 454
Echo (s) But shout and *e* play'd into each other *Foresters* II i 258
The wood is full of *e'es*, owls, elfs, „ II i 262
When horn and *e* ring, „ III 428
I am but the *e* of the lips of love. „ IV 892
Echo (verb) my wish *E'es* your Majesty's. *Pole.* It shall be so. *Queen Mary* III iii 93
Mine *e'es* both your Graces'; „ III iii 95
yells of thief And rogue and liar *e* down in Hell, *Foresters* III 324
Echo'd The trumpets of the fight had *e* down, *The Falcon* 605
Echoing *See* **Bird-echoing**
Eclipse out of the *e* Narrowing my golden hour! *Becket* II i 202
Eddicated (educated) Thy feyther *e* his darters to marry gentlefoälk, *Prom. of May* II 115
I *e* boäth on 'em to marry gentlemen, „ III 454
Eddying torrents of *e* bark! *Foresters* III 95
Eden To make this Sherwood *E* o'er again, „ II i 168
Ederunt *Sederunt principes, e pauperes.* *Becket* I iv 132
Edgar (afterwards Mr. Harold) *See also* **Harold, Hedgar, Philip, Philip Edgar, Philip Harold, Philip Hedgar**) I warrants ye'll think moor o' this young Squire *E* as ha' coomed among us— *Prom. of May* I 110
Wheer be Mr. *E*? about the premises? „ I 432
where is this Mr. *E* whom you praised so in your first letters? „ I 776
I thought Mr. *E* the best of men, and he has proved himself the worst. „ II 85
that villain, *E*, If he should ever show his face „ II 422
What *E*? *Dora.* Philip Edgar of Toft Hall „ II 437
This *E*, then, is living? *Harold.* Living? well— „ II 443
But she hates *E*. May not this Dobbins, or some other, spy *E* in Harold? „ II 672
then she will forgive *E* for Harold's sake. „ II 679
Nor am I *E*, my good fellow. „ II 701
Mr. *E*? *Allen.* Theer, Miss! You ha' naämed 'im— „ III 141
She must be crying '*E*' in her sleep. *Harold.* Who must be crying out '*E*' in her sleep? „ III 653
Happy! What? *E*? Is it so? „ III 668
Edgar (the Atheling) Who inherits? *E* the Atheling? *Harold* III i 240
Edge (*See also* **Knife-edge**) Shall I smite him with the *e* of the sword? *Becket* I iv 224
Edify (*See also* **Re-edify**) We come not to destroy, but *e*; *Queen Mary* III iii 188
Edith (ward of King Edward, the Confessor) Art thou assured By this, that Harold loves but *E*? *Harold* I ii 210
Then for thine *E*? „ II ii 422
I know the Norman license—thine own *E*— „ II ii 478
Harold, if thou love thine *E*, ay. „ II ii 622
wilt thou bring another, *E*, upon his head? „ III i 262
and on thee, *E*, if thou abide it,— „ III i 317
Look up! look up! *E*! „ III i 321
E, Tho' somewhat less a king to my true self „ III ii 52
Good even, gentle *E*. „ III ii 118
E, Hadst thou been braver, I had better braved All— „ III ii 177
E, *E*, Get thou into thy cloister as the king Will'd it: „ V i 308
E, The sign in heaven—the sudden blast at sea— „ V i 377
E, if I, the last English King of England— „ V i 383
thou art Harold, I am *E*! „ V i 392
O *E*, art thou here? „ V ii 1
O *E*, if I ever wrought against thee, „ V ii 21
O *E*, *E*, I have lost both crown And husband. „ V ii 38
E, *E*— *Edith.* What was he like, „ V ii 51
Edmund (King of the East English, martyred in 870) By St. *E* I overmeasure him. „ IV iii 119
Educated *See* **Eddicated**
Edward (the Confessor) Ask it of King *E*! „ I i 78
look, where *E* draws A faint foot hither, „ I i 143
E loves him, so Ye hate him. „ I i 427
E's prayers Were deafen'd and he pray'd them dumb, „ I ii 21
foes in *E's* hall To league against thy weal. „ I ii 32
she held with *E*, At least methought she held with holy *E*, „ I ii 50
I will demand his ward From *E* when I come again. „ I ii 60
Our wild Tostig, *E* hath made him Earl: „ I ii 186
thine host in England when I went To visit *E*. „ II ii 6
know'st my claim on England Thro' *E's* promise: „ II ii 13
did *E* know of this? „ II ii 304
Then let me hence With Wulfnoth to King *E*. „ II ii 563
And hath King *E* not pronounced his heir? „ II ii 575
if that but hung upon King *E's* will. „ II ii 601
According as King *E* promises. „ II ii 714
Thou art English, *E* too is English now, „ III i 28
E wakes!—Dazed—he hath seen a vision. „ III i 129
And *E* would have sent a host against you, „ IV i 99
Since Griffyth's head was sent To *E*, „ IV i 222
Last night King *E* came to me in dreams— (repeat) *Harold* IV i 259, 265

Edward (the Confessor) (*continued*) Take and slay me, For *E* loved me. *Harold.* *E* bad me spare thee. *Tostig.* I hate King *E*, for he join'd with thee To drive me outlaw'd. *Harold* IV ii 10
Of Alfred, or of *E* his great son, „ IV iii 52
They know King *E's* promise and thine—thine. „ V i 45
Not know that *E* cancell'd his own promise? „ V i 51
Thou didst possess thyself of *E's* ear „ V i 345
Edward (the First) In William's time, in our first *E's* time, *Queen Mary* III iii 226
Edward (the Fourth) Who's a-passing? King *E* or King Richard? „ I i 32
Edward (the Sixth) our young *E* might bequeath the crown Of England, „ I ii 26
Yet I stood out, till *E* sent for me. „ I ii 29
Have we not heard of her in *E's* time, „ I iv 18
Your pious wish to pay King *E's* debts, „ I v 111
Had mark'd her for my brother *E's* bride; „ I v 289
Did she not In Henry's time and *E's*? „ III iv 132
imprisonment, my Lord, Under young *E*. „ III iv 244
Edwin (Earl of Mercia) Morcar and *E* have stirr'd up the Thanes *Harold* II ii 288
have overthrown Morcar and *E*. „ III ii 132
Again! Morcar! *E*! What do they mean? „ IV i 133
Morcar and *E*, When will ye cease to plot „ IV i 160
Morcar and *E*, will ye, if I yield, „ IV i 175
Morcar and *E*, will ye upon oath, Help us „ IV i 179
E, my friend—Thou lingerest.—Gurth,— „ IV i 256
Gurth, Leofwin, Morcar, *E*! „ IV iii 221
Eel wriggle out of them like an *e* When the time serves. *Becket* II ii 187
Effaced he is *e*, Self-blotted out; *Queen Mary* IV i 137
Egg wi' dree hard *e's* for a good pleace at the burnin'; „ IV iii 490
sat Stone-dead upon a heap of ice-cold *e's*. *Becket* V ii 240
brood Too long o'er this hard *e*, the world, „ V ii 253
E's. *Filippo.* One, but addled. *The Falcon* 128
No not a draught of milk, no not an *e*, „ 872
and each of 'em as full of meat as an *e*, *Foresters* I i 42
or the shambles-oak, or a weasel-sucked *e*, „ IV 212
Egg-bald may give that *e-b* head The tap that silences. *Harold* V i 90
Egypt like *E's* plague, had fill'd All things with blood; *Becket* I iii 344
I heard a saying in *E*, that ambition *The Cup* I iii 137
tho' the fire should run along the ground, As once it did in *E*. *Prom. of May* I 705
Eight Seventeen—and knew *e* languages— *Queen Mary* III i 359
Eighty His *e* years Look'd somewhat crooked on him in his frieze; „ IV iii 331
Either You were the one sole man in *e* house „ III iii 253
I am the one sole man in *e* house, „ III iii 266
true To *e* function, holding it; *Becket* I iii 538
Yea, since he flouts the will of *e* realm, „ II ii 256
Oh, no, not *e* way, nor any way „ V iii 86
Elbow fray'd i' the knees, and out at *e*, *Queen Mary* I i 52
look at our suits, out at knee, out at *e*. *Foresters* I i 33
Elbowing and almost *e* her, So else they stood, *Queen Mary* II ii 76
Elder Made younger *e* son, violated the whole Tradition *Prom. of May* I 494
Eleanor (of Aquitaine, Queen of England) so this Rosamund, my true heart-wife, Not *E*! *Becket, Pro.* 132
and the soul of *E* from hell-fire. „ *Pro* 151
secret out of our loyal Thomas, I am not *E*. „ *Pro.* 467
and make Our waning *E* all but love me! „ II ii 458
Oh, Queen *E*. Yes, my lady; „ III i 203
E, *E*, have I Not heard ill things of her „ III i 230
'*E* of Aquitaine, *E* of England! Murder'd by that adulteress *E*, „ IV ii 241
Why should I swear, *E*, who am, or was, „ IV ii 403
Election dost thou think the King Forced mine *e*? *Herbert.* I do think the King Was potent in the *e*, „ I i 127
the *e* shall be made in the Chapel Royal, „ I iii 110
was thine own *e* so canonical, Good father? „ I iii 120
Eleven I am *e* years older than he is. *Queen Mary* I v 68
I am *e* years older than he, „ V v 46
Elf The wood is full of echoes, owls, *e's*, *Foresters* II i 263
E, with spiteful heart and eye, „ II ii 172
Elfin Nay, an please your *E* Grace, „ II ii 132
Elisabetta (nurse to Count Federigo degli Alberighi) you Would find it stain'd— *Count.* Silence, *E*! *The Falcon* 665
Elizabeth (Princess, afterwards Queen of England) No; it was the Lady *E*. *Queen Mary* I i 18
the Lady *E* is the more noble and royal. „ I i 72
I mean the Lady *E*. „ I i 75
be no peace for Mary till *E* lose her head.' „ I iii 5
'Long live *E* the Queen!' „ I iii 8
And get the swine to shout *E*. „ I iii 39
we'll have no pope here while the Lady *E* lives. „ I iii 44
we'll have no virgins here—we'll have the Lady *E*! „ I iii 62
If *E* lose her head—That makes for France. „ I iii 88
married The mother of *E*—a heretic Ev'n as *she* is; „ I v 32
Wyatt, shall we proclaim *E*? „ II i 239
The names of Wyatt, *E*, Courtenay, „ II ii 94
E—Her name is much abused among those traitors. „ II ii 109
whom did you say? *Messenger.* *E*? Your Royal sister. „ II iv 116
Can I strike *E*?—not now and save the life Of Devon: „ II iv 123
The proud ambitions of *E*, „ III ii 169
Quoth *E*, prisoner. „ III v 21
this re-action not re-act Yet fiercelier under Queen *E*, „ IV iii 389
You must proclaim *E* your heir. (repeat) „ V i 191, 204
E, How fair and royal—like a Queen, indeed? „ V i 234
E—To Philibert of Savoy, as you know, „ V i 246
Thou art commission'd to *E*, And not to me! „ V ii 594
A cry! What's that? *E*? revolt? „ V v 187
God save *E*, the Queen of England! „ V v 283
Elizabeth Barton *See* **Joan of Kent**
Ely (Bishop [Thirlby] of) My Lord of *E*, this. After a riot We hang the leaders, *Queen Mary* IV i 72
Ely (city) There lies a treasure buried down in *E*: *Harold* III i 11
Emboss'd many-breasted mother Artemis *E* upon it. *The Cup* II 341
Embrace on thee remains the curse, Harold, if thou *e* her: *Harold* III i 316
great and sound policy that: I could *e* him for it: *Becket, Pro.* 452
for who could *e* such an armful of joy? *Foresters* I ii 70
Wilt thou *e* thy sweetheart 'fore my face? „ II ii 28
I *E* thee with the kisses of the soul. „ III 143
E me, Marian, and thou, good Kate, „ IV 1031
Embroilment may come a crash and *e* as in Stephen's time; *Becket, Pro.* 485
Embryo every rebel birth That passes out of *e*. *Queen Mary* III vi 52
Emerald English Garter, studded with great *e's*, „ III i 85
Emperor (s) betroth'd in her babyhood to the Great *E* „ I i 119
Most goodly, Kinglike and an *E's* son,— „ I v 2
Hath he the large ability of the *E*? „ I v 324
letter which thine *E* promised Long since, „ I v 348
I am English Queen, not Roman *E*. „ I v 504
The *E* counsell'd me to fly to Flanders. „ I v 549
I fear the *E* much misvalued me. „ III ii 76
The *E's* highness happily symboll'd „ III ii 108
treaty which the *e* sent us Were mainly Gardiner's; „ III iii 69
And the *E* Approved you, and when last he wrote, „ III vi 76
prattling to her mother Of her betrothal to the *E* Charles, „ V v 233
prest upon By the fierce *E* and his Antipope. *Becket* I iii 203
When he hath shaken off the *E*, „ I iii 244
you have traffick'd Between the *E* and the Pope, „ II ii 68
Threaten our junction with the *E*— „ II ii 471
Empire Should make the mightiest *e* earth has known. *Queen Mary* V iii 70
the first Fell, and the next became an *E*. *Harold* IV i 51
push'd one way by the *E* and another by England, *Becket* II ii 327
his poor tonsure A crown of *E*. „ V i 196
Employ *E* us, heat us, quicken us, help us, *The Cup* I iii 131
Empress But—shamed of you, my *E*! *Prom. of May* III 599
Emptiness I had but *e* to set before you, *The Falcon* 870
course of that full feast That leaves but *e*. *Prom. of May* II 256
Empty Most fruitful, yet, indeed, an *e* rind, *Queen Mary* III ii 202
nave and aisles all *e* as a fool's jest! „ IV iii 286
Why then the throne is *e*. Who inherits? *Harold* III i 235
since the Sheriff left me naught but an *e* belly, *Foresters* II i 279
Encampt The Roman is *e* without your city— *The Cup* I ii 83
Enchanted the people Believe the wood *e*. *Becket* III i 36
Enclosed now you are *e* with boards of cedar, *Queen Mary* III ii 101

Encumbered *E* as we are, who would lend us any-thing? *Prom. of May* III 162
End (s) born i' the tail *e* of old Harry the Seventh. *Queen Mary* I i 42
Look to you as the one to crown their *e's*. „ I iv 172
She fear'd it might unman him for his *e*. „ III i 368
to what *e*? For yet the faith is not established there. *Gardiner*. The *e's* not come. *Pole*. No—nor this way will come, Seeing there lie two ways to every *e*, „ III iv 108
Latimer Had a brief *e*—not Ridley. „ IV ii 225
as I have come To the last *e* of life, „ IV iii 218
Might it not be the other side rejoicing In his brave *e*? „ IV iii 358
Who cannot move straight to his *e*— „ IV iii 394
sight of Danish blood Might serve an *e* not English— *Harold* IV iii 98
And to what *e*? *Becket* I ii 63
and to speak truth, nigh at the *e* of our last crust, „ III i 114
an' it 'ud be well for me in the *e*, „ III i 134
but in the *e* we flourished out into a merriment; „ III iii 137
What! Is the *e* come? „ V i 148
The *e* is mine. „ V i 151
If once our *e's* are gain'd? *The Cup* I i 32
harm at times, may even Hasten their *e*. *The Falcon* 823
At the *e* of the daäy, For the last loäd hoäm? (repeat) *Prom. of May* II 183, 194
Till the *e* of the daäy And the last loäd hoäm. „ II 208
Till the *e* o' the daäy An' the last loäd hoäm?' (repeat) „ II 238, 292
To the *e* o' the daäy An' the last loäd hoäm.' „ II 259
I came To eat him up and make an *e* of him. *Foresters* II i 125
at the far *e* of the glade I see two figures „ IV 332
To his own unprincely *e's*. „ IV 716
End (verb) Ay, if he do not *e* in smoke again. *Becket* II ii 315
So *e* all passions. Then what use in passions? *The Cup* I iii 126
Ended all things lived and *e* honestly. *Queen Mary* III v 115
Thou shalt not go. I have not *e* with thee. *Becket, Pro.* 305
That was not the way I *e* it first— „ *Pro.* 335
Our forest games are *e*, our free life, *Foresters* IV 1049
Ending (adj.) showers of blood are blown Before a never *e* blast, *Harold* III i 395
Ending (s) Other reasons There be for this man's *e*, *Queen Mary* IV iii 54
misreport His *e* to the glory of their church. „ IV iii 327
Endure Canst thou *e* to be a beggar *Foresters* I i 204
Enemy Thou speakest of the *e* of thy king. *Queen Mary* I v 327
Stand fast against our *enemies* and yours, „ II ii 242
Makes *enemies* for himself and for his king; „ II ii 399
Who will avenge me of mine *enemies*— „ III ii 166
But he was evermore mine *e*, „ V ii 91
Thou hast given it to the *e* of our house. *Harold* IV ii 31
So perish all the *enemies* of Harold! „ V i 504
So perish all the *enemies* of England! „ V i 554
Be sweet to her, she has many *enemies*. *Becket* I i 404
Is *he* thy *e*? *Henry*. He? who? ay! *Rosamund*. Thine *e* knows the secret of my bower. „ II i 262
To bless thine *enemies*—— *Becket*. Ay, mine, not Heaven's. „ V ii 25
Mine *enemies* barr'd all access to the boy. „ V ii 451
My lord, we force you from your *enemies*. „ V iii 24
Henceforth I am thy mortal *e*. *The Cup* I ii 330
I was but wounded by the *e* there And then imprison'd. *The Falcon* 388
day's bright like a friend, but the wind east like an *e*. *Prom. of May* I 80
They say, we should forgive our *enemies*. „ II 432
Red with his own and *e's* blood— *Foresters* II i 32
Enforce to *e* The long-withholden tribute: *The Cup* I i 76
Enframed powers of the house of Godwin Are not *e* in thee. *Harold* I i 317
Engelram de Trie mightiest knight of France, Sir *E d T*,— *Becket* I iii 748
England Edward might bequeath the crown Of *E*, *Queen Mary* I ii 28
not to yield His Church of *E* to the Papal wolf And Mary; „ I ii 36
—for to wed with Spain Would treble *E*— „ I v 76
I am Queen of *E*; take mine eyes, „ I v 127
Would I marry Prince Philip, if all *E* hate him? „ I v 139
Is it *E*, or a party? Now, your answer. „ I v 142
men-at-arms Guard my poor dreams for *E*. „ I v 154
if this Philip be the titular king Of *E*, „ I v 255
—after me Is heir of *E*; „ I v 286
Would make our *E*, France; Mary of *E*, joining hands with Spain, „ I v 297

England (*continued*) Heir of this *E* and the Netherlands! *Queen Mary* I v 418
Men of Kent; *E* of *E*; „ II i 157
all the rest of *E* bow'd theirs to the Norman, „ II i 159
county or a shire, but of this *E*, „ II i 163
he will be King, King of *E*, my masters; „ II i 173
and be the mightiest man This day in *E*. „ II ii 20
my father was the rightful heir Of *E*, „ II ii 171
or impair in any way This royal state of *E*, „ II ii 230
The Queen of *E*—or the Kentish Squire? „ II ii 269
The Queen of *E* or the rabble of Kent? „ II ii 273
'Who knows?' I am for *E*. „ II ii 412
They are the flower of *E*; set the gates wide. „ II iv 70
lest living Spain Should sicken at dead *E*. „ III i 28
I came to feel the pulse of *E*, „ III i 37
E now Is but a ball chuck'd between France and Spain, „ III i 109
'The Queen of *E* is delivered of a dead dog!' „ III ii 219
Presenting the whole body of this realm Of *E*, „ III iii 117
This is the loveliest day that ever smiled On *E*. „ III iii 163
But stretch it wider; say when *E* fell. „ III iii 261
Perchance in *E*, loves her like a son. „ III iii 267
We reck not tho' we lost this crown of *E*—Ay! tho' it were ten *E's*! „ III iv 56
Thou Christian Bishop, thou Lord Chancellor Of *E*! „ III iv 302
What power this cooler sun of *E* hath „ III iv 327
She troubles *E*: that she breathes in *E* „ III vi 49
I cannot be True to this realm of *E* „ IV i 27
made us lower our kingly flag To yours of *E*. „ V i 60
lower his flag To that of *E* in the seas of *E*. „ V i 66
Being Queen of *E*, I have none other. „ V i 69
he would weld France, *E*, Scotland, „ V i 137
They say your wars are not the wars of *E*. „ V i 166
The King of France the King of *E* too. „ V i 198
sharper harm to *E* and to Rome, Than Calais taken. „ V ii 29
Send out: let *E* as of old Rise lionlike, „ V ii 265
I do much fear that *E* will not care. „ V ii 282
Suffer not That my brief reign in *E* be defamed „ V ii 302
Your *E* is as loyal as myself. „ V ii 328
remember what *you* said When last you came to *E*? „ V ii 568
Welcome to *E*! „ V iii 14
What hinders but that Spain and *E* join'd, „ V iii 68
Spain would be *E* on her seas, and *E* Mistress of the Indies. „ V iii 72
E Will be the Mistress of the Indies yet, „ V iii 76
never merry world In *E*, since the Bible came among us. „ V v 241
It never will be merry world in *E*, „ V v 247
That never English monarch dying left *E* so little. „ V v 278
—we will make *E* great. „ V v 281
God save Elizabeth, the Queen of *E*! „ V v 284
Yon grimly-glaring, treble-brandish'd scourge Of *E*! *Harold* I i 5
mean The doom of *E* and the wrath of Heaven? „ I i 46
bishops down from all Their thrones in *E*! „ I i 51
is this pendent hell in heaven A harm to *E*? „ I i 77
he may tell thee, *I* am a harm to *E*. „ I i 80
War there, my son? is that the doom of *E*? „ I i 126
For all the world sees it as well as *E*. „ I i 130
but after I am gone Woe, woe to *E*! „ I i 190
E loves thee for it. „ I i 221
my father drove the Normans out Of *E*?— „ I i 253
Be there not fair woods and fields In *E*? „ I i 263
sons of Godwin Sit topmost in the field of *E*, „ I i 326
Griffyth I hated; why not hate the foe Of *E*? „ I ii 146
If he were King of *E*, I his queen, „ I ii 154
Should not *E* Love Aldwyth, „ I ii 177
Pronounced his heir of *E*. „ I ii 195
Peace-lover is our Harold for the sake Of *E's* wholeness— „ I ii 198
And bless the Queen of *E*. „ I ii 207
a whale to a whelk we have swallowed the King of *E*. „ II i 45
thine host in *E* when I went To visit Edward. „ II ii 4
know'st my claim on *E* Thro' Edward's promise: „ II ii 12
I want his voice in *E* for the crown, „ II ii 71
E our own Thro' Harold's help, „ II ii 77
Who shall be kings of *E*. I am heir Of *E* „ II ii 124
The choice of *E* is the voice of *E*. *William*. I will be king of *E* by the laws, The choice, and voice of *E*. „ II ii 128

England (*continued*) Blowing for *E*, ha? Not yet. *Harold* II ii 152
Not ever fair for *E*? „ II ii 258
for my mother's sake I love your *E*, „ II ii 269
Then for my mother's sake and *E's* sake „ II ii 274
or whether *E* Be shatter'd into fragments. *Harold.* News from *E*? „ II ii 285
Yea, yea, he would be king of *E*. „ II ii 369
And for our Mother *E*? „ II ii 425
And all thine *E* hath forgotten thee; „ II ii 443
he drove our good Normans out From *E*, „ II ii 526
sat within the Norman chair A ruler all for *E*— „ II ii 534
Why then the heir of *E*, who is he? „ II ii 568
and a child, Will *E* have him king? „ II ii 573
promised that if ever he were king In *E*. „ II ii 588
Thou art the mightiest voice in *E*, man, „ II ii 618
Foremost in *E* and in Normandy; „ II ii 631
And thou be my vice-king in *E*. „ II ii 635
Ay, brother—for the sake of *E*—ay. „ II ii 638
Swear thou to help me to the crown of *E*. „ II ii 705
I swear to help thee to the crown of *E* . . . (repeat) *Harold* II ii 713, 722
Delay is death to thee, ruin to *E*. *Harold* II ii 718
When thou art home in *E*, with thine own, „ II ii 728
The wind is fair For *E* now . . . „ II ii 767
for I am close to thee And *E*— „ III i 7
our dear *E* Is demi-Norman. „ III i 40
Our Tostig parted cursing me and *E*; „ III i 76
He hath gone to kindle Norway against *E*, „ III i 80
Crying 'the doom of *E*,' and at once He stood „ III i 134
along the highest crying 'The doom of *E*!'— „ III i 157
Be there no Saints of *E* To help us „ III i 220
he hath served me: none but he Can rule all *E*. „ III i 244
Not mean To make our *E* Norman. „ III i 250
prayer against the curse That lies on thee and *E*. „ III i 279
Who make thy good their own—all *E*, Earl. „ III i 331
whereby the curse might glance From thee and *E*. „ III i 344
thou be only King of the moment over *E*. „ III ii 51
And well for thee and *E*—and for her— „ III ii 111
And given thy realm of *E* to the bastard. „ III ii 154
thunder-cloud That lours on *E*—laughter! „ III ii 161
but our help Is Harold, king of *E*. „ IV i 11
Dane, Jute, Angle, Saxon, were or should be all One *E*, „ IV i 79
To make all *E* one, to close all feuds, „ IV i 141
one to rule All *E* beyond question, beyond quarrel. „ IV i 145
For *E*, for thy poor white dove, „ IV i 230
Thou art nothing in thine *E*, save for Norway, „ IV ii 22
To do the battle for me here in *E*, „ IV ii 70
both have life In the large mouth of *E*, „ IV iii 74
namesake, when he ask'd for *E*? „ IV iii 111
sons of those Who made this Britain *E*, „ IV iii 154
The men that guarded *E* to the South „ IV iii 209
The curse of *E*! these are drown'd in wassail, „ IV iii 223
Holy Father Hath given this realm of *E* to the Norman. „ V i 13
To do with *E's* choice of her own king? „ V i 19
Should they not know free *E* crowns herself? „ V i 48
should the King of *E* waste the fields Of *E*, „ V i 140
No Norman horse Can shatter *E*, „ V i 196
chanting that old song of Brunanburg Where *E* conquer'd. „ V i 216
our old songs are prayers for *E* too! „ V i 223
I die for *E* then, who lived for *E*— „ V i 268
I left our *E* naked to the South „ V i 289
not for myself—For *E*—yet not wholly— „ V i 307
This memory to thee!—and this to *E*, „ V i 327
Thou hast been false to *E* and to me!— „ V i 349
And not on thee—nor *E*—fall God's doom! „ V i 370
And thou art *E*! Alfred Was *E*. Ethelred was nothing. *E* Is but her king, and thou art Harold! „ V i 373
Edith, if I, the last English King of *E*— „ V i 384
The king of *E* stands between his banners. „ V i 486
So perish all the enemies of *E*! „ V i 555
Here fell the truest, manliest hearts of *E*. „ V ii 59
Why then of *E*. Madam, fear us not. „ V ii 96
When I visited *E*, Some held she was his wife „ V ii 99
I am king of *E*, so they thwart me not, „ V ii 196
I would give her to thy care in *E* *Becket, Pro.* 143

England (*continued*) I have built a secret bower in *E*, Thomas, *Becket Pro.* 153
And pass her to her secret bower in *E*. „ *Pro.* 184
Ay, ay, but swear to see to her in *E*. „ *Pro.* 191
fulminations from the side of Rome, An interdict on *E*—I will have My young son Henry crown'd the King of *E*, That so the Papal bolt may pass by *E*, „ *Pro.* 223
I loved Henry of *E*, and Henry of *E* dreamed that he loved me; „ *Pro.* 357
O thou Great Seal of *E*, Given me by my dear friend the King of *E*— „ I i 336
Barons and bishops of our realm of *E*, „ I iii 336
Flung the Great Seal of *E* in my face— „ I iii 456
he might well have sway'd All *E* under Henry, „ I iii 468
Barons of *E* and of Normandy, „ I iii 741
What say'st thou to the Chancellorship of *E*? „ II i 226
Dost thou know, my boy, what it is to be Chancellor of *E*? „ II i 232
But *E* scarce would hold Young Henry king, „ II ii 30
A hundred of the wisest heads from *E*, „ II ii 172
pushed one way by the Empire and another by *E*, „ II ii 328
till the weight of Germany or the gold of *E* brings one of them down to the dust— „ II ii 364
Save for myself no Rome were left in *E*, „ II ii 387
I strike into my former path For *E*, „ II ii 456
I came to *E* suddenly, „ III i 86
I should be back In *E* ev'n for this. „ III iii 10
My Lords of France and *E*, My friend of Canterbury „ III iii 227
And so farewell until we meet in *E*. *Becket.* I fear, my liege, we may not meet in *E*. „ III iii 237
Come, stay with us, then, Before you part for *E*. „ III iii 245
thy life Was not one hour's worth in *E* „ III iii 251
more wolves that he can tame in his woods of *E*, „ III iii 323
the wolves of *E* Must murder her one shepherd, „ III iii 343
let us move away! And thence to *E*. „ III iii 359
Of and belonging to the King of *E*, „ IV ii 23
'Eleanor of Aquitaine, Eleanor of *E*! „ IV ii 241
My liege, the Queen of *E*. *Henry.* God's eyes! *Eleanor.* Of *E*? Say of Aquitaine. I am no Queen of *E*. I had dream'd I was the bride of *E*, and a queen. *Henry.* And,—while you dream'd you were the bride of *E*,— „ V i 97
Thomas, I would thou hadst return'd to *E*, „ V ii 12
on a Tuesday pass'd From *E* into bitter banishment; „ V ii 289
such brawls and loud disturbances In *E*, „ V ii 354
Divide me from the mother church of *E*, My Canterbury. „ V ii 361
Tho' all the swords in *E* flash'd above me „ V ii 484
Priest of God, Primate of *E*. „ V iii 114
St. Denis of France and St. Alphege of *E*. „ V iii 165
your Robin, all *E's* Robin, fights not for himself but for the people of *E*. *Foresters* I i 236
I would break through them all, like the King of *E*. „ I i 326
according to the law and custom of the kingdom of *E* „ I iii 67
But shall we leave our *E*? „ I iii 92
There is no land like *E* (repeat) *Foresters* II i 1, 5, 13, 17
And these will strike for *E* *Foresters* II i 9
To sing the songs of *E* „ II i 23
King of *E* Perchance this day may sink „ II i 30
made *me* King of all the discontent Of *E* „ II i 88
one of those mercenaries that suck the blood of *E*. „ II i 175
these Barons, Devils, that make this blessed *E* hell. „ iii 127
What was this realm of *E*, all the crowns „ IV 403
I have been away from *E* all these years, „ IV 816

English but took To the *E* red and white. *Queen Mary* I v 18
I am *E* queen, not Roman Emperor. „ I v 503
E Garter, studded with great emeralds, „ III i 84
and *E* carrot's better than Spanish licorice; „ III i 219
tell you that all *E* heretics have tails. „ III i 229
and for Gardiner! being *E* citizen, „ III iii 24
being *E* churchman How should he bear the headship of the Pope? „ III iii 28
Began to batter at your *E* Church, „ III iv 186
there's An old world *E* adage to the point. „ IV i 175
I know them heretics, but right *E* ones. „ IV iii 344
to the intent That you may lose your *E* heritage. „ V i 133
The scourge and butcher of their *E* church. „ V ii 106

English (*continued*) That never *E* monarch dying left England so little. *Queen Mary* v v 277
There somewhere beats an *E* pulse in thee! *Harold* ii ii 266
Boy, thou hast forgotten That thou art *E*. „ ii ii 475
Thou art *E*, Edward too is *E* now, „ iii i 28
To Holy Peter in our *E* isle! „ iii i 207
My mother is a Dane, and I am *E*; „ iv i 55
Seven feet of *E* land, or something more, „ iv ii 54
or *E* Ironside Who fought with Knut, or Knut who coming Dane Died *E*. „ iv iii 53
sight of Danish blood Might serve an end not *E*— „ iv iii 98
'Seven feet of *E* earth, or something more, „ iv iii 112
Edith, if I, the last *E* King of England— „ v i 384
I do not hear our *E* war-cry. „ v i 651
I held it with him in his *E* halls, „ v ii 128
And where is she? There in her *E* nest? *Becket, Pro.* 178
Of Provence blew you to your *E* throne; „ v i 123
That ever blossom'd on this *E* isle. *Foresters* i ii 124
There are no hearts like *E* hearts „ ii i 3
There are no wives like *E* wives „ ii i 15
There are no maids like *E* maids „ ii i 19
the bravest *E* heart Since Hereward the Wake, „ ii i 686
Nay, no Earl am I. I am *E* yeoman. „ iii 131
when Our *E* maidens are their prey, „ iii 179
men w'll call him An Eastern tyrant, not an *E* king. „ iv 904
Look; can you make it *E*? *Queen Mary* ii i 127
Word of God In *E*! „ iii i 280
said the Miserere Mei—But all in *E*, mark you; „ iii i 392
These Spaniel-Spaniard *E* of the time, „ iii iii 240
I am ashamed that I am Bagenhall, *E*. „ iii iii 249
Peters, you know me Catholic, but *E*. „ iv iii 567
Howard is all *E*! „ v i 61
there are many *E* in your ranks To help your battle. „ v i 110
that our brave *E* Had sallied out from Calais „ v ii 255
one who fill'd All offices, all bishopricks with *E*— *Harold* ii ii 535
That art half *E*. Take them away! „ v ii 135
fought men Like Harold and his brethren, and his guard Of *E*. „ v ii 181
Make them again one people—Norman, *E*; And *E*, Norman; „ v ii 189
That's the *E* of it. *Becket* i iv 275
Not on French ground, nor any ground but *E*, „ iii iii 261
and your own name Of Harold sounds so *E* and so old *Prom. of May* iii 610

English-born Shame, shame, my masters! are you *E-b*, *Queen Mary* i iii 70

Englishman You are shy and proud like *Englishmen*, „ ii ii 257
Here swings a Spaniard—there an *E*; „ v i 87
Sailing from France, with thirty *Englishmen*, „ v i 285
There are no men like *Englishmen* *Foresters* ii i 7

Englishwoman Malet, thy mother was an *E*; *Harold* ii ii 265

Enlisted *See* **'Listed**

Enliven We might *e* you. *Queen Mary* i iii 119

Enough (*See also* **Anew**) *E*, my Lords. It is God's will, the Holy Father's will, „ iv i 183
The prison fare is good *e* for me. „ iv ii 42
old *e* To scare me into dreaming, 'what am I, „ iv ii 102
E! Thou wilt not break it! *Harold* ii ii 752
wouldst hug thy Cupid till his ribs cracked—*e* of this. *Becket, Pro.* 505
E, my lord, *e*! „ i iii 740
E, my lord. *Becket*. More than *e*. „ i iii 749
They are plagues *e* in-door. „ ii ii 91
Ay, ay! the King humbles himself *e*. „ ii ii 185
But thou art like *e* to make him thine. *Eleanor*. Becket is like *e* to make all his. „ v i 132
their spites at Rome, Is like *e* to cancel them, *The Cup* i i 92
That is *e*, Farmer Dobson. *Prom. of May* ii 118
E! *Dora*. It seem'd so; only there was left A second daughter, „ iii 769

Enrich and *e* Earth with her shadow! *The Cup* i iii 59

Ensign I, bearing this great *e*, make it clear *Becket* i iii 544

Entanglement I must free myself from this *e*. *Prom. of May* i 480

Enter Not for the seven devils to *e* in? *Queen Mary* iii ii 140
'How hard it is For the rich man to *e* into Heaven;' „ iv iii 205

Enter (*continued*) Ah!—let him *e*. Nay, you need not go: *Queen Mary* v iii 10
Why not? Let him *e*. *The Cup* ii 39
Will *e* on the larger golden age; *Prom. of May* i 590

Enter'd spirit of the twelve Apostles *e* Into thy making. *Becket* i i 50
There was a man just now that *e* here? *Foresters* ii i 240

Entertain'd Maintain'd, and *e* us royally! *Harold* ii ii 159

Entertainment My lord, we thank you for your *e*. *The Falcon* 859
I fear you scarce Will thank me for your *e* now. „ 882

Entreat does your gracious Queen *e* you kinglike? *Courtenay*. 'Fore God, I think she *e's* like a child. *Queen Mary* i iii 110
Poor Wulfnoth! do they not *e* thee well? *Harold* ii ii 404
Madam, we will *e* thee with all honour. „ v ii 199
my good lord, I do *e* thee—sign. *Becket* i iii 185
E's he may be present at our marriage. *The Cup* ii 248

Entreaty Still plied him with *e* and reproach: *Queen Mary* iv iii 577

Entrenchment A good *e* for a perilous hour! *Harold* iii i 363

Entry How can I come When you so block the *e*? *Becket* v iii 37

Envied I *e* Sinnatus when he married her. *The Cup* i i 129

Envy Spite, ignorance, *e*, Yea, honesty too, *Becket* ii i 100

Enwomb'd The babe *e* and at the breast is cursed, *Harold* v i 65

Ephesian Artemis, Artemis, hear her, *E* Artemis! *The Cup* ii 311

Ephesus seven sleepers in the cave at *E* Have turn'd *Harold* i i 192

Episcopari *Nolo* e. *Becket, Pro.* 284

Epitaph And, like the stone-cut *e*, *Queen Mary* iv iii 163

Equal (adj.) I am not *e* to it yet. *Prom. of May* iii 239
We have heard Of thy just, mild, and *e* governance; *Harold* ii ii 690
Two sisters gliding at an *e* dance, *Becket* i iii 444

Equal (s) never since have met Her *e* for pure innocence *Prom. of May* ii 372
shamed of her among The ladies, born his *e's*. „ iii 582

Equall'd Rose never blew that *e* such a bud. *Queen Mary* iii i 373

Eques *E* cum pedite Præpediatur! *Harold* v i 529

Equite Equus cum *e* Dejiciatur! „ v i 579
Equus cum *e* Præcipitatur. „ v i 598

Equity and golden provinces So that were done in *e*. *Becket* v ii 348

Equus *E* cum equite Dejiciatur! *Harold* v i 579
E cum equite Præcipitatur. „ v i 598

Err And there *e's*; As he hath ever err'd *Queen Mary* iv i 30

Err'd As he hath ever *e* thro' vanity. „ iv i 31
I have *e* with him; with him I have recanted. „ iv i 66
Thought that I knew him, *e* thro' love of him, *Becket* i iii 440

Error Repentant of his *e's*? *Queen Mary* iv iii 22

'Erse (horse) That beer be as good fur *'e's* as men. *Prom. of May* ii 315

Esaïas loons That cannot spell *E* from St. Paul, *Queen Mary* iii i 281

Escape (*See also* **'Scape**) Much less shall others in like cause *e*, „ iv iii 63
Who will be martyr when he might *e*. *Becket* v ii 280

Escaped (*See also* **Scaped**) Danaë has *e* again Her tower, and her Acrisius— „ i i 395
She hath *e*. *The Cup* i iii 121
This is my son but late *e* from prison, *Foresters* ii i 460
Gone, like a deer that hath *e* thine arrow! *Robin*. What deer when I have mark'd him ever yet *E* mine arrow? „ iv 60

Escaping charge you that ye keep This traitor from *e*. *Becket* v ii 511

Eshtree (ash-tree) wheere the big *e* cuts athurt it, *Prom. of May* iii 94

Especial A token of His more *e* Grace; *Queen Mary* iii iii 170
Our old friend Cranmer, Your more *e* love, „ iii iv 418

Essex she was passing Some chapel down in *E*, „ i v 40

Established For yet the faith is not *e* there. „ iii iv 109

Estate (condition) bland And affable to men of all *e's*, „ iii vi 81
offal of the city would not change *E's* with him; „ iv iii 78

Estate (property) that holdest thine *e's* In fee and barony *Becket* i iii 674

Esteem'd Who not alone *e* it honourable, *Queen Mary* ii ii 209

Estimation Doth not the *fewness* of anything make the fulness of it in *e*? *Becket* iii iii 303

Eternal The *E* Peter of the changeless chair, *Queen Mary* iii iv 380
our grim Walhalla, *E* war, *Harold* iii ii 75
wing'd souls flying Beyond all change and in the *e* distance „ iii ii 101
Who stands aghast at her *e* self *Becket* ii ii 404
Then with one quick short stab—*e* peace. *The Cup* i iii 124
and smile At bygone things till that *e* peace. „ i iii 173

Ethelred (**King of Saxon England, 979-1016**) Alfred Was England. *E* was nothing. *Harold* v i 374
Eucharist You do not own The bodily presence in the *E*, *Queen Mary* I ii 44
Eucharistic and retract That *E* doctrine in your book. „ IV ii 81
Europe I am the noblest blood in *E*, Madam, „ I iv 85
lord of more land Than any crown in *E*, *Becket* v i 30
oaks, Gnarl'd—older than the thrones of *E*! *Foresters* III 93
Eva (**daughter of Farmer Steer**) an' Miss Dora, an' Miss *E*, an' all! *Prom. of May* I 11
Foälks says he likes Miss *E* the best. „ I 25
Beänt Miss *E* gone off a bit of 'er good looks „ I 32
I haven't seen *E* yet. Is she anywhere in the garden? „ I 46
He's been arter Miss *E*, haän't he? „ I 121
E told me that he was taking her likeness. He's an artist. „ I 126
Hev' ony o' ye seen *E*? *Dobson.* Noä, Mr. Steer. „ I 313
I likes 'im, and *E* likes 'im. *E* can do owt wi' 'im; look for 'im, *E*, „ I 436
Jealous of me with *E*! Is it so? „ I 471
My sweet *E*, Where have you lain in ambush „ I 543
Well, *E*! *Eva.* Oh, Dora, Dora, „ I 766
Fonder of poor *E*—like everybody else. „ II 11
I hallus gi'ed soom on 'em to Miss *E* at this time o' year. „ II 16
fur Miss *E*, she set the bush by my dairy winder „ II 17
I take them, then, for *E's* sake. *Dobson.* *E's* saäke. Yeas. Poor gel, poor gel! „ II 29
or you may find me at the bottom of the river—*E*.' „ II 88
Poor *E*! O my God, if man be only A willy-nilly „ II 261
How often have I stood With *E* here! „ II 297
E! *Dora.* *E*! *Harold.* What are you? „ II 356
You knew *E*, then? „ II 367
Dear *E* Was always thought the prettier. „ II 378
tell me anything of our sweet *E* When in her brighter girlhood, „ II 520
E's eyes thro' hers—A spell upon me! Surely I loved *E* More than I knew! „ II 641
if ye be goin' to sarve our Dora as ye sarved our *E*— „ II 692
now that you have been brought to us as it were from the grave, dearest *E*, „ III 236
to saäy he's browt some of Miss *E's* roses for the sick laädy to smell on. „ III 347
E, why did you write 'Seek me at the bottom of the river'? „ III 363
E has come home. „ III 442
Be not so cast down, my sweet *E*. „ III 468
You know her, *E*. *Harold.* *E*! „ III 663
O she has fainted. Sister, *E*, sister! „ III 672
Eve if I had been *E* i' the garden I shouldn't ha' minded the apple, *Becket* III i 139
Even (adj.) a jest In time of danger shows the pulses *e*. *Queen Mary* II ii 357
Even (s) Good *e*, my good brother! *Gurth.* Good *e*, gentle Edith. *Edith.* Good *e*, Gurth. *Harold* III ii 116
yet I think these oaks at dawn and *e*, *Foresters* IV 1067
Evening When back he comes at *e* hath the door *Queen Mary* V ii 120
Event to compose the *e* In some such form „ I v 224
stay Yet for awhile, to shape and guide the *e*. „ V i 304
And the *e*—our fallows till'd, *Becket* I iii 375
Ever (*See also* **Iver**) who am your friend And *e* faithful counsellor, *Queen Mary* I v 135
Ever-closing who dream'd as blanketed In *e-c* fog, „ III ii 21
Ever-jarring *e-j* Earldoms move To music and in order— *Harold* II ii 760
Everlasting Open, ye *e* gates! The King is here!— *Queen Mary* III ii 183
Ever-rising Beneath an *e-r* sun—I see him— *The Cup* II 535
Ever-shining There—league on league of *e-s* shore „ II 533
Every Parliament can make *e* true-born man of us a bastard. *Queen Mary* I i 27
Skips *e* way, from levity or from fear. „ I iii 170
That *e* morning of your Majesty May be most good, is *e* morning's prayer „ I v 100
He is *e* way a lesser man than Charles; „ I v 330
but *e* parish tower Shall clang and clash alarum as we pass, „ II i 228
In *e* London street a gibbet stood. „ III i 7
Certain I had heard that *e* Spaniard carries a tail „ III i 223

Every (*continued*) *e* Spanish priest will tell you that all English heretics have tails. *Queen Mary* III i 228
Do here absolve you and deliver you And *e* one of you, „ III iii 215
and from all and *e* censure, Judgment, „ III iii 217
Seeing there lie two ways to *e* end, „ III iv 113
e tongue Alters it passing, till it spells and speaks „ III v 35
that she breathes in England Is life and lungs to *e* rebel birth „ III vi 51
And *e* soul of man that breathes therein. „ III vi 107
And for thy soul shall masses here be sung By *e* priest in Oxford. „ IV iii 101
Good people, *e* man at time of death Would fain set forth „ IV iii 156
In *e* article of the Catholic faith, And *e* syllable taught us by our Lord, „ IV iii 230
Let *e* craft that carries sail and gun Steer toward Calais. „ V ii 275
when our good hive Needs *e* sting to save it. *Harold* IV i 18
E man about his king Fought like a king; „ IV iii 56
E man about his king Fell where he stood. „ V ii 181
when *e* doorway blush'd, *Becket* I iii 346
When *e* baron ground his blade in blood; „ I iii 349
From *e* bond and debt and obligation Incurr'd as Chancellor. „ I iii 710
that *e* thread of thought Is broken ere it joins— „ V ii 205
I am sure of being *e* way malign'd. *The Cup* I ii 241
I would that *e* man made feast to-day „ II 225
for I've been on my knees *e* day for these half-dozen years *The Falcon* 184
The blossom had open'd on *e* bough; *Prom. of May* I 42
and sat Thro' *e* sensual course of that full feast „ II 254
might be Blown everyway with *e* gust and wreck „ III 536
is always a-telling us that *e* man, *Foresters* I i 95
Softly! softly! there may be a thief in *e* bush. „ II i 368
for being *e* inch a man I honour *e* inch of a woman. „ III 63
Ay, for old Much is *e* inch a man. „ IV 289
And loves and dotes on *e* dingle of it. „ IV 390
Everyway (*See also* **Every**) Her ghost is *e* about me here. *Prom. of May* II 353
might be Blown *e* with every gust and wreck „ III 536
Evil (adj.) She hath harken'd *e* counsel—ah! *Queen Mary* V i 54
but last night An *e* dream that ever came and went— *Harold* I ii 70
with thy goodwill that I Proceed against thine *e* councillors, *Becket* III iii 209
It may be they were *e* councillors. „ III iii 216
Whose *e* song far on into the night „ V ii 208
I fear some strange and *e* chance Coming upon me, *The Cup* I iii 74
It bears an *e* savour among women. „ I iii 86
There came some *e* fairy at my birth And cursed me, *Foresters* II ii 108
E fairy! do you hear? „ II ii 116
Evil (s) spring Of all those *e's* that have flow'd upon us; *Queen Mary* III iv 234
The Church's *e* is not as the King's, „ III iv 273
kingly touch that cures the *e* May serve to charm the tiger *Harold* I i 152
E for good, it seems, Is oft as childless of the good as *e* For *e*. „ V i 171
Evil-tongue Ingratitude, Injustice, *E-t*, Labour-in-vain. *Queen Mary* V ii 156
Evolution when the man, The child of *e*, *Prom. of May* I 585
Ewe-lamb black sheep baaed to the miller's *e-l*, *Becket* I iv 163
'*E l*, *e l*, I am here by the dam.' „ I iv 171
Exalt Hugh, how proudly you *e* your head! „ V ii 454
Example he must die, For warning and *e*. *Queen Mary* IV iii 52
Take therefore, all, *e* by this man, „ IV iii 59
Exceeding With most *e* willingness, I will; „ III v 214
Fourthly, to those that own *e* wealth, „ IV iii 201
Some hollow-hearted from *e* age— *Foresters* III 96
Exceedingly I wish you and your ladyship's father a most *e* good morning. „ I i 309
Excellent Look at the hilt. What *e* workmanship. *Becket* IV ii 315
Excess Nature's moral Against *e*. „ I i 374
Against the moral *e* No physical ache, „ I i 381
his fond *e* of wine Springs from the loneliness „ III i 38
Excessive seeing they were men Defective or *e*, „ II ii 213
Exchange we will say—*e* them For your—for your— *The Falcon* 730
Exchequer the realm is poor, The *e* at neap-tide: *Queen Mary* I v 121
I am sorry my *e* runs so low I cannot help you *Foresters* I ii 272
Excommunicate No man without my leave shall *e* My tenants or my household. *Becket*, *Pro.* 30

Excommunicate (*continued*) Ah! Thomas, *e* them all! Becket I iii 573
Smite the sheep and the shepherd will *e* thee. „ I iv 228
More like is he to *e* me. „ II i 270
my poor heretic heart would *e* His excommunication, „ II i 283
That thou wouldst *e* the King. „ V ii 90
He thought to *e* him— „ V ii 141
How could I *e* him then? *Rosamund.* And wilt thou *e* him now? „ V ii 154
to *e* The prelates whom he chose to crown his son! „ V ii 398
What! will he *e* all the world? „ V ii 466
Because thou wast *born e.* „ V ii 472
Excommunicated My lord, you have not *e* him? „ V ii 130
to absolve the bishops Whom you have *e.* „ V ii 377
I should be grateful—He hath not *e me.* „ V ii 471
Excommunicating The King condemns your *e*— „ V ii 318
Excommunication heart would excommunicate His *e.* „ II i 285
To blast my realms with *e* And interdict. „ II ii 52
Excuse must Accuse himself, *e* himself; *The Cup* II 115
Execrable With execrating *e* eyes, Glared at the citizen. *Queen Mary* II ii 67
Execrating With *e* execrable eyes, Glared at the citizen. „ II ii 67
Execute let me *e* the vengeance of the Church upon them. *Foresters* IV 915
Execution to the saving of their souls, Before your *e.* *Queen Mary* IV ii 195
Exeter Deans Of Christchurch, Durham, *E*, and Wells— „ I ii 9
Exhibited Our supplication be *e* To the Lord Cardinal Pole, „ III iii 123
Exhort *E* them to a pure and virtuous life; „ IV ii 77
Exigency But help her in this *e*, „ II ii 18
I cannot help you in this *e*; *Foresters* I ii 273
Exile (s) I know a set of *e's* over there, *Queen Mary* III i 155
long petition from the foreign *e's* To spare the life of Cranmer. „ IV i 3
This same petition of the foreign *e's* „ IV i 193
condemn The blameless *e*?— *Becket* II ii 396
'Tis not the King who is guilty of mine *e*, „ II ii 415
Send back again those *e's* of my kin „ III iii 186
On a Tuesday from mine *e* I return'd, „ V ii 293
Exile (verb) *E* me from the face of Theobald. „ I iii 43
Exit Here His turtle builds; his *e* is our adit: „ III ii 7
Expectant *E* of the rack from day to day, *Queen Mary* IV iii 437
Expectation one step in the dark beyond Our *e*, that amazes us. *The Cup* I i 213
Expedient And all our loving subjects, most *e.* *Queen Mary* II ii 211
It is *e* for one man to die, „ IV iii 17
which our Queen And Council at this present deem it not *E* to be known. „ IV iii 57
Experience And all the heap'd *e's* of life, *Becket* I i 154
Exposure *See* **Self-exposure**
Extreme your Father must be now in *e* old age. *Prom. of May* III 400
Eye (a place) Due from his castles of Berkhamstead and *E* *Becket* I iii 629
Eye I shall judge with my own *e's* *Queen Mary* I i 134
with his fast-fading *e's* Fixt hard on mine, „ I ii 30
and deep-incavern'd *e's* Half fright me. „ I iv 267
some waxen doll Thy baby *e's* have rested on, „ I v 9
take mine *e's*, mine heart, But do not lose me Calais. „ I v 127
into some more costly stone Than ever blinded *e.* „ I v 371
what, have you *e's*, ears, brains? „ II i 96
With execrating execrable *e's*, Glared at the citizen. „ II ii 67
Were your *e's* So bashful that you look'd no higher? „ III i 64
and when her innocent *e's* were bound, „ III i 405
Wore in mine *e's* the green of Paradise. „ III ii 18
Fine *e's*—but melancholy, irresolute— „ III iv 337
I read his honest horror in his *e's.* „ III v 61
And warble those brief-sighted *e's* of hers? „ III vi 155
you scarce could meet his *e* And hold your own; „ IV i 104
I am ashamed to lift my *e's* to heaven, „ IV iii 127
His *e* was like a soldier's, whom the general „ IV iii 304
Tell her to come and close my dying *e's*, „ V ii 600
Mine *e's* are dim: what hath she written? „ V v 1
I swear it, By mine own *e's*— *Harold* I ii 110
There lodged a gleaming grimness in his *e's*, „ II ii 225
He tore their *e's* out, sliced their hands away, „ II ii 389
Tear out his *e's*, And plunge him into prison. „ II ii 491
Thine 'ifs' will sear thine *e's* out—ay. „ II ii 626
whose baby *e* Saw them sufficient. „ III ii 66
I saw it in her *e's*! „ V i 368
Eye (*continued*) God's *e's*! I know all that— *Becket, Pro.* 148
God's *e's*! what a lovely cross! „ *Pro.* 371
for thine *e's* Glare stupid-wild with wine. „ I i 213
He had good *e's*! „ I ii 38
He all but pluck'd the bearer's *e's* away. „ I iii 11
God's *e's*! I had meant to make him all but king. „ I iii 464
The King's 'God's *e's*!' come now so thick and fast, „ I iii 609
by God's *e's*, we will not have him crown'd. „ II ii 3
The Church alone hath *e's*—and now I see „ II ii 436
was a pity to blindfold such *e's* as mine, „ III i 127
only there was a dare-devil in his *e*—I should say a dare-Becket. „ III iii 89
father's *e* was so tender it would have called „ III iii 101
as to the young crownling himself, he looked so malapert in the *e's*, „ III iii 109
King plucks out their *e's* Who anger him, „ IV ii 406
disciplines that clear the spiritual *e*, „ V i 43
My liege, the Queen of England. *Henry.* God's *e's*! „ V i 98
The Church! the Church! God's *e's*! „ V i 217
bust of Juno and the brows and *e's* Of Venus; *The Cup* I i 121
What follows is for no wife's *e's.* „ I ii 231
Yea,—with our *e's*,—our hearts, „ I ii 412
mark'd Her *e's* were ever on the marble floor? „ II 19
and a-spreading to catch her *e* for a dozen year, till he hasn't an *e* left *The Falcon* 100
The pleasure of his *e's*—boast of his hand— „ 221
That bright inheritor of your *e's*—your boy? „ 306
i' the poorch as soon as he clapt *e's* of 'er. *Prom. of May* I 23
Under your *e's*, Miss Dora. „ I 89
And your *e's* be as blue as— „ I 91
voice a-shaäkin', and the drop in 'er *e.* „ II 130
Eva's *e's* thro' hers—A spell upon me! „ II 641
hath the fire in her face and the dew in her *e's.* *Foresters* I i 167
Would you cast An *e* of favour on me, „ I ii 217
How close the Sheriff peer'd into thine *e's*! „ I ii 253
That if I cast an *e* of favour on him, „ I ii 261
Elf, with spiteful heart and *e*, „ II ii 172
Not an *e* to survey, „ II ii 181
Robin, the sweet light of a mother's *e*, „ IV 2
Mine *e* most true to one hair's-breadth of aim. „ IV 694
I cannot meet his *e's.* „ IV 799
Eyebrow Why do you lift your *e* at me thus? *Queen Mary* III vi 102
Eyed *See* **Far-eyed**
Eyeless —tongueless and *e*, prison'd— *Harold* II ii 496
Eyelid Mine amulet . . . This last . . . upon thine *e's*, „ I ii 125
kiss that charms thine *e's* into sleep, „ I ii 140
Eyeshot and keep me still In *e.* „ II ii 242
Eyesight play The William with thine *e* and thy tongue. „ V i 27
rend away *E* and manhood, life itself, *Becket* IV ii 285
Has lost his health, his *e*, even his mind. *Prom. of May* III 767

F

Fa I would dance too. *F*, la, la, *f* la, la. *Foresters* I ii 59
Faäce (face) plow straäit as a line right i' the *f* o' the sun, *Prom. of May* I 370
—then hup ageän i' the *f* o' the sun. „ I 372
thaw the feller's gone and maäde such a litter of his *f.* „ II 589
she niver knawed 'is *f* when 'e wur 'ere afoor; „ II 606
Fable There is a pleasant *f* in old books, *Harold* IV i 56
Face (s) (*See also* **Faäce, Janus-faces, Long-face**) wilt thou see the holy father Murdered before thy *f*? *Queen Mary* I iii 65
Is this the *f* of one who plays the tyrant? „ I v 194
Madam, methinks a cold *f* and a haughty. „ I v 197
Show me your *f's*! „ I v 307
show'd his back Before I read his *f.* „ II i 133
Here was a young mother, Her *f* on flame, „ II ii 70
The colour freely play'd into her *f*, „ II ii 321
thro' that dim dilated world of hers, To read our *f's*; „ II ii 326
before the Queen's *f* Gardiner buys them With Philip's gold. „ III i 143
there's the *f* coming on here of one Who knows me. „ III i 470
Pole has the Plantagenet *f*, „ III iv 334

Face (s) (*continued*) I have but shown a loathing *f* to you, *Queen Mary* III vi 113
See how the tears run down his fatherly *f*. „ IV iii 4
wash'd his hands and all his *f* therein, „ IV iii 338
and look upon my *f*, Not on the comet. *Harold* I i 26
I cannot read the *f* of heaven; „ I i 67
He can but read the king's *f* on his coins. *Stigand.* Ay, ay, young lord, *there* the king's *f* is power. „ I i 71
send thy saints that I may say Ev'n to their *f's*, „ II ii 787
The rosy *f*, and long down-silvering beard, „ III i 46
turn not thou Thy *f* away, „ III ii 40
The rosy *f* and long down-silvering beard— „ IV i 261
he hath risen again—he bares his *f*— „ V i 557
how he fells The mortal copse of *f's*! „ V i 589
They have so maim'd and murder'd all his *f* „ V ii 77
I left him with peace on his *f*— *Becket, Pro.* 396
Her *f* was veiled, but the back methought „ *Pro.* 469
Exile me from the *f* of Theobald. „ I iii 43
when he sign'd, his *f* was stormy-red— „ I iii 320
Flung the Great Seal of England in my *f*— „ I iii 457
he licks my *f* and moans and cries out against the King. „ I iv 99
and glass The faithful *f* of heaven— „ II i 161
Life on the *f*, the brows—clear innocence! „ II i 195
who hath withstood two Kings to their *f's* for the honour of God. „ II ii 276
as I hate the dirty gap in the *f* of a Cistercian monk, „ II ii 381
or I couldn't look your ladyship i' the *f*, „ III i 196
and to read the *f's* of men at a great show. „ III iii 83
ran a twitch across his *f* as who should say „ III iii 94
and once he strove to hide his *f*, „ III iii 104
his fine-cut *f* bowing and beaming with all that courtesy „ III iii 141
scared the red rose from your *f* Into your heart? „ IV ii 74
I will hide my *f*, Blacken and gipsyfy it; „ IV ii 99
Nay, what uncomely *f's*, could he see you! „ V i 201
These arm'd men in the city, these fierce *f's*— „ V iii 4
We will not have him slain before our *f*. „ V iii 55
shun To meet her *f* to *f* at once! *The Cup* I i 59
brows and eyes Of Venus; *f* and form unmatchable! „ I i 122
She—no, not ev'n my *f*. „ I i 132
Who are with him? I see no *f* that knows me. „ I i 183
In the full *f* of all the Roman camp? „ I ii 269
Only one, And he perhaps mistaken in the *f*. „ I ii 343
His *f* was not malignant, and he said „ I ii 451
ambition, pride So bloat and redden his *f*— „ II 170
far as the *f* goes A goodlier-looking man „ II 175
f of an angel and the heart of a—that's too positive! *The Falcon* 86
what you see you are saying afore his *f*? *Count.* Let him—he never spares me to my *f*! *Filippo.* No, my lord, I never spare your lordship to your lordship's *f*, „ 108
nor to round about and back to your lordship's *f* again, „ 115
and bless your sweet *f*, you look as beautiful „ 197
colour'd all my life, Flush'd in her *f*; „ 365
one sweet *f* Crown'd with the wreath. „ 648
her affections Will flower toward the light in some new *f*. *Prom. of May* I 487
Her bright *f* beaming starlike down upon me „ II 248
If he should ever show his *f* among us, „ II 423
the rain beating in my *f* all the way, „ III 367
'Go home;' but I hadn't the heart or *f* to do it. „ III 389
I will give thee a buffet on the *f*. *Foresters* I i 146
hath the fire in her *f* and the dew in her eyes. „ I i 167
How she looks up at him, how she holds her *f*! „ I ii 145
Why wearest thou thy cowl to hide thy *f*? „ I ii 207
bounden by a vow not to show his *f*, „ I ii 237
I hate hidden *f's*. (repeat) „ I ii 245, 251
and old *f's* Press round us, and warm hands „ I iii 19
Her *f* is thine, and if thou be as gentle „ II i 480
Wilt thou embrace thy sweetheart 'fore my *f*? „ II ii 29
Never Ob before his *f*. „ II ii 133
For ever buzzing at your lady's *f*. „ IV 11
It is not he—his *f*—tho' very like— „ IV 777
And scruplest not to flaunt it to our *f* „ IV 887
Face (verb) *f* me out of all My regal rights. *Becket* II ii 165
Faced *See* **Black-faced, Red-faced**

Facile be *f* to my hands. Now is my time. *Becket, Pro.* 218
Facility translated that hard heart into our Provençal *facilities*, „ *Pro.* 381
to spare us the hardness of your *f*? „ *Pro.* 386
Faction There is a *f* risen again for Tostig, *Harold* IV i 172
Our anti-Roman *f*? *The Cup* I ii 197
I have enough—their anti-Roman *f*. „ I ii 201
dishonour The daughters and the wives of your own *f*— *Foresters* IV 699
Fade *f* Into the deathless hell which is their doom *Queen Mary* III ii 174
we *f* and are forsaken— „ V ii 374
Faded Flower, she! Half *f*! „ I iv 61
this *f* ribbon was the mode In Florence ten years back. *The Falcon* 421
blossom of his youth, Has *f*, falling fruitless— *Prom. of May* II 334
Fading (*See also* **Fast-fading**) O my sick boy! My daily *f* Florio, *The Falcon* 236
Faggot then, who lights the *f*? Not the full faith, *Queen Mary* III iv 123
Last night, I dream'd the *f's* were alight, „ IV ii 2
Will my *f's* Be wet as his were? „ IV ii 228
bind a score All in one *f*, snap it over knee, *Harold* IV i 58
Faggot-band Snap not the *f-b* then. „ IV i 66
Fail I *f* Where he was fullest: *Queen Mary* II i 55
All traitors *f* like Tostig! *Harold* IV iii 79
Solders a race together—yea—tho' they *f*, *The Cup* I ii 163
Lest he should *f* to pay these thousand marks *Foresters* IV 454
Fail'd Few things have *f* to which I set my will. *Queen Mary* II ii 22
Wyatt was a good soldier, yet he *f*, „ III i 132
On my last voyage—but the wind has *f*— *The Cup* II 522
We ever *f* to light upon thy son. *Foresters* IV 984
Failing *F* her, my Lord, Doth not as great *Queen Mary* I iv 94
Failure but *f* it may be Of all we aim'd at. *Becket* I i 382
Fain Make me full *f* to live and die a maid. *Queen Mary* V iii 98
Faint I am somewhat *f* With our long talk. „ I iv 520
I am *f* with fear that you will come no more. „ V i 30
but look, where Edward draws A *f* foot hither, *Harold* I i 144
Tostig, I am *f* again. „ I i 266
A ghostly horn Blowing continually, and *f* battle-hymns, „ III i 373
I am *f* and sleepy. Leave me. *Becket* III i 208
I am very *f*. I must lie down. *Prom. of May* III 472
'I am *f* for your honey, my sweet.' *Foresters* IV 15
Move me no more! I am sick and *f* with pain! „ IV 599
Fainted O she has *f*. Sister, Eva, sister! *Prom. of May* III 672
Fair Even so, *f* lady. *Queen Mary* I iv 97
left about Like loosely-scatter'd jewels, in *f* order, „ II i 28
As *f* and white as angels; „ III ii 16
were much amazed To find as *f* a sun as might have flash'd „ III ii 22
you perchance were trifling royally With some *f* dame of court, „ III vi 160
And all the *f* spice-islands of the East. „ V i 49
How *f* and royal—like a Queen, indeed? „ V i 235
F island star! „ V iii 15
Were you in Spain, this fine *f* gossamer gold— „ V iii 48
I never look'd upon so *f* a likeness „ V v 28
Be there not *f* woods and fields In England? *Harold* I i 261
Then fling mine own *f* person in the gap A sacrifice to Harold, „ I ii 202
then a *f* life And bless the Queen of England. „ I ii 206
Earl, wilt thou fly my falcons this *f* day? „ II ii 146
So thou, *f* friend, will take them easily. „ II ii 207
Not ever *f* for England? „ II ii 258
Obey him, speak him *f*, „ II ii 318
O speak him *f*, Harold, for thine own sake. „ II ii 395
Look not amazed, *f* earl! „ II ii 494
The wind is *f* For England now . . . „ II ii 766
Full thanks for your *f* greeting of my bride! „ IV iii 46
Good royal customs—had them written *f* *Becket* I iii 416
And one *f* child to fondle! „ III i 12
F Sir, a happy day to you! *The Cup* I i 188
Leaving your *f* Marian alone here. *Foresters* I ii 154
There are no wives like English wives So *f* and chaste as they be. „ II i 16
Fare you well, *f* lady! „ III 243
but see *f* play Betwixt them and Sir Richard— „ IV 98
But thou art *f* as ever, my sweet sister, „ IV 1017

Fairer My sister, is far f than myself. Queen Mary I v 72
How look'd the Queen? Bagenhall. No f for her jewels. " III i 92
and the flowers Are all the f. Becket, Pro. 117
Fairest but of this England, in whose crown our Kent is the f jewel. Queen Mary II i 163
Find one a slut whose f linen seems Foul Becket V ii 202
Who art the f flower of maidenhood Foresters I ii 123
Fair-hair'd little f-h Norman maid Lived in my mother's house: Becket V ii 259
Fairly My King would know if you be f served, Queen Mary V iii 20
Fairy (adj.) What's here? A dead bat in the f ring— Foresters II ii 93
A glimpse of them and of their f Queen— " II ii 103
F realm is breaking down " II ii 134
there comes a deputation From our finikin f nation. " II ii 145
Fairy (s) wish before the word Is man's good F— Queen Mary I iv 240
I thought if I followed it I should find the fairies. Eleanor. I am the f, pretty one, a good f to thy mother. Becket IV i 24
There are good fairies and bad fairies, " IV i 28
can't sleep sound o' nights because of the bad fairies. " IV i 31
I am her good f. Geoffrey. But you don't look like a good f. Mother does. " IV i 34
And leave you alone with the good f. " IV ii 61
She may have lighted on your fairies here, Foresters II i 496
My men say The fairies haunt this glade;— " II ii 101
There came some evil f at my birth " II ii 108
Evil f! do you hear? " II ii 116
We be fairies of the wood, " II ii 118
When the f slights the crown. " II ii 135
Fairy-ring And now be skipping in their f-r's, " II i 497
Faith My flight were such a scandal to the f, Queen Mary I ii 53
long divided in itself, and sever'd from the f, " I iii 22
Bonner, who hath lain so long under bonds for the f— " I iii 36
Art thou of the true f, fellow, " I iii 45
No, being of the true f with myself. " I v 74
we two will lead The living waters of the F again " I v 88
But here's some Hebrew. F, I half forgot it. " II i 125
Good f, I was too sorry for the woman " III i 57
All greed, no f, no courage! " III i 145
'Hail, Daughter of God, and saver of the f. " III ii 82
And clasp the f in Christ; " III ii 122
Henceforth a centre of the living f. " III ii 155
The great unborn defender of the F, " III ii 165
His f shall clothe the world that will be his, " III ii 180
f that seem'd to droop will feel your light, " III iv 22
track of the true f Your lapses are far seen. " III iv 94
For yet the f is not established there. " III iv 109
because to persecute Makes a f hated, and is furthermore No perfect witness of a perfect f " III iv 116
Not the full f, no, but the lurking doubt. " III iv 124
When f is wavering makes the waverer pass " III iv 157
call they not The one true f, a loathsome idol-worship? " III iv 219
accuse you of indifference To all f's, all religion; " III iv 224
the Queen, the Holy Father, The f itself. " III vi 35
Upon the f and honour of a Spaniard, " III vi 254
Have you remain'd in the true Catholic f I left you in? Cranmer. In the true Catholic f, " IV ii 17
confess Your f before all hearers; " IV ii 80
my f would seem Dead or half-drown'd, " IV ii 96
Which frights you back into the ancient f; " IV ii 144
Power hath been given you to try f by fire— " IV ii 153
these burnings will not help The purpose of the f; " IV ii 185
he seal his f In sight of all with flaming martyrdom. " IV iii 28
proclaim Your true undoubted f, that all may hear. " IV iii 114
declare to you my very f Without all colour. " IV iii 225
In every article of the Catholic f, " IV iii 230
No f with heretics, my Lord! " IV iii 458
Died in the true f? " V ii 518
sunk rocks; no passionate f— " V v 222
Pray'd me to pay her debts, and keep the F; " V v 258
What's up is f, what's down is heresy. Harold I i 84
yet to us, in f, A happy one— " II ii 200
That runs thro' all the f's of all the world. " III i 352
all the f's Of this grown world of ours, " III ii 64
Faith (continued) Loyally and with good f, my lord Archbishop? Becket I iii 278
with all that loyalty and good f Thou still " I iii 281
Mail'd in the perfect panoply of f, " V ii 494
Die for a woman, what new f is this? The Cup I iii 67
learnt at last that all His old-world f, Prom. of May II 332
—will he ever be of one f with his wife? " III 178
Beware, man, lest thou lose thy f in me. Foresters I ii 179
on the f and honour of a king The land is his again. " IV 851
Faithful who am your friend And ever f counsellor, Queen Mary I v 135
that I live and die That true and f bride of Philip— " II iv 43
Your f friend and trusty councillor. " IV i 89
Have done my best, and as a f son, " V ii 117
herself should see That king's are f to their marriage vow. Becket I ii 78
A f traitress to thy royal fame. " II i 97
and glass The f face of heaven— " II i 161
and be to Rome More f than a Roman. The Cup I i 103
This very day the Romans crown him king For all his f services to Rome. " II 65
Our Antonius, Our f friend of Rome, " II 244
I will be f to thee till thou die. " II 330
Faithless Break thine alliance with this f John, Foresters IV 323
Falaise The F byblow! Harold IV iii 174
Falcon wilt thou fly my f's this fair day? " II ii 146
Bird-babble for my f! Let it pass. The Falcon 38
Just gone To fly his f. " 210
His f, and I come to ask for his f, " 219
his f Ev'n wins his dinner for him in the field. " 230
How can I ask for his f? " 234
'Get the Count to give me his f, " 242
How can I, dare I, ask him for his f? " 264
and once you let him fly your f. " 317
His F. Count. My f! Giovanna. Yes, your f, Federigo! " 840
Nothing but my brave bird, my noble f, " 874
Falconry The full-train'd marvel of all f, " 25
plunge and f Of heresy to the pit: Queen Mary III iv 141
Fall (s) have I that I am fixt, Fixt beyond f; " IV ii 90
It means the f of Tostig from his earldom. Harold I i 468
Except it be a soft one, And undereaten to the f. " I ii 123
Do you still suffer from your f in the hollow lane? Prom. of May III 241
She said 'It's the f of the year, Foresters IV 24
Fall (verb) Hast thou let f those papers in the palace? Queen Mary I iii 1
No—being traitor Her head will f: " I v 60
let Rebellion Roar till throne rock, and crown f. " II i 145
hoped to f Into the wide-spread arms of fealty, " II ii 263
Like dogs that set to watch their master's gate, F, " III iv 311
in the daylight truth That it may f to-day! " III v 137
If war should f between yourself and France; " V i 9
So from a clear sky f's the thunderbolt! " V iii 115
Come f not foul on me. Harold I i 460
see confusion f On thee and on thine house. " II ii 489
My prayers go up as fast as my tears f, " III i 166
F, cloud, and fill the house— " III i 190
And on it f's the shadow of the priest; " III ii 70
If the king f, may not the kingdom f? But if I f, I f, " V i 123
If I f, I f—The doom of God! " V i 135
I cannot f into a falser world— " V i 271
And not on thee—nor England—f God's doom! " V i 370
F's—and another f's. " V i 500
No, daughter, no—they f behind the horse— " V i 545
As thine own bolts that f on crimeful heads " V i 565
Charged with the weight of heaven wherefrom they f! " V i 568
They f on those within the palisade! " V i 668
As seeming his, not mine, and f abroad. Becket, Pro. 228
God make not thee, but thy foes, f. Becket. I fell. Why f? Why did He smite me? What? Shall I f off—to please the King once more? " I i 107
Thou canst not f that way. " I i 115
'When a bishoprick f's vacant, the King, " I iii 100
When thieves f out, honest men— " I iv 114
When honest men f out, thieves— " I iv 118
Shame f on those who gave it a dog's name— " II i 141
the sea-creek—the petty rill That f's into it— " II ii 295
Devil's 'if Thou wilt f down and worship me.' " III iii 286

Fall (verb) (*continued*) I could *f* down, and worship thee, my Thomas, *Becket* III iii 288
Go. See that you do not *f* in. Go. „ IV ii 59
world allows I *f* no inch Behind this Becket, „ V i 39
Ready to *f* at Henry's word or yours— „ V ii 486
I heard in Rome, This tributary crown may *f* to you. *The Cup* I i 97
So *f's* the throne of an hour. „ II 486
with as little pain As it is to *f* asleep. *Prom. of May* II 342
But for the slender help that I can give, *F* into ruin. „ II 422
I *f* before thee, clasp Thy knees. *Foresters* II i 598
When heaven *f's*, I may light on such a lark! „ III 12
he *f's* And knows no more. „ IV 526
Fallen (*See also* **Flesh-fallen**) He hath *f* out of favour with the Queen. *Queen Mary* I iv 156
We are *f*, and as I think, Never to rise again. „ III i 123
of all censures Of Holy Church that we be *f* into, „ III iii 152
we are *f* creatures; Look to your Bible, Paget! we are *f*. „ III iv 80
You sit upon this *f* Cranmer's throne; „ IV i 114
How are the mighty *f*, Master Cranmer! „ IV ii 146
From councillor to caitiff—*f* so low, „ IV iii 75
That should have *f*, and may rise again. „ V ii 6
like the bloodless head *F* on the block, „ V ii 21
Love will fly the *f* leaf, and not be overtaken; „ V ii 372
blast that came So suddenly hath *f* as suddenly— *Harold* II i 14
Many are *f* At Stamford-bridge . . . „ IV iii 214
Gurth hath leapt upon him And slain him: he hath *f*. „ V i 634
Glory to God in the Highest! *f*, *f*! „ V i 636
hath kinglike fought and *f*, His birthday, too. „ V ii 125
spouse of the Great King, thy King, hath *f*— *Becket* III iii 176
The folds have *f* from the mystery, „ IV ii 8
he hath *f* Into a sickness, and it troubles me. *The Falcon* 309
thaw I may ha' *f* out wi' ye sometimes, *Prom. of May* I 324
and now she be *f* out wi' ma, and I can't coom at 'er. „ II 600
We Steers are of old blood, tho' we be *f*. „ III 605
And darkness rises from the *f* sun. *Foresters* I iii 42
Or haply *f* a victim to the wolf. „ II i 509
we have *f* into the hands Of Robin Hood. (repeat) „ III 232, 297
my lady, Kate and I have *f* out again, „ III 412
Falling How oft the *f* axe, that never fell, *Queen Mary* III v 134
not to-night—the night is *f*. *Becket* III ii 52
blossom of his youth, Has faded, *f* fruitless— *Prom. of May* II 334
Fallow —our *f's* till'd, Much corn, *Becket* I iii 376
False (adj. and adv.) The *f* archbishop fawning on him, *Queen Mary* I v 30
O madam, if this Pembroke should be *f*? „ II iv 10
F to Northumberland, is he *f* to me? „ II iv 39
tho' a true one, Blazed *f* upon her heart. „ III i 70
And whether this flash of news be *f* or true, „ III ii 234
No pardon!—Why that was *f*: „ V v 136
Who, while ye fish for men with your *f* fires, *Harold* II i 31
So less chance for *f* keepers. „ II ii 688
Good for good hath borne at times A bastard *f* as William. „ V i 176
Thou hast been *f* to England and to me!— „ V i 349
As . . . in some sort . . . I have been *f* to thee. „ V i 352
He that was *f* in oath to me, it seems Was *f* to his own wife. „ V ii 151
And that the *f* Northumbrian held aloof, „ V ii 165
F to myself—it is the will of God (repeat) *Becket* I iii 290, 328
F to himself, but ten-fold *f* to me! „ I iii 472
F figure, Map would say. „ III iii 346
F oath on holy cross—for thou must leave him To-day, „ IV ii 209
Robin, I ever held that saying *f* That Love is blind, *Foresters* II i 643
No, no, *f* knight, thou canst not hide thyself „ II ii 23
False (s) Earth's *f's* are heaven's truths. *Becket* III iii 348
Falsehood lips that never breathed Love's *f* to true maid *Foresters* IV 73
Falsely when I sware *F* to him, the falser Norman, *Harold* V i 303
Falser I cannot fall into a *f* world— „ V i 271
when I sware Falsely to him, the *f* Norman, „ V i 303
Falter And yet methinks he *f's*: *Queen Mary* III iv 398
He *f's*, ha? 'fore God, we change and change; „ III iv 406
Falter'd old affection master'd you, You *f* into tears. *Becket* V ii 145
Faltering felt the *f* of his mother's heart, *Queen Mary* II ii 82
Fame A faithful traitress to thy royal *f*. *Henry*. *F*! what care I for *f*? *Becket* II i 98
Fame (*continued*) *F* of to-day is infamy to-morrow; Infamy of to-day is *f* to-morrow: *Becket* II i 103
—thy *f* too: I say that should be royal. „ II i 109
You heed not how you soil her maiden *f*, *Foresters* IV 480
Familiar Yea, some *f* spirit must have help'd him. *William*. Woe knave to thy *f* and to thee! *Harold* II ii 679
Family Be we not of the *f*? be we not a-supping with the head of the *f*? *Becket* I iv 178
for I am closely related to the dead man's *f*. *Prom. of May* II 715
It is the trick of the *f*, my lord. *Foresters* I iii 151
Famine Wet, *f*, ague, fever, storm, wreck, wrath,— *Queen Mary* V v 108
War, waste, plague, *f*, all malignities. *Harold* I i 466
F is fear, were it but Of being starved. „ IV iii 204
Till *f* dwarft the race— *Becket* I iii 356
if you cram me crop-full I be little better than *F* in the picture, *Foresters* I i 47
Famine-dead seen the true men of Christ lying *f-d* by scores, *Queen Mary* V iv 38
Famine-stricken Laid *f-s* at the gates of Death— *Prom. of May* III 807
Famine-wasted Who wander *f-w* thro' the world. *Becket* III iii 188
Famish'd I am footsore and *f* therewithal. *Foresters* II i 267
while *f* rats Eat them alive. *Queen Mary* V ii 196
Famishing lash'd to death, or lie *F* in black cells, „ V ii 196
Fan (s) that his *f* may thoroughly purge his floor. „ III iv 369
Fan (verb) it serves to *f* A kindled fire. „ I v 620
Fancied Have you *f* yourself in love with him? *Prom. of May* I 783
Why, my good Robin *f* me a man, *Foresters* III 20
F he saw thee clasp and kiss a man. *Kate*. Well, if *he f* that *I* fancy a man Other than *him*, „ III 23
Fancy (s) My *f* takes the burner's part, *Queen Mary* IV ii 231
this ghastly glare May heat their *fancies*. *Harold* I i 310
Who sow'd this *f* here among the people? „ IV i 147
Whether it bow'd at all but in their *f*; „ V i 109
had I fixt my *f* Upon the game I should have beaten thee, *Becket*, *Pro.* 50
And thy thoughts, thy *fancies*? „ *Pro.* 118
I speak after my *fancies*, for I am a Troubadour, „ *Pro.* 347
would she were but his paramour, for men tire of their *fancies*; but I fear this one *f* hath taken root, „ *Pro.* 480
That you may feed your *f* on the glory of it, *The Cup* II 133
And all Thro' following of my *f*. *The Falcon* 144
specially sick children, have strange *fancies*, „ 818
I have ta'en a sudden *f* to thee. *Foresters* IV 422
Fancy (verb) You must *f* that which follow'd, *Queen Mary* III i 409
Can I *f* him kneeling with me, and uttering *Prom. of May* III 179
if *he* fancied that *I f* a man Other than *him*, *Foresters* III 25
Fancy-ridd'n known a semi-madman in my time So *f-r*) *Queen Mary* II i 11
Fancy-sick *F-s*; these things are done, „ IV iii 453
Fangless he that lookt a *f* one, Issues a venomous adder. *Becket* I iii 451
Fanny *F* be the naäme i' the song, but I swopt it fur *she*. *Prom. of May* II 211
Far (*See also* **Var**) My sister, is *f* fairer than myself. *Queen Mary* I v 72
F liefer had I in my country hall Been reading some old book, „ III i 43
and rooted in *f* isles Beyond my seeing: *Harold* III i 152
at the *f* end of the glade I see two figures crawling up the hill. *Foresters* IV 331
Farce comedy meant to seem a tragedy—A feint, a *f*. *Becket* IV ii 323
You have spoilt the *f*. „ IV ii 337
There was the *f*, the feint—not mine. „ IV ii 377
Fare (s) The prison *f* is good enough for me. *Queen Mary* IV ii 42
Fare (verb) *F* you well, Sir Ralph. „ II ii 409
I must leave you. *F* you well, „ III i 473
How *f's* thy pretty boy, the little Geoffrey? *Becket* V ii 167
F you well. *Synorix*. Farewell! *The Cup* I i 158
Sir Richard and my Lady Marian *f* wellnigh as sparely as their people. *Foresters* I i 31
Where is she? and how *f's* she? „ II i 106
F you well, fair lady! „ III 242
Fared And *f* so ill in this disastrous world. *Queen Mary* V ii 344
Farewell (adj.) she means to make A *f* present to your grace. „ I iv 245
Farewell (s) heard She would not take a last *f* of him, „ III i 367
Farewell (verb, and inter.) *f*, and fly. *Cranmer*. Fly and *f*, „ I ii 103

Farewell (verb, and inter.) (*continued*) And so you may continue mine, *f*, *Queen Mary* I iv 137
Must be content with that; and so, *f*. „ I v 271
F. I am somewhat faint With our long talk. „ I v 519
F, and trust me, Philip is yours. „ I v 539
F, your Graces. „ III ii 146
F, Madam, God grant you ampler mercy „ IV i 188
For a little space, *f*; „ IV ii 46
Have you good hopes of mercy! So, *f*. „ IV ii 87
Your pardon, Sweet cousin, and *f*! „ V ii 204
F, my king. *Harold*. Not yet, but then—my queen. *Harold* I ii 137
F for ever! „ IV ii 81
F! *Harold*. Not yet. Stay. „ V i 336
Stigand will see thee safe, And so—*F*. „ V i 420
F! I am dead as Death this day to ought of earth's „ V i 424
F! *Becket*. *F*, friends! *f*, swallows! *Becket* I iv 43
that will swallow anything. *F*. „ II ii 383
And so *f* until we meet in England. „ III iii 236
f, my lord. *Becket*. *F*, my liege! „ III iii 271
F! I must follow the King. „ III iii 329
Ev'n so: but think not of the King: *f*! „ V ii 186
city is full of armed men. *Becket*. Ev'n so: *f*! „ V ii 189
Fare you well. *Synorix*. *F*! *The Cup* I i 160
Remember! Away—*f*! *Camma*. *F*! „ I iii 115
Nothing more, *f*. *Prom. of May* I 749
'*F*, *f*, my warrior Earl!' *Foresters* I i 18
We thank you, and *f*. *Robin*. *F*, *f*. „ I ii 249
F, Sir Richard: *f*, sweet Marian. „ I ii 284
F, good fellows! „ III 86
F at once, for I must hence upon The King's affair. „ IV 341
F! I left mine horse and armour with a Squire, „ IV 413
Blown like a true son of the woods. *F*! „ IV 428
Meanwhile, *f* Old friends, old patriarch oaks. „ IV 1053
Far-eyed My *f-e* queen of the winds— *The Falcon* 9
Farm (adj.) The hen cluckt late by the white *f* gate, *Prom. of May* I 38
Farm (s) her advowsons, granges, *f's*, And goodly acres— *Becket* I i 162
but the ill success of the *f*, and the debts, *Prom. of May* II 68
S'iver I mun git along back to the *f*, „ II 321
From the *f* Here, close at hand. „ II 360
I met her first at a *f* in Cumberland—Her uncle's. „ II 396
She has disappear'd, They told me, from the *f*— „ II 407
Has left his *f*, all his affairs, I fear, „ II 420
hunt him With pitchforks off the *f*, „ II 427
Allow me to go with you to the *f*. „ II 574
rose From the foul flood and pointed toward the *f*, „ II 654
The work of the *f* will go on still, but for how long? „ III 159
Father, this poor girl, the *f*, everything; „ III 212
I trust I may be able by-and-by to help you in the business of the *f*; „ III 223
And in the winter I will fire their *f's*. *Foresters* IV 95
Farm (verb) feller couldn't find a Mister in his mouth fur me, as *f's* five hoonderd haäcre. *Prom. of May* I 303
Farmer When theer wur a meeting o' *f's* at Littlechester „ I 137
Tho' you are a gentleman, I but a *f's* daughter— „ I 668
F, you should be in the hayfield looking after your men; „ II 46
How beautiful His manners are, and how unlike the *f's*! „ II 532
shamed of his poor *f's* daughter among the ladies in his drawing-room? „ III 294
if a gentleman Should wed a *f's* daughter, „ III 579
Farm-gate She gave her hand, unask'd, at the *f-g*; „ II 626
Farming Miss, the *f* men 'ull hev their dinner i' the long barn, „ I 165
Farming-men if the *f-m* be come for their wages, to send them up to me. „ III 15
Farmstead and scare lonely maidens at the *f*. *Foresters* III 201
Far-off I have a *f-o* burrow where the King Would miss her and for ever. *Becket* IV ii 158
Farther Your Grace's policy hath a *f* flight Than mine *Queen Mary* I v 312
Farthest that flower'd bowl my ancestor Fetch'd from the *f* east— *The Falcon* 485
Fashion red and white, the *f* of our land. *Queen Mary* I v 10
Is it the *f* of this clime for women „ III vi 90
Will in some lying *f* misreport His ending „ IV iii 326

Fashion (*continued*) the dead were found Sitting, and in this *f*; *Queen Mary* V ii 397
To make allowance for their rougher *f's*, *Harold* II ii 9
You are too cold to know the *f* of it. *Becket* II ii 126
Or scarce would smile that *f*. „ III iii 28
—to celebrate my birthdaäy i' this *f*. *Prom. of May* I 322
your Ladyship hath sung the old proverb out of *f*. *Foresters* I i 164
that he may see The *f* of it. „ IV 254
thou, that art churchman too In a *f*, „ IV 412
blow upon it Three mots, this *f*—listen! „ IV 425
Fashion'd (*See also* **Old-fashioned**) I have had it *f*, see, to meet my hand. *Harold* V i 422
Fast (adj. and adv.) (*See also* **Hold-fast, Friendship-fast**)
Do ye stand *f* by that which ye resolved? *Queen Mary* III iii 103
Have not I been the *f* friend of your life „ V ii 133
I dug mine into My old *f* friend the shore, *Harold* II i 7
come now so thick and *f*, *Becket* I iii 610
Fast (s) If *f* and prayer, the lacerating scourge— „ I iii 303
He fast! is that an arm of *f*? „ I iii 520
In scourgings, macerations, mortifyings, *F's*, „ V i 42
I come this day to break my *f* with you *The Falcon* 276
I have broken My *f* already. „ 575
Not having broken *f* the livelong day— *Foresters* IV 186
Fast (verb) Your Foliot *f's* and fawns too much for me. *Becket, Pro.* 264
He f's, they say, this mitred Hercules! *He f*! is that an arm of fast? „ I iii 518
F, scourge thyself, and mortify thy flesh, „ I iii 539
I love my dinner—but I can *f*, I can *f*; *Foresters* I ii 64
Fasten I will *f* thee to mine own door-post „ II i 403
Fasten'd And that myself was *f* to the stake, *Queen Mary* IV ii 3
not at the moment who had *f* About his throat— *The Cup* II 50
Faster *F* than ivy. Must I hack her arms off? *Harold* V ii 146
Come in, my friends, come in! Nay; *f*, *f*! *Becket* V iii 69
Fastest I am thy *f* friend in Normandy. *Harold* II ii 556
Fast-fading with his *f-f* eyes Fixt hard on mine, *Queen Mary* I ii 30
Fasting A life of prayer and *f* well may see *Harold* I i 199
Fat The shadows of a hundred *f* dead deer „ I ii 103
The slow, *f* fool! He drawl'd and prated so, „ IV ii 40
A-hawking, a-hawking! If I sit, I grow *f*. *Becket, Pro.* 414
One slow, *f*, white, a burthen of the hearth; „ V ii 211
That fine, *f*, hook-nosed uncle of mine, old Harold, *Prom. of May* I 509
Fatal ruling men are *f* twins that cannot Move one without the other. *Harold* III i 127
Blaze like a night of *f* stars on those Who read „ IV i 251
My *f* oath—the dead Saints—the dark dreams— „ V i 380
cowling and clouding up That *f* star, thy Beauty, *Becket* I i 312
Fatality foul *fatalities* That blast our natural passions *Prom. of May* III 723
Fate *f* Which hunted *him* when that un-Saxon blast, *Harold* II ii 29
f hath blown me hither, bound me too „ II ii 219
She is my *f*—else wherefore has my *f* *The Cup* I i 12
I fling all that upon my *f*, my star. „ I iii 27
Life yields to death and wisdom bows to *F*, „ II 90
The wheel of *F* has roll'd me to the top. „ II 221
Drew here the richest lot from *F*, „ II 442
is it thou? the *F's* are throned, not we— „ II 488
He had my *f* for it, Poison'd. „ II 516
Fated Rome is *f* To rule the world. „ II 415
Father (s) (*See also* **Feyther, God-father**) Let *f* alone, my masters! *Queen Mary* I i 38
child who had but obeyed her *f*; „ I i 95
putting by his *f's* will. „ I ii 28
you divorced Queen Catharine and her *f*; „ I ii 57
Courtenay, wilt thou see the holy *f* Murder'd before thy face? „ I iii 64
Your royal *f* (For so they say) was all pure lily „ I v 19
as tho' My *f* and my brother had not lived. „ I v 36
for doing that His *f* whipt him into doing— „ I v 63
My hard *f* hated me; „ I v 80
my royal *f*, To make the crown of Scotland one with ours, „ I v 286
Hath he the large ability of his *f*? „ I v 439
thing Was no such scarecrow in your *f's* time. „ I v 473
the child obey'd her *f*. Spite of her tears her *f* forced it on her. „ I v 494
My *f* on a birthday gave it me, And I have broken with my *f*— „ I v 527

Father (s) (*continued*) My lord, myself and my good *f* pray *Foresters* I ii 127
Not her, the *f's* power upon her. „ I iii 9
Much, the miller's son, I knew thy *f*: „ I iii 147
but my *f* will not lose his land, „ II i 522
betray'd Thy *f* to the losing of his land. „ II i 570
your good *f* had his draught of wine „ II ii 1
O my poor *f*! „ II ii 8
O lead me to my *f*! (repeat) „ II ii 22, 48
She will not marry till her *f* yield. „ II ii 82
There is a fence I cannot overleap, *My f's* will. „ III 10
And were my kindly *f* sound again, „ III 81
He was my *f*, mother, both in one. „ IV 6
And my sick *f* here has come between us „ IV 55
Quiet, quiet ! or I will to my *f*. „ IV 78
thy *f* will not grace our feast With his white beard to-day. „ IV 79
Here is my *f's* bond. „ IV 463
You scheme against her *f's* weal and hers, „ IV 481
I remain Beside my *F's* litter. „ IV 605
Speak not. I wait upon a dying *f*. „ IV 611
It seems thy *f's* land is forfeited. „ IV 640
thou shalt wed him, Or thine old *f* will go mad— „ IV 645
F, I cannot marry till Richard comes. „ IV 648
the Sheriff, *f*, Would buy me for a thousand marks „ IV 651
But pity for a *f*, it may be, „ IV 659
I grieve to say it was thy *f's* son. „ IV 811
Art thou my son? *Walter Lea.* I am, good *f*, „ IV 1020
Father (verb) No—murder *f's* murder: *Queen Mary* III i 335
Fathered had I *f* him I had given him more of the rod than the sceptre. *Becket* III iii 110
all the souls we saved and *f* here Will greet us „ V ii 223
Father-king And the *f-k*? „ III iii 100
Father-like Julius the Third Was ever just, and mild, and *f-l*; *Queen Mary* V ii 31
Fatherly See how the tears run down his *f* face. „ IV iii 4
Fathom Deep—I shall *f* him. „ I iii 158
Thou stirrest up a grief thou canst not *f*. „ III iv 299
Fatness fill all hearts with *f* and the lust Of plenty— *The Cup* II 272
Fatter yonder's *f* game for you Than this old gaping gurgoyle: *Queen Mary* I iii 79
Fatting the *f* of your calves, the making of your butter, *Prom. of May* II 92
Faugh *F*! we shall all be poisoned. Let us go. *Becket* I iv 243
Fault his *f* So thoroughly to believe in his own self. *Queen Mary* II ii 385
—this Cardinal's *f*—I have gulpt it down. „ III iv 376
To veil the *f* of my most outward foe— „ IV ii 106
O God the Son, Not for slight *f's* alone, „ IV iii 139
not *his f*, if our two houses Be less than brothers. *Harold* IV i 129
And yet she plagues me too—no *f* in her— *Becket, Pro.* 59
he had his *f's*, For which I would have laid „ V ii 337
the *f*, mebbe, wur as much mine as yours; *Prom. of May* I 325
Be that my *f*? „ II 89
making us feel guilty Of her own *f's*. „ II 270
would you beat a man for his brother's *f*? „ III 155
That last was my Father's *f*, poor man. „ III 280
Faultless The *f* Gardiner! *Queen Mary* III iv 96
Faulty Some of my former friends Would find my logic *f*; *Prom. of May* II 665
Favour He hath fallen out of *f* with the Queen. *Queen Mary* I iv 156
What makes thy *f* like the bloodless head „ V ii 19
God's *f* and king's *f* might so clash *Becket, Pro.* 295
So that you grant me one slight *f*. „ I ii 58
Would you cast An eye of *f* on me, *Foresters* I ii 217
That if I cast an eye of *f* on him, „ I ii 262
Favour'd he would pay The mortgage if she *f* him. „ I iii 7
Favourer Because they think me *f* of this marriage. *Queen Mary* I v 156
and a *f* Of players, and a courtier, *Becket* I i 78
Favourite utterly broken down By losing her—she was his *f* child— *Prom. of May* II 418
for you know, my dear, you were always his *f*— „ III 423
Fawn *f* upon him? Chime in with all? *Harold* I ii 165
Your Foliot fasts and *f's* too much for me. *Becket, Pro.* 264
f upon him For thy life and thy son's. „ IV ii 224
Fawning The false Archbishop *f* on him, *Queen Mary* I v 30
Who rub their *f* noses in the dust, „ III iii 242

Fay To a land where the *f*, *Foresters* II ii 180
Fealty Into the wide-spread arms of *f*, *Queen Mary* II ii 264
F to the King, obedience to thyself? *Becket* I iii 587
That goes against our *f* to the King. „ V ii 508
Not one to keep a woman's *f* *The Cup* I i 176
Fear (s) he brought his doubts And *f's* to me. *Queen Mary* I ii 76
Skips every way, from levity or from *f*. „ I iii 170
There lies your *f*. That is your drift. „ I v 304
I am Harry's daughter, Tudor, and not *F*. „ II iv 53
St. Peter in his time of *f* Denied his Master, „ III iv 263
my father married my good mother,—For *f* of Spain. „ III v 247
from the *f* of Him Whose ministers they be to govern you. „ IV iii 179
O father, mock not at a public *f*, *Harold* I i 75
That's a truer *f*! „ I ii 66
stuff'd the boy with *f's* that these may act „ II ii 90
Thy *f's* infect me beyond reason. Peace! „ II ii 451
Famine is *f*, were it but Of being starved. „ IV iii 204
Yet if a *f*, Or shadow of a *f*, „ V i 114
To lodge a *f* in Thomas Becket's heart *Becket* I iii 176
Nay—no *f*! More like is he to excommunicate me. „ II i 269
yet what *f*? the people Believe the wood enchanted. „ III i 35
f creeps in at the front, honesty steals out at the back, „ III iii 61
No *f*! *Grim.* No *f*, my lord. „ V ii 578
from maiden *f's* Or reverential love for him I loved, *The Cup* II 196
I do remember your first-marriage *f's*. „ II 207
I have no *f's* at this my second marriage. „ II 208
Fear (verb) I *f*, I *f*, I see you, Dear friend, *Queen Mary* I ii 102
dull life in this maiden court, I *f*, my Lord? „ I iii 115
She *f's* the Lords may side with you „ I iv 158
Do not *f* it. Of that hereafter. „ I v 130
Courtenay, Save that he *f's* he might be crack'd in using, „ II i 7
I *f* the mine is fired before the time. „ II i 123
I *f* we be too few, Sir Thomas. „ II i 224
and I *f* One scruple, this or that way, „ II ii 99
And *f* them not. I *f* them not. „ II ii 243
how to cross it balks me. I *f* we cannot. „ II iii 10
I *f* the Emperor much misvalued me. „ III ii 76
This Howard, whom they *f*, what was he saying? „ III vi 54
nor *f* but that to-day Thou shalt receive „ IV iii 84
There will be more conspiracies, I *f*. „ IV iii 433
I do much *f* that England will not care. „ V ii 282
I have given her cause—I *f* no woman. *Harold* I ii 42
Why then of England. Madam, *f* us not, „ V ii 97
that I *f* the Queen would have her life. *Becket, Pro.* 61
We *f* that he may reave thee of thine own. „ I iii 611
I *f* Church-censures like your King. „ IV ii 434
They *f* you slain: they dread they know not what. „ V ii 600
Tut—*f* me not; I ever had my victories among women. *The Cup* I i 152
I *f* not. *Synorix.* Then do not tell him. „ I ii 308
Yes, my lord, *f* not. I will answer for you. *Foresters* I ii 32
And *f* not thou! Each of us has an arrow on the cord; „ IV 606
Fear'd She *f* it might unman him for his end. *Queen Mary* III i 368
Cannot? Even so! I *f* as much. *The Falcon* 846
Fearful Paget, despite his *f* heresies, I loved the man, *Queen Mary* IV iii 633
whose *f* Priest Sits winking at the license of a king, *Becket* I ii 65
More, tenfold, than this *f* child can do; *Harold* I ii 143
thou Wast ever *f*. „ II ii 351
Too *f* still! „ II ii 412
Fearing *f* for her, sent a secret missive, *Queen Mary* II ii 121
Feast (s) No sacrifice, but a life-giving *f*! „ IV ii 112
Bring not thy hollowness On our full *f*. *Harold* IV iii 204
A doter on white pheasant-flesh at *f's*, *Becket, Pro.* 97
I would that every man made *f* to-day *The Cup* II 225
of that full *f* That leaves but emptiness. *Prom. of May* II 255
Why comest thou like a death's head at my *f*? *Foresters* I ii 211
And join your *f's* and all your forest games „ III 84
thy father will not grace our *f* With his white beard to-day. „ IV 80
Our *f* is yonder, spread beneath an oak, „ IV 189
Feast (verb) Call in the poor from the streets, and let them *f*. *Becket* I iv 73
Feed, *f*, and be merry. „ I iv 151
Feather if this Prince of fluff and *f* come *Queen Mary* I iv 162
Night, as black as a raven's *f*; *Harold* III ii 6
strike, make his *f's* Glance in mid heaven. *The Falcon* 15
We cannot flaunt it in new *f's* now: „ 42

Feather'd Breaks into *f* merriments, and flowers *Queen Mary* III v 13
Featherhead Courtenay, belike— *Mary.* A fool and *f*! „ V i 128
Feature of royal blood, of splendid *f*, „ I i 112
equal for pure innocence of nature, And loveliness of *f*. *Prom. of May* II 373
Featureless play'd at ball with And kick'd it *f*— *The Cup* II 128
Fed swoll'n and *f* With indraughts and side-currents, *Queen Mary* II i 233
F with rank bread that crawl'd upon the tongue, „ IV iii 442
pray for him who hath *f* you in the wilderness. *Becket* I iv 266
Meal enough, meat enough, well *f*; *The Falcon* 166
You be *f* with tit-bits, you, *Foresters* I i 24
I am *f* with tit-bits no more than you are, „ I i 27
those pale mouths which we have *f* will praise us— „ IV 1076
Federigo (*See also* **Federigo degli Alberighi**) my Lord *F*, he hath fallen Into a sickness, *The Falcon* 309
My lord *F*, Can I not speak with you once more „ 687
Yes, your falcon, *F*! „ 843
O *F*, *F*, I love you! Spite of ten thousand brothers, *F*. „ 897
And I am happy! *Giovanna.* And I too, *F*. „ 928
Federigo degli Alberighi Poor *F d A* Takes nothing in return „ 715
Fee (s) In *f* and barony of the King, *Becket* I iii 675
I hold Nothing in *f* and barony of the King. „ I iii 678
Take *f's* of tyranny, wink at sacrilege, „ II ii 394
And have thy *f's*, and break the law no more. *Foresters* IV 955
Fee (verb) he will *f* thee as freely as he will wrench *Harold* II i 57
if you cared To *f* an over-opulent superstition, *Prom. of May* I 693
Feeble To Dover? no, I am too *f*. *Queen Mary* III vi 221
If Rome be *f*, then should I be firm. *Becket* I iii 240
Perhaps you judge him With *f* charity: *The Cup* I ii 186
Shall I tell her he is dead? No; she is still too *f*. *Prom. of May* III 338
Feed *F*, feast, and be merry. *Becket* I iv 151
So that the fool King Louis *f* them not. „ II i 76
that the sheep May *f* in peace. „ III iii 346
That you may *f* your fancy on the glory of it, *The Cup* II 133
Feeder a *f* Of dogs and hawks, and apes, *Becket* I i 79
Feel I came to *f* the pulse of England, *Queen Mary* III i 37
faith that seem'd to droop will *f* your light, „ III iv 22
I *f* it but a duty—you will find in it Pleasure „ III iv 429
your Grace, your Grace, I *f* so happy: „ III v 250
And it were well, if thou shouldst let him *f*, *Harold* II ii 16
I can *f* for thee. *Eleanor.* Thou *f* for me!— *Becket, Pro.* 472
The man shall *f* that I can strike him yet. „ II i 78
And *f* it too. „ III iii 48
willing wives enough To *f* dishonour, honour. *The Cup* I ii 189
Will *f* no shame to give themselves the lie. „ II 117
Dost thou not *f* the love I bear to thee „ II 426
As years go on, he *f's* them press upon him, *Prom. of May* I 647
I *f* sewer, Miss Dora, that I ha' been noän too sudden wi' you, „ II 59
I *f* so much better, that I trust I may be able „ III 221
As yet I scarcely *f* it mine. „ III 613
and mighty slow To *f* offences. „ III 630
churchman too In a fashion, and shouldst *f* with him. *Foresters* IV 412
he will, He will—he *f's* it in his head. „ IV 646
That I may *f* thou art no phantom— „ IV 1013
Feeling with her poor blind hands *f*—'where is it? *Queen Mary* III i 407
F my native land beneath my foot, „ III ii 47
Feel'st thou *f* into the hands Of these same Moors *Foresters* II i 562
when thou *f* with me The ghost returns to Marian, „ III 113
Feigning *F* to treat with him about her marriage— *Queen Mary* II ii 33
Feint comedy meant to seem a tragedy—A *f*, a farce. *Becket* IV ii 323
There was the farce, the *f*—not mine. And yet I am all but sure my dagger was a *f* Till the worm turn'd— „ IV ii 377
—*this* was no *f* then? no. „ IV ii 383
No, for it came to nothing—only a *f*. „ IV ii 398
I'll swear to mine own self it was a *f*. „ IV ii 402
Fell Who stood upright when both houses *f*. *Bagenhall.* The houses *f*! *Officer.* I mean the houses knelt *Queen Mary* III iii 255
But stretch it wider; say when England *f*. „ III iii 262
God's righteous judgment *f* upon you „ III iv 240
nay, his noble mother's, Head *f*— „ III iv 296
How oft the falling axe, that never *f*, „ III v 134
owld lord *f* to 's meat wi' a will, God bless un! „ IV iii 514
Fell (*continued*) Like Peter's when he *f*, and thou wilt *Harold* III i 283
the first *F*, and the next became an Empire. „ IV i 51
Hail to the living who fought, the dead who *f*! „ IV iii 106
how he *f's* The mortal copse of faces! „ V i 588
Then all the dead *f* on him. „ V ii 50
Here *f* the truest, manliest hearts of England. „ V ii 58
Before he *f* into the snare of Guy; „ V ii 131
high altar Stand where their standard *f* . . . „ V ii 140
Every man about his king *F* where he stood. „ V ii 182
twelve stars *f* glittering out of heaven Into her bosom. *Becket* I i 46
smote me down upon the Minster floor. I *f*. „ I i 105
I *f*. Why fall? Why did He smite me? „ I i 108
they mock'd us and we *f* upon 'em, „ I ii 15
names of those who fought and *f* are like *The Cup* I ii 164
F with her motion as she rose, and she, *The Falcon* 536
how long we strove before Our horses *f* beneath us, „ 639
'er an' the owd man they *f* a kissin' o' one another *Prom. of May* I 21
f ageän coalscuttle and my kneeä gev waäy „ I 403
as I telled 'er to-daäy when she *f* foul „ II 582
I'd like to *f* 'im as deäd as a bullock! „ II 597
if ever A Norman damsel *f* into our hands, *Foresters* III 181
The deer *f* dead to the bottom, and the man *F* with him, „ IV 543
Feller (fellow) the *f* couldn't find a Mister in his mouth fur me, *Prom. of May* I 302
Why, coom then, owd *f*, I'll tell it to you; „ II 202
What *f* wur it as 'a' been a-talkin' „ II 575
thaw the *f's* gone and maäde such a litter of his faäce. „ II 588
The *f's* cleän daäzed, an' maäzed, an' maäted, „ II 728
Fellow (*See also* **Feller**) Art thou of the true faith, *f*, *Queen Mary* I iii 46
Divers honest *f's*, „ I iii 120
I will be there; the *f's* at his tricks— „ I iii 157
A goodlier-looking *f* than this Philip. „ I iv 3
and I warrant this fine *f's* life. „ II iii 84
I know some lusty *f's* there in France. „ III i 128
Ay! *f*, what! Stand staring at me! „ III i 286
Ever a rough, blunt, and uncourtly *f*— „ V v 120
Haul like a great strong *f* at my legs, *Harold* II i 11
F, dost thou catch crabs? „ II i 65
my *f's* know that I am all one scale like a fish. *Becket* I iv 212
The *f* that on a lame jade came to court, „ V i 246
He comes, a rough, bluff, simple-looking *f*. *The Cup* I i 173
I tell thee, my good *f*, *My* arrow struck the stag. „ I ii 27
I will, I will. Poor *f*! *The Falcon* 282
more than one brave *f* owed His death to the charm in it. „ 634
You hear, Filippo? My good *f*, go! „ 691
Nor am I Edgar, my good *f*. *Prom. of May* II 702
Poor *f's*! *Foresters* I i 91
there is a lot of wild *f's* in Sherwood Forest who hold by King Richard. „ I ii 73
good *f's* there in merry Sherwood That hold by Richard, „ I iii 98
A brave old *f* but he angers me. „ II i 471
Farewell, good *f's*! „ III 87
I believe thee, thou art a good *f*, though a friar. „ III 342
Thou payest easily, like a good *f*, „ IV 156
I can bring down Fourscore tall *f's* on thee. „ IV 177
now I love thee mightily, thou tall *f*. „ IV 322
Were some strong *f* here in the wild wood, „ IV 515
man of ours Up in the North, a goodly *f* too, „ IV 530
Fellow-citizen Swear with me, noble *f-c's*, all, *Queen Mary* II ii 296
Fellow-prisoner Thus Gardiner—for the two were *f-p's* „ I iv 198
Fellow-pupil Were not our *f-p's* all ladies? *Prom. of May* III 299
Fellow-trickster one should be This William's *f-t's*;— *Harold* III ii 77
Felony 'If any cleric be accused of *f*, the Church *Becket* I iii 87
Felt I have *f* within me Stirrings of some great doom *Queen Mary* I iv 259
babe in arms Had *f* the faltering of his mother's heart, „ II ii 82
The Queen hath *f* the motion of her babe! „ III ii 213
and the power They *f* in killing. „ III iv 76
if I knew you *f* this parting, Philip, As I do! „ III vi 251
I *f* his arms about me, and his lips— „ V v 99
Hate not one who *f* Some pity for thy hater! *Harold* II i 43
F the remorseless outdraught of the deep „ II i 9
I *f* it in the middle of that fierce fight „ IV iii 183
And *f* the sun of Antioch scald our mail, *Becket* II ii 93
we *f* we had laughed too long and could not stay ourselves— „ III iii 160

Fierce (*continued*) sorely prest upon By the f Emperor and his Antipope. *Becket* I iii 203
Perchance the f De Brocs from Saltwood Castle, „ V ii 249
These arm'd men in the city, these f faces— „ V iii 3
may not be seized With some f passion, *Prom. of May* II 336
Fiercelier Heaven help that this re-action not re-act Yet f under Queen Elizabeth, *Queen Mary* IV iii 389
Fiercest Out in the f storm That ever made earth tremble— *Prom. of May* III 796
Fierier That ever make him f. *Queen Mary* V ii 95
something f than fire To yield them their deserts. .. V iv 26
Fieriest And all her f partisans—are pale Before my star! „ III ii 170
Fiery And then our f Tostig, while thy hands Are palsied here, *Harold* II ii 453
Fiery-choleric And hates the Spaniard—f-c. *Queen Mary* V ii 92
Fifth This is the f conspiracy hatch'd in France; „ V i 297
Fifty We may have left their f less by five. *The Falcon* 625
F leagues Of woodland hear and know my horn, *Foresters* III 102
Fight (s) I have fought the f and go— *Harold* I i 184
I fought another f than this Of Stamford-bridge. „ IV iii 23
I felt it in the middle of that fierce f At Stamford-bridge. „ IV iii 184
power to balk Thy puissance in this f „ V i 119
I can no more—fight out the good f—die Conqueror. *Becket* V iii 189
in the front rank of the f With scarce a pang. *The Cup* I ii 154
The trumpets of the f had echo'd down, *The Falcon* 605
and with a flag of ours Ta'en in the f— „ 613
Fight (verb) who went with your train bands To f with Wyatt, *Queen Mary* II ii 28
Is he so safe to f upon her side? .. II ii 313
I trust that you would f along with us. „ III i 457
would you not f then? *Bagenhall.* I think I should f then. „ III i 466
for their heresies, Alva, they will f; „ III ii 204
Paget, You stand up here to f for heresy, „ III iv 92
I'll f it on the threshold of the grave. „ V v 189
boys will f. Leofwin would often f me, *Harold* I i 433
Even old Gurth would f. „ I i 436
Normans up To f for thee again! „ II ii 59
Well then, we must f. How blows the wind? „ III ii 134
He hath cursed thee, and all those who f for thee, „ III ii 153
Too drunk to f with thee! „ IV iii 165
F thou with thine own double, not with me, „ IV iii 167
How should the people f When the king flies? „ V i 137
Not f—tho' somehow traitor to the King— *Becket* I i 112
'I mean to f mine utmost for the Church, „ I i 123
make it clear Under what Prince I f. „ I iii 545
F for the Church, and set the Church against me! „ I iii 569
we daren't f you with our crutches, „ I iv 210
Do they not f the Great Fiend day by day? „ V ii 585
I can no more—f out the good fight—die Conqueror. „ V iii 189
We cannot f imperial Rome, *The Cup* II 92
'I go to f in Scotland With many a savage clan;' *Foresters* I i 14
if he had not gone to f the king's battles, „ I i 57
if he dare to f at all, would f for his rents, „ I i 232
f's not for himself but for the people of England. „ I i 236
I would f with any man but thee. „ II i 557
No, Sir Earl, I will not f to-day. „ II i 575
Well, I will f to-morrow. „ II i 577
he that pays not for his dinner must f for it. „ IV 200
thou f at quarterstaff for thy dinner with our Robin, „ IV 207
Fighteth The soul who f on thy side is cursed, *Harold* V i 69
Fighting And f for And dying for the people— „ V i 388
chosen by his people And f for his people! „ V i 491
Wilt thou destroy the Church in f for it, *Becket* I iii 36
they were f for her to-day in the street. „ I iv 160
to help the old man When he was f. *Foresters* II i 543
Were f underhand unholy wars „ IV 821
Figure to keep the f moist and make it hold water, *Becket* III iii 165
False f, Map would say. „ III iii 346
—a mere f. Let it go by. *Foresters* IV 221
No f, no fiction, Robin. „ IV 222
I see two f's crawling up the hill. „ IV 333
Filch a fox may f a hen by night, *Queen Mary* III v 157
f the linen from the hawthorn, *Foresters* III 198
Fili Salva F, Salva Spiritus, *Harold* V i 468

Filippo (foster brother to Count Federigo degli Alberighi) Sh—sh—F! (repeat) *The Falcon* 96, 105
Come, come, F, what is there in the larder? .. 117
out of those scraps and shreds F spoke of. .. 148
Away, F! .. 155
What is it, F? *Filippo.* Spoons, your lordship. .. 396
I thank thee, good F. .. 554
so I, F, being, with your ladyship's pardon, .. 564
F! *Giovanna.* Will you not eat with me, .. 569
Wine! F, wine! .. 577
F! will you take the word out of your master's own mouth? .. 597
I and F here had done our best, .. 607
F! *Count.* A troop of horse— .. 616
And we kill'd 'em by the score. *Elisabetta.* F! .. 622
See, my lady! *Giovanna.* I see, F! .. 655
And why, F? .. 658
tree that his lordship—— *Giovanna.* Not now, F. .. 686
You hear, F? My good fellow, go! .. 690
But the prunes that your lordship—— *Elisabetta.* F! .. 694
F! *Filippo.* Well, well! the women! .. 697
Fill no foreign prince or priest Should f my throne, *Queen Mary* III v 237
suddenly f With such fierce fire— „ III vi 161
And we will f thee full of Norman sun, *Harold* II ii 180
and f the sky With free sea-laughter— .. II ii 336
Fall, cloud, and f the house— .. III i 190
God of truth F all thine hours with peace!— „ V i 316
Thou art the man to f out the Church robe; *Becket, Pro.* 262
And f all hearts with fatness and the lust *The Cup* II 272
See here, I f it. Will you drink, my lord? .. II 366
F to the brim. *Foresters* III 343
Fill'd saw the church all f With dead men *Harold* I ii 82
one who f All offices, all bishopricks with English— .. II ii 534
God Has f the quiver, and Death has drawn the bow— „ III i 400
'And when the vacancy is to be f up, *Becket* I iii 108
like Egypt's plague, had f All things with blood; „ I iii 345
Filthy Come, you f knaves, let us pass. „ I iv 203
What f tools our Senate works with! *The Cup* I i 156
Find Whose play is all to f herself a King. *Queen Mary* I iii 164
And f's you statues. „ II ii 265
Death and the Devil—if he f I have one— „ III i 232
F out his name and bring it me. „ III i 253
thou shalt lose thine ears and f thy tongue, „ III i 256
amazed To f as fair a sun as might have flash'd „ III ii 22
Did you f a scripture, 'I come not to bring „ III iv 87
Till, by St. James, I f myself the fool. „ III vi 101
And I can f no refuge upon earth. „ IV iii 128
I shall f Heaven or else hell ready to swallow me, „ IV iii 223
And I have often found them. *Mary.* F me one! „ V ii 223
you will f written Two names, Philip and Calais; „ V v 153
You will f Philip only, policy, policy,— „ V v 158
To f the sweet refreshment of the Saints. *Harold* I i 177
and coming back F them again. .. II i 91
And, brother, we will f a way,' said he— .. II ii 367
To f a means whereby the curse might glance .. III i 342
then would f Her nest within the cloister, .. IV i 233
Know what thou dost; and we may f for thee, .. IV ii 48
until I f Which way the battle balance. .. V i 460
Harold slain?—I cannot f his body. .. V ii 20
Go further hence and f him. „ V ii 60
for I should f An easy father confessor in thee. *Becket, Pro.* 87
Thou wilt f her Back in her lodging. „ I i 399
As f a hare's form in a lion's cave. „ I iii 177
Shall I f you one? „ I iv 24
makes after it too To f it. „ II i 322
To f my stray sheep back within the fold. „ III iii 355
I thought if I followed it I should f the fairies. „ IV i 24
but I don't know if I can f the way back again. „ IV i 48
Shall I f you asleep when I come back? .. IV ii 64
this will f it there, And dig it from the root .. IV ii 75
We f that it is mightier than it seems— „ IV ii 263
Follow us, my son, and we will f it for thee— .. IV ii 373
F one a slut whose fairest linen seems Foul .. V ii 202
Here, here, here will you f me. „ V ii 514
To f Antonius here. *The Cup* I iii 55

Find (*continued*) or at least shall *f* him There in the camp. *The Cup* I iii 93
Whose winter-cataracts *f* a realm and leave it „ II 305
I sought him and I could not *f* him. „ II 397
To *f* one shock upon the field when all The harvest *The Falcon* 301
I *f* a written scroll That seems to run in rhymings. „ 431
you Would *f* it stain'd—— *Count.* Silence, Elisabetta ! „ 664
Lady, I *f* you a shrewd bargainer. „ 757
But you will *f* me a shrewd bargainer still. „ 774
An' how d'ye *f* the owd man 'ere ? *Prom. of May* I 71
feller couldn't *f* a Mister in his mouth fur me, „ I 302
You never *f* one for me, Mr. Dobson. „ I 305
or you may *f* me at the bottom of the river.— „ II 88
that we Should *f* her in the river ; „ II 412
Some of my former friends Would *f* my logic faulty ; „ II 665
Did you *f* that you worked at all the worse „ III 55
You must not expect to *f* our Father as he was five years ago. „ III 419
our carters and our shepherds Still *f* a comfort there. „ III 529
you will *f* The common brotherhood of man „ III 542
I cannot *f* the word—forgive it—Amends. „ III 789
only they that be bred in it can *f* their way a-nights in it. *Foresters* II i 265
Your worship may *f* another rhyme if you care „ II i 322
Sheriff, thou wilt *f* me at Nottingham. *Sheriff.* If anywhere, I shall *f* thee in hell. „ IV 801

Fine (adj.) If you have falsely painted your *f* Prince ; *Queen Mary* I v 598
Carew stirs In Devon : that *f* porcelain Courtenay, „ II i 6
Ay, why not, Sir Thomas ? He was a *f* courtier, he ; „ II i 33
a *f* courtier of the old Court, old Sir Thomas. „ II i 45
Ay, and I warrant this *f* fellow's life. „ II iii 83
Lord ! they be *f* ; I never stitch'd none such. „ III i 226
F eyes—but melancholy, irresolute—A *f* beard, Bonner, a very full *f* beard. „ III iv 337
Of such *f* mould, that if you sow'd therein The seed of Hate, „ IV i 170
Were you in Spain, this *f* fair gossamer gold— „ V iii 48
Is it so *f* ? Troth, some have said so. „ V iii 53
but therein Sunk rocks—they need *f* steering— „ V v 214
the *f* attractions and repulses, the delicacies, *Becket, Pro.* 499
Now let the King's *f* game look to itself. „ III ii 44
My lord, we know you proud of your *f* hand, „ IV ii 261
Here's a *f* salad for my lady, *The Falcon* 546
Here's a *f* fowl for my lady ; „ 556
And here are *f* fruits for my lady— „ 561
Well, I reckons they'll hev' a *f* cider-crop to-year *Prom. of May* I 316
but I ha taäen good care to turn out boäth my darters right down *f* laädies. „ I 337
That *f*, fat, hook-nosed uncle of mine, old Harold, „ I 509
sometimes been moved to tears by a chapter of *f* writing in a novel ; „ III 209
and prattled to each other that we would marry *f* gentlemen, „ III 277
Ay, how *f* they be in their liveries, *Foresters* I i 40
Because thou sayest such *f* things of women, „ I iii 137

Fine (s) A round *f* likelier. Your pardon. *Queen Mary* III iii 279
A *f*, a *f* ! he hath called plain Robin Hood a lord. *Foresters* III 214
A *f* ! a *f* ! He hath called plain Robin a king. „ IV 217

Fine (verb) *F* him ! *f* him ! he hath called plain Robin an earl. „ IV 150

Fine-cut his *f-c* face bowing and beaming with all that courtesy *Becket* III iii 141

Finer Margery ? no, that's a *f* thing there. How it glitters ! „ IV i 2

Finger populace, With *f's* pointed like so many daggers, *Queen Mary* I v 149
I wear Upon this *f*), ye did promise full Allegiance „ II ii 168
Would you not chop the bitten *f* off, „ III iv 206
You have a gold ring on your *f*, „ V iv 32
A lesson worth *F* and thumb—thus *Harold* I ii 55
How their pointed *f's* Glared at me ! „ II ii 790
his *f* on her harp (I heard him more than once) „ IV i 203
Yet my *f's* itch to beat him into nothing. *Becket* I iv 229
Ay, and I left two *f's* there for dead. *The Falcon* 653
ye'll think more on 'is little *f* than hall my hand at the haltar. *Prom. of May* I 112
to pass it down A *f* of that hand *Foresters* I ii 299

Finger (*continued*) she swore it never Should leave her *f*. *Foresters* II i 593

Finger'd The cardinals have *f* Henry's gold. *Becket* I iii 295

Fingernail and he's as like the King as *f* to *f*, „ III i 165

Finger-point I Scraped from your *f-p's* the holy oil ; *Queen Mary* IV ii 132

Finikin there comes a deputation From our *f* fairy nation. *Foresters* II ii 145

Finish I am your Legate ; please you let me *f*. *Queen Mary* III iv 180

Finish'd It is *f*. (repeat) *Harold* III i 177, 203, 211
They are *f*. *Synorix.* How ! *The Cup* II 422
Have you not *f*, my lord ? *Foresters* II i 341

Fire (s) (*See also* **A-hell-fire, A-vire, Fool-fire, Hell-fire, Vire**) practise on my life, By poison, *f*, shot, *Queen Mary* I iv 285
Stamp out the *f*, or this Will smoulder and re-flame, „ I v 508
it serves to fan A kindled *f*. „ I v 621
the rack, the thumbscrew, the stake, the *f*. „ II i 201
Dare-devils, that would eat *f* and spit it out „ III i 156
Rascal !—this land is like a hill of *f*, „ III i 321
I will show *f* on my side—stake and *f*— „ III i 327
Let the dead letter live ! Trace it in *f*, „ III iv 34
by the churchman's pitiless doom of *f*, „ III iv 50
Yet others are that dare the stake and *f*, „ III iv 167
I am on *f* until I see them flame. „ III iv 287
Or a second *f*, Like that which lately crackled „ III v 52
but of this *f* he says, Nay swears, „ III v 71
but they play with *f* as children do, „ III vi 28
you may strike *f* from her, Not hope to melt her. „ III vi 38
suddenly fill With such fierce *f*—had it been *f* indeed „ III vi 162
As Cranmer hath, came to the *f* on earth. „ IV i 60
Power hath been given you to try faith by *f*— „ IV ii 154
F—inch by inch to die in agony ! „ IV ii 223
makes The *f* seem crueller than it is. „ IV ii 233
Remember how God made the fierce *f* seem „ IV iii 89
The patience of St. Lawrence in the *f*. „ IV iii 95
So I may come to the *f*. „ IV iii 251
Liar ! dissembler ! traitor ! to the *f* ! „ IV iii 259
Harm him not, harm him not ! have him to the *f* ! „ IV iii 285
howsoever hero-like the man Dies in the *f*, „ IV iii 325
I say they have drawn the *f* On their own heads : „ IV iii 380
To whom the *f* were welcome, „ IV iii 438
Who follow'd with the crowd to Cranmer's *f*. „ IV iii 555
they swarm into the *f* Like flies—for what ? no dogma. „ V ii 111
sir, they hurl'd it back into the *f*, That, being but baptized in *f*, the babe Might be in *f* for ever. „ V iv 22
something fierier than *f* To yield them their deserts. „ V iv 26
in a closed room, with light, *f*, physic, tendance ; „ V iv 37
And burn the tares with unquenchable *f* ! „ V v 114
that these Three rods of blood-red *f* up yonder *Harold* I i 44
For if the North take *f*, I should be back ; „ I ii 67
while ye fish for men with your false *f's*, „ II i 31
hath blown himself as red as *f* with curses. „ V i 87
the *f*, the light, The spirit of the twelve Apostles *Becket* I i 49
Make it so hard to save a moth from the *f* ? „ I i 284
Set all on *f* against him ! „ I ii 89
the *f*, when first kindled, said to the smoke, „ II ii 317
As one that blows the coal to cool the *f*. „ V ii 549
Is that the cup you rescued from the *f* ? *The Cup* I i 71
like A bank'd-up *f* that flashes out again „ I ii 166
to the wave, to the glebe, to the *f* ! „ II 4
a red *f* woke in the heart of the town, *Prom. of May* I 50
tho' the *f* should run along the ground, „ I 703
when you put it in green, and your stack caught *f*. „ II 56
heat and *f* Of life will bring them out, „ II 286
She hath the *f* in her face and the dew in her eyes. *Foresters* I i 166
mantle of the cloud, And sets, a naked *f*. „ II i 29
Who melts a waxen image by the *f*, „ II i 671

Fire (verb) Upon their lake of Garda, *f* the Thames ; *Queen Mary* III ii 23
And in the winter I will *f* their farms. *Foresters* IV 95

Fired so in this pause, before The mine be *f*, *Queen Mary* II i 26
I fear the mine is *f* before the time. „ II i 123
The mine is *f*, and I will speak to them. „ II i 155
Your houses *f*—your gutters bubbling blood— „ II ii 280
city rose against Antonius, Whereon he *f* it, *The Cup* I ii 64

Firelike I'll have it burnish'd *f* ; *Queen Mary* I v 374

Fireside I would taäke the owd blind man to my oä *Prom. of May* II 74

Firm make their wall of shields *F* as thy cliffs, *Harold* V i 480

Firm (*continued*) by thy wisdom Hast kept it *f* from shaking; *Becket, Pro.* 204
If Rome be feeble, then should I be *f*. „ I iii 241
My hand is *f*, Mine eye most true to one hair's-breadth of aim. *Foresters* IV 693

First (adj.) are fresh and sweet As the *f* flower no bee has ever tried. *Queen Mary* I iv 63
and your worship the *f* man in Kent and Christendom, „ II i 64
In William's time, in our *f* Edward's time, „ III iii 226
as in the day of the *f* church, when Christ Jesus was King. „ V iv 55
Earl, the *f* Christian Cæsar drew to the East *Harold* V i 21
wherefore now Obey my *f* and last commandment. Go! „ V i 359
the bright link rusts with the breath of the *f* after-marriage kiss, *Becket, Pro.* 362
The *f* archbishop fled, And York lay barren for a hundred years. „ I iii 53
frosted off me by the *f* cold frown of the King. „ I iv 67
But Hereford, you know, crown'd the *f* Henry. „ III iii 202
To the fond arms of her *f* love, Fitzurse, „ IV ii 334
You kiss'd me there For the *f* time. *The Cup* I ii 419
F kiss. There then. You talk almost as if it Might be the last. „ I ii 421
He sends you This diadem of the *f* Galatian Queen, „ II 132
when Synorix, *f* King, Camma, *f* Queen o' the Realm, „ II 440
Coming to visit my lord, for the *f* time in her life too! *The Falcon* 170
I lay them for the *f* time round your neck. „ 907
But where is this Mr. Edgar whom you praised so in your *f* letters? *Prom. of May* I 777
better death With our *f* wail than life— „ II 291
My father stricken with his *f* paralysis, „ II 481
as they are arranged here according to their *f* letters. „ III 37
I do believe I lost my heart to him the very *f* time we met, „ III 284
shall I give her the *f* kiss? O sweet Kate, my *f* love, the *f* kiss, the *f* kiss! *Foresters* I i 126
but I came to give thee the *f* kiss, and thou hast given it me. „ I i 132
does it matter so much if the maid give the *f* kiss? *Little John.* I cannot tell, but I had sooner have given thee the *f* kiss. „ I i 136
if a man and a maid love one another, may the maid give the *f* kiss? „ I i 173
You shall give me the *f* kiss. „ I ii 227
The *f* part—made before you came among us— „ III 435

First (s) We strove against the papacy from the *f*, *Queen Mary* III iii 225
Who knew it from the *f*. „ III vi 114

First-marriage I do remember your *f-m* fears. *The Cup* II 206

Fish (s) I had liefer that the *f* had swallowed me, *Harold* II i 36
Rolf, what *f* did swallow Jonah? *Rolf.* A whale! „ II i 41
A sauce-deviser for thy days of *f*, *Becket, Pro.* 98
my fellows know that I am all one scale like a *f*. „ I iv 213
as to the *f*, they de-miracled the miraculous draught, „ III iii 123

Fish (verb) while ye *f* for men with your false fires, Let the great Devil *f* for your own souls. *Harold* II i 30
But 'e doänt *f* neither. *Prom. of May* I 214
Well, it's no sin in a gentleman not to *f*. „ I 216

Fisher Apostles; *they* were *f's* of men, *Harold* II i 34
Thy true King bad thee be A *f* of men; *Becket* II ii 286

Fisher (John, Bishop of Rochester) Did not More die, and *F*? he must burn. *Queen Mary* IV i 52

Fisherman We be *fishermen*; I came to see after my nets. *Harold* II i 27
Fishermen? devils! Who, while ye fish for men „ II i 29
Better have been A *f* at Bosham, my good Herbert, *Becket* II ii 292

Fist (s) and plunge His foreign *f* into our island Church *Queen Mary* III iv 364
the childish *f* That cannot strike again. *Harold* IV iii 30

Fist (verb) The boy would *f* me hard, and when we fought „ I i 444

Fit (adj.) Is the King's treasury A *f* place for the monies of the Church, *Becket* I iii 105
it is not *f* for us To see the proud Archbishop mutilated. „ I iii 613
he be *f* to bust hissen wi' spites and jalousies. *Prom. of May* II 164

Fit (verb) I measured his foot wi' the mark i' the bed, but it wouldn't *f* „ I 414

Fit *See also* **Ague-fit**

Fitter thousand times *F* for this grand function. *Becket, Pro.* 293

Fitzurse (**Reginald, knight of Henry II.'s household**) (*See also* **Reginald, Reginald Fitzurse**) *F*, that chart with the red line— *Becket Pro.* 427
what hast thou to do with this *F*? „ I i 271
And watch *F*, and if he follow thee, „ I i 330
No footfall—no *F*. We have seen her home. „ I i 367
Lord *F* reported this In passing to the Castle „ I ii 12
F—*Becket.* Nay, let him be. „ I ii 23
My lord, *F* beheld her in your lodging. „ I ii 33
Cursed *F*, and all the rest of them „ II ii 271
—*F* and his following—who would look down upon them? „ III iii 308
F, The running down the chase is kindlier „ IV ii 212
Kneel to thy lord *F*; Crouch even because thou hatest him; „ IV ii 222
My lord *F*—— *Becket.* He too! what dost thou here? „ IV ii 280
You have wrong'd *F*. I speak not of myself. „ IV ii 328
fond arms of her first love, *F*, Who swore to marry her. „ IV ii 335

Five that she met the Queen at Wanstead with *f* hundred horse, *Queen Mary* I i 78
God's righteous judgment fell upon you In your *f* years of imprisonment, „ III iv 242
My lord, the King demands *f* hundred marks, *Becket* I iii 641
Monks, knights, *f* hundred, that were there and heard. „ V ii 406
F hundred! *Count.* Say fifty! *The Falcon* 618
the feller couldn't find a Mister in his mouth fur me, as farms *f* hoonderd haäcre. *Prom. of May* I 304
It be *f* year sin' ye went afoor to him, „ II 5
We have been in such grief these *f* years, „ II 67
Poor sister, I had it *f* years ago. „ II 82
but can he trace me Thro' *f* years' absence, „ II 615
Him as did the mischief here, *f* year' sin'. „ III 140
You must not expect to find our Father as he was *f* years ago. „ III 420
F years of shame and suffering broke the heart „ III 761
and can make *F* quarts pass into a thimble. *Foresters* IV 283
Nay, my tongue tript—*f* hundred marks for use. „ IV 499

Five-fold and they rate the land *f-f* The worth of the mortgage, „ II i 149

Five-years' My *f-y* anger cannot die at once, *Prom. of May* II 462

Fixt with his fast-fading eyes *F* hard on mine, *Queen Mary* I ii 31
Well, burn me or not burn me I am *f*; „ IV ii 55
have I that I am *f*, *F* beyond fall; „ IV ii 89
had I *f* my fancy Upon the game I should *Becket, Pro.* 49
To-day they are *f* and bright—they look straight out. *The Cup* II 20

Flag made us lower our kingly *f* To yours of England. *Queen Mary* V i 59
must lower his *f* To that of England in the seas of England. „ V i 65
Our *f* hath floated for two hundred years Is France again. „ V ii 261
and with a *f* of ours Ta'en in the fight— *The Falcon* 612
But anger'd at their flaunting of our *f*, „ 628

Flame (s) (*See also* **Altar-flame, Re-flame**) Here was a young mother, Her face on *f*, *Queen Mary* II ii 70
And found it all a visionary *f*, „ IV ii 4
God will beat down the fury of the *f*, „ IV iii 98
gather'd with his hands the starting *f*, „ IV iii 337
And thrust his right into the bitter *f*; „ IV iii 610
before The *f* had reach'd his body; „ IV iii 616
Unmoving in the greatness of the *f*, „ IV iii 622
and cannot scape the *f*. *Harold* I i 13
Fling not thy soul into the *f's* of hell. *Becket* II i 316
dooms thee after death To wail in deathless *f*. „ IV ii 272
He miss the searching *f* of purgatory, „ V iii 13

Flame (verb) I am on fire until I see them *f*. *Queen Mary* III iv 288
'Tis out—mine *f's*. „ V v 124
by St. Denis, now will he *f* out, And lose his head *Becket* V ii 479

Flamed —O he *F* in brocade— *Queen Mary* III i 76
How he *f* When Tostig's anger'd earldom *Harold* III i 53

Flaming In sight of all with *f* martyrdom. *Queen Mary* IV iii 29
What with this *f* horror overhead? *Harold* I i 231
Then I saw Thy high black steed among the *f* furze, *Becket* II i 55

Flanders prince is known in Spain, in *F*, *Queen Mary* I v 207
Emperor counsell'd me to fly to *F*. „ I v 550
We heard that you w[illegible] sick in *F*, cousin. „ III ii 34

Flanders (*continued*) Why then to *F*. I will hawk and hunt In *F*. *Harold* I i 258
To follow thee to *F*! Must thou go? „ I ii 27
kisses of all kind of womankind In *F*, „ I ii 114
To-morrow—first to Bosham, then to *F*. „ I ii 240
Flap let him *f* The wings that beat down Wales! „ IV i 246
Flare fly out and *f* Into rebellions. *Queen Mary* III i 283
It glares in heaven, it *f's* upon the Thames, *Harold* I i 29
Flash (s) whether this *f* of news be false or true, *Queen Mary* III ii 234
It is the *f* that murders, the poor thunder *Harold* I ii 231
That which the *f* hath stricken. „ I ii 235
Our axes lighten with a single *f* „ V i 538
lest there should be *f'es* And fulminations *Becket, Pro.* 221
whose quick *f* splits The mid-sea mast, *The Cup* II 293
Flash (verb) Thou shalt *f* it secretly Among the good *Harold* I ii 219
I will both *f* And thunder for thee. „ I ii 228
F sometimes out of earth against the heavens. *Becket* V ii 37
fire that *f'es* out again From century to century, *The Cup* I ii 166
though my men and I *f* out at times Of festival *Foresters* I ii 274
Flash'd as might have *f* Upon their lake of Garda, *Queen Mary* III ii 22
to stay his hand Before he *f* the bolt. *Becket* II i 275
And when he *f* it Shrink from me, „ II i 276
Tho' all the swords in England *f* above me „ V ii 484
noblest light That ever *f* across my life, *Foresters* III 142
The hunter's passion *f* into the man, „ IV 539
Flashing I see the *f* of the gates of pearl— *Harold* I i 186
Flask and mine old *f* of wine Beside me, *Queen Mary* III i 46
send you down a *f* or two Of that same vintage? *Falcon* 585
Flat (adj.) but tramples *f* Whatever thwarts him; *Harold* II ii 379
and a foot to stamp it . . . *F*. „ V ii 194
This beggarly life, This poor, *f*, hedged-in field— *Prom. of May* II 344
Lusty bracken beaten *f*, Queen. *Foresters* II ii 154
Flat (s) No, nor with the *f* of it either. *Becket* I iv 225
Flatten gulf and *f* in her closing chasm Domed cities, *The Cup* II 300
Flatter You know to *f* ladies. *Queen Mary* I iv 98
I am safe enough; no man need *f* me. „ II ii 317
Will not thy body rebel, man, if thou *f* it? *Becket, Pro.* 103
—*f* And fright the Pope— „ II ii 472
You *f* me. Dear Eva Was always thought the prettier. *Prom. of May* II 378
Flatter'd Flutter'd or *f* by your notice of her, *The Falcon* 538
Flattering As if to win the man by *f* him. *Queen Mary* II ii 312
Flattery sucking thro' fools' ears The *flatteries* of corruption— *Becket* I iii 362
Flaunt We cannot *f* it in new feathers now: *The Falcon* 42
And scruplest not to *f* it to our face *Foresters* IV 887
Flaunting But anger'd at their *f* of our flag, *The Falcon* 628
Flay And *f* me all alive. *Harold* IV i 191
Flay'd starved, maim'd, flogg'd, *f*, burn'd, *Queen Mary* II i 210
Flaying Horrible! *f*, scourging, crucifying— *The Cup* I ii 235
Flea like a *f* That might have leapt upon us *Queen Mary* II ii 294
Fled (adj. and part.) our Bishops from their sees Or *f*, they say, or flying— „ I ii 5
'Sir Peter Carew *f* to France: „ II i 135
Is Peter Carew *f*? Is the Duke taken? „ II i 142
Bar the bird From following the *f* summer— *Becket* I i 259
France! Ha! De Morville, Tracy, Brito—*f* is he? „ I iv 199
Love that can shape or can shatter a life till the life shall have *f*? „ II i 12
Has *f* our presence and our feeding-grounds. „ II ii 22
Fled (verb) Left him and *f*; and thou that would'st be King, *Queen Mary* II iv 82
first archbishop *f*, And York lay barren *Becket* I iii 53
Who thief-like *f* from his own church by night, „ II ii 156
I *f*, and found thy name a charm to get me Food, „ V ii 96
Once I *f*—Never again, and you— „ V ii 498
Since Camma *f* from Synorix to our Temple, *The Cup* II 14
whereon she struck him, And *f* into the castle. *Foresters* II i 118
for Oberon *f* away Twenty thousand leagues to-day. „ II ii 142
Flee Then whither should I *f* for any help? *Queen Mary* IV iii 126
Griffyth when I saw him *f*, Chased deer-like *Harold* I ii 147
when I *f* from this For a gasp of freer air, *Becket* II i 27
then you are a dead man; *f*! „ V iii 126
Fleece hanging down from this The Golden *F*— *Queen Mary* III i 82
Fleer heard One of your Council *f* and jeer at him. „ II ii 393
The statesman that shall jeer and *f* at men, „ II ii 397
Fleet (s) Mine is the *f* and all the power at sea— „ I iv 287
Fleet (s) (*continued*) To seize upon the forts and *f*, *Queen Mary* III i 464
Hold office in the household, *f*, forts, army; „ III iii 72
and the French *f* Rule in the narrow seas. „ V i 6
collect the *f*; Let every craft that carries „ V ii 274
Fleet (verb) A breath that *f's* beyond this iron world, *Harold* III ii 197
Fleeted and makes it Foam over all the *f* wealth of kings *The Cup* II 289
Fleeth fowl that *f* o'er thy field is cursed, *Harold* V i 73
Fleeting My grayhounds *f* like a beam of light, „ I ii 129
Fleming *See* **Fox-Fleming**
Flemish Their *F* go-between And all-in-all. *Queen Mary* III vi 4
Flesh (*See also* **Pheasant-flesh**) with right reason, flies that prick the *f*. „ III iv 71
The soft and tremulous coward in the *f*? „ IV ii 107
when thou becamest Man in the *F*, „ IV iii 141
it was thought we two Might make one *f*, „ V ii 137
we were not made One *f* in happiness, no happiness here; But now we are made one *f* in misery; „ V ii 150
Where they eat dead men's *f*, *Harold* II ii 808
Treble denial of the tongue of *f*, „ III i 282
Fast, scourge thyself, and mortify thy *f*, *Becket* I iii 540
And as for the *f* at table, a whole Peter's sheet, „ III iii 128
That I would touch no *f* till he were well *The Falcon* 680
servants Are all but *f* and blood with those they serve. „ 709
And these take *f* again with our own *f*, *Prom. of May* II 277
weight of the *f* at odd times overbalance the weight of the church, *Foresters* I ii 61
and as to other frailties of the *f*— „ I ii 65
clothes itself In maiden *f* and blood, „ III 117
Flesh-fallen Look! am I not Work-wan, *f*-*f*? *Harold* I i 99
Flew in a narrow path. A plover *f* before thee. *Becket* II i 54
a bat *f* out at him In the clear noon, *Foresters* II ii 96
Crush'd my bat whereon I *f*! „ II ii 146
Flickering Pertest of our *f* mob, „ II ii 130
Fliest stay, fool, and tell me why thou *f*. *Becket* III ii 35
Flight My *f* were such a scandal to the faith, *Queen Mary* I ii 53
hath a farther *f* Than mine into the future. „ I v 312
Fling We *f* ourselves on you, my Lord. „ II ii 48
why *f* back the stone he strikes me with? „ IV ii 150
Then *f* mine own fair person in the gap *Harold* I ii 202
he *f's* His brand in air and catches it again, „ V i 493
all my doubts I *f* from me like dust, *Becket* I i 148
and *f* them out to the free air. „ I i 287
F not thy soul into the flames of hell: „ II i 316
I *f* all that upon my fate, my star. *The Cup* I iii 27
F wide the doors and let the new-made children „ II 163
f in the spices, Nard, Cinnamon, amomum, „ II 183
child of evolution, *f's* aside His swaddling-bands, *Prom. of May* I 585
To *f* myself over, when I heard a voice, „ III 374
Flint in all this, my Lord, her Majesty Is *f* of *f*, *Queen Mary* III vi 38
All your voices Are waves on *f*. „ IV i 122
crawl over knife-edge *f* Barefoot, *Becket* II i 272
I fear this Abbot is a heart of *f*, *Foresters* I ii 269
Flit We must *f* for evermore. „ II ii 123
I Titania bid you *f*, „ II ii 126
Float while the smoke *f's* from the cottage roof, „ I ii 317
Floated *f* downward from the throne Of God Almighty. *Harold* I i 17
Our flag hath *f* for two hundred years Is France again. *Queen Mary* V ii 261
Floating gonfanon of Holy Peter *F* above their helmets— *Harold* V i 550
Flock (s) your *f's* of swans, As fair and white as angels; *Queen Mary* III ii 14
doth not kill The sheep that wander from his *f*, „ III iv 103
To the poor *f*—to women and to children— „ IV ii 158
and all thy *f* should catch An after ague-fit *Becket* III iii 31
Shatter you all to pieces if ye harm One of my *f*! „ V iii 136
Home with the *f* to the fold— *The Cup* I ii 8
Flock (verb) —thousands will *f* to us. *Queen Mary* II i 192
Flogg'd I'll have you *f* and burnt too, „ I i 60
starved, maim'd, *f*, flay'd, burn'd, „ II i 210
Flood some mischance of *f*, And broken bridge, „ I v 354
like a river in *f* thro' a burst dam *Harold* II ii 465
had in it Wales, Her *f's*, her woods, her hills: „ IV i 207
from that *f* will rise the New, *Prom. of May* I 594
She rose From the foul *f* and pointed toward the farm, „ II 653
Floor that his fan may thoroughly purge his *f*. *Queen Mary* III iv 370
these chessmen on the *f*—the king's crown broken! *Becket, Pro.* 313
And smote me down upon the Minster *f*. „ I i 104

Floor (*continued*) mark'd Her eyes were ever on the marble *f*? *The Cup* II 19
Florence I left it privily At *F*, in her palace *The Falcon* 75
His grandsire struck my grandsire in a brawl At *F*, „ 252
True tears that year were shed for you in *F*. „ 385
this faded ribbon was the mode In *F* „ 423
he would marry me to the richest man In *F*; „ 749
The wildest of the random youth of *F* „ 809
Florio O my sick boy! My daily fading *F*, „ 236
My one child *F* lying still so sick, „ 678
Flourish (s) For these are no conventional *f'es*. *Prom. of May* II 562
Flourish (verb) Lift head, and *f*; *Queen Mary* III iv 24
hasn't an eye left in his own tail to *f* *The Falcon* 102
Flourished but in the end we *f* out into a merriment; *Becket* III iii 137
Flout since he *f's* the will of either realm, „ II ii 255
Flow waters of the fen they know not Which way to *f*. *Queen Mary* II ii 54
Let them *f* forth in charity, „ IV iii 208
William's or his own As wind blows, or tide *f's*: *Harold* V i 163
Colour *F's* thro' my life again, *Prom. of May* II 667
Flow'd spring Of all those evils that have *f* *Queen Mary* III iv 234
the black river *F* thro' my dreams— *Prom. of May* II 651
Flower (s) (*See also* **Wild-flower**) now would settle
Upon this *f*, now that; *Queen Mary* I iv 56
F, she! Half faded! „ I iv 60
As the first *f* no bee has ever tried. „ I iv 63
They are the *f* of England; set the gates wide. „ II iv 69
To kiss and cuff among the birds and *f's*— „ III v 259
Which in the Catholic garden are as *f's*, „ IV i 179
Love will hover round the *f's* when they first awaken; „ V ii 370
Palms, *f's*, pomegranates, golden cherubim *Harold* III i 182
A goodly *f* at times. „ IV i 151
Men are God's trees, and women are God's *f's*; *Becket, Pro.* 112
and the *f's* Are all the fairer. „ *Pro.* 116
And never a *f* at the close; (repeat) „ *Pro.* 332, 342
I love them More than the garden *f's*, „ II i 133
these golden slopes Of Solomon-shaming *f's*— „ III i 48
The brook's voice is not yours, and no *f*, „ III i 56
—would have made my pathway *f's*, „ V ii 371
mountain *f's* grew thickly round about. *The Falcon* 355
if but to guess what *f's* Had made it; „ 430
'Dead mountain *f's*, dead mountain-meadow *f's*, „ 461
You bloom again, dead mountain-meadow *f's*.' „ 471
A word with you, my lord! *Count.* 'O mountain *f's*!' „ 474
A word, my lord! *Count.* 'Dead *f's*!' „ 476
my nurse has broken The thread of my dead *f's*, „ 522
If possible, here! to crop the *f* and pass. *Prom. of May* I 253
Altho' at first he take his bonds for *f's*, „ I 646
The brook among its *f's*! Forget-me-not, „ II 298
anatomized The *f's* for her— „ II 303
but, my *f*, You look so weary and so worn! „ III 498
then the sweetest *f* of all the wolds, „ III 751
He that can pluck the *f* of maidenhood *Foresters* I ii 108
Who art the fairest *f* of maidenhood „ I ii 123
worship thee, Crown thee with *f's*; „ II ii 19
And answer it in *f's*. „ III 353
That beam of dawn upon the opening *f*, „ IV 4
Bees rather, flying to the *f* for honey. „ IV 13
The *f* said 'Take it, my dear, „ IV 16
When the *f* was wither'd and old. „ IV 22
And lie with us among the *f's*, and drink— „ IV 965
Flower (verb) and *f's* In silken pageants. *Queen Mary* III v 14
Mercy, that herb-of-grace, *F's* now but seldom. „ III vi 10
and her affections Will *f* toward the light *Prom. of May* I 486
Flower-bed but he left the mark of 'is foot i' the *f-b*; „ I 409
Flower'd that *f* bowl my ancestor Fetch'd from the farthest east— *The Falcon* 483
Flowery Nay, rather than so clip The *f* robe of Hymen, *The Cup* II 436
Flowing (part.) Two rivers gently *f* side by side— *Becket* I iii 445
And here the river *f* from the sea, *Queen Mary* III ii 26
Flowing (s) frost That help'd to check the *f* of the blood. *The Falcon* 645
Flown Our dovecote *f*! I cannot tell why monks *Becket* V ii 580
Hollow Pandora-box, With all the pleasures *f*, *Prom. of May* II 347
Fluff if this Prince of *f* and feather come *Queen Mary* I iv 162
Flung *f* them streaming o'er the battlements *Harold* II ii 391
flamed When Tostig's anger'd earldom *f* him, „ III i 54
colt winced and winnied and *f* up her heels; *Becket, Pro.* 515
F the Great Seal of England in my face— „ I iii 456

Flung (*continued*) if Thomas have not *f* himself at the King's feet. *Becket* III iii 168
never yet *F* back a woman's prayer. *The Cup* I ii 300
'He never yet *f* back a woman's prayer'— „ I ii 455
F by the golden mantle of the cloud, *Foresters* II i 28
f His life, heart, soul into those holy wars „ IV 406
Flurried with my lady's coming that had so *f* me, *The Falcon* 493
Flush coming up with a song in the *f* of the glimmering red? *Becket* II i 8
Flush'd Our bashful Legate, saw'st not how he *f*? *Queen Mary* III iv 351
colour'd all my life, *F* in her face; *The Falcon* 365
Fluster'd what hath *f* Gardiner? how he rubs His forelock! *Queen Mary* III iv 12
and is *f* by a girl's kiss. *Foresters* I i 186
your woman so *f* me that I forgot my message „ I i 296
Fluting *F*, and piping and luting 'Love, love, love'— „ III 33
Flutter (s) kill'd away at once Out of the *f*. *Queen Mary* III v 164
Flutter (verb) broken, out you *f* Thro' the new world, „ I iv 53
one half Will *f* here, one there. „ III vi 197
But he begins to *f*. *Harold* II ii 3
dove, who *f's* Between thee and the porch, „ IV i 231
f out at night? *Becket* I i 282
Begins to *f* in them, and at last Breaks *Prom. of May* I 649
Flutter'd *F* or flatter'd by your notice of her, *The Falcon* 538
he *f* his wings with a sweet little cry, *Foresters* I i 154
he *f* his wings as he gave me the lie, „ I i 159
Fluttering (part.) I found it *f* at the palace gates:— *Queen Mary* III ii 218
Fluttering (s) The leprous *f's* of the byway, „ IV iii 76
Fly (s) (*See also* **Gad-fly**) And cruel at it, killing helpless *flies*; „ III iv 65
with right reason, *flies* that prick the flesh. „ III iv 70
they swarm into the fire Like *flies*—for what? no dogma. „ V ii 112
As *flies* to the Gods; they kill us for their sport.' *Prom. of May* I 264
Cannot *he* take his pastime like the *flies*? „ I 277
that her *flies* Must massacre each other? „ I 284
would not crush The *f* that drew her blood; „ II 494
Fly (verb) Hooper, Ridley, Latimer will not *f*. *Martyr. F*, Cranmer! *Queen Mary* I ii 14
might be forgiven. I tell you, *f*, my Lord. „ I ii 43
F, my Lord, *f*! „ I ii 96
farewell, and *f*. *Cranmer. F* and farewell, „ I ii 104
I thank my God it is too late to *f*. „ I ii 112
You *f* your thoughts like kites. „ I v 390
Emperor counsell'd me to *f* to Flanders. „ I v 549
Song *flies* you know For ages. „ II i 80
Cranmer. *F* would he not, when all men bad him *f*. „ III i 171
f out and flare Into rebellions. „ III i 282
Swallows *f* again, Cuckoos cry again, „ III v 96
seems that we shall *f* These bald, blank fields, „ III v 251
Whose colours in a moment break and *f*, „ IV iii 170
Whose colours in a moment break and *f*!' „ V ii 207
Love will *f* the fallen leaf, and not be overtaken; „ V ii 372
where the black crow *flies* five, „ V v 85
who skips and *flies* To right and left, *Harold* I i 11
F thou to William; tell him we have Harold. „ II i 110
let *f* the bird within the hand, „ II ii 65
wilt thou *f* my falcons this fair day? „ II ii 146
two young wings To *f* to heaven straight with. „ III i 26
are but of spring, They *f* the winter change— „ III ii 97
Our Wessex dragon *flies* beyond the Humber, „ IV i 3
How should the people fight When the king *flies*? „ V i 138
and they *f*—the Norman *flies*. „ V i 541
They *f* once more, they *f*, the Norman *flies*! „ V i 596
Thou knowest he was forced to *f* to France; *Becket* I iii 204
When what ye shake at doth but seem to *f*, „ I iii 744
'*F* at once to France, to King Louis of France: „ I iv 53
I must *f* to France to-night. „ I iv 154
F thou too. The King keeps his forest head of game here, „ III ii 36
Linger not till the third horn. *F*! „ III ii 41
I will *f* with my sweet boy to heaven, „ IV ii 237
on a Tuesday did I *f* Forth from Northampton; „ V ii 286
I shall not *f*. Here, here, here will you find me. „ V ii 513
drag me not. We must not seem to *f*. „ V ii 637
F, *f*, my lord, before they burst the doors! „ V iii 56
I have it in my heart—to the Temple—*f*— *The Cup* I iii 112

Fly (verb) *(continued)* She—close the Temple door. Let her not *f*. *The Cup* II 461
Just gone To *f* his falcon. *The Falcon* 210
and once you let him *f* your falcon. „ 317
Should *f* like bosom friends when needed most. „ 527
Breaks thro' them, and so *flies* away for ever; *Prom. of May* I 650
Shall I say it?—*f* with me to-day. „ I 678
I will *f* to you thro' the night, the storm— „ I 701
Will he not *f* from you if he learn the story of my shame „ III 256
Tell them to *f* for a doctor. „ III 712
Their aim is ever at that which *flies* highest— *Foresters* I i 262
while the lark *flies* up and touches heaven! „ I ii 315
We must *f* from Robin Hood „ II ii 138
You see why We must leave the wood and *f*. „ II ii 174
How much? how much? Speak, or the arrow *flies*. „ III 278
Flying from their sees Or fled, they say, or *f*— *Queen Mary* I ii 5
Tut, your sonnet's a *f* ant, Wing'd for a moment. „ II i 83
and *f* to our side Left his all bare, „ II iii 3
see there the arrows *f*. „ II iv 51
and the traitor *f* To Temple Bar, „ II iv 93
A bookman, *f* from the heat and tussle, „ III iv 251
But wing'd souls *f* Beyond all change *Harold* III ii 100
Whither away, man? what are you *f* from? *Becket* III ii 18
when I was *f* from My Tetrarchy to Rome. *The Cup* I i 6
Who knows that he had ever dream'd of *f*? *Prom. of May* I 655
Prince John again. We are *f* from this John. *Foresters* II i 448
this is Maid Marian *F* from John—disguised. „ II i 680
Bees rather, *f* to the flower for honey. „ IV 12
Foälk (folk) *F's* says he likes Miss Eva the best. *Prom. of May* I 24
I knaws nowt o' what *f's* says, an' I caäres nowt neither. „ I 27
F's doesn't hallus knaw thessens; „ I 28
An' I haätes booöks an' all, fur they puts *f* off the owd waäys. „ I 222
Let ma aloän afoor *f*, wilt tha? „ II 213
Foam (s) Moon on the field and the *f*, *The Cup* I ii 3
Foam (verb) Who mouth and *f* against the Prince of Spain. *Queen Mary* II ii 250
F at the mouth because King Thomas, *Becket* V i 203
F over all the fleeted wealth of kings *The Cup* II 289
Fobbing *See* **A-fobbing**
Foe the Queen Is both my *f* and yours: *Queen Mary* I iv 42
You cannot Learn a man's nature from his natural *f*. „ I v 340
His *f's* would blame him, and I scorn'd 'em, „ I v 624
His *f's*—the Devil had suborn'd 'em. „ I v 626
make Those that we come to serve our sharpest *f's*? „ II iii 78
hath shut the gates On friend and *f*. „ II iv 62
My *f's* are at my feet and I am Queen. „ II iv 119
My *f's* are at my feet, and Philip King. „ II iv 143
To veil the fault of my most outward *f*— „ IV ii 106
seeming not as brethren, But mortal *f's*! „ IV iii 186
thou Hast broken all my *f's*, *Harold* I i 217
f's in Edward's hall To league against thy weal. „ I ii 31
Griffyth I hated: why not hate the *f* Of England? „ I ii 145
To leave the *f* no forage. „ V i 133
arm within Is Becket's, who hath beaten down my *f's*. *Becket, Pro.* 254
God make not thee, but thy *f's*, fall. „ I i 107
Serve my best friend and make him my worst *f*; „ I iii 568
No one comes, Nor *f* nor friend; „ III i 38
will you crown my *f* My victor in mid-battle? „ V i 149
a man may take good counsel Ev'n from his *f*. „ V ii 4
more of olive-branch and amnesty For *f's* at home— „ V ii 16
'O man, forgive thy mortal *f*, *Prom. of May* III 5
I am chased by my *f's*. *Foresters* II i 184
Fog who dream'd us blanketed In ever-closing *f*, *Queen Mary* III ii 21
Foible Not scorn him for the *f's* of his youth. *Becket* V ii 328
Foil man that hath to *f* a murderous aim *Harold* II ii 417
but *f's* wherein To set the precious jewel, *Becket, Pro.* 268
To *f* and spoil the tyrant *Foresters* II i 11
Foil'd And may be *f* like Tarquin, if you follow *The Cup* I i 143
Fold (as for sheep) will return into the one true *f*, *Queen Mary* I iii 22
And be regather'd to the Papal *f*? „ III ii 117
Who now recalls her to His ancient *f*. „ III iii 167
sends His careful dog to bring them to the *f*. „ III iv 105
Fold (as for sheep) *(continued)* that our wolf-Queen Is prowling round the *f*. *Becket* III iii 8
To find my stray sheep back within the *f*. „ III iii 356
Home with the flock to the *f*— *The Cup* I ii 8
Safe from the wolf to the *f*— „ I ii 20
Fold (thing folded) How dense a *f* of danger nets him round, *Harold* II ii 17
The *f's* have fallen from the mystery, *Becket* IV ii 8
Fold *See also* **Five-fold**
Folded It lies there *f*: is there venom in it? *Queen Mary* III v 216
whole life hath been *f* like a blossom in the sheath, *Foresters* I i 206
Foliot (Gilbert, Bishop of London) (*See also* **Gilbert Foliot**)
Your *F* fasts and fawns too much for me. *Becket, Pro.* 264
not the soldier As *F* swears it.— „ I i 388
F may claim the pall For London too. „ I iii 55
F, let me see what I have sign'd. „ I iii 307
I sign'd them—being a fool, as *F* call'd me. „ I iii 561
and tho' you suspend *F* or another, „ II ii 358
F is the holier man, perhaps the better. „ III iii 91
Folk (*See also* **Foälk, Volk**) Among the good Northumbrian *f*, *Harold* I ii 220
our helpless *f* Are wash'd away, wailing, „ II ii 470
blurt thy curse among our *f*, I know not— „ V i 89
sent his *f*, His kin, and all his belongings, *Becket* II i 70
Live with these honest *f*—And play the fool! *Prom. of May* I 744
Folkmote The London *f* Has made him all but king, *Foresters* I iii 80
Foller (follow) be room anew for all o' ye. *F* me. *Prom. of May* I 454
Shall I *f* 'er and ax 'er to maäke it up? „ II 131
Follow (*See also* **Foller**) it *f's* all the more that they can make thee one, *Queen Mary* I i 49
will you not *f* the procession? „ I i 129
Well, I shall *f*; „ I i 132
made you *f* The Lady Suffolk and the Lady Lennox?— „ I iv 30
I *f* your good counsel, gracious uncle. „ I iv 186
F their Majesties. „ III i 331
Mary would have it; and this Gardiner *f's*; „ III iii 231
Philip would have it; and this Gardiner *f's*! „ III iii 234
Indeed, I cannot *f* with your Grace: „ III iv 99
I do not *f*. „ III v 38
And in a moment I shall *f* him. „ V v 57
by God's grace, We'll *f* Philip's leading, „ V v 112
worst that *f's* Things that seem jerk'd *Harold* I i 136
To *f* thee to Flanders! Must thou go? „ I ii 27
F my lead, and I will make thee earl. „ I ii 216
I need thee not. Why dost thou *f* me? *Man-at-arms.* I have the Count's commands to *f* thee. „ II ii 232
debonair to those That *f* where he leads, „ II ii 320
Thy Duke will seem the darker. Hence, I *f*. „ II ii 818
'Wulfnoth is sick,' he said; 'he cannot *f*;' „ III i 85
That these will *f* thee against the Norsemen, „ IV i 157
will ye, if I yield, *F* against the Norsemen? „ IV i 177
An honest fool! *F* me, honest fool, „ V i 88
F them, *f* them, drive them to the sea! „ V i 602
They murder all that *f*. „ V i 610
F me this Rosamund day and night, *Becket, Pro.* 505
they *f* me—and I must not be known. „ I i 182
And then what *f's*? Let me *f* thee. „ I i 190
F him out! „ I i 237
And watch Fitzurse, and if he *f* thee, „ I i 330
True test of coward, ye *f* with a yell. „ I iii 745
Cross swords all of you! swear to *f* him! „ I iv 200
must we *f* All that they overdid or underdid? „ II ii 213
ran a twitch across his face as who should say what's to *f*? „ III iii 95
Farewell! I must *f* the King. „ III iii 329
I *f* out my hate and thy revenge. „ IV ii 151
F us, my son, and we will find it for thee— „ IV ii 372
if you *f* Not the dry light of Rome's straight-going policy, *The Cup* I i 144
Give him a bow and arrows—*f*—*f*. „ I i 208
What *f's* is for no wife's eyes. „ I ii 231
F my art among these quiet fields, *Prom. of May* I 743
Reaction needs must *f* revel—yet— „ II 264
'Well now you would fain *f* Wealth,' *Foresters* I i 158
And I will *f* thee, and God help us both. „ I i 277
Ay, so she did not *f* me to the wood. „ I iii 142

Follow (*continued*) But if you *f* me, you may die with me. — Foresters I iii 166
and be silent in the wood. *F* me. „ II i 366
Quick, friar, *f* them: „ II i 429
They *f* us. „ IV 579
thy match shall *f* mine. „ IV 1045
Follow'd some fifty That *f* me from Penenden Heath — Queen Mary II i 151
but *f* the device of those Her nearest kin: „ III i 379
You must fancy that which *f*, „ III i 410
boats that *f*, were as glowing-gay As regal gardens; „ III ii 12
Who *f* with the crowd to Cranmer's fire. „ IV iii 554
I *f* thee. — Harold I ii 215
Why am I *f*, haunted, harass'd, „ II ii 248
Normans left among us, Who *f* me for love! „ III i 304
She hath *f* with our host, and suffer'd all. „ IV i 28
The king's foundation, that have *f* him. „ V i 476
Last night I *f* a woman in the city here. — Becket, Pro. 468
why, my lord, I *f*—*f* one—— *Becket*. And then what follows? „ I i 188
The woman that I *f* hither. „ I i 195
My lord, I *f* Reginald Fitzurse. „ I i 235
The dog *f* his calling, my lord. „ I iv 97
Then *f* the thunder of the captains and the shouting, „ III iii 111
I thought if I *f* it I should find the fairies. „ IV i 24
I watched her and *f* her into the woods, „ IV ii 16
I *f* You and the child: he babbled all the way. „ IV ii 139
Why, these are our own monks who *f* us! „ V iii 59
I meant thee to have *f*—better thus. — The Cup II 498
She *f* thee into the forest here? — Foresters II i 486
The Sheriff! the Sheriff, *f* by Prince John „ IV 588
Followedst Art thou so sure thou *f* anything? — Becket I i 210
Follower boldness, which will give my *f's* boldness. — Queen Mary II iii 71
A worldly *f* of the wordly strong. — Becket I iii 543
He rides abroad with armed *f's*, „ V i 2
Thy holy *f* founded Canterbury— „ V iii 5
but can keep his *f's* true. — Foresters II i 77
if the *f's* Of him, who heads the movement, „ II i 700
Following (*See also* **A-follering**) but all the ladies of her *f*. — Queen Mary I I 82
hang the leaders, let their *f* go. „ IV i 74
F her like her sorrow. „ V v 11
And slew two hundred of his *f*, — Harold IV i 116
Bar the bird From *f* the fled summer— — Becket I i 259
Fitzurse and his *f*—who would look down upon them? „ III iii 308
And all Thro' *f* of my fancy. — The Falcon 144
the man, the woman, *F* their best affinities, — Prom. of May I 523
He, *f* his own instincts as his God, „ I 588
who truly loves and truly rules His *f*, — Foresters II i 77
Folly *F*, my good Lord. *Courtenay*. How *f*? — Queen Mary I iv 89
the *f* of all *follies* Is to be love-sick for a shadow. „ I v 533
if he jeer not seeing the true man Behind his *f*, „ II ii 401
His early *follies* cast into his teeth, „ V ii 124
in your chancellorship you served The *follies* of the King. *Becket*. No, not these *follies*! — Becket I ii 31
I am sure I told him that his plot was *f*. — The Cup I ii 284
Fond Unalterably and pesteringly *f*! — Queen Mary V i 120
his *f* excess of wine Springs from the loneliness of my poor bower, — Becket III i 38
To the *f* arms of her first love, Fitzurse, „ IV ii 334
But he were mighty *f* o' ye, warn't he? — Prom. of May II 9
You see, they are so *f* o' their own voices — Foresters II i 382
Fonder *F* of poor Eva—like everybody else. — Prom. of May II 11
Fondest But since the *f* pair of doves will jar, — Becket IV ii 40
Fondle And one fair child to *f*! „ III i 12
Food dogs' *f* thrown upon thy head. — Harold II ii 431
seeing now The poor so many, and all *f* so dear. — Queen Mary IV iii 209
We scarcely dare to bless the *f* we eat — Becket V i 70
found thy name a charm to get me *F*, roof, and rest. „ V ii 98
what should you know o' the *f* o' the poor? — Foresters II i 283
Fool and—the *f*—He wrecks his health — Queen Mary I v 166
It may be, thro' mine honesty, like a *f*. „ I v 237
he is thrice the *f*; „ II ii 401
He is child and *f*, and traitor to the State. „ II ii 403
some *f* that once Brake bread with us, „ III v 43

Fool (*continued*) and her priests Have preach'd, the *f's*, — Queen Mary III vi 99
Till, by St. James, I find myself the *f*. „ III vi 101
nave and aisles all empty as a *f's* jest! „ IV iii 287
—the world A most obedient beast and *f*—myself Half beast and *f* as appertaining to it; „ IV iii 414
The *f's*! (repeat) „ IV iii 521, 530
Come out, my Lord, it is a world of *f's*. „ IV iii 639
Courtenay, belike— *Mary*. A *f* and featherhead! „ V i 128
F, think'st thou I would peril mine own soul „ V v 167
hot religious *f*, Who, seeing war in heaven, — Harold I i 139
make me not *f*! Nor make the King a *f*, „ I i 289
lest I make myself a *f* Who made the King „ I i 293
F still! or wisdom there, „ I i 359
Be not a *f*! „ II i 19
To marry and have no husband Makes the wife *f*. „ II ii 310
I think I am a *f* To think it can be otherwise „ III i 102
Thou uncanonical *f*, Wilt *thou* play with the thunder? „ III i 390
F and wise, I fear This curse, and scorn it. „ III ii 67
Take and slay me, I say, Or I shall count thee *f*. „ IV ii 16
The slow, fat *f*! He drawl'd and prated so, „ IV ii 40
An honest *f*! Follow me, honest *f*, „ V i 88
Hot-headed *f's*—to burst the wall of shields! „ V i 612
Peace, *f's*! *Becket*. Peace, friends! — Becket I ii 1
F! I will make thee hateful to thy King. „ I ii 91
sucking thro' *f's'* ears The flatteries of corruption— „ I iii 360
For, like a *f*, thou knowest no middle way. „ I iii 532
I sign'd them—being a *f*, as Foliot call'd me. „ I iii 561
I play the *f* again. „ I iii 751
stay, *f*, and tell me why thou fliest. „ III ii 34
This in thy bosom, *f*, And after in thy bastard's! „ IV ii 257
The jealous *f* balk'd of her will— „ IV ii 423
honour me, obey me! Sluggards and *f's*! „ V i 241
Sluggards and *f's*, why do you stand and stare? „ V i 256
I have play'd the sudden *f*. — The Cup I iii 162
But I täākes 'im fur a bad lot and a burn *f*, — Prom. of May I 154
but I täākes 'im for a Lunnun swindler, and a burn *f*. „ I 309
Live with these honest folk—And play the *f*! „ I 745
Superstitious *f*, What brought me here? „ II 350
There, there, I am a *f*! „ III 207
More *f* he! What I that have been call'd a Socialist, „ III 583
Thou speakest like a *f* or a woman. — Foresters I i 204
There—there—be not a *f* again. „ I i 261
thou art *f* again—I am all as loyal as thyself, „ I i 293
Why do you listen, man, to the old *f*? „ II i 358
I know I have done amiss, have been a *f*. „ II ii 52
I have been a *f* and I have lost my Kate. „ II ii 78
or the head of a *f*, or the heart of Prince John, „ IV 213
See thou thwart me not, thou *f*! „ IV 745
If thou be king, Be not a *f*! „ IV 790
Fool-fire But the *f-f* of love or lust, — The Cup I i 147
Fool-friar Back, thou *f-f*! Knowest thou not the Prince? — Foresters IV 682
Foolhardy But that's *f*. *Wyatt*. No! boldness — Queen Mary II iii 69
Foolish Which found me full of *f* doubts, „ I v 530
For ever, you *f* child! What's come over you? — Prom. of May I 771
Some *f* mistake of Sally's; but what! „ III 153
And all the *f* world is pressing thither. — Foresters III 147
Fool-people The *f-p* call her a witch— „ II i 178
Foot Yearns to set *f* upon your island shore. — Queen Mary I v 367
the pebble which his kingly *f* First presses „ I v 369
It lies there in six pieces at your *feet*; „ II i 87
set no *f* theretoward unadvised Of all our Privy Council; „ II ii 204
a sound Of *feet* and voices thickening hither— „ II iv 45
My foes are at my *feet* and I am Queen. „ II iv 119
My foes are at my *feet*, and Philip King. „ II iv 143
as if her *feet* were wash'd in blood, „ III i 61
Feeling my native land beneath my *f*, „ III ii 47
Thou art much beholden to this *f* of mine, „ III ii 49
where Edward draws A faint *f* hither, — Harold I i 144
thy leave to set my *feet* On board, „ I i 228
sea shall roll me back To tumble at thy *feet*. „ I ii 115
Down thirty *feet* below the smiling day— „ II ii 430
He had but one *f*, he must have hopt away, „ II ii 675

Foot (*continued*) bright sky cleave To the very *feet* of God, *Harold* II ii 743
Seven *feet* of English land, or something more, „ IV ii 54
'Seven *feet* of English earth, or something more, „ IV iii 112
Then for the bastard Six *feet* and nothing more! „ IV iii 116
Our guardsman hath but toil'd his hand and *f*, I hand, *f*, „ V i 201
They turn on the pursuer, horse against *f*, „ V i 609
and a *f* to stamp it . . . Flat. „ V ii 192
the Archbishop washed my *feet* o' Tuesday. *Becket* I iv 234
My bank Of wild-flowers. At thy *feet*! „ II i 126
if Thomas have not flung himself at the King's *feet*. „ III iii 169
o'erleaps a jutting rock And shoots three hundred *feet*. *The Cup* I i 111
tho' Rome may set A free *f* where she will, „ II 246
My *feet* are tons of lead, They will break „ II 476
but he left the mark of 'is *f* i' the flower-bed; *Prom. of May* I 409
I measured his *f* wi' the mark i' the bed, „ I 413
I thinks I'd like to taäke the measure o' your *f*. „ I 464
is a gentleman? *Dora.* That he is, from head to *f*. „ III 282
land now And wealth, And lay both at your *feet*. „ III 616
whenever I set my own *f* on it I say to it, *Foresters* I i 335
Far from solid *f* of men, „ II ii 169
Footed *See* **Delicate-footed, Four-footed**
Footfall No *f*—no Fitzurse. We have seen her home. *Becket* I i 367
Footsore I am *f* and famish'd therewithal. *Foresters* II i 266
Footstep I thought I heard A *f*. *The Cup* I ii 12
Footstool There let them lie, your *f*! *Queen Mary* II iv 121
For *See* **Vor, Vor't**
Forage To leave the foe no *f*. *Harold* V i 133
Foraging I am *f* For Norway's army. „ IV ii 5
Forbad So royal that the Queen *f* you wearing it. *Queen Mary* I iv 77
The King *f* it. True, my liege. *Foresters* IV 865
Forbear Spare and *f* him, Harold, if he comes! *Harold* III i 299
How long shall we *f* him? *Becket* V ii 417
Forbid Shall I despair then?—God *f*! *Queen Mary* IV iii 129
No, God *f*! *Henry.* No! God *f*! *Becket* II ii 222
God *f*! (repeat) *Foresters* I ii 93, 100
Ay God *f*, But if it be so we must bear with John. „ I ii 101
save King Richard, when he comes, *f* me. „ IV 665
if the King *f* thy marrying With Robin, „ IV 874
Forbidden loved within the pale *f* By Holy Church: *Harold* III ii 23
Force (s) in full *f* Roll upon London. *Queen Mary* II i 235
so my Lord of Pembroke in command Of all her *f* be safe; „ II ii 306
Lord Pembroke in command of all our *f* „ II iv 4
jealousy Hath in it an alchemic *f* to fuse „ III vi 181
No power mine To hold their *f* together . . . *Harold* IV iii 213
Have thy two brethren sent their *f's* in? „ V i 342
Then there's no *f* in thee! „ V i 344
'A GALATIAN SERVING BY *F* IN THE ROMAN LEGION.' *The Cup* I i 47
'A GALATIAN SERVING BY *F* IN THE ROMAN LEGION.' „ I ii 75
Serve by *f*? No *f* Could make me serve by *f*. „ I ii 79
The *f* of Rome a thousand-fold our own. „ I ii 85
Force (verb) Why do you *f* me thus against my will? *Grim.* My lord, we *f* you from your enemies. *Becket.* As you would *f* a king from being crown'd. *John of Salisbury.* We must not *f* the crown of martyrdom. *Becket* V iii 21
I could not *f* or wheedle to my will. *The Cup* I iii 167
Forced Spite of her tears her father *f* it on her. *Queen Mary* I v 495
so 'z we was *f* to stick her, „ IV iii 494
When being *f* aloof from all my guard, *Harold* IV iii 15
dost thou think the King *F* mine election? *Becket* I i 127
see you yon side-beam that is *f* from under it, „ III iii 50
Forefather Beheld our rough *f's* break their Gods, *Queen Mary* III ii 120
Foreign My *f* friends, who dream'd us blanketed In ever-closing fog, „ III ii 19
That Gardiner, once so one with all of us Against this *f* marriage, „ III iii 7
and plunge His *f* fist into our island Church „ III iv 364
no *f* prince or priest Should fill my throne, „ III v 235
A long petition from the *f* exiles To spare the life of Cranmer. „ IV i 3
Shall these accuse him to a *f* prince? „ IV i 24
That Cranmer may withdraw to *f* parts, „ IV i 45
This same petition of the *f* exiles For Cranmer's life. „ IV i 193
Foreign (*continued*) how it chanced That this young Earl was sent on *f* travel, *Queen Mary* V ii 489
The *f* courts report him in his manner Noble „ V ii 511
that seem at most Sweet guests, or *f* cousins, *Becket* II i 135
Foreigner that no *f* Hold office in the household, *Queen Mary* III iii 71
Forekings fierce *f* had clench'd their private hides *Harold* IV iii 35
Forelead twin sister of the morning star, *F* the sun. *The Cup* I iii 47
Forelock That irritable *f* which he rubs, *Queen Mary* I iv 265
what hath fluster'd Gardiner? how he rubs His *f*! „ III iv 13
Foremost First of the *f* of their files, who die For God, *Becket* V ii 495
F in England and in Normandy; *Harold* II ii 631
Forenoon I was born true man at five in the *f* *Queen Mary* I i 46
Foresee For I *f* dark days. *Mary.* And so do I, sir; „ I v 275
and there was Lambert; Who can *f* himself? „ IV ii 216
Foreseeing *F*, with whate'er unwillingness, „ I v 253
Foreshorten That so *f's* greatness, „ III v 41
Forespeak I can *f* your speaking. „ I v 137
Forest (adj.) The King keeps his *f* head of game here, *Becket* III ii 37
I have shelter'd some that broke the *f* laws. *Foresters* I iii 70
up thro' all the *f* land North to the Tyne: „ II i 88
So now the *f* lawns are all as bright As ways to heaven, „ II i 630
And join our feasts and all your *f* games „ III 85
It is our *f* custom they should revel Along with Robin. „ III 174
Have ye glanced down thro' all the *f* ways „ IV 111
Ay, ay, Robin, but let him know our *f* laws: „ IV 199
Hast broken all our Norman *f* laws, „ IV 886
That thou wilt break our *f* laws again „ IV 888
They break thy *f* laws—nay, by the rood „ IV 907
Our *f* games are ended, our free life, „ IV 1049
Forest (s) King's verdurer caught him a-hunting in the *f*, *Becket* I iv 96
More sacred than his *f's* for the chase? „ IV ii 24
this door Opens upon the *f*! Out, begone! *The Cup* I ii 329
there is a lot of wild fellows in Sherwood *f* who hold by King Richard. *Foresters* I ii 73
In Sherwood *F*. I have heard of them. „ I iii 102
I believe She came with me into the *f* here. *Robin.* She follow'd thee into the *f* here? „ II i 485
myself Would guide you thro' the *f* to the sea. „ II i 638
out of the *f* and over the hills and away, „ II ii 175
most beaten track Runs thro' the *f*, „ III 90
My lord John, In wrath because you drove him from the *f*, „ III 451
To bring their counter-bond into the *f*. „ IV 90
cuirass in this *f* where I dream'd That all was peace— „ IV 130
Thou art the king of the *f*, „ IV 232
if e'er thou be assail'd In any of our *f's*, „ IV 424
Thou told'st us we should meet him in the *f*, „ IV 440
You hide this damsel in your *f* here, „ IV 476
Thou art alone in the silence of the *f* „ IV 631
Thou Robin shalt be ranger of this *f*, „ IV 954
We leave but happy memories to the *f*. „ IV 1071
Forester He was a *f* good; „ II i 319
Forest-horn if I wind This *f-h* of mine „ IV 175
Forest-life and all the better For this free *f-l*, „ II i 60
Foretold my dream *f* my martyrdom In mine own church. *Becket* V ii 632
Forfeit Or I *f* my land to the Abbot. *Foresters* I ii 151
if they were not repaid within a limited time your land should be *f*. „ IV 469
Forfeited affirms The Queen has *f* her right to reign *Queen Mary* V i 290
It seems thy father's land is *f*. *Foresters* IV 640
Forgave my father and I *f* you stealing our coals. *Prom. of May* III 69
—her last word *F*—and I forgive you. „ III 811
Forged ay; if Bonner have not *f* the bills. *Queen Mary* IV i 51
Forget (*See also* **Forgit**) you *f* That long low minster where you gave your hand „ III ii 89
may God *F* me at most need when I *f* Her foul divorce— „ IV i 80
if that May make your Grace *f* yourself a little. „ V v 81
Shall I *f* my new archbishoprick *Becket* I i 220
To rest upon thy bosom and *f* him— „ II i 31
Forgetting that *F's* me too. „ II i 50
You were. I never *f* anything. „ V ii 413
he begs you to *f* it As scarce his act:— *The Cup* II 51
I promise you that if you *f* yourself in your behaviour to this gentleman, *Prom. of May* I 161
I am old and *f*. Was Prince John there? *Foresters* I i 251

Forget (*continued*) Not till she clean f thee, noble Earl.
Marian. F *him*—never—by this Holy Cross — *Foresters* I ii 306
Till Nature, high and low, and great and small F's herself, — „ I ii 328
'Turn! turn!' but I f it. — „ I iii 155
Forgetfulness offal thrown Into the blind sea of f. — *Queen Mary* III iii 193
Forget-me-not From out a bed of thick f-m-n's, — „ V v 94
speedwell, bluebottle, succory, f-m-n? — *Prom. of May* I 98
F-m-n, meadowsweet, willow-herb. — „ II 299
Forgetting F that Forgets me too. — *Becket* II i 49
Forgit (**forget**) I ha' browt these roses to ye—I f's what they calls 'em, — *Prom. of May* II 14
Forgive She never will f you. — *Queen Mary* I ii 96
F me, Father, for no merit of mine, — „ IV iii 152
F me, brother, I will live here and die. — *Harold* II ii 803
F me thou, and help me here! — „ V ii 22
Not help me, nor f me? — „ V ii 24
I say it now, f me! — „ V ii 27
We do f you For aught you wrought against us. — *Becket* II ii 109
F me and absolve me, holy father. — „ II ii 441
and though a Roman I F thee, Camma. — *The Cup* II 506
I f her, I f her! — *The Falcon* 173
They say, we should f our enemies. — *Prom. of May* II 431
if the wretch were dead I might f him; — „ II 434
I trust I shall f him—by-and-by— — „ II 466
not So easy to f—even the dead. — „ II 486
sure am I that of your gentleness You will f him. — „ II 489
then she will f Edgar for Harold's sake. — „ II 677
said herself She would f him, by-and-by, — „ II 681
'O man, f thy mortal foe, — „ III 5
souls on earth that live To be forgiven must f. F him seventy times and seven; — „ III 8
O f me! f me! *Steer.* Who said that? — „ III 462
I do believe I could f—well, almost anything— — „ III 631
Make her happy, then, and I f you. — „ III 667
I cannot find the word—f it—Amends. — „ III 790
—her last word Forgave—and I f you. If you ever F yourself, — „ III 811
He never will f her. — *Foresters* II i 142
Thou art Her brother—I f thee. — „ II i 516
Forgiven That might be f. I tell you, fly, my Lord. — *Queen Mary* I ii 42
And, when the headsman pray'd to be f, — „ III i 394
These are f—matters of the past— — „ III iii 190
And be f for it? — „ III vi 124
to speak a single word That could not be f. — „ III vi 127
And she loved much: pray God she be f. — „ V v 272
Forgotten and f by them and thee. — *Harold* I i 255
souls on earth that live To be f must forgive. — *Prom. of May* III 8
souls in Heaven Are both forgivers and f.' — „ III 11
Didn't I say that we had f you? — „ III 75
I kneel once more to be f. — *Foresters* II i 668
Forgiveness the King—that traitor past f, — *Queen Mary* I v 29
Is now content to grant you full f, — „ III iv 389
Was there not some one ask'd me for f? — *Harold* V ii 83
Would not—if penitent—have denied him *her* F. — *Prom. of May* II 498
Go back to him and ask his f before he dies.— — „ III 401
Don't you long for Father's f! — „ III 404
Speak but one word not only of f, — *Foresters* II i 610
Forgiver souls in Heaven Are both f's and forgiven.' — *Prom. of May* III 11
Forgot some Hebrew. Faith, I half f it. — *Queen Mary* II i 126
I f to tell you He wishes you to dine along with us, — *Prom. of May* I 616
that I f my message from the Earl. — *Foresters* I i 296
Forgotten I had f How these poor libels trouble you. — *Queen Mary* V ii 201
F and forgiven by them and thee. — *Harold* I i 255
And woo their loves and have f thee; — „ II ii 438
And all thine England hath f thee; — „ II ii 443
Counts his old beads, and hath f thee. — „ II ii 447
Boy, thou hast f That thou art English. — „ II ii 474
nurse, I had f thou wast sitting there. — *The Falcon* 35
Ay, and f thy foster-brother too. — „ 36
he had not f his promise to come when I called him. — *Prom. of May* III 329
I have f my horn that calls my men together. — *Foresters* II i 185
Shame on thee, Little John, thou hast f— — „ III 238
When the Church and the law have f God's music, — „ IV 554
Forkin' And you an' your Sally was f the haäy. — *Prom. of May* II 181
When me an' my Sally was f the haäy, — „ II 192
Forlorn betray'd, defamed, divorced, f! — *Queen Mary* I v 27
and yield Full scope to persons rascal and f, — „ II ii 185
F I am, and let me look f. — „ V ii 238
The last Parthian shaft of a f Cupid at the King's left breast, — *Becket, Pro.* 339
Form to compose the event In some such f — *Queen Mary* I v 225
The public f thereof. — „ IV ii 71
face and f unmatchable! — *The Cup* I i 122
Formal a f offer of the hand Of Philip? — *Queen Mary* I v 349
The f offer of Prince Philip's hand. — „ I v 588
And that more freely than your f priest, — *Prom. of May* III 632
I believed thee to be too solemn and f to be a ruffler. — *Foresters* I i 168
Former we shall still maintain All f treaties with his Majesty. — *Queen Mary* I v 266
A bastard hate born of a f love. — *Becket* II i 174
Why then I strike into my f path For England, — „ II ii 455
To the monk-king, Louis, our f burthen, — „ IV ii 305
Some of my f friends Would find my logic faulty; — *Prom. of May* II 663
because one of the Steers had planted it there in f times. — „ III 247
Forsaken we fade and are f— — *Queen Mary* V ii 375
Forsware That he f himself for all he loved, — *Harold* V i 622
Forswear to guard the land for which He did f himself— — „ V ii 163
Forsworn realm for which thou art f is cursed, — „ V i 63
But we hold Thou art f; and no f Archbishop Shall helm the Church. — *Becket* I iii 596
Fort Spain in our ships, in our f's, — *Queen Mary* II i 179
To seize upon the f's and fleet, — „ III i 464
Hold office in the household, fleet, f's, army; — „ III iii 72
A hill, a f, a city—that reach'd a hand — *Harold* IV i 44
another hill Or f, or city, took it, — „ IV i 50
Fortifying I spent thrice that in f his castles. — *Becket* I iii 632
Fortiter *Suaviter in modo*, f *in re*, — „ V ii 539
Fortune seem'd to smile And sparkle like our f — *Queen Mary* II iii 24
still Beyond your f's, you are still the king — *The Falcon* 291
though f had born *you* into the estate of a gentleman, — *Prom. of May* II 120
Forty As haggard as a fast of f days, — *Harold* IV iii 176
Some thirty—f thousand silver marks. — *Becket* I iii 657
What! f thousand marks! — „ I iii 704
F thousand marks! f thousand devils— — „ I iv 90
These two have f gold marks between them, Robin. — *Foresters* III 202
Forward F to London with me! f to London! — *Queen Mary* II i 214
f to London! *Crowd.* F to London! — „ II i 216
A Wyatt! a Wyatt! F! — „ II i 237
To Kingston, f! — „ II iii 124
F! F! Harold and Holy Cross! — *Harold* IV i 268
Foster-brother Ay, and forgotten thy f-b too. — *The Falcon* 37
as your ladyship knows, his lordship's own f-b, — „ 566
Fought I have f the fight and go— — *Harold* I i 184
Why—how they f when boys— — „ I i 430
We f like great states for grave cause; — „ I i 440
boy would fist me hard, and when we f I conquer'd, — „ I i 445
And thou for us hast f as loyally, — „ II ii 160
Have I not f it out? — „ II ii 222
I f another fight than this Of Stamford-bridge. — „ IV iii 23
or English Ironside Who f with Knut, — „ IV iii 54
Every man about his king F like a king; — „ IV iii 57
the living Who f and would have died, — „ IV iii 71
Hail to the living who f, the dead who fell! — „ IV iii 105
hath kinglike f and fallen, His birthday too. — „ V ii 124
And but that Holy Peter f for us, — „ V ii 164
have I f men Like Harold and his brethren, — „ V ii 178
For how have f thine utmost for the Church, — *Becket* I i 117
I led seven hundred knights and f his wars. — „ I iii 639
We f in the East, And felt the sun of Antioch — „ II ii 92
But kinglike f the proud archbishop, — „ IV ii 438
names of those who f and fell are like — *The Cup* I ii 164
but we f for it back, And kill'd— — *The Falcon* 614
both f against the tyranny of the kings, the Normans. — *Foresters* I i 229
Who be those three that I have f withal? — „ II i 443
Thou shouldst have ta'en his place, and f for him. — „ II i 546
Hast thou not f for it, and earn'd it? — „ IV 344

Fought (*continued*) Give me that hand which *f* for Richard there. *Foresters* IV 1029
Foul lives Of many among your churchmen were so *f* *Queen Mary* III iv 192
may God Forget me at most need when I forget Her *f* divorce— „ IV i 81
F maggots crawling in a fester'd vice! „ V v 161
I free From this *f* charge— *Harold* II ii 518
a *f* stream Thro' fever-breeding levels,— *Becket* II i 154
slut whose fairest linen seems *F* as her dust-cloth, „ V ii 203
She rose From the *f* flood and pointed toward the farm, *Prom. of May* II 653
all the *f* fatalities That blast our natural passions into pains! „ III 723
in Nottingham they say There bides a *f* witch somewhere hereabout. *Foresters* II i 203
he has anger'd the *f* witch, „ II i 670
slut whose fairest linen seems *F* as her dust-cloth, *Becket* V ii 203
Found (*See also* **Fun'**) All my hope is now It may be *f* a scandal. *Queen Mary* I v 231
Which *f* me full of foolish doubts, „ I v 530
Happily or not, It *f* her sick indeed. „ II ii 124
I've *f* this paper; pray your worship read it; „ II iii 55
We *f* him, your worship, a plundering „ II iii 72
I *f* it fluttering at the palace gates:— „ III ii 218
yet I *f* One day, a wholesome scripture, „ III iv 83
And *f* it all a visionary flame, „ IV ii 4
I have *f* thee and not leave thee any more. „ IV ii 109
Have *f* a real presence in the stake, „ IV ii 142
so long continuing, Hath *f* his pardon; „ IV iii 50
libellous papers which I *f* Strewn in your palace. „ V ii 172
And I have often *f* them. *Mary.* Find me one! „ V ii 222
God pardon me! I have never yet *f* one. „ V ii 335
and the dead were *f* Sitting, and in this fashion; „ V ii 396
I never *f* he bore me any spite. „ V ii 474
Have you *f* mercy there, Grant it me here: „ V v 144
If he *f* me thus, Harold might hate me; *Harold* I ii 171
I *f* him all a noble host should be. „ II ii 10
because we *f* him A Norman of the Normans. „ II ii 581
Both were lost and *f* together, „ III ii 7
lost and *f* Together in the cruel river Swale „ III ii 9
Tho' we be lost and be *f* together.' „ III ii 21
I have *f* him, I am happy. „ V ii 81
That I have *f* it here again? „ V ii 116
He *f* me once alone. Nay—nay—I cannot Tell you: *Becket* I i 274
They said—her Grace's people—thou wast *f*— „ I ii 6
that had *f* a King Who ranged confusions, „ I iii 369
I *f* a hundred ghastly murders done By men, „ I iii 407
and went on till I *f* the light and the lady, „ IV ii 18
He is easily *f* again. „ IV ii 67
F out her secret bower and murder'd her. „ V i 175
f thy name a charm to get me Food, roof, and rest. „ V ii 96
have *f* together In our three married years! *The Cup* I ii 416
we *f* a goat-herd's hut and shared His fruits „ I ii 426
I never *f* the woman I could not force or wheedle „ I iii 165
f All good in the true heart of Sinnatus, „ II 86
If you had *f* him plotting against Rome, „ II 406
But had I *f* him plotting, I had counsell'd „ II 412
chaplet on the grass, And there I *f* it. *The Falcon* 370
I have *f* it once again In your own self. *Prom. of May* II 375
seen us that wild morning when we *f* Her bed unslept in, „ II 470
Has anyone *f* me out, Dora? „ III 225
We *f* a letter in your bedroom torn into bits. „ III 323
even if I *f* it Dark with the soot of slums. „ III 601
I *f* this white doe wandering thro' the wood, *Foresters* II i 95
F him dead and drench'd in dew, „ II ii 147
the warm wine, and *f* it again. „ IV 245
I never *f* one traitor in my band. „ IV 836
Foundation Waltham, my *f* For men who serve the neighbour, *Harold* V i 97
The king's *f*, that have follow'd him. „ V i 476
Fountain (adj.) Were seated sadly at a *f* side, *The Falcon* 610
Fountain (s) his wealth A *f* of perennial alms— *Queen Mary* II ii 385
Four (*See also* **Vour**) *f* guns gaped at me, Black, silent mouths: „ II iii 30
I know Some three or *f* poor priests a thousand times Fitter *Becket, Pro.* 291

GG*

Four (*continued*) And this no wife has born you *f* brave sons, *Becket* V i 125
There then, *f* hundred marks. *Foresters* IV 497
Four-and-twenty We will away in *f-a-t* hours, „ I iii 91
Four-footed all manner of game, and *f-f* things, and fowls— *Becket* III iii 130
Fourscore This forest-horn of mine I can bring down *F* tall fellows on thee. *Foresters* IV 177
Fowl (*See also* **Wild-fowl**) The *f* that fleeth o'er thy field is cursed, *Harold* V i 73
all manner of game, and four-footed things, and *f's*— *Becket* III iii 131
Here's a fine *f* for my lady; *The Falcon* 556
Fox Die like the torn *f* dumb, *Queen Mary* II ii 331
a *f* may filch a hen by night, „ III v 157
a *f* from the glen ran away with the hen, *Prom. of May* I 51
Fox-Fleming Why comes that old *f-F* back again? *Queen Mary* I v 581
Foxglove Past the bank Of *f*, then to left by that one yew. *Foresters* IV 974
Fox-lion sorrow'd for my random promise given To yon *f-l*. *Harold* III i 270
Fragment or whether England Be shatter'd into *f's*. „ II ii 286
Frail his *f* transparent hand, Damp with the sweat of death, *Queen Mary* I ii 31
Frailer At least mine own is *f*: you are laming it. *Becket* IV ii 264
Frailty and as to other *frailties* of the flesh— *Foresters* I ii 65
France *F* would not accept her for a bride *Queen Mary* I ii 67
That makes for *F*. (repeat) *Queen Mary* I iii 89, 92, 94
But we play with Henry, King of *F*, *Queen Mary* I iii 132
The King of *F*, Noailles the Ambassador, „ I iv 110
Our one point on the main, the gate of *F*! „ I v 126
The Ambassador from *F*, your Grace. „ I v 239
Would make our England, *F*; „ I v 297
Would be too strong for *F*. „ I v 300
I must needs wish all good things for *F*. „ I v 310
'Sir Peter Carew fled to *F*: „ II i 135
The King of *F* is with us; „ II i 195
The King of *F* will help to break it. *Bagenhall.* *F*! We once had half of *F*, „ III i 105
England now Is but a ball chuck'd between *F* and Spain, „ III i 110
I know some lusty fellows there in *F*. „ III i 129
Back'd by the power of *F*, and landing here, „ III i 447
Not so well holpen in our wars with *F*, „ III vi 189
Ay, ay, beware of *F*. „ IV iii 434
If war should fall between yourself and *F*; „ V i 10
To declare war against the King of *F*. „ V i 117
soon or late you must have war with *F*; „ V i 122
he would weld *F*, England, Scotland, „ V i 136
yet the Pope is now colleagued with *F*; „ V i 140
to discourage and lay lame The plots of *F*, „ V i 189
The King of *F* the King of England too. „ V i 198
There *will* be war with *F*, at last, my liege; „ V i 283
Sailing from *F*, with thirty Englishmen, „ V i 285
This is the fifth conspiracy hatch'd in *F*; „ V i 298
Our flag hath floated for two hundred years Is *F* again. „ V ii 263
You did but help King Philip's war with *F*, „ V ii 314
As far as *F*, and into Philip's heart. „ V iii 18
It was his father's policy against *F*. „ V v 45
help to build a throne Out-towering hers of *F* . . . *Harold* II ii 765
and all *F*, all Burgundy, Poitou, all Christendom „ III ii 149
Louis of *F* loved me, and I dreamed that I loved Louis of *F*: *Becket, Pro.* 355
I will have thee frighted into *F*, „ I ii 94
I mean to cross the sea to *F*, „ I iii 124
Thou knowest he was forced to fly to *F*; „ I iii 205
But I that threw the mightiest knight of *F*, „ I iii 747
'Fly at once to *F*, to King Louis of *F*: „ I iv 53
I must fly to *F* to-night. „ I iv 154
or in the land of *F* for aught I know. „ I iv 196
F! Ha! De Morville, Tracy, Brito—fled is he? „ I iv 198
one who lives for thee Out there in *F*; „ II i 310
Brother of *F*, what shall be done with Becket? „ II ii 64
claws that you perforce again Shrank into *F*. „ II ii 88
Brother of *F*, you have taken, „ II ii 154
all the Church of *F* Decide on their decision, „ II ii 177
we pray you, draw yourself from under The wings of *F*. „ II ii 249

France (*continued*) I am glad that *F* hath scouted him at last: *Becket* II ii 252
you have quenched the warmth of *F* toward you, „ II ii 311
The wine and wealth of all our *F* are yours; „ II ii 446
have I Not heard ill things of her in *F*? Oh, she's The Queen of *F*. „ III i 231
My Lords of *F* and England, My friend of Canterbury „ III iii 227
we will to *F* and be Beforehand with the King, „ IV ii 453
For once in *F* the King had been so harsh, „ V ii 139
St. Denis of *F* and St. Alphege of England, „ V iii 165

Franche-Comté (a French province) voices of *F-C*, and the Netherlands, *Queen Mary* V i 45

Frange Illorum lanceas *F* Creator! *Harold* V i 584

Frankfort To Strasburg, Antwerp, *F*, Zurich, *Queen Mary* I ii 2

Fray'd *f* i' the knees, and out at elbow, „ I i 51

Freak Her *f's* and frolics with the late Lord Admiral? „ I iv 20

Free (adj.) (*See also* **Tongue-free**) To make *f* spoil and havock of your goods. „ II ii 186
but we can save your Grace. The river still is *f*. „ II iv 25
he is *f* enough in talk, But tells me nothing. „ III ii 193
That jail you from *f* life, bar you from death. „ III v 172
with *f* wing The world were all one Araby. „ III v 208
but had rather Breathe the *f* wind from off our Saxon downs, *Harold* II ii 186
To chain the *f* guest to the banquet-board; „ II ii 193
F air! *f* field! „ II ii 230
and fill the sky With *f* sea-laughter— „ II ii 337
Should they not know *f* England crowns herself? „ V i 47
Softly, and fling them out to the *f* air. *Becket* I i 287
And weight down all *f* choice beneath the throne. „ I iii 118
couldst thou always Blurt thy *f* mind to the air? „ I iii 239
she holds it in *F* and perpetual alms, „ I iii 680
To speak without stammering and like a *f* man? „ I iv 8
but God and his *f* wind grant your lordship a happy home-return „ III iii 327
Give me the poison; set me *f* of him! „ IV ii 165
The power of life in death to make her *f*! „ V iii 101
tho' Rome may set A *f* foot where she will, *The Cup* II 246
While, had you left him *f* use of his wings, *Prom. of May* I 652
for the moment, Will leave me a *f* field. „ II 456
We should be *f* as air in the wild wood— *Foresters* I iii 124
And these will strike for England And man and maid be *f* „ II i 10
And these shall wed with freemen, And all their sons be *f*, „ II i 22
and all the better For this *f* forest-life, „ II i 60
That I might breathe for a moment *f* of shield And cuirass „ IV 128
Friends, your *f* sports have swallow'd my *f* hour. „ IV 339
while our Robin's life Hangs by a thread, but he is a *f* man. „ IV 385
Our forest games are ended, our *f* life, „ IV 1049

Free (verb) I *f* From this foul charge— *Harold* II ii 517
Take thee, or *f* thee, *F* thee or slay thee, „ IV ii 17
if thou light upon her—*f* me from her? *Becket, Pro.* 493
First, *f* thy captive from *her* hopeless prison, „ V i 183
O devil, can I *f* her from the grave? „ V i 185
That sought to *f* the tomb-place of the King *Foresters* IV 408

Freed Duke of Suffolk lately *f* from prison, *Queen Mary* I iii 121
Earl of Devon? I *f* him from the Tower, „ I v 163
he *f* himself By oath and compurgation from the charge. *Harold* II ii 519
Know that when made Archbishop I was *f*, *Becket* I iii 708
part real, part childlike, to be *f* from the dulness— „ III iii 156
I have *f* myself From all such dreams, *Prom. of May* III 594

Freedom Whereas in wars of *f* and defence *The Cup* I ii 160
The love of *f*, the desire of God, *Foresters* II i 68
maiden *f* which Would never brook the tyrant. „ III 119

Freeing For *f* my friend Bagenhall from the Tower; *Queen Mary* III vi 7

Freely that more *f* than your formal priest, *Prom. of May* III 632

Freeman wrench'd All hearts of *freemen* from thee. *Harold* V i 279
And these shall wed with *freemen*, *Foresters* II i 21

Freer and when I flee from this For a gasp of *f* air, *Becket* II i 29

Free-will now the stronger motive, Misnamed *f-w*— *Prom. of May* II 637

Freeze And, lest we *f* in mortal apathy, *The Cup* I iii 130

French (adj.) *F*, I must needs wish all goods things for France. *Queen Mary* I v 309
The *F* King winks at it. „ III i 160

French (adj.) (*continued*) not mix us any way With his *F* wars— *Queen Mary* III iii 79
and the *F* fleet Rule in the narrow seas. „ V i 6
Swine, sheep, ox—here's a *F* supper. *Becket* I iv 113
Not on *F* ground, nor any ground but English, „ III iii 260

French (s) it threatens us no more Than *F* or Norman. *Harold* I i 135
talk a little *F* like a lady; play a little like a lady? *Prom. of May* III 303

Frenchman You must be sweet and supple, like a *F*. *Queen Mary* V i 276
and driven back The *Frenchmen* from their trenches? „ V ii 258
But blaze not out before the *Frenchmen* here. *Becket* III iii 221

Frequency and so cannot suffer by the rule of *f*. „ III iii 319

Fresh but you, cousin, are *f* and sweet As the first flower *Queen Mary* I iv 61
Would fain have some *f* treaty drawn between you. *Mary*. Why some *f* treaty? „ I v 261
And put some *f* device in lieu of it— „ III i 268
Cousin Pole, You are *f* from brighter lands. „ III iv 322
Carry *f* rushes into the dining-hall, *Foresters* I i 80

Friar (*See also* **Fool-friar**) Of those two *f's* ever in my prison, *Queen Mary* IV ii 94
as he walk'd the Spanish *f's* Still plied him „ IV iii 576
f's Plied him, but Cranmer only shook his head, „ IV iii 600
overbalance the weight of the church, ha *f*? *Foresters* I ii 62
Quick, *f*, follow them: „ II i 429
Nay, nay, but softly, lest they spy thee, *f*! „ II i 438
We spoil'd the prior, *f*, abbot, monk, „ III 167
Here come three *f's*. „ III 256
Thou and thy woman are a match for three *f's*. „ III 262
How should poor *f's* have money? „ III 276
These *f's*, thieves, and liars, Shall drink „ III 312
I believe thee, thou art a good fellow, though a *f*. „ III 342
by St. Mary these beggars and these *f's* shall join you. „ III 417
This *f* is of much boldness, noble captain. „ IV 234
I am overbreathed, *F*, by my two bouts at quarterstaff. „ IV 267
our *f* is so holy That he's a miracle-monger, „ IV 280
Keep silence, bully *f*, before the King. „ IV 919
If a cat may look at a king, may not a *f* speak to one? „ IV 922
—I trust Half truths, good *f*: „ IV 950
You, good *f*, You Much, you Scarlet, you dear Little John, „ IV 1082

Friar Tuck (follower of Robin Hood) coming hither for the dance—be they not, *F T*? „ I ii 54
Besides, tho' *F T* might make us one, „ II ii 88

Friday And I was bit by a mad dog o' *F*, *Becket* I iv 218

Friend fear, I see you, Dear *f*, for the last time; *Queen Mary* I ii 103
Ay, gentle *f*, admit them. I will go. „ I ii 110
By the mass, old *f*, we'll have no pope here „ I iii 42
Unless my *f's* and mirrors lie to me, „ I iv 2
Queen Is both my foe and yours: we should be *f's*. „ I iv 43
Not many *f's* are mine, except indeed Among the many. „ I iv 135
Speak not thereof—no, not to your best *f*, „ I iv 177
who am your *f* And ever faithful counsellor, „ I v 134
call'd my *f's* together, Struck home and won. „ I v 552
His *f's* would praise him, I believed 'em, „ I v 623
His *f's*—as Angels I received 'em, „ I v 625
You as poor a critic As an honest *f*: „ II i 116
No, my *f*; war *for* the Queen's Grace— „ II i 188
world as yet, my *f*, Is not half-waked; „ II i 227
Ay, ay, my *f*; not read it? „ II iii 64
My *f's*, I have not come to kill the Queen „ II iii 116
Be happy, I am your *f*. „ II iii 123
hath shut the gates On *f* and foe. „ II iv 62
My foreign *f's*, who dream'd us blanketed „ III ii 19
St. Andrew's day; sit close, sit close, we are *f's*. „ III iii 2
My seven-years' *f* was with me, my young boy; „ III iii 47
Our old *f* Cranmer, Your more especial love, „ III iv 416
To reach the hand of mercy to my *f*. „ IV i 65
why my *f* Should meet with lesser mercy „ IV i 69
Your faithful *f* and trusty councillor. „ IV i 89
Without a *f*, a book, my faith would seem Dead „ IV ii 96
Or am I slandering my most inward *f*, „ IV ii 105
Good day, old *f*; what, you look somewhat worn; „ IV ii 115
F for so long time of a mighty King; „ IV iii 73
And I and learned *f's* among ourselves „ V i 74
Have not I been the fast *f* of your life Since mine began, „ V ii 133
He is my good *f*, and I would keep him so; „ V iii 91

Friend (*continued*) *F*, tho' so late, it is not safe to preach. Queen Mary v iv 41
Our *f's*, the Normans, holp to shake his chair. Harold I i 85
Stand by him, mine old *f*, ,, I i 113
Is not the Norman Count thy *f* and mine? ,, I i 247
F's, in that last inhospitable plunge ,, II i 1
I dug mine into My old fast *f* the shore, ,, II i 7
Thou art his *f*: thou know'st my claim on England .. II ii 11
he shall be my dear *f* As well as thine, .. II ii 80
So thou, fair *f*, will take them easily. .. II ii 207
Obey the Count's conditions, my good *f*. .. II ii 277
I am thy fastest *f* in Normandy. .. II ii 556
Be careful of thine answer, my good *f*. .. II ii 605
Harold, I am thy *f*, one life with thee, .. II ii 649
My *f*, thou hast gone too far to palter now. .. II ii 706
I, the Count—the King—Thy *f*— .. II ii 755
O *f's*, I shall not overlive the day. ,, III i 232
Edwin, my *f*—Thou lingerest.—Gurth,— .. IV i 257
F's, had I been here, Without too large self-lauding ,, IV iii 85
King Loves not as statesman, but true lover and *f*. Becket, Pro. 81
Nolo Archiepiscopari, my good *f*, Is quite another matter. ,, Pro. 286
Becket, her father's *f*, like enough staved ,, Pro. 518
F, am I so much better than thyself ,, I i 3
Henry the King hath been my *f*, my brother, ,, I i 87
my father drove him and his *f's*, De Tracy ,, I i 277
when thou seest him next, Commend me to thy *f*. What *f*? *Rosamund*. The King. ,, I i 324
My *f*, the King! . . . O thou Great Seal of England, Given me by my dear *f* the King of England— ,, I i 335
Now must I send thee as a common *f* To tell the King, my *f*, I am against him. We are *f's* no more: ,, I i 342
Go therefore like a *f* slighted by one .. I i 350
O, my dear *f*, the King! O brother!— ,, I i 359
Peace, fools! *Becket*. Peace, *f's*! ,, I ii 2
Serve my best *f* and make him my worst foe; .. I iii 567
Farewell, *f's*! farewell, swallows! .. I iv 44
may I come in with my poor *f*, my dog? .. I iv 94
My *f's*, the Archbishop bids you good night. .. I iv 261
Be *f's* with him again—I do beseech thee. .. II i 21
But since he cursed My *f's* at Veselay, ,, II i 89
I kneel to thee—be *f's* with him again. .. II i 317
Be, both, the *f's* you were. *Henry*. The *f's* we were! Co-mates we were, .. II ii 119
No one comes, Nor foe nor *f*; .. III i 38
My *f* of Canterbury and myself Are now once more .. III iii 228
It must be so, my *f*! .. III iii 342
Soon as she learnt I was a *f* of thine, ,, V ii 110
Why they, your *f's*, those ruffians, the De Brocs, ,, V ii 434
My two good *f's*, What matters murder'd here, ,, V ii 629
Come in, my *f's*, come in! ,, V iii 68
Some *f's* of mine would speak with me without. The Cup I ii 202
my *f's* may spy him And slay him as he runs. ,, I ii 390
Our Antonius, Our faithful *f* of Rome, ,, II 244
Thou art the last *f* left me upon earth— The Falcon 31
No, no—a *f* of hers. ,, 59
For fear of losing more than *f*, a son; ,, 332
Should fly like bosom *f's* when needed most. ,, 527
cold-manner'd *f* may strangely do us The truest service, ,, 642
day's bright like a *f*, but the wind east like an enemy. Prom. of May I 79
forget yourself in your behaviour to this gentleman, my father's *f*, ,, I 163
Niver man 'ed better *f's*, and I will saäy niver master 'ed better men: .. I 323
I trust, my dear, we shall be always *f's*. ,, I 632
After all that has gone between us—*f's*! What, only *f's*? .. I 634
All that has gone between us Should surely make us *f's*. .. I 638
I do not dare, like an old *f*, to shake it. ,, II 526
Some of my former *f's* Would find my logic faulty; ,, II 664
But, O dear *f*, If thro' the want of any— .. III 549
a *f* just now, One that has been much wrong'd, ,, III 574
so true a *f* of the people as Lord Robin of Huntingdon. Foresters I i 188

Friend (*continued*) This Robin, this Earl of Huntingdon —he is a *f* of Richard— Foresters I i 282
My guests and *f's*, Sir Richard, ,, I ii 77
Dost thou mistrust me? Am I not thy *f*? .. I ii 178
as I *am* thy *f*, I promise thee to make this Marian thine. .. I ii 182
I and my *f*, this monk, were here belated, .. I ii 193
Sheriff, thy *f*, this monk, is but a statue. .. I ii 233
F's, I am only merry for an hour or two .. I iii 10
Strike up a song, my *f's*, and then to bed. ,, I iii 30
Ah dear Robin? ah noble captain, *f* of the poor! ,, II i 182
Nay—that, my *f*, I am sure I did not say. ,, II i 488
He has a *f* there will advance the monies, ,, II i 628
We never robb'd one *f* of the true King. ,, III 157
Robin, the people's *f*, the King o' the woods! ,, III 347
F's, your free sports have swallow'd my free hour. .. IV 339
Meanwhile, farewell Old *f's*, old patriarch oaks. .. IV 1054
Friendly-fiendly with that *f-f* smile of his, Harold III i 86
Friendship hatred of another to us Is no true bond of *f*. Queen Mary I iv 46
I hate a split between old *f's* Becket II ii 380
No *f* sacred, values neither man Nor woman Foresters IV 713
Friendship-fast Which binds us *f-f* for ever! Harold II ii 162
Frieze Look'd somewhat crooked on him in his *f*; Queen Mary IV iii 333
Fright (s) what maäkes tha sa white? *Eva*. *F*, father! Prom. of May I 418
Since Tostig came with Norway—*f* not love. Harold IV i 173
Fright (verb) and deep-incavern'd eyes Half *f* me. Queen Mary I iv 268
Which *f's* you back into the ancient faith; ,, IV ii 143
They *f* not me. Harold I i 39
It *f's* the traitor more to maim and blind. ,, II ii 503
—flatter And *f* the Pope— Becket II ii 473
I see now Your purpose is to *f* me— ,, IV ii 180
Why do you jest with me, and try To *f* me? Prom. of May I 666
I am not deaf: you *f* me. ,, III 660
To *f* the wild hawk passing overhead, Foresters III 318
Frighted Are *f* back to Tostig. Harold IV i 119
I will have thee *f* into France, Becket I ii 93
Fringe Some golden *f* of gorgeousness beyond Old use, The Cup II 438
old woman's blessing with them to the last *f*. Foresters II i 196
Frith (John) But you were never raised to plead for *F*, Queen Mary IV ii 211
Frock What, Mr. Dobson? A butcher's *f*? Prom. of May I 94
Frog Quash'd my *f* that used to quack Foresters II ii 149
Frolic Her freaks and *f's* with the late Lord Admiral? Queen Mary I iv 20
After my *f* with his tenant's girl, Prom. of May I 493
Can have *f* and play. Foresters II ii 183
From *See* **Vro'**
Front (adj.) Would set him in the *f* rank of the fight The Cup I ii 153
Front (verb) That is Your question, and I *f* it with another: Queen Mary I v 141
Will *f* their cry and shatter them into dust. ,, II iv 5
And *f* the doom of God. Harold V i 436
I'll *f* him, cross to cross. Becket I iii 481
Frost had a touch of *f* That help'd to check The Falcon 644
How few *f's* Will chill the hearts Foresters IV 1063
Frosted *f* off me by the first cold frown of the King. Becket I iv 67
Frosty Like sun-gilt breathings on a *f* dawn— Queen Mary V iii 50
Frown (s) frosted off me by the first cold *f* of the King. Becket I iv 67
Let there not be one *f* in this one hour. ,, II i 43
Frown (verb) should not *f* as Power, but smile Harold I i 365
However kings and queens may *f* on thee. Becket I ii 19
Frowned The King hath *f* upon me. .. I iv 25
he *f* 'No mate for her, if it should come to that'— .. III i 258
Frozen snow had *f* round her, and she sat Stone-dead .. V ii 237
Fructus Sit benedictus *f* ventris tui!' Queen Mary III ii 83
Fruit should leave Some *f* of mine own body after me, ,, II ii 223
The tree that only bears dead *f* is gone. ,, III i 19
this dead *f* was ripening overmuch, ,, III i 25
Can render thanks in *f* for being sown, ,, III iii 198
when the full *f* of the royal promise might have dropt Becket III iii 275
and shared His *f's* and milk. Liar! The Cup I ii 428
strows our *f's*, and lays Our golden grain, ,, II 285
And here are fine *f's* for my lady— The Falcon 561
Fruitful Most *f*, yet, indeed, an empty rind, Queen Mary III ii 202
Drink and drink deep—our marriage will be *f*. The Cup II 381

Fugatur Pastor *f* Grex trucidatur— *Harold* V i 513
Fulfil Speak, Master Cranmer, *F* your promise made me, *Queen Mary* IV iii 112
Fulfill'd wish *f* before the word Was spoken, „ I iv 232
Full but I hear that he is too *f* of aches and broken before his day. „ I i 124
But your own state is *f* of danger here. „ I iv 168
a head So *f* of grace and beauty ! „ I v 64
in *f* force Roll upon London. „ II i 234
ye did promise *f* Allegiance and obedience to the death. „ II ii 168
and yield *F* scope to persons rascal and forlorn, „ II ii 185
And pointed *f* at Southwark ; „ II iii 46
That hastes with *f* commission from the Pope „ III ii 51
And *f* release from danger of all censures Of Holy Church „ III iii 150
Not the *f* faith, no, but the lurking doubt. „ III iv 124
A fine beard, Bonner, a very *f* fine beard. „ III iv 338
Is now content to grant you *f* forgiveness, „ III iv 389
So that you crave *f* pardon of the Legate. „ III iv 391
but it was never seen That any one recanting thus at *f*, „ IV i 59
In *f* consistory, When I was made Archbishop, „ V ii 84
with *f* proof Of Courtenay's treason ? „ V ii 498
Make me *f* fain to live and die a maid. „ V iii 98
but to pay them *f* in kind, „ V iv 14
Pour not water In the *f* vessel running out at top *Harold* I i 378
And we will fill thee *f* of Norman sun, „ II ii 180
F hope have I that love will answer love. „ IV i 237
F thanks for your fair greeting of my bride ! „ IV iii 46
The cup's *f* ! *Harold.* I saw the hand of Tostig cover it. „ IV iii 80
Bring not thy hollowness On our *f* feast. „ IV iii 204
Cramp thy crop *f*, but come when thou art call'd. „ IV iii 234
Lay hands of *f* allegiance in thy Lord's And crave his mercy, „ V i 11
My heart is *f* of tears—I have no answer. *Becket, Pro.* 406
And there stole into the city a breath *F* of the meadows, „ I i 263
if the Latin rhymes be rolled out from a *f* mouth ? „ II ii 338
What more, Thomas ? I make thee *f* amends. „ III iii 219
when the *f* fruit of the royal promise might have dropt into thy mouth „ III iii 275
Hath used the *f* authority of his Church „ V i 207
My lord, the city is *f* of armed men. „ V ii 187
But *f* mid-summer in those honest hearts. „ V ii 373
Plunder'd the vessel *f* of Gascon wine, „ V ii 441
I would stand Clothed with the *f* authority of Rome, „ V ii 493
but God's *f* curse Shatter you all to pieces „ V iii 134
In the *f* face of all the Roman camp ? *The Cup* I ii 269
All my brain is *f* of sleep. „ I ii 445
but now all drown'd in love And glittering at *f* tide— „ II 234
Thank you. Look how *f* of rosy blossom it is. *Prom. of May* I 84
when the tide Of *f* democracy has overwhelm'd This Old world, „ I 593
and sat Thro' every sensual course of that *f* feast „ II 254
with what *f* hands, may be Waiting you in the distance ? „ II 509
Why should I pay you your *f* wages ? „ III 83
Let me bring you in here where there is still *f* daylight. „ III 218
and each of 'em as *f* of meat as an egg, *Foresters* I i 42
The wood is *f* of echoes, owls, elfs, ouphes, oafs, „ II i 262
though thou wert like a bottle *f* up to the cork, „ IV 210
Rogue, I am *f* of gout. I cannot dance. „ IV 562
In this *f* tide of love, Wave heralds wave : „ IV 1042
Fullest I fail Where he was *f* : *Queen Mary* II i 56
Let all be done to the *f* in the sight *The Cup* II 433
Full-throated to close at once In one *f-t* No ! *Queen Mary* I v 634
Full-train'd The *f-t* marvel of all falconry, *The Falcon* 25
Fulmina *F*, *f* Deus vastator ! *Harold* V i 573
Fulmination flashes And *f's* from the side of Rome, *Becket, Pro.* 222
Fulness Doth not the *fewness* of anything make the *f* of it in estimation ? „ III iii 302
Fun' (found) you be a pretty squire. I ha' *f* ye out, I hev. *Prom. of May* II 689
we *f* 'im out a-walkin' i' West Field wi' a white 'at, „ III 134
Function thousand times Fitter for this grand *f*. *Becket, Pro.* 293
I will suspend myself from all my *f's*. „ I iii 301
true To either *f*, holding it ; „ I iii 538
Fundatur Illorum in lacrymas Cruor *f* ! *Harold* V i 532
Funeral look'd As grim and grave as from a *f*. *Queen Mary* II ii 65
Fungus *See* **Wood-fungus**
Furrow plow Lay rusting in the *f's* yellow weeds, *Becket* I iii 355
Vein'd marble—not a *f* yet— „ II i 197
Further Go *f* hence and find him. *Harold* V ii 60
Fury God will beat down the *f* of the flame, *Queen Mary* IV iii 98
Furze Thy high black steed among the flaming *f*, *Becket* II i 56
Fuse And in this very chamber, *f* the glass, *Queen Mary* III v 54
alchemic force to *f* Almost into one metal „ III vi 181
Iron will *f*, and marble melt ; *Prom. of May* II 505
Future hath a farther flight Than mine into the *f*. *Queen Mary* I v 313

G

Gaäme (game) a-plaäyin' the saäme *g* wi' my Dora— *Prom. of May* II 591
Gaäy (gay) Wi' the wild white rose, an' the woodbine sa *g*, „ II 175
Gad-fly deer from a dog, or a colt from a *g-f*, *Foresters* II i 434
Gaffer but if you starve me I be *G* Death himself. „ I i 48
Gaiety So winsome in her grace and *g*, *Prom. of May* III 754
Gain (s) More *g* than loss ; for of your wives *Becket* V ii 200
Gain (verb) Not to *g* paradise : no, nor if the Pope, *Queen Mary* IV iii 557
time And peace for prayer to *g* a better one. *Harold* I i 220
I may trust to *g* her then When I shall *The Cup* I i 19
Gain'd She lives—but not for him ; one point is *g*. *Becket* IV ii 416
If once our ends are *g* ? *The Cup* I i 32
I hardly *g* The camp at midnight. „ I iii 18
Gainsay which he *G's* by next sunrising— *Becket* IV ii 278
Gala-day This is the *g-d* of thy return. *Foresters* IV 959
Galahad (a knight) The veriest *G* of old Arthur's hall. *Becket, Pro.* 129
Galatia Well—I shall serve *G* taking it, *The Cup* I i 100
Must all *G* hang or drown herself ? „ I ii 87
I know of no such wives in all *G*. „ I ii 191
Then that I serve with Rome to serve *G*. „ I ii 213
my serving Rome To serve *G* : „ I ii 279
I am much malign'd. I thought to serve *G*. „ I ii 324
And I will make *G* prosperous too, „ I iii 169
tell him That I accept the diadem of *G*— „ II 158
It is our ancient custom in *G* „ II 358
The sovereign of *G* weds his Queen. „ II 432
Galatian (adj.) What is Synorix ? *Sinnatus.* *G*, and not know ? „ I ii 181
He sends you This diadem of the first *G* Queen, „ II 132
Artemis, Artemis, hear me, *G* Artemis ! „ II 313
Artemis, Artemis, hear her, *G* Artemis ! „ II 317
Thy turn, *G* King. „ II 379
Galatian (s) 'A *G* SERVING BY FORCE IN THE ROMAN LEGION.' „ I i 47
That we *G's* are both Greek and Gaul. „ I i 203
'A *G* SERVING BY FORCE IN THE ROMAN LEGION.' „ I ii 75
know myself am that *G* Who sent the cup. „ I ii 209
Galatian-born But he and I are both *G-b*, „ II 94
Thou art *G-b*. „ II 456
Gall (bile) if the truth be *g*, Cram me not thou with honey, *Harold* IV i 15
honeymoon is the *g* of love ; he dies of his honeymoon. *Becket, Pro.* 364
Ay, whether it be *g* or honey to 'em— *Foresters* IV 967
Gall (girl) I cum behind tha, *g*, and couldn't make tha hear. *Queen Mary* IV iii 465
Gall (verb) ye three must *g* Poor Tostig. *Leofwin.* Tostig, sister, *g's* himself ; *Harold* I i 419
Gallant Our *g* citizens murder'd all in vain, *The Cup* I ii 142
A *g* boy, A noble bird, each perfect of the breed. *The Falcon* 319
A *g* Earl. I love him as I hate John. *Foresters* I i 190
Who art thou, *g* knight ? „ II i 440
This *g* Prince would have me of his—what ? „ IV 701
My masters, welcome *g* Walter Lea. „ IV 1002
Gall'd His heart so *g* with thine ingratitude, *Becket* I iii 4

Gallery And I will out upon the *g*. *Queen Mary* II iv 49
In some dark closet, some long *g*, drawn, „ V ii 217
Galley more than one Row'd in that *g*—Gardiner to wit, „ IV i 87
Galley-slave now, perhaps, Fetter'd and lash'd, a *g-s*, *Foresters* II i 654
Gallop (s) On the *g*, on the *g*, Robin, like a deer „ II i 432
Gallop (verb) 'at I tell'd 'em to *g* 'im. *Prom. of May* III 433
Gallows What! the *g*? *Queen Mary* III i 24
Gamble *G* thyself at once out of my sight, „ II iii 95
Gambled has drunk and *g* out All that he had, „ II iii 87
He has *g* for his life, and lost, he hangs. „ II iii 91
Game (pastime) (*See also* **Gaäme**) The *G* of Chess. (repeat) „ I iii 127
such a *g*, sir, were whole years a playing. „ I iii 139
Strange *g* of chess! a King That with her own pawns „ I iii 161
Simon Renard spy not out our *g* Too early. „ I iii 173
With whom they play'd their *g* against the king! *Harold* V ii 13
fixt my fancy Upon the *g* I should have beaten thee, *Becket, Pro.* 51
a perilous *g* For men to play with God. „ II ii 70
Is this a *g* for thee to play at? Away. *Foresters* II i 426
All our *g's* be put to rout. „ II ii 166
And join your feasts and all your forest *g's* „ III 85
Then thou shalt play the *g* of buffets with us. „ IV 259
Our forest *g's* are ended, our free life, „ IV 1049
Game (thing hunted) fatter *g* for you Than this old gaping gurgoyle: *Queen Mary* I iii 80
well train'd, and easily call'd Off from the *g*. *Becket, Pro.* 121
When they ran down the *g* and worried it. „ *Pro.* 123
The King keeps his forest head of *g* here, „ III ii 37
let the King's fine *g* look to itself. „ III ii 44
with all manner of *g*, and four-footed things, and fowls— „ III iii 130
No rushing on the *g*—the net,—the net. *The Cup* I i 170
And I may strike your *g* when you are gone. „ I ii 36
I must lure my *g* into the camp. „ I iii 64
You run down your *g*, We ours. What pity have you for your *g*? *Foresters* IV 520
Gamekeeper Have I not seen the *g*, the groom, *Queen Mary* IV iii 371
Gamel (a Northumbrian Thane) *G*, son of Orm, What thinkest thou this means? (repeat) *Harold* I i 20, 463
Hail, *G*, son of Orm, „ I i 91
Albeit no rolling stone, my good friend *G*, „ I i 94
Is the North quiet, *G*? „ I i 107
I trust he may do well, this *G*, „ I ii 190
that was his guest, *G*, the son of Orm: „ II ii 299
murder'd thine own guest, the son of Orm, *G*, „ IV ii 39
Gamester no such *g* As, having won the stake, *The Cup* I iii 145
Gangrene this rag fro' the *g* i' my leg. *Becket* I iv 237
and *g's*, and running sores, praise ye the Lord, „ I iv 255
Gap Sheep at the *g* which Gardiner takes, *Queen Mary* III iii 236
Then fling mine own fair person in the *g* *Harold* I ii 202
as I hate the dirty *g* in the face of a Cistercian monk, *Becket* II ii 381
Could shine away the darkness of that *g* „ III i 60
thaw he niver mended that *g* i' the glebe fence *Prom. of May* I 446
Gape These fields are only green, they make me *g*. *Queen Mary* III v 8
Will the earth *g* and swallow us? *Becket* V iii 205
causest the safe earth to shudder and *g*, *The Cup* II 299
throat might *g* before the tongue could cry who? *Foresters* III 225
Gaped four guns *g* at me, Black, silent mouths: *Queen Mary* II iii 31
The nurses yawn'd, the cradle *g*, „ III vi 93
Gaping yonder's fatter game for you Than this old *g* gurgoyle: „ I iii 81
Stand staring at me! shout, you *g* rogue! „ III i 288
The pretty *g* bills in the home-nest Piping for bread— *Becket* II ii 300
When shall your parish-parson bawl our banns Before your *g* clowns? *Prom. of May* I 687
Garb These black dog-Dons *G* themselves bravely. *Queen Mary* III i 190
Garcia (Villa) *See* **Villa Garcia**
Garda might have flash'd Upon their lake of *G*, „ III ii 23
Garden (adj.) I love them More than the *g* flowers, *Becket* II i 133
matched with my Harold is like a hedge thistle by a *g* rose. *Prom. of May* III 176
Garden (s) were as glowing-gay As regal *g's*; *Queen Mary* III ii 14
Which in the Catholic *g* are as flowers, „ IV i 178
and in the midst A *g* and my Rosamund. *Becket, Pro.* 169
into a *g* and not into the world, „ III i 131
not to speak one word, for that's the rule o' the *g*, „ III i 138
Garden (s) (*continued*) if I had been Eve i' the *g* I shouldn't ha' minded the apple, *Becket* III i 139
the knights are arming in the *g* Beneath the sycamore. „ V ii 569
There sprouts a salad in the *g* still. *The Falcon* 149
I haven't seen Eva yet. Is she anywhere in the *g*? *Prom. of May* I 47
All in the castle *g*, *Foresters* I i 10
Stole on her, she was walking in the *g*, „ II i 113
The serpent that had crept into the *g* „ II i 137
Gardener the groom, *G*, and huntsman, in the parson's place, *Queen Mary* IV iii 373
Garden-stuff profess to be great in green things and in *g-s*. *The Falcon* 552
Gardiner (Bishop of Winchester and Lord Chancellor) (*See also* **Out-Gardiners, Stephen Gardiner**) *G* for one, who is to be made Lord Chancellor, *Queen Mary* I i 86
so that *G* And Simon Renard spy not out our game „ I iii 172
Thus *G*—for the two were fellow-prisoners „ I iv 198
He hath no fence when *G* questions him; „ I iv 204
this fierce old *G*—his big baldness, „ I iv 263
G is against him; The Council, „ I v 76
It then remains for your poor *G*, „ I v 220
Paget is ours. *G* perchance is ours; „ I v 386
brake into woman-tears, Ev'n *G*, all amazed, „ I v 566
G knows, but the Council are all at odds, „ II i 138
I hear that *G*, coming with the Queen, „ II ii 308
G buys them With Philip's gold. „ III i 143
a pale horse for Death and *G* for the Devil. „ III i 235
how strange That *G*, once so one with all „ III iii 6
This *G* turn'd his coat in Henry's time; „ III iii 16
Ay, and for *G*! being English citizen, „ III iii 23
which the emperor sent us Were mainly *G's*: „ III iii 71
Mary would have it; and this *G* follows; „ III iii 230
Philip would have it; and this *G* follows! „ III iii 233
Sheep at the gap which *G* takes, „ III iii 236
what hath fluster'd *G*? how he rubs His forelock! „ III iv 12
The faultless *G*! „ III iv 96
G would have my head. „ III v 118
The gray rogue, *G*, Went on his knees, „ III v 165
G out-Gardiners *G* in his heat, „ III vi 25
G burns, And Bonner burns; „ III vi 58
more than one Row'd in that galley—*G* to wit, „ IV i 87
summun towld summun o' owld Bishop *G's* end; „ IV iii 503
G wur struck down like by the hand o' God „ IV iii 515
did not *G* intercept A letter which the Count de Noailles wrote „ V ii 494
Some say that *G*, out of love for him, „ V ii 501
G burns Already; but to pay them full in kind, „ V iv 13
Garland (*See also* **Marriage-garland**) your ladyship were not Too proud to look upon the *g*, *The Falcon* 663
dead *G* Will break once more into the living blossom. „ 918
Garner *g* the wheat; And burn the tares *Queen Mary* V v 113
Garnish'd We have had it swept and *g* after him. „ III ii 139
Garrison we might withdraw Part of our *g* at Calais. „ I v 123
Garrison'd *See* **Ill-garrison'd**
Garrulous poor *g* country-wives. *Queen Mary* IV iii 547
What, daunted by a *g*, arrogant girl! *Foresters* IV 736
Garter English *G*, studded with great emeralds, *Queen Mary* III i 84
Gascon amorous Of good old red sound liberal *G* wine: *Becket, Pro.* 100
when the *G* wine mounts to my head, „ *Pro.* 113
Plunder'd the vessel full of *G* wine, „ V ii 441
Gash (s) —brave Gurth, one *g* from brow to knee! *Harold* V ii 70
Gash (verb) here I *g* myself asunder from the King, *Becket* I i 175
Gash'd Son, husband, brother *g* to death in vain, *The Cup* I ii 143
Gasp when I flee from this For a *g* of freer air, *Becket* II i 29
Gasping 'No, madam,' he said, *G*; *Queen Mary* III i 405
Gate (*See also* **Farm-gate**) Our one point on the main, the *g* of France! „ I v 125
At the park *g* he hovers with our guards. „ II iv 15
Hark, there is battle at the palace *g's*, „ II iv 47
they have shut the *g's*! „ II iv 59
hath shut the *g's* On friend and foe. „ II iv 61
cry To have the *g's* set wide again, „ II iv 65
They are the flower of England; set the *g's* wide. „ II iv 70
How oft hath Peter knock'd at Mary's *g*! „ III ii 63
Open, Ye everlasting *g's*! „ III ii 183

Gate (*continued*) I found it fluttering at the palace *g's* :— *Queen Mary* III ii 218
Like dogs that set to watch their master's *g*, „ III iv 310
I see the flashing of the *g's* of pearl— *Harold* I i 186
my men will guard you to the *g's*. *Becket* I i 403
Here is a missive left at the *g* by one from the castle. „ I iv 50
—like some loud beggar at thy *g*— „ II i 181
Close the great *g*—ho, there—upon the town. „ V ii 530
Was not the great *g* shut ? „ V iii 137
waiting To clasp their lovers by the golden *g's*. *Prom. of May* I 248
Laid famine-stricken at the *g's* of Death— „ III 807
Gate-house Last night I climb'd into the *g-h*, Brett, *Queen Mary* II iii 15
Gateway *g* to the mainland over which Our flag hath floated „ V ii 260
Gather *g* your men—Myself must bustle. „ II ii 372
g all From sixteen years to sixty ; „ V ii 272
Gathered these our companies And guilds of London, *g* here, „ II ii 129
And *g* with his hands the starting flame, „ IV iii 336
I *g* from the Queen That she would see your Grace „ V iii 102
g one From out a bed of thick forget-me-nots, „ V v 92
Was not the year when this was *g* richer ? *The Falcon* 345
confirm it now Before our *g* Norman baronage, *Harold* II ii 695
Gaul That we Galatians are both Greek and *G*. *The Cup* I i 204
Gave (*See also* **Gev, Gie'd**) That *g* her royal crown to Lady Jane. *Queen Mary* I ii 19
My father on a birthday *g* it me, „ I v 527
and in that passion *G* me my Crown. „ I v 568
where you *g* your hand To this great Catholic King. „ III ii 90
thro' the fear of death *G* up his cause, „ IV iii 28
Whereat Lord Williams *g* a sudden cry :— „ IV iii 604
G up the ghost ; and so past martyr-like— „ IV iii 623
reft me of that legateship Which Julius *g* me, „ V ii 35
Look'd hard and sweet at me, and *g* it me. „ V v 95
To the good king who *g* it—not to you— *Harold* I i 407
G his shorn smile the lie. „ II ii 226
God *g* us to divide us from the wolf ! „ IV iii 101
answer which King Harold *g* To his dead namesake, „ IV iii 109
He *g* him all the kingdoms of the West. „ V i 24
and the King *g* it to his Chancellor. *Becket, Pro.* 431
G me the golden keys of Paradise. „ I i 54
We *g* thee to the charge of John of Salisbury, „ I i 247
chart which Henry *g* you With the red line— „ I ii 61
King Stephen *g* Many of the crown lands „ I iii 149
Shame fall on those who *g* it a dog's name— „ II i 141
and *g* me a great pat o' the cheek for a pretty wench, „ III i 125
save King Henry *g* thee first the kiss of peace. „ III iii 253
By very God, the cross I *g* the King ! „ IV ii 199
life Saved as by miracle alone with Him Who *g* it. „ IV ii 369
I *g* it you, and you your paramour ; „ V i 168
His father *g* him to my care, „ V ii 335
and open arms To him who *g* it ; *The Cup* I i 85
He *g* me his hand : *The Falcon* 836
she that *g* herself to me so easily *Prom. of May* I 746
She *g* her hand, unask'd, at the farm-gate ; „ II 625
he *g* me no address, and there was no word of marriage ; „ III 332
The lady *g* a rose to the Earl, (repeat) *Foresters* I i 12, 105
The lady *g* her hand to the Earl, (repeat) „ I i 16, 92
She *g* a weeping kiss to the Earl, (repeat) „ I i 20, 119
the man had given her a rose and she *g* him another. „ I i 111
King, thy god-father, *g* it thee when a baby. „ I i 286
This ring my mother *g* me : „ I ii 293
by this Holy Cross Which good King Richard *g* me when a child— „ I ii 310
g me this morning on my setting forth. „ III 281
Gavest They have taken away the toy thou *g* me, *Harold* II ii 106
Thou *g* thy voice against me in the Council— „ IV ii 77
Thou *g* thy voice against me in my life, „ V i 252
The monk's disguise thou *g* me for my bower : *Becket* V ii 93
Gawin (going) but coom, coom ! let's be *g*. *Prom. of May* I 425
Do ye think I be *g*' to tell it to you, „ II 190
Gay (*See also* **Gaäy, Glowing-gay**) Why do you go so *g* then ? *Queen Mary* I iv 70
Dearer than when you made your mountain *g*, *The Falcon* 464
Gear Have you had enough Of all this *g* ? *Queen Mary* III i 88

Gee oop (a call to horses to start) *G o* ! whoä ! *G o* ! whoä ! (repeat) *Prom. of May* II 307, 317
Gel (girl) they be two o' the purtiest *g's* ye can see of a summer murnin'. „ I 30
Eva's saäke. Yeas. Poor *g*, poor *g* ! „ II 32
Taäke me awaäy, little *g*. It be one o' my bad daäys. „ III 465
Gem Standard of the Warrior, Dark among *g's* and gold ; *Harold* IV i 249
Gemini Nay, by St. *G*, I ha' two ; *Foresters* II i 277
General whom the *g* He looks to and he leans on as his God, *Queen Mary* IV iii 305
Poor lads, they see not what the *g* sees, „ V ii 447
When you have charm'd our *g* into mercy, *The Cup* I ii 311
Generate Is as the soul descending out of heaven Into a body *g*. *Queen Mary* IV i 36
Generous You are *g*, but it cannot be. *Prom. of May* II 76
Geneva Zurich, Worms, *G*, Basle— *Queen Mary* I ii 3
Genial I know that I am *g*, I would be Happy, *The Cup* I iii 28
Genius There is a trade of *g*, there's glory ! *Foresters* IV 375
Gentle O, kind and *g* master, the Queen's Officers *Queen Mary* I ii 107
Ay, *g* friend, admit them. I will go. „ I ii 110
Peruse it ; is it not goodly, ay, and *g* ? „ I v 195
Ah, *g* cousin, since your Herod's death, „ III ii 61
if you knew him As I do, ever *g*, and so gracious, „ IV i 156
Ay—*g* as they call you—live or die ! „ IV ii 161
and see, he smiles and goes, *G* as in life. „ V v 147
A *g*, gracious, pure and saintly man ! *Harold* II ii 584
Good even, *g* Edith. „ III ii 118
Well, well, we will be *g* with him, gracious— *Becket* II ii 128
He is *g*, tho' a Roman. *The Cup* II 502
tho' you are good and *g*, Yet if thro' any want— *Prom. of May* III 539
if thou be as *g* Give me some news of my sweet Marian. *Foresters* II i 480
he *As g* as he's brave—that such as he „ II i 659
Gentlefoälk (gentlefolk) We laäys out o' the waäy fur *g* altogither— *Prom. of May* I 211
Thy feyther eddicated his darters to marry *g*, „ II 116
I should ha' thowt they'd hed anew o' *g*, „ II 581
The Steers was all *g's* i' the owd times, an' I worked early an' laäte to make 'em all *g's* ageän. „ III 447
Gentleman he says he's a poor *g*. *Wyatt*. *G* ! a thief ! *Queen Mary* II iii 74
and *g* he was. We have been glad together ; „ II iii 89
Take thy poor *g* ! „ II iii 94
But you, my Lord, a polish'd *g*, „ III iv 250
Out, girl ! you wrong a noble *g*. „ III v 68
Peters, my *g*, an honest Catholic, „ IV iii 553
I have small hope of the *g* gout in my great toe. *The Falcon* 657
I promise you that if you forget yourself in your behaviour to this *g*, *Prom. of May* I 162
He's a Somersetshire man, and a very civil-spoken *g*. *Dobson*. *G* ! „ I 207
Well, it's no sin in a *g* not to fish. „ I 215
and now, as far as money goäs, I be a *g*, „ I 332
while I wur maäkin' mysen a *g*, „ I 335
Tho' you are a *g*, I but a farmer's daughter— „ I 666
and you, a *g*, Told me to trust you : „ I 708
And I would loove tha moor nor ony *g* 'ud loove tha. „ II 105
though fortune had born *you* into the estate of a *g*, „ II 121
drest like a *g*, too. Damn all *gentlemen*, says I ! „ II 579
and prattled to each other that we would marry fine *gentlemen*, „ III 277
And this lover of yours—this Mr. Harold—is a *g* ? „ III 281
Has he offered you marriage, this *g* ? „ III 290
I eddicated boäth on 'em to marry *gentlemen*, „ III 455
that if a *g* Should wed a farmer's daughter, „ III 578
you are tenfold more a *g*, „ III 742
He may be prince ; he is not *g*. *Foresters* IV 685
Gentlemen-at-arms your *g-a-a*, If this be not your Grace's order, *Queen Mary* II iv 62
Gentleness Lady, I say it with all *g*, *The Cup* I iii 99
G, Low words best chime with this solemnity. „ II 216
sure am I that of your *g* You will forgive him. *Prom. of May* II 488
She, you mourn for, seem'd A miracle of *g*— „ II 491

Gentlier my liege, To deal with heresy *g*. *Queen Mary* III vi 58
Geoffrey (son of Rosamund and Henry) (*See also* **Geoffrey Plantagenet, Plantagenet**) I'll call thee little *G*. *Henry*. Call him! *Rosamund*. *G*! *Becket* II i 214
if little *G* have not tost His ball into the brook! „ II i 319
the child will drown himself. *Rosamund*. *G*! *G*! „ II i 324
G! *Geoffrey*. What are you crying for, „ III i 268
G, the pain thou hast put me to! „ IV ii 10
G, my boy, I saw the ball you lost in the fork „ IV ii 56
If pretty *G* do not break his own, „ IV ii 177
How fares thy pretty boy, the little *G*? „ V ii 168
Geoffrey Plantagenet nay, *G P*, thine own husband's father— „ IV ii 249
George (patron saint of England) by the dragon of St. *G*, we shall Do some injustice, *Foresters* IV 939
Germ O Thou, that dost inspire the *g* with life, *The Cup* II 258
German for his book Against that godless *G*. *Queen Mary* V v 238
Germany till the weight of *G* or the gold of England brings one of them down to the dust— *Becket* II ii 363
Gesticulating madman, is it, *G* there upon the bridge? *Prom. of May* II 327
Get (*See also* **Git**) if I can *g* near enough I shall judge with my own eyes *Queen Mary* I i 133
And *g* the swine to shout Elizabeth. „ I iii 39
But so I *g* the laws against the heretic, „ III i 323
to *g* her baaby born; „ IV iii 523
G you home at once. „ V iv 63
Till thou wouldst *g* him all apart, *Harold* I i 447
G thee gone! He means the thing he says. „ V i 83
G thou into thy cloister as the king Will'd it: „ V i 309
g thee to thine own bed. *Becket* I i 7
G ye hence, Tell what I say to the King. „ I iii 563
G you hence! a man passed in there to-day: „ III ii 24
g you hence in haste Lest worse befall you. „ IV ii 26
found thy name a charm to *g* Food, roof, and rest. „ V ii 97
G thee back to thy nunnery with all haste; „ V ii 163
g you back! go on with the office. „ V iii 32
What can I do—what can I *g* for thee? He answers, '*G* the Count to give me his falcon, *The Falcon* 239
next time you waste them at a pot-house you *g* no more from me. *Prom. of May* III 100
Sir Richard must scrape and scrape till he *g* to the land again. *Foresters* I i 79
G thee into the closet there, „ II i 214
Getting (*See also* **A-getting**) *G* better, Mr. Dobson. *Prom. of May* I 69
which Father, for a whole life, has been *g* together, „ III 166
Gev (gave) fell ageän coalscuttle and my kneeä *g* waäy *Prom. of May* I 404
Ghastly how grim and *g* looks her Grace, *Queen Mary* V ii 390
nay, this *g* glare May heat their fancies. *Harold* I i 308
Strange and *g* in the gloom And shadowing „ III ii 157
from your *g* oubliette I send my voice across the narrow seas— „ V i 245
I found a hundred *g* murders done By men, *Becket* I iii 407
Ghittern that I can touch The *g* to some purpose. *The Falcon* 799
Ghoäst (ghost) If it be her *g*, we mun abide it. We can't keep a *g* out. *Prom. of May* III 460
Ghost (*See also* **Ghoäst**) The *g's* of Luther and Zuinglius fade Into the deathless hell *Queen Mary* III ii 174
Gave up the *g*; and so past martyr-like— „ IV iii 623
shadows of a hundred fat dead deer For dead men's *g's*. *Harold* I ii 104
One *g* of all the *g's*—as yet so new, *The Cup* II 141
haunted by The *g's* of the dead passions *Prom. of May* II 275
To see her grave? her *g*? Her *g* is everyway „ II 352
I was afear'd it was the *g*, your worship. *Prince John*. *G*! did one in white pass? *Foresters* II i 226
oafs, *g's* o' the mist, wills-o'-the-wisp; „ II i 263
Love himself Seems but a *g*, but when thou feel'st with me The *g* returns „ III 113
They must have sprung like *G's* from underground, „ IV 592
Ghostly A *g* horn Blowing continually, and faint battle-hymns, *Harold* III i 372
at Pontigny came to me The *g* warning of my martyrdom; *Becket* V ii 292
and make a *g* wail ever and anon to scare 'em. *Foresters* II i 215
Giant (adj.) He, and the *g* King of Norway, Harold Hardrada, *Harold* III ii 122
Giant (s) as the heathen *g* Had but to touch the ground, *Queen Mary* III ii 43
or something more, Seeing he is a *g*. *Harold* IV ii 56
or something more, Seeing he is a *g*!' „ IV iii 114
spiritual *g* with our island laws And customs, *Becket* IV ii 444
Giant-king Their *g-k*, a mightier man-in-arms *Harold* V i 399
Gibbet In every London street a *g* stood. *Queen Mary* III i 7
witness the brawls, the *g's*. „ V i 86
He will come to the *g* at last? *Foresters* II i 328
Gibbeted *See* **Cliff-gibbeted**
Giddy I can bear all, And not be *g*. *Harold* I i 486
Gie (give) fur he'll *g* us a big dinner, *Prom. of May* I 9
Gi'e (give) and s'pose I kills my pig, and *g's* it among 'em, „ I 147
Weänt ye *g* me a kind answer at last? „ II 63
fur owd Dobson 'll *g* us a bit o' supper. „ II 216
Owd Steer *g's* nubbut cowd tea to '*is* men, and owd Dobson *g's* beer. „ II 223
G us a buss fust, lass. „ II 228
d'ye think *I'd g* 'em the fever? „ III 49
and wheere the big eshtree cuts athurt it, it *g's* a turn like, „ III 95
Gie'd (gave) but I hallus *g* soom on 'em to Miss Eva „ II 15
Gift A diamond, And Philip's *g*, as proof of Philip's love, *Queen Mary* III i 67
An honest *g*, by all the Saints, *Harold* I i 344
thro' The random *g's* of careless kings, *Becket* I i 159
Then he took back not only Stephen's *g's*, „ I iii 154
I thought it was a *g*; „ I iii 646
Shall God's good *g's* be wasted? „ I iv 71
child We waited for so long—heaven's *g* at last— „ III i 14
A strange *g* sent to me to-day. *The Cup* I ii 52
is another sacred to the Goddess, The *g* of Synorix; „ II 347
In honour of his *g* and of our marriage, „ II 351
And this last costly *g* to mine own self, *The Falcon* 228
Yet I come To ask a *g*. „ 299
g I ask for, to *my* mind and at this present „ 777
Gig and he sent me wi' the *g* to Littlechester to fetch 'er; *Prom. of May* I 20
Gilbert Becket (father of Thomas Becket) me, Thomas, son Of *G B*, London Merchant. *Becket* II ii 231
Gilbert Foliot (Bishop of London) (*See also* **Foliot**) There's *G F*. *Henry*. He! too thin, too thin. „ *Prc.* 260
But hast thou heard this cry of *G F* „ I i 36
Ay, For *G F* held himself the man. „ I i 43
If it were not, *G F*, I mean to cross the sea to France, „ I iii 123
And bid him re-create me, *G F*. „ I iii 126
Thou still hast owed thy father, *G F*. „ I iii 276
Thou still hast shown thy primate, *G F*. „ I iii 282
G F, A worldly follower of the worldly strong. „ I iii 541
Cursed be John of Oxford, Roger of York, And *G F*! „ II ii 267
Gild It *g's* the greatest wronger of her peace, *Queen Mary* V ii 415
Gilded over His *g* ark of mummy-saints, *Harold* V i 304
Gilt *See* **Sun-gilt**
Gingerbread He speaks As if it were a cake of *g*. *Becket* II i 230
Giovanna (*See also* **Monna Giovanna**) the Lady *G*, who hath been away so long, *The Falcon* 2
G here! Ay, ruffle thyself—*be* jealous! „ 21
yet if *G* Be here again—No, no! „ 27
G, my dear lady, in this same battle „ 601
G, dear *G*, I that once The wildest „ 806
Yes, *G*, But he will keep his love to you for ever! „ 891
Gipsyfy I will hide my face, Blacken and *g* it; *Becket* IV ii 100
Gipsy-stuff Life on the hand is naked *g-s*; „ II i 194
Girl (*See also* **Gall, Gel**) A king to be,—is he not noble, *g*? *Queen Mary* I v 4
that young *g* who dared to wear your crown? „ I v 491
G; hast thou ever heard Slanders against Prince Philip „ I v 569
No, *g*; most brave and loyal, „ II iv 11
G never breathed to rival such a rose; „ III i 372
There's whitethorn, *g*. „ III v 9
But truth of story, which I glanced at, *g*, „ III v 33
Out, *g*! you wrong a noble gentleman. „ III v 67

Girl (*continued*) Lord Devon, *g's*! what are you whispering here? *Queen Mary* v ii 485
I could not, *g*, Not this way— „ v v 170
That art the Queen; ye are boy and *g* no more: *Harold* i i 455
My *g*, what was it? „ i ii 73
My *g*, thou hast been weeping: „ iii ii 38
thou art not A holy sister yet, my *g*, „ iii ii 82
Ay, my *g*, no tricks in him— „ v i 401
I tell thee, *g*, I am seeking my dead Harold. „ v ii 42
Not true, my *g*, here is the Queen! „ v ii 91
Where is he, *g*? *The Cup* i i 106
My *g*, I am the bride of Death, „ ii 28
My *g*, At times this oracle of great Artemis „ ii 32
and she, A *g*, a child, then but fifteen, *The Falcon* 537
After my frolic with his tenant's *g*, *Prom. of May* i 493
may not a *g's* love-dream have too much romance in it „ iii 184
Father, this poor *g*, the farm, everything; „ iii 211
Can't a *g* when she loves her husband, and he her, „ iii 304
I heard a voice, '*G*, what are you doing there?' „ iii 375
Come, come, my *g*, enough Of this strange talk. „ iii 619
and is flustered by a *g's* kiss. *Foresters* i i 186
but O *g*, *g*, I am almost in despair. „ i i 262
Thou hast robb'd my *g* of her betrothal ring. „ ii i 586
to mistrust the *g* you say you love Is to mistrust your own love for your *g*! „ ii ii 57
Come, *g*, thou shalt along with us on the instant. „ iv 678
What, daunted by a garrulous, arrogant *g*! „ iv 737
Risk not the love I bear thee for a *g*. „ iv 742

Girlhood tell me anything of our sweet Eva When in her brighter *g*, *Prom. of May* ii 521

Git (get) Did 'e *g* into thy chaumber? „ i 399
an' we'll *g* 'im to speechify for us arter dinner. „ i 439
G along wi' ye, do! „ ii 235
S'iver I mun *g* along back to the farm, „ ii 321
I mun *g* out on 'is waäy now, or I shall be the death on 'im. „ ii 609
I'll *g* the book ageän, and larn mysen the rest, „ iii 12

Give (*See also* **Gie, Gi'e, Gi'ed**) to *g* us all that holy absolution which— *Queen Mary* i iii 28
grant me my prayer: *G* me my Philip; „ i v 87
G it me quick. „ i v 592
Have for thine asking aught that I can *g*, „ ii iii 7
G me a piece of paper! „ ii iii 66
boldness, which will *g* my followers boldness. „ ii iii 71
'You will *g* me my true crown at last, „ iii i 395
I come for counsel and ye *g* me feuds, „ iii iv 307
I will *g* your message. „ iii vi 40
Ay, but to *g* the poor. „ iv ii 43
To *g* the poor—they *g* the poor who die. „ iv ii 52
It is the last. *Cranmer*. *G* it me, then. „ iv ii 65
I not doubt that God will *g* me strength, „ iv ii 234
Or *g* thee saintly strength to undergo. „ iv iii 99
For death *g's* life's last word a power to live, „ iv iii 161
G to the poor, Ye *g* to God. „ iv iii 212
G me the lute. He hates me! „ v ii 362
g the Devil his due, I never found he bore me any spite. „ v ii 472
in happy state To *g* him an heir male. „ v ii 573
Ay, ever *g* yourselves your own good word. *Harold* i i 342
As much as I can *g* thee, man; „ i i 479
thou didst stand by her and *g* her thy crabs, „ ii i 49
And I'll *g* her my crabs again, „ ii i 52
would *g* his kingly voice To me as his successor. „ ii ii 588
G me thy keys. „ ii ii 681
Stigand shall *g* me absolution for it— „ ii ii 798
I may *g* that egg-bald head The tap that silences. „ v i 90
I *g* my voice against thee from the grave— „ v i 254
We *g* our voice against thee out of heaven! „ v i 260
We will not *g* him A Christian burial: „ v ii 153
I would *g* her to thy care in England *Becket, Pro.* 143
G him a bone, *g* him a bone! „ i iv 107
Is the Archbishop a thief who *g's* thee thy supper? „ i iv 116
Something good, or thou wouldst not *g* it me. „ ii i 234
but *g* it me, and I promise thee not to turn the world „ ii i 241
Kind of the witch to *g* thee warning tho'. „ iii ii 29

Give (*continued*) *G* me thy hand. My Lords of France and England, *Becket* iii iii 225
I sware I would not *g* the kiss of peace, „ iii iii 259
here is a golden chain I will *g* thee „ iv i 40
G her to me. „ iv ii 135
G her to me to make my honeymoon. „ iv ii 142
G me the poison; set me free of him! „ iv ii 164
G to the King the things that are the King's, „ v ii 461
You should attend the office, *g* them heart. „ v ii 598
I *g* you here an order To seize upon him. *The Cup* i i 163
G him a bow and arrows—follow—follow. „ i i 208
Will feel no shame to *g* themselves the lie. „ ii 117
And *g* him limbs, then air, and send him forth „ ii 261
G it me again. It is the cup belonging our own Temple. „ ii 343
Well, Madam, I will *g* your message to him. *The Falcon* 217
'Get the Count to *g* me his falcon, „ 241
I *g* it my sick son, and if you be Not quite recover'd „ 589
I can *g* my time To him that is a part of you, „ 790
If the good Count would *g* me——' *Count*. *G* me. „ 838
G her a month or two, and her affections *Prom. of May* i 484
Come, *g* me your hand and kiss me „ i 563
But for the slender help that I can *g*, „ ii 421
But *g* me first your hand: „ ii 525
And he may die before he *g's* it; „ iii 407
will *g* him, as they say, a new lease of life. „ iii 423
G me your arm. Lead me back again. „ iii 473
I *g* him back to you again. „ iii 675
shall I *g* her the first kiss? *Foresters* i i 126
I came to *g* thee the first kiss, and thou hast given it me. „ i i 132
matter so much if the maid *g* the first kiss? „ i i 136
now thou hast given me the man's kiss, let me *g* thee the maid's. „ i i 143
I will *g* thee a buffet on the face. „ i i 146
Wilt thou not *g* me rather the little rose for Little John? „ i i 147
may the maid *g* the first kiss? „ i i 173
said that whenever I married he would *g* me away, „ i i 288
there is no other man that shall *g* me away. „ i i 291
I would *g* thee any gold So that myself „ i ii 165
You shall *g* me the first kiss. „ i ii 227
G me thy hand and tell him— „ i ii 241
what we wring from them we *g* the poor. „ ii i 56
I would *g* my life for thee, „ ii i 189
I can spell the hand. *G* me thine. „ ii i 351
I will *g* thee a silver penny if thou wilt show „ ii i 359
O your honour, I pray you too to *g* me an alms. „ ii i 389
G me a draught of wine. „ ii i 458
Take him, good Little John, and *g* him wine. „ ii i 469
G me some news of my sweet Marian. „ ii i 481
G me thy glove upon it. „ ii i 579
G it me, by heaven, Or I will force it from thee. „ ii i 593
g us guides To lead us thro' the windings of the wood. „ ii i 632
'Sell all thou hast and *g* it to the poor;' Take all they have and *g* it to thyself! „ iii 169
Bitters before dinner, my lady, to *g* you a relish. „ iii 435
love that children owe to both I *g* To him alone. „ iv 7
G me thy hand on that? *Marian*. Take it. „ iv 66
I am glad of it. *G* him back his gold again. „ iv 182
that will *g* thee a new zest for it, „ iv 208
G him the quarterstaff. „ iv 250
I *g* thee A buffet, and thou me. „ iv 262
G me thy hand, Much; I love thee. At him, Scarlet! „ iv 309
G him another month, and he will pay it. *Justiciary*. We cannot *g* a month. „ iv 443
G me my bow and arrows. „ iv 603
g me one sharp pinch upon the cheek „ iv 1011
G me that hand which fought for Richard there. „ iv 1029

Given They have *g* me a safe conduct: *Queen Mary* i ii 100
g A token of His more especial Grace; „ iii iii 169
God hath *g* Grace to repent and sorrow for their schism; „ iii iii 176
we by that authority Apostolic *G* unto us, „ iii iii 211
God hath *g* your Grace a nose, or not, „ iii v 203
Power hath been *g* you to try faith by fire— „ iv ii 153
Done right against the promise of this Queen Twice *g*. „ iv iii 457

Given (*continued*) We have *g* the church-lands back: *Queen Mary* V i 170
I have *g* her cause—I fear no woman. *Harold* I ii 40
God and the sea have *g* thee to our hands— „ II ii 548
Stigand hath *g* me absolution for it. „ III i 213
sorrow'd for my random promise *g* To yon fox-lion. „ III i 269
king Hath *g* his virgin lamb to Holy Church „ III i 334
And *g* thy realm of England to the bastard. „ III ii 154
Thou hast *g* it to the enemy of our house. „ IV ii 31
Holy Father Hath *g* this realm of England to the Norman. „ V i 13
G me by my dear friend the King of England— *Becket* I i 337
I pray God I haven't *g* thee my leprosy, „ I iv 214
kingly promise *g* To our own self of pardon, „ II ii 432
warder of the bower hath *g* himself Of late to wine. „ III i 30
had I fathered him I had *g* him more of the rod than the sceptre. „ III iii 110
I think, time *g*, I could have talk'd „ IV ii 311
had she but *g* Plain answer to plain query? „ IV ii 385
your ladyship has *g* him bitters enough in this world, *The Falcon* 192
the man had *g* her a rose and she gave him another. *Foresters* I i 110
I came to give thee the first kiss, and thou hast *g* it me. „ I i 133
but I had sooner have *g* thee the first kiss. „ I i 138
now thou hast *g* me the man's kiss, let me give thee the maid's. „ I i 143
g my whole body to the King had *he* asked for it, „ II i 305
but the cow? *Robin.* She was *g* me. „ II i 315
Giver if *g* And taker be but honest! *Harold* I i 345
if She knew the *g*; but I bound the seller *The Falcon* 72
Giving (*See also* **Life-giving**) My liberality perforce is dead Thro' lack of means of *g*. „ 297
Glad We have been *g* together; let him live. *Queen Mary* II iii 90
Cranmer, be thou *g*. This is the work of God. „ IV iii 81
g to wreak our spite on the rosefaced minion *Becket, Pro.* 528
I am *g* that France hath scouted him at last: „ II ii 251
She will be *g* at last to wear my crown. *The Cup* I iii 168
I am *g* I shall not see it. „ II 512
an' owd Dobson should be *g* on it. *Prom. of May* II 147
I am *g* it pleases you; „ II 543
There, I am *g* my nonsense has made you smile! „ III 314
if this life of ours Be a good *g* thing, *Foresters* I iii 13
I am *g* of it. Give him back his gold again. „ IV 182
Glade My men say The fairies haunt this *g*;— „ II ii 101
See that men be set Along the *g's* and passes of the wood „ III 457
Look, Robin, at the far end of the *g* „ IV 332
Gladness Breathing an easy *g* . . . not like Aldwyth . . . *Harold* I ii 174
Glance (s) Philip with a *g* of some distaste, *Queen Mary* III i 99
No *g* yet Of the Northumbrian helmet on the heath? *Harold* V i 142
Dark even from a side *g* of the moon, *Becket* IV ii 148
to 'scape The *g* of John— *Foresters* III 463
Glance (verb) Before I dare to *g* upon your Grace. *Queen Mary* III v 186
whereby the curse might *g* From thee and England. *Harold* III i 343
Tho' in one moment she should *g* away, *Foresters* II i 161
Glanced But truth of story, which I *g* at, girl, *Queen Mary* III v 33
Has never *g* upon me when a child. *Foresters* IV 5
Have ye *g* down thro' all the forest ways „ IV 110
Glancing a Boleyn, too, *G* across the Tudor— *Queen Mary* V v 228
Then, *g* thro' the story of this realm, *Becket* I iii 410
now and then *g* about him like a thief at night „ III iii 97
G at the days when his father was only Earl of Anjou, „ III iii 149
Glare (s) this ghastly *g* May heat their fancies. *Harold* I i 309
from the squint Of lust and *g* of malice. *Becket* I i 313
Like sudden night in the main *g* of day. „ II i 57
Glare (verb) It *g's* in heaven, it flares upon the Thames, *Harold* I i 29
for thine eyes *G* stupid-wild with wine. *Becket* I i 214
Glared execrable eyes, *G* at the citizen. *Queen Mary* II ii 68
How their pointed fingers *G* at me! *Harold* II ii 791
How the clown *g* at me! that Dobbins, is it, *Prom. of May* II 611
Glaring *See* **Grimly-glaring**
Glass (barometer) weather's well anew, but the *g* be a bit shaäky. *Prom. of May* II 51
Glass (substance) and my poor chronicle Is but of *g*. *Queen Mary* III v 47
fuse the *g*, And char us back again into the dust „ III v 54
Glass (verb) and *g* The faithful face of heaven— *Becket* II i 160
Glasses (spectacles) You see thro' warping *g*. *Queen Mary* I v 212
Glassy-smooth So far my course, albeit not *g-s*, *Becket* I iii 379
Gleam *G* upon gloom, „ III i 277
Gleam (*continued*) Gloom upon *g*, *Becket* III i 281
I never spied in thee one *g* of grace. „ V ii 474
man perceives that The lost *g* of an after-life *Prom. of May* I 503
This world of mud, on all its idiot *g's* Of pleasure, „ III 722
Gleaming There lodged a *g* grimness in his eyes, *Harold* II ii 224
Glebe (adj.) thaw he niver mended that gap i' the *g* fence *Prom. of May* I 446
Glebe (s) to the wave, to the *g*, to the fire! *The Cup* II 4
Glen a fox from the *g* ran away with the hen, *Prom. of May* I 51
Lead us thou to some deep *g*, *Foresters* II ii 168
Glide Seem'd as a happy miracle to make *g*— *Queen Mary* III ii 30
There is an arm'd man ever *g's* behind! *Harold* II ii 247
G like a light across these woodland ways! *Foresters* II i 159
Glided so she *g* up into the heart O' the bottle, „ IV 244
Gliding Corpse-candles *g* over nameless graves— *Harold* III i 381
Two sisters *g* in an equal dance, *Becket* I iii 444
Glimmer twilight of the coming day already *g's* in the east. *Foresters* I ii 248
Glimmering One coming up with a song in the flush of the *g* red? *Becket* II i 8
Glimpse Rome has a *g* of this conspiracy; *The Cup* I ii 233
catch A *g* of them and of their fairy Queen— *Foresters* II ii 103
Glitter He *g's* on the crowning of the hill. *Harold* V i 488
that's a finer thing there. How it *g's*! *Becket* IV i 2
Glittering all drown'd in love And *g* at full tide— *The Cup* II 234
Gloom I crept along the *g* and saw *Queen Mary* II iii 17
g of Saul Was lighten'd by young David's harp. „ V ii 358
Strange and ghastly in the *g* *Harold* III ii 158
Gleam upon *g*, *Becket* III i 277
G upon gleam, „ III i 281
Glorified He is *g* In thy conversion: *Queen Mary* IV iii 82
But that Thy name by man be *g*, „ IV iii 153
Die with him, and be *g* together. *Becket* V iii 31
Glorify God grant me grace to *g* my God! *Queen Mary* IV iii 166
Glorifying *See* **A-glorifying**
Glorious O blessed saint, O *g* Benedict,— *Becket* V iii 1
Glory there's no *g* Like his who saves his country: *Queen Mary* II i 109
But for the wealth and *g* of our realm, „ II ii 210
misreport His ending to the *g* of their church. „ IV iii 327
I have wrought miracles—to God the *g*— *Harold* I i 182
and our marriage and thy *g* Been drunk together! „ IV iii 8
whether it symbol'd ruin Or *g*, who shall tell? „ V i 111
G to God in the Highest! fallen, fallen! „ V i 636
All I had I lavish'd for the *g* of the King; I shone from him, for him, his *g*, his Reflection: now the *g* of the Church Hath swallow'd up the *g* of the King; *Becket* I iii 663
Power and great *g*—for thy Church, O Lord— „ V iii 194
The *g* and grief of battle won or lost *The Cup* I ii 161
Hear thy priestesses hymn thy *g*! „ II 7
That you may feed your fancy on the *g* of it, „ II 134
and send him forth The *g* of his father— „ II 263
make them happy in the long barn, for father is in his *g*, *Prom. of May* I 792
There is a trade of genius, there's *g*! *Foresters* IV 375
Gloss his manners want the nap And *g* of court; *Queen Mary* III v 71
Glo'ster (Gloucester) and she brew'd the best ale in all *G*, *Becket* III i 197
Glove Give me thy *g* upon it. *Foresters* II i 579
A pair of *g's*, a pair of *g's*, sir; ha? *Queen Mary* III i 270
The man shall paint a pair of *g's*. „ III i 274
Glow Dost thou not feel the love I bear to thee *G* thro' thy veins? *Synorix.* The love I bear to thee *G's* thro' my veins *The Cup* II 427
Glowing-gay were as *g-g* As regal gardens; *Queen Mary* III ii 12
Glowworm yellow silk here and there, and it looked pretty like a *g*, *Becket* IV i 23
No, by wisp and *g*, no. *Foresters* II ii 136
Glum What maäkes 'im allus sa *g*? *Sally Allen.* *G*! he be wuss nor *g*. *Prom. of May* II 148
Gnarl'd hundreds of huge oaks, *G*— *Foresters* III 92
Gnat A *g* that vext thy pillow! *Harold* I ii 71
Gnawed The rats have *g* 'em already. *Foresters* I i 88
Go (*See also* **Goä, Gwo**) God be with you! *G*. *Queen Mary* I ii 83
gentle friend, admit them. I will *g*. „ I ii 111
My mother said, *G* up; and up I went. „ I iii 98

Go (*continued*) there are messengers That *g* between us. *Queen Mary* I iii 138
g zigzag, now would settle Upon this flower, " I iv 54
Why do you *g* so gay then? " I iv 70
Come, come, I will *g* with you to the Queen. " I iv 297
Your people, and I *g* with them so far, " I v 188
Bad you *g* softly with your heretics here, " I v 392
some believe that he will *g* beyond him. " I v 441
she *goes*, I warrant, not to hear the nightingales, " I v 463
Your apple eats the better. Let them *g*. They *g* like those old Pharisees in John " II ii 7
Sir Thomas, pray you *g* away, " II iii 99
Don't ye now *g* to think that we be for Philip o' Spain. " II iii 105
come to save you all, And I'll *g* further off. " II iii 119
Pray you *g* on. (repeat) " III i 374, 389
I will *g* with you to the waterside. " III ii 148
No, my Lord Legate, the Lord Chancellor *goes*. " III ii 152
His sceptre shall *g* forth from Ind to Ind! " III ii 177
We might *g* softlier than with crimson rowel " III iv 182
And if he *g* not with you— " III iv 348
not like a word, That comes and *goes* in uttering. " III v 30
leisure wisdom of his Queen, Before he *g*, " III vi 24
for women To *g* twelve months in bearing " III vi 91
And *goes* to-morrow. " III vi 119
O Philip! Nay, must you *g* indeed? " III vi 192
But must you *g*? " III vi 207
Your Majesty shall *g* to Dover with me, " III vi 218
I will *g* to Greenwich, So you will have me with you; " III vi 221
hang the leaders, let their following *g*. " IV i 75
you must look to Calais when I *g*. *Mary*. *G*? must you *g*, indeed— " V i 17
G in, I pray you. " V i 214
Say *g*; but only say it lovingly. " V i 216
And panting for my blood as I *g* by. " V ii 219
Ah!—let him enter. Nay, you need not *g*: " V iii 11
You had best *g* home. What are you? " V iv 43
Why, you long-winded—— Sir, you *g* beyond me. " V iv 58
Good night! *G* home. Besides, you curse so loud, " V iv 61
Thou light a torch that never will *g* out! " V v 122
see, he smiles and *goes*, Gentle as in life. *Alice*. Madam, who *goes*? King Philip? *Mary*. No, Philip comes and *goes*, but never *goes*. " V v 146
before I *g*, To find the sweet refreshment of the Saints. *Harold* I i 176
I have fought the fight and *g*— " I i 185
if it pass. *G* not to Normandy—*g* not to Normandy. " I i 235
I pray thee, do not *g* to Normandy. " I i 249
Harold, I will not yield thee leave to *g*. " I i 257
G—the Saints Pilot and prosper all thy wandering " I i 263
How *goes* it then with thy Northumbria? " I i 332
To follow thee to Flanders! Must thou *g*? " I ii 28
When Harold *goes* and Tostig, shall I play " I ii 163
And when doth Harold *g*? *Morcar*. To-morrow— " I ii 238
—I will *g* with thee to-morrow— " II ii 204
'I pray you do not *g* to Normandy.' " II ii 218
G not to Normandy— (repeat) " II ii 327
yield this iron-mooded Duke To let me *g*. " II ii 341
'Marry, the Saints must *g* along with us, " II ii 365
the lark sings, the sweet stars come and *g*, " II ii 435
Or lash'd his rascal back, and let him *g*. " II ii 507
And let him *g*? To slander thee again! " II ii 508
My prayers *g* up as fast as my tears fall, " III i 166
not so with us—No wings to come and *g*. " III ii 99
I am weary—*g*: make me not wroth with thee! " V i 31
Gurth, Leofwin, *g* once more about the hill— " V i 182
G round once more; See all be sound and whole. " V i 192
Leave me. No more—Pardon on both sides—*G*! " V i 354
Obey my first and last commandment. *G*! " V i 359
After the battle—after the battle. *G*. *Aldwyth*. I *g*. " V i 363
G further hence and find him. " V ii 60
business Of thy whole kingdom waits me: let me *g*. *Becket*, *Pro*. 279
Thou shalt not *g*. I have not ended with thee. " *Pro*. 305
Follow me this Rosamund day and night, whithersoever she *goes*; " *Pro*. 507
That I should *g* against the Church with him, And I shall *g* against him with the Church, " I i 93

Go (*continued*) *G* home, and sleep thy wine off, for thine eyes *Becket* I i 212
What shall it be? I'll *g* as a nun. " I i 301
G like a monk, cowling and clouding up " I i 311
G therefore like a friend slighted by one " I i 350
Not slighted—all but moan'd for: thou must *g*. " I i 353
G with her—at once—To-night— " I i 400
G, *g*—no more of this! " I ii 20
Customs, traditions,—clouds that come and *g*; " I iii 23
for if thou *g* against thy King, Then must he likewise *g* against thy King, " I iii 207
Let us *g* in to the Council, where our bishops " I iii 547
I am confounded by thee. *G* in peace. " I iii 731
Ay, *g* in peace, caitiff, caitiff! " I iii 735
No; yet all but all. *G*, *g*! " I iv 28
Wilt thou not say, 'God bless you,' ere we *g*? " I iv 33
Well, then, how does it *g*? " I iv 118
we shall all be poisoned. Let us *g*. " I iv 244
I'll *g* back again. I hain't half done yet. " I iv 258
then to be made Archbishop and *g* against the King " II i 237
G try it, play. " II i 246
I must *g*; but when thou layest thy lip To this, " II i 305
Mince and *g* back! his politic Holiness " II ii 45
that none may dream I *g* against God's honour— " II ii 168
said to the smoke, '*G* up, my son, straight to Heaven.' And the smoke said, 'I *g*;' " II ii 318
it was in him to *g* up straight if the time had been quieter. " II ii 324
there they *g*—both backs are turn'd to me— " II ii 453
I *g* to have young Henry crown'd by York. " II ii 478
Must you *g*, my liege, So suddenly? " III i 84
all on us ha' had to *g*, bless the Saints, " III i 146
G, you shall tell me of her some other time. " III i 190
Nay—*g*. What! will you anger me? " III i 208
I hear Margery: I'll *g* play with her. " III i 274
I *g* myself—so many alleys, " IV ii 6
G. See that you do not fall in. *G*. " IV ii 58
you bid me *g*, and I'll have my ball anyhow. " IV ii 63
let me *g* With my young boy, and I will hide my face, " IV ii 97
Wilt thou *g* with him? he will marry thee. " IV ii 162
The worm! shall I let her *g*? " IV ii 197
G, lest I blast thee with anathema, " IV ii 287
Lest I remember thee to the lion, *g*. " IV ii 292
rather *g* beyond In scourgings, macerations, mortifyings, " V i 40
That *goes* against our fealty to the King. " V ii 508
Valour and holy life should *g* together. " V ii 587
I *g* to meet my King! " V ii 620
It is God's will. *G* on. " V ii 635
get you back! *g* on with the office. " V iii 33
Back, I say! *G* on with the office. " V iii 39
I will *g* out and meet them. " V iii 52
Wake me before you *g*, I'll after you— *The Cup* I ii 447
Shall I *g*? Shall I *g*? Death, torture— " I ii 452
I *g*, but I will have my dagger with me. " I ii 457
whither *g* you now? *Camma*. To lodge this cup " I iii 51
Pray you, *G* on with the marriage rites. " II 399
G on with the marriage rites. " II 421
I will *g* To meet him, crown'd! " II 518
There *goes* a musical score along with them, *The Falcon* 452
That seem'd to come and *g*. " 650
You hear, Filippo? My good fellow, *g*! " 691
Ay, prune our company of thine own and *g*! " 696
I *g*. Master Dobson, did you hear what I said? *Prom. of May* I 171
to come together again in a moment and to *g* on together again, " I 775
Now I must *g*. " II 524
Allow me to *g* with you to the farm. " II 574
Let bygones be bygones. *G* home! Good-night! " III 157
Courage, courage! and all will *g* well. " III 215
so that you do not copy his bad manners? *G*, child. " III 362
'*G* home;' but I hadn't the heart or face to do it. " III 389
G back to him and ask his forgiveness before he dies.— " III 401
You see she is lamed, and cannot *g* down to him. " III 416
to the grave he *goes* to, Beneath the burthen of years. " III 516
Than even I can well believe you, *G*! " III 815
'I *g* to fight in Scotland With many a savage clan;' *Foresters* I i 14
I am all but sure of him. I will *g* to him. " I i 276

Go (*continued*) but I know not if I will let thee *g*.
Marian. I mean to *g*. *Foresters* I i 312
Well, thou shalt *g*, but O the land! the land! „ I i 327
More water *goes* by the mill than the miller wots of,
and more *goes* to make right „ I ii 48
G now and ask the maid to dance with thee, „ I ii 185
What say you? shall we *g*? „ I iii 126
Then, Scarlet, thou at least wilt *g* with me. „ I iii 145
G with him. I will talk with thee anon. „ II i 132
I saw a man *g* in, my lord. „ II i 207
let me *g* to make the mound: bury me in the mound, „ II i 311
Shall we not *g*? „ II i 349
I pray thee *g*, *g*, for tho' thou wouldst bar „ II i 354
there *goes* one in the moonlight. Shoot! „ II i 394
Missed! There *goes* another. Shoot, Sheriff! „ II i 397
But *g* not yet, stay with us, and when thy brother— „ II i 640
Yet are they twins and always *g* together. *Kate.*
Well, well, until they cease to *g* together, „ II ii 66
Wherefore, wherefore should we *g* „ II ii 125
Only wherefore should we *g*? „ II ii 137
One half of this shall *g* to those they have wrong'd, „ III 303
—a mere figure. Let it *g* by. „ IV 221
is not he that *goes* against the king and the law „ IV 229
I *g* to Nottingham. „ IV 799
What! *g* to slay his brother, and make *me* „ IV 804
Goä (go) Theer ye *g's* ageän, Miss, *Prom. of May* I 106
But let that *g* by. „ I 199
noän o' the parishes *g's* by that naäme 'ereabouts. „ I 268
and now, as far as money *g's*, I be a gentleman, „ I 331
winder at the end o' the passage, that *g's* by thy
chaumber. „ I 397
Theer she *g's*! Shall I foller 'er and ax 'er „ II 130
I weänt *g* to owd Dobson; „ II 218
and wants a hand, and I'll *g* to him. „ II 222
Scizzars an' Pumpy was good uns to *g* (repeat) „ II 308, 319
says the master *g's* cleän off his 'eäd when he 'eärs the
naäme on 'im; „ III 132
I warrants that ye *g's* By haäfe a scoor o' naämes— „ III 728
Goal I see the *g* and half the way to it.— *Harold* I ii 196
in the racing toward this golden *g* He turns „ II ii 377
Goat *See* **Scape-goat, She-goat**
Goat-herd we found a *g-h's* hut and shared *The Cup* I ii 426
Go-between Their Flemish *g-b* And all-in-all. *Queen Mary* III vi 4
God (s) (*See also* **Warrior-god**) *G* save her Grace; „ I i 66
By *G's* light a noble creature, right royal! „ I i 68
G be with you. Go. „ I II 82
I wrote it, and *G* grant me power to burn! „ I ii 98
I thank my *G* it is too late to fly. „ I ii 112
'Fore *G*, I think she entreats me like a child. „ I iii 111
some great doom when *G's* just hour Peals— „ I iv 261
my good mother came (*G* rest her soul) „ I v 11
O, just *G*! Sweet mother, „ I v 22
G hath sent me here To take such order with all
heretics „ I v 33
I am all thanks To *G* and to your Grace: „ I v 186
Pray *G* he do not be the first to break them, „ I v 269
G change the pebble which his kingly foot „ I v 368
G lay the waves and strow the storms at sea, „ I v 381
I pray *G* No woman ever love you, „ I v 601
By *G*, you are as poor a poet, Wyatt, „ II i 113
and if Philip come to be King, O, my *G*! „ II i 200
Or—if the Lord *G* will it—on the stake. „ II i 251
—'fore *G*, the rogues— „ II ii 96
G send her well; Here comes her Royal Grace. „ II ii 125
I thank *G*, I have lived a virgin, and I noway doubt
But that with *G's* grace, I can live so still. Yet
if it might please *G* that I should leave Some fruit „ II ii 217
Speak! in the name of *G*? „ II ii 272
I trust this day, thro' *G*, I have saved the crown. „ II ii 302
But o' *G's* mercy don't ye kill the Queen here, „ II iii 110
And I, by *G*, believe myself a man. „ III i 168
G save their Graces! (repeat) *Queen Mary* III i 177, 187, 342, 412
G's passion! knave, thy name? *Queen Mary* III i 248
Ha — Verbum Dei — verbum — word of *G*! *G's*
passion! do you know the knave that painted it? „ III i 263

God (s) (*continued*) Word of *G* In English! *Queen Mary* III i 279
trusted *G* would save her thro' the blood „ III i 386
Their Graces, our disgraces! *G* confound them! „ III i 415
which *G's* hand Wrote on her conscience, „ III i 421
But all is well; 'twas ev'n the will of *G*, „ III ii 77
'Hail, Daughter of *G*, and saver of the faith. „ III ii 82
Beheld our rough forefathers break their *G's*, „ III ii 121
Serve *G* and both your Majesties. „ III iii 159
G to this realm hath given A token „ III iii 168
first whom *G* hath given Grace to repent „ III iii 175
By him who sack'd the house of *G*; „ III iii 195
Julius, *G's* Vicar and Viceregent upon earth, „ III iii 213
Trembled for her own *g's*, for these were trembling— „ III iv 128
For which *G's* righteous judgment fell upon you „ III iv 240
Nay, *G's* passion, before me! speak! „ III iv 285
G upon earth! what more? what would you have? „ III iv 383
He falters, ha? 'fore *G*, we change and change; „ III iv 406
G grant it last, And witness to your Grace's innocence, „ III v 49
G save the Queen! „ III v 170
G hath blest or cursed me with a nose— „ III v 178
O *G*, sir, do you look upon your boots, „ III v 191
G hath given your Grace a nose, or not, „ III v 203
Pray *G*, we 'scape the sunstroke. „ III v 279
These are the means *G* works with, „ III vi 68
To whom he owes his loyalty after *G*, „ IV i 23
may *G* Forget me at most need when I forget Her
foul divorce— „ IV i 79
It is *G's* will, the Holy Father's will, „ IV i 184
G grant you ampler mercy at your call „ IV i 189
May *G* help you Thro' that hard hour! *Cranmer.*
And may *G* bless you, Thirlby! „ IV ii 195
I not doubt that *G* will give me strength, „ IV ii 234
Cranmer, be thou glad. This is the work of *G*. „ IV iii 82
Remember how *G* made the fierce fire „ IV iii 89
if thou call on *G* and all the saints, *G* will beat
down the fury of the flame, „ IV iii 96
O *G*, Father of Heaven! O Son of *G*, Redeemer
of the world! „ IV iii 116
Three persons and one *G*, have mercy on me, „ IV iii 121
Shall I despair then?—*G* forbid! O *G*. For thou
art merciful, refusing none That come to Thee „ IV iii 129
O Lord *G*, although my sins be great, „ IV iii 135
O *G* the Son, Not for slight faults alone, „ IV iii 138
O *G* the Father, not for little sins „ IV iii 143
truth of *G*, which I have proven and known. „ IV iii 149
G grant me grace to glorify my *G*! „ IV iii 166
'Love of this world is hatred against *G*.' Again,
I pray you all that, next to *G*, „ IV iii 174
Albeit he think himself at home with *G*, „ IV iii 193
Give to the poor, Ye give to *G*. „ IV iii 214
I do believe in *G*, Father of all; „ IV iii 228
G bless him! „ IV iii 256
He looks to and he leans on as his *G*, „ IV iii 306
died As manfully and boldly, and, 'fore *G*, „ IV iii 343
beast might roar his claim To being in *G's* image, „ IV iii 369
owld lord fell to 's meat wi' a will, *G* bless un!
but Gardiner wur struck down like by the hand
o' *G* „ IV iii 515
There's nought but the vire of *G's* hell ez can burn
out that. „ IV iii 527
Why then to heaven, and *G* ha' mercy on him. „ IV iii 631
Is *G's* best dew upon the barren field. „ V i 102
and therefore *G* Is hard upon the people. „ V i 175
and mine own natural man (It was *G's* cause); „ V ii 104
I hoped I had served *G* with all my might! „ V ii 296
G pardon me! I had never yet found one. „ V ii 334
Mother of *G*, Thou knowest never woman „ V ii 341
G help me, but methinks I love her less „ V ii 420
by *G's* providence a good stout staff Lay near me; „ V ii 468
light enough, *G* knows, And mixt with Wyatt's
rising— „ V ii 477
as I love The people! whom *G* aid! „ V iii 36
G's death! and wherefore spake you not before? „ V iii 106
Then I and he will snaffle your '*G's* death,' „ V iii 119
G's death, forsooth—you do not know King Philip. „ V iii 123

God (s) (*continued*) G curse her and her Legate ! *Queen Mary* v iv 12
cries continually with sweat and tears to the Lord G „ v iv 46
Poor enough in G's grace ! „ v v 50
I trust that G will make you happy yet. „ v v 76
O G ! I have been too slack, too slack ; „ v v 100
but by G's grace, We'll follow Philip's leading, „ v v 111
Ay, Madam, but o' G's mercy— „ v v 165
O G, I have kill'd my Philip ! „ v v 180
G guide me lest I lose the way. „ v v 209
she loved much : pray G she be forgiven. „ v v 271
G save Elizabeth, the Queen of England ! *Bagenhall.* G save the Crown ! the Papacy is no more. „ v v 283
G save the Queen ! „ v v 288
floated downward from the throne Of G Almighty. *Harold* I i 19
in Normanland G speaks thro' abler voices, „ I i 167
But dreading G's revenge upon this realm „ I i 172
I have wrought miracles—to G the glory— „ I i 181
Pray G the people choose thee for their king ! „ I i 314
that the shipwreckt are accursed of G ;— „ II i 101
by the splendour of G, no guest of mine. „ II ii 26
My G, I should be there. „ II ii 310
Our Duke is all about thee like a G ; „ II ii 316
G and the sea have given thee to our hands— „ II ii 548
bright sky cleave To the very feet of G, „ II ii 743
O G, that I were in some wide, waste field „ II ii 777
That sun may G speed ! „ III i 72
G bless thee, wedded daughter. „ III i 293
for the king Is holy, and hath talk'd with G, „ III i 355
Pray G that come not suddenly ! „ III i 364
G Has fill'd the quiver, and Death has drawn the bow— „ III i 399
O G ! I cannot help it, but at times „ III ii 63
when that which reign'd Call'd itself G.— „ III ii 167
The Lord was G and came as man—the Pope Is man and comes as G.— „ III ii 172
But I dare. G with thee ! „ III ii 188
G help me ! I know nothing— „ III ii 193
in the name of the great G, so be it ! „ IV i 240
peace with what G gave us to divide us „ IV iii 101
Here's to him, sink or swim ! *Thane.* G sink him ! „ IV iii 135
By G, we thought him dead— „ IV iii 148
Hath harried mine own cattle—G confound him ! „ IV iii 190
And all the Heavens and very G : they heard— „ v i 43
Tell him that G is nobler than the Saints, „ v i 57
And bide the doom of G. „ v i 61
If I fall, I fall—The doom of G ! „ v i 136
A snatch of sleep were like the peace of G. „ v i 181
great G of truth Fill all thine hours with peace !— „ v i 315
And not on thee—nor England—fall G's doom ! „ v i 371
And front the doom of G. „ v i 436
O G of battles, make their wall of shields „ v i 478
G save King Harold ! „ v i 489
Harold and G Almighty ! „ v i 526
O G of battles, make his battle-axe keen „ v i 562
O G of battles, they are three to one, „ v i 575
O G, the G of truth hath heard my cry. „ v i 600
Glory to G in the Highest ! fallen, fallen ! „ v i 636
Whisper ! G's angels only know it. „ v ii 31
my G, They have so maim'd and murder'd all his face „ v ii 75
build a church to G Here on the hill of battle ; „ v ii 137
till that blighted vow Which G avenged to-day. „ v ii 157
by the splendour of G—have I fought men „ v ii 177
pray G My Normans may but move as true „ v ii 183
I would to G thou wert, for I should find *Becket, Pro.* 86
Men are G's trees, and women are G's flowers ; „ *Pro.* 111
No, my liege, no !—not once—in G's name, no ! „ *Pro.* 126
G's eyes ! I know all that— „ *Pro.* 148
Would G she were—no, here within the city. „ *Pro.* 179
G's favour and king's favour might so clash „ *Pro.* 295
G's eyes ! what a lovely cross ! „ *Pro.* 370
And spake to the Lord G, and said, „ I i 74
' O Lord my G, Henry the King hath been my friend, „ I i 86
G make not thee, but thy foes, fall. „ I i 106
'Fore G, I am a mightier man than thou. „ I i 223
By G's death, thou shalt stick him like a calf ! „ I iii 183

God (s) (*continued*) it is the will of G To break me, *Becket* I iii 291
' False to myself ! It is the will of G ! ' *Henry.* G's will be what it will, „ I iii 328
The King's will and G's will and justice ; „ I iii 420
G's eyes ! I had meant to make him all but king. „ I iii 464
The will of G—why, then it is my will— „ I iii 473
The King's ' G's eyes ! ' come now so thick and fast, „ I iii 609
For the King's pleasure rather than G's cause „ I iii 697
G from me withdraws Himself, And the King too. „ I iii 701
That thou obey, not me, but G in me, „ I iii 721
Wilt thou not say, ' G bless you, 'ere we go ? *Becket.* ' G bless you all ! G redden your pale blood ! But mine is human-red ; „ I iv 33
and see it mounting to Heaven, my G bless you, „ I iv 38
Shall G's good gifts be wasted ? „ I iv 70
his paws are past help. G help him. „ I iv 111
dawns darkly and drearily over the house of G— „ I iv 146
I pray G I haven't given thee my leprosy, „ I iv 214
this beast-body That G has plunged my soul in— „ II i 150
May G grant No ill befall or him or thee „ II i 259
by G's eyes, we will not have him crown'd. „ II ii 3
a perilous game For men to play with G. „ II ii 71
and pray G she prove True wife to you. „ II ii 77
Saving G's honour ! „ II ii 140
—that Is clean against G's honour— „ II ii 163
that none may dream I go against G's honour— „ II ii 168
Would G they had torn up all By the hard root, „ II ii 207
to suppress G's honour for the sake Of any king that breathes. No, G forbid ! *Henry.* No ! G forbid ! „ II ii 220
No G but one, and Mahound is his prophet. „ II ii 225
you shall have None other G but me— „ II ii 229
who hath withstood two Kings to their faces for the honour of G. „ II ii 277
I pray G pardon mine infirmity. „ II ii 353
Yet you both love G. „ II ii 376
O G, how many an innocent Has left his bones „ II ii 407
Deny not thou G's honour for a king. „ II ii 424
surrendering G's honour to the pleasure of a man. „ II ii 440
Son, I absolve thee in the name of G. „ II ii 443
G bless the great Archbishop ! „ II ii 451
G help her, That she was sworn to silence. „ III i 77
G help her, she had 'em from her mother, „ III i 185
O G ! some dreadful truth is breaking on me— „ III i 265
puffed out such an incense of unctuosity into the nostrils of our G's of Church and State, „ III iii 116
before G I promise you the King hath many „ III iii 321
G and his free wind grant your lordship a happy home-return „ III iii 326
The boy so late ; pray G, he be not lost. „ IV ii 2
and G will be our guide. „ IV ii 104
By very G, the cross I gave the King ! „ IV ii 199
Strike ! I challenge thee to meet me before G. „ IV ii 254
G's grace and Holy Church deliver'd us. „ IV ii 309
If G would take him in some sudden way— „ v i 93
My liege, the Queen of England. *Henry.* G's eyes ! „ v i 98
The Church ! the Church ! G's eyes ! „ v i 217
Thou hast waged G's wars against the King ; „ v ii 46
York against Canterbury, York against G ! „ v ii 67
G bless him for it. „ v ii 146
G save him from all sickness of the soul ! „ v ii 174
this mother, runs thro' all The world G made— „ v ii 243
G help thee ! „ v ii 296
things that are the King's, And those of G to G. „ v ii 463
scare me from my loyalty To G and to the Holy Father. „ v ii 483
foremost of their files, who die For G, „ v ii 496
to people heaven in the great day When G makes up his jewels. „ v ii 497
G's will be done ! (repeat) *Becket* v ii 565, 567
It is G's will. Go on. *Becket* v ii 634
No traitor to the King, but Priest of G, „ v iii 113
G pardon thee and these, but G's full curse „ v iii 133
I do commend my cause to G, the Virgin, „ v iii 163
O G, O noble knights, O sacrilege ! „ v iii 178
O G's ! She is my fate— *The Cup* I i 11
Rome Made war upon the peoples not the G's. „ I ii 61

Golden yet stay, this *g* chain—My father on a birthday gave it me, *Queen Mary* I v 526
hanging down from this The *G* Fleece— „ III i 82
Your Philip hath gold hair and *g* beard ; „ v iii 57
Some few of Gothic blood have *g* hair, „ v iii 61
With *g* deeds and iron stakes that brought Thy war with Brittany *Harold* II ii 47
For in the racing toward this *g* goal He turns not right or left, „ II ii 377
Lay thou thy hand upon this *g* pall ! „ II ii 699
Set forth our *g* Dragon, let him flap The wings „ IV i 245
saw thy willy-nilly nun Vying a tress against our *g* fern. „ v i 149
for marriage, rose or no rose, has killed the *g* violet. *Becket, Pro.* 351
Gave me the *g* keys of Paradise. „ I i 54
winter after summer, and the *g* leaves, „ I iv 65
Yea, thou my *g* dream of Love's own bower, „ II i 34
out of the eclipse Narrowing my *g* hour ! „ II i 203
Only the *g* Leopard printed in it Such hold-fast claws „ II ii 85
these *g* slopes Of Solomon-shaming flowers— „ III i 46
The *g* ornaments are stolen from her— „ III iii 180
Come, here is a *g* chain I will give thee „ IV i 40
and *g* provinces So that were done in equity. „ v ii 346
And roll the *g* oceans of our grain, *The Cup* II 269
and lays Our *g* grain, and runs to sea and makes it „ II 287
we would add Some *g* fringe of gorgeousness beyond Old use, „ II 438
for wasn't my lady born with a *g* spoon in her ladyship's mouth, and we haven't never so much as a silver one for the *g* lips of her ladyship. *The Falcon* 401
like the Moslem beauties waiting To clasp their lovers by the *g* gates. *Prom. of May* I 248
Will enter on the larger *g* age ; „ I 590
Who can tell What *g* hours, with what full hands, „ II 509
Flung by the *g* mantle of the cloud, *Foresters* II i 28

Goldenest Less than a star among the *g* hours Of Alfred, *Harold* IV iii 51

Goldsmiths (Immanuel) *See* **Immanuel Goldsmiths**

Goliasing There again, *G* and Goliathising ! *Becket* III iii 126

Goliath There is one Come as *G* came of yore— *Harold* v i 493

Goliathising There again, Goliasing and *G* ! *Becket* III iii 127

Gone he will not come Till she be *g*. *Queen Mary* I v 513
The Duke hath *g* to Leicester ; „ II i 4
had *g* over to him With all his men, „ II ii 28
tree that only bears dead fruit is *g*. „ III i 19
Hence, let's be *g*. *Usher.* Well that you be not *g*, My Lord. „ III iv 385
The civil wars are *g* for evermore : „ III v 150
She has *g*, Maid Marian to her Robin— „ III v 155
should her love when you are *g*, my liege, „ III vi 173
Be somewhat pitiful, after I have *g*, „ IV ii 157
G narrowing down and darkening to a close. „ IV iii 431
in pursuing heresy I have *g* beyond your late Lord Chancellor,— „ v ii 98
G beyond him and mine own natural man „ v ii 102
Philip *g* ! And Calais *g* ! Time that I were *g* too ! „ v ii 319
Calais *g*—Guisnes *g*, too—and Philip *g* ! „ v v 22
Charles, the lord of this low world, is *g* ; „ v v 55
but after I am *g* Woe, woe to England ! *Harold* I i 189
—That was many a summer *g*— „ I i 254
thou art not *g* so wild But thou canst hear „ I i 299
Yea,—get thee *g* ! „ II ii 117
My friend, thou hast *g* too far to palter now. „ II ii 707
He hath *g* to kindle Norway against England, „ III i 79
Many are *g*—Drink to the dead who died for us, „ IV iii 68
Get thee *g* ! He means the thing he says. „ v i 83
Over and *g* with the roses, (repeat) *Becket, Pro.* 326, 333
And over and *g* with the sun. „ *Pro.* 327
Not over and *g* with the rose. „ *Pro.* 344
I more than once have *g* against the Church. „ I i 29
—a chink—he's out, *G* ! „ I i 261
Hadst thou not sign'd, I had *g* along with thee ; „ I iii 522
No ill befall or him or thee when I Am *g*. „ II i 261
I stay myself—Puff—it is *g*. „ II ii 151
g to the King And taken our anathema with him. „ v ii 6
he had *g* too far Into the King's own woods ; „ v ii 107
Going or *g* to-day To hunt with Sinnatus. *The Cup* I i 64

Gone (*continued*) And I may strike your game when you are *g*. *The Cup* I ii 37
He is *g* already. Oh, look,— „ I ii 393
Just *g* To fly his falcon. *The Falcon* 209
Beänt Miss Eva *g* off a bit of 'er good looks o' laäte ? *Prom. of May* I 33
if I could ha' *g* on wi' the plowin' „ I 376
After all that has *g* between us—friends ! „ I 633
All that has *g* between us Should surely make us friends. „ I 636
He has *g* to London. „ I 780
and now she be *g*, will ye taäke 'em, Miss Dora ? „ II 21
who came to us three years after you were *g*, how should she know you ? „ III 233
Pledge the Plantagenet, Him that is *g*. *Foresters* I ii 8
Now that the sun our King is *g*, „ I ii 83
All *g* !—my ring—I am happy— „ I iii 1
make us merry Because a year of it is *g* ? „ I iii 15
G, and it may be *g* for evermore ! „ II i 155
G, like a deer that hath escaped thine arrow ! „ IV 60
By old St. Vitus Have you *g* mad ? „ IV 616
Where be they *g* to ? „ IV 629

Gonfanon and have sent him back A holy *g*, *Harold* III ii 148
g of Holy Peter Floating above their helmets— „ v i 549

Good and of the *g* Lady Jane as a poor innocent child *Queen Mary* I i 94
I know it, my *g* Lord. „ I ii 92
—and now that your *g* bishop, Bonner, „ I iii 34
I shall fathom him. *G* morning, Noailles. „ I iii 159
G now, my Lady Queen, tho' by your age, „ I iv 11
Folly, my *g* Lord. „ I iv 89
Not very dangerous that way, my *g* uncle. „ I iv 167
I follow your *g* counsel, gracious uncle. „ I iv 186
Do they say so, *g* uncle ? „ I iv 214
Ay, *g* niece ! You should be plain and open with me, „ I iv 216
No, *g* uncle. „ I iv 220
to have the wish before the word Is man's *g* Fairy— „ I iv 240
But my *g* mother came (God rest her soul) Of Spain, „ I v 11
G morning, my *g* Lord. „ I v 98
That every morning of your Majesty May be most *g*, „ I v 102
G, then, they will revolt : but I am Tudor, „ I v 174
Bid him come in. *G* morning, Sir de Noailles. „ I v 242
and your *g* master, Pray God he do not be the first to break them, „ I v 267
French, I must needs wish all *g* things for France. „ I v 309
G Madam, when the Roman wish'd to reign, „ I v 497
G Lord ! but I have heard a thousand such. „ I v 578
Why, *g* Lord, Write you as many sonnets as you will. „ II i 94
By God, you are as poor a poet, Wyatt, As a *g* soldier. „ II i 114
that *g* helpless creature, starved, maim'd, flogg'd, „ II i 209
And see the citizens arm'd. *G* day ; *g* day. „ II ii 378
and they With their *g* battleaxes will do you right „ II iv 66
G, was it splendid ? „ III i 49
G faith, I was too sorry for the woman To mark the dress. „ III i 57
Wyatt was a *g* soldier, yet he fail'd, „ III i 132
Methinks the *g* land heard me, for to-day My heart beats twenty, „ III ii 57
True, *g* cousin Pole ; „ III ii 68
G news have I to tell you, news to make Both of us happy— „ III ii 186
G ! Well, Madam, this new happiness of mine ? „ III ii 207
G sir, for this, if Philip— „ III iii 82
Why, *g* ! what then ? granted !—we are fallen creatures ; „ III iv 78
And tropes are *g* to clothe a naked truth, „ III iv 150
With that vile Cranmer in the accursed lie Of *g* Queen Catharine's divorce— „ III iv 232
Ha ! *g* ! it seems then I was summon'd hither „ III iv 268
But this most noble prince Plantagenet, Our *g* Queen's cousin— „ III iv 292
Upon the *g* Queen's mercy ; ay, when, my Lord ? „ III v 168
Before my father married my *g* mother,— „ III v 245
G morrow, my Lord Cardinal ; „ IV i 42
These are but natural graces, my *g* Bishop, „ IV i 176
And bad me have *g* courage ; „ IV ii 8
The prison fare is *g* enough for me. „ IV ii 42

Good (*continued*) And drown all poor self-passion in the sense Of public *g*? — *The Cup* II 103
Did not some old Greek Say death was the chief *g*? — „ II 515
G mother, happy was the prodigal son, — *The Falcon* 140
And yet to speak white truth, my *g* old mother, — „ 504
G! let it be but one. — „ 511
You hear, Filippo? My *g* fellow, go! — „ 690
I have anger'd your *g* nurse; — „ 707
'I should be well again If the *g* Count would give me——' — „ 838
Beänt Miss Eva gone off a bit of 'er *g* looks o' laäte? — *Prom. of May* I 33
G day! *Wilson.* *G* day, sir. — „ I 294
G day, then, Dobson. *Dobson.* '*G* daäy then, Dobson!' — „ I 299
G murnin', neighbours, and the saäme to you, my men. — „ I 317
but I ha taäen *g* care to turn out boäth my darters right down fine laädies. — „ I 335
Coom, coom, that's a *g* 'un. — „ I 467
G wishes, not reproaches; — „ I 526
you have robb'd poor father Of ten *g* apples. — „ I 616
You had better attend to your hayfield. *G* afternoon. — „ II 123
Scizzars an' Pumpy was *g* uns to goä (repeat) — „ II 308, 318
That beer be as *g* fur 'erses as men. — „ II 315
And you Seem my *g* angel who may help me from it. — „ II 388
Now am I Edgar, my *g* fellow. — „ II 701
My name is Harold! *G* day, Dobbins! — „ II 726
Naäy, but '*G* daäy, Dobbins.' — „ II 732
'*G* daäy, Dobbins.' Dang tha! — „ II 741
G afternoon, my friends. — „ III 20
You are as *g* as a man in the hayfield. — „ III 106
and the man has doubtless a *g* heart, — „ III 171
though I can be sorry for him—as the *g* Sally says, — „ III 173
Come, come, keep a *g* heart! Better for me! That's *g*. — „ III 252
and tho' you are *g* and gentle, Yet if thro' any want— — „ III 538
G; then what is it That makes you talk so dolefully? — „ III 571
but I keep a *g* heart and make the most of it, — *Foresters* I i 28
he hath wasted his revenues in the service of our *g* king Richard — „ I i 194
I wish you and your ladyship's father a most exceedingly *g* morning. — „ I i 309
God's *g* Angel Help him back hither, — „ I ii 10
myself and my *g* father pray Thy thirtieth summer may be thirty-fold — „ I ii 127
G Prince, art thou in need of any gold? — „ I ii 162
O *g* Sir Richard, I am sorry my exchequer runs so low — „ I ii 271
by this Holy Cross Which *g* King Richard gave me when a child— — „ I ii 310
if this life of ours Be a *g* glad thing, — „ I iii 13
There be *g* fellows there in merry Sherwood — „ I iii 98
Not now, *g* Much! And thou, dear Little John, — „ I iii 158
O my *g* lord, I am but an angel by reflected light. — „ II i 107
The fool-people call her a witch—a *g* witch to me! — „ II i 179
Quick, *g* mother, quick! — „ II i 193
He was a forester *g*; — „ II i 319
Take him, *g* Little John, and give him wine. — „ II i 469
Knight, your *g* father had his draught of wine — „ II ii 1
We be neither bad nor *g*. — „ II ii 119
Why, my *g* Robin fancied me a man, — „ III 19
O *g* Kate—If my man-Robin were but a bird-Robin, — „ III 38
Farewell, *g* fellows! — „ III 87
Art thou not hard upon them, my *g* Robin? — „ III 222
G! Roll it in here. — „ III 311
I believe thee, thou art a *g* fellow, though a friar. — „ III 342
Quiet, *g* Robin, quiet! — „ IV 9
G! but having lived For twenty days and nights in mail, — „ IV 122
Thou payest easily, like a *g* fellow, — „ IV 156
G, *g*, I love thee for that! — „ IV 173
Up, *g* Much. — „ IV 284
G, now I love thee mightily, thou tall fellow, — „ IV 321
For if he did me the *g* grace to kick me — „ IV 364
My *g* friend Robin, Earl of Huntingdon, For Earl thou art again, — „ IV 828
O my *g* liege, we did believe you dead. — „ IV 845
I thank thee, *g* Sir Richard. — „ IV 858

Good (*continued*) But if the King forbid thy marrying With Robin, our *g* Earl of Huntingdon. — *Foresters* IV 876
I trust Half truths, *g* friar: — „ IV 950
The king's *g* health in ale and Malvoisie. — „ IV 968
O *g* Sir Richard, I am like the man In Holy Writ, — „ IV 980
I am, *g* father, I am. — „ IV 1020
Embrace me, Marian, and thou, *g* Kate, Kiss and congratulate me, my *g* Kate. — „ IV 1031
You, *g* friar, You Much, you Scarlet, you dear Little John, — „ IV 1081

Good-bye I'll say something for you—so—*g-b*. — *Queen Mary* IV ii 168
G-b. *James.* Gi'e us a buss fust, lass. — *Prom. of May* ii 227

Good-day (*See also* **Good**) *G-d*, my Lord of Devon; — *Queen Mary* I iii 95
G-d, my Lord. — „ I iii 160
And see the citizens arm'd. *G d*; *g d*. — „ II ii 378
G d! Wilson. *G d*, sir. — *Prom. of May* I 294
G d, then, Dobson. — „ I 299
My name is Harold! *G d*, Dobbins! — „ II 726

Goodlier and yet, methinks, I have seen *g*. — *Queen Mary* I v 7
Yet she's no *g*; — „ II ii 345
brought Thy war with Brittany to a *g* close Than else had been, — *Harold* II ii 49
as brave a soldier as Henry and a *g* man: — *Becket, Pro.* 437

Goodlier-looking A *g-l* fellow than this Philip. — *Queen Mary* I iv 3
A *g-l* man than Sinnatus. — *The Cup* II 176

Goodliest *That* makes or man or woman look their *g*. — *Queen Mary* II ii 330

Goodly Most *g*, Kinglike and an Emperor's son,— — „ I v 2
G enough, your Grace, and yet, methinks, I have seen goodlier. — „ I v 5
Peruse it; is it not *g*, ay, and gentle? — „ I v 195
Ay, true—a *g* one. I would his life Were half as *g*. — „ I v 200
I have never seen her So queenly or so *g*. — „ II ii 327
And all men cry, She is queenly, she is *g*. — „ II ii 344
Should look more *g* than the rest of us. — „ II ii 349
G? I feel most *g* heart and hand, — „ II ii 351
says she will live And die true maid—a *g* creature too. — „ III vi 46
My liege, I bring you *g* tidings. — „ V i 279
But is Don Carlos such a *g* match? — „ V iii 86
Who knows what sows itself among the people? A *g* flower at times. — *Harold* IV i 151
G news! *Morcar.* Doubt it not thou! — „ IV i 219
have graspt Her livings, her advowsons, granges, farms, And *g* acres— — *Becket* I i 163
Well—if that isn't *g* wine—— *Beggar.* Then there isn't a *g* wench to serve him with it: — „ I iv 157
the *g* way of women Who love, for which I love them. — „ II i 256
O bestial! O how unlike our *g* Sinnatus. — *The Cup* I 173
True, she is a *g* thing. — *Foresters* II ii 140
There was a man of ours Up in the north, a *g* fellow too, — „ IV 530

Goodman I mean your *g*, your husband, my lady, — *Becket* III i 158
Where is thy *g-m*? — *Foresters* II i 370

Good-night *G n*! Go home. Besides, you curse so loud. — *Queen Mary* V iv 61
G-n, and dream thyself Their chosen Earl. — *Harold* I ii 247
G n! *g n*! — *Becket* I i 313
Both, *g n*! — „ I i 406
My friends, the Archbishop bids you *g n*. — „ I iv 261
Thou—coming my way too—Camma—*g-n*. — *The Cup* II 493
Let bygones be bygones. Go home! *G-n*! — *Prom. of May* III 157

Goods Confiscate lands, *g*, money— — *Queen Mary* II i 102
To make free spoil and havock of your *g*. — „ II ii 187
thou art dispossessed of all thy lands, *g*, and chattels; — *Foresters* I iii 60
Sheriff had taken all our *g* for the King without paying, — „ II i 190

Goodwill If but to prove your Majesty's *g*, — *Queen Mary* I v 260
With *g w*; Yea, take the Sacrament upon it, — *Harold* IV i 182
is it then with thy *g* that I Proceed against thine evil councillors, — *Becket* III iii 207

Goose father's eye was so tender it would have called a *g* off the green, — „ III iii 102
Venison, and wild boar, hare, *geese*, — *Foresters* IV 191
Geese, man! for how canst thou be allied With John, and serve King Richard save thou be A traitor or a *g*? — „ IV 349

Goosewing By arrow and gray *g*, — „ III 427

Gorge (*See also* **Side-gorge**) not like thine To *g* a heretic whole, — *Queen Mary* III iv 344

Gorgeous the *g* Indian shawl That Philip brought me in our happy days!— *Queen Mary* v ii 538
Gorgeousness Some golden fringe of *g* beyond *The Cup* ii 438
Gospeller and the Hot *G's* will go mad upon it. *Queen Mary* i i 115
Yon gray old *G*, sour as midwinter, „ i iii 40
Not dream'd of by the rabidest *g*. „ iii vi 138
there be two old gossips—*g's*, I take it; „ iv iii 460
There are Hot *G's* even among our guards— „ v v 102
Gossamer Were you in Spain, this fine fair *g* gold— „ v iii 48
Gossip Hist! there be two old *g's*—gospellers, „ iv iii 460
Gossiping with no fear Of the world's *g* clamour, *Prom. of May* i 528
Got And I *g* it. I woke Sir Henry— *Queen Mary* iii v 59
afoor I coomed up he *g* thruff the winder ageän. *Eva. G* thro' the window again? *Prom. of May* i 405
Then she *g* me a place as nursery governess, „ iii 385
Gothic Some few of *G* blood have golden hair, *Queen Mary* v iii 60
Gotten Owd Steer's *g* all his grass down and wants a hand, *Prom. of May* ii 221
The beer's *g* oop into my 'eäd, „ ii 320
Gout small hope of the gentleman *g* in my great toe. *The Falcon* 657
'I hope your Lordship is quite recovered of your *g*?' *Prom. of May* iii 309
Rogue, I am full of *g*. I cannot dance. *Foresters* iv 562
Sweat out your *g*, friend, for by my life, „ iv 565
Govern Whose ministers they be to *g* you. *Queen Mary* iv iii 180
Ye *g* milder men. *Harold* i i 339
Governance Against thy brother Tostig's *g*; „ ii ii 290
We have heard Of thy just, mild, and equal *g*; „ ii ii 690
Governess Then she got me a place as a nursery *g*, *Prom. of May* iii 385
Government We have made them milder by just *g*. *Harold* i i 341
and by the advice of his *G*.' *Becket* i iii 113
Gown Disguise me—thy *g* and thy coif. *Foresters* ii i 186
Ay, ay, *g*, coif, and petticoat, „ ii i 194
Graäy (gray) Wi' the briar sa green, an' the willer sa *g*, *Prom. of May* ii 187
Grace (s) (*See also* **Herb-of-grace**) God save her *G*; *Queen Mary* i i 67
whether her *G* incline to this splendid scion of Plantagenet. „ i i 134
The Queen would see your *G* upon the moment. „ i iv 222
Your *G* will hear her reasons from herself. „ i iv 230
Whereof 'tis like enough she means to make A farewell present to your G. „ i iv 245
Goodly enough, your *G*, and yet, methinks, I have seen goodlier. „ i v 5
By your *G's* leave Your royal mother came of Spain, „ i v 15
I cannot, and I dare not, tell your *G* What Lady Jane replied. „ i v 49
—a head So full of *g* and beauty! „ i v 64
I say your *G* is loved. „ i v 131
I am all thanks To God and to your *G*: „ i v 186
Hath your *G* so sworn? „ i v 217
In some such form as least may harm your *G*. „ i v 226
your *G* And kingdom will be suck'd into the war, „ i v 256
Nay, pure phantasy, your *G*. „ i v 280
but I protest Your *G's* policy hath a farther flight „ i v 312
Who waits? *Usher*. The Ambassador of Spain, your *G*. „ i v 343
Nay, your *G*, it hath not reach'd me. „ i v 351
You are happy in him there, Chaste as your *G*! „ i v 456
What slanders? I, your *G*; no, never. *Mary*. Nothing? *Alice*. Never, your G. „ i v 572
I scarce had left your *G's* presence „ i v 583
must we levy war against the Queen's *G*? *Wyatt*. No, my friend, war *for* the Queen's *G*—to save her from herself and Philip— „ ii i 187
When will her *G* be here? „ ii ii 13
Here comes her Royal *G*. „ ii ii 126
But that with God's *G*, I can live so still. „ ii ii 219
but we can save your *G*. The river still is free. „ ii iv 24
No, no, your *G*; see there the arrows flying. „ ii iv 50
The porter, please your *G*, hath shut the gates On friend and foe. Your gentlemen-at-arms, If this be not your *G's* order, „ ii iv 61
I do not love your *G* should call me coward. *Messenger*. Over, your G, all crush'd; „ ii iv 88
God save their *G's*. (repeat). *Queen Mary* iii i 178, 187, 343, 413
Grace (s) (*continued*) Seventeen—a rose of *g*! *Queen Mary* iii i 371
Their *G's*, our disgraces! God confound them! „ iii i 415
Farewell, your *G's*. „ iii ii 146
Mine echoes both your *G's'*; „ iii iii 96
Lo! once again God to this realm hath given A token of His more especial *G*; „ iii iii 170
G to repent and sorrow for their schism; „ iii iii 177
their two *G's* Do so dear-cousin and royal-cousin him, „ iii iv 398
Why do they keep us here? Why still suspect your *G*? „ iii v 17
And witness to your *G's* innocence, „ iii v 50
Before I dare to glance upon your *G*. „ iii v 186
See, I lay it here, For I will come no nearer to your *G*; „ iii v 200
And God hath given your *G* a nose, or not, „ iii v 203
O Lord! your *G*, your *G*, „ iii v 248
And had your *G* a Robin? „ iii v 273
A *g* to me! Mercy, that herb-of-grace, „ iii vi 9
when last he wrote, declared His comfort in your *G* „ iii vi 79
Your *G* hath a most chaste and loving wife. „ iii vi 129
Your *G's* business will not suffer, sire, „ iii vi 244
Crave, in the same cause, hearing of your *G*. „ iv i 9
Health to your *G*! Good morrow, my Lord Cardinal; We make our humble prayer unto your *G* „ iv i 41
Ay, ay, your *G*; but it was never seen That any one recanting thus at full, „ iv i 57
These are but natural *g's*, my good Bishop, „ iv i 176
After this, Your *G* will hardly care to overlook „ iv i 192
By Heaven's *g*, I am more and more confirm'd. „ iv ii 21
Sire, if your *G* hath mark'd it, so have I. „ v i 231
That if your *G* hath mark'd her, so have I. „ v i 239
and your *G*, So you will take advice of mine, „ v i 300
Your *G* hath been More merciful to many a rebel head „ v ii 4
what sin Beyond all *g*, all pardon? „ v ii 340
Your *G* hath a low voice. „ v ii 378
Good Lord! how grim and ghastly looks her *G*, „ v ii 390
Ay, so your *G* would bide a moment yet. „ v ii 546
I trust your *G* is well. „ v ii 551
But shall I take some message from your *G*? „ v ii 597
Then I may say your *G* will see your sister? Your *G* is too low-spirited. „ v ii 603
But as to Philip and your *G*—consider,— „ v iii 64
I gather'd from the Queen That she would see your *G* before she—died. „ v iii 104
Poor enough in God's *g*! „ v v 50
I will, if that May make your *G* forget yourself a little. „ v v 81
by God's *g*, We'll follow Philip's leading, „ v v 111
I never spied in thee one gleam of *g*. *Becket* v ii 474
Is strength less strong when hand-in-hand with *g*? „ v ii 541
and 'your *G*' are all growing old-fashioned *Prom. of May* iii 318
So winsome in her *g* and gaiety, „ iii 754
Nay, an please your Elfin *G*, *Foresters* ii ii 132
For if he did me the good *g* to kick me „ iv 364
Not now, not now—with after-dinner *g*. „ iv 938
Grace (verb) To *g* his memory. *Queen Mary* ii i 31
My cottage, while you *g* it, is a palace. *The Falcon* 288
thy father will not *g* our feast With his white beard to-day. *Foresters* iv 80
Graced Much *g* are we that our Queen Rome in you *The Cup* ii 335
Graceless That were a *g* hospitality To chain the free guest *Harold* ii ii 192
Gracious seeing that our *g* Virgin Queen hath— *Queen Mary* i iii 23
—and since our *G* Queen, let me call her our second Virgin Mary, „ i iii 56
But does your *g* Queen entreat you kinglike? „ i iii 109
I follow your good counsel, *g* uncle. „ i iv 186
would that mine Were half as *g*! „ i v 66
A *g* guard Truly; shame on them! they have shut the gates! „ ii iv 56
That by your *g* means and intercession „ iii iii 121
and there watch All that is *g* in the breath of heaven „ iii vi 224
O, Madam, if you knew him As I do, ever gentle, and so *g*, „ iv i 156
Such weeds make dunghills *g*. „ iv i 182
He had his *g* moment, Altho' you'll not believe me. „ v v 37
A gentle, *g*, pure, and saintly man! *Harold* ii ii 584
Well, well, we will be gentle with him, *g*—Most *g*. *Becket* ii ii 129
will not your Holiness Vouchsafe a *g* answer to your Queen? „ iv ii 359

Gracious (*continued*) So *g* toward women, never yet Flung back a woman's prayer. *The Cup* I ii 299
And be you *G* enough to let me know the boon *The Falcon* 765
It will be all the more *g* of her if she do. *Foresters* I i 175
Grafted And *g* on the hard-grain'd stock of Spain— *Queen Mary* IV iii 426
Grain (corn) And roll the golden oceans of our *g*, *The Cup* II 269
strows our fruits, and lays Our golden *g*, „ II 287
and why ye have so few *g's* to peck at. *Foresters* I i 77
Grain (particle) My one *g* of good counsel which you will not swallow. *Becket* II ii 378
second *g* of good counsel I ever proffered thee, „ III iii 317
Grain'd *See* **Hard-grain'd**
Gramercy *G* for thy preachment! *Foresters* IV 397
Granada *G*, Naples, Sicily, and Milan,— *Queen Mary* V i 44
Grand a thousand times Fitter for this *g* function. *Becket, Pro.* 293
Grandfather My *g*—of him They say, that women— *Prom. of May* II 271
my great great great *g*, my great great *g*, my great *g*, my *g*, and my own father— *Foresters* I i 329
Grandsire Lost in desuetude, of my *g's* day— *Becket* I iii 413
His *g* struck my *g* in a brawl At Florence, and my *g* stabb'd *The Falcon* 250
Grandson only *g* To Wulfnoth, a poor cow-herd. *Harold* IV i 69
cottage of yours where your *g* had the fever. *Prom. of May* III 44
Grange her advowsons, *g's*, farms, And goodly acres— *Becket* I i 161
Granny *G* says marriages be maäde i' 'eaven. *Prom. of May* III 709
Grant I wrote it, and God *g* me power to burn! *Queen Mary* I ii 98
g me my prayer: Give me my Philip; „ I v 85
Sir Thomas, we may *g* the wine. „ II i 40
Is now content to *g* you full forgiveness, „ III iv 389
God *g* it last, And witness to your Grace's innocence, „ III v 49
God *g* your ampler mercy at your call „ IV i 189
God *g* me grace to glorify my God! „ IV iii 166
If ever, as heaven *g*, we clash with Spain, „ IV iii 346
By loss of Calais. *G* me Calais. „ V ii 305
Have you found mercy there, *G* it me here: „ V v 145
So that you *g* me one slight favour. *Becket* I ii 58
we *g* when kings are dangerous The Church must play „ I ii 67
he would *g* thee The crown itself. „ I iii 29
G me one day To ponder these demands. „ I iii 667
May God *g* No ill befall or him or thee „ II i 259
we *g* the Church King over this world's kings, „ II ii 241
God and his free wind *g* your lordship a happy home-return „ III iii 327
By granting which, if aught be mine to *g*, *The Falcon* 768
Then they would *g* you what they call a licence *Prom. of May* I 694
Granted Old Sir Thomas always *g* the wine. *Queen Mary* II i 42
Why, good! what then? *g*!— „ III iv 78
It shall be *g* him, my king; *Harold* III i 227
Granting let me know the boon By *g* which, *The Falcon* 767
Grape These *g's* are for the house of Sinnatus— *The Cup* I i 51
may this mouth Never suck *g* again, *Foresters* IV 394
Grape-bunches sway the long *g-b* of our vines, *The Cup* II 270
Grapple stand beside thee One who might *g* with thy dagger, *Becket* IV ii 230
He would *g* with a lion like the King, *Foresters* I i 185
Grappling and the mitre *G* the crown— *Becket* I i 27
Grasp (s) in his *g* a sword Of lightnings, *Harold* III i 136
Why, what a cold *g* is thine— *Foresters* I ii 242
Grasp (verb) should have a hand To *g* the world with, *Harold* V ii 192
Graspt have *g* Her livings, her advowsons, *Becket* I i 160
Grass balmy wind to robe our hills with *g*, *The Cup* II 266
she had thrown my chaplet on the *g*, *The Falcon* 369
Had she not thrown my chaplet on the *g*, „ 378
if you'd like to measure your own length upon the *g*. *Prom. of May* I 466
Owd Steer's gotten all his *g* down and wants a hand, „ II 221
Grasshopper *G*, *g*, Whoop—you can hear. *Becket* III i 102
Grateful All the church is *g*. *Queen Mary* I v 179
Most loyal and most *g* to the Queen. „ V iii 25
You should be *g* to my master, too. „ V iii 27
And *g* to the hand that shielded him, *Harold* II ii 586
—am *g* for thine honest oath, „ II ii 755
For which she should be duly *g*. *Becket* I ii 74
I should be *g*—He hath not excommunicated *me*. „ V ii 470
g that I show'd her The weakness *The Cup* I i 21
and the Goddess, being For this most *g*, „ II 349
That one, then, should be *g* for your preference. *Prom. of May* II 556

Grateful (*continued*) one that should be *g* to me overseas, a Count in Brittany— *Foresters* I i 270
so you would make it two I should be *g*. „ III 195
Gratefully O Dora, he signed himself 'Yours *g*'— fancy, Dora, '*g*'! 'Yours *g*'! *Prom. of May* III 334
Gratefulness If ever man by bonds of *g*— *Becket* I iii 435
Gratia Ave Maria, *g* plena, Benedicta tu in mulieribus. *Queen Mary* III ii 1
Grating Close to the *g* on a winter morn *The Falcon* 441
Gratior G *in pulchro corpore virtus.* *Becket* V ii 542
Grave (adj.) look'd As grim and *g* as from a funeral. *Queen Mary* II ii 65
We fought like great states for *g* cause; *Harold* I i 440
Grave (s) Dug from the *g* that yawns for us beyond; *Queen Mary* V ii 163
A low voice from the dust and from the *g* „ V ii 386
And wear my crown, and dance upon my *g*. „ V ii 602
I'll fight it on the threshold of the *g*. „ V v 190
With dead men upright from their *g's*, *Harold* I ii 83
And thou art upright in thy living *g*, „ II ii 440
Corpse-candles gliding over nameless *g's*— „ III i 382
I give my voice against thee from the *g*— „ V i 255
He commends me now From out his *g* *Becket, Pro.* 420
And I shall live to trample on thy *g*. „ I ii 95
spire of Holy Church may prick the *g's*— „ I iii 554
O devil, can I free her from the *g*? „ V i 186
I should seem to be dancing upon a *g*. *Prom. of May* I 431
And *he* would hear you even from the *g*. „ I 763
I told her I should hear her from the *g*. „ II 245
To see her *g*? her ghost? „ II 352
as they call it so truly, to the *g* at the bottom, „ III 193
O *g's* in daisies drest, „ III 204
But now that you have been brought to us as it were from the *g*, „ III 235
to the *g* he goes to, Beneath the burthen of years. „ III 515
stillness in the *g* By the last trumpet. *Foresters* II i 47
Gravedigger like the *g's* child I have heard of, trying to ring the bell, *Becket* III iii 73
Graveness Had put off levity and put *g* on. *Queen Mary* V ii 510
Gray (*See also* **Graäy**) Yon *g* old Gospeller, sour as midwinter, „ I iii 40
he loved the more His own *g* towers, „ II i 49
Ah, *g* old castle of Alington, green field Beside the brimming Medway, „ II i 243
And scared the *g* old porter and his wife. „ II iii 16
The *g* rogue, Gardiner, Went on his knees, „ III v 164
And the *g* dawn Of an old age that never will be mine „ V ii 234
and dumb'd his carrion croak From the *g* sea for ever. *Harold* IV iii 67
the green field—the *g* church— *Becket* II ii 296
He will pass to-morrow In the *g* dawn before the Temple doors. *The Cup* I ii 295
I rise to-morrow In the *g* dawn, and take this holy cup „ I ii 434
And *g* before his time as thou art, Much. *Foresters* I iii 149
By arrow and *g* goosewing, „ III 427
Grayhound My *g's* fleeting like a beam of light, *Harold* I ii 129
Graze would not *g* The Prince of Spain. *Queen Mary* I v 453
Grazing Our horses *g* by us, when a troop, *The Falcon* 611
Greasy so *g*, and smell so vilely that my Lady Marian *Foresters* I i 82
that very word '*g*' hath a kind of unction in it, „ I i 86
Great Was she not betroth'd in her babyhood to the *G* Emperor himself? *Queen Mary* I i 118
How folly? a *g* party in the state Wills me to wed her. „ I iv 91
Doth not as *g* a party in the state Will you to wed me? „ I iv 95
Is no *g* party in the state as yet. „ I iv 102
G, said you? nay, you shall be *g*. I love you, „ I iv 103
I have felt within me Stirrings of some *g* doom when God's just hour Peals— „ I iv 261
Let the *g* angel of the church come with him; „ I v 377
Spain in all the *g* offices of state; „ II i 178
were to do *G* things, my Lord. „ II ii 390
and round his knee, misplaced, Our English Garter, studded with *g* emeralds, „ III i 84
where you gave your hand To this *g* Catholic King. „ III ii 92
The *g* unborn defender of the Faith, „ III ii 165
Ay, sir; Inherit the *G* Silence. „ III ii 199
Saying, O Lord God, although my sins be *g*, For thy *g* mercy have mercy! „ IV iii 136

Green (s) Bagenhall, I see The Tudor *g* and white. *Queen Mary* III i 180
The colours of our Queen are *g* and white, „ III v 5
father's eye was so tender it would have called a goose off the *g*, *Becket* III iii 103
Greenwich I will go to *G*, So you will have me *Queen Mary* III vi 221
Greenwood Beneath the *g* tree. (repeat) *Foresters* II i 12, 24
'Grees (agree) thaw me and 'im we niver *'g* about the tithe; *Prom. of May* I 444
Greet Wessex dragon flies beyond the Humber, No voice to *g* it. *Harold* IV i 5
Will *g* us as our babes in Paradise. *Becket* V ii 225
And music there to *g* my lord the king. *The Cup* II 191
Greeting Makes me his mouth of holy *g*. *Queen Mary* III ii 80
And scarce a *g* all the day for me— „ III vi 118
Full thanks for your fair *g* of my bride! *Harold* IV iii 46
G and health from Synorix! (repeat) *The Cup* II 40, 130
Gregory (Pope) no croucher to the *Gregories* That tread the kings *Becket, Pro.* 212
G bid St. Austin here Found two archbishopricks, „ I iii 48
Not to a *G* of my throning! No. „ V i 33
Gresham (Sir Thomas) *See* **Thomas Gresham**
Grew thus baptized in blood *G* ever high and higher, *Harold* III i 148
like a barren shore That *g* salt weeds, *The Cup* II 232
mountain flowers *g* thickly round about. *The Falcon* 355
and when the children *g* too old for me, *Prom. of May* III 386
Grex Pastor fugatur *G* trucidatur— *Harold* V i 514
Grey (Lady Jane) *See* **Jane**
Grief Thou stirrest up a *g* thou canst not fathom. *Queen Mary* III iv 298
mine own, a *g* To show the scar for ever— *Becket* I i 177
O *g* for the promise of May, (repeat) *Prom. of May* I 59, 60, 750, 752
We have been in such *g* these five years, *Prom. of May* II 66
how should I, with this *g* still at my heart, „ II 91
One that has been much wrong'd, whose *g's* are mine, „ III 577
Whate'er thy *g's*, in sleep they fade away. *Foresters* I iii 45
Grieve Death would not *g* him more. *Queen Mary* IV i 25
I bring your Majesty such grievous news I *g* to bring it „ V ii 241
I *g* I cannot; but, indeed— *Prom. of May* I 621
I *g* I am the Raven who croaks it. *Foresters* III 447
I *g* to say it was thy father's son. „ IV 810
Grieved I am vastly *g* to leave your Majesty. *Queen Mary* III vi 255
I am *g* to know as much. *Becket, Pro.* 4
I am *g*, my daughter. „ V ii 82
The Sheriff—I am *g* it was the Sheriff; *Foresters* II i 449
Grievous And first I say it is a *g* case, *Queen Mary* IV iii 167
I bring your Majesty such *g* news I grieve to bring it. „ V ii 240
in their mood May work them *g* harm at times, *The Falcon* 821
Griffyth (King of Wales) *G* I hated: why not hate the foe Of England? *G* when I saw him flee, Chased deer-like up his mountains, all the blood That should have only pulsed for *G*, *Harold* I ii 145
Since *G's* head was sent To Edward, „ IV i 221
With a love Passing thy love for *G*? „ V i 357
Grim (adj.) look'd As *g* and grave as from a funeral. *Queen Mary* II ii 65
how *g* and ghastly looks her Grace, „ V ii 389
Our cancell'd warrior-gods, our *g* Walhalla, *Harold* III ii 73
Grim (a monk) Thou art but yesterday from Cambridge, *G*; *Becket* V ii 55
Grimly-glaring Yon *g-g*, treble-brandish'd scourge Of England! *Harold* I i 3
Grimness There lodged a gleaming *g* in his eyes, „ II ii 224
Grip The black fiend *g* her? *Foresters* III 380
Griping and *g* mine, Whisper'd me, *Queen Mary* I ii 34
Grisly Spite of this *g* star ye three must gall Poor Tostig. *Harold* I i 418
Groan (s) cries, and clashes, and the *g's* of men; „ III i 375
Misheard their snores for *g's*. „ V i 213
Groan (verb) They *g* amen; they swarm into the fire *Queen Mary* V ii 110
Groan'd crept Up even to the tonsure, and he *g*, *Becket* I iii 327
Groaning *See* **A-groänin'**
Groining The *g* hid the heavens; *Foresters* II i 62
Groom (a servant) clowns and *g's* May read it! *Queen Mary* III iv 36
the *g*, Gardener, and huntsman, in the parson's place, „ IV iii 372
Groom (bridegroom) (*See also* **Bridegroom**) there is one Death stands behind the *G*, „ V ii 166
Groove Moved in the iron *g's* of Destiny? *Prom. of May* II 267
Gross invade their hive Too *g* to be thrust out, *Queen Mary* III iii 55
Who so bolster'd up The *g* King's headship of the Church, „ III iv 246
your Priests *G*, worldly, simoniacal, unlearn'd! *Harold* I i 162
Grossness Delight to wallow in the *g* of it, *Becket* II ii 343
Ground We but seek Some settled *g* for peace *Queen Mary* I v 315
as the heathen giant Had but to touch the *g*, „ III ii 44
bit his shield, and dash'd it on the *g*, *Harold* V i 406
tho' the fire should run along the *g*, *Prom. of May* I 704
Not while the swallow skims along the *g*, *Foresters* I ii 314
Group Many such *g's*. *Queen Mary* II ii 93
Grove Oh look,—yon *g* upon the mountain, *The Cup* I ii 394
Grovel He *g's* to the Church when he's black-blooded, *Becket* IV ii 436
Grow I shall *g* into it—I shall be the Tower. *Queen Mary* II iv 105
Daisies *g* again, Kingcups blow again, „ III v 89
Perhaps our vines will *g* the better for it. *Harold* I i 68
If e'er the Norman *g* too hard for thee, „ III i 12
old men must die, or the world would *g* mouldy, *Becket, Pro.* 409
If I sit, I *g* fat. „ *Pro.* 414
How the boy *g's*! „ II i 217
—her main law Whereby she *g's* in beauty— *Prom. of May* I 283
So the child *g* to manhood: „ II 289
What rightful cause could *g* to such a heat *Foresters* II i 698
Growing *G* dark too—but light enough to row. *The Cup* II 523
I have heard that 'your Lordship,' and 'your Ladyship,' and 'your Grace' are all *g* old-fashioned! *Prom. of May* III 318
He hath been hurt, was *g* whole again, *Foresters* IV 451
Grown Why, she's *g* bloodier! *Queen Mary* III i 416
How doubly aged this Queen of ours hath *g* „ V i 228
all the faiths Of this *g* world of ours, *Harold* III ii 65
were he living And *g* to man and Sinnatus will'd it, *The Cup* I ii 151
Growth did not wholly clear The deadly *g's* of earth, *Becket* II ii 203
Grudge tho' I *g* the pretty jewel, that I Have worn, *Prom. of May* I 473
Grunting These beastly swine make such a *g* here, *Queen Mary* I iii 12
Guard (s) I trust the Queen comes hither with her *g's*. „ II ii 2
I must set The *g* at Ludgate. „ II ii 409
I saw Lord William Howard By torchlight, and his *g*; „ II iii 30
At the park gate he hovers with our *g's*. „ II iv 16
These Kentish ploughmen cannot break the *g's*. „ II iv 18
broken thro' the *g's* And gone to Ludgate. „ II iv 20
The *g's* are all driven in, skulk into corners „ II iv 54
A gracious *g* Truly; shame on them! „ II iv 57
And tear you piecemeal: so you have a *g*. „ IV ii 37
There are Hot Gospellers even among our *g's*— „ V v 103
When being forced aloof from all my *g*, *Harold* IV iii 16
fought men Like Harold and his brethren, and his *g* Of English. V ii 180
I have my *g* about me. *The Cup* I iii 14
Guard (verb) men-at-arms *G* my poor dreams for England. *Queen Mary* I v 154
To *g* and keep you whole and safe „ II ii 246
The lion needs but roar to *g* his young; „ III v 123
not the living rock Which *g's* the land. *Harold* I ii 121
voice of any people is the sword That *g's* them, „ II ii 136
to *g* the land for which He did forswear himself— „ V ii 161
To *g* this bird of passage to her cage; *Becket* I i 329
my men will *g* you to the gates. „ I i 402
G from the stroke that dooms thee after death „ IV ii 270
high Heaven *g* thee from his wantonness, *Foresters* I ii 121
And there be men-at-arms to *g* her. „ I ii 158
Guarded The men that *g* England to the South *Harold* IV iii 209
Guardsman Our *g* hath but toil'd his hand and foot, „ V i 200
Our *guardsmen* have slept well, since we came in? „ V i 207
Guernsey in *G*, I watch'd a woman burn; *Queen Mary* V iv 16
Guess *G* what they be. *Edith.* He cannot *g* who knows. *Harold* I ii 135
But on conditions. Canst thou *g* at them? „ II ii 343
might chance—perchance—To *g* their meaning. „ IV i 139
How should *you g* What manner of beast it is? *The Cup* I ii 370
if but to *g* what flowers Had made it; *The Falcon* 429
Guess'd You are more than *g* at as a heretic, *Queen Mary* III iv 93

H

Hail'd As we past, Some *h*, some hiss'd us. *Queen Mary* II ii 61
Hair (*See also* **'Air**) her red *h* all blown back, She shrilling „ II ii 70
as red as she In *h* and cheek ; „ II ii 76
The common barber clipt your *h*, „ IV ii 131
No *h* is harm'd. „ V i 161
and held up by the *h* ? „ V ii 22
Let me first put up your *h* ; „ V ii 232
Philip ! quick ! loop up my *h* ! „ V ii 535
Your Philip hath gold *h* and golden beard ; There must be ladies many with *h* like mine. *Feria.* Some few of Gothic blood have golden *h*, „ V iii 56
Heard, heard— *Harold.* The wind in his *h* ? *Harold* III i 371
and a blessed *h* Of Peter, and all France, „ III ii 148
Holy Father strangled him with a *h* Of Peter, „ V ii 46
I ask'd A ribbon from her *h* to bind it with ; *The Falcon* 359
a bat flew out at him In the clear noon, and hook'd him by the *h*, *Foresters* II ii 98
Hair'd *See* **Fair-hair'd**
Hair's-breadth Mine eye most true to one *h-b* of aim. „ IV 694
Hale (robust) *See* **Haäle**
Hale (verb) stop the heretic's mouth ! *H* him away ! *Queen Mary* IV iii 283
H him hence ! *Harold* II i 108
Haled *H* thy shore-swallow'd, armour'd Normans „ II ii 57
Ye *h* this tonsured devil into your courts ; *Becket* I iii 387
Half (*See also* **Haäfe**) Flower, she ! *H* faded ! *Queen Mary* I iv 61
His buzzard beak and deep-incavern'd eyes *H* fright me. „ I iv 268
and the remission Of *h* that subsidy levied on the people, „ I v 115
which every now and then Beats me *h* dead : „ I v 525
The sire begets Not *h* his likeness in the son. „ II i 55
And the *h* sight which makes her look so stern, „ II ii 322
'tis not written *H* plain enough. „ II iii 66
Thine is a *h* voice and a lean assent. „ III i 311
Out crept a wasp, with *h* the swarm behind. „ III iii 49
one *h* Will flutter here, one there. „ III vi 196
Till I myself was *h* ashamed for him. „ IV ii 171
myself *H* beast and fool as appertaining to it ; „ IV iii 415
There's *h* an angel wrong'd in your account ; „ V iii 1
I say not this, as being *H* Norman-blooded, *Harold* I i 169
That marriage was *h* sin. „ I ii 53
I see the goal and *h* the way to it.— „ I ii 196
And yon huge keep that hinders *h* the heaven. „ II ii 228
Better leave undone Than do by *halves*— „ II ii 496
Thou art *h* English. Take them away ! „ V ii 135
an' I be *h* dog already by this token, *Becket* I iv 218
I'll go back again. I hain't *h* done yet. „ I iv 259
or foreign cousins, not *h* speaking The language of the land. „ II i 135
Not *h her* hand—no hand to mate with *her*, „ II i 189
But the King hath bought *h* the College of Redhats. „ II ii 374
Trodden one *h* dead ; one *h*, but half-alive, „ V i 63
He loses *h* the meed of martyrdom Who will be martyr when he might escape. „ V ii 278
Hugh, I know well thou hast but *h* a heart „ V iii 129
They are thronging in to vespers—*h* the town. „ V iii 139
One *h* besotted in religious rites. *The Cup* I i 74
close not yet the door upon a night That looks *h* day. „ I ii 389
If I be not back in *h* an hour, Come after me. „ I ii 438
How many of you are there ? *Publius.* Some *h* a score. „ I iii 13
The camp is *h* a league without the city ; „ I iii 89
Beside this temple *h* a year ago ? „ II 393
H a breakfast for a rat ! *The Falcon* 123
H a tit and a hern's bill. „ 131
Have we not *h* a score of silver spoons ? *Filippo.* *H* o' one, my lord ! *Count.* How *h* of one ? „ 405
H an hour late ! why are you loitering here ? *Prom. of May* II 324
I am *h* afraid to pass. „ II 328
H a score of them, all directed to me— „ II 721
could it look But *h* as lovely. „ III 491
they have trodden it for *h* a thousand years, *Foresters* I i 333
and he hath seized On *h* the royal castles. „ I iii 83
Half (*continued*) I have paid him *h*. That other thousand— *Foresters* II i 465
I trust *H* truths, good friar : „ IV 950
Some hunter in day-dreams or *h* asleep. „ IV 1088
Halfabitical (alphabetical) *H* ! Taäke one o' the young 'uns fust, *Prom. of May* III 31
Half-afraid Still I am *h-a* to meet her now. „ I 488
Half-Alfgar thence a king may rise Half-Godwin and *h-A*, *Harold* IV i 144
Half-alive one half, but *h-a*, Cries to the King. *Becket* V i 64
Half-born I must—I will !—Crush it *h-b* ! *Harold* I i 359
Half-dozen for I've been on my knees every day for these *h-d* years *The Falcon* 185
Half-drown'd my faith would seem Dead or *h-d*, *Queen Mary* IV ii 98
Half-Godwin thence a king may rise *H-G* and half-Alfgar, *Harold* IV i 144
Half-hanged he hath *h-h* himself in the rope of the Church, *Becket* III iii 75
Half-rag *h-r*, half-sore—beggars, poor rogues „ I iv 81
Half-ruin'd The house *h-r* ere the lease be out ; *Queen Mary* V ii 66
Half-shamed I seem *h-a* at times to be so tall. „ V ii 423
Half-sore half-rag, *h-s*—beggars, poor rogues *Becket* I iv 82
Half-Spanish Hard-natured Queen, *h-S* in herself, *Queen Mary* IV iii 424
Half-waked world as yet, my friend, Is not *h-w* ; „ II i 228
Half-way I am *h-w* down the slope—will no man stay me ? *Becket* II ii 148
Those sweet tree-Cupids *h-w* up in heaven, *Foresters* III 35
Half-witted *H-w* and a witch to boot ! „ II i 375
But sickly, slight, *h-w* and a child, *Harold* II ii 571
Halidome By my *h* I felt him at my leg still. *Foresters* IV 627
Hall (*See also* **Dining-hall**) Far liefer had I in my country *h* *Queen Mary* III i 43
Is this a place To wail in, Madam, what ! a public *h*. „ V i 213
foes in Edward's *h* To league against thy weal. *Harold* I i 32
And Tostig in his own *h* on suspicion „ II ii 295
At banquet in this *h*, and hearing me— „ IV iii 93
I held it with him in his English *h's*, „ V ii 128
The veriest Galahad of old Arthur's *h*. *Becket*, *Pro.* 129
In mine own *h*, and sucking thro' fools' ears „ I iii 360
trumpets in the *h's*, Sobs, laughter, cries : „ V ii 367
Philip Edgar of Toft *H* in Somerset. *Prom. of May* II 438
One Philip Edgar of Toft *H* in Somerset Is lately dead. „ II 445
I have been telling her of the death of one Philip Edgar of Toft *H*, Somerset. „ II 706
'O' the 17th, Philip Edgar, o' Toft *H*, Soomerset.' „ II 712
last time When I shall hold my birthday in this *h* : *Foresters* I ii 90
sat Among my thralls in my baronial *h* „ II i 61
Hall (all) ye'll think more on 'is little finger than *h* my hand at the haltar. *Prom. of May* I 112
Hall-door Shut the *h-d's*. *Becket* V ii 532
Hallus (always) Foälks doesn't *h* knaw thessens ; *Prom. of May* I 28
h a-fobbing ma off, tho' ye knaws I love ye. „ I 107
thaw 'e knaws I was *h* ageän heving schoolmaster i' the parish ! „ I 186
h hup at sunrise, and I'd drive the plow straäit as a line „ I 368
H about the premises ! „ I 434
but I *h* gi'ed soom on 'em to Miss Eva at this time o' year. „ II 15
But *h* ud stop at the Vine-an'-the-Hop, „ II 311
and I wur *h* scaäred by a big word ; „ III 33
Ye sees the holler laäne be *h* sa dark i' the arternoon, „ III 93
Halt That business which we have in Nottingham—— *Little John.* *H* ! *Foresters* III 231
Church and Law, *h* and pay toll ! „ IV 429
Haltar (altar) ye'll think more on 'is little finger than hall my hand at the *h*. *Prom. of May* I 113
Haman will hang as high As *H*. *Foresters* IV 752
Hammer (s) Anvil on *h* bang— *Harold* IV iii 161
H on anvil, *h* on anvil. „ IV iii 162
set the Church This day between the *h* and the anvil— *Becket* I iii 585
Hampton Court In *H C* My window look'd upon the corridor ; *Queen Mary* V ii 458
Hand (s) (*See also* **Left-hand**) took her *h*, call'd her sweet sister, „ I i 80
h, Damp with the sweat of death, „ I ii 32

Hand (s) (*continued*) I love you, Lay my life in your *h's*. *Queen Mary* I iv 105
I left her with rich jewels in her *h*, " I iv 242
Mary of England, joining *h's* with Spain, " I v 298
a formal offer of the *h* Of Philip ? " I v 349
For Philip comes, one *h* in mine, " I v 515
The formal offer of Prince Philip's *h*. " I v 588
counts on you And on myself as her two *h's* ; " II ii 105
And arm and strike as with one *h*, " II ii 292
I feel most goodly heart and *h*, " II ii 352
His in whose *h* she drops ; " III i 112
I cannot lift my *h's* unto my head. " III i 240
See there be others that can use their *h's*. " III i 243
She had no desire for that, and wrung her *h's*, " III i 385
with her poor blind *h's* feeling—' where is it ? " III i 407
which God's *h* Wrote on her conscience, " III i 421
where you gave your *h* To this great Catholic King. " III ii 91
From stirring *h* or foot to wrong the realm. " III iii 60
The sword Is in her Grace's *h* to smite with. " III iv 90
What, if a mad dog bit your *h*, my Lord, " III iv 205
Their hour is hard at *h*, " III iv 426
with my *h's* Milking the cow ? (repeat) *Queen Mary* III v 87, 94, 101
Rose *h* in *h*, and whisper'd, ' come away ! *Queen Mary* III v 148
By seeking justice at a stranger's *h* " IV i 20
To reach the *h* of mercy to my friend. " IV i 65
By mine own self—by mine own *h* ! O thin-skinn'd *h* and jutting veins, " IV ii 203
papers by my *h* Sign'd since my degradation—by this *h* " IV iii 243
since my *h* offended, having written Against my heart, my *h* shall first be burnt, So I may come to the fire. " IV iii 247
gather'd with his *h's* the starting flame, And wash'd his *h's* and all his face therein, " IV iii 336
Gardiner wur struck down like by the *h* o' God " IV iii 516
I could see that many silent *h's* Came from the crowd " IV iii 582
Then Cranmer lifted his left *h* to heaven, " IV iii 608
' This hath offended—this unworthy *h* ! ' " IV iii 614
they clapt their *h's* Upon their swords when ask'd ; " V i 173
The *h's* that write them should be burnt clean off " V ii 190
And, like a thief, push'd in his royal *h* ; " V ii 467
How her *h* burns ! (repeat) " V ii 552, 616
your *h* Will be much coveted ! What a delicate one ! " V iii 43
King in armour there, his *h* Upon his helmet. " V v 30
there is the right *h* still Beckons me hence. " V v 137
To sleek and supple himself to the king's *h*. *Harold* I i 150
Our Tostig loves the *h* and not the man. " I i 156
to turn and bite the *h* Would help thee " I i 382
Join *h's*, let brethren dwell in unity ; " I i 397
I have but bark'd my *h's*. " II i 5
Run thou to Count Guy ; he is hard at *h*. " II i 55
let fly the bird within the *h*, " II ii 66
Thou hast but seen how Norman *h's* can strike, " II ii 171
have thy conscience White as a maiden's *h*, " II ii 284
He tore their eyes out, sliced their *h's* away, " II ii 389
while thy *h's* Are palsied here, " II ii 454
God and the sea have given thee to our *h's*— " II ii 549
And grateful to the *h* that shielded him, " II ii 586
Lay thou thy *h* upon this golden pall ! " II ii 699
but take back thy ring. It burns my *h*— " III ii 186
that reach'd a *h* Down to the field beneath it, " IV i 44
Somewhere hard at *h*. Call and she comes. " IV i 185
join our *h's* before the hosts, That all may see. " IV i 241
these poor *h's* but sew, Spin, broider— " IV iii 9
I saw the *h* of Tostig cover it. " IV iii 81
Cannot *h's* which had the strength To shove " IV iii 136
And be thy *h* as winter on the field, " V i 132
Our guardsman hath but toil'd his *h* and foot, I *h*, foot, " V i 201
Fain had I kept thine earldom in thy *h's* " V i 276
I have had it fashion'd, see, to melt my *h*. " V i 423
Stigand, With *h's* too limp to brandish iron— " V i 449
wicked sister clapt her *h's* and laugh'd ; " V ii 48
we should have a *h* To grasp the world with, " V ii 191

Hand (s) (*continued*) be facile to my *h's*. Now is my time. *Becket*, *Pro.* 219
Thou hast but to hold out thy *h*. " *Pro.* 412
He sued my *h*. I shook at him. " I i 273
May the *h* that next Inherits thee be but as true " I i 357
Hath often laid a cold *h* on my heats, " I i 384
Church must play into the *h's* of kings ; " I ii 68
Shall *h's* that do create the Lord be bound " I iii 94
lay My crozier in the Holy Father's *h's*, " I iii 125
For, like a son, I lift my *h's* to thee. " I iii 264
He sat down there And dropt it in his *h's*, " I iii 324
wouldst deliver Canterbury To our King's *h's* again, " I iii 581
Which came into thy *h's* when Chancellor. " I iii 653
Cornwall's *h* or Leicester's : they write marvellously alike. " I iv 51
if thou hast not laid *h's* upon me ! " I iv 212
let the *h* of one To whom thy voice is all her music, " II i 176
happy boldness of this *h* hath won it Love's alms, " II i 182
Not half *her h*—no *h* to mate with *her*, " II i 189
Life on the *h* is naked gipsy-stuff ; " II i 193
to stay his *h* Before he flash'd the bolt. " II i 274
I here deliver all this controversy Into your royal *h's*. " II ii 137
primm'd her mouth and put Her *h's* together— " III i 76
Give me thy *h*. My Lords of France and England, " III iii 226
I might deliver all things to thy *h*— " III iii 270
bosom never Heaved under the King's *h* " IV ii 189
My lord, we know you proud of your fine *h*, " IV ii 261
so still I reach'd my *h* and touch'd ; " V ii 235
I cannot bear a *h* upon my person, " V iii 20
At the right *h* of Power— " V iii 193
Into Thy *h's*, O Lord—into Thy *h's* !— " V iii 196
There is my *h*—if such a league there be. *The Cup* I ii 103
For I have always play'd into their *h's*, " I iii 150
More than once You have refused his *h*. " II 43
clasp a *h* Red with the sacred blood of Sinnatus ? " II 83
So shook within my *h*, that the red wine Ran down " II 202
See here—I stretch my *h* out—hold it there. " II 210
and my *h's* are too sleepy To lift it off. " II 530
Shame on her that she took it at thy *h's*, *The Falcon* 61
The pleasure of his eyes—boast of his *h*— " 222
who could trace a *h* So wild and staggering ? " 438
having his right *h* Lamed in the battle, " 444
He gave me his *h* : " 836
ye'll think more on 'is little finger than hall my *h* at the haltar. *Prom. of May* I 112
fur him as be handy wi' a book bean't but haäfe a *h* at a pitchfork. " I 188
he's walking to us, and with a book in his *h*. " I 220
storm is hard at *h* will sweep away Thrones, " I 517
Come, give me your *h* and kiss me " I 564
Owd Steer's gotten all his grass down and wants a *h*, " II 222
From the farm Here, close at *h*. " II 361
what full *h's*, may be Waiting you in the distance ? " II 510
But give me first your *h* : " II 525
She gave her *h*, unask'd, at the farm-gate ; " II 625
should walk *h* in *h* together down this valley of tears, " III 191
The lady gave her *h* to the Earl, The maid her *h* to the man. (repeat) *Foresters* I i 16, 92
That is no true man's *h*. I hate hidden faces. " I ii 245
A finger of that *h* which should be mine " I ii 299
and warm *h's* close with warm *h's*, " I iii 20
Your *h's*, your *h's* ! " I iii 127
Your *h's* again. " I iii 164
old hag tho' I be, I can spell the *h*. " II i 351
And capering *h* in *h* with Oberon. " II i 498
fell'st into the *h's* Of these same Moors " II i 563
What sparkles in the moonlight on thy *h* ? " II i 583
O hold thy *h* ! this is our Marian. " II ii 36
call Kate when you will, for I am close at *h*. " III 51
bulrush now in this right *h* For sceptre, " III 76
all that live By their own *h's*, the labourer, the poor priest ; " III 165
if ever A Norman damsel fell into our *h's*, " III 181

Hand (s) (*continued*) we have fallen into the *h's* Of Robin Hood. (repeat) *Foresters* III 233, 298
Give me thy *h* on that? *Marian.* Take it. „ IV 66
Give me thy *h*, Much; I love thee. At him, Scarlet! „ IV 309
My *h* is firm, Mine eye most true to one hair's-breadth of aim. „ IV 693
Our rebel Abbot then shall join your *h's*, „ IV 934
Give me that *h* which fought for Richard there. „ IV 1029
Hand (verb) *H* me the casket with my father's sonnets. *Queen Mary* II i 43
H it me, then! I thank you. „ IV ii 44
King would act servitor and *h* a dish to his son; *Becket* III iii 139
Might not your courtesy stoop to *h* it me? „ IV ii 296
Handed *See* **Two-handed**
Handedness *See* **Left-handedness, Under-handedness**
Hand-in-hand (*See also* **Hand**) Is strength less strong when *h-i-h* with grace? *Becket* V ii 540
Handle In all that *h's* matter of the state *Harold* I i 412
h all womankind gently, and hold them in all honour, *Foresters* I i 99
Handled They shall be *h* with all courteousness. „ IV 102
Handsome and he so *h*—and bless your sweet face, *The Falcon* 197
Handy fur him as be *h* wi' a book bean't but haäfe a hand at a pitchfork. *Prom. of May* I 187
Hang All *h's* on her address, And upon you, Lord Mayor. *Queen Mary* II ii 54
Gentleman? a thief! Go *h* him. „ II iii 76
H him, I say. „ II iii 80
He has gambled for his life, and lost, he *h's*. „ II iii 92
may but *h* On the chance mention of some fool „ III v 42
After a riot We *h* the leaders, „ IV i 74
H's all my past, and all my life to be, „ IV iii 219
A man may *h* gold bracelets on a bush, *Harold* II i 87
they should *h* Cliff-gibbeted for sea-marks; „ II i 96
Were there no boughs to *h* on, Rivers to drown in? *The Cup* I ii 78
Must all Galatia *h* or drown herself? „ I ii 87
I am like to *h* myself on the hooks. *The Falcon* 121
while our Robin's life *H's* by a thread, *Foresters* IV 385
You will all of you *h*. „ IV 580
Let us *h*, so thou dance meanwhile; „ IV 581
we will *h thee*, prince or no prince, sheriff or no sheriff. „ IV 583
twist it round thy neck and *h* thee by it. „ IV 688
will *h* as high As Haman. „ IV 750
Hang'd (*See also* **Half-hanged**) A hundred here and hundreds *h* in Kent. *Queen Mary* III i 2
There were not many *h* for Wyatt's rising. „ V ii 8
I hope they whipt him. I would have *h* him. *Becket, Pro.* 16
ye but degraded him Where I had *h* him. „ I iii 392
H at mid-day, their traitor of the dawn *The Cup* II 123
thaw they *h* ma at 'Size fur it. *Prom. of May* II 697
Hanging (*See also* **A-lolluping**) *h* down from this The Golden Fleece— *Queen Mary* III i 80
Hapless *H* doom of woman happy in betrothing! „ V ii 364
Our *h* brother, Tostig—He, and the giant King of Norway, *Harold* III ii 121
O *h* Harold! King but for an hour! „ V i 257
Happen *See* **'Appen**
Happen'd ever have *h* thro' the want Of any or all of them. *Prom. of May* III 546
Happier it would seem this people Care more for our brief life in their wet land, Than yours in *h* Spain. *Queen Mary* III vi 64
H he than I. „ V ii 520
upon thine eyelids, to shut in A *h* dream. *Harold* I ii 127
and pray in thy behalf For *h* homeward winds „ II ii 198
the living Who fought and would have died, but *h* lived, If *h* be to live; „ IV iii 72
Whispering 'it will be *h*,' and old faces Press round us, *Foresters* I iii 18
I should be *h* for it all the year. „ II i 163
Thou art *h* than thy king. Put him in chains. „ IV 837
Happiest but after that Might not St. Andrew's be her *h* day? *Queen Mary* III ii 123
Sit down here: Tell me thine *h* hour. „ V v 79
Happiest (*continued*) being King And happy! *h*, Lady, in my power To make you happy. *The Cup* II 239
Happily Ay, Madam, *h*. *Mary.* Happier he than I. *Queen Mary* V ii 519
Happiness Well, Madam, this new *h* of mine? „ III ii 208
we were not made One flesh in *h*, no *h* here; „ V ii 150
What is the strange thing *h*? „ V v 78
My liege, your will and *h* are mine. *Becket* III iii 43
I would that *h* were gold, that I *The Cup* II 223
If marriage ever brought a woman *h* *Prom. of May* III 639
But lack of *h* in a blatant wife. *Foresters* I iii 132
Happy (*See also* **'Appy**) Well, sir, I look for *h* times, *Queen Mary* I i 99
A *h* morning to your Majesty. *Mary.* And I should some time have a *h* morning; „ I v 243
You are *h* in him there, „ I v 454
I am *h* in him there. *Renard.* And would be altogether *h*, Madam, „ I v 457
Be *h*, I am your friend. „ II iii 123
Seem'd as a *h* miracle to make glide— „ III ii 29
No, cousin, *h*—*H* to see you; never yet so *h* „ III ii 86
True, cousin, I am *h*. „ III ii 113
Good news have I to tell you, news to make Both of us *h*— „ III ii 188
by and by Both *h*! „ III v 157
your Grace, your Grace, I feel so *h*: „ III v 250
My life is not so *h*, no such boon, „ IV i 130
ever looking to the *h* haven Where he shall rest at night, „ IV iii 579
Hapless doom of woman *h* in betrothing! „ V ii 364
gorgeous Indian shawl That Philip brought me in our *h* days!— „ V ii 540
it was hoped Your Highness was once more in *h* state „ V ii 571
I am *h* you approve it. „ V iii 63
Dead or alive you cannot make him *h*. „ V v 71
I trust that God will make you *h* yet. „ V v 76
and babble all the way As if itself were *h*. „ V v 87
Ah, those days Were *h*. „ V v 240
A *h* one—whereby we came to know Thy valour *Harold* II ii 201
Ay, and perchance a *h* one for thee, „ II ii 203
Ay, that *h* day! A birthday welcome! *h* days and many! „ V i 430
I have found him, I am *h*. „ V ii 81
And Harold was most *h*. „ V ii 134
thou wast not *h* taking charge Of this wild Rosamund *Becket* I i 391
Nor am I *h* having charge of her— „ I i 394
at her side, Among these *h* dales, „ II i 157
The *h* boldness of this hand hath won it Love's alms, „ II i 182
and known Nothing but him—*h* to know no more, „ III i 224
So many *h* hours alone together, „ III iii 39
but God and his free wind grant your lordship a *h* home-return „ III iii 327
I am not so *h* I could not die myself, „ IV ii 87
Fair Sir, a *h* day to you! *The Cup* I i 188
our hearts, our prophet hopes Let in the *h* distance, „ I ii 414
I would be *H*, and make all others *h* so „ I iii 29
speak I now too mightily, being King And *h*! happiest, Lady, in my power To make you *h*. „ II 239
make me *h* in my marriage! „ II 274
Drink and drink deep, and thou wilt make me *h*. „ II 383
Thou hast drunk deep enough to make me *h*. „ II 425
This all too *h* day, crown—queen at once. „ II 451
h was the prodigal son, For he return'd *The Falcon* 140
and tell her all about it and make her *h*? „ 183
made more *h* than I hoped Ever to be again. „ 769
And I am *h*! *Giovanna.* And I too, Federigo. „ 927
Many *h* returns of the day, father. *Prom. of May* I 350
I am sure I wish her *h*. „ I 479
that should make you *h*, if you love her! „ I 547
all the world is beautiful If we were *h*, „ I 578
As *h* as the bees there at their honey „ I 606
I have been in trouble, but I am *h*—I think, quite *h* now. „ I 788
and make them *h* in the long barn, „ I 791
'O *h* lark, that warblest high Above thy lowly nest, „ III 199
He said we had been most *h* together, „ III 327
I doubt not I can make you *h*. *Dora.* You make me *H* already. „ III 641

Happy (*continued*) Make her *h*, then, and I forgive you. *Dora.* *H*! *Prom. of May* III 666
So *h* in herself and in her home— „ III 756
As *h* as any of those that went before. *Foresters* I ii 129
—my ring—I am *h*—should be *h*. „ I iii 2
Sleep, *h* soul! all life will sleep at last. „ I iii 48
Both be *h*, and adieu for ever and for evermore— „ II ii 196
Shall I be *h*? *H* vision, stay. „ II ii 199
Could live as *h* as the larks in heaven, „ III 82
We leave but *h* memories to the forest. „ IV 1070
I am most *h*—Art thou not mine?—and *h* that our King „ IV 1096

Harass'd Why am I follow'd, haunted, *h*, watch'd? *Harold* II ii 248

Harbour At last a *h* opens; but therein Sunk rocks— *Queen Mary* V v 213

Harbour (arbour) Didn't I spy 'em a-sitting i' the woodbine *h* togither? *Prom. of May* I 125

Hard (*See also* **Stone-hard**) That's a *h* word, legitimate; what does it mean? *Queen Mary* I i 11
My *h* father hated me; „ I v 80
And that were *h* upon you, my Lord Chancellor. „ I v 158
And those *h* men brake into woman-tears, „ I v 564
the provinces Are *h* to rule and must be hardly ruled; „ III ii 201
You are *h* to please. „ III iv 154
Their hour is *h* at hand, their 'dies Iræ,' „ III iv 426
H upon both. „ III v 18
This *h* coarse man of old hath crouch'd to me „ IV ii 169
May God help you Thro' that *h* hour! „ IV ii 196
'How *h* it is For the rich man to enter into Heaven;' Let all rich men remember that *h* word. „ IV iii 203
and awaay betimes wi' dree *h* eggs for a good pleace at the burnin'; „ IV iii 489
and therefore God Is *h* upon the people. „ V i 176
strike *h* and deep into The prey they are rending from her— „ V ii 267
Look'd *h* and sweet at me, and gave it me. „ V v 95
Tostig says true; my son, thou art too *h*, *Harold* I i 206
The boy would fist me *h*, and when we fought I conquer'd, „ I i 444
Run thou to Count Guy; he is *h* at hand. „ II i 55
would make the *h* earth rive To the very Devil's horns, „ II ii 739
If e'er the Norman grow too *h* for thee, „ III i 12
a war-crash, and so *h*, So loud, that, by St. Dunstan, old St. Thor— „ IV iii 145
Harsh is the news! *h* is our honeymoon! „ IV iii 229
Take it and wear it on that *h* heart of yours—there. *Becket, Pro.* 373
On this left breast before so *h* a heart, „ *Pro.* 376
Nay, if I took and translated that *h* heart into our Provençal facilities, „ *Pro.* 380
Make it so *h* to save a moth from the fire? „ I i 283
What doth *h* murder care For degradation? „ I iii 393
Would God they had torn up all By the *h* root, „ II ii 209
To assail our Holy Mother lest she brood Too long o'er this *h* egg, „ V ii 253
it is thou Hath set me this *h* task, *The Falcon* 237
It will be *h*, I fear, To find one shock upon the field „ 300
She smiles at him—how *h* the woman is! „ 661
My brother! my *h* brother! „ 895
The storm is *h* at hand will sweep away Thrones, *Prom. of May* I 517
I fear this Abbot is a heart of flint, *H* as the stones of his abbey. *Foresters* I ii 270
Our cellar is *h* by. Take him, good Little John, and give him wine. „ II i 468
Art thou not *h* upon them, my good Robin? „ III 221
I should be *h* beset with thy fourscore. „ IV 179

Harder might be *h* upon thee, if met in a black lane „ III 223

Hardest The *h*, cruellest people in the world, *Queen Mary* II i 100

Hard-grain'd And grafted on the *h-g* stock of Spain— „ IV iii 426

Hard-hearted Out upon all *h-h* maidenhood! *Foresters* IV 50

Hard-natured *H-n* Queen, half-Spanish in herself, *Queen Mary* IV iii 424

Hardness spare us the *h* of your facility? *Becket, Pro.* 386
Father, I am so tender to all *h*! „ I i 316

Hardrada (King of Norway) (*See also* **Harold**) the giant King of Norway, Harold *H*— *Harold* III ii 123

HH

Hardrada (King of Norway) (*continued*) little help without our Saxon carles Against *H*. *Harold* IV i 36
striking at *H* and his madmen I had wish'd „ IV iii 17
May all invaders perish like *H*! „ IV iii 78

Hard Tillery (artillery) 'Listed for a soädger, Miss, i' the Queen's Real *H T*. *Prom. of May* III 109

Hardy Too *h* with thy king! *Harold* I i 198

Hare As find a *h's* form in a lion's cave. *Becket* I iii 177
Venison, and wild boar, *h*, geese, *Foresters* IV 191

Harebell Bluebell, *h*, speedwell, bluebottle, *Prom. of May* I 97

Harem new term Brought from the sacred East, his *h*? *Foresters* IV 705

Harfleur To-morrow we will ride with thee to *H*, *Harold* II ii 196
To-morrow will we ride with thee to *H*. „ II ii 648
To-morrow will I ride with thee to *H*. „ II ii 770
For when I rode with William down to *H*, „ III i 83

Hark *H*! the trumpets. *Queen Mary* I i 64
H, there is battle at the palace gates, „ II iv 47
H, how those Roman wolfdogs howl and bay him! „ IV iii 354
H! Madam! *Eleanore.* Ay, *Becket* III ii 14
H! Is it they? Coming! „ V iii 15
The murderers, *h*! Let us hide! „ V iii 46
H! Dora, some one is coming. *Prom. of May* III 339

Harken'd She hath *h* evil counsel— *Queen Mary* I v 54

Harlot She play the *h*! never. „ III vi 136
They are so much holier than their *h's* son *Harold* V ii 11
kill with knife or venom One of his slanderous *h's*? *Becket* IV ii 411

Harm (s) and thou canst not come to *h*. *Queen Mary* I iii 68
sharper *h* to England and to Rome, Than Calais taken. „ V ii 29
What *h*? She hath but blood enough to live, *Harold* I ii 160
He meant no *h* nor damage to the Church. *Becket* I iii 216
and should *h* come of it, it is the Pope Will be to blame— „ I iii 220
or any *h* done to the people if my jest be in defence of the Truth? „ II ii 339
I never meant you *h* in any way. „ IV ii 106
May work them grievous *h* at times, *The Falcon* 821
And what *h* will that do you, *Prom. of May* III 360

Harm (verb) If they dared To *h* you, I would blow this Philip *Queen Mary* I iv 290
In some such form as least may *h* your Grace. „ I v 225
That our commission is to heal, not *h*; „ III iii 185
Than you would *h* your loving natural brother „ IV iii 189
H him not, *h* him not! have him to the fire! „ IV iii 284
scorn'd her too much To *h* her. *Becket* IV ii 394
God's full curse Shatter you all to pieces if ye *h* One of my flock! „ V iii 135
They shall not *h* My guest within my house. *The Cup* I ii 326
It is but pastime—nay, I will not *h* thee. *Foresters* II i 554
Came stepping o'er him, so as not to *h* him— „ IV 538

Harm'd No hair is *h*. *Queen Mary* V i 161
the poor thunder Never *h* head. *Harold* I ii 233

Harming And bind him in from *h* of their combs. *Queen Mary* III iii 57
came and went before our day, Not *h* any: *Harold* I i 133

Harmony This burst and bass of loyal *h*, *Queen Mary* II ii 285

Harold (Earl of Wessex, afterwards King of England) (*See also* **Harold the Saxon**) *H*, I will not yield thee leave to go. *Harold* I i 256
Son *H*, I will in and pray for thee. „ I i 267
My wise head-shaking *H*? „ I i 361
H always hated him. „ I i 429
How *H* used to beat him! „ I i 432
lest the king Should yield his ward to *H's* will. „ I ii 159
When *H* goes and Tostig, shall I play The craftier Tostig with him? „ I ii 163
If he found me thus, *H* might hate me; „ I ii 172
H Hear the king's music, all alone with him, „ I ii 193
Peace-lover is our *H* for the sake Of England's „ I ii 197
A sacrifice to *H*, a peace-offering, „ I ii 203
thou assured By this, that *H* loves but Edith? „ I ii 210
that I—That *H* loves me—yea, and presently That I and *H* are betroth'd—and last—Perchance that *H* wrongs me; „ I ii 222
And when doth *H* go? *Morcar.* To-morrow— „ I ii 237
H? Earl of Wessex! „ II i 82
Fly thou to William; tell him we have *H*. „ II i 111
they are not like to league With *H* against *me*. „ II ii 54

Harold (Earl of Wessex, afterwards King of England) (*continued*)
England our own Thro' *H's* help, *Harold* II ii 79
that these may act On *H* when they meet. „ II ii 92
I can but love this noble, honest *H*. „ II ii 95
Yea, lord *H*. „ II ii 243
Thou canst not, *H*; Our Duke is all between thee „ II ii 313
'This *H* is not of the royal blood, „ II ii 354
O speak him fair, *H*, for thine own sake. „ II ii 395
H, I do not counsel thee to lie. „ II ii 416
H, for my sake and for thine own! „ II ii 607
H, if thou love thine Edith, ay. „ II ii 622
H, I am thy friend, one life with thee, „ II ii 649
Am I *H*, *H*, son Of our great Godwin? „ II ii 791
Ask me for this at thy most need, son *H*, „ III i 15
Come, *H*, shake the cloud off! „ III i 73
Let *H* serve for Tostig! *Queen.* *H* served Tostig so ill, he cannot serve for Tostig! „ III i 159
H? Gurth, where am I? „ III i 193
Sign it, my good son *H*, Gurth, and Leofwin, „ III i 199
No, no, but *H*. I love him: „ III i 241
but their Saints Have heard thee, *H*. „ III i 254
Spare and forbear him, *H*, if he comes! „ III i 299
And let him pass unscathed; he loves me, *H*! „ III i 302
on thee remains the curse, *H*, if thou embrace her: „ III i 316
noble *H*, I would thou couldst have sworn. „ III i 325
It is *H*! *H* the King! *Harold.* Call me not King, but *H*. „ III ii 31
H, *H*! *Harold.* The voice of Gurth! „ III ii 114
can but pray For *H*—pray, pray, pray— „ III ii 195
but our help Is *H*, king of England. „ IV i 11
Hear King *H*! he says true! „ IV i 60
And Alfgar hates King *H*. „ IV i 125
Old man, *H* Hates nothing; „ IV i 128
Aldwyth, *H*, Aldwyth! „ IV i 132
Thine own meaning, *H*, To make all England one, „ IV i 140
H, *H* and Aldwyth! „ IV i 244
Forward! Forward! *H* and Holy Cross! „ IV i 269
O brother, brother, O *H*— „ IV ii 63
Conjured the mightier *H* from his North „ IV ii 68
Hail! *H*! Aldwyth! hail, bridegroom and bride! „ IV iii 1
Hail, *H*, Aldwyth! Bridegroom and bride! „ IV iii 42
answer which King *H* gave To his dead namesake, „ IV iii 109
'To thrust our *H's* throne from under him? „ IV iii 126
Thou hast lost thine even temper, brother *H*! „ V i 95
A lake that dips in William As well as *H*. „ V i 187
Son *H*, I thy King, who came before To tell thee „ V i 234
O hapless *H*! King but for an hour! „ V i 258
O *H*! husband! Shall we meet again? „ V i 360
England Is but her king, and thou art *H*! „ V i 376
thou art *H*, I am Edith! „ V i 392
H and Holy Cross! (repeat) *Harold* V i 439, 519, 662
I have a power—would *H* ask me for it— *Harold* V i 451
Power now from *H* to command thee hence „ V i 455
God save King *H*! „ V i 489
So perish all the enemies of *H*! „ V i 505
H and God Almighty! „ V i 526
Against the shifting blaze of *H's* axe! „ V i 587
Look out upon the hill—is *H* there? „ V i 670
O *H*, *H*—Our *H*—we shall never see him more. „ V ii 2
H slain?—I cannot find his body. „ V ii 18
I tell thee, girl, I am seeking my dead *H*. „ V ii 43
H? Oh no—nay, if it were—my God, „ V ii 74
And what body is this? *Edith.* *H*, thy better! „ V ii 88
with all his rooftree ringing '*H*,' „ V ii 130
When all men counted *H* would be king, And *H* „ V ii 132
have I fought men Like *H* and his brethren, „ V ii 179

Harold (King of Norway) (*See also* **Hardrada**) the giant King of Norway, *H* Hardrada— „ III ii 123
as having been so bruised By *H*, king of Norway; „ IV i 10

Harold (Mr. Philip Edgar) (*See also* **'Arold, Edgar, Philip, Philip Edgar, Philip Harold, Philip Hedgar**) That fine, fat, hook-nosed uncle of mine, old *H*, *Prom. of May* I 510
Not *H*! 'Philip Edgar, Philip Edgar!' „ II 240
Might I ask your name? *Harold.* *H*. „ II 394

Harold (Mr. Philip Edgar) (*continued*) Nay—now—not one, for I am Philip *H*. *Prom. of May* II 451
Dobbins, or some other, spy Edgar in *H*? Well then, I must make her Love *H* first, and then she will forgive Edgar for *H's* sake. „ II 675
Half a score of them, all directed to me—*H*. „ II 723
My name is *H*! Good day, Dobbins! „ II 726
an' whether thou calls thysen Hedgar or *H*, „ II 738
matched with my *H* is like a hedge thistle by a garden rose. „ III 175
And this lover of yours—this Mr. *H*—is a gentleman? „ III 281
your own name Of *H* sounds so English „ III 610
Master Hedgar, *H*, or whativer They calls ye, „ III 726

Harold the Saxon (Earl of Wessex, afterwards King of England) (*See also* **Harold**) have loved *H t S*, or Hereward the Wake. *Foresters* I i 228

Ha Rou *H R*! *H R*! (repeat) *Harold* V i 437, 528, 631, 650, 661, 664

Harp (s) his finger on her *h* (I heard him more than once) *Harold* IV i 204
gloom of Saul Was lighten'd by young David's *h*. *Queen Mary* V ii 359

Harp (verb) That he should *h* this way on Normandy? *Harold* I i 270

Harried Hath *h* mine own cattle—God confound him! „ IV iii 190

Harrowing *See* **A-harrowin'**

Harry (great ship) he look'd the Great *H*, You but his cockboat; *Queen Mary* V ii 146

Harry (Henry) Bolingbroke such a one As *H B* hath a lure in it. „ I iv 10
H o B Had holpen Richard's tottering throne to stand, Could *H* have foreseen that all our nobles „ III i 112

Harry (Henry the Eighth) (*See also* **Henry**) Mary, the lawful and legitimate daughter of *H* the Eighth! „ I i 9
Our sovereign Lady by King *H's* will; „ II ii 268
I am *H's* daughter, Tudor, and not Fear. „ II iv 52
But then what's here? King *H* with a scroll. „ III i 260
I am *H's* daughter: „ III v 116
then King *H* look'd from out a cloud, „ IV ii 6

Harry (Henry the Seventh) born i' the tail end of old *H* the Seventh. „ I i 43
born true man at five in the forenoon i' the tail of old *H*, „ I i 46

Harry (Henry the Sixth?) It's *H*! *Third Citizen.* It's Queen Mary. „ I i 34

Harsh *H* is the news! hard is our honeymoon! *Harold* IV iii 229
but my voice is *h* here, not in tune, *Becket, Pro.* 349
For once in France the King had been so *h*, „ V ii 140
Even this brawler of *h* truths— *Foresters* IV 948

Hartist (artist) What's a *h*? I doänt believe he's iver *Prom. of May* I 129

Harvest (adj.) the *h* moon is the ripening of the harvest, *Becket, Pro.* 362

Harvest (s) Were scatter'd to the *h* . . . *Harold* IV iii 211
which we Inheriting reap an easier *h*. *Becket* II ii 194
find one shock upon the field when all The *h* has been carried. *The Falcon* 302

Harvestless *H* autumns, horrible agues, plague— *Queen Mary* V i 98

Harwich On all the road from *H*, night and day; „ V ii 579

Haste (s) with what *h* I might To save my royal cousin. „ II iv 77
in *h* put off the rags They had mock'd his misery with, „ IV iii 589

Haste (verb) That *h's* with full commission from the Pope „ III ii 51

Hasten harm at times, may even *H* their end. *The Falcon* 823

Hastings (Francis, second Earl of Huntingdon) Sent Cornwallis and *H* to the traitor, *Queen Mary* II ii 31

Hastings (town in Sussex) lay them both upon the waste sea-shore At *H*, *Harold* V ii 161

Hat *See* **'At**

Hatch But *h* you some new treason in the woods. *Queen Mary* I v 465

Hatch'd This is the fifth conspiracy *h* in France; „ V i 297

Hatchet before you can eat it you must hack it with a *h*, *Foresters* II i 285

Hate (s) (*See also* **Heart-hate**) her *h* Will burn till you are burn'd. *Queen Mary* I ii 58
In hope to charm them from their *h* of Spain. „ III vi 82
to fuse Almost into one metal love and *h*,— „ III vi 182
sow'd therein The seed of *H*, it blossom'd Charity. „ IV i 172
carrion-nosing mongrel vomit With *h* and horror. „ IV iii 450
when she touch'd on thee, She stammer'd in her *h*; *Harold* I ii 37
If *H* can kill, And Loathing wield a Saxon battle-axe— „ V i 412
his, a *h* Not ever to be heal'd. *Becket* I i 178
We have but one bond, her *h* of Becket. „ II i 165

Hate (s) (*continued*) And mine a bitterer illegitimate *h*, A bastard *h* — *Becket* II i 173
That sow this *h* between my lord and me! — „ II ii 272
I follow out my *h* and thy revenge. — „ IV ii 151
And private *h's* with our defence of Heaven. — „ V ii 52
and all her loves and *h's* Sink again into chaos. — *Foresters* I ii 329

Hate (verb) (*See also* **Haäte**) this bald priest, and she that *h's* me, — *Queen Mary* I iv 282
My sister cowers and *h's* me. — „ I v 83
Would I marry Prince Philip, if all England *h* him? — „ I v 139
Lord of Devon is a pretty man. I *h* him. — „ I v 616
no old news that all men *h* it. — „ II i 17
and the beds I know. I *h* Spain. — „ II i 185
Ay, since you *h* the telling it. — „ III i 89
With all the rage of one who *h's* a truth — „ III vi 143
H me and mine: — „ V i 85
They *h* *me* also for my love to you, My Philip; — „ V i 95
He *h's* Philip; He is all Italian, and he *h's* the Spaniard; — „ V ii 54
but I know it of old, he *h's* me too; — „ V ii 60
And *h's* the Spaniard—fiery-choleric, — „ V ii 92
Clarence, they *h* me; even while I speak — „ V ii 214
'Your people *h* you as your husband *h's* you.' — „ V ii 336
My people *h* me and desire my death. — „ V ii 345
My husband *h's* me, and desires my death. — „ V ii 347
I *h* myself, and I desire my death. — „ V ii 351
Give *me* the lute. He *h's* me! — „ V ii 363
Even for that he *h's* me. — „ V ii 380
Edward loves him, so Ye *h* him. — *Harold* I i 429
I am sure she *h's* thee, Pants for thy blood. — „ I ii 38
H not one who felt Some pity for thy hater! — „ I ii 43
H him? I could love him More, — „ I ii 141
Griffyth I hated: why not *h* the foe Of England? — „ I ii 145
If he found me thus, Harold might *h* me; — „ I ii 172
many among our Norman lords *H* thee for this, — „ II ii 546
Juggler and bastard—bastard—he *h's* that most— — „ II ii 773
Our sister *h's* us for his banishment; — „ III i 78
And Alfgar *h's* King Harold. — „ IV i 125
Old man, Harold *H's* nothing; — „ IV i 129
Morcar, it is all but duty in her To *h* me; I have heard she *h's* me. — „ IV i 154
If not, they cannot *h* the conqueror. — „ IV i 215
I *h* King Edward, for he join'd with thee — „ IV ii 12
I *h* myself for all things that I do. — „ IV ii 45
I *h* thee, and despise thee, and defy thee. — „ IV ii 79
I loved him as I *h* This liar who made me liar. — „ V i 411
how your Grace must *h* him. *Eleanor*. *H* him? — *Becket*, *Pro.* 434
break down our castles, for the which I *h* him. — „ *Pro.* 448
The Church will *h* thee. — „ I iii 566
He *h's* my will, not me. — „ II ii 27
I *h* a split between old friendships as I *h* the dirty gap — „ II ii 380
I *h* him for his insolence to all. — „ V i 226
I *h* him for I *h* him is my reason, And yet I *h* him for a hypocrite. — „ V i 230
I *h* the man! What filthy tools our Senate — *The Cup* I i 155
I could *h* her for it But that she is distracted. — „ II 178
My brother *h's* him, scorns The noblest-natured man — *The Falcon* 257
I *h* tears. Marriage is but an old tradition. I *h* Traditions, ever since my narrow father, — *Prom. of May* I 489
It seems to me that I *h* men, ever since my sister left us. — „ II 79
But she *h's* Edgar. — „ II 672
Scorn! I *h* scorn! A soul with no religion— — „ III 531
A gallant Earl. I love him as I *h* John. — *Foresters* I i 191
yet I *h* him for his want of chivalry. — „ I ii 107
I *h* him, I *h* the man. I may not *h* the King — „ I ii 113
Beware of John! *Marian*. I *h* him. — „ I ii 215
I *h* hidden faces. (repeat) — „ I ii 245, 250

Hated (*See also* **World-hated**) My hard father *h* me; My brother rather *h* me — *Queen Mary* I v 81
Old Sir Thomas would have *h* it. — „ II i 18
So *h* here! I watch'd a hive of late; — „ III iii 46
because to persecute Makes a faith *h*, — „ III iv 116
Harold always *h* him. — *Harold* I i 429
Griffyth I *h*: why not hate the foe Of England? — „ I ii 145
There spake Godwin, Who *h* all the Normans; — „ III i 252
Hated (*continued*) Out, beast monk! I ever *h* monks. — *Harold* V i 76
Roger of York, you always *h* him, — *Becket* V i 9
I always *h* boundless arrogance. — „ V i 12
I held for Richard, and I *h* John. — *Foresters* II i 52

Hateful make her as *h* to herself and to the King, — *Becket*, *Pro.* 526
Fool! I will make thee *h* to thy King. — „ I ii 92
Save from some *h* cantrip of thine own. — „ V i 140

Hate-philtre such A strong *h-p* as may madden him— — „ IV ii 458

Hater Hate not one who felt Some pity for thy *h*! — *Harold* I ii 44

Hatest Thou *h* him, *h* him. — „ III i 172
Crouch even because thou *h* him; — *Becket* IV ii 223

Hating *See* **World-hating**

Hatred the *h* of another to us Is no true bond — *Queen Mary* I iv 44
h of the doctrines Of those who rule, which *h* by and by Involves the ruler — „ III iv 159
'Love of this world is *h* against God.' — „ IV iii 173
yet what *h* Christian men Bear to each other, — „ IV iii 182

Haughtiness have marked the *h* of their nobles; — „ II i 168

Haughty Madam, methinks a cold face and a *h*. — „ I v 197
They call him cold, *H*, ay, worse. — „ I v 432
Why, ev'n the *h* prince, Northumberland, — „ III i 147

Haul *H* like a great strong fellow at my legs, — *Harold* II i 11

Haunt There *h* some Papist ruffians hereabout — *Queen Mary* III v 174
My men say The fairies *h* this glade;— — *Foresters* II ii 101

Haunted Why am I follow'd, *h*, harrass'd, — *Harold* II ii 248
A lying devil Hath *h* me— — „ V i 318
is *h* by The ghosts of the dead passions of dead men; — *Prom. of May* II 274

Haven looking to the happy *h* Where he shall rest — *Queen Mary* IV iii 579
bays And *h's* filling with a blissful sea. — *The Cup* II 236

Haveringatte-Bower nightingales in *H-B* Sang out — *Harold* I ii 18

Havings Your *h* wasted by the scythe and spade— — *Queen Mary* II ii 276

Havock To make free spoil and *h* of your goods. — „ II ii 186

Havock'd That *h* all the land in Stephen's day. — *Becket* I i 242

Hawk (s) Sick for an idle week of *h* and hound — *Harold* I i 103
a feeder Of dogs and *h's*, and apes, — *Becket* I i 80
H, buzzard, jay, the mavis and the merle, — *Foresters* I iii 115
To fright the wild *h* passing overhead, — „ III 318

Hawk (verb) and hunt and *h* beyond the seas! — *Harold* I i 229
I will *h* and hunt In Flanders. — „ I i 259
had past me by To hunt and *h* elsewhere, — „ II ii 28

Hawking (*See also* **A-hawking**) Gone *h* on the Nene, — *Becket* I iii 2
when he came last year To see me *h*, he was well enough: — *The Falcon* 313

Hawking-phrases then I taught him all our *h-p*. — „ 314

Hawthorn filch the linen from the *h*, — *Foresters* III 199

Haxed (asked) Why if Steer han't *h* schoolmaster to dinner, — *Prom. of May* I 185

Hay *See* **Haäy**

Haycock *See* **Haäycock**

Hayfield (*See also* **Haäyfield**) you should be in the *h* looking after your men; — *Prom. of May* II 47
You had better attend to your *h*. — „ II 123
that you did not come into the *h*. — „ III 82
You are as good as a man in the *h*. — „ III 106

Haystack and a plum-pudding as big as the round *h*. — „ I 794

Head (s) (*See also* **'Eäd**) draw back your *h's* and your horns — *Queen Mary* I i 4
be no peace for Mary till Elizabeth lose her *h*.' — „ I iii 5
If Elizabeth lose her *h*— — „ I iii 88
with an ass's, not a horse's *h*, — „ I iii 169
Stand further off, or you may lose your *h*. *Courtenay*. I have a *h* to lose for your sweet sake. — „ I iv 129
No—being traitor Her *h* will fall: — „ I v 60
a *h* So full of grace and beauty! — „ I v 63
When the *h* leapt—so common! — „ I v 477
For all that I can carry it in my *h*. — „ II i 88
If you can carry your *h* upon your shoulders. — „ II i 89
I'll have my *h* set higher in the state; — „ II i 250
Have made strong *h* against ourselves and you. — „ II ii 146
I cannot lift my hands unto my *h*. — „ III i 240
He, whom the Father hath appointed *H* — „ III iii 207
I had held my *h* up then. — „ III iii 246
What! will she have my *h*? — „ III iii 278
lost the *h's* Wherewith they plotted in their treasonous malice, — „ III iv 3

Head (s) (*continued*) Lift *h*, and flourish; *Queen Mary* III iv 24
his brother's, nay, his noble mother's, *H* fell— „ III iv 296
I kept my *h* for use of Holy Church; „ III iv 359
Gardiner would have my *h*. „ III v 118
I never lay my *h* upon the pillow But that I think, „ III v 131
Cranmer is *h* and father of these heresies, „ IV i 76
I say they have drawn the fire On their own *h's*: „ IV iii 381
become Hideously alive again from *h* to heel, „ IV iii 447
but Cranmer only shook his *h*, „ IV iii 602
and of his holy *h*—For Alva is true son of the true church— „ V i 158
I have broken off the *h*. „ V ii 3
More merciful to many a rebel *h* That should have fallen, „ V ii 5
like the bloodless *h* Fall'n on the block, „ V ii 20
He drew this shaft against me to the *h*, „ V ii 81
Methought some traitor smote me on the *h*. „ V ii 253
sent on foreign travel, Not lost his *h*. „ V ii 491
and make Down for their *h's* to heaven! „ V iv 8
all the sins of both The houses on mine *h*— *Harold* I ii 206
the poor thunder Never harm'd *h*. „ I ii 233
Upon the *h's* of those who walk'd within— „ II ii 393
dogs' food thrown upon thy *h*. „ II ii 432
The crime be on his *h*—not bounden—no. „ II ii 670
Tostig, raise my *h*! „ III i 158
raise his *h*, for thou hast laid it low! „ III i 163
wilt thou bring another, Edith, upon his *h*? „ III i 262
and the second curse Descend upon thine *h*, „ III ii 49
Since Griffyth's *h* was sent To Edward, „ IV i 221
may give that egg-bald *h* The tap that silences. „ V i 91
hand and foot, I hand, foot, heart and *h*. „ V i 202
and *h's* And arms are sliver'd off and splinter'd „ V i 539
As thine own bolts that fall on crimeful *h's* „ V i 566
And when the Gascon wine mounts to my *h*, *Becket, Pro.* 114
That rang Within my *h* last night, „ I i 71
be we not a-supping with the *h* of the family? „ I iv 179
A hundred of the wisest *h's* from England, „ II ii 171
asked our mother if I could keep a quiet tongue i' my *h*, „ III i 119
He bows, he bares his *h*, he is coming hither. „ III iii 34
with the Holy Father astride of it down upon his own *h*. „ III iii 78
Hugh, how proudly you exalt your *h*! „ V ii 455
And lose his *h* as old St. Denis did. „ V ii 480
Save that dear *h* which now is Canterbury, „ V iii 6
They howl for thee, to rend thee *h* from limb. *The Cup* I ii 321
that same *h* they would have play'd at ball with „ II 126
and rears his root Beyond his *h*, „ II 285
you that have *not* the *h* of a toad, *The Falcon* 90
And softly placed the chaplet on her *h*. „ 363
Set, as you say, so lightly on her *h*, „ 535
and dipt your sovereign *h* Thro' these low doors, „ 867
I think I scarce could hold my *h* up there. *Prom. of May* I 689
has promised to keep our *h's* above water; „ III 170
—is a gentleman? *Dora*. That he is, from *h* to foot. „ III 282
Now if she kiss him, I will have his *h*. *Foresters* I ii 146
Why comest thou like a death's *h* at my feast? „ I ii 210
She broke my *h* on Tuesday with a dish. „ I iii 133
A houseless *h* beneath the sun and stars, „ II i 64
A price is set On this poor *h*; „ II i 74
or the *h* of a fool, or the heart of Prince John, „ IV 212
he will, He will—he feels it in his *h*. „ IV 646
Then on the instant I will break thy *h*. „ IV 681
Thou hast saved my *h* at the peril of thine own. „ IV 795

Head (verb) And *h* them with a lamer rhyme of mine, *Queen Mary* II i 29
He *h's* the Church against the King with thee. *Becket* I iii 245
if the followers Of him, who *h's* the movement, *Foresters* II i 701

Headache And heal your *h*. *Queen Mary* I iv 146
what *h*? Heartache, perchance; not *h*. „ I iv 147
to snore away his drunkenness Into the sober *h*,— *Becket* I i 373
I have a dizzying *h*. Let me rest. „ V i 88

Headed *See* **Bull-headed, Hot-headed**

Heading *H* the holy war against the Moslem, *Foresters* IV 818

Headless To make me *h*. *Queen Mary* I i 41

Headlong both of us Too *h* for our office. *Becket* II ii 290
The cataract typed the *h* plunge and fall Of heresy to the pit: *Queen Mary* III iv 140

Head-shaking My wise *h-s* Harold? *Harold* I i 361

Headship So fierce against the *H* of the Pope, *Queen Mary* III iii 11
How should he bear the *h* of the Pope? „ III iii 29
bolster'd up The gross King's *h* of the Church, „ III iv 246

Headsman when the *h* pray'd to be forgiven, „ III i 393

Headstone Then have my simple *h* by the church, „ III v 113

Headstrong A strain of hard and *h* in him. *Becket, Pro.* 234

Heal And *h* your headache. *Queen Mary* I iv 146
That our commission is to *h*, not harm; „ III iii 185
We two together Will help to *h* your son— *The Falcon* 923

Heal'd Cannot be *h* by stroking. *Queen Mary* III iv 274
his, a hate, Not ever to be *h*. *Becket* I i 179

Health He wrecks his *h* and wealth on courtesans, *Queen Mary* I v 167
H to your Grace! „ IV i 41
yet it is a day to test your *h* Ev'n at the best: „ IV ii 117
Here—all of you—my lord's *h*. *Becket* I iv 156
That *h* of heart, once ours, „ III iii 266
Greeting and *h* from Synorix! (repeat) *The Cup* II 41, 130
Has lost his *h*, his eyesight, even his mind. *Prom. of May* III 767
Shall drink the *h* of our new woodland Queen. *Foresters* III 314
till the green earth drink Her *h* along with us „ III 351
Drink to the *h* of our new Queen o' the woods, „ III 368
We drink the *h* of thy new Queen o' the woods. „ III 372
The king's good *h* in ale and Malvoisie. „ IV 968

Healthful A right rough life and *h*. *Queen Mary* III v 260

Heap she sits naked by a great *h* of gold in the middle of the wood, *Becket* III ii 21
she sat Stone-dead upon a *h* of ice-cold eggs. „ V ii 239

Heap'd And all the *h* experiences of life, „ I i 154

Hear (*See also* **'Ëär**) Did you *h* (I have a daughter in her service *Queen Mary* I i 75
I *h* that he too is full of aches and broken „ I i 124
h what the shaveling has to say for himself. „ I iii 17
Hush—*h*! *Bourne*. —and so this unhappy land, „ I iii 19
Peace! *h* him; let his own words damn the Papist. „ I iii 52
Her Majesty *H's* you affect the Prince— „ I iv 82
She *h's* you make your boast that after all „ I iv 87
If Mary will not *h* us—well—conjecture— „ I iv 117
You speak too low, my Lord; I cannot *h* you. „ I iv 125
Nay, if by chance you *h* of any such, „ I iv 175
Your Grace will *h* her reasons from herself. „ I iv 230
I will not *h* of him. „ I v 173
Madam, my master *h's* with much alarm, „ I v 249
Will you *h* why? Mary of Scotland,— „ I v 283
I see but the black night, and *h* the wolf. „ I v 413
not to *h* the nightingales, But hatch you some new treason „ I v 464
See that you neither *h* them nor repeat! „ I v 576
It breaks my heart to *h* her moan at night „ I v 603
I *h* them stirring in the Council Chamber. „ I v 628
I do not *h* from Carew or the Duke „ II i 1
Doesn't your worship *h*? „ II i 20
Until I *h* from Carew and the Duke. „ II i 122
from Penenden Heath in hope To *h* you speak. „ II i 153
Your Highness *h's* This burst and bass of loyal harmony, „ II ii 284
H us now make oath To raise your Highness „ II ii 288
I *h* that Gardiner, coming with the Queen, „ II ii 308
I have ears to *h*. *Gardiner*. Ay, rascal, if I leave thee ears to *h*. „ III i 250
I *h* this Legate's coming To bring us absolution „ III i 430
You'll *h* of me again. *Bagenhall*. Upon the scaffold. „ III i 474
Ay; but I *h* she hath a dropsy, lad, „ III ii 223
Did you *h* 'em? were you by? „ III iv 395
Well, they shall *h* my recantation there. „ IV ii 199
Ye *h* him, and albeit there may seem „ IV iii 31
Yourselves shall *h* him speak. „ IV iii 110
proclaim Your true undoubted faith, that all may *h*. „ IV iii 115
H him, my good brethren. „ IV iii 227
H what I might—another recantation Of Cranmer at the stake. *Paget*. You'd not *h* that. „ IV iii 299
Nay, you sicken *me* To *h* you. „ IV iii 452
I cum behind tha, gall, and couldn't make tha *h*. „ IV iii 466
'not till I *h's* ez Latimer and Ridley be a-vire;' „ IV iii 508
I *h* unhappy rumours—nay, I say not, I believe. „ V i 34
Alas! the Council will not *h* of war. „ V i 164
Lost in a wilderness where none can *h*! „ V ii 383
She neither sees nor *h's*, „ V ii 405

Hear (*continued*) And love to *h* bad tales of Philip. *Queen Mary* v ii 429
Much changed, I *h*, Had put off levity „ v ii 509
There's the Queen's light. I *h* she cannot live. „ v iv 11
you curse so loud, The watch will *h* you. „ v iv 63
speak him sweetly, he will *h* thee. *Harold* I i 117
When didst thou *h* from thy Northumbria? *Tostig.* When did I *h* aught but this '*When*' from thee? „ I i 281
But thou canst *h* the best and wisest of us. „ I i 300
yet *h*! thine earldom, Tostig, hath been a kingdom. „ I i 303
I fain would *h* him coming! . . . „ I ii 5
And *h* my peregrine and her bells in heaven; „ I ii 131
Harold *H* the king's music, all alone with him, „ I ii 194
Come, Malet, let us *h*! „ II i 211
No more! I will not *h* thee—William comes. „ II ii 479
We *h* he hath not long to live. „ II ii 565
H King Harold! he says true! „ IV i 60
I *h* no more. *Margot.* *H* me again—for the last time. „ V i 7
H me again! Our Saints have moved the Church „ V i 39
H it thro' me. „ V i 62
I do not *h* our English war-cry. „ V i 651
That thou wilt *h* no more o' the customs. *Becket* I iii 255
Dost thou not *h*? „ I iii 267
till I *h* from the Pope I will suspend myself „ I iii 299
Art thou deaf? *Becket.* I *h* you. *Hilary.* Dost thou *h* those others? *Becket.* Ay! „ I iii 605
H first thy sentence! The King and all his lords— *Becket.* Son, first *h me*! „ I iii 670
Nay, but *h* thy judgment. „ I iii 682
H me son. As gold Outvalues dross, „ I iii 713
and when ye shall *h* it is poured out upon earth, „ I iv 36
wind of the dawn that I *h* in the pine overhead? „ II i 1
I will not *h* it. „ II i 211
we shall *h* him presently with clapt wing „ II ii 48
Out! I *h* no more. „ II ii 233
Grasshopper, grasshopper, Whoop—you can *h*. „ III i 103
I did not *h* aright, „ III i 235
I would not *h* him. „ III i 257
I *h* Margery: I'll go play with her. „ III i 274
I holla'd to him, but he didn't *h* me: „ III ii 26
I *h* the yelping of the hounds of hell. „ III ii 48
when he *h's* a door open in the house and thinks 'the master.' „ III iii 98
Did you *h* the young King's quip? „ III iii 146
The King shall never *h* of me again, „ IV ii 102
Do you *h* me? Believe or no, I care not. „ IV ii 352
Threats! threats! ye *h* him. „ V ii 465
You *h* them, brother John; „ V ii 534
Can you not *h* them yonder like a storm, „ V ii 624
Do you *h* that? strike, strike. „ V iii 161
Artemis, Artemis, *h* us, O Mother, *h* us, and bless us! *The Cup* II 1
H thy people who praise thee! „ II 5
H thy priestesses hymn thy glory! „ II 7
Artemis, Artemis, *h* him, Ionian Artemis! „ II 277
all the fleeted wealth of kings And peoples, *h*. „ II 290
hurls the victor's column down with him That crowns it, *h*. „ II 297
gulf and flatten in her closing chasm Domed cities, *h*. Whose lava-torrents blast and blacken a province To a cinder, *h*. Whose winter-cataracts find a realm and leave it A waste of rock and ruin, *h*. „ II 301
Artemis, Artemis, *h* her, Ephesian Artemis! *Camma.* Artemis, Artemis, *h* me, Galatian Artemis! „ II 310
Why then the Goddess *h's*. „ II 388
H that, my bird! Art thou not jealous of her? *The Falcon* 5
h that you are saying behind his back „ 106
by your leave if you would *h* the rest, The writing. „ 529
H that, my lady! (repeat) „ 636, 652
You *h*, Filippo? My good fellow, go! „ 690
Master Dobson, did you *h* what I said? *Prom. of May* I 172
Heaven *h's* you, Philip Edgar! „ I 760
And *he* would *h* you even from the grave. „ I 762
p'raps ye *h's* 'at I soomtimes taäkes a drop too much; „ II 107
I told her I should *h* her from the grave. „ II 244
You—did *you h* a cry? „ III 652
Sweet, do you *h* me? „ III 678
You wrong me there! *h*, *h* me! „ III 775

Hear (*continued*) You *h*! *Sheriff.* Yes, my lord, fear not. *Foresters* I ii 31
but no! We *h* he is in prison. „ II i 34
Did we not *h* the two would pass this way? „ II i 197
Ay, do you *h*? There may be murder done. „ II i 339
Evil fairy! do you *h*? „ II ii 116
Up with you, all of you, out of it! *h* and obey. „ II ii 184
Fifty leagues Of woodland *h* and know my horn, „ III 104
will you not *h* one of these beggars' catches? „ III 405
You *h* your Queen, obey! „ III 464
Will *h* our arrows whizzing overhead, „ IV 1090

Heard (*See also* **'Eärd, Heärd, Heerd**) Have we not *h* of her in Edward's time, *Queen Mary* I iv 18
I have *h*, the tongue yet quiver'd with the jest „ I v 475
hast thou ever *h* Slanders against Prince Philip „ I v 569
but I have *h* a thousand such. „ I v 579
and your worship's name *h* into Maidstone market, „ II i 63
I have *h* One of your Council fleer and jeer „ II ii 392
I had *h* that every Spaniard carries „ III i 222
h She would not take a last farewell of him, „ III i 366
We *h* that you were sick in Flanders, cousin. „ III ii 33
Methinks the good land *h* me, „ III ii 57
I *h* An angel cry 'There is more joy in Heaven,'— „ IV ii 9
yet have *h* Of all their wretchedness. „ IV iii 211
Our prayers are *h*! „ IV iii 255
Have I not *h* them mock the blessed Host „ IV iii 365
And *h* these two, there might be sport for him. „ V ii 212
I never *h* him utter worse of you „ V ii 431
If ever I *h* a madman,—let's away! „ V iv 56
I had *h* of him in battle over seas, „ V v 33
I *h* from my Northumbria yesterday. *Harold* I i 331
I *h* from thy Northumberland to-day. „ I i 350
And he spoke—I *h* him— „ II ii 353
hast thou never *h* His savagery at Alençon,— „ II ii 381
I have *h* the Normans Count upon this confusion— „ II ii 457
We have *h* Of thy just, mild, and equal governance; „ II ii 689
Would he *h* me! O God, that I were in some wide, „ II ii 776
I have *h* a saying of thy father Godwin, „ III i 111
but their Saints Have *h* thee, Harold. „ III i 254
but those heavenly ears have *h*, „ III i 259
H, *h*— *Harold.* The wind in his hair? „ III i 370
that Archdeacon Hildebrand His master, *h* him, „ III ii 146
I have *h* she hates me. „ IV i 154
Ye *h* one witness even now. „ IV i 170
his finger on her harp (I *h* him more than once) „ IV i 205
but our old Thor *H* his own thunder again, „ IV iii 150
H how the war-horn sang, „ IV iii 157
H how the shield-wall rang, „ IV iii 159
And all the Heavens and very God: they *h*— „ V i 44
who made And *h* thee swear— „ V i 121
Nor seen, nor *h*; thine, „ V i 161
Our scouts have *h* the tinkle of their bells. „ V i 220
O God, the God of truth hath *h* my cry. „ V i 601
And I am *h*. „ V i 635
hast thou *h* this cry of Gilbert Foliot *Becket* I i 36
I *h* him swear revenge. „ I i 280
And *h* her cry 'Where is this bower of mine?' „ I ii 42
I have *h* him say He means no more; „ I iii 191
Yea, *h* the churl against the baron— „ I iii 365
have *h* say that if you boxed the Pope's ears „ II ii 369
have I Not *h* ill things of her in France? „ III i 231
like the gravedigger's child I have *h* of, trying to ring the bell, „ III iii 74
But I *h* say he had had a stroke, or you'd have *h* his horn „ IV i 53
I have *h* of such that range from love to love, „ IV ii 119
I have *h* of such—yea, even among those „ IV ii 123
Have we not *h* Raymond of Poitou, thine own uncle— „ IV ii 246
I *h* your savage cry. „ IV ii 320
knights, five hundred, that were there and *h*. Nay, you yourself were there: you *h* yourself. „ V ii 407
I *h* in Rome, This tributary crown may fall to you. *The Cup* I i 95
I have *h* them say in Rome, „ I i 136
I thought I *h* a footstep. „ I ii 11
you *h* him on the letter. „ I ii 279
I *h* a saying in Egypt, that ambition Is like the sea wave, „ I iii 137
I never *h* of this request of thine. „ II 394

Heard (*continued*) I have *h* these poisons May be walk'd down. *The Cup* II 474
I have *h* That, thro' his late magnificence *The Falcon* 226
Oh, Philip, Father *h* you last night. *Prom. of May* I 557
I have *h* of you. The likeness Is very striking. „ II 364
I never *h* her mention you. „ II 395
The painful circumstances which I *h*— „ II 402
I never *h* that he had a brother. „ III 152
I have *h* that 'your Lordship,' and 'your Ladyship,' and 'your Grace' are all growing old-fashioned! „ III 316
I *h* a voice, 'Girl, what are you doing there?' „ III 375
You *h* him say it was one of his bad days. „ III 469
I have *h* the Steers Had land in Saxon times; „ III 607
I may be outlaw'd, I have *h* a rumour. *Foresters* I ii 91
I *h* this Sheriff tell her he would pay „ I iii 5
I have *h* of them. Have they no leader? „ I iii 103
I have *h* him swear he will be even wi' thee. „ II i 344
silent blessing of one honest man Is *h* in heaven— „ III 322
Shamed a too trustful widow whom you *h* In her confession; „ III 386
I have *h* 'em in the market at Mansfield. „ III 406
We *h* Sir Richard Lea was here with Robin. „ IV 978
Heärd I ha' *h* 'im a-gawin' on 'ud make your 'air—God bless it!—stan' on end. *Prom. of May* I 134
and I *h* the winder—that's the winder at the end o' the passage, „ I 395
Heardst He said (thou *h* him) that I must not *Harold* II ii 260
Hearer confess Your faith before all *h's*; *Queen Mary* IV ii 80
Hearing Crave, in the same cause, *h* of your Grace. „ IV i 8
At banquet in this hall, and *h* me— *Harold* IV iii 93
If *h*, would have spurn'd her; *Becket* IV ii 346
the man himself, When *h* of that piteous death, *Prom. of May* II 500
Heart (*See also* **'Eart, Lion-heart**) A bold *h* yours to beard that raging mob! *Queen Mary* I iii 96
I meant True matters of the *h*. „ I iv 100
My h, my Lord, Is no great party in the state „ I iv 101
I have the jewel of a loyal *h*. „ I iv 247
You've a bold *h*; keep it so. „ I iv 269
Make all tongues praise and all *h's* beat for you. „ I v 117
take mine eyes, mine *h*, But do not lose me Calais. „ I v 128
I am not Queen Of mine own *h*, „ I v 523
It breaks my *h* to hear her moan at night „ I v 603
felt the faltering of his mother's *h*, „ II ii 83
I scarce have *h* to mingle in this matter, „ II ii 113
They have betray'd the treason of their *h's*: „ II ii 157
come to cast herself On loyal *h's* and bosoms, „ II ii 263
never whine Like that poor *h*, Northumberland, „ II ii 333
I feel most goodly *h* and hand, „ II ii 352
And hast not *h* nor honour. „ II iv 84
Blazed false upon her *h*. „ III i 70
and hurl'd our battles Into the *h* of Spain; „ III i 109
Her dark dead blood is in my *h* with mine. „ III i 349
If you have *h* to do it! „ III i 411
to-day My *h* beats twenty, when I see you, cousin. „ III ii 59
Is like the cleaving of a *h*; „ III vi 196
A day may save a *h* from breaking too. „ III vi 240
beget A kindness from him, for his *h* was rich, „ IV i 169
My *h* is no such block as Bonner's is: „ IV ii 174
Pray with one breath, one *h*, one soul for me. „ IV iii 104
doubt The man's conversion and remorse of *h*, „ IV iii 109
Against the truth I knew within my *h*, „ IV iii 241
since my hand offended, having written Against my *h*, „ IV iii 249
That might live always in the sun's warm *h*, „ V i 23
Reginald Pole, what news hath plagued my *h*? „ V ii 18
I am sad at *h* myself. „ V ii 159
I used to love the Queen with all my *h*— „ V ii 419
As far as France, and into Philip's *h*. „ V iii 19
Women, when I am dead, Open my *h*, „ V v 153
Adulterous to the very *h* of Hell. „ V v 163
Brave, wary, sane to the *h* of her— „ V v 224
I swear I have no *h* To be your Queen. „ V v 264
strike Their *h's*, and hold their babies up to it. *Harold* I i 35
will make his nippers meet in thine *h*; „ II i 77
It is the arrow of death in his own *h*— „ III i 405
where Tostig lost The good *h's* of his people. „ III ii 30

Heart (*continued*) hand and foot, I hand, foot, *h* and head. *Harold* V i 202
violent will that wrench'd All *h's* of freemen from thee. „ V i 279
Here fell the truest, manliest *h's* of England. „ V ii 58
Take it and wear it on that hard *h* of yours— *Becket, Pro.* 373
On this left breast before so hard a *h*, „ *Pro.* 376
translated that hard *h* into our Provençal facilities, „ *Pro.* 380
That the *h* were lost in the rhyme and the matter „ *Pro.* 383
My *h* is full of tears—I have no answer. „ *Pro.* 406
His *h* so gall'd with thine ingratitude, „ I iii 4
To lodge a fear in Thomas Becket's *h* „ I iii 176
That my poor heretic *h* would excommunicate „ II i 283
And push'd our lances into Saracen *h's*. „ II ii 95
in the dark *h* of the wood I hear the yelping „ III ii 47
That health of *h*, once ours, „ III iii 266
scared the red rose from your face Into your *h*? „ IV ii 75
While this but leaves me with a broken *h*, „ IV ii 174
shall not I, the Queen, Tear out her *h*— „ IV ii 409
and send Her whole *h's* heat into it, „ V ii 255
full mid-summer in those honest *h's*. „ V ii 374
You should attend the office, give them *h*. „ V ii 599
I know well thou hast but half a *h* „ V iii 130
I thank you from my *h*. *The Cup* I ii 211
Yea,—with our eyes,—our *h's*, „ I ii 412
That this brave *h* of mine should shake me so, „ I iii 38
I have it in my *h*—to the Temple—fly— „ I iii 111
found All good in the true *h* of Sinnatus, „ II 87
I have no *h* to do it. „ II 166
As in the midmost *h* of Paradise. „ II 186
fill all *h's* with fatness and the lust Of plenty— „ II 272
The stately widow has no *h* for me. *The Falcon* 30
you that have the face of an angel and the *h* of a—that's too positive! You that have a score of lovers and have not a *h* for any of them— „ 87
and *not* a *h* like the jewel in it— „ 91
cheek like a peach and a *h* like the stone in it— „ 93
Pride of his *h*—the solace of his hours— „ 223
I had no *h* to part with her for money. „ 326
We mounted, and we dash'd into the *h* of 'em. „ 630
best *h* that ever Beat for one woman. „ 667
No other *h* Of such magnificence in courtesy „ 722
a red fire woke in the *h* of the town, *Prom. of May* I 50
small *h* have I to dance. „ I 429
Keep up your *h* until we meet again. „ I 754
I wear it next my *h*. „ II 82
how should I, with this grief still at my *h*, „ II 91
O sir, you seem to have a *h*; „ II 468
But wherefore waste your *h* In looking „ II 503
the man has doubtless a good *h*, and a true and lasting love for me: „ III 171
Come, come, keep a good *h*! „ III 253
I do believe I lost my *h* to him the very first time we met, „ III 283
'Go home;' but I hadn't the *h* or face to do it. „ III 389
What is it Has put you out of *h*? „ III 501
It puts me in *h* Again to see you; but indeed the state Of my poor father puts me out of *h*. „ III 502
I think That I should break my *h*, „ III 556
—the *h*, O God!—the poor young *h* Broken „ III 679
broke the *h* That only beat for you; „ III 762
sits and eats his *h* for want of money to pay the Abbot. *Foresters* I i 4
but I keep a good *h* and make the most of it, „ I i 28
it answers, I am thine to the very *h* of the earth— „ I i 337
I fear this Abbot is a *h* of flint, „ I ii 268
when I loved A maid with all my *h* „ I ii 297
Sleep, mournful *h*, and let the past be past! „ I iii 47
There are no *h's* like English *h's* Such *h's* of oak „ II i 3
I have shot her thro' the *h*. *Kate.* He lies, my lord. I have shot *him* thro' the *h*. „ II i 98
That I had shot *him* thro' the *h*, „ II i 123
my *h* so down in my heels that if I stay, I can't run. „ II i 346
how to charm and waste the *h's* of men. „ II i 502
And drains the *h* and marrow from a man. „ II i 672
the bravest English *h* Since Hereward the Wake, „ II i 687
Elf, with spiteful *h* and eye, „ II ii 172

Heart (*continued*) And that would quite *un*man him, *h* and soul. *Foresters* III 30
And let them warm thy *h* to Little John. „ III 44
but I hold thee The husband of my *h*, „ III 140
and thy legs, and thy *h*, and thy liver, „ IV 204
or the head of a fool, or the *h* of Prince John, „ IV 213
so she glided up into the *h* O' the bottle, „ IV 244
flung His life, *h*, soul into those holy wars „ IV 407
He drove his knife into the *h* of the deer, „ IV 541
A woman's *h* is but a little thing, „ IV 656
Will chill the *h's* that beat for Robin Hood ! „ IV 1064

Heartache what headache ? *H*, perchance ; *Queen Mary* I iv 149

Heart-comfort *H-c* and a balsam to thy blood ? *Becket* I i 14

Hearted *See* **Brave-hearted, Great-hearted, Hard-hearted, High-hearted, Hollow-hearted, Poor-hearted**

Heartedest *See* **Human-heartedest**

Hearth with mine old hound Couch'd at my *h*, *Queen Mary* III i 46
The stranger at his *h*, and all his house— „ IV i 163
King Henry warms your traitors at his *h*. „ V i 124
Translating his captivity from Guy To mine own *h* at Bayeux, *Harold* II ii 43
Dabble your *h's* with our own blood. „ II ii 751
son of Orm, Gamel, at thine own *h*. „ IV ii 39
none could sit By his own *h* in peace ; *Becket* I iii 342
a son stone-blind Sat by his mother's *h* : „ V ii 106
One slow, fat, white, a burthen of the *h* ; „ V ii 212
I wouldn't have thy blood on my *h*. *Foresters* II i 356

Heart-hate fierce resolve and fixt *h-h* in men *Queen Mary* III vi 32

Heart-sick Better than *h-s*, friar. *Foresters* IV 674

Heart-wife so this Rosamund, my true *h-w*, Not Eleanor— *Becket, Pro.* 130

Heat (s) There must be *h*—there must be *h* enough *Queen Mary* III iv 26
A bookman, flying from the *h* and tussle, „ III iv 251
It is the *h* and narrowness of the cage „ III v 207
Gardiner out-Gardiners Gardiner in his *h*, „ III vi 26
men should bear their earthly *h's* Into yon bloodless world, *Harold* V i 284
Hath often laid a cold hand on my *h's*, *Becket* I i 384
Besides, we came away in such a *h*, „ II i 294
do much To rake out all old dying *h's*, „ II ii 114
Hell's own *h* So dwelt on that they rose „ II ii 204
Henry Says many a thing in sudden *h's*, „ IV ii 276
and send Her whole heart's *h* into it, „ V ii 255
h and fire Of life will bring them out, *Prom. of May* II 285
In that great *h* to wed her to the Sheriff *Foresters* II i 584
The bee buzz'd up in the *h*. „ IV 14
And the bee buzz'd down from the *h*. „ IV 20

Heat (verb) this ghastly glare May *h* their fancies. *Harold* I i 310
secret matter which would *h* the King against thee. *Becket, Pro.* 487
Why should you *h* yourself for such as these ? „ V ii 544
Employ us, *h* us, quicken us, help us, *The Cup* I iii 131
How few Junes Will *h* our pulses quicker ! *Foresters* IV 1062

Heated —we have eaten—we are *h*. Wine ! *The Cup* I ii 46

Heath ten thousand men on Penenden *H* all calling after *Queen Mary* II i 61
They roar for you On Penenden *H*, „ II i 106
fifty That follow'd me from Penenden *H* in hope „ II i 151
Of the Northumbrian helmet on the *h* ? *Harold* V i 145
No, but a shoal of wives upon the *h*, „ V i 147

Heath (Sir Nicholas) *See* **Nicholas, Nicholas Heath**

Heathen (adj.) Ay, cousin, as the *h* giant Had but to touch the ground, *Queen Mary* III ii 43
The *h* priesthood of a *h* creed ! *Becket* I iii 63
Cold, but look how the table steams, like a *h* altar ; „ I iv 69

Heathen (s) Why do the *h* rage ? „ V ii 628

Heathendom Out of the deep, deep night of *h*, *Queen Mary* III iii 173

Heathenism that Lucullus or Apicius might have sniffed it in their Hades of *h*, *Becket* III iii 118

Heather Walk'd at night on the misty *h* ; *Harold* III ii 5

Heaved that bosom never *H* under the King's hand *Becket* IV ii 189

Heaven (*See also* **'Eaven**) To him within there who made *H* and Earth ? *Queen Mary* I v 47
banks rolling incense, as of old, To *h*, „ I v 93
Yea, by *H*, The text—Your Highness knows it, „ I v 450
in his scared prayers *H* and earth's Maries ; „ II ii 88

Heaven (*continued*) Ah, *h* ! *Pole.* Unwell, your Grace ? *Queen Mary* III ii 84
Rise to the *h's* in grateful praise of Him „ III iii 165
With *h* for earth. „ III iii 201
That *h* wept and earth blush'd. „ III iv 193
pray *H* That you may see according to our sight. „ III iv 330
To yield the remnant of his years to *h*, „ III vi 211
All that is gracious in the breath of *h* „ III vi 225
soul descending out of *h* Into a body generate. „ IV i 35
An angel cry ' There is more joy in *H*,'— „ IV ii 11
By *H's* grace, I am more and more confirm'd. „ IV ii 21
On earth ; but saved in *h* By your recanting. „ IV ii 179
O God, Father of *H* ! O Son of God, „ IV iii 117
I have offended against *h* and earth „ IV iii 124
I am ashamed to lift my eyes to *h*, „ IV iii 127
' How hard it is For the rich man to enter into *H* ; ' „ IV iii 205
Either to live with Christ in *H* with joy, „ IV iii 220
find *H* or else hell ready to swallow me, „ IV iii 224
If ever, as *h* grant, we clash with Spain, „ IV iii 346
H help that this re-action not re-act „ IV iii 388
Then Cranmer lifted his left hand to *h*, „ IV iii 609
Why then to *h*, and God ha' mercy on him. „ IV iii 631
Have courage, your reward is *H* itself. „ V ii 109
and make Down for their heads to *h* ! „ V iv 8
It glares in *h*, it flares upon the Thames, *Harold* I i 29
To have the *h's* clear. „ I i 38
mean The doom of England and the wrath of *H* ? „ I i 47
Why should not *H* be wroth ? „ I i 53
Is there no reason for the wrath of *H* ? *Leofwin.* Why then the wrath of *H* hath three tails, The devil only one. „ I i 59
Stigand should know the purposes of *H*. *Stigand.* Not I. I cannot read the face of *h* ; „ I i 65
is this pendent hell in *h* A harm to England ? „ I i 76
religious fool, Who, seeing war in *h*, for *h's* credit „ I i 140
In *h* signs ! Signs upon earth ! „ I i 159
see Deeper into the mysteries of *h* Than thou, „ I i 200
Not stagger'd by this ominous earth and *h* : But *h* and earth are threads „ I i 208
Did not *H* speak to men in dreams of old ? „ I ii 94
and her bells in *h* ; And other bells on earth, which yet are *h's* ; „ I ii 132
thunder moulded in high *h* To serve the Norman purpose, „ II ii 33
yon huge keep that hinders half the *h*. „ II ii 229
Cleave *h*, and send thy saints that I may say „ II ii 785
two young wings To fly to *h* straight with. „ III i 26
swear To consecrate my virgin here to *h*— „ III i 276
all promises Made in our agony for help from *h* ? „ III i 288
more the love, the more acceptable The sacrifice of both your loves to *h*. No sacrifice to *h*, no help from *h* ; „ III i 349
there are signs in *h*— „ III i 358
H yield us more ! for better, „ III ii 71
Yon *h* is wroth with *thee* ? „ V i 39
And all the *H's* and very God : they heard— „ V i 43
a sigh With these low-moaning *h's*. „ V i 152
We give our voice against thee out of *h* ! „ V i 261
The sign in *h*—the sudden blast at sea— „ V i 378
Charged with the weight of *h* wherefrom they fall ! „ V i 567
Ye that are now of *h*, and see beyond „ V i 618
The Norman sends his arrows up to *H*, „ V i 667
twelve stars fell glittering out of *h* Into her bosom. *Becket* I i 47
Why should not *H* have so inspired the King ? „ I i 130
I ask no more. *H* bless thee ! hence ! „ I i 321
Lest there be battle between *H* and Earth, „ I iii 226
Strong—not in mine own self, but *H* ; „ I iii 537
and see it mounting to *H*, my God bless you, „ I iv 38
beggars, poor rogues (*H* bless 'em) „ I iv 83
and glass The faithful face of *h*— „ II i 161
dwelt on that they rose and darken'd *H*. „ II ii 206
said to the smoke, ' Go up, my son, straight to *H*.' „ II ii 319
if he move at all, *H* stay him, is fain to diagonalise. „ II ii 329
like Mahound's coffin hung between *h* and earth— „ II ii 362
child We waited for so long—*h's* gift at last— „ III i 14

Heaven (*continued*) All praise to *H*, and sweet St. Magdalen ! *Becket* III iii 234
Earth's falses are *h's* truths. " III iii 348
H help you ; get you hence in haste " IV ii 26
thy true home—the *h's*—cry out for thee " IV ii 132
I will fly with my sweet boy to *h*, " IV ii 238
To bless thine enemies—— *Becket.* Ay, mine, not *H's*. " V ii 26
lightnings that we think are only *H's* Flash sometimes out of earth against the *h's*. " V ii 36
And private hates with our defence of *H*. " V ii 53
to people *h* in the great day When God makes up his jewels. " V ii 496
He is not here—Not yet, thank *h*. O save him ! " V iii 17
Shall not *H* be served Tho' earth's last earthquake " V iii 39
Seen by the Church in *H*, the Church on earth— " V iii 98
open'd out The purple zone of hill and *h* ; *The Cup* I ii 408
cloudless *h* which we have found together " I ii 415
drew the light From *h* to brood upon her, " I iii 58
strike, make his feathers Glance in mid *h*. *The Falcon* 16
O *h's* ! the very letters seem to shake With cold, " 447
Here, or else well in *H*, where all is well. " 682
No other heart Of such magnificence in courtesy Beats—out of *h*. " 724
And so return—*H* help him !—to our son. " 861
H hears you, Philip Edgar ! *Prom. of May* I 760
H curse him if he come not at your call ! " I 764
The body !—*H's* ! I come ! " II 572
For all the blessed souls in *H* " III 10
to be realised all at once, or altogether, or anywhere but in *H* ? " III 187
I pray *H* we may not have to take to the rushes. *Foresters* I i 89
for the sake of the great blessed Mother in *h*, " I i 97
come as freely as *h's* air and mother's milk ? " I i 210
The high *H* guard thee from his wantonness, " I ii 121
while the lark flies up and touches *h* ! " I ii 316
topmost tree, that shoots New buds to *h*, " I iii 26
that worship for me which *H* knows I ill deserve— " I iii 161
and the blessed Queen of *H*, " II i 39
The groining hid the *h's* ; " II i 62
Thou comest a very angel out of *h*. " II i 105
Your *h* is vacant of your angel. " II i 109
—the Sheriff, and by *h*, Prince John himself " II i 173
Give it me, by *h*, Or I will force it from thee. " II i 594
Thou seem'st a saintly splendour out from *h*, " II i 607
forest lawns are all as bright As ways to *h*, " II i 632
When *h* falls, I may light on such a lark ! " III 12
Those sweet tree-Cupids half-way up in *h*, " III 36
Could live as happy as the larks in *h*, " III 83
silent blessing of one honest man Is heard in *h*— " III 322
Sweet *h's*, I could wish that all the land " IV 666
I breathe *H's* air, and *H* looks down on me, " IV 725

Heavenly I know He knew not, but those *h* ears have heard, *Harold* III i 258

Heavier Is it so much *h* than thy Chancellor's robe ? *Becket* I i 20
Not *h* than thine armour at Thoulouse ? " I i 25
Beware, Lord Legate, of a *h* crime Than heresy is itself ; *Queen Mary* III iv 221

Heavy Too *h* for me, this, off with it, Herbert ! *Becket* I i 18
h As thine own bolts that fall on crimeful heads *Harold* V i 564

Hebrew But here's some *H*. *Queen Mary* II i 125

Hedgar (**Edgar**) What dost a knaw o' this Mr. *H* as be a-lodgin' wi' ye ? *Prom. of May* I 200
but if iver I cooms upo' Gentleman *H* ageän, " II 137
Philip *H* o' Soomerset ! (repeat) " II 586
whether thou be *H*, or *H's* business man, " II 734
an' whether thou calls thysen *H* or Harold, " II 737
Master *H*, Harold, or whativer They calls ye, " III 726

Hedge matched with my Harold is like a *h* thistle by a garden rose. " III 176

Hedged-in This poor, flat, *h-i* field—no distance— " II 344

Hedge-pig besides *H-p's*, a savoury viand, *Foresters* IV 193

Hedge-priest He is but *h-p*, Sir King. " IV 930

Hedge-rose like the wild *h-r* Of a soft winter, *Queen Mary* III vi 14

Heed (*See also* **Take heed**) You *h* not how you soil her maiden fame, *Foresters* IV 479
I have had a year of prison-silence, Robin, And *h* him not— *Foresters* IV 925

Heel (*See also* **Under-heel**) bursten at the toes, and down at *h's*. *Queen Mary* I i 53
Her cap would brush his *h's*. " III i 14
become Hideously alive again from head to *h*, " IV iii 447
colt winced and whinnied and flung up her *h's* ; *Becket, Pro.* 516
less loyalty in it than the backward scrape of the clown's *h*— " III iii 144
not yield To lay your neck beneath your citizen's *h*. " V i 32
my heart so down in my *h's* that if I stay, I can't run. *Foresters* II i 347

Heerd (**heard**) I *h* summat as summun towld summun o' owld Bishop Gardiner's end ; *Queen Mary* IV iii 501

Height (*See also* **Eagle-height**) from that *h* something was said to me *Becket* II i 59
Blared from the *h's* of all the thrones of her kings, " V ii 489
What breadth, *h*, strength—torrents of eddying bark ! *Foresters* III 94

Heir You, The *h* presumptive. *Queen Mary* I iv 33
—after me Is *h* of England ; " I v 286
H of this England and the Netherlands ! " I v 418
my father was the rightful *h* Of England, " II ii 170
You must proclaim Elizabeth your *h*. (repeat) " V i 191, 204
in happy state To give him an *h* male. " V ii 573
Mary hath acknowledged you her *h*. " V iii 31
She knew me, and acknowledged me her *h*, " V v 256
Pronounced his *h* of England. *Harold* I ii 195
I am *h* Of England by the promise of her king. " II ii 124
Why then the *h* of England, who is he ? " II ii 567
hath King Edward not pronounced his *h* ? " II ii 576
leave the royalty of my crown Unlessen'd to mine *h's*. *Becket* II i 108
citizen's *h* hath conquer'd me For the moment. " II ii 60
left his *h*, Born, happily, with some sense of art, *Prom. of May* I 496
And cursed me, as the last *h* of my race : *Foresters* II ii 109

Held the boy she *h* Mimick'd and piped her 'Wyatt,' *Queen Mary* II ii 73
this day be *h* in after years More solemn " III iii 89
I had *h* my head up then. " III iii 246
were he wroth indeed, You *h* it less, or not at all. " IV i 107
That when I was Archbishop *h* with me. " IV ii 160
So *h* it till it all was burn'd, " IV iii 615
and *h* up by the hair ? " V ii 21
But *h* from you all papers sent by Rome, " V ii 45
nor as some have *h*, Because I love the Norman better— *Harold* I i 170
she *h* with Edward, At least methought she *h* with holy Edward, " I ii 49
yet he *h* that Dane, Jute, Angle, Saxon, " IV i 75
He *h* with Morcar.— " IV ii 43
were man's to have *h* The battle-axe by thee ! " IV iii 12
whether that which *h* it Had weaken'd, " V i 105
Some *h* she was his wife in secret— " V ii 100
I *h* it with him in his English halls, " V ii 128
And that the false Northumbrian *h* aloof, " V ii 165
For Gilbert Foliot *h* himself the man. *Becket* I i 43
I that *h* the orange blossom Dark as the yew ? *Prom. of May* II 629
True, I have *h* opinions, hold some still, " III 622
I *h* for Richard, and I hated John. *Foresters* II i 52
I ever *h* that saying false That Love is blind, " II i 642
who heads the movement, *h* him craven ? " II i 701
Tho' you should queen me over all the realms *H* by King Richard, " IV 709
but all those that *h* with him, Except I plead for them, " IV 748

Hell (*See also* **A-hell-fire**) Look at the New World—a paradise made *h* ; *Queen Mary* II i 208
Traced in the blackest text of *H*—' Thou shalt ! ' " III i 426
Into the deathless *h* which is their doom " III ii 175
The unity of Universal *H*, " III iii 232
He burns in Purgatory, not in *H*. " IV i 56
Or to be still in pain with devils in *h* ; " IV iii 222
find Heaven or else *h* ready to swallow me, " IV iii 224
There's nought but the vire of God's *h* ez can burn out that. " IV iii 527
Adulterous to the very heart of *H*. " V v 163
like a spirit in *H* who skips and flies *Harold* I i 11

Hell (*continued*) is this pendent *h* in heaven A harm to England ? *Harold* I i 76
Is thy wrath *H*, that I should spare to cry, „ v i 37
H take thy bishop then, and my kingship too ! *Becket, Pro.* 93
With a wanton in thy lodging—*H* requite 'em ! „ I ii 9
I scatter all their cowls to all the *h's*. „ II i 93
Fling not thy soul into the flames of *h* : „ II i 316
which *H's* own heat So dwelt on that they rose „ II ii 204
I hear the yelping of the hounds of *h*. „ III ii 48
I would the Church were down in *h* ! „ v i 218
Too late on earth may be too soon in *h*. „ v ii 528
She lies ! They are made in *H*. *Prom. of May* III 711
By all the devils in and out of *H* ! *Foresters* II ii 27
Devils, that make this blessed England *h*. „ III 128
yells of thief And rogue and liar echo down in *H*, „ III 324
Maid ? *Friar.* Paramour ! *Friar.* *H* take her ! „ III 403
Or, like the Devils they are, straight up from *H*. „ IV 595
If anywhere, I shall find thee in *h*. „ IV 803
Hellebore madden Against his priest beyond all *h*. *Becket* IV ii 460
Hell-fire and the soul of Eleanor from *h-f*. „ *Pro.* 151
Hellstow Into Godstow, into *H*, Devilstow ! „ v i 215
Helm (armour for the head) Cowl, *h* ; and crozier, battle-axe. *Harold* v i 444
Helm (as of a boat) Cranmer, as the helmsman at the *h* Steers, *Queen Mary* IV iii 578
Helm (verb) wherefore not *H* the huge vessel of your state, „ v i 73
and no forsworn Archbishop Shall *h* the Church. *Becket* I iii 598
Helmet his hand Upon his *h*. *Queen Mary* v v 31
Of the Northumbrian *h* on the heath ? *Harold* v i 144
gonfanon of Holy Peter Floating above their *h's*— „ v i 550
Helmeted not courtly to stand *h* Before the Queen. *Queen Mary* v v 36
Helmsman Cranmer, as the *h* at the helm Steers, „ IV iii 578
Help (s) thro' thine *h* we are come to London Bridge ; „ II iii 8
Then whither should I flee for any *h* ? „ IV iii 126
Without the *h* of Spain. „ v iii 78
England our own Thro' Harold's *h*, *Harold* II ii 79
all promises Made in our agony for *h* from heaven ? „ III i 288
No sacrifice to heaven, no *h* from heaven ; „ III i 350
pray, pray, pray—no *h* but prayer, „ III ii 195
but our *h* Is Harold, king of England. „ IV i 10
old crown Were little *h* without our Saxon carles „ IV i 35
Call not for *h* from me. I knew him not. „ v ii 54
butts him from his chair, Will need my *h*— *Becket, Pro.* 218
Past *h* ! his paws are past *h*. God help him ! „ I iv 110
Man's *h* ! but we, we have the Blessed Virgin „ v ii 219
But for the slender *h* that I can give, *Prom. of May* II 421
Help (verb) I cannot *h* it. *Queen Mary* I ii 60
I will *h* you, Madam, Even to the utmost. „ I v 177
But *h* her in this exigency, „ II ii 18
The King of France will *h* to break it. „ III i 105
H it can I ? with my hands Milking the cow ? „ III v 101
H me : what think you, Is it life or death ? „ III v 192
I'll *h* you, if I may. „ III v 205
these burnings will not *h* The purpose of the faith ; „ IV ii 184
May God *h* you Thro' that dark hour ! „ IV ii 195
are profitless to the burners, And *h* the other side. „ IV ii 220
Heaven *h* that this re-action not re-act „ IV iii 388
Not to *h me* ? They hate *me* also for my love to you, „ v i 94
many English in your ranks To *h* your battle. „ v i 112
Will you not *h* me here ? „ v i 161
You did but *h* King Philip's war with France, „ v ii 313
God *h* me, but methinks I love her less „ v ii 420
Drugs—but he knows they cannot *h* me— „ v v 61
—*H* me hence. „ v v 200
Would *h* thee from the trap. *Harold* I i 383
H the good ship, showing the sunken rock, „ II ii 100
Good, good, and thou wilt *h* me to the crown ? „ II ii 614
I ask thee, wilt thou *h* me to the crown ? „ II ii 627
Swear thou to *h* me to the crown of England. „ II ii 705
I swear to *h* thee to the crown of England . . . (repeat) *Harold* II ii 712, 721
h to build a throne Out-towering hers of France . . . *Harold* II ii 763
To *h* us from their brethren yonder ? „ III i 221
Oh God ! I cannot *h* it, but at times They seem to me „ III ii 63

Help (verb) (*continued*) God *h* me ! I know nothing— *Harold* III ii 193
To *h* the realm from scattering. „ IV i 106
will ye upon oath, *H* us against the Norman ? „ IV i 181
I cannot find his body. O *h* me thou ! „ v ii 20
Forgive me thou, and *h* me here ! „ v ii 22
Not *h* me, nor forgive me ? „ v ii 24
thou didst *h* me to my throne In Theobald's time, *Becket, Pro.* 200
Shall I not *h* your lordship to your rest ? „ I i 1
better than thyself That thou shouldst *h* me ? „ I i 5
H me off, Herbert, with this— „ I i 10
Past help ! his paws are past help. God *h* him ! „ I iv 110
God *h* her, That she was sworn to silence. „ III i 77
Heaven *h* you ; get you hence in haste „ IV ii 26
H ! *h* ! *Eleanor.* They say that walls have ears ; „ IV ii 78
God *h* thee ! „ v ii 296
laid mine own life down To *h* him from them, „ v ii 340
I cannot *h* the mould that I was cast in. *The Cup* I iii 25
Employ us, heat us, quicken us, *h* us, „ I iii 131
O *h* us from all that oppress us ! „ II 5
Will hardly *h* to make him sane again. *The Falcon* 83
Not quite recover'd of your wound, the wine Might *h* you. „ 592
And so return—Heaven *h* him !—to our own. „ 861
We two together Will *h* to heal your son— „ 923
H me to move this bench for him into the sun. *Prom. of May* I 80
Seem my good angel who may *h* me from it. „ II 388
How can I *h* him ? „ II 392
I trust I may be able by-and-by to *h* you in the business of the farm ; „ III 222
and I asked her once more to *h* me, „ III 388
And I will follow thee, and God *h* us both. *Foresters* I i 278
God's good Angel *H* him back hither, „ I ii 11
I must pass overseas to one that I trust will *h* me. „ I ii 153
I cannot *h* you in this exigency ; „ I ii 273
A worthy messenger ! how should he *h* it ? „ I iii 86
for, God *h* us, we lie by nature. „ II i 237
to *h* the old man When he was fighting. „ II i 541
balms and simples of the field To *h* a wound. „ II ii 13
Robin's an outlaw, but he *h's* the poor. While Richard hath outlaw'd himself, and *h's* Nor rich, nor poor. „ IV 358
—God *h* the mark— „ IV 714
Hail, knight, and *h* us. „ IV 765
Help'd-helpt (*See also* **Holp, Holpen**) Pole Will tell you that the devil *helpt* them thro' it. *Queen Mary* IV iii 352
some familiar spirit must have *help'd* him. *Harold* II ii 677
The Norseman's raid Hath *helpt* the Norman, „ v i 292
and his brother Tostig *helpt* ; „ v ii 47
King Stephen gave Many of the crown lands to those that *helpt* him ; *Becket* I iii 151
King Louis, Who *helpt* me when none else. „ III iii 249
frost That *help'd* to check the flowing of the blood. *The Falcon* 645
Helping as she was *h* to build the mound against the city. *Foresters* II i 308
Helpless the red man, that good *h* creature, starved, maim'd, flogg'd, *Queen Mary* II i 209
And cruel at it, killing *h* flies ; „ III iv 65
our *h* folk Are wash'd away, wailing, in their own blood— *Harold* II ii 470
Helpt *See* **Help'd**
Heman (a singer) sing, Asaph ! clash The cymbal, *H* ! „ III i 188
Hen (*See also* **Sitting-hen**) a fox may filch a *h* by night, *Queen Mary* III v 157
Who stole the widow's sitting *h* o' Sunday, *Becket* I iv 121
Sitting *h* ! Our Lord Becket's our great sitting-hen cock, „ I iv 124
The *h* cluckt late by the white farm gate, *Prom. of May* I 38
a fox from the glen ran away with the *h*, „ I 52
Henceforward none shall hold them in his house and live, *H*. *Queen Mary* IV i 98
Henry (Bedingfield) (*See also* **Henry Bedingfield**) I woke Sir *H*—and he's true to you— „ III v 60
Henry (King of France) but we play with *H*, King of France, „ I iii 131
King *H* warms your traitors at his hearth. „ v i 123
this *H* Stirs up your land against you „ v i 130
Henry (son of Henry II.) I will have My young son *H* crown'd the King of England, *Becket, Pro.* 224

Heretic (s) (*continued*) And there be many *h's* in the town, *Queen Mary* IV ii 30
Did I call him *h*? A huge heresiarch! „ IV iii 45
Ay, stop the *h's* mouth! Hale him away! „ IV iii 282
I know them *h's*, but right English ones. „ IV iii 344
I have seen *h's* of the poorer sort, „ IV iii 436
No faith with *h's*, my Lord! „ IV iii 458
Than *h* of these times; „ IV iii 599
blood and sweat of *h's* at the stake Is God's best dew „ V i 101
But she's a *h*, and, when I am gone, „ V i 200
So brands me in the stare of Christendom, A *h*! „ V ii 63
all my lifelong labour to uphold The primacy—a *h*. „ V ii 71
A *h*! He drew his shaft against me to the head, „ V ii 79
have sent me Legate hither, Deeming me *h*? „ V ii 89
I, a *h*? Your Highness knows that in pursuing heresy „ V ii 95
the Pope Pointing at me with 'Pole, the *h*, „ V ii 175
H and rebel Point at me and make merry. „ V ii 316
Heretical Touch him upon his old *h* talk, „ III iv 352
I will take Such order with all bad, *h* books „ IV i 95
Hereward the Wake have loved Harold the Saxon, or *H t W*. *Foresters* I i 228
our great Earl, the bravest English heart Since *H t W*, „ II i 688
Heritage to the intent That you may lose your English *h*. *Queen Mary* V i 133
Yea, let a stranger spoil his *h*, *Becket* II ii 259
Hern No bird? *Filippo*. Half a tit and a *h's* bill. *The Falcon* 131
Hern (hers) Our Daisy's butter's as good 'z *h*. *Queen Mary* IV iii 482
Herod since your *H's* death, How oft hath Peter „ III ii 61
Herod-Henry When *H-H* first Began to batter „ III iv 184
Hero-like howsoever *h-l* the man Dies in the fire, „ IV iii 324
Herring-pond liest as loud as the black *h-p* behind thee. *Harold* II i 26
Herring-shoal here's a crowd as thick as *h-s's*. *Queen Mary* III i 182
Hers *See* **Hern**
Herse (horse) Blacksmith, thaw be niver shoes a *h* to my likings; *Prom. of May* I 448
Herse-pond (horse-pond) I'd like to drag 'im thruff the *h-p*, and she to be a-lookin' at it. „ II 593
Hew His sword shall *h* the heretic peoples down! *Queen Mary* III ii 178
Hewn I'll have the drawbridge *h* into the Thames, „ II ii 376
They had *h* the drawbridge down into the river. „ II iii 18
Hid with his brother Odo The Bayeux bishop, and I *h* myself. *Harold* II ii 348
I was afraid of her, and I *h* myself. *Prom. of May* I 551
She *h* this sister, told me she was dead— „ III 689
The groining *h* the heavens; *Foresters* II i 62
Hidden Then *h* in the street He watch'd her pass *Becket* I ii 39
From all the *h* by-ways of the world „ III iii 15
I hate *h* faces. (repeat) *Foresters* I ii 245, 251
Hide (skin) town Hung out raw *h's* along their walls, *Harold* II ii 383
clench'd their pirate *h's* To the bleak church doors, „ IV iii 36
Hide (verb) and *h* himself and die; *Queen Mary* IV i 142
To *h* the scar left by thy Parthian dart. *Becket, Pro.* 377
Save me, father, *h* me—they follow me— „ I i 181
and once he strove to *h* his face, „ III iii 103
I will *h* my face, Blacken and gipsyfy it; „ IV ii 98
But these arm'd men—will you not *h* yourself? „ V ii 247
Pray you, *h* yourself. „ V ii 257
The murderers, hark! Let us *h*! let us *h*! „ V iii 47
Why wearest thou thy cowl to *h* thy face? *Foresters* I ii 206
thou canst not *h* thyself From her who loves thee. „ II ii 24
You *h* this damsel in your forest here, „ IV 476
Hide and seek You play at *h a s*. *Queen Mary* I v 305
Higgins (a farm labourer) *H*, Jackson, Luscombe, Nokes, *Prom. of May* III 52
High Before our own *H* Court of Parliament, *Queen Mary* II ii 234
There stands a man, once of so *h* degree, „ IV iii 68
And bolts of thunder moulded in *h* heaven To serve the Norman purpose, *Harold* II ii 32
that thus baptized in blood Grew ever *h* and higher, „ III i 148
let our *h* altar Stand where their standard fell . . . „ V ii 138
Then I saw Thy *h* black steed among the flaming furze, *Becket* II i 55
And is the King's *if* too *h* a stile for your lordship to overstep „ III iii 281
But crowns must bow when mitres sit so *h*. „ IV ii 298
The *h* Heaven guard thee from his wantonness, *Foresters* I ii 121
Till Nature, *h* and low, and great and small Forgets herself, „ I ii 326
Highback'd The deer, the *h* polecat, the wild boar, *Foresters* I iii 119
High-dropsy Or a *h-d*, as the doctors call it. *Queen Mary* III ii 225
Higher I'll have my head set *h* in the state; „ II i 250
eyes So bashful that you look'd no *h*? „ III i 65
O *h*, holier, earlier, purer church, „ IV ii 108
Grew ever high and *h*, beyond my seeing, *Harold* III i 148
Your ladyship lives *h* in the sun. *The Falcon* 583
strain to make ourselves Better and *h* than Nature, *Prom. of May* I 604
Highest That all of you, the *h* as the lowest, *Queen Mary* IV iii 64
great Angel past along the *h* Crying *Harold* III i 133
Angel rose And past again along the *h* „ III i 156
Glory to God in the *H*! fallen, fallen! „ V i 636
High-hearted Then the maid is not *h-h* enough. *Foresters* I i 258
High-priest I have it . . . My lord Paramount, Our great *H-p*, *Becket* IV ii 357
High-set sitting here Between the two most *h-s* thrones on earth, *Queen Mary* III ii 106
Hildebrand (afterwards Pope Gregory VII.) and that Archdeacon *H* His master, *Harold* III ii 144
Hill this land is like a *h* of fire, *Queen Mary* III i 321
signs on earth! Knowest thou Senlac *h*? *Harold* III i 361
passing by that *h* three nights ago— „ III i 366
And dreadful shadows strove upon the *h*, „ III i 378
A *h*, a fort, a city—that reach'd a hand „ IV i 44
another *h* Or fort, or city, took it, „ IV i 49
had in it Wales, Her floods, her woods, her *h's*: „ IV i 207
and yet I saw thee drive him up his *h's*— „ IV i 211
Scatter thy people home, descend the *h*, „ V i 10
tell him we stand arm'd on Senlac *H*, „ V i 60
Gurth, Leofwin, go once more about the *h*— „ V i 183
To tell thee thou shalt die on Senlac *h*— „ V i 242
He glitters on the crowning of the *h*. „ V i 488
All the Norman foot Are storming up the *h*. „ V i 523
axes lighten with a single flash About the summit of the *h*, „ V i 539
their horse Swallow the *h* locust-like, „ V i 560
The horse and horseman roll along the *h*, „ V i 595
Look out upon the *h*—is Harold there? „ V i 669
build a church to God Here on the *h* of battle; „ V ii 138
open'd out The purple zone of *h* and heaven; *The Cup* I ii 408
whose breath Is balmy wind to robe our *h's* with grass, „ II 265
storm was drawing hither Across the *h's* „ II 320
there is Monna Giovanna coming down the *h* from the castle. *The Falcon* 161
out of the forest and over the *h's* and away, *Foresters* II ii 176
Old as the *h's*. „ IV 301
I see two figures crawling up the *h*. „ IV 333
Hillo *H*, the stag! What, you are all unfurnish'd? *The Cup* I i 205
H! *H*! „ I i 214
Hilt Look at the *h*. What excellent workmanship. *Becket* IV ii 314
Himself *See* **'Issen**
Hinder I'd make a move myself to *h* that: *Queen Mary* III i 127
What *h's* but that Spain and England join'd, „ V iii 68
What *h's* me to hold with mine own men? *Harold* II i 102
yon huge keep that *h's* half the heaven. „ II ii 228
Hindering *See* **Burial-hindering**
Hinted Yet her—what her? he *h* of some her— *Becket* III i 243
Hip Back and side and *h* and rib, *Foresters* II ii 120
Hiss and *h* Against the blaze they cannot quench— *Harold* III i 395
Hiss'd As we past, Some hail'd, some *h* us. *Queen Mary* II ii 61
And *h* against the sun? *Becket* V iii 45
Hissing Stab me in fancy, *h* Spain and Philip; *Queen Mary* I v 150
Whose doings are a horror to the east, A *h* in the west!' *Becket* IV ii 245
History how often in old *histories* have the great men *Foresters* I i 242
Hit This is the likelier tale. We have *h* the place. *Becket* III i 43
This is no bow to *h* nightingales; *Foresters* II i 391
H! Did I not tell you an old woman could shoot better? „ II i 406
Hive So hated here! I watch'd a *h* of late; *Queen Mary* III iii 46
bees, If any creeping life invade their *h* „ III iii 54
when our good *h* Needs every sting to save it. *Harold* IV i 17
Hoäm (home) *H* wi' it, then. *Haymaker*. Well, it be the last loäd *h*. *Prom. of May* II 143
as I said afoor, it be the last loäd *h*; do thou and thy sweet'art sing us *h* to supper— „ II 169
—'The Last Loäd *H*.' (repeat) „ II 171, 172

Hoäm (home) (*continued*) At the end of the daäy,
For the last loäd *h*? (repeat) *Prom. of May* ii 184, 195
Till the end of the daäy And the last loäd *h*. " ii 209
Till the end o' the daäy An' the last loäd *h*.' " ii 239
To the end o' the daäy An' the last loäd *h*.' " ii 260
An' the last loäd *h*, Loäd *h*.' " ii 293
H? fro' the bottom o' the river? " iii 443
Hoäm-maäde (home-made) and Baäker, thaw I
sticks to *h-m*— " i 449
Hoarse I have, my Lord, shouted till I am *h*. *Queen Mary* iii i 291
Hobnail'd Your rights and charters *h* into slush— " ii ii 278
Hodge *H* 'ud ha' been a-harrowin' o' white peasen i' the
outfield— " iv iii 491
Hog The *h* hath tumbled himself into some corner, *Becket* i i 369
Hoist But I would *h* the drawbridge, like thy master. *Foresters* i i 318
Hold (s) (*See also* **Holt**) hottest *h* in all the devil's den *Queen Mary* v iv 15
Hold (verb) (*See also* **'Owd**) Seek to possess our
person, *h* our Tower, " ii ii 158
I may be wrong, sir. This marriage will not *h*. " iii i 103
There's a brave man, if any. *Bagenhall*. Ay; if it *h*. " iii i 176
that no foreigner *H* office in the household, " iii iii 72
So then you *h* the Pope— *Gardiner*. I *h* the Pope!
What do I *h* him? what do I *h* the Pope? " iii iv 371
none shall *h* them in his house and live, " iv i 96
could scarce meet his eye And *h* your own; " iv i 105
I *h* by all I wrote within that book. " iv iii 275
I do *h* The Catholic, if he have the greater right, " iv iii 381
strike Their hearts, and *h* their babies up to it. *Harold* i i 35
much ado To *h* mine own against old Gurth. " i i 438
thine eyelids into sleep, Will *h* mine waking. " i ii 141
H thine own, if thou canst! " ii i 79
my men *H* that the shipwreckt are accursed of God;—
What hinders me to *h* with mine own men? " ii i 100
We *h* our Saxon woodcock in the springe, " ii ii 1
Yet I *h* out against them, as I may, Yea—would *h* out, " ii ii 552
Better to be a liar's dog, and *h* My master honest, " iii i 125
And Morcar *h's* with us. " iv ii 46
must *h* The sequel had been other than his league " iv iii 87
No power mine To *h* their force together . . . " iv iii 213
This is the hottest of it: *h*, ash! *h*, willow! " v i 628
The Church should *h* her baronies of me, *Becket, Pro.* 24
Thou hast but to *h* out thy hand. " *Pro.* 412
And many a baron *h's* along with me— " i ii 52
among you those that *h* Lands reft from Canterbury. " i iii 140
And mean to *h* it, or—— *Becket*. To have my life. " i iii 162
Wilt thou *h* out for ever, Thomas Becket? " i iii 265
h's his cross before him thro' the crowd, " i iii 477
I *h* not by my signing. " i iii 563
But we *h* Thou art forsworn; " i iii 595
I *h* Nothing in fee and barony of the King. Whatever
the Church owns—she *h's* it in Free and perpetual alms, " i iii 677
If the King *h* his purpose, I am myself a beggar. " i iv 89
England scarce would *h* Young Henry king, " ii ii 31
We *h* by his defiance, not his defect. " ii ii 218
cursed those De Brocs That *h* our Saltwood Castle from
our see! " ii ii 269
Map scoffs at Rome. I all but *h* with Map. " ii ii 385
keep the figure moist and make it *h* water, " iii iii 166
the lady *h's* the cleric Lovelier than any soldier, " v i 193
Who *h* With York, with York against me. " v ii 62
De Morville, *H* her away. *De Morville*. I *h* her. " v iii 173
See here—I stretch my hand out—*h* it there. *The Cup* ii 210
I am sinking—*h* me—Let me alone. " ii 478
I think I scarce could *h* my head up there. *Prom. of May* i 689
True, I have held opinions, *h* some still, " iii 622
Lady Marian *h's* her nose when she steps across it. *Foresters* i i 83
handle all womankind gently, and *h* them in all honour, " i i 99
there is a lot of wild fellows in Sherwood Forest who *h*
by King Richard. " i ii 73
last time When I shall *h* my birthday in this hall: " i ii 89
How she looks up at him, how she *h's* her face! " i ii 144
I fear you be of those who *h* more by John than Richard. " i ii 198
good fellows there in merry Sherwood That *h* by Richard, " i iii 100
They *h* by Richard—the wild wood! " i iii 110
O *h* thy hand! this is our Marian. " ii ii 36

Hold (verb) (*continued*) but I *h* thee The husband of my heart, *Foresters* iii 139
You hope to *h* and keep her for yourself, " iv 477
mate with one that *h's* no love is pure, " iv 711
if you *h* us here Longer from our own venison. " iv 941
Holdest thou, De Broc, that *h* Saltwood Castle— *Becket* i iii 160
that *h* thine estates In fee and barony " i iii 674
Hold-fast Such *h-f* claws that you perforce again " ii ii 86
Holding true To either function, *h* it; " i iii 538
Hold'st Thou *h* with him? (repeat) *Foresters* ii i 526, 530
Hole skulk into corners Like rabbits to their *h's*. *Queen Mary* ii iv 56
creep down into some dark *h* Like a hurt beast, " iv i 141
crawl down thine own black *h* To the lowest Hell. *The Cup* ii 495
Holiday a boon, my king, Respite, a *h*: *Harold* i i 227
Holier O higher, *h*, earlier, purer church, *Queen Mary* iv ii 108
They are so much *h* than their harlot's son *Harold* v ii 11
Foliot is the *h* man, perhaps the better. *Becket* iii iii 92
Holiest From all the *h* shrines in Normandy! *Harold* ii ii 735
The *H* of our *H* one should be This William's fellow-
tricksters; " iii ii 76
More, what the mightiest and the *h* Of all his predecessors *Becket* ii ii 179
Holiness that you might not seem To disobey his *H*. *Queen Mary* v ii 53
his politic *H* Hath all but climb'd the Roman perch *Becket* ii ii 45
His *H*, pushed one way by the Empire and another by
England, " ii ii 327
will not your *H* Vouchsafe a gracious answer " iv ii 358
Holla'd (shouted) I *h* to him, but he didn't hear me: " iii ii 25
Holler (hollow) Dan Smith's cart hes runned ower a
laädy i' the *h* laäne, *Prom. of May* ii 569
Ye sees the *h* laäne be hallus sa dark i' the arternoon, " iii 92
Hollow (adj.) (*See also* **Holler**) —no distance—this *H*
Pandora-box, " ii 346
when you lamed the lady in the *h* lane. " iii 90
Do you still suffer from your fall in the *h* lane. " iii 241
Scarlet hacking down A *h* ash, a bat flew out at him *Foresters* ii ii 96
though thou wert like a bottle full up to the cork, or
as *h* as a kex, " iv 211
Hollow (verb) voice of the deep as it *h's* the cliffs of the land. *Becket* ii i 4
tho' the drop may *h* out the dead stone, *Becket* iii iii 315
Hollow'd All *h* out with stinging heresies; *Queen Mary* iii ii 203
Hollow-hearted Some *h-h* from exceeding age— *Foresters* iii 96
Hollowness Bring not thy *h* On our full feast. *Harold* iv iii 203
Holocaust wherein have been Such *h's* of heresy! *Queen Mary* iii iv 108
Holp (*See also* **Help'd**) he *h* the King to break down our
castles, *Becket, Pro.* 446
I do believe he *h* Northumberland Against me. *Queen Mary* i v 278
Holpen (*See also* **Help'd**) Had *h* Richard's tottering
throne to stand, " iii i 114
Not so well *h* in our wars with France, " iii vi 188
All widows we have *h* pray for us, *Foresters* iv 1078
Holt (hold) and tells un ez the vire has tuk *h*. *Queen Mary* iv iii 512
Holy —hath sent for the *h* legate of the *h* father
the Pope, Cardinal Pole, to give us all that
absolution which— " i iii 26
H absolution! *h* Inquisition! " i iii 31
Son Courtenay, wilt thou see the *h* father Murdered " i iii 64
No, by the *h* Virgin, being noble, But love me only: " i v 70
H Virgin, Plead with thy blessed Son; " i v 83
Makes me his mouth of *h* greeting. " iii ii 80
sent here as Legate From our most *H* Father Julius,
Pope, " iii iii 126
Against the *H* Father's primacy, " iii iii 131
of all censures Of *H* Church that we be fall'n into, " iii iii 152
Unto the *h* see and reigning Pope Serve God " iii iii 158
Our Lord and *H* Father, Julius, God's Vicar " iii iii 212
or more Denied the *H* Father! " iii iv 248
I kept my head for use of *H* Church; " iii iv 359
range Among the pleasant fields of *H* Writ " iii v 80
As once the *H* Father did with mine, " iii v 243
Against the King, the Queen, the *H* Father, " iii vi 33
The *H* Virgin will not have me yet Lose the sweet hope " iii vi 199
The *H* Father in a secular kingdom Is as the soul " iv i 34
It is God's will, the *H* Father's will, " iv i 184
and I Scraped from your finger-points the *h* oil; " iv ii 132
As if he had been the *H* Father, sat And judged it. " iv iii 44
For if our *H* Queen not pardon him, " iv iii 61

Holy (*continued*) O *H* Ghost! proceeding from them both, *Queen Mary* IV iii 119
Who deems it a most just and *h* war. „ V i 147
and of his *h* head— „ V i 157
And yet I must obey the *H* Father, „ V ii 38
We have made war upon the *H* Father All for your sake: „ V ii 307
No, Madam, not against the *H* Father; „ V ii 312
And done such mighty things by *H* Church, „ V v 74
set up The *H* Office here—garner the wheat, „ V v 113
H Father Has ta'en the legateship from our cousin Pole— „ V v 125
Our *h* Norman bishops down from all Their thrones in England? *Harold* I i 50
I have builded the great Church of *H* Peter: „ I i 180
And, *H* Mary! How Harold used to beat him! „ I i 431
At least methought she held with *h* Edward, „ I ii 51
'O blessed relics!' O *H* Peter!' „ I ii 171
And that the *H* Saints of Normandy When thou art home in England, „ II ii 727
The *h* bones of all the Canonised „ II ii 734
I would I were As *h* and as passionless as he! „ III i 43
H? ay, ay, forsooth, A conscience for his own soul, „ III i 61
loftiest minster ever built To *H* Peter in our English isle! „ III i 206
And all our just and wise and *h* men That shall be born hereafter. „ III i 209
Our *h* king Hath given his virgin lamb to *H* Church „ III i 334
for the king Is *h*, and hath talk'd with God, „ III i 355
loved within the pale forbidden By *H* Church: „ III ii 24
Kiss me—thou art not A *h* sister yet, my girl, „ III ii 81
and have sent him back A *h* gonfanon, „ III ii 148
Forward! Forward! Harold and *H* Cross! „ IV i 269
H Father Hath given this realm of England to the Norman. „ V i 12
H Father To do with England's choice of her own king? „ V i 17
the *H* Rood had lean'd And bow'd above me; „ V i 102
made too good an use of *H* Church To break her close! „ V i 312
the *H* Rood That bow'd to me at Waltham— „ V i 382
Harold and *H* Cross! (repeat) *Harold* V i 439, 519, 662
What power, *h* father? *Harold* V i 454
gonfanon of *H* Peter Floating above their helmets— „ V i 549
His oath was broken—O *h* Norman Saints, „ V i 616
The *H* Father strangled him with a hair Of Peter, „ V ii 45
And but that *H* Peter fought for us, „ V ii 164
to whom thou art bound By *H* Church. *Becket*, *Pro.* 68
I, true son Of *H* Church—no croucher to the Gregories „ *Pro.* 211
the *H* Father, while This Barbarossa butts him from his chair, „ *Pro.* 215
Name him; the *H* Father will confirm him. „ *Pro.* 244
Our *h* mother Canterbury, who sits With tatter'd robes. „ I i 156
O, *h* father, when thou seest him next, „ I i 322
Knowing how much you reverence *H* Church, „ I ii 48
Are not so much at feud with *H* Church „ I ii 54
and lay My crozier in the *H* Father's hands, „ I iii 125
Have I the orders of the *H* Father? „ I iii 233
The secret whisper of the *H* Father. „ I iii 236
The spire of *H* Church may prick the graves— „ I iii 553
Becket shall be king, and the *H* Father shall be king, „ I iv 270
The *h* Thomas! Brother, you have traffick'd Between the Emperor and the Pope, „ II ii 66
H Church May rock, but will not wreck, „ II ii 102
thanks of *H* Church are due to those That went before us „ II ii 190
Thee, thou *h* Thomas! I would that thou hadst been the *H* Father. „ II ii 398
I would have done my most to keep Rome *h*, „ II ii 401
Forgive me and absolve me, *h* father. „ II ii 441
with the *H* Father astride of it down upon his own head. „ III iii 77
False oath on *h* cross—for thou must leave him To-day, „ IV ii 209
God's Grace and *H* Church deliver'd us. „ IV ii 309
sometimes I have overshot My duties to our *H* Mother Church, „ V i 38
crying On *H* Church to thunder out her rights „ V ii 31
Nor make me traitor to my *h* office. „ V ii 149
To assail our *H* Mother lest she brood Too long „ V ii 251

Holy (*continued*) scare me from my loyalty To God and to the *H* Father. *Becket* V ii 483
Valour and *h* life should go together. „ V ii 587
Thy *h* follower founded Canterbury— „ V iii 5
and take this *h* cup To lodge it in the shrine of Artemis. *The Cup* I ii 434
To lodge this cup Within the *h* shrine of Artemis, „ I iii 53
H mother! To breakfast! Oh sweet saints! *The Falcon* 214
I keep it For *h* vows made to the blessed Saints *Foresters* I ii 175
he is a *h* Palmer, bounden by a vow not to show his face, „ I ii 236
till he join King Richard in the *H* Land. *Robin.* Going to the *H* Land to Richard! „ I ii 239
by this *H* Cross Which good King Richard gave me „ I ii 309
For playing upside down with *H* Writ. „ III 168
And you three *h* men, „ III 382
In the sweat of thy brow, says *H* Writ, shalt thou eat bread, „ IV 201
The *H* Virgin Stand by the strongest. „ IV 263
our friar is so *h* That he's a miracle-monger, „ IV 280
he flung His life, heart, soul into those *h* wars „ IV 407
Heading the *h* war against the Moslem, „ IV 818
like the man In *H* Writ, who brought his talent back; „ IV 981
And join'd my banner in the *H* Land, „ IV 1000
Holy Ghost O *H G*! proceeding from them both, *Queen Mary* IV iii 119
Homage Then here she stands! my *h*. „ V v 254
all manner of *h's*, and observances, and circumbendibuses. *Foresters* I i 103
Home (*See also* **Hoäm**) Struck *h* and won. *Queen Mary* I v 554
nearer *h*, the Netherlands, Sicily, Naples, „ II i 212
A smile abroad is oft a scowl at *h*. „ III i 213
bring it *H* to the leisure wisdom of his Queen, „ III vi 23
thou art reclaim'd; He brings thee *h*: „ IV iii 84
Albeit he think himself at *h* with God, „ IV iii 192
When I should guide the Church in peace at *h*, „ V ii 68
You had best go *h*. What are you? „ V iv 43
Good night! Go *h*. Besides, you curse so loud, The watch will hear you. Get you *h* at once. „ V iv 61
Thy life at *h* Is easier than mine here. *Harold* I i 96
I pray thee, let me hence and bring him *h*. „ I i 242
I should let him *h* again, my lord. „ II ii 63
Since thou hast promised Wulfnoth *h* with us, Be *h* again with Wulfnoth. „ II ii 167
poor lad! how sick and sad for *h*! „ II ii 326
When thou art *h* in England, with thine own, „ II ii 728
No footfall—no Fitzurse. We have seen her *h*. *Becket* I i 368
We be a-going *h* after our supper in all humbleness, „ I iv 206
thy true *h*—the heavens—cry out for thee „ IV ii 132
Moon bring him *h*, bring him *h* *The Cup* I ii 5
H, sweet moon, bring him *h*, *H* with the flock „ I ii 7
A miracle that they let him *h* again, „ I ii 270
Strange that the words at *h* with me so long *The Falcon* 525
how long you have been away from *h*! *Prom. of May* I 768
Close by that alder-island in your brook, 'The Angler's *H*.' „ II 536
Let bygones be bygones. Go *h*! Good-night! „ III 157
'Go *h*;' but I hadn't the heart or face to do it. „ III 389
Eva has come *h*. *Steer.* Hoäm? „ III 442
So happy in herself and in her *h*— „ III 756
we should have better battels at *h*. *Foresters* I i 58
Cleave to him, father! he will come *h* at last. „ I i 198
till King Richard come *h* again. „ I ii 141
Now the King is *h* again, and nevermore to roam again, Now the King is *h* again, the King will have his own again, *H* again, *h* again, and each will have his own again, All the birds in merry Sherwood sing and sing him *h* again. „ IV 1103
Homely You have but trifled with our *h* salad, *The Falcon* 672
Home-made *See* **Hoäm-maäde**
Home-nest gaping bills in the *h-n* Piping for bread— *Becket* II ii 300
Home-return God and his free wind grant your lordship a happy *h-r* „ III iii 328
Homeward prosper all thy wandering out And *h*. *Harold* I i 266
and pray in thy behalf For happier *h* winds „ II ii 198
Homo *H* sum. I love my dinner— *Foresters* I ii 63
H sum, sed virgo sum, „ I ii 66

Honest (*See also* **Stupid-honest**) Divers *h* fellows, *Queen Mary* I iii 119
You as poor a critic As an *h* friend: „ II i 116
For all that, Most *h*, brave, and skilful; „ II ii 383
I read his *h* horror in his eyes. „ III v 61
Right *h* and red-cheek'd; Robin was violent, „ III v 106
Peters, my gentleman, an *h* Catholic, „ IV iii 553
He is passionate but *h*. *Harold* I i 118
An *h* gift, by all the Saints, if giver And taker be but *h*! „ I i 344
he is broad and *h*, Breathing an easy gladness . . . „ I ii 173
I can but love this noble, *h* Harold. „ II ii 95
I, the Count—the King—Thy friend—am grateful for thine *h* oath, „ II ii 755
Better to be a liar's dog, and hold My master *h*, „ III i 126
He hath blown himself as red as fire with curses. An *h* fool! Follow me, *h* fool, „ V i 88
To be *h* is to set all knaves against thee. *Becket* I iii 571
When thieves fall out, *h* men— „ I iv 114
When *h* men fall out, thieves—no, it can't be that. „ I iv 118
H John! To Rome again! the storm begins again. „ II ii 467
but most on 'em know an *h* woman and a lady when they see her, „ III i 179
for I never knew an *h* woman that could make songs, „ III i 182
but none on 'em ever made songs, and they are all *h*. „ III i 189
and tho' I count Henry *h* enough, „ III iii 61
My *h* lord, you are known Thro' all the courts of Christendom „ IV ii 323
But full mid-summer in those *h* hearts. „ V ii 373
Would clap his *h* citizens on the back, *The Cup* I ii 358
Did he, *h* man? „ I ii 376
God rest his *h* soul, he bought 'em for me, *The Falcon* 49
for I'm *h*, your lordship. „ 116
Live with these *h* folk—And play the fool! *Prom. of May* I 744
You are an *h* pair. I will come to your wedding. „ III 114
H daisy deadly bruised, Queen. *Foresters* II ii 156
The silent blessing of one *h* man Is heard in heaven— „ III 321
So that they deal with us like *h* men, „ IV 101
Honester bolder than the rest, Or *h* than all? *Queen Mary* III i 439
Honesty It may be, thro' mine *h*, like a fool. „ I v 237
Yea, *h* too, paint her what way they will. *Becket* II i 101
fear creeps in at the front, *h* steals out at the back, „ III iii 62
Honey if the truth be gall, Cram me not thou with *h*, *Harold* IV i 16
As happy as the bees there at their *h* *Prom. of May* I 606
Here's a pot o' wild *h* from an old oak, *Foresters* II i 295
Bees rather, flying to the flower for *h*. „ IV 13
'I am faint for your *h*, my sweet.' „ IV 15
'Have you still any *h*, my dear?' „ IV 23
Ay, whether it be gall or *h* to 'em— „ IV 967
Honeycomb She is none of those who loathe the *h*. *Queen Mary* V i 278
Honeying then the King came *h* about her, *Becket, Pro.* 516
Honeymaking So rare the household *h* bee, „ V ii 217
Honeymoon Harsh is the news! hard is our *h*! *Harold* IV iii 229
and the *h* is the gall of love; he dies of his *h*. *Becket, Pro.* 364
Give her to me to make my *h*. „ IV ii 143
For she shall spend her *h* with me. *Foresters* IV 757
Honour (s) And hast not heart nor *h*. *Queen Mary* II iv 84
Upon the faith and *h* of a Spaniard, „ III vi 254
so wounded in his *h*, He can but creep down „ IV i 139
Win thro' this day with *h* to yourself, „ IV ii 165
For the pure *h* of our common nature, „ IV iii 297
H to thee? thou art perfect in all *h*! *Harold* II ii 691
Madam, we will entreat thee with all *h*. „ V ii 200
Saving the *h* of my order—ay. *Becket* I iii 20
Save the King's *h* here before his barons. „ I iii 187
As thou hast *h* for the Pope our master, „ I iii 200
Saving God's *h*! „ II ii 140
Saving the Devil's *h*, his yes and no. „ II ii 142
—that Is clean against God's *h*— „ II ii 163
that none may dream I go against God's *h*— „ II ii 168
to suppress God's *h* for the sake Of any king „ II ii 220
Deny not thou God's *h* for a king. „ II ii 424
surrendering God's *h* to the pleasure of a man. „ II ii 440
'great *h*,' says he, 'from the King's self to the King's son.' „ III iii 144
Thro' chastest *h* of the Decalogue „ V i 206
willing wives enough To feel dishonour, *h*. *The Cup* I ii 189
In *h* of his gift and of our marriage, „ II 351
Honour (s) (*continued*) handle all womankind gently, and hold them in all *h*, *Foresters* I i 100
O your *h*, I pray you too to give me an alms. „ II i 389
H to thee, brave Marian, and thy Kate. „ III 299
we have made a song in your *h*, so your ladyship care to listen. „ III 414
Do you call that in my *h*? „ III 433
on the faith and *h* of a king The land is his again. „ IV 852
Honour (verb) you would *h* my poor house to-night, *Queen Mary* I iii 117
For the which I *h* him. *Becket, Pro.* 449
No man to love me, *h* me, obey me! „ V i 239
Who deign to *h* this my thirtieth year, *Foresters* I ii 79
All here will prize thee, *h*, worship thee, „ II ii 17
being every inch a man I *h* every inch of a woman. „ III 64
Why art thou mute? Dost thou not *h* woman? „ III 68
Honourable Who not alone esteem'd it *h*, *Queen Mary* II ii 209
How, Malet, if they be not *h*! *Harold* II ii 279
Most *h* Sheriff! *Foresters* II i 153
Honour'd I am much *h*—yes—Do what I told thee. *The Falcon* 278
No, my most *h* and long-worshipt lady, „ 713
Honouring I that wedded Henry, *H* his manhood— *Becket* IV ii 421
h all womankind, and more especially my lady Marian, *Foresters* III 55
Hood (a cowl) Put on your *h* and see me to the bounds. *Becket* III i 94
Hood (Robin) *See* **Huntingdon, Robin, Robin Hood, Robin of Huntingdon**
Hook (*See also* **Pruning-hook**) Shelves and *h's*, shelves and *h's*, and when I see the shelves I am like to hang myself on the *h's*. *The Falcon* 119
Hook'd bat flew out at him In the clear noon, and *h* him by the hair, *Foresters* II ii 97
Hook-nosed That fine, fat, *h-n* uncle of mine, old Harold, *Prom. of May* I 509
Hoonderd (hundred) feller couldn't find a Mister in his mouth fur me, as farms five *h* haäcre. „ I 304
I, mun ha' plowed it moor nor a *h* times; „ I 368
and ower a *h* pounds worth o' rings stolen. „ I 393
Hooper (Bishop of Gloucester and Worcester) *H*, Ridley, Latimer will not fly. *Queen Mary* I ii 14
Cranmer and *H*, Ridley and Latimer, „ III iv 424
H burn'd Three-quarters of an hour. „ IV ii 225
Hoot Our men and boys would *h* him, stone him, *Prom. of May* II 425
Hope (s) All my *h* is now It may be found a scandal. *Queen Mary* I v 230
from Penenden Heath in *h* To hear you speak. „ II i 152
In *h* to charm them from their hate of Spain. *Philip*. In *h* to crush all heresy under Spain. „ III vi 82
Lose the sweet *h* that I may bear a prince. „ III vi 201
Have you good *h's* of mercy! So, farewell. „ IV ii 86
Good *h's*, not theirs, have I that I am fixt, „ IV ii 88
There is no *h* of better left for him, „ IV iii 79
Since she lost *h* of bearing us a child? „ V i 229
There yet is *h*. „ V ii 279
Count de Feria waits without, In *h's* to see your Highness. „ V ii 401
Full *h* have I that love will answer love. *Harold* IV i 237
our prophet *h's* Let in the happy distance, *The Cup* I ii 413
in *h* that the saints would send us this blessed morning; *The Falcon* 185
small *h* of the gentleman gout in my great toe. „ 656
not even *H* Left at the bottom! *Prom. of May* ii 348
but *H* Smiles from the threshold of the year *Foresters* I iii 15
The *h* of larger life hereafter, „ II i 69
Hope (verb) (*See also* **'Oäpe**) may strike fire from her, Not *h* to melt her. *Queen Mary* III vi 40
I *h* they whipt him. I would have hang'd him. *Becket, Pro.* 14
We *h* not, my lord. „ I iv 41
Not in my chin, I *h*! That threatens double. „ II i 250
Richard, if he *be* mine—I *h* him mine. „ V i 130
Mercy, mercy, As you would *h* for mercy. „ V iii 176
May lead them on to victory—I *h* so— *The Cup* I ii 168
I *h* he be not underdone, for we be undone in the doing of him. *The Falcon* 557
'I *h* your Lordship is quite recovered of your gout?' *Prom. of May* III 308
What did you *h* to make? (repeat) „ III 784, 788
You *h* to hold and keep her for yourself, *Foresters* IV 477

Hoped *h* to fall Into the wide-spread arms of fealty, *Queen Mary* II ii 263
I *h* I had served God with all my might! „ V ii 296
it was *h* Your Highness was once more in happy state „ V ii 570
H, were he chosen archbishop, *Becket* I iii 442
I would not be bold, Yet *h* ere this you might— „ III i 65
made more happy than I *h* Ever to be again. *The Falcon* 770
I wish'd, I *h* To make, to make— *Prom. of May* III 782
Hopeful and leaves me As *h*. *Queen Mary* I v 532
Hopeless (*See also* **Wholly-hopeless**) Ho there! thy rest of life is *h* prison, *Becket* V i 180
First, free thy captive from *her h* prison. „ V i 183
Hopt He had but one foot, he must have *h* away, *Harold* II ii 675
Horder (order) if tha can't keep thy one cow i' *h*, how can tha keep all thy scholards i' *h*? *Prom. of May* I 197
Horizon past is like a travell'd land now sunk Below the *h*— *The Cup* II 231
Horn (*See also* **Forest-horn, ar-horn**) draw back your heads and your *h's* *Queen Mary* I i 5
Pope has pushed his *h's* beyond his mitre— „ V i 152
Alva will but touch him on the *h's*, And he withdraws; „ V i 156
Had I been by, I would have spoil'd his *h*. *Harold* I ii 73
would make the hard earth rive To the very Devil's *h's*, „ II ii 741
A ghostly *h* Blowing continually, „ III i 372
How ghostly sounds that *h* in the black wood! *Becket* III ii 16
when the *h* sounds she comes out as a wolf. „ III ii 23
when that *h* sounds, a score of wolf-dogs are let loose „ III ii 38
Linger not till the third *h*. Fly! „ III ii 41
or you'd have heard his *h* before now. „ IV i 55
have forgotten my *h* that calls my men together. *Foresters* II i 185
Fifty leagues Of woodland hear and know my *h*, „ III 104
Wherever the *h* sound and the buck bound, „ III 345
Wherever the buck bound, and the *h* sound, „ III 355
When *h* and echo ring, „ III 428
Accept this *h*! if e'er thou be assail'd „ IV 423
Wait till he blow the *h*. „ IV 787
Why blowest thou not the *h*? „ IV 791
I blow the *h* against this rascal rout! „ IV 794
And catch the winding of a phantom *h*. „ IV 1092
Horologe always in suspense, like the tail of the *h*— *Becket* II ii 366
Horrible scourge Of England! *Courtier. H!* *Harold* I i 6
From all the holiest shrines in Normandy! *Harold. H!* „ II ii 736
Harvestless autumns, *h* agues, plague— *Queen Mary* V i 99
H! flaying, scourging, crucifying— *The Cup* I ii 235
Horror I read his honest *h* in his eyes. *Queen Mary* III v 61
carrion-nosing mongrel vomit With hate and *h*. „ IV iii 450
What with this flaming *h* overhead? *Harold* I i 232
hath talk'd with God, and seen A shadowing *h*; „ III i 357
Whose doings are a *h* to the east, A hissing in the west!' *Becket* IV ii 244
And make thee a world's *h*. „ IV ii 288
And blanch the crowd with *h*. *The Cup* II 154
Horse (*See also* **'Erse, Herse**) she met the Queen at Wanstead with five hundred *h*, *Queen Mary* I i 78
with an ass's, not a *h's* head, „ I iii 169
that's a noble *h* of yours, my Lord. „ I iv 143
And broken bridge, or spavin'd *h*, „ I v 355
a pale *h* for Death and Gardiner for the Devil. „ III i 234
Your boots are from the *h's*. „ III v 180
I had *h's* On all the road from Dover, „ V ii 576
H's there, without! „ V iii 109
Why did you keep me prating? *H's*, there! „ V iii 113
Because I broke The *h's* leg— *Harold* II ii 110
Thousands of *h's*, like as many lions „ IV iii 196
No Norman *h* Can shatter England, „ V i 195
No *h*—thousands of *h's*—our shield wall— „ V i 231
range of knights Sit, each a statue on his *h*, „ V i 525
they fall behind the *h*—Their *h* are thronging „ V i 546
all their *h* Swallow the hill locust-like, „ V i 559
The *h* and horseman cannot meet the shield, The blow that brains the horseman cleaves the *h*, The *h* and horseman roll along the hill, „ V i 591
They turn on the pursuer, *h* against foot, „ V i 608
No, no, his *h*—he mounts another— „ V i 638
Three *h's* had I slain beneath me: „ V ii 171
I could tear him asunder with wild *h's* *Becket* II i 267
Our *h's* grazing by us, when a troop, *The Falcon* 611
Horse (*continued*) A troop of *h*—— *Filippo.* Five hundred! *The Falcon* 617
how long we strove before Our *h's* fell beneath us; „ 639
lanker than an old *h* turned out to die on the common. *Foresters* I i 51
our *h* and our little cart— „ II i 191
when the Sheriff took my little *h* for the King without paying for it— „ II i 301
I left mine *h* and armour with a Squire, „ IV 414
A *h*! a *h*! I must away at once; „ IV 797
Horseback How should a baron love a beggar on *h*, *Becket, Pro.* 444
Horseman The horse and *h* cannot meet the shield, The blow that brains the *h* cleaves the horse, The horse and *h* roll along the hill, *Harold* V i 591
Horse-pond *See* **Herse-pond**
Horsiness To rose and lavender my *h*, *Queen Mary* III v 185
Hospitable and seeing the *h* lights in your castle, *Foresters* I ii 194
Hospital *See* **Spital**
Hospitality a graceless *h* To chain the free guest *Harold* II ii 192
knowing the fame of your *h*, we ventured in uninvited. *Foresters* I ii 196
Host (a consecrated wafer) Have I not heard them mock the blessed *H* *Queen Mary* IV iii 366
Host (array of men) and send her *h's* Of injured Saints *Harold* II ii 744
And Edward would have sent a *h* against you, „ IV i 99
join our hands before the *h's*, That all may see. „ IV i 242
Host (entertainer of guests) He was thine *h* in England when I went To visit Edward. „ II ii 4
I found him all a noble *h* should be. „ II ii 10
She hath follow'd with our *h*, and suffer'd all. „ IV i 29
A cleric violated The daughter of his *h*, *Becket* I iii 383
Hostage four of her poor Council too, my Lord, As *h's*. *Queen Mary* II ii 44
Is not my brother Wulfnoth *h* there *Harold* I i 239
Poor brother! still a *h*! „ II ii 329
They did thee wrong who made thee *h*; „ II ii 350
Remain a *h* for the loyalty Of Godwin's house.' „ III i 90
Hostis *H* in Angliam Ruit prædator, „ V i 506
H per Angliae Plagas bacchatur; „ V i 510
Hot and the *H* Gospellers will go mad upon it. *Queen Mary* I i 115
But you so bubbled over with *h* terms Of Satan, „ I ii 94
And *h* desire to imitate; „ III iv 171
There are *H* Gospellers even among our guards— „ V v 102
jerk'd out of the common rut Of Nature in the *h* religious fool, *Harold* I i 139
H blood, ambition, pride So bloat and redden his face— *The Cup* II 168
Thou blowest *h* and cold. Where is she then? *Foresters* II i 490
Hot-blooded *H-b*! I have heard them say in Rome, *The Cup* I i 135
Hot-headed *H-h* fools—to burst the wall of shields! *Harold* V i 612
I can see further into a man than our *h-h* Henry, *Becket, Pro.* 463
Hottest This is the *h* of it: hold, ash! hold, willow! *Harold* V i 628
The *h* hold in all the devil's den Were but a sort of winter; *Queen Mary* V iv 15
Hound with mine old *h* Couch'd at my hearth, „ III i 45
Sick for an idle week of hawk and *h* *Harold* I i 103
I hear the yelping of the *h's* of hell. *Becket* III ii 48
Huntsman, and *h*, and deer were all neck-broken! *The Cup* I ii 23
You saw my *h's* True to the scent; „ I ii 110
Hounded We never *h* on the State at home To spoil the Church. *Becket* II ii 96
Hour Ay, that was in her *h* of joy; *Queen Mary* I i 84
some great doom when God's just *h* Peals— „ I iv 262
What do and say Your Council at this *h*? „ II ii 46
Who knows? the man is proven by the *h*. *White.* The man should make the *h*, not this the man; „ II ii 364
An *h* will come When they will sweep her from the seas. „ III i 160
do triumph at this *h* In the reborn salvation „ III iii 181
tolerate the heretic, No, not an *h*. „ III iv 211
Their *h* is hard at hand, „ III iv 426
Ay, for an *h* in May. „ III v 10
It shall be all my study for one *h* „ III v 184
in strange *h's*, After the long brain-dazing colloquies, „ IV ii 91
May God help you Thro' that hard *h*! „ IV ii 196
Hooper burn'd Three-quarters of an *h*. „ IV ii 227
the *h* has come For utter truth and plainness; „ IV iii 272
Make us despise it at odd *h's*, my Lord. „ IV iii 386
Brook for an *h* such brute malignity? „ IV iii 544

Hour (*continued*) O would I were My father for an *h*! *Queen Mary* V ii 294
And may not speak for *h's*. „ V ii 406
Sit down here: Tell me thine happiest *h*. „ V v 79
worse than that—not one *h* true to me! „ V v 159
A good entrenchment for a perilous *h*! *Harold* III i 363
among the goldenest *h's* Of Alfred, „ IV iii 51
O hapless Harold! King but for an *h*! „ V i 258
God of truth Fill all thine *h's* with peace!— „ V i 316
But the *h* is past, and our brother, Master Cook, *Becket* I iv 59
I have but one *h* with thee— „ II i 24
Let there not be one frown in this one *h*. „ II i 44
out of the eclipse Narrowing my golden *h*! „ II i 203
Come, come, mine *h*! I bargain for mine *h*. „ II i 212
our mother 'ill sing me old songs by the *h*, „ III i 185
We have had so many *h's* together, Thomas, So many happy *h's* „ III iii 37
bound For that one *h* to stay with good King Louis, „ III iii 247
thy life Was not one *h's* worth in England „ III iii 251
Your Grace will never have one quiet *h*. „ V i 79
tho' it be their *h*, the power of darkness, But my *h* too, „ V iii 93
If I be not back in half an *h*, Come after me. *The Cup* I ii 438
So falls the throne of an *h*. „ II 486
Pride of his heart—the solace of his *h's*— *The Falcon* 224
Ay, haäfe an *h* ago. She be in theer now. *Prom. of May* I 14
Half an *h* late! why are you loitering here? „ II 324
Who can tell What golden *h's*, with what full hands, „ II 509
What feller wur it as 'a' been a-talkin' fur haäfe an *h* wi' my Dora? „ II 576
niver 'a been talkin' haäfe an *h* wi' the divil 'at killed her oän sister, „ II 603
may drop off any day, any *h*. You must see him at once. „ III 407
the light Of these dark *h's*; *Foresters* I ii 85
We make but one *h's* buzz, „ I ii 277
I am only merry for an *h* or two Upon a birthday: „ I iii 11
We will away in four-and-twenty *h's*, „ I iii 91
My lonely *h*! The king of day hath stept „ II i 25
to carve One lone *h* from it, „ II i 43
Why break you thus upon my lonely *h*? „ II i 94
The ruler of an *h*, but lawful King, „ IV 47
Try me an *h* hence. „ IV 276
your free sports have swallow'd my free *h*. „ IV 340
No, not an *h*: the debt is due to-day. „ IV 447
are delivered here in the wild wood an *h* after noon. „ IV 509

Houris whose cheerless *H* after death Are Night and Silence, *Prom. of May* I 249

House (*See also* **Ale-house, Gate-house, Treasure-house**)
So you would honour my poor *h* to-night, *Queen Mary* I iii 118
To Ashridge, or some other country *h*. „ I iv 226
seek In that lone *h*, to practise on my life, „ I iv 284
my *h* hath been assaulted, „ I v 146
Spain in our ships, in our forts, in our *h's*, in our beds? „ II i 180
Your *h's* fired—your gutters bubbling blood— „ II ii 280
a plundering o' Bishop Winchester's *h*; „ II iii 73
Here by this *h* was one; „ III i 9
You are of the *h*? what will you do, Sir Ralph? „ III i 435
there were those within the *h* Who would not have it. „ III ii 66
also those without the *h* Who would not have it. „ III ii 70
When will you that we summon both our *h's* „ III ii 115
My lords of the upper *h*, And ye, my masters, of the lower *h*, „ III iii 102
sole man in either *h* Who stood upright when both the *h's* fell. *Bagenhall.* The *h's* fell! *Officer.* I mean the *h's* knelt „ III iii 253
I am the one sole man in either *h*, „ III iii 266
The *h* is all in movement. Hence, and see. „ III v 83
play with fire as children do, And burn the *h*. „ III vi 30
none shall hold them in his *h* and live, „ IV i 96
The stranger at his hearth, and all his *h*— „ IV i 164
The *h* half-ruin'd ere the lease be out; „ V ii 66
When Wyatt sack'd the Chancellor's *h* in Southwark. „ V ii 505
light enough for Alfgar's *h* To strike thee down *Harold* I i 307
powers of the *h* of Godwin Are not enframed in thee. „ I i 316

House (*continued*) running out at top To swamp the *h*. *Harold* I i 379
Unwholesome talk For Godwin's *h*! „ I i 391
It means the lifting of the *h* of Alfgar. „ I i 473
all the sins of both The *h's* on mine head— „ I ii 206
see confusion fall On thee and on thine *h*. „ II ii 490
Remain a hostage for the loyalty Of Godwin's *h*.' „ III i 91
I have built the Lord a *h*— (repeat) *Harold* III i 178, 181, 186
Fall, cloud, and fill the *h*— *Harold* III i 190
not *his* fault, if our two *h's* Be less than brothers. „ IV i 130
When will ye cease to plot against my *h*? „ IV i 162
Thou hast given it to an enemy of our *h*. „ IV ii 32
Thou hast no passion for the *H* of Godwin— „ IV ii 72
When I and thou were youths in Theobald's *h*, *Becket* I iii 41
Not he That is not of the *h*, but from the street „ I iii 689
dawns darkly and drearily over the *h* of God— „ I iv 146
Sudden change is a *h* on sand; „ III iii 60
when he hears a door open in the *h* and thinks 'the master.' „ III iii 99
I will be Sole master of my *h*. „ V i 151
and in thy name I pass'd From *h* to *h*. „ V ii 104
little fair-hair'd Norman maid Lived in my mother's *h*: „ V ii 261
yet threaten your Archbishop In his own *h*. „ V ii 506
dost thou know the *h* of Sinnatus? *The Cup* I i 49
These grapes are for the *h* of Sinnatus— „ I i 51
this pious cup Is passport to their *h*, „ I i 83
They shall not harm My guest within my *h*. „ I ii 327
The child, a thread within the *h* of birth, „ II 259
feud between our *h's* is the bar I cannot cross; *The Falcon* 254
My comrade of the *h*, and of the field. „ 875
O this mortal *h*, Which we are born into, *Prom. of May* II 273
would fight for his rents, his leases, his *h's*, *Foresters* I i 233
whose return Builds up our *h* again? „ IV 1009

House-breäker Beänt there *h-b's* down i' Littlechester, Dobson— *Prom. of May* I 388

House-dog filch the linen from the hawthorn, poison the *h-d*, *Foresters* III 200

Household (adj.) The *h* dough was kneaded up with blood; *Becket* I iii 351
So rare the *h* honeymaking bee, „ V ii 217
to cast All threadbare *h* habit, *Foresters* I iii 112

Household (s) Your lavish *h* curb'd, *Queen Mary* I v 113
no foreigner Hold office in the *h*, fleet, „ III iii 72
No man without my leave shall excommunicate My tenants or my *h*. *Becket, Pro.* 32
And when I was of Theobald's *h*, once— „ I i 60
you have put so many of the King's *h* out of communion, „ III iii 311
Prince would have me of his—what? *H*? *Foresters* IV 703

Houseless A *h* head beneath the sun and stars, „ II i 64

House-side and there is a piece of beef like a *h-s*, *Prom. of May* I 793

Hover At the park gate he *h's* with our guards. *Queen Mary* II iv 15
Love will *h* round the flowers when they first awaken; „ V ii 370
That *h's* round your shoulder— „ V iii 52
sea-bird rouse himself and *h* Above the windy ripple, *Harold* II ii 335

How *See* **'Ow**

Howard (Lord William, Lord High Admiral) (*See also* **William, William Howard**) had *H* spied me there And made them speak, *Queen Mary* II iii 32
This *H*, whom they fear, what was he saying? „ III vi 54
And if he did I care not, my Lord *H*. „ IV i 129
Lord *H*, Sending an insolent shot that dash'd „ V i 56
H is all English! „ V i 61

Howiver (however) my rheumatizy be that bad *h* be I to win to the burnin'. „ IV iii 474

Howl if your wolf the while should *h* for more, „ I v 419
how those Roman wolfdogs *h* and bay him! „ IV iii 354
note Whereat the dog shall *h* and run, *Harold* I ii 192
if it suit their purpose to *h* for the King, *Becket* III iii 324
They *h* for thee, to rend thee head from limb. *The Cup* I ii 321

Howsoever *See* **Howsomiver, S'iver**

Howsomiver (howsoever) but a had to bide *h*, *Queen Mary* IV iii 506

Hug thou wouldst *h* thy Cupid till his ribs cracked— *Becket, Pro.* 504

Huge or else swam heavily Against the *h* corruptions of the Church, *Queen Mary* IV ii 100
Did I call him heretic? A *h* heresiarch! „ IV iii 46
But wherefore not Helm the *h* vessel of your state, „ V i 73

Huge (*continued*) I watch'd you dancing once With your *h* father ; *Queen Mary* v ii 145
And yon *h* keep that hinders half the heaven. *Harold* II ii 228
I have always told Father that the *h* old ashtree there would cause an accident some day ; *Prom. of May* III 244
hundreds of *h* oaks, Gnarl'd—older than the thrones of Europe— *Foresters* III 90
Hugest therefore have we shatter'd back The *h* wave from Norseland ever yet Surged on us, *Harold* IV iii 62
Hugh (de Morville, knight of the household of King Henry II.) (*See also* **De Morville**) *H*, *H*, how proudly you exalt your head ! *Becket* v ii 454
H, I know well thou hast but half a heart „ v iii 129
Hum thick as bees below, They *h* like bees,— *Harold* I i 32
So come, come ! ' '*H* !' *Foresters* IV 19
But come, come !' '*H* !' „ IV 26
Human What *h* reason is there why my friend Should meet *Queen Mary* IV i 68
not for little sins Didst thou yield up thy Son to *h* death ; „ IV iii 144
to cancel and abolish all bonds of *h* allegiance, „ v iv 50
He dyed, He soak'd the trunk with *h* blood, *Harold* III i 143
not strange ! This was old *h* laughter in old Rome „ III ii 163
It's humbling—it smells o' *h* natur'. *Becket* I iv 238
Were I *h*, were I *h*, I could love you like a woman. *Foresters* II ii 190
Human-heartedest Thou art the *h-h*, Christian-charitiest of all crab-catchers. *Harold* II i 62
Humankind After his death and better *h* ; *Queen Mary* IV iii 160
Human-red God redden your pale blood ! But mine is *h-r* ; *Becket* I iv 36
Humber (river) all the North of *H* is one storm. *Harold* II ii 291
We could not move from Dover to the *H* „ II ii 537
Are landed North of *H*, and in a field „ III ii 126
Our Wessex dragon flies beyond the *H*, „ IV i 4
Humble So wife-like *h* to the trivial boy *Queen Mary* III i 364
Do make most *h* suit unto your Majesties, „ III iii 118
So to set forth this *h* suit of ours „ III iii 145
Sir, I attend the Queen To crave most *h* pardon— „ III iv 432
We make our *h* prayer unto your Grace „ IV i 43
Therefore I come ; *h* myself to Thee ; „ IV iii 133
Ay, ay ! the King *h's* himself enough. *Becket* II ii 184
Humbleness We be a-going home after our supper in all *h*, my lord ; for the Archbishop loves *h*, „ I iv 207
Humblest Loyal and royal cousin, *h* thanks. *Queen Mary* III ii 4
Our *h* thanks for your blessing. Farewell ! *Becket* I iv 42
Humbling It's *h*—it smells o' human natur'. „ I iv 238
Humiliated Being so crush'd and so *h* We scarcely dare „ v i 69
Humiliation bow'd herself to meet the wave Of *h*, „ IV ii 390
Humour man not prone to jealousies, Caprices, *h's*, *Prom. of May* III 627
Humpt Ay, ay, no doubt ; and were I *h* behind, *Becket* II i 255
Hundred (*See also* **Hoonder'd**) that she met the Queen at Wanstead with five *h* horse, *Queen Mary* I i 78
And when I sleep, a *h* men-at-arms Guard my poor dreams „ I v 152
I would not ; but a *h* miles I rode, „ I v 551
'Whosoever will apprehend the traitor Thomas Wyatt shall have a *h* pounds for reward.' „ II iii 61
A *h* here and *h's* hang'd in Kent. „ III i 1
in Guisnes Are scarce two *h* men, „ v i 5
That gateway to the mainland over which Our flag hath floated for two *h* years Is France again. „ v ii 261
The shadows of a *h* fat dead deer For dead men's ghosts. *Harold* I ii 103
Red gold—a *h* purses—yea, and more ! „ III i 18
lost and found Together in the cruel river Swale A *h* years ago ; „ III ii 11
And caked and plaster'd with a *h* mires, „ IV iii 177
a *h* thousand men—Thousands of horses, „ IV iii 194
A *h* pathways running everyway, *Becket, Pro.* 163
And York lay barren for a *h* years. „ I iii 54
I found a *h* ghastly murders done By men, „ I iii 407
My lord, the King demands three *h* marks, „ I iii 626
My lord, the King demands seven *h* marks, „ I iii 634
I led seven *h* knights and fought his wars. „ I iii 638

Hundred (*continued*) My lord, the King demands five *h* marks, *Becket* I iii 641
crawl over knife-edge flint Barefoot, a *h* leagues, „ II i 273
I warrant Thou hast sworn on this my cross a *h* times „ IV ii 206
Monks, knights, five *h*, that were there and heard. „ v ii 406
But after rain o'erleaps a jutting rock And shoots three *h* feet. *The Cup* I i 111
It is old, I know not How many *h* years. „ II 343
My bird ? a *h* Gold pieces once were offer'd by the Duke. *The Falcon* 323
A troop of horse—— *Filippo.* Five *h* ! *Count.* Say fifty ! „ 618
A *h* times more worth a woman's love, Than this, *Prom. of May* III 743
She was murdered here a *h* year ago, *Foresters* II i 245
Ay, ay, but there is use, four *h* marks. „ IV 496
There then, four *h* marks. „ IV 497
What did I say ? Nay, my tongue tript—five *h* marks for use. „ IV 499
A *h* more ? There then, a *h* more. „ IV 502
a *h* lovers more To celebrate this advent of our King ! „ IV 1046
And here perhaps a *h* years away Some hunter in day-dreams „ IV 1087
Hung town *H* out raw hides along their walls, *Harold* II ii 383
if that but *h* upon King Edward's will. „ II ii 600
like Mahound's coffin *h* between heaven and earth— *Becket* II ii 361
Hunger (s) when I was down in the fever, *she* was down with the *h*, *Harold* II i 48
Hunger (verb) crowd that *h's* for a crown in Heaven *Becket* II ii 282
Who *h* for the body, not the soul— *Foresters* IV 700
Hunger-nipt on a land So *h-n* and wretched ; *Queen Mary* v i 168
Hunt (s) tho' a stranger fain would be allow'd To join the *h*. *The Cup* I i 197
a random guest Who join'd me in the *h*. „ I ii 109
Hunt (verb) Nay, I know They *h* my blood. *Queen Mary* III v 78
and *h* and hawk beyond the seas ! *Harold* I i 229
I will hawk and *h* In Flanders. „ I i 259
had past me by To *h* and hawk elsewhere, „ II ii 28
Going or gone to-day To *h* with Sinnatus. *The Cup* I i 65
Have let him *h* the stag with you to-day. „ I ii 379
h him With pitchforks off the farm, *Prom. of May* II 426
They *h* in couples, and when they look at a maid *Foresters* I i 255
Hunted Which *h* him when that un-Saxon blast, *Harold* II ii 30
not fear the crowd that *h* me Across the woods, *The Cup* I iii 16
Hunter he stood there Staring upon the *h*. „ I ii 123
And take a *h's* vengeance on the meats. „ I ii 43
and the *h's*, if caught, are blinded, or worse than blinded. *Foresters* IV 226
The *h's* passion flash'd into the man, „ IV 539
Some *h* in day-dreams or half asleep „ IV 1088
Hunting (*See also* **A-hunting**) I once was at the *h* of a lion. *The Cup* I ii 116
Why, is not man a *h* animal ? *Foresters* IV 223
Huntingdon (Robin Hood, Earl of) (*See also* **Robin, Robin Hood, Robin of Huntingdon**) I pray you, look at Robin Earl of *H's* men. „ I i 36
as true a friend of the people as Lord Robin of *H*. „ I i 189
me who worship Robin the great Earl of *H* ? „ I i 226
God bless our well-beloved Robin, Earl of *H*. „ I i 248
This Robin, this Earl of *H*—he is a friend of Richard— „ I i 281
Thou, Robin Hood Earl of *H*, art attainted and hast lost thine earldom of *H*. „ I iii 57
by virtue of this writ, whereas Robin Hood Earl of *H* „ I iii 62
Robin Hood Earl of *H* is outlawed and banished. „ I iii 68
Art thou that banish'd lord of *H*, „ IV 140
My good friend Robin, Earl of *H*, „ IV 829
if the King forbid thy marrying With Robin, our good Earl of *H*. „ IV 876
Huntsman Gardener, and *h*, in the parson's place, *Queen Mary* IV iii 373
H, and hound, and deer were all neck-broken ! *The Cup* I ii 23
Hup (up) hallus *h* at sunrise, and I'd drive the plow straäit as a line right i' the faäce o' the sun, then back ageän, a-follering my oän shadder—then *h* ageän *Prom. of May* I 369
Huppads (upwards) an' then I wur turned *h* o' sixty. „ I 363

Hurl *H's* his soil'd life against the pikes and dies. *Queen Mary* IV iii 311
if his Northumbrians rise And *h* him from them,— *Harold* II ii 457
And *h* the dread ban of the Church on those *Becket* III iii 210
And *h's* the victor's column down with him *The Cup* II 295
Hurl'd and *h* our battles Into the heart of Spain; *Queen Mary* III i 107
sir, they *h* it back into the fire, „ V iv 22
and *h* it from him Three fields away, *Harold* III i 138
Hurrah *H*! Vive le Roy! *Becket* I iv 274
Hurry (s) I trod upon him even now, my lord, in my *h*, and broke him. *The Falcon* 410
Hurry (verb) Why do they *h* out there? *Queen Mary* II ii 4
Hurt He can but creep down into some dark hole Like a *h* beast, „ IV i 142
H no man more Than you would harm „ IV iii 187
He had been *h*, And bled beneath his armour. *Foresters* II ii 4
He hath been *h*, was growing whole again, „ IV 451
Husband The traitor *h* dangled at the door, *Queen Mary* III i 10
happily symboll'd by The King your *h*, „ III ii 110
Oh, Philip, *h*! now thy love to mine Will cling „ III ii 159
Philip's no sudden alien—the Queen's *h*, „ III iii 43
parting of a *h* and a wife Is like the cleaving of a heart; „ III vi 194
not were he ten times king, Ten times our *h*, „ V i 64
'Your people hate you as your *h* hates you.' „ V ii 337
My *h* hates me, and desires my death. „ V ii 347
the child came not, and the *h* came not; „ V ii 581
To marry and have no *h* Makes the wife fool. *Harold* II ii 309
Who did discrown thine *h*, unqueen thee? Didst thou not love thine *h*? „ IV i 193
I had rather She would have loved her *h*. „ IV i 224
O Harold! *h*! Shall we meet again? „ V i 360
because I love The *h* of another! „ V i 649
I have lost both crown And *h*. „ V ii 40
What was he like, this *h*? like to thee? „ V ii 52
I mean your goodman, your *h*, my lady, *Becket* III i 159
for her *h*, King Louis—— *Rosamund.* Hush! „ III i 170
whom you call—fancy—my *h's* brother's wife. „ III i 202
Son, *h*, brother gash'd to death in vain, *The Cup* I ii 143
To draw you and your *h* to your doom. „ I ii 222
And if you should betray me to your *h*— „ I ii 243
Still—I should tell My *h*. „ I ii 304
She may, perchance, to save this *h*. „ I iii 33
And for the sake of Sinnatus your *h*, „ I iii 101
So much of *h* in it still—that if „ II 145
Can't a girl when she loves her *h*, and he her, *Prom. of May* III 305
but I hold thee The *h* of my heart, *Foresters* III 140
Husbanded nor yet so amorous That I must needs be *h*; *Queen Mary* II ii 216
Husband-in-law *H-i-l*, our smooth-shorn suzerain, *Becket* II ii 40
Hush *H*—hear! *Bourne.* —and so this unhappy land, *Queen Mary* I iii 19
H! *h*! You wrong the Chancellor: „ III iii 66
H, father, *h*! *Harold* III i 389
for her husband, King Louis—— *Rosamund.* *H*! *Becket* III i 171
O *h*! O peace! This violence ill becomes *The Cup* II 214
Husk If we may judge the kernel by the *h*, „ I i 175
Hut we found a goat-herd's *h* and shared His fruits „ I ii 427
Here is the witch's *h*. *Foresters* II i 178
They must have past. Here is a woodman's *h*. „ II i 200
Not in this *h* I take it. „ II i 205
There is but one old woman in the *h*. „ II i 242
Hymen rather than so clip The flowery robe of *H*, *The Cup* II 436
Hymn (s) (*See also* **Battle-hymns, 'Ymn**) chants and *h's* In all the churches, *Becket* V ii 366
standing up side by side with me, and singing the same *h*? *Prom. of May* III 182
Hymn (verb) Hear thy priestesses *h* thy glory! *The Cup* II 7
Hypocrisy never burn out the *h* that makes the water in her. *Queen Mary* IV iii 525
Hypocrite And yet I hate him for a *h*. *Becket* V i 232
From whom he knows are *h's* and liars. *Foresters* IV 380

I

Ibyci And one an *uxor pauperis I*. *Becket* V ii 216
Iceberg To shove that stranded *i* off our shores, *Harold* IV iii 138
Ice-cold Stone-hard, *i-c*—no dash of daring in him. *Queen Mary* I v 331
sat Stone-dead upon a heap of *i-c* eggs. *Becket* V ii 239
Iceland —Scotland, Ireland, *I*, Orkney, *Harold* III ii 124
Icy white cells, beneath an *i* moon— „ V i 325
Iden And he will prove an *I* to this Cade, *Queen Mary* II ii 369
Idiot This world of mud, on all its *i* gleams Of pleasure, *Prom. of May* III 722
Idiotcies What are all these? *Harold.* Utopian *i*. „ III 588
Idle But this is *i* of you. Well, sir, well, *Queen Mary* IV ii 75
other things As *i*; a weak Wyatt! „ V i 292
Sick for an *i* week of hawk and hound Beyond the seas— *Harold* I i 103
Peace, friends! what *i* brawl is this? *Becket* I ii 2
Idol-worship one true faith, a loathsome *i-w*? *Queen Mary* III iv 219
Idyll This Dobson of your *i*? *Prom. of May* III 563
If Thine '*i's*' will sear thine eyes out—ay. *Harold* II ii 625
He fenced his royal pomise with an *i*. *Becket* III iii 279
is the King's *i* too high a stile for your lordship to overstep „ III iii 280
Ay, if this *i* be like the Devil's '*i* „ III iii 284
Ignorance Wyatt, who hath tamper'd with A public *i*, *Queen Mary* II ii 182
And I crying in the streets, „ IV iii 377
Spite, *i*, envy, Yea, honesty too, *Becket* II i 100
Ignorant She is *i* of all but that I love her. „ *Pro.* 185
Ignorantly I am sure (Knowing the man, he wrought it *i*, *Queen Mary* III i 276
Ill The Queen is *i* advised: shall I turn traitor? „ I iv 5
i counsel! These let them keep at present; „ I v 405
I am *i* disguised. „ III i 33
And fared so *i* in this disastrous world. „ V ii 344
My Lord Count, Her Highness is too *i* for colloquy. „ V ii 613
I news for guests, ha, Malet! More? What more? *Harold* II ii 302
Harold served Tostig so *i*, he cannot serve for Tostig! „ III i 162
I news hath come! Our hapless brother, Tostig— „ III ii 120
Madam, you do *i* to scorn wedded love. *Becket*, *Pro.* 353
May God grant No *i* befall or him or thee when I Am gone. „ II i 260
Eleanor, Eleanor, have I Not heard *i* things of her in France? „ III i 231
This violence *i* becomes The silence of our Temple. *The Cup* II 215
but you turn right ugly when you're in an *i* temper; *Prom. of May* I 160
but the *i* success of the farm, and the debts, „ II 68
and so *i* in consequence all Monday, „ III 80
But *i* befitting such a festal day *Foresters* I iii 37
Who hast that worship for me which Heaven knows I *i* deserve— „ I iii 162
Illa Their 'dies *I*,' which will test their sect. *Queen Mary* III iv 428
Ill-bested A maiden now Were *i-b* in these dark days of John, *Foresters* II ii 45
Illegitimate And mine a bitterer *i* hate, *Becket* II i 173
Ill-garrison'd Calais is but *i-g*, in Guisnes *Queen Mary* V i 4
Illogically but unsymmetrically, preposterously, *i*, *Becket*, *Pro.* 336
Image beast might roar his claim To being in God's *i*, *Queen Mary* IV iii 369
set up your broken *i's*; Be comfortable to me. „ V ii 300
Who melts a waxen *i* by the fire, *Foresters* II i 671
Imagine And can you not *i* that the wreath, *The Falcon* 534
I said you might *i* it was so. „ 545
Imitate And hot desire to *i*; *Queen Mary* III iv 171
Imitative A Parliament of *i* apes! „ III iii 235
Immanuel Goldsmiths *I G* was broke into o' Monday night, *Prom. of May* I 391
Immediate and they threaten The *i* thunder-blast of interdict: *Becket* III iii 26
Immemorial so violated the *i* usage of the Church, „ III iii 72
Immortal Lovers hold True love *i*. *Foresters* II i 616
You seem, as it were, *I*, and we mortal. „ IV 1060
We have respect for man's *i* soul, *Harold* II ii 501

Imp Venal *i*! What say'st thou to the Chancellorship *Becket* II i 224
Impair or *i* in any way This royal state of England, *Queen Mary* II ii 229
Imperial What your *i* father said, my liege, To deal with heresy gentlier. „ III vi 56
We cannot fight *i* Rome, *The Cup* II 92
let the new-made children Of our *i* mother see the show. „ II 165
Implore I thus *i* you, low upon my knees, *Queen Mary* IV i 64
Import It much *i's* me I should know her name. *Becket* I i 192
it may *i* her all as much Not to be known. „ I i 197
Importance policy in some matter Of small *i* *Queen Mary* III vi 168
Impossible *I*; Except you put Spain down. „ V iii 79
Impress And she *i* her wrongs upon her Council, „ III vi 183
Imprison Degrade, *i* him—Not death for death. *Becket* I iii 400
Too politic for that. *I* me? „ IV ii 397
Imprison'd I was but wounded by the enemy there And then *i*. *The Falcon* 389
Imprisonment In your five years of *i*, *Queen Mary* III iv 242
Impugn Which might *i* or prejudice the same; „ III iii 133
Impute it is the traitor that *i's* Treachery to his King! *Becket* I iii 484
Weak natures that *i* Themselves to their unlikes, *Foresters* II i 691
Incalculable Yea, even such as mine, *i*, *Queen Mary* IV iii 147
Incapable Old, miserable, diseased, *I* of children. „ V v 179
Incarnate Whose life was all one battle, *i* war, *Harold* V i 397
Incavern'd *See* **Deep-incavern'd**
Incense parch'd banks rolling *i*, as of old, *Queen Mary* I v 91
puffed out such an *i* of unctuosity into the nostrils of our Gods of Church and State, *Becket* III iii 115
Incenselike All her breath should, *i*, Rise *Queen Mary* III iii 164
Incest As being born from *i*; „ I ii 69
Incestuous Peter, I'll swear for him He *did* believe the bond *i*. „ I ii 77
Inch Fire—*i* by *i* to die in agony! „ IV ii 223
If thou draw one *i* nearer, *Foresters* I i 145
being every *i* a man I honour every *i* of a woman. „ III 63
for old Much is every *i* a man, „ IV 290
Incline whether her Grace *i* to this splendid scion of Plantagenet. *Queen Mary* I i 134
Included The *i* Danaë has escaped again Her tower, *Becket* I i 395
Inconsistency Nay, for bare shame of *i*, *Queen Mary* I ii 39
Incurr'd every bond and debt and obligation *I* as Chancellor. *Becket* I iii 712
Ind His sceptre shall go forth from *I* to *I*! *Queen Mary* III ii 177
Indeterminate But a weak mouth, an *i*—ha? „ III iv 340
Indian *I* shawl That Philip brought me in our happy days!— „ V ii 538
Indies Spain would be England on her seas, and England Mistress of the *I*. „ V iii 74
England Will be Mistress of the *I* yet, „ V iii 77
Indifference accuse you of *i* To all faiths, all religion; „ III iv 223
Indignation begets An admiration and an *i*, „ III iv 170
In-door They are plagues enough *i-d*. *Becket* II ii 91
Indraught swoll'n and fed With *i's* and side-currents, *Queen Mary* II i 234
Indungeon'd *I* from one whisper of the wind, *Becket* IV ii 146
Infallible of her most Royal, *I*, Papal Legate-cousin. *Queen Mary* III iv 433
Infamous *I* wretch. Shall I tell her he is dead? *Prom. of May* III 336
Infamy Fame of to-day is *i* to-morrow; *I* of to-day is fame to-morrow; *Becket* II i 103
Infant (adj.) I had to cuff the rogue For *i* treason. *Queen Mary* III iii 52
Infant (s) blast your *i's*, dash The torch of war among *Harold* II ii 747
Infatuated —*i*—To sue you for his life? *Queen Mary* IV i 10
Infect Thy fears *i* me beyond reason. Peace! *Harold* II ii 451
Infinite that it would please Him out of His *i* love to break down all kingship and queenship, *Queen Mary* V iv 47
Infirmity And *I*, that knew mine own *i*, *Becket* I iii 696
I pray God pardon mine *i*. „ II ii 353
Ingratitude *I*, Injustice, Evil-tongue, Labour-in-vain. *Queen Mary* V ii 156
His heart so gall'd with thine *i*, *Becket* I iii 4
Inhabitant altho' the *i's* Seem semi-barbarous. *Prom. of May* II 541
not only love the country, But its *i's* too; „ II 546
Then one at least of its *i's* „ II 552
Inherit Ay, sir; *I* the Great Silence. *Queen Mary* III ii 199
Why then the throne is empty. Who *i's*? *Harold* III i 235
Inherit (*continued*) Who *i's*? Edgar the Atheling? *Harold* III i 239
hand that next *I's* thee be but as true to thee *Becket* I i 358
Thou wilt *i* the land, And so wouldst sell *Foresters* II i 534
Inherited some will say because I have *i* my Uncle. *Prom. of May* III 598
True, and I have an *i* loathing of these black sheep of the Papacy. *Becket, Pro.* 460
Inheriting which we *I* reap an easier harvest. *Becket* II ii 194
Inheritor That bright *i* of your eyes—your boy? *The Falcon* 306
Inhospitable Friends, in that last *i* plunge Our boat hath burst her ribs; *Harold* II i 1
Injure That none should wrong or *i* your Archbishop. *Becket* I iii 754
Injured send her hosts Of *i* Saints to scatter sparks of plague *Harold* II ii 745
Injury not be wanting Those that will urge her *i*— *Queen Mary* III vi 176
Injustice Ingratitude, *I*, Evil-tongue, Labour-in-vain. „ V ii 156
Shall *we* too work *i*? *Foresters* I iii 87
we must at times have wrought Some great *i*, „ III 156
If the king and the law work *i*, „ IV 229
Do some *i*, if you hold us here Longer „ IV 941
Ink is written in invisible *i's* 'Lust, Prodigality, *Prom. of May* II 283
Inland we two Have track'd the King to this dark *i* wood; *Becket* III ii 3
Inmost weight of the very land itself, Down to the *i* centre. *Foresters* IV 1027
Inn at the wayside *i* Close by that alder-island *Prom. of May* II 534
Innocence And witness to your Grace's *i*, *Queen Mary* III v 50
Life on the face, the brows—clear *i*! *Becket* II i 195
i's that will cry From all the hidden by-ways „ III iii 14
equal for pure *i* of nature, And loveliness of feature. *Prom. of May* II 372
Except she could defend her *i*. *Foresters* II ii 47
Innocent (adj.) and of the good Lady Jane as a poor *i* child who had but obeyed her father; *Queen Mary* I i 94
perchance A child more *i* than Lady Jane. „ I v 502
No, no; her *i* blood had blinded me. „ III i 345
and when her *i* eyes were bound, She, „ III i 405
And love is joyful, *i*, beautiful, And jealousy is wither'd, sour and ugly: *Foresters* II ii 64
and another—worse!—An *i* maid. „ III 389
Innocent (s) O God, how many an *i* Has left his bones *Becket* II ii 408
Inquisition Holy absolution! holy *I*! *Queen Mary* I iii 32
cited me to Rome, for heresy, Before his *I*. „ V ii 43
Insane That palate is *i* which cannot tell *Becket, Pro.* 104
Insolence I hate him for his *i* to all. *De Tracy.* And I for all his *i* to thee. „ V i 226
Insolent Sending an *i* shot that dash'd the seas Upon us, *Queen Mary* V i 57
I clown. Shall I smite him with the edge of the sword? *Becket* I iv 223
Inspire O Thou, that dost *i* the germ with life, *The Cup* II 257
Inspired Why should not Heaven have so *i* the King? *Becket* I i 130
Instant (adj.) It craves an *i* answer, Ay or No. *Mary.* An *i* Ay or No! the Council sits. Give it me quick. *Queen Mary* I v 589
and had my constant 'No' For all but *i* battle. *Harold* V i 7
Instant (s) You are to come to Court on the *i*; *Queen Mary* III v 223
Come, girl, thou shalt along with us on the *i*. *Friar Tuck.* Then on the *i* I will break thy head. *Foresters* IV 679
Instinct following his own *i's* as his God, *Prom. of May* I 588
Insured I were *i*, Miss, an' I lost nowt by it. „ II 57
Intent to the *i* That you may lose your English heritage. *Queen Mary* V i 132
Intercept did not Gardiner *i* A letter which „ V ii 495
Intercession That by your gracious means and *i* „ III iii 121
by your *i* May from the Apostolic see obtain, „ III iii 146
Interdict from the side of Rome, An *i* on England— *Becket, Pro.* 223
To blast my realms with excommunication And *i*. „ II ii 53
The immediate thunder-blast of *i*: „ III iii 26
bell-silencing, anti-marrying, burial-hindering *i* „ III iii 56
King at last is fairly scared by this cloud—this *i*. „ III iii 64
Intermeddling This Godstow-Becket *i* such „ IV ii 457
Interpreter Is he thy mouthpiece, thine *i*? *Foresters* I ii 212
Interwoven See here—an *i* H and E! *Harold* I ii 57
Invade bees, If any creeping life *i* their hive *Queen Mary* III iii 54
Invader May all *i's* perish like Hardrada! *Harold* IV iii 77
Inverted *I* Æsop—mountain out of mouse. *Queen Mary* II i 67
Invisible There, there, is written in *i* inks *Prom. of May* II 283

Involve which hatred by and by *I's* the ruler *Queen Mary* III iv 161
Inward Or am I slandering my most *i* friend, „ IV ii 105
Inwrought white satin his trunk-hose, *I* with silver,— „ III i 78
Ionian Artemis, Artemis, hear him, *I* Artemis ! *The Cup* II 277
Iræ Their hour is hard at hand, their ' dies *I*,' *Queen Mary* III iv 426
Ireland —Scotland, *I*, Iceland, Orkney, *Harold* III ii 124
Iron (adj.) The Duke Of Alva, an *i* soldier. *Queen Mary* III i 194
With golden deeds and *i* strokes that brought *Harold* II ii 47
A breath that fleets beyond this *i* world, „ III ii 197
knowing that he *must* have Moved in the *i* grooves of Destiny ? *Prom. of May* II 267
Iron (s) *I* on *i* clang, *Harold* IV iii 160
With hands too limp to brandish *i*— „ V i 449
flask or two Of that same vintage. There is *i* in it. *The Falcon* 586
I will fuse, and marble melt ; *Prom. of May* II 505
Iron-mooded make yield this *i-m* Duke To let me go. *Harold* II ii 339
Ironside or English *I* Who fought with Knut, „ IV iii 53
Irregular This is *i* and the work of John. [' *I*, *i* ! *Foresters* I iii 71
Irresolute Fine eyes—but melancholy, *i*— *Queen Mary* III iv 337
Irreverent St. Cupid, that is too *i*. *Becket* V i 198
Irritable That *i* forelock which he rubs, *Queen Mary* I iv 265
Iscariot Not red like *I's*. „ III i 217
Island (adj.) Yearns to set foot upon your *i* shore. „ I v 367
and plunge His foreign fist into our *i* Church „ III iv 364
Fair *i* star ! *Elizabeth*. I shine ! „ V iii 15
And send thee back among thine *i* mists With laughter. *Harold* II ii 181
The spiritual giant with our *i* laws And customs, *Becket* IV ii 444
Island (s) (*See also* **Alder-island, Spice-island**) or the stout old *i* will become A rotten limb *Queen Mary* II i 104
The *i's* call'd into the dawning church „ III iii 172
We parted like the brook yonder about the alder *i*, *Prom. of May* I 773
Island-Church would make Our *i-C* a schism from Christendom, *Becket* I iii 116
Islander Because these *i's* are brutal beasts ? *Queen Mary* III vi 153
Isle and rooted in far *i's* Beyond my seeing : *Harold* III i 153
To Holy Peter in our English *i* ! „ III i 207
Keep him away from the lone little *i*. *Becket* II i 16
Row to the blessed *I's* ! the blessed *I's* ! *The Cup* II 525
That ever blossom'd on this English *i*. *Foresters* I ii 124
Islip it be a var waay vor my owld legs up vro' *I*. *Queen Mary* IV iii 473
Dumble's the best milcher in *I*. (repeat) „ IV iii 478, 497
'Issen (himself) the owd man's coom'd ageän to *'i*, *Prom. of May* III 703
Issue (s) Yea, were there *i* born to her, *Queen Mary* I v 301
Issue (verb) he that lookt a fangless one, *I's* a venomous adder. *Becket* I iii 453
Istis *Non defensoribus i*, Walter Map. „ II ii 346
Italian Catholic church as well Without as with the *I* ? *Queen Mary* III iii 99
He is all *I*, and he hates the Spaniard ; „ V ii 55
Italy I have seen A pine in *I* that cast „ III iv 136
Tainted with Lutheranism in *I*. „ III iv 227
In your soft *I* yonder ! „ III iv 254
To plump the leaner pouch of *I*. „ III iv 365
You make your wars upon him down in *I* :— „ V i 142
Your troops were never down in *I*. „ V ii 315
and with him who died Alone in *I*. „ V ii 508
Itch (s) Crutches, and *i'es*, and leprosies, and ulcers, *Becket* I iv 254
Itch (verb) Yet my fingers *i* to beat him into nothing. „ I iv 229
Iver (ever) I doänt believe he's *i* a 'eart under his waistcoat. *Prom. of May* I 130
but if *i* I cooms upo' Gentleman Hedgar ageän, „ II 136
burnin' o' the owld archbishop 'll burn the Pwoap out o' this 'ere land vor *i* and *i*. *Queen Mary* IV iii 536
Ivy Faster than *i*. Must I hack her arms off ? *Harold* V ii 146
Your names will cling like *i* to the wood. *Foresters* IV 1085

J

Jachin (a brass pillar, entrance to Solomon's temple) lo ! my two pillars, *J* and Boaz !— *Harold* III i 192
Jackson (labourer to Farmer Dobson) Higgins, *J*, Luscombe, Nokes, *Prom. of May* III 53
Jacta *J* tonitrua Deus bellator ! *Harold* V i 569
Jade fellow that on a lame *j* came to court, *Becket* V i 246
Jail whose bolts, That *j* you from free life, *Queen Mary* III v 172
Jailor My *j*— *Bedingfield*. One, whose bolts, „ III v 170
Hast thou such trustless *j's* in thy North ? *Harold* II ii 685
Jalousies (jealousies) he be fit to bust hissen wi' spites and *j*. *Prom. of May* II 165
James *J*, didst thou ever see a carrion crow *Queen Mary* IV iii 5
James, St. *See* **St. James**
Jane (Lady Jane Grey) and of the good Lady *J* as a poor innocent child „ I i 94
That gave her royal crown to Lady *J*. „ I ii 19
saying of this Lady *J*, Now in the Tower ? „ I v 37
Lady *J* stood up Stiff as the very backbone „ I v 42
tell your Grace What Lady *J* replied. „ I v 50
A child more innocent than Lady *J*. „ I v 502
Or Lady *J* ? *Wyatt*. No, poor soul ; no. „ II i 241
And Lady *J* had left us. „ II iv 139
Lady *J* ? *Crowd*. God save their Graces ! „ III i 341
Cried no God-bless-her to the Lady *J*, „ III iv 45
Janus-faces But *J-f* looking diverse ways. „ III ii 75
Jar since the fondest pair of doves will *j*, *Becket* IV ii 41
that Dobbins, is it, With whom I used to *j* ? *Prom. of May* II 613
Jarr'd but suddenly *J* on this rock. *Becket* I iii 382
Jarring *See* **Ever-jarring**
Javelin Our *j's* Answer their arrows. *Harold* V i 521
Jay Hawk, buzzard, *j*, the mavis and the merle, *Foresters* I iii 115
Jealous (*See also* **Childlike-jealous**) and thou in thy way shouldst be *j* of the King, *Becket, Pro.* 511
will he not mock at me The *j* fool balk'd of her will— „ IV ii 423
Art thou not *j* of her ? *The Falcon* 6
Ay, ruffle thyself—*be j* ! Thou shouldst be *j* of her. „ 22
J of me with Eva ! Is it so ? *Prom. of May* I 471
Jealousy (*See also* **Jalousies**) and *j* Hath in it an alchemic force *Queen Mary* III vi 180
Did you not tell me he was crazed with *j*, *Prom. of May* III 566
I am a man not prone to *jealousies*, „ III 626
O Kate, true love and *j* are twins, *Foresters* II ii 63
And *j* is wither'd, sour and ugly : „ II ii 65
J, *j* of the king. „ II ii 141
Elf, with spiteful heart and eye, Talk of *j* ? „ II ii 173
Jean *they* were fishers of men, Father *J* says. *Harold* II i 35
Jeer heard One of your Council fleer and *j* at him. *Queen Mary* II ii 393
nursery-cocker'd child will *j* at aught „ II ii 395
The statesman that shall *j* and fleer at men, „ II ii 397
if he *j* not seeing the true man Behind his folly, „ II ii 400
if he see the man and still will *j*, „ II ii 402
Jenny here's little Dickon, and little Robin, and little *J*— „ II iii 113
Jeopardy being in great *j* of his life, he hath made *Becket* I iv 263
Jerk Let be thy jokes and thy *j's*, man ! *The Falcon* 133
Jerk'd Things that seem *j* out of the common rut *Harold* I i 137
Jerusalem table steams, like a heathen altar ; nay, like the altar at *J*. *Becket* I iv 70
smell o' the mou'd 'ud ha' maäde ma live as long as *J*. *Prom. of May* I 378
Jest (s) the tongue yet quiver'd with the *j* *Queen Mary* I v 476
a *j* In time of danger shows the pulses even. „ II ii 356
And the Dutchman, Now laughing at some *j* ? „ III i 196
nave and aisles all empty as a fool's *j* ! „ IV iii 287
Thy *j*—no more. Why—look—is this a sleeve *Becket, Pro.* 249
Then for thy barren *j* Take thou mine answer „ *Pro.* 281
—That were a *j* indeed ! „ *Pro.* 297
There's no *j* on the brows of Herbert there. „ *Pro.* 390
good old man would sometimes have his *j*— „ I i 62
J or prophecy there ? *Herbert*. Both, Thomas, both. „ I i 67
or any harm done to the people if my *j* be in defence of the Truth ? „ II ii 339
if the *j* be so done that the people Delight „ II ii 341
Bandy their own rude *j's* with them, *The Cup* I ii 360
Jest (verb) Ha ! ha ! sir ; but you *j* ; I love it : *Queen Mary* II ii 355
Thou angerest me, man : I do not *j*. *Becket, Pro.* 300
We did but *j*. „ *Pro.* 389
Why do you *j* with me, and try To fright me ? *Prom. of May* I 664
Jester Thou art a *j* and a verse-maker. *Becket* II ii 334

Jesting if you be not *j*, Neither the old world, *Prom. of May* I 673
They are *j* at us yonder, mocking us? *Foresters* IV 676
Jesus Christ (*See also* **Christ, Christ Jesus**) save her thro' the blood Of *J C* *Queen Mary* III i 388
Jetsam range with *j* and with offal thrown „ III iii 191
Jew He calls us worse than *J's*, Moors, Saracens. „ V i 150
There is Antwerp and the *J's*. „ V i 183
Advanced thee at his instance by the *J's*, *Becket* I iii 644
Jewel (adj.) Beetle's *j* armour crack'd, Queen. *Foresters* II ii 160
Jewel (s) I left her with rich *j's* in her hand, *Queen Mary* I iv 242
I have the *j* of a loyal heart. „ I iv 247
left about Like loosely-scatter'd *j's*, „ II i 28
in whose crown our Kent is the fairest *j*. „ II i 164
How look'd the Queen? *Bagenhall.* No fairer for her *j's*. „ III i 92
To set that precious *j*, Roger of York. *Becket, Pro.* 270
God's eyes! what a lovely cross! what *j's*! „ *Pro.* 371
to people heaven in the great day When God makes up his *j's*. „ V ii 497
Behold the *j* of St. Pancratius *Harold* II ii 700
tho' I grudge the pretty *j*, that I Have worn, *Prom. of May* I 473
and *not* a heart like the *j* in it— *The Falcon* 91
Outvalues all the *j's* upon earth. „ 779
Jingling Has my simple song set you *j*? *Becket, Pro.* 379
Joan (country wife) Pwoaps be pretty things, *J*, *Queen Mary* IV iii 469
Our Daisy's as good 'z her. *Tib.* Noä, *J*. *Joan.* Our Daisy's butter's as good 'z hern. *Tib.* Noä, *J*. *Joan.* Our Daisy's cheeses be better. *Tib.* Noä, *J*. „ IV iii 480
Ay, *J*, and my owld man wur up and awaay „ IV iii 488
Ay, *J*; and Queen Mary gwoes on a burnin' „ IV iii 522
but tek thou my word vor't, *J*,— „ IV iii 533
Joan of Kent (Elizabeth Barton, executed 1534) 'twas you That sign'd the burning of poor *J o K*; „ IV ii 206
Jocelyn (Bishop of Salisbury) (*See also* **Salisbury**) No saying of mine—*J* of Salisbury. *Becket* II ii 372
John (Gospel of St.) They go like those old Pharisees in *J* *Queen Mary* II ii 8
John (Little) *See* **Little John**
John (of Oxford, called the Swearer) (*See also* **John of Oxford, John the Swearer**) See if our pious—what shall I call him, *J*?— *Becket* II ii 39
J, Thou hast served me heretofore with Rome— „ II ii 459
Honest *J*! To Rome again! the storm begins again. „ II ii 467
John (of Salisbury) (*See also* **John of Salisbury, Salisbury**)
Our good *J* Must speed you to your bower „ I i 290
Dan *J* with a nun, That Map, „ I i 305
—*J*, and out of breath! „ I i 388
Why, *J*, my kingdom is not of this world. „ V ii 18
Dan *J*, how much we lose, we celibates, „ V ii 197
You hear them, brother *J*; Why do you stand so silent, brother *J*? „ V ii 534
Is it so, Dan *J*? well, what should I have done? „ V ii 552
My counsel is already taken, *J*. „ V ii 561
Methought they would have brain'd me with it, *J*. „ V ii 613
John (Prince, afterwards King of England) and these are the days of Prince *J*: *Foresters* I i 178
A gallant Earl. I love him as I hate *J*. „ I i 191
in the service of our good king Richard against the party of *J*, „ I i 195
This *J*—this Norman tyranny— „ I i 238
I am old and forget. Was Prince *J* there? *Marian.* The Sheriff of Nottingham was there—not *J*. *Sir Richard.* Beware of *J* and the Sheriff of Nottingham. „ I i 251
he hath sold himself to that beast *J*— „ I i 268
Down with *J*! (repeat) *Foresters* I ii 4, 12, 16, 17, 30
Perfect—who should know you for Prince *J*, *Foresters* I ii 21
ye did wrong in crying 'Down with *J*;' For be he dead, then *J* may be our King. „ I ii 97
But if it be so we must bear with *J*. „ I ii 102
I fear you be of those who hold more by *J* than Richard. *Sheriff.* True, for through *J* I had my sheriffship. I am *J's* till Richard come back again, and then I am Richard's. „ I ii 199
Beware of *J*! *Marian.* I hate him. „ I ii 214
John (Prince, afterwards King of England) (*continued*) Bad me beware Of *J*: what maid but would beware of *J*? *Foresters* I ii 256
This is irregular and the work of *J*. „ I iii 71
How should we cope with *J*? „ I iii 79
I held for Richard, and I hated *J*. „ II i 52
Our vice-king *J*, True king of vice— „ II i 82
our *J* By his Norman arrogance and dissoluteness, „ II i 84
J—Shame on him!—Stole on her, „ II i 110
the Sheriff, and by heaven, Prince *J* himself „ II i 173
Prince *J*, the Sheriff, and a mercenary. *Sir Richard.* Prince *J* again. We are flying from this *J*. „ II i 445
be there wolves in Sherwood? *Marian.* The wolf, *J*! „ II i 513
this is Maid Marian Flying from *J*—disguised. „ II i 680
break, Far as he might, the power of *J*— „ II i 696
A maiden now Were ill-bested in these dark days of *J*, „ II ii 46
That *J* last week return'd to Nottingham, „ III 147
We robb'd the traitors that are leagued with *J*; „ III 160
My lord *J*, In wrath because you drove him from the forest, „ III 449
to 'scape The glance of *J*—— „ III 463
The bee should buzz about the Court of *J*. No ribald *J* is Love, no wanton Prince, „ IV 45
Art thou for Richard, or allied to *J*? *Richard.* I am allied to *J*. „ IV 136
But being o' *J's* side we must have thy gold. „ IV 157
But I am more for Richard than for *J*. „ IV 160
or the head of a fool, or the heart of Prince *J*, „ IV 213
Break thine alliance with this faithless *J*, „ IV 324
Still I am more for Richard than for *J*. „ IV 330
for how canst thou be thus allied With *J*, „ IV 351
The Sheriff! the Sheriff, follow'd by Prince *J* „ IV 588
My liege, Prince *J*—— *Richard.* Say thou no word against my brother *J*. „ IV 823
John (St.) *See* **John (Gospel of St.), St. John**
John of Oxford (*See also* **John, John the Swearer**) I, *J o O*, The President of this Council, *Becket* I iii 74
For *J o O* here to read to you. „ I iii 417
Cursed be *J o O*, Roger of York, And Gilbert Foliot! „ II ii 265
John of Salisbury (*See also* **John, Salisbury**) We gave thee to the charge of *J o S*, „ I i 247
J o S Hath often laid a cold hand on my heats, „ I i 383
He watch'd her pass with *J o S* „ I ii 40
priest whom *J o S* trusted Hath sent another. „ III i 69
J o S committed The secret of the bower, „ III iii 4
I know him; our good *J o S*. „ V ii 77
make me not a woman, *J o S*, „ V ii 148
John the Swearer (*See also* **John, John of Oxford**) They call thee *J t S*. „ II ii 462
Join To *j* a voice, so potent with her Highness, *Queen Mary* IV i 117
May the great angels *j* their wings, „ V iv 6
J hands, let brethren dwell in unity; *Harold* I i 397
j our hands before the hosts, That all may see. „ IV i 241
And then thy King might *j* the Antipope, *Becket* I iii 211
every thread of thought Is broken ere it *j's*— „ V ii 207
I'll *j* with him: I may reap something from him— *The Cup* I i 177
tho' a stranger fain would be allow'd To *j* the hunt. „ I i 197
And *j* your life this day with his, „ II 135
Well, my child, let us *j* them. *Prom. of May* I 797
till he *j* King Richard in the Holy Land. *Foresters* I ii 238
And *j* our feasts and all your forest games „ III 84
by St. Mary these beggars and these friars shall *j* you. „ III 417
J them and they are a true marriage; „ III 420
Our rebel Abbot then shall *j* your hands, „ IV 933
Join'd What hinders but that Spain and England *j*, *Queen Mary* V iii 69
he *j* with thee To drive me outlaw'd. *Harold* IV ii 13
a random guest Who *j* me in the hunt. *The Cup* I ii 109
And *j* my banner in the Holy Land, *Foresters* IV 1000
Joining Mary of England, *j* hands with Spain, *Queen Mary* I v 298
Joke Let be thy *j's* and thy jerks, man! *The Falcon* 132
Jolt Against the unpleasant *j's* of this rough road *Prom. of May* I 228
Jonah that the fish had swallowed me, Like *J*, *Harold* II i 38
Rolf, what fish did swallow *J*? *Rolf.* A whale! „ II i 42
Jostle winds so cross and *j* among these towers. „ II ii 155
Journey I am an old man wearied with my *j*, *Queen Mary* III ii 128
make ready for the *j*. „ III v 278

Journey (*continued*) so much worse For last day's *j*. *The Falcon* 834
Joy Ay, that was in her hour of *j*; *Queen Mary* I i 84
wearied with my journey, Ev'n with my *j*. „ III ii 129
An angel cry 'There is more *j* in Heaven,'— „ IV ii 10
Either to live with Christ in Heaven with *j*, „ IV iii 221
I wish you *j* o' the King's brother. *Becket* III i 155
O *j* for the promise of May, (repeat) *Prom. of May* I 43, 44, 723, 725
I reel beneath the weight of utter *j*— *The Cup* II 450
for who could embrace such an armful of *j*? *Foresters* I ii 71
Whate'er thy *j's*, they vanish with the day; „ I iii 44
Joyful And love is *j*, innocent, beautiful, „ II ii 64
Judas-lover *J-l* of our passion-play Hath track'd us hither. *Becket* IV ii 136
Judge (s) *J's* had pronounced That our young Edward *Queen Mary* I ii 24
if I'm any *j*, By God, you are as poor a poet, „ II i 112
sat in mine own courts Judging my *j's*, *Becket* I iii 369
Doubtless, like *j's* of another bench, *Foresters* III 153
Judge (verb) I shall *j* with my own eyes *Queen Mary* I i 133
From thine own mouth I *j* thee— „ I iii 54
You cannot *j* the liquor from the lees. „ IV iii 550
Who but the bridegroom dares to *j* the bride. *Becket* I iii 685
If we may *j* the kernel by the husk, *The Cup* I i 174
Perhaps you *j* him With feeble charity: „ I ii 185
Sit here, my queen, and *j* the world with me. *Foresters* III 152
But will the King, then, *j* us all unheard? „ IV 897
Judged As if he had been the Holy Father, sat And *j* it. *Queen Mary* IV iii 45
The Lord be *j* again by Pilate? No! *Becket* I iii 97
make my cry to the Pope, By whom I will be *j*; „ I iii 725
Judgement what a day! nigh upo' *j* daay loike. *Queen Mary* IV iii 468
Judging sat in mine own courts *J* my judges, *Becket* I iii 369
Judgment (*See also* **Judgement**) *J*, and pain accruing thereupon; *Queen Mary* III iii 219
This was the cause, and hence the *j* on her. „ III iv 187
For which God's righteous *j* fell upon you „ III iv 240
and these *j's* on the land— „ V i 96
You must abide my *j*, and my father's, „ V i 145
And our great lords will sit in *j* on him. *Becket* I iii 549
Sons sit in *j* on their father!— „ I iii 551
decline The *j* of the King? „ I iii 676
Nay, but hear thy *j*. The King and all his barons——
Becket. *J*! Barons! „ I iii 682
Ay, the princes sat in *j* against me, „ I iv 129
yea, and in the day of *j* also, „ I iv 147
there are men Of canker'd *j* everywhere— „ V ii 61
by the *j* of the officers of the said lord king, *Foresters* I iii 64
Judgment-seat drag The cleric before the civil *j-s*, *Becket* I iii 84
Juggle What game, what *j*, what devilry are you playing? „ V i 153
Juggled She knew me from the first, she *j* with me, *Prom. of May* III 687
Juggler *J* and bastard—bastard—he hates that most— *Harold* II ii 773
And for *my* part therein—Back to that *j*, „ V i 54
Julius (the Third, Pope) Legate From our most Holy Father *J*, Pope, *Queen Mary* III iii 126
Our Lord and Holy Father, *J*, „ III iii 212
J the Third Was ever just, and mild, and father-like; „ V ii 30
reft me of that legateship Which *J* gave me, „ V ii 35
July King closed with me last *J* That I should pass the censures of the Church *Becket* V ii 389
Jumiéges Did ye not outlaw your archbishop Robert, Robert of *J*— *Harold* I i 57
Robert the Archbishop! Robert of *J*, „ II ii 530
Jumped or the cow that *j* over the moon. *Foresters* II i 435
Junction Threaten our *j* with the Emperor— *Becket* II ii 471
June They did not last three *J's*. *Prom. of May* III 589
How few *J's* Will heat our pulses quicker! *Foresters* IV 1061
Juno bust of *J* and the brows and eyes Of Venus; *The Cup* I i 120
Jupiter O all ye Gods—*J*!—*J*! „ II 453
Just O, *j* God! Sweet mother, you had time and cause enough *Queen Mary* I v 22
His learning makes his burning the more *j*. „ IV i 160
Who deems it a most *j* and holy war. „ V i 147
Julius the Third Was ever *j*, and mild, and father-like; „ V ii 31
We have heard Of thy *j*, mild, and equal governance; *Harold* II ii 690
And all our *j* and wise and holy men That shall be born hereafter. „ III i 209
Just (*continued*) for it seem'd to me but *j* The Church should pay her scutage like the lords. *Becket* I i 33
All that you say is *j*. I cannot answer it Till better times, „ III i 1
Justice Your courts of *j* will determine that. *Queen Mary* II iv 130
By seeking *j* at a stranger's hand „ IV i 20
make his battle-axe keen As thine own sharp-dividing *j*, *Harold* V i 564
Ay, and the King of kings, Or *j*; *Becket* I i 33
I trust I have not; Not mangled *j*. „ I i 356
churl against the baron—yea, And did him *j*; „ I iii 367
The King's will and God's will and *j*; „ I iii 420
he's no respect for the Queen, or the parson, or the *j* o' peace, or owt. *Prom. of May* I 133
That were a wild *j* indeed. „ III 156
how often *j* drowns Between the law and the letter of the law! *Foresters* IV 512
Was *j* dead because the King was dead? „ IV 847
We dealt in the wild *j* of the woods. „ IV 1072
Justiciary Before the Prince and chief *J*, *Becket* I iii 709
I have sent to the Abbot and *j* *Foresters* IV 88
The Abbot of York and his *j*. „ IV 335
You, my lord Abbot, you *J*, I made you Abbot, you *J*: „ IV 842
Jute Angle, *J*, Dane, Saxon, Norman, *Harold* II ii 762
yet he held that Dane, *J*, Angle, Saxon, „ IV i 77
Jutting O thin-skinn'd hand and *j* veins, *Queen Mary* IV ii 204
But after rain o'erleaps a *j* rock And shoots three hundred feet. *The Cup* I i 110

K

Kate (attendant on Marian) You do well, Mistress *K*, to sing and to gather roses. *Foresters* I i 23
I would like to show you, Mistress *K*, „ I i 49
O sweet *K*, my first love, the first kiss, „ I i 126
I have played at the foils too with *K*: „ I i 218
to stand between me and your woman, *K*. „ I i 305
Speak to me, *K*, and say you pardon me! „ II ii 53
O *K*, true love and jealousy are twins, „ II ii 62
I have been a fool and I have lost my *K*. „ II ii 79
O good *K*—If my man-Robin were but a bird-Robin, „ III 38
call *K* when you will, for I am close at hand. „ III 50
Why, where is *K*? *Marian*. *K*! „ III 258
Search them, *K*, and see if they have spoken truth. „ III 288
Honour to thee, brave Marian, and thy *K*. „ III 300
my lady, *K* and I have fallen out again, „ III 411
come between me and my *K* and make us one again. „ III 422
Embrace me, Marian, and thou, good *K*, Kiss and congratulate me, my good *K*. „ IV 1032
Katekin I have lodged my pretty *K* in her bower. „ II i 418
Keen Take heed, take heed! The blade is *k* as death. *Queen Mary* V v 175
make his battle-axe *k* As thine own sharp-dividing justice, *Harold* V i 563
Keep (s) he is here, And yonder is thy *k*.' „ II ii 359
Keep (verb) Stand back, *k* a clear lane! *Queen Mary* I i 1
Have you, my Lord? Best *k* it for your own. „ I iv 133
You've a bold heart; *k* it so. „ I iv 269
That I may *k* you thus, who am your friend „ I v 133
These let them *k* at present; „ I v 407
To bind me first by oaths I could not *k*, And *k* „ I v 557
To guard and *k* you whole and safe from all „ II ii 246
He *k's*, they say, some secret that may cost „ III i 200
Why do they *k* us here? „ III v 15
He is my good friend, and I would *k* him so; „ V iii 91
Why did you *k* me prating? Horses, there! „ V iii 113
Pray'd me to pay her debts, and *k* the Faith; „ V v 257
and *k* me still In eyeshot. *Harold* II ii 241
arm'd men Ever *k* watch beside my chamber door, „ II ii 245
He did not mean to *k* his vow. „ III i 248
K that for Norman William! „ IV iii 169
chart here mark'd '*Her Bower*,' Take, *k* it, friend. *Becket*, *Pro.* 161
Wast thou not told to *k* thyself from sight? „ I i 251
And mean to *k* them, In spite of thee! „ I iii 142
K him away from the lone little isle. „ II i 15

Keep (verb (*continued*) That if they *k* him longer as their guest, *Becket* II i 91
You did your best or worse to *k* her Duchy. „ II ii 83
we make the time, we *k* the time, ay, and we serve the time; „ II ii 368
I would have done my most to *k* Rome holy, „ II ii 401
asked our mother if I could *k* a quiet tongue i' my head, „ III i 119
The King *k's* his forest head of game here, „ III ii 37
to *k* the figure moist and make it hold water, „ III iii 165
k her Indungeon'd from one whisper of the wind, „ IV ii 145
Rest you easy, For I am easy to *k*. „ V ii 513
That in the summer *k's* the mountain side, *The Cup* I i 108
Not one to *k* a woman's fealty when Assailed „ I i 176
k it, or you sell me To torment and to death. „ I ii 214
k us From seeing all too near that urn, „ I iii 132
Then *k* your wreath, But you will find me *The Falcon* 772
I cannot *k* your diamonds, for the gift I ask for, „ 776
But he will *k* his love to you for ever! „ 892
Owd Steer wur afeärd she wouldn't be back i' time to *k* his birthdaäy, *Prom. of May* I 17
I came back to *k* his birthday. *Dobson.* Well I be coomed to *k* his birthdaäy an' all. „ I 74
She *will* break fence. I can't *k* her in order. „ I 194
if tha can't *k* thy one cow i' horder, how can tha *k* all thy scholards i' horder? „ I 196
Let him *k* awaäy, then; but coom, „ I 424
if the child could *k* Her counsel. „ I 477
But *k* us lovers. „ I 639
K up your heart until we meet again. „ I 753
Noä, noä! *K* 'em. But I hed a word to saäy to ye. „ II 44
has promised to *k* our heads above water; „ III 170
Come, come, *k* a good heart! „ III 252
but I *k* a good heart and make the most of it, *Foresters* I i 28
Shall I *k* one little rose for Little John? „ I i 112
so that you *k* the cowl down and speak not? „ I ii 21
I *k* it For holy vows made to the blessed Saints „ I ii 174
but can *k* his followers true. „ II i 77
Why did ye *k* us at the door so long? „ II i 223
I *k* it to kill nightingales. „ II i 380
He is old and almost mad to *k* the land. „ II i 528
I *k* it for her. *Robin.* Nay, she swore it never „ II i 591
You hope to hold and *k* her for yourself, „ IV 477
We all *k* watch. „ IV 608
And we shall *k* the land. „ IV 637
K silence, bully friar, before the King. „ IV 919
Keeper So less chance for false *k's*. *Harold* II ii 688
With Cain's answer, my lord. Am I his *k*? *Becket* I iv 187
Keepest that thou *k* a record of his birthdays? *Foresters* I i 221
Keeping Might strengthen thee in *k* of thy word, *Harold* II ii 730
Is guiltier *k* this, than breaking it. „ III i 231
I have done wrong in *k* your secret; *Prom. of May* III 399
Kennel if the city be sick, and I cannot call the *k* sweet, *Becket* II ii 349
Kent your worship the first man in *K* and Christendom, *Queen Mary* II i 64
Men of *K*; England of England; „ II i 157
in whose crown our *K* is the fairest jewel. „ II i 163
Or tamperers with that treason out of *K*. „ II ii 12
these rebels out of *K* Have made strong head „ II ii 145
The Queen of England or the rabble of *K*? „ II ii 274
And strong to throw ten Wyatts and all *K*. „ II ii 354
he was my neighbour once in *K*. „ II iii 86
A hundred here and hundreds hang'd in *K*. „ III i 2
'twas you That sign'd the burning of poor Joan of *K*; „ IV ii 206
happy home-return and the King's kiss of peace in *K*. *Becket* III iii 329
Kentish The Queen of England—or the *K* Squire? *Queen Mary* II ii 269
These *K* ploughmen cannot break the guards. „ II iv 17
Kept you that have *k* your old customs upright, „ II i 158
I *k* my head for use of Holy Church; „ III iv 359
I had *k* My Robins and my cows in sweeter order „ III v 269
thou hast sworn an oath Which, if not *k*, *Harold* II ii 739
Fain had I *k* thine earldom in thy hands „ V i 275
by thy wisdom Hast *k* it firm from shaking; *Becket, Pro.* 204
she *k* the seventh commandment better than some I know on, „ III i 193
We never *k* a secret from each other; *Prom. of May* I 552
you *k* your veil too close for that when they carried you in; „ III 226
Kernel If we may judge the *k* by the husk, *The Cup* I i 174
Kex like a bottle full up to the cork, or as hollow as a *k*, *Foresters* IV 211
Key Give me thy *k's*. *Harold* II ii 681
See here this little *k* about my neck! „ III i 10
Gave me the golden *k's* of Paradise. *Becket* I i 54
Kick if he did me the good grace to *k* me *Foresters* IV 364
Kick'd the cow *k*, and all her milk was spilt. *Queen Mary* III v 266
thou hast *k* down the board. I know thee of old. *Becket, Pro.* 315
slave that eat my bread has *k* his King! „ V i 242
play'd at ball with And *k* it featureless— *The Cup* II 128
Kill We do not *k* the child for doing that *Queen Mary* I v 62
we know that ye be come to *k* the Queen, „ II iii 108
don't ye *k* the Queen here, Sir Thomas; „ II iii 110
we pray you to *k* the Queen further off, „ II iii 114
I have not come to *k* the Queen Or here or there: „ II iii 117
We *k* the heretics that sting the soul— „ III iv 68
the shepherd doth not *k* The sheep that wander „ III iv 102
you must *k* him if you would have him rest— „ V v 69
If Hate can *k*, And Loathing wield a Saxon battle-axe— *Harold* V i 413
k, *k* with knife or venom One of his slanderous harlots? *Becket* IV ii 409
s'pose I *k's* my pig, and gi'es it among 'em, *Prom. of May* I 147
'As flies to the Gods; they *k* us for their sport.' „ I 264
It is Nature *k's*, And not for *her* sport either. „ I 272
That hold by Richard, tho' they *k* his deer. *Foresters* I iii 100
I keep it to *k* nightingales. „ II i 380
if we *k* a stag, our dogs have their paws cut off, „ IV 224
Kill'd Thy *k* but for their pleasure and the power *Queen Mary* III iv 74
and *k* away at once Out of the flutter. „ III v 163
O God, I have *k* my Philip! „ V v 181
rose or no rose, has *k* the golden violet. *Becket, Pro.* 351
K half the crew, dungeon'd the other half „ V ii 444
a rumour then That you were *k* in battle. *The Falcon* 382
but we fought for it back, And *k*— „ 615
And we *k* 'em by the score! „ 620
mastiff, That all but *k* the beggar, *Prom. of May* I 559
niver 'a been talkin' haäfe an hour wi' the divil 'at *k* her oän sister, „ II 604
If it had *k* one of the Steers there the other day, „ III 249
K the sward where'er they sat, *Foresters* II ii 152
Killing And cruel at it, *k* helpless flies; *Queen Mary* III iv 65
and the power They felt in *k*. „ III iv 76
Kin but follow'd the device of those Her nearest *k*: „ III i 380
Let kith and *k* stand close as our shield-wall, *Harold* I i 398
His *k*, all his belongings, overseas; *Becket* II i 71
restore his *k*, Reseat him on his throne of Canterbury, „ II ii 117
Send back again those exiles of my *k* „ III iii 187
From whom, as being too *k*, you know, „ IV ii 307
I dare not brave my brother, Break with my *k*. *The Falcon* 257
Kind O, *k* and gentle master, the Queen's Officers, *Queen Mary* I ii 107
she had seen the Archbishop once, So mild, so *k*. *Becket* V ii 120
Weänt ye gi'e me a *k* answer at last? *Prom. of May* II 63
saints were so *k* to both on us that he was dead before he was born. *Foresters* II i 372
Kindle He hath gone to *k* Norway against England, *Harold* III i 79
And *k* all our vales with myrtle-blossom, *The Cup* II 267
Kindled sparkles out as quick Almost as *k*; *Queen Mary* I ii 74
and *k* with the palms Of Christ! „ I v 93
you should know that whether A wind be warm or cold, it serves to fan A *k* fire. „ I v 621
after much smouldering and smoking, be *k* again upon your quarter. *Becket* II ii 313
the fire, when first *k*, said to the smoke, „ II ii 318
Kindlier The running down the chase is *k* sport „ IV ii 213
and will pray for you That *you* may thrive, but in some *k* trade. *Foresters* III 253
Kindliest The *k* man I ever knew; *Queen Mary* IV iii 421
Kindly Be *k* to the Normans left among us, *Harold* III i 303
A *k* rendering Of 'Render unto Cæsar.' . . . „ III ii 167
Thou art too *k*. „ IV iii 32
Not *k* to them? *Sinnatus.* *K*? O the most *k* Prince in all the world! *The Cup* I ii 354
Yet he seem'd *k*, And said he loathed the cruelties „ I ii 372
he always took you so *k*, he always took the world so *k*. *The Falcon* 187
made a wry mouth at it, but he took it so *k*, „ 191

Kindly (*continued*) he always took you so *k*— *The Falcon* 195
And were my *k* father sound again, *Foresters* III 81
Kindness beget A *k* from him, for his heart was rich, *Queen Mary* IV i 169
O Bonner, if I ever did you *k*— „ IV ii 152
but smile As *k*, watching all, *Harold* I i 367
King (*See also* **Baby-king, Boy-king, Co-king, Father-king, Giant-king, Mock-king, Monk-king, Vice-king**) and this wrought Upon the *k*; *Queen Mary* I ii 71
You look'd a *k*. „ I iii 103
but we play with Henry, *K* of France, „ I iii 131
The *K* is skilful at it? „ I iii 144
And so you well attend to the *k's* moves, „ I iii 152
a *K* That with her own pawns plays against a Queen, Whose play is all to find herself a *K*. „ I iii 161
make him *K* belike. „ I iv 212
A *k* to be—is he not noble, girl? „ I v 4
then the *K*—that traitor past forgiveness, „ I v 28
What says the *K* your master? „ I v 248
if this Philip be the titular *k* Of England, „ I v 254
but your *k* stole her a babe from Scotland „ I v 291
Thou speakest of the enemy of thy *k*. „ I v 327
he will be *K*, *K* of England, my masters; „ II i 173
and if Philip come to be *K*, O my God! „ II i 199
to whom The *k*, my father, did commit his trust; „ II ii 208
To be your *k*, ye would rejoice thereat, „ II ii 224
Makes enemies for himself and for his *k*; „ II ii 399
Their cry is, Philip never shall be *k*. „ II iv 2
Left him and fled; and thou that would'st be *K*, „ II iv 83
My foes are at my feet, and Philip *K*. „ II iv 143
Nay, he is *K*, you know, the *K* of Naples. The father ceded Naples, that the son Being a *K*, might wed a Queen— „ III i 72
The *K* of France will help to break it. „ III i 105
The French *K* winks at it. „ III i 160
Long live the *K* and Queen, Philip and Mary! „ III i 208
There be both *K* and Queen, Philip and Mary. Shout! „ III i 296
where you gave your hand To this great Catholic *K*. „ III ii 92
happily symboll'd by The *K* your husband, „ III ii 110
The *K* is here!—My star, my son! „ III ii 183
He's here, and *k*, or will be—yet cocksbody! „ III iii 44
The *K* and I, my Lords, now that all traitors „ III iv 1
the *K* And you together our two suns in one; „ III iv 18
bolster'd up The gross *K's* headship of the Church, „ III iv 246
The Church's evil is not as the *K's*, „ III iv 273
But not the force made them our mightiest *k's*. „ III iv 336
Crown'd slave of slaves, and mitred *k* of *k's*. „ III iv 381
'It is the *K's* wish, that you should wed Prince Philibert of Savoy. „ III v 221
Why then the *K*! for I would have him bring it „ III vi 21
Against the *K*, the Queen, the Holy Father, „ III vi 33
'The *K* hath wearied of his barren bride.' „ III vi 140
K and Queen, To whom he owes his loyalty „ IV i 21
Stood out against the *K* in your behalf, „ IV i 126
And when the *K's* divorce was sued at Rome, „ IV iii 41
Friend for so long time of a mighty *K*; „ IV iii 73
Obey your *K* and Queen, and not for dread „ IV iii 177
I conclude the *K* a beast; Verily a lion if you will— „ IV iii 411
Here is the *K*. „ V i 15
There is no *k*, not were he ten times *k*, „ V i 62
The *K* of France the *K* of England too. „ V i 198
Madam, I brought My *K's* congratulations; „ V ii 570
My *K* would know if you be fairly served. „ V iii 20
I take it that the *k* hath spoken to you; „ V iii 85
Ay, tell the *K* that I will muse upon it; „ V iii 89
But I am much beholden to your *K*. „ V iii 99
I am much beholden to your *K*, your master. „ V iii 111
the one *K*, the Christ, and all things in common, as in the day of the first church, when Christ Jesus was *K*. „ V iv 53
fair a likeness As your great *K* in armour „ V v 29
He can but read the *k's* face on his coins. *Stigand*. Ay, ay, young lord, *there* the *k's* face is power. *Harold* I i 71
To sleek and supple himself to the *k's* hand. „ I i 149
Too hardy with thy *k*! „ I i 198
after those twelve years a boon, my *k*, „ I i 226

King (*continued*) What lies upon the mind of our good *k* *Harold* I i 269
Brother, the *k* is wiser than he seems; And Tostig knows it; Tostig loves the *k*. *Harold*. And love should know; and—be the *k* so wise,— „ I i 272
The *k* hath made me Earl; make me not fool! Nor make the *K* a fool, who made me Earl! „ I i 288
Who made the *K* who made thee, make thee Earl. „ I i 294
Pray God the people choose thee for their *k*! „ I i 315
And thou art ever here about the *K*: „ I i 321
To the good *k* who gave it—not to you— „ I i 407
The *k*! the *k* is ever at his prayers; „ I i 410
In all that handles matter of the state I am the *k*. „ I i 413
thou hast taught the *k* to spoil him too; „ I i 451
Farewell, my *k*. *Harold*. Not yet, but then—my queen. „ I ii 137
If he were *K* of England, I his queen, „ I ii 154
lest the *k* Should yield his ward to Harold's will. „ I ii 158
'O thou more saint than *k*!' „ I ii 168
Tostig, Edward hath made him Earl: he would be *k*:— „ I ii 187
Harold Hear the *k's* music, all alone with him, „ I ii 194
Who knows I may not dream myself their *k*! „ I ii 252
a whale to a whelk we have swallowed the *K* of England. „ II i 45
Who shall be *k's* of England. I am heir Of England by the promise of her *k*. „ II ii 123
there the great Assembly choose their *k*, „ II ii 127
I will be *k* of England by the laws, „ II ii 130
More kinglike he than like to prove a *k*. „ II ii 143
What said the *K*? 'I pray you do not „ II ii 217
Yea, yea, he would be *k* of England. „ II ii 369
And he our lazy-pious Norman *K*, „ II ii 444
our good *K* Kneels mumbling some old bone— „ II ii 468
The *k*, the lords, the people clear'd him of it. „ II ii 522
and a child, Will England have him *k*? „ II ii 573
promised that if ever he were *k* In England, „ II ii 587
Ay . . . if the *k* have not revoked his promise. „ II ii 609
Thou shalt be verily *k*—all but the name— „ II ii 632
I, the Count—the *K*—Thy friend— „ II ii 754
Then our great Council wait to crown thee *K*— „ III i 4
sickness of our saintly *k*, for whom My prayers „ III i 164
Nay—but the council, and the *k* himself, „ III i 171
It lies beside thee, *k*, upon thy bed. „ III i 195
Let me be buried there, and all our *k's*, „ III i 208
It shall be granted him, my *k*; „ III i 228
we be not bound by the *k's* voice In making of a *k*, yet the *k's* voice „ III i 236
my lord, my *k*! He knew not whom he sware by. „ III i 255
I did not dream then I should be *k*.— „ III i 271
and dear son, swear When thou art *k*, „ III i 306
but to please our dying *k*, and those Who make „ III i 329
Our holy *k* Hath given his virgin lamb to Holy Church „ III i 333
for the *k* Is holy, and hath talk'd with God, „ III i 354
And our great Council wait to crown thee *K*. „ III i 407
Crown'd, crown'd and lost, crown'd *K*— „ III ii 2
Harold the *K*! *Harold*. Call me not *K*, but Harold. *Edith*. Nay, thou art *K*! „ III ii 32
Thine, thine, or *K* or churl! „ III ii 36
rather let me be *K* of the moment to thee, „ III ii 41
than to reign *K* of the world without it. „ III ii 45
thou be only *K* of the moment over England. „ III ii 51
Tho' somewhat less a *k* to my true self „ III ii 53
nor priestly *k* to cross Their billings ere they nest. „ III ii 93
He, and the giant *K* of Norway, „ III ii 122
The *K* hath cursed him, if he marry me; „ III ii 189
Let not our great *k* Believe us sullen—only shamed to the quick Before the *k*—as having been so bruised By Harold, *k* of Norway; but our help Is Harold, *k* of England. Pardon us, thou! Our silence is our reverence for the *k*! „ IV i 6
old Northumbrian crown, And *k's* of our own choosing. „ IV i 33
Had in him kingly thoughts—a *k* of men, „ IV i 83
Not made but born, like the great *k* of all, „ IV i 85
bad the *k* Who doted on him, „ IV i 102
K! thy brother, If one may dare to speak the truth, „ IV i 107
good *k* would deign to lend an ear Not overscornful, „ IV i 135
thence a *k* may rise Half-Godwin and half-Alfgar, „ IV i 142
The *k* can scarcely dream that we, „ IV i 163

King (*continued*) Who dares arraign us, *k*, of such a plot? *Harold* IV i 168
Yea, take the Sacrament upon it, *k*. ,, IV i 183
The nimble, wild, red, wiry, savage *k*— ,, IV i 198
Thou hast but cared to make thyself a *k*— ,, IV ii 75
Every man about his *k* Fought like a *k*; the *k* like his own man, ,, IV iii 56
My lord the *K*! William the Norman, ,, IV iii 180
To do with England's choice of her own *k*? ,, V i 20
If the *k* fall, may not the kingdom fall? But if I fall, I fall, and thou art *k*; And, if I win, I win, and thou art *k*; ,, V i 123
How should the people fight When the *k* flies? ,, V i 138
How should the *K* of England waste the fields Of England, ,, V i 140
That scared the dying conscience of the *k*, ,, V i 212
I thy *k*, who came before To tell thee ,, V i 235
O hapless Harold! *K* but for an hour! ,, V i 258
The *k's* last word—'the arrow!' ,, V i 266
advise the *k* Against the race of Godwin. ,, V i 281
Get thou into thy cloister as the *k* Will'd it: ,, V i 309
I have not spoken to the *k* One word; ,, V i 335
The *k* commands thee, woman! ,, V i 340
England Is but her *k*, and thou art Harold! ,, V i 376
Edith, if I, the last English *K* of England— ,, V i 384
all the monks of Peterboro' Strike for the *k*; ,, V i 447
k of England stands between his banners. ,, V i 486
They have broken the commandment of the *k*! ,, V i 615
With whom they play'd their game against the *k*! *Aldwyth*. The *k* is slain, the kingdom overthrown! ,, V ii 14
being the true wife Of this dead *K*, ,, V ii 85
And this dead *k's* Who, *k* or not, ,, V ii 123
When all men counted Harold would be *k*, ,, V ii 133
Every man about his *k* Fell where he stood. ,, V ii 181
I am *K* of England, so they thwart me not, ,, V ii 196
Look to your *k*. *Becket*, *Pro*. 33
my bishop Hath brought your *k* to a standstill. ,, *Pro*. 44
Why, there then—down go bishop and *k* together. ,, *Pro*. 48
to the statesman Who serves and loves his *k*, and whom the *k* Loves not as statesman, ,, *Pro*. 78
That tread the *k's* their children under-heel— ,, *Pro*. 213
My young son Henry crown'd the *K* of England, ,, *Pro*. 224
K, Church, and State to him but foils wherein ,, *Pro*. 268
God's favour and *k's* favour might so clash ,, *Pro*. 295
Parthian shaft of a forlorn Cupid at the *K's* left breast, ,, *Pro*. 340
and the *K* gave it to his Chancellor. ,, *Pro*. 431
but because he had the love of the *K*. ,, *Pro*. 443
retinue of three *k's* behind him, outroyalling royalty? ,, *Pro*. 445
he holp the *K* to break down our castles, ,, *Pro*. 446
you could not see the *K* for the kinglings. ,, *Pro*. 453
she, whom the *K* loves indeed, is a power in the State. ,, *Pro*. 482
Rival!—ay, and when the *K* passes, ,, *Pro*. 484
secret matter which would heat the *K* against thee ,, *Pro*. 488
thou in thy way shouldst be jealous of the *K*, ,, *Pro*. 512
then the *K* came honeying about her, ,, *Pro*. 516
make her as hateful to herself and to the *K*, ,, *Pro*. 527
wreak our spite on the rosefaced minion of the *K*, and bring her to the level of the dust, so that the *K*— ,, *Pro*. 530
To please the *K*! *Becket*. Ay, and the *K* of *k's*, ,, I i 31
Shall I fall off—to please the *K* once more? ,, I i 110
Not fight—tho' somehow traitor to the *K*— ,, I i 113
'I mean to fight mine utmost for the Church, Against the *K*'? *Becket*. But dost thou think the *K* Forced mine election? *Herbert*. I do think the *K* Was potent in the election, and why not? Why should not Heaven have so inspired the *K*? ,, I i 125
The rift that runs between me and the *K*. ,, I i 141
thro' The random gifts of careless *k's*, ,, I i 159
here I gash myself asunder from the *K*, ,, I i 175
What friend! *Rosamund*. The *K*. ,, I i 326
My friend, the *K*! . . . O thou Great Seal of England, Given me by my dear friend the *K* of England— ,, I i 335
To tell the *K*, my friend, I am against him. ,, I i 343
O, my dear friend, the *K*! O brother!— ,, I i 360
Let the Great Seal be sent Back to the *K* to-morrow. ,, I i 376
The *K* may rend the bearer limb from limb. ,, I i 378
Of this wild Rosamund to please the *K*, ,, I i 393

King (*continued*) However *k's* and queens may frown on thee. *Becket* I ii 18
in your chancellorship you served The follies of the *K*. ,, I ii 31
Priest Sits winking at the license of a *k*, Altho' we grant when *k's* are dangerous The Church must play into the hands of *k's*; ,, I ii 66
That *k's* are faithful to their marriage vow. ,, I ii 78
Where I shall meet the Barons and my *K*. ,, I ii 85
Stir up the *K*, the Lords! ,, I ii 88
I will make thee hateful to thy *K*. ,, I ii 92
Where is the *K*? *Roger*. Gone hawking on the Nene, ,, I iii 1
But by the *K's* command, are written down, And by the *K's* command I, John of Oxford, ,, I iii 72
whether between laymen or clerics, shall be tried in the *K's* court.' ,, I iii 81
he shall answer to the summons of the *K's* court to be tried therein.' ,, I iii 89
the *K*, till another be appointed, shall receive the revenues thereof.' ,, I iii 100
Is the *K's* treasury A fit place for the monies of the Church, ,, I iii 104
the *K* shall summon the chapter of that church to court, ,, I iii 108
with the consent of our lord the *K*, and by the advice ,, I iii 112
Without the license of our lord the *K*. ,, I iii 130
Are ye my masters, or my lord the *K*? ,, I iii 135
The *K* is quick to anger; ,, I iii 164
sheathe your swords, ye will displease the *K*. ,, I iii 180
Save the *K's* honour here before his barons. ,, I iii 187
He pray'd me to pray thee to pacify Thy *K*; for if thou go against thy *K*, Then must he likewise go against thy *K*, And then thy *K* may join the Antipope, ,, I iii 207
K swore to our cardinals He meant no harm ,, I iii 215
He told me thou shouldst pacify the *K*, ,, I iii 225
He heads the Church against the *K* with thee. ,, I iii 245
I came, your *K*! Nor dwelt alone, ,, I iii 357
that had found a *K* Who ranged confusions, ,, I iii 370
The master of his master, the *K's* *k*.—God's eyes! I had meant to make him all but *k*. Chancellor-Archbishop, he might well have sway'd All England under Henry, the young *K*, ,, I iii 462
it is the traitor that imputes Treachery to his *K*! ,, I iii 485
The *K* will not abide thee with thy cross. ,, I iii 488
Make not thy *K* a traitorous murderer. ,, I iii 500
Arm'd with thy cross, to come before the *K*? ,, I iii 510
Nay, nay, my lord, thou must not brave the *K*. ,, I iii 515
Now as Archbishop goest against the *K*; ,, I iii 531
Ay, ay! but art thou stronger than the *K*? ,, I iii 535
I promised The *K* to obey these customs, ,, I iii 557
Tell what I say to the *K*. ,, I iii 564
deliver Canterbury To our *K's* hands again, ,, I iii 581
Fealty to the *k*, obedience to thyself? ,, I iii 587
But the *K* rages—most are with the *K*; ,, I iii 591
The *K's* 'God's eyes!' come now so thick and fast, ,, I iii 609
the *K* demands three hundred marks, ,, I iii 626
Tell the *K* I spent thrice that in fortifying his castles. ,, I iii 631
the *K* demands seven hundred marks, Lent at the siege of Thoulouse by the *K*. ,, I iii 634
the *K* demands five hundred marks, ,, I iii 641
For which the *K* was bound security, ,, I iii 645
K Demands a strict account of all those revenues ,, I iii 649
my good lord Leicester, The *K* and I were brothers. All I had I lavish'd for the glory of the *K*; ,, I iii 661
The *K* and all his lords—— *Becket*. Son, first hear *me*! ,, I iii 671
In fee and barony of the *K*, decline The judgment of the *K*? *Becket*. The *K*! I hold Nothing in fee and barony of the *K*. ,, I iii 675
The *K* and all his barons—— *Becket*. Judgment! Barons! ,, I iii 683
K would throne me in the great Archbishoprick: ,, I iii 693
For the *K's* pleasure rather than God's cause ,, I iii 697
God from me withdraws Himself, And the *K* too. ,, I iii 703
Why thou, the *K*, the Pope, the Saints, the world, ,, I iii 705
I refuse to stand By the *K's* censure, ,, I iii 723
The *K*, these customs, all the Church, ,, I iii 726
K commands you, upon pain of death, ,, I iii 752
The *K* hath frowned upon me. ,, I iv 25
there be those about our *K* who would have thy blood.' ,, I iv 55

King (*continued*) frosted off me by the first cold frown of the *K*. *Becket* I iv 68
The Church is ever at variance with the *k's*, „ I iv 79
If the *K* hold his purpose, I am myself a beggar. „ I iv 89
K's verdurer caught him a-hunting in the forest, „ I iv 95
he licks my face and moans and cries out against the *K*. „ I iv 100
Were the Church *k*, it would be otherwise. „ I iv 104
K's meat! By the Lord, „ I iv 140
Becket shall be *k*, and the Holy Father shall be *k*, and the world shall live by the *K's* venison „ I iv 270
A greater *K* Than thou art, Love, „ II i 115
It is, my boy, to side with the *K* when Chancellor, and then to be made Archbishop and go against the *K* „ II i 236
England scarce would hold Young Henry *k*, „ II ii 32
for any rough sea Blown by the breath of *k's*. „ II ii 108
rift he made May close between us, here I am wholly *k*, „ II ii 133
Ay, ay! the *K* humbles himself enough. „ II ii 184
suppress God's honour for the sake Of any *k* „ II ii 221
we grant the Church *K* over this world's *k's*, yet, my good lord, We that are *k's* are something in this world, „ II ii 243
who hath withstood two *K's* to their faces for the honour of God. „ II ii 276
I thank you, sons; when *k's* but hold by crowns, The crowd that hungers for a crown in Heaven Is my true *k*. „ II ii 280
Thy true *K* bad thee be A fisher of men; „ II ii 285
I am too like the *K* here; „ II ii 288
But the *K* hath bought half the College of Redhats. „ II ii 373
shakes at mortal *k's*—her vacillation, Avarice, craft— „ II ii 405
The *K* had had no power except for Rome. 'Tis not the *K* who is guilty of mine exile, „ II ii 412
Deny not thou God's honour for a *k*. The *K* looks troubled. „ II ii 424
being ever duteous to the *K*, „ II ii 464
I am the *K*, his father, And I will look to it. „ III i 26
and I ha' seen the *K* once at Oxford, and he's as like the *K* „ III i 163
thought at first it was the *K*, only you know the *K's* married, „ III i 166
I thought if it were the *K's* brother he had a better bride than the *K*, „ III i 173
Myself confused with parting from the *K*. „ III i 238
Have track'd the *K* to this dark inland wood; „ III ii 3
Our woodland Circe that hath witch'd the *K*? „ III ii 33
The *K* keeps his forest head of game here, „ III ii 37
let the *K's* fine game look to itself. „ III ii 44
There is the *K* talking with Walter Map? „ III iii 22
K at last is fairly scared by this cloud—this interdict. I have been more for the *K* than the Church in this matter— „ III iii 63
He thought less of two *k's* than of one Roger the *k* of the occasion. „ III iii 90
like the Greek *k* when his daughter was sacrificed, „ III iii 104
K would act servitor and hand a dish to his son; „ III iii 138
part royal, for *K* and kingling both laughed, „ III iii 157
if Thomas have not flung himself at the *K's* feet. „ III iii 169
Ay, *K*! for in thy kingdom, as thou knowest, The spouse of the Great *K*, thy *K*, hath fallen— „ III iii 173
ere Pope or *K* Had come between us! „ III iii 267
is the *K's if* too high a stile for your lordship to overstep „ III iii 280
You wrong the *K*: he meant what he said to-day. „ III iii 299
K hath many more wolves than he can tame „ III iii 321
if it suit their purpose to howl for the *K*, „ III iii 324
Farewell. I must follow the *K*. „ III iii 330
Did the *K* Speak of the customs? „ III iii 332
The *K's* not like to die for that which dies; „ III iii 338
I am mine own self Of and belonging to the *K*. The *K* Hath divers ofs and ons, ofs and belongings, „ IV ii 30
The *K* shall never hear of me again, „ IV ii 102
burrow where the *K* Would miss her and for ever. „ IV ii 158
By very God, the cross I gave the *K*! „ IV ii 199

King (*continued*) Has wheedled it off the *K's* neck to her own. *Becket* IV ii 201
We thought to scare this minion of the *K* Back from her churchless commerce with the *K* „ IV ii 331
The *K* himself, for love of his own sons, „ IV ii 344
You have lost The ear of the *K*. „ IV ii 355
The world hath trick'd her—that's the *K*; „ IV ii 376
K plucks out their eyes Who anger him, „ IV ii 405
Madam, I am as much man as the *k*. Madam, I fear Church-censures like your *K*. „ IV ii 433
we will to France and be Beforehand with the *K*, „ IV ii 455
Before you made him *k*. But Becket ever moves against a *k*. „ V i 24
The Church is all—the crime to be a *k*. „ V i 27
one half, but half-alive, Cries to the *K*. „ V i 65
The brideless Becket is thy *k* and mine: „ V i 108
I dream'd I was the consort of a *k*, „ V i 144
What made the *K* cry out so furiously? „ V i 220
he did his best To break the barons, and now braves the *K*. *Eleanor*. Strike, then, at once, the *K* would have him— „ V i 236
slave that eat my bread has kick'd his *K*! „ V i 243
gone to the *K* And taken our anathema with him. „ V ii 7
Can the *K* de-anathematise this York? „ V ii 10
Thou hast waged God's war against the *K*; „ V ii 47
That thou wouldst ex-communicate the *K*. „ V ii 91
he had gone too far Into the *K's* own woods; „ V ii 108
Cried out against the cruelty of the *K*. I said it was the *K's* courts, not the *K*; „ V ii 113
and she wish'd The Church were *k*: „ V ii 118
when I was Chancellor to the *K*, I fear I was as cruel as the *K*. „ V ii 123
For once in France the *K* had been so harsh, „ V ii 139
'The *K* is sick and almost unto death.' „ V ii 152
Liker the *K*. *Becket*. No, daughter. *Rosamund*. Ay, but wait Till his nose rises; he will be very *k*. *Becket*. Ev'n so: but think not of the *K*: „ V ii 181
breathe one prayer for my liege-lord the *K*, „ V ii 192
we bring a message from the *K* Beyond the water; „ V ii 302
The *K* condemns your excommunicating— „ V ii 317
Now, sirs, the *K's* commands! *Fitzurse*. The *K* beyond the water, thro' our voices, Commands you to be dutiful and leal To your young *K* on this side of the water, „ V ii 322
broken Your bond of peace, your treaty with the *K*— „ V ii 351
K commands you to absolve the bishops „ V ii 375
The *K* commands you. We are all *K's* men. „ V ii 383
K's men at least should know That their own *K* „ V ii 386
What! dare you charge the *K* with treachery? „ V ii 397
He makes the *K* a traitor, me a liar. „ V ii 415
If this be so, complain to your young *K*, „ V ii 449
I ask no leave of *K*, or mortal man, „ V ii 458
Give to the *K* the things that are the *K's*, „ V ii 461
Blared from the heights of all the thrones of her *k's*, „ V ii 490
That goes against our fealty to the *K*. „ V ii 508
I go to meet my *K*! *Grim*. To meet the *K*? „ V ii 620
As you would force a *k* from being crown'd. „ V iii 25
Here, here, *K's* men! „ V iii 102
Where is this treble traitor to the *K*? „ V iii 108
No traitor to the *K*, but Priest of God, „ V iii 112
The Pope, the *K*, will curse you— „ V iii 182
and throne One *k* above them all, *The Cup* I i 93
The *k*, the crown! their talk in Rome? „ I i 98
We have had our leagues of old with Eastern *k's*. „ I ii 102
There then I rest, Rome's tributary *k*. „ I iii 156
This very day the Romans crown him *k* „ II 64
—and blast the *k* and me, „ II 152
Lay down the Lydian carpets for the *k*. The *k* should pace on purple to his bride, „ II 188
And music there to greet my lord the *k*. „ II 192
Hail, *K*! *Synorix*. Hail, Queen! „ II 219
speak I now too mightily, being *K* And happy! „ II 238
Foam over all the fleeted wealth of *k's* And peoples, „ II 289
Words are not always what they seem, my *K*. „ II 329
Thy turn, Galatian *K*. „ II 379

King (*continued*) Synorix, first K, Camma, first Queen o' the Realm, *The Cup* II 440
you are still the k Of courtesy and liberality. *The Falcon* 292
He would grapple with a lion like the K, *Foresters* I i 186
We will be beggar'd then and be true to the K. „ I i 202
both fought against the tyranny of the k's, the Normans. „ I i 230
the K, thy god-father, gave it thee when a baby. „ I i 285
I would break through them all, like the K of England. „ I i 326
Now that the sum our K is gone, „ I ii 83
For be he dead, then John may be our K. „ I ii 99
I may not hate the K For aught I know, „ I ii 115
I think they will be mightier than the k. „ I ii 120
I trust he brings us news of the K's coming. „ I iii 53
by force and arms hath trespassed against the k in divers manners, „ I iii 63
The London folkmote Has made him all but k, „ I iii 81
Traitors are rarely bred Save under traitor k's. Our vice-king John, True k of vice— „ II i 81
Hath made *me* k of all the discontent Of England „ II i 87
Sheriff had taken all our goods for the K without paying, „ II i 191
when the Sheriff took my little horse for the K without paying for it— „ II i 301
given my whole body to the K had *he* asked for it, „ II i 306
I ha' served the K living, says she, and let me serve him dead, „ II i 310
He was the k o' the wood. „ II i 321
Jealousy, jealousy of the k. „ II ii 141
We never robb'd one friend of the true K. „ III 158
Our Robin, K o' the woods, „ III 344
Robin, the people's friend, the K o' the woods ! „ III 347
We care so much for a K ; (repeat) *Foresters* III 429, 443
The ruler of an hour, but lawful K, *Foresters* IV 47
if these knaves should know me for their K ? „ IV 134
Great woodland k, I know not quarterstaff. *Little John.* A fine ! a fine ! He hath called plain Robin a k. „ IV 215
did ye not call me k in your song ? „ IV 220
Is that to be a k ? If the k and the law work injustice, is not he that goes against the k and the law the true k in the sight of the K of k's ? Thou art the k of the forest, and I would thou wert the k of the land. „ IV 228
We had it i' the Red K's time, „ IV 303
for I must hence upon The K's affair. „ IV 342
Richard's the k of courtesy, „ IV 362
and call it courtesy, For he's a k. „ IV 368
Richard, again, is k over a realm He hardly knows, and Robin k of Sherwood, „ IV 387
if the land Were ruleable by tongue, thou shouldst be k. And yet thou know'st how little of thy k ! „ IV 400
free the tomb-place of the K Of all the world ? „ IV 409
You, Prince, our k to come— „ IV 696
Woe to that land shall own thee for her k ! „ IV 760
It is the K Who bears all down. „ IV 783
If thou be k, Be not a fool ! „ IV 789
fighting underhand unholy wars Against your lawful k. „ IV 822
Thou art happier than thy k. Put him in chains. „ IV 838
You both are utter traitors to your k. „ IV 844
Was justice dead because the K was dead ? „ IV 848
on the faith and honour of a k The land is his again. „ IV 852
God save the K ! „ IV 857
The K forbad it. True, my liege. *King Richard.* How if the K command it ? „ IV 865
if the K forbid thy marrying With Robin, „ IV 874
My k, I am but the echo of the lips of love. „ IV 891
But will the K, then, judge us all unheard ? „ IV 896
If the K Condemn us without trial, men will call him An Eastern tyrant, not an English k. „ IV 901
Beware, O K, the vengeance of the Church. „ IV 913
Keep silence, bully friar, before the K. *Friar Tuck.* If a cat may look at a k, may not a friar speak to one ? „ IV 920
He is but hedge-priest, Sir K. „ IV 931
The k's good health in ale and Malvoisie. „ IV 968
To celebrate this advent of our K ! „ IV 1048
And we must hence to the K's court. „ IV 1050

King (*continued*) and happy that our K Is here again, *Foresters* IV 1098
Now the K is home again, and nevermore to roam again, Now the K is home again, the K will have his own again, „ IV 1103
Kingcup Daisies grow again, K's blow again, *Queen Mary* III v 90
Kingdom your Grace And k will be suck'd into the war, „ I v 257
Not for myself, but for the k— „ III i 455
make Both of us happy—ay, the K too. „ III ii 188
The bond between the k's be dissolved ; „ III iii 76
A secular k is but as the body Lacking a soul ; „ IV i 32
The Holy Father in a secular k Is as the soul „ IV i 34
thine earldom, Tostig, hath been a k. *Harold* I i 304
The k's of this world began with little, „ IV i 42
He gave him all the k's of the West. „ V i 24
If the king fall, may not the k fall ? „ V i 123
The king is slain, the k overthrown ! „ V ii 16
the business Of thy whole k waits me : *Becket, Pro.* 278
it was but the sacrifice of a k to his son, a smaller matter ; „ III iii 107
in thy k, as thou knowest, The spouse of the Great King, „ III iii 173
Why, John, my k is not of this world. „ V ii 18
Kinghood Your father was a man Of such colossal k, *Queen Mary* IV i 101
Kingless While thou and others in our k realms Were fighting *Foresters* IV 819
Kinglier which will make My kingship k to me *Harold* III ii 44
Kingliest The k Abbey in all Christian lands, „ III i 204
Kinglike does your gracious Queen entreat you k ? *Queen Mary* I iii 110
Most goodly, K and an Emperor's son,— „ I v 2
Here comes the would-be what I will be . . . k . . . *Harold* II ii 139
More k he than like to prove a king. „ II ii 142
hath k fought and fallen, His birthday, too. „ V ii 124
But k fought the proud archbishop,— *Becket* IV ii 438
—k Defied the Pope, and, like his kingly sires, „ IV ii 439
Kingling—you could not see the King for the k's. „ *Pro.* 453
part royal, for King and k both laughed, „ III iii 157
Kingly God change the pebble which his k foot First presses *Queen Mary* I v 369
made us lower our k flag To yours of England. „ V i 59
I trust the k touch that cures the evil May serve *Harold* I i 151
he would give his k voice To me as his successor. „ II ii 588
Nor k priest, nor priestly king to cross Their billings „ III ii 93
Ay, but thou art not k, only grandson To Wolfnoth, „ IV i 68
Had in him k thoughts—a king of men, „ IV i 83
despite his k promise given To our own self of pardon, *Becket* II ii 431
Nay, can I send her hence Without his k leave ? „ III i 220
and, like his k sires, The Normans, „ IV ii 440
that stale Church-bond which link'd me with him To bear him k sons. „ IV ii 449
King-parliament So your k-p suffer him to land, *Queen Mary* I v 365
Kingship to break down all k and queenship, „ V iv 48
which will make My k kinglier to me *Harold* III ii 44
I should beat Thy k as my bishop hath beaten it. *Henry.* Hell take thy bishop then, and my k too ! *Becket, Pro.* 91
Queen should play his k against thine ! „ *Pro.* 236
King Henry sware That, saving his King's k, „ I iii 28
mother Would make him play his k against mine. „ II ii 11
Kingston (adj.) we must round By K Bridge, *Queen Mary* II iii 48
Kingston (s) Be happy, I am your friend. To K, forward ! „ II iii 124
Kinsman They blinded my young k, Alfred— *Harold* II ii 511
Kiss (s) k'es of all kind of womankind In Flanders, „ I ii 113
The k that charms thine eyelids into sleep, „ I ii 139
Shall see the dewy k of dawn no more „ II ii 331
and command That k my due when subject, „ III ii 42
There might be more than brother in my k, „ III ii 84
For there was more than sister in my k, „ V ii 6
link rusts with the breath of the first after-marriage k, *Becket, Pro.* 362
thy k—Sacred ! I'll kiss it too. „ II i 184
To-day I almost fear'd your k was colder— „ III i 18
K in the bower, Tit on the tree ! „ III i 104
save King Henry gave thee first the k of peace. „ III iii 253
I sware I would not give the k of peace, „ III iii 259
happy home-return and the King's k of peace in Kent. „ III iii 328
First k. There then. You talk almost as if it *The Cup* I ii 421
by this true k, *you* are the first I ever *Prom. of May* III 647

Kiss (s) (*continued*) She gave a weeping *k* to the Earl,
And the maid a *k* to the man. *Foresters* I i 20
She gave a weeping *k* to the Earl, The maid a *k* to the man. „ I i 119
shall I give her the first *k* ? O sweet Kate, my first love, the first *k*, the first *k* ! „ I i 126
I came to give thee the first *k*, and thou hast given it me. „ I i 132
does it matter so much if the maid give the first *k* ? *Little John*. I cannot tell, but I had sooner have given thee the first *k*. „ I i 136
now thou hast given me the man's *k*, let me give thee the maid's. „ I i 143
may the maid give the first *k* ? „ I i 173
and is flustered by a girl's *k*. „ I i 186
You shall give me the first *k*. „ I ii 228
In *k'es*. *Kate*. You, how dare you mention *k'es* ? „ II i 126
Take thou this light *k* for thy clumsy word. „ III 134
I Embrace thee with the *k'es* of the soul. „ III 143

Kiss (verb) *K* me would you ? with my hands Milking the cow ? *Queen Mary* III v 87
Come, Robin, Robin, Come and *k* me now ; „ III v 100
Come behind and *k* me milking the cow ! „ III v 105
To *k* and cuff among the birds and flowers— „ III v 258
K me—thou art not A holy sister yet, *Harold* III ii 80
thy kiss—Sacred ! I'll *k* it too. *Becket* II i 185
K me, little one, Nobody near ! „ III i 100
Sinnatus, *k* me now. *The Cup* I ii 419
and *k* me This beautiful May-morning. *Prom. of May* I 564
I *k* it as a prelude to that privilege „ II 528
Now if she *k* him, I will have his head. *Foresters* I ii 146
Is it made up ? Will you *k* me ? „ I ii 226
I thought I saw thee clasp and *k* a man „ II ii 72
Thou see me clasp and *k* a man indeed. „ II ii 76
Fancied he saw thee clasp and *k* a man. „ III 23
K me again. *Marian*. Robin, I will not *k* thee, „ III 136
K him, Sir Richard—*k* him, my sweet Marian. „ IV 1003
K and congratulate me, my good Kate. „ IV 1033
I have seen thee clasp and *k* a man indeed, „ IV 1035
Well then, who *k'es* first ? *Little John*. *K* both together. „ IV 1040

Kiss'd *k* not her alone, but all the ladies *Queen Mary* I i 80
you came and *k* me milking the cow. (repeat) „ III v 91, 98
K me well I vow ; „ III v 93
You *k* me there For the first time. *The Cup* I ii 417
should have told us how the man first *k* the maid. *Foresters* I i 123

Kissin' 'er an' the owd man they fell a *k* o' one another *Prom. of May* I 21

Kissing *See* **A-bussin', Kissin'**

Kite (a toy) You fly your thoughts like *k's*. *Queen Mary* I v 390

Kite (bird) And the stock-dove coo'd, till a *k* dropt down, *Prom. of May* I 55
To the bleak church doors, like *k's* upon a barn. *Harold* IV iii 37

Kith Let *k* and kin stand close as our shield-wall, „ I i 398

Knave Shout, *k's* ! *Queen Mary* I i 9
Say for ten thousand ten—and pothouse *k's*, „ II i 70
K, wilt thou wear thy cap before the Queen ? „ III i 236
Thy name, thou *k* ? *Man*. I am nobody, my Lord. „ III i 246
God's passion ! *k*, thy name ? „ III i 249
K, thou shalt lose thine ears and find thy tongue, „ III i 255
God's passion ! do you know the *k* that painted it ? „ III i 264
What hast thou shouted, *k* ? „ III i 293
K, there be two. There be both King and Queen, „ III i 295
Must it be so, my Lord ? *Gardiner*. Ay, *k*. „ III i 308
Where, *k*, where ? *Man*. Sign of the Talbot. „ III i 318
The *k's* are easily cow'd. „ III i 329
K, hast thou let thy prisoner scape ? *Harold* II ii 672
Woe *k* to thy familiar and to thee ! „ II ii 679
To be honest is to set all *k's* against thee. *Becket* I iii 572
Come, you filthy *k's*, let us pass. „ I iv 203
K, there is a lot of wild fellows in Sherwood Forest *Foresters* I ii 72
Sit there, *k's*, till the captain call for you. „ III 219
I know them arrant *k's* in Nottingham. „ III 301
Louder, louder, ye *k's*. „ III 396
mark'd if those two *k's* from York be coming ? „ IV 112
if these *k's* should know me for their King ? „ IV 133

Knaw (know) I *k's* nowt o' what foälks says, an' I caäres nowt neither. Foälks doesn't hallus *k* thessens ; *Prom. of May* I 26
hallus a-fobbing ma off, tho' ye *k's* I love ye. „ I 108
Squire Edgar as ha' coomed among us—the Lord *k's* how— „ I 111
tha 'e *k's* I was hallus ageän heving schoolmaster i' the parish ! „ I 186
What dost a *k* o' this Mr. Hedgar as be a-lodgin' wi' ye ? „ I 199
and I *k's* what men be, and what masters be, „ I 328
—ye all *k's* the ten-aäcre— „ I 367
Noä ; I *k's* a deäl better now. „ II 26
doänt tha *k* he be sweet upo' Dora Steer, „ II 160
k's the back on 'im—drest like a gentleman, „ II 578
fur I haätes 'im afoor I *k's* what 'e be. „ II 585
I'll maäke her *k* ! (repeat) „ II 608
dosta *k* this paäper ? Ye dropt it upo' the road. „ II 687
dosta *k* what tha meäns wi' by-and-by ? „ II 690
thou hesn't naw business 'ere wi' *my* Dora, as I *k's* on, „ II 736

Knaw'd (knew) *k* better nor to cast her sister's misfortin inter 'er teeth „ II 126
Fur boäth on 'em *k* as well as mysen „ II 313
she niver *k* 'is faäce when 'e wur 'ere afoor ; „ II 606
I *k* 'im when I seed 'im ageän an I telled feyther on 'im. „ III 121
I beänt sa sewer o' that, fur Sally *k* 'im ; „ III 147

Knaw'd (known) fur they be *k* as far as Littlechester. „ I 213

Kneaded household dough was *k* up with blood ; *Becket* I iii 351

Knee (*See also* **Kneeä**) fray'd i' the *k's*, and out at elbow, *Queen Mary* I i 51
Cast myself down upon my *k's* before them, „ I v 562
we'll pray for you all on our bended *k's*. „ II iii 109
on our *k's*, we pray you to kill the Queen „ II iii 114
pray for you on our bended *k's* till our lives' end. „ II iii 122
round his *k*, misplaced, Our English Garter, „ III i 82
gray rogue, Gardiner, Went on his *k's*, „ III v 166
I thus implore you, low upon my *k's*, „ IV i 64
I would dandle you upon my *k* At lisping-age. „ V ii 142
With both her *k's* drawn upward to her chin. „ V ii 391
bind a score All in one faggot, snap it over *k*, *Harold* IV i 58
This old Wulfnoth Would take me on his *k's* „ IV i 72
—brave Gurth, one gash from brow to *k* ! „ V ii 71
been on my *k's* every day for these half-dozen years *The Falcon* 184
I seed tha a-limpin' up just now wi' the roomatics i' the *k*. *Prom. of May* I 385
I laäme't my *k* last night running arter a thief. „ I 387
look at our suits, out at *k*, out at elbow. *Foresters* I i 33
I fall before thee, clasp Thy *k's*. „ II i 600

Kneeä (knee) fell ageän coalscuttle and my *k* gev waäy *Prom. of May* I 404

Kneel prelates *k* to you.— *Queen Mary* I iv 83
And worse than all, you had to *k* to *me* ; „ IV ii 134
good King *K's* mumbling some old bone— *Harold* II ii 469
I *k* to thee—be friends with him again. *Becket* II i 317
K to thy lord Fitzurse ; Crouch even „ IV ii 221
I *k* once more to be forgiven. *Foresters* II i 667
he *k's* ! he has anger'd the foul witch, „ II i 669

Kneeling Behold thy father *k* to thee, Becket. *Becket* I iii 252
Can I fancy him *k* with me, and uttering the same prayer ; *Prom. of May* III 180

Knelt *k* And blubber'd like a lad, *Queen Mary* III i 149
Then *k* and said the Miserere Mei— „ III i 390
I mean the houses *k* Before the Legate. „ III iii 257

Knew (*See also* **Knaw'd**) I *k* they would not do me any wrong, „ I iii 100
if I either thought or *k* This marriage „ II ii 226
Seventeen—and *k* eight languages— „ III i 358
she thought they *k* the laws. But for herself, she *k* but little law, „ III i 380
Who *k* it from the first. „ III vi 114
O if I *k* you felt this parting, Philip, As I do ! „ III vi 251
if you *k* him As I do, ever gentle, and so gracious, „ IV i 155
Against the truth I *k* within my heart, „ IV iii 241
I *k* it would be so. „ IV iii 252
The kindliest man I ever *k* ; „ IV iii 421

Knew (*continued*) I *k* it, cousin, But held from you all papers *Queen Mary* v ii 44
What then, he *k* I was no Lutheran. „ v ii 78
I thought you *k* me better. „ v ii 186
Too young! And never *k* a Philip. „ v ii 361
She *k* me, and acknowledged me her heir, „ v v 255
I *k* thy purpose; he and Wulfnoth never Have met, *Harold* ii ii 84
I never *k* thee check thy will for ought „ ii ii 120
Far as he *k* in this poor world of ours— „ ii ii 363
He *k* not whom he sware by. „ iii i 256
I know He *k* not, but those heavenly ears have heard, „ iii i 258
Stigand believed he *k* not what he spake. „ iii ii 61
I *k* him brave: he loved his land: „ iv i 201
I smote him suddenly, I *k* not what I did. „ iv ii 43
by whom I *k* not that I sware,—not for myself— „ v i 305
Call not for help from me. I *k* him not. „ v ii 54
Since I *k* battle, And that was from my boyhood, „ v ii 174
I *k* thy father; he would be mine age Had he lived now; *Becket* i iii 249
Thought that I *k* him, err'd thro' love of him, „ i iii 440
And I, that *k* mine own infirmity, „ i iii 696
something was said to me I *k* not what. „ ii i 61
I never *k* an honest woman that could make songs, „ iii i 182
I never saw any such, Never *k* any such, „ iv ii 127
Your Becket *k* the secret of your bower. „ v i 177
I think our Abbess *k* it and allow'd it. „ v ii 95
They *k* he loved me. „ v ii 453
wrong'd Without there, *k* thee with Antonius. *The Cup* i ii 320
One of the men there *k* him. „ i ii 341
He *k* not at the moment who had fasten'd „ ii 49
but he *k* I meant to marry him. *The Falcon* 51
if She *k* the giver; but I bound the seller „ 72
I *k* it would come to this. (repeat) „ 156, 174
I always *k* it would come to this! (repeat) „ 158, 175
You *k* Eva, then? *Prom. of May* ii 367
Surely I loved Eva More than I *k*! „ ii 644
She *k* me from the first, she juggled with me, „ iii 687
Much, the miller's son, I *k* thy father: *Foresters* i iii 146
So hollowly we *k* not which was which. „ ii i 260
far as we *k*, We never robb'd one friend „ iii 156

Knife Hast thou a *k*? *Queen Mary* v v 164
callous with a constant stripe, Unwoundable. The *k*! „ v v 173
Becket, beware of the *k*! *Becket* i iv 133
As at this loveless *k* that stirs the riot, „ iv ii 191
kill, with *k* or venom One of his slanderous harlots? „ iv ii 409
And my *k* there—and blast the king and me, *The Cup* ii 152
He drove his *k* into the heart of the deer, *Foresters* iv 541

Knife-edge crawl over *k-e* flint Barefoot, *Becket* ii i 272

Knight Call him a *K*, That, with an ass's, *Queen Mary* i iii 168
They have taken away the toy thou gavest me, The Norman *k*. *Harold* ii ii 107
thou shalt have another Norman *k*! „ ii ii 114
range of *k's* Sit, each a statue on his horse, „ v i 524
I led seven hundred *k's* and fought his wars. *Becket* i iii 638
But I that threw the mightiest *k* of France, „ i iii 746
K's, bishops, earls, this London spawn— „ ii ii 143
Monks, *k's*, five hundred, that were there and heard. „ v ii 406
the *k's* are arming in the garden Beneath the sycamore. „ v ii 569
A score of *k's* all arm'd with swords and axes— „ v iii 71
O God, O noble *k's*, O sacrilege! „ v iii 178
Did two *k's* pass? *Foresters* ii i 230
Take thou mine arm. Who art thou, gallant *k*? „ ii i 440
Seize on the *k*! wrench his sword from him! „ ii i 676
we saw thee cowering to a *k* And thought thou wert bewitch'd. „ ii i 683
K, your good father had his draught of wine „ ii ii 1
No, no, false *k*, thou canst not hide thyself „ ii ii 23
Quick with thy sword! the yoeman braves the *k*. „ ii ii 31
Art thou a *k*? „ iv 116
How much is it, Robin, for a *k*? „ iv 152
He hath got it from the bottle, noble *k*. „ iv 237
Shall I undertake The *k* at quarterstaff, „ iv 248
Thou seest, Sir *K*, our friar is so holy „ iv 279
Hail, *k*, and help us. „ iv 765

Knit ere two souls be *k* for life and death, *The Cup* ii 359

Knock *K* off his cap there, some of you about him! *Queen Mary* iii i 241
K, and it shall be open'd. *Becket* v iii 64
it be i' *my* natur to *k* 'im o' the 'eäd now; *Prom. of May* i 288
K again! *k* again! *Foresters* ii i 212

Knock'd How oft hath Peter *k* at Mary's gate! *Queen Mary* iii ii 63

Knot And here a *k* of ruffians all in rags, „ ii ii 66
thro' this common *k* and bond of love, „ ii ii 198

Know (*See also* **Knaw**) thou shouldst *k*, for thou art as white as three Christmasses. „ i i 29
I *k* not if you *k*. „ i i 101
child by child, you *k*, Were momentary sparkles „ i ii 72
I *k* it, my good Lord. „ i ii 92
and then, who *k's*— „ i iv 25
Why do you ask? you *k* it. „ i iv 35
You *k* to flatter ladies. „ i iv 98
You *k* your Latin—quiet as a dead body. „ i iv 181
You do right well. I do not care to *k*; „ i iv 189
because they *k* him The last White Rose, „ i iv 206
I do but bring the message, *k* no more. „ i iv 229
I am of sovereign nature, that I *k*, „ i iv 258
yet I *k* well, Your people, and I go with them so far, „ i v 186
Ay, Simon Renard *k's* it. „ i v 218
I *k* it a scandal. „ i v 229
I *k* not wherefore—some mischance of flood, „ i v 353
Yet I *k* the Prince, „ i v 364
The text—Your Highness *k's* it, „ i v 451
you should *k* that whether A wind be warm or cold, „ i v 619
Song flies you *k* For ages. „ ii i 81
You *k* I *k* all this. „ ii i 120
Gardiner *k's*, but the Council are all at odds, „ ii i 138
I *k* Spain. I have been there with my father; „ ii i 166
and the beds I *k*. I hate Spain. „ ii i 185
ye *k*, my masters, that wherever Spain hath ruled „ ii i 205
You *k* that after The Captain Brett, „ ii ii 25
K too what Wyatt said. „ ii ii 35
I *k* it. What do and say Your Council at this hour? „ ii ii 45
waters of the fen they *k* not Which way to flow. „ ii ii 52
at once may *k* The wherefore of this coming, „ ii ii 137
To tell you what indeed ye see and *k*, „ ii ii 144
Now what I am ye *k* right well—your Queen; „ ii ii 162
Ye *k* my father was the rightful heir „ ii ii 170
I *k* you loyal. „ ii ii 271
Who *k's*? the man is proven by the hour. „ ii ii 363
'Who *k's*?' I am for England. But who *k's*, That *k's* „ ii ii 411
I *k* not my letters; the old priests taught me nothing. „ ii iii 57
we *k* that ye be come to kill the Queen, „ ii iii 107
he is King, you *k*, the King of Naples. „ iii i 73
studded with great emeralds, Rubies, I *k* not what. „ iii i 86
I *k* some lusty fellows there in France. „ iii i 128
I *k* a set of exiles over there, „ iii i 155
God's passion! do you *k* the knave that painted it? „ iii i 264
there's the face coming on here of one Who *k's* me. „ iii i 472
I *k* that she was ever sweet to me. „ iii ii 228
—all times for aught I *k*. „ iii iv 67
for you *k* Right well that you yourself „ iii iv 224
He *k's* not where he stands, „ iii iv 420
Nay, I *k* They hunt my blood. „ iii v 77
You *k* I never come till I be call'd. „ iii v 215
Best wisdom is to *k* the worst at once. „ iii v 220
I *k* that these are breeding A fierce resolve „ iii vi 30
Simon Renard *K's* me too well to speak „ iii vi 126
but, my Lord, you *k* what Virgil sings, „ iii vi 133
you *k* my father, Retiring into cloistral solitude „ iii vi 208
Not sued for that—he *k's* it were in vain. „ iv i 13
I *k* not if he did; „ iv i 128
your Highness *k's* The saying, 'Martyr's blood— „ iv i 145
You *k* that you recanted all you said „ iv iii 261
Of recantation yield again, who *k's*? „ iv iii 315
I *k* them heretics, but right English ones. „ iv iii 344
but I do *k* ez Pwoaps and vires be bad things; „ iv iii 500
Peters, you *k* me Catholic, but English. „ iv iii 566
K's where he nested—ever comes again. „ v i 26
and you *k* The crown is poor. „ v i 169
Elizabeth—To Philibert of Savoy, as you *k*, We meant to wed her; „ v i 247

Know (*continued*) but I *k* it of old, he hates me too ; *Queen Mary* v ii 60
Your Highness *k's* that in pursuing heresy „ v ii 96
They *k* nothing ; They burn for nothing. „ v ii 113
who said that ? I *k* not—true enough ! „ v ii 208
Our drooping Queen should *k* ! „ v ii 457
and you *k* me strong of arm ; „ v ii 469
light enough, God *k's*, And mixt with Wyatt's rising— „ v ii 478
And tell him that I *k* he comes no more. Tell him at last I *k* his love is dead, „ v ii 589
My King would *k* if you be fairly served, „ v ii 20
Who *k* my right, and love me, „ v iii 34
God's death, forsooth—you do not *k* King Philip. „ v iii 123
Drugs—but he *k's* they cannot help me— „ v v 60
I took it, tho' I did not *k* I took it, „ v v 97
Who *k's* if Boleyn's daughter be my sister ? „ v v 194
Stigand should *k* the purposes of Heaven. *Harold* I i 64
I *k* it, son ; I am not thankless : „ I i 215
And Tostig *k's* it ; Tostig loves the king. *Harold.* And love should *k* ; and—be the king so wise,— „ I i 274
He cannot guess who *k's*. „ I ii 136
Who *k's* I may not dream myself their king ! „ I ii 251
we came to *k* Thy valour and thy value, „ II ii 201
did Edward *k* of this ? „ II ii 304
I *k* the Norman license— „ II ii 477
Edward not pronounced his heir ? *Harold.* Not that I *k*. „ II ii 577
None that I *k* . . . if that but hung „ II ii 599
But hath he done it then ? *Harold.* Not that I *k*. „ II ii 612
He is a liar who *k's* I am a liar, „ II ii 667
I *k* your Norman cookery is so spiced, „ II ii 810
Yea, I *k* He knew not, but those heavenly ears „ III i 257
I *k* all Sussex ; A good entrenchment for a perilous hour ! „ III i 362
Do they ? I did not *k* it. „ III ii 106
God help me ! I *k* nothing— „ III ii 193
Who *k's* what sows itself among the people ? „ IV i 149
who *k* His prowess in the mountains of the West, „ IV i 164
K what thou dost ; and we may find for thee, „ IV ii 48
They *k* King Edward's promise and thine — thine. *Harold.* Should they not *k* free England crowns herself ? Nor *k* that he nor I had power to promise ? Not *k* that Edward cancell'd his own promise ? „ V i 45
blurt thy curse among our folk, I *k* not— „ V i 90
Whisper ! God's angels only *k* it. Ha ! „ V ii 31
I am grieved to *k* as much. *Becket, Pro.* 4
dost thou *k* I am not wedded to her. *Becket.* How should I *k* ? „ *Pro.* 72
I love thee and I *k* thee, I *k* thee, „ *Pro.* 95
How shouldst thou *k* that never hast loved one ? „ *Pro.* 140
God's eyes ! I *k* all that— „ *Pro.* 148
Nay—I *k* not, Thomas. „ *Pro.* 197
I *k* Some three or four good priests „ *Pro.* 290
thou hast kicked down the board. I *k* thee of old. „ *Pro.* 316
The people *k* their Church a tower of strength, „ I i 15
It much imports me I should *k* her name. „ I i 193
let me pass, my lord, for I must *k*. „ I i 206
And *k* the ways of Nature. „ I i 257
Well—you *k*—the minion, Rosamund. „ I ii 36
Shame, wrath, I *k* not what. „ I iii 322
K that when made Archbishop I was freed, „ I iii 707
or in the land of France for aught I *k*. „ I iv 197
my fellows *k* that I am all one scale like a fish. „ I iv 213
cursed My friends at Veselay, I have let them *k*, „ II i 90
—thine ! thine ! *Rosamund.* I *k* it. „ II i 163
Dost thou *k*, my boy, what it is to be Chancellor of England ? „ II i 231
Thine enemy *k's* the secret of my bower. „ II i 264
You are too cold to *k* the fashion of it. „ II ii 126
I would have made Rome *k* she still is Rome— „ II ii 402
Bee mustn't buzz, Whoop—but he *k's*. (repeat) *Becket* III i 99, 241
what's an apple, you *k*, save to a child, *Becket* III i 141
only you *k* the King's married, for King Louis— „ III i 166
most on 'em *k* an honest woman and a lady when they see her, „ III i 179
she kept the seventh commandment better than some I *k* on, „ III i 195

Know (*continued*) known Nothing but him—happy to *k* no more, *Becket* III i 224
Whoop—but he *k's*, Whoop—but he *k's*. „ III i 263
I *k* Thy meaning. „ III iii 18
Hereford, you *k*, crown'd the first Henry. „ III iii 201
Even now—Who *k's* ?—I might deliver all things „ III iii 269
Why ? *Geoffrey.* Don't *k* why. „ IV i 14
but I don't *k* if I can find the way back again. „ IV i 48
K you not this bower is secret, „ IV ii 21
none shall *k* me ; The King shall never hear „ IV ii 100
Who *k's* but that thy lover May plead so pitifully, „ IV ii 215
we *k* you proud of your fine hand, „ IV ii 260
you *k* thro' all this quarrel I still have cleaved „ V i 46
I *k*—could swear—as long as Becket breathes, „ V i 76
and yet You *k* me easily anger'd. „ V i 84
Do you *k* this cross, my liege ? „ V i 161
I *k* him ; our good John of Salisbury. „ V ii 77
Deal not with things you *k* not. *Rosamund.* I *k him*. „ V ii 133
I *k* not why You call these old things „ V ii 269
I marvel at you—Ye *k* what is between us. „ V ii 500
K you not You have spoken to the peril „ V ii 515
He *k's* the twists and turnings of the place. „ V ii 576
Hugh, I *k* well thou hast but half a heart „ V iii 129
Boy, dost thou *k* the house of Sinnatus ? *The Cup* I i 49
You *k* the waterfall That in the summer „ I i 107
She *k's* it ? Ha ! „ I i 131
Who are with him ? I see no face that *k's* me. „ I i 183
k That we Galatians are both Greek and Gaul. „ I i 202
Scarce *k* what she has done. „ I ii 135
I *k* of no such wives in all Galatia. „ I ii 191
k myself am that Galatian Who sent the cup. „ I ii 209
I *k* they mean to torture him to death. I dare not tell him how I came to *k* it ; „ I ii 273
I say it to you—you are wiser—Rome *k's* all, But you *k* not the savagery of Rome. „ I ii 286
is there danger ? *Camma.* Nay, None that I *k* : „ I ii 442
Will she come to me Now that she *k's* me Synorix ? „ I iii 21
I *k* that I am genial, I would be Happy, „ I iii 28
as you *k* The camp is half a league without the city ; „ I iii 88
We will let her *k*. „ II 13
the world may *k* You twain are reconciled, „ II 68
It is old, I *k* not How many hundred years. „ II 342
She not *k* ? She *k's* There's none such other— *The Falcon* 77
He loves me, and he *k's* I *k* he loves me ! „ 245
as your ladyship *k's*, his lordship's own foster-brother, „ 566
You *k*, my lord, I told you I was troubled. „ 676
you *k* the saying—' Better a man without riches, „ 749
let me *k* the boon By granting which, „ 765
You *k* that I can touch The ghittern „ 797
You *k* sick people, More specially sick children, „ 815
I don't *k* why I sing that song ; I don't love it. *Prom. of May* I 61
He's been arter Miss Eva, haän't he ? *Dora.* Not that I *k*. „ I 123
She *k's* nothing. Man only *k's*, „ I 273
Who *k's* that he had ever dream'd of flying ? „ I 654
That's all nonsense, you *k*, such a baby as you are. „ I 784
Perhaps you *k* him ? „ II 439
then you would *k* it is not So easy to forgive— „ II 484
has suffer'd More than we *k*. „ II 502
When you shall *k* me better. „ II 529
who came to us three years after you were gone, how should she *k* you ? „ III 234
was a mockery, you *k*, for he gave me no address, and there was no word of marriage ; „ III 331
for you *k*, my dear, you were always his favourite— „ III 422
Be he dead ? *Dora.* Not that I *k*. „ III 434
He will be sure to *k* you to-morrow. „ III 470
I *k* more fully that *he* can What poor earthworms „ III 634
You *k* her, Eva. *Harold.* Eva ! „ III 663
She—she *k's* me—now . . . „ III 686
but now ye *k* why we live so stintedly, *Foresters* I i 76
I *k* not, but he may save the land, „ I i 282
but I *k* not if I will let thee go. „ I i 311
Him that is gone. Who *k's* whither ? „ I ii 9
Perfect—who should *k* you for Prince John, „ I ii 20

L

Lady (*continued*) lily and rose In his youth, and like a *l*. *Queen Mary* I v 21
Our sovereign *L* by King Harry's will; „ II ii 268
Ay, my *L*. When next there comes a missive „ III v 181
Our Spanish *ladies* have none such— „ V iii 46
There must be *ladies* with hair like mine. „ V iii 58
up and down, poor *l*, up and down. „ V v 6
Nay, dearest *L*, see your good physician. „ V v 58
War, my dear *l*! *Harold* I i 22
Mightily, my dear *l*! „ I i 24
War, my dear *l*, War, waste, plague, „ I i 465
told me he would advance me to the service of a great *l*, *Becket* III i 124
but more a woman o' the world than my *l* here, „ III i 143
I am as well-shaped as my *l* here, „ III i 150
for here comes my *l*, and, my *l*, „ III i 153
most on 'em know an honest woman and a *l* when they see her, „ III i 180
and went on and on till I found the light and the *l*, „ IV ii 19
the *l* holds the cleric Lovelier than any soldier, „ V i 193
Your cleric hath your *l*. „ V i 200
O dearest *l*, Think,—torture,—death,— *The Cup* I ii 313
L, I say it with all gentleness, „ I iii 99
happiest, *L*, in my power To make you happy. „ II 239
if we *will* buy diamond necklaces To please our *l*, *The Falcon* 45
Welcome to this poor cottage, my dear *l*. „ 271
L, you bring your light into my cottage „ 283
A *l* that was beautiful as day Sat by me „ 349
wasn't my *l* born with a golden spoon in her ladyship's mouth, „ 401
with my *l's* coming that had so flurried me, „ 492
No, my most honour'd and long-worshipt *l*, „ 714
L, I find you a shrewd bargainer. „ 756
when you lamed the *l* in the hollow lane. *Prom. of May* III 89
marry fine gentlemen, and played at being fine *ladies*? „ III 278
shamed of his poor farmer's daughter among the *ladies* in his drawing-room? „ III 295
Wasn't Miss Vavasour, our schoolmistress at Littlechester, a *l* born? Were not our fellow-pupils all *ladies*? Wasn't dear mother herself at least by one side a *l*? Can't I speak like a *l*; pen a letter like a *l*; talk a little French like a *l*; play a little like a *l*? „ III 298
The sick *l* here might have been asleep. „ III 343
Say that the sick *l* thanks him! „ III 349
Tell him I cannot leave the sick *l* just yet. „ III 353
Tell him that I and the *l* here wish to see him. „ III 414
Sooner or later shamed of her among The *ladies*, „ III 582
The *l* loved the master well, *Foresters* I i 8
The *l* gave a rose to the Earl, (repeat) „ I i 12, 105
The *l* gave her hand to the Earl, (repeat) „ I i 16, 92
part to the shrine of our *L*. „ III 207
I have sworn by our *L* if they come „ IV 96
Our *L's* blessed shrines throughout the land „ IV 1079
Ladylike *L*! Lilylike in her stateliness *Prom. of May* II 620
Laggard Where is this *l* Richard of the Lea? *Foresters* IV 449
Lagoon He caught a chill in the *l's* of Venice, *Queen Mary* V ii 515
Laic *L's* and barons, thro' The random gifts *Becket* I i 157
Laid spousal ring whereof, Not ever to be *l* aside, *Queen Mary* II ii 167
attainder *l* on us By him who sack'd the house of God; „ III iii 194
raise his head, for thou hast *l* it low! *Harold* III i 163
Hath often *l* a cold hand on my heats, *Becket* I i 384
There now, if thou hast not *l* hands upon me! „ I iv 212
I would have *l* mine own life down „ V ii 338
L famine-stricken at the gates of Death— *Prom. of May* III 807
Lain Bonner, who hath *l* so long under bonds for the faith— *Queen Mary* I iii 35
Long have I *l* in prison, yet have heard „ IV iii 210
Where have you *l* in ambush all the morning? *Prom. of May* I 544
Lais With Phryne, Or *L*, or thy Rosamund, *Becket, Pro.* 56
My Rosamund is no *L*, Thomas Becket; „ *Pro.* 57
Laity I am but of the *l*, my Lord Bishop, *Queen Mary* III iv 81
Lake might have flash'd Upon their *l* of Garda, „ III ii 23
Senlac! Sanguelac, The *L* of Blood! *Harold* III i 386
—a *l*, A sea of blood—we are drown'd in blood „ III i 397
call it—Sanguelac, The *l* of blood? „ V i 185
Lake (*continued*) A *l* that dips in William As well as Harold. *Harold* V i 186
Lamb (*See also* **Ewe-lamb**) king Hath given his virgin *l* to Holy Church „ III i 334
Our Church in arms—the *l* the lion— „ V i 441
'Ewe *l*, ewe *l*, I am here by the dam.' *Becket* I iv 171
Lambert there was *L*; Who can foresee himself? *Queen Mary* IV ii 215
Lambeth (adj.) And unto no dead world; but *L* palace, „ III ii 154
Lambeth (s) seen your steps a mile From me and *L*? „ I ii 82
Permit me to withdraw. To *L*? „ III ii 131
Ay, *L* has ousted Cranmer. „ III ii 132
was not meet the heretic swine should live In *L*. „ III ii 136
Lame And further to discourage and lay *l* The plots of France, „ V i 188
The fellow that on a *l* jade came to court, *Becket* V i 246
Lamed (*See also* **Laäme't**) arm; I do believe I *l* his Majesty's *Queen Mary* V ii 471
And *l* and maim'd to dislocation, *Becket* IV ii 266
having his right hand *L* in the battle, *The Falcon* 445
when you *l* the lady in the hollow lane. *Prom. of May* III 89
You see she is *l*, and cannot go down to him. „ III 416
Lamentation I should say rather, the lacrymation of a *l*; *Becket* III iii 167
Lamer And head them with a *l* rhyme of mine, *Queen Mary* II i 29
Lamester How should this old *l* guide us? *Foresters* II i 370
Laming At least mine own is frailer: you are *l* it. *Becket* IV ii 265
Lammas And that's at latter *L*—never perhaps. *Foresters* II ii 86
Lamp loom Across their *l's* of revel, *Harold* II ii 407
Lamplight river, black, slimy, swirling under me in the *l*, *Prom. of May* III 370
Lance for how their *l's* snap and shiver *Harold* V i 585
And push'd our *l's* into Saracen hearts. *Becket* II ii 94
Lanceas Illorum *l* Frange Creator! *Harold* V i 583
Land (s) (*See also* **Church-land**) so this unhappy *l*, long divided in itself, *Queen Mary* I iii 20
red and white, the fashion of our *l*. „ I v 10
And here at *l* among the people! „ I v 383
stir not yet This matter of the Church *l's*. „ I v 409
Confiscate *l's*, goods, money— „ II i 102
I have seen them in their own *l*; „ II i 168
clash alarum as we pass, And pour along the *l*, „ II i 232
Rascal!—this *l* is like a hill of fire, „ III i 321
Feeling my native *l* beneath my foot, „ III ii 47
'Ah, native *l* of mine, Thou art much beholden „ III ii 48
Methinks the good *l* heard me, „ III ii 57
In the reborn salvation of a *l* So noble. „ III iii 182
The ruler of a *l* Is bounden by his power „ III iv 211
You are fresh from brighter *l's*. Retire with me. „ III iv 322
Care more for our brief life in their wet *l*, „ III vi 63
So weary am I of this wet *l* of theirs, „ III vi 106
Draw with your sails from our poor *l*, „ III vi 226
Unhappy *l*! Hard-natured Queen, „ IV iii 423
'll burn the Pwoap out o' this 'ere *l* vor iver and iver. „ IV iii 536
this Henry Stirs up your *l* against you „ V i 131
They will not lay more taxes on a *l* „ V i 167
not the living rock Which guards the *l*. *Harold* I ii 121
get himself wrecked on another man's *l*? „ II i 61
Large lordship there of *l's* and territory. „ II ii 83
In mine own *l* I should have scorn'd the man, „ II ii 505
in thine own *l* in thy father's day „ II ii 510
The kingliest Abbey in all Christian *l's*, „ III i 205
Thou art Tostig's brother, Who wastes the *l*. *Harold*. This brother comes to save Your *l* from waste; „ IV i 93
I knew him brave: he loved his *l*: „ IV i 201
He looks for *l* among us, he and his. „ IV ii 53
Seven feet of English *l*, or something more, „ IV ii 54
Hath wasted all the *l* at Pevensey— „ IV iii 189
Neighing and roaring as they leapt to *l*— „ IV iii 198
And waste the *l* about thee as thou goest, „ V i 131
to guard the *l* for which He did forswear himself— „ V ii 161
That havock'd all the *l* in Stephen's day. *Becket* I i 242
among you those that hold *L's* reft from Canterbury. „ I iii 141
Many of the crown *l's* to those that helpt him; „ I iii 150
Claim'd some of our crown *l's* for Canterbury— „ I iii 459
With Cain belike, in the *l* of Nod, or in the *l* of France „ I iv 196
voice of the deep as it hollows the cliffs of the *l*. „ II i 4
not half speaking The language of the *l*. „ II i 137

Land (s) (*continued*) from the salt lips of the *l* we two Have track'd — *Becket* III ii 2
lord of more *l* Than any crown in Europe, „ v i 29
And wrought his worst against his native *l*, *The Cup* I ii 178
past is like a travell'd *l* now sunk Below the horizon— „ II 230
I never saw The *l* so rich in blossom as this year. *The Falcon* 342
'The *l* belongs to the people!' *Prom. of May* I 140
s'pose my pig's the *l*, and you says it belongs to the parish, „ I 144
violated the whole Tradition of our *l*, „ I 496
Who leaves me all his *l* at Littlechester, „ I 511
pacing my new *l's* at Littlechester, „ II 647
We shall have to sell all the *l*, „ III 165
The *l* belonged to the Steers i' the owd times, „ III 450
I have heard the Steers Had *l* in Saxon times; „ III 608
I have *l* now And wealth, and lay both at your feet. „ III 615
not with all your wealth, Your *l*, your life! „ III 796
if they be not paid back at the end of the year, the *l* goes to the Abbot. *Foresters* I i 70
Sir Richard must scrape and scrape till he get to the *l* again. „ I i 79
must be paid in a year and a month, or I lose the *l*. „ I i 269
but he may save the *l*, (repeat) „ I i 283
Well, thou shalt go, but O the *l*! the *l*! „ I i 328
and I shall lose my *l* also. „ I i 339
Or I forfeit my *l* to the Abbot. „ I ii 151
pay My brother all his debt and save the *l*. „ I ii 219
till he join King Richard in the Holy *L*. *Robin*. Going to the Holy *L* to Richard! „ I ii 239
pay his mortgage to his brother, And save the *l*. „ I ii 265
thou art dispossessed of all thy *l's*, goods, and chattels; „ I iii 60
There is no *l* like England (repeat) *Foresters* II i 1, 5, 13, 17
thro' all the forest *l* North to the Tyne: being outlaw'd in a *l* Where law lies dead, *Foresters* II i 88
—if so the *l* may come To Marian, and they rate the *l* fivefold The worth of the mortgage, and who marries her Marries the *l*. „ II i 147
and couldst never pay The mortgage on my *l*. „ II i 454
but my father will not lose his *l*, „ II i 523
He is old and almost mad to keep the *l*. „ II i 529
what sort of man art thou For *l*, not love? Thou wilt inherit the *l*, „ II i 534
betray'd Thy father to the losing of his *l*. „ II i 570
Now he cries 'The *l*! the *l*!' Come to him. „ II ii 7
To a *l* where the fay, „ II ii 180
thou seest the *l* has come between us, „ IV 53
and I would thou wert the king of the *l*. „ IV 233
if the *l* Were ruleable by tongue, „ IV 398
if they were not repaid within a limited time your *l* should be forfeit. „ IV 468
The *l*! the *l*! (repeat) *Foresters* IV 470, 491, 854
one thousand marks, Or else the *l*. *Foresters* IV 475
old Sir Richard might redeem his *l*. He is all for love, he cares not for the *l*. „ IV 488
Out of our treasury to redeem the *l*. „ IV 493
And Sir Richard cannot redeem his *l*. „ IV 565
And we shall keep the *l*. „ IV 637
It seems thy father's *l* is forfeited. „ IV 640
He shall wed thee: The *l* shall still be mine. „ IV 643
I could wish that all the *l* Were plunged „ IV 667
Woe to that *l* shall own thee for her king! „ IV 759
on the faith and honour of a king The *l* is his again. „ IV 853
I am crazed no longer, so I have the *l*. „ IV 856
The gold—my son—my gold, my son, the *l*— „ IV 988
And join'd my banner in the Holy *L*, „ IV 1000
weight of the very *l* itself, Down to the inmost centre. „ IV 1025
Our Lady's blessed shrines throughout the *l* „ IV 1080
Land (verb) So your king-parliament suffer him to *l*, *Queen Mary* I v 366
Landed Are *l* North of Humber, and in a field *Harold* III ii 126
William hath *l*, ha? *Thane*. *L* at Pevensey—I am from Pevensey— „ IV iii 185
Landing Back'd by the power of France, and *l* here, *Queen Mary* III i 448
Landless Specially not this *l* Philibert Of Savoy; „ III v 240
Landlord fur I wur nobbut a laäbourer, and now I be a *l*— *Prom. of May* I 330
Land-surveyor and I taäked 'im fur soom sort of a *l-s*—but a beänt. *Prom. of May* I 204
Lane (*See also* **Laäne**) Stand back, keep a clear *l*! *Queen Mary* I i 2
when you lamed the lady in the hollow *l*. *Prom. of May* III 90
Do you still suffer from your fall in the hollow *l*? „ III 241
if met in a black *l* at midnight: *Foresters* III 224
Language Seventeen—and knew eight *l's*— *Queen Mary* III i 359
not half speaking The *l* of the land. *Becket* II i 137
His wickedness is like my wretchedness—Beyond all *l*. *Prom. of May* III 748
Lanker I be *l* than an old horse turned out to die on the common. *Foresters* I i 51
Lap Milk? *Filippo*. Three *l's* for a cat! *The Falcon* 125
Lapse track of the true faith Your *l's* are far seen. *Queen Mary* III iv 95
Lapwing The *l's* lies, says 'here' when they are there. „ III v 124
Larder Come, come, Filippo, what is there in the *l*? *The Falcon* 118
then there is anything in your lordship's *l* at your lordship's service, „ 137
Large Hath he the *l* ability of the Emperor? *Queen Mary* I v 323
Hath he the *l* ability of his father? „ I v 438
They have brought it in *l* measure on themselves. „ IV iii 363
thou thyself shalt have *L* lordship there of lands and territory. *Harold* II ii 83
they both have life In the *l* mouth of England, „ IV iii 74
Without too *l* self-lauding I must hold The sequel „ IV iii 87
Larger Will enter on the *l* golden age; *Prom. of May* I 590
The hope of *l* life hereafter, more Tenfold than under roof. *Foresters* II i 69
Largess Might cast my *l* of it to the crowd! *The Cup* II 224
Lark Spit them like *l's* for aught I care. *Queen Mary* I v 395
The *l* above, the nightingale below, „ II i 52
the *l* sings, the sweet stars come and go, *Harold* II ii 434
l first takes the sunlight on his wing, *The Cup* I iii 43
thou that canst soar Beyond the morning *l*, *The Falcon* 11
and the *l's* 'ud sing i' them daäys, *Prom. of May* I 374
'O happy *l*, that warblest high Above thy lowly nest, „ III 199
while the *l* flies up and touches heaven! *Foresters* I ii 315
When heaven falls, I may light on such a *l*! „ III 13
Could live as happy as the *l's* in heaven, „ III 82
Larn (learn, teach) Wheer did they *l* ye that? *Dora*. In Cumberland, Mr. Dobson. *Prom. of May* I 64
I'll git the book ageän, and *l* mysen the rest, „ III 12
Them be what they *l's* the childer' at school, „ III 39
Larned (learned, taught) 'at I ha' nobbut *l* mysen haäfe on it. „ III 4
Lash (verb) If they prance, Rein in, not *l* them, *Harold* I i 372
Lash (whip) with crimson rowel And streaming *l*. *Queen Mary* III iv 184
Lash'd *l* to death, or lie Famishing in black cells, „ v ii 194
scorn'd the man, Or *l* his rascal back, *Harold* II ii 507
now, perhaps, Fetter'd and *l*, a galley-slave, *Foresters* II i 654
Lashing storm and shower *l* Her casement, *Prom. of May* II 472
Lass Ay, *l*, but when thou be as owd as me „ I 380
Why, *l*, what maäkes tha sa red? „ I 398
and the lads and *l'es* 'ull hev a dance. „ I 428
Last Dear friend, for the *l* time; farewell, and fly. *Queen Mary* I ii 103
because they know him the *l* White Rose, the *l* Plantagenet „ I iv 207
L night I climb'd into the gate-house, Brett, „ II iii 14
Did not his *l* breath Clear Courtenay and the Princess „ III i 134
I have heard She would not take a *l* farewell of him, „ III i 367
Laughs at the *l* red leaf, and Andrew's Day. „ III iii 87
Thou *l* of all the Tudors, come away! With us is peace!' The *l*? It was a dream; „ III v 151
A missive from the Queen: *l* time she wrote, I had like to have lost my life: „ III v 188
L night, I dream'd the faggots were alight, „ IV ii 1
It is the *l*. *Cranmer*. Give it me, then. „ IV ii 64
For death gives life's *l* word a power to live, „ IV iii 161
forasmuch as I have come To the *l* end of life, „ IV iii 218
This *l*—I dare not read it her. „ v ii 183
and I say it For the *l* time perchance, *Harold* I i 176
but *l* night An evil dream that ever came and went— „ I ii 69
Friends, in that *l* inhospitable plunge Our boat hath burst her ribs; „ II i 1
L night King Edward came to me in dreams—(repeat) *Harold* IV i 259, 265

Last (*continued*) Hear me again—for the *l* time. *Harold* v i 8
Then for the *l* time, monk, I ask again „ v i 15
Peace! The king's *l* word—'the arrow!' I shall die— „ v i 266
wherefore now Obey my first and *l* commandment. Go! „ v i 359
Edith, if I, the *l* English King of England— „ v i 384
but our sun in Aquitaine *l's* longer. *Becket, Pro.* 328
The *l* Parthian shaft of a forlorn Cupid at the King's left breast, „ *Pro.* 339
and his *l* words were a commendation of Thomas Becket „ *Pro.* 400
L night I followed a woman in the city here. „ *Pro.* 468
That rang Within my head *l* night, „ I i 71
at *l* tongue-free To blast my realms with excommunication „ II ii 50
nigh at the end of our *l* crust, and that mouldy, „ III i 114
He hath the Pope's *l* letters, and they threaten „ III iii 24
Take thy one chance; Catch at the *l* straw. „ IV ii 221
Let this be thy *l* trespass. „ V ii 165
King closed with me *l* July That I should pass the censures of the Church „ V ii 388
Shall not Heaven be served Tho' earth's *l* earthquake clash'd the minster-bells, „ V iii 41
I need not fear the crowd that hunted me Across the woods, *l* night. *The Cup* I iii 17
He entreats you now For your *l* answer. „ II 46
O would it were His third *l* apoplexy! „ II 172
I had a touch of this *l* year—in—Rome. „ II 446
crown'd victor of my will—On my *l* voyage— „ II 521
came back *l* night with her son to the castle. *The Falcon* 3
Thou art the *l* friend left me upon earth— „ 31
And this *l* costly gift to mine own self, „ 228
when he came *l* year To see me hawking, „ 312
My *l* sight ere I swoon'd was one sweet face Crown'd „ 647
so much weaker, so much worse For *l* day's journey. „ 834
tha looks haäle anew to *l* to a hoonderd. *Steer.* An' why shouldn't I *l* to a hoonderd? *Prom. of May* I 355
Noä; I laäme't my knee *l* night running arter a thief. „ I 387
Oh, Philip, Father heard you *l* night. „ I 557
but you must not be too sudden with it either, as you were *l* year, „ II 54
The *l* on it, eh? *Haymaker.* Yeas. „ II 141
Well, it be the *l* loäd hoäm. „ II 144
Well but, as I said afoor, it be the *l* loäd hoäm; „ II 169
'The *L* Loäd Hoäm.' (repeat) „ II 171
At the end of the daäy, For the *l* loäd hoäm? (repeat) „ II 184, 195
Till the end of the daäy And the *l* loäd hoäm. „ II 209
Till the end o' the daäy An' the *l* loäd hoäm.' (repeat) „ II 239, 293
To the end o' the daäy, An' the *l* loäd hoäm „ II 260
Only *l* week at Littlechester, drove me From out her memory. „ II 404
Oh, *l* night, Tired, pacing my new lands at Littlechester, „ II 645
spent all your *l* Saturday's wages at the ale-house; „ III 78
It is almost the *l* of my bad days, I think. „ III 471
They did not *l* three Junes. „ III 589
But she there—her *l* word Forgave—and I forgive you. „ III 810
Nay, this may be the *l* time When I shall hold my birthday in this hall: *Foresters* I ii 87
from their stillness in the grave By the *l* trumpet. „ II i 48
and the old woman's blessing with them to the *l* fringe. „ II i 196
We have him at *l*; we have him at advantage. „ II i 414
There came some evil fairy at my birth And cursed me, as the *l* heir of my race: „ II ii 109
is it true?—That John *l* week return'd to Nottingham, „ III 147

Lasting and the man has doubtless a good heart, and a true and *l* love for me: *Prom. of May* III 172

Late (adj. and adv.) my daughter said that when there rose a talk of the *l* rebellion, *Queen Mary* I i 92
I will go. I thank my God it is too *l* to fly. „ I ii 112
Her freaks and frolics with the *l* Lord Admiral? „ I iv 20
My Lord, you *l* were loosed from out the Tower, „ I iv 49
Who loathe you for your *l* return to Rome, „ IV ii 32
in pursuing heresy I have gone beyond your *l* Lord Chancellor,— „ V ii 98

Late (adj. and adv.) (*continued*) Friend, tho' so *l*, it is not safe to preach. *Queen Mary* V iv 41
Am I too *l*? Cecil . . . God guide me lest I lose the way. „ V v 208
Ay, but what *l* guest, As haggard as a fast of forty days, *Harold* IV iii 175
Too *l*, my lord: you see they are signing there. *Becket* I iii 288
The boy so *l*; pray God, he be not lost. „ IV ii 1
Is it too *l* for me to save your soul? „ V ii 524
Becket, it *is* too *l*. *Becket.* Is it too *l*? Too *l* on earth may be too soon in hell. „ V ii 526
Too *l*—thought myself wise—A woman's dupe. *The Cup* II 480
—and better *l* than never— *The Falcon* 200
I have heard That, thro' his *l* magnificence of living „ 227
I am too *l* then with my quarterstaff! *Foresters* II i 427

Late (s) There was one here of *l*—William the Silent *Queen Mary* III ii 191

Later Sooner or *l* shamed of her among The ladies, *Prom. of May* III 581

Lateran When had the *L* and the Holy Father *Harold* V i 17
leave *L* and Vatican in one dust of gold— *Becket* II ii 475

Latimer (Bishop of Worcester) Hooper, Ridley, *L* will not fly. *Queen Mary* I ii 14
Cranmer and Hooper, Ridley and *L*, „ III iv 424
L Had a brief end—not Ridley. „ IV ii 224
I saw the deaths of *L* and Ridley. „ IV iii 295
And you saw *L* and Ridley die? *L* was eighty, was he not? „ IV iii 328
'not till I hears ez *L* and Ridley be a-vire;' „ IV iii 508
When we had come where Ridley burnt with *L*, „ IV iii 586
L! Sir, we are private with our women here— „ V v 118

Latimer-sailor Our Ridley-soldiers and our *L-s's* „ IV iii 348

Latin (adj.) for my verses if the *L* rhymes be rolled out from a full mouth? *Becket* II ii 337
That's a delicate *L* lay Of Walter Map: „ V i 191

Latin (s) You know your *L*—quiet as a dead body. *Queen Mary* I iv 181

Laugh And that's at *l* Lammas—never perhaps. *Foresters* II ii 86
Oh *L's* at the last red leaf, and Andrew's Day. *Queen Mary* III iii 87
so! *l* not! . . . Strange and ghastly *Harold* III ii 157

Latter we could not but *l*, as by a royal necessity— *Becket* III iii 158

Lauding *See* **Self-lauding**

Laugh'd William *l* and swore that might was right, *Harold* II ii 361
The wicked sister clapt her hands and *l*; „ V ii 49
part royal, for King and kingling both *l*, *Becket* III iii 158
when we felt we had *l* too long and could not stay ourselves— „ III iii 160
such a comedy as our court of Provence Had *l* at. „ V i 191

Laughing (*See also* **A-laughin'**) And the Dutchman, Now *l* at some jest? *Queen Mary* III i 196

Laughter (*See also* **Sea-laughter**) among thine island mists With *l*. *Harold* II ii 183
thunder-cloud That lours on England—*l*! „ III ii 161
human *l* in old Rome Before a Pope was born, „ III ii 163
great motion of *l* among us, part real, part childlike, *Becket* III iii 155
trumpets in the halls, Sobs, *l*, cries: „ V ii 368
I Shall not be made the *l* of the village, *Prom. of May* I 720

Lava-torrents Whose *l-t* blast and blacken a province *The Cup* II 302

Lavender To rose and *l* my horsiness, *Queen Mary* III v 185

Lavish Spare not thy tongue! be *l* with our coins, *Becket* II ii 469
Your *l* household curb'd, and the remission *Queen Mary* I v 113

Lavish'd All I had I *l* for the glory of the King; *Becket* I iii 663

Law (s) the Queen, and the *l's*, and the people, his slaves. *Queen Mary* II i 174
when I was wedded to the realm And the realm's *l's* „ II ii 165
seeks To bend the *l's* to his own will, „ II ii 184
But so I get the *l's* against the heretic, „ III i 323
she thought she knew the *l's*. But for herself, she knew but little *l*, „ III i 381
Either in making *l's* and ordinances „ III iii 130
Of all such *l's* and ordinances made; „ III iii 142
I will be King of England by the *l's*, *Harold* II ii 131
For I shall rule according to your *l's*, „ II ii 759
I will rule according to their *l's*. „ V ii 198
Like other lords amenable to *l*. I'll have them written down and made the *l*. *Becket, Pro.* 25
sign'd These ancient *l's* and customs of the realm. „ I iii 7
to obey These ancient *l's* and customs of the realm? „ I iii 18

Law (s) (continued) and l From madness. Becket I iii 374
There wore his time studying the canon l „ II i 86
Co-kings we were, and made the l's together. „ II ii 123
spiritual giant with our island l's And customs, „ IV ii 444
it is the l, not he; The customs of the realm. „ V ii 126
—her main l Whereby she grows in beauty— Prom. of May I 282
according to the l and custom of the kingdom of England Foresters I iii 66
I have shelter'd some that broke the forest l's. „ I iii 70
being outlaw'd in a land Where l lies dead, we make ourselves the l. „ II i 91
An outlaw's bride may not be wife in l. „ II ii 91
We robb'd the lawyer who went against the l; „ III 162
chief of these outlaws who break the l? „ IV 142
being out of the l how should we break the l? if we broke into it we should break the l, „ IV 144
Ay, ay, Robin, but let him know our forest l's: „ IV 199
If the king and the l work injustice, is not he that goes against the king and the l the true king „ IV 228
Church and L, halt and pay toll! „ IV 429
you see the bond and the letter of the l. „ IV 505
Between the l and letter of the l! O God, I would the letter of the l Were some strong fellow „ IV 513
When the Church and the l have forgotten God's music, „ IV 554
Sweet Marian, by the letter of the l „ IV 639
You crost him with a quibble of your l. „ IV 850
Hast broken all our Norman forest l's, „ IV 886
That thou wilt break our forest l's again „ IV 888
They break thy forest l's—nay, by the rood „ IV 907
And have thy fees, and break the l no more. „ IV 955
Law (inter.) (See also **Lor**) O l—yeäs, Sir! I'll run fur 'im mysen. Prom. of May III 713
Law-bench Spain in the pulpit and on the l-b; Queen Mary II i 178
Lawful Long live Queen Mary, the l and legitimate daughter Of Harry the Eighth! „ I i 8
with your l Prince Stand fast against our enemies and yours, „ II ii 240
Your l Prince hath come to cast herself On loyal hearts and bosoms, „ II ii 261
The ruler of an hour, but l King, Foresters IV 47
Were fighting underhand unholy wars Against your l king, „ IV 822
Lawn forest l's are all as bright As ways to heaven, „ II i 630
Thro' wood and l and ling, „ III 425
Lawrence (Saint) The patience of St. L in the fire. Queen Mary IV iii 95
Lawyer leästwaäys, I should be wi' a l. Prom. of May III 34
We robb'd the l who went against the law; Foresters III 161
Lay (s) That's a delicate Latin l Of Walter Map: Becket V i 192
Lay (verb, trans.) (See also **Laäy**) I love you, L my life in your hands. Queen Mary I iv 105
God l the waves and strow the storms „ I v 381
'Will you take it off Before I l me down?' „ III i 403
I never l my head upon the pillow But that I think, „ III v 131
See, I l it here, For I will come no nearer „ III v 198
They will not l more taxes on a land „ V i 167
to discourage and l lame The plots of France, „ V i 188
L thou thy hand upon this golden pall! Harold II ii 699
L hands of full allegiance in thy Lord's „ V i 11
l them both upon the waste sea-shore At Hastings, „ V ii 159
l My crozier in the Holy Father's hands, Becket I iii 124
not yield To l your neck beneath your citizen's heel. „ V i 31
Where to l on her tribute—heavily here And lightly there. The Cup II 98
L down the Lydian carpets for the king. „ II 187
strows our fruits, and l's Our golden grain, „ II 286
But l them there for a moment! The Falcon 763
I l them for the first time round your neck. „ 907
land now And wealth, and l both at your feet. Prom. of May III 616
Lay (past tense [of Lie]) by God's providence a good stout staff L near me; Queen Mary V ii 469
And York l barren for a hundred years. Becket I iii 54
plow L rusting in the furrow's yellow weeds, „ I iii 355
The town l still in the low sun-light, Prom. of May I 37
She l so long at the bottom of her well Foresters IV 242
The man l down—the delicate-footed creature „ IV 535
Layest (intrans.) thou That l so long in heretic bonds with me; Queen Mary III iv 280
Layest (trans.) but when thou l thy lip To this, Becket II i 306
Laying I saw the covers l. Philip. Let us have it. Queen Mary III vi 258
Layman whether between laymen or clerics, shall be tried in the King's court.' Becket I iii 80
Laymen-criminals be bound Behind the back like l-c? „ I iii 96
Lazar I marked a group of l's in the marketplace— „ I iv 81
Lazarus Am I a prisoner? Leicester. By St. L, no! „ I iii 730
Lazy We dally with our l moments here, Queen Mary V iii 108
Lazy-pious And he our l-p Norman King, Harold II ii 444
Lea I come here to see this daughter of Sir Richard of the L Foresters I ii 27
Robin, I am Sir Richard of the L. „ II i 442
Where is this old Sir Richard of the L? „ IV 438
Where is this laggard Richard of the L? „ IV 450
Lea (Sir Richard) See **Richard, Richard Lea, Richard of the Lea**
Lea (Walter) See **Walter, Walter Lea**
Lead (direction) Follow my l, and I will make thee earl. Morcar. What l then? Harold I ii 216
Lead (metal) My feet are tons of l, They will break in the earth— The Cup II 476
Lead (verb) we two will l The living waters of the Faith Queen Mary I v 87
l on; ye loose me from my bonds. „ IV ii 240
debonair to those That follow where he l's, Harold II ii 320
Thy voice will l the Witan—shall I have it? „ II ii 619
if thou wilt l me to thy mother. Becket IV i 41
Save by that way which l's thro' night to light. „ V iii 88
and at last May l them on to victory— The Cup I ii 168
Give me your arm. L me back again. Prom. of May III 474
To l us thro' the windings of the wood. Foresters II i 634
O l me to my father! (repeat) „ II ii 22, 48
L us thou to some deep glen, „ II ii 168
Leader the people Claim as their natural l— Queen Mary I iv 210
All arm'd, waiting a l; „ II i 108
and ye have called me to be your l. „ II i 165
Northumberland, The l of our Reformation, „ III i 149
After a riot We hang the l's, „ IV i 74
I am no soldier, as he said—at least No l. Becket I iii 299
'Antonius l of the Roman Legion.' The Cup I i 167
I have heard of them. Have they no l? Foresters I iii 104
Be thou their l and they will all of them „ I iii 106
and their own want Of manhood to their l! „ II i 694
Leädin' so ta'en up wi' l the owd man about all the blessed murnin' Prom. of May III 2
Leading (See also **Leädin'**) by God's grace, We'll follow Philip's l, Queen Mary V v 112
Leaf (See also **Lettuce-leaf**) Laughs at the last red l, and Andrew's Day. „ III iii 87
Love will fly the fallen l, and not be overtaken; „ V ii 372
golden leaves, these earls and barons, that clung to me, Becket I iv 65
all the l of this New-wakening year. The Falcon 339
I tear away The leaves were darken'd by the battle— „ 913
How happily would we lilt among the leaves Foresters III 41
When all the leaves are green; (repeat) „ III 426, 441
By all the leaves of spring, „ III 439
I scent it in the green leaves of the wood. „ IV 944
You see the darkness thro' the lighter l. „ IV 976
Leaf-sky Pillaring a l-s on their monstrous boles, „ III 100
League (alliance) may he not make A l with William, Harold II ii 461
sequel had been other than his l With Norway, „ IV iii 88
We have had our l's of old with Eastern kings. The Cup I ii 101
There is my hand—if such a l there be. „ I ii 103
League (measure) crawl over knife-edge flint Barefoot, a hundred l's, Becket II i 273
The camp is half a l without the city; The Cup I iii 89
There—l on l of ever-shining shore „ II 533
for Oberon flew away Twenty thousand l's to-day. Foresters II ii 143
Fifty l's Of woodland hear and know my horn, „ III 103
League (verb) foes in Edward's hall To l against thy weal. Harold I ii 33
they are not like to l With Harold against me. „ II ii 53
Leagued l together To bar me from my Philip. Queen Mary I iv 139
We robb'd the traitors that are l with John; Foresters III 159
Leal Commands you to be dutiful and l To your young King Becket V ii 325
Lean (adj.) worse off than any of you, for I be l by nature, Foresters I i 45

Lean (adj.) (*continued*) I distrust thee. Thine is a half voice and a *l* assent. *Queen Mary* III i 311
Lean (verb) He looks to and he *l's* on as his God, „ IV iii 306
I marvel why you never *l* On any man's *Becket* V ii 550
Lean'd the Holy Rood had *l* And bow'd above me ; *Harold* V i 103
Leaner To plump the *l* pouch of Italy. *Queen Mary* III iv 365
Leaning A faint foot hither, *l* upon Tostig. *Harold* I i 144
Leap thro' the blood the wine *l's* to the brain *Foresters* I iii 22
Nor care to *l* into each other's arms. „ III 7
Leapt When the head *l*—so common ! *Queen Mary* I v 477
That might have *l* upon us unawares. „ II ii 295
Neighing and roaring as they *l* to land— *Harold* IV iii 197
Gurth hath *l* upon him And slain him : „ V i 632
Lear (Shakespeare's play) 'What are we,' says the blind old man in *L* ? *Prom. of May* I 263
Then the owd man i' *L* should be shaämed of hissen, „ I 267
Learn (*See also* **Larn**) Your people have begun to *l* your worth. *Queen Mary* I v 109
You cannot *L* a man's nature from his natural foe. „ I v 340
and so *l* Your royal will, and do it.— „ II ii 138
to *l* That ev'n St. Peter in his time of fear „ III iv 262
Will let you *l* in peace and privacy „ III iv 326
May *l* there is no power against the Lord. „ IV iii 66
Knowest thou this ? *Harold.* I *l* it now. *Harold* II ii 591
Let me *l* at full The manner of his death, *Becket, Pro.* 425
I *l* but now that those poor Poitevins, „ II ii 427
Nor you, nor I Have now to *l*, my lord, „ IV ii 274
Will he not fly from you if he *l* the story of my shame *Prom. of May* III 256
And *l* from her if she do love this Earl. *Foresters* I ii 187
Learned-Learn'd (adj.) but you still preferr'd Your *learned* leisure. „ III iv 258
And tell this *learned* Legate he lacks zeal. „ III iv 272
And I and *learned* friends among ourselves „ V ii 74
I have done my best. I am not *learn'd.* *Becket* III i 25
Taught her the *learned* names, anatomized The flowers for her— *Prom. of May* II 302
Learned (verb) *See* **Larned**
Learning (part.) Or *l* witchcraft of your woodland witch, *Foresters* II i 500
Learning (s) and her *l* Beyond the churchmen ; *Queen Mary* III i 361
The light of this new *l* wanes and dies : „ III ii 172
New *l* as they call it ; „ IV i 78
ever gentle, and so gracious, With all his *l*— „ IV i 157
His *l* makes his burning the more just. „ IV i 159
Your *l*, and your stoutness, and your heresy, „ IV ii 125
Brings the new *l* back. „ V i 202
Learnt Thou hast *learnt* Thy lesson, and I mine. *Queen Mary* V ii 584
He hath *learnt* to love our Tostig much of late. *Leofwin.* And *he* hath *learnt*, despite the tiger in him, *Harold* I i 145
Thou hast not *learnt* thy quarters here. „ II ii 153
When all the world hath *learnt* to speak the truth, „ III i 68
'We have *learnt* to love him, let him a little longer „ III i 88
but belike Thou hast not *learnt* his measure. „ IV iii 118
Soon as she *learnt* I was a friend of thine, *Becket* V ii 110
When man has surely *learnt* at last that all *Prom. of May* II 330
Lease The house half-ruin'd ere the *l* be out ; *Queen Mary* V ii 66
will give him, as they say, a new *l* of life. *Prom. of May* III 424
would fight for his rents, his *l's*, his houses, *Foresters* I i 233
Least (adj.) out of which Looms the *l* chance of peril to our realm. *Queen Mary* II ii 238
even now You seem the *l* assassin of the four. *Becket* V ii 522
Anyhow we must Move in the line of *l* resistance *Prom. of May* II 670
Least (s) Ev'n to the *l* and meanest of my own, *Becket* II ii 181
Then one at *l* of its inhabitants *Prom. of May* II 552
Leather (beat) I'd like to *l* 'im black and blue, and she to be a-laughin' at it. „ II 595
all on us, wi' your leave, we wants to *l* 'im. „ III 137
Then you mun be his brother, an' we'll *l* '*im.* „ III 151
Leave (permission) By your Grace's *l* Your royal mother *Queen Mary* I v 15
thy *l* to set my feet On board, *Harold* I i 228
Harold, I will not yield thee *l* to go. „ I i 257
No man without my *l* shall excommunicate *Becket, Pro.* 30
Leave (permission) (*continued*) No man without my *l* shall cross the seas *Becket Pro.* 34
can I send her hence Without his kingly *l* ? „ III i 220
By thy *l*, beauty. Ay, the same ! „ IV ii 203
—I have still thy *l* to speak. „ V ii 44
mount with your lordship's *l* to her ladyship's castle, *The Falcon* 413
by your *l* if you would hear the rest, The writing. „ 529
Leave (verb) I dare not *l* my post. *Queen Mary* I ii 55
You offend us ; you may *l* us. „ I v 210
we will *l* all this, sir, to our council. „ I v 317
and *l's* me As hopeful. „ I v 531
that I should *l* Some fruit of mine own body „ II ii 222
I *l* Lord William Howard in your city, „ II ii 245
And *l* the people naked to the crown, „ III i 119
Ay, rascal, if I *l* thee ears to hear. „ III i 251
And shalt be thankful if I *l* thee that. „ III i 257
I must *l* you. Fare you well, „ III i 472
L me now, Will you, „ III v 210
pass And *l* me, Philip, with my prayers for you. „ III vi 228
I am vastly grieved to *l* your Majesty. „ III vi 255
I have found thee and not *l* thee any more. „ IV ii 109
Tell me that, or *l* All else untold. „ IV iii 568
my Queen is like enough To *l* me by and by. *Feria.* To *l* you, sire ? „ V i 243
so my Queen Would *l* me—as—my wife. „ V i 252
L me alone, brother, with my Northumbria : *Harold* I i 285
I *l* thee, brother. „ I i 461
And *l* them for a year, and coming back „ II i 89
I *l* thee to thy talk with him alone ; „ II ii 324
Better *l* undone Than do by halves— „ II ii 495
L them ! and thee too, Aldwyth, must I *l*— „ IV iii 227
To *l* the Pope dominion in the West. „ V i 23
but *l* this day to me. „ V i 128
To *l* the foe no forage. „ V i 133
L me. No more—Pardon on both sides—Go ! „ V i 353
L them. Let them be ! „ V ii 149
L me with Herbert, friend. *Becket* I i 9
I *l* that, Knowing how much you reverence Holy Church, „ I ii 47
My lord, permit us then to *l* thy service. „ I iv 10
My Lord, we *l* thee not without tears. „ I iv 16
I wrong the bird ; she *l's* only the nest she built, they *l* the builder. „ I iv 45
I must *l* you to your banquet. „ I iv 150
I mean to *l* the royalty of my crown Unlessen'd „ II i 107
Not *l* these countryfolk at court. „ II i 129
the Pope will not *l* them in suspense, „ II ii 359
l Lateran and Vatican in one dust of gold— „ II ii 474
—And to meet it I needs must *l* as suddenly. „ III i 92
I am faint and sleepy. *L* me. „ III i 208
And *l* you alone with the good fairy. „ IV ii 60
I cannot *l* him yet. „ IV ii 85
While this but *l's* thee with a broken heart, „ IV ii 173
sworn on this my cross a hundred times Never to *l* him— „ IV ii 207
for thou must *l* him To-day, but not quite yet. „ IV ii 210
L it, daughter ; Come thou with me to Godstow nunnery, „ IV ii 365
and *l* it A waste of rock and ruin, hear. *The Cup* II 306
And if he *l* me—all the rest of life— *The Falcon* 334
And thou too *l* us, my dear nurse, alone. „ 700
Ay, the dear nurse will *l* you alone ; „ 703
An' how did ye *l* the owd uncle i' Coomberland ? *Prom. of May* I 67
but *l's* him A beast of prey in the dark, „ I 503
Who *l's* me all his land at Littlechester, „ I 511
I must *l* you, love, to-day. *Eva.* *L* me, to-day ! „ I 624
that full feast That *l's* but emptiness. „ II 256
this, for the moment, Will *l* me a free field. „ II 456
Tell him I cannot *l* the sick lady just yet. „ III 352
Milly, my dear, how did you *l* Mr. Steer ? „ III 410
But shall we *l* our England ? *Foresters* I iii 92
You see why We must *l* the wood and fly. „ II ii 174
L it with him and add a gold mark thereto. „ III 210
L them each what they say is theirs, „ III 293
We *l* but happy memories to the forest. „ IV 1070
Leaven the old *l* sticks to my tongue yet. *Queen Mary* I iii 48
so much of the anti-papal *l* Works in him yet, „ IV i 15

Leaven (*continued*) be something Of this world's *l* in thee too, *Becket* V ii 29
Leaving But *l* light enough for Alfgar's house *Harold* I i 307
L so many foes in Edward's hall „ I ii 31
Tho' *l* each, a wound; *Becket* I i 176
To steel myself against the *l* her? *Prom. of May* I 293
How could I think of *l* him? „ II 71
L your fair Marian alone here. *Foresters* I ii 154
Led they *l* Processions, chanted litanies, *Queen Mary* III vi 94
I *l* seven hundred knights and fought his wars. *Becket* I iii 638
S'iver we've *l* moäst on it. *Prom. of May* II 52
O Lord, I am easily *l* by words, *Foresters* I ii 39
Ledge He met a stag there on so narrow a *l*— „ IV 532
Lees You cannot judge the liquor from the *l*. *Queen Mary* IV iii 550
Left (adj.) The last Parthian shaft of a forlorn Cupid at the King's *l* breast, *Becket*, *Pro.* 340
On this *l* breast before so hard a heart, „ *Pro.* 375
Take the *l* leg for the love of God. *Foresters* IV 577
Left (s) reels Now to the right, then as far to the *l*, *Queen Mary* IV iii 396
Left (verb) I shall be *l* alone. No: „ I ii 13
I *l* her with rich jewels in her hand, „ I iv 242
I scarce had *l* your Grace's presence „ I v 583
As tho' the nightmare never *l* her bed. „ I v 605
l about Like loosely-scatter'd jewels, „ II i 27
flying to our side *L* his all bare, „ II iii 5
Their voice had *l* me none to tell you this. „ II iii 36
Where is Pembroke? *Courtenay.* I *l* him somewhere in the thick of it. *Mary.* *L* him and fled; and thou that would'st be King, „ II iv 80
And Lady Jane had *l* us. „ II iv 139
L Mary a wife-widow here alone, „ III i 462
Have you remain'd in the true Catholic faith I *l* you in? „ IV ii 19
When *l* alone in my despondency, „ IV ii 95
There is no hope of better *l* for him, „ IV iii 79
Her life, since Philip *l* her, and she lost „ IV iii 428
Methinks there is no manhood *l* among us. „ V ii 284
I *l* her lying still and beautiful, „ V v 261
Be kindly to the Normans *l* among us, *Harold* III i 303
Then *l* him for the meaner! thee!— „ IV ii 71
I saw her even now: She hath not *l* us. „ V i 159
I *l* our England naked to the South To meet thee „ V i 289
I *l* him with peace on his face— *Becket*, *Pro.* 395
Save for myself no Rome were *l* in England, „ II ii 386
how many an innocent Has *l* his bones upon the way to Rome „ II ii 409
darkness of the gap *L* by that lack of love. „ III i 61
Hath not thy father *l* us to ourselves? „ III i 271
And *l* all naked, I were lost indeed. „ IV ii 9
Well—well—too costly to be *l* or lost. „ IV ii 299
live what may be *l* thee of a life Saved „ IV ii 367
I surely should have *l* That stroke to Rome. *The Cup* I iii 159
Thou art the last friend *l* me upon earth— *The Falcon* 31
and I *l* it privily At Florence, in her palace. „ 74
hasn't an eye *l* in his own tail to flourish „ 101
Ay, ay! stare at it: it's all you have *l* us. „ 163
We may have *l* their fifty less by five. „ 625
They *l* us there for dead! „ 651
Ay, and I *l* two fingers there for dead. „ 653
I *l* him there for dead too! „ 659
had you *l* him free use of his wings, *Prom. of May* I 652
Hesn't he *l* ye nowt? *Dora.* No, Mr. Dobson. „ II 7
Since I *l* her Here weeping, I have ranged the world, „ II 251
L but one dreadful line to say, „ II 411
Some of our workmen have *l* us, „ III 28
—all still—and nothing *l* To live for. „ III 681
I Was *l* alone, and knowing as I did *Foresters* II i 122
since the Sheriff *l* me naught but an empty belly, „ II i 278
He dozes. I have *l* her watching him. „ II ii 80
I *l* mine horse and armour with a Squire, „ IV 414
Left-hand Absolve the *l-h* thief and damn the right? *Becket* II ii 392
Left-handedness all *l-h* and under-handedness. „ *Pro.* 341
Leg about our *l's* till we cannot move at all; *Queen Mary* II i 204
it be a var waay vor my owld *l's* up vro' Islip. „ IV iii 472
Haul like a great strong fellow at my *l's*, *Harold* II i 11
Leg (*continued*) Because I broke The horse's *l*— *Harold* II ii 110
And may I break his *l's*? „ II ii 116
this rag fro' the gangrene i' my *l*. *Becket* I iv 237
On my *l's*. *Eleanor.* And mighty pretty *l's* too. „ IV i 5
and thy *l's*, and thy heart, and thy liver, *Foresters* IV 204
I have a swollen vein in my right *l*, „ IV 569
Take the left *l* for the love of God. „ IV 577
By my halidome I felt him at my *l* still. „ IV 628
Legacy My *l* of war against the Pope *Harold* V i 328
Legate holy *l* of the holy father the Pope, Cardinal Pole, *Queen Mary* I iii 26
L's coming To bring us absolution from the Pope. „ III i 431
Well said, Lord *L*. „ III ii 93
Lord Paget Waits to present our Council to the *L*. „ III ii 98
No, my Lord *L*, the Lord Chancellor goes. „ III ii 151
all one mind to supplicate The *L* here for pardon, „ III iii 107
L From our most Holy Father Julius, Pope, „ III iii 125
authority Apostolic Given unto us, his *L*, „ III iii 211
I mean the houses knelt Before the *L*. „ III iii 258
You brawl beyond the question; speak, Lord *L*! „ III iv 98
I am your *L*; please you let me finish. „ III iv 179
Beware, Lord *L*, of a heavier crime Than heresy „ III iv 221
You, Lord *L* And Cardinal-Deacon, „ III iv 260
And tell this learned *L* that he lacks zeal. „ III iv 272
Your violence and much roughness to the *L*, „ III iv 319
yet the *L* Is here as Pope and Master of the Church, „ III iv 346
Our bashful *L*, saw'st not how he flush'd? „ III iv 350
So that you crave full pardon of the *L*. „ III iv 392
the duty which as *L* He owes himself, „ III iv 401
it would more become you, my Lord *L*, „ IV i 116
And how should he have sent me *L* hither, „ V ii 87
God curse her and her *L*! „ V iv 12
Legate-cousin Royal, Infallible, Papal *L-c*. „ III iv 433
Legateship reft me of that *l* Which Julius gave me, and the *l* Annex'd to Canterbury— „ V ii 34
Holy Father Has ta'en the *l* from our cousin Pole— „ V v 126
Legg'd *See* **Two-legg'd**
Legion 'A Galatian serving by force in the Roman *L*.' *The Cup* I i 48
'Antonius leader of the Roman *L*.' „ I i 167
'A Galatian serving by force in the Roman *L*.' „ I ii 76
Let him come—a *l* with him, if he will. „ II 250
Legitimate Long live Queen Mary, the lawful and *l* daughter of Harry the Eighth! *Queen Mary* I i 8
That's a hard word, *l*; what does it mean? „ I i 12
Leicester (Lord) How much might that amount to, my lord *L*? *Becket* I iii 656
my good lord *L*, The King and I were brothers. „ I iii 660
Cornwall's hand or *L's*: they write marvellously alike. „ I iv 51
Was not my lord of *L* bidden to our supper? „ I iv 56
Leicester (town) The Duke hath gone to *L*; *Queen Mary* II i 4
Leisure (adj.) for I would have him bring it Home to the *l* wisdom of his Queen, „ III vi 23
Leisure (s) but you still preferr'd Your learned *l*. „ III iv 258
Lend would deign to *l* an ear Not overscornful, *Harold* IV i 136
Encumbered as we are, who would *l* us anything? *Prom. of May* III 163
Length if you'd like to measure your own *l* upon the grass. „ I 466
Lenient I was too *l* to the Lutheran, *Queen Mary* V ii 73
Lennox The Lady Suffolk and the Lady *L*?— „ I iv 31
Lent *L* at the siege of Thoulouse by the King. *Becket* I iii 636
Those two thousand marks *l* me by the Abbot *Foresters* I i 264
Leofric *L*, and all the monks of Peterboro' *Harold* V i 446
Leofwin (Earl of Kent and Essex) Ask thou Lord *L* what he thinks of this! *Morcar.* Lord *L*, dost thou believe, that these „ I i 40
as well as with mine earldom, *L's* and Gurth's. „ I i 338
L, thou hast a tongue, „ I i 391
Vex him not, *L*. „ I i 403
L would often fight me, and I beat him. „ I i 434
Sign it, my good son Harold, Gurth, and *L*, „ III i 200
Gurth, *L*, Morcar, Edwin! „ IV iii 220
And, *L*, art thou mad? „ V i 138
Gurth, *L*, go once more about the hill— „ V i 182
And *L* is down! „ V i 644
And here is *L*. *Edith.* And here is *He*! „ V i 72

Lie (verb) (*continued*) that I think, 'Wilt thou *l* there to-morrow?' *Queen Mary* III v 132
It *l's* there folded: is there venom in it? „ III v 216
lash'd to death, or *l* Famishing in black cells, „ v ii 195
Come thou down. *L* there. „ v v 180
What *l's* upon the mind of our good king *Harold* I i 268
That *l's* within the shadow of the chance. „ II ii 463
Nay let them *l*. Stand there and wait my will. „ II ii 682
There *l's* a treasure buried down in Ely: „ III i 11
It *l's* beside thee, king, upon thy bed. „ III i 195
curse That *l's* on thee and England. „ III i 279
Where *l* the Norsemen? on the Derwent? „ IV i 253
He *l's* not here: not close beside the standard. „ v ii 56
their standards fell . . . where these two *l*. „ v ii 141
So then our good Archbishop Theobald *L's* dying. *Becket, Pro.* 3
—there *l's* the secret of her whereabouts, „ *Pro.* 430
The daughter of Zion *l's* beside the way— „ III iii 177
All that *L's* with Antonius. *The Cup* I ii 293
We *l* too deep down in the shadow here. *The Falcon* 581
l down there together in the darkness which would seem but for a moment, *Prom. of May* III 194
I am very faint. I must *l* down. „ III 473
Where *l's* that cask of wine whereof *Foresters* III 306
And *l* with us among the flowers, and drink— „ IV 965
Lied To sit high Is to be *l* about. *Queen Mary* I v 430
Some said it was thy father's deed. *Harold.* They *l*. *Harold* II ii 514
l like a lad That dreads the pendent scourge, „ II ii 656
Of all the lies that ever men have *l*, „ III i 99
Lief we'd as *l* talk o' the Divil afoor ye as 'im, *Prom. of May* III 130
Liefer Far *l* had I in my country hall *Queen Mary* III i 43
I had *l* that the fish had swallowed me, *Harold* II i 36
But I had *l* than this gold again— *Foresters* IV 184
Liege My *l's* and my lords, The thanks of Holy Church *Becket* II ii 189
Liege-lord breathe one prayer for my *l-l* the King, „ v ii 191
Liest thou *l* as loud as the black herring-pond *Harold* II i 25
Norman, thou *l*! liars all of you, „ v ii 104
Lieth do you good to all As much as in you *l*. *Queen Mary* IV iii 187
So he said who *l* here. *Foresters* II ii 117
Lieu put some fresh device in *l* of it— *Queen Mary* III i 268
Life (*See also* **After-life, Forest-life**) Old Bourne to the *l*! „ I iii 30
You've but a dull *l* in this maiden court, I fear, my Lord? *Courtenay.* A *l* of nods and yawns. „ I iii 113
like a butterfly in a chrysalis, You spent your *l*; „ I iv 52
I love you, Lay my *l* in your hands. „ I iv 105
to practise on my *l*, By poison, fire, shot, stab— „ I iv 284
I would his *l* Were half as goodly. „ I v 201
If cold, his *l* is pure. „ I v 333
A very wanton *l* indeed. „ I v 336
Of a pure *l*? „ I v 448
And wastes more *l*. „ I v 507
plain *l* and letter'd peace, „ II i 49
and I warrant this fine fellow's *l*. „ II iii 84
He has gambled for his *l*, and lost, he hangs. „ II iii 91
pray for you on our bended knees till our *lives'* end. „ II iii 122
La, to whistle out my *l*, „ II iv 109
and save the *l* Of Devon: if I save him, „ II iv 123
some secret that may cost Philip his *l*. „ III i 202
you would fling your *lives* into the gulf. „ III i 459
scarlet thread of Rahab saved her *l*; „ III ii 39
bees, If any creeping *l* invade their hive „ III iii 54
To take the *lives* of others that are loyal, „ III iv 48
Paget, you are all for this poor *l* of ours, And care but little for the *l* to be. „ III iv 59
Watch'd children playing at *their l* to be, „ III iv 63
the *lives* Of many among your churchmen „ III iv 190
it is an age Of brief *l*, and brief purpose, „ III iv 413
For there was *l*—And there was *l* in death— „ III v 145
whose bolts, That jail you from free *l*, „ III v 172
I had like to have lost my *l*: „ III v 189
what think you, Is it *l* or death? „ III v 194
A right rough *l* and healthful. „ III v 260
Is *l* and lungs to every rebel birth „ III vi 51
Care more for our brief *l* in their wet land, „ III vi 62
The sunshine sweeps across my *l* again. „ III vi 250
To spare the *l* of Cranmer. „ IV i 4

Life (*continued*) To sue you for his *L*? *Mary.* His *l*? Oh, no; *Queen Mary* IV i 11
Or into private *l* within the realm. „ IV i 47
once he saved your Majesty's own *l*; „ IV i 125
My *l* is not so happy, no such boon, „ IV i 130
if he have to live so loath'd a *l*, „ IV i 152
petition of the foreign exiles For Cranmer's *l*. „ IV i 194
Exhort them to a pure and virtuous *l*; „ IV ii 77
For death gives *l's* last word a power to live, „ IV iii 161
as I have come To the last end of *l*, and thereupon Hangs all my past, and all my *l* to be, „ IV iii 218
Or said or done in all my *l* by me; „ IV iii 239
Written for fear of death, to save my *l*, „ IV iii 242
have been a man loved plainness all my *l*; „ IV iii 271
Hurls his soil'd *l* against the pikes and dies. „ IV iii 311
his best Of *l* was over then. „ IV iii 330
Her *l*, since Philip left her, and she lost „ IV iii 428
Philip is as warm in *l* As ever. „ v ii 24
fast friend of your *l* Since mine began, „ v ii 134
Your Majesty has lived so pure a *l*, „ v v 73
see, he smiles and goes, Gentle as in *l*. „ v v 147
More beautiful than in *l*. „ v v 262
Her *l* was winter, for her spring was nipt: „ v v 269
Thy *l* at home Is easier than mine here. *Harold* I i 96
I have lived a *l* of utter purity: „ I i 178
A *l* of prayer and fasting well may see „ I i 199
Love will stay for a whole *l* long. „ I ii 17
praised The convent and lone *l*—within the pale— „ I ii 47
then a fair *l* And bless the Queen of England. „ I ii 206
We seldom take man's *l*, except in war; „ II ii 502
Archbishop Robert hardly scaped with *l*. „ II ii 527
Harold, I am thy friend, one *l* with thee, „ II ii 650
Is naked truth actable in true *l*? „ III i 110
silent, cloister'd, solitary *l*, A *l* of life-long prayer „ III i 277
'Love for a whole *l* long' When was that sung? „ III ii 88
they both have *l* In the large mouth of England, „ IV iii 73
Thou gavest thy voice against me in my *l*, „ v i 253
Whose *l* was all one battle, incarnate war, „ v i 397
that I fear the Queen would have her *l*. *Becket, Pro.* 62
The *l* of Rosamund de Clifford more Than that „ *Pro.* 70
not my purveyor Of pleasures, but to save a *l*—her *l*; „ *Pro.* 150
And all the heap'd experiences of *l*, „ I i 154
And mean to hold it, or—— *Becket.* To have my *l*. „ I iii 163
since your canon will not let you take *L* for a *l*, „ I iii 391
being in great jeopardy of his *l*, he hath made „ I iv 263
or can shatter a *l* till the *l* shall have fled? „ II i 12
Love that can lift up a *l* from the dead. „ II i 14
O my *l's l*, not to smile Is all but death „ II i 39
There may be crosses in my line of *l*. „ II i 188
L on the hand is naked gipsy-stuff; *L* on the face, „ II i 193
He said thy *l* Was not one hour's worth „ III iii 250
Thy *l* is worth the wrestle for it: „ IV ii 194
fawn upon him For thy *l* and thy son's. „ IV ii 225
to take a *l* which Henry bad me Guard „ IV ii 268
rend away Eyesight and manhood, *l* itself, „ IV ii 285
a *l* Saved as by miracle alone with Him Who gave it. „ IV ii 367
not *l* shot up in blood, But death drawn in;— „ IV ii 380
To take my *l* might lose him Aquitaine. „ IV ii 396
thy rest of *l* is hopeless prison. „ v i 180
Thanks in this *l*, and in the *l* to come. „ v ii 161
drowning man, they say, remembers all The chances of his *l*, „ v ii 274
laid mine own *l* down To help him from them, „ v ii 339
You have spoken to the peril of your *l*? „ v ii 516
Valour and holy *l* should go together. „ v ii 587
Save him, he saved my *l*, he saved my child, „ v iii 8
The power of *l* in death to make her free! „ v iii 100
What would ye have of me? *Fitzurse.* Your *l*. *De Tracy.* Your *l*. „ v iii 117
But in this narrow breathing-time of *l* *The Cup* I i 29
courtesans for aught I know Whose *l* is one dishonour. „ I ii 194
However I thank thee; thou hast saved my *l*. „ I ii 333
loveliest *l* that ever drew the light From heaven „ I iii 56
To warm the cold bounds of our dying *l* „ I iii 129
He saved my *l* too. Did he? „ I iii 160

Life (*continued*) thou that art *l* to the wind, to the wave, *The Cup* II 3
L yields to death and wisdom bows to Fate, „ II 89
And join your *l* this day with his, „ II 135
For all my truer *l* begins to-day. „ II 229
that dost inspire the germ with *l*, The child, „ II 258
ere two souls be knit for *l* and death, „ II 359
came To plead to thee for Sinnatus's *l*, „ II 392
Coming to visit my lord, for the first time in her *l* too! *The Falcon* 171
And if he leave me—all the rest of *l*— „ 334
A colour, which has colour'd all my *l*, „ 364
I'd slaäve out my *l* fur 'er. *Prom. of May* I 178
And long *l* to boath on 'em. „ I 345
I have all my *l* before me—so has she— „ I 482
heat and fire Of *l* will bring them out, „ II 287
better death With our first wail than *l*— „ II 291
not so much for Death As against *L*! „ II 338
This beggarly *l*, This poor, flat, hedged-in field— „ II 343
Colour Flows thro' my *l* again, „ II 667
which Father, for a whole *l*, has been getting together, „ III 165
O Love and *L*, how weary am I, „ III 205
will give him, as they say, a new lease of *l*. „ III 424
niver been surprised but once i' my *l*, and I went blind upon it. „ III 440
Had threaten'd ev'n your *l*, and would say anything? „ III 567
'Twere best to make an end of my lost *l*. „ III 786
not with all your wealth, Your land, your *l*! „ III 796
whose whole *l* hath been folded like a blossom in the sheath, *Foresters* I i 205
I saved his *l* once in battle. „ I i 272
A question that every true man asks of a woman once in his *l*. „ I ii 139
if this *l* of ours Be a good glad thing, „ I iii 12
Sleep, happy soul! all *l* will sleep at last. „ I iii 48
mix with all The lusty *l* of wood and underwood, „ I iii 114
The hope of larger *l* hereafter, „ II i 69
I would give my *l* for thee, „ II i 189
Ay, ay, the line o' *l* is marked enow; „ II i 352
Mislead us, and I will have thy *l*! „ II i 377
L, *l*. I know not death. „ II i 621
Our Robin beaten, pleading for his *l*! „ II i 675
noblest light That ever flash'd across my *l*, „ III 142
Whose writ will run thro' all the range of *l*. „ IV 49
Their *lives* unsafe in any of these our woods, „ IV 93
in the fear of thy *l* shalt thou eat the King's venison— „ IV 205
Richard risks his *l* for a straw, So lies in prison—while our Robin's *l* Hangs by a thread, „ IV 382
flung His *l*, heart, soul into those holy wars „ IV 407
for by my *l*, you shall dance till he can. „ IV 566
Thou hast risk'd thy *l* for mine: bind these two men. „ IV 894
Our forest games are ended, our free *l*, „ IV 1049
Life-giving No sacrifice, but a *l-g* feast! *Queen Mary* IV ii 112
Life-green a thousand summers Robe you *l-g* again. *Foresters* IV 1058
Life-long To plunge thee into *l-l* prison here:— *Harold* II ii 550
A life of *l-l* prayer against the curse „ III i 278
she hath begun Her *l-l* prayer for thee. „ III i 324
And all my *l* labour to uphold The primacy—a heretic. *Queen Mary* V ii 70
I am a *l-l* lover of the chase, *The Cup* I i 194
Lift I cannot *l* my hands unto my head. *Queen Mary* III i 240
L head, and flourish; „ III iv 24
Why do you *l* your eyebrow at me thus? „ III vi 102
I am ashamed to *l* my eyes to heaven, „ IV iii 127
death is death, or else *L's* us beyond the lie. *Harold* III ii 80
For, like a son, I *l* my hands to thee. *Becket* I iii 264
Love that can *l* up a life from the dead. „ II i 14
I pray you *l* me And make me walk awhile. *The Cup* II 472
my hands are too sleepy To *l* it off. „ II 531
Lifted Then Cranmer *l* his left hand to heaven, *Queen Mary* IV iii 608
L our produce, driven our clerics out— *Becket* V ii 432
Lifting It means the *l* of the house of Alfgar. *Harold* I i 472
Light (adj.) My Lord of Devon—*l* enough, God knows, *Queen Mary* V ii 477
Growing dark too—but *l* enough to row. *The Cup* II 523
Take thou this *l* kiss for thy clumsy word. *Foresters* III 134

Light (s) By God's *l* a noble creature, *Queen Mary* I i 68
The *l* of this new learning wanes and dies: „ III ii 172
faith that seem'd to droop will feel your *l*, „ III iv 23
yet not *l* alone, There must be heat— „ III iv 24
springs to *l* That Centaur of a monstrous Commonweal, „ III iv 162
White as the *l*, the spotless bride of Christ, „ III iv 199
in a pale *l*, Rose hand in hand, „ III v 147
Cool as the *l* in old decaying wood; „ IV ii 5
Unpardonable,—sin against the *l*, „ IV iii 148
Is not yon *l* in the Queen's chamber? „ V iv 1
There's the Queen's *l*. I hear she cannot live. „ V iv 10
in a closed room, with *l*, fire, physic, tendance; „ V iv 36
My grayhounds fleeting like a beam of *l*, *Harold* I ii 130
dog, with thy lying *l's* Thou hast betray'd „ II i 22
villains with their lying *l's* have wreck'd us! „ II i 84
be as the shadow of a cloud Crossing your *l*. „ II ii 178
dreadful *l's* crept up from out the marsh— „ III i 379
Lost, lost, the *l* of day, „ III ii 12
But a little *l*!—And on it falls the shadow „ III ii 69
A *l* among the oxen. „ IV i 87
Lower the *l*. He must be here. „ V ii 63
the fire, the *l*, The spirit of the twelve Apostles *Becket* I i 49
moon Divides the whole long street with *l* and shade. „ I i 365
As gold Outvalues dross, *l* darkness, „ I iii 715
L again! *l* again! Margery? „ IV i 1
and went on and on till I found the *l* and the lady, „ IV ii 18
Save by that way which leads thro' night to *l*. „ V iii 89
I am not in the darkness but the *l*, „ V iii 97
the dry *l* of Rome's straight-going policy, *The Cup* I i 145
drew the *l* From heaven to brood upon her, „ I iii 57
Lady, you bring your *l* into my cottage *The Falcon* 283
her affections Will flower toward the *l* in some new face. *Prom. of May* I 486
to be wakened again together by the *l* of the resurrection, „ III 196
the *l* Of these dark hours; *Foresters* I ii 84
and seeing the hospitable *l's* in your castle, „ I ii 194
I am but an angel by reflected *l*. „ II i 108
Glide like a *l* across these woodland ways! „ II i 159
l of the seas by the moon's long-silvering ray! „ II ii 178
noblest *l* That ever flash'd across my life, „ III 141
Robin, the sweet *l* of a mother's eye, „ IV 2
Light (to come upon) if thou *l* upon her—free me from her? *Becket, Pro.* 493
Light (to kindle) then, who *l's* the faggot? Not the full faith, *Queen Mary* III iv 122
Thou *l* a torch that never will go out! „ V v 122
Lighted (come upon) And I have *l* On a new pleasure. *Prom. of May* II 668
She may have *l* on your fairies here, *Foresters* II i 496
Lighted (shone) A twilight conscience *l* thro' a chink; *Harold* III i 65
Lighten (to brighten) these lilies to *l* Sir Richard's black room, *Foresters* I i 3
Lighten (to gleam) Our axes *l* with a single flash *Harold* V i 537
Lighten'd gloom of Saul Was *l* by young David's harp. *Queen Mary* V ii 359
l for me The weight of this poor crown, *Harold* I i 217
Lighter Much *l* than a thousand marks in gold; *Foresters* IV 657
You see the darkness thro' the *l* leaf. „ IV 975
Lightning sword Of *l's*, wherewithal he cleft the tree *Harold* III i 137
This *l* before death Plays on the word,— „ III i 387
are sliver'd off and splinter'd by Their *l*— „ V i 541
The *l's* that we think are only Heaven's Flash *Becket* V ii 35
Lightning-like swoops down upon him Eagle-like, *l-l*— *The Falcon* 14
Like (adj. and adv.) These princes are *l* children, must be physick'd, *Queen Mary* I v 234
Is this *l* him? *Renard.* Ay, somewhat; „ I v 442
Rascal!—this land is *l* a hill of fire, „ III i 321
Much less shall others in *l* cause escape, „ IV iii 62
How fair and royal—*l* a Queen, indeed? „ V i 235
methinks my Queen is *l* enough To leave me by and by. „ V i 242
I mean not *l* to live. Elizabeth— „ V i 245
There must be ladies many with hair *l* mine. „ V iii 58
To draw him nearer with a charm *L* thine to thine. *Harold* I ii 9
What was he *l*, this husband? *l* to thee? „ V ii 52
have I fought men *L* Harold and his brethren, „ V ii 179
A pretty lusty boy. *Rosamund.* So *l* to thee; *L* to be liker. *Becket* II i 248

(*continued*) *L*! we are Danes, Who conquer'd what we walk on, our own field. *Harold* IV i 37
He calls us *l*! *Harold.* The kingdoms of this world began with *l*, „ IV i 41
Keep him away from the lone *l* isle. *Becket* II i 15
I'll call thee *l* Geoffrey. „ II i 214
Look, look! if *l* Geoffrey have not tost His ball into the brook! „ II i 319
Kiss me, *l* one, Nobody near! „ III i 100
Come to me, *l* one. How camest thou hither? „ IV i 3
We can't all of us be as pretty as thou art—*l* bastard. „ IV i 39
How fares thy pretty boy, the *l* Geoffrey? „ V ii 167
There was a *l* fair-hair'd Norman maid „ V ii 259
Nay, see, why she turns down the path through our *l* vineyard, *The Falcon* 168
When he was a *l* one, and I put the bitters on my breast to wean him, „ 189
ye'll think more on 'is *l* finger than hall my hand at the haltar. *Prom. of May* I 112
How gracefully there she stands Weeping—the *l* Niobe! „ I 736
into nescience with as *l* pain As it is to fall asleep „ II 341
The *l* 'ymn? Yeäs, Miss; „ III 1
an' axed ma to be 'is *l* sweet-art, „ III 120
Poor blind Father's *l* guide, Milly, „ III 231
talk a *l* French like a lady; play a *l* like a lady? „ III 303
Who said that? Taäke me awaäy, *l* gell. „ III 465
Child, read a *l* history, you will find The common brotherhood „ III 542
and if you cram me crop-full I be *l* better than Famine in the picture, *Foresters* I i 46
and for the love of his own *l* mother on earth, „ I i 98
O the sacred *l* thing! What a shape! „ I i 108
Shall I keep one *l* rose for Little John? No. „ I i 112
But he flutter'd his wings with a sweet *l* cry, „ I i 154
But then your Sheriff, your *l* man, „ I i 231
and our *l* Sheriff will ever swim with the stream! „ I i 239
the Sheriff had taken all our goods for the King without paying, our horse and our *l* cart— „ II i 192
for when the Sheriff took my *l* horse for the King without paying for it— „ II i 301

Littlechester (adj.) and we dragg'd The *L* river all in vain: *Prom. of May* II 414

Littlechester (s) When theer wur a meeting o' farmers at *L* t'other daäy, „ I 137
fur they be knaw'd as far as *L*. „ I 214
Beänt there house-breäkers down i' *L*, Dobson— „ I 389
Who leaves me all his land at *L*, „ I 511
afoor she went to school at *L*— „ II 19
fur she tell'd me to taäke the cart to *L*. „ II 323
Only last week at *L*, drove me From out her memory. „ II 404
pacing my new lands at *L*, „ II 647
Wasn't Miss Vavasour, our schoolmistress at *L*, a lady born? „ III 298
that dreadful night! that lonely walk to *L*, „ III 367

Little John (a follower of Robin Hood) She hath looked well at one of 'em, *L J*. *Foresters* I i 39
Shall I keep one little rose for *L J*? No. „ I i 113
Wilt thou not give me rather the little rose for *L J*? „ I i 148
thou hast ruffled my woman, *L J*. „ I i 166
starched stiff creature, *L J*, the Earl's man. „ I i 184
L J, Who hast that worship for me „ I iii 159
Take him, good *L J*, and give him wine. „ II i 469
thou That hast not made it up with *L J*! *Kate.* I wait till *L J* makes up to *me*. „ III 15
L J Fancied he saw thee clasp and kiss a man. „ III 21
And let them warm thy heart to *L J*. „ III 44
I *L J*, he Much the miller's son, and he Scarlet, „ III 54
I *L J*, he, young Scarlet, and he, old Much, and all the rest of us. „ III 60
Search them, *L J*. „ III 201
Shame on thee, *L J*, thou hast forgotten— „ III 237
Play the air, *L J*. „ III 418
Strike up our music, *L J*. „ IV 559
You, good friar, You Much, you Scarlet, you dear *L J*, „ IV 1083

Live Long *l* Queen Mary, (repeat) *Queen Mary* I i 7, 65
'Long *l* Elizabeth the Queen!' „ I iii 7
we'll have no pope here while the Lady Elizabeth *l's*. „ I iii 44
But that with God's grace, I can *l* so still. „ II ii 219
never Consent thereto, nor marry while I *l*; „ II ii 231
Long *l* Queen Mary! Down with Wyatt! The Queen! „ II ii 252
We have been glad together; let him *l*. „ II iii 90
I *l* and die The true and faithful bride of Philip— „ II iv 41
Long *l* the King and Queen, Philip and Mary! „ III i 208
Long *l* Queen Mary! „ III i 294
Where dost thou *l*? *Man.* In Cornhill. „ III i 316
was not meet the heretic swine should *l* In Lambeth. „ III ii 135
Let the dead letter *l*! Trace it in fire, „ III iv 33
says she will *l* And die true maid— „ III vi 45
none shall hold them in his house and *l*, „ IV i 97
if he have to *l* so loath'd a life, „ IV i 152
Ay—gentle as they call you—*l* or die! „ IV ii 162
set forth some saying that may *l* After his death and better humankind; For death gives life's last word a power to *l*, „ IV iii 159
I pray you all to *l* together Like brethren; „ IV iii 181
Either to *l* with Christ in Heaven with joy, „ IV iii 220
That might *l* always in the sun's warm heart, „ V i 22
I mean not like to *l*. „ V i 245
Long *l* your Majesty! Shall Alice sing you „ V ii 353
Make me full fain to *l* and die a maid. „ V iii 98
There's the Queen's light. I hear she cannot *l*. „ V iv 11
She hath but blood enough to *l*, not love.— *Harold* I ii 161
We hear he hath not long to *l*. „ II ii 565
Forgive me, brother, I will *l* here and die. „ II ii 804
but happier lived, If happier be to *l*; „ IV iii 73
l or die, I would I were among them! „ V i 463
And if I *l*, No man without my leave *Becket, Pro.* 29
For we would *l* and die for thee, my lord, „ I ii 16
And I shall *l* to trample on thy grave. „ I ii 95
and the world shall *l* by the King's venison „ I iv 271
one who *l's* for thee Out there in France; „ II i 309
Long *l* the good King Louis! „ II ii 450
I *l* to die for it, I die to *l* for it. „ III iii 335
They call her—But she *l's* secret, you see. „ IV i 12
Madam, let her *l*. „ IV ii 157
And *l* what may be left thee of a life „ IV ii 367
She *l's*—but not for him; one point is gain'd. „ IV ii 415
I will go *l* and die in Aquitaine. (repeat) „ V i 109, 142
Here is the great Archbishop! He *l's*! he *l's*! „ V iii 30
A woman I could *l* and die for. *The Cup* I iii 65
Might I not *l* for that, And drown all poor self-passion „ II 99
to *l* And die together. „ II 443
as I *l*, there is Monna Giovanna coming down the hill from the castle. *The Falcon* 159
Your ladyship *l's* higher in the sun. „ 583
For her sick son, if he were like to *l*, „ 854
What can a man, then, *l* for but sensations, *Prom. of May* I 241
smell o' the mou'd 'ud ha' maäde ma *l* as long as Jerusalem. „ I 378
with some sense of art, to *l* By brush and pencil. „ I 498
L with these honest folk—And play the fool! „ I 744
if you cared To *l* some time among them. „ II 550
For all the souls on earth that *l* „ III 7
will be willing that you and Father should *l* with us; „ III 261
in our spring-and-winter world If we *l* long enough! „ III 512
—all still—and nothing left To *l* for. „ III 682
She said 'all still. Nothing to *l* for.' „ III 685
but now ye know why we *l* so stintedly, *Foresters* I i 76
a Count in Brittany—he *l's* near Quimper. „ I i 272
Long *l* Richard, (repeat) „ I ii 1, 3
Long *l* Robin, Robin and Richard! Long *l* Robin, „ I ii 13
'Long *l* King Richard!' „ I ii 25
O Lord, I will *l* and die for King Richard— „ I ii 37
We will *l* and die with thee, (repeat) „ I iii 168
I believe there *l's* No man who truly loves „ II i 75
You gentles that *l* upo' manchet-bread and marchpane, „ II i 281
Then I roast 'em, for I have nought else to *l* on. „ II i 388
Could *l* as happy as the larks in heaven, „ III 82
L thou maiden! Thou art more my wife so feeling, „ III 121

Live (*continued*) all that *l* By their own hands, the labourer, the poor priest; *Foresters* III 164
And *l* with us and the birds in the green wood. „ IV 325
We needs must *l*. Our bowmen are so true „ IV 523
Then will I *l* for ever in the wild wood. „ IV 878
Lived (*See also* **Short-lived**) as tho' My father and my brother had not *l*. *Queen Mary* I v 36
I thank God, I have *l* a virgin, „ II ii 218
You *l* among your vines and oranges, „ III iv 253
And all things *l* and ended honestly. „ III v 115
Your Majesty has *l* so pure a life, „ v v 73
I have *l* a life of utter purity: *Harold* I i 178
but happier *l*, If happier be to live; „ IV iii 72
I die for England then, who *l* for England— „ v i 268
he would be mine age Had he *l* now; *Becket* I iii 250
I have *l*, poor bird, from cage to cage, „ III i 222
little fair-hair'd Norman maid *L* in my mother's house: „ v ii 261
having *l* For twenty days and nights in mail, *Foresters* IV 123
Livelong Not having broken fast the *l* day— „ IV 186
Liver and thy legs, and thy heart, and thy *l*, „ IV 205
Livery Ay, how fine they be in their *liveries*, „ I i 41
Living (adj. and part.) and we two will lead The *l* waters of the Faith again *Queen Mary* I v 88
And had to be removed lest *l* Spain Should sicken at dead England. „ III i 27
Will stir the *l* tongue and make the cry. „ III i 354
but Lambeth palace, Henceforth a centre of the *l* faith. „ III ii 155
not the *l* rock Which guards the land. *Harold* I ii 119
And thou art upright in thy *l* grave, „ II ii 440
and sell not thou Our *l* passion for a dead man's dream; „ III ii 60
the *l* Who fought and would have died, „ IV iii 70
Hail to the *l* who fought, the dead who fell! „ IV iii 105
And dying for the people—*Edith*. *L*—*l*! „ v i 390
doth not the *l* skin thicken against perpetual whippings? *Becket* III iii 316
were he *l* And grown to man and Sinnatus will'd it, *The Cup* I ii 150
dead garland Will break once more into the *l* blossom. *The Falcon* 919
We know not whether he be dead or *l*. *Prom. of May* II 436
This Edgar, then, is *l*? *Harold*. *L*? well— „ II 443
were she *l*, Would not—if penitent—have denied „ II 495
Will he not fly from you if he learn the story of my shame and that I am still *l*? „ III 258
Is yours yet *l*? *Harold*. No—I told you. „ III 505
I never said As much before to any woman *l*. „ III 645
L . . . dead . . . She said 'all still. „ III 683
I ha' served the King *l*, says she, and let me serve him dead, *Foresters* II i 310
Living (s) have graspt Her *l's*, her advowsons, *Becket* I i 161
That, thro' his late magnificence of *l* *The Falcon* 227
Hath served me better than her *l*— „ 901
Loäd Well, it be the last *l* hoäm. *Prom. of May* II 145
as I said afoor, it be the last *l* hoäm; „ II 169
'The Last *L* Hoäm.' (repeat) „ II 171, 172
At the end of the daäy, For the last *l* hoäm? (repeat) „ II 184, 195
Till the end of the daäy And the last *l* hoäm. „ II 209
Till the end o' the daäy An' the last *l* hoäm.' „ II 239
To the end o' the daäy An' the last *l* hoäm.' „ II 260
An' the last *l* hoäm, *L* hoäm.' „ II 293
Loan raise us *l's* and subsidies Among the merchants; *Queen Mary* v i 179
Loathe Who *l* you for your late return to Rome, „ IV ii 32
She is none of those who *l* the honeycomb. „ v i 277
I *l* being beaten; had I fixt my fancy *Becket, Pro.* 49
Loath'd if he have to live so *l* a life, *Queen Mary* IV i 152
and great baseness *l* as an exception: *Becket* III iii 304
worship whom she *l*, I should have let her be, „ IV ii 391
l the cruelties that Rome Wrought on her vassals. *The Cup* I ii 373
Loathing (adj.) I have but shown a *l* face to you, *Queen Mary* III vi 113
Loathing (s) Beauty passes like a breath and love is lost in *l*: „ v ii 366
And *L* wield a Saxon battle-axe— *Harold* v i 414
I have an inherited *l* of these black sheep of the Papacy. *Becket, Pro.* 461
sane and natural *l* for a soul Purer, „ II i 171
Loathsome call they not The one true faith, a *l* idol-worship? *Queen Mary* III iv 219
make Thy body *l* even to thy child; *Becket* IV ii 172
Lobster-basket The simple *l-b*, and the mesh— *Becket* II ii 297
Locusting Come *l* upon us, eat us up, *Queen Mary* II i 101
Locust-like their horse Swallow the hill *l-l*, *Harold* v i 560
Lodge To *l* a fear in Thomas Becket's heart *Becket* I iii 176
take this holy cup To *l* it in the shrine of Artemis. *The Cup* I ii 435
To *l* this cup Within the holy shrine of Artemis, „ I ii 52
in some of these may *l* That baseness *Foresters* II ii 705
Lodged if you be fairly served, And *l*, and treated. *Queen Mary* v iii 22
There *l* a gleaming grimness in his eyes, *Harold* II ii 224
I have *l* my pretty Katekin in her bower. *Foresters* II i 417
Lodging (*See also* **A-lodgin'**) You see the *l*, sir, *Queen Mary* v iii 23
track her, if thou canst, even into the King's *l*, *Becket, Pro.* 508
Thou wilt find her Back in her *l*. „ I i 400
With a wanton in thy *l*—Hell requite 'em! „ I ii 9
My lord, Fitzurse, beheld her in your *l*. „ I ii 34
Lodging-house went into service—the drudge of a *l-h*— *Prom. of May* III 392
Loftiest The lordliest, *l* minster ever built To Holy Peter *Harold* III i 206
Logic Some of my former friends Would find my *l* faulty; *Prom. of May* II 665
Loiter Come, come, why do ye *l* here? *Foresters* I i 80
Loitering Half an hour late! why are you *l* here? *Prom. of May* II 324
Lollardism That those old statutes touching *L* *Queen Mary* III iv 7
Lolluping *See* **A-lolluping**
Lombardy the Netherlands, Sicily, Naples, *L*. „ II i 213
London (adj.) (*See also* **Lunnon**) For thro' thine help we are come to *L* Bridge; „ II iii 9
On over *L* Bridge We cannot: stay we cannot; „ II iii 41
In every *L* street a gibbet stood. „ III i 7
To this son of a *L* merchant—how your Grace must hate him. *Becket, Pro.* 433
Knights, bishops, earls, this *L* spawn—by Mahound, „ II ii 143
Thomas, son Of Gilbert Becket, *L* merchant. „ II ii 231
The *L* folkmote Has made him all but king, *Foresters* I iii 80
London (bishop) Who made thee *L*? Who, but Canterbury? *Becket* I iii 66
Bishops—York, *L*, Chichester, Westminster— „ I iii 385
hath in this crowning of young Henry by York and *L* „ III iii 71
crowning thy young son by York, *L* and Salisbury—not Canterbury. „ III iii 196
London (bishoprick) Found two archbishopricks, *L* and York? „ I iii 50
Foliot may claim the pall For *L* too. „ I iii 57
London (city) Forward to *L* with me! forward to *L*! *Queen Mary* II i 214
forward to *L*! *Crowd*. Forward to *L*! „ II i 217
in full force Roll upon *L*. „ II i 236
these our companies And guilds of *L*, gathered here, „ II ii 129
I, Lord Mayor Of *L*, and our guilds and companies. „ II ii 141
You droop in your dim *L*. „ v ii 609
Draw thou to *L*, there make strength to breast *Harold* v i 126
For *L* had a temple and a priest *Becket* I iii 59
Do I wish it? *Edgar*. In *L*. *Prom. of May* I 698
He has gone to *L*. „ I 780
Lone seek In that *l* house, to practise on my life, *Queen Mary* I iv 284
she so praised The convent and *l* life—within the pale— *Harold* I ii 47
Thine ear, *Becket*. That's *l* enough. *Becket, Pro.* 158
Keep him away from the *l* little isle. „ II i 15
I am as *l* and loveless as thyself. *The Falcon* 20
Loneliness Springs from the *l* of my poor bower, *Becket* III i 40
Lonely And if I walk within the *l* wood, *Harold* II ii 246
And it is so *l* here—no confessor. *Becket* II i 290
that dreadful night! that *l* walk to Littlechester, *Prom. of May* III 366
My *l* hour! The king of day hath stept from off his throne, *Foresters* II i 25
Why break you thus upon my *l* hour? „ II i 93
and scare *l* maidens at the farmstead. „ III 200
You caught a *l* woodman of our band, „ III 359
Long (adj. and adv.) Nay; not so *l* I trust. *Queen Mary* I iii 141
I am somewhat faint With our *l* talk. „ I v 521
L live Queen Mary! „ III i 294
you forget That *l* low minster where you gave your hand To this great Catholic King. „ III ii 90
And do declare our penitence and grief For our *l* schism and disobedience, „ III iii 129
thou That layest so *l* in heretic bonds with me; „ III iv 280

Long (adj. and adv.) (*continued*) How many names in the *l* sweep of time That so foreshortens greatness, *Queen Mary* III v 40
A *l* petition from the foreign exiles To spare the life of Cranmer. „ IV i 3
After the *l* brain-dazing colloquies, „ IV ii 92
Friend for so *l* time of a mighty King: „ IV iii 73
L have I lain in prison, yet have heard Of all their wretchedness. „ IV iii 210
His *l* white beard, which he had never shaven Since Henry's death, „ IV iii 592
Look! I have play'd with this poor rose so *l* I have broken off the head. „ V ii 2
That all day *l* hath wrought his father's work, „ V ii 118
listening In some dark closet, some *l* gallery, drawn, „ V ii 217
The rosy face, and *l* down-silvering beard, *Harold* III i 46
The rosy face and *l* down-silvering beard— „ IV i 261
O rare, a whole *l* day of open field. *Becket* I i 296
and the moon Divides the whole *l* street with light and shade. „ I i 365
Their *l* bird-echoing minster-aisles,— „ III i 44
We have watch'd So *l* in vain, he hath pass'd out again, „ III ii 12
And sway the *l* grape-bunches of our vines, *The Cup* II 270
'Tis *l* since we have met! *The Falcon* 274
Be thou a-gawin' to the *l* barn? *Prom. of May* I 2
and 'e telled all on us to be i' the *l* barn by one o'clock, „ I 8
Why coöm awaäy, then, to the *l* barn. „ I 36
Miss, the farming men 'ull hev their dinner i' the *l* barn, „ I 166
And *l* life to boath on' em. „ I 345
the smell o' the mou'd 'ud ha' maäde ma live as *l* as Jerusalem. „ I 378
They ha' broached a barrel of äale i' the *l* barn, „ I 426
and I've hed the *l* barn cleared out of all the machines, „ I 451
Oh, Dora, Dora, how *l* you have been away from home! „ I 767
Come, then, and make them happy in the *l* barn, „ I 791
And plaäy the pianner, if ye liked, all daäy *l*, like a laädy, „ II 101
Whoy, O lor, Miss! that wur so *l* back, and the walls sa thin, „ III 71
the state we all Must come to in our spring-and-winter world If we live *l* enough! „ III 512
and how often in the *l* sweep of years to come *Foresters* I i 244
L live Richard, Robin and Richard! *L* live Richard! „ I ii 1
L live Robin, Robin and Richard! *L* live Robin, „ I ii 13
'*L* live King Richard!' „ I ii 25
To sleep! to sleep! The *l* bright day is done, „ I iii 41
Why did ye keep us at the door so *l*? „ II i 224
She lay so *l* at the bottom of her well In the cold water „ IV 242
Long (verb) And how I *l* for rest.' *Prom. of May* III 206
Longed he *l* much to see your Grace and the Chancellor ere he past, *Becket, Pro.* 398
Less lovely than her own, and *l* for it. *The Falcon* 56
Longer should be No *l* a dead letter, but requicken'd. *Queen Mary* III iv 10
Stays *l* here in our poor north than you:— „ V i 24
these customs are no *l* As Canterbury calls them, *Becket* I iii 69
That if they keep him *l* as their guest, II i 91
And were it *l*—well—I should not do it. „ V ii 159
and then we were no *l* outlaws. *Foresters* IV 147
The land! the land! I am crazed no *l*, so I have the land. „ IV 855
if you hold us here *L* from our own venison. „ IV 942
Long-face Who's the *l-f* there, *Queen Mary* III i 191
Longing have strange fancies, Strange *l's*; *The Falcon* 819
Long-silvering Up thro' the light of the seas by the moon's *l-s* ray! *Foresters* II ii 179
Long-tugged-at *l-t-a*, threadbare-worn Quarrel of Crown and Church— *Becket* II ii 54
Long-winded Why, you *l-w*—Sir, you go beyond me. *Queen Mary* V iv 58
Long-withholden to enforce The *l-w* tribute: *The Cup* I i 77
Long-worshipt my most honour'd and *l-w* lady, *The Falcon* 714
Look (s) tho' by your age, And by your *l's* *Queen Mary* I iv 13
She calls you beauty, but I don't like her *l's*. *Becket* IV ii 62
Beänt Miss Eva gone off a bit of 'er good *l's* o' laäte? *Prom. of May* I 33
Look (verb) She *l's* comelier than ordinary to-day; *Queen Mary* I i 70

Look (verb) (*continued*) Well, sir, I *l* for happy times. *Queen Mary* I i 98
l you there—The Prince of Spain coming to wed „ I iii 81
L's it not right royal? „ I iv 74
L to you as the one to crown their ends. „ I iv 171
L to it, niece, He hath no fence when Gardiner „ I iv 201
L you, Master Wyatt, Tear up that woman's work „ II i 74
L; can you make it English? „ II i 127
L at the New World—a paradise made hell; „ II i 207
chance That I shall never *l* upon you more. „ II i 246
the half sight which makes her *l* so stern, „ II ii 322
That makes or man or woman *l* their goodliest. „ II ii 329
Should *l* more goodly than the rest of us. „ II ii 349
Be merry! yet, Sir Ralph, you *l* but sad. „ II ii 358
L's very Spain of very Spain? „ III i 192
But then he *l's* so merry. „ III i 203
L to your Bible, Paget! we are fallen. „ III iv 80
L to the Netherlands, wherein have been „ III iv 106
And make it *l* more seemly. „ III iv 152
let 'em *l* to it, Cranmer and Hooper, „ III iv 423
O God, sir, do you *l* upon your boots, „ III v 191
what, you *l* somewhat worn; „ IV ii 116
He *l's* to and he leans on as his God, „ IV iii 306
And you must *l* to Calais when I go. „ V i 17
L! I have play'd with this poor rose so long „ V ii 1
L you here—the Pope Pointing at me with 'Pole, „ V ii 173
how grim and ghastly *l's* her Grace, „ V ii 390
she *l's* a corpse. „ V ii 397
Doth he not *l* noble? „ V v 32
L you, there's a star That dances in it *Harold* I i 7
and *l* upon my face, Not on the comet. „ I i 25
L to the skies, then to the river, „ I i 34
L! am I not Work-wan, flesh-fallen? „ I i 97
but *l*, where Edward draws A faint foot „ I i 142
She is *my* mistress, let *me l* to her! „ I i 287
L thee, Rolf, when I was down in the fever, „ II i 46
L, he's here! He'll speak for himself! „ II i 78
L thou, here is Wulfnoth! „ II ii 322
L not amazed, fair earl! „ II ii 494
L at him—The rosy face, „ III i 44
L up! *l* up! Edith! „ III i 320
He *l's* for land among us, he and his. „ IV ii 53
I am Edith! *L* not thus wan! *Edith.* What matters how I *l*? „ V i 393
L, I will bear thy blessing into the battle „ V i 434
L out upon the battle—is he safe? (repeat) *Harold* V i 484, 654
L, daughter, *l*. *Edith.* Nay, father, *l* for *me*! *Harold* V i 535
L out upon the battle! „ V i 623
L out upon the hill—is Harold there? „ V i 669
L you, we never meant to part again. „ V ii 80
For *l*, our marriage ring! „ V ii 108
L to your king. *Becket, Pro.* 33
L, this line—The rest you see is colour'd green— „ *Pro.* 169
L! I would move this wanton from his sight „ I ii 70
L on me as I were thy bodily son, „ I iii 263
L to it, your own selves! „ I iii 397
It is not safe for me to *l* upon him. „ I iii 486
l how the table steams, like a heathen altar; „ I iv 68
L rather thou all-royal as when first I met thee. „ II i 46
L, *l*! if little Geoffrey have not tost His ball „ II i 319
will but *l* into The wrongs you did him, „ II ii 115
The King *l's* troubled. „ II ii 425
I am the King, his father, And I will *l* to it. „ III i 27
for there were great ones who would *l* after me, „ III i 135
or I couldn't *l* your ladyship i' the face, „ III i 195
L! He bows, he bares his head, „ III iii 33
were all, my lord, as noble as yourself, who would *l* up to you? „ III iii 306
Fitzurse and his following—who would *l* down upon them? „ III iii 309
But you don't *l* like a good fairy. Mother does. „ IV i 35
L at the hilt. What excellent workmanship. „ IV ii 313
L! how this love, this mother, runs thro' all „ V ii 241
Why do you *l* at her so lingeringly? *The Cup* I i 123
To-day they are fixt and bright—they *l* straight out. „ II 21
L for me! „ II 167

Look (verb) (*continued*) I wonder if I *l* as pale as she? *The Cup* II 322
Deigns to *l* in upon our barbarisms. „ II 337
you *l* as beautiful this morning as the very Madonna *The Falcon* 198
your ladyship were not Too proud to *l* upon the garland, „ 663
'Coomly to *l* at,' says she—but she said it spiteful-like. To *l* at—yeas, *Prom. of May* I 179
tha *l's* haäle anew to last to a hoonderd. „ I 354
and you *l* thin and pale. Is it for his absence? „ I 781
sweet upo' Dora Steer, and she weänt sa much as *l* at 'im? „ II 162
How worn he *l's*, poor man! who is it, I wonder. „ II 390
l to thysen, for, by the Lord, I'd think „ II 695
L there—under the deaths. „ II 710
I had to *l* over his letters. „ II 720
could it *l* But half as lovely. „ III 490
but, my flower, You *l* so weary and so worn! „ III 499
L up! One word, or do but smile! „ III 675
Yes, deathlike! Dead? I dare not *l*: if dead, „ III 717
How she *l's* up at him, how she holds her face! *Foresters* I ii 144
He often *l's* in here by the moonshine. „ II i 336
L, my lord, there goes one in the moonlight. „ II i 394
O *l*! before the shadow of these dark oaks „ II i 604
L! *l*! he kneels! he has anger'd the foul witch, „ II i 669
L, there comes a deputation „ II ii 144
warm thy heart to Little John. *L* where he comes! „ III 46
and *l's* at once Maid Marian, „ III 117
I *l* on the King's venison as my own. „ IV 197
If a cat may *l* at a king, may not a friar speak to one? „ IV 921

Look'd-looked-lookt You *look'd* a king. *Queen Mary* I iii 103
So that your sister were but *look'd* to closer. „ I v 460
How *look'd* the city When you past it? Quiet? „ II ii 57
and *look'd* As grim and grave as from a funeral. „ II ii 64
And *look'd* as bloodless. „ II ii 84
eyes So bashful that you *look'd* no higher? „ III i 65
How *look'd* the Queen? „ III i 91
then King Harry *look'd* from out a cloud, „ IV ii 6
His eighty years *Look'd* somewhat crooked on him „ IV iii 332
I do assure you, that it must be *look'd* too: „ V i 2
It must be *look'd* to, If war should fall „ V i 8
It shall be *look'd* to; „ V i 12
he *look'd* the Great Harry, You but his cockboat; „ V ii 145
In Hampton Court My window *look'd* upon the corridor; „ V ii 459
I never *look'd* upon so fair a likeness „ V v 28
L hard and sweet at me, and gave it me. „ V v 95
but he that *lookt* a fangless one, Issues *Becket* I iii 451
as to the young crownling himself, he *looked* so malapert in the eyes, „ III iii 109
yellow silk here and there, and it *looked* pretty like a glowworm, „ IV i 22
wine Ran down the marble and *lookt* like blood, *The Cup* II 204
Glows thro' my veins since first I *look'd* on thee. „ II 429
You never had *look'd* in on me before, *The Falcon* 865
for the past *Look'd* thro' the present, *Prom. of May* II 641
She hath *looked* well at one of 'em, Little John. *Foresters* I i 38

Lookest Why *l* thou so amazed? „ I i 130

Looketh 'Whosoever *L* after a woman,' *Queen Mary* I v 453

Lookin' (*See also* **A-lookin'**) I coom'd upon 'im t'other daäy *l* at the coontry, *Prom. of May* I 201

Looking (part) (*See also* **Lookin', Nobler-looking, Goodlier-looking, Simple-looking**) But Janus-faces *l* diverse ways. *Queen Mary* III ii 75
ever *l* to the happy haven Where he shall rest at night, „ IV iii 579
Have you been *l* at the 'Dance of Death'? „ V ii 169
l thro' my reign, I found a hundred ghastly murders *Becket* I iii 406
you should be in the hayfield *l* after your men; *Prom. of May* II 47

Looking (s) With *l* on the dead. Am I so white? *Harold* II ii 815
In *l* on a chill and changeless Past? *Prom. of May* II 504

Lookt *See* **Look'd**

Loom (s) heaven and earth are threads of the same *l*, *Harold* I i 210

Loom (verb) out of which *L's* the least chance of peril *Queen Mary* II ii 238
blackness of my dungeon *l* Across their lamps *Harold* II ii 406

Loon the brainless *l's* That cannot spell *Queen Mary* III i 280

Loop Philip! quick! *l* up my hair! „ V ii 534

Loose (adj.) a score of wolf-dogs are let *l* that will tear thee piecemeal. *Becket* III ii 39

Loose (verb) going now to the Tower to *l* the prisoners *Queen Mary* I i 109
lead on; ye *l* me from my bonds. „ IV ii 240

Loosed you late were *l* from out the Tower, „ I iv 50

Loosely-scatter'd left about Like *l-s* jewels, „ II i 28

Loove (love) And I would *l* tha moor nor ony gentleman 'ud *l* tha. *Prom. of May* II 104

Lor (inter.) (*See also* **Law**) Whoy, O *l*, Miss! that wur sa long back, „ III 71
O *l*, Miss! noä, noä, noä! „ III 91

Lord (*See also* **Liege-lord, My-lord**) Gardiner for one, who is to be made *L* Chancellor, *Queen Mary* I i 87
Her freaks and frolics with the late *L* Admiral? „ I iv 20
She fears the *L's* may side with you „ I iv 158
The *L* Chancellor (I count it as a kind of virtue in him, „ I iv 191
Why, my *l* Bishop? (repeat) *Queen Mary* I iv 223, 227
Who waits, sir? *Usher*. Madam, the *L* Chancellor. *Queen Mary* I v 96
that were hard upon you, my *L* Chancellor. „ I v 159
The *L* Chancellor himself is on our side. „ II i 193
Or—if the *L* God will it—on the stake. „ II i 251
All hangs on her address, And upon you, *L* Mayor. „ II ii 56
I, the *L* Mayor, and these our companies And guilds „ II ii 127
I, *L* Mayor Of London, and our guilds and companies. „ II ii 139
tho' my *L* Mayor here, By his own rule, „ II ii 345
new *L's* Are quieted with their sop of Abbeylands, „ III i 141
No, my *L* Legate, the *L* Chancellor goes. „ III ii 151
We, the *L's* Spiritual and Temporal, „ III iii 113
The *L* who hath redeem'd us With His own blood, „ III iii 202
I am but of the laity, my *L* Bishop, „ III iv 81
Yet my *L* Cardinal— *Pole*. I am your Legate; „ III iv 178
Till when, my *L's*, I counsel tolerance. „ III iv 203
Thou Christian Bishop, thou *L* Chancellor Of England! „ III iv 300
My *L* Chancellor, You have an old trick of offending us; „ III iv 313
O *L*! your Grace, your Grace, „ III v 248
I told my *L* He should not vex her Highness; „ III vi 65
And my *L* Paget and *L* William Howard, „ IV i 6
Good morrow, my *L* Cardinal; „ IV i 42
My *L* of Ely, this. After a riot We hang the leaders, „ IV i 72
And if he did I care not, my *L* Howard. „ IV i 129
You are too politic for me, my *L* Paget. „ IV i 150
May learn there is no power against the *L*. „ IV iii 67
And be with Christ the *L* in Paradise. „ IV iii 88
O *L* God, although my sins be great, „ IV iii 135
And every syllable taught us by our *L*, „ IV iii 231
No, here's *L* William Howard. What, my *L*, „ IV iii 288
Thank the *L* therevore. (repeat) *Queen Mary* IV iii 496, 520, 529
there wur an owld *l* a-cum to dine wi' un, *Queen Mary* IV iii 504
'I wunt dine,' says my *L* Bishop, „ IV iii 507
the owld *l* fell to 's meat wi' a will, God bless un! „ IV iii 514
but when I came to wed your majesty, *L* Howard, „ V i 56
I have gone beyond your late *L* Chancellor,— „ V ii 98
cries continually with sweat and tears to the *L* God „ V iv 46
Charles, the *l* of this low world, is gone; „ V v 54
Ask thou *L* Leofwin what he thinks of this! *Harold* I i 40
L Leofwin, dost thou believe, „ I i 42
Yea, *l* Harold. „ II ii 243
The king, the *l's*, the people clear'd him of it, „ II ii 522
many among our Norman *l's* Hate thee for this, „ II ii 545
I have built the *L* a house— (repeat) *Harold* III i 178, 180, 186
the *L* hath dwelt In darkness. *Harold* III i 178
The *L* was God and came as man— „ III ii 172
Thou art one of those Who brake into *L* Tostig's treasure-house „ IV i 114
Lay hands of full allegiance in thy *L's* „ V i 11
Like other *l's* amenable to law. *Becket, Pro.* 25
Church should pay her scutage like the *l's*. „ I i 35
And spake to the *L* God, and said 'O *L*, I have been a lover of wines, „ I i 74
And the *L* answer'd me, 'Thou art the man, (repeat) „ I i 82, 98
'O *L* my God, Henry the King hath been my friend, „ I i 86
Stir up the King, the *L's*! „ I ii 88
Is not the Church the visible *L* on earth? Shall hands that do create the *L* be bound „ I iii 92
The *L* be judged again by Pilate? No! „ I iii 97
My *l* Archbishop, that we too should sign? „ I iii 272
Loyally and with good faith, my *l* Archbishop? „ I iii 279

Lord (*continued*) dwelt alone, like a soft *l* of the East, *Becket* I iii 358
And our great *l's* will sit in judgment on him. „ I iii 549
I would, my *l* Thomas of Canterbury, „ I iii 577
How much might that amount to, my *l* Leicester ? „ I iii 656
O my good *l* Leicester, The King and I were brothers. „ I iii 660
The King and all his *l's*—— *Becket.* Son, first hear *me* ! „ I iii 671
Blessed is he that cometh in the name of the *L* ! „ I iii 759
My *l* Archbishop, wilt thou permit us— „ I iv 5
That is the parable of our blessed *L*. *Becket.* And why should not the parable of our blessed *L* be acted again ? „ I iv 75
our *l's* and masters in Christ Jesus. „ I iv 87
My *l* Archbishop, may I come in with my poor friend, my dog ? „ I iv 93
and the *L* hath prepared your table— „ I iv 130
Where is my *l* Archbishop ? „ I iv 184
because the *L* hath set his mark upon him „ I iv 191
for I be his *l* and master i' Christ, „ I iv 241
gangrenes, and running sores, praise ye the *L*, „ I iv 256
world shall live by the King's venison and the bread o' the *L*, „ I iv 272
since we would be *l* of our own manor, „ II ii 19
My lieges and my *l's*, The thanks of Holy Church „ II ii 189
That sow this hate between my *l* and me ! „ II ii 272
by-things of the *L* Are the wrong'd innocences „ III iii 13
If . . . but I say no more . . . farewell, my *l*. „ III iii 272
It must be so—my visions in the *L* : „ III iii 341
l of more land Than any crown in Europe, „ V i 28
Thomas, *l* Not only of your vassals but amours, „ V i 204
for thy Church, O *L*—Into thy hands, O *L*— „ V iii 195
The *L* bless boäth on 'em ! *Prom. of May* I 341
—the *L* bless 'er—'er oän sen ; „ II 39
it be the *L's* doin', noän o' mine ; „ III 48
I would set my men-at-arms to oppose thee, like the *L* of the Castle. *Foresters* I i 324
O *L*, I will live and die for King Richard— „ I ii 37
O *L*, I am easily led by words, „ I ii 39
L's and Commons will bow down before him— *Queen Mary* III i 433

Lordliest The *l*, loftiest minster ever built To Holy Peter in our English isle ! *Harold* III i 206

Lordship Large *l* there of lands and territory. *Harold* II ii 83

Lose be no peace for Mary till Elizabeth *l* her head.' *Queen Mary* I iii 5
If Elizabeth *l* her head— „ I iii 88
Stand further off, or you may *l* your head. *Courtenay.* I have a head to *l* for your sweet sake. „ I iv 128
what have you done to *l* her ? „ I iv 296
But do not *l* me Calais. „ I v 129
To go back Were to *l* all. „ II iii 40
I pass to Windsor and I *l* my crown. „ II iv 29
thou shalt *l* thine ears and find thy tongue, „ III i 255
L the sweet hope that I may bear a prince. „ III vi 201
Or you will *l* your Calais. „ V i 11
to the intent That you may *l* your English heritage. „ V i 133
God guide me lest I *l* the way. „ V v 209
Yet thee I would not *l*, and sell not thou *Harold* III ii 58
To take my life might *l* him Aquitaine. *Becket* IV ii 396
He *l's* half the meed of martyrdom „ V ii 278
And *l* his head as old St. Denis did. „ V ii 480
which well May make you *l* yourself, *The Cup* I i 149
I might plunge And *l* myself for ever. *Prom. of May* II 306
and I shall *l* my land also. *Foresters* I i 339
Beware, man, lest thou *l* thy faith in me. „ I ii 179
but my father will not *l* his land, „ II i 523
Or *l* all hope of pardon from us— „ IV 935

Losing would dare the chance Of double, or *l* all. *The Cup* I iii 148
For fear of *l* more than friend, a son ; *The Falcon* 332
poor father, utterly broken down By *l* her— *Prom. of May* II 418
betray'd Thy father to the *l* of his land. *Foresters* II i 570

Loss This marriage should bring *l* or danger to you, *Queen Mary* II ii 227
angry chronicles hereafter By *l* of Calais. „ V ii 305
More gain than *l* ; for of your wives *Becket* V ii 201

Lost To the Pleiads, uncle ; they have *l* a sister. *Queen Mary* I iv 294
I have *l* mine office, „ I v 235
He has gambled for his life, and *l*, he hangs. „ II iii 92
Madam, I much fear That all is *l* ; „ II iv 23

Lost (*continued*) All *l*, all *l*, all yielded ! A barge, a barge ! *Queen Mary* II iv 71
traitors Against our royal state have *l* the heads „ III iv 3
We reck not tho' we *l* this crown of England— „ III iv 55
I had like to have *l* my life : „ III v 189
l Her fierce desire of bearing him a child, „ IV iii 428
a star beside the moon Is all but *l* ; „ V i 81
So ; but it is not *l*—Not yet. „ V ii 264
Beauty passes like a breath and love is *l* in loathing : „ V ii 365
L in a wilderness where none can hear ! „ V ii 382
sent on foreign travel, Not *l* his head. „ V ii 491
was *l* When Wyatt sack'd the Chancellor's house „ V ii 503
For having *l* myself to save myself, *Harold* II ii 654
thro' his dying sense Shrills '*l* thro' thee.' „ III i 35
Crown'd, crown'd and *l*, crown'd King—and *l* to me ! „ III ii 1
Both were *l* and found together, „ III ii 7
l and found Together in the cruel river Swale „ III ii 9
L, *l*, the light of day, „ III ii 12
L, *l*, we have *l* the way. „ III ii 15
into the river, Where we two may be *l* together, And *l* for ever ? 'Oh ! never, oh ! never, Tho' we be *l* and be found together.' „ III ii 18
the truth Was *l* in that fierce North, where *they* were *l*, Where all good things are *l*, where Tostig *l* „ III ii 26
I have *l* Somewhat of upright stature „ III ii 55
I have *l* the boy who play'd at ball with me, „ IV iii 21
Thou hast *l* thine even temper, brother Harold ! „ V i 94
when all was *l*, he yell'd, And bit his shield, „ V i 403
I have *l* both crown And husband. „ V ii 38
I *l* it somehow—I *l* it, playing with it „ V ii 109
twice I thought that all was *l*. „ V ii 173
That the heart were *l* in the rhyme *Becket, Pro.* 383
certain wholesome usages, *L* in desuetude, „ I iii 413
I think so. So I *l* mine. „ II i 64
I have *l* all trust in him. „ II ii 434
The boy so late ; pray God, he be not *l*. „ IV ii 2
nay, if I *l* him, now The folds have fallen from the mystery, And left all naked, I were *l* indeed. „ IV ii 7
l her and went on and on till I found the light and the lady, „ IV ii 17
I saw the ball you *l* in the fork of the great willow over the brook. „ IV ii 57
Well—well—too costly to the left or *l* „ IV ii 299
You have *l* The ear of the King. „ IV ii 354
L in the common good, the common wrong, „ V ii 40
have I *l* authority among you ? „ V iii 66
The glory and grief of battle won or *l*. *The Cup* I ii 161
I have *l* a friend of late. *The Falcon* 329
there wudn't be a dinner for nawbody, and I should ha' *l* the pig. *Prom. of May* I 149
and man perceives that The *l* gleam of an after-life but leaves him „ I 503
I were insured, Miss, an' I *l* nowt by it. „ II 58
I have *l* myself, and am *l* for ever to you and my poor father. „ II 83
I do believe I *l* my heart to him the very first time we met, „ III 283
but I couldn't buy my darter back ageän when she *l* hersen, „ III 454
an' one on 'em went an' *l* hersen i' the river. „ III 456
Has *l* his health, his eyesight, even his mind. „ III 767
'Twere best to make an end of my *l* life. „ III 786
I have *l* my gold, I have *l* my son, *Foresters* I i 338
art attainted, and hast *l* thine earldom of Huntingdon. „ I iii 58
I fear me we have *l* our labour, then. „ II i 232
I have *l* a cow from my meadow. „ II i 326
I have been a fool and I have *l* my Kate. „ II ii 79
In the cold water that she *l* her voice, „ IV 243
Have I *l* her then ? „ IV 618
L her ? O no, we took Advantage of the letter— „ IV 619

Lot The *l* of Princes. To sit high Is to be lied about. *Queen Mary* I v 428
I say no more—only this, their *l* is yours. „ II i 214
Is that it ? That's a big *l* of money. „ II iii 62
Drew here the richest *l* from Fate, *The Cup* II 442
That never be thy *l* or mine !— *Foresters* III 98

Loud And dazzled men and deafen'd by some bright *L* venture, *Queen Mary* III i 453
Not so *l* ! Our Clarence there Sees ever an aureole „ v ii 411
Not so *l*. Lord Devon, girls ! „ v ii 484
Go home. Besides, you curse so *l*. „ v iv 62
So *l*, that, by St. Dunstan, old St. Thor— *Harold* IV iii 146
Why there—like some *l* beggar at thy gate— *Becket* II i 180
Wakening such brawls and *l* disturbances In England, „ v ii 352
L disturbances ! Oh, ay—the bells rang out even to deafening, „ v ii 362
Have our *l* pastimes driven them all away ? *Foresters* II ii 105
Louder *L* ! *l* ! Maid Marian, Queen o' the woods ! „ III 374
L, *l*, ye knaves. „ III 396
Loud-lung'd Tho' all the *l-l* trumpets upon earth *Becket* v II 487
Louis (King of France) *L* of France loved me, and I dreamed that I loved *L* of France : „ *Pro.* 355
King *L* had no paramours, and I loved him „ *Pro.* 474
'Fly at once to France, to King *L* of France : „ I iv 53
So that the fool King *L* feed them not. „ II i 76
brave The Pope, King *L*, and this turbulent priest. „ II i 312
O good son *L*, do not counsel me, „ II ii 219
My lord, I see this *L* Returning, ah ! „ II ii 417
Long live the good King *L* ! „ II ii 451
know the King's married for King *L*—— *Rosamund.* Married ! *Margery.* Years and years, my lady, for her husband, King *L*—— *Rosamund.* Hush ! „ III i 167
bound For that one hour to stay with good King *L*, „ III iii 248
He said so ? *L*, did he ? „ III iii 255
When I was in mine anger with King *L*, „ III iii 258
my much constancy To the monk-king, *L*, „ IV ii 305
I, that thro' the Pope divorced King *L*, „ IV ii 418
You were but Aquitaine to *L*—no wife ; „ v i 116
Lours thunder-cloud That *l's* on England—laughter ! *Harold* III ii 161
Lousiest Thou the lustiest and *l* of this Cain's brotherhood, answer. *Becket* I iv 185
Lout that all the *l's* to whom Their A B C is darkness, *Queen Mary* III iv 34
L, churl, clown ! *Prom. of May* III 739
Love (adj.) What matters ? State matters ? *l* matters ? *Becket, Pro.* 320
Love (s) O, my lord to be, My *l*, for thy sake only. *Queen Mary* I v 67
not with gold, But dearest links of *l*. „ I v 539
deem This *l* by you return'd as heartily ; And thro' this common knot and bond of *l*, „ II ii 197
A diamond, And Philip's gift, as proof of Philip's *l*, „ III i 67
She cast on him a vassal smile of *l*, „ III i 98
thy *l* to mine Will cling more close, „ III ii 159
make me shamed and tongue-tied in my *l*. „ III ii 163
Cranmer, Your more especial *l*, „ III iv 418
should her *l* when you are gone, my liege, „ III vi 172
should her *l*—And I have known such women „ III vi 177
to fuse Almost into one metal *l* and hate,— „ III vi 182
'*L* of this world is hatred against God.' „ IV iii 173
They hate *me* also for my *l* to you, My Philip ; „ v i 95
Beauty passes like a breath and *l* is lost in loathing : „ v ii 365
L will hover round the flowers when they first awaken ; „ v ii 370
L will fly the fallen leaf, and not be overtaken ; „ v ii 372
Some say that Gardiner, out of *l* for him, „ v ii 502
he sends his veriest *l*, And says, he will come quickly. „ v ii 564
Tell him at last I know his *l* is dead, „ v ii 590
that it would please Him out of His infinite *l* „ v iv 47
And *l* should know ; and—be the king so wise,— *Harold* I i 276
Cling to their *l* ; for, now the sons of Godwin „ I i 324
Thy *l* ? *Aldwyth.* As much as I can give thee, „ I i 478
And thy *l* ? *Aldwyth.* As much as thou canst bear. „ I i 483
L is come with a song and a smile, Welcome *L* with a smile and a song : *L* can stay but a little while. „ I ii 10
L will stay for a whole life long. „ I ii 17
Sang out their *l's* so loud, „ I ii 20
And woo their *l's* and have forgotten thee ; „ II ii 438
Normans left among us, Who follow'd me for *l* ! „ III i 304
The more the *l*, the mightier is the prayer ; The more the *l*, the more acceptable The sacrifice of both your *l's* to heaven. „ III i 346
'*L*, I will guide thee.' „ III ii 16
'*L* for a whole life long' When was that sung ? „ III ii 88
Since Tostig came with Norway—fright not *l*. „ IV i 174

Love (s) (*continued*) Full hope have I that *l* will answer *l*. *Harold* IV i 273
—a sin against The truth of *l*. „ v i 171
With a *l* Passing thy *l* for Griffyth ! „ v i 356
What matters ? State matters ? love matters ? *Henry.* My *l* for thee, and thine for me. *Becket, Pro.* 321
Madam, you do ill to scorn wedded *l*. „ *Pro.* 354
honeymoon is the gall of *l* ; he dies of his honeymoon. „ *Pro.* 364
Not for my *l* toward him, but because he had the *l* of the King. „ *Pro.* 441
thou shalt have our *l*, our silence, and our gold— „ *Pro.* 492
My Courts of *L* would have held thee guiltless of *l*— „ *Pro.* 498
worldly bond between us is dissolved, Not yet the *l* : „ I i 348
Ye make this clashing for no *l* o' the customs „ I iii 136
Thought that I knew him, err'd thro' *l* of him, „ I iii 441
Took it upon me—err'd thro' *l* of him. „ I iii 699
L that is born of the deep coming up with the sun from the sea. (repeat) „ II i 9, 19
L that can shape or can shatter a life „ II i 11
L that can lift up a life from the dead. „ II i 13
thou my golden dream of *L's* own bower, „ II i 34
A greater King Than thou art, *L*, „ II i 116
A bastard hate born of a former *l*. „ II i 174
Speak only of thy *l*. „ II i 179
boldness of this hand hath won it *L's* alms, „ II i 184
O by thy *l* for me, all mine for thee, „ II i 314
the gap Left by the lack of *l*. *Henry.* The lack of *l* ! „ III i 61
bound me by his *l* to secrecy Till his own time. „ III i 228
stray'd From *l's* clear path into the common bush, „ III i 247
L is the only gold. „ IV i 43
I have heard of such that range from *l* to *l*, Like the wild beast—if you can call it *l*. „ IV ii 120
Come with me, *l*, And I will love thee . . . „ IV ii 155
King himself, for *l* of his own sons, „ IV ii 344
in aiming at your *l*, It may be sometimes „ v i 36
Would he were dead ! I have lost all *l* for him. „ v i 92
Lacking the *l* of woman and of child. „ v ii 199
how this *l*, this mother, runs thro' all „ v ii 241
But the fool-fire of *l* or lust, *The Cup* I i 147
woman's fealty when Assailed by Craft and *L*. „ I i 177
I love you—for your *l* to the great Goddess. „ I ii 218
there You told your *l* ; and like the swaying vines— „ I ii 410
—if I win her *l*, They too will cleave to me, „ I iii 153
all else Was *l* for you : he prays you to believe him. „ II 55
from maiden fears Or reverential *l* for him I loved, „ II 197
all drown'd in *l* And glittering at full tide— „ II 233
l I bear to thee Glow thro' thy veins ? „ II 426
The *l* I bear to thee Glows thro' my veins „ II 428
But hath she yet return'd thy *l* ? *The Falcon* 67
I'll be bound to confess her *l* to him at last. „ 172
Will he not pray me to return his *l*— „ 247
Hath she return'd thy *l* ? *Count.* Not yet ! „ 513
For that would seem accepting of your *l*. „ 740
It should be *l* that thus outvalues all. You speak like *l*, and yet you love me not. I have nothing in this world but *l* for you. *Lady Giovanna.* *L* ? it *is l*, *l* for my dying boy, „ 780
—the *l* you said you bore me— „ 857
But he will keep his *l* to you for ever ! „ 892
for the senses, *l*, are for the world ; *Prom. of May* I 580
if you *will* bind *l* to one for ever, „ I 644
That was only *true l* ; and I trusted— „ I 712
Have you fancied yourself in *l* with him ? „ I 783
all of them Loved her, and she was worthy of all *l*. „ II 430
the man has doubtless a good heart, and a true and lasting *l* for me : „ III 172
O *L* and Life, how weary am I, „ III 205
But the *l* of sister for sister can never be old-fashioned. „ III 319
A hundred times more worth a woman's *l*, „ III 744
for the *l* of his own little mother on earth, *Foresters* I i 97
come at their *l* with all manner of homages, „ I i 102
L flew in at the window As Wealth walk'd „ I i 150
as I am a true believer in true *l* myself, „ I i 162
and all her *l's* and hates Sink again into chaos. „ I ii 328
'Tis for no lack of *l* to you, my lord, „ I iii 130

Love (s) (*continued*) The *l* of freedom, the desire of God, *Foresters* II i 68
Thou hast crost him in *l*, „ II i 343
what sort of man art thou For land, not *l*? „ II i 534
Mortal enough, If *l* for thee be mortal. Lovers hold True *l* immortal. „ II i 614
ever held that saying false That *L* is blind, „ II i 644
Stay with us here, sweet *L*, Maid Marian, „ II ii 14
How should you love if you mistrust your *l*? *Little John.* O Kate, true *l* and jealousy are twins, And *l* is joyful, innocent, beautiful, „ II ii 61
Tit, for *l* and brevity, Not for *l* of levity. „ II ii 128
Fluting, and piping and luting '*L*, *l*, *l*'— „ III 33
lilt among the leaves '*L*, *l*, *l*, *l*'— „ III 42
take and wear this symbol of your *l*; „ III 80
L himself Seems but a ghost, „ III 111
Ha, brother. Toll, my dear? the toll of *l*. „ III 271
The *l* that children owe to both I give „ IV 7
No, sweetheart! out of tune with *L* and me. „ IV 31
No ribald John is *L*, no wanton Prince, „ IV 46
lips that never breathed *L's* falsehood to true maid will seal *L's* truth „ IV 73
He is all for *l*, he cares not for the land. „ IV 489
mate with one that holds no *l* is pure, „ IV 711
Risk not the *l* I bear thee for a girl. „ IV 742
I am but the echo of the lips of *l*. „ IV 892
In this full tide of *l*, Wave heralds wave: „ IV 1043

Love (verb) up, son, and save him! They *l* thee, *Queen Mary* I iii 67
I *l* not to be called a butterfly: „ I iv 68
I *l* you, Lay my life in your hands. „ I iv 104
as a mastiff dog May *l* a puppy cur „ I iv 195
you are one Who *l* that men should smile upon you, „ I iv 274
by the holy Virgin, being noble, But *l* me only: „ I v 71
I pray God No woman ever *l* you, „ I v 602
If ye *l* your liberties or your skins, „ II i 216
cannot tell How mothers *l* their children; yet, methinks, A prince as naturally may *l* his people As these their children; and be sure your Queen So *l's* you, „ II ii 190
Ha! ha! sir; but you jest; I *l* it: „ II ii 355
flying to our side Left his all bare, for which I *l* thee, Brett. „ II iii 5
I do not *l* your Grace should call me coward. „ II iv 88
It was a sin to *l* her married, dead I cannot choose but *l* her. „ III i 339
Perchance in England, *l's* her like a son. „ III iii 267
wholesome scripture, 'Little children, *L* one another.' „ III iv 86
To sing, *l*, marry, churn, brew, bake, and die, „ III v 111
Here by the side of her who *l's* you most? „ V i 75
altho' you *l* her not, You must proclaim Elizabeth „ V i 189
I used to *l* the Queen with all my heart— „ V ii 418
I *l* her less For such a dotage upon such a man. „ V ii 420
And *l* to hear bad tales of Philip. „ V ii 429
and *l* me, as I *l* The people! whom God aid! „ V iii 34
He never loved me—nay, he could not *l* me. „ V v 44
He hath learnt to *l* our Tostig much of late. *Harold* I i 145
Our Tostig *l's* the hand and not the man. „ I i 156
Because I *l* the Norman better—no, „ I i 171
England *l's* thee for it. „ I i 221
thyself wast wont To *l* the chase: „ I i 228
And Tostig knows it; Tostig *l's* the king. „ I i 274
I *l* the man but not his phantasies. „ I i 279
Edward *l's* him, so Ye hate him. „ I i 427
I *l* thee for it—ay, but stay a moment; „ I ii 3
Hate him? I could *l* him More, „ I ii 142
I *l* him or think I *l* him. „ I ii 152
Nay, I do *l* him.— „ I ii 155
She hath but blood enough to live, not *l*.— „ I ii 162
not like Aldwyth . . . For which I strangely *l* him. Should not England *L* Aldwyth, „ I ii 176
Art thou assured By this, that Harold *l's* but Edith? „ I ii 210
that I—That Harold *l's* me—yea, „ I ii 222
I can but *l* this noble, honest Harold. *William.* *L* him! why not? thine is a loving office, „ II ii 94
The Normans *l* thee not, nor thou the Normans, „ II ii 253
for my mother's sake I *l* your England, But for my father I *l* Normandy. „ II ii 269

Love (verb) (*continued*) Harold, if thou *l* thine Edith, ay. *Harold* II ii 622
'We have learnt to *l* him, let him a little longer „ III i 88
No, no, but Harold. I *l* him: he hath served me: „ III i 242
They *l* the white rose of virginity, „ III i 273
Son, there is one who *l's* thee: „ III i 289
Bless thou too That brother whom I *l* beyond the rest, „ III i 295
And let him pass unscathed; he *l's* me, Harold! „ III i 301
Care not for me who *l* thee. „ III ii 113
—but I *l* thee and thou me— „ III ii 180
and I *l* him now, for mine own father Was great, „ IV i 89
Canst thou *l* one Who did discrown thine husband, unqueen thee? Didst thou not *l* thine husband? „ IV i 192
women Cling to the conquer'd, if they *l*, the more; „ IV i 213
Canst thou *l* me, thou knowing where I *l*? „ IV i 226
Canst thou *l* one, who cannot *l* again? „ IV i 235
save for Norway, Who *l's* not thee but war. „ IV ii 24
because I *l* The husband of another! „ V i 648
I cannot *l* them, For they are Norman saints— „ V ii 8
Take them away, I do not *l* to see them. „ V ii 142
to the statesman Who serves and *l's* his king, and whom the king *L's* not as statesman, *Becket*, *Pro.* 78
I *l* thee and I know thee, I know thee, „ *Pro.* 95
Well, who *l's* wine *l's* woman. „ *Pro.* 108
whom I *l* indeed As a woman should be loved— „ *Pro.* 132
how should he *l* A woman, as a woman should be loved? „ *Pro.* 138
She is ignorant of all but that I *l* her. „ *Pro.* 185
and tho' I *l* him heartily, I can spy already „ *Pro.* 233
but thou—dost thou *l* this Chancellor, „ *Pro.* 438
How should a baron *l* a beggar on horseback, „ *Pro.* 443
she, whom the King *l's* indeed, is a power in the State. „ *Pro.* 482
for the Archbishop *l's* humbleness, „ I iv 208
I *l* them More than the garden flowers, „ II i 132
I *l* *them* too, Yes. „ II i 137
something I had to say—I *l* thee none the less— „ II i 207
—the goodly way of women Who *l*, for which I *l* them. „ II i 258
Yet you both *l* God. „ II ii 376
and make Our waning Eleanor all but *l* me! „ II ii 458
There is no woman that I *l* so well. „ III i 9
Of one we *l*. Nay, I would not be bold, „ III i 63
I do not *l* her. Must you go, my liege, „ III i 83
So that he loved me—and he *l's* me— „ III i 226
Wilt thou *l* me? *Geoffrey.* No; I only *l* mother. „ IV i 8
I *l* thy mother, my pretty boy. „ IV i 44
so, if you *l* him—Nay, if you *l* him, „ IV ii 92
there are those Who say you do not *l* him— „ IV ii 97
Come with me, love, And I will *l* thee . . . „ IV ii 156
if he *l* thee, Thy life is worth the wrestle „ IV ii 193
'None of such?' I *l* her none the more. „ IV ii 413
I am not so sure But that I *l* him still. „ IV ii 451
I think ye four have cause to *l* this Becket. „ V i 224
I do not *l* him, for he did his best To break the barons, „ V i 233
No man to *l* me, honour me, obey me! „ V i 239
The people *l* thee, father. „ V ii 120
And *l* him next after my lord his father. „ V ii 342
L her, do you? *The Cup* I i 127
I *l* you—for your love to the great Goddess. „ I ii 218
Camma for my bride—The people *l* her— „ I iii 153
And *l* thee and thou me, yet if Giovanna *The Falcon* 26
He *l's* me, and he knows I know he *l's* me! „ 245
You speak like love, and yet you *l* me not. „ 782
O Federigo, Federigo, I *l* you! „ 897
I will make Your brother *l* me. „ 912
I don't know why I sing that song; I don't *l* it. *Prom. of May* I 62
hallus a-fobbing ma off, tho' ye knaws I *l* ye. „ I 108
that should make you happy, if you *l* her! „ I 548
Oh, I *l* her so, I was afraid of her, „ I 550
Child, do you *l* me now? „ I 640
Then you should wish us both to *l* for ever. „ I 643
they that *l* do not believe that death Will part them. „ I 662
I cannot *l* you; nay, I think I never can be brought to *l* any man. „ II 77
not only *l* the country, But its inhabitants too; „ II 544
Well then, I must make her *L* Harold first, „ II 677

M

Madonna Come in, *M*, come in. *The Falcon* 176
you look as beautiful this morning as the very *M* „ 199
No, no, not quite, *M*, not yet, not yet. „ 392
This was penn'd, *M*, Close to the grating „ 440
I bear with him no longer. *Count.* No, *M* ! „ 886
Mad-woman O murderous *m-w* ! I pray you lift *The Cup* II 471
Magdalen (a character in "Queen Mary") Ah, *M*, sin is bold as well as dull. *Queen Mary* V ii 442
Magdalen (St. Mary) Thanks to the blessed *M*, whose day it is. *Becket* III iii 171
All praise to Heaven, and sweet St. *M* ! „ III iii 235
Maggot Foul *m's* crawling in a fester'd vice ! *Queen Mary* V v 161
Magistrate all the *m's*, all the nobles, and all the wealthy ; „ V iv 50
Magnificence I have heard That, thro' his late *m* of living *The Falcon* 227
No other heart Of such *m* in courtesy Beats— „ 723
Magpie Peace, *m* ! Give him the quarterstaff. *Foresters* IV 249
Mahound by *M*, I had sooner have been born a Mussulman— *Becket* II ii 144
No God but one, and *M* is his prophet. „ II ii 225
like *M's* coffin hung between heaven and earth— „ II ii 361
By *M* I could dine with Beelzebub ! *Foresters* IV 970
Maid says she will live And die true *m*— *Queen Mary* III vi 46
Make me full fain to live and die a *m*. „ V iii 98
little fair-hair'd Norman *m* Lived in my mother's house : *Becket* V ii 260
The *m* to her dairy came in from the cow, *Prom. of May* I 39
The *m* she loved the man. *Foresters* I i 9
The *m* a rose to the man. (repeat) *Foresters* I i 13, 106
The *m* her hand to the man. (repeat) „ I i 17, 93
the *m* a kiss to the man. (repeat) „ I i 21, 120
should have told us how the man first kissed the *m*. „ I i 124
if a man and a *m* care for one another, does it matter so much if the *m* give the first kiss ? „ I i 134
now thou hast given me the man's kiss, let me give thee the *m's*. „ I i 144
if a man and a *m* love one another, may the *m* give the first kiss ? „ I i 172
when they look at a *m* they blast her. „ I i 256
Then the *m* is not high-hearted enough. „ I i 258
Go now and ask the *m* to dance with thee, „ I ii 185
what *m* but would beware of John ? „ I ii 256
when I loved A *m* with all my heart to pass it down „ I ii 297
man and *m* be free To foil and spoil the tyrant „ II i 10
There are no *m's* like English *m's* „ II i 19
' This boy will never wed the *m* he loves, „ II ii 111
and another—worse !—An innocent *m*. „ III 388
—to this *m*, this Queen o' the woods. „ III 394
M ! *Friar.* Paramour ! *Friar.* Hell take her ! „ III 401
Air and word, my lady, are *m* and man. „ III 420
lips that never breathed Love's falsehood to true *m* „ IV 73
For so this *m* would wed our brother, „ IV 483
Maiden (adj.) You've but a dull life in this *m* court, I fear, my Lord ? *Queen Mary* I iii 114
Would not for all the stars and *m* moon „ V ii 455
whether from *m* fears Or reverential love for him I loved, *The Cup* II 196
Modest *m* lily abused, Queen. *Foresters* II ii 158
clothes itself In *m* flesh and blood, „ III 117
Live thou *m* ! Thou art more my wife so feeling, „ III 122
You heed not how you soil her *m* fame, „ IV 479
Maiden (s) (*See also* **Bower-maiden**) My pretty *m*, tell me, did you ever Sigh for a beard ? *Queen Mary* I v 607
my pretty *m*, A pretty man for such a pretty *m*. „ I v 612
Then, pretty *m*, you should know that whether „ I v 618
Peace, pretty *m*. I hear them stirring „ I v 627
have thy conscience White as a *m's* hand, *Harold* II ii 284
A *m* slowly moving on to music Among her *m's* to this Temple— *The Cup* I i 9
When first he meets his *m* in a bower. „ I iii 41
I am none of your delicate Norman *m's* *Foresters* I i 212
A *m* now Were ill-bested in these dark days „ II ii 44
and all your forest games As far as *m* might. „ III 86
when Our English *m's* are their prey, „ III 179
and scare lonely *m's* at the farmstead. „ III 200
Save for this *m* and thy brother Abbot, „ IV 632

Maidenhood He that can pluck the flower of *m* *Foresters* I ii 108
Who art the fairest flower of *m* „ I ii 123
Out upon all hard-hearted *m* ! „ IV 50
Maiden-white Make blush the *m-w* of our tall cliffs, *Harold* II ii 332
Maiden-wife O *m-w*, The oppression of our people *Foresters* III 108
Maid Marian (daughter of Sir Richard Lea) (*See also* **Marian**) She has gone, *M M* to her Robin— *Queen Mary* III v 156
this is *M M* Flying from John—disguised. *Men.* *M M* ? she ? *Foresters* II i 679
Stay with us here, sweet love, *M M*, „ II ii 15
and looks at once *M M*, „ III 119
M M, Queen o' the woods ! (repeat) *Foresters* III 357, 374, 376, 397, 399
M M. *Marian.* Yes, King Richard. *Foresters* IV 859
Maidstone The bells are ringing at *M*. *Queen Mary* II i 19
and your worship's name heard into *M* market, „ II i 63
Mail I wear beneath my dress A shirt of *m* : „ I v 146
And felt the sun of Antioch scald our *m*, *Becket* II ii 93
having lived For twenty days and nights in *m*, *Foresters* IV 124
Mail'd *M* in the perfect panoply of faith, *Becket* V ii 494
Maim when he springs And *m's* himself against the bars, *Queen Mary* V v 67
It frights the traitor more to *m* and blind. *Harold* II ii 503
Maim'd starved, *m*, flogg'd, flay'd, burn'd, *Queen Mary* II i 209
They have so *m* and murder'd all his face *Harold* V ii 76
And lamed and *m* to dislocation, *Becket* IV ii 266
Not caught, *m*, blinded him. *The Cup* I ii 271
Main (adj.) Madam, I loved according to the *m* purpose and intent of nature. *Becket, Pro.* 502
Like sudden night in the *m* glare of day. „ II i 57
That I am his *m* paramour, his sultana. „ IV ii 39
her *m* law Whereby she grows in beauty— *Prom. of May* I 281
Main (s) Calais ! Our one point on the *m*, *Queen Mary* I v 125
Had prosper'd in the *m*, but suddenly Jarr'd *Becket* I iii 381
Mainland gateway to the *m* over which Our flag *Queen Mary* V ii 260
Maintain we shall still *m* All former treaties „ I v 265
I trust I still *m* my courtesy ; *The Falcon* 294
Maintain'd *M*, and entertain'd us royally ! *Harold* II ii 159
Majestic Be somewhat less—*m* to your Queen. *Queen Mary* III vi 149
Majesty When will her *M* pass, sayst thou ? „ I i 2
Her *M* Hears you affect the Prince— „ I iv 81
A happy morning to your *M*. „ I v 244
maintain All former treaties with his *M*. „ I v 266
Follow their *Majesties*. „ III i 331
my wish Echoes your *M's*. *Pole.* It shall be so. „ III iii 93
Do make most humble suit unto your *Majesties*, „ III iii 119
Whereon we humbly pray your *Majesties*, „ III iii 143
Serve God and both your *Majesties*. „ III iii 159
My Lords, you cannot see her *M*. „ III vi 20
in all this, my Lord, her *M* Is flint of flint, „ III vi 37
Your *M* shall go to Dover with me, „ III vi 218
Then one day more to please her *M*. „ III vi 248
I am vastly grieved to leave your *M*. „ III vi 255
Long live your *M* ! Shall Alice sing you „ V ii 354
Your *M* has lived so pure a life, „ V v 72
Make (*See also* **Maäke**) *m* what noise you will with your tongues, „ I i 5
didn't the Parliament *m* her a bastard ? „ I i 16
Parliament can *m* every true-born man of us a bastard. Old Nokes, can't it *m* thee a bastard ? „ I i 27
so they can't *m* me a bastard. „ I i 47
if Parliament can *m* the Queen a bastard, why, it follows all the more that they can *m* thee one, „ I i 49
To *m* me headless. „ I ii 41
These beastly swine *m* such a grunting here, „ I iii 12
That *m's* for France. (repeat) „ I iii 89, 92, 94
His Highness *m's* his moves across the Channel, „ I iii 134
m your boast that after all She means to wed you. „ I iv 87
That you shall marry him, *m* him King belike. „ I iv 212
she means to *m* A farewell present to your Grace. „ I iv 244
M all tongues praise and all hearts beat for you. „ I v 117
To *m* the crown of Scotland one with ours, „ I v 287
Would *m* our England, France ; „ I v 297
I can *m* allowance for thee, „ I v 326
M no allowance for the naked truth. „ I v 328
Pope would have you *m* them render these ; „ I v 403

Make (*continued*) Your Highness is all trembling. *Mary.* *M* way. *Queen Mary* I v 595
Look ; can you *m* it English ? „ II i 127
m Your city loyal, and be the mightiest man „ II ii 18
To *m* free spoil and havock of your goods. „ II ii 186
Hear us now *m* oath To raise your Highness „ II ii 288
the half sight which *m's* her look so stern, „ II ii 322
Courage, sir, *That m's* a man or woman „ II ii 329
man should *m* the hour, not this the man ; „ II ii 365
M's enemies for himself and for his king ; „ II ii 399
Shall we *m* Those that we come to serve our sharpest foes ? „ II iii 76
you'll *m* the White Tower a black 'un „ II iii 100
cloth of gold, Could *m* it so. „ III i 55
I'd *m* a move myself to hinder that : „ III i 127
You would but *m* us weaker, Thomas Stafford. „ III i 130
They *m* amends for the tails. „ III i 227
M themselves drunk and mad, „ III i 282
Will stir the living tongue and *m* the cry. „ III i 354
She could not *m* it white— „ III i 424
and *m* us A Spanish province ; „ III i 465
Seem'd as a happy miracle to *m* glide— „ III ii 29
I return As Peter, but to bless thee : *m* me well.' „ III ii 56
M's me his mouth of holy greeting. „ III ii 80
That *m* me shamed and tongue-tied in my love. „ III ii 162
news to *m* Both of us happy—ay, the Kingdom too. „ III ii 187
Do *m* most humble suit unto your Majesties, „ III iii 118
because to persecute *M's* a faith hated, „ III iv 116
And *m* it look more seemly. „ III iv 152
m's the waverer pass Into more settled hatred „ III iv 157
These fields are only green, they *m* me gape. „ III v 7
One of those wicked wilfuls that men *m*, „ III v 76
And *m* a morning outcry in the yard ; „ III v 158
narrowness of the cage That *m's* the captive testy ; „ III v 208
m ready for the journey. „ III v 277
Than any sea could *m* me passing hence, „ III vi 87
We *m* our humble prayer unto your Grace „ IV i 43
His learning *m's* his burning the more just. „ IV i 159
M out the writ to-night. „ IV i 195
No man can *m* his Maker— „ IV ii 58
And *m* you simple Cranmer once again. „ IV ii 129
and *m's* The fire seem even crueller than it is. „ IV ii 232
I wish some thunderbolt Would *m* this Cole a cinder, „ IV iii 11
M us despise it at odd hours, my Lord. „ IV iii 386
I cum behind tha, gall, and couldn't *m* tha hear. „ IV iii 466
never burn out the hypocrisy that *m's* the water in her. „ IV iii 525
'*M* short ! *m* short !' and so they lit the wood. „ IV iii 606
You *m* your wars upon him down in Italy :— „ V i 141
What *m's* thy favour like the bloodless head „ V ii 19
wines, That ever *m* him fierier. „ V ii 95
it was thought we two Might *m* one flesh, „ V ii 137
and *m* Musters in all the counties ; „ V ii 271
Heretic and rebel Point at me and *m* merry. „ V ii 318
Should *m* the mightiest empire earth has known. „ V iii 70
M me full fain to live and die a maid. „ V iii 98
And break your paces in, and *m* you tame ; „ V iii 121
and *m* Down for their heads to heaven ! „ V iv 7
Dead or alive you cannot *m* him happy. „ V v 71
I trust that God will *m* you happy yet. „ V v 76
if that May *m* your Grace forget yourself „ V v 81
—we will *m* England great. „ V v 281
for heaven's credit *M's* it on earth : *Harold* I i 142
m me not fool ! Nor *m* the King a fool, who made me Earl ! *Harold.* No, Tostig—lest I *m* myself a fool Who made the King who made thee, *m* thee Earl. „ I i 288
M not thou The nothing something. „ I i 362
the true *must* Shall *m* her strike as Power : „ I i 369
would but shame me, Rather than *m* me vain. „ I ii 117
Follow my lead, and I will *m* thee earl. „ I ii 217
Count-crab will *m* his nippers meet in thine heart ; „ II i 76
To *m* allowance for their rougher fashions, „ II ii 8
To marry and have no husband *M's* the wife fool. „ II ii 310
M blush the maiden-white of our tall cliffs, „ II ii 332

Make (*continued*) may he not *m* A league with William, *Harold* II ii 460
M thou not mention that I spake with thee. „ II ii 483
And I will *m* thee my great Earl of Earls, „ II ii 629
And *m's* believe that he believes my word— „ II ii 668
would *m* the hard earth rive To the very Devil's horns, „ II ii 739
m your ever-jarring Earldoms move To music „ II ii 760
If thou canst *m* a wholesome use of these „ III i 20
as the libertine repents who cannot *M* done undone, „ III i 33
Not mean To *m* our England Norman. „ III i 250
and those Who *m* thy good their own— „ III i 330
which will *m* My kingship kinglier to me „ III ii 43
To *m* all England one, to close all feuds, „ IV i 141
Thou hast but cared to *m* thyself a king— „ IV ii 74
M not our Morcar sullen : it is not wise. „ IV iii 102
I am weary—go : *m* me not wroth with thee ! „ V i 31
there *m* strength to breast Whatever chance, „ V i 126
m their wall of shields Firm as thy cliffs, „ V i 478
m his battle-axe keen As thine own sharp-dividing justice, „ V i 562
M thou one man as three to roll them down ! „ V i 577
M them again one people—Norman, English ; „ V ii 188
A more awful one. *M me* Archbishop ! *Becket, Pro.* 289
m her as hateful to herself and to the King, „ *Pro.* 526
M an Archbishop of a soldier ? „ I i 41
we will *m* her whole ; Not one rood lost. „ I i 163
M it so hard to save a moth from the fire ? „ I i 283
if he follow thee, *M* him thy prisoner. „ I i 332
I will *m* thee hateful to thy King. „ I ii 91
Ye *m* this clashing for no love o' the customs „ I iii 136
I had meant to *m* him all but king. „ I iii 464
M not thy King a traitorous murderer. „ I iii 500
m it clear Under what Prince I fight. „ I iii 544
Serve my best friend and *m* him my worst foe ; „ I iii 568
m my cry to the Pope, By whom I will be judged ; „ I iii 723
he *m's* moan that all be a-getting cold. *Becket.* And I *m* my moan along with him. „ I iv 61
We can *m* a black sin white. „ I iv 169
let him *m* it his own, let him reign in it— „ II i 17
who cares not for the word, *M's* 'care not'— „ II i 118
m's after it too To find it. „ II i 321
mother Would *m* him play his kingship against mine. „ II ii 11
So we *m* our peace with him. „ II ii 62
we *m* the time, we keep the time, ay, and we serve the time ; „ II ii 367
and *m* Our waning Eleanor all but love me ! „ II ii 457
and to *m* me a woman of the world, „ III i 116
they say, she *m's* songs, and that's against her, for I never knew an honest woman that could *m* songs, „ III i 181
tho' you *m* your butt too big, you overshoot it. „ III iii 121
keep the figure moist and *m* it hold water, „ III iii 166
I *m* thee full amends. „ III iii 219
How, do you *m* me a traitor ? „ III iii 240
Doth not the *fewness* of anything *m* the fulness of it in estimation ? „ III iii 302
she says she can *m* you sleep o' nights. „ IV ii 19
Give her to me to *m* my honeymoon. „ IV ii 142
m Thy body loathsome even to thy child ; „ IV ii 171
baseness as would *m* me Most worthy of it : „ IV ii 235
And *m* thee a world's horror. „ IV ii 288
But thou art like enough to *m* him thine. „ V i 132
m me not a woman, John of Salisbury, Nor *m* me traitor „ V ii 147
you would *m* his coronation void By cursing „ V ii 329
He *m's* a King a traitor, me a liar. „ V ii 415
They seek—you *m*—occasion for your death. „ V ii 558
Ay, *m* him prisoner, do not harm the man. „ V iii 145
which well May *m* you lose yourself, *The Cup* I i 149
I would be Happy, and *m* all others happy so „ I iii 29
And I will *m* Galatia prosperous too, „ I iii 169
You will not easily *m* me credit that. „ II 25
—*m* me happy in my marriage ! „ II 274
To *m* my marriage prosper to my wish ! „ II 308
See first I *m* libation to the Goddess, „ II 377
Thou hast drunk deep enough to *m* me happy. „ II 425
Will hardly help to *m* him sane again. *The Falcon* 83
and tell her all about it and *m* her happy ? „ 183

Make (*continued*) to give me his falcon, And that will *m* me well.' *The Falcon* 243
I ha' heärd 'im a-gawin' on 'ud *m* your 'air—God bless it !—stan' on end. *Prom. of May* I 134
you *m* The May and morning still more beautiful, „ I 572
When the great Democracy *M's* a new world— „ I 672
and *m* them happy in the long barn, „ I 791
turn back at times, and *m* Courtesy to custom ? „ II 634
I could *m* his age A comfort to him— „ II 660
Well then, I must *m* her Love Harold first, „ II 676
m herself anything he wishes her to be ? „ III 305
I couldn't *m* it out. What was it ? „ III 324
I mounted upon the parapet—— *Dora.* You *m* me shudder ! „ III 373
then what is it That *m's* you talk so dolefully ? „ III 572
I doubt not I can *m* you happy. *Dora.* You *m* me Happy already. „ III 641
M her happy, then, and I forgive you. „ III 666
I wish'd, I hoped To *m*, to *m*—— *Dora. What* did you hope to *m* ? *Harold.* 'Twere best to *m* an end of my lost life. O Dora, Dora ! *Dora. What* did you hope to *m* ? *Harold. M, m* ! „ III 783
I keep a good heart and *m* the most of it, *Foresters* I i 29
What *m's* thee so down in the mouth ? „ I ii 42
My Lady Marian you can *m* it so If you will deign „ I ii 131
I promise thee to *m* this Marian thine. „ I ii 183
We *m* but one hour's buzz, „ I ii 277
m us merry Because a year of it is gone ? „ I iii 14
Where law lies dead, we *m* ourselves the law. „ II i 91
I came To eat him up and *m* an end of him. „ II i 125
To *m* this Sherwood Eden o'er again, „ II i 168
M for the cottage then ! „ II i 210
and *m* a ghostly wail ever and anon to scare 'em. „ II i 215
let me go to *m* the mound : „ II i 312
but *m* haste then, and be silent in the wood. „ II i 364
Besides, tho' Friar Tuck might *m* us one, „ II ii 88
What *m's* you seem so cold to Robin, lady ? *Marian.* What *m's* thee think I seem so cold to Robin ? „ III 1
I wait till Little John *m's* up to *me.* „ III 17
so you would *m* it two I should be grateful. „ III 194
come between me and my Kate and *m* us one again. „ III 423
and can *m* Five quarts pass into a thimble. „ IV 282
M at him, all of you, a traitor coming „ IV 780
m me The monkey that should roast „ IV 804
Maker (God) No man can make his *M*— *Queen Mary* IV ii 58
Maker *See* **Verse-maker**
Mak'st Thou *m* me much ashamed „ III iv 304
Making (part.) (*See also* **A-makin', Maäkin'**) *M* libation to the Goddess. *The Cup* II 364
m us feel guilty Of her own faults. *Prom. of May* II 269
Making (s) (*See also* **Bastard-making, Sonnet-making**)
Either in *m* laws and ordinances *Queen Mary* III iii 130
we be not bound by the king's voice In *m* of a king, yet the king's voice Is much toward his *m.* *Harold* III i 237
spirit of the twelve Apostles enter'd Into thy *m.* *Becket* I i 51
the *m* of your butter, and the managing of your poultry ? *Prom. of May* II 93
Malapert as to the young crownling himself, he looked so *m* in the eyes, *Becket* III iii 109
Male it was hoped Your Highness was once more in happy state To give him an heir *m.* *Queen Mary* V ii 573
Malet Come *M*, let us hear ! *Harold* II ii 211
M, thy mother was an Englishwoman ; „ II ii 264
How, *M*, if they be not honourable ! „ II ii 278
I should be there, *M*, I should be there ! „ II ii 293
Ill news for guests, ha, *M* ! „ II ii 302
M, I vow to build a church to God „ V ii 137
Pluck the dead woman off the dead man, *M* ! „ V ii 145
Malice he wrought it ignorantly, And not from any *m.* *Queen Mary* III i 278
Wherewith they plotted in their treasonous *m*, „ III iv 5
from the squint Of lust and glare of *m.* *Becket* I i 313
Twice did thy *m* and thy calumnies Exile me „ I iii 42
Malign For whether men *m* thy name, or no, *The Cup* I iii 84
Malignant His face was not *m*, and he said „ I ii 451
Malign'd I am sure of being every way *m.* *The Cup* I ii 241
I am much *m.* I thought to serve Galatia. „ I ii 323
and he said That men *m* him. „ I ii 452
Malignity Brook for an hour such brute *m* ? *Queen Mary* IV iii 544
War, waste, plague, famine, all *malignities.* *Harold* I i 466
Malvoisie (a malmsey wine) I marvel is it sack or *M* ? *Foresters* III 332
The king's good health in ale and *M.* „ IV 969
Man (*See also* **Farming-men, Goodman, Man-in-arms, Men-at-arms**), That was after, *m* ; that was after. *Queen Mary* I i 19
Parliament can make every true-born *m* of us a bastard „ I i 27
I was born true *m* at five in the forenoon „ I i 45
was born of a true *m* and a ring'd wife, „ I i 54
thinkest thou that anyone Suspected thee to be my *m* ? „ I iii 176
wish before the word Is *m's* good Fairy— „ I iv 240
Who love that *men* should smile upon you, „ I iv 274
Men would murder me, „ I v 155
He is every way a lesser *m* than Charles ; „ I v 330
You cannot Learn a *m's* nature from his natural foe. „ I v 340
And those hard *men* brake into woman-tears, „ I v 564
A pretty *m* for such a pretty maiden. *Alice.* My Lord of Devon is a pretty *m.* „ I v 613
no old news that all *men* hate it. „ II i 17
ten thousand *men* on Penenden Heath all calling „ II i 61
your worship the first *m* in Kent and Christendom, „ II i 64
Men of Kent ; England of England ; „ II i 157
If this *m* marry our Queen, „ II i 170
the red *m*, that good helpless creature, „ II i 208
I have striven in vain to raise a *m* for her. „ II ii 17
and be the mightiest *m* This day in England. „ II ii 19
had gone over to him With all his *men*, „ II ii 29
To raise your Highness thirty thousand *men*, „ II ii 291
As if to win the *m* by flattering him. „ II ii 312
If not, there's no *m* safe. *White.* Yes, Thomas White. I am safe enough ; no *m* need flatter me. *Second Alderman.* Nay, no *m* need ; but did you mark our Queen ? „ II ii 315
That makes or *m* or woman look their goodliest. „ II ii 329
The *m* had children, and he whined for those. Methinks most *men* are but poor-hearted, „ II ii 335
all *men* cry, She is queenly, she is goodly. „ II ii 343
Who knows ? the *m* is proven by the hour. *White.* The *m* should make the hour, not this the *m* ; „ II ii 363
gather your *men*—Myself must bustle. „ II ii 373
The statesman that shall jeer and fleer at *men*, „ II ii 398
if he jeer not seeing the true *m* Behind his folly, he is thrice the fool ; And if he see the *m* and still will jeer, „ II ii 400
There, any *m* can read that. „ II iii 68
Stafford, I am a sad *m* and a serious. „ III i 41
We have no *men* among us. „ III i 140
No *men* ? Did not Lord Suffolk die like a true *m* ? Is not Lord William Howard a true *m* ? „ III i 163
And I, by God, believe myself a *m.* Ay, even in the church there is a *m*—Cranmer. Fly would he not when all *men* bad him fly. „ III i 168
There's a brave *m*, if any. „ III i 175
Thou art one of Wyatt's *men* ? *Man.* No, my Lord, no. „ III i 244
The *m* shall paint a pair of gloves. „ III i 274
(Knowing the *m*) he wrought it ignorantly, „ III i 276
I say There is no *m*—there was one woman with us— „ III i 337
dazzled *men* and deafen'd by some bright „ III i 451
I am an old *m* wearied with my journey, „ III ii 127
You were the one sole *m* in either house Who stood upright „ III iii 252
I say you were the one sole *m* who stood. *Bagenhall.* I am the one sole *m* in either house, „ III iii 264
Well, you one *m*, because you stood upright, „ III iii 268
If any *m* in any way would be The one *m*, „ III iii 274
when *men* are tost On tides of strange opinion, „ III iv 118
Lest *men* accuse you of indifference To all faiths, „ III iv 223
Smiles that burn *men.* „ III iv 404
Men now are bow'd and old, the doctors tell you, „ III iv 408
One of those wicked wilfuls that *men* make, „ III v 75

Man (*continued*) Are you so small a *m*? *Queen Mary* III v 192
all boots were ever made Since *m* went barefoot. „ III v 198
fierce resolve and fixt heart-hate in *men* „ III vi 32
bland And affable to *men* of all estates, „ III vi 81
And every soul of *m* that breathes therein. „ III vi 107
Your father was a *m* Of such colossal kinghood, „ IV i 100
Your father had a will that beat *men* down; Your father had a brain that beat *men* down— „ IV i 108
No *m* can make his Maker— „ IV ii 58
At your trial Never stood up a bolder *m* than you; „ IV ii 122
I must obey the Queen and Council, *m*. „ IV ii 164
This hard coarse *m* of old hath crouch'd to me „ IV ii 169
Repeat your recantation in the ears Of all *men*, „ IV ii 194
It is expedient for one *m* to die, „ IV iii 17
Those of the wrong side will despise the *m*, „ IV iii 25
That any *m* so writing, preaching so, „ IV iii 47
Other reasons There be for this *m's* ending, „ IV iii 54
Take therefore, all, example by this *m*, „ IV iii 60
There stands a *m*, once of so high degree, „ IV iii 68
doubt The *m's* conversion and remorse of heart, „ IV iii 108
Most miserable sinner, wretched *m*. „ IV iii 123
when thou becamest *M* in the Flesh, „ IV iii 141
But that Thy name by *m* be glorified, And Thy most blessed Son's, who died for *m*. Good people, every *m* at time of death Would fain set forth „ IV iii 153
After the vanish'd voice, and speak to *men*. „ IV iii 165
yet what hatred Christian *men* Bear to each other, „ IV iii 183
Hurt no *m* more Than you would harm „ IV iii 187
'How hard it is For the rich *m* to enter into Heaven;' Let all rich *men* remember that hard word. „ IV iii 205
Dissemble not; play the plain Christian *m*. „ IV iii 268
I have been a *m* loved plainness all my life; „ IV iii 270
And watch a good *m* burn. „ IV iii 293
the *m* Hurls his soil'd life against the pikes and dies. „ IV iii 310
howsoever hero-like the *m* Dies in the fire, „ IV iii 324
and all *men* Regarding her? „ IV iii 378
My lord, the world is like a drunken *m*, „ IV iii 393
men Have hardly known what to believe, „ IV iii 404
The kindliest *m* I ever knew; „ IV iii 421
ez thou hast wi' thy owld *m*. *Tib.* Ay, Joan, and my owld *m* wur up and awaay „ IV iii 487
Thou's thy way wi' *m* and beast, Tib. „ IV iii 498
till his *m* cum in post vro' here, „ IV iii 510
I loved the *m*, and needs must moan for him; „ IV iii 635
in Guisnes Are scarce two hundred *men*, „ V i 5
I am not certain but that Philibert Shall be the *m*; „ V i 265
and mine own natural *m* (It was God's cause); „ V ii 103
and cleave unto each other As *m* and wife? „ V ii 139
Our altar is a mound of dead *men's* clay, „ V ii 162
love her less For such a dotage upon such a *m*. „ V ii 421
It is the low *m* thinks the woman low; „ V ii 439
throat of mine, Barer than I would wish a *m* to see it,— „ V ii 462
I will see no *m* hence for evermore, „ V ii 525
seen the true *men* of Christ lying famine-dead by scores, „ V iv 38
I was walking with the *m* I loved. „ V v 88
weak and meek old *m*, Seven-fold dishonour'd „ V v 132
Till all *men* have their Bible, rich and poor. „ V v 248
Not he the *m*—for in our windy world *Harold* I i 83
Our Tostig loves the hand and not the *m*. „ I i 157
Thou art the *m* to rule her! „ I i 223
I love the *m* but not his phantasies. „ I i 279
Thou art the quietest *m* in all the world— „ I i 312
Waits till the *m* let go. „ I i 329
Ye govern milder *men*. „ I i 339
As much as I can give thee, *m*; „ I i 480
a dead *m* Rose from behind the altar, „ I ii 78
saw the church all fill'd With dead *men* upright from their graves, and all The dead *men* made at thee to murder thee, „ I ii 83
Did not Heaven speak to *men* in dreams of old? „ I ii 94
fat dead deer For dead *men's* ghosts. „ I ii 104
while ye fish for *men* with your false fires, „ II i 30

Man (*continued*) Apostles; *they* were fishers of *men*, *Harold* II i 34
get himself wrecked on another *m's* land? „ II i 61
A *m* may hang gold bracelets on a bush, „ II i 87
Thou art a mighty *m* In thine own earldom! „ II i 92
my *men* Hold that the shipwreckt are accursed of God;— What hinders me to hold with mine own *men*? „ II i 99
The Christian manhood of the *m* who reigns! „ II i 105
I have commission'd thee to save the *m*: „ II ii 99
arm'd *men* Ever keep watch beside my chamber door, „ II ii 244
There is an arm'd *m* ever glides behind! „ II ii 247
The *m* that hath to foil a murderous aim „ II ii 417
Words are the *m*. „ II ii 419
And *men* are at their markets, in their fields, „ II ii 436
We have the *m* that rail'd against thy birth. „ II ii 485
Better methinks have slain the *m* at once! „ II ii 499
We have respect for *m's* immortal soul, „ II ii 500
scorn'd the *m*, Or lash'd his rascal back, „ II ii 506
A gentle, gracious, pure and saintly *m*! „ II ii 585
Thou art the mightiest voice in England, *m*, „ II ii 618
Let all *men* bear witness of our bond! „ II ii 698
Where they eat dead *men's* flesh, „ II ii 807
Of all the lies that ever *men* have lied, „ III i 99
That, were a *m* of state nakedly true, *Men* would but take him for the craftier liar. *Leofwin.* Be *men* less delicate than the Devil himself? „ III i 113
that lying And ruling *men* are fatal twins „ III i 127
and holy *men* That shall be born hereafter. „ III i 209
Alas! poor *m*, *His* promise brought it on me. „ III i 337
cries, and clashes, and the groans of *men*; „ III i 376
Our living passion for a dead *m's* dream; „ III ii 60
The Lord was God and came as *m*—the Pope Is *m* and comes as God.— „ III ii 173
What would ye, *men*? „ IV i 30
Had in him kingly thoughts—a king of *men*, „ IV i 84
plots against him Had madden'd tamer *men*. „ IV i 112
Old *m*, Harold Hates nothing; „ IV i 128
Morcar, collect thy *men*; Edwin, my friend— „ IV i 256
No *m* would strike with Tostig, save for Norway. „ IV ii 20
Never shall any *m* say that I that Tostig „ IV ii 66
were *m's* to have held The battle-axe by thee! „ IV iii 12
Every *m* about his king Fought like a king; the king like his own *m*, „ IV iii 56
Sound sleep to the *m* Here by dead Norway „ IV iii 121
A thousand ships—a hundred thousand *men*— „ IV iii 195
The *men* that guarded England to the South „ IV iii 209
selfless *m* Is worth a world of tonguesters. „ V i 81
Waltham, my foundation For *men* who serve the neighbour, „ V i 98
What did the dead *m* call it—Sanguelac, „ V i 184
second-sighted *m* That scared the dying conscience „ V i 210
What nobler? *men* must die. „ V i 270
I have done no *m* wrong. „ V i 272
That mortal *men* should bear their earthly heats „ V i 283
Make thou one *m* as three to roll them down! „ V i 577
There is no *m* can swear to him. „ V ii 78
When all *men* counted Harold would be king, „ V ii 132
Pluck the dead woman off the dead *m*, Malet! „ V ii 144
have I fought *men* Like Harold and his brethren, „ V ii 178
Every *m* about his king Fell where he stood. „ V ii 181
we must have a mightier *m* than he For his successor. *Becket*, *Pro.* 7
No *m* without my leave shall excommunicate „ *Pro.* 30
No *m* without my leave shall cross the seas „ *Pro.* 34
Will not thy body rebel, *m*, if thou flatter it? „ *Pro.* 102
Men are God's trees, and women are God's flowers; „ *Pro.* 111
if a *m* Wastes himself among women, „ *Pro.* 136
A *m* of this world and the next to boot. „ *Pro.* 259
Thou art the *m* to fill out the Church robe; „ *Pro.* 262
Thou angerest me, *m*: I do not jest. „ *Pro.* 299
old *men* must die, or the world would grow mouldy, „ *Pro.* 408
dead *m's* dying wish should be of weight. „ *Pro.* 422
as brave a soldier as Henry and a goodlier *m*: „ *Pro.* 437
I can see further into a *m* than our hot-headed Henry, „ *Pro.* 463
would she were but his paramour, for *men* tire of their fancies; „ *Pro.* 479

Man (*continued*) Together more than mortal *m* can bear. *Becket* I i 24
That I am not the *m* to be your Primate, „ I i 38
For Gilbert Foliot held himself the *m*. *Becket*. Am I the *m*? My mother, ere she bore me, „ I i 43
good old *m* would sometimes have his jest— „ I i 61
Am I the *m*? That rang Within my head „ I i 70
Am *I* the *m*? And the Lord answer'd me, 'Thou art the *m*, and all the more the *m*.' (repeat) „ I i 82, 98
Thou art the *m*—be thou A mightier Anselm. „ I i 132
I do believe thee, then. I am the *m*. „ I i 136
Back *m*! *Fitzurse*. Then tell me who and what she is. „ I i 207
Back, *m*, I tell thee! „ I i 218
'Fore God, I am a mightier *m* than thou. „ I i 223
Herbert, take out a score of armed *men* „ I i 328
my *men* will guard you to the gates. „ I i 402
the *m* shall seal, Or I will seal his doom. „ I iii 330
bounden by my coronation oath To do *men* justice. „ I iii 397
a hundred ghastly murders done By *men*, „ I iii 408
If ever *m* by bonds of gratefulness— „ I iii 435
Deal gently with the young *m* Absalom. „ I iii 757
To speak without stammering and like a free *m*? „ I iv 8
When thieves fall out, honest *men*— „ I iv 114
When honest *men* fall out, thieves— „ I iv 118
Lord hath set his mark upon him that no *m* should murder him. „ I iv 192
The *m* shall feel that I can strike him yet. „ II i 78
a perilous game For *men* to play with God. „ II ii 71
Out upon thee, *m*! Saving the Devil's honour, „ II ii 141
I am half-way down the slope—will no *m* stay me? „ II ii 149
fled from his own church by night, No *m* pursuing. „ II ii 158
seeing they were *men* Defective or excessive, „ II ii 212
Poor *m*, beside himself—not wise. „ II ii 235
I told the Pope what manner of *m* he was. „ II ii 253
Thy true King bad thee be A fisher of *men*; „ II ii 286
surrendering God's honour to the pleasure of a *m*. „ II ii 440
ever spread into the *m* Here in our silence? „ III i 22
Whither away, *m*? what are you flying from? „ III ii 18
a *m* passed in there to-day: I holla'd to him, „ III ii 24
and to read the faces of *men* at a great show. „ III iii 83
Foliot is the holier *m*, perhaps the better. „ III iii 92
Have I not promised, *m*, to send them back? „ III iii 190
when my voice Is martyr'd mute, and this *m* disappears, „ III iii 350
Come hither, *m*; stand there. „ IV ii 219
if he Had aught of *m*, or thou of woman; „ IV ii 232
My pleasure is to have a *m* about me. „ IV ii 430
Madam, I am as much *m* as the King „ IV ii 432
Thou as much *m*! No more of that; „ IV ii 452
No *m* to love me, honour me, obey me! „ V i 239
You are no King's *men*—you—you—you are Becket's *men*. „ V i 258
Will no *m* free me from this pestilent priest? *Eleanor*. *Are* ye king's *men*? I am king's woman, I. *Knights*. King's *men*! King's *men*! „ V i 262
a *m* may take good counsel Ev'n from his foe. „ V ii 2
there are *men* Of canker'd judgment everywhere— „ V ii 60
Did not a *m's* voice ring along the aisle, „ V ii 150
My lord, the city is full of armed *men*. „ V ii 188
M's help! but we, we have the Blessed Virgin „ V ii 219
she told us of arm'd *men* Here in the city. „ V ii 227
But these arm'd *men*—will you not hide yourself? „ V ii 247
drowning *m*, they say, remembers all The chances „ V ii 272
but these arm'd *men*—will *you* drown *yourself*? „ V ii 276
Reginald, all *men* know I loved the Prince. „ V ii 333
King commands you. We are all King's *men*. *Becket*. King's *men* at least should know „ V ii 385
I ask no leave of king, or mortal *m*, „ V ii 458
sworn Yourselves my *men* when I was Chancellor— „ V ii 502
On any *m's* advising but your own. „ V ii 551
Ay, monks, not *men*. „ V ii 602
These arm'd *men* in the city, these fierce faces— „ V iii 3
Those arm'd *men* in the cloister. „ V iii 49
Here, here, King's *men*! „ V iii 102
then you are a dead *m*; flee! „ V iii 126
Ay, make him prisoner, do not harm the *m*. „ V iii 146
Thou art my *m*, thou art my vassal. „ V iii 153

Man (*continued*) I hate the *m*! What filthy tools our Senate works with! *The Cup* I i 155
What would you with me, *m*? „ I i 193
were he living And grown to *m* and Sinnatus will'd it, „ I ii 151
My lord, the *men*! „ I ii 195
One of the *men* there knew him. „ I ii 341
Did he, *honest m*? „ I ii 376
and he said That *men* malign'd him. „ I ii 452
Or *m*, or woman, as traitors unto Rome. „ I iii 9
For whether *men* malign thy name, or no, „ I iii 84
drink too much, as *men* Have done on rafts of wreck— „ I iii 141
—having proof enough Against the *m*, „ I iii 159
that *m* from Synorix, who has been So oft to see the Priestess, „ II 9
Did not this *m* Speak well? „ II 91
A goodlier-looking *m* than Sinnatus. „ II 176
I would that every *m* made feast to-day „ II 225
or after slayest him As boy or *m*, „ II 281
Let be thy jokes and thy jerks, *m*! *The Falcon* 133
scorns The noblest-natured *m* alive, and I— „ 259
Why—no, *m*. Only see your cloth be clean. „ 419
he would marry me to the richest *m* In Florence; „ 748
'Better a *m* without riches, than riches without a *m*.' „ 751
A nobler breed of *men* and women. „ 755
Why, o' coorse, fur it be the owd *m's* birthdaäy. *Prom. of May* I 6
'er an' the owd *m* they fell a kissin' o' one another „ I 21
But he'll never be the same *m* again. *Dobson*. An' how d'ye find the owd *m* 'ere? „ I 70
The owd *m* be heighty to-daäy, beänt he? „ I 76
he cooms up, and he calls out among our oän *men*, „ I 140
the farming *men* 'ull hev their dinner i' the long barn, „ I 166
He's a Somersetshire *m*, and a very civil-spoken gentleman. „ I 206
all but proving *m* An automatic series of sensations, „ I 225
What can a *m*, then, live for but sensations, „ I 241
men of old would undergo Unpleasant for the sake of pleasant ones Hereafter, „ I 243
'What are we, says the blind old *m* in Lear? „ I 263
Then the owd *m* i' Lear should be shaämed of hissen, „ I 266
M only knows, the worse for him! „ I 275
Good murnin', neighbours, and the saäme to you, my *men*. „ I 318
Niver *m* 'ed better friends, and I will saäy niver master 'ed better *men*: „ I 322
thaw I says it mysen, niver *men* 'ed a better master—and I knaws what *men* be, „ I 327
theer be noän o' my *men*, thinks I to mysen, „ I 410
and *m* perceives that The lost gleam of an after-life „ I 501
Then the *m*, the woman, Following their best affinities, „ I 521
And when the *m*, The child of evolution, „ I 584
I seed how the owd *m* wur vext. „ II 27
an' ony o' Steer's *men*, an' ony o' my *men* „ II 34
you should be in the hayfield looking after your *men*; „ II 47
as long as the *m* sarved for 'is sweet'art i' Scriptur'. „ II 62
I would taäke the owd blind *m* to my oän fireside. „ II 74
I think I never can be brought to love any *m*. It seems to me that I hate *men*, ever since my sister left us. „ II 78
I thought Mr. Edgar the best of *men*, and he has proved himself the worst. „ II 86
Owd Steer gi'es nubbut cowd tea to *'is men*, and owd Dobson gi'es beer. „ II 224
if *m* be only A willy-nilly current of sensations— „ II 262
The ghosts of the dead passions of dead *men*; „ II 276
That beer be as good fur 'erses as *men*. „ II 316
When *m* has surely learnt at last that all „ II 330
How worn he looks, poor *m*! who is it, I wonder. „ II 391
Our *men* and boys would hoot him, stone him, „ II 425
the *m* himself, When hearing of that piteous death, „ II 498
Well, my *m*, it seems that you can read. „ II 709
for I am closely related to the dead *m's* family. „ II 715
whether thou be Hedgar, or Hedgar's business *m*, „ II 735
so ta'en up wi' leädin' the owd *m* about all the blessed murnin' „ III 3
'O *m*, forgive thy mortal foe, „ III 5
You are as good as a *m* in the hayfield. „ III 106
He's dead, *m*—dead; gone to his account— „ III 144
would you beat a *m* for his brother's fault? „ III 155

Manners and those bleak m thaw, Queen Mary III ii 161
like his cloak, his m want the nap And gloss of court; „ III v 69
Am I to change my m, Simon Renard, „ III vi 151
How beautiful His m are, and how unlike the farmer's! Prom. of May II 531
so that you do not copy his bad m? „ III 362
M be so corrupt, and these are the days of Prince John. Foresters I i 176
Manor since we would be lord of our own m, Becket II ii 20
They slew my stags in mine own m here, „ V ii 438
Man-Robin If my m-R were but a bird-Robin, Foresters III 39
Mansfield I have heard 'em in the market at M. „ III 407
Mantle Flung by the golden m of the cloud, „ II i 28
Many Thro' m voices crying right and left, Queen Mary I ii 48
The downfall of so m simple souls, „ I ii 54
for the two were fellow-prisoners So m years in yon accursed Tower— „ I iv 200
there were m wolves among you Who dragg'd the scatter'd limbs „ I v 399
For tho' we touch'd at m pirate ports, Foresters IV 983
Many-breasted The m-b mother Artemis Emboss'd upon it. The Cup II 340
Map (See also **Walter Map**) That M, and these new railers at the Church Becket I i 306
M scoffs at Rome. I all but hold with M. „ II ii 384
M, tho' you make your butt too big, you overshoot it. „ III iii 121
False figure, M would say. „ III iii 346
Mar as one That m's a cause with over-violence. „ IV ii 327
Marah this bitter world again—These wells of M. „ V ii 82
Marble (adj.) have you not mark'd Her eyes were ever on the m floor? The Cup II 19
Marble (s) Vein'd m—not a furrow yet— Becket II i 197
wine Ran down the m and lookt like blood, The Cup II 204
Iron will fuse, and m melt; Prom. of May II 505
This is mere m. Old hag, how should thy one tooth Foresters II i 275
March may not those, who m Before their age, Prom. of May II 632
Marchpane You gentles that live upo' manchet-bread and m, Foresters II i 282
Margery I hear M: I'll go play with her. Becket III i 274
M? no, that's a finer thing there. How it glitters! „ IV i 1
I sent this M, and she comes not back; „ IV ii 3
You said you couldn't trust M, „ IV ii 16
Maria Ave M, gratia plena, Benedicta tu in mulieribus. Queen Mary III ii 1
Marian (daughter of Sir Richard Lea) (See also **Maid Marian**)
These roses for my Lady M; Foresters I i 2
Sir Richard and my Lady M fare wellnigh as sparely as their people. „ I i 30
Lady M holds her nose when she steps across it. „ I i 83
M! Marian. Father! „ I i 179
Lady M, your woman so flustered me that I forgot „ I i 295
My Lady M you can make it so If you will deign „ I ii 130
Leaving your fair M alone here. „ I ii 154
I promise thee to make this M thine. „ I ii 183
Farewell, Sir Richard; farewell, sweet M. „ I ii 285
thou art the very woman who waits On my dear M. „ II i 103
She struck him, my brave M, struck the Prince, „ II i 134
Sheriff Would pay this cursed mortgage to his brother If M would marry him; „ II i 146
—if so the land may come To M, „ II i 149
Thou wilt not see My M more. „ II i 456
Give me some news of my sweet M. Where is she? Marian. Thy sweet M? I believe She came with me „ II i 481
O thou unworthy brother of my dear M! „ II i 539
O my dear M, Is it thou, is it thou? „ II i 597
O hold thy hand! this is our M. „ II ii 37
You shall wed your M. She is true, and you are true, „ II ii 193
honouring all womankind, and more especially my lady M, „ III 57
thou feel'st with me The ghost returns to M, „ III 115
M, thou and thy woman, Why, where is Kate? „ III 257
Honour to thee, brave M, and thy Kate. „ III 300
And they shall pledge thee, M, „ III 316
M! Marian. Speak not. „ IV 609
Sweet M, by the letter of the law It seems „ IV 638
would clutch Our pretty M for his paramour, „ IV 767
On those two here, Robin and M. „ IV 929
Kiss him, Sir Richard—kiss him, my sweet M. „ IV 1004

Marian (daughter of Sir Richard Lea) (continued) Embrace me, M, and thou, good Kate, Foresters IV 1031
these old oaks will murmur thee M along with Robin. „ IV 1095
Maries in his scared prayers Heaven and earth's M; Queen Mary II ii 88
Mark (an object) (See also **Sea-marks**) Wide of the m ev'n for a madman's dream. „ V iii 81
Mark (coin) the King demands three hundred m's, Becket I iii 627
the King demands seven hundred m's, „ I iii 635
the King demands five hundred m's, „ I iii 642
Some thirty—forty thousand silver m's. „ I iii 658
What! forty thousand m's! „ I iii 704
Forty thousand m's! forty thousand devils— „ I iv 90
ransomed for two thousand m's in gold. Foresters I i 65
Those two thousand m's lent me by the Abbot „ I i 264
I ran into my debt to the Abbot, Two thousand m's in gold. „ II i 464
These two have forty gold m's between them, Robin. „ III 203
Leave it with him and add a gold m thereto. „ III 211
Take his penny and leave him his gold m. „ III 218
I have one m in gold which a pious son of the Church „ III 280
Well, as he said, one m in gold. „ III 285
One m in gold. „ III 287
they have each ten m's in gold. „ III 292
take the twenty-seven m's to the captain's treasury. „ III 295
How much is it, Robin, for a knight? Robin. A m. „ IV 153
I had one m. Robin. What more. „ IV 165
Where he would pay us down his thousand m's. „ IV 442
Lest he should fail to pay these thousand m's „ IV 455
What more? one thousand m's, Or else the land. „ IV 474
Here be one thousand m's Out of our treasury „ IV 492
Ay, ay, but there is use, four hundred m's. Robin. There then, four hundred m's. „ IV 496
my tongue tript—five hundred m's for use. „ IV 499
Would buy me for a thousand m's in gold— „ IV 652
Much lighter than a thousand m's in gold; „ IV 657
Is weightier than a thousand m's in gold. „ IV 660
Thou art worth thy weight in all those m's of gold, „ IV 1024
Mark (impression) Lord hath set his m upon him that no man should murder him. Becket I iv 192
but he left the m of 'is foot i' the flower-bed; Prom. of May I 408
I measured his foot wi' the m i' the bed, but it wouldn't fit—seeäms to me the m wur maäde by a Lunnun boot. „ I 414
Mark (verb) I'll have one m it And bring it me. Queen Mary I v 372
no man need; but did you m our Queen? „ II ii 320
I was too sorry for the woman To m the dress. „ III i 59
said the Miserere Mei—But all in English, m you; „ III i 392
Nor m the sea-bird rouse himself and hover Harold II ii 334
hereafter Shall m out Vice from Virtue Prom. of May I 540
Mark'd Had m her for my brother Edward's bride; Queen Mary I v 289
have m the haughtiness of their nobles; „ II i 168
And m me ev'n as Cain, „ III ii 55
I stood near—M him— „ IV iii 618
Hast thou not m—come closer to mine ear— „ V i 225
if your Grace hath m it, so have I. Philip. Hast thou not likewise m Elizabeth, „ V i 231
That if your Grace hath m her, so have I. „ V i 239
m the sons of those Who made this Britain England, Harold IV iii 152
M how the war-axe swang, „ IV iii 156
M how the spear-head sprang, „ IV iii 158
This chart here m 'Her Bower,' Becket, Pro. 160
I m a group of lazars in the marketplace— „ I iv 80
m Her eyes were ever on the marble floor? The Cup II 18
Ay, ay, the line o' life is m enow; Foresters II i 352
They are all m men. „ III 290
What deer when I have m him ever yet Escaped mine arrow? „ IV 63
m if those two knaves from York be coming? „ IV 112
Market And your worship's name heard into Maidstone m, Queen Mary II i 63
men are at their m's, in their fields, Harold II ii 436
have won Their value again—beyond all m's— The Falcon 905
I have heard 'em in the m at Mansfield. Foresters III 407
Marketplace I marked a group of lazars in the m— Becket I iv 81
Marriage (adj.) While this same m question was being argued, Queen Mary II ii 37

Master (*continued*) You, *M* Hedgar, Harold, or whativer They calls ye, *Prom. of May* III 726
The lady loved the *m* well, *Foresters* I i 8
My *m*, Robin the Earl, is always a-telling us „ I i 94
I would hoist the drawbridge, like thy *m*. „ I i 319
I am a virgin, my *m's*, I am a virgin. *Much.* And a virgin, my *m's*, three yards about the waist „ I ii 67
My *m's*, welcome gallant Walter Lea. „ IV 1002
Strike up a stave, my *m's*, all is well. „ IV 1101
Master'd old affection *m* you, You falter'd into tears. *Becket* V ii 143
Mastiff (adj.) as a *m* dog May love a puppy cur for no more reason *Queen Mary* I iv 194
Mastiff (s) Our savage *m*, That all but kill'd the beggar, *Prom. of May* I 558
Match (an equal) Thou and thy woman are a *m* for three friars. *Foresters* III 262
Match (marriage) But is Don Carlos such a goodly *m*? *Queen Mary* V iii 86
That was, my lord, a *m* of policy. *Harold* IV i 199
thy *m* shall follow mine. *Foresters* IV 1044
Match (verb) If such a one as you should *m* with Spain, *Queen Mary* V iii 66
Match'd You do misname me, *m* with any such, *Becket* IV ii 128
and *m* with my Harold is like a hedge thistle by a garden rose. *Prom. of May* III 175
Mate (s) (*See also* **Co-mate, Määte**) News, *m's*! a miracle, a miracle! *Queen Mary* III ii 209
Mad for thy *m*, passionate nightingale . . . *Harold* I ii 1
They are not so true, They change their *m's*. „ III ii 105
he frown'd 'No *m* for her, if it should come to that'— *Becket* III i 259
I would thou hadst a *m*! *The Falcon* 17
Mate (verb) Let York bear his to *m* with Canterbury. *Becket* I iii 512
Not half *her* hand—no hand to *m* with *her*, „ II i 190
As *m* with one that holds no love is pure, *Foresters* IV 711
Mated *See* **Määted**
Mater Salva patriam, Sancta *M*. *Harold* V i 471
Matilda (or Maud, daughter of Henry I.) So did *M*, the King's mother. *Becket* I iii 152
Matter (s) stir not yet This *m* of the Church lands. *Queen Mary* I v 409
I scarce have heart to mingle in this *m*, „ II ii 114
These are forgiven—*m's* of the past— „ III iii 190
might it not be policy in some *m* Of small importance „ III vi 167
And if you be not secret in this *m*, „ V i 272
That were too small a *m* for a comet! *Harold* I i 470
No *m*! *Aldwyth.* How no *m*, Harold slain?— „ V ii 17
No *m*! *Aldwyth.* Not help me, „ V ii 23
my mind was set upon other *m's*. *Eleanor.* What *m's*? State *m's*? love *m's*? *Becket, Pro.* 318
and the *m* in the metre. „ *Pro.* 384
that secret *m* which would heat the King against thee. „ *Pro.* 487
And on a *m* wholly spiritual. „ I iii 85
You have had the better of us In secular *m's*. „ II ii 81
I have been more for the King than the Church in this *m*— „ III iii 66
it was but the sacrifice of a kingdom to his son, a smaller *m*; „ III iii 107
This is no secret, but a public *m*. „ V ii 320
No *m*! see your cloth be white as snow! *The Falcon* 498
A moment for some *m* of no moment! *Foresters* II i 474
Matter (verb) No, no; what *m's*? Forlorn I am, *Queen Mary* V ii 237
What *m's* how I look? *Harold* V i 394
That doth not *m* either. „ V ii 62
What *m's*? Royal—I mean to leave the royalty *Becket* II i 106
That *m's* not. Take thou this cup and leave it *The Cup* I i 66
Savage, is he? What *m's*? *Prom. of May* I 563
Maurice (*See also* **Maurice Berkeley**) told Sir *M* there was one Cognisant of this, *Queen Mary* II iv 99
Maurice Berkeley there by Sir *M B* Was taken prisoner. „ II iv 94
Mavis Hawk, buzzard, jay, the *m* and the merle, *Foresters* I iii 115
May Ay, for an hour in *M*. But court is always *M*, buds out in masques, *Queen Mary* III v 10
which a breeze of *M* Took ever and anon, *The Cup* I ii 406
Richer than all the wide world-wealth of *M*, *The Falcon* 467
O joy for the promise of *M*, of *M*, O joy for the promise of *M*. (repeat) *Prom. of May* I 43, 723

May (*continued*) O grief for the promise of *M*, of *M*, O grief for the promise of *M*. (repeat) *Prom. of May* I 59, 750
most beautiful *M* we have had for many years! „ I 567
Is the most beautiful morning of this *M*. „ I 570
you make The *M* and morning still more beautiful, You, the most beautiful blossom of the *M*. „ I 573
So lovely in the promise of her *M*, „ III 753
Maybe *See* **Mebbe**
May-morning and kiss me This beautiful *M-m*. *Prom. of May* I 565
Mayn't and she *m* be so fur out theer. „ I 181
Mayor All hangs on her address, And upon you, Lord *M*. *Queen Mary* II ii 56
I, the Lord *M*, and these our companies And guilds „ II ii 127
I, Lord *M* Of London, and our guilds and companies. „ II ii 139
tho' my Lord *M* here, By his own rule, „ II ii 345
May-time It was *M-t*, And I was walking „ V v 87
or a stump-tailed ox in *M-t*, *Foresters* II i 435
Maze This labyrinthine brickwork *m* in *m*, *Becket, Pro.* 166
Mazed *See* **Määzed**
Meadow (*See also* **Midder, Mountain-meadow**) there stole into the city a breath Full of the *m's*, *Becket* I i 263
With other beauties on a mountain *m*, *The Falcon* 352
I have lost a cow from my *m*. *Foresters* II i 326
Meadowsweet Forget-me-not, *m*, willow-herb. *Prom. of May* II 299
Meal (ground corn) so dusted his back with the *m* in his sack, *Becket* I iv 174
M enough, meat enough, well fed; *The Falcon* 165
Meal (repast) make Thy slender *m* out of those scraps and shreds „ 146
Mean That's a hard word, legitimate; what does it *m*? *Second Citizen.* It *m's* a bastard. *Third Citizen.* Nay, it *m's* true-born. *Queen Mary* I i 12
I *m* the Lady Elizabeth. „ I i 74
boast that after all She *m's* to wed you. „ I iv 89
she *m's* to counsel your withdrawing To Ashridge, „ I iv 224
she *m's* to make A farewell present to your Grace. „ I iv 243
they *m* to pardon me. „ IV ii 50
I *m* not like to live. „ V i 245
Do you *m* to drive me mad? „ V ii 200
Gamel, son of Orm, What thinkest thou this *m's*? (repeat) *Harold* I i 21, 464
m The doom of England and the wrath of Heaven? „ I i 45
And cannot answer sanely . . . What it *m's*? „ I i 89
It *m's* the fall of Tostig from his earldom. „ I i 468
It *m's* the lifting of the house of Alfgar. „ I i 472
What did he *m*? „ II ii 223
He did not *m* to keep his vow. *Harold.* Not *m* To make our England Norman. „ III i 248
Morcar! Edwin! What do they *m*? „ IV i 134
Look you, we never *m* to part again. „ V ii 80
I have heard him say He *m's* no more; *Becket* I iii 193
sworn upon his side, And ever *m* to do it. „ II ii 466
What is it you *m*? *Margery.* I *m* your goodman, „ III i 157
I *m* her whom you call—fancy— „ III i 201
Meän'd (meant) I *m* they be as blue as violets. *Prom. of May* I 103
Meaner Then left him for the *m*! thee!— *Harold* IV ii 71
Meanest Ev'n to the least and *m* of my own, *Becket* II ii 181
Meaning might chance—perchance—To guess their *m*. *Morcar.* Thine own *m*, Harold, To make all England one, *Harold* IV i 139
I know Thy *m*. Perish she, I, all, *Becket* III iii 19
And smiles at my best *m's*, *Foresters* IV 727
Means stakes high? *Noailles.* But not beyond your *m*. *Queen Mary* I iii 147
That by your gracious *m* and intercession „ III iii 121
These are the *m* God works with, „ III vi 68
My liberality perforce is dead Thro' lack of *m* of giving. *The Falcon* 297
How hadst thou then the *m* to buy a cow? *Foresters* II i 303
Meant (*See also* **Meän'd**) I *m* True matters of the heart. *Queen Mary* I iv 99
Elizabeth—To Philibert of Savoy, as you know, We *m* to wed her; „ V i 248
Thou knowest never woman *m* so well, „ V ii 342
Said 'ay' when I *m* 'no,' lied like a lad *Harold* II ii 656
He *m* no harm nor damage to the Church. *Becket* I iii 216
I had *m* to make him all but king. „ I iii 464

Meant (*continued*) I never *m* you harm in any way. *Becket* IV ii 106
Not if you *m* it, I am sure. „ IV ii 184
I *m* thee to have follow'd—better thus. *The Cup* II 498
but he knew I *m* to marry him. *The Falcon* 51
Why? because I *m* it!— *Prom. of May* III 365
Measure (s) (*See also* **Over-measure**) still All within *m*—nay, *Queen Mary* I v 436
They have brought it in large *m* on themselves. „ IV iii 363
And he is with you in a *m* still. „ V v 27
but belike Thou hast not learnt his *m*. *Harold* IV iii 118
I thinks I'd like to taäke the *m* o' your foot. *Prom. of May* I 464
If you will deign to tread a *m* with me. *Foresters* I ii 132
Measure (verb) if you'd like to *m* your own length upon the grass. *Prom. of May* I 465
Measured an' I *m* his foot wi' the mark i' the bed, „ I 413
Meat owld lord fell to 's *m* wi' a will, God bless un! *Queen Mary* IV iii 514
I have been a lover of wines, and delicate *m's*, *Becket* I i 77
King's *m*! By the Lord, „ I iv 140
And take a hunter's vengeance on the *m's* *The Cup* I ii 44
Meal enough, *m* enough, well fed; *The Falcon* 165
each of 'em as full of *m* as an egg. *Foresters* I i 42
Mebbe (maybe) the fault, *m*, wur as much mine as yours; *Prom. of May* I 325
and Parson *m*, thaw he niver mended that gap „ I 445
Meddle I'll not *m* wi' 'im if he doänt *m* wi' meä. „ I 173
I promised one of the Misses I wouldn't *m* wi' ye, „ I 470
She telled me once not to *m* wi' 'im, „ II 599
Medicine I have a wholesome *m* here Puts that belief asleep. *Becket* IV ii 50
It has been much commended as a *m*. *The Falcon* 588
Meditate so to *m* Upon my greater nearness *Foresters* II i 43
Medway (river) green field Beside the brimming *M*, *Queen Mary* II i 244
Meek yet so *m*, so modest, So wife-like humble „ III i 362
Ah, weak and *m* old man, „ V v 131
Meet When do you *m*? *Noailles*. To-night. „ I iii 154
these shall *m* upon St. Andrew's day. „ III ii 125
It was not *m* heretic swine should live In Lambeth. „ III ii 134
We *m* at Brussels. „ III vi 214
why my friend Should *m* with a lesser mercy „ IV i 70
you scarce could *m* his eye And hold your own; „ IV i 104
Count-crab will make his nippers *m* in thine heart; *Harold* II i 76
shall they *m* In private? „ II ii 87
fears that these may act On Harold when they *m*. *William*. Then let them *m*! „ II ii 92
To *m* thee in the North. „ V i 290
O Harold! husband! Shall we *m* again? „ V i 361
I have had it fashion'd, see, to *m* my hand. „ V i 422
And no David To *m* him? „ V i 497
The horse and horseman cannot *m* the shield, „ V i 591
Where I shall *m* the Barons and my King. *Becket* I ii 84
—And to *m* it I needs must leave as suddenly. „ III i 91
And so farewell until we *m* in England. *Becket*. I fear, my liege, we may not *m* in England. „ III iii 237
Strike! I challenge thee to *m* me before God. „ IV ii 254
bow'd herself to *m* the wave Of humiliation, „ IV ii 388
But he and he must never *m* again. „ IV ii 425
I go to *m* my King! *Grim*. To *m* the King? „ V ii 620
I will go out and *m* them. „ V iii 52
shun To *m* her face to face at once! *The Cup* I i 59
When first he *m's* his maiden in a bower. „ I iii 41
walk with me we needs must *m* Antonius coming, „ I iii 92
I will go To *m* him, crown'd! „ II 519
Why comes he not to *m* me? „ II 528
Still I am half-afraid to *m* her now. *Prom. of May* I 488
Keep up your heart until we *m* again. „ I 754
If that should break before we *m* again? „ I 756
and he trusted that some time we should *m* again, „ III 329
If ever I *m* thee there, I will break thy sconce *Foresters* I ii 74
they can *m* upon anything thro' a millstone. „ II i 280
I will not *m* him yet, I'll watch him „ III 47
Thou told'st us we should *m* him in the forest, „ IV 439
I cannot *m* his eyes. „ IV 799
Meeting (part) Gardiner, coming with the Queen, And *m* Pembroke, *Queen Mary* II ii 310
Meeting (s) When theer wur a *m* o' farmers at Littlechester t'other daäy, *Prom. of May* I 137
Melancholy Fine eyes—but *m*, irresolute— *Queen Mary* III iv 337
Mellow and as sleek and as round-about as a *m* codlin. *Foresters* I i 43
Melt Till doomsday *m* it. *Queen Mary* III v 51
may strike fire from her, Not hope to *m* her. „ III vi 40
Iron will fuse, and marble *m*; *Prom. of May* II 505
Who *m's* a waxen image by the fire, *Foresters* II i 671
Memorial wear it as *m* of a morning *Queen Mary* I v 529
Memory This *m* to thee!—and this to England, *Harold* V i 326
My *m* is as dead. *The Falcon* 524
drove me From out her *m*. *Prom. of May* II 405
We leave but happy *memories* to the forest. *Foresters* IV 1070
Menace if Philip *m* me, I think that I will play *Queen Mary* III v 241
Menaced whereupon I *m* her with this, *Becket* IV ii 348
Men-at-arms *m-a-a* Guard my poor dreams for England. *Queen Mary* I v 152
I would set my *m-a-a* to oppose thee, *Foresters* I i 323
and there be *m-a-a* to guard her. „ I ii 158
Mended he niver *m* that gap i' the glebe fence as I tell'd 'im; *Prom. of May* I 446
Mene *M*, *M*, Tekel! Is thy wrath Hell, *Harold* V i 35
Mention (s) hang On the chance *m* of some fool *Queen Mary* III v 43
Make thou not *m* that I spake with thee. *Harold* II ii 483
Mention (verb) I never heard her *m* you. *Prom. of May* II 395
An' we weänt *m* naw naämes, „ III 129
You, how dare you *m* kisses? *Foresters* II i 127
Mentioned You haven't even *m* him in your last? *Prom. of May* I 778
you *m* her name too suddenly before my father. „ II 23
And if she never *m* me, „ II 400
Mercenary one of those *mercenaries* that suck the blood of England. *Foresters* II i 174
Strike, Sheriff! Strike, *m*! „ II i 416
Prince John, the Sheriff, and a *m*. „ II i 446
Is coming with a swarm of *mercenaries* „ III 452
follow'd by Prince John And all his *mercenaries*! „ IV 589
Merchant raise us loans and subsidies Among the *m's*; *Queen Mary* V i 180
To this son of a London *m*— *Becket, Pro.* 434
Thomas, son Of Gilbert Becket, London *m*. „ II ii 231
Mercians Earl of the *M*! if the truth be gall, *Harold* IV i 14
Merciful It were more *m* to burn him now. *Queen Mary* IV i 153
O God, For thou art *m*, refusing none „ IV iii 131
Your Grace hath been More *m* to many a rebel head „ V ii 5
Mercy Yet too much *m* is a want of *m*, „ I v 505
He by His *m* absolve you! „ III iii 208
to cast myself Upon the good Queen's *m*; „ III v 168
M, that herb-of-grace, Flowers now but seldom. „ III vi 9
To reach the hand of *m* to my friend. „ IV i 65
why my friend Should meet with lesser *m* than myself? „ IV i 70
God grant you ampler *m* at your call „ IV i 189
Will they have *m* on me? *Villa Garcia*. Have you good hopes of *m*! So, farewell. „ IV ii 84
Three persons and one God, have *m* on me, „ IV iii 121
For thy great *m* have *m*! „ IV iii 137
Thy *m* must be greater than all sin. „ IV iii 151
Why then to heaven, and God ha' *m* on him. „ IV iii 632
Have you found *m* there, Grant it me here: „ V v 144
Ay, Madam, but o' God's *m*— „ V v 166
allegiance in thy Lord's And crave his *m*, *Harold* V i 12
Have *m* on us! (repeat) *Harold* V i 501, 611, 643, 645
The child . . . No . . . *m*! No! *Becket* IV ii 186
M, *m*, As you would hope for *m*. „ V iii 175
When you have charm'd our general into *m*, *The Cup* I ii 312
a Sister of *M*, come from the death-bed of a pauper, *Prom. of May* III 376
Mere (adj.) *M* compliments and wishes. *Queen Mary* V ii 596
The *m* wild-beast! *Prom. of May* III 736
This is *m* marble. *Foresters* II i 275
A shadow, a poetical fiction—did ye not call me king in your song?—a *m* figure. „ IV 221
Mere (s) The brows unwrinkled as a summer *m*.— *Harold* III i 49
A summer *m* with sudden wreckful gusts „ III i 50
Merit (s) Forgive me, Father, for no *m* of mine, *Queen Mary* IV iii 152
Merit (verb) and that *m's* death—False oath on holy cross— *Becket* IV ii 207
Merle Hawk, buzzard, jay, the mavis and the *m*, *Foresters* I iii 116
Merriest beyond The *m* murmurs of their banquet clank *Harold* II ii 408

Merriment Breaks into feather'd *m's*, *Queen Mary* III v 13
in the end we flourished out into a *m*; *Becket* III iii 138
Merry Be *m*! yet, Sir Ralph, you look but sad. *Queen Mary* II ii 358
But then he looks so *m*. „ III i 203
Heretic and rebel Point at me and make *m*. „ V ii 318
It was never *m* world In England, since the Bible came among us. „ V v 240
It never will be *m* world in England, „ V v 246
Thou hast misread this *m* dream of thine, *Harold* I ii 98
To-night we will be *m*. (repeat) *Harold* II ii 768, 771
Feed, feast, and be *m*. *Becket* I iv 152
let us be *m* to-night at the banquet. *Foresters* I i 344
I am only *m* for an hour or two Upon a birthday: „ I iii 11
why should we make us *m* Because a year of it is gone? „ I iii 14
There be good fellows there in *m* Sherwood That hold by Richard, „ I iii 98
'Love, love, love, love'—what *m* madness—listen! „ III 42
All the birds in *m* Sherwood sing and sing him home again. „ IV 1109
Mesh Tho' scarce at ease; for, save our *m'es* break, *Harold* II ii 140
The simple lobster-basket, and the *m*— *Becket* II ii 298
Message I do but bring the *m*, know no more. *Queen Mary* I iv 228
I will give your *m*. „ III vi 41
But shall I take some *m* from your Grace? „ V ii 597
we bring a *m* from the King Beyond the water; *Becket* V ii 301
Had you then No *m* with the cup? *The Cup* I ii 68
Well, Madam, I will give your *m* to him. *The Falcon* 217
that I forgot my *m* from the Earl. *Foresters* I i 297
Messenger and there are *m's* That go between us. *Queen Mary* I iii 137
I chanced upon the *m* Who brings that letter „ I v 585
Not thee, my son: some other *m*. *Harold* I i 244
—thou art but a *m* of William. „ V i 29
I am the *m* of God, His Norman Daniel! „ V i 33
The *m* from Synorix who waits Before the Temple? *The Cup* II 37
too rich a prize To trust with any *m*. *The Falcon* 726
It is a royal *m*, my lord: *Foresters* I iii 52
A worthy *m*! how should he help it? „ I iii 85
Met she *m* the Queen at Wanstead *Queen Mary* I i 77
hands Came from the crowd and *m* his own; „ IV iii 583
Thou hast rounded since we *m*. *Harold* I i 95
he and Wulfnoth never Have *m*, except in public; „ II ii 86
Look rather thou all-royal as when first I *m* thee. *Becket* II i 47
I *m* a robber once, I told him I was bound „ V ii 98
'Tis long since we have *m*! *The Falcon* 274
never since have *m* Her equal for pure innocence *Prom. of May* II 371
I *m* her first at a farm in Cumberland—Her uncle's. „ II 396
he tells me that he *m* you once in the old times, „ III 262
I do believe I lost my heart to him the very first time we *m*, „ III 284
if *m* in a black lane at midnight: *Foresters* III 224
He *m* a stag there on so narrow a ledge— „ IV 531
Metal to fuse Almost into one *m* love and hate,— *Queen Mary* III vi 182
Meteor These *m's* came and went before our day, *Harold* I i 131
Methinks and yet, *m*, I have seen goodlier. *Queen Mary* I v 6
Madam, *m* a cold face and a haughty. „ I v 196
m, A prince as naturally may love his people „ II ii 191
M most men are but poor-hearted, „ II ii 337
M the good land heard me, „ III ii 57
M that under our Queen's regimen We might go „ III iv 181
And yet *m* he falters: „ III iv 398
M that would you tarry one day more „ III vi 232
m my Queen is like enough To leave me by and by. „ V i 241
M there is no manhood left among us. „ V ii 284
m I love her less For such a dotage upon such a man. „ V ii 420
M I am all angel, that I bear it „ V iii 3
so *m*, my boy, Thy fears infect me beyond reason. *Harold* II ii 450
Better *m* have slain the man at once! „ II ii 498
Methought glance of some distaste, Or so *m*, return'd. *Queen Mary* III i 101
Methusaleh live as long as Jerusalem. *Eva*. *M*, father. *Prom. of May* I 379
Metre and the matter in the *m*. *Becket, Pro.* 384
Metropolitan He here, this heretic *m*, *Queen Mary* IV iii 43
Mexico The voices of Peru and *M*, „ V i 47
Michaelmas At *M*, Miss, please God. *Prom. of May* III 112
Mid strike, make his feathers Glance in *m* heaven. *The Falcon* 16
Mid-battle will you crown my foe My victor in *m-b*? *Becket* V i 150
Mid-day Hang'd at *m-d*, their traitor of the dawn *The Cup* II 123
Midder (meadow) An' the *m's* all mow'd, an' the sky sa blue— (repeat) *Prom. of May* II 176, 188, 200
Middle (adj.) For, like a fool, thou knowest no *m* way. *Becket* I iii 532
Middle (s) in the *m* of that fierce fight At Stamfordbridge. *Harold* IV iii 183
Midland or wreckt And dead beneath the *m* ocean, *Foresters* II i 657
Midmost As in the *m* heart of Paradise. *The Cup* II 186
Midnight I hardly gain'd The camp at *m*. „ I iii 19
dead *m* when I came upon the bridge; *Prom. of May* III 368
if met in a black lane at *m*: *Foresters* III 224
Midriff-shaken many *m-s* even to tears, as springs gush out after earthquakes— *Becket* III iii 162
Mid-sea whose quick flash splits The *m-s* mast, *The Cup* II 293
Mid-summer full *m-s* in those honest hearts. *Becket* V ii 373
Midwinter Yon gray old Gospeller, sour as *m*, *Queen Mary* I iii 40
'Tis known you are *m* to all women, *Becket* I ii 27
Save that it was *m-w* in the street, „ V ii 372
Might (s) 'Thine is the right, for thine the *m*; *Harold* II ii 357
William laugh'd and swore that *m* was right, „ II ii 362
Waste not thy *m* before the battle! „ V i 415
Might (verb) *See* **Mowt**
Mightier but those of Normanland Are *m* than our own. *Harold* III i 225
The more the love, the *m* is the prayer; „ III i 347
that Tostig Conjured the *m* Harold from his North „ IV ii 68
Their giant-king, a *m* man-in-arms Than William. „ V i 399
But we must have a *m* man than he For his successor. *Becket, Pro.* 6
Thou art the man—be thou A *m* Anselm. „ I i 134
'Fore God, I am a *m* man than thou. „ I i 223
We find that it is *m* than it seems— „ IV ii 263
I think they will be *m* than the king. *Foresters* I ii 119
Mightiest (adj.) and be the *m* man This day in England. *Queen Mary* II ii 19
But not the force made them our *m* kings. „ III iv 335
You are the *m* monarch upon earth, I but a little Queen: „ V i 52
Bride of the *m* sovereign upon earth? „ V ii 544
Should make the *m* empire earth has known. „ V iii 70
Thou art the *m* voice in England, man, *Harold* II ii 617
But I that threw the *m* knight of France, *Becket* I iii 746
Mightiest (s) More, what the *m* and the holiest Of all his predecessors „ II ii 179
Mighty (adj. and adv.) For I am *m* popular with them, Noailles. *Queen Mary* I iii 101
Ay, ay, but *m* doctors doubted there. „ IV i 83
Friend for so long time of a *m* King; „ IV iii 73
And done such *m* things by Holy Church, „ V v 74
Thou art a *m* man In thine own earldom! *Harold* II i 92
And *m* pretty legs too. Thou art the prettiest child I ever saw. *Becket* IV i 6
But my sister wrote that he was *m* pleasant, *Prom. of May* I 116
But he were *m* fond o' ye, warn't he? „ II 9
ready To make allowances, and *m* slow To feel offences. „ III 629
Mighty (s) How are the *m* fallen, Master Cranmer! *Queen Mary* IV ii 146
Milan (town) Granada, Naples, Sicily, and *M*,— „ V i 44
Milcher (milch-cow) Dumble's the best *m* in Islip. (repeat) „ IV iii 478, 497
Mild Your *m* Legate Pole Will tell you that the devil helpt them thro' it. „ IV iii 351
Julius the Third Was ever just, and *m*, and father-like; „ V ii 31
We have heard Of thy just, *m*, and equal governance; *Harold* II ii 690
she had seen the Archbishop once, So *m*, so kind. *Becket* V ii 120
Milder Ye govern *m* men. *Gurth*. We have made them *m* by just government. *Harold* I i 339
Mile seen your steps a *m* From me and Lambeth? *Queen Mary* I ii 81
I would not; but a hundred *m's* I rode, „ I v 551
we must round By Kingston Bridge. *Brett*. Ten *m's* about. „ II iii 49
brook across our field For twenty *m's*, „ V v 84
I ha' carried him ever so many *m's* in my arms, *Becket* I iv 98
What be he a-doing here ten *m* an' moor fro' a raäil? *Prom. of May* I 209
Militant Thou hast roll'd over the Church *m* *Foresters* IV 273

Milk mute as death, And white as her own *m*; *Queen Mary* II ii 80
the cow kick'd, and all her *m* was spilt. „ III v 266
and shared His fruits and *m*. Liar! *The Cup* I ii 428
M? *Filippo*. Three laps for a cat! *The Falcon* 124
No not a draught of *m*, no not an egg, „ 871
come as freely as heaven's air and mother's *m*? *Foresters* I i 210
Sour *m* and black bread. „ II i 272
and her bread is beyond me: and the *m*—faugh! „ II i 293
wouldst bar me fro' the *m* o' my cow, „ II i 355
Milking with my hands *M* the cow? (repeat) *Queen Mary* III v 88, 95, 102
you came and kiss'd me *m* the cow. (repeat) „ III v 91, 98
Come behind and kiss me *m* the cow! „ III v 105
take to the *m* of your cows, the fatting of your calves, *Prom. of May* II 92
Milkmaid I would I were a *m*, To sing, *Queen Mary* III v 110
I wish'd myself the *m* singing here, „ III v 256
Your Highness such a *m*? „ III v 268
Mill More water goes by the *m* than the miller wots of, *Foresters* I ii 48
Old as the *m*. „ IV 302
Miller black sheep baaed to the *m's* ewe-lamb, The *m's* away for to-night: *Becket* I iv 163
But the *m* came home that night, „ I iv 173
She beautiful: sleep as a *m's* mouse! *The Falcon* 165
Thou Much, *m's* son, hath not the Earl right? *Much*. More water goes by the mill than the *m* wots of, *Foresters* I ii 46
Much, the *m's* son, I knew thy father: „ I iii 146
they can meet upon anything thro' a *m*. „ II i 280
I Little John, he Much the *m's* son, and he Scarlet, „ III 55
Millwheel The *m* turn'd in blood; *Becket* I iii 353
Milly (servant to Farmer Dobson) ye ringed fur that, Miss, didn't ye? *Dora*. No, *M*; *Prom. of May* III 15
no one has seen you but myself. *Eva*. Yes—this *M*. *Dora*. Poor blind Father's little guide, *M*, „ III 230
It is only *M*. *Dora*. Well, *M*, why do you come in so roughly? „ III 341
M, my dear, how did you leave Mr. Steer? „ III 409
Mimick'd boy she held *M* and piped her *Queen Mary* II ii 74
Mince *M* and go back! his politic Holiness *Becket* II ii 45
Mind (s) to my *m* the Lady Elizabeth is the more noble *Queen Mary* I i 71
all one *m* to supplicate The Legate here for pardon, „ III iii 105
We are all one *m*. „ III iii 110
To my *m*, The cataract typed the headlong plunge „ III iv 139
as one whose *m* Is all made up, „ IV iii 588
To be nor mad, nor bigot—have a *m*— „ V v 216
What lies upon the *m* of our good king *Harold* I i 268
I have a *m* that thou shalt catch no more. „ II i 70
I have a *m* to brain thee with mine axe. „ II i 73
my *m* was set upon other matters. *Becket, Pro.* 317
Blurt thy free *m* to the air? „ I iii 239
run my *m* out to a random guest Who join'd me *The Cup* I ii 107
Hath she made up her *m* to marry him? „ II 22
who call'd the *m* Of children a blank page, *Prom. of May* II 281
Has lost his health, his eyesight, even his *m*. „ III 768
Mind (remind) *M*, ma o' summun. „ II 583
Minded it *m* me Of the sweet woods of Clifford, *Becket* I i 263
Mine (poss.) *M*—but not yet all *m*. *Queen Mary* I v 542
May I have it as *m*, till *m* Be *m* again? *Becket* II i 298
Mine (s) in this pause, before The *m* be fired, *Queen Mary* II i 26
I fear the *m* is fired before the time. „ II i 123
The *m* is fired, and I will speak to them. „ II i 155
Mingle I scarce have heart to *m* in this matter, „ II ii 113
Minion glad to wreak our spite on the rosefaced *m* *Becket, Pro.* 529
Well—you know—the *m*, Rosamund. „ I ii 37
We thought to scare this *m* of the King „ IV ii 330
Minister Whose *m's* they be to govern you. *Queen Mary* IV iii 180
Minnow if you care to drag your brains for such a *m*. *Foresters* II i 324
Minster (adj.) And smote me down upon the *M* floor. *Becket* I i 104
Minster (s) as the new-made couple Came from the *M*, *Queen Mary* III i 95
That long low *m* where you gave your hand „ III ii 90
Methought I stood in Canterbury *M*, *Becket* I i 73
loftiest *m* ever built To Holy Peter *Harold* III i 206
Minster-aisle Their long bird-echoing *m-a's*,— *Becket* III i 44
Minster-bell Tho' earth's last earthquake clash'd the *m-b's*, „ V iii 42
Minute In some few *m's*. She will address your guilds *Queen Mary* II ii 14
Your pardon for a *m*. She must be waked. *Prom. of May* III 657

Miracle Our voyage by sea was all but *m*; *Queen Mary* III ii 25
Seem'd as a happy *m* to make glide— „ III ii 29
News, mates! a *m*, a *m*! news! „ III ii 209
—would be deem'd a *m*. „ V iii 55
I have wrought *m's*—to God the glory—And *m's* *Harold* I i 181
For Henry could not work a *m*— *Becket* I i 40
life Saved as by *m* alone with Him Who gave it. „ IV ii 368
A *m* that they let him home again, *The Cup* I ii 270
Why now I count it all but *m*, „ I iii 37
She, you mourn for seem'd A *m* of gentleness— *Prom. of May* II 491
Miracled *See* **De-miracled**
Miracle-monger our friar is so holy That he's a *m-m*, *Foresters* IV 281
Miraculous For as to the fish, they de-miracled the *m* draught, *Becket* III iii 124
Mire caked and plaster'd with a hundred *m's*, *Harold* IV iii 178
from the street Stain'd with the *m* thereof. *Becket* I iii 691
From off the stalk and trample it in the *m*, *Foresters* I ii 111
Mirror Unless my friends and *m's* lie to me, *Queen Mary* I iv 2
Mischance some *m* of flood, And broken bridge, „ I v 353
Mischief Him as did the *m* here, five year' sin.' *Prom. of May* III 139
Miser Close as a *m's* casket. Listen: *Queen Mary* I iv 108
Miserable scum And offal of the city would not change Estates with him; in brief, so *m*. „ IV iii 78
Most *m* sinner, wretched man. „ IV iii 123
The *m* see-saw of our child-world, „ IV iii 385
Old, *m*, diseased, „ V v 178
And poor old father not die *m*. *Prom. of May* I 722
and father Will not die *m*.' „ II 660
Miserere Mei said the *M M*—But all in English, mark you; *Queen Mary* III i 391
Misery put off the rags They had mock'd his *m* with, „ IV iii 590
But now we are made one flesh in *m*; „ V ii 153
pauper, who had died in his *m* blessing God, *Prom. of May* III 378
Misfortin (misfortune) knaw'd better nor to cast hes sister's *m* inter 'er teeth „ II 127
Mishandled If she should be *m*. *Queen Mary* II ii 115
Misheard *M* their snores for groans. *Harold* V i 213
Mislead *M* us, and I will have thy life! *Foresters* II i 376
Misleader were there but three or four Of these *m's*, *Queen Mary* III iv 174
Mismatch'd *M* with her for policy! „ III i 365
Misname You do *m* me, match'd with any such, *Becket* IV ii 128
Misnamed now the stronger motive, *M* free-will— *Prom. of May* II 637
Misplaced round his knee, *m*, Our English Garter, *Queen Mary* III i 83
Misread Thou hast *m* this merry dream of thine, *Harold* I ii 98
Misreport Will in some lying fashion *m* His ending *Queen Mary* IV iii 326
One that would neither *m* nor lie, „ IV iii 556
Miss (s) (*See also* **Misses**) and häafe th' parish 'll be theer, an' *M* Dora, an' *M* Eva, an' all! *Man*. *M* Dora be coomed back, then? *Prom. of May* I 10
Foälks says he likes *M* Eva the best. „ I 25
Beänt *M* Eva gone off a bit of 'er good looks o' läate? „ I 32
Noä, *M*. I ha'n't seed 'er neither. „ I 48
Blessings on your pretty voice, *M* Dora. „ I 64
Theer be redder blossoms nor them, *M* Dora. „ I 86
Under your eyes, *M* Dora. „ I 89
Noä, *M* Dora; as blue as— (repeat) „ I 95, 99
Theer ye goäs ageän, *M* niver believing owt I says to ye— „ I 106
He'll be arter you now, *M* Dora. „ I 118
He's been arter *M* Eva, haän't he? „ I 121
And I tells ye what, *M* Dora: „ I 131
I thank you for that, *M* Dora, onyhow. „ I 157
M, the farming men 'ull hev their dinner i' the long barn, „ I 165
So the owd uncle i' Coomberland be deäd, *M* Dora, „ II 2
Not like me, *M* Dora; „ II 13
but I hallus gi'ed soom on 'em to *M* Eva at this time o' year. Will ya täake 'em? fur *M* Eva, „ II 16
and now she be gone, will ye täake 'em, *M* Dora? „ II 21
an' weänt ye täake 'em now, *M* Dora, „ II 41
I were insured, *M*, an' I lost nowt by it. But I weänt be too sudden wi' it; and I feel sewer, *M* Dora, „ II 57
but that be all along o' you, *M*, „ II 109
M Dora, Dan Smith's cart hes runned ower a läady „ II 567

Miss (s) (*continued*) ye ringed fur that, *M*, didn't ye? *Dora.* No, Milly; but if the farming-men be come for their wages, to send them up to me. *Milly.* Yeäs, *M*. *Prom. of May* III 14
Taäke one o' the young 'uns fust, *M*? „ III 32
Noä, *M*; we worked naw wuss upo' the cowd tea; „ III 58
All right, *M*; and thank ye kindly. „ III 66
Whoy, O lor, *M*! „ III 71
O lor, *M*! noä, noä, noä! „ III 91
Yeäs, *M*; but he wur so rough wi' ma, „ III 103
'Listed for a soädger, *M*, i' the Queen's Real Hard Tillery. „ III 108
At Michaelmas, *M*, please God. „ III 112
An' I thanks ye fur that, *M*, moor nor fur the waäge. „ III 116
'A cotched ma about the waaist, *M*, „ III 119
Why, *M* Dora, meä and my maätes, us three, we wants to hev three words wi' ye. *Higgins.* That be 'im, and meä, *M*. *Jackson.* An' meä, *M*. „ III 124
Theer, *M*! You ha' naämed 'im—not me. „ III 142
Wasn't *M* Vavasour, our schoolmistress at Littlechester, „ III 297
Pleäse, *M*, Mr. Dobson telled me to saäy he's browt some of *M* Eva's roses for the sick laädy to smell on. „ III 345
Yeäs, *M*; and he wants to speak to ye partic'lar. „ III 350
Yeäs, *M*; but he says he wants to tell ye summut very partic'lar. „ III 354
Why, *M*? I be afeard I shall set him a-sweäring like onythink. „ III 358
You see she is lamed, and cannot go down to him. *Milly.* Yeäs, *M*, I will. „ III 417
M Dora! *M* Dora! *Dora.* Quiet! quiet! What is it? *Milly.* Mr. 'Arold, *M*. *Dora.* Below? *Milly.* Yeäs, *M*. „ III 475
Tell him, then, that I'm waiting for him. *Milly.* Yeäs, *M*. „ III 485

Miss (verb) I *m* something. The tree that only bears *Queen Mary* III i 18
To strike too soon is oft to *m* the blow. „ III vi 72
burrow where the King Would *m* her and for ever. *Becket* IV ii 159
He *m* the searching flame of purgatory, „ V iii 13
Why didst thou *m* thy quarry yester-even? *The Falcon* 150
if thou *m* I will fasten thee to thine own door-post *Foresters* II i 403

Missed *M*! There goes another. Shoot, Sheriff! *Sheriff.* *M*! „ II i 396
They have *m* the vein. „ IV 636

Misses (*See also* **Miss**) but I promised one of the *M* I wouldn't meddle wi' ye, and I weänt. *Prom. of May* I 469

Missive fearing for her, sent a secret *m*, *Queen Mary* II ii 121
When next there comes a *m* from the Queen „ III v 182
A *m* from the Queen: „ III v 187
Here is a *m* left at the gate by one from the castle. *Becket* I iv 49

Misstate Swear and unswear, state and *m* thy best! „ II ii 476

Mist among thine island *m's* With laughter. *Harold* II ii 182
oafs, ghosts o' the *m*, wills-o'-the-wisp; *Foresters* II i 263

Mistake (s) I see it—some confusion, Some strange *m*. *Becket* III i 235
Some foolish *m* of Sally's; *Prom. of May* III 153
No, Father, that was a *m*. She's here again. „ III 445

Mistake (verb) You do *m*. I am not one to change. *Queen Mary* V i 217
No, daughter, you *m* our good Archbishop; *Becket* V ii 138

Mistaken Only one, And he perhaps *m* in the face. *The Cup* I ii 343

Mister (*See also* **Master, Mr.**) feller couldn't find a *M* in his mouth fur me, as farms five hoonderd haäcre. *Prom. of May* I 303
Pleäse *M* 'Arold. *Harold.* Well? „ III 700

Mistradition Monsters of *m*, old enough *Queen Mary* IV ii 102

Mistress Spain would be England on her seas, and England *M* of the Indies. „ V iii 74
England Will be the *M* of the Indies yet, „ V iii 77
She is *my m*, let *me* look to her! *Harold* I i 287
I shall have my tetrarchy restored By Rome, our *m*, *The Cup* I i 21
when the *m* died, and I appealed to the Sister again, *Prom. of May* III 393
You do well, *M* Kate, *Foresters* I i 23
I would like to show you, *M* Kate. „ I i 49
Pretty *m*! *Robin.* What art thou, man? „ I ii 189
Pretty *m*, will you dance? „ I ii 203

Mistress (*continued*) She is my queen and thine, The *m* of the band. *Foresters* II ii 42
I remain *M* of mine own self and mine own soul. „ IV 729

Mistrust Doth thou *m* me? Am I not thy friend? „ I ii 177
to *m* the girl you say you love Is to *m* your own love „ II ii 57
How should you love if you *m* your love? „ II ii 60

Misty Walk'd at night on the *m* heather; *Harold* III ii 5
I am *m* with my thimbleful of ale. *Foresters* IV 278

Misuse Who *m's* a dog would *m* a child— *Becket* I iv 108

Misused she will not have thee, Thou hast *m* her: *Harold* IV ii 35

Misvalued I fear the Emperor much *m* me. *Queen Mary* III ii 76

Mite Cheese? *Filippo.* A supper for twelve *m's*. *The Falcon* 127
Cast them into our treasury, the beggars' *m's*. *Foresters* III 205

Mitre Wanting the Papal *m*. *Queen Mary* III iv 148
The Pope has pushed his horns beyond his *m*— „ V i 153
He took his *m* off, and set it on me, *Becket* I i 63
and the *m* Grappling the crown— „ II i 26
Who made the second *m* play the first, And acted me? „ III iii 212
crowns must bow when *m's* sit so high. „ IV ii 297
The *M*! *Salisbury.* Will you wear it?— „ V ii 616

Mitred Crown'd slave of slaves, and *m* king of kings, *Queen Mary* III iv 381
He fasts, they say, this *m* Hercules! *Becket* I iii 518

Mix *M* not yourself with any plot I pray you; *Queen Mary* I iv 173
Philip should not *m* us any way With his French wars— „ III iii 78
m our spites And private hates with our defence *Becket* V ii 50
m with all The lusty life of wood and underwood, *Foresters* I iii 112

Mixing Catholic, Mumbling and *m* in his scared prayers *Queen Mary* II ii 86
M our bloods, that thence a king may rise *Harold* IV i 142

Mixt And *m* with Wyatt's rising— *Queen Mary* V ii 479
I fear my dear lord *m* With some conspiracy *The Cup* I ii 15

Moan (s) he never uttered *m* of pain: *Queen Mary* IV iii 618
But your *m* is useless now: „ IV iii 638
he makes *m* that all be a-getting cold. *Becket* I iv 61
And I make my *m* along with him. „ I iv 63

Moan (verb) It breaks my heart to hear her *m* at night *Queen Mary* I v 603
and needs must *m* for him; O Cranmer! „ IV iii 635
he licks my face and *m's* and cries out against the King. *Becket* I iv 99

Moan'd Ran sunless down, and *m* against the piers. *Queen Mary* II iii 26
Not slighted—all but *m* for: thou must go. *Becket* I i 352

Moaning *See* **A-moänin', Low-moaning**

Moänt (must not) Here! she *m* coom here. *Prom. of May* III 458

Moat And I would swim the *m*, like an otter. *Foresters* I i 321

Mob A bold heart yours to beard that raging *m*! *Queen Mary* I iii 97
Pertest of our flickering *m*, *Foresters* II ii 130

Mock (adj.) (*See also* **Mock-king**) All the church is grateful. You have ousted the *m* priest, *Queen Mary* I v 180

Mock (verb) Have I not heard them *m* the blessed Host „ IV iii 365
O father, *m* not at a public fear, *Harold* I i 74
M me not. I am not even a monk. *Becket, Pro.* 247
They *m* us; he is here. „ I iv 202
will he not *m* at me The jealous fool balk'd „ IV ii 422

Mock'd summon'd hither But to be *m* and baited. *Queen Mary* III iv 270
put off the rags They had *m* his misery with, „ IV iii 590
then they *m* us and we fell upon 'em, *Becket* I ii 15

Mockery And if your penitence be not *m*, *Queen Mary* III iii 179
that was a *m*, you know, for he gave me no address, and there was no word of marriage; *Prom. of May* III 331

Mocking but thou art *m* me. Thou art Her brother— *Foresters* II i 515
They are jesting at us yonder, *m* us? „ IV 676
If Cranmer's spirit were a *m* one, *Queen Mary* V ii 211

Mock-king *M-k*, I am the messenger of God, *Harold* V i 33

Mode this faded ribbon was the *m* In Florence *The Falcon* 422

Model as a sculptor clay, To their own *m*. *Queen Mary* III iii 34
Statesmen that are wise Take truth herself for *m*. „ III iii 37

Moderate I pride myself on being *m*. „ V iv 60

Moderately Methought I answer'd *m* enough. *Becket* V ii 546

Modest yet so meek, so *m*, *Queen Mary* III i 363
Then our *m* women—I know the Norman license— *Harold* II ii 476
I thought that naked Truth would shame the Devil The Devil is so *m*. „ III i 120
M maiden lily abused, Queen. *Foresters* II ii 158

Modo *Suaviter in* m, *fortiter in re*, *Becket* V ii 539

Moist tho', to keep the figure *m* and make it hold water, „ III iii 166

Molehill My nurse would tell me of a *m* *Harold* IV iii 128

Moon (*continued*) light of the seas by the *m's* long-silvering ray! *Foresters* II ii 179
Moonlight (adj.) And how her shadow crosses one by one The *m* casements *Queen Mary* V v 9
Moonlight (s) there goes one in the *m*. Shoot! *Foresters* II i 395
What sparkles in the *m* on thy hand? „ II i 582
Moonshine He often looks in here by the *m*. „ II i 337
Moor I remember it well. There on the *m's*. *Becket* II i 52
Moor (more) I warrants ye'll think *m* o' this young Squire Edgar as ha' coomed among us— *Prom. of May* I 109
What be he a-doing here ten mile an' *m* fro' a raäil? „ I 209
I' mun ha' plowed it *m* nor a hoonderd times; „ I 368
And I would loove tha *m* nor ony gentleman 'ud loove tha. „ II 104
I'd think na *m* o' maäkin' an end o' tha nor a carrion craw— „ II 696
An' I thanks ye fur that, Miss, *m* nor fur the waäge. „ III 117
Moorish or closed For ever in a *M* tower, *Foresters* II i 656
Moors He calls us worse than Jews, *M*, Saracens. *Queen Mary* V i 150
the boy was taken prisoner by the *M*. *Foresters* I i 61
fell'st into the hands Of these same *M* „ II i 564
Mooted whene'er your royal rights Are *m* in our councils— *Becket* I iii 431
Moraine I have seen it like the snow on the *m*. *The Falcon* 506
Moral (adj.) Against the *m* excess No physical ache, *Becket* I i 381
Moral (s) Nature's *m* Against excess. „ I i 373
His swaddling-bands, the *m's* of the tribe, *Prom. of May* I 586
Morcar (Earl of Northumbria) *M*! Why creep'st thou like a timorous be st *Harold* I ii 211
M and Edwin have stirr'd up the Thanes „ II ii 288
have overthrown *M* and Edwin. „ III ii 132
Tostig's banishment, and choice of *M*, „ IV i 105
Again! *M*! Edwin! What do they mean? „ IV i 133
M, it is all but duty in her To hate me; „ IV i 153
M and Edwin, When will ye cease to plot „ IV i 160
M and Edwin, will ye, if I yield, „ IV i 175
M and Edwin, will ye upon oath, Help us „ IV i 179
We never—oh! good *M*, speak for us, „ IV i 216
M, collect thy men; Edwin, my friend— „ IV i 256
He held with *M*.— „ IV ii 44
And *M* holds with us. „ IV ii 46
Make not our *M* sullen: it is not wise. „ IV iii 103
Gurth, Leofwin, *M*, Edwin! „ IV iii 220
Nought of *M* then? „ V i 160
I married her for *M*—a sin against The truth of love. „ V i 169
More *See* **Moor**
More (Sir Thomas, Lord Chancellor) Did not *M* die, and Fisher? he must burn. *Queen Mary* IV i 52
Moreing thou and thy youngsters are always muching and *m* me. *Foresters* IV 296
Morn (*See also* **Marriage-morn**) Close to the grating on a winter *m* *The Falcon* 441
Morning (adj.) Brain-dizzied with a draught of *m* ale. *Queen Mary* II i 71
And make a *m* outcry in the yard; „ III v 158
But you, twin sister of the *m* star, *The Cup* I iii 45
Their shield-borne patriot of the *m* star „ II 122
thou that canst soar Beyond the *m* lark, *The Falcon* 11
Morning (s) (*See also* **May-morning, Murnin'**) Good *m*, Noailles. *Queen Mary* I iii 159
Good *m*, my good Lord. *Gardiner*. That every *m* of your Majesty May be most good, „ I v 98
Good *m*, Sir de Noailles. *Noailles*. A happy *m* to your Majesty. *Mary*. And I should some time have a happy *m*; „ I v 242
take And wear it as memorial of a *m* „ I v 529
I am sure Her *m* wanted sunlight, *Harold* I ii 45
on that *m* when I came To plead to thee *The Cup* II 390
and I sneezed three times this *m*. *The Falcon* 169
in hope that the saints would send us this blessed *m*; „ 186
you look as beautiful this *m* as the very Madonna „ 198
Where have you lain in ambush all the *m*? *Prom. of May* I 545
Is the most beautiful *m* of this May. „ I 569
you make The May and *m* still more beautiful, „ I 573
seen us that wild *m* when we found Her bed unslept in, „ II 469
and I wish you and your ladyship's father a most exceeding good *m*. *Foresters* I i 309
Morning (s) (*continued*) Who breaks the stillness of the *m* thus? *Foresters* I iii 51
gave me this *m* on my setting forth. „ III 282
Only this *m* in his agony „ IV 453
Morrow Good *m*, my Lord Cardinal; *Queen Mary* IV i 42
Morsel (*See also* **Mossel**) Come, come, the *m* stuck—this Cardinal's fault— „ III iv 375
Not a *m*, not one *m*. I have broken My fast already. *The Falcon* 573
Mortal seeming not as brethren, But *m* foes! *Queen Mary* IV iii 186
Because I loved thee in my *m* day, *Harold* V i 240
Is it possible That *m* men should bear their earthly heats „ V i 283
how he fells The *m* copse of faces! „ V i 589
but the Chancellor's and the Archbishop's Together more than *m* man can bear. *Becket* I i 24
Who stands aghast at her eternal self And shakes at *m* kings— „ II ii 405
I ask no leave of king, or *m* man, „ V ii 458
Out, begone! Henceforth I am thy *m* enemy. *The Cup* I ii 330
And, lest we freeze in *m* apathy, „ I iii 130
O this *m* house, Which we are born into, *Prom. of May* II 273
'O man, forgive thy *m* foe, „ III 5
But to show thou art *m*. *Marian*. *M* enough, If love for thee be *m*. *Foresters* II i 612
Not *m*! after death, if after death— „ II i 619
would cower to any Of *m* build. „ II i 690
You seem, as it were, Immortal, and we *m*. „ IV 1060
Mortality As may be consonant with *m*. *Queen Mary* IV iii 419
Mortally I am *m* afear'd o' thee, thou big man, *Foresters* IV 316
Mortgage thou shouldst marry one who will pay the *m*. „ I i 280
Himself would pay this *m* to his brother, „ I ii 263
he would pay The *m* if she favour'd him. „ I iii 7
Sheriff Would pay this cursed *m* to his brother „ II i 144
rate the land fivefold The worth of the *m*, „ II i 151
and couldst never pay The *m* on thy land. „ II i 454
Mortgaged I am *m* as thyself. „ I ii 280
Mortice Hath no more *m* than a tower of cards; *Queen Mary* III i 442
Mortify Fast, scourge thyself, and *m* thy flesh, *Becket* I iii 539
Mortifying In scourgings, macerations, *m's*, Fasts, „ V i 41
Moslem like the *M* beauties waiting To clasp *Prom. of May* I 246
I that have turn'd their *M* crescent pale— *Foresters* IV 793
Heading the holy war against the *M*, „ IV 818
And cleft the *M* turban at my side. „ IV 1001
Mossel (morsel) avore a could taste a *m*, *Queen Mary* IV iii 517
Most I do my *m* and best. „ II ii 24
Mot blow upon it Three *m's*, this fashion—listen! *Foresters* IV 425
Moth Make it so hard to save a *m* from the fire? *Becket* I i 283
would not blur A *m's* wing by the touching; *Prom. of May* II 492
Mother My *m* said, Go up; and up I went. *Queen Mary* I iii 98
my good *m* came (God rest her soul) Of Spain, „ I v 11
Your royal *m* came of Spain, „ I v 16
m, you had time and cause enough To sicken „ I v 23
married The *m* of Elizabeth—a heretic „ I v 32
Here was a young *m*, Her face on flame, „ II ii 69
felt the faltering of his *m's* heart, „ II ii 82
I, that was never *m*, cannot tell How *m's* „ II ii 189
nay, his noble *m's*, Head fell— „ III iv 295
Before my father married my good *m*,— „ III v 246
Her foul divorce—my sainted *m*—No!— „ IV i 81
M of God, Thou knowest never woman meant so well, „ V ii 340
and in her agony The *m* came upon her— „ V iv 20
prattling to her *m* Of her betrothal „ V v 232
Malet, thy *m* was an Englishwoman; *Harold* II ii 264
for my *m's* sake I love your England, „ II ii 268
Speak for thy *m's* sake, and tell me true. *Malet*. Then for my *m's* sake, and England's sake „ II ii 271
And for our *M* England? „ II ii 425
for he Who vows a vow to strangle his own *m* „ III i 230
My *m* is a Dane, and I am English; „ IV i 54
Trampling thy *m's* bosom into blood? „ IV ii 26
A cleric lately poison'd his own *m*, *Becket, Pro.* 11
My *m*, ere she bore me, Dream'd that twelve stars „ I i 44
So did Matilda, the King's *m*. „ I iii 152
took back not only Stephen's gifts, But his own *m's*, „ I iii 155
Age, orphans, and babe-breasting *m's*— „ II i 73

Mother (*continued*) Babes, orphans, *m's*! is that royal, Sire? *Becket* II i 80
that the *m* Would make him play his kingship „ II ii 10
Father Philip that has confessed our *m* for twenty years, „ III i 112
asked our *m* if I could keep a quiet tongue i' my head, „ III i 118
our *m* 'ill sing me old songs by the hour, „ III i 184
she had 'em from her *m*, and her *m* from her *m* back „ III i 186
The crown! who? *Margery. M.* „ III i 200
but Salisbury was a calf cowed by *M* Church, „ III iii 96
I only love *m*. *Eleanor*. Ay; and who is thy *m*? „ IV i 9
a good fairy to thy *m*. Take me to her. „ IV i 26
But you don't look like a good fairy. *M* does. You are not pretty, like *m*. „ IV i 36
golden chain I will give thee if thou wilt lead me to thy *m*. *Geoffrey*. No—no gold. *M* says gold spoils all. „ IV i 41
I love thy *m*, my pretty boy. „ IV i 44
M, you told me a great fib: „ IV ii 370
I have overshot My duties to our Holy *M* Church, „ V i 38
a son stone-blind Sat by his *m's* hearth: „ V ii 106
and the poor *m*, Soon as she learnt I was a friend „ V ii 109
and our *M* Church for bride; „ V ii 221
this love, this *m*, runs thro' all The world „ V ii 241
To assail our Holy *M* lest she brood Too long „ V ii 251
Divide we from the *m* church of England, My Canterbury. „ V ii 360
Artemis, Artemis, hear us, O *M*, hear us, and bless us! *The Cup* II 1
new-made children Of our imperial *m* see the show. „ II 165
many-breasted *m* Artemis Emboss'd upon it. „ II 340
Good *m*, happy was the prodigal son, *The Falcon* 140
Holy *m*! To breakfast! „ 214
yet to speak white truth, my good old *m*, „ 504
easier for you to make Allowance for a *m*— „ 826
I was just out of school, I had no *m*— *Prom. of May* I 707
Wasn't dear *m* herself at least by one side a lady? „ III 300
she moänt coom here. What would her *m* saäy? „ III 459
My *m* used to say that such a one Was without rudder, „ III 533
for the sake of the great blessed *M* in heaven, and for the love of his own little *m* on earth, *Foresters* I i 97
come as freely as heaven's air and *m's* milk? „ I i 210
they were born and bred on it—it was their *m*— „ I i 333
This ring my *m* gave me: „ I ii 293
My *m*, For whose sake, and the blessed Queen „ II i 37
Quick, good *m*, quick! „ II i 193
That by the blessed *M* no man, „ III 239
Robin, the sweet light of a *m's* eye, „ IV 2
He was my father, *m*, both in one. „ IV 6

Mother-wit Put thou thyself and *m-w* together. *Harold* II i 17

Motion The Queen hath felt the *m* of her babe! *Queen Mary* III ii 213
great *m* of laughter among us, part real, part childlike, *Becket* III iii 154
Fell with her *m* as she rose, and she, *The Falcon* 536

Motive now the stronger *m*, Misnamed free-will— *Prom. of May* II 636
when The stronger *m* rules. „ II 671

Mou'd (mould) and the smell o' the *m* an' all. „ I 375
the smell o' the *m* 'ud ha' maäde ma live as long as Jerusalem. „ I 377

Mould (earth) (*See also* **Mou'd**) such fine *m*, that if you sow'd therein *Queen Mary* IV i 170

Mould (shape) I cannot help the *m* that I was cast in. *The Cup* I iii 25
Not yet, but here comes one of bigger *m*. *Foresters* IV 115

Mould (verb) I could *m* myself To bear your going better; *Queen Mary* III vi 234

Moulded bolts of thunder *m* in high heaven *Harold* II ii 32

Mouldwarp wild hawk passing overhead, The *m* underfoot. *Foresters* III 319

Mouldy old men must die, or the world would grow *m*, *Becket, Pro.* 409
nigh at the end of our last crust, and that *m*, „ III i 115

Moult bird that *m's* sings the same song again, „ I iii 447

Mound Our altar is a *m* of dead men's clay, *Queen Mary* V i 161
as she was helping to build the *m* against the city. *Foresters* II i 309
let me go to make the *m*: bury me in the *m*, „ II i 312

Mount No, no, his horse—he *m's* another— *Harold* V i 639
when the Gascon wine *m's* to my head, *Becket, Pro.* 113
m with your lordship's leave to her ladyship's castle, *The Falcon* 412

Mountain (adj.) You know the waterfall That in the summer keeps the *m* side, *The Cup* I i 108
This *m* shepherd never dream'd of Rome. „ I i 17
With other beauties on a *m* meadow, *The Falcon* 351
The *m* flowers grew thickly round about. „ 355
'Dead *m* flowers, dead mountain-meadow flowers, „ 461
'O *m* flowers!' „ 474
Dead *m* flowers'— „ 519

Mountain (s) Inverted Æsop—*m* out of mouse. *Queen Mary* II i 67
Chased deer-like up his *m's*, *Harold* I ii 148
who know His prowess in the *m's* of the West, „ IV i 165
crying To a *m* 'Stand aside and room for me!' „ IV iii 130
climb The *m* opposite and watch the chase. *The Cup* I i 117
Oh look,—yon grove upon the *m*, „ I ii 394
'Dead *m*.' Nay, for who could trace a hand *The Falcon* 437
Dearer than when you made your *m* gay, „ 463
snow yonder on the very tip-top o' the *m*. „ 502

Mountain-meadow (*See also* **Meadow**) 'Dead mountain flowers, dead *m-m* flowers, „ 461
You bloom again, dead *m-m* flowers.' „ 470

Mounted We *m*, and we dash'd into the heart of 'em. „ 629
I was no mad, that I *m* upon the parapet— *Prom. of May* III 372

Mounting and see it *m* to Heaven, my God bless you, *Becket* I iv 37

Mourn She, you *m* for, seem'd A miracle of gentleness— *Prom. of May* II 489

Mournful Sleep, *m* heart, and let the past be past! *Foresters* I iii 47

Mouse Inverted Æsop—mountain out of *m*. *Queen Mary* II i 68
She beautiful: sleek as a miller's *m*! *The Falcon* 165

Mouth (s) From thine own *m* I judge thee— *Queen Mary* I iii 54
four guns gaped at me, Black, silent *m's*: „ II iii 32
Makes me his *m* of holy greeting. „ III ii 80
But a weak *m*, an indeterminate—ha? *Bonner*. Well, a weak *m*, perchance. „ III iv 340
stop the heretic's *m*! Hale him away! „ IV iii 282
tongue on un cum a-lolluping out o' 'is *m* „ IV iii 519
both have life In the large *m* of England, *Harold* IV iii 74
The *m* is only Clifford, my dear father. *Becket* II i 220
Out of th *m's* of babes and sucklings, praise! „ II ii 278
for my verses if the Latin rhymes be rolled out from a full *m*? „ II ii 338
primm'd her *m* and put Her hands together— „ III i 75
cold corners of the King's *m* began to thaw, „ III iii 153
royal promise might have dropt into thy *m* „ III iii 276
Foam at the *m* because King Thomas, „ V i 203
he made a wry *m* at it, but he took it so kindly, *The Falcon* 191
and he never made a wry *m* at you, „ 194
wasn't my lady born with a golden spoon in her ladyship's *m*, „ 402
will you take the word out of your master's own *m*? „ 598
feller couldn't find a Mister in his *m* fur me, as farms five hoonderd haäcre. *Prom. of May* I 303
What makes thee so down in the *m*? *Foresters* I ii 42
though I be down in the *m*, I will swear „ I ii 44
may this *m* Never suck grape again, „ IV 393
those pale *m's* which we have fed will praise us— „ IV 1076

Mouth (verb) Who *m* and foam against the Prince of Spain. *Queen Mary* II ii 250

Mouthpiece Is he thy *m*, thine interpreter? *Foresters* I ii 212

Move (s) His Highness makes his *m's* across the Channel, *Queen Mary* I iii 134
so you well attend to the king's *m's*, „ I iii 152
I'd make a *m* myself to hinder that: „ III i 127
if I And others made that *m* I touch'd upon, „ III i 445
It is your *m*. *Becket, Pro.* 17

Move (verb) Why should he *m* against you? *Queen Mary* I v 282
and till then I should not *m*. „ II i 3
I must not *m* Until I hear from Carew and the Duke. „ II i 121
M, if you *m*, at once.' „ II i 141
if we *m* not now, yet it will be known „ II i 197
If we *m* not now, Spain *m's*, „ II i 201
about our legs till we cannot *m* at all; „ II i 204
dark dead blood that ever *m's* with mine „ III i 352
Who cannot *m* straight to his end— „ IV iii 394
Sir, I will *m* them in your cause again, „ V i 178
could not *m* from Dover to the Humber *Harold* II ii 536

Murder (verb) *(continued)* Robert of Jumiéges—well-nigh *m* him too ? *Harold* I i 57
The dead men made at thee to *m* thee, „ I ii 85
It is the flash that *m's*, the poor thunder „ I ii 231
but a voice Among you : *m*, martyr me if ye will— „ V i 78
They *m* all that follow. „ V i 610
for he would *m* his brother the State. *Becket* I iv 190
Lord hath set his mark upon him that no man should *m* him. „ I iv 193
the wolves of England Must *m* her one shepherd, „ III iii 344
They stood on Dover beach to *m* me, „ V ii 436
Win me you cannot, *m* me you may, *Foresters* IV 721
Murder'd see the holy father *M* before thy face ? *Queen Mary* I iii 65
You would not have him *m* as Becket was ? „ III i 334
And I the race of *m* Buckingham— „ III i 454
The little *m* princes, in a pale light, „ III v 147
Hast *m* thine own guest, the son of Orm, *Harold* IV ii 37
They have so maim'd and *m* all his face „ V ii 76
A cleric violated The daughter of his host, and *m* him. *Becket* I iii 383
Say that a cleric *m* an archbishop, „ I iii 399
Am I to be *m* to-night ? „ I iv 47
M by that adulteress Eleanor, „ IV ii 243
Dead ! you have *m* her, Found out her secret bower and *m* her. „ V i 173
What matters *m* here, or *m* there ? „ V ii 630
Our gallant citizens *m* all in vain, *The Cup* I ii 142
She was *m* here a hundred year ago, *Foresters* II i 245
Murderer Make not thy King a traitorous *m*. *Becket* I iii 500
The *m's*, hark ! Let us hide ! „ V iii 46
Murderess *M* ! *Eleanor.* My lord, we know you proud „ IV ii 259
Murderous Were such *m* liars In Wessex— *Harold* II i 94
The man that hath to foil a *m* aim May, „ II ii 417
braced and brazen'd up with Christmas wines For any *m* brawl. *Becket* V ii 425
O *m* mad-woman ! I pray you lift me And make me walk awhile. *The Cup* II 471
Murmur (s) there be *m's*, for thy brother breaks us *Harold* I i 108
merriest *m's* of their banquet clank The shackles „ II ii 408
Murmur (verb) these old oaks will *m* thee Marian along with Robin. *Foresters* IV 1094
Murnin' (morning) and he wur in a tew about it all the *m* ; *Prom. of May* I 19
they be two o' the purtiest gels ye can see of a summer *m*. „ I 31
Good *m*, neighbours, and the saäme to you, my men. „ I 317
sa ta'en up wi' leädin' the owd man about all the blessed *m* „ III 3
nine o'clock, upo' Tuesday *m*, „ III 136
He wur sa bellows'd out wi' the wind this *m*, „ III 432
Muse I will not *m* upon it. *Queen Mary* IV ii 230
tell the King that I will *m* upon it ; „ V iii 90
that made me *m*, Being bounden by my coronation oath *Becket* I iii 395
Music in *m* Peerless—her needle perfect, *Queen Mary* III i 359
Thou art my *m* ! *Harold* I ii 25
Harold Hear the king's *m*, all alone with him, „ I ii 194
ever-jarring Earldoms move To *m* and in order— „ II ii 762
hand of one To whom thy voice is all her *m*, *Becket* II i 177
A maiden slowly moving on to *m* *The Cup* I i 9
And *m* there to greet my lord the king. „ II 191
Repeat them to their *m*. *Count.* You can touch No chord in me that would not answer you In *m*. *The Falcon* 454
When the Church and the law have forgotten God's *m*, they shall dance to the *m* *Foresters* IV 555
Strike up our *m*, Little John. „ IV 559
Musical There goes a *m* score along with them, *The Falcon* 452
Musically That is *m* said. „ 458
Musing What are you *m* on, my Lord of Devon ? *Queen Mary* I iv 26
Well, I was *m* upon that ; „ I iv 40
For I was *m* on an ancient saw, *Becket* V ii 537
Mussulman I had sooner have been born a *M*— „ II ii 145
and turn me *M* ! No God but one, „ II ii 224
Almost as many as your true *M*— „ IV ii 34
Must *See* **Moänt, Mun**

Muster and make *M's* in all the counties ; *Queen Mary* V ii 272
Mutable Woman is various and most *m*. „ III vi 135
Mute another, *m* as death, And white as her own milk ; „ II ii 78
And when my voice Is martyr'd *m*, and this man disappears, *Becket* III iii 350
Why art thou *m* ? Dost thou not honour woman ? *Foresters* III 67
Mutilated *M*, poor brute, my sumpter-mule, *Becket* V ii 440
Mutter What is that you *m* ? *Queen Mary* I v 203
Muttering And *m* to himself as heretofore. „ III i 16
My-lord Why do you so *m-l* me, Who am disgraced ? „ IV ii 176
Myriad sent his *m's* hither To seize upon the forts „ III i 463
Myrtle apricot, Vine, cypress, poplar, *m*, *The Cup* I i 3
Myrtle-blossom And kindle all our vales with *m-b*, „ II 267
Mysen (myself) I niver thowt o' *m* i' that waäy ; *Prom. of May* I 176
and, thaw I says it *m*, niver men 'ed a better master— „ I 327
fur I 'ednt naw time to maäke *m* a scholard while I wur maäkin' *m* a gentleman, „ I 333
now theer be noän o' my men, thinks I to *m*, „ I 410
fur I'd ha' done owt fur 'er *m* ; „ II 33
Fur boäth on 'em knawed as well as *m* „ II 314
'at I ha' nobbut larned *m* haäfe on it. „ III 4
But I'll git the book ageän, and larn *m* the rest, „ III 13
O law—yeäs, Sir ! I'll run fur 'im *m*. „ III 714
Mystery was the great *m* wrought ; *Queen Mary* IV iii 141
see Deeper into the *mysteries* of heaven *Harold* I i 200
The folds have fallen from the *m*, *Becket* IV ii 8
Mystic Clothed with the *m* silver of her moon. *Foresters* II i 608

N

Naäiled (nailed) I'll hev the winder *n* up, and put Towser under it. *Prom. of May* I 420
Naäme (name) noän o' the parishes goäs by that *n* 'ereabouts. „ I 268
then he called me a rude *n*, and I can't abide 'im. „ II 159
Fanny be the *n* i' the song, but I swopt it fur *she*. „ II 211
An' we weänt mention naw *n's*, „ III 130
says the master goäs cleän off his 'eäd when he 'eärs the *n* on 'im ; „ III 133
I warrants that ye goäs By haäfe a scoor o' *n's*— „ III 729
Naämed (named) Theer, Miss ! You ha' *n* 'im—not me. „ III 142
Naäy (nay) *N*, I knaws nowt o' what foälks says, „ I 26
N then. I meän'd they be as blue as violets. „ I 103
N, but I hev an owd woman as 'ud see to all that ; „ II 95
N, but I mun git out on 'is waäy now, „ II 609
Nail tigress had unsheath'd her *n's* at last, *Queen Mary* III i 3
But one that pares his *n's* ; to me ? „ III v 65
There you strike in the *n*. „ V ii 437
Nailed *See* **Naäiled**
Naked Make no allowance for the *n* truth. *Queen Mary* I v 329
And leave the people *n* to the crown, And the crown *n* to the people ; „ III i 119
And tropes are good to clothe a *n* truth, „ III iv 151
To ours in plea for Cranmer than to stand On *n* self-assertion. „ IV i 120
and then Cast on the dunghill *n*, „ IV iii 446
Thy *n* word thy bond ! confirm it now *Harold* II ii 693
I that so prized plain word and *n* truth Have sinn'd against it— „ III i 93
Is *n* truth actable in true life ? „ III i 109
I thought that *n* Truth would shame the Devil The Devil is so modest. „ III i 118
I left our England *n* to the South To meet thee in the North. „ V i 289
They are stripping the dead bodies *n* yonder, „ V ii 34
Life on the hand is *n* gipsy-stuff ; *Becket* II i 193
she sits *n* by a great heap of gold in the middle of the wood, „ III ii 21
And left all *n*, I were lost indeed. „ IV ii 9
but *n* Nature In all her loveliness. *Prom. of May* I 598
Flung by the golden mantle of the cloud, And sets, a *n* fire. *Foresters* II i 29

Nakedly That, were a man of state *n* true, *Harold* III i 113
Nakedness to spy my *n* In my poor North ! „ I i 352
Name (s) (*See also* **Naäme**) your *n* Stands first of those who sign'd *Queen Mary* I i 16
your worship's *n* heard into Maidstone market, „ II i 62
The *n's* of Wyatt, Elizabeth, Courtenay, „ II ii 94
Elizabeth—Her *n* is much abused „ II ii 110
Speak ! in the *n* of God ! „ II ii 271
Thy *n*, thou knave ? *Man.* I am nobody, my Lord. „ III i 246
God's passion ! knave, thy *n* ? „ III i 249
Find out his *n* and bring it me. „ III i 253
What is thy *n* ? *Man.* Sanders. „ III i 312
In our own *n* and that of all the state, „ III iii 120
How many *n's* in the long sweep of time „ III v 39
But that Thy *n* by man be glorified, „ IV iii 153
Ay, but they use his *n*. „ V i 129
you will find written Two *n's*, Philip and Calais ; „ V v 155
miracles will in my *n* be wrought Hereafter.— *Harold* I i 183
Thou shalt be verily king—all but the *n*— „ II ii 633
Why cry thy people on thy sister's *n* ? „ IV i 21
in the *n* of the great God, so be it ! „ IV i 239
no !—not once—in God's *n*, no ! *Becket, Pro.* 126
It much imports me I should know her *n*. „ I i 193
May plaister his clean *n* with scurrilous rhymes ! „ I i 308
When Canterbury hardly bore a *n*. „ I iii 60
I'll have the paper back—blot out my *n*. „ I iii 287
Blessed is he that cometh in the *n* of the Lord ! „ I iii 758
Shame fall on those who give it a dog's *n*— „ II i 142
Son, I absolve thee in the *n* of God. „ II ii 443
found thy *n* a charm to get me Food, roof, and rest. „ V ii 96
in thy *n* I pass'd From house to house. „ V ii 102
if Rosamund is The world's rose, as her *n* imports „ V ii 263
in his *n* we charge you that ye keep This traitor „ V ii 509
Save him, his blood would darken Henry's *n* ; „ V iii 11
Your *n* ? *Synorix.* Strato, my *n*. *Sinnatus.* No Roman *n* ? *Synorix.* A Greek, my lord ; *The Cup* I i 198
n's of those who fought and fell are like „ I ii 164
For whether men malign thy *n*, or no, „ I iii 84
in your lordship's and her ladyship's *n*, *The Falcon* 415
mentioned her *n* too suddenly before my father. *Prom. of May* II 23
Her phantom call'd me by the *n* she loved. „ II 242
Taught her the learned *n's*, anatomized „ II 302
Might I ask your *n* ? *Harold.* Harold. „ II 393
five years' absence, and my change of *n*, „ II 616
My *n* is Harold ! Good day, Dobbins ! „ II 726
I spoke of your *n's*, Allen, „ III 35
your own *n* Of Harold sounds so English „ III 609
And *what* was Your *n* before ? „ III 618
O yes ! In the *n* of the Regent. *Foresters* I iii 55
Ay, ay, because I have a *n* for prowess. „ II i 560
in the *n* of all our woodmen, present her with „ III 57
a traitor coming In Richard's *n*— „ IV 781
Your *n's* will cling like ivy to the wood. „ IV 1085
Name (verb) *N* him ; the Holy Father will confirm him. *Becket, Pro.* 244
My fault to *n* him ! „ II i 175
when those, that *n* themselves Of the King's part, „ V ii 428
Named (*See also* **Naämed**) proud of my ' Monk-King,' Whoever *n* me ; „ II ii 102
Nameless Corpse-candles gliding over *n* graves— *Harold* III i 381
Namesake your Scottish *n* marrying The Dauphin, *Queen Mary* V i 134
which King Harold gave To his dead *n*, *Harold* IV iii 110
Nap his manners want the *n* And gloss of court ; *Queen Mary* III v 70
Napkin I will bind up his wounds with my *n*. *Becket* I iv 107
Naples the Netherlands, Sicily, *N*, Lombardy. *Queen Mary* II i 212
he is King, you know, the King of *N*. The father ceded *N*, that the son Being a King, „ III i 73
Granada, *N*, Sicily, and Milan,— „ V i 44
The Pope would cast the Spaniard out of *N* : „ V i 149
Napoleon make the soil For Cæsars, Cromwells, and *N's* *Prom. of May* III 593
Nard *N*, Cinnamon, amomum, benzoin. *The Cup* II 184
Narrow and the French fleet Rule in the *n* seas. *Queen Mary* V i 7
but at times They seem to me too *n*, *Harold* III ii 64
I send my voice across the *n* seas— „ V i 246
Narrow (*continued*) And in a *n* path. A plover flew before thee. *Becket* II i 53
But in this *n* breathing-time of life *The Cup* I i 29
I hate Traditions, ever since my *n* father, *Prom. of May* I 492
He met a stag there on so *n* a ledge— *Foresters* IV 531
Narrowing Gone *n* down and darkening to a close. *Queen Mary* IV iii 431
out of the eclipse *N* my golden hour ! *Becket* II i 203
Narrowness It is the heat and *n* of the cage *Queen Mary* III v 207
God's revenge upon this realm For *n* and coldness : *Harold* I i 174
Nation comes a deputation From our finikin fairy *n*. *Foresters* II ii 145
Native Feeling my *n* land beneath my foot, I said thereto : ' Ah, *n* land of mine, *Queen Mary* III ii 47
And wrought his worst against his *n* land, *The Cup* I ii 177
Natur (nature) *N* ! *N* ! Well, it be i' *my n* to knock *Prom. of May* I 287
Natur' (nature) It's humbling—it smells o' human *n*. *Becket* I iv 238
Natural the people Claim as their *n* leader— *Queen Mary* I iv 210
You cannot Learn a man's nature from his *n* foe. „ I v 340
Nay swears, it was no wicked wilfulness, Only a *n* chance. „ III v 73
By seeking justice at a stranger's hand Against my *n* subject. „ IV i 21
These are but *n* graces, my good Bishop, „ IV i 176
Hurt no man more Than you would harm your loving *n* brother „ IV iii 189
Gone beyond him and mine own *n* man (It was God's cause) ; „ V ii 102
A sane and *n* loathing for a soul Purer, *Becket* II i 171
all the foul fatalities That blast our *n* passions into pains ! *Prom. of May* III 724
Naturally *N* enough ; for I am closely related „ II 714
N again ; for as I used to transact all his business „ II 718
Nature (*See also* **Natur**) I am of sovereign *n*, that I know, *Queen Mary* I iv 258
You cannot Learn a man's *n* from his natural foe. „ I v 340
Nor shame to call it *n*. „ III v 77
craft that do divide The world of *n* ; „ III v 121
For the pure honour of our common *n*, „ IV iii 298
Why, *n's* licensed vagabond, the swallow, „ V i 20
Does he think Low stature is low *n*, „ V ii 434
Things that seem jerk'd out of the common rut Of *N* *Harold* I i 139
I loved according to the main purpose and intent of *n*. *Becket, Pro.* 502
And know the ways of *N*. „ I i 257
N's moral Against excess. „ I i 373
when murder common As *n's* death, „ I iii 344
I doubt not from your nobleness of *n*, *The Falcon* 804
my nobleness Of *n*, as you deign to call it, „ 811
It is *N* kills, And not for *her* sport either. *Prom. of May* I 272
—is not that the course of *N* too, „ I 279
this poor *N* ! *Dobson.* Natur ! Natur ! „ I 286
but naked *N* In all her loveliness. „ I 599
strain to make ourselves Better and higher than *N*, „ I 604
N a liar, making us feel guilty Of her own faults. „ II 269
equal for pure innocence of *n*, And loveliness of feature. „ II 372
Here crawling in this boundless *N*. „ III 637
worse off than any of you, for I be lean by *n*, *Foresters* I i 45
Till *N*, high and low, and great and small „ I ii 326
for, God help us, we lie by *n*. „ II i 238
Weak *n's* that impute Themselves to their unlikes, „ II i 690
Of a *n* Stronger, sadder than my own, „ II ii 188
yet in tune with *N* and the bees. „ IV 32
Natured *See* **Hard-natured, Noblest-natured**
Naught (*See also* **Nought**) and since the Sheriff left me *n* but an empty belly, *Foresters* II i 279
Nave *n* and aisles all empty as a fool's jest ! *Queen Mary* IV iii 286
Navy and might have sunk a *n*— *Becket* III iii 125
Naw (no) thaw I beänt *n* scholard, fur I 'ednt *n* time to maäke mysen a scholard *Prom. of May* I 332
He 'ant *n* pride in 'im, and we'll git 'im to speechify for us arter dinner. „ I 439
thou hesn't *n* business 'ere wi' *my* Dora, „ II 735
we worked *n* wuss upo' the cowd tea ; „ III 58
An' we weänt mention *n* naämes, „ III 130
Nawbody (nobody) why there wudn't be a dinner for *n*, „ I 149

Nawbody (nobody) (*continued*) When ye thowt there were *n* watchin' o' you, *Prom. of May* II 179
Nay *See* **Naäy**
Neap-tide the realm is poor, The exchequer at *n-t*: *Queen Mary* I v 121
Near They call me *n*, for I am close to thee And England— *Harold* III i 6
Stay !—too *n* is death. *The Cup* I iii 104
Nearer For I will come no *n* to your Grace ; *Queen Mary* III v 200
No *n* to me ! back ! *Foresters* IV 692
Nearest (adj.) She had but follow'd the device of those Her *n* kin : *Queen Mary* III i 380
Nearest (s) Who stands the *n* to her. „ v ii 416
The Atheling is *n* to the throne. *Harold* II ii 569
Nearness Upon my greater *n* to the birthday *Foresters* II i 44
Necessity Statesmen that are wise Shape a *n*, *Queen Mary* III iii 33
bound To that *n* which binds us down ; *Harold* V i 108
so we could not but laugh, as by a royal *n*— *Becket* III iii 159
Neck on his *n* a collar, Gold, thick with diamonds ; *Queen Mary* III i 78
and weight of all the world From off his *n* to mine. „ III vi 214
rear and run And break both *n* and axle. *Harold* I i 374
See here this little key about my *n* ! „ III i 10
swear nay to that by this cross on thy *n*. *Becket, Pro.* 370
Has wheedled it off the King's *n* to her own. „ IV ii 201
not yield To lay your *n* beneath your citizen's heel. „ V i 31
upon a *n* Less lovely than her own, *The Falcon* 55
I wore the lady's chaplet round my *n* ; „ 631
I lay them for the first time round your *n*. „ 908
Swear to me by that relic on thy *n*. *Prince John.* I swear then by this relic on my *n*— *Foresters* I ii 170
twist it round thy *n* and hang thee by it. „ IV 688
Neck-broken Huntsman, and hound, and deer were all *n-b* ! *The Cup* I ii 24
Necklace if we *will* buy diamond *n's* To please our lady, *The Falcon* 44
She should return thy *n* then. „ 70
Need (s) Ask me for this at thy most *n*, son Harold, At thy most *n*— *Harold* III i 14
No *n* ! no *n* ! . . . There is a bench. *Becket* II i 123
Good Prince, art thou in *n* of any gold ? *Foresters* I ii 162
Need (verb) I *n* thee not. Why dost thou follow me ? *Harold* II ii 231
Needed fly like bosom friends when *n* most. *The Falcon* 527
Needle —in music Peerless—her *n* perfect, *Queen Mary* III i 360
Negative (*See also* **Positive-negative**) Or answer'd them in smiling *n's* ; „ IV iii 603
not a heart like a jewel in it—that's too *n* ; *The Falcon* 92
Neighbour he was my *n* once in Kent. *Queen Mary* II iii 85
good *n*, There should be something fierier than fire „ V iv 25
my foundation For men who serve the *n*, *Harold* V i 98
Good murnin', *n's*, and the saäme to you, my men. *Prom. of May* I 317
Neighing *N* and roaring as they leapt to land— *Harold* IV iii 197
Neither No friendship sacred, values *n* man Nor woman save as tools— *Foresters* IV 713
Nene (river) Gone hawking on the *N*, *Becket* I iii 3
Nescience Back into *n* with as little pain *Prom. of May* II 341
Nest (s) (*See also* **Home-nest**) then would find Her *n* within the cloister, *Harold* IV i 234
A *n* in a bush. *Becket.* And where, my liege ? *Becket, Pro.* 155
And where is she ? There in her English *n* ? „ *Pro.* 178
I wrong the bird ; she leaves only the *n* she built, „ I iv 46
came upon A wild-fowl sitting on her *n*, „ V ii 234
lark, that warblest high Above thy lowly *n*, *Prom. of May* III 200
all in all to one another from the time when we first peeped into the bird's *n*, „ III 274
When I and thou will rob the *n* of her. *Foresters* I ii 161
So that myself alone may rob the *n*. *Prince John.* Well, well then, thou shalt rob the *n* alone. „ I ii 166
Nest (verb) nor priestly king to cross Their billings ere they *n*. *Harold* III ii 95
Nested Knows where he *n*—ever comes again. *Queen Mary* V i 26
Net (s) We be fishermen ; I came to see after my *n's*. *Harold* II i 27
thou hast them in thy *n*. *Becket* II ii 287
No rushing on the game—the *n*,—the *n*. *The Cup* I i 170
Net (verb) How dense a fold of danger *n's* him round, *Harold* II ii 17
Netherlands Heir of this England and the *N* ! *Queen Mary* I v 418
nearer home, the *N*, Sicily, Naples, Lombardy. „ II i 212
Netherlands (*continued*) Look to the *N*, wherein have been *Queen Mary* III iv 106
The voices of Franche-Comté, and the *N*, „ V i 46
Never *See* **Niver**
Never-dawning Shall mark out Vice from Virtue in the gulf Of *n-d* darkness ? *Prom. of May* I 542
New (adj.) out you flutter Thro' the *n* world, go zigzag, *Queen Mary* I iv 54
But hatch you some *n* treason in the woods. „ I v 465
None so *n*, Sir Thomas, and none so old, Sir Thomas. No *n* news that Philip comes to wed Mary, no old news that all men hate it. „ II i 14
Look at the *N* World—a paradise made hell ; „ II i 207
The *n* Lords Are quieted with their sop of Abbey-lands, „ III i 140
The light of this *n* learning wanes and dies : „ III ii 172
Well, Madam, this *n* happiness of mine ? „ III ii 208
N learning as they call it ; „ IV i 78
in the Testaments, Both Old and *N*. „ IV iii 234
But she's a heretic, and when I am gone, Brings the *n* learning back. „ V i 202
But this *n* Pope Caraffa, Paul the Fourth, „ V ii 32
A *n* Northumberland, another Wyatt ? „ V v 188
That palate is insane which cannot tell A good dish from a bad, *n* wine from old. *Becket, Pro.* 106
I care not for thy *n* archbishoprick. „ I i 217
Shall I forget my *n* archbishoprick And smite thee „ I i 220
It well befits thy *n* archbishoprick To take the vagabond woman „ I i 225
That Map, and these *n* railers at the Church „ I i 306
What, this ! and this !—what ! *n* and old together ! „ I iii 309
Die for a woman, what *n* faith is this ? *The Cup* I iii 67
One ghost of all the ghosts—as yet so *n*, „ II 142
We cannot flaunt it in *n* feathers now : *The Falcon* 42
and her affections Will flower toward the light in some *n* face. *Prom. of May* I 486
tide Of full democracy has overwhelm'd This Old World, from that flood will rise the *N*, „ I 595
When the great Democracy Makes a *n* world— „ I 672
Neither the old world, nor the *n*, nor father, „ I 674
Oh, last night, Tired, pacing my *n* lands at Littlechester, „ II 647
and I have lighted On a *n* pleasure. „ II 669
will give him, as they say, a *n* lease of life. „ III 424
but this *n* moon, I fear, Is darkness. *Foresters* I ii 85
whereon the throstle rock'd Sings a *n* song to the *n* year— „ I iii 28
We must fly from Robin Hood And this *n* queen of the wood. „ II ii 139
Shall drink the health of our *n* woodland Queen. „ III 314
Drink to the health of our *n* Queen o' the woods, „ III 368
We drink the health of thy *n* Queen o' the woods. „ III 372
so thou fight at quarterstaff for thy dinner with our Robin, that will give thee a *n* zest for it, „ IV 209
or shall I call it by that *n* term Brought from the sacred East, „ IV 704
New (adv.) Ay, that am I, *n* converted, but the old leaven sticks to my tongue yet. *Queen Mary* I iii 47
New-made *n-m* children Of our imperial mother see the show. *The Cup* II 164
And I could see that as the *n-m* couple Came from the Minster, *Queen Mary* III i 93
News *N* to me ! It then remains for your poor Gardiner, „ I v 219
N abroad, William ? „ II i 13
No new *n* that Philip comes to wed Mary, no old *n* that all men hate it. „ II i 16
There *is n*, there *is n*, „ II i 58
Good *n* have I to tell you, *n* to make „ III ii 186
N, mates ! a miracle, a miracle ! *n* ! „ III ii 209
whether this flash of *n* be false or true, „ III ii 234
whether it bring you bitter *n* or sweet, „ III v 201
(The *n* was sudden) I could mould myself „ III vi 234
Reginald Pole, what *n* hath plagued thy heart ? „ V ii 17
Madam, he may bring you *n* from Philip. „ V ii 229
I bring your Majesty such grievous *n* „ V ii 240

News (*continued*) there is a post from over seas With *n* for thee. *Harold* II ii 210
N from England? „ II ii 287
Ill *n* for guests, ha, Malet! „ II ii 302
Ill *n* hath come! Our hapless brother, „ III ii 120
but worse *n*: this William sent to Rome, „ III ii 140
Goodly *n*! *Morcar.* Doubt it not thou! „ IV i 219
Harsh is the *n*! hard is our honeymoon! „ IV iii 229
And thou, my carrier-pigeon of black *n*, „ IV iii 233
disappear'd, They told me, from the farm—and darker *n*. *Prom. of May* II 408
No *n* of young Walter? *Foresters* I i 72
but we have no *n* of Richard yet, „ I ii 94
I trust he brings us *n* of the King's coming. „ I iii 53
Give me some *n* of my sweet Marian. „ II i 481
Black *n*, black *n* from Nottingham! „ III 446
we have certain *n* he died in prison. „ IV 778

Newspaäper (newspaper) —what's the *n* word, Wilson? —celebrate— *Prom. of May* I 320

New-wakening all the leaf of this *N-w* year. *The Falcon* 340

New year Sings a new song to the *n y*— *Foresters* I iii 28

Next Who shall crown him? Canterbury is dying. *Becket.* The *n* Canterbury. *Becket, Pro.* 241
And is the King's *if* too high a stile for your lordship to over-step and come at all things in the *n* field? „ III iii 282
which he Gainsays by *n* sunrising— „ IV ii 278
A child's sand-castle on the beach For the *n* wave— *The Cup* I ii 255
the *n* time you waste them at a pothouse you get no more from me. *Prom. of May* III 99

Nicholas (Archbishop of York and Lord Chancellor) (*See also* **Nicholas Heath**) I wish you a good morning, good Sir *N*: *Queen Mary* V i 14
Sir *N* tells you true, „ V i 16
Sir *N*! I am stunn'd—Nicholas Heath? „ V ii 250
Spite of your melancholy Sir *N*, „ V ii 327

Nicholas Heath Sir *N H*, the Chancellor, Would see your Highness. „ V ii 225
Madam, your Chancellor Sir *N H*. *Mary.* Sir Nicholas! I am stunn'd—*N H*? „ V ii 249

Nicholas (Saint) By St. *N* I have a sudden passion *Foresters* I iii 121
By St. *N* They must have sprung like Ghosts „ IV 591

Niece Prince of fluff and feather come To woo you, *n*, *Queen Mary* I iv 164
Look to it, *n*, He hath no fence when Gardiner „ I iv 202
Ay, good *n*! You should be plain and open with me, *n*. „ I iv 216
love that men should smile upon you, *n*. „ I iv 275
They will not, *n*. Mine is the fleet „ I iv 286

Night (*See also* **Good-night, To-night**) I see but the black *n*, and hear the wolf. „ I v 413
It breaks my heart to hear her moan at *n* „ I v 604
Last *n* I climb'd into the gate-house, Brett, „ II iii 14
Out of the dead, deep *n* of heathendom, „ III iii 173
Those damp, black, dead *N's* in the Tower; „ III v 139
a fox may filch a hen by *n*, „ III v 157
Last *n*, I dream'd the faggots were alight, „ IV ii 1
happy haven Where he shall rest at *n*, „ IV iii 580
horses On all the road from Dover, day and *n*; On all the road from Harwich, *n* and day; „ V ii 578
Good *n*! Go home. Besides, you curse so loud, „ V iv 61
there once more—this is the seventh *n*! *Harold* I i 2
last *n* An evil dream that ever came and went— „ I ii 69
beast of prey Out of the bush by *n*? „ I ii 214
passing by that hill three *n's* ago— „ III i 366
Walk'd at *n* on the misty heather; *N*, as black as a raven's feather; „ III ii 5
banner, Blaze like a *n* of fatal stars „ IV i 251
Last *n* King Edward came to me in dreams— (repeat) *Harold* IV i 259, 265
I have ridden *n* and day from Pevensey— „ IV iii 192
Last *n* I followed a woman in the city here. *Becket, Pro.* 468
Follow me this Rosamund day and *n*, „ *Pro.* 506
That rang Within my head last *n*, „ I i 71
flutter out at *n*? „ I i 282
Good *n*! good *n*! „ I i 313
Both, good *n*! „ I i 406

KK*

Night (*continued*) But the miller came home that *n*, *Becket* I iv 173
My friends, the Archbishop bids you good *n*. „ I iv 262
to bid you this *n* pray for him who hath fed „ I iv 266
Like sudden *n* in the main glare of day. „ II i 57
Who thief-like fled from his own church by *n*, „ II ii 157
Madam, not to-night—the *n* is falling. „ III ii 52
she says she can make you sleep o' *n's*. „ IV ii 20
evil song far on into the *n* Thrills to the topmost tile— „ V ii 208
Save by that way which leads thro' *n* to light. „ V iii 88
close not yet the door upon a *n* That looks half day. *The Cup* I ii 388
crowd that hunted me Across the woods, last *n*. „ I iii 17
came back last *n* with her son to the castle. *The Falcon* 3
The *n*, As some cold-manner'd friend „ 641
The stock-dove coo'd at the fall of *n*, *Prom. of May* I 41
whose cheerless Houris after death Are *N* and Silence, „ I 251
I laäme't my knee last *n* running arter a thief. „ I 387
Immanuel Goldsmiths was broke into o' Monday *n*, „ I 393
Who shrieks by day at what she does by *n*, „ I 533
Oh, Philip, Father heard you last *n*. „ I 557
I will fly to you thro' the *n*, the storm— „ I 702
last *n* Tired, pacing my new lands at Littlechester, „ II 646
that dreadful *n*! that lonely walk to Littlechester, „ III 366
I cannot sleep o' *n's* by cause on 'em. *Foresters* II i 384
In the *n*, in the day, „ II ii 182
having lived For twenty days and *n's* in mail, „ IV 124
Or in the balmy breathings of the *n*, „ IV 1068

Nightingale not to hear the *n's*, But hatch you some new treason *Queen Mary* I v 464
The lark above, the *n* below, „ II i 52
Mad for thy mate, passionate *n* . . . *Harold* I ii 2
The *n's* in Haveringatte-Bower „ I ii 18
I dumb thee too, my wingless *n*! „ I ii 24
Here to the *n's*. „ III ii 90
not in tune, a *n* out of season; *Becket, Pro.* 350
I keep it to kill *n's*. *John.* *N's*? *Foresters* II i 380
This is no bow to hit *n's*; „ II i 391

Nightmare As tho' the *n* never left her bed. *Queen Mary* I v 605
Must be the *n* breaking on my peace *Becket* II i 36

Nihilist I that have been call'd a Socialist, A Communist, a *N*— *Prom. of May* III 585

Nimble The *n*, wild, red, wiry, savage king— *Harold* IV i 197

Nine The conduit painted—the *n* worthies—ay! *Queen Mary* III i 258
And I ha' *n* darters i' the spital that be dead *Becket* I iv 249
And the other *n*? *Filippo.* Sold! *The Falcon* 411

Ninepin more of a man than to be bowled over like a *n*. *Foresters* IV 305

Nineteen After the *n* winters of King Stephen— *Becket* I iii 338

Ninetieth This is my *n* birthday. (repeat) *Harold* IV i 121, 127

Niobe How gracefully there she stands Weeping—the little *N*! *Prom. of May* I 736

Nip *N*, *n* him for his fib. *Foresters* II ii 121
N him not, but let him snore. „ II ii 122

Nipper Count-crab will make his *n's* meet *Harold* II i 76

Nipt Her life was winter, for her spring was *n*: *Queen Mary* V v 270

Niver (never) Theer ye goäs agean, Miss, *n* believing owt I says to ye— *Prom. of May* I 107
I *n* thowt o' mysen i' that waäy; „ I 176
leästwaäys they *n* cooms 'ere but fur the trout „ I 212
N man 'ed better friends, and I will saäy *n* master 'ed better men; „ I 322
and, thaw I says it mysen, *n* men 'ed a better master— „ I 327
I *n* 'es sa much as one pin's prick of paäin; „ I 359
fur I *n* touched a drop of owt till my oän wedding-daäy, „ I 361
thaw me and 'im we *n* 'grees about the tithe; „ I 444
thaw he *n* mended that gap i' the glebe fence „ I 445
Blacksmith, thaw he *n* shoes a herse to my likings „ I 447
he tell'd me 'at sweet'arts *n* worked well togither; „ II 156
Fur she'd *n* 'a been talkin' haäfe an hour „ II 603
Fur she *n* knawed 'is faäce when 'e wur 'ere afoor; „ II 606
I ha *n* been surprised but once i' my life, „ III 439

No *See* **Naw, Noä**

Noä (No) *N*, Joan. (repeat) *Queen Mary* IV iii 480, 483, 485
N, not a bit. *Prom. of May* I 34
N, Miss. I ha'n't seed 'er neither. „ I 48
N, Miss Dora; as blue as— (repeat) „ I 95, 99
N, but I haätes 'im. „ I 217

Noä (no) (*continued*) *N*, fur thou be nobbut schoolmaster; *Prom. of May* I 307
N, Mr. Steer. „ I 314
N; I laäme't my knee last night running arter a thief. „ I 386
N; I knaws a deäl better now. „ II 26
N, *n*! Keep 'em. „ II 44
N, not yet. „ II 132
Philip Hedgar o' Soomerset!—*N*—yeas— „ II 588
It mun be *him*. *N*! „ II 602
n—thaw they hanged ma at 'Size fur it. „ II 697
N, Miss; we worked naw wuss upo' the cowd tea; „ III 58
O lor, Miss! *n*, *n*, *n*! „ III 92

Noailles (French Ambassador) I am mighty popular with them, *N*. *Queen Mary* I iii 102
Good morning, *N*. „ I iii 159
King of France, *N* the Ambassador, „ I iv 110
Good morning, Sir de *N*. „ I v 242
A letter which the Count de *N* wrote „ V ii 496

Noän (none) but *n* o' the parishes goäs by that name 'ereabouts. *Prom. of May* I 268
now theer be *n* o' my men, thinks I to mysen, „ I 409
Miss Dora, that I ha' been *n* too sudden wi' you, „ II 60
Meä? why, it be the Lord's doin', *n* o' mine; „ III 49

Nobbut (only) (*See also* **Nubbut**) Noä, fur thou be *n* schoolmaster; „ I 307
fur I wur *n* a laäbourer, „ I 329
if I could ha' gone on wi' the plowin' *n* the smell o' the mou'd „ I 376
and it seems to me *n* t'other day. „ II 6
and if ye would *n* hev me, „ II 73
'at I ha' *n* larned mysen haäfe on it. „ III 4

Noble (adj.) By God's light a *n* creature, right royal! *Queen Mary* I i 69
but to my mind the Lady Elizabeth is the more *n* and royal. „ I i 72
Well, that's a *n* horse of yours, my Lord. „ I iv 143
A king to be,—is he not *n*, girl? „ I v 4
No, by the holy Virgin, being *n*, „ I v 70
Swear with me, *n* fellow-citizens, all, „ II ii 296
And that this *n* realm thro' after years „ III iii 156
do triumph at this hour In the reborn salvation of a land So *n*. „ III iii 183
But this most *n* prince Plantagenet, Our good Queen's cousin—dallying over seas Even when his brother's, nay, his *n* mother's, Head fell— „ III iv 291
Out, girl, you wrong a *n* gentleman. „ III v 68
N as his young person and old shield. „ V ii 513
Doth he not look *n*? I had heard of him in battle over seas, „ V v 32
Courage, *n* Aldwyth! Let all thy people bless thee! *Harold* I ii 182
I found him all a *n* host should be. „ II ii 10
I can but love this *n*, honest Harold. „ II ii 94
whereby we came to know Thy valour and thy value, *n* earl. „ II ii 202
Thou must swear absolutely, *n* Earl. „ II ii 716
'If ye side with William Ye are not *n*.' „ II ii 789
O *n* Harold, I would thou couldst have sworn. „ III i 325
This is *n*! That sounds of Godwin. „ IV ii 57
N Gurth! Best son of Godwin! If I fall, I fall— „ V i 134
dashes it on Gurth, and Gurth, Our *n* Gurth, is down! „ V i 642
for were all, my lord, as *n* as yourself, who would look up to you? *Becket* III iii 306
O God, O *n* knights, O sacrilege! „ V iii 178
A *n* anger! but Antonius To-morrow will demand your tribute— *The Cup* I ii 95
A gallant boy, A *n* bird, each perfect of the breed. *The Falcon* 320
A *n* saying—and acted on would yield A nobler breed of men and women. „ 753
Nothing but my brave bird, my *n* falcon, „ 873
Why then the dying of my *n* bird Hath served me better than her living— „ 900
Ay, *n* Earl, and never part with it. *Foresters* I ii 303
Not till she clean forget thee, *n* Earl. „ I ii 306
Ay dear Robin! ah *n* captain, friend of the poor! „ II i 182
N Robin. „ III 185
I thank you, *n* sir, the very blossom Of bandits. „ III 246
I thank you, *n* sir, and will pray for you „ III 250

Noble (adj.) (*continued*) This friar is of much boldness, *n* captain. *Robin*. He hath got it from the bottle, *n* knight. *Foresters* IV 235
Damsel, is this the truth? *Marian*. Ay, *n* knight. „ IV 771

Noble (s) have marked the haughtiness of their *n's*; *Queen Mary* II i 169
Spain moves, bribes our *n's* with her gold, „ II i 202
Could Harry have foreseen that all our *n's* Would perish „ III i 117
We have given the church-lands back: The *n's* would not; „ V i 172
all the magistracy, all the *n's*, and all the wealthy; „ V iv 51
N's we dared not touch. „ V v 104
he speaks to a *n* as tho' he were a churl, and to a churl as if he were a *n*. *Becket, Pro.* 455

Nobleness I doubt not from your *n* of nature, *The Falcon* 803

Nobler Tell him the Saints are *n* than he dreams, Tell him that God is *n* than the Saints, *Harold* V i 55
What *n*? men must die. „ V i 270
Go therefore like a friend slighted by one That hath climb'd up to *n* company. *Becket* I i 351
A sane and natural loathing for a soul Purer, and truer and *n* than herself; „ II i 172
and acted on would yield A *n* breed of men and women. *The Falcon* 755
n The victim was, the more acceptable Might be the sacrifice. „ 879
if our true Robin Be not the *n* lion of the twain. *Foresters* IV 396

Nobler-looking Ay, but *n-l*. *Queen Mary* I v 322

Noblest I am the *n* blood in Europe, Madam, „ I iv 84
the *n* light That ever flash'd across my life, *Foresters* III 140

Noblest-natured scorns The *n-n* man alive, and I— *The Falcon* 259

Nobody (*See also* **Nawbody**) Thy name, thou knave? *Man*. I am *n*, my Lord. *Queen Mary* III i 247

Nod A life of *n's* and yawns. „ I iii 116
With Cain belike, in the land of *N*, *Becket* I iv 196

No-hows (unsatisfactorily) and so brought me *n-h* as I may say, „ III i 129

Noise make what *n* you will with your tongues, *Queen Mary* I i 6
What *n* was that? she told us of arm'd men *Becket* V ii 226

Nokes (a character in Queen Mary) Old *N*, can't it make thee a bastard? *Queen Mary* I i 28
No, old *N*. *Old Nokes*. It's Harry! „ I i 33

Nokes (a farm hand) Luscombe, *N*, Oldham, Skipworth! *Prom. of May* III 53

Nolo N *episcopari*. *Henry*. Ay, but N *Archiepiscopari*, *Becket, Pro.* 284

None *See* **Noän**

Nonsense That's all *n*, you know, such a baby as you are. *Prom. of May* I 784
I am glad my *n* has made you smile! „ III 314

Noon a bat flew out at him In the clear *n*, *Foresters* II ii 97
monies should be paid in to the Abbot of York, at the end of the month at *n*, and they are delivered here in the wild wood an hour after *n*. „ IV 508

Norfolk (Duke of) when the Duke of *N* moved against us *Queen Mary* II iii 2

Norman (adj.) (*See also* **Demi-Norman**) Did ye not cast with bestial violence Our holy *N* bishops down from all Their thrones *Harold* I i 50
I have a *N* fever on me, son, And cannot answer sanely . . . „ I i 87
Is not the *N* Count thy friend and mine? „ I i 247
And bolts of thunder moulded in high heaven To serve the *N* purpose, „ II ii 34
They have taken away the toy thou gavest me, The *N* knight. „ II ii 107
Well, thou shalt have another *N* knight! „ II ii 114
Stay—as yet Thou hast but seen how *N* hands can strike, But walk'd our *N* field, „ II ii 171
And we will fill thee full of *N* sun, „ II ii 180
And he our lazy-pious *N* King, „ II ii 444
Then our modest women—I know the *N* license—thine own Edith— „ II ii 477
if there sat within the *N* chair A ruler all for England— „ II ii 533
We could not move from Dover to the Humber Saving thro' *N* bishopricks— „ II ii 538
Ay, ay, but many among our *N* lords Hate thee for this, „ II ii 544
confirm it now Before our gather'd *N* baronage, „ II ii 695
I know your *N* cookery is so spiced, It masks all this. „ II ii 810

Norman (adj.) (*continued*) They have built their castles here;
Our priories are *N*; the *N* adder Hath bitten us; *Harold* III i 37
To save thee from the wrath of *N* Saints. *Stigand.*
N enough! „ III i 217
Not mean To make our England *N*. „ III i 250
Or *N*? *Voices.* No! „ IV i 64
Who shook the *N* scoundrels off the throne, „ IV i 81
Keep that for *N* William! „ IV iii 169
William the *N*, for the wind had changed— „ IV iii 181
His *N* Daniel! Mene, Mene, Tekel! „ V i 35
No *N* horse Can shatter England, standing shield by shield; „ V i 194
But by all Saints— *Leofwin.* Barring the *N*! „ V i 225
The *N* arrow! „ V i 483
All the *N* foot Are storming up the hill. „ V i 522
The *N* Count is down. „ V i 553
Truth! no; a lie; a trick, a *N* trick! „ V i 607
His oath was broken—O holy *N* Saints, „ V i 617
and see beyond Your *N* shrines, pardon it, pardon it, „ V i 620
I cannot love them, For they are *N* saints— „ V ii 9
Make them again one people—*N*, English; And English, *N*; „ V ii 188
There was a little fair-hair'd *N* maid Lived in my mother's house: *Becket* V ii 260
that he calls you oversea To answer for it in his *N* courts. „ V ii 355
I am none of your delicate *N* maidens who can only broider *Foresters* I i 212
This John—this *N* tyranny—the stream is bearing us all down, „ I i 238
our John By his *N* arrogance and dissoluteness, „ II i 85
Dear, in these days of *N* license, when Our English maidens are their prey, if ever A *N* damsel fell into our hands, „ III 178
Where lies that cask of wine whereof we plunder'd The *N* prelate? „ III 308
Earl, thou when we were hence Hast broken all our *N* forest laws, „ IV 886

Norman (s) rest of England bow'd theirs to the *N*, *Queen Mary* II i 160
Our friends, the *N's*, holp to shake his chair. I have a Norman fever on me, son, *Harold* I i 85
it threatens us no more Than French or *N*. „ I i 135
Because I love the *N* better—no, „ I i 171
my father drove the *N's* out Of England?— „ I i 252
N's up To fight for thee again! „ II ii 58
Count of the *N's*, thou hast ransom'd us, „ II ii 157
The *N's* love thee not, nor thou the *N's*, „ II ii 253
And he our lazy-pious Norman King, With all his *N's* round him once again, „ II ii 445
I have heard the *N's* Count upon this confusion— „ II ii 458
Descends the ruthless *N*— „ II ii 467
thou and he drove our good *N's* out From England, „ II ii 525
Saving thro' Norman bishopricks—I say Ye would applaud that *N* who should drive „ II ii 539
because we found him A *N* of the *N's*. „ II ii 582
Angle, Jute, Dane, Saxon, *N*, „ II ii 763
let earth rive, gulf in These cursed *N's*— „ II ii 783
If e'er the *N* grow too hard for thee, „ III i 12
wholesome use of these To chink against the *N*, „ III i 22
Not mean To make our England Norman. *Edward.* There spake Godwin, Who hated all the *N's*; „ III i 252
Be kindly to the *N's* left among us, „ III i 303
will ye upon oath, Help us against the *N*? „ IV i 181
Holy Father Hath given this realm of England to the *N*. „ V i 14
The *N*, What is he doing? „ V i 217
Call when the *N* moves— „ V i 230
The Norseman's raid Hath helpt the *N*, „ V i 292
when I sware Falsely to him, the falser *N*, „ V i 303
The *N* moves! „ V i 438
and they fly—the *N* flies. „ V i 541
They fly once more, they fly, the *N* flies! „ V i 596
The *N* sends his arrows up to Heaven, „ V i 666
N, thou liest! liars all of you, „ V ii 104
My *N's* may but move as true with me „ V ii 184
like his kingly sires, The *N's*, striving still *Becket* IV ii 442
both fought against the tyranny of the kings, the *N's*. *Foresters* I i 230

Norman-blooded I say not this, as being Half *N-b*, *Harold* I i 169

Normandy if it pass, Go not to *N*—go not to *N*. *Harold.* And wherefore not, my king, to *N*? „ I i 235
And why not me, my lord, to *N*? „ I i 246
I pray thee, do not go to *N*. „ I i 250
That he should harp this way on *N*? „ I i 271
'I pray you do not go to *N*.' „ II ii 218
But for my father I love *N*. „ II ii 270
Go not to *N*— (repeat) „ II ii 327
I am thy fastest friend in *N*. „ II ii 556
When he was here in *N*, He loved us and we him, „ II ii 579
Foremost in England and in *N*; „ II ii 631
For I shall most sojourn in *N*; „ II ii 634
And that the Holy Saints of *N* „ II ii 727
From all the holiest shrines in *N*! „ II ii 735
And Wulfnoth is alone in *N*. „ III i 81
Praying for *N*; „ V i 219
When I am out in *N* or Anjou. *Becket, Pro.* 144
Barons of England and of *N*, „ I iii 742
A hundred, too, from *N* and Anjou: „ II ii 173

Normanism He hath clean repented of his *N*. *Harold* III i 30

Normanize—Plays on the word,—and *N's* too! „ III i 388

Normanland in *N* God speaks thro' abler voices, „ I i 165
but those of *N* Are mightier than our own. „ III i 223

Norseland hugest wave from *N* ever yet Surged on us, „ IV iii 62
Have we not broken Wales and *N*? „ V i 395

Norseman Would ye be *Norsemen*? *Voices.* No! „ IV i 62
That these will follow thee against the *Norsemen*, „ IV i 158
will ye, if I yield, Follow against the *N*? „ IV i 177
Where lie the *Norsemen*? on the Derwent? „ IV i 253
Why didst thou let so many *Norsemen* hence? „ IV iii 33
The *N's* raid Hath helpt the Norman, „ V i 290

North Stays longer here on our poor *n* than you:— *Queen Mary* V i 24
Hath taken Scarboro' Castle, *n* of York; „ V i 287
Is the *N* quiet, Gamel? *Harold* I i 107
to spy my nakedness In my poor *N*! „ I i 353
For if the *N* take fire, I should be back; „ I ii 67
shake the *N* With earthquake and disruption— „ I ii 199
And all the *N* of Humber is one storm. „ II ii 291
Hast thou such trustless jailors in thy *N*? „ II ii 685
N and South Thunder together, „ III i 391
the truth Was lost in that fierce *N*, „ III ii 26
Are landed *N* of Humber, and in a field „ III ii 126
Well then, we will to the *N*. „ III ii 139
Should care to plot against him in the *N*. „ IV i 167
Conjured the mightier Harold from his *N* „ IV ii 69
send the shatter'd *N* again to sea, „ IV iii 140
Who made this Britain England, break the *N*: „ IV iii 155
in South and *N* at once I could not be. „ IV iii 218
To meet thee in the *N*. „ V i 290
—your *n* chills me. *Becket, Pro.* 330
thro' all the forest land *N* to the Tyne: *Foresters* II i 89
There was a man of ours Up in the *n*, „ IV 530

Northampton on a Tuesday did I fly Forth from *N*; *Becket* V ii 287

North-east the *N-e* took and turned him South-west, then the South-west turned him *N-e*, „ II ii 320

Northumberland (Northumbria) Thou art a great voice in *N*! *Harold* I i 114
I heard from thy *N* to-day. „ I i 350
Wash up that old crown of *N*. „ V i 167

Northumberland (Earl of) and death to *N*! *Queen Mary* I i 67
she spoke even of *N* pitifully, „ I i 93
I do believe he holp *N* „ I v 278
when you put *N* to death, „ I v 485
never whine Like that poor heart, *N*, „ II ii 333
Was not Lord Pembroke with *N*? „ II iv 8
His breaking with *N* broke *N*. „ II iv 13
False to *N*, is he false to me? „ II iv 39
Why, ev'n the haughty prince, *N*, „ III i 147
The stormy Wyatts and *N's*, „ III ii 168
A new *N*, another Wyatt? „ V v 188

Northumbria (ancient earldom) When didst thou hear from thy *N*? *Harold* I i 281
Leave me alone, brother, with my *N*: „ I i 286
I heard from my *N* yesterday. „ I i 331
How goes it then with thy *N*? „ I i 333

Northumbria (ancient earldom) (*continued*) fain had calcined all *N* To one black ash, *Harold* III i 56
I come for mine own Earldom, my *N*; „ IV ii 30
N threw thee off, she will not have thee, „ IV ii 33
Northumbrian (adj.) Among the good *N* folk, „ I ii 220
Our old *N* crown, And kings of our own choosing. „ IV i 31
Of the *N* helmet on the heath? „ V i 144
Northumbrian (s) if his *N's* rise And hurl him from them,— „ II ii 455
Thou didst arouse the fierce *N's*! „ V i 347
And that the false *N* held aloof, „ V ii 165
Norway (country) and the giant King of *N*, Harold Hardrada— „ III ii 122
as having been so bruised By Harold, king of *N*; „ IV i 10
Norway (King) He hath gone to kindle *N* against England, „ III i 79
Since Tostig came with *N*— „ IV i 173
I am foraging For *N's* army. „ IV ii 6
Free thee or slay thee, *N* will have war; No man would strike with Tostig, save for *N*. „ IV ii 18
Thou art nothing in thine England, save for *N*, „ IV ii 23
What for *N* then? He looks for land among us, „ IV ii 52
sequel had been other than his league With *N*, „ IV iii 89
Here by dead *N* without dream or dawn! „ IV iii 122
Nose cackling of bastardy under the Queen's own *n*? *Queen Mary* I i 59
Who rub their fawning *n's* in the dust, „ III iii 242
God hath blest or cursed me with a *n*— „ III v 179
God hath given your Grace a *n*, or not, „ III v 203
rose but pricks his *n* Against the thorn, *Harold* I i 422
when I was a-getting o' bluebells for your ladyship's *n* to smell on— *Becket* iii i 162
wait Till his *n* rises; he will be very king. „ V ii 184
Lady Marian holds her *n* when she steps across it. *Foresters* I i 84
Nosing *See* **Carrion-nosing**
Nostril puffed out such an incense of unctuosity into the *n's* of our Gods of Church and State, *Becket* III iii 116
Note He never yet could brook the *n* of scorn. „ V ii 299
play the *n* Whereat the dog shall howl *Harold* I ii 191
Nothing (*See also* **Naught, Nought, Nowt, Something-nothing**) *N*? *Alice.* Never, your Grace. *Queen Mary* I v 574
What such a one as Wyatt says is *n*: „ III i 139
And *n* of the titles to the crown; „ III i 383
he is free enough in talk, But tells me *n*. „ III ii 194
They know *n*; They burn for *n*. „ V ii 113
but say the world is *n*— „ V ii 368
N, Madam, Save that methought I gather'd „ V iii 101
N; but 'come, come, come,' and all awry, „ V v 15
quiet, ay, as yet—*N* as yet. *Harold* I i 111
Make not thou The *n* something. „ I i 363
On a sudden—at a something—for a *n*— „ I i 443
Anything or *n*? *The Falcon* 133
he would answer *n*, I could make *n* of him; *Prom. of May* III 496
N from you! (repeat) „ III 802, 809
we be beggars, we come to ask o' you. We ha' *n*. *Second Beggar.* Rags, *n* but our rags. *Foresters* III 190
Notice I have *n* from our partisans Within the city *Queen Mary* II iii 51
A *n* from the priest, *Becket* III iii 3
Flutter'd or flatter'd by your *n* of her, *The Falcon* 538
Nottingham Thou knowest that the Sheriff of *N* loves thee. *Foresters* I i 223
The Sheriff of *N* was there—not John. „ I i 252
Beware of John and the Sheriff of *N*. „ I i 255
What art thou, man? Sheriff of *N*? „ I ii 191
in *N* they say There bides a foul witch „ II i 202
if thou wilt show us the way back to *N*. „ II i 361
is it true?—That John last week return'd to *N*, „ III 147
Part shall go to the almshouses at *N*, „ III 206
That business which we have in *N*— „ III 230
And may your business thrive in *N*! „ III 245
I know them arrant knaves in *N*. „ III 302
Black news, black news from *N*! „ III 447
I go to *N*. Sheriff, thou wilt find me at *N*. „ IV 800
No, let him be. Sheriff of *N*, „ IV 815
Nought (nothing) There's *n* but the vire of God's hell *Queen Mary* IV iii 526
Novel sometimes been moved to tears by a chapter of fine writing in a *n*; *Prom. of May* III 209
Noviciate Breaking already from thy *n* *Becket* V ii 80
Small peace was mine in my *n*, „ V ii 87
Noway and I *n* doubt But that with God's grace, I can live so still. *Queen Mary* II ii 218
Nowt (nothing) I knaws *n* o' what foälks says, *Prom. of May* I 27
N—what could he saäy? „ I 152
But if that be *n* to she, then it be *n* to me. „ I 182
Hesn't he left ye *n*? *Dora.* No, Mr. Dobson. „ II 7
I were insured, Miss, an' I lost *n* by it. „ II 58
Out o' the chaumber! I'll mash tha into *n*. „ III 735
Nubbut (only) (*See also* **Nobbut**) Owd Steer gi'es *n* cowd tea to '*is* men, and owd Dobson gi'es beer. „ II 224
Numb'd Has often *n* me into apathy Against the „ I 227
Number'd We dally with our lazy moments here, And hers are *n*. *Queen Mary* V iii 109
Nun Thou art *my n*, thy cloister in mine arms. *Harold* I ii 63
saw thy willy-nilly *n* Vying a tress „ V i 148
What shall it be? I'll go as a *n*. *Becket.* No. *Rosamund.* What, not good enough Even to play at *n*? *Becket.* Dan John with a *n*, That Map, *Becket* I i 301
thy solitude among thy *n's*, May that save thee! „ V ii 176
Nunnery Put her away into a *n*! „ *Pro.* 65
Come thou with me to Godstow *n*, „ IV ii 366
To put her into Godstow *n*. (repeat) *Becket* V i 208, 210
He bad me put her into a *n*— *Becket* V i 214
Get thee back to thy *n* with all haste; „ V ii 163
Nurse (s) The *n's* yawn'd, the cradle gaped, *Queen Mary* III vi 93
My *n* would tell me of a molehill *Harold* IV iii 128
My good old *n*, I had forgotten thou wast sitting there. *The Falcon* 34
You can take it, *n*! „ 490
my *n* has broken The thread of my dead flowers, „ 521
I thank you, my good *n*. „ 560
And thou too leave us, my dear *n*, alone. „ 701
Ay, the dear *n* will leave you alone; „ 702
I have anger'd your good *n*; „ 707
Our old *n* crying as if for her own child, *Prom. of May* II 479
Nursery (adj.) Then she got me a place as *n* governess, „ III 385
Nursery (s) That may seem strange beyond his *n*. *Queen Mary* II ii 396
Nursery-cocker'd The *n-c* child will jeer at aught „ II ii 394
Nursery-tale That *n-t* Still read, then? *Prom. of May* III 525
Nut woodland squirrel sees the *n* Behind the shell, *Foresters* II i 647
On *n's* and acorns, ha! Or the King's deer? „ IV 882

O

Oaf *o's*, ghosts o' the mist, wills-o'-the-wisp; *Foresters* II i 263
Oak (*See also* **Shambles-oak**) Pine, beech and plane, *o*, walnut, *The Cup* I i 1
whose storm-voice Unsockets the strong *o*, „ II 283
Such hearts of *o* as they be. *Foresters* II i 4
And these rough *o's* the palms of Paradise! „ II i 169
Here's a pot o' wild honey from an old *o*, „ II i 296
before the shadow of these dark *o's* „ II i 605
hundreds of huge *o's*, Gnarl'd— „ III 91
In that *o*, where twelve Can stand upright, „ III 309
Our feast is yonder, spread beneath an *o*, „ IV 190
Meanwhile, farewell Old friends, old patriarch *o's*. „ IV 1054
yet I think these *o's* at dawn and even, „ IV 1066
these old *o's* will murmur thee Marian along with Robin. „ IV 1093
Oaken present her with this *o* chaplet as Queen of the wood, „ III 59
Oak-tree Come from out That *o-t*! „ IV 998
Oän (own) and he calls out among our *o* men, 'The land belongs to the people!' *Prom. of May* I 140
fur I niver touched a drop of owt till my *o* wedding-daäy, „ I 362
then back ageän, a-follering my *o* shadder— „ I 371
an' them theer be soom of her *o* roses, „ II 38
the Lord bless 'er—'er *o* sen; „ II 40
I would taäke the owd blind man to my *o* fireside. „ II 74

Oän (own) (*continued*) and you should sit i' your *o* parlour quite like a laädy, ye should ! *Prom. of May* II 97
Fur she'd niver 'a been talkin' haäfe an hour wi' the divil 'at killed her *o* sister, „ II 604
'Oäpe (hope) They can't be many, my dear, but I *'o's* they'll be 'appy. „ I 353
Oath To bind me first by *o's* I could not keep, *Queen Mary* I v 557
he freed himself By *o* and compurgation *Harold* II ii 520
he hath not bound me by an *o*—Is ' ay ' an *o* ? is ' ay ' strong as an *o* ? „ II ii 661
same sin to break my word As break mine *o* ? „ II ii 665
thou hast sworn an *o* Which, if not kept, „ II ii 738
—am grateful for thine honest *o*, „ II ii 756
Hast thou had absolution for thine *o* ? „ III i 212
O son, when thou didst tell me of thine *o*, „ III i 268
my son ! Are all *o's* to be broken then, „ III i 286
lost Somewhat of upright stature thro' mine *o*, „ III ii 57
will ye upon *o*, Help us against the Norman ? „ IV i 180
devil Hath haunted me—mine *o*—my wife— „ V i 318
My fatal *o*—the dead Saints—the dark dreams— „ V i 380
His o was broken—O holy Norman Saints, „ V i 616
He that was false in *o* to me, „ V ii 151
Being bounden by my coronation *o* To do men justice. *Becket* I iii 396
that merits death,—False *o* on holy cross— „ IV ii 209
Ob Wouldst thou call my Oberon *O* ? *Foresters* II ii 131
Never *O* before his face. „ II ii 133
Obedience promise full Allegiance and *o* to the death. *Queen Mary* II ii 169
in this unity and *o* Unto the holy see „ III iii 157
His tractate upon True *O*, „ IV i 92
serviceable In all *o*, as mine own hath been : *Harold* III i 292
by that canonical *o* Thou still hast owed *Becket* I iii 275
Fealty to the King, *o* to thyself ? „ I iii 587
Obedient —the world A most *o* beast and fool— *Queen Mary* IV iii 414
Oberon And capering hand in hand with *O*. *Foresters* II i 498
Wouldst thou call my *O* Ob ? „ II ii 131
for *O* fled away Twenty thousand leagues to-day. „ II ii 142
Obey Well, well, you must *o* ; *Queen Mary* I iv 253
I must *o* the Queen and Council, man. „ IV ii 164
O your King and Queen, and not for dread „ IV iii 177
Sire, I *o* you. Come quickly. „ V i 220
And yet I must *o* the Holy Father, „ V ii 38
O the Count's conditions, my good friend. *Harold* II ii 276
Seem to *o* them. „ II ii 280
O him, speak him fair, „ II ii 317
O my first and last commandment. Go ! „ V i 359
Didst thou not promise Henry to *o* These ancient laws *Becket* I iii 17
Sign and *o* ! „ I iii 132
Sign, and *o* the crown ! „ I iii 144
And swear to *o* the customs. „ I iii 270
I promised The King to *o* these customs, „ I iii 557
That thou *o*, not me, but God in me, „ I iii 721
since we likewise swore to *o* the customs, „ V i 54
No man to love me, honour me, *o* me ! „ V i 240
Still I must *o* them. Fare you well. *The Cup* I i 158
Up with you, all of you, out of it ! hear and *o*. *Foresters* II ii 185
You hear your Queen, *o* ! „ III 464
Obeyed who had but *o* her father ; *Queen Mary* I i 95
the child *o* her father. „ I v 494
crown Would cleave to me that but *o* the crown, *Becket* V i 50
Obligation With bitter *o* to the Count— *Harold* II ii 221
every bond and debt and *o* Incurr'd as Chancellor. *Becket* I iii 710
Obliged you worked well enough, and I am much *o* to all of you. *Prom. of May* III 62
Observance all manner of homages, and *o's*, and circumbendibuses. *Foresters* I i 103
Obtain by your intercession May from the Apostolic see *o*, *Queen Mary* III iii 147
Occasion on a great *o* sure to wake As great a wrath in Becket— *Becket* III i 87
They seek—you make—*o* for your death. „ V ii 558
two-legg'd dogs Among us who can smell a true *o*, *The Cup* I ii 113
but this day has brought A great *o*. *The Falcon* 489
Occupy that anyone Should seize our person, *o* our state, *Queen Mary* II ii 178
Ocean And roll the golden *o's* of our grain, *The Cup* II 269
or wreckt And dead beneath the midland *o*, *Foresters* II i 657
Odd (adj.) Make us despise it at *o* hours, my Lord. *Queen Mary* IV iii 386
I have to pray you, some *o* time, „ V i 258
But doth not the weight of the flesh at *o* times overbalance the weight of the church, ha friar ? *Foresters* I ii 61
Odd (s) They are all too much at *o's* to close at once *Queen Mary* I v 632
Gardiner knows, but the Council are all at *o's*, „ II i 139
But seeing valour is one against all *o's*, *Foresters* IV 318
Odo (Bishop of Bayeux) coming with his brother *O* The Bayeux bishop, *Harold* II ii 347
and *O* said, ' Thine is the right, „ II ii 356
Odour Let all the air reel into a mist of *o*, *The Cup* II 185
O'erleap after rain *o's* a jutting rock And shoots „ I i 110
Offal with *o* thrown Into the blind sea of forgetfulness. *Queen Mary* III iii 191
scum And *o* of the city would not change „ IV iii 77
men, the scum and *o* of the Church ; *Becket* I iii 408
Offence As persons undefiled with our *o*, *Queen Mary* III iii 144
and mighty slow To feel *o's*. *Prom. of May* III 630
Offend You *o* us ; you may leave us. *Queen Mary* I v 210
You *o* us. *Gardiner*. These princes are like children, „ I v 232
It is the crown *O's* him— *The Cup* II 530
Offended I have *o* against heaven and earth *Queen Mary* IV iii 124
since my hand *o*, having written Against my heart, „ IV iii 247
' This hath *o*—this unworthy hand ! ' „ IV iii 613
Offending You have an old trick of *o* us ; „ III iv 315
Offer a formal *o* of the hand Of Philip ? „ I v 349
The formal *o* of Prince Philip's hand. „ I v 588
Offer'd has *o* her his son Philip, the Pope and the Devil. „ I i 105
a hundred Gold pieces once were *o* by the Duke. *The Falcon* 324
Has he *o* you marriage, this gentleman ? *Prom. of May* III 289
Offering *See* **Peace-offering**
Office I have lost mine *o*, *Queen Mary* I v 236
Spain in all the great *o's* of state ; „ II i 178
no foreigner Hold *o* in the household, „ III iii 72
set up The Holy *O* here—garner the wheat, „ V v 113
tell the cooks to close The doors of all the *o's* below. „ V v 117
Love him ! why not ? thine is a loving *o*, *Harold* II ii 97
fill'd All *o's*, all bishopricks with English— „ II ii 535
I had been so true To Henry and mine *o* *Becket* I iii 693
both of us Too headlong for our *o*. „ II ii 290
Nor make me traitor to my holy *o*. „ V ii 149
You should attend the *o*, give them heart. „ V ii 598
He said, ' Attend the *o*.' *Becket*. Attend the *o* ? „ V ii 608
get you back ! go on with the *o*. „ V iii 33
Back, I say ! Go on with the *o*. „ V iii 39
Officer the Queen's *O's* Are here in force *Queen Mary* I ii 108
by the judgment of the *o's* of the said lord king, *Foresters* I iii 65
Ofs King Hath divers *o* and ons, *o* and belongings, *Becket* IV ii 32
Oftener But you were *o* there. I have none but you. „ III i 53
Oil I Scraped from your finger-points the holy *o* ; *Queen Mary* IV ii 133
Olaf (a Norwegian king) St. *O*, not while I am by ! *Harold* I i 395
Old (adj.) (*See also* **Owd, Owld**) *O* Nokes, can't it make thee a bastard ? *Queen Mary* I i 28
No, *o* Nokes. *Old Nokes*. It's Harry. „ I i 33
for thou was born i' the tail end of *o* Harry the Seventh. „ I i 42
I was born true man at five in the forenoon i' the tail of *o* Harry, „ I i 46
but I and my *o* woman 'ud burn upon it, „ I i 56
Ay, but he's too *o*. „ I i 121
O Bourne to the life ! „ I iii 30
Yon gray *o* Gospeller, sour as midwinter, Begin with him. „ I iii 40
By the mass, *o* friend, we'll have no pope here „ I iii 42
Ay, that am I, new converted, but the *o* leaven sticks to my tongue yet. „ I iii 48
but this fierce *o* Gardiner—his big baldness, „ I iv 263
or wave And wind at their *o* battle : he must have written. „ I v 357
Not yet ; but your *o* Traitors of the Tower— „ I v 483
Why comes that *o* fox-Fleming back again ? „ I v 581
None so new, Sir Thomas, and none so *o*, Sir Thomas. No new news that Philip comes to wed Mary, no *o* news that all men hate it. *O* Sir Thomas would have hated it. „ II i 15

Old (adj.) (*continued*) *O* Sir Thomas always granted the wine. *Queen Mary* II i 41
Ay—sonnets—a fine courtier of the *o* court, *o* Sir Thomas. „ II i 46
Wake, or the stout *o* island will become A rotten limb of Spain. „ II i 104
you that have kept your *o* customs upright, „ II i 158
I have been there with *o* Sir Thomas, and the beds I know. „ II i 184
Ay, gray *o* castle of Alington, green field Beside the brimming Medway, „ II i 243
They go like those *o* Pharisees in John Convicted by their conscience, „ II ii 8
And scared the gray *o* porter and his wife. „ II iii 16
I know not my letters; the *o* priest taught me nothing. „ II iii 57
Far liefer had I in my country hall Been reading some *o* book, with mine *o* hound Couch'd at my hearth, and mine *o* flask of wine Beside me, „ III i 44
I am an *o* man wearied with my journey, Ev'n with my joy. „ III ii 127
and are well agreed That those *o* statutes touching Lollardism „ III iv 7
O Rome, that first made martyrs in the Church, „ III iv 126
You have an *o* trick of offending us; „ III iv 315
Touch him upon his *o* heretical talk, „ III iv 352
Men now are bow'd and *o*, the doctors tell you, „ III iv 408
Our *o* friend Cranmer, Your more especial love, „ III iv 416
there's An *o* world English adage to the point. „ IV i 175
Cool as the light in *o* decaying wood; „ IV ii 5
Monsters of mistradition, *o* enough To scare me into dreaming, „ IV ii 102
Good day, *o* friend; what, you look somewhat worn; „ IV ii 115
in the Testaments, Both *O* and New. „ IV iii 234
Crying, 'Forward!'—set our *o* church rocking, „ IV iii 403
Hist! there be two *o* gossips—gospellers, „ IV iii 460
And the gray dawn Of an *o* age that never will be mine „ V ii 234
Probing an *o* state-secret—how it chanced That this young Earl „ V ii 487
Noble as his young person and *o* shield. „ V ii 513
Ah, weak and meek *o* man, Seven-fold dishonour'd „ V v 132
O, miserable, diseased, „ V v 178
I am a harm to England. *O* uncanonical Stigand— *Harold* I i 81
Stand by him, mine *o* friend, „ I i 112
So says *o* Gurth, not I: yet hear! thine earldom, Tostig, hath been a kingdom. Their *o* crown Is yet a force among them, „ I i 302
and I beat him. Even *o* Gurth would fight. I had much ado To hold mine own against *o* Gurth. *O* Gurth, „ I i 436
I dug mine into My *o* fast friend the shore, „ II i 7
Counts his *o* beads, and hath forgotten thee. „ II ii 447
our good King Kneels mumbling some *o* bone— „ II ii 469
I, *o* shrivell'd Stigand, I, Dry as an *o* wood-fungus on a dead tree, „ III i 7
I do believe My *o* crook'd spine would bud out two young wings „ III i 24
No, not strange This was *o* human laughter in *o* Rome „ III ii 163
Our *o* Northumbrian crown, And kings of our own choosing. „ IV i 31
Your *o* crown Were little help without our Saxon carles „ IV i 34
There is a pleasant fable in *o* books, „ IV i 56
This *o* Wulfnoth Would take me on his knees and tell me tales „ IV i 71
O man, Harold Hates nothing; not *his* fault, „ IV i 128
So loud, that, by St. Dunstan, *o* St. Thor— „ IV iii 146
but our *o* Thor Heard his own thunder again, „ IV iii 149
O dog, Thou art drunk, *o* dog! „ IV iii 163
Wash up that *o* crown of Northumberland. „ V i 167
And chanting that *o* song of Brunanburg Where England conquer'd. „ V i 215
And our *o* songs are prayers for England too! „ V i 222
but I, *o* wretch, *o* Stigand, With hands too limp to brandish iron— „ V i 447

Old (adj.) (*continued*) He is chanting some *o* warsong. *Harold* V i 495
War-woodman of *o* Woden, how he fells The mortal copse of faces! „ V i 588
and most amorous Of good *o* red sound liberal Gascon wine: *Becket, Pro.* 100
believe thee The veriest Galahad of *o* Arthur's hall. „ *Pro.* 129
Well, well, *o* men must die, or the world would grow mouldy, „ *Pro.* 408
The good *o* man would sometimes have his jest— „ I i 61
You will do much To rake out all *o* dying heats, „ II ii 114
I hate a split between *o* friendships as I hate the dirty gap „ II ii 380
And that *o* priest whom John of Salisbury trusted Hath sent another. „ III i 69
for to be sure it's no more than a week since our *o* Father Philip „ III i 110
tho' to be sure our mother 'ill sing me *o* songs „ III i 184
for the *o* King would act servitor and hand a dish to his son; „ III iii 138
Mine *o* friend, Thomas, I would there were that perfect trust between us, „ III iii 262
You could not—*o* affection master'd you, „ V ii 143
I know not why You call these *o* things back again, „ V ii 270
The *o* King's present, carried off the casks, „ V ii 442
And lose his head as *o* St. Denis did. „ V ii 480
May they not say you dared not show yourself In your *o* place? „ V ii 596
I am not mad, not sick, not *o* enough To doat on one alone. *The Cup* I iii 69
It is *o*, I know not How many hundred years. „ II 342
we would add Some golden fringe of gorgeousness beyond *O* use, „ II 439
Did not some *o* Greek Say death was the chief good? „ II 513
This *o* thing here they are but blue beads—my Piero, *The Falcon* 47
Ay, my lady, but won't you speak with the *o* woman first, „ 182
And yet to speak white truth, my good *o* mother, „ 504
It's the *o* Scripture text, 'Let us eat and drink, for to-morrow we die.' *Prom. of May* I 258
'What are we,' says the blind *o* man in Lear? „ I 263
I hate tears. Marriage is but an *o* tradition. „ I 491
That fine, fat, hook-nosed uncle of mine, *o* Harold, „ I 510
will each Bid their *o* bond farewell with smiles, not tears; „ I 524
for when the tide Of full democracy has overwhelm'd This *O* world, „ I 594
Tut! you talk *O* feudalism. „ I 670
Neither the *o* world, nor the new, nor father, „ I 674
And poor *o* father not die miserable. „ I 722
Our *o* nurse crying as if for her own child, „ II 479
I do not dare, like an *o* friend, to shake it. „ II 526
I have always told Father that the huge *o* ashtree there would cause an accident some day; „ III 244
for, indeed, he tells me that he met you once in the *o* times, „ III 263
and when the children grew too *o* for me, „ III 387
your Father must be now in extreme *o* age. „ III 400
We Steers are of *o* blood, tho' we be fallen. „ III 604
and your own name Of Harold sounds so English and so *o* „ III 610
I be lanker than an *o* horse turned out to die on the common. *Foresters* I i 51
and your Ladyship hath sung the *o* proverb out of fashion. „ I i 164
And how often in *o* histories have the great men striven against the stream, „ I i 242
I am *o* and forget. Was Prince John there? „ I i 250
o faces Press round us, and warm hands close with warm hands, „ I iii 18
Ay, ay, gown, coif, and petticoat, and the *o* woman's blessing with them to the last fringe. „ II i 195
Except this *o* hag have been bribed to lie. *Robin.* We *o* hags should be bribed to speak truth, „ II i 234
There is but one *o* woman in the hut. „ II i 241
There is yet another *o* woman. „ II i 244
O hag, how should thy one tooth drill thro' this? „ II i 275

Old (adj.) (*continued*) There's for you, and there's for you—and the *o* woman's welcome. *Foresters* II i 290
The *o* wretch is mad, and her bread is beyond me: „ II i 291
Here's a pot o' wild honey from an *o* oak, „ II i 296
And, *o* hag tho' I be, I can spell the hand. „ II i 350
Why do you listen, man, to the *o* fool? „ II i 358
All the sweet saints bless your worship for your alms to the *o* woman! „ II i 364
How should this *o* lamester guide us! „ II i 369
Why, an *o* woman can shoot closer than you two. „ II i 400
and make thine *o* carcase a target for us three. „ II i 404
Did I not tell you an *o* woman could shoot better? „ II i 407
Thou art no *o* woman—thou art disguised—thou art one of the thieves. „ II i 410
O as I am, I will not brook to see Three upon two. „ II i 422
A brave *o* fellow but he angers me. „ II i 471
He is *o* and almost mad to keep the land. „ II i 528
thou wast by And never drewest sword to help the *o* man „ II i 541
The *o* man dotes. „ II ii 83
And I, *o* Much, say as much, for being every inch a man I honour every inch of a woman. „ III 62
When the flower was wither'd and *o*. „ IV 22
at last I crawl'd like a sick crab from my *o* shell, „ IV 126
Ay, for *o* Much is every inch a man. „ IV 289
Because thou art always so much more of a man than my youngsters *o* Much. *Much.* Well, we Muches be *o*. *Robin.* *O* as the hills. *Much.* *O* as the mill. „ IV 299
Where is this *o* Sir Richard of the Lea? „ IV 438
and thus This *o* Sir Richard might redeem his land. „ IV 487
By *o* St. Vitus Have you gone mad? „ IV 614
And this *o* crazeling in the litter there. „ IV 634
Child, thou shalt wed him, Or thine *o* father will go mad—he will, „ IV 645
Carry her off, and let the *o* man die. „ IV 677
Meanwhile, farewell *O* friends, *o* patriarch oaks. „ IV 1054
And surely these *o* oaks will murmur thee Marian along with Robin. „ IV 1093
Old (s) and watch The parch'd banks rolling incense, as of *o*, *Queen Mary* I v 92
Should not this day be held in after years More solemn than of *o*? „ III iii 91
This hard coarse man of *o* hath crouch'd to me „ IV ii 169
but I know it of *o*, he hates me too; „ V ii 60
Did not Heaven speak to men in dreams of *o*? *Harold.* Ay—well—of *o*. *Harold* I ii 95
What, this! and this!—what! new and *o* together! *Becket* I iii 310
We have had our leagues of *o* with Eastern kings. *The Cup* I ii 101
Perhaps I thought with those of *o*, *The Falcon* 878
Olden Is like a word that comes from *o* days, *Queen Mary* III v 34
Let these decide on what was customary In *o* days, *Becket* II ii 176
Older I am eleven years *o* than he is. *Queen Mary* I v 68
I am eleven years *o* than he, Poor boy! „ V v 46
oaks, Gnarl'd—*o* than the thrones of Europe— *Foresters* III 92
Oldest Becket, I am the *o* of the Templars; *Becket* I iii 247
I am the *o* of thy men, and thou and thy youngsters *Foresters* IV 294
Old-fashioned I have heard that 'your Lordship,' and 'your Ladyship,' and 'your Grace' are all growing *o-f*! *Prom. of May* III 318
But the love of sister for sister can never be *o-f*. „ III 320
Oldham Luscombe, Nokes, *O*, Skipworth! „ III 53
Old-world There was an *o-w* tomb beside my father's, *Queen Mary* V ii 393
these *o-w* servants Are all but flesh and blood *The Falcon* 707
full democracy has overwhelm'd This *O w*, *Prom. of May* I 594
learnt at last that all His *o-w* faith, „ II 332
Olive-branch more of *o-b* and amnesty For foes at home— *Becket* V ii 15
Ominous Not stagger'd by this *o* earth and heaven: *Harold* I i 207
Ommost (almost) Seeäms I *o* knaws the back on 'im— *Prom. of May* II 577
One There is but *o* thing against them. *Queen Mary* I i 100
and sever'd from the faith, will return into the *o* true fold, „ I iii 22
Calais! Our *o* point on the main, the gate of France! „ I v 125
Spain and we, *O* crown, might rule the world. „ I v 303
But Philip never writes me *o* poor word, „ I v 360

One (*continued*) For Philip comes, *o* hand in mine, and *o* Steadying the tremulous pillars of the Church— *Queen Mary* I v 515
They are all too much at odds to close at once In *o* full-throated No! „ I v 634
you stroke me on *o* cheek, Buffet the other. „ II i 117
So I say Your city is divided, and I fear *O* scruple, „ II ii 100
Am I Thomas White? *O* word before she comes. „ II ii 109
And arm and strike as with *o* hand, „ II ii 292
moving side by side Beneath *o* canopy, „ III i 97
They smile as if content with *o* another. „ III i 211
O crater opens when another shuts. „ III i 322
but I say There is no man—there was *o* woman with us— „ III i 337
Nay come with me—*o* moment! „ III ii 189
You were the *o* sole man in either house Who stood upright „ III iii 252
I say you were the *o* sole man who stood. „ III iii 263
I am the *o* sole man in either house, „ III iii 265
Well, you *o* man, because you stood upright, „ III iii 268
If any man in any way would be The *o* man, he shall be so to his cost. „ III iii 276
yet I found *O* day, a wholesome scripture, „ III iv 84
call they not The *o* true faith, a loathsome idol-worship? „ III iv 219
there comes a missive from the Queen It shall be all my study for *o* hour „ III v 184
with free wing The world were all *o* Araby. „ III v 210
o half Will flutter here, *o* there. „ III vi 196
Methinks that would you tarry *o* day more (The news was sudden) „ III vi 233
For *o* day more, so far as I can tell. „ III vi 246
Then *o* day more to please her Majesty. „ III vi 247
return'd To the *o* Catholic Universal Church, Repentant of his errors? „ IV iii 21
Pray with *o* breath, *o* heart, *o* soul for me. „ IV iii 104
What, not *o* day? „ V i 209
and it was thought we two Might make *o* flesh, „ V ii 137
No—we were not made *O* flesh in happiness, no happiness here; But now we are made *o* flesh in misery; „ V ii 150
And there is *o* Death stands behind the Groom, And there is *o* Death stands behind the Bride— „ V ii 165
and to send us again, according to His promise, the *o* King, the Christ, „ V iv 53
Ay, worse than that—not *o* hour true to me! „ V v 159
Why then the wrath of Heaven hath three tails, The devil only *o*. *Harold* I i 62
But heaven and earth are threads of the same loom, Play into *o* another, „ I i 211
It is but for *o* moon. „ I ii 30
And all the North of Humber is *o* storm. „ II ii 291
Harold, I am thy friend, *o* life with thee, „ II ii 649
Sir Count, He had but *o* foot, he must have hopt away, „ II ii 675
were or should be all *O* England, for this cow-herd, like my father, „ IV i 79
Ye heard *o* witness even now. „ IV i 170
I have not spoken to the king *O* word; and *o* I must. Farewell! „ V i 336
Whose life was all *o* battle, incarnate war, „ V i 397
Make thou *o* man as three to roll them down! „ V i 577
No, no—brave Gurth, *o* gash from brow to knee! „ V ii 70
But *o* woman! Look you, we never mean to part again. „ V ii 79
Death!—and enough of death for this *o* day, „ V ii 120
Of *o* self-stock at first, Make them again *o* people— „ V ii 186
True, *o* rose will outblossom the rest, *o* rose in a bower. *Becket, Pro.* 345
but I fear this *o* fancy hath taken root, „ *Pro.* 480
And goodly acres—we will make her whole; Not *o* rood lost. „ I i 165
So that you grant me *o* slight favour. „ I ii 58
And some are reeds, that *o* time sway to the current, „ I iii 593
Grant me *o* day To ponder these demands. „ I iii 668
she holds it in Free and perpetual alms, unsubject to *O* earthy sceptre. „ I iii 681

One (*continued*) Who stole the widow's *o* sitting hen o' Sunday, when she was at mass ? *Becket* I iv 121
And I ha' nine darters i' the spital that be dead ten times o'er i' *o* day wi' the putrid fever ; „ I iv 251
With Becket ! I have but *o* hour with thee— „ II i 24
Let there not be *o* frown in this *o* hour. „ II i 43
We have but *o* bond, her hate of Becket. „ II i 165
My *o* grain of good counsel which you will not swallow. „ II ii 378
leave Lateran and Vatican in *o* dust of gold— „ II ii 475
And *o* fair child to fondle ! „ III i 12
I but ask'd her *O* question, and she primm'd her mouth „ III i 74
and bad me whatever I saw not to speak *o* word, „ III i 133
and then not to speak *o* word, for that's the rule o' the garden, „ III i 137
tho' I shouldn't speak *o* word, I wish you joy o' the King's brother. „ III i 154
Yet *o* thing more. Thou hast broken thro' the pales Of privilege, „ III iii 192
I am bound For that *o* hour to stay with good King Louis, „ III iii 247
He said thy life Was not *o* hour's worth in England „ III iii 251
O word further. Doth not the *fewness* of anything make the fulness of it in estimation ? „ III iii 301
the wolves of England Must murder her *o* shepherd, „ III iii 344
Could you keep her Indungeon'd from *o* whisper of the wind, „ IV ii 146
Take thy *o* chance ; Catch at the last straw. „ IV ii 220
O downward plunge of his paw would rend away Eyesight „ IV ii 283
Rosamund hath not answer'd you *o* word ; Madam, I will not answer you *o* word. „ IV ii 362
She lives—but not for him ; *o* point is gain'd. „ IV ii 415
Your Grace will never have *o* quiet hour. „ V i 78
But *o* question—How fares thy pretty boy, the little Geoffrey ? „ V ii 165
And breathe *o* prayer for my liege-lord the King, „ V ii 191
O slow, fat, white, a burthen of the hearth ; „ V ii 211
I never spied in thee *o* gleam of grace. „ V ii 474
I pray you for *o* moment stay and speak. „ V ii 525
and throne *O* king above them all, *The Cup* I i 93
It is the *o* step in the dark beyond Our expectation, „ I i 212
put forth *o* paw, Slew four, and knew it not, „ I ii 126
There may be courtesans for aught I know Whose life is *o* dishonour. „ I ii 194
No, not *o* step with thee. „ I iii 96
Then with *o* quick short stab—eternal peace. „ I iii 124
Tell him there is *o* shadow among the shadows, *O* ghost of all the ghosts— „ II 139
The shout of Synorix and Camma sitting Upon *o* throne, „ II 148
They two should drink together from *o* cup, „ II 361
and *o* plate of dried prunes be all-but-nothing, *The Falcon* 135
Oh sweet saints ! *o* plate of prunes ! „ 215
His *o* companion here—nay, I have heard That, „ 225
It will be hard, I fear, To find *o* shock upon the field „ 301
we have but *o* piece of earthenware to serve the salad in to my lady, „ 481
My *o* thing left of value in the world ! „ 496
And *o* word more. Good ! let it be but *o*. „ 510
I cannot, Not a morsel, not *o* morsel. „ 573
I am sure that more than *o* brave fellow owed His death to the charm in it. „ 633
My last sight ere I swoon'd was *o* sweet face „ 647
My *o* child Florio lying still so sick, „ 678
who comes To rob you of your *o* delight on earth. „ 828
and 'er an' the owd man they fell a kissin' o' *o* another *Prom. of May* I 21
I seed that *o* cow o' thine i' the pinfold ageän as I wur a-coomin' 'ere. „ I 190
An' if tha can't keep thy *o* cow i' horder, „ I 197
I niver 'es sa much as *o* pin's prick of paäin ; „ I 359
but when thou be as owd as me thou'll put *o* word fur another as I does. „ I 381
but *o* time's vice may be The virtue of another ; „ I 534
I could put all that o' *o* side eäsy anew. „ II 111
when meä and my sweet'art was a workin' along o' *o* side wi' *o* another, „ II 152

One (*continued*) wasn't thou and me a-bussin' o' *o* another t'other side o' the haäycock, *Prom. of May* II 231
Left but *o* dreadful line to say, that we Should find her in the river ; „ II 411
will he ever be of *o* faith with his wife ? „ III 178
Wasn't dear mother herself at least by *o* side a lady ? „ III 301
Look up ! *O* word, or do but smile ! „ III 677
and to her you came Veiling *o* sin to act another. „ III 773
The shelter of *your* roof—not for *o* moment— „ III 800
Shall I keep *o* little rose for Little John ? No. *Foresters* I i 112
But if a man and a maid care for *o* another, „ I i 135
If thou draw *o* inch nearer, I will give thee a buffet on the face. „ I i 145
if a man and a maid love *o* another, may the maid give the first kiss ? „ I i 172
Cloud not thy birthday with *o* fear for me. „ I ii 126
We make but *o* hour's buzz, are only like The rainbow „ I ii 277
I have reign'd *o* year in the wild wood. „ II i 36
to carve *O* lone hour from it, „ II i 43
Tho' in *o* moment she should glance away, „ II i 161
There is but *o* old woman in the hut. „ II i 241
Old hag, how should thy *o* tooth drill thro' this ? „ II i 276
Speak but *o* word not only of forgiveness, „ II i 610
We never robb'd *o* friend of the true King. „ III 157
I have but *o* penny in pouch, „ III 193
I have *o* mark in gold which a pious son of the Church gave me „ III 280
Well, as he said, *o* mark in gold. *Marian.* And thou ? *Friar.* *O* mark in gold. „ III 284
O half of this shall go to those they have wrong'd, *O* half shall pass into our treasury. „ III 303
How much hast thou about thee ? *King Richard.* I had *o* mark. „ IV 165
What more ? *o* thousand marks, Or else the land. „ IV 473
Here be *o* thousand marks Out of our treasury to redeem the land. „ IV 492
Mine eye most true to *o* hair's-breadth of aim. „ IV 694
I never found *o* traitor in my band. „ IV 836
Past the bank Of foxglove, then to left by that *o* yew. „ IV 974
No—there's yet *o* other : I will not dine without him. „ IV 994
Here—give me *o* sharp pinch upon the cheek „ IV 1011
Only (*See also* **Nobbut, Nubbut**) I am the *o* rose of all the stock That never thorn'd him ; *Harold* I i 425
Mother says gold spoils all. Love is the *o* gold. *Becket* IV i 43
'Till death us part'—those are the *o* words, *Prom. of May* I 658
Ons King Hath divers ofs and *o*, ofs and belongings, *Becket* IV ii 32
Ony (any) or *o* waäy, I'd slaäve out my life fur 'er. *Prom. of May* I 177
Hev' *o* o' ye seen Eva ? „ I 313
afoor *o* o' ye wur burn— „ I 366
doänt ye hear of *o* ? „ I 390
an' *o* o' Steer's men, an' *o* o' my men „ II 34
an' she wur as sweet as *o* on 'em— „ II 39
And I would loove tha moor nor *o* gentleman 'ud loove tha. „ II 105
Onyhow (anyhow) I thank you fur that, Miss Dora, *o*. „ I 158
Onythink (anything) Why, Miss, I be afeard I shall set him a-sweäring like *o*. „ III 359
Oop (up) The beer's gotten *o* into my 'eäd. „ II 320
but I thinks he be wakkenin' *o*. „ III 413
Ooze All *o's* out ; yet him— *Queen Mary* I iv 205
Open (adj.) You should be plain and *o* with me, niece. „ I iv 217
In clear and *o* day were congruent With that vile Cranmer „ III iv 230
O rare, a whole long day of *o* field. *Becket* I i 296
I am *o* to him. „ V ii 68
No, look ! the door is *o* : let him be. „ V ii 316
and *o* arms To him who gave it ; *The Cup* I i 83
Smitten with fever in the *o* field, *Prom. of May* III 806
Open (verb) *O* the window, Knyvett : *Queen Mary* II i 154
One crater *o's* when another shuts. „ III i 322
O, Ye everlasting gates ! „ III ii 182
Women, when I am dead, *O* my heart, „ V v 153
o his,—So that he have one,— „ V v 155
At last a harbour *o's* ; but therein Sunk rocks— „ V v 213
this door *O's* upon the forest ! Out, begone ! *The Cup* I ii 329
O, *o*, or I will drive the door from the door-post. *Foresters* II i 219

Open'd this was *o*, and the dead were found Sitting, *Queen Mary* V ii 395

into thy mouth hadst thou but *o* it to thank him. *Becket* III iii 277

Knock, and it shall be *o*. „ V iii 64

o out The purple zone of hill and heaven; *The Cup* I ii 407

The blossom had *o* on every bough; *Prom. of May* I 42

Opening Beware of *o* out thy bosom to it, *Becket* III iii 30

That beam of dawn upon the *o* flower, *Foresters* IV 3

Opinion when men are tost On tides of strange *o*, *Queen Mary* III iv 119

True, I have held *o's*, hold some still, *Prom. of May* III 622

Opportunity our *o* When I and thou will rob the nest of her. *Foresters* I ii 160

Oppose I would set my men-at-arms to *o* thee, „ I i 323

Opposite we will climb The mountain *o* and watch the chase. *The Cup* I i 117

Oppress The walls *o* me, And yon huge keep *Harold* II ii 227

O help us from all that *o* us! *The Cup* II 6

Oppression The *o* of our people moves me so, *Foresters* III 109

Opulent *See* **Over-opulent**

Oracle this *o* of great Artemis Has no more power than other *o's* *The Cup* II 33

Oran (in Algeria) Tunis, and *O*, and the Philippines, *Queen Mary* V i 48

Orange (plant) You lived among your vines and *o's*, „ III iv 253

I that held the *o* blossom Dark as the yew? *Prom. of May* II 629

Orange (town) William of *O*, William the Silent. *Queen Mary* III i 197

Order (arrangement, etc.) Like loosely-scatter'd jewels, in fair *o*, „ II i 28

my cows in sweeter *o* Had I been such. „ III v 271

ever-jarring Earldoms move To music and in *o*— *Harold* II ii 762

She *will* break fence. I can't keep her in *o*. *Prom. of May* I 195

Order (command, etc.) (*See also* **Horder**) To take such *o* with all heretics *Queen Mary* I v 34

If this be not your Grace's *o*, „ II iv 64

Have I the *o's* of the Holy Father? *Philip de Eleemosyna.* *O's*, my lord—why, no; for what am I? *Becket* I iii 232

I give you here an *o* To seize upon him. *The Cup* I i 164

Will *you* betray him by this *o*? „ I ii 245

Is this your brother's *o*? *The Falcon* 745

Order (rank, etc.) Saving the honour of my *o*—ay. *Becket* I iii 21

Saving thine *o*! „ I iii 26

Saving thine *o*, Thomas, Is black and white „ I iii 30

Ordered pity this poor world myself that it is no better *o*. „ *Pro.* 367

Ordinance Either in making laws and *o's* *Queen Mary* III iii 130

Of all such laws and *o's* made; „ III iii 142

Against the solemn *o* from Rome, *Becket* I iii 505

Ordinary She looks comelier than *o* to-day; *Queen Mary* I i 71

Ordnance there is *o* On the White Tower and on the Devil's Tower, „ II iii 43

Organ *O* and pipe, and dulcimer, chants and hymns *Becket* V ii 365

Original Cleaving to your *o* Adam-clay, *Queen Mary* IV iii 418

Orkney —Scotland, Ireland, Iceland, *O*, *Harold* III ii 125

Orm Gamel, son of *O*, What thinkest thou this means? (repeat) „ I i 20, 463

Hail, Gamel, son of *O*! „ I i 92

that was his guest, Gamel, the son of *O*: „ II ii 299

murder'd thine own guest, the son of *O*, Gamel, „ IV ii 38

Ornament The golden *o's* are stolen from her— *Becket* III iii 180

Orphan (adj.) a widow And *o* child, whom one of thy wild barons— „ *Pro.* 188

Orphan (s) Age, *o's*, and babe-breasting mothers— „ II i 72

Babes, *o's*, mothers! is that royal, Sire? „ II i 80

Orthodoxy He'll burn a diocese to prove his *o*. *Queen Mary* III iv 353

Other (*See also* **T'other**) counsel your withdrawing To Ashridge, or some *o* country house. „ I iv 226

As Thirlby says, are profitless to the burners, And help the *o* side. „ IV ii 220

O reasons There be for this man's ending, „ IV iii 53

Might it not be the *o* side rejoicing In his brave end? „ IV iii 356

o things As idle; a weak Wyatt! „ V i 291

Not thee, my son: some *o* messenger. *Harold* I i 244

And *o* bells on earth, which yet are heaven's; „ I ii 133

Like *o* lords amenable to law. *Becket, Pro.* 25

Than that of *o* paramours of thine? „ *Pro.* 71

True enough, my mind was set upon *o* matters. „ *Pro.* 318

Ay, my lord, and divers *o* earls and barons. „ I iv 59

Other (*continued*) look you, you shall have None *o* God but me— *Becket* II ii 229

then the South-west turned him North-west, and so of the *o* winds; „ II ii 323

Go, you shall tell me of her some *o* time. „ III i 191

he hath pass'd out again, And on the *o* side. „ III ii 13

Then speak; this is my *o* self, „ V ii 74

dungeon'd the *o* half In Pevensey Castle— „ V ii 444

At times this oracle of great Artemis Has no more power than *o* oracles *The Cup* II 34

With *o* beauties on a mountain meadow, *The Falcon* 351

And the *o* nine? *Filippo.* Sold! „ 411

No *o* heart Of such magnificence in courtesy Beats— „ 721

Is there no *o* way? *Prom. of May* I 691

If it had killed one of the Steers there the *o* day, „ III 250

there is no *o* man that shall give me away. *Foresters* I i 290

That *o* thousand—shall I ever pay it? „ II i 466

Other-world that sweet *o-w* smile, which will be reflected *Becket, Pro.* 396

Otter And I would swim the moat, like an *o*. *Foresters* I i 321

Oubliette but in our *o's* Thou shalt or rot or ransom. *Harold* II i 107

And deeper still the deep-down *o*, „ II ii 429

from my ghastly *o* I send my voice „ V i 245

Oublietted And *o* in the centre—No! *Becket* IV ii 150

Ought (*See also* **Aught, Owt**) I am dead as Death this day to *o* of earth's *Harold* V i 425

Ouphe *o's*, oafs, ghosts o' the mist, wills-o'-the-wisp; *Foresters* II i 263

Oust Stir up thy people: *o* him! *Harold* I i 482

would *o* me from his will, if I Made such a marriage. *Prom. of May* I 513

Ousted You have *o* the mock priest, *Queen Mary* I v 180

Ay, Lambeth has *o* Cranmer. „ III ii 132

Outblossom one rose will *o* the rest, one rose in a bower. *Becket, Pro.* 345

Out-Bonner Bonner cannot *o-B* his own self— *Queen Mary* III vi 27

Outcry And make a morning *o* in the yard; „ III v 158

Outdoor One of much *o* bluster. „ II ii 380

Outdraught Felt the remorseless *o* of the deep *Harold* II i 9

Outfield (outlying field) Hodge 'ud ha' been a-harrowin' o' white peasen i' the *o* *Queen Mary* IV iii 492

Out-Gardiners Gardiner *o-G* Gardiner in his heat, „ III vi 25

Outlander wrench this *o's* ransom out of him— *Harold* II i 58

Outlaw (s) Thou art an *o*, and couldst never pay *Foresters* II i 452

An *o's* bride may not be wife in law. „ II ii 90

The chief of these *o's* who break the law? „ IV 141

and then we were no longer *o's*. „ IV 147

Robin's an *o*, but he helps the poor. „ IV 358

my liege, these men are *o's*, thieves, „ IV 906

Outlaw (verb) Did ye not *o* your archbishop Robert, *Harold* I i 55

Outlaw'd he join'd with thee To drive me *o*. „ IV ii 14

I may be *o*, I have heard a rumour. *Foresters* I ii 91

Robin Hood Earl of Huntingdon is *o* and banished. „ I iii 68

I am *o*, and if caught, I die. „ I iii 163

Am I worse or better? I am *o*. „ II i 50

being *o* in a land Where law lies dead, „ II i 89

While Richard hath *o* himself, „ IV 360

Out-passion'd with our great Council against Tostig, *O-p* his! *Harold* III i 61

Outraged Wasted our diocese, *o* our tenants, *Becket* V ii 431

Out-towering help to build a throne *O-t* hers of France . . . *Harold* II ii 765

Outvalue As gold *O's* dross, light darkness, *Becket* I iii 715

wreath That once you wore *o's* twenty-fold *The Falcon* 759

O's all the jewels upon earth. „ 779

It should be love that thus *o's* all. „ 781

Outward To veil the fault of my most *o* foe— *Queen Mary* IV ii 106

Outwoman'd She could not be unmann'd—no, nor *o*— „ III i 370

Over *See* **Ower**

Overbalance weight of the flesh at odd times *o* the weight of the church, *Foresters* I ii 61

Overbold Thou art *o*. *Robin.* My king, „ IV 890

Over-breathed I am *o-b*, Friar, by my two bouts at quarterstaff. „ IV 265

Over-confident Brave—ay—too brave, too *o-c*, *The Cup* I ii 262

Overdid must we follow All that they *o* or underdid? *Becket* II ii 214

Overhead loud enough To fright the wild hawk passing *o*, *Foresters* III 318

Overleap There is a fence I cannot *o*, My father's will. „ III 9

Overlive O friends, I shall not *o* the day. *Harold* III i 232

Overlook would hardly care to *o* This same petition *Queen Mary* IV i 192

Over-measure By St. Edmund I *o-m* him. *Harold* IV iii 120
Overmuch Sir, this dead fruit was ripening *o*, *Queen Mary* III i 26
Then without tropes, my Lord, An *o* severeness, „ III iv 156
Over-opulent if you cared To fee an *o-o* superstition, *Prom. of May* I 693
Overscornful would deign to lend an ear Not *o*, *Harold* IV i 137
Oversea And *o* they say this state of yours *Queen Mary* III i 441
His kin, all his belongings, *o's*; *Becket* II i 71
calls you *o* To answer for it in his Norman courts. „ V ii 354
one that should be grateful to me *o's*, a Count in Brittany— *Foresters* I i 271
I must pass *o's* to one that I trust will help me. „ I ii 152
And I and he are passing *o's*: „ II i 627
Overshoot tho' you make your butt too big, you *o* it, *Becket* III iii 122
Overshot I have *o* My duties to our Holy Mother Church, „ V i 37
Overstep is the King's *if* too high a stile for your lordship to *o* „ III iii 281
Overtaken Love will fly the fallen leaf, and not be *o*; *Queen Mary* V ii 372
Over-taxing for thy brother breaks us With *o-t*— *Harold* I i 110
Overthrown Doubt not they will be speedily *o*. *Queen Mary* II ii 200
have *o* Morcar and Edwin. *Harold* III ii 131
The king is slain, the kingdom *o*! „ V ii 16
Overturn when they seek to *o* our rights, *Becket* V ii 456
Over-violence as one That mars a cause with *o-v*. „ IV ii 327
Overwhelm'd We shall be *o*. Seize him and carry him! „ V iii 141
full democracy has *o* This Old world, *Prom. of May* I 593
'Ow (how) and *'o* should I see to laäme the laädy, „ III 95
'Owd (hold) they'll hev' a fine cider-crop to-year if the blossom *'o's*. „ I 317
Owd (old) Why, o' coorse, fur it be the *o* man's birthdaäy. „ I 6
O Steer wur afeärd she wouldn't be back i' time to keep his birthdaäy, „ I 16
and 'er an' the *o* man they fell a-kissin' o' one another „ I 21
An' how did ye leäve the *o* uncle i' Coomberland? „ I 68
An' how d'ye find the *o* man 'ere? „ I 71
The *o* man be heighty to-daäy, beänt he? „ I 76
An' I haätes boooks an' all, fur they puts foälk off the *o* waäys. „ I 222
Then the *o* man i' Lear should be shaämed of hissen, „ I 266
but when thou be as *o* as me thou'll put one word fur another as I does. „ I 381
So the *o* uncle i' Coomberland be deäd, Miss Dora, beänt he? „ II 1
I seed how the *o* man wur vext. „ II 27
I would taäke the *o* blind man to my oän fireside. „ II 74
Naäy, but I hev an *o* woman as 'ud see to all that: „ II 95
Yeas, an' *o* Dobson should be glad on it. „ II 146
Why, coom then, *o* feller, I'll tell it to you; „ II 202
Ye shall sing that ageän to-night, fur *o* Dobson 'll gi'e us a bit o' supper. *Sally.* I weänt goä to *o* Dobson; „ II 216
O Steer's gotten all his grass down and wants a hand, and I'll goä to him. „ II 220
O Steer gi'es nubbut cowd tea to *'is* men, and *o* Dobson gi'es beer. *Sally.* But I'd like *o* Steer's cowd tea better nor Dobson's beer. Good-bye. „ II 223
when *o* Dobson coom'd upo' us? „ II 232
but I wur so ta'en up wi' leädin' the *o* man about all the blessed murnin' „ III 2
The Steers was all gentlefoälks i' the *o* times, „ III 448
The land belonged to the Steers i' the *o* times, „ III 451
He be saäyin' a word to the *o* man, but he'll coom up if ye lets 'im. „ III 481
The *o* man's coom'd ageän to 'issen, an' wants To hev a word wi' ye „ III 702
Owe the duty which as Legate He *o's* himself, *Queen Mary* III iv 402
To whom he *o's* his loyalty after God, „ IV i 23
unto him you *o* That Mary hath acknowledged „ V iii 29
you That *o* to me your power over me— *Becket* II ii 152
I *o* you thanks for ever. *The Cup* I ii 249
love that children *o* to both I give To him alone. *Foresters* IV 7
Owed Thou still hast *o* thy father, Gilbert Foliot. *Becket* I iii 276
more than one brave fellow *o* His death *The Falcon* 634
Ower (over) I should saay 'twur *o* by now. *Queen Mary* IV iii 475
and *o* a hoonderd pounds worth o' rings stolen. *Prom. of May* I 393
Ower (over) (*continued*) Dan Smith's cart hes runned *o* a laädy i' the holler laäne, *Prom. of May* II 568
and my missus a-gittin' *o* 'er lyin'-in, „ III 74
Owl (*See also* **Scritch-owl**) The wood is full of echoes, *o's*, elfs, *Foresters* II i 263
Owld (old) it be a var waay vor my *o* legs up vro' Islip. *Queen Mary* IV iii 472
Eh, then ha' thy waay wi' me, Tib; ez thou hast wi' thy *o* man. „ IV iii 487
Ay, Joan, and my *o* man wur up and awaay betimes „ IV iii 488
I heerd summat as summun towld summun o' *o* Bishop Gardiner's end; „ IV iii 503
there wur an *o* lord a-cum to dine wi' un, and a wur so *o* a couldn't bide vor his dinner, „ IV iii 504
and the *o* lord fell to 's meat wi' a will, „ IV iii 514
the burnin' o' the *o* archbishop 'll burn the Pwoap out o' this 'ere land vor iver and iver. „ IV iii 535
Own (adj.) (*See also* **Oän**) What are you cackling of bastardy under the Queen's *o* nose? „ I i 59
I shall judge with my *o* eyes whether her Grace incline „ I i 134
Peace! hear him; let his *o* words damn the Papist. From thine *o* mouth I judge thee—tear him down! „ I iii 53
a King That with her *o* pawns plays against a Queen, „ I iii 162
But your *o* state is full of danger here. „ I iv 168
'Tis mine *o* wish fulfill'd before the word Was spoken, „ I iv 232
Tho' Queen, I am not Queen Of mine *o* heart, „ I v 523
he loved the more His *o* gray towers, „ II i 49
Well, for mine *o* work, „ II i 86
I have seen them in their *o* land; „ II i 167
mute as death, And white as her *o* milk; „ II ii 80
on you, In your *o* city, as her right, my Lord, For you are loyal. „ II ii 106
From your *o* royal lips, at once may know „ II ii 136
In mine *o* person am I come to you, „ II ii 142
seeks To bend the laws to his *o* will, „ II ii 184
that I should leave Some fruit of mine *o* body after me, „ II ii 223
Before our *o* High Court of Parliament, „ II ii 234
By his *o* rule, he hath been so bold to-day, „ II ii 347
his fault So thoroughly to believe in his *o* self. „ II ii 386
Yet thoroughly to believe in one's *o* self, So one's *o* self be thorough, „ II ii 388
Well, the tree in Virgil, sir, That bears not its *o* apples. „ III i 23
the Pope's Holiness By mine *o* self. „ III ii 112
Statesmen that are wise Shape a necessity, as a sculptor clay, To their *o* model. „ III iii 34
In our *o* name and that of all the state, „ III iii 120
As well for our *o* selves as all the realm, „ III iii 136
The Lord who hath redeem'd us With his *o* blood, „ III iii 203
and not sure Of their *o* selves, they are wroth with their *o* selves, „ III iv 120
Trembled for her *o* gods, for these were trembling— „ III iv 128
But the wench Hath her *o* troubles; she is weeping now; „ III v 262
Bonner cannot out-Bonner his *o* self— „ III vi 27
he hath pray'd me not to sully Mine *o* prerogative, „ IV i 18
Yet once he saved your Majesty's *o* life; Stood out against the King in your behalf, At his *o* peril. „ IV i 125
By mine *o* self—by mine *o* hand! „ IV ii 202
The parson from his *o* spire swung out dead, „ IV iii 375
I say they have drawn the fire On their *o* heads: „ IV iii 381
I could weep for them And her, and mine *o* self and all the world. „ V ii 12
Gone beyond him and mine *o* natural man (It was God's cause); „ V ii 102
That his *o* wife is no affair of his. „ V ii 561
Nay, but I speak from mine *o* self, not him; „ V iii 42
Seven-fold dishonour'd even in the sight Of thine *o* sectaries— „ V v 134
Ay, ever give yourselves your *o* good word. *Harold* I i 343
I swear it, By mine *o* eyes—and these two sapphires— „ I ii 110
Swear thou to-day, to-morrow is thine *o*. „ II ii 711
A cleric lately poison'd his *o* mother, *Becket, Pro.* 11
what shall I call it, affect her thine *o* self. „ *Pro.* 513

Own (adj.) (*continued*) Thou art wearied out With this day's work, get thee to thine *o* bed. *Becket* I i 8
And was thine *o* election so canonical, Good father? „ I iii 120
But his *o* mother's, lest the crown should be Shorn of ancestral splendour. This did Henry. Shall I do less for mine *o* Canterbury? „ I iii 155
Ringing their *o* death-knell thro' all the realm. „ I iii 172
when none could sit By his *o* hearth in peace; „ I iii 342
In mine *o* hall, and sucking thro' fools' ears The flatteries of corruption— „ I iii 360
sat in mine *o* courts Judging my judges, „ I iii 367
Look to it, your *o* selves! „ I iii 398
Strong—not in mine *o* self, but Heaven; „ I iii 536
And I, that knew mine *o* infirmity, „ I iii 696
I warrant you, or your *o* either. „ I iv 23
be we not in my lord's *o* refractory? „ I iv 180
Yea, thou my golden dream of Love's *o* bower, „ II i 35
But, since we would be lord of our *o* manor, „ II ii 19
cherish'd him Who thief-like fled from his *o* church by night, „ II ii 156
which Hell's *o* heat So dwelt on that they rose and darken'd Heaven. „ II ii 204
Yea—on mine *o* self The King had had no power except for Rome. „ II ii 411
despite his kingly promise given To our *o* self of pardon, „ II ii 433
and to win my *o* bread, whereupon he asked our mother „ III i 117
And bound me by his love to secrecy Till his *o* time. „ III i 229
or rather pulled all the Church with the Holy Father astride of it down upon his *o* head. „ III iii 78
so that the smell of their *o* roast had not come across it— „ III iii 119
Your *o* child brought me hither! „ IV ii 13
Child, I am mine *o* self Of and belonging to the King. „ IV ii 29
Have we not heard Raymond of Poitou, thine *o* uncle—nay, Geoffrey Plantagenet, thine *o* husband's father— „ IV ii 247
that The King himself, for love of his *o* sons, If hearing, „ IV ii 344
I'll swear to mine *o* self it was a feint. „ IV ii 401
In mine *o* cause I strove against him there, „ V i 14
And what would my *o* Aquitaine say to that? „ V i 181
crying On Holy Church to thunder out her rights And thine *o* wrong so pitilessly? „ V ii 33
Strikes truest ev'n for his *o* self. „ V ii 42
he had gone too far Into the King's *o* woods; „ V ii 108
His child and mine *o* soul, and so return. „ V ii 193
Shall I not smite him with his *o* cross-staff? „ V ii 313
For which I would have laid mine *o* life down „ V ii 338
That their *o* King closed with me last July „ V ii 388
They slew my stags in mine *o* manor here, „ V ii 438
Not punish of your *o* authority? „ V ii 450
and yet threaten your Archbishop In his *o* house. „ V ii 506
Take refuge in your *o* cathedral, Thomas. „ V ii 584
I say, take refuge in your *o* cathedral. „ V ii 590
And yet my dream foretold my martyrdom In mine *o* church. „ V ii 634
Why, these are our *o* monks who follow'd us! „ V iii 58
Strike our Archbishop in his *o* cathedral! „ V iii 180
else wherefore has my fate Brought me again to her *o* city? *The Cup* I i 14
Is vengeance for its *o* sake worth the while, „ I i 30
That your *o* people cast you from their bounds, „ I i 137
Save for some slight report in her *o* Senate „ I ii 133
His *o* true people cast him from their doors Like a base coin. „ I ii 351
Bandy their *o* rude jests with them, „ I ii 360
Then for your *o* sake, Lady, I say it with all gentleness, „ I iii 98
Good! mine *o* dagger driven by Synorix found All good „ II 85
I call on our *o* Goddess in our *o* Temple. „ II 314
It is the cup belonging our *o* Temple. „ II 345
That Synorix should drink from his *o* cup. „ II 353
poor worm, crawl down thine *o* black hole To the lowest Hell. „ II 495
Thou art one With thine *o* people, and though a Roman I Forgive thee, Camma. „ II 504
till he hasn't an eye left in his *o* tail to flourish among the peahens, *The Falcon* 102
you look as beautiful this morning as the very Madonna her *o* self— „ 199

Own (adj.) (*continued*) And this last costly gift to mine *o* self, *The Falcon* 228
and so descend again with some of her ladyship's *o* appurtenances? „ 417
his lordship's *o* foster-brother, would commend them to your ladyship's most peculiar appreciation. „ 566
Filippo! will you take the word out of your master's *o* mouth? „ 598
Ay, if you'd like to measure your *o* length upon the grass. *Prom. of May* I 466
He, following his *o* instincts as his God, „ I 588
Nature a liar, making us feel guilty Of her *o* faults. „ II 270
And these take flesh again with our *o* flesh, „ II 277
I have found it once again In your *o* self. „ II 377
Our old nurse crying as if for her *o* child, „ II 479
so be more at peace With mine *o* self. „ II 663
For her *o* sake *then*, if not for mine—not now—But by-and-by. „ II 683
and your *o* name Of Harold sounds so English and so old „ III 608
till we be only bones our *o* selves. *Foresters* I i 26
and for the love of his *o* little mother on earth, „ I i 98
my great great grandfather, my great grandfather, my grandfather, and my *o* father— „ I i 331
and whenever I set my *o* foot on it I say to it, „ I i 335
This ring my mother gave me: it was her *o* Betrothal ring. „ I ii 294
You see, they are so fond o' their *o* voices „ II i 383
and if thou miss I will fasten thee to thine *o* doorpost „ II i 403
What! do I not know mine *o* ring? „ II i 590
and their *o* want Of manhood to their leader! „ II i 693
Is to mistrust your *o* love for your girl! „ II ii 59
all that live By their *o* hands, the labourer, the poor priest; „ III 165
so His *o* true wife came with him, „ III 240
you that dishonour The daughters and the wives of your *o* faction— „ IV 699
God help the mark—To his *o* unprincely ends. „ IV 716
I remain Mistress of mine *o* self and mine *o* soul. „ IV 729
hast thou no fetters For those of thine *o* band who would betray thee? „ IV 832
if you hold us here Longer from our *o* venison. „ IV 942
Then by thine *o* account thou shouldst be mine. „ IV 1038

Own (s) you scarce could meet his eye And hold your *o*; *Queen Mary* IV i 105
But softly as a bridegroom to his *o*. *Harold* II ii 758
When Henry came into his *o* again, *Becket* I iii 153
We fear that he may reave thee of thine *o*. „ I iii 612
Now the King is home again, the King will have his *o* again, Home again, home again, and each will have his *o* again, *Foresters* IV 1106

Own (verb) You do not *o* The bodily presence in the Eucharist, *Queen Mary* I ii 43
And you, that would not *o* the Real Presence, „ IV ii 140
Whatever the Church *o's*—she holds it in Free and perpetual alms, *Becket* I iii 679
then each man That *o's* a wife or daughter, *Foresters* III 460
Woe to that land shall *o* thee for her king! „ IV 759

Own'd —for I have not *o* My sister, and I will not,— *Queen Mary* I v 284

Owt (anything) (*See also* **Aught, Ought**) Theer ye goäs ageän, Miss, niver believing *o* I says to ye— *Prom. of May* I 107
or the parson, or the justice o' peace, or *o*. „ I 133
fur I niver touched a drop of *o* till my oän wedding-daäy, „ I 362
Eva can do *o* wi' 'im; „ I 437
fur I'd ha' done *o* fur 'er mysen; „ II 33
an' all the parish 'ud ha' done *o* fur 'er, „ II 36
Let 'im bust hissen, then, fur *o* I cares. „ II 167
Deäd! It mun be true, fur it wur i' print as black as *o*. „ II 731

Ox A light among the *oxen*. *Harold* IV i 87
Swine, sheep, *o*—here's a French supper. *Becket* I iv 112
his monies, his *oxen*, his dinners, himself. *Foresters* I i 234
or a stump-tailed *o* in May-time, „ II i 435

Oxford (adj.) Right as an *O* scholar, „ I i 59

Oxford (s) masses here be sung By every priest in *O*. *Queen Mary* IV iii 101
John of *O*, The President of this Council, *Becket* I iii 74
For John of *O* here to read to you. „ I iii 417
Cursed be John of *O*, Roger of York, And Gilbert Foliot! „ II ii 265
and I ha' seen the King once at *O*, „ III i 164

P

Paäin (pain) I niver 'es sa much as one pin's prick of *p*; *Prom. of May* I 360
Paäper (paper) then a-scrattin upon a bit o' *p*, then a-lookin' ageän; „ I 203
dosta knaw this *p*? Ye dropt it upo' the road. „ II 687
Pace (s) break your *p's* in, and make you tame; *Queen Mary* V iii 121
Pace (verb) king should *p* on purple to his bride, *The Cup* II 189
Pacify pray'd me to pray thee to *p* Thy King; *Becket* I iii 206
He told me thou shouldst *p* the King, „ I iii 224
Pacing *p* my new lands at Littlechester, *Prom. of May* II 647
But I am weary *p* thro' the wood. *Foresters* II i 129
Packt So *p* with carnage that the dykes and brooks *Harold* III ii 128
Padua (city of Venetia) And died in *P*. *Queen Mary* V ii 516
Pagan The *p* temple of a *p* Rome! *Becket* I iii 61
Page who call'd the mind Of children a blank *p*, *Prom. of May* II 282
Pageant second actor in this *p* That brings him in; *Queen Mary* III iii 14
and flowers In silken *p's*. „ III v 15
Paget (Lord) *P* is for him—for to wed with Spain „ I v 75
P is ours. Gardiner perchance is ours; „ I v 386
Lord *P's* 'Ay' is sure—who else? „ I v 630
Spite of Lord *P* and Lord William Howard, „ III i 324
Lord *P* Waits to present our Council to the Legate. „ III ii 97
If we could burn out heresy, my Lord *P*, „ III iv 54
P, you are all for this poor life of ours, „ III iv 59
Look to your Bible, *P*! we are fallen. „ III iv 80
P, You stand up here to fight for heresy, „ III iv 91
they are many, As my Lord *P* says. „ III iv 177
my Lord *P* and Lord William Howard, Crave, „ IV i 6
You are too politic for me, my Lord *P*. „ IV i 151
Ay, ay, *P*, They have brought it in large measure „ IV iii 362
yet, *P*, I do hold The Catholic, „ IV iii 381
O *P*, *P*! I have seen heretics of the poorer sort, „ IV iii 435
P, despite his fearful heresies, „ IV iii 633
Paid he *p* his ransom back. *Harold* II ii 50
I have once more *p* them all. *Prom. of May* III 158
if they be not *p* back at the end of the year, the land goes to the Abbot. *Foresters* I i 69
must be *p* in a year and a month, or I lose the land. „ I i 268
You shall wait for mine till Sir Richard has *p* the Abbot. „ I ii 232
I have *p* him half. That other thousand— „ II i 465
these monies should be *p* in to the Abbot at York, „ IV 507
The debt hath not been *p*. „ IV 612
Has it been *p*? *Abbot*. O yes. „ IV 616
Not *p* at York—the wood—prick me no more! „ IV 623
Sir Richard *p* his monies to the Abbot. „ IV 849
Pain (*See also* **Paäin**) Judgment, and *p* accruing thereupon; *Queen Mary* III iii 219
Or to be still in *p* with devils in hell; „ IV iii 222
he never uttered moan of *p*: „ IV iii 619
evilly used And put to *p*. *Becket* II ii 434
Geoffrey, the *p* thou hast put me to! „ IV ii 10
This *p*—what is it?—again? *The Cup* II 445
With cold, with *p* perhaps, poor prisoner! *The Falcon* 449
And if my pleasure breed another's *p*, *Prom. of May* I 278
with as little *p* As it is to fall asleep. „ II 341
to spare myself, And her too, *p*, *p*, *p*? „ III 720
That blast our natural passions into *p's*! „ III 725
Move me no more! I am sick and faint with *p*! *Foresters* IV 599
Painful perhaps The *p* circumstances which I heard— *Prom. of May* II 402
Paint Tell him to *p* it out, *Queen Mary* III i 267
The man shall *p* a pair of gloves. „ III i 274
honesty too, *p* her what way they will. *Becket* II i 101
Painted If you have falsely *p* your fine Prince; *Queen Mary* I v 598
The conduit *p*—the nine worthies—ay! „ III i 258
God's passion! do you know the knave that *p* it? „ III i 265
Pair But since the fondest *p* of doves will jar, *Becket* IV ii 40
You are an honest *p*. I will come to your wedding. *Prom. of May* III 114
Pair'd Ay, if Wisdom *P* not with Good. *Harold* V i 178
Palace (adj.) Hark, there is battle at the *p* gates, *Queen Mary* II iv 47
I found it fluttering at the *p* gates:— „ III ii 218
Palace (s) Hast thou let fall those papers in the *p*? „ I iii 2
And unto no dead world; but Lambeth *p*, „ III ii 154
There was a paper thrown into the *p*, „ III vi 139
which I found Strewn in your *p*. „ V ii 173
I left it privily At Florence, in her *p*. *The Falcon* 75
And welcome turns a cottage to a *p*. „ 273
Who never deign'd to shine into my *p*. „ 286
My *p* wanting you was but a cottage; My cottage, while you grace it, is a *p*. „ 287
In cottage or in *p*, being still Beyond your fortunes, „ 290
Palate That *p* is insane which cannot tell *Becket, Pro.* 104
Pale (adj.) The word has turn'd your Highness *p*; *Queen Mary* I v 471
How deathly *p*! a chair, your Highness. „ I v 636
a *p* horse for Death and Gardiner for the Devil. „ III i 234
Mary rubb'd out *p*— „ III i 423
fieriest partisans—are *p* Before my star! „ III ii 170
The little murder'd princes, in a *p* light, „ III v 147
Peters, how *p* you look! you bring the smoke „ IV iii 560
Brother! why so *p*? *Harold* I i 28
God redden your *p* blood! *Becket* I iv 35
I wonder if I look as *p* as she? *The Cup* II 322
more blessed were the rags Of some *p* beggar-woman *The Falcon* 852
and you look thin and *p*. Is it for his absence? *Prom. of May* I 782
You are *p*, my Dora! but the ruddiest cheek „ III 486
I that have turn'd their Moslem crescent *p*— *Foresters* IV 793
All those *p* mouths which we have fed will praise us— „ IV 1076
Pale (s) praised The convent and lone life—within the *p*— *Harold* I ii 48
loved within the *p* forbidden By Holy Church: „ III ii 22
Thou hast broken thro' the *p's* Of privilege, *Becket* III iii 193
Paleness a *p*, Like the wan twilight after sunset, „ I iii 325
Palisade The trenches dug, the *p's* uprear'd *Harold* V i 189
strengthen their *p's*! „ V i 481
They fall on those within the *p*! „ V i 668
Pall Lay thou thy hand upon this golden *p*! „ II ii 699
Foliot may claim the *p* For London too. *Becket* I iii 56
The *P*! I go to meet my King! „ V ii 619
Pallium Who had my *p* from an Antipope! *Harold* I i 82
Because I had my Canterbury *p*, „ III i 106
Palm and kindled with the *p's* of Christ! *Queen Mary* I v 93
P's, flowers, pomegranates, golden cherubim *Harold* III i 182
And these rough oaks the *p's* of Paradise! *Foresters* II i 169
Palmer he is a holy *P*, bounden by a vow not to show „ I ii 236
Palsied while thy hands Are *p* here, *Harold* II ii 455
Palsy In this low pulse and *p* of the state, *Queen Mary* II ii 103
Palter My friend, thou hast gone too far to *p* now. *Harold* II ii 707
Why do you *p* with the ceremony? *The Cup* II 419
Pan Swarm to thy voice like bees to the brass *p*. *Foresters* I iii 109
Pancratius (St. Pancras) jewel of St. *P* Woven into the gold. *Harold* II ii 700
Pander I am your subject, not your—— *Henry*. *P*. *Becket, Pro.* 147
Profligate *p*! *Fitzurse*. Do you hear that? „ V iii 160
Pandora-box this Hollow *P-b*, With all the pleasures flown, *Prom. of May* II 346
Pang in the front rank of the fight With scarce a *p*. *The Cup* I ii 155
Panoply Mail'd in the perfect *p* of faith, *Becket* V ii 494
Pant sure she hates thee, *P's* for thy blood. *Harold* I ii 39
Panting And *p* for my blood as I go by. *Queen Mary* V ii 219
Papacy We strove against the *p* from the first, „ III iii 225
God save the Crown! the *P* is no more. „ V v 286
inherited loathing of these black sheep of the *P*. *Becket, Pro.* 462
that would shake the *P* as it stands. „ I iii 213
Papal (*See also* **Anti-papal**) not to yield His Church of England to the *P* wolf And Mary; *Queen Mary* I ii 36
And be regather'd to the *P* fold? „ III ii 117
Wanting the *P* mitre. „ III iv 148
of her most Royal, Infallible, *P* Legate-cousin. „ III iv 433
That so the *P* bolt may pass by England, *Becket, Pro.* 226
Paper (*See also* **Paäper**) Hast thou let fall those *p's* in the palace? *Queen Mary* I iii 2
I've found this *p*; pray your worship read it; „ II iii 56
This *p*, Dickon. I found it fluttering at the palace gates:— „ III ii 217
There was a *p* thrown into the palace, „ III vi 139

Paper (*continued*) when you are gone, my liege, Witness these *p's*, *Queen Mary* III vi 174
Pray you write out this *p* for me, Cranmer. „ IV ii 61
the *p's* by my hand Sign'd since my degradation— „ IV iii 243
might not after all those *p's* Of recantation yield again, who knows? *Paget.* *P's* of recantation! Think you then That Cranmer read all *p's* that he sign'd? „ IV iii 314
But held from you all *p's* sent by Rome, „ V ii 45
these libellous *p's* which I found Strewn in your palace. „ V ii 171
Nay, Madam, there be loyal *p's* too, „ V ii 221
There! there! another *p*! Said you not „ V ii 329
I'll have the *p* back—blot out my name. *Becket* I iii 286
hath he sign'd? show me the *p's*! „ I iii 317
This *p* sign'd Antonius—will you take it, *The Cup* I ii 225
Yes; it was in the Somersetshire *p's*. *Prom. of May* III 149
Paphlagonia Have you alliances? Bithynia, Pontus, *P*? *The Cup* I ii 100
Papist (adj.) There haunt some *P* ruffians hereabout Would murder you. *Queen Mary* III v 174
Papist (s) for we are many of us Catholics, but few *P's*, „ I i 115
Down with the *P*! „ I iii 33
let his own words damn the *P*. „ I iii 53
Parable That is the *p* of our blessed Lord. *Becket* I iv 74
why should not the *p* of our blessed Lord be acted again? „ I iv 77
Paradise Look at the New World—a *p* made hell; *Queen Mary* II i 208
Wore in mine eyes the green of *P*. „ III ii 18
And be with Christ the Lord in *P*. „ IV iii 88
Not to gain *p*; no, nor if the Pope, „ IV iii 557
and be driven out of her *p*. *Becket, Pro.* 533
Gave me the golden keys of *P*. „ I i 54
Will greet us as our babes in *P*. „ V ii 225
And pass at once perfect to *P*. „ V iii 14
As in the midmost heart of *P*. *The Cup* II 186
And these rough oaks the palms of *P*! *Foresters* II i 170
Paralysis My father stricken with his first *p*, *Prom. of May* II 481
He is stricken with a slight *p*. *Foresters* IV 456
Paramount I have it . . . My lord *P*, Our great High-priest, *Becket* IV ii 356
Paramour Well—some believed she was his *p*. *Harold* V ii 102
Bury him and his *p* together. „ V ii 150
more Than that of other *p's* of thine? *Becket, Pro.* 71
was Rosamund—his *p*—thy rival. „ *Pro.* 471
p—rival! King Louis had no *p's*, „ *Pro.* 473
I would she were but his *p*, for men tire of their fancies; „ *Pro.* 479
Belongings, *p's*, whom it pleases him To call his wives; „ IV ii 35
That I am his main *p*, his sultana. „ IV ii 39
I gave it you, and you your *p*; „ V i 169
Maid? *Friar.* *P*! *Friar.* Hell take her! *Foresters* III 402
clutch Our pretty Marian for his *p*, „ IV 767
Parapet I was so mad, that I mounted upon the *p*— *Prom. of May* III 372
Parch'd and watch The *p* banks rolling incense, as of old. *Queen Mary* I v 91
Parchment be not wroth at the dumb *p*. *Foresters* I i 342
Pardon (s) all one mind to supplicate The Legate here for *p*, *Queen Mary* III iii 107
A round fine likelier. Your *p*. „ III iii 280
So that you crave full *p* of the Legate. „ III iv 391
I attend the Queen To crave most humble *p*— „ III iv 432
Your *p*, then; It is the heat and narrowness „ III v 206
According to the canons *p* due To him that so repents, „ IV iii 33
so long continuing, Hath found his *p*; „ IV iii 50
Your *p*, Sweet cousin, and farewell! „ V ii 203
what sin Beyond all grace, all *p*? „ V ii 340
No *p*!—Why that was false: „ V v 135
hard is our honeymoon! Thy *p*. *Harold* IV iii 230
Leave me. No more—*P* on both sides—Go! „ V i 353
—I pray your *p*. *Becket, Pro.* 37
kingly promise given To our own self of *p*, „ II ii 433
A policy of wise *p* Wins here as well as there. „ V ii 23
I crave Thy *p*—I have still thy leave to speak. „ V ii 44
Your *p*. *Salisbury.* He said, 'Attend the office.' „ V ii 606
Thy *p*, Priestess! *The Cup* II 373
with your ladyship's *p*, and as your ladyship knows, *The Falcon* 565
Your *p* for a minute. She must be waked. *Prom. of May* III 657
I crave your worship's *p*. *Foresters* II i 243
Or lose all hope of *p* from us— „ IV 935
Pardon (verb) She said—pray *p* me, and pity her— *Queen Mary* I v 52
they mean to *p* me. „ IV ii 50
For if our Holy Queen not *p* him, „ IV iii 61
God *p* me! I have never yet found one. „ V ii 334
P us, thou! Our silence is our reverence *Harold* IV i 11
see beyond Your Norman shrines, *p* it, *p* it, „ V i 620
I pray God *p* mine infirmity. *Becket* II ii 353
God *p* thee and these, but God's full curse „ V iii 133
Pray, *p* me! *The Falcon* 395
I pray you *p* me again! „ 478
Will *p* me for asking what I ask. „ 805
you are young, and—*p* me—As lovely as your sister. *Prom. of May* II 507
And *p* me for saying it— „ III 552
P him, my lord: he is a holy Palmer, *Foresters* I ii 235
P him again, I pray you; „ I ii 246
Speak to me, Kate, and say you *p* me! „ II ii 53
And it was but a woman. *P* me. „ II ii 73
When Richard comes he is soft enough to *p* His brother; „ IV 747
Pardonablest lies that ever men have lied, Thine is the *p*. *Harold* III i 100
Pardon'd That must be *p* me; *Queen Mary* I v 311
Why surely ye are *p*, *Foresters* IV 947
Pare But one that *p's* his nails; to me? *Queen Mary* III v 65
Parish (adj.) every *p* tower Shall clang and clash alarum „ II i 228
Parish (s) and haäfe th' *p* 'll be theer, an' Miss Dora, an' Miss Eva, an' all! *Prom. of May* I 10
and you says it belongs to the *p*, and theer be a thousand i' the *p*, „ I 145
thaw 'e knaws I was hallus ageän heving schoolmaster i' the *p*! „ I 187
noän o' the *p'es* goäs by that naäme 'ereabouts. „ I 268
an' all the *p* 'ud ha' done out fur 'er, „ II 36
if the fever spread, the *p* will have to thank you for it. „ III 47
Parish-parson When shall your *p-p* bawl our banns „ I 685
Park At the *p* gate he hovers with our guards. *Queen Mary* II iv 15
Parleying This comes of *p* with my Lord of Devon. „ I iv 251
Still *P* with Renard, all the day with Renard, „ III vi 116
Parliament (*See also* **King-Parliament**) didn't the *P* make her a bastard? „ I i 15
they be both bastards by Act of *P* and Council. *Citizen.* Ay, the *P* can make every true-born man of us a bastard. „ I i 24
But if *P* can make the Queen a bastard, „ I i 48
Council, people, *P* against him; „ I v 78
But for our heretic *P*— „ I v 388
That, soon or late, your *P* is ours. „ I v 424
shall we have Spain on the throne and in the *p*; „ II i 176
Council, The *P* as well, are troubled waters; „ II ii 50
Corroborate by your acts of *P*: „ II ii 173
Before our own High Court of *P*, „ II ii 234
And others of our *P*, revived, „ III i 326
And Commons here in *P* assembled, „ III iii 114
A *P* of imitative apes! „ III iii 235
And these again upon her *P*— „ III vi 185
Tell my mind to the Council—to the *P*: „ V ii 289
Parlour and you should sit i' your oän *p* quite like a laädy, *Prom. of May* II 97
Parson (*See also* **Parish-parson**) Gardener, and huntsman, in the *p's* place, The *p* *Queen Mary* IV iii 373
he's no respect for the Queen, or the *p*, or the justice o' peace, or owt. *Prom. of May* I 133
and *P* mebbe, thaw he niver mended that gap „ I 445
Part (s) you are art and *p* with us In purging heresy, *Queen Mary* III iv 316
And for *my p* therein—Back to that juggler, *Harold* V i 53
I could but read a *p* to-day, because— *Becket* I iii 422
when those, that name themselves Of the King's *p*, „ V ii 429
The first *p*—made before you came among us— *Foresters* III 435
Part (verb) To *p* me from the woman that I loved! *Harold* V i 346
Look you, we never meant to *p* again. „ V ii 80
Must I hack her arms off? How shall I *p* them? „ V ii 148
'Till death us *p*'—those are the only words, *Prom. of May* I 658
they that love do not believe that death Will *p* them. „ I 664

Past-Pass'd (*continued*) *Past* help! his paws are *past* help. *Becket* I iv 110
he hath *pass'd* out again, And on the other side. „ III ii 12
a man *passed* in there to-day: I holla'd to him, „ III ii 24
and in thy name I *pass'd* From house to house. „ V ii 103
on a Tuesday *pass'd* From England into bitter banishment; „ V ii 288
She *past* me here Three years ago when I was flying *The Cup* I i 4
in a city thro' which he *past* with the Roman army: „ I i 43
in some city where Antonius *past*. „ I ii 58
having *pass'd* unwounded from the field, *The Falcon* 608
but they, the shadows of ourselves, Have *past* for ever. *Prom. of May* I 272
You never told her, then, of what has *past* Between us. „ I 729
Sleep, mournful heart, and let the past be *past*! *Foresters* I iii 47
She and Sir Richard Have *past* away, „ II i 120
They must have *past*. Here is a woodman's hut. „ II i 199
You see he is *past* himself. What would you more? „ IV 471
Past the bank Of foxglove, then to left by that one yew. „ IV 973
Pastime While you can take your *p* in the woods. *The Cup* I i 190
Cannot *he* take his *p* like the flies? *Prom. of May* I 277
It is but *p*—nay, I will not harm thee. *Foresters* II i 554
Have our loud *p's* driven them all away? „ II ii 105
Pastor *P* fugatur Grex trucidatur— *Harold* V i 513
Pastoral The polish'd Damon of your *p* here, *Prom. of May* III 562
Pat gave me a great *p* o' the cheek for a pretty wench, *Becket* III i 125
Patch I must *p* up a peace— „ II ii 53
Patent your name Stands first of those who sign'd the Letters *P* *Queen Mary* I ii 18
State secrets should be *p* to the statesman *Becket, Pro.* 76
Pater Salva patriam Sancte *P*, *Harold* V i 467
Path in a narrow *p*. A plover flew before thee. *Becket* II i 53
I strike into my former *p* For England, „ II ii 455
stray'd From love's clear *p* into the common bush, „ III i 247
so many alleys, crossings, *P's*, avenues— „ IV ii 7
she turns down the *p* through our little vineyard, *The Falcon* 167
Pathway A hundred *p's* running everyway, *Becket, Pro.* 163
—would have made my *p* flowers, „ V ii 370
Patience age Of brief life, and brief purpose, and brief *p*, *Queen Mary* III iv 414
The *p* of St. Lawrence in the fire. „ IV iii 95
Patient with that sweet worn smile Among thy *p* wrinkles— „ V v 200
till now, by the *p* Saints, she's as crabb'd as ever. *Harold* II i 50
Patriam Salva *p* Sancte Pater, „ V i 466
Salva *p*, Sancta Mater. „ V i 470
Patriarchal And die upon the *P* throne Of all my predecessors? *Becket* V iii 75
Patrimony When I was ruler in the *p*, *Queen Mary* V ii 72
That be the *p* of the poor? *Becket* I iii 106
Patriot (adj.) but that thy *p* passion Siding with our great Council against Tostig, *Harold* III i 57
Patriot (s) Their shield-borne *p* of the morning star *The Cup* II 121
Patriotism you suspect This Sinnatus of playing *p*, „ I i 78
Pattern'd moonlight casements *p* on the wall, *Queen Mary* V v 9
Paul (Saint) (*See also* **St. Paul**) what saith *P*? 'I would they were cut off „ III iv 31
Paul the Fourth (Pope) But this new Pope Caraffa, *P t F*, „ V ii 32
Pauper a Sister of Mercy, come from the death-bed of a *p*, *Prom. of May* III 377
Pauper'd Why then, my lord, we are *p* out and out. *The Falcon* 268
Pauperes *Sederunt principes, ederunt* p. *Becket* I iv 132
Pauperis And one an *uxor* p *Ibyci.* „ V ii 216
Pauperism Sunk in the deepest pit of *p*, *Prom. of May* III 803
Pause (s) so in this *p*, before The mine be fired, *Queen Mary* II i 25
Pause (verb) Wherefore *p* you—what? „ V iii 39
Pavement To bathe this sacred *p* with my blood. *Becket* V iii 131
Paw King's verdurer caught him a-hunting in the forest, and cut off his *p's*. „ I iv 96
Past help! his *p's* are past help. „ I iv 111
One downward plunge of his *p* would rend away „ IV ii 283
if we kill a stag, our dogs have their *p's* cut off, *Foresters* IV 225
Pawn a King That with her own *p's* plays against a Queen, *Queen Mary* I iii 162

Pawn (*continued*) Courtenay seems Too princely for a *p*. *Queen Mary* I iii 167
Pay Your pious wish to *p* King Edward's debts, „ I v 111
but to *p* them full in kind, „ V iv 14
Pray'd me to *p* her debts, and keep the Faith; „ V v 257
What conditions? *p* him back His ransom? *Harold* II ii 213
Church should *p* her scutage like the lords. *Becket* I i 34
and he *p's* me regular every Saturday. *Prom. of May* I 311
Why should I *p* you your full wages? „ III 83
sits and eats his heart for want of money to *p* the Abbot. *Foresters* I i 5
thou shouldst marry one who will *p* the mortgage. „ I i 280
I would *p* My brother all his debt and save the land. „ I ii 217
Himself would *p* this mortgage to his brother, „ I ii 263
he would *p* The mortgage if she favour'd him. „ I iii 6
Sheriff Would *p* this cursed mortgage to his brother „ II i 144
and couldst never *p* The mortgage on my land. „ II i 453
That other thousand—shall I ever *p* it? „ II i 466
Take thou my bow and arrow and compel them to *p* toll. „ III 263
he that *p's* not for his dinner must fight for it. „ IV 199
Church and Law, halt and *p* toll! „ IV 430
Where he would *p* us down his thousand marks. „ IV 441
Give him another month, and he will *p* it. „ IV 444
Lest he should fail to *p* these thousand marks „ IV 454
he Would *p* us all the debt at once, „ IV 485
Payest Thou *p* easily, like a good fellow, „ IV 155
Paying but the schoolmaster looked to the *p* you *Prom. of May* III 23
Sheriff had taken all our goods for the King without *p*, *Foresters* II i 191
when the Sheriff took my little horse for the King without *p* for it— „ II i 302
Pea *See* **Peasen**
Peace be no *p* for Mary till Elizabeth lose her head.' *Queen Mary* I iii 4
P! hear him! let his own words damn the Papist. „ I iii 52
Ay, tho' you long for *p*; „ I v 258
Some settled ground for *p* to stand upon. „ I v 315
P, pretty maiden. I hear them stirring „ I v 627
plain life and letter'd *p*, „ II i 50
P. False to Northumberland, is he false to me? „ II iv 38
The second Prince of *P*— „ III ii 164
P—the Queen, Philip, and Pole. „ III iii 83
'I come not to bring *p* but a sword'? „ III iv 88
P, madman! Thou stirrest up a grief „ III iv 297
Will let you learn in *p* and privacy „ III iv 326
With us is *p*!' The last? It was a dream; „ III v 152
P among you, there! „ IV iii 199
When I should guide the Church in *p* at home, „ V ii 67
P, cousin, *p*! I am sad at heart myself. „ V ii 159
It gilds the greatest wronger of her *p*, „ V ii 415
sleeping after all she has done, in *p* and quietness, „ V iv 35
Then clasp't the cross, and pass'd away in *p*. „ V v 260
P is with the dead. „ V v 267
P with the dead, who never were at *p*! „ V v 273
left me time And *p* for prayer to gain *Harold* I i 220
Ay, ay and wise in *p* and great in war— „ I i 313
Thy fears infect me beyond reason. *P*! „ II ii 452
P be with him! „ IV iii 89
p with them Likewise, if *they* can be at *p* „ IV iii 98
A snatch of sleep were like the *p* of God. „ V i 180
Come yet once more, from where I am at *p*, „ V i 239
P! The king's last word—'the arrow!' „ V i 265
God of truth Fill all thine hours with *p*!— „ V i 316
P to his soul! *Becket, Pro.* 394
I left him with *p* on his face— „ *Pro.* 395
P, fools! *Becket*. *P*, friends! „ I ii 1
P, *p*, my lords! these customs are no longer „ I iii 68
none could sit By his own hearth in *p*; „ I iii 342
To our King's hands again, and be at *p*. „ I iii 582
I am confounded by thee. Go in *p*. *De Broc*. In *p* now—but after. Take that for earnest. „ I iii 731
Ay, go in *p*, caitiff, caitiff! „ I iii 735
P! *Beggar*. The black sheep baaed to the miller's ewe-lamb, „ I iv 161
P! *Beggar*. 'Ewe lamb, ewe lamb, „ I iv 170
the nightmare breaking on my *p* With 'Becket.' „ II i 37
I must patch up a *p*— „ II ii 53
So we make our *p* with him. „ II ii 63

Peace (*continued*) what it is you doubt? Behold your *p* at hand. *Becket* II ii 200
but this day he proffer'd *p*. „ II ii 240
Rest in our realm, and be at *p* with all. „ II ii 448
save King Henry gave thee first the kiss of *p*. „ III iii 254
I sware I would not give the kiss of *p*, „ III iii 259
happy home-return and the King's kiss of *p* in Kent. „ III iii 328
that the sheep May feed in *p*. „ III iii 346
I thought that I had made a *p* for thee. „ V ii 84
Small *p* was mine in my noviciate, „ V ii 86
brken Your bond of *p*, your treaty with the King— „ V ii 350
Then with one quick short stab—eternal *p*. *The Cup* I iii 125
and smile At bygone things till that eternal *p*. „ I iii 173
O hush! O *p*! This violence ill becomes „ II 214
No more feuds, but *p*, *P* and conciliation! *The Falcon* 910
he's no respect for the Queen, or the parson, or the justice o' *p*, or owt. *Prom. of May* I 133
—so be more at *p* With mine own self. „ II 662
P, let him be: it is the chamber of Death! „ III 740
P, my lord; the Earl and Sir Richard come this way. *Foresters* I ii 147
capering hand in hand with Oberon. *Robin.* *P*! „ II i 499
cuirass in this forest where I dream'd That all was *p*— „ IV 131
P, magpie! Give him the quarterstaff. „ IV 249
O *p*! Father, I cannot marry till Richard comes. „ IV 647
Peaceful and no more feuds Disturb our *p* vassalage to Rome. *The Cup* II 71
Peace-lover *P-l* is our Harold for the sake *Harold* I ii 197
Peace-offering a *p-o*, A scape-goat marriage— „ I ii 203
Peach a cheek like a *p* and a heart like the stone in it— *The Falcon* 93
Peacock Never *p* against rain Scream'd as you did *Queen Mary* III v 56
Peacocking *See* **A-peacocking**
Peahen eye left in his own tail to flourish among the *p's*, *The Falcon* 102
Peal some great doom when God's just hour *P's*— *Queen Mary* I iv 263
Pearl set it round with gold, with *p*, with diamond. „ I v 375
Some six or seven Bishops, diamonds, *p's*, „ III i 53
I see the flashing of the gates of *p*— *Harold* I i 186
prize The *p* of Beauty, even if I found it *Prom. of May* III 601
Peasen (peas) Hodge 'ud ha' been a-harrowin' o' white *p* i' the outfield— *Queen Mary* IV iii 492
Pebble God change the *p* which his kingly foot „ I v 368
Peck and why ye have so few grains to *p* at. *Foresters* I i 77
Peculiar would commend them to your ladyship's most *p* appreciation. *The Falcon* 568
Pedite Eques cum *p* Præpediatur! *Harold* V i 529
Peeped all in all to one another from the time when we first *p* into the bird's nest, *Prom. of May* III 274
Peer And is not York the *p* of Canterbury? *Becket* I iii 47
Peer'd How close the Sheriff *p* into thine eyes! *Foresters* I ii 253
Peerless in music *P*—her needle perfect, *Queen Mary* III i 360
Pell-mell Church in the *p-m* of Stephen's time *Becket, Pro.* 19
Pelt After him, boys! and *p* him from the city. *Queen Mary* I iii 85
Pembroke (Earl of) so my Lord of *P* in command Of all her force be safe; „ II ii 305
Gardiner, coming with the Queen, And meeting *P*, „ II ii 310
Lord *P* in command of all our force „ II iv 3
Was not Lord *P* with Northumberland? O mad-man, if this *P* should be false? „ II iv 7
The traitor! treason! *P*! „ II iv 36
Where is *P*? *Courtenay.* I left him somewhere in the thick of it. „ II iv 79
Pen Can't I speak like a lady; *p* a letter like a lady; *Prom. of May* III 302
Pencil with some sense of art, to live By brush and *p*. „ I 499
Pendent But tell us, is this *p* hell in heaven A harm to England? *Harold* I i 76
lied like a lad That dreads the *p* scourge, „ II ii 658
Penenden Heath ten thousand men on *P H* all calling after your worship, *Queen Mary* II i 61
They roar for you On *P H*, „ II i 106
some fifty That follow'd me from *P H* in hope To hear you speak. „ II i 151
Penitence declare our *p* and grief For our long schism „ III iii 128
And if your *p* be not mockery, „ III iii 179
Penitent So that we may, as children *p*, „ III iii 153
Thou shalt receive the *p* thief's award, „ IV iii 86
Would not—if *p*—have denied him *her* Forgiveness. *Prom. of May* II 496
Penn'd This was *p*, Madonna, Close to the grating *The Falcon* 440
Penny I will give thee a silver *p* if thou wilt show *Foresters* II i 360
I have but one *p* in pouch, „ III 193
He hath, as he said, but one *p*. „ III 209
Take his *p* and leave him his gold mark. „ III 217
People (s) (*See also* **Fool-people**) council and all her *p* wish her to marry. *Queen Mary* I i 113
And if her *p*, anger'd thereupon, „ I iii 90
The *p* there so worship me— „ I iv 120
the *p* Claim as their natural leader— „ I iv 209
The Council, *p*, Parliament against him; „ I v 78
Your *p* have begun to learn your worth. „ I v 109
remission Of half that subsidy levied on the *p*, „ I v 116
Your *p*, and I go with them so far, „ I v 188
And here at land among the *p*! „ I v 383
The hardest, cruellest *p* in the world, „ II i 100
the Queen, and the laws, and the *p*, his slaves. „ II i 175
A prince as naturally may love his *p* „ II ii 192
And leave the *p* naked to the crown, And the crown naked to the *p*; „ III i 119
and the *p* so unquiet— „ III i 453
His sword shall hew the heretic *p's* down! „ III ii 178
For as this *p* were the first of all „ III iii 171
bounden by his power and place to see His *p* be not poison'd. „ III iv 213
And passes thro' the *p's*: „ III v 35
seem this *p* Care more for our brief life „ III vi 61
read your recantation Before the *p* in St. Mary's Church. „ IV ii 29
You are to beg the *p* to pray for you; „ IV ii 76
Yea, for the *p*, lest the *p* die. „ IV iii 18
Good *p*, every man at time of death „ IV iii 156
your *p* will not crown me—Your *p* are as cheerless „ V i 81
The *p's* are unlike as their complexion; „ V i 89
and therefore God Is hard upon the *p*. „ V i 176
Ah, Madam, but your *p* are so cold; „ V ii 280
'Your *p* hate you as your husband hates you.' „ V ii 336
My *p* hate me and desire my death. „ V ii 345
No, not to her nor him; but to the *p*, „ V iii 33
love me, as I love The *p*! whom God aid! „ V iii 36
The *p* are as thick as bees below, *Harold* I i 31
Pray God the *p* choose thee for their king! „ I i 314
Stir up thy *p*: oust him! „ I i 482
Let all thy *p* bless thee! „ I ii 184
shown And redden'd with his *p's* blood „ I ii 243
voice of any *p* is the sword That guards them, „ II ii 134
The king, the lords, the *p* clear'd him of it. „ II ii 522
where Tostig lost The good hearts of his *p*. „ III ii 30
What! are thy *p* sullen from defeat? „ IV i 1
Why cry thy *p* on thy sister's name? „ IV i 20
She hath won upon our *p* thro' her beauty, „ IV i 23
For when your *p* banish'd Tostig hence, „ IV i 97
Who sow'd this fancy here among the *p*? *Morcar.* Who knows what sows itself among the *p*? „ IV i 148
the *p* stupid-sure Sleep like their swine . . . „ IV iii 215
Scatter thy *p* home, descend the hill, „ V i 10
How should the *p* fight When the king flies? „ V i 137
waste the fields Of England, his own *p*?— „ V i 142
First of a line that coming from the *p*, And chosen by the *p*— *Harold.* And fighting for And dying for the *p*— „ V i 386
chosen by his *p* And fighting for his *p*! „ V i 491
Make them again one *p*—Norman, English; „ V ii 188
—like a song of the *p*. *Becket, Pro.* 338
Was not the *p's* blessing as we past „ I i 12
The *p* know their Church a tower of strength, „ I i 15
They said—her Grace's *p*—thou wast found— „ I ii 5
spied my *p's* ways; Yea, heard the churl against „ I iii 363
any harm done to the *p* if my jest be in defence of the Truth? *Becket.* Ay, if the jest be so done that the *p* Delight „ II ii 339
the *p* Believe the wood enchanted. „ III i 35
p do say that he is bad beyond all reckoning—and—— *Rosamund.* The *p* lie. „ III i 174
of the *p* there are many with me. „ III iii 292
The *p* love thee, father. „ V ii 120
What do these *p* fear? „ V iii 48
your own *p* cast you from their bounds, *The Cup* I i 137

People (s) (*continued*) Rome Made war upon the *p's* not the Gods. *The Cup* I ii 60
His own true *p* cast him from their doors „ I ii 351
Camma for my bride—The *p* love her— „ I iii 153
Hear thy *p* who praise thee! „ II 5
throned together in the sight Of all the *p*, „ II 68
teach this Rome—from knowledge of our *p*— „ II 97
all the fleeted wealth of kings And *p's*, hear. „ II 290
if my *p* must be thralls of Rome, „ II 500
Thou art one With thine own *p*, and though a Roman „ II 504
You know sick *p*, More specially sick children, *The Falcon* 816
'The land belongs to the *p*!' *Prom. of May* I i 141
So loved by all the village *p* here, „ III 755
Sir Richard and my Lady Marian fare wellnigh as sparely as their *p*. *Foresters* I i 31
so true a friend of the *p* as Lord Robin of Huntingdon. „ I i 188
fights not for himself but for the *p* of England. „ I i 237
to save his country, and the liberties of his *p*! „ I i 247
My *p* are all scattered I know not where. „ II i 176
The oppression of our *p* moves me so, „ III 109
Robin, the *p's* friend, the King o' the woods! „ III 347
These be the lies the *p* tell of us, „ III 392
People (verb) to *p* heaven in the great day When God makes up his jewels. *Becket* V ii 496
Perceive man *p's* that The lost gleam of an after-life *Prom. of May* I i 502
Perch his politic Holiness Hath all but climb'd the Roman *p* *Becket* II ii 46
Perch'd Him *p* up there? I wish some thunderbolt *Queen Mary* IV iii 9
Pereant *P*, *p*, Anglia precatur. *Harold* V i 533
Peregrine And hear my *p* and her bells in heaven; „ I ii 131
Perennial and his wealth A fountain of *p* alms— *Queen Mary* II ii 385
Perfect No! the disguise was *p*. Let's away. „ I iii 178
her needle *p*, and her learning Beyond the churchmen; „ III i 360
and is furthermore No *p* witness of a *p* faith In him who persecutes: „ III iv 117
Thou art manlike *p*. *Becket* II i 253
My friend of Canterbury and myself Are now once more in *p* amity. „ III iii 229
I would there were that *p* trust between us, „ III iii 264
That *p* trust may come again between us, „ III iii 351
Mail'd in the *p* panoply of faith, „ V ii 494
Honour to thee! thou art *p* in all honour! *Harold* II ii 691
But wherefore slur the *p* ceremony? *The Cup* II 431
A gallant boy, A noble bird, each *p* of the breed. *The Falcon* 320
And yet I had once a vision of a pure and *p* marriage, *Prom. of May* III 188
Shall I be known? is my disguise *p*? *Sheriff.* *P*— who should know you for Prince John, *Foresters* I ii 19
Perhaps *See* **P'raps**
Peril Looms the least chance of *p* to our realm. *Queen Mary* II ii 238
are you not in *p* here? *Stafford.* I think so. „ III i 34
in your behalf, At his own *p*. „ IV i 127
day of *p* that dawns darkly and drearily *Becket* I iv 145
At their *p*, at their *p*— „ III iii 313
Thou hast saved my head at the *p* of thine own. *Foresters* IV 796
Perilous Many points weather'd, many *p* ones, *Queen Mary* V v 212
A good entrenchment for a *p* hour! *Harold* III i 363
a *p* game For men to play with God. *Becket* II ii 70
all these walks are Robin Hood's And sometimes *p*. *Foresters* IV 121
Perish Would *p* on the civil slaughter-field, *Queen Mary* III i 118
May all invaders *p* like Hardrada! *Harold* IV iii 77
So *p* all the enemies of Harold! „ V i 504
So *p* all the enemies of England! „ V i 554
P she, I, all, before The Church should suffer wrong! *Becket* III iii 20
Perjured And thou art *p*, and thou wilt not seal. „ I iii 526
And that too, *p* prelate—and that, turncoat shaveling! „ I iii 736
Perjury-mongering the *p-m* Count Hath made too good an use *Harold* V i 310
Permission *P* of her Highness to retire To Ashridge, *Queen Mary* I iv 236
Permit *P* me to withdraw To Lambeth? „ III ii 129
P me, my good lord, to bear it for thee, *Becket* I iii 490
wilt thou *p* us—— *Becket.* To speak without stammering „ I iv 6
My lord, *p* us then to leave thy service. „ I iv 9
Perpendicular Your lordship affects the unwavering *p*; „ II ii 326
Perpetual Their wafer and *p* sacrifice: *Queen Mary* I ii 45
Perpetual (*continued*) she holds it in Free and *p* alms, *Becket* I iii 680
the voice Of the *p* brook, these golden slopes „ III i 46
doth not the living skin thicken against *p* whippings? „ III iii 316
Close to the grating on a winter morn In the *p* twilight of a prison, *The Falcon* 441
Persecute the worse is here To *p*, because to *p* *Queen Mary* III iv 115
of a perfect faith In him who *p's*: „ III iv 118
Person demanded Possession of her *p* and the Tower. „ II ii 41
In mine own *p* am I come to you, „ II ii 142
Seek to possess our *p*, hold our Tower, „ II ii 158
that anyone Should seize our *p*, occupy our state, „ II ii 178
yield Full scope to *p's* rascal and forlorn, „ II ii 185
As *p's* undefiled with our offence, „ III iii 144
first In Council, second *p* in the realm, „ IV iii 72
Three *p's* and one God, have mercy on me, „ IV iii 121
Noble as his young *p* and old shield. „ V ii 513
if our *p* be secured From traitor stabs— „ V v 280
Then fling mine own fair *p* in the gap A sacrifice *Harold* I ii 202
I cannot bear a hand upon my *p*, *Becket* V iii 20
I came In *p* to return them. *The Falcon* 727
Persuaded She would have *p* me to come back here, *Prom. of May* III 383
Pertest *P* of our flickering mob, *Foresters* II ii 130
Peru The voices of *P* and Mexico, *Queen Mary* V i 47
Peruse *P* it; is it not goodly, ay, and gentle? „ I v 195
wherefore dost thou so *p* it? *Becket* II i 186
Pesteringly Unalterably and *p* fond! *Queen Mary* V i 120
Pestilent Will no man free me from this *p* priest? *Becket* V i 262
Peter The Eternal *P* of the changeless chair, *Queen Mary* III iv 380
Peter (Peter Martyr) *P*, I'll swear for him He *did* believe „ I ii 76
Peter (Saint) (*See also* **St. Peter**) and I return As *P*, but to bless thee: „ III ii 56
How oft hath *P* knock'd at Mary's gate! „ III ii 63
The Church on *P's* rock? never! „ III iv 134
I have builded the great church of Holy *P*: *Harold* I i 180
'O blessed relics!' 'O Holy *P*!' „ I ii 171
loftiest minster ever built To Holy *P* „ III i 207
Like *P's* when he fell, and thou wilt have To wail for it like *P*. „ III i 283
and a blessed hair Of *P*, and all France, „ III ii 149
gonfanon of Holy *P* Floating above their helmets— „ V i 549
Holy Father strangled him with a hair Of *P*, „ V ii 47
And but that Holy *P* fought for us, „ V ii 164
The customs of the Church are *P's* rock. *Becket* i III 24
Which even *P* had not dared? „ II ii 395
And as for the flesh at table, a whole *P's* sheet, „ III iii 129
Peterboro' Leofric, and all the monks of *P* *Harold* V i 446
Peter Carew (*See also* **Carew**) Sir *P C* and Sir Thomas Wyatt, *Queen Mary* I iii 123
Duke of Suffolk and Sir *P C*, „ I iv 112
'Sir *P C* fled to France: „ II i 135
Is *P C* fled? Is the Duke taken? „ II i 142
Peters (Gentleman of Lord Howard) *P*, my gentleman, an honest Catholic, „ IV iii 553
P, how pale you look! you bring the smoke „ IV iii 560
P, you know me Catholic, but English. „ IV iii 566
Ay, Master *P*, tell us. „ IV iii 573
Petition long *p* from the foreign exiles To spare „ IV i 3
This same *p* of the foreign exiles For Cranmer's life. „ IV i 193
Petticoat Ay, ay, gown, coif, and *p*, *Foresters* II i 195
Petty To still the *p* treason therewithin, *Queen Mary* III i 13
the sea-creek—the *p* rill That falls into it— *Becket* II ii 293
Petulancy Thou goest beyond thyself in *p*! „ I iii 65
Pevensey dungeon'd the other half In *P* Castle— „ V ii 446
Landed at *P*—I am from *P*—Hath wasted all the land at *P*— *Harold* IV iii 188
I have ridden night and day from *P*— „ IV iii 192
Phantasy Nay, pure *p*, your Grace. *Queen Mary* I v 280
Not as from me, but as your *p*; „ V i 260
This coarseness is a want of *p*. „ V ii 438
I love the man but not his *phantasies*. *Harold* I i 279
Phantom (adj.) The *p* cry! *You*—did *you* hear a cry? *Prom. of May* III 651
And catch the winding of a *p* horn. *Foresters* IV 1091
Phantom (s) to victory—I hope so—Like *p's* of the Gods. *The Cup* I ii 170
Her *p* call'd me by the name she loved. *Prom. of May* II 242
That I may feel thou art no *p*— *Foresters* IV 1013

Philip Harold (Philip Edgar) Nay—now—not one, for I am P H. Prom. of May II 451
Philip Hedgar (Edgar) P H o' Soomerset! (repeat) „ II 586
Philippines Tunis, and Oran, and the P, Queen Mary V i 48
Philosopher A poor p who call'd the mind Prom. of May II 281
Phœbe P, that man from Synorix, who has been The Cup II 9
Phrase Do not scrimp your p, Queen Mary III iii 260
now I see That I was blind—suffer the p— Becket II ii 438
If the p 'Return' displease you, we will say— The Falcon 728
Phryne With P, Or Lais, or thy Rosamund, Becket, Pro. 55
Physic in a closed room, with light, fire, p, tendance; Queen Mary V iv 37
Physical Against the moral excess No p ache, Becket I i 382
Physician Nay, dearest Lady, see your good p. Queen Mary V v 59
Physick'd These princes are like children, must be p, „ I v 234
Pianner (piano) plaäy the p, if ye liked, all daäy long, like a laädy, Prom. of May II 100
Pick What should I say, I cannot p my words— Queen Mary III vi 147
Picture we prize The statue or the p all the more Prom. of May I 738
poor Steer looks The very type of Age in a p, „ III 514
More like the p Of Christian in my 'Pilgrim's Progress' „ III 518
if you cram me crop-full I be little better than Famine in the p, Foresters I i 47
Piece Henry broke the carcase of your church To p's, Queen Mary I v 399
It lies there in six p's at your feet; „ II i 87
Give me a p of paper! „ II iii 66
A p in this long-tugged-at, threadbare-worn Quarrel Becket II ii 54
I dash myself to p's—I stay myself— „ II ii 150
God's full curse Shatter you all to p's if ye harm „ V iii 135
I tear it all to p's, never dream'd Of acting on it. The Cup I ii 247
a hundred Gold p's once were offer'd by the Duke. The Falcon 324
but one p of earthenware to serve the salad in to my lady, „ 481
Towser'ill tear him all to p's. Prom. of May I 423
and there is a p of beef like a house-side, „ I 793
break it all to p's, as you would break the poor, Foresters II i 285
Piecemeal And tear you p: so you have a guard. Queen Mary IV ii 36
a score of wolf-dogs are let loose that will tear thee p. Becket III ii 40
Pier Ran sunless down, and moan'd against the p's. Queen Mary II iii 27
Pierced Tho' we have p thro' all her practices; Harold V i 156
Piero they are but blue beads—my P, The Falcon 48
Pig (See also **Hedge-pig**) s'pose I kills my p, and gi'es it among 'em, why there wudn't be a dinner for nawbody, and I should ha' lost the p. Prom. of May I 147
Pigeon See **Carrier-pigeon**
Pike Hurls his soil'd life against the p's and dies. Queen Mary IV iii 311
Pilate The Lord be judged again by P? No! Becket I iii 97
Piled dead So p about him he can hardly move. Harold V i 658
'Pilgrim's Progress' More like the picture Of Christian in my 'P P' Prom. of May III 519
Pillage (s) The p of his vassals. Foresters III 107
Richard sacks and wastes a town With random p, „ IV 378
Pillage (verb) they p Spain already. Queen Mary III i 158
Pillar Steadying the tremulous p's of the Church— „ I v 517
Be limpets to this p, or we are torn „ III i 184
stand behind the p here; „ IV iii 462
But thou didst back thyself against a p, Harold I ii 88
Taken the rifted p's of the wood „ I ii 100
lo! my two p's, Jachin and Boaz!— „ III i 191
Pillaring P a leaf-sky on their monstrous boles, Foresters III 100
Pillow I never lay my head upon the p Queen Mary III v 131
A gnat that vext thy p! Harold I ii 71
Pilot Saints P and prosper all thy wandering out „ I i 265
Pincer fiends that utter them Tongue-torn with p's, Queen Mary V ii 194
Pinch give me one sharp p upon the cheek Foresters IV 1011
Pine (tree) I have seen A p in Italy that cast its shadow Athwart a cataract; firm stood the p— Queen Mary III iv 136
the p was Rome. You see, my Lords, „ III iv 142
wind of the dawn that I hear in the p overhead? Becket II i 2
P, beech and plane, oak, walnut, The Cup I i 1
Beneath the shadow of our p's and planes! „ II 227
Pine (verb) poor Pole p's of it, As I do, to the death. Queen Mary V v 128
Pinfold I seed that one cow 'o thine i' the p ageän Prom. of May I 191
Pinned What's here? a scroll P to the wreath. The Falcon 425
Pious Your p wish to pay King Edward's debts, Queen Mary I v 111
it were a p work To string my father's sonnets, „ II i 26
Here a p Catholic, Mumbling and mixing up in his scared prayers „ II ii 84
See if our p—what shall I call him, John?— Becket II ii 38
now this p cup Is passport to their house, The Cup I i 81
I have one mark in gold which a p son of the Church gave me this morning Foresters III 281
Pipe Organ and p, and dulcimer, chants and hymns Becket V ii 365
Piped boy she held Mimick'd and p her Queen Mary II ii 74
Pipest thou, my bird, thou p Becket, Becket— Becket II i 32
Piping gaping bills in the home-nest P for bread— „ II ii 301
Fluting, and p and luting 'Love, love, love'— Foresters III 33
Pirate Thy fierce forekings had clench'd their p hides To the bleak church doors, Harold IV iii 36
For tho' we touch'd at many p ports, Foresters IV 983
Pit plunge and fall Of heresy to the p: Queen Mary III iv 142
Sunk in the deepest p of pauperism, Prom. of May III 803
Pitchfork fur him as be handy wi' a book bean't but haäfe a hand at a p. „ I 189
hunt him With p's off the farm, „ II 427
Piteous perhaps the man himself, When hearing of that p death, „ II 500
Pitiful Be somewhat p, after I have gone, Queen Mary IV ii 157
P to this p heresy? „ IV ii 163
Pitiless And by the churchman's p doom of fire, „ III iv 49
Pity (s) Hate not one who felt Some p for thy hater! Harold I ii 44
the Pope our master, Have p on him, Becket I iii 202
P, my lord, that you have quenched the warmth „ II ii 310
said it was a p to blindfold such eyes as mine „ III i 126
more the p then That thy true home— „ IV ii 131
I have wasted p on her—not dead now— Prom. of May III 691
Have you no p? must you see the man? Foresters IV 457
Have you no p? „ IV 519
What p have you for your game? „ IV 521
P, p!—There was a man of ours Up in the north, „ IV 528
I fear I had small p for that man.— „ IV 547
But p for a father, it may be, „ IV 659
Pity (verb) She said—pray pardon me, and p her— Queen Mary I v 53
I could p this poor world myself that it is no better ordered. Becket, Pro. 365
and I have none—to p thee. „ IV ii 81
Plaäy (play) And p the pianner, if ye liked, all daäy long, like a laädy, Prom. of May II 100
Wi' the butterflies out, and the swallers at p, „ II 199
Place (s) (See also **Pleace, Tomb-place**) Is bounden by his power and p to see Queen Mary III iv 212
No p for worse. „ IV iii 80
Gardener, and huntsman, in the parson's p, „ IV iii 374
Is this a p To wail in, Madam? „ V i 212
battle-axe Was out of p; it should have been the bow.— Harold I ii 106
yea, and thou Chair'd in his p. „ I ii 247
Then shalt thou step into my p and sign. Becket I iii 15
A fit p for the monies of the Church, „ I iii 105
This is the likelier tale. We have hit the p. „ III ii 43
And weeps herself into the p of power; „ V ii 214
He knows the twists and turnings of the p. „ V ii 577
not show yourself In your old p? „ V ii 596
Thou shouldst have ta'en his p, and fought for him. Foresters II i 546
Place (verb) P and displace our councillors, Queen Mary II ii 160
We therefore p ourselves Under the shield Becket I iii 599
let me p this chair for your ladyship. The Falcon 178
Placed freed him from the Tower, p him at Court; Queen Mary I v 163
And softly p the chaplet on her head. The Falcon 362
will be p Beneath the window, Philip. Prom. of May I 560
Plagas Hostis per Angliae P bacchatur; Harold V i 511
Plague (s) so the p Of schism spreads; Queen Mary III iv 171
Harvestless autumns, horrible agues, p— „ V i 99
War, waste, p, famine, all malignities. Harold I i 466
Saints to scatter sparks of p Thro' all your cities, „ II ii 746
like Egypt's p, had fill'd All things with blood; Becket I iii 344
They are p's enough in-door. „ II ii 91
The p's That smite the city spare the solitudes. „ V ii 172
Whose arrow is the p—whose quick flash The Cup II 291
Push'd from all doors as if we bore the p, Prom. of May III 805

Plague (verb) And yet she *p's* me too—no fault in her— *Becket, Pro.* 59
Plagued what news hath *p* thy heart? *Queen Mary* V ii 18
Plain You should be *p* and open with me, niece. „ I iv 217
he loved the more His own gray towers, *p* life and letter'd peace. „ II i 49
'tis not written Half *p* enough. Give me a piece of paper! „ II iii 66
play the *p* Christian man. „ IV iii 267
I that so prized *p* word and naked truth *Harold* III i 93
Thou wert *p* Thomas and not Canterbury, *Becket* I iii 578
had she but given *P* answer to *p* query? „ IV ii 386
Cannot you understand *p* words, Mr. Dobson? *Prom. of May* II 112
Henceforth I am no more Than *p* man to *p* man. *Tuck.* Well, then, *p* man, *Foresters* I iii 96
A fine, a fine! he hath called *p* Robin a lord. „ III 215
I am the yeoman, *p* Robin Hood, „ IV 143
Fine him! fine him! he hath called *p* Robin an earl. „ IV 151
A fine! a fine! He hath called *p* Robin a king. „ IV 218
Plainer Be *p*, Master Cranmer. *Queen Mary* IV iii 235
Plainness I have been a man loved *p* all my life; I *did* dissemble, but the hour has come For utter truth and *p*; „ IV iii 270
Plaister May *p* his clean name with scurrilous rhymes! *Becket* I i 308
Plane Pine, beech and *p*, oak, walnut, *The Cup* I i 1
Beneath the shadow of our pines and *p's*! „ II 228
Planed That all was *p* and bevell'd smooth again, *Becket* V i 138
Plantagenet (*See also* **Geoffrey, Geoffrey Plantagenet**)
whether her Grace incline to this splendid scion of *P*. *Queen Mary* I i 135
The last White Rose, the last *P* „ I iv 207
But this most noble prince *P*, „ III iv 291
Pole has the *P* face, „ III iv 333
My son a Clifford and *P*. *Becket* IV ii 227
Pledge the *P*, Him that is gone. *Foresters* I ii 7
Planted tree that my lord himself *p* here in the blossom of his boyhood— *The Falcon* 563
because one of the Steers had *p* it there in former times. *Prom. of May* III 247
Plaster'd caked and *p* with a hundred mires, *Harold* IV iii 177
Plate and one *p* of dried prunes be all-but-nothing, *The Falcon* 135
O sweet saints! one *p* of prunes! „ 216
Play (s) (*See also* **Passion-play**) Whose *p* is all to find herself a King. *Queen Mary* I iii 164
True king of vice—true *p* on words— *Foresters* II i 83
Can have frolic and *p*. „ II ii 183
but see fair *p* Betwixt them and Sir Richard— „ IV 98
Play (verb) (*See also* **Plaäy**) we *p*. *Courtenay.* At what? *Noailles.* The Game of Chess. *Queen Mary* I iii 125
I can *p* well, and I shall beat you there. *Noailles.* Ay, but we *p* with Henry, King of France, „ I iii 129
with her own pawns *p's* against a Queen, „ I iii 162
You should not *p* upon me. „ I iv 219
Pope nor Spaniard here to *p* The tyrant, „ I v 190
Is this the face of one who *p's* the tyrant? „ I v 194
You *p* at hide and seek. „ I v 305
And he will *p* the Walworth to this Wat; „ II ii 370
Should *p* the second actor in this pageant „ III iii 13
Then must I *p* the vassal to this Pole. „ III iii 111
I think that I will *p* with Philibert,— „ III v 242
but they *p* with fire as children do, „ III vi 28
She *p* the harlot! never. „ III vi 136
Dissemble not; *p* the plain Christian man. „ IV iii 267
P into one another, and weave the web *Harold* I i 211
shall I *p* The craftier Tostig with him? „ I ii 164
this Gamel, whom I *p* upon, that he may *p* the note „ I ii 191
May, surely, *p* with words. „ II ii 418
This lightning before death *P's* on the word,— „ III i 388
Wilt *thou p* with the thunder? „ III i 391
I have a mind to *p* The William with thine eyesight „ V i 26
Queen should *p* his kingship against thine! *Becket, Pro.* 236
I could so *p* about it with the rhyme— „ *Pro.* 381
What, not good enough Even to *p* at nun? „ I i 304
Church must *p* into the hands of kings; „ I ii 68
I *p* the fool again. „ I iii 750
to turn anyway and *p* with as thou wilt— „ II i 245
Play (verb) (*continued*) Go try it, *p*. *Becket* II i 246
mother Would make him *p* his kingship „ II ii 11
a perilous game For men to *p* with God. „ II ii 71
I hear Margery: I'll go *p* with her. „ III i 274
Who made the second mitre *p* the first, And acted me? „ III iii 212
—a troubadour You *p* with words. „ IV ii 182
P! . . . that bosom never Heaved under the King's hand „ IV ii 187
Lest thou shouldst *p* the wanton there again. „ V i 112
Live with these honest folk—And *p* the fool! *Prom. of May* I 745
talk a little French like a lady; *p* a little like a lady? „ III 303
Is this a game for thee to *p* at? Away. *Foresters* II i 426
P the air, Little John. „ III 418
but thyself Shalt *p* a bout with me, „ IV 252
Then thou shalt *p* the game of buffets with us. „ IV 258
Play'd The colour freely *p* into her face, *Queen Mary* II ii 321
I have *p* with this poor rose so long „ V ii 1
We have so *p* the coward; „ V v 110
I have lost the boy who *p* at ball with me, *Harold* IV iii 22
With whom they *p* their game against the king! „ V ii 13
For I have always *p* into their hands, *The Cup* I iii 150
I have *p* the sudden fool. „ I iii 162
same head they would have *p* at ball with „ II 127
marry fine gentlemen, and *p* at being fine ladies? *Prom. of May* III 277
I have *p* at the foils too with Kate: *Foresters* I i 217
But shout and echo *p* into each other „ II i 258
Player Upon the skill and swiftness of the *p's*. *Queen Mary* I iii 143
I'm the first of *p's*. I shall win. „ I iii 149
and a favourer Of *p's*, and a courtier, *Becket* I i 79
both of us are *p's* In such a comedy as our court „ V i 188
Playest Thou *p* in tune. *Harold* I i 384
Playing (*See also* **A-plaäyin'**) such a game, sir, were whole years a *p*. *Queen Mary* I iii 140
Watch'd children *p* at *their* life to be, „ III iv 63
I lost it, *p* with it when I was wild. *Harold* V ii 110
Did she not tell me I was *p* on her? *Becket* IV ii 399
What game, what juggle, what devilry are you *p*? „ V i 154
you suspect This Sinnatus of *p* patriotism, *The Cup* I i 78
No! acting, *p* on me, both of them. *Prom. of May* III 693
P on me—not dead now—a swoon— „ III 696
For *p* upside down with Holy Writ. *Foresters* III 168
Thou art *p* with us. How should poor friars have money? „ III 275
Plea To ours in *p* for Cranmer than to stand *Queen Mary* IV i 119
Pleace (place) wi' dree hard eggs for a good *p* at the burnin'; „ IV iii 490
Plead Holy Virgin, *P* with thy blessed Son; „ I v 85
But you were never raised to *p* for Frith, „ IV ii 210
Who knows but that thy lover May *p* so pitifully, *Becket* IV ii 217
P to him, I am sure you will prevail. *The Cup* I ii 300
Will he let you *p* for him To a Roman? „ I ii 305
came To *p* to thee for Sinnatus's life, „ II 392
but all those that held with him, Except I *p* for them, *Foresters* IV 750
Pleaded Some have *p* for him, *Becket* I iii 590
Pleading Our Robin beaten, *p* for his life! *Foresters* II i 674
Pleasant Had you a *p* voyage up the river? *Queen Mary* III ii 5
Among the *p* fields of Holy Writ I might despair. „ III v 80
Which was not *p* for you, Master Cranmer. „ IV ii 136
God made the fierce fire seem To those three children like a *p* dew. „ IV iii 91
Shall Alice sing you One of her *p* songs? „ V ii 355
There is a *p* fable in old books, *Harold* IV i 56
But my sister wrote that he was mighty *p*, *Prom. of May* I 117
What can a man, then, live for but sensations, *P* ones? men of old would undergo Unpleasant for the sake of *p* ones Hereafter, „ I 243
whose cheerless Houris after death Are Night and Silence, *p* ones— „ I 251
Pleasantness thro' her beauty, And *p* among them. *Harold* IV i 24
Pleasaunce A royal *p* for thee, in the wood, *Becket* II i 128
Please (*See also* **Pleäse**) setting up a mass at Canterbury To *p* the Queen. *Queen Mary* I ii 89
Your Council is in Session, *p* your Majesty. „ I v 544
it might *p* God that I should leave Some fruit „ II ii 221
porter, *p* your Grace, hath shut the gates „ II iv 60

Please (*continued*) You are hard to *p*. *Queen Mary* III iv 154
Then one day more to *p* her Majesty. „ III vi 247
So *p* your Majesty, A long petition „ IV i 2
Might I not say—to *p* your wife, the Queen? „ V i 307
that it would *p* Him out of His infinite love „ V iv 46
to *p* our dying king, and those Who make *Harold* III i 328
Well, well, I swear, but not to *p* myself. *Becket, Pro.* 193
Doth it *p* you? Take it and wear it on that hard heart „ *Pro.* 372
To *p* the King? „ I i 31
Shall I fall off—to *p* the King once more? „ I i 110
Of this wild Rosamund to *p* the King, „ I i 392
whom it *p's* him To call his wives; „ IV ii 35
if we *will* buy diamond necklaces To *p* our lady, *The Falcon* 45
I am glad it *p's* you; *Prom. of May* II 543
Nay, an *p* your Elfin Grace, *Foresters* II ii 132
Pleäse *P*, Miss, Mr. Dobson telled me to saäy *Prom. of May* III 345
Pleased All *p* you so at first. *Becket* III i 50
and the master 'ud be straänge an' *p* if you'd step in fust, *Prom. of May* I 168
Pleasure Thou hast shouted for thy *p*, shout for mine! *Queen Mary* III i 304
They kill'd but for their *p* and the power „ III iv 74
you will find in it *P* as well as duty, „ III iv 430
For thine own *p*? *Harold* III i 327
not my purveyor Of *p's*, but to save a life— *Becket, Pro.* 150
and the walks Where I could move at *p*, „ I i 266
For the King's *p* rather than God's cause „ I iii 697
daily want supplied—The daily *p* to supply it. „ II ii 303
for I have *p* in the *p* of crowds, „ III iii 82
Here, Madam, at your *p*. *Eleanor*. My *p* is to have a man about me. „ IV ii 428
She would have robb'd me then of a great *p*. *The Falcon* 65
The *p* of his eyes—boast of his hand— „ 221
And if my *p* breed another's pain, *Prom. of May* I 278
Have I the *p*, friend, of knowing you? „ I 297
No *p* then taboo'd: for when the tide Of full democracy „ I 591
Hollow Pandora-box, With all the *p's* flown, „ II 347
and I have lighted On a new *p*. „ II 669
on all its idiot gleams Of *p*, „ III 723
Not *p's*, women's matters. *Foresters* I ii 176
Plebeian Pride of the *p*! *Fitzurse*. And this *p* like to be Archbishop! *Becket, Pro.* 457
Pledge (s) I be ready to taäke the *p*. *Prom. of May* III 85
Pledge (verb) I *p* you, Strato. *Synorix*. And I you, my lord. *The Cup* I ii 49
I will *p* you. Wine! Filippo, wine! *The Falcon* 575
P the Plantagenet, Him that is gone. *Foresters* I ii 7
And they shall *p* thee, Marian, „ III 316
They p me, Robin? „ III 320
Pleiads To the *P*, uncle; they have lost a sister. *Queen Mary* I iv 293
Plenty will be *p* to sunder and unsister them again: „ I i 84
fill all hearts with fatness and the lust Of *p*— *The Cup* II 274
Plied Still *p* him with entreaty and reproach: *Queen Mary* IV iii 577
and still the friars *P* him, „ IV iii 601
Plot (s) Mix not yourself with any *p* I pray you; „ I iv 173
to discourage and lay lame The *p's* of France, „ V i 189
the *p's* against him Had madden'd tamer men. *Harold* IV i 110
P's and feuds! This is my ninetieth birthday. (repeat) „ IV i 120, 125
Who dares arraign us, king, of such a *p*? „ IV i 169
Hath Sinnatus never told you of this *p*? *Camma*. What *p*? *The Cup* I ii 251
I am sure I told him that his *p* was folly. „ I ii 283
Plot (verb) When will ye cease to *p* against my house? *Harold* IV i 161
Should care to *p* against him in the North. „ IV i 166
Plotted Wherewith they *p* in their treasonous malice, *Queen Mary* III iv 4
Plotting They have been *p* here! *Harold* IV i 40
If you had found him *p* against Rome, *The Cup* II 406
But had I found him *p*, I had counsell'd him „ II 412
Ploughman-Plowman These Kentish *ploughmen* cannot break the guards. *Queen Mary* II iv 17
burn a *plowman*, and now, as far as money goäs, *Prom. of May* I 330
That ever charm'd the *plowman* of your wolds „ III 488
Plover in a narrow path. A *p* flew before thee. *Becket* II i 54
Plow *p* Lay rusting in the furrow's yellow weeds, „ I iii 354
and I'd drive the *p* straäit as a line *Prom. of May* I 369
Plowed I ha' *p* the ten-aäcre—it be mine now— *Prom. of May* I 365
I mun ha' *p* it moor nor a hoonderd times; „ I 367
Plowest steer wherewith thou *p* thy field is cursed, *Harold* V i 71
Plowin' if I could ha' gone on wi' the *p* *Prom. of May* I 376
Pluck *P* the dead woman off the dead man, Malet! *Harold* V ii 144
King *p's* out their eyes Who anger him, *Becket* IV ii 405
He that can *p* the flower of maidenhood *Foresters* I ii 108
Pluck'd He all but *p* the bearer's eyes away. *Becket* I iii 11
Plumed My princess, of the cloud my *p* purveyor, *The Falcon* 7
Plump To *p* the leaner pouch of Italy. *Queen Mary* III iv 365
Plum-pudding and a *p-p* as big as the round haystack. *Prom. of May* I 794
Plunder they *p*—yea, ev'n bishops, Yea, even arch-bishops— *Foresters* IV 909
Plunder'd *P* the vessel full of Gascon wine, *Becket* V ii 441
cask of wine whereof we *p* The Norman prelate? *Foresters* III 307
Plundering a *p* o' Bishop Winchester's house; *Queen Mary* II iii 73
Plunge (s) Our short-lived sun, before his winter *p*, „ III iii 86
headlong *p* and fall Of heresy to the pit: „ III iv 140
last inhospitable *p* Our boat hath burst her ribs; *Harold* II i 2
One downward *p* of his paw would rend *Becket* IV ii 283
Plunge (verb) and *p* His foreign fist into our island Church *Queen Mary* III iv 363
Tear out his eyes, And *p* him into prison. *Harold* II ii 492
To *p* thee into life-long prison here:— „ II ii 550
To *p* into this bitter world again— *Becket* V ii 81
I might *p* And lose myself for ever. *Prom. of May* II 305
Plunged beast-body That God has *p* my soul in— *Becket* II i 150
Were *p* beneath the waters of the sea, *Foresters* IV 668
Pocket but he would *p* the purse. *Becket* II ii 371
Pœna Illorum scelera *P* sequatur! (repeat) *Harold* V i 518, 605
Poet you are as poor a *p*, Wyatt, As a good soldier. *Queen Mary* II i 113
There! my lord, you are a *p*, *The Falcon* 533
Poetical A shadow, a *p* fiction—did ye not call me king in your song? *Foresters* IV 219
Poinet (John, Bishop of Winchester) *P*, Barlow, Bale, Scory, Coverdale; *Queen Mary* I ii 5
Point (s) (*See also* **Finger-point**) Calais! Our one *p* on the main, „ I v 125
then to cede A *p* to her demand? „ III vi 170
there's An old world English adage to the *p*. „ IV i 175
Many *p's* weather'd, many perilous ones, „ V v 211
The *p* you aim'd at, and pray God she prove *Becket* II ii 77
She lives—but not for him; one *p* is gain'd. „ IV ii 415
Point (verb) Heretic and rebel *P* at me and make merry. *Queen Mary* V ii 318
Shouts something—he *p's* onward— *Harold* V i 558
Pointed With fingers *p* like so many daggers, *Queen Mary* I v 149
And *p* full at Southwark; „ II iii 46
How their *p* fingers Glared at me! *Harold* II ii 789
rose From the foul flood and *p* toward the farm, *Prom. of May* II 653
Pointing the Pope *P* at me with 'Pole, the heretic, *Queen Mary* V ii 175
Poison (s) practise on my life, By *p*, fire, shot, stab— „ I iv 285
Lest your whole body should madden with the *p*? „ III iv 208
Give me the *p*; set me free of him! *Becket* IV ii 164
I have heard these *p's* May be walk'd down. *The Cup* II 474
Poison (verb) filch the linen from the hawthorn, *p* the house-dog, *Foresters* III 199
Poison'd to see His people be not *p*. *Queen Mary* III iv 213
the Norman adder Hath bitten us; we are *p*: *Harold* III i 39
A cleric lately *p* his own mother, *Becket, Pro.* 10
we shall all be *p*. Let us go. „ I iv 244
I am *p*. She—close the Temple door. *The Cup* II 459
He had my fate for it, *P*. „ II 517
Poisoning So *p* the Church, so long continuing, *Queen Mary* IV iii 48
Poitevins I learn but now that those poor *P* *Becket* II ii 427
Poitou and all France, all Burgundy, *P*, all Christendom *Harold* III ii 150
Have we not heard Raymond of *P*, thine own uncle— *Becket* IV ii 247
Pole (Reginald, Cardinal and Papal Legate) (*See also* **Reginald Pole**) holy legate of the holy father the Pope, Cardinal *P*, *Queen Mary* I iii 28
(Nay, there is Cardinal *P*, too), „ I iv 208
So would your cousin, Cardinal *P*; „ I v 405
True, good cousin, *P*; And there were also those „ III ii 68
Peace—the Queen, Philip, and *P*. „ III iii 84
Then must I play the vassal to this *P* „ III iii 112

Pole (Reginald, Cardinal and Papal Legate) (*continued*)
Our supplication be exhibited To the Lord Cardinal *P*, *Queen Mary* III iii 124
Cousin *P*, You are fresh from brighter lands. „ III iv 321
P has the Plantagenet face, „ III iv 333
Doth *P* yield, sir, ha! „ III iv 394
I am sorry for it If *P* be like to turn. „ III iv 416
Write to him, then. *Pole.* I will. *Mary.* And sharply, *P*. „ IV i 39
P Will tell you that the devil helpt them thro' it. „ IV iii 351
Reginald *P*, what news hath plagued thy heart? „ V ii 17
the Pope Pointing at me with '*P*, the heretic, „ V ii 175
for the death Of our accursed Queen and Cardinal *P*.' „ V ii 182
let my cousin *P* Seize him and burn him „ V ii 244
Saving my confessor and my cousin *P*. „ V ii 527
They say she's dying. *First.* So is Cardinal *P*. „ V iv 5
Holy Father Has ta'en the legateship from our cousin *P*—Was that well done? and poor *P* pines of it, As I do, to the death. „ V v 127
'twas I and Bonner did it, And *P*; „ V v 143
Polecat The deer, the highback'd *p*, the wild boar, *Foresters* I iii 119
Policy (*See also* **Church-policy, State-policy**) Your Grace's *p* hath a farther flight *Queen Mary* I v 312
Mismatch'd with her for *p*! „ III i 365
Were but a thankless *p* in the crown, „ III iv 51
might it not be *p* in some matter „ III vi 166
It was his father's *p* against France. „ V v 45
You will find Philip only, *p*, *p*,— „ V v 158
That was, my lord, a match of *p*. *Harold* IV i 199
A great and sound *p* that: I could embrace him for it: *Becket, Pro.* 451
A *p* of wise pardon Wins here as well as there. „ V ii 22
the dry light of Rome's straight-going *p*, *The Cup* I i 146
The One Who shifts his *p* suffers something, „ II 113
And apt at arms and shrewd in *p*. *Foresters* I ii 104
Polish'd But you, my Lord, a *p* gentleman, *Queen Mary* III iv 250
Politic You are too *p* for me, my Lord Paget. „ IV i 150
If this be *p*, And well for thee and England— *Harold* III ii 110
his *p* Holiness Hath all but climb'd the Roman perch again, *Becket* II ii 45
Too *p* for that. Imprison me? „ IV ii 397
Pomegranate Palms, flowers, *p's*, golden cherubim *Harold* III i 182
Pompey *See* **Pumpy**
Pond *See* **Herring-pond, Herse-pond**
Ponder Grant me one day To *p* these demands. *Becket* I iii 669
Ponthieu (adj.) drave and crack'd His boat on *P* beach; *Harold* II ii 36
Ponthieu (s) Guy, Count of *P*? „ II i 81
winds than that which crack'd Thy bark at *P*,— „ II ii 200
Pontigny He shelter'd in the Abbey of *P*. *Becket* II i 84
On a Tuesday at *P* came to me The ghostly warning „ V ii 290
Pontus Have you alliances? Bithynia, *P*, Paphlagonia? *The Cup* I ii 100
Pooh *P*, *p*, my Lord! poor garrulous country-wives. *Queen Mary* IV iii 546
Pool stormless shipwreck in the *p's* Of sullen slumber, *Harold* V i 296
I only wish This *p* were deep enough, *Prom. of May* II 304
Poor (adj.) and of the good Lady Jane as a *p* innocent child *Queen Mary* I i 94
So you would honour my *p* house to-night, „ I iii 118
the realm is *p*, The exchequer at neap-tide: „ I v 120
a hundred men-at-arms Guard my *p* dreams for England „ I v 154
It then remains for your *p* Gardiner, „ I v 220
But Philip never writes me one *p* word, „ I v 360
but, if I'm any judge, By God, you are as *p* a poet, Wyatt, As a good soldier. „ II i 113
You as *p* a critic As an honest friend: „ II i 115
No, *p* soul; no. „ II i 242
And four of her *p* Council too, my Lord, As hostages. „ II ii 42
he says he's a *p* gentleman. „ II iii 74
He's *p* enough, has drunk and gambled out All that he had, „ II iii 87
Take thy *p* gentleman! „ II iii 94
She, with her *p* blind hands feeling—' where is it? „ III i 407
Amplier than any field on our *p* earth Can render thanks „ III iii 197
Paget, you are all for this *p* life of ours, „ III iv 59
So they have sent *p* Courtenay over sea. „ III v 1
and my *p* chronicle Is but of glass. „ III v 46
Draw with your sails from our *p* land, „ III vi 226

Poor (adj.) (*continued*) To the *p* flock—to women and to children— *Queen Mary* IV ii 158
but my *p* voice Against them is a whisper to the roar Of a spring-tide. „ IV ii 185
'twas you That sign'd the burning of *p* Joan of Kent; „ IV ii 206
Pooh, pooh, my Lord! *p* garrulous country-wives. „ IV iii 546
Stays longer here in our *p* north than you:— „ V i 24
and you know The crown is *p*. „ V i 170
I have play'd with this *p* rose so long I have broken off the head. „ V ii 2
And the *p* son turn'd out into the street To sleep, „ V ii 125
I still will do mine utmost with the Pope. *P* cousin! „ V ii 132
I had forgotten How these *p* libels trouble you. „ V ii 202
P lads, they see not what the general sees, „ V ii 447
this *p* throat of mine, Barer than I should wish a man to see it,— „ V ii 460
I would she could have wedded that *p* youth, „ V ii 476
There—up and down, *p* lady, up and down. „ V v 6
I am eleven years older than he, *P* boy! „ V v 47
P enough in God's grace! „ V v 50
and *p* Pole pines of it, As I do, to the death. „ V v 128
Why would you vex yourself, *P* sister? „ V v 264
lighten'd for me The weight of this *p* crown, *Harold* I i 218
From spies of thine to spy my nakedness In my *p* North! „ I i 353
Spite of this grisly star ye three must gall *P* Tostig. „ I i 420
the *p* thunder Never harm'd head. „ I ii 231
How wan, *p* lad! how sick and sad for home! „ II ii 325
P brother! still a hostage! „ II ii 329
Far as he knew in this *p* world of ours— „ II ii 363
P Wulfnoth! do they not entreat thee well? „ II ii 403
Alas! *p* man, *His* promise brought it on me. „ III i 337
only grandson To Wulfnoth, a *p* cow-herd. „ IV i 70
For England, for thy *p* white dove, who flutters „ IV i 230
these *p* hands but sew, Spin, broider— „ IV iii 9
thy victories Over our own *p* Wales, „ IV iii 27
Tostig, *p* brother, Art *thou* so anger'd? „ V i 272
Praying perchance for this *p* soul of mine In cold, „ V i 323
I know Some three or four *p* priests a thousand times *Becket, Pro.* 291
I could pity this *p* world myself that it is no better ordered. „ *Pro.* 366
P bird of passage! so I was; but, father, „ I i 253
P soul! *p* soul! My friend, the King! . . . „ I i 334
p rogues (Heaven bless 'em) who never saw nor dreamed of such a banquet. „ I iv 82
My lord Archbishop, may I come in with my *p* friend, my dog? „ I iv 94
P beast! *p* beast! set him down. „ I iv 105
That my *p* heretic heart would excommunicate His excommunication, „ II i 283
P man, beside himself—not wise. „ II ii 235
I learn but now that those *p* Poitevins, „ II ii 427
his fond excess of wine Springs from the loneliness of my *p* bower, „ III i 40
I have lived, *p* bird, from cage to cage, „ III i 222
In our *p* west We cannot do it so well. „ IV ii 316
his *p* tonsure A crown of Empire. „ V i 194
p mother, Soon as she learnt I was a friend of thine, „ V ii 109
Mutilated, *p* brute, my sumpter-mule, „ V ii 440
And drown all *p* self-passion in the sense Of public good? *The Cup* II 101
Thy way? *p* worm, crawl down thine own black hole „ II 494
Welcome to this *p* cottage, my dear lady. *The Falcon* 270
I will, I will. *P* fellow! „ 281
you have said so much Of this *p* wreath that I was bold enough „ 427
very letters seem to shake With cold, with pain perhaps, *p* prisoner! „ 449
P Federigo degli Alberighi Takes nothing in return „ 715
that her flies Must massacre each other? this *p* Nature! *Prom. of May* I 285
you have robb'd *p* father Of ten good apples. „ I 615
And *p* old father not die miserable. „ I 722
Fonder of *p* Eva—like everybody else. „ II 11
Eva's saäke. Yeas. *P* gel, *p* gel! „ II 31
P sister, I had it five years ago. „ II 82

Porter And scared the gray old *p* and his wife. *Queen Mary* II iii 16
The *p*, please your Grace, hath shut the gates „ II iv 60
Positive and the heart of a—that's too *p*! *The Falcon* 87
heart like the stone in it—that's *p* again— „ 94
Positive-negative not a heart for any of them—that's *p-n*: „ 89
Possess Seek to *p* our person, hold our Tower, *Queen Mary* II ii 158
Thou didst *p* thyself of Edward's ear *Harold* V i 345
Possession demanded *P* of her person and the Tower. *Queen Mary* II ii 41
Possible hedge-rose Of a soft winter, *p*, not probable, „ III vi 16
Is it *p* That mortal men should bear their earthly heats *Harold* V i 282
Post (messenger) there is a *p* from over seas With news for thee. *Harold* II ii 208
Post (position) I dare not leave my *p*. *Queen Mary* I ii 59
Post (post-haste) till his man cum in *p* vro' here, *Queen Mary* IV iii 511
Post *See* **Door-post**
Pot Here's a *p* o' wild honey from an old oak, *Foresters* II i 295
Potato *See* **Taäter**
Potent To join a voice, so *p* with her Highness, *Queen Mary* IV i 117
I do think the King Was *p* in the election, *Becket* I i 129
Pothouse next time you waste them at a *p* you get no more from me. *Prom. of May* III 99
Pouch To plump the leaner *p* of Italy. *Queen Mary* III iv 365
I have but one penny in *p*, *Foresters* III 194
Poultry making of your butter, and the managing of your *p*? *Prom. of May* II 94
Pounce *p* like a wild beast out of his cage *Queen Mary* I i 87
Pound shall have a hundred *p's* for reward.' „ II iii 61
Pour as we pass, And *p* along the land, „ II i 232
P not water In the full vessel running out at top *Harold* I i 376
Poured and when ye shall hear it is *p* out upon earth, *Becket* I iv 37
Pout Nay, *p* out, cousin. *Queen Mary* I iv 134
Poverty I But add my *p* to thine. *The Falcon* 143
P crept thro' the door. *Foresters* I i 157
Powder Until the *p* suddenly blew him dead. *Queen Mary* IV iii 340
Power and God grant me *p* to burn! „ I ii 99
Mine is the fleet and all the *p* at sea— „ I iv 287
may fence round his *p* with restriction, „ II i 172
Back'd by the *p* of France, and landing here, „ III i 447
and the *p* They felt in killing. „ III iv 75
Is bounden by his *p* and place to see „ III iv 212
What would'st thou do hadst thou his *p*, „ III iv 279
What *p* this cooler sun of England hath „ III iv 327
P hath been given you to try faith by fire— „ IV ii 153
May learn there is no *p* against the Lord. „ IV iii 66
I am but a woman, I have no *p*.— „ V v 131
ay, young lord, *there* the king's face is *p*. *Harold* I i 73
p's of the house of Godwin Are not enframed „ I i 316
Crush it at once With all the *p* I have!— „ I i 357
Wisdom when in *p* And wisest, should not frown as *P*, „ I i 364
the true *must* Shall make her strike as *P*: „ I i 369
Come hither, I have a *p*; „ III i 5
wood-fungus on a dead tree, I have a *p*! „ III i 9
when Tostig hath come back with *p*, „ IV i 118
No *p* mine To hold their force together . . . „ IV iii 212
Not know that he nor I had *p* to promise? „ V i 49
p to balk Thy puissance in this fight „ V i 117
I have a *p*—would Harold ask me for it—I have a *p*. „ V i 451
What *p*, holy father? *Stigand.* *P* now from Harold to command thee hence „ V i 454
she, whom the King loves indeed, is a *p* in the State. *Becket, Pro.* 483
you That owe to me your *p* over me— „ II ii 152
The King had had no *p* except for Rome. „ II ii 412
who am, or was, A sovereign *p*? „ IV ii 405
And weeps herself into the place of *p*; „ V ii 215
tho' it be their hour, the *p* of darkness, But my hour too, the *p* of light „ V iii 93
The *p* of life in death to make her free! „ V iii 100
At the right hand of *P*—*P* and great glory— „ V iii 193
have you *p* with Rome? use it for him! *The Cup* I ii 289
Alas! I have no such *p* with Rome. „ I ii 292
Has no more *p* than other oracles „ II 34
happiest, Lady, in my *p* To make you happy. „ II 240
and Napoleons To root their *p* in. *Prom. of May* III 594
Not her, the father's *p* upon her. *Foresters* I iii 9
break, Far as he might, the *p* of John— „ II i 696

Power (*continued*) In this dark wood when all was in our *p* *Foresters* III 183
Practice Tho' we have pierced thro' all her *p's*; *Harold* V i 156
Practise to *p* on my life, By poison, fire, shot, stab— *Queen Mary* I iv 284
I am tender enough. Why do you *p* on me? *Synorix.* Why should I *p* on you? *The Cup* I ii 238
Præcipitatur Equus cum equite *P*. *Harold* V i 599
Prædator Hostis in Angliam Ruit *p*, „ V i 507
Præpediatur Equus cum pedite *P*! „ V i 530
Praise (s) in grateful *p* of Him Who now recalls *Queen Mary* III iii 165
Out of the mouths of babes and sucklings, *p*! *Becket* II ii 279
All *p* to Heaven, and sweet St. Magdalen! „ III iii 234
Praise (verb) Make all tongues *p* and all hearts beat for you. *Queen Mary* I v 117
His friends would *p* him, I believed 'em, „ I v 623
P the Saints. It is over. No more blood! *Harold* V ii 194
gangrenes, and running sores, *p* ye the Lord, *Becket* I iv 256
Hear thy people who *p* thee! *The Cup* II 5
those pale mouths which we have fed will *p* us— *Foresters* IV 1077
Praised *P*, where you should have blamed him, *Queen Mary* I v 600
she so *p* The convent and lone life— *Harold* I ii 46
where is this Mr. Edgar whom you *p* so in your first letters? *Prom. of May* I 777
Prance If they *p*, Rein in, not lash them, *Harold* I i 371
P'raps (perhaps) And *p* ye hears 'at I soomtimes taäkes a drop too much; *Prom. of May* II 107
Prate Come, sirs, we *p*; hence all— *Queen Mary* II ii 372
P not of bonds, for never, oh, never again *Becket* V ii 356
yet they *p* Of mine, my brawls, when those, „ V ii 426
Prated fat fool! He drawl'd and *p* so, *Harold* IV ii 41
Prating Why did you keep me *p*? Horses, there! *Queen Mary* V iii 113
Prattled and *p* to each other that we would marry fine gentlemen, *Prom. of May* III 276
Prattling *p* to her mother Of her betrothal *Queen Mary* V v 231
Save for the *p* of thy little ones. *Harold* II ii 122
Pray *P*—consider— *Queen Mary* I iv 141
Mix not yourself with any plot I *p* you; „ I iv 173
And so take heed I *p* you— „ I iv 273
P God he do not be the first to break them, „ I v 269
I *p* God No woman ever love you, „ I v 601
and we *p* That we, your true and loyal citizens, „ II ii 134
I've found this paper; *p* your worship read it; „ II iii 56
Sir Thomas, *p* you go away, „ II iii 99
we'll *p* for you all on our bended knees. „ II iii 109
we *p* you to kill the Queen further off, „ II iii 114
we'll *p* for you on our bended knees „ II iii 121
Pass then, I *p* your Highness, to the Tower. „ II iv 31
P you go on. (repeat) „ III i 374, 389
Whereon we humbly *p* your Majesties, „ III iii 143
And *p* Heaven That you may see according to our sight. „ III iv 329
P God, we 'scape the sunstroke. „ III v 279
P you write out this paper for me, Cranmer. „ IV ii 60
You are to beg the people to *p* for you; „ IV ii 76
So, so; this will I say—thus will I *p*. „ IV ii 114
P you, remembering how yourself have changed, „ IV ii 155
P for him. *Cranmer.* Ay, one and all, dear brothers, *p* for me; *P* with one breath, „ IV iii 101
Again, I *p* you all that, next to God, „ IV iii 175
I *p* you all to live together Like brethren; „ IV iii 181
Go in, I *p* you. „ V i 214
I have to *p* you, some odd time, „ V i 257
I *p* you be not so disconsolate; „ V ii 129
'We *p* continually for the death Of our accursed Queen „ V ii 180
she loved much: *p* God she be forgiven. „ V v 271
I *p* thee, let me hence and bring him home. *Harold* I i 241
I *p* thee, do not go to Normandy. „ I i 249
Son Harold, I will in and *p* for thee. „ I i 267
P God the people choose thee for their king! „ I i 314
p in thy behalf For happier homeward winds „ II ii 197
'I *p* you do not go to Normandy.' „ II ii 218
can but *p* For Harold—*p*, *p*, *p*— „ III ii 194
p God My Normans may but move as true with me —I *p* your pardon. „ V ii 183
My liege, I *p* thee let me hence: *Becket, Pro.* 36
May we not *p* you, Madam, to spare us the hardness „ *Pro.* 186
pray'd me to *p* thee to pacify Thy King; „ *Pro.* 385
„ I iii 206

Pray (*continued*) won't we *p* for your lordship ! *Becket* I iv 141
I *p* God I haven't given thee my leprosy, „ I iv 214
bid you this night *p* for him who hath fed „ I iv 266
and *p* God she prove True wife to you. „ II ii 77
I *p* you, Do not defend yourself. „ II ii 111
we *p* you, draw yourself from under The wings of France. „ II ii 247
I *p* you come and take it. „ II ii 263
I *p* you then to take my sleeping-draught; „ IV ii 69
but *p* you do not work upon me. „ V i 81
I could not eat, sleep, *p*: „ V ii 92
P for me too: much need of prayer have I. „ V ii 195
P you, hide yourself. „ V ii 257
I *p* you for one moment stay and speak. „ V ii 525
he *p's* you to believe him. *Camma.* I *p* him to believe —that I believe him. *The Cup* II 55
Are you so sure? I *p* you wait and see. „ II 106
P you, Go on with the marriage rites. „ II 397
I *p* you lift me And make me walk awhile. „ II 472
P thee make Thy slender meal out of those scraps *The Falcon* 144
Will he not *p* me to return his love— „ 247
P, pardon me ! „ 395
I *p* you pardon me again ! „ 478
Nay, nay, I *p* you rise. „ 921
I *p* you, look at Robin Earl of Huntingdon's men. *Foresters* I i 35
Spare me thy spare ribs, I *p* thee; „ I i 54
I *p* Heaven we may not have to take to the rushes. „ I i 89
I *p* you, my lady, if a man and a maid love one another, „ I i 171
he *p's* your ladyship and your ladyship's father „ I i 299
I *p* you, my lady, to stand between me „ I i 303
My lord, myself and my good father *p* „ I ii 127
Pardon him again, I *p* you; „ I ii 246
I *p* thee go, go, for tho' thou wouldst bar „ II i 354
O your honour, I *p* you too to give me an alms. „ II i 389
I *p* thee give us guides To lead us „ II i 632
and will *p* for you That *you* may thrive, „ III 251
and I *p* you to come between us again, „ III 412
I *p* you, my lady, come between me and my Kate „ III 421
I *p* you, my liege, let me execute the vengeance of the Church upon them. „ IV 915
I *p* thee, for the moment strike the bonds „ IV 961
All widows we have holpen *p* for us, „ IV 1078
Pray'd when the headsman *p* to be forgiven, *Queen Mary* III i 393
and *p* me to confess In Wyatt's business, „ III v 166
p me not to sully Mine own prerogative, „ IV i 16
P me to pay her debts, and keep the Faith; „ V v 257
Edward's prayers Were deafen'd and he *p* them dumb, *Harold* I ii 22
He *p* me to pray thee to pacify Thy King; *Becket* I iii 206
She *p* me when I loved A maid with all my heart *Foresters* I ii 295
Prayer grant me my *p*: Give me my Philip; *Queen Mary* I v 86
is every morning's *p* Of your most loyal subject, „ I v 103
Catholic, Mumbling and mixing up in his scared *p's* „ II ii 87
leave me, Philip, with my *p's* for you. „ III vi 228
doubtless I shall profit by your *p's*. „ III vi 231
We make our humble *p* unto your Grace „ IV i 43
Our *p's* are heard ! „ IV iii 254
A life of *p* and fasting well may see *Harold* I i 199
and left me time And peace for *p* „ I i 220
the king is ever at his *p's*; „ I i 411
Edward's *p's* Were deafen'd and he pray'd them dumb, „ I ii 21
My *p's* go up as fast as my tears fall, „ III i 166
A life of life-long *p* against the curse „ III i 278
she hath begun Her life-long *p* for thee. „ III i 324
more the love, the mightier is the *p*; „ III i 347
pray, pray, pray—no help but *p*, „ III ii 196
our old songs are *p's* for England too ! „ V i 222
let not my strong *p* Be weaken'd in thy sight, „ V i 647
If fast and *p*, the lacerating scourge— *Becket* I iii 303
your *p's* will do more for me in the day „ I iv 144
breathe one *p* for my liege-lord the King, „ V ii 191
Pray for me too: much need of *p* have I. „ V ii 196
never yet Flung back a woman's *p*. *The Cup* I ii 300
'He never yet flung back a woman's *p*.'— „ I ii 456
Can I fancy him kneeling with me, and uttering the same *p*; *Prom. of May* III 181
Praying I cast me down prone, *p*; *Harold* V i 100

Praying (*continued*) *P* for Normandy; *Harold* V i 219
P perchance for this poor soul of mine „ V i 323
Preach bad my chaplain, Castro, *p* Against these burnings. *Queen Mary* III vi 74
Friend, tho' so late, it is not safe to *p*. „ V iv 42
Preach'd and her priests Have *p*, the fools, „ III vi 99
By all the truths that ever priest hath *p*, *Harold* III i 98
Preaching That any man so writing, *p* so, *Queen Mary* IV iii 47
Preachment Gramercy for thy *p* ! *Foresters* IV 398
Precatur Pereant, pereant, Anglia *p*. *Harold* V i 534
Precedent It is against all *p* to burn One who recants; *Queen Mary* IV ii 48
Precious the State to him but foils wherein To set that *p* jewel, Roger of York, *Becket, Pro.* 270
Would wrest from me the *p* ring I promised Never to part with— *Foresters* II i 660
Precipice break of *p* that runs Thro' all the wood, *The Cup* I i 21
A *p* above, and one below— *Foresters* IV 533
Predecessor Of all his *p's* may have done *Becket* II ii 180
die upon the Patriarchal throne Of all my *p's*? „ V iii 76
Predetermined wolf Mudded the brook and *p* all. *Harold* V i 3
Preface Be the rough *p* of some closer bond? *Queen Mary* I iv 48
Prefer He did *p* me to the chancellorship, *Becket, Pro.* 415
Preference That one, then, should be grateful for your *p*. *Prom. of May* II 556
Preferr'd but you still *p* Your learned leisure. *Queen Mary* III iv 257
Prejudice Which might impugn or *p* the same; „ III iii 133
Prelacy and queenship, all priesthood and *p*; „ V iv 49
Prelate *p's* kneel to you.— „ I iv 82
Chief *p* of our Church, archbishop, „ IV iii 70
For how should reverend *p* or throned prince „ IV iii 542
P, The Saints are one, *Harold* III i 222
Nay, if I cannot break him as the *p*, *Becket* I iii 333
And that too, perjured *p*— „ I iii 736
to excommunicate The *p's* whom he chose to crown his son; „ V ii 399
To all the archbishops, bishops, *p's*, barons, „ V ii 404
cask of wine whereof we plunder'd The Norman *p*? *Foresters* III 308
Prelude I kiss it as a *p* to that privilege *Prom. of May* II 528
Premises Wheer be Mr. Edgar? about the *p*? *Dobson.* Hallus about the *p* ! „ I 433
Prepare I ought to *p* you. You must not expect to find „ III 418
Prepared (*See also* **All-prepared**) and the Lord hath *p* your table— *Becket* I iv 131
I am *p* to die. „ V ii 562
Prerogative pray'd me not to sully Mine own *p*, *Queen Mary* IV i 18
Presence You do not own The bodily *p* in the Eucharist, „ I ii 44
I scarce had left your Grace's *p* „ I v 584
our lowliest thanks For your most princely *p*; „ II ii 133
I sign it with my *p*, if I read it. „ IV ii 73
And you, that would not own the Real *P*, Have found a real *p* in the stake, „ IV ii 141
Has fled our *p* and our feeding-grounds. *Becket* II ii 22
Before these bandits brake into your *p*. „ V ii 557
this world Is brighter for his absence as that other Is darker for his *p*. *Prom. of May* II 459
I cannot tell, tho' standing in her *p*. „ II 558
Present (gift) means to make A farewell *p* to your Grace. *Queen Mary* I iv 245
The old King's *p*, carried off the casks, *Becket* V ii 442
My lord, I have a *p* to return you, . *The Falcon* 711
Present (time) These let them keep at *p*; *Queen Mary* I v 407
at this *p* deem it not Expedient to be known. „ IV iii 56
for the past Look'd thro' the *p*, *Prom. of May* II 641
Enough at any rate for the *p*. „ III 19
to whom all things, up to this *p*, *Foresters* I i 209
Present (verb) Lord Paget Waits to *p* our Council to the Legate. *Queen Mary* III ii 98
p her with this oaken chaplet as Queen of the wood, *Foresters* III 58
Presentation 'All causes of advowsons and *p's*, *Becket* I iii 79
Presenting *P* the whole body of this realm Of England, *Queen Mary* III iii 116
President I, John of Oxford, The *P* of this Council, *Becket* I iii 76
Press pebble which his kingly foot First *p'es* *Queen Mary* I v 370
So *p* on him the duty which as Legate „ III iv 401
Hate thee for this, and *p* upon me— *Harold* II ii 546
As years go on, he feels them *p* upon him, *Prom. of May* I 647
old faces *P* round us, and warm hands *Foresters* I iii 20

Pressing And all the foolish world is *p* thither. *Foresters* III 149
Pressure By too much *p* on it, I would fain, *Harold* II ii 165
almost think she half return'd the *p* Of mine. *Prom. of May* II 628
Prest *p* upon By the fierce Emperor and his Antipope. *Becket* I iii 202
Presume Wherefore dost thou *p* to bear thy cross, „ I iii 503
Why dost thou *p*, Arm'd with thy cross. „ I iii 507
Presumed So—so—I have *p* Beyond my strength. *Foresters* II i 456
Presumptive You, The heir *p*. *Queen Mary* I iv 33
Presumptuous a traitor so *p* As this same Wyatt, „ II ii 179
Pretext That was their *p*—so they spake at first— „ II ii 150
Prettier Dear Eva Was always thought the *p*. *Prom. of May* II 379
P than that same widow which you wot of. *Foresters* III 268
Prettiest (*See also* **Purtiest**) Thou art the *p* child I ever saw. *Becket* IV i 7
Prettily *p* you did it, And innocently. *Queen Mary* V ii 147
Pretty That's not a *p* question. „ I v 610
I mean, my *p* maiden, A *p* man for such a *p* maiden.
Alice. My Lord of Devon is a *p* man. I hate him. „ I v 612
Then, *p* maiden, you should know that whether „ I v 618
Peace, *p* maiden. I hear them stirring in the Council Chamber. „ I v 627
Pwoaps be *p* things, Joan, but they wunt set i' the Lord's cheer o' that daay. „ IV iii 469
A *p* lusty boy. *Becket* II i 247
The *p* gaping bills in the home-nest Piping for bread— „ II ii 300
and gave me a great pat o' the cheek for a *p* wench, „ III i 126
And mighty *p* legs too. „ IV i 6
P one, how camest thou? „ IV i 20
I am the fairy, *p* one, a good fairy to thy mother. „ IV i 25
You are not *p*, like mother. *Eleanor*. We can't all of us be as *p* as thou art—little bastard. „ IV i 37
I love thy mother, my *p* boy. „ IV i 45
Then is thy *p* boy a bastard? „ IV ii 112
over which If *p* Geoffrey do not break his own, „ IV ii 177
How fares thy *p* boy, the little Geoffrey? „ V ii 167
Blessings on your *p* voice, Miss Dora. *Prom. of May* I 63
Well, tho' I grudge the *p* jewel, that I Have worn, „ I 473
Ay, you be a *p* squire. „ II 689
and meä coomin' along *p* sharp an' all? „ III 97
P mistress! *Foresters* I ii 189
P mistress, will you dance? „ I ii 203
I have lodged my *p* Katekin in her bower. „ II i 417
Behold a *p* Dian of the wood, „ III 267
Here is one would clutch Our *p* Marian for his paramour, „ IV 767
Prevail Plead to him, I am sure you will *p*. *The Cup* I ii 302
Prey The *p* they are rending from her— *Queen Mary* V ii 268
leaves him A beast of *p* in the dark, *Prom. of May* I 505
when Our English maidens are their *p*, *Foresters* III 179
Price A *p* is set On this poor head; „ II i 72
Prick with right reason, flies that *p* the flesh. *Queen Mary* III iv 70
rose but *p*'s his nose Against the thorn, *Harold* I i 422
spire of Holy Church may *p* the graves— *Becket* I iii 553
This wild one—nay, I shall not *p* myself—Is sweetest. „ II i 144
not thorn enough to *p* him for it, Ev'n with a word? „ III i 251
were I taken They would *p* out my sight. *Foresters* II i 72
P 'em in the calves with the arrow-points—*p* 'em in the calves. „ IV 560
P him in the calves! „ IV 567
and if thou *p* me there I shall die. *Robin*. *P* him where thou wilt, so that he dance. „ IV 569
Not paid at York—the wood—*p* me no more! „ IV 623
What *p*'s thee save it be thy conscience, man? „ IV 625
Prick'd be those I fear who *p* the lion To make him spring, *Harold* IV iii 94
Prick'st There thou *p* me deep. „ II ii 423
Pride (s) *P* of the plebeian! *Becket, Pro.* 457
O bolster'd up with stubbornness and *p*, „ I iii 35
Smooth thou his *p*—thy signing is but form; „ I iii 218
ambition, *p* So bloat and redden his face— *The Cup* II 169
P of his heart—the solace of his hours— *The Falcon* 223
my sister wrote that he was mighty pleasant, and had no *p* in him. *Prom. of May* I 117
He 'ant naw *p* in 'im, and we'll git 'im „ I 439
Pride (verb) I *p* myself on being moderate. *Queen Mary* V iv 60
Priest (*See also* **Hedge-priest, High-priest**) Perinde ac cadaver—as the *p* says, „ I iv 180
And this bald *p*, and she that hates me, „ I iv 282

Priest (*continued*) You have ousted the mock *p*, *Queen Mary* I v 180
the cruelty of their *p*'s. „ II i 169
every Spanish *p* will tell you that all „ III i 229
The bible is the *p*'s. „ III i 286
no foreign prince or *p* Should fill my throne, „ III v 236
her *p*'s Have preach'd, the fools, „ III vi 98
spare to take a heretic *p*'s, Who saved it „ IV i 132
masses here be sung By every *p* in Oxford. „ IV iii 101
burnt The heretic *p*, workmen, and women and children. „ V v 106
I will see none except the *p*. Your arm. „ V v 196
Nor let *P*'s talk, or dream of worlds to be, „ V v 217
your *P*'s Gross, worldly, simoniacal, unlearn'd! *Harold* I i 161
By all the truths that ever *p* hath preach'd, „ III i 97
blow the trumpet, priest! „ III i 189
And on it falls the shadow of the *p*; „ III ii 70
Nor kingly *p*, nor priestly king to cross „ III ii 93
three or four poor *p*'s a thousand times *Becket, Pro.* 291
fearful *P* Sits winking at the license of a king, „ I ii 65
For London had a temple and a *p* „ I iii 59
brave The Pope, King Louis, and this turbulent *p*. „ II i 313
Less clashing with their *p*'s— „ II ii 147
old *p* whom John of Salisbury trusted Hath sent another. „ III i 69
A notice from the *p*, „ III iii 3
The *p*'s of Baal tread her underfoot— „ III iii 179
madden Against his *p* beyond all hellebore. „ IV ii 460
Not one whose back his *p* has broken. „ V i 145
Will no man free me from this pestilent *p*? „ V i 263
No traitor to the King, but *P* of God, „ V iii 112
How the good *p* gods himself! „ V iii 149
that more freely than your formal *p*, *Prom. of May* III 633
than if my wife And siding with these proud *p*'s, *Foresters* III 125
all that live By their own hands, the labourer, the poor *p*; „ III 166
Priestess Hear thy *p*'*es* hymn thy glory! *The Cup* II 7
who has been So oft to see the *P*, „ II 11
for her beauty, stateliness, and power, Was chosen *P* „ II 17
wills, thro' me her *P*, In honour of his gift „ II 350
Thy pardon, *P*! „ II 374
Priesthood and queenship, all *p* and prelacy; *Queen Mary* V iv 48
The heathen *p* of a heathen creed! *Becket* I iii 63
Priestly nor *p* king to cross Their billings ere they nest. *Harold* III ii 93
Primacy and acknowledge The *p* of the Pope? *Queen Mary* III iii 109
Against the Holy Father's *p*, „ III iii 131
all my lifelong labour to uphold The *p*—a heretic. „ V ii 71
Primal Have I climb'd back into the *p* church, „ I ii 49
Primate That I am not the man to be your *P*, *Becket* I i 39
Thou still hast shown thy *p*, Gilbert Foliot. „ I iii 282
bravest in our roll of *P*'s down From Austin— „ V ii 58
Priest of God, *P* of England. „ V iii 114
Primm'd *p* her mouth and put Her hands together— „ III i 74
Prince Her Majesty Hears you affect the *P*— *Queen Mary* I iv 82
if this *P* of fluff and feather come To woo you, „ I iv 162
this Philip, the proud Catholic *p*, And this bald priest, „ I iv 281
The *p* is known in Spain, in Flanders, „ I v 207
These *p*'s are like children, must be physick'd, „ I v 233
Yet I know the *P*, „ I v 364
Why do they talk so foully of your *P*, Renard? „ I v 426
The lot of *P*'s. To sit high Is to be lied about. „ I v 428
the most princelike *P* beneath the sun. „ I v 445
If you have falsely painted your fine *P*; „ I v 599
Now as your *P*, I say, I, „ II ii 188
A *p* as naturally may love his people „ II ii 192
your lawful *P* Stand fast against our enemies „ II ii 241
Your lawful *P* hath come to cast herself „ II ii 261
But this proud *P*— *Bagenhall*. Nay, he is King, „ III i 71
Why, ev'n the haughty *p*, Northumberland, „ III i 147
The second *P* of Peace— „ III ii 164
little murder'd *p*'s, in a pale light, „ III v 147
no foreign *p* or priest Should fill my throne, „ III v 235
dance into the sun That shines on *p*'s. „ III v 254
of this fair *p* to come; „ III vi 100
that I may bear a *p*. If such a *p* were born „ III vi 202
I should be here if such a *p* were born. „ III vi 206
Shall these accuse him to a foreign *p*? „ IV i 24

Prince (*continued*) how should reverend prelate or throned *p* — *Queen Mary* IV iii 543
make it clear Under what *P* I fight. — *Becket* I iii 545
Before the *P* and chief Justiciary, — „ I iii 709
Ay, the *p's* sat in judgment against me, — „ I iv 129
Like some wise *p* of this world from his wars, — „ V ii 13
Reginald, all men know I loved the *P*. — „ V ii 334
And you a *P* and Tetrarch in this province— — *The Cup* I ii 89
O the most kindly *P* in all the world! — „ I ii 356
Good *P*, art thou in need of any gold? — *Foresters* I ii 162
She struck him, my brave Marian, struck the *P*, — „ II i 135
might Betray me to the wild *P*. — „ II i 708
No ribald John is Love, no wanton *P*, — „ IV 46
We told the *P* and the Sheriff of our coming. — „ IV 575
we will hang *thee*, *p* or no *p*, sheriff or no sheriff. — „ IV 583
Knowest thou not the *P*? — „ IV 683
He may be *p*; he is not gentleman. — „ IV 685
You, *P*, our king to come— — „ IV 696
This gallant *P* would have me of his— — „ IV 701

Princelike but your Philip Is the most *p* Prince beneath the sun. — *Queen Mary* I v 445

Princely Courtenay seems Too *p* for a pawn. — „ I iii 167
Your star will be your *p* son, — „ I v 416
beseech Your Highness to accept our lowliest thanks For your most *p* presence; — „ II ii 133

Princess The *P* there? If I tried her and la— — „ I iv 16
Also this Wyatt did confess the *P* Cognisant thereof, — „ II iv 112
Clear Courtenay and the *P* from the charge — „ III i 135
To sound the *P* carelessly on this; — „ V i 259
My *p* of the cloud, my plumed purveyor, — *The Falcon* 7

Principes *Sederunt* p, *ederunt pauperes*. — *Becket* I iv 131

Print It mun be true, fur it wur i' *p* as black as owt. — *Prom. of May* II 731

Printed Only the golden Leopard *p* in it — *Becket* II ii 85

Prior We spoil'd the *p*, friar, abbot, monk, — *Foresters* III 167

Priory Our *priories* are Norman; — *Harold* III i 37

Prison (adj.) The *p* fare is good enough for me. — *Queen Mary* IV ii 42

Prison (s) Duke of Suffolk lately freed from *p*, — „ I iii 122
Of those two friars ever in my *p*, — „ IV ii 94
Long have I lain in *p*, yet have heard — „ IV iii 210
Tear out his eyes, And plunge him into *p*. — *Harold* II ii 492
To plunge thee into life-long *p* here:— — „ II ii 550
Except I clap thee into *p* here, — *Becket* V i 111
Ho there! thy rest of life is hopeless *p*. — „ V i 180
First, free thy captive from *her* hopeless *p*. — „ V i 184
In the perpetual twilight of a *p*, — *The Falcon* 442
but no! We hear he is in *p*. — *Foresters* II i 34
This is my son but late escaped from *p*, — „ II i 461
Richard risks his life for a straw, So lies in *p*— — „ IV 384
No, no! we have certain news he died in *p*. — „ IV 779
This young warrior broke his *p* — „ IV 999

Prison'd —tongueless and eyeless, *p*— — *Harold* II ii 497

Prisoner (*See also* **Fellow-prisoner**) She is going now to the Tower to loose the *p's* — *Queen Mary* I i 109
I shall but be their *p* in the Tower. — „ II iv 33
there by Sir Maurice Berkeley Was taken *p*. — „ II iv 96
Quoth Elizabeth, *p*. — „ III v 21
But I am royal, tho' your *p*, — „ III v 177
where he sits My ransom'd *p*. — *Harold* II ii 45
but he had *p's*, He tore their eyes out, — „ II ii 388
Knave, hast thou let thy *p* scape? — „ II ii 673
We have few *p's* in mine earldom there, — „ II ii 686
if he follow thee, Make him thy *p*. — *Becket* I i 332
Am I a *p*. *Leicester*. By St. Lazarus, no! — „ I iii 729
Come with us—nay—thou art our *p*— — „ V iii 143
Ay, make him *p*, do not harm the man. — „ V iii 145
Come; as he said, thou art our *p*. — „ V iii 156
I might have sent him *p* to Rome. — *The Cup* II 418
With cold, with pain perhaps, poor *p*! — *The Falcon* 450
the boy was taken *p* by the Moors. — *Foresters* I i 60

Prison-silence I have had a year of *p-s*, Robin, — „ IV 924

Privacy Will let you learn in peace and *p* — *Queen Mary* III iv 326

Private Or into *p* life within the realm. — „ IV i 47
We'll have no *p* conference. — „ V iii 13
Sir, we are *p* with our women here— — „ V v 119
My bed, where ev'n the slave is *p*—he— — *Becket* V i 251

Private (*continued*) mix our spites And *p* hates with our defence of Heaven. — *Becket* V ii 52

Privilege Thou hast broken thro' the pales Of *p*, — „ III iii 194
I kiss it as a prelude to that *p* — *Prom. of May* II 528

Privy Those that are now her *P* Council, sign'd Before me: — *Queen Mary* I ii 22
theretoward unadvised Of all our *P* Council; — „ II ii 205

Prize (s) too rich a *p* To trust with any messenger. — *The Falcon* 725

Prize (verb) we *p* The statue or the picture all the more — *Prom. of May* I 737
p The pearl of Beauty, even if I found it — „ III 600
All here will *p* thee, honour, worship thee, — *Foresters* II ii 17

Prized I that so *p* plain word and naked truth — *Harold* III i 93
Is not virtue *p* mainly for its rarity — *Becket* III iii 303

Probable wild hedge-rose Of a soft winter, possible, not *p*, — *Queen Mary* III vi 17

Probing *P* an old state-secret— — „ V ii 486

Proceed is it then with thy goodwill that I *P* against thine evil councillors, — *Becket* III iii 209
I love you all the same. *P*. — *Foresters* III 438

Proceeding O Holy Ghost! *p* from them both, — *Queen Mary* IV iii 119

Procession will you not follow the *p*? — „ I i 129
they led *P's*, chanted litanies, — „ III vi 95

Proclaim Wyatt, shall we *p* Elizabeth? — „ II i 238
and *p* Your true undoubted faith, — „ IV iii 112
You must *p* Elizabeth your heir. (repeat) — „ V i 191, 204
P's himself protector, and affirms The Queen — „ V i 289
P it to the winds. — „ V ii 290

Prodigal happy was the *p* son, For he return'd to the rich father; — *The Falcon* 141

Prodigality 'Lust, *P*, Covetousness, Craft, — *Prom. of May* II 284

Produce Lifted our *p*, driven our clerics out— — *Becket* V ii 432

Profess and *p* to be great in green things and in garden-stuff. — *The Falcon* 551

Proffer'd but this day he *p* peace. — *Becket* II ii 240
second grain of good counsel I ever *p* thee, — „ III iii 318

Profit doubtless I shall *p* by your prayers. — *Queen Mary* III vi 230

Profitless are *p* to the burners, And help the other side. — „ IV ii 218

Profligate *P* pander! *Fitzurse*. Do you hear that? — *Becket* V iii 160

Promise (s) Speak, Master Cranmer, Fulfil your *p* made me, — *Queen Mary* IV iii 112
Done right against the *p* of this Queen Twice given. — „ IV iii 455
and to send us again, according to His *p*, — „ V iv 53
That thou wouldst have his *p* for the crown? — *Harold* I i 203
know'st my claim on England Thro' Edward's *p*: — „ II ii 13
I am heir Of England by the *p* of her king. — „ II ii 125
Ay . . . if the king have not revoked his *p*. — „ II ii 610
sorrow'd for my random *p* given To yon fox-lion. — „ III i 269
all *p's* Made in our agony for help from heaven? — „ III i 286
poor man, *His p* brought it on me. — „ III i 338
They know King Edward's *p* and thine—thine. — „ V i 45
Not know that Edward cancell'd his own *p*? — „ V i 52
kingly *p* given To our own self of pardon, — *Becket* II ii 431
and the more shame to him after his *p*, — „ III i 131
Nothing, so thy *p* be thy deed. — „ III iii 224
royal *p* might have dropt into thy mouth — „ III iii 275
He fenced his royal *p* with an *if*. — „ III iii 278
Hath broken all his *p's* to thyself, — „ V i 3
O joy for the *p* of May, (repeat) — *Prom. of May* I 43, 44, 723, 725
O grief for the *p* of May, (repeat) — „ I 59, 60, 750, 752
he had not forgotten his *p* to come when I called him. — *Prom. of May* III 330
So lovely in the *p* of her May, — „ III 753
She is mine. I have thy *p*. — *Foresters* IV 754

Promise (verb) ye did *p* full Allegiance and obedience — *Queen Mary* II ii 168
According as King Edward *p's*. — *Harold* II ii 714
Not know that he nor I had power to *p*? — „ V i 50
Didst thou not *p* Henry to obey These ancient laws — *Becket* I iii 16
I *p* thee on my salvation That thou wilt hear — „ I iii 254
and I *p* thee not to turn the world upside down — „ II i 241
before God I *p* you the King hath many more wolves — „ III iii 321
I *p* you that if you forget yourself in your behaviour to this gentleman, — *Prom. of May* I 161
Did *I* not *p* not to listen to him, — „ III 569
I *p* thee to make this Marian thine. — *Foresters* I ii 183

Promised letter which thine Emperor p Long since, Queen Mary I v 348
Wyatt, but now you p me a boon. „ II iii 81
Since thou hast p Wulfnoth home with us, Harold II ii 167
He p that if ever he were king In England, „ II ii 587
I p The King to obey these customs, Becket I iii 556
Have I not p to restore her, Thomas, „ III iii 182
Have I not p, man, to send them back? „ III iii 190
I p one of the Misses I wouldn't meddle wi' ye, Prom. of May I 469
has p to keep our heads above water; „ III 169
bit by bit—for she p secrecy—I told her all. „ III 380
precious ring I p Never to part with— Foresters II i 661
fair play Betwixt them and Sir Richard—p too, „ IV 99
Promising By this our supplication p, Queen Mary III iii 135
Prona Acies Acies, P sternatur! Harold V i 582
Prone I cast me down p, praying; „ V i 100
I am a man not p to jealousies, Prom. of May III 626
Pronounce Thou shalt p the blessing of the Church Foresters IV 927
Pronounced Judges had p That our young Edward Queen Mary I ii 24
He is p anathema. „ IV i 187
P his heir of England. Harold I ii 195
hath King Edward not p his heir? „ II ii 576
Proof A diamond, And Philip's gift, as p of Philip's love, Queen Mary III i 67
There was no p against him. „ V ii 492
with full p Of Courtenay's treason? „ V ii 498
You have yet No p against him: The Cup I i 81
—having p enough Against the man, „ I iii 157
Prophecy Dream, Or p, that? Becket I i 56
Well, dream and p both. „ I i 57
Jest or p there? Herbert. Both, Thomas, both. „ I i 67
Prophet (adj.) our hearts, our p hopes Let in the happy distance, The Cup I ii 413
Prophet (s) His p's, and apostles, in the Testaments, Queen Mary IV iii 232
No God but one, and Mahound is his p. Becket II ii 226
Thou art no p, Nor yet a p's son. „ II ii 421
And some of you were p's that I might be Foresters I ii 81
Prosper Saints Pilot and p all thy wandering out Harold I i 265
If you p, Our Senate, wearied of their tetrarchies, The Cup I i 88
To make my marriage p to my wish! „ II 308
Prosper'd Had p in the main, but suddenly Becket I iii 381
Prosperous And I will make Galatia p too, The Cup I iii 169
Protect 'If any cleric be accused of felony, the Church shall not p him; Becket I iii 88
No: it must p me. „ I iii 493
Protector Proclaims himself p, and affirms The Queen Queen Mary V i 289
Protest I p Your Grace's policy hath a farther flight „ I v 311
we do p That our commission is to heal, „ III iii 184
By St. James I do p, „ III vi 253
Proud But if this Philip, the p Catholic prince, „ I iv 280
You are shy and p like Englishmen, „ II ii 257
But this p Prince— Bagenhall. Nay, he is King, you know, „ III i 71
As p as Becket. „ III i 332
The p ambitions of Elizabeth, And all her fieriest partisans— „ III ii 169
it is not fit for us To see the p Archbishop mutilated. Becket I iii 614
I am p of my 'Monk-King,' „ II ii 101
we know you p of your fine hand, „ IV ii 261
But kinglike fought the p Archbishop,—kinglike „ IV ii 438
p Ev'n of that stale Church-bond which link'd „ IV ii 446
ladyship were not Too p to look upon the garland, The Falcon 663
fur we was all on us p on 'er, Prom. of May II 37
I am sure you must be p of it. „ III 611
than if my wife And siding with these p priests, Foresters III 125
Prove If but to p your Majesty's goodwill, Queen Mary I v 260
And Thomas White will p this Thomas Wyatt, And he will p an Iden „ II ii 367
He'll burn a diocese to p his orthodoxy. „ III iv 353
More kinglike he than like to p a king. Harold II ii 142
p me nothing of myself! Becket I iii 292
and pray God she p True wife to you. „ II ii 78
to p Bigger in our small world than thou art. „ V i 127
I fear I might p traitor with the sheriff. Foresters IV 872
Proved I thought Mr. Edgar the best of men, and he has p himself the worst. Prom. of May II 86
Proven (adj.) And thou thyself a p wanton? Becket IV ii 115
Proven (verb) Who knows? the man is p by the hour. Queen Mary II ii 364
Much suspected, of me Nothing p can be. „ III v 20
However you have p it. „ III vi 17
The truth of God, which I had p and known. „ IV iii 149
That Love is blind, but thou hast p it true. Foresters II i 644
Provençal translated that hard heart into our P facilities, Becket, Pro. 380
Provence Of P blew you to your English throne; „ V i 123
such a comedy as our court of P Had laugh'd at. „ V i 189
Proverb your Ladyship hath sung the old p out of fashion. Foresters I i 164
'Much would have more,' says the p; „ IV 308
Provided perchance a happy one for thee, P— Harold II ii 204
Providence by God's p a good stout staff Lay near me; Queen Mary V ii 468
Province and make us A Spanish p; „ III i 466
Sometime the viceroy of those p's— „ III ii 196
p's Are hard to rule and must be hardly ruled; „ III ii 200
beyond his mitre—Beyond his p. „ V i 154
I am the Dean of the p: let me bear it. Becket I iii 498
Out of thy p? „ I iii 506
With revenues, realms, and golden p's „ V ii 346
you a Prince and Tetrarch in this p— Sinnatus. P! The Cup I ii 90
they call it so in Rome. Sinnatus. P! „ I ii 94
Whose lava-torrents blast and blacken a p To a cinder, „ II 303
Proving all but p man An automatic series of sensations, Prom. of May I 225
Provoke Would I could move him, P him any way! The Cup I ii 137
Prow Our silver cross sparkled before the p, Queen Mary III ii 9
Prowess who know His p in the mountains of the West, Harold IV i 165
Ay, ay, because I have a name for p. Foresters II i 560
Prowling that our wolf-Queen Is p round the fold. Becket III iii 8
Prune (s) and one plate of dried p's be all-but-nothing, The Falcon 136
Oh sweet saints! one plate of p's! „ 216
p's, my lady, from the tree that my lord „ 562
the p's, my lady, from the tree that his lordship— „ 684
But the p's that your lordship— „ 692
Prune (verb) Ay, p our company of thine own and go! „ 695
Pruning-hook not Spear into p-h— Harold V i 442
Psalm-singing Ay, the p-s weavers, cobblers, scum— Queen Mary III iv 289
Psalter They scarce can read their P; Harold I i 163
Public (adj.) Wyatt, who hath tamper'd with A p ignorance, Queen Mary II ii 182
The p form thereof. „ IV ii 71
Is this a place To wail in, Madam? what! a p hall. „ V i 213
O father, mock not at a p fear, Harold I i 74
This is no secret, but a p matter. Becket V ii 319
And drown all poor self-passion in the sense Of p good? The Cup II 103
Public (s) he and Wulfnoth never Have met, except in p; Harold II ii 86
Publius P! Publius. Here! The Cup I iii 1
P! P! No, „ I iii 119
Pudding See **Plum-pudding**
Puddle I raised him from the p of the gutter, Becket I iii 436
Puff (s) And that a p would do it— Queen Mary III i 444
Puff (inter.) I stay myself—P—it is gone. Becket II ii 151
Puffed p out such an incense of unctuosity into the nostrils of our Gods of Church and State, „ III iii 114
Puissance And all the p of the warrior, „ I i 152
Pull 'P him down! Away with him!' Queen Mary IV iii 280
Pulled or rather p all the Church with the Holy Father Becket III iii 76
Pulpit Spain in the p and on the law-bench; Queen Mary II i 177
Would make this Cole a cinder, p and all. „ IV iii 11
Pulpited See **Re-pulpited**
Pulse In this low p and palsy of the state, .. II ii 103
a jest In time of danger shows the p's even. „ II ii 357
I came to feel the p of England, „ III i 37
There somewhere beats an English p in thee! Harold II ii 266
How few Junes Will heat our p's quicker! Foresters IV 1062
Pulsed blood That should have only p for Griffyth, Harold I ii 150
Pumpy (Pompey, name of horse) Scizzars an' P was good uns to goä (repeat) Prom. of May II 308, 318
Punish Not p of your own authority? Becket V ii 450
Punishment My p is more than I can bear. Harold V ii 201
Pupil See **Fellow-pupil**
Puppy as a mastiff dog May love a p cur for no more reason Queen Mary I iv 195
Purchase To p for Himself a stainless bride; „ III iii 205

Q

Queen (s) (*continued*) our gracious Virgin *Q* hath——
Crowd. No pope ! no pope ! *Queen Mary* I iii 23
our Gracious *Q*, let me call her our second Virgin Mary, „ I iii 57
Prince of Spain coming to wed our *Q* ! „ I iii 84
Arise against her and dethrone the *Q*— „ I iii 91
does your gracious *Q* entreat you kinglike ? „ I iii 110
with her own pawns plays against a *Q*, „ I iii 163
The *Q* is ill advised : „ I iv 5
my Lady *Q*, tho' by your age, „ I iv 11
Has not the *Q*— *Elizabeth.* Done what, Sir ? „ I iv 28
I am utterly submissive to the *Q*. „ I iv 39
the *Q* Is both my foe and yours : „ I iv 41
you have solicited The *Q*, and been rejected. „ I iv 59
So royal that the *Q* forbad you wearing it. „ I iv 76
Your ear ; You shall be *Q*. „ I iv 122
He hath fallen out of favour with the *Q*. „ I iv 157
Q would see your Grace upon the moment. „ I iv 221
the *Q* is yours. I left her with rich jewels „ I iv 240
Come, come, I will go with you to the *Q*. „ I iv 298
I am English *Q*, not Roman Emperor. „ I v 503
Tho' *Q*, I am not *Q* Of mine own heart, „ I v 521
when I, their *Q*, Cast myself down upon my knees „ I v 561
for the *Q's* down, and the world's up, „ II i 65
but, for appearance sake, stay with the *Q*. „ II i 138
and the *Q* hath no force for resistance. „ II i 140
If this man marry our *Q*, „ II i 170
the *Q*, and the laws, and the people, his slaves. „ II i 174
must we levy war against the *Q's* Grace ? „ II i 187
war *for* the *Q's* Grace—to save her „ II i 189
I trust the *Q* comes hither with her guards. „ II ii 1
Q in that distress Sent Cornwallis and Hastings „ II ii 29
Nay the *Q's* right to reign— „ II ii 96
now the *Q* In this low pulse and palsy „ II ii 102
Q had written her word to come to court : „ II ii 117
your *Q* ; To whom, when I was wedded to the realm „ II ii 163
and be sure your *Q* So loves you, „ II ii 194
Long live Queen Mary ! Down with Wyatt ! The *Q* ! „ II ii 252
The *Q* of England—or the Kentish Squire ? „ II ii 269
The *Q* of England or the rabble of Kent ? „ II ii 273
No ! No ! The *Q* ! the *Q* ! „ II ii 282
Gardiner, coming with the *Q*, And meeting Pembroke, „ II ii 309
no man need ; but did you mark our *Q* ? „ II ii 320
Q stands up, and speaks for her own self ; „ II ii 341
That knows the *Q*, the Spaniard, and the Pope, „ II ii 413
Whether I be for Wyatt, or the *Q* ? „ II ii 415
we know that ye be come to kill the *Q*, „ II iii 108
don't ye kill the *Q* here, Sir Thomas ; „ II iii 111
we pray you to kill the *Q* further off, Sir Thomas.
Wyatt. My friends, I have not come to kill the *Q* „ II iii 115
The *Q* must to the Tower. „ II iv 73
My foes are at my feet and I am *Q*. „ II iv 119
that the son Being a King, might wed a *Q*— „ III i 75
How look'd the *Q* ? „ III i 91
before the *Q's* face Gardiner buys them „ III i 143
Long live the King and *Q*, Philip and Mary ! „ III i 208
wilt thou wear thy cap before the *Q* ? „ III i 237
There be both King and *Q*, Philip and Mary. Shout ! „ III i 296
The *Q* comes first, Mary and Philip. „ III i 299
The *Q* hath felt the motion of her babe ! „ III ii 213
'The *Q* of England is delivered of a dead dog !' „ III ii 219
The *Q* would have him ! „ III iii 27
The *Q* would have it ! „ III iii 31
Philip's no sudden alien—the *Q's* husband, „ III iii 42
if the *Q* should die without a child, „ III iii 74
Peace—the *Q*, Philip, and Pole. „ III iii 83
Her Grace the *Q* commands you to the Tower. „ III iii 270
under our *Q's* regimen We might go softlier „ III iv 181
I would not, were I *Q*, tolerate the heretic, „ III iv 209
And done your best to bastardise our *Q*, „ III iv 239
Our good *Q's* cousin—dallying over seas „ III iv 292
Q, most wroth at first with you, „ III iv 387
colours of our *Q* are green and white, „ III v 5
to cast myself Upon the good *Q's* mercy ; ay, when, my Lord ? God save the *Q* ! „ III v 168

Queen (s) (*continued*) When next there comes a missive from the *Q* *Queen Mary* III v 183
A missive from the *Q* : „ III v 187
and think of this in your coming. 'Mary the *Q*.' „ III v 225
I think the *Q* may never bear a child ; I think that I may be some time the *Q*, Then, *Q* indeed : „ III v 231
You cannot see the *Q*. Renard denied her, „ III vi 1
Q hath been three days in tears For Philip's going— „ III vi 12
bring it Home to the leisure wisdom of his *Q*, „ III vi 23
Against the King, the *Q*, the Holy Father, „ III vi 33
Would *she* had been the *Q* ! „ III vi 47
The *Q* of Philip should be chaste. „ III vi 131
Be somewhat less—majestic to your *Q*. „ III vi 150
King and *Q*, To whom he owes his loyalty after God, „ IV i 22
Declare the *Q's* right to the throne ; „ IV ii 78
I must obey the *Q* and Council, man. „ IV ii 164
causes Wherefore our *Q* and Council at this time „ IV iii 36
which our *Q* And Council at this present „ IV iii 55
For if our Holy *Q* not pardon him, „ IV iii 61
Obey your King and *Q*, and not for dread „ IV iii 177
Hard-natured *Q*, half-Spanish in herself, „ IV iii 424
Done right against the promise of this *Q* Twice given. „ IV iii 456
I but a little *Q* ; and, so indeed, „ V i 53
A little *Q* ! but when I came to wed your majesty, „ V i 55
Being *Q* of England, I have none other. „ V i 69
She stands between you and the *Q* of Scots. *Mary.* The *Q* of Scots at least is Catholic. „ V i 192
The *Q* in tears ! „ V i 223
How doubly aged this *Q* of ours hath grown „ V i 227
Elizabeth, How fair and royal—like a *Q*, indeed ? „ V i 235
methinks my *Q* is like enough To leave me „ V i 242
so my *Q* Would leave me—as—my wife. „ V i 251
and I shall urge his suit Upon the *Q*, „ V i 267
affirms The *Q* has forfeited her right to reign „ V i 290
Might I not say—to please your wife, the *Q* ? „ V i 308
for the death Of our accursed *Q* and Cardinal Pole.' „ V ii 181
Unhappiest Of *Q's* and wives and women ! „ V ii 408
Sees ever such an aureole round the *Q*, „ V ii 414
I used to love the *Q* with all my heart— „ V ii 418
Our drooping *Q* should know ! „ V ii 457
Most loyal and most grateful to the *Q*. „ V iii 26
You will be *Q*, And, were I Philip— „ V iii 37
gather'd from the *Q* That she would see your Grace „ V iii 103
Is not yon light in the *Q's* chamber ? „ V iv 1
There's the *Q's* light. I hear she cannot live. „ V iv 10
not courtly to stand helmeted Before the *Q*. „ V v 37
The *Q* of Scots is married to the Dauphin, „ V v 52
How is the good *Q* now ? „ V v 229
The *Q* is dying, or you dare not say it. *Elizabeth.* The *Q* is dead. „ V v 250
I swear I have no heart To be your *Q*. „ V v 265
God save Elizabeth, the *Q* of England ! „ V v 283
God save the *Q* ! „ V v 288
Thou art the *Q* ; ye are boy and girl no more : *Harold* I i 455
Not yet, but then—my *q*. „ I ii 138
If he were King of England, I his *q*, „ I ii 154
And bless the *Q* of England. „ I ii 207
Sign it, my *q* ! „ III i 201
They shout as they would have her for a *q*. „ IV i 27
The *Q* of Wales ! Why, Morcar, „ IV i 152
Not true, my girl, here is the *Q* ! „ V ii 92
Wast thou his *Q* ? *Aldwyth.* I was the *Q* of Wales. „ V ii 94
that I fear the *Q* would have her life. *Becket, Pro.* 61
The *Q* should play his kingship against thine ! „ *Pro.* 236
Dead is he, my *Q* ? „ *Pro.* 368
However kings and *q's* may frown on thee. „ I ii 18
Ay, Madam, and *q's* also. *Eleanor.* And *q's* also ! „ I ii 80
Remember the *Q* ! „ I iv 201
Vouchsafe a gracious answer to your *Q* ? „ IV ii 360
shall not I, the *Q*, Tear out her heart— „ IV ii 408
My liege, the *Q* of England. *Henry.* God's eyes ! „ V i 96
Of England ? Say of Aquitaine. I am no *Q* of England. „ V i 101
I had dream'd I was the bride of England, and a *q*. „ V i 103
He sends you This diadem of the first Galatian *Q*, *The Cup* II 132
I wait him his crown'd *q*. „ II 161

Queen (s) (*continued*) Hail, King! *Synorix.* Hail, *Q*! *The Cup* II 220
Much graced are we that our *Q* Rome in you „ II 335
The sovereign of Galatia weds his *Q*. „ II 432
Synorix, first King, Camma, first *Q* o' the Realm, „ II 440
This all too happy day, crown—*q* at once. „ II 451
She too—she too—the bride! the *Q*! and I— „ II 468
My far-eyed *q* of the winds— *The Falcon* 9
I whisper'd, Let me crown you *Q* of Beauty, „ 360
with the same crown my *Q* of Beauty. „ 915
he's no respect for the *Q*, or the parson, or the justice o' peace, or owt. *Prom. of May* I 132
and the blessed *Q* of Heaven, *Foresters* II i 38
O would she stood before me as my *q*, „ II i 167
She is my *q* and thine, The mistress of the band. „ II ii 41
catch A glimpse of them and of their fairy *Q*— „ II ii 104
Tit, my *q*, must it be so? „ II ii 124
And this new *q* of the wood. „ II ii 139
Found him dead and drench'd in dew, *Q*. (repeat) *Foresters* II ii 148, 151, 153, 155, 157, 159, 161, 163, 171
present her with this oaken chaplet as *Q* of the wood, *Foresters* III 59
I were like a *q* indeed. „ III 77
Sit here, my *q*, and judge the world with me. „ III 151
Shall drink the health of our new woodland *Q*. „ III 315
The *Q* o' the woods, „ III 353
Maid Marian, *Q* o' the woods! (repeat) *Foresters* III 357, 375, 377, 398, 400
Drink to the health of our new *Q* o' the woods, *Foresters* III 368
We drink the health of thy new *Q* o' the woods. „ III 372
Drink to the *Q* o' the woods, „ III 388
—to this maid, this *Q* o' the woods. „ III 394
We care not much for a *Q*— „ III 430
For a *Q*, for a *Q* o' the woods. (repeat) „ III 431, 445
That we would die for a *Q*— „ III 444
You hear your *Q*, obey! „ III 464
And thou their *Q*. „ IV 932
Queen (verb) Tho' you should *q* me all over the realms „ IV 707
Queenlike So—am I somewhat *Q*, *Queen Mary* V ii 543
Queenly I have never seen her So *q* or so goodly. „ II ii 327
all men cry, She is *q*, she is goodly. „ II ii 343
Queen's 'Listed for a soädger, Miss, i' the *Q* Real Hard Tillery. *Prom. of May* III 109
Queenship to break down all kingship and *q*, *Queen Mary* V iv 48
Quell'd Not to be *q*; and I have felt within me „ I iv 259
Quench hiss Against the blaze they cannot *q*— *Harold* III i 396
Which it will *q* in blood! *Becket* IV ii 192
Quenched *q* the warmth of France toward you, „ II ii 311
And *q* it there for ever. *The Cup* II 88
Query had she but given Plain answer to plain *q*? *Becket* IV ii 386
Question (s) That is Your *q*, and I front it with another: *Queen Mary* I v 141
That's not a pretty *q*. „ I v 610
While this same marriage *q* was being argued, „ II ii 37
And by their answers to the *q* ask'd, „ II ii 153
You brawl beyond the *q*; speak, Lord Legate! „ III iv 97
one to rule All England beyond *q*, beyond quarrel. *Harold* IV i 145
I but ask'd her One *q*, and she primm'd *Becket* III i 74
But one *q*—How fares thy pretty boy, „ V ii 166
I have been unwilling to trouble you with *q's*, *Prom. of May* III 321
My Lady, will you answer me a *q*? *Foresters* I ii 136
A *q* that every true man asks of a woman once in his life. „ I ii 138
Question (verb) hath no fence when Gardiner *q's* him; *Queen Mary* I iv 203
Nor yet to *q* things already done; „ III iii 189
Cranmer, I come to *q* you again; „ IV ii 15
charged me not to *q* any of those About me. *Becket* III i 210
May she not tempt me, being at my side, To *q her*? „ III i 218
Question'd she *q me.* Did she not slander *him*? „ III i 212
Questioning he's past your *q*. *Queen Mary* I i 39
Quibble You crost him with a *q* of your law. *Foresters* IV 850
Quick Were momentary sparkles out as *q* Almost as kindled; *Queen Mary* I ii 73
That now we be and ever shall be *q*, „ III iii 137

Quick (*continued*) Away now—*Q*! *Queen Mary* V ii 295
The King is *q* to anger; if thou anger him, *Becket* I iii 164
his monarch mane Bristled about his *q* ears— *The Cup* I ii 121
Then with one *q* short stab—eternal peace. „ I iii 124
whose *q* flash splits The mid-sea mast, „ II 291
Q, good mother, *q*! *Foresters* II i 193
Quicken Employ us, heat us, *q* us, help us, *The Cup* I iii 131
Quicker How few Junes Will heat our pulses *q*! *Foresters* IV 1062
Quiet *Q* a moment, my masters; *Queen Mary* I iii 16
You know your Latin—*q* as a dead body. „ I iv 181
Q as a dead body. „ I iv 187
In *q*—home your banish'd countryman. „ III ii 31
Is the North *q*, Gamel? *Harold* I i 107
q, ay, as yet—Nothing as yet. „ I i 110
Q! *q*! *Harold.* Count! „ II ii 531
My lord, the town is *q*, and the moon Divides *Becket* I i 364
he asked our mother if I could keep a *q* tongue i' my head, „ III i 119
Your Grace will never have one *q* hour. „ V i 78
Follow my art among these *q* fields, *Prom. of May* I 743
Q! *q*! What is it? „ III 476
Q, good Robin, *q*! *Foresters* IV 9
Q, *q*! or I will to my father. „ IV 77
Quieted new Lords Are *q* with their sop of Abbey-lands, *Queen Mary* III i 142
Quieter it was in him to go up straight if the time had been *q*. *Becket* II ii 325
Quietest Thou art the *q* man in all the world— *Harold* I i 312
Quietist made me A *Q* taking all things easily. *Prom. of May* I 232
A *Q* taking all things easily— „ I 290
Quietness sleeping after all she has done, in peace and *q*, *Queen Mary* V iv 35
Quimper a Count in Brittany—he lives near *Q*. *Foresters* I i 272
Quip Did you hear the young King's *q*? *Becket* III iii 147
Quiring Are those the blessed angels *q*, father? *Harold* V i 473
Quiver for God Has fill'd the *q*, „ III i 400
Quiver'd the tongue yet *q* with the jest *Queen Mary* I v 475

R

Rabbit skulk into corners Like *r's* to their holes. *Queen Mary* II iv 56
stick to tha like a weasel to a *r*, I will. Ay! and I'd like to shoot tha like a *r* an' all. *Prom. of May* II 740
Rabble The Queen of England or the *r* of Kent? *Queen Mary* II ii 273
Rabidest Not dream'd of by the *r* gospeller. „ III vi 138
Race And I the *r* of murder'd Buckingham— „ III i 454
advise the king Against the *r* of Godwin. *Harold* V i 282
Till famine dwarft the *r*— *Becket* I iii 356
Wretched *r*! And once I wish'd to scourge *The Cup* I i 26
Solders a *r* together—yea—tho' they fail, „ I ii 162
And cursed me, as the last heir of my *r*: *Foresters* II ii 110
Racing in the *r* toward this golden goal *Harold* II ii 377
Rack the rope, the *r*, the thumbscrew, *Queen Mary* II i 200
Expectant of the *r* from day to day, „ IV iii 437
wrung his ransom from him by the *r*, *Harold* II ii 39
Raft as men Have done on *r's* of wreck—it drives you mad. *The Cup* I iii 142
Rag (*See also* **Half-rag**) this *r* fro' the gangrene i' my leg. *Becket* I iv 237
Rage (s) With all the *r* of one who hates a truth *Queen Mary* III vi 143
'Adulterous dog!' that red-faced *r* at me! *The Cup* I iii 122
Rage (verb) But the King *r's*—most are with the King; *Becket* I iii 591
Why do the heathen *r*? „ V ii 628
Ragged A *r* cloak for saddle—he, he, he, „ V i 248
Raging A bold heart yours to beard that *r* mob! *Queen Mary* I iii 96
Rags And here a knot of ruffians all in *r*, „ II ii 66
R, nothing but our *r*. *Foresters* III 191
Rahab scarlet thread of *R* saved her life; *Queen Mary* III ii 38
Raid The Norseman's *r* Hath helpt the Norman, *Harold* V i 291
Rail and *r's* against the rose. „ I i 423
He shall not *r* again. „ II ii 488
Rail'd We have the man that *r* against thy birth. „ II ii 485

Railer That Map, and these new *r's* at the Church *Becket* I i 306
Raiment and soft *r* about your body; *Queen Mary* V iv 33
they spread their *r* down Before me— *Becket* V ii 369
Rain Never peacock against *r* Scream'd as you did *Queen Mary* III v 57
It is a day of *r*. „ IV ii 229
Ay, but he's taken the *r* with him. *Becket* III i 273
after *r* o'erleaps a jutting rock And shoots *The Cup* I i 110
the *r* beating in my face all the way, *Prom. of May* III 367
Rainbow *R*, stay, (repeat) *Becket* III i 276, 279
O *r* stay. „ III i 283
are only like The *r* of a momentary sun. *Foresters* I ii 279
Raining It is *r*, Put on your hood *Becket* III i 93
Raise I have striven in vain to *r* a man for her. *Queen Mary* II ii 17
make oath To *r* your Highness thirty thousand men, „ II ii 290
we will *r* us loans and subsidies „ V i 179
Tostig, *r* my head! *Harold* III i 157
r his head, for thou hast laid it low! „ III i 163
To *r* that tempest which will set it trembling *Becket, Pro.* 208
tho' I am none of those that would *r* a storm between you, „ III iii 296
Raised *r* the rood again, And brought us back the mass. *Queen Mary* I v 182
But you were never *r* to plead for Frith, „ IV ii 210
Poitou, all Christendom is *r* against thee; *Harold* III ii 150
I *r* him from the puddle of the gutter, *Becket* I iii 436
I cannot brook the turmoil thou hast *r*. „ I iii 576
better Than *r* to take a life which Henry „ IV ii 268
thou hast *r* the world against thee. „ V ii 16
Rake do much To *r* out all old dying heats, „ II ii 114
Ralph (Sir Ralph Bagenhall) (*See also* **Bagenhall, Ralph Bagenhall**) Be merry! yet, Sir *R*, you look but sad. *Queen Mary* II ii 358
Fare you well, Sir *R*. „ II ii 410
It is Sir *R*, And muttering to himself „ III i 15
I swear you do your country wrong, Sir *R*. „ III i 154
You are of the house? what will you do, Sir *R*? „ III i 436
Ralph Bagenhall Sir *R B*! *Bagenhall*. What of that? „ III iii 250
Rampant Such *r* weeds Strangle each other, die, *Prom. of May* III 590
Ran (*See also* **Runned**) *R* sunless down, and moan'd against the piers. *Queen Mary* II iii 26
And then I rose and *r*. *Harold* II i 12
How *r* that answer which King Harold gave „ IV iii 108
r in upon us And died so, „ V i 409
When they *r* down the game and worried it. *Becket, Pro.* 123
r a twitch across his face as who should say what's to follow? „ III iii 93
vast vine-bowers *R* to the summit of the trees, *The Cup* I ii 403
wine *R* down the marble and lookt like blood. „ II 204
there *r* a rumour then That you were kill'd *The Falcon* 381
a fox from the glen *r* away with the hen, *Prom. of May* I 51
waded in the brook, *r* after the butterflies, „ III 275
And ever a tear down *r*. *Foresters* I i 19
For whom I *r* into my debt to the Abbot, „ II i 462
Random I sorrow'd for my *r* promise given To yon fox-lion. *Harold* III i 269
Laics and barons, thro' The *r* gifts of careless kings, *Becket* I i 159
And run my mind out to a *r* guest *The Cup* I ii 107
he begs you to forget it As scarce his act:—a *r* stroke: „ II 53
I that once The wildest of the *r* youth of Florence *The Falcon* 808
this Richard sacks and wastes a town With *r* pillage, *Foresters* IV 378
Randulf Robert, The apostate monk that was with *R* *Becket* V ii 574
Rang (*See also* **Ringed**) Heard how the shield-wall *r*, *Harold* IV iii 159
That *r* Within my head last night, *Becket* I i 70
—the bells *r* out even to deafening, „ V ii 363
her cry *r* to me across the years, *Prom. of May* II 655
Range (s) daily *r* Among the pleasant fields of Holy Writ *Queen Mary* III v 79
The *r* of knights Sit, each a statue on his horse, *Harold* V i 523
Range (verb) *r* with jetsam and with offal thrown *Queen Mary* III iii 191
Ranged that had found a King Who *r* confusions, *Becket* I iii 371
Since I left her Here weeping, I have *r* the world, *Prom. of May* II 252
Ranger Thou Robin shalt be *r* of this forest, *Foresters* IV 954
Rank (adj.) Fed with *r* bread that crawl'd upon the tongue, *Queen Mary* IV iii 442
Rank (line) many English in your *r's* To help your battle. *Queen Mary* V i 111
Would set him in the front *r* of the fight *The Cup* I ii 153
Rank (social station) Thrones, churches, *r's*, traditions, customs, *Prom. of May* I 519
Rankle Normans out From England, and this *r's* in us yet. *Harold* II ii 526
Ransom (s) wrench this outlander's *r* out of him— „ II i 58
Ransom (verb) in our oubliettes Thou shalt or rot or *r*. „ II i 108
wrung his *r* from him by the rack, „ II ii 38
he paid his *r* back. „ II ii 50
What conditions? pay him back His *r*? „ II ii 214
for the *r* of my son Walter— *Foresters* I i 265
Whose *r* was our ruin, „ IV 1007
Ransom'd where he sits My *r* prisoner. *Harold* II ii 45
Count of the Normans, thou hast *r* us, „ II ii 158
Sir Richard was told he might be *r* *Foresters* I i 64
Rare O *r*, a whole long day of open field. *Becket* I i 296
O *r* again! We'll baffle them, „ I i 298
So *r* the household honeymaking bee, „ V ii 217
Rascal (adj.) and yield Full scope to persons *r* and forlorn, *Queen Mary* II ii 185
Or lash'd his *r* back, and let him go. *Harold* II ii 507
I blow the horn against this *r* rout! *Foresters* IV 794
Rascal (s) Ay, *r*, if I leave thee ears to hear. *Queen Mary* III i 251
R!—this land is like a hill of fire, „ III i 321
Rat scurrying of a *r* Affrighted me, „ III v 143
tongue on un cum a-lolluping out o' 'is mouth as black as a *r*. „ IV iii 520
while famish'd *r's* Eat them alive. „ V ii 197
No bread? *Filippo*. Half a breakfast for a *r*! *The Falcon* 123
And a cat to the cream, and a *r* to the cheese; *Prom. of May* I 53
The *r's* have gnawed 'em already. *Foresters* I i 88
Rate What do you *r* her at? *Count*. My bird? *The Falcon* 322
Rated Hath *r* for some backwardness *Queen Mary* IV iii 307
Rave *r* thy worst, but in our oubliettes *Harold* II i 106
Raven Night, as black as a *r's* feather; „ III ii 6
and our battle-axes broken The *R's* wing, „ IV iii 65
I grieve I am the *R* who croaks it. *Foresters* III 448
Raven-croak With *r-c's* of death and after death? „ II i 624
Raw To gorge a heretic whole, roasted or *r*. *Queen Mary* III iv 344
the town Hung out *r* hides along their walls, *Harold* II ii 383
Ray light of the seas by the moon's long-silvering *r*! *Foresters* II ii 179
Raymond of Poitou Have we not heard *R o P*, thine own uncle— *Becket* IV ii 247
Re *Suaviter in modo, fortiter in* r, „ V ii 539
Reach (*See also* **Win**) To *r* the hand of mercy to my friend. *Queen Mary* IV i 65
shout of Synorix and Camma sitting Upon one throne, should *r* it, *The Cup* II 148
Reach'd your Grace, it hath not *r* me. *Queen Mary* I v 352
If Ludgate can be *r* by dawn to-morrow. „ II iii 53
They had not *r* right reason; little children! „ III iv 72
Whose dogmas I have *r*: „ IV ii 212
before The flame had *r* his body; „ IV iii 616
that *r* a hand Down to the field beneath it, *Harold* IV i 44
so still I *r* my hand and touch'd; *Becket* V ii 235
Re-act this re-action not *r-a* Yet fiercelier under Queen Elizabeth, *Queen Mary* IV iii 388
Re-action Action and *r-a*, The miserable see-saw „ IV iii 384
this *r-a* not re-act Yet fiercelier under Queen Elizabeth, „ IV iii 388
R needs must follow revel—yet— *Prom. of May* II 264
Read To *r* and rhyme in solitary fields, *Queen Mary* II i 51
show'd his back Before I *r* his face. „ II i 133
thro' that dim dilated world of hers, To *r* our faces; „ II ii 326
I've found this paper; pray your worship *r* it; „ II iii 56
Ay, ay, my friend; not *r* it? „ II iii 64
There, any man can *r* that. „ II iii 68
clowns and grooms May *r* it! „ III iv 37
And may not *r* your Bible, „ III iv 83
I *r* his honest horror in his eyes. „ III v 61
She came upon it, *r* it, and then rent it, „ III vi 142
Hath not your Highness ever *r* his book, „ IV i 90
Then never *r* it. The truth is here. „ IV i 99
r your recantation Before the people in St Mary's Church. „ IV ii 27

Read (*continued*) I sign it with my presence, if I *r* it. *Queen Mary* IV ii 73
That Cranmer *r* all papers that he sign'd ? „ IV iii 318
This last—I dare not *r* it her— „ V ii 183
I never *r*, I tear them ; „ V ii 187
I may die Before I *r* it. Let me see him at once. „ V ii 550
to *r* the letter which you bring. „ V ii 555
what hath she written ? *r*. „ V v 2
I cannot *r* the face of heaven ; *Harold* I i 66
He can but *r* the king's face on his coins. „ I i 70
They scarce can *r* their Psalter ; „ I i 163
on those Who *r* their doom and die. „ IV i 252
President of this Council, *r* them. *Becket.* *R* ! *Becket* I iii 76
For John of Oxford here to *r* to you. „ I iii 417
I could but *r* a part to-day, because— „ I iii 422
and to *r* the faces of men at a great show. „ III iii 83
paper sign'd Antonius—will you take it, *r* it ? *The Cup* I ii 226
Might I *r* ? *Count.* Ay, if you will. *The Falcon* 433
Shall I Sit by him, *r* to him, tell him my tales, „ 795
Well, my man, it seems that you can *r*. *Prom. of May* II 710
tho' you can't *r*, you could whitewash that cottage „ III 42
That nursery-tale Still *r*, then ? „ III 526
Child, *r* a little history, you will find „ III 542
Readier I am *r* to be slain, than thou to slay. *Becket* V iii 128
Readiness Have him away ! I sicken of his *r*. *Queen Mary* V ii 611
Reading (*See also* **A-reädin'**) Been *r* some old book, „ III i 44
Ready make *r* for the journey. Pray God, we 'scape the sunstroke. *R* at once. „ III v 277
Simon, is supper *r* ? „ III vi 256
We are *r* To take you to St. Mary's, Master Cranmer. „ IV ii 237
I be *r* to taäke the pledge. *Dora.* And as *r* to break it again. *Prom. of May* III 84
but very *r* To make allowances, and mighty slow To feel offences. „ III 628
Real And you, that would not own the *R* Presence, Have found a *r* presence in the stake, *Queen Mary* IV ii 140
there was a great motion of laughter among us, part *r*, part childlike, to be freed from the dulness— *Becket* III iii 155
Real Hard Tillery (**Royal Artillery**) 'Listed for a soädger, Miss, i' the Queen's *R H T*. *Prom. of May* III 109
Realised to be *r* all at once, or altogether, or anywhere but in Heaven ? „ III 186
Realm the *r* is poor, The exchequer at neap-tide : *Queen Mary* I v 119
when I was wedded to the *r* And the *r's* laws „ II ii 164
But for the wealth and glory of our *r*, „ II ii 210
To be of rich advantage to our *r*, „ II ii 235
Looms the least chance of peril to our *r*. „ II ii 239
From stirring hand or foot to wrong the *r*. „ III iii 61
Presenting the whole body of this *r* Of England, „ III iii 116
As well for our own selves as all the *r*, „ III iii 136
this noble *r* thro' after years May in this unity „ III iii 156
God to this *r* hath given A token „ III iii 168
all the *r* And its dominions from all heresy, „ III iii 215
I think they fain would have me from the *r* ; „ III v 230
a day may sink or save a *r*. „ III vi 239
and degrade the *r* By seeking justice „ IV i 19
I cannot be True to this *r* of England and the Pope „ IV i 27
Or into private life within the *r*. „ IV i 47
A shaker and confounder of the *r* ; „ IV iii 40
first In Council, second person in the *r*, „ IV iii 72
God's revenge upon this *r* For narrowness *Harold* I i 173
A conscience for his own soul, not his *r* ; „ III i 64
And given thy *r* of England to the bastard. „ III ii 154
To help the *r* from scattering. „ IV i 106
Holy Father Hath given this *r* of England to the Norman. „ V i 13
The *r* for which thou art forsworn is cursed, „ V i 63
But by the royal customs of our *r* *Becket, Pro.* 23
For my *r's* sake, myself must be the wizard „ *Pro.* 206
sign'd These ancient laws and customs of the *r*. „ I iii 8
to obey These ancient laws and customs of the *r* ? „ I iii 19
Ringing their own death-knell thro' all the *r*. „ I iii 173
Barons and bishops of our *r* of England, „ I iii 336
Much corn, repeopled towns, a *r* again. „ I iii 377
Then, glancing thro' the story of this *r*, „ I iii 411
To blast my *r's* with excommunication And interdict. „ II ii 52

Realm (*continued*) since he flouts the will of either *r*, *Becket* II ii 256
Louis Returning, ah ! to drive thee from his *r*. „ II ii 419
Rest in our *r*, and be at peace with all. „ II ii 448
it is the law, not he ; The customs of the *r*. „ V ii 127
With revenues, *r's*, and golden provinces „ V ii 346
On those that crown'd young Henry in this *r*, „ V ii 393
Whose winter-cataracts find a *r* and leave it *The Cup* II 305
Synorix, first King, Camma, first Queen o' the *R*, „ II 441
Fairy *r* is breaking down *Foresters* II ii 134
Richard, again, is king over a *r* He hardly knows, „ IV 387
What was this *r* of England, all the crowns „ IV 403
Tho' you should queen me over all the *r's* Held by King Richard, „ IV 708
thou and others in our kingless *r's* Were fighting „ IV 820
Reap which we Inheriting *r* an easier harvest. *Becket* II ii 194
I may *r* something from him—come upon *her* *The Cup* I i 179
Rear lest they *r* and run And break both *Harold* I i 372
and *r's* his root Beyond his head, *The Cup* II 283
Reason mastiff dog May love a puppy cur for no more *r* *Queen Mary* I iv 195
Your Grace will hear her *r's* from herself. „ I iv 230
with right *r*, flies that prick the flesh. „ III iv 70
They had not reach'd right *r* ; little children ! „ III iv 73
What human *r* is there why my friend „ IV i 68
Other *r's* There be for this man's ending, „ IV iii 53
Is there no *r* for the wrath of Heaven ? *Harold* I i 59
Thy fears infect me beyond *r*. Peace ! „ II ii 451
Why, that is *r* ! Warrior thou art, „ II ii 542
And with good *r* too, *Becket* I iii 58
ay, or himself In any *r*, „ II ii 170
For this *r*, That, being ever duteous to the King, „ II ii 463
I hate him for I hate him is my *r*, „ V i 231
Reave We fear that he may *r* thee of thine own. „ I iii 611
Rebel (adj.) that she breathes in England Is life and lungs to every *r* birth *Queen Mary* III vi 51
Your Grace hath been More merciful to many a *r* head „ V ii 5
Our *r* Abbot then shall join your hands, *Foresters* IV 933
Rebel (s) (*See also* **Co-rebels**) How traitorously these *r's* out of Kent *Queen Mary* II ii 145
spoil and sackage aim'd at by these *r's*, „ II ii 249
Charing Cross ; the *r's* broke us there, „ II iv 76
Heretic and *r* Point at me and make merry. „ V ii 317
Rebel (verb) Will not thy body *r*, man, if thou flatter it ? *Becket, Pro.* 102
Rebellion when there rose a talk of the late *r*, *Queen Mary* I i 92
and all *r's* lie Dead bodies without voice. „ II i 79
let *R* Roar till throne rock, and crown fall. „ II i 144
fly out and flare Into *r's*. „ III i 284
so you quash *r* too, „ III iv 37
Reborn In the *r* salvation of a land So noble. „ III iii 182
Rebuilt Saints, I have *r* Your shrines, „ V ii 299
Rebuked And Herbert hath *r* me even now. *Becket* I i 385
Recall Who now *r's* her to His ancient fold. *Queen Mary* III iii 167
Recant It is against all precedent to burn One who *r's* ; „ IV ii 50
Recantation read your *r* Before the people in St. Mary's Church. „ IV ii 27
Repeat your *r* in the ears Of all men, „ IV ii 193
Well, they shall hear my *r* there. „ IV ii 199
another *r* Of Cranmer at the stake. „ IV iii 299
after all those papers Of *r* yield again, „ IV iii 315
Papers of *r* ! Think you then That Cranmer read „ IV iii 316
Recanted on the scaffold *R*, and resold himself to Rome. „ III i 152
He hath *r* all his heresies. „ IV i 49
He hath *r*, Madam. „ IV i 54
I have err'd with him ; with him I have *r*. „ IV i 67
And so you have *r* to the Pope. „ IV ii 145
you *r* all you said Touching the sacrament „ IV iii 261
Recanting any one *r* thus at full, As Cranmer hath, „ IV i 59
but saved in heaven By your *r*. „ IV ii 180
Receive Thou shalt *r* the penitent thief's award, „ IV iii 86
the King, till another be appointed, shall *r* the revenues thereof.' *Becket* I iii 101
R it from one who cannot at present write *The Cup* I i 44
Dare beg him to *r* his diamonds back— *The Falcon* 262

Received His friends—as Angels I *r* 'em, *Queen Mary* I v 625
again *r* into the bosom And unity of Universal Church; „ III iii 154
Reck We *r* not tho' we lost this crown of England— „ III iv 55
You *r* but little of the Roman here, *The Cup* I i 189
Reckon I *r's* they'll hev' a fine cider-crop to-year if the blossom 'owds. *Prom. of May* I 315
Reckoning people do say that his is bad beyond all *r*, and—— *Rosamund.* The people lie. *Becket* III i 175
Reclaimed thou art *r*; He brings thee home: *Queen Mary* IV iii 83
Recognise Now you, that would not *r* the Pope, „ IV ii 138
Recommend I can *r* our Voltigeur.' *Prom. of May* III 311
Reconcile We come not to condemn, but *r*; *Queen Mary* III iii 186
Reconciled Is *r* the word? the Pope again? „ III iii 3
the world may know You twain are *r*, *The Cup* II 69
Record that thou keepest a *r* of his birthdays? *Foresters* I i 221
Recover Stay with us in this wood, till he *r*. „ II ii 10
Recover'd Methought I had *r* of the Becket, *Becket* V i 136
I see you quite *r* of your wound. *The Falcon* 391
if you be Not quite *r* of your wound, „ 590
'I hope your Lordship is quite *r* of your gout?' *Prom. of May* III 309
Recoverer but our *r* and upholder of customs hath *Becket* III iii 69
Re-create And bid him *r-c* me, Gilbert Foliot. „ I iii 126
Recrost Crost and *r*, a venomous spider's web— „ II i 199
Recurring And thousand-times *r* argument Of those two friars *Queen Mary* IV ii 93
Red (*See also* **Blood-red, Human-red, Stormy-red**) All *r* and white, the fashion of our land. „ I v 10
but took To the English *r* and white. „ I v 18
Her face on flame, her *r* hair all blown back, „ II ii 70
as *r* as she In hair and cheek; „ II ii 74
She wore *r* shoes! *Stafford.* *R* shoes! „ III i 59
Not *r* like Iscariot's. „ III ii 217
Laughs at the last *r* leaf, and Andrew's Day. „ III iii 87
R gold—a hundred purses—yea, and more! *Harold* III i 18
The nimble, wild, *r*, wiry, savage king— „ IV i 197
He hath blown himself as *r* as fire with curses. „ V i 87
and most amorous Of good old *r* sound liberal Gascon wine: *Becket, Pro.* 100
This chart with the *r* line! her bower! whose bower? „ *Pro.* 308
Fitzurse, that chart with the *r* line—thou sawest it—her bower. „ *Pro.* 428
A sight of that same chart which Henry gave you With the *r* line—'her bower.' „ I ii 62
Dash'd *r* with that unhallow'd passover; „ I iii 348
coming up with a song in the flush of the glimmering *r*? „ II i 8
What! have I scared the *r* rose from your face Into your heart? „ IV ii 73
hand *R* with the sacred blood of Sinnatus? *The Cup* II 84
HE! . . . HE, with that *r* star between the ribs, „ II 150
that the *r* wine Ran down the marble and lookt like blood, „ II 202
and seen the *r* of the battle-field, *The Falcon* 549
But a *r* fire woke in the heart of the town, *Prom. of May* I 50
Why, lass, what maäkes tha sa *r*? „ I 399
R with his own and enemy's blood— *Foresters* II i 32
We had it i' the *R* King's time, „ IV 303
Red-blooded And, when again *r-b*, speak again; *Harold* IV iii 208
Red-cheek'd Right honest and *r-c*; *Queen Mary* III v 106
Redden God *r* your pale blood! But mine is human-red; *Becket* I iv 35
How the good Archbishop *r's*! „ V ii 298
ambition, pride So bloat and *r* his face— *The Cup* II 170
Redden'd shown And *r* with his people's blood *Harold* I ii 243
Redder Theer be *r* blossoms nor them, Miss Dora. *Prom. of May* I 85
Redeem old Sir Richard might *r* his land. *Foresters* IV 487
Out of our treasury to *r* the land. „ IV 493
And Sir Richard cannot *r* his land. „ IV 565
Redeem'd who hath *r* us With His own blood, *Queen Mary* III iii 202
Redeemer O Son of God, *R* of the world! „ IV iii 118
Red-faced 'Adulterous dog!' that *r-f* rage at me! *The Cup* I iii 122
Redhats But the King hath bought half the College of *R.* *Becket* II ii 374
Redress He shall absolve you . . . you shall have *r*. „ V i 87
Reed some are *r's*, that one time sway to the current, „ I iii 593
R I rock'd upon broken-back'd, *Foresters* II ii 162
Re-edify hath begun to *r-e* the true temple— *Queen Mary* I iii 58

Reeking The *r* dungfork master of the mace! *Queen Mary* II ii 275
Reel *r's* Now to the right, then as far to the left, „ IV iii 395
Let all the air *r* into a mist of odour, *The Cup* II 185
I *r* beneath the weight of utter joy— „ II 450
Refer *R* my cause, my crown to Rome! . . . *Harold* V i 1
r myself, The King, these customs, *Becket* I iii 725
Re-flame Stamp out the fire, or this Will smoulder and *r-f*, *Queen Mary* I v 509
Reflected will be *r* in the spiritual body among the angels. *Becket, Pro.* 397
O my good lord, I am but an angel by *r* light. *Foresters* II i 108
Reflection I shone from him, for him, his glory, his *R*: *Becket* I iii 665
Reformation Northumberland, The leader of our *R*, *Queen Mary* III i 149
Reformer disaffected, heretics, *r's*, Look to you „ I iv 170
Refractory be we not in my lord's own *r*? *Becket* I iv 180
Refrain We will *r*, and not alone from this, *Queen Mary* II ii 236
Refreshment To find the sweet *r* of the Saints. *Harold* I i 177
Reft Not only *r* me of that legateship *Queen Mary* V ii 34
Refuge And I can find no *r* upon earth. „ IV iii 128
Take *r* in your own cathedral, (repeat) *Becket* V ii 583, 590
Refuse and *r*, Reject him, and abhor him. *Queen Mary* IV iii 278
I *r* to stand By the King's censure, *Becket* I iii 722
Refused More than once You have *r* his hand. *The Cup* II 43
Refusing *r* none That come to Thee for succour, *Queen Mary* IV iii 131
Regal were as glowing-gay As *r* gardens; „ III ii 14
face me out of all My *r* rights. *Becket* II ii 166
Regard even drown you In the good *r* of Rome. *The Cup* I i 151
Regarding and all men *R* her? *Queen Mary* IV iii 379
Regather'd And be *r* to the Papal fold? „ III ii 117
Regent O yes! In the name of the *R.* *Foresters* I iii 56
Regimen Sir, no woman's *r* Can save us. *Queen Mary* III i 122
under our Queen's *r* We might go softlier „ III iv 181
Reginald (Fitzurse, knight) (*See also* **Fitzurse, Reginald Fitzurse**) Ay! what wouldst thou, *R*? *Becket* I i 186
R, all men know I loved the Prince. „ V ii 333
I spake no word of treachery, *R.* „ V ii 402
No, *R*, he is dead. „ V iii 204
Reginald Fitzurse My lord, I follow'd *R F.* „ I i 236
R F! *Fitzurse.* Here, Madam, at your pleasure. „ IV ii 426
Reginald Pole (**Cardinal and Papal Legate**) (*See also* **Pole**) again to her cousin *R P*, now Cardinal; *Queen Mary* I i 123
R P, what news hath plagued thy heart? „ V ii 17
Reg'lar and see that all be right and *r* fur 'em afoor he coöm. *Prom. of May* I 169
Reign (s) Suffer not That my brief *r* in England *Queen Mary* V ii 302
The *r* of the roses is done— (repeat) *Becket, Pro.* 303, 325
A *r* which was no *r*, „ I iii 340
looking thro' my *r*, I found a hundred ghastly murders „ I iii 406
Reign (verb) Madam, when the Roman wish'd to *r*, *Queen Mary* I v 498
Ay, for the Saints are come to *r* again. „ II i 22
we will teach Queen Mary how to *r*. „ II i 148
Nay the Queen's right to *r*— „ II ii 96
forfeited her right to *r* By marriage with an alien— „ V i 290
To *r* is restless fence, Tierce, quart, and trickery. „ V v 265
The Christian manhood of the man who *r's*! *Harold* II i 105
than to *r* King of the world without it. „ III ii 44
let him make it his own, let him *r* in it— *Becket* II i 18
Reign'd when that which *r* Call'd itself God.— *Harold* III ii 166
I have *r* one year in the wild wood. *Foresters* II i 36
Reigning Unto the holy see and *r* Pope Serve God *Queen Mary* III iii 158
Rein (s) no more *r* upon thine anger Than any child! „ III iv 302
Rein (verb) If they prance, *R* in, not lash them, *Harold* I i 372
Reject and refuse, *R* him, and abhor him. *Queen Mary* IV iii 279
Rejected you have solicited The Queen, and been *r*. „ I iv 59
Rejoice To be your king, ye would *r* thereat, „ II ii 224
blessed angels who *r* Over one saved „ III iii 180
I shall *r* To find my stray sheep back *Becket* III iii 354
Rejoicing Might it not be the other side *r* In his brave end? *Queen Mary* IV iii 357
Relate some *r* that it was lost When Wyatt sack'd „ V ii 503
Related for I am closely *r* to the dead man's family. *Prom. of May* II 715
Release full *r* from danger of all censures *Queen Mary* III iii 150
Relent O yet *r*. O, Madam, if you knew him „ IV i 154
Relic 'O blessed *r's*!' 'O Holy Peter!' *Harold* I ii 170
Swear to me by that *r* on thy neck. *Prince John.* I swear then by this *r* on my neck— *Foresters* I ii 169

Religion accuse you of indifference To all faiths, all *r*; *Queen Mary* III iv 224
A soul with no *r*—My mother used to say *Prom. of May* III 532
Yet if thro' any want— *Harold.* Of this *r*? „ III 541
Wrong'd by the cruelties of his *r's* „ III 545
Religious Things that seem jerk'd out of the common rut Of Nature is the hot *r* fool, *Harold* I i 139
One half besotted in *r* rites. *The Cup* I i 74
Relish a kind of unction in it, a smack of *r* about it. *Foresters* I i 87
Bitters before dinner, my lady, to give you a *r*. „ III 435
Remain It then *r's* for your poor Gardiner, *Queen Mary* I v 220
r After the vanish'd voice, and speak to men. „ IV iii 163
R within the chamber, but apart. „ V iii 12
bishops down from all Their thrones in England? I alone *r*. *Harold* I i 52
R a hostage for the loyalty Of Godwin's house.' „ III i 90
Then on thee *r's* the curse, „ III i 314
R's beyond all chances and all churches, „ III ii 182
I *r*! *Stigand.* Yea, so will I, daughter, „ V i 458
the Past *R's* the Past. *Prom. of May* II 506
but he sent me an alphabetical list of those that *r*, „ III 29
three yards about the waist is like to *r* a virgin, *Foresters* I ii 70
I *r* Beside my Father's litter. „ IV 604
I *r* Mistress of mine own self and mine own soul. „ IV 728
Remain'd Have you *r* in the true Catholic faith *Queen Mary* IV ii 17
had they *r* true to me whose bread they have partaken. *Becket* I iv 149
Remainest thou *r* Gilbert Foliot, A worldly follower „ I iii 541
Remember thou could'st drink in Spain if I *r*. *Queen Mary* II i 39
R how God made the fierce fire „ IV iii 89
R, too, The triumph of St. Andrew on his cross, „ IV iii 93
R that sore saying spoken once By Him „ IV iii 202
Let all rich men *r* that hard word. „ IV iii 206
I *r* How I would dandle you upon my knee „ V ii 140
do *you r* what *you* said When last you came „ V ii 567
burnt for heresy, not for treason, *R* that! „ V v 141
I shall *r* this. *Becket* I i 232
I shall *r* this Discourtesy. „ I i 238
R the Queen! „ I iv 201
I *r* it well. There on the moors. „ II i 51
R also one who lives for thee Out there in France; „ II i 309
I shall *R* this. *Becket.* I *do r* thee; Lest I *r* thee to the lion, go. „ IV ii 290
He dared not—liar! yet, yet I *r*—I do *r*. „ V i 211
Doth he *r* me? *Rosamund.* I warrant him. „ V ii 177
drowning man, they say, *r's* all The chances of his life, „ V ii 273
I told thee that I should *r* thee! „ V iii 158
Sinnatus, you *r*—yea, you must, *The Cup* I ii 400
Do you *r* what I told you? „ I iii 3
R! Away—farewell! „ I iii 114
Dost thou *r* when I wedded Sinnatus? „ II 193
I do *r* your first-marriage fears. „ II 206
I *r* Her bright face beaming starlike *Prom. of May* II 247
I *r*, Scarlet hacking down A hollow ash, *Foresters* II ii 95
Rememberest Ha, Becket! thou *r* our talk! *Becket, Pro.* 404
Remembering *r* how yourself have changed, *Queen Mary* IV ii 155
r One who died for thee, *Becket* II i 307
Remission *r* Of half that subsidy levied *Queen Mary* I v 114
Remnant To yield the *r* of his years to heaven, „ III vi 210
Remorse doubt The man's conversion and *r* of heart, „ IV iii 108
yet—Why feel *r*, he, knowing that he *must* *Prom. of May* II 265
R then is a part of Destiny, „ II 268
Remorseless Felt the *r* outdraught of the deep Haul like a great strong fellow *Harold* II i 9
Remove Your Lordship may not have so long to wait. *R* him! *Queen Mary* II iv 108
Removed had to be *r* lest living Spain „ III i 27
Renard (**Simon, Spanish Ambassador**) (*See also* **Simon, Simon Renard**) O *R*, I am much beset, „ I v 384
talk so foully of your Prince, *R*? „ I v 427
No, *R*; it must never come to this. „ I v 481
O, Master *R*, Master *R*, If you have falsely painted „ I v 596
No woman ever love you, Master *R*. „ I v 602
Methought I smelt out *R* in the letter, „ II ii 119
Bear witness, *R*, that I live and die „ II iv 41
Renard (**Simon, Spanish Ambassador**) (*continued*) *R* and the Chancellor sharpen'd them. *Queen Mary* III i 5
there's no *R* here to 'catch her tripping.' „ III v 159
R denied her, Ev'n now to me. „ III vi 2
But, *R*, I am sicker staying here „ III vi 86
With *R*. Still Parleying with *R*, all the day with *R*, „ III vi 115
Good! *R*, I will stay then. „ V i 305
Ay, *R*, if you care to put it so. „ V i 309
Rend —ay, and *r* The renders too. „ V ii 269
The King may *r* the bearer limb from limb. *Becket* I i 378
Quarrel of Crown and Church—to *r* again. „ II ii 56
Take heed he do not turn and *r* you too: „ II ii 160
would *r* away Eyesight and manhood, „ IV ii 284
They howl for thee, to *r* thee head from limb. *The Cup* I ii 321
Render (s) ay, and rend The *r's* too. *Queen Mary* V ii 270
Render (verb) Pope would have you make them *r* these; „ I v 404
kindly rendering Of '*R* unto Cæsar.' . . . The Good Shepherd! Take this, and *r* that. *Harold* III ii 168
Rendering kindly *r* Of 'Render unto Cæsar.' . . . „ III ii 167
Rending The prey they are *r* from her— *Queen Mary* V ii 268
Renounce —I here *r* them all; „ IV iii 245
Rent (s) would fight for his *r's*, his leases, his houses, *Foresters* I i 233
Rent (verb) She came upon it, read it, and then *r* it, *Queen Mary* III vi 142
tore away My marriage ring, and *r* my bridal veil; *Harold* I ii 80
Repaid if they were not *r* within a limited time your land should be forfeit. *Foresters* IV 467
Repay Do here and now *r* you sixty-fold, *Queen Mary* III iii 199
Repeal Towards the abrogation and *r* Of all such laws „ III iii 141
Repeat I'll *r* it. *Elizabeth.* No! „ I iv 126
See that you neither hear them nor *r*! „ I v 577
An overmuch severeness, I *r*, „ III iv 156
R your recantation in the ears Of all men, „ IV ii 193
R them to their music. *The Falcon* 454
Repeated Ay, and *r* them as often—mum! *Queen Mary* I v 580
Repeating I will not vex you by *r* them— *Prom. of May* II 405
Repent Grace to *r* and sorrow for their schism; *Queen Mary* III iii 177
pardon due To him that so *r's*, „ IV iii 34
as the libertine *r's* who cannot Make done undone, *Harold* III i 31
if thou didst *r* thy courtesy even in the doing it. *Foresters* I ii 243
Repentant *R* of his errors? *Queen Mary* IV iii 22
Repented As for what I did I suffer'd and *r*. „ III iv 259
He hath clean *r* of his Normanism. *Harold* III i 30
Repeopled Much corn, *r* towns, a realm again. *Becket* I iii 377
Replace cut the canvas out; We can *r* it. *Queen Mary* V v 184
Report (s) I have to make *r* of my good earldom *Harold* I i 406
Save for some slight *r* in her own Senate *The Cup* I ii 133
and if her beauties answer their *r*. *Foresters* I ii 28
Report (verb) and hundreds more; So they *r*: *Queen Mary* I ii 13
foreign courts *r* him in his manner „ V ii 511
Reported (I have a daughter in her service who *r* it) „ I i 76
Lord Fitzurse *r* this In passing to the Castle *Becket* I ii 12
Reproach Still plied him with entreaty and *r*: *Queen Mary* IV iii 577
We have parted from our wife without *r*, *Harold* V i 155
smiles, not tears; Good wishes, not *r's*; *Prom. of May* I 526
Re-pulpited *r-p* The Shepherd of St. Peter, *Queen Mary* I v 180
Repulse the fine attractions and *r's*, *Becket, Pro.* 500
Request I never heard of this *r* of thine. *The Cup* II 394
Requesting if you, At my *r*, will but look into *Becket* II ii 115
Requicken'd be No longer a dead letter, but *r*. *Queen Mary* III iv 10
Before these bitter statutes be *r*. „ III iv 197
Require can deny Nothing to you that you *r* of him. *Lady Giovanna.* Then I *r* you to take back your diamonds— *The Falcon* 718
Requite With a wanton in thy lodging—Hell *r* 'em! *Becket* I ii 10
Rescue Or seek to *r* me. I thank the Council. *Queen Mary* IV ii 38
Rescued sends you this cup *r* from the burning *The Cup* I i 41
Is that the cup you *r* from the fire? „ I i 71
Reseat *R* him on his throne of Canterbury, *Becket* II ii 118
Resistance and the Queen hath no force for *r*. *Queen Mary* II i 140
I had counsell'd him To rest from vain *r*. *The Cup* II 414
we must Move in the line of least *r* *Prom. of May* II 670
Resold on the scaffold Recanted, and *r* himself to Rome. *Queen Mary* III i 152
Resolve fierce *r* and fixt heart-hate in men „ III vi 32
Resolved Do ye stand fast by that which ye *r*? „ III iii 103

Respect We have *r* for man's immortal soul, *Harold* II ii 500
he's no *r* for the Queen, or the parson, or the justice o' peace, or owt. *Prom. of May* I 132
Respite a boon, my king, *R*, a holiday: *Harold* I i 227
Rest (remainder) the *r* of England bow'd theirs to the Norman, *Queen Mary* II i 159
Should look more goodly than the *r* of us. „ II ii 349
why should I be bolder than the *r*, „ III i 438
Bless thou too That brother whom I love beyond the *r*, *Harold* III i 295
The *r* you see is colour'd green— *Becket, Pro.* 171
Cursed Fitzurse, and all the *r* of them „ II ii 271
Coom along then, all the *r* o' ye! *Prom. of May* I 442
I'll git the book ageän, and larn mysen the *r*, „ III 13
he, young Scarlet, and he, old Much, and all the *r* of us. *Foresters* III 61
Rest (repose) says That *r* is all—tells me I must not think— *Queen Mary* V v 62
All is well then; *r*—I will to *r*; he said, I must have *r*. „ V v 186
Shall I not help your Lordship to your *r*? *Becket* I i 2
He hath retired to *r*, and being in great jeopardy „ I iv 262
And how I long for *r*.' *Prom. of May* III 206
Rest (verb) my good mother came (God *r* her soul) *Queen Mary* I v 11
the happy haven Where he shall *r* at night, „ IV iii 580
That you might *r* among us, till the Pope, „ V ii 47
Let dead things *r*. „ V ii 506
That I must *r*—I shall *r* by and by. „ V v 64
maims himseif against the bars, say '*r*': Why, you must kill him if you would have him *r*— „ V v 68
Nay, *r* a week or two, *Harold* II ii 179
That I might *r* as calmly! „ III i 44
I needs must *r*. „ V i 229
To *r* upon thy bosom and forget him— *Becket* II i 31
R in our realm, and be at peace with all. „ II ii 448
Let me *r*. I'll call you by and by. „ V i 89
R you easy, For I am easy to keep. „ V ii 512
I had counsell'd him To *r* from vain resistance. *The Cup* II 414
God *r* his honest soul, he bought 'em for me, *The Falcon* 49
Show me some cave or cabin where I may *r*. *Foresters* II i 131
Rested some waxen doll Thy baby eyes have *r* on, *Queen Mary* I v 9
Restless To reign is *r* fence, „ V v 265
Restore we *r* you to the bosom And unity of Universal Church. „ III iii 220
and *r* his kin, Reseat him on his throne *Becket* II ii 116
Have I not promised to *r* her, Thomas, „ III iii 183
Restored I shall have my tetrachy *r* By Rome, *The Cup* I i 20
Restriction may fence round his power with *r*, *Queen Mary* II i 172
Resurrection to be wakened again together by the light of the *r*, *Prom. of May* III 197
Retinue with the *r* of three kings behind him, outroyalling royalty? *Becket, Pro.* 444
Retire Permission of her Highness to *r* To Ashridge, *Queen Mary* I iv 236
You are fresh from brighter lands. *R* with me. „ III iv 322
Her Highness is unwell. I will *r*. „ V ii 247
There was no room to advance or to *r*. *Foresters* IV 534
Retired He hath *r* to rest, and being in great jeopardy *Becket* I iv 262
Retiring (part.) *R* into cloistral solitude To yield *Queen Mary* III vi 209
Retiring (s) or is it but the past That brightens in *r*? *Prom. of May* II 645
Retract and *r* That Eucharistic doctrine in your book. *Queen Mary* IV ii 80
Return (s) (*See also* **Home-return**) Who loathe you for your late *r* to Rome, „ IV ii 32
Takes nothing in *r* from you except *R* of his affection— *The Falcon* 716
Many happy *r's* of the day, father. *Prom. of May* I 350
I trust that your *r*—for you know, my dear, „ III 421
This is the gala-day of thy *r*. *Foresters* IV 960
whose *r* Builds up our house again? „ IV 1008
Return (verb) will *r* into the one true fold, *Queen Mary* I iii 22
and I *r* As Peter, but to bless thee: „ III ii 55
Yet will I be your swallow and *r*— „ V i 91
R, And tell him that I know he comes no more. „ V ii 588
R to Sens, where we will care for you. *Becket* II ii 444
Return (verb) (*continued*) And, being scratch'd, *r's* to his true rose, *Becket* III i 249
His child and mine own soul, and so *r*. „ V ii 194
I here *r* like Tarquin—for a crown. *The Cup* I i 142
R's with this Antonius. „ I ii 179
You, Strato, make good cheer till I *r*. „ I ii 206
Or tell him, if you will, when you *r*, „ I ii 310
R and tell him Synorix is not here. „ I ii 334
Within the holy shrine of Artemis, And so *r*. „ I iii 54
I trust she *will r*. „ I iii 61
She should *r* thy necklace then. *The Falcon* 69
Will he not pray me to *r* his love— „ 247
Was yet too bashful to *r* for it? „ 540
My lord, I have a present to *r* you, „ 711
I came In person to *r* them. „ 727
If the phrase '*R*' displease you, we will say— „ 729
Shall I *r* to the castle with you? „ 793
And so *r*—Heaven help him!—to our son. „ 861
And when will you *r*? *Edgar.* I cannot tell precisely; *Prom. of May* I 627
but call for Philip when you will, And he *r's*. „ I 759
Never to *r* again, *Foresters* II ii 170
thou feel'st with me The ghost *r's* to Marian, „ III 115
When wilt thou *r*? *Richard.* *R*, I? when? when Richard will *r*. „ IV 417
I trust We shall *r* to the wood. „ IV 1052
Return'd deem This love by you *r* as heartily; *Queen Mary* II ii 197
glance of some distaste, Or so methought, *r*. „ III i 101
that hath *r* To the one Catholic Universal Church, „ IV iii 20
Thomas, I would thou hadst *r* to England, *Becket* V ii 12
On a Tuesday from mine exile I *r*, „ V ii 293
But hath she yet *r* thy love? *The Falcon* 66
happy was the prodigal son, For he *r* to the rich father; „ 142
Hath she *r* thy love? *Count.* Not yet! „ 513
They say your sister, Dora, has *r*, *Prom. of May* I 546
almost think she half *r* the pressure Of mine. „ II 627
That John last week *r* to Nottingham, *Foresters* III 147
Returning Louis *R*, ah! to drive thee from his realm. *Becket* II ii 418
Revel (s) loom Across their lamps of *r*, *Harold* II ii 407
Reaction needs must follow *r*—yet— *Prom. of May* II 264
Revel (verb) It is our forest custom they should *r* Along with Robin. *Foresters* III 174
Reveller *See* **Co-reveller**
Revelling You see they have been *r*, and I fear *Becket* V ii 421
Revelry So the wine run, and there be *r*, *Queen Mary* III ii 236
Thou and I will still their *revelries* presently. *Foresters* I ii 24
Revenge But dreading God's *r* upon this realm *Harold* I i 172
Of this dead King, who never bore *r*. „ V ii 85
I heard him swear *r*. *Becket* I i 280
I follow out my hate and my *r*. „ IV ii 151
You bad me take *r* another way— „ IV ii 152
Revenged Thus then thou art *r*— *Harold* V i 288
Revenue Meanwhile the *r's* are mine. *Becket, Pro.* 413
King, till another be appointed, shall receive the *r's* thereof.' „ I iii 101
King Demands a strict account of all those *r's* „ I iii 651
With *r's*, realms, and golden provinces „ V ii 346
wasted his *r's* in the service of our good king Richard *Foresters* I i 193
Reverence (s) Our silence is our *r* for the king! *Harold* IV i 13
Who have that *r* for him that I scarce *The Falcon* 260
honey from an old oak, saving your sweet *r's*. *Foresters* II i 297
Reverence (verb) Knowing how much you *r* Holy Church, *Becket* I ii 48
I *r* all women, bad me, dying, *Foresters* II i 40
Reverend Thro' this most *r* Father, absolution, *Queen Mary* III iii 148
For how should *r* prelate or throned prince Brook for an hour „ IV iii 542
Reverential whether from maiden fears Or *r* love for him I loved, *The Cup* II 197
Reversed Ye have *r* the attainder laid on us *Queen Mary* III iii 194
R his doom, and that you might not seem „ V ii 51
Revived And others of our Parliament, *r*, „ III i 326
Revoked Ay . . . if the king have not *r* his promise. *Harold* II ii 610
Revolt (s) all of us abhor The venomous, bestial, devilish *r* Of Thomas Wyatt. *Queen Mary* II ii 287

Revolt (s) *(continued)* A cry! What's that? Elizabeth? *r*? *Queen Mary* V v 187
Revolt (verb) Good, then, they will *r*: „ I v 174
would hold out, yea, tho' they should *r*— *Harold* II ii 554
Reward shall have a hundred pounds for *r*.' *Queen Mary* II iii 61
Have courage, your *r* is Heaven itself. „ V ii 108
Rheumatics *See* **Roomatics**
Rheumatizy (Rheumatism) Eh, my *r* be that bad howiver *Queen Mary* IV iii 475
Rhyme (s) And head them with a lamer *r* of mine, „ II i 29
A true *r*. *Lady*. Cut with a diamond; „ III v 24
I could so play about it with the *r*—— *Henry*. That the heart were lost in the *r* *Becket, Pro.* 382
May plaister his clean name with scurrilous *r's*! „ I i 309
for my verses if the Latin *r's* be rolled out from a full mouth? „ II ii 337
shall we say this wreath and your sweet *r's*? *The Falcon* 735
Your worship may find another *r* if you care *Foresters* II i 322
Rhyme (verb) To read and *r* in solitary fields, *Queen Mary* II i 51
Rhyming written scroll That seems to run in *r's*. *The Falcon* 432
Rib plunge Our boat hath burst her *r's*; *Harold* II i 3
thou wouldst hug thy Cupid till his *r's* cracked— *Becket, Pro.* 504
with that red star between the *r's*, *The Cup* II 151
how bare and spare I be on the *r*: *Foresters* I i 50
Spare me thy spare *r's*, I pray thee; „ I i 53
Back and side and hip and *r*, „ II ii 120
Ribald No *r* John is Love, no wanton Prince, „ IV 46
Ribaldry O drunken *r*! Out, beast! out, bear! *Becket* I i 230
Ribbon I ask'd A *r* from her hair to bind it with; *The Falcon* 359
this faded *r* was the mode In Florence „ 422
Rich I left her with *r* jewels in her hand, *Queen Mary* I iv 242
To be of *r* advantage to our realm, „ II ii 235
for his heart was *r*, Of such fine mould, „ IV i 169
'How hard it is For the *r* man to enter into Heaven;' Let all *r* men remember that hard word. „ IV iii 205
Till all men have their Bible, *r* and poor. „ V v 248
She *r* enough to have bought it for herself! *The Falcon* 62
happy was the prodigal son, For he return'd to the *r* father; „ 142
And yet I never saw The land so *r* in blossom as this year. „ 342
They seem'd too *r* a prize To trust with any messenger. „ 725
I remember Her bright face beaming starlike down upon me Thro' that *r* cloud of blossom. *Prom. of May* II 250
I'll cleave to you *r* or poor. *Foresters* I i 155
green earth drink Her health along with us in this *r* draught, „ III 351
And this *r* Sheriff too has come between us; „ IV 57
While Richard hath outlaw'd himself, and helps Nor *r*, nor poor. „ IV 362
Richard (de Brito, knight of the household of King Henry II.) *(See also* **Brito, De Brito)** *R*, if he *be* mine—I hope him mine. *Becket* V i 130
Richard (Lea) *(See also* **Richard Lea, Richard of the Lea)**
these lilies to lighten Sir *R's* black room, *Foresters* I i 3
Sir *R* and my Lady Marian fare wellnigh as sparely as their people. „ I i 30
Sir *R* was told he might be ransomed „ I i 63
Sir *R* must scrape and scrape till he get to the land again. „ I i 78
My guests and friends, Sir *R*, „ I ii 78
the Earl and Sir *R* come this way. „ I ii 148
You shall wait for mine till Sir *R* has paid the Abbot. „ I ii 232
O good Sir *R*, I am sorry my exchequer „ I ii 271
Farewell, Sir *R*; farewell, sweet Marian. „ I ii 284
She and Sir *R* Have past away, „ II i 119
but see fair play Betwixt them and Sir *R*— „ IV 99
Sir *R*, it was agreed when you borrowed „ IV 465
and thus This old Sir *R* might redeem his land. „ IV 487
And Sir *R* cannot redeem his land. „ IV 564
Sir *R* paid his monies to the Abbot. „ IV 849
I thank thee, good Sir *R*. „ IV 858
O good Sir *R*, I am like the man In Holy Writ, „ IV 980
Sir *R*, let that wait till we have dined. „ IV 991
Kiss him, Sir *R*—kiss him, my sweet Marian. „ IV 1003
Richard (the First, Cœur de Lion) wasted his revenues in the service of our good king *R* against the party of John, as I have done, as I have done: and where is *R*? *Foresters* I i 194
I believed this Abbot of the party of King *R*, „ I i 267
This Robin, this Earl of Huntingdon—he is a friend of *R*— „ I i 282
Long live *R*, Robin and *R*! Long live *R*! „ I ii 1
Love live Robin, Robin and *R*! „ I ii 14
'Long live King *R*!' „ I ii 25
O Lord, I will live and die for King *R*— „ I ii 38
there is a lot of wild fellows in Sherwood Forest who hold by King *R*. „ I ii 74
but we have no news of *R* yet, „ I ii 95
not answer it, my lord, till King *R* come home again. „ I ii 141
you be of those who hold more by John than *R*. „ I ii 199
I am John's till *R* come back again, and then I am *R's*. „ I ii 202
I cannot answer thee till *R* come. „ I ii 221
till he join King *R* in the Holy Land. *Robin*. Going to the Holy Land to *R*! „ I ii 238
by this Holy Cross Which good King *R* gave me „ I ii 310
good fellows there in merry Sherwood That hold by *R*, „ I iii 100
They hold by *R*—the wild wood! „ I iii 110
I held for *R*, and I hated John. „ II i 52
she will not marry till *R* come, „ II ii 84
Art thou for *R*, or allied to John? „ IV 135
But I am more for *R* than for John. „ IV 160
Still I am more for *R* than for John. „ IV 329
and serve King *R* save thou be A traitor or a goose? „ IV 351
For Robin is no scatterbrains like *R*, Robin's a wise man, *R* a wiseacre, „ IV 356
While *R* hath outlaw'd himself, „ IV 360
R's the king of courtesy, „ IV 362
R sacks and wastes a town With random pillage, „ IV 376
R risks his life for a straw, So lies in prison— „ IV 382
R, again, is king over a realm He hardly knows, „ IV 387
Again this *R* is the lion of Cyprus, „ IV 391
to *R* when he flung His life, heart, „ IV 405
Return, I? when? when *R* will return. „ IV 419
Father, I cannot marry till *R* comes. „ IV 648
save King *R*, when he comes, forbid me. „ IV 664
Tho' you should queen me over all the realms Held by King *R*, „ IV 709
When *R* comes he is soft enough to pardon „ IV 746
and she will not marry till *R* come. „ IV 773
a traitor coming In *R's* name— „ IV 781
Maid Marian. *Marian*. Yes, King *R*. *King Richard*. Thou wouldst marry This Sheriff when King *R* came „ IV 860
Give me that hand which fought for *R* there. „ IV 1030
Richard (the Third) Who's a-passing? King Edward or King *R*? *Queen Mary* I i 32
Had holpen *R's* tottering throne to stand, „ III i 114
Richard Lea *(See also* **Richard, Richard of the Lea)** We heard Sir *R L* was here with Robin. *Foresters* IV 978
Richard of the Lea *(See also* **Richard, Richard Lea)** I come here to see this daughter of Sir *R o t L* „ I ii 27
Robin, I am Sir *R o t L*. „ II i 441
Where is this old Sir *R o t L*? „ IV 438
Where is this laggard *R o t L*? „ IV 449
Richer Was not the year when this was gather'd *r*? *The Falcon* 345
R than all the wide world-wealth of May, „ 466
Our Lady's blessed shrines throughout the land Be all the *r* for us. *Foresters* IV 1081
Riches 'Better a man without *r*, than *r* without a man.' *The Falcon* 751
Richest Drew here the *r* lot from Fate, to live And die together. *The Cup* II 442
For he would marry me to the *r* man In Florence; *The Falcon* 747
Rid This last to *r* thee of a world of brawls! *Becket* V iii 198
Ridden *(See also* **Fancy-ridd'n)** I have *r* night and day from Pevensey— *Harold* IV iii 192
tho' we have been a soldier, and *r* by his lordship's side, *The Falcon* 548
Ride To-morrow we will *r* with thee to Harfleur, *Harold* II ii 195

Ride (*continued*) To-morrow will we *r* with thee to Harfleur. *Harold* II ii 647
To-morrow will I *r* with thee to Harfleur. „ II ii 769
He *r's* abroad with armed followers, *Becket* V i 2
'Will your Ladyship *r* to cover to-day? *Prom. of May* III 310
mayhap *r* a-hawking with the help of the men. *Foresters* I i 213
Ridley (Bishop of London) Hooper, *R*, Latimer will not fly. *Queen Mary* I ii 14
Cranmer and Hooper, *R* and Latimer, „ III iv 424
Latimer Had a brief end—not *R*. „ IV ii 225
I saw the deaths of Latimer and *R*. „ IV iii 295
And you saw Latimer and *R* die? „ IV iii 328
R was longer burning; but he died As manfully „ IV iii 342
'not till I hears ez Latimer and *R* be a-vire;' „ IV iii 509
When we had come where *R* burnt with Latimer, „ IV iii 585
Ridley-soldier Our *R-s's* and our Latimer-sailors „ IV iii 348
Rift (s) The *r* that runs between me and the King. *Becket* I i 140
that the *r* he made May close between us, „ II ii 131
Rift (verb) and *r's* the tower to the rock, *The Cup* II 293
Rifted Taken the *r* pillars of the wood For smooth stone columns of the sanctuary, *Harold* I ii 100
Right (adj. and adv.) By God's light a noble creature, *r* royal! *Queen Mary* I i 69
He says *r*; by the mass we'll have no mass here. „ I iii 50
This dress was made me as the Earl of Devon To take my seat in; looks it not *r* royal? „ I iv 74
You do *r* well—I do not care to know; „ I iv 188
Now what I am ye know *r* well—your Queen; „ II ii 162
R, your Grace. Paget, you are all for this poor life of ours, „ III iv 58
They, with *r* reason, flies that prick the flesh. „ III iv 70
They had not reach'd *r* reason; little children! „ III iv 73
for you know *R* well that you yourself have been supposed „ III iv 225
R honest and red cheek'd; Robin was violent, „ III v 106
A *r* rough life and healthful. „ III v 260
I know them heretics, but *r* English ones. „ IV iii 344
Said I not *r*? For how should reverend prelate or throned prince „ IV iii 541
there is the *r* hand still Beckons me hence. „ V v 136
Knowing *r* well with what a tenderness He loved my son. *Becket* V i 20
At the *r* hand of Power—Power and great glory— „ V iii 193
R. Back again. How many of you are there? *The Cup* I iii 11
having his *r* hand Lamed in the battle, wrote it with his left. *The Falcon* 443
Ay, but you turn *r* ugly when you're in an ill temper; *Prom. of May* I 159
and see that all be *r* and reg'lar fur 'em afoor he coöm. „ I 169
and I'd drive the plow straäit as a line *r* i' the faäce o' the sun, „ I 370
But now you will set all *r* again, „ I 718
Come, you will set all *r* again, and father Will not die miserable.' „ II 658
Count the money and see if it's all *r*. „ III 65
Sister Agatha is *r*. „ III 403
R as an Oxford scholar, but the boy was taken prisoner by the Moors. *Foresters* I i 59
There, there! You see I was *r*. „ I i 115
Had I a bulrush now in this *r* hand For sceptre, „ III 76
Rogue, I have a swollen vein in my *r* leg, „ IV 569
Right (s) Nay the Queen's *r* to reign— *Queen Mary* II ii 96
on you, In your own city, as her *r*, my Lord, „ II ii 106
and his *r* came down to me, „ II ii 171
Your *r's* and charters hobnail'd into slush— „ II ii 278
And let the Pope trample our *r's*, „ III iv 362
Declare the Queen's *r* to the throne; „ IV ii 78
I do hold The Catholic, if he have the greater *r*, „ IV iii 382
reels Now to the *r*, then as far to the left, „ IV iii 396
And thrust his *r* into the bitter flame; „ IV iii 610
Who know my *r*, and love me, „ V iii 34
what *r* had he to get himself wrecked *Harold* II i 59
Can have no *r* to the crown,' and Odo said, 'Thine is the *r*, for thine the might; „ II ii 355
William laugh'd and swore that might was *r*, „ II ii 362
Right (s) (*continued*) bad me seal against the *r's* of the Church, *Becket* I iii 312
whene'er your royal *r's* Are mooted in our councils— „ I iii 430
face me out of all My regal *r's*. „ II ii 166
And trampled on the *r's* of Canterbury. „ V ii 394
when they seek to overturn our *r's*, „ V ii 457
Thou art in the *r*. This blessing is for Synorix *The Cup* II 375
I am easily led by words, but I think the Earl hath *r*. Scarlet, hath not the Earl *r*? *Foresters* I ii 41
Thou Much, miller's son, hath not the Earl *r*? „ I ii 47
more goes to make *r* than I know of, but for all that I will swear the Earl hath *r*. „ I ii 50
Righteous For which God's *r* judgment fell upon you *Queen Mary* III iv 240
Rightful Ye know my father was the *r* heir Of England, „ II ii 170
What *r* cause could grow to such a heat *Foresters* II i 698
Rill the sea-creek—the petty *r* That falls into it— *Becket* II ii 294
Rind Most fruitful, yet, indeed, an empty *r*, *Queen Mary* III ii 202
Ring (s) (*See also* **Fairy-ring**) spousal *r* whereof, Not even to be laid aside, „ II ii 165
You have a gold *r* on your finger, „ V iv 32
Take thou this *r*; *Harold* I ii 58
tore away My marriage *r*, and rent my bridal veil; „ I ii 80
but take back thy *r*. It burns my hand— „ III ii 185
The *r* thou darest not wear, „ V i 421
And thou art come to rob them of their *r's*! „ V ii 37
For look, our marriage *r*! „ V ii 108
and ower a hoonderd pounds worth o' *r's* stolen. *Prom. of May* I 394
R, trinket of the Church, „ I 598
This *r* my mother gave me: it was her own Betrothal *r*. *Foresters* I ii 293
All gone!—my *r*—I am happy—should be happy. She took my *r*. I trust she loves me—yet „ I iii 1
Thou hast robb'd my girl of her betrothal *r*. „ II i 587
What! do I not know mine own *r*? „ II i 590
the precious *r* I promised Never to part with— „ II i 660
What's here? a dead bat in the fairy *r*— „ II ii 94
All our *r's* be trampled out. „ II ii 167
The Sheriff! This *r* cries out against thee. Say it again, And by this *r* the lips that never breathed Love's falsehood „ IV 69
Ring (verb) The bells must *r*; Te Deums must be sung; *Queen Mary* III ii 211
like the gravedigger's child I have heard of, trying to *r* the bell, *Becket* III iii 74
Did not a man's voice *r* along the aisle, „ V ii 150
When horn and echo *r*, *Foresters* III 428
What shouts are these that *r* along the wood? „ IV 763
Ringdove *R's* coo again, All things woo again. *Queen Mary* III v 103
Ring'd I was born of a true man and a *r* wife, „ I i 55
Ringed (rang) ye *r* fur that, Miss, didn't ye? *Prom. of May* III 14
Ringing The bells are *r* at Maidstone. *Queen Mary* II i 19
with all his rooftree *r* 'Harold,' *Harold* V ii 129
R their own death-knell thro' all the realm. *Becket* I iii 172
Riot After a *r*, We hang the leaders, *Queen Mary* IV i 73
As at this loveless knife that stirs the *r*, *Becket* IV ii 191
Ripen'd Who, waiting till the time had *r*, *Queen Mary* III ii 78
Ripening (part) this dead fruit was *r* overmuch, „ III i 26
Ripening (s) harvest moon is the *r* of the harvest, *Becket, Pro.* 363
Ripple The *r's* twinkled at their diamond-dance, *Queen Mary* III ii 10
and hover Above the windy *r*, *Harold* II ii 336
Rise At his coming Your star will *r*. *Queen Mary* I v 411
We are fallen, and as I think, Never to *r* again. „ III i 125
He comes, and my star *r's*. „ III ii 167
R to the heavens in grateful praise „ III iii 165
That should have fallen, and may *r* again. „ V ii 6
let England as of old *R* lionlike, „ V ii 267
if his Northumbrians *r* And hurl him from them,— *Harold* II ii 456
thence a king may *r* Half-Godwin and half-Alfgar, „ IV i 143
wait Till his nose *r's*; he will be very king. *Becket* V ii 184
I *r* to-morrow In the gray dawn, *The Cup* I ii 433
it would *r* HE! . . . HE with that red star „ II 149
R—I could almost think that the dead garland *The Falcon* 917
Nay, nay, I pray you *r*. „ 921
from that flood will *r* the New, *Prom. of May* I 594
And darkness *r's* from the fallen sun. *Foresters* I iii 42
Risen And Mary would have *r* and let him in, *Queen Mary* III ii 64

Robin (Hood, Earl of Huntingdon) (*continued*) Fine him! fine him! he hath called plain *R* an earl. How much is it, *R*, for a knight? *Foresters* IV 151
R, he hath no more. He hath spoken truth. „ IV 180
Nay, *R*, I am like thyself in that „ IV 195
Ay, ay, *R*, but let him know our forest laws: „ IV 198
thou fight at quarterstaff for thy dinner with our *R*, „ IV 208
A fine! a fine! He hath called plain *R* a king. „ IV 218
No figure, no fiction, *R*. „ IV 223
Try, thyself, valorous *R*! „ IV 315
I cannot break it, *R*, if I wish'd. „ IV 328
Look, *R*, at the far end of the glade „ IV 331
but stay with *R*; For *R* is no scatterbrains like Richard, *R's* a wise man, Richard a wiseacre, *R's* an outlaw, „ IV 354
But *R* is a thief of courtesy „ IV 370
R takes From whom he knows are hypocrites „ IV 378
while our *R's* life Hangs by a thread, „ IV 384
R king of Sherwood, And loves and dotes „ IV 388
R, the lion of Sherwood— „ IV 392
if our true *R* Be not the nobler lion of the twain. „ IV 395
And all I love, *R*, and all his men, „ IV 722
R! *Robin.* I am here, my arrow on the cord. „ IV 731
R, shall we not move? „ IV 782
My good friend *R*, Earl of Huntingdon, „ IV 829
if the King forbid thy marrying With *R*, our good Earl of Huntingdon. „ IV 876
I have had a year of prison-silence, *R*, „ IV 924
On those two here, *R* and Marian. „ IV 929
Thou *R* shalt be ranger of this forest, „ IV 954
We heard Sir Richard Lea was here with *R*. „ IV 979
For our brave *R* is a man indeed. „ IV 1037
these old oaks will mumur thee Marian along with *R*. „ IV 1095
Robing And I was *r*;—this poor throat of mine, *Queen Mary* V ii 460
Robin Hood (Earl of Huntingdon) (*See also* **Huntingdon, Robin, Robin of Huntingdon**) Thou, *R H* Earl of Huntingdon, art attainted *Foresters* I iii 56
by virtue of this writ, whereas *R H* Earl of Huntingdon „ I iii 61
R H Earl of Huntingdon is outlawed and banished. „ I iii 67
as you would hack at *R H* if you could light upon him „ II i 287
R H was it? I thought as much. „ II i 326
We must fly from *R H* „ II ii 138
And over this *R H's* bay! „ II ii 177
we have fallen into the hands Of *R H*. (repeat) „ III 234, 298
And *R H* hath sworn— „ III 235
R H, These be the lies the people tell of us, „ III 391
all these walks are *R H's* And sometimes perilous. „ IV 119
That all was peace—not even a *R H*— „ IV 131
I am the yeoman, plain *R H*, „ IV 143
Here Abbot, Sheriff—no—no, *R H*. „ IV 989
Will chill the hearts that beat for *R H*! „ IV 1064
Will whisper evermore of *R H*. „ IV 1069
Robin of Huntingdon (Robin Hood) so true a friend of the people as Lord *R o H*. „ I i 189
Rochester first to *R*, to take the guns From out *Queen Mary* II i 220
Rock (s) I spy the *r* beneath the smiling sea. „ I iv 278
The Church on Peter's *r*? never! „ III iv 134
You beat upon the *r*. „ V i 210
therein Sunk *r's*—they need fine steering— „ V v 214
sunk *r's*; no passionate faith— „ V v 221
not the living *r* Which guards the land. *Harold* I ii 120
Thou hast betray'd us on these *r's* of thine! „ II i 23
Help the good ship, showing the sunken *r*, „ II ii 101
customs of the Church are Peter's *r*. *Becket* I iii 25
but suddenly Jarr'd on this *r*. „ I iii 382
after rain o'erleaps a jutting *r* And shoots *The Cup* I i 110
and rifts the tower to the *r*, „ II 294
and leave it A waste of *r* and ruin, hear. „ II 307
with every gust and wreck On any *r*; *Prom. of May* III 538
Rock (verb) let Rebellion Roar till throne *r*, and crown fall. *Queen Mary* II i 145
Holy Church May *r*, but will not wreck, *Becket* II ii 104
Rock'd New buds to heaven, whereon the throstle *r* *Foresters* I iii 27
Reed I *r* upon broken-back'd, „ II ii 162
Rocking Crying, ' Forward!'—set our old church *r*, *Queen Mary* IV iii 404
Rod To say ' I did not?' and my *r's* the block. „ III v 130
Rod (*continued*) that these Three *r's* of blood-red fire up yonder *Harold* I i 44
had I fathered him I had given him more of the *r* than the sceptre. *Becket* III iii 111
Rode I would not; but a hundred miles I *r*, *Queen Mary* I v 551
when I *r* with William down to Harfleur, *Harold* III i 82
Roger (Archbishop of York) (*See also* **Roger of York**) Roger of York. *Henry.* *R* is Roger of York. *Becket, Pro.* 266
He thought less of two kings than of one *R* „ III iii 91
Roger (a servant) Friend *R*, steal thou in among the crowd, *Queen Mary* I iii 37
R, thinkest thou that anyone Suspected thee „ I iii 174
Roger of York *R o Y*. *Henry.* Roger is *R o Y*. *Becket Pro.* 266
To set that precious jewel, *R o Y*. „ *Pro.* 270
R o Y, When I and thou were youths in Theobald's house, „ I iii 39
Cursed be John of Oxford, *R o Y*, And Gilbert Foliot! „ II ii 266
And how did *R o Y* confort himself? „ III iii 84
R o Y, you always hated him, „ V i 8
Rogers (John, martyr) *R* and Ferrar, for their time is come, *Queen Mary* III iv 425
Rogue —'fore God, the *r's*— „ II ii 97
Stand staring at me! shout, you gaping *r*! „ III i 289
gray *r*, Gardiner, Went on his knees, „ III v 164
beggars, poor *r's* (Heaven bless 'em) *Becket* I iv 82
R's, have you no manhood? *Foresters* II i 421
you are sturdy *r's* that should be set to work. „ III 197
yells of thief And *r* and liar echo down in Hell, „ III 324
Here, you three *r's*. „ III 358
R, we have thy captain's safe-conduct; though he be the chief of *r's*, he hath never broken his word. „ IV 431
R, I am full of gout. I cannot dance. „ IV 562
R, I have a swollen vein in my right leg, „ IV 568
R, we come not alone. „ IV 573
Rolf (a Ponthieu fisherman) *R*, what fish did swallow Jonah? *Rolf.* A whale! *Harold* II i 41
Look thee, *R*, when I was down in the fever, „ II i 46
I thank thee, *R*. „ II i 54
Roll (s) If this war-storm in one of its rough *r's* Wash up „ V i 166
bravest in our *r* of Primates down From Austin— *Becket* V ii 58
Roll (verb) And *r's* himself in carrion like a dog. *Queen Mary* I v 169
in full force *R* upon London. „ II i 236
sea shall *r* me back To tumble at thy feet. *Harold* I ii 114
The sea may *r* Sand, shingle, shore-weed, „ I ii 118
Make thou one man as three to *r* them down! „ V i 577
The horse and horseman *r* along the hill, „ V i 595
And *r* the golden oceans of our grain, *The Cup* II 269
Good! *R* it in here. *Foresters* III 312
Roll'd It *r* black as death; *Queen Mary* II iii 20
for my verses if the Latin rhymes be *r* out *Becket* II ii 338
The wheel of Fate has *r* me to the top. *The Cup* II 221
And the white cloud is *r* along the sky! *Foresters* I ii 319
Thou hast *r* over the Church militant „ IV 272
Rolling parch'd banks *r* incense, as of old, *Queen Mary* I v 91
Albeit no *r* stone, my good friend Gamel, *Harold* I i 93
Roman (adj.) (*See also* **Anti-Roman**) I am English Queen, not *R* Emperor. *Queen Mary* I v 504
For thou and thine are *R* to the core. „ III ii 230
Hark, how those *R* wolfdogs howl and bay him! „ IV iii 354
his politic Holiness Hath all but climb'd the *R* perch again, *Becket* II ii 46
sends you this cup rescued from the burning of one of her shrines in a city thro' which he past with the *R* army: *The Cup* I i 43
' A GALATIAN SERVING BY FORCE IN THE *R* LEGION.' „ I i 48
There ' Antonius leader of the *R* Legion.' „ I i 167
Strato, my name. *Sinnatus.* No *R* name? „ I i 200
' A GALATIAN SERVING BY FORCE IN THE *R* LEGION.' „ I ii 76
In the full face of all the *R* camp? „ I ii 269
The *R* Senate, For I have always play'd into their hands, „ I iii 148
Most like it was the *R* soldier shouted. „ II 119
But that might bring a *R* blessing on us. „ II 372
O women, Ye will have *R* masters. „ II 511

Roman (s) Madam, when the *R* wish'd to reign, *Queen Mary* I v 498
who shall be true To the *R*: *The Cup* I i 95
and be to Rome More faithful than a *R*. „ I i 103
I am a *R* now, they dare not touch me. „ I i 185
You reck but little of the *R* here, „ I i 189
The *R* is encamp without your city— „ I ii 83
The *R's* sent me here a spy upon you, „ I ii 220
Will he let you plead for him To a *R*? „ I ii 307
These *R's* dare not violate the Temple. „ I iii 62
This very day the *R's* crown him king „ II 63
He is gentle, tho' a *R*. „ II 502
and though a *R* I Forgive thee, Camma. „ II 505
Romance may not a girl's love-dream have too much *r* in it *Prom. of May* III 185
Rome on the scaffold Recanted, and resold himself to *R*. *Queen Mary* III i 152
And from the Apostolic see of *R*; „ III iii 127
Old *R*, that first made martyrs in the Church, „ III iv 126
But when did our *R* tremble? „ III iv 130
the pine was *R*. „ III iv 142
Who loathe you for your late return to *R*, „ IV ii 33
when the King's divorce was sued at *R*, „ IV iii 42
sharper harm to England and to *R*, Than Calais taken. „ V ii 29
He has cited me to *R*, for heresy, „ V ii 42
But held from you all papers sent by *R*, „ V ii 46
To compass which I wrote myself to *R*, „ V ii 50
But—he would have me Catholic of *R*, „ V iii 93
but worse news: this William sent to *R*, *Harold* III ii 141
human laughter in old *R* Before a Pope was born, „ III ii 164
Refer my cause, my crown to *R*! . . . „ V i 2
flashes And fulminations from the side of *R*, *Becket, Pro.* 222
This Canterbury is only less than *R*, „ I i 147
The pagan temple of a pagan *R*! „ I iii 62
If *R* be feeble, then should I be firm. „ I iii 240
And *R* is venal ev'n to rottenness. „ I iii 296
Against the solemn ordinance from *R*, „ I iii 505
Map scoffs at *R*. I all but hold with Map. Save for myself no *R* were left in England, „ II ii 384
Why should this *R*, this *R*, Still choose Barabbas „ II ii 389
I would have done my most to keep *R* holy, I would have made *R* know she still is *R*— „ II ii 401
Has left his bones upon the way to *R* „ II ii 409
The King had had no power except for *R*. 'Tis not the King who is guilty of mine exile, But *R*, *R*, *R*! „ II ii 413
Thou hast served me heretofore with *R*— „ II ii 461
To *R* again! the storm begins again. „ II ii 468
stand Clothed with the full authority of *R*, „ V ii 493
when I was flying from My Tetrarchy to *R*. *The Cup* I i 7
if he be conspirator, *R* will chain, Or slay him. „ I i 18
I shall have my tetrarchy restored By *R*, „ I i 21
quarrels with themselves, their spites at *R*, „ I i 91
I heard in *R*, This tributary crown may fall to you. „ I i 96
The king, the crown! their talk in *R*? „ I i 99
and be to *R* More faithful than a Roman. „ I i 102
I have heard them say in *R*, „ I i 136
violence to a woman, As *R* did Tarquin. „ I i 140
the dry light of *R's* straight-going policy, „ I i 145
even drown you In the good regard of *R*. „ I i 151
I am most true to *R*. „ I i 154
They say that *R* Sprang from a wolf. „ I ii 13
This mountain shepherd never dream'd of *R*. „ I ii 18
R Made war upon the peoples not the Gods. „ I ii 59
The force of *R* a thousand-fold our own. „ I ii 85
they call it so in *R*. *Sinnatus.* Province! „ I ii 93
R Will crush you if you wrestle with her; „ I ii 130
If Synorix, who has dwelt three years in *R* „ I ii 176
Then that I serve with *R* to serve Galatia. „ I ii 213
Camma, *R* has a glimpse of this conspiracy; *R* never yet hath spar'd conspirator. „ I ii 233
—all seen,—all calculated, All known by *R*. „ I ii 257
with this black thunderbolt of *R* Above him, „ I ii 266
my serving *R* To serve Galatia: „ I ii 278
I say it to you—you are wiser—*R* knows all, „ I ii 285
But you know not the savagery of *R*. *Camma.* O—have you power with *R*? use it for him! *Synorix.* Alas! I have no such power with *R*. „ I ii 288
Rome (*continued*) He steep'd himself In all the lust of *R*. *The Cup* I ii 369
loathed the cruelties that *R* Wrought on her vassals. „ I ii 374
When you cry '*R*, *R*,' to seize On whomsoever „ I iii 5
Or man, or woman, as traitors unto *R*. „ I iii 10
R! *R*! *Sinnatus.* Adulterous dog! „ I iii 107
There then I rest, *R's* tributary king. „ I iii 156
I surely should have left That stroke to *R*. „ I iii 160
R! *R*! Twice I cried *R*. „ I iii 174
For all his faithful services to *R*. „ II 65
no more feuds Disturb our peaceful vassalage to *R*. „ II 71
We cannot fight imperial *R*, „ II 93
he and I Might teach this *R*— „ II 96
Our Antonius, Our faithful friend of *R*, tho' *R* „ II 244
R in you Deigns to look in upon our barbarisms. „ II 336
If you had found him plotting against *R*, „ II 407
R is fated To rule the world. „ II 414
I might have sent him prisoner to *R*. „ II 418
I had a touch of this last year—in—*R*. „ II 447
Dost thou cry out upon the Gods of *R*? „ II 455
by the Gods of *R* and all the world, „ II 465
tell the Senate I have been most true to *R*— „ II 483
if my people must be thralls of *R*, „ II 501
Rood by the *R* I will. *Queen Mary* I i 61
He swears by the *R*. Whew! „ I i 63
raised the *r* again, And brought us back the mass. „ I v 183
They told me that the Holy *R* had lean'd And bow'd above me; *Harold* V i 102
and the *R* itself were bound To that necessity „ V i 106
the Holy *R* That bow'd To me at Waltham— „ V i 382
we will make her whole; Not one *r* lost. *Becket* I i 165
nay, by the *r* They have done far worse— *Foresters* IV 908
Roof your loving natural brother Of the same *r*, same breast. *Queen Mary* IV iii 191
found thy name a charm to get me Food, *r*, and rest. *Becket* V ii 98
To the chapel of St. Blaise beneath the *r*! „ V iii 83
The shelter of *your r*—not for one moment— *Prom. of May* III 800
while the smoke floats from the cottage *r*, *Foresters* I ii 318
larger life hereafter, more Tenfold than under *r*. „ II i 70
Rooftree with all his *r* ringing 'Harold,' *Harold* V ii 129
Room (apartment) in a closed *r*, with light, fire, physic, tendance; *Queen Mary* V iv 36
The *r* she sleeps in—is not this the way? „ V v 205
How dark your *r* is! *Prom. of May* III 217
these lilies to lighten Sir Richard's black *r*, *Foresters* I i 3
Room (space) there is barely *r* to shift thy side, *Harold* II ii 441
crying To a mountain 'Stand aside and *r* for me!' „ IV iii 130
and theer'll be *r* anew for all o' ye. *Prom. of May* I 454
There was no *r* to advance or to retire. *Foresters* IV 534
Roomatics (rheumatics) I seed tha a-limping' up just now wi' the *r* i' the knee. *Prom. of May* I 385
Root (s) heat enough To scorch and wither heresy to the *r*. *Queen Mary* III iv 28
burn and blast them *r* and branch? „ III iv 283
this one fancy hath taken *r*, and borne blossom too, *Becket, Pro.* 481
Would God they had torn up all By the hard *r*, „ II ii 209
And dig it from the *r* for ever. „ IV ii 77
and rears his *r* Beyond his head, *The Cup* II 284
Root (verb) and Napoleons To *r* their power in. *Prom. of May* III 594
Rooted and *r* in far isles Beyond my seeing: *Harold* III i 152
Rope the *r*, the rack, the thumbscrew, the stake, *Queen Mary* III i 200
he hath half-hanged himself in the *r* of the Church, *Becket* III iii 75
In the church *r*?—no. „ III iii 80
I will take the *r* from off thy waist *Foresters* IV 687
Rosamund (de Clifford) (*See also* **Clifford, Rosamund de Clifford**) With Phryne, Or Lais, or thy *R*, or another? *Henry.* My *R* is no Lais, Thomas Becket; *Becket, Pro.* 56
And so this *R*, my true-heart wife, Not Eleanor— „ *Pro.* 130
and in the midst A garden and my *R*. „ *Pro.* 169
her bower. *Fitzurse.* *R's*? „ *Pro.* 429
was *R*—his paramour—thy rival. „ *Pro.* 471
Follow me this *R* day and night, „ *Pro.* 506
taking charge Of this wild *R* to please the King, „ I i 392
Well—you know—the minion, *R*. „ I ii 37
O *R*, I would be true—would tell thee all— „ II i 204

Rosamund (de Clifford) (*continued*) *R* hath not answer'd you one word; *Becket* IV ii 361
if *R* is The world's rose, as her name imports „ v ii 261
Rosamund de Clifford wherefore should she seek The life of *R d C* „ *Pro.* 70
R d C! *Rosamund.* Save me, father, „ I i 180
R d C. Rosamund. Here am I. „ I i 244
Rosary It served me for a blessed *r*. *The Falcon* 632
Rose (s) (*See also* **Hedge-rose, White Rose**) was all pure lily and *r* In his youth, *Queen Mary* I v 20
To sicken of his lilies and his *r's*. „ I v 25
Seventeen—a *r* of grace! Girl never breathed to rival such a *r*; *R* never blew that equall'd such a bud. „ III i 371
I have play'd with this poor *r* so long „ v ii 2
He cannot smell a *r* but pricks his nose Against the thorn, and rails against the *r*. *Queen.* I am the only *r* of all the stock That never thorn'd him; *Harold* I i 422
They love the white *r* of virginity, „ III i 273
The reign of the *r's* is done— (repeat) *Becket, Pro.* 303, 325
Over and gone with the *r's*, (repeat) „ *Pro.* 326, 333,343
Not over and gone with the *r*. True, one *r* will outblossom the rest, one *r* in a bower. *Becket, Pro.* 344
r or no *r*, has killed the golden violet. „ *Pro.* 351
The rosebud of my *r*!— „ II i 68
But, my liege, I am sure, of all the *r's*— „ II i 140
Thou *r* of the world! Thou *r* of all the *r's*! „ II i 146
My brave-hearted *R*! Hath he ever been to see thee? „ II i 287
Babble in bower Under the *r*! „ III i 97
And, being scratch'd, returns to his true *r*, „ III i 250
scared the red *r* from your face Into your heart? „ IV ii 73
if Rosamund is The world's *r*, as her name imports „ v ii 263
I ha' browt these *r's* to ye—I forgits what they calls 'em, *Prom. of May* II 14
soom of her oän *r's*, an' she wur as sweet as ony on 'em— „ II 38
but I thowt I'd bring tha them *r's* fust. „ II 50
Wi' the wild white *r*, an' the woodbine sa gaäy, „ II 174
matched with my Harold is like a hedge thistle by a garden *r*. „ III 176
to saäy he's browt some of Miss Eva's *r's* for the sick laädy to smell on. „ III 347
Might wish its *r* a lily, „ III 490
These *r's* for my Lady Marian; *Foresters* I i 2
The lady gave a *r* to the Earl, The maid a *r* to the man. (repeat) *Foresters* I i 12, 105
You do well, Mistress Kate, to sing and to gather *r's*. „ I i 23
A *r* to the man! Ay, the man had given her a *r* and she gave him another. *Kate.* Shall I keep one little *r* for Little John? „ I i 109
Wilt thou not give me rather the little *r* for Little John? „ I i 148
Rose (verb) To *r* and lavender my horsiness, *Queen Mary* III v 185
Rose (past tense) when there *r* a talk of the late rebellion, „ I i 91
r again, And, when the headsman pray'd „ III i 392
R hand in hand, and whisper'd 'come away! „ III v 148
a dead man *R* from behind the altar, *Harold* I ii 79
And then I *r* and ran. „ II i 12
great Angel *r* And past again along the highest „ III i 155
when I *r*, They told me that the Holy Rood „ v i 101
So dwelt on that they *r* and darken'd Heaven. *Becket* II ii 205
Most like the city *r* against Antonius, *The Cup* I ii 62
And presently all *r*, and so departed. *The Falcon* 367
Fell with her motion as she *r*, and she, „ 536
She *r* From the foul flood and pointed *Prom. of May* II 652
Rosebud The *r* of my rose!— *Becket* II i 68
Rosefaced I and all would be glad to wreak our spite on the *r* minion of the King, „ *Pro.* 529
Rosy The *r* face, and long down-silvering beard, *Harold* III i 46
The *r* face and long down-silvering beard— „ IV i 261
Thank you. Look how full of *r* blossom it is. *Prom. of May* I 84
Rot in our oubliettes Thou shalt or *r* or ransom. *Harold* II i 108
Rotted Until they died of *r* limbs; and then Cast on the dunghill naked, *Queen Mary* IV iii 445
Rotten (adj.) Wake, or the stout old island will become A *r* limb of Spain. *Queen Mary* II i 105
swirling under me in the lamplight, by the *r* wharfs— *Prom. of May* III 371
Rotten (s) cut out the *r* from your apple, *Queen Mary* II ii 5
Rou Ha *R*! Ha *R*! (repeat) *Harold* v i 437, 528, 631, 650, 661, 664
Rough Might it not Be the *r* preface of some closer bond? *Queen Mary* I iv 48
Beheld our *r* forefathers break their Gods, „ III ii 120
A right *r* life and healthful. „ III v 260
Ever a *r*, blunt, and uncourtly fellow— „ v v 120
Like the *r* bear beneath the tree, good brother, *Harold* I i 327
If this war-storm in one of its *r* rolls „ v i 165
He comes, a *r*, bluff, simple-looking fellow. *The Cup* I i 172
nor our Archbishop Stagger on the slope decks for any *r* sea *Becket* II ii 106
Against the unpleasant jolts of this *r* road *Prom. of May* I 228
Yeäs, Miss; but he wur so *r* wi' ma, I couldn't abide 'im. *Dora.* Why should he be *r* with you? „ III 104
And these *r* oaks the palms of Paradise! *Foresters* II i 169
Rougher To make allowance for their *r* fashions, *Harold* II ii 8
Roughness Your violence and much *r* to the Legate, *Queen Mary* III iv 318
Round A *r* fine likelier. Your pardon. „ III iii 279
and a plum-pudding as big as the *r* haystack. *Prom. of May* I 794
Round-about as sleek and as *r-a* as a mellow codlin. *Foresters* I i 43
Rounded Thou hast *r* since we met. *Harold* I i 95
Rouse Not so dead, But that a shock may *r* her. *Queen Mary* III i 30
sea-bird *r* himself and hover Above the windy ripple, *Harold* II ii 334
R the dead altar-flame, fling in the spices, *The Cup* II 182
Roused *R* by the clamour of the chase he woke, „ I ii 117
Rout (s) All our games be put to *r*. *Foresters* II ii 166
I blow the horn against this rascal *r*! „ IV 794
Row but light enough to *r*. *R* to the blessed Isles! *The Cup* II 245
Row'd more than one *R* in that galley—Gardiner to wit, *Queen Mary* IV i 87
Rowel softlier than with crimson *r* And streaming lash. „ III iv 183
Roy Hurrah! Vive le *R*! *Becket* I iv 274
Royal (*See also* **All-royal, Real Hard Tillery**) By God's light a noble creature, right *r*! *Queen Mary* I i 69
but to my mind the Lady Elizabeth is the more noble and *r*. „ I i 73
and among them Courtenay, to be made Earl of Devon, of *r* blood, „ I i 111
That gave her *r* crown to Lady Jane. „ I ii 19
This dress was made me as the Earl of Devon To take my seat in; looks it not right *r*? *Elizabeth.* So *r* that the Queen forbad you wearing it. „ I iv 75
By your Grace's leave Your *r* mother came of Spain, „ I v 16
Your *r* father (For so they say) was all pure lily and rose In his youth, „ I v 19
Our *r* word for that! and your good master, „ I v 267
after me Is heir of England; and my *r* father, „ I v 286
God send her well; Here comes her *R* Grace. „ II ii 126
From your own *r* lips, at once may know The wherefore of this coming, and so learn Your *r* will, and do it.— „ II ii 136
or impair in any way This *r* state of England, „ II ii 230
And I sped hither with what haste I might To save my *r* cousin. „ II iv 78
Elizabeth, Your *R* sister. „ II iv 117
That *r* commonplace too, cloth of gold, Could make it so. „ III i 54
Loyal and *r* cousin, humblest thanks. „ III ii 3
We had your *r* barge, and that same chair, „ III ii 6
now that all traitors Against our *r* state have lost the heads „ III iv 3
He owes himself, and with such *r* smiles— „ III iv 402
of her most *R*, Infallible, Papal Legate-cousin. „ III iv 433
But I am *r*, tho' your prisoner, „ III v 177
How fair and *r*—like a Queen, indeed? „ v i 235
And, like a thief, push'd in his *r* hand; „ v ii 466
Your *r* sister cannot last; your hand Will be much coveted! „ v iii 43
Madam, your *r* sister comes to see you. „ v v 191
'This Harold is not of the *r* blood, *Harold* II ii 354

Royal (*continued*) But by the *r* customs of our realm The Church should hold — *Becket, Pro.* 23
No; too *r* for me. And I'll have no more Anselms. „ *Pro.* 274
And for these *R* customs, These ancient *R* customs—they *are R*, Not of the Church— „ I i 165
and the election shall be made in the Chapel *R*, „ I iii 111
Good *r* customs—had them written fair For John of Oxford here to read to you. „ I iii 415
As is his wont Too much of late whene'er your *r* rights „ I iii 429
Babes, orphans, mothers! is that *r*, Sire? *Henry.* And I have been as *r* with the Church. „ II i 81
And is that altogether *r*? „ II i 95
A faithful traitress to thy *r* fame. „ II i 98
What matters? *R*— „ II i 106
Still—thy fame too: I say that should be *r*. „ II i 110
I bad them clear A *r* pleasaunce for thee, in the wood, „ II i 128
I here deliver all this controversy Into your *r* hands. „ II ii 137
part *r*, for King and kingling both laughed, and so we could not but laugh, as by a *r* necessity— „ III iii 157
when the full fruit of the *r* promise might have dropt into thy mouth hadst thou but opened it to thank him. *Becket.* He fenced his *r* promise with an *if*. „ III iii 275
We trust your *R* Grace, lord of more land Than any crown in Europe, „ V i 28
My *r* liege, in aiming at your love, „ V i 35
It is a *r* messenger, my lord: *Foresters* I iii 52
and he hath seized On half the *r* castles. „ I iii 83
Royal-cousin their two Graces Do so dear-cousin and *r-c* him, *Queen Mary* III iv 400
Royalty retinue of three kings behind him, outroyalling *r*? *Becket, Pro.* 446
leave the *r* of my crown Unlessen'd to mine heirs. „ II i 107
Rub That irritable forelock which he *r's*, *Queen Mary* I iv 265
Who *r* their fawning noses in the dust, „ III iii 242
what hath fluster'd Gardiner? how he *r's* His forelock! „ III iv 12
Rubb'd Mary *r* out pale— „ III i 422
Ruby emeralds, *Rubies*, I know not what. „ III i 86
eyes—and these two sapphires—these Twin *rubies*— *Harold* I ii 112
Rudder such a one Was without *r*, anchor, compass— *Prom. of May* III 534
Ruddiest You are pale, my Dora! but the *r* cheek „ III 487
Rude Bandy their own *r* jests with them, *The Cup* I ii 360
and then he call'd me a *r* naäme, and I can't abide 'im. *Prom. of May* II 159
he wur *r* to me i' tha hayfield, and he'll be *r* to me ageän to-night. „ II 219
Ruffian And here a knot of *r's* all in rags, *Queen Mary* II ii 66
some Papist *r's* hereabout Would murder you. „ III v 174
your friends, those *r's*, the De Brocs, *Becket* V ii 434
Ruffle Ay, *r* thyself—*be* jealous! *The Falcon* 21
Ruffled but thou hast *r* my woman, Little John. *Foresters* I i 165
Ruffler too solemn and formal to be a *r*. Out upon thee! *Little John.* I am no *r*, my lady; „ I i 169
Ruffling that I bear it Without more *r*. *Queen Mary* V iii 4
Ruin (s) the general sees, A risk of utter *r*. „ V ii 449
Delay is death to thee, *r* to England. *Harold* II ii 718
whether it symbol'd *r* Or glory, who shall tell? „ V i 110
and leave it A waste of rock and *r*, hear. *The Cup* II 307
But for the slender help that I can give, Fall into *r*. *Prom. of May* II 422
Whose ransom was our *r*, *Foresters* IV 1007
Ruin (verb) Too like to *r* himself, and you, and me! *The Cup* I ii 263
Ruin'd (*See also* **Half-ruin'd**) and the race of Godwin Hath *r* Godwin. *Harold* V i 294
Rule (s) my Lord Mayor here, By his own *r*, *Queen Mary* II ii 347
by this *r*, Foliot may claim the pall For London *Becket* I iii 55
not to speak one word, for that's the *r* o' the garden, „ III i 138
and so cannot suffer by the *r* of frequency. „ III iii 319
Rule (verb) Spain and we, One crown, might *r* the world. *Queen Mary* I v 303
provinces Are hard to *r* and must be hardly ruled; „ III ii 201
hatred of the doctrines Of those who *r*, „ III iv 160
So that she come to *r* us. „ IV iii 390
and the French fleet *R* in the narrow seas. „ V i 7
Rule (verb) (*continued*) Thou art the man to *r* her! *Harold* I i 223
For I shall *r* according to your laws, „ II ii 759
he hath served me: none but he Can *r* all England. „ III i 244
one to *r* All England beyond question, beyond quarrel. „ IV i 144
I will *r* according to their laws. „ V ii 198
Rome is fated To *r* the world. *The Cup* II 416
when The stronger motive *r's*. *Prom. of May* II 671
No man who truly loves and truly *r's* *Foresters* II i 76
Ruleable if the land Were *r* by tongue, „ IV 399
Ruled wherever Spain hath *r* she hath wither'd *Queen Mary* II i 206
provinces Are hard to rule and must be hardly *r*; „ III ii 201
Ruler which hatred by and by Involves the *r* „ III iv 161
The *r* of a land Is bounden by his power „ III iv 211
When I was *r* in the patrimony, „ V ii 72
sat within the Norman chair A *r* all for England— *Harold* II ii 534
The *r* of an hour, but lawful King, *Foresters* IV 47
Ruling And *r* men are fatal twins that cannot Move *Harold* III i 127
Rumour *r* that Charles, the master of the world, *Queen Mary* I i 104
I trust it is but a *r*. „ I i 107
I hear unhappy *r's*—nay, I say not, I believe. „ V i 35
a *r* then That you were kill'd in battle. *The Falcon* 381
I may be outlaw'd, I have heard a *r*. *Foresters* I ii 92
Run (*See also* **Runned**) So the wine *r*, and there be revelry, *Queen Mary* III ii 236
See how the tears *r* down his fatherly face. „ IV iii 4
There *r's* a shallow brook across our field „ V v 83
lest they rear and *r* And break both neck and axle. *Harold* I i 373
play the note Whereat the dog shall howl and *r*, „ I ii 192
R thou to Count Guy; he is hard at hand. „ II i 54
That *r's* thro' all the faiths of all the world. „ III i 352
r in upon her and devour her, one and all *Becket, Pro.* 525
The rift that *r's* between me and the King. „ I i 140
Among these happy dales, *r* clearer, „ II i 157
this love, this mother, *r's* thro' all The world „ V ii 241
Why, whither *r's* the boy? *The Cup* I i 70
break of precipice that *r's* Thro' all the wood, „ I ii 21
r my mind out to a random guest Who join'd me „ I ii 107
my friends may spy him And slay him as he *r's*. „ I ii 392
r's to sea and makes it Foam over all the fleeted wealth „ II 287
a written scroll That seems to *r* in rhymings. *The Falcon* 432
tho' the fire should *r* along the ground, *Prom. of May* I 703
O law—yeäs, Sir! I'll *r* fur 'im mysen. „ III 714
I am sorry my exchequer *r's* so low *Foresters* I ii 272
if I hadn't a sprig o' wickentree sewn into my dress, I should *r*. „ II i 251
my heart so down in my heels that if I stay, I can't *r*. „ II i 348
most beaten track *R's* thro' the forest, „ III 90
And thou wouldst *r* more wine than blood. „ III 337
Whose writ will *r* thro' all the range of life. „ IV 48
You *r* down your game, We ours. „ IV 520
Runned (ran) I *r* arter thief i' the dark, *Prom. of May* I 402
Runned (run) Dan Smith's cart hes *r* ower a laädy i' the holler laäne, „ II 568
Running In the full vessel *r* out at top *Harold* I i 378
A hundred pathways *r* everyway, *Becket, Pro.* 163
and leprosies, and ulcers, and gangrenes, and *r* sores, „ I iv 256
r down the chase is kindlier sport Ev'n than the death. „ IV ii 213
I laäme't my knee last night *r* arter a thief. *Prom. of May* I 387
Rush Carry fresh *r'es* into the dining-hall, *Foresters* I i 81
I pray Heaven we may not have to take to the *r'es*. „ I i 90
Rushing No *r* on the game—the net,—the net. *The Cup* I i 170
Rust link *r's* with the breath of the first after-marriage kiss, *Becket, Pro.* 361
Rustic Is not this wood-witch of the *r's* fear „ III ii 31
A lady that was beautiful as day Sat by me at a *r* festival *The Falcon* 350
he, your *r* amourist, The polish'd Damon of your pastoral here, *Prom. of May* III 561
Rusting plow Lay *r* in the furrow's yellow weeds, *Becket* I iii 355
Rut Things that seem jerk'd out of the common *r* Of Nature *Harold* I i 138
Ruthless And like a river in flood thro' a burst dam Descends the *r* Norman— „ II ii 467

S

Saäke (sake) fur 'er *s* an' fur my *s* an' all? *Prom. of May* II 41
Saäme (same) a-plaäyin' the *s* gaäme wi' my Dora— I'll Soomerset tha. „ II 591
Saäve (save) if she weänt listen to me when I be a-tryin' to *s* 'er— „ II 694
Saäy (say) I should *s* 'twur ower by now. *Queen Mary* IV iii 475
Nowt—what could he *s*? *Prom. of May* I 152
and I will *s* niver master 'ed better men: „ I 323
But I hed a word to *s* to ye. „ II 45
What did ye do, and what did ye *s*, „ II 173
What did ye *s*, and what did ye do, (repeat) „ II 178, 196
What did we do, and what did we *s*, „ II 185
What we mowt *s*, and what we mowt do, „ II 191
But what 'ud she *s* to that? „ II 598
and *s* it to ye afoor dark; „ III 13
to *s* he's browt some of Miss Eva's roses for the sick laädy to smell on. „ III 346
she moänt coom here. What would her mother *s*? „ III 459
Saäyin' (saying) What hasta been *s* to *my* Dora? „ II 704
He be *s* a word to the owd man, „ III 480
Sack (a wine) I marvel is it *s* or Malvoisie? *Foresters* III 331
Sack (bag) so dusted his back with the meal in his *s*, *Becket* I iv 175
and the *s's*, and the taäters, and the mangles, *Prom. of May* I 452
Sack (verb) Richard *s's* and wastes a town With random pillage, *Foresters* IV 376
Sackage safe from all The spoil and *s* aim'd *Queen Mary* II ii 248
Sack'd By him who *s* the house of God; „ III iii 195
When Wyatt *s* the Chancellor's house in Southwark. „ V ii 504
Sacrament Touching the *s* in that same book „ IV iii 263
Yea, take the *S* upon it, King. *Harold* IV i 183
Sacred thy kiss—*S*! I'll kiss it too. *Becket* II i 185
More *s* than his forests for the chase? „ IV ii 24
To bathe this *s* pavement with my blood. „ V iii 131
A *s* cup saved from a blazing shrine Of our great Goddess, *The Cup* I ii 54
and the *s* shrine By chance was burnt along with it. „ I ii 64
that you should clasp a hand Red with the *s* blood of Sinnatus? „ II 84
Antonius. Here is another *s* to the Goddess, „ II 346
O the *s* little thing. What a shape! *Foresters* I i 107
And coil'd himself about her *s* waist. „ II i 138
or shall I call it by that new term Brought from the *s* East, his harem? „ IV 705
No friendship *s*, values neither man Nor woman save as tools— „ IV 713
Sacrifice Their wafer and perpetual *s*: *Queen Mary* I ii 45
A holy supper, not a *s*; „ IV ii 57
No *s*, but a life-giving feast! „ IV ii 112
A *s* to Harold, a peace-offering, *Harold* I ii 203
The more the love, the more acceptable The *s* of both your loves to heaven. No *s* to heaven, no help from heaven; „ III i 349
And *s* there must be, for the king Is holy, „ III i 354
it was but the *s* of a kingdom to his son, *Becket* III iii 106
nobler The victim was, the more acceptable Might be the *s*. *The Falcon* 881
Sacrificed like the Greek king when his daughter was *s*, *Becket* III iii 105
Sacrilege Take fees of tyranny, wink at *s*, „ II ii 394
O God, O noble knights, O *s*! „ V iii 179
Sad Be merry! yet, Sir Ralph, you look but *s*. *Queen Mary* II ii 359
Stafford, I am a *s* man and a serious. „ III i 41
Peace, cousin, peace! I am *s* at heart myself. „ V ii 159
poor lad! how sick and *s* for home! *Harold* II ii 325
Why art thou *s*? „ IV iii 20
but they were *s*, And somewhat sadden'd me. „ V i 112
Sadden'd but they were sad, And somewhat *s* me. „ V i 113
Sadder Of a nature Stronger, *s* than my own, *Foresters* II ii 189
Saddle A ragged cloak for *s*—he, he, he, *Becket* V i 248
Saddle-bow bent to his *s-b*, As if to win the man *Queen Mary* II ii 311
Sadness There is a touch of *s* in it, my lord, *Foresters* I iii 35
I have a touch of *s* in myself. „ I iii 38
Safe They have given me a *s* conduct: *Queen Mary* I ii 101
and keep you whole and *s* from all The spoil „ II ii 246
Is he so *s* to fight upon her side? „ II ii 313
If not, there's no man *s*. „ II ii 315
Yes, Thomas White. I am *s* enough; „ II ii 317
Friend, tho' so late, it is not *s* to preach. „ V iv 42
See him out *s*! (repeat) *Harold* V i 85, 93
into thy cloister as the king Will'd it: be *s*: „ V i 310
Stigand will see thee *s*, And so—Farewell. „ V i 419
And see thee *s* from Senlac. „ V i 457
Look out upon the battle—is he *s*? (repeat) „ V i 485, 655
S enough there from her to whom thou art bound *Becket, Pro.* 66
that is *s* with me as with thyself: „ *Pro.* 489
It is not *s* for me to look upon him. „ I iii 486
S from the dark and the cold, *The Cup* I ii 6
Home with the flock to the fold—*S* from the wolf— „ I ii 9
S from the wolf to the fold— „ I ii 19
charm'd our general into mercy, And all is *s* again. „ I ii 313
Who causest the *s* earth to shudder and gape, „ II 298
Safe-conduct Rogue, we have thy captain's *s-c*; *Foresters* IV 432
Safeguard Under the shield and *s* of the Pope, *Becket* I iii 600
Safelier you had *s* have slain an archbishop than a she-goat: „ III iii 68
Safer I fear you come to carry it off my shoulders, And sonnet-making's *s*. *Queen Mary* II i 93
Said my daughter *s* that when there rose „ I i 91
she *s* that no one in her time should be burnt for heresy. „ I i 96
Know too what Wyatt *s*. „ II ii 35
What Wyatt *s*, or what they *s* he *s*, „ II iv 127
He *s* it. *Gardiner*. Your courts of justice „ II iv 129
s she was condemn'd to die for treason; „ III i 377
Then knelt and *s* the Miserere Mei— „ III i 390
Well *s*, Lord Legate. *Mary*. Nay, not well *s*; I thought of you, my liege, „ III ii 93
Or *s* or done in all my life by me; „ IV iii 239
you recanted all you *s* Touching the sacrament „ IV iii 262
I have *s*. *Cries*. 'Pull him down! „ IV iii 279
S I not right? For how should reverend prelate „ IV iii 541
Have I not *s*? Madam, I came to sue Your Council „ V i 106
Why, who *s* that? I know not—true enough! „ V ii 208
What *s* you, my good Lord, that our brave English „ V ii 254
S you not Many of these were loyal? „ V ii 329
what *you s* When last you came to England? „ V ii 567
you *s* more; You *s* he would come quickly. „ V ii 574
Is it so fine? Troth, some have *s* so. „ V iii 54
He *s* it was not courtly to stand helmeted „ V v 35
He *s* (thou heardst him) that I must not hence Save on conditions. *Malet*. So in truth he *s*. *Harold* II ii 260
He *s* that he should see confusion fall „ II ii 489
Some *s* it was thy father's deed. *Harold*. They lied. „ II ii 513
S 'ay' when I meant 'no,' lied like a lad „ II ii 656
The Devil is so modest. *Gurth*. He never *s* it! „ III i 121
Since Griffyth's head was sent To Edward, she hath *s* it. „ IV i 222
Monk, Thou hast *s* thy say, „ V i 5
The manner of his death, and all he *s*. *Becket, Pro.* 426
And I have *s* no word of this to him: „ I i 97
They *s*—her Grace's people—thou wast found— „ I ii 4
And what *s* the black sheep, my masters? „ I iv 167
from that height something was *s* to me I knew not what. „ II i 59
He *s* as much before. „ II ii 420
from those, as I *s* before, there may come a conflagration— „ III iii 164
He *s* so? Louis, did he? „ III iii 255
You wrong the King: he meant what he *s* to-day. „ III iii 299
You *s* you couldn't trust Margery, „ IV ii 15
ready To tear himself for having *s* as much. „ IV ii 279
I *s* it was the King's courts, not the King; „ V ii 114
Why *s* you not as much to my brave Sinnatus? *The Cup* I ii 259
Not say as much? I all but *s* as much. „ I ii 281
And *s* he loathed the cruelties that Rome „ I ii 373
As I *s* before, you are still too early. „ I iii 80
Do what I *s*; (repeat) *The Falcon* 265, 269
you have *s* so much Of this poor wreath „ 426
That is musically *s*. „ 459
I *s* you might imagine it was so. „ 545
Master Dobson, did you hear what I *s*? *Prom. of May* I 172

Said (*continued*) Well but, as I *s* afoor, it be the last loäd hoäm; *Prom. of May* II 168
She *s* herself She would forgive him, „ II 679
He *s* we had been most happy together, „ III 327
O forgive me! forgive me! *Steer.* Who *s* that? „ III 464
I never *s* As much before to any woman living. „ III 644
he *s* that whenever I married he would give me away, *Foresters* I i 287
I care not what he *s*. „ I ii 259
therefore by the judgment of the officers of the *s* lord king, „ I iii 65
So he *s* who lieth here. „ II ii 117
He hath, as he *s*, but one penny. „ III 208
S I not, I loved thee, man? „ IV 740
Saidest So thou *s*. *Harold* V ii 26
Sail Stand on the deck and spread his wings for *s*! *Queen Mary* I v 379
Draw with your *s's* from our poor land, „ III vi 226
every craft that carries *s* and gun Steer toward Calais. „ V ii 275
her six and thirty *s* Of Provence blew you *Becket* V i 122
Sailing *S* from France, with thirty Englishmen, *Queen Mary* V i 285
Sailor *See* **Latimer-sailor**
Saint (*See also* **Mummy-saints, Saint's-day**) Ay, for the *S's* are come to reign again. „ II i 21
if thou call on God and all the *s's*, „ IV iii 97
S's, I have rebuilt Your shrines, „ V ii 299
O *S* of Aragon, with that sweet worn smile „ V v 198
To find the sweet refreshment of the *S's*. *Harold* I i 177
the *S's* Pilot and prosper all thy wandering „ I i 264
Thank the *S's*, no! „ I i 318
An honest gift, by all the *S's*, „ I i 345
'O thou more *s* than king!' „ I ii 167
by the patient *S's*, she's as crabb'd as ever. „ II i 51
'Marry, the *S's* must go along with us, „ II ii 365
Holy *S's* of Normandy When thou art home in England, „ II ii 727
S's to scatter sparks of plague Thro' all your cities, „ II ii 745
send thy *s's* that I may say Ev'n to their faces, „ II ii 785
To save thee from the wrath of Norman *S's*. *Stigand.* Norman enough! Be there no *S's* of England To help us „ III i 218
The *S's* are one, but those of Normanland Are mightier „ III i 223
but their *S's* Have heard thee, Harold. „ III i 253
My son, the *S's* are virgins; „ III i 271
All the sweet *S's* bless him! „ III i 297
Eternal war, than that the *S's* at peace „ III ii 75
Swearing thou swearest falsely by his *S's*: „ III ii 143
Our *S's* have moved the Church that moves the world, „ V i 41
Tell him the *S's* are nobler than he dreams, „ V i 55
Tell him that God is nobler than the *S's*, „ V i 58
lest the strange *S's* By whom thou swarest, „ V i 116
But by all *S's*— *Leofwin.* Barring the Norman! „ V i 224
My fatal oath—the dead *S's*—the dark dreams— „ V i 380
His oath was broken—O holy Norman *S's*, „ V i 617
And so the *s's* were wroth. I cannot love them, For they are Norman *s's*— „ V ii 7
liars all of you, Your *S's* and all! „ V ii 106
arrow which the *S's* Sharpen'd and sent against him— „ V ii 168
Praise the *S's*. It is over. No more blood! „ V ii 194
Why thou, the King, the Pope, the *S's*, the world, *Becket* I iii 706
And wake with it, and show it to all the *S's*. „ II i 304
My lord, you will be greater than the *S's*, „ II ii 197
all on us ha' had to go, bless the *S's*, „ III i 146
And shriek to all the *s's* among the stars: „ IV ii 239
O blessed *s*, O glorious Benedict,— „ V iii 1
And all the tutelar *S's* of Canterbury. „ V iii 167
Why, bless the *s's*! *The Falcon* 171
in hope that the *s's* would send us this blessed morning; „ 186
—they are made by the blessed *s's*—these marriages. „ 203
Oh sweet *s's*! one plate of prunes! „ 215
and by all the *s's* I can shoot almost as closely *Foresters* I i 215
For holy vows made to the blessed *S's* „ I ii 175
sweet *s's* bless your worship for your alms „ II i 363
s's were so kind to both on us that he was dead „ II i 372
by all the *s's* and all the devils ye shall dance. „ IV 552
St. Alphege *See* **Alphege**
St. Andrew (*See also* **Andrew's**) Might not *S A's* be her happiest day? *Mary.* Then these shall meet upon *S A's* day. *Queen Mary* III ii 123
St. Andrew (*continued*) *S A's* day; sit close, sit close, we are friends. *Queen Mary* III iii 1
The triumph of *S A* on his cross, „ IV iii 94
St. Blaise *See* **Blaise**
St. Calixtus *See* **Calixtus**
St. Cupid *See* **Cupid**
St. Denis *See* **Denis**
St. Dunstan *See* **Dunstan**
Sainted yea, may God Forget me at most need when I forget Her foul divorce—my *s* mother— *Queen Mary* IV i 81
St. Edmund *See* **Edmund**
St. George *See* **George**
St. James Till, by *S J*, I find myself the fool. *Queen Mary* III vi 101
By *S J* I do protest, „ III vi 253
St. John What saith *S J*:—'Love of this world is hatred against God.' „ IV iii 172
St. Lawrence *See* **Lawrence**
Saintly Or give thee *s* strength to undergo. *Queen Mary* IV iii 99
A gentle, gracious, pure and *s* man! *Harold* II ii 585
The sickness of our *s* king, „ III i 164
Save him till all as *s* as thyself *Becket* V iii 12
Thou seem'st a *s* splendour out from heaven, *Foresters* II i 606
St. Mary's read your recantation Before the people in *S M* Church. *Queen Mary* IV ii 29
farewell; Until I see you in *S M* Church. „ IV ii 47
We are ready To take you to *S M*, Master Cranmer. „ IV ii 238
St. Olaf *See* **Olaf**
St. Pancratius *See* **Pancratius**
St. Paul (*See also* **Paul**) loons That cannot spell Esaïas from *S P*, *Queen Mary* III i 281
St. Peter (*See also* **Peter**) re-pulpited The shepherd of *S P*, „ I v 182
ev'n *S P* in his time of fear Denied his Master, „ III iv 263
They crucified *S P* downward. *Becket* I iii 619
greater than the Saints, More than *S P*? „ II ii 198
if they were defective as *S P* Denying Christ, „ II ii 215
Saint's-day Most like it is a *S-d*. *Queen Mary* II i 23
St. Valery Against *S V* And William. *Harold* III ii 136
St. Vitus *See* **Vitus**
Sake (*See also* **Saäke**) I have a head to lose for your sweet *s*. *Queen Mary* I iv 131
O, my lord to be, My love, for thy *s* only. „ I v 67
for appearance *s*, stay with the Queen. „ II i 137
We have made war upon the Holy Father All for your *s*: „ V ii 309
for the *s* Of England's wholeness— *Harold* I ii 197
for my mother's *s* I love your England, „ II ii 268
Speak for thy mother's *s*, and tell me true. *Malet.* Then for my mother's *s* and England's *s* „ II ii 271
O speak him fair, Harold, for thine own *s*. „ II ii 396
But for my *s*, oh brother! oh! for my *s*! „ II ii 401
Not ev'n for thy *s*, brother, would I lie. „ II ii 420
Harold, for my *s* and for thine own! „ II ii 607
Ay, brother—for the *s* of England—ay. „ II ii 638
for mine own *s*, for thine, For England, „ IV i 229
for their *s* who stagger betwixt thine Appeal, *Becket* I iii 621
for the *s* of the Church itself, if not for my own, „ I iv 152
Agree with him quickly again, even for the *s* of the Church. „ II ii 377
Then for your own *s*, Lady, I say it with all gentleness, And for the *s* *The Cup* I iii 98
For *my s*—or they seize on thee. „ I iii 113
For her own *s then*, if not for mine— *Prom. of May* II 683
Salad There sprouts a *s* in the garden still. *The Falcon* 149
one piece of earthenware to serve the *s* in „ 482
Here's a fine *s* for my lady, „ 546
You have but trifled with our homely *s*, „ 672
Saladdeen Nay, ev'n the accursed heathen *S*— *Becket* IV ii 251
Salisbury (Jocelyn, Bishop of) (*See also* **Jocelyn**) No saying of mine—Jocelyn of *S*. „ II ii 373
but *S* was a calf cowed by Mother Church, „ III iii 95
crowning thy young son By York, London and *S*—not Canterbury. „ III iii 196
York and myself, and our good *S* here, „ V i 56
Salisbury (John of) (*See also* **John, John of Salisbury**) We gave thee to the charge of John of *S*, „ I i 247

Salisbury (John of) (*continued*) John of *S* Hath often laid a cold hand on my heats, *Becket* I i 383
He watch'd her pass with John of *S* „ I ii 40
priest whom John of *S* trusted Hath sent another. „ III i 69
John of *S* committed The secret of the bower, „ III iii 4
I know him; our good John of *S*. „ V ii 77
make me not a woman, John of *S*, „ V ii 148
Sallied that our brave English Had *s* out from Calais *Queen Mary* V ii 256
Sally (Allen, servant to Farmer Dobson) (*See also* **Sally Allen**) wheniver 'e sees two sweet'arts togither like thou and me, *S*, *Prom. of May* II 164
And you an' your *S* was forkin' the haäy, „ II 181
When me an' my *S* was forkin' the haäy, „ II 192
For me an' my *S* we sweär'd to be true, „ II 204
I can't let tha aloän if I would, *S*. „ II 234
but us three, arter *S'd* telled us on 'im, „ III 133
I beänt sa sewer o' that, fur *S* knaw'd 'im; „ III 147
Some foolish mistake of *S's*; „ III 154
as the good *S* says, 'I can't abide him'— „ III 174
Sally Allen *S A*, you worked for Mr. Dobson, didn't you? „ III 101
Salt (adj.) Up from the *s* lips of the land we two *Becket* III ii 1
like a barren shore That grew *s* weeds, *The Cup* II 232
And a *s* wind burnt the blossoming trees; *Prom. of May* I 57
Salt (s) Have I sown it in *s*? I trust not, *Becket* III iii 320
Saltwood (adj.) thou, De Broc, that holdest *S* Castle— „ I iii 160
cursed those De Brocs That hold our *S* Castle „ II ii 269
Perchance the fierce De Brocs from *S* Castle, „ V ii 249
Saltwood (s) but an he come to *S*, By God's death, „ I iii 182
Salva *S* patriam Sancte Pater, *S* Fili, *S* Spiritus, *S* patriam, *Harold* V i 466
Salvation In the reborn *s* of a land So noble. *Queen Mary* III iii 182
I promise thee on my *s* That thou wilt hear *Becket* I iii 254
Same (*See also* **Saäme**) While this *s* marriage question was being argued, *Queen Mary* II ii 37
and that *s* tide Which, coming with our coming, „ II iii 20
We had your royal barge, and that *s* chair, „ III ii 7
the clauses added To that *s* treaty which the emperor sent us „ III iii 69
Crave, in the *s* cause, hearing of your Grace. „ IV i 8
This *s* petition of the foreign exiles For Cranmer's life. „ IV i 193
Hurt no man more Than you would harm your loving natural brother Of the *s* roof, *s* breast. „ IV iii 191
Touching the sacrament in that *s* book „ IV iii 263
But heaven and earth are threads of the *s* loom, *Harold* I i 210
A sight of that *s* chart which Henry gave you *Becket* I ii 60
The bird that moults sings the *s* song again, „ I iii 447
The *s* smile still. „ III ii 44
And that *s* head they would have play'd at ball with *The Cup* II 126
Have I not drunk of the *s* cup with thee? „ II 463
If I might send you down a flask or two Of that *s* vintage? *The Falcon* 586
Giovanna, my dear lady, in this *s* battle We had been beaten— „ 602
crown you Again with the *s* crown my Queen of Beauty. „ 915
But he'll never be the *s* man again. *Prom. of May* I 70
Can I fancy him kneeling with me, and uttering the *s* prayer; standing up side by side with me, and singing the *s* hymn? „ III 181
I believe thou fell'st into the hands Of these *s* Moors *Foresters* II i 564
Prettier than that *s* widow which you wot of. „ III 268
or by that *s* love of God we will hang *thee*, prince or no prince, „ IV 582
Sanction *s* your decree Of Tostig's banishment, *Harold* IV i 103
He s thee to excommunicate The prelates *Becket* V ii 398
Sanctuary For smooth stone columns of the *s*, *Harold* I ii 101
As one that puts himself in *s*. *Becket* I iii 479
Antonius would not suffer me to break Into the *s*. *The Cup* I iii 121
Sand sea may roll *S*, shingle, shore-weed, *Harold* I ii 119
from the liquid *s's* of Coesnon Haled „ II ii 56
Sudden change is a house on *s*; *Becket* III iii 60
Sand-castle A child's *s-c* on the beach *The Cup* I ii 253
Sanders What is thy name? *Man. S.* *Queen Mary* III i 313
Sane Brave, wary, *s* to the heart of her— „ V v 224
A *s* and natural loathing for a soul Purer, *Becket* II i 170
Will hardly help to make him *s* again. *The Falcon* 83
Sang *S* out their loves so loud, *Harold* I ii 20
Heard how the war-horn *s*, „ IV iii 157
Sanguelac Senlac! *S*, The Lake of Blood! „ III i 385
S! *S*! the arrow! the arrow! „ III i 402
the dead man call it—*S*, The lake of blood? „ V i 184
thou shalt die on Senlac hill—*S*! „ V i 243
dear brother, nevermore—*S*! „ V i 249
my voice against thee from the grave—*S*! „ V i 256
S! *S*! The arrow! the arrow! „ V i 262
S—*S*—the arrow—the arrow!—away! „ V i 671
Sank I *s* so low that I went into service— *Prom. of May* III 391
Sap Like April *s* to the topmost tree, *Foresters* I iii 24
Sapphire eyes—and these two *s's*—these Twin rubies, *Harold* I ii 110
Saracen (adj.) And push'd our lances into *S* hearts. *Becket* II ii 94
Saracen (s) He calls us worse than Jews, Moors, *S's*. *Queen Mary* V i 151
Sarve (serve) if ye be goin' to *s* our Dora as ye sarved our Eva— *Prom. of May* II 691
Sarved (served) fur I ha' *s* for ye well nigh as long as the man *s* for 'is sweet'art i' Scriptur'. „ II 61
if ye be goin' to sarve our Dora as ye *s* our Eva— „ II 692
Sat As if he had been the Holy Father, *s* And judged it. *Queen Mary* IV iii 44
if there *s* within the Norman chair A ruler *Harold* II ii 532
He *s* down there And dropt it in his hands, *Becket* I iii 323
s in mine own courts Judging my judges, „ I iii 367
Ay, the princes *s* in judgment against me, „ I iv 129
a son stone-blind *S* by his mother's hearth: „ V ii 106
s Stone-dead upon a heap of ice-cold eggs. „ V ii 238
S by me at a rustic festival *The Falcon* 350
and *s* Thro' every sensual course of that full feast *Prom. of May* II 253
while I *s* Among my thralls in my baronial hall *Foresters* II i 60
Kill'd the sward where'er they *s*, „ II ii 152
Satan terms Of *S*, liars, blasphemy, Antichrist, *Queen Mary* I ii 95
A spice of *S*, ha! „ III iv 77
betwixt thine Appeal, and Henry's anger, yield. *Becket.* Hence, *S*! *Becket* I iii 624
Satin white *s* his trunk-hose, Inwrought with silver,— *Queen Mary* III i 76
Satisfaction we cannot yield thee an answer altogether to thy *s*. *Becket* I iv 22
Satisfy Have I not writ enough to *s* you? *Queen Mary* IV ii 63
Saturday and he pays me regular every *S*. *Prom. of May* I 311
spent all your last *S's* wages at the ale-house; „ III 78
Sauce-deviser A *s-d* for thy days of fish, *Becket, Pro.* 98
Saul (first Hebrew King) gloom of *S* Was lighten'd by young David's harp. *Queen Mary* V ii 358
Savage The nimble, wild, red, wiry, *s* king— *Harold* IV i 197
I heard your *s* cry. *Becket* IV ii 320
You have spoilt the farce. My *s* cry? „ IV ii 338
Our *s* mastiff, That all but kill'd the beggar, *Prom. of May* I 557
S, is he? What matters? „ I 562
'I go to fight in Scotland With many a *s* clan;' *Foresters* I i 15
Savagery hast thou never heard His *s* at Alençon,— *Harold* II ii 382
But you know not the *s* of Rome. *The Cup* I ii 287
Save (verb) (*See also* **Saäve**) up, son, and *s* him! They love thee, *Queen Mary* I iii 66
To *s* your crown that it must come to this. „ I v 479
no glory Like his who *s's* his country: „ II i 110
to *s* her from herself and Philip— „ II i 189
I come to *s* you all, And I'll go further off. „ II iii 118
but we can *s* your Grace. The river still is free. „ II iv 23
with what haste I might To *s* my royal cousin. „ II iv 78
and *s* the life Of Devon: if I *s* him, „ II iv 123
Sir, no woman's regimen Can *s* us. „ III i 123
God *s* their Graces! (repeat) *Queen Mary* III i 177, 187, 342, 412
trusted God would *s* her thro' the blood Of Jesus Christ *Queen Mary* III i 386
God *s* the Queen! „ III v 170
a day may sink or *s* a realm. *Mary.* A day may *s* a heart from breaking too. „ III vi 239
Yet to *s* Cranmer were to serve the Church, „ IV i 135
Written for fear of death, to *s* my life, „ IV iii 242
Tell, tell me; *s* my credit with myself. „ V ii 452
God *s* Elizabeth, the Queen of England! „ V v 283
God *s* the Queen! „ V v 288
Their saver, save thou *s* him from himself. *Harold* II ii 61

Save (verb) (*continued*) I have commission'd thee to *s* the man: *Harold* II ii 98
For having lost myself to *s* myself, „ II ii 654
To *s* thee from the wrath of Norman Saints. „ III i 217
lamb to Holy Church To *s* thee from the curse. „ III i 336
when our good hive Needs every sting to *s* it. „ IV i 18
This brother comes to *s* Your land from waste; „ IV i 94
not my purveyor Of pleasures, but to *s* a life— *Becket, Pro.* 150
S me, father, hide me—they follow me— „ I i 181
Make it so hard to *s* a moth from the fire? „ I i 283
S the King's honour here before his barons. „ I iii 187
God *s* him from all sickness of the soul! „ V ii 174
thy solitude among thy nuns, May that *s* thee! „ V ii 177
Is it too late for me to *s* your soul? „ V ii 524
S that dear head which now is Canterbury, *S* him, he saved my life, he saved my child, *S* him, his blood would darken Henry's name; *S* him till all as saintly as thyself „ V iii 6
He is not here—Not yet, thank heaven. O *s* him! „ V iii 17
That way, or this! *S* thyself either way. „ V iii 85
And *s* her from herself, and be to Rome *The Cup* I i 101
She may, perchance, to *s* this husband. „ I iii 33
but he may *s* the land, (repeat) *Foresters* I i 283
pay My brother all his debt and *s* the land. „ I ii 218
pay this mortgage to his brother, And *s* the land. „ I ii 265
God *s* the King! „ IV 857

Save (quasi-prep. and conj.) *S* for my daily range Among the pleasant fields *Queen Mary* III v 78
s for the fate Which hunted *him* *Harold* II ii 28
Their saver, *s* thou save him from himself. „ II ii 61
S for the prattling of thy little ones. „ II ii 122
I must not hence *S* on conditions. „ II ii 262
S for thy wild and violent will that wrench'd „ V i 277
S for some once or twice, *Becket, Pro.* 122
S from the throne of thine archbishoprick? „ I i 119

Saved I trust this day, thro' God, I have *s* the crown. *Queen Mary* II ii 303
scarlet thread of Rahab *s* her life; „ III ii 39
blessed angels who rejoice Over one *s* „ III iii 181
once he *s* your Majesty's own life; „ IV i 124
Who *s* it or not *s*. „ IV i 133
but *s* in heaven By your recanting. „ IV ii 178
I thank thee for having *s* thyself. *Harold* II ii 653
save Your land from waste; I *s* it once before, „ IV i 95
I have *s* many of 'em. *Becket* I i 285
for to-night ye have *s* our Archbishop! „ I iv 257
life *S* as by miracle alone with Him Who gave it. „ IV ii 368
but *s* From all that by our solitude. „ V ii 170
all the souls we *s* and father'd here „ V ii 223
Save him, he *s* my life, he *s* my child, „ V iii 8
sacred cup *s* from a blazing shrine *The Cup* I ii 54
However I thank thee; thou hast *s* my life. „ I ii 333
He *s* my life too. Did he? „ I iii 160
I *s* his life once in battle. He has monies. I will go to him. I *s* him. I will try him. *Foresters* I i 272
Thou hast *s* my head at the peril of thine own. „ IV 795

Saver 'Hail, Daughter of God, and *s* of the faith. *Queen Mary* III ii 82
Their *s*, save thou save him from himself. *Harold* II ii 61

Saving to the *s* of their souls, Before your execution. *Queen Mary* IV ii 194
S my confessor and my cousin Pole. „ V ii 527
S thro' Norman bishopricks— *Harold* II ii 538
And even as I should bless thee *s* mine, „ II ii 651
S the honour of my order—ay. *Becket* I iii 20
S thine order! But King Henry sware That, *s* his King's kingship, „ I iii 26
S thine order, Thomas, Is black and white at once, „ I iii 30

Savour Burn!—Fie, what a *s*! *Queen Mary* V v 116
It bears an evil *s* among women. *The Cup* I iii 86

Savoury geese, beside Hedge-pigs, a *s* viand, *Foresters* IV 193

Savoy 'It is the King's wish, that you should wed Prince Philibert of *S*. *Queen Mary* III v 222
Specially not this landless Philibert Of *S*; „ III v 240
She will not have Prince Philibert of *S*, „ III vi 43
Elizabeth—To Philibert of *S*, as you know, „ V i 247
She will not have Prince Philibert of *S*. „ V i 254

Saw (maxim) For I was musing on an ancient *s*, *Becket* V ii 538

Saw (verb) (*See also* **Seed**) and *s* They had hewn the drawbridge *Queen Mary* II iii 17
I *s* Lord William Howard By torchlight, „ II iii 28
than have seen it: yet I *s* it. „ III i 48
changed not colour when she *s* the block, „ III i 399
I never *s* your Highness moved till now. „ III vi 103
Ay, my liege, I *s* the covers laying. „ III vi 258
I *s* the deaths of Latimer and Ridley. „ IV iii 295
And you *s* Latimer and Ridley die? „ IV iii 328
You *s* him how he past among the crowd; „ IV iii 574
s the church all fill'd With dead men *Harold* I ii 81
Griffyth when I *s* him flee, Chased deer-like „ I ii 146
I *s* him over there. „ II i 46
I *s* him coming with his brother Odo „ II ii 347
whose baby eye *S* them sufficient. „ III ii 67
and yet I *s* thee drive him up his hills— „ IV i 211
I *s* the hand of Tostig cover it. „ IV iii 81
someone *s* thy willy-nilly nun Vying a tress „ V i 148
I *s* her even now: She hath not left us. „ V i 158
I *s* it in her eyes! „ V i 368
I *s* that door Close even now upon the woman. *Becket* I i 201
who never *s* nor dreamed of such a banquet. „ I iv 83
Then I *s* Thy high black steed among the flaming furze, „ II i 54
bad me whatever I *s* not to speak one word, „ III i 133
s your ladyship a-parting wi' him even now „ III i 159
Thou art the prettiest child I ever *s*. „ IV i 7
I *s* the ball you lost in the fork of the great willow „ IV ii 56
I never *s* any such, Never knew any such, „ IV ii 125
I *s* you there. *Fitzurse.* I was not. „ V ii 411
You *s* my hounds True to the scent; *The Cup* I ii 109
When last I *s* you, You all but yielded. „ II 44
that ye *s* me crown myself withal. „ II 159
She *s* it at a dance, upon a neck Less lovely *The Falcon* 54
I never *s* The land so rich in blossom as this year. „ 341
Before I *s* you—all my nobleness Of nature, „ 810
I *s* a man go in, my lord. *Foresters* II i 207
Captain, we *s* thee cowering to a knight „ II i 682
I thought I *s* thee clasp and kiss a man „ II ii 71
I never *s* them: yet I could believe „ II ii 107

Saw *See also* **See-saw**

Saw'st Our bashful Legate, *s* not how he flush'd? *Queen Mary* III iv 350
that chart with the red line—thou *s* it— *Becket, Pro.* 428

Saxon (*See also* **Un-Saxon, West Saxon**) We hold our *S* woodcock in the springe, *Harold* II ii 1
Breathe the free wind from off our *S* downs, „ II ii 186
Angle, Jute, Dane, *S*, Norman, „ II ii 763
little help without our *S* carles Against Hardrada. „ IV i 35
yet he held that Dane, Jute, Angle, *S*, „ IV i 77
And Loathing wield a *S* battle-axe— „ V i 414
Ay, there springs a *S* on him, „ V i 498
I have heard the Steers Had land in *S* times; *Prom. of May* III 608
have loved Harold the *S*, or Hereward the Wake. *Foresters* I i 228
True soul of the *S* churl for whom song has no charm. „ II i 385

Say (s) Monk, Thou hast said thy *s*, *Harold* V i 5
Say all thy *s*, But blaze not out before the Frenchmen *Becket* III iii 220

Say (verb) (*See also* **Saäy**) from their sees Or fled, they *s*, or flying— *Queen Mary* I ii 5
hear what the shaveling has to *s* for himself. „ I iii 17
He *s*'s right; by the mass we'll have no mass „ I iii 50
Perinde ac cadaver—as the priest *s*'s, „ I iv 180
some *s*, That you shall marry him, make him King belike. *Elizabeth.* Do they *s* so, good uncle? „ I iv 211
But why *s* that? what have you done to lose her? „ I iv 295
Your royal father (For so they *s*) „ I v 20
I *s* your Grace is loved. „ I v 131
What *s*'s the King your master? „ I v 247
No, *s* I come. I won by boldness once. „ I v 547
S for ten thousand ten—and pothouse knaves, „ II i 69
I *s* no more—only this, their lot is yours. „ II i 213
What do and *s* Your Council at this hour? „ II ii 45
So I *s* Your city is divided, „ II ii 98
I *s*, I, that was never mother, cannot tell „ II ii 188
he *s*'s he's a poor gentleman. „ II iii 74
Hang him, I *s*. „ II iii 80
whom—whom did you *s*? *Messenger.* Elizabeth, „ II iv 115

Say (verb) (*continued*) What such a one as Wyatt *s's* is nothing : *Queen Mary* III i 139
He keeps, they *s*, some secret that may cost „ III i 200
I *s* There is no man—there was one woman with us— „ III i 336
oversea they *s* this state of yours Hath no more mortice „ III i 441
What *s* you ? *Bagenhall.* We talk and talk. „ III iii 37
But stretch it wider ; *s* when England fell. „ III iii 261
I *s* you were the one sole man who stood. „ III iii 263
yet I would not *s* Burn ! „ III iv 174
there are many, As my Lord Paget *s's*. „ III iv 177
beware, I *s*, Lest men accuse you of indifference „ III iv 222
But truth, they *s*, will out, „ III v 28
To *s* ' I did not ? ' and my rod's the block. „ III v 130
she would *s* These are the means God works with, „ III vi 67
What should I *s*, I cannot pick my words— „ III vi 147
You *s* true, Madam. „ III vi 198
I *s*, Your father had a will that beat men down ; „ IV i 107
So, so ; this will I *s*—thus will I pray. „ IV ii 113
I'll *s* something for you—so—good-bye. „ IV ii 167
And first I *s* it is a grievous case, „ IV iii 167
I *s*, I hold by all I wrote within that book. „ IV iii 274
I *s* they have drawn the fire On their own heads : „ IV iii 379
' Now,' *s's* the Bishop, *s's* he, ' we'll gwo to dinner ; ' „ IV iii 512
I hear unhappy rumours—nay, I *s* not, I believe. „ V i 36
They *s* your wars are not the wars of England. „ V i 165
S go ; but only *s* it lovingly. „ V i 216
Might I not *s*—to please your wife, the Queen ? „ V i 307
They *s* the gloom of Saul Was lighten'd „ V ii 358
but *s* the world is nothing— „ V ii 367
How dare you *s* it ? „ V ii 379
And *s's*, he will come quickly. „ V ii 565
Then I may *s* your Grace will see your sister ? „ V ii 603
They *s* she's dying. *First.* So is Cardinal Pole. „ V iv 4
s's That rest is all—tells me I must not think— „ V v 61
And who *s's* that ? *Alice.* It is a saying among the Catholics. „ V v 243
The Queen is dying, or you dare not *s* it. „ V v 251
I needs must *s*—That never English monarch „ V v 276
I *s* not this, as being Half Norman-blooded, *Harold* I i 168
and I *s* it For the last time perchance, „ I i 174
So *s's* old Gurth, not I : „ I i 302
I *s*, thou hast a tongue, „ I i 400
What do they *s* ? did Edward know of this ? *Malet.* They *s*, his wife was knowing and abetting. *Harold.* They *s*, his wife !— „ II ii 304
I *s* Ye would applaud that Norman who should drive „ II ii 538
send thy saints that I may *s* Ev'n to their faces, „ II ii 786
forbidden By Holy Church : but who shall *s* ? „ III ii 24
They *s* thou art to wed the Lady Aldwyth. *Harold.* They *s*, they *s*. „ III ii 107
Never shall any man *s* that I, that Tostig „ IV ii 66
He means the thing he *s's*. See him out safe ! „ V i 84
I *s* it now, forgive me ! „ V ii 27
S, The Queen should play his kingship *Becket, Pro.* 235
They *s* that you are wise in winged things, „ I i 255
We are friends no more : he will *s* that, not I. „ I i 345
I have heard him *s* He means no more ; „ I iii 192
S that a cleric murder'd an archbishop, „ I iii 399
What did the traitor *s* ? „ I iii 471
Tell what I *s* to the King. „ I iii 564
What *s* the bishops ? „ I iii 589
S that he blind thee and tear out thy tongue. „ I iii 615
Wilt thou not *s*, ' God bless you,' ere we go ? „ I iv 33
Call them in, I *s*. „ I iv 85
and they do *s* the very breath catches. „ I iv 222
And I *s*, I care not for thy saying. (repeat) „ II i 111
I almost fear to *s* That my poor heretic heart „ II i 282
I *s* that those Who went before us „ II ii 201
All that you *s* is just. I cannot answer it „ III i 1
and so brought me no-hows as I may *s*, „ III i 130
people do *s* that his is bad beyond all reckoning, and—— *Rosamund.* The people lie. „ III i 174
that is to *s* in her time when she had the ' Crown.' „ III i 197
S all thy say, But blaze not out before the Frenchmen „ III iii 219
but I *s* no more . . . farewell, my lord. „ III iii 271

Say (verb) (*continued*) base as—who shall I *s*—Fitzurse and his following— *Becket* III iii 308
False figure, Map would *s*. „ III iii 347
she *s's* she can make you sleep o' nights. „ IV ii 19
They *s* that walls have ears ; „ IV ii 79
there are those Who *s* you do not love him— „ IV ii 97
See, I can *s* no more. *Eleanor.* Will you not *s* you are not married to him ? *Rosamund.* Ay, Madam, I can *s* it, if you will. „ IV ii 107
And what would my own Aquitaine *s* to that ? „ V i 182
York will *s* anything. What is he saying now ? „ V ii 5
What *s* ye there of Becket ? „ V ii 56
They *s* that Rome Sprang from a wolf. *The Cup* I ii 12
Do not *s* so. I know of no such wives „ I ii 190
I have much to *s*, no time to *s* it in. „ I ii 207
Not *s* as much ? I all but said as much. „ I ii 281
I *s* it to you—you are wiser—Rome knows all, „ I ii 285
What did that villain Synorix *s* to you ? „ I ii 336
What did he *s* ? *Camma.* What *should* he *s* ? *Sinnatus.* What *should* he *s*, „ I ii 345
He should *s* this, that being Tetrarch once „ I ii 349
What should he *s* ? He should *s* nothing „ I ii 365
Lady, I *s* it with all gentleness, „ I iii 99
How dare she *s* it ? I could hate her for it „ II 177
some old Greek *S* death was the chief good ? „ II 515
Call him back and *s* I come to breakfast with him. *The Falcon* 212
for when I *s* What can I do— „ 238
How long since do you *s* ? „ 372
How can your lordship *s* so ? „ 508
I did not *s*, my lord, that it was so ; „ 544
shall we *s* this wreath and your sweet rhymes ? „ 734
And what did *you s* to that ? *Prom. of May* I 142
And what did he *s* to that ? „ I 151
thaw I *s's* it mysen, niver men 'ed a better master— „ I 326
Shall I *s* it ?—fly with me to-day. „ I 678
Didn't I *s* that we had forgiven you ? „ III 75
S that the sick lady thanks him ! „ III 348
but he *s's* he wants to tell ye summut „ III 354
some will *s* because I have inherited my Uncle. „ III 596
I *s* to it, Thou art mine, and it answers, *Foresters* I i 335
What did he *s* to thee ? „ I ii 254
Do you doubt me when I *s* she loves me, man ? „ II i 520
Speak to me, Kate, and *s* you pardon me ! „ II ii 53
Leave them each what they *s* is theirs, „ III 294
Out on it, I *s*, as out of tune and time ! „ IV 34
S it again, And by this ring the lips „ IV 69
What did I *s* ? Nay, my tongue tript— „ IV 498

Saying (part.) (*See also* **Saäyin**) I cannot catch what Father Bourne is *s*. *Queen Mary* I iii 15
What wast thou *s* of this Lady Jane, „ I v 37
This Howard, whom they fear, what was he *s* ? „ III vi 55
hear that you are *s* behind his back what you see you are *s* afore his face ? *The Falcon* 106

Saying (s) It is a *s* among the Catholics. *Queen Mary* V v 244
I have heard a *s* of thy father Godwin, *Harold* III i 111
And I say, I care not for thy *s*. (repeat) *Becket* II i 112
No *s* of mine—Jocelyn of Salisbury. „ II ii 372
slopes Of Solomon-shaming flowers—that was your *s*, „ III i 49
I heard a *s* in Egypt, that ambition Is like the sea wave, *The Cup* I iii 137
you know the *s*—' Better a man without riches, *The Falcon* 750
A noble *s*—and acted on would yield A nobler breed „ 753

Sayst Why (*smiling*), no, indeed. *Mary.* *S* thou ? *Queen Mary* I v 335

Scaäred (scared) I be a bit deaf, and I wur hallus *s* by a big word ; *Prom. of May* III 33

Scabbard Down *s*, and out sword ! *Queen Mary* II i 143

Scaffold on the *s* Recanted, and resold himself to Rome. „ III i 151
She came upon the *s*, „ III i 376
You'll hear of me again. *Bagenhall.* Upon the *s*. „ III i 475

Scald And felt the sun of Antioch *s* our mail, *Becket* II ii 93

Scale (for weighing) always in suspense, like the *s*, *Becket* II ii 363
But lest we turn the *s* of courtesy *Harold* II ii 164

Scale (of a fish) my fellows know that I am all one *s* like a fish. *Becket* I iv 213

Scandal My flight were such a *s* to the faith, *Queen Mary* I ii 53
I'll have the *s* sounded to the mud. I know it a *s*. *Gardiner*. All my hope is now It may be found a *s*. „ I v 227
Scandalous but I am small and *s*, „ v ii 428
Scant I had *s* time to do him in. *The Falcon* 556
Scape (escape) flies To right and left, and cannot *s* the flame. *Harold* I i 12
Knave, hast thou let thy prisoner *s*? „ II ii 673
Pray God, we '*s* the sunstroke. *Queen Mary* III v 279
let him bury her Even in the bowels of the earth to '*s* The glance of John— *Foresters* III 463
Scaped (escaped) Archbishop Robert hardly *s* with life. *Harold* II ii 527
Scape-goat A sacrifice to Harold, a peace-offering, A *s-g* marriage— „ I ii 204
Scar To hide the *s* left by thy Parthian dart. *Becket, Pro.* 377
mine own, a grief To show the *s* for ever— „ I i 178
Scarboro' Castle Hath taken *S C*, north of York; *Queen Mary* V i 287
Scare old enough To *s* me into dreaming, „ IV ii 103
We thought to *s* this minion of the King *Becket* IV ii 330
Ye think to *s* me from my loyalty „ V ii 481
and speak small to 'em, and not *s* 'em, *Foresters* I i 101
make a ghostly wail ever and anon to *s* 'em. „ II i 216
that *s's* The Baron at the torture of his churls, „ III 105
Scarecrow no such *s* in your father's time. *Queen Mary* I v 473
We be more like *s's* in a field than decent serving men; *Foresters* I i 34
Scared (*See also* **Scaäred**) Mumbling and mixing up in his *s* prayers Heaven and earth's Maries; *Queen Mary* II ii 86
And *s* the gray old porter and his wife. „ II iii 16
S by the Church— *Harold* III ii 87
That *s* the dying conscience of the king, „ V i 211
Too *s*—so young! *Becket* II i 67
King at last is fairly *s* by this cloud—this interdict. „ III iii 63
have I *s* the red rose from your face Into your heart? „ IV ii 73
And he was *s* and slew it. *Foresters* II ii 99
We be *s* with song and shout. „ II ii 164
Scarlet (a companion of Robin Hood) *S*, hath not the Earl right? *Foresters* I ii 41
You, *S*, you are always moody here. „ I iii 128
Then, *S*, thou at least wilt go with me. „ I iii 144
I remember, *S* hacking down A hollow ash, „ II ii 95
I Little John, he Much the miller's son, and he *S*, „ III 55
he, young *S*, and he, old Much, and all the rest of us. „ III 60
Friend *S*, art thou less a man than Much? „ III 65
Then let her pass as an exception, *S*. „ III 72
S told me—is it true?— „ III 145
S, begin. „ III 423
Give me thy hand, Much; I love thee. At him, *S*! „ IV 311
You, good friar, You Much, you *S*, you dear Little John, „ IV 1083
Scarlet (adj.) *S*, as if her feet were wash'd in blood, *Queen Mary* III i 61
The *s* thread of Rahab saved her life; „ III ii 38
Scatter Saints to *s* sparks of plague Thro' all your cities, *Harold* II ii 745
S thy people home, descend the hill, „ V i 10
Winnow and *s* all scruples to the wind, *Becket* I i 150
I *s* all their cowls to all the hells. „ II i 93
To break our band and *s* us to the winds. *Foresters* III 453
Scatterbrains For Robin is no *s* like Richard, „ IV 355
Scatter'd (*See also* **Loosely-scatter'd**) Were *s* to the harvest . . . *Harold* IV iii 211
Smite the shepherd and the sheep are *s*. *Becket* I iv 227
Who dragg'd the *s* limbs into their den. *Queen Mary* I v 401
My people are all *s* I know not where. *Foresters* II i 176
Scattering To help the realm from *s*. *Harold* IV i 106
The crowd are *s*, let us move away! *Becket* III iii 357
Scelera Illorum *s* Pœna sequatur! (repeat) *Harold* V i 517, 604
Scene —not dead now—a swoon—a *s*— *Prom. of May* III 697
Scent (s) You saw my hounds True to the *s*; *The Cup* I ii 111
Scent (verb) I *s* it in the green leaves of the wood. *Foresters* IV 944
Sceptre His *s* shall go forth from Ind to Ind! *Queen Mary* III ii 177
unsubject to One earthly *s*. *Becket* I iii 681
S and crozier clashing, and the mitre „ II i 25
had I fathered him I had given him more of the rod than the *s*. „ III iii 111
bulrush now in this right hand For *s*, *Foresters* III 77
Scheme You *s* against her father's weal and hers, „ IV 481
Schism and grief For our long *s* and disobedience, *Queen Mary* III iii 129
Grace to repent and sorrow for their *s*; „ III iii 178
All *s*, and from all and every censure, „ III iii 217
so the plague Of *s* spreads; „ III iv 172
make Our island-Church a *s* from Christendom, *Becket* I iii 116
Scholar (*See also* **Scholard**) Right as an Oxford *s*, *Foresters* I i 59
Scholard (scholar) how can tha keep all thy *s's* i' horder? *Prom. of May* I 198
thaw I beänt naw *s*, fur I 'ednt naw time to maäke mysen a *s* „ I 332
School I was just out of *s*, I had no mother— „ I 706
afoor she went to *s* at Littlechester— „ II 19
Them be what they larns the childer' at *s*, „ III 40
School-boy More like a *s-b* that hath broken bounds, *Queen Mary* I v 170
School'd a Tudor *S* by the shadow of death— „ V v 226
Schoolin-time but I were burn afoor *s-t*. *Prom. of May* III 40
Schoolmaster *S*! Why if Steer han't haxed *s* to dinner, thaw 'e knaws I was hallus ageän heving *s* i' the parish! „ I 184
An' thou doänt understan' it neither—and thou *s* an' all. „ I 239
Noä, fur thou be nobbut *s*; „ I 308
but the *s* looked to the paying you your wages when I was away, „ III 23
Schoolmen The Canonists and *S* were with me. *Queen Mary* I ii 61
Schoolmistress Wasn't Miss Vavasour, our *s* at Littlechester, *Prom. of May* III 298
Science I had some smattering of *s* then, „ II 301
and *s* now could drug and balm us Back into nescience „ II 339
Scindatur Illorum, Domine, Scutum *s*! *Harold* V i 509
Scion whether her Grace incline to this splendid *s* of Plantagenet. *Queen Mary* I i 135
Scizzars (Cæsar, name of horse) *S* an' Pumpy was good uns to goä (repeat) *Prom. of May* II 308, 318
Sconce I will break thy *s* with my quarterstaff. *Foresters* I ii 75
Scope yield Full *s* to persons rascal and forlorn, *Queen Mary* II ii 185
Scorch heat enough To *s* and wither heresy to the root. „ III iv 28
Score (*See also* **Three-score**) There goes a musical *s* along with them, *The Falcon* 452
How many of you are there? *Publius*. Some half a *s*. *The Cup* I iii 13
Half a *s* of them, all directed to me— *Prom. of May* II 721
Scorn (s) He never yet could brook the note of *s*. *Becket* V ii 300
S! I hate *s*. A soul with no religion— *Prom. of May* III 531
Scorn (verb) dost thou *s* me, Because I had my Canterbury pallium, *Harold* III i 105
Fool and wise, I fear This curse, and *s* it. „ III ii 68
Madam, you do ill to *s* wedded love. *Becket, Pro.* 353
Church must *s* herself whose fearful Priest „ I ii 64
Not *s* him for the foibles of his youth. „ V ii 328
s's The noblest-natured man alive, *The Falcon* 258
Scorn'd His foes would blame him, and I *s* 'em, *Queen Mary* I v 624
tho' some of you Have *s* me— *Harold* I i 188
have *s* the man, Or lash'd his rascal back, „ II ii 506
s her too much To harm her. *Becket* IV ii 392
Scorning divorced King Louis, *S* his monkery,— „ IV ii 419
Scory (Bishop) Poinet, Barlow, Bale, *S*, Coverdale; *Queen Mary* I ii 7
Scotland Mary of *S*,—for I have not own'd My sister, „ I v 284
To make the crown of *S* one with ours, „ I v 287
but your king stole her a babe from *S* „ I v 292
Mary of *S*, married to your Dauphin, „ I v 295
he would weld France, England, *S*, „ V i 137
—*S*, Ireland, Iceland, Orkney, *Harold* III ii 124
'I go to fight in *S* With many a savage clan;' *Foresters* I i 14
Scots (Mary, Queen of) (*See also* **Mary of Scotland**) She stands between you and the Queen of *S*. *Mary*. The Queen of *S* at least is Catholic. *Queen Mary* V i 193
The Queen of *S* is married to the Dauphin, „ V v 52
Scottish your *S* namesake marrying The Dauphin, „ V i 134
Scoundrel Trusted than trust—the *s*— „ II ii 39
Who shook the Norman *s's* off the throne, *Harold* IV i 81
Scourge (s) they call me now, The *s* and butcher *Queen Mary* V ii 106
Yon grimly-glaring, treble-brandish'd *s* Of England! *Harold* I i 4
lied like a lad That dreads the pendent *s*, „ II ii 658
If fast and prayer, the lacerating *s*— *Becket* I iii 304

Scourge (verb) Threaten the child; 'I'll *s* you if you did it:' *Queen Mary* III v 126
Fast, *s* thyself, and mortify thy flesh, *Becket* I iii 539
once I wish'd to *s* them to the bones. *The Cup* I i 27
Scourging In *s's*, macerations, mortifyings, Fasts, *Becket* V i 41
Horrible! flaying, *s*, crucifying— *The Cup* I ii 235
Scout Our *s's* have heard the tinkle of their bells. *Harold* V i 220
Scouted I am glad that France hath *s* him at last: *Becket* II ii 252
Scowl A smile abroad is oft a *s* at home. *Queen Mary* III i 213
Scowl'd *S* that world-hated and world-hating beast, „ II ii 90
Scrape (s) less loyalty in it than the backward *s* of the clown's heel— *Becket* III iii 143
Scrape (verb) Sir Richard must *s* and *s* till he get to the land again. *Foresters* I i 78
Scraped I *S* from your finger-points the holy oil; *Queen Mary* IV ii 132
Scraps make Thy slender meal out of those *s* and shreds *The Falcon* 146
Scratch'd And, being *s*, returns to his true rose, *Becket* III i 249
Scratching *See* **A-scrattin**
Scream the *s* of some wild woodland thing. *Foresters* II i 252
Scream'd *S* as you did for water. *Queen Mary* III v 58
Scrimp Do not *s* your phrase, „ III iii 259
Scriptur' as long as the man sarved for 'is sweet'art i' *S*. *Prom. of May* II 63
Scripture (adj.) It's the old *S* text, 'Let us eat and drink, „ I 258
Scripture (s) (*See also* **Scriptur'**) wholesome *s*, 'Little children Love one another.' *Queen Mary* III iv 84
Did you find a *s*, 'I come not to bring peace „ III iv 87
Scritch-owl Anger the *s-o*. *Mercenary*. But, my lord, the *s-o* bodes death, my lord. *Foresters* II i 331
Scroll But then what's here? King Harry with a *s*. *Queen Mary* III i 261
What's here? a *s* Pinned to the wreath. *The Falcon* 424
a written *s* That seems to run in rhymings. „ 431
Scruple and I fear One *s*, this or that way, *Queen Mary* II ii 100
Winnow and scatter all *s's* to the wind, *Becket* I i 150
Scruplest And *s* not to flaunt it to our face *Foresters* IV 887
Sculptor as a *s* clay, To their own model. *Queen Mary* III iii 33
Scum the psalm-singing weavers, cobblers, *s*— „ III iv 290
s And offal of the city would not change Estates „ IV iii 76
men, the *s* and offal of the Church; *Becket* I iii 408
Scurrilous May plaister his clean name with *s* rhymes! „ I i 309
Scurrying the *s* of a rat Affrighted me, *Queen Mary* III v 143
Scutage Church should pay her *s* like the lords. *Becket* I i 34
Scuttle *S* his cockle-shell? *Harold* IV iii 142
Scutum Illorum, Domine, *S* scindatur! „ V i 509
Scythe Your havings wasted by the *s* and spade— *Queen Mary* II ii 276
Sea (*See also* **Mid-sea,**) I spy the rock beneath the smiling *s*. „ I iv 279
Mine is the fleet and all the power at *s*— „ I iv 288
God lay the waves and strow the storms at *s*, „ I v 382
When they will sweep her from the *s's*. „ III i 162
Our voyage by *s* was all but miracle; „ III ii 25
And here the river flowing from the *s*, „ III ii 26
offal thrown Into the blind *s* of forgetfulness. „ III iii 193
dallying over *s's* Even when his brother's, „ III iv 293
So they have sent poor Courtenay over *s*. „ III v 2
I am sicker staying here Than any *s* could make me passing hence, Tho' I be ever deadly sick at *s*. „ III vi 87
and the French fleet Rule in the narrow *s's*. „ V i 7
Sending an insolent shot that dash'd the *s's* Upon us, „ V i 58
must lower his flag To that of England in the *s's* „ V i 66
A voice of shipwreck on a shoreless *s*! „ V ii 384
Spain would be England on her *s's*, and England Mistress of the Indies. „ V iii 72
I had heard of him in battle over *s's*, „ V v 33
Beyond the *s's*—a change! *Harold* I i 104
and hunt and hawk beyond the *s's*! „ I i 230
s shall roll me back To tumble at thy feet. „ I ii 114
The *s* may roll Sand, shingle, shore-weed, „ I ii 117
there is a post from over *s's* With news for thee. „ II ii 209
I'll hack my way to the *s*. „ II ii 312
Our Duke is all between thee and the *s*, „ II ii 315
God and the *s* have given thee to our hands— „ II ii 548
a lake, A *s* of blood—we are drown'd in blood— „ III i 398
dumb'd his carrion croak From the gray *s* for ever. „ IV iii 67
Sea (*continued*) send the shatter'd North again to *s*, *Harold* IV iii 141
I send my voice across the narrow *s's*— „ V i 246
Till the *s* wash her level with her shores, „ V i 331
The sign in heaven—the sudden blast at *s*— „ V i 379
Follow them, follow them, drive them to the *s*! „ V i 603
No man without my leave shall cross the *s's* *Becket, Pro.* 35
I mean to cross the *s* to France, „ I iii 124
Wilt not be suffer'd so to cross the *s's* „ I iii 129
Love that is born of the deep coming up with the sun from the *s*. (repeat) „ II i 10, 20
for any rough *s* Blown by the breath of kings. „ II ii 107
Shall the waste voice of the bond-breaking *s* „ V ii 359
bays And havens filling with a blissful *s*. *The Cup* II 236
runs to *s* and makes it Foam over all the fleeted wealth „ II 287
The sky? or the *s* on a blue day? *Prom. of May* I 101
myself Would guide you thro' the forest to the *s*. *Foresters* II i 639
light of the *s's* by the moon's long-silvering ray! „ II ii 178
Were plunged beneath the waters of the *s*, „ IV 669
Sea-bird Nor mark the *s-b* rouse himself and hover Above the windy ripple, *Harold* II ii 334
Sea-creek the *s-c*—the petty rill That falls into it— *Becket* II ii 293
Seal (s) Let the Great *S* be sent Back to the King to-morrow. „ I i 374
O thou Great *S* of England, Given me by my dear friend „ I i 336
Send the Great *S* by daybreak. „ I i 405
Thy sending back the Great *S* madden'd him, „ I iii 9
Flung the Great *S* of England in my face— „ I iii 456
Seal (verb) except he *s* his faith In sight of all *Queen Mary* IV iii 28
My lord Archbishop, thou hast yet to *s*. *Becket* I iii 306
S? If a seraph shouted from the sun, And bad me *s* „ I iii 311
I will not *s*. „ I iii 315
He would not *s*. „ I iii 319
the man shall *s*, Or I will *s* his doom. „ I iii 330
And thou art perjured, and thou wilt not *s*. „ I iii 527
Sign? *s*? I promised The King to obey these customs, „ I iii 555
will *s* Love's truth On those sweet lips *Foresters* IV 73
Sea-laughter and fill the sky With free *s-l*— *Harold* II ii 337
Seal'd Sign'd and not *s*! How's that? *Becket* I iii 318
Seaman Perhaps; but we have *seamen*. *Queen Mary* V iii 84
Sea-marks they should hang Cliff-gibbeted for *s-m*; *Harold* II i 97
Sea-mew our *s-m* Winging their only wail! „ II i 97
Sear Thine 'ifs' will *s* thine eyes out—ay. „ II ii 626
Search *S* them, Little John. *Foresters* III 201
S this other. „ III 207
S them, Kate, and see if they have spoken truth. „ III 288
s him then. How much hast thou about thee? „ IV 163
S me then. I should be hard beset with thy fourscore. „ IV 178
Search'd But how then if I will not bide to be *s*? „ IV 169
Searching He miss the *s* flame of purgatory, *Becket* V iii 13
Sea-saw The miserable *s-s* of our child-world, *Queen Mary* IV iii 385
Sea-shore lay them both upon the waste *s-s* At Hastings, *Harold* V ii 159
Sea-sick so should all the love-sick be *s-s*. *Foresters* IV 673
Season not in tune, a nightingale out of *s*; *Becket, Pro.* 350
Seat (*See also* **Jugdment-seat**) This dress was made me as the Earl of Devon To take my *s* in; *Queen Mary* I iv 74
Throw cushions on that *s*, and make it throne-like. „ V ii 536
Seated Were *s* sadly at a fountain side, *The Falcon* 610
Sea-will-o'-the-wisp Wicked *s-w-o'-t-w*! *Harold* II i 20
Second let me call her our *s* Virgin Mary, *Queen Mary* I iii 57
The *s* Prince of Peace— „ III ii 164
Should play the *s* actor in this pageant That brings him in; „ III iii 13
Or a *s* fire, Like that which lately crackled underfoot „ III v 52
first In Council, *s* person in the realm, „ IV iii 72
and the *s* curse Descend upon thine head, *Harold* III ii 47
Who made the *s* mitre play the first, And acted me? *Becket* III iii 212
This is the *s* grain of good counsel I ever proffered thee, „ III iii 317
and I Became his *s* father: „ V ii 336
I have no fears at this my *s* marriage. *The Cup* II 209
It seem'd so; only there was left A *s* daughter, *Prom. of May* III 772
Second-sight Or some strange *s-s*, the marriage cup *The Cup* II 198
Second-sighted Your *s-s* man That scared the dying *Harold* V i 210
Secrecy bound me by his love to *s* Till his own time. *Becket* III i 228
Secret (adj.) And fearing for her, sent a *s* missive, *Queen Mary* II ii 121
And if you be not *s* in this matter, „ V i 271
I have built a *s* bower in England, Thomas, *Becket, Pro.* 153

Secret (adj.) (*continued*) We take her from her *s* bower in Anjou And pass her to her *s* bower in England. — *Becket Pro.* 181
that *s* matter which would heat the King against thee — „ *Pro.* 487
To pass thee to thy *s* bower to-morrow. — „ I i 249
The *s* whisper of the Holy Father. — „ I iii 236
And that old priest whom John of Salisbury trusted Hath sent another. *Henry.* *S*? — „ III i 72
Henry. *S*, then? — „ III i 82
Know you not this bower is *s*, — „ IV ii 22
Found out her *s* bower and murder'd her. — „ V i 175

Secret (s) (*See also* **State-secret**) some *s* that may cost Philip his life. — *Queen Mary* III i 201
That is my *s*, Thomas. *Becket.* State *s's* should be patent to the statesman — *Becket, Pro.* 75
—there lies the *s* of her whereabouts, — „ *Pro.* 430
I do not then charm this *s* out of our loyal Thomas, — „ *Pro.* 466
Thine enemy knows the *s* of my bower. — „ II i 265
Is our *s* ours? Have you had any alarm? — „ III i 27
John of Salisbury committed The *s* of the bower, — „ III iii 6
This is no *s*, but a public matter. — „ V ii 319
That is my *s*: keep it, or you sell me — *The Cup* I ii 214
We never kept a *s* from each other; — *Prom. of May* I 552
I have done wrong in keeping your *s*; — „ III 399

Sect Their 'dies Illa,' which will test their *s*. — *Queen Mary* III iv 428
worthy Bonner,—To test their *s*. — „ III iv 431

Sectaries dishonour'd even in the sight Of thine own *s*— — „ V v 134

Secular A *s* kingdom is but as the body Lacking a soul; and in itself a beast. The Holy Father in a *s* kingdom Is as the soul descending out of heaven Into a body generate. — „ IV i 32
he was deliver'd To the *s* arm to burn; — „ IV ii 214
I have been a lover of wines, and delicate meats, And *s* splendours, — *Becket* I i 78
You have had the better of us In *s* matters. — „ II ii 81

Secured if our person be *s* From traitor stabs— — *Queen Mary* V v 280

Security Ay, ay, but what *s*, — „ III iii 81

Sederunt S *principes, ederunt pauperes.* — *Becket* I iv 131

See (a bishoprick) And from the Apostolic *s* of Rome; — *Queen Mary* III iii 127
by your intercession May from the Apostolic *s* obtain, — „ III iii 147
obedience Unto the holy *s* and reigning Pope — „ III iii 158
our Bishops from their *s's* Or fled, — „ I ii 4
From all the vacant *s's* and abbacies, — *Becket* I iii 652
That hold our Saltwood Castle from our *s*! — „ II ii 270

See (verb) fear, I *s* you, Dear friend, for the last time; — *Queen Mary* I ii 102
my Lord; I *s* you in the Tower again. — „ I iv 80
S that you neither hear them nor repeat! — „ I v 576
To tell you what indeed ye *s* and know, — „ II ii 144
And *s* the citizens arm'd. Good day; — „ II ii 378
if he *s* the man and still will jeer, — „ II ii 402
I could *s* that as the new-made couple — „ III i 93
Bagenhall, I *s* The Tudor green and white. — „ III i 179
S there be others that can use their hands. — „ III i 243
Did you *s* her die? — „ III i 344
No, cousin, happy—Happy to *s* you; — „ III ii 87
Ay; but *s* here! *First Page.* *S* what? — „ III ii 215
pray Heaven That you may *s* according to our sight. — „ III iv 331
You cannot *s* the Queen. Renard denied her, — „ III vi 1
My Lords, you cannot *s* her Majesty. — „ III vi 19
Can I not *s* him? *Renard.* Not now. — „ III vi 35
farewell; Until I *s* you in St. Mary's Church. — „ IV ii 47
You have not gone to *s* the burning? — „ IV iii 290
I could *s* that many silent hands Came from the crowd — „ IV iii 582
Not to *s* me? *Philip.* Ay, Madam, to *s* you. — „ V i 118
Count de Feria waits without, In hopes to *s* your Highness. — „ V ii 401
She neither *s's* nor hears, — „ V ii 404
Our Clarence there *S's* ever such an aureole — „ V ii 413
Sin is too dull to *s* beyond himself. — „ V ii 441
they *s* not what the general *s's*, A risk of utter ruin. — „ V ii 447
throat of mine, Barer than I should wish a man to *s* it,— — „ V ii 462
I will *s* no man hence for evermore, — „ V ii 525
I may die Before I read it. Let me *s* him at once. — „ V ii 550

See (verb) (*continued*) Then I may say your Grace will *s* your sister? — *Queen Mary* V ii 604
You *s* the lodging, sir, — „ V iii 23
That she would *s* your Grace before she—died. — „ V iii 104
Nay, dearest Lady, *s* your good physician. — „ V v 59
your royal sister comes to *s* you. *Mary.* I will not *s* her. — „ V v 192
I will *s* none except the priest. Your arm. — „ V v 196
For all the world *s's* it as well as England. — *Harold* I i 129
I *s* the flashing of the gates of pearl— — „ I i 186
s Deeper into the mysteries of heaven — „ I i 199
S's he into thine, That thou wouldst have — „ I i 202
S here—an interwoven H and E! — „ I ii 57
thou shalt *s* My grayhounds fleeting — „ I ii 128
I *s* the goal and half the way to it.— — „ I ii 196
We be fishermen; I came to *s* after my nets. — „ II i 27
He came not to *s* me, had past me by To hunt — „ II ii 27
He *s's* me not—and yet he dreams of me. — „ II ii 144
And *s* thee shipt, and pray in thy behalf — „ II ii 197
I Shall *s* the dewy kiss of dawn no more — „ II ii 331
I *s* the blackness of my dungeon loom — „ II ii 405
s confusion fall On thee and on thine house. — „ II ii 489
S here this little key about my neck! — „ III i 10
to *s* my solemn vow Accomplish'd. — „ III i 306
join our hands before the hosts, That all may *s*. — „ IV i 243
cannot *s* the world but thro' their wines! — „ IV iii 225
S him out safe! (repeat) — „ V i 84, 93
S all be sound and whole. — „ V i 194
I *s* it in thine. And not on thee— — „ V i 369
Stigand will *s* thee safe, And so—Farewell. — „ V i 418
And *s* thee safe from Senlac. — „ V i 457
I can *s* it From where we stand: — „ V i 462
I *s* the gonfanon of Holy Peter — „ V i 549
and *s* beyond Your Norman shrines, — „ V i 618
Our Harold—we shall never *s* him more. — „ V ii 3
Take them away, I do not love to *s* them. — „ V ii 142
s my bishop Hath brought your king to a standstill. — *Becket, Pro.* 42
Ay! blood, perchance, except thou *s* to her. — „ *Pro.* 176
Ay, ay, but swear to *s* to her in England. — „ *Pro.* 190
longed much to *s* your Grace and the Chancellor ere he past, — „ *Pro.* 399
you could not *s* the King for the kinglings. — „ *Pro.* 452
I can *s* further into a man than our hot-headed Henry, — „ *Pro.* 462
I stand and *s* The rift that runs between me — „ I i 139
herself should *s* That kings are faithful — „ I ii 77
He will not *s* thy face till thou hast sign'd — „ I iii 5
I *s* it, I *s* it. — „ I iii 297
Foliot, let me *s* what I have sign'd. — „ I iii 307
To *s* the proud Archbishop mutilated. — „ I iii 614
and *s* it mounting to Heaven, my God bless you, — „ I iv 37
s here, my lord, this rag fro' the gangrene i' my leg. — „ I iv 236
My brave-hearted Rose! Hath he ever been to *s* thee? — „ II i 288
S if our pious—what shall I call him, John?— — „ II ii 38
How should you *s* this rightly? — „ II ii 98
now I *s* That I was blind—suffer the phrase— — „ II ii 437
Bird mustn't tell, Whoop—he can *s*. (repeat) — „ III i 107, 256
I *s* it—some confusion, Some strange mistake. — „ III i 233
S here! *Herbert.* What's here? — „ III iii 1
Do you *s*, my lord, There is the King — „ III iii 21
Do you *s* that great black cloud — „ III iii 45
And *s* you yon side-beam that is forced from under it, — „ III iii 49
Ay, but some one comes to *s* her now and then. — „ IV i 16
we shall *s* the silk here and there, and I want my supper. — „ IV i 56
S, I can say no more. — „ IV ii 107
what uncomely faces, could he *s* you! — „ V i 201
I told him I was bound to *s* the Archbishop; — „ V ii 100
You *s* they have been revelling, and I fear — „ V ii 421
Who are with him? I *s* no face that knows me. — *The Cup* I i 183
Had you then No Message with the cup? *Camma.* Why, yes, *s* here. — „ I ii 69
a brave one Which you shall *s* to-morrow. — „ I ii 432
S, *s*, my white bird stepping toward the snare. — „ I iii 35
who has been So oft to *s* the Priestess, — „ II 11
Are you so sure? I pray you wait and *s*. — „ II 107
S here—I stretch my hand out—hold it there. — „ II 210

See (verb) *(continued)* I am glad I shall not *s* it. *The Cup* II 513
Beneath an ever-rising sun—I *s* him— „ II 535
s, why she turns down the path through our little vineyard, *The Falcon* 167
I *s* you quite recover'd of your wound. „ 391
I *s* There goes a musical score along with them, „ 451
S, my lady! *Giovanna.* I *s*, Filippo! „ 654
and *s* that all be right and reg'lar fur 'em afoor he coöm. *Prom. of May* I 168
S that you do not do so again! „ II 24
And wheniver 'e *s's* two sweet'arts togither like thou and me, Sally, „ II 163
Which told us we should never *s* her more— „ II 477
Letters! Yeas, I *s's* now. „ III 38
Ye *s's* the holler laäne be hallus so dark i' the arternoon, „ III 92
I cannot and I will not *s* anybody. „ III 340
may drop off any day, any hour. You must *s* him at once. „ III 408
Tell him that I and the lady here wish to *s* him. You *s* she is lamed, „ III 415
It puts me in heart Again to *s* you; „ III 503
I *s* it all now. O she has fainted. „ III 670
you *s* her there! Only fifteen when first you came on her, „ III 749
There, there! You *s* I was right. *Foresters* I i 114
She doesn't *s* me. Shall I be bold? „ I i 124
I could *s* her for a moment Glide like a light „ II i 157
You *s*, they are so fond o' their own voices „ II i 382
I will not brook to *s* Three upon two. „ II i 423
S whether there be more of 'em in the wood. „ II i 430
Thou wilt not *s* My Marian more. „ II i 455
S, thou hast wrong'd my brother and myself. „ II i 665
S then, I kneel once more to be forgiven. „ II i 667
Thou *s* me clasp and kiss a man indeed, „ II ii 76
that he may *s* The fashion of it. „ IV 253
left mine horse and armour with a Squire, And I must *s* to 'em. „ IV 416
You *s* he is past himself. What would you more? „ IV 471
S you not They are jesting at us yonder, „ IV 675
S thou thwart me not, thou fool! „ IV 744

Seeäms (seems) *S* I ommost knaws the back on 'im— *Prom. of May* II 577

Seed (s) 'Martyr's blood—*s* of the Church.' *Queen Mary* IV i 146
sow'd therein The *s* of Hate, it blossom'd Charity. „ IV i 172
The *s* thou sowest in thy field is cursed, *Harold* V i 70

Seed (saw) I *s* that one cow 'o thine i' the pinfold *Prom. of May* I 190
I *s* tha a-limpin' up just now wi' the roomatics i' the knee. „ I 384
I *s* how the owd man wur vext. „ II 27
I knaw'd 'im when I *s* 'im ageän „ III 121

Seed (seen) Noä, Miss. I ha'n't *s* 'er neither. „ I 48

Seeing (part.) *s* that our gracious Virgin Queen hath— *Queen Mary* I iii 23
if he jeer not *s* the true man Behind his folly, „ II ii 400
S there lie two ways to every end, „ III iv 113
s now The poor so many, and all food so dear. „ IV iii 208
And, *s* in a moment, I shall find Heaven „ IV iii 223
religious fool, Who, *s* war in heaven, *Harold* I i 140
and *s* the hospitable lights in your castle, *Foresters* I ii 194

Seeing (s) Grew ever high and higher, beyond my *s*, *Harold* III i 149
and rooted in far isles Beyond my *s*: „ III i 154
keep us From *s* all too near that urn, *The Cup* I iii 133

Seek *s* In that lone house, to practise on my life, *Queen Mary* I iv 283
You play at hide and *s*. „ I v 305
We but *s* Some settled ground for peace „ I v 314
S to possess our person, hold our Tower, „ II ii 158
s's To bend the laws to his own will, „ II ii 183
Or *s* to rescue me. I thank the Council. „ IV ii 38
I am not vext,—Altho' ye *s* to vex me, *Harold* I i 405
wherefore should she *s* The life of Rosamund de Clifford *Becket, Pro.* 69
where to *s*? I have been about the city. „ I i 397
when they *s* to overturn our rights, „ V ii 456
They *s*—you make—occasion for your death. „ V ii 558
I am he ye *s*. What would ye have of me? „ V iii 115
S not for me, or you may find me at the bottom of the river.— *Prom. of May* II 87
why did you write '*S* me at the bottom of the river'? *Prom. of May* III 363
Because we *s* to curb their viciousness. *Foresters* III 393

Seeking By *s* justice at a stranger's hand *Queen Mary* IV i 20
I am *s* one who wedded me in secret. *Harold* V ii 29
I tell thee, girl, I am *s* my dead Harold. „ V ii 43
pale beggar-woman *s* alms For her sick son, *The Falcon* 852

Seem (*See also* **Seeäms**) it *s's* that we shall fly These bald, blank fields, *Queen Mary* III v 250
even now You *s* the least assassin of the four. *Becket* V ii 522

Seem'd *S* thro' that dim dilated world of hers, *Queen Mary* II ii 324
s to smile And sparkle like our fortune „ II iii 22
S as a happy miracle to make glide— „ III ii 29
it *s* to me but just The Church should pay *Becket* I i 33
It *s* to me that we were parted for ever. *Prom. of May* I 769
It *s* so; only there was left A second daughter, „ III 770

Seeming *s* not as brethren, But mortal foes! *Queen Mary* IV iii 184
As *s* his, not mine, and fall abroad. *Becket, Pro.* 228

Seen (*See also* **Seed**) I have *s* enough for this day. *Queen Mary* I i 130
should already have *s* your steps a mile „ I ii 80
do not you Be *s* in corners with my Lord of Devon. „ I iv 154
and yet, methinks, I have *s* goodlier. „ I v 7
Have you *s* Philip ever? *Noailles.* Only once. „ I v 319
I have *s* them in their own land; „ II i 167
I have never *s* her So queenly or so goodly. „ II ii 326
flask of wine Beside me, than have *s* it: yet I saw it. „ III i 48
track of the true faith Your lapses are far *s*. „ III iv 95
I have *s* A pine in Italy that cast its shadow „ III iv 135
when she once more is *s* White as the light, „ III iv 198
Brief-sighted tho' they be, I have *s* them, „ III vi 158
never *s* That any one recanting thus at full, „ IV i 58
It will be *s* now, then. „ IV i 62
Have I not *s* the gamekeeper, the groom, „ IV iii 371
I have *s* heretics of the poorer sort, „ IV iii 436
old age that never will be mine Is all the clearer *s*. „ V ii 236
s the true men of Christ lying famine-dead by scores, „ V iv 37
Thou hast but *s* how Norman hands can strike, *Harold* II ii 171
I dare not well be *s* in talk with thee. „ II ii 481
Edward wakes!—Dazed—he hath *s* a vision. „ III i 131
hath talk'd with God, and *s* A shadowing horror; „ III i 356
Nor *s*, nor heard; thine, „ V i 161
I have *s* The trenches dug, the palisades uprear'd „ V i 188
No footfall—no Fitzurse. We have *s* her home. *Becket* I i 367
The world had never *s* the like before. „ II ii 125
and I ha' *s* what I ha' *s*, (repeat) *Becket* III i 109, 143, 151
and to be sure I ha' *s* great ones to-day— *Becket* III i 136
and I ha' *s* the King once at Oxford, „ III i 163
she had *s* the Archbishop once, So mild, so kind. „ V ii 118
S by the Church in Heaven, the Church on earth— „ V iii 98
S in the thicket at the bottom there *The Cup* I i 113
—all *s*,—all calculated, All known by Rome. „ I ii 255
It may be I had never *s* the wars. *The Falcon* 379
I have *s* it like the snow on the moraine. „ 505
and *s* the red of the battle-field, „ 548
I haven't *s* Eva yet. Is she anywhere in the garden? *Prom. of May* I 46
I can't tell, for I have never *s* him. „ I 115
She would have *s* at once into my trouble, „ I 553
if you Had *s* us that wild morning when we found „ II 469
—had you been one of us And *s* all this, „ II 484
I have *s* the world—And cheer his blindness „ II 513
since then, no one has *s* you but myself. „ III 228
I have *s* thee clasp and kiss a man indeed, *Foresters* IV 1035

See-saw The miserable *s-s* of our child-world, *Queen Mary* IV iii 385

Seest when thou *s* him next, Commend me to thy friend. *Becket* I I 323
Thou *s*, Sir Knight, our friar is so holy *Foresters* IV 279

Seethed She *s* with such adulteries, *Queen Mary* III iv 189

Seize that anyone Should *s* our person, „ II ii 178
To *s* upon the forts and fleet, „ III i 464
S him and burn him for a Lutheran. „ V ii 245
Stumble not in the darkness, Lest they should *s* thee. *Becket* V iii 80
We shall be overwhelm'd. *S* him and carry him! „ V iii 141
I give you here an order To *s* upon him. *The Cup* I i 165
'You are to *s* on Sinnatus,—if——' „ I ii 228

Seize (*continued*) to *s* On whomsover may be talking with you, *The Cup* I iii 6
For *my* sake—or they *s* on thee. „ I iii 113
Why come we now? Whom shall we *s* upon? „ I iii 178
S on the knight? wrench his sword from him! *Foresters* II i 676
S him and truss him up, and carry her off. „ IV 690
S her and carry her off into my castle. „ IV 738
Seized may not be *s* With some fierce passion, *Prom. of May* II 335
he hath *s* On half the royal castles. *Foresters* I iii 82
Self The Queen stands up, and speaks for her own *s*; *Queen Mary* II ii 342
his fault So thoroughly to believe in his own *s*. „ II ii 386
Yet thoroughly to believe in one's own *s*, So one's own *s* be thorough, „ II ii 388
the Pope's Holiness By mine own *s*. „ III ii 112
As well for our own *selves* as all the realm, „ III iii 136
and not sure Of their own *selves*, they are wroth with their own *selves*, „ III iv 120
Bonner cannot out-Bonner his own *s*— „ III vi 27
By mine own *s*—by mine own hand! „ IV ii 202
and mine own *s* and all the world. „ V ii 12
but I speak from mine own *s*, not him; „ V iii 42
—yea and mine own *s*. *Harold* II ii 784
Tho' somewhat less a king to my true *s* „ III ii 53
where mine own *s* Takes part against myself! „ V i 299
what shall I call it, affect her thine own *s*. *Becket, Pro.* 513
Look to it, your own *selves*! „ I iii 398
Strong—not in mine own *s*, but Heaven; „ I iii 537
Who stands aghast at her eternal *s* „ II ii 404
on mine own *s* The King had had no power „ II ii 411
kingly promise given To our own *s* of pardon, „ II ii 433
'great honour,' says he, 'from the King's *s* to the King's son.' „ III iii 145
I am mine own *s* Of and belonging to the King. „ IV ii 29
I'll swear to mine own *s* it was a feint. „ IV ii 401
The soldier, when he lets his whole *s* go Lost in the common good, the common wrong, Strikes truest ev'n for his own *s*. „ V ii 39
Then speak; this is my other *s*, „ V ii 74
as beautiful this morning as the very Madonna her own *s*— *The Falcon* 199
And this last costly gift to mine own *s*, „ 228
Vice and Virtue Are but two masks of *s*; *Prom. of May* I 538
I have found it once again In your own *s*. „ II 377
—so be more at peace With mine own *s*. „ II 663
till we be only bones our own *selves*. *Foresters* I i 26
I remain Mistress of mine own *s* and mine own soul. „ IV 729
Self-assertion than to stand On naked *s-a*. *Queen Mary* IV i 120
Self-blotted he is effaced, *S-b* out; „ IV i 138
Self-disdain for a spark Of *s-d* born in me when I sware *Harold* V i 302
Self-exposure Why will you court it By *s-e*? *Becket* I i 282
Self-lauding Without too large *s-l* I must hold *Harold* IV iii 87
Selfless The simple, silent, *s* man Is worth a world of tonguesters. „ V i 81
Self-murder lying were *s-m* by that state „ III i 70
Self-passion drown all poor *s-p* in the sense Of public good? *The Cup* II 101
Self-stock Of one *s-s* at first, Make them again *Harold* V ii 186
Self-uncertain and yet We are *s-u* creatures, *Becket* V ii 48
Sell *s* not thou Our living passion for a dead man's dream; *Harold* III ii 58
keep it, or you *s* me To torment and to death. *The Cup* I ii 214
We shall have to *s* all the land, *Prom. of May* III 164
And so wouldst *s* thy sister to the Sheriff, *Foresters* II i 536
'*S* all thou hast and give it to the poor;' „ III 169
S me again perchance for twice as much. „ IV 654
Seller but I bound the *s* To silence, *The Falcon* 73
Semi-barbarous altho' the inhabitants Seem *s-b*. *Prom. of May* II 542
Semi-madman known a *s-m* in my time So fancy-ridd'n) *Queen Mary* II i 9
Senate Our *S*, wearied of their tetrarchies, *The Cup* I i 89
What filthy tools our *S* works with! „ I i 156
Save for some slight report in her own *S* „ I ii 134
Roman *S*, For I have always play'd into their hands, „ I iii 149
tell the *S* I have been most true to Rome— „ II 482
Send God *s* her well; Here comes her Royal Grace. *Queen Mary* II ii 125
s's His careful dog to bring them to the fold. „ III iv 104
S out: let England as of old Rise lionlike, „ V ii 265
Send (*continued*) *S* out, *s* out, and make Musters in all the counties; *Queen Mary* V ii 270
S out; I am too weak to stir abroad: „ V ii 286
he *s's* his veriest love, And says, he will come quickly. „ V ii 563
and to *s* us again, according to His promise, „ V iv 52
s thee back among thine island mists With laughter. *Harold* II ii 181
s her hosts Of injured Saints to scatter sparks „ II ii 743
and *s* thy saints that I may say Ev'n to their faces, „ II ii 785
And *s* the shatter'd North again to sea, „ IV iii 140
I *s* my voice across the narrow seas— „ V i 246
The Norman *s's* his arrows up to Heaven, „ V i 666
I *s* thee as a common friend To tell the King, *Becket* I i 341
S the Great Seal by daybreak. „ I i 405
S for him back. „ I iii 334
he *s's* me to bid you this night pray for him „ I iv 265
can I *s* her hence Without his kingly leave? „ III i 218
And *s* thee back again to Canterbury? „ III iii 184
S back again those exiles of my kin „ III iii 186
Have I not promised, man, to *s* them back? „ III iii 191
She *s's* it back, as being dead to earth, „ V i 170
and *s* Her whole heart's heat into it, „ V ii 254
s's you this cup rescued from the burning *The Cup* I i 41
I *s* it to the wife of Sinnatus, „ I i 72
—*s's* you this cup—the cup we use in our marriages— „ I ii 72
He *s's* you This diadem of the first Galatian Queen, „ II 131
and *s* him forth The glory of his father— „ II 261
in hope that the saints would *s* us this blessed morning; *The Falcon* 186
I might *s* you down a flask or two „ 584
if the farming-men be come for their wages, to *s* them up to me. *Prom. of May* III 16
Sending Lord Howard, *S* an insolent shot that dash'd *Queen Mary* V i 57
Thy *s* back the Great Seal madden'd him, *Becket* I iii 9
Seneschal and confer with her ladyship's *s*, *The Falcon* 416
Senlac (adj.) signs on earth! Knowest thou *S* hill? *Harold* III i 361
tell him we stand arm'd on *S* Hill, „ V i 59
To tell thee thou shalt die on *S* hill— „ V i 241
Senlac (s) over nameless graves— *Harold.* At *S*? *Aldred.* *S*. „ III i 383
S! Sanguelac, The Lake of Blood! „ III i 385
And see thee safe from *S*. „ V i 457
Sens (a French town) Return to *S*, where we will care for you. *Becket* II ii 444
Sensation all but proving man An automatic series of *s's*, *Prom. of May* I 226
What can a man, then, live for but *s's*, „ I 242
if man be only A willy-nilly current of *s's*— „ I 263
Sense thro' his dying *s* Shrills 'lost thro' thee.' *Harold* III i 34
Which in your *s* is treason. *The Cup* I i 79
for the *s's*, love, are for the world; That for the *s's*. *Prom. of May* I 580
Sensual and sat Thro' every *s* course of that full feast „ II 254
Sent I stood out, till Edward *s* for me. *Queen Mary* I ii 29
hath *s* for the holy legate of the holy father „ I iii 26
God hath *s* me here To take such order „ I v 33
You have *s* her from the court, „ I v 462
S out my letters, call'd my friends together, „ I v 552
S Cornwallis and Hastings to the traitor, „ II ii 31
And fearing for her, *s* a secret missive, „ II ii 121
But we *s* divers of our Council to them, „ II ii 152
s his myriads hither To seize upon the forts „ III i 463
which the emperor *s* us Were mainly Gardiner's: „ III iii 70
s here as Legate From our most Holy Father „ III iii 124
You were *s* for, You were appeal'd to, „ III iv 255
I am *s* to fetch you. „ III iv 393
So they have *s* poor Courtenay over sea. „ III v 1
But held from you all papers *s* by Rome, „ V ii 45
And how should he have *s* me Legatic hither, „ V ii 87
this young Earl was *s* on foreign travel, „ V ii 489
and have *s* him back A holy gonfanon, *Harold* III ii 146
And Edward would have *s* a host against you, „ IV i 99
Since Griffyth's head was *s* To Edward, „ IV i 221
Have thy two brethren *s* their forces in? „ V i 342
arrow which the Saints Sharpen'd and *s* against him— „ V ii 169
Let the Great Seal be *s* Back to the King to-morrow. *Becket* I i 375
s his folk, His kin, all his belongings, „ II i 69
priest whom John of Salisbury trusted Hath *s* another. „ III i 71

Sent (*continued*) I *s* this Margery, and she comes not back;
I *s* another, and she comes not back. *Becket* IV ii 3
A strange gift *s* to me to-day. *The Cup* I ii 52
know myself am that Galatian Who *s* the cup. „ I ii 210
The Romans *s* me here a spy upon you, „ I ii 220
I might have *s* him prisoner to Rome. „ II 418
and he *s* me wi' the gig to Littlechester to fetch 'er; *Prom. of May* I 19
cotched 'im once a-steälin' coäls an' I *s* fur 'im, „ I 413
and he *s* 'im awaäy to t'other end o' the field; „ II 153
but he *s* me an alphabetical list of those that remain, „ III 28
What hasta *s* fur me, then, fur? „ III 435
I have *s* to the Abbot and justiciary *Foresters* IV 87
I had despair'd of thee—that *s* me crazed, „ IV 1022
Sentence The *s* having past upon them all, *Queen Mary* I v 487
Hear first thy *s*! *Becket* I iii 670
Sequatur Illorum scelera Pœna *s*! (repeat) *Harold* V i 518, 605
Sequel The *s* had been other than his league With Norway, „ IV iii 88
Seraph If a *s* shouted from the sun, *Becket* I iii 311
Serf All those poor *s's* whom we have served will bless us, *Foresters* IV 1074
Series all but proving man An automatic *s* of sensations, *Prom. of May* I 226
Serious Stafford, I am a sad man and a *s*. *Queen Mary* III i 42
Serjeant *See* **Drill-serjeant**
Serpent *s* that hath slough'd will slough again. *Queen Mary* III iii 18
Tut, then we all are *s's*. „ III iii 21
Let her eat it like the *s*, *Becket, Pro.* 533
s that had crept into the garden And coil'd himself *Foresters* II i 136
Servant these old-world *s's* Are all but flesh and blood *The Falcon* 708
Serve (*See also* **Sarve**) it *s's* to fan A kindled fire. *Queen Mary* I v 620
make Those that we come to *s* our sharpest foes? „ II iii 77
S God and both your Majesties. „ III iii 159
Yet to save Cranmer were to *s* the Church, „ IV i 136
but I am not sure She will not *s* me better— „ V i 250
May *s* to charm the tiger out of him. *Harold* I i 153
thunder moulded in high heaven To *s* the Norman purpose, „ II ii 34
Let Harold *s* for Tostig! *Queen.* Harold served Tostig so ill, he cannot *s* for Tostig! „ III i 160
sight of Danish blood Might *s* an end not English— „ IV iii 98
my foundation For men who *s* the neighbour, „ V i 98
to the statesman Who *s's* and loves his king, *Becket, Pro.* 78
I am his no more, and I must *s* the Church. „ I i 145
S my best friend and make him my worst foe; „ I iii 567
Then there isn't a goodly wench to *s* him with it: „ I iv 159
tongue lick him whole again To *s* your will? „ II ii 26
wriggle out of them like an eel When the time *s's*. „ II ii 188
we make the time, we keep the time, ay, and we *s* the time; „ II ii 368
Well—I shall *s* Galatia taking it, *The Cup* I i 100
S by force? No force Could make me *s* by force. „ I ii 79
Then that I *s* with Rome to *s* Galatia. „ I ii 212
my serving Rome To *s* Galatia: „ I ii 279
I am much malign'd. I thought to *s* Galatia. *Sinnatus.* *S* thyself first, villain! They shall not harm „ I ii 324
Well used, they *s* us well. „ I iii 136
one piece of earthenware to *s* the salad in to my lady, *The Falcon* 481
servants Are all but flesh and blood with those they *s*. „ 710
I ha' served the King living, says she, and let me *s* him dead, *Foresters* II i 311
and *s* King Richard save thou be A traitor or a goose? „ IV 351
Served (*See also* **Sarved, Well-served**) I hoped I had *s* God with all my might! *Queen Mary* V ii 296
if you be fairly *s*, And lodged, and treated. „ V iii 21
For I have *s* thee long and honestly. *Harold* I i 214
Harold *s* Tostig so ill, he cannot serve for Tostig! „ III i 161
No, no, but Harold. I love him: he hath *s* me: „ III i 242
I *s* our Theobald well when I was with him; *Becket* I i 142
I *s* King Henry well as Chancellor; „ I i 144
in your chancellorship you *s* The follies of the King. „ I ii 30
Thou hast *s* me heretofore with Rome— „ II ii 460
Heaven be *s* Tho' earth's last earthquake „ V iii 40
It *s* me for a blessed rosary. *The Falcon* 632
Hath *s* me better than her living— „ 901
I ha' *s* the King living, says she, and let me serve him dead, *Foresters* II i 310
those poor serfs whom we have *s* will bless us, „ IV 1075
Service (I have a daughter in her *s* who reported it) *Queen Mary* I i 76
This chains me to your *s*, „ I v 537
Twelve years of *s*! *Harold* I i 221
My lord, permit us then to leave thy *s*. *Becket* I iv 10
told me he would advance me to the *s* of a great lady, „ III i 123
which our loyal *s*, And since we likewise „ V i 53
For all his faithful *s's* to Rome. *The Cup* II 65
then there is anything in your lordship's larder at your lordship's *s*, *The Falcon* 138
cold-manner'd friend may strangely do us The truest *s*, „ 644
I sank so low that I went into *s*— *Prom. of May* III 392
wasted his revenues in the *s* of our good king Richard *Foresters* I i 193
All thanks for all your *s*; „ I iii 165
Do me the *s* to tap it, and thou wilt know. „ III 333
I would tap myself in thy *s*, Robin. „ III 336
And both at thy *s*, Robin. „ III 339
Serviceable so she be *s* In all obedience, *Harold* III i 291
Serving (**adj. and part.**) We be more like scarecrows in a field than decent *s* men; *Foresters* I i 35
'A Galatian *s* by force in the Roman Legion.' *The Cup* I i 47
'A Galatian *s* by force in the Roman Legion.' *S* by force! „ I ii 75
Serving (**s**) my *s* Rome To serve Galatia: „ I ii 277
Servitor King would act *s* and hand a dish to his son; *Becket* III iii 139
Session Your Council is in *S*, please your Majesty. *Queen Mary* I v 543
Set (**s**) I know a *s* of exiles over there, „ III i 155
Set (**sit**) they wunt *s* i' the Lord's cheer o' that daay. „ IV iii 470
Set (**verb**) was a wheedling monk *S* up the mass. „ I ii 91
s yourselves by hundreds against one? „ I iii 72
Yearns to *s* foot upon your island shore. „ I v 367
s it round with gold, with pearl, with diamond. „ I v 375
I'll have my head *s* higher in the state; „ II i 250
Few things have fail'd to which I *s* my will. „ II ii 22
s no foot theretoward unadvised Of all our Privy Council; „ II ii 204
I am not so *s* on wedlock as to choose „ II ii 214
I must *s* The guard at Ludgate. „ II ii 408
you'll *s* the Divil's Tower a-spitting, „ II iii 102
cry To have the gates *s* wide again, „ II iv 65
They are the flower of England; *s* the gates wide. „ II iv 70
S up a viceroy, sent his myriads hither To seize „ III i 463
So to *s* forth this humble suit of ours „ III iii 145
Like dogs that *s* to watch their master's gate, „ III iv 309
Would fain *s* forth some saying that may live „ IV iii 158
For there be writings I have *s* abroad „ IV iii 240
Crying, 'Forward!'—*s* our old church rocking, „ IV iii 403
s up your broken images; Be comfortable to me. „ V ii 300
and *s* up The Holy office here— „ V v 112
thy leave to *s* my feet On board, *Harold* I i 228
a sun *s* But leaving light enough for Alfgar's house „ I i 306
and *s* her up again, till now, „ II i 50
And over thee the suns arise and *s*, „ II ii 433
sunder'd tree again, and *s* it Straight on the trunk, „ III i 145
S forth our golden Dragon, „ IV i 245
shall cross the seas To *s* the Pope against me— *Becket, Pro.* 36
will *s* it trembling Only to base it deeper. „ *Pro.* 208
To *s* that precious jewel, Roger of York. „ *Pro.* 270
True enough, my mind was *s* upon other matters. „ *Pro.* 318
Has my simple song *s* you jingling? „ *Pro.* 378
He took his mitre off, and *s* it on me, „ I i 63
S all on fire against him! „ I ii 89
Strike, and ye *s* these customs by my death „ I iii 170
Fight for the Church, and *s* the Church against me! *Herbert.* To be honest is to *s* all knaves against thee. „ I iii 569
s the Church This day between the hammer and the anvil— „ I iii 584
Poor beast! poor beast! *s* him down. „ I iv 106
Lord hath *s* his mark upon him that no man should murder him. „ I iv 192
I brought them In from the wood, and *s* them here. „ II i 131
and *s's* the church-tower over there all a-hell-fire as it were? „ III iii 51
Give me the poison; *s* me free of him! „ IV ii 164

Set (verb) (*continued*) To *s* them straight again. *Becket* V ii 459
Not *s* myself abroach And run my mind *The Cup* I ii 106
Would *s* him in the front rank of the fight „ I ii 153
And that *s's* her against me—for the moment. „ I iii 163
tho' Rome may *s* A free foot where she will, „ II 245
it is thou Hath *s* me this hard task, *The Falcon* 237
S, as you say, so lightly on her head, „ 535
I had but emptiness to *s* before you, „ 870
But now you will *s* all right again, *Prom. of May* I 718
she *s* the bush by my dairy winder afoor „ II 18
Come, you will *s* all right again, „ II 658
I be afeard I shall *s* him a-sweäring like onythink. „ III 359
I would *s* my men-at-arms to oppose thee, like the Lord of the Castle. *Foresters* I i 322
whenever I *s* my own foot on it I say to it, „ I i 334
mantle of the cloud, And *s's*, a naked fire. „ II i 29
a price is *s* On this poor head; „ II i 73
Well, *s* them forth. I could eat anything. „ II i 273
you are sturdy rogues that should be *s* to work. „ III 197
See that men be *s* Along the glades „ III 456
Set *See* **High-set**
Setting slander'd you For *s* up a mass at Canterbury „ I ii 88
gave me this morning on my *s* forth. *Foresters* III 282
Settle now would *s* Upon this flower, *Queen Mary* I iv 55
in the eternal distance To *s* on the Truth. *Harold* III ii 103
Settled We but seek Some *s* ground for peace to stand upon. *Queen Mary* I v 315
pass Into more *s* hatred of the doctrines Of those who rule, „ III iv 159
but you will stay your going Somewhat beyond your *s* purpose? „ V i 207
Seven (*See also* **Twenty-seven**) Some six or *s* Bishops, diamonds, pearls, „ III i 52
Not for the *s* devils to enter in? „ III ii 140
The *s* sleepers in the cave at Ephesus Have turn'd from right to left. *Harold* I i 192
S feet of English land, or something more, Seeing he is a giant. „ IV ii 54
'*S* feet of English earth, or something more, Seeing he is a giant!' „ IV iii 112
My lord, the King demands *s* hundred marks, *Becket* I iii 634
I led *s* hundred knights and fought his wars. „ I iii 638
Forgive him seventy times and *s*; *Prom. of May* III 9
Seven-fold weak and meek old man, *S-f* dishonour'd *Queen Mary* V v 133
Seventeen *S*—and knew eight languages— „ III i 358
S—a rose of grace! „ III i 371
Seventh Lo! there once more—this is the *s* night! *Harold* I i 2
only she kept the *s* commandment better than some I know on, *Becket* III i 194
Seventy Forgive him *s* times and seven; *Prom. of May* III 9
Seven-years' My *s-y* friend was with me, my young boy; *Queen Mary* III iii 47
Several In *s* bills and declarations, Madam, „ IV i 48
Sever'd long divided in itself, and *s* from the faith, „ I iii 21
My arm is *s*. I can no more— *Becket* V iii 188
Severeness An overmuch *s*, I repeat, *Queen Mary* III iv 156
Sew these poor hands but *s*, Spin, broider— *Harold* IV iii 10
Sewer (sure) Ay, to be *s*! Be thou? *Prom. of May* I 3
but *s* I be, they be two o' the purtiest gels ye can see of a summer murnin'. „ I 29
and I feel *s*, Miss Dora, that I ha' been noän too sudden wi' you, „ II 59
I be Farmer Dobson, *s* anew; „ II 136
I beänt sa *s* o' that, fur Sally knaw'd im; Now then? „ III 146
Sewer In breathless dungeons over steaming *s's*, *Queen Mary* IV iii 441
Sewn if I hadn't a sprig o' wickentree *s* into my dress, *Foresters* II i 250
Shaäky (shaky) The weather's well anew, but the glass be a bit *s*. *Prom. of May* II 52
Shaämed (ashamed) Then the owd man i' Lear should be *s* of hissen, „ I 267
Shackle The *s's* that will bind me to the wall. *Harold* II ii 410
Shadder (shadow) then back ageän, a-follering my oän *s*— *Prom. of May* I 372
Shade moon Divides the whole long street with light and *s*. *Becket* I i 366

Shadow (*See also* **Shadder**) Is to be love-sick for a *s*. *Queen Mary* I v 535
pine in Italy that cast its *s* Athwart a cataract; firm stood the pine—The cataract shook the *s*. „ III iv 136
It was the *s* of the Church that trembled; Your church was but the *s* of a church, „ III iv 144
And how her *s* crosses one by one „ V v 7
a Tudor School'd by the *s* of death— „ V v 226
s's of a hundred fat dead deer For dead men's ghosts. *Harold* I ii 103
dog that snapt the *s*, dropt the bone.— „ I ii 188
be as the *s* of a cloud Crossing your light. „ II ii 177
That lies within the *s* of the chance. „ II ii 463
And dreadful *s's* strove upon the hill, „ III i 377
And on it falls the *s* of the priest; „ III ii 70
Yet if a fear, Or *s* of a fear, „ V i 115
Surely too young Even for this *s* of a crown; *Becket, Pro.* 231
That were but as the *s* of an assent. „ I iii 195
cloud that hath come over the sun and cast us all into *s*? „ III iii 47
Your *s*. Synorix— *The Cup* I ii 450
and enrich Earth with her *s*! „ I iii 60
Tell him there is one *s* among the *s's*, „ II 139
Beneath the *s* of our pines and planes! „ II 227
We lie too deep down in the *s* here. *The Falcon* 581
but they, the *s's* of ourselves, Have past for ever. *Prom. of May* I 271
would she moved beside me like my *s*! *Foresters* II i 165
O look! before the *s* of these dark oaks „ II i 604
A *s*, a poetical fiction— „ IV 219
Shadowing hath talk'd with God, and seen A *s* horror; *Harold* III i 357
And *s* of this double thunder-cloud „ III ii 159
Shaft He drew this *s* against me to the head, *Queen Mary* V ii 80
Parthian *s* of a forlorn Cupid at the King's left breast, *Becket, Pro.* 339
Shake Our friends, the Normans, holp to *s* his chair. *Harold* I i 85
to *s* the North With earthquake and disruption— „ I ii 198
Come, Harold, *s* the cloud off! „ III i 73
that would *s* the Papacy as it stands. *Becket* I iii 213
When what ye *s* at doth but seem to fly, „ I iii 743
s's at mortal kings—her vacillation, Avarice, craft— „ II ii 405
To *s* my throne, to push into my chamber— „ V i 249
That this brave heart of mine should *s* me so, *The Cup* I iii 39
the very letters seem to *s* With cold, *The Falcon* 448
I do not dare it, like an old friend, to *s* it. *Prom. of May* II 527
Shaken When he hath *s* off the Emperor, *Becket* I iii 244
dead Are *s* from their stillness in the grave *Foresters* II i 46
Shaker A *s* and confounder of the realm; *Queen Mary* IV iii 40
Shakest thou *s*! Here, here—a cup of wine— *Foresters* I iii 88
Shaking (*See also* **A-shaäkin', Head-shaking**) by thy wisdom Hast kept it firm from *s*; *Becket, Pro.* 204
Shaky *See* **Shaäky**
Shallow There runs a *s* brook across our field For twenty miles, *Queen Mary* V v 83
But thou hast drain'd them *s* by thy tolls, *Harold* I i 319
Shambles-oak or the *s-o*, or a weasel-sucked egg, *Foresters* IV 211
Shame (s) Nay, for bare *s* of inconsistency, *Queen Mary* I ii 39
S, *s*, my masters! are you English-born, „ I iii 69
A gracious guard Truly; *s* on them! „ II iv 58
S upon you, Robin, *S* upon you now! „ III v 85
And bring us all to *s*? *Becket* I iii 38
S, wrath, I know not what. „ I iii 322
and the more *s* to him after his promise, „ III i 130
Will feel no *s* to give themselves the lie. *The Cup* II 117
S on her that she took it at thy hands, *The Falcon* 60
it's all you have left us. *S* on you! „ 163
S on her then! „ 206
I scarce believe it! *Elisabetta*. *S* upon her then! „ 518
I shall go mad for utter *s* and die. *Prom. of May* I 682
Will he not fly from you if he learn the story of my *s* „ III 257
Five years of *s* and suffering broke the heart „ III 761
John—*S* on him!—Stole on her, *Foresters* II i 111
S on thee, Little John, thou hast forgotten— „ III 237
Shame (verb) Nor *s* to call it nature. *Queen Mary* III v 77
no need For Philip so to *s* himself again. „ V ii 587
That would but *s* me, Rather than make me vain. *Harold* I ii 116
thought that naked Truth would *s* the Devil „ III i 118
I *s* to quote 'em—caught, my lord, *Becket* I ii 7
Shamed (*See also* **Half-shamed**) make me *s* and tongue-tied in my love. *Queen Mary* III ii 162

Shamed (*continued*) only *s* to the quick Before the king— *Harold* IV i 7
s of his poor farmer's daughter among the ladies in his drawing-room? *Prom. of May* III 294
S of me in a drawing-room! (repeat) „ III 296, 306
Sooner or later *s* of her among The ladies, „ III 581
But—*s* of you, my Empress! „ III 599
S a too trustful widow whom you heard In her confession; *Foresters* III 385
Shaming *See* **Solemn-shaming**
Shape (s) struck a *s* from out the vague, *Becket* I iii 373
my sleeping-draught May bloat thy beauty out of *s*, „ IV ii 170
What a *s*! what lovely arms! *Foresters* I i 108
Shape (verb) Statesmen that are wise *S* a necessity, *Queen Mary* III iii 33
stay Yet for awhile, to *s* and guide the event. „ V i 303
Love that can *s* or can shatter a life *Becket* II i 11
Shaped *See* **Well-shaped**
Share Come, come! thou hadst thy *s* on her. „ I iv 124
S and *s* alike! *Harold* II i 64
Shared and *s* His fruits and milk. Liar! *The Cup* I ii 427
Sharp stake and fire—*S* work and short. *Queen Mary* III i 329
Here—give me one *s* pinch upon the cheek *Foresters* IV 1011
Sharp-dividing battle-axe keen As thine own *s-d* justice, *Harold* V i 564
Sharpen'd Renard and the Chancellor *s* them. *Queen Mary* III i 5
arrow which the Saints *S* and sent against him— *Harold* V ii 169
Sharper A *s* harm to England and to Rome, Than Calais taken. *Queen Mary* V ii 29
Sharpest Shall we make Those that we come to serve our *s* foes? „ II iii 77
Shatter Will front their cry and *s* them into dust. „ II iv 5
No Norman horse Can *s* England, *Harold* V i 196
Love that can shape or can *s* a life *Becket* II i 11
God's full curse *S* you all to pieces „ V iii 135
Shatter'd or whether England Be *s* into fragments. *Harold* II ii 286
have we *s* back The hugest wave from Norseland „ IV iii 60
And send the *s* North again to sea, „ IV iii 140
Shaveling hear what the *s* has to say for himself. *Queen Mary* I iii 17
—and that, turncoat *s*! *Becket* I iii 737
Shaven beard, which he had never *s* Since Henry's death, *Queen Mary* IV iii 593
Shawl Indian *s* That Philip brought me in our happy days!— „ V ii 539
Sheath Take up your dagger; put it in the *s*. *Becket* IV ii 294
whose whole life hath been folded like a blossom in the *s*, *Foresters* I i 206
Sheathe *s* your swords, ye will displease the King. *Becket* I iii 178
Shed True tears that year were *s* for you in Florence. *The Falcon* 384
Sheep *S* at the gap which Gardiner takes, *Queen Mary* III iii 236
doth not kill The *s* that wander from his flock, „ III iv 103
inherited loathing of these black *s* of the Papacy. *Becket, Pro.* 461
But thou the shepherd hast betray'd the *s*, „ I iii 525
Swine, *s*, ox—here's a French supper. „ I iv 112
black *s* baaed to the miller's ewe-lamb, „ I iv 162
Black *s*, quoth she, too black a sin for me. And what said the black *s*, my masters? „ I iv 165
That he made the black *s* white. „ I iv 176
Out from among us; thou art our black *s*. „ I iv 181
S, said he? And *s* without the shepherd, too. „ I iv 182
Smite the shepherd and the *s* are scattered. Smite the *s* and the shepherd will excommunicate thee. „ I iv 227
that the *s* May feed in peace. „ III iii 345
To find my stray *s* back within the fold. „ III iii 355
Sheet And as for the flesh at table, a whole Peter's *s*, „ III iii 129
Sheeted when all the *s* dead Are shaken from their stillness in the grave *Foresters* II i 45
She-goat you had safelier have slain an archbishop than a *s-g*: *Becket* III iii 69
Shelf *Shelves* and hooks, *shelves* and hooks, and when I see the *shelves* *The Falcon* 119
Shell (*See also* **Cockle-shell**) she that has eaten the yolk is scarce like to swallow the *s*. „ 705
woodland squirrel sees the nut Behind the *s*, *Foresters* II i 648
I crawl'd like a sick crab from my old *s*, „ IV 127
Shelter (s) The *s* of *your* roof—not for one moment— *Prom. of May* III 800
Shelter (verb) We *s* you no more. *Becket* II ii 249
I will *s* here. *Foresters* II i 180
Shelter'd Ah! much heresy *S* in Calais. *Queen Mary* V ii 299
He *s* in the Abbey of Pontigny. *Becket* II i 84
I have *s* some that broke the forest laws. *Foresters* I iii 69
Shepherd re-pulpited The *s* of St. Peter, *Queen Mary* I v 182
the *s* doth not kill The sheep that wander „ III iv 101
The Good *S*! Take this, and render that. *Harold* III ii 169
But thou the *s* hast betray'd the sheep, *Becket* I iii 524
And sheep without the *s*, too. „ I iv 183
Smite the *s* and the sheep are scattered. Smite the sheep and the *s* will excommunicate thee. „ I iv 226
the wolves of England Must murder her one *s*, „ III iii 344
This mountain *s* never dream'd of Rome. *The Cup* I ii 17
our carters and our *s's* Still find a comfort there. *Harold.* Carters and *s's*! *Prom. of May* III 527
Sheriff Thou knowest that the *S* of Nottingham loves thee. *Marian.* The *S* dare to love me? *Foresters* I i 223
But then your *S*, your little man, „ I i 231
our little *S* will ever swim with the stream! „ I i 240
The *S* of Nottingham was there—not John. „ I i 252
Beware of John and the *S* of Nottingham. „ I i 255
What art thou, man? *S* of Nottingham? „ I ii 190
S, thy friend, this monk, is but a statue. „ I ii 233
How close the *S* peered into thine eyes! „ I ii 253
Did he say so, the *S*? „ I ii 267
I heard this *S* tell her he would pay „ I iii 5
after some slight speech about the *S* „ II i 115
the *S* Would pay this cursed mortgage to his brother „ II i 143
Most honourable *S*! „ II i 154
the *S*, and by heaven, Prince John himself „ II i 173
the *S* had taken all our goods for the King without paying, „ II i 190
since the *S* left me naught but an empty belly, „ II i 278
when the *S* took my little horse for the King without paying for it— „ II i 300
Missed! There goes another. Shoot, *S*! „ II i 397
Strike *S*! Strike, mercenary! „ II i 416
Prince John, the *S*, and a mercenary. „ II i 445
The *S*—I am grieved it was the *S*; „ II i 449
Rather than that would wed her with the *S*. „ II i 525
And so wouldst sell thy sister to the *S*, „ II i 537
That such a brother—*she* marry the *S*! „ II i 551
In that great heat to wed her to the *S* „ II i 585
Thou shalt not marry The *S*, but abide with me „ II i 602
Then you will wed the *S*? „ III 11
And this rich *S* too has come between us; „ IV 57
The *S*! This ring cries out against thee. „ IV 68
What wilt thou do with the *S*? „ IV 107
We told the Prince and the *S* of our coming. „ IV 576
we will hang *thee*, prince or no prince, *s* or no *s*. „ IV 584
The *S*! the *S*, follow'd by Prince John „ IV 587
But, Sir, the *S*— *Sir Richard.* Let me be, I say! The *S* will be welcome! „ IV 600
And then the *S*! *Marian.* Ay, the *S*, father, „ IV 650
I cannot love the *S*. „ IV 662
S, Who thought to buy your marrying me „ IV 717
S, thou wilt find me at Nottingham. „ IV 801
No, let him be. *S* of Nottingham, „ IV 815
Thou wouldst marry This *S* when King Richard came „ IV 862
If you would marry me with a traitor *s*, I fear I might prove traitor with the *s*. „ IV 871
Here Abbot, *S*—no—no, Robin Hood. „ IV 989
Sheriffship True, for through John I had my *s*. „ I ii 201
Sherwood (adj.) there is a lot of wild fellows in *S* Forest who hold by King Richard. „ I ii 73
In *S* Forest. I have heard of them. „ I iii 102
Sherwood (s) good fellows there in merry *S* That hold by Richard, „ I iii 99
To make this *S* Eden o'er again, „ II i 168
Tut! be there wolves in *S*? „ II i 512
Robin king of *S*, And loves and dotes „ IV 389
Robin, the lion of *S*— „ IV 392
All the birds in merry *S* sing and sing him home again. „ IV 1109
Shield (adj.) our *s* wall—Wall—break it not—break not—break— *Harold* V i 232
Shield (s) Noble as his young person and old *s*. *Queen Mary* V ii 513
No Norman horse Can shatter England, standing *s* by *s*; *Harold* V i 196

Shield (s) (*continued*) bit his *s*, and dash'd it on the ground, *Harold* V i 405
make their wall of *s's* Firm as thy cliffs, „ V i 479
The horse and horseman cannot meet the *s*, „ V i 592
Hot-headed fools—to burst the wall of *s's*! „ V i 613
Under the *s* and safeguard of the Pope, *Becket* I iii 600
See there our *s*. *Prom. of May* III 606
That I might breathe for a moment free of *s* *Foresters* IV 129
Shield-borne Their *s-b* patriot of the morning star *The Cup* II 121
Shielded You are doubly fenced and *s* sitting here *Queen Mary* III ii 104
And grateful to the hand that *s* him, *Harold* II ii 586
Shield-wall Let kith and kin stand close as our *s-w*, „ I i 399
Heard how the *s-w* rang, „ IV iii 159
Shift (s) a *s*, a trick Whereby to challenge, *Becket* II ii 163
Shift (verb) Will *s* the yoke and weight of all the world *Queen Mary* III vi 212
the currents So *s* and change, „ IV iii 409
there is barely room to *s* thy side, *Harold* II ii 441
The One Who *s's* his policy suffers something, *The Cup* II 113
Shifting for how their lances snap and shiver Against the *s* blaze of Harold's axe! *Harold* V i 587
Shine so the beams of both may *s* upon us, *Queen Mary* III iv 20
dance into the sun That *s's* on princes. „ III v 254
you want the sun That *s's* at court; „ III v 277
I *s*! What else, Sir Count? „ V iii 16
Our day beside the Derwent will not *s* Less than a star *Harold* IV iii 50
Could *s* away the darkness of that gap *Becket* III i 59
What are you crying for, when the sun *s's*? „ III i 270
Who never deign'd to *s* into my palace. *The Falcon* 285
how the sun 'ud *s*, and the larks 'ud sing *Prom. of May* I 373
Shingle sea may roll Sand, *s*, shore-weed, *Harold* I ii 119
Shining *See* **Ever-shining**
Ship Spain in our *s's*, in our forts, *Queen Mary* II i 179
Help the good *s*, showing the sunken rock, *Harold* II ii 100
A thousand *s's*—a hundred thousand men— „ IV iii 194
lest ye should draw together like two *s's* in a calm. *Becket* III iii 298
Shipt And see thee *s*, and pray in thy behalf *Harold* II ii 197
Shipwreck A voice of *s* on a shoreless sea! *Queen Mary* V ii 384
stormless *s* in the pools Of sullen slumber, *Harold* V i 296
Shipwreckt that the *s* are accursed of God;— „ II i 100
Shire is not the cause of a county or a *s*, *Queen Mary* II i 162
Shirt I wear beneath my dress A *s* of mail: „ I v 146
Shiver lances snap and *s* Against the shifting *Harold* V i 586
Shoal (*See also* **Herring-shoal**) No, but a *s* of wives upon the heath, „ V i 146
His Holiness cannot steer straight thro' *s's*, *Becket* II ii 59
Shock Not so dead, But that a *s* may rouse her. *Queen Mary* III i 30
To find one *s* upon the field when all The harvest has been carried. *The Falcon* 301
Shock'd Hath *s* me back into the daylight truth *Queen Mary* III v 135
Shoe (s) She wore red *s's*! *Stafford.* Red *s's*! „ III i 59
Shoe (verb) Blacksmith, thaw he niver *s's* a herse to my likings; *Prom. of May* I 448
Shone I *s* from him, for him, his glory, his Reflection: *Becket* I iii 664
Shook The cataract *s* the shadow. *Queen Mary* III iv 138
but Cranmer only *s* his head, „ IV iii 601
He *s* so that he scarce could out with it— *Harold* III i 368
Who *s* the Norman scoundrels off the throne, „ IV i 81
He sued my hand. I *s* at him. *Becket* I i 273
So *s* within my hand, that the red wine *The Cup* II 202
Shoot By the hard root, which *s's* again; *Becket* II ii 209
o'erleaps a jutting rock And *s's* three hundred feet. *The Cup* I i 111
and I'd like to *s* tha like a rabbit an' all. *Prom. of May* II 740
I can *s* almost as closely with the bow *Foresters* I i 216
that *s's* New buds to heaven, „ I iii 25
there goes one in the moonlight. *S*! *Prince John.* Missed! There goes another. *S*, Sheriff! „ II i 395
an old woman can *s* closer than you two. *Prince John.* *S* then, and if thou miss I will fasten thee „ II i 400
Did I not tell you an old woman could *s* better? „ II i 407
Shore (*See also* **Sea-shore**) Yearns to set foot upon your island *s*. *Queen Mary* I v 367
your *s's* Wore in mine eyes the green of Paradise. „ III ii 17
I dug mine into My old fast friend the *s*, *Harold* II i 7
Wolf of the *s*! dog, with thy lying lights „ II i 21
To shove that stranded iceberg off our *s's*, „ IV iii 139
Till the sea wash her level with her *s's*, „ V i 331

Shore (*continued*) like a barren *s* That grew salt weeds, *The Cup* II 231
There—league on league of ever-shining *s* „ II 534
Shoreless A voice of shipwreck on a *s* sea! *Queen Mary* V ii 384
Shore-swallow'd *s-s*, armour'd Normans up To fight *Harold* II ii 57
Shore-weed sea may roll Sand, shingle, *s-w*, „ I ii 119
Shorn (*See also* **Smooth-shorn**) lest the crown should be *S* of ancestral splendour. *Becket* I iii 157
Gave his *s* smile the lie. *Harold* II ii 226
Short stake and fire—Sharp work and *s*. *Queen Mary* III i 329
Hast not thou drawn the *s* straw? *Becket* I iv 3
Daughter, my time is *s*, I shall not do it. „ V ii 157
Then with one quick *s* stab—eternal peace. *The Cup* I iii 124
Short-lived Our *s-l* sun, before his winter plunge, *Queen Mary* III iii 85
Shot (s) practise on my life, By poison, fire, *s*, stab— „ I iv 285
insolent *s* that dash'd the seas Upon us, „ V i 57
Shot (verb) clash'd their bells, *S* off their lying cannon, „ III vi 97
s out sidelong boughs across the deep *Harold* III i 150
not life *s* up in blood, But death drawn in;— *Becket* IV ii 380
I have *s* her thro' the heart. *Kate.* He lies, my lord. I have *s him* thro' the heart. *Foresters* II i 97
That I had *s* him thro' the heart, „ II i 123
Turk *s* her as she was helping to build the mound „ II i 308
Shou'der (shoulder) and doänt laäy my cartwhip athurt 'is *s's*, *Prom. of May* II 138
Shoulder (*See also* **Shou'der**) If you can carry your head upon your *s's*. *Wyatt.* I fear you come to carry it off my *s's*, *Queen Mary* II i 90
over his bow'd *s* Scowl'd that world-hated „ II ii 89
and brush This Wyatt from our *s's*, „ II ii 294
That hovers round your *s*— „ V iii 52
and the weight of the church to boot on my *s's*, *Foresters* I ii 58
Shout (s) Came with a sudden splendour, *s*, and show, *Queen Mary* III i 449
s of Synorix and Camma sitting Upon one throne, *The Cup* II 146
But *s* and echo play'd into each other *Foresters* II i 258
We be scared with song and *s*. „ II ii 164
What *s's* are these that ring along the wood? „ IV 762
Shout (verb) *S*, knaves! *Queen Mary* I i 9
And get the swine to *s* Elizabeth. „ I iii 39
Who are those that *s* below there? „ II i 149
Stand staring at me! *s*, you gaping rogue! „ III i 288
There be both King and Queen, Philip and Mary. *S*! „ III i 297
S, then, Mary and Philip! „ III i 300
Thou hast shouted for thy pleasure, *s* for mine! „ III i 304
They *s* as they would have her for a queen. *Harold* IV i 26
S's something—he points onward— „ V i 558
Shouted (*See also* **Holla'd**) I have, my Lord, *s* till I am hoarse. *Gardiner.* What hast thou *s*, knave? *Queen Mary* III i 290
Thou hast *s* for thy pleasure, shout for mine! „ III i 304
But *s* in Queen Mary. „ III iv 46
If a seraph *s* from the sun, *Becket* I iii 311
Most like it was the Roman soldier *s*. *The Cup* II 120
We *s*, and *they s*, as I thought, *Foresters* II i 256
Shouting Then followed the thunder of the captains and the *s*, *Becket* III iii 113
Shove To *s* that stranded iceberg off our shores, *Harold* IV iii 138
Show (s) Came with a sudden splendour, shout, and *s*, *Queen Mary* III i 450
To stand at ease, and stare as at a *s*, „ IV iii 292
and to read the faces of men at a great *s*. *Becket* III iii 83
new-made children Of our imperial mother see the *s*. *The Cup* II 165
Show (verb) *S* me your faces! *Queen Mary* I v 307
Philip *s's* Some of the bearing of your blue blood— „ I v 433
So doubtless will ye *s* yourselves to me. „ II ii 175
a jest In time of danger *s's* the pulses even. „ II ii 357
I will *s* fire on my side— „ III i 327
They *s* their teeth upon it; „ V i 299
Too small! a comet would not *s* for that! *Harold* I i 475
S him by whom he hath sworn. „ II ii 732
mine own, a grief To *s* the scar for ever— *Becket* I i 178
hath he sign'd? *s* me the papers! „ I iii 317
And wake with it, and *s* it to all the Saints. „ II i 303
S me where thou camest out of the wood. „ IV i 45
May they not say you dared not *s* yourself „ V ii 595
If he should ever *s* his face among us, *Prom. of May* II 423
I would like to *s* you, Mistress Kate, *Foresters* I i 49

Show (verb) (*continued*) a tenderness toward me, but is too shy to *s* it. *Foresters* I i 116
bounden by a vow not to *s* his face, „ I ii 237
S me some cave or cabin where I may rest. „ II i 130
if thou wilt *s* us the way back to Nottingham. „ II i 360
But to *s* thou art mortal. „ II i 612
And *s* thyself more of a man than me. „ IV 285
Show'd *s* his back Before I read his face. *Queen Mary* II i 131
s her The weakness and the dissonance *The Cup* I i 22
Shower *s's* of blood are blown Before a never ending blast, *Harold* III i 393
storm and *s* lashing Her casement, *Prom. of May* II 471
Showing Help the good ship, *s* the sunken rock, *Harold* II ii 100
Shown and brief patience, As I have *s* to-day. *Queen Mary* III iv 415
I have but *s* a loathing face to you, „ III vi 113
Than you have *s* to Cranmer. „ IV i 190
have *s* And redden'd with his people's blood *Harold* I ii 242
Thou still hast *s* thy primate, Gilbert Foliot. *Becket* I iii 282
You have *s* me that, though fortune had born you *Prom. of May* II 119
Shrank you perforce again *S* into France. *Becket* II ii 88
Shreds make Thy slender meal out of those scraps and *s* *The Falcon* 147
Shrew Is broken ere it joins—a *s* to boot, *Becket* V ii 207
Shrewd I find you a *s* bargainer. *The Falcon* 757
But you will find me a *s* bargainer still. „ 774
And apt at arms and *s* in policy. *Foresters* I ii 104
Shriek And *s* to all the saints among the stars: *Becket* IV ii 239
Who *s's* by day at what she does by night, *Prom. of May* I 532
Shrill thro' his dying sense *S's* 'lost thro' thee.' *Harold* III i 35
Shrilling She *s* 'Wyatt,' while the boy she held *Queen Mary* II ii 72
Shrine Saints, I have rebuilt Your *s's*, „ V ii 300
as He dwells In statelier *s's*. *Harold* I i 168
From all the holiest *s's* in Normandy! „ II ii 735
and see beyond Your Norman *s's*, „ V i 620
rescued from the burning of one of her *s's* *The Cup* I i 42
cup saved from a blazing *s* Of our great Goddess, „ I ii 55
sacred *s* By chance was burnt along with it. „ I ii 65
take this holy cup To lodge it in the *s* of Artemis. „ I ii 435
To lodge this cup Within the holy *s* of Artemis „ I iii 53
part to the *s* of our Lady. *Foresters* III 207
Our Lady's blessed *s's* throughout the land „ IV 1079
Shrink And when he flash'd it *S* from me, *Becket* II i 277
Shrivell'd I, old *s* Stigand, I, Dry as an old wood-fungus on a dead tree, *Harold* III i 7
Shroud But after they had stript him to his *s*, *Queen Mary* IV iii 334
I'll have it with me in my *s*, *Becket* II i 302
Shudder causest the safe earth to *s* and gape, *The Cup* II 298
I mounted upon the parapet—— *Dora.* You make me *s*! *Prom. of May* III 373
Shun Who is he? let me *s* him. *Queen Mary* III ii 405
and now but *s's* The semblance of defeat; *Becket* I iii 190
s To meet her face to face at once! *The Cup* I i 58
Shut shame on them! they have *s* the gates! *Queen Mary* II iv 58
hath *s* the gates On friend and foe. „ II iv 61
One crater opens when another *s's*. „ III i 322
Have *s* you from our counsels. „ III iv 320
hath the door *S* on him by the father whom he loved, „ V ii 122
She to *s* up my blossom in the dark! *Harold* I ii 62
to *s* in A happier dream. „ I ii 126
S the hall-doors. *Becket* V ii 532
S the doors! We will not have him slain „ V iii 53
Was not the great gate *s*? „ V iii 138
Shut-up There were citizens Stood each before his *s-u* booth. *Queen Mary* II ii 63
Shy You are *s* and proud like Englishmen, „ II ii 257
a tenderness toward me, but is too *s* to show it. *Foresters* I i 116
Sicily the Netherlands, *S*, Naples, Lombardy. *Queen Mary* II i 212
Granada, Naples, *S*, and Milan,— „ V i 44
Sick (*See also* **Fancy-sick, Heart-sick, Love-sick, Sea-sick**) sent a secret missive, Which told her to be *s*. Happily or not, It found her *s* indeed. „ II ii 122
We heard that you were *s* in Flanders, cousin. „ III ii 33
Tho' I be ever deadly *s* at sea. So *s* am I „ III vi 88
didst thou ever see a carrion crow Stand watching a *s* beast before he dies? „ IV iii 7
Sick (*continued*) Art thou *s*, good Earl? *Harold.* *S* as an autumn swallow for a voyage, *S* for an idle week of hawk and hound *Harold* I i 100
poor lad! how *s* and sad for home! „ II ii 325
'Wulfnoth is *s*,' he said; 'he cannot follow;' „ III i 84
so if the city be *s*, and I cannot call the kennel sweet, *Becket* II ii 348
'The King is *s* and almost unto death.' „ V ii 152
I am not mad, not *s*, not old enough *The Cup* I iii 69
O my *s* boy! My daily fading Florio, *The Falcon* 235
S! is it so? why, when he came last year „ 311
I give it my *s* son, and if you be Not quite recover'd of your wound, „ 589
My one child Florio lying still so *s*, „ 678
You know *s* people, More specially *s* children, have strange fancies, „ 816
How often has my *s* boy yearn'd for this! „ 829
more blessed were the rags Of some pale beggar-woman seeking alms For her *s* son, „ 854
The *s* lady here might have been asleep. *Prom. of May* III 343
Mr. Dobson telled me to saäy he's browt some of Miss Eva's roses for the *s* laädy to smell on. *Dora.* Take them, dear. Say that the *s* lady thanks him! „ III 347
Tell him I cannot leave the *s* lady just yet. „ III 353
And my *s* father here has come between us *Foresters* IV 55
Being so *s* How should he, Robin? „ IV 82
at last I crawl'd like a *s* crab from my old shell, „ IV 126
Move me no more! I am *s* and faint with pain! „ IV 599
Sicken To *s* of his lilies and his roses. *Queen Mary* I v 25
lest living Spain Should *s* at dead England. „ III i 28
Nay, you *s me*, To hear you. „ IV iii 451
Have him away! I *s* of his readiness. „ V ii 611
they cried Sinnatus Not so long ago—they *s* me. *The Cup* II 111
And wake the Devil, and I may *s* by 'em. *Foresters* III 325
Sickening *S* himself with sweets. *Queen Mary* I v 172
Sicker I am *s* staying here Than any sea could make me „ III vi 86
Sickly But *s*, slight, half-witted and a child, *Harold* II ii 571
Sickness The *s* of our saintly king, for whom „ III i 164
I ha' three sisters a-dying at home o' the sweating *s*. *Becket* I iv 247
No fever, cough, croup, *s*? „ V ii 169
God save him from all *s* of the soul! „ V ii 174
he hath fallen Into a *s*, and it troubles me. *The Falcon* 310
Side (adj.) Dark even from a *s* glance of the moon, *Becket* IV ii 148
Side (s) The Council, the Court itself, is on our *s*. The Lord Chancellor himself is on our *s*. *Queen Mary* II i 193
Is he so safe to fight upon her *s*? „ II ii 313
moving *s* by *s* Beneath one canopy, „ III i 95
I will show fire on my *s*—stake and fire— „ III i 327
are profitless to the burners, And help the other *s*. „ IV ii 220
Those of the wrong *s* will despise the man, „ IV iii 24
Might it not be the other *s* rejoicing In his brave end? „ IV iii 357
Here by the *s* of her who loves you most? „ V i 75
there is barely room to shift thy *s*, *Harold* II ii 442
when at thy *s* He conquer'd with thee. „ IV iii 28
we might take your *s* against the customs— *Becket* I ii 56
Two rivers gently flowing *s* by *s*— „ I iii 445
I evermore have sworn upon his *s*, „ II ii 465
he hath pass'd out again, And on the other *s*. „ III ii 13
That in the summer keeps the mountain *s*, *The Cup* I i 109
You on this *s* the altar. You on that. „ II 254
tho' we have been a soldier, and ridden by his lordship's *s*, *The Falcon* 548
Were seated sadly at a fountain *s*, „ 610
I could put all that o' one *s* eäsy anew. *Prom. of May* II 111
meä and my sweet'art was a workin' along o' one *s* wi' one another, „ II 153
standing up *s* by *s* with me, and singing the same hymn? „ III 181
But being o' John's *s* we must have thy gold. *Foresters* IV 157
And cleft the Moslem turban at my *s*. „ IV 1001
Side (verb) 'If ye *s* with William Ye are not noble.' *Harold* II ii 787
It is, my boy, to *s* with the King when Chancellor, *Becket* II i 235
Side-beam see you yon *s-b* that is forced from under it, „ III iii 49
Side-cousin —though she's but a *s-c*— *Queen Mary* II iii 113
Side-current swoll'n and fed With indraughts and *s-c's*, „ II i 234

Side-gorge with sudden wreckful gusts From a *s-g.* *Harold* III i 52
Sidelong And shot out *s* boughs across the deep „ III i 150
Side-smile that hath squeezed out this *s-s* upon Canterbury, *Becket* III iii 56
Sideway Lest thou be *s's* guilty of the violence. *Harold* I i 458
Siding *S* with our great Council against Tostig, „ III i 59
Siege Lent at the *s* of Thoulouse by the King. *Becket* I iii 636
Sigh (s) a *s* With these low-moaning heavens. *Harold* V i 151
Sigh (verb) tell me, did you ever *S* for a beard? *Queen Mary* I v 609
Wherefore do you *s*? *Count.* I have lost a friend of late. *Lady Giovanna.* I could *s* with you For fear of losing more than friend, *The Falcon* 328
Sight (*See also* **Second-sight**) the half *s* which makes her look so stern, *Queen Mary* II ii 322
Gamble thyself at once out of my *s*, „ II iii 95
pray Heaven That you may see according to our *s*. „ III iv 331
Behold him—— *People.* Oh, unhappy *s*! „ IV iii 2
dishonour'd even in the *s* Of thine own sectaries— „ V v 133
s of Danish blood Might serve an end not English— *Harold* IV iii 96
My *s* is eagle, but the strife so thick— „ V i 627
let not my strong prayer Be weaken'd in thy *s*, „ V I 648
Wast thou not told to keep thyself from *s*? *Becket* I i 252
A *s* of that same chart which Henry gave you „ I ii 60
I would move this wanton from his *s* „ I ii 71
throned together in the *s* Of all the people, *The Cup* II 67
to the fullest in the *s* Of all the Gods. „ II 433
My last *s* ere I swoon'd was one sweet face *The Falcon* 647
and I haätes the very *s* on him. *Prom. of May* I 154
were I taken They would prick out my *s*. *Foresters* II i 72
Sighted (*See also* **Brief-sighted, Second-sighted**) We *s* 'em Only this moment. „ IV 589
Sign (s) if yon weird *s* Not blast us in our dreams.— *Harold* I i 121
In heaven *s's*! *S's* upon earth! *s's* everywhere! „ I i 159
there are *s's* in heaven— „ III i 357
And *s's* on earth! Knowest thou Senlac hill? „ III i 360
The *s* in heaven—the sudden blast at sea— „ V i 378
Where, knave, where? *Man.* *S* of the Talbot. *Queen Mary* III i 319
Sign (verb) Now *s*. *Cranmer.* I have sign'd enough, and I will *s* no more. „ IV ii 66
I *s* it with my presence, if I read it. „ IV ii 73
Will you not *s* it now? *Cranmer.* No, Villa Garcia, I *s* no more. „ IV ii 82
S, *s* at once—take, *s* it, Stigand, Aldred! *S* it, my good son Harold, Gurth, and Leofwin, *S* it, *Harold* III i 197
Then shalt thou step into my place and *s*. *Becket* I iii 15
that I cannot *s*: for that would drag The cleric „ I iii 82
And that I cannot *s*. (repeat) *Becket* I iii 91, 103, 114
That, too, I cannot *s*. *S* and obey! *Becket* I iii 131
S, and obey the crown! „ I iii 144
O my good lord, I do entreat thee—*s*. „ I iii 186
He hath sworn that thou shouldst *s*, „ I iii 189
so if thou *s*, my lord, That were but as the shadow „ I iii 193
Cannot the Pope absolve thee if thou *s*? „ I iii 231
Why—there then—there—I *s*, „ I iii 269
that we too should *s*? „ I iii 273
S? seal? I promised The King to obey these customs, „ I iii 555
order To seize upon him. Let me *s* it. *The Cup* I i 165
Sign'd first of those who *s* the Letters Patent *Queen Mary* I ii 17
Those that are now her Privy Council, *s* Before me: „ I ii 23
then I could no more—I *s*. „ I ii 38
'Thou shalt!' And *s* it—Mary! *Stafford.* Philip and the Pope Must have *s* too. „ III i 428
I have *s* enough, and I will sign no more. *Villa Garcia.* It is no more than what you have *s* already, „ IV ii 67
'twas you That *s* the burning of poor Joan of Kent; „ IV ii 206
papers by my hand *S* since my degradation—by this hand Written and *s*— „ IV iii 244
That Cranmer read all papers that he *s*? Or *s* all those they tell us that he *s*? „ IV iii 319
We have *s* it. *Harold* III i 202
s These ancient laws and customs of the realm. *Becket* I iii 6
'Twould seem too like the substance, if I *s*. „ I iii 197
Foliot, let me see what I have *s*. „ I iii 308
hath he *s*! show me the papers! *S* and not seal'd! „ I iii 317
when he *s*, his face was stormy-red— „ I iii 320
Sign'd (*continued*) Hadst thou not *s*, I had gone along with thee; *Becket* I iii 522
true too, that when written I *s* them— „ I iii 561
This paper *s* Antonius—will you take it, *The Cup* I ii 225
O Dora, he *s* himself 'Yours gratefully'! *Prom. of May* III 334
Signing Smooth thou his pride—thy *s* is but form; *Becket* I iii 218
Too late, my lord: you see they are *s* there. „ I iii 289
I hold not by my *s*. „ I iii 563
Sign of the Talbot Where, knave, where? *Man.* *S o t T.* *Queen Mary* III i 319
Silence (s) (*See also* **Prison-silence**) Ay, sir; Inherit the great *S*. „ III ii 199
They can but weep in *s*. „ IV iii 361
Our *s* is our reverence for the king! *Harold* IV i 13
thou shalt have our love, our *s*, and our gold— *Becket, Pro.* 492
ever spread into the man Here in our *s*? „ III i 23
God help her, That she was sworn to *s*. „ III i 78
This violence ill becomes The *s* of our Temple. *The Cup* II 216
whose cheerless Houris after death Are Night and *S*, *Prom. of May* I 251
Thou art alone in the *s* of the forest *Foresters* IV 630
Silence (verb) may give that egg-bald head The tap that *s's*. *Harold* V i 92
Silenced Little doubt This buzz will soon be *s*; *Queen Mary* V i 293
Silencing *See* **Bell-silencing**
Silent four guns gaped at me, Black, *s* mouths: *Queen Mary* II iii 32
William of Orange, William the *S*. „ III i 198
And I could see that many *s* hands Came from the crowd „ IV iii 582
even while I speak There lurks a *s* dagger, „ V ii 216
And both were *s*, letting the wild brook Speak for us— „ V v 90
The *s*, cloister'd, solitary life, *Harold* III i 277
The simple, *s*, selfless man Is worth a world of tonguesters. „ V i 81
Why do you stand so *s*, brother John? *Becket* V ii 535
All *s* there, Yes, deathlike! Dead? *Prom. of May* III 715
I am a *s* man myself, and all the more wonder at our Earl. *Foresters* I ii 34
but make haste then, and be *s* in the wood. Follow me. „ II i 365
The *s* blessing of one honest man Is heard in heaven— „ III 321
Silk There was a bit of yellow *s* here and there, *Becket* IV i 22
shall see the *s* here and there, and I want my supper. „ IV i 56
Silken Breaks into feather'd merriments, and flowers In *s* pageants. *Queen Mary* III v 15
Silking *See* **A-silking**
Silver (adj.) Our *s* cross sparkled before the prow, *Queen Mary* III ii 9
Some thirty—forty thousand *s* marks. *Becket* I iii 658
and we haven't never so much as a *s* one for the golden lips of her ladyship. *Count.* Have we not half a score of *s* spoons? *The Falcon* 403
I will give thee a *s* penny if thou wilt show us the way back to Nottingham. *Foresters* II i 359
Silver (s) white satin his trunkhose, Inwrought with *s*,— *Queen Mary* III i 78
Clothed with the mystic *s* of her moon. *Foresters* II i 608
if his backward-working alchemy Should change this gold to *s*, why, the *s* Were dear as gold, „ IV 40
Silvering *See* **Down-silvering, Long-silvering**
Simon (Renard, Spanish Ambassador) (*See also* **Renard, Simon Renard**) *S*, is supper ready? *Queen Mary* III vi 256
Simoniacal your Priests Gross, worldly, *s*, unlearn'd! *Harold* I i 162
Simon Renard so that Gardiner And *S R* spy not out *Queen Mary* I iii 173
Ay, *S R* knows it. „ I v 218
trust him somewhat less Than *S R*, „ I v 223
Thou art ever welcome, *S R*. „ I v 345
S R!—This Howard, whom they fear, „ III vi 53
May *S R* speak a single word? „ III vi 121
S R Knows me too well to speak a single word „ III vi 125
Am I to change my manners, *S R*, „ III vi 152
Well, *S R*, shall we stop a day? „ III vi 242
Simple The downfall of so many *s* souls, „ I ii 54
Then have my *s* headstone by the church, „ III v 113
And make you *s* Cranmer once again. „ IV ii 129
S! let fly the bird within the hand, *Harold* II ii 65
The *s*, silent, selfless man Is worth a world of tonguesters. „ V i 81
Has my *s* song set you jingling? *Becket, Pro.* 378
The *s* lobster-basket, and the mesh— „ II ii 297

Simple (*continued*) This author, with his charm of *s* style And close dialectic, *Prom. of May* I 224
And out upon all *s* batchelors! *Foresters* IV 52
Simple-looking He comes, a rough, bluff, *s-l* fellow. *The Cup* I i 173
Sin It was a *s* to love her married, *Queen Mary* III i 339
With His own blood, and wash'd us from our *s's*, „ III iii 204
O Lord God, although my *s's* be great, „ IV iii 135
not for little *s's* Didst thou yield up thy Son to human death; But for the greatest *s* that can be sinn'd, „ IV iii 143
Unpardonable,—*s* against the light, „ IV iii 148
Thy mercy must be greater than all *s*. „ IV iii 151
what *s* Beyond all grace, all pardon? „ V ii 339
S is too dull to see beyond himself. *Alice.* Ah, Magdalen, *s* is bold as well as dull. „ V ii 441
That marriage was half *s*. *Harold* I ii 53
s's of both The houses on mine head— „ I ii 204
Or is it the same *s* to break my word „ II ii 664
—a *s* against The truth of love. „ V i 170
Black sheep, quoth she, too black a *s* for me. *Becket* I iv 165
We can make a black *s* white. „ I iv 169
Thou shalt confess all thy sweet *s's* to me. „ II i 292
Well, it's no *s* in a gentleman not to fish. *Prom. of May* I 215
Bow'd to the dust beneath the burthen of *s*. *Harold.* *S*! What *s*? „ III 522
Veiling one *s* to act another. „ III 773
Sin' (since) It be five year *s* ye went afoor to him, *Prom. of May* II 5
Him as did the mischief here, five year' *s*. „ III 140
Sing To *s*, love, marry, churn, brew, bake, and die, *Queen Mary* III v 111
but, my Lord, you know what Virgil *s's*, „ III vi 134
Shall Alice *s* you One of her pleasant songs? „ V ii 354
the lark *s's*, the sweet stars come and go, *Harold* II ii 434
s, Asaph! clash The cymbal, Heman! „ III i 186
bird that moults *s's* the same song again, *Becket* I iii 447
our mother 'ill *s* me old songs by the hour, „ III i 184
tell him my tales, *S* him my songs? *The Falcon* 797
I don't know why I *s* that song; I don't love it. *Prom. of May* I 61
and the larks 'ud *s* i' them daäys, „ I 374
do thou and thy sweet'art *s* us hoäm to supper— „ II 170
Ye shall *s* that ageän to-night, „ II 215
You do well, Mistress Kate, to *s* and to gather roses. *Foresters* I i 23
S's a new song to the new year— „ I iii 28
I have a touch of sadness in myself. *S*. „ I iii 40
I can *s* it. *Robin.* Not now, good Much! „ I iii 157
To *s* the songs of England Beneath the greenwood tree. „ II i 23
S, and by St. Mary these beggars and these friars „ III 416
And all the birds that *s* „ III 440
Did I not *s* it in tune? „ IV 29
Till thou thyself shalt come to *s* it—in time. „ IV 37
Let the birds *s*, and do you dance to their song. „ IV 557
All the birds in merry Sherwood *s* and *s* him home again. „ IV 1109
Singing (*See also* **Psalm-singing**) I wish'd myself the milkmaid *s* here, *Queen Mary* III v 256
standing up side by side with me, and *s* the same hymn? *Prom. of May* III 182
Single May Simon Renard speak a *s* word? *Queen Mary* III vi 121
Simon Renard Knows me too well to speak a *s* word That could not be forgiven. „ III vi 126
Our axes lighten with a *s* flash About the summit of the hill, *Harold* V i 538
But dallied with a *s* lettuce-leaf; *The Falcon* 673
He loves the chivalry of his *s* arm. *Foresters* IV 786
Sing-songing and you sit *S-s* here; *Queen Mary* II i 112
Sink a day may *s* or save a realm. „ III vi 238
Here's to him, *s* or swim! *Thane.* God *s* him! *Harold* IV iii 133
and all her loves and hates *S* again into chaos. *Foresters* I ii 330
Perchance this day may *s* as gloriously, „ II i 31
Sinking I am *s*—hold me—Let me alone. *The Cup* II 478
Sinnatus (a Tetrarch) married Since—married *S*, the Tetrarch „ I i 16
'To the admired Camma, wife of *S*, the Tetrarch, „ I i 37
Boy, dost thou know the house of *S*? *Boy.* These grapes are from the house of *S*— „ I i 50
and this cup to Camma, The wife of *S*. *Boy.* Going or gone to-day To hunt with *S*. „ I i 63
I send it to the wife of *S*, „ I i 73
Sinnatus (a Tetrarch) (*continued*) you suspect This *S* of playing patriotism, *The Cup* I i 78
I envied *S* when he married her. „ I i 129
Nor *S* either? *Synorix.* No, nor *S*. „ I i 133
If you track this *S* In any treason, „ I i 162
No *S* yet—and there the rising moon. „ I ii 1
Lord *S*, I once was at the hunting of a lion. „ I ii 115
were he living And grown to man and *S* will'd it, „ I ii 151
'You are to seize on *S*,—if——' „ I ii 229
Hath *S* never told you of this plot? „ I ii 250
No chance for *S*. „ I ii 258
Why said you not as much to my brave *S*? „ I ii 260
S, you remember—yea, you must, „ I ii 400
S, kiss me now. „ I ii 419
Not if *S* Has told her all the truth about me. „ I iii 22
And for the sake of *S* your husband, „ I iii 100
body of that dead traitor *S*. Bear him away. „ I iii 180
To marry him who stabb'd her *S*. „ II 24
When he struck at *S*— „ II 47
hand Red with the sacred blood of *S*? „ II 84
found All good in the true heart of *S*, „ II 87
So they cried *S* Not so long since— „ II 110
O how unlike our goodly *S*. „ II 173
A goodlier-looking man than *S*. „ II 176
Dost thou remember when I wedded *S*? „ II 194
came To plead to thee for *S's* life, „ II 392
Would you have tortured *S* to death? „ II 408
S! Why comes he not to meet me? „ II 527
'Camma, Camma!' *S*, *S*! „ II 536
Sinn'd But for the greatest sin that can be *s*, *Queen Mary* IV iii 146
Have *s* against it—all in vain. *Harold* III i 95
Sinner Most miserable *s*, wretched man. *Queen Mary* IV iii 123
We are *s's* all, The best of all not all-prepared *Becket* V ii 563
Sire The *s* begets Not half his likeness *Queen Mary* II i 53
like his kingly *s's*, The Normans, *Becket* IV ii 441
Sister took her hand, call'd her sweet *s*, *Queen Mary* I i 80
To the Pleiads, uncle; they have lost a *s*. „ I iv 294
bastard sprout, My *s*, is far fairer than myself. „ I v 72
My *s* cowers and hates me. „ I v 83
—for I have not own'd My *s*, and I will not.— „ I v 285
So that your *s* were but look'd to closer. „ I v 460
whom did you say? *Messenger.* Elizabeth, Your Royal *s*. „ II iv 117
And your so loving *s*? *Mary.* She shall die. „ II iv 141
Our little *s* of the Song of Songs! „ III ii 103
Then I may say your Grace will see your *s*? „ V ii 604
Your royal *s* cannot last; your hand Will be much coveted! „ V iii 43
My *s's* marriage, and my father's marriages, „ V iii 96
Madam, your royal *s* comes to see you. „ V v 192
Who knows if Boleyn's daughter be my *s*? „ V v 195
Why would you vex yourself, Poor *s*? „ V v 264
Tostig, *s*, galls himself; *Harold* I i 421
Nay, my good *s*— „ I i 462
Our *s* hates us for his banishment; „ III i 78
thou art not A holy *s* yet, my girl, „ III ii 82
And more than *s* in thine own. „ III ii 85
Why cry thy people on thy *s's* name? „ IV i 21
Where is thy *s*? „ IV i 184
For there was more than *s* in my kiss, „ V ii 5
wicked *s* clapt her hands and laugh'd; „ V ii 48
Two *s's* gliding in an equal dance, *Becket* I iii 444
I ha' three *s's* a-dying at home o' the sweating sickness. „ I iv 246
twin *s* of the morning star, Forelead the sun. *The Cup* I iii 45
my *s* wrote that he was mighty pleasant, and had no pride in him. *Prom. of May* I 116
nor father, *S*, nor you, shall ever see me more. „ I 676
My *s* far away—and you, a gentleman, „ I 708
Speak not so loudly; that must be your *s*. „ I 727
not only on my *s's* account, but the ill success of the farm, „ II 67
It seems to me that I hate men, ever since my *s* left us. „ II 80
Poor *s*, I had it five years ago. „ II 82
knaw'd better nor to cast her *s's* misfortin inter 'er teeth „ II 127
Are you—you are—that Dora, The *s*. „ II 364
you are young, and—pardon me—As lovely as your *s*. „ II 508

Sister (*continued*) niver 'a been talkin' haäfe an hour wi' the divil 'at killed her oän *s*, *Prom. of May* II 604
But the love of *s* for *s* can never be old-fashioned. „ III 319
a *S* of Mercy, come from the death-bed of a pauper, „ III 376
S took me to her house, and bit by bit— „ III 379
I appealed to the *S* again, her answer— „ III 394
O she has fainted. *S*, Eva, *s*! „ III 672
She hid this *s*, told me she was dead— „ III 689
And so wouldst sell thy *s* to the Sheriff, *Foresters* II i 536
But thou art fair as ever, my sweet *s*. „ IV 1018
Sit (*See also* **Set**) To *s* high Is to be lied about. *Queen Mary* I v 428
burn the throne Where you should *s* with Philip: „ I v 511
Sir, let them *s*. I must have time to breathe. „ I v 545
An instant Ay or No! the Council *s's*. „ I v 591
and you *s* Sing-songing here; „ II i 111
S down here, all; „ III ii 99
St. Andrew's day; *s* close, *s* close, we are friends. „ III iii 1
You *s* upon this fallen Cranmer's throne; „ IV i 114
S down here: Tell me thine happiest hour. „ V v 78
sons of Godwin *S* topmost in the field of England, *Harold* I i 326
where he *s's* My ransom'd prisoner. „ II ii 44
S down, *s* down, and eat, „ IV iii 206
range of knights *S*, each a statue on his horse, „ V i 525
If I *s*, I grow fat. *Becket, Pro.* 414
mother Canterbury, who *s's* With tatter'd robes. „ I i 156
Priest *S's* winking at the license of a king, „ I ii 66
none could *s* By his own hearth in peace; „ I iii 341
And our great lords will *s* in judgment on him. „ I iii 549
Sons *s* in judgment on their father!— „ I iii 551
There is a bench. Come, wilt thou *s*? „ II i 124
she *s's* naked by a great heap of gold in the middle of the wood, „ III ii 21
even among those Who *s* on thrones— „ IV ii 125
crowns must bow when mitres *s* so high. „ IV ii 297
S and eat, And take a hunter's vengeance *The Cup* I ii 41
Shall I *S* by him, read to him, tell him my tales, *The Falcon* 795
and you should *s* i' your oän parlour quite like a laädy, *Prom. of May* II 97
s's and eats his heart for want of money to pay the Abbot. *Foresters* I i 4
S here by me, where the most beaten track „ III 88
S here, my queen, and judge the world with me. „ III 151
S there, knaves, till the captain call for you. „ III 219
S there till you be called for. „ III 295
Sitting (*See also* **A-sitting**) *s* here Between the two most high-set thrones *Queen Mary* III ii 104
and the dead were found *S*, and in this fashion; „ V ii 397
Who stole the widow's one *s* hen o' Sunday, *Becket* I iv 121
S hen! Our Lord Becket's our great sitting-hen cock, we shouldn't ha' been *s* here if the barons and bishops hadn't been a-sitting on the Archbishop. „ I iv 124
shout of Synorix and Camma *s* Upon one throne, *The Cup* II 146
nurse, I had forgotten thou wast *s* there. *The Falcon* 35
Sitting-hen (*See also* **Sitting**) Our Lord Becket's our great *s-h* cock, *Becket* I iv 124
S'iver (Howsoever) *S* we've led moäst on it. *Prom. of May* II 52
S I mun git along back to the farm, „ II 321
Six It lies there in *s* pieces at your feet; *Queen Mary* II i 87
Some *s* or seven Bishops, diamonds, pearls, „ III i 52
Then for the bastard *S* feet and nothing more! *Harold* IV iii 116
Yet this no wife—her *s* and thirty sail Of Provence *Becket* V i 122
She was there *s* years ago. *Prom. of May* II 399
Dan Smith, they tell me that you—and you have *s* children—spent all your last Saturday's wages at the ale-house; „ III 77
Sixteen gather all From *s* years to sixty; *Queen Mary* V ii 273
Sixty And Counts, and *s* Spanish cavaliers, „ III i 51
gather all From sixteen years to *s*; „ V ii 273
Sixty-fold Do here and now repay you *s-f*, „ III iii 199
'Size (assize) thaw they hanged ma at *'S* fur it. *Prom. of May* II 698
Sketching but I Take some delight in *s*, „ II 539
Skilful The King is *s* at it? *Queen Mary* I iii 144
For all that, Most honest, brave, and *s*; „ II ii 383
Skill Upon the *s* and swiftness of the players. „ I iii 143
Skill (*continued*) with this *s* of fence! let go mine arm. *Foresters* II ii 38
Skim Not while the swallow *s's* along the ground, „ I ii 313
Skin If ye love your liberties or your *s's*, *Queen Mary* II i 216
doth not the living *s* thicken against perpetual whippings? *Becket* III iii 316
Skinn'd *See* **Thin-skinn'd**
Skip *S's* every way, from levity or from fear. *Queen Mary* I iii 170
who *s's* and flies To right and left, *Harold* I i 11
Skipping And now be *s* in their fairy-rings, *Foresters* II i 497
Skipworth (a farm labourer) Luscombe, Nokes, Oldham, *S*! *Prom. of May* III 54
Skulk *s* into corners Like rabbits to their holes. *Queen Mary* II iv 54
Skull And smite thee with my crozier on the *s*? *Becket* I i 222
Sky (*See also* **Leaf-sky**) So from a clear *s* falls the thunderbolt! *Queen Mary* V iii 115
Look to the *skies*, then to the river, *Harold* I i 34
and fill the *s* With free sea-laughter— „ II ii 336
the bright *s* cleave To the very feet of God, „ II ii 741
dash us down Our dinner from the *skies*. *The Falcon* 154
The *s*? or the sea on a blue day? *Prom. of May* I 101
An' the midders all mow'd, an' the *s* sa blue—(repeat) *Prom. of May* II 176, 188, 200
O tower spiring to the *s*, *Prom. of May* III 203
And the white cloud is roll'd along the *s*! *Foresters* I ii 320
Slack O God! I have been too *s*, too *s*; *Queen Mary* V v 100
Slain and there be more As villainously *s*. *Harold* II ii 300
Better methinks have *s* the man at once! „ II ii 498
s, Whose life was all one battle, „ V i 396
Gurth hath leapt upon him And *s* him: „ V i 634
The king is *s*, the kingdom overthrown! „ V ii 15
Three horses had I *s* beneath me: „ V ii 171
you had safelier have *s* an archbishop than a she-goat: *Becket* III iii 68
They fear you *s*; they dread they know not what. „ V ii 600
We will not have him *s* before our face. „ V iii 54
And will you bolt them out, and have *them s*? „ V iii 61
I am readier to be *s*, than thou to slay. „ V iii 128
Slander (s) heard *S's* against Prince Philip in our Court? *Alice.* What *s's*? *Queen Mary* I v 570
Slander (verb) And let him go? To *s* thee again? *Harold* II ii 508
she question'd *me*. Did she not *s him*? *Becket* III i 214
Slander'd when they *s* you For setting up a mass *Queen Mary* I ii 86
Slandering Or am I *s* my most inward friend, „ IV ii 105
Slanderous kill, kill with knife or venom One of his *s* harlots? *Becket* IV ii 411
Slaughter peril mine own soul By *s* of the body? *Queen Mary* V v 169
Slaughter-field Would perish on the civil *s-f*, „ III i 118
Slave (*See also* **Galley-slave**) the Queen, and the laws, and the people, his *s's*. „ II i 175
Crown'd *s* of *s's*, and mitred king of kings, „ III iv 381
S, if he love thee, Thy life is worth the wrestle *Becket* IV ii 192
The *s* that eat my bread has kick'd his King! „ V i 242
My bed, where ev'n the *s* is private— „ V i 251
Slay I could take and *s* thee. *Harold* IV ii 7
Take and *s* me, For Edward loved me. „ IV ii 9
Take and *s* me, I say, Or I shall count thee fool. „ IV ii 14
Free thee or *s* thee, Norway will have war; „ IV ii 18
dash thyself against me that I may *s* thee! *Becket* IV ii 196
I am readier to be slain, than thou to *s*. „ V iii 128
if he be conspirator, Rome will chain, Or *s* him. *The Cup* I i 19
my friends may spy him And *s* him as he runs. „ I ii 392
true woodman's bow of the best yew-wood to *s* the deer. *Foresters* II i 393
What! go to *s* his brother, and make *me* „ IV 804
O Thou that *s* the babe within the womb *The Cup* II 278
Slayest or after *s* him As boy or man, „ II 280
Sleek To *s* and supple himself to the king's hand. *Harold* I i 149
She beautiful: *s* as a miller's mouse! *The Falcon* 164
as *s* and as round-about as a mellow codlin. *Foresters* I i 42
Sleep (s) kiss that charms thine eyelids into *s*, *Harold* I ii 140
Sound *s* to the man Here by dead Norway „ IV iii 120
A snatch of *s* were like the peace of God. „ V i 180
The Virgin, in a vision of my *s*, *Becket* I i 53
All my brain is full of *s*. *The Cup* I ii 446
He's been a-moänin' and a-groänin' in 'is *s*, *Prom. of May* III 412

Sleep (s) (*continued*) She must be crying out 'Edgar' in her *s*. *Harold.* Who must be crying out 'Edgar' in her *s*? *Prom. of May* III 654
'To *s*! to *s*!' (repeat) *Foresters* I iii 34, 41, 43, 46, 49
Whate'er thy griefs, in *s* they fade away. *Foresters* I iii 45
Why so I said, *my* arrow. Well, to *s*. *The Cup* I ii 386
Sleep (verb) when I *s*, a hundred men-at-arms *Queen Mary* I v 152
I couldn't *s* in Spain. „ II i 36
son turn'd out into the street To *s*, to die— „ V ii 127
The room she *s's* in—is not this the way? „ V v 205
let them turn from left to right And *s* again. *Harold* I i 197
S, *s*, and thou shalt see My grayhounds „ I ii 127
the people stupid-sure *S* like their swine . . . „ IV iii 217
Go home, and *s* thy wine off, for thine eyes *Becket* I i 212
I sometimes think he *s's* When he would watch; „ III i 33
can't *s* sound o' nights because of the bad fairies. „ IV i 30
she shall *s* sound enough if thou wilt take me to her. „ IV i 33
she says she can make you *s* o' nights. „ IV ii 20
I could not eat, *s*, pray: „ V ii 92
S, mournful heart, and let the past be past! *S*, happy soul! all life will *s* at last. *Foresters* I iii 47
I cannot *s* o' nights by cause on 'em. „ II i 383
Sleeper seven *s's* in the cave at Ephesus Have turn'd *Harold* I i 192
like a careless *s* in the down; *Foresters* I i 207
Sleeping *s* after all she has done, in peace and quietness, *Queen Mary* V iv 34
S or dying there? If this be death, *Harold* III i 1
Sleeping-draught I pray you then to take my *s-d*; *Becket* IV ii 69
my *s-d* May bloat thy beauty out of shape, „ IV ii 168
Sleepy I am faint and *s*. Leave me. „ III i 208
and my hands are too *s* To lift it off. *The Cup* II 530
Sleeve look—is this a *s* For an archbishop? *Becket, Pro.* 250
Slender Pray thee make Thy *s* meal out of those scraps and shreds *The Falcon* 146
But for the *s* help that I can give, *Prom. of May* II 421
Slept Our guardsmen have *s* well, since we came in? *Leofwin.* Ay, *s* and snored. *Harold* V i 207
when I *s* Methought I stood in Canterbury Minster, *Becket* I i 72
Slew *s* not him alone who wore the purple, *Queen Mary* I v 499
And *s* two hundred of his following, *Harold* IV i 116
They *s* my stags in mine own manor here, *Becket* V ii 438
And he was scared and *s* it. *Foresters* II ii 99
Sliced He tore their eyes out, *s* their hands away, *Harold* II ii 389
Slight (adj.) Not for *s* faults alone, when thou becamest Man in the Flesh, *Queen Mary* IV iii 139
But sickly, *s*, half-witted and a child, *Harold* II ii 571
So that you grant me one *s* favour. *Becket* I ii 58
then Save for some *s* report in her own Senate *The Cup* I ii 133
And after some *s* speech about the Sheriff He caught her round the waist, *Foresters* II i 114
He is stricken with a *s* paralysis. „ IV 456
Slight (verb) When the fairy *s's* the crown. „ II ii 135
Slighted like a friend *s* by one That hath climb'd up to nobler company. Not *s*—all but moan'd for: thou must go. *Becket* I i 350
Slimy the river, black, *s*, swirling under me in the lamplight, *Prom. of May* III 369
Slink Why did you *s* away so like a cur? *Becket* IV ii 431
Sliver'd are *s* off and splinter'd by Their lightning— *Harold* V i 540
Slope (adj.) nor our Archbishop Stagger on the *s* decks for any rough sea *Becket* II ii 106
Slope (s) I am half-way down the *s*—will no man stay me? „ II ii 148
golden *s's* Of Solomon-shaming flowers— „ III i 47
Slouch Dares the bear *s* into the lion's den? „ IV ii 282
Slough serpent that hath slough'd will *s* again. *Queen Mary* III iii 19
snake that *s's* comes out a snake again. *Becket* I iii 449
Slough'd serpent that hath *s* will slough again. *Queen Mary* III iii 18
Slow The *s*, fat fool! He drawl'd and prated so, I smote him suddenly, *Harold* IV ii 40
One *s*, fat, white, a burthen of the hearth; *Becket* V ii 211
but very ready To make allowances, and mighty *s* To feel offences. *Prom. of May* III 629
Sluggard honour me, obey me! *S's* and fools! *Becket* V i 241
S's and fools, why do you stand and stare? „ V i 256
Slum even if I found it Dark with the soot of *s's*. *Prom. of May* III 602
Slumber stormless shipwreck in the pools Of sullen *s*, *Harold* V i 297
Slur But wherefore *s* the perfect ceremony? *The Cup* II 431
Slush Your rights and charters hobnail'd into *s*— *Queen Mary* II ii 279
Thruf *s* an' squad When roäds was bad, *Prom. of May* II 309
Slut a *s* whose fairest linen seems Foul as her dust-cloth, *Becket* V ii 202
Smack kind of unction in it, a *s* of relish about it. *Foresters* I i 87
Small Are you so *s* a man? *Queen Mary* III v 192
matter Of *s* importance now and then to cede A point to her demand? „ III vi 168
Beyond his aim—but I am *s* and scandalous, „ V ii 427
That were too *s* a matter for a comet! *Harold* I i 470
Too *s*! a comet would not show for that! *Aldwyth.* Not *s* for thee, if thou canst compass it. „ I i 474
Bigger in our *s* world than thou art. *Becket* V i 128
S peace was mine in my noviciate, father. „ V ii 86
And the *s* state more cruelly trampled on *The Cup* I ii 145
And I have *s* hope of the gentleman gout in my great toe. *The Falcon* 656
Dance! *s* heart have I to dance. *Prom. of May* I 429
Till Nature, high and low, and great and *s* Forgets herself, *Foresters* I ii 327
I fear I had *s* pity for that man.— „ IV 547
Smaller it was but the sacrifice of a kingdom to his son, a *s* matter; *Becket* III iii 107
Smash (*See also* **Mash**) he'll *s* all our bits o' things worse than Philip o' Spain. *Queen Mary* II iii 103
Smattering I had some *s* of science then, *Prom of May* II 301
Smell (s) Wilt thou smell it, my lord? for the Archbishop likes the *s* on it, my lord; *Becket* I iv 240
so that the *s* of their own roast had not come across it— „ III iii 119
and the *s* o' the mou'd an' all. *Prom. of May* I i 375
the *s* o' the mou'd 'ud ha' maäde ma live as long as Jerusalem. „ I i 377
Smell (verb) He cannot *s* a rose but pricks his nose *Harold* I i 422
It's humbling—it *s's* of human natur'. Wilt thou *s* it, my lord? for the Archbishop likes the smell on it, *Becket* I iv 238
Do but *s*! „ II i 145
when I was a-getting o' bluebells for your ladyship's nose to *s* on— „ III i 163
two-legg'd dogs Among us who can *s* a true occasion, *The Cup* I ii 113
Yes; how sweet they *s*! *Prom. of May* I 608
to saäy he's browt some of Miss Eva's roses for the sick laädy to *s* on. „ III 347
so greasy, and *s* so vilely that my Lady Marian *Foresters* I i 82
Smelt Methought I *s* out Renard in the letter, *Queen Mary* II ii 119
Smile (s) (*See also* **Side-smile**) She cast on him a vassal *s* of love, „ III i 98
A *s* abroad is oft a scowl at home. „ III i 212
and with such royal *s's*— *Gardiner.* *S's* that burn men. „ III iv 403
with a cheerful *s*, as one whose mind Is all made up, „ IV iii 587
sweet worn *s* Among thy patient wrinkles— „ V v 199
Love is come with a song and a *s*, Welcome Love with a *s* and a song: *Harold* I ii 10
Gave his shorn *s* the lie. „ II ii 226
Then with that friendly-fiendly *s* of his, „ III i 86
that sweet other-world *s*, which will be reflected *Becket, Pro.* 396
Still with a *s*. „ III iii 36
The same *s* still. „ III iii 44
Bid their old bond farewell with *s's*, not tears; *Prom. of May* I 524
Smile (verb) love that men should *s* upon you, niece. They'd *s* you into treason— *Queen Mary* I iv 274
seem'd to *s* And sparkle like our fortune „ II iii 23
They *s* as if content with one another. „ III i 210
How he *s's* As if he loved me yet! „ V v 40
and see, he *s's* and goes, Gentle as in life. „ V v 145
but *s* As kindness, watching all, *Harold* I i 366
Why dost thou *s* So dolorously? *Becket, Pro.* 134
not to *s* Is all but death to me. „ II i 40
Or scarce would *s* that fashion. „ III iii 28
that they began to *s* at it. „ III iii 312
and *s* At bygone things till that eternal peace. *The Cup* I iii 171
She *s's* at him—how hard the woman is! *The Falcon* 660
Nay, you must *s* upon me! *Prom. of May* I 571
I am glad my nonsense has made you *s*! „ III 315

Smile (verb) (*continued*) One word, or do but *s* ! *Prom. of May* III 677
but Hope *S's* from the threshold of the year *Foresters* I iii 16
I could but sneak and *s* and call it courtesy, „ IV 366
And *s's* at my best meanings, „ IV 727
Smiled loveliest day that ever *s* On England. *Queen Mary* III iii 162
Smiling I spy the rock beneath the *s* sea. „ I iv 279
He pass'd out *s*, and he walk'd upright; „ IV iii 302
Or answer'd them in *s* negatives; „ IV iii 603
Down thirty feet below the *s* day— *Harold* II ii 430
Smite The sword Is in her Grace's hand to *s* with. *Queen Mary* III iv 90
I fell. Why fall? Why did He *s* me? *Becket* I i 109
And *s* thee with my crozier on the skull? „ I i 221
Shall I *s* him with the edge of the sword? „ I iv 224
S the shepherd and the sheep are scattered. *S* the sheep and the shepherd will excommunicate thee. „ I iv 226
plagues That *s* the city spare the solitudes. „ V ii 173
Shall I not *s* him with his own cross-staff? „ V ii 313
Smith (Dan) *See* **Dan Smith**
Smitten our good Gurth hath *s* him to the death. *Harold* V i 503
S with fever in the open field, *Prom. of May* III 806
Smoke you bring the *s* Of Cranmer's burning with you. *Queen Mary* IV iii 561
s of Cranmer's burning wrapt me round. „ IV iii 564
a candle in the sun Is all but *s*— „ V i 79
Ay, if he do not end in *s* again. *Becket* II ii 316
said to the *s*, 'Go up, my son, straight to Heaven.' And the *s* said, 'I go;' „ II ii 318
while the *s* floats from the cottage roof, *Foresters* I ii 317
Smoking after much smouldering and *s*, be kindled again upon your quarter. *Becket* II ii 313
Smooth (adj.) Taken the rifted pillars of the wood For *s* stone columns of the sanctuary, *Harold* I ii 101
Cannot a *s* tongue lick him whole again To serve your will? *Becket* II ii 24
That all was planed and bevell'd *s* again, „ V i 138
Smooth-Smoothe (verb) *Smooth* thou my way, before he clash with me; *Harold* II ii 69
Smoothe thou his pride—thy signing is but form; *Becket* I iii 218
Smooth-shorn Husband-in-law, our *s-s* suzerain, „ II ii 40
Smote Methought some traitor *s* me on the head. *Queen Mary* V ii 252
I *s* him suddenly, I knew not what I did. *Harold* IV ii 41
And *s* me down upon the Minster floor. *Becket* I i 104
Smoulder or this Will *s* and re-flame, *Queen Mary* I v 509
Smouldering after much *s* and smoking, be kindled again upon your quarter. *Becket* II ii 313
Snaffle Then I and he will *s* your 'God's death,' *Queen Mary* V iii 119
Snake A *s*—and if I touch it, it may sting. „ III v 218
s that sloughs comes out a *s* again. *S*—ay, *Becket* I iii 449
Snake-like creeps *s-l* about our legs *Queen Mary* II i 203
Snap bind a score All in one faggot, *s* it over knee, *Harold* IV i 58
S not the faggot-band then. „ IV i 66
lances *s* and shiver Against the shifting blaze „ V i 586
Snapt dog that *s* the shadow, dropt the bone.— „ I ii 188
Snare Before he fell into the *s* of Guy; „ V ii 131
my white bird stepping toward the *s*. *The Cup* I iii 36
Snatch A *s* of sleep were like the peace of God. *Harold* V i 180
Sneak I could but *s* and smile and call it courtesy, *Foresters* IV 366
Sneezed and I *s* three times this morning. *The Falcon* 168
Sniffed that Lucullus or Apicius might have *s* it in their Hades of heathenism, *Becket* III iii 118
Snore (s) Misheard their *s's* for groans. *Harold* V i 213
Snore (verb) to *s* away his drunkenness Into the sober headache,— *Becket* I i 371
Nip him not, but let him *s*. *Foresters* II ii 122
Snored Ay, slept and *s*. *Harold* V i 209
Snow And winter again and the *s's*. *Becket, Pro.* 334
I am *s* to mud. „ IV ii 130
s had frozen round her, and she sat Stone-dead „ V ii 237
In the sweet moon as with a lovelier *s* ! *The Cup* I ii 397
see your cloth be white as *s* ! *The Falcon* 499
as the *s* yonder on the very tip-top o' the mountain. „ 501
I have seen it like the *s* on the moraine. „ 505
Soä (so) An' *s* they be. *Man.* *S* they be! *s* they be! *Prom. of May* I 338
an' *s* I know'd 'im when I seed 'im ageän „ III 121

Soädger (soldier) 'Listed for a *s*, Miss, i' the Queen's Real Hard Tillery. *Prom. of May* III 108
Soak'd he *s* the trunk with human blood, *Harold* III i 142
Soar thou that canst *s* Beyond the morning lark, *The Falcon* 10
Sob trumpets in the halls, *S's*, laughter, cries: *Becket* V ii 368
Sober to snore away his drunkenness Into the *s* headache,— „ I i 373
Socialist I that have been call'd a *S*, A Communist, *Prom. of May* III 584
Soft You lived among your vines and oranges, In your *s* Italy yonder! *Queen Mary* III iv 254
What weapon hath the child, save his *s* tongue, „ III v 129
like the wild hedge-rose Of a *s* winter, possible, „ III vi 16
The *s* and tremulous coward in the flesh? „ IV ii 107
You have a gold ring on your finger, and *s* raiment about your body; „ V iv 32
on a *s* bed, in a closed room, with light, fire, physic, tendance; „ V iv 36
Except it be a *s* one, And undereaten to the fall. *Harold* I ii 122
Nor dwelt alone, like a *s* lord of the East, *Becket* I iii 358
When Richard comes he is *s* enough to pardon His brother; *Foresters* IV 746
Softlier We might go *s* than with crimson rowel And streaming lash. *Queen Mary* III iv 182
Soil (s) make the *s* For Cæsars, Cromwells, and Napoleons *Prom. of May* III 592
Soil (verb) You heed not how you *s* her maiden fame, *Foresters* IV 479
Soil'd and the man Hurls his *s* life against the pikes and dies. *Queen Mary* IV iii 311
Sojourn For I shall most *s* in Normandy; *Harold* II ii 634
Solace Pride of his heart—the *s* of his hours— *The Falcon* 223
Sold Thou hast *s* me for a cry.— *Harold* IV ii 76
And *s* thine own To buy it for her. *The Falcon* 76
And the other nine? *Filippo.* *S* ! „ 412
and he hath *s* himself to that beast John— *Foresters* I i 267
Soldan I had it from an Arab *s*, who, *Becket* IV ii 300
Solder *S's* a race together—yea—tho' they fail, *The Cup* I ii 162
Soldier (*See also* **Soädger**) you are as poor a poet, Wyatt, As a good *s*. *Queen Mary* II i 114
Wyatt was a good *s*, yet he fail'd, „ III i 132
The Duke Of Alva, an iron *s*. „ III i 194
His eye was like a *s's*, „ IV iii 304
Stupid *s's* oft are bold. „ V ii 445
A *s's*, not a spiritual arm. *Henry.* I lack a spiritual *s*, Thomas— *Becket, Pro.* 255
as brave a *s* as Henry and a goodlier man: „ *Pro.* 437
Make an Archbishop of a *s* ? „ I i 41
not the *s* As Foliot swears it.— „ I i 387
I am no *s*, as he said—at least No leader. „ I iii 298
the lady holds the cleric Lovelier than any *s*, „ V i 194
The *s*, when he lets his whole self go „ V ii 39
You come here with your *s's* to enforce *The Cup* I i 75
Most like it was the Roman *s* shouted. „ II 120
tho' we have been a *s*, and ridden by his lordship's side, *The Falcon* 547
Sole I say you were the one *s* man who stood. *Bagenhall.* I am the one *s* man in either house, *Queen Mary* III iii 263
I will be *S* master of my house. *Becket* V i 151
Solemn Should not this day be held in after years More *s* than of old? *Queen Mary* III iii 91
swear When thou art king, to see my *s* vow Accomplish'd. *Harold* III i 306
Against the *s* ordinance from Rome, *Becket* I iii 505
I bound myself, and by a *s* vow, *The Falcon* 679
I believed thee to be too *s* and formal to be a ruffler. *Foresters* I i 168
Solemnity Low words best chime with this *s*. *The Cup* II 217
Solicited you have *s* The Queen, and been rejected. *Queen Mary* I iv 58
Solid Far from *s* foot of men, Never to return again, *Foresters* II ii 169
Solitary To read and rhyme in *s* fields, *Queen Mary* II i 51
The silent, cloister'd, *s* life, *Harold* III i 277
Solitude Retiring into cloistral *s* To yield *Queen Mary* III vi 209
but saved From all that by our *s*. The plagues That smite the city spare the *s's*. *Becket* V ii 171
thy *s* among thy nuns, May that save thee! „ V ii 176
Solomon-shaming golden slopes Of *S-s* flowers— „ III i 48

Some (*See also* **Soom**) Might it not Be the rough preface of *s* closer bond? *Queen Mary* I iv 48
counsel your withdrawing To Ashridge, or *s* other country house. „ I iv 226
I have felt within me Stirrings of *s* great doom when God's just hour Peals— „ I iv 261
Some one *See* **Summun**
Somerset-Somersetshire (*See also* **Soomerset**) He's a *Somersetshire* man, and a very civil-spoken gentleman. *Prom. of May* I 206
Philip Edgar of Toft Hall In *Somerset.* „ II 439
One Philip Edgar of Toft Hall in *Somerset* Is lately dead. „ II 445
I have been telling her of the death of one Philip Edgar of Toft Hall, *Somerset.* „ II 707
Yes; it was in the *Somersetshire* papers. „ III 148
Something (*See also* **Summat, Summut**) I miss *s.* The tree that only bears dead fruit is gone. *Queen Mary* III i 18
I'll say *s* for you—so—good-bye. „ IV ii 167
and our Latimer-sailors Will teach her *s.* „ IV iii 350
There should be *s* fierier than fire „ V iv 26
Make not thou The nothing *s.* *Harold* I i 363
On a sudden—at a *s*—for a nothing— „ I i 442
and *s* I had to say—I love thee none the less—Which will so vex thee. *Rosamund.* *S* against *me*? *Becket* II i 206
We that are kings are *s* in this world, „ II ii 245
S that would displease me. „ III i 245
may there not be *s* Of this world's leaven in thee too, „ V ii 28
Something-nothing Some daily *s-n.* „ III i 80
Sometime (*See also* **Soomtimes**) It may be *s's* I have overshot My duties „ V i 37
s's been moved to tears by a chapter of fine writing in a novel; *Prom. of May* III 208
Somewhat (*See also* **Summat, Summut**) trust him *s* less Than Simon Renard, *Queen Mary* I v 221
S beyond your settled purpose? „ V i 207
Son has offer'd her his *s* Philip, the Pope and the Devil. „ I i 106
S Courtenay, wilt thou see the holy father Murdered before thy face? up, *s*, and save him! They love thee, „ I iii 63
Most goodly, Kinglike and an Emperor's *s*,— „ I v 3
Holy Virgin, Plead with thy blessed *S*; „ I v 85
And be stepmother of a score of *s's*! „ I v 206
princely *s*, Heir of this England and the Netherlands! „ I v 417
sire begets Not half his likeness in the *s.* „ II i 55
that the *s* Being a King, might wed a Queen— „ III i 74
The King is here!—My star, my *s*! „ III ii 184
Perchance in England, loves her like a *s.* „ III iii 267
O *S* of God, Redeemer of the world! „ IV iii 118
O God the *S*, Not for slight faults alone, „ IV iii 138
Didst thou yield up thy *S* to human death; „ IV iii 144
And Thy most blessed *S's*, who died for man. „ IV iii 154
For Alva is true *s* of the true church— „ V i 159
Have done my best, and as a faithful *s*, „ V ii 117
And the poor *s* turn'd out into the street „ V ii 125
Gamel, *s* of Orm, What thinkest thou this means? (repeat) *Harold* I i 20, 463
I have a Norman fever on me, *s*, „ I i 87
Hail, Gamel, *s* of Orm! „ I i 92
War there, my *s*? is that the doom of England? „ I i 125
Tostig says true; my *s*, thou art too hard, „ I i 205
I know it, *s*; I am not thankless: „ I i 215
Not thee, my *s*: some other messenger. „ I i 243
now the *s's* of Godwin Sit topmost in the field „ I i 324
feuds that part The *s's* of Godwin from the *s's* of Alfgar „ I ii 180
that was his guest, Gamel, the *s* of Orm: „ II ii 299
O *s*, when thou didst tell me of thine oath, „ III i 267
My *s*, the Saints are virgins; „ III i 271
O my *s*! Are all oaths to be broken then, „ III i 285
S, there is one who loves thee: „ III i 289
and dear *s*, swear When thou art king, „ III i 304
O good *s*! That knowledge made him all the carefuller „ III i 339
Come thou back, and be Once more a *s* of Godwin. „ IV ii 60
Of Alfred, or of Edward his great *s*, „ IV iii 52
mark'd the *s's* of those Who made this Britain England, „ IV iii 152
Noble Gurth! Best *s* of Godwin! „ V i 135

Son (*continued*) They are so much holier than their harlot's *s* *Harold* V ii 12
I, true *s* Of Holy Church—no croucher *Becket, Pro.* 210
To this *s* of a London merchant— „ *Pro.* 433
Look on me as I were thy bodily *s*, For, like a *s*, „ I iii 263
My burgher's *s*—Nay, if I cannot break him „ I iii 332
S's sit in judgment on their father!— „ I iii 551
S, first hear *me*! „ I iii 672
Hear me, *s.* As gold Outvalues dross, „ I iii 713
I thank you, *s's*; when kings but hold by crowns, „ II ii 280
Thou art no prophet, Nor yet a prophet's *s.* „ II ii 422
S, I absolve thee in the name of God. „ II ii 442
it was but the sacrifice of a kingdom to his *s*, a smaller matter; „ III iii 107
King would act servitor and hand a dish to his *s*; „ III iii 140
'great honour,' says he, 'from the King's self to the King's *s.*' „ III iii 146
'Should not an earl's *s* wait on a king's *s*?' „ III iii 151
crowning thy young *s* by York, London and Salisbury—not Canterbury. „ III iii 194
fawn upon him For thy life and thy *s's*. *Rosamund.* I am a Clifford, My *s* a Clifford and Plantagenet. „ IV ii 225
King himself, for love of his own *s's*, „ IV ii 345
link'd me with him To bear him kingly *s's*. „ IV ii 449
Stirr'd up a party there against your *s*— „ V i 7
I cannot think he moves against my *s*, Knowing right well with what a tenderness He loved my *s.* „ V i 19
that but obey'd the crown, Crowning your *s*; „ V i 52
this no wife has born you four brave *s's*, „ V i 126
In one a *s* stone-blind Sat by his mother's hearth: „ V ii 104
The prelates whom he chose to crown his *s*! „ V ii 400
S, husband, brother gash'd to death in vain, *The Cup* I ii 143
came back last night with her *s* to the castle. *The Falcon* 3
How couldst thou do it, my *s*? „ 52
happy was the prodigal *s*, For he return'd to the rich father; „ 141
For fear of losing more than friend, a *s*; „ 333
White? I warrant thee, my *s*, as the snow „ 500
O my dear *s*, be not unkind to me. „ 509
give my time To him that is a part of you, your *s.* „ 792
I would you had a *s*! „ 824
beggar-woman seeking alms For her sick *s*, „ 854
We two together Will help to heal your *s*—your *s* „ 923
After my frolic with his tenant's girl, Made younger elder *s*, *Prom. of May* I 494
I have lost my gold, I have lost my *s*, *Foresters* I i 338
Thou Much, miller's *s*, hath not the Earl right? „ I ii 46
Much, the miller's *s*, I knew thy father: „ I iii 146
And all their *s's* be free, „ II i 22
and the *s* Is most like dead— „ II i 146
This is my *s* but late escaped from prison, „ II i 460
I Little John, he Much the miller's *s*, and he Scarlet, „ III 55
which a pious *s* of the Church gave me this morning „ III 281
Blown like a true *s* of the woods. „ IV 427
I grieve to say it was thy father's *s.* „ IV 811
We ever fail'd to light upon thy *s.* „ IV 984
The gold—my *s*—my gold, my *s*, the land— „ IV 987
Art thou my *s*? *Walter Lea.* I am, good father, „ IV 1019
Song According to the *s.* *Queen Mary* I v 622
And answer them in *s.* „ II i 53
S flies you know For ages. „ II i 80
Our little sister of the *S* of *S's*! „ III ii 103
mock the blessed Host In *s's* so lewd, „ IV iii 367
Shall Alice sing you One of her pleasant *s's*? „ V ii 355
Love is come with a *s* and a smile, Welcome Love with a smile and a *s*: *Harold* I ii 10
And chanting that old *s* of Brunanburg „ V i 215
our old *s's* are prayers for England too! „ V i 222
—like a *s* of the people. *Becket, Pro.* 338
Has my simple *s* set you jingling? „ *Pro.* 378
bird that moults sings the same *s* again, „ I iii 447
coming up with a *s* in the flush of the glimmering red? „ II i 7
they say, she makes *s's*, and that's against her, for I never knew an honest woman that could make *s's*, tho' to be sure our mother 'ill sing me old *s's* by the hour, „ III i 181

Song (*continued*) none on 'em ever made *s's*, and they were all honest. *Becket* III i 189
Whose evil *s* far on into the night „ v ii 208
tell him my tales, Sing him my *s's*? *The Falcon* 797
I don't know why I sing that *s*; I don't love it. *Prom. of May* I 61
Fanny be the naäme i' the *s*, but I swopt it fur *she.* „ II 212
Sings a new *s* to the new year—and you Strike up a *s*, *Foresters* I iii 28
There was a *s* be made to the turning wheel— „ I iii 153
To sing the *s's* of England Beneath the greenwood tree. „ II i 23
True soul of the Saxon churl for whom *s* has no charm. „ II i 386
We be scared with *s* and shout. „ II ii 164
we have made a *s* in your honour, so your ladyship care to listen. „ III 414
Out on thy *s*! „ IV 28
did ye not call me king in your *s*? „ IV 220
Let the birds sing, and do you dance to their *s*. „ IV 557
Songing *See* **Sing-songing**
Son-in-law For, Robin, he must be my *s-i-l*. *Foresters* II i 451
Sonnet (*See also* **Sonnet-making**) were a pious work To string my father's *s's*, *Queen Mary* II i 27
Hand me the casket with my father's *s's*. *William.* Ay—*s's*— „ II i 44
Tut, your *s's* a flying ant, „ II i 83
Write you as many *s's* as you will. „ II i 95
Sonneteer Or would you have me turn a *s*, „ III vi 154
Sonnet-making and no call for sonnet-sorting now, nor for *s-m* either, „ II i 60
And *s-m's* safer. „ II i 93
Sonnet-sorting and no call for *s-s* now, nor for sonnet-making either, „ II i 59
Sonnetting Come, now, you're *s* again. „ II i 247
Soom (**some**) and I taäked 'im fur *s* sort of a land-surveyor— *Prom. of May* I 204
but I hallus gi'ed *s* on 'em to Miss Eva at this time o' year. „ II 15
so I allus browt soom on 'em to her; „ II 20
an' them theer be *s* of her oän roses, „ II 38
Soomerset (**Somerset**) Philip Hedgar o' *S*! (repeat) „ II 587
—I'll *S* tha. „ II 592
'O' the 17th, Philip Edgar, o' Toft Hall, *S*.' „ II 712
Soomtimes (**sometimes**) And p'raps ye hears 'at I *s* taäkes a drop too much; „ II 108
Sooner He'd *s* be, While this same marriage question *Queen Mary* II ii 36
At thy most need—not *s*. *Harold.* So I will. *Harold* III i 16
S or later shamed of her among The ladies, *Prom. of May* III 581
No *s*? when will that be? *Foresters* IV 420
Soot even if I found it Dark with the *s* of slums. *Prom. of May* III 602
Sop new Lords Are quieted with their *s* of Abbey-lands, *Queen Mary* III i 142
Sore (**adj.**) (*See also* **Half-sore**) Remember that *s* saying spoken once By Him „ IV iii 202
Sore (**s**) gangrenes, and running *s's*, praise ye the Lord, *Becket* I iv 256
Sorrier thou canst not be *s* than I am. *Foresters* I ii 282
Sorrow Grace to repent and *s* for their schism; *Queen Mary* III iii 177
Following her like her *s*. „ v v 11
Sorrow'd I *s* for my random promise given *Harold* III i 269
Have *s* for her all these years in vain. *Prom. of May* II 415
Sorry Good faith, I was too *s* for the woman To mark the dress. *Queen Mary* III i 57
I am *s* for it If Pole be like to turn. „ III iv 415
I'm *s* for it, for, tho' he never comes to church, *Prom. of May* I 260
I am *s* Mr. Steer still continues too unwell to attend to you, „ III 21
though I can be *s* for him—as the good Sally says, „ III 173
'I am *s* that we could not attend your Grace's party on the 10th!' „ III 312
I am *s* my exchequer runs so low *Foresters* I ii 272
Here is thy gold again. I am *s* for it. „ IV 985
Sort What *s* of brothers then be those that lust *Queen Mary* IV iii 196
I have seen heretics of the poorer *s*, „ IV iii 436
I think that in some *s* we may. „ IV iii 551
Were but a *s* of winter; „ v iv 16
As . . . in some *s* . . . I have been false to thee. *Harold* v i 351
Yes, in some *s* I do. *Foresters* II i 527
I tell thee, in some *s*. *Robin.* *S*! *s*! what *s*? what *s* of man art thou For land, „ II i 531

Sorting *See* **Sonnet-sorting**
Sought I *s* him and I could not find him. *The Cup* II 396
That *s* to free the tomb-place of the King *Foresters* IV 408
Soul The downfall of so many simple *s's*, *Queen Mary* I ii 54
my good mother came (God rest her *s*) „ I v 12
Or Lady Jane? *Wyatt.* No, poor *s*; no. „ II i 242
We kill the heretics that sting the *s*— „ III iv 69
And every *s* of man that breathes therein. „ III vi 107
A secular kingdom is but as the body Lacking a *s*; „ IV i 33
Is as the *s* descending out of heaven „ IV i 35
to the saving of their *s's*, Before your execution. „ IV ii 194
for thy *s* shall masses here be sung „ IV iii 100
Pray with one breath, one heart, one *s* for me. „ IV iii 104
peril mine own *s* By slaughter of the body? „ v v 168
Let the great Devil fish for your own *s's*. *Harold* II i 32
We have respect for man's immortal *s*, „ II ii 501
A conscience for his own *s*, not his realm; „ III i 63
But wing'd *s's* flying Beyond all change „ III ii 100
one for all, and all for one, One *s*! „ IV iii 60
The *s* who fighteth on thy side is cursed, „ v i 69
Praying perchance for this poor *s* of mine „ v i 323
and the *s* of Eleanor from hell-fire. *Becket, Pro.* 151
Peace to his *s*! „ *Pro.* 394
Poor *s*! poor *s*! My friend, the King! . . . „ I i 334
The *s* the body, and the Church the Throne, „ I iii 717
loathing for a *s* Purer, and truer and nobler „ II i 171
Fling not thy *s* into the flames of hell: „ II i 316
And break the *s* from earth. „ v i 44
God save him from all sickness of the *s*! „ v ii 175
His child and mine own *s*, and so return. „ v ii 193
all the *s's* we saved and father'd here Will greet us „ v ii 223
Is it too late for me to save your *s*? „ v ii 524
ere two *s's* be knit for life and death, *The Cup* II 359
God rest his honest *s*, he bought 'em for me, *The Falcon* 49
For all the *s's* on earth that live *Prom. of May* III 7
For all the blessed *s's* in Heaven „ III 10
A *s* with no religion—My mother used to say „ III 532
Sleep, happy *s*! all life will sleep at last. *Foresters* I iii 48
The *s* of the woods hath stricken thro' my blood, „ II i 66
True *s* of the Saxon churl for whom song has no charm. „ II i 385
And that would quite *un*man him, heart and *s*. „ III 30
I Embrace thee with the kisses of the *s*. „ III 143
flung His life, heart, *s* into those holy wars „ IV 407
Who hunger for the body, not the *s*— „ IV 700
Marriage is of the *s*, not of the body. „ IV 720
I remain Mistress of mine own self and mine own *s*. „ IV 730
Sound (**adj.**) *S* sleep to the man Here by dead Norway without dream or dawn! *Harold* IV iii 120
Go round once more; See all be *s* and whole. „ v i 194
and most amorous Of good old red *s* liberal Gascon wine: *Becket, Pro.* 100
A great and *s* policy that: I could embrace him for it: „ *Pro.* 451
And were my kindly father *s* again, *Foresters* III 81
S at the core as we are. „ III 102
Sound (**s**) What is that whirring *s*? (repeat) *Harold* v i 482, 665
Sound (**verb**) To *s* the Princess carelessly on this; *Queen Mary* v i 259
That is noble! That *s's* of Godwin. *Harold* IV ii 58
How ghostly *s's* that horn in the black wood! *Becket* III ii 16
when the horn *s's* she comes out as a wolf. „ III ii 23
when that horn *s's*, a score of wolf-dogs are let loose „ III ii 38
all that *s's* so wicked and so strange; *Prom. of May* I 656
name Of Harold *s's* so English and so old „ III 610
Wherever the horn *s*, and the buck bound, *Foresters* III 345
Wherever the buck bound, and the horn *s*, „ III 356
Sounded I'll have the scandal *s* to the mud. *Queen Mary* I v 227
Sour Yon gray old Gospeller, *s* as midwinter, „ I iii 40
S milk and black bread. *Foresters* II i 272
And jealousy is wither'd, *s* and ugly: „ II ii 65
South North and *S* Thunder together, *Harold* III i 392
The men that guarded England to the *S* „ IV iii 210
in *S* and North at once I could not be. „ IV iii 217
I left our England naked to the *S* „ v i 289
Southern The tan of *s* summers and the beard? *Prom. of May* II 617
Southwark Wyatt comes to *S*; *Queen Mary* II ii 375
And pointed full at *S*; „ II iii 46

Speak (*continued*) You brawl beyond the question;
s, Lord Legate! — Queen Mary III iv 98
S, friend Bonner, And tell this learned Legate — „ III iv 270
Nay, God's passion, before me! s! — „ III iv 286
till it spells and s's Quite other than at first. — „ III v 36
May Simon Renard s a single word? — „ III vi 121
to s a single word That could not be forgiven. — „ III vi 126
Yourselves shall hear him s. S, Master Cranmer, — „ IV iii 110
After the vanish'd voice, and s to men. — „ IV iii 164
see, see, I s of him in the past. — „ IV iii 422
even while I s There lurks a silent dagger, — „ V ii 215
Low, my lute; s low, my lute, — „ V ii 367
And may not s for hours. — „ V ii 406
When he we s of drove the window back, — „ V ii 464
but I s from mine own self, not him; — „ V iii 41
letting the wild brook S for us— — „ V v 92
—they cannot s—for awe; — Harold I i 32
s him sweetly, he will hear thee. — „ I i 116
in Normanland God s's thro' abler voices, — „ I i 167
Did not Heaven s to men in dreams of old? — „ I ii 94
He'll s for himself! Hold thine own, if thou canst! — „ II i 79
S for thy mother's sake, and tell me true. — „ II ii 271
Obey him, s him fair, — „ II ii 317
Is it not better still to s the truth? — „ II ii 373
O s him fair, Harold, for thine own sake. — „ II ii 395
Oh no, no—s him fair! — „ II ii 413
thou be my vice-king in England. S. — „ II ii 636
When all the world hath learnt to s the truth, — „ III i 68
If one may dare to s the truth, — „ IV i 108
We never—oh! good Morcar, s for us, — „ IV i 216
And, when again red-blooded, s again; — „ IV iii 208
I s after my fancies, for I am a Troubadour, — Becket, Pro. 346
he s's to a noble as tho' he were a churl, — „ Pro. 454
And all that s for them anathema. — „ I i 171
Do thou s first. — „ I iv 1
To s without stammering and like a free man? — „ I iv 7
Who misuses a dog would misuse a child—they
cannot s for themselves— — „ I iv 110
S only of thy love. — „ II i 179
He s's As if it were a cake of gingerbread. — „ II i 229
and to s truth, night at the end of our last crust, — „ III i 113
and not s till I was spoke to, — „ III i 120
bad me whatever I saw not to s one word, — „ III i 133
not to s one word, for that's the rule o' the garden, — „ III i 137
tho' I shouldn't s one word, — „ III i 154
tho' I be sworn not to s a word, I can tell you all
about her, — „ III i 205
That I would s with you once more alone. — „ III iii 40
Did the King S of the customs? — „ III iii 333
You have wrong'd Fitzurse. I s not of myself. — „ IV ii 328
—I have still thy leave to s. — „ V ii 45
Can I s with you Alone, my father? — „ V ii 69
Then s; this is my other self, — „ V ii 73
Better perhaps to s with them apart. — „ V ii 310
S with them privately on this hereafter. — „ V ii 419
As I shall s again. — „ V ii 517
I pray you for one moment stay and s. — „ V ii 525
Some friends of mine would s with me without. — The Cup I ii 203
no more power than other oracles To s directly.
Phœbe. Will you s to him, The messenger
from Synorix — „ II 35
Did not this man S well? — „ II 92
Nor s I now too mightily, being King And happy! — „ II 237
These are strange words to s to Artemis. — „ II 326
S freely, tho' to call a madman mad — The Falcon 81
Can I s with the Count? — „ 179
won't you s with the old woman first, — „ 182
yet to s white truth, my good old mother, — „ 503
Can I not s with you once more alone? — „ 688
You s like love, and yet you love me not. — „ 782
No more, but s. Giovanna. I will. — „ 814
And s for him after—you that are so clever! — Prom. of May I 619
S not so loudly; that must be your sister. — „ I 726
Did you s, Philip? — „ I 748
Is not this To s too pitilessly of the dead? — „ II 461

Speak (*continued*) will you not s with Father to-day? — Prom. of May III 237
Can't I s like a lady; pen a letter like a lady; — „ III 301
and he wants to s to ye partic'lar. — „ III 351
What ails you? Harold. S. — „ III 662
and s small to 'em, and not scare 'em — Foresters I i 100
I will s with her. — „ I i 306
so that you keep the cowl down and s not? — „ I ii 22
nor to s word to anyone, — „ I ii 237
We old hags should be bribed to s truth, — „ II i 237
S straight out, crookback. — „ II i 270
I beseech you all to s lower. — „ II i 334
S but one word not only of forgiveness, — „ II i 610
S to me, I am like a boy now going to be whipt; — „ II ii 49
S to me, Kate, and say you pardon me! Kate. I
never will s word to thee again. — „ II ii 53
How much? how much? S, or the arrow flies. — „ III 278
S not. I wait upon a dying father. — „ IV 610
If a cat may look at a king, may not a friar s to one? — „ IV 922

Speaker It would have burnt both s's. — Queen Mary III vi 164
for thou Art known a s of the truth, — Harold II ii 517

Speakest Thou s of the enemy of thy king. — Queen Mary I v 327
Thou s like a fool or a woman. — Foresters I i 203
Thou standest straight. Thou s manlike. — „ II i 409

Speaking I can forespeak your s. — Queen Mary I v 137
or by s aught Which might impugn or prejudice — „ III iii 132
not half s The language of the land. — Becket II i 136
I was s with Your father, asking — Prom. of May III 491

Spear not S into pruning-hook— — Harold V i 442

Spear-head Mark'd how the s-h sprang, — „ IV iii 158

Sped And I s hither with what haste — Queen Mary II iv 77

Speech after some slight s about the Sheriff — Foresters II i 114

Speechify and we'll git 'im to s for us arter dinner. — Prom. of May I 440

Speed That sun may God s! — Harold I i 72
Must s you to your bower at once. — Becket I i 291

Speedwell Bluebell, harebell, s, bluebottle, — Prom. of May I 97

Spell (s) Eva's eyes thro' hers—A s upon me! — „ II 643
Weary—weary As tho' a s were on me. — Foresters II ii 115

Spell (verb) loons That cannot s Esaïas from St. Paul, — Queen Mary III i 281
till it s's and speaks Quite other than at first. — „ III v 36
old hag tho' I be, I can s the hand. — Foresters II i 351

Spend For she shall s her honeymoon with me. — „ IV 757

Spent like a butterfly in a chrysalis, You s your life; — Queen Mary I iv 52
I s thrice that in fortifying his castles. — Becket I iii 632
s all your last Saturday's wages at the ale-house; — Prom. of May III 78

Spice Some s of wisdom in my telling you, — Queen Mary II iv 134
A s of Satan, ha! — „ III iv 77
fling in the s's, Nard, Cinnamon, — The Cup II 183

Spiced I know your Norman cookery is so s, — Harold II ii 811

Spice-islands And all the fair s-i's of the East. — Queen Mary V i 49

Spider Crost and recrost, a venomous s's web— — Becket II i 199
Then I would drop from the casement, like a s. — Foresters I i 317

Spied had Howard s me there And made them speak, — Queen Mary II iii 32
s my people's ways; — Becket I iii 363
I never s in thee one gleam of grace. — „ V ii 474

Spilt the cow kick'd, and all her milk was s. — Queen Mary III v 267

Spin these poor hands but sew, S, broider— — Harold IV iii 11

Spine My old crook'd s would bud out — „ III i 24

Spire parson from his own s swung out dead, — Queen Mary IV iii 375
s of Holy Church may prick the graves— — Becket I iii 553

Spiring O tower s to the sky, — Prom. of May III 203

Spirit If Cranmer's s were a mocking one, — Queen Mary V ii 210
like a s in Hell who skips and flies — Harold I i 10
some familiar s must have help'd him. — „ II ii 677
s of the twelve Apostles enter'd Into thy making. — Becket I i 50
and mortify thy flesh, Not s— — „ I iii 541
talk not of cows. You anger the s. — Foresters II i 330

Spiritual We, the Lords S and Temporal, — Queen Mary III iii 113
A soldier's, not a s arm. Henry. I lack a soldier,
Thomas— — Becket, Pro. 255
that sweet other-world smile which will be reflected
in the s body among the angels. — „ Pro. 397
And on a matter wholly s. — „ I iii 85
striving still to break or bind The s giant with our
island laws And customs, — „ IV ii 444
Fasts, disciplines that clear the s eye, — „ V i 42

Spiritus Salva Fili, Salva *S*, *Harold* V i 469
Spit *S* them like larks for aught I care. *Queen Mary* I v 395
Dare-devils, that would eat fire and *s* it out „ III i 156
Spital (hospital) I ha' nine darters i' the *s* that be dead *Becket* I iv 250
Spite (s) *S* of her tears her father forced it on her. *Queen Mary* I v 495
S of Lord Paget and Lord William Howard, „ III i 324
Sir Henry Bedingfield May split it for a *s*. „ III v 48
S of your melancholy Sir Nicholas, „ V ii 327
I never found he bore me any *s*. „ V ii 474
S of this grisly star ye three must gall *Harold* I i 418
glad to wreak our *s* on the rosefaced minion *Becket, Pro.* 529
And mean to keep them, In *s* of thee! „ I iii 143
S, ignorance, envy, Yea, honesty too, „ II i 100
mix our *s's* And private hates with our defence „ V ii 51
quarrels with themselves, their *s's* at Rome, *The Cup* I i 91
S of ten thousand brothers, Federigo. *The Falcon* 898
he be fit to bust hissen wi' *s's* and jalousies. *Prom. of May* II 165
Spite (verb) I wear it then to *s* her. *Queen Mary* I iv 78
Spiteful Elf, with *s* heart and eye, Talk of jealousy? *Foresters* II ii 172
Spiteful-like 'Coomly to look at,' says she—but she said it *s-l*. *Prom. of May* I 180
Spitting *See* **A-spitting**
Splendid and among them Courtenay, to be made Earl of Devon, of royal blood, of *s* feature, *Queen Mary* I i 111
I shall judge with my own eyes whether her Grace incline to this *s* scion of Plantagenet. „ I i 135
Good, was it *s*? „ III i 49
you couldn't have more *s* weather. *Prom. of May* II 48
Splendour Came with a sudden *s*, shout, and show, *Queen Mary* III i 449
by the *s* of God, no guest of mine. *Harold* II ii 25
scarce touch'd or tasted The *s's* of our Court. „ II ii 175
by the *s* of God—have I fought men Like Harold „ V ii 177
secular *s's*, and a favourer Of players, *Becket* I i 78
lest the crown should be Shorn of ancestral *s*. „ I iii 157
Rather than dim the *s* of his crown „ V ii 343
Thou seem'st a saintly *s* out from heaven, *Foresters* II i 606
Splinter'd are sliver'd off and *s* by Their lightning— *Harold* V i 540
Split (s) I hate a *s* between old friendships *Becket* II ii 380
Split (verb) Sir Henry Bedingfield May *s* it for a spite. *Queen Mary* III v 48
whose quick flash *s's* The mid-sea mast, *The Cup* II 292
Spoil (s) To make free *s* and havock of your goods. *Queen Mary* II ii 186
safe from all The *s* and sackage aim'd „ II ii 248
Spoil (verb) thou hast taught the king to *s* him too; *Harold* I i 451
We never hounded on the State at home To *s* the Church. *Becket* II ii 97
Yea, let a stranger *s* his heritage, „ II ii 258
No—no gold. Mother says gold *s's* all. „ IV i 43
To foil and *s* the tyrant *Foresters* II i 11
Spoil'd-Spoilt Now the *spoilt* child sways both. *Harold* I i 453
Had I been by, I would have *spoil'd* his horn. „ I ii 73
You have *spoilt* the farce. *Becket* IV ii 337
We *spoil'd* the prior, friar, abbot, monk, *Foresters* III 167
Spoke (*See also* **Spake**) she *s* even of Northumberland pitifully, *Queen Mary* I i 92
I thought of you, my liege, Ev'n as I *s*. „ III ii 96
What traitor *s*? Here, let my cousin Pole „ V ii 243
He *s* of this; and unto him you owe „ V iii 29
And he *s*! I heard him— *Harold* II ii 352
Who *s*? *Beggar*. Nobody, my lord. *Becket* I iv 134
I *s* of late to the boy, he answer'd me, „ II ii 5
and not speak till I was *s* to, and I answered for myself that I never *s* more than was needed, „ III i 120
out of those scraps and shreds Filippo *s* of. *The Falcon* 148
brooding Upon a great unhappiness when you *s*. *Prom. of May* II 384
I *s* of your names, Allen, „ III 35
Spoken (*See also* **Civil-spoken**) wish fulfill'd before the word Was *s*, *Queen Mary* I iv 234
I scarce have *s* with you Since when?— „ IV ii 118
saying *s* once By Him that was the truth, „ IV iii 202
I take it that the King hath *s* to you; „ V iii 85
I have not *s* to the king One word; *Harold* V i 334
There have I *s* true? *Becket* II i 119
You have *s* to the peril of your life? „ V ii 516
Well *s*, wife. *Synorix*. Madam, so well I yield. *The Cup* I ii 171
He hath *s* truth in a world of lies. *Foresters* III 211
Search them, Kate, and see if they have *s* truth. „ III 289
Spoken (*continued*) Robin, he hath no more. He hath *s* truth. *Foresters* IV 181
Spoon What is it, Filippo. *Filippo*. *S's* your lordship. *Count*. *S's*! *The Falcon* 398
wasn't my lady born with a golden *s* in her ladyship's mouth, „ 401
Have we not half a score of silver *s's*? „ 406
Sport And heard these two, there might be *s* for him. *Queen Mary* V ii 213
Co-mates we were, and had our *s* together, *Becket* II ii 121
'As flies to the Gods; they kill us for their *s*.' *Prom. of May* I 265
It is Nature kills, And not for *her s* either. „ I 273
your free *s's* have swallow'd my free hour. *Foresters* IV 339
Spotless White as the light, the *s* bride of Christ, *Queen Mary* III iv 199
Spousal (the *s* ring whereof, Not ever to be laid aside, I wear Upon this finger), „ II ii 165
Spouse The *s* of the Great King, thy King, hath fallen— *Becket* III iii 175
Sprang Mark'd how the spear-head *s*, *Harold* IV iii 158
They say that Rome *S* from a wolf. *The Cup* I ii 14
Spread (*See also* **Wide-spread**) Stand on the deck and *s* his wings for sail! *Queen Mary* I v 379
so the plague Of schism *s's*; „ III iv 172
ever *s* into the man Here in our silence? *Becket* III i 22
they *s* their raiment down Before me— „ V ii 368
if the fever *s*, the parish will have to thank you for it. *Prom. of May* III 46
Our feast is yonder, *s* beneath an oak, *Foresters* IV 189
Spreading *See* **A-spreading**
Sprig if I hadn't a *s* o' wickentree sewn into my dress, *Foresters* II i 249
Spring (fountain) the *s* Of all those evils that have flow'd *Queen Mary* III iv 233
midriff-shaken even to tears, as *s's* gush out after earthquakes— *Becket* III iii 162
Spring (season) Her life was winter, for her *s* was nipt: *Queen Mary* V v 269
They are but of *s*, They fly the winter change— *Harold* III ii 96
By all the leaves of *s*, *Foresters* III 439
For now is the *s* of the year. „ IV 17
Spring (verb) there *s's* to light That Centaur *Queen Mary* III iv 161
char us back again into the dust We *s* from. „ III v 56
when he *s's* And maims himself against the bars, „ V v 66
Tostig, thou look'st as thou wouldst *s* upon him. *Harold* I i 394
be those I fear who prick'd the lion To make him *s*, „ IV iii 96
Ay, there *s's* a Saxon on him, „ V i 498
S's from the loneliness of my poor bower, *Becket* III i 40
By all the deer that *s* Thro' wood and lawn *Foresters* III 424
Spring-and-winter Must come to in our *s-a-w* world *Prom. of May* III 510
Springe We hold our Saxon woodcock in the *s*, *Harold* II ii 2
Spring-tide whisper to the roar Of a *s-t*. *Queen Mary* IV ii 188
Sprout (s) bastard *s*, My sister, is far fairer than myself. „ I v 71
Sprout (verb) There *s's* a salad in the garden still. *The Falcon* 149
Sprung They must have *s* like Ghosts from underground, *Foresters* IV 592
Spurn'd If hearing, would have *s* her; *Becket* IV ii 346
Spy (s) We have our *spies* abroad to catch *Queen Mary* I v 467
From *spies* of thine to spy my nakedness *Harold* I i 351
The Romans sent me here a *s* upon you, *The Cup* I ii 220
Spy (verb) *s* not out our game Too early. *Queen Mary* I iii 173
I *s* the rock beneath the smiling sea. „ I iv 278
to *s* my nakedness In my poor North! *Harold* I i 351
Lest thy fierce Tostig *s* me out alone, „ IV i 190
I can *s* already A strain of hard and headstrong *Becket, Pro.* 233
my friends may *s* him And slay him as he runs. *The Cup* I ii 391
Didn't I *s* 'em a-sitting i' the woodbine harbour togither? *Prom. of May* I 124
Dobbins, or some other, *s* Edgar in Harold? „ II 674
but softly, lest they *s* thee, friar! *Foresters* II i 438
Squad (mud) Thruf slush an' *s* When roäds was bad, *Prom. of May* II 309
Squeamish so thou be *S* at eating the King's venison. *Foresters* IV 194
Squeezed I stand so *s* among the crowd *Queen Mary* III i 238
that hath *s* out this side-smile upon Canterbury, whereof may come conflagration. *Becket* III iii 56
Squint from the *s* Of lust and glare of malice. „ I i 312
Squire The Queen of England—or the Kentish *S*? *Queen Mary* II ii 270
S!—if so be you be a *s*. *Prom. of May* I 457
you be a pretty *s*. I ha' fun' ye out, I hev. „ II 689

Squire (*continued*) I left mine horse and armour with a *S*, *Foresters* IV 415
Squirrel The tawny *s* vaulting thro' the boughs, „ I iii 117
your woodland *s* sees the nut Behind the shell, „ II i 646
Stab (s) practise on my life, By poison, fire, shot, *s*— *Queen Mary* I iv 285
if our person be secured From traitor *s's*— „ V v 281
Then with one quick short *s*—eternal peace. *The Cup* I iii 124
Stab (verb) *S* me in fancy, hissing Spain and Philip; *Queen Mary* I v 150
That I could *s* her standing there! *Harold* V i 365
Steady enough to *s* him! *The Cup* II 213
Stabb'd To marry him who *s* her Sinnatus. „ II 23
and my grandsire *s* him there. *The Falcon* 252
Stack when you put it in green, and your *s* caught fire. *Prom. of May* II 56
Staff (*See also* **Cross-staff**) by God's providence a good stout *s* Lay near me; *Queen Mary* V ii 468
Stafford (Sir Thomas) (*See also* **Thomas Stafford**) *S*, I am a sad man and a serious. „ III i 41
Stag They slew my *s's* in mine own manor here, *Becket* V ii 438
The *s* is there? *Maid.* Seen in the thicket *The Cup* I i 112
Hillo, the *s*! What, you are all unfurnish'd? „ I i 205
my good fellow, *My* arrow struck the *s*. „ I ii 28
we will not quarrel about the *s*. „ I ii 39
would have chased the *s* to-day In the full face „ I ii 267
Have let him hunt the *s* with you to-day. *Sinnatus.* I warrant you now, he said *he* struck the *s*. *Camma.* Why no, he never touched upon the *s*. „ I ii 379
You will believe Now that he never struck the *s*— „ I ii 430
if we kill a *s*, our dogs have their paws cut off, *Foresters* IV 225
He met a *s* there on so narrow a ledge— „ IV 531
Stagger for their sake who *s* betwixt thine Appeal, *Becket* I iii 621
nor our Archbishop *S* on the slope decks „ II ii 106
if you boxed the Pope's ears with a purse, you might *s* him, „ II ii 371
Stagger'd Not *s* by this ominous earth and heaven: *Harold* I i 207
Staggering who could trace a hand So wild and *s*? *The Falcon* 439
Stain'd from the street *S* with the mire thereof. *Becket* I iii 691
you Would find it *s*— *Count.* Silence, Elisabetta! *Elisabetta.* *S* with the blood of the best heart *The Falcon* 664
Stainless To purchase for Himself a *s* bride; *Queen Mary* III iii 205
Stake (a post) the thumbscrew, the *s*, the fire. „ II i 201
Or—if the Lord God will it—on the *s*. „ II i 251
I will show fire on my side—*s* and fire— „ III i 327
To bring the heretic to the *s*, „ III iv 9
Yet others are that dare the *s* and fire, „ III iv 167
And that myself was fasten'd to the *s*, „ IV ii 3
Have found a real presence in the *s*, „ IV ii 142
another recantation Of Cranmer at the *s*. „ IV iii 300
chain, Wherewith they bound him to the *s*, „ IV iii 596
blood and sweat of heretics at the *s* „ V i 101
Stake (a wager) And the *s's* high? „ I iii 146
no such gamester As, having won the *s*, *The Cup* I iii 146
Stale And customs, made me for the moment proud Ev'n of that *s* Church-bond *Becket* IV ii 447
Stalk From off the *s* and trample it in the mire, *Foresters* I ii 110
Stamford-bridge on the Derwent? ay At *S-b*. *Harold* IV i 255
On to *S-b*! „ IV ii 82
I fought another fight than this Of *S-b*. „ IV iii 25
What's Brunanburg To *S-b*? „ IV iii 144
middle of that fierce fight At *S-b*. „ IV iii 185
Many are fallen At *S-b*. . . . „ IV iii 215
To tell thee thou shouldst win at *S-b*, „ V i 236
Stammer'd when she touch'd on thee, She *s* in her hate; „ I ii 37
Stammering To speak without *s* and like a free man? *Becket* I iv 7
Stamp *S* out the fire, or this Will smoulder *Queen Mary* I v 507
and a foot to *s* it . . . Flat. *Harold* V ii 193
Stan' I ha' heärd 'im a-gawin' on 'ud make your 'air—God bless it!—*s* on end, *Prom. of May* I 135
Stand (*See also* **Stan'**) *S* back, keep a clear lane! *Queen Mary* I i 1
your name *S's* first of those who sign'd „ I ii 17
S first it may, but it was written last: „ I ii 20
s within the porch, and Christ with me: „ I ii 51
S from me. If Elizabeth lose her head— „ I iii 87
S further off, or you may lose your head. „ I iv 128
Some settled ground for peace to *s* upon. „ I v 315
S on the deck and spread his wings for sail! „ I v 379
with your lawful Prince *S* fast against „ II ii 242
Stand (*continued*) The Queen *s's* up, and speaks for her own self; *Que^ Mary* II ii 341
I dare avouch you'd *s* up for yourself, „ II ii 360
they will *s* by us If Ludgate can be reach'd „ II iii 52
Had holpen Richard's tottering throne to *s*, „ III i 115
I *s* so squeezed among the crowd I cannot lift „ III i 238
S staring at me! shout, you gaping rogue! „ III i 288
Do ye *s* fast by that which ye resolved? „ III iii 103
Paget, You *s* up here to fight for heresy, „ III iv 92
He knows not where he *s's*, „ III iv 420
than to *s* On naked self-assertion. „ IV i 119
ever see a carrion crow *S* watching a sick beast „ IV iii 7
There *s's* a man, once of so high degree, „ IV iii 68
To *s* at ease, and stare as at a show, „ IV iii 292
s behind the pillar here; „ IV iii 462
She *s's* between you and the Queen of Scots. „ V i 192
there is one Death *s's* behind the Groom, And there is one Death *s's* behind the Bride— „ V ii 165
Who *s's* the nearest to her. „ V ii 416
not courtly to *s* helmeted Before the Queen. „ V v 35
Then here she *s's*! my homage. „ V v 253
S by me then, and look upon my face, *Harold* I i 25
S by him, mine old friend, „ I i 112
S thou by him! „ I i 118
thou didst *s* by her and give her thy crabs, „ II i 49
S out of earshot then, „ II ii 240
S there and wait my will. „ II ii 682
crying To a mountain '*S* aside and room for me!' „ IV iii 130
tell him we *s* arm'd on Senlac Hill, „ V i 59
I can see it From where we *s*: „ V i 463
He *s's* between the banners with the dead „ V i 656
high altar *S* where their standard fell . . . „ V ii 140
I *s* and see The rift that runs between me *Becket* I i 139
And that would shake the Papacy as it *s's*. „ I iii 214
I refuse to *s* By the King's censure, „ I iii 722
Who *s's* aghast at her eternal self „ II ii 404
nor any ground but English, Where his cathedral *s's*. „ III iii 262
Come hither, man; *s* there. „ IV ii 219
s beside thee One who might grapple with thy dagger, „ IV ii 228
Sluggards and fools, why do you *s* and stare? „ V i 256
s Clothed with the full authority of Rome, „ V ii 492
Why do you *s* so silent, brother John? „ V ii 535
Some would *s* by you to the death. „ V ii 605
S by, make way! „ V iii 67
S aside, *S* aside; here she comes! *The Cup* I i 104
S apart. „ I ii 317
How gracefully there she *s's* Weeping— *Prom. of May* I 735
to *s* between me and your woman, Kate. *Foresters* I i 304
where twelve Can *s* upright, nor touch each other. „ III 310
I *s* up here, thou there. „ IV 261
The Holy Virgin *S* by the strongest. „ IV 265
Standard Advance our *S* of the Warrior, *Harold* IV i 248
He lies not here: not close beside the *s*. „ V ii 57
high altar Stand where their *s* fell . . . „ V ii 140
As once he bore the *s* of the Angles, So now he bears the *s* of the angels. *Becket* I iii 494
Standest Thou *s* straight. Thou speakest manlike. *Foresters* II i 408
Standing dash The torch of war among your *s* corn, *Harold* II ii 749
No Norman horse Can shatter England, *s* shield by shield; „ V i 196
That I could stab her *s* there! „ V i 365
I cannot tell, tho' *s* in her presence. *Prom. of May* II 557
s up side by side with me, and singing the same hymn? „ III 181
Standstill my bishop Hath brought your king to a *s*. *Becket, Pro.* 44
Star At his coming Your *s* will rise. *Mary.* My *s*! *Queen Mary* I v 411
What *s*? *Renard.* Your *s* will be your princely son, „ I v 415
He comes, and my *s* rises. „ III ii 167
fieriest partisans—are pale Before my *s*! „ III ii 171
which is their doom Before my *s*! „ III ii 176
The King is here!—My *s*, my son! „ III ii 184
a *s* beside the moon Is all but lost; „ V i 79
Would nor for all the *s's* and maiden moon „ V ii 455
Fair island *s*! *Elizabeth.* I shine! „ V iii 15
s That dances in it as mad with agony! *Harold* I i 8
Spite of this grisly *s* ye three must gall „ I i 418

Star (*continued*) the lark sings, the sweet *s's* come and go, *Harold* II ii 434
banner, Blaze like a night of fatal *s's* „ IV i 251
shine Less than a *s* among the goldenest hours „ IV iii 51
Dream'd that twelve *s's* fell glittering out of heaven *Becket* I i 46
cowling and clouding up That fatal *s*, thy Beauty, „ I i 312
Her crypt among the *s's*. „ I iii 555
And shriek to all the saints among the *s's* : „ IV ii 240
I fling all that upon my fate, my *s*. *The Cup* I iii 27
twin sister of the morning *s*, Forelead the sun. „ I iii 45
This shield-borne patriot of the morning *s* „ II 122
with that red *s* between the ribs, „ II 150
A houseless head beneath the sun and *s's*, *Foresters* II i 65
Starched That strange *s* stiff creature, Little John, the Earl's man. „ I i 183
Stare Sluggards and fools, why do you stand and *s* ? *Becket* V i 257
To stand at ease, and *s* as at a show, *Queen Mary* IV iii 292
Philip shall not *S* in upon me in my haggardness ; „ V v 177
Stops and *s's* at our cottage. Ay, ay ! *s* at it : *The Falcon* 162
Staring Stand *s* at me ! shout, you gaping rogue ! *Queen Mary* III i 288
he stood there *S* upon the hunter. *The Cup* I ii 123
Stark but *s* as death To those that cross him.— *Harold* II ii 320
Starting And gather'd with his hands the *s* flame, *Queen Mary* IV iii 336
Starve —there to beg, *s*, die— *Becket* II i 74
but if you *s* me I be Gaffer Death himself. *Foresters* I i 48
Starved *s*, maim'd, flogg'd, flay'd, burn'd, *Queen Mary* II i 209
Famine is fear, were it but Of being *s*. *Harold* IV iii 206
State (adj.) (*See also* **state-secret**) *S* secrets should be patent to the statesman *Becket, Pro.* 76
What matters ? *S* matters ? love matters ? „ *Pro.* 319
State (body politic) I should be still A party in the *s* ; *Queen Mary* I iv 24
great party in the *s* Wills me to wed her. „ I iv 92
as great a party in the *s* Will you to wed me ? „ I iv 95
My heart, my Lord, Is no great party in the *s* „ I iv 102
Spain in all the great offices of *s* ; „ II i 179
I'll have my head set higher in the *s* ; „ II i 250
In this low pulse and palsy of the *s*, „ II ii 103
or impair in any way This royal *s* of England, „ II ii 230
He is child and fool, and traitor to the *S*. „ II ii 404
they say this *s* of yours Hath no more mortice „ III i 441
In our own name and that of all the *s*, „ III iii 120
wherefore not Helm the huge vessel of your *s*, „ V i 73
In all that handles matter of the *s* I am the king. *Harold* I i 412
We fought like great *s's* for grave cause ; „ I i 440
lying were self-murder by that *s* Which was the exception. „ III i 70
That, were a man of *s* nakedly true, „ III i 113
King, Church, and *S* to him but foils wherein *Becket, Pro.* 268
she, whom the King loves indeed, is a power in the *S*. „ *Pro.* 483
for he would murder his brother the *S*. „ I iv 190
We never hounded on the *S* at home To spoil the Church. „ II ii 96
puffed out such an incense of unctuosity into the nostrils of our Gods of Church and *S*, „ III iii 116
The *S* will die, the Church can never die. „ III iii 336
And the small *s* more cruelly trampled on *The Cup* I ii 145
if a *s* submit At once, she may be blotted out „ I ii 156
State (condition) But your own *s* is full of danger here. *Queen Mary* I iv 168
in happy *s* To give him an heir male. „ V i 572
that I am in *s* to bring forth death— „ V ii 592
the *s* Of my poor father puts me out of heart. *Prom. of May* III 503
s we all Must come to in our spring-and-winter world „ III 509
State (chair of state) that anyone Should seize our person, occupy our *s*, *Queen Mary* II ii 178
State (verb) Swear and unswear, *s* and misstate thy best ! *Becket* II ii 476
Stated It is *s* there that these monies should be paid *Foresters* IV 506
Statelier while in Normanland God speaks thro' abler voices, as He dwells In *s* shrines. *Harold* I i 168
The trees are all the *s*, and the flowers Are all the fairer. *Becket, Pro.* 115
Stateliest You are the *s* deer in all the herd— *Queen Mary* V ii 425
Stateliness Why do you move with such a *s* ? *Becket* V ii 623
Lilylike in her *s* and sweetness ! *Prom. of May* II 621
Stately 'My young Archbishop—thou wouldst make A *s* Archbishop !' *Becket* I i 67
Camma the *s*, Camma the great-hearted, *The Cup* I iii 72
The *s* widow has no heart for me. *The Falcon* 30
State-policy *S-p* and church-policy are conjoint, *Queen Mary* III ii 73
State-secret (*See also* **State (adj.)**) Probing an old *s-s*— *Queen Mary* V ii 487
Statesman The *s* that shall jeer and fleer at men, „ II ii 397
Statesmen that are wise Shape a necessity, „ III iii 31
Statesmen that are wise Take truth herself „ III iii 35
State secrets should be patent to the *s* *Becket, Pro.* 77
and whom the king Loves not as *s*, „ *Pro.* 80
S not Churchman he. „ *Pro.* 450
that hast been a *s*, couldst thou always „ I iii 237
Statesmanship but in *s* To strike too soon is oft to miss the blow. *Queen Mary* III vi 71
Statue And finds you *s's*. „ II ii 265
like a *s*, Unmoving in the greatness of the flame, „ IV iii 621
range of knights Sit, each a *s* on his horse, *Harold* V i 525
we prize The *s* or the picture all the more *Prom. of May* I 738
Sheriff, thy friend, this monk, is but a *s*. *Foresters* I ii 234
Stature Does he think Low *s* is low nature, *Queen Mary* V ii 434
lost Somewhat of upright *s* tho' mine oath, *Harold* III ii 56
Statured *See* **Low-statured**
Statute That those old *s's* touching Lollardism *Queen Mary* III iv 7
Before these bitter *s's* be requicken'd. „ III iv 197
Why ? that these *s's* may be put in force, „ III iv 367
that since these *s's* past, „ III vi 24
Stave (s) Strike up a *s*, my masters, all is well. *Foresters* IV 1101
Stave (verb) *S* off the crowd upon the Spaniard there. *Queen Mary* I iii 77
Staved like enough *s* us from her. *Becket, Pro.* 518
Stay for all that I dare not *s*. *Queen Mary* I ii 102
yet *s*, this golden chain—My father on a birthday „ I v 525
for appearance sake, *s* with the Queen. „ II i 138
On over London Bridge We cannot : *s* we cannot ; „ II iii 42
S's longer here in our poor north than you :— „ V i 24
I will, I will ; and you will *s* ? „ V i 105
And you will *s* your going ? „ V i 185
Then it is done ; but you will *s* your going „ V i 206
should *s* Yet for awhile, „ V i 302
Good ! Renard, I will *s* then. „ V i 305
but *s* a moment ; *He* can but *s* a moment : *Harold* I ii 3
Love can *s* but a little while. Why cannot he *s* ? „ I ii 13
Love will *s* for a whole life long. „ I ii 17
if she *s* the feuds that part The sons of Godwin „ I ii 178
S—as yet Thou hast but seen how Norman hands „ II ii 170
I *s* with these, Lest thy fierce Tostig „ IV i 189
Farewell ! *Harold*. Not yet. *S*. „ V i 338
Tears ? Why not *s* with me then ? *Becket* I iv 18
s it But for a breath. „ II i 177
to *s* his hand Before he flash'd the bolt. „ II i 273
I am half-way down the slope—will no man *s* me ? „ II ii 149
I *s* myself—Puff—it is gone. „ II ii 150
if he move at all, Heaven *s* him, is fain to diagonalise. „ II ii 329
Should she *s* here ? „ III i 215
Rainbow, *s*, (repeat) *Becket* III i 276, 279
O rainbow *s*. *Becket* III i 283
I daren't *s*—I daren't *s* ! „ III ii 27
Again ! *s*, fool, and tell me why thou fliest. „ III ii 34
when we felt we had laughed too long and could not *s* ourselves— „ III iii 161
Come, *s* with us, then, Before you part for England. „ III iii 244
bound For that one hour to *s* with good King Louis, „ III iii 247
I pray you for one moment *s* and speak. „ V ii 525
S !—too near is death. *The Cup* I iii 103
S, *s*, I am most unlucky, most unhappy. *The Falcon* 863
To *s*—Follow my art among these quiet fields, *Prom. of May* I 742
But I shall have to thwack her if I *s*. *Foresters* I iii 139
my heart so down in my heels that if I *s*, I can't run. „ II i 347
Young Walter, nay, I pray thee, *s* a moment. „ II i 472
But go not yet, *s* with us, and when thy brother— „ II i 640
S with us in this wood, till he recover. „ II ii 9
S with us here, sweet love, Maid Marian, „ II ii 13
Shall I be happy ? Happy vision, *s*. „ II ii 199
S, Dine with my brethren here, „ IV 345
but *s* with Robin ; For Robin is no scatterbrains „ IV 353
Stay'd should be *s* From passing onward. „ III 241
Staying I am sicker *s* here Than any sea *Queen Mary* III vi 86
However, *s* not to count how many, *The Falcon* 627
You are *s* here ? *Prom. of May* II 533
Not to-day. What are you *s* for ? „ III 357

Stolen (*continued*) For thou hast *s* my will, and made it thine. *Foresters* III 329
Stone (adj.) For smooth *s* columns of the sanctuary, *Harold* I ii 101
Stone (s) into some more costly *s* Than ever blinded eye. *Queen Mary* I v 370
why fling back the *s* he strikes me with? „ IV ii 150
Albeit no rolling *s*, my good friend Gamel, *Harold* I i 93
tho' the drop may hollow out the dead *s*, *Becket* III iii 315
a cheek like a peach and a heart like the *s* in it— *The Falcon* 94
Hard as the *s's* of his abbey. *Foresters* I ii 270
I am but a *s* and a dead stock to thee. „ II ii 69
Stone (verb) Our men and boys would hoot him, *s* him, *Prom. of May* II 425
Stone-blind a son *s-b* Sat by his mother's hearth: *Becket* V ii 105
Stone-cut And, like the *s-c* epitaph, *Queen Mary* IV iii 163
Stone-dead sat *S-d* upon a heap of ice-cold eggs. *Becket* V ii 239
Stone-hard *S-h*, ice-cold—no dash of daring in him. *Queen Mary* I v 331
Stood I *s* out, till Edward sent for me. „ I ii 29
Lady Jane *s* up Stiff as the very backbone „ I v 42
citizens *S* each before his shut-up booth, „ II ii 63
and almost elbowing her, So close they *s*, „ II ii 78
In every London street a gibbet *s*. „ III i 7
Who *s* upright when both the houses fell. „ III iii 254
Well, you one man, because you *s* upright, „ III iii 269
firm *s* the pine—The cataract shook „ III iv 137
S out against the King in your behalf, „ IV i 126
At your trial Never *s* up a bolder man than you; „ IV ii 122
He *s* upright, a lad of twenty-one, „ IV iii 335
s More like an ancient father of the Church, „ IV iii 597
I *s* near—Mark'd him— „ IV iii 616
while we *s* together, a dead man Rose *Harold* I ii 78
and at once He *s* beside me, „ III i 136
Every man about his king Fell where he *s*. „ V ii 182
Methought I *s* in Canterbury Minster, *Becket* I i 73
as the case *s*, you had safelier have slain an archbishop than a she-goat: „ III iii 67
They *s* on Dover beach to murder me, „ V ii 436
he *s* there Staring upon the hunter. *The Cup* I ii 121
How often have I *s* With Eva here! *Prom. of May* II 296
O would she *s* before me as my queen, *Foresters* II i 166
Stoop Might not your courtesy *s* to hand it me? *Becket* IV ii 296
could I *s* so low As mate with one that holds *Foresters* IV 709
Stoop'd he *s* and gather'd one From out a bed *Queen Mary* V v 92
Stop Well, Simon Renard, shall we *s* a day? „ III vi 243
s the heretic's mouth! Hale him away! „ IV iii 282
S's and stares at our cottage. *The Falcon* 161
But hallus ud *s* at the Vine-an'-the-Hop, *Prom. of May* II 311
Storm (*See also* **War-storm**) and strow the *s's* at sea, *Queen Mary* I v 381
Wet, famine, ague, fever, *s*, wreck, wrath,— „ V v 108
all the North of Humber is one *s*. *Harold* II ii 292
To Rome again! the *s* begins again. *Becket* II ii 468
tho' I am none of those that would raise a *s* between you, III iii 296
Can you not hear them yonder like a *s*, „ V ii 625
the *s* was drawing hither Across the hills *The Cup* II 319
The *s* is hard at hand will sweep away Thrones, *Prom. of May* I 517
I will fly to you thro' the night, the *s*— „ I 702
s and shower lashing Her casement, „ II 471
Out in the fiercest *s* That ever made earth tremble— „ III 797
Storming All the Norman foot Are *s* up the hill. *Harold* V i 523
Stormless No—our waking thoughts Suffer a *s* shipwreck in the pools „ V i 296
Storm-voice whose *s-v* Unsockets the strong oak, *The Cup* II 282
Stormy The *s* Wyatts and Northumberlands, *Queen Mary* III ii 168
Stormy-red when he sign'd, his face was *s-r*— *Becket* I iii 320
Story But truth of *s*, which I glanced at, *Queen Mary* III v 33
Then, glancing thro' the *s* of this realm, *Becket* I iii 410
The *s* of your battle and your wound. *The Falcon* 594
Will he not fly from you if he learn the *s* of my shame *Prom. of May* III 257
Stout Wake, or the *s* old island will become A rotten limb of Spain. *Queen Mary* II i 104
But by God's providence a good *s* staff Lay near me; „ V ii 468
And Tostig is not *s* enough to bear it. *Harold* I i 402
I have a *s* crabstick here, which longs to break itself across their backs. *Foresters* IV 917
Stoutness Your learning, and your *s*, and your heresy, *Queen Mary* IV ii 125
Straäit (straight) hallus hup at sunrise, and I'd drive the plow *s* as a line right i' the faäce o' the sun, *Prom. of May* I 370
Straänge (strange) and the master 'ud be *s* an' pleased if you'd step in fust, „ I 167
Straight (*See also* **Straäit**) and set it *S* on the trunk, *Harold* III i 146
Speak *s* out, crookback. *Foresters* II i 271
Straight-going the dry light of Rome's *s-g* policy, *The Cup* I i 145
Strain (s) A *s* of hard and headstrong in him. *Becket, Pro.* 234
Strain (verb) if we did not *s* to make ourselves Better *Prom. of May* I 602
Strain'd I cannot cope with him: my wrist is *s*. *Foresters* IV 313
Strand voice coming up with the voice of the deep from the *s*, *Becket* II i 6
Stranded To shove that *s* iceberg off our shores, *Harold* IV iii 138
Strange (*See also* **Straänge**) *S* game of chess: a King That with her own pawns plays against a Queen, *Queen Mary* I iii 160
S in a wooer! „ I v 363
A *s* youth Suddenly thrust in on me, whisper'd, „ II i 128
That may seem *s* beyond his nursery. „ II ii 396
how *s*, That Gardiner, once so one with all of us Against this foreign marriage, should have yielded So utterly!—*s*! „ III iii 5
when men are tost On tides of *s* opinion, „ III iv 119
however, in *s* hours, After the long brain-dazing colloquies, „ IV ii 90
His Highness is so vex'd with *s* affairs— „ V ii 560
What is the *s* thing happiness? Sit down here: „ V v 77
S and ghastly in the gloom And shadowing of this double thunder-cloud *Harold* III ii 157
No, not *s* This was old human laughter in old Rome „ III ii 162
lest the *s* Saints By whom thou swarest, „ V i 115
I see it—some confusion, Some *s* mistake. *Becket* III i 235
A *s* gift sent to me to-day. *The Cup* I ii 52
So mad, I fear some *s* and evil chance Coming upon me, for by the Gods I seem *S* to myself. „ I iii 74
So *s* among them—such an alien there, „ II 143
Or some *s* second-sight, the marriage cup Wherefrom „ II 198
Surely—yet These are *s* words to speak to Artemis. „ II 326
S that the words at home with me so long Should fly *The Falcon* 525
sick people, More specially sick children, have *s* fancies, *S* longings; „ 817
But all that sounds so wicked and so *s*; *Prom. of May* I 657
Come, come, my girl, enough Of this *s* talk. „ III 620
That *s* starched stiff creature, Little John, the Earl's man. *Foresters* I i 183
Stranger (adj.) A *s* monk desires access to you *Becket* V ii 65
Stranger (compar.) strange! but *s* still that he, So fierce against the Headship of the Pope, *Queen Mary* III iii 9
Stranger (s) By seeking justice at a *s's* hand „ IV i 20
The *s* at his hearth, and all his house— „ IV i 163
Norman who should drive The *s* to the fiends! *Harold* II ii 541
Yea, let a *s* spoil his heritage, *Becket* II ii 258
Have you had any alarm? no *s*? „ III i 28
tho' a *s* fain would be allow'd To join the hunt. *The Cup* I i 196
And you, that seldom brook the *s* here, „ I ii 378
Strangle for he Who vows a vow to *s* his own mother *Harold* III i 229
Such rampant weeds *S* each other, *Prom. of May* III 591
Strangled Holy Father *s* him with a hair Of Peter, *Harold* V ii 45
Strasburg To *S*, Antwerp, Frankfort, Zurich, *Queen Mary* I ii 1
Strato Your name? *Synorix*. *S*, my name. *The Cup* I i 199
Who is our guest? *Sinnatus*. *S* he calls himself. *Sinnatus*. I pledge you, *S*. *Synorix*. And I you, my lord. „ I ii 48
You, *S*, make good cheer till I return. „ I ii 205
Straw Hast not thou drawn the short *s*? *Becket* I iv 4
Take thy one chance; Catch at the last *s*. „ IV ii 221
Richard risks his life for a *s*, So lies in prison— *Foresters* IV 383
Stray not here I shall rejoice To find my *s* sheep back within the fold. *Becket* III iii 355
Stray'd Hath he *s* From love's clear path into the common bush, „ III i 246
Stream foul *s* Thro' fever-breeding levels,—at her side, „ II i 155
—the *s* is bearing us all down, *Foresters* I i 238

Stream (*continued*) our little Sheriff will ever swim with the *s* ! *Foresters* I i 240
have the great men striven against the *s*, „ I i 243
Streamer and dropt Their *s's* earthward, *The Cup* I ii 405
Streaming We might go softlier than with crimson rowel And *s* lash. *Queen Mary* III iv 184
And flung them *s* o'er the battlements *Harold* II ii 391
Street Cries of the moment and the *s*— *Queen Mary* II iv 128
In every London *s* a gibbet stood. „ III i 7
And might assail you passing through the *s*, „ IV ii 35
And Ignorance crying in the *s's*, „ IV iii 377
son turn'd out into the *s* To sleep, to die— „ V ii 126
To take the vagabond woman of the *s* Into thine arms ! *Becket* I i 228
moon Divides the whole long *s* with light and shade. „ I i 365
Then hidden in the *s* He watch'd her „ I ii 39
from the *s* Stain'd with the mire thereof. „ I iii 690
Call in the poor from the *s's*, and let them feast. „ I iv 72
they were fighting for her to-day in the *s*. „ I iv 160
Save that it was mid-winter in the *s*, „ V ii 372
Strength I not doubt that God will give me *s*, *Queen Mary* IV ii 235
Or give thee saintly *s* to undergo. „ IV iii 99
s To shove that stranded iceberg off our shores, *Harold* IV iii 137
there make *s* to breast Whatever chance, „ V i 126
The people know their Church a tower of *s*, *Becket* I i16
Is *s* less strong when hand-in-hand with grace ? „ V ii 540
Curse on your brutal *s* ! I cannot pass that way. *Prom. of May* III 732
So—so—I have presumed Beyond my *s*. *Foresters* II i 458
What breadth, height, *s*—torrents of eddying bark ! „ III 94
Strengthen Might *s* thee in keeping of thy word, *Harold* II ii 730
s their palisades ! „ V i 480
Strengthen'd yet he fail'd, And *s* Philip. *Queen Mary* III i 133
Stretch Do not scrimp your phrase, But *s* it wider ; „ III iii 261
See here—I *s* my hand out—hold it there. *The Cup* II 210
Strew *See* **Strow**
Strewn which I found *S* in your palace. *Queen Mary* V ii 173
Stricken (*See also* **Famine-stricken**) My father *s* with his first paralysis, *Prom. of May* II 481
soul of the woods hath *s* thro' my blood, *Foresters* II i 66
I think I should have *s* him to the death. „ II i 140
He is *s* with a slight paralysis. „ IV 456
Strict The King Demands a *s* account of all those revenues *Becket* I iii 650
Strife My sight is eagle, but the *s* so thick— *Harold* V i 627
Strike And arm and *s* as with one hand, *Queen Mary* II ii 292
Can I *s* Elizabeth ?—not now and save the life Of Devon : „ II iv 122
he and his Are bound to me—may *s* hereafter. „ II iv 125
you may *s* fire from her, Not hope to melt her. „ III vi 38
To *s* too soon is oft to miss the blow. „ III vi 72
why fling back the stone he *s's* me with ? „ IV ii 150
He *s's* thro' me at Philip and yourself. „ V ii 58
s hard and deep into The prey they are rending „ V ii 267
There you *s* in the nail. „ V ii 436
s Their hearts, and hold their babies up to it. *Harold* I i 34
light enough for Alfgar's house To *s* thee down „ I i 308
the true *must* Shall make her *s* as Power : but when to *s*— „ I i 369
And *s* among them with thy battle-axe— „ I ii 89
Thou hast but seen how Norman hands can *s*, „ II ii 172
No man would *s* with Tostig, save for Norway. „ IV ii 20
the childish fist That cannot *s* again. „ IV iii 31
all the monks of Peterboro' *S* for the king ; „ V i 447
We wait but the King's word to *s* thee dead. *Becket.* *S*, and I die the death of martyrdom ; *S*, and ye set these customs by my death Ringing *Becket* I iii 166
The man shall feel that I can *s* him yet. „ II i 78
Why then I *s* into my former path For England, „ II ii 455
S ! I challenge thee to meet me before God. „ IV ii 253
S, then, at once, the King would have him— „ V i 237
S's truest ev'n for his own self. „ V ii 42
Do you hear that ? *s*, *s*. „ V iii 162
S him, Tracy ! *Rosamund.* No, No, No, No ! „ V iii 169
S, I say. „ V iii 177
S our Archbishop in his own cathedral ! „ V iii 180
Answer not, but *s*. „ V iii 186

Strike (*continued*) And I may *s* your game when you are gone. *The Cup* I ii 36
Why did I *s* him ?—having proof enough „ I iii 157
s, make his feathers Glance in mid heaven. *The Falcon* 14
Nor ever *s* him blow for blow ; *Prom. of May* iii 6
you *S* up a song, my friends, and then to bed. *Foresters* I iii 30
these will *s* for England And man and maid be free „ II i 9
S, Sheriff ! *S*, mercenary ! „ II i 415
They *s* the deer at once to death— „ IV 525
S up our music, Little John. „ IV 558
s the bonds From these three men, „ IV 961
S up a stave, my masters, all is well. „ IV 1101
Striking And *s* at Hardrada and his madmen *Harold* IV iii 17
I have heard of you. The likeness Is very *s*. *Prom. of May* II 366
String were a pious work To *s* my father's sonnets, *Queen Mary* II i 27
Strip A thousand winters Will *s* you bare as death, *Foresters* IV 1056
Stripe callous with a constant *s*, Unwoundable. *Queen Mary* V v 172
Stripping They are *s* the dead bodies naked yonder, *Harold* V ii 34
Stript But after they had *s* him to his shroud, *Queen Mary* IV iii 334
Strive And in thy cause I *s* against him now. *Becket* V i 16
great man *s* against it again to save his country, *Foresters* I i 245
Striven I have *s* in vain to raise a man for her. *Queen Mary* II ii 17
have the great men *s* against the stream, *Foresters* I i 243
Striving Not *s* still, however much in vain, *Becket* III iii 232
s still to break or bind The spiritual giant „ IV ii 442
Stroke (s) Toll of a bell, *S* of a clock, *Queen Mary* III v 143
and iron *s's* that brought Thy war with Brittany *Harold* II ii 47
But I heard say he had had a *s*, *Becket* IV i 54
Guard from the *s* that dooms thee after death „ IV ii 270
I surely should have left That *s* to Rome. *The Cup* I iii 160
As scare his act :—a random *s* : „ II 53
Stroke (verb) you *s* me on one cheek, Buffet the other. *Queen Mary* II i 116
Stroking Cannot be heal'd by *s*. „ III iv 274
Strong Would be too *s* for France. „ I v 300
Have made *s* head against ourselves and you. „ II ii 146
And *s* to throw ten Wyatts and all Kent. „ II ii 353
or we are torn Down the *s* wave of brawlers. „ III i 186
And their *s* torment bravely borne, „ III iv 168
A drinker of black, *s*, volcanic wines, „ V ii 93
I would I were as tall and *s* as you. „ V ii 422
and you know me *s* of arm ; „ V ii 469
Haul like a great *s* fellow at my legs, *Harold* II i 11
Is 'ay' an oath ? is 'ay' *s* as an oath ? „ II ii 662
let not my *s* prayer Be weaken'd in thy sight, „ V i 647
S—not in mine own self, but Heaven ; *Becket* I iii 536
A *s* hate-philtre as may madden him— „ IV ii 458
Is strength less *s* when hand-in-hand with grace ? „ V ii 540
whose storm-voice Unsockets the *s* oak, and rears his root Beyond his head, *The Cup* II 283
Were some *s* fellow here in the wild wood, *Foresters* IV 515
Stronger Ay, ay, but art thou *s* than the King ? *Becket* I iii 534
and now the *s* motive, Misnamed free-will— *Prom. of May* II 635
Anyhow we must Move in the line of least resistance when The *s* motive rules. „ II 671
only differing as the *s* and the weaker, „ III 190
Of a nature *S*, sadder than my own, *Foresters* II ii 189
Strongest Well, well, be it so, thou *s* thief of all, „ III 327
The Holy Virgin Stand by the *s*. „ IV 265
Strong-wing'd the best, *s-w* against the wind. *Harold* II ii 148
Strove We *s* against the papacy from the first, *Queen Mary* III iii 224
And dreadful shadows *s* upon the hill, *Harold* III i 377
and once he *s* to hide his face, *Becket* III iii 103
s To work against her license for her good, „ IV ii 339
In mine own cause I *s* against him there, „ V i 14
I cannot tell how long we *s* before *The Falcon* 638
Strow and *s* the storms at sea, *Queen Mary* I v 381
s's our fruits, and lays Our golden grain, *The Cup* II 285
Struck *S* home and won. *Queen Mary* I v 554
Gardiner wur *s* down like by the hand o' God „ IV iii 516
And *s* a shape from out the vague, *Becket* I iii 373
Very bad. Somebody *s* him. „ IV i 50
I tell thee, my good fellow, *My* arrow *s* the stag. *The Cup* I ii 28
I am sure *I s* him. *Synorix.* And I am just as sure, my lord, *I s* him. „ I ii 33
I warrant you now, he said, *he s* the stag. „ I ii 382

Struck (*continued*) You will believe Now that he never *s* the stag— *The Cup* I ii 430
When he *s* at Sinnatus— „ II 46
His grandsire *s* my grandsire in a brawl *The Falcon* 250
whereon she *s* him, And fled into the castle. *Foresters* II i 117
She *s* him, my brave Marian, *s* the Prince, „ II i 134
Stubbornness O bolster'd up with *s* and pride, *Becket* I iii 34
Stuck Come, come, the morsel *s*—this Cardinal's fault— *Queen Mary* III iv 375
Studded English Garter, *s* with great emeralds, „ III i 84
Study retire To Ashridge, and pursue my *studies* there. „ I iv 237
It shall be all my *s* for one hour „ III v 184
Studying There wore his time *s* the canon law *Becket* II i 85
Stuff *See* **Garden-stuff, Gipsy-stuff**
Stuff'd *s* the boy with fears that these may act *Harold* II ii 90
Stumble *S* not in the darkness, Lest they should seize thee. *Becket* V iii 78
fear not I should *s* in the darkness, „ V iii 91
Stumbled Hath *s* on our cups? *Harold* IV iii 179
Stump-tailed or a *s-t* ox in May-time, *Foresters* II i 434
Stung your wise bees had *s* him first to death. *Queen Mary* III iii 64
Stunn'd Sir Nicholas! I am *s*— „ V ii 250
Stupid *S* soldiers oft are bold. „ V ii 445
that you were *s* drunk all Sunday, and so ill in consequence all Monday, *Prom. of May* III 79
Stupid-honest Be thou not *s-h*, brother Gurth! *Harold* III i 122
Stupid-sure the people *s-s* Sleep like their swine . . . „ IV iii 216
Stupid-wild thine eyes Glare *s-w* with wine. *Becket* I i 214
Sturdy Beggars, you are *s* rogues that should be set to work. *Foresters* III 196
Style with his charm of simple *s* And close dialectic, *Prom. of May* I 224
Suaviter S *in modo, fortiter in re,* *Becket* V ii 539
Subject is every morning's prayer Of your most loyal *s*, *Queen Mary* I v 104
marriage should bring loss or danger to you, My *s's*, „ II ii 229
And all our loving *s's*, most expedient. „ II ii 211
Against my natural *s*. „ IV i 21
I am your *s*, not your—— *Henry*. Pander. *Becket, Pro.* 145
I'll crush him as the *s*. „ I iii 334
Submission Except they make *s* to the Church. „ V iii 122
Submissive I am utterly *s* to the Queen. *Queen Mary* I iv 39
Submit *S*; I promise thee on my salvation *Becket* I iii 254
They have but to *s*. „ V ii 382
to *s* at once Is better than a wholly-hopeless war, *The Cup* I ii 140
if a state *s* At once, she may be blotted out „ I ii 156
Suborn'd His foes—the Devil had *s* 'em. *Queen Mary* I v 626
Subscribe Will you *s* the customs? *Becket* I ii 46
Subsidy remission Of half that *s* levied *Queen Mary* I v 115
raise us loans and *subsidies* Among the merchants; „ V i 179
Substance 'Twould seem too like the *s*, if I sign'd. *Becket* I iii 197
Subtlety repulses, the delicacies, the *subtleties*. „ *Pro.* 500
Sub-writing as you suspended yourself after *s-w* to the customs. „ II ii 351
Success this or that way, of *s* Would turn it thither. *Queen Mary* II ii 100
but the ill *s* of the farm, and the debts, *Prom. of May* II 68
Successor give his kingly voice To me as his *s*. *Harold* II ii 589
we must have a mightier man than he For his *s*. *Becket, Pro.* 8
as his *s* in the archbishoprick. „ *Pro.* 402
Succory speedwell, bluebottle, *s*, forget-me-not? *Prom. of May* I 98
Succour refusing none That come to Thee for *s*, *Queen Mary* IV iii 132
Such Answer thou for him, then! thou'rt no *s* cockerel thyself, „ I i 41
My flight were *s* a scandal to the faith, „ I ii 53
These beastly swine make *s* a grunting here, „ I iii 12
Why, *s* a game, sir, were whole years a playing. „ I iii 139
to be *s* a one As Harry Bolingbroke hath a lure in it. „ I iv 9
but God hath sent me here To take *s* order with all heretics „ I v 34
to compose the event In some *s* form as least may harm your Grace. „ I v 225
the thing Was no *s* scarecrow in your father's time. „ I v 473
A pretty man for *s* a pretty maiden. „ I v 613
Many *s* groups. „ II ii 92
Should play the second actor in this pageant That brings him in; *s* a cameleon he! „ III iii 15
Towards the abrogation and repeal Of all *s* laws and ordinances made; „ III iii 142
wherein have been *S* holocausts of heresy! to what end? „ III iv 108

Such (*continued*) She seethed with *s* adulteries, and the lives *Queen Mary* III iv 189
And I have known *s* women more than one— „ III vi 178
If *s* a prince were born and you not here! „ III vi 203
Your father was a man Of *s* colossal kinghood, „ IV i 101
My heart is no *s* block as Bonner's is: „ IV ii 174
but methinks I love her less For *s* a dotage upon *s* a man. V ii 421
Come, thou shalt dream no more *s* dreams; I swear it, *Harold* I ii 108
Like Jonah, than have known there were *s* devils. „ II i 38
Hast thou *s* trustless jailors in thy North? „ II ii 684
She hath wean'd me from it with *s* bitterness. „ IV ii 28
Wakening *s* brawls and loud disturbances In England, *Becket* V ii 352
I never felt *s* passion for a woman. *The Cup* I i 34
I know of no *s* wives in all Galatia. „ I ii 191
Alas! I have no *s* power with Rome. „ I ii 291
I will be no *s* wreck, „ I iii 144
We have been in *s* grief these five years, *Prom. of May* II 66
I have freed myself From all *s* dreams, „ III 596
Suck one of those mercenaries that *s* the blood of England. *Foresters* II i 175
may this mouth Never *s* grape again, „ IV 394
Suck'd (*See also* **Weasle-sucked**) And kingdom will be *s* into the war, *Queen Mary* I v 257
Sucking *s* thro' fools' ears The flatteries of corruption— *Becket* I iii 360
Suckling Out of the mouths of babes and *s's*, praise! „ II ii 279
Sudden Came with a *s* splendour, shout, and show, *Queen Mary* III i 449
Philip's no *s* alien—the Queen's husband, „ III iii 42
Whereat Lord Williams gave a *s* cry:— „ IV iii 604
Methinks that would you tarry one day more (The news was *s*) „ III vi 234
s touches For him, or him—sunk rocks; „ V v 219
but Tostig On a *s*—at a something—for a nothing— *Harold* I i 442
A summer mere with *s* wreckful gusts From a side-gorge. „ III i 50
Edith, The sign in heaven—the *s* blast at sea— „ V i 378
Like *s* night in the main glare of day. *Becket* II i 57
S change is a house on sand; „ III iii 59
that our good Henry Says many a thing in *s* heats, „ IV ii 276
If God would take him in some *s* way— „ V i 93
Did he? It seem'd so. I have play'd the *s* fool. *The Cup* I iii 162
To-day? Too *s*. I will brood upon it. „ II 72
Ay! but you must not be too *s* with it either, *Prom. of May* II 54
But I weänt be too *s* wi' it; and I feel sewer, Miss Dora, that I ha' been noän too *s* wi' you, „ II 59
By St. Nicholas I have a *s* passion for the wild wood— *Foresters* I iii 122
but look, there is a cross line o' *s* death. „ II i 354
But I have ta'en a *s* fancy to thee. „ IV 422
Sue —infatuated—To *s* you for his life? *Queen Mary* IV i 11
I came to *s* Your Council and yourself (repeat) „ V i 107, 114
Sued Not *s* for that—he knows it were in vain. „ IV i 13
when the King's divorce was *s* at Rome, „ IV iii 41
He *s* my hand. I shook at him. *Becket* I i 272
Suffer So your king-parliament *s* him to land, *Queen Mary* I v 365
Your Grace's business will not *s*, sire, „ III vi 245
We talk and Cranmer *s's*. „ IV iii 420
S not That my brief reign in England „ V ii 301
That *s's* in the daily want of thee, *Harold* II ii 275
S a stormless shipwreck in the pools „ V i 296
Perish she, I, all, before The Church should *s* wrong! *Becket* III iii 20
and so cannot *s* by the rule of frequency. „ III iii 319
The One Who shifts his policy *s's* something, *The Cup* II 113
Do you still *s* from your fall in the hollow lane? *Prom. of May* III 240
they that *s* by him call the blossom Of bandits. *Foresters* IV 371
Suffer'd As for what I did I *s* and repented. *Queen Mary* III iv 259
She hath followed with our host, and *s* all. *Harold* IV i 29
Wilt not be *s* so to cross the seas *Becket* I iii 129
has *s* More than we know. *Prom. of May* II 501
Suffering Five years of shame and *s* broke the heart „ III 761
Sufficient whose baby eye Saw them *s*. *Harold* III ii 67
S for the day, dear father! *Foresters* I i 343
Suffolk (Duke of) Duke of *S* lately freed from prison, *Queen Mary* I iii 121
Duke of *S* and Sir Peter Carew, „ I iv 112
Spared you the Duke of *S*, Guildford Dudley, „ I v 489
I do not hear from Carew or the Duke Of *S*, „ II i 3
Till Guildford Dudley and the Duke of *S*, „ II iv 138
Did not Lord *S* die like a true man? „ III i 164

Sure (*continued*) I am *s* (Knowing the man) he wrought it — *Queen Mary* III i 275
I should fight then. *Stafford.* I am *s* of it. — „ III i 469
and not *s* Of their own selves, — „ III iv 119
Of this be *s*, he is whole worlds away. — „ IV iii 194
but I am not *s* She will not serve me better— — „ V i 249
Papacy is no more. *Paget.* Are we so *s* of that? — „ V v 287
I am *s* she hates thee, Pants for thy blood. — *Harold* I ii 37
I his queen, I might be *s* of it. — „ I ii 155
I am *s* this body Is Alfwig, the king's uncle. — „ V ii 67
Art thou so *s* thou followedst anything? — *Becket* I i 210
But, my liege, I am *s*, of all the roses— — „ II i 139
for to be *s* it's no more than a week since our old Father Philip — „ III i 109
be *s* they be, but he blinded 'em for all that, — „ III i 128
and to be *s* I ha' seen great ones to-day— — „ III i 136
tho' to be *s* if I had been Eve i' the garden I shouldn't ha' minded the apple, — „ III i 139
to be *s* if I hadn't minded it we should all — „ III i 144
tho' to be *s* our mother 'ill sing me old songs by the hour, — „ III i 184
You had never used so many, Not if you meant it, I am *s*. — „ IV ii 184
And yet I am all but *s* my dagger was a feint Till the worm turn'd— — „ IV ii 379
I am not so *s* But that I love him still. — „ IV ii 450
I am *s I* struck him. *Synorix.* And I am just as *s*, my lord, *I* struck him. — *The Cup* I ii 34
Wise I am *s* as she is beautiful, — „ I ii 139
I am *s* of being every way malign'd. — „ I ii 241
I am *s* I told him that his plot was folly. — „ I ii 283
Plead to him, I am *s* you will prevail. — „ I ii 302
I am *s* you will not marry him. *Camma.* Are you so *s*? — „ II 104
I am all but *s* that some one spake. — „ II 404
I am most *s* that some one call'd. — „ II 509
I am *s* that more than one brave fellow — *The Falcon* 633
but be *s* That I shall never marry again, my lord! *Count.* *S*? — „ 741
I am *s* I wish her happy. — *Prom. of May* I 478
But *s* am I that of your gentleness You will forgive him. — „ II 487
and that, I am *s*, would be the death of him. — „ III 167
and he loves me too, I am quite *s* of that. — „ III 214
I am *s* that when we are married he will be willing — „ III 259
are you quite *s* that after marriage this gentleman — „ III 292
He will be *s* to know you to-morrow. — „ III 470
But there I am *s* the ballad is at fault. — *Foresters* I i 122
I am all but *s* of him. I will go to him. — „ I i 275
Nay—that, my friend, I am *s* I did not say. — „ II i 489

Surgas *S* e tenebris, Sis vindicator! — *Harold* V i 571
Surged hugest wave from Norseland ever yet *S* on us, — „ IV iii 64
Surname He must deserve his *s* better. — *Queen Mary* III ii 197
Surprise Well, Father, I have a *s* for you. — *Prom. of May* III 438
Surprised niver been *s* but once i' my life, and I went blind upon it. — „ III 439
Surrendering *s* God's honour to the pleasure of a man. — *Becket* II ii 439
Survey Not an eye to *s*, — *Foresters* II ii 181
Surveyor *See* **Land-surveyor**
Suspect Why still *s* your Grace? — *Queen Mary* III v 17
you *s* This Sinnatus of playing patriotism, — *The Cup* I i 77
Suspected anyone *S* thee to be my man? — *Queen Mary* I iii 176
Much *s*, of me Nothing proven can be. — „ III v 19
Suspend I will *s* myself from all my functions. — *Becket* I iii 301
your lordship would *s* me from verse-writing, — „ II ii 349
and tho' you *s* Foliot or another, — „ II ii 358
Suspended as you *s* yourself after sub-writing to the customs. — „ II ii 350
tho' you *s* yourself, The Pope let you down again; — „ II ii 356
Suspense the Pope will not leave them in *s*, for the Pope himself is always in *s*, — „ II ii 359
—always in *s*, like the scales, — „ II ii 362
always in *s*, like the tail of the horologe— — „ II ii 365
Sussex I know all *S*; A good entrenchment — *Harold* III i 362
Suzerain Husband-in-law, our smooth-shorn *s*, — *Becket* II ii 40
Swaddling-band flings aside His *s-b's*, — *Prom. of May* I 586
Swale in the cruel river *S* A hundred years ago; — *Harold* III ii 10

Swaller (swallow) Wi' the butterflies out, and the *s's* at plaäy, — *Prom. of May* II 198
Swallow (s) (*See also* **Swaller**) *S's* fly again, Cuckoos cry again, — *Queen Mary* III v 96
Why, nature's licensed vagabond, the *s*, — „ V i 21
Yet will I be your *s* and return— — „ V i 91
Sick as an autumn *s* for a voyage, — *Harold* I i 101
Farewell, friends! farewell, *s's*! — *Becket* I iv 45
Not while the *s* skims along the ground, — *Foresters* I ii 313
Swallow (verb) find Heaven or else hell ready to *s* me, — *Queen Mary* IV iii 224
Rolf, what fish did *s* Jonah? *Rolf.* A whale! — *Harold* II i 41
all their horse *S* the hill locust-like, — „ V i 560
My one grain of good counsel which you will not *s*. — *Becket* II ii 379
that will *s* anything. Farewell. — „ II ii 382
Will the earth gape and *s* us? — „ V iii 206
she that has eaten the yolk is scarce like to *s* the shell. — *The Falcon* 705
Swallowed (*See also* **Shore-swallow'd**) I had liefer that the fish had *s* me, — *Harold* II i 37
whale to a whelk we have *s* the King of England. — „ II i 45
glory of the Church Hath *s* up the glory of the King; — *Becket* I iii 666
And *s* in the conqueror's chronicle. — *The Cup* I ii 158
your free sports have *s* my free hour. — *Foresters* IV 339
Swam or else *s* heavily Against the huge corruptions — *Queen Mary* IV ii 98
Swamp running out at tōp To *s* the house. — *Harold* I i 379
Swan flocks of *s's*, As fair and white as angels; — *Queen Mary* III ii 15
Swang Mark'd how the war-axe *s*, — *Harold* IV iii 156
Swapped *See* **Swopt**
Sward Kill'd the *s* where'er they sat, — *Foresters* II ii 152
Sware (*See also* **Swore**) He knew not whom he *s* by. — *Harold* III i 256
and I *s* To consecrate my virgin here — „ III i 275
born in me when I *s* Falsely to him, — „ V i 302
by whom I knew not that I *s*,— — „ V i 305
King Henry *s* That, saving his King's kingship, — *Becket* I iii 27
I *s* I would not give the kiss of peace, — „ III iii 259
Swarest Swearing thou *s* falsely by his Saints: — *Harold* III ii 142
lest the strange Saints By whom thou *s*, — „ V i 117
Thou *s* falsely by our blessed bones, — „ V i 259
Swarm (s) Philip and the black-faced *s's* of Spain, — *Queen Mary* II i 98
Out crept a wasp, with half the *s* behind. — „ III iii 49
Is coming with a *s* of mercenaries To break — *Foresters* III 452
Swarm (verb) they *s* into the fire Like flies—for what? no dogma. — *Queen Mary* V ii 110
S to thy voice like bees to the brass pan. — *Foresters* I iii 108
Swarming Swallow the hill locust-like, *s* up. — *Harold* V i 560
Sway Now the spoilt child *s's* both. — „ I i 453
that one time *s* to the current, And to the wind another. — *Becket* I iii 593
And *s* the long grape-bunches of our vines, — *The Cup* II 270
Sway'd might well have *s* All England under Henry, — *Becket* I iii 467
Swaying And *s* his two-handed sword about him, — *Harold* V i 407
and like the *s* vines—Yea,—with our eyes,— — *The Cup* I ii 410
Swear (*See also* **Sweär**) He *s's* by the Rood. Whew! — *Queen Mary* I i 62
Peter, I'll *s* for him He *did* believe — „ I ii 76
S with me, noble fellow-citizens, all, — „ II ii 296
We *s*! *Mary.* We thank your Lordship and your loyal city. — „ II ii 299
I *s* you do your country wrong, Sir Ralph. — „ III i 153
but of this fire he says, Nay *s's*, — „ III v 72
I *s* I have no heart To be your Queen. — „ V v 264
I *s* it, By mine own eyes— — *Harold* I ii 109
to *s* Vows that he dare not break. — „ II ii 76
S thou on this! *Harold.* What should I *s*? Why should I *s* on this? *William.* *S* thou to help me to the crown of England. — „ II ii 701
S thou to-day, to-morrow is thine own. — „ II ii 709
I *s* to help thee to the crown of England . . . (repeat) — *Harold* II ii 712, 721
Thou must *s* absolutely, noble Earl. — „ II ii 715
S, dearest brother, I beseech thee, *s*! — „ II ii 719
I made thee *s*.—Show him by whom he hath sworn. — „ II ii 732
and dear son, *s* When thou art king, — „ III i 305
for I have sworn Not to *s* falsely twice. *Edward.* Thou wilt not *s*? *Harold.* I cannot. — „ III i 311
For I can *s* to that, but cannot *s* That these will follow thee — „ IV i 156

Swine These beastly *s* make such a grunting here, *Queen Mary* I iii 12
And get the *s* to shout Elizabeth. „ I iii 39
was not meet the heretic *s* should live In Lambeth. „ III ii 134
No, for we trust they parted in the *s*. „ III ii 143
the people stupid-sure Sleep like their *s* . . . *Harold* IV iii 217
S, sheep, ox—here's a French supper. *Becket* I iv 112
Swing (s) Two deaths at every *s*, ran in upon us *Harold* V i 409
Swing (verb) Here *s's* a Spaniard—there an Englishman; *Queen Mary* V i 87
Which way soever the vane-arrow *s*, *Harold* II ii 257
Swirling river, black, slimy, *s* under me in the lamplight, *Prom. of May* III 370
Swoll'n *s* and fed With indraughts and side-currents, *Queen Mary* II i 232
Rogue, I have a *s* vein in my right leg, *Foresters* IV 568
Swoon (s) —not dead now—a *s*—a scene— *Prom. of May* III 696
Swoon (verb) being thwarted ever *s's* And weeps herself *Becket* V ii 213
Swoon'd He hath *s*! Death? . . . no, as yet a breath. *Harold* III i 318
My last sight ere I *s* was one sweet face *The Falcon* 647
had his draught of wine And then he *s* away. *Foresters* II ii 3
Swoop *s* down upon him Eagle-like, lightning-like— *The Falcon* 12
Swopt Fanny be the naäme i' the song, but I *s* it fur *she*. *Prom. of May* II 212
Sword Down scabbard, and out *s*! *Queen Mary* II i 143
His *s* shall hew the heretic peoples down! „ III ii 178
'I come not to bring peace but a *s*'? The *s* Is in her Grace's hand to smite with. „ III iv 88
Into one *s* to hack at Spain and me. „ V i 138
they clapt their hands Upon their *s's* when ask'd; „ V i 174
voice of any people is the *s* That guards them, or the *s* that beats them down. *Harold* II ii 135
s Of lightnings, wherewithal he cleft the tree „ III i 136
swaying his two-handed *s* about him, „ V i 407
sheathe your *s's*, ye will displease the King, *Becket* I iii 179
Did not your barons draw their *s's* against me? „ I iii 502
than the *s's* of the craven sycophants „ I iv 147
Cross *s's* all of you! swear to follow him! „ I iv 199
Shall I smite him with the edge of the *s*? „ I iv 224
Tho' all the *s's* in England flash'd above me „ V ii 484
score of knights all arm'd with *s's* and axes— „ V iii 71
Clashing of *s's*—three upon one, and that one our Robin! *Foresters* II i 419
And never drewest *s* to help the old man „ II i 541
Seize on the knight! wrench his *s* from him! „ II i 676
Quick with thy *s*! the yeoman braves the knight. „ II ii 30
Down with thy *s*! She is my queen and thine, „ II ii 40
Robin fancied me a man, And drew his *s* upon me, „ III 21
Swore (*See also* **Sware, Swear'd**) William laugh'd and *s* that might was right, *Harold* II ii 362
King *s* to our cardinals He meant no harm *Becket* I iii 215
arms of her first love, Fitzurse, Who *s* to marry her. „ IV ii 336
since we likewise *s* to obey the customs, „ V i 54
Nay, she *s* it never Should leave her finger. *Foresters* II i 592
Sworn *s* this Spanish marriage shall not be. *Queen Mary* I iv 115
I have *s* upon the body and blood of Christ „ I v 214
Hath your Grace so *s*? „ I v 217
Show him by whom he hath *s*. *Harold* II ii 733
thou hast *s* an oath Which, if not kept, „ II ii 737
for I have *s* Not to swear falsely twice. „ III i 310
noble Harold, I would thou couldst have *s*. „ III i 326
I would thou couldst have *s*. „ III i 333
—brother—*I* have not *s*— „ V i 122
thou hast *s* a voluntary allegiance to him? *Becket, Pro.* 439
He hath *s* that thou shouldst sign, „ I iii 189
I evermore have *s* upon his side, „ II ii 465
God help her, That she was *s* to silence. „ III i 78
tho' I be *s* not to speak a word, I can tell you all about her, „ III i 204
s on this my cross a hundred times Never to leave him— „ IV ii 205
Ye have *s* Yourselves my men when I was Chancellor— „ V ii 501
on this cross I have *s* that till I myself pass away, *Foresters* I i 289
And Robin Hood hath *s*— „ III 236
I have *s* by our Lady if they come „ IV 96
Swung parson from his own spire *s* out dead, *Queen Mary* IV iii 375

Sycamore the knights are arming in the garden Beneath the *s*. *Becket* V ii 570
Sycophant than the swords of the craven *s's* „ I iv 148
Syllable And every *s* taught us by our Lord, *Queen Mary* IV iii 231
Symbol In *s* of their married unity, *The Cup* II 363
take and wear this *s* of your love; *Foresters* III 79
or any other *s* of vacuity. „ IV 214
Symbol'd-symboll'd happily *symboll'd* by The King your husband, *Queen Mary* III ii 108
whether it *symbol'd* ruin Or glory, who shall tell? *Harold* V i 110
Synorix (an ex-tetrarch) If *S*, who has dwelt three years in Rome *The Cup* I ii 175
What is *S*? *Sinnatus.* Galatian, and not know? This *S* Was Tetrarch here, and tyrant also— „ I ii 180
Thou art that *S*! One whom thou hast wrong'd „ I ii 318
Return and tell them *S* is not here. What did that villain *S* say to you? *Camma.* Is *he—that—S*? „ I ii 335
S—His face was not malignant, „ I ii 450
Will she come to me Now that she knows me *S*? „ I iii 21
that man from *S*, who has been So oft to see the Priestess, „ II 10
Since Camma fled from *S* to our Temple, „ II 14
You will not marry *S*? „ II 27
and only Marry the dead. *Priestess.* Not *s* then? „ II 31
messenger from *S* who waits Before the Temple? „ II 37
Greeting and health from *S*! (repeat) „ II 41, 131
mine own dagger driven by *S* found All good „ II 86
'*S*! *S*!' *Camma.* *S*, *S*! „ II 108
shout of *S* and Camma sitting Upon one throne, „ II 146
Call first upon the Goddess, *S*. „ II 256
Here is another sacred to the Goddess, The gift of *S*; „ II 347
That *S* should drink from his own cup. „ II 353
This blessing is for *S* and for me. „ II 376
S, first King, Camma, first Queen o' the Realm, „ II 440

T

Taäen (taken) but I ha *t* good care to turn out boäth my darters right down fine laädies. *Prom. of May* I 335
Taäke (take) But I *t's* 'im fur a bad lot and a burn fool, „ I 153
but if she'd *t* to ma i' that waäy, or ony waäy, „ I 177
but I *t's* 'im fur a Lunnon swindler, and a burn fool. „ I 308
I *t's* it kindly of all o' you that you be coomed— „ I 318
an' I can *t* my glass wi' the youngest, „ I 360
I thinks I'd like to *t* the measure o' your foot. „ I 463
Will ya *t* 'em? fur Miss Eva, „ II 17
and now she be gone, will ye *t* 'em, Miss Dora? „ II 21
an' weänt ye *t* 'em now, Miss Dora, „ II 41
I would *t* the owd blind man to my oän fireside. „ II 74
p'raps ye hears 'at I soomtimes *t's* a drop too much; „ II 108
fur she tell'd ma to *t* the cart to Littlechester. „ II 322
T one o' the young 'uns fust, Miss, „ III 31
I be ready to *t* the pledge. „ III 84
T me awaäy, little gell. It be one o' my bad daäys. „ III 464
Taäked (took) and I *t* 'im fur soom sort of a land-surveyor— „ I 204
Taäkin' (taking) theer be a thousand i' the parish, *t* in the women and childer; „ I 146
I likes 'er all the better fur *t* me down, „ II 133
Taäter (potato) and the sacks, and the *t's*, and the mangles, „ I 453
Table look how the *t* steams, like a heathen altar; *Becket* I iv 68
and the Lord hath prepared your *t*— „ I iv 131
And as for the flesh at *t*, a whole Peter's sheet, „ III iii 129
Taboo'd No pleasure then *t*: for when the tide *Prom. of May* I 591
Tabor Like Christ himself on *T*, *Queen Mary* III iv 201
Tabula rasa a blank page, a *t r*. *Prom. of May* II 282
Ta'en (taken) and they ha' *t* the body up inter your chaumber, „ II 569
Tail (adj.) for thou was born i' the *t* end of old Harry the Seventh. *Queen Mary* I i 42
Tail (s) I was born true man at five in the forenoon i' the *t* of old Harry, „ I i 46

Taken (*continued*) York *t*? *Gurth.* Yea, Tostig hath
t York! *Harold* III ii 174
Brother of France, you have *t*, cherish'd him *Becket* II ii 154
Ay, but he's *t* the rain with him. „ III i 273
gone to the King And *t* our anathema with him. „ V ii 8
You should have *t* counsel with your friends „ V ii 555
My counsel is already *t*, John. „ V ii 560
and was much *t* with you, my dear. *Eva.* *T*
with me; *Prom. of May* III 263
the boy was *t* prisoner by the Moors. *Foresters* I i 60
were I *t* They would prick out my sight. „ II i 71
Sheriff had *t* all our goods for the King without paying, „ II i 190
Taker if giver And *t* be but honest! *Harold* I i 346
Taking (*See also* **Taäkin'**) thou wast not happy *t* charge
Of this wild Rosamund *Becket* I i 391
that *t* The Fiend's advantage of a throne, „ II i 151
Well—I shall serve Galatia *t* it, *The Cup* I i 100
made me A Quietist *t* all things easily. *Prom. of May* I 232
A Quietist *t* all things easily— „ I 290
Talbot Where, knave, where? *Man.* Sign of the *T*. *Queen Mary* III i 319
Tale (*See also* **Nursery-tale**) And love to hear bad *t's*
of Philip. „ V ii 429
tell me *t's* Of Alfred and of Athelstan the Great *Harold* IV i 73
This is the likelier *t*. We have hit the place. *Becket* III ii 42
tell him my *t's*, Sing him my songs? *The Falcon* 796
And cheer his blindness with a traveller's *t's*? *Prom. of May* II 516
Talent like the man In Holy Writ, who brought his *t*
back; *Foresters* IV 981
Talk (s) when there rose a *t* of the late rebellion, *Queen Mary* I i 92
I am somewhat faint With our long *t*. „ I v 521
—he is free enough in *t*, But tells me nothing. „ III ii 193
Touch him upon his old heretical *t*, „ III iv 352
Nor let Priests' *t*, or dream of worlds to be, „ V v 217
More *t* of this to-morrow, if yon weird sign *Harold* I i 120
Unwholesome *t* For Godwin's house! „ I i 390
I leave thee to thy *t* with him alone; „ II ii 324
I dare not well be seen in *t* with thee. „ II ii 482
Ha, Becket! thou rememberest our *t*! *Becket, Pro.* 405
The king, the crown! their *t* in Rome? *The Cup* I i 99
That must be *t*, not truth, but truth or *t*, *The Falcon* 232
Come, come, my girl, enough Of this strange *t*. *Prom. of May* III 620
Talk (verb) when your Highness *t's* of Courtenay— *Queen Mary* I v 198
Why do they *t* so foully of your Prince, „ I v 425
We *t* and *t*. *Member.* Ay, and what use to *t*? „ III iii 39
We *t* and Cranmer suffers. „ IV iii 420
I warrant you they *t* about the burning. „ IV iii 463
You *t* almost as if it Might be the last. *The Cup* I ii 422
Tut! you *t* Old feudalism. *Prom. of May* I 669
we'd as lief *t* o' the Divil afoor ye as 'im, „ III 130
t a little French like a lady; „ III 302
then what is it That makes you *t* so dolefully? „ III 572
Go with him. I will *t* with thee anon. *Foresters* II i 132
O sweet sir, *t* not of cows. „ II i 329
Elf, with spiteful heart and eye, *T* of jealousy? „ II ii 173
Talked They've almost *t* me into it: *Queen Mary* I iv 7
When last we *t*, that Philip would not come „ II iv 135
Have *t* together, and are well agreed „ III iv 6
I *t* with her in vain—says she will live „ III vi 44
Council (I have *t* with some already) are for war. „ V i 295
I have often *t* with Wulfnoth, *Harold* II ii 88
for the king Is holy, and hath *t* with God, „ III i 355
Hath Henry told thee? hast thou *t* with him? *Becket* I iii 258
I could have *t* him out of His ten wives into one. „ IV ii 311
Talkin' she'd niver 'a been *t* haäfe an hour wi' the
divil 'at killed her oän sister, *Prom. of May* II 603
Talking (*See also* **A-talkin', Talkin'**) what's the good of
my *t* to myself, *Becket* III i 152
There is the King *t* with Walter Map? „ III iii 22
to seize On whomsoever may be *t* with you, *The Cup* I iii 7
Tall I would I were as *t* and strong as you. *Lady
Magdalen.* I seem half-shamed at times to
be so *t*. *Queen Mary* V ii 422
Make blush the maiden-white of our *t* cliffs, *Harold* II ii 332
So *t* and bold as they be. *Foresters* II i 8
I can bring down Fourscore *t* fellows on thee. „ IV 177

Tall (*continued*) Good, now I love thee mightily, thou
t fellow. *Foresters* IV 322
Tame (adj.) And break your paces in, and make
you *t*; *Queen Mary* V iii 122
Tame (verb) King hath many more wolves than he can *t* *Becket* III iii 322
Tamer but the plots against him Had madden'd *t* men. *Harold* IV i 112
Tamper'd Wyatt, who hath *t* with A public ignorance, *Queen Mary* II ii 180
Tamperer Or *t's* with that treason out of Kent. „ II ii 11
Tan The *t* of southern summers and the beard? *Prom. of May* II 617
Tann'd Thou art *t* almost beyond my knowing, brother. *Foresters* IV 1015
Tanner and cried 'Work for the *t*.' *Harold* II ii 385
William the *t's* bastard! „ II ii 775
The *t's* bastard! „ IV iii 173
Tap (s) may give that egg-bald head The *t* that silences. „ V i 92
Tap (verb) Do me the service to *t* it, and thou wilt know.
Friar Tuck. I would *t* myself in thy service,
Robin. *Foresters* III 333
Tare burn the *t's* with unquenchable fire! *Queen Mary* V v 114
Target and make thine old carcase a *t* for us three. *Foresters* II i 404
Tarquin (II., the seventh and last King of Rome) violence
to a woman, As Rome did *T*. *The Cup* I i 140
I here return like *T*—for a crown. *Antonius.* And
may be foil'd like *T*, if you follow „ I i 142
Tarry Methinks that would you *t* one day more *Queen Mary* III vi 232
Task it is thou Hath set me this hard *t*, *The Falcon* 237
Taste by the hand o' God avore a could *t* a
mossel, *Queen Mary* IV iii 517
Not *t* his venison first? *Foresters* IV 343
Tasted scarce touch'd or *t* The splendours of our Court. *Harold* II ii 174
This Almoner hath *t* Henry's gold. *Becket* I iii 294
Tatter'd Our holy mother Canterbury, who sits With *t* robes. „ I i 157
Taught (*See also* **Larned**) the old priests *t* me
nothing. *Queen Mary* II iii 58
And every syllable *t* us by our Lord, „ IV iii 231
thou hast *t* the king to spoil him too; *Harold* I i 451
then I *t* him all our hawking-phrases. *The Falcon* 314
T her the learned names, anatomized *Prom. of May* II 302
for you have *t* me To love you. „ III 557
Tawny The *t* squirrel vaulting thro' the boughs, *Foresters* I iii 117
Tax They will not lay more *t'es* on a land *Queen Mary* V i 167
Taxing *See* **Over-taxing**
Tea Owd Steer gi'es nubbut cowd *t* to 'is men, *Prom. of May* II 224
But I'd like owd Steer's cowd *t* better nor
Dobson's beer. „ II 227
worked at all the worse upon the cold *t* than you
would have done upon the beer? „ III 56
we worked naw wuss upo' the cowd *t*; „ III 59
Teach (*See also* **Larn**) we will *t* Queen Mary how to
reign. *Queen Mary* II i 147
if this pass, We two shall have to *t* him; „ III iv 422
and our Latimer-sailors Will *t* her something. „ IV iii 350
he and I Might *t* this Rome— *The Cup* II 96
Tear (s) (*See also* **Woman-tears**) Spite of her *t's* her
father forced it on her. *Queen Mary* I v 495
those hard men brake into woman *t's*, Ev'n Gardiner, „ I v 565
Queen hath been three days in *t's* „ III vi 13
See how the *t's* run down his fatherly face. „ IV iii 3
The Queen in *t's*! „ V i 223
cries continually with sweat and *t's* to the Lord God „ V iv 45
And blotted by her *t's*. This cannot last. „ V v 17
My prayers go up as fast as my *t's* fall, *Harold* III i 166
Vying a *t* with our cold dews, „ V i 150
My heart is full of *t's*—I have no answer. *Becket, Pro.* 406
My lord, we leave thee not without *t's*. *Becket.* *T's*?
Why not stay with me then? „ I iv 17
many midriff-shaken even to *t's*, as springs gush out
after earthquakes— „ III iii 162
old affection master'd you, You falter'd into *t's*. „ V ii 145
True *t's* that year were shed for you in Florence. *The Falcon* 384
I hate *t's*. Marriage is but an old tradition. *Prom. of May* I 490
Bid their old bond farewell with smiles, not *t's*; „ I 525
That desolate letter, blotted with her *t's*, „ II 476
should walk hand in hand together down this valley
of *t's*, „ III 192
T's! I have sometimes been moved to *t's* „ III 207

Tell (*continued*) I cannot t; but I came to give thee — Foresters I i 131
I cannot t, but I had sooner have given — „ I i 137
I cannot t. Manners be so corrupt, — „ I i 176
Give me thy hand and t him— — „ I ii 241
I heard this Sheriff t her he would pay — „ I iii 5
T me, t me of her. — „ II i 103
Did I not t you an old woman could shoot better? — „ II i 406
I t thee, in some sort. — „ II i 531
These be the lies the people t of us, — „ III 392
when will that be? canst thou t? — „ IV 421
Telled (told) and 'e t all on us to be i' the long barn by one o'clock, — Prom. of May I 7
he niver mended that gap i' the glebe fence as I t 'im; — „ I 447
he t me 'at sweet'arts niver worked well togither; and I t 'im 'at sweet'arts allus worked best togither; — „ II 155
I t tha to let ma aloän! — „ II 229
fur she t ma to taäke the cart to Littlechester. — „ II 322
as I t 'er to-daäy when she fell foul upo' me. — „ II 581
She t me once not to meddle wi' 'im, — „ II 599
I knaw'd 'im when I seed 'im ageän an I t feyther on 'im. — „ III 122
but us three, arter Sally'd t us on 'im, — „ III 134
Mr. Dobson t me to saäy he's browt — „ III 346
'at I t 'em to gallop 'im. — „ III 432
Telling (part.) (*See also* **A-telling**) What was my Lord of Devon t you? — Queen Mary I iv 183
I have been t her of the death of one Philip Edgar — Prom. of May II 705
Telling (s) Some spice of wisdom in my t you, — Queen Mary II iv 134
Ay, since you hate the t it. — „ III i 89
Temper Thou hast lost thine even t, brother Harold! — Harold V i 95
but you turn right ugly when you're in an ill t; — Prom. of May I 160
Tempest To raise that t which will set it trembling — Becket, Pro. 208
Templars Becket, I am the oldest of the T; — „ I iii 248
I am the youngest of the T, — „ I iii 261
Temple (adj.) In the gray dawn before the T doors. — The Cup I ii 295
She—close the T door. Let her not fly. — „ II 460
Temple (s) hath begun to re-edify the true t— — Queen Mary I iii 59
For London had a t and a priest When Canterbury — Becket I iii 59
The pagan t of a pagan Rome! — „ I iii 61
Among her maidens to this T— — The Cup I i 10
beheld you afar off worshipping in her T, — „ I i 40
house of Sinnatus—Close to the T. — „ I i 53
'tis but a step from here To the T. — „ I ii 444
These Romans dare not violate the T. — „ I iii 63
I have it in my heart—to the T—fly— — „ I iii 111
The women of the T drag her in. — „ I iii 118
waits once more Before the T. — „ II 12
Since Camma fled from Synorix to our T, — „ II 15
messenger from Synorix who waits Before the T? — „ II 38
And where? *Messenger*. Here by your t. — „ II 77
This violence ill becomes The silence of our T. — „ II 216
Welcome, my lord Antonius, to our T. — „ II 253
I call on our own Goddess in our own T. — „ II 315
It is the cup belonging our own T. — „ II 345
Beside this t half a year ago? — „ II 393
Temple Bar and the traitor flying To T B, — Queen Mary II iv 94
Temporal We, the Lords Spiritual and T, — „ III iii 113
Temporize Call it to t: and not to lie; — Harold II ii 415
Tempt May she not t me, being at my side, To question *her*? — Becket III i 216
Tempted ever Be t into doing what might seem — Prom. of May III 554
Ten but t thousand men on Penenden Heath all calling after your worship, — Queen Mary II i 60
Say for t thousand t—and pothouse knaves, — „ II i 69
And strong to throw t Wyatts and all Kent. — „ II ii 353
T miles about. *Wyatt*. Ev'n so. — „ II iii 49
Ay! tho' it were t Englands! — „ III iv 57
and I bean't wrong not twice i' t year— — „ IV iii 534
There is no king, not were he t times king, T times our husband, — „ V i 62
And I ha' nine darters i' the spital that be dead t times o'er i' one day — Becket I iv 250
I could have talk'd him out of His t wives into one. — „ IV ii 313
Alas, t summers! — The Falcon 348
this faded ribbon was the mode In Florence t years back. — „ 423

Ten (*continued*) Spite of t thousand brothers, Federigo. — The Falcon 898
What be he a-doing here t mile an' moor fro' a raäil? — Prom. of May I 209
you have robb'd poor father Of t good apples. — „ I 616
they have each t marks in gold. — Foresters III 292
Ten-aäcre (acre) I ha' plowed the t-a—it be mine now —afoor ony o' ye wur burn—ye all knaws the t-a— — Prom. of May I 365
Tenant shall excommunicate My t's or my household. — Becket, Pro. 32
Wasted our diocese, outraged our t's, — „ V ii 431
After my frolic with his t's girl, — Prom. of May I 493
Tendance in a closed room, with light, fire, physic, t; — Queen Mary V iv 37
Tender Father, I am so t to all hardness! — Becket I i 315
The father's eye was so t it would have called a goose off the green, — „ III iii 102
I am t enough. Why do you practise on me? — The Cup I ii 237
Tenderness with what a t He loved my son. — Becket V i 20
She had a t toward me, — Foresters I i 115
Tenebris Surgas e t, Sis vindicator! — Harold V i 571
Tenfold t, than this fearful child can do; — „ I ii 143
False to himself, but t-f false to me! — Becket I iii 472
Sir, you are t more a gentleman, — Prom. of May III 742
larger life hereafter, more T than under roof. — Foresters II i 70
Term with hot t's Of Satan, liars, — Queen Mary I ii 94
call it by that new t Brought from the sacred East, — Foresters IV 704
Territory Large lordship there of lands and t. — Harold II ii 83
Test (s) True t of coward, ye follow with a yell. — Becket I iii 745
Test (verb) Their 'dies Illa,' which will t their sect. — Queen Mary III iv 428
worthy Bonner,—To t their sect. — „ III iv 431
yet it is a day to t your health — „ IV ii 117
Testament in the T's, Both Old and New. — „ IV iii 232
Testy It is the heat and narrowness of the cage That makes the captive t; — „ III v 208
Tetrarch married Since—married Sinnatus, the T — The Cup I i 16
'To the admired Camma, wife of Sinnatus, the T, — „ I i 37
And you a Prince and T in this province— — „ I ii 89
This Synorix Was T here, and tyrant also— — „ I ii 183
being as you tell me T, there might be willing wives — „ I ii 187
being T once His own true people cast him — „ I ii 349
Tetrarchy when I was flying from My T to Rome. — „ I i 7
I shall have my t restored By Rome, — „ I i 20
Our Senate, wearied of their *tetrarchies*, — „ I i 89
Tew (worry) and he wur in a t about it all the murnin'; — Prom. of May I 18
Text by Heaven, The t—Your Highness knows it, — Queen Mary I v 451
Traced in the blackest t of Hell—'Thou shalt!' — „ III i 426
It's the old Scripture t, 'Let us eat and drink, — Prom. of May I 258
Thames I'll have the drawbridge hewn into the T, — Queen Mary II ii 377
Upon their lake of Garda, fire the T; — „ III ii 24
It glares in heaven, it flares upon the T, — Harold I i 30
Thane Morcar and Edwin have stirr'd up the T's — „ II ii 289
Hath massacred the T that was his guest, — „ II ii 297
Earls and T's! Full thanks for your fair greeting — „ IV iii 45
Earls, T's, and all our countrymen! — „ IV iii 48
Thank I t my God it is too late to fly. — Queen Mary I ii 112
I t God, I have lived a virgin, — „ II ii 216
We t your Lordship and your loyal city. — „ II ii 300
I t you heartily, sir, — „ III v 176
I came to t her Majesty For freeing — „ III vi 5
Or seek to rescue me. I t the Council. — „ IV ii 39
Hand it me, then! I t you. — „ IV ii 45
T the Lord therevore. (repeat) — Queen Mary IV iii 496, 520, 529
T the Saints, no! — Harold I i 318
I t thee, Rolf. — „ II i 54
I t thee, but had rather Breathe the free wind — „ II ii 184
I t thee now for having saved thyself. — „ II ii 653
T thee, father! Thou art English, — „ III i 27
I t you, sons; when kings but hold by crowns, — Becket II ii 280
into thy mouth hadst thou but opened it to t him. — „ III iii 277
He is not here—Not yet, t heaven. O save him! — „ V iii 17
I t you from my heart. — The Cup I ii 211
However I t thee; thou hast saved my life. — „ I ii 331
I t thee, Camma,—I t thee. (repeat) — „ II 331, 355
Who touch'd me then? I t you. — „ II 532
I t thee, good Filippo. — The Falcon 553

Thank (*continued*) I *t* you, my good nurse. *The Falcon* 559
I *t* you heartily for that—and you, „ 801
My lord, we *t* you for your entertainment. „ 859
scarce Will *t* me for your entertainment now. „ 882
T you. Look how full of rosy blossom it is. *Prom. of May* I 83
I *t* you for that, Miss Dora, onyhow. „ I 157
saäme to you, Master Steer, likewise. *Steer.* *T* ye. „ I 348
I *t* you. They tell me that yesterday „ II 22
if the fever spread, the parish will have to *t* you for it. „ III 47
But I *t's* ye all the saäme, Miss. „ III 50
All right, Miss; and *t* ye kindly. „ III 66
An' I *t's* ye fur that, Miss, moor nor fur the waäge. „ III 116
Say that the sick lady *t's* him! „ III 349
I *t* you, my lady, and I wish you *Foresters* I i 307
We *t* you, and farewell. „ I ii 248
Comrades, I *t* you for your loyalty, „ III 78
I *t* thee. *Marian.* Scarlet told me— „ III 144
I *t* you, my lord. „ III 213
I *t* you, noble sir, the very blossom Of bandits. Curtsey to him, wife, and *t* him. *Wife.* I *t* you, noble sir, and will pray for you „ III 246
There is our bond. *Robin.* I *t* thee. „ IV 436
Here is my father's bond. *Robin.* I *t* thee, dear. „ IV 464
I *t* thee, good Sir Richard. „ IV 858

Thank'd She *t* her father sweetly for his book *Queen Mary* V v 236

Thankful And shalt be *t* if I leave thee that. „ III i 257

Thankless Were but a *t* policy in the crown, „ III iv 51
I know it, son; I am not *t*: *Harold* I i 216

Thanks I am all *t* To God and to your Grace: *Queen Mary* I v 185
beseech Your Highness to accept our lowliest *t* „ II ii 132
T, Sir Thomas, we be beholden to you, „ II iii 120
Loyal and royal cousin, humblest *t*. „ III ii 4
Can render *t* in fruit for being sown, „ III iii 198
Madam, my *t*. „ V i 184
T, truthful Earl; I did not doubt thy word, *Harold* II ii 723
Full *t* for your fair greeting of my bride! „ IV iii 46
T, Gurth! The simple, silent, selfless man „ V i 80
Our humblest *t* for your blessing. *Becket* I iv 42
t of Holy Church are due to those That went „ II ii 190
T to the blessed Magdalen, whose day it is. „ III iii 171
T in this life, and in the life to come. „ V ii 161
I owe you *t* for ever. *The Cup* I ii 249
My *t*. But, look, how wasteful of the blossom *Prom. of May* I 611
Yeäs; and *t* to ye. „ III 26
T, my lady—inasmuch as I am a true believer *Foresters* I i 161
All *t* for all your service; „ I iii 164

Thaw and those bleak manners *t*, *Queen Mary* III ii 161
cold corners of the King's mouth began to *t*, *Becket* III iii 154

Thaw (though) *t* 'e knaws I was hallus ageän heving schoolmaster i' the parish! *Prom. of May* I 185
fur *t* I may ha' fallen out wi' ye sometimes, „ I 324
and, *t* I says it mysen, niver men 'ed a better master— „ I 326
I be a gentleman, *t* I beänt naw scholard, „ I 332
fur *t* I be heighty this very daäy, „ I 358
But, Steer, *t* thou be haäle anew I seed tha a-limpin' up just now „ I 383
Churchwarden be a coomin', *t* me and 'im we niver 'grees about the tithe; and Parson mebbe, *t* he niver mended that gap i' the glebe fence as I telled 'im; and Blacksmith, *t* he niver shoes a herse to my likings; and Baäker, *t* I sticks to hoäm-maäde— „ I 443
Noä—yeas—*t* the feller's gone and maäde such a litter of his faäce. „ II 588
noä—*t* they hanged ma at 'Size fur it. „ II 697

Themselves *See* **Thessens**

Theobald (Archbishop of Canterbury) So then our good Archbishop *T* Lies dying. *Becket, Pro.* 2
thou didst help me to my throne In *T's* time, „ *Pro.* 202
when I was of *T's* household, once— „ I i 59
I served our *T* well when I was with him; „ I i 142
I and thou were youths in *T's* house, „ I iii 40
Exile me from the face of *T*. „ I iii 43
Even when you both were boys at *T's*. „ V i 11

Therevore (therefore) Thank the Lord *t*. (repeat) *Queen Mary* IV iii 496, 520, 529

Therewithin To still the petty treason *t*, *Queen Mary* III i 13

Thessens (themselves) Foälks doesn't hallus knaw *t*; *Prom. of May* I 29

Thick (adj.) on his neck a collar, Gold, *t* with diamonds; *Queen Mary* III i 80
And here's a crowd as *t* as herring-shoals. „ III i 182
till he stoop'd and gather'd one From out a bed of *t* forget-me-nots, „ V v 94
The people are as *t* as bees below, *Harold* I i 31
And wattled *t* with ash and willow-wands; „ V i 190
My sight is eagle, but the strife so *t*— „ V i 627
The King's 'God's eyes!' come now so *t* and fast, *Becket* I iii 610

Thick (s) I left him somewhere in the *t* of it. *Queen Mary* II iv 81

Thicken doth not the living skin *t* against perpetual whippings? *Becket* III iii 316

Thicket Seen in the *t* at the bottom there *The Cup* I i 113

Thief Gentleman! a *t*! Go hang him. *Queen Mary* II iii 75
when the *t* is ev'n within the walls, „ III iv 311
Thou shalt receive the penitent *t's* award, „ IV iii 86
And, like a *t*, push'd in his royal hand; „ V ii 466
When *thieves* fall out, honest men— *Becket* I iv 113
Is the Archbishop a *t* who gives thee thy supper? „ I iv 116
When honest men fall out, *thieves*— „ I iv 119
Absolve the left-hand *t* and damn the right? „ II ii 392
like a *t* at night when he hears a door open „ III iii 97
I laäme't my knee last night running arter a *t*. *Prom. of May* I 387
I runned arter *t* i' the dark, „ I 402
I am a *t*, ay, and a king of *thieves*. *Foresters* II i 53
By a *t*. *Sheriff.* Who, woman, who? „ II i 317
Softly! softly! there may be a *t* in every bush. „ II i 368
thou art disguised—thou art one of the *thieves*. „ II i 411
It is the very captain of the *thieves*! „ II i 413
These friars, *thieves*, and liars, Shall drink „ III 312
yells of *t* And rogue and liar echo down in Hell, „ III 323
Well, well, be it so, thou strongest *t* of all, „ III 327
But Robin is a *t* of courtesy „ IV 370
There—to be a *t* of courtesy— „ IV 373
my liege, these men are outlaws, *thieves*, „ IV 906

Thief-like Who *t-l* fled from his own church by night, *Becket* II ii 156

Thimble and can make Five quarts pass into a *t*. *Foresters* IV 283

Thimbleful I am misty with my *t* of ale. „ IV 278

Thin He! too *t*, too *t*. *Becket, Pro.* 261
Ay, child; and you look *t* and pale. *Prom. of May* I 781
that wur sa long back, and the walls sa *t*, „ III 72
It is but *t* and cold, Not like the vintage *The Falcon* 578

Thing There is but one *t* against them. *Queen Mary* I i 101
but all *t's* here At court are known; „ I iv 56
I must needs wish all good *t's* for France. „ I v 309
the *t* Was no such scarecrow in your father's time. „ I v 472
Few *t's* have fail'd to which I set my will. „ II ii 22
were to do Great *t's*, my Lord. „ II ii 390
smash all our bits o' *t's* worse than Philip o' Spain. „ II iii 104
These are the *t's* that madden her. Fie upon it! „ III ii 221
By bonds of beeswax, like your creeping *t*; „ III iii 63
Nor yet to question *t's* already done; „ III iii 189
Ringdoves coo again, All *t's* woo again. „ III v 104
all *t's* lived and ended honestly. „ III v 115
Fancy-sick; these *t's* are done, „ IV iii 453
Pwoaps be pretty *t's*, Joan, „ IV iii 469
I do know ez Pwoaps and vires be bad *t's*; „ IV iii 501
other *t's* As idle; a weak Wyatt! „ V i 291
Let dead *t's* rest. „ V ii 506
the one King, the Christ, and all *t's* in common, „ V iv 54
And done such mighty *t's* by Holy Church, „ V v 74
What is the strange *t* happiness? „ V v 77
dream of worlds to be, Miscolour *t's* about her— „ V v 219
worst that follows *T's* that seem jerk'd *Harold* I i 137
thou be a wild *t* Out of the waste, „ I i 380
where *they* were lost, Where all good *t's* are lost, „ III ii 28
I hate myself for all *t's* that I do. „ IV ii 45
He means the *t* he says. See him out safe! „ V i 84
They say that you are wise in winged *t's*, *Becket* I i 256
like Egypt's plague, had fill'd All *t's* with blood; „ I iii 346
have I Not heard ill *t's* of her in France? „ III i 231

Thing (*continued*) Some dreadful *t* is coming on me. *Becket* III i 267
all manner of game, and four-footed *t's*, and fowls— „ III iii 130
And all manner of creeping *t's* too? „ III iii 133
Yet one *t* more. Thou hast broken thro' the pales „ III iii 192
I might deliver all *t's* to thy hand— „ III iii 270
to overstep and come at all *t's* in the next field? „ III iii 282
that's a finer *t* there. How it glitters! „ IV i 2
Henry Says many a *t* in sudden heats, „ IV ii 276
Deal not with *t's* you know not. „ V ii 133
I know not why You call these old *t's* back „ V ii 270
and smile At bygone *t's* till that eternal peace. *The Cup* I iii 172
This old *t* here they are but blue beads— *The Falcon* 47
My one *t* left of value in the world! „ 496
and profess to be great in green *t's* and in garden-stuff. „ 551
made me A Quietist taking all *t's* easily. *Prom. of May* I 232
A Quietist taking all *t's* easily— „ I 290
O the sacred little *t*! What a shape! *Foresters* I i 108
to whom all *t's*, up to this present, „ I i 209
if this life of ours Be a good glad *t*, „ I iii 13
Because thou sayest such fine *t's* of women, „ I iii 137
the scream of some wild woodland *t*. „ II i 253
criedst 'I yield' almost before the *t* was ask'd, „ II i 566
True, she is a goodly *t*. „ II ii 140
A woman's heart is but a little *t*, „ IV 656

Think I *t* she entreats me like a child. *Queen Mary* I iii 111
I *t* you may. „ I iii 153
I *t* she means to counsel your withdrawing „ I iv 224
I *t* my time will come. „ I iv 256
Because they *t* me favourer of this marriage. „ I v 156
I do *t* To save your crown that it must come to this. „ I v 478
And *t* not we shall be alone— „ II i 191
I'll *t* upon it, Knyvett. „ II i 240
Don't ye now go to *t* that we be for Philip o' Spain. „ II iii 106
are you not in peril here? *Stafford.* I *t* so. „ III i 36
I *t* with you. The King of France will help „ III i 104
We are fallen, and as I *t*, Never to rise again. „ III i 124
I *t* I should fight then. „ III i 468
that I *t*, 'Wilt thou lie there to-morrow?' „ III v 132
Help me: what *t* you, Is it life or death? „ III v 193
and *t* of this in your coming. 'MARY THE QUEEN.' „ III v 224
T! I have many thoughts; I *t* there may be birdlime here for me; I *t* they fain would have me from the realm; I *t* the Queen may never bear a child; I *t* that I may be some time the Queen, „ III v 226
I *t* I will not marry anyone, „ III v 239
I *t* that I will play with Philibert,— „ III v 242
Albeit he *t* himself at home with God, „ IV iii 192
T you then That Cranmer read all papers „ IV iii 316
I *t* that in some sort we may. But see, „ IV iii 551
Does he *t* Low stature is low nature, „ V ii 433
It is the low man *t's* the woman low; „ V ii 439
T you That I might dare to tell her that the Count— „ V ii 522
tells me I must not *t*—That I must rest— „ V v 63
I *t* that they would Molochize them too, *Harold* I i 36
Ask thou Lord Leofwin what he *t's* of this! „ I i 40
I love him or *t* I love him. „ I ii 152
As I *t* He was thine host in England „ II ii 3
I *t* it so, I *t* I am a fool To *t* it can be otherwise „ III i 102
Some *t* they loved within the pale forbidden „ III ii 22
I *t* that this is Thurkill. „ V ii 65
I will not *t* so, Thomas. *Becket, Pro.* 238
dost thou *t* the king Forced mine election? *Herbert.* I do *t* the King Was potent in the election, „ I i 126
T on it again. „ I i 380
t of me as thy father! „ I iii 250
I ask'd the way. *Rosamund.* I *t* so. „ II i 63
I sometimes *t* he sleeps When he should watch; „ III i 32
when he hears a door open in the house and *t's* 'the master.' „ III iii 99
I *t*, time given, I could have talk'd „ IV ii 311
I cannot *t* he moves against my son, „ V i 18
I *t* ye four have cause to love this Becket. „ V i 224
lightnings that we *t* are only Heaven's Flash „ V ii 35
I *t* our Abbess knew it and allow'd it. „ V ii 95

Think (*continued*) but *t* not of the King: farewell! *Becket* V ii 185
T,—torture,—death,—and come. *The Cup* I ii 314
I warrants ye'll *t* moor o' this young Squire Edgar *Prom. of May* I 109
ye'll *t* more on 'is little finger than hall my hand „ I 111
Dobbins, I *t*. *Dobson.* Dobbins, you *t's*; and I *t's* ye wears „ I 459
I *t's* I'd like to taäke the measure o' your foot. „ I 463
I can't abeär to *t* on 'er now, „ II 32
How could I *t* of leaving him? „ II 71
Do ye *t* I be gawin' to tell it to you, „ II 190
almost *t* she half return'd the pressure Of mine. „ II 627
I'd *t* na moor o' maäkin' an end o' tha nor a carrion craw— „ II 695
d'ye *t* I'd gi'e 'em the fever? „ III 49
Do you *t* that I may? No, not yet. „ III 238
her answer—I *t* I have it about me—yes, there it is! „ III 395
I *t* That I should break my heart, „ III 555
I am easily led by words, but I *t* the Earl hath right. *Foresters* I ii 40
I *t* they will be mightier than the king. „ I ii 119
What makes thee *t* I seem so cold to Robin? „ III 3
That when I *t* of it hotly, Love himself Seems „ III 111
Robin—I crave pardon, I always *t* of you as my lord, „ III 410

Thinkest Roger, *t* thou that anyone Suspected thee *Queen Mary* I iii 174
Gamel, son of Orm, What *t* thou this means? (repeat) *Harold* I i 21, 464

Thinking —I was *t* of her when—O yes, *Prom. of May* II 368

Thin-skinn'd O *t-s* hand and jutting veins, *Queen Mary* IV ii 204

Third Linger not till the *t* horn. Fly! *Becket* III ii 40
O would it were His *t* last apoplexy! *The Cup* II 172

Thirlby (Bishop of Ely) (*See also* **Ely**) Bishop *T*, And my Lord Paget *Queen Mary* IV i 5
Weep not, good *T*. „ IV ii 172
Will they burn me, *T*? „ IV ii 182
And may God bless you, *T*! „ IV ii 198
these burnings, As *T* says, are profitless „ IV ii 218

Thirst which the more you drink, The more you *t*— *The Cup* I iii 140

Thirtieth To-day he hath accomplished his *t* birthday, *Foresters* I i 298
all of you Who deign to honour this my *t* year, „ I ii 79
pray Thy *t* summer may be thirty-fold As happy „ I ii 128

Thirty To raise your Highness *t* thousand men, *Queen Mary* II ii 290
Sailing from France, with *t* Englishmen, „ V i 285
Down *t* feet below the smiling day— *Harold* II ii 430
Some *t*—forty thousand silver marks. *Becket* I iii 657
her six and *t* sail Of Provence blew you to your English throne; „ V i 122

Thirty-fold Thy thirtieth summer may be *t-f* *Foresters* I ii 128

This *t* Gardiner for one, who is to be made Lord Chancellor, *Queen Mary* I i 85
My masters, yonder's fatter game for you Than *t* old gaping gurgoyle: „ I iii 81
but *t* fine blue-blooded Courtenay seems Too princely for a pawn. „ I iii 165
now would settle Upon *t* flower, now that; „ I iv 56
T dress was made me as the Earl of Devon To take my seat in; „ I iv 72
Have sworn *t* Spanish marriage shall not be. „ I iv 115
And if *t* Prince of fluff and feather come To woo you, niece, „ I iv 162
He commends me now From out his grave to *t* archbishoprick. *Becket, Pro.* 420
and I do not then charm *t* secret out of our loyal Thomas, „ *Pro.* 466
Follow me *t* Rosamund day and night, whithersoever she goes; „ *Pro.* 506
and *t* Becket, her father's friend, like enough staved us from her. „ *Pro.* 517
And mine uplifter in *t* world, and chosen me For *t* thy great archbishoprick, „ I i 89
and I sneezed three times *t* morning. *The Falcon* 169
To make amends I come *t* day to break my fast with you. „ 276

Thistle matched with my Harold is like a hedge *t* by a garden rose. *Prom. of May* III 176

Thomas (Becket, Chancellor of England, afterwards Archbishop of Canterbury) (*See also* **Becket, Thomas Becket, Thomas of Canterbury**) That is my secret, *T*. *Becket, Pro.* 75

Thomas (Becket, Chancellor of England, afterwards Archbishop of Canterbury) (*continued*) I have built a secret bower in England, *T*, *Becket Pro.* 154
Nay—I know not, *T*. „ *Pro.* 197
I will not think so, *T*. „ *Pro.* 238
And who shall he be, my friend *T*? „ *Pro.* 243
I lack a spiritual soldier, *T*— „ *Pro.* 258
chart is not mine, but Becket's: take it, *T*. „ *Pro.* 311
I do not then charm this secret out of our loyal *T*, „ *Pro.* 467
Jest or prophecy there? *Herbert.* Both, *T*, both. „ I i 69
T, thou art moved too much. „ I i 172
T, thou wast not happy taking charge „ I i 390
Saving thine order, *T*, Is black and white „ I iii 31
Where's *T*? hath he sign'd? „ I iii 316
Ah! *T*, excommunicate them all! „ I iii 573
Thou wert plain *T* and not Canterbury, „ I iii 578
The holy *T*? Brother, you have traffick'd „ II ii 66
Ah, *T*, *T*, Thou art thyself again, *T* again. „ II ii 138
me, *T*, son Of Gilbert Becket, London merchant. „ II ii 229
Ah, *T*, You had not borne it, no, not for a day. „ II ii 304
Our *T* never will diagonalise. „ II ii 333
condemn The blameless exile?— *Herbert.* Thee, thou holy *T*! „ II ii 397
We have had so many hours together, *T*, „ III iii 38
Were I *T*, I wouldn't trust it. „ III iii 58
As magnificently and archiepiscopally as our *T* would have done: „ III iii 87
but look if *T* have not flung himself at the King's feet. „ III iii 168
Have I not promised to restore her, *T*, „ III iii 183
What more, my lord Archbishop? What more, *T*? „ III iii 218
T, I would there were that perfect trust between us, „ III iii 263
Oh, *T*, I could fall down and worship thee, my *T*, „ III iii 287
T, lord Not only of your vassals but amours, „ V i 204
T, I would thou hadst return'd to England, „ V ii 11
T, The lightnings that we think are only Heaven's „ V ii 34
T You could not—old affection master'd you, „ V ii 142
T, Why should you heat yourself for such as these? „ V ii 543
Take refuge in your own cathedral, *T*. „ V ii 584

Thomas (Wyatt, insurrectionary leader) (*See also* **Thomas Wyatt, Wyatt**) None so new, Sir *T*, and none so old, Sir *T*. *Queen Mary* II i 14
Ay, why not, Sir *T*? „ II i 32
I hate Spain, Sir *T*. „ II i 37
Sir *T*, we may grant the wine. „ II i 40
But, Sir *T*, must we levy war against the Queen's Grace? „ II i 186
I fear we be too few, Sir *T*. „ II i 225
Sir *T*, I've found this paper; „ II iii 55
Sir *T*— *Wyatt.* Hang him, I say. „ II iii 79
O Sir *T*, Sir *T*, pray you go away, Sir *T*, „ II iii 98
don't ye kill the Queen here, Sir *T*; „ II iii 111
we pray you to kill the Queen further off, Sir *T*. „ II iii 115
Thanks, Sir *T*, we be beholden to you, „ II iii 120

Thomas (Wyatt, the elder) Old Sir *T* would have hated it. „ II i 18
Old Sir *T* always granted the wine. „ II i 41
a fine courtier of the old Court, old Sir *T*. „ II i 46
I have been there with old Sir *T*, and the beds I know. „ II i 184

Thomas Becket (Chancellor of England, afterwards Archbishop of Canterbury) (*See also* **Becket, Thomas, Thomas of Canterbury**) My Rosamund is no Lais, *T B*; *Becket, Pro.* 58
last words were a commendation of *T B* to your Grace „ *Pro.* 401
ye are all as like To lodge a fear in *T B's* heart „ I iii 176
Wilt thou hold out for ever, *T B*? „ I iii 266
Where is the Archbishop, *T B*? „ V iii 110

Thomas Gresham and Sir *T G* Will aid us. *Queen Mary* V i 180

Thomas of Canterbury (Becket) I would, my lord *T o C*, Thou wert plain Thomas and not Canterbury, *Becket* I iii 577

Thomas Stafford (insurrectionary leader) (*See also* **Stafford**) Sir *T S*, and some more— *Queen Mary* I iii 124
I believe Sir *T S*? „ III i 32
You would but make us weaker, *T S*. „ III i 131
Carew is there, and *T S* there. „ V i 125
Sir *T S*, a bull-headed ass, „ V i 284

Thomas White (Lord Mayor of London) I am *T W*. Few things have fail'd to which I set my will. „ II ii 21

Thomas White (Lord Mayor of London) (*continued*)
Am I *T W*? One word before she comes. *Queen Mary* II ii 108
Yes, *T W*. I am safe enough; „ II ii 316
And *T W* will prove this Thomas Wyatt, „ II ii 367

Thomas Wyatt (insurrectionary leader) (*See also* **Thomas, Wyatt**) Sir Peter Carew and Sir *T W*, „ I iii 123
Sir *T W*, I myself, some others, „ I iv 113
all of us abhor The venomous, bestial, devilish revolt Of *T W*. „ II ii 288
And Thomas White will prove this *T W*, „ II ii 368
'Whosoever will apprehend the traitor *T W* „ II iii 60

Thor by St. Dunstan, old St. *T*—By God, we thought him dead—but our old *T* Heard his own thunder again, *Harold* IV iii 147

Thorn rose but pricks his nose Against the *t*, „ I i 423
not *t* enough to prick him for it, Ev'n with a word? *Becket* III i 251

Thorn'd only rose of all the stock That never *t* him; *Harold* I i 427

Thorough Yet thoroughly to believe in one's own self, So one's own self be *t*, *Queen Mary* II ii 389

Though *See* **Thaw**

Thought (s) You fly your *t's* like kites. *Queen Mary* I v 390
Think! I have many *t's*; „ III v 226
Had in him kingly *t's*—a king of men, *Harold* IV i 83
our waking *t's* Suffer a stormless shipwreck „ V i 295
And thy *t's*, thy fancies? *Becket, Pro.* 118
every thread of *t* Is broken ere it joins— „ V ii 206
I have no *t* of marriage, my friend. *Prom. of May* II 65
No *t* was mine of torture or of death, *The Cup* II 410
when *T* Comes down among the crowd, *Prom. of May* I 500

Thought (verb) (*See also* **Thowt**) *t* To bind me first by oaths I could not keep, *Queen Mary* I v 556
it is *t* the Duke will be taken. „ II i 136
if I either *t* or knew This marriage should bring loss „ II ii 226
I *t* this Philip had been one of those black devils of Spain, „ III i 214
but I *t* he was a beast. „ III i 220
she *t* they knew the laws. „ III i 380
(for they *t* not of our tides), „ III ii 27
I *t* of you, my liege, Ev'n as I spoke. „ III ii 94
I *t* not on my boots; „ III v 195
when it was *t* I might be chosen Pope, „ V ii 82
and it was *t* we two Might make one flesh, „ V ii 135
I *t* you knew me better. „ V ii 186
but I *t* I was not loved. „ V v 89
I *t* that naked Truth would shame the Devil *Harold* III i 118
By God, we *t* him dead— „ IV iii 148
twice I *t* that all was lost. „ V ii 173
Have you *t* of one? *Becket, Pro.* 9
and I *t* Lo! I must out or die. „ I i 267
T that I knew him, err'd thro' love of him, „ I iii 440
I *t* it was a gift; (repeat) „ I iii 646
and I *t* at first it was the King, „ III i 165
I *t* if it were the King's brother he had a better bride than the King, „ III i 172
He *t* less of two kings than of one Roger the king of the occasion. „ III iii 90
I *t* if I followed it I should find the fairies. „ IV i 23
We *t* to scare this minion of the King „ IV ii 330
I *t* that I had made a peace for thee. „ V ii 84
He *t* to excommunicate him— „ V ii 141
De Morville, I had *t* so well of you; „ V ii 520
I am much malign'd. I *t* to serve Galatia. *The Cup* I ii 324
Too late—*t* myself wise—A woman's dupe. „ II 480
Perhaps I *t* with those of old, *The Falcon* 878
We shouted, and *they* shouted, as I *t*, *Foresters* II i 257
Robin Hood was it? I *t* as much. „ II i 327
And *t* thou wert bewitch'd. „ II i 684
I *t* I saw thee clasp and kiss a man „ II ii 71
Who *t* to buy your marrying me with gold. „ IV 718

Thoulouse (Toulouse) Not heavier than thine armour at *T*? *Becket* I i 26
Lent at the siege of *T* by the King. „ I iii 636

Thousand Good Lord! but I have heard a *t* such. *Queen Mary* I v 579
but ten *t* men on Penenden Heath all calling after your worship, „ II i 60
Say for ten *t* ten—and pothouse knaves, „ II i 69

Thousand (*continued*) And think not we shall be alone—*t's* will flock to us. *Queen Mary* II i 191
To raise your Highness thirty *t* men, „ II ii 290
A hundred, yea, a *t* thousand-fold, „ III iii 300
A *t* ships—a hundred *t* men—*T's* of horses, *Harold* IV iii 194
I know Some three or four poor priests a *t* times Fitter for this grand function. *Becket*, *Pro.* 291
Some thirty—forty *t* silver marks. „ I iii 657
What! forty *t* marks! „ I iii 704
Forty *t* marks! forty *t* devils—and these craven bishops! „ I iv 90
Spite of ten *t* brothers, Federigo. *The Falcon* 898
I took it For some three *t* acres. *Prom. of May* III 614
And Sir Richard was told he might be ransomed for two *t* marks in gold. *Foresters* I i 64
Those two *t* marks lent me by the Abbot „ I i 264
they have trodden it for half a *t* years, „ I i 334
Two *t* marks in gold. I have paid him half. That other *t*— „ II i 464
for Oberon fled away Twenty *t* leagues to-day. „ II ii 143
Where he would pay us down his *t* marks. „ IV 441
Lest he should fail to pay these *t* marks „ IV 454
What more? one *t* marks, Or else the land. „ IV 473
Here be one *t* marks Out of our treasury to redeem the land. „ IV 492
Would buy me for a *t* marks in gold— „ IV 652
Is weightier than a *t* marks in gold, „ IV 660
A *t* winters Will strip you bare as death, a *t* summers Robe you life-green again. „ IV 1055
Thousand-fold A hundred, yea, a thousand *t-f*, *Queen Mary* III iii 200
The force of Rome a *t-f* our own. *The Cup* I ii 85
Thousand-times And *t-t* recurring argument Of those two friars *Queen Mary* IV ii 93
Thowt (thought) Coomly, says she. I niver *t* o' mysen i' that waäy; *Prom. of May* I 176
So I *t*, and I heärd the winder— „ I 395
but I *t* I'd bring tha them roses fust. „ II 50
When ye *t* there were nawbody watchin' o' you, „ II 179
I should ha' *t* they'd hed anew o' gentlefoälk, „ II 580
Thrall if my people must be *t's* of Rome, *The Cup* II 500
sat Among my *t's* in my baronial hall *Foresters* II i 61
The scarlet *t* of Rahab saved her life; *Queen Mary* III ii 38
Thread heaven and earth are *t's* of the same loom, *Harold* I i 209
that every *t* of thought Is broken ere it joins— *Becket* V ii 205
The child, a *t* within the house of birth, *The Cup* II 259
my nurse has broken The *t* of my dead flowers, *The Falcon* 522
while our Robin's life Hangs by a *t*, *Foresters* IV 385
Threadbare to cost All *t* household habit, „ I iii 112
Threadbare-worn long-tugged at, *t-w* Quarrel of Crown and Church— *Becket* II ii 54
Threat *T's*! *t's*! ye hear him. „ V ii 464
Threaten *T* the child; 'I'll scourge you if you did it:' *Queen Mary* III v 126
it *t's* us no more Than French or Norman. *Harold* I i 133
and *t* us thence Unschool'd of Death? „ V i 285
Not in my chin, I hope! That *t's* double. *Becket* II i 251
T our junction with the Emperor— „ II ii 471
they *t* The immediate thunder-blast of interdict: „ III iii 25
as when we *t* A yelper with a stick. „ IV ii 349
yet *t* your Archbishop In his own house. „ V ii 504
Threaten'd Had *t* ev'n your life, and would say anything? *Prom. of May* III 567
Three (*See also* **Dree**) for thou art as white as *t* Christmasses. *Queen Mary* I i 30
T voices from our guilds and companies! „ II ii 255
Because the Queen hath been *t* days in tears „ III vi 12
God made the fierce fire seem To those *t* children like a pleasant dew. „ IV iii 91
T persons and one God, have mercy on me, „ IV iii 121
that these *T* rods of blood-red fire up yonder mean *Harold* I i 44
Why then the wrath of Heaven hath *t* tails, The devil only one. „ I i 61
and hurl'd it from him *T* fields away, „ III i 140
There is one Who passing by that hill *t* nights ago— „ III i 366
T horses had I slain beneath me: „ V ii 171

Three (*continued*) I know Some *t* or four poor priests a thousand times *Becket*, *Pro.* 291
with the retinue of *t* kings behind him, outroyalling royalty? „ *Pro.* 445
My lord, the King demands *t* hundred marks, „ I iii 626
My lord, I ha' *t* sisters a-dying at home „ I iv 245
She past me here *T* years ago when I was flying from My Tetrarchy to Rome. *The Cup* I i 6
But after rain o'erleaps a jutting rock And shoots *t* hundred feet. „ I i 111
who has dwelt *t* years in Rome And wrought his worst against his native land, „ I ii 175
That there *t* years ago—the vast vine-bowers „ I ii 401
cloudless heaven which we have found together In our *t* married years! „ I ii 417
T laps for a cat! *The Falcon* 125
and I sneezed *t* times this morning. „ 169
Yeas, yeas! *T* cheers for Mr. Steer! *Prom. of May* I 455
Why, Miss Dora, meä and my maätes, us *t*, we wants to hev *t* words wi' ye. „ III 126
Milly, who came to us *t* years after you were gone, „ III 232
They did not last *t* Junes. „ III 589
I took it For some *t* thousand acres. „ III 614
t yards about the waist is like to remain a virgin, *Foresters* I ii 69
Here come *t* beggars. „ III 187
Here come *t* friars. „ III 256
Thou and thy woman are a match for *t* friars. „ III 262
Here, you *t* rogues, „ III 358
blow upon it *T* mots, this fashion—listen! „ IV 425
for the moment strike the bonds From these *t* men, „ IV 963
Three-score the doctors tell you, At *t-s* years; *Queen Mary* III iv 410
Threshold I'll fight it on the *t* of the grave. „ V v 189
Hope Smiles from the *t* of the year to come *Foresters* I iii 16
Threw Northumbria *t* thee off, she will not have thee, *Harold* IV ii 33
But I that *t* the mightiest knight of France, *Becket* I iii 746
Thrill *T's* to the topmost tile—no hope but death; „ V ii 209
Thrive And may your business *t* in Nottingham! *Foresters* III 244
That *you* may *t*, but in some kindlier trade. „ III 252
Throat heretic *t's* Cried no God-bless-her *Queen Mary* III iv 44
this poor *t* of mine, Barer than I should wish a man to see it,— „ V ii 460
I have my dagger here to still their *t's*. *Becket* III ii 50
Madam, I saw your dagger at her *t*; „ IV ii 319
not at the moment who had fasten'd About his *t*— *The Cup* II 51
t might gape before the tongue could cry who? *Foresters* III 225
Throated *See* **Full-throated**
Throne (s) Until your *t* had ceased to tremble. *Queen Mary* I v 393
But his assessor in the *t*, „ I v 501
burn the *t* Where you should sit with Philip: „ I v 510
let Rebellion Roar till *t* rock, and crown fall. „ II i 145
shall we have Spain on the *t* and in the parliament; „ II i 176
Had holpen Richard's tottering *t* to stand, „ III i 114
same chair, Or rather *t* of purple, on the deck. „ III ii 8
Between the two most high-set *t's* on earth, „ III ii 106
no foreign prince or priest Should fill my *t*, „ III v 237
You sit upon this fallen Cranmer's *t*; „ IV i 114
Declare the Queen's right to the *t*; „ IV ii 78
floated downward from the *t* Of God Almighty. *Harold* I i 18
bishops down from all Their *t's* in England? „ I i 51
The Atheling is nearest to the *t*. „ II ii 570
help to build a *t* Out-towering hers of France . . . „ II ii 764
Why then the *t* is empty. Who inherits? „ III i 234
Who shook the Norman scoundrels off the *t*, „ IV i 82
To thrust our Harold's *t* from under him? „ IV iii 126
Hath climb'd the *t* and almost clutch'd the crown; *Becket*, *Pro.* 21
thou didst help me to my *t* In Theobald's time, „ *Pro.* 201
A bulwark against *T* and Baronage. „ I i 17
weight down all free choice beneath the *t*. „ I iii 119
The soul the body, and the Church the *T*, „ I iii 718
I, that taking The Fiend's advantage of a *t*, „ II i 152
Reseat him on his *t* of Canterbury, „ II ii 118
yea, even among those Who sit on *t's*— „ IV ii 125
Of Provence blew you to your English *t*; „ V i 124
Lest Becket thrust you even from your *t*. „ V i 160
To shake my *t*, to push into my chamber— „ V i 249

Throne (s) (*continued*) Blared from the heights of all the *t's* of her kings, *Becket* v ii 489
die upon the Patriarchal *t* Of all my predecessors? „ v iii 75
and wear it Beside him on his *t*. *The Cup* II 137
shout of Synorix and Camma sitting Upon one *t*, „ II 148
He climbs the *t*. Hot blood, „ II 168
So falls the *t* of an hour. *Synorix*. *T*? is it thou? „ II 486
T's, churches, ranks, traditions, customs, *Prom. of May* I 519
king of day hath stept from off his *t*, *Foresters* II i 27
oaks, Gnarl'd—older than the *t's* of Europe— „ III 92
Throne (verb) King Would *t* me in the great Archbishoprick: *Becket* I iii 694
and *t* One king above them all, *The Cup* I i 92
T him—and then the marriage—ay and tell him „ II 156
Throned For how should reverend prelate or *t* prince *Queen Mary* IV iii 543
And so be *t* together in the sight *The Cup* II 67
is it thou? the Fates are *t*, not we— „ II 488
Throne-like Throw cushions on that seat, and make it *t-l*. *Queen Mary* v ii 537
Thronging Their horse are *t* to the barricades; *Harold* v i 547
They are *t* in to vespers—half the town. *Becket* v iii 139
Throning Not to a Gregory of my *t*! No. „ v i 34
Throstle New buds to heaven, whereon the *t* rock'd *Foresters* I iii 27
Throttle say nothing to my wife if I Were by to *t* him! *The Cup* I ii 367
Throw strong to *t* ten Wyatts and all Kent. *Queen Mary* II ii 353
T cushions on that seat, and make it throne-like. „ v ii 536
Why, I could *t* four o' ye; *Prom. of May* I 468
Thrown offal *t* Into the blind sea of forgetfulness. *Queen Mary* III iii 192
There was a paper *t* into the palace, „ III vi 139
dogs' food *t* upon thy head. *Harold* II ii 431
she had *t* my chaplet on the grass, *The Falcon* 368
Had she not *t* my chaplet on the grass, „ 377
Thrush *See* **Mavis**
Thrust A strange youth Suddenly *t* it on me, *Queen Mary* II i 129
brave Lord William *T* him from Ludgate, „ II iv 92
invade their hive Too gross to be *t* out, „ III iii 55
And *t* his right into the bitter flame; „ IV iii 610
To *t* our Harold's throne from under him? *Harold* IV iii 126
Why do you *t* this Becket on me again? *Becket* v i 155
Thumb A lesson worth Finger and *t*—thus *Harold* I ii 55
Thumbscrew the *t*, the stake, the fire. *Queen Mary* II i 200
Thunder (s) the poor *t* Never harm'd head. *Harold* I ii 232
But *t* may bring down That which the flash „ I ii 234
And bolts of *t* moulded in high heaven „ II ii 32
Wilt *thou* play with the *t*? „ III i 391
but our old Thor Heard his own *t* again, „ IV iii 150
T! Ay, ay, the storm was drawing hither *The Cup* II 318
Thunder (verb) I will both flash And *t* for thee. *Harold* I ii 229
North and South *T* together, „ III i 393
They *t* again upon the barricades. „ v i 625
crying On Holy Church to *t* out her rights *Becket* v ii 31
Thunder-blast The immediate *t-b* of interdict: „ III iii 26
Thunderbolt I wish some *t* Would make this Cole a cinder, *Queen Mary* IV iii 10
So from a clear sky falls the *t*! „ v iii 116
with this black *t* of Rome Above him, *The Cup* I ii 265
Thunder-cloud shadowing of this double *t-c* That lours *Harold* III ii 159
Thurkill I think that this is *T*. „ v ii 65
Thwack But I shall have to *t* her if I stay. *Foresters* I iii 139
Thwack'd I would have *t* the woman, but I did not, „ I iii 135
Thwart That shalt thou never be If I can *t* thee. *Harold* I i 415
but tramples flat Whatever *t's* him; „ II ii 380
Thysen (thyself) Why, Wilson, tha 'eärd 'im *t*— *Prom. of May* I 302
Maäke *t* eäsy. „ I 419
if she weänt—look to *t*, „ II 695
an' whether thou calls *t* Hedgar or Harold, „ II 737
Tib (country wife) Why, it be *T*! *Queen Mary* IV iii 464
I must set down myself, *T*; „ IV iii 471
Eh, then ha' thy waay wi' me, *T*; „ IV iii 487
Thou's thy way wi' man and beast, *T*. „ IV iii 499
Tick-tack like the tail of the horologe—to and fro—*t-t*— *Becket* II ii 367
Tide same *t* Which, coming with our coming, *Queen Mary* II iii 21
(for they thought not of our *t's*), „ III ii 28
when men are tost On *t's* of strange opinion, „ III iv 119
William's or his own As wind blows, or *t* flows: *Harold* v i 163
all drown'd in love And glittering at full *t*— *The Cup* ii 234
Tide (*continued*) for when the *t* Of full democracy *Prom. of May* I 592
In this full *t* of love, Wave heralds wave: *Foresters* IV 1043
Tidings My liege, I bring you goodly *t*. *Queen Mary* v i 280
Tied (*See also* **Tongue-tied**) that the twain have been *t* up together, „ I iv 196
Tierce To reign is restless fence, *T*, quart, and trickery. „ v v 267
Tiger And *he* hath learnt, despite the *t* in him, *Harold* I i 148
May serve to charm the *t* out of him. *Leofwin*. He hath as much of cat as *t* in him. „ I i 153
Tigress *t* had unsheath'd her nails at last, *Queen Mary* III i 3
Tile Thrills to the topmost *t*—no hope but death; *Becket* v ii 209
Till'd —our fallows *t*, Much corn, „ I iii 376
Time (*See also* **Breathing-time, Thousand-times**) no one in her *t* should be burnt for heresy. *Queen Mary* I i 97
Well, sir, I look for happy *t's*. „ I i 99
am I trenching on the *t* That should already „ I ii 79
fear, I see you, Dear friend, for the last *t*; „ I ii 103
These birds of passage come before their *t*: „ I iii 76
Have we not heard of her in Edward's *t*, „ I iv 19
Your *t* will come. *Elizabeth*. I think my *t* will come. „ I iv 255
you had *t* and cause enough To sicken „ I v 23
I should some *t* have a happy morning; „ I v 245
no such scarecrow in your father's *t*. „ I v 474
let them sit. I must have *t* to breathe. „ I v 546
known a semi-madman in my *t* So fancy-ridd'n) „ II i 10
I fear the mine is fired before the *t*. „ II i 123
a jest In *t* of danger shows the pulses even. „ II ii 357
There yet is *t*, take boat and pass to Windsor. „ II iv 27
Who, waiting till the *t* had ripen'd, „ III ii 78
This Gardiner turn'd his coat in Henry's *t*; „ III iii 17
In William's *t*, in our first Edward's *t*, And in my master Henry's *t*; „ III iii 226
These spaniel-Spaniard English of the *t*, „ III iii 241
I have some *t*, for curiousness, my Lord, „ III iv 61
Such is our *t*—all *t's* for aught I know. „ III iv 66
Did she not In Henry's *t* and Edward's? „ III iv 132
St. Peter in his *t* of fear Denied his Master, „ III iv 263
In those *t's*, Thou knowest we had to dodge, „ III iv 356
For a *t*, for a *t*. „ III iv 366
Rogers and Ferrar, for their *t* is come, „ III iv 425
How many names in the long sweep of *t* „ III v 40
last *t* she wrote, I had like to have lost my life: „ III v 188
I think that I may be some *t* the Queen, „ III v 233
Wherefore our Queen and Council at this *t* „ IV iii 37
Friend for so long *t* of a mighty King; „ IV iii 73
every man at *t* of death Would fain set forth „ IV iii 156
I have not *t* for more: „ IV iii 207
Than heretic of these *t's*; „ IV iii 599
not were he ten *t's* king, Ten *t's* our husband, „ v i 62
I have to pray you, some odd *t*, „ v i 258
even now, when bow'd before my *t*, „ v ii 65
T that I were gone too! „ v ii 320
I seem half-shamed at *t's* to be so tall. „ v ii 424
and I say it For the last *t* perchance, *Harold* I i 176
left me *t* And peace for prayer to gain a better one. „ I i 219
but at *t's* They seem to me too narrow, „ III ii 63
A goodly flower at *t's*. „ IV i 151
Hear me again—for the last *t*. „ v i 9
Then for the last *t*, monk, I ask again „ v i 15
Good for good hath borne at *t's* „ v i 175
Church in the pell-mell of Stephen's *t* *Becket, Pro.* 20
—be facile to my hands. Now is my *t*. „ *Pro.* 220
thousand *t's* Fitter for this grand function. „ *Pro.* 292
Madam, I have loved her in my *t*. „ *Pro.* 496
And Earth should get the better—for the *t*. „ I iii 229
that be dead ten *t's* o'er i' one day wi' the putrid fever; „ I iv 250
wriggle out of them like an eel When the *t* serves. „ II ii 188
we make the *t*, we keep the *t*, ay, and we serve the *t*; „ II ii 367
I cannot answer it Till better *t's*, „ III i 3
That which you ask me Till better *t's*. „ III i 7
you shall tell me of her some other *t*. „ III i 191
that is to say in her *t* when she had the 'Crown.' „ III i 198
bound me by his love to secrecy Till his own *t*. „ III i 229
sworn on this my cross a hundred *t's* Never to leave him— „ IV ii 206
Daughter, my *t* is short, I shall not do it. „ v ii 157

Time (*continued*) I have much to say, no *t* to say it in. *The Cup* I ii 208
As I have many a *t* declared to you— „ II 48
and I sneezed three *t's* this morning. Coming to visit my lord, for the first *t* in her life too! *The Falcon* 169
fine fowl for my lady; I had scant *t* to do him in. „ 556
What? my *t*? Is it my *t*? Well, I can give my *t* „ 789
and they was all a-crying out at the bad *t's*, *Prom. of May* I 139
fur I 'ednt naw *t* to maäke mysen a scholard „ I 333
I mun ha' plowed it moor nor a hoonderd *t's*; „ I 368
Forgive him seventy *t's* and seven; „ III 9
next *t* you waste them at a pot-house you get no more from me. „ III 99
because one of the Steers had planted it there in former *t's*. „ III 248
he tells me that he met you once in the old *t's*, „ III 263
all in all to one another from the *t* when we first peeped „ III 273
and he trusted that some *t* we should meet again, „ III 328
The Steers was all gentlefoälks i' the owd *t's*, „ III 448
The land belonged to the Steers i' the owd *t's*, „ III 451
A hundred *t's* more worth a woman's love, „ III 743
weight of the flesh at odd *t's* overbalance the weight of the church, *Foresters* I ii 61
last *t* When I shall hold my birthday in his hall: „ I ii 88
Till better *t's*. *Robin.* But if the better *t's* „ I ii 286
And if the worst *t* come? „ I ii 290
Why then I will be better than the *t*. „ I ii 292
we must at *t's* have wrought Some great injustice, „ III 154
Out on it, I say, out of tune and *t*! *Marian.* Till thou thyself shall come to sing it—in *t*. *Robin.* *T*! if his backward-working alchemy „ IV 35
We had it i' the Red King's *t*, „ IV 303
if they were not repaid within a limited *t* your land should be forfeit. „ IV 468
Timorous Why creep'st thou like a *t* beast of prey *Harold* I ii 212
Tinkle Our scouts have heard the *t* of their bells. „ V i 220
Tipsy —and I fear you were *t* then, too— *Prom. of May* III 88
Tip-top snow yonder on the very *t-t* o' the mountain. *The Falcon* 501
Tire would she were but his paramour, for men *t* of their fancies; *Becket, Pro.* 479
Tired last night, *T*, pacing my new lands *Prom. of May* II 647
Tit Kiss in the bower, *T* on the tree! *Becket* III i 105
No bird? *Filippo.* Half a *t* and a hern's bill. *The Falcon* 131
T, my queen, must it be so? *Foresters* II ii 124
And you dare to call me *T*. *T*, for love and brevity, „ II ii 127
Titania I *T* bid you flit, „ II ii 126
Tit-bit You be fed with *t-b's*, you, „ I i 24
I am fed with *t-b's* no more than you are, „ I i 27
Tithe thaw me and 'im we niver 'grees about the *t*; *Prom. of May* I 445
Title And nothing of the *t's* to the crown; *Queen Mary* III i 383
Titular That if this Philip be the *t* king Of England, „ I v 254
Toad you that have *not* the head of a *t*, *The Falcon* 91
Tod Like a *t* of wool from wagon into warehouse. *Foresters* IV 274
To-daäy (**to-day**) The owd man be heighty *t-d*, beänt he? *Prom. of May* I 77
as I telled 'er *t-d* when she fell foul upo' me. „ II 581
To-day (*See also* **To-daäy**) She looks comelier than ordinary *t-d*; *Queen Mary* I i 71
I trust that he will carry you well *t-d*, „ I iv 145
he hath been so bold *t-d*, „ II ii 348
They are down *t-d*. „ III i 8
for *t-d* My heart beats twenty, „ III ii 57
and brief patience, As I have shown *t-d*. „ III iv 415
into the daylight truth That it may fall *t-d*! „ III v 137
That you *t-d* should read your recantation „ IV ii 27
t-d Thou shalt receive the penitent thief's award, „ IV iii 85
When camest thou hither? *Gamel.* *T-d*, good Earl. *Harold* I i 106
I heard from thy Northumberland *t-d*. „ I i 350
Lady Aldwyth Was here *t-d*, „ I ii 35
Swear thou *t-d*, to-morrow is thine own. „ II ii 710
we must use our battle-axe *t-d*. „ V i 205
Thy death!—*t-d*! Is it not thy birthday? „ V i 428
that blighted vow Which God avenged *t-d*. „ V ii 157
I could but read a part *t-d*, because— *Becket* I iii 422
they were fighting for her *t-d* in the street. „ I iv 160

To-day (*continued*) Fame of *t-d* is infamy to-morrow; Infamy of *t-d* is fame to-morrow; *Becket* II i 103
He warmed to you *t-d*, and you have chilled him again. „ II ii 375
T-d I almost fear'd your kiss was colder— „ III i 16
and to be sure I ha' seen great ones *t-d*— „ III i 136
a man passed in there *t-d*: I holla'd to him, „ III ii 25
You wrong the King: he meant what he said *t-d*. „ III iii 299
for thou must leave him *T-d*, but not quite yet. „ IV ii 211
Going or gone *t-d* To hunt with Sinnatus. *The Cup* I i 64
come upon *her* Again, perhaps, *t-d*—*her*. „ I i 181
A strange gift sent to me *t-d*. „ I ii 53
Have let him hunt the stag with you *t-d*. „ I ii 379
T-d they are fixt and bright—they look straight out. „ II 20
T-d? Too sudden. I will brood upon it. „ II 72
I would that every man made feast *t-d* „ II 225
For all my truer life begins *t-d*. „ II 229
T-d, my beauty, thou must dash us down *The Falcon* 152
Sweeter than any violet of *t-d*, „ 465
but *t-d* I dared not—so much weaker, „ 831
I must leave you, love, *t-d*. *Eva.* Leave me, *t-d*! *Prom. of May* I 625
Shall I say it?—fly with me *t-d*. „ I 678
will you not speak with Father *t-d*? „ III 237
'Will your Ladyship ride to cover *t-d*? „ III 310
but you seem somewhat better *t-d*. „ III 322
Not *t-d*. What are you staying for? „ III 356
but is not *t-d* his birthday? *Foresters* I i 219
T-d he hath accomplished his thirtieth birthday, „ I i 297
No, Sir Earl, I will not fight *t-d*. „ II i 575
for Oberon fled away Twenty thousand leagues *t-d*. „ II ii 143
thy father will not grace our feast With his white beard *t-d*. „ IV 81
No, not an hour: the debt is due *t-d*. „ IV 448
Toe bursten at the *t's*, and down at heels. *Queen Mary* I i 53
small hope of the gentleman gout in my great *t*. *The Falcon* 657
Toft Hall Philip Edgar of *T H* In Somerset. *Prom. of May* II 438
One Philip Edgar of *T H* in Somerset Is lately dead. „ II 445
I have been telling her of the death of one Philip Edgar of *T H*, Somerset. „ II 706
'O' the 17th, Philip Edgar, o' *T H*, Soomerset.' „ II 712
Togither (**together**) Didn't I spy 'em a-sitting i' the woodbine harbour *t*? „ I 125
he tell'd me 'at sweet'arts niver worked well *t*; and I telled '*im* 'at sweet'arts allus worked best *t*; „ II 156
And wheniver 'e sees two sweet'arts *t* like thou and me, Sally, „ II 163
Toil we have him in the *t's*. *Harold* II ii 14
Toil'd Our guardsman hath but *t* his hand and foot, „ V i 201
Token given A *t* of His more especial Grace; *Queen Mary* III iii 170
an' I be half dog already by this *t*, *Becket* I iv 219
Told (*See also* **Telled, Towld**) Whether he *t* me anything or not, *Queen Mary* I iv 184
secret missive, Which *t* her to be sick. „ II ii 122
'Tis said he *t* Sir Maurice there was one Cognisant „ II iv 98
I *t* my Lord He should not vex her Highness; „ III vi 64
He *t* me I should conquer:— *Harold* IV i 263
And *t* me we should conquer. „ IV i 267
They *t* me that the Holy Rood had lean'd „ V i 102
how been made Archbishop hadst thou *t* him, *Becket* I i 122
Wast thou not *t* to keep thyself from sight? „ I i 251
He *t* me thou shouldst pacify the King, „ I iii 224
Hath Henry *t* thee? hast thou talk'd with him? „ I iii 258
'Tis true what Becket *t* me, that the mother „ II ii 9
I *t* the Pope what manner of man he was. „ II ii 253
t me he would advance me to the service of a great lady, „ III i 122
you *t* me a great fib: it wasn't in the willow. „ IV ii 370
I *t* him I was bound to see the Archbishop; „ V ii 100
she *t* us of arm'd men Here in the city. „ V ii 226
but I *t* them I would wait them here. „ V ii 592
I *t* thee that I should remember thee! „ V iii 158
Hath Sinnatus never *t* you of this plot? *The Cup* I ii 250
I am sure I *t* him that his plot was folly. „ I ii 283
there You *t* your love; and like the swaying vines— „ I ii 410
Do you remember what I *t* you? „ I iii 4
Not if Sinnatus Has *t* her all the truth about me. „ I iii 23
She *t* thee as much? *The Falcon* 58

Told (*continued*) Do what I *t* thee. Must I do it myself? *The Falcon* 279
None has ever *t* me yet The story of your battle „ 592
You know, my lord, I *t* you I was troubled. „ 676
Eva *t* me that he was taking her likeness. He's an artist. *Prom. of May* I 126
and you, a gentleman, *T* me to trust you: „ I 710
You never *t* her, then, of what has past „ I 728
I *t* her I should hear her from the grave. „ II 244
She has disappear'd, They *t* me, from the farm— „ II 407
Which *t* us we should never see her more— „ II 477
always *t* Father that the huge old ashtree there would cause an accident some day; „ III 243
Have you *t* him I am here? *Dora.* No; do you wish it; „ III 266
bit by bit—for she promised secrecy—I *t* her all. „ III 380
Is yours yet living? *Harold.* No—I *t* you. „ III 506
I *t* you—My father. „ III 573
Can it be? They *t* me so. Yes, yes! „ III 670
She hid this sister, *t* me she was dead— „ III 689
Sir Richard was *t* he might be ransomed *Foresters* I i 63
It should have *t* us how the man first kissed the maid. „ I i 123
Scarlet *t* me—is it true?— „ III 145
They have *t* but a tenth of the truth: „ III 291
We *t* the Prince and the Sheriff of our coming. „ IV 575
Told'st Thou *t* us we should meet him in the forest, „ IV 439
Tolerance Till when, my Lords, I counsel *t*. *Queen Mary* III iv 203
Tolerate I would not, were I Queen, *t* the heretic, „ III iv 209
T them! Why? do they *t* you? „ III iv 213
Toll *T* of a bell, Stroke of a clock, „ III v 141
thou hast drain'd them shallow by thy *t's*, *Harold* I i 320
T! *Beggar.* Eh! we be beggars, *Foresters* III 188
Take thou my bow and arrow and compel them to pay *t*. *Marian.* *T*! „ III 264
Ha, brother. *T*, my dear? the *t* of love. „ III 270
Church and Law, halt and pay *t*! „ IV 430
Toll'd A passing bell *t* in a dying ear— *Queen Mary* V ii 41
Tomb There was an old-world *t* beside my father's, „ V ii 393
Tomb-place free the *t-p* of the King Of all the world? *Foresters* IV 408
To-morrow If Ludgate can be reach'd by dawn *t-m*. *Queen Mary* II iii 53
Come to me *t-m*.— „ III i 320
that I think, 'Wilt thou lie there *t-m*?' „ III v 132
And goes *t-m*. „ III vi 119
More talk of this *t-m*, if yon weird sign *Harold* I i 120
No more now: *t-m*. „ I i 487
T-m—first to Bosham, then to Flanders. „ I ii 239
T-m we will ride with thee to Harfleur, „ II ii 195
I will go with thee *t-m*— „ II ii 204
T-m will we ride with thee to Harfleur. „ II ii 647
Swear thou to-day, *t-m* is thine own. „ II ii 710
T-m will I ride with thee to Harfleur. „ II ii 769
To-night we will be merry—and *t-m*— „ II ii 772
Come to me *t-m*. *Becket, Pro.* 411
To pass thee to thy secret bower *t-m*. „ I i 249
Let the Great Seal be sent Back to the King *t-m*. „ I i 376
Fame of to-day is infamy *t-m*; Infamy of to-day is fame *t-m*; „ II i 103
and crown Young Henry there *t-m*. „ III ii 10
Who shall vouch for his *t-m's*? One word further. „ III iii 300
Antonius *T-m* will demand your tribute— *The Cup* I ii 97
He will pass *t-m* In the gray dawn „ I ii 294
—a brave one Which you shall see *t-m*. *Camma.* I rise *t-m* In the gray dawn, „ I ii 432
'Let us eat and drink, for *t-m* we die.' *Prom. of May* I 259
He will be sure to know you *t-m*. „ III 470
T-m then? *Marian.* Well, I will fight *t-m*. *Foresters* II i 576
Tongue (*See also* **Evil-tongue**) make what noise you will with your *t's*, *Queen Mary* I i 6
old leaven sticks to my *t* yet. „ I iii 48
Make all *t's* praise and all hearts beat for you. „ I v 117
t yet quiver'd with the jest When the head leapt— „ I v 475
thou shalt lose thine ears and find thy *t*, „ III i 256
Will stir the living *t* and make the cry. „ III i 354
every *t* Alters it passing, till it spells „ III v 35
What weapon hath the child, save his soft *t*, „ III v 129
More grievously than any *t* can tell. „ IV iii 125

NN

Tongue (*continued*) Fed with rank bread that crawl'd upon the *t*, *Queen Mary* IV iii 443
the *t* on un cum a-lolluping out o' 'is mouth as black as a rat. „ IV iii 518
Leofwin, thou hast a *t*! *Harold* I i 392
I say, thou hast a *t*, „ I i 401
Tear out his *t*. *Officer.* He shall not rail again. „ II ii 487
Treble denial of the *t* of flesh, „ III i 281
play The William with thine eyesight and thy *t*. „ V i 28
Say that he blind thee and tear out thy *t*. *Becket* I iii 616
Cannot a smooth *t* lick him whole again „ II ii 25
Spare not thy *t*! be lavish with our coins, „ II ii 469
asked our mother if I could keep a quiet *t* i' my head, „ III i 119
So charged with *t*, that every thread „ V ii 205
Well, well, well! I bite my *t*. *The Falcon* 624
throat might gape before the *t* could cry who? *Foresters* III 225
if the land Were ruleable by *t*, „ IV 399
Nay, my *t* tript—five hundred marks for use. „ IV 499
Tongue-free Crow over Barbarossa—at last *t-f* *Becket* II ii 50
Tongueless —*t* and eyeless, prison'd— *Harold* II ii 496
Tonguester selfless man Is worth a world of *t's*. „ V i 82
Tongue-tied make me shamed and *t-t* in my love. *Queen Mary* III ii 162
Tongue-torn fiends that utter them *T-t* with pincers, „ V ii 194
To-night you would honour my poor house *t-n*, „ I iii 118
When do you meet? *Noailles.* *T-n*. „ I iii 155
Make out the writ *t-n*. „ IV i 195
T-n we will be merry. *Harold* II ii 767
T-n we will be merry—and to-morrow— „ II ii 771
Go with her—at once—*T-n*— *Becket* I i 402
T-n. *Retainer.* *T-n*, my lord. „ I iv 13
Am I to be murdered *t-n*? „ I iv 48
I must fly to France *t-n*. „ I iv 154
The miller's away for *t-n*. „ I iv 164
for *t-n* ye have saved our Archbishop! „ I iv 257
not *t-n*—the night is falling. What can be done *t-n*? „ III ii 51
Ye shall sing that ageän *t-n*, *Prom. of May* II 216
and he'll be rude to me ageän *t-n*, „ II 220
prays your ladyship and your ladyship's father to be present at his banquet *t-n*. *Foresters* I i 301
let us be merry *t-n* at the banquet. „ I i 344
Tonitrua Jacta *t* Deus bellator! *Harold* V i 569
Tonsure crept Up even to the *t*, and he groan'd, *Becket* I iii 327
his poor *t* A crown of Empire. „ V i 195
Tonsured Ye haled this *t* devil into your courts; „ I iii 387
Took (*See also* **Täaked**) *t* her hand, call'd her sweet sister, *Queen Mary* I i 79
but *t* To the English red and white. „ I v 17
For the wrong Robin *t* her at her word. „ III v 264
I *t* it, tho' I did not know I *t* it, „ V v 97
another hill Or fort, or city, *t* it, *Harold* IV i 50
if I *t* and translated that hard heart *Becket, Pro.* 379
He *t* his mitre off, and set it on me, „ I i 63
Then he *t* back not only Stephen's gifts, „ I iii 154
rather than God's cause *T* it upon me— „ I iii 699
North-east *t* and turned him South-west, „ II ii 321
t me ever so far away, and gave me a great pat „ III i 124
which a breeze of May *T* ever and anon, *The Cup* I ii 407
Shame on her that she *t* it at thy hands, *The Falcon* 61
he always *t* you so kindly, he always *t* the world so kindly. „ 187
he made a wry mouth at it, but he *t* it so kindly, „ 191
he always *t* you so kindly— „ 194
the Sister *t* me to her house, and bit by bit— *Prom. of May* III 379
I *t* it For some three thousand acres. „ III 613
She *t* my ring. I trust she loves me—yet *Foresters* I iii 3
when the Sheriff *t* my little horse for the King „ II i 300
and *t* His monies. „ III 362
O no, we *t* Advantage of the letter— „ IV 620
Tool What filthy *t's* our Senate works with! *The Cup* I i 156
values neither man Nor woman save as *t's*— *Foresters* IV 714
Tooth They show their *teeth* upon it; *Queen Mary* V i 299
His early follies cast into his *teeth*, „ V ii 124
the *teeth* That shall be broken by us— *Harold* I ii 244
knaw'd better nor to cast her sister's misfortin inter 'er *teeth* *Prom. of May* II 128
how should thy one *t* drill thro' this? *Foresters* II i 276

Top (*See also* **A-top**) wheel of Fate has roll'd me to the *t*. *The Cup* II 222
Topmost Thrills to the *t* tile—no hope but death; *Becket* V ii 209
wine leaps to the brain Like April sap to the *t* tree, *Foresters* I iii 24
Torch Thou light a *t* that never will go out! *Queen Mary* V v 122
dash The *t* of war among your standing corn, *Harold* II ii 749
Torchlight I saw Lord William Howard By *t*, *Queen Mary* II iii 30
Tore *t* away My marriage ring, and rent my bridal veil; *Harold* I ii 79
He *t* their eyes out, sliced their hands away, „ II ii 389
Torment And their strong *t* bravely borne, *Queen Mary* III iv 168
keep it, or you sell me To *t* and to death. *The Cup* I ii 216
Torn (*See also* **Tongue-torn**) Die like the *t* fox dumb, but never whine *Queen Mary* II ii 331
or we are *t* Down the strong wave of brawlers. „ III i 185
Would God they had *t* up all By the hard root, *Becket* II ii 208
We found a letter in your bedroom *t* into bits. *Prom. of May* III 323
Torrent (*See also* **Lava-torrents**) What breadth, height, strength—*t's* of eddying bark! *Foresters* III 94
Torture (s) Think,—*t*,—death,—and come. *The Cup* I ii 314
Shall I go? Shall I go? Death, *t*— „ I ii 454
No thought was mine of *t* or of death, „ II 411
scares The Baron at the *t* of his churls, *Foresters* III 106
Torture (verb) I know they mean to *t* him to death. *The Cup* I ii 273
Tortured Would you have *t* Sinnatus to death? „ II 408
Tost when men are *t* On tides of strange opinion, *Queen Mary* III iv 118
Geoffrey have not *t* His ball into the brook! *Becket* II i 320
Tostig (Earl of Northumbria) A faint foot hither, leaning upon *T*. He hath learnt to love our *T* much of late. *Harold* I i 144
Our *T* loves the hand and not the man. „ I i 156
T says true; my son, thou art too hard, „ I i 205
Thou art the man to rule her! *Aldwyth.* So, not *T*! „ I i 224
T, I am faint again. „ I i 266
And *T* knows it; *T* loves the king. „ I i 274
Then *T* too were wiser than he seems. „ I i 278
No, *T*—lest I make myself a fool „ I i 292
thine earldom, *T*, hath been a kingdom. „ I i 304
I may tell thee, *T*, I heard from thy Northumberland to-day. „ I i 349
O *T*, O dear brother—If they prance, „ I i 371
T, thou look'st as thou wouldst spring upon him. „ I i 393
And *T* is not stout enough to bear it. „ I i 402
ye three must gall Poor *T*. *Leofwin.* *T*, sister, galls himself; „ I i 420
but *T*—On a sudden—at a something— „ I i 441
Side not with *T* in any violence, „ I i 457
It means the fall of *T* from his earldom. „ I i 468
This *T* is, or like to be, a tyrant; „ I i 481
Yea, but Earl *T*— „ I ii 65
When Harold goes and *T*, shall I play The craftier *T* „ I ii 163
Our wild *T*, Edward hath made him Earl: „ I ii 185
Down with *T*! That first of all.— „ I ii 236
Not to come back till *T* shall have shown „ I ii 242
Against thy brother *T's* governance; „ II ii 290
T in his own hall on suspicion Hath massacred „ II ii 295
our fiery *T*, while thy hands Are palsied here, „ II ii 453
flamed When *T's* anger'd earldom flung him, „ III i 54
Siding with our great Council against *T*, „ III i 60
Our *T* parted cursing me and England; „ III i 76
T, raise my head! *Harold.* Let Harold serve for *T*! *Queen.* Harold served *T* so ill, he cannot serve for *T*! „ III i 157
hath mainly drawn itself From lack of *T*— „ III i 168
I love beyond the rest, My banish'd *T*. „ III i 296
where *T* lost The good hearts of his people. „ III ii 29
Our hapless brother, *T*—He, „ III ii 121
Yea, *T* hath taken York! „ III ii 176
Thou art *T's* brother, Who wastes the land. „ IV i 92
For when your people banish'd *T* hence, „ IV i 97
sanction your decree Of *T's* banishment, „ IV i 104
Who brake into Lord *T's* treasure-house „ IV i 114
when *T* hath come back with power, Are frighted back to *T*. „ IV i 117
There is a faction risen again for *T*, Since *T* came with Norway— „ IV i 172
Lest thy fierce *T* spy me out alone, „ IV i 190
Tostig (Earl of Northumbria) (*continued*) Who is it comes this way? *T*? *Harold* IV ii 2
No man would strike with *T*, save for Norway. „ IV ii 20
that *T* Conjured the mightier Harold from his North „ IV ii 67
All traitors fail like *T*! „ IV iii 79
I saw the hand of *T* cover it. Our dear, dead, traitor-brother *T*, him Reverently we buried. „ IV iii 81
T, poor brother, Art *thou* so anger'd? „ V i 272
and his brother *T* helpt; „ V ii 47
T'other (other) When theer wur a meeting o' farmers at Littlechester *t* daäy, *Prom. of May* I 137
I coom'd upon 'im *t* daäy lookin' at the coontry, „ I 201
It be five year sin' ye went afoor to him, and it seems to me nobbut *t* day. „ II 7
and he sent 'im awaäy to *t* end o' the field; „ II 154
wasn't thou and me a-bussin' o' one another *t* side o' the haäycock, „ II 231
Tottering Harry of Bolingbroke Had holpen Richard's *t* throne to stand, *Queen Mary* III i 114
Touch (s) sudden *t'es* For him, or him— „ V v 220
I trust the kingly *t* that cures the evil *Harold* I i 151
I had a *t* of this last year—in—Rome. *The Cup* II 446
There is a *t* of sadness in it, my lord, *Foresters* I iii 35
I have a *t* of sadness in myself. „ I iii 38
Touch (verb) you *t* upon the rumour that Charles, *Queen Mary* I i 104
cannot *t* you save that you turn traitor; „ I iv 271
as the heathen giant Had but to *t* the ground, „ III ii 44
T him upon his old heretical talk, „ III iv 352
A snake—and if I *t* it, it may sting. „ III v 218
Alva will but *t* him on the horns, And he withdraws; „ V i 155
Nobles we dared not *t*. „ V v 104
I *t* mine arms, My limbs— *Harold* II ii 793
As far as *t'es* Wulfnoth I that so prized „ III i 91
And *t'es* Him that made it. „ III ii 198
T me not! *De Brito.* How the good priest gods himself! *Becket* V iii 147
I will not only *t*, but drag thee hence. „ V iii 151
I am a Roman now, they dare not *t* me. *The Cup* I i 185
You can *t* No chord in me that would not *The Falcon* 455
That I would *t* no flesh till he were well „ 680
know that I can *t* The ghittern to some purpose. „ 798
Shall I be bold? shall I *t* her? *Foresters* I i 125
while the lark flies up and *t'es* heaven! „ I ii 315
where twelve Can stand upright, nor *t* each other. „ III 310
He dies who dares to *t* thee. „ IV 734
Touch'd if I And others made that move I *t* upon, *Queen Mary* III i 445
when she *t* on thee, She stammer'd in her hate; *Harold* I ii 35
scarce *t* or tasted The splendours of our Court. „ II ii 174
so still I reach'd my hand and *t*; *Becket* V ii 235
I almost *t* her—A maiden slowly *The Cup* I i 7
Why no, he never *t* upon the stag. „ I ii 383
Who *t* me then? I thank you. „ II 532
niver *t* a drop of owt till my oän wedding-daäy, *Prom. of May* I 362
For tho' we *t* at many pirate ports, *Foresters* IV 983
Touching That those old statutes *t* Lollardism *Queen Mary* III iv 7
T the sacrament in that same book „ IV iii 263
Yet he can scarce be *t* upon those, *Becket* III iii 27
would not blur A moth's wing by the *t*; *Prom. of May* II 492
Toulouse (*See also* **Thoulouse**) and won the violet at *T*; *Becket, Pro.* 348
Tourney He wore thy colours once at a *t*. *Foresters* I i 250
Tower (*See also* **Church-tower, Tree-tower**) going now to the *T* to loose the prisoners *Queen Mary* I i 109
Officers Are here in force to take you to the *T*. „ I ii 109
you late were loosed from out the *T*, „ I iv 50
my Lord; I see you in the *T* again. „ I iv 80
So many years in yon accursed *T*— „ I iv 200
saying of this Lady Jane, Now in the *T*? „ I v 38
Earl of Devon? I freed him from the *T*, „ I v 163
then if caught, to the *T*. *Renard.* The *T*! „ I v 469
but your old Traitors of the *T*— „ I v 484
he loved the more His own gray *t's*, „ II i 49
every parish *t* Shall clang and clash alarum „ II i 228
demanded Possession of her person and the *T*. „ II ii 41
Seek to possess our person, hold our *T*, „ II ii 159
ordnance On the White *T* and on the Devil's *T*, „ II iii 44

Tower (*continued*) you'll make the White *T* a black 'un — *Queen Mary* II iii 100
you'll set the Divil's *T* a-spitting, „ II iii 102
Pass, then, I pray your Highness, to the *T*. „ II iv 32
I shall but be their prisoner in the *T*. „ II iv 34
The Queen must to the *T*. „ II iv 73
To the *T* with *him* ! (repeat) „ II iv 97, 102
the *T*, the *T*, always the *T*, I shall grow into it— I shall be the *T*. „ II iv 103
To the *T* with *her* ! „ II iv 118
Hath no more mortice than a *t* of cards ; „ III i 442
Her Grace the Queen commands you to the *T*. „ III iii 271
By the river to the *T*. „ III iii 281
damp, black, dead Nights in the *T* ; „ III v 139
For freeing my friend Bagenhall from the *T* ; „ III vi 8
winds so cross and jostle among these *t's*. *Harold* II ii 156
The people know their Church a *t* of strength, *Becket* I i 16
Danaë has escaped again Her *t*, and her Acrisius— „ I i 396
and rifts the *t* to the rock, *The Cup* II 293
O *t* spiring to the sky, *Prom. of May* III 203
or closed For ever in a Moorish *t*, *Foresters* II i 656
Towering *See* **Out-towering**
Towld (told) summun *t* summun o' owld Bishop Gardiner's end ; *Queen Mary* IV iii 502
Town and we cannot burn whole *t's* ; they are many, „ III iv 175
And there be many heretics in the *t*, „ IV ii 31
the *t* Hung out raw hides along their walls, *Harold* II ii 382
My lord, the *t* is quiet, and the moon Divides *Becket* I i 364
Much corn, repeopled *t's*, a realm again. „ I iii 377
Close the great gate—ho, there—upon the *t*. „ V ii 531
They are thronging in to vespers—half the *t*. „ V iii 140
The *t* lay still in the low sun-light, *Prom. of May* I 37
a red fire woke in the heart of the *t*, „ I 50
Richard sacks and wastes a *t* With random pillage, *Foresters* IV 377
Towser (a dog's name) I'll hev the winder naäiled up, and put *T* under it. *Prom. of May* I 420
T'll tear him all to pieces. „ I 423
Toy They have taken away the *t* thou gavest me, *Harold* II ii 106
I like to have my *t's*, and break them too. „ II ii 112
To-year (this year) they'll hev' a fine cider-crop *t-y* if the blossom 'owds. *Prom. of May* I 316
Trace Let the dead letter live ! *T* it in fire, *Queen Mary* III iv 34
who could *t* a hand So wild and staggering ? *The Falcon* 438
but can he *t* me Thro' five years' absence, *Prom. of May* II 614
Traced *T* in the blackest text of Hell—' Thou shalt ! ' *Queen Mary* III i 426
Track (s) most beaten *t* Runs thro' the forest, *Foresters* III 89
Track (verb) *t* her, if thou canst, even into the King's lodging, *Becket, Pro.* 507
If you *t* this Sinnatus In any treason, *The Cup* I i 162
Track'd Have *t* the King to this dark inland wood ; *Becket* III ii 3
Judas-lover of our passion-play Hath *t* us hither. „ IV ii 138
Tractate His *t* upon True Obedience, *Queen Mary* IV i 92
Tracy (Sir William de, knight of the household of King Henry II.) (*See also* **De Tracy**) *T*, what dost thou here ? *Becket* I i 234
France ! Ha ! De Morville, *T*, Brito—fled is he ? „ I iv 199
—on a Tuesday—*T* ! God help thee ! „ V ii 295
Strike him, *T* ! *Rosamund.* No, No, No, No ! „ V iii 169
Nay, nay, good *T*. *Fitzurse.* Answer not, „ V iii 185
Trade With all your *t's*, and guilds, and companies. *Queen Mary* II ii 297
That *you* may thrive, but in some kindlier *t*. *Foresters* III 253
There is a *t* of genius, there's glory ! „ IV 375
Tradition Customs, *t's*,—clouds that come and go ; *Becket* I iii 22
Marriage is but an old *t*. I hate *T's*, *Prom. of May* I 491
violated the whole *T* of our land, „ I 496
Thrones, churches, ranks, *t's*, customs, „ I 519
Traffick'd you have *t* Between the Emperor and the Pope, *Becket* II ii 67
Tragedy A comedy meant to seem a *t*— „ IV ii 322
Tragic You are too *t* : both of us are players „ V i 187
Train Captain Brett, who went with your *t* bands To fight with Wyatt, *Queen Mary* II ii 27
Train'd (*See also* **Full-train'd**) Good dogs, my liege, well *t*, *Becket, Pro.* 120
Traitor (adj.) She cannot pass her *t* council by, *Queen Mary* I ii 40
The *t* husband dangled at the door, And when the *t* wife came out for bread „ III i 10

Traitor (adj.) (*continued*) But with Cecil's aid And others, if our person be secured From *t* stabs— *Queen Mary* V v 281
Traitors are rarely bred Save under *t* kings. *Foresters* II i 81
If you would marry me with a *t* sheriff, „ IV 870
Traitor (s) down with all *t's* ! *Queen Mary* I i 66
shall I turn *t* ? „ I iv 6
He cannot touch you save that you turn *t* ; „ I iv 272
the King—that *t* past forgiveness, „ I v 28
being *t* Her head will fall : „ I v 59
but your old *T's* of the Tower— „ I v 484
Sent Cornwallis and Hastings to the *t*, „ II ii 32
Her name is much abused among these *t's*. „ II ii 111
a *t* so presumptuous As this same Wyatt, „ II ii 179
He is child and fool, and *t* to the State. „ II ii 403
' Whosoever will apprehend the *t* Thomas Wyatt „ II iii 60
The *t* ! treason ! Pembroke ! „ II iv 35
will do you right Against all *t's*. „ II iv 68
and the *t* flying To Temple Bar, „ II iv 92
As *t*, or as heretic, or for what ? „ III iii 272
all *t's* Against our royal state have lost the heads „ III iv 2
For heretic and *t* are all one : „ III iv 38
He hath been a *t*, „ IV iii 39
Liar ! dissembler ! *t* ! to the fire ! „ IV iii 259
King Henry warms your *t's* at his hearth. „ V i 123
What *t* spoke ? Here, let my cousin Pole „ V ii 243
Methought some *t* smote me on the head. „ V ii 252
Noailles wrote To that dead *t*, Wyatt, „ V ii 498
It frights the *t* more to maim and blind. *Harold* II ii 503
All *t's* fail like Tostig ! „ IV iii 79
Not fight—tho' somehow *t* to the King— *Becket* I i 112
Let *t* be ; For how have fought thine utmost „ I i 116
What did the *t* say ? „ I iii 470
it is the *t* that imputes Treachery to his King ! „ I iii 483
There, there, there ! *t*, *t*, *t* ! „ I iii 737
How, do you make me a *t* ? „ III iii 241
Nor make me *t* to my holy office. „ V ii 149
He makes the King a *t*, me a liar. „ V ii 416
charge you that ye keep This *t* from escaping. „ V ii 511
Where is the *t* Becket ? *Becket* V iii 103
Where is this treble *t* to the King ? „ V iii 108
No *t* to the King, but Priest of God, „ V iii 112
The *t* 's dead, and will arise no more. „ V iii 200
Or man, or woman, as *t's* unto Rome. *The Cup* I iii 9
Hang'd at mid-day, their *t* of the dawn „ II 123
T's are rarely bred Save under traitor kings. *Foresters* II i 79
We robb'd the *t's* that are leagued with John ; „ III 159
serve King Richard save thou be A *t* or a goose ? „ IV 353
a *t* coming In Richard's name— „ IV 780
I never found one *t* in my band. „ IV 836
You both are utter *t's* to your king. „ IV 844
If you would marry me with a traitor sheriff, I fear I might prove *t* with the sheriff. „ IV 872
I can defend my cause against the *t's* Who fain would make me *t*. „ IV 899
Traitor-brother Our dear, dead, *t-b*, Tostig, *Harold* IV iii 83
Traitor-heretic So there be Some *t-h*, *Queen Mary* III iv 47
Centaur of a monstrous Commonweal, The *t-h*) „ III iv 165
Traitorous Make not thy King a *t* murderer. *Becket* I iii 500
Traitress *T* ! *Rosamund.* A faithful *t* to thy royal fame. „ II i 96
Tramp You are those that *t* the country, *Foresters* III 198
Trample And let the Pope *t* our rights, *Queen Mary* III iv 362
but *t's* flat Whatever thwarts him ; *Harold* II ii 378
And I shall live to *t* on thy grave. *Becket* I ii 95
From off the stalk and *t* it in the mire, *Foresters* I ii 110
Trampled And *t* on the rights of Canterbury. *Becket* V ii 394
state more cruelly *t* on Than had she never moved. *The Cup* I ii 145
Crush'd, hack'd at, *t* underfoot. *The Falcon* 640
And boast that he hath *t* it. *Foresters* I ii 112
All our rings be *t* out. „ II ii 167
Trampling *T* thy mother's bosom into blood ? *Harold* IV ii 26
Trance Wait he must—Her *t* again. *Queen Mary* V ii 404
Transact as I used to *t* all his business for him, *Prom. of May* II 719
Translated if I took and *t* that hard heart *Becket, Pro.* 379
Translating *T* his captivity from Guy *Harold* II ii 42

Trouble (verb) (*continued*) I had forgotten How these poor libels *t* you. *Queen Mary* v ii 202
he hath fallen Into a sickness, and it *t's* me. *The Falcon* 310
I have been unwilling to *t* you with questions, *Prom. of May* III 321
Troubled The King looks *t*. *Becket* II ii 425
The Parliament as well, are *t* waters; *Queen Mary* II ii 50
You know, my lord, I told you I was *t*. *The Falcon* 677
But you look *t*. *Prom. of May* I 549
Trout leästwaäys they niver cooms 'ere but fur the *t* i' our beck, „ I 212
Trow Nay, I *t* not: and you shall see, *Queen Mary* IV iii 322
Trucida Illos *t*, Domine. *Harold* v i 515
Trucidatur Pastor fugatur Grex *t*— „ v i 514
Truckled For you yourself have *t* to the tyrant, *Queen Mary* III iv 236
Truckler And let him call me *t*. „ III iv 355
What, what, a *t*! a word-eating coward! *Foresters* IV 161
True I was born *t* man at five in the forenoon *Queen Mary* I i 45
I was born of a *t* man and a ring'd wife, „ I i 54
T, Mary was born, „ I ii 65
and sever'd from the faith, will return into the one *t* fold, „ I iii 22
Art thou of the *t* faith, fellow, „ I iii 45
hath begun to re-edify the *t* temple— „ I iii 58
the hatred of another to us Is no *t* bond of friendship. „ I iv 46
Nay, I meant *T* matters of the heart. „ I iv 100
No, being of the *t* faith with myself. „ I v 74
And when your Highness talks of Courtenay—Ay, *t*—a goodly one. „ I v 200
Indeed, if that were *t*—For Philip comes, one hand in mine, „ I v 514
and we pray That we, your *t* and loyal citizens, „ II ii 135
And if he jeer not seeing the *t* man Behind his folly, „ II ii 400
that I live and die The *t* and faithful bride of Philip— „ II iv 43
tho' a *t* one, Blazed false upon her heart. „ III i 68
Did not Lord Suffolk die like a *t* man? Is not Lord William Howard a *t* man? „ III i 164
t enough Her dark dead blood is in my heart with mine. „ III i 347
Said 'You will give me my *t* crown at last, „ III i 395
T, good cousin Pole; „ III ii 68
T, cousin, I am happy. „ III ii 113
T, and I am the Angel of the Pope. „ III ii 144
T; the provinces Are hard to rule and must be hardly ruled; „ III ii 200
And whether this flash of news be false or *t*, „ III ii 235
And on the steep-up track of the *t* faith Your lapses are far seen. „ III iv 94
call they not The one *t* faith, a loathsome idol-worship? „ III iv 219
What hath your Highness written? *Elizabeth*. A *t* rhyme. „ III v 24
I woke Sir Henry—and he's *t* to you—I read his honest horror in his eyes. *Elizabeth*. Or *t* to you? *Lady*. Sir Henry Bedingfield! I will have no man *t* to me, your Grace, „ III v 60
says she will live And die *t* maid—a goodly creature too. „ III vi 46
You say *t*, Madam. „ III vi 198
I cannot be *T* to this realm of England „ IV i 27
His tractate upon *T* Obedience, Writ by himself and Bonner? „ IV i 92
Of the *t* Church; but his is none, nor will be. „ IV i 148
Have you remain'd in the *t* Catholic faith I left you in? „ IV ii 17
In the *t* Catholic faith, By Heaven's grace, I am more and more confirm'd. „ IV ii 20
and proclaim Your *t* undoubted faith, that all may hear. „ IV iii 114
Sir Nicholas tells you *t*, And you must look to Calais when I go. „ v i 16
For Alva is *t* son of the *t* church— „ v i 159
Why, who said that? I know not—*t* enough! „ v ii 209
Died in the *t* faith? „ v ii 518
and I have seen the *t* men of Christ lying famine-dead by scores, „ v iv 38
Ay, worse than that—not one hour *t* to me! „ v v 159
Tostig says *t*; my son, thou art too hard, *Harold* I i 205
till the *t* *must* Shall make her strike as Power: „ I i 367
T, that the battle-axe Was out of place; „ I ii 104

True (*continued*) And that were *t* enough. *Harold* I ii 169
Speak for thy mother's sake, and tell me *t*. „ II ii 272
Is naked truth actable in *t* life? „ III i 109
That, were a man of state nakedly *t*, „ III i 113
Tho' somewhat less a king to my *t* self „ III ii 53
They are not so *t*, They change their mates. „ III ii 104
Hear King Harold! he says *t*! „ IV i 61
That is *t*! (repeat) „ IV i 67, 88
I yield it freely, being the *t* wife Of this dead King, „ v ii 84
Not *t*, my girl, here is the Queen! „ v ii 91
Will none among you all Bear me *t* witness—only for this once— „ v ii 115
pray God My Normans may but move as *t* with me To the door of death. „ v ii 184
whom the king Loves not as statesman, but *t* lover and friend. *Becket, Pro.* 80
And so this Rosamund, my *t* heart-wife, „ *Pro.* 130
I, *t* son Of Holy Church—no croucher to the Gregories „ *Pro.* 210
T enough, my mind was set upon other matters. „ *Pro.* 317
T, one rose will outblossom the rest, one rose in a bower. „ *Pro.* 345
T, and I have an inherited loathing of these black sheep of the Papacy. „ *Pro.* 460
May the hand that next Inherits thee be but as *t* to thee As mine hath been! „ I i 358
T! Tho' she that binds the bond, „ I ii 75
t To either function, holding it; „ I iii 537
t too, that when written I sign'd them—being a fool, „ I iii 559
I had been so *t* To Henry and mine office „ I iii 692
T test of coward, ye follow with a yell. „ I iii 745
had they remained *t* to me whose bread they have partaken. „ I iv 149
O Rosamund, I would be *t*—would tell thee all— „ II i 205
'Tis *t* what Becket told me, that the mother Would make him play „ II ii 9
and pray God she prove *T* wife to you. „ II ii 79
The crowd that hungers for a crown in Heaven Is my *t* king. *Herbert*. Thy *t* King bad thee be A fisher of men; „ II ii 284
And, being scratch'd, returns to his *t* rose, „ III i 249
Almost as many as your *t* Mussulman— „ IV ii 34
The more the pity then That thy *t* home—the heavens—cry out for thee „ IV ii 132
Play! . . . that bosom never Heaved under the King's hand with such *t* passion „ IV ii 190
Why? for I *am* *t* wife, and have my fears Lest Becket thrust you „ v i 157
who shall be *t* To the Roman: *The Cup* I i 94
I am most *t* to Rome. „ I i 154
You saw my hounds *T* to the scent; and we have two-legg'd dogs Among us who can smell a *t* occasion, „ I ii 111
that being Tetrarch once His own *t* people cast him from their doors „ I ii 351
T; and my friends may spy him And slay him as he runs. „ I ii 390
Yet if she be a *t* and loving wife She may, „ I iii 32
mine own dagger driven by Synorix found All good in the *t* heart of Sinnatus, „ II 87
Antonius, tell the Senate I have been most *t* to Rome—would have been *t* To *her*—if—if— „ II 483
I can tell you *T* tears that year were shed for you in Florence. *The Falcon* 384
T; for the senses, love, are for the world; *Prom. of May* I 580
The *t* ones—nay, and those not *t* enough, „ I 660
That was the only *t* love; and I trusted— „ I 712
For me an' my Sally we sweär'd to be *t*, „ II 205
'To be *t* to each other, let 'appen what maäy, (repeat) *Prom. of May* II 206, 236, 257
It mun be *t*, fur it wur i' print as black as owt. *Prom. of May* II 730
and a *t* and lasting love for me: „ III 172
which is my dream of a *t* marriage. „ III 179
If thro' the want of any—I mean the *t* one— „ III 550
T, I have held opinions, hold some still, „ III 622
No! by this *t* kiss, *you* are the first I ever have loved truly. „ III 647
inasmuch as I am a *t* believer in *t* love myself, *Foresters* I i 162
There never was an Earl so *t* a friend of the people „ I i 188
We will be beggar'd then and be *t* to the King. „ I i 202

True (*continued*) A question that every *t* man asks of a woman once in his life. *Foresters* I ii 138
T, for through John I had my sheriffship. „ I ii 200
That is no *t* man's hand. I hate hidden faces. „ I ii 244
T, were I taken They would prick out my sight. „ II i 71
there lives No man who truly loves and truly rules His following, but can keep his followers *t*. „ II i 78
T king of vice—*t* play on words— „ II i 83
T soul of the Saxon churl for whom song has no charm. „ II i 385
this is a *t* woodman's bow of the best yew-wood „ II i 392
Lovers hold *T* love immortal. „ II i 616
I ever held that saying false That Love is blind, but thou hast proven it *t*. „ II i 645
O Kate, *t* love and jealousy are twins, „ II ii 62
T, she is a goodly thing. „ II ii 140
She is *t*, and you are *t*, „ II ii 194
Scarlet told me—is it *t*? „ III 146
We never robb'd one friend of the *t* King. „ III 157
so His own *t* wife came with him, „ III 240
Join them and they are a *t* marriage; „ III 421
Love's falsehood to *t* maid will seal Love's truth „ IV 73
is not he that goes against the king and the law the *t* king in the sight of the King of kings? „ IV 230
if our *t* Robin Be not the nobler lion of the twain. „ IV 394
Blown like a *t* son of the woods. Farewell! „ IV 427
Our bowmen are so *t* They strike the deer at once to death— „ IV 524
Mine eye most *t* to one hair's-breadth of aim. „ IV 694
The King forbad it. *T*, my liege. „ IV 865

True-born Nay, it means *t-b*. *Queen Mary* I i 14
Parliament can make every *t-b* man of us a bastard. „ I i 27

Truer That's a *t* fear! *Harold* I ii 66
Purer, and *t* and nobler than herself; *Becket* II i 172
For all my *t* life begins to-day. *The Cup* II 229

Truest Here fell the *t*, manliest hearts of England. *Harold* V ii 58
As some cold-manner'd friend may strangely do us The *t* service, *The Falcon* 644

Trumpet Hark! the *t's*. *Queen Mary* I i 64
And after that, the *t* of the dead. Why, there are *t's* blowing now: what is it? „ IV ii 12
Why are the *t's* blowing, Father Cole? „ IV ii 23
blow the *t*, priest! *Harold* III i 188
Were the great *t* blowing doomsday dawn, „ V i 227
t's in the halls, Sobs, laughter, cries: *Becket* V ii 367
Tho' all the loud-lung'd *t's* upon earth „ V ii 487
The *t's* of the fight had echo'd down, *The Falcon* 605
stillness in the grave By the last *t*. *Foresters* II i 48

Trunk cleft the tree From off the bearing *t*, *Harold* III i 138
he soak'd the *t* with human blood, „ III i 142
sunder'd tree again, and set it Straight on the *t*, „ III i 146

Trunk-hose white satin his *t-h*, Inwrought with silver,— *Queen Mary* III i 76
tail like a devil under his *t-h*. *Tailor*. Ay, but see what *t-h's*! „ III i 224

Truss Seize him and *t* him up, and carry her off. *Foresters* IV 690

Trust (s) to whom The king, my father, did commit his *t*; *Queen Mary* II ii 208
I have lost all *t* in him. *Becket* II ii 434
Thomas, I would there were that perfect *t* between us, „ III iii 264
That perfect *t* may come again between us, „ III iii 351

Trust (verb) I *t* it is but a rumour. *Queen Mary* I i 107
Nay; not so long I *t*. „ I iii 141
I *t* that he will carry you well to-day, „ I iv 145
So you still care to *t* him somewhat less „ I v 221
Farewell, and *t* me, Philip is yours. „ I v 540
I *t* the Queen comes hither with her guards. „ II ii 1
Trusted than *t*—the scoundrel— „ II ii 39
I will *t* you. We fling ourselves on you, „ II ii 47
And it would be your comfort, as I *t*; „ II ii 225
And will not *t* your voices. „ II ii 259
I *t* this day, thro' God, I have saved the crown. „ II ii 302
I *t* by this your Highness will allow „ II iv 132
I *t* that you would fight along with us. „ III i 457
No, for we *t* they parted in the swine. „ III ii 142
You will be, we *t*, Sometime the viceroy „ III ii 195
I *t* your Grace is well. „ V ii 551
I *t* that God will make you happy yet. „ V v 76

Trust (verb) (*continued*) I *t* the kingly touch that cures the evil *Harold* I i 151
Nay, I *t* not, For I have served thee long „ I i 213
I *t* he may do well, this Gamel, „ I ii 190
Were I Thomas, I wouldn't *t* it. *Becket* III iii 59
Have I sown it in salt? I *t* not, „ III iii 320
You said you couldn't *t* Margery, „ IV ii 15
We *t* your Royal Grace, lord of more land „ V i 28
I durst not *t* him with—my serving Rome *The Cup* I ii 277
I *t*, my dear, we shall be always friends. *Prom. of May* I 631
and you, a gentleman, Told me to *t* you: „ I 710
I *t* I shall forgive him—by-and-by— „ II 465
I *t* I may be able by-and-by to help you in the business of the farm; „ III 222
I *t* he will, but if he do not I and thou *Foresters* II 199
can I *t* myself With your brave band? „ II i 703
I *t* We shall return to the wood. „ IV 1051
never I *t* to roam So far again, „ IV 1099

Trusted *T* than trust—the scoundrel— *Queen Mary* II ii 39
And *t* God would save her thro' the blood „ III i 386
priest whom John of Salisbury *t* Hath sent another. *Becket* III i 70
That was the only *true* love; and I *t*— *Prom. of May* I 713
and he *t* that some time we should meet again, „ III 328

Trustful A child, and all as *t* as a child! „ III 759
one of you Shamed a too *t* widow whom you heard *Foresters* III 385

Trustless Hast thou such *t* jailors in thy North? *Harold* II ii 685

Trusty Your faithful friend and *t* councillor. *Queen Mary* IV i 89

Truth in *t* I had meant to crave Permission „ I iv 234
Make no allowance for the naked *t*. „ I v 329
Statesmen that are wise Take *t* herself for model. „ III iii 37
tropes are good to clothe a naked *t*, „ III iv 151
Cut with a diamond; so to last like *t*. *Elizabeth*. Ay, if *t* last. *Lady*. But *t*, they say, „ III v 26
T, a word! The very *T* and very Word are one. „ III v 31
But *t* of story, which I glanced at, girl, „ III v 33
into the daylight *t* That it may fall to-day! „ III v 136
rage of one who hates a *t* He cannot but allow. „ III vi 144
Then never read it. The *t* is here. „ IV i 100
The *t* of God, which I had proven and known. „ IV iii 149
saying spoken once By Him that was the *t*, „ IV iii 203
Against the *t* I knew within my heart, „ IV iii 241
hour has come For utter *t* and plainness; „ IV iii 273
So in *t* he said. *Harold* II ii 263
Is it not better still to speak the *t*? „ II ii 374
Welshman says, 'The *T* against the World,' Much more the *t* against myself. „ II ii 398
for thou Art known a speaker of the *t*, „ II ii 517
When all the world hath learnt to speak the *t*, „ III i 69
I that so prized plain word and naked *t* „ III i 94
By all the *t's* that ever priest hath preach'd, „ III i 97
Is naked *t* actable in true life? „ III i 109
thought that naked *T* would shame the Devil „ III i 118
the *t* Was lost in that fierce North, „ III ii 25
in the eternal distance To settle on the *T*. „ III ii 103
if the *t* be gall, Cram me not thou with honey, „ IV i 15
If one may dare to speak the *t*, „ IV i 108
—a sin against The *t* of love. „ V i 171
the God of *t* hath heard my cry. „ V i 600
T! no; a lie; a trick, a Norman trick! „ V i 606
or any harm done to the people if my jest be in defence of the *T*? *Becket* II ii 340
Till *T* herself be shamed of her defender. „ II ii 344
some dreadful *t* is breaking on me— „ III i 266
Earth's falses are heaven's *t's*. „ III iii 348
But for the *t* of this I make appeal „ V ii 403
Not if Sinnatus Has told her all the *t* about me. *The Cup* I iii 23
That must be talk, not *t*, but *t* or talk, *The Falcon* 232
yet to speak white *t*, my good old mother, „ 503
and *t* to say, Sir Richard and my Lady Marian *Foresters* I i 29
We old hags should be bribed to speak *t*, „ II i 237
They have told but a tenth of the *t*: „ III 291
will seal Love's *t* On those sweet lips „ IV 74
Boldness is in the blood, *T* in the bottle. „ IV 240
Damsel, is this the *t*? *Marian*. Ay, noble knight. „ IV 770
Even this brawler of harsh *t's*—I trust Half *t's*, „ IV 948

Truthful being t wrought upon to swear Vows — *Harold* II ii 76
For thou art t, and thy word thy bond. — „ II ii 645
Thanks, t Earl; I did not doubt thy word, — „ II ii 723
And wise, yea t, till that blighted vow — „ V ii 155
Try Are you the bee to t me? — *Queen Mary* I iv 64
Shall I t If this be one of such? — „ V ii 331
Go t it, play. — *Becket* II i 246
Why do you jest with me, and t To fright me? — *Prom. of May* I 665
I saved him. I will t him. — *Foresters* I i 274
Well, then, let me t. — „ IV 256
Take him and t him, friar. — „ IV 268
T me an hour hence. — „ IV 276
T, thyself, valorous Robin! — „ IV 314
Trying (*See also* **A-tryin'**) like the gravedigger's child I have heard of, t to ring the bell, — *Becket* III iii 74
Tuck (Friar) *See* **Friar Tuck**
Tudor but I am T, And shall control them. — *Queen Mary* I v 175
I am Harry's daughter, T, and not Fear. — „ II iv 52
Bagenhall, I see The T green and white. — „ III i 180
Thou last of all the T's, come away! — „ III v 151
a T School'd by the shadow of death— — „ V v 225
a Boleyn, too, Glancing across the T— — „ V v 228
Tuesday the Archbishop washed my feet o' T. — *Becket* I iv 234
What day of the week? T? *Salisbury.* T, my lord. *Becket.* On a T was I born, and on a T Baptized; and on a T did I fly Forth from Northampton; on a T pass'd From England into bitter banishment; On a T at Pontigny came to me The ghostly warning of my martyrdom; On a T from mine exile I return'd, And on a T—on a T— — „ V ii 282
nine o'clock, upo' T murnin', — *Prom. of May* III 136
She broke my head on T with a dish. — *Foresters* I iii 133
Tuk (taken) and tells un ez the fire has t holt. — *Queen Mary* IV iii 512
Tumble first put up your hair: It t's all abroad. — „ V ii 233
sea shall roll me back To t at thy feet. — *Harold* I ii 115
Tumbled The hog hath t himself into some corner, — *Becket* I i 369
Tune Thou playest in t. — *Harold* I i 384
my voice is harsh here, not in t, — *Becket, Pro.* 349
Did I not sing it in t? *Robin.* No, sweetheart! out of t with Love and me. *Marian.* And yet in t with Nature and the bees. *Robin.* Out on it, I say, as out of t and time! — *Foresters* IV 29
Tunis T, and Oran, and the Philippines, — *Queen Mary* V i 48
Turban And cleft the Moslem t at my side. — *Foresters* IV 1001
Turbulent for I must hence to brave The Pope, King Louis, and this t priest. — *Becket* II i 312
Turk T shot her as she was helping to build — *Foresters* II i 308
Turmoil I cannot brook the t thou hast raised. — *Becket* I iii 575
Turn (s) Thy t, Galatian King. — *The Cup* II 379
wheere the big eshtree cuts athurt it, it gi'es a t like, — *Prom. of May* III 95
Turn (verb) shall I t traitor? — *Queen Mary* I iv 5
cannot touch you save that you t traitor; — „ I iv 271
this or that way, of success Would t it thither. — „ II ii 101
I am sorry for it If Pole be like to t. — „ III iv 416
Or would you have me t a sonneteer, — „ III vi 154
She t's again. — „ V v 12
let them t from left to right And sleep again. — *Harold* I i 195
to t and bite the hand Would help thee from the trap. — „ I i 381
But lest we t the scale of courtesy — „ II ii 164
He t's not right or left, but tramples flat — „ II ii 378
t not thou Thy face away, — „ III ii 38
They t on the pursuer, horse against foot, — „ V i 608
and t the world upside down. — *Becket* II i 238
I promise thee not to t the world upside down. — „ II i 242
to t anyway and play with as thou wilt— — „ II i 244
Take heed he do not t and rend you too: — „ II ii 160
and t me Mussulman! — „ II ii 223
she t's down the path through our little vineyard, — *The Falcon* 167
And welcome t's a cottage to a palace. — „ 272
but you t right ugly when you're in an ill temper; — *Prom. of May* I 159
to t out boäth my darters right down fine laädies. — „ I 336
Theer! he t's round. — „ II 586
t back at times, and make Courtesy to custom? — „ II 633
'T! t!' but I forget it. — *Foresters* I iii 155
Turncoat —and that, t shaveling! — *Becket* I iii 736
Turn'd The word has t your Highness pale; — *Queen Mary* I v 471
This Gardiner t his coat in Henry's time; — „ III iii 16
hath t so often, He knows not where he stands, — „ III iv 418
And the poor son t out into the street — „ V ii 125
Have t from right to left. — *Harold* I i 193
then I t, and saw the church all fill'd — „ I ii 81
The millwheel t in blood; — *Becket* I iii 353
North-east took and t him South-west, then the South-west t him North-east, — „ II ii 321
there they go—both backs are t to me— — „ II ii 454
sure my dagger was a feint Till the worm t— — „ IV ii 380
an' then I wur t huppads o' sixty. — *Prom. of May* I 363
lanker than an old horse t out to die on the common. — *Foresters* I i 51
I that have t their Moslem crescent pale— — „ IV 792
Turning (adj.) There was a song he made to the t wheel— — „ I iii 153
Turning (s) He knows the twists and t's of the place. — *Becket* V ii 576
Turtle Here His t builds; his exit is our adit: — „ III ii 7
Tussle flying from the heat and t, — *Queen Mary* III iv 252
Tut T, t, I have absolved thee: — *Harold* III i 104
T, t! did we convene This conference — *Becket* II ii 88
T, the chance gone, She lives— — „ IV ii 413
Tutelar And all the t Saints of Canterbury. — „ V iii 167
Twang Why, that wur the very t on 'im. — *Prom. of May* II 733
Twelve To go t months in bearing of a child? — *Queen Mary* III vi 90
Don Carlos, Madam, is but t years old. — „ V iii 87
T years of service! England loves thee for it. — *Harold* I i 221
And after those t years a boon, my king, — „ I i 225
Dream'd that t stars fell glittering out of heaven — *Becket* I i 46
The spirit of the t Apostles enter'd Into thy making. — „ I i 50
A supper for t mites. — *The Falcon* 127
Twenty (*See also* **Four-and-twenty**) Thus, after t years of banishment, — *Queen Mary* III ii 46
After my t years of banishment, — „ V ii 69
There runs a shallow brook across our field For t miles, — „ V v 84
Father Philip that has confessed our mother for t years, — *Becket* III i 112
No, to the crypt! T steps down. — „ V iii 78
Not t steps, but one. — „ V iii 90
where t years ago Huntsman, and hound, and deer — *The Cup* I ii 22
for Oberon fled away T thousand leagues to-day. — *Foresters* II i 143
but having lived For t days and nights in mail, — „ IV 124
Twenty-cubit cherubim With t-c wings from wall to wall— — *Harold* III i 184
Twenty-fold outvalues t-f The diamonds that you — *The Falcon* 759
Twenty-seven and take the t-s marks to the captain's treasury. — *Foresters* III 294
Twilight (adj.) A t conscience lighted thro' a chink; — *Harold* III i 65
Twilight (s) a paleness, Like the wan t after sunset, — *Becket* I iii 326
made the t day, And struck a shape from out the vague, — „ I iii 371
In the perpetual t of a prison, — *The Falcon* 442
t of the coming day already glimmers in the east. — *Foresters* I ii 247
Twin (adj.) these T rubies, that are amulets against all The kisses — *Harold* I ii 112
But you, t sister of the morning star, — *The Cup* I iii 45
Twin (s) that lying And ruling men are fatal t's — *Harold* III i 127
O Kate, true love and jealousy are t's, — *Foresters* II ii 63
Yet are they t's and always go together. — „ II ii 66
Twinkled The ripples t at their diamond-dance, — *Queen Mary* III ii 10
Twist (s) He knows the t's and turnings of the place. — *Becket* V ii 576
Twist (verb) And t it round thy neck and hang thee by it. — *Foresters* IV 688
Twitch ran a t across his face as who should say what's to follow? — *Becket* III iii 93
Two Bad me to tell you that she counts on you And on myself as her t hands; — *Queen Mary* II ii 105
sitting here Between the t most high-set thrones on earth, — „ III ii 106
the King And you together our t suns in one; — „ III iv 19
T vipers of one breed—an amphisbæna, Each end a sting: — „ III iv 39
Seeing there lie t ways to every end, — „ III iv 113
their t Graces Do so dear-cousin and royal-cousin him, — „ III iv 398
Of those t friars ever in my prison, — „ IV ii 94
Hist! there be t old gossips—gospellers, I take it; — „ IV iii 460
in Guisnes Are scarce t hundred men, — „ V i 5
Nay, not t hundred. — „ V ii 10
mainland over which Our flag hath floated for t hundred years Is France again. — „ V ii 261

Two (*continued*) and there you will find written *T* names, Philip and Calais; *Queen Mary* v v 155
By mine own eyes—and these *t* sapphires—these Twin rubies, *Harold* I ii 110
I do believe My old crook'd spine would bud out *t* young wings „ III i 24
lo! my *t* pillars, Jachin and Boaz!— „ III i 191
T young lovers in winter weather, „ III ii 3
And slew *t* hundred of his following, „ IV i 116
if our *t* houses Be less than brothers. „ IV i 129
Have thy *t* brethren sent their forces in? „ V i 342
T deaths at every swing, ran in upon us And died so, „ V i 409
Gregory bid St. Austin here Found *t* archbishopricks, London and York? *Becket* I iii 50
T sisters gliding in an equal dance, *T* rivers gently flowing side by side— „ I iii 444
who hath withstood *t* Kings to their faces for the honour of God. „ II ii 276
He thought less of *t* kings than of one Roger the king of the occasion. „ III iii 90
lest ye should draw together like *t* ships in a calm. „ III iii 298
My *t* good friends, What matters murder'd here, or murder'd there? „ V ii 629
That ere *t* souls be knit for life and death, *The Cup* II 359
Ay, and I left *t* fingers there for dead. *The Falcon* 653
they fell a kissin' o' one another like *t* sweet'arts i' the poorch *Prom. of May* I 22
and Vice and Virtue Are but *t* masks of self; „ I 538
And wheniver 'e sees *t* sweet'arts togither like thou and me, Sally, „ II 163
And Sir Richard was told he might be ransomed for *t* thousand marks in gold. *Foresters* I i 64
Those *t* thousand marks lent me by the Abbot for the ransom of my son Walter— „ I i 263
Did *t* knights pass? „ II i 230
For whom I ran into my debt to the Abbot, *T* thousand marks in gold. „ II i 464
And mark'd if those *t* knaves from York be coming? „ IV 112
Friar, by my *t* bouts at quarterstaff. „ IV 267
at the far end of the glade I see *t* figures crawling up the hill. „ IV 333
Thou hast risk'd thy life for mine: bind these *t* men. „ IV 894
Two-handed And swaying his *t-h* sword about him, *Harold* V i 407
Two-legg'd *t-l* dogs Among us who can smell *The Cup* I ii 111
'Twur (it were, it was) I should saay *'t* ower by now. *Queen Mary* IV iii 475
Tyne (river) thro' all the forest land North to the *T*: *Foresters* II i 89
Type poor Steer looks The very *t* of Age in a picture, *Prom. of May* III 514
Typed cataract *t* the headlong plunge and fall *Queen Mary* III iv 140
Tyranny Take fees of *t*, wink at sacrilege, *Becket* II ii 394
both fought against the *t* of the kings, the Normans. *Foresters* I i 230
This John—this Norman *t*— „ I i 238
Tyrant brook nor Pope nor Spaniard here to play The *t*, *Queen Mary* I v 191
Is this the face of one who plays the *t*? „ I v 194
you yourself have truckled to the *t*, „ III iv 237
This Tostig is, or like to be, a *t*; *Harold* I i 481
This Synorix Was Tetrarch here, and *t* also— *The Cup* I ii 183
To foil and spoil the *t* Beneath the greenwood tree. *Foresters* II i 11
maiden freedom which Would never brook the *t*. „ III 121
men will call him An Eastern *t*, not an English king. „ IV 904

U

Ugly Ay, but you turn right *u* when you're in an ill temper; *Prom. of May* I 159
And jealousy is wither'd, sour and *u*: *Foresters* II ii 65
Ulcer Crutches, and itches, and leprosies, and *u's*, *Becket* I iv 255
Unadvised theretoward *u* Of all our Privy Council; *Queen Mary* II ii 204
Unalterably *U* and pesteringly fond! „ V i 120
Unarmour'd And walkest here *U*? *Foresters* IV 119
Unask'd She gave her hand, *u*, at the farm-gate; *Prom. of May* II 625
Unaware That might have leapt upon us *u's*. *Queen Mary* II ii 295
Unbearded As helplessly as some *u* boy's *The Cup* I iii 40
Unborn The great *u* defender of the Faith, *Queen Mary* III ii 165
Unbrotherlike O brother, most *u* to me, *Harold* V i 251
Uncanonical Old *u* Stigand—ask of *me* Who had my pallium from an Antipope! „ I i 81
Thou *u* fool, Wilt *thou* play with the thunder? „ III i 390
Uncared upon the way to Rome Unwept, *u* for. *Becket* II ii 410
Uncertain *See* **Self-uncertain**
Uncle Not very dangerous that way, my good *u*. *Queen Mary* I iv 167
I follow your good counsel, gracious *u*. „ I iv 186
Do they say so, good *u*? „ I iv 215
You should not play upon me. *Elizabeth.* No, good *u*. „ I iv 220
U, I am of sovereign nature, „ I iv 257
To the Pleiads, *u*; they have lost a sister. „ I iv 293
I am sure this body Is Alfwig, the king's *u*. *Harold* V ii 68
Have we not heard Raymond of Poitou, thine own *u*— *Becket* IV ii 247
An' how did ye leäve the owd *u* i' Coomberland? *Prom. of May* I 68
That fine, fat, hook-nosed *u* of mine, old Harold, „ I 509
So the owd *u* i' Coomberland be deäd, Miss Dora, „ II 1
I met her first at a farm in Cumberland—Her *u's*. „ II 398
some will say because I have inherited my *U*. „ III 598
Uncomely Nay, what *u* faces, could he see you! *Becket* V i 201
Uncourtly Ever a rough, blunt, and *u* fellow— *Queen Mary* V v 120
Uncouth and your churches, *U*, unhandsome, *Harold* I i 165
Unction that very word 'greasy' hath a kind of *u* in it, *Foresters* I i 87
Unctuosity puffed out such an incense of *u* into the nostrils of our Gods of Church and State, *Becket* III iii 115
Undefiled As persons *u* with our offence, *Queen Mary* III iii 144
Underdid must we follow All that they overdid or *u*? *Becket* II ii 214
Underdone I hope he be not *u*, for we be undone in the doing of him. *The Falcon* 557
Undereaten Except it be a soft one, And *u* to the fall. *Harold* I ii 123
Underfoot the wild hawk passing overhead, The mouldwarp *u*. *Foresters* III 319
crackled *u* And in this very chamber, *Queen Mary* III v 53
and *u* An earthquake; „ IV iii 397
The priests of Baal tread her *u*— *Becket* III iii 179
Crush'd, hack'd at, trampled *u*. *The Falcon* 640
Undergo Or give thee saintly strength to *u*. *Queen Mary* IV iii 99
men of old would *u* Unpleasant for the sake of pleasant ones Hereafter, *Prom. of May* I 243
Underground They must have sprung like Ghosts from *u*, *Foresters* IV 593
Underhand Were fighting *u* unholy wars Against your lawful king. „ IV 821
Under-handedness and all left-handedness and *u-h*. *Becket, Pro.* 341
Under-heel That tread the kings their children *u-h*— „ *Pro.* 213
Understan' summat wrong theer, Wilson, fur I doänt *u* it. *Prom. of May* I 235
An' thou doänt *u* it neither—and thou schoolmaster an' all. „ I 239
Cannot you *u* plain words, Mr. Dobson? „ II 112
Understand (*See also* **Understan'**) *u* We made thereto no treaty of ourselves, *Queen Mary* II ii 202
U: Your lawful Prince hath come „ II ii 259
because I am not certain: You *u*, Feria. „ V i 269
You *u* me there, too? „ V i 273
Undertake Shall I *u* The knight at quarterstaff, *Foresters* IV 247
Underwood mix with all The lusty life of wood and *u*, „ I iii 114
Undescendible Steam'd upward from the *u* Abysm. *Harold* I i 15
Undone I hope he be not underdone, for we be *u* in the doing of him. *The Falcon* 558
Undoubted and proclaim Your true *u* faith, that all may hear. *Queen Mary* IV iii 114
Unfamiliar marvell'd at Our *u* beauties of the west; *Becket* IV ii 303
Unfurnish'd you are all *u*? Give him a bow and arrows— *The Cup* I i 207
Unhallow'd Dash'd red with that *u* passover; *Becket* I iii 348
Unhandsome and your churches Uncouth, *u*, *Harold* I i 165
Unhappiest *U* Of Queens and wives and women! *Queen Mary* V ii 407
Unhappiness brooding Upon a great *u* when you spoke. *Prom. of May* II 383
Unhappy and so this *u* land, long divided in itself, *Queen Mary* I iii 20
Behold him— *People.* Oh, *u* sight! „ IV iii 2
U land! Hard-natured Queen, half-Spanish in herself, „ IV iii 422
Voices—I hear *u* rumours—nay, I say not, I believe. „ V i 34
O this *u* world! How shall I break it to him? *The Falcon* 846
I am most unlucky, most *u*. „ 864
Unheard But will the King, then, judge us all *u*? *Foresters* IV 897

Unholy Were fighting underhand *u* wars Against your lawful king. *Foresters* IV 821
Uninvited knowing the fame of your hospitality, we ventured in *u*. „ I ii 196
Unity again received into the bosom And *u* of Universal Church; *Queen Mary* III iii 155
in this *u* and obedience Unto the holy see „ III iii 157
to the bosom And *u* of Universal Church. „ III iii 221
but now, The *u* of Universal Church, „ III iii 229
The *u* of Universal Hell, „ III iii 232
Join hands, let brethren dwell in *u*; *Harold* I i 397
In symbol of their married *u*, *The Cup* II 363
Universal Like *u* air and sunshine! Open, *Queen Mary* III ii 182
Be once again received into the bosom And unity of *U* Church; „ III iii 155
And also we restore you to the bosom And unity of *U* Church. „ III iii 221
but now, The unity of *U* Church, Mary would have it; and this Gardiner follows; The unity of *U* Hell, „ III iii 229
Yet wherefore should he die that hath return'd To the one Catholic *U* Church, „ IV iii 21
Unkind O my dear son, be not *u* to me. *The Falcon* 509
Unkingly *U* should I be, and most unknightly, *Becket* III iii 230
Unknightly Unkingly should I be, and most *u*, „ III iii 230
Unlearn'd your Priests Gross, wordly, simoniacal, *u*! *Harold* I i 162
Unlike The peoples are *u* as their complexion; *Queen Mary* V i 89
O how *u* our goodly Sinnatus. *The Cup* II 173
Weak natures that impute Themselves to their *u's*, *Foresters* II i 692
Unlord after that, We had to dis-archbishop and *u*, *Queen Mary* IV ii 128
Unlucky I am most *u*, most unhappy. *The Falcon* 864
Unman She fear'd it might *u* him for his end. *Queen Mary* III i 368
And that would quite *u* him, heart and soul. *Foresters* III 29
Unmann'd She could not be *u*—no, nor outwoman'd— *Queen Mary* III i 369
Unmatchable face and form *u*! *The Cup* I i 122
Unmoving *U* in the greatness of the flame, *Queen Mary* IV iii 622
Unpardonable Yea, even such as mine, incalculable, *U*,— „ IV iii 148
Unpleasant Against the *u* jolts of this rough road *Prom. of May* I 228
men of old would undergo *U* for the sake of pleasant ones Hereafter, „ I 245
Unprincely For some *u* violence to a woman, *The Cup* I i 139
God help the mark—To his own *u* ends. *Foresters* IV 716
Unqueen Who did discrown thine husband, *u* thee? *Harold* IV i 193
Unquenchable And burn the tares with *u* fire! *Queen Mary* V v 114
Unquiet and the people so *u*— „ III i 453
Unriddle Stigand, *u* This vision, canst thou? *Stigand.* Dotage! *Harold* III i 174
Unsafe Their lives *u* in any of these our woods, *Foresters* IV 93
Un-Saxon Which hunted *him* when that *u-S* blast, *Harold* II ii 30
Unscathed And let him pass *u*; he loves me, Harold! „ III i 301
Unschool'd and threaten us thence *U* of Death? „ V i 287
Unsheath'd tigress had *u* her nails at last, *Queen Mary* III i 3
Unsister plenty to sunder and *u* them again: „ I i 85
Unslept seen us that wild morning when we found Her bed *u* in, *Prom. of May* II 471
Unsocket whose storm-voice *U's* the strong oak, *The Cup* II 283
Unsubject *u* to One earthly sceptre. *Becket* I iii 680
Unswear Swear and *u*, state and misstate thy best! „ II ii 476
Unsymmetrically but *u*, preposterously, illogically, „ *Pro.* 336
Untold Tell me that, or leave All else *u*. *Queen Mary* IV iii 569
Unwavering Your lordship affects the *u* perpendicular; *Becket* II ii 326
Unwell Ah, heaven! *Pole.* *U*, your Grace? *Queen Mary* III ii 85
Her Highness is *u*. I will retire. „ V ii 246
I am sorry Mr. Steer still continues too *u* to attend to you, *Prom. of May* III 22
Unwept upon the way to Rome *U*, uncared for. *Becket* II ii 410
Unwholesome *U* talk For Godwin's house! *Harold* I i 390
Unwilling I have been *u* to trouble you with questions, *Prom. of May* III 321
Unwillingness Foreseeing, with whate'er *u*, *Queen Mary* I v 253
Unworthy 'This hath offended—this *u* hand!' „ IV iii 613
O thou *u* brother of my dear Marian! *Foresters* II i 538
Unwoundable callous with a constant stripe, *U*. *Queen Mary* V v 173
Unwounded having passed *u* from the field, *The Falcon* 608
Unwrinkled The brows *u* as a summer mere.— *Harold* III i 48
Up *See* **Hup, Oop, Shut-up, Steep-up**
Uphold all my lifelong labour to *u* The primacy—a heretic. *Queen Mary* V ii 70
Wilt *thou* *u* my claim? *Harold* II ii 602
Upholder our recoverer and *u* of customs hath in this crowning *Becket* III iii 70
Uplifter And mine *u* in this world, „ I i 89
Upper My lords of the *u* house, *Queen Mary* III iii 101
Uprear'd The trenches dug, the palisades *u* *Harold* V i 189
Upright you that have kept your old customs *u*, *Queen Mary* II i 159
Well, you one man, because you stood *u*, „ III iii 269
He pass'd out smiling, and he walk'd *u*; „ IV iii 303
He stood *u*, a lad of twenty-one, „ IV iii 335
and saw the church all fill'd With dead men *u* from their graves, *Harold* I ii 83
And thou art *u* in thy living grave, „ II ii 440
for I have lost Somewhat of *u* stature thro' mine oath, „ III ii 56
Uproar —made an *u*. *Henry.* And Becket had my bosom *Becket* I iii 432
Upshot and there bide The *u* of my quarrel, *Queen Mary* II iv 86
Upwards *See* **Huppads**
Urge not be wanting Those that will *u* her injury— *Queen Mary* III vi 176
and I shall *u* his suit Upon the Queen, „ V i 265
She will *u* marriage on me. *Prom. of May* I 489
Urn keep us From seeing all too near that *u*, *The Cup* I iii 133
Usage I came on certain wholesome *u's*, *Becket* I iii 412
so violated the immemorial *u* of the Church, „ III iii 72
Use (s) Ay, and what *u* to talk? *Queen Mary* III iii 40
I kept my head for *u* of Holy Church; „ III iv 359
wholesome *u* of these To chink against the Norman, *Harold* III i 20
made too good an *u* of Holy Church To break „ V i 312
Not yet. Stay. *Edith.* To what *u*? „ V i 339
fringe of gorgeousness beyond Old *u*, *The Cup* II 439
had you left him free *u* of his wings, *Prom. of May* I 652
but there is *u*, four hundred marks. *Foresters* IV 495
my tongue tript—five hundred marks for *u*. „ IV 500
You have the monies and the *u* of them. „ IV 548
Use (verb) Well, we shall *u* him somehow, *Queen Mary* I iii 171
and *u* Both us and them according as they will. „ II ii 160
Ay, but they *u* his name. „ V i 129
we must *u* our battle-axe to-day. *Harold* V i 205
King's courts would *u* thee worse than thy dog— *Becket* I iv 102
it is the cup we *u* in our marriages. *The Cup* I i 44
sends you this cup—the cup we *u* in our marriages— „ I ii 72
have you power with Rome? *u* it for him! „ I ii 290
we never *u* it For fear of breakage— *The Falcon* 486
—take and *u* your moment, while you may. *Foresters* II i 476
Used evilly *u* And put to pain. *Becket* II ii 433
You had never *u* so many, „ IV ii 183
Hath *u* the full authority of his Church „ V i 207
Foul as her dust-cloth, if she *u* it— „ V ii 203
Well *u*, they serve us well. *The Cup* I iii 135
Used (was accustomed) I *u* to love the Queen with all my heart— *Queen Mary* V ii 418
that Dobbins, is it, With whom I *u* to jar? *Prom. of May* II 613
as I *u* to transact all his business for him, „ II 719
Useless But your moan is *u* now: *Queen Mary* IV iii 638
Using fears he might be crack'd in *u*, „ II i 8
Usurper And thou, *u*, liar— *Harold.* Out, beast monk! *Harold* V i 74
Utmost I will help you, Madam, Even to the *u*. *Queen Mary* I v 178
To do to the *u* all that in us lies „ III iii 140
Utopian What are all these? *Harold.* *U* idiotcies. *Prom. of May* III 588
Utter (adj.) but the hour has come For *u* truth and plainness; *Queen Mary* IV iii 273
Poor lads, they see not what the general sees, A risk of *u* ruin. „ V ii 449
I have lived a life of *u* purity: *Harold* I i 178
I reel beneath the weight of *u* joy— *The Cup* II 450
I shall go mad for *u* shame and die. *Prom. of May* I 682
You both are *u* traitors to your king. *Foresters* IV 844
Utter (verb) fiends that *u* them Tongue-torn with pincers, *Queen Mary* V ii 192
I never heard him *u* worse of you Than that „ V ii 431
Uttered he never *u* moan of pain: „ IV iii 618

Uttering not like a word, That comes and goes in *u*. *Queen Mary* III v 30
Can I fancy him kneeling with me, and *u* the same prayer; *Prom. of May* III 180
Utterly I am *u* submissive to the Queen. *Queen Mary* I iv 39
Uxor And one an *u pauperis Ibyci*. *Becket* v ii 216

V

Vacancy 'And when the *v* is to be filled up, *Becket* I iii 108
Vacant 'When a bishoprick falls *v*, the King, till another be appointed, shall receive the revenues thereof.' „ I iii 100
King Demands a strict account of all those revenues From all the *v* sees and abbacies, „ I iii 652
Your heaven is *v* of your angel. *Foresters* II i 109
Vacillation shakes at mortal kings—her *v*, Avarice, craft— *Becket* II ii 405
Vacuity or any other symbol of *v*. *Foresters* IV 214
Vagabond (adj.) To take the *v* woman of the street Into thine arms! *Becket* I i 227
Vagabond (s) Why, nature's licensed *v*, the swallow, *Queen Mary* v i 20
I should have beaten thee, But that was *v*. *Becket, Pro.* 53
Vague struck a shape from out the *v*, „ I iii 373
Vain Surely, not all in *v*. *Queen Mary* v ii 158
—And all in *v*! The Queen of Scots is married „ v v 51
I had counsell'd him To rest from *v* resistance. *The Cup* II 414
Vale And kindle all our *v's* with myrtle-blossom, „ II 267
Valery Against St. *V* And William. *Harold* III ii 136
Valhalla *See* **Walhalla**
Valley should walk hand in hand together down this *v* of tears, *Prom. of May* III 192
Valorous Try, thyself, *v* Robin! *Foresters* IV 314
Valour came to know Thy *v* and thy value, *Harold* II ii 202
V and holy life should go together. *Becket* v ii 587
But seeing *v* is one against all odds, *Foresters* IV 318
Value came to know Thy valour and thy *v*, *Harold* II ii 202
My one thing left of *v* in the world! *The Falcon* 496
have won Their *v* again—beyond all markets— „ 905
v's neither man Nor woman save as tools— *Foresters* IV 713
Vane-arrow Which way soever the *v-a* swing, *Harold* II ii 257
Vanish Whate'er thy joys, they *v* with the day; *Foresters* I iii 44
Vanish'd (adj.) remain After the *v* voice, and speak to men. *Queen Mary* IV iii 164
Vanish'd (verb) And somewhere hereabouts he *v*. *Becket* III ii 5
Vanity As he hath ever err'd thro' *v*. *Queen Mary* IV i 31
Vanquish'd Our Artemis Has *v* their Diana. *The Cup* II 457
Var (far) it be a *v* waay vor my owld legs up vro' Islip. *Queen Mary* IV iii 472
Variance The Church is ever at *v* with the kings, *Becket* I iv 79
Various Woman is *v* and most mutable. *Queen Mary* III vi 135
Vassal (adj.) She cast on him a *v* smile of love, „ III i 98
Vassal (s) Then must I play the *v* to this Pole. „ III iii 111
Thomas, lord Not only of your *v's* but amours, *Becket* v i 205
sworn Yourselves my men when I was Chancellor—My *v's*— „ v ii 504
Thou art my man, thou art my *v*. „ v iii 154
loathed the cruelties that Rome Wrought on her *v's*. *The Cup* I ii 375
The pillage of his *v's*. *Foresters* III 107
Vassalage no more feuds Disturb our peaceful *v* to Rome. *The Cup* II 71
Vast the *v* vine-bowers Ran to the summit of the trees, „ I ii 401
Vastly I am *v* grieved to leave your Majesty. *Queen Mary* III vi 255
Vatican leave Lateran and *V* in one dust of gold— *Becket* II ii 475
Vaulted When I *v* on his back, *Foresters* II ii 150
Vaulting The tawny squirrel *v* thro' the boughs, „ I iii 117
Vavasour Wasn't Miss *V*, our schoolmistress at Littlechester, a lady born? *Prom. of May* III 297
Veer *V* to the counterpoint, and jealousy *Queen Mary* III vi 180
Veil (s) tore away My marriage ring, and rent my bridal *v*; *Harold* I ii 80
Like the Love-goddess, with no bridal *v*, *Prom. of May* I 597
you kept your *v* too close for that when they carried you in; „ III 226
Veil (verb) To *v* the fault of my most outward foe— *Queen Mary* IV ii 106
Veiled Her face was *v*, but the back methought *Becket, Pro.* 470
Veiling and no need Of *v* their desires. *Prom. of May* I 530

Veiling (*continued*) *V* one sin to act another. *Prom. of May* III 773
Vein O thin-skinn'd hand and jutting *v's*, *Queen Mary* IV ii 204
love I bear to thee Glow thro' thy *v's*? *Synorix.* The love I bear to thee Glows thro' my *v's* *The Cup* II 427
I have a swollen *v* in my right leg, *Foresters* IV 569
O Lord, the *v*! Not paid at York— „ IV 622
They have missed the *v*. „ IV 636
Velvet (*See also* **A-velveting**) *V* and gold. This dress was made me *Queen Mary* I iv 71
Venal And Rome is *v* ev'n to rottenness. *Becket* I iii 296
V imp! What say'st thou to the Chancellorship of England? „ II i 224
Vengeance Is *v* for its own sake worth the while, *The Cup* I i 30
And take a hunter's *v* on the meats. „ I ii 43
Beware, O King, the *v* of the Church. *Foresters* IV 913
let me execute the *v* of the Church upon them. „ IV 916
the *v* of the Church! Thou shalt pronounce the blessing of the Church „ IV 925
Venice He caught a chill in the lagoons of *V*, *Queen Mary* v ii 515
Venison What's that, my lord? *Becket. V. Beggar. V*? *Becket* I iv 137
and the world shall live by the King's *v* „ I iv 272
V, and wild boar, hare, geese, *Foresters* IV 191
so thou be Squeamish at eating the King's *v*. „ IV 194
I look on the King's *v* as my own. „ IV 197
in the fear of thy life shalt thou eat the King's *v*— „ IV 206
Not taste his *v* first? „ IV 343
if you hold us here Longer from our own *v*. „ IV 942
Venom It lies there folded: is there *v* in it? *Queen Mary* III v 217
Venomous all of us abhor The *v*, bestial, devilish revolt Of Thomas Wyatt. „ II ii 287
but he that lookt a fangless one, Issues a *v* adder. *Becket* I iii 453
and hers Crost and recrost, a *v* spider's web— „ II i 199
Ventris Sit benedictus fructus *v* tui!' *Queen Mary* III ii 83
Venture and deafen'd by some bright Loud *v*, „ III i 453
Ventured knowing the fame of your hospitality, we *v* in uninvited. *Foresters* I ii 196
Venus bust of Juno and the brows and eyes Of *V*; *The Cup* I i 122
Verbum Ha—*V* Dei—*v*—word of God! *Queen Mary* III i 262
Verdurer King's *v* caught him a-hunting in the forest, *Becket* I iv 95
Veriest Nay, Madam, nay! he sends his *v* love, *Queen Mary* v ii 564
believe thee The *v* Galahad of old Arthur's hall. *Becket, Pro.* 129
Verily Thou shalt be *v* king—all but the name— *Harold* II ii 632
Veritas *In vino* v. *Foresters* IV 247
Vermin In breeding godless *v*. *Queen Mary* III iv 329
Verse for my *v's* if the Latin rhymes be rolled out from a full mouth? *Becket* II ii 337
Verse-maker Thou art a jester and a *v-m*. „ II ii 334
Verse-writing your lordship would suspend me from *v-w*, „ II ii 350
Very but Lady Jane stood up Stiff as the *v* backbone of heresy. *Queen Mary* I v 44
A *v* wanton life indeed. „ I v 336
A fine beard, Bonner, a *v* full fine beard. „ III iv 338
The *v* Truth and *v* Word was one. „ III v 32
And in this *v* chamber, fuse the glass, „ III v 54
would make the hard earth rive To the *v* Devil's horns, the bright sky cleave To the *v* feet of God, *Harold* II ii 741
And all the Heavens and *v* God: they heard— „ v i 43
I want to bite, and they do say the *v* breath catches. *Becket* I iv 222
But ha! what's here? By *v* God, the cross I gave the King! „ IV ii 199
Ay, but wait Till his nose rises; he will be *v* king. „ v ii 184
This *v* day the Romans crown him king *The Cup* II 63
you look as beautiful this morning as the *v* Madonna her own self— *The Falcon* 199
That was the *v* year before you married. „ 373
O heavens! the *v* letters seem to shake With cold, „ 448
as the snow yonder on the *v* tip-top o' the mountain. „ 501
He be heighty this *v* daäy, *Prom. of May* I 7
But I taäkes 'im fur a bad lot and a burn fool, and I haätes the *v* sight on him. „ I 154
He's a Somersetshire man, and a *v* civil-spoken gentleman. „ I 207
fur thaw I be heighty this *v* daäy, „ I 358
I have heard of you. The likeness Is *v* striking. „ II 366
Why, that wur the *v* twang on 'im. „ II 733
and poor Steer looks The *v* type of Age in a picture, „ III 514

Very (*continued*) Why there, now! that *v* word 'greasy' hath a kind of unction in it, *Foresters* I i 86
I am thine to the *v* heart of the earth— „ I i 337
My God, thou art the *v* woman who waits On my dear Marian. „ II i 101
Thou comest a *v* angel out of heaven. „ II i 105
and what dost thou with that who art more bow-bent than the *v* bow thou carriest? „ II i 378
It is the *v* captain of the thieves! „ II i 412
I thank you, noble sir, the *v* blossom Of bandits. „ III 247
It is not he—his face—tho' *v* like—No, no! „ IV 777
Yea, and the weight of the *v* land itself, „ IV 1025
Veselay But since he cursed My friends at *V*, *Becket* II i 89
Vesper I will but pass to *v's*, And breathe one prayer „ V ii 190
In your old place? and *v's* are beginning. „ V ii 596
Come, then, with us to *v's*. „ V iii 35
They are thronging in to *v's*—half the town. „ V iii 139
Vessel guns From out the *v's* lying in the river. *Queen Mary* II i 222
wherefore not Helm the huge *v* of your state, „ V i 73
In the full *v* running out at top *Harold* I i 378
Plunder'd the *v* full of Gascon wine, *Becket* V ii 441
Vex *V* him not, Leofwin. *Tostig.* I am not vext,—Altho' ye seek to *v* me, *Harold* I i 403
I told my Lord He should not *v* her Highness; *Queen Mary* III vi 66
Why do you *v* me? „ IV i 134
Why would you *v* yourself, Poor sister? „ V v 263
Which will so *v* thee. *Becket* II i 208
I will not *v* you by repeating them— *Prom. of May* II 403
Why do you *v* me With raven-croaks *Foresters* II i 623
Vex'd-Vext His Highness is so *vex'd* with strange affairs— *Queen Mary* V ii 559
No, I am not *vext*,—Altho' ye seek to vex me, *Harold* I i 404
—I am not *vext* at all. „ I i 409
A gnat that *vext* thy pillow! „ I ii 71
I seed how the owd man wur *vext*. *Prom. of May* II 28
Viand besides Hedge-pigs, a savoury *v*, *Foresters* IV 193
Vicar Julius, God's *V* and Vicegerent upon earth, *Queen Mary* III iii 213
and adore This *V* of their *V*. „ III iii 244
Vice Foul maggots crawling in a fester'd *v*! „ V v 162
Would call this *v*; but one time's *v* may be The virtue of another; and *V* and Virtue Are but two masks of self; and what hereafter Shall mark out *V* from Virtue *Prom. of May* I 534
Our vice-king John,—True king of *v*— *Foresters* II i 83
Vicegerent Julius, God's Vicar and *V* upon earth, *Queen Mary* III iii 213
Vice-king And thou be my *v-k* in England. *Harold* II ii 635
Our *v-k* John, True king of vice— *Foresters* II i 81
Viceroy Set up a *v*, sent his myriads *Queen Mary* III i 463
Sometime the *v* of those provinces— „ III ii 196
Viciousness Because we seek to curb their *v*. *Foresters* III 393
Victim nobler The *v* was, the more acceptable Might be the sacrifice. *The Falcon* 880
Or happy fallen a *v* to the wolf. *Foresters* II i 509
Victor will you crown my foe My *v* in mid-battle? *Becket* V i 150
crown'd *v* of my will— *The Cup* II 519
Victory wines Of wedding had been dash'd into the cups Of *v*, *Harold* IV iii 8
thy *victories* Over our own poor Wales, „ IV iii 26
I ever had my *victories* among women. *The Cup* I i 153
at last May lead them on to *v*— „ I ii 168
Vile With that *v* Cranmer in the accursed lie Of good Queen Catharine's divorce— *Queen Mary* III iv 231
Villa Garcia No man can make his Maker—*V G.* „ IV ii 58
No, *V G*, I sign no more. „ IV ii 83
Village (adj.) His *v* darling in some lewd caress *Becket* IV ii 200
So loved by all the *v* people here, *Prom. of May* III 755
Village (s) I Shall not be made the laughter of the *v*, „ I 721
Villain *v's* with their lying lights have wreck'd us! *Harold* II i 83
Serve thyself first, *v*! They shall not harm *The Cup* I ii 325
that *v*, Edgar, If he should ever show *Prom. of May* II 422
Vindicator Surgas e tenebris, Sis *v*! *Harold* V i 572
Vine You lived among your *v's* and oranges, *Queen Mary* III iv 253
Perhaps our *v's* will grow the better for it. *Harold* I i 68
apricot, *V*, cypress, poplar, myrtle, *The Cup* I i 3
and like the swaying *v's*—Yea,— „ I ii 411
Vine (*continued*) we will chirp among our *v's*, and smile *The Cup* I iii 170
sway the long grape-bunches of our *v's*, „ II 271
Vine-an'-the-Hop (inn sign) But hallus ud stop at the *V-a-t-H*, *Prom. of May* II 311
Vine-bower vast *v-b's* Ran to the summit of the trees, *The Cup* I ii 402
Vineyard she turns down the path through our little *v*, *The Falcon* 168
Vino *In* v *veritas.* *Foresters* IV 247
Vintage Not like the *v* blowing round your castle. *The Falcon* 579
send you down a flask or two Of that same *v*? „ 586
Violate These Romans dare not *v* the Temple. *The Cup* I iii 62
Violated A cleric *v* The daughter of his host, *Becket* I iii 382
so *v* the immemorial usage of the Church, „ III iii 72
v the whole Tradition of our land, *Prom. of May* I 494
Violence (*See also* **Over-violence**) Your *v* and much roughness to the Legate, *Queen Mary* III iv 318
—a sweet *v*, And a sweet craft. „ III v 108
v and the craft that do divide The world „ III v 120
cast with bestial *v* Our holy Norman bishops *Harold* I i 49
Side not with Tostig in any *v*, „ I i 457
For some unprincely *v* to a woman, *The Cup* I i 139
This *v* ill becomes The silence of our Temple. „ II 215
Violent Robin was *v*, And she was crafty— *Queen Mary* III v 107
Save for thy wild and *v* will that wrench'd All hearts of freemen from thee. *Harold* V i 277
Violet and won the *v* at Toulouse; *Becket, Pro.* 348
rose or no rose, has killed the golden *v*. „ *Pro.* 352
Sweeter than any *v* of to-day, *The Falcon* 465
I meän'd they be as blue as *v's*. *Prom. of May* I 104
Viper Two *v's* of one breed—an amphisbæna, *Queen Mary* III iv 39
Vire (fire) I do know ez Pwoaps and *v's* be bad things; „ IV iii 501
and tells un ez the *v* has tuk holt. „ IV iii 512
There's nought but the *v* of God's hell ez can burn out that. „ IV iii 527
Virgil Well, the tree in *V*, sir, „ III i 22
but, my Lord, you know what *V* sings, „ III vi 134
Virgin (adj.) seeing that our gracious *V* Queen hath— „ I iii 23
Virgin (s) (*See also* **Mary**) let me call her our second *V* Mary, „ I iii 57
V Mary! we'll have no virgins here— „ I iii 60
we'll have no *v's* here—we'll have the Lady Elizabeth! „ I iii 61
by the holy *V*, being noble, But love me only: „ I v 70
Holy *V*, Plead with thy blessed Son; „ I v 84
I thank God, I have lived a *v*, „ II ii 218
Holy *V* will not have me yet Lose the sweet hope „ III vi 199
My son, the Saints are *v's*; *Harold* III i 272
I have been myself a *v*; and I swear To consecrate my *v* here „ III i 275
Yea, by the Blessed *V*! *Becket, Pro.* 520
The *V*, in a vision of my sleep, „ I i 53
we have the Blessed *V* For worship, „ V ii 220
I do commend my cause to God, the *V*, „ V iii 164
I am a *v*, my masters, I am a *v*. *Much.* And a *v*, my masters, three yards about the waist is like to remain a *v*, *Foresters* I ii 67
And you three holy men, You worshippers of the *V*, „ III 383
The Holy *V* Stand by the strongest. „ IV 264
Our holy king Hath given his *v* lamb to Holy Church *Harold* III i 334
Virginity They love the white rose of *v*, „ III i 273
Virgo Homo sum, sed *v* sum, *Foresters* I ii 66
Virtue (I count it as a kind of *v* in him, *Queen Mary* I iv 193
Is not *v* prized mainly for its rarity *Becket* III iii 303
one time's vice may be The *v* of another; and Vice and *V* Are but two masks of self; and what hereafter Shall mark out Vice from *V* *Prom. of May* I 536
Virtuous Exhort them to a pure and *v* life; *Queen Mary* IV ii 77
Virtus *Gratior in pulchro corpore* v. *Becket* V ii 542
Visible Is not the Church the *v* Lord on earth? „ I iii 92
Vision I have had a *v*; *Harold* I i 191
Edward wakes!—Dazed—he hath seen a *v*. „ III i 131
Stigand, unriddle This *v*, canst thou? *Stigand.* Dotage! „ III i 175
The Virgin, in a *v* of my sleep, *Becket* I i 53
It will be so—my *v's* in the Lord: „ III iii 341
I had once a *v* of a pure and perfect marriage, *Prom. of May* III 188
Shall I be happy? Happy *v*, stay. *Foresters* II ii 199
Visionary And found it all a *v* flame, *Queen Mary* IV ii 4

Visit thine host in England when I went To *v* Edward. *Harold* II ii 6
Coming to *v* my lord, for the first time in her life too! *The Falcon* 170
Visited When I *v* England, Some held she was his wife *Harold* V ii 99
Vitus (Saint) By old St. *V* Have you gone mad? *Foresters* IV 614
Vive le Roy Hurrah! *V l R*! *Becket* I iv 274
Voice (*See also* **Storm-voice**) Thro' many *v's* crying right and left, *Queen Mary* I ii 48
and all rebellions lie Dead bodies without *v*. „ II i 80
Three *v's* from our guilds and companies! „ II ii 255
And will not trust your *v's*. „ II ii 259
Their *v* had left me none to tell you this. „ II iii 36
A sound Of feet and *v's* thickening hither— „ II iv 45
Thine is a half *v* and a lean assent. „ III i 311
To join a *v*, so potent with her Highness, „ IV i 117
All your *v's* Are waves on flint. „ IV i 121
my poor *v* Against them is a whisper to the roar „ IV ii 186
remain After the vanish'd *v*, „ IV iii 164
crying, in his deep *v*, more than once, „ IV iii 611
Ay, ay; but many *v's* call me hence. *Mary*. *V's* —I hear unhappy rumours—nay, „ V i 32
What *v's* call you Dearer than mine „ V i 36
Alas, my Lord! what *v's* and how many? *Philip*. The *v's* of Castille and Aragon, „ V i 40
v's of Franche-Comté, and the Netherlands, The *v's* of Peru and Mexico, „ V i 45
if the fetid gutter had a *v* And cried „ V ii 323
Your Grace hath a low *v*. „ V ii 378
A low *v* Lost in a wilderness where none can hear! A *v* of shipwreck on a shoreless sea! A low *v* from the dust and from the grave „ V ii 381
No, that way there are *v's*. Am I too late? „ V v 207
Thou art a great *v* in Northumberland! *Harold* I i 114
in Normanland God speaks thro' abler *v's*, „ I i 167
I want his *v* in England for the crown, I want thy *v* with him to bring him round; „ II ii 71
The choice of England is the *v* of England. *William*. I will be king of England by the laws, The choice, and *v* of England. „ II ii 128
v of any people is the sword That guards them, „ II ii 134
would give his kingly *v* To me as his successor. „ II ii 588
Thou art the mightiest *v* in England, man, Thy *v* will lead „ II ii 617
we be not bound by the king's *v* In making of a king, yet the king's *v* „ III i 236
The *v* of Gurth! Good even, my good brother! „ III ii 115
Wessex dragon flies beyond the Humber, No *v* to greet it. „ IV i 5
Thou gavest thy *v* against me in the Council— „ IV ii 77
till *her v* Die with the world. „ IV iii 75
I am but a *v* Among you: murder, martyr me „ V i 77
I send my *v* across the narrow seas— „ V i 246
Thou gavest thy *v* against me in my life, I give my *v* against thee from the grave— „ V i 252
We give our *v* against thee out of heaven! „ V i 260
My battle-axe against your *v's*. „ V i 265
my *v* is harsh here, not in tune, *Becket, Pro.* 349
v of the deep as it hollows the cliffs of the land. „ II i 3
a *v* coming up with the *v* of the deep from the strand, „ II i 5
hand of one To whom thy *v* is all her music, „ II i 177
the *v* Of the perpetual brook, „ III i 45
The brook's *v* is not yours, and no flower, „ III i 55
when my *v* Is martyr'd mute, and this man disappears, „ III iii 349
Did not a man's *v* ring along the aisle, „ V ii 150
The King beyond the water, thro' our *v's*, „ V ii 324
Shall the waste *v* of the bond-breaking sea „ V ii 358
Blessings on your pretty *v*, Miss Dora. *Prom. of May* I 64
arter she'd been a-reädin' me the letter wi' 'er *v* a-shaäkin', „ II 129
And *her* charm Of *v* is also yours; „ II 381
I heard a *v*, 'Girl, what are you doing there?' „ III 375
Swarm to thy *v* like bees to the brass pan. *Foresters* I iii 108
they are so fond o' their own *v's* „ II i 383
Thou art her brother, and her *v* is thine, „ II i 479
In the cold water that she lost her *v*, „ IV 243
Void you would make his coronation *v* By cursing those who crown'd him. *Becket* V ii 330
Volcanic A drinker of black, strong, *v* wines, *Queen Mary* V ii 93
Volk (folk) and a-makin' o' *v* madder and madder; „ IV iii 532
Voltigeur I can recommend our *V*.' *Prom. of May* III 311
Voluntary that thou hast sworn a *v* allegiance to him? *Becket, Pro.* 439
Vomit Made even the carrion-nosing mongrel *v* *Queen Mary* IV iii 449
Vor (for) it be a var waay *v* my owld legs up vro' Islip. „ IV iii 472
the burnin' o' the owld archbishop 'll burn the Pwoap out o' this 'ere land *v* iver and iver. „ IV iii 536
Vor't (for it) but tek thou my word *v*, Joan,— „ IV iii 533
Vouch Who shall *v* for his to-morrows? One word further. *Becket* III iii 300
Vouchsafe *V* a gracious answer to your Queen? „ IV ii 359
Vour (four) and so they bided on and on till *v* o' the clock, *Queen Mary* IV iii 510
Vow (s) to swear *V's* that he dare not break. *Harold* II ii 77
for he Who vows a *v* to strangle his own mother „ III i 229
He did not mean to keep his *v*. „ III i 248
to see my solemn *v* Accomplish'd. „ III i 307
that blighted *v* Which God avenged to-day. „ V ii 156
That kings are faithful to their marriage *v*. *Becket* I ii 78
I bound myself, and by a solemn *v*, *The Falcon* 679
but what a *v*! what a *v*! *Foresters* I i 294
For holy *v's* made to the blessed Saints „ I ii 175
bounden by a *v* not to show his face, „ I ii 236
Vow (verb) Kiss'd me well I *v*; *Queen Mary* III v 93
for he Who *v's* a vow to strangle his own mother *Harold* III i 229
I *v* to build a church to God Here on the hill of battle; „ V ii 137
Voyage Had you a pleasant *v* up the river? *Queen Mary* III i 5
Our *v* by sea was all but miracle; „ III ii 25
Sick as an autumn swallow for a *v*, *Harold* I i 102
On my last *v*—but the wind has fail'd— *The Cup* II 521
Vro' (from) and it be a var waay vor my owld legs up *v* Islip. *Queen Mary* IV iii 473
till his man cum in post *v* here, „ IV iii 511
Vying saw thy willy-nilly nun *V* a tress against our golden fern. *Harold*. *V* a tear with our cold dews, *Harold* V i 149

W

Waäge (wage) An' I thanks ye fur that, Miss, moor nor fur the *w*. *Prom. of May* III 117
Waäist (waist) 'A cotched ma about the *w*, Miss, „ III 119
Waäy (way) it be a var *w* vor my owld legs up vro' Islip. *Queen Mary* IV iii 472
Eh, then ha' thy *w* wi' me, Tib; „ IV iii 486
I niver thowt o' mysen i' that *w*; but if she'd taäke to ma i' that *w*, or ony *w*, *Prom. of May* I 176
We laäys out o' the *w* fur gentlefoälk altogither— „ I 210
An' I haätes boooks an' all, fur they puts foälk off the owd *w's*. „ I 222
fell ageän coalscuttle and my kneeä gev *w* „ I 404
I mun git out on 'is *w* now, or I shall be the death on 'im. „ II 609
Waded As if she had *w* in it. *Queen Mary* III i 63
w in the brook, ran after the butterflies, *Prom. of May* III 275
Wafer Their *w* and perpetual sacrifice: *Queen Mary* I ii 45
Waged Thou hast *w* God's war against the King; *Becket* V ii 46
Wages (*See also* **Waäge**) if the farming-men be come for their *w*, to send them up to me. *Prom. of May* III 16
but the schoolmaster looked to the paying you your *w* when I was away, „ III 24
spent all your last Saturday's *w* at the ale-house; „ III 78
Why should I pay you your full *w*? „ III 83
there are your *w*; the next time you waste „ III 98
Wagon Like a tod of wool from *w* into warehouse. *Foresters* IV 274
Wail (s) our sea-mew Winging their only *w*! *Harold* II i 98
better death With our first *w* than life— *Prom. of May* II 291
—how she made her *w* as for the dead! „ III 698
and make a ghostly *w* ever and anon to scare 'em. *Foresters* II i 216
Wail (verb) Is this a place To *w* in, Madam? *Queen Mary* V i 213
thou wilt have To *w* for it like Peter. *Harold* III i 285
dooms thee after death To *w* in deathless flame. *Becket* IV ii 272

Wailing helpless folk Are wash'd away, *w*, in their own blood— *Harold* II ii 471
W ! not warring ? Boy, thou hast forgotten „ II ii 473
her poor spaniel *w* for her, *Prom. of May* II 473
Waist (*See also* **Waaist**) three yards about the *w* is like to remain a virgin, *Foresters* I ii 69
He caught her round the *w*, „ II i 116
And coil'd himself about her sacred *w*. „ II i 139
I will take the rope from off thy *w* „ IV 687
Waistcoat I doänt believe he's iver a 'eart under his *w*. *Prom. of May* I 130
Wait Who *w's*, sir ? *Usher*. Madam, the Lord Chancellor. *Queen Mary* I v 95
Who *w's* ? *Usher*. The Ambassador from France, „ I v 238
Who *w's* ? *Usher*. The Ambassador of Spain, „ I v 341
Your Lordship may not have so long to *w*. Remove him ! „ II iv 107
Lord Paget *W's* to present our Council to the Legate. „ III ii 98
And *w* my coming back. „ III vi 219
Madam, the Count de Feria *w's* without, „ V ii 400
W he must—Her trance again. „ V ii 402
W's till the man let go. *Harold* I i 329
Stand there and *w* my will. „ II ii 683
Then our great Council *w* to crown thee King— „ III i 3
And our great Council *w* to crown thee King. „ III i 406
knights Sit, each a statue on his horse, and *w*. „ V i 525
the business Of thy whole kingdom *w's* me: *Becket, Pro.* 278
We *w* but the King's word to strike thee dead. „ I iii 166
'Should not an earl's son *w* on a king's son?' „ III iii 152
w Till his nose rises; he will be very king. „ V ii 183
I told them I would *w* them here. „ V ii 593
w's once more Before the Temple. *The Cup* II 11
messenger from Synorix who *w's* Before the Temple ? „ II 37
Are you so sure ? I pray you *w* and see. „ II 107
He *w's* your answer. „ II 137
I *w* him his crown'd queen. „ II 161
Well, you must *w* till then. *Foresters* I ii 223
You shall *w* for mine till Sir Richard has paid the Abbot. „ I ii 231
thou art the very woman who *w's* On my dear Marian. „ II i 102
I *w* till Little John makes up to *me*. „ III 17
W and see. (repeat) „ IV 106, 108
Speak not. I *w* upon a dying father. „ IV 610
W till he blow the horn. „ IV 787
Sir Richard, let that *w* till we have dined. „ IV 991
Waited Who brings that letter which we *w* for— *Queen Mary* I v 586
child We *w* for so long—heaven's gift at last— *Becket* III i 14
Waiting (part.) All arm'd, *w* a leader; *Queen Mary* II i 108
Who, *w* till the time had ripen'd, „ III ii 78
like the Moslem beauties *w* To clasp *Prom. of May* I 247
what full hands, may be *W* you in the distance ? „ II 511
Tell him, then, that I'm *w* for him. „ III 483
Waiting (s) Good counsel yours—No one in *w* ? *Queen Mary* V v 203
Wake (s) have loved Harold the Saxon, or Hereward the *W*. *Foresters* I i 228
our great Earl, bravest English heart Since Hereward the *W*, „ II i 688
Wake (verb) *W*, or the stout old island will become *Queen Mary* II i 104
Edward *w's* !—Dazed—he hath seen a vision. *Harold* III i 130
And *w* with it, and show it to all the Saints. *Becket* II i 303
on a great occasion sure to *w* As great a wrath in Becket— „ III i 87
W me before you go, I'll after you— *The Cup* I ii 447
And *w* the Devil, and I may sicken by 'em. *Foresters* III 325
Waked She must be *w*. *Harold*. Who must be *w* ? *Prom. of May* III 658
Wakened to be *w* again together by the light of the resurrection, „ III 196
Wakening (*See also* **New-wakening, Wakkenin'**) *W* such brawls and loud disturbances *Becket* V ii 352
Waking thine eyelids into sleep, Will hold mine *w*. *Harold* I ii 141
our *w* thoughts Suffer a stormless shipwreck in the pools Of sullen slumber, „ V i 294
Wakkenin' (wakening) but I thinks he be *w* oop. *Prom. of May* III 413
Wales The Queen of *W* ? Why, Morcar, *Harold* IV i 152
had in it *W*, Her floods, her woods, her hills: „ IV i 206
let him flap The wings that beat down *W* ! „ IV i 247
thy victories Over our own poor *W*, „ IV iii 27
Have we not broken *W* and Norseland ? „ V i 395
I was the Queen of *W*. „ V ii 95
Walhalla for better, Woden, all Our cancell'd warrior-gods, our grim *W*, Eternal war, *Harold* III ii 74
Walk (s) and the *w's* Where I could move at pleasure, *Becket* I i 265
that dreadful night ! that lonely *w* to Littlechester, *Prom. of May* III 366
He was the cock o' the *w*; *Foresters* II i 320
all these *w's* are Robin Hood's And sometimes perilous. „ IV 119
Walk (verb) And when I *w* abroad, the populace, *Queen Mary* I v 148
And if I *w* within the lonely wood, *Harold* II ii 246
we are Danes, Who conquer'd what we *w* on, „ IV i 38
If you will *w* with me we needs must meet *The Cup* I iii 91
I pray you lift me And make me *w* awhile. „ II 473
should *w* hand in hand together down this valley of tears, *Prom. of May* III 191
Walk'd He pass'd out smiling, and he *w* upright; *Queen Mary* IV iii 302
as he *w* the Spanish friars Still plied him „ IV iii 576
But *w* our Norman field, *Harold* II ii 173
Upon the heads of those who *w* within— „ II ii 393
W at night on the misty heather; „ III ii 5
I have heard these poisons May be *w* down. *The Cup* II 475
As Wealth *w* in at the door. *Foresters* I i 151
Walkest And *w* here Unarmour'd ? „ IV 118
Walking (*See also* **A-walkin'**) I was *w* with the man I loved. *Queen Mary* V v 88
he's *w* to us, and with a book in his hand. *Prom. of May* I 219
Stole on her, she was *w* in the garden, *Foresters* II i 112
Wall (*See also* **Shield-wall**) And carve my coat upon the *w's* again ! *Queen Mary* II iv 110
when the thief is ev'n within the *w's*, „ III iv 312
moonlight casements pattern'd on the *w*, „ V v 10
The *w's* oppress me, And yon huge keep *Harold* II ii 226
town Hung out raw hides along their *w's*, „ II ii 383
shackles that will bind me to the *w*. „ II ii 411
cherubim With twenty-cubit wings from *w* to *w*— „ III i 184
our shield *w*—*W*—break it not—break not— „ V i 232
make their *w* of shields Firm as thy cliffs, „ V i 479
Hot-headed fools—to burst the *w* of shields ! „ V i 613
They say that *w's* have ears; *Becket* IV ii 79
Battering the doors, and breaking thro' the *w's* ? „ V ii 627
and the *w's* sa thin, and the winders brokken, *Prom. of May* III 72
Wallow Delight to *w* in the grossness of it, *Becket* II ii 343
Walnut *w*, apricot, Vine, cypress, poplar, myrtle, *The Cup* I i 2
Walter (Lea, son of Sir Richard Lea) (*See also* **Walter Lea**)
No news of young *W* ? *Foresters* I i 73
for the ransom of my son *W*— „ I i 265
Young *W*, nay, I pray thee, stay a moment. „ II i 472
to dream that he My brother, my dear *W*— „ II i 652
O *W*, *W*, is it thou indeed Whose ransom was our ruin, „ IV 1005
Walter Lea I ask you all, did none of you love young *W L* ? „ I i 55
My masters, welcome gallant *W L*. „ IV 1002
W L, Give me that hand which fought for Richard „ IV 1028
Walter Map (*See also* **Map**) But bear with *W M*, *Becket* II ii 307
Non defensoribus istis, W M. „ II ii 346
There is the King talking with *W M* ? „ III iii 22
That's a delicate Latin lay Of *W M*: „ V i 193
Waltham *W*, my foundation For men who serve the neighbour, *Harold* V i 97
the Holy Rood That bow'd to me at *W*— „ V i 383
No, daughter, but the canons out of *W*, „ V i 475
Walworth And he will play the *W* to this Wat; *Queen Mary* II ii 370
Wan The *w* boy-king, with his fast-fading eyes Fixt hard on mine, „ I ii 30
How *w*, poor lad ! how sick and sad for home ! *Harold* II ii 325
thou art Harold, I am Edith ! Look not thus *w* ! „ V i 393
Like the *w* twilight after sunset, crept Up even to the tonsure, *Becket* I iii 326
Wander doth not kill The sheep that *w* from his flock, *Queen Mary* III iv 103
Who *w* famine-wasted thro' the world. *Becket* III iii 188
Wander'd so long Have *w* among women,— „ II i 154
Wandering (adj. and part.) I found this white doe *w* through the wood, *Foresters* II i 96
As Canterbury calls them, *w* clouds, *Becket* I iii 70
Wandering (s) prosper all thy *w* out And homeward. *Harold* I i 265
Wane light of this new learning *w's* and dies: *Queen Mary* III ii 172

Waning and make Our w Eleanor all but love me! Becket II ii 458
Wanstead she met the Queen at W Queen Mary I i 77
Want (s) Yet too much mercy is a w of mercy, " I v 506
This coarseness is a w of phantasy. " V ii 438
Thine absence well may seem a w of care. Harold I i 322
That suffers in the daily w of thee, " II ii 275
daily w supplied—The daily pleasure to supply it. Becket II ii 301
Yet if thro' any w— Harold. Of this religion? Prom. of May III 540
ever have happen'd thro' the w Of any or all of them. " III 547
If thro' the w of any—I mean the true one— " III 550
who never hast felt a w, to whom all things, Foresters I i 208
and their own w Of manhood to their leader! " II i 693
Want (verb) his manners w the nap And gloss of court; Queen Mary III v 70
you w the sun That shines at court; " III v 276
I w his voice in England for the crown, I w thy voice with him to bring him round; Harold II ii 71
and I w to bite, I w to bite, Becket I iv 221
shall see the silk here and there, and I w my supper. " IV i 57
Do you w them back again? Prom. of May II 43
Owd Steer's gotten all his grass down and w's a hand, " II 222
Miss Dora, meä and my maätes, us three, we w's to hev three words wi' ye. " III 125
all on us, wi' your leave, we w's to leather 'im. " III 137
and he w's to speak to ye partic'lar. " III 350
says he w's to tell ye summut very partic'lar. " III 355
an w's To hev a word wi' ye about the marriage. " III 703
Wanted I am sure Her morning w sunlight, Harold I ii 45
Wanting W the Papal mitre. Queen Mary III iv 148
not be w Those that will urge her injury— " III vi 175
My palace w you was but a cottage; The Falcon 287
Wanton (adj.) A very w life indeed. Queen Mary I v 336
No ribald John is Love, no w Prince, Foresters IV 46
Wanton (s) With a w in thy lodging—Hell requite 'em! Becket I ii 9
I would move this w from his sight " I ii 70
And thou thyself a proven w? " IV ii 116
Lest thou shouldst play the w there again. " V i 112
This w here. De Morville, Hold her away. " V iii 171
Wantonness high Heaven guard thee from his w, Foresters I ii 122
War and at w with him, your Grace And kingdom will be suck'd into the w, Queen Mary I v 255
must we levy w against the Queen's Grace? Wyatt. No, my friend; w for the Queen's Grace—to save her from herself and Philip —w against Spain. " II i 187
the world is with us—w against Spain! " II i 196
not mix us any way With his French w's— " III iii 79
The civil w's are gone for evermore: " III v 150
Not so well holpen in our w's with France, " III vi 188
If w should fall between yourself and France; " V i 9
came to sue Your Council and yourself to declare w. (repeat) " V i 109, 116
soon or late you must have w with France; " V i 121
You make your w's upon him down in Italy:— " V i 141
Who deems it a most just and holy w. " V i 147
Alas! the Council will not hear of w. They say your w's are not the w's of England. " V i 164
There will be w with France, at last, my liege; " V i 282
the Council (I have talk'd with some already) are for w. " V i 296
He cannot dream that I advised the w; " V ii 57
We have made w upon the Holy Father All for your sake: " V ii 307
You did but help King Philip's w with France, " V ii 313
Dear Madam, Philip is but at the w's; " V v 25
And all his w's and wisdoms past away; " V v 56
W, my dear lady! Harold I i 22
W there, my son? is that the doom of England? " I i 124
W? the worst that follows Things that seem " I i 135
religious fool, Who, seeing w in heaven, " I i 140
Ay, ay and wise in peace and great in w— " I i 313
W, my dear lady, W, waste, plague, " I i 465
brought Thy w with Brittany to a goodlier close " II ii 49
We seldom take man's life, except in w; " II ii 502
dash The torch of w among your standing corn, " II ii 749
War (continued) Eternal w, than that the Saints at peace Harold III ii 75
Free thee or slay thee, Norway will have w; " IV ii 19
save for Norway, Who loves not thee but w. " IV ii 24
My legacy of w against the Pope " V i 328
Whose life was all one battle, incarnate w, " V i 398
I led seven hundred knights and fought his w's. Becket I iii 639
You will have w; and tho' we grant " II ii 241
Like some wise prince of this world from his w's, " V ii 14
Thou hast waged God's w against the King; " V ii 46
Rome Made w upon the peoples not the Gods. The Cup I ii 60
you, Can you make w? Have you alliances? " I ii 99
submit at once Is better than a wholly-hopeless w, " I ii 141
Whereas in w's of freedom and defence " I ii 160
When I was married you were at the w's. The Falcon 376
It may be I had never seen the w's. " 379
flung His life, heart, soul into those holy w's Foresters IV 407
Heading the holy w against the Moslem, " IV 818
fighting underhand unholy w's Against your lawful king. " IV 821
War-axe Mark'd how the w-a swang, Harold IV iii 156
Warble And w those brief-sighted eyes of hers? Queen Mary III vi 155
Warblest 'O happy lark, that w high Prom. of May III 199
War-club wields His w-c, dashes it on Gurth, Harold V i 640
War-crash a w-c, and so hard, So loud, that, " IV iii 144
War-cry I do not hear our English w-c. " V i 652
Ward lest the king Should yield his w to Harold's will. " I ii 159
Warden When thou thereof wast w. Becket I iii 630
Warder The w of the bower hath given himself " III i 30
Where's the w? Geoffrey. Very bad. " IV i 49
Warehouse Like a tod of wool from wagon into w. Foresters IV 275
War-horn Heard how the w-h sang, Harold IV iii 157
Warm (adj.) know that whether A wind be w or cold, Queen Mary I v 620
That might live always in the sun's w heart, " V i 22
Philip is as w in life As ever. " V ii 24
I would we had you, Madam, in our w Spain. " V ii 607
Cold after w, winter after summer, Becket I iv 64
old faces Press round us, and w hands close with w hands, Foresters I iii 20
so she glided up into the heart O' the bottle, the w wine, " IV 245
Warm (verb) King Henry w's your traitors at his hearth. Queen Mary V i 123
To w the cold bounds of our dying life The Cup I iii 128
And let them w thy heart to Little John. Foresters III 44
Warmed He w to you to-day, and you have chilled him again. Becket II ii 374
Warmth quenched the w of France toward you, " II ii 311
Warn To w us of his coming! Foresters III 458
Warning (part.) Was w me that if a gentleman Prom. of May III 578
Warning (s) he must die, For w and example. Queen Mary IV iii 52
Kind of the witch to give thee w thro'. Becket III ii 30
The ghostly w of my martyrdom; " V ii 292
Warping You see thro' w glasses. Queen Mary I v 212
Warrant but then she goes, I w, " I v 464
and I w this fine fellow's life. " II iii 83
I w you. Cole. Take, therefore, " IV iii 58
I w you they talk about the burning. " IV iii 463
I w thee! thou wouldst hug thy Cupid Becket, Pro. 503
We'll baffle them, I w. " I i 299
I w you, or your own either. " I iv 23
So we will—so we will, I w thee. " I iv 269
Ay, and I w the customs. " III iii 331
Doth he remember me? Rosamund. I w him. " V ii 179
there I w I worm thro' all their windings. The Cup I i 86
I w you now, he said he struck the stag. " I ii 381
White? I w thee, my son, as the snow The Falcon 500
I w's ye'll think moor o' this young Squire Edgar Prom. of May I 109
I w's that ye goäs By haäfe a scoor o' naämes— " III 728
I w thee—thou canst not be sorrier Foresters I ii 281
Warring Wailing! not w? Boy, thou hast forgotten Harold II ii 473
Warrior (adj.) The w Earl of Allendale, He loved the Lady Anne; Foresters I i 6
'Farewell, farewell, my w Earl!' " I i 18
Warrior (s) And I would have my w all in arms. Queen Mary V v 34
W thou art, and mighty wise withal! Harold II ii 543
Advance our Standard of the W, " IV i 248

Warrior (s) (*continued*) yet he was a *w*, And wise, yea truthful, *Harold* v ii 154
—a *w*—ay, And but that Holy Peter fought for us, „ v ii 163
And all the puissance of the *w*, *Becket* I i 152
This young *w* broke his prison *Foresters* iv 998
Warrior-god all Our cancell'd *w-g's*, our grim Walhalla, *Harold* III ii 73
Warsong He is chanting some old *w*. „ v i 495
War-storm If this *w-s* in one of its rough rolls Wash up „ v i 165
War-woodman W-*w* of old Woden, how he fells „ v i 588
Wary I will be wise and *w*, not the soldier As Foliot swears it.— *Becket* I i 387
Brave, *w*, sane to the heart of her—a Tudor *Queen Mary* v v 225
Was *W* it so indeed? *w* it so? *w* it so? *The Falcon* 541
Wash *W* up that old crown of Northumberland. *Harold* v i 167
Till the sea *w* her level with her shores, „ v i 331
Wash'd as if her feet were *w* in blood, *Queen Mary* III i 62
With His own blood, and *w* us from our sins, „ III iii 203
w his hands and all his face therein, „ IV iii 338
our helpless folk Are *w* away, wailing, *Harold* II ii 471
the Archbishop *w* my feet o' Tuesday. *Becket* I iv 234
Washerwoman The *w's* brat! *Harold* IV iii 171
Wasp Out crept a *w*, with half the swarm behind. *Queen Mary* III iii 49
Wassail The curse of England! these are drown'd in *w*, *Harold* IV iii 224
the *w* yells of thief And rogue and liar echo down in Hell, *Foresters* III 322
Waste (adj.) *w* field With nothing but my battle-axe and him To spatter his brains! *Harold* II ii 777
And lay them both upon the *w* sea-shore At Hastings, „ v ii 159
never again Shall the *w* voice of the bond-breaking sea *Becket* v ii 358
Waste (s) thou be a wild thing Out of the *w*, *Harold* I i 381
War, *w*, plague, famine, all malignities. „ I i 466
This brother comes to save Your land from *w*; „ IV i 95
Moon on the *w* and the wold, *The Cup* I ii 4
and leave it A *w* of rock and ruin, hear. „ II 307
Waste (verb) And *w's* more life. *Queen Mary* I v 507
Thou art Tostig's brother, Who *w's* the land. *Harold* IV i 93
And *w* the land about thee as thou goest, „ v i 130
should the King of England *w* the fields Of England, „ v i 140
W not thy might before the battle! „ v i 415
if a man *W's* himself among women, *Becket, Pro.* 137
But wherefore *w* your heart In looking *Prom. of May* II 503
next time you *w* them at a pot-house you get no more from me. „ III 99
Than this, this—but I *w* no words upon him: „ III 745
how to charm and *w* the hearts of men. *Foresters* II i 502
Richard sacks and *w's* a town With random pillage, „ IV 376
Wasted (*See also* **Famine-wasted**) Your havings *w* by the scythe and spade— *Queen Mary* II ii 276
Hath *w* all the land at Pevensey— *Harold* IV iii 189
wells of Castaly are not *w* upon the desert. *Becket, Pro.* 388
Shall God's good gifts be *w*? „ I iv 71
W our diocese, outraged our tenants, „ v ii 431
I have *w* pity on her—not dead now— *Prom. of May* III 691
w his revenues in the service of our good king Richard *Foresters* I i 193
Wasteful look, how *w* of the blossom you are! *Prom. of May* I 612
Wat And he will play the Walworth to this *W*; *Queen Mary* II ii 371
Watch (verb) and *w* The parch'd banks rolling incense, *Queen Mary* I v 90
Like dogs that set to *w* their master's gate, „ III iv 309
I must not dream, not wink, but *w*. „ III v 154
w All that is gracious in the breath of heaven „ III vi 223
And *w* a good man burn. „ IV iii 293
belike he *w'es*, If this war-storm in one of its rough rolls *Harold* v i 164
And *w* Fitzurse, and if he follow thee, *Becket* I i 330
I sometimes think he sleeps When he should *w*; „ III i 34
W! he will out again, and presently, „ III ii 8
climb The mountain opposite and *w* the chase. *The Cup* I i 117
I'll *w* him from behind the trees, *Foresters* III 48
Watch (vigil) (*See also* **Death-watch**) arm'd men Ever keep *w* beside my chamber door, *Harold* II ii 245
We all keep *w*. *Foresters* IV 608
Watch (watchman) you curse so loud, The *w* will hear you. *Queen Mary* v iv 63
Watch'd So hated here! I *w* a hive of late; *Queen Mary* III iii 46
W children playing at *their* life to be, „ III iv 63
Watch'd (*continued*) I *w* you dancing once With your huge father; *Queen Mary* v ii 143
in Guernsey, I *w* a woman burn; „ v iv 18
Why am I follow'd, haunted, harass'd, *w*? *Harold* II ii 249
He *w* her pass with John of Salisbury *Becket* I ii 40
We have *w* So long in vain, he hath pass'd out again, „ III ii 11
and I *w* her and followed her into the woods, „ IV ii 16
Watchin' When ye thowt there were nawbody *w* o' you, *Prom. of May* II 180
Watching (*See also* **Watchin'**) ever see a carrion crow Stand *w* a sick beast *Queen Mary* IV iii 7
but smile As kindness, *w* all, *Harold* I i 367
I have had a weary day in *w* you. *The Cup* I ii 40
He dozes. I have left her *w* him. *Foresters* II ii 81
Water lead The living *w's* of the Faith again *Queen Mary* I v 88
Council, The Parliament as well, are troubled *w's*; And yet like *w's* „ II ii 51
Scream'd as you did for *w*. „ III v 58
And putrid *w*, every drop a worm, „ IV iii 444
Pour not *w* In the full vessel *Harold* I i 377
tho' I can drink wine I cannot bide *w*, *Becket* I iv 220
keep the figure moist and make it hold *w*, „ III iii 166
we bring a message from the King Beyond the *w*; „ v ii 303
The King beyond the *w*, thro' our voices, „ v ii 323
To your young King on this side of the *w*, „ v ii 327
has promised to keep our heads above *w*; *Prom. of May* III 170
More *w* goes by the mill than the miller wots of, *Foresters* I ii 48
In the cold *w* that she lost her voice, „ IV 243
Were plunged beneath the *w's* of the sea, „ IV 668
Waterfall You know the *w* That in the summer *The Cup* I i 107
Waterside I will go with you to the *w*. *Queen Mary* III ii 148
Wattled And *w* thick with ash and willow-wands; *Harold* v i 190
Wave or *w* And wind at their old battle: *Queen Mary* I v 356
God lay the *w's* and strow the storms „ I v 381
torn Down the strong *w* of brawlers. „ III i 186
All your voices Are *w's* on flint. „ IV i 122
shatter'd back The hugest *w* from Norseland *Harold* IV iii 62
child's sand-castle on the beach For the next *w*— *The Cup* I ii 255
heard a saying in Egypt, that ambition Is like the sea *w*, „ I iii 138
to the *w*, to the glebe, to the fire! „ II 4
In this full tide of love, *W* heralds *w*: *Foresters* IV 1044
Waver'd The Pope himself *w*; *Queen Mary* IV i 85
Waverer makes the *w* pass Into more settled hatred „ III iv 157
Wavering When faith is *w* makes the waverer pass „ III iv 157
Waxen some *w* doll Thy baby eyes have rested on, belike; „ I v 8
Who melts a *w* image by the fire, *Foresters* II i 671
Way (*See also* **Half-way, Waäy**) Skips every *w*, from levity or from fear. *Queen Mary* I iii 170
He is every *w* a lesser man than Charles; „ I v 330
Your Highness is all trembling. *Mary.* Make *w*. „ I v 595
and I fear One scruple, this or that *w*, „ II ii 100
But Janus-faces looking diverse *w's*. „ III ii 75
If any man in any *w* would be The one man, „ III iii 274
No—nor this *w* will come, Seeing their lie two *w's* „ III iv 111
Thou's thy *w* wi' man and beast, Tib. „ IV iii 498
bound and babble all the *w* As if itself were happy, „ v v 86
is not this the *w*? No, that *w* there are voices. „ v v 206
God guide me lest I lose the *w*. „ v v 210
That he should harp this *w* on Normandy? *Harold* I i 270
I see the goal and half the *w* to it.— „ I ii 196
Smooth thou my *w*, before he clash with me; „ II ii 69
I'll tell them I have had my *w* with thee. „ II ii 119
Which *w* soever the vane-arrow swing, „ II ii 257
I'll hack my *w* to the sea. „ II ii 312
And, brother, we will find a *w*,' said he— „ II ii 367
but thou must not this *w* answer *him*. „ II ii 371
Lost, lost, we have lost the *w*. „ III ii 15
Who is it comes this *w*? Tostig? „ IV ii 1
the counter *w*—Cowl, helm; and crozier, „ v i 443
until I find Which *w* the battle balance. „ v i 461
That was not the *w* I ended it first— *Becket, Pro.* 335
Thou canst not fall that *w*. „ I i 115
Take it not that *w*—balk not the Pope's will. „ I iii 242
spied my people's *w's*; „ I iii 364

Way (*continued*) like a fool, thou knowest no middle *w*. *Becket* I iii 533
I ask'd the *w*. *Rosamund*. I think so. „ II i 62
the goodly *w* of women Who love, „ II i 256
daughter of Zion lies beside the *w*— „ III iii 178
Well, well, then—have thy *w*! „ III iii 215
If God would take him in some sudden *w*— „ V i 94
That *w*, or this! Save thyself either *w*. *Becket*. Oh,
no, not either *w*, nor any *w* Save by that *w* „ V iii 84
Slowly but surely—till I see my *w*. *The Cup* I i 211
Thou—coming my *w* too—Camma—good-night.
Camma. Thy *w*? poor worm, crawl down thine
own black hole „ II 492
No, not that *w*—here, under the apple tree. *Prom. of May* I 82
yet that might be The best *w* out of it, „ I 476
Is there no other *w*? „ I 691
the rain beating in my face all the *w*, „ III 368
I was dreaming of it all the *w* hither. *Foresters* I i 139
Dream of it, then, all the *w* back, „ I i 140
Glide like a light across these woodland *w's*! „ II i 160
Did we not hear the two would pass this *w*? „ II i 198
only they that be bred in it can find their *w* a-nights in it. „ II i 265
forest lawns are all as bright As *w's* to heaven, „ II i 632
Have ye glanced down thro' all the forest *w's* „ IV 111
So now which *w* to the dinner? „ IV 972
Wayside Yes, at the *w* inn Close by that alder-island
in your brook, *Prom. of May* II 534
Weak But a *w* mouth, an indeterminate—ha?
Bonner. Well, a *w* mouth, perchance. *Queen Mary* III iv 340
what is *w* must lie; „ III v 121
other things As idle; a *w* Wyatt! „ V i 292
Send out; I am too *w* to stir abroad: „ V ii 286
Ah, *w* and meek old man, „ V v 131
W natures that impute Themselves to their unlikes, *Foresters* II i 690
Weaken'd whether that which held it Had *w*, *Harold* V i 106
let not my strong prayer Be *w* in thy sight, „ V i 648
Weaker You would but make us *w*, Thomas Stafford. *Queen Mary* III i 130
so much *w*, so much worse For last day's journey. *The Falcon* 832
where the man and the woman, only differing as
the stronger and the *w*, *Prom. of May* III 191
Weakness was it boldness Or *w* that won there? *Queen Mary* I v 560
The *w* and the dissonance of our clans, *The Cup* I i 23
Weal foes in Edward's hall To league against thy *w*. *Harold* I ii 33
You scheme against her father's *w* and hers, *Foresters* IV 481
Wealth (*See also* **World-wealth**) He wrecks his health
and *w* on courtesans, *Queen Mary* I v 167
Which in his absence had been all my *w*. „ I v 362
But for the *w* and glory of our realm, „ II ii 210
his *w* A fountain of perennial alms— „ II ii 384
to those that own exceeding *w*, „ IV iii 201
The wine and *w* of all our France are yours; *Becket* II ii 446
Foam over all the fleeted *w* of kings *The Cup* II 289
Than all my childless *w*, if mine must die. *The Falcon* 855
I have land now And *w*, and lay both at your feet. *Prom. of May* III 616
not with all your *w*, Your land, your life! „ III 795
As *W* walk'd in at the door. 'You have come for you
saw *W* coming,' *Foresters* I i 151
W dropt out of the window, „ I i 156
'Well now you would fain follow *W*,' „ I i 158
What a *w* of words—O Lord, I will live „ I ii 36
Wealthy all the magistracy, all the nobles, and all
the *w*; *Queen Mary* V iv 51
Wean I put the bitters on my breast to *w* him, *The Falcon* 190
Wean'd She hath *w* me from it with such bitterness. *Harold* IV ii 27
Weänt (will not) Well, it be i' *my* natur to knock 'im
o' the 'eäd now; but I *w*. *Prom. of May* I 289
but I promised one of the Misses I wouldn't meddle
wi' ye, and I *w*. „ I 470
an' *w* ye taäke 'em now, Miss Dora, „ II 40
But I *w* be too sudden wi' it; „ II 58
W ye gi'e me a kind answer at last? „ II 63
but that be all along o' you, Miss, because ye *w* hev me; „ II 110
and she *w* sa much as look at 'im? „ II 161
I *w* goä to owd Dobson; „ II 218
then, by-and-by, if she *w* listen to me when I be
a-tryin' to saäve 'er—if she *w*— „ II 693

Weänt (will not) (*continued*) An' we *w* mention
naw naämes, *Prom. of May* III 129
Weapon What *w* hath the child, save his soft tongue, *Queen Mary* III v 128
I had wish'd for any *w*. *Harold* IV iii 19
Wear (*See also* **Weär**) I *w* it then to spite her. *Queen Mary* I iv 78
I *w* beneath my dress A shirt of mail: „ I v 144
Ev'n that young girl who dared to *w* your crown? „ I v 491
w it as memorial of a morning Which found me „ I v 529
I *w* Upon this finger), ye did promise full Allegiance „ II ii 167
wilt thou *w* thy cap before the Queen? „ III i 236
And *w* my crown, and dance upon my grave. „ V ii 601
I dare not *w* it. *Harold* III ii 187
The ring thou darest not *w*, „ V i 421
Take it and *w* it on that hard heart of yours *Becket, Pro.* 373
The Mitre! *Salisbury*. Will you *w* it?— „ V ii 617
She will be glad at last to *w* my crown. *The Cup* I iii 168
and *w* it Beside him on his throne. „ II 136
The diamonds that you never deign'd to *w*. *The Falcon* 762
I *w* it next my heart. *Prom. of May* II 81
Will you have it? Will you *w* it? *Foresters* I ii 302
And take and *w* this symbol of your love; „ III 79
Weär and I thinks ye *w's* a Lunnon boot. *Prom. of May* I 461
Wearest Why *w* thou thy cowl to hide thy face? *Foresters* I ii 206
Wearied I am an old man *w* with my journey, *Queen Mary* III ii 127
King hath *w* of his barren bride.' „ III vi 140
Thou art *w* out With this day's work, *Becket* I i 6
Our Senate, *w* of their tetrarchies, *The Cup* I i 89
Wearier Yours must have been a *w*. „ I ii 41
Wearing So royal that the Queen forbad you *w* it. *Queen Mary* I iv 77
Weary So *w* am I of this wet land of theirs, „ III vi 105
I am *w*—go; make me not wroth with thee! *Harold* V i 31
I have had a *w* day in watching you. *The Cup* I ii 40
O Love and Life, how *w* am I, *Prom. of May* III 205
but, my flower, You look so *w* and worn! „ III 499
But I am *w* pacing thro' the wood. *Foresters* II i 129
I am *w*. What's here? „ II ii 92
W—*w* As tho' a spell were on me. „ II ii 114
Weasel stick to tha like a *w* to a rabbit, I will. *Prom. of May* II 739
Weasel-sucked or the shambles-oak, or a *w-s* egg, *Foresters* IV 212
Weather Two young lovers in winter *w*, *Harold* III ii 3
you couldn't have more splendid *w*. *Prom. of May* II 48
The *w's* well anew, but the glass be a bit shaäky. „ II 51
the winders brokken, and the *w* sa cowd, „ III 73
Weather'd Many points *w*, many perilous ones, *Queen Mary* V v 211
Weave *w* the web That may confound thee yet. *Harold* I i 211
Weaver the psalm-singing *w's*, cobblers, scum— *Queen Mary* III iv 290
Web weave the *w* That may confound thee yet. *Harold* I i 211
Crost and recrost, a venomous spider's *w*— *Becket* II i 200
Wed 'Thou shalt not *w* thy brother's wife.' *Queen Mary* I ii 63
Prince of Spain coming to *w* our Queen! „ I iii 83
that after all She means to *w* you. „ I iv 89
great party in the state Wills me to *w* her. „ I iv 93
as great a party in the state Will you to *w* me? „ I iv 96
—for to *w* with Spain Would treble England— „ I v 75
No new news that Philip comes to *w* Mary, „ II i 16
Philip shall not *w* Mary; „ II i 164
They would not have me *w* the Prince of Spain; „ II ii 148
that the son Being a King, might *w* a Queen— „ III i 75
'It is the King's wish, that you should *w* Prince
Philibert of Savoy. „ III v 222
when I came to *w* your majesty, Lord Howard, „ V i 56
as you know, We meant to *w* her; „ V i 248
Why then, thou must not *w* him. *Harold* III i 265
They say thou art to *w* the Lady Aldwyth. „ III ii 107
The sovereign of Galatia *w's* his Queen. *The Cup* II 432
if a gentleman Should *w* a farmer's daughter, *Prom. of May* III 579
And these shall *w* with freemen, *Foresters* II i 21
Rather than that would *w* her with the Sheriff. „ II i 524
In that great heat to *w* her to the Sheriff „ II i 584
till thou *w* what man thou wilt. „ II ii 15
'This boy will never *w* the maid he loves, „ II ii 111
You shall *w* your Marian. She is true, and you are
true, „ II ii 193
Then you will *w* the Sheriff? „ III 11
For so this maid would *w* our brother, „ IV 483

Wed (*continued*) He shall *w* thee : The land shall still be mine. Child, thou shalt *w* him, Or thine old father will go mad— *Foresters* IV 642
But thou wilt *w* him? „ IV 663
Wedded Were I in Devon with my *w* bride, *Queen Mary* I iv 119
when I was *w* to the realm And the realm's laws „ II ii 164
I would she could have *w* that poor youth, „ V ii 475
God bless thee, *w* daughter. *Harold* III i 293
I am seeking one who *w* me in secret. „ V ii 29
How dost thou know I am not *w* to her? *Becket, Pro.* 73
Madam, you do ill to scorn *w* love. „ *Pro.* 354
W? *Rosamund.* Father! „ I i 318
I that *w* Henry, Honouring his manhood— „ IV ii 419
I be wife to one That only *w* me for Aquitaine? „ V i 121
Dost thou remember when I *w* Sinnatus? *The Cup* II 194
Wedding wines Of *w* had been dash'd into the cups Of victory, *Harold* IV iii 7
You are an honest pair. I will come to your *w*. *Prom. of May* III 115
Wedding-daäy (day) niver touched a drop of owt till my oän *w-d*, „ I 362
Wedlock I am not so set on *w* as to choose *Queen Mary* II ii 214
Weed (*See also* **Shore-weed**) But on the heretic dunghill only *w's*. „ IV i 180
Such *w's* make dunghills gracious. „ IV i 181
plow Lay rusting in the furrow's yellow *w's*, *Becket* I iii 355
like a barren shore That grew salt *w's*, *The Cup* II 232
Such rampant *w's* Strangle each other, *Prom. of May* III 590
Week Sick for an idle *w* of hawk and hound *Harold* I i 103
Nay, rest a *w* or two, „ II ii 179
I ha' been but a *w* here and I ha' seen *Becket* III i 108
What day of the *w*? Tuesday? „ V ii 281
Only last *w* at Littlechester, drove me *Prom. of May* II 404
That John last *w* return'd to Nottingham, *Foresters* III 147
Why then a *w*. *Justiciary.* No, not an hour: „ IV 446
Weep *W* not, good Thirlby. *Queen Mary* IV ii 172
Who would not *w*? „ IV ii 175
Behold him, brethren: he hath cause to *w*!—So have we all: *w* with him if ye will, Yet—— „ IV iii 14
They can but *w* in silence. „ IV iii 361
I could *w* for them And her, and mine own self „ V ii 11
And *w's* herself into the place of power; *Becket* V ii 214
Weeping she is *w* now; For the wrong Robin took her *Queen Mary* III v 262
My girl, thou hast been *w*: *Harold* III ii 38
I was *w* for him; He gave me his hand: *The Falcon* 834
How gracefully there she stands *W*— *Prom. of May* I 736
Since I left her Here *w*, I have ranged the world, „ II 252
She gave a *w* kiss to the Earl, (repeat) *Foresters* I i 20, 119
Weigh the cause that *w's* Upon my conscience *Queen Mary* IV iii 237
Which *w's* even on me. *Becket* III i 42
Weight (s) Will shift the yoke and *w* of all the world *Queen Mary* III vi 212
lighten'd for me The *w* of this poor crown, *Harold* I i 218
Charged with the *w* of heaven wherefrom they fall! „ V i 567
dead man's dying wish should be of *w*. *Becket, Pro.* 423
till the *w* of Germany or the gold of England brings one of them down to the dust— „ II ii 363
I reel beneath the *w* of utter joy— *The Cup* II 450
but that I am a man of *w*, and the *w* of the church to boot *Foresters* I ii 57
doth not the *w* of the flesh at odd times overbalance the *w* of the church, „ I ii 60
Thou art worth thy *w* in all those marks of gold, Yea, and the *w* of the very land „ IV 1023
Weight (verb) And *w* down all free choice beneath the throne. *Becket* I iii 118
Weightier Is *w* than a thousand marks in gold. *Foresters* IV 660
Weird if yon *w* sign Not blast us in our dreams.— *Harold* I i 120
Welcome (adj.) Thou art ever *w*, Simon Renard. *Queen Mary* I v 345
To whom the fire were *w*, „ IV iii 438
but all on 'em *w*, all on 'em *w*; *Prom of May* I 450
You are *w*, though I fear you be of those *Foresters* I ii 197
Let me be, I say! The Sheriff will be *w*! „ IV 602
Welcome (inter.) *W* to England! *Queen Mary* V iii 13
W to this poor cottage, my dear lady. *The Falcon* 270
Welcome (s) And *w* turns a cottage to a palace. *The Falcon* 272
Will bid you *w*, and will listen to you. *Prom. of May* II 522
Welcome (s) (*continued*) and there's for you—and the old woman's *w*. *Foresters* II i 290
Welcome (verb) let us *w* him, Love that can lift up *Becket* II i 13
My masters, *w* gallant Walter Lea. *Foresters* IV 1002
Weld he would *w* France, England, Scotland, *Queen Mary* V i 136
Welfare Believe it will be better for your *w*. „ I iv 254
be curious About the *w* of their babes, *The Cup* I ii 362
Well (adj. and adv.) God send her *w*; Here comes her Royal Grace. *Queen Mary* II ii 125
Now what I am ye know right *w*—your Queen; „ II ii 162
But all is *w*; 'twas ev'n the will of God, „ III ii 77
Can we not have the Catholic church as *w* Without as with the Italian? „ III iii 98
Philip, can that be *w*? „ V i 143
Thou knowest never woman meant so *w*, „ V ii 343
I trust your Grace is *w*. „ V ii 551
I am not *w*, but it will better me, „ V ii 553
All is *w* then; rest—I will to rest; he said, I must have rest. „ V v 185
a Boleyn, too, Glancing across the Tudor—not so *w*. „ V v 228
And it is *w* with me, tho' some of you Have scorn'd me— *Harold* I i 187
w, *w*—a dream—no more! „ I ii 92
Ay—*w*—of old. I tell thee what, my child; „ I ii 96
And it were *w*, if thou shouldst let him feel, „ II ii 15
And *w* for thee and England—and for her— „ III ii 111
Tho' we have pierced thro' all her practices; And that is *w*. „ V i 157
That is *w*. The Norman, What is he doing? „ V i 217
W? *Fitzurse.* Nay, let me pass, my lord, for I must know. *Becket* I i 204
an' it 'ud be *w* for me in the end, „ III i 134
W—*w*—away. „ III ii 54
I mean to marry him—if that be *w*. *The Cup* II 62
Great Artemis! O Camma, can it be *w*, „ II 81
'Get the Count to give me his falcon, And that will make me *w*.' *The Falcon* 243
when he came last year To see me hawking, he was *w* enough: „ 313
It might have been as *w* for me. „ 386
Here, or else *w* in Heaven, where all is *w*. „ 682
He gave me his hand: 'I should be *w* again If the good Count would give me——' „ 836
As *w* as ever. I came back to keep his birthday. *Prom. of May* I 73
The weather's *w* anew, but the glass be a bit shaäky. „ II 51
Eh, but I be *w* to do; „ II 72
Courage, courage! and all will go *w*. „ III 215
Crown thee with flowers; and he will soon be *w*: All will be *w*. *Foresters* II ii 20
Then all is *w*. In this full tide of love, Wave heralds wave: „ IV 1042
Strike up a stave, my masters, all is *w*. „ IV 1102
Well (s) The *w's* of Castaly are not wasted upon the desert. *Becket, Pro.* 387
this bitter world again—These *w's* of Marah. „ V ii 82
We are almost at the bottom of the *w*: *Prom. of May* III 161
She lay so long at the bottom of her *w* *Foresters* IV 242
Well-beloved God bless our *w-b* Robin, Earl of Huntingdon. „ I i 248
Wells Deans Of Christchurch, Durham, Exeter, and *W*— *Queen Mary* I ii 10
Well-served I am *w-s*, and am in everything „ V iii 24
Well-shaped I am as *w-s* as my lady here, *Becket* III i 150
Well to do but I be *w t d*; and if ye would nobbut hev me, *Prom. of May* II 72
Welsh had I been his, I had been all *W*. *Aldwyth.* Oh, ay—all *W*—and yet I saw thee drive him up his hills— *Harold* IV i 209
Welshman Your *W* says, 'The Truth against the World,' „ II ii 397
Wench But the *w* Hath her own troubles; *Queen Mary* III v 261
Then there isn't a goodly *w* to serve him with it: *Becket* I iv 159
gave me a great pat o' the cheek for a pretty *w*, „ III i 126
Went My mother said, Go up; and up I *w*. *Queen Mary* I iii 99
who *w* with your train bands To fight with Wyatt, „ II ii 26
gray rogue, Gardiner, *W* on his knees, „ III v 166
all boots were ever made Since man *w* barefoot. „ III v 198
These meteors came and *w* before our day, *Harold* I i 131
wouldst thou that it *w* aught else than well? „ I i 334

Went (*continued*) I would it *w* as well as with mine earldom, *Harold* I i 336
An evil dream that ever came and *w*— „ I ii 70
thine host in England when I *w* To visit Edward. „ II ii 5
Your comet came and *w*. „ III i 359
w abroad Thro' all my counties, *Becket* I iii 362
due to those That *w* before us for their work, „ II ii 192
those Who *w* before us did not wholly clear „ II ii 202
lost her and *w* on and on till I found the light and the lady, „ IV ii 18
besides the wind *W* with *my* arrow. *The Cup* I ii 32
It be five year sin' ye *w* afoor to him, *Prom. of May* II 5
I sank so low that I *w* into service— „ III 391
an' one on 'em *w* an' lost hersen i' the river. „ III 456
As happy as any of those that *w* before. *Foresters* I ii 129
Wept then all *w* but she, Who changed not colour *Queen Mary* III i 397
That heaven *w* and earth blush'd. „ III iv 193
under no ceiling but the cloud that *w* on them, „ V iv 40
Wessex (adj.) Our *W* dragon flies beyond the Humber, *Harold* IV i 3
Wessex (s) (kingdom of the West Saxons) Harold, Earl of *W*! „ II i 82
Art thou not Earl of *W*? „ II i 85
Were such murderous liars In *W*— „ II i 95
West (adj.) we fun' 'im out a-walkin' i' *W* Field wi' a white 'at, *Prom. of May* III 135
Yet Thou art but a *W* Saxon: *we* are Danes! *Harold* IV i 53
West (s) (*See also* **South-west**) Tho' charged with all the wet of all the *w*. „ II ii 189
who know His prowess in the mountains of the *W*, „ IV i 165
To leave the Pope dominion in the *W*. He gave him all the kingdoms of the *W*. „ V i 23
Whose doings are a horror to the east, A hissing in the *w*!' *Becket* IV ii 245
marvell'd at Our unfamiliar beauties of the *w*; „ IV ii 303
In our poor *w* We cannot do it so well. „ IV ii 316
Westminster (abbey and city) Where is the charter of our *W*? *Harold* III i 194
Seeing he must to *W* and crown Young Henry *Becket* III ii 9
Westminster (Bishop) Bishops—York, London, Chichester, *W*— „ I iii 386
West Saxon Thou art but a *W S*: *we* are Danes! *Harold* IV i 53
Wet (adj.) it would seem this people Care more for our brief life in their *w* land, *Queen Mary* III vi 62
So weary am I of this *w* land of theirs, „ III vi 105
Will my faggots Be *w* as his were? „ IV ii 229
Wet (s) Eh, the wind and the *w*! „ IV iii 467
barrin' the *w*, Hodge 'ud ha' been a-harrowin' „ IV iii 491
W, famine, ague, fever, storm, wreck, wrath,— „ V v 108
Tho' charged with all the *w* of all the west. *Harold* II ii 188
Whale Rolf, what fish did swallow Jonah? *Rolf.* A *w*! *Fisherman.* Then a *w* to a whelk we have swallowed the King of England. „ II i 43
Wharf swirling under me in the lamplight, by the rotten *w's*— *Prom. of May* III 371
Wharton (Lady Anne) *See* **Anne, Anne Wharton**
Wheat garner the *w*, And burn the tares *Queen Mary* V v 113
Wheedle I could not force or *w* to my will. *The Cup* I iii 167
Wheedled Has *w* it off the King's neck to her own. *Becket* IV ii 201
Wheedling It was a *w* monk Set up the mass. *Queen Mary* I ii 90
Wheel(s) The *w* of Fate has roll'd me to the top. *The Cup* II 221
There was a song he made to the turning *w*— *Foresters* I iii 154
Wheel (verb) and howsoe'er Thy quarry wind and *w*, *The Falcon* 12
Whelk whale to a *w* we have swallowed the King of England. *Harold* II i 44
Whelmest corpse thou *w* with thine earth is cursed, „ V i 67
When When did I hear aught but this '*W*' from thee? „ I i 284
Whew He swears by the Rood. *W*! *Queen Mary* I i 63
Whine never *w* Like that poor heart, Northumberland, „ II ii 332
Whined The man had children, and he *w* for those. „ II ii 336
Whinnied colt winced and *w* and flung up her heels; *Becket, Pro.* 515
Whipping doth not the living skin thicken against perpetual *w's*? „ III iii 317
Whipt for doing that His father *w* him into doing— *Queen Mary* I v 63
I hope they *w* him. I would have hang'd him. *Becket, Pro.* 15
I am like a boy now going to be *w*; *Foresters* II ii 50
Whirl in the *w* of change may come to be one. *Queen Mary* I iii 106
Whirring What is that *w* sound? (repeat) *Harold* V i 482, 665
Whisking And *w* round a corner, show'd his back *Queen Mary* II i 131
Whisper (s) voice Against them is a *w* to the roar „ IV ii 187
The secret *w* of the Holy Father. *Becket* I iii 236
Indungeon'd from one *w* of the wind, „ IV ii 146
Thro' all closed doors a dreadful *w* crept „ V ii 88
Whisper (verb) *W*! God's angels only know it. Ha! *Harold* V ii 31
You never *w* close as lovers do, *Foresters* III 5
Will *w* evermore of Robin Hood. „ IV 1069
Whisper'd *W* me, if I loved him, not to yield *Queen Mary* I ii 35
w, 'Wyatt,' And whisking round a corner, „ II i 129
Rose hand in hand, and *w*, 'come away! „ III v 148
I *w*, Let me crown you Queen of Beauty, *The Falcon* 360
Whispering *W*—leagued together To bar me *Queen Mary* I iv 139
Lord Devon, girls! what are you *w* here? „ V ii 485
year to come *W* 'it will be happier,' *Foresters* I iii 18
Whistle La, to *w* out my life, *Queen Mary* II iv 109
I *w* to the bird has broken cage, And all in vain. „ V v 19
Arrows *w* all about. *Foresters* II ii 165
White (*See also* **Maiden-white**) for thou art as *w* as three Christmasses. *Queen Mary* I i 30
because they know him The last *W* Rose, the last Plantagenet „ I iv 207
All red and *w*, the fashion of our land. „ I v 10
but took To the English red and *w*. „ I v 18
another, mute as death, And *w* as her own milk; „ II ii 80
there is ordnance On the *W* Tower and on the Devil's Tower, „ II iii 44
or you'll make the *W* Tower a black 'un for us this blessed day. „ II iii 100
w satin his trunkhose, Inwrought with silver,— „ III i 76
Bagenhall, I see The Tudor green and *w*. „ III i 180
Mary rubb'd out pale—She could not make it *w*— „ III i 424
and your flocks of swans, As fair and *w* as angels; „ III ii 16
So after that when she once more is seen *W* as the light, „ III iv 199
The colours of our Queen are green and *w*, „ III v 6
Hodge 'ud ha' been a-harrowin' o' *w* peasen i' the outfield „ IV iii 492
Charged him to do it—he is *w* as death. „ IV iii 558
and all in *w*, His long *w* beard, which he had never shaven „ IV iii 591
Choose therefore whether thou wilt have thy conscience *W* as a maiden's hand, *Harold* II ii 284
My lord! thou art *w* as death. „ II ii 813
Am I so *w*? Thy Duke will seem the darker. Hence, I follow. „ II ii 816
They love the *w* rose of virginity, The cold, *w* lily blowing in her cell: „ III i 273
For England, for thy poor *w* dove, who flutters Between thee and the porch, „ IV i 230
In cold, *w* cells beneath an icy moon— „ V i 325
A doter on *w* pheasant-flesh at feasts, *Becket, Pro.* 97
Is black and *w* at once, and comes to nought. „ I iii 32
We can make a black sin *w*. „ I iv 169
That he made the black sheep *w*. „ I iv 176
w In the sweet moon as with a lovelier snow! *The Cup* I ii 395
See, see, my *w* bird stepping toward the snare. „ I iii 35
No matter! see your cloth be *w* as snow! *The Falcon* 498
W? I warrant thee, my son, as the snow yonder on the very tip-top o' the mountain. „ 500
And yet to speak *w* truth, my good old mother, „ 503
The hen cluckt late by the *w* farm gate, *Prom. of May* I 38
Why, now, what maäkes tha sa *w*? „ I 417
Wi' the wild *w* rose, an' the woodbine sa gaäy, „ II 174
And the *w* cloud is roll'd along the sky! *Foresters* I ii 319
I found this *w* doe wandering thro' the wood, „ II i 95
Ghost! did one in *w* pass? „ II i 228
thy father will not grace our feast With his *w* beard to-day. „ IV 81
White (Sir Thomas) *See* **Thomas White**
White Rose The last *W R*, the last Plantagenet *Queen Mary* I iv 207
Whitethorn There's *w*, girl. „ III v 9
Whitewash you could *w* that cottage of yours *Prom. of May* III 43
Whizzing Will hear our arrows *w* overhead, *Foresters* IV 1090
Whoä (stop) Gee oop! *w*! Gee oop! *w*! (repeat) *Prom. of May* II 307, 317

Wife (*continued*) they put it upon me because I have a bad *w*. *Foresters* III 438
then each man That owns a *w* or daughter, „ III 460
dishonour The daughters and the *wives* of your own faction— „ IV 698
Wife-like So *w-l* humble to the trivial boy Mismatch'd with her for policy! *Queen Mary* III i 364
Wife-widow Left Mary a *w-w* here alone, „ III i 462
Wild and will pounce like a *w* beast out of his cage to worry Cranmer. „ I i 88
You are *w*; what headache? „ I iv 147
like the *w* hedge-rose Of a soft winter, possible, „ III vi 14
Catch the *w* cat, cage him, and when he springs „ V v 65
letting the *w* brook Speak for us— „ V v 90
Thou knowest I soon go *w*. *Harold* I i 297
Come, come! as yet thou art not gone so *w* „ I i 299
Nor thou be a *w* thing Out of the waste, „ I i 380
Our *w* Tostig, Edward hath made him Earl: he would be king:— „ I ii 185
W as he, born so: „ IV i 110
The nimble, *w*, red, wiry, savage king— „ IV i 197
Save for thy *w* and violent will that wrench'd All hearts „ V i 277
I lost it, playing with it when I was *w*. „ V ii 110
a widow And orphan child, whom one of thy *w* barons— *Becket, Pro.* 188
Thomas, thou wast not happy taking charge Of this *w* Rosamund to please the King, „ I i 392
This *w* one—nay, I shall not prick myself— „ II i 143
And I could tear him asunder with *w* horses Before he would betray it. „ II i 267
Like the *w* beast—if you can call it love. „ IV ii 121
Nay, for who could trace a hand So *w* and staggering? *The Falcon* 439
Wi' the *w* white rose, an' the woodbine sa gaäy, *Prom. of May* II 174
if you Had seen us that *w* morning when we found Her bed unslept in, „ II 469
That were a *w* justice indeed. „ III 156
Knave, there is a lot of *w* fellows in Sherwood Forest *Foresters* I ii 72
They hold by Richard—the *w* wood! „ I iii 111
the highback'd polecat, the *w* boar, The burrowing badger—By St. Nicholas I have a sudden passion for the *w* wood—We shall be free as air in the *w* wood— „ I iii 120
I have reign'd one year in the *w* wood. „ II i 36
Tut! tut! the scream of some *w* woodland thing. „ II i 253
Here's a pot o' *w* honey from an old oak, „ II i 295
might Betray me to the *w* Prince. „ II i 708
loud enough To fright the *w* hawk passing overhead, „ III 318
Venison, and *w* boar, hare, geese, besides Hedge-pigs, „ IV 191
and they are delivered here in the *w* wood an hour after noon. „ IV 509
Were some strong fellow here in the *w* wood, „ IV 515
When the Church and the law have forgotten God's music, they shall dance to the music of the *w* wood. „ IV 556
Then will I live for ever in the *w* wood. „ IV 879
We dealt in the *w* justice of the woods. „ IV 1072
Wild-beast The mere *w-b*! *Dobson.* Out o' the chaumber, *Prom. of May* III 736
Wilderness Lost in a *w* where none can hear! *Queen Mary* V ii 382
pray for him who hath fed you in the *w*. *Becket* I iv 267
Wildest The *w* of the random youth of Florence *The Falcon* 808
Wild-flower My bank Of *w-f's*. At thy feet! *Becket* II i 126
Wild-fowl we came upon A *w-f* sitting on her nest, „ V ii 234
Wilful One of those wicked *w's* that men make, *Queen Mary* III v 75
W, *w*. Go—the Saints Pilot *Harold* I i 263
Wilfulness was no wicked *w*, Only a natural chance. *Queen Mary* III v 72
Will (s) (*See also* **Free-will**) putting by his father's *w*. „ I ii 28
Few things have fail'd to which I set my *w*. „ II ii 23
and so learn Your royal *w*, and do it.— „ II ii 139
seeks To bend the laws to his own *w*, „ II ii 184
Our sovereign Lady by King Harry's *w*; „ II ii 268
But all is well; 'twas ev'n the *w* of God, „ III ii 77
Your father had a *w* that beat men down; „ IV i 108
It is God's *w*, the Holy Father's *w*, And Philip's *w*, „ IV i 184
Stand there and wait my *w*. *Harold* II ii 683
Help us against the Norman? *Morcar.* With good *w*; „ IV i 182

Will (s) (*continued*) Take it not that way—balk not the Pope's *w*. *Becket* I iii 243
Is it thy *w*, My lord Archbishop, „ I iii 271
it is the *w* of God To break me, „ I iii 290
'False to myself! It is the *w* of God!' *Henry.* God's *w* be what it will, „ I iii 328
The King's *w* and God's *w* and justice; „ I iii 420
The *w* of God—why, then it is my *w*— „ I iii 473
tongue lick him whole again To serve your *w*? *Henry.* He hates my *w*, not me. „ II ii 26
since he flouts the *w* of either realm, „ II ii 256
My liege, your *w* and happiness are mine. „ III iii 42
God's *w* be done! (repeat) „ V ii 565, 567
It is God's *w*. Go on. „ V ii 634
Why do you force me thus against my *w*? „ V iii 22
I could not force or wheedle to my *w*. *The Cup* I iii 167
would oust me from his *w*, if I Made such a marriage. *Prom. of May* I 513
There is a fence I cannot overleap, My father's *w*. *Foresters* III 10
For thou hast stolen my *w*, and made it thine. „ III 329
Will (verb) Or—if the Lord God *w* it—on the stake. *Queen Mary* II i 251
and use Both us and them according as they *w*. „ II ii 161
As you *w*. *Fitzurse.* Nay, as *you w*. *Becket.* Nay, as *you w*. *Becket* V ii 306
I *w*, I *w*. And I *w* not betray you. *The Cup* I ii 315
I *w*, I *w*. Poor fellow! *The Falcon* 281
Will'd Get thou into thy cloister as the king *W* it: *Harold* V i 310
were he living And grown to man and Sinnatus *w* it, *The Cup* I ii 151
Willer (willow) Wi' the briar sa green, an' the *w* sa graäy, *Prom. of May* II 186
William (Lord William Howard) (*See also* **Howard, William Howard**) News abroad, *W*? *Queen Mary* II i 13
brave Lord *W* Thrust him from Ludgate, „ II iv 91
William (the Conqueror) (*See also* **William the First**) Fly thou to *W*; tell him we have Harold. *Harold* II i 110
W laugh'd and swore that might was right, „ II ii 361
That had anger'd *me* Had I been *W*. „ II ii 387
may he not make A league with *W*, „ II ii 461
I will not hear thee—*W* comes. „ II ii 480
W the tanner's bastard! „ II ii 775
'If ye side with *W* Ye are not noble.' „ II ii 788
when I rode with *W* down to Harfleur, „ III i 82
one should be This *W's* fellow-tricksters;— „ III ii 77
Against St. Valery And *W*. „ III ii 137
but worse news: this *W* sent to Rome, „ III ii 141
Keep that for Norman *W*! *Thane.* Down with *W*! „ IV iii 169
W the Norman, for the wind had changed— „ IV iii 181
W hath landed, ha? „ IV iii 185
play The *W* with thine eyesight and thy tongue. „ V i 27
—thou art but a messenger of *W*. „ V i 30
W's or his own As wind blows, or tide flows: „ V i 162
hath borne at times A bastard false as *W*. „ V i 176
A lake that dips in *W* As well as Harold. „ V i 186
a mightier man-in-arms Than *W*. „ V i 400
Save *W's* death or mine. „ V i 427
William (the First) (*See also* **William the Conqueror**) In *W's* time, in our first Edward's time, *Queen Mary* III iii 226
There was no Canterbury in *W's* time. *Becket* III iii 200
William Howard (Lord, Lord High Admiral) (*See also* **Howard, William**) I leave Lord *W H* in your city, *Queen Mary* II ii 245
I saw Lord *W H* By torchlight, „ II iii 28
Is not Lord *W H* a true man? „ III i 165
Spite of Lord Paget and Lord *W H*, „ III i 324
my Lord Paget and Lord *W H*, Crave, „ IV i 6
No, here's Lord *W H*. „ IV iii 288
William of Orange *W o O*, William the Silent. „ III i 197
Williams (Lord, of Thame) Whereat Lord *W* gave a sudden cry:— „ IV iii 604
William the Silent (William of Orange) William of Orange, *W t S*. „ III i 198
W t S They call him— „ III ii 191
Willing he will be *w* that you and Father should live with us; *Prom. of May* III 260

Willing (*continued*) there might be *w* wives enough To feel dishonour, honour. *The Cup* I ii 187
Willingly Full *w*, my lord. *Foresters* I ii 134
Willingness With most exceeding *w*, I will; *Queen Mary* III v 214
Will not *See* **Weänt, Wunt**
Willow (*See also* **Willer**) This is the hottest of it: hold, ash! hold, *w*! *Harold* V i 629
saw the ball you lost in the fork of the great *w* *Becket* IV ii 58
you told me a great fib: it wasn't in the *w*. „ IV ii 371
Willow-herb Forget-me-not, meadowsweet, *w-h*. *Prom. of May* II 299
Willow-wands And wattled thick with ash and *w-w*; *Harold* V i 190
Wills-o'-the-wisp (*See also* **Wisp**) oafs, ghosts o' the mist, *w-o'-t-w*; *Foresters* II i 264
Willy-nilly if man be only A *w-n* current of sensations— *Prom. of May* II 263
And someone saw thy *w-n* nun Vying a tress *Harold* V i 148
This other, *w-n*, for his bride. *Foresters* IV 768
Wilson (a schoolmaster) Well, *W*. I seed that one cow o' thine *Prom. of May* I 190
summat wrong theer, *W*, fur I doänt understan' it. „ I 234
Why, *W*, tha 'eärd 'im thysen— „ I 301
—what's the newspaäper word, *W*?—celebrate— „ I 320
Win I'm the first of players. I shall *w*. *Queen Mary* I iii 149
As if to *w* the man by flattering him. „ II ii 312
W thro' this day with honour to yourself, „ IV ii 165
And, if I *w*, I *w*, and thou art king; *Harold* V i 125
To tell thee thou shouldst *w* at Stamford-bridge, „ V i 236
and to *w* my own bread, *Becket* III i 117
A policy of wise pardon *W's* here as well as there. „ V ii 24
—if I *w* her love, They too will cleave to me, *The Cup* I iii 153
his falcon Ev'n *w's* his dinner for him in the field. *The Falcon* 231
W me you cannot, murder me you may, *Foresters* IV 721
Win (reach) Eh, my rheumatizy be that bad howiver be I to *w* to the burnin'. *Queen Mary* IV iii 474
Winced colt *w* and whinnied and flung up her heels; *Becket, Pro.* 515
Winchester a plundering o' Bishop *W's* house; *Queen Mary* II iii 73
same book You wrote against my Lord of *W*; „ IV iii 265
Henry of *W*? *Henry*. Him who crown'd Stephen— *Becket, Pro.* 272
Wind (s) or wave And *w* at their old battle: *Queen Mary* I v 357
know that whether A *w* be warm or cold, „ I v 620
Eh, the *w* and the wet! „ IV iii 466
but Dumble wur blow'd wi' the *w*, „ IV iii 477
barrin' the *w*, Dumble wur blow'd wi' the *w*, „ IV iii 493
Proclaim it to the *w's*. „ V ii 290
As few as I may in a *w*, *Harold* II i 68
the best, strong-wing'd against the *w*. „ II ii 149
The *w's* so cross and jostle among these towers. „ II ii 155
Breathe the free *w* from off our Saxon downs, „ II ii 186
For happier homeward *w's* than that which crack'd „ II ii 198
But wherefore is the *w*, „ II ii 256
The *w* is fair For England now . . . „ II ii 766
Heard, heard— *Harold*. The *w* in his hair? „ III i 371
we must fight. How blows the *w*? „ III ii 135
William the Norman, for the *w* had changed— „ IV iii 181
William's or his own As *w* blows, or tide flows: „ V i 163
Winnow and scatter all scruples to the *w*, *Becket* I i 151
that one time sway to the current, And to the *w* another. „ I iii 595
Is it the *w* of the dawn that I hear „ II i 1
and so of the other *w's*; „ II ii 323
God and his free *w* grant your lordship a happy home-return „ III iii 327
Indungeon'd from one whisper of the *w*, „ IV ii 147
besides the *w* Went with *my* arrow. *The Cup* I ii 31
thou that art life to the *w*, to the wave, „ II 3
Thou whose breath Is balmy *w* to robe „ II 265
On my last voyage—but the *w* has fail'd— „ II 521
My far-eyed queen of the *w's*— *The Falcon* 9
And a salt *w* burnt the blossoming trees; *Prom. of May* I 57
day's bright like a friend, but the *w* east like an enemy. „ I 79
He wur sa bellows'd out wi' the *w* this murnin', „ III 432
To break our band and scatter us to the *w's*. *Foresters* III 454
Wind (verb) and howsoe'er Thy quarry *w* and wheel, *The Falcon* 12
if I *w* This forest-horn of mine *Foresters* IV 174
Winder (window) and I heärd the *w*—that's the *w* at the end o' the passage, *Prom. of May* I 396
afoor I coomed up he got thruff the *w* ageän. „ I 406

Winder (window) (*continued*) I'll hev the *w* naäiled up, and put Towser under it. *Prom. of May* I 420
she set the bush by my dairy *w* „ II 18
the walls sa thin, and the *w's* brokken, „ III 72
Winding I warrant I worm thro' all their *w's*. *The Cup* I i 87
To lead us thro' the *w's* of the wood. *Foresters* II i 634
And catch the *w* of a phantom horn. „ IV 1091
Window (*See also* **Winder**) Open the *w*, Knyvett; *Queen Mary* II i 154
My *w* look'd upon the corridor; „ V ii 459
When he we speak of drove the *w* back, „ V ii 464
Got thro' the *w* again? *Prom. of May* I 407
will be placed Beneath the *w*, Philip. I 561
Love flew in at the *w* *Foresters* I i 150
Wealth dropt out of the *w*, „ I i 156
Windsor There yet is time, take boat and pass to *W*. *Mary*. I pass to *W* and I lose my crown. *Queen Mary* II iv 28
Windy for in our *w* world What's up is faith, *Harold* I i 83
Nor mark the sea-bird rouse himself and hover Above the *w* ripple, „ II ii 336
Wine we may grant the *w*. Old Sir Thomas always granted the *w*. *Queen Mary* II i 41
and mine old flask of *w* Beside me, „ III i 47
So the *w* ran, and there be revelry, „ III ii 236
what an acrid *w* has Luther brew'd, „ IV iii 545
A drinker of black, strong, volcanic *w's*, „ V ii 94
Would the *w's* Of wedding had been dash'd *Harold* IV iii 6
cannot see the world but thro' their *w's*! „ IV iii 226
Some *w*! Too much! „ V i 203
amorous Of good old red sound liberal Gascon *w*: *Becket, Pro.* 101
A good dish from a bad, new *w* from old. *Henry*. Well, who loves *w* loves woman. „ *Pro.* 106
when the Gascon *w* mounts to my head, „ *Pro.* 113
I have been a lover of *w's*, and delicate meats, „ I i 76
Go home, and sleep thy *w* off, for thine eyes Glare stupid-wild with *w*. „ I i 212
Well—if that isn't goodly *w*— „ I iv 157
that tho' I can drink *w* I cannot bide water, „ I iv 220
The *w* and wealth of all our France are yours; „ II ii 446
warder of the bower hath given himself Of late to *w*. „ III i 32
his fond excess of *w* Springs from the loneliness „ III i 39
Are braced and brazen'd up with Christmas *w's* „ V ii 424
Plunder'd the vessel full of Gascon *w*, „ V ii 441
—we have eaten—we are heated. *W*! *The Cup* I ii 46
red *w* Ran down the marble and lookt like blood, „ II 203
Bring me The costly *w's* we use in marriages. „ II 365
W! Filippo, *w*! *Count*. It is but thin and cold, *The Falcon* 576
Not quite recover'd of your wound, the *w* Might help you. „ 591
thro' the blood the *w* leaps to the brain *Foresters* I iii 22
Here, here—a cup of *w*—drink and begone! „ I iii 89
Give me a draught of *w*. „ II i 459
A draught of *w*. *Robin*. Our cellar is hard by. „ II i 467
Take him, good little John, and give him *w*. „ II i 470
your good father had his draught of *w* „ II ii 2
Where lies that cask of *w* whereof „ III 306
And thou wouldst run more *w* than blood. „ III 338
the warm *w*, and found it again. „ IV 245
Wine-press For thou hast trodden this *w-p* alone. *Becket* III iii 290
Wing on the deck and spread his *w's* for sail! *Queen Mary* I v 379
hardly, save by boat, swimming, or *w's*. „ II iii 13
free *w* The world were all one Araby. „ III v 209
May the great angels join their *w's*, „ V iv 6
Would their *w's* were mine To follow thee *Harold* I ii 26
two young *w's* To fly to heaven straight with. „ III i 25
cherubim With twenty-cubit *w's* from wall to wall— „ III i 184
not so with us—No *w's* to come and go. „ III ii 99
let him flap The *w's* that beat down Wales! „ IV i 247
and our battle-axes broken The Raven's *w*, „ IV iii 65
hear him presently with clapt *w* Crow over Barbarossa— *Becket* II ii 49
we pray you, draw yourself from under The *w's* of France. „ II ii 249
lark first takes the sunlight on his *w*, *The Cup* I iii 44
had you left him the free use of his *w's*, *Prom. of May* I 653
would not blur A moth's *w* by the touching; „ II 492
he flutter'd his *w's* with a sweet little cry, *Foresters* I i 154
he flutter'd his *w's* as he gave me the lie, „ I i 159

Wing'd (*See also* **Strong-wing'd**) sonnet's a flying ant, *W* for a moment. *Queen Mary* II i 85
But *w* souls flying Beyond all change *Harold* III ii 100
They say that you are wise in *w* things, *Becket* I i 255
Winging our sea-mew *W* their only wail! *Harold* II i 98
Wingless and thus I dumb thee too, my *w* nightingale! „ I ii 24
Wink The French King *w's* at it. *Queen Mary* III i 160
I must not dream, not *w*, but watch. „ III v 154
Take fees of tyranny, *w* at sacrilege, *Becket* II ii 394
Winking Priest Sits *w* at the license of a king, „ I ii 66
Winnow *W* and scatter all scruples to the wind, „ I i 150
Winsome So *w* in her grace and gaiety, *Prom. of May* III 754
Winter (adj.) (*See also* **Spring-and-winter**) Tho' all the world should bay like *w* wolves. *Queen Mary* II ii 361
Our short-lived sun, before his *w* plunge, „ III iii 86
Two young lovers in *w* weather, *Harold* III ii 3
They are but of spring, They fly the *w* change— „ III ii 97
W sunshine! Beware of opening out thy bosom to it, *Becket* III iii 29
Close to the grating on a *w* morn *The Falcon* 441
Winter (s) (*See also* **Midwinter**) like the wild hedge-rose Of a soft *w*, *Queen Mary* III vi 16
Hath, like a brief and bitter *w's* day, „ IV iii 430
Were but a sort of *w*; „ V iv 16
Her life was *w*, for her spring was nipt: „ V v 269
And be thy hand as *w* on the field, *Harold* V i 132
And *w* again and the snows. *Becket, Pro.* 334
After the nineteen *w's* of King Stephen— „ I iii 338
Cold after warm, *w* after summer, „ I iv 64
And in the *w* I will fire their farms. *Foresters* IV 95
A thousand *w's* Will strip you bare as death, „ IV 1055
Winter-cataracts Whose *w-c* find a realm and leave it *The Cup* II 305
Wiry The nimble, wild, red, *w*, savage king— *Harold* IV i 197
Wisdom Some spice of *w* in my telling you, *Queen Mary* II iv 134
Best *w* is to know the worst at once. „ III v 220
bring it Home to the leisure *w* of his Queen, „ III vi 23
And all his wars and *w's* past away; „ V v 56
Fool still? or *w* there, *Harold* I i 359
W when in power And wisest, should not „ I i 363
Ay, if *W* Pair'd not with Good. „ V i 177
by thy *w* Hast kept it firm from shaking; *Becket, Pro.* 203
And all the *w* of the Chancellor, „ I i 153
Life yields to death and *w* bows to Fate, *The Cup* II 89
Wise (*See also* **Stupid-wise**) Statesmen that are *w* Shape a necessity, *Queen Mary* III iii 32
Statesmen that are *w* Take truth herself for model. „ III iii 36
But your *w* bees that stung him first to death. „ III iii 64
And love should know; and—be the king so *w*,— *Harold* I i 277
Ay, ay and *w* in peace and great in war— „ I i 313
Fool still? or wisdom there, My *w* head-shaking Harold? „ I i 361
Warrior thou art, and mighty *w* withal! „ II ii 543
And all our just and *w* and holy men „ III i 209
Fool and *w*, I fear This curse, and scorn it. „ III ii 67
Make not our Morcar sullen: it is not *w*. „ IV iii 104
but I am wiser now . . . I am too *w* . . . „ V ii 113
And *w*, yea truthful, till that blighted vow „ V ii 155
They say that you are *w* in winged things, *Becket* I i 255
I will be *w* and wary, not the soldier „ I i 387
Poor man, beside himself—not *w*. „ II ii 235
Like some *w* prince of this world from his wars, „ V ii 13
A policy of *w* pardon Wins here as well as there. „ V ii 22
Camma, *W* I am sure as she is beautiful, *The Cup* I ii 139
Or good, or *w*, that you should clasp a hand „ II 82
W! Life yields to death and wisdom „ II 88
Too late—thought myself *w*—A woman's dupe. „ II 480
However *w*, we must at times have wrought Some great injustice, *Foresters* III 154
Robin's a *w* man, Richard a wiseacre, „ IV 357
Wiseacre Robin's a wise man, Richard a *w*, „ IV 357
Wisely Have I done *w*, then, in accepting him? *Prom. of May* III 183
Wiser Brother, the king is *w* than he seems; *Harold* I i 272
Then Tostig too were *w* than he seems. „ I i 278
but I am *w* now . . . I am too wise . . . „ V ii 111
The *w* choice, because my sleeping-draught *Becket* IV ii 168
Woman again!—but I am *w* now. *The Cup* I i 169
I say it to you—you are *w*—Rome knows all, „ I ii 285
Wisest But thou canst hear the best and *w* of us. *Harold* I i 300
Wisdom when in power And *w*, „ I i 365
choose A hundred of the *w* heads from England, *Becket* II ii 171
wisdom bows to Fate, Is *w*, doing so. *The Cup* II 91
Wish (s) mine own *w* fulfill'd before the word *Queen Mary* I iv 232
to have the *w* before the word Is man's „ I iv 238
Your pious *w* to pay King Edward's debts, „ I v 111
my *w* Echoes your Majesty's. *Pole.* It shall be so. „ III iii 92
' It is the King's *w*, that you should wed Prince Philibert of Savoy. „ III v 221
Mere compliments and *w'es*. „ V ii 596
Amen to all Your *w*, and further. „ V iv 29
dead man's dying *w* should be of weight. *Becket, Pro.* 422
To make my marriage prosper to my *w*! *The Cup* II 309
smiles, not tears; Good *w'es*, not reproaches; *Prom. of May* I 526
Wish (verb) council and all her people *w* her to marry. *Queen Mary* I i 113
I must needs *w* all good things for France. „ I v 309
I *w* some thunderbolt Would make this Cole a cinder, „ IV iii 10
I *w* you a good morning, good Sir Nicholas: „ V i 13
I *w* her Highness better. „ V ii 615
I *w* you joy o' the King's brother. *Becket* III i 155
I am sure I *w* her happy. *Prom. of May* I 478
He *w'es* you to dine along with us, „ I 618
Then you should *w* us both to love for ever. „ I 642
Do you *w* it? *Eva.* *Do* I *w* it? „ I 696
I only *w* This pool were deep enough, „ II 303
Have you told him I am here? *Dora.* No; do you *w* it? „ III 267
make herself anything he *w'es* her to be? „ III 306
Tell him that I and the lady here *w* to see him. „ III 415
Might *w* its rose a lily, „ III 490
I *w* you and your ladyship's father a most exceedingly good morning. *Foresters* I i 308
I could *w* that all the land Were plunged „ IV 666
Wish'd Madam, when the Roman *w* to reign, *Queen Mary* I v 498
sometime I have *w* That I were caught, „ III v 162
I *w* myself the milkmaid singing here, „ III v 256
I had *w* for any weapon. *Harold* IV iii 19
and she *w* The Church were king: *Becket* V ii 117
once I *w* to scourge them to the bones. *The Cup* I i 27
Oh, how often I have *w* for you! *Prom. of May* I 769
asking his consent—you *w* me— „ III 494
I *w*, if you—— *Dora.* If I—— „ III 776
I *w*, I hoped To make, to make—— „ III 782
I cannot break it, Robin, if I *w*. *Foresters* IV 328
Wisp (*See also* **Wills-o'-the-wisp**) No, by *w* and glowworm, no. „ II ii 136
Wit (*See also* **Mother-wit**) The man is able enough—no lack of *w*, „ I ii 103
Witan Ay . . . if the *W* will consent to this. *Harold* II ii 615
Thy voice will lead the *W*— „ II ii 619
Witch (*See also* **Wood-witch**) But then she was a *w*. *Queen Mary* IV ii 208
what are you flying from? *Countryman.* The *w*! the *w*! *Becket* III ii 20
he'll never out again, the *w* has got him. „ III ii 26
Kind of the *w* to give thee warning tho'. „ III ii 29
Here is the *w's* hut. The fool-people call her a *w*—a good *w* to me! *Foresters* II i 178
in Nottingham they say There bides a foul *w* „ II i 203
Half-witted and a *w* to boot! „ II i 375
Or learning witchcraft of your woodland *w*, „ II i 501
he kneels! he has anger'd the foul *w*, „ II i 670
Witchcraft Or learning *w* of your woodland witch, „ II i 500
Witch'd Our woodland Circe that hath *w* the King? *Becket* III ii 32
Withdraw we might *w* Part of our garrison at Calais. *Queen Mary* I v 122
Permit me to *w*. To Lambeth? „ III ii 129
That Cranmer may *w* to foreign parts, „ IV i 45
Alva will but touch him on the horns, And he *w's*; „ V i 157
God from me *w's* Himself, And the King too. *Becket* I iii 701
Will you not *w*? „ V ii 228
speak with them apart. Let us *w*. „ V ii 311
Withdrawing means to counsel your *w* To Ashridge, *Queen Mary* I iv 225
Withdrew thought I might be chosen Pope, But then *w* it. „ V ii 84

Wither heat enough To scorch and *w* heresy to the root. *Queen Mary* III iv 28
marriage-garland *w's* even with the putting on, *Becket, Pro.* 360
Wither'd wherever Spain hath ruled she hath *w* *Queen Mary* II i 206
That *w* wreath were of more worth to me. *The Falcon* 335
That *w* wreath is of more worth to me. „ 337
And jealousy is *w*, sour and ugly : *Foresters* II ii 65
When the flower was *w* and old. „ IV 22
Withholden *See* **Long-withholden**
Within-door They burn themselves *w-d.* *Becket* I i 289
Withstood who hath *w* two Kings to their faces for the honour of God. „ II ii 275
Witness (s) Bear *w*, Renard, that I live and die *Queen Mary* II iv 41
No perfect *w* of a perfect faith In him who persecutes : „ III iv 117
Let all men here bear *w* of our bond ! *Harold* II ii 698
Ye heard one *w* even now. „ IV i 170
Bear me true *w*—only for this once— „ V ii 115
Witness (verb) And *w* to your Grace's innocence, *Queen Mary* III v 50
you are gone, my liege, *W* these papers, „ III vi 174
w the brawls, the gibbets. „ V i 85
Witted *See* **Half-witted**
Wizard myself must be the *w* To raise that tempest *Becket, Pro.* 207
Woden *W*, all Our cancell'd warrior-gods, *Harold* III ii 72
War-woodman of old *W*, how he fells „ V i 588
Woe *W* knave to thy familiar and to thee ! „ II ii 679
Woke I *w* Sir Henry—and he's true to you— *Queen Mary* III v 60
and *w* and came Among us again, *Harold* IV iii 150
Roused by the clamour of the chase he *w*, *The Cup* I ii 118
a red fire *w* in the heart of the town, *Prom. of May* I 50
Wold Moon on the waste and the *w*, *The Cup* I ii 4
That ever charm'd the plowman of your *w's* *Prom. of May* III 489
then the sweetest flower of all the *w's*, „ III 752
Wolf not to yield His Church of England to the Papal *w* And Mary ; *Queen Mary* I ii 36
there were many *wolves* among you Who dragg'd „ I v 399
black night, and hear the *w*. „ I v 414
if your *w* the while should howl for more, „ I v 419
Tho' all the world should bay like winter *wolves*. „ II ii 362
W of the shore ! dog, with thy lying lights *Harold* II i 21
The *w* ! the beast ! „ II ii 301
God gave us to divide us from the *w* ! „ IV iii 101
The *w* Mudded the brook and predetermined all. „ V i 2
Mannerless *wolves* ! *Becket* I iii 739
when the horn sounds she comes out as a *w*. „ III ii 23
King hath many more *wolves* than he can tame „ III iii 322
wolves of England Must murder her one shepherd, „ III iii 342
with the flock to the fold—Safe from the *w*— *The Cup* I ii 9
They say that Rome Sprang from a *w*. „ I ii 14
With some conspiracy against the *w*. „ I ii 16
Safe from the *w* to the fold— „ I ii 19
Or haply fallen a victim to the *w*. *Foresters* II i 510
be there *wolves* in Sherwood ? *Marian.* The *w*, John ! „ II i 511
Wolfdog how those Roman *w's* howl and bay him ! *Queen Mary* IV iii 354
a score of *w-d's* are let loose that will tear thee piecemeal. *Becket* III ii 39
Wolf-queen that our *w-Q* Is prowling round the fold. „ III iii 6
Woman (*See also* **Beggar-woman, Mad-woman, Yeo-woman**) I and my old *w* 'ud burn upon it, *Queen Mary* I i 56
' Whosoever Looketh after a *w*,' „ I v 453
I pray God No *w* ever love you, „ I v 602
All the *women* loved him. „ II i 34
Tear up that *w's* work there. „ II i 75
That makes or man or *w* look their goodliest. „ II ii 329
Away ! *Women* and children ! „ II iii 97
I was too sorry for the *w* To mark the dress. „ III i 58
Sir, no *w's* regimen Can save us. „ III i 122
I say There is no man—there was one *w* with us— „ III i 337
for *women* To go twelve months in bearing „ III vi 90
W is various and most mutable. „ III vi 135
—And I have known such *women* more than one— „ III vi 178
To the poor flock—to *women* and to children— „ IV ii 158
Thou knowest never *w* meant so well, „ V ii 342
Hapless doom of *w* happy in betrothing ! „ V ii 364
Unhappiest Of Queens and wives and *women* ! „ V ii 408
or all *women's* Low as his own ? „ V ii 434

Woman (*continued*) It is the low man thinks the *w* low ; *Queen Mary* V ii 439
in Guernsey, I watch'd a *w* burn ; „ V iv 18
the *w* up yonder sleeping after all she has done, „ V iv 34
burnt The heretic priest, workmen, and *women* and children. „ V v 106
we are private with our *women* here— „ V v 119
Women, the Holy Father Has ta'en the legateship „ V v 124
I am but a *w*, I have no power.— „ V v 130
Women, when I am dead, Open my heart, „ V v 152
I have given her cause—I fear no *w*. *Harold* I ii 42
Then our modest *women*— „ II ii 476
and *women* Cling to the conquer'd, „ IV i 212
I am no *w* to put faith in dreams. „ IV i 264
The king commands thee, *w* ! „ V i 341
To part me from the *w* that I loved ! „ V i 346
no man can swear to him. *Edith.* But one *w* ! „ V ii 79
Who be these *w* ? And what body is this ? „ V ii 86
Pluck the dead *w* off the dead man, Malet ! „ V ii 144
Well, who loves wine loves *w*. *Becket, Pro.* 109
Men are God's trees, and *women* are God's flowers ; „ *Pro.* 111
whom I love indeed As a *w* should be loved— „ *Pro.* 133
if a man Wastes himself among *women*, how should he love A *w*, as a *w* should be loved ? „ *Pro.* 137
Last night I followed a *w* in the city here. „ *Pro.* 469
The *w* that I follow'd hither. „ I i 195
I saw that door Close even now upon the *w*. „ I i 203
To take the vagabond *w* of the street Into thine arms ! „ I i 227
'Tis known you are midwinter to all *women*, „ I ii 28
so long Have wander'd among *women*— „ II i 154
the goodly way of *women* Who love, „ II i 257
There is no *w* that I love so well. *Rosamund.* No *w* but should be content with that— „ III i 9
and to make me a *w* of the world, „ III i 117
more a *w* o' the world than my lady here, „ III i 142
most on 'em know an honest *w* and a lady when they see her, „ III i 179
I never knew an honest *w* that could make songs, „ III i 183
there were Abbots—but they did not bring their *women* ; „ III iii 136
if he Had aught of man, or thou of *w* ; „ IV ii 232
Are ye king's men ? I am king's *w*, I. „ V i 265
make me not a *w*, John of Salisbury, „ V ii 147
Lacking the love of *w* and of child. „ V ii 199
I never felt such passion for a *w*. *The Cup* I i 34
With all my range of *women* should yet shun „ I i 57
For some unprincely violence to a *w*, „ I i 139
I ever had my victories among *women*. „ I i 153
W again !—but I am wiser now. „ I i 168
Not one to keep a *w's* fealty when Assailed „ I i 176
Antonius, So gracious toward *women*, never yet Flung back a *w's* prayer. „ I ii 299
' He never yet flung back a *w's* prayer '— „ I ii 455
Or man, or *w*, as traitors unto Rome. „ I iii 9
A *w* I could live and die for. What ! Die for a *w*, what new faith is this ? „ I iii 65
It bears an evil savour among *women*. „ I iii 86
It is not easy to disarm a *w* ? „ I iii 106
The *women* of the Temple drag her in. „ I iii 118
I never found the *w* I could not force „ I iii 166
thought myself wise—A *w's* dupe. „ II 481
O *women*, Ye will have Roman masters. „ II 510
Ah, the *women*, the *women* ! *The Falcon* 84
won't you speak with the old *w* first, „ 182
She smiles at him—how hard the *w* is ! „ 661
best heart that ever Beat for one *w*. „ 668
Well, well ! the *women* ! „ 699
A nobler breed of men and *women*. „ 755
theer be a thousand i' the parish, taäkin' in the *women* and childer ; *Prom. of May* I 146
Then the man, the *w*, Following their best affinities, „ I 522
but I hev an owd *w* as 'ud see to all that ; „ II 96
My grandfather—of him They say, that *women*— „ II 272
where the man and the *w*, only differing as the stronger and the weaker, „ III 189
If marriage ever brought a *w* happiness „ III 639

Woman (*continued*) I never said As much before to any *w* living. Prom. of May III 645
A hundred times more worth a *w*'s love, „ III 743
in the *w*, and the man must bring it out of her. Foresters I i 117
thou hast ruffled my *w*, Little John. „ I i 166
Thou speakest like a fool or a *w*. „ I i 204
your *w* so flustered me that I forgot my message „ I i 296
to stand between me and your *w*, Kate. „ I i 305
A question that every true man asks of a *w* once in his life. „ I ii 139
Not pleasures, *women's* matters. „ I ii 176
Because thou sayest such fine things of *women*, „ I iii 138
I reverence all *women*, bad me, dying, „ II i 40
thou art the very *w* who waits On my dear Marian. „ II i 102
and the old *w*'s blessing with them to the last fringe. „ II i 195
There is but one old *w* in the hut. „ II i 241
There is yet another old *w*. „ II i 244
there's for you—and the old *w*'s welcome. „ II i 290
like the *w* at Acre when the Turk shot her „ II i 307
bury me in the mound, says the *w*. „ II i 313
By a thief. Sheriff. Who, *w*, who? „ II i 318
sweet saints bless your worship for your alms to the old *w*! „ II i 364
an old *w* can shoot closer than you two. „ II i 400
Did I not tell you an old *w* could shoot better? „ II i 407
Thou art no old *w*—thou art disguised— „ II i 410
kiss a man And it was but a *w*. „ II ii 73
I could love you like a *w*. „ II ii 191
being every inch a man I honour every inch of a *w*. „ III 64
Why art thou mute? Dost thou not honour *w*? „ III 68
And if a *w* pass— „ III 176
We never wrong'd a *w*. „ III 184
Marian, thou and thy *w*, Why, where is Kate? „ III 257
Thou and thy *w* are a match for three friars. „ III 261
A *w*'s heart is but a little thing, „ IV 656
values neither man Nor *w* save as tools— „ IV 714

Womankind kisses of all kind of *w* In Flanders, Harold I ii 113
handle all *w* gently, and hold them in all honour, Foresters I i 99
honouring all *w*, and more especially my lady Marian, „ III 56

Woman-tears And those hard men brake into *w-t*, Queen Mary I v 564

Womb O Thou that slayest the babe within the *w* The Cup II 279

Won I *w* by boldness once. The Emperor counsell'd Queen Mary I v 547
Struck home and *w*. „ I v 554
was it boldness Or weakness that *w* there? „ I v 560
possibly The Lutheran may be *w* to her again; „ III iv 202
She hath *w* upon our people thro' her beauty, Harold IV i 22
The day is *w*! „ IV i 270
Stigand, O father, have we *w* the day? „ V i 544
and *w* the violet at Toulouse; Becket, Pro. 348
boldness of this hand hath *w* it Love's alms, „ II i 183
The glory and grief of battle *w* or lost The Cup I ii 161
no such gamester As, having *w* the stake, „ I iii 146
have *w* Their value again—beyond all markets— The Falcon 904

Wonder I *w* at tha', it beats me! Queen Mary IV iii 499
shall not *w* If Synorix, who has dwelt three years The Cup I ii 174
I *w* if I look as pale as she? „ II 322
Sometimes I *w*, When man has surely learnt Prom. of May II 329
How worn he looks, poor man! who is it, I *w*. „ II 391
you yourself are ashamed of me, and I do not *w* at it. Dora. But I should *w* at myself if it were so. „ III 270
I am a silent man myself, and all the more *w* at our Earl. Foresters I ii 35

Wonder'd But *w* more at my much constancy Becket IV ii 304

Woo Prince of fluff and feather come To *w* you, Queen Mary I iv 164
Ringdoves coo again, All things *w* again. „ III v 104
And *w* their loves and have forgotten thee; Harold II ii 438

Wood But hatch you some new treason in the *w*'s. Queen Mary I v 466
Cool as the light in old decaying *w*; „ IV ii 5
'Make short! make short!' and so they lit the *w*. „ IV iii 607
Be there not fair *w*'s and fields In England? Harold I i 261
Taken the rifted pillars of the *w* „ I ii 100
And if I walk within the lonely *w*, „ II ii 246
had in it Wales, Her floods, her *w*'s, her hills: „ IV i 207

Wood (*continued*) See, first, a circling *w*, A hundred pathways Becket, Pro. 162
And then another *w*, and in the midst „ Pro. 168
it minded me Of the sweet *w*'s of Clifford, „ I i 264
A royal pleasaunce for thee, in the *w*, „ II i 128
I brought them In from the *w*, and set them here. „ II i 131
the people Believe the *w* enchanted. „ III i 36
Have track'd the King to this dark inland *w*; „ III ii 4
How ghostly sounds that horn in the black *w*! „ III ii 17
she sits naked by a great heap of gold in the middle of the *w*, „ III ii 22
in the dark heart of the *w* I hear the yelping „ III ii 47
more wolves than he can tame in his *w*'s of England, „ III iii 323
Show me where thou camest out of the *w*. „ IV i 46
I watched her and followed her into the *w*'s, „ IV ii 17
he had gone too far Into the King's own *w*'s; „ V ii 108
While you can take your pastime in the *w*'s. The Cup I i 191
break of precipice that runs Thro' all the *w*, „ I ii 22
Came to the front of the *w*— „ I ii 119
not fear the crowd that hunted me Across the *w*'s, „ I iii 17
They hold by Richard—the wild *w*! Foresters I iii 111
mix with all The lusty life of *w* and underwood, „ I iii 114
I have a sudden passion for the wild *w*— „ I iii 123
We should be free as air in the wild *w*— „ I iii 125
Would it be better for thee in the *w*? Scarlet. Ay, so she did not follow me to the *w*. „ I iii 141
I have reign'd one year in the wild *w*. „ II i 36
soul of the *w*'s hath stricken thro' my blood, „ II i 66
I found this white doe wandering thro' the *w*, „ II i 96
But I am weary pacing thro' the *w*. „ II i 129
The *w* is full of echoes, owls, elfs, „ II i 262
He was the king o' the *w*. „ II i 321
but make haste then, and be silent in the *w*. „ II i 365
See whether there be more of 'em in the *w*. „ II i 431
To lead us thro' the windings of the *w*. „ II i 635
Stay with us in this *w*, till he recover. „ II ii 9
We be fairies of the *w*, „ II ii 118
And this new queen of the *w*. „ II ii 139
You see why We must leave the *w* and fly. „ II ii 174
with you, out of it, over the *w* and away! „ II ii 201
present her with this oaken chaplet as Queen of the *w*, „ III 59
In this dark *w* when all was in our power „ III 182
Behold a pretty Dian of the *w*, „ III 267
Our Robin, King o' the *w*'s, „ III 344
Robin, the people's friend, the King o' the *w*'s! „ III 348
The Queen o' the *w*'s, „ III 354
Maid Marian, Queen o' the *w*'s! (repeat) Foresters III 357, 375, 377, 398, 400
Drink to the health of our new Queen o' the *w*'s, Foresters III 369
We drink the health of thy new Queen o' the *w*'s. „ III 373
Drink to the Queen o' the *w*'s, „ III 389
—to this maid, this Queen o' the *w*'s. „ III 395
Thro' *w* and lawn and ling, „ III 425
For a Queen, for a Queen o' the *w*'s, (repeat) „ III 431, 445
Along the glades and passes of the *w* „ III 457
Their lives unsafe in any of these our *w*'s, „ IV 94
And live with us and the birds in the green *w*. „ IV 326
Blown like a true son of the *w*'s. „ IV 427
are delivered here in the wild *w* an hour after noon. „ IV 509
Were some strong fellow here in the wild *w*, „ IV 516
they shall dance to the music of the wild *w*. „ IV 556
Not paid at York—the *w*—prick me no more! „ IV 623
What shouts are these that ring along the *w*? „ IV 763
Then will I live for ever in the wild *w*. „ IV 879
I scent it in the green leaves of the *w*. „ IV 944
I trust We shall return to the *w*. „ IV 1052
We dealt in the wild justice of the *w*'s. „ IV 1073
Your names will cling like ivy to the *w*. „ IV 1086

Woodbine (adj.) Didn't I spy 'em a-sitting i' the *w* harbour togither? Prom. of May I 125

Woodbine (s) Wi' the wild white rose, an' the *w* sa gaäy, „ II 174

Woodcock We hold our Saxon *w* in the springe, Harold II ii 1

Wood-fungus Dry as an old *w-f* on a dead tree, „ III i 8

Woodland (adj.) Glide like a light across these *w* ways! Foresters II i 159

Woodland (adj.) (*continued*) Tut! tut! the scream of some wild *w* thing. *Foresters* II i 253
Or learning witchcraft of your *w* witch, „ II i 501
Why—even your *w* squirrel sees the nut Behind the shell, „ II i 646
Shall drink the health of our new *w* Queen. „ III 314
Great *w* king, I know not quarterstaff. „ IV 215
Then, if ye cannot breathe but *w* air, „ IV 952
Woodland (s) Fifty leagues Of *w* hear and know my horn, „ III 104
Woodman (*See also* **War-woodman**) They must have past. Here is a *w's* hut. „ II i 199
true *w's* bow of the best yew-wood to slay the deer. „ II i 392
in the name of all our *woodmen*, present her with „ III 58
You caught a lonely *w* of our band, „ III 359
Woodstock banish'd us to *W* and the fields. *Queen Mary* III v 3
Wood-witch Is not this *w-w* of the rustic's fear *Becket* III ii 31
Wooer Strange in a *w*! *Queen Mary* I v 363
Wool Like a tod of *w* from wagon into warehouse. *Foresters* IV 274
Word That's a hard *w*, legitimate; what does it mean? *Queen Mary* I i 11
let his own *w's* damn the Papist. „ I iii 53
yet the *w* Affrights me somewhat: „ I iv 8
'Tis mine own wish fulfill'd before the *w* Was spoken, „ I iv 233
wish before the *w* Is man's good Fairy— „ I iv 239
Our royal *w* for that! „ I v 267
Philip never writes me one poor *w*, „ I v 360
The *w* has turn'd your Highness pale; „ I v 471
One *w* before she comes. „ II ii 109
Queen had written her *w* to come to court: „ II ii 117
No, no, my *w's* my *w*. „ II iii 93
Ha—Verbum Dei—verbum—*w* of God! „ III i 262
W of God In English! „ III i 279
Is reconciled the *w*? the Pope again? „ III iii 3
I have changed a *w* with him In coming, and may change a *w* again. „ III iv 14
not like a *w*, That comes and goes in uttering. „ III v 29
Truth, a *w*! The very Truth and very *W* are one. „ III v 31
Is like a *w* that comes from olden days, „ III v 34
For the wrong Robin took her at her *w*. „ III v 265
May Simon Renard speak a single *w*? „ III vi 122
to speak a single *w* That could not be forgiven. „ III vi 126
What should I say, I cannot pick my *w's*— „ III vi 148
For death gives life's last *w* a power to live, „ IV iii 161
Let all rich men remember that hard *w*. „ IV iii 206
but tek thou my *w* vor't, Joan,— „ IV iii 533
ever give yourselves your own good *w*. *Harold* I i 343
May, surely, play with *w's*. *Harold*. *W's* are the man. „ II ii 418
at thy *w*, for thou Art known a speaker „ II ii 516
For thou art truthful, and thy *w* thy bond. „ II ii 645
Or is it the same sin to break my *w* As break mine oath? He call'd my *w* my bond! „ II ii 664
And makes believe that he believes my *w*— „ II ii 669
Thy naked *w* thy bond! „ II ii 693
Thanks, truthful Earl; I did not doubt thy *w*, But that my barons might believe thy *w*, „ II ii 724
Might strengthen thee in keeping of thy *w*, „ II ii 731
I that so prized plain *w* and naked truth „ III i 93
This lightning before death Plays on the *w*,— „ III i 388
The king's last *w*—' the arrow!' „ V i 266
I have not spoken to the king One *w*; „ V i 336
Nay, then, I take thee at thy *w*— *Becket*, *Pro*. 128
his last *w's* were a commendation of Thomas Becket „ *Pro*. 400
And I have said no *w* of this to him: „ I i 97
We wait but the King's *w* to strike thee dead. „ I iii 166
who cares not for the *w*, Makes ' care not '— „ II i 117
The *w* should come from him. „ II ii 134
W's! he will wriggle out of them „ II ii 186
bad me whatever I saw not to speak one *w*, „ III i 133
not to speak one *w*, for that's the rule o' the garden, „ III i 137
tho' I shouldn't speak one *w*, „ III i 155
tho' I be sworn not to speak a *w*, I can tell you all about her, if—— *Rosamund*. No *w* now. „ III i 205
not thorn enough to prick him for it, Ev'n with a *w*? „ III i 253
One *w* further. Doth not the *fewness* of anything „ III iii 301
we had *w's* of late, And thereupon he call'd „ IV ii 42
Word (*continued*) —a troubadour You play with *w's*. *Becket* IV ii 182
Rosamund hath not answer'd you one *w*; Madam, I will not answer you one *w*. „ IV ii 362
I spake no *w* of treachery, Reginald. „ V ii 401
Ready to fall at Henry's *w* or yours— „ V ii 486
Low *w's* best chime with this solemnity. *The Cup* II 217
These are strange *w's* to speak to Artemis. „ II 326
W's are not always what they seem, my King. „ II 328
My lord, a *w* with you. *The Falcon* 394
Well, Tell me the *w's*—or better— „ 451
A *w* with you, my lord! „ 472
A *w*, my lord! *Count*. ' Dead flowers!' *Elisabetta*. A *w*, my lord! „ 475
one *w* more. *Count*. Good! let it be but one. „ 510
Strange that the *w's* at home with me so long „ 525
will you take the *w* out of your master's own mouth? „ 598
I will never change *w* with you again. *Prom. of May* I 163
—what's the newspaäper *w*, Wilson?—celebrate— „ I 320
thou'll put one *w* fur another as I does. „ I 381
' Till death us part '—those are the only *w's*, „ I 659
But I hed a *w* to saäy to ye. „ II 45
Cannot you understand plain *w's*, Mr Dobson? „ II 113
I be a bit deaf, and I wur hallus scaäred by a big *w*; „ III 33
Miss Dora, meä and my maätes, us three, we wants to hev three *w's* wi' ye. „ III 126
he gave me no address, and there was no *w* of marriage; „ III 333
He be saäyin' a *w* to the owd man, „ III 481
One *w*, or do but smile! „ III 677
and wants To hev a *w* wi' ye about the marriage. „ III 704
Than this, this—but I waste no *w's* upon him: „ III 745
I cannot find the *w*—forgive it—Amends. „ III 790
—her last *w* Forgave—and I forgive you— „ III 810
that very *w* ' greasy ' hath a kind of unction in it, *Foresters* I i 86
What a wealth of *w's*—O Lord, I will live „ I ii 36
O Lord, I am easily led by *w's*, „ I ii 40
nor to speak *w* to anyone, „ I ii 237
True king of vice—true play on *w's*— „ II i 83
Speak but one *w* not only of forgiveness, „ II i 610
I never will speak *w* to thee again. „ II ii 55
Then *I* am yeo-woman. O the clumsy *w*! *Robin*. Take thou this light kiss for thy clumsy *w*. „ III 133
Air and *w*, my lady, are maid and man. „ III 419
though he be the chief of rogues, he hath never broken his *w*. „ IV 434
Say thou no *w* against my brother John. „ IV 824
Why then, my liege, I have no *w* to say. „ IV 827
Word-eating what, a truckler! a *w-e* coward! „ IV 162
Word-monger Diagonalise! thou art a *w-m*. *Becket* II ii 332
Wore slew not him alone who *w* the purple, *Queen Mary* I v 499
She *w* red shoes! *Stafford*. Red shoes! „ III i 59
your shores *W* in mine eyes the green „ III ii 18
There *w* his time studying the canon law *Becket* II i 85
he answer'd me, As if he *w* the crown already— „ II ii 7
I *w* the lady's chaplet round my neck; *The Falcon* 631
wreath That once you *w* outvalues twenty-fold „ 759
He *w* thy colours once at a tourney. *Foresters* I i 249
Work (s) were a pious *w* To string my father's sonnets, *Queen Mary* II i 26
Tear up that woman's *w* there. „ II i 75
Well, for mine own *w*, „ II i 86
Sharp *w* and short. „ III i 329
Cranmer, be thou glad. This is the *w* of God. „ IV iii 82
That all day long hath wrought his father's *w*, „ V ii 119
and cried ' *W* for the tanner.' *Harold* II ii 385
Thou art wearied out With this day's *w*, *Becket* I i 7
due to those That went before us for their *w*, „ II ii 192
The *w* of the farm will go on still, but for how long? *Prom. of May* III 159
Work (verb) Your master *w's* against me in the dark. *Queen Mary* I v 277
These are the means God *w's* with, „ III vi 68
so much of the anti-papal leaven *W's* in him yet, „ IV i 16
For Henry could not *w* a miracle— *Becket* I i 40
studying the canon law To *w* it against me. „ II i 87
strove To *w* against her license for her good, „ IV ii 340
but pray you do not *w* upon me. „ V i 81

Worldly your Priests Gross, *w*, simoniacal, unlearn'd ! *Harold* I i 162
The *w* bond between us is dissolved, *Becket* I i 347
Gilbert Foliot, A *w* follower of the *w* strong. „ I iii 543
World-wealth Richer than all the wide *w-w* of May, *The Falcon* 466
Worm (s) And putrid water, every drop a *w*, *Queen Mary* IV iii 444
The *w* ! shall I let her go ? *Becket* IV ii 197
sure my dagger was a feint Till the *w* turn'd— „ IV ii 380
Becket hath trodden on us like *w's*, „ V i 61
poor *w*, crawl down thine own black hole *The Cup* II 494
Worm (verb) I warrant I *w* thro' all their windings. „ I i 87
Worms Zurich, *W*, Geneva, Basle— *Queen Mary* I ii 2
Worn (*See also* **Threadbare-worn**) what, you look somewhat *w* ; „ IV ii 116
O Saint of Aragon, with that sweet *w* smile „ V v 198
I am somewhat *w*, A snatch of sleep *Harold* V i 179
But have you ever *w* my diamonds ? *The Falcon* 736
tho' I grudge the pretty jewel, that I Have *w*, *Prom. of May* I 474
How *w* he looks, poor man ? who is it, I wonder. „ II 390
but, my flower, You look so weary and so *w* ! „ III 499
I have ; but these were never *w* as yet. *Foresters* IV 835
Worried boil'd, buried alive, *w* by dogs ; *Queen Mary* II i 211
When they ran down the game and *w* it. *Becket, Pro.* 124
dog I cramm'd with dainties *w* me ! „ V i 244
Worry (*See also* **Tew**) out of his cage to *w* Cranmer. *Queen Mary* I i 88
Worrying To *w* one another. „ III iv 313
Worse (*See also* **Wuss**) They call him cold, Haughty, ay, *w*. „ I v 432
—that were *w* than all. „ II i 183
and he'll smash all our bits o' things *w* than Philip o' Spain. „ II iii 104
A better and a *w*—the *w* is here „ III iv 114
And *w* than all, you had to kneel to *me* ; „ IV ii 134
No place for *w*. „ IV iii 80
He calls us *w* than Jews, Moors, Saracens. „ V i 150
but *w*—And yet I must obey the Holy Father, „ V ii 37
w than all, A passing bell toll'd in a dying ear— „ V ii 39
w than that—not one hour true to me ! „ V v 159
Ay, but *w* news : this William sent to Rome, *Harold* III ii 140
The King's courts will use thee *w* than thy dog— *Becket* I iv 102
get you hence in haste Lest *w* befall you. „ IV ii 28
We can do *w*. Madam, I saw your dagger „ IV ii 318
so much *w* For last day's journey. *The Falcon* 833
I be *w* off than any of you, for I be lean by nature, *Foresters* I i 44
Then I shall be no *w*. „ I ii 289
Am I *w* or better ? I am outlaw'd. „ II i 49
I am none the *w* for that. (repeat) „ II i 50, 58
and another—*w* !—An innocent maid. „ III 387
I *am* allied to John. *Robin.* The *w* for thee. „ IV 138
and the hunters, if caught, are blinded, or *w* than blinded. „ IV 227
nay, by the rood They have done far *w*— „ IV 909
Worship (s) (*See also* **Idol-worship**) we have the Blessed Virgin For *w*, *Becket* V ii 221
Who hast that *w* for me which Heaven knows *Foresters* I iii 160
Worship (verb) The people there so *w* me— *Queen Mary* I iv 120
Devil's '*if* Thou wilt fall down and *w* me.' *Becket* III iii 286
me who *w* Robin the great Earl of Huntingdon ? *Foresters* I i 225
All here will prize thee, honour, *w* thee, „ II ii 17
Worshipper With a crowd of *w's*, *Becket* I iii 476
And you three holy men, You *w's* of the Virgin, *Foresters* III 383
Worshipping beheld you afar off *w* in her Temple, *The Cup* I i 39
Worshipt (*See also* **Long-worshipt**) So *w* of all those that came across him ; *Queen Mary* IV i 161
w whom she loathed, I should have let her be, *Becket* IV ii 390
Worst (adj.) Serve my best friend and make him my *w* foe ; „ I iii 568
And if the *w* time come ? *Foresters* I ii 290
Worst (s) Come, come, the *w* ! Best wisdom is to know the *w* at once. *Queen Mary* III v 219
He was not of the *w*. *Harold* IV iii 91
And wrought his *w* against his native land, *The Cup* I ii 177
Worsted That where he was but *w*, he was wrong'd. *Harold* I i 449
Worth (adj.) by your looks you are not *w* the having, *Queen Mary* I iv 13
A lesson *w* Finger and thumb—thus *Harold* I ii 54
selfless man Is *w* a world of tonguesters. „ V i 82
Thy life is *w* the wrestle for it : arise, *Becket* IV ii 194
central diamond, *w*, I think, Half of the Antioch „ V i 165
Worth (adj.) (*continued*) Is vengeance for its own sake *w* the while, *The Cup* I i 30
A hundred times more *w* a woman's love, *Prom. of May* III 743
Thou art *w* thy weight in all those marks of gold, *Foresters* IV 1023
Worth (s) Your people have begun to learn your *w*. *Queen Mary* I v 110
That wither'd wreath were of more *w* to me. *The Falcon* 335
wither'd wreath is of more *w* to me Than all the blossom, „ 338
rate the land fivefold The *w* of the mortgage, *Foresters* II i 151
Worthies The conduit painted—the nine *w*—ay ! *Queen Mary* III i 258
Worthy you will find in it Pleasure as well as duty, *w* Bonner,— „ III iv 430
My most *w* brother, Thou art the quietest man in all the world— *Harold* I i 311
I am not *w* of her—this beast-body That God has plunged my soul in— *Becket* II i 148
or I Would bow to such a baseness as would make me Most *w* of it : „ IV ii 236
for all of them Loved her, and she was *w* of all love. *Prom. of May* II 429
you should ever Be tempted into doing what might seem Not altogether *w* of you, „ III 555
A *w* messenger ! how should he help it ? *Foresters* I iii 85
Wound Tho' leaving each, a *w* ; *Becket* I i 176
I will bind up his *w's* with my napkin. „ I iv 107
I see you quite recover'd of your *w*. *The Falcon* 391
if you be Not quite recover'd of your *w*, „ 590
The story of your battle and your *w*. „ 594
balms and simples of the field To help a *w*. *Foresters* II ii 13
Wounded so *w* in his honour, He can but creep *Queen Mary* IV i 138
This Canterbury, like a *w* deer, *Becket* II ii 21
I was but *w* by the enemy there And then imprison'd. *The Falcon* 388
Woven jewel of St. Pancratius *W* into the gold. *Harold* II ii 701
Wrap *W* them together in a purple cloak „ V ii 158
Wrapt smoke of Cranmer's burning *w* me round. *Queen Mary* IV iii 564
Wrath Wet, famine, ague, fever, storm, wreck, *w*,— „ V v 109
mean The doom of England and the *w* of Heaven ? *Harold* I i 46
Is there no reason for the *w* of Heaven ? *Leofwin.* Why then the *w* of Heaven hath three tails, The devil only one. „ I i 59
To save thee from the *w* of Norman Saints. „ III i 217
Is thy *w* Hell, that I should spare to cry, „ V i 37
Shame, *w*, I know not what. *Becket* I iii 322
My lord John, In *w* because you drove him from the forest, *Foresters* III 450
Wreak glad to *w* our spite on the rosefaced minion *Becket, Pro.* 529
crowd May *w* my wrongs upon my wrongers. *Prom. of May* I 507
Wreath That wither'd *w* were of more worth to me. *The Falcon* 335
wither'd *w* is of more worth to me Than all the blossom, „ 337
I made a *w* with some of these ; „ 357
What's here ? a scroll Pinned to the *w*. My lord, you have said so much Of this poor *w* „ 425
And can you not imagine that the *w*, „ 534
one sweet face Crown'd with the *w*. „ 649
shall we say this *w* and your sweet rhymes ? „ 735
The *w* That once you wore outvalues twenty-fold „ 758
Then keep your *w*, But you will find me „ 773
Wreck (s) Wet, famine, ague, fever, storm, *w*, wrath,— *Queen Mary* V v 108
as men Have done on rafts of *w*—it drives you mad. *The Cup* I iii 142
I will be no such *w*, am no such gamester „ I iii 144
Wreck (verb) He *w's* his health and wealth on courtesans, *Queen Mary* I v 167
Holy Church May rock, but will not *w*, *Becket* II ii 104
Blown everyway with every gust and *w* On any rock ; *Prom. of May* III 537
Wrecked-Wreckt get himself *wrecked* on another man's land ? *Harold* II i 60
villains with their lying lights have *wreck'd* us ! „ II i 84
Or he is *wreckt* for ever. „ II ii 102
or *wreckt* And dead beneath the midland ocean, *Foresters* II i 656
Wreckful A summer mere with sudden *w* gusts From a side-gorge. *Harold* III i 51
Wrench *w* this outlander's ransom out of him— „ II i 58
Seize on the knight ! *w* his sword from him ! *Foresters* II i 676
Wrench'd violent will that *w* All hearts of freemen from thee. *Harold* V i 278
Wrest Would *w* from me the precious ring *Foresters* II i 660
Wrestle (s) Thy life is worth the *w* for it : *Becket* IV ii 194
Wrestle (verb) Rome Will crush you if you *w* with her ; *The Cup* I ii 131
Wretch but I, old *w*, old Stigand, With hands too limp *Harold* V i 447
if the *w* were dead I might forgive him ; *Prom. of May* II 433

Wretch (*continued*) Infamous *w* ! Shall I tell her he is dead? *Prom. of May* III 336
The old *w* is mad, and her bread is beyond me: *Foresters* II i 291
Wretched Most miserable sinner, *w* man. *Queen Mary* IV iii 123
on a land So hunger-nipt and *w*; „ V i 168
W race! And once I wish'd to scourge them to the bones. *The Cup* I i 25
Wretchedness yet have heard Of all their *w*. *Queen Mary* IV iii 212
His wickedness is like my *w*— *Prom. of May* III 747
Wriggle he will *w* out of them like an eel *Becket* II ii 187
Wring what we *w* from them we give the poor. *Foresters* II i 56
Wrinkle sweet worn smile Among thy patient *w's*— *Queen Mary* V v 200
silver Were dear as gold, the *w* as the dimple. *Foresters* IV 42
Wrist I cannot cope with him: my *w* is strain'd. „ IV 313
Writ (s) range Among the pleasant fields of Holy *W* *Queen Mary* III v 80
Make out the *w* to-night. „ IV i 195
by virtue of this *w*, whereas Robin Hood Earl of Huntingdon *Foresters* I iii 61
For playing upside down with Holy *W*. „ III 168
Whose *w* will run thro' all the range of life. „ IV 48
In the sweat of thy brow, says Holy *W*, shalt thou eat bread, „ IV 201
like the man In Holy *W*, who brought his talent back; „ IV 981
Writ (verb) (*See also* **Written**) *W* by himself and Bonner? *Queen Mary* IV i 93
Have I not *w* enough to satisfy you? „ IV ii 62
Write Philip never *w's* me one poor word, „ I v 359
yet—to *w* it down. „ II i 56
W you as many sonnets as you will. „ II i 95
W to him, then. *Pole.* I will. „ IV i 37
Pray you *w* out this paper for me, Cranmer. „ IV ii 60
hands that *w* them should be burnt clean off „ V ii 190
Cornwall's hand or Leicester's: they *w* marvellously alike. *Becket* I iv 52
cannot at present *w* himself other than *The Cup* I i 45
cannot at present *w* himself other than „ I ii 73
You will *w* to me? *Edgar.* I will. *Prom. of May* I 699
Eva, why did you *w* 'Seek me at the bottom of the river'? „ III 363
Writhed never stirr'd or *w*, but, like a statue, *Queen Mary* IV iii 620
Writing (part.) That any man so *w*, preaching so, „ IV iii 47
Writing (s) (*See also* **Sub-writing, Verse-writing**)
For these be *w's* I have set abroad „ IV iii 240
by your leave if you would hear the rest, The *w*. *The Falcon* 531
sometimes been moved to tears by a chapter of fine *w* in a novel; *Prom. of May* III 209
Written (*See also* **Writ**) Stand first it may, but it was *w* last: *Queen Mary* I ii 21
'Tis *w*, 'They shall be childless.' „ I ii 64
he must have *w*. „ I v 358
Queen had *w* her word to come to court: „ II ii 117
'tis not *w* Half plain enough. „ II iii 65
What hath your Highness *w*? „ III v 23
Hath he not *w* himself—infatuated— „ IV i 10
You have *w* much, But you were never raised „ IV ii 209
W for fear of death, to save my life, „ IV iii 242
by this hand *W* and sign'd— „ IV iii 245
since my hand offended, having *w* Against my heart, „ IV iii 248
what hath she *w*? read. „ V v 2
What hath she *w* now? „ V v 13
you will find *w* Two names, Philip and Calais; „ V v 154
I'll have them *w* down and made the law. *Becket, Pro.* 26
But by the King's command are *w* down, „ I iii 72
Good royal customs—had them *w* fair „ I iii 416
not yet *w*, Saving mine order; true too, that when *w* I sign'd them— „ I iii 558
What have I *w* to her? *The Cup* I i 35
and I find a *w* scroll That seems to run in rhymings. *The Falcon* 431
is *w* in invisible inks 'Lust, Prodigality, *Prom. of May* II 283
Wrong (adj.) I may be *w*, sir. This marriage will not hold. *Queen Mary* III i 102
For the *w* Robin took her at her word. „ III v 264
Those of the *w* side will despite the man, „ IV iii 24
—and I bean't *w* not twice i' ten year— „ IV iii 534
summut *w* theer, Wilson, fur I doänt understan' it. *Prom. of May* I 234
Wrong (s) I knew they would not do me any *w*, *Queen Mary* I iii 100
You did me *w*, I love not to be called „ I iv 67
Wrong (s) (*continued*) And she impress her *w's* upon her Council, *Queen Mary* III vi 183
To do him any *w* was to beget A kindness „ IV i 167
Ye do him *w*, ye do him *w*; *Harold* I ii 16
They did thee *w* who made thee hostage; „ II ii 349
I have done no man *w*. „ V i 272
We mean thee no *w*. *Becket* I iv 32
wilt but look into The *w's* you did him, „ II ii 116
before The Church should suffer *w*! „ III iii 20
if you love him, there is great *w* done Somehow; „ IV ii 94
Holy Church to thunder out her rights And thine own *w* „ V ii 33
Lost in the common good, the common *w*, „ V ii 41
crowd May wreak my *w's* upon my wrongers. *Prom. of May* I 507
I have done *w* in keeping your secret; „ III 399
ye did *w* in crying 'Down with John;' *Foresters* I ii 96
to such a heat As burns a *w* to ashes, „ II i 700
Wrong (verb) From stirring hand or foot to *w* the realm. *Queen Mary* III iii 60
Hush, hush! You *w* the Chancellor: „ III iii 67
Out, girl! you *w* a noble gentleman. „ III v 67
Perchance that Harold *w's* me; *Harold* I ii 225
That none should *w* or injure your Archbishop. *Becket* I iii 754
I *w* the bird; she leaves only the nest she built, „ I iv 45
You *w* the King: he meant what he said to-day. „ III iii 298
Perhaps, my lord, you *w* us. „ V ii 604
Why should I practise on you? How you *w* me! *The Cup* I ii 240
You *w* him surely; far as the face goes „ II 174
You *w* me there! hear, hear me! *Prom. of May* III 775
but we rob the robber, *w* the wronger, *Foresters* II i 54
Wrong'd There's half an angel *w* in your account; *Queen Mary* V iii 2
I were whole devil if I *w* you, Madam. „ V iii 7
That where he was but worsted, he was *w*. *Harold* I i 450
If one may dare to speak the truth, was *w*. „ IV i 109
believing that our brother Had *w* you; *Becket* II ii 239
The by-things of the Lord Are the *w* innocences that will cry „ III iii 14
You have *w* Fitzurse. I speak not of myself. „ IV ii 328
One whom thou hast *w* Without there, *The Cup* I ii 319
W by the cruelties of his religions *Prom. of May* III 545
One that has been much *w*, whose griefs are mine, „ III 576
thou hast *w* my brother and myself. *Foresters* II i 665
We never *w* a woman. „ III 184
One half of this shall go to those they have *w*, „ III 304
Wronger It gilds the greatest *w* of her peace, *Queen Mary* V ii 415
In the great day against the *w*. *Becket* III iii 17
crowd May wreak my wrongs upon my *w's*. *Prom. of May* I 507
but we rob the robber, wrong the *w*, *Foresters* II i 55
Wrote letter you *w* against Their superstition *Queen Mary* I ii 85
I *w* it, and God grant me power to burn! „ I ii 98
And what a letter he *w* against the Pope! „ III i 173
which God's hand *W* on her conscience, „ III i 422
last time she *w*, I had like to have lost my life: „ III v 188
when last he *w*, declared His comfort „ III vi 77
same book You *w* against my Lord of Winchester; „ IV iii 265
I hold by all I *w* within that book. „ IV iii 275
To compass which I *w* myself to Rome, „ V i 49
letter which the Count de Noailles *w* „ V ii 497
right hand Lamed in the battle, *w* it with his left. *The Falcon* 445
my sister *w* he was mighty pleasant, and had no pride in him. *Prom. of May* I 116
Wroth they are *w* with their own selves, *Queen Mary* III iv 120
That I was for a moment *w* at thee. „ III iv 306
The Queen, most *w* at first with you, „ III iv 387
Except when *w*, you scarce could meet his eye And hold your own; and were he *w* indeed, You held it less, or not at all. „ IV i 103
Why should not Heaven be *w*? *Harold* I i 53
I am weary—go: make me not *w* with thee! „ V i 31
Yon heaven is *w* with *thee*? „ V i 39
And so the saints were *w*. „ V ii 7
be not *w* at the dumb parchment. *Foresters* I i 342
Wrought and this *w* Upon the king; *Queen Mary* I ii 70
he *w* it ignorantly, And not from any malice. „ III i 276
was the great mystery *w*; „ IV iii 142
That all day long hath *w* his father's work, „ V ii 118

Wrought (*continued*) I have *w* miracles—to God the glory—
And miracles will in my name be *w* Hereafter.— *Harold* I i 181
w upon to swear Vows that he dare not break. „ II ii 76
Yea, *w* at them myself. „ V i 192
O Edith, if I ever *w* against thee, „ V ii 21
We long have *w* together, thou and I— *Becket* I i 339
forgive you For aught you *w* against us. „ II ii 110
And *w* his worst against his native land, *The Cup* I ii 177
we must at times have *w* Some great injustice, *Foresters* III 155

Wrung She had no desire for that, and *w* her hands, *Queen Mary* III i 384
w his ransom from him by the rack, *Harold* II ii 38

Wry he made a *w* mouth at it, but he took it so kindly, *The Falcon* 191
and he never made a *w* mouth at you, he always took you so kindly— „ 194

Wulfnoth Is not my brother *W* hostage there *Harold* I i 239
he and *W* never Have met, except in public; „ II ii 85
I have often talk'd with *W*, „ II ii 89
Since thou hast promised *W* home with us, Be home again with *W*. „ II ii 167
Look thou, here is *W*! „ II ii 323
No, *W*, no. *Wulfnoth.* And William laugh'd „ II ii 360
Poor *W*! do they not entreat thee well? „ II ii 403
let me hence With *W* to King Edward. „ II ii 563
O *W*, *W*, brother, thou hast betray'd me! „ II ii 801
And *W* is alone in Normandy. „ III i 81
'*W* is sick,' he said; 'he cannot follow;' „ III i 84
As far as touches *W* I that so prized „ III i 92
only grandson To *W*, a poor cow-herd. *Harold.* This old *W* Would take me on his knees „ IV i 70

Wunt (will not) but they *w* set i' the Lord's cheer o' that daay. *Queen Mary* IV iii 469

Wuss (worse) And *w* nor that. *Prom. of May* I 136
Glum! he be *w* nor glum. „ II 149
Noä, Miss; we worked naw *w* upo' the cowd tea; „ III 59

Wyatt (Sir Thomas, insurrectionary leader) (*See also* **Thomas, Thomas Wyatt**) Look you, Master *W*, Tear up that woman's work *Queen Mary* II i 74
W, *W*, Wake, or the stout old island „ II i 102
you are as poor a poet, *W*, As a good soldier. „ II i 113
whisper'd, '*W*,' And whisking round a corner, „ II i 130
A *W*! a *W*! *Wyatt.* But first to Rochester, „ II i 219
A *W*! a *W*! Forward! *Knyvett.* *W*, „ II i 237
who went with your train bands To fight with *W*, „ II ii 28
Know too what *W* said. „ II ii 35
She shrilling '*W*,' while the boy she held Mimick'd and piped her '*W*,' „ II ii 72
names of *W*, Elizabeth, Courtenay, „ II ii 94
W, who hath tamper'd with A public ignorance, „ II ii 180
Long live Queen Mary! Down with *W*! The Queen! „ II ii 253
and brush This *W* from our shoulders, „ II ii 294
strong to throw ten *W's* and all Kent. „ II ii 353
W comes to Southwark; „ II ii 374
Whether I be for *W*, or the Queen? „ II ii 415
Thou cried'st 'A *W*!' and flying to our side „ II iii 3
W, but now you promised me a boon. „ II iii 81
W, your Grace, hath broken thro' the guards „ II iv 19
Also this *W* did confess the Princess „ II iv 111
What *W* said, or what they said he said, „ II iv 127
W was a good soldier, yet he fail'd, „ III i 132
What such a one as *W* says is nothing: „ III i 139
Thou art one of *W's* men? *Man.* No, my Lord, no. „ III i 244
The stormy *W's* and Northumberlands, „ III ii 168
pray'd me to confess In *W's* business, „ III v 167
other things As idle; a weak *W*! „ V i 292
There were not many hang'd for *W's* rising. „ V ii 9
Noailles wrote To that dead traitor *W*, „ V ii 498
lost When *W* sack'd the Chancellor's house „ V ii 504
A new Northumberland, another *W*? „ V v 188

Y

Yard And make a morning outcry in the *y*; *Queen Mary* III v 158
three *y's* about the waist is like to remain a virgin, *Foresters* I ii 69

Yawn (s) A life of nods and *y's*. *Queen Mary* I iii 116

Yawn (verb) Dug from the grave that *y's* for us beyond; „ V ii 163

Yawn'd The nurses *y*, the cradle gaped, „ III vi 93

Year (*See also* **Five-years', New Year, Seven-years', To-year**) such a game, sir, were whole *y's* a playing. „ I iii 140
So many *y's* in yon accursed Tower— „ I iv 200
I am eleven *y's* older than he is. „ I v 68
Thus, after twenty *y's* of banishment, „ III ii 46
this day be held in after *y's* More solemn „ III iii 90
this noble realm thro' after *y's* May in this unity „ III iii 156
In your five *y's* of imprisonment, „ III iv 242
But not for five-and-twenty *y's*, my Lord. „ III iv 267
the doctors tell you, At three-score *y's*; „ III iv 410
To yield the remnant of his *y's* to heaven, „ III vi 210
His eighty *y's* Look'd somewhat crooked „ IV iii 331
—and I bean't wrong not twice i' ten *y*— „ IV iii 534
After my twenty *y's* of banishment, „ V ii 69
Our flag hath floated for two hundred *y's* Is France again. „ V ii 262
gather all From sixteen *y's* to sixty; „ V ii 273
Don Carlos, Madam, is but twelve *y's* old. „ V iii 88
I am eleven *y's* older than he, Poor boy! „ V v 46
Twelve *y's* of service! *Harold* I i 221
after those twelve *y's* a boon, my king, „ I i 225
And leave them for a *y*, and coming back Find them again. „ II i 89
in the cruel river Swale A hundred *y's* ago; „ III ii 11
thou in after *y's* Praying perchance for this poor soul „ V i 322
And York lay barren for a hundred *y's*. *Becket* I iii 54
Ye have eaten of my dish and drunken of my cup for a dozen *y's*. „ I iv 30
Father Philip that has confessed our mother for twenty *y's*, „ III i 112
Y's and *y's*, my lady, for her husband, King Louis— „ III i 169
She past me here Three *y's* ago *The Cup* I i 6
one who *y's* ago, himself an adorer of our great goddess, „ I i 37
To see if *y's* have changed her. „ I i 125
where twenty *y's* ago Huntsman, and hound, „ I ii 22
If Synorix, who has dwelt three *y's* in Rome „ I ii 175
three *y's* ago—the vast vine-bowers „ I ii 401
found together In our three married *y's*! „ I ii 417
It is old, I know not How many hundred *y's*. „ II 343
Beside this temple half a *y* ago? „ II 393
I had a touch of this last *y*—in—Rome. „ II 446
a-spreading to catch her eye for a dozen *y*, *The Falcon* 101
been on my knees every day for these half-dozen *y's* „ 185
when he came last *y* To see me hawking, „ 312
all the leaf of this New-wakening *y*. „ 340
I never saw The land so rich in blossom as this *y*. *Count.* Was not the *y* when this was gather'd richer? „ 343
That was the very *y* before you married. „ 373
True tears that *y* were shed for you in Florence. „ 384
faded ribbon was the mode In Florence ten *y's* back. „ 423
most beautiful May we have had for many *y's*! *Prom. of May* I 567
As *y's* go on, he feels them press upon him, „ I 647
It be five *y* sin' ye went afoor to him, „ II 5
hallus gi'ed soom on 'em to Miss Eva at this time o' *y*. „ II 16
you must not be too sudden with it either, as you were last *y*, „ II 55
We have been in such grief these five *y's*, „ II 67
Poor sister, I had it five *y's* ago. „ II 82
Many *y's* back, and never since have met „ II 370
She was there six *y's* ago. „ II 399
Have sorrow'd for her all these *y's* in vain. „ II 415
can he trace me Thro' five *y's* absence, „ II 615
her cry rang to me across the *y's*, „ II 656

Year (*continued*) Him as did the mischief here, five *y'* sin'. — *Prom. of May* III 140
who came to us three *y's* after you were gone, — „ III 232
You must not expect to find our Father as he was five *y's* ago. — „ III 420
grave he goes to, Beneath the burthen of *y's*. — „ III 517
Five *y's* of shame and suffering broke the heart — „ III 761
if they be not paid back at the end of the *y*, the land goes to the Abbot. — *Foresters* I i 70
in the long sweep of *y's* to come must the great man — „ I i 244
must be paid in a *y* and a month, or I lose the land. — „ I i 269
they have trodden it for half a thousand *y's*, — „ I i 334
Who deign to honour this my thirtieth *y*, — „ I ii 80
Must you have these monies before the *y* and the month end? — „ I ii 150
make us merry Because a *y* of it is gone? but Hope Smiles from the threshold of the *y* to come — „ I iii 15
Sings a new song to the new *y*— — „ I iii 28
I have reign'd one *y* in the wild wood. — „ II i 36
I should be happier for it all the *y*. — „ II i 163
She was murdered here a hundred *y* ago, — „ II i 245
For now is the spring of the *y*. — „ IV 17
She said 'It's the fall of the *y*, — „ IV 24
I have been away from England all these *y's*, — „ IV 817
I have had a *y* of prison-silence, Robin, — „ IV 923
And here perhaps a hundred *y's* away — „ IV 1087

Yearn *Y's* to set foot upon your island shore. — *Queen Mary* I v 367

Yearn'd How often has my sick boy *y* for this! — *The Falcon* 829

Yeäs (yes) *Y*, *y*! I'll not meddle wi' 'im if he doänt meddle wi' meä. — *Prom. of May* I 173
To look to—*y*, 'coomly'; — „ I 180
Y; but I haätes 'im, — „ I 312
Y, *y*! Three cheers for Mr. Steer! — „ I 455
Eva's saäke. *Y*. — „ II 31
The last on it, eh? *Haymaker*. *Y*. — „ II 142
Y, an' owd Dobson should be glad on it. — „ II 146
Noä—*y*—thaw the feller's gone and maäde such a litter of his faäce. — „ II 588
Y! Fur she niver knawed 'is faäce when 'e wur 'ere afoor; — „ II 606
The little 'ymn? *Y*, Miss; — „ III 1
Y, Miss. (repeat) — *Prom. of May* III 18, 480, 485
Y; and thanks to ye. — *Prom. of May* III 26
Letters! *Y*, I sees now. — „ III 38
Y, Miss; but he wur so rough wi' ma, — „ III 103
Y, Miss; and he wants to speak to ye partic'lar. — „ III 350
Y, Miss; but he says he wants to tell ye summut very partic'lar. — „ III 354
Y, Miss, I will. — „ III 417
Y, the marriage. — „ III 708
O law—*y*, Sir! I'll run fur 'im mysen. — „ III 713

Yell (s) True test of coward, ye follow with a *y*. — *Becket* I iii 745
wassail *y's* of thief And rogue and liar — *Foresters* III 322

Yell (verb) whenever a murder is to be done again she *y's* out i' this way— — „ II i 247

Yell'd when all was lost, he *y*, — *Harold* V i 404

Yellow I thought this Philip had been one of those black devils of Spain, but he hath a *y* beard. — *Queen Mary* III i 216
the wholesome plow Lay rusting in the furrow's *y* weeds, — *Becket* I iii 355
There was a bit of *y* silk here and there, — „ IV i 21

Yelper as when we threaten A *y* with a stick. — „ IV ii 350

Yelping I hear the *y* of the hounds of hell. — „ III ii 48

Yeoman Quick with thy sword! the *y* braves the knight. — *Foresters* II ii 30
Nay, no Earl am I. I am English *y*. — „ III 131
I am the *y*, plain Robin Hood, — „ IV 143

Yeo-woman Then *I* am *y-w*. O the clumsy word! — „ III 132

Yes *See* **Yeas**

Yesterday (*See also* **Yisterdaäy**) I heard from my Northumbria *y*. — *Harold* I i 331
y you mentioned her name too suddenly before my father. — *Prom. of May* II 23

Yestereven It seems but *y* I held it with him — *Harold* V ii 126
Seen in the thicket at the bottom there But *y-e*. — *The Cup* I i 115
Why didst thou miss thy quarry *y-e*? — *The Falcon* 151

Yew I that held the orange blossom Dark as the *y*? — *Prom. of May* II 631
Past the bank Of foxglove, then to left by that one *y*. — *Foresters* IV 974

Yew-wood true woodman's bow of the best *y-w* to slay the deer. — „ II i 393

Yield not to *y* His Church of England — *Queen Mary* I ii 35
I do believe she'd *y*. — „ I iv 22
y Full scope to persons rascal and forlorn, — „ II ii 184
Doth Pole *y*, sir, ha! — „ III iv 394
To *y* the remnant of his years to heaven, — „ III vi 210
Didst thou *y* up thy Son to human death; — „ IV iii 144
after all those papers Of recantation *y* again. — „ IV iii 315
fierier than fire To *y* them their deserts. — „ V iv 27
Harold, I will not *y* thee leave to go. — *Harold* I i 256
Thou canst make *y* this iron-mooded Duke — „ II ii 339
Ask me not, Lest I should *y* it, — „ III ii 47
Heaven *y* us more! for better, — „ III ii 71
will ye, if I *y*, Follow against the Norseman? — „ IV i 176
I *y* it freely, being the true wife — „ V ii 84
betwixt thine Appeal, and Henry's anger, *y*. — *Becket* I iii 623
My lord, we cannot *y* thee an answer — „ I iv 21
not *y* To lay your neck beneath your citizen's heel. — „ V i 30
Well spoken, wife. *Synorix*. Madam, so well I *y*. — *The Cup* I ii 173
O *y* them all their desire! — „ II 8
Life *y's* to death and wisdom bows to Fate, — „ II 89
Will *y* herself as easily to another. — *Prom. of May* I 747
y A nobler breed of men and women. — *The Falcon* 754
let them be, man, let them be. We *y*. — *Foresters* I iii 78
criedst 'I *y*' almost before the thing was ask'd, — „ II i 566
She will not marry till her father *y*. — „ II ii 82
I *y*, I *y*. I know no quarterstaff. — „ IV 257

Yielded should have *y* So utterly!—strange! — *Queen Mary* III iii 8
When last I saw you, You all but *y*. — *The Cup* II 45

Yisterdaäy (yesterday) He coom'd up to me *y* i' the haäyfield, — *Prom. of May* II 150

'Ymn (hymn) The little '*y*? Yeäs, Miss; — „ III 1

Yoke Will shift the *y* and weight of all the world — *Queen Mary* III vi 212

Yolk she that has eaten the *y* is scarce like to swallow the shell. — *The Falcon* 704

Yon *Y* gray old Gospeller, sour as midwinter, — *Queen Mary* I iii 40
for the two were fellow-prisoners So many years in *y* accursed Tower— — „ I iv 200
Is not *y* light in the Queen's chamber? — „ V iv 1
Y grimly-glaring, treble-brandish'd scourge Of England! — *Harold* I i 3
More talk of this to-morrow, if *y* weird sign Not blast us in our dreams.— — „ I i 120
And *y* huge keep that hinders half the heaven. — „ II ii 228
I sorrow'd for my random promise given To *y* fox-lion. — „ III i 270
Y heaven is wroth with *thee*? — „ V i 39
drop The mud I carried, like *y* brook, — *Becket* II i 159
And see you *y* side-beam that is forced from under it, — „ III iii 49

Yore There is one Come as Goliath came of *y*— — *Harold* V i 493

York Hath taken Scarboro' Castle, north of *Y*; — *Queen Mary* V i 288
They have taken *Y*. — *Harold* III ii 171
Y taken? *Gurth*. Yea, Tostig hath taken *Y*! — „ III ii 174
To *Y* then. Edith, Hadst thou been braver, — „ III ii 177
Roger of *Y*. *Henry*. Roger is Roger of *Y*. — *Becket, Pro.* 267
To set that precious jewel, Roger of *Y*. — „ *Pro.* 270
Roger of *Y*, When I and thou were youths in Theobald's house, — „ I iii 39
Now I am Canterbury and thou art *Y*. *Roger of York*. And is not *Y* the peer of Canterbury? — „ I iii 45
Found two archbishopricks, London and *Y*? — „ I iii 51
And *Y* lay barren for a hundred years. — „ I iii 54
Bishops—*Y*, London, Chichester, Westminster— — „ I iii 385
Let *Y* bear his to mate with Canterbury. — „ I iii 512
My Lord of *Y*, Let us go in to the Council, — „ I iii 546
There's *Y*, my liege. — „ II ii 28
hold Young Henry king, if only crown'd by *Y*, And that would stilt up *Y* — „ II ii 33
Cursed be John of Oxford, Roger of *Y*, And Gilbert Foliot! — „ II ii 266
I go to have young Henry crown'd by *Y*. — „ II ii 479
hath in this crowning of young Henry by *Y* and London — „ III iii 71
And how did Roger of *Y* comport himself? — „ III iii 84
my Lord of *Y*—his fine-cut face bowing — „ III iii 140

Z

A CONCORDANCE TO THE POEMS

CONTAINED IN THE LIFE OF

ALFRED, LORD TENNYSON.

A

Abyss The starr'd *a'es* of the sky, *'Tis not alone* 2
Accept *A's* the song you gave, and he sends *Little Aubrey* 2
A on this your golden bridal day *Remembering him* 3
Ache Till heart and sight and hearing *a* *How strange it is* 3
Act (s) Steersman, be not precipitate in thine *a* Of steering *Steersman* 1
Act (verb) *a* on Eternity To keep thee here *That is his portrait* 39
Admire *A* that stalwart shape, those ample brows, „ 4
Æon In the vast Of the rolling of the *a's*, *Little Aubrey* 6
Aerial Whose trumpet-tongued, *a* melody *O God, make this age* 3
Affectation Let it cry an *a*, *Immeasurable sadness!* 6
Affection To thee with whom my true *a's* dwell, *To thee with whom* 1
Afraid Truth-seeking he and not *a*, *He was too good* 5
Age when your *a* had somewhat riper grown, *Hear you the sound* 54
O God, make this *a* great that we may be *O God, make this age* 1
O'er the bow'd shoulder of a bland old *A*, *That is his portrait* 36
To hold the Spirit of the *A* Against the Spirit *They wrought, etc.* 47
Agony An energy, an *a*, A labour working to an end. *Youth, lapsing ii* 3
Aileth What *a* thee, O bird divine, *Full light aloft* 5
Aim So lived I without *a* or choice, *Youth, lapsing i* 37
Air (*See also* **Under-air**) gaily spring In that unwholesome *a*, *Far off in the dun* 10
glooms were spread Around in the chilling *a*, „ 102
With pleasant hymns they soothe the *a* Of death, „ 109
there Hovering, thoughtful, poised in *a*. *Not to Silence* 12
Airy On her forehead undefiled I will print an *a* kiss: *Not a whisper* 12
Ait Streaming thro' his osier'd *a's*! *Vicar of this* 20
Akin Great spirits grow *a* to base. *They wrought, etc.* 16
Alarum May blow *a* loud to every wind, *O God, make this age* 4
Ale lifts The creaming horn of corny *a*! *Yon huddled cloud* 4
Gives stouter *a* and riper port „ 7
Alfred little *A* in the East *Little Aubrey* 1
All *A* things please you, nothing vex you, *Vicar of this* 9
that give The difference of *a* things to the sense, *Why suffers* 10
An orb repulsive of *a* hate, A will concentric with *a* fate, A life four-square to *a* the winds. *Young is the grief* 14
And how *a* things become the past. *Youth, lapsing i* 28
And the guard gasp'd out '*A's* right.' *Far off in the dun* 88
A freedom vanish'd— *Rise, Britons, rise* 3
All-perfect but rather bless The *A-p* Framer, *That is his portrait* 48
Alma At the battle of *A* River. *Frenchman, etc.* 4
That rests by the *A* River. „ 12
Aloft Full light *a* doth the laverock spring *Full light aloft* 1
Alone 'Tis not *a* the warbling woods, *'Tis not alone* 1
Along voice Cried in the future 'Come *a*.' *Youth, lapsing i* 40
Altar bind Falsehood beneath the *a* of great Truth: *O God, make this age* 8
Alternation With click-clack *a* to and fro, *Half after midnight!* 8
Ambrosial and make beneath *A* gloom. *Hear you the sound* 30
Amethyst Of beryl, and of *a* Was the spiritual frame. *Far off in the dun* 123
Ample Admire that stalwart shape, those *a* brows, *That is his portrait* 4
Anacaona happy as *A*, The beauty of Espagnola, repeat) *A dark Indian maiden* 10, 22
Anacaona (*continued*) Indian queen, *A*, Dancing on the blossomy plain *A dark Indian maiden* 28
Happy happy was *A*, The beauty of Espagnola, „ 34
Happy, happy *A*, The beauty of Espagnola, „ 46
they smiled on *A*, The beauty of Espagnola, „ 58
No more in Xaraguay Wander'd happy *A*, „ 70
Anadyomenè more fair to me Than aught of *A*! *Not to Silence* 16
Anana By the crimson-eyed *a*, *A dark Indian maiden* 4
Ancestor battlemented towers Of my old *a's*! *Hear you the sound* 13
Ancient (*See also* **Antient**) He cares, if *a* usage fade, *They wrought, etc.* 33
Anger victim, Broken in this *a* of Aphrodite, *Faded ev'ry violet* 3
Ankle floating snake Roll'd round her *a's*, *One was the Tishbite* 10
Anon 'Tis a clear night, they will be here *a*. *Hear you the sound* 6
Another Into *a* shape, born of the first, As beautiful, but yet *a* world. *That is his portrait* 29
and I will show to you *A* countenance, one yet more dear, „ 45
Antient (*See also* **Ancient**) And somewhat loftier *a* heights Touch'd with Heaven's latest lights. *Thy soul is like* 11
Apart Not with this age wherefrom ye stand *a*, *Therefore your Halls* 11
Ape (s) We come from *a's*—and are far removed— *How is it that men* 4
Ape (verb) And the voice that *a's* a nation— *Immeasurable sadness!* 5
Aphrodite victim, Broken in this anger of *A*, *Faded ev'ry violet* 3
Apparel For they were kingly in *a*, *A dark Indian maiden* 63
Approach what lights *a* With heavenly melodies? *Far off in the dun* 105
Arch (s) look you what an *a* the brain has built *That is his portrait* 10
Beneath those double *a'es* lie Fair with green fields *Youth, lapsing ii* 35
Arch (verb) thick dark oaks, that *a* their arms above, *Hear you the sound* 11
Archangel And a bright *a* drove. *Far off in the dun* 116
Areyto moving To her *A's* mellow ditty, *A dark Indian maiden* 50
Aristocrat proud *a's* whose lordly shadows, *Hear you the sound* 21
Arm thick dark oaks, that arch their *a's* above, „ 11
With one *a* stretch'd out bare, *One was the Tishbite* 3
this one smiled, that other waved his *a's*, *That is his portrait* 22
Armed A sound of blows on *a* breasts! And individual interests Becoming bands of *a* foes! *They wrought, etc.* 18
Array And though girt in glad *a*, *The lamps were bright* 23
Art *A* for *A's* sake! Hail, *Art for Art's sake!* 1
I hate the trim-set plots of *a*!' *I keep no more* 14
A, Science, Nature, everything is full, *Why suffers* 7
Artist Like some wise *a*, Nature gives, *'Tis not alone* 6
Ash by fits the lady *a* With twinkling finger *Townsmen, etc.* 9
Ask *a* you whether you would be A great man in your time, *Hear you the sound* 56
Asleep sound of the deep when the winds are *a*; *That the voice* 3
Asphaltus slime Which from *A* flows. *Far off in the dun* 40
Athwart as 'twere *a* a colour'd cloud, *That is his portrait* 35
A the bloomy morn. *Full light aloft* 4
Atrophy And his name was *A*! *Far off in the dun* 56
Attire And rich was their *a*: „ 126
Attitude Down to his slightest turns and *a's*— *That is his portrait* 24
Aubrey Little *A* in the West! little Alfred in the East *Little Aubrey* 1
Austral *Your flag thro'* A *ice is borne,* *The noblest men* 6

Avenue through The knotted boughs of this long *a* *Hear you the sound* 10
Awe And looks to *a* the standers by, *Because she bore* 4
Awful Our *a* inner ghostly sense Unroused, *How strange it is* 5
Awry mould you all *a* and mar your worth; *Old ghosts* 11

B

Babble cuckoo-voice that loves To *b* its own name. *I, loving Freedom* 8
we, Poor devils, *b* 'we shall last.' *Well, as to Fame* 8
Babe Father will come to his *b* in the nest, *Bright is the moon* 11
Baby and knit your *b* brows Into your father's frown, *Hear you the sound* 48
Back voices mourn'd In distant fields, 'Come *b*, come *b*.' *Youth, lapsing i* 44
Bad When a great man's found to be *b* and base, *How is it that men* 2
Balmy And softly blow the *b* skies; *Life of the Life* 4
Band (a company) Becoming *b's* of armed foes! *They wrought, etc.* 20
Band (strip) We drest her in the Proctor's *b's*, *Sweet Kitty Sandilands* 3
Bang *B* thy stithy stronger and stronger, *Wherever evil* 8
Banish'd The true men *b*— *Rise, Britons, rise* 4
Bank Whate'er the crowd on either *b* may say, *Steersman* 7
child was sitting on the *b* Upon a stormy day, *The child was sitting* 1
Bar rivulet, Rippling by cressy isles or *b's* of sand, *Townsmen, etc.* 6
Bare With one arm stretch'd out *b*, *One was the Tishbite* 3
Barkless And above the *b* trees They saw the green verge of the pleasant earth, *Far off in the dun* 62
Barley Full fields of *b* shifting tearful lights *Townsmen, etc.* 8
Barren If night, what *b* toil to be! *Gone into darkness* 6
Base When a great man's found to be bad and *b*, *How is it that men* 2
Great spirits grow akin to *b*. *They wrought, etc.* 16
Bathe *B* with me in the fiery flood, *Life of the life* 5
Bathing *B* in the slumbrous coves, *A dark Indian maiden* 7
Battle Every mile a *b*, Every *b* a victory. *Bold Havelock* 3
At the *b* of Alma River. *Frenchman, etc.* 4
Battlemented Coeval with the *b* towers Of my old ancestors! *Hear you the sound* 12
Bay Dancing by a palmy *b*, *A dark Indian maiden* 18
With her maidens to the *b*; „ 42
With her damsels by the *b*; „ 54
wreath'd with green *b's* were the gorgeous lamps, *Far off in the dun* 115
Beaker He brims his *b* to the top, *Yon huddled cloud* 13
Beam Bright are the cliffs in her *b*, *Bright is the moon* 2
Warm *b's* across the meadows stole; *The night, etc.* 3
Ray'd round with *b's* of living light. *Youth, lapsing ii* 52
Bear Although the merry bridegroom *B's* the bride away, *The lamps were bright* 12
Beard He strokes his *b* before he speaks; *Yon huddled cloud* 10
Bearest Thou *b* from the threshold of thy friends *Woman of noble* 3
Beat And the *b* of the horny heels? *Far off in the dun* 96
Long as the heart *b's* life within her breast, *Long as the heart* 1
sorrows of as pure a heart As e'er *b* time to Nature, *Woman of noble* 5
Warm *b's* my blood, my spirit thirsts; *Youth, lapsing ii* 45
Beauteous Nor Sorrow *b* in her youth, *Are those the far-famed* 7
Beautiful Into another shape, born of the first, As *b*, *That is his portrait* 30
E'en scorn looks *b* on human lips! *Why suffers* 4
Beauty happy as Anacaona, The *b* of Espagnola, (repeat) *A dark Indian maiden* 11, 23
Happy, happy was Anacaona, The *b* of Espagnola, „ 35
happy Anacaona, The *b* of Espagnola, (repeat) „ 47, 71
they smiled on Anacaona, The *b* of Espagnola, „ 59
B, Good and Knowledge are three sisters . . . *Beauty, Good, etc.* 1
Strange *beauties* from the sky. *Far off in the dun* 32
Beckon father's frown, and *b* me Away. *Hear you the sound* 49
Bed damn'd that writhe Upon their *b's* of flame, *Half after midnight!* 11
Clusters and *b's* of worlds, *Hither, when all* 7
Bedimm'd The tears *b* their sight: *Far off in the dun* 86
Bee-like *b-l* swarms Of suns, and starry streams. *Hither, when all* 7
Began Old ghosts whose day was done ere mine *b*, *Old ghosts* 1
The months, ere they *b* to rise, *Youth, lapsing i* 9
they *b* at last To speak of what had gone before, „ 26
Begin The May *b's* to breathe and bud, *Life of the Life* 3
Beginning In thy *b's* in the past, *Young is the grief* 11
Behind *B* the burning Sun: *Far off in the dun* 2
Behold *B*, ye cannot bring but good, *Are those the far-famed* 5
Belie To make me thus *b* my constant heart *To thee with whom* 11

Bend That streams about the *b*; *Steersman* 5
Take thou the '*b*,' 'twill save thee many a day. „ 8
showing every *b* Of each dark hill *Thy soul is like* 5
Beryl Of *b*, and of amethyst Was the spiritual frame. *Far off in the dun* 123
Best And God's *b* blessing on each dear head That rests by the Alma River. *Frenchman, etc.* 11
Bigger But rejoice when a *b* brother has proved *How is it that men* 5
Bind when Poesy shall *b* Falsehood beneath the altar *O God, make this age* 7
Bird What aileth thee, O *b* divine, *Full light aloft* 5
Like *b's* of passage, to return with thee *Woman of noble* 8
Birth That Inn was built at the *b* of Time: *Far off in the dun* 37
and tell me you were great Already in your *b*. *Hear you the sound* 60
high *b* Had writ nobility upon my brow. „ 63
She whose *b* brought on my bliss: *Not a whisper* 10
Bitter Whoever walks that *b* ground His limbs beneath him fail; *Far off in the dun* 25
On the *b*, *b* bridal, The *b* bridal-day. *The lamps were bright* 53
a stranger tale to tell Than if the vine had borne the *b* sloe. *To thee with whom* 4
Black They mounted slow in their long *b* cloaks, *Far off in the dun* 85
And why her *b* eyes burn With a light so wild and stern?' *The lamps were bright* 15
What is that I hear? The night is *b* and still; *What rustles* 3
Bland O'er the bow'd shoulder of a *b* old Age, *That is his portrait* 36
Blast the ricketty *b* runs shrilly and fast *Far off in the dun* 11
Blatant We help the *b* voice abroad To preach the freedom of despair, *He was too good* 9
Bleat deer *B* as with human voices in the park. *What rustles* 4
Blend A noise of winds that meet and *b*, *Youth, lapsing ii* 2
Bless child will *b* thee, guardian mother mild, *Long as the heart* 2
but rather *b* The All-perfect Framer, *That is his portrait* 47
God *b* the little isle where a man may still be true!
God *b* the noble isle that is Mistress of the Seas! *They say, etc.* 17
Bless'd-Blest thy memory will be *bless'd* By children *Long as the heart* 3
They see the light of their *blest* firesides, *Far off in the dun* 65
Were I not a spirit *blest*, *Not a whisper* 7
Blessing And God's best *b* on each dear head *Frenchman, etc.* 11
Blest *See* **Bless'd**
Blind then Is this *b* flight the winged Powers. *Are those the far-famed* 4
Bliss She whose birth brought on my *b*: *Not a whisper* 10
Something of pain—of *b*—of Love, *'Tis not alone* 11
Blissful That wash'd her shores with *b* sounds: *Youth, lapsing i* 4
Blithe she seeming *b* Declined her head: *One was the Tishbite* 13
Blood 'I am of Havelock's *b*!' *Bold Havelock* 16
The tingling *b* grew chill, *Far off in the dun* 78
Whose *b* in its liveliest course would not pause „ 93
My Spanish *b* ran proudly in my veins. *Hear you the sound* 45
Life of the Life within my *b*, (repeat) *Life of the Life* 1, 7
what madness moved my *b* To make me thus belie *To thee with whom* 10
Sent thro' my *b* a prophet voice *Youth, lapsing i* 10
Warm beats my *b*, my spirit thirsts; „ *ii* 45
Bloom'd Indian maiden, Warbling in the *b* liana, *A dark Indian maiden* 2
Bloomy And chants in the golden wakening Athwart the *b* morn. *Full light aloft* 4
Blossomy Dancing on the *b* plain To a woodland melody: *A dark Indian maiden* 29
Blow (s) A sound of words that change to *b's*! A sound of *b's* on armed breasts! *They wrought, etc.* 17
Blow (verb) And softly *b* the balmy skies; *Life of the Life* 4
May *b* alarum loud to every wind, *O God, make this age* 4
With that long horn she loves to *b*, *Well, as to Fame* 2
Behind yon hill the trumpets *b*, *Youth, lapsing ii* 11
Blowing Watch your standard roses *b*, *Vicar of this* 12
Blown *Your name is* b *on every wind*, *The noblest men* 5
Blue (adj.) With fair *b* eyes and winning sweet, *Because she bore* 3
From dawn till sunset looking far away On the *b* mountains, *Hear you the sound* 40
Blue (s) pall of the sky Leave never an inch of *b*; *Far off in the dun* 22
Body heads without *bodies* and shapes without heads „ 103
Bold *B* Havelock march'd, (repeat) *Bold Havelock* 1, 5, 9, 13
Bone (*See also* **Skull and Cross-bones**) eyes glared fiercely thro' The windows of shaven *b*. *Far off in the dun* 48
There was not a tinge on each high cheek *b*, „ 51
His *b's* crack'd loud, as he stept thro' the crowd, „ 75
threw up the dust Of dead men's pulverised *b's*. „ 92

Bony But the ricketty blast runs shrilly and fast Thro' the *b* branches there. *Far off in the dun* 12
Book your golden bridal day The *B* of Prayer. *Remembering him* 4
full God-bless-you with this *b* of song, *Take, Lady,* 2
I give this faulty b *to you,* *The noblest men* 9
Boot And his *b's* creak'd heavily. *Far off in the dun* 76
Booth The hubbub of the market and the *b's*: *That is his portrait* 21
Bore Because she *b* the iron name Of him *Because she bore* 1
And *b* the child away. *The child was sitting* 7
the merry bridegroom *B* the bride away! *The lamps were bright* 4
Born This chamber she was *b* in! *Along this glimmering* 3
All Nature is the womb whence Man is *b*. *Hold thou, my friend* 2
Into another shape, *b* of the first, *That is his portrait* 29
Borne (*See also* **Wind-borne**) merry bridegroom Hath *b* the bride away— (repeat) *The lamps were bright* 20, 26, 38, 44
a merry bridegroom Had *b* the bride away, „ 50
Your flag thro' Austral ice is b, *The noblest men* 6
Than if the vine had *b* the bitter sloe. *To thee with whom* 4
Bough through The knotted *b's* of this long avenue *Hear you the sound* 10
Bound (limit) transgressing the low *b* Of mortal hope, *That is his portrait* 38
The river rose and burst his *b*, *The child was sitting* 4
Bound (verb) When corny Lammas *b* the sheaves: *Youth, lapsing i* 16
Bounded leaders *b*, the guard's horn sounded: *Far off in the dun* 89
Boundless And rushes o'er a *b* field. *Youth, lapsing ii* 32
Through all that *b* depth of fires is heard *Half after midnight!* 13
Bow With all his groves he *b's*, he nods, *Youth, lapsing ii* 49
Bow'd O'er the *b* shoulder of a bland old Age, The face of placid Death.' *That is his portrait* 36
Bower Now idly in my natal *b's*, *Youth, lapsing i* 49
Box (driver's seat) grim old coachee strode to the *b*, *Far off in the dun* 87
Box (house) snug brick *b* Of some sleek citizen. *Hear you the sound* 19
Boy And the laugh of their rose-lipp'd *b's*. *Far off in the dun* 38
Thou dost remember, Michael, How, when a *b*, *Hear you the sound* 31
we jar like *b's*: And in the hurry and the noise *They wrought, etc.* 14
Brain His heart throbs thick, his *b* reels sick: *Far off in the dun* 27
The *b* is moulded,' she began, *From shape to shape* 2
Is thy mad *b* drunk with the merry, red wine, *Full light aloft* 7
what an arch the *b* has built Above the ear! *That is his portrait* 10
dark form glances quick Thro' her worn *b*, *The lamps were bright* 28
With reason cloister'd in the *b*: *Young is the grief* 4
Brake How every *b* and flower spread and rose, *That is his portrait* 26
Branch Waving a palm *b*, wondering, loving, *A dark Indian maiden* 51
Thro' the bony *b'es* there. *Far off in the dun* 12
singing lustily Among the moss-grown *b'es*, *Hear you the sound* 42
Brave whole world shall not *b* us! (repeat) *They say, etc.* 6, 13, 20
Break (s) Dancing at the *b* of day, *A dark Indian maiden* 66
At the very *b* of light? *Full light aloft* 8
Break (verb) would have call'd you down to *b* your fast, *Hear you the sound* 47
Lightly lisping, *b's* away; *Not to Silence* 32
To *b* the pride of Britain, *They say, etc.* 2
To *b* the noble pride of the Mistress of the Seas. „ 4
Not he that *b's* the dams, but he *They wrought, etc.* 29
B thro' with the hammer of iron rhyme, *Wherever evil* 2
Breast Long as the heart beats life within her *b*, *Long as the heart* 1
And veils a *b* more fair to me *Not to Silence* 15
And that large table of the *b* dispread, *That is his portrait* 5
A sound of blows on armed *b's*! *They wrought, etc.* 18
These only do not move the *b*; *'Tis not alone* 5
An idle hope was in my *b*, *What rustles* 11
Breathe The May begins to *b* and bud, *Life of the Life* 3
Bred *The noblest men methinks are* b *The noblest men* 1
Breeze *B's* from the palm and canna *A dark Indian maiden* 14
Brick or the snug *b* box Of some sleek citizen. *Hear you the sound* 19
Brickwork Inextricable *b* maze in maze? *What rustles* 8
Bridal (adj.) Accept on this your golden *b* day *Remembering him* 3
Bridal (s) bitter, bitter *b*, The bitter bridal-day. *The lamps were bright* 53
A merry, merry *b*, a merry bridal-day! (repeat) „ 5, 13
Bridal-day lamps were bright and gay On the merry *b-d*, „ 2
A merry, merry bridal, A merry *b-d*! (repeat) „ 6, 14
the bitter, bitter bridal, The bitter *b-d*. „ 54
Bride the merry bridegroom Bore the *b* away! „ 4
Why the *b* is white as clay, Although the merry bridegroom Bears the *b* away, „ 10
Bride (*continued*) the merry bridegroom Hath borne the *b* away—(repeat) *The lamps were bright* 20, 26, 38, 44
tho' the merry bridegroom Might lead the *b* away, *The lamps were bright* 32
he a merry bridegroom Had borne the *b* away, „ 50
Bridegroom the merry *b* Bore the bride away! „ 3
Although the merry *b* Bears the bride away, „ 11
the merry *b* Hath borne the bride away— (repeat) „ 19, 25 37, 43
tho' the merry *b* Might lead the bride away, „ 31
he a merry *b* Had borne the bride away, „ 49
Bridge I stepp'd upon the old mill *b*? *Remember you* 4
Brief Or sleep thro' one *b* dream upon the grass,— *Townsmen, etc.* 4
Bright *B* is the moon on the deep, *B* are the cliffs in her beam, *Bright is the moon* 1
And a *b* archangel drove. *Far off in the dun* 116
his forehead heavenly *b* From the clear marble *One was the Tishbite* 6
lamps were *b* and gay On the merry bridal-day, *The lamps were bright* 1
And Heaven is dark and *b* by turns. *Youth, lapsing ii* 16
A mountain *b* with triple peaks: „ 48
Brim He *b's* his beaker to the top, *Yon huddled cloud* 13
Bring Behold, ye cannot *b* but good, *Are those the far-famed* 5
break the pride of Britain, and *b* her on her knees, *They say, etc.* 2
Bringing *b* To happy Hayti the new-comer, *A dark Indian maiden* 37
Brink but ever drawn Under either grassy *b* *Not to Silence* 25
Upon the *b* A solitary fortress burns, *Youth, lapsing ii* 13
Britain every man in *B* Says 'I am of Havelock's blood!' *Bold Havelock* 15
To break the pride of *B*, *They say, etc.* 2
you gleam reset In *B's* lyric coronet. *We lost you* 4
Briton let an honest *B* sit at home at ease: *They say, etc.* 9
Broad below The highway, *b* and flat, *Far off in the dun* 98
Broke They *b* the ground with hoofs of fire „ 128
Broken victim, *B* in this anger of Aphrodite, *Faded ev'ry violet* 3
Brook Partly river, partly *b*, *Not to Silence* 29
Brother But rejoice when a bigger *b* has proved *How is it that men* 5
Brought Then she *b* the guava fruit, *A dark Indian maiden* 41
She whose birth *b* on my bliss: *Not a whisper* 10
Brow His *b* is clammy and pale. *Far off in the dun* 28
the white fly leapt About his hairless *b*. „ 84
knit your baby *b's* Into your father's frown, *Hear you the sound* 48
high birth Had writ nobility upon my *b*. „ 64
Admire that stalwart shape, those ample *b's*, *That is his portrait* 4
These careful and those candid *b's*, „ 23
Brush *B'es* of fire, hazy gleams, *Hither, when all* 6
Brush'd As the quick wheels *b*, *Far off in the dun* 91
Bud May begins to breathe and *b*, *Life of the Life* 3
Build Not to Silence would I *b* A temple *Not to Silence* 1
Built (*See also* **Slight-built**) That Inn was *b* at the birth of Time: *Far off in the dun* 37
what an arch the brain has *b* Above the ear! *That is his portrait* 10
Burn hearts that in them *b* With power *Far off in the dun* 29
her black eyes *b* With a light so wild and stern?' *The lamps were bright* 15
Upon the brink A solitary fortress *b's*, *Youth, lapsing ii* 14
Burning (*See also* **Ever-burning**) Far off in the dun, dark occident, Behind the *b* Sun: *Far off in the dun* 2
Cemented with the *b* slime Which from Asphaltus flows. „ 39
With a silver sound the wheels went round, The wheels of *b* flame, „ 122
Hard by the *b* throne of my great grandsire, *Half after midnight!* 6
Burst (s) With a solemn *b* of thrilling light, *Far off in the dun* 119
Burst (verb) The river rose and *b* his bound, *The child was sitting* 4
I could *b* into a psalm of praise, *Why suffers* 2
Out *b's* a rainbow in the sky— *Youth, lapsing ii* 33
from the golden vapour *b's* A mountain bright „ 47
Butterfly Before the first white *butterflies,* „ *i* 11

C

Caesar A *C* of a punier dynasty *Here, I that stood* 5
Call You were wont to *c* it Your throne. *Hear you the sound* 35
C to the freshly-flower'd hill. *Remember you* 12
C to its mate when nothing stirr'd „ 15

Call'd would have *c* you down to break your fast, *Hear you the sound* 47
Calm Before his eyes so grim and *c* *Far off in the dun* 77
Came And the host *c* forth, and stood alone „ 49
There *c* a gaunt man from the dark Inn door, „ 73
wind *c* singing lustily Among the moss-grown branches, *Hear you the sound* 41
I *c* And would have call'd you down „ 46
Candid These careful and those *c* brows, how each— *That is his portrait* 23
Canna Breezes from the palm and *c* *A dark Indian maiden* 14
Cap Jauntily sat the Proctor's *c* *Sweet Kitty Sandilands* 11
Capacious *C* both of Friendship and of Love. *That is his portrait* 51
Care He *c's*, if ancient usage fade, *They wrought, etc.* 33
Careful These *c* and those candid brows, how each— *That is his portrait* 23
Carmel-steeps As when he stood on *C-s* *One was the Tishbite* 2
Carol Following her wild *c* She led them *A dark Indian maiden* 61
Carolling *C* 'Happy, happy Hayti!' „ 52
Carouse no revelling tones Of *c* were heard within: *Far off in the dun* 42
Carved forms Of the unfading marble *c* upon them, *Hear you the sound* 26
First shaped, and *c*, and set me in my place. *Here, I that stood* 4
Casement The *c's* sparkle on the plain, *Youth, lapsing ii* 39
Cast every line Wore the pale *c* of thought, *Methought I saw* 2
Castle Up the street we took her As far as to the *C*, *Sweet Kitty Sandilands* 10
Cataract This goes straight forward to the *c*: *Steersman* 4
But tho' the *c* seem the nearer way, „ 6
Caterwaul If the world *c*, lay harder upon her *Wherever evil* 6
Cause great *c* of Freedom round and round. *First drink a health* 60
Carven Wax-lighted chapels, and rich *c* screens *Therefore your Halls* 4
Cease These voices did not *c* to cry *Youth, lapsing i* 22
Ceasing Confused, and *c* from my quest, „ 45
Cedar-wooded *c-w* paradise Of still Xaraguay: *A dark Indian maiden* 20
Cellar For he, whose *c* is his pride, *Yon huddled cloud* 6
Cemented *C* with the burning slime *Far off in the dun* 39
Century Which speak of us to other *centuries*, *Hear you the sound* 27
Cessation There may be short *c* of their wails, *Half after midnight!* 12
Chamber This *c* she was born in! *Along this glimmering* 3
tho' the faults be thick as dust In vacant c's, *The noblest men* 11
Chance lest it by *c* should mark The life that haunts *How strange it is* 6
pleasant spot Where it was my *c* to marry, *Vicar of this* 2
Change (s) of the *c's* of the suns? *Little Aubrey* 6
Mature, harbour'd from *c*, contemplative, *That is his portrait* 12
overhaste Should fire the many wheels of *c*! *They wrought, etc.* 24
to repair With seasonable *c's* fair „ 35
When from *c* to *c*, Led silently by power divine, *Thou may'st remember* 8
Thro' every *c* that made thee what thou art? *To thee with whom* 14
Change (verb) A sound of words that *c* to blows! *They wrought, etc.* 17
Changed when the winds Are fallen or *c*; *Woman of noble* 10
Channel river here, my friend, Parts in two *c's*, *Steersman* 3
thro' the *c's* of the state Convoys *They wrought, etc.* 30
Chant And *c's* in the golden wakening *Full light aloft* 3
Chanted He *c* some old doleful rhyme. *Youth, lapsing i* 36
Chapel *c's* vaulted gloom Was misted with perfume. *The lamps were bright* 7
Charged *C* with his gallant few, *Bold Havelock* 6
Charnel-place tomb And *c-p* of purpose dead, *Thou may'st remember* 4
Chase Uncertain of ourselves we *c* The clap of hands; *They wrought, etc.* 13
Chatter That they chuckle and *c* and mock? *How is it that men* 3
Chattering The *c* of the fleshless jaws, *Far off in the dun* 95
Cheek There was not a tinge on each high *c* bone, „ 51
Those thoughtful furrows in the swarthy *c*; *That is his portrait* 3
eyes Are swallow'd in his pamper'd *c's*. *Yon huddled cloud* 12
Chequer'd *C* with moonlight's variation, *Hear you the sound* 22
Chief This tavern is their *c* resort, *Yon huddled cloud* 5
Child A *c* she loved to play; *Along this glimmering* 2
Thy *c* will bless thee, guardian mother mild, *Long as the heart* 2
bless'd By children of the children of thy *c*. „ 4
In that cradle sleeps my *c*, *Not a whisper* 9
c was sitting on the bank Upon a stormy day, *The child was sitting* 1
Took the *c* from off the ground, And bore the *c* away. „ 6
O the *c* so meek and wise, „ 8
Childhood All her loving *c* Breezes from the palm *A dark Indian maiden* 13
Children memory will be bless'd By *c* of the *c* *Long as the heart* 4
Chill The tingling blood grew *c*, *Far off in the dun* 78
Chilling There lies a land of *c* storms, *Far off in the dun* 5
Vast wastes of starless glooms were spread Around in the *c* air, „ 102
Chimney Moan'd in her *c's* and her eaves; *Youth, lapsing i* 30
Choice So lived I without aim or *c*, „ 37
Chuckle That they *c* and chatter and mock? *How is it that men* 3
Cinchona Crown'd with garlands of *c*, *A dark Indian maiden* 26
Citizen snug brick box Of some sleek *c*. *Hear you the sound* 20
Whence your own *c's*, for their own renown, *Here, I that stood* 7
he, the *c*, Deep-hearted, moderate, firm, *They wrought, etc.* 9
Claim those whom Freedom *c's* As patriot-martyrs *Not such were those* 1
Clammy His brow is *c* and pale. *Far off in the dun* 28
Clap Uncertain of ourselves we chase The *c* of hands; *They wrought, etc.* 14
Clapperclaw Till she *c* no longer, *Wherever evil* 7
Clasp I *c* her slender waist, We kiss, *How glad am I* 5
Clay Why the bride is white as *c*, *The lamps were bright* 10
Clear 'Tis a *c* night, they will be here anon. *Hear you the sound* 6
oak Which towers above the lake that ripples out In the *c* moonshine. „ 34
From the *c* marble pouring glorious scorn, *One was the Tishbite* 7
Remember you the *c* moonlight *Remember you* 1
Rang like a trumpet *c* and dry, *Youth, lapsing i* 19
Clear-edged *C-e*, and showing every bend *Thy soul is like* 5
Clearer A *c* day Than our poor twilight dawn on earth— *Gone into darkness* 4
Cleave land of many days that *c's* In two great halves, *They wrought, etc.* 26
Clever Shadows of statesmen, *c* men! „ 12
Click-clack With *c-c* alternation to and fro, *Half after midnight!* 8
Cliff Bright are the *c's* in her beam, *Bright is the moon* 2
Cloak They mounted slow in their long black *c's*, *Far off in the dun* 85
his *c* wind-borne Behind, *One was the Tishbite* 5
Clock There is a *c* in Pandemonium, *Half after midnight!* 5
What's the *c*? *Mich.* Half way toward midnight. *Hear you the sound* 3
Cloister'd With reason *c* in the brain: *Young is the grief* 4
Clomb Shudder'd with silent stars, she *c*, *Hither, when all* 2
Close I met in all the *c* green ways, *I met in all* 1
Cloud *c's* are sunder'd toward the morning-rise; *O God, make this age* 9
a colour'd *c*, O'er the bow'd shoulder of a bland old Age, *That is his portrait* 35
A momentary *c* upon me fell: *To thee with whom* 6
Yon huddled *c* his motion shifts, *Yon huddled cloud* 1
The *c's* unswathe them from the height, *Youth, lapsing ii* 50
Cloudless With him you love, be *c* and be long! *Take, Lady* 4
Cloudy things of past days with their horrible eyes Look out from the *c* vast. *Far off in the dun* 20
And the moaning wind before it drives Thick wreaths of *c* dew. „ 24
Fast by me flash the *c* streaks, *Youth, lapsing ii* 46
Clue think a cunning hand has found the *c*— *What rustles* 14
Cluster *C's* and beds of worlds, *Hither, when all* 7
Coach there stood a dark *c* at an old Inn door *Far off in the dun* 35
As the *c* ran on, and the sallow lights shone „ 99
those are the lights of the Paradise *c*, „ 107
Coachee (coachman) grim old *c* strode to the box, „ 87
O *C*, *C*, what lights approach With heavenly melodies? „ 105
Coat A dreadnought *c* had he: „ 74
Cockroach As the *c* crept, and the white fly leapt „ 83
Cocoa-shadow'd In the *c-s* coves, *A dark Indian maiden* 8
Coeval *C* with the battlemented towers *Hear you the sound* 12
Cold *C* words I spoke, yet loved thee warm and well. *To thee with whom* 8
Seem'd I so *c*? what madness moved my blood „ 10
Coldness My *c* was mistimed like summer-snow, „ 7
Colour'd At the end, as 'twere athwart a *c* cloud, *That is his portrait* 35
Come Father will *c* to thee soon, *Bright is the moon* 9
Father will *c* to his babe in the nest, „ 11
'And thro' all phases of all thought I *c* *From shape to shape* 3
We *c* from apes—and are far removed— *How is it that men* 4
The crowd have *c* to see thy grave, *I keep no more* 2
The year, that *c's*, may *c* with shame, *I, loving Freedom* 6
mock'd and said, '*C*, cry aloud, he sleeps.' *One was the Tishbite* 4
That would have *c* to woo her. *Sweet Kitty Sandilands* 8
Thro' spiritual dark we *c* Into the light *Thou may'st remember* 5
far off from England's shore, He *c's* no more. *What rustles* 10
voice Cried in the future '*C* along.' *Youth, lapsing i* 40

D

Day (*See also* **Bridal-day**) All *d* long with laughing eyes, *A dark Indian maiden* 17
upon the shore Dancing at the break of *d*, „ 66
things of past *d's* with their horrible eyes *Far off in the dun* 19
Ere the *d* be well-nigh done; *Full light aloft* 10
clearer *d* Than our poor twilight dawn on earth— *Gone into darkness* 4
I see the world's renewed youth A long *d's* dawn, *O God, make this age* 7
Old ghosts whose *d* was done ere mine began, *Old ghosts* 1
That none can truly write his single *d*, „ 13
Take thou the 'bend,' 'twill save thee many a *d*. *Steersman* 8
child was sitting on the bank Upon a stormy *d*, *The child was sitting* 2
In the hall, at close of *d*, *The lamps were bright* 35
A land of many *d's* that cleaves In two great halves, *They wrought, etc.* 26
D by *d* Watch your standard roses blowing, *Vicar of this* 11
The image of the sun by *d*, *Youth, lapsing i* 7
Down from the summit sweeps the *d* „ *ii* 31
Dead (adj.) March'd and fought himself *d*. *Bold Havelock* 12
They lifted their eyes to the *d*, pale skies, *Far off in the dun* 61
and threw up the dust Of *d* men's pulverised bones. „ 92
'The dead are *d* and let them be.' *I keep no more* 8
'From the tomb And charnel-place of purpose *d*, *Thou may'st remember* 4
Dead (s) Then pledge we our glorious *d*, *Frenchman, etc.* 9
and so many *d*, And him the last. *Gone into darkness* 10
'The *d* are dead and let them be.' *I keep no more* 8
Deal Not *d's* in threats, but works with hope, *They wrought, etc.* 39
Dear And God's best blessing on each *d* head *Frenchman, etc.* 11
one yet more *d*, More *d*, for what is lost is made more *d*; 'More *d*' *That is his portrait* 45
Was I so harsh? Ah *d*, it could not be. *To thee with whom* 9
Dearest Speak to me, *d*, lest I die. *Speak to me* 4
Death That ride to *d* the griefs of men? *Are those the far-famed* 2
The *D* for which you mourn is Life.' *Early-wise* 8
pleasant hymns they soothe the air Of *d*, *Far off in the dun* 110
The face of a placid *D*.' *That is his portrait* 37
silent Guardians But true till *D*; *Woman of noble* 7
Declined she seeming blithe *D* her head: *One was the Tishbite* 14
Deemed I *d* her one of stately frame *Because she bore* 3
Deep (adj.) In the *d* wood no more,—By the *d* sea no more,— *A dark Indian maiden* 67
D glens I found, and sunless gulfs, *Deep glens I found* 1
D dells of snow sunk on each side below The highway, *Far off in the dun* 97
Full light aloft doth the laverock spring From under the *d*, sweet corn, *Full light aloft* 2
Hither, when all the *d* unsounded skies *Hither, when all* 1
Often *d* beyond the sight, *Not to Silence* 22
Yet her own *d* soul says nay: *The lamps were bright* 24
Then a scream of wild dismay Thro' the *d* hall forced its way, „ 42
'Come' and I come, the vale is *d*, *Youth, lapsing ii* 27
Deep (s) Bright is the moon on the *d*, *Bright is the moon* 1
Father is over the *d*, „ 8
sound in her ears like the sound of the *d*, Like the sound of the *d* *That the voice* 2
Deepening Crown'd with soft shade her *d* floods *Youth, lapsing i* 3
Deeper past, in sleep, away By night, into the *d* night! The *d* night? *Gone into darkness* 3
But his was minted in a *d* mould, *That is his portrait* 17
Lower and *d* evermore They grew, *Youth, lapsing i* 25
Deep-hearted citizen, *D-h*, moderate, firm, *They wrought, etc.* 10
Deep-mouth'd mutter of *d-m* thunderings *Far off in the dun* 15
Deer *d* Bleat as with human voices in the park. *What rustles* 3
Delicious Which in one *d* nook, *Not to Silence* 30
Delight Nor proved I such *d* as he, *That is his portrait* 19
Dell Deep *d's* of snow sunk on each side *Far off in the dun* 97
Demure how *d* a smile, How full of wisest humour *That is his portrait* 6
Depth Through all that boundless *d* of fires *Half after midnight!* 13
Deserve Yet grief *d's* a nobler name: *Young is the grief* 5
Desire And lights at length on his *d*: *They wrought, etc.* 40
The sharp *d* of knowledge still with knowing! *Why suffers* 6
Despair To preach the freedom of *d*, *He was too good* 10
Despising Contends, *d* party-rage, *They wrought, etc.* 46
Despot The *d's* over yonder, let 'em do whate'er *They say, etc.* 16
Devil and we, Poor *d's*, babble 'we shall last.' *Well, as to Fame* 8
and the *d*——*l* take the parties! *They say, etc.* 10
Dew wind before it drives Thick wreaths of cloudy *d*. *Far off in the dun* 24
'I love the daisy weeping *d*, *I keep no more* 13
Die Of him who doomed the king to *d*, *Because she bore* 2
Speak to me, dearest, lest I *d*. *Speak to me* 4
When I *d*, the GHOULS! ! ! *While I live* 2
Died Bold Havelock *d*, Tender and great *Bold Havelock* 13
Difference The *d* of all things to the sense, And all the likeness in the *d*. *Why suffers* 10
Dignity It show'd the seeds of innate *d* *Hear you the sound* 52
Dim Wherefore should your eyes be *d*? *Early-wise* 5
D grief did wait upon her, *The lamps were bright* 33
Dimly sallow lights shone *D* and blurly *Far off in the dun* 100
Disappear I have seen the four great empires *d*! *Here, I that stood* 9
Disarrange hands that *d* The social engine! *They wrought, etc.* 21
Discourse owning more *D*, more widely wise.' *From shape to shape* 8
Dishonest There's a treaty, so they tell us, of some *d* fellows *They say, etc.* 3
Dismay Then a scream of wild *d* *The lamps were bright* 41
Disploding *D* globes of roaring fire. *Deep glens I found* 4
Dispread that large table of the breast *d*, *That is his portrait* 5
Dissipation Unto the *d* of this Earth. *Half after midnight!* 4
Dissolve *D* a world, condense a star, *Are those the far-famed* 14
Distant He sees his father in *d* lands, *Bright is the moon* 5
low sweet voices mourn'd In *d* fields, 'Come back, come back.' *Youth, lapsing i* 44
Distress I keep no more a lone *d*, *I keep no more* 1
Ditty moving To her Areyto's mellow *d*, *A dark Indian maiden* 50
Divine What aileth thee, O bird *d*, *Full light aloft* 5
Most eloquent, who spake of things *d*. *Methought I saw* 3
When from change to change, Led silently by power *d*, *Thou may'st remember* 9
Dizzy Yet am I *d* in the track, *Youth, lapsing ii* 43
Doctor Kitty Sandilands, The daughter of the *d*, *Sweet Kitty Sandilands* 2
Doleful He chanted some old *d* rhyme. *Youth, lapsing i* 36
Dome her keen eyes Pierced thro' the mystic *d*, *Hither, when all* 4
Done Ere the day be well-nigh *d*; *Full light aloft* 10
And there is something greatly *d*: *Youth, lapsing ii* 12
Doomed Of him who *d* the king to die, *Because she bore* 2
Door there stood a dark coach at an old Inn *d* *Far off in the dun* 35
There came a gaunt man from the dark Inn *d*, „ 73
Step thro' these *d's*, and I will show to you *That is his portrait* 44
Beside my *d* at morning stood The tearful spirit *Youth, lapsing i* 33
Doorway stood alone And still in the dark *d*: *Far off in the dun* 50
Double Beneath those *d* arches lie Fair with green fields the realms of Love. *Youth, lapsing ii* 35
Doubt I knew him in his hour Of darkest *d*, and in his power, To fling his *d's* into the street. *He was too good* 3
Unvext by *d's* I cannot solve, *Youth, lapsing i* 50
Doubtful Where the *d* shadows play, *Not to Silence* 31
Dragon on every side The *d's* curves melted, *One was the Tishbite* 15
Dragon-fly The *d-f* and scarlet crane, *A dark Indian maiden* 32
Drank and *d* The sweet sad tears of wisdom.' *Methought I saw* 5
Draw To *d* strange comfort from the earth, *Far off in the dun* 31
Drawn but ever *d* Under either grassy brink *Not to Silence* 24
Dreadnought A *d* coat had he: *Far off in the dun* 74
Dream (*See also* **Half-dream**) And kisses him there in a *d*, *Bright is the moon* 6
See, she dreameth happy *d's*, *Not a whisper* 13
sleep thro' one brief *d* upon the grass,— *Townsmen, etc.* 4
Dreameth See, she *d* happy dreams, *Not a whisper* 13
Dreaming In the *d* of past things: *The lamps were bright* 22
Dreamt And *d* not of the miller's daughter. *I met in all* 8
Drest We *d* her in the Proctor's bands, *Sweet Kitty Sandilands* 3
Drew sun *D* down the West his feeble lights; *Deep glens I found* 6
Thro' strange seas *d* me to your monster town. *Here, I that stood* 8
Drifted That mystic field of *d* light In mid Orion, *Hither, when all* 10
Drink Let us *d* to the health of thine and mine *Frenchman, etc.* 3
It is not good to *d* strong wine *Full light aloft* 9
Shall *d* the fulness of thy victory, *O God, make this age* 13
Dripping I grieved as woods in *d* rains *Youth, lapsing i* 31
Drive moaning wind before it *d's* Thick wreaths *Far off in the dun* 23
To *d* them where he will. „ 80
Drop And sometimes with a twinkling *d*, *Yon huddled cloud* 15

G

H

Hail *H*, truest Lord of Hell! *H* Genius, Master of the Moral Will! — *Art for Art's sake!* 1
Hair and threw back Your floating *h*. — *Hear you the sound* 43
Hairless and the white fly leapt About his *h* brow. — *Far off in the dun* 84
Haled *h* me toward the Mediterranean sea, — *Here, I that stood* 6
Half (adj.) What's the clock? *Mich.* *H* way toward midnight. — *Hear you the sound* 4
But to one of finer sense, Her *h* sister, Reticence. — *Not to Silence* 6
Half (s) that cleaves In two great *halves*, — *They wrought, etc.* 27
Half-consciousness With some *h-c* of inward power, — *That is his portrait* 8
Half-dream Ye know that History is *h-d*— — *Old ghosts* 3
Hall In the *h*, at close of day, — *The lamps were bright* 35
Thro' the deep *h* forced its way, — „ 42
Hamlet Townsmen, or of the *h*, young or old, — *Townsmen, etc.* 1
Hammer (*See also* **Rhyme-hammer**) Break thro' with the *h* of iron rhyme, — *Wherever evil* 2
Hand (*See also* **Left**) And longed to kiss her *h* and lie — *Because she bore* 7
Wrought with his *h* and his head, — *Bold Havelock* 10
Look he smiles, and opens his *h's*, — *Bright is the moon* 4
The skin hung lax on his long thin *h's*; — *Far off in the dun* 53
Frenchman, a *h* in thine! — *Frenchman, etc.* 1
And long'd to take his *h* in mine. — *I met in all* 4
Her *h's* are folded quietly, — *Not a whisper* 14
but with right *h* Moving toward her lip, — *Not to Silence* 10
left *h* holds Her up-gather'd garment folds, — „ 13
Further and further reaching *h's* — *They wrought, etc.* 3
Uncertain of ourselves we chase The clap of *h's*; — „ 14
h's that disarrange The social engine! — „ 21
And think a cunning *h* has found the clue— — *What rustles* 14
Hang mockery to *h* it O'er the thatch'd cottage, — *Hear you the sound* 18
Happy Who was so *h* as Anacaona, — *A dark Indian maiden* 10
None were so *h* as Anacaona, — „ 22
H, *h* was Anacaona, The beauty of Espagnola, — „ 34
bringing To *h* Hayti the new-comer, — „ 38
H, *h* Anacaona, The beauty of Espagnola, — „ 46
Carolling '*H*, *h* Hayti!' — „ 52
No more in Xaraguay Wander'd *h* Anacaona, — „ 70
H, *h* be your lot In the Vicarage — *Vicar of this* 3
They glitter'd with a stedfast light, The *h* spirits within; — *Far off in the dun* 130
The *h* maiden's tears are free — *I keep no more* 5
See, she dreameth *h* dreams, — *Not a whisper* 13
Like birds of passage, to return with thee Some *h* Summer morning, — *Woman of noble* 9
Harbour'd Mature, *h* from change, contemplative, — *That is his portrait* 12
Hard that heart of his *H*, and the slave of vice; — *A surface man* 4
H by the burning throne of my great grandsire, — *Half after midnight!* 6
But what, were *h* to say. — *'Tis not alone* 12
Hark *H*! they are coming. — *Hear you the sound* 65
It is the early morning, *H*! — *Youth, lapsing ii* 6
Harsh That I was *h* to thee, let no one know; — *To thee with whom* 2
Tho' I was *h*, my nature is not so: — „ 5
Was I so *h*? Ah dear, it could not be. — „ 9
Hasten'd That would have *h* to her, — *Sweet Kitty Sandilands* 6
Hate (s) An orb repulsive of all *h*, — *Young is the grief* 14
Hate (verb) I *h* the trim-set plots of art!' — *I keep no more* 14
Haunt life that *h's* the emptiness And horrors — *How strange it is* 7
Havelock (General Sir Henry) Bold *H* march'd, (repeat) — *Bold Havelock* 1, 5, 9
Bold *H* died, Tender and great and good, — „ 13
'I am of *H's* blood!' — „ 16
Hayti Espagnola, The golden flower of *H*? (repeat) — *A dark Indian maiden* 12, 24, 36, 48, 60, 72
bringing To happy *H* the new-comer, — *A dark Indian maiden* 38
Carolling 'Happy, happy *H*!' — „ 52
Hazel Tempers the peaceful light of *h* eyes, — *That is his portait* 13
Hazy Brushes of fire, *h* gleams, — *Hither, when all* 6
Head Else this wild whisper round my *h* — *Are those the far-famed* 11
Wrought with his hand and his *h*, — *Bold Havelock* 10
Head (*continued*) *h's* without bodies and shapes without *h's* — *Far off in the dun* 103
God's best blessing on each dear *h* — *Frenchman, etc.* 11
she seeming blithe Declined her *h*: — *One was the Tishbite* 14
noblest place, Madam, is yours, our Queen and H. — *The noblest men* 4
some foreign powers have laid their *h's* together — *They say, etc.* 1
Health Let us drink to the *h* of thine and mine — *Frenchman, etc.* 3
Here's a *h* to the Queen of the Isles. — *That the voice* 4
Hear They *h* each household voice: — *Far off in the dun* 66
H you the sound of wheels? — *Hear you the sound* 1
Little poet, *h* the little poet's epigram! — *Little Aubrey* 7
The stream is loud: I cannot *h*!' — *Remember you* 8
I heard, as I have seem'd to *h*, — „ 9
Speak to me, let me *h* or see! — *Speak to me* 5
A step? a footfall? What is that I *h*? — *What rustles* 2
And see and *h* the world revolve: — *Youth, lapsing i* 52
ear Be tickled with the loud '*h*, *h*,' — *They wrought, etc.* 7
Heard no revelling tones Of carouse were *h* within: — *Far off in the dun* 42
And *h* the roar of her seas. — „ 64
is *h* The shrill and solemn warning 'Ever, Never': — *Half after midnight!* 13
I *h* you whisper from above, — *Remember you* 5
I *h*, as I have seem'd to hear, — „ 9
I *h*, as I have often *h*, — „ 13
This is the man of whom you *h* me speak. — *That is his portrait* 15
With jokes you never *h* before, — *Yon huddled cloud* 14
I *h* Spring laugh in hidden rills, — *Youth, lapsing i* 13
Faint shouts are *h* across the glen, — „ *ii* 22
Hearing Till heart and sight and *h* ache — *How strange it is* 3
Heart that *h* of his Hard, and the slave of vice; — *A surface man* 3
His *h* throbs thick, his brain reels sick: — *Far off in the dun* 27
some have *h's* that in them burn With power — „ 29
And from the *h* of all things fair To pluck — *He was too good* 11
Till *h* and sight and hearing ache — *How strange it is* 3
My friend, thou speakest from the *h*, — *I keep no more* 15
Long as the *h* beats life within her breast, — *Long as the heart* 1
Every *h* is lain to rest, — *Not a whisper* 5
may the life, which, *h* in *h*, you live — *Take, Lady* 3
All-perfect Framer, Him, who made the *h*, — *That is his portrait* 48
And teach us nothing, feeding not the *h*. — *Therefore your Halls* 14
To make me thus belie my constant *h* — *To thee with whom* 11
Seeing the *h* so wondrous in her ways, — *Why suffers* 3
as pure a *h* As e'er beat time to Nature, — *Woman of noble* 4
My *h* is dark, but yet I come. — *Youth, lapsing ii* 28
Hearted *See* **Deep-hearted**
Hearties Up, Jack Tars, my *h*! — *They say, etc.* 10
Heaven If earth be seen from your conjectured *h*, — *Old ghosts* 2
It were, O *H*, a stranger tale to tell — *To thee with whom* 3
Of each dark hill against the *H*, — *Thy soul is like* 6
Touch'd with *H's* latest lights. — „ 12
And *H* is dark and bright by turns. — *Youth, lapsing ii* 16
Heavenly O Coachee, Coachee, what lights approach With *h* melodies? — *Far off in the dun* 106
his forehead *h* bright From the clear marble — *One was the Tishbite* 6
Heel And the beat of the horny *h's*? — *Far off in the dun* 96
Height confused The shadows from the icy *h's*. — *Deep glens I found* 8
And somewhat loftier antient *h's* — *Thy soul is like* 11
The clouds unswathe them from the *h*, — *Youth, lapsing ii* 50
Hell Hail, truest Lord of *H*! — *Art for Art's sake!* 1
So prone are we toward the broad way to *H*. — „ 6
Sound 'Ever, Never' thro' the courts of *H*, — *Half after midnight!* 9
Help Than which of us most shall *h* the world, — *Frenchman, etc.* 7
We *h* the blatant voice abroad To preach — *He was too good* 9
Here I am *h* again with him. — *Early-wise* 6
H, I that stood in On beside the flow — *Here, I that stood* 1
I was when London was not! I am *h*! — „ 10
Why, they should be *h*. *Mich.* 'Tis a clear night, — *Hear you the sound* 5
A lute-toned whisper, 'I am *h*!' — *Remember you* 6
Heroic Hush! there floats upward from the gulf A murmur of *h* song, — *Youth, lapsing ii* 19
Hidden I heard Spring laugh in *h* rills, — „ *i* 13
Hide Those holly-thickets only *h* Her grave— — *Along this glimmering* 7
High But some have hearts that in them burn With power and promise *h*, — *Far off in the dun* 30
There was not a tinge on each *h* cheek bone, — „ 51

High (*continued*) but ye still shall flourish In your *h* pomp of shade, *Hear you the sound* 29
Ev'n then the force of nature and *h* birth Had writ nobility upon my brow. „ 63
A voice, when night had crept on *h*, *Youth, lapsing i* 17
Highland Lady over wood and *h*, *A dark Indian Maiden* 27
Highway sunk on each side below The *h*, *Far off in the dun* 98
Hill The summer *h's* they see; „ 70
Call to the freshly-flower'd *h*. *Remember you* 12
The wind is loud in holt and *h*, *Speak to me* 2
Of each dark *h* against the Heaven, *Thy soul is like* 6
The silent *h's*, the stormy floods, *'Tis not alone* 3
These *h's* were plains within the past, *Well, as to Fame* 6
a voice ran round the *h's* When corny Lammas *Youth, lapsing i* 15
Behind yon *h* the trumpets blow, „ *ii* 11
Hist *H*! what was that! *Mich.* The night gale *Hear you the sound* 7
History Ye know that *H* is half-dream— *Old ghosts* 3
Hoary And *h* holts on uplands green, *Thy soul is like* 10
Hold Nor Love that *h's* a constant mood. *Are those the far-famed* 8
H thou, my friend, no lesser life in scorn, *Hold thou, my friend* 1
left hand *h's* Her up-gather'd garment folds, *Not to Silence* 13
To *h* the Spirit of the Age Against the Spirit *They wrought, etc.* 47
Hollow-stemm'd *h-s* and well-nigh leafless oak *Hear you the sound* 32
Holly-thickets Those *h-t* only hide Her grave— *Along this glimmering* 7
Holt The wind is loud in *h* and hill, *Speak to me* 2
And hoary *h's* on uplands green, *Thy soul is like* 10
Home We quarrel here at *h*, *They say, etc.* 8
will not let an honest Briton sit at *h* at ease: „ 9
Homer Little *H*, little Dante, little Shakespeare, *Little Aubrey* 4
Honest They will not let an *h* Briton sit at home at ease: *They say, etc.* 9
Honour In glory and in *h*. *The lamps were bright* 34
Thy rhyme-hammer *shall* have *h*. *Wherever evil* 9
Hoof They broke the ground with *h's* of fire *Far off in the dun* 128
Hope Am large in *h* that these expectant eyes *O God, make this age* 12
transgressing the low bound Of mortal *h*, *That is his portrait* 39
Not deals in threats, but works with *h*, *They wrought, etc.* 39
An idle *h* was in my breast, My *h* is false, my terror's true! *What rustles* 11
but let them go in *h*, Like birds of passage, *Woman of noble* 7
Horn leaders bounded, the guard's *h* sounded: *Far off in the dun* 89
With that long *h* she loves to blow, *Well, as to Fame* 2
lifts The creaming *h* of corny ale! *Yon huddled cloud* 4
Horny And the beat of the *h* heels? *Far off in the dun* 96
Horrible And the things of past days with their *h* eyes „ 19
Horror emptiness And *h's* of the formless dark. *How strange it is* 8
Horse Yoked the skeleton *h's* to. *Far off in the dun* 60
Horseman The thirsty *h*, nodding, lifts *Yon huddled cloud* 3
Host the *h* came forth, and stood alone *Far off in the dun* 49
No jolly *h* was he; „ 54
Mine *h* is fat, and gray, and wise, *Yon huddled cloud* 9
Hot Thro' her worn brain, *h* and sick.' *The lamps were bright* 28
And his *h* steeds never run: *Far off in the dun* 4
Hour Are those the far-famed Victor *H's* *Are those the far-famed* 1
At the solemn midnight *h*. *Far off in the dun* 36
Remembering all the golden *h's* Now silent, *Gone into darkness* 9
Pointing to the unheeded lapse of *h's*, *Half after midnight!* 2
Methinks my tongue runs twenty knots an *h*: „ 19
I knew him in his *h* Of darkest doubt, *He was too good* 2
All this so stirr'd him in his *h* of joy, *That is his portrait* 31
would you waste an *h*, *Townsmen, etc.* 3
House All the *h* is fast in sleep, *Not a whisper* 6
Household They hear each *h* voice: *Far off in the dun* 66
Hovering there *H*, thoughtful, poised in air. *Not to Silence* 12
Howling *H* in outer darkness.' *Beauty, Good, etc.* 5
A *h* of the mountain wolf; *Youth, lapsing ii* 20
Hubbub The *h* of the market and the booths: *That is his portrait* 21
Huddled Yon *h* cloud his motion shifts, *Yon huddled cloud* 1
Hue Thro' his own nature, well mingled *h's*, *That is his portrait* 28
Millions of forms, and *h's*, and shades, *Why suffers* 9
Human Large as a *h* eye the sun Drew down the West his feeble lights; *Deep glens I found* 5
And startle the dull ears of *h* kind! *O God, make this age* 5
the deer Bleat as with *h* voices in the park. *What rustles* 4
Why suffers *h* life so soon eclipse? *Why suffers* 1
E'en scorn looks beautiful on *h* lips! „ 4
Humming Still *h* snatches of old song, *Youth, lapsing i* 38
Humour How full of wisest *h* and of love, *That is his portrait* 7
The *h's* of the polling and the wake, „ 20
Hung skin *h* lax on his long thin hands; *Far off in the dun* 53
And from it *h* the tassel. *Sweet Kitty Sandilands* 12
Hurl'd Thence, across the summit *h*, *Not to Silence* 33
Hurry in the *h* and the noise Great spirits *They wrought, etc.* 15
Hush *H*! there floats upward from the gulf *Youth, lapsing ii* 18
Hustings To which the slight-built *h* shake; *They wrought, etc.* 8
Hymn With pleasant *h's* they soothe the air *Far off in the dun* 109

I

Ice *Your flag thro' Austral* i *is borne,* *The noblest men* 6
Icy night, all moons, confused The shadows from the *i* heights. *Deep glens I found* 8
Idler An *i* hope was in my breast, *What rustles* 11
Were *i* than a flight of rooks. *Are those the far-famed* 12
Idly Now *i* in my natal bowers, *Youth, lapsing ii* 49
Ill (adv.) 'The filthiest of all paintings painted well Is mightier than the purest painted *i*!' *Art for Art's sake!* 4
Ill (s) he would weep For *i's* himself had practised *A surface man* 5
Image The *i* of the sun by day, The *i* of the moon by night *Youth, lapsing i* 7
Imitative She spurs an *i* will; *Young is the grief* 6
Immeasurable *I* sadness! (repeat) *Immeasurable sadness!* 1, 4, 11
Inch pall of the sky Leave never an *i* of blue; *Far off in the dun* 22
Ind *And floats in either golden* I. *The noblest men* 8
Indian A dark *I* maiden, Warbling in the bloom'd liana, *A dark Indian maiden* 1
I queen, Anacaona, Dancing on the blossomy plain „ 28
Individual And *i* interests Becoming bands of armed foes! *They wrought, etc.* 19
Inextricable The man that round me wove *I* brickwork maze in maze? *Why rustles, etc.* 8
Infancy Mine was no vulgar mind in *i*, *Hear you the sound* 62
heart That watch't with love thine earliest *i*, *To thee with whom* 12
Infernal but in them slept A red *i* glow; *Far off in the dun* 82
Inn (adj.) there stood a dark coach at an old *I* door „ 35
There came a gaunt man from the dark *I* door, „ 73
Inn (s) That *I* was built at the birth of Time: „ 37
Swung creaking before the *I*. „ 44
Innate It show'd the seeds of *i* dignity That were within me; *Hear you the sound* 52
Inner They pass'd (an *i* spirit fed Their ever-burning fires,) *Far off in the dun* 117
common objects that moved keep Our awful *i* ghostly sense Unroused, *How strange it is* 5
Lit as with *i* light. *One was the Tishbite* 8
Innovation And *i* grade by grade: *They wrought, etc.* 36
Intent *I* to follow on the track, *Youth, lapsing i* 42
Interest individual *i's* Becoming bands of armed foes! *They wrought, etc.* 19
Inward With some half-consciousness of *i* power, *That is his portrait* 8
Iron Because she bore the *i* name *Because she bore* 1
Break thro' with the hammer of *i* rhyme, *Wherever evil* 2
Iron'd From *i* limbs and tortured nails! *First drink a health* 16
Island In the purple *i*, Crown'd with garlands *A dark Indian maiden* 25
Isle God bless the little *i* where a man may still be true! *They say, etc.* 17
God bless the noble *i* that is Mistress of the Seas! „ 18
rivulet, Rippling by cressy *i's* or bars of sand, *Townsmen, etc.* 6
Thro' wooded *i's* the river shines, *Youth, lapsing ii* 38
Here's a health to the Queen of the *I's*. *That the voice* 4

J

Jack Up, *J* Tars, and save us! (repeat) *They say, etc.* 5, 12, 19
Up, *J* Tars, my hearties! „ 10
The lasses and the little ones, *J* Tars, they look to you! „ 15
James *See* **St. James**

Jar we *j* like boys: And in the hurry and the noise *They wrought, etc.* 14
Jaw The chattering of the fleshless *j's*, *Far off in the dun* 95
Jesu The 'Mercy *J*' in the rain! *I keep no more* 11
Joint Unsocket all the *j's* of war, *Are those the far-famed* 15
Joke With *j's* you never heard before, *Yon huddled cloud* 14
Jolly He look'd so *j* and so good— *I met in all* 5
No *j* host was he; *Far off in the dun* 54
Joy No sound of *j*, no revelling tones „ 41
There's not a *j* beyond. *How glad am I* 8
All this so stirr'd him in his hour of *j*, *That is his portrait* 31
My *j* was only less than thine. *Thou may'st remember* 12
One only *j* I know, the *j* of life. *Why suffers* 14
Joy'd I *j* to place me on The hollow-stemm'd *Hear you the sound* 31
Joyful *j* when The wanton wind came singing „ 40
Joyfully But did not sound so *j*: *Youth, lapsing i* 24
Just Knowing those laws are *j* alone That contemplate a mighty plan, *They wrought, etc.* 41

K

Kate Sweetly flow your life with *K's*, *Vicar of this* 16
Keen And as with optic glasses her *k* eyes Pierced thro' the mystic dome, *Hither when all* 3
Keep objects that would *k* Our awful inner *How strange it is* 4
I *k* no more a lone distress, *I keep no more* 1
act on Eternity To *k* thee here amongst us! *That is his portrait* 40
voice of a satisfied people may *k* A sound in her ears *That the voice* 1
Keys With twinkling finger sweeps her yellow *k*. *Townsmen, etc.* 10
Kind (adj.) He was too good and *k* and sweet, *He was too good* 1
It is not *k* to be so still: *Speak to me* 3
I can trust Your woman's nature k *and true.* *The noblest men* 12
Kind (s) And startle the dull ears of human *k*! *O God, make this age* 5
King Of him who doomed the *k* to die, *Because she bore* 2
Is it the *k*; is it my love Coming along *What rustles* 5
King-craft Till priest-craft and *k-c* sicken, *Wherever evil* 3
Kingliest A Pharaoh, *k* of his kingly race, *Here, I that stood* 3
Kingly For they were *k* in apparel, *A dark Indian maiden* 63
A Pharaoh, kingliest of his *k* race, *Here, I that stood* 3
Kiss (s) And mingle *k'es*, tears, and sighs, *Life of the Life* 6
I will print an airy *k*: *Not a whisper* 12
Kiss (verb) And longed to *k* her hand and lie *Because she bore* 7
And *k'es* him there in a dream, *Bright is the moon* 6
I *k* her o'er and o'er. *How glad am I* 4
We *k*, we are so fond, „ 6
Kitty Sandilands Sweet *K S*, The daughter of the doctor, *Sweet Kitty Sandilands* 1
Knee was wont to dandle you upon My *k*, *Hear you the sound* 56
To break the pride of Britain, and bring her on her *k's*, *They say, etc.* 2
Knew Ev'n when I *k* him in his hour *He was too good* 2
Knit *k* your baby brows Into your father's frown, *Hear you the sound* 48
You were he that *k* the knot! *Vicar of this* 5
Knot my tongue runs twenty *k's* an hour: *Half after midnight!* 19
You were he that knit the *k*! *Vicar of this* 5
Knotted round her waist *K*, *One was the Tishbite* 11
The *k* boughs of this long avenue Of thick dark oaks, *Hear you the sound* 10
Know And I *k* it as a poet, *Immeasurable sadness!* 2
But I *k* it as a poet, „ 8
Ye *k* that History is half-dream— *Old ghosts* 3
whatsoever *k's* us truly, *k's* That none „ 12
That I was harsh to thee, let no one *k*; *To thee with whom* 2
I *k* a little of her worth, *Well, as to Fame* 3
And I will tell you what I *k*— „ 4
One only joy I *k*, the joy of life. *Why suffers* 14
Yet well I *k* that nothing stays, *Youth, lapsing i* 53
Knowing *K* those laws are just alone *They wrought, etc.* 41
sharp desire of knowledge still with *k*! *Why suffers* 6
Knowledge Beauty, Good and *K* are three sisters . . . *Beauty, Good, etc.* 1
sharp desire of *k* still with knowing! *Why suffers* 6

L

Labour A *l* working to an end. *Youth, lapsing ii* 4
Laden *See* **Flower-laden**
Lady (adj.) by fits the *l* ash With twinkling finger sweeps her yellow keys. *Townsmen, etc.* 9
Lady (s) *L* of the green Savannah: *A dark Indian maiden* 16
L over wood and highland, „ 27
Take, *L*, what your loyal nurses give, *Take, Lady* 1
Laid foreign powers have *l* their heads together *They say, etc.* 1
Lain Every heart is *l* to rest, *Not a whisper* 5
Lake *l* that ripples out In the clear moonshine. *Hear you the sound* 33
Lammas When corny *L* bound the sheaves: *Youth, lapsing i* 16
Lamp wreath'd with green bays were the gorgeous *l's*, *Far off in the dun* 115
l's were bright and gay On the merry bridal-day, *The lamps were bright* 1
Land He sees his father in distant *l's*, *Bright is the moon* 5
There lies a *l* of chilling storms, *Far off in the dun* 5
A *l* of thin faces and shadowy forms, „ 7
A pure example to the *l's*, *They wrought, etc.* 2
A *l* of many days that cleaves In two great halves, „ 26
The whole *l* glitters after rain, *Youth, lapsing ii* 37
Landskip Thy soul is like a *l*, friend, *Thy soul is like* 1
Lapse Pointing to the unheeded *l* of hours, *Half after midnight!* 2
Lapsing Youth, *l* thro' fair solitudes, *Youth, lapsing i* 1
Large *L* as a human eye the sun Drew down the West his feeble lights; *Deep glens I found* 5
Am *l* in hope that these expectant eyes *O God, make this age* 12
And that *l* table of the breast dispread, *That is his portrait* 5
Larger Or, if the sense of most require A precedent of *l* scope, *They wrought, etc.* 38
Lark *See* **Laverock**
Lass The *l'es* and the little ones, Jack Tars, *They say, etc.* 15
Last (s) so many dead, And him the *l*. *Gone into darkness* 11
Last (verb) can they *l* In the vast Of the rolling of the æons, *Little Aubrey* 4
we, Poor devils, babble 'we shall *l*.' *Well, as to Fame* 8
Later Sooner or *l* from the haze The second voice *Youth, lapsing i* 55
Latest *L* of her worshippers, *Not to Silence* 7
loftier antient heights Touch'd with Heaven's *l* lights. *Thy soul is like* 12
The *l* thunder-peal hath peal'd, *Youth, lapsing ii* 30
Laugh (s) And the *l* of their rose-lipp'd boys. *Far off in the dun* 68
Laugh (verb) when he *l's*, his little eyes *Yon huddled cloud* 11
I heard Spring *l* in hidden rills, *Youth, lapsing i* 13
Laughable 'twas *l*, and yet It show'd *Hear you the sound* 51
Laugh'd I *l* to see him as he stood, *I met in all* 7
Laughing All day long with *l* eyes, *A dark Indian maiden* 17
And they saw *her* standing by, With a *l* crazed eye, *The lamps were bright* 52
Lava The walls of *l* rose, *Far off in the dun* 38
Laverock *l* spring From under the deep, *Full light aloft* 1
Law Knowing those *l's* are just alone *They wrought, etc.* 41
Lawn Here and there about the *l* Wholly mute, *Not to Silence* 23
Steeple, and stream, and forest *l*, *Thy soul is like* 2
Lay See, The cradle where she *l*! *Along this glimmering* 4
Then they found him where *l* *The lamps were bright* 47
l harder upon her Till she clapperclaw *Wherever evil* 6
Lead Which *l* the noblest life. *Frenchman, etc.* 8
tho' the merry bridegroom Might *l* the bride away, *The lamps were bright* 32
Leader The *l's* bounded, the guard's horn sounded: *Far off in the dun* 89
Leaf summer plains with their shining *leaves*, „ 69
dark vine *leaves* round the rustling eaves, „ 71
Summer thro' all her sleepy *leaves* *Youth, lapsing i* 14
Sigh over all their fallen *leaves*; „ 32
Leafless The hollow-stemm'd and well-nigh *l* oak *Hear you the sound* 32
Leafy The nightingale in *l* woods Call to its mate *Remember you* 14
League Flooded fifty *l's* around, *The child was sitting* 5
Lean Tall, eager, *l* and strong, his cloak *One was the Tishbite* 5
Leaping shapes without heads Went *l* *Far off in the dun* 104
Leapt white fly *l* About his hairless brow. „ 83
Leave pall of the sky *L* never an inch of blue; „ 22

Leave (*continued*) O *l* not thou thy son forlorn; *O leave not thou* 1
each one *l's* The middle road of sober thought! *They wrought, etc.* 27
Led (*See also* **Wisdom-led**) She *l* them down the pleasant places, *A dark Indian maiden* 62
L silently by power divine, *Thou may'st remember* 9
Left To *l* or right but falling floods. *Remember you* 16
the *l* hand holds Her up-gather'd garment folds, *Not to Silence* 13
Length And lights at *l* on his desire: *They wrought, etc.* 40
Lengthen'd Far away thro' the night ran the *l* tones: *Far off in the dun* 90
Less But these shall see it none the *l*. *I keep no more* 4
My joy was only *l* than thine. *Thou may'st remember* 12
Lesser Hold thou, my friend, no *l* life in scorn, *Hold thou, my friend* 1
Letter Their lies the *l*, but it is not he *Old ghosts* 5
The man's life in the *l's* of the man. „ 4
Level Thames along the silent *l*, *Vicar of this* 19
Liana Indian maiden, Warbling in the bloom'd *l*, *A dark Indian maiden* 2
Lie on her threshold *l*, Howling *Beauty, Good etc.* 4
l A thousand summers at her feet. *Because she bore* 7
There *l's* a land of chilling storms, *Far off in the dun* 5
Evermore The simpler essence lower *l's*, *From shape to shape* 6
There *l's* the letter, but it is not he *Old ghosts* 5
Beneath those double arches *l* *Youth, lapsing ii* 35
Life The Death for which you mourn is *L*.' *Early-wise* 8
Which lead the noblest *life*. *Frenchman, etc.* 8
What *l*, so maim'd by night, were worth *Gone into darkness* 7
my friend, no lesser *l* in scorn, *Hold thou, my friend* 1
mark The *l* that haunts the emptiness *How strange it is* 7
L of the *L* within my blood, (repeat) *Life of the Life* 1, 7
Long as the heart beats *l* within her breast, *Long as the heart* 1
The man's *l* in the letters of the man. *Old ghosts* 4
Alas, my *l* is frail and weak: *Speak to me* 6
may the *l*, which, heart in heart, you live *Take, Lady* 3
I look thro' all my glimmering *l*, *That is his portrait* 34
Thro' one whole *l* an overflowing urn, „ 50
come Into the light of spiritual *l*. *Thou may'st remember* 6
Sweetly, smoothly flow your *l*. *Vicar of this* 6
Sweetly flow your *l* with Kate's, „ 16
Why suffers human *l* so soon eclipse? *Why suffers* 1
Would I could pile fresh *l* on *l*, „ 5
One only joy I know, the joy of *l*. „ 14
A *l* four-square to all the winds. *Young is the grief* 16
L, to this wind, turn'd all her vanes, *Youth, lapsing i* 29
Lift he spake: 'I *l* the eyes of thought, *That is his portrait* 33
l's The creaming horn of corny ale! *Yon huddled cloud* 3
Lifted They *l* their eyes to the dead, pale skies, *Far off in the dun* 61
Light (adj.) A *l* wind wafts me from my feet. *Youth, lapsing ii* 44
Light (adv.) Full *l* aloft doth the laverock spring *Full light aloft* 1
Light (come upon) And *l's* at length on his desire: *They wrought, etc.* 40
Light (s) sun Drew down the West his feeble *l's*; *Deep glens I found* 6
A region void of *l*, *Far off in the dun* 6
No taper's *l* look'd out on the night, „ 45
They see the *l* of their blest firesides, „ 65
sallow *l's* shone Dimly and blurly „ 99
what *l's* approach With heavenly melodies? „ 105
those are the *l's* of the Paradise coach, „ 107
With a solemn burst of thrilling *l*, „ 119
They glitter'd with a stedfast *l*, „ 129
At the very break of *l*? *Full light aloft* 8
Gone into darkness, that full *l* Of friendship! *Gone into darkness* 1
That mystic field of drifted *l* In mid Orion, *Hither when all* 10
L of the *L* within mine eyes, (repeat) *Life of the Life* 2, 8
Often shallow, pierced with *l*, *Not to Silence* 21
Lit as with inner *l*. *One was the Tishbite* 8
peaceful *l* of hazel eyes, Observing all things. *That is his portrait* 13
eyes burn With a *l* so wild and stern?' *The lamps were bright* 16
come Into the *l* of spiritual life.' *Thou may'st remember* 6
Touch'd with Heaven's latest *l's*. *Thy soul is like* 12
Full fields of barley shifting tearful *l's* *Townsmen, etc.* 8
Drove into lines and studs of *l* *Youth, lapsing i* 6
Now one faint line of *l* doth glow, „ *ii* 9
Ray'd round with beams of living *l*. „ 52
Like (*See also* **Bee-like**) *L* to one of us she seems, *Not a whisper* 15
Likeness And all the *l* in the difference. *Why suffers* 11
Lily The two fair *lilies* growing at thy side *Woman of noble* 11
Limb His *l's* beneath him fail: *Far off in the dun* 26
Limb (*continued*) woman's youthful pride Of rounded *l's*— *One was the Tishbite* 17
Limb'd *See* **Dark-limb'd**
Line While walking with my rod and *l*, *I met in all* 2
a face whose every *l* Wore the pale cast *Methought I saw* 1
Drove into *l's* and studs of light *Youth, lapsing i* 6
Now one faint *l* of light doth glow, „ *ii* 9
Link In many a silver loop and *l* *Not to Silence* 26
Lip with right hand Moving toward her *l*, *Not to Silence* 11
Her perfect *l's* to taste, *One was the Tishbite* 12
Sleeps round those quiet *l's*; not quite a smile; *That is his portrait* 9
E'en scorn looks beautiful on human *l's*! *Why suffers* 4
Because the *l's* of little children preach Against you, *Therefore your Halls* 12
Lipp'd *See* **Finger-lipt, Rose-lipp'd**
Lisping Lightly *l*, breaks away; *Not to Silence* 32
Lit *L* as with inner light. *One was the Tishbite* 8
Little That *l* garden was her pride, *Along this glimmering* 5
Sleep, my *l* one, sleep! *Bright is the moon* 3
How is it that men have so *l* grace, *How is it that men* 1
L Aubrey in the West! *l* Alfred in the East *Little Aubrey* 1
L Homer, *l* Dante, *l* Shakespeare, can they last „ 4
L poet, hear the *l* poet's epigram! „ 7
The lasses and the *l* ones, Jack Tars, they look to you! *They say, etc.* 15
God bless the *l* isle where a man may still be true! „ 17
when he laughs, his *l* eyes Are swallow'd in his pamper'd cheeks. *Yon huddled cloud* 11
Live And he prays that you may *l*. *Little Aubrey* 3
Teach me, great Nature: make me *l*. *O leave not thou* 2
life, which heart in heart, you *l* With him you love, *Take, Lady* 3
Yet he *l's*; His and my friendship *That is his portrait* 40
to each that *l's* A hint of somewhat unexprest. *'Tis not alone* 7
L and prosper! Day by day Watch your standard roses *Vicar of this* 11
While I *l*, the owls! *While I live* 1
I thank thee, God, that thou hast made me *l*: *Why suffers* 12
Lived Prince, whose Father *l* in you, *Early-wise* 2
So *l* I without aim or choice, *Youth, lapsing i* 37
Liveliest Whose blood in its *l* course would not pause *Far off in the dun* 93
Living were worth Our *l* out? *Gone into darkness* 8
there sit figures as of gods Ray'd round with beams of *l* light. *Youth, lapsing ii* 52
Lock fingers in these *l's* (They are gray now) *Hear you the sound* 58
Loftier somewhat *l* antient heights Touch'd with Heaven's latest lights. *Thy soul is like* 11
Loins gird up thy *l* for fight, And get thee forth *O God, make this age* 10
Loiter'd I *l* in the middle way, *Youth, lapsing i* 46
London I was when *L* was not! *Here, I that stood* 10
This *L* once was middle sea, *Well, as to Fame* 5
Lone I keep no more a *l* distress, *I keep no more* 1
Lonely I shudder in my *l* nest, *What rustles, etc.* 13
Long The skin hung lax on his *l* thin hands; *Far off in the dun* 53
They mounted slow in their *l* black cloaks, „ 85
The knotted boughs of this *l* avenue Of thick dark oaks, *Hear you the sound* 10
L as the heart beats life within her breast, *Long as the heart* 1
With *l* tracts of murmuring, Partly river, partly brook, *Not to Silence* 28
Methinks I see the world's renewed youth A *l* day's dawn, *O God, make this age* 7
you live With him you love, be cloudless and be *l*! *Take, Lady* 4
who strides the earth With that *l* horn she loves to blow, *Well, as to Fame* 2
Pour'd by *l* glades and meadowy mounds, *Youth, lapsing i* 2
Longed And *l* to kiss her hand and lie *Because she bore* 7
And *l* to take his hand in mine. *I met in all* 4
Longer lay harder upon her Till she clapperclaw no *l*, *Wherever evil* 7
Look (s) Ye must be wiser than your *l's*, *Are those the far-famed* 9
And *l's* to awe the standers by, *Because she bore* 4
Look (verb) *L* he smiles, and opens his hands, *Bright is the moon* 4
L out from the cloudy vast. *Far off in the dun* 20
How beautifully *l's* the moonbeam *Hear you the sound* 9
I never *l* upon them but I glow „ 14
You would *l* down and knit your baby brows „ 48
But *l*, for these are nature too. *I keep no more* 16
L on those manly curls so glossy dark, *That is his portrait* 2

Look (verb) (*continued*) *l* you what an arch the brain has built *That is his portrait* 10
I *l* thro' all my glimmering life, „ 34
lasses and the little ones, Jack Tars, they *l* to you! *They say, etc.* 15
E'en scorn *l's* beautiful on human lips! *Why suffers* 4
Look'd No taper's light *l* out on the night, *Far off in the dun* 45
Dimly the travellers *l* thro' the glooms, „ 57
He *l* so jolly and so good— *I met in all* 5
Looking *l* far away On the blue mountains, *Hear you the sound* 39
Loom *l* or plough To weigh them as they *He was too good* 7
Loop In many a silver *l* and link *Not to Silence* 26
Lord Hail, truest *L* of Hell! *Art for Art's sake!* 1
Lordly Ye proud aristocrats whose *l* shadows, *Hear you the sound* 21
Loss Another whispers sick with *l*: *I keep no more* 9
His and my friendship have not suffer'd *l*, *That is his portrait* 41
Lost for what is *l* is made more dear; „ 46
We *l* you for how long a time, *We lost you* 1
Lot happy be your *l* In the Vicarage *Vicar of this* 3
Loud *l* the roar Of wind and mingled shower, *Far off in the dun* 33
The stream is *l*: I cannot hear!' *Remember you* 8
The wind is *l* in holt and hill, *Speak to me* 2
wanton ear Be tickled with the *l* 'hear, hear,' *They wrought, etc.* 7
Love (s) Nor *L* that holds a constant mood. *Are those the far-famed* 8
he that shuts out *L*, in turn shall be Shut out from *L*, *Beauty, Good, etc.* 3
whisper'd *l* of the fair young wives; *Far off in the dun* 67
I glow With an enthusiastic *l* of them. *Hear you the sound* 15
I murmur'd 'Speak again, my *l*, *Remember you* 7
They are not want of *l* for thee. *Speak to me* 8
How full of wisest humour and of *l*, *That is his portrait* 7
Capacious both of Friendship and of *L*. „ 51
For *L* flew over grove and field, *The night, etc.* 4
Something of pain—of bliss—of *L*, *'Tis not alone* 11
heart That watch't with *l* thine earliest infancy, *To thee with whom* 12
is it my *l* Coming along the secret ways? *What rustles* 5
Fair with green fields the realms of *L*. *Youth, lapsing ii* 36
Love (verb) 'I *l* the daisy weeping dew, *I keep no more* 13
cuckoo-voice that *l's* To babble its own name. *I, loving Freedom* 7
heart in heart, you live With him you *l*, *Take, Lady* 4
With that long horn she *l's* to blow, *Well, as to Fame* 2
Loved A child she *l* to play; *Along this glimmering* 2
This is he I *l*, This is the man *That is his portrait* 14
He *l* the river's roaring sound; *The child was sitting* 3
Cold words I spoke, yet *l* thee warm and well. *To thee with whom* 8
Loving All her *l* childhood Breezes from the palm *A dark Indian maiden* 13
wondering, *l*, Carolling 'Happy, „ 51
I, *l* Freedom for herself, *I, loving Freedom* 1
Low The *l* voice of the glad New Year Call to the freshly-flower'd hill. *Remember you* 11
And that large table of the breast dispread, Between *l* shoulders; *That is his portrait* 6
long May my strong wish, transgressing the *l* bound Of mortal hope, „ 38
Again the *l* sweet voices mourn'd In distant fields, *Youth, lapsing i* 43
Lower Evermore The simpler essence *l* lies, *From shape to shape* 6
L and deeper evermore They grew, *Youth, lapsing i* 25
Loyal Take, Lady, what your *l* nurses give, *Take, Lady*, 1
Lucid Regions of *l* matter taking forms, *Hither, when all* 5
Lured *L* by the cuckoo-voice that loves *I, loving Freedom* 7
Lute-toned A *l-t* whisper, 'I am here!' *Remember you* 6
Luxuriant My fancy was the more *l*, *That is his portrait* 16
Lyre And a sound of stringed *l's*. *Far off in the dun* 120
Lyric and you gleam reset In Britain's *l* coronet. *We lost you* 4

M

Mad Is thy *m* brain drunk with the merry, red wine, *Full light aloft* 7
Madam *the noblest place*, M, *is yours*, *The noblest men* 4
Made I thank thee, God, that thou hast *m* me live: *Why suffers* 12
for what is lost is *m* more dear; *That is his portrait* 46
All-perfect Framer, Him, who *m* the heart, „ 48
Thro' every change that *m* thee what thou art? *To thee with whom* 14
Madness Or a fancy or a *m*,— *Immeasurable sadness!* 7
what *m* moved my blood To make me thus belie *To thee with whom* 10
Mahomet Like the flower of *M*. *Spurge with fairy* 2
Maiden A dark Indian *m*, Warbling in the bloom'd liana, *A dark Indian maiden* 1
With her *m's* to the bay; „ 42
But found a *m* tender, shy, *Because she bore* 5
The happy *m's* tears are free *I keep no more* 5
Maim'd What life, so *m* by night, were worth *Gone into darkness* 7
Main That thou singest with *m* and with might? *Full light aloft* 6
Maize-bread *M* and the yuccaroot, *A dark Indian maiden* 44
Make and *m* beneath Ambrosial gloom. *Hear you the sound* 29
Sender and sent-to go to *m* up this, *Old ghosts* 7
Who *m* you utter things you did not say, „ 10
Teach me great Nature: *m* me live. *O leave not thou* 2
To *m* me thus belie my constant heart *To thee with whom* 11
The thunder cannot *m* thee dumb; *Youth, lapsing ii* 26
Man The white *m's* white sail, bringing *A dark Indian maiden* 37
She gave the white *men* welcome all, „ 53
Than the *men* of Xaraguay, „ 57
That ride to death the grief's of *men*? *Are those the far-famed* 2
A surface *m* of many theories, *A surface man* 1
Ten *men* fought a thousand, Slew them *Bold Havelock* 7
every *m* in Britain Says 'I am of Havelock's blood!' „ 15
There came a gaunt *m* from the dark Inn door, *Far off in the dun* 73
threw up the dust Of dead *men's* pulverised bones. „ 92
I come Unto the perfect *m*. *From shape to shape* 4
ask you whether you would be A great *m* *Hear you the sound* 57
The true *men* banish'd— *Rise, Britons, rise* 4
All Nature is the womb whence *M* is born. *Hold thou, my friend* 2
How is it that *men* have so little grace, When a great *m's* found to be bad and base, *How is it that men* 1
a good old *m*, Most eloquent, who spake *Methought I saw* 2
The *m's* life in the letters of the *m*. *Old ghosts* 4
All the *men* ran from her (repeat) *Sweet Kitty Sandilands* 5, 7
This is the *m* of whom you heard me speak. *That is his portrait* 15
The noblest men *methinks are bred* *The noblest men* 1
God bless the little isle where a *m* may still be true! *They say, etc.* 17
Shadows of statesmen, clever *men*! *They wrought, etc.* 12
fears that waste The strength of *men*, „ 23
The frame, the mind, the soul of *m*, „ 43
The *m* that round me wove Inextricable brickwork *What rustles* 7
And in the pauses groans of *men*. *Youth, lapsing ii* 24
Manly Look on those *m* curls so glossy dark, *That is his portrait* 2
Many lest overhaste Should fire the *m* wheels of change! *They wrought, etc.* 24
A voice like *m* voices cries, *Youth, lapsing ii* 7
A moan of *m* waterfalls, „ ii 23
Mar mould you all awry and *m* your worth; *Old ghosts* 11
Marble forms Of the unfading *m* carved upon them, *Hear you the sound* 26
From the clear *m* pouring glorious scorn, *One was the Tishbite* 7
March'd Bold Havelock *m*, (repeat) *Bold Havelock* 1, 5, 9
M and thought and fought, „ 11
M and fought himself dead. „ 12
Mark by chance should *m* The life that haunts *How strange it is* 6
to *m* The humours of the polling and the wake, *That is his portrait* 19
Market The hubbub of the *m* and the booths: „ 21
Married That mystic field of drifted light In mid Orion, and the *m* stars. *Hither, when all* 11
Marry spot Where it was my chance to *m*, *Vicar of this* 2
Mars She saw the snowy poles and Moons of *M*, *Hither, when all* 9
Martyr *See* **Patriot-martyrs**
Master (adj.) A *m* mind with *m* minds, *Young is the grief* 13
Master (s) Genius, *M* of the Moral Will! *Art for Art's sake* 2
Mate Call to its *m* when nothing stirr'd *Remember you* 15
Matter Regions of lucid *m* taking forms, *Hither, when all* 5
Mature and what a settled mind, *M*, *That is his portrait* 12
May (hawthorn-bloom) The *M* begins to breathe and bud, *Life of the Life* 3
May (month) terrace growing Green and greener every *M*! *Vicar of this* 15
Maze Inextricable brickwork *m* in *m*? *What rustles* 8
Meadow Warm beams across the *m* stole; *The night, etc.* 3
Meadowy Pour'd by long glades and *m* mounds, *Youth, lapsing i* 2
Mealy The miller with his *m* face, *I met in all* 3
Meant whose whims were *m* For virtue's servants, *A surface man* 2
Meat *See* **Pap-meat-pamper**
Mediterranean Thence haled me toward the *M* sea, *Here, I that stood* 6

Moving *m* To her Areyto's mellow ditty, — *A dark Indian maiden* 49
but with right hand *M* toward her lip, — *Not to Silence* 11
Parts in two channels, *m* to one end— — *Steersman* 3
Murmur The *m's* of the rivulet, Rippling — *Townsmen, etc.* 5
floats upward from the gulf A *m* of heroic song, — *Youth, lapsing ii* 19
Murmur'd I *m* 'Speak again, my love, — *Remember you* 7
Summer thro' all her sleepy leaves *M*: — *Youth, lapsing i* 15
Murmuring With long tracts of *m*, — *Not to Silence* 28
Music The southern stars a *m* peal'd, — *The night, etc.* 2
Mute there about the lawn Wholly *m*, — *Not to Silence* 24
Half after midnight! these *m* moralizers, — *Half after midnight!* 1
Mutter the *m* of deep-mouth'd thunderings — *Far off in the dun* 15
Myriad-volumed Your gardens, *m-v* libraries, — *Therefore your Halls* 3
Mystery A rumour of a *m*, — *Youth, lapsing ii* 1
Mystic And as with optic glasses her keen eyes Pierced thro' the *m* dome, — *Hither, when all* 4
That *m* field of drifted light In mid Orion, — „ 10

N

Naked orange groves *N*, and dark-limb'd, — *A dark Indian maiden* 6
N, without fear moving To her Areyto's mellow ditty, — „ 49
Not to Silence would I build A temple in her *n* field; — *Not to Silence* 2
Name she bore the iron *n* Of him who doomed — *Because she bore* 1
And his *n* was Atrophy! — *Far off in the dun* 56
cuckoo-voice that loves To babble its own *n*. — *I, loving Freedom* 8
They were not slaves that *n's* mislead, Nor traitors that mislead by *n's*! — *Not such were those* 3
Your n *is blown on every wind*, — *The noblest men* 5
His *n* is pure, his fame is free: — *They wrought, etc.* 32
Yet grief deserves a nobler *n*: — *Young is the grief* 5
Natal Now idly in my *n* bowers, — *Youth, lapsing i* 49
Nation And the voice that apes a *n*— — *Immeasurable sadness!* 5
Nature All *n* widens upward. — *From shape to shape* 5
Ev'n then the force of *n* and high birth — *Hear you the sound* 63
All *N* is the womb whence Man is born. — *Hold thou, my friend* 2
But look, for these are *n* too. — *I keep no more* 16
Teach me, great *N*: make me live. — *O leave not thou* 2
And took in more of *N* than mine own: — *That is his portrait* 18
which he compell'd once more Thro' his own *n*, — „ 28
I can trust Your woman's n *kind and trve.* — *The noblest men* 12
Like some wise artist, *N* gives, — *'Tis not alone* 6
Tho' I was harsh, my *n* is not so: — *To thee with whom* 5
Art, Science, *N*, everything is full, — *Why suffers* 7
as pure a heart As e'er beat time to *N*, — *Woman of noble* 5
Nearer But tho' the cataract seem the *n* way, — *Steersman* 6
Necessity Forethinking its twinfold *n*, — *That is his portrait* 49
Neck and folded once about her *n*, — *One was the Tishbite* 11
Nest Father will come to his babe in the *n*, — *Bright is the moon* 11
I shudder in my lonely *n*, — *What rustles* 13
New And ever *n* the tale she tells, — *Young is the grief* 2
The low voice of the glad *N* Year — *Remember you* 11
New-comer bringing To happy Hayti the *n-c*, — *A dark Indian maiden* 38
New Year low voice of the glad *N Y* — *Remember you* 11
Night (adj.) The *n* gale in those trees. — *Hear you the sound* 8
Night (s) then a *n*, all moons, confused The shadows — *Deep glens I found* 7
Of vapors, and mist, and *n*. — *Far off in the dun* 8
When the shadow of *n's* eternal wings — „ 13
Dark was the *n*, and loud the roar Of wind — „ 33
No taper's light look'd out on the *n*, — „ 45
Far away thro' the *n* ran the lengthen'd tones: — „ 90
away By *n*, into the deeper *n*! The deeper *n*? — *Gone into darkness* 3
If *n*, what barren toil to be! What life, so maim'd by *n*, were worth Our living out? — „ 6
'Tis a clear *n*, they will be here anon. — *Hear you the sound* 6
The *n* with sudden odour reel'd, — *The night, etc.* 1
The *n* is black and still; the deer Bleat — *What rustles* 3
The image of the moon by *n* — *Youth, lapsing i* 8
A voice, when *n* had crept on high, — „ 17
Nightingale The *n* in leafy woods Call — *Remember you* 12
Nile beside the flow Of sacred *N*, — *Here, I that stood* 4
Nobility high birth Had writ *n* upon my brow. — *Hear you the sound* 64
Noble But near the dwelling of some *n* race; — „ 17
To break the *n* pride of the Mistress of the Seas. — *They say, etc.* 4
God bless the *n* isle that is Mistress of the Seas! — „ 18
Woman of *n* form and *n* mind! — *Woman of noble* 1
Nobler Yet grief deserves a *n* name: — *Young is the grief* 5
Noblest Which lead the *n* life. — *Frenchman, etc.* 8
The n *men methinks are bred* — *The noblest men* 1
Nod With all his groves he bows, he *n's*, — *Youth, lapsing ii* 49
Nodding The thirsty horseman, *n*, lifts — *Yon huddled cloud* 3
Noise And in the hurry and the *n* Great spirits — *They wrought, etc.* 15
A *n* of hands that disarrange The social engine! — „ 21
A *n* of winds that meet and blend, — *Youth, lapsing ii* 2
Nook Which in one delicious *n*, — *Not to Silence* 30
Noon At *n* and eve, because your manner sorts — *Therefore your Halls* 10
Norman *See* **Saxo-Norman**
Northern *And glimmers to the* n *morn*, — *The noblest men* 7
Nurse Take, Lady, what your loyal *n's* give, — *Take, Lady* 1

O

Oak (*See also* **Oak-tree**) this long avenue Of thick dark *o's*, — *Hear you the sound* 11
leafless *o* Which towers above the lake — „ 32
Oak-tree *o-t* never should be planted — „ 16
Object ache For common *o's* that would keep — *How strange it is* 4
Observing light of hazel eyes, *O* all things. — *That is his portrait* 14
Occident Far off in the dun, dark *o*, — *Far off in the dun* 1
Odour The night with sudden *o* reel'd, — *The night, etc.* 1
Office I must unto mine *o*. — *Half after midnight!* 20
Offspring I and my son's son and our *o*, — *Hear you the sound* 24
Their *o* of this union. — *Old ghosts* 8
Old When there stood a dark coach at an *o* Inn door — *Far off in the dun* 35
The grim *o* coachee strode to the box, — „ 87
Coeval with the battlemented towers Of my *o* ancestors! — *Hear you the sound* 13
Wore the pale cast of thought, a good *o* man, — *Methought I saw* 2
O ghosts whose day was done ere mine began, — *Old ghosts* 1
And on me Frown not, *o* ghosts, — „ 9
I stepp'd upon the *o* mill bridge? — *Remember you* 4
O'er the bow'd shoulder of a bland *o* Age, The face of placid Death.' — *That is his portrait* 36
Townsmen, or of the hamlet, young or *o*, — *Townsmen, etc.* 1
He chanted some *o* doleful rhyme. — *Youth, lapsing i* 36
Still humming snatches of *o* song, — „ 38
Older When I was somewhat *o* grown — „ 21
Olympias One was *O*: the floating snake — *One was the Tishbite* 9
One (adj.) As when he stood on Carmel-steeps With *o* arm stretch'd out bare, — „ 3
Parts in two channels, moving to *o* end— — *Steersman* 3
Thro' *o* whole life an overflowing urn, — *That is his portrait* 50
Or sleep thro' *o* brief dream upon the grass,— — *Townsmen, etc.* 4
O only joy I know, the joy of life. — *Why suffers* 14
Now *o* faint line of light doth glow, — *Youth, lapsing ii* 9
One (pron. and s) Sleep, my little *o*, sleep! — *Bright is the moon* 3
Sleep, my pretty *o*, sleep! — „ 10
O was the Tishbite whom the raven fed, — *One was the Tishbite* 1
O was Olympias: the floating snake — „ 9
The lasses and the little *o's*, Jack Tars, — *They say, etc.* 15
Only One *o* joy I know, the joy of life. — *Why suffers* 14
Open Look he smiles, and *o's* his hands, — *Bright is the moon* 4
Said, 'O, Rosebud, *o*, yield Thy fragrant soul.' — *The night, etc.* 5
Optic And as with *o* glasses her keen eyes Pierced — *Hither, when all* 3
Orange Wantoning in *o* groves Naked, — *A dark Indian maiden* 5
Orb An *o* repulsive of all hate, — *Young is the grief* 14
Orbit But as Earth her *o* runs, — *Little Aubrey* 3
Orion field of drifted light In mid *O*, — *Hither, when all* 11
Osier'd Streaming thro' his *o* aits! — *Vicar of this* 20
Other Henceforward no *o* strife— — *Frenchman, etc.* 6
Which speak of us to *o* centuries, — *Hear you the sound* 27
Outer Howling in *o* darkness.' — *Beauty, Good, etc.* 5
Overdealt praise Is neither *o* nor idly won. — *That is his portrait* 43

Overdrawn delicately *o* With the first twilight *Thy soul is like* 3
Overflow as never *o's* With flush of rain, *Not to Silence* 19
Overflowing As my own soul is full, to *o*— *Why suffers* 8
Thro' one whole life an *o* urn, *That is his portrait* 50
Overhaste lest *o* Should fire the many wheels *They wrought, etc.* 23
Overthrew Slew them and *o*. *Bold Havelock* 8
Owl While I live, the *o's*! *While I live* 1
Own Whence your *o* citizens, for their *o* renown, *Here, I that stood* 7
Lured by the cuckoo-voice that loves To babble its *o* name. *I, loving Freedom* 8
Yet her *o* deep soul says nay: *The lamps were bright* 24
which he compell'd once more Thro' his *o* nature, *That is his portrait* 28
When thine *o* spirit was at strife With thine *o* spirit. *Thou may'st remember* 2
As my *o* soul is full, to overflowing— *Why suffers* 8
Owning *o* more Discourse, more widely wise.' *From shape to shape* 7

P

Pain Something of *p*—of bliss—of Love, *'Tis not alone* 11
Painted filthiest of all paintings *p* well Is mightier than the purest *p* ill!' Yes, mightier than the purest *p* well, *Art for Art's sake!* 3
That is his portrait *p* by himself. *That is his portrait* 1
Painting filthiest of all *p's* painted well *Art for Art's sake!* 3
Pale His brow is clammy and *p*. *Far off in the dun* 28
They lifted their eyes to the dead, *p* skies, „ 61
Methought I saw a face whose every line Wore the *p* cast of thought, *Methought I saw* 2
Pall the *p* of the sky Leave never an inch *Far off in the dun* 21
Palm (a tree) Breezes from the *p* and canna *A dark Indian maiden* 14
Waving a *p* branch, wondering, „ 51
Palm (of the hand) As each put a farthing into his *p*, *Far off in the dun* 79
Palmy All day long with laughing eyes, Dancing by a *p* bay, *A dark Indian maiden* 18
Pamper *See* **Pap-meat-pamper**
Pamper'd his little eyes Are swallow'd in his *p* cheeks. *Yon huddled cloud* 12
Pandemonium There is a clock in *P*, *Half after midnight!* 5
Papao Beneath the *p* tree! *A dark Indian maiden* 33
Pap-meat-pamper But *p-m-p* not the time *Wherever evil* 4
Paradise (adj.) those are the lights of the *P* coach, *Far off in the dun* 107
Paradise (s) In the wooded *p*, The cedar-wooded *p* *A dark Indian maiden* 19
Parish *P* feud, or party strife, *Vicar of this* 8
Park deer Bleat as with human voices in the *p*. *What rustles* 4
Part river here, my friend, *P's* in two channels, *Steersman* 3
Party (adj.) Parish feud, or *p* strife, *Vicar of this* 8
Party (s) and the d——l take the *parties*! *They say, etc.* 10
Party-rage Contends, despising *p-r*, *They wrought, etc.* 46
Pass'd *See* **Past**
Passion-wrought Ill fares a people *p-w*, *They wrought, etc.* 25
Past (adj.) things of *p* days with their horrible eyes *Far off in the dun* 19
Her thoughts have found their wings In the dreaming of *p* things: *The lamps were bright* 22
Past (s) These hills were plains within the *p*, *Well, as to Fame* 6
In thy beginnings in the *p*, *Young is the grief* 11
And how all things become the *p*. *Youth, lapsing i* 28
Past-Pass'd (verb) They *pass'd* (an inner spirit fed Their ever-burning fires,) *Far off in the dun* 117
past, in sleep, away By night, *Gone into darkness* 2
And *past* her for the Proctor. *Sweet Kitty Sandilands* 4
Path who sees His *p* before him? *They wrought, etc.* 11
Patriot-martyrs Freedom claims As *p-m* of her creed: *Not such were those* 2
Pause (s) And in the *p's* groans of men. *Youth, lapsing ii* 24
Pause (verb) not *p* At the strife of the shadowy wheels, *Far off in the dun* 93
brief dream upon the grass,—*P* here. *Townsmen, etc.* 5
Pausing So *p* 'twixt the East and West, *Youth, lapsing i* 47
Peaceful Tempers the *p* light of hazel eyes, *That is his portrait* 13
Peak A mountain bright with triple *p's*: *Youth, lapsing ii* 48
Peal (s) *See* **Thunder-peal**
Peal (verb) The second voice will *p* again. *Youth, lapsing i* 56
Peal'd The southern stars a music *p*, *The night, etc.* 2
Peal'd (*continued*) The latest thunder-peal hath *p*, *Youth, lapsing ii* 30
Pearl True *P* of our poetic prime! *We lost you* 2
Pendulum The slow vibrations of whose *p*, *Half after midnight!* 7
People And fuse the *p's* into one. *Are those the far-famed* 16
That the voice of a satisfied *p* *That the voice* 1
Did the *p* dance and play, *The lamps were bright* 36
Ill fares a *p* passion-wrought, *They wrought, etc.* 25
Convoys the *p's* wish, is great; „ 31
Perfect (*See also* **All-perfect**) 'And thro' all phases of all thought I come Unto the *p* man. *From shape to shape* 4
More complex is more *p*, owning more Discourse, „ 7
Her *p* lips to taste, *One was the Tishbite* 12
Perfume chapel's vaulted gloom Was misted with *p*. *The lamps were bright* 8
Perish and our offspring, all Shall *p*, *Hear you the sound* 25
speak of us to other centuries, Shall *p* also, „ 28
Perplex But questions that *p* us now— *He was too good* 6
Never tithe unpaid *p* you, *Vicar of this* 7
Phantom Mix'd with the *p* of his coming fame, *That is his portrait* 32
Pharaoh A *P*, kingliest of his kingly race, *Here, I that stood* 3
Phase thro' all *p's* of all thought I come *From shape to shape* 3
Pierced eyes *P* thro' the mystic dome, *Hither, when all* 4
Often shallow, *p* with light, *Not to Silence* 21
Piercing *P* the wrung ears of the damn'd *Half after midnight!* 10
Pile Would I could *p* fresh life on life, *Why suffers* 5
Place (s) (*See also* **Charnel-place**) She led them down the pleasant *p's*, *A dark Indian maiden* 62
shaped, and carved, and set me in my *p*. *Here, I that stood* 4
And in the world the noblest p, *The noblest men* 3
Place (verb) joy'd to *p* me on The hollow-stemm'd *Hear you the sound* 31
Placid O'er the bow'd shoulder of a bland Old Age, The face of *p* Death.' *That is his portrait* 37
Plain Anacaona, Dancing on the blossomy *p* *A dark Indian maiden* 29
summer *p's* with their shining leaves, *Far off in the dun* 69
These hills were *p's* within the past, There will be *p's* again, and we, *Well, as to Fame* 6
And I must traverse yonder *p*: *Youth, lapsing i* 54
The casements sparkle on the *p*, „ *ii* 39
Plan That contemplate a mighty *p*, *They wrought, etc.* 42
Planted oak-tree never should be *p* But near *Hear you the sound* 16
Play (s) And your three young things at *p*, *Vicar of this* 13
Her silver eddies in their *p* Drove into lines *Youth, lapsing i* 5
Play (verb) A child she loved to *p*; *Along this glimmering* 2
Where the doubtful shadows *p*, *Not to Silence* 31
Did the people dance and *p*, *The lamps were bright* 36
Playing *P* with the scarlet crane, *A dark Indian maiden* 31
Pleasant She led them down the *p* places, „ 62
They saw the green verge of the *p* earth, *Far off in the dun* 63
With *p* hymns they soothe the air Of death, „ 109
Are *p* from the early Spring to when, *Townsmen, etc.* 7
Vicar of this *p* spot Where it was my chance to marry, *Vicar of this* 1
Please The despots over yonder, let 'em do whate'er they *p*! *They say, etc.* 16
All things *p* you, nothing vex you, *Vicar of this* 9
Pledge Then *p* we our glorious dead, *Frenchman, etc.* 9
Plot (s) I hate the trim-set *p's* of art!' *I keep no more* 14
Plot (verb) and they *p* against us yonder, *They say, etc.* 8
Plough loom or *p* To weigh them as they should *He was too good* 7
Pluck To *p* the sanction of a God. „ 12
Poesy when *P* shall bind Falsehood beneath *O God, make this age* 7
Poet I know it as a *p*, (repeat) *Immeasurable sadness!* 2, 8
Little *p*, hear the little *p's* epigram! *Little Aubrey* 7
'You're no *P*'—the critics cried! 'Why?' said the *P*. 'You're unpopular!' *Popular, Popular* 2
'You're no *P*!' 'Why?'—'You're popular!' „ 5
Poetic True Pearl of our *p* prime! *We lost you* 2
Pointing *P* to the unheeded lapse of hours, *Half after midnight!* 2
Poised there Hovering, thoughtful, *p* in air. *Not to Silence* 12
Pole thunderings Shakes all the starless *p*, *Far off in the dun* 16
She saw the snowy *p's* and Moons of Mars, *Hither, when all* 9
Polling The humours of the *p* and the wake, *That is his portrait* 20
Pomp ye still shall flourish In your high *p* of shade, *Hear you the sound* 29
Poor A clearer day Than our *p* twilight dawn on earth— *Gone into darkness* 5
P devils, babble 'we shall last.' *Well, as to Fame* 8
Pop-gun *P-g*, Popular and Unpopular! *Popular, Popular* 6

Q

R

Retire As he *r's* into himself and is: *Old ghosts* 6
Return to *r* with thee Some happy Summer morning, *Woman of noble* 8
Revel (s) But the *r* still goes on. *The lamps were bright* 40
Revel (verb) 'They *r* as they may,' „ 17
Revelling no *r* tones Of carouse were heard within: *Far off in the dun* 41
Revere They wrought a work which Time *r's*, *They wrought, etc.* 1
Revolve And see and hear the world *r*: *Youth, lapsing i* 52
Rhyme Break thro' with the hammer of iron *r*, *Wherever evil* 2
He chanted some old doleful *r*. *Youth, lapsing i* 36
Rhyme-hammer Thy *r-h shall* have honour. *Wherever evil* 9
Rich And *r* was their attire: *Far off in the dun* 126
Ricketty But the *r* blast runs shrilly and fast „ 11
Ride That *r* to death the griefs of men? *Are those the far-famed* 2
With psaltery they *r*. *Far off in the dun* 112
Ridge moonlight That whiten'd all the eastern *r*, *Remember you* 2
Right Finger-lipt, but with *r* hand Moving toward her lip, *Not to Silence* 10
To left or *r* but falling floods. *Remember you* 16
And the guard gasp'd out 'All's *r*.' *Far off in the dun* 88
Rill I heard Spring laugh in hidden *r's*, *Youth, lapsing i* 13
Ripening *See* **Slow-ripening**
Riper when your age had somewhat *r* grown, *Hear you the sound* 54
Gives stouter ale and *r* port Than any in the country-side. *Yon huddled cloud* 7
Ripple lake that *r's* out In the clear moonshine. *Hear you the sound* 33
Rippling rivulet, *R* by cressy isles or bars of sand, *Townsmen, etc.* 6
Rise (s) *See* **Morning-rise**
Rise (verb) These whispers *r*, and fall away, *'Tis not alone* 10
The months, ere they began to *r*, *Youth, lapsing i* 9
Now shall I rest or shall I *r*? „ *ii* 5
Rising At the *r* of the sun. *Full light aloft* 12
River I would have a *r* run, *Not to Silence* 18
Partly *r*, partly brook, „ 29
the *r* here, my friend, Parts in two channels, *Steersman* 2
He loved the *r's* roaring sound; *The child was sitting* 3
The *r* rose and burst his bound, „ 4
Thro' wooded isles the *r* shines, *Youth, lapsing ii* 38
At the battle of Alma *R*. *Frenchman, etc.* 4
That rests by the Alma *R*. „ 12
Rivulet *r*, Rippling by cressy isles or bars of sand, *Townsmen, etc.* 5
Road The middle *r* of sober thought! *They wrought, etc.* 28
Roam Where'er you *r* from, would you waste an hour, *Townsmen, etc.* 3
Roar loud the *r* Of wind and mingled shower, *Far off in the dun* 33
And heard the *r* of her seas. „ 64
Roaring monstrous rocks from craggy snouts Disploding globes of *r* fire. *Deep glens I found* 4
He loved the river's *r* sound; *The child was sitting* 3
Rock monstrous *r's* from craggy snouts *Deep glens I found* 3
Rod While walking with my *r* and line, *I met in all* 2
Roll'd floating snake *R* round her ankles, *One was the Tishbite* 10
Rolling In the vast Of the *r* of the æons, *Little Aubrey* 6
Rook Were idler than a flight of *r's*. *Are those the far-famed* 12
Room We may glide from *r* to *r*, *Not a whisper* 3
Rose (s) Faded ev'ry violet, all the *r's*; *Faded ev'ry violet* 1
Watch your standard *r's* blowing, *Vicar of this* 12
Rose (verb) The walls of lava *r*, *Far off in the dun* 38
How every brake and flower spread and *r*, *That is his portrait* 26
The river *r* and burst his bound, *The child was sitting* 4
Rosebud *R*, open, yield Thy fragrant soul.' *The night, etc.* 6
Rose-lipp'd And the laugh of their r-*l* boys. *Far off in the dun* 68
Rounded mingled with The woman's youthful pride Of *r* limbs— *One was the Tishbite* 17
Roundelay she said her say—This was her *r*— *The lamps were bright* 30
Rumour A *r* of a mystery, *Youth lapsing ii* 1
Run And his hot steeds never *r*: *Far off in the dun* 4
the ricketty blast *r's* shrilly and fast „ 11
Methinks my tongue *r's* twenty knots an hour: *Half after midnight!* 19
But as Earth her orbit *r's*, *Little Aubrey* 3
I would have a river *r*, *Not to Silence* 18
Rush And *r'es* o'er a boundless field. *Youth, lapsing ii* 32
Rustle What *r's* hither in the dark? *What rustles* 1
Rustling The dark vine leaves round the *r* eaves, *Far off in the dun* 71
Rusty But the *r* sign of a skull and cross-bones „ 43

S

Sackbut With *s*, and with dulcimer, *Far off in the dun* 111
Sacred I that stood in On beside the flow Of *s* Nile, three thousand years ago!— *Here, I that stood* 2
The *s* sorrows of as pure a heart As e'er beat time to Nature, *Woman of Noble* 4
Sad At some *s* tale of wrong, and do the wrong He wept for, *A surface man* 6
and drank The sweet *s* tears of wisdom.' *Methought I saw* 6
Sadness Immeasurable *s*! (repeat) *Immeasurable sadness!* 1, 4, 11
Said she *s* her say—This was her roundelay— *The lamps were bright* 29
Thou may'st remember what I *s* *Thou may'st remember* 1
Sail The white man's white *s*, bringing *A dark Indian maiden* 37
Silver *s's* all out of the West, *Bright is the moon* 12
St. James Ha! by *S J* Mine was no vulgar mind *Hear you the sound* 61
Sake Art for Art's *s*! *Art for Art's sake!* 1
They worshipt Freedom for her *s*; *They wrought, etc.* 5
Salaam and he sends you his *S*; *Little Aubrey* 2
Sallow and the *s* lights shone Dimly and blurly with simmering fat. *Far off in the dun* 99
Sanction To pluck the *s* of a God. *He was too good* 12
Sand rivulet, Rippling by cressy isles or bars of *s*, *Townsmen, etc.* 6
Sandilands (Kitty) *See* **Kitty Sandilands**
Sat Jauntily *s* the Proctor's cap *Sweet Kitty Sandilands* 11
Satisfied That the voice of a *s* people may keep *That the voice* 1
Savannah Lady of the green *S*: *A dark Indian maiden* 16
Save Take thou the 'bend,' 'twill *s* thee many a day. *Steersman* 8
Up, Jack Tars, and *s* us! (repeat) *They say, etc.* 5, 12, 19
Up and *s* the pride of the Mistress of the Seas! (repeat) „ 7, 11, 14
If *you* will *s* the pride of the Mistress of the Seas. „ 21
Saw *s* the green verge of the pleasant earth, *Far off in the dun* 63
She *s* the snowy poles and Moons of Mars, *Hither, when all* 9
'Methought I *s* a face whose every line *Methought I saw* 1
And they *s her* standing by, *The lamps were bright* 51
Saxo-Norman *are bred Of ours the* S-N *race*; *The noblest men* 2
Say (s) she said her *s*—This was her roundelay— *The lamps were bright* 29
Say (verb) If you could speak, would you not *s*: *Early-wise* 3
And I *s* it, and repeat it, *Immeasurable sadness!* 10
Who make you utter things you did not *s*, *Old ghosts* 10
Whate'er the crowd on either bank may *s*, *Steersman* 7
'More dear' I will not *s*, but rather bless *That is his portrait* 47
That skinny witch did *s*, *The lamps were bright* 18
They *s* some foreign powers have laid *They say, etc.* 1
But what, were hard to *s*. *'Tis not alone* 12
Scale Thy thought did *s* a purer range *Thou may'st remember* 10
Scan who did *s* His countenance so grand *Methought I saw* 4
Scar To snowy crofts and winding *s's*, *Youth, lapsing i* 18
Scarlet Playing with the *s* crane, The dragon-fly and *s* crane, *A dark Indian maiden* 31
Scentless I sit among the *s* flowers *Youth, lapsing i* 51
Science Art, *S*, Nature, everything is full, *Why suffers* 7
Scope A precedent of larger *s*, *They wrought, etc.* 38
Scorn my friend, no lesser life in *s*, *Hold thou, my friend* 1
From the clear marble pouring glorious *s*, *One was the Tishbite* 7
E'en *s* looks beautiful on human lips! *Why suffers* 4
Scream shrill *s's* arise Along the sunless waste, *Far off in the dun* 17
Then a *s* of wild dismay Thro' the deep hall *The lamps were bright* 41
Sea In the deep *s* no more,— *A dark Indian maiden* 68
And heard the roar of her *s's*. *Far off in the dun* 64
Thence haled me toward the Mediterranean *s*, *Here, I that stood* 6
Thro' strange *s's* drew me to your monster town. „ 8
This London once was middle *s*, *Well, as to Fame* 5
To break the noble pride of the Mistress of the *S's*. *They say, etc.* 4
Up and save the pride of the Mistress of the *S's*! (repeat) „ 7, 11, 14
God bless the noble isle that is Mistress of the *S's*! „ 18
If *you* will save the pride of the Mistress of the *S's*. „ 21
Sea-marge Over the dark *s-m* springing, *A dark Indian maiden* 39
Seasonable To shape, to settle, to repair With *s* changes fair *They wrought, etc.* 35

Second Sooner or later from the haze The *s* voice will peal again. *Youth, lapsing i* 56
Secret is it my love Coming along the *s* ways? *What rustles* 6
And where the *s* streams rejoice. *Youth, lapsing i* 12
See *S*, The cradle where she lay! *Along the glimmering* 3
And *s*, ye dare not touch the truth, *Are those the far-famed* 6
He *s's* his father in distant lands, *Bright is the moon* 5
They *s* the light of their blest firesides *Far off in the dun* 65
The summer hills they *s*; „ 70
The crowd have come to *s* thy grave, *I keep no more* 2
But these shall *s* it none the less. „ 4
I laugh'd to *s* him as he stood, *I met in all* 7
S, she dreameth happy dreams, *Not a whisper* 13
Methinks I *s* the world's renewed youth *O God, make this age* 6
Speak to me, let me hear or *s*! *Speak to me* 5
I *s* At the end, as 'twere athwart *That is his portrait* 34
who *s's* His path before him? *They wrought, etc.* 10
Whate'er I *s*, where'er I move, *'Tis not alone* 9
And *s* and hear the world revolve: *Youth, lapsing i* 52
Seed It show'd the *s's* of innate dignity *Hear you the sound* 52
Seeing He, *s* far an end sublime, *They wrought, etc.* 45
S the heart so wondrous in her ways, *Why suffers* 3
Seeking *See* **Truth-seeking**
Seem 'I *s*, but am not, far away; *Early-wise* 4
Like to one of us she *s's*, *Not a whisper* 15
But tho' the cataract *s* the nearer way, *Steersman* 6
Seem'd I heard, as I have *s* to hear, *Remember you* 9
S I so cold? what madness moved my blood *To thee with whom* 10
Seen I have *s* the four great empires disappear! *Here, I that stood* 9
If earth be *s* from your conjectured heaven, *Old ghosts* 2
Considering what mine eyes have *s*, *Young is the grief* 9
Seest *S* thou my faults and wilt not speak? *Speak to me* 7
Self-control range Of prospect up to *s-c*, *Thou may'st remember* 11
Send and he *s's* you his Salaam; *Little Aubrey* 2
Sender *S* and sent-to go to make up this, *Old ghosts* 7
Sense keep Our awful inner ghostly *s* Unroused, *How strange it is* 5
But to one of finer *s*, *Not to Silence* 5
Or, if the *s* of most require *They wrought, etc.* 37
The difference of all things to the *s*, *Why suffers* 10
Sent Where his gilding ray is never *s*, *Far off in the dun* 3
S thro' my blood a prophet voice *Youth, lapsing i* 10
Sent-to Sender and *s-t* go to make up this, *Old ghosts* 7
Servant whose whims were meant For virtue's *s's*, *A surface man* 3
Set (*See also* **Trim-set**) *S* round with many a toppling spire, *Deep glens I found* 2
shaped, and carved, and *s* me in my place. *Here, I that stood* 4
Spurge with fairy crescent *s*, *Spurge with fairy* 1
Settle To shape, to *s*, to repair *They wrought, etc.* 34
Settled and what a *s* mind, Mature, *That is his portrait* 11
Shade ye still shall flourish In your high pomp of *s*, *Hear you the sound* 29
Millions of forms, and hues, and *s's*, *Why suffers* 9
Crown'd with soft *s* her deepening floods *Youth, lapsing i* 3
Shadow confused The *s's* from the icy heights. *Deep glens I found* 8
When the *s* of night's eternal wings *Far off in the dun* 13
Ye proud aristocrats whose lordly *s's*, *Hear you the sound* 21
Where the doubtful *s's* play, *Not to Silence* 31
S's of statesmen, clever men! *They wrought, etc.* 12
And *s's* strike and *s's* sink, *Youth, lapsing ii* 15
Away with *s's*! On they move! „ 34
Shadow'd *See* **Cocoa-shadow'd**
Shadowy A land of thin faces and *s* forms, *Far off in the dun* 7
As the shrivell'd forms of the *s* grooms Yoked the skeleton horses to. „ 59
Whose blood in its liveliest course would not pause At the strife of the *s* wheels, „ 94
Shake thunderings *S's* all the starless pole, „ 16
To which the slight-built hustings *s*; *They wrought, etc.* 8
Shaken They were *s* from the dance.— *The lamps were bright* 46
Shakespeare Little Homer, little Dante, little *S*, *Little Aubrey* 4
Shallow Often *s*, pierced with light, *Not to Silence* 21
Shame The year, that comes, may come with *s*, *I, loving Freedom* 6
'Tis *s* to fail so far, and still My failing shall be less my *s*: *Young is the grief* 7
Shank his *s's* were shrunken to willow wands *Far off in the dun* 55
Shape (s) heads without bodies and *s's* without heads *Far off in the dun* 103
From *s* to *s* at first within the womb *From shape to shape* 1
Admire that stalwart *s*, those ample brows, *That is his portrait* 4
Into another *s*, born of the first, „ 29
Shape (verb) To *s*, to settle, to repair *They wrought, etc.* 34
Shaped *s*, and carved, and set me in my place. *Here, I that stood* 4
Sharp and dull The *s* desire of knowledge still with knowing! *Why suffers* 6
Sharper Till suddenly a *s* voice Cried in the future 'Come along.' *Youth, lapsing i* 39
Shaven Strange fiery eyes glared fiercely thro' The windows of *s* bone. *Far off in the dun* 48
Sheaf When corny Lammas bound the *sheaves*: *Youth, lapsing i* 16
Shift Yon huddled cloud his motion *s's*, *Yon huddled cloud* 1
Shifting Full fields of barley *s* tearful lights *Townsmen, etc.* 8
Shine Thro' wooded isles the river *s's*, *Youth, lapsing ii* 38
Shining The summer plains with their *s* leaves, *Far off in the dun* 69
Shook And *s* the frosty winter stars. *Youth, lapsing i* 20
Shone sallow lights *s* Dimly and blurly *Far off in the dun* 99
As stars they *s*, in raiment white, „ 131
Shore never more upon the *s* Dancing *A dark Indian maiden* 65
How glad am I to walk With Susan on the *s*! *How glad am I* 2
far off from England's *s*, He comes no more. *What rustles* 9
That wash'd her *s's* with blissful sounds: *Youth, lapsing i* 4
Short Thick sobs and *s* shrill screams arise Along the sunless waste, *Far off in the dun* 17
and whensoe'er There may be *s* cessation of their wails, *Half after midnight!* 12
Shoulder Down from the *s* moved: *One was the Tishbite* 13
breast dispread Between low *s's*; *That is his portrait* 6
O'er the bow'd *s* of a bland old Age, „ 36
Shout (s) Faint *s's* are heard across the glen, *Youth, lapsing ii* 22
Shout (verb) shriek and *s* to drown the thrilling noise. *Half after midnight!* 16
Show I will *s* to you Another countenance, *That is his portrait* 44
Show'd It *s* the seeds of innate dignity *Hear you the sound* 52
Shower (s) loud the roar Of wind and mingled *s*, *Far off in the dun* 34
Shower (verb) *S's* in a whisper o'er the world. *Not to Silence* 34
Showing *s* every bend Of each dark hill *Thy soul is like* 5
Shriek *s* and shout to drown the thrilling noise. *Half after midnight!* 16
Shrill Thick sobs and short *s* screams arise Along the sunless waste, *Far off in the dun* 17
is heard The *s* and solemn warning 'Ever, Never': *Half after midnight!* 14
Shrine (s) Not to her would raise a *s*: *Not to Silence* 3
Near the *s*, but half in sun, „ 17
Shrine (verb) I would *s* her in my verse! „ 8
Shrivell'd As the *s* forms of the shadowy grooms Yoked the skeleton horses to. *Far off in the dun* 59
Shrunken his shanks were *s* to willow wands „ 55
Shudder I *s* in my lonely nest, *What rustles* 13
Shudder'd *S* with silent stars, she clomb, *Hither, when all* 2
Shut he that *s's* out Love, in turn shall be *S* out from Love, *Beauty, Good, etc.* 3
Shy But found a maiden tender, *s*, *Because she bore* 5
Sick His heart throbs thick, his brain reels *s*: *Far off in the dun* 27
Another whispers *s* with loss: *I keep no more* 9
Thro' her worn brain, hot and *s*.' *The lamps were bright* 28
Sicken Till priest-craft and king-craft *s*, *Wherever evil* 3
Side Deep dells of snow sunk on each *s* *Far off in the dun* 97
on every *s* The dragon's curves melted, *One was the Tishbite* 14
Sigh (s) And mingle kisses, tears, and *s's*, *Life of the Life* 6
Sigh (verb) *S* over all their fallen leaves; *Youth, lapsing i* 32
Sight The tears bedimm'd their *s*: *Far off in the dun* 86
Till heart and *s* and hearing ache *How strange it is* 3
Often deep beyond the *s*, *Not to Silence* 22
Sign rusty *s* of a skull and cross-bones *Far off in the dun* 43
Silence Not to *S* would I build A temple *Not to Silence* 1
Not like *S* shall she stand, „ 9
Silent Floated in the *s* summer: *A dark Indian maiden* 40
Remembering all the golden hours Now *s*, *Gone into darkness* 10
Shudder'd with *s* stars, she clomb, *Hither, when all* 2
The *s* hills, the stormy floods, *'Tis not alone* 3
Thames along the *s* level, *Vicar of this* 19

Silent (*continued*) take with thee Our warmest wishes, *s* Guardians But true till death ; *Woman of noble* 6
Silver *S* sails all out of the West, Under the *s* moon, *Bright is the moon* 12
With a *s* sound the wheels went round, *Far off in the dun* 121
In many a *s* loop and link Variously from its far spring, *Not to Silence* 26
Her *s* eddies in their play Drove into lines and studs of light *Youth, lapsing i* 5
Simmering sallow lights shone Dimly and blurly with *s* fat. *Far off in the dun* 100
Simple Those holly-thickets only hide Her grave—a *s* stone ! *Along this glimmering* 8
' O let the *s* slab remain ! *I keep no more* 10
Simpler Evermore The *s* essence lower lies, *From shape to shape* 6
Sin And free from taint of *s*. *Far off in the dun* 132
Singest That thou *s* with main and with might ? *Full light aloft* 6
Singing The wanton wind came *s* lustily *Hear you the sound* 41
Single knows That none can truly write his *s* day, *Old ghosts* 13
Sink And shadows strike and shadows *s*, *Youth, lapsing ii* 15
Sister Beauty, Good and Knowledge are three *s's* . . . *Beauty, Good, etc.* 1
S's, I could almost weep ! *Not a whisper* 8
Her half *s*, Reticence. *Not to Silence* 6
Sit You'd *s* there From dawn till sunset *Hear you the sound* 38
will not let an honest Briton *s* at home at ease : *They say, etc.* 9
I *s* among the scentless flowers *Youth, lapsing i* 51
And there *s* figures as of Gods „ *ii* 51
Sitting The child was *s* on the bank *The child was sitting* 1
Skeleton As the shrivell'd forms of the shadowy grooms Yoked the *s* horses to. *Far off in the dun* 60
Skin The *s* hung lax on his long thin hands ; „ 53
Skinny ' They revel as they may,' That *s* witch did say, *The lamps were bright* 18
Skull and Cross-bones (Inn sign) rusty sign of a *s a c-b* *Far off in the dun* 43
Sky the pall of the *s* Leave never an inch of blue ; „ 21
Strange beauties from the *s*. „ 32
lifted their eyes to the dead, pale *skies*, „ 61
when all the deep unsounded *skies* *Hither, when all* 1
And softly blow the balmy *skies* ; *Life of the Life* 4
Speak to me from the stormy *s* ! *Speak to me* 1
The starr'd abysses of the *s*, *'Tis not alone* 2
Out bursts a rainbow in the *s*— *Youth, lapsing ii* 33
Slab ' O let the simple *s* remain ! *I keep no more* 10
Slave heart of his Hard, and the *s* of vice ; *A surface man* 4
They were not *s's* that names mislead, *Not such were those* 3
Slay Whom the wedded wife did *s*, *The lamps were bright* 48
Sleek or the snug brick box Of some *s* citizen. *Hear you the sound* 20
Sleep (s) past, in *s*, away By night, *Gone into darkness* 2
All the house is fast in *s*, *Not a whisper* 6
Sleep (verb) *S*, my little one, *s* ! *Bright is the moon* 3
kisses him there in a dream, *S*, *s*. „ 7
S, my pretty one, *s* ! „ 10
Under the silver moon, *S*, *s* ! „ 14
To watch and wake while others *s*, *How strange it is* 2
In that cradle *s's* my child, *Not a whisper* 9
mock'd and said, ' Come, cry aloud, he *s's*.' *One was the Tishbite* 4
S's round those quiet lips ; not quite a smile ; *That is his portrait* 9
Or *s* thro' one brief dream upon the grass,— *Townsmen, etc.* 4
' Come ' and I come, no more I *s* : *Youth, lapsing ii* 25
Sleepy Summer thro' all her *s* leaves Murmur'd : „ *i* 14
Slender I clasp her *s* waist, We kiss, we are so fond, *How glad am I* 5
Slept in them *s* A red infernal glow ; *Far off in the dun* 81
Slew *S* them and overthrew. *Bold Havelock* 8
Slight-built To which the *s-b* hustings shake ; *They wrought, etc.* 8
Slightest Down to his *s* turns and attitudes— *That is his portrait* 24
Slime Cemented with the burning *s* *Far off in the dun* 39
Slip Her garment *s's*, the left hand holds *Not to Silence* 13
Sloe Than if the vine had borne the bitter *s*. *To thee with whom* 4
Slow The *s* vibrations of whose pendulum, *Half after midnight !* 7
Slow-ripening *S-r* to the grace of womanhood, *To thee with whom* 13
Slumber *S* not now, gird up thy loins for fight, *O God, make this age* 10
Slumbrous Bathing in the *s* coves, *A dark Indian maiden* 7
Small *S* thanks or credit shall I have, *I keep no more* 3
Smile (s) how demure a *s*, How full *That is his portrait* 6

Smile (s) (*continued*) Sleeps round those quiet lips ; not quite a *s* ; *That is his portrait* 9
Smile (verb) Look he *s's*, and opens his hands, *Bright is the moon* 4
Smiled And they *s* on Anacaona, *A dark Indian maiden* 58
this one *s*, that other waved his arms, *That is his portrait* 22
Smooth *S* as Thames below your gates, *Vicar of this* 18
Snake floating *s* Roll'd round her ankles, *One was the Tishbite* 9
Snatch Still humming *s'es* of old song, *Youth, lapsing i* 38
Snout monstrous rocks from craggy *s's* *Deep glens I found* 3
Snow (*See also* **Summer-snow**) Deep dells of *s* sunk on each side *Far off in the dun* 97
With flush of rain, or molten *s's*, *Not to Silence* 20
Snowy She saw the *s* poles and Moons of Mars, *Hither, when all* 9
To *s* crofts and winding scars, *Youth, lapsing i* 18
Snug or the *s* brick box Of some sleek citizen. *Hear you the sound* 19
Sob Thick *s's* and short shrill screams *Far off in the dun* 17
Sober when each one leaves The middle road of *s* thought ! *They wrought, etc.* 28
Social A noise of hands that disarrange The *s* engine ! „ 22
Socket His *s's* were eyeless, but in them slept A red infernal glow ; *Far off in the dun* 81
Soft Crown'd with *s* shade her deepening floods *Youth, lapsing i* 3
Solemn When there stood a dark coach at an old Inn door At the *s* midnight hour. *Far off in the dun* 36
With a *s* burst of thrilling light, „ 119
is heard The shrill and *s* warning ' Ever, Never ' : *Half after midnight !* 14
Stately and mild, and all between Valleys full of *s* sound, *Thy soul is like* 9
Solitary Upon the brink A *s* fortress burns, *Youth, lapsing ii* 14
Solitude Youth, lapsing thro' fair *s's*, „ *i* 1
Solve Unvext by doubts I cannot *s*, „ 50
Sombre Nor wanting many a *s* mound, *Thy soul is like* 7
Something Was *s* that another could not be, *That is his portrait* 25
And there is *s* greatly done : *Youth, lapsing ii* 12
Son I and my *s's s's* and our offspring, *Hear you the sound* 24
O leave not thou thy *s* forlorn ; *O leave not thou* 1
Song air Of death, with *s's* of pride : *Far off in the dun* 110
Accepts the *s's* you gave, and he sends *Little Aubrey* 2
full God-bless-you with this book of *s*, *Take, Lady* 2
Still humming snatches of old *s*, *Youth, lapsing i* 38
from the gulf A murmur of heroic *s*, „ *ii* 19
Sooner *S* or later from the haze „ *i* 55
Soothe With pleasant hymns they *s* the air *Far off in the dun* 109
Sorrow Nor *S* beauteous in her youth, *Are those the far-famed* 7
I reck not for the *s* or the strife : *Why suffers* 13
The sacred *s's* of as pure a heart *Woman of noble* 4
Soul Yet her own deep *s* says nay : *The lamps were bright* 24
Rosebud, open, yield Thy fragrant *s*.' *The night, etc.* 6
The frame, the mind, the *s* of man, *They wrought, etc.* 43
God walk'd the waters of thy *s*, *Thou may'st remember* 7
Thy *s* is like a landskip, friend, *Thy soul is like* 1
God be gracious to my *s* ! *What rustles* 15
As my own *s* is full, to overflowing— *Why suffers* 8
Sound (s) No *s* of joy, no revelling tones *Far off in the dun* 41
And a *s* of stringed lyres. „ 120
With a silver *s* the wheels went round, „ 121
Hear you the *s* of wheels ? *Hear you the sound* 1
may keep A *s* in her ears like the *s* of the deep, Like the *s* *That the voice* 2
He loved the river's roaring *s* ; *The child was sitting* 3
A *s* of words that change to blows ! *They wrought, etc.* 17
A *s* of blows on armed breasts ! „ 18
between Valleys full of solemn *s*, *Thy soul is like* 9
That wash'd her shores with blissful *s's* : *Youth, lapsing i* 4
When to this *s* my face I turn'd, „ 41
Sound (verb) *S* ' Ever, Never ' thro' the courts of Hell, *Half after midnight !* 9
But did not *s* so joyfully : *Youth, lapsing i* 24
Sounded leaders bounded, the guard's horn *s* : *Far off in the dun* 89
Southern The *s* stars a music peal'd, *The night, etc.* 2
Spake man, Most eloquent, who *s* of things *Methought I saw* 3
he *s* : ' I lift the eyes of thought, *That is his portrait* 33
Spanish My *S* blood ran proudly in my veins. *Hear you the sound* 45

Sparkle The casements *s* on the plain, *Youth, lapsing ii* 39
Speak If you could *s*, would you not say : *Early-wise* 3
Which *s* of us to other centuries, *Hear you the sound* 27
I murmur'd '*S* again, my love, *Remember you* 7
S to me from the stormy sky ! *Speak to me* 1
S to me, dearest, lest I die. „ 4
S to me, let me hear or see ! „ 5
Seest thou my faults and wilt not *s* ? „ 7
This is the man of whom you heard me *s*. *That is his portrait* 15
He strokes his beard before he *s's* ; *Yon huddled cloud* 10
To *s* of what had gone before, *Youth, lapsing i* 27
Speakest My friend, thou *s* from the heart, *I keep no more* 15
Spear On growing *s's*, by fits the lady ash *Townsmen, etc.* 9
Spire Set round with many a toppling *s*, *Deep glens I found* 2
Spirit an inner *s* fed Their ever-burning fires,) *Far off in the dun* 117
The happy *s's* within ; „ 130
I mourn in *s* when I think The year, *I, loving Freedom* 5
Were I not a *s* blest, *Not a whisper* 7
Great *s's* grow akin to base. *They wrought, etc.* 16
To hold the *S* of the Age Against the *S* of the Time. „ 47
When thine own *s* was at strife With thine own *s*. *Thou may'st remember* 2
stood The tearful *s* of the time ; *Youth, lapsing i* 34
Warm beats my blood, my *s* thirsts ; „ *ii* 45
Spiritual Of beryl, and of amethyst Was the *s* frame. *Far off in the dun* 124
Thro' *s* dark we come Into the light of *s* life.' *Thou may'st remember* 5
Spoke Cold words I *s*, yet loved thee warm and well. *To thee with whom* 8
Spot *s* Where it was my chance to marry, *Vicar of this* 1
Spread were *s* Around in the chilling air, *Far off in the dun* 101
How every brake and flower *s* and rose, *That is his portrait* 26
Spring (fountain) Variously from its far *s*, *Not to Silence* 27
Spring (season) Are pleasant from the early *S* to when, *Townsmen, etc.* 7
I heard *S* laugh in hidden rills, *Youth, lapsing i* 13
Spring (verb) never green thing will gaily *s* In that *Far off in the dun* 9
the laverock *s* From under the deep, *Full light aloft* 1
That he *s's* from the common stock. *How is it that men* 6
Springing Over the dark sea-marge *s*, *A dark Indian maiden* 39
Spur She *s's* an imitative will ; *Young is the grief* 6
Spurge *S* with fairy crescent set, *Spurge with fairy* 1
Square *See* **Four-square**
Stalwart Admire that *s* shape, those ample brows, *That is his portrait* 4
Stand Wherefore *s* I here ? *Half after midnight !* 18
Not like Silence shall she *s*, *Not to Silence* 9
Not with this age wherefrom ye *s* apart, *Therefore your Halls* 11
Standard Day by day Watch your *s* roses blowing, *Vicar of this* 12
Standers by And looks to awe the *s b*, *Because she bore* 4
Standing And they saw *her s* by, *The lamps were bright* 51
Star Dissolve a world, condense a *s*, *Are those the far-famed* 14
As *s's* they shone, in raiment white, *Far off in the dun* 131
Shudder'd with silent *s's*, she clomb, *Hither, when all* 2
light In mid Orion, and the married *s's*. „ 11
The southern *s's* a music peal'd, *The night, etc.* 2
And shook the frosty winter *s's*. *Youth, lapsing i* 20
Staring And, *s* as in trance, *The lamps were bright* 45
Starless mutter of deep-mouth'd thunderings Shakes all the *s* pole, *Far off in the dun* 16
Vast wastes of *s* glooms were spread Around „ 101
Starr'd The *s* abysses of the sky, *'Tis not alone* 2
Starry and bee-like swarms Of suns, and *s* streams. *Hither, when all* 8
Startle *s* the dull ears of human kind ! *O God, make this age* 5
State Wed to no faction in the *s*, *I, loving Freedom* 3
thro' the channels of the *s* Convoys *They wrought, etc.* 30
Stately I deemed her one of *s* frame *Because she bore* 3
S and mild, and all between Valleys full of solemn sound, *Thy soul is like* 8
two fair lilies growing at thy side Have slowly prosper'd into *s* flowers. *Woman of noble* 12
Statesman Shadows of *statesmen*, clever men ! *They wrought, etc.* 12
Stay I found the Present where I *s* : *Youth, lapsing i* 48
Yet well I know that nothing *s's*, „ 53
Stedfast They glitter'd with a *s* light, *Far off in the dun* 129
Steed And his hot *s's* never run : „ 4
Their *s's* were strong exceedingly : „ 125
Steeple *S*, and stream, and forest lawn, *Thy soul is like* 2
Steering be not precipitate in thine act Of *s*, *Steersman* 2
Steersman *S*, be not precipitate in thine act „ 1
Stemm'd *See* **Hollow-stemm'd**
Step (s) A *s* ? a footfall ? What is that I hear ? *What rustles* 2
Step (verb) *S* thro' these doors, and I will show *That is his portrait* 44
Stepp'd-Stept as he *stept* thro' the crowd, *Far off in the dun* 75
I *stepp'd* upon the old mill bridge ? *Remember you* 4
Stepping *S* lightly flower-laden, *A dark Indian maiden* 3
Loftily *s* with fair faces. „ 64
Stept *See* **Stepp'd**
Stern burn With a light so wild and *s* ? ' *The lamps were bright* 16
Still The night is black and *s* ; the deer *What rustles* 3
The cedar-wooded paradise Of *s* Xaraguay : *A dark Indian maiden* 21
Still'd waters of thy soul, And *s* them. *Thou may'st remember* 8
Stir Not a whisper *s's* the gloom, *Not a whisper* 1
Stirr'd Call to its mate when nothing *s* *Remember you* 15
this so *s* him in his hour of joy, *That is his portrait* 31
Stithy Bang thy *s* stronger and stronger, *Wherever evil* 8
Stock That he springs from the common *s*. *How is it that men* 6
Stole Warm beams across the meadows *s* ; *The night, etc.* 3
Stone Her grave—a simple *s* ! *Along this glimmering* 8
Stood there *s* a dark coach at an old Inn door *Far off in the dun* 35
s alone And still in the dark doorway : „ 49
I that *s* in On beside the flow *'Here, I that stood* 1
I laugh'd to see him as he *s*, *I met in all* 7
As when he *s* on Carmel-steeps *One was the Tishbite* 2
s The tearful spirit of the time ; *Youth, lapsing i* 33
Storm There lies a land of chilling *s's*, *Far off in the dun* 5
A voice before the *s*, *I, loving Freedom* 4
Stormy Speak to me from the *s* sky ! *Speak to me* 1
The child was sitting on the bank Upon a *s* day, *The child was sitting* 2
The silent hills, the *s* floods, *'Tis not alone* 3
Stouter Gives *s* ale and riper port Than any in the country-side. *Yon huddled cloud* 7
Strand I took delight in this fair *s* and free ; *Here often when a child* 2
Strange To draw *s* comfort from the earth, *S* beauties from the sky. *Far off in the dun* 31
S fiery eyes glared fiercely thro' The windows of shaven bone. „ 47
Thro' *s* seas drew me to your monster town. *Here, I that stood* 8
How *s* it is, O God, to wake, *How strange it is* 1
Stranger It were, O Heaven, a *s* tale to tell *To thee with whom* 3
Streak Fast by me flash the cloudy *s's*, *Youth, lapsing ii* 46
Stream (s) Before them flow'd a fiery *s* ; *Far off in the dun* 127
swarms Of suns, and starry *s's*. *Hither, when all* 8
The *s* is loud : I cannot hear ! ' *Remember you* 8
Steeple, and *s*, and forest lawn, *Thy soul is like* 2
And where the secret *s's* rejoice. *Youth, lapsing i* 12
Stream (verb) That *s's* about the bend ; *Steersman* 5
Streaming *S* thro' his osier'd aits ! *Vicar of this* 20
Street To fling his doubts into the *s*. *He was too good* 4
Up the *s* we took her As far as to the Castle, *Sweet Kitty Sandilands* 9
Strength fears that waste The *s* of men, *They wrought, etc.* 23
all the *s* thou wouldst have been : *Young is the grief* 12
Stretch'd With one arm *s* out bare, *One was the Tishbite* 3
Stricken *See* **Thunder-stricken**
Stride as to Fame, who *s's* the earth *Well, as to Fame* 1
Strife not pause At the *s* of the shadowy wheels, *Far off in the dun* 94
Henceforward no other *s*— *Frenchman, etc.* 6
When thine own spirit was at *s* *Thou may'st remember* 2
Parish feud, or party *s*, *Vicar of this* 8
I reck not for the sorrow or the *s* : *Why suffers* 13
Strike And shadows *s* and shadows sink, *Youth, lapsing ii* 15
A tempest *s's* the craggy walls, „ 21
Stringéd And a sound of *s* lyres. *Far off in the dun* 120
Strode grim old coachee *s* to the box, „ 87
Stroke He *s's* his beard before he speaks ; *Yon huddled cloud* 10
Strong Their steeds were *s* exceedingly : *Far off in the dun* 125
It is not good to drink *s* wine Ere the day be well-nigh done ; *Full light aloft* 9
Tall, eager, lean and *s*, his cloak wind-borne Behind, *One was the Tishbite* 5
Long, Eustace, long May my *s* wish, transgressing the low bound Of mortal hope, *That is his portrait* 38
' Come ' and I come, the wind is *s* : *Youth, lapsing ii* 17
Stronger Bang thy stithy *s* and *s*, *Wherever evil* 8
Stud Drove into lines and *s's* of light *Youth, lapsing i* 6

Sublime He, seeing far an end *s*, *They wrought, etc.* 45
Such Nor proved I *s* delight as he, to mark The humours of the polling and the wake, *That is his portrait* 19
Sudden The night with *s* odour reel'd, *The night, etc.* 1
Suffer Why *s's* human life so soon eclipse? *Why suffers* 1
Suffer'd His and my friendship have not *s* loss, *That is his portrait* 41
Summer (adj.) The *s* plains with their shining leaves, The *s* hills they see; *Far off in the dun* 69
to return with thee Some happy *S* morning, *Woman of noble* 9
Summer (s) Floated in the silent *s*: *A dark Indian maiden* 40
and lie A thousand *s's* at her feet. *Because she bore* 8
S thro' all her sleepy leaves Murmur'd: *Youth, lapsing i* 14
Summer-snow My coldness was mistimed like *s-s*, *To thee with whom* 7
Summit Thence, across the *s* hurl'd, *Not to Silence* 33
Down from the *s* sweeps the day *Youth, lapsing ii* 31
Sun *s* Drew down the West his feeble lights; *Deep glens I found* 5
Behind the burning *S*: *Far off in the dun* 2
At the rising of the *s*. *Full light aloft* 12
bee-like swarms Of *s's*, and starry streams. *Hither, when all* 8
of the changes of the *s's*? *Little Aubrey* 6
Near the shrine, but half in *s*, *Not to Silence* 17
The image of the *s* by day, *Youth, lapsing i* 7
I follow to the morning *s*, „ *ii* 10
Sunbright cocoa-shadow'd coves, Of *s* Xaraguay, *A dark Indian maiden* 9
Sunder'd That never can be *s* without tears. *Beauty, Good, etc.* 2
clouds are *s* toward the morning-rise; *O God, make this age* 9
Sunk Deep dells of snow *s* on each side *Far off in the dun* 97
Sunless Deep glens I found, and *s* gulfs, *Deep glens I found* 1
Thick sobs and short shrill screams arise Along the *s* waste, *Far off the dun* 18
Sunset You'd sit there From dawn till *s* *Hear you the sound* 39
Surface A *s* man of many theories, And yet not true to one: *A surface man* 1
Susan to walk With *S* on the shore! *How glad am I* 2
Swallow'd eyes Are *s* in his pamper'd cheeks. *Yon huddled cloud* 12
Swarm bee-like *s's* Of suns, and starry streams. *Hither, when all* 7
Swarthy Those thoughtful furrows in the *s* cheek; *That is his portrait* 3
Swear *S* to be one for ever, *Frenchman, etc.* 10
Sweep With twinkling finger *s's* her yellow keys. *Townsmen, etc.* 10
Down from the summit *s's* the day *Youth, lapsing ii* 31
Sweet Maizebread and the yuccaroot, Of *s* Xaraguay: *A dark Indian maiden* 45
With fair blue eyes and winning *s*, *Because she bore* 6
the laverock spring From under the deep, *s* corn, *Full light aloft* 2
But thou hast drunk of the merry, *s* wine, „ 11
He was too good and kind and *s*, *He was too good* 1
and drank The *s* sad tears of wisdom.' *Methought I saw* 6
S Kitty Sandilands, The daughter of the doctor, *Sweet Kitty Sandilands* 1
These voices did not cease to cry Only they took a *s* tone, *Youth, lapsing i* 23
Again the low *s* voices murmur'd In distant fields, „ *i* 43
and all comes back Which in that early voice was *s*, „ *ii* 42
Sweetness the *s* which thou wast In thy beginnings *Young is the grief* 10
Swung *S* creaking before the Inn. *Far off in the dun* 44

T

Table that large *t* of the breast dispread, *That is his portrait* 5
Tacit Become a *t* eloquent reproach Unto the dissipation of this Earth. *Half after midnight!* 3
Taint And free from *t* of sin. *Far off in the dun* 132
Take And long'd to *t* his hand in mine. *I met in all* 4
T thou the 'bend,' 'twill save thee many a day. *Steersman* 8
T, Lady, what your loyal nurses give, *Take, Lady* 1
and the d——l *t* the parties! *They say, etc.* 10
t with thee Our warmest wishes, *Woman of noble* 5
Taking Regions of lucid matter *t* forms, *Hither, when all* 5
Tale At some sad *t* of wrong, and do the wrong *A surface man* 6
a stranger *t* to tell Than if the vine *To thee with whom* 3
And ever new the *t* she tells, *Young is the grief* 2
Talk How glad am I to *t*! I kiss *How glad am I* 3
Tall For they were fair-faced and *t*, They were more fair-faced and *t*, *A dark Indian maiden* 55
T, eager, lean and strong, his cloak *One was the Tishbite* 5
Taper No *t's* light look'd out on the night, *Far off in the dun* 45
Tar Up, Jack *T's*, and save us! (repeat) *They say, etc.* 5, 12, 19
Up, Jack *T's*, my hearties! „ 10
The lasses and the little ones, Jack *T's*, they look to you! „ 15
Tarry Methinks they *t* somewhat. What's the clock? *Hear you the sound* 3
Tasse And from it hung the *t*. *Sweet Kitty Sandilands* 12
Taste Her perfect lips to *t*, *One was the Tishbite* 12
'To those who will not *t* it more!' *Yon huddled cloud* 16
Taught with thee, Mother, *t* us first to pray, *Remembering him* 2
Tavern by the *t* in the dale, The thirsty horseman, *Yon huddled cloud* 2
This *t* is their chief resort, „ 5
Teach *T* me, great Nature: make me live. *O leave not thou* 2
And *t* us nothing, feeding not the heart. *Therefore your Halls* 14
Tear That never can be sunder'd without *t's*. *Beauty, Good, etc.* 2
The *t's* bedimm'd their sight: *Far off in the dun* 86
The happy maiden's *t's* are free *I keep no more* 5
And mingle kisses, *t's*, and sighs, *Life of the Life* 6
drank The sweet sad *t's* of wisdom.' *Methought I saw* 6
water'd by thy *t's*, The two fair lilies *Woman of noble* 10
Tearful Full fields of barley shifting *t* lights On growing spears, *Townsmen, etc.* 8
Beside my door at morning stood The *t* spirit of the time; *Youth, lapsing i* 34
Tell *t* me you were great Already in your birth. *Hear you the sound* 59
'Now, *t* me, mother, pray, *The lamps were bright* 9
There's a treaty, so they *t* us, *They say, etc.* 3
a stranger tale to *t* Than if the vine *To thee with whom* 3
And I will *t* you what I know— *Well, as to Fame* 4
And ever new the tale she *t's*, *Young is the grief* 2
Temper *T's* the peaceful light of hazel eyes, *That is his portrait* 13
Tempest A *t* strikes the craggy walls, *Youth, lapsing ii* 21
Temple build A *t* in her naked field; *Not to Silence* 2
Ten *T* men fought a thousand, Slew them and overthrew. *Bold Havelock* 7
Tender But found a maiden *t*, shy, *Because she bore* 5
Havelock died, *T* and great and good, *Bold Havelock* 14
Terrace your triple *t* growing Green and greener *Vicar of this* 14
Terror My hope is false, my *t's* true! *What rustles* 12
Thames Smooth as *T* below your gates, *Vicar of this* 18
T along the silent level, „ 19
Thank I *t* thee, God, that thou hast made me live: *Why suffers* 12
Thanks Small *t* or credit shall I have, *I keep no more* 3
Thatch'd For it were almost mockery to hang it O'er the *t* cottage, *Hear you the sound* 19
Theory A surface man of many *theories*, *A surface man* 1
Thick *T* sobs and short shrill screams arise *Far off in the dun* 17
And the moaning wind before it drives *T* wreaths of cloudy dew. „ 24
His heart throbs *t*, his brain reels sick: „ 27
The knotted boughs of this long avenue Of *t* dark oaks, *Hear you the sound* 11
For, tho' the faults be t *as dust In vacant chambers*, *The noblest men* 10
Thicken Wherever evil customs *t*, *Wherever evil* 1
Thicket *See* **Holly-thickets**
Thin A land of *t* faces and shadowy forms, *Far off in the dun* 7
The skin hung lax on his long *t* hands; „ 53
Thing never green *t* will gaily spring „ 9
t's of past days with their horrible eyes „ 19
And from the heart of all *t's* fair *He was too good* 11
man, Most eloquent, who spake of *t's* divine. *Methought I saw* 3
Who make you utter *t's* you did not say, *Old ghosts* 10
light of hazel eyes, Observing all *t's*. *That is his portrait* 14
In the dreaming of past *t's*: *The lamps were bright* 22
All *t's* please you, nothing vex you, *Vicar of this* 9
And your three young *t's* at play, „ 13
Glancing off from all *t's* evil, „ 17
The difference of all *t's* to the sense, *Why suffers* 10
And how all *t's* become the past. *Youth, lapsing i* 28
Think when I *t* The year, that comes, *I, loving Freedom* 5
t a cunning hand has found the clue— *What rustles* 14
Thirst Warm beats my blood, my spirit *t's*; *Youth, lapsing ii* 45

Thirsty The *t* horseman, nodding, lifts The creaming horn of corny ale ! — *Yon huddled cloud* 3
Thought (s) thro' all phases of all *t* I come — *From shape to shape* 3
every line Wore the pale cast of *t*, — *Methought I saw* 2
he spake : 'I lift the eyes of *t*, — *That is his portrait* 33
Her *t's* have found their wings — *The lamps were bright* 21
The middle road of sober *t* ! — *They wrought, etc.* 28
Thy *t* did scale a purer range — *Thou may'st remember* 10
Thought (verb) What time (he *t*) have loom or plough — *He was too good* 7
March'd and *t* and fought, — *Bold Havelock* 11
Thoughtful there Hovering, *t*, poised in air. — *Not to Silence* 12
Those *t* furrows in the swarthy cheek ; — *That is his portrait* 3
Thousand And longed to kiss her hand and lie A *t* summers at her feet. — *Because she bore* 8
I that stood in On beside the flow Of sacred Nile, three *t* years ago !— — *Here, I that stood* 2
Threat Not deals in *t's*, but works with hope, — *They wrought, etc.* 39
Three Beauty, Good and Knowledge are *t* sisters . . . — *Beauty, Good, etc.* 1
I that stood in On beside the flow Of sacred Nile, *t* thousand years ago !— — *Here, I that stood* 2
And your *t* young things at play, — *Vicar of this* 13
Threshold on her *t* lie, Howling in outer darkness.' — *Beauty, Good, etc.* 4
bearest from the *t* of thy friends — *Woman of noble* 3
Threw *t* up the dust Of dead men's pulverised bones. — *Far off in the dun* 91
and *t* back Your floating hair. — *Hear you the sound* 42
Thrilling With a solemn burst of *t* light, — *Far off in the dun* 119
And shriek and shout to drown the *t* noise. — *Half after midnight !* 16
Throb His heart *t's* thick, his brain reels sick : — *Far off in the dun* 27
Throbbing Comes hither *t* thro' the dark ; — *Youth, lapsing ii* 8
Throne Go forward ! crumble down a *t*, — *Are those the far-famed* 13
Hard by the burning *t* of my great grandsire, — *Half after midnight !* 6
You were wont to call it Your *t*. — *Hear you the sound* 36
Thunder The *t* cannot make thee dumb ; — *Youth, lapsing ii* 26
Thundering mutter of deep-mouth'd *t's* Shakes — *Far off in the dun* 15
Thunder-peal The latest *t-p* hath peal'd, — *Youth, lapsing ii* 30
Thunder-stricken With the flock of the *t-s*. — *Wherever evil* 5
Tickled ear Be *t* with the loud 'hear, hear,' — *They wrought, etc.* 7
Tide Then they cried at the turn of the *t*— — *Popular, Popular* 4
Time That Inn was built at the birth of *T* : — *Far off in the dun* 37
you would be A great man in your *t*, — *Hear you the sound* 57
What *t* (he thought) have loom or plough — *He was too good* 7
They wrought a work which *T* reveres, — *They wrought, etc.* 1
Against the Spirit of the *T*. — „ 48
We lost you for how long a *t*, — *We lost you* 1
But pap-meat-pamper not the *t* — *Wherever evil* 4
pure a heart As e'er beat *t* to Nature, — *Woman of noble* 5
stood The tearful spirit of the *t* ; — *Youth, lapsing i* 34
Tinge not a *t* on each high cheek bone, — *Far off in the dun* 51
Tingling Before his eyes so grim and calm The *t* blood grew chill, — „ 78
Tishbite One was the *T* whom the raven fed, — *One was the Tishbite* 1
Tithe Never *t* unpaid perplex you, — *Vicar of this* 7
Toil If night, what barren *t* to be ! — *Gone into darkness* 6
Tomb 'From the *t* And charnel-place — *Thou may'st remember* 3
Tone no revelling *t's* Of carouse were heard — *Far off in the dun* 41
thro' the night ran the lengthen'd *t's* : — „ 90
Only they took a sweeter *t*, — *Youth, lapsing i* 23
Toned *See* **Lute-toned**
Tongue my *t* runs twenty knots an hour : — *Half after midnight !* 19
Tongued *See* **Trumpet-tongued**
Took *t* her As far as to the Castle, — *Sweet Kitty Sandilands* 9
t in more of Nature than mine own : — *That is his portrait* 18
T the child from off the ground, — *The child was sitting* 6
Only they *t* a sweeter tone, — *Youth, lapsing i* 23
Top He brims his beaker to the *t*, — *Yon huddled cloud* 13
Toppling Set round with many a *t* spire, — *Deep glens I found* 2
Toss bitterly I trow they turn and *t* — *Half after midnight !* 15
Touch see, ye dare not *t* the truth, — *Are those the far-famed* 6
Touch'd *T* with Heaven's latest lights. — *Thy soul is like* 12
Tower (s) battlemented *t's* Of my old ancestors ! — *Hear you the sound* 12
The *t's* gleam among the vines ; — *Youth, lapsing ii* 40
Tower (verb) leafless oak Which *t's* above the lake — *Hear you the sound* 33
Town drew me to your monster *t*. — *Here, I that stood* 8
Townsman *Townsmen*, or of the hamlet, young or old, — *Townsmen, etc.* 1
Track Intent to follow on the *t*, — *Youth, lapsing i* 42
Track (*continued*) Yet am I dizzy in the *t*, — *Youth, lapsing ii* 43
Tract With long *t's* of murmuring, — *Not to Silence* 28
Traitor Nor *t's* that mislead by names ! — *Not such were those* 4
Trance And, staring as in *t*, — *The lamps were bright* 45
Transgressing *t* the low bound Of mortal hope, — *That is his portrait* 38
Traveller Dimly the *t's* look'd thro' the glooms, — *Far off in the dun* 57
Traverse And I must *t* yonder plain : — *Youth, lapsing i* 54
Treaty There's a *t*, so they tell us, — *They say, etc.* 3
Tree (*See also* **Oak-tree**) Beneath the papao *t* ! — *A dark Indian maiden* 33
above the barkless *t's* They saw the green verge — *Far off in the dun* 62
The night gale in those *t's*. — *Hear you the sound* 8
Trim-set I hate the *t-s* plots of art !' — *I keep no more* 14
Triple And your *t* terrace growing Green and greener every May ! — *Vicar of this* 14
A mountain bright with *t* peaks : — *Youth, lapsing ii* 48
Trow Worn and wan was their gaze, I *t*, — *Far off in the dun* 58
Then bitterly I *t* they turn and toss — *Half after midnight !* 15
True man of many theories, And yet not *t* to one : — *A surface man* 2
Early-wise, and pure, and *t*, — *Early-wise* 1
That man's the *t* Conservative — *First drink a health* 7
The *t* men banish'd— — *Rise, Britons, rise* 4
I can trust Your woman's nature kind and t. — *The noblest men* 12
God bless the little isle where a man may still be *t* ! — *They say, etc.* 17
To thee with whom my *t* affections dwell, — *To thee with whom* 1
T Pearl of our poetic prime ! — *We lost you* 2
My hope is false, my terror's *t* ! — *What rustles* 12
take with thee Our warmest wishes, silent Guardians But *t* till Death ; — *Woman of noble* 7
Truest Art for Art's sake ! Hail, *t* Lord of Hell ! — *Art for Art's sake !* 1
Trumpet Rang like a *t* clear and dry, — *Youth, lapsing i* 19
Behind yon hill the *t's* blow, — „ *ii* 11
Trumpet-tongued Mind, Whose *t-t*, aerial melody — *O God, make this age* 3
Trust *I can* t *Your woman's nature* — *The noblest men* 11
Truth see, ye dare not touch the *t*, — *Are those the far-famed* 6
bind Falsehood beneath the altar of great *T* : — *O God, make this age* 8
Truth-seeking *T-s* he and not afraid, — *He was too good* 5
Turn (s) in *t* shall be Shut out from Love, — *Beauty, Good, etc.* 3
Then they cried at the *t* of the tide— — *Popular, Popular* 4
Down to his slightest *t's* and attitudes— — *That is his portrait* 24
And Heaven is dark and bright by *t's*. — *Youth, lapsing ii* 16
Turn (verb) bitterly I trow they *t* and toss — *Half after midnight !* 15
Turn'd Life, to this wind, *t* all her vanes, — *Youth, lapsing i* 29
When to this sound my face I *t*, — „ 41
Twenty Methinks my tongue runs *t* knots an hour : — *Half after midnight !* 19
Twilight Than our poor *t* dawn on earth— — *Gone into darkness* 5
With the first *t* of the even, — *Thy soul is like* 4
Twinfold Forethinking its *t* necessity, — *That is his portrait* 49
Twinkling—by fits the lady ask With *t* finger sweeps her yellow keys. — *Townsmen, etc.* 10
And sometimes with a *t* drop, — *Yon huddled cloud* 15
Two Parts in *t* channels, moving to one end— — *Steersman* 3
A land of many days that cleaves In *t* great halves, — *They wrought, etc.* 27
The *t* fair lilies growing at thy side Have slowly prosper'd into stately flowers. — *Woman of noble* 11

U

Uncertain *U* of ourselves we chase — *They wrought, etc.* 13
Unconscious Tho' thou art all *u* of thy Might. — *O God, make this age* 14
Undefiled On her forehead *u* I will print — *Not a whisper* 11
Under-air When all the *u-a* was still, — *Remember you* 10
Unexprest A hint of somewhat *u*. — *'Tis not alone* 8
Unfading with forms Of the *u* marble carved upon them, — *Hear you the sound* 26
Unheeded Pointing to the *u* lapse of hours, — *Half after midnight !* 2
Union Their offspring of this *u*. — *Old ghosts* 8
Unpaid Never tithe *u* perplex you, — *Vicar of this* 7
Unpopular Popular, Popular, *U* ! — *Popular, Popular* 1
'Why ?' said the Poet. 'You're *u* !' — „ 3
Pop-gun, Popular and *U* ! — „ 6

Unroused keep Our awful inner ghostly sense *U*, *How strange it is* 6
Unschool'd Yet one *u* in want will say *I keep no more* 7
Unsocket *U* all the joints of war, *Are those the far-famed* 15
Unsounded when all the deep *u* skies Shudder'd with silent stars, *Hither, when all* 1
Unswathe The clouds *u* them from the height, *Youth, lapsing ii* 50
Unvext *U* by doubts I cannot solve, „ *i* 50
Unwholesome There never green thing will gaily spring In that *u* air, *Far off in the dun* 10
These fear not the mists of *u* damps That through that region rove, „ 113
Up-gather'd left hand holds Her *u-g* garment folds, *Not to Silence* 14
Uplands And hoary holts on *u* green, *Thy soul is like* 10
Urn Thro' one whole life an overflowing *u*, *That is his portrait* 50
Usage He cares, if ancient *u* fade, *They wrought, etc.* 33

V

Vacant *For, tho' the faults be thick as dust In* v *chambers*, *The noblest men* 11
Vale ' Come ' and I come, the *v* is deep, *Youth, lapsing ii* 27
Valley between *V's* full of solemn sound, *Thy soul is like* 9
Vane Life, to this wind, turn'd all her *v's*, *Youth, lapsing i* 29
Vanish'd All freedom *v*— *Rise, Britons, rise* 3
Vapor-Vapour Of *vapors*, and mist, and night. *Far off in the dun* 8
from the golden *vapour* bursts *Youth, lapsing ii* 47
Variation Chequer'd with moonlight's *v*, *Hear you the sound* 22
Various How every brake and flower spread and rose, A *v* world ! *That is his portrait* 27
Vast (adj.) *V* wastes of starless glooms were spread Around in the chilling air, *Far off in the dun* 101
Vast (s) Look out from the cloudy *v*. „ 20
can they last In the *v* Of the rolling æons, *Little Aubrey* 5
Vaulted And the chapel's *v* gloom Was misted with perfume. *The lamps were bright* 7
Veil And *v's* a breast more fair to me *Not to Silence* 15
Vein My Spanish blood ran proudly in my *v's*. *Hear you the sound* 45
Verge saw the green *v* of the pleasant earth, *Far off in the dun* 63
Verse I would shrine her in my *v* ! *Not to Silence* 8
Very till the *v* wrong itself Had found him out. *A surface man* 7
At the *v* break of light ? *Full light aloft* 8
Vex All things please you, nothing *v* you, *Vicar of this* 9
Vibration The slow *v's* of whose pendulum, *Half after midnight !* 7
Vicar *V* of this pleasant spot *Vicar of this* 1
Vicarage In the *V* by the quarry. „ 4
Vice heart of his Hard, and the slave of *v* ; *A surface man* 4
Victim and the *v*, Broken in this anger *Faded ev'ry violet* 2
Victor (adj). Are those the far-famed *V* Hours *Are those the far-famed* 1
Victor (s) Yields to the *v*. *Faded ev'ry violet* 4
Victory Every battle a *v*. *Bold Havelock* 4
Shall drink the fulness of thy *v*, *O God, make this age* 13
Vine (adj.) dark *v* leaves round the rustling eaves, *Far off in the dun* 71
Vine (s) Than if the *v* had borne the bitter sloe. *To thee with whom* 4
The towers gleam among the *v's* ; *Youth, lapsing ii* 40
Violet Faded ev'ry *v*, all the roses ; *Faded ev'ry violet* 1
Virtue whose whims were meant For *v's* servants, *A surface man* 3
Voice (*See also* **Cuckoo-voice**) They hear each household *v* : *Far off in the dun* 66
We help the blatant *v* abroad *He was too good* 9
A *v* before the storm, *I, loving Freedom* 4
And the *v* that apes a nation— *Immeasurable sadness !* 5
The low *v* of the glad New Year *Remember you* 11
That the *v* of a satisfied people *That the voice* 1
deer Bleat as with human *v's* in the park. *What rustles* 4
Sent thro' my blood a prophet *v* *Youth, lapsing i* 10
a *v* ran round the hills When corny Lammas „ 15
A *v*, when night had crept on high, „ 17
These *v's* did not cease to cry, „ 22
a sharper *v* Cried in the future ' Come along.' „ 39
Again the low sweet *v's* mourn'd „ 43
The second *v* will peal again. „ 56
A *v* like many *v's* cries, „ *ii* 7
The *v* cries, ' Come.' „ 13
Voice (*continued*) Which in that early *v* was sweet, *Youth lapsing ii* 42
Void A region *v* of light, *Far off in the dun* 6
Volumed *See* **Myriad-volumed**
Vulgar Ha ! by St. James Mine was no *v* mind in infancy, *Hear you the sound* 62

W

Waft A light wind *w's* me from my feet. *Youth, lapsing ii* 44
Wail There may be short cessation of their *w's*, *Half after midnight !* 12
Waist I clasp her slender *w*, *How glad am I* 5
round her *w* Knotted, *One was the Tishbite* 10
Wait Remembering him who *w's* thee far away, *Remembering him* 1
Dim grief did *w* upon her, *The lamps were bright* 33
Wake (festival) humours of the polling and the *w*, *That is his portrait* 20
Wake (verb) How strange it is, O God, to *w*, To watch and *w* while others sleep, *How strange it is* 1
Wakening And chants in the golden *w* *Full light aloft* 3
Walk Whoever *w's* that bitter ground *Far off in the dun* 25
How glad am I to *w* With Susan *How glad am I* 1
Walk'd God *w* the waters of thy soul, *Thou may'st remember* 7
Walking While *w* with my rod and line, *I met in all* 2
Wall The *w's* of lava rose, *Far off in the dun* 38
Richly and darkly girdle these gray *w's*,— *Hear you the sound* 23
A tempest strikes the craggy *w's*, *Youth, lapsing ii* 21
Wan Worn and *w* was their gaze, I trow, *Far off in the dun* 58
Wand shanks were shrunken to willow *w's* „ 55
Wander Whithersoever you may *w* now, *Townsmen, etc.* 2
He moan'd, ' I *w* from my good ! ' *Youth, lapsing i* 35
Wander'd No more in Xaraguay *W* happy Anacaona, *A dark Indian maiden* 70
Want Yet one unschool'd in *w* will say *I keep no more* 7
They are not *w* of love for thee. *Speak to me* 8
Wanting Nor *w* many a sombre mound, *Thy soul is like* 7
Wanton The *w* wind came singing lustily Among the moss-grown branches, *Hear you the sound* 41
We faint unless the *w* ear Be tickled with the loud ' hear, hear,' *They wrought, etc.* 6
Wantoning *W* in orange groves Naked, *A dark Indian maiden* 5
War Unsocket all the joints of *w*, *Are those the far-famed* 15
Warbling Indian maiden, *W* in the bloom'd liana, *A dark Indian maiden* 2
'Tis not alone the *w* woods, *'Tis not alone* 1
Warm *W* beams across the meadow stole ; *The night, etc.* 3
Cold words I spoke, yet loved thee *w* and well. *To thee with whom* 8
W beats my blood, my spirit thirsts ; *Youth, lapsing ii* 45
Warmest take with thee Our *w* wishes, *Woman of noble* 6
Warning The shrill and solemn *w* ' Ever, Never ' : *Half after midnight !* 14
Warrant Ay, Ay, I *w* you, and when I came *Hear you the sound* 46
Wash'd That *w* her shores with blissful sounds : *Youth, lapsing i* 4
Waste (s) screams arise Along the sunless *w*, *Far off in the dun* 18
Vast *w's* of starless glooms were spread „ 101
Waste (verb) fears that *w* The strength of men, *They wrought, etc.* 22
would you *w* an hour, *Townsmen, etc.* 3
Watch To *w* and wake while others sleep, *How s range it is* 2
W your standard roses blowing, *Vicar of this* 12
Watch't heart That *w* with love thine earliest infancy, *To thee with whom* 12
Water (*See also* **Milldam-water**) When o'er the *w* dancing white *Remember you* 3
God walk'd the *w's* of thy soul, *Thou may'st remember* 7
Water'd *w* by thy tears, The two fair lilies *Woman of noble* 10
Waterfall A moan of many *w's*, *Youth, lapsing ii* 23
Waved Our flags have *w* together ! *Frenchman, etc.* 2
this one smiled, that other *w* his arms, *That is his portrait* 22
Waving *W* a palm branch, wondering, *A dark Indian maiden* 51
Waxen You'd weave your *w* fingers in these locks (They are gray now) *Hear you the sound* 58
Way So prone are we toward the broad *w* to Hell. *Art for Art's sake !* 6
What's the clock ? *Mich.* Half *w* toward midnight. *Hear you the sound* 4
she will weep and give them *w* ; *I keep no more* 6
I met in all the close green *w's*, *I met in all* 1

Way (*continued*) tho' the cataract seem the nearer *w*, *Steersman* 6
Thro' the deep hall forced its *w*, *The lamps were bright* 42
my love Coming along the secret *w's*? *What rustles* 6
Seeing the heart so wondrous in her *w's*, *Why suffers* 3
I loiter'd in the middle *w*, *Youth, lapsing i* 46
Up hither have I found my *w*, " *ii* 29
Weak Alas, my life is frail and *w*: *Speak to me* 6
Weave *w* your waxen fingers in these locks *Hear you the sound* 58
Wed *W* to no faction in the state, *I, loving Freedom* 3
Wedded Then they found him where he lay Whom the *w* wife did slay, *The lamps were bright* 48
Weep he would *w* For ills himself had practised *A surface man* 4
And she will *w* and give them way; *I keep no more* 6
Sisters, I could almost *w*! *Not a whisper* 8
Weeping O Mother-Queen, and *w* Wife, *Early-wise* 7
'I love the daisy *w* dew, *I keep no more* 13
Weigh To *w* them as they should be weighed? *He was too good* 8
Weighed To weigh them as they should be *w*? " 8
Welcome She gave the white men *w* all, *A dark Indian maiden* 53
Well Yes, mightier than the purest painted *w*, *Art for Art's sake!* 5
Thro' his own nature, with *w* mingled hues, *That is his portrait* 28
Cold words I spoke, yet loved thee warm and *w*. *To thee with whom* 8
Went Many a mile *w* he, *Bold Havelock* 2
shapes without heads *W* leaping here and there. *Far off in the dun* 104
With a silver sound the wheels *w* round, " 121
Wept and do the wrong He *w* for, *A surface man* 7
West Silver sails all out of the *W*, *Bright is the moon* 12
sun Drew down the *W* his feeble lights; *Deep glens I found* 6
Little Aubrey in the *W*! *Little Aubrey* 1
So pausing 'twixt the East and *W*, *Youth, lapsing i* 47
Wheel As the quick *w's* brush'd, *Far off in the dun* 91
not pause At the strife of the shadowy *w's*, " 94
With a silver sound the *w's* went round, The *w's* " 121
Hear you the sound of *w's*? *Hear you the sound* 1
Should fire the many *w's* of change! *They wrought, etc.* 24
Wherefrom Not with this age *w* ye stand apart, *Therefore your Halls* 11
Whim whose *w's* were meant For virtue's servants, *A surface man* 2
Whisper (s) Else this wild *w* round my head *Are those the far-famed* 11
Not a *w* stirs the gloom, *Not a whisper* 1
Showers in a *w* o'er the world. *Not to Silence* 34
A lute-toned *w*, 'I am here!' *Remember you* 6
These *w's* rise, and fall away, *'Tis not alone* 10
Whisper (verb) Another *w's* sick with loss: *I keep no more* 9
I heard you *w* from above, *Remember you* 5
Whisper'd The *w* love of the fair young wives; *Far off in the dun* 67
White The *w* man's *w* sail, bringing To happy Hayti the new-comer, *A dark Indian maiden* 37
She gave the *w* men welcome all, " 53
and the *w* fly leapt About his hairless brow. *Far off in the dun* 83
As stars they shone, in raiment *w*, " 131
Why the bride is *w* as clay, *The lamps were bright* 10
Sent thro' my blood a prophet voice Before the first *w* butterflies, *Youth, lapsing i* 11
Whiten'd moonlight That *w* all the eastern ridge, *Remember you* 2
Whole (adj.) Thro' one *w* life an overflowing urn, *That is his portrait* 50
The *w* world shall not brave us! (repeat) *They say, etc.* 6, 13, 20
The *w* land glitters after rain, *Youth, lapsing ii* 37
Whole (s) When the shadow of night's wings Envelopes the gloomy *w*, *Far off in the dun* 14
Widely owning more Discourse, more *w* wise.' *From shape to shape* 8
Widen All nature *w's* upward. " 5
Wife O Mother-Queen, and weeping *W*, *Early-wise* 7
whisper'd love of the fair young *wives*; *Far off in the dun* 67
Whom the wedded *w* did slay, *The lamps were bright* 48
You have given me such a *w*! *Vicar of this* 10
Wild Following her *w* carol She led them down the pleasant places, *A dark Indian maiden* 61
Else this *w* whisper round my head Were idler than a flight of rooks. *Are those the far-famed* 11
And why her black eyes burn With a light so *w* and stern?' *The lamps were bright* 16
Then a scream of *w* dismay Thro' the deep hall forced its way, " 41
Wilderness thro' the *w* Thou bearest from the threshold *Woman of noble* 2
Wildwood Fann'd this queen of the green *w*, *A dark Indian maiden* 15
Will Genius, Master of the Moral *W*! *Art for Art's sake!* 2
She spurs an imitative *w*; *Young is the grief* 6
A *w* concentric with all fate, " 15
Willow shanks were shrunken to *w* wands *Far off in the dun* 55
Wind moaning *w* before it drives Thick wreaths " 23
loud the roar Of *w* and mingled shower, " 34
The wanton *w* came singing lustily *Hear you the sound* 41
May blow alarum loud to every *w*, *O God, make this age* 4
The *w* is loud in holt and hill, *Speak to me* 2
sound of the deep when the *w's* are asleep; *That the voice* 3
Your name is blown on every w, *The noblest men* 5
when the *w's* Are fallen or changed; *Woman of noble* 9
A life four-square to all the *w's*. *Young is the grief* 16
Life, to this *w*, turn'd all her vanes, *Youth, lapsing i* 29
A noise of *w's* that meet and blend, " *ii* 2
'Come' and I come, the *w* is strong: " 17
A light *w* wafts me from my feet. " 44
Wind-borne his cloak *w-b* Behind, *One was the Tishbite* 5
Winding To snowy crofts and *w* scars, *Youth, lapsing i* 18
Window thro' The *w's* of shaven bone. *Far off in the dun* 48
Wine Is thy mad brain drunk with the merry, red *w*, *Full light aloft* 7
It is not good to drink strong *w* " 9
But thou hast drunk of the merry, sweet *w*, " 11
Wing night's eternal *w's* Envelopes the gloomy whole, *Far off in the dun* 13
Her thoughts have found their *w's* *The lamps were bright* 21
Winged then Is this blind flight the *w* Powers. *Are those the far-famed* 4
Winning fair blue eyes and *w* sweet, *Because she bore* 6
Winter And shook the frosty *w* stars. *Youth, lapsing i* 20
Wisdom drank The sweet sad tears of *w*.' *Methought I saw* 6
Wisdom-led Or wise yourselves, or *w-l*, *Are those the far-famed* 10
Wise (*See also* **Early-wise**) Or *w* yourselves, or wisdom-led, " 10
owning more Discourse, more widely *w*.' *From shape to shape* 8
O the child so meek and *w*, Who made *us w* and mild! *The child was sitting* 8
Like some *w* artist, Nature gives, *'Tis not alone* 6
Mine host is fat, and gray, and *w*, *Yon huddled cloud* 9
Wiser Ye must be *w* than your looks, *Are those the far-famed* 9
Wisest How full of *w* humour and of love, *That is his portrait* 7
" 38
Wish Eustace, long May my strong *w*, *They wrought, etc.* 31
Convoys the people's *w*, is great; *Woman of noble* 6
take with thee Our warmest *w's*,
Witch That skinny *w* did say, *The lamps were bright* 18
Wolf A howling of the mountain *w*; *Youth, lapsing ii* 20
Woman *w's* youthful pride Of rounded limbs— *One was the Tishbite* 16
I can trust Your w's *nature kind and true.* *The noblest men* 12
W of noble form and noble mind! *Woman of noble* 1
Womanhood Slow-ripening to the grace of *w*, *To thee with whom* 13
Womb shape to shape at first within the *w* *From shape to shape* 1
All Nature is the *w* whence Man is born. *Hold thou, my friend* 2
Won praise Is neither overdealt, nor idly *w*. *That is his portrait* 43
Wondering *w*, loving, Carolling 'Happy, *A dark Indian maiden* 51
Wondrous Seeing the heart so *w* in her ways, *Why suffers* 3
Woo That would have come to *w* her. *Sweet Kitty Sandilands* 8
Wood Lady over *w* and highland, *A dark Indian maiden* 27
In the deep *w* no more,— " 67
The nightingale in leafy *w's* *Remember you* 14
'Tis not alone the warbling *w's*, *'Tis not alone* 1
I grieved as *w's* in dripping rains *Youth, lapsing i* 31
Wooded (*See also* **Cedar-wooded**) Dancing by a palmy bay, In the *w* paradise, *A dark Indian maiden* 19
Thro' *w* isles the river shines, *Youth, lapsing ii* 38
Woodland Dancing on the blossomy plain To a *w* melody: *A dark Indian maiden* 30
Word A sound of *w's* that change to blows! *They wrought, etc.* 17
Cold *w's* I spoke, yet loved thee warm *To thee with whom* 8
Wore face whose every line *W* the pale cast *Methought I saw* 2
Work (s) They wrought a *w* which Time reveres, *They wrought, etc.* 1
Nature gives, Thro' all her *w's*, *'Tis not alone* 7
Work (verb) Not deals in threats, but *w's* with hope, *They wrought, etc.* 39
Working A labour *w* to an end. *Youth, lapsing ii* 4
World Dissolve a *w*, condense a star, *Are those the far-famed* 14
which of us most shall help the *w*, *Frenchman, etc.* 7

X

Y

A CONCORDANCE TO THE SUPPRESSED POEMS

OF

ALFRED, LORD TENNYSON

(1830-1868)

A

Abide So swiftly, that they nowhere would *a*, *Love and Sorrow* 15
in him light and joy and strength *a's*; *Love* 42
We will *a* in the golden vale Of the Lotos-land, *Lotos-Eaters* 26
Absorbed torrent of quick thought *A* me *Timbuctoo* 142
Abstraction The still serene *a*; *The Mystic* 5
Abyss The blossoming *a'es* of your hills? *Timbuctoo* 44
showering circular *a* Of radiance. „ 173
Accent In *a's* of majestic melody, „ 192
Accident All on-set of capricious *A*, „ 26
Accurate I know not if I shape These things with *a* similitude „ 134
Aching We beat upon our *a* hearts with rage; *Love* 18
Acorn on an oaken sprout A goodly *a* grew; But winds from heaven shook the *a* out, *Lost Hope* 6
Acropolis retir'd At midnight, in the lone *A*. *Timbuctoo* 32
Act (s) Yours are the public *a's* of public men, *Sugg. by Reading* 21
Act (verb) she did *a* the step-dame to mine eyes, *Lover's Tale i* 664
Adage widow'd, like the cur In the child's *a*? „ 770
Adore all men *a* thee; Heaven crieth after thee; *Love* 25
Afresh And being there they did break forth *a* *Lover's Tale i* 731
Afric whose rapid interval Parts *A* from green Europe, *Timbuctoo* 3
cried 'Wide *A*, doth thy Sun Lighten, „ 58
Again And yet *a*, *a* and evermore, *The Mystic* 19
Should war's mad blast *a* be blown, *Hands all Round* 41
Age and old *a* Is but to know thee: *Love* 15
for your manner sorts Not with this *a*, *Cambridge* 11
Agglomerated *A* swiftness, I had lived *Lover's Tale i* 495
Aggression Nor seek to bridle His vile *a's*, *Britons, guard* 53
Agony Wake on, my soul, nor crouch to *a*: *Though night* 5
serpent in his *agonies* Awestricken Indians; *Love* 30
in mine *a*, Did I make bare of all *Lover's Tale ii* 50
Ailment whom woful *a's* Of unavailing tears „ *i* 818
Air ev'n as flame draws *a*; *Timbuctoo* 18
As *a* is th' life of flame: „ 20
Blown round with happy *a's* of odorous winds? „ 46
The indistinctest atom in deep *a*, „ 100
Pure without heat, into a larger *a* Upburning, *The Mystic* 44
And as light as *a*; *The Grasshopper* 25
globefilled arch that, cleaving *a*, *Chorus* 25
Filled with a finer *a*: *D. of F. Women* 8
happy *a* shall woo The wither'd leaf *Lover's Tale i* 621
nor breathe What *a's* he pleased! „ 693
Airily Keen-eyed Sisters, singing *a* *Hesperides, Song i* 25
Airy Vaulting on thine *a* feet. *The Grasshopper* 10
Airy-fashioned There be some hearts so *a-f*, *Lover's Tale i* 848
Alarm Weariness and wild *a*, *Lotos-Eaters* 2
Albion New-risen o'er awakened *A*— *Cambridge* 7
Alchemy And dross to gold with glorious *a*, *Though night* 7
All Shadows to which, despite *a* shocks of Change, *Timbuctoo* 25
And circled with the glory of living light And alternations of *a* hues, „ 76
Man is the measure of *a* truth Unto himself. *οἱ ῥέοντες* 3
A things are not told to *a*, *Hesperides, Song iii* 12
and ceasing from A contemplation of *a* forms, *Lover's Tale i* 67
The centre of *a* splendours, *a* unworthy Of such a shrine— „ 69
And *a* the quaint old scraps of ancient crones, „ 288
And throwing by *a* consciousness of self, „ 787
Yet hands *a* round! *Hands all Round* 21
Alley Thro' yonder poplar *a* Below, *Check every outflash* 4
Allied God keep their lands *a*, *God bless our Prince* 2
Almeida Weep not, *A*, that I said to thee *Love and Sorrow* 3
A, if my heart were substanceless, „ 13
Aloft and *a* Winnow the purple, bearing *Timbuctoo* 153
a Upon his renown'd Eminence bore globes „ 170
Alone why muse you here *a* Upon the Mountain, „ 77
A she is there: *I' the glooming light* 8
Ever *a* She maketh her moan: „ 16
To fight thy mother here *a*, *Hands all Round* 43
All *a* she sits and hears Echoes *Home they brought him* 3
Altarthrone Offered to Gods upon an *a*; *To* —— 7
Altercating Alas, Church writers, *a* tribes— *Sugg. by Reading* 73
Alternate Dappled with hollow and *a* rise Of inter-penetrated arc, *Timbuctoo* 130
Alternation And *a's* of all hues, he stood. „ 76
Amiss For my doubts and fears were all *a*, *The Ringlet* 19
Anakim Piled by the strong and sunborn *A* *A fragment* 20
Anarchy To shapes of wildest *a*, *Chorus* 4
Ancient *A* dream as frail as those of *a* Time?' *Timbuctoo* 62
There standeth our *a* enemy; (repeat) *English War Song* 23, 45
Hark! he shouteth—the *a* enemy! „ 24
For his *a* heart is drunk with overwatchings night and day, *Hesperides, Song ii* 12
And the *a* secret revealèd. „ *iii* 5
In the valley some, and some On the *a* heights divine; *Lotos-Eaters* 17
Therefore your halls, your *a* colleges, *Cambridge* 1
Our *a* boast is this—we reverence law. *Sugg. by Reading* 34
And trust an *a* manhood and the cause Of England „ 39
And all the quaint old scraps of *a* crones, *Lover's Tale i* 288
Anew Evermore it is born *a*; *Hesperides, Song i* 18
Angel (adj.) *a* mind which look'd from out The starry glowing *Timbuctoo* 88
Angel (s) *A's* have talked with him, and showed him thrones: *The Mystic* 1
Over heaven's parapets the *a's* lean. *To a Lady Sleep.* 10
What an *a*! How clothed with beams! *Lover's Tale i* 351
I became to her A tutelary *a* „ 388
the *a's*, The watchers at heaven's gate, „ 615

Anger must your noble *a* blaze out more — *Blow ye the trumpet* 9
Horrible with the *a* and the heat — *Lover's Tale i* 681
Angry Flooding its *a* cheek with odorous tears. — „ *i* 565
Annoy Basing thy throne above the world's *a.* — *Though night* 8
Another He hath not *a* dart; — *Burial of Love* 10
Antelope Sure never yet was *A* Could skip — *Skipping-rope* 1
Anxious Beat like a far wave on my *a* ear. — *Timbuctoo* 114
Apart *a* In intellect and power and will, — *The Mystic* 37
Apathy Shall hollow-hearted *a*, The cruellest form — *Burial of Love* 17
Ape and our mirth *A's* the happy vein, — *Every day, etc.* 13
Appeal I honour much, I say, this man's *a.* — *Sugg. by Reading* 49
Apple The golden *a*, the golden *a*, the hallowed fruit, — *Hesperides, Song i* 1
Guard the *a* night and day, — „ 28
and the golden *a* be stol'n away, — „ *ii* 11
If the golden *a* be taken The world — „ 21
The golden *a* stol'n away, — „ *iii* 4
Make the *a* holy and bright, — „ *iv* 10
But the *a* of gold hangs over the sea, — „ „ 23
The golden *a*, the golden *a*, the hallowed fruit, — „ 30
Dear room, the *a* of my sight, — *O darling room* 2
April Young fishes, on an *A* morn, — *Rosalind* 21
Green springtide, *A* promise, glad new year — *Lover's Tale i* 277
Arabian from his mother's eyes Flow over the *A* bay, — *A Fragment* 24
Arc alternate rise Of interpenetrated *a*, — *Timbuctoo* 131
Arch With triple *a* of everchanging bows, — „ 74
globefilled *a* that, cleaving air, — *Chorus* 25
in and out the woodbine's flowery *a'es* — *Check every outflash* 11
Stays on the flowering *a* of the bough, — *Hesperides, Song iv* 18
Arch'd wheel in wheel, *A* the wan Sapphire. — *Timbuctoo* 111
Archetype To its *A* that waits Clad in light — *Germ of 'Maud'* 31
Arching *A* blue-glossèd necks beneath — *Dualisms* 13
A the billow in his sleep; — *Hesperides, Song iv* 3
Arch-mock This was the very *a-m* And insolence — *Lover's Tale i* 687
Archway All night through *a's* of the bridgèd pearl — *Though night* 3
Argent windeth through The *a* streets o' the City, — *Timbuctoo* 231
Pleached with her hair, in mail of *a* light Shot into gold, — *Pallid thunderstricken* 12
Parted on either side her *a* neck, — *Lover's Tale i* 740
Argosy broad-blown *Argosies* Drave into haven? — *A Fragment* 7
Aright And my eyes read, they read *a*, her heart Was Lionel's: — *Lover's Tale i* 602
Arise *A*, brave Poles, the boldest of the bold; — *Blow ye the trumpet* 3
Arm I dare not fold My *a's* about thee— — *Oh, Beauty* 6
Arms Than vanquish all the world in *a.* — *Hands all Round* 28
Arrested love too high to be express'd *A* in its sphere, — *Lover's Tale i* 66
Arrogant It looks too *a* a jest— — *New Timon* 42
Arrow Love is dead; His last *a* sped; — *Burial of Love* 9
Arrowy borne Adown the sloping of an *a* stream, — *Timbuctoo* 144
Art We know him, out of Shakespeare's *a*, — *New Timon* 1
An artist, Sir, should rest in *a*, — „ 21
Strung in the very negligence of *A*, Or in the *a* of Nature, — *Lover's Tale i* 562
Artist An *a*, Sir, should rest in art, — *New Timon* 21
Ashes I lay! White as quench'd *a*, — *Lover's Tale i* 620
Ask I only *a* to sit beside thy feet. — *Oh, Beauty* 13
Assimilated Perchance *a* all our tastes — *Lover's Tale i* 238
Assyrian Some vast *A* doom to burst upon our race. — *Sugg. by Reading* 42
Astonishment full of strange *A* and boundless change. (repeat) — *Chorus* 10, 20, 30
Atalantis Divinest *A*, whom the waves Have buried deep, — *Timbuctoo* 22
Atlantic-Atlantick That ran bloombright into the *Atlantic* blue, — *The Hesperides* 9
O rise, our strong *Atlantic* sons, — *Hands all Round* 49
when the Sun Had fall'n below th' *Atlantick*, — *Timbuctoo* 4
Atmosphere Thou foldest, like a golden *a*, — *Love* 5
drew the happy *a* Of my unhappy sighs, — *Lover's Tale i* 673
Atom The indistinctest *a* in deep air, — *Timbuctoo* 100
Attain teach him to *a* By shadowing forth the Unattainable; — „ 196
Austrian The Russian whips and *A* rods— — *Hands all Round* 18
Author Refused to look his *a* in the face, — *Lover's Tale i* 697
Autocrat We must not dread in you the nameless *a.* — *Sugg. by Reading* 18
Autumn in red *A* when the winds are wild — *Timbuctoo* 202
The troublous *a's* sallow gloom, — *Chorus* 17
bitter blasts the screaming *a* whirl, — *Though night* 2
Avail Shall not *a* you when the day-beam sports — *Cambridge* 6
Awake He often lying broad *a*, — *The Mystic* 36
Awakened when the day-beam sports New-risen o'er *a* Albion— — *Cambridge* 7
Awakening *See* **Earth-awakening**
Awestricken As on a serpent in his agonies *A* Indians; — *Love* 31
Awful Before the *a* Genius of the place Kneels the pale Priestess in deep faith, — *Timbuctoo* 33
A with most invariable eyes. — *The Mystic* 24
Hallowed in *a* chasms of wheeling gloom, — *Love* 22
And in his writhings *a* hues begin To wander down his sable sheeny sides, — „ 38
A Memnonian countenances calm Looking athwart the burning flats, — *A Fragment* 16
Five and three (Let it not be preached abroad) make an *a* mystery. — *Hesperides, Song i* 16
But grow upon them like *a* glorious vision Of unconceived and *a* happiness, — *Lover's Tale i* 798
Aye Merry England! England for *a*! (repeat) — *English War Song* 11, 22, 33, 44, 55

B

Balanced and swum with *b* wings To some tall mountain. — *Lover's Tale i* 304
Ball Till your *b's* fly as their true shafts have flown. — *Britons, guard* 47
Think you hearts are tennis *b's* To play with, — *Rosalind* 32
Balloon As when a man, that sails in a *b*, — *D. of F. Women* 1
Balm Thy locks are dripping *b*; — *Hero to Leander* 20
Baltic on the *B* shore Boleslas drove the Pomeranian. — *Blow ye the trumpet* 13
Banbury '*B* Cross,' 'The Gander' — *Lover's Tale i* 286
Bandbox to take *his* name You *b.* — *New Timon* 44
Banded Although we fought the *b* world alone, — *Britons, guard* 59
Banished The true men *b*, — „ 10
Bank (*See also* **Brookbank**) Gray sand *b's* and pale sunsets —dreary wind, — *Mablethorpe* 7
Banner On the ridge of the hill his *b's* rise; — *English War Song* 25
Barbarian Low-built, mud-walled, *B* settlement, — *Timbuctoo* 248
Bare Her shoulders are *b*; — *I' the glooming light* 10
The *b* word kiss hath made my inner soul To tremble — *Oh, Beauty* 12
Bark (of a tree) Creeping under the fragrant *b*, — *Hesperides, Song i* 23
Bark (vessel) winedark wave our weary *b* did carry. — *Lotos-Eaters* 9
Based *See* **Broad-based**
Basing *B* thy throne above the world's annoy. — *Though night* 8
Bathe *B's* the cold hand with tears, — *Timbuctoo* 38
Come *b* me with thy kisses, — *Hero to Leander* 12
Bathed I have *b* thee with the pleasant myrrh; — „ 19
Battailing *B* with the glooms of my dark will, — *Lover's Tale i* 782
Battle (s) gather from afar The hosts to *b*: — *Blow ye the trumpet* 2
To blow the *b* from their oaken sides. — *Britons, guard* 38
We won old *b's* with our strength, the bow. — „ 44
Battle (verb) Will he dare to *b* with the free? — *English War Song* 46
Battled Or loyally disloyal *b* for our rights. — *Sugg. by Reading* 36
Battlement Illimitable range of *b* On *b*, — *Timbuctoo* 164
Bay Your flowering Capes and your gold-sanded *b's* — „ 45
from his mother's eyes Flow over the Arabian *b*, — *A Fragment* 24
Past Thymiaterion, in calmèd *b's*, — *The Hesperides* 4
Through vineyards from an island *b.* — *Rosalind* 29
Bayard The *B* of the meadow. — *The Grasshopper* 21
Bayona In old *B*, nigh the Southern Sea— — *There are three things* 11
Beam (*See also* **Day-beam**) What an angel! How clothed with *b's*! — *Lover's Tale i* 352
Bear *b* them upward through the trackless fields — *Timbuctoo* 159
There must no man go back to *b* the tale: No man to *b* it—Swear it! We swear it! — *Britons, guard* 56
Bearded Her tears are mixed with the *b* dews. — *I' the glooming light* 11
Bearing *b* on both sides Double display — *Timbuctoo* 154
As *b* no essential fruits of excellence. — *Lover's Tale i* 385
So *b* on thro' Being limitless The triumph — „ 514
Beast wondrous tones Of man and *b* — *Chorus* 9
Beat *B* like a far wave on my anxious ear. — *Timbuctoo* 114
Thy heart *b's* through thy rosy limbs — *Hero to Leander* 16
the brazen *b* Of their broad vans, — *Shall the hag* 7
We *b* upon our aching hearts with rage; — *Love* 18
B upon his father's shield— — *Home they brought him* 9
heart *b* Twice to the melody of hers. — *Lover's Tale i* 73

Blue (adj.) The ocean with the morrow light Will be both *b* and calm; *Hero to Leander* 26
all the day heaven gathers back her tears Into her own *b* eyes so clear and deep, *Tears of Heaven* 7
black eyes, and brown and *b*; I hold them all most dear; *There are three things* 6
That ran bloombright into the Atlantic *b*, *The Hesperides* 9
Stream from beneath him in the broad *b* noon, *D. of F. Women* 3
Blue (s) chasms of deep, deep *b* Slumber'd unfathomable, *Timbuctoo* 7
With eyes dropt downward through the *b* serene, *To a Lady Sleep.* 9
Blue-glossèd Arching *b-g* necks beneath *Dualisms* 13
Blue-green Through yonder poplar alley Below, the *b-g* river windeth slowly; *Check every outflash* 5
Blush'd Ringlet, She *b* a rosy red, *The Ringlet* 36
Boast Our ancient *b* is this—we reverence law. *Sugg. by Reading* 34
Boat And sailing on Pactolus in a *b*, *Pallid thunderstricken* 3
Body and yet Remaining from the *b*, *The Mystic* 37
You cannot let a *b* be: *New Timon* 30
Crept like the drains of a marsh thro' all my *b*; *Lover's Tale ii* 56
Unto the growth of *b* and of mind; „ 74
Bold no men like Englishmen, So tall and *b* as they be. *National Song* 8
nothing seems to me so wild and *b*, *Oh, Beauty* 7
Caucasus is *b* and strong. *Hesperides, Song iii* 7
B, subtle, careless Rosalind, *Rosalind* 2
Arise, brave Poles, the boldest of the *b*; *Blow ye the trumpet* 3
Bolder child in our cradles is *b* than he; *English War Song* 35
Boldest Arise, brave Poles, the *b* of the bold; *Blow ye the trumpet* 3
Bole gnarlèd *b* of the charmèd tree, *Hesperides, Song iv* 29
Boleslas on the Baltic shore *B* drove the Pomeranian. *Blow ye the trumpet* 14
Bond Thy spirit fetter'd with the *b* of clay: *Timbuctoo* 83
Bone they plunge their doubts among old rags and *b's*. *Sugg. by Reading* 72
dead skin withering on the fretted *b*, *Lover's Tale i* 678
Boot A dapper *b*—a little hand— *New Timon* 35
Bore *b* globes Of wheeling suns, or stars, *Timbuctoo* 171
waves, which *b* The reflex of my City „ 238
b downward with the wave. *Lover's Tale i* 375
Born (*See also* **Sunborn**) We laugh, we cry, we are *b*, we die, *The 'How' and the 'Why'* 8
Through whose dim brain the wingèd dreams are *b*, *To a Lady Sleep.* 2
Far better, far better he never were *b* *English War Song* 16
Evermore it is *b* anew; *Hesperides, Song i* 18
Borne (*See also* **Blastborne**) *b* Adown the sloping of an arrowy stream, *Timbuctoo* 143
Through dark and bright Wingèd hours are *b*; *Every day, etc.* 4
b abroad By the loud winds, *Love* 8
Bosom My heart is warmer surely than the *b* of the main. *Hero to Leander* 9
each rose Doth faint upon the *b* *Lover's Tale i* 564
Both So that with hasty motion I did veil My vision with *b* hands, *Timbuctoo* 69
bearing on *b* sides Double display of starlit wings „ 154
Yet on *b* sides at once thou canst not shine: *Love and Sorrow* 7
Bottom Creep down into the *b* of the flower. *Lover's Tale i* 560
Bough great bird sits on the opposite *b*, *The 'How' and the 'Why'* 28
Stays on the flowering arch of the *b*, *Hesperides, Song iv* 18
And a titmarsh in the *b*. *A gate and a field* 4
fall'n in the woods, or blasted Upon this *b*? *Lover's Tale i* 623
Bought ruthless host is *b* with plunder'd gold, *Britons, guard* 7
hosts to battle: be not *b* and sold. *Blow ye the trumpet* 2
She that gave you 's *b* and sold, *The Ringlet* 33
Bound (s) The herald lightning's starry *b*, *Chorus* 14
verge and *b* alone Of full beatitude. *Timbuctoo* 95
Bound (verb) spirit With supernatural excitation *b* Within me, „ 91
Carol clearly, *b* along. (repeat) *The Grasshopper* 4, 30
Bound (past of Bind) With a silken cord I *b* it. *Anacreontics* 8
Bound (part.) sisters three, *B* about the golden tree. *Hesperides, Song ii* 25
B about All round about The gnarlèd bole „ *iv* 27
Half bursten from the shroud, in cere cloth *b*, *Lover's Tale i* 677
Bounding The fierceness of the *b* element? *Timbuctoo* 148
Boundless Through length of porch and lake and *b* hall, „ 180
Astonishment and *b* change. (repeat) *Chorus* 10, 20, 30
Bow With triple arch of everchanging *b's*, *Timbuctoo* 74
His *b* unstrung With the tears he hath shed, *Burial of Love* 5
We won old battles with our strength, the *b*. *Britons, guard* 44
Bow'd As towards the gracious light I *b*, *What time I wasted* 4
lithe limbs *b* as with a heavy weight *Lover's Tale i* 126
Bower the light of vernal *b's*, *Could I outwear* 6
Bowing *B* the seeded summerflowers. *The Grasshopper* 8
Bowman Now practise, yeomen, Like those *bowmen*, *Britons, guard* 46
Boy Who killed the girls and thrill'd the *b's* *New Timon* 9
The *b* began to leap and prance, *Home they brought him* 7
Let them so love that men and *b's* may say, *Lover's Tale i* 801
Brain hurried through The riv'n rapt *b*: *Timbuctoo* 121
my human *b* Stagger'd beneath the vision, „ 185
Through whose dim *b* the wingèd dreams are born, *To a Lady Sleep.* 2
b could keep afloat The subtle spirit. *Oh, Beauty* 10
And a juggle of the *b*. *Germ of 'Maud'* 8
On those first-moved fibres of the *b*. *Lover's Tale i* 21
They flash across the darkness of my *b*, „ 53
All unawares, into the poet's *b*; „ 557
Bramble matted *b* and the shining gloss Of ivy-leaves, „ 373
Branching And *b* silvers of the central globe, *Pallid thunderstricken* 8
Brassy between whose limbs Of *b* vastness broad-blown Argosies Drave into haven? *A Fragment* 7
Brave Arise, *b* Poles, the boldest of the bold; *Blow ye the trumpet* 3
Brazen Would shatter and o'erbear the *b* heat Of their broad vans, *Shall the hag* 7
Bread He shall eat the *b* of common scorn; *English War Song* 13
Breadth With moral *b* of temperament. *New Timon* 28
Break spheres Which *b* upon each other, *Timbuctoo* 126
world will not change, and her heart will not *b*. *I' the glooming light* 22
deep salt wave *b's* in above *Hero to Leander* 34
B through your iron shackles—fling them far. *Blow ye the trumpet* 4
summer winds *b* their soft sleep with sighs, *Lover's Tale i* 559
they did *b* forth afresh In a new birth, „ 731
Breast Zone of flashing gold beneath His *b*, *Timbuctoo* 73
Breath lips so cruel dumb Should have so sweet a *b*! *The lintwhite* 18
redolent *b* Of this warm seawind ripeneth, *Hesperides, Song iv* 1
Which waste with the *b* that made 'em. *Lover's Tale i* 475
blood, the *b*, the feeling and the motion, „ *ii* 75
Breath-Breathe Before the face of God didst *breath* and move, *Love* 3
Breathe on thy wingèd throne, and it shall move „ 27
Breathes low into the charmed ears of morn *A Fragment* 25
nor *breathe* What airs he pleased! *Lover's Tale i* 692
Breathèd the new year warm *b* on the earth, *Love* 33
With roses musky *b*, *Anacreontics* 1
Intense delight and rapture that I *b*, *Lover's Tale i* 381
for which I lived and *b*: „ *ii* 73
Breathing And the low west wind, *b* afar, *Hesperides, Song iv* 8
Brere They from the blosmy *b* Call *The lintwhite* 4
Brethren (*See also* **Brother**) Over their crowned *b* On and Oph? *A Fragment* 21
Bride I can shadow forth my *b* *Germ of 'Maud'* 9
God bless our Prince and *B*! *God bless our Prince* 1
Bridge Your *b's* and your busted libraries, *Cambridge* 3
With shouts from off the *b*, *Lover's Tale i* 369
Upon the tremulous *b*, that from beneath „ 406
Bridgèd All night through archways of the *b* pearl *Though Night* 3
Bridle Nor seek to *b* His vile aggressions, *Britons, guard* 52
Brief Could I outwear my present state of woe With one *b* winter, *Could I outwear* 2
Bright (*See also* **Bloombright**) The *b* descent Of a young Seraph! *Timbuctoo* 64
Through dark and *b* Wingèd hours are borne; *Every day, etc.* 3
There is no *b* form Doth not cast a shade— „ 9
Thine is the *b* side of my heart, and thine My heart's day, *Love and Sorrow* 8
I am so dark, alas! and thou so *b*, *Me my own fate* 13
Make the apple holy and *b*, Holy and *b*, round and full, *b* and blest, *Hesperides, Song iv* 10
No little room so warm and *b* Wherein to read, *O darling room* 5
Not any room so warm and *b*, Wherein to read, „ 17
Brightness hearts of all on Earth Toward their *b*, *Timbuctoo* 18
it was wonderful With its exceeding *b*, „ 87
Brilliance beneath Two doors of blinding *b*, „ 178
Brilliant soon yon *b* towers Shall darken with the waving of her wand; „ 244
Brine roaring *b* Will rend thy golden tresses; *Hero to Leander* 23
melancholy home At the limit of the *b*, *Lotos-Eaters* 21
Bring Hoarded wisdom *b's* delight. *Hesperides, Song ii* 6
And careless what this hour may *b*, *New Timon* 18
Bringeth Laughter *b* tears: *Every day, etc.* 18

C

Cerement spiced *c's* in old grots Rock-hewn *A Fragment* 30
Chain Five links, a golden *c*, are we, *Hesperides, Song ii* 23
Five links, a golden *c*, are we, „ *iv* 24
Chance Jesuit laughs, and reckoning on his *c*, *Britons, guard* 32
Change (s) Shadows to which, despite all shocks of *C*, *Timbuctoo* 25
All is *c*, woe or weal; *Every day, etc.* 23
woes of many a fiery *c* Had purified, *The Mystic* 9
full of strange Astonishment and boundless *c*. (repeat) *Chorus* 10, 20, 30
All truth is *c*: *οἱ ῥέοντες* 4
Glory in glory, without sense of *c*. *Lover's Tale i* 516
Updrawn in expectation of her *c*— „ 597
Change (verb) Her light shall into darkness *c*; *Burial of Love* 27
world will not *c*, and her heart will not break. *I' the glooming light* 22
by a spell Did *c* them into gall; *Love, Pride, etc.* 10
Kingdoms lapse, and climates *c*, and races die; *Hesperides, Song ii* 4
Why *c* the titles of your streets? *Hands all Round* 31
This cannot *c*, nor yet can I.' *The Ringlet* 12
If this can *c*, why so can I.' (repeat) „ 24, 42
as tho' a red rose Should *c* into a white one *Lover's Tale i* 727
Changed How *c* from this fair City!' *Timbuctoo* 249
C into fire, and blown about with sighs. *To* —— 9
Changeful Yet endure unscathed Of *c* cycles the great Pyramids *A Fragment* 9
Changing *See* **Everchanging**
Channel Thro' the *c* windeth far *Germ of 'Maud'* 29
Chapel Wax-lighted *c's* and rich carved screens, *Cambridge* 4
Chaplet mine wove *c's* of the self-same flower, *Lover's Tale i* 333
Character'd I feel Exception to be *c* in fire. *Sugg. by Reading* 52
Charge *c* to the fight: *C*! *c* to the fight! *English War Song* 47
Charged I straightly would commend the tears to creep From my *c* lids; *Could I outwear* 11
Charm Whom martial progress only *c's*? *Hands all Round* 26
To *c* a lower sphere of fulminating fools. *Sugg. by Reading* 30
Charmed Breathes low into the *c* ears of morn *A Fragment* 25
Standing about the *c* root. *Hesperides, Song i* 4
All round about The gnarlèd bole of the *c* tree, „ *iv* 29
Standing about the *c* root, „ *iv* 34
Chasm *c's* of deep, deep blue Slumber'd unfathomable, *Timbuctoo* 7
Hallowed in awful *c's* of wheeling gloom, *Love* 22
to link The earthquake-shattered *c*, *Lover's Tale i* 408
Chaste English wives, So fair and *c* as they be. *National Song* 22
Chastened Had purified, and *c*, and made free. *The Mystic* 10
Chastise To raise the people and *c* the times *Sugg. by Reading* 5
Chaunt And *c's* 'how? how?' the whole of the night. *The 'How' and the 'Why'* 31
Check *C* every outflash, every ruder sally *Check every outflash* 1
Cheek Hateful with hanging *c's*, a withered brood, *Shall the hag* 4
As with one kiss to touch thy blessèd *c*. *Oh, Beauty,* 8
old mark of rouge upon your *c's*. *New Timon* 38
Flooding its angry *c* with odorous tears. *Lover's Tale i* 565
Chiefest But this *c*, Next to her presence „ 421
Child (*See also* **Children**) 'O *c* of man, why muse you here alone *Timbuctoo* 77
C of Man, See'st thou yon river, „ 228
The echo, feeble *c* of sound, *Chorus* 12
SHALL the hag Evil die with the *c* of Good, *Shall the hag* 1
The *c* in our cradles is bolder than he; *English War Song* 35
A *c* with a broken slate, *A gate and a field* 3
How often, when a *c* I lay reclined, *Mablethorpe* 1
A woful man had thrust his wife and *c* *Lover's Tale i* 368
Misery, like a fretful, wayward *c*, „ 696
widow'd, like the cur In the *c's* adage? „ 770
Children (*See also* **Child**) Two *c* lovelier than love, adown the lea *Dualisms* 14
Fair year, fair year, thy *c* call, *The lintwhite* 10
words of little *c* preach Against you,— *Cambridge* 12
Chilling Then never *c* touch of Time Will turn it silver-gray; *The Ringlet* 5
Now never *c* touch of Time Can turn thee silver-gray; „ 15
One very dark and *c* night Pride came beneath and held a light. *Love, Pride, etc.* 5
Chimeth In the ear, from far and near, *C* musically clear. *Rosalind* 8
Chimney-pot And a house with a *c-p*? *The 'How' and the 'Why'* 35
Chink'd brain, Now seam'd and *c* with years— *Lover's Tale i* 131
Chirrup Carol clearly, *c* sweet *The Grasshopper* 12
Choice This man is France, the man they call her *c*. *Britons, guard* 20
Choir murmurous planets' rolling *c*, *Chorus* 24
Chose Could he not walk what paths he *c*, *Lover's Tale i* 692
Christ With decent dippings at the name of *C*! *Sugg. by Reading* 64
C cried: Woe, woe, to Pharisees and Scribes! „ 75
Christian *See* **Un-Christian**
Christopher late review my lays, Crusty *C*; *To C. North* 2
mingle blame and praise, Rusty *C*. „ 4
forgave you all the blame, Musty *C*; „ 7
could *not* forgive the praise, Fusty *C*. „ 9
Chrysolite Her obelisks of rangèd *C*, *Timbuctoo* 235
Chrystal I saw A wilderness of spires, and *c* pile Of rampart upon rampart, „ 162
Two bees within a *c* flowerbell rockèd *Dualisms* 1
Church (adj.) Alas, *C* writers, altercating tribes— *Sugg. by Reading* 73
Church (s) Why a *c* is with a steeple built; *The 'How' and the 'Why'* 34
The *C* caress'd him; *Britons, guard* 4
The Court, the *C*, the Parliament, the crowd. *Sugg. by Reading* 16
Alas, our *C*! alas, her growing ills, „ 67
The vessel and your *C* may sink in storms. „ 74
Circle Ye were yet within The narrower *c*; *The Mystic* 42
Circled (*See also* **Golden-circled**) *c* with the glory of living light *Timbuctoo* 75
Thy spirit, *c* with a living glory, *Me my own fate* 3
Circling *c* round their emerald cones In coronals *Timbuctoo* 52
Circular showering *c* abyss Of radiance. „ 173
Circumference With such a vast *c* of thought, „ 93
Circumfus'd Fill'd with Divine effulgence, *c*, „ 50
Circumstance Of wayward vary coloured *c*, *The Mystic* 12
City some great *C* where the walls Shake, *Timbuctoo* 28
thy hills enfold a *C* as fair As those „ 59
Moon's white *cities*, and the opal width „ 101
windeth through The argent streets o' the *C*, „ 231
reflex of my *C* in their depths. Oh *C*! „ 239
How chang'd from this fair *C*!' „ 249
Her frantic *c's* flashing heats But fire, *Hands all Round* 29
Civic Severe and quick to feel a *c* sin, *Sugg. by Reading* 4
To soothe a *c* wound or keep it raw, „ 32
Clad *C* in light by golden gates, *C* in light the Spirit waits *Germ of 'Maud'* 32
Claim And wave a little of his *c*; *New Timon* 22
Clan Than when from Sobieski, *c* by *c*, *Blow ye the trumpet* 10
Clap *C* thy shielded sides and carol, *The Grasshopper* 11
Let them *c* together, foam and fall. *Hesperides, Song iii* 9
Nathless she ever *c's* the marble knees, *Timbuctoo* 37
Clay Thy spirit fetter'd with the bond of *c*: „ 83
Clear and the stars Were flooded over with *c* glory and pale. „ 9
Flowing between the *c* and polish'd stems, „ 51
The *c* Galaxy Shorn of its hoary lustre, wonderful, „ 105
Most pale and *c* and lovely distances. *The Mystic* 35
all the day heaven gathers back her tears Into her own blue eyes so *c* and deep, *Tears of Heaven* 7
THE lintwhite and the throstlecock Have voices sweet and *c*; *The lintwhite* 2
C melody flattering the crisped Nile By columned Thebes. *A Fragment* 26
Clearest Unroof the shrines of *c* vision, *To a Lady Sleep.* 3
Clearness my present mind With its past *c*, *Timbuctoo* 140
Cleave scorn of the many shall *c* To the man *English War Song* 5
Clever Alas, our youth, so *c* yet so small, *Sugg. by Reading* 79
Cliff a highland leaning down a weight Of *c's*, *The Hesperides* 11
Show'd me vast *c's* with crown of towers, *What time I wasted* 3
thro' the black-wall'd *c* the rapid brook *Lover's Tale i* 371
Climate Kingdoms lapse, and *c's* change, and races die; *Hesperides, Song ii* 4
Climb And the waves *c* high and fast. *Hero to Leander* 4
Climbed Night hath *c* her peak of highest noon, *Though night* 1
Clinging Or moisture of the vapour, left in *c*, *Lover's Tale ii* 46
Clip a snake her forehead *c's* And skins *Pallid thunderstricken* 13
Clipt Ringlet, She *c* you from her head, *The Ringlet* 38
Clique That spilt his life about the *c's*. *New Timon* 40
Clogg'd sense is *c* with dull mortality, *Timbuctoo* 82
Close and of waters Betraying the *c* kisses of the wind— „ 209
Closed And never *c* again. *Lover's Tale i* 299
Closer Oh kiss me ere we part; Grow *c* to my heart. *Hero to Leander* 8
Cloth from the shroud, in cere *c* bound, *Lover's Tale i* 677

Crisping Upon the *c's* of the dappled waves *Lover's Tale i* 46
Crocodile *C's* in briny creeks Sleep and stir not: *Hesperides, Song i* 8
Crone all the quaint old scraps of ancient *c's*, *Lover's Tale i* 288
Cross 'Banbury *C*,' 'The Gander' „ 286
Crouch Wake on, my soul, nor *c* to agony: *Though night* 5
hollow at heart shall *c* forlorn, *English War Song* 12
Crowd Court, the Church, the Parliament, the *c*. *Sugg. by Reading* 16
Crown (s) thou of many *c's*, white-robèd love, *Love* 24
from his brows a *c* of living light Looks through „ 43
I wove a *c* before her, *Anacreontics* 5
Show'd me vast cliffs with *c* of towers, *What time I wasted* 3
Crown (verb) *C* them with happiness, *God bless our Prince* 5
Crowned (adj.) Over their *c* brethren ON and OPH? *A Fragment* 21
Crown'd (verb) As I said, with these She *c* her forehead. *Lover's Tale i* 349
Cruel The *c* vapours went through all, *Love, Pride, etc.* 7
Alas! that lips so *c* dumb Should have so sweet a breath! *The lintwhite* 17
Cruellest The *c* form of perfect scorn, *Burial of Love* 18
Crumbling *c* from their parent slope At slender interval, *Timbuctoo* 123
Crush'd *C* link on link into the beaten earth, *Lover's Tale i* 859
Crushing *c* the thick fragrant reeds he lies, *Love* 32
Crusty YOU did late review my lays, *C* Christopher; *To C. North* 2
Cry (s) blow back Their wild *cries* down their cavern-throats, *Shall the hag* 10
'God save the Queen' is here a truer *c*. *Britons, guard* 26
Cry (verb) We laugh, we *c*, we are born, we die, *The 'How' and the 'Why'* 8
We *c* for thee: we deem the world thy tomb. *Love* 19
Crystalline Thou art my heart's sun in love's *c*: *Love and Sorrow* 6
Culver the *c's* mourn All the livelong day. *Every day, etc.* 29
Cup And filled the *c* with dew. *Lost Hope* 8
Cupola When even to Moscow's *c's* were rolled *Blow ye the trumpet* 7
Cur widow'd, like the *c* In the child's adage? *Lover's Tale i* 769
Curled Round about the hallowed fruit tree *c*— *Hesperides, Song ii* 13
Current The slope into the *c* of my years, *Lover's Tale ii* 76
Curse (s) And those fine *c's* which he spoke; *New Timon* 2
Curse (verb) We *c* the crimes of Southern kings, *Hands all Round* 17
Cursed Who was *c* But I? *Lover's Tale i* 626
Curve (s) A *c* of whitening, flashing, ebbing light! *Timbuctoo* 63
Curve (verb) where the Rhene *C's* towards Mentz, *O darling room* 12
Cushion makes *C's* of yellow sand; *Lover's Tale i* 537
Cut *See* **Drain-cut**
Cycle Of changeful *c's* the great Pyramids *A Fragment* 9
Cypress Like a lone *c*, through the twilight hoary, *Me my own fate* 6
One *c* on an inland promontory. „ 8
Czar ere the *C* Grew to this strength *Blow ye the trumpet* 5

D

Daffodilly And drooping *d*, *Anacreontics* 2
Dame *See* **Step-dame**
Damn'd And *d* unto his loathed tenement. *Lover's Tale i* 683
Dance colour'd spots as *d* athwart the eyes *Timbuctoo* 70
Dandy With *d* pathos when you wrote, *New Timon* 10
Dapper A *d* boot—a little hand— „ 35
Dappled (adj. and part.) Upon the crispings of the *d* waves That blanched upon its side. *Lover's Tale i* 46
D with hollow and alternate rise *Timbuctoo* 130
Dappled (verb) smallest grain that *d* the dark Earth. „ 99
Dare Will he *d* to battle with the free? *English War Song* 46
knowest I *d* not look into thine eyes, *Oh, Beauty* 4
I *d* not fold My arms about thee—scarcely *d* to speak. „ 5
Daring Hath *d* fancies of her own, *Rosalind* 26
Dark (*See also* **Winedark**) I saw The smallest grain that dappled the *d* Earth, *Timbuctoo* 99
and the Moon Had fallen from the night, and all was *d*! „ 253
Go—carry him to his *d* deathbed; *Burial of Love* 11
Through *d* and bright Wingèd hours are borne; *Every day, etc.* 3
The night is *d* and vast; *Hero to Leander* 2
One very *d* and chilly night Pride came beneath and held a light. *Love, Pride, etc.* 5
and mightily outgrow The wan *d* coil of faded suffering— *Could I outwear* 4
Driven back the billow of the dreamful *d*. *To a Lady Sleep.* 6
And all the haunted place is *d* and holy. *Check every outflash* 8
Dark (*continued*) I am so *d*, alas! and thou so bright, *Me my own fate* 13
And the *d* pine weeps, *Lotos-Eaters* 33
From the root Drawn in the *d*, Up to the fruit, *Hesperides, Song i* 21
And you, *d* Senate of the public pen, *Sugg. by Reading* 19
There hang within the heavens a *d* disgrace, „ 41
And onward floating in a full, *d* wave, *Lover's Tale i* 739
Battailing with the glooms of my *d* will, „ 782
Darken towers Shall *d* with the waving of her wand; *Timbuctoo* 245
D, and shrink and shiver into huts, „ 246
world's last tempest *d's* overhead; *Britons, guard* 2
And why was I to *d* their pure love, *Lover's Tale i* 765
Darken'd Because my own was *d*? „ 767
Darkling They with dim eyes Behold me *d*. *Timbuctoo* 213
Darkly-wreathed And ivy *d-w*, *Anacreontics* 4
Darkness wave, Forth issuing from *d*, *Timbuctoo* 230
Her light shall into *d* change; *Burial of Love* 27
They flash across the *d* of my brain, *Lover's Tale i* 53
Darling (adj.) O *D* room, my heart's delight, *O darling room* 1
Darling (s) Mid May's *d* goldenlockèd, *Dualisms* 21
Darmstadt Bingen in *D*, where the Rhene *O darling room* 11
Dart He hath not another *d*; *Burial of Love* 10
Daughter *D's* of time, divinely tall, *The Mystic* 26
and sisters three, *D's* thee, *Hesperides, Song iv* 26
Rome's dearest *d* now is captive France, *Britons, guard* 31
Gigantic *d* of the West, *Hands all Round* 37
Dawn (s) So in thine hour of *d*, the body's youth, *Though night* 13
Purplefringed with even and *d*. *Hesperides, Song iii* 14
Fresh as the *d* before the day, *Rosalind* 27
Dawn (verb) such a one As *d's* but once a season. *Lover's Tale i* 302
Day (*See also* **Marriage-day, To-day, Week-day**) Upon some earth-awakening *d* of spring *Timbuctoo* 152
EVERY *d* hath its night: *Every day, etc.* 1
Golden calm and storm Mingle *d* by *d*. „ 8
the culvers mourn All the livelong *d*. „ 30
there stood before him, night and *d*, *The Mystic* 11
all things creeping to a *d* of doom. „ 40
The *d*, the diamonded light, *Chorus* 11
all the *d* heaven gathers back her tears *Tears of Heaven* 6
showering down the glory of lightsome *d*, „ 8
and thine My heart's *d*, *Love and Sorrow* 9
Making their *d* dim, so we gaze on thee. *Love* 23
Looks through the thickstemmed woods by *d* and night „ 44
Where'er the light of *d* be; (repeat) *National Song* 2, 6, 20, 24
As round the rolling earth night follows *d*: *Me my own fate* 10
Guard the apple night and *d*, *Hesperides, Song i* 28
heart is drunk with over-watchings night and *d*, „ *ii* 12
Father Hesper, watch, watch, night and *d*, „ *iii* 1
The end of *d* and beginning of night „ *iv* 9
Watch it warily *d* and night; „ 13
Fresh as the dawn before the *d*, *Rosalind* 27
O for those *d's* of Piast, ere the Czar *Blow ye the trumpet* 5
To kiss it night and *d*, *The Ringlet* 4
Ringlet, I kiss'd you night and *d*, „ 26
many pleasant *d's*, the moonlit nights, *Lover's Tale i* 54
Oh, happy, happy outset of my *d's*! „ 276
On that *d* the year First felt his youth „ 305
May their *d's* be golden *d's*, „ 794
Day-beam Shall not avail you when the *d-b* sports *Cambridge* 6
Dazzle Till it *d* and blind his eyes. *English War Song* 28
Dazzled *d* to the heart with glorious pain. *There are three things* 14
Dazzling upsprung the *d* Cones Of Pyramids, *Timbuctoo* 168
Dead Love is *d*; (repeat) *Burial of Love* 8, 13
And when thou art *d*, Leander, *Hero to Leander* 30
The *d* skin withering on the fretted bone, *Lover's Tale i* 678
RISE, Britons, rise, if manhood be not *d*; *Britons, guard* 1
Deaf (Shame fall 'em they are *d* and blind) *The Grasshopper* 6
But thou art *d* as death; *The lintwhite* 11
Deal You may not, like yon tyrant, *d* in spies. *Sugg. by Reading* 20
Dean Your doctors and your proctors and your *d's* *Cambridge* 5
Dear black eyes, and brown and blue; I hold them all most *d*; *There are three things* 7
D room, the apple of my sight, *O darling room* 2
To our *d* kinsmen of the West, my friends, *Hands all Round* 59
Dearest SAINTED Juliet! *d* name! *To ——* 1
Rome's *d* daughter now is captive France, *Britons, guard* 31

E

Edge Could link his shallop to the fleeting *e*, *Timbuctoo* 145
Edict *e's* of his fear Are mellowed into music, *Love* 7
Effect each th' *e* Of separate impulse, *Timbuctoo* 126
Effulgence Fill'd with Divine *e*, circumfus'd, „ 50
Egypt Mysterious *E*, are thine obelisks *A Fragment* 12
Either Which droops low hung on *e* gate of life, *The Mystic* 32
Parted on *e* side her argent neck, *Lover's Tale i* 740
Eld Keen knowledges of low-embowèd *e*) *The Mystic* 30
An honourable *e* shall come upon thee. *Though night* 14
Elder which starr'd the night o' the *E* World? *Timbuctoo* 60
Eldorado Imperial *E* roof'd with gold: „ 24
Element The fierceness of the bounding *e*? „ 148
with the heat Of their infolding *e*; *Lover's Tale i* 615
Eloquence when hope died, part of her *e* Died „ 751
Elysian Seraphtrod, Wound thro' your great *E* solitudes, *Timbuctoo* 48
Embalming *E* with sweet tears the vacant shrine, *Lost Hope* 3
Emblem obelisks Graven with gorgeous *e's* undiscerned? *A Fragment* 13
Embowed *See* **Low-embowèd**
Embrace the billow will *e* thee with a kiss *Hero to Leander* 27
Spirit waits To *e* me in the sky. *Germ of 'Maud'* 34
Embracing thoughts Involving and *e* each with each *Timbuctoo* 116
Emerald And ever circling round their *e* cones In coronals and glories, „ 52
Shooting, singing, ever springing In and out the *e* glooms, *The Grasshopper* 42
Eminence aloft Upon his renown'd *E* *Timbuctoo* 171
Empereur 'Vive l'*E*' may follow by and bye; *Britons, guard* 25
Empery thine *e* Is over all: *Love* 10
Emphatic Who make the *e* One, by whom is all, *Sugg. by Reading* 81
Emptiness But lose themselves in utter *e*. *Love and Sorrow* 16
Empty All alone she sits and hears Echoes in his *e* hall, *Home they brought him* 4
I, screaming, from me flung The *e* phantom: *Lover's Tale ii* 213
Encircled *See* **Moon-encircled**
End Till the *e* of fears Cometh in the shroud, *Every day, etc.* 20
The *e* of day and beginning of night *Hesperides, Song iv* 9
For better so you fight for public *e's*; *Sugg. by Reading* 26
Endue *See* **Indue**
Endure Yet *e* unscathed Of changeful cycles *A Fragment* 8
Enduring But men of long *e* hopes, *New Timon* 17
not *e* To carry through the world *Timbuctoo* 237
Enemy There standeth our ancient *e*; (repeat) *English War Song* 23, 45
Hark! he shouteth—the ancient *e*! „ 24
Enfold thy hills *e* a City as fair *Timbuctoo* 59
Athwart the veils of evil which *e* thee *Love* 17
England Shout for *E*! Ho! for *E*! George for *E*! Merry *E*! *E* for aye! (repeat) *English War Song* 7, 18, 29, 40, 51
Than to shame merry *E* here. „ 17
Hold up the Lion of *E* on high (repeat) „ 27, 49
There is no land like *E* (repeat) *National Song* 1, 5, 19, 23
A health to *E*, every guest; *Hands all Round* 2
And the great name of *E* round and round. (repeat) „ 24, 48, 60
The thinking men of *E*, loathe a tyranny. *Sugg. by Reading* 12
Of *E* and her health of commonsense— „ 40
Farewell our *E's* flower, *God bless our Prince* 9
English There are no hearts like *E* hearts, Such hearts of oak as they be. *National Song* 3
There are no wives like *E* wives, „ 21
There are no maids like *E* maids, „ 25
Englishmen There are no men like *E*, „ 7
Enough Matter *e* for deploring *1865-1866* 8
Entwine *e* The indecision of my present mind *Timbuctoo* 138
Envenom heart deep moans Feed and *e*, *Lover's Tale i* 820
Enwoven *See* **Inwoven**
Epitaph An *e* that all may spy? *Burial of Love* 23
Eras'd pillars high Long time *e* from Earth: *Timbuctoo* 13
Erewhile E'en so my thoughts, *e* so low, „ 157
Essence Nor *e* nor eternal laws: *οἱ ῥέοντες* 11
An *e* less concentred than a man! *Sugg. by Reading* 82
Essential As bearing no *e* fruits of excellence. *Lover's Tale i* 385
Eternal The very throne of the *e* God: *Love* 6
Nor essence nor *e* laws: *οἱ ῥέοντες* 11
We shall lose *e* pleasure, Worth *e* want of rest. *Hesperides, Song i* 11
Eternity In *e* no future, In *e* no past. *The 'How' and the 'Why'* 6
Eternity (*continued*) One reflex from *e* on time, *The Mystic* 22
lived That intense moment thro' *e*. *Lover's Tale i* 496
Ether and an *e* of black hue, *The Mystic* 45
Ethereal if gold it were Or metal more *e*, *Timbuctoo* 177
Europe whose rapid interval Parts Afric from green *E*, „ 3
A health to *E's* honest men! *Hands all Round* 13
To *E's* better health we drink, „ 23
O speak to *E* through your guns! „ 51
Evanisheth Our life *e*: Oh! stay. *The lintwhite* 15
Even (*See also* **Evening**) Purplefringed with *e* and dawn. *Hesperides, Song iii* 14
thunders through your vacant courts At morn and *e*; *Cambridge* 10
Even-fall They brought him home at *e-f*: *Home they brought him* 2
Evening Hesper hateth Phosphor, *e* hateth morn. *Hesperides, Song iii* 15
Everchanging With triple arch of *e* bows, *Timbuctoo* 74
Every Expanding momently with *e* sight „ 118
Reacheth to *e* corner under Heaven, „ 224
E day hath its night: *E* night its morn: *Every day, etc.* 1
CHECK *e* outflash, *e* ruder sally Of thought and speech; *Check every outflash* 1
Looking warily *E* way, *Hesperides, Song i* 27
E flower and *e* fruit the redolent breath „ *iv* 1
A health to England, *e* guest; *Hands all Round* 2
a land of Love; Where Love was worshipp'd upon *e* height, Where Love was worshipp'd under *e* tree— *Lover's Tale i* 323
One rainy night, when *e* wind blew loud, „ 367
Evil (adj.) We likewise have our *e* things; *Hands all Round* 19
Like to the wild youth of an *e* king, *Lover's Tale i* 344
Evil (s) What hast thou to do with *e* (repeat) *The Grasshopper* 34, 40
selfwrought *e's* of unnumbered years, *Tears of Heaven* 4
SHALL the hag *E* die with the child of Good, *Shall the hag* 1
Athwart the veils of *e* which enfold thee *Love* 17
Evocation With mighty *e*, had updrawn *Lover's Tale i* 668
Ewe *e's* bleat On the solitary steeps, *Lotos-Eaters* 29
Exceeding his face, for it was wonderful With its *e* brightness, *Timbuctoo* 87
Excellence memory of that mental *e* Comes o'er me, „ 137
As bearing no essential fruits of *e*. *Lover's Tale i* 385
Exception I feel *E* to be character'd in fire. *Sugg. by Reading* 52
Excess Lest you go wrong from power in *e*. „ 10
Excitation spirit With supernatural *e* bound Within me, *Timbuctoo* 91
Excite She loves a little scandal which *e's*; *Sugg. by Reading* 57
Existence fields Of undefin'd *e* far and free. *Timbuctoo* 160
Expanding *E* momently with every sight And sound „ 118
Expectation Updrawn in *e* of her change— *Lover's Tale i* 597
Experience The stern *e's* of converse lives, *The Mystic* 8
Exploring 'Science enough and *e* *1865-1866* 6
Express'd love too high to be *e* Arrested in its sphere, *Lover's Tale i* 65
Exquisite There is no room so *e*, *O darling room* 4
A little room so *e*, „ 15
Extreme even Misery Forgot herself in that *e* distress, *Lover's Tale i* 628
Eye (*See also* **Eyne**) gazeth on Those *e's* which wear no light *Timbuctoo* 39
colour'd spots as dance athwart the *e's* „ 70
Open thine *e* and see.' „ 84
The starry glowing of his restless *e's*. „ 89
my mental *e* grew large With such a vast circumference „ 92
till the *e's* in vain Amid the wild unrest „ 128
the *e* could scan Through length of porch „ 179
fill'd My *e's* with irresistable sweet tears, „ 191
Visit his *e's* with visions, and his ears „ 206
They with dim *e's* Behold me darkling. „ 212
mystery of loveliness Unto all *e's*, „ 242
HIS *e's* in eclipse, Pale cold his lips, *Burial of Love* 1
In the weathered light Of the tearless *e* „ 22
My heart is lighted at thine *e's*, *To ——* 8
With glazèd *e* She looks at her grave: *I' the glooming light* 14
E's are worn away Till the end of fears *Every day, etc.* 19
Thine *e* in drops of gladness swims. *Hero to Leander* 18
Ye could not read the marvel in his *e*, *The Mystic* 4
Awful with most invariable *e's*. „ 24
with shining *e's* Smiling a godlike smile „ 27
Into her own blue *e's* so clear and deep, *Tears of Heaven* 7
e's dropt downward through the blue serene, *To a Lady Sleep.* 9
From my cold *e's* and melted it again. *Could I outwear* 14
strain Weak *e's* upon the glistering sands *Pallid thunderstricken* 5
Strain the hot spheres of his convulsèd *e's*, *Love* 37

Fear (verb) Who *f's* to die? Who *f's* to die? Is there any here who *f's* to die He shall find what he *f's*, and none shall grieve For the man who *f's* to die: — *English War Song* 1
scorn of the many shall cleave To the man who *f's* to die. — „ 6
Self-poised, nor *f's* to fall. — *D. of F. Women* 12
Take care thou dost not *f* to fall!' — *What time I wasted* 9
I *f* for you, as for some youthful king, — *Sugg. by Reading* 9
An honest isolation need not *f* The Court, — „ 15
Fearful weak lamp dips and winks Unto the *f* summoning without: — *Timbuctoo* 36
With which the *f* springtide flecks the lea, — *Love and Sorrow* 2
And with a *f* self-impelling joy Saw round her feet — *Lover's Tale i* 389
Feather two birds of glancing *f* Do woo each other, — *Dualisms* 8
Fed Memory tho' *f* by Pride Did wax — *Love, Pride, etc.* 11
unhappy sighs. *f* with my tears, — *Lover's Tale i* 674
Feeble The echo, *f* child of sound, — *Chorus* 12
Feed heart deep moans *F* and envenom, — *Lover's Tale i* 820
When the shrill storm blast *f's* it from behind, — „ *ii* 47
Feeding taught nothing, *f* on the soul. — *Cambridge* 14
Eye *f* upon eye with deep intent; — *Lover's Tale i* 64
Feel and to *f* My fullness; — *Timbuctoo* 214
I *f* there is something; but how and what? — *The 'How' and the 'Why'* 23
Severe and quick to *f* a civic sin, — *Sugg. by Reading* 4
I *f* the thousand cankers of our State, — „ 43
I *f* Exception to be character'd in fire. — „ 51
She *f's* not how the social frame is rack'd. — „ 56
Feeling A little *f* is a want of tact. — „ 58
blood, the breath, the *f* and the motion, — *Lover's Tale ii* 75
Feign No Tithon thou as poets *f* — *The Grasshopper* 5
Fell Came down upon my eyelids, and I *f*. — *Timbuctoo* 187
The Moslem myriads *f*, and fled before— — *Blow ye the trumpet* 11
falling, they *f* too, Crush'd link on link — *Lover's Tale i* 858
had shatter'd from The mountain, till they *f*, — „ *ii* 49
Felt I *f* my soul grow mighty, — *Timbuctoo* 90
now *f* Unutterable buoyancy and strength — „ 157
not *f* and known A higher than they see: — „ 211
hath *f* The vanities of after and before; — *The Mystic* 5
the year First *f* his youth and strength, — *Lover's Tale i* 306
Fere Thy art the fairest of thy *f's*, — *The lintwhite* 35
Fetter'd Thy spirit *f* with the bond of clay: — *Timbuctoo* 83
Fibre On those first-moved *f's* of the brain. — *Lover's Tale i* 21
Fibred wings which burn Fanlike and *f*, — *Timbuctoo* 156
Fie O *f*, you golden nothing, *f* You golden lie. — *The Ringlet* 43
Field (*See also* **Sandfield**) *f's* Of undefin'd existence far and free. — *Timbuctoo* 159
A gate and a *f* half ploughed, — *A gate and a field* 1
Sun peeped in from open *f*, — *Home they brought him* 6
Fierce The *f* old man—to take *his* name You bandbox. — *New Timon* 43
whose low-hung tresses, dipp'd In the *f* stream, — *Lover's Tale i* 375
Fierceness The *f* of the bounding element? — *Timbuctoo* 148
Fiery Part of a throne of *f* flame, — „ 181
The linkèd woes of many a *f* change Had purified, — *The Mystic* 9
Fight (s) charge to the *f*: Charge! charge to the *f*! — *English War Song* 47
We still were loyal in our wildest *f's*, — *Sugg. by Reading* 35
Fight (verb) Till we were left to *f* for truth alone. — *Britons, guard* 35
To *f* thy mother here alone, — *Hands all Round* 43
For better so you *f* for public ends; — *Sugg. by Reading* 26
Fill There are three things that *f* my heart with sighs — *There are three things* 1
Fill'd (*See also* **Globefilled**) *F* with Divine effulgence, circumfus'd, — *Timbuctoo* 50
dreams of old Which *f* the Earth with passing loveliness, — „ 79
f My eyes with irresistible sweet tears, — „ 190
I have *f* thy lips with power. — „ 215
And *f* the cup with dew. — *Lost Hope* 8
F with a finer air: — *D. of F. Women* 8
Film'd *f* the margents of the recent wound. — *Lover's Tale i* 764
Find He shall *f* what he fears, — *English War Song* 3
f The drain-cut levels of the marshy *l*,— — *Mablethorpe* 5
Fine And those *f* curses which he spoke; — *New Timon* 2
Finer Filled with a *f* air: — *D. of F. Women* 8
Fire Rapid as *f*, inextricably link'd, — *Timbuctoo* 117
Changed into *f*, and blown about with sighs. — *To ——* 9

Fire (*continued*) By secret *f* and midnight storms That wander — *Chorus* 5
flings Grand Music and redundant *f*, — „ 22
They stream like *f* in the skies; — *English War Song* 26
Through the water and the *f*. (repeat) — *National Song* 14, 32
The world is wasted with *f* and sword, — *Hesperides, Song iv* 22
But *f*, to blast the hopes of men. — *Hands all Round* 30
I feel Exception to be character'd in *f*. — *Sugg. by Reading* 52
Firmament Seemed with a cobweb *f* to link — *Lover's Tale i* 407
First I have rais'd thee higher to the Spheres of Heaven, Man's *f*, last home: — *Timbuctoo* 217
O Maiden, fresher than the *f* green leaf — *Love and Sorrow* 1
For the two *f* were not, but only seemed One shadow — *The Mystic* 20
First-moved begins to play On those *f-m* fibres of the brain. — *Lover's Tale i* 21
Fish Young *f'es*, on an April morn, — *Rosalind* 21
Five *F* links, a golden chain, are we, — *Hesperides, Song ii* 23
F links, a golden chain, are we, — „ *iv* 24
Fixed he in the centre *f*, Saw far on each side — *The Mystic* 33
My eyes, *f* upon hers, — *Lover's Tale i* 352
By the shuddering moonlight, *f* his eyes — 680
Flag takes his *f's* and waves them to the mob — *D. of F. Women* 5
Flake thick snow falls on her *f* by *f*, — *I' the glooming light* 20
Flame (s) ev'n as *f* draws air; But had their being in the heart of Man As air is th' life of *f*: — *Timbuctoo* 18
Part of a throne of fiery *f*, — „ 181
Love unreturn'd is like the fragrant *f* — *To ——* 5
a region of white *f*, Pure without heat, — *The Mystic* 43
Ringlet, I doom you to the *f*. — *The Ringlet* 50
Flame (verb) To *f* and sparkle and stream as of old, — „ 8
Flash (s) As with a momentary *f* of light — *Timbuctoo* 97
With a *f* of frolic scorn And keen delight, — *Rosalind* 15
Flash (verb) They *f* across the darkness of my brain, — *Lover's Tale i* 53
Flashing A curve of whitening, *f*, ebbing light! — *Timbuctoo* 63
Girt with a Zone of *f* gold beneath His breast, — „ 72
Her frantic city's *f* heats But fire, — *Hands all Round* 29
Flat Looking athwart the burning *f's*, — *A Fragment* 17
Flattering melody *f* the crisped Nile By columned Thebes. — „ 26
Fleck which the fearful springtide *f's* the lea, — *Love and Sorrow* 2
Flecked *See* **Silverfleckèd**
Fled The Moslem myriads fell, and *f* before— — *Blow ye the trumpet* 11
Fleet more *f* and strong Than its precursor, — *Timbuctoo* 127
Though thou art *f* of wing, Yet stay. — *The lintwhite* 24
Fleeting Could link his shallop to the *f* edge, — *Timbuctoo* 145
They from the blosmy brere Call to the *f* year, — *The lintwhite* 5
the great Pyramids Broad-based amid the *f* sands, — *A Fragment* 10
Fleetness nature of itself With its own *f*. — *Timbuctoo* 143
Fling from the centre *f's* Grand music — *Chorus* 21
Thy golden largess *f*, — *The lintwhite* 22
Break through your iron shackles—*f* them far. — *Blow ye the trumpet* 4
Flinging Then *f* myself down upon my knees — *Lover's Tale i* 789
Flit Lets the great world *f* from him, — *D. of F. Women* 10
Float Down an ideal stream they ever *f*, — *Pallid thunderstricken* 2
Floating Like a swol'n river's gushings in still night Mingled with *f* music, — *Timbuctoo* 194
Nor blot with *f* shades the solar light. — *Shall the hag* 14
And onward *f* in a full, dark wave, — *Lover's Tale i* 739
Flood We drink to thee across the *f*, — *Hands all Round* 38
Flooded stars Were *f* over with clear glory — *Timbuctoo* 9
Flooding freshflushing springtime calls To the *f* waters cool, — *Rosalind* 20
F its angry cheek with odorous tears. — *Lover's Tale i* 565
Flow Nor the rivers *f*, nor the sweet birds sing, — *Burial of Love* 29
How scorn and ruin, pain and hate could *f*: — *Pallid thunderstricken* 10
And all things *f* like a stream. (repeat) — *οἱ ῥέοντες* 8, 16
from his mother's eyes *F* over the Arabian bay, — *A Fragment* 24
Flower (s) (*See also* **Summerflowers**) Moving his crest to all sweet plots of *f's* — *Could I outwear* 7
I smelt a wildweed *f* alone; — *O sad no more!* 4
From an old garden where no *f* bloometh, — *Me my own fate* 7
Every *f* and every fruit the redolent breath — *Hesperides, Song iv* 1
Farewell our England's *f*, — *God bless our Prince* 9
Creep down into the bottom of the *f*. — *Lover's Tale i* 560
Flower (verb) Seasons *f* and fade; — *Every day, etc.* 6
Flowerbell Two bees within a chrystal *f* rockèd — *Dualisms* 1
Flowerèd Pushing the thick roots aside Of the singing *f* grasses, — *The Grasshopper* 38
Through and through the *f* heather. — *Dualisms* 5

Flowering Your f Capes and your gold-sanded bays — Timbuctoo 45
Stays on the f arch of the bough, — Hesperides, Song iv 18
Flowery And in and out the woodbine's f arches — Check every outflash 11
Floweth And the sap to three-fold music f, — Hesperides, Song i 19
Flowing faery light or cloud, F Southward, — Timbuctoo 7
F between the clear and polish'd stems, — „ 51
lordly music f from Th' illimitable years. — „ 218
Time f in the middle of the night, — The Mystic 39
Seas at my feet were f Waves on the shingle — 1865-1866 10
Flown Till your balls fly as their true shafts have f. — Briton's, guard 47
Flung f strange music on the howling winds, — Timbuctoo 80
would have f himself From cloud to cloud, — Lover's Tale i 303
Flush'd face Was starry-fair, not pale, tenderly f — „ 75
Flushing See **Freshflushing**
Flute See **Lotosflute**
Fly rocks stand still, and the light clouds f? — The 'How' and the 'Why' 14
Then I lose it: it will f: — Germ of 'Maud' 25
How fairy-like you f! — Skipping-rope 6
Till your balls f as their true shafts have flown. — Britons, guard 47
Foam (s) no more roam, On the loud hoar f, — Lotos-Eaters 19
Foam (verb) Let them clash together, f and fall. — Hesperides, Song iii 9
Foamfountains narwhale swalloweth His f in the sea. — Lotos-Eaters 8
Foam-white And the f-w waters pour; — „ 32
Foe Our freedom's foemen are her f's, — Hands all Round 55
For her there lie in wait millions of f's, — Sugg. by Reading 59
Foeman Our freedom's foemen are her foes, — Hands all Round 55
Fold See **Three-fold**
Fold (s) Rolled together in purple f's. — Hesperides, Song ii 10
Fold (verb) I dare not f My arms about thee— — Oh, Beauty 5
Folded See **Triple-folded**
Foldest Thou f, like a golden atmosphere, — Love 5
Folding F the slaughter of the sacrifice — To —— 6
Follow My soul shall f thee! — Hero to Leander 31
go not, go not yet, Or I will f thee. — „ 41
But yet my lonely spirit f's thine, As round the rolling earth night f's day: — Me my own fate 9
'Vive l'Empereur' may f by and bye; — Britons, guard 25
Following and f, plunged Into the dizzy chasm — Lover's Tale i 369
Fool You f's, you'll want them all again. — Hands all Round 32
That wish to keep their people f's; — „ 54
To charm a lower sphere of fulminating f's. — Sugg. by Reading 30
O f's, we want a manlike God and Godlike men! — „ 84
And a f may say his say; — The Ringlet 18
Foot (See also **Mountain-foot**) Vaulting on thine airy feet. — The Grasshopper 10
I only ask to sit beside thy feet. — Oh, Beauty 3
Seas at my feet were flowing Waves on the shingle — 1865-1866 10
Saw round her feet the country far away, — Lover's Tale i 390
Planting my feet against this mound of time — „ 492
Forehead unfading f's of the Saints in Heaven? — Timbuctoo 54
a snake her f clips And skins the colour — Pallid thunderstricken 13
About her f wound it, — Anacreontics 11
As I said, with these She crown'd her f. — Lover's Tale i 349
Did brush my f in their to-and-fro: — „ 736
Foreign Why stay they there to guard a f throne? — Britons, guard 41
Foretaste The triumph of this f, — Lover's Tale i 515
Forgave I f you all the blame, — To C. North 6
Forgive I could not f the praise, — „ 8
Forgot Almost f even to move again. — Lover's Tale i 353
Misery F herself in that extreme distress, — „ 628
Known when their faces are f in the land. — „ 804
Forgotten (See also **Half-forgotten**) Thy pleasant wiles F, — Burial of Love 16
Forlorn love! art thou f, And unrevenged? — „ 14
Be not all f; — Every day, etc. 31
Because the earth hath made her state f — Tears of Heaven 3
The hollow at heart shall crouch f, — English War Song 12
Form The cruellest f of perfect scorn, — Burial of Love 18
Colossal, without f, or sense, or sound, — The Mystic 14
the countless f's Of living things, — Chorus 7
There is no bright f Doth not cast a shade— — Every day, etc. 9
Fair maiden f's moving like melodies), — There are three things 3
Like them, you bicker less for truth than f's. — Sugg. by Reading 76
ceasing from All contemplation of all f's, — Lover's Tale i 67
Forward One f, one respectant, three but one; — The Mystic 18
Fought Although we f the banded world alone, — Britons, guard 59
Found The cause is nowhere f in rhyme. — Who can say 8
Fountain (See also **Foamfountains**) Calls to him by the f to uprise. — Love 35
Fountainpregnant f mountains riven To shapes — Chorus 3
Four Why two and two make f? — The 'How' and the 'Why' 13
Fourfacèd to f corners of the sky; — The Mystic 16
Four-and-twenty 'The f-a-t Blackbirds' 'Banbury Cross,' — Lover's Tale i 286
Fourfacèd presences F to four corners of the sky; — The Mystic 16
Fragrance in The f of its complicated glooms — Timbuctoo 227
The blossom and the f. — Lover's Tale i 626
Fragrant Love unreturned is like the f flame — To —— 5
And crushing the thick f reeds he lies, — Love 32
Creeping under the f bark, — Hesperides, Song i 23
Frail A dream as f as those of ancient Time?' — Timbuctoo 62
Frailest Hopes did sway from that Which hung the f: — Lover's Tale i 858
Frame She feels not how the social f is rack'd. — Sugg. by Reading 56
France We hate not F, but this man's heart of stone. — Britons, guard 17
We hate not F, but F has lost her voice This man is F, the man they call her choice. — „ 19
Rome's dearest daughter now is captive F, — „ 31
What health to F, if F be she Whom martial progress — Hands all Round 25
To F, the wiser F, we drink, my friends, — „ 35
To that half-pagan harlot kept by F! — Sugg. by Reading 70
Frantic Her f city's flashing heats But fire, — Hands all Round 29
Free through the trackless fields Of undefin'd existence far and f. — Timbuctoo 160
linkèd woes of many a fiery change Had purified, and chastened, and made f. — The Mystic 10
Thou art so glad and f, And as light as air; — Grasshopper 24
But a short youth sunny and f. — „ 29
Come along! we alone of the earth are f; — English War Song 34
He is weak! we are strong; he is slave, we are f; — „ 38
Will he dare to battle with the f? — „ 46
We are the sons of freedom, We are f. (repeat) — National Song 18, 36
Yet winds the pathway f to all!— — What time I wasted 8
better to be f Than vanquish all the world in arms. — Hands all Round 27
And the f speech that makes a Briton known. — Britons, guard 29
F subjects of the kindliest of all thrones, — Sugg. by Reading 71
Was not the wide world f, — Lover's Tale i 693
Freedom Our glory is our f, (repeat) — National Song 15, 33
We are the sons of f, We are free. (repeat) — „ 17, 35
All f vanish'd, — Britons, guard 9
And murder was her f overthrown. — „ 23
When war against our f springs! — Hands all Round 50
Our f's foemen are her foes, — „ 55
Whereby to guard our F from offence— — Sugg. by Reading 38
Freeman A f is, I doubt not, freest here; — „ 13
Freest A freeman is, I doubt not, f here; — „ 13
French For the F the Pope may shrive 'em, (repeat) — National Song 9, 27
As for the F, God speed 'em (repeat) — „ 11, 29
Frequent Her gardens f with the stately Palm, — Timbuctoo 233
Fresh and indue i' the spring Hues of f youth, — Could I outwear 3
F as the dawn before the day, F as the early seasmell blown — Rosalind 27
Fresher O Maiden, f than the first green leaf — Love and Sorrow 1
Freshflushing f springtime calls To the flooding waters — Rosalind 19
Freshness that never falls Away from f, — „ 17
Fretful But Misery, like a f, wayward child, — Lover's Tale i 696
Fretted The dead skin withering on the f bone, — „ 678
Friend Europe's better health we drink, my f's, — Hands all Round 23
To France, the wiser France, we drink, my f's, — „ 35
kinsmen of the West, my f's, (repeat) — „ 47, 59
You should be all the nobler, O my f's. — Sugg. by Reading 28
Frightful Go, f omens. — „ 85
Fringèd (See also **Purplefringed**) O thou whose f lids I gaze upon, — To a Lady Sleep. 1
Frockèd Both in blosmwhite silk are f: — Dualisms 16
Frolic With a flash of f scorn And keen delight, — Rosalind 15
Front Stood out a pillar'd f of burnish'd gold — Timbuctoo 175
Fronting yet again, three shadows, f one, — The Mystic 17
Frozen This to itself hath drawn the f rain From my cold eyes — Could I outwear 13
Fruit And doth the f of her dishonour reap. — Tears of Heaven 5
The golden apple, the golden apple, the hallowed f, — Hesperides, Song i 1
Up to the f, Creeping under the fragrant bark, — „ 22
Round about the hallowed f tree curled— — „ ii 13
Every flower and every f the redolent breath — „ iv 1

Fruit (*continued*) The golden apple, the golden apple, the hallowed *f*, *Hesperides, Song* 30
As bearing no essential *f's* of excellence. *Lover's Tale i* 385
Fruitage The luscious *f* clustereth mellowly, *Hesperides, Song iv* 19
Fruit-tree How many the mystic *f-t* holds, „ *ii* 8
Full Upon the outward verge and bound alone Of *f* beatitude. *Timbuctoo* 96
Till Love have his *f* revenge. *Burial of Love* 30
are *f* of strange Astonishment and boundless change. (repeat) *Chorus* 9, 19, 29
Alas! that eyes so *f* of light Should be so wandering! *The lintwhite* 26
Thy locks are *f* of sunny sheen In rings of gold yronne, „ 28
Holy and bright, round and *f*, bright and blest, *Hesperides, Song iv* 11
Her eyes, I saw, were *f* of tears in the morn, *Lover's Tale i* 728
And onward floating in a *f*, dark wave, „ 739
laden with mournful thanks, From my *f* heart: „ 749
Solemn but splendid, *f* of shapes and sounds, „ 799
Fullfaced But when the *f* sunset yellowly Stays on the flowering arch of the bough, *Hesperides, Song iv* 17
Fullness and to feel My *f*; *Timbuctoo* 215
Fullsailed Rosalind *F* before a vigorous wind, *Rosalind* 10
Full-voiced when *f-v* Winter roofs The headland *Timbuctoo* 203
Fulminating To charm a lower sphere of *f* fools. *Sugg. by Reading* 30
Furrowed *See* **Deep-furrowed**
Fusty I could *not* forgive the praise, *F* Christopher. *To C. North* 9
Future In eternity no *f*, In eternity no past. *The 'How' and the 'Why'* 6
Perchance assimilated all our tastes And *f* fancies. *Lover's Tale i* 239

G

Gain pallid thunderstricken sigh for *g*, *Pallid thunderstricken* 1
Galaxy clear *G* Shorn of its hoary lustre, *Timbuctoo* 105
Gall by a spell Did change them into *g*; *Love, Pride, etc.* 10
Memory tho' fed by Pride Did wax so thin on *g*, „ 12
Gallant A *g* cavalier *Sans peur et sans reproche*, *The Grasshopper* 18
Gambol (s) when the winds are wild With *g's*, *Timbuctoo* 203
The summer midges wove their wanton *g*, *Check every outflash* 12
Gambol (verb) As they *g*, lilygarlands ever stringing: *Dualisms* 15
Gander 'The *G*' and 'The man of Mitylene,' *Lover's Tale i* 287
Garden Her *g's* frequent with the stately Palm, *Timbuctoo* 233
From an old *g* where no flower bloometh, *Me my own fate* 7
Garland (*See also* **Lilygarlands**) A *g* for Lenora. *Anacreontics* 7
Garment The snowy skirting of a *g* hung, *Timbuctoo* 182
Gate low hung on either *g* of life, *The Mystic* 32
Saw far on each side through the grated *g's* „ 34
Clad in light by golden *g's*, *Germ of 'Maud'* 32
A *G* and a field half ploughed, *A gate and a field* 1
the angels, The watchers at heaven's *g*, *Lover's Tale i* 616
Gather all the day heaven *g's* back her tears *Tears of Heaven* 6
g from afar The hosts to battle: *Blow ye the trumpet* 1
Gathering from this impulse Continuing and *g* ever, *Lover's Tale i* 494
Gave She that *g* you 's bought and sold, *The Ringlet* 33
Ringlet, She *g* you me, and said, „ 40
Gay *See* **Golden-gay**
Gaze (s) where no *g* Might rest, stood open, *Timbuctoo* 178
Methinks I could have sooner met that *g*! *Lover's Tale i* 684
Gaze (verb) Of those that *g* upon the noonday Sun. *Timbuctoo* 71
THOU whose fringèd lids I *g* upon, *To a Lady Sleep.* 1
Albeit we *g* not on thy glories near, *Love* 2
Making their day dim, so we *g* on thee. „ 23
And now—methinks I *g* upon thee now, „ 29
Gaz'd I *g* upon the sheeny coast beyond, *Timbuctoo* 10
So *g* I on the ruins of that thought *Lover's Tale ii* 71
Gazeth *g* on Those eyes which wear no light *Timbuctoo* 38
Gazing whose eyes are dim With *g* on the light *Lover's Tale i* 486
Genius Before the awful *G* of the place *Timbuctoo* 33
Gentleman Nor like a *g* at ease With moral breadth *New Timon* 27
George *G* for England! (repeat) *English War Song* 9, 20, 31, 42, 53
Get Go, *g* you gone, you muse and mope— *Skipping-rope* 7
Ghastful Oh! rather had some loathly *g* brow, *Lover's Tale i* 676
Ghastly and the streets with *g* faces throng'd *Timbuctoo* 29
Tho' its *g* sister glide And be moved around me still *Germ of 'Maud'* 18
Ghost By a dull mechanic *g* „ 7
Giant where the *G* of old Time infixed *Timbuctoo* 11
WHERE is the *G* of the Sun, *A Fragment* 1
Gigantic *G* daughter of the West, *Hands all Round* 37
Gilded somewhere in death They sleep with staring eyes and *g* lips, *A Fragment* 29
Gird such as *g* The unfading foreheads *Timbuctoo* 53
Girded *See* **Planet-girded**
Girding The heavy thunder's *g* might, *Chorus* 13
Girl Who killed the *g's* and thrill'd the boys *New Timon* 9
And a lad may wink, and a *g* may hint, *The Ringlet* 17
Girt *G* with a Zone of flashing gold *Timbuctoo* 72
Give speak low, and *g* up wholly Thy spirit *Check every outflash* 2
If you will *g* me one, but one, *The Ringlet* 3
Given I have *g thee* To understand my presence, *Timbuctoo* 213
Has *g* all my faith a turn? *The Ringlet* 52
earth beneath me yawning *g* Sign of convulsion; *Lover's Tale i* 611
Giveth It *g* out a constant melody That drowns „ 534
Glad Thou art so *g* and free, *The Grasshopper* 24
Green springtide, April promise, *g* new year Of Being, *Lover's Tale i* 277
Gladness Thine eye in drops of *g* swims. *Hero to Leander* 18
self-upborne With such *g*, as, *Rosalind* 18
Glancing Over a stream two birds of *g* feather *Dualisms* 8
Glare The lawless comets as they *g*, *Chorus* 27
Glazèd With *g* eye She looks at her grave: *I' the glooming light* 14
Glide Both alike, they *g* together Side by side: *Dualisms* 10
Tho' its ghastly sister *g* *Germ of 'Maud'* 18
Glimpse And *g* of multitudes of multitudes *Timbuctoo* 183
Glistering Weak eyes upon the *g* sands that robe The understream. *Pallid thunderstricken* 5
Globe bore *g's* Of wheeling suns, or stars, *Timbuctoo* 171
And branching silvers of the central *g*, *Pallid thunderstricken* 8
Glows rubylike the far-up crimson *g*, *D. of F. Women* 7
Globefilled The *g* arch that, cleaving air, *Chorus* 25
Gloom springing In and out the emerald *g's*, *The Grasshopper* 42
your moonlight halls, your cedarn *g's*, *Timbuctoo* 43
Do pass from *g* to glory, „ 153
complicated *g's* And cool impleachèd twilights. „ 227
The troublous autumn's sallow *g*, *Chorus* 17
shalt thou pierce the woven *g's* of truth; *Though night* 11
Hallowed in awful chasms the wheeling *g*, *Love* 22
Gloometh Alone my hopeless melancholy *g*, *Me my own fate* 5
Glooming I' the *g* light Of middle night, *I' the glooming light* 1
Glorious When I must render up this *g* home To keen *Discovery*: *Timbuctoo* 243
And dross to gold with *g* alchemy, *Though night, etc.* 7
And dazzled to the heart with *g* pain. *There are three things* 14
By diminution made most *g*, *Lover's Tale i* 71
I well remember, It was a *g* morning, „ 301
But grow upon them like a *g* vision „ 797
Glory stars Were flooded over with clear *g* *Timbuctoo* 9
round their emerald cones In coronals and *glories*, „ 53
it was play'd about With its peculiar *g*. „ 57
And circled with the *g* of living light „ 75
Do pass from gloom to *g*, „ 153
But the *g* of the place Stood out „ 174
wrapt about with clouds Of *g* of Heaven. „ 200
showering down the *g* of lightsome day, *Tears of Heaven* 8
Albeit we gaze not on thy *glories* near, *Love* 2
Our *g* is our freedom, (repeat) *National Song* 15, 33
In the midnoon the *g* of old Rhodes, *A Fragment* 2
Thy spirit, circled with a living *g*, *Me my own fate* 3
The *g* unsealèd, *Hesperides, Song iii* 3
with many a name Whose *g* will not die. *D. of F. Women* 16
I had merged *G* in *g*, *Lover's Tale i* 516
Glory-circled and thou wert then A center'd *g-c* Memory, *Timbuctoo* 21
Gloss bramble and the shining *g* Of ivy-leaves, *Lover's Tale i* 373
Glossed *See* **Blue-glossèd**
Glossy Burn, you *g* heretic, burn, Burn, burn. *The Ringlet* 53
Glow (s) And in the *g* of sallow Summertide, *Timbuctoo* 201
Glow (verb) *G's* rubylike the far-up crimson globe, *D. of F. Women* 7
Glowing light Of the great angel mind which look'd from out The starry *g* of his restless eyes. *Timbuctoo* 89
and the opal width Of her small *g* lakes, „ 102
The naked summer's *g* birth, *Chorus* 16

Gnarlèd All round about The *g* bole of the charmèd tree, *Hesperides, Song iv* 29
Go The world is somewhat; it *goes* on somehow; *The 'How' and the 'Why'* 21
Why the life *goes* when the blood is spilt? „ 32
G—carry him to his dark deathbed; *Burial of Love* 11
OH *g* not yet, my love, (repeat) *Hero to Leander* 1, 32
Leander! *g* not yet. „ 38
Oh! *g* not, *g* not yet, „ 40
Let the dismal face *g* by, *Germ of 'Maud'* 23
G, get you gone, you muse and mope— *Skipping-rope* 7
There must no man *g* back to bear the tale: *Britons, guard* 56
Lest you *g* wrong from power in excess. *Sugg. by Reading* 10
G, frightful omens. „ 85
God Offered to *G's* upon an altarthrone; *To —* 7
Before the face of *G* didst breath and move, *Love* 3
The very throne of the eternal *G*: „ 6
Shout for *G* and our right! *English War Song* 50
As for the French, *G* speed 'em (repeat) *National Song* 11, 29
'*G* save the Queen' is here a truer cry. *G* save the Nation, The toleration, *Britons, guard* 26
Too much we make our Ledgers, *G's*. *Hands all Round* 20
G the tyrant's cause confound! (repeat) „ 22, 34, 46, 58
O fools, we want a manlike *G* and Godlike men! *Sugg. by Reading* 84
G bless our Prince and Bride! *G* keep their lands allied, *God bless our Prince* 1
G save the Queen! (repeat) „ 3, 7, 10
G bless thy marriage-day, *G* bless the Queen. „ 13
I pray'd aloud to *G* that he would hold *Lover's Tale i* 791
Goddess shall see The British *G*, *Sugg. by Reading* 54
Godlike Who looks for *G* greatness here „ 53
O fools, we want a manlike God and *G* men! „ 84
with shining eyes Smiling a *g* smile *The Mystic* 28
Goest Thou *g* and returnest to His Lips *Love* 12
Going Wanderers coming and *g* *1865-1866* 7
Gold Imperial Eldorado roof'd with *g*: *Timbuctoo* 24
Zone of flashing *g* beneath His breast, „ 72
front of burnish'd *g* Interminably high, if *g* it were „ 175
And dross to *g* with glorious alchemy, *Though night* 7
Cathedralled caverns of thick-ribbèd *g* *Pallid thunderstricken* 7
But Hatred in a *g* cave sits below, „ 11
in mail of argent light Shot into *g*, „ 13
Liquid *g*, honeysweet thro' and thro'. *Hesperides, Song i* 24
the apple of *g* hangs over the sea, „ *iv* 23
ruthless host is bought with plunder'd *g*, *Britons, guard* 7
Thy locks are full of sunny sheen In rings of *g* yronne, *The lintwhite* 29
then shall I know it is all true *g* *The Ringlet* 7
I that took you for true *g*, „ 32
Golden *G* calm and storm Mingle day by day. *Every day, etc.* 7
To-night the roaring brine Will rend thy *g* tresses *Hero to Leander* 24
Lighting on the *g* blooms? *The Grasshopper* 44
Thou foldest, like a *g* atmosphere, *Love* 5
they roam together Under a summervault of *g* weather; *Dualisms* 18
Thy *g* largess fling, *The lintwhite* 22
The *g* apple, the *g* apple, the hallowed fruit, *Hesperides, Song i* 1
Look to him, father, lest he wink, and the *g* apple be stol'n away. „ *ii* 11
If the *g* apple be taken The world will be overwise. „ 21
Five links, a *g* chain, are we, Hesper, the dragon, and sisters three, Bound about the *g* tree „ 23
The *g* apple stol'n away, „ *iii* 4
Five links, a *g* chain, are we, „ *iv* 24
The *g* apple, the *g* apple, the hallowed fruit, „ 30
We will abide in the *g* vale Of the Lotos-land, *Lotos-Eaters* 26
To its Archetype that waits Clad in light by *g* gates, *Germ of 'Maud'* 32
O fie, you *g* nothing, fie You *g* lie. *The Ringlet* 43
And from the *g* threshold had down-roll'd Their heaviest thunder, *Lover's Tale i* 617
May their days be *g* days, „ 794
Erewhile close couch'd in *g* happiness, „ *ii* 79
Golden-circled A center'd *g-c* Memory, *Timbuctoo* 21
Goldencored fruitage clustereth mellowly, Goldenkernalled, *g*, *Hesperides, Song iv* 20
Golden-gay ringlets, That look so *g-g*, *The Ringlet* 2
'My ringlet, my ringlet, That art so *g-g*, „ 14
Golden-gay (*continued*) O Ringlet, You still are *g-g*, *The Ringlet* 28
Goldenkernelled fruitage clustereth mellowly, *G*, goldencored, *Hesperides, Song iv* 20
Goldenlockèd Mid May's darling *g*, *Dualisms* 21
Gold-sanded Your flowering Capes and your *g-s* bays *Timbuctoo* 45
Gone Delight is with thee *g*, Oh! stay. *The lintwhite* 33
Old Memphis hath *g* down: *A Fragment* 27
Surely all pleasant things had *g* before, *O sad no more!* 7
Go, get you *g*, you muse and mope— *Skipping-rope* 7
Good SHALL the hag Evil die with the child of *G*, *Shall the hag* 1
Nor *g* nor ill, nor light nor shade, *οἱ ῥέοντες* 10
O you, the Press! what *g* from you might spring! *Sugg. by Reading* 7
All *g* things are in the west, *Hesperides, Song iv* 14
'Tis a phantom fair and *g* I can call it to my side, *Germ of 'Maud'* 15
'They call this man as *g* as *me*.' *New Timon* 32
Goodly So on an oaken sprout A *g* acorn grew; *Lost Hope* 6
Gorgeous are thine obelisks Graven with *g* emblems undiscerned? *A Fragment* 13
Graceful Backward drooping his *g* head. *Burial of Love* 7
Gracious As towards the *g* light I bow'd, *What time I wasted* 4
Grain I saw The smallest *g* that dappled *Timbuctoo* 99
Grand Each sun which from the centre flings *G* music and redundant fire, *Chorus* 22
Grant I *g* you one of the great Powers on earth, *Sugg. by Reading* 23
Grasp costly casket in the *g* Of memory? *Lover's Tale i* 101
Grass For her the green *g* shall not spring, *Burial of Love* 28
Of the singing flowerèd *g'es*, *The Grasshopper* 38
where the *g* was warm where I had lain, *Lover's Tale i* 790
Grassgreen tuskèd seahorse walloweth In a stripe of *g* calm, *Lotos-Eaters* 5
Grasshopper I would dwell with thee, Merry *g*, *The Grasshopper* 23
Grated Saw far on each side through the *g* gates *The Mystic* 34
Grave she hath half delved her own deep *g*. *I' the glooming light* 7
With glazèd eye She looks at her *g*: „ 15
Come along! we will dig their *g's*. *English War Song* 39
Will it lead me to the *g*? *Germ of 'Maud'* 24
and with the shock Half dug their own *g's*), *Lover's Tale ii* 50
Graven obelisks *G* with gorgeous emblems *A Fragment* 13
Gray (*See also* **Silver-gray**) *G* sand banks and pale sunsets —dreary wind, *Mablethorpe* 7
Great As when in some *g* City where the walls Shake, *Timbuctoo* 28
Wound thro' your *g* Elysian solitudes, „ 48
and the light Of the *g* angel mind which look'd „ 88
All th' intricate and labyrinthine veins Of the *g* vine of *Fable*, „ 222
And the *g* bird sits on the opposite bough, *The 'How' and the 'Why'* 28
but only seemed One shadow in the midst of a *g* light, *The Mystic* 21
Of changeful cycles the *g* Pyramids *A Fragment* 9
the poet at his will Lets the *g* world flit from him, *D. of F. Women* 10
To this *g* cause of Freedom drink, my friends, *Hands all Round* 11
And the *g* name of England round and round. (repeat) „ 24, 48, 60
To our *g* kinsmen of the West, my friends, „ 47
With such a heat as lives in *g* creative rhymes. *Sugg. by Reading* 6
I grant you one of the *g* Powers on earth, „ 23
The hogs who can believe in nothing *g*, „ 45
Greatness We move so far from *g*, that I feel „ 51
Who looks for Godlike *g* here shall see „ 53
Grecian And here the *G* ships did seem to be. *Mablethorpe* 4
Green (*See also* **Blue-green, Grassgreen**) whose rapid interval Parts Afric from *g* Europe, *Timbuctoo* 3
Where are ye Thrones of the Western wave, fair Islands *g*? „ 42
For her the *g* grass shall not spring, *Burial of Love* 28
O MAIDEN, fresher than the first *g* leaf *Love and Sorrow* 1
And Oberwinter's vineyards *g*, *O darling room* 8
G springtide, April promise, glad new year *Lover's Tale i* 277
Think not thy tears will make my name grow *g*,— „ 806
Greenness And taken away the *g* of my life, „ 625
Grew my mental eye *g* large With such a vast circumference *Timbuctoo* 92
G thrillingly distinct and keen. „ 98
So on an oaken sprout A goodly acorn *g*; *Lost Hope* 6
ere the Czar *G* to this strength among his deserts cold; *Blow ye the trumpet* 6
Grief *G* and sadness steal Symbols of each other; *Every day, etc.* 25
bitter *g* Doth hold the other half in sovranty. *Love and Sorrow* 4
O *G* and Shame if while I preach of laws *Sugg. by Reading* 37

Grief (*continued*) And still bewept my *g*. *Lover's Tale i* 733
Grieve none shall *g* For the man who fears to die: *English War Song* 3
Groan Why the heavy oak *g's*, *The 'How' and the 'Why'* 15
Gross and few there be So *g* of heart *Timbuctoo* 211
Grot old *g's* Rock-hewn and sealed for ever. *A Fragment* 30
Ground had birth In that blest *g* *Timbuctoo* 56
You cast to *g* the hope which once was mine, *Lost Hope* 1
solid shining *g* Stream from beneath him *D. of F. Women* 2
Grovell'd *g* in the slime Of this dull world, *Timbuctoo* 149
Grow I felt my soul *g* mighty, „ 90
G closer to my heart. *Hero to Leander* 8
But *g* upon them like a glorious vision *Lover's Tale i* 797
Think not thy tears will make my name *g* green,— „ 806
Growing The *g* murmurs of the Polish war! *Blow ye the trumpet* 8
Alas, our Church! alas, her *g* ills, *Sugg. by Reading* 67
Growth *g* of shadowing leaf and clusters rare, *Timbuctoo* 223
Unto the *g* of body and of mind; *Lover's Tale ii* 74
Guard *G* it well, *g* it warily, *Hesperides, Song i* 2
G the apple night and day, „ 28
G it well, *g* it warily, „ *iv* 31
So to *g* my life from ill, *Germ of 'Maud'* 17
Britons, *G* your own. (repeat) *Britons, guard* 6, 12, 18, 24, 30, 36
Why stay they there to *g* a foreign throne? Seamen, *g* your own. *Britons, guard* 41
Yeomen, *g* your own. „ 48
We swear to *g* our own. „ 60
Heaven *g* them from her tyrants' jails! *Hands all Round* 14
Whereby to *g* our Freedom from offence— *Sugg. by Reading* 38
Guest A health to England, every *g*; *Hands all Round* 2
Gulf Have hallowed out a valley and a *g* *Lover's Tale i* 26
Gulph he passeth by, And *g's* himself in sands, *Timbuctoo* 237
Gun O speak to Europe thro' your *g's*! *Hands all Round* 51
Gushed both my eyes *g* out with tears. *O sad no more!* 6
Gushing Like a swol'n river's *g's* in still night *Timbuctoo* 193

H

Hag Shall the *h* Evil die with the child of Good, *Shall the hag* 1
Hail With points of blastborne *h* their heated eyne! „ 11
Hair her *h* falls loose; Her shoulders are bare; *I' the glooming light* 9
Pleached with her *h*, in mail of argent light *Pallid thunderstricken* 12
Looking under silver *h* with a silver eye. *Hesperides, Song ii* 2
Half that I said to thee That thou hast *h* my heart, for bitter grief Doth hold the other *h* in sovranty. *Love and Sorrow* 4
H round the mantling night is drawn, *Hesperides, Song iii* 13
A gate and a field *h* ploughed, *A gate and a field* 1
You never look but *h* content: *New Timon* 26
If *h* the little soul is dirt? „ 36
Mantling her form *h* way. *Lover's Tale i* 741
Half-bursten brow, *H-b* from the shroud, „ 677
Half-forgotten Less vivid than a *h-f* dream, *Timbuctoo* 136
Half-light *H-l*, half-shadow, let my spirit sleep *Love and Sorrow* 17
Half-open From an *h-o* lattice looked at *me*. *There are three things* 12
Half-pagan To that *h-p* harlot kept by France! *Sugg. by Reading* 70
Half-shadow Half-light, *h-s*, let my spirit sleep *Love and Sorrow* 17
Hall your moonlight *h's*, your cedarn glooms, *Timbuctoo* 43
length of porch and lake and boundless *h*, „ 180
Therefore your *h's*, your ancient colleges, *Cambridge* 1
sits and hears Echoes in his empty *h*, *Home they brought him* 4
Hallowed *H* in awful chasms of wheeling gloom, *Love* 22
The golden apple, the golden apple, the *h* fruit, *Hesperides, Song i* 1
Round about the *h* fruit tree curled— „ *ii* 13
The golden apple, the golden apple, the *h* fruit, „ *iv* 30
Fair fall this *h* hour, *God bless our Prince* 8
Hamlet Tilth, *h*, mead and mound: *D. of F. Women* 4
Hand Bathes the cold *h* with tears, *Timbuctoo* 38
I did veil My vision with both *h's*, „ 69
With ministering *h* he rais'd me up; „ 188
Might I but kiss thy *h*! *Oh, Beauty* 5
A dapper boot—a little *h*— *New Timon* 35
Yet *h's* all round! *Hands all Round* 21
You hide the *h* that writes: *Sugg. by Reading* 25
Hand (*continued*) In eager haste I shook him by the *h*; *Lover's Tale i* 788
pray'd aloud to God that he would hold The *h* of blessing over Lionel, „ 792
Hang the apple of gold *h's* over the sea, *Hesperides, Song iv* 23
take my skipping-rope And *h* yourself thereby. *Skipping-rope* 12
There *h* within the heavens a dark disgrace, *Sugg. by Reading* 41
Hanging Hateful with *h* cheeks, a withered brood, *Shall the hag* 4
Hanno Zidonian *H*, voyaging beyond *The Hesperides* 2
Happiness Crown them with *h*, *God bless our Prince* 5
glorious vision Of unconceived and awful *h*, *Lover's Tale i* 798
Erewhile close couch'd in golden *h*, „ *ii* 79
Happy Blown round with *h* airs of odorous winds? *Timbuctoo* 46
When we laugh, and our mirth Apes the *h* vein, *Every day, etc.* 13
My *h* falcon, Rosalind, *Rosalind* 25
Oh, *h*, *h* outset of my days! *Lover's Tale i* 276
What *h* air shall woo The wither'd leaf fall'n in the woods, „ 621
The lover Lionel, the *h* Lionel, All joy; who drew the *h* atmosphere „ 672
Hard But you, Sir, you are *h* to please; *New Timon* 25
Hardship unto both Delight from *h* to be overcome, *Lover's Tale i* 379
Hark *H* how the wild rain hisses, *Hero to Leander* 14
H! he shouteth—the ancient enemy! *English War Song* 24
H! how sweet the horned ewes bleat *Lotos-Eaters* 29
Harlot To that half-pagan *h* kept by France! *Sugg. by Reading* 70
Harmony *h* of planet-girded Suns And moon-encircled planets, *Timbuctoo* 109
With *harmonies* of wind and wave and wood „ 207
Harsh But did the while your *h* decree deplore, *Lost Hope* 2
Haste In eager *h* I shook him by the hand; *Lover's Tale i* 788
Hasty So that with *h* motion I did veil My vision with both hands, *Timbuctoo* 68
Hate (s) How scorn and ruin, pain and *h* could flow: *Pallid thunderstricken* 10
Hate (verb) I *h* that silly sigh. *Skipping-rope* 8
We *h* not France, but this man's heart of stone. *Britons, guard* 17
We *h* not France, but France has lost her voice „ 19
Hateful With languor of most *h* smiles, *Burial of Love* 19
H with hanging cheeks, a withered brood, *Shall the hag* 4
as the milky blood Of *h* herbs a subtle-fanged snake, *Lover's Tale i* 821
Hater Peace-lovers, *h's* Of shameless traitors, *Britons, guard* 15
Hateth Hesper *h* Phosphor, evening *h* morn. *Hesperides, Song iii* 15
Hatred But *H* in a gold cave sits below, *Pallid thunderstricken* 11
Haunted And all the *h* place is dark and holy. *Check every outflash* 8
Haven broad-blown Argosies Drave into *h*? *A Fragment* 8
Head (*See also* **Hoarhead**) Above her *h* the weak lamp dips and winks *Timbuctoo* 35
Backward drooping his graceful *h*. *Burial of Love* 7
Ringlet, She clipt you from her *h*, *The Ringlet* 38
Headland Winter roofs The *h* with inviolate white snow, *Timbuctoo* 204
Headlong *H* they plunge their doubts *Sugg. by Reading* 72
Healèd Lest the old wound of the world be *h*, *Hesperides, Song iii* 2
Health First drink a *h*, this solemn night, A *h* to England every guest; *Hands all Round* 1
A *h* to Europe's honest men! „ 13
To Europe's better *h* we drink, „ 23
What *h* to France, if France be she Whom martial progress „ 25
cause Of England and her *h* of commonsense— *Sugg. by Reading* 40
my refluent *h* made tender quest Unanswer'd, *Lover's Tale, i* 742
Hear If that he would them *h* And stay. *The lintwhite* 6
And longer *h* us sing; „ 23
I *h* a thunder though the skies are fair, *Sugg. by Reading* 89
All alone she sits and *h's* Echoes *Home they brought him* 3
Heard hath *h* Time flowing in the middle of the night, *The Mystic* 38
H neither warbling of the nightingale, *The Hesperides* 6
And shook its earthly socket, for we *h*, *Lover's Tale, i* 61
I *h* in thought Those rhymes, 'The Lion and the Unicorn' „ 284
Hearing *H* apart the echoes of his fame. *D. of F. Women* 13
Heart whilome won the *h's* of all on Earth *Timbuctoo* 17
being in the *h* of Man As air is th' life of flame: „ 19
Spirit than I to sway The *h* of Man: „ 196
I play about his *h* a thousand ways, „ 205
few there be So gross of *h* who have not felt „ 211
Bury him in the cold, cold *h*— *Burial of Love* 12

Heart (*continued*) My h is lighted at thine eyes, To—— 8
world will not change, and her h will not break. I' the glooming light 22
Grow closer to my h. My h is warmer surely than the bosom of the main. Hero to Leander 8
My h of h's art thou. „ 11
Thy h beats through thy rosy limbs „ 16
Albeit, his spirit and his secret h The Mystic 7
ERE yet my h was sweet Love's tomb, Love, Pride, etc. 1
My h the honey-comb. „ 4
My h, where Hope had been and was no more. Lost Hope 4
I said to thee That thou hast half my h, Love and Sorrow 4
Thou art my h's sun in love's crystalline: „ 6
Thine is the bright side of my h, and thine My h's day, but the shadow of my h, „ 8
my h's night Thou canst not lighten even with thy light, „ 10
Almeida, if my h were substanceless, „ 13
Some vital heat as yet my h is wooing: Could I outwear 12
thou dost ever brood above The silence of all h's, Love 14
We beat upon our aching h's with rage; „ 18
The hollow at h shall crouch forlorn, English War Song 12
For where is the h and strength of slaves? „ 36
There are no h's like English h's, National Song 3
Unto their h's desire, (repeat) „ 12, 30
THERE are three things that fill my h with sighs There are three things 1
And dazzled to the h with glorious pain. „ 14
h is drunk with overwatchings night and day, Hesperides, Song ii 12
Think you h's are tennis balls To play with, Rosalind 32
O DARLING room, my h's delight, O darling room 1
Lest my h be overborne, Germ of 'Maud' 5
The old Timon, with his noble h, New Timon 3
To have the deep poetic h „ 23
We hate not France, but this man's h of stone. Britons, guard 17
as my h beat Twice to the melody of hers. Lover's Tale i 73
And my eyes read, they read aright, her h Was Lionel's: „ 602
and h deep moans Feed and envenom, „ 819

Hearted See **Hollow-hearted**

Hearth But be not you the blatant traitors of the h. Sugg. by Reading 24

Heat (s) region of white flame, Pure without h, The Mystic 44
In thy h of summerpride, The Grasshopper 36
Some vital h as yet my heart is wooing: Could I outwear 12
wind which bloweth cold or h Would shatter Shall the hag 6
Her frantic city's flashing h's But fire, Hands all Round 29
With such a h as lives in great creative rhymes. Sugg. by Reading 6
with the h Of their infolding element; Lover's Tale i 614
the h Of the remorseful soul alive within, „ 681

Heat (verb) But knowing all your power to h or cool, Sugg. by Reading 31

Heated and slake With points of blastborne hail their h eyne! Shall the hag 11

Heather Through and through the flowered h. Dualisms 5

Heave 'Gan rock and h upon that painted sea; Lover's Tale ii 199

Heaven silent H's were blench'd with faery light, Timbuctoo 5
unfading foreheads of the Saints in H? „ 54
Earth's As H than Earth is fairer. „ 170
landing-place is wrapt about with clouds Of glory of H. „ 200
I have rais'd thee higher to the Spheres of H, „ 216
Reacheth to every corner under H, „ 224
Larks in h's cope Sing: Every day, etc. 28
The white moon is hid in her h above, Hero to Leander 3
THE varied earth, the moving h, Chorus 1
But winds from h shook the acorn out, Lost Hope 7
H weeps above the earth all night till morn, Tears of Heaven 1
And all the day h gathers back her tears „ 6
Over h's parapets the angels lean. To a Lady Sleep. 10
H crieth after thee; earth waileth for thee: Love 26
Till all the comets in h are cold, The Ringlet 9
H guard them from her tyrants' jails! Hands all Round 14
There hang within the h's a dark disgrace, Sugg. by Reading 41
had the angels, The watchers at h's gate, Lover's Tale i 616
from that H in whose light I bloom'd „ 624

Heavenward Then parted H on the wing: Timbuctoo 251

Heaviest And from the golden threshold had down-roll'd Their h thunder, Lover's Tale i 618

Heavy Why the h oak groans, and the white willows sigh? The 'How' and the 'Why' 15
The h thunder's girding might, Chorus 13

Heavy (*continued*) And the h melon sleeps On the level of the shore: Lotos-Eaters 35
Dim shores, dense rains, and h clouded sea. Mablethorpe 8
The lithe limbs bow'd as with a h weight Lover's Tale i 126

Heed For the devil a whit we h 'em, (repeat) National Song 10, 28

Height her silver h's Unvisited with dew of vagrant cloud, Timbuctoo 102
Imperial h Of Canopy o'ercanopied. „ 165
and some On the ancient h's divine; Lotos-Eaters 17
When Love was worshipp'd upon every h, Lover's Tale i 323

Held Pride came beneath and h a light. Love, Pride, etc. 6

Herald The h lightning's starry bound, Chorus 14

Herb as the milky blood Of hateful h's Lover's Tale i 821

Heretic Burn, you glossy h, burn, The Ringlet 53

Hesper Father H, Father H, watch, watch, ever and aye, Hesperides, Song ii 1
H, the dragon, and sisters three, „ 24
Father H, Father H, watch, watch, night and day, „ iii 1
H hateth Phosphor, evening hateth morn. „ 15
H, the dragon, and sisters three, „ iv 25

Hewn See **New-hewn, Rock-hewn**

Hid white moon is h in her heaven above, Hero to Leander 3
H now and then with sliding cloud. What time I wasted 6

Hide You h the hand that writes: Sugg. by Reading 25

High pillars h Long time eras'd from Earth: Timbuctoo 12
glory of the place Stood out a pillar'd front of burnish'd gold Interminably h, „ 176
Why deep is not h, and h is not deep? The 'How' and the 'Why' 16
They seem'd h palaces and proud, What time I wasted 5
And mine, with love too h to be express'd Lover's Tale i 65

Higher few there be So gross of heart who have not felt and known A h than they see: Timbuctoo 212
I have rais'd thee h to the Spheres of Heaven, „ 216
H thro' secret splendours mounting still, D. of F. Women 11

Highest THOUGH Night hath climbed her peak of h noon, Though night 1

Highland a h leaning down a weight Of cliffs, The Hesperides 10

Highland-steep Broken by the h-s, Hesperides, Song iv 5

High-necked far off Seen by the h-n camel on the verge Journeying southward? A Fragment 18

Highness His soldier-ridden H might incline Britons, guard 49

Hill The blossoming abysses of your h's? Timbuctoo 44
thy h's enfold a City as fair As those „ 59
On the ridge of the h his banners rise; English War Song 25
between The h's to Bingen have I been, O darling room 10
About sunset We came unto the h of woe, Lover's Tale i 365
With all her interchange of h and plain „ 694

Hillbrow light Is shut out by the round of the tall h; Hesperides, Song iv 16

Himla Father, old H weakens, „ iii 7

Hindrance to both of us It was delight, not h: Lover's Tale i 378

Hinge Which was the h on which the door of Hope, „ 297

Hint And a lad may wink, and a girl may h, The Ringlet 17

Hiss Hark how the wild rain h'es, Hero to Leander 14

Hit my skipping-rope Will h you in the eye. Skipping-rope 4

Hive I was the h and Love the bee, Love, Pride, etc. 3

Hoar On the loud h foam, Lotos-Eaters 19

Hoarded H wisdom brings delight. Hesperides, Song ii 6

Hoarhead The h winter paving earth With sheeny white, Chorus 18

Hoary The clear Galaxy Shorn of its h lustre, Timbuctoo 106
Like a lone cypress, through the twilight h, Me my own fate 6
Zidonian Hanno, voyaging beyond The h promontory of Soloë Past Thymiaterion, The Hesperides 3

Hog h's who can believe in nothing great, Sugg. by Reading 45

Hold ever h aloft the cloud Which droops low The Mystic 31
grief Doth h the other half in sovranty. Love and Sorrow 5
H up the lion of England on high (repeat) English War Song 27, 49
I h them all most dear; but oh! black eyes, There are three things 7
How many the mystic fruit-tree h's, Hesperides, Song ii 8
But the thing I h in scorn, Germ of 'Maud' 6
I pray'd aloud to God that he would h The hand of blessing over Lionel, Lover's Tale i 791

Hollow (adj.) In the h rosy vale to tarry, Lotos-Eaters 12

Hollow (s) And the unsounded, undescended depth Of her black h's. Timbuctoo 105
Dappled with h and alternate rise Of interpenetrated arc, „ 130

Hollow-hearted Shall *h-h* apathy, The cruellest form of perfect scorn, *Burial of Love* 17
Holy And all the haunted place is dark and *h*. *Check every outflash* 8
The end of day and beginning of night Make the apple *h* and bright, *H* and bright, round and full, *Hesperides, Song iv* 10
Home Heaven, Man's first, last *h*: *Timbuctoo* 217
render up this glorious *h* To keen *Discovery*: „ 243
To the melancholy *h* At the limit of the brine, *Lotos-Eaters* 20
Call *h* your ships across Biscayan tides, *Britons, guard* 37
H they brought him slain with spears. They brought him *h* at even-fall: *Home they brought him* 1
Honest A health to Europe's *h* men! *Hands all Round* 13
An *h* isolation need not fear The Court, *Sugg. by Reading* 15
Honey (adj.) To him the *h* dews of orient hope. *Lover's Tale i* 675
Honey (s) Love laboured *h* busily. *Love, Pride, etc.* 2
Honey-comb My heart the *h-c*. „ 4
Lotos, sweet As the yellow *h*, *Lotos-Eaters* 15
Honeysweet Liquid gold, *h* thro' and thro'. *Hesperides, Song i* 24
Honour (s) In *h* of the silverfleckèd morn: *To a Lady Sleep.* 4
H comes with mystery; *Hesperides, Song ii* 5
Honour (verb) I *h* much, I say, this man's appeal. *Sugg. by Reading* 49
Honourable An *h* eld shall come upon thee. *Though night* 14
Honour'd The precious jewel of my *h* life, *Lover's Tale ii* 78
Hope (s) Men clung with yearning *H* which would not die. *Timbuctoo* 27
men's *h's* and fears take refuge in The fragrance „ 226
The light of his *h's* unfed, *Burial of Love* 3
Let us weep in *h*— *Every day, etc.* 32
You cast to ground the *h* which once was mine, *Lost Hope* 1
My heart, where *H* had been and was no more. „ 4
But men of long enduring *h's*, *New Timon* 17
But fire, to blast the *h's* of men. *Hands all Round* 30
hinge on which the door of *H*, Once turning, *Lover's Tale i* 297
cold as were the *h's* Of my lorn love! „ 620
To him the honey dews of orient *h*. „ 675
when *h* died, part of her eloquence Died with her? „ 751
I To stand within the level of their *h's*, „ 768
Because my *h* was widow'd, „ 769
The course of *H* is dried,— „ 808
For me all other *H's* did sway from that „ 857
Hope (verb) For she will not *h*. *I' the glooming light* 19
Could I thus *h* my lost delights renewing, *Could I outwear* 9
Nay, dearest, teach me how to *h*, *Skipping-rope* 9
Hopeless Alone my *h* melancholy gloometh, *Me my own fate* 5
Horizon lights on my *h* shine Into my night „ 11
Horn Between the Southern and the Western *H*, *The Hesperides* 5
Horned Hark! how sweet the *h* ewes bleat On the solitary steeps, *Lotos-Eaters* 29
Horrible *H* with the anger and the heat *Lover's Tale i* 681
Horrid and tho' *h* rifts Sent up the moaning of unhappy spirits „ 612
As men do from a vague and *h* dream, „ 786
Host gather from afar The *h's* to battle: *Blow ye the trumpet* 2
His ruthless *h* is bought with plunder'd gold, *Britons, guard* 7
Hot Strain the *h* spheres of his convulsèd eyes, *Love* 37
Hour (*See also* **Summerhours**) Wingèd *h's* are borne; *Every day, etc.* 4
For him the silent congregated *h's*, *The Mystic* 25
In thy *h* of love and revel, *The Grasshopper* 35
So in thine *h* of dawn, the body's youth, *Though night* 13
And careless what this *h* may bring, *New Timon* 18
What time I wasted youthful *h's* *What time I wasted* 1
Should he land here, and for one *h* prevail, *Britons, guard* 55
Fair fall this hallow'd *h*, *God bless our Prince* 8
Move with me to that *h*, *Lover's Tale i* 296
since that *h*, My voice had somewhat falter'd— „ 749
House (s) And a *h* with a chimney-pot? *The 'How' and the 'Why'* 35
House (verb) worms which *h* Beneath unshaken waters, *Timbuctoo* 150
Household But yours are not their *h* privacies. *Sugg. by Reading* 22
How Who will riddle me the *h* and the *why*? (repeat) *The 'How' and the 'Why'* 9, 20
H you are you? Why I am I? „ 19
I feel there is something; but *h* and what? „ 23
And stares in his face and shouts '*h? h?*' „ 29
And chaunts '*h? h?*' the whole of the night. „ 31
Who will riddle me the *h* and the what? 36
Howling Which flung strange music on the *h* winds, *Timbuctoo* 80
Hue And alternations of all *h's*, he stood. „ 76
an ether of black *h*, Investeth and ingirds *The Mystic* 45
indue i' the spring *H's* of fresh youth, *Could I outwear* 3
in his writhings awful *h's* begin To wander *Love* 38
Dimples, roselips, and eyes of any *h*. *There are three things* 4
Huge even as the sea When weary of wild inroad buildeth up *H* mounds *Timbuctoo* 15
Close by our ears, the *h* roots strain and creak), *Lover's Tale i* 63
(*H* splinters, which the sap of earliest showers, „ *ii* 45
Hum (s) the *h* of men, Or other things talking *Timbuctoo* 111
Hum (verb) *H* a lovelay to the westwind at noontide. *Dualisms* 2
Both alike, they *h* together „ 4
Stands in her pew and *h's* her decent psalm *Sugg. by Reading* 63
Human for my *h* brain Stagger'd beneath the vision, *Timbuctoo* 185
With stony smirks at all things *h* and divine! *Sugg. by Reading* 48
Hung (*See also* **Low-hung**) The snowy skirting of a garment *h*, *Timbuctoo* 182
Pagods *h* with music of sweet bells: „ 234
low *h* on either gate of life, *The Mystic* 32
earthquake-shattered chasm, *h* with shrubs, *Lover's Tale i* 408
Or as the dew-drops on the petal *h*, „ 558
Hopes did sway from that Which *h* the frailest: „ 858
Hurried *h* through The riv'n rapt brain: *Timbuctoo* 120
Hush 'Oh *h*, my joy, my sorrow.' *Home they brought him* 10
Hut Darken, and shrink and shiver into *h's*, *Timbuctoo* 246

I

I How you are you? Why *I* am *I*, *The 'How' and the 'Why'* 19
Ideal Down an *i* stream they ever float, *Pallid thunderstricken* 2
Idle Why waste they yonder Their *i* thunder? *Britons, guard* 40
Shall we stand *i*, Nor seek to bridle „ 51
Idol A perfect *I*, with profulgent brows *A Fragment* 3
Thy shadowy *I's* in the solitudes, „ 15
Ilion Here stood the infant *I* of the mind, *Mablethorpe* 3
Ill Nor good nor *i*, nor light nor shade, *οἱ ῥέοντες* 10
So to guard my life from *i*, *Germ of 'Maud'* 17
Alas, our Church! alas, her growing *i's*, *Sugg. by Reading* 67
Illimitable *I* range of battlement On battlement, *Timbuctoo* 164
Listenest the lordly music flowing from Th' *i* years. „ 219
Image did pause To worship mine own *i*, *Lover's Tale i* 68
mine *i* in her eyes, „ 70
Imaging *i* The soft inversion of her tremulous Domes; *Timbuctoo* 231
Imbue presence of his eyes To *i* his lustre; *Lover's Tale i* 419
Immingled In a new birth, *i* with my own, „ 732
Immortality No withered *i*, *The Grasshopper* 28
Impelling *See* **Self-impelling**
Imperial and thou of later name *I* Eldorado roof'd with gold: *Timbuctoo* 24
and the *I* height Of Canopy o'ercanopied. „ 165
Imperishable The *i* presences serene, *The Mystic* 13
Impleachèd The fragrance of its complicated glooms And cool *i* twilights. *Timbuctoo* 228
Imprison'd unhappy spirits *I* in her centre, *Lover's Tale i* 614
Impulse The issue of strong *i*, hurried through *Timbuctoo* 120
each th' effect Of separate *i*, „ 127
from this *i* Continuing and gathering ever, *Lover's Tale i* 493
Increasing level calm Is ridg'd with restless and *i* spheres *Timbuctoo* 125
Indecision entwine The *i* of my present mind „ 139
Indian serpent in his agonies Awestricken *I's*; *Love* 31
Indistinctest The *i* atom in deep air, *Timbuctoo* 100
Indue *i* i' the spring Hues of fresh youth, *Could I outwear* 2
Ineffable Then with a mournful and *i* smile, *Timbuctoo* 189
Infant Here stood the *i* Ilion of the mind, *Mablethorpe* 3
Infinite Where are the *i* ways which, Seraphtrod, *Timbuctoo* 47
Infixed Giant of old Time *i* The limits „ 11
Infolding with the heat Of their *i* element; *Lover's Tale i* 615
Inform wherewith Her phantasy *i's* them. *Timbuctoo* 40
Ingird Investeth and *i's* all other lives. *The Mystic* 46
Inland One cypress on an *i* promontory. *Me my own fate* 8
Through vineyards from an *i* bay. *Rosalind* 29
Inmost The written secrets of her *i* soul Lay like an open scroll *Lover's Tale i* 600

J

K

Know (*continued*) I *k* not, faith: *Lover's Tale i* 695
Knowest *k* I dare not look into thine eyes, *Oh, Beauty* 4
Knoweth *k* not Beyond the sound he lists: *Lover's Tale i* 657
Knowing But *k* all your power to heat or cool, *Sugg. by Reading* 31
Have ye aught that is worth the *k*? *1865-1866* 5
But aught that is worth the *k*?' „ 9
Knowledge Keen *k's* of low-embowèd eld) *The Mystic* 30
Known felt and *k* A higher than they see: *Timbuctoo* 211
the free speech that makes a Briton *k*. *Britons, guard* 29
K when their faces are forgot in the land. *Lover's Tale i* 804

L

Labour He said, 'The *l* is not small; *What time I wasted* 7
the shore Than *l* in the ocean, *Lotos-Eaters* 39
Laboured Love *l* honey busily. *Love, Pride, etc.* 2
Labyrinthine All th' intricate and *l* veins Of the great vine of *Fable*, *Timbuctoo* 221
Lad And a *l* may wink, and a girl may hint, *The Ringlet* 17
Laden Strove to uprise, *l* with mournful thanks, *Lover's Tale i* 748
Laid Beside her are *l*, Her mattock and spade, *I' the glooming light* 5
what time *l* low And crushing the thick fragrant reeds *Love* 31
Lain I had *l* as still, And blind and motionless *Lover's Tale i* 618
new-hewn sepulchre, Where man had never *l*, „ 714
the grass was warm where I had *l*, „ 790
Lake opal width Of her small glowing *l's*, *Timbuctoo* 102
large *l* From pressure of descendant crags, „ 121
length of porch and *l* and boundless hall, „ 180
Lameness strangling sorrow weigh Mine utterances with *l*. *Lover's Tale i* 25
Lamp Above her head the weak *l* dips and winks *Timbuctoo* 35
Lance Rode upon his father's *l*, *Home they brought him* 8
Land (s) (*See also* **Lotos-land**) In music and in light o'er *l* and sea. *Love* 28
There is no *l* like England (repeat) *National Song* 1, 5, 19, 23
Mellowed in a *l* of rest; *Hesperides, Song iv* 12
God keep their *l's* allied, *God bless our Prince* 2
Known when their faces are forgot in the *l*. *Lover's Tale i* 804
Land (verb) Should he *l* here, and for one hour prevail, *Britons, guard* 55
Landing-place *l-p* is wrapt about with clouds *Timbuctoo* 199
Land-wind But the *l-w* wandereth, *Hesperides, Song iv* 4
Languor With *l* of most hateful smiles, *Burial of Love* 19
Lapse descendant crags, which *l* Disjointed, *Timbuctoo* 122
Kingdoms *l*, and climates change, and races die; *Hesperides, Song ii* 4
Lapt Which, *l* in seeming dissolution, *Lover's Tale i* 507
Larch Warbled from yonder knoll of solemn *l'es*, *Check every outflash* 10
Large and my mental eye grew *l* With such a vast circumference of thought, *Timbuctoo* 92
as when in some *l* lake From pressure of descendant crags, „ 121
Larger Pure without heat, into a *l* air Upburning, *The Mystic* 44
Largess Thy golden *l* fling, *The lintwhite* 22
Lark *L's* in heaven's cope Sing: *Every day, etc.* 28
Though long ago listening the poisèd *l*, *To a Lady Sleep.* 8
Last (adj.) I have rais'd thee higher to the Spheres of Heaven, Man's first, *l* home: *Timbuctoo* 217
Love is dead; His *l* arrow sped; *Burial of Love* 9
The world's *l* tempest darkens overhead; *Britons, guard* 2
Last (s) Lest thy kiss should be the *l*. *Hero to Leander* 6
he had well nigh reached The *l*, *The Mystic* 43
Lasting ME my own fate to *l* sorrow doometh: *Me my own fate* 1
Later and thou of *l* name Imperial Eldorado roof'd with gold: *Timbuctoo* 23
Latest Oh City! Oh *l* Throne! where I was rais'd To be a mystery of loveliness „ 240
Lattice From an half-open *l* looked at *me*. *There are three things* 12
Laugh We *l*, we cry, we are born, we die, *The 'How' and the 'Why'* 8
When we *l*, and our mirth Apes the happy vein, *Every day, etc.* 12
L not loudly; watch the treasure Of the wisdom *Hesperides, Song i* 13
Jesuit *l's*, and reckoning on his chance, *Britons, guard* 32
Laugheth Madness *l* loud: *Every day, etc.* 17
Laughing *l* clearly A light and thrilling laughter, *Anacreontics* 9
Laughter *L* bringeth tears: *Every day, etc.* 18
laughing clearly A light and thrilling *l*, *Anacreontics* 10
Laved mine own image, *l* in light, *Lover's Tale i* 68
Law wondrous *l's* which regulate The fierceness *Timbuctoo* 147
Law (*continued*) Nor essence nor eternal *l's*: *οἱ ῥέοντες* 11
Our ancient boast is this—we reverence *l*. *Sugg. by Reading* 34
O Grief and Shame if while I preach of *l's* „ 37
Lawless The *l* comets as they glare, *Chorus* 27
Lay (s) (*See also* **Lovelay**) YOU did late review my *l's*, *To C. North* 1
Lay (verb) wave unshockèd *L's* itself calm and wide, *Dualisms* 7
How often, when a child I *l* reclined, *Mablethorpe* 1
L like an open scroll before my view, *Lover's Tale i* 601
And blind and motionless as then I *l*! „ 619
Lea which the fearful springtide flecks the *l*, *Love and Sorrow* 2
Two children lovelier than love, adown the *l* are singing, *Dualisms* 14
At noon-tide beneath the *l*; *Lotos-Eaters* 6
The drain-cut levels of the marshy *l*,— *Mablethorpe* 6
Lead turretstairs are wet That *l* into the sea. *Hero to Leander* 37
Will it *l* me to the grave? *Germ of 'Maud'* 24
Oh! *l* me tenderly, for fear the mind *Lover's Tale i* 23
Leaf (*See also* **Ivy-leaves**) growth of shadowing *l* and clusters rare, *Timbuctoo* 223
O MAIDEN, fresher than the first green *l* *Love and Sorrow* 1
What happy air shall woo The wither'd *l* *Lover's Tale i* 622
Lean Over heaven's parapets the angels *l*. *To a Lady Sleep.* 10
Leander And when thou art dead, *L*, *Hero to Leander* 30
L! go not yet. „ 38
Leaneth my wish *l* evermore Still to believe it— *Lover's Tale i* 270
Leaning Beneath a highland *l* down a weight Of cliffs, *The Hesperides* 10
Leap *L* the little waterfalls That sing *Rosalind* 23
And the merry lizard *l's*, *Lotos-Eaters* 31
The boy began to *l* and prance, *Home they brought him* 7
Leaping Ever *l*, ever singing, *The Grasshopper* 43
Learn lest we *l* A sharper lesson than we ever knew. *Sugg. by Reading* 87
For what is this which now I *l*, *The Ringlet* 51
Learnt-Learn'd They never *learnt* to love who never knew to weep. *Love and Sorrow* 18
When I *learnt* from whom it came, *To C. North* 5
Because she *learn'd* them with me. *Lover's Tale i* 290
Leave If thou dost *l* the sun, *The lintwhite* 32
Leaved *See* **Silverleaved**
Led By such men *l*, our press had ever been *Sugg. by Reading* 2
Ledgers Too much we make our *L*, Gods. *Hands all Round* 20
Left (hand) In any town, to *l* or right, *O darling room* 14
Left (verb) and I Was *l* alone on Calpe, *Timbuctoo* 252
Till we were *l* to fight for truth alone. *Britons, guard* 35
Or moisture of the vapour, *l* in clinging, *Lover's Tale ii* 46
And, trampled on, *l* to its own decay. „ 81
Legend And much I mus'd on *l's* quaint and old *Timbuctoo* 16
hill of woe, so call'd Because the *l* ran that, *Lover's Tale i* 366
Length *l* of porch and lake and boundless hall, *Timbuctoo* 180
Lenora A garland for *L*. *Anacreontics* 7
L, laughing clearly A light and thrilling laughter, „ 9
Lesson lest we learn A sharper *l* than we ever knew. *Sugg. by Reading* 88
Lethargised So *l* discernment in the sense, *Lover's Tale i* 663
Level (adj.) the *l* calm Is ridg'd with restless and increasing spheres *Timbuctoo* 124
Level (s) melon sleeps On the *l* of the shore: *Lotos-Eaters* 36
The drain-cut *l's* of the marshy lea,— *Mablethorpe* 6
I To stand within the *l* of their hopes, *Lover's Tale i* 768
Levelling Rapidly *l* eager eyes. *Hesperides, Song ii* 18
Liar Peace-lovers we—but who can trust a *l*?— *Britons, guard* 14
Libraries Your bridges and your busted *l*, *Cambridge* 3
Libyan *See* **Lybian**
Lid THOU whose fringèd *l's* I gaze upon, *To a Lady Sleep.* 1
commend the tears to creep From my charged *l's*. *Could I outwear* 11
Lie (s) fie You golden *l*. *The Ringlet* 44
Lie (verb) What the life is? where the soul may *l*? *The 'How' and the 'Why'* 33
crushing the thick fragrant reeds he *l's*, *Love* 32
For her there *l* in wait millions of foes, *Sugg. by Reading* 59
Life The precious jewel of my honour'd *l*, *Lover's Tale ii* 78
As air is th' *l* of flame: *Timbuctoo* 20
notes of busy *l* in distant worlds Beat „ 113
The permeating *l* which courseth through „ 220
Some say this *l* is pleasant, *The 'How' and the 'Why'* 3
Why the *l* goes when the blood is spilt? „ 32
What the *l* is? where the soul may lie? „ 33
If to love be *l* alone, *To ——* 2

Life (*continued*) The stern experiences of converse *lives*, The Mystic 8
cloud Which droops low hung on either gate of *l*, „ 32
Investeth and ingirds all other *lives*. „ 46
L of the summerhours, The Grasshopper 3
subtle *l*, the countless forms Of living things, Chorus 7
Our *l* evanisheth : Oh ! stay. The lintwhite 15
To whom the slope and stream of *l*, Rosalind 5
The *l* before, the *l* behind, „ 6
That trouble *l* in early years, „ 14
In the silence of my *l*— Germ of 'Maud' 13
So to guard my *l* from ill, „ 17
That spilt his *l* about the cliques. New Timon 40
And taken away the greenness of my *l*, Lover's Tale i 625
And their long *l* a dream of linked love, „ 795
Hope is dried,—the *l* o' the plant— „ 808
The wreck of ruin'd *l*, and shatter'd thought, „ ii 62
Lift We'll *l* no more the shattered oar, Lotos-Eaters 23
Lifted So, *l* high, the poet at his will D. of F. Women 9
Light (s) (*See also* **Half-light**) silent Heavens were blench'd with faery *l*, Timbuctoo 5
Uncertain whether faery *l* or cloud, „ 6
no *l* but that wherewith Her phantasy informs them. „ 39
A curve of whitening, flashing, ebbing *l* ! „ 63
And circled with the glory of living *l* „ 75
l Of the great angel mind which look'd „ 87
As with a momentary flash of *l* Grew „ 97
with sharp points of *l* Blaze within blaze, „ 107
Behind, In diamond *l*, upsprung the dazzling Cones „ 168
With earliest *L* of Spring, „ 200
The *l* of his hopes unfed, Burial of Love 3
For ever write In the weathered *l* „ 21
Her *l* shall into darkness change ; „ 27
I' the glooming *l* Of middle night, I' the glooming light 1
ocean with the morrow *l* Will be both blue and calm ; Hero to Leander 25
One shadow in the midst of a great *l* The Mystic 21
l Of earliest youth pierced through and through „ 28
Pride came beneath and held a *l*. Love, Pride, etc. 6
The day, the diamonded *l*, Chorus 11
Thou canst not lighten even with *thy l*, Love and Sorrow 11
wave of the virgin *l* Driven back the billow To a Lady Sleep. 5
A sheeny snake, the *l* of vernal bowers, Could I outwear 6
Turn cloud to *l*, and bitterness to joy, Though night 6
Nor blot with floating shades the solar *l*. Shall the hag 14
in mail of argent *l* Shot into gold, Pallid thunderstricken 12
In music and in *l* o'er land and sea. Love 28
Like *l* on troubled waters : „ 40
And in him *l* and joy and strength abides ; „ 42
from his brows a crown of living *l* Looks through „ 43
Where'er the *l* of day be ; (repeat) National Song 2, 6, 20, 24
Nor good nor ill, nor *l* nor shade, οἱ ῥέοντες 10
When thy *l* perisheth That from thee issueth, The lintwhite 13
eyes so full of *l* Should be so wandering ! „ 26
thy *l's* on my horizon shine Into my night Me my own fate 11
When we two meet there's never perfect *l*. „ 14
Till midnoon the cool east *l* Is shut out Hesperides, Song iv 15
Clad in *l* by golden gates, Clad in *l* the Spirit waits Germ of 'Maud' 32
As towards the gracious *l* I bow'd, What time I wasted 4
To worship mine own image, laved in *l*, Lover's Tale i 68
A *l*, methought, flash'd even from her white robe, „ 361
Even from that Heaven in whose *l* I bloom'd „ 624
came in O'erhead the white *l* of the weary moon, „ 659
Light (adj.) Why the rocks stand still, and the *l* clouds fly ? The 'How' and the 'Why' 14
Thou art so glad and free, And as *l* as air ; The Grasshopper 25
Lenora, laughing clearly A *l* and thrilling laughter, Anacreontics 10
and mine Were dim with floating tears, that shot the sunset, In *l* rings round me ; Lover's Tale i 438
Light (verb) Waiting to *l* him with his purple skies, Love 34
Lighted (*See also* **Wax-lighted**) My heart is *l* at thine eyes, To —— 8
Lighten 'Wide Afric, doth thy sun *L*, Timbuctoo 59
Thou canst not *l* even with *thy* light, Love and Sorrow 11
Lighting *L* on the golden blooms ? The Grasshopper 44
Lightning The herald *l's* starry bound, Chorus 14
goest and returnest to His Lips Like *l* : Love 13
a *l* stroke had come Even from that Heaven Lover's Tale i 623
Lightsome And showering down the glory of *l* day, Tears of Heaven 8
Like *L*, unlike, they roam together Dualisms 17
L, unlike, they sing together Side by side ; „ 19
Lily And silverleaved *l*, Anacreontics 3
Lilygarlands As they gambol, *l* ever stringing : Dualisms 15
Limb Thy heart beats through thy rosy *l's* Hero to Leander 16
their wan *l's* no more might come between Shall the hag 12
between whose *l's* Of brassy vastness A Fragment 6
From iron *l's* and tortured nails ! Hands all Round 16
lithe *l's* bow'd as with a heavy weight Lover's Tale i 126
Limit infixed The *l's* of his prowess, Timbuctoo 12
melancholy home At the *l* of the brine, Lotos-Eaters 21
Limitless So bearing on thro' Being *l* The triumph of this foretaste, Lover's Tale i 514
Link (s) Five *l's*, a golden chain, are we, Hesperides, Song ii 23
Five *l's*, a golden chain, are we, „ iv 24
Crush'd *l* on *l* into the beaten earth, Lover's Tale i 859
Link (verb) Could *l* his shallop to the fleeting edge, Timbuctoo 145
firmament to *l* The earthquake-shattered chasm, Lover's Tale i 407
Link'd Rapid as fire, inextricably *l*, Timbuctoo 117
Linkèd The *l* woes of many a fiery change Had purified, The Mystic 9
And their long life a dream of *l* love, Lover's Tale i 795
Lintwhite The *l* and the throstlecock Have voices sweet and clear ; The lintwhite 1
Lion Hold up the *L* of England on high (repeat) English War Song 27, 49
A *L*, you, that made a noise, New Timon 11
heard in thought Those rhymes, 'The *L* and the Unicorn' Lover's Tale i 285
Lionel her heart Was *L's* : „ i 603
It was the man she loved, even *L*, The lover *L*, the happy *L*, „ 671
pray'd aloud to God that he would hold The hand of blessing over *L*, „ 792
Lip (*See also* **Roselip**) I have fill'd thy *l's* with power. Timbuctoo 215
His eyes in eclipse, Pale cold his *l's*, Burial of Love 2
skins the colour from her trembling *l's*. Pallid thunderstricken 14
goest and returnest to His *L's* Like lightning : Love 12
Alas ! that *l's* so cruel dumb Should The lintwhite 17
peaceful *l's* are kissed With earliest rays, A Fragment 22
They sleep with staring eyes and gilded *l's*, „ 29
name to which her seraph *l's* Did lend Lover's Tale i 451
Liquid *L* gold, honeysweet thro' and thro'. Hesperides, Song i 24
List knoweth not Beyond the sound he *l's* : Lover's Tale i 658
Listenest *L* the lordly music flowing Timbuctoo 218
Listening Though long ago *l* the poisèd lark, To a Lady Sleep. 8
Lithe But an insect *l* and strong, The Grasshopper 7
And the *l* vine creeps, Lotos-Eaters 34
The *l* limbs bow'd as with a heavy weight Lover's Tale i 126
Little The *l* bird pipeth 'why ! why !' The 'How' and the 'Why' 26
Leap the *l* waterfalls That sing into the pebbled pool. Rosalind 23
The *l* isle of Ithaca, beneath the day's decline. Lotos-Eaters 22
No *l* room so warm and bright Wherein to read, O darling room 5
A *l* room so exquisite, „ 15
Because the words of *l* children preach Against you,— Cambridge 12
Can pardon *l* would-be Popes And Brummels, New Timon 19
A dapper boot—a *l* hand—If half the *l* soul is dirt ? „ 35
She loves a *l* scandal which excites ; A *l* feeling is a want of tact. Sugg. by Reading 57
Lower down Spreads out a *l* lake, that, flooding, Lover's Tale i 536
Live I love thee, and *l* ; To —— 4
For which I *l*—black eyes, and brown and blue ; There are three things 6
black eyes, I *l* and die, and only die for you. „ 8
such a heat as *l's* in great creative rhymes. Sugg. by Reading 6
by that name was wont to *l* in her speech, Lover's Tale i 571
Lived Awhile she scarcely *l* at all, Love, Pride, etc. 13
I had *l* That intense moment thro' eternity. Lover's Tale i 495
So each with each inwoven *l* with each, „ 566
for which I *l* and breathed : „ ii 73
Livelong the culvers mourn All the *l* day. Every day, etc. 30
Living And circled with the glory of *l* light Timbuctoo 75
Deep-rooted in the *l* soil of truth : „ 225
The subtle life, the countless forms Of *l* things, Chorus 8
And from his brows a crown of *l* light Love 43
Thy spirit, circled with a *l* glory, Me my own fate 3
rare pity had stolen The *l* bloom away, Lover's Tale i 726

Made (*continued*) By diminution m most glorious, *Lover's Tale i* 71
Which waste with the breath that m 'em. „ 475
The very spirit of Paleness m still paler „ 679
my refluent health m tender quest Unanswer'd, „ 742
drove them onward—m them sensible; „ *ii* 77
Madness M laugheth loud: *Every day, etc.* 17
Mahmoud Better wild M's war-cry once again! *Sugg. by Reading* 83
Maid There are no m's like English m's, *National Song* 25
Maiden (adj.) (when I view Fair m forms moving like melodies), *There are three things* 3
Maiden (s) O M, fresher than the first green leaf *Love and Sorrow* 1
beauteous face Of the m, that I lost, *Germ of 'Maud'* 3
Mail in m of argent light Shot into gold, *Pallid thunderstricken* 12
Mailèd Thou art a m warrior in youth and strength complete; *The Grasshopper* 13
Main My heart is warmer surely than the bosom of the m. *Hero to Leander* 9
Majestic In accents of m melody, *Timbuctoo* 192
The mighty disk of their m sun, *Love* 21
Make Why two and two m four? *The 'How' and the 'Why'* 13
If ye sing not, if ye m false measure, *Hesperides, Song i* 10
Five and three (Let it not be preached abroad) m an awful mystery. „ 16
M the apple holy and bright, „ *iv* 10
the free speech that m's a Briton known. *Britons, guard* 29
M their cause your own. „ 54
Too much we m our Ledgers, Gods. *Hands all Round* 20
Who m the emphatic One, by whom is all, *Sugg. by Reading* 81
I call on you To m opinion warlike, „ 87
lake, that, flooding, m's Cushions of yellow sand; *Lover's Tale i* 536
her whom he would m his wedded wife, Camilla! „ 793
Think not thy tears will m my name grow green,— „ 806
Maketh Ever alone She m her moan: *I' the glooming light* 17
Making M their day dim, so we gaze on thee. *Love* 23
Man being in the heart of M As air is th' life of flame: *Timbuctoo* 19
Men clung with yearning Hope which would not die. „ 27
'O child of m, why muse you here alone „ 77
the hum of men, Or other things talking „ 111
Spirit than I to sway The heart of m: „ 196
Heaven, M's first, last home: „ 217
men's hopes and fears take refuge in The fragrance „ 226
Child of M, See'st thou yon river, „ 228
I am any m's suitor, If any will be my tutor: *The 'How' and the 'Why'* 1
wondrous tones Of m and beast are full of strange Astonishment *Chorus* 9
all men adore thee; Heaven crieth after thee; *Love* 25
none shall grieve For the m who fears to die: *English War Song* 4
scorn of the many shall cleave To the m who fears to die. „ 6
There are no men like Englishmen, *National Song* 7
M is the measure of all truth Unto himself. *οἱ ῥέοντες* 3
All men do walk in sleep, „ 5
Men of Ithaca, this is meeter, *Lotos-Eaters* 11
As when a m, that sails in a balloon, *D. of F. Women* 1
The padded m—that wears the stays— *New Timon* 8
But men of long enduring hopes, „ 17
'They call this m as good *as me*.' „ 32
fierce old m—to take *his* name You bandbox. „ 43
The true men banished, *Britons, guard* 10
We hate not France, but this m's heart of stone. „ 17
This m is France, the m they call her choice. „ 20
There must no m go back to bear the tale: No m to bear it—Swear it! We swear it! „ 56
A health to Europe's honest men! *Hands all Round* 13
But fire, to blast the hopes of men. „ 30
By such men led, our press had ever been *Sugg. by Reading* 2
The thinking men of England, loathe a tyranny. „ 12
Yours are the public acts of public men, „ 21
I honour much, I say, this m's appeal. „ 49
An essence less concentred than a m! „ 82
we want a manlike God and Godlike men! „ 84
I turn To you that mould men's thoughts; „ 86
'The Gander' and 'The m of Mitylene,' *Lover's Tale i* 287
A woful m had thrust his wife and child „ 368
Man (*continued*) It was the m she loved, even Lionel, *Lover's Tale i* 671
new-hewn sepulchre Where m had never lain. „ 714
As men do from a vague and horrid dream, „ 786
Let them so love that men and boys may say, „ 801
Mane And shook a m en papillotes. *New Timon* 12
Manhood Rise, Britons, rise, if m be not dead; *Britons, guard* 1
And trust an ancient m and the cause *Sugg. by Reading* 39
Manlike we want a m God and Godlike men! „ 84
Manly How much I love this writer's m style! „ 1
Manner for your m sorts Not with this age, *Cambridge* 10
Mantling Half round the m night is drawn, *Hesperides, Song iii* 13
Many Come, thou of m crowns, white-robèd love, *Love* 24
The m pleasant days, the moonlit nights, *Lover's Tale i* 54
Marble Nathless she ever clasps the m knees, *Timbuctoo* 37
The deep salt wave breaks in above Those m steps below. *Hero to Leander* 35
Margent Had film'd the m's of the recent wound. *Lover's Tale i* 764
Mark old m of rouge upon your cheeks. *New Timon* 38
Marksman We were the best of marksmen long ago, *Britons, guard* 43
Marriage-day God bless thy m-d, *God bless our Prince* 13
Marshy The drain-cut levels of the m lea,— *Mablethorpe* 6
Martial if France be she Whom m progress only charms? *Hands all Round* 26
Marvel (s) Ye could not read the m in his eye, *The Mystic* 4
What m that she died? *Love, Pride, etc.* 14
Marvel (verb) Would m from so beautiful a sight *Pallid thunderstricken* 9
Matted built above With m bramble and the shining gloss Of ivy-leaves, *Lover's Tale i* 373
Matter M enough for deploring *1865-1866* 8
Mattock Beside her are laid Her m and spade, *I' the glooming light* 6
May Mid M's darling goldenlockèd, *Dualisms* 21
All in the bloomèd M. (repeat) *The lintwhite* 3, 12, 21, 30
Farewell, fair rose of M! *God bless our Prince* 11
Maze m of piercing, trackless, thrilling thoughts *Timbuctoo* 115
Mead Tilth, hamlet, m and mound: *D. of F. Women* 4
Meadow The Bayard of the m. *The Grasshopper* 21
Meaning But what is the m of *then* and *now*! *The 'How' and the 'Why'* 22
where, alack, is Bewick To tell the m now? *A gate and a field* 6
Measure Man is the m of all truth *οἱ ῥέοντες* 3
If ye sing not, if ye make false m, *Hesperides, Song i* 10
Meat Over their scrips and shares, their m's and wine, *Sugg. by Reading* 47
Mechanic By a dull m ghost And a juggle of the brain. *Germ of 'Maud'* 7
Meditation 'Tis a beautiful And pleasant m, *Lover's Tale i* 240
Meek shall the blessing of the m be on thee; *Though night* 12
Meet When we two m there's never perfect light. *Me my own fate* 14
Yet never did there m my sight, *O darling room* 13
I said, 'O years that m in tears, *1865-1866* 4
Meeter Men of Ithaca, this is m, *Lotos-Eaters* 11
Melancholy (adj.) To the m home At the limit of the brine, „ 20
Melancholy (s) Thy spirit to mild-minded M; *Check every outflash* 3
Alone my hopeless m gloometh, *Me my own fate* 5
Mellow And the black owl scuds down the m twilight, *The 'How' and the 'Why'* 30
Mellowed edicts of his fear Are m into music, *Love* 8
M in a land of rest; *Hesperides, Song iv* 12
Melodious M thunders through your vacant courts At morn and even; *Cambridge* 9
Melody In accents of majestic m, *Timbuctoo* 192
Clear m flattering the crisped Nile *A Fragment* 26
Fair maiden forms moving like *melodies*), *There are three things* 3
Nor m o' the Lybian lotusflute *The Hesperides* 7
as my heart beat Twice to the m of hers. *Lover's Tale i* 74
It giveth out a constant m That drowns „ 534
heavy m sleeps On the level of the shore: *Lotos-Eaters* 35
Melted From my cold eyes and m it again. *Could I outwear* 14
note Hath m in the silence that it broke. *Oh, Beauty* 14
Memnon Thy M, when his peaceful lips are kissed *A Fragment* 22
Memnonian Awful M countenances calm „ 16
Memory A center'd golden-circled M, *Timbuctoo* 21
m of that mental excellence Comes o'er me, „ 137
M tho' fed by Pride Did wax so thin on gall, *Love, Pride, etc.* 11
While I spoke thus, the seedsman, M, *D. of F. Women* 14
a costly casket in the grasp Of m? *Lover's Tale i* 102
m of that sound With mighty evocation, „ 667
Memphis Old M hath gone down: *A Fragment* 27

Moved (*continued*) That is *m* not of the will. *Germ of 'Maud'* 21
she has *m* in that smooth way so long, *Sugg. by Reading* 65
M with their motions, as those eyes were *m* *Lover's Tale i* 72
from his spring *M* smiling toward his summer. „ 307
Moving *M* his crest to all sweet plots of flowers *Could I outwear* 7
(when I view Fair maiden forms *m* like melodies), *There are three things* 3
The varied earth, the *m* heaven, *Chorus* 1
moved around me still With the *m* of the blood *Germ of 'Maud'* 20
Mud-walled Low-built, *m-w*, Barbarian settlement, *Timbuctoo* 248
Multitude *m's* of *m's* That minister'd around it— „ 183
Murder And *m* was her freedom overthrown. *Britons, guard* 23
Murmur rolled The growing *m's* of the Polish war! *Blow ye the trumpet* 8
Murmurous The *m* planets' rolling choir, *Chorus* 24
Muse (s) tried the *M's* too: You fail'd, Sir: *New Timon* 13
Muse (verb) why *m* you here alone Upon the Mountain, *Timbuctoo* 77
And *m* midway with philosophic calm „ 146
Go, get you gone, you *m* and mope— *Skipping-rope* 7
Mus'd And much I *m* on legends quaint and old *Timbuctoo* 16
while I *m* At sunset, underneath a shadowy plane *There are three things* 9
Music flung strange *m* on the howling winds, *Timbuctoo* 80
Mingled with floating *m*, thus he spake: „ 194
lordly *m* flowing from Th' illimitable years. „ 218
Pagods hung with *m* of sweet bells: „ 234
flings Grand *m* and redundant fire, *Chorus* 22
edicts of his fear Are mellowed into *m*, *Love* 8
In *m* and in light o'er land and sea. „ 28
For the blossom unto three-fold *m* bloweth; *Hesperides, Song i* 17
And the sap to three-fold *m* floweth, „ 19
Musical And Oberwinter's vineyards green, *M* Lurlei; *O darling room* 9
Musically The crispèd waters whisper *m*, *Check every outflash* 7
Chimeth *m* clear. *Rosalind* 8
Musky With roses *m* breathed, *Anacreontics* 1
Musty I forgave you all the blame, *M* Christopher; *To C. North* 7
Mute *M* his tongue, *Burial of Love* 4
Round about all is *m*, *Hesperides, Song i* 5
Sleep and stir not: all is *m*. „ 9
Myriad The Moslem *m's* fell, and fled before— *Blow ye the trumpet* 11
Myrrh I have bathed thee with the pleasant *m*; *Hero to Leander* 19
Mysterious but where, *M* Egypt, are thine obelisks *A Fragment* 12
Mystery was rais'd To be a *m* of loveliness *Timbuctoo* 241
make an awful *m*. *Hesperides, Song i* 16
Honour comes with *m*; „ *ii* 5
Mystic Number, tell them over and number How many the *m* fruit-tree holds, „ 8

N

Nail From iron limbs and tortured *n's*! *Hands all Round* 16
Naked The *n* summer's glowing birth, *Chorus* 16
Name thou of later *n* Imperial Eldorado *Timbuctoo* 23
Sainted Juliet! dearest *n*! *To ——* 1
with many a *n* Whose glory will not die. *D. of F. Women* 15
And the great *n* of England round and round (repeat) *Hands all Round* 24, 48, 60
fierce old man—to take *his n* You bandbox. *New Timon* 43
With decent dippings at the *n* of Christ! *Sugg. by Reading* 64
Think not thy tears will make my *n* grow green,— *Lover's Tale i* 806
Named underneath the star *N* of the Dragon— *A Fragment* 6
Nameless We must not dread in you the *n* autocrat. *Sugg. by Reading* 18
Narrow I stood upon the Mountain which o'erlooks The *n* seas; *Timbuctoo* 2
Narrower Ye were yet within The *n* circle; *The Mystic* 42
Narwhale monstrous *n* swalloweth His foamfountains *Lotos-Eaters* 7
Nathless *N* she ever clasps the marble knees, *Timbuctoo* 37
Nation God save the *N*, The toleration, *Britons, guard* 27
Native That man's the best cosmopolite Who loves his *n* country best. *Hands all Round* 4
Nature Absorbed me from the *n* of itself *Timbuctoo* 142
You prate of *n*! you are he That spilt *New Timon* 39
Thin dilletanti deep in *n's* plan, *Sugg. by Reading* 80
Or in the art of *N*, *Lover's Tale i* 563
Warping their *n*, till they minister'd „ 665

Neck blue-glossèd *n's* beneath the purple weather. *Dualisms* 13
Parted on either side her argent *n*, *Lover's Tale i* 740
Necked *See* **High-necked**
Negligence Strung in the very *n* of Art, „ 562
Nerve Can it overlast the *n's*? *Germ of 'Maud'* 26
New (adj.) When the *n* year warm breathèd on the earth, *Love* 33
Already with the pangs of a *n* birth „ 36
And *N* Year and Old Year met, *1865-1866* 2
And *N* Year blowing and roaring. „ 13
Green springtide, April promise, glad *n* year Of Being, *Lover's Tale i* 277
And being there they did break forth afresh In a *n* birth, „ 732
New (s) So died the Old: here comes the *N*: *New Timon* 5
New-hewn *n-h* sepulchre, Where man had never lain. *Lover's Tale i* 713
New-risen *N-r* o'er awakened Albion— *Cambridge* 7
Newstarrèd The Northwind fall'n, in the *n* night Zidonian Hanno, *Hesperides* 1
New Year And *N Y* and Old Year met, *1865-1866* 2
And *N Y* blowing and roaring. „ 13
Nigh the time is well *n* come When I must render up *Timbuctoo* 242
Nigher As with a sense of *n* Deity, *Lover's Tale i* 382
Night those which starr'd the *n* o' the Elder World? *Timbuctoo* 60
the thick *n* Came down upon my eyelids, „ 186
Like a swol'n river's gushings in still *n* „ 193
Moon Had fallen from the *n*, and all was dark! „ 253
chaunts 'how?' 'how?' the whole of the *n*. *The 'How' and the 'Why'* 31
I' the glooming light Of middle *n*, *I' the glooming night* 2
Every day hath its *n*: Every *n* its morn: *Every day, etc.* 1
The *n* is dark and vast; *Hero to Leander* 2
Always there stood before him, *n* and day, *The Mystic* 11
Time flowing in the middle of the *n*, „ 39
One very dark and chilly *n* Pride came *Love, Pride, etc.* 5
Heaven weeps above the earth all *n* till morn, *Tears of Heaven* 1
my heart's *n* Thou canst not lighten *Love and Sorrow* 10
Thou all unwittingly prolongest *n*, *To a Lady Sleep.* 7
N hath climbed her peak of highest noon, *Though night* 1
All *n* through archways of the bridgèd pearl „ 3
between The moon and the moon's reflex in the *n*; *Shall the hag* 13
n and pain and ruin and death reign here. *Love* 4
Looks through the thickstemmed woods by day and *n* „ 44
As round the rolling earth *n* follows day: *Me my own fate* 10
horizon shine Into my *n* thou art far away; „ 12
Northwind fall'n, in the newstarrèd *n* *The Hesperides* 1
Guard the apple *n* and day, „ *Song i* 28
heart is drunk with overwatchings *n* and day, „ *ii* 12
Father Hesper, watch, watch, *n* and day, „ *iii* 1
Half round the mantling *n* is drawn, „ 13
The end of day and beginning of *n* „ *iv* 9
Watch it warily day and *n*; „ 13
First drink a health, this solemn *n*, *Hands all Round* 1
To kiss it *n* and day, *The Ringlet* 4
Ringlet, I kiss'd you *n* and day, „ 26
The many pleasant days, the moonlit *n's*, *Lover's Tale i* 54
One rainy *n*, when every wind blew loud, „ 367
Nightingale The *n*, with long and low preamble, *Check every outflash* 9
Heard neither warbling of the *n*, *The Hesperides* 6
Nile The placid Sphinxes brooding o'er the *N*? *A Fragment* 14
melody flattering the crisped *N* By columned Thebes. „ 26
Noble Now must your *n* anger blaze out more *Blow ye the trumpet* 9
The old Timon, with his *n* heart, *New Timon* 3
our press had ever been The public conscience of our *n* isle, *Sugg. by Reading* 3
Be *n*, you! nor work with faction's tools „ 29
Nobler You should be all the *n*, O my friends. „ 28
Nod The bulrush *n's* unto his brother *The 'How' and the 'Why'* 10
Noise A Lion, you, that made a *n*, *New Timon* 11
Noisome From wronged Poerio's *n* den, *Hands all Round* 15
No more O sad *N m*! O sweet *N m*! O strange *N m*! *O sad No more!* 1
Low-buried fathom deep beneath with thee, *N M*! „ 9
Nonnenwerth For I the *N* have seen, *O darling room* 7
Noon (*See also* **Midnoon**) Night hath climbed her peak of highest *n*, *Though night* 1
sloped Into the slumberous summer *n*; *A Fragment* 11
Stream from beneath him in the broad blue *n*, *D. of F. Women* 3

Noonday Of those that gaze upon the *n* Sun. *Timbuctoo* 71
Noontide Hum a lovelay to the westwind at *n*. *Dualisms* 2
At *n-t* beneath the lea ; *Lotos-Eaters* 6
Northwind *N* fall'n, in the newstarrèd night *The Hesperides* 1
Note And *n's* of busy life in distant worlds *Timbuctoo* 113
ere the *n* Hath melted in the silence that it broke. *Oh, Beauty* 13
Nothing For *n* is, but all is made, *οἱ ῥέοντες* 12
O fie, you golden *n*, *The Ringlet* 43
Now But what is the meaning of *then* and *n* ! *The ' How ' and the ' Why '* 22
Number *N*, tell them over and *n* *The Hesperides, Song ii* 7

O

Oak Why the heavy *o* groans, *The ' How ' and the ' Why '* 15
Such hearts of *o* as they be. *National Song* 4
Oaken So on an *o* sprout A goodly acorn grew ; *Lost Hope* 5
To blow the battle from their *o* sides. *Britons, guard* 38
Oar We'll lift no more the shattered *o*, *Lotos-Eaters* 23
and rowing with the *o*, „ 39
Obelisk Her *o's* of rangèd Chrysolite, *Timbuctoo* 235
Egypt, are thine *o's* Graven with gorgeous emblems *A Fragment* 12
Oberwinter And *O's* vineyards green, *O darling room* 8
Object From visible *o's*, for but dimly now, *Timbuctoo* 135
Oblivion Did fall away into *o*. *Lover's Tale i* 630
Ocean The *o* with the morrow light *Hero to Leander* 25
Tossing on the tossing *o*, *Lotos-Eaters* 3
the shore Than labour in the *o*, „ 39
Odorous Blown round with happy airs of *o* winds ? *Timbuctoo* 46
Flooding its angry cheek with *o* tears. *Lover's Tale i* 565
Odour And *o's* rapt from remote Paradise ? *Timbuctoo* 81
No western *o's* wander On the black *Hero to Leander* 28
O'erbear Would shatter and *o* the brazen beat *Shall the hag* 7
O'ercanopied Imperial height Of Canopy *o*. *Timbuctoo* 166
Offence Whereby to guard our Freedom from *o*— *Sugg. by Reading* 38
Offered *O* to Gods upon an altarthrone ; *To ——* 7
Old (adj.) There where the Giant of *o* Time infixed *Timbuctoo* 11
And much I mus'd on legends quaint and *o* „ 16
To know thee is all wisdom, and *o* age Is but to know thee : *Love* 15
which stood In the midnoon the glory of *o* Rhodes, *A Fragment* 2
O Memphis hath gone down : „ 27
Wrapped round with spiced cerements in *o* grots „ 30
From an *o* garden where no flower bloometh, *Me my own fate* 7
underneath a shadowy plane In *o* Bayona, nigh the Southern Sea— *There are three things* 11
Lest the *o* wound of the world be healèd, *The Hesperides, Song iii* 2
Father, *o* Himla weakens, Caucasus is bold and strong. „ 7
Your portals statued with *o* kings and queens, *Cambridge* 2
The *o* Timon, with his noble heart, *New Timon* 3
why we see The *o* mark of rouge upon your cheeks. „ 38
The fierce *o* man—to take *his* name You bandbox. „ 43
We won *o* battles with our strength, the bow. *Britons, guard* 44
Headlong they plunge their doubts among *o* rags and bones. *Sugg. by Reading* 72
And New Year and *O* Year met, *1865-1866* 2
O Year roaring and blowing „ 12
And all the quaint *o* scraps of ancient crones, *Lover's Tale i* 288
Old (s) So died the *O* : here comes the New : *New Timon* 5
Older For he is *o* than the world. *The Hesperides, Song ii* 16
Old Year And New Year and *O Y* met, *1865-1866* 2
O Y roaring and blowing „ 12
Omen Go, frightful *o's*. *Sugg. by Reading* 85
On Over their crowned brethren *O* and Oph ? *A Fragment* 21
One but only seemed *O* shadow in the midst of a great light, *O* reflex from eternity on time, *O* mighty countenance of perfect calm, *The Mystic* 21
O very dark and chilly night Pride came beneath and held a light. *Love, Pride, etc.* 5
Could I outwear my present state of woe With *o* brief winter, *Could I outwear* 2
O cypress on an inland promontory. *Me my own fate* 8
As with *o* kiss to touch thy blessèd cheek. *Oh, Beauty* 8
Should he land here, and for *o* hour prevail, *Britons, guard* 55
O rainy night, when every wind blew loud, *Lover's Tale i* 367
One (*continued*) And yet again, three shadows, fronting *o*, *O* forward, *o* respectant, three but *o* ; *The Mystic* 17
Who make the emphatic *O*, by whom is all, *Sugg. by Reading* 81
On-set All *o-s* of capricious Accident, *Timbuctoo* 26
Onward drove them *o*—made them sensible ; *Lover's Tale ii* 77
Opal *o* width Of her small glowing lakes, *Timbuctoo* 101
Open (adj.) (*See also* **Half-open**) where no gaze Might rest, stood *o*, „ 179
The Sun peeped in from *o* field, *Home they brought him* 6
The written secrets of her inmost soul Lay like an *o* scroll before my view, *Lover's Tale i* 601
Was not the South, The East, the West, all *o*, „ 699
Open (verb) *O* thine eye and see.' *Timbuctoo* 84
Open'd *o* far into the outward, And never closed again. *Lover's Tale i* 298
Oph Over their crowned brethren On and *O* ? *A Fragment* 21
Opinion I call on you To make *o* warlike, *Sugg. by Reading* 87
Opposite And the great bird sits on the *o* bough, *The ' How ' and the ' Why '* 28
Orb With his unutterable, shining *o's*, *Timbuctoo* 67
Organ-pipe Nor yet your solemn *o-p's* that blow *Cambridge* 8
Orient To him the honey dews of *o* hope. *Lover's Tale i* 675
Other Or *o* things talking in unknown tongues, *Timbuctoo* 112
Investeth and ingirds all *o* lives. *The Mystic* 46
for bitter grief Doth hold the *o* half in sovranty. *Love and Sorrow* 5
Then might thy rays pass thro' to the *o* side, „ 14
Continuous till he reached the *o* sea. *The Hesperides* 13
such as in *o* minds Had film'd the margents of the recent wound. *Lover's Tale i* 763
For me all *o* Hopes did sway from that Which hung the frailest : „ 857
Outflash Check every *o*, every ruder sally *Check every outflash* 1
Outgrow *o* The wan dark coil of faded suffering— *Could I outwear* 3
Outset Oh, happy, happy *o* of my days ! *Lover's Tale i* 276
Outspread *o* With growth of shadowing leaf *Timbuctoo* 222
Outward (adj.) I seem'd to stand Upon the *o* verge „ 95
Is one of those who know no strife Of inward woe or *o* fear ; *Rosalind* 4
With her to whom all *o* fairest things *Lover's Tale i* 383
Outward (s) open'd far into the *o*, And never closed again. „ 298
Outwear Could I *o* my present state of woe *Could I outwear* 1
Overborne Lest my heart be *o*, *Germ of ' Maud '* 5
Overcome unto both Delight from hardship to be *o* *Lover's Tale i* 379
Overdoing *o* of her part Did fall away into oblivion. „ 629
Overhead world's last tempest darkens *o* ; *Britons, guard* 2
Overlast Can it *o* the nerves ? *Germ of ' Maud '* 26
Overleap but *o* All the petty shocks and fears *Rosalind* 12
Overlive Can it *o* the eye ? *Germ of ' Maud '* 27
Overthrown And murder was her freedom *o*. *Britons, guard* 23
Overwatching heart is drunk with *o's* night and day, *The Hesperides, Song ii* 12
Overwise The world will be *o*. „ 22
Owl black *o* scuds down the mellow twilight, *The ' How ' and the ' Why '* 30
Own Absorbed me from the nature of itself With its *o* fleetness. *Timbuctoo* 143
For she hath half delved her *o* deep grave. *I' the glooming light* 7
Into her *o* blue eyes so clear and deep, *Tears of Heaven* 7
Issue of its *o* substance, my heart's night *Love and Sorrow* 10
Shall be steeped in his *o* salt tear : *English War Song* 15
Me my *o* fate to lasting sorrow doometh : *Me my own fate* 1
did pause To worship mine *o* image, laved in light, *Lover's Tale i* 68
and with the shock Half dug their *o* graves), „ *ii* 50
And, trampled on, left to its *o* decay. „ 81
In a new birth, immingled with my *o*, „ *i* 732

P

Pactolus And sailing on *P* in a boat, *Pallid thunderstricken* 3
Padded What, it's you The *p* man—that wear the stays— *New Timon* 8
Pagan *See* **Half-pagan**
Pagod Her *P's* hung with music of sweet bells : *Timbuctoo* 234
Pain so kin to earth Pleasaunce fathers *p*— *Every day, etc.* 15
How scorn and ruin, *p* and hate could flow : *Pallid thunderstricken* 10
Though night and *p* and ruin and death reign here. *Love* 4
dazzled to the heart with glorious *p*. *There are three things* 14

Paint And I *p* the beauteous face — *Germ of 'Maud'* 2
Painted 'Gan rock and heave upon that *p* sea; — *Lover's Tale ii* 199
Palace They seem'd high *p's* and proud, — *What time I wasted* 5
Pale and the stars Were flooded over with clear glory and *p*. — *Timbuctoo* 9
Before the awful Genius of the place Kneels the *p* Priestess in deep faith, — „ 34
His eyes in eclipse, *P* cold his lips, — *Burial of Love* 2
Most *p* and clear and lovely distances. — *The Mystic* 35
With the blissful Lotos-eaters *p* We will abide in the golden vale — *Lotos-Eaters* 25
Gray sand banks and *p* sunsets—dreary wind, — *Mablethorpe* 7
her cheek was *p*, Oh! very fair and *p*: — *Lover's Tale i* 724
Paleness very spirit of *P* made still paler — „ 679
Paler very spirit of Paleness made still *p* — „ 679
Pallid The *p* thunderstricken sigh for gain, — *Pallid thunderstricken* 1
Palm gardens frequent with the stately *P*, — *Timbuctoo* 233
Palpitating And sound which struck the *p* sense, — „ 119
Pang Already with the *p's* of a new birth — *Love* 36
Papillote And shook a mane en *p's*. — *New Timon* 12
Paradise And odours rapt from remote *P*? — *Timbuctoo* 81
Parapet Over heaven's *p's* the angels lean. — *To a Lady Sleep.* 10
Pardon Can *p* little would-be Popes — *New Timon* 19
Parent crumbling from their *p* slope At slender interval, — *Timbuctoo* 123
Parliament The Court, the Church, the *P*, the crowd. — *Sugg. by Reading* 16
Part (s) *P* of a throne of fiery flame, — *Timbuctoo* 181
And with the overdoing of her *p* — *Lover's Tale i* 629
when hope died, *p* of her eloquence Died — „ 751
Part (verb) whose rapid interval *P's* Afric from green Europe, — *Timbuctoo* 3
Oh kiss me ere we *p*; — *Hero to Leander* 7
Parted Then *p* Heavenward on the wing: — *Timbuctoo* 251
P on either side her argent neck, — *Lover's Tale i* 740
Pass Do *p* from gloom to glory, — *Timbuctoo* 153
might thy rays *p* thro' to the other side, — *Love and Sorrow* 14
We pri' thee *p* not on; (repeat) — *The lintwhite* 31, 36
Let it *p*, the dreary brow, — *Germ of 'Maud'* 22
Passed We *p* with tears of rapture. — *Lover's Tale i* 409
Passeth he *p* by, And gulphs himself in sands, — *Timbuctoo* 236
Passing *P* through thee the edicts of his fear — *Love* 7
Which fill'd the Earth with *p* loveliness, — *Timbuctoo* 79
Oh, Beauty, *p* beauty! sweetest Sweet! — *Oh, Beauty* 1
Past (adj.) The indecision of my present mind With its *p* clearness, — *Timbuctoo* 140
Past (s) In eternity no future, In eternity no *p*. — *The 'How and the 'Why'* 7
Pastured Though hourly *p* on the salient blood? — *Shall the hag* 5
Path *p* was steep and loosely strewn with crags — *Lover's Tale i* 376
Could he not walk what *p's* he chose, — „ 692
Pathos With dandy *p* when you wrote, — *New Timon* 10
Pathway Yet winds the *p* free to all:— — *What time I wasted* 8
Pause (s) There is no rest, no calm, no *p*, — *οἱ ῥέοντες* 9
Pause (verb) did *p* To worship mine own image, — *Lover's Tale i* 67
Paving winter *p* earth With sheeny white, — *Chorus* 18
Peace unshaken *p* hath won thee: — *Though night* 10
Peace-lovers we—sweet *P* we all desire— — *Britons, guard* 13
Sneering bedridden in the down of *P* — *Sugg. by Reading* 46
Peaceful Thy Memnon, when his *p* lips are kissed With earliest rays, — *A Fragment* 22
Peace-lover *P-l's* we—sweet Peace we all desire— — *Britons, guard* 13
P-l's we—but who can trust a liar?— — „ 14
P-l's, haters Of shameless traitors, — „ 15
Peak (*See also* **Mountain-peak**) Night hath climbed her *p* of highest noon, — *Though night* 1
Pearl All night through archways of the bridgèd *p* — „ 3
Pebbled Leap the little waterfalls That sing into the *p* pool. — *Rosalind* 24
Peculiar In that blest ground but it was play'd about With its *p* glory. — *Timbuctoo* 57
Peeped Sun *p* in from open field, — *Home they brought him* 6
Pen you, dark Senate of the public *p*, — *Sugg. by Reading* 19
People That wish to keep their *p* fools; — *Hands all Round* 54
To raise the *p* and chastise the times — *Sugg. by Reading* 5
Let both the *p's* say, — *God bless our Prince* 12
Perfect The cruellest form of *p* scorn, — *Burial of Love* 18
One mighty countenance of *p* calm, — *The Mystic* 23
A *p* Idol, with profulgent brows — *A Fragment* 3
When we two meet there's never *p* light. — *Me my own fate* 14
Perilous And scorn of *p* seeming: — *Lover's Tale i* 380
Perisheth When thy light *p* That from thee issueth, — *The lintwhite* 13
Permeating I am the Spirit, The *p* life which courseth through — *Timbuctoo* 220
Permit *P* not thou the tyrant powers — *Hands all Round* 42
Pertness What unheroic *p*? what un-Christian spite! — *Sugg. by Reading* 78
Petal Or as the dew-drops on the *p* hung, — *Lover's Tale i* 558
Petty but overleap All the *p* shocks and fears — *Rosalind* 13
Peur cavalier *Sans* p *et sans reproche*, — *The Grasshopper* 19
Pew Stands in her *p* and hums her decent psalm — *Sugg. by Reading* 63
Phantasy wherewith Her *p* informs them. — *Timbuctoo* 40
Phantom 'Tis a *p* of the mind. — *Germ of 'Maud'* 14
'Tis a *p* fair and good I can call it to my side, — „ 15
Pharaoh The *P's* are no more: — *A Fragment* 28
Pharisees Christ cried: Woe, woe, to *P* and Scribes! — *Sugg. by Reading* 75
Philosophic And muse midway with *p* calm — *Timbuctoo* 146
Phosphor Hesper hateth *P*, evening hateth morn. — *The Hesperides, Song iii* 15
Piast O for those days of *P*, ere the Czar — *Blow ye the trumpet* 5
Pierce shalt thou *p* the woven glooms of truth; — *Though night* 11
Pierced *p* through and through with all Keen knowledges — *The Mystic* 29
Piercing A maze of *p*, trackless, thrilling thoughts — *Timbuctoo* 115
Pile chrystal *p* Of rampart upon rampart, — „ 162
Piled *P* by the strong and sunborn Anakim — *A Fragment* 20
Pillar *p's* high Long time eras'd from Earth: — *Timbuctoo* 12
Pillar'd Stood out a *p* front of burnish'd gold — „ 175
Pine And the dark *p* weeps, — *Lotos-Eaters* 33
And close above us, sang the wind-tost *p*, — *Lover's Tale i* 60
Pinewood all the white-stemmed *p* slept above— — *Check every outflash* 13
Pipe *See* **Organ-pipe**
Pipeth The little bird *p* 'why! why!' — *The 'How' and the 'Why'* 26
Pity rare *p* had stolen The living bloom — *Lover's Tale i* 725
Place (*See also* **Landing-place**) Before the awful Genius of the *p* — *Timbuctoo* 33
But the glory of the *p* Stood out — „ 174
This is the *p*. — *Check every outflash* 4
all the haunted *p* is dark and holy. — „ 8
But she tarries in her *p* — *Germ of 'Maud'* 1
Placid Thy *p* Sphinxes brooding o'er the Nile? — *A Fragment* 14
Plain (*See also* **Summerplain**) With all her interchange of hill and *p* — *Lover's Tale i* 694
Plaining Drooping and beaten with the *p* wind, — „ 735
Plan Thin dilletanti deep in nature's *p*, — *Sugg. by Reading* 80
Plane underneath a shadowy *p* In old Bayona, — *There are three things* 10
Planet planet-girded Suns And moon-encircled *p's*, — *Timbuctoo* 110
The murmurous *p's'* rolling choir, — *Chorus* 24
As dwellers in lone *p's* look upon The mighty disk — *Love* 20
Planet-girded *p-g* Suns And moon-encircled planets, — *Timbuctoo* 109
Plant Hope is dried,—the life o' the *p*— — *Lover's Tale i* 808
Planting *P* my feet against this mound of time — „ 492
Play I *p* about his heart a thousand ways, — *Timbuctoo* 205
you hearts are tennis balls To *p* with, — *Rosalind* 33
Play'd it was *p* about With its peculiar glory. — *Timbuctoo* 56
Playmate that thought Which was the *p* of my youth— — *Lover's Tale ii* 72
Pleached *P* with her hair, in mail of argent light — *Pallid thunderstricken* 12
the *p* ivy tress had wound Round my worn limbs, — *Lover's Tale i* 637
Pleasant Some say this life is *p*, — *The 'How' and the 'Why'* 3
Thy *p* wiles Forgotten, and thine innocent joy? — *Burial of Love* 15
I have bathed thee with the *p* myrrh; — *Hero to Leander* 19
The *p* stars have set! — „ 39
Surely all *p* things had gone before, — *O sad No more!* 7
The many *p* days, the moonlit nights, — *Lover's Tale i* 54
'Tis a beautiful And *p* meditation, — „ 240
Pleasaunce so kin to earth *P* fathers pain— — *Every day, etc.* 15
Please But you, Sir, you are hard to *p*; — *New Timon* 25
Pleased nor breathe What airs he *p*! — *Lover's Tale i* 693
Pleasure We shall lose eternal *p*, — *The Hesperides, Song i* 11
Plot Moving his crest to all sweet *p's* of flowers — *Could I outwear* 7
Ploughed A gate and a field half *p*, — *A gate and a field* 1
Plunder'd His ruthless host is bought with *p* gold, — *Britons, guard* 7
Plunge they *p* their doubts among old rags and bones. — *Sugg. by Reading* 72
Plunged and following, *p* Into the dizzy chasm — *Lover's Tale i* 369
Poerio From wronged *P's* noisome den, — *Hands all Round* 15
Poet No Tithon thou as *p's* feign — *The Grasshopper* 5
p at his will Lets the great world flit from him, — *D. of F. Women* 9
All unawares, into the *p's* brain; — *Lover's Tale i* 557
Poetic To have the deep *p* heart Is more than all *p* fame. — *New Timon* 23
Point Distinct and vivid with sharp *p's* of light — *Timbuctoo* 107
With *p's* of blastborne hail their heated eyne! — *Shall the hag* 11

Poisèd (*See also* **Self-poised**) Though long ago listening the *p* lark, *To a Lady Sleep.* 8
Poles Arise, brave *P*, the boldest of the bold; *Blow ye the trumpet* 3
Polish rolled The growing murmurs of the *P* war! „ 8
Polish'd Flowing between the clear and *p* stems, *Timbuctoo* 51
Pomeranian on the Baltic shore Boleslas drove the *P*. *Blow ye the trumpet* 14
Pool waterfalls That sing into the pebbled *p*. *Rosalind* 24
Poor *P* soul! behold her: what decorous calm! *Sugg. by Reading* 61
Pope For the French the *P* may shrive 'em, (repeat) *National Song* 9, 27
pardon little would-be *P's* And Brummels, *New Timon* 19
The *P* has bless'd him; *Britons, guard* 3
Poplar Through yonder *p* alley Below, *Check every outflash* 4
Poppy So I wove Even the dull-blooded *p*, *Lover's Tale i* 342
Porch length of *p* and lake and boundless hall, *Timbuctoo* 180
Portal *p's* of pure silver walks the moon. *Though night* 4
Your *p's* statued with old kings and queens, *Cambridge* 2
Pour And the foam-white waters *p*; *Lotos-Eaters* 32
Pouring Waves on the shingle *p*, *1865-1866* 11
Power I have fill'd thy lips with *p*. *Timbuctoo* 215
and apart In intellect and *p* and will, *The Mystic* 38
One of the shining wingèd *p's*, *What time I wasted* 2
Permit not thou the tyrant *p's* *Hands all Round* 42
What *p* is yours to blast a cause or bless! *Sugg. by Reading* 8
Lest you go wrong from *p* in excess. „ 10
I grant you one of the great *P's* on earth, „ 23
But knowing all your *p* to heat or cool, „ 31
Powerful All *p* in beauty as thou art. *Love and Sorrow* 12
Practise Now *p*, yeomen, Like those bowmen, *Britons, guard* 45
Praise You did mingle blame and *p*, *To C. North* 3
I could *not* forgive the *p*, „ 8
Prance The boy began to leap and *p*, *Home they brought him* 7
Prate *You p* of nature! you are he That spilt his life *New Timon* 39
Pray *See* **Pri' thee**
Pray'd He worked for both: he *p* for both: *Lover's Tale i* 223
I *p* aloud to God that he would hold „ 791
Preach words of little children *p* Against you,— *Cambridge* 12
O Grief and Shame if while I *p* of laws *Sugg. by Reading* 37
Preached Five and three (Let it not be *p* abroad) *The Hesperides, Song i* 16
Preamble nightingale, with long and low *p*, *Check every outflash* 9
Precious The *p* jewel of my honour'd life, *Lover's Tale ii* 78
Precursor more fleet and strong Than its *p*, *Timbuctoo* 128
Pregnant *See* **Fountain pregnant**
Prepare loud and long, the warning-note: *P*! *Sugg. by Reading* 90
Presence I have given *thee* To understand my *p*, *Timbuctoo* 214
The imperishable *p's* serene, *The Mystic* 13
p's Fourfacèd to four corners of the sky; „ 15
Present (adj.) The indecision of my *p* mind With its past clearness, *Timbuctoo* 139
Could I outwear my *p* state of woe *Could I outwear* 1
Present (s) In time there is no *p*, *The 'How' and the 'Why'* 5
Press *p* had ever been The public conscience *Sugg. by Reading* 2
O you, the *P*! what good from you might spring! „ 7
nor the *P*! and look you well to that— „ 17
Pressure lake From *p* of descendant crags, *Timbuctoo* 122
Prevail Should he land here, and for one hour *p*, *Britons, guard* 55
Pride (*See also* **Summerpride**) *P* came beneath and held a light. *Love, Pride, etc.* 6
P took Love's sweets, and by a spell „ 9
Memory tho' fed by *P* Did wax so thin on gall, „ 11
in the *p* of beauty issuing A sheeny snake, *Could I outwear* 5
Priest By lying *p's* the peasant's votes controlled. *Britons, guard* 8
Priestess Kneels the pale *P* in deep faith, *Timbuctoo* 34
Prime dewy *p* Of youth and buried time? *Who can say* 6
Prince God bless our *P* and Bride! *God bless our Prince* 1
Pri' thee We *p t* pass not, (repeat) *The lintwhite* 31, 36
Privacy But yours are not their homestead *privacies*. *Sugg. by Reading* 22
Privilege Take heed of your wide *p's*! „ 11
Proctor Your doctors and your *p's* and your deans *Cambridge* 5
Profess ye that did *p* to teach And have taught nothing „ 13
Profit What *p's* now to understand *New Timon* 33
what *p's* it To tell ye that her father died, *Lover's Tale, i* 290
Profulgent A perfect Idol, with *p* brows *A Fragment* 3
Progress if France be she Whom martial *p* only charms? *Hands all Round* 26
Promontory One cypress on an inland *p*. *Me my own fate* 8
voyaging beyond The hoary *p* of Soloë *The Hesperides* 3
Propagate Or *p* again her loathèd kind, *Shall the hag* 2
Proud They seem'd high palaces and *p*, *What time I wasted* 5
Prove *P* their falsehood and thy quarrel, *The Grasshopper* 9
Proved Now *p* counterfeit, was shaken out, *Lover's Tale ii* 80
Proverb till their love Shall ripen to a *p* „ *i* 803
Prowess infixed The limits of his *p*, *Timbuctoo* 12
Psalm Stands in her pew and hums her decent *p* *Sugg. by Reading* 63
Public The *p* conscience of our noble isle, „ 3
And you, dark Senate of the *p* pen, „ 19
Yours are the *p* acts of *p* men, „ 21
For better so you fight for *p* ends; „ 26
Pure *P* without heat, into a larger air Upburning, *The Mystic* 44
And portals of *p* silver walks the moon. *Though night, etc.* 4
And why was I to darken their *p* love, *Lover's Tale i* 765
Purest starr'd at slender intervals With blossom tufts of *p* white; „ 400
Purified Had *p*, and chastened, and made free. *The Mystic* 10
Purple Waiting to light him with his *p* skies, *Love* 34
Arching blue-glossèd necks beneath the *p* weather. *Dualisms* 13
Far sheening down the *p* seas to those *A Fragment* 4
Lest the redcombed dragon slumber Rolled together in *p* folds. *The Hesperides, Song ii* 10
Purplefringed *P* with even and dawn. „ *iii* 14
Purport Keeping unchanged The *p* of their coinage. *Lover's Tale i* 734
Push'd watcher's at heaven's gate, *p* them apart, „ 616
Pushing *P* the thick roots aside *The Grasshopper* 37
Put 'Then take it, love, and *p* it by; *The Ringlet* 11
'Then kiss it, love, and *p* it by: „ 23
'Come, kiss it, love, and *p* it by: „ 41
Ringlet, You *p* me much to shame, „ 48
Pyramids upsprung the dazzling Cones Of *P*, *Timbuctoo* 169
P Broad-based amid the fleeting sands, *A Fragment* 9

Q

Quaint And much I mus'd on legends *q* and old *Timbuctoo* 16
And all the *q* old scraps of ancient crones, *Lover's Tale i* 288
Quarrel Prove their falsehood and thy *q*, *The Grasshopper* 9
Queen Your portals statued with old kings and *q's*, *Cambridge* 2
'God save the *Q*' is here a truer cry. *Britons, guard* 26
You must not mix our *Q* with those *Hands all Round* 53
God save the *Q*! (repeat) *God bless our Prince* 3, 7, 10
God bless the *Q*. „ 14
Quench'd White as *q* ashes, cold as were the hopes Of my lorn love! *Lover's Tale i* 620
Quest my refluent health made tender *q* „ 742
Quick Severe and *q* to feel a civic sin, *Sugg. by Reading* 4
As even then the torrent of *q* thought Absorbed me *Timbuctoo* 141

R

Race Kingdoms lapse, and climates change, and *r's* die; *The Hesperides, Song ii* 4
She comprehends the *r* she rules. *Hands all Round* 56
Some vast Assyrian doom to burst upon our *r*. *Sugg. by Reading* 42
Rack'd She feels not how the social frame is *r*, „ 56
Radiance showering circular abyss Of *r*. *Timbuctoo* 174
Rag they plunge their doubts among old *r's* and bones. *Sugg. by Reading* 72
Rage We beat upon our aching hearts with *r*; *Love* 18
Rain (s) Hark how the wild *r* hisses, *Hero to Leander* 14
hath drawn the frozen *r* From my cold eyes *Could I outwear* 13
Dim shores, dense *r's*, and heavy clouded sea. *Mablethorpe* 8
the dew, the sun, the *r*, Under the growth of body *Lover's Tale ii* 73
Rain (verb) for fear the mind *R* thro' my sight, „ *i* 24
Rainy One *r* night, when every wind blew loud, „ 367
Raise To *r* the people and chastise the times *Sugg. by Reading* 5
Rais'd I *r* My voice and cried 'Wide Afric, *Timbuctoo* 57
With ministering hand he *r* me up; „ 188
I have *r* thee higher to the Spheres of Heaven, „ 216
I was *r* To be a mystery of loveliness „ 240
Rampart chrystal pile Of *r* upon *r*, dome on dome, „ 163
Ran That *r* bloombright into the Atlantic blue, *The Hesperides* 9
legend *r* that, long time since, One rainy night, *Lover's Tale i* 366
Range *r* of battlement On battlement, *Timbuctoo* 164
Rangèd Her obelisks of *r* Chrysolite, „ 235

Rapid whose *r* interval Parts Afric from green Europe, *Timbuctoo* 2
Involving and embracing each with each *R* as fire, „ 117
The *r* waste of roving sea, *Chorus* 2
Up and down a *r* river, Leap the little waterfalls *Rosalind* 22
Sheer thro' the black-wall'd cliff the *r* brook *Lover's Tale i* 371
Rapt And odours *r* from remote Paradise? *Timbuctoo* 81
hurried through The riv'n *r* brain: „ 121
Rapture Intense delight and *r* that I breathed, *Lover's Tale i* 381
We passed with tears of *r*. „ 409
Rare outspread With growth of shadowing leaf and clusters *r*, *Timbuctoo* 223
r pity had stolen The living bloom away, *Lover's Tale i* 725
Ravish'd and thou with *r* sense Listenest the lordly music flowing from Th' illimitable years. *Timbuctoo* 217
Raw To soothe a civic wound or keep it *r*, *Sugg. by Reading* 32
Ray might thy *r's* pass thro' to the other side, *Love and Sorrow* 14
peaceful lips are kissed With earliest *r's*, *A Fragment* 23
Reached he had well nigh *r* The last, *The Mystic* 42
Continuous till he *r* the other sea. *The Hesperides* 13
Reacheth *R* to every corner under Heaven, *Timbuctoo* 224
Read Ye could not *r* the marvel in his eye, *The Mystic* 4
Wherein to *r*, wherein to write. (repeat) *O darling room* 6, 18
I sorrow when I *r* the things you write, *Sugg. by Reading* 77
And my eyes *r*, they *r* aright, *Lover's Tale i* 602
Reap doth the fruit of her dishonour *r*. *Tears of Heaven* 5
Recall *r's* the dewy prime Of youth *Who can say* 6
Recent Had film'd the margents of the *r* wound. *Lover's Tale i* 764
Reckoning Jesuit laughs, and *r* on his chance, *Britons, guard* 32
Reclined How often, when a child I lay *r*, *Mablethorpe* 1
Red (adj.) And in *r* Autumn when the winds are wild With gambols, *Timbuctoo* 202
So I wove Even the dull-blooded poppy, 'whose *r* flower Hued with the scarlet of a fierce sunrise, *Lover's Tale i* 342
as tho' a *r* rose Should change into a white one suddenly. „ 726
Red (s) Ringlet, She blush'd a rosy *r*, *The Ringlet* 36
Redcombed Lest the *r* dragon slumber Rolled together in purple folds. *The Hesperides, Song ii* 9
Redolent Every flower and every fruit the *r* breath „ *iv* 1
Redundant Each sun which from the centre flings Grand music and *r* fire, *Chorus* 22
Reed crushing the thick fragrant *r's* he lies, *Love* 32
Referr'd by the busy mind *r*, compared, *Lover's Tale i* 384
Reflex waves, which bore The *r* of my City in their depths. *Timbuctoo* 239
One *r* from eternity on time, *The Mystic* 22
between The moon and the moon's *r* in the night; *Shall the hag* 13
Refluent After my *r* health made tender quest *Lover's Tale i* 742
Refuge men's hopes and fears take *r* in The fragrance *Timbuctoo* 226
Refused *R* to look his author in the face, *Lover's Tale i* 697
Regard comes the New: *R* him: *New Timon* 6
Region with which a *r* of white flame, *The Mystic* 43
Regulate wondrous laws which *r* The fierceness *Timbuctoo* 147
Reign *R* thou above the storms of sorrow *Though night* 9
night and pain and ruin and death *r* here. *Love* 4
Remaining and yet *R* from the body, *The Mystic* 37
Remember I well *r*, It was a glorious morning, *Lover's Tale i* 300
Remorseful and the heat Of the *r* soul alive within, „ 682
Remote And odours rapt from *r* Paradise? *Timbuctoo* 81
Rend roaring brine Will *r* thy golden tresses; *Hero to Leander* 24
Oh! *r* the veil in twain: *Love* 25
Render I must *r* up this glorious home *Timbuctoo* 243
Renewing I thus hope my lost delights *r*, *Could I outwear* 9
Renown'd Upon his *r* Eminence bore globes Of wheeling suns, *Timbuctoo* 171
Reproche cavalier *Sans peur et sans* r, *The Grasshopper* 19
Respectability The British Goddess, sleek *R*. *Sugg. by Reading* 54
Respectant One forward, one *r*, three but one; *The Mystic* 18
Rest (s) There is no *r*, no calm, no pause, *οἱ ῥέοντες* 9
Worth eternal want of *r*. *The Hesperides, Song i* 12
Mellowed in a land of *r*; „ *iv* 12
Rest (verb) where no gaze Might *r*, stood open, *Timbuctoo* 179
An artist, Sir, should *r* in art, *New Timon* 21
Off, and let him *r*. „ 44
Rested Wherein we *r* sleeping or awake, *Lover's Tale i* 227
Restless The starry glowing of his *r* eyes. *Timbuctoo* 89
the level calm Is ridg'd with *r* and increasing spheres „ 125
Resumeth In summer still a summer joy *r*. *Me my own fate* 4
Retir'd *r* At midnight, in the lone Acropolis. *Timbuctoo* 31
Return islanders of Ithaca, we will *r* no more. *Lotos-Eaters* 40
some you strike can scarce *r* the blow; *Sugg. by Reading* 27
Returnest Thou goest and *r* to His Lips Like lightning: *Love* 12
Revealèd And the ancient secret *r*. *The Hesperides, Song iii* 5
Revel In thine hour of love and *r*, *The Grasshopper* 35
Revenge Till Love have his full *r*. *Burial of Love* 30
Reverence Our ancient boast is this—we *r* law. *Sugg. by Reading* 34
Review You did late *r* my lays, *To C. North* 1
Rhene (Rhine) where the *R* Curves towards Mentz, *O darling room* 11
Rhine (*See also* **Rhene**) To take Sardinia, Belgium, or the *R*: *Britons, guard* 50
Rhodes In the midnoon the glory of old *R*, *A Fragment* 2
Rhyme The cause is nowhere found in *r*. *Who can say* 8
such a heat as lives in great creative *r's*. *Sugg. by Reading* 6
Those *r's*, 'The Lion and the Unicorn' *Lover's Tale i* 285
Ribbèd *See* **Thick-ribbèd**
Rich Wax-lighted chapels and *r* carved screens, *Cambridge* 4
Ridden *See* **Soldier-ridden**
Riddle Who will *r* me the *how* and the *why?* (repeat) *The 'How' and the 'Why'* 9, 20
Who will *r* me the how and the what? Who will *r* me the what and the why? „ 36
Ridge he stood beside me There on the *r*, *Timbuctoo* 66
On the *r* of the hill his banners rise; *English War Song* 25
Ridg'd *r* with restless and increasing spheres *Timbuctoo* 125
Rift horrid *r's* Sent up the moaning *Lover's Tale i* 612
Right Shout for God and our *r*! *English War Song* 50
In any town, to left or *r*, *O darling room* 14
Or loyally disloyal battled for our *r's*. *Sugg. by Reading* 36
Righteousness Clothe them with *r*, *God bless our Prince* 4
Ring The burning belts, the mighty *r's*, *Chorus* 23
In *r's* of gold yronne, *The lintwhite* 29
shot the sunset, In light *r's* round me; *Lover's Tale i* 438
Ringing There was a *r* in my ears, *O sad No more!* 5
It's always *r* in your ears, *New Timon* 31
Ringlet 'Your *r's*, your *r's*, *The Ringlet* 1
'My *r*, my *r*, That art so golden-gay, „ 13
O *R*, O *R*, I kiss'd you night and day, „ 25
And *R*, O *R*, You still are golden-gay, „ 27
But *R*, O *R*, You should be silver-gray: „ 29
O *R*, O *R*, She blush'd a rosy red, „ 35
When *R*, O *R*, She clipt you from her head, „ 37
And *R*, O *R*, She gave you me, „ 39
O *R*, O *R*, I count you much to blame, „ 45
For *R*, O *R*, You put me much to shame, „ 47
So *R*, O *R*, I doom you to the flame. „ 49
r's, Drooping and beaten with the plaining wind, *Lover's Tale i* 734
Ripen till their love Shall *r* to a proverb „ 803
Ripened Sunset *r*, above on the tree, *The Hesperides, Song iv* 21
Ripeneth redolent breath Of this warm seawind *r*, „ 2
Rise (s) alternate *r* Of interpenetrated arc, *Timbuctoo* 130
Rise (verb) On the ridge of the hill his banners *r*; *English War Song* 25
R, Britons, *r*, if manhood be not dead; *Britons, guard* 1
O *r*, our strong Atlantic sons, *Hands all Round* 49
Risen *See* **New-risen**
Rising In *r* and in falling with the tide, *Lover's Tale i* 62
Riven mountains *r* To shapes of wildest anarchy, *Chorus* 3
hurried through The *r* rapt brain: *Timbuctoo* 121
River Like a swol'n *r's* gushings in still night „ 193
See'st thou yon *r*, whose translucent wave, „ 229
Nor the *r's* flow, nor the sweet birds sing, *Burial of Love* 29
the blue-green *r* windeth slowly; *Check every outflash* 5
Up and down a rapid *r*, *Rosalind* 22
Roam they *r* together Under a summervault *Dualisms* 17
And no more *r*, On the loud hoar foam, *Lotos-Eaters* 18
Roar And the loud sea *r's* below. *Hero to Leander* 15
storms of sorrow and ruth That *r* beneath; *Though night* 10
But let thy broadsides *r* with ours. *Hands all Round* 44
Roaring And winds were *r* and blowing; *1865-1866* 3
Old Year *r* and blowing And New Year blowing and *r*. „ 12
To-night the *r* brine Will rend thy golden tresses; *Hero to Leander* 23
Robe glistering sands that *r* The understream. *Pallid thunderstricken* 5
Robèd *See* **White-robèd**

Rock Why the *r's* stand still, *The 'How' and the 'Why'* 14
'Gan *r* and heave upon that painted sea; *Lover's Tale ii* 199
Rockèd Two bees within a chrystal flowerbell *r* *Dualisms* 1
Rock-hewn grots *R-h* and sealed for ever. *A Fragment* 31
Rod The Russian whips and Austrian *r's*— *Hands all Round* 18
Rode *R* upon his father's lance, *Home they brought him* 8
Roll nor with the thoughts that *r*, *Cambridge* 11
Rolled (*See also* **Down-roll'd**) *R* together in purple folds. *The Hesperides, Song ii* 10
r The growing murmurs of the Polish war! *Blow ye the trumpet* 7
Rolling The murmurous planets' *r* choir, *Chorus* 24
As round the *r* earth night follows day: *Me my own fate* 10
Rome *R's* dearest daughter now is captive France, *Britons, guard* 31
Roof (s) the *r* and crown Of all I hoped and fear'd? *Lover's Tale ii* 27
Roof (verb) Winter *r's* The headland with inviolate *Timbuctoo* 203
Roof'd Imperial Eldorado *r* with gold: „ 24
Room O DARLING *r*, my heart's delight, Dear *r*, the apple of my sight, *O darling room* 1
There is no *r* so exquisite, No little *r* so warm and bright „ 4
A little *r* so exquisite, „ 15
Not any *r* so warm and bright, „ 17
Root Pushing the thick *r's* aside *The Grasshopper* 37
Standing about the charmèd *r*. *The Hesperides, Song i* 4
From the *r* Drawn in the dark, „ 20
Standing about the charmèd *r*. „ *iv* 34
by our ears, the huge *r's* strain and creak), *Lover's Tale i* 63
Rooted *See* **Deep-rooted**
Rosalind MY *R*, my *R*, Bold, subtle, careless *R*, *Rosalind* 1
My falconhearted *R* Fullsailed „ 9
My happy falcon, *R*, „ 25
My *R*, my *R*, Because no shadow on you falls, „ 30
hearts are tennis balls To play with, wanton *R*? „ 33
Rose (s) WITH *r's* musky breathed, *Anacreontics* 1
Farewell, fair *r* of May! *God bless our Prince* 11
each *r* Doth faint upon the bosom of the other, *Lover's Tale i* 563
a red *r* Should change into a white one „ 726
„ 388
Rose (verb) A tutelary angel as she *r*, *There are three things* 4
Roselip Dimples, *r's*, and eyes of any hue. *Hero to Leander* 16
Rosy Thy heart beats through thy *r* limbs *Lotos-Eaters* 12
In the hollow *r* vale to tarry, *The Ringlet* 36
O Ringlet, O Ringlet, She blush'd a *r* red, *New Timon* 38
Rouge old mark of *r* upon your cheeks. *Burial of Love* 26
Round Nor the *r* sun that shineth to all; *Hands all Round* 21
Yet hands all *r* „ 24, 48, 60
And the great name of England *r* and *r* (repeat) *The 'How' and the 'Why'* 13
Why *r* is not square? *The Hesperides, Song i* 5
R about all is mute, „ *iv* 11
Holy and bright, *r* and full, bright and blest, *Chorus* 2
Roving The rapid waste of *r* sea, *Lotos-Eaters* 39
Rowing Than labour in the ocean, and *r* with the oar, *The lintwhite* 19
Royal Fair year, with brows of *r* love Thou comest, *D. of F. Women* 7
Rubylike Glows *r* the far-up crimson globe, *Lover's Tale i* 796
Rude From which may *r* Death never startle them, *Check every outflash* 1
Ruder every *r* sally Of thought and speech; *Pallid thunderstricken* 10
Ruin How scorn and *r*, pain and hate could flow: *Lover's Tale ii* 71
So gazed I on the *r's* of that thought *Love* 4
night and pain and *r* and death reign here. *Lover's Tale ii* 62
Ruin'd The wreck of *r* life and shatter'd thought, *Sugg. by Reading* 33
Rule (s) Be loyal, if you wish for wholesome *r*: „ 60
yet the 'not too much' is all the *r* she knows. *Hands all Round* 56
Rule (verb) She comprehends the race she *r's*. *Timbuctoo* 61
Rumour Or is the *r* of thy Timbuctoo *Love* 41
Rusheth Anon he *r* forth with merry din, *Hands all Round* 18
Russian The *R* whips and Austrian rods— *Timbuctoo* 64
Rustling A *r* of white wings! *To C. North* 4
Rusty You did mingle blame and praise, *R* Christopher. *Though night* 9
Ruth storms of sorrow and *r* That roar beneath; *Britons, guard* 7
Ruthless His *r* host is bought with plunder'd gold,

S

Sable To wander down his *s* sheeny sides, *Love* 39
Sacrifice Folding the slaughter of the *s* *To* —— 6
Sad O s *No more!* O sweet *No more!* *O sad No more!* 1
Sadness Grief and *s* steal Symbols of each other; *Every day, etc.* 25
Said *s* to thee That thou hast half my heart, *Love and Sorrow* 3
As I *s*, with these She crown'd her forehead. *Lover's Tale i* 348
Sail (s) No more unfurl the straining *s*; *Lotos-Eaters* 24
Sail (verb) As when a man, that *s's* in a balloon, *D. of F. Women* 1
Sailed (*See also* **Fullsailed**) to those Who *s* from Mizraim *A Fragment* 5
Sailing And *s* on Pactolus in a boat, *Pallid thunderstricken* 3
Saint unfading foreheads of the *S's* in Heaven? *Timbuctoo* 54
Sainted *S* Juliet! dearest name! *To* —— 1
Salient Though hourly pastured on the *s* blood? *Shall the hag* 5
Sallow And in the glow of *s* Summertide, *Timbuctoo* 201
The troublous autumn's *s* gloom, *Chorus* 17
Sally every ruder *s* Of thought and speech; *Check every outflash* 1
Salt The deep *s* wave breaks in above Those marble steps below. *Hero to Leander* 34
It shall be steeped in the *s*, *s* tear, Shall be steeped in his own *s* tear: *English War Song* 14
Same *See* **Self-same**
Sand (adj.) Gray *s* banks and pale sunsets—dreary wind, *Mablethorpe* 7
Sand (s) he passeth by, And gulphs himself in *s's*, *Timbuctoo* 237
Black specks amid a waste of dreary *s*, „ 247
glistering *s's* that robe The understream. *Pallid thunderstricken* 5
Pyramids Broad-based amid the fleeting *s's*, *A Fragment* 10
lake, that, flooding, makes Cushions of yellow *s*; *Lover's Tale i* 537
Sanded *See* **Gold-sanded**
Sandfield As the *s* at the mountain-foot. *The Hesperides, Song i* 7
Sang close above us, *s* the wind-tost pine, *Lover's Tale i* 60
Sap And the *s* to three-fold music floweth, *The Hesperides, Song i* 19
Huge splinters, which the *s* of earliest showers, *Lover's Tale ii* 45
Sapphire wheel in wheel, Arch'd the wan *S*. *Timbuctoo* 111
And thunder thro' the *s* deeps In wayward strength, *Chorus* 28
Sardinia To take *S*, Belgium, or the Rhine: *Britons, guard* 50
Save 'God *s* the Queen' is here a truer cry. „ 26
God *s* the Nation, The toleration, „ 27
God *s* the Queen! (repeat) *God bless our Prince* 3, 7, 10
Saw *s* before me Such colour'd spots *Timbuctoo* 69
I *s* The smallest grain that dappled the dark Earth, „ 98
within the South methought I *s* A wilderness of spires, „ 161
if I *s* These things distinctly, „ 184
S far on each side through the grated gates *The Mystic* 34
I *s* no more only those eyes— *There are three things* 13
S round her feet the country far away, *Lover's Tale i* 390
eyes, I *s*, were full of tears in the morn, „ 728
Say (s) And a fool may say his *s*; *The Ringlet* 18
Say (verb) nothing visible, they *s*, had birth *Timbuctoo* 55
Some *s* this life is pleasant, *The 'How' and the 'Why'* 3
What is it they *s*? What do they there? „ 12
WHO can *s* Why To-day To-morrow will be yesterday? *Who can say* 1
I honour much, I *s*, this man's appeal. *Sugg. by Reading* 49
Let both the peoples *s*, *God bless our Prince* 12
And a fool may *s* his say; *The Ringlet* 18
Let them so love that men and boys may *s*, *Lover's Tale i* 801
Scale step by step to *s* that mighty stair *Timbuctoo* 198
Scalèd Lest his *s* eyelid drop, *The Hesperides, Song ii* 15
Scan would *s* Definite round. *Timbuctoo* 131
eye could *s* Through length of porch and lake „ 179
Scandal She loves a little *s* which excites; *Sugg. by Reading* 57
Scatter feeds it from behind, And *s's* it before, *Lover's Tale ii* 48
Scene Rhene Curves towards Mentz, a woody *s*. *O darling room* 12
Science '*S* enough and exploring *1865-1866* 6
Scorn The cruellest form of perfect *s*, *Burial of Love* 18
Ye scorned him with an undiscerning *s*: *The Mystic* 3
How *s* and ruin, pain and hate could flow: *Pallid thunderstricken* 10
withering *s* of the many shall cleave *English War Song* 5
He shall eat the bread of common *s*; „ 13
With a flash of frolic *s* And keen delight, *Rosalind* 15
By the thing I hold in *s*, *Germ of 'Maud'* 6
And *s* of perilous seeming: *Lover's Tale i* 380
Scorned Ye *s* him with an undiscerning *s*: *The Mystic* 3
Scrap all the quaint old *s's* of ancient crones, *Lover's Tale i* 288
Screaming *s*, from me flung The empty phantom: „ *ii* 212
And bitter blasts the *s* autumn whirl, *Though night, etc.* 2
Screen Wax-lighted chapels and rich carved *s's*, *Cambridge* 4
Scribe Christ cried: Woe, woe, to Pharisees and *S's*! *Sugg. by Reading* 75
Scrip Over their *s's* and shares, their meats and wine, „ 47
Scroll Lay like an open *s* before my view, *Lover's Tale i* 601

Stop sing aloud and evermore in the wind, without *s*, *The Hesperides, Song ii* 14
Storm calm and *s* Mingle day by day. *Every day, etc.* 7
By secret fire and midnight *s's* *Chorus* 5
s's of sorrow and ruth That roar beneath; *Though night* 9
vessel and your Church may sink in *s's*. *Sugg. by Reading* 74
Storm-blast the shrill *s-b* feeds it from behind, *Lover's Tale ii* 47
Strain *s* Weak eyes upon the glistering sands *Pallid thunderstricken* 4
S the hot spheres of his convulsèd eyes, *Love* 37
Close by our ears, the huge roots *s* and creak), *Lover's Tale i* 63
Straining No more unfurl the *s* sail; *Lotos-Eaters* 24
Strange Which flung *s* music on the howling winds, *Timbuctoo* 80
are full of *s* Astonishment and boundless change. (repeat) *Chorus* 9, 19, 29
All visions wild and *s*; *οἱ ῥέοντες* 2
O SAD *No more!* O sweet *No more!* O *s No more! O sad No more!* 2
Strangling *s* sorrow weigh Mine utterance with lameness. *Lover's Tale i* 24
Stream (s) (*See also* **Understream**) borne Adown the sloping of an arrowy *s*, *Timbuctoo* 144
Down an ideal *s* they ever float, *Pallid thunderstricken* 2
Over a *s* two birds of glancing feather *Dualisms* 8
And all things flow like a *s*. (repeat) *οἱ ῥέοντες* 8, 16
Two *s's* upon the violet deep: *The Hesperides, Song iv* 6
To whom the slope and *s* of life, *Rosalind* 5
low-hung tresses, dipp'd In the fierce *s*, *Lover's Tale i* 375
the chillness of the mountain *s* Smote on my brow, „ 652
the loud *s*, Awoke me not, but were a part of sleep; „ *ii* 123
Stream (verb) They *s* like fire in the skies; *English War Song* 26
solid shining ground *S* from beneath him *D. of F. Women* 3
To flame and sparkle and *s* as of old, *The Ringlet* 8
Street and the *s's* with ghastly faces throng'd *Timbuctoo* 29
windeth through The argent *s's* o' the City, „ 231
Why change the titles of your *s's*? *Hands all Round* 31
Strength buoyancy and *s* To bear them upward *Timbuctoo* 158
mailèd warrior in youth and *s* complete; *The Grasshopper* 13
thro' the sapphire deeps In wayward *s*, *Chorus* 29
in him light and joy and *s* abides; *Love* 42
For where is the heart and *s* of slaves? Oh! where is the *s* of slaves? *English War Song* 36
ere the Czar Grew to this *s* *Blow ye the trumpet* 6
We won old battles with our *s*, the bow. *Britons, guard* 44
On that day the year First felt his youth and *s*, *Lover's Tale i* 306
Strewn path was steep and loosely *s* with crags „ 376
Stricken *See* **Awestricken, Thunderstricken**
Strife know no *s* Of inward woe or outward fear; *Rosalind* 3
Strike some you *s* can scarce return the blow; *Sugg. by Reading* 27
String *See* **Lutestring**
Stringing As they gambol, lilygarlands ever *s*: *Dualisms* 15
Stripe In a *s* of grassgreen calm, *Lotos-Eaters* 5
Stroke a lightning *s* had come Even from that Heaven *Lover's Tale i* 623
Strong The issue of *s* impulse, hurried through The riv'n rapt brain: *Timbuctoo* 120
more fleet and *s* Than its precursor, „ 127
But an insect lithe and *s*, *The Grasshopper* 7
Where are thy monuments Piled by the *s* and sunborn Anakim *A Fragment* 20
He is weak! we are *s*; he a slave, we are free; *English War Song* 38
O rise, our *s* Atlantic sons, *Hands all Round* 49
Caucasus is bold and *s*. *The Hesperides, Song iii* 7
Stronger May Freedom's oak for ever live With *s* life from day to day; *Hands all Round* 6
Strove *S* to uprise, laden with mournful thanks, *Lover's Tale i* 748
Struck sound which *s* the palpitating sense, *Timbuctoo* 119
Strung *S* in the very negligence of Art, *Lover's Tale i* 562
Style How much I love this writer's manly *s*! *Sugg. by Reading* 1
Subaltern who are to you As captain is to *s*. *New Timon* 16
Subject Free *s's* of the kindliest of all thrones, *Sugg. by Reading* 71
Substance Issue of its own *s*, *Love and Sorrow* 10
Substanceless Almeida, if my heart were *s*, „ 13
Subterranean and the streets with ghastly faces throng'd Do utter forth a *s* voice, *Timbuctoo* 30
Subtle The *s* life, the countless forms Of living things, *Chorus* 7
no control Within the thrilling brain could keep afloat The *s* spirit. *Oh, Beauty* 11
Bold, *s*, careless Rosalind, *Rosalind* 2
Subtle-fanged blood Of hateful herbs a *s-f* snake. *Lover's Tale i* 821
Such There are no hearts like English hearts, *S* hearts of oak as they be. *National Song* 4
Of late *s* eyes looked at me—while I mused At sunset, *There are three things* 9
self-upborne With *s* gladness, as, *Rosalind* 18
With two *s* couches soft and white; *O darling room* 16
The centre of the splendours, all unworthy Of *s* a shrine— *Lover's Tale i* 70
I well remember, It was a glorious morning, *s* a one As dawns but once a season. Mercury On *s* a morning would have flung himself From cloud to cloud, „ 301
There was no *s* thing.— „ 670
Suffer She hardly can believe that she shall *s* wrong. *Sugg. by Reading* 66
Suffering wan dark coil of faded *s*— *Could I outwear* 4
Sufficed with her week-day worldliness *s*, *Sugg. by Reading* 62
Suitor I am any man's *s*, If any will be my tutor: *The 'How' and the 'Why'* 1
Summer (adj.) and sloped Into the slumberous *s* noon; *A Fragment* 11
The *s* midges wove their wanton gambol, *Check every outflash* 12
In summer still a *s* joy resumeth. *Me my own fate* 4
When *s* winds break their soft sleep with sighs, *Lover's Tale i* 559
Summer (s) A *s* of loud song, *The Grasshopper* 32
The naked *s's* glowing birth, *Chorus* 16
A *s* still a summer joy resumeth. *Me my own fate* 4
S's tanling diamondeyed. *Dualisms* 22
from his spring Moved smiling toward his *s*. *Lover's Tale i* 307
Summerflowers Bowing the seeded *s*. *The Grasshopper* 8
Summerhours Life of the *s*, „ 3
Summerplain Joy of the *s*, „ 2
Summerpride In thy heat of *s*, „ 36
Summertide And in the glow of sallow *S*, *Timbuctoo* 201
Summervault Under a *s* of golden weather; *Dualisms* 18
Summerwind VOICE of the *s*, *The Grasshopper* 1
Summerwood In the *s's* when the sun falls low, *The 'How' and the 'Why'* 27
Summoning Unto the fearful *s* without: *Timbuctoo* 36
Sun when the *S* Had fall'n below th' Atlantick, „ 3
'Wide Afric, doth thy *S* Lighten, „ 58
Of those that gaze upon the noonday *S*. „ 71
planet-girded *S's* And moon-encircled planets, „ 109
bore globes Of wheeling *s's*, or stars, „ 172
In the summerwoods when the *s* falls low, *The 'How' and the 'Why'* 27
Nor the round *s* that shineth to all; *Burial of Love* 26
Each *s* which from the centre flings *Chorus* 21
Thou art my heart's *s* in love's crystalline: *Love and Sorrow* 6
The mighty disk of their majestic *s*, *Love* 21
If thou dost leave the *s*, *The lintwhite* 32
WHERE is the Giant of the *S*, *A Fragment* 1
For the western *s* and the western star, *The Hesperides, Song iv* 7
S peeped in from open field, *Home they brought him* 6
the dew, the *s*, the rain, Unto the growth *Lover's Tale ii* 73
Sunborn Where are thy monuments Piled by the strong and *s* Anakim *A Fragment* 20
Sunlight In *s* and in shadow, *The Grasshopper* 20
Sunny But a short youth *s* and free. „ 29
Thy locks are full of *s* sheen *The lintwhite* 28
Sunset while I mused At *s*, underneath a shadowy plane *There are three things* 10
fullfaced *s* yellowly Stays on the flowering arch *The Hesperides, Song iv* 17
S ripened, above on the tree, „ 21
Gray sand banks and pale *s's*—dreary wind, *Mablethorpe* 7
About *s* We came unto the hill of woe, *Lover's Tale i* 364
Supernatural and my spirit With *s* excitation bound Within me, *Timbuctoo* 91
Surpassing *s* Earth's As Heaven than Earth „ 169
Swalloweth narwhale *s* His foamfountains in the sea. *Lotos-Eaters* 7
Sway no mightier Spirit than I to *s* The heart *Timbuctoo* 195
Hopes did *s* from that Which hung the frailest: *Lover's Tale i* 857
Swear No man to bear it—*S* it! We *s* it! *Britons, guard* 58
We *s* to guard our own. „ 60
And I *s* henceforth by this and this, *The Ringlet* 20
Sweet (*See also* **Double-sweet**) for a moment fill'd My eyes with irresistible *s* tears, *Timbuctoo* 191
Her Pagods hung with music of *s* bells: „ 234